THE SOCIETY OF DISTINGUISHED AMERICAN HIGH SCHOOL STUDENTS

"The Nation's Leading High School Honorary"

Editors:
L.B. Siegelman, Jr.
E. Vinson Givens

The Society of Distinguished American High
School Students reserves the right to edit all
copy to preserve the general flow and
homogeneity of the biographies and is not
responsible for errors occurring in editing or
typography. Any information not listed was
either not submitted, submitted illegibly, or
incongruent with the biographical form.

Published by: The Society of Distinguished
American High School Students
Post Office Box 7641A,
Birmingham, Alabama

THE SOCIETY

The Society of Distinguished American High School Students strives to further the pursuance of high academic achievement and civic responsibility on the part of every high school student.

To accomplish this aim The Society conducts a scholarship award program for the nation's highest achievers. The Society's National Awards Program remains one of the largest of its kind in the United States.

Recognition for Society members is attained through this published volume which is distributed nationally. Thousands of news releases provide additional publicity for the students in their home towns.

Due to the honor associated with membership in The Society, younger students are encouraged to excel academically early in their high school careers.

THE STUDENTS

The Society accepts for membership only young men and women who have distinguished themselves as the nation's highest achievers.

The students listed in this volume were nominated by high school and church officials. They are representative of all ethnic, religious and socio-economic groups in the United States.

These students are being recognized and rewarded for outstanding achievement in leadership and academics. While devoting themselves to their secondary education, at the same time, they have made a meaningful contribution to their schools, communities and the country. The members honored here have truly earned a place in The Society of Distinguished American High School Students—an honor for which all members may be justly proud.

THE COLLEGES

Since its inception, The Society's scholarship and awards program has grown rapidly to become the largest of its kind in the country.

The Society wishes to recognize the following institutions, which rank among the most distinguished names in America's education, for their efforts on behalf of the members of The Society of Distinguished American High School Students.

Bethany College

COLLEGIUM BETHANIENSIS

VERITAS

MDCCCXL

Bethany College is a four year, coeducational, liberal arts college. For more than 130 years, the College has operated as a private institution. The founder believed that a close environment, personal attention, individual stimulation, independent study and concern for others breeds a well educated man. At Bethany, students become acquainted with values as well as facts. The spectrum is wide. It spans areas of arts, sciences, and humanities. Each person becomes a participant, rather than a spectator in the unmasking of truths. He is invited to question, to search, and to discover his own responses to the interpretations of history, the realities of today, and the presumptions of tomorrow. He is challenged to build a foundation of knowledge that will ignite a zest for continuing education throughout life.

Bethany possesses a beautiful country campus with over 1,300 acres of fields, trails, timber land, and picnic areas all easily accessible to students. It is located in the foothills of the Allegheny Mountains in the Northern Panhandle of West Virginia. The main 60 acre sector of the campus is situated 2 miles from Pennsylvania, 7 miles from Ohio. The regenerated city of Pittsburgh is less than an hour's drive to the northeast. The College is served by one of the country's finest airports, Pittsburgh International, 55 minutes away by limousine.

The new curriculum, called the Bethany Plan, provides for maximum individualization of the academic program. Bethany believes students should make decisions. Gone are the old required courses and lock-step ordering of prerequisites. Students are expected to design their own program in consultation with a faculty adviser. They can even develop their own inter-disciplinary major if one of the regular departmental concentrations fails to meet special needs.

Bradford College

Bradford is a New England college with an international enrollment of 375 men and women. Its 70-acre wooded campus is located in northeastern Massachusetts in the residential community of Bradford, a part of the city of Haverhill. Boston with its colleges and universities, historic sites, and cultural, entertainment, and shopping resources is 30 miles away. Altantic ocean beaches and the New Hampshire and Vermont mountains are also within easy driving distance.

Bradford is proud of its 175-year tradition of quality education. Consistently since its founding in 1803 as an academy, it has concentrated on providing personal education in the liberal arts. The college's emphasis on personal education extends to the teaching of English composition through the freshman tutorial, in which students work individually with a faculty member throughout the year to sharpen writing skills while conducting research in a subject of interest to them. Additional opportunities to work outside of the regular class structure include workshops, reading seminars, and individually-designed independent and advanced study courses.

The college offers both Bachelor of Arts and Associate in Arts programs aimed at sound personal development. Internships and counseling link classroom studies to career goals. Broad-based B.A. majors are offered in Administrative Studies, American Culture, Creative Arts, Human Studies, and Urban Studies.

Bradford seeks well qualified candidates from all backgrounds—cultural, social, economic, religious, and geographic. About 40% of its students receive financial aid. A transcript of secondary school work and the scores of the Scholastic Aptitude Test or of the test of the American College Testing Program are required. There is no application fee.

For information write:
Director of Admissions
Bradford College
Bradford, Mass. 01830
(617) 372-7161

College of St. Benedict

Saint Benedict's is located in Saint Joseph, Minnesota, and enrolls 1400 from 22 states and 14 foreign countries. Ninety percent of our students live on-campus in dormitories, apartments or mobile homes. Over 100 faculty members, full and part time, offer an attractive student-teacher ratio of 15-1.

In many parts of America people are talking about restoring "quality of life": clean air, clear lakes, quiet when you want it, freedom for work and celebration, friends a door or a block away. In Minnesota, we talk about keeping it, protecting it. Drive 70 miles northwest of Minneapolis-Saint Paul or ten miles west of Saint Cloud and you'll find the College of Saint Benedict, a liberal arts college directed by Benedictine women. Our campus, with a variety of recreational opportunities and the best of the fine arts, illustrates quality of life at its best.

Saint Benedict's conducts a full academic exchange with Saint John's University, a College for men, enrollment 1750, just four miles away. Together Saint Benedict's and Saint John's offer 41 majors, 8 pre-professional programs and 7 special programs. In addition to the four-year program, Saint Benedict's also offers two-year degrees in criminal justice, music and liberal arts.

Situated on 700 acres of wooded campus, Saint Benedict's Benedicta Arts Center is one of the finest art-drama-music-dance facilities in the Midwest. A swimming pool and a horsemanship center, and campus center, have added to a wide range of recreational activities. The college also participates in several inter-collegiate sports.

The school calendar is 4-1-4: two semesters and a four-week January Term. Opportunities to study abroad for a full semester or during January are plentiful. Over seventy percent of our students are receiving financial aid in the form of scholarships, loans, work programs and grants.

Drew University

Drew University, consisting of the College of Liberal Arts, the Graduate School, and the School of Theology, is located in Madison, New Jersey, an attractive suburban city of 15,000 located 30 miles west of New York City. The college is small (1450) highly residential (95%) and coed (50-50). A Freshman class of 400 is enrolled annually through a selective admissions process. Class rank, counselor recommendations, school and community contributions, and SAT College Board scores form the basis for selection. The college draws mainly from the Mid-Atlantic and New England areas. Twenty-five states and twelve foreign countries were, however, represented in the most recent Freshman class.

The college awards the Bachelor of Arts degree only and offers a major in 24 subject areas. Advanced placement and credit is granted to qualified students and there are opportunities for independent study.

A distinctive faculty has 95% of its members above the rank of instructor holding the earned PhD. Excellent facilities for learning are highlighted by a library which houses 440,000 volumes, subscribes to more than 1200 journals and periodicals, and has 4000 microfilms and numerous specialized collections.

A unique feature of the Drew experience is the opportunity for off-campus study. Included are the United Nations, Art, the Washington Semester, Miami Semester, London and Brussels Semesters, and the Junior Year Abroad.

An active co-curricular program includes varsity and intramural sports for men and women, clubs and honor societies, student government, publications, campus radio station, and musical organizations.

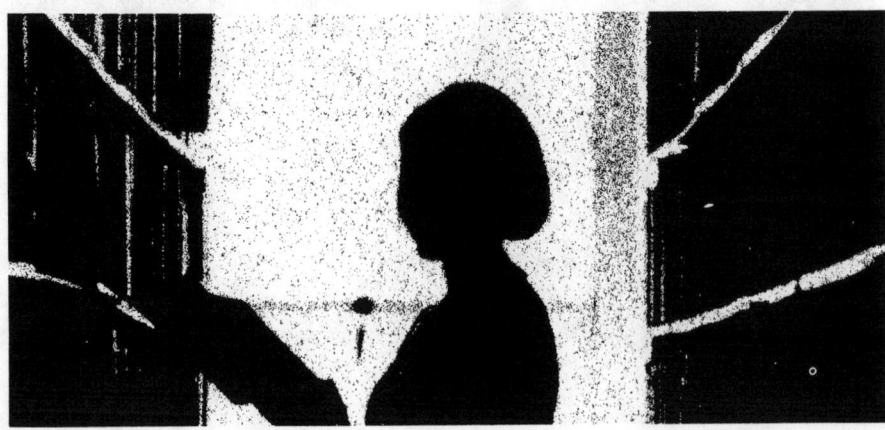

Eckerd College

Eckerd College is a school that has always been at the forefront of higher education in the United States today. Begun in 1958 as Florida Presbyterian College, the Eckerd College Concept in its entirety is an approach to learning that is unique in college education today. Among our programs you will find the Autumn Term, a three week period when freshmen and faculty have an opportunity to work together intensively; mentorship, close

associations between students and faculty in interest areas; the 4-1-4 calendar with Winter Term in January (we were the first school in the United States to adopt this); modular scheduling, provides maximum flexibility in designing your course load; interest collegia of faculties who are associated by common methods of exploration rather than traditional subject departments; the freedom and guidance to allow you to construct a major in light of your individual needs, (an emphasis on independent study); and a variety of programs in virtually all parts of the world. Between sixty and seventy percent of our graduates have either completed or are currently engaged in graduate work. Over the past seven years, 70% of our students who applied to medical schools were accepted. Of graduates applying to Law school, 78% have gained admission over the past three years.

The Eckerd College campus has just under a thousand students on its two hundred eighty-one acres in southwest St. Petersburg, of which a mile and a quarter is waterfront. From the beginning of the Autumn Term till the time you complete your senior year, the Eckerd program is designed to allow you to become exposed to and participate in a wide range of educational experiences. In turn, this approach requires a high degree of ability, motivation, and maturity in its students. We feel that members of The Society of Distinguished American High School Students would both gain and contribute should they decide to join us.

If you would like further information please write or call: Director of Admissions, Eckerd College, St. Petersburg, Florida 33733 (813) 867-1166.

Jamestown College

Jamestown College is an old college where new ideas thrive. Enrolling about 500 students, we consider our small size to be our strength. Concern for the personal and academic development of the student and his adjustment to college life is demonstrated by a comprehensive counseling program and a student-faculty ratio of 15:1. In addition, a new, individually designed curriculum was adopted in which students may design their own college program with the aid of their advisor.

Jamestown College is North Dakota's oldest private liberal arts college. The curriculum includes 17 departments and 28 major areas of study, including nursing, teacher education, business administration, medical technology, pre-optometry, pre-dentistry, and pre-medicine.

In 1966, Jamestown College broke the bonds of the traditional semester system and adopted the 4-1-4 calendar which we feel is a partial answer to the students' quest for putting textbook knowledge to practical use. Under the 4-1-4 calendar, which includes a one-month special study term in January between two traditional semesters, students select small group projects or pursue their own independent areas of interest on or off campus. Jamestown College students broaden their knowledge in a wide range of subjects over a vast geographical area . . . the world is literally their classroom.

Kansas Wesleyan

Educational experience—in its truest sense—is the aim of Kansas Wesleyan, a four-year liberal arts college in Salina, KS. Founded in 1886 and affiliated with the United Methodist Church, Kansas Wesleyan does not confine the learning experience to the classroom.

Kansas Wesleyan strives to educate and prepare its students for a rich and full life—professionally and personally. For nearly 92 years, the college has dedicated itself to providing quality Christian education for its students.

KANSAS WESLEYAN HAS:

- 14 "traditional" majors and minors
- Individual majors tailored to student needs
- Creative programs for students wanting non-traditional degree options

- 2-year Associate degrees in business administration, criminal justice and parish services
- A cooperative degree program in agricultural education with Kansas State University
- A January Interterm with classes held both on—and off—the campus
- Courses available on 7 other college campuses through the ACCK and Salina College Consortium
- Physical and social activity programs to develop a well-rounded person

Kansas Wesleyan operates on a 4-1-4 calendar. The one-month Interterm allows students the time for independent study, travel or a special project. Cooperation with the Associated Colleges of Central Kansas (Kansas Wesleyan, Bethany, Bethel, McPherson, Sterling and Tabor—all located within a 60-mile radius) allows students to broaden their educational horizons beyond one campus. Cooperation with Marymount College and Kansas Technical Institute of Salina allows students to cross-register without additional cost.

Kansas Wesleyan participates in such diverse programs as the Columbia Combined Plan in Engineering; Washington, DC, Semester, and United Nations Semester plus other effective cooperative programs.

At Kansas Wesleyan, the emphasis is on the individual and, because of this, openess is encouraged. As a completely open and honest institution, we hope to set an example, not only for individuals, but also for other institutions in our society.

The Kansas Wesleyan experience is varied; it suits the individual and it lasts a lifetime.

Morehouse College

Accreditation: Southern Association of Colleges and Schools

Student Body: Commute: 33%
Geographic distribution: 35% in state
65% out of state
From public schools: 90%
Racial composition: 99% black
Who begin, graduate: 59%
To graduate study: 62%

Faculty:
With doctorates: 65%
Faculty—student ratio: 1 to 16

Government: Student Government Association. Three students vote on Board of Trustees; students are voting members on faculty committees; students have equal representation with faculty on disciplinary committee.

Degrees: B.A., B.S.
Majors: 28
Graduation Credits: 128 semester hours.
Special Programs: Dual-degree programs in engineering, law, and pharmacy; Law Enforcement Education Program; Afro-American studies; community psychology; critical languages; humanities; social welfare; urban studies; international studies; oral history

Extracurricular Activities: 16
Fraternities: 4
Honor Societies: Phi Beta Kappa, Delta Sigma Rho, Phi Alpha Theta, Phi Delta Phi

Student Newspaper: The Maroon Tiger, monthly

Sports: 8 varsity, intramurals

Religion:
Facilities: Sale Hall Chapel and Danforth Chapel

Nearby Colleges: 11

Size of Campus: 40 acres
Setting: Urban, about two miles west of downtown Atlanta

Number of Buildings: 25
Library: 250,000 volumes
Housing:
Number accommodated: 800
Kinds available: Dormitories, fraternity houses

Admission Deadlines:
Regular Admissions: April 15
Early Admission: December 1
Financial Aid: April 15

For further information, write:

Director of Admissions
Morehouse College
Atlanta, Georgia 30314
(404) 681-2800

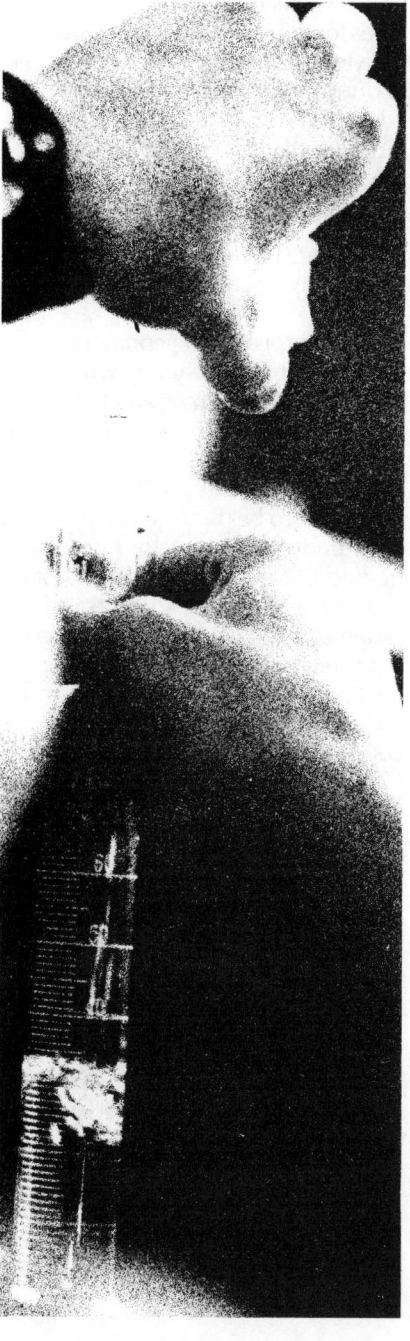

Northland College

Northland College, founded in 1892, is a four-year, co-educational, liberal arts environmental college located on the southern edge of Ashland, Wisconsin. The campus consists of 20 buildings situated on 76 acres. Dormitory facilities provide living accommodations for 260 men and 100 women. Approximately 60% of the student body graduated in the top half of the high school class, 30% in the top quarter, and 5% in the highest tenth.

Special financial aid is available for economically handicapped students and 60% of students recently received some form of financial assistance. Nearly 65% of a previous freshman class returned to the campus for the second year.

Affiliated with the United Church of Christ, the college offers undergraduate degree programs in arts and sciences and is accredited by the North Central Association of Colleges and Secondary Schools and American Chemical Society. It is also accredited by the Wisconsin State Department of Public Instruction for the education of teachers for the elementary and secondary schools in Wisconsin.

A new program, "The Northland Plan", includes a core of liberal studies to replace the existing general studies program covering the student's first two years. 4-4-1 replaces the quarter system. Short spring term offers opportunities for study in Europe or at any of nine cooperating colleges.

A faculty of 58 gives a faculty-student ratio of 1-14. Vocal and instrumental music groups, inter-collegiate and intramural athletics and Air Force ROTC are offered. Also offered is a Cooperative Education Program (alternating work and class periods) in environmental studies.

Olivet College

Olivet College was founded in 1844 by Father John J. Shipherd, a Congregational minister and 39 followers who came to this oak grove for the purpose of founding a coeducational Christian college open to all students of both sexes, and all races. The integrity and strength of character exhibited by those first settlers has given us a tradition to build upon.

Today there are about 800 students from 30 states and 15 foreign countries, and 50 faculty members. These people, working together for a common goal, are the main ingredient in the "Olivet experience." Olivet College is a place that cares, cares for you as a person and your individual talents and character, cares about your future, believing that education is an important building block for that future, and cares about the world of which you are such a vital part.

College life has more than one dimension. Your college years will be many faceted. The "Olivet experience" is flexible enough to allow you to choose your own course of study in determining what you want to get out of Olivet, and making sure that happens. The college recently assessed its goals and objectives to be these: to deliver a basic understanding of the liberal arts tradition; to prepare the student for a career; to instruct the students in a systematic and controlled approach to problem solving; to enrich the quality of the student's personal and social life, both during and after college.

Variety and flexibility are an important Olivet concept. You create your own academic schedule here, and to help you do that we offer you certain freedom of choice options, including: the independent study, experimental courses, exploratory courses, and the professional semester, and the pre-legal and pre-professional option.

If you are interested in Olivet, why not contact?:

Mr. William Wilkinson
Director of Admissions
Olivet College
Olivet, MI. 49076

Pepperdine University

Pepperdine University is an independent, liberal arts, Christian University offering year-round education under the trimester plan. Students have the option to earn a bachelor's degree in less than three years.

This fully accredited, rapidly growing University offers a School of Law in Anaheim, a "Year-in-Europe" in Heidelberg, its original urban campus in Los Angeles, and a dramatic new campus overlooking the ocean at Malibu.

Pepperdine Los Angeles is centrally located in a metropolitan area of over seven million people. This means involvement, challenges, and opportunities—factors that make for a meaningful, exciting educational experience. The pleasant, convenient campus offers its students the opportunity to study and grow in close association with faculty and fellow students.

The curriculum gives special emphasis to urban-oriented studies, while continuing the standard majors

of college study. In 1972 beginning students were offered twenty-nine bachelors degrees, fifteen graduate degrees and seven teaching credentials. General education requirements have been made more flexible to facilitate transfer from other colleges. Pepperdine Los Angeles offers an exciting urban education where relevance, experimentation, and Christian concern are key factors.

Pepperdine Malibu is a very new kind of place. The curriculum is built around the concept of unity of knowledge where all of the various disciplines are grouped in six major subject areas. The inter-relationships of all areas of learning with one another and with life in general is emphasized. This is a new adventure in education.

The new Pepperdine Malibu campus is one of the most beautiful college campuses in America. Above the breathtaking panorama of the Pacific Ocean, the campus buildings rise quietly to meet the California sun, like some Mediterranean hill-town of yesterday. The peaceful scene from the great knoll on which the Academic Complex sprawls is in sharp contrast to the exciting educational, personal, and spiritual challenges presented inside.

Would you like to know more about Pepperdine? Write:

Dean of Admissions
Pepperdine University
24255 Pacific Coast Highway
Malibu, CA 90265
(213) 456-4392

or

8035 South Vermont Avenue
Los Angeles, CA 90044
(213) 971-7503

Saint Mary's College

Saint Mary's is a Catholic women's liberal arts college with career orientation. The academic program of 29 major fields of study prepares women for a career within a liberal arts context leading to the degrees of Bachelor of Arts, Bachelor of Science, Bachelor of Fine Arts, Bachelor of Business Administration and Bachelor of Music. The curriculum for each degree is designed to fulfill the physical, social, intellectual and religious needs of the individual. It begins, therefore, with a general education in the freshman and sophomore years. A major is selected in the sophomore year. Nursing, preprofessional studies, business, and a new dual degree engineering program in cooperation with the University of Notre Dame are just a few of the career options available to Saint Mary's students.

An opportunity to study abroad is provided on Saint Mary's Rome campus. Saint Mary's also sponsors a program at St. Patrick's College in Maynooth, Ireland. A cooperative program with Notre Dame enables Saint Mary's students to study in Angers, France; Innsbruck, Austria; Tokyo, Japan; and Mexico City, Mexico.

Started by four sisters of the Holy Cross, Saint Mary's became the first legally chartered Catholic College for women in the United States in 1855. It is located in Notre Dame, Indiana— long recognized as a center of Catholic education—and is situated across from the University of Notre Dame, providing a co-exchange program for students from both campuses. In addition, Saint Mary's and four other colleges form the Northern Indiana Consortium for Education (NICE) through which Indiana University South Bend, Bethel College, Holy Cross Junior College, Indiana Vocational School and Saint Mary's exchange students, faculty, and library facilities.

Saint Mary's enrollment of 1700 students represents 48 states and 26 foreign countries. Its 275 acre campus houses more than 20 buildings, a lake, tennis courts, a swimming pool and a new athletic building.

For further information contact:

Admissions Director
St. Mary's College
Notre Dame, Indiana 46556

Saint Mary's Dominican College

The purpose of St. Mary's Dominican College is to educate its students to be more useful members of society and to assist in the development of individuals committed to the betterment of mankind through love of God and love of neighbor.

It is a Catholic liberal arts college primarily for women. However, because of the introduction of such timely majors as Respiratory Therapy and Cytotechnology as well as the establishment of a consortium with Loyola and Xavier Universities, male students are admitted.

Dominican draws students from many different states and foreign countries; moreover, the availability of a Program of English as a Second Language attracts numerous students from Central and South America. Air-conditioned dormitories provide living accommodations for the resident women students and up-to-date facilities afford opportunities to pursue an education in surroundings conducive to learning.

A sound liberal arts program supplemented by several degree offerings in community oriented services makes Dominican an ideal place to study. For it enjoys a superb spot in the University Section of New Orleans, a city which gives added dimensions to a college curriculum. To enter into the life of an international city, to share in the many attractions and stimulating encounters a city such as New Orleans offers is to enrich campus life and formal study with "lagniappe" that is beyond price.

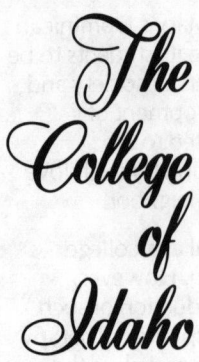

The College of Idaho

The College of Idaho, a Presbyterian-related, coeducational, liberal arts college, was founded in 1891. The attractive tree-lined campus, with some of the finest facilities in the West, is located in Caldwell, a residential community 25 miles west of the capital city of Boise. This natural setting in one of the great year around recreation areas offers some of the finest skiing in the nation.

The Bachelor of Arts and Bachelor of Science degrees are offered in 28 major fields with over 300 courses available in the humanities, arts, natural and social sciences, and education. Over 85% of the 47 faculty members hold earned doctorates and the student faculty ratio is 13 to 1.

The College of Idaho calendar of two thirteen-week semesters separated by a six-week winter session is designed to provide a maximum opportunity for innovative approaches to teaching and learning. This unique calendar, highlighted by the mid-year mini-semester, places emphasis on meeting the needs of the individual student and allows unusual opportunities for extended field trips, independent study, projects, and internships.

A diversified program of extracurricular activities provides balance and perspective to the college experience. There are many social, athletic, and cultural events and a broad variety of organizations and interest groups.

Financial aid in the form of scholarships, grants, loans, and employment is available to qualified applicants. Over 60% of the students receive some form of financial assistance. Specific information may be obtained by contacting the Office of Admissions.

Westminster College

Westminster College, founded in 1851, is a private four-year liberal arts college for men. The College is located in Fulton, Missouri, about 100 miles west of St. Louis and 150 miles east of Kansas City.

Despite student population pressures, Westminster adheres to the philosophy that small classes and close student-faculty relationships enable the student to derive the maximum benefits from his collegiate experience. Enrollment, therefore, is limited so that a faculty-student ratio of approximately 1:15 may be maintained.

Westminster's student body is composed of about 750 young men from more than 30 states and several foreign countries, representing many religious backgrounds. Eighty-five per cent are graduates of public high schools, while 15 per cent attended private secondary schools.

Since the strength of an educational institution depends largely upon the competence of its faculty, Westminster concentrates on assembling a highly qualified group of teachers and scholars. Over half of the faculty hold the Ph.D. degree, and all of them are actively engaged in classroom teaching.

Westminster's liberal arts and pre-professional curriculum is designed to prepare a student to live, as well as make a living. The college offers the Bachelor of Arts and Bachelor of Fine Arts degrees, with majors available in twenty-two fields. Independent study, internships, and overseas programs are available for all students.

A cooperative program with William Woods College for women, also located in Fulton, makes possible a co-educational campus environment and a normal social program. A voluntary Army ROTC unit operates at Westminster, and a wide variety of extra-curricular activities enhance life outside the classroom. Financial aid is available for any student demonstrating a need for assistance.

Located on the Westminster Campus is the Winston Churchill Memorial and Library, which commemorates Sir Winston's visit to Westminster in 1946.

The Abbreviations

Abbr	Meaning	Abbr	Meaning	Abbr	Meaning
A	Award	FBLA	Future Business Leaders of America	NFL	National Forensic League
A Cap Choir	A Capella Choir			NHS	National Honor Society
A-Ed	Assistant Editor	Fed	Federation Federal	NMF	National Merit Finalist
Acad	Academy	FFA	Future Farmers of America	NML	National Merit Letter
Acct	Accounting			NMS	National Merit Semifinalist
Adm	Administration	Fin	Finalist	Ntl	National
Adv	Advisory, Advanced	FHA	Future Homemakers of America	Nurs	Nursing
AFS	American Field Service			Off	Office, Officer
Agr	Agriculture	FNA	Future Nurses of America	Opt	Optimist
Alg	Algebra	Found	Foundation	Orch	Orchestra
Alt	Alternate	Fr	French		
Amer	America, American	FTA	Future Teachers of America	PA	Perfect Attendance
Amer Leg	American Legion			Parl	Parliamentarian
Ann	Annual	Ftbl	Football	Phar	Pharmacy
ARC	American Red Cross			Phys Ed	Physical Education
Arch	Archery	GAA	Girls Athletic Association	Pol Sci	Political Science
Assn	Association	Geol	Geology	Pres	President
Asst	Assistant	Geom	Geometry	Psych	Psychology
Ath	Athletics	Ger	German	Pub	Public
Aux Lat	Auxilum Latinum	Gl C	Glee Club		
Avg	Average	Gov Honor Prog	Governor's Honors Program	Q & S	Quill and Scroll
		GS	Girls State	Qn	Queen
B Mgr	Business Manager	GSct	Girl Scout	Quar	Quarter
BC	Beta Club	Gym	Gymnastics		
Bio	Biology			Rep	Representative
Bkbl	Basketball	Hist	History	Rptr	Reporter
Bowl	Bowling	HKg, Qn, Ct.	Homecoming King, Queen Court	S-T	Secretary-Treasurer
BS	Boys State			Sal	Salutatorian
Bsbl	Baseball	Hmrm	Homeroom	SC	Student Council
BSct	Boy Scout	H of Fame	Hall of Fame	Sch	School
Bstr	Booster Club	Hon	Honor	Sch P	School Paper
Bus	Business	Hon Prog	Honors Program	Schol	Scholar, Scholarship
Bus Adm	Business Administration	Hon Soc	Honor Society	Sci	Science
		HR	Honor Roll	Secy	Secretary
C	Club	HS	High School	Sem	Seminary
Cand	Candidate			Semi-Fin	Semifinalist
Cath	Catholic	Ind	Independent	Sen	Senator, Senate
Ch	Chairman	Inst	Institute	Sftbl	Softball
Chem	Chemistry			Soph	Sophomore
Chldr	Cheerleader	JA	Junior Achievement	Span	Spanish
Chor	Chorus	JC	Junior Chamber of Commerce	Spch	Speech
Chpt	Chapter	JETS	Junior Engineering Technical Society	Spkr	Speaker
Citz	Citizenship			Sq	Squad
Cl	Class	Journ	Journalism	Sr	Senior
Cl Fav	Class Favorite	Jr	Junior	St	State
Co	County	JV	Junior Varsity	Stu	Students, Studies
Co-Ch	Co-Chairman			Sup	Superior
Co-Cpt	Co-Captain	K of C	Knights of Columbus	Swtht	Sweetheart
Co-Ed	Co-Editor	Kg	King	Sym	Symposium
COM	Certificate of Merit	Kn	Knight	Symph	Symphony
Comm	Committee, Community				
Comp	Competition	Lang	Language	Thes	Thespians
Conf	Conference	Lat	Latin	Tm	Team
Coun	Council	Ldr	Leader	Tn	Teen
Cpt	Captain	Leg	Legislature	Tnns	Tennis
Cr-Ctry	Cross Country	Lib	Library	Tourn	Tournament
CSF	California Scholarship Federation	Lit Mag	Literary Magazine	Tr	Track
		Lit Ral	Literary Rally	Tres	Treasurer
Ctry	Country	Ltr	Letter	Trng	Training
CYO	Catholic Youth Organization	Ltrman	Letterman		
				U	University
Dbte Tm	Debate Team	Md	Maid		
Del	Delegate	Med	Medicine	Val	Valedictorian
Dist	District	Mem	Memorial	Var	Varsity
		Mgr	Manager	Vice-Ch	Vice Chairman
Ed	Editor, Education	Mjrte	Majorette	Vlbl	Volleyball
Engr	Engineering	MLS	Most Likely to Succeed	V of Dem	Voice of Democracy
Ensm	Ensemble	Mod Mus Mas	Modern Music Masters	Vol	Volume, Volunteer
		Mod UN	Model UN	VP	Vice President
F-Ed	Feature Editor	Mus	Music	Win	Winner
Fav	Favorite	MVP	Most Valuable Player	Wk	Week
				Wrest	Wrestling
				WW	Who's Who
				Yrbk	Yearbook
				Yth	Youth
				Yth Fel	Youth Fellowship
				Yth Leg	Youth Legislature

THE BIOGRAPHIES

A Biographical Compilation of the Most
Distinguished High School Students in
America

A

AAKJAR, Linda May
Ossining HS; Ossining High, NY; Orch; Secy, Soph Cl; Hockey; Span A; Church Choir; Pres, MYF; Northeastern Col; Special Ed.

AAMOT, Jeffrey Scott
Roosevelt HS; Minneapolis, MN (60-700) A Cap Choir; Spch C; JV, Ftbl; Opt A; Spch A; St Olaf; Archeology.

AARDEMA, Steven Duane
Zeeland HS; Zeeland, MI (2-200) Band; Ensm; Lat C; Model UN; NHS; Mgr, Bsbl; Hon Prog; Pres, Church Yth Group; Hope Col; Math.

AARON, James Robert
Lexington HS; Lexington, TN (15-172) BS; Lat C; NHS; F-Ed, Sch P; Span C; SC; Bsbl; Bkbl; Cpt, Ftbl; Amer Leg A; All Conf, Coach's Trophy, Ftbl; Most Athletic; Most Versatile; US Air Force Acad; Engr.

AARON, Leonard
Etowah HS; Attalla, AL; Tri-HiY; Bkbl; Tr.

AARON, Roberta
Parkway Delta HS; Philadelphia, PA; Chor; Most Congenial; Most Efficient; U of Mexico; Special Ed.

AARONSON, Wendy Ilene
El Camino Real HS; Woodland Hills, CA; City Conf; Hmrm; NHS; Pres, Span C; Secy, SC; Pres, Jr Cl; VP, Soph Cl; Tnns; CSF; Most Out; Best Sportsmanship Tnns Tm; UCLA; Pre-Law.

ABADIE, Debra Ann
Lutcher HS; Lutcher, LA (2-200) BC; Pres, FBLA; Hmrm; SC; Sal; Dance Tm; Miss LHS; Outst Bus A; Periquette Swtht; Eng A; Bat Girl; Semi-Fin, Miss La Ntl Tnagr Pageant; Cath Daughters of Amer A; Nicholls Col; Off Adm.

ABAJIAN, Tony James
Warren HS; Downey, CA; Cpt, Wrest; Biola Col; Bible.

ABAJIAN, William David
W Essex HS; N Caldwell, NJ (50%-415) Band; Chor; Demolay; Hmrm; Key C; Pres, Ski C; SC; Var C; Sr Cl; Ftbl; Sftbl; Lacross; NorthEastern U; Bus.

ABBEY, Kristin Lee
Robert E Lee HS; Tyler, TX (25%-620) City Conf; Community Yth Symph; ARC; Sch Achieve Tm; Citz A; Star Student; Yth Fel; 700 Vol Hours, Candystriper; Tyler Jr Col; Bus Adm.

ABBEY, Marilyn Louise
Anchor Bay HS; New Baltimore, MI (20-250) A-Ed, Ann; NHS; Pres, Span C; Var C; Cpt, Bkbl; Cpt, Tr; Most Out; MVP, Bkbl; Macomb Comm Col; Bus.

ABBEY, Mark Raymond
Rogers Sr HS; Michigan City, IN (187-540) Demolay; Ftbl; Tr.

ABBOTT, Anita Irene
P K Yonge Lab Sch; Gainesville, FL (10%-90) Chor; Ensm; Vlbl; Adm Board; Pres, Sr High Division of Yth; Pres, Yth Choir; Coun of Ministeries.

ABBOTT, Annie Mae
Northeastern HS; Detroit, MI (7-200) JETS; NHS; Pol Sci C; COM; Citz A; Hon Prog; MLS; Teacher's Pet; Top Ten A; Service A; Art A; Mary Grove Col; Engr.

ABBOTT, Carlise Wilsonia
Camden HS; Camden, NC (32-101) Cpt, Chldr; FHA; Hmrm; Mjrte; Bus.

ABBOTT, Donna Joanna
Oak Lawn Comm HS; Oak Lawn, IL (35-800) Band; Thes; Eng.

ABBOTT, Georgia Snow
Sanford Central HS; Sanford, NC (24-350) Band; Mod Mus Mas; NHS; SC; VP, Soph Cl; Citz A; Kiwanis A; Pres A; Rotary A; Civinettes; All St Band; Nom, Gov's Sch; Mus.

ABBOTT, Karen Jenell
John F Hodge HS; St James, MO (14-106) Chldr; Fr C; Jr Miss Pagent; Sci C; Pres, Sr Cl; VP, Jr Cl; Most Out; Vlbl; Art A; Chldr A; Burge Sch of Nurs; Nurs.

ABBOTT, Melanie Hope
Lancaster HS; Lancaster, VA (10-95) BC; Chldr; Chor; Fr C; Hmrm; Sci C; Bkbl; COM; VP, Art C; VP, Tri-Lingua C; Old Dominion U; Dental Hygiene.

ABBOTT, Ramona Susan
Bradford HS; Bradford, TN; Rptr, BC; Pres, Bus C; Pres, FHA; 4H; Var C; Secy, Sr Cl; Secy, Jr Cl; Secy, Soph Cl; Bkbl; HQn; VP, FHA; Best Attitude & Hustle, Bkbl As; U of Tenn at Martin; Acct.

ABBOTT, Randall Lee
Whiteland Comm HS; Whiteland, IN (120-208) Band; Var C; JV, Ftbl; Tr; Wrest; Sound Engr.

ABBOTT, Rena Fay
Bellmont HS; Decatur, IN (10%-307).

ABBOTT, Susan Elizabeth
Fremont Ross HS; Fremont, OH; Ann; Band; Drama; Ensm; COM; Hist A; Superior Ratings, Solo & Ensm; Capital U; Mus.

ABBOTT, Tamara Lynn
Robert E Lee HS; San Antonio, TX (55-585) Bus C; FHA; NHS; ARC; Span C; Span NHS; COM; Opt A; ARC A; Executive Secretaries; Shorthand A; Acct A; Artist A; Trinity U; Acct.

ABBOTT, Thomas Michael
Desoto HS; DeSoto, TX; Pres, Ger C; Pres, Jr Cl; JV, Bsbl; Ftbl; Cl Fav.

ABBOTT, Tyler Alan
Northgate HS; Walnut Creek, CA (1-500) CSF; Hon Prog; Outst, Span; Astrophysics.

ABDELLA, Stephen Martin
Jamestown HS; Jamestown, NY (20-520) Band; Dbte Tm; NHS; Ski C; Tres, SC; Tres, Sr Cl; Tres, Jr Cl; Tres, Soph Cl; Bsbl; Hon Prog; NEDT; Regent Schol; St Scholar; All St Band; Col of William & Mary; Hist.

ABDO, Mona S
Hazelwood E HS; St Louis, MO (5-500) Chor; NHS; Rptr, Sch P; Drill Tm; Pom Pon; Job's Daughters; Stephens Col; Eng.

ABEE, Melvin Neal
N Gaston HS; Dallas, NC (50-200) Band; Key C; Order/Arrow; Order/Arrow A; Pres A; All St Band; Gaston Col; Elec.

ABEL, James Henry III
Forrest City HS; Forrest City, AR (29-330) BC; BS; Hmrm; SC; Cpt, Bsbl; Bkbl; Ftbl; MVP, Bsbl; All Conf, All St, Ftbl; Miss St U; Bus Adm.

ABEL, Pamela Sue
Landmark Christian Sch; Cincinnati, OH (3-36) Band; Chor; Pres, FHA; Hmrm; Orch; SC; Secy, Sr Cl; COM; Moody Bible Inst; Christian Ed.

ABEL, Sally Ruth
Cocoa Beach HS; Cocoa Beach, FL (12-240) A Cap Choir; BC; Chldr; Chor; Ensm; Mu Alpha Theta; NHS; Var C; Tr; Most Popular; Chor A; Clemson U.

ABELL, Marcia Lea
Butler HS; Louisville, KY; Chor; Drama; Hmrm; Mod Mus Mas; COM; PTA A; U of Louisville; Nurs.

ABELL, Rick Warner
Harrisburg HS; Harrisburg, IL (4-158) Pres, HiY; Key C; Pres, Lat C; NHS; A-Ed, Sch P; Var C; Bsbl; Ftbl; WW; SE Ill Col; Bus Adm.

ABELS, Karen Sue
Mansfield Christian HS; Mansfield, OH (30-60) Ensm; Secy, 4H; Tr; DARGCA; Prom Art; Nationwide Beauty Sch; Cosmotology.

ABENDROTH, Rosemary Ann
Bancroft Pub Sch; Bancroft, NE (4-28) Ann; Chldr; Chor; NHS; Sch P; Sci C; Spch C; Tr; Spch A; Pres, Yth Fel; Banner Carrier, Band; Fin, Comm C Schol; WW; Mgr, Vlbl; U of Nebr; Home Ec.

ABENS, Janice Mae
Aurora W HS; Aurora, IL (95-601) A Cap Choir; Pres, Chor; VP, Yth Fel; HR; 1st, St Solo & Ensm Contest; Bethel Col; Bus.

ABERCROMBIE, Lesa Ann
Bauxite HS; Bauxite, AR (10-30) VP, FBLA; Pres, FTA; GS; Rptr, NHS; Sch P; Sci C; VP, Sr Cl; Sftbl; HCt; Counselor at GS.

ABERNATHY, Joanie Lucy
Giles Co HS; Pulaski, TN (50-150) Drama; FBLA; Hmrm; Lat C; Sch P; Spch C; Thes; Rotary A; U of Miss; Law.

ABERNATHY, Lisa Kirk
Suffolk HS; Suffolk, VA (13-118) Bus Mgr, Ann; Co-Cpt, Chldr; Drama; Hmrm; Lat C; S-T, Monogram; NHS; Ch, SC; Thes; Tri-HiY; Tnns; WW; Nom, Ntl Tn Pagent; VPI; Environmental Engr.

ABERNATHY, Michael Andrew
Grace Christain Sch; Blackstone, VA;

ABERNETHY, Everett Thomas
Lenoir HS; Lenoir, NC (50-120) Band; Chess C; Monogram; Ski C; Span C; Tnns; Band As; Tnns As; ASU; Bus.

ABLES, Kee Alice
Sherman HS; Sherman, TX (57-460) Bus C; Tres, Lat C; NHS; Tnns; N Tex St U; Phys Ed.

ABNER, Trudy Lynn
Bourbon Co HS; Paris, KY; FHA; Jr Degree, FHA; Billy Graham Correspondence Course; Westminster Col; Nurs.

ABNEY, Carol Elizabeth
Columbus HS; Columbus, GA; Chor; Secy, FHA; Math C; NHS; Sci C; SC; Gov Honor Prog; Hist A; Hon Prog; Sci A; Pres, Art C; Art A; U of Ga; Art.

1

ABNEY, Kathy Lorraine
Columbus HS; Columbus, GA; F-Ed, Ann; BC; Secy, Drama; Ch, FHA; NHS; Secy, Sci C; Hist A; Hon Prog; Secy, Art C; Rptr, Sci C; St Win, Sci C Scrapbook Competition; Art A; Art Schola; *Columbus Col; Art.*

ABNEY, Mark Wesley
Covina HS; Covina, CA; JV, Bkbl; Tr.

ABRAHAM, Bobby
Flint Central HS; Flint, MI; City Conf; Cr-Ctry; Soccer; Citz A; Hon Prog; NHS Nom; Graduation Marshal; Donald H Fogell A; Bentley Prog; General Motor's Inst Sci C; Sch C, Explor Diversified Subjects; *U of Mich; Med.*

ABRAHAM, Carrie Lee
Homestead HS; Mequon, WI (82-430) AFS; Chldr; Chor; Tres, Hmrm; Ski C; Span C; Tres, SC; Tres, Jr Cl; Soph Cl; Pres, Swim; COM; HCt; Hon Prog; Skiing; VP, Curling; Tr Court.

ABRAHAM, David John
Adrian HS; Adrian, MI; Lat C; Photo C; *Rochester Inst; Chem.*

ABRAHAM, David Thomas
Vicksburg HS; Vicksburg, MS (8-244) AFS; F-Ed, Ann; Band; BS; Chor; VP, Key C; Lat C; Math C; NHS; Sch P; VP, SC; VP, Soph Cl; Amer Leg A; H of F; HCt; MLS; NEDT; VofDEM; Yth Leg; Pres, SC; Most Intellectual; *Vanderbilt U; Pre-Law.*

ABRAHAM, Michelle Legaspi
George Washington Sr HS; Mangilao, GUAM; Rptr, Sch P; SC; Pres, Soph Cl; Most Out; Sal; *Temple U; Phys Therapy.*

ABRAHAM, Muriel Annette
Myrtle Beach HS; Myrtle Beach, SC; COM; Hist A; *U of SC-Columbia; Nurs.*

ABRAHAM, Robert Eugene
Myrtle Beach HS; Myrtle Beach, SC; Chor; Bsbl; Ftbl.

ABRAM, Susan Marie
Raytown S HS; Raytown, MO (15-585) Ann; Chldr; NHS; Secy, SC; VP, Sr Cl; VP, Jr Cl; VP, Soph Cl; B Crocker A; COM; Regent Schol; Cand, Prom Qn; *U of Mo.*

ABRAMOVITZ, Jay David
Clear Creek HS; League City, TX (1-453) AFS; Semi-Fin, BS; Pres, Chem C; Drama; Pres, JETS; Mu Alpha Theta; VP, NHS; Phys C; Bsbl; Soccer; Chem A; Hon Prog; Ntl Sci Found; Val; Mood Hon Schol; *Rice U; Biomed Engr.*

ABRAMS, Connie Louise
Martin Luther King Jr Acad; Gary, IN; Hon Prog; Ind U; *Social Worker.*

ABRAMS, Lisa Gail
Skyview Baptist Acad; Memphis, TN; BC; Lat C; Sci C; *Memphis St; Sci.*

ABRAMS, Sherman
Barringer HS; Newark, NJ (193-650) *Air Force; Aviation Mechanic.*

ABRAMSON, Thomas Joel
Holdrege Sr HS; Holdrege, NE (74-120) Band; Chor; Ensm; Order/Arrow; Ftbl; Wrest; Order/Arrow A; Band A; *Central Nebr Tech Col; Elec.*

ABREU, Alberto Nadruz
St Francis Prep Sch; Spring Grove, PA (3-26) Fin, NHS; Pres, Span C; Var C; Cr-Ctry; Cpt, Soccer; Tr; COM; Hon Prog; *Georgetown U; Foreign Service.*

ABREU, Andres
Francisco Mendoza HS; Isabela, PR; CYO; Bsbl; Cpt, Bkbl; Sftbl; Hon Stu; *Aguadilla Regional Col; Pol Sci.*

ABREU, Jane Ann
St Joseph's Notre Dame HS; Alameda, CA (4-56) Chor; Fr C; NHS; Sci C; Ski C; CSF; Hon Prog; Hist A; Eng A; Religion A; *U of San Francisco; Psych.*

ABROM, Kenneth Leon
Bell Voc HS; Washington, DC; Bsbl; Bkbl; Ftbl; Citz A; ROTC A; PA; Excellence A; *Easton Col; Plumbing.*

ABSHER, Connie Elaine
Foothill HS; Bakersfield, CA; JV, Chldr; Ger C; Chldr As; *Ecology.*

ABSHER, Delores Ann
Wetumka HS; Wetumka, OK (14-48) Band; Chor; Pres, FHA; Sch P; Journ A; *East Central U; Voc Home Ec.*

ABSHER, Roger Keith
Wetumka HS; Wetumka, OK (14-49) BS; Tres, FFA; Sch P; Bsbl; Ftbl; Tr; *E Central U; Industrial Arts.*

ABSHIER, Susan Lynette
Groveton HS; Groveton, TX (1-46) Ed, Ann; Secy, Band; Secy, BC; S-T, FHA; Co-Cpt, Mjrte; A-Ed, Sch P; Span C; SC; Rptr, Sr Cl; Mgr, Tr; Coun of Teach A; Hon Prog; MLS; Star Student; Val; *Sam Houston St U; Bus Adm.*

ABSHIRE, Marvin Ray
Randolph Sou Jr-Sr HS; Lynn, IN (4-76) Band; NHS; Chem A; St Scholar; Band A; Pol Sci A; *Anderson Col; Pre-Law.*

ABSON, Charlotte Yvette
Lynwood HS; Lynwood, CA; Drama; CSF; Citz A; Spch A; *Calif St U; Pre-Med.*

ABSTON, Connie Sue
Chesterton HS; Chesterton, IN (1-430) NHS; Span C; Spch C; Citz A; Hon Prog; Math A; Spch A; Type A; *Bethel Col; Secy Studies.*

ACEVEDO, Ray Manuel
Colegio Universit de Sagrado; Santurce, PR (2-37) Most Out; Summa Cum Laude; *Georgetown U; Pre-Med.*

ACEVEJO, Larisa Dianette
Antilles HS; Fort Buchanan, PR (1-118) Drama; Hmrm; COM; Hon Prog; JA A; NJHS; DAHSS; Keyettes; Tres, Ecology C; Lib Aide A; *MIT; Sci Research.*

ACHOR, Janet Lynn
Hillsboro HS; Hillsboro, OH (10-180) Ed, Ann; Band; Chor; Ensm; S-T, 4H; VP, Lat C; NHS; COM; 4H A; Hon Prog; Yth Fel; *Social Work.*

ACHORD, Lynne Marie
E Ascension Acad; Gonzales, LA (4-21) Sch P; Rptr, Jr Cl; Most Courteous; *LSU; Kindergarten Teacher.*

ACHORN, Leesa Ann
Brewer HS; Brewer, ME; Chldr; Chor; Drama; Fr C; Secy, Rainbow; Ski C; JV, Bkbl; Co-Cpt, Tr; Hist A; MLS; Most Out; Sci A; *U of Maine; Psych.*

ACKAL, Kalil Anthony
Catholic HS; New Iberia, LA; Lit Ral; VP, SC; Var C; Pres, Sr Cl; Pres, Jr Cl; VP, Soph Cl; Bsbl; Ftbl; Soccer; Wrest; Citz A; Cl Fav; DARGCA; Hist A; Math A; *U of SW La; Elec Engr.*

ACKER, Brian James
Colonie Central HS; Albany, NY (53-714) Band; Ensm; NHS; Orch; Sci C; Pres, VP, Church Yth Group; JV Vlbl; Area & All St Orch.

ACKER, Deborah Ann
S Cobb HS; Austell, GA; Ann; BC; COM; *Art Inst of Atlanta; Comm Art.*

ACKER, Gina LaVonne
Stevenson HS; Stevenson, WA (3-98) Ensm; Hmrm; Secy, NHS; Rptr, Sch P; Tr; B Crocker A; Masonic A; Fin, Miss United Tnager Pageant; Most Outst, Gym; Ltrwomen Pres; Girl o-t Month; *Multnomah Sch o-t Bible; Bible.*

ACKER, Karen Sue
Wapakoneta Sr HS; Wapakoneta, OH (4-291) Co-Ed, Ann; Pres, Ntl Teachers C; Rptr, Sch P; Span C; Span NHS; Secy, SC; Y-Tns; Mgr, Tr; Hon Prog; NEDT; Sal; 3-D Gym A; *Wittenberg U; Elem Ed.*

ACKER, Mary Beth
Mercy HS; Albany, NY (9-108) *Siena Col; Psych.*

ACKER, Melody Lynn
Thompson HS; Alabaster, AL (1-163) Band; Drama; Mjrte; Orch; Eng A; *U of Montevallo; Math.*

ACKER, Ramona Kay
New Braunfels HS; New Braunfels, TX; Band; Ensm; Ger C; InterClub Coun; Pres, Math C; Pres, Mu Alpha Theta; NHS; Sci C; Secy, SC; NEDT; Eng A; *Med Tech.*

ACKER, Shella Deeann
McMullen Co ISD HS; Tilden, TX (3-6) A-Ed, Ann; FFA; FHA; 4H; Jr Miss Pagent; Secy, NHS; Secy, Sr Cl; Secy, Jr Cl; VP, Soph Cl; Mgr, Bkbl; Tr; B Crocker A; WW; *Tex A&M U; Lib Sci.*

ACKERMAN, April Rene
Wade Hampton Acad; Orangeburg, SC; Chor; Lat C; Span C; Bkbl; NEDT; Conservation Essay A; *Clemson U.*

ACKERMAN, Carol Mae
Hazen HS; Hazen, ND (22-48) Band; Chldr; Chor; Ch, FHA; Pres, Soph Cl; Bkbl; Tr; Yth Fel.

ACKERMAN, Cherol Kay
Hazen HS; Hazen, ND (24-48) Band; Chldr; Chor; FHA; Secy, Hmrm; Bkbl; Tr; HCt; Yth Fel; VP, Tn Challenge.

ACKERMAN, Michael Jon
Thompson Pub Sch; Thompson, ND (5-28) 4H; Key C; F-Ed, Sch P; S-T, Sr Cl; VP, Jr Cl; Secy, Soph Cl; Bkbl; Cr-Ctry; Ftbl; 4H A; I Dare You; Spch A; Yth Leg; *U of ND; Personnel Mgr.*

ACKERMAN, Peter Joseph
Hazen HS; Hazen, ND (20-49) Band; Drama; Ensm; FFA; *Westmar Col; Computer Sci.*

ACKERSON, Corine
Marvell HS; Marvell, AR (7-118) Hmrm; SC; Phys Ed, Home Ec, A's; HR; WW.

ACKLIN, JoAnn
Bethel Baptist HS; Memphis, TN (5-20) Ann; Band; Chldr; Chor; Stu o-t Mo, Christian Ed Assn; Miss Most Faithful; *Tri-St Baptist Col; Primary Ed.*

ACKMANN, Sheila Rena
Hickman HS; Columbia, MO; Chor; Citz A; Hon Prog; Yth Fel; Alt, SC; PA; Show Me Yth Chorale Tour; *U of Mo at Columbia; Nurs.*

ACOL, Jose Chris
University of San Diego HS; San Diego, CA (88-311) CYO; Cum Laude Soc; Parl, Hmrm; Model UN; VP, SC; UN Council; Var C; Pres, Soph Cl; Ftbl; Tr; HCt; Hon Prog; *U of Calif; Pre-Med.*

ACOSTA, Beatriz Eugenia
Juan Jose Osuna HS; Baldrich, PR (2-150) Band; Pres, Chldr; Chem C; Drama; Hmrm; ARC; Rptr, Sch P; SC; Tr; Alg A; Amer Leg Orator A; COM; Chem A; Hon Prog; Sal; Star Student; *U of PR; Engr.*

ACOSTA, Edgardo
Luis Munoz Rivera HS; Lajas, PR (1-175) CYO; Tres, Drama; Pres, Hmrm; Sch Achieve Tm; Alg A; COM; Hon Prog; JA A; Sacristan; Star Student; *Cath U of PR; Priest.*

ACOSTA, Enrique Nunez
Amer Military Acad; Guaynabo, PR (4-18) JV, Bsbl; Ftbl; *UPR.*

ACOSTA, Eva
Luis Munoz Rivera HS; Lajas, PR; CYO; Chor; 4H; Lit Mag; 4H A; ARC A; *U of PR; Nurs.*

ACOSTA, Juan
Barringer HS; Newark, NJ (5%-450) Drama; FNA; Hmrm; NHS; SC; Up Bound; Soccer; COM; Chem A; Citz A; Phy A; Sci A; SEED A, NJIT; Achv A; Hon Soc A; *Pre-Med.*

ACOSTA, Waldo A
Luis Munoz Rivera HS; Lajas, PR (2-170) Drama; Bsbl; Cpt, Bkbl; Alg A; Bausch & Lomb A; COM; Hon Prog; Math A; Star Student; Theater A; *CAAM Mayaguez; Chem Engr.*

ACRED, Joy Annette
Treadwell HS; Memphis, TN (4-200) F-Ed, Ann; S-T, Band; Ensm; S-T, Math C; S-T, Mu Alpha Theta; NHS; Tres, Phys C; Rainbow; Span C; Span NHS; Parl, SC; Tnns; HCt; Ntl Sci Found; NML; *U of Miss; Chem.*

ACREE, Lynn Dawson
Rosemark Acad HS; Millington, TN (15-49) Mjrte; Nurs.*

ACREE, Mark Alan
Jenks HS; Jenks, OK (10-256) Bus C; Chess C; Hmrm; Key C; NHS; Ntl Yth Conf; Orch; Order/Arrow; ARC; Sch Achieve Tm; SC; Arch; Co-Cpt, Soccer; Sftbl; Swim; Amer Leg A; COM; Chamber of Comm A; Citz A; Hist A; Hon Prog; JA A; Masonic A; Ntl Sci Symposium; Order/Arrow A; ARC A; Spch A; St Scholar; St Defensive Driving A; Ok Safety Commission A of Merit; *Tulsa U; Acct.*

ACRES, Karen Joy
Layton HS; Layton, UT; VP, FHA; Art C; Pep C; *Weber St U; General.*

ACRES, Mark Elliott
Layton HS; Layton, UT; Cr-Ctry; Tr; Ltrman C.

ACTON, Cynthia Rae
Riverton HS; Riverton, WY (20%-215) Ger C; WW; Hist C; *Central Wy Col; Sociology.*

ADAIR, Horace Randolph III
Union HS; Union, MS (6%-47) Ann; BC; Hmrm; VP, SC; Ftbl; COM; Eagle Sct; *U of Miss; Med.*

ADAIR, Nancy Kathryn
Parkway N Sr HS; St Louis, MO (35-538) Chor; Dbte Tm; NHS; Ed, Sch P; SC; Sftbl; COM; Citz A; Cl Fav; Hon Prog; Journ A; Vlbl; Straight 'A' Bsbl Tickets; 1st Cl, GSct; Best All Around; Ath A; *David Libscomb Col; Span.*

ADAIR, Tracy Lynne
Harlingen HS; Harlingen, TX (10%-600) A Cap Choir; Band; Ensm; Madrigal; NHS; Alg A; Hist A; All St Choir; All Region Band; *U of Tex; Elem Ed.*

ADAM, Barry Neil
Fleetwood Area HS; Fleetwood, PA (22-149) Band; Chess C; Ensm; Hmrm; NHS; Orch; Tres, Soph Cl; JV, Bsbl; JV, Soccer; *Computer Tech.*

ADAME, Mark Joseph
San Jose HS; San Jose, CA (30-350) Span C; SC; Var C; Cpt, Bsbl; Bkbl; Cpt, Ftbl; CSF; HKg; Most Out; St Scholar; Excalibur; *U of Calif; Biol.*

ADAMOWICH, Donna Susan
St Paul Cath HS; Bristol, CT (60%-245) Sodality; Span C; *Tunkis Comm Col; Dental Assistant.*

ADAMS, Alecia Dianne
Frost HS; Frost, TX (1-17) Ann; Dbte Tm; Tres, FHA; Hmrm; Ed, Sch P; SC; Bkbl; Tnns; Cl Fav; HCt; FFA Swtht; *Med.*

ADAMS, Amanda Alice
Zwolle HS; Zwolle, LA (10-72) Cpt, Chldr; Secy, FHA; 4H; NHS; Sftbl; COM; Yth Fel; Most Sch Spirit; Most Energetic; *Grambling U; Counseling.*

ADAMS, Bonnie Lynn
Kansas City Christian HS; Merriam, KS (4-25) Ann; Band; Bus C; Chor; Ensm; NHS; Sch P; Sftbl; Tnns; Tr; COM; Citz A; Type A; Yth Fel; All Sch Bus, Shorthand, Mus, A's; Vlbl; 1st Pl, St Mus Competition; Semi-Fin, Ntl Mus Competition.

ADAMS, Brenda Joyce
E Central HS; Tulsa, OK (201-614) Chor; Drama; FHA; Hmrm; ARC; Thes; Sftbl; Swim; Hon Prog; *NE Okla A&M.*

ADAMS, Brenda Sue
E Buchanan HS; Gower, MO; Band; BC; Chor; Drama; FHA; FTA; S-T, NFL; ARC; Spch C; Amer Leg Orator A; Spch A; Type A.

ADAMS, Bruce Hadley
Classicol HS; Springfield, MA (251-518) Band; Ensm; Orch; Sch P; *Dean Jr Col; Correction.*

ADAMS, Carmen Angela
Trenton Central HS; Trenton, NJ; Drama; Hmrm; Ntl Yth Conf; Delta Sigma Theta A; Hon Prog; Yth Fel; VP, Delta Tns; VP, Debutants; *Journ.*

ADAMS, Carol Jean
Martinsville HS; Martinsville, VA (2-277) A-Ed, Ann; Drama; NHS; Bausch & Lomb A; HCt; Hon Prog; I Dare You; Sal; 1st Cl, GSct; *Va Polytechnical Inst; Chem.*

ADAMS, Catherine Elaine
Sterling Heights HS; Sterling Heights, MI (101-801) A Cap Choir; Cpt, Chldr; MVP, Chor; Drama; Ensm; Hmrm; Madrigal; SC; MLS; Most Out; Swtht; *Mus.*

ADAMS, Charles III
Cartersville HS; Cartersville, GA (14-156) BC; FTA; Hmrm; Secy, Key C; Mu Alpha Theta; Order/Arrow; Sci C; SC; Pres, Jr Cl; Ftbl; Tr; Mayor, Civics Yth Day; Eagle Sct; *Auburn U; Engr.*

ADAMS, Cheryl Anne
Brighton HS; Salt Lake City, UT (122-800) Dbte Tm.

ADAMS, Cheryl Lynn
N College Hill HS; Cincinnati, OH (1-160) Cpt, Chldr; Hmrm; Tres, NHS; Span C; SC; COM; Yth Fel; City Chor; Chldr A; HR; Pep C; Poster A; Top Pl Voice, Mus Contest; *Journ.*

ADAMS, Cheryl Monica Maria
Woodham HS; Pensacola, FL (24-530) Ann; BC; Hon Prog; *Pensacola Jr Col; Dental Hygiene.*

ADAMS, Cindy Denise
Rossville Comp HS; Rossville, GA (3-212) Ann; Secy, BC; Y-Tns; Alg A; COM; Gov Honor Prog; Hist A; Hon Prog; Star Student; Yth Fel; Presbyterian Col Jr Fellow; Pep C; Soc Stu A; Page St Leg; Pom Pom Sq; Eng A; Millers Tn Board; Beta C Outst Sr; Seekers Yth Choir; *Dalton Jr Col; Bus Adm.*

ADAMS, Colby Susan
Boston Latin Acad Sch; Dorchester, MA (88-176) Chor; Dbte Tm; Drama; Hmrm; Bus Mgr, Lit Mag; Bsbl; COM; Hist A; NEDT; Candystriper; Sailing; Art As; *Middlebury Col; Eng.*

ADAMS, Craig Alan
Denver S HS; Denver, CO (54-550) Demolay; Ski C; Ftbl; Cpt, Wrest; Ntl Coun of Teachers of Eng A.

ADAMS, Cynthia Jean
Wilburton HS; Wilburton, OK (10-60) Ann; Drama; FHA; FTA; Spch C; St Hon Soc; Win, Rural Elec Essay; Superintendent's HR; *E Okla St U; Elem Ed.*

ADAMS, Daniel Edward
Cache HS; Cache, OK; VP, Band; Tres, BC; VP, Jr Cl; Tres, Soph Cl; Bsbl; Co-Cpt, Bkbl; Ftbl; Tr; Alg A; Hist A; Sci A; Star Student; WW; Secy of St A; Top 10, Band; *Camron U; Aerodynamics.*

ADAMS, Dari
Burbank HS; Burbank, CA; AFS; Citz A; *Pierce Junior; Fine Arts.*

ADAMS, David Ray
Cache HS; Cache, OK; Band; Ensm; Orch; ARC; Bsbl; Bkbl; Ftbl; Swim; Tnns; Tr; Wrest; Sci A; Band Top 10; *SW Okla U; Band.*

ADAMS, Debbie Lynn
Wheeler Co HS; Alamo, GA (5-79) Secy, BC; Chldr; Chor; Drama; Ensm; Pres, FBLA; NHS; Secy, Y-Tns; Hon Prog; Sportsmanship A; Top Ten, Pageant; Yth Rep, District Baptist; *Optometry.*

ADAMS, Deborah Sue
Wood River-E Alton HS; Wood River, IL (18-313) A Cap Choir; Band; Chor; Ensm; Hmrm; A-Ed, Sch P; Tnns; Yth for Christ; Big Sisters.

ADAMS, Debra Ann
Morton Jr-Sr HS; Morton, WA (7-38) AFS; CYO; Chor; Ensm; Fr C; FHA; FNA; FTA; Secy, NHS; Bkbl; MVP, Tnns; Mgr, Tr; *Seattle U; Ed.*

ADAMS, Debra Jan
Science Hill HS; Johnson City, TN; A Cap Choir; Band; VP, SC; Bible Bowl Tm; *E Tenn St U; Nurs.*

ADAMS, Dexter Cornelius
Weequahie HS; Newark, NJ (219-749) Ed, Ann; Band; Chess C; Hmrm; SC; Up Bound; Val; All City Band; Yth Against Drugs; Upward Bound; *Fla A&M Col; Mus Ed.*

ADAMS, Freddie Lee
Center HS; Center, TX (11-157) A Cap Choir; F-Ed, Ann; Fr C; FHA; FTA; NHS; Rainbow; Sch Achieve Tm; A-Ed, Sch P; SC; Journ A; Type A; *E Tex Baptist Col; Eng.*

ADAMS, Gail Ann
Sci Hill HS; Johnson City, TN (44-442) A Cap Choir; Chor; Pres, Lat C; Bible Bowl; Lat Silver Key; All-Star Bible Bowl Tm Trophies; *Milligan Col; Med.*

ADAMS, Georgia LaVerne
Carlmont HS; Belmont, CA; Cl Fav; Miss Saint John Qn; *U of Southern Col; Prof Model.*

ADAMS, Glen Phillip
Cherry Hill HS W; Cherry Hill, NJ (225-700) Band; Bus Mgr, Ski C; JV, Cr-Ctry; JV, Tr; Pres A; Most Dedicated Diver; Arrow of Flight; *Ozark Bible Col; Theology.*

ADAMS, Gregory Bryant
Sequoyah HS; Clarmore, OK (1-68) Alg A; Math A; Val.

ADAMS, Holly Ann
Columbia HS; Richland, WA (100-450) NHS; COM; Hon Prog; NEDT; People- to-People Stu Ambassador; *Elem.*

ADAMS, James Griffin
Decatur HS; Decatur, AL (80-420) Fr C; Key C; *U of Ala; Med.*

ADAMS, James Robert
Haynesville HS; Haynesville, LA (18-49) Bus Mgr, Sch P; Spch C; Tres, Sr Cl; Ftbl; Cl Fav; *Northeast La U; Building Construction.*

ADAMS, Jayme Leigh
Justin F Kimball HS; Dallas, TX; Fin, A Cap Choir; Chor; Ensm; Secy, Hmrm; Secy, SC; Yth Fel; Yth Leg; Musicals; *Texas Tech; Interior Design.*

ADAMS, Jeri Lee
Lake Wales Sr HS; Lake Wales, FL (10%-327) A Cap Choir; Band; Chor; Ensm; GS; Hmrm; Pres, ARC; Span C; SC; Sftbl; COM; Hon Prog; Phys Fitness; *Fla Mem Col; Math.*

ADAMS, Jerie Lynn
Sulphur HS; Sulphur, OK; Band; Chor; 4H; Band Qn; *Okla U; Pol Sci.*

ADAMS, John Steven
Hannibal HS; Hannibal, MO (50-300) Band; Ensm; Key C; NHS; Ed, Sch P; Ftbl; Journ A; Q&S A; Ch, Lettermen's C; Outst Jazz Soloist As; *William Jewell Col; Communications.*

ADAMS, Joseph David
Croton-Harmon HS; Croton- on-Hudson, NY (50-190) AFS; Fin, BS; Span C; Pres, Var C; Bsbl; Cpt, Ftbl; Tr; Wrest; Hospital Vol; Sunday Sch Teacher; Lay Reader; *Hobart Col; Sci.*

ADAMS, Judi Bettina
Lee-Davis HS; Mechanicsville, VA (4-450) AFS; BC; Chor; Drama; Hmrm; NHS; Span C; SC; S-T, Thes; Sftbl; Swim; NEDT; Job's Daughters; Fin, Forensics A; *U of Richmond; Span.*

ADAMS, Judy Rowan
New Trier E HS; Winnetka, IL (104-950) Chor; JV, Golf; Swim; Hon Prog; St Scholar; Yth Fel; Bridge C; Solo, Asst Director, Water Ballet; *Miami of Ohio Col; Bus.*

ADAMS, Karen Diane
Vanguard HS; Ocala, FL (11-350) FBLA; NHS; *Central Fla Comm Col; Bus.*

ADAMS, Karen Elaine
Choctaw HS; Choctaw, OK (10%-300) Chor; NHS; COM; Most Talented; *Oscar Rose Jr Col; Bus.*

ADAMS, Kelley Anne
Gaston Day Sch; Gastonia, NC (1-29) A-Ed, Ann; BC; Chor; Monogram; Ed, Sch P; Var C; VP, Sr Cl; Cpt, Bkbl; Cpt, Sftbl; Journ A; Yth Fel; Worthy Advisor, Rainbow Girls; Cpt, MVP, Vlbl; Jr Heart Board; Jr Marshal; Journ A; *Auburn U; Vet Sci.*

ADAMS, Kimberly Leigh
Winyah HS; Georgetown, SC; Yth Fel; *U of Colo; Forestry.*

ADAMS, Larry Joel
Crestview Sr HS; Crestview, FL (5-220) A Cap Choir; Anchor C; Chor; Ensm; Key C; Madrigal; Cpt, Golf; MVP, Golf; *Fla St U; Bus Adm.*

ADAMS, Lynn DeVon
Foothills Christian Heritage Sch; Montrose, CO (2-5) Band; Chor; Drama; VP, NHS; Sch P; Sci C; Pres, SC; VP, Var C; VP, Sr Cl; Pres, Jr Cl; Parl, Soph Cl; Bkbl; Cpt, Cr-Ctry; Ftbl; Sftbl; Tr; Citz A; God & Country A; HCt; Phy A; ROTC A; Sal; Swtht; Shorthand A; *Elec.*

ADAMS, Marcia Diane
Commodore Perry HS; Hadley, PA; Band; Cpt, Chldr; Chor; Drama; Ensm; VP, Fr C; FHA; FNA; 4H; Ed, Sch P; Var C; Scorekeeper, Tr; *Thiel Col; Nurs.*

ADAMS, Marie Anita
Central Valley Pub Sch; Buxton, ND (1-32) Ann; Chldr; FHA; Pres, Soph Cl; Bkbl; Sftbl; Sci A.

ADAMS, Mark
Florence Twp Mem HS; Florence, NJ (10-125) Math C; JV, Bsbl; Cr-Ctry; Tr; Math A; *U of Calif; Acct.*

ADAMS, Mark Aaron
Charlotte Jr Sr HS; Rochester, NY; Fr C; Orch; Cpt, Sftbl; Swim; Hon Prog; Most Improved Swimmer; *Space Sci.*

ADAMS, Mark Owen
George Rogers Clark HS; Winchester, KY (150-300) FFA; Order/Arrow; God & Country A; WW; *Morehead St U; Agr.*

ADAMS, Marvin Lee
Ethel HS; Ethel, MS (1-50) Rptr, BC; Pres, FFA; F-Ed, Sch P; Pres, Sr Cl; Bkbl; Ftbl; MVP, Tr; Star Student; Type A; Val; WW; *Miss St U; Nuclear Engr.*

ADAMS, Mary Elisabeth
Peach Co HS; Fort Valley, GA (3%-199) Ann; Cpt, Band; Pres, BC; Chor; Ensm; Hmrm; Lit Mag; Cpt, Model UN; Orch; Sch Achieve Tm; Ed, Sch P; Tri-HiY; Mgr, Bsbl; Hon Prog; Most Out; NEDT; Sci A; Spch A; Mus A; Spelling A; Drum Major; Stu Nutrition Coun; AKA COM; Essay A; *Rice U; Math Sci.*

ADAMS, Mary J
Northwest HS; St Louis, MO (3-728) Hmrm; Tnns; *Law.*

ADAMS, Mary Lou
Central Valley Pub Sch; Buxton, ND (3-31) Band; JV, Chldr; Chor; Drama; FHA; Rptr, 4H; Mgr, Bkbl; Sftbl; Tr; *AVTI; Nurse's Aid.*

ADAMS, Mary Louise
Gaston Day Sch; Gastonia, NC; Monogram; Var C; Bkbl; Sftbl; Yth Fel; Vlbl; Yth Coun; *Phys Ed.*

ADAMS, Melissa Ann
Evadale HS; Evadale, TX (2-30) Band; Cpt, Chldr; Drama; FHA; Math C; Rptr, Sch P; Bkbl; B Crocker A; HQn; Journ A; Math A; PTA A; *Lamar U; Nurs.*

ADAMS, Melodie Joy
Forbush HS; East Bend, NC (45-244) Band; Fr C; FBLA; FTA; Tres, 4H; Hmrm; Cpt, Mjrte; NHS; SC; Sftbl; Tnns; 4H A; PTA A; *NC St U; Engr.*

ADAMS, Merrill Jerome
Holly Springs HS; Holly Springs, MS (5-180) BS; NHS; Sch P; SC; Pres, Soph Cl; Ftbl; Alg A; DECA; *Acct.*

ADAMS, Michael Yong
N Nash Sr HS; Rocky Mount, NC (15-382) Co-Ed, Ann; BS; Chess C; VP, Monogram; NHS; Rptr, Sch P; VP, SC; Bsbl; JV, Ftbl; Q&S A; *U of NC; Chem.*

ADAMS, Nancy Lynn
Abraham Lincoln HS; Council Bluffs, IA (15%-430) Band; Chor; Madrigal; NHS; Thes; Secy, Job's Daughters; Demolay Swtht; *Iowa St U; Chem.*

ADAMS, Patricia Ann
Thomasville HS; Thomasville, AL (10%-73) Ann; BC; Fr C; FBLA; FHA; Tres, Hmrm; Tri-HiY; Beauty; HCt; *Patrick Henry Jr Col; Elem Ed.*

ADAMS, Patricia Mae
York Comp HS; York, SC (3-272) V-Ch, Hmrm; NHS; Span C; Marshal; *Winthrop Col.*

ADAMS, Phyllis Marie
Madonna HS; Chicago, IL (132-238) Band; JV, Chldr; Fr C; Sci C; SC; Secy, Soph Cl; *U of Ill; Nurs.*

ADAMS, Rebecca Carolyn
Amarillo HS; Amarillo, TX (194-612) Ch, A Cap Choir; Chor; Pres, Ensm; FHA; Pres, Madrigal; FCA; Mus Medals; Secy, Wrest Spirit; All St Choir; Judy Parker Mem Schol; *N Tex St U; Sociology.*

ADAMS, Ricky Franklin
Volunteer St Baptist Acad; Ripley, TN (1-14) Chor; FBLA; FFA; Pres, Hmrm; Pres, Sr Cl; Pres, Bkbl; Cpt, Sftbl; Cl Fav; God & Country A; Hon Prog; Most Out; Ntl Achv Schol; Opt Out Tn; Pres A; Sal; Yth Fel; *Tenn Temple Col; Ed.*

ADAMS, Robert Franklin
W Side Sr HS; Gary, IN (74-686) BS; Drama; Fr C; F-Ed, Sch P; SC; Up Bound; K of C A; Spch A; Most Studious; *N Eastern U; Mass Communications.*

ADAMS, Robert Freeman Jr
Thomasville HS; Thomasville, AL; BC; Ftbl.

ADAMS, Robert Warren
Sesser-Valier HS; Sesser, IL (15-48) Band; Thes; S-T, Soph Cl; Bsbl; Cpt, Bkbl; Ftbl; Outst Ath; Jim Flatt A; *Harding Christian Col.*

ADAMS, Roseanna
John Bartram HS; Philadelphia, PA (37-800) Rptr, Sch P; Type A; Ath Assn; 1st Runner-Up, Prom Qn; Bible Cl; JA Mgt Soc; HR; Shorthand Cert; Stu Assn; Chapel Chor; Secy, Yng Adult Ushers; *Peirce Jr Col; Adm Secretarial.*

ADAMS, Ross Willard III
Evanston Township HS; Evanston, IL (20%-1000) Math C; SC; Ftbl; Tr; NMF; NMS; Fin, Award Rm; *U of Ill; Computer Engr.*

ADAMS, Roxane
Living Word Acad; Oklahoma City, OK (6-17) Chor; Fr C; 4H; NHS; Rptr, Sch P; Sci C; Bkbl; Sftbl; COM; Sch & St Mus A's; Chor & Phys Ed, A's; *OCU; Mus.*

ADAMS, Sandra Diane
All Saints Cathedral Sch; St Thomas, VI (1-21) Dbte Tm; Pres, Jr Cl; Hon Prog; Math A; Debate A; *Computer Sci.*

ADAMS, Sandra Renee
Chicago Vocational HS; Chicago, IL (71-975) Hmrm; Rptr, Sch P; SC; VP, Jr Cl; COM; Hon Prog; Gym Leader A; *Northern U; Journ.*

ADAMS, Sara Elizabeth
Conestoga Valley HS; Lancaster, PA (5-315) JV, Chldr; Chor; Community Yth Symph; NHS; Orch; SC; Tres, Jr Cl; Tnns; Musical Art Soc Schol; All Co Orch; All Co Chor; Dist Orch; *Bucknell U; Social Sci.*

ADAMS, Scott Arthur
Carson HS; Carson City, NV (9-380) CYO; Pres, NHS; Ski C; Bausch & Lomb A; 4H A; NMS; *Havard U; Physics.*

ADAMS, Shafton Trennis
Gordon Jr HS; Washington, DC; Chor; Parl, Fr C; ARC; Rptr, Sch P; Pres, Jr Cl; COM; Citz A; Cl Fav; Hon Prog; JA A; Yth Fel; VP, Acolytes; Church Yth Rep; *Mary McCloud Bethune Cookman Col.*

ADAMS, Sheri
E St Louis HS; E St Louis, IL (11-500) Chldr; Dbte Tm; NHS; Sftbl; *Math.*

ADAMS, Spencer Dwight
Palm Beach Gardens HS; Palm Beach Gardens, FL; ARC; Ftbl; Citz A; Order/Arrow A; Art A; Sunday Sch Teacher; *Fla Mem Col; Guidance Coun.*

ADAMS, Stephen Michael
Greenwood HS; Springfield, MO (10-25) Fr C; Model UN; Rptr, Sch P; SC; Bkbl; Ftbl; Sftbl; Rotary A; *SW Mo St U.*

ADAMS, Thomas Avent
Westminster Christian HS; Miami, FL (50-103) Lat C; *Auburn U; Forestry.*

ADAMS, Timothy Kennedy
Newton Co Comp HS; Covington, GA (33%-507) Band; Fr C; 4H; Ch, Hmrm; Key C; Cpt, Orch; SC; Pres, Soph Cl; Pres, Yth Fel; Fin, Kiwanis A; Fin, Gov Pro; Al-St Bnd; Fin, 4-H C; Dist Clinic Band; Section Ldr; Fin, Gov Prog; *Mus.*

ADAMS, Tommy Jefrey
Forest Grove HS; Forest Grove, OR (25%-268) Bsbl; Ftbl; Swim; Wrest; Church Yth Activities; *SW Baptist Col; Psych.*

ADAMS, William Oliver
Washington Co HS; Sandersville, GA; Band; Drama; FFA; 4H; Span C; Bsbl; *Elec.*

ADAMSON, Patrick Doyal
Appalachian HS; Oneonta, AL (1-38) Ann; BC; Tres, FFA; Sch P; Tres, Var C; Bkbl; DARGCA; Val; FFA St Farmer; *Gadsden St Jr Col; Journ.*

ADAMSON, Ruth Ellen
Van-Far HS; Vandalia, MO (2-90) A-Ed, Ann; Band; Chor; Madrigal; NHS; Var C; Bkbl; JV, Golf; Sftbl; *Mus.*

ADAY, Stacy Lynet
Chanute Sr HS; Chanute, KS; Co-Ch, Band; 4H; ARC; Sftbl; Tr; 4H A; Pres A; Yth Fel; Swim Instructor; YLC; *Neosho Co Jr Col; Teaching Handicapped.*

ADCOCK, Dorothy Elizabeth
St Mary's Jr Col; Raleigh, NC (6-103) BC; Fr C; NHS; Pol Sci C; *Wake Forest U; Med.*

ADCOCK, Michael Wayne
Model HS; Rome, GA; Secy, Dbte Tm; VP, FBLA; 4H; Sci C; Sci A; *Law.*

ADCOCK, Paul Dean
Assumption Jr-Sr HS; Assumption, IL (10%-56) Secy, FFA; 4H; Var C; Y-Tns; VP, Soph Cl; Bsbl; Bkbl; Ftbl; 4H A; Yth Fel.

ADCOCK, Regina
Trinity Christian HS; Chattanooga, TN; Ann; Co-Cpt, Chldr; VP, SC; Pres, Jr Cl; Cpt, Bkbl; Spch A.

ADCOCK, Talmadge Keith
Tabernacle Christian Acad; San Diego, CA (1-7) Band; Pres, SC; Fin, Sr Cl; Tr; Citz A; God & Country A; Hist A; MLS; Val.

ADDINGTON, Chris Lee
Merced HS; Merced, CA (2%-900) Chess C; Demolay; Swim; CSF; Cpt, Water Polo; *Vet Sci.*

ADDIS, Mike Jeffrey
Zanesville HS; Zanesville, OH; Chor; Mod Mus Mas; Ftbl; Interlochen Ntl Mus; *Mus.*

ADDISON, Anna Maria
Cardinal Newman HS; Columbia, SC (2-70) Ed, Ann; Fr C; Pres, NHS; SC; Pres, Sr Cl; Pres, Jr Cl; Pres, Soph Cl; Alg A; Bio A; COM; Chem A; Hist A; HCt; Hon Prog; Math A; MLS; NMF; NMS; NEDT; Sal; Sci A; St Scholar; Bicentennial Courier-France; Highest Acad A; Eng A; Outst Stu; *U of SC; Bus Adm.*

ADDISON, Gregory Paul
Leesville HS; Leesville, LA; CYO; Fr C; 4H; Hmrm; Lit Ral; Mgr, Bkbl; *Aviation.*

ADDISON, Shirisa M
Oxon Hill Sr HS; Oxon Hill, MD; *Georgetown U; Personnel Mgt.*

ADDO, Deborah Elizabeth
McKinley HS; Washington, DC (1-34) Band; Chor; VP, Drama; French NHS; NHS; Alg A; Bio A; Citz A; Hist A; Hon Prog; Math A; PTA A; Sci A; Val; VFW A; Stu Coun; Fr A; PA; Band A; *Howard U; Med.*

ADDY, Ken Alan
Enterprise HS; Enterprise, AL (10%-400) Band; Drama; NHS; Thes; *Auburn U; Dentistry.*

ADKINS, Aimee Ryan
St Teresa's Acad; Kansas City, MO (74-112) Chor; Drama.

ADKINS, Becky Lynn
Greenup Co HS; Greenup, KY; Rainbow; Tri-HiY; MLS; *Morehead St U; Med Asst.*

ADKINS, Caldwell Gavin
Bishop HS; Bishop, TX (35-200) A Cap Choir; FHA; Hmrm; SC; Bsbl; Bkbl; Cr-Ctry; Ftbl; Soccer; Sftbl; Swim; Tnns; Tr; *Tex A&I; Bus.*

ADKINS, Dawn Marie
Lely HS; Naples, FL (5%-300) Tres, Ann; A-Ed, Lit Mag; NHS; COM; NMS; Opt A; Octagon C; *Math.*

ADKINS, Julia Ann
Dan River HS; Ringgold, VA (35-238) F-Ed, Ann; BC; FHA; VP, Span C; Tri-HiY; *Danville Mem Hosp Sch of Nurs; Nurs.*

ADKINS, Karla Jean
Bishop Dunne HS; Dallas, TX (6-50) BC; Drama; Span C; Spch C; Drill Tm; *N Tex St U; Journ.*

ADKINS, Kathryn Lynn
Falls Church HS; Falls Church, VA (300-600) Band; Church Choir; All Region Band.

ADKINS, Lisa
Kemper Acad; DeKalb, MS (8-42) Ed, Ann; BC; Ed, Sch P; Var C; Bkbl; Sftbl; Mgr, Tr; Sci A; Type A; Sr o-t Mo; *E Miss Jr Col; Sci.*

4

ADKINS, Peter John
Coon Rapids Sr HS; Coon Rapids, MN (475-650) CYO; Ski C; Span C; Var C; Ftbl; Hon Prog; Sci A; Ski Tm; Fin, Sci A; *St John's U; Law.*

ADKINS, Sharon Denise
Greenup Co HS; Greenup, KY (65-315) Ann; GS; Lat C; Rainbow; Sch P; Tri-HiY; Journ A; Secy, Hist C; Essay Win.

ADKINS, Sherry Lynn
Millard HS; Pikeville, KY (15-118) SC; HR; *Pikeville Col; Bus.*

ADKINS, Timothy
Bell Voc HS; Washington, DC; Bkbl; *Maryland U; Elec.*

ADKINS, William Harold
Santa Monica HS; Santa Monica, CA (8%-900) VP, Demolay; NHS; Bsbl; COM; Christian Fel C; UMW A; *UCLA; Aeronautical Engr.*

ADKINSON, Timothy Allen
Vanguard HS; Ocala, FL (4-350) Mu Alpha Theta; NHS; Golf; Alg A; COM; *Concordia Lutheran Col; Ministry.*

ADKISSON, Frank Mark
Long Beach Polytechnic HS; Long Beach, CA (1-601) Math C; NHS; Orch; DARGCA; Hon Prog; Math A; Phy A; Sci A; Pres Schol; Alumni Schol; Harnett Mem Fund Win; Foreign Lang A; *UCLA; Bio.*

ADLER, Beth Jane
Robert E Lee HS; Baytown, TX; Anchor C; Drama; S-T, Rainbow; ARC; Rptr, Sch P; Thes; JV, Swim; 4H A; *San Jacinto Jr Col; Drama.*

ADLER, Marie
Paramus HS; Paramus, NJ (56-581) Pres, AFS; Hmrm; Semi-Fin, Jr Miss Pa; NHSt; Pres, Ski C; SC; Type A; Grl's Singles Champ, Table Tnns; Stu Adv Paramus Ed Committee; Open Door Exchng Stu to Argentina; *George Washington U; Bus Adm.*

ADLIS, Kim Diane
Strandquist HS; Strandquist, MN (1-13) Co-Ed, Ann; Pres, CYO; Drama; Pres, 4H; NHS; Rptr, Sch P; Tres, Sr Cl; S-T, Jr Cl; Secy, Soph Cl; Mgr, Bkbl; B Crocker A; 4H A; Pres A; Val; Church Organist; Jr Ldrship A; Sunday Sch Teacher; *Moorhead St Col; Social Work.*

ADOLPHS, Darrel Gene
New Hartford Community HS; New Hartford, IA (1-32) Band; Chor; NHS; SC; Var C; Pres, Sr Cl; Pres, Soph Cl; MVP, Bkbl; Ftbl; Gov Honor Prog; St Scholar; Val; Co-Cpt, Bkbl; Century III Ldrship Schol; *Central Col; Math.*

ADRINE, Ethel Marie
Byron Jr HS; Shaker Heights, OH (70-273) Chor; Drama; Ensm; F-Ed, Sch P; Sftbl; Morning Announcer; Secondary Adv Coun; Gym; *Jour.*

ADUCCI, Elizabeth Ann
Swissvale Area HS; Swissvale, PA (30-200) Chldr; Chor; Rptr, Hmrm; Span C; Y-Tns; Hon Prog; Chldr A; *Ind U of Pa; Nurs.*

ADUCCI, Michael Richard
Swissvale Area HS; Pittsburgh, PA (60-196) Band; CYO; Co-Ed, Chess C; Chor; Math C; Orch; Span C; Var C; Bkbl; Mgr, Ftbl; Art C; *Plumbing Apprentice.*

AEPPLI, Rick Lee
Struthers HS; Struthers, OH (110-300) A Cap Choir; Chor; Ensm; ARC; Bkbl; Sftbl; Mgr, Tr; ARC A; Pres, Yth Fel; Solo, Chor, PA, A's.

AETONU, Vila Loa
Marist Brothers' HS; Pago Pago, AMERICAN SAMOA (1-50) Co-Ed, Ann; Dbte Tm; Hmrm; Sch P; Span C; COM; Hon Prog; Sci A; *Pepperdine U; Psych.*

AGARD, Garrie Lynne
Del Rio HS; Del Rio, TX (34-425) Secy, Lat C; Hist A; *SW Tex St U.*

AGEE, Linda Leath
Venice Sr HS; Venice, FL (97-420) Ed, Ann; Drama; GS; Co-Ed, Lit Mag; Var C; Bkbl; COM; All Conf, Most Improved, Bkbl; *U of Fla; Psychiatry.*

AGEE, Lisa Gay
New Caney HS; Porter, TX (25%-280) Chldr; Hmrm; SC; Secy, Jr Cl; Sftbl; Tnns; Beauty; Cl Fav; HCt; YCC; *U of Houston; Bio.*

AGEE, Susan Parker
Huntington HS; Huntington, WV; Fr C; ARC; SC; Tri-HiY; *Salem Col; Biol.*

AGETON, Timothy Sheldon
Lincoln Sr HS; Sioux Falls, SD; Band; VP, 4H; Monogram; Ftbl; Tr; 4H A; Spch A; Pres, Law Enforcement Explorers; Ch, EPA; Ntl Explorers Congress, Wash DC; *U of SD; Psych.*

AGIN, Becky Lynne
Antelope Valley HS; Lancaster, CA; A Cap Choir; Band; Hon Prog; Ch, Candystriper; Mus As; *Antelope Valley Col; Child Development.*

AGLEHAM, Montserrat Fidelino
St Joseph's Notre Dame HS; Alameda, CA (1-78) Span C; *U of Calif.*

AGLUBAT, Elizabeth Manalisay
George Washington Sr HS; Mangilao, GUAM; Ann; Tres, SC; Cr-Ctry; Gov Honor Prog; Math A; Most Out; Sal; Tnns C; Mgr, Vlbl; Top Ten; *USC; Pre-Med.*

AGNESS, Mark Steven
Acalanes HS; Lafayette, CA (40-320) AFS; Drama; Sch Achieve Tm; SC; VP, Sr Cl; Ftbl; Wrest; CSF; HKg; Regent Schol; Pres, Young Life; All League Ftbl; 3rd Pl, League Wrest; Eagle Sct; Baccalaureate Prayer; *Stanford U; Pre-Med.*

AGNEW, Charles Allen
Penn Hills HS; Penn Hills, PA (1-1250) F-Ed, Ann; Fr C; Ger C; Bkbl; MVP, Vlbl; *Allegheny Col; Fr.*

AGNOR, Jeffrey Todd
High Point HS; Beltsville, MD; Pres, Ensm; SC; COM; Ger A; *U of Md; Law.*

AGOFF, Edith Elaine
Sweet Home HS; Sweet Home, OR (1-225) AFS; Band; Chess C; NHS; Secy, SC; Bkbl; Tnns; Amer Leg A; Most Out; NMS; Social Stu, Geom, A's; GAA; *Colo Sch of Mines; Engr.*

AGOSTI, James Charles
Marian HS; Tamaqua, PA (32-153) CYO; Hmrm; Bkbl; Co-Cpt, Ftbl; Swim; *Bus Adm.*

AGOSTI, Joseph Ermano
Marian HS; Tamaqua, PA (64-177) CYO; Chess C; Hmrm; Bkbl; MVP, Ftbl; Swim; Schol Ath; *Bus Adm.*

AGUAYO, Maribel Teresa
Colegio Puertorriqueno de Ninas; Caparra Heights, PR (4-70) Drama; NHS; Sci C; Secy, Span C; UN Council; COM; Cultural C; PA; 2nd Pl, Sci Fair; Social Action C; Peer Group Counseling; Second Hon A; *MIT.*

AGUIGUI, Kenneth Cruz
George Washington Sr HS; Mangilao, GUAM; Chess C; Soccer; COM; Citz A; Math A; Phys Ed A; *U of Guam; Elec.*

AGUILAR, Cynthia Elaine
Althoff Catholic HS; Belleville, IL (45-290) Bus C; CYO; Chor; Hon Prog; VFW A; *Belleville Area Col; Bus Adm.*

AGUILAR, Irene
Kelly HS; Chicago, IL (1-689) Hmrm; Key C; NHS; Orch; Tr; COM; Citz A; Hon Prog; Journ A; Kiwanis A; Most Out; NEDT; Sci A; VofDEM; *U of Chicago; Biological Sci.*

AGUINAGA, Connie Linda
Castle Park HS; Chula Vista, CA (147-400) Chldr; HQn.

AGUON, Lourdes Perez
John F Kennedy HS; Tumon, GUAM (21-511) Hmrm; NHS; SC; Pres, Sr Cl; Pres, Soph Cl; Sftbl; Career Ed; Islander A; Stu Govt; Phys Ed; *Col o-t Holy Names; Pol Sci.*

AHERRON, Renee Catharine
The Bolles Sch; Jacksonville, FL (26-157) Anchor C; Secy, Bkbl; Span C; Hon Prog; Yth Fel; Serteen; Agape Singers; *Med.*

AHLEFELDER, Gail Arlene
Melbourne HS; Melbourne, FL; SC; Sftbl; HCt; Librarian Band; Keyettes; Band As; *Brevard Comm Col; Social Sci.*

AHLEMEYER, Beth Ann
Brazil HS; Brazil, IN (5-156) A-Ed, Ann; Band; Drama; FHA; NHS; Sch P; Pres, Sci C; Span C; Thes; Journ A; Q&S A; Scholastic A; Drama A; *Ind St U.*

AHLERS, Amy Fae
Wautoma Sr HS; Wautoma, WI (43-126) Drama; 4H; Type A; Member, Library C; Spelling A; Attendance A; *Bus.*

AHLERS, Jennifer Susan
Wautoma Sr HS; Wautoma, WI (24-101) Drama; Fr C; 4H; Thes; 4H A; Type A; Member, STOP; Member, Library C; *Lakeland Col; Nurs.*

AHLERS, Kay Lynn
Cedar Rapids HS; Cedar Rapids, NE (7-23) Chldr; Chor; Spch C; Bkbl; Sftbl; Tr; Amer Leg A; Lion A; Pres A; Type A; Vlbl; *Hastings Col; Phys Ed.*

AHLERS, Mark Carl
Audubon HS; Audubon, NJ (4-213) Ger C; NHS; JV, Cr-Ctry; *Drexel U; Engr.*

AHLERT, Gregory Leo
Southside HS; Fort Smith, AR (96-430) BS; Pres, InterAct C; Order/Arrow; Ftbl; *U of Ark; Advertising.*

AHLMAN, Richard Ernest
Geneva HS; Geneva, OH (4-250) Chor; Lat C; NHS; Amer Leg A; Hon Prog; *Ohio St U; Physics.*

AHNSTEDT, Sarah Lee
Longmont Sr HS; Longmont, CO (35-600) NHS; Orch; Mgr, Swim; FCA; *U of N Colo; Sociology.*

AHRENDT, Christine Marie
Simley HS; Inver Grove Hgts, MN; Band; Chor; Pres, 4H; Spch C; Mgr, Tr; 4H A.

AHRENS, Cynthia Dee
Castle Park HS; Chula Vista, CA (1-425) Hmrm; InterClub Coun; St Stu Congress; SC; Tres, Sr Cl; CSF; Val; Drill Tm; Pres, Pep C; Schol A; *San Diego St U; Health Sci.*

AHRENS, Lori Louise
Marion HS; Marion, IN (10%-632) Ger C; Madrigal; NHS; Camping Life; Christian Sing Group; Ger Cert; Top 10; *ORU; Special Ed.*

AHRENS, Mark Jeffrey
Central HS; St Joseph, MO (5,-575) Band; Chor; Ensm; Orch; Citz A; Hon Prog; *Mus.*

AHRENS, Paul David
Oakland-Craig HS; Oakland, NE (4-46) Ann; Chor; Pres, Drama; 4H; HiY; Pres, NHS; Spch C; Pres, SC; Var C; Pres, Jr Cl; Bkbl; Tr; 4H A; Hon Prog; *VofDEM; U of Nebr; Bus Adm.*

AHRENS, Yvonne Kay
Superior HS; Superior, NE (50-80) Chor; FBLA; FHA; Pres, 4H; Arch; Tnns; 4H A; *Central Tech Comm Col; Commercial Horticulture.*

AHRNDT, Julie Marie
Washington HS; Two Rivers, WI (14-250) Chor; Pres, 4H; Madrigal; NHS; Bkbl; Sftbl; Swim; Tnns; 4H A; JA A; Kiwanis A; Type A; VP, Secy, 4 H C; High Point A'S, Horse Shows.

AIELLO, Darlene Rose
Temple Christian Sch; Detroit, MI (3-67) Chor; Ski C; Secy, Soph Cl; Bkbl; Sftbl; Type A; Art C; Vlbl.

AIKEN, Faith Love
John Overton HS; Nashville, TN; Chldr; Hmrm; Tnns; Mgr, Tr; Bio A; Gym A; FCA; Civinettes C; Delta Gamma Beta A; *David Lipscomb Col; Pediatric Therapy.*

AIKEN, Mark Allen
Saint Regis Falls Central HS; Saint Regis Falls, NY (4-30) CYO; Fr C; Pres, Hmrm; Math C; Order/Arrow; Pres, Soph Cl; Bkbl; Citz A; Hon Prog; Order/Arrow A; *Math.*

AIKEN, Wallace Dale
Clayton HS; Clayton, NC (10-200) BC; Chess C; Sftbl; *NC St U; Elec Engr.*

AINLEY, Frank Charles Jr
Woodlake Union HS; Woodlake, CA; Rptr, Dbte Tm; FFA; Hmrm; Ed, Sch P; SC; MVP, Bsbl; JV, Bkbl; Cpt, Ftbl; Bank Of Amer A; Co- cpt, Ftbl; Pres, Boys Block W Christian C.

AINLEY, Lori Helen
Graduate of Visalia Adult Sch; Visalia, CA (13-155).

AINSLIE, April Ann
Bellevue HS; Bellevue, MI (12-95) Band; NHS; Ski C; Tres, Sr Cl; Pres, Jr Cl; Tres, Soph Cl; HCt; MLS; *Kellogg Comm Col; Dietician*

5

AINSWORTH, Sherri Lyn
Irving HS; Irving, TX (148-600) Drama; Span C; Tr; *Southwestern U; Ed.*

AINSWORTH, Walter Joseph
Fayetteville Terry Sanford HS; Fayetteville, NC; Campbell Col; Ministry.

AIRHART, Janet Marie
Hastings Sr HS; Hastings, MN (50-430) Dbte Tm; Drama; Fr C; Secy, FHA; NFL; NHS; VofDEM; OEA; NFL Cert; *Oral Roberts U; Social Work.*

AITKEN, Dennis Lynn
Wichita HS S; Wichita, KS; Cpt, Swim.

AITKEN, Jeffery Lee
Sparta HS; Sparta, IL (9-160) Chor; Tres, FBLA; Pres, FTA; VP, 4H; NHS; HCt; I Dare You; Rotary A; Yth Fel; Friendliest; *E Ill U; Acct.*

AITKEN, Mark Wayne
Wichita HS S; Wichita, KS (29-575) Math C; NHS; Order/Arrow; Cr-Ctry; Cpt, Swim; Hon Prog; St Scholar; *Kans St U; Engr.*

AKAGI, Donald George
Ulysses HS; Ulysses, KS; Band; Ensm; NHS; VP, SC; Bkbl; Ftbl; Tr; St Scholar; *Dodge City Comm Col; Lab Sci.*

AKAMINE, Lorna Kiyoko
Waimea HS; Waimea, HI (4-199) NHS; Tres, SC; Y-Tns; DARGCA; St Secy, FTA; *Central Washington Col; Ed.*

AKARD, Julie Ruth
Antlers HS; Antlers, OK (15-94) VP, FHA; Semi-Fin, GS; NHS; Sci C; Bkbl; Cl Fav; HCt; Masonic A; SC Activity A; *E Central St Col; Nurs.*

AKENS, Hazel Irene
McMann Co HS; Athens, TN; A Cap Choir; Band; Chor; FHA; 4H; Sci C; Alg A; 4H A; Spch A; Mus A.

AKER, Deborah Katherine
Lakeview HS; Battle Creek, MI (8-450) Band; Community Yth Symph; Ensm; NHS; Orch; Ftbl; Swim; Hon Prog; *Ferris St Col; Phar.*

AKER, Pamela Jo
Estancia HS; Estancia, NM (2-68) Band; Drama; Secy, FHA; SC; Var C; Bio A; COM; Type A; Most Schol; *Lubbock Christian Col.*

AKERS, Donna Joy
Deer Park HS; Deer Park, TX (25%-450) A Cap Choir; Mu Alpha Theta; Rainbow; Hon Prog; Math A; *Baylor U; Sci.*

AKERS, Johnie
Dilce Combs Mem HS; Jeff, KY (3-150) BC; Hon Prog; *E Ky U; Forestry.*

AKERS, Johnny Lee
Jess Lanier HS; Bessemer, AL; Band; Parl, FHA; Tri-HiY; JV, Bkbl; *U of Ala.*

AKERS, Laura Lynn
Waynesboro HS; Waynesboro, VA (11-210) BC; Hmrm; Lit Mag; NHS; Rptr, Sch P; Sci C; Chem A; Hon Prog; NEDT; WW; *Madison Col; Rehabilitative.*

AKERS, Sherry Denice
Wister HS; Wister, OK (15%-31) Bus C; Chldr; Chor; Pres, FBLA; Pres A; Carnival Attendant Qn; *Amer Col; Bus.*

AKERS, Steve Ronald
Wister HS; Wister, OK (4-38) VP, FFA; NHS; Sci C; Bkbl; Bkbl; COM; HCt; Acad Achv Hon Schol; Most Friendly; *Math.*

AKERS, Susan Gail
J D Bassett HS; Bassett, VA (9-210) Chor; Drama; Tr; *Radford Col; Nurs.*

AKERS, Tammy Jo
Lubbock Christian HS; Lubbock, TX; Ch, Chor; Ensm; FHA; Madrigal; NHS; Amer Heritage C; *York Christian Col; HS Guidance Counselor.*

AKERS, Timothy Dale
Estacada HS; Estacada, OR; NHS; Var C; JV, Ftbl; Soccer; Wrest; COM; *Clackamas Comm Col; Elec.*

AKEY, Linda Coleen
Haigler HS; Haigler, NE (4-8) Cpt, Chldr; Chor; Rptr, 4H; Fin, Jr Miss Pagent; Pres, Soph Cl; Cpt, Bkbl; MVP, Sftbl; Tr; Beauty; 4H A; Most Out; Cpt, Vlbl; Livestock Judging Tm; Driver's Ed A; *U of Nebr; Animal Sci.*

AKIN, Starlotte Gwen
Waco HS; Waco, TX (25%-200) Chor; Ensm; Madrigal; NHS; Span C; All Region Choir; Div I Rating, UIL Solo Comp; *McClennan Comm Col; Bus Adm.*

AKINS, David Lee
Poteau Sr HS; Poteau, OK; FFA; Secy, Hmrm; Bsbl; Ftbl; *Okla St Tech; Air Conditioning.*

AKINS, Donna Lynn
Zion-Benton HS; Zion, IL (10%-500) AFS; Chor; Secy, Fr C; NHS; SC; Hon Prog; Outst Fr Stu; *Mus.*

AKINS, Mary Amelia
Berrien Co HS; Nashville, GA (11-202) Band; Ensm; Secy, Tri-HiY; COM; Hon Prog; Top 10 Fresh & Soph; Fresh & Soph Band A's; *Emery U; Med.*

AKINS, Tanya Renee
Livingston HS; Livingston, CA; Chor; SC; Citz A; Play Ldr A; Hall Monitor A; *Pepperdine U; Bus.*

AKRIDGE, April Kimberly
Inkster HS; Inkster, MI; Chldr; NHS; Orch; Var C; Chor.

ALAKS, Kathleen Christine
Elk Grove HS; Elk Grove Village, IL (25%-550) Drama; Lit Mag; Span C; COM; Cum Laude, Rite, Span; *U of Ill; Humanities.*

ALAMO, Maria del Carmen
Antilles HS; Fort Buchanan, PR (2-118) SC; Pres, Soph Cl; COM; NJHS; Sch Ltr, Vlbl; DAHSS SC As; Drill Tm; NJHS As; Keyettes; Vlbl; *Bio.*

ALANIVA, Beverly Dolores
Nashwauk-Keewatin Sr HS; Nashwauk, MN (22-88) AFS; Ann; Cpt, Chldr; Rptr, Sch P; Bkbl; Secy, AYF.

ALARCIO, Milgrace Tuzon
John F Kennedy HS; Tumon, GUAM (4-511) FNA; NHS; Alg A; Citz A; Top Ten A; Foreign Lang A; *U of Hawaii; Acct.*

ALBAN, Barbara Lee
Westminster Sr HS; Westminster, MD (10-550) F-Ed, Ann; Cpt, Band; Pres, CYO; Fr C; S-T, FTA; NHS; SC; Bkbl; Sftbl; Swim; COM; Cl Fav; JA A; Most Out; Pres A; VP, JA; Bowl; Keyettes; Tres, Hosp Aux; Asst Ldr, GScts; *U of Del.*

ALBAN, Theodore Frederick
Westminster Sr HS; Westminster, MD (10-575) VP, CYO; Key C; Lat C; NHS; ARC; Y-Tns; Secy, Bkbl; Sftbl; COM; Swim Instructor; Ch, Secy, Bowl Tm; JA; Outst Yth A, CYO; *Mortuary Sci.*

ALBANDOZ, Carmen I
Consuelo Escalona Private Sch; Carolina, PR (4-28) Drama; 4H; Math C; COM; Chem A; Hon Prog; *U of PR; Med.*

ALBANO, Carrie Lee
Meadowdale HS; Lynn Wood, WA; Orch; Var C; Bkbl; Tr; St Champ, Shot Put; *U of Wash; Vet.*

ALBANO, Debra Ann
Riverview Garden HS; St Louis, MO; A Cap Choir; Chor; Soccer; Sftbl; GAA A; *Flow Valley Col; Law Enforcement.*

ALBAUGH, Edward Allen
Belmont Harrison Area Voc Sch; St Clairsville, OH (3-15) Hmrm; Span C; SC; *Tex Bible Col; Evangelism.*

ALBAUGH, Kathryn Irene
Derry Sr HS; Derry, PA (8-335) AFS; Chor; Monogram; NHS; Co-Ed, Sch P; Pres, SC; Bkbl; DARGCA; Adam Eidemiller A; *Westmoreland Comm Col.*

ALBEE, Lori Jean
Ephrata Sr HS; Ephrata, WA (40-154) Band; Pres, 4H; Pres, Jr Cl; 4H A; S-T, 4-H C; *Wash St U; Fine Arts.*

ALBERS, Carla Ann
Center Pub HS; Center, ND; Band; Bus C; CYO; Chldr; Chor; Ger C; 4H; Co-Ed, Sch P; 4H A; Type A; Degree Ch, FHA; Tr A; Bkbl A; Shorthand A; Gym A; S-T & VP, Lt; Band A; Chor A; Tr Carriers Assn for Jr.

ALBERS, Geri Ann
Gilman HS; Gilman, WI (6-70) Ann; Band; Cpt, Chldr; Pres, Chor; GS; 4H; VP, NHS; SC; Var C; MVP, Tr; 4H A; Hon Prog; Co Cpt, Vlbl; GSct; Fin, Wisc Miss Ntl Tn-Ager; Tres, Interntl Fellowship; Secy, Yth Group; *Valparaiso U; Nurs.*

ALBERS, Rebecca Ann
Mendota HS; Mendota, IL (100-240) FNA; Treas, Compton Luther League; Library Page; Hospital Vol; Bible Sch Teacher; *Ill Valley Comm Col; Law Enforcement.*

ALBERSON, Nancy Dealonnia
Northeast HS; N Little Rock, AR; Chor; Ensm; Bible A; Alt, Bible Contest; Mus A; 2nd Pl, Voice & Piano As; Poetry A; Spch A; *UALR.*

ALBERT, Alexander Scott
Battle Mountain HS; Minturn, CO (6-68) Band; Bkbl; Tnns; *Colo St U; Elec Engr.*

ALBERT, Anne Marie
Archmere Acad; Claymont, DE; CYO; Chor; Drama; GS; NHS; ARC; F-Ed, Sch P; Spch C; VP, Span NHS; Ch, SC; Spch A; VofDEM; Ursaline Acad Schol; Archmere Acad Schol; Cabrini Col Schol; *Cabrini Col; Special Ed.*

ALBERT, Diana
M B Smiley HS; Houston, TX (5-400) Math C; Mu Alpha Theta; NHS; Sci C; Bio A; Hist A; Sci A; *U of Houston; Med.*

ALBERT, Diana Jill
Clark HS; Clark, SD (16-66) AFS; Band; Chor; Ensm; FHA; Orch; Var C; Bkbl; Tr; Co Tn Ch, Easter Seal; Marimba Soloist; S-T, Luther League; Church Vocal Soloist; *Ntl Col of Bus; Bus.*

ALBERT, Karla Denise
Lincoln HS; Dallas, TX; Pres, Hmrm; SC; VP, Soph Cl; Cl Fav; Hon Prog; MLS; Phy A; *Sou Methodist U; Law.*

ALBERT, Susan Kerry
Le Mars Comm HS; Le Mars, IA; Chor; Dbte Tm; Drama; Ger C; 4H; Bkbl.

ALBERTI, Regina Lynn
Moberly Sr HS; Moberly, MO (13-214) A Cap Choir; Secy, Chor; Madrigal; Span C; Secy, Soph Cl; Soph Pilgrimage A; *U of Mo; Home Ec.*

ALBERTO, Angelo
Kingsway Regional HS; Swedesboro, NJ (1-136) Semi-Fin, BS; Hmrm; Key C; NHS; Pres, Ski C; SC; Ftbl; Cpt, Tnns; Amer Leg Orator A; J Bently Sci Day; *Cornell U; Architecture.*

ALBERTSON, James Mark
Reseda HS; Reseda, CA (10%-650) VP, Magic C; *Calif Tech Col; Plumbing.*

ALBERTSON, Sue Jane
Hoehne HS; Hoehne, CO (2-34) Ann; FHA; Secy, 4H; Hmrm; NHS; Rptr, Sch P; SC; Tres, Var C; Tres, Jr Cl; Mgr, Bkbl; Tr; 4H A; Semi- fin, Rodeo C; Home Ec A; *U of Wy; Dentistry.*

ALBRECHT, Arnold Arthur
Saint Martin HS; Biloxi, MS (2-200) BC; BS; VP, Drama; Pres, Math C; NHS; Sci C; NEDT; Most Outst Sen, Amer Leg BS; Del, Miss Jr Sci & Humanities Sym; Civil Air Patrol.

ALBRECHT, Daniel Ronald
Crystal Lake Comm HS; Crystal Lake, IL (32-620) A Cap Choir; Chor; Ger C; Madrigal; NHS; SAE; *Concordia Teachers Col; Elem Ed.*

ALBRECHT, Helen Melissa
Tiskilwa HS; Tiskilwa, IL (3-32) A-Ed, Ann; Chor; Ensm; 4H; Secy, NHS; Tres, SC; Secy, Sr Cl; Amer Leg A; Citz A; *U of Ill; Agr.*

ALBRECHT, Janet Eileen
Crystal Lake Comm HS; Crystal Lake, IL (30-615) A Cap Choir; Chor; FNA; Hon Prog; *Nurs.*

ALBRECHT, Michael Robert
N Kitsap Sr HS; Poulsbo, WA (4-300) NHS; SC; Bkbl; Gr Marshal; Sport Ltr; *U of Wash; Forestry.*

ALBRECHT, Richard Joseph
W Holt HS; Atkinson, NE (55-76) Dbte Tm; *Agr.*

ALBRIGHT, Allison Leigh
Hardaway HS; Columbus, GA (40-376) Hmrm; NHS; SC; Bkbl; Ltr Var; NHS; *Converse Col; Math.*

ALBRIGHT, Bonnie Lynn
Person Co HS; Roxboro, NC (6%-450) Band; Fr C; Mjrte; NHS; Orch; COM; I Dare You; Keywanettes; GSct; Explorer Sct; *Med.*

ALBRIGHT, David Eugene Jr
Hapeville HS; Hapeville, GA (34-96) Ed, Ann; Chor; Ensm; SC; Var C; Bsbl; Cpt, Ftbl; Cpt, Wrest; Rotary A; U of S Swanee, A of Excellence; Exchange C Stu o-t Mon; Christian Ath A; *Phys Ed.*

ALBRIGHT, Dawn Marie
Havre HS; Havre, MT; Bkbl; Candystripers; Royal Neighbors; GScts; *Nurs.*

ALBRIGHT, Elvin Carl
Lenora HS; Lenora, KS (1-25) Chor; NHS; SC; Var C; Bsbl; Bkbl; Ftbl; Tr; Alg A; COM; Citz A; Hon Prog; Math A; Ntl Sci Found; Regent Schol; Rensselaer A; Spch A; St Scholar; Val; *Goodland Vo Tech Col; Elec.*

ALBRIGHT, James F
Pottsgrove HS; Pottstown, PA (13-195) Chor; Hmrm; NHS; Rptr, Sch P; Span C; Sr Cl; Sci A; NMS Win; Firestone Schol; Hon Stu; Ursinus Centennial Schol; *Ursinus Col; Pol Sci.*

ALBRIGHT, Robert Harrison
Pottstown Sr HS; Pottstown, PA (25-300) Pres, Chess C; Chor; VP, Fr C; NHS; SC; *Messiah Col; Philosophy.*

ALBRIGHT, Susan Lynn
Robert E Lee HS; Baytown, TX (10%-483) NHS; Hist A; Hon Prog; Sci A; Church Chor; WW; Homemaker o-t Yr A; *Lee Col; Home Ec.*

ALCANTARA, Belinda Charing
University of San Diego HS; San Diego, CA (82-374) Pres, Soph Cl; MVP, Bkbl; MVP, Tnns; *U of San Diego; Law.*

ALCAZAR, Jose
Dr Pila HS; Ponce, PR (4-688) Hmrm; Lion A; Sci A; *PRU; Med.*

ALCORN, Jonathan Andrew
Battle Ground Acad; Franklin, TN (10-76) Chem C; Key C; Lat C; Math C; Var C; Tres, Soph Cl; Bkbl; JV, Tr; Alg A; Hon Prog; Math A; NEDT; *NCSU; Acct.*

ALCORN, Renee Ruth
Hanford Joint Union HS; Hanford, CA (15-515) Pres, FBLA; Pres, 4H; InterClub Coun; SC; Bank Of Amer A; 4H A; Yth Fel; VP, Parl Procedure, FBLA; Secy, Tres, Rptr, 4-H C; Rep, Jr & Sr Cl; 4-H All Star; Gen Mills, Shorthand, A; *Col o-t Sequoias; Legal Secy.*

ALCORN, Shelley Kay
Rowan Center HS; Hattiesburg, MS (5%-500) Ensm; Pres, Hmrm; A-Ed, Sch P; Y-Tns; COM; St Piano A.

ALCOSER, Sandra Sue
Wm B Travis HS; Austin, TX; Hmrm; Sch P; Span C; Sargeant at Arms, CYO; Best Dixie Bell.

ALCOTT, Lorraine Nadine
Karlsruhe Amer HS; Karlsruhe, GERMANY; Ed, Ann; Band; Ger C; Band Cert; *Acct.*

ALDAG, Betty Lou
Carlyle HS; Carlyle, IL; Band; Bus C; Chldr; FBLA; Vlbl; *Kaskaskia Col; Secy.*

ALDAG, Phyllis Jean
New Holland-Middletown HS; New Holland, IL (5-31) Band; Pres, Chor; Ensm; FHA; Rptr, 4H; NHS; Span C; 4H A; Vocal A; Instrumental A; *Lincoln Col; Child Care.*

ALDAY, Pearlene
Grand Ridge HS; Grand Ridge, FL (12-65) Star Student; *Chipola Jr Col; Elem Ed.*

ALDEN, Kelley Denise
Penney HS; Hamilton, MO (8-81) S-T, Band; Chldr; VP, FHA; Mjrte; Amer Leg A; Amer Leg Orator A; Spch A; Amer A; Oratory A; *Mo W U; Pub Relations.*

ALDEN, Kimberley Ann
Auburn HS; Auburn, NE (5-97) A Cap Choir; Band; Chor; GS; Pres, 4H; Math C; Sci C; Span C; Bkbl; Citz A; 4H A; 4-H Ldrship, Conservation Camp; Alt Win, St 4-H Home Environmen A; *Nebr Wesleyan U; Math.*

ALDER, Jacqueline Diane
London HS; London, OH (13-98) Band; Lat C; Lit Mag; NHS; Rptr, Sch P; *Ohio St U; Elem Ed.*

ALDERMAN, Cheryl Lynn
Miller Co R III HS; Tuscumbia, MO (10-27) Ann; Chldr; Chor; Sch P; SC; Sftbl.

ALDERSON, Rhonda Kaye
River Forest HS; Hobart, IN; *Secretarial.*

ALDRICH, Allison Ruth
Concord HS; Concord, NH; A Cap Choir; Drama; Lat C; NHS; Thes; COM; Hon Prog; *Eng.*

ALDRICH, Celia Louise
Miami Palmetto Sr HS; Miami, FL (600-1800) Mus, Conversational Span Hon, A's; *Miami Dade Comm Col; Med.*

ALDRICH, David Alan
William J Palmer HS; Colorado Springs, CO (38-525) Band; Swim; Alg A; COM; Hon Prog; Math A; Water Polo; Bowler o-t Yr.

ALDRICH, Mary Elizabeth
Belmond Comm HS; Belmond, IA (34-83) F-Ed, Ann; Band; Chor; FHA; GS; VP, 4H; Ch, Madrigal; Ntl Yth Conf; Span C; Thes; 4H A; St Yth Power; *Iowa St U; Dietetics.*

ALDRIDGE, Gracellen
Corona Sr HS; Corona, CA; Band; Chldr; Tr; Pres, MYF; Jobs Daughters; Gym; *Cal-Poly at Pomona; Sci.*

ALDRIDGE, Jeff Gene
Lemon-Monroe HS; Monroe, OH; Arch; JV, Ftbl; Golf; Wrest; Citz A; Yth Fel; *Wildlife.*

ALDRIDGE, Jesse Philmore
Independence HS; Charlotte, NC; Fr C; Tr; *Engr.*

ALDRIDGE, Leslie Gerhard
Bloomington HS; Bloomington, IL; Chor; Spch C; Barbershop Singer; *Ill St U; Jet Pilot.*

ALDRIDGE, Lori Lynn
Greenon HS; Springfield, OH (115-320) FHA; Tres, Rainbow; Ski C; Yth Fel; *Interior Design.*

ALDRIDGE, Mark Donald
Lemon-Monroe HS; Monroe, OH (25%-375) SC; JV, Bkbl; Cr-Ctry; Tr; Citz A.

ALDRIDGE, Michael Dewayne
Wayne Co HS; Jesup, GA (5%-450) Hmrm; F-Ed, Sch P; Parl, Span C; SC; Bkbl; Ftbl; Tr; Hon Prog; Nom, Gov Honor Prog; Sgt-At-Arms; *U of Ga; Med.*

ALDRIDGE, Robert Allen Jr
Western Guilford Sr HS; Greensboro, NC; BC; Sch P; Mgr, Tr; JA A; Newspaper Staff; *Math.*

ALEGRE, David Max
Prescott HS; Prescott, AZ (17-450) BS; Chess C; Key C; NHS; Span C; Pres, SC; Var C; Cr-Ctry; Tr; Mgr, Wrest; Hon Prog; MLS; ROTC A; Eng Lit A; *US Military Acad; Engr.*

ALEGRIA, Anselmo A
Edward R Murrow HS; Brooklyn, NY; *Law.*

ALEKNA, John Norman
Don Bosco Tech HS; Boston, MA (5-177) CYO; VP, Hmrm; Ski C; SC; Swim; Hon Prog; *Harvard U; Bus.*

ALEMAN, Gladys Higdalia
Consuelo Escalona Private Sch; Carolina, PR (3-56) Ch, CYO; Co-Cpt, Chldr; Chor; Drama; FTA; Fin, Jr Miss Pagent; Secy, ARC; Rptr, Sch P; SC; Cpt, Swim; Bio A; COM; Hon Prog; Magna Cum Laude; Sci A; Ldrship Medal; Hon Medals; *De Paul U; Chem.*

ALEMANY, Edgard
Lola Rodriguez de Tio; San German, PR (30-300) CYO; Chor; Pres, Hmrm; COM; Masonic A; Cooperation A; Art A; High Hon; Western Sci Fair; *Col Agr de Mayaguez; Phar.*

ALEMAR, Jose Ramon
Central HS; Santurce, PR; FBLA; Bsbl; Bkbl; JA A; Math A; Sci A; Star Student; *U of Puerto Rico; Phar.*

ALEN, Maria Elena
Colegio Espiritu Santo; Hato Rey, PR (14-96) Ed, Ann; Secy, NHS; A-Ed, Sch P; Secy, Spch C; Tres, SC; Semi-Fin, Tr; COM; Hon Prog; Spch A; *Lafayette Col; Bus Adm.*

ALERS, Paul Etzler
Surrattsville Sr HS; Clinton, MD; Mgr, Tr; Wrest; Soph Float; Mini-Marathon; Gold Crpt, Acolyte; Church Yth Activities.

ALEWINE, Jack Jean
Portsmouth Sr HS; Portsmouth, NH (57-505) Fr C; Sch P; Bkbl; Ftbl; Soccer; Tr; 2nd, Maine, 5th, New England, Fr A; 9th, US, Ntl Fr A; *Bethany Col; Pre-Med.*

ALEWINE, Loretta Elise
R L Osborne Sr HS; Marietta, GA (2-400) Band; VP, BC; Community Yth Symph; Ensm; Lat C; NHS; Orch; COM; Citz A; Cl Fav; H of F; Magna Cum Laude; Most Out; Sal; Star Student; Summa Cum Laude; Cpt, Rifle Corp; Sr o-t Mo; *Berry Col; Mus.*

ALEWINE, Marianne Elizabeth
Riverside HS; Greer, SC (10-214) BC; Chldr; Chor; Pres, Hmrm; Span C; Graduation Marshall.

ALEXAKOS, George Leo
Robinson HS; San Juan, PR (7-37) NHS; VP, Sr Cl; Pres, Soph Cl; Bsbl; Bkbl; Mgr, Ftbl; Soccer; *Dartmouth U; Bus.*

ALEXANDER, Adrienne Colleen
Great Bridge HS; Chesapeake, VA; Chor; Lit Mag; Madrigal; Sch P; All City Chor; All Regional Choir; 1st Perfect Score, All Reg Chor Aud; NCIE Schol; Win, Norfolk Comm; *Norfolk St Col; Mus.*

ALEXANDER, Ann Lynette
N Daviess HS; Elnora, IN (2-100) BC; Chor; Lat C; NHS; Sch P; S-T, Soph Cl; Sal; Social Stu, Eng, A's; *Lincoln Christian Col; Christian Ed.*

ALEXANDER, Anthony
Monticello HS; Monticello, MS (8-130) BC; Hmrm; SC; *Jackson St U; Med.*

ALEXANDER, Brenda Joy
Farmington Sr HS; Farmington, MO (43-269) Band; Chor; FNA; 4H; Mjrte; Candystriper; *Med.*

ALEXANDER, Carla Belle
William Brown HS; Sturgis, SD (32-214) A Cap Choir; Chor; Drama; NHS; Thes; COM; Drama A; *Jamestown Col.*

ALEXANDER, Carmen Patrice
Southwest HS; Atlanta, GA; BC; Dbte Tm; Pres, Hmrm; Math C; Mu Alpha Theta; NHS; Bkbl; Cr-Ctry; MVP, Sftbl; Tr; Bio A; Hon Prog; K of C A; Math A; Sci A; Essay Published; Tr A; Eng A; Sftbl A; *Phys Therapy.*

ALEXANDER, Cecille Lanne
Eastern Hills HS; Fort Worth, TX (25%-390) Pres, Band; Community Yth Symph; Fin, Hmrm; Orch; Sch P; Drill Tm; *Baylor U.*

ALEXANDER, Charysse Lynn
Westminster Christian Acad; Huntsville, AL (2-6) Ann; Chor; Drama; Ensm; ARC; Ed, Sch P; VP, SC; Soccer; Tnns; Sci A; Vlbl; *Covenant Col; Hist.*

ALEXANDER, Chris Allen
N Daviess Sr HS; Elnora, IN (29-101) Arch; Chess C; Chor; FFA; Spch C; Mgr, Bkbl; Cr-Ctry; Golf; Tr; Semester HR; 3rd Pl, Ctznship Essay Contest A; *Vincennes U; Police Work.*

ALEXANDER, Debbie Denise
Stratford HS; Nashville, TN; Semi-Fin, GS; SC; Civitan C; Tn Board; Prom Comm.

ALEXANDER, Denise
Carver Area HS; Chicago, IL; Chor; COM; Citz A; Hon Prog; *Chicago St Col; Bus Adm.*

ALEXANDER, Don Eric
John Marshall HS; Oklahoma City, OK; Demolay; Hist A; Math A; Type A; Gym.

ALEXANDER, Eric Daniel
Danville Comm HS; Danville, IN; A Cap Choir; Band; Chor; Dbte Tm; Drama; 4H; Span C; Spch C; SC; Thes; Ftbl; Tr; MLS; Opt A; Spch A; Dist Mus As; *Ind U; Mus.*

ALEXANDER, Gary Charles
Mary Brantley Smiley HS; Houston, TX (11-461) Band; Ensm; Pres, Hmrm; Math C; NHS; Sch P; Sci C; SC; Parl, Jr Cl; Bio A; Hon Prog; Math A; Sci A; Eng A; *U of Houston; Journ.*

ALEXANDER, Gay Antoinette
Northwest HS; St Louis, MO (9-652) Drama; *Nurs.*

ALEXANDER, Jan Maureen
Hoisington HS; Hoisington, KS (6-82) Dbte Tm; Pres, Ger C; VP, NFL; Rainbow; Sftbl.

ALEXANDER, Jane Hart
Western Alamance HS; Elon College, NC (12-230) Band; Fr C; Secy, Hmrm; NHS; SC; Bkbl; Tr; Hon Prog; MIP, Bkbl; Cpt, Vlbl; *Wake Forest U; Law.*

ALEXANDER, Jesse Nelson
Montclair HS; Montclair, NJ; NHS; Pres, Sci C; *Howard U; Elec Engr.*

ALEXANDER, Jill Lynn
Montgomery Co HS; Clayton, OH (12-175) Tres, FHA; GS; Hmrm; NHS; SC; World Affairs C; Parl, Sr Cl; Hon Prog; Yth Fel; JV Vlbl; Sunday Sch Teacher; Semi-Fin, OEA Qn; Top Sch Banquet; Ntl Conven, Juvenile Delinquency; Semi-Fin, Records Mgr Contest; *Paralegal.*

ALEXANDER, June Rena
John Adams HS; Cleveland, OH (20%-850) VP, A Cap Choir; Ch, Fr C; NHS; Bkbl; Tr; Citz A; Hist A; Math A; ARC A; Type A; Vlbl; GAA; Gym Cpt; *U of Cinncinati; Archt.*

ALEXANDER, Junia Lorraine
Westminster Christian Acad; Huntsville, AL (2-7) Ann; Chldr; Chor; Ensm; Hmrm; Co-Ed, Sch P; S-T, SC; Soccer; Val; Vlbl; *Wheaton Col; Mus.*

ALEXANDER, Karen Faye
Cherry Hill HS; Inkster, MI (54-333) NHS; *Radiology Tech.*

ALEXANDER, Kathy
Saginaw HS; Saginaw, MI (33%-225) Pres, Chor; Fr C; FHA; 4H; Hmrm; SC; Citz A; JA A; Pres A; Yth Fel; Pres & A, Christian Yth Fel; Secy, Church Sch; Attendance; A Board of Christian Ed; Vocal A; VP, Yth Adv Coun; *Delta Col; Bus Ed.*

ALEXANDER, Kathy Lynn
Ashbrook HS; Gastonia, NC (18-496) Band; Bus C; Chor; Fr C; French NHS; 4H; Pres, Hmrm; NHS; SC; 4H A; Hon Prog; Math A; Type A; Hon Sct; Sewing A; *U of NC; Nurs.*

ALEXANDER, Kevin Charles
Chester HS; Chester, PA; Pres, Soph Cl; Bsbl; Bkbl; Ftbl; *Communication.*

ALEXANDER, Lisa Ann
Rio Americana HS; Sacramento, CA; Band; NHS; Bank of Amer A; CSF; Pres, Rptr, GSct; Pres, Drill Tm; Phys Fitness A; Cadette o-t Yr A; *Calif St U; Ed.*

ALEXANDER, Lisa Anne
N Gaston HS; Dallas, NC (25-200) Band; BC; Bus C; FBLA; NHS; Sftbl; *U of NC; Acct.*

ALEXANDER, Lisa Marie
Dallas Christian HS; Dallas, TX (4-55) A-Ed, Ann; Chem C; Secy, Drama; Fr C; FHA; NHS; Sci C; Secy, Spch C; Var C; VP, Jr Cl; Cpt, Bkbl; Sftbl; Tnns; Hon Prog; Fr A; *Okla Christian Col; Special Ed.*

ALEXANDER, Margaret Marie
Mountain Brook HS; Mountain Brook, AL; AFS; *U of Ala; General Stu.*

ALEXANDER, Marsha Renee
Bruriah HS; Elizabeth, NJ (8-26) Tres, Hmrm; Ed, Sch P.

ALEXANDER, Matthew Quinn
Delavan Comm Unit Sch; Delavan, IL (16-54) Tres, FFA; Pres, 4H; NHS; Pres, SC; Cpt, Wrest; Citz A; DARGCA; 4H A; Most Out; Yth Fel; Sch Carnival Kg; Pres, Art C; 48 Delavan Wrest Tourn; Stu o-t Month in 1975-76.

ALEXANDER, Melissa Ann
Rossville HS; Rossville, GA (3-225) BC; COM; Math A; Sci A; Val.

ALEXANDER, Pamela Leslie
University HS; Los Angeles, CA (265-600) Ger C; *W LA Comm Col; Bus.*

ALEXANDER, Paul Garvin
Cohn HS; Nashville, TN; Drama; Pres, Hmrm; InterClub Coun; NFL; NHS; Span C; Pres, SC; Pres, Jr Cl; Pres, Soph Cl; Bsbl; Mgr, Bkbl; Tr; Alg A; MLS; *USC; Pre-Med.*

ALEXANDER, Penny Renee
Weequahie HS; Newark, NJ; Nurs.

ALEXANDER, Rebecca Lorraine
Ulysses HS; Ulysses, KS (9-125) Chor; Dbte Tm; Drama; Ensm; Madrigal; NFL; NHS; SC; Pres, Y-Tns; DARGCA; HQn; *Gulf Coast Bible Col; Mus.*

ALEXANDER, Rita Ellen
N Gwinnett HS; Suwanee, GA (15%-120) Secy, BC; Pres, FHA; GS; 4H; Ch, Span C; Beauty; COM; Citz A; Gov Honor Prog; 4H A; MLS; Sen Pro-temp, GS; FHA Girl o-t Yr; Agribus Coun A; WSB-TV Yng Am A; Qns Regent with Septer-Acteens A; St VP, FHA; Outst Home Ec Stu A; *Gainesville Jr Col; Child Developement.*

ALEXANDER, Sandra Dean
John C Fremont HS; Los Angeles, CA; Pres, FHA; Span C; COM; *Pepperdine U; Sci.*

ALEXANDER, Sharon Kaye
Cherry Hill HS; Inkster, MI (52-333) NHS; *X-Ray Tech.*

ALEXANDER, Terry Lynn
Hammond HS; Hammond, IN (118-235) 4H A; Ind St U; *Social Work.*

ALEXANDER, Terry Ralph
Littlefield Jr Sr HS; Lumberton, NC; BC; Chor; Fr C; Pres, Math C; Alg A.

ALEXANDER, Thomas Bower
Beaufort Acad; Beaufort, SC (3-38) Fr C; NHS; Parl, SC; Cpt, Golf; Soccer; Gr Marshal; Hon Prog; NMS; MVP, Golf; *UNC at Chapel Hill.*

ALEXANDER, Timothy Brown
Amory HS; Amory, MS (50%-160) BS; Parl, Bus C; FBLA; FFA; Hmrm; Span C; Thes; Var C; Secy, Jr Cl; Secy, Soph Cl; Secy, SC; Bkbl; Ftbl; Tnns; Tr; Cl Fav; HCt; Yth Fel; Yth Leg; *Miss St U; Commercial Art.*

ALEXANDER, Timothy Gerald
Stone Mountain HS; Stone Mountain, GA (108-300) Chor; Fr C; Var C; Cr-Ctry; Tr; FCA; *Mus.*

ALEXANDER, Tony Earl
Starkville HS; Starkville, MS; Band.

ALEXANDER, Vickie Denise Evans
Powell Valley HS; Speedwell, TN; Ann; Rptr, BC; Bus Mgr, Bus C; FFA; Pres, 4H; Rainbow; Ed, Sch P; SC; Tri-HiY; Cr-Ctry; Tr; Cl Fav; 4H A; Poet A; Pres A; Swtht; 1st Aid A; *Lincoln Mem U; Phys Ed.*

ALEXANDROFF, Lilliana Carmen
St Joseph HS; Jeanerette, LA (3-28) Ann; Chldr; Fin, Lit Ral; NHS; VP, Jr Cl; COM; Type A; Fr A; *U of Southwestern La.*

ALEXANDROVICH, Joanne Marie
Syosset HS; Syosset, NY; Secy, SC; Type A; Dance C; Home Ec A; *Math.*

ALEYWINE, Annette Lee
Edward H White Sr HS; Jacksonville, FL; Chor; Ensm; ARC; Co-Cpt, Bkbl; Co-Cpt, Swim; Swim A; Chorus A; *U of Fla; Med Tech.*

ALFARO, Lisette
Colegio San Antonio; Isabela, PR (2-33) Chor; Drama; Ger C; Sci C; Span C; Spch C; Pres, SC; Var C; Bsbl; Bkbl; Fin, Cr-Ctry; Sftbl; Beauty; COM; Hon Prog; JA A; Most Out; Spch A; Dental A; Tn Involvement A; *U of Puerto Rico; Psych.*

ALFARO, Wendy Gay
Tilden HS; Chicago, IL (5-408) NHS; SC; HCt; Hon Prog; Vlbl; Teacher's Aid; Soph & Jr Lrdship Conference; *Col of Tampa; Secretarial.*

ALFIERI, Michael Joseph
Browning Sch; New York, NY (5-27) Chor; Drama; Fr C; Hmrm; ARC; Rptr, Sch P; Spch C; SC; Var C; Pres, Soph Cl; Bsbl; Soccer; Citz A; Hon Prog; ARC A; Spch A; St Sebastian Ath A; Achv A; *Colgate U; Hist.*

ALFONSI, Shawn Mario
St Joseph HS; Ogden, UT (8-36) NHS; JV, Bsbl; JV, Bkbl; Cr-Ctry; JV, Tr; Tres, Fresh Cl; *Col of Idaho; Computers.*

ALFORD, Connie Ramona
Grand Ridge HS; Grand Ridge, FL (1-65) Pres, BC; Chor; FTA; NHS; Ed, Sch P; Sci C; Citz A; Hon Prog; Sci A; Type A; Yth Fel; PA.

ALFORD, Daniel Richard
John T Hoggard Sr HS; Wilmington, NC (5-24) Secy, Chess C; Chor; Span C; Bsbl; Sftbl; Wrest; Alg A; COM; Citz A; Math A; Eng A; *Wake Forest U; Mus.*

ALFORD, Kenneth Mathews
Jefferson Davis HS; Montgomery, AL (33-742) Fr C; VP, French NHS; Mu Alpha Theta; NHS; NEDT; *Auburn U; Archt.*

ALFRED, Sandra Lynn
Immaculata HS; Chicago, IL (20-171) Hmrm; COM; *Mundeline Col; Law.*

ALFT, Julie Faye
Merrill Sr HS; Merrill, WI (63-325) Chor; Ensm; Tres, FBLA; Church Yth Choir; Church Sch Teacher; Honored Qn, Job's Daughters; Yth Serv Recogn & Apprec A; *N Central Tech Inst; Insurance.*

ALGEO, Mary Margaret
Lansdale Cath HS; Lansdale, PA (10-170) Math C; Secy, NHS; Co-Cpt, Bkbl; Hockey; MVP, Tnns; MVP, Bkbl; 1st Hons; Best Female Ath.

ALGER, Lisa Gay
Columbia Christian Acad; Ghent, NY; Mgr, Sftbl; COM; Vlbl; Achv Phys Fitness; *Tenn Temple Col; Bible.*

ALHOLM, Jeffery James
Shawnee Mission S; Overland Park, KS (100-850) Co-Ed, Ann; Order/Arrow; Co-Ed, Sch P; SC; Thes; Cr-Ctry; Tr; COM; Hon Prog; Journ A; Order/Arrow A; Q&S A; Pres, Yth Fel; Royalty Nom; Planning Comm Ch, Chrch Conf; *Kans U; Engr.*

ALICEA, Alida
Yauco HS; Yauco, PR; Commercial C; FBLA; *Bradley U; Computers Programming.*

ALISON, Bruce Lanville
Arvada HS; Arvada, CO (188-578) A Cap Choir; Ger C; Bus Mgr, Key C; Madrigal; Thes; Var C; Co-Cpt, Ftbl; Tr; Chamber of Comm A; Kiwanis A; Most Out; Yth Fel; MVP, Ftbl; *U of Colo; Bus.*

ALKEMA, Carla Sue
Gull Lake HS; Richland, MI (136-248) Pep C; Pres, Yth Group; VP, Bible C.

ALLAIN, Deborah Mary
Tignish Regional HS; Tignish, CANADA; Fr C; Sci A; *Holland Col; Secy.*

ALLAIN, Diane Catherine
Northside HS; Atlanta, GA (1-330) Hmrm; NHS; COM; HCt; Drill Tm; Northside HS Beauty Pageant; *Fla St U; Home Ec.*

ALLAIN, Theresa Mary
Tignish Regional HS; Tignish, CANADA; Canadian Legion A; Sons of Temperance A; Atlantic Canada Inst A; *Holland Col; Journ.*

ALLAMAN, Daniel Charles
Union HS; Biggsville, IL (10%-75) Band; Chess C; FFA; NHS; *Farm Mgt.*

ALLBRITTON, Denise JoAnn
Georgia Christian Sch; Valdosta, GA (7-23) A Cap Choir; Chor; Bkbl; Sftbl; Ga Bible Camp Bible Stu A; *David Liscomb Col; Acct.*

ALLBRITTON, Samuel III
Great Bridge HS; Chesapeake, VA (142-349) Monogram; Ftbl; MVP, Tr; *Va St Col; Sociology.*

ALLEE, David Ray
St Xavier HS; Cincinnati, OH (1-330) Parl, Hmrm; SC; *Law.*

ALLEGREZZA, Sandra Teresa
Madison-Ridgeland Acad; Canton, MS; Ann; CYO; Chor; Ensm; Secy, Hmrm; Cl Fav; Most Dependable; *Miss St U; Bus.*

ALLEGRO, Joann Helene
Karlsruhe Amer HS; Karlsruhe, GERMANY; Co-Ed, Ann; Co-Cpt, Chldr; NHS; ARC; Ed, Sch P; VP, SC; Secy, Jr Cl; Bkbl; Tnns; COM; Type A; Phys Ed, Chldr, Hon Soc, A's.

ALLELY, Craig Martin
University HS; Greeley, CO; Key C; SC; JV, Bkbl; JV, Tr; Spch A; Eagle Sct.

ALLELY, Eric Bruce
University HS; Greeley, CO; Ann; BS; Dbte Tm; Demolay; Drama; VP, Key C; Math C; Model UN; NFL; NHS; Secy, Order/Arrow; Sci C; Pres, Spch C; SC; Thes; Pres, Sr Cl; Citz A; Opt A; Spch A; Eagle Sct; *U of Colo; Med.*

ALLEMAND, Theresa Ann
Beaver Dam Sr HS; Beaver Dam, WI (20-317) Band; Chldr; Ensm; Ski C; Var C; Cpt, Tnns; MVP, Tnns; *U of Wisc; Phys Ed.*

ALLEN, Amber Crowley
Vista HS; Vista, CA (53-780) Chor; NHS; COM; Panther Christian Fel; Yth Group; Pre- sch Church Teacher; *Ed.*

ALLEN, Amy Darlene
Big Sandy HS; Big Sandy, TX (4-45) FHA; Secy, Soph Cl; Cl Fav; HCt; Vlbl; *Pub Relations.*

ALLEN, Anna Marie
Galena Park HS; Galena Park, TX (10%-300) A Cap Choir; Band; Fr C; Tres, NHS; SC; Sftbl; S-T, Yth For Christ; Attendance A; *Houston Baptist Col.*

ALLEN, Anne Louise
Western Hills HS; Ft Worth, TX; CYO; COM; Jr Chamber of Com A; Outst, Jr C of C Pub Sch Art Show; *Art.*

ALLEN, Barbara Grace
Cameron HS; Cameron, MO; BC; Chldr; Chor; Jr Miss Pagent; VP, Span C; Type A; Phys Fitness A; Epsilom Beta; Lib Asst; Concert Choir; WW; Grls Sextet; Grl's Glee C; 2nd A, 2nd Rating, Dist Concrt Chor; *Brigham Young U; Phys Ed.*

ALLEN, Barbara Jean
Dewey HS; Dewey, OK (4-94) Band; Secy, Chor; Ensm; Secy, FHA; Jr Miss Pagent; Mjrte; NHS; Span C; Y-Tns; Chor Qn; Chor Jr Attendant; WW; *Ozark Bible Col; Mus.*

ALLEN, Becky Lynn
Dallas HS; Dallas, OR (5%-200) Co-Ed, Ann; Chor; Fr C; FBLA; NHS; SC; JV, Bkbl; Journ A; Type A; Fire Prevention Qn; Bkbl, Badminton, Ltrs; Poetry A; *U of Chicago; Ed.*

ALLEN, Bradly Gayle
Wheaton R-III HS; Wheaton, MO (5-31) Ch, FFA; NHS; SC; Var C; Co-Cpt, Bsbl; Bkbl; Cr-Ctry; Tr; HCt; Math A; Sci A; Yth Fel; *Sou Mo St U; Agr Mgmt.*

ALLEN, Brenda Doris
Plainfield HS; Plainfield, NJ (60-434) Chldr; B Crocker A; *Taylor Bus Inst; Fashion Merchandising.*

ALLEN, Brenda Lou
Rogers HS; Michigan City, IN (27-530) Band; Fr C; Hmrm; NHS; Citz A; Bronze, Silver & Gold Schol Pins; *Moody Bible Col; Missions.*

ALLEN, Brent D
Sky View HS; Smithfield, UT (6-611) A Cap Choir; Chor; Drama; Ftbl; Citz A; God & Country A; Math A; Schol A; Life Sct; Attendance A; *Utah St U; Engr.*

ALLEN, Brently Cliff
Roy Miller HS; Corpus Christi, TX; Order/Arrow; Bsbl; JV, Ftbl; God & Country A; Order/Arrow A; *Tex St Tech Inst; Civil Engr.*

ALLEN, Brigette Ann
Pass Christian HS; Pass Christian, MS (25%-110) BC; Hon Prog; *St Mary's Dominican Col; Sci.*

ALLEN, Bruce Eldon
Albert City-Truesdale HS; Albert City, IA (4-45) Pres, Band; VP, FFA; 4H; NHS; SC; VP, Sr Cl; VP, Jr Cl; Bsbl; Co-Cpt, Bkbl; Ftbl; Golf; Tr; HCt; Spch A; Yth Fel; NMS Ltr of Commendation; Star Greenhand, FFA; 2nd Tm, All Conf, Bsbl & Ftbl; *Iowa St U.*

ALLEN, Bryan C
Valentine HS; Valentine, NE (14-75) Band; Chess C; Orch; Arch; Swim; Tr; Bowl; Fin, Hist A; *Phar.*

ALLEN, Bryan Carter
Nw Cabarrus HS; Concord, NC (2%-275) Ann; Band; BC; FTA; Pres, 4H; VP, Hmrm; Order/Arrow; Wrest; Opt A; *NW Cabarrus Hs; Law.*

ALLEN, Carol Jean
Midway Indpt Sch; Waco, TX (25%-255) Sftbl; Pres A; Gym; Worker, Deaf Children; 1st Crochet Co Fair; *Baylor U; Special Ed.*

ALLEN, Carol Lynn
Chaffey HS; Ontario, CA (10%-1000) A Cap Choir; *Azusa Pacific Col.*

ALLEN, Carolyn Joyce
Percy L Julian HS; Chicago, IL; Bus C; MVP, Chor; Dbte Tm; COM; Hon Prog; Great Book A; Bible Quiz Trophy; *Mac Cormac Jr Bus Col; Stenography.*

ALLEN, Charles Brett
Battle Ground Acad; Franklin, TN (14-64) Key C; SC; Var C; Bkbl; Cpt, Ftbl; Tr; Varsity As; *Auburn U; Architecture.*

ALLEN, Charlton Reef
Belle Plaine HS; Belle Plaine, KS (15-65) Band; Ensm; Pres, 4H; Span C; Spch C; SC; 4H A; Hon Prog; Spch A; Yth Fel; *Kans St U; Med.*

ALLEN, Cindy Ann
South Lake HS; St Clair Shores, MI; Chor; Rainbow; Tres, Swim; *Dental Asst.*

ALLEN, Clay Parks
Roy Miller HS; Corpus Christi, TX; Arch; Order/Arrow; God & Country A; Order/Arrow A; Ntl Eagle Assn; *E Tex St U; Aerospace-Aviation.*

ALLEN, Cora Elizabeth
Durham HS; Durham, NC (10%-400) Secy, BC; Secy, Fr C; Hmrm; Tnns; Hist A; HCt; Hon Prog; Val; *NC St U; Engr.*

ALLEN, Craig Cecil
John Graham HS; Warrenton, NC (95-250) Band; Chess C; JV, Bkbl; JV, Ftbl; *E Carolina U; Marine Biol.*

ALLEN, Dawn Layne
Princeton HS; Princeton, WV (26-300) A Cap Choir; NHS; Sci C; *Bluefield St Col; Nurs.*

ALLEN, Debbie Jo
Breckinridge Co HS; Harned, KY (15%-207) Band; FTA; Pres, 4H; NHS; Span C; Var C; Bkbl; Outst Phys Ed Stu.*

ALLEN, Diane Gay
Meridian HS; Meridian, TX (8-36) Ann; Secy, BC; Cpt, Chldr; Secy, FHA; MVP, Bkbl; Fin, Tr; HCt; Girl o-t Mo; Halloween Rep; *Sam Houston St U; Health.*

ALLEN, Diane Marie
Spencer HS; Spencer, IA; Span C; Sftbl; FCA; Vlbl; *Sociology.*

ALLEN, Donna Lyn
Classical HS; Springfield, MA (160-515) Chor; Hmrm; Rptr, Lit Mag; Madrigal; Mjrte; Ski C; SC; Citz A; JA A; *The King's Col; Pre-Nurs.*

ALLEN, Doris Yvonne
Northwest HS; St Louis, MO (11-433) Bus C; Drama; FBLA; Hmrm; Cpt, Mjrte; Secy, Sr Cl; Hon Prog; MLS; Type A; *Central Mo St U; Acct.*

ALLEN, Earl Snow
Anderson Union HS; Anderson, CA; Phys C; SC; Co-Cpt, Ftbl; *Med.*

ALLEN, Elisabeth Maria
Columbus HS; Columbus, GA (10%-379) Hmrm; Bkbl; Sftbl; Hon Prog.

ALLEN, Elizabeth Jane
Kimball HS; Royal Oak, MI (4-700) VP, NHS; Secy, Orch; Var C; Tnns; Tr.

ALLEN, Elizabeth Jane
Delavan HS; Delavan, IL (3-55) Band; Chor; Pres, Drama; Pres, 4H; NHS; Rptr, Sch P; Ch, SC; Ch, Thes; Pres, Jr Cl; Ch, Soph Cl; Citz A; 4H A; HCt; Hon Prog; Rotary A; Yth Fel; GAA; Seventeen's Advisory Board; Amer Angus Assn; Del, Yth Citizenship Course.

ALLEN, Eric Robert
Cleveland HS; St Louis, MO (5%-663) Wrest; *U of Mo at St Louis; Journ.*

ALLEN, Fontello Ricardo
Saint Francis HS; La Canda, CA; Cr-Ctry; Tr; Secy, Pep C; *U of Sou Calif; Psych.*

ALLEN, Gay Lynn
Upper Arlington HS; Columbus, OH (85-698) Chor; Fr C; Hon Prog; *Wheaton Col; Lib Arts.*

ALLEN, Gina R
Montgomery HS; Semmes, AL; Chldr; FHA; Sch P; Bsbl; Sftbl; Swim; Beauty; HCt.

ALLEN, Gloria June
Wonderview HS; Hattieville, AR (10%-40) Pres, FHA; 4H; Rptr, Jr Cl; Bkbl; Sftbl; Beauty; HCt; Sci A; *Crowleys Ridge Col.*

ALLEN, Gregory
Dunbar HS; Baltimore, MD (100-675) Band; Hmrm; Var C; Cpt, Bsbl; Co-Cpt, Bkbl; Cpt, Ftbl; *Frostburg St Col; Drafting.*

ALLEN, Gretchen Denise
John Ehret HS; Marrero, LA (89-550) A Cap Choir; Secy, Chor; Community Yth Symph; Hmrm; Secy, SC; COM; Hist A; Opt Out Tn; Vof-DEM; *Loyola U; Journ.*

ALLEN, Gwen Marie
Evangelical Christian Sch; Memphis, TN; CYO; Chor; Drama; Sci C; Sftbl; Bio A; Hon Prog; Yth Fel; Headmaster's List; PA; *U of Tenn; Vet Med.*

ALLEN, Helen Christine
Montclair HS; Montclair, NJ (10%-500) All Amer Yth; Band; SC; *Howard U; Law.*

ALLEN, Helen Ruth
York Acad; Shacklefords, VA (7-45) Arch; Hmrm; Lat C; Sci C; Cpt, Arch; MVP, Hockey; Co-Cpt, Soccer; Tr; HCt; Journ A; MLS; *Freed-Hardeman Col; Eng.*

ALLEN, Howard Keith
Jones Co HS; Gray, GA (5%-200) Rptr, BC; MVP, Chess C; Hmrm; Math C; NHS; Sci C; Bio A; COM; HCt; Hon Prog; JA A; Sci A; *Ga Southwestern Col; Bio.*

ALLEN, James Scott
Pendleton HS; Pendleton, OR (2-285) Ger C; NHS; Ftbl; Wrest; Citz A; Order/Arrow A; *Hist.*

ALLEN, Jamie Sue
Treadwell HS; Memphis, TN; Bus C; *Secy.*

ALLEN, Janet Diane
Bradford HS; Bradford, TN (10-60) Secy, BC; Rptr, 4H; HCt; Historian, FHA; *Union U; Bus.*

ALLEN, Janice Lee
Sparks HS; Sparks, NV (14-380) FHA; NHS; S-T, SC; Tr; Pres A; *Stanford U; Pre Med.*

ALLEN, Janie Mae
S Gwinnett HS; Snellville, GA; Band; Drama; Span C; Thes; PTA Drama A; Gov Hons Nom; Regional Win, One-Act Play; St Thespian A of Excellence; *St Mary's Col; Drama.*

ALLEN, Jennifer Lynn
Springbrook Sr HS; Silver Spring, MD (40%-601) A Cap Choir; Chor; Ensm; Hmrm; Bus Mgr, Mod Mus Mas; Orch; SC; *Towson St U; Mus Ed.*

ALLEN, Jerold Wade
Lake Worth HS; Ft Worth, TX (30-116) Ann; VP, FFA; Tr; Cl Fav; Semi-Fin, Mr Personality; Semi-Fin, Most Friendly; *Tarlton St Col; Agr-Bus.*

ALLEN, Jill Marie
Science Hill HS; Johnson City, TN (6-400) Co-Ed, Ann; BC; Chor; Ensm; Fr C; COM; PTA A; Fiction A; Most Intelligent; *Wake Forest U; Eng.*

ALLEN, Joanne Sue
Melbourne HS; Melbourne, FL; Pres, MYF; Ntl Ldrship Contest; VP, DECA; Del DECA St Ldrshp Con; 2nd Pl, DECA Dist Food Mktng Cont; 2nd Pl, Marketing Research Manual; *Brevald Comm Col; Bus Mgt.*

ALLEN, John William
Cleveland HS; St Louis, MO (4%-663) *UMSL; Psych.*

ALLEN, Julia Emily
Aledo HS; Aledo, IL (10%-135) AFS; Chor; Ensm; Bkbl; *U of Iowa; Med.*

ALLEN, Julie Ann
Ben Davis HS; Indianapolis, IN (5%-1000) Band; Pres, Chor; Drama; Fr C; 4H; SC; Thes; Sftbl; Amer Leg A; 4H A; Fr A; HR; Solo, Chor; *Eng.*

ALLEN, June Elizabeth
Plant City Sr HS; Plant City, FL (375-650) Band; Ensm; 4H; Orch; Band Ltr; Lead Chair, Stage Band; Bible C; *Mus.*

ALLEN, Kathy J
Carlynton HS; Carnegie, PA (5%-260) Bus Mgr, Ann; Chor; Drama; Mjrte; NHS; Sch P; Span C; SC; Mgr, Bkbl; Journ A; JA A; Carnegie Civil C Schol; St Clair Mem Hospital Schol; GAR Schol; Silver Medalion; Vol Hosp Silver Medalion A; U of Pittsburgh; Pre-Med.

ALLEN, Kaywin
Freeport Sr HS; Freeport, IL (40%-550) A Cap Choir; Band; Chor; Drama; Madrigal; Cpt, Mjrte; Span C; Thes; Spch A; Span, Mus, Drama, A's; Elmhurst Col; Drama.

ALLEN, Kevin Donald
Maries R-L HS; Vienna, MO (20%-86) Ann; Band; Tres, FFA; JV, Cr-Ctry; Tr; Math A; Chapter Farmer; U of Mo; Engr.

ALLEN, Kevin Walter
Silsbee HS; Silsbee, TX (23-240) Ann; Chess C; Demolay; VP, JETS; Key C; NHS; SC; 1st Pl, Drafting A; Photography A; Oreg St U; Engr.

ALLEN, Kimberly
Pensacola HS; Pensacola, FL (150-450) Jr Miss Pagent; Span NHS; Ch, Childrens Church; Lang Arts.

ALLEN, Kyle Richard
Chillicothe HS; Chillicothe, OH (12%-415) Chor; VP, Fr C; Secy, Key C; NHS; Ftbl; Pres, Key C; Biol.

ALLEN, LaVeda Dianne
Baker HS; Columbus, GA; Co-Cpt, Chldr; FTA; Hmrm; SC; Most Out; Yth Fel; Spelman Col; Med.

ALLEN, Linda Jean
Lake Clifton Sr HS; Baltimore, MD (10%-350) FBLA; Hmrm; NHS; JA A; Yth Fel; A-Ed, Yrbk; Hon Soc A; Co-Cpt, Vlbl; Dance; Outst Bus A; U of Md at Col; Computer Programming.

ALLEN, Linda Lue
Sanford HS; Sanford, ME (19-260) Math C; NHS; Sci C; Bkbl; Hon Prog; Yth Fel; Bowl; Vlbl; Endicott Col; Occupational Therapy.

ALLEN, Lisa Gaye
Littlefield HS; Lumberton, NC (20-96) Cpt, Chldr; Chor; Secy, FHA; Sftbl; Cl Fav; HCt; Most Out; Type A; MVP, Chldr; Church Organist-Pianist; WW; Pembroke St U; Bus Ed.

ALLEN, Lisa Maria
S Dade Sr HS; Homestead, FL (70-820) Band; FBLA; InterClub Coun; Key C; Co-Cpt, Mjrte; Co-Ch, Model UN; Tres, Mod Mus Mas; Pres, SC; Secy, World Affairs; Pres, Sr Cl; HCt; Type A; Miami Dade Comm Col; Bus Ed.

ALLEN, Lori Denise
Woodmont HS; Piedmont, SC (33%-163) Drama; FHA; Star Student; HR; Principal HR; Greenville Tec Col; Off Occupations.

ALLEN, Lorraine
Wilton HS; Wilton, CT (51-441) Barrington Col; Bus.

ALLEN, Mark Paul
Roseburg Sr HS; Roseburg, OR; A Cap Choir; MVP, Band; Chor; Ger C; Orch; Order/Arrow; Citz A; Order/Arrow A; Fin, Band; 3rd, St Solo Contest; I Rating, Dist Solo Contest; 1st Chair of Amer A; Most Improved Choir Member; U of Oreg; Mus Ed.

ALLEN, Melissa Jane
Glenbrook S HS; Glenview, IL (10%-400) Hon Prog; Sci A; Yth Fel; Eng A; Span A.

ALLEN, Michael Wayne
Columbus HS; Columbus, GA; Band; Chess C; Mu Alpha Theta; NHS; Span C; Soccer; Hon Prog; Opt A; Opt Out Tn; Auburn U; Civil Engr.

ALLEN, Mike David
Rider HS; Wichita, TX; Chess C; Order/Arrow; Span C; Sftbl; JV, Tnns; Order/Arrow A; Life Sct A; Sct o-t Yr; Sct Ldrship A; Sr Patrol Ldr; Midwestern St U; Med.

ALLEN, Patricia Lynn
Martinsville HS; Martinsville, IN; 4H; Mgr, Swim; Jobs Daughters; Franklin Col; Nurs.

ALLEN, Patrick Albert
Fowler HS; Fowler, CO (13-60) Band; BS; Bus C; Chor; Drama; VP, FBLA; Madrigal; Spch C; SC; Thes; COM; Hon Prog; Type A; Alt, BS; Ark-Valley Hon Band; Stu Coun Rep, Jr Cl; Western St Hon Bnd; Beef-Empire Bnd; Beef-Empire Band; Colo St U; Bus.

ALLEN, Peggy Sue
Permian HS; Odessa, TX (400-800) A Cap Choir; Fr C; Bkbl; Christian Ed.

ALLEN, Peter Tyrone
H M Turner HS; Atlanta, GA; Parl, SC; Bkbl; Cr-Ctry; Hist A; Social Sci.

ALLEN, Phyllis Victoria
Sw Miami HS; Miami, FL; Chor; Hmrm; SC; Beauty; COM; Citz A; Cl Fav; Hon Prog; Poet A; Pres A; Sci A; Yth Fel; Ltr of Merit; Driver Ed Cert; Dancing A; Pres, JA; Tr & Field A; Patriotic Essay A; Service A; Eng A; Pres, Sr HS Fel; Pepperdine U; Pol Sci.

ALLEN, Roger Lee
Mineral Wells HS; Mineral Wells, TX (50-234) Band; Chem C; Sci C; Span C; Ftbl; Ftbl A's; Wetherford Col; Elec.

ALLEN, Ronald Earl
Littlefield HS; Lumberton, NC (23-98) Chor; Fr C; FFA; Pres, SC; Tr; Asst Trng Union Director; Tr A's; Asst Yth Director; Pres, Sunday Sch Cl; Yth Choir; Royal Ambassadors.

ALLEN, Ronald Jay
E Ascension Acad; Gonzales, LA (11-37) SC; VP, Soph Cl; Bsbl; Bkbl; Ftbl; Phys Ed.

ALLEN, Sandra Sue
Wheaton R III; Wheaton, MO (5-34) Secy, Band; Chldr; Secy, Chor; FHA; Mjrte; NHS; Tres, SC; Var C; Pres, Soph Cl; Cpt, Bkbl; Sftbl; Tr; Hist A; Math A; Sci A; Val; Yth Fel; Pianist, Chor; S-T, Pep C; Scholastic A; Semi-Fin, HQn; Sou Mo St U; Legal Secy.

ALLEN, Sharon B
Westport HS; Louisville, KY (50-300) Band; Bkbl; Tr; Col of Idaho; Mus.

ALLEN, Sharon Lee
T C Roberson HS; Skyland, NC (29-230) BC; Cpt, Color Guard; Graduation Usher; WW; Greensboro Col.

ALLEN, Sharon Lynn
Wyoming HS; Cincinnati, OH; VP, FHA; Cpt, Bsbl; Cl Fav; I Dare You; Yth Foundation; HERO; Raymond Walters Col; Elem Ed.

ALLEN, Shelley Marie
Hannibal HS; Hannibal, MO (158-326) FTA; Semi-Fin, Arch; Sftbl; JV, Tr; Sci A; Home Ec Sew A; Gem City Bus Col; Mgr of Fashion.

ALLEN, Shelly Dee
Hudson Sr HS; Hudson, FL; Fla St U; Home Ec.

ALLEN, Sherri Ann
Old Mill Sr HS; Glen Burnie, MD; FBLA; SC; Bus.

ALLEN, Sherry Rae
Odell HS; Odell, IL (2-45) Ann; Band; Chor; Fr C; Sch P; Hon Prog; Yth Fel; Ill St U; General Math.

ALLEN, Sidney Earl
Milford Township HS; Milford, IL (5-68) Order/Arrow; Bsbl; JV, Bkbl; Ftbl; Lincoln Christian Col; Ministry.

ALLEN, Susan Elizabeth
Phoebus HS; Hampton, VA (7-391) AFS; Tres, Drama; Span C; Tres, Thes; Sci A; Cornell U; Vet Med.

ALLEN, Susan Lynn
Dover HS; Dover, NH (25-380) Band; Pres, Mu Alpha Theta; NHS; Rainbow; Lesley Col; Early Childhood Ed.

ALLEN, Tamara Lynn
United Twp HS; E Moline, IL (45-792) Chor; Marksman, Sharpshooter, As; Lutheran Sch of Nurs; Nurs.

ALLEN, Teresa Jo
Vista HS; Vista, CA; Band; Sci A; Drama A.

ALLEN, Teresa Marie
W Jefferson HS; W Jefferson, OH (20%-140) Ed, Ann; Band; CYO; Drama; FHA; 4H; Semi-Fin, NHS; Span C; Bkbl; Cpt, Sftbl; Tr; 4H A; Journ A; Q&S A; Type A; VofDEM; Ath A; Mt Carmel Sch of Nurs; Nurs.

ALLEN, Terri Lynn
Patterson Cooperative HS; Dayton, OH (82-400) Bus C; Secy, Chor; Hmrm; Secy, SC; Hon Prog; Type A; Shorthand A; Delta Debutante; Fisk U; Law.

ALLEN, Terri Lynn
Old Mill Sr HS; Glen Burnie, MD; Tres, SC.

ALLEN, Terrie Ann
Milford Township HS; Milford, IL (2-57) Chor; Ensm; Hist A; Sal; St Vocal Mus A's; Ill St U; Elem Ed.

ALLEN, Therese Marie
Marillac HS; Northfield, IL (6-222) Band; Chor; Ensm; Pres, NHS; Orch; COM; Opt A; St Scholar; Quincy Col; Mus Ed.

ALLEN, Thomas Francis
Loyola HS; Mankato, MN (15-78) Chor; Bsbl; Bkbl; JV, Ftbl; Solo, Drama, A's; Mankato St Col; Acct.

ALLEN, Timothy Wayne
Harrodsburg HS; Harrodsburg, KY (50%-100) Golf; Sci A; Yth Fel; Pep C; Soc Stu A; Statistician, Bkbl.

ALLEN, Toni Lanese
Bethel HS; Shawnee, OK (5%-112) Band; Ensm; Secy, 4H; NHS; Sci C; Bkbl; Sftbl; Swim; Tnns; Citz A; 4H A; Hist A; Math A; Sci A; OSU; Sci.

ALLEN, Tracey Joy
Burbank HS; Burbank, CA (25-275) A Cap Choir; Chor; Drama; NHS; SC; Bsbl; Tnns; Tr; Cl Fav; Yth Fel; Gym; Pierce Col; Nursery Sch Aide.

ALLEN, Trina Lee
Marymount HS; Richmond, VA; SC; Sftbl; Pres, Sewing C; Gym; U of SC; Art.

ALLEN, Valerie Jean
Washington HS; Los Angles, CA; SC; Cpt, Tr; Citz A; Hon Prog; Los Angles City Col; Dental Asst.

ALLEN, Vivian Lee
Galena Park HS; Galena Park, TX (10%-300) A Cap Choir; Bus C; Fr C; Bsbl; Span A; Ed.

ALLEN, Wendy Darlene
Mary G Montgomery HS; Semmes, AL (11-230) Co-Ed, Ann; Cum Laude Soc; FBLA; Hmrm; SC; VP, Sr Cl; Beauty; Cl Fav; HCt; Magna Cum Laude; Swtht; Prom Qn; Lee Col; Elem Ed.

ALLEN, William Dean
Beaver Local HS; Lisbon, OH (1-280) Band; BS; Drama; Fr C; NHS; Thes; Var C; Pres, Jr Cl; Cr-Ctry; Tr; Eng Hon C; Summi Decem; PA; St Schol Achv Tests; Med.

ALLEN, Yolandra Gail
Melville HS; Melville, LA; Band; BC; FBLA; Cpt, Bkbl; Sftbl; Bio A; COM; Hist A; HCt; Swtht; Type A; Geography, Band, A's; Grambling U; Mus.

ALLENBACH, Conroad Park
Valley Local HS; Lucasville, OH (25-92) Pres, Jr Cl; Bkbl; Cpt, Ftbl; Cpt, Tr; U of Calif; Aeronautical Engr.

ALLENSO, Amina
Marshall Island HS; Majuro, MARSHALL ISLANDS; Bsbl; Sftbl; Tnns; Hon Prog; Star Student.

ALLERTON, Susan Jane
Abraham Lincoln HS; Denver, CO; Band; Orch; Hon Prog; Type A; Yth Fel; JV Gym; Handbell Choir; Mus.

ALLES, Deborah Kay
Clarksville Sr HS; Clarksville, IN (33%-192) F-Ed, Ann; Chor; Drama; Fr C; FTA; F-Ed, Sch P; COM; Co Cpt, Vlbl; Pep C; Secy, Qua Amicae Sorority; Choir; Ind U; Journ.

ALLEY, Nancy Marie
Western Hills HS; Cincinnati, OH; Tres, Chldr; Fr C; Span C; Mgr, Tnns; Mgr, Tr; Math A; Nurs.

ALLEY, Ralph Timothy
Western Hills HS; Cincinnati, OH (150-875) Rptr, FFA; Ch, Hmrm; ARC; Sci C; Pres, Span C; Alg A; DARGCA; Sci A; U of Cincinnati; Environmental Mgt.

ALLEY, Sandra Jeanne
N Mercer R III HS; Mercer, MO (4-24) Band; Chor; Sch P; SC; Sftbl; Tr; Asst Lib.

ALLEYNE, Nilsa Josefina
Rainbow City Jr-Sr HS; Rainbow City, CANAL ZONE; Chor; Dbte Tm; Rptr, Sch P; Pres, SC; Bsbl; Sftbl; Tr; Alg A; Hist A; Math A; Sci A; *Balboa Col; Med.*

ALLGOOD, Greta Anne
Lufkin HS; Lufkin, TX (20%-475) A Cap Choir; Band; Drama; FTA; JETS; Mjrte; Span C; SC; Thes; Swim; Tr; Cl Fav; Tres, Leo C; Panther Pride Drill Tm; *Baylor U; Elem Ed.*

ALLGOOD, Pamela Anne
Pineville HS; Pineville, LA (15%-300) A-Ed, Ann; InterAct C; Rainbow; Spch C; Y-Tns; Sftbl; *La Tech; Phys Therapy.*

ALLGOOD, Ronnie Lee
Shawnee HS; Louisville, KY (20-242) Lat C; Var C; JV, Bkbl; Ftbl; Cpt, Soccer; COM; Math A; *Western Col; Sports Med.*

ALLISON, Chris Louis
W P Davidson HS; Mobile, AL (29-475) Band; 4H; NHS; Sch P; SC; Tnns; Citz A; Sci A; *Asbury Col; Theology.*

ALLISON, Cynthia
Ahrens HS; Louisville, KY; NHS; JV, Bkbl; Fr A; *U of Ky; Med Technology.*

ALLISON, Darlene Grace
Columbiana HS; Columbiana, OH (20-104) A Cap Choir; Bus Mgr, Ann; Chor; Drama; Ensm; Hmrm; Madrigal; NHS; Secy, SC; Tri-HiY; HCt; Hon Prog; Spch A; Service A; 1st Pl, Prepared Verbal Comm; *Ky Christian Col; Secy Sci.*

ALLISON, Diane Louise
Highland HS; Salt Lake City, UT (10%-455) Chor; FBLA; NHS; Presidential Schol; COM; Singing Group; *Westminster Col; Psych.*

ALLISON, James Edward
Blairsville Sr HS; Blairsville, PA; Chess C; Chor; Tr; Rotary A; Co Chor; *Williamsport Area Comm Col; Toolmaking Tech.*

ALLISON, JoAnn
Lawrenceville HS; Lawrenceville, IL (36-176) Chem C; Drama; FNA; 4H; Span C; Spch C; SC; Drill Tm; *Nurs.*

ALLISON, Joan Marie
Clear Creek HS; League City, TX (25%-635) Chldr; NHS; Cl Fav; Cl VP; *Law.*

ALLISON, Laurie Ruth
Pattonville Sr HS; Maryland Heights, MO (235-895) Chor; Hmrm; Sch P; SC; Tr; Hon Prog; Acteens; Church Yth Group; *UMS; Home Ec.*

ALLISON, Linda Gail
Franklin Co HS; Frankfort, KY (60-425) Ann; BC; Chor; Drama; Rptr, FHA; FTA; Math C; Mu Alpha Theta; NHS; Span C; *Georgetown Col; Elem Ed.*

ALLISON, Selina Marie
Ahrens HS; Louisville, KY; Chor; Hmrm; Tres, NHS; SC; COM; *Georgetown U; Social Work.*

ALLISON, Tyson Renard
Kinston HS; Kinston, NC (6-330) A Cap Choir; Band; Chem C; Chor; Fr C; French NHS; Hmrm; JETS; SC; Var C; Mgr, Bkbl; Cr-Ctry; Ftbl; Tr; Wrest; Ath A; *Elec Engr.*

ALLISTER, Shawna Marie
Granite Hills HS; El Cajon, CA (10%-500) CSF; Citz A; Hon Prog; *U of Calif; Vet Med.*

ALLMAN, Tod Jay
Benson Polytechnic HS; Portland, OR (12-375) Chess C; NHS; Var C; Bkbl; Cr-Ctry; Chem A; Math A; Fin, Calculus Contest; *Harvey Mudd Col; Physics.*

ALLMOND, Steven Duane
Danville Christian Sch; Danville, VA (4-30) Bsbl; JV, Bkbl; Ftbl; Math A; Yrbk Photographer.

ALLRED, Aaron
Beaumont HS; St Louis, MO; Cr-Ctry; Ftbl; Tr; *Morehouse Col; Law.*

ALLRED, Brian J
Sky View HS; Smithfield, UT (1-611) Community Yth Symph; Pres, 4H; Orch; Pres, Order/Arrow; Ftbl; Tr; Citz A; God & Country A; 4H A; Order/Arrow A; Sci A; Eagle Sct; *Utah St U.*

ALLRED, Cynthia Jeanette
Sw Acad; Ruth, MS (4-12) Ann; BC; Bus C; Chldr; FBLA; Sci C; SC; Co-Cpt, Var C; MVP, Bkbl; Sftbl; Tnns; Beauty; HCt; Most Beautiful; Sr Maid; *Co-Lin Jr Col; Data Processing.*

ALLRED, James LeRoy
Altamont HS; Altamont, UT (1-41) Pres, Band; Cpt, Dbte Tm; Drama; 4H; Spch C; Spch A; St Champion Debator; Drama A; Most Ambitious Stu; Outst Band Stu; Outst Debator; *Brigham Young U; Commercial Art.*

ALLRED, Laurie Gwen
Pleasant Hill HS; Pleasant Hill, OR (9-122) A Cap Choir; Band; Ensm; 4H; NHS; SC; All-Northwest Choir; Amer Yth in Concert; Most Dedicated, Swing Choir; *Portland Comm Col; Optical Technology.*

ALLRED, Tawna
Star Valley HS; Afton, WY (1-100) Rptr, Band; Pres, Drama; Fr C; FHA; VP, FTA; GS; NHS; Ed, Sch P; Pres, Spch C; SC; Amer Leg A; Citz A; Journ A; MLS; Q&S A; Spch A; Val; Alt, NHS Schol; St U Poetry Contest Win; St Supt of Pub Instructions, GS; Runner-Up, Miss Teenage Wy.

ALLRED, Tish Autumn
Dalton HS; Dalton, GA (18-245) Secy, Anchor C; Secy, Chor; Drama; Ensm; Fin, Jr Miss Pagent; NHS; Sci C; SC; COM; Hon Prog; Kiwanis A; Alpha Delta Kappa Schol; Ntl Choral A; Best Female Musician; 1st Pl, Talent Show; Co Jr Miss Talent A & Runner-Up; *U of Ga; Mus.*

ALMAND, Lisa Ellen
Jones Co HS; Gray, GA; Sci C; *Nurs.*

ALMODOVAR, Roberto
Dr Pila HS; Ponce, PR (19-703) Chess C; Hmrm; Math C; Sci C; VP, Sr Cl; Lion A; *Mayaguez Col; Chem Engr.*

ALMODOVAR, Wilda A
Luis Munoz Rivera HS; Lajas, PR (3-170) Sch P; Tr; Hon Prog; Magna Cum Laude; *Recinto Universitario Mayaguez; Pre-Medica.*

ALMOND, Byron Dennis
Los Angeles HS; Los Angeles, CA; Band; Ftbl; *Annapolis Acad; Eng.*

ALMQUIST, Sue Marian
Arvada W HS; Arvada, CO (170-706) A Cap Choir; Band; Chor; Drama; Ensm; Madrigal; Thes; Mus, Band, Theatre, Ltrs; *U of N Colo; Occupational Therapy.*

ALMS, Debra Sue
Steeleville HS; Steeleville, IL (3-69) Co-Ed, Ann; Chldr; Secy, FBLA; FHA; S-T, NHS; Tres, SC; Golf; Sftbl; Cl Fav; HCt; Type A; Shorthand, Annual, A's; Hon Stu; *Belleville Area Col; Legal Secy.*

ALMS, James Elmer
Chester HS; Chester, IL (10-94) NHS; JV, Bsbl; Fleischman Schol; Hon Prog; *Belleville Area Col; Elec.*

ALOE, Lisa Frances
Our Lady of Good Counsel HS; Newark, NJ (5-77) Tres, NHS; Hon Prog; *Essex Co Voc Sch; Dental Asst.*

ALOFS, Derek Owen
Springbrook HS; Silver Spring, MD (207-619) SC; Sci A; *Md U; Bus.*

ALOJIPAN, Emily Jane
Kenmore W Sr HS; Kenmore, NY; Band; Soccer.

ALOJIPAN, Louella Mae
Kenmore W Sr HS; Kenmore, NY; Chor; Tr.

ALONSO, Steven
St Peters Prep HS; Jersey City, NJ (40-259) CYO; Pres, Hmrm; Co-Ch, SC; Bkbl; Cpt, Ftbl; Sftbl; Hon Prog; Hon Pin; *Holy Cross Col; Med.*

ALREAD, Kerry Dee
Round Rock HS; Round Rock, TX (134-286) Secy, FHA; V-Ch, Orch; Mgr, Tr; Chem A; Most Out; Sci A; Rptr, FHA; *SW Tex St U; Home Ec.*

ALREAD, Michael Lee
Evans HS; Evans, GA (10%-310) Bus C; Parl, FBLA; 4H; InterAct C; Lit Ral; Span C; Bkbl; Hon Prog; Math A; Phi Beta Kappa; ARC A; Type A; Mr EOT, FBLA; Eagle Sct; *Atlanta Christian Col; Christian Ed.*

ALSAYBAR, Norla Darlene
Glendale Acad; Glendale, CA; A Cap Choir; Secy, Chor; Secy, Soph Cl; St Scholar; *Loma Linda U at La Sierra; Nurs.*

ALSINA, Victor Miguel
Manuela Toro HS; Caguas, PR; *U of Puerto Rico; Engr.*

ALSTON, Cynthia Denise
Rocky Mount Sr HS; Rocky Mount, NC; AFS; Cpt, Chldr; Hmrm; Secy, SC; Bkbl; Tr; Citz A; Gr Marshal; HCt; Opt A; Rotary A; Yth Fel; *Sociology.*

ALSTON, Daphne Annette
Sch w-O Walls; Washington, DC; CYO; Chldr; Chess C; Lit Mag; MVP, Sftbl; Swim; Bio A; Type A; Social Services A; *Rochester Inst of Tech; Photography.*

ALSTON, Lee Ann
SW DeKalb HS; Decatur, GA (33%-400) Band; Chor; Ensm; Sftbl; Swim; COM; Band Ltr; Band Bar; Superior Ensm; Superior Symph; *Mus.*

ALSTON, Margaret Leora
Howell HS; Farmingdale, NJ (45-350) NHS; Mgr, Bkbl; Mgr, Tr; Span A; Secy, Afro-Lat C; *Lincoln U; Ed.*

ALSTON, Parenza Marie
Howard HS; Georgetown, SC; A Cap Choir; Chldr; Chor; 4H; Bkbl; Swim; *Benedict Col; Data-Processing.*

ALSTON, Rita Yvette
Indian River HS; Chesapeake, VA (20-416) FBLA; NHS; *Va Union U; Bus Adm.*

ALSTON, William Jr
Central HS; Philadelphia, PA (142-385) Bkbl; COM; Hist A; Hon Prog; Star Student; Distinguished Stu A; *Fisk U; Pre-Law.*

ALSUP, Jeana Renee
Western Heights HS; Oklahoma City, OK; Chor; Beauty; Hist A; Equipment Ch, Chor; Pres Church Sr High Dpt; Homemak A; Secy, Church Camp; Rptr-Historian, Yth Kally; *S Okla City Jr Col; Bus Ed.*

ALSUP, Susan Elizabeth
Walnut HS; Walnut, MS (10-55) Ann; Secy, BC; Chor; FHA; VP, Hmrm; Bio A; COM; H of F; MLS; Eng A; WW; *Blue Mountain Col; Law.*

ALT, Nancy J
St Joseph-Ogden HS; St Joseph, IL (39-92) Chor; Pres, FHA; Home Ec A; B Section Ed, Yrbk; Vlbl.

ALTABE, Richard Jonathan
Hillel HS; Lawrence, NY (10-46) Ed, Ann; Cpt, Chess C; Drama; Cpt, Math C; NHS; Mgr, Bkbl; COM; NMS; Regent Schol; *NYU; AB DDS Prog.*

ALTAMOS, Barry Richard
Rochester HS; Rochester, PA (66-177) Ger C; JA A; Camera C; Win Conf Quiz Tm; JA; *Roberts Wesleyan; Forestry.*

ALTAMURA, Regina Marie
St Joseph o-t Palisades HS; W New York, NJ (11-225) FBLA; Tres, NHS; Span NHS; Hon Prog; *Pace U; Acct.*

ALTEMUS, Anne Louise
Heritage HS; Littleton, CO (1-451) A Cap Choir; Chor; Hon Prog; Graduation Jr Escort; Sunday Sch Teacher; Sr High Yth Group; Nom Comm; Asst, Associate Pastor; *Math.*

ALTHEIDE, Richard Wayne
Hannibal Sr HS; Hannibal, MO (18-326) Band; Order/Arrow; Ch, Sci C; Bkbl; JV, Tnns; Top 10%; *U of Mo; Engr.*

ALTHOFF, Theresa Rose
Guttenberg HS; Guttenberg, IA; Chor; Tres, FHA; NHS.

ALTIMIER, Paul Vance
Russell HS; Flatwoods, KY (50-250) BC; Secy, BS; Dbte Tm; Pres, HiY; Hmrm; Model UN; Order/ Arrow; Parl, SC; Ch, UN Council; Tres, Sr Cl; Tnns; God & Country A; Spch A; Yth Leg; WW; *U of Ky; Law.*

ALTLAND, Robert Scott
Wm Penn Sr HS; York, PA (27-420) Band; NHS; JV, Golf; JV, Tr; *Pa St U; Earth & Mineral Sci.*

ALTMAN, Janice Marie
Sanger HS; Sanger, CA; Dbte Tm; Co-Ch, Model UN; NFL; A-Ed, Sch P; Spch C; UN Council; Spch A; Rptr, Sch P; Secy, Church Coun; Secy, Yth League; Ch, Yth Rally; Jr Cl Activities Comm; *Pepperdine U; Journ.*

ALTMAN, Joseph Allen
Estill HS; Estill, SC; A Cap Choir; Chor; Ensm; Madrigal.

ALTMAN, Nancy Emily
Winyan HS; Georgetown, SC; VP, Fr C; Hmrm; Mu Alpha Theta; Tres, NHS; VP, SC; Pres, Church Yth Fel; Tres, Jr Civinettes; Lieutenant Gov, Jr Civitans.

ALTMAN, William David
Aynor HS; Aynor, SC (3-85) Bus Mgr, Ann; BC; Fin, BS; Fr C; Sci C; Var C; Ftbl; Co-Cpt, Tr; Furman Schol; Presbyterian Schol; *Clemson U; Vet.*

ALTMARK, Alan Charles
Park Hill Sr HS; Kansas City, MO; Band; Span C; Span A; *U of Mo; Elec.*

ALUND, Amy Lou
McKeesport Sr HS; McKeesport, PA; JV, Chldr; Hmrm; Tres, SC; Swim; *Drafting.*

ALVARADO, Esther Lorraine
S Lafourche HS; Galliano, LA (25%-292) Band; Chor; Drama; Ensm; FTA; Beauty; COM; Hon Prog; Sci A; Dist Hon Choir; All St Chor; *Nicholls St U; Special Ed.*

ALVARADO, Grace Hernandez
Lasalle Extension U; Chicago, IL; Yth Fel; Yth Leg; *Midland Col; Art.*

ALVARADO, Julie R
Stamford HS; Stamford, TX (35-70) CYO; FHA; Span C; Bkbl.

ALVARADO, Marilu
English HS; Boston, MA; Chldr; Lat C; Span C; Sftbl; Vlbl; Sch Span A; *Boston U; Lib Arts.*

ALVAREZ, Betsy
Luis Munoz Marin HS; Cabo Rojo, PR (6-200) Dbte Tm; Drama; FHA; COM; Hon Prog; Math A; *Colegio de Agricultura; Math.*

ALVAREZ, Denise Margaret
Maple Shade HS; Maple Shade, NJ (8-241) GS; *Douglass Col; Foreign Lang.*

ALVAREZ, Lourdes Maria
Acad o-t Holy Names; Tampa, FL (5-68) Chor; Hmrm; NHS; VP, Span C; Span NHS; Secy, SC; Hon Prog; Star Student; Gold Scholastic Key A; *U of S Fla; Math.*

ALVAREZ, Patricia
Thomas A Edison HS; San Antonio, TX; VP, Bus C; CYO; Chor; VP, FBLA; Hmrm; Sch Achieve Tm; Span C; SC; Bsbl; JA A; Chaplin, FTA; Princess and Qn; Various Social C; Modeling; *Southwest Tex Col; Eng.*

ALWINE, Cynthia Lee
Westmont Hilltop HS; Johnstown, PA; A Cap Choir; Chor; Drama; Ensm; FTA; Fin, Jr Miss Pagent; Ntl Yth Conf; Sch P; Span C; JV, Bkbl; Sftbl; Swim; Tnns; Hon Prog; Journ A; Yth Fel; Best Actress; HS Mus; Reg Choir; JA; Sr Cl Play; Jr Cl Play; Yth Ed Assn; Children's Theater; Band Announcer; Mixed Quartet; *Hood Col; Bus Adm.*

ALY, Cathy Lynn
Pope Co HS; Golconda, IL; A Cap Choir; Band; Chldr; Chor; FHA; Ch, FTA; Pres, 4H; Var C; Bkbl; Sftbl; 4H A; Vlbl; Church Pianist & Organist; St 4-H A; Cand, Deer Festival Qn; 'A' Rating, St Mus Festival; *SE Ill Col; General Bus.*

AMACHER, Julie Elaine
Fort Sr HS; Fort Atkinson, WI; A Cap Choir; Ann; Chor; Ensm; Rainbow; Yth Fel; Section Ldr, Pep C; Art League; Redskins; HR.

AMADIO, Patricia Ann
Struthers HS; Struthers, OH (32-275) Bus C; Chor; NHS; Y-Tns; *Youngstown St Col; Child Development.*

AMAN, Janet Lee
Spearfish HS; Spearfish, SD (22-127) A Cap Choir; VP, AFS; VP, Band; Chor; Drama; Ensm; Semi-Fin, GS; 4H; Jr Miss Pagent; Madrigal; NHS; Ski C; SC; HCt; Yth Fel; WW; NHS A; Alt, St Piano Auditions; *U of SD; Mus.*

AMAN, Pamela Dian
Fairfield Comm HS; Fairfield, IL (1-190) Ann; Band; Ensm; Tres, FTA; InterAct C; Lat C; Math C; NHS; Orch; Sci C; WW; DAR Hist A; Alt, GS; *E Ill U; Acct.*

AMAN, Paula Ann
Lamar R-1 HS; Lamar, MO (23-83) AFS; Band; NFL; Rainbow; S-T, Jr Cl; Sftbl; Pep C; Semi-Fin, Qn Contest; Explorer's C; Cert of Appr, Vol Wrk; Bookkeep Cert; Nurses' Aid Trng Cer; Leon Couch Mem Fund Schol; *Nev Vo-tech Col; Nurs.*

AMAN, Rebecca Kay
Pollock HS; Pollock, SD (2-28) Chor; Bausch & Lomb A; B Crocker A; DARGCA; Math A; Val; Pol Sci A; Chor Ltr; *Presentation Col; Med Technology.*

AMATO, Stephanie Marie
Saint John Vianney HS; Holmdel, NJ (65-208) Co-Cpt, Mjrte; NHS; Order/Arrow; Co-Cpt, Tr; HCt; Gold & White A; *Montclair St Col; Bus Adm.*

AMAYA, Rosaura
Cerritos HS; Cerritos, CA; Fr C; Span C; CSF; *U of Calif; Med.*

AMBLE, Gary Jay
Iola HS; Iola, KS (90-150) BS; Tres, Drama; Hmrm; NFL; SC; Thes; Tres, Var C; Ftbl; Tr.

AMBROS, Leandro Jr
Goodrich HS; Goodrich, TX (5-30) CYO; FFA; Span C; Bsbl; Bkbl; JV, Ftbl; JV, Tr; *U of Tex; Law.*

AMBROSE, Charles Monroe
Cherry Hill HS E; Cherry Hill, NJ (40%-1100) Orch; JV, Soccer; *Wake Forest U; Med.*

AMBROSE, Steven Wayne
Lincoln HS; Lincoln, CA (1-209) Chess C; 4H; SC; JV, Bsbl; Ftbl; CSF; 4H A; Alt, BS; Pres, CSF C; Math.

AMBROSE, Susan Elizabeth
Lincoln HS; Lincoln, CA (3-165) Band; Chor; Drama; Secy, 4H; Sci C; CSF; Citz A; 4H A; *Sierra Col; Computer Prog.*

AMBROSE, William Page
Aynor HS; Aynor, SC (15%-85) Ann; Chem C; Hmrm; Sci C; Span C; SC; Var C; Y-Tns; Bkbl; Yth Leg; Bus.

AMBRUSTER, Judith Ann
Neshaminy Maple Point HS; Langhorne, PA (20-400) Chldr; Chor; Hmrm; NHS; Sch P; Ski C; SC; Var C; Hockey; Tr; HCt; Gym Night; *Pa St U; Bio Sci.*

AMEN, Bryan Donald
Sheridan HS; Englewood, CO; BS; Chor; 4H; NHS; Var C; Ftbl; Wrest; COM; 4H A; Prom Escort; Del, Civitan; *Aviation.*

AMENT, Michael Richard
Oakland-Craig HS; Oakland, NE (3-51) Band; Order/Arrow; Pres, Soph Cl; Ftbl; Tr; Mgr, Wrest; Eagle Sct; HR; PA; *Agr.*

AMENT, Pauline Frances
Oakland-Craig HS; Oakland, NE (20-47) Chor; FHA; GS; Pres, 4H; Mjrte; ARC; Rptr, Sch P; Mgr, Bkbl; Ftbl; 4H A; Q&S A; Leadership A; Achv A; *Northeast Comm Tech; Recreation.*

AMERSON, Pamela Vera
W Craven HS; Vanceboro, NC (14-160) BC; Bus C; 4H; Monogram; Secy, NHS; Span C; Var C; Bkbl; HQn; Hon Prog; Jr Civitan; Drivers Ed A; Phys Ed A; *E Carolina U; Phys Therapy.*

AMES, Anita Marie
Del Campo HS; Fair Oaks, CA (2-500) NHS; Pres, Sch P; CSF; Sal; 1st Pl, Vocal As; Gifted Stu Prog; Outst Horsemanship A; Hon Men, Art Show; Candlebearer; Biola Col Mus Schol; *Biola Col; Mus.*

AMES, Barry Allan
Hillsboro HS; Hillsboro, HS (40-220) Bsbl; Bkbl; Ftbl; Tr; Alg A; Sci A; *Mich U; Secondary Ed.*

AMES, Christine Darlene
Northern Chester Co Tech Sch; Phoenixville, PA (10%-132) Ed, Ann; Ski C; Var C; Hockey; Tr; *Penn St U; Bio.*

AMES, Tambrea Leigh
Forest Hills N HS; Grand Rapids, MI; Span C; *Okla Baptist U; Ed.*

AMICK, Dave James
Highland Sr HS; Highland, IN (109-582) NHS; Soccer; Tr; Health Careers C; PA; *Sci.*

AMICK, Linda Kathryn
NW Classen HS; Okla City, OK (171-460) A Cap Choir; JV, Chldr; Chor; Community Yth Symph; Ensm; Madrigal; Pres, Orch; COM; *U of Okla; Vocal & Instrumental Mus Ed.*

AMICONE, Robin Frances
St Mary's HS; Lynn, MA (10-146) Hmrm; Ftbl; Sftbl; Swim; COM; Eng, Span, A's.

AMILL, Dayra
Dr Pila HS; Ponce, PR (22-845) CYO; Chem C; Chor; Ensm; Hmrm; Math C; NHS; Bio A; COM; Lion A; Vlbl; Guide, Ponce Museum; Peers Counselor; Dance; *Med.*

AMIRAULT, Mona Elaine
Susquehanna Comm HS; Susquehanna, PA (2-110) Band; Chess C; Chor; Drama; Rainbow; COM; Dist Band Medal; Soph Progress Medal; 1st Prize, Drug Essay Contest As; *Brigham Young U; Pre-Med.*

AMIRI, Tamela Mina
Lorain Cath HS; Lorain, OH (1-250) Community Yth Symph; HiY; Hmrm; NHS; Orch; Ski C; SC; Alg A; HCt; NEDT; Cert of Meritorious Service; I Rating, Mus Auditions; Dist, St, Mus Competition; *Case Western Reserve U; Med.*

AMMALA, Darwin Edward
McGregor HS; McGregor, MN (4-72) 4H; NHS; Sch P; Sci C; SC; Var C; Mgr, Bkbl; Tr; 4H A; *UMD; Acct.*

AMMENTORP, Wayne Joel
William Howard Taft HS; Chicago, IL (58-810) Bus Mgr, Hmrm; Bkbl; Sftbl; COM; Hon Prog; NEDT; Span A; Hon C; Leader Church Yth; Church Yth Singing Group; *U of Ill; Archt.*

AMMESON, Carol Ann
Williams Bay HS; Williams Bay, WI (2-45) Bus Mgr, Ann; Band; Cpt, Chldr; VP, Chor; Dbte Tm; Drama; Ensm; 4H; Madrigal; Mjrte; NFL; VP, NHS; VP, Rainbow; Sch P; Ski C; VP, Soph Cl; MVP, Bkbl; Sftbl; Bio A; 4H A; Hon Prog; MLS; Most Out; Cpt, Bkbl; Hon Men, Vlbl; Cpt, Vlbl; All Conf, Bkbl; MVP, Bowl; Alt, GS; *Moody Bible Inst; Christian Ed.*

AMMONS, Dawn Marie
Norman Thomas HS For Comm Ed; New York, NY; NHS; COM; Hon Prog; *Pace U; Acct.*

AMMONS, Janice Marie
W Mecklenburg HS; Charlotte, NC; Rptr, Ann; Chor; Drama; Hmrm; InterAct C; ARC; Ski C; Span C; SC; Mgr, Soccer; Sftbl; Yth Fel; 1st Cl Sct; *Interior Design.*

AMMONS, Walter Logan
Sam Rayburn HS; Pasadena, TX (250-575) Band; S-T, Demolay; FFA; Tnns; Cpt, Bowl; *San Jacinto Col; Acct.*

AMOND, Hermud
Emmaus HS; Koror, PALAU, WESTERN CAROLINE ISLANDS (3-13) A Cap Choir; Chem C; Math C; Bkbl; Hon Prog.

AMORE, Vicky Kay
Utica Sr HS; Utica, OH (145-200) Chor; Sftbl; Most Out; Yth Fel; Organ A; Table Tennis A; *Mount Vernon Nazarene Col; Mus.*

AMORUSO, Patricia Joanne
John Adams HS; Ozone Park, NY (2-1076) Chor; Ed, Lit Mag; Secy, Math C; NHS; F-Ed, Sch P; Secy, SC; COM; Citz A; Regent Schol; Val; Fr Medal; Service Medal; *Eng.*

AMOS, Albert Lynn
Walnut Hills HS; Cincinnati, OH (33%-440).

AMOS, Gena Renee
Independence Sr HS; Charlotte, NC (65-647)
Band; Ensm; Fr C; FTA; NHS; Hon Prog; Color-
guard; Fine Arts Hon Soc; Band Director's Ldrship
A; WW; *U of Pittsburgh; Nurs.*

AMOS, Richard Glenn
Penncrest HS; Media, PA (10-473) A Cap Choir;
Chor; Hmmr; Madrigal; Mu Alpha Theta; SC; VP,
Soph Cl; JV, Soccer; Swim; Amer Leg A; MLS;
Most Out; *Duke U; Med.*

AMOS, Richard William
Virgil I Grissom HS; Huntsville, AL (10%-610)
Band; Key C; Hon Prog; NEDT; Yth Fel; Jr NHS;
Church Choir; Jazz Band; *Auburn U; Engr.*

AMOTH, Julie Kay
Willows HS; Willows, CA (6-148).

AMRHEIN, Charlotte Grace
Westminster Sr HS; Westminster, MD (10%-600)
Ed, Ann; Band; Co-Ch, CYO; Lat C; NHS; Sftbl;
Med.

AMRHEIN, Michele Rose
Westminster Sr HS; Westminster, MD; Ed, Ann;
Secy, CYO; Chor; NHS; COM; *Elem Ed.*

AMSTUTZ, Amy Ruth
Lake Highlands HS; Dallas, TX (65-694) Hmrm;
A-Ed, Lit Mag; VP, Math C; Mu Alpha Theta;
NHS; Y-Tns; Hon Prog; Math A; U of TX, Sum-
mer Research Prog; *Tex A&M U; Chem.*

AMSTUTZ, Brice Emerson
S Adams Comm Sch; Berne, IN; A Cap Choir;
Band; Ensm; Madrigal; Orch; Span C; *Bethel Col;
Mus.*

AMUNDSON, Debra Ann
Royal HS; Simi Valley, CA (112-964) Band; Ensm;
Secy, Jr Cl; Cl Fav.

AMUNRUD, Nadine Ruth
N Salinas HS; Salinas, CA (5-450) A Cap Choir;
Band; Chor; Ger C; NHS; CSF; Pres, Candystrip-
ing C; *Nurs.*

ANACKER, Marc Anthony
Gateway HS; Aurora, CO (24-440) Bus C; Fr C;
Math C; Mu Alpha Theta; Tr; Math A; Sci A; *U of
Colo at Denver; Acct.*

ANCHETA, Junell Celis
San Leandro HS; San Leandro, CA (17-325) Band;
Parl, Hmrm; NHS; JV, Bkbl; Hon Prog; Pres A; Yth
Fel; Co-Ch, CCYM; VP, CSF; Church Bkbl Tm;
Pres, UMYF; *UC Davis; Med.*

ANCHRUM, Jonathan
Mumford HS; Detroit, MI; Chess C; Chor; SC;
Bsbl; Ftbl; *U of Mich; Elec.*

ANDERS, Derrick Elliott
Seward Park HS; New York, NY (398-627) JV,
Bkbl; Yth Fel; *Jackson St U; Sociology.*

ANDERS, Julie Louise
Grundy Center Comm Sch; Grundy Center, IA;
Band; Chor; Drama; Sch P; Thes; Journ A; Type A;
Mus A; *Ellsworth Col; Bus.*

ANDERS, Linda Marie
A G Lane Tech HS; Chicago, IL (202-1151) Orch;
St Scholar; Ntl Merit Commended Stu; *Ill Wes-
leyan U; Mus.*

ANDERSEN, Clifford James
Newfield HS; Selden, NY (30-488) Chess C; Chor;
Hmrm; Cr-Cntry; Tr; Fencing; *Annapolis Acad; Mil-
itary Sci.*

ANDERSEN, Cynthia Lynn
Tabernacle Baptist Sch; Va Beach, VA (1-13) Band;
Co-Cpt, Chldr; Dbte Tm; Drama; Pres, FHA;
Secy, FNA; Pres, FTA; Hmrm; NHS; S-T, Orch;
Span C; Spch C; Secy, Sr Cl; Secy, Jr Cl; Sftbl; Fin,
Tr; Alg A; COM; Hist A; Math A; Most Out; Ntl
Achv Schol; Spch A; Val; Fin, Table Tnns; Princi-
pal's HR; Highest Acad Avg; *Bob Jones U; Mis-
sions.*

ANDERSEN, Elizabeth Jane
Tabernacle Baptist Sch; Virginia Beach, VA (1-27)
Cpt, Chldr; Chor; FHA; FNA; NFL; Sch P; Span C;
Secy, Jr Cl; Tres, Soph Cl; Alg A; COM; Citz A;
Most Out; Sci A; Bible A; Eng A; *Pensacola Chris-
tian Col; Med Missions.*

ANDERSEN, Ellen Eileen
Columbia HS; Columbia Station, OH; F-Ed, Ann;
Band; Ch, Chor; Ch, Drama; FHA; FTA; Sch
Achieve Tm; Pres, Ski C; Span C; Thes; Hon Prog;
Sci A; Tres, Church Yth Fel; Ohio Dist Board of
Yth Ministries; Pep C; Organizer, Ski C; St Yth
Del, Lutheran Intrntl Conv; *Kent St U; Special Ed.*

ANDERSEN, Gary Wayne
Freeport Sr HS; Freeport, IL (100-530) Hmrm;
Bsbl; Bkbl; Ftbl; *U of Ill; Park and Recreation.*

ANDERSEN, Janet Lynn
Lee's Summit HS; Lee's Summit, MO (17-476) BC;
Chldr; Hmrm; NHS; Swim; Type A; Pres, Unity
Church; 2nd VP, Unity Village; Drill Tm; Vol,
Mentally Retarded & Spec Olymp; *Working With
Retarded Children.*

ANDERSEN, Joan Marie
Lee's Summit HS; Lee's Summit, MO (7-476) Tres,
BC; Co-Cpt, Chldr; NHS; Swim; Cl Fav; Type A;
VP, Tres, Atlanta Yth of Unity; 1st VP, Unity Vil-
lage Yth Group; Special Ed Vol; Coaches A, Swim
Tm; Drill Tm; *Special Ed.*

ANDERSEN, Karen Kay
Northwest HS; Omaha, NE (16-545) A Cap Choir;
Band; Chor; Community Yth Symph; Co-Ch,
Ensm; Co-Ch, 4H; Math C; NHS; Orch; Span C;
Span NHS; SC; Thes; Tr; Citz A; 4H A; Hon Prog;
Math A; Pres A; Type A; 1st Grange Sewing Con-
test; Achv A, Home Ec, Eng, Art, Sci, Geo; 1st &
3rd Pl, Grange Talent Contest; Ntl Fed Mus C
Superior Rating; *Mus Therapy.*

ANDERSEN, Karen Marie
University of San Diego HS; San Diego, CA
(6-311) CYO; Cum Laude Soc; NHS; ARC; Co-Ch,
Sodality; Secy, SC; CSF; *U of Calif; Psych.*

ANDERSEN, Monne Kay
Salina HS; Salina, KS (25-367) VP, HiY; Hmrm;
Lat C; NFL; Orch; Ed, Sch P; Ch, SC; Chamber of
Comm A; Journ A; St Scholar; Yth Leg; Secy of St,
Model Legislature; Kans U Alumni A; Fresh Cl
Off; *Kans U; Journ.*

ANDERSEN, Nancy Braga
Klein HS; Spring, TX (128-620) Ski C; Span C; JV,
Bkbl; Tr; *Tex A&M U; Pre-Law.*

ANDERSEN, Pamela Elizabeth
Atherton HS; Burton, MI (80-225) Drama; Fr C;
ARC; Sci C; Arch; Bsbl; Sftbl; Swim; Tnns; ARC A;
GSct As; *Mott Col; Nurs.*

ANDERSEN, Paul Eric
Orestimba HS; Newman, CA (25%-180) Pres,
CYO; JV, Ftbl; Tnns; Wrest; Sacristan; Sanctuary
Soc; *Chico St Col; Vet Med.*

ANDERSON, Aaron Michael
Lewis Central HS; Council Bluffs, IA (15%-300)
Band; Demolay; 4H; Mgr, Ftbl.

ANDERSON, Aaron Wade
St Ignatius HS; St Ignatius, MT (12-30) Ann; F-Ed,
Sch P; Outst Draftsman; Outst Woodworker;
Northern Mont Col; Voc.

ANDERSON, Alexis Laquita
Benjamin Bosse HS; Evansville, IN; VP, Chor;
Cum Laude Soc; Fin, Ensm; GS; NHS; SC; Thes;
Up Bound; Tres, Jr Cl; Tnns; Kiwanis A; *Oberlin
Conservatory Col; Mus.*

ANDERSON, Alice Elizabeth
Oregon Comm HS; Oregon, IL (18-114) A Cap
Choir; A-Ed, Ann; S-T, Band; Pres, Chor; Madri-
gal; NHS; 4H A; WW; 4 Yr School A; Schol Bowl
Tm; *Souk Valley Jr Col; Commercial Art.*

ANDERSON, Allen Kenneth
S Mecklenburg Sr HS; Pinville, NC; Band; Alg A;
Gov Honor Prog; Boy o-t Yr, Church; *NC St U;
Archt.*

ANDERSON, Amy Louise
Susquehanna Comm HS; Susquehanna, PA (2-110)
Band; Chldr; Chor; Drama; Ski C; Thes; Secy, Soph
Cl; Mgr, Bsbl; Co-Cpt, Bkbl; Tr; COM; *Law.*

ANDERSON, Angela Rose
Galva HS; Galva, IL (1-86) JV, Chldr; Drama; Fr
C; Tres, FHA; FTA; Tres, SC; Bsbl; Sftbl; Tr; Amer
Leg A; HCt; Hon Prog; *Health.*

ANDERSON, Anita Lynn
Adolfo Camarillo HS; Camarillo, CA (5%-500)
Secy, Band; Community Yth Symph; FHA; Sftbl;
Amer Leg A; CSF; COM; Hon Prog; Most Out;
Yth Fel; Gym; Sunday Sch Teacher; *Cal St at
Northridge; Phys Therapy.*

ANDERSON, Anne Louise
Peru HS; Peru, IN; Chor; Ftbl; Girls League; *U of
Tampa; Nurs.*

ANDERSON, Arethia Phenise
Carolina HS; Greenville, SC (20-230) Fr C; VP,
FBLA; VP, FHA; 4H; Sch P; VP, Sr Cl; Beauty; 4H
A; JA A; Spch A; Distributive Ed C; Prom Comm;
SC St Col; Bus Adm.

ANDERSON, Axel Alberto
Dra Maria Cadilla de Martinez HS; Arecibo, PR
(6-429) Chem C; Drama; FTA; Pres, Hmrm; Phys
C; Sci C; Alg A; COM; Chem A; Hist A; Hon Prog;
Math A; Rotary A; Sci A; *Universidad de Puerto
Rico; Phar.*

ANDERSON, Barbara Sue
American Acad; Bogalusa, LA (3-32) Band; Chldr;
4H; Hmrm; SC; Bkbl; Yth Fel; Bells & Beaus
Beauty Pageant; Qn with Scepter, Acteens; Vol,
Assn for Retarded Children; *Harvard U; Med.*

ANDERSON, Bert Andrew
York HS; York, NE (15%-160) VP, A Cap Choir;
Ann; Chor; Sch P; SC; JV, Bkbl; Art A; Sch Car-
toonist; Sup, Dist Barbershop Qrt, Mus Cont; *U of
Nebr; Archt.*

ANDERSON, Beverly Jo
Will Rogers HS; Tulsa, OK (120-500) Cpt, Chldr;
Fr C; Secy, SC; Var C; Cl Fav; Hist A; HQn; HCt;
Hon Prog; Masque & Gavel A; Spch A; Young Life
Christian Group; Secy, Damsel Social C; *Bethany
Nazarene Col; Secretarial.*

ANDERSON, Birgitta Marianne
Martin Luther HS; Maspeth, NY (17-113) A Cap
Choir; Ann; Chor; Span C; COM; PA; *Social Work.*

ANDERSON, Bradley Donald
Thomas Jefferson Sr HS; Rockford, IL (44-380)
NHS; Order/Arrow; Kiwanis A; Order/Arrow A;
WW; *Bethel Col; Bus.*

ANDERSON, Brenda Jane
Park Center Sr HS; Brooklyn Park, MN (103-579)
Band; Drama; Ensm; Hmrm; Ski C; SC; Fin, Tr;
Hon Prog; Job's Daughters; Most Spirit, Vlbl; *Col
of St Benedict; Psych.*

ANDERSON, Brenda Kay
John F Kennedy HS; Bloomington, MN (94-600)
Chor; NHS; Rptr, Sch P; HQn; Kennedy Kolleens;
Normandale Jr Col.

ANDERSON, Brenda Kay
Sunset HS; Beaverton, OR; Band; 4H; *NW Nazarene Col; Bus.*

ANDERSON, Brenda Lee
Bradley Bourbonnais Comm HS; Bradley, IL;
Chor; Ensm; Swim.

ANDERSON, Brenda Rae
Denfeld HS; Duluth, MN (10-400) Chor.

ANDERSON, Bruce Robert
Batavia HS; Batavia, IL; AFS; Band; CYO; 4H;
Math C; NHS; SC; Pres, Sr Cl; Pres, Soph Cl; Co-
Cpt, Ftbl; Tr; COM; 4H A; St Scholar; Val; Ntl
Merit Commended Stu; *Saint Joseph's Col; Bio.*

ANDERSON, Camron Call
Skyline HS; Salt Lake City, UT; Chor; Lit Mag;
Cpt, Bkbl; JV, Tr; God & Country A; Hon Prog;
Eagle Sct; *U of Utah; Engr.*

ANDERSON, Carey Glenn
Berkeley HS; Berkeley, CA; *Hayward St U; Bus
Adm.*

ANDERSON, Carol Anne
Citrus HS; Inverness, FL (9-250) Pres, Fr C; FFA;
Hmrm; NHS; Sftbl; H of F; Hon Prog; NMS; Ntl
Sci Found; *U of Fla; Vet Med.*

ANDERSON, Carolyn
Reseda HS; Reseda, CA (20%-650) Chor; Rptr, Sch
P; S-T, Ski C; VP, SC; Bank Of Amer A;
DARGCA; Hon Prog; Kiwanis A; Mayor, GS;
Girls League; Secy, CSF; Soph, Jr, Sr, Cl Coun;
Photo C; *Occidental Col; Pre-Med.*

ANDERSON, Cathy Fay
King's Garden HS; Seattle, WA (50-64) Band; Chldr; Chor; NHS; Hon Prog; *Shoreline Comm Col; Home Ec.*

ANDERSON, Charles Cragin
Battle Ground Acad; Franklin, TN (14-76) Chem C; Lat C; Math C; Var C; Swim; Hon Prog; NEDT; *U of Va; Architecture.*

ANDERSON, Charles Edward
N Natchez Adams HS; Natchez, MS (40-70) Band; Band A; *Valley St U; Ed.*

ANDERSON, Christina Louise
Durham Acad; Durham, NC (6-46) F-Ed, Ann; Lat C; Math C; Sci C; 1st Pl, Durham Woman's C Art Show; NMS Ltr; Effort A; WW.

ANDERSON, Christine Isabelle
Durham Acad; Durham, NC (3-60) VP, AFS; F-Ed, Ann; Chor; SC; Bkbl; Sftbl.

ANDERSON, Christine Lesie
Gibraltar HS; Fish Creek, WI; Band; Chldr; NFL; Secy, Jr Cl; Tr; Vlbl; *Bethel Col.*

ANDERSON, Cindy Kay
Hot Springs Co HS; Thermopolis, WY (3-93) A Cap Choir; Band; Chor; GS; Madrigal; VP, NFL; NHS; Spch C; VP, SC; Pres, Thes; Pres, Soph Cl; Golf; Citz A; Cl Fav; Elk A; I Dare You; Kiwanis A; MLS; Spch A; Girl's Nation Secy o-t Interior; Hon Qn, Jobs Daughters; *U of Wy.*

ANDERSON, Darrell Lee
Amarillo HS; Amarillo, TX; A Cap Choir; Chor; Ensm; Hmrm; Bsbl; Bkbl; Tnns; *Baylor U; Coaching.*

ANDERSON, David Alan
Carpio Pub HS; Carpio, ND (1-17) Band; BS; S-T, Chess C; Chor; Ensm; 4H; NHS; F-Ed, Sch P; Tres, Soph Cl; Mgr, Bkbl; 4H A; Math A; Val; *Mary Col; Acct.*

ANDERSON, David Brian
Masonic Home And Sch; Ft Worth, TX (2-15) Ann; Band; Dbte Tm; Demolay; Drama; Ed, Sch P; Spch C; Pres, SC; Bsbl; Cr-Ctry; Ftbl; Soccer; Tnns; Tr; Masonic A; Opt A; *Real Estate Trng Inst; Real Estate.*

ANDERSON, David John
Don Bosco Tech HS; Boston, MA (3-211) Band; NHS; VP, SC; Bsbl; Bkbl; Hockey; Sci A; Reading A; *MIT; Elec Engr.*

ANDERSON, David Keith
Athens HS; Athens, AL; Tr; *U of Ala; Drafting.*

ANDERSON, David Paul
Badger HS; Lake Geneva, WI; Golf; Math A; Grand Cr of Color, Rainbow Grl; *U of Wis; Computer Sci.*

ANDERSON, David Rowe
N B Forrest HS; Jacksonville, FL (50-700) Cr-Ctry; Tr; Math A; Most Out; Sch Calendar; Sch Fitness A; Pres Phys Fitness A; *Newberry Col; Religion.*

ANDERSON, David Scott
Nederland HS; Nederland, TX (95-546) Band; PA; *Lamar U; Mus.*

ANDERSON, David Scott
Holdrege Sr HS; Holdrege, NE; Chor; JV, Ftbl; Tr; Wrest; *Hist.*

ANDERSON, Dawn Danette
Winthrop Comm HS; Winthrop, MN; Ann; Band; Drama; Ensm; Sch P; VP, Soph Cl; Sftbl; HCt; Vlbl; *Nurs.*

ANDERSON, Debbie Sue
Cooper HS; Abilene, TX; Var C; Chaplain, Tri-Hi-Y; Christian C; Gym; *Abilene Christian U; Phys Ed.*

ANDERSON, Debbie Sue
Richwoods HS; Peoria, IL (1-520) Band.

ANDERSON, Deborah Fay
Terrell Co HS; Dawson, GA (10%-147) SC; Chor; FBLA; NHS; Hist A; Hon Prog; Sci A; Type A; Eng A; *U of Ga; Bus Adm.*

ANDERSON, Debra Kaye
Hernando HS; Brooksville, FL; FHA; Bkbl; Bkbl A; *Fla A&M U; Secy.*

ANDERSON, Debra Pauline
Dows Comm HS; Dows, IA (6-30) Ann; Band; Chor; Ensm; Secy, FHA; JV, Bkbl; Tr.

ANDERSON, Delores
Frederick Douglass HS; Baltimore, MD (85-450) 4H; Rptr, Hmrm; NHS; SC; VP, Var C; Cpt, Bkbl; Cpt, Tr; COM; 4H A; Hon Prog; Math A; Most Out; Type A; Vlbl; PA A; Gov's Comm On Children & Yth; *Early Childhood Development.*

ANDERSON, Delores Chrystal Theresa
Warwick HS; Lititz, PA (100-260) Band; FBLA; Ger C; Type A; Yth Fel; *Nurs.*

ANDERSON, Denise
Vashon HS; St Louis, MO; A Cap Choir; All Amer Yth; AFS; CYO; Chldr; Drama; Hmrm; Jr Miss Pagent; Ntl Yth Conf; Rainbow; Spch C; SC; God & Country A; JA A; Most Out; Sanctuary Soc; Spch A; Type A; *Heutis Teacher Col; Social Work.*

ANDERSON, Denise Kay
West HS; Columbus, OH; Drama; Sch P; SC; Yth Fel; HR.

ANDERSON, Donald Mark
Cache HS; Cache, OK (8-44) BC; Pres, FFA; Span C; Co-Cpt, Var C; Tres, Jr Cl; Pres, Soph Cl; Cpt, Bkbl; Co-Cpt, Ftbl; Cl Fav; *Cameron U; Agr Ec.*

ANDERSON, Donna Jean
Permian HS; Odessa, TX (15-668) Dbte Tm; Rptr, NHS; S-T, Spch C; JV, Tnns; H of F; Opt A; Opt Out Tn; Regent Schol; Spch A; VofDEM; Pres, Candy Stripers; Sup Rating, Ntl Fed of Mus C; *McMurry Col; Med Tech.*

ANDERSON, Donna Renee
Daviess Co HS; Owensboro, KY (60-330) A Cap Choir; Chor; Ensm; Bio A; Sci A; Swtht; Drill Corps; Church Yth Conf; Mus A; *Ky Wesleyan Col; Mus.*

ANDERSON, Doris Ann
Canton Acad; Canton, MS; Band; CYO; Chldr; 4H; Y-Tns; 4H A; HCt; *Holmes Jr Col.*

ANDERSON, Doris Evelyn
Norquay HS; Norquay, CANADA (3-22) Rptr, Sch P; *STI; Secy.*

ANDERSON, Douglas Paul
Belmond Community HS; Belmond, IA (4-95) Chor; Ensm; Madrigal; NHS; Order/Arrow; Thes; Amer Leg A; God & Country A; NMS; Order/Arrow A; Eagle Sct; Win, Soc of Actuaries Math Tests; *Iowa St U; Mech Engr.*

ANDERSON, Eddie Charles
Ribault Sr HS; Jacksonville, FL; A Cap Choir; VP, Chor; SC; Swim; Most Out; *Med.*

ANDERSON, Edward Elmo
Lake City HS; Lake City, TN (32-110) F-Ed, Ann; FBLA; Sch P; SC; Bsbl; Hist A; Yth Fel; *Roane St Comm Col; Elec.*

ANDERSON, Eric Matthew
Red Lion Area Sr HS; Red Lion, PA (35-400) Band; BS; Chor; Ensm; Madrigal; Mod Mus Mas; Yth Fel; *Data Processing.*

ANDERSON, Erick Bertel
Timberline HS; Weippe, ID (12-48) Ann; CYO; Chem C; Phys C; A-Ed, Sch P; VP, Ski C; Var C; VP, Jr Cl; Bkbl; Ftbl; Tnns; 4H A; Hon Prog; Journ A; Spch A; Yth Leg; *U of Idaho; Engr.*

ANDERSON, Erin Gaye
Science Hill HS; Johnson City, TN (30%-400) Lat C; Span C; *E Tenn St U; Speech Therapy.*

ANDERSON, Erna Mae
Whitewater HS; Whitewater, WI (23-172) Band; Ensm; Fr C; Rptr, FFA; Math C; COM; FFA As; *Platteville Col; Horticulture.*

ANDERSON, F James Jr
Jamestown HS; Jamestown, NY (50-600) Band; Lat A; *U at Buffalo; Sci.*

ANDERSON, Faye Frances
James H Hammond Acad; Columbia, SC; Chldr; Fr C; Hmrm; Jr Miss Pagent; ARC; SC; NEDT; *Sweet Briar Col.*

ANDERSON, Fernandez
W Fulton HS; Atlanta, GA; MVP, Bsbl; Ftbl; Alg A; Math A; ROTC A; ROTC Merit A & Academic Wreath; Best Drill Sq & Platoon A's; B-Tm Chldr Escort; *Engr.*

ANDERSON, Floretha
Woodrow Wilson Sr HS; Washington, DC (501-237) Band; Chor; Dbte Tm; Demolay; Hmrm; ARC; Sch P; Cpt, Sftbl; Co-Cpt, Swim; Tnns; Tr; Cl Fav; Hist A; ARC A; Type A; *U of Md; Interior Design.*

ANDERSON, Franceia
Compton HS; Compton, CA (35-800) CYO; Fr C; Secy, Sr Cl; CSF; Hon Prog; *U of Calif; Elem Ed.*

ANDERSON, Frank
South Side HS; Memphis, TN (10%-370) NFL; Pres, Spch C; Citz A; Opt A; Spch A; *Memphis St U; Acct.*

ANDERSON, Gary Lynn
Franklin Co HS; Rocky Mount, VA;

ANDERSON, Georgia Lynne
Daviess Co HS; Owensboro, KY; Chldr; 4H; Tnns; Cl Fav; HQn; Swtht; *Stephens Col; Equestrian Sci.*

ANDERSON, Gregory Dean
Rowan Center HS; Hattiesburg, MS (5%-500) Pres, Demolay; Mu Alpha Theta; Ntl Fed of Mus C Sup A; *U of Sou Miss; Math.*

ANDERSON, Gretchen Renee
Wayzata Sr HS; Wayzata, MN (90-600) Chldr; NHS; Swim; Tr.

ANDERSON, Harriet Denise
Clarkrange HS; Clarkrange, TN; VP, Band; BC; Chor; FHA; 4H; F-Ed, Sch P; Sci C; Spch C; MVP, Bkbl; Sci A; *Health Occupation.*

ANDERSON, Jane Ellen
Glenbrook N HS; Northbrook, IL; Chor; Ensm; Tr; Sci A; Spch A; Pres, Dance C; Stu Govt; Dance Tour Group; Bell Choir; *Natural Sci.*

ANDERSON, Jane Emilie
Glen Ridge HS; Glen Ridge, NJ (58-179) AFS; Band; Secy, Chor; Hmrm; Cpt, Mjrte; Secy, Sr Cl; Mgr, Tr; COM; Citz A; VP, Girl's C; Colorguard; *Keuka Col; Med Tech.*

ANDERSON, Janet Rose
St Josephs o-t Palisades; W New York, NJ (1-225) Ed, Ann; Drama; NHS; Span NHS; Hon Prog; MLS; WW; *Syracuse U; Journ.*

ANDERSON, Janine Diane
Laurel Valley Jr Sr HS; New Florence, PA (8-135) AFS; Band; Chldr; Chor; Drama; Hmrm; VP, NHS; Co-Ed, Sch P; VP, SC; Var C; Tnns, Jr Cl; Bkbl; Sftbl; Amer Leg A; Citz A; DARGCA; Hon Prog; Most Sch Spirit; *U of Pittsburgh; Eng.*

ANDERSON, Jeanne Ellen
Oceanside Sr HS; Oceanside, NY; JV, Chldr; Chor; Ensm; NHS; COM; JA A; Yth Fel; Girls Sportnite; Big Buddy Prog; Choir; Bible Stu; Chor & Sunday Sch Pianist.

ANDERSON, John Durant
Fort Myers HS; Fort Myers, FL; Lat C; Bus Mgr, Sch P; Yth Fel; Church Librarian; Church Adm Board; *Fla Sou Col; Bus Adm.*

ANDERSON, Jon Hayward
Bloomfield Sr HS; Bloomfield, NJ (239-651) Band; Ensm; Orch; Order/Arrow; ARC; *Engr.*

ANDERSON, Joseph Alvin
Galva HS; Galva, IL (17-79) Hmrm; NHS; Order/Arrow; SC; Var C; S-T, Soph Cl; Ftbl; Co-Cpt, Wrest; HCt; Order/Arrow A; St Scholar; MVP, Wrest; *U of Ill; Forestry.*

ANDERSON, Joseph Keith
Washington HS; Lake Charles, LA; Pres, Chor; Fr C; Spch C; Var C; JV, Ftbl; Tr; COM; Hon Prog; JA A; Math A; Spch A; Type A; Yth Fel; Chor, Hon Soc, A's; *Voice.*

ANDERSON, Joy Annette
Asher HS; Asher, OK (5%-21) Chldr; FHA; Sch P; Secy, Jr Cl; Bkbl; Bio A; Hist A; HCt; Sci A; *ECU; Elem Ed.*

ANDERSON, Joyce Marie
S Oak Cliff HS; Dallas, TX; Chor; FHA; Hmrm; Jr Miss Pagent; Math C; NHS; ARC; SC; Pres, Bsbl; Pres, Bkbl; Pres, Soccer; Pres, Sftbl; Hist A; Drill Tm A; *Data Processing.*

ANDERSON, Judith
Stonington HS; Pawcatuck, CT (140-210) Pres, Rainbow; Yth Fel; *Briarwood Sch for Women; Travel.*

ANDERSON, Judith Lynne
Roosevelt HS; Saint Louis, MO (3-423) Band; Chem C; VP, Ger C; GS; Math C; Mu Alpha Theta; Pres, NHS; Orch; ARC; COM; Citz A; Curator A; Hon Prog; Co-Cpt, Vlbl; God-Home-Ctry A; 1st Cl Sct; Win-A-Rama Jr-Sr A; *U of Mo-Columbia; Chem.*

ANDERSON, Julie Marlene
William J Palmer HS; Colo Springs, CO (1-450) Band; Madrigal; NHS; Tr; Hon Prog; Val; NML; Lazenby Chem Schol; University Schol; *Sou Methodist U; Chem.*

ANDERSON, Julius Lee
Amite Co Attendance Center; Gloster, MS (5-40) Band; Tres, BC; Drama; Ensm; VP, FFA; Hmrm; Orch; SC; COM; Citz A; Hon Prog; *Miss Valley St U; Acct.*

ANDERSON, Karen Christine
Livermore HS; Livermore, CA (1-503) Drama; Bank Of Amer A; Val; S-T, Interntl Exchange C; CSF Life Member; Amer Bus Woman's Assn Schol; WW; St Mary's Col Academic Schol; *St Mary's Col; Govt.*

ANDERSON, Karen Jean
Evergreen Pk HS; Evergreen Park, IL (127-454) Band; Drama; ARC; Span C; Thes; ARC A; Yth Fel; Candystriper; Nurse's Aid; Yth Worker; *Morraine Valley Comm Col; Nurs.*

ANDERSON, Karen Jean
Washington Co Ind Sch; Sandersville, GA (25%-38) BC; Chldr; Chor; Sch P; JV, Bkbl; Sftbl; Tr; *Georgia Col.*

ANDERSON, Karen Sue
Dunlap Comm Sch; Dunlap, IA (35-60) Chor; FHA; Swim; 4H A; *Secretarial Work.*

ANDERSON, Katherine Jean
Conway HS; Conway, SC (25%-400) Span C; Type A; Cpt, Vlbl; Pres, Church Yth Fel; GSct; Piano Stu; *Sweet Briar Col; Mus.*

ANDERSON, Kathy Irene
Acalanes HS; Lafayette, CA (20%-350) AFS; Tres, Chldr; Fr C; FHA; 4H; Ski C; Span C; Var C; Tnns; CSF; 4H A; *Pediatrics.*

ANDERSON, Kathy Jo
Willard HS; Willard, MO (30-219) Chor; Madrigal; Sftbl; *Stephens Col; Ed.*

ANDERSON, Katrina Sue
Chapman HS; Inman, SC (6-143) BC; Chor; Fr C; Hmrm; Hist A; Hon Prog; WW; Service A; Helen J Bruce; PC Schol; Ann Todd Wofford Schol; Congressional Medal of Merit; *Converse Col; Med Tech.*

ANDERSON, Kelly Lee
St Francis HS; St Francis, MN (17-260) Band; Cpt, Chldr; NHS; Sch P; Ski C; SC; Tres, Jr Cl; Tr; Miss SFHS; Superior, St Flute Duet; *Nurs.*

ANDERSON, Kelly Lin
Jamestown HS; Jamestown, NY (65-470) Band; Hmrm; NHS; *Jamestown Comm Col; Sci.*

ANDERSON, Kevin John
Carpio HS; Carpio, ND (10%-23) MVP, Chess C; 4H; NHS; Var C; Bkbl; Ftbl.

ANDERSON, Kevin Walter
Ithaca HS; Richland Center, WI (19-43) Band; Drama; Tres, FFA; Pres, 4H; Co-Cpt, Bsbl; MVP, Ftbl; Sftbl; Co-Cpt, Wrest; 4H A; HKg; All Conf, Bsbl, Ftbl; *U of Wisc; Animal Sci.*

ANDERSON, Kimathie Joan
Litchfield Sr HS; Litchfield, MN; Band; Chor; FHA; Hmrm; Madrigal; ARC; Sch P; COM; *Normandale Jr Col; Fashion.*

ANDERSON, Kimberly Ardelle
Pendleton HS; Pendleton, SC (2-120) Ann; BC; Chldr; Fr C; Ch, InterClub Coun; VP, SC; Beauty; Citz A; HCt.

ANDERSON, Kimberly Jean
Red Lion Area Sr HS; Red Lion, PA (6-375) Secy, 4H; Lat C; Rptr, Sch P; Hon Prog; Journ A; Most Out; *Pa St U; Hist.*

ANDERSON, Kimberly Sue
Burnsville HS; Burnsville, MN (64-712) Bkbl; Young Life C; Girls Triple Trio; Church Choir; *Christian Ed.*

ANDERSON, Kristen Louise
Northwood HS; Silver Spring, MD; Pres, Band; Drama; Orch; Sch Ltr; *Mus.*

ANDERSON, Kurt David
Denfeld HS; Duluth, MN (38-450) A Cap Choir; Chor; Bsbl; Co-Cpt, Hockey; COM; Hon Prog; *Concordia Col; Bio.*

ANDERSON, Kyle Raymond
Southside HS; Southside, AR (1-480) Key C; NHS; Span C; VP, Soph Cl; Bsbl; JV, Ftbl; Journ A; *MIT; Sci.*

ANDERSON, Laura Jean
Ardmore HS; Ardmore, OK (20%-300) Ann; Band; Sch P; SC; Sci A; Band As; *Okal St U.*

ANDERSON, Laura Kay
Plainfield Jr-Sr HS; Plainfield, IN (25-290) Ed, Ann; Chor; Ger C; NHS; Cert of Hon; *Ind St U; Eng.*

ANDERSON, Laurie Ann
Paris HS; Paris, IL; Band; Chldr; Chor; Fr C; Tres, 4H; ARC; Var C; Tnns; JV, Tr; 4H A; Hon Ltrs; *U of Ill; Math.*

ANDERSON, Laurie Nadine
Holyoke HS; Holyoke, CO (7-61) Ann; Band; FBLA; VP, 4H; Ed, Lit Mag; Pres, NHS; Pol Sci C; Ed, Sch P; Sci C; SC; Var C; Pres, Jr Cl; Bkbl; Tr; COM; 4H A; Hist A; Journ A; Attd, Miss HHS; *Ft Lewis Col; Engr.*

ANDERSON, Laurita Maria
S Mecklenburg Sr HS; Pineville, NC;

ANDERSON, Leigh Ellen
Bloomfield HS; Bloomfield, NJ; Band; Tr.

ANDERSON, Leonard Charles
Chelan HS; Chelan, WA (2-48) Band; Cpt, Chor; Hmrm; Pres, NHS; Order/Arrow; Pres, SC; Var C; Bsbl; Ftbl; Tr; Gr Marshal; ROTC A; Eagle Sct.

ANDERSON, Leroy
W Charlotte HS; Charlotte, NC (490-800) Fr C; Tnns; Bkbl; Phys Ed A; *A&T St U; Math.*

ANDERSON, Lila Rose
Parkway W Sr HS; Ballwin, MO (17-619) Swim; Excel, Russian; Fin, NETC.

ANDERSON, Linda Frances
John T Hoggard HS; Wilmington, NC; ARC; Y-Tns; Tr; *Early Childhood Ed.*

ANDERSON, Linda Sue
S Clay Comm HS; Gillett Grove, IA (5-30) Band; Chldr; Chor; Drama; 4H; Rptr, Sch P; Spch C; 4H A; Spch A; Yth Fel; Tres, Ostomy Assn.

ANDERSON, Lori Beth
Rocky Grove HS; Franklin, PA (2-134) Band; Chor; Ensm; VP, NHS; Orch; *Grove City Col; Chem.*

ANDERSON, Lori Corinne
W F West HS; Chehalis, WA (38-177) ARC; Var C; Bkbl; Sftbl; Tr; 4H A; Most Out; ARC A; Most Inspirational, Tr & Vlbl; Cpt, MVP, Vlbl; Girl Ath o-t Yr; *Centralia Col; Lab Tech.*

ANDERSON, Lori Louise
Ridgefied HS; Ridgefield, CT; A Cap Choir; Chor.

ANDERSON, Lori Lynn
Maddock Pub HS; Maddock, ND (3-28) Ann; Band; Secy, Chor; Tres, FHA; GS; Rptr, Sch P; Thes; VP, Sr Cl; B Crocker A; Hon Prog; *U of ND; Bus Adm.*

ANDERSON, Lori Lynn
Hamilton Union HS; Hamilton City, CA (2-45) Chldr; FFA; Pres, FHA; Semi-Fin, GS; Secy, 4H; Tres, SC; Pres, Sr Cl; Secy, Jr Cl; Bkbl; Sftbl; CSF; COM; 4H A; Most Out; Type A; Older Girls Conf; Eng A; HR; Secy, GAA; DAR Essay A, Win; Vlbl; FFA Chpt Swtht.

ANDERSON, Lucy Lynn
Canton Acad; Canton, MS (15-95) Band; Tres, BC; Secy, CYO; Ch, Chldr; 4H; Mjrte; Sci C; Y-Tns; Alg A; 4H A; Lion A; Math A; Sci A; Master Bandsman; *Holmes Jr Col; Elem Ed.*

ANDERSON, Lynn Yvonne
James W Robinson Secondary Sch; Fairfax, VA (94-501) InterAct C; Key C; Mjrte; NHS; Ski C; Span NHS; Tres, Church Yth; NML; *U of Va; Eng.*

ANDERSON, Malcolm Craig
York HS; Monterey, CA (10-25) Bkbl; *UC Davis; Elec Engr.*

ANDERSON, Malinda Faye
Bullock Co HS; Union Springs, AL (3-150) Secy, FBLA; 4H; Hmrm; Pres, NHS; Rptr, Sch P; SC; Hist A; HCt; Hon Prog; Sci A; Service, Schol Achv, Eng, A's; May Day Qn; *Tuskegee Inst; Acct.*

ANDERSON, Marc Charles
Richardson HS; Richardson, TX (237-980) Order/Arrow; Order/Arrow A; Yth Fel; Church Coun; *Stetson Col; Law.*

ANDERSON, Marcia Jane
Evangelical Christian Sch; Cordova, TN; Hmrm; ARC; Sftbl; Sci A; Pep C; PA; Appher A; Andrew C; 100 Mile C; Home Ec C.

ANDERSON, Margaret Lynn
White Oak HS; White Oak, TX (1-95) Band; Math C; Sch Achieve Tm; MYF; Scholastic Roll; All Dist Band; I, UIL Solo & Ensm Contest; HR; *Kilgore Jr Col; Engr.*

ANDERSON, Mark Allen
Long Prairie HS; Long Prairie, MN (8-130) A Cap Choir; A-Ed, Ann; Chem C; Chor; Ensm; Ger C; Madrigal; Math C; NHS; JV, Bkbl; Hon Prog; *Wheaton Col; Chem.*

ANDERSON, Mark Christian
Ponchatoula HS; Ponchatoula, LA (1-325) Band; Ensm; Semi-Fin, Lit Ral; Hon Prog; Most Out; St Mus Ed Dist Hon Band & A's; Superior A, Interst Jazz Festival; *Loyola U; Mus.*

ANDERSON, Mark Edwin
Ysleta HS; El Paso, TX (50-700) Band; NHS; Phys C; Sci C; JA A; Math A; Ntl Conf Chr & Jews; Sci A; *U of Tex; Elec Engr.*

ANDERSON, Mark Holden
Clearwater HS; Clearwater, FL; BS; InterAct C; NHS; Var C; Ftbl; Amer Leg A; Sr Scholastic A, Ftbl; *Baylor U; Religion.*

ANDERSON, Mark Jerome
Cambridge Sr HS; Cambridge, MN (10-350) Bsbl; Swim; Hon Prog.

ANDERSON, Marvin John
Gladstone HS; Gladstone, MI; 4H; Arch; Bsbl; Bkbl; Swim; Wrest; *Northland Col; Ministry.*

ANDERSON, Maurice Dean Jr
Montgomery Bell Acad; Nashville, TN (16-87) Fr C; Hon Prog; NEDT.

ANDERSON, Michael Allen
Vashon HS; St Louis, MO (3-35) *Forest Park Col; Auto Mech.*

ANDERSON, Michael Eugene
Mason City HS; Mason City, IA (25%-500) Model UN; Bsbl; Hockey; *U of Iowa; Bus.*

ANDERSON, Michael Laverne
Vanguard HS; Ocala, FL (19-350) Pres, Band; Tres, Key C; Mu Alpha Theta; Tres, SC; COM; Most Out; Sci A; Swtht; *Fla St U; Law.*

ANDERSON, Michael Scott
Burnsville Sr HS; Burnsville, MN (84-892) Drama; Ger C; F-Ed, Sch P; Thes.

ANDERSON, Mitchell Lee
Meriden-Cleghorn HS; Cleghorn, IA (4-36) Spch C; Var C; Bsbl; Bkbl; Ftbl; Tr; Spch A; Yth Fel.

ANDERSON, Nancy Jean
Minnehaha Acad; Minneapolis, MN (14-170) Cpt, Chldr; Tres, Chor; VP, Ger C; GS; Pres, NHS; Ski C; Cr-Ctry; Tr; HCt; Hon Prog; VFW A; VofDEM; AAU Swim; *U of Minn; Bio.*

ANDERSON, Nancy Lee
Highland Park Sr HS; St Paul, MN; Band; Co-Cpt, Chldr; Hmrm; Orch; SC; Mgr, Bkbl; Cr-Ctry; Sftbl; Tr; Alg A; Math A; Pres A; Sci A; Sportsmanship Trophy; Mgr, Gym; MVP, Vlbl; Awana Hon A; *U of Minn; Teaching.*

ANDERSON, Nancy Louise
Washington HS; Washington, PA; A Cap Choir; AFS; Band; Tres, Bus C; Chor; Ensm; Y-Tns.

ANDERSON, Pamela Jean
Laurelwood Adventist Acad; Gaston, OR; A Cap Choir; Band; Ski C; SC; VP, Associated Stu Body; Secy-Treas, Girls C; *Meritt-Davis Bus Col; Receptionist.*

15

ANDERSON, Pamela Marie
Cannon Falls HS; Cannon Falls, MN (5-142) Chor; Dbte Tm; Ch, FFA; Pres, 4H; NHS; Spch C; 4H A; K of C A; Spch A; FFA, 4-H Key, A's; *U of Wis; Home Ec.*

ANDERSON, Pamela Sue
Mullens HS; Mullens, WV (4-144) BC; Bus Mgr, FBLA; COM; Hist A; Type A; *Concord Col; Bus.*

ANDERSON, Patricia Louise
Middle Park HS; Granby, CO (2-72) Secy, Band; Dbte Tm; Ensm; 4H; NFL; Spch C; Secy, Soph Cl; Bkbl; 4H A; Kiwanis A; Spch A; Mgr, Vlbl; St Solo A's; Phi Cappa Delta.

ANDERSON, Patricia Steel
Wilton HS; Wilton, CT (70-400) A Cap Choir; Bus Mgr, Chor; VP, Drama; Pres, Hmrm; Madrigal; Thes; JV, Bkbl; All St Chor; *Rollins Col; Mus.*

ANDERSON, Paula Jean
Nevis HS; Nevis, MN (4-24) FHA; Rptr, Sch P; VP, SC; Tr; *Moorhead St U; Communications.*

ANDERSON, Peter Duncan
Guilford HS; Rockford, IL; A Cap Choir; Chor; Drama; Ensm; Madrigal; Thes; Costume Designer; Dancer & Singer, Musicals; Choreographer, Jenny Lind Soc Var; *Mus Theater.*

ANDERSON, Philip Louis
Shorecrest HS; Seattle, WA (10-580) Chor; NHS; Spch A; Interntl Bible Quiz; *MIT; Econ.*

ANDERSON, Rachel Ann
Forest Lake HS; Forest Lake, MN; A Cap Choir; Drama; Ensm; ARC; Fin, Spch C; Swim; God & Country A; Spch A; *Gustavus Adolphus; Nurs.*

ANDERSON, Rebecca Joyce
Luther HS N; Chicago, IL (50%-300) Chldr; ARC; Ski C; VP, Sr Cl; Secy, Jr Cl; Tres, Soph Cl; Bkbl; Tr; COM; Hist A; Hon Prog; Vlbl; Pep C; Ski C; Canoe C; Tr As; Field Hockey; Girls Service C; Treas, Girls Serv C; Equestrian C; Bowl Tm; Chldr As; DAR Essay A; *U of Okla Norman; Med.*

ANDERSON, Rebekah Lynn
Hillcrest Acad; Fergus Falls, MN (3-64) Dbte Tm; 4H; NHS; Orch; Bkbl; 4H A; Sal; Spch A; All-Conf Vlbl; *U of Wis at Eau Claire; Med.*

ANDERSON, Regina Veronica
Morse HS; San Diego, CA (300-604) Chor; Ensm; Hmrm; *U of Calif; Mus.*

ANDERSON, Richard Clayton Jr
The King's Temple Christian Sch; Seattle, WA (1-4) BS; Chess C; Cpt, Dbte Tm; Key C; NFL; F-Ed, Sch P; Cpt, Spch C; St Stu Congress; Swim; Amer Leg A; Kiwanis A; Masonic A; Pres A; Spch A; *The King's Temple Bible Acad; Ministry.*

ANDERSON, Richard Louis
Monroe Co HS; Monroeville, AL; Ann; Key C; Sch P; SC; Var C; Bsbl; Ftbl; Yth Fel; Yth Leg.

ANDERSON, Rita Helene
Chicago Voc HS; Chicago, IL (58-1214) Dbte Tm; FBLA; Scholastic Ltr; HR; *Roosevelt Col; Bus.*

ANDERSON, Robert Farold
Central HS; St Louis, MO; Band; Ftbl; Tnns; Citz A; PA; Tallest, Band; Pres, Jr Usher Board; *Ohio St U; Mortuary Sci.*

ANDERSON, Robert M Jr
Jonathan Alder HS; Plain City, OH (7-121) Band; Semi-Fin, BS; Pres, Chor; Drama; Ensm; FTA; HiY; Hmrm; NHS; Orch; Sch Achieve Tm; Pres, Span C; Pres, SC; Tr; Elk A; Yth Fel; Ldrship A; WW; WW, Mus; *NW U; Theatre.*

ANDERSON, Robert Morse Jr
Jonathan Alder HS; Plain City, OH (6-127) Band; Pres, Chor; Drama; Ensm; FTA; HiY; Hmrm; NHS; Orch; Pres, Span C; Pres, SC; Elk A; WW, HS Stu; WW, Mus Stu; *Northwestern U; Theatre.*

ANDERSON, Robin Jane
S Hills HS; Pittsburgh, PA (107-530) NHS; Drill Tm; *U of Pittsburgh; Bus.*

ANDERSON, Roger Dale
S Gwinnett HS; Snellville, GA (7-255) F-Ed, Ann; BC; Math C; Order/Arrow; ARC; COM; Cl Fav; Gov Honor Prog; Q&S A; NML; *U of Ga; Pre-Med.*

ANDERSON, Sammie Paul
Ware Shoals HS; Ware Shoals, SC (5-106) Pres, BC; Chem C; VP, Fr C; Hmrm; NHS; Phys C; SC; VP, Var C; Pres, Jr Cl; Pres, Soph Cl; Bsbl; Bkbl; MVP, Ftbl; Tr; Chem A; Gr Marshal; Most Out; Co-Cpt, Ftbl; *Phys Ed.*

ANDERSON, Scott Allen
Stoughton HS; Stoughton, WI (72-300) *Parker Col; Aeronautics.*

ANDERSON, Scott Bradley
Sioux Falls-Lincoln Sr HS; Sioux Falls, SD (23-600) Band; Chess C; JV, Dbte Tm; Co-Cpt, HiY; NFL; Orch; Sci C; St Stu Congress; Tri-HiY; MVP, Bsbl; Bkbl; Ftbl; Golf; Sftbl; Tnns; Tr; Wrest; COM; Math A; Most Out; Spch A; Distinction of Excel, Hon & Merit; St Record, Most NFL Points; *Augustana Col; Law.*

ANDERSON, Scott Edward
Denfeld HS; Duluth, MN (250-450) A Cap Choir; Chor; Ensm; Y-Tns; Bsbl; Cr-Ctry; JV, Hockey; Co-Cpt, Swim; Tr; COM; HCt; *Mesabi St Col; Law Enforcement.*

ANDERSON, Shannon Marie
Punahou Sch; Honolulu, HI (206-417) Drama; Rptr, Hmrm; Pres, Yth of Unity; Chapel Comm; Service C; Co-Ch Make Up Crew; Stage Crew, Set Dsgn Crew, Shows; Church Talent Show; *Theater.*

ANDERSON, Sonja Marie
Lake Washington HS; Kirkland, WA; Fin, A Cap Choir; Fin, Ensm; *Northwest Nazarene Col; Mus.*

ANDERSON, Sonja Renea
Medina HS; Medina, TN (10%-25) BC; Chldr; Rptr, FHA; VP, Hmrm; Tres, SC; Var C; VP, Soph Cl; Cl Fav; HCt; Swtht.

ANDERSON, Stacey Lyn
Arvada Sr HS; Arvada, CO (13-545) Chor; NHS; ARC; Alt, GS; VP, Russian C; *Fine Arts.*

ANDERSON, Stanley
Glenville HS; Cleveland, OH; Band; Ensm; Math C; Orch; Tnns; *Ohio St U; Mus.*

ANDERSON, Steven
Glenville HS; Cleveland, OH; Band; Ensm; *Ohio St U; Mus.*

ANDERSON, Steven Joe
Greenland HS; Greenland, AR (1-45) Ann; BS; CYO; Hmrm; NHS; Sch P; SC; Var C; Bkbl; Cpt, Ftbl; Tr; Alg A; Cl Fav; Hist A; HKg; Hon Prog; Math A; Most Out; Val; Bookkeeping A; *U of Ark; Bus.*

ANDERSON, Steven Karl
Falls Church HS; Falls Church, VA (69-449) Band; *Naval Acad; Aviation.*

ANDERSON, Steven Robert
Crescent HS; Joyce, WA (2-31) Ann; CYO; NHS; Sch P; Soph Cl; Kiwanis A; NEDT; *Elec.*

ANDERSON, Stuart Mark
Crescent HS; Joyce, WA (1-18) Bus Mgr, Ann; NHS; Sch P; Sci C; SC; Pres, Jr Cl; Alg A; COM; Math A; NMS; NEDT; Val; Bookkeeping Champion; 2nd, Spelling Bee; *Seattle U; Math.*

ANDERSON, Suelaine Mae
Burlington Comm HS; Burlington, IA (5-475) Band; Dbte Tm; Model UN; NFL; NHS; Orch; ARC; Sci C; Span C; Spch C; NMS; ARC A; 1st Cl GSct; God & Comm A; *Bio.*

ANDERSON, Susan Denise
W Charlotte HS; Charlotte, NC; AFS; Band; VP, Chor; Hmrm; Key C; A-Ed, Lit Mag; Orch; Ski C; SC; *Art.*

ANDERSON, Susan Lynn
La Porte HS; LaPorte, TX (64-343) Chldr; NHS; Thes; Tr; COM; Swtht; Honorable Men, Art; Hon Graduate; WW; *San Jacinto Col; Bus.*

ANDERSON, Susan Marie
West HS; Madison, WI (140-596) Yth Fel; West HS Stu o-t Yr; Nom, Yth Achv; Co-Op Ed Prog; *MATC; Bus.*

ANDERSON, Tamela Jo
Century HS; Bismarck, ND (20-265) Band; JV, Chldr; Span C; Tr.

ANDERSON, Tamira J
Morse HS; San Diego, CA (10%-700) Bus Mgr, Model UN; Hockey; Swim; CSF; Hon Prog; MLS; Poet A; Type A; Ind Stu Prog; *Saint Marys Col; Humanities.*

ANDERSON, Tammi Lynne
Franklin Co HS; Rocky Mount, VA; Pres, Hmrm; SC; Tri-HiY; Sftbl; Tr.

ANDERSON, Tammy Jo
Eastwood HS; El Paso, TX (25%-1000) FHA; Tnns; Tr; Sci A; Spch A; Rptr, VOE; VOE A; Gym; *Pepperdine U; Bio.*

ANDERSON, Tammy Sue
Milton Sr HS; Milton, WI (34-188) Band; Drama; Secy, Fr C; 4H; Math C; 4H A; Yth Fel; Pres, Yth Group; Church Choir; *U of Wis; Nurs.*

ANDERSON, Tanya Lynn
Reidsville Sr HS; Reidsville, NC (66-344) Tres, AFS; Cpt, Chldr; Pres, Fr C; Ch, SC; *UNC-Greensboro; Anesthesiology.*

ANDERSON, Teresa Ann
Green Forest HS; Green Forest, AR (9-50) Ann; Band; BC; FBLA; FHA; Sch P; Sci C; Bkbl; *Evangel Col; Ed.*

ANDERSON, Terry Ann
La Sierra HS; Carmichael, CA (7-430) Band; Chor; 4H; Hmrm; Secy, SC; Sftbl; COM; 4H A; Hon Prog; Sci A; Pioneer Girls; Horsemanship, Mus, Achv, A's.

ANDERSON, Terry J
McEachern HS; Powder Springs, GA; Ann; Band; Fr C; HiY; Hmrm; Span C.

ANDERSON, Terry Lynn
Sunset HS; Beaverton, OR (50%-450) 4H; Orch; *Portland Comm Col; Childhood Ed.*

ANDERSON, Thomas Arthur
Paris HS; Paris, IL (18-240) Band; Tres, Key C; Tres, NHS; Pres, SC; Var C; Mgr, Bsbl; Ftbl; JV, Tnns; Wrest; Amer Leg A; Elk A; St Scholar; WW; Hon Ltr; *U of Ill; Lib Arts.*

ANDERSON, Thomas Elliott
Brandon HS; Brandon, FL; Key C; Cpt, Bsbl; Cpt, Ftbl; Amer Leg A; H of F; HCt; Pres, Stu Adv; *S Fla Jr Col; Phy Ed.*

ANDERSON, Timothy Reed
Greeley W HS; Greeley, CO (7-290) Ann; Chess C; Key C; Model UN; Sch P; Pres, SC; Var C; JV, Ftbl; Tnns; Hist A; Math A; Most Contributive; *U of Colo; Bus.*

ANDERSON, Timothy Wayne
Carl Schurz HS; Chicago, IL (47-696) Pres, Band; NHS; Orch; Co-Cpt, Ftbl; Hon Prog; St Scholar; Solo Trumpel, All City Band; Coaches A, Ftbl; *NE Ill U; Ed.*

ANDERSON, Tony Wayne
Chillicothe HS; Chillicothe, TX (5%-25) Ann; Dbte Tm; FFA; VP, Sr Cl; Bsbl; Bkbl; Cpt, Ftbl; Tnns; HCt; *Vernon Regional Jr Col; Agr.*

ANDERSON, Valerie Probin
Southwestern Central HS; Jamestown, NY; Chldr; Chor; Fr C; Ski C; Secy, Jr Cl; VP, Soph Cl; HCt; Win, Chldr Comp; Cand, Princess, Duchess; *Ashland Col; Sociology.*

ANDERSON, Vanessa
Surry Co HS; Elbron, VA (8-200) *Va St Col; Private Investigation.*

ANDERSON, Vanora Lauren
Francis T Maloney HS; Meriden, CT (10-350) Drama; Rptr, Sch P; Foreign Exchange Stu; *Journ.*

ANDERSON, Vickie Jane
Center HS; Center, TX; FHA; 4H; Tr; 4H A; *E Texas Baptist Col.*

ANDERSON, Virginia Dianne
Wakulla HS; Medart, FL; Ann; FBLA; Hmrm; Lit Mag; NHS; SC; Tres, Sr Cl; Tres, Jr Cl; Spch A; *Tallahassee Comm Col; Law.*

ANDERSON, Wanda Marie
Ashland HS; Ashland, WI (7-213) A Cap Choir; Ann; Band; Chor; FBLA; Hmrm; Model UN; NHS; SC; VP, Jr Cl; JV, Bkbl; Hon Prog; Vlbl; Jr Prom Court; *Bus.*

ANDERSON, William Eugene Jr
Paint Valley HS; Bainbridge, OH (7-89) BS; Chor; Lat C; NHS; Sci C; Span C; Mgr, Bsbl; Mgr, Bkbl; *Ohio St U; Law.*

ANDERSON, William Perry
Warwick Sr HS; Lititz, PA (90-260) Band; Chess C; Chor; Drama; Ensm; FFA; Hockey; Hon Choir; AVDA A; Co Chorus; Stage Band; Co Band; *Air Force Acad; Aircraft Mechanics.*

ANDERSON, William Robert
Vian HS; Vian, OK (1-60) Band; FFA; NHS; Masonic A; FFA A; *Northeastern Okla St U; Law.*

ANDERSON, Willie James
Benjamin Franklin HS; Rochester, NY (20-375) Chess C; Drama; Ger C; Hmrm; Ftbl; Tr; Wrest; Hon Prog; JA A; Masonic A; NEDT; *Hastings Col; Lit.*

ANDERZON, David Lane
Rockford E HS; Rockford, IL (93-607) Band; Chess C; NHS; Ftbl; Tr; *Rock Valley Col; Bus Mgt.*

ANDING, Bill David
Hopkins Eisenhower HS; Hopkins, MN; Chor; Sci C; Home Ec Dept Stu o-t Mon; Nursing Home Worker; Law Enforcement Explorer Post UP; *Alexandria Vo-tech Col; Law-Enforcement.*

ANDINO, Rosaura
Centro Oportunidad Edu Buchanan HS; Guaynabo, PR; Chor; Cooperacion A; *Universidad de Puerto Rico; Acct.*

ANDIS, Debbie Lee
Spencer HS; Spencer, IA; NHS; Rainbow; Ed, Sch P; Pres, Span C; Swim; Secy, Yth Fel.

ANDOL, Shirley Jane
Huron HS; Huron, SD (22-322) Band; Chldr; Chor; Dbte Tm; FBLA; Ger C; Fin, GS; Hmrm; Madrigal; NFL; Tres, Soph Cl; Type A; All St Band; *Augustana Col.*

ANDOW, Trudy Ayako
Kailua HS; Kailua, HI (200-570) FBLA; Hmrm; SC; Sr Cl; *Chaminade Col; Bus Adm.*

ANDRADA, John Henry
Haskell HS; Haskell, TX; Pres, CYO; FFA; 4H; JV, Bkbl; JV, Ftbl; JV, Tr; COM; *Tex Tech; Voc Agr.*

ANDRADE, Ana Esther
University Col o-t Sacred Heart; Santurce, PR (1-25) NHS; Alg A; COM; Hist A; Phy A; Sci A; Summa Cum Laude; Span A; Sociology A; Eng A.

ANDRE, Amy Elizabeth
Karns City Area HS; Karns City, PA; Band; Chor; Ensm; Mjrte; Rainbow; Bkbl; Cr-Ctry; Sftbl; Tr; Yth Fel; Worthy Advisor, Rainbow Girls; *Jameson Memorial Hos Sch of Nurs; Nurs.*

ANDRE, Katherine Ann
Bellevue Sr HS; Bellevue, NE (156-851) FBLA; *Central Col; Bus Adm.*

ANDRE, Lavergne Marcia
Colonie Central HS; Colonie, NY (35-627) Chor; NHS; Bkbl; Sftbl; Hon Prog; *Andrews U; Pre-Med.*

ANDREAS, Alisyn Arden
Winfield HS; Winfield, KS (44-215) Dbte Tm; Drama; NHS; Orch; JV, Tnns; *Kans U; Lib Arts.*

ANDREASSEN, James Allen
E Waterloo HS; Waterloo, IA; Band; Orch; Sch P; Bsbl; Cpt, Bkbl; *Bus.*

ANDREOZZI, Jonathan
S Philadelphia HS; Philadelphia, PA (8-1200) VP, A Cap Choir; VP, Chor; Drama; Amer Leg A; COM; Hon Prog; SC A; *Oral Roberts U; Pre-Med.*

ANDRESEN, Brenda Jean
Westside HS; Omaha, NE (76-760) Band; Fr C; FBLA; NHS; ARC; Tres, JA; Secy, Yth Fel; Outst Bus Stu; *Bethel Col; Bus.*

ANDRESEN, David William
Pass Christian HS; Pass Christian, MS (5-110) BC; COM; PTA A; Civics A; *Perkinston Jr Col; Marine Bio.*

ANDRESEN, Randall Ray
Chadwick HS; Chadwick, IL (1-23) Citz A; Val; High HR.

ANDREW, Mark Alan
Oak Hills HS; Cincinnati, OH (4-830) Demolay; NHS; Sftbl; Hon Prog; Intramural, Ftbl; Mary Rowe A; *Northwestern U; Physics.*

ANDREW, Sarah Emily
La Farge Pub HS; La Farge, WI (5-25) F-Ed, Ann; Band; Chor; Ensm; Ed, Sch P; COM; VofDEM; Yth Fel.

ANDREWARTHA, John Michael
Winston Churchill HS; San Antonio, TX (12-870) A Cap Choir; Band; Ensm; Lit Mag; Model UN; NHS; COM; Hist A; Hon Prog; Dist, Sweepstakes, Bands; 1st, Solo & Ensm; Outst Eng Stu A; *Baylor U; Mus.*

ANDREWS, Ashley Taylor
Darlington Sch; St Petersburg, FL; Chor; JV, Ftbl; JV, Soccer; *Acting.*

ANDREWS, Carolyn Ruth
Westfield HS; Westfield, NJ (128-660) A Cap Choir; Community Yth Symph; Fr C; Madrigal; VP, Mod Mus Mas; Orch; Ski C; Y-Tns; Interlochen Ntl Mus; Yth Fel; *Gettysburg Col; Mus.*

ANDREWS, Cathy M
Marcus Comm Sch; Marcus, IA; Co-Cpt, Bkbl; Tr; Tres, Church Yth; Vlbl; MVP, All St, All Conf, Bkbl; All Conf, St Meet, Tr; Most Improved, Bkbl; *Col of St Mary's; Recreation Ldr.*

ANDREWS, Charles Kenneth
Pine Forest Sr HS; Fayetteville, NC (200-500) Span C; Tnns; *Louisburg Col; Bio.*

ANDREWS, Cyril Blythe
King HS; Tampa, FL; *Talladega Col; Journ.*

ANDREWS, Damon Rodney
Round Rock HS; Round Rock, TX (30-300) Pres, A Cap Choir; NHS; Span C; Tr; All St Choir; *Baylor U; Acct.*

ANDREWS, Deborah Kay
Springfield SE HS; Springfield, IL (61-403) Bus C; Chor; FBLA; Hmrm; ARC; SC; Citz A; Hon Prog; Mus Fed A; *Cincinnati Bible Col; Church Secy.*

ANDREWS, Dena
Little Rock Central HS; Little Rock, AR; BC; Southernaires; NEDT Cert; *Rice U; Eng.*

ANDREWS, Denise
R C Mahar Reg HS; Orange, MA (6-170) Ann; Band; Chor; NHS; Rptr, Sch P; Pres, SC; Var C; Co-Cpt, Bkbl; Co-Cpt, Sftbl; MAC C; HR; Sci Fair; Outing C; Secy, SC; Fish & Game C; Usher; VP, Fresh Cl; Winter Carnival; Co-Cpt, Field Hockey; SC A; *U of Mass; Chem Engr.*

ANDREWS, Dorothy Jean
Manley HS; Chicago, IL (8-219) Secy, Bus C; Chor; FBLA; NHS; SC; MLS; Type A; Eng A; Chor A; *Bradly U; Bus Mgt.*

ANDREWS, Eileen Marie
Cary Grove Comm HS; Cary, IL (11-326) Band; CYO; Chor; Secy, NHS; Span C; Hon Prog; Sci A; St Scholar; *Col of Saint Benedict; Phys Therapy.*

ANDREWS, Elizabeth Waties
Liggett HS; Grosse Pointe, MI (5-75) A Cap Choir; Cum Laude Soc; Drama; Fr C; Ed, Lit Mag; Thes; COM; Harvard Book A; NMF; Phi Beta Kappa; Summa Cum Laude; Gym C; Sch Plays; Pres, Literary Mag; Grosse Pointe Alliance Francaise Cn; Hon Men, Mich Arts Coun, Poetry; *Smith Col; Theatre.*

ANDREWS, Helen Courtenay
Hardaway HS; Columbus, GA (25%-500) SC; MOD; HR; *Sweet Briar Col.*

ANDREWS, James Allen
Carver HS; Montgomery, AL; Pres, Chess C; Math C; Mu Alpha Theta; NHS; Sci C; SC; VP, Sr Cl; Hon Prog; ROTC A; Huntingdon Schol A; Drill Tm Ltr; *Huntingdon Col; Religion.*

ANDREWS, James Scott
Hernando HS; Brooksville, FL (29-412) Order/ Arrow; God & Country A; Eagle Sct; *Pasco-Hernando Comm Col; Sci.*

ANDREWS, Jay Ernest
Dodge Co HS; Eastman, GA; Anchor C; BS; HiY; Bsbl; Bkbl; Co-Cpt, Ftbl; Amer Leg A; 4H A; Journ A; Coaches Trophy; *Ed.*

ANDREWS, Jenny Leigh
I C Norcom HS; Portsmouth, VA; Band; Fr C; Sci A; *Shenandoah Conservatory.*

ANDREWS, Jill Lanette
Temple Heights Christian Sch; Tampa, FL; Band; Chor; NHS; COM; Sci A; Sci Fair; Band A; *Pensacola Christian Col; Nurs.*

ANDREWS, Kurt Charles
Perry HS; Perry, OK (12-88) BS; Hmrm; Pres, NHS; SC; MVP, Bsbl; Co-Cpt, Bkbl; Co-Cpt, Golf; Tr; Amer Leg A; Citz A; Hist A; HCt; Hon Prog; Lion A; Masonic A; Most Out; House of Reps, BS; Pep Coun; SC Del to St Conf; All Sch Revue; St Champion, High Jump; All Tourn, Bkbl; *U of Okla-Norman; Petroleum Engr.*

ANDREWS, Laurie Lou
Roseburg Sr HS; Roseburg, OR; 4H A; *UMPQUA Comm Col; Nurs.*

ANDREWS, Laverne Carroll
St Vincent Acad; Newark, NJ (9-70) Band; Chldr; Drama; NHS; Bkbl; Cpt, Soccer; Sftbl; Swim; Tr; Alg A; COM; Cl Fav; Math A; MLS; Gym A; Most Ath; *Computer Sci.*

ANDREWS, Linda Elaine
Fort Pierce Central HS; Fort Pierce, FL (46-587) Hmrm; VP, NHS; Ftbl; Tr, St Stu Congress; SC; Hon Prog; Most Out; Pres, Sigma Lambda Chi Service C; Pres, Distributive Ed; *Indian River Comm Col; Radiology.*

ANDREWS, Linda Marie
Hancock Central HS; Sparta, GA; Chor; 4H; NHS; Sci C; Up Bound; *Atlanta Area Tech Sch; Med Asst.*

ANDREWS, Lisa Louise
Arcadia HS; Arcadia, CA; A Cap Choir; Hmrm; Pres, Pol Sci C; ARC; Mgr, Tr; *Law.*

ANDREWS, Lisa Maria
Red Hill HS; Bridgeport, IL (13-118) Ann; Secy, Band; Chor; Ensm; NHS; Sch P; *Brigham Young U; Special Ed.*

ANDREWS, Lori June
S Kitsap HS; Port Orchard, WA (5-555) A Cap Choir; Chor; Spirit, 4 0 GPA, A's; *Fort Stelicome Comm Col; Acct.*

ANDREWS, Mary Helen
Brandon HS; Brandon, FL (15%-1200) Mjrte; HR; *FSU.*

ANDREWS, Michael John
Clear Creek HS; League City, TX (1-550) BS; Fr C; Math C; Model UN; Mu Alpha Theta; Secy, NHS; A-Ed, Sch P; St Stu Congress; JV, Bkbl; Alg A; Journ A; Math A; Q&S A; *Baylor U; Law.*

ANDREWS, Michael Wayne
Robert E Lee HS; Tyler, TX (97-606) NHS; SC; Thes; Var C; Ftbl; COM; Hon Prog; NEDT; Rotary A; *Tyler Jr Col; Bus.*

ANDREWS, Michelle Annette
Inglewood HS; Inglewood, CA (84-360) Fr C; Hmrm; Maranatha Bco Schol; *Calif St U; Law.*

ANDREWS, Mollie Mae
Roseburg Sr HS; Roseburg, OR; Chor; 4H; COM; 4H A; Schol Achv A; Elem Atheics A; *Umpqua Comm Col; Sci.*

ANDREWS, Nancy Rai
King HS; Tampa, FL; Chldr; Beauty; COM; Learned Lions; *Fisk U; Bio.*

ANDREWS, Paige Lynne
Cambridge S Dorchester HS; Cambridge, MD (6-286) NHS; JV, Hockey; *Nurs.*

ANDREWS, Robin Craig
Hillcrest HS; Memphis, TN (45-230) Band; Chess C; Key C; Math C; Tnns; WW; *Memphis St U; Pre-Med.*

ANDREWS, Scott Kevin
Port Huron HS; Port Huron, MI; Work Study Prog Grant; *St Clair Co Comm Col; Law Enforcement.*

ANDREWS, Shirley
St Joseph's Notre Dame HS; Alameda, CA (1-78) NHS; Span C; Alg A; CSF; COM; Citz A; Hist A; Hon Prog; NEDT; Spch A; *U of Cal at Hayward; Psych.*

ANDREWS, Susan Fay
King HS; Tampa, FL (86-619) VP, Anchor C; Hmrm; Lat C; NHS; Y-Tns; Tnns; COM; HCt; Vlbl; *Fisk U; Biol.*

ANDREWS, Tanner Robert
Penncrest HS; Media, PA (53-470) Mu Alpha Theta; Math Tm; *Computer Software.*

ANDREWS, Teresa Ann
Tuscaloosa HS; Tuscaloosa, AL (295-561) Band; Chor; FBLA; Ch, Hmrm; Jr Civitan; Marching Band; Central Ala Yth Fel Off; Candystriper A; *U of Ala; Legal Secy.*

ANDREWS, Tony
Halter HS; Wellston, MO (4-150) Chor; Rptr, Sch P; Pres, Soph Cl; Wrest; Alg A; Hon Prog; Wrestling A; *Math.*

ANDREWS, Valorie Lynn
Los Alamitos HS; Los Alamitos, CA (83-683) NHS; CSF; *Calif St Col; Special Ed.*

ANDREWS, Vanessa Renee
The Summit Ctry Day Sch; Cincinnati, OH (24-37) Chor; *Social Psych.*

ANDREWS, Vickie Elaine
W S Neal HS; Brewton, AL (20-130) *Jefferson Davis Jr Col; Bus.*

ANDREWS, William Thomas
Struthers HS; Struthers, OH (17-275) Band; Bus C; Drama; FTA; NHS; Thes; Mus A's; Bookkeeping Cert; *Youngstown Col of Bus; Acct.*

ANDRS, Allen Frank
Thomas Dale HS; Chester, VA; Band; Bkbl; JV, Tr; Math A; Pres A; Church Sftbl.

ANDRUS, Daniel Mark
Iver C Ranum HS; Denver, CO (89-625) *Asbury Col.*

ANDRUS, Denise Lynn
Elmira Southside HS; Elmira, NY (1-475) Band; Ensm; NHS; Sch Achieve Tm; Span C; Sftbl; Hon Prog; Math A.

ANDRUS, Elizabeth Kaye
Robert H Goddard HS; Roswell, NM; VP, Chor; Rainbow; All-St Choir; Worthy Adv; Grand Cross of Color; Outst Jr Girl; *WTSU; Elem Ed.*

ANDRUS, Robert Herman
Oakdale HS; Oakdale, LA; Key C; NHS; Order/ Arrow; A-Ed, Sch P; H of F; Hon Prog; Fr A; *LSU; Animal Sci.*

ANEX, Patrick Lawrence
Highline Sr HS; Seattle, WA (100-450) VP, Chem C; Ftbl; Soccer; Fin, Sftbl; Fin, Tr; VP, VICA; *Highline Col; Bus.*

ANEY, Julie Aney
U S Grant HS; Portland, OR; A Cap Choir; Chor; Ensm; Madrigal; Model UN; ARC; *East Oreg St; Pre-Nurs.*

ANGEL, Margaret Ann
West HS; Knoxville, TN; Drama; VP, FHA; NFL; Spch C; Y-Tns; COM; Spch A; *U of Tenn; Home Ec.*

ANGEL, Mark Brantley
Hibriten HS; Lenoir, NC (30-170) Band; Monogram; Order/Arrow; SC; Pres, Soph Cl; Bkbl; Ftbl; God & Country A; Order/Arrow A; Yth Fel; Eagle Sct; Pres, Stu Body; Pres, Fresh Cl; *UNC; Pol Sci.*

ANGEL, Richard Lance
Searcy HS; Searcy, AR (1-233) BC; Key C; NHS; Sch P; Span C; Bsbl; Bkbl; Ftbl; Tr; Math A; *Med.*

ANGELETY, Cheryl Ann
Francis T Nicholls Sr HS; New Orleans, LA; CYO; Fr C; IBM; VASAU; Service A; *U of New Orleans; Computer Prog.*

ANGELL, Deborah Lynn
Central Sr HS; Providence, RI (6-288) Chldr; FNA; Sci C; Chem A; DARGCA; Hon Prog; Phy A; Sci A; RI Hon Soc; Tel Fad; Med Explorer; Eng A; *Indiana U; Phys Therapy.*

ANGELL, Mary Scott
Claremont HS; Claremont, CA; Chor; Community Yth Symph; Ensm; Key C; Orch; CSF; Bell Choir; John Child Walker Mus A; *U of Calif; Psych.*

ANGELL, Samuel John Bowne
Rhinebeck HS; Rhinebeck, NY (1-130) Band; Chor; Hmrm; VP, Lat C; NHS; Orch; SC; Alg A; Elk A; NEDT; Area All-St, Orch; 2nd, Elks C A; *Earlham Col; Pol Sci.*

ANGELLE, Guy
Cecilia HS; Cecilia, LA (2-300) Parl, K of C; Ftbl; Sftbl; Sci A; *U of SW La; Mech Engr.*

ANGIONE, Maria Louise
St Joseph's o-t Palisades HS; W New York, NJ (10-289) Secy, Span NHS; Sal.

ANGLEA, Faye Eileen
Central Baptist HS; Hampton, VA (3-14) Band; Chor; Ensm; Monogram; A-Ed, Sch P; Sftbl; COM; DARGCA; H of F; Hist A; Hon Prog; Type A; DAR Hist A; Most Ath; Most Studious; *Bob Jones U; Secondary Ed.*

ANGLIN, Dale Edwin
Athens HS; Troy, MI (22-406) A Cap Choir; Pres, Band; Chess C; Drama; NHS; MVP, Orch; Order/ Arrow; Var C; Tnns; God & Country A; Hon Prog; Order/Arrow A; Megaphone A; *Olivet Nazarene Col; Engr.*

ANGLIN, Glenda A
N Gwinnett HS; Suwanee, GA (10%-120) BC; Tres, FBLA; FHA.

ANGLIN, Michael George
Forest Park Sr HS; Forest Park, GA (7-600) BC; Dbte Tm; Hmrm; VP, Span C; Parl, SC; Alg A; COM; PC Jr Fel; Eng A; *Chem.*

ANGOTTI, John David
Notre Dame HS; Clarksburg, WV (2-55) Key C; Lat C; VP, SC; Ftbl; Tnns; Alg A; Math A; NEDT; *W Va U; Med.*

ANICH, Barbara Katherine
Ashland HS; Ashland, WI (23-208) Ann; Community Yth Symph; Model UN; Orch; Pres, Ski C; Secy, SC; Pres, Var C; MVP, Bkbl; Sftbl; Tr; Cpt, Bkbl; Ntl HS Orch A; *U-W at LaCrosse; Phys Therapy.*

ANIKIN, Donna Bernadette
Carmel HS; Carmel, NY (11-320) Band; Bus C; Chldr; VP, Chor; Drama; Ensm; Hmrm; NHS; Orch; COM; NYSSMA Mus Solo A; Frederick Chopin Piano A; *SUNY at Albany; Bus Adm.*

ANKROM, Karen Darlene
Madison Heights HS; Anderson, IN (27-293) Band; Chem C; Chor; Tres, Drama; Ger C; Rainbow; Sci C; Tres, Thes; Chamber of Comm A; *International Bus Col; Fashion Merchandising.*

ANKROM, Karen Karlene
Madison Heights HS; Anderson, IN (27-373) Band; Chor; Tres, Drama; Ger C; Rainbow; Sci C; Tres, Thes; Chamber of Comm A; *International Bus Col; Fashion Merchandizing.*

ANKROM, Sandra Jean
Zane Trace HS; Old Washington, OH (1-65) Ann; Band; Secy, Chor; VP, 4H; NHS; SC; Secy, Soph Cl; Alg A; 4H A; St Missionette Qn; Geom A; *Christian Service.*

ANNALA, Nancy Jean
Luther L Wright HS; Ironwood, MI (9-178) Co-Ed, Ann; Secy, Drama; Fr C; Thes; NMS; *Mich Tech U; Computer Sci.*

ANNEN, Janelle Louise
Winnebago HS; Winnebago, MN (15%-36) Chor; Drama; FHA; Ger C; Bkbl; Sftbl; Swim.

ANNIBALLI, Dean Robert
Newburgh Free Acad; Newburgh, NY (62-850) Band; Chor; Regent Schol; Tres, Yth Fel; Church Bkbl; *St U of NY; Phar.*

ANNIS, Douglas Wayne
Chamberlain HS; Tampa, FL; *U of S Fla; Bus.*

ANNIS, Laurie Jean
Merrill Sr HS; Merrill, WI (102-345) Bus Mgr, Ann; Chor; Span C; SC; Journ A; *U of Wis; Social Work.*

ANNIS, Tamara Gwyn
Tabernacle Baptist Sch; Va Beach, VA; FTA; ARC; Hyles-Anderson Col; *Elem Ed.*

ANNIS, William Phillip
Hesperia HS; Hesperia, MI (9-80) *Gustavus Adolphus Col; Med.*

ANNUNZIATA, Janet Lee
Norfolk Cath HS; Norfolk, VA; Co-Ed, Ann; FFA; Pol Sci C; Bkbl; Powderpuff Ftbl; *Horticulture.*

ANNUNZIO, Zoan Ruth
Park Hill Sr HS; Kansas City, MO (13-450) Band; FBLA; FHA; Hmrm; Pres, NHS; Cpt, Ski C; Tres, SC; VP, Var C; Cpt, Bkbl; JV, Tnns; Tr; COM; Pres A; Regent Schol; Cand, St Cl Qn; Quietest Girls Tr Tm; Cl Offices; *Phillips U; Med Tech.*

ANOBILE, Graciela Elvira
Glendale Acad; Glendale, CA (8-68) Chor; Lit Ral; Span C; Bsbl; Bkbl; Ftbl; Sftbl; Citz A; *Loma Linda U; Nurs.*

ANONSEN, Tammy Lynn
Central Baptist Sch; Hampton, VA (3-21) Ann; Chor; Secy, Hmrm; COM; Citz A; Type A.

ANSCHUTZ, Janet Ann
Topeka HS; Topeka, KS (10%-500) Hon Prog; Type A; 'B' Avg A; *Washburn U; Bus.*

ANSTETT, William Joseph
Las Vegas HS; Las Vegas, NV (25%-320) City Conf; Dbte Tm; NHS; Spch C; Var C; Sftbl; Cpt, Tnns; COM; Hon Prog; MVP, Tnns; Bowl; *Bus.*

ANSTEY, Toni Yvonne
Chula Vista HS; Chula Vista, CA; Lt, Cpt, Drill Tm; *Pacific Col; Med Receptionist.*

ANTAL, Martha Ann
Chaney HS; Youngstown, OH (42-367) Band; NHS; Span C; Church Choir; Secy, Church Yth Group; *Youngstown St U; Nurs.*

ANTAL, Thomas Jess
Chaney HS; Youngstown, OH (8-486) A Cap Choir; Band; Chor; NHS; Bio A; NMF; *U of Dayton; Computer Sci.*

ANTES, Jeffery Scott
Elmira Southside HS; Elmira, NY (10-300) Band; Chor; Community Yth Symph; VP, Key C; Model UN; Tres, NHS; Sch P; Span C; Thes; Cr-Ctry; Hon Prog; Lion A; Regent Schol.

ANTHON, Michael Dwayne
Middletown HS; Middletown, RI; Bsbl; Bkbl; Ftbl; ROTC A; Yth Fel; Drill Tm; HR; Yth For Christ C.

ANTHONY, Avril Dawn
Hillcrest HS; Queens, NY; Chor; Rptr, Sch P; Sci C; Yth Leg; Sunday Sch Teacher; Domestic Sci Cl; Acolyte's Group; *Med.*

ANTHONY, Connie June
Oceanside HS; Oceanside, CA; Chldr; Bkbl; Soccer; Swim; COM; *Mira Costa Col; Court Stenographer.*

ANTHONY, Donna Marie
Eustace HS; Eustace, TX (5-61) BC; FHA; Parl, 4H; ARC; A-Ed, Sch P; Mgr, Bkbl; Mgr, Tr; 4H A; MLS; ARC A; *X-Ray Technology.*

ANTHONY, Kathy Francine
Venus HS; Venus, TX (2-11) Ed, Ann; Drama; FHA; Sch P; Spch C; Pres, Sr Cl; Secy, Jr Cl; Bkbl; Semi-Fin, Tr; Citz A; HQn; Math A; 'A' HR; Miss VHS; PA; Home Ec A; Best All Around Girl; *N Tex St U; Commercial Art.*

ANTHONY, Kristi Elizabeth
Kenton Ridge HS; Springfield, OH (38-200) VP, FHA.

ANTHONY, Lamar
Motley HS; Columbus, MS (10-81) Rptr, HiY; Bkbl; Cl Fav; *U of Ga; Bus Adm.*

ANTHONY, Marjorie Ann
Reynolds HS; Greenville, PA (1-207) Band; Chor; Span C; Tres, Soph Cl.

ANTHONY, Marnice
Northwest HS; St Louis, MO (11-652) *Military.*

ANTHONY, Michael Lamar
Glenn HS; Birmingham, AL (4-126) Ann; Pres, NHS; Sch P; Span C; Pres, SC; Cl Fav; Hon Prog; ROTC A; *Samford U; Law.*

ANTINOZZI, Joseph Rudolph
Marian HS; Hometown, PA (32-150) MVP, CYO; Chor; NHS; SC; Var C; MVP, Bkbl; Cr-Ctry; Tr; *Notre Dame Col; Sci.*

ANTLEY, Sandra Deanne
Orangeburg Wilkinson HS; Orangeburg, SC (20%-400) Bus C; *U of SC; Child Care.*

ANTOLINI, Cynthia Elaine
Elkins HS; Elkins, WV (6-240) Co-Ed, Ann; VP, CYO; GS; 4H; NHS; VP, SC; Tres, Tri-HiY; Var C; Tnns; Exchange Stu; Cl Couns; Scholastic Achv A; *W Va Wesleyan Col.*

ANTONACCI, Dominic Anthony Jr
Brimfield HS District 309; Brimfield, IL (1-53) Band; Pres, FFA; 4H; K of C; NHS; Ntl Yth Conf; SC; Var C; Bkbl; Cr-Ctry; Tr; COM; 4H A; I Dare You; JA A; St Scholar; Val; Pres, Section V FFA; St Farmer FFA; *Ill Central Col; Agr.*

ANTONELLIS, Pamela Marie
Sparta HS; Sparta, IL (21-160) Dbte Tm; WW; Best Novice Tm Trophy; Lit A; Sociology Cert of A; Debate Excel Cert; *Sou Ill U; Psych.*

ANTONIUK, Sonia Julia
Immaculate Conception HS; Hamtramck, MI (6-44) Co-Cpt, Chldr; Chor; NHS; MVP, Chldr; *Wayne St U; Optometry.*

ANTONSON, Kristi Arlene
Westview HS; Braham, MN; FHA; Mjrte; Rptr, Sch P; Tres, Soph Cl; Snow-Daze Qn Cand; B-HR; *St Cloud Beauty Col; Cosmetology.*

ANTONSON, Peggy Sue
Eisenhower Sr HS; Lawton, OK (85-560) Hmrm; Madrigal; NHS; Span C; Tri-HiY; *Baylor U; Spch Pathology and Audiology.*

ANTRIM, Melissa Lynn
Pompano Bch HS; Pompano Bch, FL (26-527) Cpt, Chldr; Secy, Lit Mag; NHS; Sch P; Kiwanis A; Pres A; Yth Fel; WW; *Fla Atlantic U; Ed.*

ANTTILA, Janice Kay
Ralston HS; Ralston, NE (37-296) Band; Chor; Fr C; NHS; Thes; Fr A; Band Serv A; *U of Nebr-Lincoln.*

ANTWINE, Cornelius Martin
Vicksburg HS; Vicksburg, MS (33-244) Pres, Band; CYO; Pres, Drama; NHS; SC; Cl Fav; *Alcorn St U; Mus.*

APEL, Betty Jane
Madison C-3 HS; Madison, MO (2-29) BC; Fr A; WW; *Northeast Mo St U; Acct.*

APKE, Susan Carol
John T Hoggard HS; Wilmington, NC (87-590) Band; Ger C; Sch P; Mgr, Bsbl; Bkbl; Sftbl; COM; MLS; All Conf, Bkbl; *UNC; Computer Sci.*

APODACA, Shirley Jean
Post Falls HS; Post Falls, ID; Drama; A-Ed, Sch P; SC; Bkbl; Hon Prog; Journ A; Spch A; VFW Orator Win; VofDEM; Pep C; Drill Tm; Vlbl; Gym; *N Idaho Col; Communication Arts.*

APONTE, Diana Felisa
Nuestra Senora de la Providencia; Rio Piedras, PR (2-32) Tres, CYO; Chor; Secy, 4H; Pres, Hmrm; COM; 4H A; Hon Prog; Yth Foundation A; Conduct A; *U of Puerto Rico; Med.*

APONTE, Noel
Barringer HS; Newark, NJ; Hon Prog; *Rutgers U; Med.*

APONTE, Rafael
Notre Dame HS; Caguas, PR (4-136) VP, Chem C; Chess C; Drama; JETS; NHS; Tr; Alg A; COM; Chem A; Hon Prog; Most Out; Ntl Sci Found; Sci A; Spch A; *Cornell U; Chem.*

APPEL, Daniel Mark
Mercy HS; Red Bluff, CA (1-30) Drama; Fr C; Secy, Jr Cl.

APPEL, Gene Brian
Lincoln Comm HS; Lincoln, IL (18-340) Band; Thes; Pres, Jr Cl; Civics, Band Directors Key, A's; *Lincoln Christian Col; Ministry.*

APPEL, Jerry Richard
Northwood-Kensett HS; Northwood, IA (10-65) Pres, 4H; NHS; SC; JV, Cr-Ctry; Tr; 4H A; *Iowa St U Ames; Law.*

APPEL, Ruth Ann
Milford Township HS; Milford, IL (8-56) Band; Chor; Ensm; FHA; Pres, 4H; NHS; Bkbl; Sftbl; Tr; 4H A; Hon Prog; *Parkland Jr Col; Mus.*

APPELL, Jeffrey Leonard
Hebrew Acad HS; Yonkers, NY (3-16) Chess C; Math C; F-Ed, Sch P; Span NHS; Var C; Bkbl; Cpt, Ftbl; MVP, Hockey; Tr; *Harvard U; Law.*

APPERSON, Mark Wayne
Colo HS; Colo City, TX (2-95) Ann; Band; Ensm; NHS; Journ A; NMS; Sal; Swtht; *Baylor U; Math.*

APPLEBY, Audrey Ann
Elgin HS; Elgin, OK (2-70) Chor; FHA; NHS; Rainbow; Secy, SC; Alg A; Masonic A; MLS; Type A; Chaplain, Band; Most Intelligent; All Region Band; John Philip Sousa Band A; *Okla St U; Law.*

APPLEGATE, Cynthia Annette
Neshaminy Maple Point HS; Langhorne, PA (24-388) Secy, NHS; Mgr, Swim; *Temple U; Biol.*

APPLEGATE, David Glenn
Monterey Bay Acad; Watsonville, CA (15%-150) Ger C; ARC; Ski C; Pres, SC; JV, Bsbl; JV, Ftbl; Soccer; Fin, Tr; *Pacific Union Col; Journ.*

APPLEGATE, Martha Elizabeth
Scotland HS; Laurinburg, NC (10%-500) Drama; Span C; NEDT; Nom, Gov Sch.

APPLEGATE, Michael Dale
Scotland HS; Laurinburg, NC (10%-400) Ann; Chess C; VP, NHS; Pres, Sci C; Mgr, Bsbl; Mgr, Bkbl; Cr-Ctry; Bio A; Gov Honor Prog; Math A; NMF; NMS; NEDT; Spch A; Annual Photographer; Carswell Schol; *Wake Forest U; Biol.*

APPLEGATE, Stephen Mason
Woodford Co HS; Versailles, KY (20%-323) BC; Key C; SC; JV, Bkbl; Tnns; Yth Fel; Folk & Ctry Dance Tm; Exchange Stu, Denmark; *U of Ky.*

APPLEGATE, Tina Marie
Melvin-Sibley HS; Melvin, IL; Band; Chor; Ensm; FHA; Madrigal; *Parkland Col; Bus.*

APPLETON, Forrest Ronald
Taylors Falls HS; Taylors Falls, MN (5-41) A Cap Choir; Rptr, Ann; Band; Chor; Hmrm; Orch; Sci C; SC; Var C; Bsbl; Bkbl; Ftbl; Tr; HCt; Best Free Throw Bkbl; *Bemidji St U; Communications Media.*

APPLING, James Walter
Rebecca Comer HS; Eufaula, AL (3-64) Drama; FFA; 4H; Hmrm; NHS; SC; 4H A; Sci A; Spch A; Art C; *Sci.*

APPLING, Valerie Jean
Baker HS; Columbus, GA; Chor; Military Ball Qn; JA; Team Lift; HS ROTC; *Clark Col; Acct.*

APRIL, Nancy Lee
Chester HS; Chester, PA (17-673) Band; Chor; Key C; Tnns; *Washington And Jefferson Col; Biol.*

AQUINO, Bernadette J
Kohala HS; Kapaau, HI (1-78) AFS; Band; Tres, FHA; Hmrm; Mjrte; NHS; F-Ed, Sch P; SC; *Cannons Interntl Bus Col; Secretarial.*

AQUINO, Floriza Rose
St Joseph's Notre Dame HS; Alameda, CA (4-78) CYO; NHS; Cr-Ctry; Tr; CSF; COM; Ca; Hist A; Hon Prog; Spch A; *U of San Francisco; Computer Sci.*

ARABIE, Ramona Rosalie
St Charles Borromeo HS; Destrehan, LA; BC; Co-Cpt, Chldr; Secy, Sr Cl; Tres, Soph Cl; Bkbl; Sftbl; HQn; HCt; All Dist, Bkbl; *Nicholl's St Col; Acct.*

ARABIS, Thomas Anthony
Neshaminy Maple Point HS; Langhorne, PA (10-415) NHS; Var C; Soccer; Tr; Cpt, Wrest; HR; WW; *NE Bible Col; Bible.*

ARANGO, Anna Maria
Miami Springs Sr HS; Miami Springs, FL (30-750) Anchor C; Band; CYO; Ger C; Hmrm; Secy, Sci C; COM; Hon Prog; MLS; Foreign Lang Hon Soc; Girls Soccer Supporting C; *U of Miami; Sci.*

ARANT, Darrell Ray
Hanahan HS; Hanahan, SC; Band; NHS; JV, Ftbl; Tr; *U of SC; Elec.*

ARANT, Lynda Carol
Indianola Acad; Indianola, MS (5-100) Chor; S-T, 4H; Secy, Hmrm; Lat C; Madrigal; NHS; VP, Y-Tns; Bkbl; Alg A; Amer Leg A; 4H A; Most Outst Choral A; *Miss St U; Acct.*

ARBANASIN, Robert Mark
St Mary's HS; Stockton, CA (14-204) CYO; Fr C; Hmrm; Tres, Key C; Lit Mag; Model UN; NHS; Phys C; Ed, Sch P; Tres, SC; Var C; Tres, Sr Cl; Tres, Jr Cl; Tres, Soph Cl; Co-Cpt, Ftbl; Tr; CSF; COM; DARGCA; Hist A; Hon Prog; Journ A; Most Out; NEDT; Rotary A; Yth Leg; All League, All City, Ftbl; *U o-t Pacific; Phar.*

ARBES, Debra Kay
El Reno HS; El Reno, OK (10%-250) Bus C; Chor; Ensm; FHA; Secy, Hmrm; SC; Secy, Jr Cl; Mgr, Tr; COM; OSU Academic Achv A; Psych A; *Okla St U; Psych.*

ARBOGAST, Myra Lynn
Old Mill Sr HS; Glen Burnie, MD (10%-650) Fr C; 4H; Ed, Lit Mag; NHS; SC; Var C; Cpt, Swim; Semi-Fin, Tr; 4H A; Sci A; Pom-Pom; Mus A; MVP, Swim; Cpt, Fin, Gym; Art A; *Psych.*

ARBUCKLE, Andrea Dawn
Manual HS; Peoria, IL (27-410) *U of Ill; Med.*

ARBUCKLE, Elana Lanye
Manual HS; Peoria, IL (141-360) Afro-Amer C.

ARBUCKLE, James Edward
Permian HS; Odessa, TX (140-668) Band; Ensm; Orch; Ftbl; Tr; Most Out; Spch A; Star Student; Pres, VICA; Pres, Dist VICA; All St, All Region Bands; Outst Drafting A; Outst Band; VP, St VICA; *Odessa Col; Mech Engr.*

ARBUTHNOT, Becky Ann
Weber HS; Pleasant View, UT (23%-525) Band; Community Yth Symph; Ger C; Hon Prog; W-Pin; Excel, Ntl Ger Exam; Excel, Wrld Bnd Comp, Switzerland; *U of Utah; Ed.*

ARCE, Jorge Alberto
St Augustine HS; Laredo, TX (3-68) Math C; MLS; HR; *Laredo Jr Col; Acct.*

ARCE, Maria De Lourdes
St Augustine HS; Laredo, TX (10%-70) Ann; GS; Math C; NHS; HR; Essay A; *Laredo Jr Col.*

ARCE, Martha Abigail
Tabernacle Christian Acad; San Diego, CA (1-8) Chldr; Co-Cpt, Dbte Tm; Drama; Fr C; ARC; Spch C; Cl Fav; Poet A; ARC A; Spch A.

ARCH, Janet Ruth
Cherokee HS; Cherokee, NC; VP, BC; Monogram; SC; Tr; Gr Marshal; Most Out; Corresponding Secy, SC; Achv A; *Med.*

ARCHE, Arturo C
Notre Dame HS; Caguas, PR (10%-137) Chem C; JETS; Lit Mag; COM; Hon Prog; Phy A; Sci A; Span A; *Princeton U; Sci.*

ARCHER, Delwin Eugene
Justin F Kimball HS; Dallas, TX (37-530) FBLA; Mu Alpha Theta; NHS; Span C; Span NHS; JV, Bsbl; JV, Bkbl; COM; Hon Prog; Yth Fel; Geom A; *Dallas Baptist Col; Psych.*

ARCHER, Lora Faye
Winnetonka HS; Kansas City, MO; Ch, Bus C; Chor; Ch, FBLA; ARC; COM; PTA A; Vlbl; *Law.*

ARCHER, Lori Rochelle
Sandusky HS; Sandusky, MI (12-146) Band; Chldr; NHS; *Central Mich U.*

ARCHER, Marjorie Mary
Westwood Christian HS; Miami, FL; Chldr; Sftbl; Sal; Home Ec A; HR; *Dade South Col; Primary Ed.*

ARCHER, Rhonda Jean
U S Grant HS; Oklahoma City, OK; Tres, Band; NHS; Span C; Outst Sr; Mus, US Grant Band; *Central Baptist Col; Special Ed.*

ARCHER, Sonya Gail
McMinn Co HS; Athens, TN; BC; FHA; Campus Life; Tn for Christ; Tenn Office Ed C.

ARCHER, Virginia Ina Jo
Sangre De Criste Christian Sch; Canon City, CO; Chldr; Chor; Sftbl; Citz A; Cl Fav; Mus, Art, Drama, A's; Vlbl; *Hyle's U; Missionary.*

ARCHEY, Caroline Elizabeth
Denbigh HS; Newport News, VA (59-488) Fr C; *Va Commonwealth U; Med Tech.*

ARCHIBALD, Janice Michele
Music and Art HS; New York, NY (169-524) Band; Chor; Mus Hon A; *Marymount Man Col; Spch and Hearing.*

ARCHIBALD, Willa Jennett
Wasatch Sr HS; Heber, UT; Band; Fr C; Ch, FFA; Ch, SC; Chamber of Comm A; Val; St HS Short Story Contest; *Utah St U; Vet Med.*

ARCHIE, Andrea Pearl
Richard J Reynolds Sr HS; Winston-Salem, NC (330-825) Chor; Tres, FHA; *Forsyth Tech Inst; X-Ray Tech.*

ARCHIE, Hazel Elise
Paisley HS; Winston-Salem, NC (219-668) Chor; MVP, Sftbl; MVP, Tnns; Tr; Beauty; Delta Sigma Theta A; God & Country A; HQn; Most Out; Yth Fel; *Bus.*

ARCHILLA, Wanda Ivelisse
Our Lady of Pilar HS; Hato Rey, PR (10%-148) VP, Chor; Model UN; Spch C; Tres, Span NHS; COM; *Gainesville Col; Architecture.*

ARCHULETA, Lori
Dell City HS; Dell City, TX (2-33) Chldr; 4H; NHS; SC; Bkbl; Tnns; Tr; Hist A; Ready Writing A.

ARD, Susan Annette
J J Pearce HS; Richardson, TX; NHS; JV, Bkbl; DARGCA; Hon Prog; Church Yth Coun; Ntl Piano Guild; Church Yth Choir; *Baylor U.*

ARDOVINO, Vincent Jarvis
Harry S Truman HS; Bronx, NY (16-700) VP, Ann; BS; Chess C; Dbte Tm; Hmrm; Pres, Key C; Lit Mag; Math C; VP, NHS; ARC; Sci C; Ski C; Ftbl; JV, Hockey; JV, Soccer; COM; Hon Prog; Magna Cum Laude; Regent Schol; Summa Cum Laude; UFT Schol; *City Col of NY; Med.*

AREHART, Theresa Viola
Upper Scioto Valley HS; Guffey, OH (7-46) Secy, BC; Tres, FHA; NHS; Sup Ratng, Sch Sci Fair; Fitness; Alt, GS; Yth Conf, St FFA; Home Ec Cert, St Fair; *Columbus Tech Col; Elec.*

AREL, Paul Norman
London HS; London, OH (6-187) Tr; Cpt, in The Know; *Computer Programming.*

ARELONG, Florence
Marshall Islands HS; Majuro, MARSHALL IS-LANDS; Alg A; Hon Prog; Math A; Most Out; Star Student.

ARELONG, Moana
Marshall Island HS; Majuro, MARSHALL IS-LANDS (1-103) Semi-Fin, AFS; Alg A; Bio A; Hon Prog; Star Student; *Maui Comm Col; Acct.*

ARENAS, Ortencia
Palo Duro HS; Amarillo, TX (20-445) Bus Mgr, Band.

ARENCIBIA, Amarily
Our Lady of Good Counsel HS; Newark, NJ (2-60) CYO; Chor; NHS; Span C; SC; Pres, Jr Cl; Rptr, Chaplain, Co-Ed-Y; Eng A; Pep C; Powder-Puff Ftbl; Rifle Drill Tm; All Co Band; *Georgetown U; Therapeutic Recreation.*

ARENCIBIA, Marisela Caridad
Our Lady of Good Counsel HS; Newark, NJ (10-84) CYO; Chor; NHS; Span C; SC; Citz A; Teacher.

ARENDSHORST, Jane Ellen
Holland HS; Holland, MI (16-310) JV, Chldr; NHS; Orch; Var C; Tres, Sr Cl; Tnns; Hon Prog; Interlochen Ntl Mus; Journ A; *Ohio Wesleyan U; Spch Pathology.*

ARENDT, Judy Carol
St Croix Lutheran HS; W Saint Paul, MN (15-47) Ann; Chor; Drama; Hmrm; Tr; *Sociology.*

ARENDT, Roberta Lynn
Gainesville HS; Gainesville, TX (3-184) Chor; Pres, NHS; NEDT; All St Choir; Ceramic A's; *Cooke Co Col; Mus.*

ARENSMANN, Frank Wesley Jr
E Alton-Wood River Comm HS; Wood River, IL (20-320) Pres, Ger C; Tnns; *St Louis Col of Phar; Phar.*

ARENSMEYER, Anthony Sim
Munford HS; Munford, AL; Math C; A-Ed, Sch P; Var C; Ftbl; Aerospace A; *Eckard Col; Pilotry.*

AREVALO, Alvin D
Cumberland Valley HS; New Kingstown, PA (24-622) Band; Tres, NHS; Pres, SC; Var C; Bkbl; *Med.*

AREVALO, Thomas Vincent
St Joseph o-t Palisades HS; W New York, NJ (19-225) French NHS; Math C; NHS; Cr-Ctry; Co-Cpt, Soccer; Tr; COM; Hon Prog; K of C A; *Newark Col; Sci.*

AREY, Janet
Wade Hampton HS; Greenville, SC (10%-400) Pres, Hmrm; NHS; Span NHS; SC; Co-Cpt, Tnns; *Clemson Col; Economics.*

ARGENTO, B John
S Charleston HS; S Charleston, WV (220-300) Order/Arrow; ARC; SC; Tr; *W Va Tech Col; Vet Med.*

ARGUELLES, Joaquin
Marine Military Acad; Harlingen, TX (2-58) Var C; Ftbl; Swim; Superintendent List.

ARGUESO, Dolly Margarita
Our Lady of Pilar HS; Rio Piedras, PR (20%-166) Chem C; Hmrm; Lit Ral; Secy, Model UN; NFL; COM; *Yale U; Biochem.*

ARHUTHNOT, Michele Rae
Montpelier HS; Montpelier, OH (14-104) Cpt, Band; Fr C; NHS; Pres, Rainbow; ARC; Var C; Tr; *Bus Adm.*

ARIMA, Mark T
Dinuba Joint Union HS; Dinuba, CA (1-160) AFS; InterAct C; InterClub Coun; Span C; SC; Pres, Sr Cl; Pres, Jr Cl; MVP, Golf; Bank Of Amer A; Bausch & Lomb A; Bio A; CSF; COM; Chamber of Comm A; Citz A; DARGCA; I Dare You; MLS; NEDT; PTA A; Rotary A; Type A; Val; CSF Seymour Mem Fin A; Central Ca Dist Coun; Japan Amer Citzn League Achv A; *Reedley Col; Phar.*

ARISMENDI, Christopher Mark
St Mary's HS; Stockton, CA (5-256) JV, Bkbl; JV, Tnns; Hon Prog; Star Student; Span A.

ARKET, Joe Anthony
Notre Dame-Bishop Gibbons HS; Schenectady, NY (15-160) NHS; JV, Bkbl; Ftbl; Tr; Hon Prog; *Niagara Col; Law.*

ARKWRIGHT, Daryl Lynn
Parchment HS; Parchment, MI (10-200) FNA; NHS; Rptr, Sch P; Span C; Var C; Tr; Hon Prog; Future Nurs A; *Western Mich U; Med Research.*

ARLINE, Wanda Lee
John F Kennedy HS; Suffolk, VA (50-230) Band; Chem C; Citz A; HCt; HR; PA; *Va St U; Pediatrician.*

ARLT, Karma Kae
Ritzville HS; Ritzville, WA; Band; Ger C; Fin, Jr Miss Pagent; NHS; ARC; Bkbl; MVP, Tr; Most Out; Pres A; Vlbl; Most Inspirational; *CWSC; Vet Sci.*

ARMACOST, Martha Hayden
Ottawa HS; Ottawa, KS (25-197) Drama; Pres, Span C; Parl, SC; Hist A; VP, GAA; Drill Tm; Gym; Eng A; Pep C; Drill Tm A; Gym Ltrs; Baptist Yth Fel; Secy, Guild Girls; Presidential Phys Fitness A; *U of Redlands.*

ARMAN, Timothy Mark
Harbor Springs HS; Harbor Springs, MI (10-74) Band; FFA; Bkbl; Ftbl; Cpt, Sftbl; *Mich St U; Vet Med.*

ARMAND, Harry Richard
Brooklyn Tech HS; Brooklyn, NY; Amer Leg A; Sci A; Traffic Engr; *Bradley U; Structural Engr.*

ARMEL, Bryan Nevin
Latrobe Sr HS; Latrobe, PA (15-518) AFS; Ger C; 4H; NHS; Sci C; Sftbl; Bio A; COM; Chem A; Hon Prog; NML; *VPI; Forestry.*

ARMENDARIZ, Veronica
Hobbs HS; Hobbs, NM (61-497) GS; Pres, NHS; SC; COM; JA A; Pres A; *Saint Mary's Col; Communications.*

ARMENT, Kelley Renae
Columbus Sr HS; Columbus, NE; Sftbl; Yth Fel; Ch, DECA; Vlbl; DECA Blue Seal; *Med.*

ARMGARD, Christine Lynne
Glenbard S HS; Glen Ellyn, IL (10%-323) Chldr; Hmrm; Ski C; SC; COM; Hon Prog; Dance C; Semi-Fin, St Gym.

ARMINGTON, Deborah Ruth
Geneva Secondary Sch; Geneva, OH (50%-250) Band; Drama; Fr C; 4H; Ski C; Thes; Amer Leg A; 4H A; *Psych.*

ARMSTEAD, Katherine
Norman Thomas HS; NY, NY (166-805) FBLA; Hmrm; Sch Achieve Tm; Hon Prog; Bookkeeping & Bus Law Certs; *Pace U; Acct.*

ARMSTEAD, Roy Richard Jr
Robert E Lee HS; Montgomery, AL; A-Ed, Ann; Key C; Mu Alpha Theta; VP, SC; Cl Fav; Fav, Anchor C; Fel of Christian Stu; Rptr, Gym C; Friendliest; *Ed.*

ARMSTRONG, Alice Camille
Clarksdale HS; Clarksdale, MS (3-30) BC; Drama; 4H; Hmrm; SC; Bkbl; HCt; Type A; *U of Sou Miss; Archt.*

ARMSTRONG, Anna Vernice
Simon Gratz HS; Philadelphia, PA (1-450) FTA; Hmrm; NHS; St Scholar; Val; WW; *U of Pitts; Med Technology.*

ARMSTRONG, Anne Elizabeth
Jefferson Co HS; Dandridge, TN (20%-473) AFS; Band; Ensm; Ger C; ARC; Swim; COM; God & Country A; 4H A; Hon Band; Pom Pon Ltr; Candystriper; Ntl Piano Guild, Mus C, Poetry, A's; 1st Cl Sr Plan Brd, Women in Action; Sailing C; Opportunity, G Scts; *Med.*

ARMSTRONG, Arlene
Thornton Township HS; Harvey, IL (234-893) Chor; Drama; Spch C; Thes; S-T, Thorton Theatre Tech; Rep Congress C; Purple X C; *Manchester Col; Journ.*

ARMSTRONG, Cheryl Kay
Triway HS; Wooster, OH (40-170) Band; Cpt, Chldr; Chor; Drama; Ensm; 4H; SC; Hon Prog; Spch A; Yth Fel; Prom Qn; Miss Triway; Ways and Means Comm; *Bus.*

ARMSTRONG, Cleotha Napoleon
Callaway HS; Jackson, MS; Bsbl; JV, Bkbl; Ftbl; *Jackson St U.*

ARMSTRONG, Constance Priscilla
Lincoln HS; Dallas, TX; Band; Key C; Math C; NHS; Sci C; Chem A; Cl Fav; JA A; Algebra Cert; Keywanetes C, Advanced Band A's; *Sou Methodist U; Chem Engr.*

ARMSTRONG, Deanna Lynn
Issequah HS; Issaquah, WA; Community Yth Symph; NHS; Orch; Mgr, Tr; Vlbl; *Seattle Pacific U; Teaching.*

ARMSTRONG, Denise R
Louisville Sr HS; Louisville, OH; SC; Secy, Sr Cl; JA A; *Mo Baptist Bible Col; Bible Study.*

ARMSTRONG, Derek Anthony
Eatern Sr HS; Washington, DC (17-626) Co-Ch, Chor; Citz A; Hon Prog; Humanities A; Consecutive Hon; Superintendent's A; *U of Pittsburgh; Pol Sci.*

ARMSTRONG, Dewey Thurman Jr
Goodlettsville HS; Goodlettsville, TN (10%-185) Hmrm; VP, Lat C; Sch Achieve Tm; SC; Pres, Jr Cl; Bsbl; Bkbl; Ftbl; *Vanderbilt U; Math.*

ARMSTRONG, Jana Lou
Fort Scott Sr HS; Fort Scott, KS; Chldr; Dbte Tm; Drama; Fr C; Pres, NFL; Ch, SC; Thes; Tr; NMF; NMS; Regent Schol; Val; VofDEM; *U of Kans; Math.*

ARMSTRONG, Joey Carroll
Chico HS; Chico, TX (2-30) Ed, Ann; BC; FFA; VP, Jr Cl; Pres, Soph Cl; Bsbl; Bkbl; Ftbl; Tr; Alg A; COM; Chem A; Hon Prog; Math A; MLS; Most Out; Sci A; Spch A; Star Student; Agr A; Eng A; Fin, St Beta P; *Tex Tech at Lubbock; Engr.*

ARMSTRONG, John Allen
Lincoln HS; Lincoln, CA (2-169) Band; Chess C; Drama; VP, 4H; Sch P; Pres, Span C; VP, SC; Cpt, Ftbl; Golf; Cpt, Wrest; Bank Of Amer A; CSF; NMF; Chem Engr; Semi-Fin, PG&E Schol; *U of Sou Calif; Chem Engr.*

ARMSTRONG, Karen Lavona
Sumner HS; St Louis, MO (72-419) FBLA; Hon Prog; Type A; Attendance; *Forest Park Jr Col; Morticianing.*

ARMSTRONG, Kathy Louise
Amarillo HS; Amarillo, TX (300-546) Chor; FHA; Hmrm; SC; FCA; *Amarillo Col; Homemaking.*

ARMSTRONG, Kimberly Nan
Thornwell HS; Clinton, SC (2-30) Ann; Band; BC; Cpt, Chldr; Fr C; VP, 4H; Secy, Hmrm; Bkbl; Sftbl; 4H A; Hist A; *Clemson U.*

ARMSTRONG,
 Lawrence Channing
Menchville HS; Newport News, VA; Key C; Lat C; Pres, Order/Arrow; Cr-Ctry; Tr; Order/Arrow A; Pres A; Eagle Sct; Exchange Stu; Order o-t Arrow A Brotherhood.

ARMSTRONG, Lisa Kaye
Central HS; Savannah, TN (47-271) Secy, FHA; Pres, Lat C; Tres, Jr Cl; FHA Chor; Alt, GS.

ARMSTRONG, Lori Anne
Abingdon Sr HS; Abingdon, IL (3-120) Band; Ensm; Span C; Church Choir; High Hon A; Bowl Tm; Alpha Gamma Nu Sorority; *Carl Sandburg Jr Col; Math.*

ARMSTRONG, Maria Gloria
Milpitas HS; Milpitas, CA (8-304) CYO; Hmrm; MVP, Swim; Bank Of Amer A; Gemco A; *San Jose City Col; Bus.*

ARMSTRONG, Mark Jordan
Alfred Bonnabel HS; Metairie, LA (36-530) A Cap Choir; BS; Chor; Ensm; Pres, FBLA; Key C; Semi-Fin, Lit Ral; NHS; Tres, SC; COM; Cl Fav; Pres A; Type A; All St Chor; Dist Hon Chor; Stu Activity Coordinator A; Chor A; *Loyola U; Mus Ed.*

ARMSTRONG, Mary Elizabeth
St Joseph HS; Toms River, NJ (10-250) CYO; Tr; Amer Leg A; Citz A; Hon Prog; K of C A; Most Dependable.

ARMSTRONG, Patricia Ann
James H Bowen HS; Chicago, IL (101-518) Bowl; Daisy A, GSct; *N Ill U; Pre-Med.*

ARMSTRONG, Rebecca Jean
Kickapoo HS; Springfield, MO; A Cap Choir; Anchor C; Band; Secy, CYO; Chor; Secy, FTA; *Drury Col; Elem Ed.*

ARMSTRONG, Richard Anthony
Baker HS; Baker, LA (44-374) Pres, HiY; Co-Cpt, Ftbl; Outst Christian Athlete A; Sportsmanship A; *U of Southwestern La; Ed.*

ARMSTRONG, Richard Whitney
Haverlin Central Sch; Bath, NY (50%-210) Pres, VP, Tres, NYI; *Wanakena Col; Conservation.*

ARMSTRONG,
 Robert Eugene Jr
Kickapoo HS; Springfield, MO; A Cap Choir; Key C; Math C; VP, Sci C; Span C; Math A; Sci A; Spch A; Gold Medal, Math Relay; *Sou Mo St U; Engr.*

ARMSTRONG, Robert Wilburn
High Point HS; Beltsville, MD; Chor; *Mus.*

ARMSTRONG, Robyn Michelle
Kalamazoo Jr Acad; Kalamazoo, MI (2-8) Ed, Sch P; *Andrews U; Math.*

ARMSTRONG, Terry Micah
Lake Clifton Sr HS; Baltimore, MD; Fr C; NHS; SC; Tnns; Hist A; Hon Prog; Sci A; Scholastic Points A; Service A; Extra Curricular Points A; Tnns As; Fr A; PA.

ARMSTRONG, Valerie Ann
Whitehall HS; Whitehall, MI (25%-150) Band; JV, Chldr; NHS; SC; JV, Bkbl; Tr; Co Yth Advisory Bd; 1st Cl, GSct; Sun Sch Teacher; *Olivet Col; Med.*

ARNDT, Barbara Jean
Leeton HS; Leeton, MO (5-21) Chldr; Chor; VP, FHA; Madrigal; Pres, SC; Secy, Jr Cl; Pres, Soph Cl; Bkbl; Sftbl; HCt; Pres, Pep C; Bkbl, Sftbl, A's; *Central Mo St U; Phys Ed.*

ARNDT, Cheri Monique
Ossining HS; Ossining, NY (60-390) All Amer Yth; NHS; Cpt, Sftbl; MVP, Sftbl; Woman Sport Ath o-t Yr; Field Hockey; JA; Most Ath, Sr Cl; All-Co Sftbl; Columbus Lod Bst Female Sch Ath; *Bentley Col; Acct.*

ARNDT, Cherizelle Monique
Ossining HS; Ossining, NY (60-375) All Amer Yth; Tres, Bus C; CYO; NHS; Cpt, Hockey; Cpt, Sftbl; Most Ath; HS All-Amer; Woman Sport Ath o-t Yr; *Bentley Col; Acct.*

ARNDTSEN, Karen Marie
Arlington Sr HS; Poughkeepsie, NY (11-735) Mjrte; Fin, Swim; Hon Prog.

ARNDTSON, Bruce Arnold
Hastings Sr HS; Hastings, MN (270-506) 4H; Cpt, Soccer; 4H A; All Conf Hon Men, Soccer; Ch, March of Dimes; Bike- a- thon.

ARNEACH, Teresa Elaine
Cherokee Central HS; Cherokee, NC (3-55) Band; VP, BC; Mjrte; Monogram; Tres, Jr Cl; Bkbl; Sftbl; Gr Marshal; Math A; Jr Cl Academic A; *U of NC at Chapel Hill; Phys Therapy.*

ARNESON, Connie Kay
Timberline HS; Weippe, ID (5-80) Ann; Chldr; 4H; NHS; Sch P; Ski C; S-T, Soph Cl; 4H A; 1860 Days Princess.

ARNETT, Jeffrey David
Huntsville HS; Huntsville, AL; Sch P Photographer.

ARNETT, Julie Ann
Salem HS; Salem, MO (24-179) Secy, Drama; Jr Miss Pagent; Art C; Dramatic Schol; Vlbl; Powder Puff Ftbl & Bkbl; Best Female Actor; *SW Mo St U; Dramatics.*

ARNETT, Patricia Ruth
Wheelersburg HS; Wheelersburg, OH (34-126) Band; Chess C; Chor; Ensm; Fr C; 4H; Lat C; Sch P; Sci C; Sftbl; Tr; 4H A; Spch A; High Point, Tr; Rescue Trng Cert; 1st Pl, Art Show; *Ohio St U; Biol.*

ARNEY, Kristi Kay
Lindale HS; Lindale, TX (33%-100) Ann; Arch; Cpt, Chldr; Arch; Bkbl; Golf; Tnns; HCt; Soph Duchess; Ann Staff Swtht; *Tex A&M U; Vet.*

ARNOLD, Abigail
Gilmer Co HS; Glenville, WV (30-122) Band; Chldr; Chor; Mjrte; ARC; Var C; Bkbl; Tr; *Fairmont St Col; Vet Med.*

ARNOLD, Anna Melissa
Corsicana HS; Corsicana, TX (10%-319) A Cap Choir; Band; S-T, FHA; SC; JV, Tnns; DARGCA; Most Outst Soph Girl, NHS; Eng A; Co Yth Exposition Outst Stu.

ARNOLD, Bryce Elliott
Lutcher Stark HS; Orange, TX; *Lamar U.*

ARNOLD, Cheryl Ann
Gorman HS; Gorman, TX (3-32) Chldr; Drama; FHA; A-Ed, Sch P; Span C; Spch C; VP, Jr Cl; Secy, Soph Cl; Mgr, Bkbl; Tr; Beauty; Hon Prog; VP, Church Yth Group; *Psych.*

ARNOLD, Craig Steven
Eastern HS; Middletown, KY (22-288) Bus C; Chor; Ger C; NHS; Bkbl; Citz A; Hon Prog; Speed Scientific Sch; Engr.

ARNOLD, Daniel Edward
Herbert Hoover Jr HS; Kenmore, NY; Ann; Ger C; Math C; NHS; Hon Prog; Yth Fel; BSct.

ARNOLD, Diane Susan
East Peoria Comm HS; E Peoria, IL (50%-500) AFS; Band; Ger C; Secy, Jr Cl.

ARNOLD, Edwina Marie
Lely HS; Naples, FL (21-288) Anchor C; Chor; Dbte Tm; Secy, InterAct C; NHS; Spch C; SC; Elk A; Hon Prog; Spch A; *Trevecca Nazarene Col; Religion.*

ARNOLD, Joey Lynn
Constantine HS; Constantine, MI (50%-136) Band; 4H; Var C; Y-Tns; JV, Ftbl; Tnns; Tr; Wrest; COM; Rotary A; Most Improved Wrestler; Var Ltr.

ARNOLD, Karen Denise
Rossville HS; Rossville, GA (11-212) Ann; Band; BC; Hmrm; Y-Tns; Sftbl; Math A; Star Student; Type A; Tres, Pom Pom Sq; Yth Church Choir; Tres, Pep C; Homecoming Queen; GAA; Attendance A; *Dalton Jr Col; Computer Programming.*

ARNOLD, Laura Elizabeth
Oak Hills HS; Cincinnati, OH; Chor; Ensm; Rptr, Hmrm; ARC; SC; Tr; COM; Citz A; Hist A; Math A; PTA A; Camper of Week; *Christian Service.*

ARNOLD, Lonnie Dale
Cleveland HS; Seattle, WA; A Cap Choir; Chor; Fin, Ntl Yth Conf; Bkbl; Kiwanis A; Comm Service Bureau; *Southwestern Christian Col; Bible.*

ARNOLD, Lori Kay
Texas City HS; Texas City, TX (115-473) Band; Community Yth Symph; FHA; Lit Ral; Mjrte; Orch; Thes; Career C; *U of Tex; Med Lab Tech.*

ARNOLD, Mary Caroleen
Oak Hills HS; Cincinnati, OH (30-860) Chor; Drama; Ensm; Tres, NHS; Cpt, Sch Achieve Tm; Tr; Citz A; Hon Prog; NMS; Pres A; Comm A; 'It's Academic' Tm; Bsbl Statistican; *Milligan Col; Nurs.*

ARNOLD, Pamela Ann
Eden Valley-Watkins HS; Eden Valley, MN; Band; Chor; FHA; Orch; Ski C; Star Student; *Bus.*

ARNOLD, Paula Rene
Bay City HS; Bay City, TX (250-900) Band; Ensm; ARC; ARC A; Flag Rank; Gym.

ARNOLD, Russell Eugene
Monroe Area Comp HS; Monroe, GA (48-192) FFA; Bsbl; Tres, FCA; *Athens Tech U; Off Mach Repair.*

ARNOLD, Sandra Darlene
Crestview Sr HS; Crestview, FL; Band; FTA; *U of Fla; Math.*

ARNOLD, Susan Joy
Smoky Hill HS; Denver, CO (5-493) A Cap Choir; JV, Chldr; NHS; JV, Swim; JV, Tnns; Opt A; *Concordia Col; Elem Ed.*

ARNOLD, Suzette Michelle
Lindale HS; Lindale, TX (10%-110) All Amer Yth; Band; Drama; FHA; Mjrte; NHS; Sch P; Spch C; SC; Beauty; Hon Prog; Q&S A; Swtht; WW; Ftbl Swtht; Miss Tyler Tn Cinderella; Drum Major; FFA Swtht; *TCU; Elem Ed.*

ARNOLD, Walter Richard
Kings Park Sr HS; Kings Park, NY (116-480) Hmrm; Math C; Pol Sci C; Rptr, Sch P; Sci C; Co-Ch, Var C; Bkbl; Ftbl; Cpt, Soccer; Alg A; I Dare You; Math A; Sci A; Coach, Cath Yth; Win, Project Aim; Cpt, LaCrosse; Litergury C; Coast Guard Auxiliary; Stu Advisor; Secy, Acad C; *US Coast Guard Acad; Oceanography.*

ARNOLD, William Michael
Herrin HS; Herrin, IL (4-251) Chor; NHS; Hon Prog; St Scholar; *Sou Ill U; Math.*

ARNWINE, Perry Dean
McCurtain HS; McCurtain, OK (2-14) BS; Bus C; Chem C; Math C; NHS; Co-Cpt, Bsbl; Co-Cpt, Bkbl; Hist A; HKg; Sal; *Eastern Okla St; Engr.*

AROLA, Margaret Louise
William Kelley HS; Silver Bay, MN (25%-147) AFS; Band; Chldr; Chem C; Drama; Fr C; NHS; Pres, Ski C; SC; Tnns; Tr; NMS; Sci A; VFW A; Yth Fel; Fr C; Interntl Sci Fair; Cr-Ctry Ski Tm; Band A; Americans Abroad; *The Col of Saint Catherine; Bio.*

ARON, Barbara Joann
Arsenal Tech HS; Indianapolis, IN;

ARONSON, Elaine Tracy
Hebrew Acad of Nassau Co; Uniondale, NY; Chor; Drama; NHS; Rptr, Sch P; COM; PTA A; Hon Cert; Fr A; Mem A; *MIT; Chem.*

ARPAJIAN, George Girard
Upper Darby Sr HS; Upper Darby, PA; Band; Hmrm; Orch; SC; Tr; DAR Essay A; Mus A; Orch A; *Mus.*

ARRANTS, George Reed Jr
Athens Jr HS; Athens, TN (7-94) Chor; Hmrm; NHS; Order/Arrow; SC; Tnns; God & Country A; HCt; Kiwanis A; Order/Arrow A; Eagle Sct.

ARRIAGA,
 Francisco Byron Caleb
Farragut HS; Chicago, IL (18-280) VP, Lat C; NHS; VP, SC; VP, Sr Cl; Alg A; COM; Cl Fav; Hon Prog; *Ill Inst of Tech; Elec Engr.*

ARRIAGA, Moises Alberto
Jesuit HS; New Orleans, LA (6-230) Chess C; Pres, Dbte Tm; Lat C; Lit Ral; NFL; Sci C; Pres, Spch C; Secy, SC; Soccer; Amer Leg Orator A; COM; Journ A; Spch A; 1st Pl, Lit Rally; Best Elocutionist; Greek A; Eng A; *Med.*

ARRINGTON, Belinda Renee
Music And Art HS; New York, NY; Fr C; Bkbl; Tr; Sci A; Tr & Dancing A's.

ARRINGTON, Darlean Smith
W S Creecy HS; Rich Square, NC (10-42) 4H; VP, Hmrm; COM; 4H A; Eng, Bookkeeping, A's.

ARRINGTON, Dexter Edwin
Alma J Brown Lab HS; Grambling, LA (2-50) Co-Cpt, Band; Ensm; FTA; VP, 4H; Semi-Fin, Lit Ral; Sci C; Spch C; SC; Pres, Soph Cl; Mgr, Bkbl; Bio A; Chem A; Citz A; 4H A; Hon Prog; Math A; NEDT; Phy A; Sci A; Span A; Hist, SC; Career Poster, Fr, A's; *La Tech U; Med.*

ARRINGTON, Felecia Arleen
Norview HS; Norfolk, VA (192-642) Pres, FHA; FNA; Y-Tns; *Nurs.*

ARRINGTON, Ted William
Hillside HS; Durham, NC; MVP, Soccer.

ARRINGTON, Velina Joyce
HS of Music And Art; New York, NY (268-495) Band; Chor; Sch Achieve Tm; Tr; COM; Hon Prog; Ntl Achv Schol; Phys Ed & Reading A's; *Wooster Col; Psych.*

ARROUES, Denise Michele
San Gorgonio HS; San Bernardino, CA (60-900) Chldr; Semi-Fin, GS; Hmrm; Tres, NHS; SC; JV, Bkbl; Tnns; CSF; COM; Citz A; HCt; *Westmont Col; Eng.*

ARROYO, Ana Ivelyse
Colegio Universit Sagrado Corazon; Santurce, PR (1-39) Band; Swim; Hon Prog; *Marine Bio.*

ARROYO, Blanca I
Superior Dr Pila HS; Ponce, PR; Chor; Hmrm; SC; COM; Cl Fav; Lion A; Type A; *Interamericana-San German; Techologia Medica.*

ARROYO, Francisco
Adlai E Stevenson HS; Bronx, NY (29-788) Cpt, Gym; *Biochem.*

ARROYO, Luz Ivette
Luis Munoz Marin HS; Cabo Rojo, PR (8-200) CYO; Dbte Tm; Bus Mgr, FHA; 4H; InterAct C; Lit Ral; ARC; Sci C; Span C; SC; Alg A; COM; Hon Prog; ARC A; *Recinto Universitario Mayaguez; Farmacia.*

ARSEMENT, Phyllis Kay
Nederland HS; Nederland, TX; Anchor C; CYO; Bus Mgr, Chldr; Drama; Secy, FHA; FTA; Co-Ed, Sch P; Spch C; Math A; HR; Tex Readers C; *Lamar U; Teacher.*

ARTEAGA, Isabel Priscilla
Juan Jose Osuna HS; Hato Rey, PR (5-150) Chldr; Chor; Fin, Dbte Tm; Pres, Hmrm; ARC; Alg A; COM; Citz A; Cl Fav; Hist A; Hon Prog; Lion A; Math A; Sci A; Star Student; Vlbl; Good Behavior A; *U of Puert Rico; Bus Adm.*

ARTECHE, Danny
Deming HS; Deming, NM; Band; Pres, CYO; Tnns; Mgr, Wrest; *NM St U; Criminology.*

ARTER, Michelle Patrice
Jamaica HS; Jamaica, NY; Band; NHS; ARC; COM; Citz A; Hon Prog; ARC A; Cert of Hon; Service League; Creative Arts Soc; Arista; *Med.*

ARTHUR, Jacqueline Ann
Kountze HS; Kountze, TX; Math C; Phys C; *Tex Tech Col; Med.*

ARTHUR, John Michael
Coppell HS; Coppell, TX (1-22) Ed, Ann; Band; Pres, BC; Chor; Pres, Drama; Ed, Sch P; Pres, SC; Pres, Thes; Pres, Sr Cl; VP, Jr Cl; Pres, Soph Cl; Ftbl; Tnns; Hon Prog; MLS; Val; Mr CHS; Board Member, Pub Lib; Interntl Thespian; *N Tex St U; Mus.*

ARTHUR, Laura Jean
Northwest HS; Indianapolis, IN; Cpt, Band; Chor; Rptr, Sch P; Sci C; Span C; SC; VP, Thes; Y-Tns; Tnns; COM; Spelling Bee A; Choir A; Drama A; *Journ.*

ARTHUR, Mary Julia
Grimsley Sr HS; Greensboro, NC (15%-625) Bkbl; VP, Yth Fel; Page for Gov; Exchange Stu, Switzerland; *Calif St U; Law.*

ARTHURS, Robert Lee
E Central HS; Tulsa, OK (25%-650) Chess C; Pres, Bsbl; HR; *Central Bible Col; Ministry.*

ARTISON, Edmonay Wanda
Thomas Jefferson HS; Los Angeles, CA; Secy, Chor; Up Bound; *UCLA; Law.*

ARTMAN, Jeffrey Mark
Falls Church HS; Falls Church, VA (100-500) NHS; Span NHS; JV, Ftbl; Tr; JV, Wrest; *Pa St U; Engr.*

ARTMAN, Scot Andrew
Reynolds HS; Greenville, PA (5-183) AFS; A-Ed, Ann; Band; Drama; Secy, Lat C; Thes; Var C; Mgr, Wrest; Gov Honor Prog; Art Service C; HR; Blue Ribbons, Art; *Art.*

ARTUSO, Renee Michele
Maple Shade HS; Maple Shade, NJ; CYO; Hmrm; Tres, SC; *Chestnut Hill Col; Psych.*

ARTZ, Dynda Lou
Springfield HS; Springfield, IL (2-479) A Cap Choir; AFS; Chor; Drama; Hmrm; Math C; NHS; Tres, SC; VP, Sr Cl; VP, Jr Cl; VP, Soph Cl; HCt; Tres & Pres, Span C; Stu o-t Week; Hugh O'Brien Yth Ldr; Optimists Stu o-t Week.

ARVIN, Sharon Jean
Central Sr HS; York, PA (100-300) Drama; Yth Fel; Pres, Yth Fel; Swim A; Bowl A.

ASA, Sandra Jayne
San Marcos HS; Santa Barbara, CA; Band; Chor; ARC; Bkbl; Hockey; Sftbl; Swim; Tr; Improvement A; Sailing C; Trackettes; Pep C; *W Nebr Sch of Nurs; Nurs.*

ASBILL, Dale Lewis
Trinity Sr HS; Trinity, NC; Band; Fr C; Yth Fel; *Math.*

ASBURY, Anthony Bash
Sam Houston HS; Arlington, TX (350-700) A Cap Choir; Chor; Secy, Drama; Ensm; NFL; Order/Arrow; Sch Achieve Tm; Spch C; Secy, Thes; World Affairs C; Opt A; Outst Achv, Drama; Best Actor, Dist, Area & Region; *Amer Acad of Dramatic Arts; Theatre.*

ASBURY, Gilla Louise
Eufaula HS; Eufaula, OK (16-98) *Tulsa Jr Col; Acct.*

ASCENZI, Daniel James
Pennsville Mem HS; Pennsville, NJ (40%-250) JV, Bsbl; JV, Bkbl; COM; *Engr.*

ASENCIO,
 Andria Mercedes Salva
Academia San Jorge; Santurce, PR; Chor; Fr C; InterAct C; Pres, Model UN; NHS; Span C; Tres, Soph Cl; COM; Chem A; Eng Phorensic A; *Universidad de Puerto Rico; Psych.*

ASH, Catherine Susan
Gustine HS; Gustine, CA (7-85) FBLA; FHA; Vlbl; *PCBBC; Mus.*

ASH, Jerry Richard
Mt Healthy HS; Mt Healthy, OH (40-496) BC; Hmrm; NHS; Y-Tns; Co-Cpt, Bsbl; *Ohio St U; Horticulture.*

ASH, Kellee Delaine Katherine
Bishop Moore HS; Orlando, FL (2-198) Ann; CYO; Drama; NHS; Bkbl; Math A; Sal; Scholastic Achv A; *St Mary's Col; Math.*

ASH, Kenneth Patrick
North HS; Bakersfield, CA; Ger C; JV, Tr; JV, Wrest; CSF; Pres A; *Math.*

ASHAMALLA, Rosemarie Ann
The Buckley Sch; Sherman Oaks, CA (8-52) F-Ed, Ann; NHS; COM; Chem A; Hon Prog; Math A; NMS; NEDT; HR; Director's List; *Stanford U; Biological Sci.*

ASHBEE, James Cleveland
University Military Sch; Mobile, AL (20-60) Hmrm; Key C; SC; Swim; Hon Coun AE Fraternity; Gayfers Tn Board; *U of Ala; Optometry.*

ASHBROOK, Myrna Suzanne
Big Wlanut HS; Sunbury, OH; A Cap Choir; FHA; Swim.

ASHBURN, Anna Priscilla
Savannah Ctry Day Sch; Savannah, GA (14-67) Ann; Cpt, Chldr; Chor; Pres, Commercial C; Lit Mag; NHS; JV, Bkbl; Hon Prog; *Davidson Col; Advertising.*

ASHBURN, Donna Jean
Shawnee Mission W HS; Overland Park, KS (12-600) Bus C; Fr C; Pep C; Hostess, Wrest; HD Shotwell Fr A; *Juco Col; Ed.*

ASHBURN, Kristen Joy
Torrington HS; Torrington, CT (25-550) Drama; Hmrm; Ch, Span C; Hon Prog; Math A; *Med.*

ASHBURN, Wanda Rose
Clarkrange HS; Clarkrange, TN; BC; FHA; Sch P; Spch C; *Bus.*

ASHBY, Charles Roger Jr
Iroquois HS; Louisville, KY; Amer Leg A; Opt A.

ASHBY, Donna Gayle
Ketron HS; Kingsport, TN (20-160) Anchor C; Ed, Ann; Tres, BC; GS; Hmrm; Tres, SC; Pres, Y-Tns; VP, Jr Cl; Bkbl; Sftbl; Tnns; Cl Fav; Opt Out Tn; Pres, Hiking C; Astra C; Tn o-t Wk; *E Tenn St U; Hist.*

ASHCRAFT, Ricky Jack
Elmore Co HS; Eclectic, AL; Pres, Band; BC; Pres, Ensm; Bus Mgr, Sch P; H of F; All St Band; *Auburn U; Mus.*

ASHCRAFT, Sandra Jean
Mannington HS; Mannington, WV (20-109) Drama; VP, Fr C; Hmrm; Mjrte; VP, NHS; SC; *Fairmont St Col; Allied Health.*

ASHCRAFT, Shari Lynn
Davenport HS; Davenport, IA (130-803) Fr C; FTA; Hmrm; Lit Mag; Sch P; Span C; Hon Prog; Journ A; Q&S A; Yth Fel; Co-Ed, Yrbk; Off, Tns for Crippled Children; Pres, Yth Group; Pres, Church Choir; *Palmer Jr Col; Communications.*

ASHER, Gregory Brian
Westminster HS; Westminster, CO (4-789) Chor; NHS; Bsbl; *Colo Sch of Mines; Engr.*

ASHER, Rhonda Lee
Eastwood HS; El Paso, TX (20-989) Band; Chor; Ensm; NHS; Orch; COM; Spch A; Jr NHS; Flute Solo, A; Span Spch Tm; Woodwind Ensm, A; Hon Ment, Art & Sci; Top 10 Tns; Handicapped Vol, A; *Counseling of Young People.*

ASHFORD, Ruth Ellen
Franklin Road Christian Sch; Murfreesboro, TN; Cpt, Chldr; Drama; Ensm; Spch C; Most Outst, Chldr; *Hyles Anderson Col; Seconday Ed.*

ASHFORD, Sandra Denise
Alma J Brown HS; Grambling, LA; 4H A; Sci A; Social Stu A; Theater Drama A; *Tuskegee Inst; Pre Law.*

ASHKIE, Carmelita
Chinle HS; Chinle, AZ (15-130) FHA; Span C; Secy, SC; *Mesa Comm Col; Ed.*

ASHLEY, Cathy Jo
Appleton City HS R2; Appleton City, MO (12-63) A Cap Choir; Chldr; Chor; FHA; FTA; Pres, 4H; 4H A; Secy, Rptr, 4-H C.

ASHLEY, Leissa Diane
Rossville HS; Rossville, GA (22-225) Bkbl; Type A; Outst Gym Stu.

ASHLEY, Lillian Ann
Booker T Washington HS; Shreveport, LA (3-323) Band; 4H; HiY; Hmrm; Lat NHS; Mjrte; NHS; Sch P; Tri-HiY; 4H A; Hon Prog; Sal; *La St U; Acct.*

ASHLEY, Michael Dean
Andrew Lewis HS; Salem, VA; Co-Ed, Lit Mag; Co-Ed, Sch P; COM; Yth Pastor A; *Va W Col; Gen.*

ASHLEY, Phillip Wayne
Elk City HS; Elk City, OK (45-140) BS; Chor; Ensm; FBLA; FHA; Pres, SC; Bsbl; Ftbl; Sftbl; Tr; Amer Leg A; Chamber of Comm A; Citz A; HCt; FBLA Swtht; All-Dist Ftbl; Chor Royalty; *Southwestern Okla St Col; Bus.*

ASHLEY, Wallace
Smithfield-Selma HS; Smithfield, NC; VP, Fr C; Key C; Order/Arrow; SC; Bsbl; Ftbl; God & Country A; Order/Arrow A.

ASHMORE, Athena Diane
El Camino Real HS; Woodland Hills, CA (30-1095) VP, A Cap Choir; Secy, Chor; Pres, Drama; Ensm; Hmrm; Jr Miss Pagent; Madrigal; Pres, Thes; CSF; COM; Hon Prog; *UC at Los Angeles; Dance.*

ASHMORE, David Mack
Wade Hampton HS; Greenville, SC; *Clemson U; Civil Engr.*

ASHMORE, Susan Gayle
Tivy HS; Kerrville, TX (50-350) Band; SC; Sftbl; Secy, Fresh Cl; FCA; Vlbl; Tex Readers C; *Teaching.*

ASHMORE, Wayne Craig
Northglenn HS; Northglenn, CO; Chor; Tnns; Tres, Yth Fel.

ASHTON, James William
Wood River HS; Hailey, ID (80-89) BS; Ger C; NHS; Order/Arrow; Ski C; Cpt, Cr-Ctry; Tr; Order/Arrow A; Eagle Sct; *Wash St U; Geology.*

ASHTON, Tamara Lea
Arvada W HS; Arvada, CO; Chor; Spch C; Close-Up Prog; *Colo U; Math.*

ASHWILL, Mark Douglas
Connersville Sr HS; Connersville, IN; Tres, Span C; JV, Ftbl; Pres, Gun C; *Huntington Col; Forestry.*

ASHWORTH, Donna Ellen
Hamilton HS E; Trenton, NJ (255-755) Chor; FNA; InterAct C; ARC; Circle Singers; Vol Hospital Service; Spartan o-t Wk; *Nurs.*

ASIMUS, Mark Anthony
O'Neill Pub HS; O'Neill, NE (12-74) BC; Chor; Ensm; NHS; Sch P; Pres, Soph Cl; Ftbl; Tr; *Wheaton Col; Hist.*

ASK, Paul Edward
Lanesboro HS; Lanesboro, MN (33%-33) Chor; FFA; SC; Tres, Soph Cl; Bkbl; Ftbl; Tr; Amer Leg A; Hon Prog; *Winona St U; Bus.*

ASKEGARD, Karen Marie
Kerkhoven-Sunburg HS; Kerkhoven, MN (7-60) Ann; Chor; FHA; NHS; Sch P; Span C; Tr; COM; Hon Prog; FHA As; *Mounds-Midway Sch of Nurs; Registered Nurs.*

ASKER, Barbara Ann
Soap Lake HS; Soap Lake, WA; Ann; Chor; FHA; GS; Rptr, Sch P; B Crocker A; I Dare You; MLS; VP & Pres, FBLA; *Eastern Wash St Col; Bus.*

ASKER, David Micheal
Soap Lake Jr-Sr HS; Soap Lake, WA; Var C; JV, Bkbl; Ftbl; Tr; HR; Special Eng A.

ASKEW, Angela Alice
Putnam City W HS; Oklahoma City, OK (350-700) Mu Alpha Theta; Bkbl; Sftbl; Sci A; *Okla St U; Vet Med.*

ASKEY, Donald Fredrick Jr
Hopewell HS; Aliquippa, PA; Order/Arrow; Ftbl; Wrest.

ASKINS, John William Jr
Bellaire HS; Bellaire, TX; Chldr; Key C; Order/Arrow; SC; JV, Bkbl; Cr-Ctry; Mgr, Ftbl; Tr; Ntl Ed Assn A; Off Diabetes Bikeathon Worker; Ready For Zion; *Tex A&M U; Chem Engr.*

ASKINS, Lillian Judith
Marion HS; Marion, SC (9-245) Bus Mgr, Ann; Chess C; FHA; Semi-Fin, GS; Hmrm; NHS; Var C; Bkbl; Tnns; St Scholar; *Clemson U; Nurs.*

ASMAN, Adriane Anne
Lutheran HS; Denver, CO; Chor; Swim; *Colo St U; Bus Adm.*

ASMUS, Aaron Joel
W Fargo HS; West Fargo, ND (10%-211) AFS; BS; Chess C; Chor; Ensm; Madrigal; VP, NHS; Parl, SC; Thes; Bsbl; Mgr, Bkbl; Tnns; Math A; *Concordia Col; Teaching.*

ASMUSSEN, Loris Carl
Tift Area Acad; Tifton, GA (20%-350) Chem C; Pres, Order/Arrow; Rptr, Sch P; Spch C; Cpt, Bsbl; Cpt, Bkbl; Ftbl; V Order/Arrow A; Sci A; Eagle Sct A's; 2nd Pl, St Sci Fair.

ASPENSON, Kenneth Duane
Belvidere HS; Belvidere, IL (83-365) AFS; Ger C; NHS; SC; Var C; Co-Cpt, Bkbl; Yth Fel; Ger & Ath Hon Soc's; *Rock Valley Col; Bus.*

ASPENWALL, Jeffrey Dale
John F Kennedy HS; Bloomington, MN (77-668) Band; NHS; JV, Bsbl; Drum Major; *Devry Inst of Technology; Computer Sci.*

ASPER, Wilbert Ryan
John F Kennedy HS; Tumon, GUAM (1-511) NHS; Soccer; Tr; JA A; *U of Ill.*

ASPEY, Bobby Scott
Weld Central HS; Keenesburg, CO (18-98) A Cap Choir; Pres, Band; BS; Chor; Ensm; VP, Sci C; Ski C; Var C; Bsbl; Ntl Choir A; Best Sr Bandman; Top of Nation Band; *York Col; Bus.*

ASSALITA, Mary Beth
Marian Cath HS; Tamaqua, PA; CYO; Mgr, Bsbl; Hockey; *Bloomsburg St Col; Elem Ed.*

ASSELMEIER, Kimberly Helen
Valmeyer HS; Valmeyer, IL (6-41) Band; Chldr; VP, Chor; Ensm; FHA; Mjrte; Math C; NHS; Sftbl; Tr; Cl Fav; Math A; Yth Fel; Pep C; 1st, Ill St Mus Contest; Secy, Ath C; MVP, JV, Vlbl; MVP, Vlbl; Chor & Church Accompanist; *U of Ill; Bus.*

ASSENHEIMER, Suzanne E
Becton Regional HS; E Rutherford, NJ (30-200) Chor; Lit Mag; NHS; Orch; SC; Tr; Hon Prog; Yth Fel; Cl Mus; Hon Guard; *Eisenhower Col.*

ASSINI, Mary Ellen
Mercy HS; Albany, NY (7-135) CYO; Chldr; Chor; Hmrm; Lat C; Ski C; Pres, Spch C; SC; Cpt, Sftbl; K of C A; Math A; NEDT; Spch A.

ASTACIO, Maria Del Carmen
Colegio San Antonio HS; Rio Piedras, PR (7-100) Chess C; Hmrm; Math C; NHS; ARC; Secy, SC; Swim; Beauty; COM; Hon Prog; Yale Book A; *Colo St U; Arts.*

ASTRAUSKAS, Colleen Ann
Maria HS; Chicago, IL (183-341) Lat C; ARC; Sftbl; COM; ARC A; Yth Fel; Red Cross 2 Mile Swim; Panel Spkr; *Zoology.*

ATCHISON, Paul Ray
Homewood HS; Homewood, AL (3-236) Math C; Mu Alpha Theta; NHS; Cr-Ctry; Tr; Math A; NEDT; Art C; Art Excel A's; *Samford U; Pre-Med.*

ATCHISON, Steven Joseph
Valhalla HS; El Cajon, CA (97-532) BS; Pres, Sr Cl; Pres, Jr Cl; Cpt, Soccer; JV, Tnns; *UC at Santa Barbara; Humanities.*

ATCHLEY, Connie Marcella
Russell County HS; Russell Springs, KY (15-150) NHS; Bkbl; Cr-Ctry; Tr; *Western Ky U; Phys Ed.*

ATEN, Jennifer Susan
Glenbrook S HS; Glenview, IL (76-597) Swim; Onward House Tutoring C; Scholastic Art A; Span A.

ATER, Lori Christina
Chillicothe HS; Chillicothe, OH (6-383) Band; Fr C; Mjrte; NHS; Hon Prog; Yth Fel; *Ohio St U; Phar.*

ATES, Lashunda Deonne
Pascagoula HS; Pascagoula, MS; Chor; Ensm; Rainbow; *William Carey Col; Mus.*

ATHANASIADES, Caryl Jean
Rosati-Kain HS; St Louis, MO (2-110) Band; Dbte Tm; Ensm; Hmrm; Orch; Spch C; Up Bound; Hon Prog; JA A; Spch A; *Bus.*

ATHERTON, Cindy Lynn
Warren Central HS; Indianapolis, IN (20-900) S-T, Chor; Ger C; Pres, 4H; NHS; COM; 4H A; Hon Prog; Yth Fel; *Butler Col; Phys Therapy.*

ATHMER, Mary Theresa
Central Comm HS; Breese, IL (15-157) FHA; Type A; Art A; Clothing As; Sup A, Ill St Historical Soc.

ATKINS, Brenda Faye
Williamston HS; Williamston, NC (75-218) FFA; Hmrm; *Bible Training Inst; Theology.*

ATKINS, Diana Majoria
Albion Sr HS; Albion, MI; Chldr; SC; HCt; *Kellog Comm Col; Bus.*

ATKINS, Heidi Elizabeth
Cowan HS; Muncie, IN (14-70) Chldr; Chem C; Pres, NHS; Co-Ed, Sch P; SC; Var C; Bkbl; Sftbl; COM; Chem A; Math A; Vlbl; *Ball St U; Nurs.*

ATKINS, Julie Elizabeth
Lyndon Baines Johnson HS; Austin, TX; Drama; FHA; COM; Hon Prog; Type A; St Readers C, Reading Tutor, A's; Performance of Lit, Service, A's; *Baylor U; Elem Ed.*

ATKINS, Kenneth Wayne
Hillsborough HS; Tampa, FL (99-640) Chor; Ensm; Most Out; WW; *Hillsborough Comm Col; Mus.*

ATKINS, Linda Marie
Amherst Central HS; Buffalo, NY (37-469) VP, Key C; NHS; Hon Prog; Bowling Trophies; Pres, Tapen C; Sharpshooter; Rifle C; Riding C; Marksman 1st Cl; Color Guard; Backpacking; Tres, Sorority; *SUNY at Albany; Math.*

ATKINS, Philip Reginald
John Bowne HS; Flushing, NY (259-911) FFA; SC; Acolyte; *Kans St U; Agr.*

ATKINS, Rebecca Hope
Tuscola HS; Waynesville, NC (80-370) Band; Chor; Ensm; Sandy Townsand A; 'B' HR; *Clemson U; Computer Sci.*

ATKINS, Rebecca Ruth
Edgewater HS; Orlando, FL; FCA; Soccerette; *U of Fla; Decorating.*

ATKINS, Sandra Alesia
Overbrook HS; Philadelphia, PA (73-832) Ann; Pres, Band; Chldr; Chor; MVP, Community Yth S; Ensm; Hmrm; MVP, Orch; Tres, SC; Secy, Y-Tns; Citz A; Most Out; Ntl Jr Hon Soc; PSFS Bank A; Outst Stu in Instrumental Mus; Samuel Rudofker Schol; McDonald's Nom A; *W Chester St Col; Mus.*

ATKINS, Sheila Vernice
Albion Sr HS; Albion, MI; Chldr; FBLA; 4H; Hmrm; Ski C; SC; Bkbl; Tr; Citz A; Cl Fav; Spch A; Most Improved; *Ga St U; Child Care.*

ATKINS, Susan Kaye
James Monroe HS; Fredericksburg, VA (22-180) Chor; Drama; Span C; *Va Tech U; Vet Sci.*

ATKINS, Sylvia June
King William HS; King William, VA (10-107) Secy, BC; Fr C; Tres, FBLA; Citz A; *Rappahanoch Comm Col; Bus.*

ATKINS, Terry Kim
Parma Sr HS; Parma, OH (100-1009) Band; Bus C; City Conf; Hmrm; Lat C; Mjrte; SC; Cpt, Sftbl; COM; God & Country A; JA A; Type A; Pres, Christian Yth Fel; 1st Cl GSct; *Cleveland St U; Acct.*

ATKINS, Wiletta Nadine
John Marshall HS; Indianapolis, IN (238-623) FTA; SC; COM; *Morehouse Col; Computer Programming.*

ATKINSON, Daniel Thomas
Clairemont Sr HS; San Diego, CA (1-839) Lat C; Ch, Lit Ral; NHS; CSF; Hon Prog; *Westmont Col; Eng Lit.*

ATKINSON, Julie Marie
Douglas Byrd Sr HS; Fayetteville, NC; BC; Chor; Ensm; Fin, Jr Miss Pagent; Bkbl; Cpt, Sftbl; Beauty; God & Country A; MLS; Type A; Yth Fel; Acct A; Shorthand A; *Fayetteville Tech Inst; Bus.*

ATKINSON, Keith Alan
Redmond HS; Redmond, OR (30-227) Band; NHS; VP, Jr Cl; MVP, Bkbl; Ftbl; Tr; *Concordia Col; Special Ed.*

ATKINSON, Laura Lee
Newton-Conover HS; Newton, NC (22-200) BC; Fr C; Pres, Hmrm; JV, Bkbl; Citz A; Drum Mjrte; Pres, Jr Civitan; 2nd Pl, Drum Major Tm; *NC St U; Engr.*

ATKINSON, Linda Sue
Steubenville HS; Steubenville, OH (9-185) Co-Ed, Ann; Pres, Bus C; Dbte Tm; GS; Orch; Rptr, Sch P; Tres, Sci C; Y-Tns; Amer Leg A; Summa Cum Laude; Secy, Russian C; Women's C School; Proficiency in Russian A; Pres, Church Yth; WW; *Col of Wooster; Russian.*

ATKINSON, Margaret Louise
Neshaminy Langhorne HS; Langhorne, PA (60-722) Band; Chor; Ensm; NHS; SC; World Affairs C; Hon Prog; Champs of Ireland Band; Church Conf; Co-Pres, Yth Fel; Acolyte; Church Board of Directors; *Temple Col; Phys Therapy.*

ATKINSON, Marisa Elizabeth
Se HS; Bradenton, FL (71-319) Band; Orch; Golf; COM; God & Country A; Yth Fel; Para- med; *Manatee Jr Col; Nurs.*

ATKINSON, Patrick John
St Mary's Central HS; Bismarck, ND (58-180) Rptr, Ann; MVP, Band; BS; Pres, CYO; Drama; Fr C; ARC; Pres, Sr Cl; Pres, Jr Cl; Ftbl; Tnns; Wrest; Louis Armstrong Band A; Yth Ldrship; Eagle Sct; *Moorhead St U; Psych.*

ATKINSON, Teresa Louise
N Bullitt HS; Shepherdsville, KY (9-250) BC; Ed, Sch P; VP, Sci C; COM; Chem A; Sci A; Pres, Med Explorers; *David Lipscombe Col; Pre-Med.*

ATKINSON, Thomas Wayne
Clay City HS; Clay City, IN (1-84) BS; Pres, FFA; Math C; VP, NHS; Parl, SC; St Win, FFA Fresh Pub Spkg; St Win FFA Soils Tm; *Purdue U; Agr.*

ATKINSON, Von Eric
Soldan HS; St Louis, MO; A Cap Choir; Chor; Span C; Mgr, Bkbl; *St Louis U; Med Tech.*

ATOR, James Eric
West HS; Columbus, OH (50-300) Semi-Fin, BS; Drama; FTA; Hmrm; NHS; Orch; Ski C; PA A; *Archt.*

ATRIA, Joseph John
Glenbard W HS; Glen Ellyn, IL (77-508) Band; Chor; Pres, Var C; Ftbl; Tr; Wrest; Pres, Yth Center; Dist Champ, Wrest; Planning Committee, Young Life; FCA; NML; All St, Ftbl; All Conf, Hon Men All Area, Ftbl; *de Pauw Col; Biol.*

ATTEBERRY, Kimberly Gayle
Rosepine HS; Rosepine, LA (16-45) A Cap Choir; VP, Chor; Ensm; FBLA; F-Ed, FHA; 4H A; Hon Choir; Dist & St Solo & Ensm; Dist Tn Talent; *McNeese St Col; Psych.*

ATTEBERRY, Nancy Jean
Superior HS; Superior, NE; Chor; Church Nursery Teacher; Awana A; Valentine Swtht Qn, Church; Church Bus Ministry; Church Tn Choir; *Olivet Nazarene Col; Missionary Teacher.*

ATTLES, Keith
Seton Hall Prep HS; S Orange, NJ (335-360) SC; Tr; Drums A; *Computer Prog.*

ATTLES, Michelle
St Vincent Acad; Newark, NJ (25-70) Chor; Ensm; Madrigal; Sch P; Bkbl; Swim; Tnns; Reading Tutor; Hospital Vol; Child Aide; HR; *Psych.*

ATWATER, Anna Louise
Asheboro HS; Asheboro, NC (10%-300) BC; Chor; *St Marys Col.*

ATWATER, John Waldo
Weymouth N HS; Weymouth, MA (30-450) Key C; Bkbl; JV, Ftbl; Tr; Part- time Work; *Wheaton Col; Pre-Law.*

ATWATER, Paul Wendell
Weymouth N HS; E Weymouth, MA (20-467) Key C; Pres, NHS; Bkbl; Co-Cpt, Ftbl; Tr; MLS; Ath Coun Schol-Ath A; *Wheaton Col; Bible.*

ATWELL, Patrick Earl
Andover Central Sch; Andover, NY (8-43) Span C; Var C; Bsbl; Co-Cpt, Bkbl; Cr-Ctry; Soccer; Tr; Hon Prog; Outst Fresh Ath.

ATWELL, Sandra Jo
Northern HS; Baltimore, MD (109-644) SC; Hon Prog; *Essex Comm Col; Special Ed.*

ATWOOD, Mary Patricia
St Mary's Acad; Alexandria, VA (4-102) CYO; JV, Chldr; Drama; Hmrm; SC; Soccer; Sftbl; COM; Hon Prog; *U of Va; Med.*

ATWOOD, Sherita Rochelle
J M Tate HS; Gonzalez, FL; Band; Secy, FHA; NHS; Span C; JV, Bkbl; Cr-Ctry; Tr; HCt; Spch A; Swtht; WW; A-B HR Cert; *Pensacola Jr Col; Med.*

AU, James Kwok Hing
Burbank HS; Burbank, CA (5%-700) Orch; Ch, SC; CSF; Chem A; *U of Calif; Engr.*

AUBE, Marianne
Dover HS; Dover, NH (19-396) S-T, Fr C; Mu Alpha Theta; NHS; Hon Prog; St Paul's Sch Adv Stu Prog; *NH Voc-Tech Col; Practical Nurs.*

AUBERT, Raymond George
Bishop Guertin HS; Nashua, NH (1-150) Ann; BS; Math C; NHS; A-Ed, Sch P; SC; Bkbl; Hist A; Hon Prog; Val; Yth Leg; Eng A; *Worcester Polytechnic Inst; Applied Math.*

AUBLEY, George Leonid
Neshaminy Maple Point HS; Langhorne, PA (5-388) Math C; NHS; ARC; Co-Cpt, Cr-Ctry; Cpt, Tr; DARGCA; MVP, Cr-Ctry; Sch Ath A; *Biol.*

AUBREY, Debbie Francis
Alexander Galt Regional HS; Lennoxville, CANADA (24-539) Hon Prog; Type A; Fitness A.

AUDILET, Allison Alexandra
St Mary's Acad; Alexandria, VA (4-64) Cpt, Chldr; French NHS; Key C; Math C; Pres, NHS; Cpt, Tr; Chem A; Hon Prog; NEDT; Trig A; Fr A; *U of Va; Chem.*

AUDINO, Michael John
Colonie Central HS; Albany, NY (160-716) Mu Alpha Theta; Sch P; Sci C; Golf; Yth Fel; Yth Rep, Parish Coun; *Engr.*

AUDRAIN, Jeanne Marie
Rosati-Kain HS; St Louis, MO (4-94) VP, NHS; COM; Hon Prog; Math A; Summa Cum Laude; Scholastic Art A; NMS Commended; Mo Sch Col A; *Fontbonne Col; Special Ed.*

AUDREY, Cynthia Denese
W Charlotte Sr HS; Charlotte, NC; AFS; Band; Drama; Fr C; Hmrm; NHS; Ski C; SC; Secy, Soph Cl; Secy, Yth Group; Chldr A; SC A; Secy, Jr Usher's Board; PA; Jr Chor; Ldrshp Med; Chldrn's Thrte; Jr Missionary; Jr Fire Marshal.

AUE, Jenifer Lynne
Potter HS; Potter, NE (14-21) Ann; JV, Chldr; Chor; Drama; Secy, 4H; Lit Mag; Secy, Soph Cl; Bsbl; Bkbl; Mgr, Wrest; 4H A; *Colo Inst of Art; Commercial Artist.*

AUFFARTH, Mark Richard
Newark HS; Newark, DE; Band; Soccer; JV, Wrest; All St Band; *Covenant Col.*

AUGER, Patricia Joan
Ridgewood HS; Ridgewood, NJ (50%-600) Bkbl; MVP, Sftbl; MVP, Tnns; Bowl; Teacher, Church Yth Group; Pres Phy Fitness A; Del to NW Bergen Convocation.

AUGSBURGER, Paul Daniel
Flanagan HS; Flanagan, IL (5-35) FFA; Bsbl; Bkbl; Ftbl; Sftbl; Tr; Amer Leg A; Most Out; *Recreation.*

AUGSTAD, Kim Shiree
Chester Area HS; Chester, SD (5-40) All Amer Yth; Band; Chldr; Secy, Chor; Dbte Tm; Drama; Ensm; FBLA; FHA; GS; S-T, NHS; Pres, SC; Sftbl; Swim; Tr; Amer Leg A; Citz A; Ntl Amer Legion Essay Contest; WW; SDAHSS; All St, Chor & Hon Choir; *Augustana Col.*

AUGUSTIN, Don Marty
St Thomas Pub HS; St Thomas, ND (2-17) Pres, Band; BS; Chem C; VP, Chor; Ensm; Pres, 4H; Var C; Bsbl; Bkbl; Cpt, Ftbl; Citz A; 4H A; Hon Prog; All Conf Ftbl; Ltrman A; Gray Gown; *A VIT; Farm Mgt.*

AUGUSTIN, Jeffrey Lee
Notre Dame HS; Portsmouth, OH; Chess C; Dbte Tm; K of C; Span C; Pres, Sr Cl; Co-Cpt, Bkbl; Tr; *Shawnee St Col; Elec Engr.*

AUGUSTINE, David Andrew
Hopkins-Charles A Lindbergh HS; Hopkins, MN (12-396) Band; Band A; Church Memorization A; *Wheaton Col; Pre-Med.*

AUGUSTINE, Kathy Marie
Western HS; Louisville, KY (10%-350) Secy, Chor; Hmrm; Mjrte; Tri-HiY; Excel A'S, Drill Tm; Creativity A; *Secy Work.*

AUGUSTINE, Walter Lee
Starmount HS; Boonville, NC (24-152) Cpt, Ftbl; Tr.

AULD, Sandra Lynn
Hazelwood E HS; St Louis, MO (4-455) Cpt, Chldr; JETS; NHS; VP, SC; Pres, Sr Cl; Secy, Soph Cl; Tr; COM; PTA A; Pep C; Athena A; PTA Schol; WW; Faculty Mem Schol St Louis Col Phar; WW Chldr; *St Louis Col of Phar; Phar.*

AULD, Timothy Jon
Hobbs HS; Hobbs, NM; Pres, Ann; JV, Cr-Ctry; JV, Ftbl; Cpt, Tr; DA, Annual; Amateur Ath Union; Explorers; *NM Jr Col; Photography.*

AULI, Lisa Marie
Eastside HS; Paterson, NJ (5-850) Sci C; Sftbl; V-Ch, 'Z' C; Horsemanship C; Hon A; *Health.*

AULT, Barry Ralph
Detroit Lakes Comm HS; Detroit Lakes, MN (85-350) 4H; Ftbl; Golf; Sftbl; 4H A.

AUMAN, Kay Frances
Allen Jay HS; High Point, NC (8-92) Band; BC; Tres, Fr C; Mjrte; Band A; *Guilford Tech Inst; Dental Hygiene.*

AUMAN, Kyle Dean
Allen Jay HS; High Point, NC (15-100) Band; BC; Ensm; Fr C; Monogram; Sch P; Bsbl; Tr; John Philip Sousa Band A; Tr & Band Ltrs; *U of NC; Mus.*

AUNE, Katherine Louise
Westview HS; Braham, MN (3-100) Chldr; Pres, Chor; Pres, FHA; VP, 4H; NHS; Span C; Spch C; Bkbl; COM; 4H A; Spch A; Cl Rep, Band; FHA A; GS Alt; Graduation Hon Guard; Vlbl; Band A; Choir A; Snow-Daze Ct; *Augsburg Col; Pol Sci.*

AURAND, Dawn Rene
Bellmont HS; Decatur, IN (97-350) Chor; Ensm; Rainbow; Span C; Sftbl; Cert of Comp, Bible Inst; *Phys Ed.*

AURAND, Susan Christene
Logan Sr HS; Logan, OH; Band; 4H; Sftbl; Tr; 4H A; Band A; *Bethany Col; Nurs.*

AUSBURY, David Bradley
Pennfield HS; Battle Creek, MI (20-179) Band; Chor; NHS; Orch; Tnns; Hist A; Drafting A; *Mus.*

AUSEN, Eileen Kay
Jasper HS; Jasper, MN; Ann; Band; Chor; Ensm; FHA; Madrigal; COM; Tres, Yth Group; Amer Yth in Concert, Tour Europe; *Bethany Lutheran Col; Natural Sci.*

AUSKALNIS, Toni Lynn
Maria HS; Chicago, IL (4-370) CYO; Co-Cpt, Chldr; Chor; Hmrm; NHS; Orch; Sodality; Hon Prog; Kiwanis A; Math A; Schoenstadt Schol; Ntl Essay Publication; High Hons A; *Northwestern U; Acct.*

AUST, Wallace Michael
Kemper Acad; DeKalb, MS (2-42) Sch P; SC; Var C; Secy, Sr Cl; Ftbl; MLS; Sci A; Most Dependable; *E Miss Jr Col; Forestry.*

AUSTAD, Linda Jean
Central HS; Minneapolis, MN (26-282) Chldr; Hmrm; NHS; Bkbl; Co-Cpt, Swim; H of F; Chldr Mascot; Badminton; Cl Clown; Most Spirited; *Augsburg Col; Ed.*

AUSTELL, Millicent
Grimsley HS; Greensboro, NC (10%-500) Chor; Ensm; Fr C; FHA; Hmrm; Madrigal; NHS; SC; Mus A; *Wake Forest U; Psych.*

AUSTIN, Aldean
Russell HS; Hurtsboro, AL (10%-75) Cpt, Chldr; Chor; FHA; 4H; Lit Mag; NHS; SC; Up Bound; Pres, Soph Cl; 4H A; Hist A; Hon Prog; ROTC A; *Engr.*

AUSTIN, Ann Blair
Smithfield-Selma Sr HS; Smithfield, NC (70-350) Ann; Band; Chor; Drama; Fr C; Golf; Chldr; Key C; Cpt, Mjrte; SC; Secy, Sr Cl; Sub-Jr Women's C; VP, Pep C; *Salem Col; Mus.*

AUSTIN, Arlene Michele
Forest Glen HS; Suffolk, VA (10-151) F-Ed, Ann; BC; Co-Cpt, Chldr; Tres, Chor; Parl, FBLA; FHA; Madrigal; S-T, Monogram; Secy, Span C; SC; Tres, Soph Cl; Sftbl; Hon Graduate; Outst, Sci; WW; WW, Chldr; *Bus Adm.*

AUSTIN, Barry Rustin
Tuscaloosa HS; Tuscaloosa, AL (16-561) Pres, Mu Alpha Theta; NHS; Order/ Arrow; Span C; Band & Country A; Gov Honor Prog; Math A; Most Out; Eagle Sct; *U of Ala; Microbio.*

AUSTIN, Bonnie Lynn
Seminole HS; Sanford, FL (10%-482) Secy, Anchor C; Mu Alpha Theta; NHS; *Stetson U; Acct.*

AUSTIN, Bryan Leigh
Fruitport HS; Fruitport, MI (50%-330) Order/ Arrow; Bsbl; Bkbl; Ftbl; Sftbl; Tnns; Order/Arrow A; *Muskegon Bus Col; Acct.*

AUSTIN, Clint Dean
S Haven HS; S Haven, KS (2-15) A-Ed, Ann; Chor; Secy, FFA; VP, Hmrm; Var C; VP, Jr Cl; Ftbl; Tr; MLS; Sal; *Agr Mech.*

AUSTIN, Cynthia Ashley
St Joseph HS; Ogden, UT; Drama; French NHS; GS; Cpt, Mjrte; Model UN; VP, SC; Mgr, Tnns; Tr; Cpt, Vlbl; Hugh O'Brian Ldrship A; Fr Hons A; *Potomic Horse Center; Horsemanship.*

AUSTIN, Daivd Wayne
Treadwell HS; Memphis, TN; Tres, Chem C; Math C; Mu Alpha Theta; NHS; Secy, Span C; Pres, Jr Cl; Bsbl; JV, Bkbl; Golf; *U of Miss; Acct.*

AUSTIN, Dan Alan
Fruitport HS; Fruitport, MI; All Amer Yth; Drama; *Muskeyon Bus Col; Bus.*

AUSTIN, Delilah Jan
Hillsborough HS; Tampa, FL (30-650) Chor; Ensm; NHS; Hon Prog; *USF; Mus.*

AUSTIN, Diane Elizabeth
Eldorado HS; Albuquerque, NM (1-744) Co-Ch, CYO; Drama; Hmrm; Math C; NHS; Spch C; Pres, Span NHS; Cpt, Swim; Citz A; Coun of Teach A; Hon Prog; Math A; Q&S A; Spch A; Val; Yth Leg; Amateur Ath Union; UP, SC; Tres, Conservation Action League; Girls Nation; Yth & Govt C; Keyette; Pres & Secy, Sierra C; *Tex Christian U; Environmental Sci.*

AUSTIN, Donald Mark
E Central HS; Tulsa, OK (100-650) Band; NHS; Jazz Band; Bowl League; *Okla St U; Bus Adm.*

AUSTIN, Elizabeth Ann
Jackson Mem HS; Jackson, NJ (12-389) CYO; NHS; Hon Prog; NEDT; Academic Achv A; *Col of New Rochelle; Interntl Bus.*

AUSTIN, Jennifer Laird
Newnan HS; Newnan, GA; Span C; Span NHS; *LaGrange Col; Registered Nurs.*

AUSTIN, Julie Lynn
Savannah Ctry Day Sch; Savannah, GA; Ann; Chor; FNA; Sci A; Historian, Sci C; St Sci Fair A; *Med.*

AUSTIN, Kathryn Ann
Lakewood HS; Lakewood, OH (407-909) Chor; Ensm; Fr C; Choir Citation; *Mus.*

AUSTIN, Kevin Patric
Sweet Home HS; Sweet Home, OR; A Cap Choir; Chor; Mod Mus Mas; Bkbl; Tr; *U of Oreg; Mus.*

AUSTIN, Lewell Harmon III
Oak Ridge HS; Orlando, FL (178-784) VP, Key C; *Fla Technological U; Bus.*

AUSTIN, Lillian Loerine
Compton Sr HS; Compton, CA (8-800) Pres, Band; Dbte Tm; Drama; Pres, Ger C; NHS; Orch; Sci C; Spch C; Swim; Cpt, Tr; CSF; COM; Citz A; MLS; Most Out; Spch A; WW; *U of Wash; Med.*

AUSTIN, Lynda Karen
Bend Sr HS; Bend, OR; Ensm; NHS; Secy, SC; Tnns; *Biola Col; Communications.*

AUSTIN, Marlin Lee Wayne
Irvin HS; El Paso, TX (200-500) Chess C; Ftbl.

AUSTIN, Michael Dean
Richwoods HS; Peoria, IL; Chor; ARC; Var C; JV, Ftbl; Swim; Tr; Wrest; PTA A; Pres A; ARC A; Yth Fel; Most Outst Bradley U; *Trinety Bible Col; Bible Theology.*

AUSTIN, Neal Evan
Pine View Prog for the Gifted; Sarasota, FL; Key C; Bkbl; Cr-Ctry; Soccer; Tnns; Tr; Pres A; Art Merit A; *Aerospace.*

AUSTIN, Patricia Diane
F O Alexander HS; Starkville, MS (30-59) Y-Tns; Bkbl; Tr; *Miss St U; Secy.*

AUSTIN, Sallie Marie
Ottawa HS; Ottawa, KS (12-215) Band; Chess C; Ensm; Fr C; 4H; NHS; Orch; Cpt, Bkbl; Sftbl; Tr; Hon Prog; *Kans U; Med Tech.*

AUSTIN, Scott Francis
Fremont Sr HS; Fremont, NE (25%-400) Band; Orch; Tr; Band Ltr A; Cert of Apprec, Chamber of Commerce; *St Paul Bible Col; Theology.*

AUSTIN, Susan Frances
Millbrook HS; Raleigh, NC; Chor; Drama; Ensm; Hmrm; Bkbl; Sftbl; Swim; JV, Tnns; *Mus.*

AUSTIN, Susan Gail
Ygnacio Valley HS; Concord, CA (86-490) Chor; CSF; Hon Prog; Yth Fel; Sr Women's Service Organization; Bowl Tm; *Westmont Col.*

AUSTIN, Tammy Rhea
Livingston Acad; Livingston, TN (5-150) BC; SC; Var C; Bkbl; Vlbl; *Tenn Technological U; Law.*

AUSTIN, Trevor Alvin
Simon Gratz HS; Philadelphia, PA; Cr-Ctry; *Pa St U; Computer Engr.*

AUTAUBO, Evelyn Grace
Preston HS; Preston, OK (10%-11) NHS; Pres, Sr Cl; Gov Honor Prog; Hist A; Journ A; Sci A; Type A; Val; Hon Soc A; Home Ec A; Eng A; *Northeastern Okla St U; Pol Sci.*

AUTEN, Karen Deline
W Meck HS; Charlotte, NC; Fr C; Bkbl; Swim; Tnns; W Meck Civinette.

AUTEN, Thomas Edward
Northwestern HS; Rock Hill, SC (122-460) Tr; Church Sftb Tm; All Area, Tr; Best Field Event Performer A; *York Tech Col.*

AUTERY, Miriam Renee
McAdory HS; McCalla, AL; FHA; Sftbl; *Ala A&M U.*

AUTHEMENT, Mona Jane
Destrehan HS; Destrehan, LA (3-227) BC; GS; Lit Ral; Ed, Sch P; Span C; Amer Leg A; Bio A; Tres, Film Acad; GS Medal; Eng, Service, A's; *U of New Orleans; Math.*

AUTIO, Christine Elaine
Ralph Mahar Reg HS; Orange, MA; Band; Chor; Mgr, Fr C; JV, Bkbl; JV, Hockey; JV, Sftbl; Sci A; NJHS; Quabloin Valley Mus Festival; Gym Tm Exhibition; Church Yth Group; *Law.*

AUTON, James Christopher
W Lincoln HS; Lincolnton, NC; SC; Ftbl; Wrest.

AUTRY, Connie Cordarrell
Booker T Washington HS; Shreveport, LA; Band; Chor; FHA; Secy, 4H; Hmrm; Y-Tns; Bsbl; Sftbl; Swim; Cl Fav; 4H A; MLS; Yth Foundation; *Pepperdine U; Mus.*

AUTRY, Walter Douglas
MacArthur HS; San Antonio, TX (50%-610) Pre-Law C; Stu Trainer, Ftbl; Elec C; *U of Tex of San Antonio; Pre-Law.*

AUWARTER, Rodney Blake
Greene Central HS; Greene, NY (9-144) Band; Chem C; NHS; Order/Arrow; Sci C; SC; VP, Sr Cl; Bsbl; Mgr, Ftbl; Golf; Soccer; Hon Prog; Order/Arrow A; Regent School; *Oneonta Col; Pre-Med.*

AUXIER, Anne Marie
St Mary's Acad; Portland, OR (28-151) Band; CYO; Ger C; Var C; Co-Cpt, Bkbl; Sftbl; Tr; Mus A; *U of Portland; Ed.*

AVALLONE, Curt Vincent
Archmere Acad; Claymont, DE; Band; Dbte Tm; K of C; Lit Mag; Rptr, Sch P; Sci C; Span C; Spch C; Span NHS; Bsbl; Bkbl; Ftbl; Tr; Amer Leg A; Amer Leg Orator A; Hon Prog; Spch A; Optimist Ntl Spch Semi-Fin; *U of Penn; Bio.*

AVANT, Clyde
Independence HS; Independence, MS (10-118) FBLA; Sch P; Bsbl; Bkbl; Ftbl; Tr; *U of Tenn; Bus.*

AVANT, Denise Rena
Foreman HS; Chicago, IL (13-373) Chor; Hmrm; Math C; Mu Alpha Theta; NHS; A-Ed, Sch P; SC; Amer Leg A; COM; Hon Prog; Journ A; Most Out; Q&S A; VFW A; Century III Ldrs; Sch Service, Hon, A's; *U of Notre Dame; Journ.*

AVANT, Dorothy Irene
Independence HS; Independence, MS (15%-106) Tres, BC; FBLA; FHA; *Med.*

AVANT, Mike
Winyah HS; Georgetown, SC; BS; City Conf; Order/Arrow; SC; Var C; Bsbl; Bkbl; Ftbl; God & Country A; Eagle Sct; *U of SC; Bus.*

AVELAR, Charlie
Gladys Porter HS; Brownsville, TX (20%-302) Bsbl; Dist Pres, VICA; *Tex Southmost Col; Bus Adm.*

AVEN, Susan Marie
Kickapoo HS; Springfield, MO; Co-Cpt, Band; VP, Fr C; Drum Corps; *Sou Mo St U; Forestry.*

AVERHART, Paula Evette
Leesville HS; Leesville, LA (80-262) Parl, BC; Chor; Ensm; FHA; GS; Span C; SC; VP, Jr Cl; HCt; *Northwestern St U; Nurs.*

AVERSA, Jill Patrice
South Plantation HS; Plantation, FL (6-650) Band; Chldr; Hmrm; Fin, Jr Miss Pagent; Tres, NHS; Sch Achieve Tm; SC; Tres, Sr Cl; Beauty; COM; Elk A; Kiwanis A; Most Out; NEDT; Opt A Smith Col Book C A; Prom Qn; Exchange Girl o-t Yr; Exchange Girl o-t Month; *U of Fla; Banking & Finance.*

AVERY, Bryan Waddell
Mount Vernon HS; Fairfax County, VA; Band; Key C; Lit Mag; Orch; Order/Arrow; Co-Ch, Jr Cl; Eagle Sct; *Pre-Med.*

AVERY, Debbie Mae
Forest Lake Sr HS; Forest Lake, MN (10%-450) A Cap Choir; Drama; VP, FHA; 4H; Ski C; SC; JV, Tnns; *Nurs.*

AVERY, Melody Lanessa
Northside HS; Atlanta, GA; Chor; Hmrm; SC; Secy, Sr Cl; Hon Prog; Debutante, Sigma Gamma Rho; *U of Ariz; Criminal Justice.*

AVERY, Norine Margaret
Guysborough Municipal HS; Guysborough, CANADA; Young Christians Stu.

AVERY, Robert Brian
Newton Co Comprehensive HS; Covington, GA (10-250) BC; Pres, HiY; Key C; Semi-Fin, Lit Ral; SC; Bkbl; Golf; Tnns; Alg A; COM; Chem A; Hist A; Math A; Phy A; Rotary A; Sci A; Yth Leg; *U of Ga; Finance.*

AVERY, Scott Ryan
Deerfield Beach HS; Deerfield Beach, FL (9-700) Band; Ensm; NHS; DARGCA; K of C A; NEDT.

AVERY, Veronica Gail
West End HS; Birmingham, AL; Pres, SC; Hist A.

AVEY, Tammy Lee
Thomas S Wootton HS; Rockville, MD (20-380) NHS; Yth Fel; Seekers; Servants; Handbell Choir; *E Tenn St U; Child Psych.*

AVILES, Elizabeth
Manuela Toro HS; Caguas, PR; Pres, FHA; Secy, Sftbl; Vlbl; Theater Cl A; *U of Puerto Rico; Pub Relations.*

AVILES, Nestor J
Jose de Diego HS; Mayaguez, PR (3-276) Chem C; Cum Laude Soc; Dbte Tm; Math C; ARC; COM; Chem A; Hist A; Magna Cum Laude; Sci A; *U of Puerto Rico at Mayaguez; Chem Engr.*

AVIOTTI, Mary Christine
Bishop Byrne HS; Memphis, TN (18-183) CYO; Secy, Drama; NHS; Span C; GSct; Christmas Belle Ct; *Memphis St U.*

AVOLA, Shelley Ann
Eastside HS; Paterson, NJ (10-519) Co-Ed, Ann; Hmrm; VP, NHS; VP, 'Z' C; Horsemanship C; Bowl Tm; HR Certs; *Alfred U; Pol Sci.*

AWTREY, Cheryl Ann
Central HS; La Crosse, WI (1-555) Secy, Drama; Hmrm; NFL; NHS; Spch C; Amer Leg Orator A; Spch A; *Law.*

AXBERG, Julie Anne
East HS; Rockford, IL (110-800) Bkbl; Sftbl; Vlbl; *Phys Ed.*

AXILE, Mark Edward
Seekonk HS; Seekonk, MA (19-224) NHS; Karate; *Southeastern Mass U; Elec Engr.*

AXT, Amy
Richwoods HS; Peoria, IL (38-500) AFS; Band; Sch P; God & Country A; Hon Prog; 1st Cl GSct; Sch Yrbk Staff; Pres, Sct Troop; *U of Ill; Chem.*

AXTELL, Karen Lynne
Callaway HS; Callaway, NE (2-30) Band; Chor; Drama; FHA; GS; Tres, 4H; NHS; Sch P; Spch C; Thes; Tr; Amer Leg A; 4H A; Spch A; Star Student; Yth Fel; Vlbl; *Mus.*

AYALA, Ana Sol
Centro Oportunides Educativas de B; Guaynabo, PR; *Colegio Regional; Secretaria Ejecutiva.*

AYALA, Irmel Adalillies
La Merced HS; Hato Rey, PR (2-108) CYO; Chor; ARC; Alg A; Beauty; Bio A; Chem A; Hist A; Hon Prog; Math A; Most Out; Phy A; Sal; Sci A; Span A; Eng A; Appreciation Cert; *Med.*

AYALA, Mary Lou
Mission HS; Mission, TX (37-365) Pres, CYO; Span C; SC; Y-Tns; H of F; Lion A; Rotary A; PA; HR; *Pan American U; Ed.*

AYARS, Barbara Lynn
Central HS; Cheyenne, WY (29-375) Band; Orch; Sci C; Sci A; HR; Superior Mus A; All St, Band; *U of Wyo; Wildlife Mgt.*

AYBAR, Jose Alberto
Amer Military Acad; Guaynabo, PR (5-68) CYO; Bkbl; Soccer; Alg A; COM; Phy A; Sci A; Attendance A; Conduct A; Military Sci A; *UPR; Laws.*

AYCOCK, Edward Bryan
Princeton HS; Princeton, NC (50-75) Chor; Dbte Tm; FFA; FTA; JV, Ftbl; Tr; MLS; *US Army; Aviation.*

AYCOCK, James Robert
N Side HS; Ft Worth, TX; SC; Bsbl; JV, Ftbl; Cl Fav; Drafting A; *Tex Tech U; Industrial Arts.*

AYCOCK, June Carol
S Dade Sr HS; Homestead, FL; VP, SC; *Duke U.*

AYCOCK, Sheryl Rose
John Graham HS; Warrenton, NC; Ann; Fr C; GS; NHS; Alg A; Chem A; Gr Marshal; Hon Prog; Fr Stu o-t Yr As; *UNC-Greensboro; Social Sci.*

AYDELOTTE, Johanna Kathryn
Delmar Public HS; Delmar, De (1-100) Band; GS; VP, NHS; SC; Var C; Hockey; Sftbl; Bausch & Lomb A; Crisco A; DARGCA; NEDT; Val; Parl, VP & Pres, FHA; *Salisbury St U.*

AYER, Margaret Ann
Kaimuki HS; Honolulu, HI (126-300) Math C.

AYERS, Angela
Fremont HS; Oakland, CA; Hmrm; SC; Bkbl; Sftbl; Tnns; JA A; Yth Fel; Fin, Block Ltr; *Bus Adm.*

AYERS, Becky Lynn
New Brighton HS; New Brighton, PA (110-250) Band; Drama; FTA; Tri-HiY; Bicentennial A; *Edinboro Col; Elem Ed.*

AYERS, Brock Edward
Freeburg Comm HS; Freeburg, IL (6-137) Band; Model UN; NHS; Pres, Sci C; Pres, SC; UN Council; VP, Var C; JV, Bsbl; Co-Cpt, Cr-Ctry; Swim; Tr; Amer Leg A; Bio A; Citz A; DARGCA; HCt; Hon Prog; Sci A; Yth Fel; 2nd Pl, St Amer Leg Essay Contest; Best of Exposition, St Sci Fair; Distinguished Service A; Outst Attitude A; *Westminster Col; Pre-Law.*

AYERS, Gregory Alan
Ft Wayne Christian HS; Ft Wayne, IN; Ch, Chor; Pres, Spch C; VP, Soph Cl; Bsbl; Bkbl; Soccer; Outst Ath o-t Yr; Outst Vocalist o-t Yr; *Oral Roberts U; Missionary.*

AYERS, Jean Marie
St Croix HS; Solor Springs, WI (1-33) Secy, Chor; 4H; NFL; Pres, NHS; Ed, Sch P; Secy, Jr Cl; VP, Soph Cl; 4H A; MLS; Pres A; Spch A; *Eau Claire U; Journ.*

AYERS, Kathryn Irene
Sherwood HS; Creighton, MO (22-75) NHS.

AYERS, Kelly Denise
Willington Acad; Orangeburg, SC (12-43) Co-Ed, Ann; S-T, Fr C; Var C; Sftbl; Hon Prog; Yth Fel; Alt, GS; Yth Choir; *Midlands Tech Col; Dental Hygiene.*

AYERS, Warren Brett
Reidsville Sr HS; Reidsville, NC (4-344) AFS; Fr C; Math C; NHS; Sci C; VP, SC; JV, Bkbl; MVP, Cr-Ctry; MVP, Tr; B Crocker A; Gov Honor Prog; Most Out; NEDT; Rotary A; Gov's Sch, NC; Marshal; Morehead Schol; NCTE Writing Fin; *U of NC-CHAPEL Hill; Dentistry.*

AYLESWORTH, Robin Ann
Bemidji Sr HS; Bemidji, MN (44-384) F-Ed, Ann; Band; Chor; Dbte Tm; Rptr, Sch P; Spch C; Pres, Thes; DARGCA; H of F; Alt, GS; *Amer Acad of Dramatic Arts; Theatre.*

AYLOR, Charlotte Catherine
Ranney Sch; Tinton Falls, NJ (3-35) Drama; Fr C; Lat C; Lit Mag; Math C; Co-Ed, Sch P; Secy, SC; Bkbl; Hockey; Co-Cpt, Sftbl; Swim; NMS; Bowl; Sr Lifesaving; Lat A; Fr A; High HR; *Pol Sci.*

AYME, Keah Marie
Destrehan HS; Destrehan, LA (8-300) BC; CYO; Chldr; FTA; Hmrm; Pres, Key C; SC; HCt; Secy, Ecology C; Fr A; *SE La U; Special Ed.*

AYMOND, Denise Marlene
Bolton HS; Alexandria, LA; GS; Hmrm; NHS; SC; Secy, Y-Tns; Pres, Boosters; Pres, Acteens; *La Tech U; Med.*

AYRES, Kathryn Dale
Fairfield HS; Fairfield, AL (10%-174) Ann; Band; InterClub Coun; Orch; Pres, Y-Tns; *Math.*

AYRES, Mary Rebecca
Penney HS; Hamilton, MO (5%-77) Band; FHA; Mgr, Bkbl; Golf; FHA A; Ltr Ms C; *U of Mo-Columbia.*

AYRES, Wendy E
Collingswood Sr HS; Collingswood, NJ (125-360) Chor; Fr C; Var C; Tnns; Mgr, Wrest; Bowl Tm; *Nurs.*

AYSCUE, Margaret Patricia
Columbus HS; Columbus, GA; NHS; *Auburn U; Phar.*

AYTES, Natalie Rochelle
Flint Acad; Flint, MI (1-9) VP, SC; VP, Jr Cl; Co-Cpt, Bkbl; Cpt, Sftbl; Cl Fav; Hon Prog; MVP, Sftbl; Outst Stu Gov Off; *U of Mich; Criminal Justice.*

AZARI, Robert Joseph
Granite City HS S; Granite City, IL (2-634) Chess C; NEDT; Hon Men, Math Field Day A; *Nuclear Engr.*

AZBELL, Richard Munford
Sidney Lanier HS; Montgomery, AL; Pres, Lat C; Lat NHS; Math C; NHS; Tres, SC; World Affairs C; Hist A; Math A; NEDT; Yth Fel; Most Intelligent; Area Yth Coun; Schol A; Win, Opt Oratory.

B

BAADE, Kim Marie
Elmhurst HS; Fort Wayne, IN (3-456) Band; Fr C; Alg A; Bio A; COM; Hon Prog; Math A; Most Out; *Ball St U.*

BABA, Lynelle Naema
Bishop Carroll HS; Wichita, KS (7-211) Fr C; NHS; SC; COM; Citz A; HQn; Hon Prog; St Scholar; WW; Executive HS Intern; *Emporia Kans St Col; Registered Nurs.*

BABA, Stephanie Alice
Neshaminy HS; Langhorne, PA (50-735) Cpt, Chldr; Chor; Drama; FTA; Lit Mag; NHS; Bkbl; Mgr, Tnns; Pres A; *Long Island U; Pol Sci.*

BABB, Martha Ann
Van-Far Sr HS; Vandalia, MO (7-64) Band; Ensm; FHA; 4H; Tres, Sr Cl; God & Country A; 4H A; *Culver-Stockton Col; Bus Adm.*

BABB, Sherry Darlene
Smithfield HS; Smithfield, VA; Rptr, FBLA; Hmrm; Alg A; Hon Prog; *Math.*

BABBS, Adrienne Michele
The HS of Mus; Manhattan, NY; Chor; Drama.

BABBS, Jade Anglyn
Cotton Plant HS; Cotton Plant, AR (4-35) Ann; Parl, BC; Co-Cpt, Chldr; Chor; Drama; VP, FHA; 4H; Fin, Jr Miss Pagent; NHS; A-Ed, Sch P; VP, Soph Cl; Bkbl; Beauty; Cl Fav; MLS; *U of A at Fayetteville; Eng.*

BABCHECK, Andria
Uniontown Area Sr HS; Uniontown, PA; Chldr; Drama; Fr C; Pres, Hmrm; InterAct C; Ski C; Secy, Jr Cl; Beauty; Chamber of Comm A; Jr Chamber of Com A; *NC Sch o-t Arts; Art.*

BABCOCK, Brian Keith
Trott Voc HS; Niagara Falls, NY (18-150) Band; CYO; Chess C; Drama; Hmrm; ARC; Sci C; Span C; Var C; Pres, Jr Cl; Tres, Soph Cl; Bsbl; Wrest; HCt; Ntl Conf Chr & Jews; Yth Fel; Pres, Yth Group; *Niagara Co Comm HS; Drafting.*

BABCOCK, Heather Ann
Madison Comprehensive HS; Mansfield, OH (30-457) Tres, Band; Chor; Secy, Drama; FHA; Lit Mag; NHS; Orch; Secy, Spch C; Span NHS; JV, Bkbl; Tr; Hon Prog; Most Out; VV, Vlbl; Exec Comm, Sr Cl; Most Outst Bandsman; John Philip Sousa A; *Miami U; Ed Psych.*

BABEL, David Joseph
Lutheran HS; Racine, WI (3-90) Band; Hmrm; NHS; JV, Bsbl; JV, Bkbl; JV, Ftbl; JV, Tnns; *Math.*

BABIARZ, Edward Edward
Auburn HS; Auburn, NY (69-607) NHS; Bsbl; Amer Leg A; Regent Schol; Commended Stu Ntl Merit Schol; *SUNY at Oswego; Psych.*

BABICZ, Marcelline Therese
St Louise de Marillac HS; Northfield, IL (10-175) Ann; Cpt, Chldr; Ski C; Sftbl; Marian A; 1st Cl GSet.

BABILONIA, Priscilla
Wesleyan Acad; Guaynabo, PR (2-31) Chor; NHS; Bkbl; Sftbl; COM; Val; Girl o-t Month; *Med.*

BABIN, Lucy Lynn
Clear Creek HS; League City, TX (25%-635) Tres, CYO; Rptr, Hmrm; Cl Fav.

BABINEAUX, Antoine Todd
Catholic HS; New Iberia, LA; Pres, CYO; Pres, Key C; Mu Alpha Theta; Pres, NHS; Bsbl; Bkbl; Ftbl; COM; Hon Prog; Opt Out Tn; Spch A; Torch of Knowleage; WW; *U of SW La; Pre-Med.*

BABINGTON, Miles Anthony
Edward Lee McClain HS; Greenfield, OH (1-161) Drama; Fr C; NHS; Sch Achieve Tm; Span C; SC; Type A; Val; Span Scholastic Achv; Drama C; *Georgetown U; Foreign Lang.*

BACA, Cynthia Margaret
Los Lunas HS; Los Lunas, NM (15-240) Spch C; SC; Tr; Hon Prog; Spch A; Vlbl; Pom Pom Girl; *Pepperdine U; Spch.*

BACA, Laura L
Albuquerque HS; Albuquerque, NM; FHA; MVP, Bkbl; Composer, Sr Cl Song; *Pepperdine U; Mus.*

BACA, Patricia Anne
Deming HS; Deming, NM (23-252) S-T, CYO; Pres, FHA; GS; Hmrm; Lit Mag; NHS; Span C; Pres, SC; Secy, Jr Cl; Secy, Soph Cl; Tnns; Amer Leg A; Cl Fav; HQn; *Columbia Col; Psych.*

BACA, Roseann Theresa
Cardinal Mooney HS; Youngstown, OH (13-337) Math C; NHS; Ski C; Span C; Bio A; Chem A; Hon Prog; Math Tm; Religion A; Teacher's Aid; Bowl Tm; Health A; *Med Tech.*

BACAS, Susan Constantine
Brooklyn Tech HS; Brooklyn, NY (54-1350) Chldr; NHS; Alg A; Chem A; Hist A; Hon Prog; Math A; Phy A; Sci A; Yth Fel; Secy, Longfellow Soc; Church Bkbl; Church Choir; Archt Department Draftsman; Yrbk 'Blueprint'; *Columbia U; Engr.*

BACH, Elizabeth Ann
Goodrich HS; Goodrich, MI (18-125) Chor; Tres, 4H; Ski C; Tres, Soph Cl; Bkbl; Swim; Tnns; Spelling A; *Concordia Col; Psych.*

BACH, Gary Donald
Hutchinson HS; Hutchinson, MN (22-217) NHS; Ftbl; Tnns; Citz A; Opt A; Ch, FCA; Church Choir; Ath o-t Wk, Ftbl; Win, Opt Oratorical Contest; H C; *Concordia Col; Ed.*

BACH, Lisa Claire
McCallum HS; Austin, TX (36-253) Tres, FHA; SC; Beauty; Yth Fel; Pres, Yth Group; Yth Group; Yth Coun; Yth Choir; *Tex A&M U; Horticulture.*

BACHER, Francis Lee
Campbell Central Sch; Campbell, NY (5-33) Band; Chor; Fr C; Mgr, Bsbl; JV, Soccer; COM; All Co Chor.

BACHIER, Jose M
Academia Ste Monica; Santurce, PR (1-53) Ann; NHS; VP, SC; COM; Math A; *UPR-RECINTO; Engr.*

BACHINI, Linda Marie
Havre HS; Havre, MT (1-249) Fr C; NHS; Sch P; Pres, Sr Cl; Golf; Opt A; VP, DECA; UN Pilgramage For Yth; Soroptomist Yth Citz A; *Concordia Col; Acct.*

BACHMAN, Cheryl Lynne
Madisonville N Hopkins HS; Madisonville, KY (6-296) Ann; BC; Cum Laude Soc; Ch, Hmrm; Model UN; Rainbow; St Stu Congress; Tri-HiY; Mgr, Bkbl; Tnns; Bio A; HQn; HCt; Hon Prog; Sal; Art, Span, A's; *U of Louisville; Sci.*

BACHMANN, Heidi
Richardson HS; Richardson, TX (13-909) Pres, FTA; Pres, 4H; InterClub Coun; NHS; SC; Secy, Tri-HiY; Secy, Soph Cl; 4H A; Math A; NMS; Opt A; Spch A; Type A; WW; *Tex A&M U; Vet Sci.*

BACHMANN, John Charles
University City Sr HS; University City, MO; Ger C; Soccer; Tnns; HR; *Aviation.*

BACHMANN, Regina Nanette
Shamrock HS; Shamrock, TX (6-50) Band; Chldr; FBLA; FHA; Hmrm; NHS; Rainbow; Bkbl; Cl Fav; Spch A; Yth Fel; *Tex Tech U; Bookkeeping.*

BACHMANN, Rhonda Ranae
Shamrock HS; Shamrock, TX (11-48) FBLA; VP, FHA; Mu Alpha Theta; Rainbow; Bkbl; Tnns; COM; Miss Congenialty; *Tex Tech U; Home Ec.*

BACHTELL, Kimberly Sue
Catoosa HS; Catoosa, OK; Ann; Co-Cpt, Chldr; Pres, Rainbow; Mgr, Bkbl; Bio A; Masonic A; Church, Dist & Regional Bible Quiz; *Okla U; Biol Research.*

BACHTOLD, Anne Madeline
St Joseph's Notre Dame HS; Alameda, CA (4-72) Fr C; NHS; Ski C; Bio A; CSF; Hist A; Most Out; NEDT.

BACICH, Dan Joseph
N Syracuse HS; North Syracuse, NY (6-521) Pres, Fr C; Lat C; Ed, Lit Mag; Math C; NHS; Ed, Sch P; Pres, SC; Amer Leg A; COM; Elk A; Hon Prog; Journ A; MLS; NHS; Opt A; Opt Out Tn; Regent Schol; Gold Medal Art A; *Harvard U; Art.*

BACK, Barbara Jean
Shawnee HS; Louisville, KY; VP, Jr Cl; Citz A; 4H A; Hon Prog; *U of Louisville; Guidance Counselor.*

BACK, Karen Adelle
Riverheads HS; Staunton, VA; 4H; Span C; *Madison Col.*

BACK, Michael James
Anderson HS; Cincinnati, OH (350-750) Var C; JV, Bkbl; Cpt, Ftbl; Co-Cpt, Sftbl; Yth Fel; Campus Crusade for Christ; Bible Study Ldr; *Northern Ky U; Bus.*

BACK, Sharon Elaine
Riverheads HS; Greenville, VA; 4H; Span C; *Madison Col.*

BACK, Walter Michael
Riverheads HS; Greenville, VA (4-104) Dbte Tm; NHS; Sch P; VP, Sci C; WW; 3rd, District Debate Sci Fair; *VPI; Vet.*

BACKBERG, Blaine Roger
Midpark HS; Middleburg Hts, OH; Tres, NHS; Co-Cpt, Bkbl; MVP, Bkbl; Outst Acad Achv A; *Concordia Col; Pre-Law.*

BACKE, John Patrick
Hammond Tech-Voc HS; Hammond, IN (8-243) Ed, Ann; BS; Drama; Ed, Lit Mag; NHS; Ed, Sch P; Pres, SC; Thes; World Affairs C; VP, Jr Cl; Pres, Soph Cl; COM; Cl Fav; Hon Prog; Journ A; MLS; Most Out; St Scholar; VofDEM; Prom Kg; Best Supporting Actor; 4-Yr HR Stu; *Purdue Univ W Lafayette; Engineering.*

BACKES, Sheila Maria
Saint Joseph Acad; McSherrystown, PA (1-15) CYO; Chor; Drama; Fr C; Rainbow; SC; Bkbl; Hockey; Sftbl; Hon Prog; Ntl Cath Mus Ed Asn; Wll; Choir Excel A; *Mt St Mary's Col; Med.*

BACKHAUS, Judy Kay
Rockdale HS; Rockdale, TX; Chem C; VP, FHA; NHS; Bkbl; Tr; Vlbl; *Temple Jr Col; Nurs.*

BACKHAUS, Peter Fritz
Martin Co HS; Stuart, FL (16-500) Fr C; FBLA; Ger C; Span C; Soccer; Bookkeeping A; *Indian River Comm Col; Acct.*

BACKHUUS, Michael William
Bennington HS; Bennington, NE (4-40) Band; Chor; Ensm; Pres, 4H; Math C; NHS; Tres, SC; Tres, Var C; Rptr, Jr Cl; Co-Cpt, Bkbl; Ftbl; Co-Cpt, Tr; HCt; *U of Nebr; Agr.*

BACKMAN, Julie Anne
Moses Lake HS; Moses Lake, WA (180-300) A Cap Choir; Chor; SC; *Big Bend Comm Col; Beauty.*

BACKMAN, Novia Lyndel
Radford HS; Honolulu, HI; Dbte Tm; Rainbow; NJHS; Rainbow Grls, Past Worthy Adv,; St Off, Tres, Mast o-t Grand & Cros; *U of Hawaii at Manoa; Communications.*

BACKSTROM, Debora Sue
Drury Sr HS; North Adams, MA (5%-280) Band; Chor; Fr C; Hon Prog; Yth Fel; Pep C; Skiing; Rep, Yrbk; Yth Rep, Active Pulpit Comm; *Ed.*

BACKSTROM, Eunice Joy
Hillcrest Lutheran Acad; Fergus Falls, MN; A Cap Choir; Band; Chldr; NHS; Bkbl; *Bismarck Jr Col; Engr.*

BACKSTROM, Valerie
Hillsdale HS; San Mateo, CA; Rptr, Sch P; Bsbl; Ftbl; Hockey; Tnns; Tr; *Col of San Mateo; Nurs.*

BACON, Aaron Jay
Calvary Baptist HS; Menomonee Falls, WI (1-8) VP, SC; MVP, Bkbl; Ftbl; Sftbl; *Waukesha Tech; Acct.*

BACON, Billy O'Neal
Frankston Sch; Frankston, TX (10-45) FFA; Rptr, Jr Cl; Citz A; Cl Fav; Livestock Production A; *Tyler Jr Col; Bus.*

BACON, Heidi Roberta
Kearsarge Regional HS; Sutton, NH; Band; Drama; 4H; Model UN; ARC; Bkbl; Cr-Ctry; Hockey; Cpt, Sftbl; Tr; COM; 4H A; Pres A; ARC A; VFW A; Yth Fel; GSct; *Computer Tech.*

BACON, Katherine Elizabeth
Dulaney Sr HS; Baltimore, MD;

BACON, Margaret Elizabeth
Kearsarge Regional HS; N Sutton, NH; Chor; Drama; Secy, 4H; Model UN; Pres, Rainbow; ARC; COM; 4H A; ARC A; Secy, Yth Fel; G Sct; Chamber, All St, 4-H, Chrch, Chors; Sunday Sch Teacher; *Working With Children.*

BACON, Mary Rita
London HS; London, OH (5-180) CYO; Chldr; 4H; InterAct C; NHS; A-Ed, Sch P; Secy, SC; Pres, Jr Cl; Swim; Tr; Kiwanis A; *Miami U; Phys Ed.*

BACON, Richard Keith
William Nottingham HS; Syracuse, NY (20%-300) Drama; Soccer; Yth Fel; *Applied Arts.*

BACON, Scott Mitchell
Augusta Sr HS; Augusta, KS (15-156) Var C; Ftbl; Wrest; All League, Ftbl; St Tourney, Wrest; FCA; Tres, Church Yth; *U of Nebr; Journ.*

BACON, Sheryl Ann
First Assembly Acad; New Orleans, LA (2-36) Chor; Dbte Tm; Lit Ral; Sftbl; Bio A; Citz A; *Bob Jones U; Missions.*

BACON, Sue Lynn
Ottawa HS; Ottawa, IL (99-575) CYO; Chor; Drama; Ensm; 4H; ARC; Spch C; Bkbl; Sftbl; Swim; 4H A; Pink Striper Hospital; *Sci.*

BACON, Tanya
Pittsburg Learning Lab Cntr; Pittsburgh, PA (1-127) All Amer Yth; Chor; Dbte Tm; S-T, FTA; Pres, Hmrm; Rptr, Lit Mag; Pres, Sr Cl; Sftbl; Hon Prog; Journ A; Math A; MLS; Star Student; *U of Pittsburgh; Ed.*

BADE, Daniel
E Windsor HS; E Windsor, CT; Band; Co-Cpt, Ftbl; Tr; *Sci.*

BADGETT, Katherine Ann
West HS; Knoxville, TN; Y-Tns; Citz A; 4H A; VP & Secy, 4-H C.

BADGLEY, Janet Lea
Potosi HS; Potosi, MO (5-265) Secy, 4H; Hon Prog; *Mineral Area Col; Fr.*

BADGLEY, Renee Arlene
Oconto HS; Oconto, NE (2-5) Ann; Band; Chldr; Chor; Fin, GS; S-T, Sr Cl; Sftbl; Tr; HQn; HCt; Hon Prog; Sci A; Ch, Nebr Coun of Yth; Cpt, Vlbl; *Med.*

BADILLO, Nancy Ivellise
Esc Sup Antonio S Pedreira; Moca, PR (4-45) CYO; 4H; Span C; Alg A; Beauty; Hist A; *UPR-CORA Reg; Biologia.*

BADJE, Lynda Suzanne
Columbus Sr HS; Columbus, NE (25%-350) Chor; Orch; JV, Tnns; *Grand Island Sch of Bus; Bus.*

BADY, Henry E
Westside HS; Augusta, GA (150-280) *Bethune Col; Bus Ed.*

BAECHER, Anne Victoria
Cave Spring HS; Roanoke, VA; Chldr; Span C; *Va Tech Col.*

BAEDER, James Douglas
University HS; Los Angeles, CA (5-950) Chor; Ensm; Sci C; Tres, SC; Citz A; DARGCA; Hon Prog; Gifted Stu; *Sci.*

BAEHLER, Kathy Lynn
Alton Sr HS; Alton, IL; A Cap Choir; Band; Orch; Yth Fel; Published Author.

BAEHR, Christian Robert
Arcadia HS; Arcadia, CA; Bkbl; Campus Life; Pres, Church Yth; WW; Co- cpt, Vlbl; *Pasadena City Col; Emergency Med Tech.*

BAER, Belinda Lee
Berne Union HS; Sugar Grove, OH; Band; Chldr; Fr C; 4H; Bkbl; Sftbl; Tr; Yth Fel; *Eckerd Col; Foreign Lang.*

BAER, Bryan Lee
Kenmore HS; Akron, OH; Pres, Band; Orch; COM; Citz A; Christian Ldrship A; *Akron St U; Bus Mgt.*

BAER, Debra Jean
Apollo-Ridge HS; Spring Church, PA (35-240) Chor; Ensm; Madrigal; NHS; Secy, Pol Sci C; Rainbow; SC; HCt; Mem Schol; WW, Mus Stu; Ntl Sch Choral A; St Chor; *Westminster Col; Mus Ed.*

BAEZ, Aracelis
Consuelo Escalona Private Sch; Carolina, PR (1-38) CYO; SC; Pres, Sr Cl; Tres, Jr Cl; COM; Hon Prog; Loyalty A; Faculty A; *Bradley U; Bus Adm.*

BAEZ, Carlos Ulises
York Comm HS; Elmhurst, IL; Band; Drama; Pres, Order/Arrow; Swim; Order/Arrow A; Eagle Sct; Pres, BSct, Explorer Scts; *Mass Media.*

BAEZ, John Paul
York HS; Elmhurst, IL; Band; Drama; Order/ Arrow; Thes; Cr-Ctry; Swim; Tr; Order/Arrow A; Pres, BScts; VP, Explorers.

BAEZ, Katheryn Yevonne
Sacred Heart HS; Kingston, MA (9-54) Chor; Jr Miss Pagent; Spch C; Tnns; COM; Hon Prog; VFW A; Dancing C; Fr A; Chor Cert; *Burdett Col; Secretarial.*

BAGAASON, Sarah Michal
Mayo HS; Rochester, MN (1-611) A Cap Choir; NHS; Sci C; Var C; Tr; Regent Schol; Val; *Luther Col; Early Childhood Ed.*

BAGBY, John Robert Jr
E Peoria Comm HS; E Peoria, IL (164-391) Ann; 2nd Pl, Women's C Art Contest; Hon Men, W Ill U, Ind Ed Exhibit; *Ill Central Col; Archt.*

BAGDONAS, Dalia Louise
Curie HS; Chicago, IL (7-769) CYO; Cpt, Chldr; Chor; VP, Sodality; COM; Math A; Ger Hon Soc; *Loyola U; Bus.*

BAGDONAS, Teresa Maria
Kelly HS; Chicago, IL (11-485) Band; Secy, FNA; FTA; Pres, Math C; V-Ch, NHS; Tres, ARC; Sodality; Span NHS; COM; Hon Prog; Math A; Tres, Lib Guild; Pep C; Stu Exec Bd; Lithuanian C; *Aurora Col; Acct.*

BAGG, Melodie Ann
Grandview Park Baptist HS; Des Moines, IA (4-23) F-Ed, Ann; Chor; Pres, Hmrm; Sch P; Ch, SC; Pres, Jr Cl; Bkbl; Sftbl; Tr; Sci A; Athletic Letter; *Cedarville Col; Phys Ed.*

BAGGARLEY, Eva Ruth
Brunswick HS; Brunswick, GA (7-416) Band; Drama; FBLA; Hmrm; NHS; COM; Hon Speaker, Graduation; Dixie O'Brien Schol; *Armstrong St Col; Dental Hygiene.*

BAGGETT, Carolyn Faye
Western Hills HS; Fort Worth, TX (165-650) MVP, Sftbl; Tr; *Tex Tech Col; Ed.*

BAGGETT, Jewell Margaret
Acad o-t Sacred Heart; Grand Coteau, LA (10-55) Drama; 4H; Bkbl; 4H A; Sup Rating, Fr Lang Festival; Stu o-t Wk; Hon Men, Piano; *Spring Hill Col; Marine Bio.*

BAGGETTE, Wade Ross Jr
Battle Ground Acad; Franklin, TN (43-64) A-Ed, Ann; VP, Lat C; JV, Ftbl; COM; NEDT; *Vanderbilt U; Med.*

BAGGOTT, Wanda Maria
Eastern Sr HS; Washington, DC (1-520) CYO; Cum Laude Soc; Hmrm; Lat NHS; NHS; Tres, SC; Tres, Sr Cl; Alg A; Amer Leg A; Bio A; Citz A; Hon Prog; Magna Cum Laude; Math A; Most Out; Ntl Achv Schol; Phy A; Type A; Val; Rptr & Secy, Sch Paper; Eng A; Women's Bar Assn A; Georgetown A; Most Studious; Geo Washington A; Erl Howard Gld Md; *Cath U; Nurs.*

BAGGS, Gina Marie
James B Conant HS; Hoffman Estates, IL (83-646) Fr C; COM; Church Yth Ministry; HS Schol A; Jr Vol, Med Center; Med Careers C; Attendance Recogn; JV Badminton; Med Center Serv A; *Loyola U; Nurs.*

BAGGS, Ramona Lynn
Battiest HS; Battiest, OK (1-24) F-Ed, Ann; Chor; FHA; NHS; Co-Head, Librarian.

BAGLEY, Anita Marie
Saint Mary's HS; Stockton, CA (1-204) NHS; CSF; Hon Prog; NEDT; Span, Eng, A's; *Law.*

BAGLEY, Bernadette Claire
St Mary's HS; Stockton, CA (1-204) Ed, Ann; Fin, GS; NHS; Bank Of Amer A; CSF; Hon Prog; NMF; NMS; Yth in City Govt A; *Calif St U; Bus Adm.*

BAGLEY, Dennis Alan
N Mercer R III HS; Mercer, MO (5-13) Ann; Chor; VP, Soph Cl; Bkbl; Sftbl; Tr; DARGCA; WW.

BAGLEY, James Tyler
Mooresville HS; Mooresville, IN (1-310) AFS; BS; Fr C; French NHS; Math C; Sci C; St Stu Congress; Pres, Jr Cl; Pres, Soph Cl; Bsbl; Bkbl; MVP, Tnns; Elk A; Lion A; *Phys Sci.*

BAGLEY, Pamela Mae
Kress HS; Kress, TX (2-31) Ann; Chldr; FHA; FTA; S-T, Sr Cl; Tres, Jr Cl; Tres, Soph Cl; Bkbl; JV, Tnns; Tr; Citz A; Cl Fav; HCt; Sal; Lion's C Swtht; *W Tex St U; Commercial Art.*

BAGNELL, Terri Kay
Washington HS; Washington, KS (5-33) Band; Co-Cpt, Chldr; Parl, FHA; 4H; Mjrte; SC; Bkbl; Tr; Prom Server; Secy, Pep C; Vlbl; *Phys Ed.*

BAGSTAD, Becky Jo
Huntington Beach HS; Huntington Beach, CA (500-750) Pres, A Cap Choir; Band; Pres, Chor; Ensm; InterClub Coun; Madrigal; Orch; Ski C; Most Out; Tower A, Clrm Excel Fin; *Orange Coast Col; Mus.*

BAGUHN, Kathleen Joy
Merrill Sr HS; Merrill, WI (32-343) A Cap Choir; FBLA; 4H; Type A; VP, Secy, Mat Maids C; Secy, Rackett Squad; Bicentennial Committee; Participation A'S, Bus Skills Cont; *U of Wis; Recreational Adm.*

BAGWELL, Clarissa Jane
Cass HS; Cassville, GA (10%-190) BC; Chor; FHA; Pres, Math C; Sci C; Tri-Hi-Y; Var C; Cpt, Bkbl; MVP, Sftbl; Tnns; Tr; COM; Chem A; Math A; MVP, Bkbl; All Amer, Sftbl; All St Bkbl; *Berry Col.*

BAGWELL, Cynthia Lynn
Cartersville HS; Cartersville, GA (33-152) Band; Chor; Ensm; All St Chor; *Vocal Mus.*

BAGWELL, James Donald
Tyner HS; Chattanooga, TN (19-261) Ann; BS; Hmrm; Key C; NHS; SC; Pres, Sr Cl; Bsbl; Ftbl; Soccer; Swtht; *W Point Military Acad; Sci.*

BAGWELL, Jeffrey Howard
St Joseph's Prep Sch; Philadelphia, PA (75-115) Band; Chess C; Ensm; Fr C; Orch; Swim; Ntl Cath Mus Ed Asn; NMS; ARC A; Mus Cert; Band Ltrs & Trophies; Hospital Vol; *La Salle Col; Phys Therapy.*

BAGWELL, Laurie Ann
Osborne Sr HS; Marietta, GA (25-400) Band; BC; Chor; Key C; NHS; VP, SC; Lion A; Opt A; Rotary A; *Mercer Col; Mus.*

BAGWELL, Susan Elaine
Spartanburg HS; Spartanburg, SC; Fr C; Drama, Bkbl, Sftbl, Church; VP, Church Yth Coun; Pres, Acteens; *U of SC; Nurs.*

BAHNEMAN, Wendy Jeanne
Thompson Pub Sch; Thompson, ND (2-28) Ann; Chldr; Chor; Drama; Ensm; GS; 4H; Bkbl; Tr; DARGCA; WW; *U of ND; Aviation.*

BAIAMONTE, Barbara Michelle
Flintridge Sacred Heart Acad; Pasadena, CA (12-80) VP, Drama; Fr C; SC; Stu Christian Involvement; Drama A; Semi-Fin, Venice Drama; Sem-Fin, Shakesperian Drama Fest; *U of Calif; Dramatics.*

BAIER, Barbara Ann
Cissna Park HS; Cissna Park, IL (20-41) Cpt, Chldr; Chor; FHA; Co-Cpt, Bkbl; JV, Sftbl; Qn, Old Sell Lers; *Parkland Jr Col; Marketing.*

BAIER, Joseph Mark
Breckinridge Co HS; Harned, KY (5%-250) Golf; *U of Ky; Archt.*

BAIER, Marie Genevieve
Altario HS; Altario, CANADA (1-15) Tres, 4H; Ch, Hmrm; SC; Bkbl; Tr; 4H A; PTA A; Sci A; Spch A; *U of Alberta; Law.*

BAILES, Melanie Denise
York Comp HS; York, SC (7-272) A-Ed, Ann; FTA; Ch, Hmrm; Span C; HCt; Jr Steering Comm; Jr Marshal; *Winthrop Col; Bus Adm.*

BAILES, Sandy Lee
Eldorado HS; El Dorado, AR (20%-500) Tres, Soph Cl; Hon Prog; Yth Fel; FCA; Jr Civitan; Yth Church; *Phys Therapy.*

BAILESS, Jeffrey Glenn
Gretna Sr HS; Gretna, VA (10%-370) Band; BS; Span C; *Central Va Comm Col; Bus Adm.*

BAILEY, Adrian Wayne
Rockdale HS; Rockdale, TX (20-140) Ann; Pres, Band; Chem C; Chor; VP, Drama; Fin, Lit Ral; NHS; Orch; Order/Arrow; Sci C; SC; 'R' A; *U of Houston; Pre-Law.*

BAILEY, Anne Louise
Parkersburg HS; Parkersburg, WV (3-821) A Cap Choir; JV, Chldr; GS; 4H; Hmrm; Madrigal; Mjrte; NFL; ARC; Spch C; SC; VP, Jr Cl; COM; Elk A; 4H A; Math A; Sci A; Spch A; Yth Fel; SC Adv Comm; Church Choir; Symphonic Choir; Drill Tm; Pres, Tres, Church Yth Group; Spch Tourn.

BAILEY, Arnold Judson III
Hart Co HS; Hartwell, GA; Band; Chess C; 4H; VP, Hmrm; Sci C; SC; Pres, Jr Cl; Ftbl; MVP, Golf; Chaplin, Hi-Y; *Ga Sou Col; Ind Mgt.*

BAILEY, Babbi Diane
Erwin HS; Erwin, NC (12-103) Chor; FHA; Inter-Club Coun; Span C; SC; Best Alto; Home Ec A; *Mus.*

BAILEY, Babbie Diane
Erwin HS; Erwin, NC (12-103) Chor; FBLA; FHA; InterClub Coun; Span C; SC; Sftbl; Best Alto; Outst Achv; *Mus.*

BAILEY, Bertram Cass
P S DuPont HS; Wilmington, De; BS; CYO; Chess C; Pres, Fr C; Secy, NHS; Cr-Ctry; Cpt, Swim; Tr; Chess Champ; Fr A; *Princeton U; Chem.*

BAILEY, Beth Ann
Park Center HS; Minneapolis, MN; Band; Hmrm; Sch P; Secy, SC; VP, Soph Cl; Bkbl; Soccer; Swim; Hon Prog; Most Out; Pres A; MVP, Vlbl; St Yth Coun; Prs Yth Fl; Handball; Dist Coun On Ministries; Church Admin Board; Stu o-t Wk; Most Spirited, Vlbl & Bkbl; *Psych.*

BAILEY, Billye Carol
Mission HS; Mission, TX; Pres, Chor; Rptr, Sch P; SC; Y-Tns; H of F; Hon Prog; Rotary A; Sci A; Lead, Mus; Superior Medals, Singing; Rotary Pianist; Dist UIL A; *E Tex St U; Mus Ed.*

BAILEY, Brenda Joyce
Chester HS; Chester, PA (10%-720) A Cap Choir; Band; *Pa St U; Vet.*

BAILEY, Carla
Skyline HS; Salt Lake City, UT (1-675) Ann; NHS; Hon Prog; Pres, Young Women; Trustee's Schol, BYU; *Brigham Young U;; Math.*

BAILEY, Cassandea Ann
Hoover HS; San Diego, CA; City Conf; Pres, 4H; Cpt, Sftbl; *Grossmont Col; Nurs.*

BAILEY, Charisse Annette
Southwestern Sr HS; Baltimore, MD (25%-650) Drama; NHS; *Howard U; Phar.*

BAILEY, Cheryl Lynn
Manhattan Sr HS; Manhattan, KS (177-425) FHA; Y-Tns; Pres & Parl, 4-H C; *Wichita St U; Dental Hygiene.*

BAILEY, Chris M
Lordstown HS; Warren, OH (1-56) F-Ed, Ann; Band; BS; VP, Chess C; NHS; Order/Arrow; F-Ed, Sch P; Tres, Jr Cl; VP, Soph Cl; MVP, Cr-Ctry; Tr; Amer Leg A; God & Country A; Val; Eagle Sct; *Ohio U; Journ.*

BAILEY, Cindy Lynn
Hopkinsville HS; Hopkinsville, KY (45-357) Band; ARC; Sch Achieve Tm; COM; Interlochen Ntl Mus; *Hopkinsville Comm Col; Nurs.*

BAILEY, Dana Jo
Kalamazoo Central HS; Kalamazoo, MI; Hon Prog; Sci A; Church Ed Comm; Dist Yth Rep, MYF; *Western Mich U; Special Ed.*

BAILEY, Dana Lea
Timberline HS; Weippe, ID; Chldr; Chor; 4H; NHS; Secy, Soph Cl; Bkbl; Tr; 4H A; Hon Prog.

BAILEY, David Crockett
Hannibal Central Sch; Hannibal, NY; Band; NHS; Cr-Ctry; Tr; *Oswego Col; Engr.*

BAILEY, Donna Jean
E Syracuse-Minoa Sr HS; E Syracuse, NJ; Tres, Bus C; Chor; Drama; NHS; Y-Tns; COM; Hon Prog; JA A; Pres, JA; Chor, Lib, Merit Roll, Bowl, A's; *Bradford Col; Ed.*

BAILEY, Dwayne Allen
Warren Area HS; Warren, PA (40-396) A Cap Choir; Chor; Math C; NHS; Alg A; COM; Hon Prog; Math A; Yth Fel; *Allegheny Col; Pre-Med.*

BAILEY, Earnest Edward
Surry Co HS; Surry, VA; Fr C; FBLA; Bsbl; Bkbl; Ftbl; Ntl Achv Schol; Bkbl Trainer; *Elec.*

BAILEY, Elizabeth Marie
Lutheran HS S; St Louis, MO (17-157) Chor; Hon Prog; Concert Choir; *Nutrition.*

BAILEY, Elizabeth Nadean
Herndon HS; Herndon, VA (35%-500) Span C; Bkbl; Ftbl; Sftbl; Tr; Yth Fel; Jr Festival Mus A; Ntl Piano Playing Auditions; Comm Girls Sftbl Champions.

BAILEY, Frank Wayne
Charleston HS; Charleston, IL (100-248) Band; Chor; 4H; Orch; ARC; Spch C; Bio A; COM; Sci A; Spch A; Band A's; *E Ill U; Mus.*

BAILEY, Glenda Ann
Lordstown HS; Lordstown, OH (1-56) Band; VP, 4H; Pres, Soph Cl; Bkbl; Sftbl; Tr; Amer Leg A; 4H A; Hon Prog; *Phys Ed.*

BAILEY, Gregory Lee
Man HS; Man, WV (17-180) Band; Ensm; InterAct C; NHS; ARC; Span C; Lit A; All Area, All Co, Bands; *W Va U; Engr.*

BAILEY, Gwendolyn Faye
Pearl HS; Nashville, TN; MLS; *Nash Tech; Acct.*

BAILEY, Howard H
Wyndmere HS; Wyndmere, ND (9-50) Chor; Madrigal; Math C; Tres, NHS; Pres, Jr Cl; Bsbl; MVP, Bkbl; Cpt, Ftbl; Tr; Cpt, Bkbl; All St Vocal; Stu o-t Wk; *U of ND.*

28

BAILEY, Hoy A
Southern HS; Wymore, NE (35-70) Band; Chor; 4H; Madrigal; Var C; Bsbl; Bkbl; Tr; 4H A.

BAILEY, James Tranter
Warren Area HS; Warren, PA (10%-435) Band; Drama; Ensm; Lat C; Orch; Hon Prog; Civic Orch; *Med.*

BAILEY, Janice Marie
Tyrone Area HS; Tyrone, PA (130-290) Band; Chor; InterAct C; Span C.

BAILEY, Jennifer Elizabeth
McGavock HS; Nashville, TN; Bkbl; Sftbl.

BAILEY, Jennifer Leigh
Pennsville Mem HS; Pennsville, NJ (38-269) Band; Chor; Hmrm; NHS; Orch; SC; Yth Fel; God & Country A; Drum Mjrte, Marching Band; Fencing; Stage Band; Al-Co Bnd; Most Talent; All-Sch Musicals; All-Co Chor; Gym; All-S Jersey Chor; MIP, Chor; *W Chester St Col; Mus.*

BAILEY, Joseph Michael
Haynesville HS; Haynesville, LA (17-49) Chor; Drama; FBLA; FFA; 4H; F-Ed, Sch P; Bkbl; Ftbl; Tr; WW; *NW Voc Col; Industrial Instruments.*

BAILEY, Kandie J
Clovis Sr HS; Clovis, NM; Band; *Lubbock Christian Col; Home Ec.*

BAILEY, Katherine Anne
Lincoln HS; Stockton, CA; Drama; Thes; *Alan Hancock Col; Cosmotology.*

BAILEY, Keith Middleton
Montgomery HS; Santa Rosa, CA (2-600) Band; Chor; Lat C; Math C; NHS; Order/Arrow; Var C; Swim; COM; DARGCA; Hon Prog; Math A; Order/Arrow A; Rotary A; VFW A; Eagle Sct; *Oral Roberts U; Math.*

BAILEY, Kenneth James
David Anderson HS; Lisbon, OH (13-120) A-Ed, Ann; Fr C; NHS; Church Sftbl; Comm Swim; *Ohio St U; Vet Med.*

BAILEY, Kimberly Renee
Calhoun HS; Hardin, IL (8-59) Co-Ed, Ann; Secy, Band; NHS; SC; Secy, Sr Cl; JV, Bkbl; JV, Sftbl; Pom-Pom; GAA; Vlbl; *Passavant Area Sch of Nurs; Register Nurs.*

BAILEY, LaGenia
Quincy Sr HS I; Quincy, IL (81-800) Chor; Ch, Ensm; Madrigal; Orch; Rainbow; Span C; Hon Prog; NEDT; Outst Mus, Instrumental; Theater A; Orch A; Pam Bedford Dance Company; Fine Arts C.

BAILEY, Laurie Ann
E Syracuse-Minoa HS; E Syracuse, NY (32-900) FBLA; *Word of Life Bible Inst; Bible.*

BAILEY, Leasha Ann
Detroit Lakes HS; Detroit Lakes, MN (2-260) A Cap Choir; JV, Chldr; Drama; Ensm; Lat C; Math C; Mgr, Tr; *Northland Col; Math.*

BAILEY, Lillian Frances
Warren Co Sr HS; McMinnville, TN (38-390) InterAct C; NHS; ARC; Mgr, Bkbl; Sftbl; Swim; 1st Cl, GS; Marketing Medal; Top 10%; 1st Pl Dist, 4th Pl, St, Marketing; *Tenn Tech U; Special Ed.*

BAILEY, Lori Ann
Park Jr-Sr HS; Fairplay, CO (1-12) Bus Mgr, Ann; JV, Chldr; FBLA; SC; Mgr, Bkbl; COM; HQn; Hon Prog; Val; Prom Qn; *Mesa Col; Bus Adm.*

BAILEY, Lynn Sue
Harbor HS; Ashtabula, OH (12-183) AFS; Rptr, Band; Fr C; Hmrm; ARC; 1st Cl GSct; *Wittenberg Col; Math.*

BAILEY, Margaret
Pearl HS; Nashville, TN; Chldr; Chor; Dbte Tm; FHA; FTA; Span C; SC; Y-Tns; Sftbl; *Tex St U; Hist.*

BAILEY, Mariana
Putnam City HS; Oklahoma City, OK; A-Ed, Ann; Co-Ch, Lat C; NHS; SC; Hon Prog; Drill Tm; Dist Off, Okla Christian Yth Fel; *Computer Analysis.*

BAILEY, Marilyn Fern
Siloam Springs HS; Siloam Springs, AR; VP, Band; BC; FBLA; Span C; VP, Soph Cl; *John Brown U; Secy Sci.*

BAILEY, Martha Susan
Webster Groves Sr HS; Webster Groves, MO (95-484) S-T, SC; Vol Swim Teacher, Red Cross; Sr Service A; Trea, Sr Yth League; Young Life; Pep C; *Valparaiso U.*

BAILEY, Mary Beth
Lincoln Sr HS; Sioux Falls, SD (72%-557) Ger C; Lit Mag; Y-Tns; Golf; Tnns; Tr; Q&S A; *U of SD; Special Ed.*

BAILEY, Monica Lynn
Cambridge HS; Cambridge, OH; Chor.

BAILEY, Nancy Kaye
Whitewater HS; Whitewater, WI (26-176) AFS; S-T, Band; Chor; Ensm; Hmrm; NHS; Ski C; Secy, SC; Sftbl; Tr; HCt; Hon Prog; Sci A; GAA; Vlbl; *Fashion Design.*

BAILEY, Rex Clifford
Huron Sr HS; Huron, SD (7-257) A Cap Choir; Chor; FBLA; Madrigal; NHS; Gov Honor Prog; All St Chor; *Sioux Falls Col; Math.*

BAILEY, Richard Daniels
Parkway W Sr HS; St Louis, MO (220-650) Ch, Hmrm; ARC; Bkbl; Ftbl; Tr; Hon Prog; Yth Fel; Presidential Phys Fitness A; Prom Ct; *Southern Methodist U; Bus.*

BAILEY, Robert Eugene
Canadian HS; Canadian, TX (32-60) Band; NHS; Bkbl; Ftbl; Golf; Yth Fel; Stu Trnr, Ftbl; Outst Marcher, Band; I Rating, Ensm; *Panhandle St U; Med.*

BAILEY, Ronald Lee
Montabella HS; Edmore, MI (25-150) 4H; Ski C; Tr; JV, Wrest; *Miss St U; Vet.*

BAILEY, Russell Robinson Jr
Smithfield HS; Smithfield, VA; Bkbl; Letter of Merit, Bkbl; *Bus.*

BAILEY, Samuel Henry
Warren Area HS; Warren, PA (53-414) Band; Drama; Ensm; Fr C; Pres, Mod Mus Mas; NHS; Orch; Tnns; Hon Prog; Dist Band; Yrbk Board; Bowl; *Mansfield Col; Secondary Ed.*

BAILEY, Sandra Lynn
Sissonville HS; Charleston, WV (4-195) Ed, Ann; Fr C; Mu Alpha Theta; NHS; 4H A; MLS; Miss Sissonian; *W Va U.*

BAILEY, Sandra Lynn
Detroit Lakes HS; Detroit Lakes, MN (3-255) Pres, A Cap Choir; AFS; Dbte Tm; Drama; Ensm; Lat C; Math C; NFL; NHS; Rptr, Sch P; Secy, SC; St Debate Tourn; St Ensm; *Saint Benedict Col; Engr.*

BAILEY, Saundra Maria
Phineas Banning HS; Wilmington, CA; FBLA; GS; Hmrm; Ch, SC; Pres, Sr Cl; Secy, Jr Cl; Tres, Soph Cl; Tnns; CSF; PTA A; Drill Tm; Sr Cl A; *Cal St Dominquez; Public Adm.*

BAILEY, Sheila Renay
Martin Luther King Acad; Gary, IN; Chor; Hmrm; Bkbl; Soccer; Sftbl; Hon Prog; *Ind U NW; Nurs.*

BAILEY, Sidney Wayne
Collinsville HS; Collinsville, OK (50%-140) Band; Pres, Chor; Drama; Ensm; Spch C; H of F; Drum Major; Arion A; Most Talented; *Mus.*

BAILEY, Susan Fern
Tuscaloosa HS; Tuscaloosa, AL; VP, Anchor C; Band; Fr C; Hmrm; Lat C; NHS; SC; Sftbl; JV, Tnns; Tr; Beauty; Cl Fav; HCt; Sci A; 1st, Dist Sci Fair; Philadelphia Freedoms Found; Talent Show Win; *Ga Tech U; Civil Engr.*

BAILEY, Suzanne Marie
The Cecilian Acad; Philadelphia, PA (4-29) Pres, Fr C; World Affairs C; NMS; *Tyler Col of Art; Illustration.*

BAILEY, Terrilyn Gail
Sparkman HS; Toney, AL (15%-140) Ann; Cpt, Chldr; FTA; Hmrm; Secy, InterAct C; Tres, NHS; Rptr, Sch P; SC; Var C; Tres, Jr Cl; Beauty; HCt; Hon Prog; *Auburn U; Marketing.*

BAILEY, Thomas Alben
Chelan HS; Chelan, WA; NHS; Span C; Tnns.

BAILEY, Thomas Waring
Pinewood HS; Summerville, SC (2-3) Ann; Drama; Sch P; Pres, SC; Drivers Ed Cert; *Elem Ed.*

BAILEY, Vici Lyne
Southgate HS; Southgate, MI (21-365) Tres, NHS; Ski C; NHS A; *Asbury Col; Pre-Med.*

BAILEY, Walter Bernard
Garfield Sr HS; Hamilton, OH (48-445) Chor; Dbte Tm; Drama; Ensm; Fr C; Pres, Spch C; SC; Thes; COM; Citz A; Opt A; Spch A; *U of Cincinnati; Chem.*

BAILIFF, Cheryl Lynn
Plantation HS; Plantation, FL (68-618) Pres, Chor; Span C; SC; Cr-Ctry; Tr; Yth Fel; Outst Marcher; Pres's Phys Fitness A; Amer Wilderness Ldrship Schol; Tr Achv A.

BAILIN, David
Paramus HS; Paramus, NJ (14-581) All Amer Yth; Cpt, Band; VP, Dbte Tm; HiY; Lit Mag; Model UN; VP, NFL; Tres, NHS; Secy, Orch; Ed, Sch P; Ch, SC; UN Council; Tnns; Hon Prog; Sci A; Spch A; Yth Leg; Eng A; Calculus A; Ntl Forensic Leg Sprtsmanshp A; *Amherst U; Pol Sci.*

BAILLY, Deborah Lynn
Green Mountain HS; Lakewood, CO (25%-500) *Trinity Col; Art.*

BAILY, Scott Alan
Adrian Sr HS; Adrian, MI (87-430) A Cap Choir; Pres, Chor; Ensm; Madrigal; Order/Arrow; SC; Tres, Var C; Pres, Sr Cl; Co-Cpt, Swim; Tr; God & Country A; HKg; Order/Arrow A; Rotary A; Yth Fel; MVP, Swim; Eagle Sct; Jr Exchangeite; Tn o-t Mo; *Alma Col; Bus.*

BAILY, Todd Michael
Adrian Sr HS; Adrian, MI (25%-420) A Cap Choir; Band; BS; Chor; Ensm; Madrigal; Order/Arrow; St Stu Congress; Swim; God & Country A; Order/Arrow A; Yth Fel; Yth Leg; Eagle Sct; Jr Exchangeite.

BAIN, Debra Sue
Cape Fear HS; Fayetteville, NC (40-400) Ann; Band; BC; Fr C; InterAct C; Pres, Rainbow; Sci C; Bio A; Masonic A; Q&S A; Med Self-Help Trng Course; *W Carolina U; Nurs.*

BAIN, Heather Lind
Dalton Sch; New York City, NY (33%-88) Chor; Dbte Tm; Drama; Model UN; Rptr, Sch P; Var C; Bkbl; Sftbl; March of Dimes Walk-A-Thon Patch; Bkbl Trophy; Vlbl Trophy; Ath Patch.

BAIN, Hillary Ann
Niskayuna HS; Schenectady, NY (20%-400) Chor; Hmrm; SC; Church Yth Group; Rep, Consistory of Church; Amer Assn of Teachers of Fr A; *Pol Sci.*

BAIN, Philip Edward
Valley Head HS; Valley Head, AL; Pres, BC; FFA; Var C; Bsbl; Ftbl; H of F; Best Defensive Back; All Star, Bsbl; Bsbl Player o-t Yr; *U of Ala; Acct.*

BAIN, Pierre Walter
Los Angeles Baptist HS; Sepulveda, CA (50-100) Attendance A; *U of Nev; Conservation.*

BAINES, Leonard Meredith
Granada HS; Livermore, CA (201-560) A Cap Choir; Band; Ensm; Var C; Tnns; Bausch & Lomb A.

BAINTER, Debbie May
Los Amigos HS; Fountain Valley, CA (68-375) Band; Ensm; Orch; Sftbl; Hon Prog; Yth Fel; Cpt, MVP, JV Vlbl; *Orange Coast Col.*

BAINTER, Gregory Lee
Lewistown Comm HS; Lewistown, IL; Chor; Drama; FTA; 4H; Bsbl.

BAINTER, James David
Lewistown Comm HS; Lewistown, IL (43-100) Chor; Dbte Tm; Ensm; A-Ed, Sch P; Span C; Bsbl; JV, Golf; 1st Pl, Co Sr Bowl.

BAIR, Delci Jean
Turlock HS; Turlock, CA (26-370) Chor; Ensm; S-T, SC; CSF; COM; Type A; Yth Fel; Bible Memory Assn; Leader, Awana Yth Assn; Church Choirs; Soloist; *Calif St Col; Mus.*

BAIR, Guy Donald
Forest Hill HS; W Palm Beach, FL (3-580) SC; Pres, Soph Cl; Chem A; Hist A; Hon Prog; Sci A; DAC Hist A; Acad Letter; Phys Fitness A; *Penn St U; Psych.*

BAIR, Kevin John
Forest Hill HS; W Palm Beach, FL (10-425) NHS; Ed, Sch P; Wrest; COM; Boy o-t Mo; Sports Letter; Acad Letter; Temple U; Journ.

BAIR, Randal Alan
S Page Comm Sch; College Springs, IA; Tres, FFA; Pres, 4H; Tres, Jr Cl; Pres, Soph Cl; Bsbl; Bkbl; Co-Cpt, Ftbl; Tr; 4H A; Hon Prog; FFA A.

BAIR, Susie P
Rochester Comm HS; Rochester, IN (8-179) Tres, Drama; FFA; Secy, FTA; Ger C; GS; 4H; Hmrm; NHS; SC; Co-Cpt, Bkbl; Semi-Fin, Sftbl; MVP, Tnns; Tr; Elk A; 4H A; Hon Prog; Pres A; Type A; Semi-Fin, Bkbl; GAA St A; Cpt, Tnns; Army Schol Ath; Cpt, MVP, Semi-Fin, Vlbl; FCA Ntl Outst Girl Ath; Prom Dutch; Ind St U; Phys Ed.

BAIRD, Andrea Marie
Jonesboro Sr HS; Jonesboro, GA (20%-1800) F-Ed, Ann; Band; VP, BC; Span C; WW; Clayton Jr Col.

BAIRD, Denese Valerie
George W Wingate HS; Brooklyn, NY (5-25) Band; CYO; Dbte Tm; FHA; FTA; InterAct C; Math C; Sch P; Spch C; Span NHS; Bkbl; Tnns; Tr; Alg A; Bio A; Citz A; Cl Fav; God & Country A; H of F; Hist A; I Dare You; Interlochen Ntl Mus; Math A; Most Out; Sci A; Spch A; Star Student; Type A; Yth Fel; Yth Foundation; Yth Foundation A; Yth Leg; Acting A; Brooklyn Col; TV Production & Direction.

BAIRD, Diane Louise
Kailua HS; Kailua, HI (119-683).

BAIRD, Eric Charleton
E Valley HS; Spokane, WA (40-186) MVP, Dbte Tm; Fr C; Pres, SC; Var C; Cpt, Tnns; Masonic A; Spch A; St Debate; Top 5 Jr Boys; Patrl Ldr, Asst Sr Patrl, Ldr, B St; Wash St U; Agr Engr.

BAIRD, George Clifford III
Westminster HS; Atlanta, GA (1-99) Cl, Cum Laude Soc; Pres, NHS; Cpt, Tr; Bio A; COM; Harvard Book A; NMF; NMS; Val; MVP, Tr; Fr A; Yale U; Engr.

BAIRD, Jami Kay
Palo Duro HS; Amarillo, TX (15-285) Bus C; FBLA; NHS; Ed, Sch P; JV, Cr-Ctry; Tr; Journ A; Yth Fel; Trainer, Bkbl, Vlbl; Stu o-t Mo; N Tex St U; Phys Ed.

BAIRD, Joyce Lynne
Whispering Hills Christian Acad; Nashville, TN (5-20) Ed, Ann; Co-Cpt, Chldr; Chor; Rainbow; Pres, Jr Cl; MVP, Sftbl; Hist A; Superlatives; U of Tenn at Nashville; Nurs.

BAIRD, Richard Alan
Father Geibel HS; Connellsville, PA (70-99) Chess C; Model UN; SC; Pres, Soph Cl; Co-Cpt, Bkbl; Cr-Ctry; Penn St U; Bus Adm.

BAIRD, Susan Duncan
Colonial Heights HS; Colonial Heights, VA (40-315) Chor; Drama; Hmrm; VP, Lat C; SC; Yth Fel; Keyettes; U of Commonwealth U; Special Ed.

BAISDEN, Deleana Faye
Kermit HS; Kermit, WV; All Amer Yth; Ann; Chldr; FHA; Sch P; Span C; SC; Secy, Sr Cl; Cpt, Bkbl; Sftbl; Swtht; Outst Chldr; WW; Marshall U; Coach.

BAISDEN, Denise Lynn
Huntington E HS; Huntington, WV (2-375) Chor; Fr C; Hmrm; Lat C; NHS; SC; Sal; Marshall U; Pre-Med.

BAISLEY, Vivian Ann
Dalton HS; Dalton, GA; Chor; FHA; Hmrm; Cpt, Bkbl; Sftbl; Tnns; Cl Fav; HCt; Yth Fel; Miss April; Pep C; Mus.

BAIZE, David Michael
Mount Carmel HS; Mt Carmel, IL (41-170) VP, Demolay; Bsbl; JV, Bkbl; JV, Ftbl; Mgr, Wrest; NEDT; DeMolay Merit As; Wabash Valley Col; Acct.

BAJEMA, Bryan Gordon
San Rafael HS; San Rafael, CA (20-400) Co-Ed, Lit Mag; Math C; Pres, Model UN; Bank Of Amer A; CSF; Badminton; UC Berkley Alumni Schol; U of Calif at Berkeley; Foreign Lang.

BAJO, Teresa Manuela
St Joseph's o-t Palisades HS; W New York, NJ (18-289) French NHS; Beauty; COM; 1st Hons; St Peter's Col; Acct.

BAK, Evan John
Maui HS; Kahului, HI (6-299) Dbte Tm; NHS; Sci C; B Crocker A; Math A; NMS; Cal Tech; Astronomy.

BAKANAUSKAS, Paul
Collegiate Sch; Passaic, NJ (2-20) NHS; RPI; Med.

BAKER, Ann Laree
Brookhaven Acad; Brookhaven, MS; Ed, Ann; BC; Cpt, Chldr; Fr C; Fin, Jr Miss Pagent; HCt; Best Sch Spirit; Miss BA; Miss St U; Art.

BAKER, Barbara Elaine
Towers HS; Decatur, GA (36-360) Pres, BC; Co-Cpt, Chldr; Hmrm; Ch, InterClub Coun; NHS; Tres, SC; Secy, Soph Cl; MVP, Bkbl; Tnns; DARGCA; HCt; Nom, WSB Great Young Amer A; Runner Up, Homecoming; Sr Superlative; Sch Service A; Ga Tech; Acct.

BAKER, Benita Joy
Van-Far HS; Vandalia, MO; Secy, FHA; NHS.

BAKER, Billy James Jr
T L Hanna HS; Anderson, SC (7-325) Band; Community Yth Symph; VP, Ger C; Mu Alpha Theta; NHS; VP, Orch; NMF; NMS; NEDT; Commencement Marshal; All St Orch; Piano Guild Early Buch A; Piano Guild Sonatina A; Anderson Col; Mus.

BAKER, Bonnie Joy
Coon Rapids Sr HS; Coon Rapids, MN (253-654) Band; Orch; Marching Band; Cpt, Color Guard; Solo Star, Instrumental Mus; U of Wisc-Stout; Home Ec.

BAKER, Brenda Grace
J E B Stuart HS; Falls Church, VA (25-415) Chor; FBLA; Tres, Mjrte; NHS; Bkbl; Golf; Sftbl; Swtht; Best All Around; Madison U; Bus.

BAKER, Brian Kirk
Lindsay HS; Lindsay, OK (10-120) Ann; Amer Leg A; MLS; Most Out; Eng Merit A; St Hon Soc; U of Okla.

BAKER, Britt Allan
Pearland HS; Pearland, TX (10-350) Band; NHS; Bsbl; Ftbl; JV, Tr; Cl Fav; All Dist Ftbl; U of Houston; Engr.

BAKER, Bryan
Chaffey HS; Ontario, CA (255-918) Band; Chess C; Chor; Ensm; Orch; Cr-Ctry; Arts & Crafts A; Cert of Achv, Boy's Foods & Health; Chaffey City Col; Mus.

BAKER, Carol Ann
Ladysmith HS; Ladysmith, VA (19-75) Ann; Band; Chldr; Drama; VP, FHA; FTA; Secy, 4H; Sch P; Rptr, SC; Bkbl; Sftbl; Band A; Outst Achv, SCA; Lynchburg Sch of Nurs; Nurs.

BAKER, Carolyn Lavon
Messmer HS; Milwaukee, WI; Chldr; Chor; Jr Miss Pagent; Ntl Yth Conf; SC; Jr Cl; CSF; HCt; Most Out; Northland Col; Mus.

BAKER, Charlotte Jean
Hartshorne HS; Hartshorne, OK (7-70) Band; Chor; Ensm; Alg A; Hist A; Sci A; Band Attendant; Tympani Solo; SE St Col.

BAKER, Charmetrea Denise
Guthrie HS; Gutherie, OK; Chldr; Chor; Ensm; Bkbl; Sftbl; Swim; Tr; Hon Prog; Kiwanis A; Masonic A; Qn of Church; Essay Contest; Supt, Sunday Sch; Secy, YPPU; Central St Col; Bus.

BAKER, Christine Ann
Clarke Comm HS; Osceola, IA (24-110) Co-Ed, Ann; Band; Chldr; Chor; Dbte Tm; SC; Var C; Mgr, Bkbl; JV, Sftbl; Tnns; JV, Tr; Pres, Yth Conservation Committee; Art C; FCA; Iowa Methodist Med Center; Radiological Tech.

BAKER, Curtis Duane
Herbert Hoover HS; Glendale, CA (7-700) AFS; Pres, Dbte Tm; Ger C; Lat C; Pres, Model UN; Order/Arrow; Pres, SC; Var C; Cr-Ctry; Tr; Amer Leg A; Amer Leg Orator A; CSF; Lion A; Magna Cum Laude; NEDT; USC; Pol Sci.

BAKER, Daniel Paul
North HS; Omaha, NE (10%-509) Band; Chor; Drama; Ensm; Lat C; SC; Thes; U of Nebr; Mus.

BAKER, Davetta Lorine
Middleton Jr HS; Tampa, FL; Drew U; Art.

BAKER, David Lee
Brookfield Central HS; Brookfield, WI; Order/Arrow; Wrest; Order/Arrow A; Eagle Sct A; Waukesha Co Tech Inst; Police Sci.

BAKER, Deborah Lynne
Lancaster HS; Lancaster, OH; A Cap Choir; Cpt, Chldr; Chor; Drama; Ensm; Pres, 4H; Hmrm; SC; Var C; COM; 4H A; HCt; NEDT; Z C; GAA; Hon Stu; Ohio St U; Dental Hygiene.

BAKER, Deborah Rene
Northwest HS; St Louis, MO (37-433) FBLA; Hmrm; SC; COM; Citz A; HQn; Sci A; Outst Sigma Gamma Rhoe Service; Outst Soph; U of Mo; Radiology.

BAKER, Denise Renee
Canton S HS; Canton, OH (50%-300) Band; Bus C; Spch C; Thes; Tri-HiY; Spch A; Akron U.

BAKER, Douglas Vance
Cushing HS; Cushing, OK (18-145) VP, Band; Pres, Demolay; NHS; SC; Bsbl; Bkbl; Ftbl; Golf; Tr; Wrest; Amer Leg A; Ntl Achv Schol; Found, Shop, A's; Traveling PMC A; DeMolay Rep; Okla St U; Engr.

BAKER, Eddie B
Tupelo HS; Tupelo, MS; BC; Key C; U of Miss; Bus.

BAKER, Elizabeth Ann
High Point HS; Beltsville, MD (5%-773) Ski C; Swim; Md U; Med.

BAKER, James Bryant
Englewood Christian Sch; Independence, MO; Band; Chess C; Chor; Community Yth Symph; Ensm; Math C; Orch; Span C; Gold Key A; Jr Photo League; Band A; VP, Church Yth; Orch A; Civics C.

BAKER, James Mark
Lookeba-Sickles HS; Lookeba, OK (1-25) BS; Chor; Secy, FFA; NHS; Pres, Jr Cl; Bsbl; Bkbl; COM; Math A; Sci A; Val; FFA Crop Production A; Southwestern St U; Pol Sci.

BAKER, James Patrick
Tampa Cath HS; Tampa, FL (160-330) Mgr, Bsbl; Mgr, Ftbl; Hillsboro Comm Col.

BAKER, Janice Maureen
Lincoln HS; Sioux Falls, SD (86%-525) Bus C; FBLA; Type A; Gregg Shorthand A; 10 Key Silver Cert; Evangel Col; Bus.

BAKER, Jeanne Marie
College View Acad; Lincoln, NE; Band; Chor; NHS; Ski C; Tres, Jr Cl; Hon Prog; Union Col.

BAKER, Jeffrey Lance
Cushing HS; Cushing, OK (84-114) Demolay; Bsbl; Ftbl; Tr; Tonkawa Col; Welding.

BAKER, Jerry Leonard
E Union Acad; Marion, LA (9-18) MVP, Bsbl; MVP, Bkbl; Cl Fav; Church Sftbl; Yth Ldr, Church; Substitute Choir Director; Most Ath; NE La U; Phys Ed.

BAKER, John Franklin
High Point HS; Beltsville, MD (10%-840) Co-Cpt, Ger C; Ski C; Mgr, Bsbl; Bkbl; MVP, Soccer; MVP, Swim; Tr; COM; Citz A; Most Out; Yth Fel; 1st Cl, BSA; CSA; Coun.

BAKER, Joyce Elaine
Rockdale HS; Rockdale, TX (7-133) Band; Pres, FHA; NHS; Tnns; Home Ec A; Outst Graduating FHA Member; Navy.

BAKER, Julia Ellen
Portsmouth HS; Portsmouth, OH (27-267) Band; VP, 4H; Tres, Hmrm; Lat C; VP, NHS; Swim; Tnns; Yth Fel; Drum Major; VP, Yth Fel; WW.

BAKER, Karen Sue
Beth Haven Christian HS; Louisville, KY (3-57) Chldr; Orch; Rainbow; COM; Hist A; HCt; Math A; Type A; Eng, Shorthand, Bible, Acct, A's; Western U; Secy.

BAKER, Kathy Lynn
Riverview Gardens Sr HS; St Louis, MO (104-654) Hockey; MVP, Sftbl; Tr; Historian, Pep C; HR; Phys Ed.

BAKER, Kelley Jo
James B Dudley Sr HS; Greensboro, NC; Drama; FHA; Sci C; JA A; Spch A; Pres A, Ntl Christian Yth Coun; *Western Carolina U; Law.*

BAKER, Kenneth David
Stratford Sr HS; Houston, TX (68-435) Lat C; Math C; Mu Alpha Theta; Order/Arrow; JV, Bkbl; God & Country A; Hon Prog; Order/Arrow A; Sci A; Summa Cum Laude; Yth Fel; *Southwestern U; Law.*

BAKER, Kimberly Anne
Centennial HS; Pueblo, CO (95-350) Band; Rptr, Lit Mag; God & Country A; Jobs Daughters; Gym; Yth Group; *Sterling Col; Eng.*

BAKER, Larry
University HS; San Diego, CA (200-400) Tres, Band; Pres, CYO; Chldr; Chess C; Crown & Scepter; Fin, Dbte Tm; Drama; Parl, Hmrm; Lit Mag; Rptr, Sch P; Sci C; Fin, Spch C; SC; Lion A; Spch A; AIFS; *San Diego St U; Hist.*

BAKER, Larry Dean
Claiborne Acad; Haynesville, LA (2-41) Lit Ral; Pres, NHS; Pres, Jr Cl; Bkbl; JV, Ftbl; Golf; *NE La U; Phar.*

BAKER, Lauren Sue
Hartford HS; Hartford, MI (50-119) Ann; FHA; Ski C; *Grand Rapids Baptist Col; Bus.*

BAKER, Linda June
Newton Local; Pleasant Hill, OH (25-60) Ann; Band; Chor; FHA; Span C; JV, Bkbl; Sftbl; JV, Tr; Pres, SMM; VP, ACT; Sunday Sch Teacher; Bible Sch Teacher; *Grace Col; Phys Therapy.*

BAKER, Lisa Ann
Lee Acad; Clarksdale, MS (25-100) Band; JV, Bkbl; Sftbl; Citz A; Math A; Gourmet Cooking C; Eng A.

BAKER, Lisa Ann
Mount Notre Dame HS; Reading, OH (2-137) Hmrm; VP, NHS; Alg A; Math A; Xavier Pres Schol; Schmidtlap Found; *Xavier U; Ed.*

BAKER, Lisa Joy
Northern Sr HS; Baltimore, MD (6-34) Chor; French NHS; Alg A; NJHS.

BAKER, Mark Edward
Los Alamitos HS; Los Alamitos, CA; Mgr, Band; MVP, Order/Arrow; *Sou Calif Col; Mus.*

BAKER, Martha Lisa
Cedar Bluff HS; Cedar Bluff, AL; Ann; VP, BC; Chldr; Math C; Var C; Tnns; Beauty.

BAKER, Mary Jane
McCluer N HS; Florissant, MO (143-764) Hon Prog; Regent Schol; *Northeast Mo St U; Nurs.*

BAKER, Melody Kim
Frankston HS; Frankston, TX; Ann; Secy, BC; FHA; Secy, Sch P; Rptr, Soph Cl; Bkbl; Cl Fav; HQn; Best Dressed Girl; *Tyler Jr Col.*

BAKER, Michael Lee
Guilford HS; Rockford, IL (135-680) BS; Bus C; JV, Bkbl; Hon Prog; *Augustona Col; Acct.*

BAKER, Michelle Maxine
McMinn Co HS; Athens, TN (20%-280) Chess C; Sci C; Secy, Span C; SC; Tri-HiY; Opt A; *Cleveland St Comm Col; Health.*

BAKER, Neville Donnahue
Newtown HS; Elmhurst, NY (10-30) A Cap Choir; Chor; Yth Fel; *Oral Roberts U; Engr.*

BAKER, Nick Joseph
Middle Park Jr Sr HS; Granby, CO (9-76) SC; Bsbl; Ftbl; Cpt, Wrest; HCt; *W St Col; Psych.*

BAKER, Pamela Baxter
Mannington HS; Mannington, WV (10-105) Band; Drama; GS; Mjrte; NHS; Yth Fel; Wrest Matmaid; Prom Court; Cl Off; Forensics Tm; *Fairmont St Col; Art.*

BAKER, Randal Joe
Guilford Sr HS; Rockford, IL (273-778) FBLA; Lat C; Phys C; Wrest; Hon Prog.

BAKER, Robert Leland
S Hills HS; W Covina, CA (1-400) Pres, SC; Bkbl; JV, Ftbl; I Dare You; Opt Out Tn; Val; CSF; Boys Service C; JV Vlbl; Most Sch Service; *Pomona Col; Pre-Med.*

BAKER, Ruth Ann
Lutheran HS; Burbank, CA; A Cap Choir; AFS; Secy, Band; Chor; NHS; Orch; Bkbl; Sftbl; CSF; Seal Bearer; *Loyola Marymount U; Pre-Med.*

BAKER, Sharon Cardalle
Rockdale Comprehensive HS; Conyers, GA (105-419) Band; Fr C; FBLA; Ntl Yth Conf; *Ga Sou Col; Bus Adm.*

BAKER, Sharon Lynn
Triway HS; Wooster, OH (20-200) Ann; Band; Chor; Ensm; Semi-Fin, GS; Pres, 4H; NHS; Orch; Span C; God & Country A; 4H A; *Milligan Col; Mus.*

BAKER, Sherri Renee
Avondale HS; Avondale Estates, GA (125-257) Dbte Tm; Fr C; FBLA; FHA; Sch P; Sftbl; Tnns; Pres, Church Yth Group; Nat Hon A; *Dekalb Comm Col; Radiology.*

BAKER, Sherry Lynn
Phil Campbell HS; Phil Campbell, AL (12-72) Band; FHA; 4H; NHS; Bkbl; Beauty; Artist, Sch Paper; Most Outst Jr Civitan A; Pres, Jr Civitan; *U of Ala at Birmingham; Phys Therapy.*

BAKER, Sonya Valjean
Woodmont HS; Piedmont, GA; CYO; Fr C; Tres, FHA; Citz A; JA A; 2nd Runner-Up, FHA Pageant; Tres, CYO; Sch Baker A; *Savannah St U; Respiratory Therapy.*

BAKER, Tamare Julie
The King's Temple Christian Sch; Seattle, WA; A Cap Choir; Chor; Ensm; Hmrm; Sch Achieve Tm; COM; Hon Prog; Yth Fel; *Bus.*

BAKER, Theresa Faye
Phil Campbell HS; Phil Campbell, AL (10-80) VP, FHA; St Rep FHA Meeting; Pres, Jr Civitan C; A-HR; March of Dimes Super Walk; *U of Ala; Psych.*

BAKER, Tonya Lorraine
Aledo HS; Aledo, IL (10%-135) AFS; Chor; Pres, 4H; Span C; 4H A; *Med.*

BAKER, Valerie Fay
Bement HS; Bement, IL (1-60) Drama; Pres, FHA; Lat C; NHS; Rptr, Sch P; Thes; DARGCA; NEDT; Poem Published in Anthology; *Ill St U; Social Work.*

BAKER, William Ludlow
Lincoln HS; Sioux Falls, SD (50-630) Bus Mgr, Bus C; Dbte Tm; HiY; Span C; Tr; COM; Tr Ltr; *Drake U; Bus Adm.*

BAKER, Yvonna Carol
Phelps HS; Phelps, KY (5-74) Rptr, Drama; VP, FHA; FTA; NHS; Rptr, Spch C; COM; 4H A; Hon Prog; Grade A; *Eastern Ky U; Pre-Med.*

BAKES, Margaret Moore
Westfield Sr HS; Westfield, NJ (67-669) Cpt, Chldr; Chor; GS; Hmrm; NHS; SC; Pres, Sr Cl; Sftbl; Amer Leg A; Citz A; Choir; Women's C; Emerald Book; Choraleers; Summer Stock; Broadway Singers; VP, Fresh Cl; Ldrship, Schol & Citz A; *Lafayette Col; Econ.*

BAKIE, Sandy Sue
Sycamore HS; Cincinnati, OH; Chor; Gov Honor Prog; Schol Art A's; *Art.*

BAKKE, Erik Samson
Ingraham HS; Seattle, WA (10%-600) Band; VP, Bus C; Pres, Demolay; Key C; Orch; Co-Ed, Sch P; Bsbl; Bkbl; Soccer; Sftbl; Swim; COM; Masonic A; MLS; Most Out; Rep DeMolay A; *Pacific Lutheran U; Orthodontics.*

BAKKE, Karen Erna
Arundel Sr HS; Gambrills, MD (20-400) NHS; ARC; Citz A; Hon Prog; ARC A; Secy, GScts; NRA; *Phys Therapy.*

BAKKE, Teresa Lyn
Irene HS; Irene, SD (6-29) Chor; FHA; NHS; Span C; Tr; Hon Prog; *Stewarts Hairstyling Col; Hairstyling.*

BAKOULIS, Marion Gordon
Princeton HS; Princeton, NJ; Chor; Fr C; InterAct C; Lit Mag; Ed, Sch P; SC; Hockey; Poet A; Sr High Fellowship; Outing C; 2nd Pl, Princeton Packet Essay Cont; *Eng.*

BAKSA, Matthew Joseph
Mathews HS; Vienna, OH;

BALABAN, Debora Lee
San Ramon HS; Danville, CA (51-336) Chldr; Ski C; SC; VP, Jr Cl; Co-Cpt, Tnns; CSF; COM; Yth Fel; GAA; VP, Girl's Adv Coun; GScts; Phys Ed A; Pres, Spiritldr's C; Powder Puff Ftbl; Vol Service A; Jr Lifesaving; Off Asst; Flag Girl; *UC Berkeley; Law.*

BALABAN, Marie Therese
Lourdes HS; Chicago, IL (2-263) NHS; Rptr, Sch P; SC; Alg A; COM; Hon Prog; Journ A; Outst NHS Member A.

BALADAD, Joe Russell
Elk Grove Sr HS; Elk Grove, CA (10-497) Alg A; Sci A.

BALAGUER, Victor Ramon
Dr P Perea Fajardo Voc HS; Mayaguez, PR; COM; Hon Medal; *Elec Engr.*

BALAY, Richard Wallace
Arkadelphia HS; Arkadelphia, AR (8-168) BS; Rptr, Chess C; Fr C; NHS; Sch P; SC; Tnns; Math A; MLS; *U of Ark; Pre-Med.*

BALBIN, Sandy Ralleta
George Washington Sr HS; Mangilao, GUAM; FNA; NHS; F-Ed, Sch P; Amer Lung Assn A; Outst Achv, Poetry; *Med.*

BALDI, Lisa Elaine
St Marie Goretti HS; Philadelphia, PA; Chor; Tnns; *La Salle Col; Social Worker.*

BALDREE, David Wilford
Chaminade Col Prep; St Louis, MO (3-118) Chess C; Pres, NHS; Rptr, Sch P; Ch, SC; Pres, Sr Cl; Mgr, Cr-Ctry; Cpt, Golf; COM; NEDT; St Scholar; Summa Cum Laude; *Northwestern U; Med.*

BALDRIDGE, David Wayne
Centralia HS; Centralia, IL (16-360) Key C; VP, Lat C; NHS; Mgr, Tr; Hon Prog; Magna Cum Laude; *Kaskaskia Jr Col; Hist.*

BALDUS, Paul Lawrence
Kuemper HS; Carroll, IA (15-270) Chor; InterAct C; Key C; Pres, Lat C; Monogram; Bsbl; Bkbl; Cr-Ctry; Tr; COM; Sci A; Spch A; Ath, Newspaper, A's; *Iowa St U; Eng.*

BALDWIN, Brenda Sue
Forst HS; Ocala, FL; Band; VP, 4H; 4H A; Secy, 4-H C; Bible Quiz Tm; *Phys Therapy.*

BALDWIN, Cathy Jo
Attica Jr-Sr HS; Attica, IN (13-120) JV, Chldr; Tr; *Nurs.*

BALDWIN, Cheryl Lynn
Plainfield Jr-Sr HS; Plainfield, IN (1-300) Ann; Chor; Drama; Fr C; GS; Jr Miss Pagent; NHS; Phys C; Sch P; SC; Thes; VP, Sr Cl; VP, Jr Cl; JV, Tnns; COM; Hon Prog; Journ A; Val; Vlbl; 2nd St Poetry Contest; Senate Page; *Butler U; Sci.*

BALDWIN, Denise Marie
Rio Linda Sr HS; Rio Linda, CA;

BALDWIN, Gail Lynne
Ashville HS; Ashville, AL; FBLA; FHA; FNA; 4H; 4H A; *Gasden St Bus Col; Secretarial.*

BALDWIN, Jo Shannon
Richland HS; Fort Worth, TX; A Cap Choir; Chldr; Drama; Ensm; VP, FHA; Hmrm; SC; Sftbl; Cl Fav; Swtht; WW.

BALDWIN, Mary Annette
Little Wolf HS; Manawa, WI (10%-98) Ann; Chor; FHA; Secy, 4H; Sftbl; Citz A; 4H A; Spch A; *Psych.*

BALDWIN, Mollie Beth
Dublin HS; Dublin, GA; Band; Drama; Spch A; Cpt, Flag Corp; Most Improved, Outst Soph, Band; Rookie o-t Yr, Band; *Fla St U; Mus Ed.*

BALDWIN, Rebecca Jean
Carter HS; Carter, OK (2-12) Chldr; Chor; Pres, FHA; MVP, Bkbl; Tr; COM; HCt; Okla St U Top 10%; Soap Box Derby Champ; *Bus Adm.*

BALDWIN, Rosie Lee
North HS; Wichita, KS;

BALDWIN, Sharon Mae
Parkview HS; Springfield, MO; Chor; Drama; Ensm; Rptr, Fr C; Orch; Thes; Sftbl; Drum Corp.

BALDWIN, Susan Jane
Eastside HS; Taylors, SC; A Cap Choir; Chor; Community Yth Symph; Ensm; Orch; MVP, Bkbl; Sftbl; COM; Hist A; *Mus.*

BALDWIN, Sylvia Fern
St Mary's Acad; Englewood, CO (2-54) French NHS; Tnns; Hon Prog; *Rosary Col; Lang.*

BALENGER, Sharon Ann
Musselman HS; Bunker Hill, WV (3-92) Band; Tres, FTA; VP, NHS; ARC; *W Va U; Chem Engr.*

BALENTINE, Roy Anthony
Weir HS; Weir, MS (10-50) Ed, Ann; BC; Chor; Pres, FFA; Spch C; VP, Soph Cl; H of F; HKg; Mr WHS; Dignified Sr; *Miss St U; Pol Sci.*

BALES, Deborah Sue
McArthur HS; Hollywood, FL; *Broward Comm Col; Court Reporting.*

BALES, Grace Clorinda
Weed HS; Weed, CA; Bus Mgr, Ann; Chldr; Semi-Fin, GS; Ski C; SC; Tres, Jr Cl; CSF; Lion A; Ed, Annual; WW; *Col o-t Siskiyous; Bus Ed.*

BALES, Karri Renee
Yukon HS; Yukon, OK (15%-325) Secy, Chor; FHA; JV, Bkbl; Yth Fel; Rep, UN, DC; Yth Coun; Church Choir; *Okla St U; Child Developement.*

BALES, Melody Jo
Raytown S HS; Raytown, MO (77-560) Chor; Drama; NHS; COM; HQn; Regent Schol; Time Keeper, Swim, Tr; Pres, Pep Squad; PTSA; *Bus.*

BALESTRUCCI, Donna Marie
Kingsway Regional HS; Swedesboro, NJ (10-166) Cpt, Mjrte; NHS; SC; COM; Hon Prog.

BALEY, George David
Bowie HS; Bowie, TX; Rptr, Ann; Co-Ch, Chess C; Phys C; Span C; Var C; Mgr, Bkbl; Trainer, Ftbl, Tr; *TCU-Ft Worth; Ftbl Trainer.*

BALEY, Marsha Gay
Reagan Co HS; Big Lake, TX; Dbte Tm; *Oral Roberts U.*

BALIAN, Habib Fredrick
John Muir HS; Pasadena, CA; Bus Mgr, A Cap Choir; Rptr, Hmrm; Rptr, InterClub Coun; Rptr, Mod Mus Mas; SC; CSF; Choir Service; Saint Elizabeth Sch Serv; *Lib Arts.*

BALIKIAN, Seta Joy
Venice HS; Los Angeles, CA; Band; Hmrm; *Santa Monica City Col; Bus Adm.*

BALK, Lavern Leroy
Fulton HS; Fulton, IL (14-120) Band; VP, 4H; Tnns; DARGCA; 4H A; *Augustana Col; Acct.*

BALKE, Rebecca Renee
Reseda HS; Reseda, CA (19-816) NHS; Ski C; CSF; Hon Prog; Gifted Prog; Val, Jr HS; *USC; Sci.*

BALL, Angelene
Morgan Co HS; Hartselle, AL (59-235) *U of Ala; Med.*

BALL, Brian Douglas
Bentworth HS; Bentleyville, PA (40-163) Band; Drama; Tres, Var C; Ftbl; *W Va U.*

BALL, Daniel Joseph
Kaukauna HS; Kaukauna, WI (15%-425) Bsbl; Bkbl; Ftbl.

BALL, Darnella Karen
Winnfield Sr HS; Winnfield, LA; Chor; Drama; FBLA; Spch C; Sftbl; Beauty; Masonic A; Most Versatile, Ebony Elite Pagent; *Sou U; Vocal Mus.*

BALL, David Roy
White Station HS; Memphis, TN (79-419) F-Ed, Ann; Chor; Ensm; VP, Key C; Mod Mus Mas; NHS; Order/Arrow; Ftbl; Tr; Service A; *Memphis St U; Civil Engr.*

BALL, Edward Bernard
Washington HS; Greenville, MS; Secy, Lat C; Lat NHS; Secy, Mu Alpha Theta; Var C; JV, Bkbl; Ftbl; Tr; COM; Chem A; Cl Fav; Hist A; Math A; NEDT; *Med.*

BALL, Helen Yvette
Denham Springs HS; Denham Springs, LA (3-250) Chldr; Chor; NHS; Phys Fitness A; Nom, WW; *LSU; Bus.*

BALL, Julian Allen Jr
Lancaster HS; Lancaster, VA (15-134) Chess C; Fr C; FFA; NHS; F-Ed, Sch P; Sci C; Var C; Tres, Soph Cl; JV, Bkbl; Cpt, Ftbl; Tnns; MVP, Tr; Hon Prog; I Dare You; MVP, Ftbl; WW; *U of Md; Bio.*

BALL, Kathy Jean
Timberline HS; Weippe, ID (1-41) Cl Fav; 4H A; Q&S A; Star Student; Val; VFW Orator Win; Yth Leg; *U of Idaho; Vet Sci.*

BALL, Luana Jean
Luverne HS; Luverne, MN (33%-130) Band; Chldr; Chor; FHA; FTA; Sftbl; Tr; Pres A; Teachers Aide; GAA; *Optometric Field.*

BALL, Marilyn Louise
Cumberland Valley HS; Mechanicsburg, PA (23-649) Drama; NHS; NEDT; *VPI; Pre-Vet.*

BALL, Mark Eden
Olathe HS; Olathe, KS (53-460) Chor; Ensm; Madrigal; Orch; SC; 1st Pl, Piano Comp; *U of Tex-Austin; Mus.*

BALL, Marlesa Lynn
Central HS; Thomasville, GA; A Cap Choir; Band; Co-Ch, Chldr; Chor; Hmrm; Fin, Lit Ral; VP, Tri-HiY; Kiwanis A; Swtht; Mus & Drama Troupe; Superior, Solo & Ensm; 1st Pl, Lit Meet; *Lee Col; Mus.*

BALL, Mary Stephanie
Holy Rosary Acad; Louisville, KY; Drama; NHS; ARC; Hon Prog; Bellarmine Col Academic Schol; *Bellarmine Col; Spch.*

BALL, Michael
Evanston Township HS; Evanston, IL (10%-1100) Chor; Gym; Master Singers; CS A; *Span.*

BALL, Patricia Jeanne
Manalapan HS; Englishtown, NJ (22-425) Drama; Lit Mag; Co-Cpt, Mjrte; *Wheaton Col.*

BALL, Sonya Gayle
Waynoka HS; Waynoka, OK (7-29) Ann; Chldr; VP, FHA; Ch, FTA; F-Ed, Sch P; Rptr, Jr Cl; Ftbl; Type A; Annual Qn; *NW Okla St U; Special Ed.*

BALL, Steven Lee
Weld Central HS; Keenesburg, CO (1-100) Band; Fin, BS; Ensm; FFA; NHS; Spch C; Var C; JV, Bkbl; Cpt, Cr-Ctry; Tr; Amer Leg A; Amer Leg Orator A; Hist A; Masonic A; Pres A; VFW Orator Win; VofDEM; Win, St UN Essay; Hon Band; FFA Contest; AAU Champion; St Jr Olympics Champ; Superior & Excel Ratings, St FFA.

BALL, Wanda Cheryl
Baker HS; Baker, FL (20-75) FHA; Bsbl; Bkbl; Sftbl; Swim; Tnns; Mrs Swtht, Southside Baptist.

BALL, Wendi Dawne
Midland HS; Midland, TX (55-640) Chor; Ensm; Hmrm; NHS; Span C; Span NHS; SC; Bkbl; Sftbl; Tnns; Hon Prog; Yth Fel; *Tex Tech U; Acct.*

BALL, William Lee
Crystal Lake Comm HS; Crystal Lake, IL (29-537) Dbte Tm; Lat C; NFL; NHS; Order/Arrow; Spch C; St Stu Congress; God & Country A; Order/Arrow A; Spch A; St Scholar; Eagle Sct; WW; Reg Qualifier Bicen Yth Debates; Co Win, Reader's Dig B Sct Spch Con; *N Ill U; Biol.*

BALLANCE, Sharon
Mattamuskeet HS; Swan Quarter, NC (26-71) Bus Mgr, Ann; Pres, 4H; Arch; Tnns; 4H A; Hist A; Secy, Rptr, 4-H C; *E Carolina U; Occupational Therapy.*

BALLARD, Brenda Fay
Akron HS; Akron, CO (28-43) Band; Chor; FHA; Span C; 4H A; Sci A; Art C; Tres, Lutheran Yth For Today; Lib Aide A.

BALLARD, Kathryn Lea
Holy Rosary Acad; Louisville, KY (8-85) Drama; Pres, Hmrm; Jr Miss Pagent; NHS; ARC; Rptr, Sch P; Pres, SC; JV, Bkbl; Tnns; Tr; COM; NEDT; Opt A; ARC A; WW; *Western Ky U; Theatre Arts.*

BALLARD, Patricia
Paul Laurence Dunbar Voc HS; Chicago, IL (9-450) Secy, NHS; Rptr, Sch P; SC; COM; Hon Prog; Q&S A; WW; *Columbia Col; Broadcasting.*

BALLARD, Patricia
Colonel Zadok Magruder HS; Rockville, MD (3-423) Drama; FHA; Hon Prog; Pres A; *Allied Health Fields.*

BALLARD, Rhonda Renee
L D Bell HS; Hurst, TX (25%-800) Dbte Tm; Drama; FTA; Ger C; Lit Mag; NFL; Sch P; Spch C; SC; Thes; Secy, Soph Cl; COM; HCt; Cpt, Drill Tm; WW; Sr Superlative; WW in Raiderettes; *Abilene Christian U; Phys Therapy.*

BALLARD, Stephanie Jo
Pascagoula HS; Pascagoula, MS; *Child Development.*

BALLARD, Suzette Marie
Baker Sr HS; Baker, LA (29-374) A Cap Choir; BC; Chor; Dbte Tm; Rptr, FHA; VP, 4H; Madrigal; SC; Bkbl; Sftbl; Mgr, Tr; Citz A; 4H A; Pres A; Spch A; *LSU; Law Enforcement.*

BALLARD, Valerie Grayce
W Memphis Sr HS; W Memphis, AR (38-394) BC; Drama; Spch C; VofDEM.

BALLARD, Vanessa Kay
Narrows HS; Narrows, VA (5-100) Band; Chor; Fr C; 4H; Mjrte; NHS; Cr-Ctry; COM; 4H A; Lion A; Pres A; Spch A; Keyettes; Demolay Swtht; *Roanoke Col.*

BALLARD, Virginia Ann
Scott HS; Madison, WV; VP, FNA; Co-Ed, Sch P; Thes; Bio A; *Marshall Col; Nurs.*

BALLARD, William Hillman
Dobyns Bennet HS; Kingsport, TN; VP, CYO; Span C; Wrest; Knox New Sentnel A; *U of Tenn; Bus Adm.*

BALLENGER, Brian W
London HS; London, OH (6-100) Band; BS; 4H; NHS; Orch; Ed, Sch P; Sci C; Hist A; Journ A; Kiwanis A; Q&S A; Sci A; Type A; Homecoming Escort; Top Twenty; Art C; *Wittenberg U; Pre-Dent.*

BALLENTINE, Susan Melanie
Columbia HS; Columbia, SC (89-286) Chor; Fr C; Secy, Hmrm; VP, Yth Choir; Tres, Sr High Sunday Sch; Alt, Yth Coun On Ministries; *Columbia Col; Mus.*

BALLESTEROS, Martin Rene
Conroe HS; Conroe, TX (15%-860) NHS; Span C; Spch C; Bkbl; Tr; Hon Prog; Leadership Program; *Sam Houston St U; Mus.*

BALLEW, Laura Lisa
E Gaston HS; Mt Holly, NC (33%-330) Chldr; Chor; Drama; Rainbow; Spch C; Var C; *Fashion Sch of Tech; Buying and Selling.*

BALLEW, Seron Yanette
Wehrle HS; Columbus, OH (69-105) *Fashion.*

BALLINGALL, Beatrice Evelyn
Roxborough HS; Philadelphia, PA; Rptr, Sch P; COM; Citz A; Hon Prog; Bowl.

BALLINGALL, Christina Louise
Roxborough HS; Philadelphia, PA; Chldr; Amer Leg A; COM; Citz A.

BALLINGER, Timothy Lee
Santa Barbara HS; Santa Barbara, CA; Rptr, Sch P; Q&S A; *Santa Barbara City Col.*

BALLINGER, Wade Lurlan
Sidney Comm HS; Sidney, IA (6-40) BS; Var C; Bsbl; Ftbl; Tr; MVP, Wrest; COM; HCt; *Wildlife Bio.*

BALLOU, Judith Kristine
Exira HS; Exira, IA (5-50) Co-Ed, Ann; Band; S-T, 4H; NHS; Ed, Sch P; MVP, Bkbl; Sftbl; Tr; 4H A; Vlbl; Ch, Luther League; Secy, Conf Luther League; *NW Mo St U; Phys Ed.*

BALLS, Pamela Mary
Rosati-Kain HS; St Louis, MO (7-93) NHS; Ed, Sch P; Hon Prog; Ntl Achv Schol; Summa Cum Laude; Mo Sch-Col A; Scholastic Art A; R-K Newspaper A; *Wash U; Journ.*

BALM, Brian Scott
Le Mars Comm Sch; Le Mars, IA (1%-204) Pres, Band; VP, NHS; Var C; Golf; Cpt, Wrest; Rotary A; St Scholar; Val; Pres, Church Yth Fel; John Philip Sousa A; *Westmar Col; Bio.*

BALMER, Brenda Carolyn
Glenbrook N HS; Northbrook, IL (200-700) Chor; Community Yth Symph; Drama; Orch; Thes; *Northern Ill U; Phys Therapy.*

32

BALSAM, Sheri Lee
Hillel HS; Lawrence, NY (2-46) Ed, Ann; Math C; NHS; Span C; NMS; *Queens Col; Secondary Ed.*

BALSBAUGH, Amy Beth
E Lebanon Co HS; Myerstown, PA (50-200) Band; 4H; SC; Tri-HiY; Hockey; Tnns; 4H A; NEDT; Spch A; Silver Spirit, Gold Key, A's; St Essay Win; *Pa St U; Home Ec.*

BALTHAZAR, Catherine
St Matthew HS; Melrose, LA; FBLA; FHA; GS; Alg A; Hon Prog; Type A; Val; *Northwestern St U; Bus Adm.*

BALTHAZOR, Bart Alan
Clyde HS; Clyde, KS (9-40) Band; CYO; Chor; Drama; Ensm; Madrigal; Thes; Tres, Jr Cl; Secy, Soph Cl; Bkbl; Ftbl; Golf; Tr; Lion A; VofDEM; Hugh O'Brien Outst Soph A; *Engr.*

BALTHROP, Diana Marie
Thurston HS; Springfield, OR (4-250) A Cap Choir; Chor; Drama; Ensm; Hmrm; NHS; SC; COM; JA A; St Scholar; VP, UICA; *Drafting.*

BALTHROP, Randall Scott
Bryan Adams HS; Dallas, TX (25%-700) Chor; De-molay; COM; Hist A; Math A; Sci A; NJHS; Hon Choir; Bowl; Mus A; Lang Arts A; Concert Choir; *Texas Tech U; Mus.*

BALTZ, Deborah Sue
Sylvan Hills HS; Sherwood, AR; A Cap Choir; Chldr; Ensm; SC; Type A; *Ark St U; Mus.*

BALTZELL, David Guy
Ogallala; Ogallala, NE (6-126) Pres, 4H; NHS; Or-der/Arrow; Cr-Ctry; JV, Ftbl; DARGCA; God & Country A; 4H A; I Dare You; Eagle A; BSct; Co 4-H King; *U of Nebr; Pre-Vet Med.*

BAME, Michael Allen
Blacksburg HS; Blacksburg, VA (50-300) Drama; Tres, FFA; Order/Arrow; Mgr, Cr-Ctry; Mgr, Ftbl; Mgr, Wrest; God & Country A; Order/Arrow A; Stage Crew; *VPI; Theatre Arts.*

BAME, Richard William
Glenwood Springs HS; Glenwood Springs, CO (45-146) Pres, Drama; Tres, Drama; Math C; *Worcester Poly-tech Inst; Mech Engr.*

BANCROFT, Barbara Ann
Leeton HS; Leeton, MO; Sci C; Co-Cpt, Bkbl; Sftbl; *Central Mo St U; Phys Ed.*

BANCROFT, John David
Hubbard HS; Hubbard, OH;

BANCROFT, Thomas Richard
Hubbard HS; Hubbard, OH (69-342) Band; Merit Roll; *Youngstown St U; Elec Engr.*

BANCROFT, Troy Douglas
Ovid-Elsie HS; Elsie, MI (60-153) BS; FFA; 4H; Hmrm; Ed, Sch P; Pres, Var C; Ftbl; Co-Cpt, Wrest; HCt; St Wrest; Pres, Church Yth Group; *Lansing Comm Col; Surveying.*

BANDEMER, Cindy Ann
Geneva Pub HS; Geneva, NE (6-45) Band; Chor; FHA; NHS.

BANDY, Beverly Sue
Hendersonville HS; Hendersonville, TN; FHA; Hero; *Trevecca Nazarene Col; Child Care.*

BANDY, Jack Todd
St Louis Park HS; St Louis Park, MN (50-610) NHS; ARC; Mgr, Cr-Ctry; Swim; Mgr, Tr; Asst Coach Girls Swim; Co-Cpt, Water Polo; *U of Minn at Mpls; Math Ed.*

BANDY, Rebecca Higgins
Newton-Conover HS; Newton, NC (18-230) AFS; Co-Ed, Ann; S-T, Band; BC; VP, FHA; Pres, FTA; InterAct C; InterClub Coun; Mjrte; Span C; SC; WW; Leo C; Pep C; S-T, MYF; Page, NC House of Reps; Del, Civitan Yth Conf; S-T, Jr Civit C; S-T, Dist Yth Conf; *Appalachian St U; Primary Ed.*

BANE, Agnes Regina
Windham HS; Wilimantic, CT (10-250) CYO; Cr-Ctry; Tr; Hon Prog; Tr A; Gym A; Cr-Ctry A; Winter Tr A; *NY Fashion Inst; Fashion Merchan-dising.*

BANE, Linda Carol
Mullens HS; Mullens, WV (2-110) Ann; BC; Rptr, FBLA; VP, FHA; Pres, Rainbow; Secy, SC; Secy, Soph Cl; Sci A; *Concord Col; Ed.*

BANEY, Donna Ellen
Clearfield Area HS; Clearfield, PA (33-350) Chor; Dbte Tm; Drama; VP, FTA; Model UN; Orch; Rptr, Sch P; Span C; Thes; *Ind U of Penn; Sociol-ogy.*

BANFIELD, Glenn Ivan
Denison HS; Denison, TX (25-498) Order/Arrow; Sci C; Span C; JV, Ftbl; Tr; *Tex Tech U; Enviro-mental Design.*

BANFIELD, John Eric
Denison Sr HS; Denison, TX; Order/Arrow; Tr; COM; Order/Arrow A; FCA; United Service C; Jr NHS; *U of Tex; Archt.*

BANG, Marna Lorraine
Central Sr HS; Albert Lea, MN (44-596) Ensm; 4H; Orch; Tnns; Citz A; 4H A; *Waldorf Jr Col; Early Childhood Ed.*

BANGEL, Bruce Dean
Kewanna HS; Kewanna, IN (8-18) Ann; Band; Chor; Drama; Ensm; 4H; Math C; Bsbl; Bkbl; Cr-Ctry; Ftbl; Sftbl; Tnns; Tr; Cl Fav; 4H A; MLS; Yth Fel; Most Improved, Cr-Ctry; *IUF Tech Col; Elec.*

BANGS, Caroline Royce
Algona HS; Algona, IA (30-140) Co-Ed, Ann; Chor; Drama; F-Ed, Lit Mag; Span C; JV, Bkbl; JV, Golf; Kiwanis A; Drama A; *U of Minn; Theatre Arts.*

BANGS, Elizabeth Ruth
Algona HS; Algona, IA (6-172) JV, Bkbl; Tnns; FCA; JV, Vlbl; *Smith Col.*

BANISTER, Randy Dale
Hart Co HS; Hartwell, GA (25%-300) VP, Hmrm; InterAct C; Sci C; Ftbl; *U of Ga; Bus Mgt.*

BANKEN, Charles Henry Jr
Henderson Co HS; Henderson, KY; BC; Chem C; Chess C; Lat C; Math C; NHS; Sci C.

BANKER, Sarah Ruth
Finneytown HS; Cincinnati, OH; Chor; Ensm; Orch; Sftbl; COM; Citz A; *Mus.*

BANKORD, Melisa Dawn
Belvidere HS; Belvidere, IL (92-390) Secy, A Cap Choir; FBLA; 4H; Jr Miss Pagent; Ski C; VP, SC; Pom Pon; Parl, 'Z' C; YMCA Instructor; *Bradley U; Bus Mgt.*

BANKS, Ann Carol
J H Rose Sr HS; Greenville, NC; Band; All-St Band; *Mus.*

BANKS, David Michael
Bedford HS; Temperance, MI (87-446) Ann; Band; Drama; Ensm; Band As.

BANKS, Denise Lynn
Gardena HS; Gardena, CA; Chor; Hist Rep; *U of Sou Calif; Theatrical Arts.*

BANKS, Gail Wydean
Russell HS; Hurtsboro, AL (2-72) Co-Cpt, Chldr; Rptr, FHA; Pres, 4H; Lit Mag; NHS; Sftbl; B Crocker A; COM; Cl Fav; 4H A; Hist A; ROTC A; *Huntingdon St Col; Computer Sci.*

BANKS, James Alan
Rocky Mount Sr HS; Rocky Mount, NC (37-900) AFS; Pres, Hmrm; Order/Arrow; Cr-Ctry; Tr; Citz A; God & Country A; Tres, Service C; Ed, CYF; Pres, Art C; Eagle Sct; Pres, Scts; Explorers; *NC St U; Archt.*

BANKS, Jill Teresa
Winter Park HS; Winter Park, FL (229-911) Chor; Hmrm; St Stu Congress; SC; Tri-HiY; COM; Hist A; Fr Congress.

BANKS, Justine Marie
Marysville-Pilchuck HS; Marysville, WA (30-419) Ger C; Sci C; SC; Most Out; Sci A; Service A; PTSA; Guitar Group; Mgr, Vlbl; Church Member-ship Comm; A-Ed, Church Paper; Pres, Campfire; *U of Wash; Med.*

BANKS, Kevin Cooper
Greenville Sr HS; Greenville, TX; Ed, Ann; Band; FTA; F-Ed, Sch P; Span C; Jr Cl; Journ A; Stage Band; VP, Conf Yth Coun; Pres, Church Yth; De-signed, City Bicentennial Logo; *McMurry Col; Counseling & Guidance.*

BANKS, Kimberly Jenise
Woodrow Wilson HS; Washington, DC (130-560) Co-Cpt, Chldr; Hmrm; SC; Var C; Secy, Soph Cl; Bkbl; Sftbl; Swim; Tr; Cl Fav; HQn; HCt; Most Out; ARC A; Del, Girl Service C Conf; Ntl Coun of Negro Women; HR; *Psych.*

BANKS, Linda Gale
East HS; Columbus, OH (5-350) WW; WW Among Amer HS Mus Stu; *Spelman Col.*

BANKS, Michelle Denise
Camden HS; Camden, NJ; Band; Pres, Chor; NHS; *Law.*

BANKS, Natalie Elaine
Indian River Sr HS; Frankford-Dagsboro, De (10-200) Band; JV, Chldr; Chor; Drama; Ensm; Fr C; Hmrm; NHS; SC; VP, Jr Cl; NEDT; PTA A; Past Hon Qn, Jobs Daughters; Ldrship A, SC; Hon Band; Co Choir; *U of Del; Pol Sci.*

BANKS, Patricia Ann
Simon Gratz HS; Philadelphia, PA (13-450) FTA; NHS; Vlbl; *Penn St U; Bio.*

BANKS, Robin Timothy
Washington HS; Washington, NC (50-280) Band; Pres, Bus C; Chor; NHS; Bsbl; Hon Prog; Stu o-t Yr; *E Carolina U; Med.*

BANKS, Rochelle Marie
Evanston Township HS; Evanston, IL;

BANKS, Sarah Nell
Grand Ridge Sch; Grand Ridge, FL (4-49) F-Ed, Ann.

BANKS, Wanda Gail
Denbigh HS; Newport News, VA; FBLA; Mgr, Tr; COM; Citz A; Phys Fitness A; HR.

BANKSON, Timothy Paul
Abraham Lincoln HS; Denver, CO (50%-750) SC; Var C; Bsbl; Mgr, Ftbl; Sr Cl Rep; *U of Northern Colo; Phys Ed.*

BANKSTON, Tommy Lyn
Winnfield Sr HS; Winnfield, LA (18-130) Anchor C; Ann; BC; Rptr, Drama; Tres, FBLA; Pres, FTA; Spch C; SC; Bsbl; Co-Cpt, Ftbl; Tr; Spch A; All Amer, Ftbl; *La Tech U; Phys Ed.*

BANNERT, Karen Lynn
Ole Main HS; N Little Rock, AR (5-430) A-Ed, Ann; Chem C; Drama; Mu Alpha Theta; NHS; Hon Prog; Q&S A; Exchange Stu, Brazil; *U of Houston; Bus.*

BANNING, Lori Lee
Sharpstown Sr HS; Houston, TX; SC.

BANNISTER, Brandt D
Weston-McEwen HS; Athena, OR (2-61) Parl, Dbte Tm; FFA; Span C; Var C; Bkbl; Ftbl; Tnns; Tr; Hon Prog; Photography C; *BMCC.*

BANNISTER, Deborah Kay
Hopkinsville HS; Hopkinsville, KY (10%-320) Band; BC; COM; All Dist, All St, Bands; Superior Mus A.

BANNISTER, Dennis Keith
Central HS; Thomasville, GA; FFA; Key C; Bsbl; Stu o-t Mo; *Abraham Baldwin Agr Col; Wildlife Mgt.*

BANNISTER, Robin Sue
Marquette Sr HS; Marquette, MI (219-411) Band; Chor; Drama; Parl, FHA; Thes; Amer Leg A; FHA A; *N Mich U; Mus.*

BANSCHBACH, Neil Anthony
Valparaiso HS; Valparaiso, IN; Beauty; Boy Sct; VP & Tres, Lutheran Yth Org; *Ohio St U; Architec-ture.*

BANTA, Charles Damian
Eastside HS; Paterson, NJ (25-500) Chess C; Ed, Lit Mag; Math C; Ed, Sch P; SC; Mgr, Bsbl; Cr-Ctry; Tr; COM; Journ A; Ath Cert's; *Cornell U; Hotel Adm.*

BAPTISTA, Joanne
St Raphael Acad; Pawtucket, RI (15-130) NHS; *Providence Col; Teaching Handicapped.*

BARABBA, Tracy Ann
Sylmar HS; Sylmar, CA; Silver Seal; *Cal St U at Northridge; Bus Adm.*

33

BARAJAS, Michael A
Aquinas HS; San Bernardino, CA; CYO; Bsbl; Cpt, Bkbl; Cpt, Ftbl; Cpt, Tr; COM; Sportsmanship A; Inspirational A; Perry Winstea Mem A; *San Bdno Vally Col.*

BARAN, David Theodore
Glenbard E HS; Lombard, IL (10-950) Sch P; Span C; Bsbl; Cpt, Bkbl; Co-Cpt, Ftbl; MVP, Ftbl; *Valparaiso U; Physics.*

BARANOWSKI, Joel William
Manchester HS; Manchester, CT; Chess C; Cr-Ctry; Tr.

BARANYK, Irene Anna
Immaculate Conception Ukrainian HS; Hamtramck, MI; CYO; Chor; NHS; Hon Prog; Hon Cert; *Wayne St U; Fashion Illustration.*

BARANYK, Marta Zenia
Immaculate Conception HS; Hamtramck, MI (6-30) Co-Ed, Ann; Chldr; Chor; NHS; Sch P; SC; Secy, Soph Cl; HQn; HCt; Hon Prog; Kiwanis A; *Wayne St U; Ecology.*

BARBA, Deborah Anne
University HS; San Diego, CA (16-315) CYO; NHS; Sch Achieve Tm; SC; Var C; Pres, Jr Cl; VP, Soph Cl; Tnns; CSF; Hon Prog; Pep C; Loyalty & Service A; *Math.*

BARBA, Denis Luke
University HS; San Diego, CA (25-311) Pres, CYO; Cum Laude Soc; Drama; NHS; Ch, SC; Pres, Jr Cl; Bkbl; JV, Cr-Ctry; HCt; Hon Prog; Magna Cum Laude; Jr Loyalty & Service; Most Inspirational, V Bkbl; Pep C; *Stanford Col; Pre-Med.*

BARBATO, Thomas Robert
S Broward HS; Hollywood, FL; DCT; *Elec.*

BARBEAU, Cynthia Marie
Southgate HS; Southgate, MI (25%-360) Ed, Ann; Drama; Church Band & Ensm; S-T, Church Chor; *U of Mich; Psych.*

BARBEITO, Rosa Maria
Colegio Espiritu Santo; Hato Rey, PR (6-96) A-Ed, Ann; Chor; Drama; VP, Hmrm; Math C; Pres, NHS; Semi-Fin, Tr; COM; Hon Prog; Pres, Ecology C; *La Fayette Col; Biological Sci.*

BARBER, Alvin T Jr
St Anne HS; St Anne, IL (25%-115) Ftbl; Tnns; Tr; HKg; HCt; Prom King; Prep C; Afro C; Newspaper A; *Depaul U; Bus Adm.*

BARBER, Brenda Marie
White Oak Sr HS; Jacksonville, NC; *Coastal Carolina Comm Col; Agr.*

BARBER, Elaine Marie
Christian Acad; Waverly, NY; Chor; FHA; NHS.

BARBER, Freda Gale
White Oak HS; Jacksonville, NC; Band; FBLA; FFA; Bkbl; *Coastal Carolina Comm Col; Police Sci.*

BARBER, George Caston
Indian Springs Acad; Jackson, GA (4-13) VP, Key C; NHS; Sch Achieve Tm; SC; Bsbl; Bkbl; COM; Cl Fav; Sports Ed, Sch P; Highest Avg For Boy, Jr Yr; EMC Essay Win; *Gordon Jr Col; Pre-Phar.*

BARBER, Janice Lynne
Johnstown Central HS; Johnstown, PA (20-430) Secy, Band; Chor; Key C; Tres, NHS; Amer Leg A; Journ A; *Penn St U; Sci.*

BARBER, Joyce Rene
Reynolds HS; Greenville, PA (19-212) Band; 1st Cl, GSct A; WW; *Allegheny Comm Col; Hotel-Motel Mgt.*

BARBER, Lesia Katherine
Catlemont HS; Oakland, CA; Tres, A Cap Choir; Chor; NHS; Sftbl; CSF; Dance C; Cpt, Bowl Tm; *UCLA; Med.*

BARBER, Mary Loren
Lindsay HS; Lindsay, OK (11-108) Band; Chor; Ensm; FBLA; Rptr, Span C; COM; JA A; St Scholar; Type A; Worthy Advisor, Rainbow Girls; Superior, Twirling; Pep C; Superintendent's Off Asst; Jr Deaconess; *U of Okla; Phar.*

BARBER, Meredith Anne
Herndon HS; Herndon, VA; Band; Span NHS; Secy, Yth Group; All Regional Band; Ntl Brethren Yth Church Coun; *Shenandoah Col; Mus Therapy.*

BARBER, Randal David
Bend Sr HS; Bend, OR (25-450) Band; NHS; ARC; Bkbl; Math A; Airplane Pilot; Advance Stage Band; Sr Wind Ensm; *Oreg St U; Elec Engr.*

BARBER, Ruth Ann
Red Bluff Union HS; Red Bluff, CA (19-353) Fr C; Pres, FNA; F-Ed, Lit Mag; NHS; Bank Of Amer A; B Crocker A; CSF; Kiwanis A; Secy, Church Yth Group; Church Choir; Sunday Sch Teacher; Church Lib; *Biola Col; Nurs.*

BARBER, Terri Marie
Cottage Grove HS; Cottage Grove, OR (5-240) Chldr; Pres, FBLA; GS; Hmrm; NHS; SC; Bkbl; Tnns; COM; Elk A; Hon Prog; *Oreg St U; Acct.*

BARBERIE, Nancy Jean
Richwoods HS; Peoria, IL (9-460) A Cap Choir; Fin, AFS; Madrigal; NHS; SC; God & Country A; Hon Prog; Sterling Merit A; Top 10; All St Choir; *U of Ill; Lib Arts.*

BARBERIS, Maria Ann
St Mary's Acad; Portland, OR (5-169) NHS; ARC; SC; VP, Jr Cl; Mgr, Bkbl; *Med.*

BARBIER, Ann Lorraine
Lamarque HS; La Marque, TX (20%-350) Ed, Ann; Rptr, Bus C; Chor; Ensm; Madrigal; Mod Mus Mas; NHS; Sch P; Journ A; Q&S A; *Houston Baptist U; Bio.*

BARBKNECHT, Mary Rose
Dunkirk Sr HS; Dunkirk, NY; Chor; *Bus Mgt.*

BARBOSA, Janette Liz
Colegio Santa Rita; Bayamon, PR (1-33) Chor; Hmrm; NHS; ARC; SC; Excellence; PA; Principal A; *Greighton U; Natural Sci.*

BARBOUR, Christy Suzanne
Turner HS; Kans City, KS (11-350) Board Member, Kayettes; Vlbl; *William Jewell Col; Elem Ed.*

BARBOUR, Douglas Sheridan
Myers Park HS; Charlotte, NC; Band; *NC St Col; Mech Engr.*

BARBOUR, John Herman
Turner HS; Kans City, KS (15-310) Band; BS; NHS; Tres, Var C; Ftbl; Tr; Hon Prog; *William Jewell Col; Sci.*

BARBREE, Jeffery Wayne
Bainbridge HS; Bainbridge, GA; FFA; Pres, Sci C; Sci A.

BARCLAY, Alan Wayne
Lawrence HS N; Lawrenceville, NJ (118-246) Band; JV, Tnns; Church Choir; Christian Service Brigade; Cpt, Word of Life C; *Liberty Baptist Col; Missions.*

BARCLAY, Lester Lloyd
Calumet HS; Chicago, IL (17-475) Band; Chem C; Chor; Secy, 4H; Model UN; VP, NHS; Pres, Pol Sci C; SC; Up Bound; VP, Sr Cl; Tres, Soph Cl; JV, Ftbl; Amer Leg A; COM; Citz A; Cl Fav; 4H A; Hon Prog; JA A; Spch A; Yth Leg; *Oberlin Col.*

BARCLAY, Patrick George
Robert Lindblom Tech HS; Chicago, IL (25%-450) A Cap Choir; Band; Chor; Madrigal; Tr; COM; Citz A; Jr NHS; NML; *Beloit Col; Psych.*

BARCLIFT, Michael Ray
Rantoul Twp HS; Rantoul, IL (25%-350) Hmrm; A-Ed, Lit Mag; SC; JV, Bsbl; JV, Ftbl; JV, Wrest; Math A; *Air Force Acad.*

BARDELL, Christine Lynn
Westfield HS; Westfield, IL (3-19) Secy, Band; Chldr; Chor; 4H; Tres, Hmrm; Span C; VP, SC; Tres, Jr Cl; Bkbl; Sftbl; Tr; HCt; Type A.

BARDILL, Carol Lee
Central HS; LaCrosse, WI; SC; Secy, Vandalism Comm; Pep C; Candystriper; Bible Sch Helper; Job's Daughters; Medany Infant Care; Summer Friends Program; *U of Wisc; Social Work.*

BARDWELL, Betty Ann
Central HS; San Angelo, TX (10-671) Band; NHS; S-T, Orch; Math A; NML; Fr, Area Band, A's; *Angelo St U; Bus.*

BARE, Sandra Eileen
St Joseph Acad; McSherrystown, PA (3-12) Ann; Chor; 4H; Ed, Sch P; 4H A; Hon Prog; *Pa St U; General Arts.*

BAREA, Jaime Eduardo
Notre Dame HS; Caguas, PR (1-140) Var C; Cpt, Swim; Semi-Fin, Tr; COM; Sci A; *U of Puerto Rico; Sci.*

BAREFIELD, Debbie Ann
M B Smiley HS; Houston, TX (27-400) Mu Alpha Theta; NHS; Bio A; COM; Bookkeeping, A; Ntl Fr Exam, Soc Stu, A's.

BAREFIELD, Mark Darryl
Panama City Christian Sch; Panama City, FL (3-20) Chess C; Chor; VP, Lat C; Bkbl; Ftbl; Sci A; Most Intellectual; Bowl Tm Champ, Jaycee HS Quiz; *Politics.*

BAREFIELD, Melvin Karl
Eudora HS; Eudora, AR; Ann; Sch P; VP, SC; Bkbl; Hon Prog; Church Choir.

BAREFOOT, Phyllis Marie
Midway HS; Rual, NC; Monogram; Sftbl.

BARELA, Joseph Lee
Estancia HS; Estancia, NM (10-40) A-Ed, Ann; Band; Semi-Fin, BS; Pres, Bus C; Secy, CYO; Secy, Drama; VP, NHS; Secy, Sci C; Pres, Span C; SC; JV, Bkbl; JV, Ftbl; Tr; Hist A; Type A; Acct, Bus PA, Shorthand, A's; *U of NM; Bus.*

BARELA, Leticia Yvonne
Albuquerque HS; Albuquerque, NM; CYO; Bkbl; Hon Prog; *U of NM; Bus Adm.*

BARELA, Mark Eric
Albuquerque HS; Albuquerque, NM (50%-485) Pres, CYO; Drama; Thes; *U of NM; Bus Adm.*

BARENKAMP, Shari Lynne
Paris HS; Paris, IL (25-249) Band; Chor; Drama; NHS; Span C; Hon Prog; Band A; *Wayne St Col; Phys Therapy.*

BARES, Allen Wayne
Lafayette HS; Lafayette, LA (20%-650) FBLA; Ch, Hmrm; Bsbl; Bkbl; Yth Fel; VP, Yth Fellowship; *SW La U; Agr.*

BARFIELD, Daphne Gay
Wayne Ctry Day Sch; Goldsboro, NC (7-33) Ann; Parl, Jr Cl; Pres, Soph Cl; Bkbl; MVP, Sftbl; HCt; Hon Prog; NEDT; *U of NC.*

BARFIELD, Judy Lynn
Oak Grove HS; San Jose, CA; Chor; Hon Prog; Church Yth Choir; Christian C; Acteen; Secy, NHS; Outreach Ldr, Sundy Sch; *Calif Baptist Col; Bus Adm.*

BARFIELD, Lisa Annette
Bethel Christian Sch; Ruston, LA (5-12) Ann; Chldr; Fin, Lit Ral; SC; Pres, Soph Cl; Bkbl; Sftbl; Alg A; Beauty; Citz A; HCt; Hon Men, Dist Bkbl; Most Improved, Free Throw %, Bkbl; *La Tech U; Secy.*

BARG, Elisabeth Ann
Ladysmith-Hawkins HS; Ladysmith, WI (24-110) Band; Chldr; Chor; FHA; Fin, Jr Miss Pagent; Madrigal; WW, Mus; *UW-Superior; Mus.*

BARGDILL, Nancy JoLynn
Eastern Hills HS; Fort Worth, TX (28-450) Band; Bus C; NHS; Sci C; Span C; Citz A; Hist A; Hon Prog; Opt A; Summa Cum Laude; Type A; 2nd Cl; Drill Tm; Church Choir; Sr Hi MYF; *Texas Christian U; Bus.*

BARGE, Jody Lynn
Winona Sr HS; Winona, MN (20-560) Chor; Fr C; NHS; *U of Minn; Hist.*

BARGER, Blane Rene
Coppell Ind HS; Coppell, TX (5%-50) BC; SC; Pres, Jr Cl; Bkbl; Ftbl; Golf; JV, Tnns; Tr; *Tex Tech U; Engr.*

BARGER, Elaine Marie
Winchester HS; Winchester, MA (104-444) Chor; Fr C; Madrigal; Sch P; Les Troubadors; 50 Hr Candystriper; Los Companeros; Philosophy C; 1st Cl GSct.

BARGER, Kym William
Lamar HS; Lamar, MO; Bus Mgr, Band; Ensm; Var C; Bkbl; MVP, Cr-Ctry; Tr; Hon Prog; Coach, Girl's Sftbl.

BARGER, Larry Ashley
Springfield Shawnee HS; Springfield, OH; 4H; *Clark Tech Col; Automotive Engr.*

34

BARGER, Traci Lynn
Salisbury HS; Salisbury, NC (45-250) Chor; Span C; Hon Prog; Jr Civitan; *U of Tenn; Interior Design.*

BARGO, Sarah Lynne
Sprayberry HS; Marietta, GA (13-600) Chldr; Chor; Drama; Hmrm; Lat C; NHS; SC; COM; Citz A; JA A; Math A; *Mus.*

BARHAM, Edward Ellison
Independence HS; Independence, MS (10%-120) BC; FFA; Pres, Soph Cl; Bsbl; Ftbl; *Northwest Jr Col; Agr.*

BARHAM, Emil R
Edison HS; Huntington Beach, CA (11-891) Fr C; SC; Tr; Hon Prog; *USC; Bio.*

BARHAM, Janie Marie
Independence HS; Independence, MS (5%-72) Ann; Band; Rptr, BC; Ensm; FBLA; FHA; Tres, 4H; COM; 4H A; Sci A; Yth Fel; Drum Major; Mid-South Hon Band; Pres, UMYF; *Northwest Jr Col.*

BARIL, Marlene Mae
George Washington Sr HS; Mangilao, GUAM; Band; Chor; Fr C; Tres, FNA; NHS; Rptr, Sch P; Bio A; Most Out; Sci A; Tres A; Service A; Art A; *Nurs.*

BARIONI, Donald Vic II
Imperial HS; Imperial, CA (7-92) Rptr, Ann; Drama; S-T, FFA; 4H; ARC; Thes; Wrest; CSF; Hon Prog; Photography C; Pres, Video Tape C; Certified Diver, Scuba; *The U of Calif at San Diego; Med.*

BARK, David Karl
Broadmoor HS; Baton Rouge, LA (20-450) BC; BS; Hmrm; S-T, InterAct C; S-T, NHS; JV, Bsbl; Ftbl; Tr; Hon Prog; MLS; NEDT; Eagle Sct; Highest Scholastic Avg; *LSU; Engr.*

BARKAN, Jeremy Myles
Hebrew Acad HS; Yonkers, NY (4-16) Chess C; Community Yth Symph; Dbte Tm; Ensm; Fr C; Mgr, Math C; Ed, Sch P; SC; Cpt, Tr; COM, Ntl Fr Assn Contest; *Biochem.*

BARKER, Betty Brown
Halifax Co Sr HS; S Boston, VA (5%-550) F-Ed, Ann; Drama; VP, 4H; Hmrm; Lat C; Lit Mag; NHS; Sch P; Secy, Sci C; SC; Y-Tns; Pres, Soph Cl; Tnns; 4H A; Med Explorers Sec; All A's; Most Versatile Actress; *U of Va; Law.*

BARKER, Cheryl Catherine
Springfield HS; Springfield, PA (43-431) Chor; Ensm; Hmrm; Choir A.

BARKER, Danita Monique
MacDuffie Sch; Springfield, MA; Chor; Drama; Math C; Rptr, Sch P; JV, Bkbl; Am As of Tchrs of Fr Ntl Contest; *Harvard U; Med.*

BARKER, Dewain Timothy
Greenville HS; Greenville, TX (9-310) Math C; Pres, NHS; Order/Arrow; Soccer; Tr; Balfour A; Cl Fav; HCt; Kiwanis A; MLS; Academic Excellence A; *Tex Tech U; Wildlife Mgt.*

BARKER, Douglas Keith
Central HS; Louisville, KY (75-300) VP, Thes; Cpt, Bkbl; Mgr, Ftbl; Mgr, Wrest; *Boston U; Bus.*

BARKER, James William
West Carter Co HS; Olive Hill, KY (5%-130) BC; Alg A; *Morehead St U; Med Sci.*

BARKER, Julie Ann
Mississinewa HS; Gas City, IN (45-250) Fr C; Pres, FTA; Tri-HiY; Dist DECA A; Shorthand A; *Ball St U; Elem Ed.*

BARKER, Kasandra Kay
Northeastern HS; Detroit, MI; Band; Chem C; Chor; NHS; Span C; Swim; COM; Service A; *Wayne U; Phar.*

BARKER, Lisa Ann
Boyd Co HS; Ashland, KY (14-314) Band; BC; FBLA; FHA; Pres, FTA; GS; Hmrm; Jr Miss Pageant; Mjrte; Co-Ed, Sch P; SC; Hon Prog; JA A.

BARKER, Lisa Kaye
John Overton HS; Nashville, TN (173-421) FHA; Hmrm; SC; Y-Tns; Service, Church, A's; Outst Eng Stu, Attendance, A's; *Middle Tenn St U; Bus.*

BARKER, Marquetta
W Carter HS; Olive Hill, KY (4-127) Ann; BC; FBLA; FHA; 4H; Secy, Sci C; Math A; Type A; *Morehead St Col; Nurs.*

BARKER, Mary Frances
Alvin HS; Alvin, TX (21-365) A Cap Choir; VP, Dbte Tm; Drama; Madrigal; NFL; NHS; JV, Tnns; Most Out; Yth Fel; 1st Cl GSct; Region & Area Choir; *Southwest Tex St U; Bus.*

BARKER, Melanie Joy
Abraham Lincoln Sr HS; Bloomington, MN (6-586) Secy, Chor; Pioneer Girls; JA; *Bethel Col; Bio.*

BARKER, Neil Evan
Fairfield HS; Fairfield, AL (25%-180) Chor; Bsbl; Ftbl; Wrest; COM; *U of Ala; Med.*

BARKER, Patricia Isabel
Adlai E Stevenson HS; Bronx, NY (48-777) Citz A; Attendance A; Outst Stu A; Schol A; Deaconess; Service A; Punctuality A; *Oakwood Col; Math.*

BARKER, Philip Lawrence
Lincoln Sr HS; Bloomington, MN (5-530) Chor; NHS; Order/Arrow; Wrest; NMS; Order/Arrow A; Rensselaer A; *Bethel Col; Sci.*

BARKER, Rachel Ann
Barberton HS; Barberton, OH (120-522) FHA; Hmrm; SC; B Crocker A; *Fla Col; Nurs.*

BARKER, Ryne Allen
Van Buren Comm HS; Keosauqua, IA (15-96) Band; VP, 4H; JV, Ftbl; 4H A; Spch Tm; R & M Quiz Tm; V Ltr; *Iowa St U; Genetics.*

BARKER, Sandra Kaye
Boyd Co HS; Cannonsburg, KY (170-550) FHA; Span C; Sftbl; *Morehead St U; Nurs.*

BARKER, Sherry Ann
LeRoy HS; LeRoy, IL (34-68) Semi-Fin, GS; Co-Cpt, Bkbl; MVP, Sftbl; Most Out; Mgr, Co-Cpt, Vlbl; Church Swtht Banquet Qn; *Cincinnati Bible Col; Bible.*

BARKER, Susan Elaine
Beaverton HS; Beaverton, OR (12-525) Co-Ed, Ann; NHS; Elk A; Hon Prog; Journ A; Q&S A; Type A; *Portland St U; Bus Adm.*

BARKETT, Ronald William
Dover HS; Dover, OH (30-273) VP, Band; Chor; Ensm; NHS; Pres, Orch; Spch C; Thes; Hon Prog; Math A; Spch A; Sup & Excellence, Solo & Ensm; OMEA, Voice & Tuba; *U of Cincinnati; Vocal Mus.*

BARKKARI, Dawn Elizabeth
Eisenhower HS; Washington, MI (7-650) Bus Mgr, CYO; Fr C; 4H; NHS; Orch; Ski C; Secy, Span C; SC; Pres, Jr Cl; Sftbl; Tnns; *Saint Mary's Col; Social Sci.*

BARKLEY, John Phillip
Newton Conover HS; Newton, NC (10-250) Fin, AFS; S-T, BC; Pres, Dbte Tm; Pres, Drama; Inter-Club Coun; Fin, Ntl Yth Conf; Span C; SC; Hon Prog; NEDT; Fin, Morehead Schol; AFS Exchange Stu to Italy; YMCA Rep to Constitutional Congre; Page, NC Leg; *U of NC at Chapel Hill; Econs.*

BARKLEY, Julia Annette
E Peoria Comm HS; E Peoria, IL (8-508) Chldr; Fr C; A-Ed, Sch P; SC; *Bus.*

BARKLEY, Karen Sue
DuPont Sr HS; Hermitage, TN (17-350) Bus Mgr, Ann; BC; Hmrm; NHS; Rainbow; SC; Outst Sr; Top 10%; *Memphis St U; Bus Adm.*

BARKS, Melissa Ann
Jackson HS; Jackson, MO (2-210) Co-Ed, Ann; Band; Pres, Drama; NHS; Span C; Spch C; Secy, SC; Curator A; HCt; Journ A; MLS; Sal; Spch A; *U of Mo; Acct.*

BARKSDALE, Robert Joe III
Kensington HS; Buffalo, NY; Band; Chor; Ensm; Ftbl; Tr; Cl Fav; Yth Fel; *Morehouse Col; Pre-Med.*

BARLAND, Keith Kim
Joel E Ferris HS; Spokane, WA; FFA; Ger C; Tnns; COM; *Eastern Washington U.*

BARLAR, Connie Rene
Beech Hill HS; Pulaski, TN; Chor; FHA; Secy, 4H; Secy, Jr Cl; Tres, Soph Cl; Bkbl; COM; 4H A; HCt; *U of Tenn; Mus.*

BARLAR, Emily Kate
Giles Co HS; Pulaski, TN (17-150) A-Ed, Ann; VP, BC; Drama; Thes; Win, Century III Schol; *Martin Col; Sci.*

BARLAZ, Rachel Ann
Bruriah HS; Elizabeth, NJ (2-26) Drama; NHS; Co-Ed, Sch P; Pres, Jr Cl; Hon Prog; Cast, Sch Play; Tutor Comm; Art C.

BARLICH, Patty Cloretta
Speedway HS; Speedway, IN (6-200) Band; Chor; Hmrm; SC; COM; Hon Prog; Lion A; Type A; 500 Flag Corp; *Elem Ed.*

BARLOW, Darcy Lee
N Kitsap HS; Poulsbo, WA; A-Ed, Ann; Chldr; Chor; Secy, Drama; Hmrm; Bsbl; Bkbl; Soccer; H of F; HCt; Secy Foreign Exchange Prog; VP, Fresh Cl; Art for the Gifted Child; *Wash St Col; Bus.*

BARLOW, David James
E Valley HS; Yakima, WA (20-154) Chor; Ensm; Span C; Mgr, Ftbl; Wrest; *Yakima Valley Col; Art.*

BARLOW, James Alfred
Pickwick South Side HS; Counce, TN (3-34) Pres, BC; Rptr, FFA; Pres, 4H; SC; Pres, Soph Cl; Bkbl; 4H A; Journ A; Math A; Spch A; Yth Fel; BSct; *U of Tenn; Math.*

BARLOW, John Scott
Maryville HS; Maryville, TN (10%-195) Band; Chem C; Key C; Lat C; Mu Alpha Theta; NHS; Cpt, Cr-Ctry; Cpt, Tr; Hon Prog; Sci A; Hon Band; All East Tenn Band; *U of Tenn; Engr.*

BARLOW, Mary Anne
Charleston HS; Charleston, IL (13-272) Pres, AFS; Bus Mgr, Ann; Chor; Drama; Fr C; VP, FTA; Madrigal; NHS; SC; *U of Ariz.*

BARLOW, Phoebe Sue
Port St Joe Jr Sr HS; Port St Joe, FL (10-120) Band; Drama; Secy, Ensm; NHS; Span C; Thes; Bkbl; *Med.*

BARLOW, Shirley Denise
Momence HS; Momence, IL (14-135) Band; NHS; Span C; Tr; *Bradley U; Law.*

BARMETTLER, Cheryl Mari
Royal HS; Simi Valley, CA; Band; Commercial C; Drama; Hmrm; Ski C; Span C; Alg A; COM; Citz A; Eng A; *Moorpark Col; Art.*

BARNACASTLE, Jeffrey Curtis
Northeast Lauderdale HS; Meridian, MS (20-84) VP, FFA; Parl, Key C; Bsbl; Bkbl; Ftbl; Admiral Parl, Anchor C; Most Ath; Hustle A; Dekalb Agr Accomplishment A; *Meridian Jr Col; Mech.*

BARNARD, David Alan
David Lipscomb HS; Nashville, TN; Sci C; Tr; *Middle Tenn St U; Aviation.*

BARNARD, Elaine Tyree
Thomas Jefferson HS; Los Angeles, CA; Bus C; Citz A; Hon Prog; Sci A; Type A; *Pepperdine U; Bus.*

BARNARD, Glenn Douglas
Mountlake Terrace HS; Mountlake Terrace, WA; Ger C; NHS; Var C; Bsbl; Bkbl; Ftbl; Coaches A, Bsbl; Most Improved, Bkbl & Bsbl; *U of Wash; Law Enforcement.*

BARNARD, Linda Kay
Cascade Union HS; Turner, OR (6-160) Chldr; FFA; Hmrm; NHS; Orch; SC; JV, Bkbl; HCt; Yth Fel; Yth Foundation; VP, Girl's League; Pres, GAA; MVP, Vlbl; *Northwest Col; Christian Ed.*

BARNARD, Pamela Sean
Nitro HS; Nitro, WV; Band; Pres, Hmrm; NHS; Span C; Bio A; Hist A; MLS; Val; *Morris Harvey Col; Bus.*

BARNER, Althea Charisse
Walter F George HS; Atlanta, GA (10-176) Ann; BC; Fr C; FHA; Hmrm; InterClub Coun; Model UN; NHS; SC; SC; Tnns; Hon Prog; Journ A; JA A; Acad Excel, Calculus, A's; Outst Achv Pin; Top 10%, Cl; *Dillard U; Econ.*

BARNER, Bryan Dwain
Odessa R-VII HS; Odessa, MO; Band; BS; NHS; Var C; Bsbl; Sftbl; Wrest; God & Country A; Hon Prog; *NW Mo St U; Dentistry.*

35

BARNER, Cassandra Ann
San Juan HS; Citrus Heights, CA (10%-500) CYO; Semi-Fin, Chldr; 4H; Sch P; SC; COM; Citz A; SG; Co-Ch, Rally C; HR; Church Yth Organizations; Homecoming Comm; Campus Adv Board; U of San Francisco; Nurs.

BARNER, Debra Leigh
Belle Plaine HS; Belle Plaine, KS (15-75) Ed, Ann; Band; Chldr; Ensm; 4H; Sch P; SC; COM; HCt; Type A; Dist, Stage, Bands; Shorthand A; Kans St U; Instrumental Mus Ed.

BARNER, Dennis Alan
San Juan HS; Citrus Heights, CA (33%-500) Band; CYO; 4H; ARC; Span C; COM; ARC A; Amer Legion Band; Greek Cath Fraternal Union; Span C, Band, A's; Stanford U; Med.

BARNES, Arletha Marie
St Willibrord HS; Chicago, IL (10-97) Chldr; Hmrm; Monogram; NHS; Tres, Sci C; SC; Mgr, Bkbl; JV, Soccer; Loyola U; Med.

BARNES, Arva Lisa
Kalamazoo Central HS; Kalamazoo, MI (159-517) Alpha Kappa Alpha; Sorority A; Mich St U; Bus Adm.

BARNES, Barbara Ellen
Broken Arrow Sr HS; Broken Arrow, OK; SC; WW; Drill Tm; Tres, Jr Executive Board; HR; Okla St U; Fashion Designing.

BARNES, Barry
F O Alexander HS; Starkville, MS (10-59) SC; Bsbl; Elem Ed.

BARNES, Beckham Bloyd
Russell Co HS; Jamestown, KY (5-152) Band; BC; Chess C; Dbte Tm; Drama; Hmrm; Math C; NHS; Bsbl; Bkbl; Ftbl; Sftbl; Tr; COM; H of F; HCt; Hon Prog; Pres A; ARC A; U of Ky; Civil Engr.

BARNES, Bennie Wayne
M B Smiley HS; Houston, TX (8-400) Hmrm; Mu Alpha Theta; NHS; SC; JV, Bkbl; Bio A; COM; Chem A; MLS; NMS; Sci A; Span A; Rice U; Sociology.

BARNES, Carrie Lafane
Germantown HS; Philadelphia, PA; Chor; NHS; Swim; Tnns; Hist A; Howard Col; Phys Therapy.

BARNES, Charles Elwyn
Obion Co Central HS; Troy, TN (3-180) Pres, A Cap Choir; All Amer Yth; A-Ed, Ann; VP, BC; BS; Chem C; Pres, Chor; Cum Laude Soc; FBLA; Hmrm; Math C; Rptr, NHS; SC; Var C; Bsbl; Cpt, Bkbl; Cr-Ctry; Sftbl; Tnns; Tr; Amer Leg A; H of F; Yth Fel; U of Tenn; Pre-Optometry.

BARNES, Christina Louise
Redlands Sr HS; Redlands, CA; Exotic Animal Care.

BARNES, Cidra Lamana
Suffolk HS; Suffolk, VA (17-118) Chor; Secy, FHA; Hmrm; NFL; SC; VP, Soph Cl; Citz A; Yth Fel; Va Commonwealth U; Fashion Design.

BARNES, Cynthia Murray
Watertown HS; Watertown, CT (60-303) AFS; Band; Rainbow; Yth Fel; Ed, Yrbk; Church Choir; Acolytes; U of Maine; Psych.

BARNES, Daphne Renee
Marianna HS; Marianna, FL; Co-Ch, Hmrm; Pres A; ROTC A; ROTC Qn; Chipola Jr Col; Bus.

BARNES, Darda Ann
Highmore HS; Highmore, SD (12-44) Chor; FHA; 4H; 4H A; SD St U; Home Ec.

BARNES, Denice Marie
E Peoria Comm HS; E Peoria, IL (10-400) Chem C; Chor; Fr C; Madrigal; NHS; Bausch & Lomb A; Sterling Merit A; Ill Weslyan U; Biol.

BARNES, Donna Faye
Southwest HS; Macon, GA (1-850) Bus Mgr, Band; Pres, BC; Ensm; 4H; Hmrm; Math C; SC; Sftbl; COM; 4H A; Hon Prog; Math A; Most Out; Sci A; Star Student; Val; Comm Band; 1st Cl Sct; Mus Achv, PA, A's; HR; NML; Ga SW Col; Nurs.

BARNES, Donna Lynne
Belen HS; Belen, NM (6-316) 4H; 4H A; Math A; Sci A; Type A; OEA; Rodeo C; Auto Mech A.

BARNES, Eric Christian
Shawnee Mission N HS; Shawnee Mission, KS (87-562) Dbte Tm; Ensm; Pres, NFL; NHS; SC; Cr-Ctry; Tr; Outst Jr Eng St, Brown U A; PSAT Ltr of Commendation; Grinnel Col; Eng.

BARNES, Felicia Dorothea
William Penn HS; Philadelphia, PA (20%-600) Math C; NHS; Pres, Sci C; COM; 4H A; Hon Prog; Math A; Art A; Beaver Col; Bio.

BARNES, Glenda Jean
Camp Verde HS; Camp Verde, AZ (8-56) Ann; Chor; 4H; Tres, NHS; Rptr, Sch P; SC; Bkbl; Sftbl; Cpt, Tr; 4H A; H of F; Type A; Pres, Pep C; Cpt, Vlbl; Ltrwomen; St Champion; Tr; VP, HERO; MVP, Tr; President's Phys Fitness A; Northern Ariz U; Psych.

BARNES, Gloria Jean
Santa Ana Valley HS; Santa Ana, CA; Amer Leg A; Hon Prog; Peppedine Col; Child Development.

BARNES, Greg Duane
Burnsville Sr HS; Burnsville, MN; Chor; Ensm; Ski C; Tnns; Yth Fel.

BARNES, Gregory Kent
Gainesville HS; Gainesville, TX (10-185) Pres, Chor; Dbte Tm; Parl, Drama; Ensm; Pres, FTA; Tres, Key C; NHS; Order/Arrow; Parl, Spch C; JV, Ftbl; COM; God & Country A; NEDT; Order/Arrow A; Eagle Sct; Excellent Rating, St Solo Contest; Howard Payne U; Mus Ed.

BARNES, James Mark
Terre Haute S Vigo HS; Terre Haute, IN (100-500) Band; BS; Community Yth Symph; Ensm; Hmrm; Mod Mus Mas; Orch; Sch P; SC; Mgr, Ftbl; Mgr, Wrest; Amer Leg A; Cl Fav; MLS; Most Out; Yth Leg; WW, HS Mus; Ind St U; Mus.

BARNES, Janis Lea
Arapahoe HS; Littleton, CO (120-560) Community Yth Symph; SC; Sftbl; Hon Prog; Flag Twirler; Social Ch, Pep C; Dist Six Textbook Comm; Baylor U; Special Ed.

BARNES, Jean Annette
University HS; Spokane, WA (71-370) Chor; Hmrm; SC; Secy, Sr Cl; Bkbl; Ftbl; Sftbl; Howard Payne U; Bus.

BARNES, Joseph Scott
Marine Military Acad; Harlingen, TX (2-41) Band; BS; Demolay; Drama; NHS; Citz A; Spch A; Vof-DEM; Marine Corps League Distin Serv A; U of Minn; Engr.

BARNES, Joyleeta Louine
Warrior Acad; Eutaw, AL; BC; Chor; Ensm; Fr C; Math C; Rptr, Sch P; Beauty.

BARNES, Julia Annette
Wellston HS; Wellston, OK (4-51) A Cap Choir; F-Ed, Ann; Band; Chor; Drama; Ensm; Rptr, FHA; Rptr, 4H; NHS; Rptr, Sch P; Sci C; Span C; Tres, SC; Rptr, Soph Cl; Bsbl; Co-Cpt, Bkbl; Tr; Amer Leg A; COM; Citz A; Cl Fav; Hist A; HCt; Hon Prog; Journ A; JA A; Sal; St Hon Soc; Superintendent's HR; Mus Contest A's; Phys Ed.

BARNES, Karen Diane
McCluer N Sr HS; Florissant, MO (20-780) Chor; Ensm; Madrigal; Hon Prog; Concert Choir; Mus A; Top Ten As; Psych.

BARNES, Karen Louise
Lynbrook HS; San Jose, CA (1-550) NHS; Tr; Vlbl; Northwest Christian Col; Sci.

BARNES, Karen Sue
Lancaster HS; Lancaster, OH (28-750) Chor; Ensm; 2nd Pl, Span Fair; Lib Asst; Church Bible Quiz Tm; Ohio U at Lancaster; Secretarial Sci.

BARNES, Kenneth Ray
Yreka HS; Yreka, CA (25-185) Chldr; SC; Var C; Ftbl; Cpt, Tr; CSF; Rotary A; Best Wit, Sr Cl; All Around Stu; Pt Loma Col.

BARNES, Kristy Elizabeth
Burnsville Sr HS; Burnsville, MN (15-800) A Cap Choir; Madrigal; NHS; Pres, Span C; Tnns; NMS; Stanford U; Pre-Med.

BARNES, Lori Faye
Medina HS; Medina, TN (10%-27) Ann; Secy, BC; FHA; Pres, Hmrm; Rptr, SC; Mgr, Var C; Pres, Jr Cl; Mgr, Bkbl; Cl Fav; HCt; U of Tenn; Biol.

BARNES, Marty Don
Burnsville HS; Burnsville, MS; SC; Bsbl; Bkbl; Ftbl; Tr; Sportmanship A.

BARNES, Mary Cheryl
Assumption Jr-Sr HS; Assumption, IL (10%-56) Band; FHA; Tnns; Hon Prog; Vlbl; SAA; Math.

BARNES, Mary Kristin
Rockville HS; Rockville, IN (4-84) Band; Chor; Ensm; FHA; 4H; Lat C; NHS; Rainbow; Sci C; Secy, Soph Cl; Swim; God & Country A; St Scholar; Statistician, Bsbl; Outst Musician; Mus A; Amer Yth Symph Band; Oral Roberts U; Special Ed.

BARNES, Melvin Henry Jr
Cromwell Acad; Washington, DC; Pres, NHS; Rptr, Sch P; Citz A; Math A; Ntl Sci Found; Sci A; Ldrship A; Dependability & Effort A; Pub Speaking A; Math.

BARNES, Nerrissia Sadie
Hyde Park Career Acad; Chicago, IL; Band; VP, Chor; Bkbl; Oral Roberts U; Mus.

BARNES, Phyllis Juanita
Wingfield HS; Jackson, MS (11-237) Fr C; Mjrte; NHS; St Stu Congress; SC; COM; H of F; NMF; NMS; NEDT; Yth Leadership A; Tougaloo Col; Bio.

BARNES, Richard Jefferson
Carbon Hill HS; Carbon Hill, AL (33%-80) Chess C; HiY; Sci C; Var C; Bkbl; Ftbl; Pres, Leo C.

BARNES, Rita Pamela
Assumption HS; Assumption, IL (3-49) Fr C; Secy, FHA; Sch P; Secy, Soph Cl; MVP, Tnns; Journ A; Fr A.

BARNES, Robert Richard III
Grissom HS; Huntsville, AL (200-730) Soccer; Anthropology.

BARNES, Roger Allen
Marshall Sr HS; Marshall, MO (41-219) AFS; Chor; Drama; Parl, FFA; 4H; Spch C; 4H A; FFA A; Skill Tractor Driving; U of Mo; Agr.

BARNES, Ronnie Olaf
Abraham Lincoln Sr HS; Houston, TX (9-72) A-Ed, Ann; Band; Chor; Pres, FHA; InterAct C; Secy, NHS; Var C; Bkbl; Cl Fav; MLS; HR; PA; Photography A; Tex Sou U; Marketing Research.

BARNES, Ruth Ellen
Johnstown-Monroe HS; Johnstown, OH (2-134) Band; Chor; FTA; Math C; VP, NHS; Alg A; Math A; Band A; Eng A; Otterbein Col; Mus.

BARNES, Sheila Elaine
Ritenour Sr HS; Overland, MO (121-826) Drama; Rptr, Sch P; SC; COM; Outst Performance, Drama; Bradley U; Social Services.

BARNES, Sherry Elaine
Red Bank HS; Red Bank, TN (43-403) Band; Pres, BC; Fr C; FHA; GS; Hmrm; Span C; SC; COM; Star Student; Rifle Corp; Church Bkbl & Sftbl; Work Schol, Tenn Tech; Tenn Tech U; Vet Med.

BARNES, Sherry Yvette
Woodside HS; Woodside, CA; Chor; City Conf; Pres, Drama; SC; Bkbl; Soccer; Sftbl; UCLA; Bus.

BARNES, Steven Byard
Winnfield Sr HS; Winnfield, LA (22-124) Anchor C; FBLA; FFA; Tres, Var C; Ftbl; La Col.

BARNES, Steven Garth
Cody-Kilgore Unified Sch; Cody, NE (2-15) Band; BS; VP, FFA; Pres, 4H; NHS; Pres, Soph Cl; JV, Bkbl; Cpt, Ftbl; Tr; Citz A; HCt; U of Nebr; Agr Mech.

BARNES, Tamera Renee
Mountain View HS; Mtn View, OK (3-25) Ann; Band; Chldr; Chor; Ensm; FHA; NHS; Rainbow; Rptr, Sch P; SC; S-T, Sr Cl; S-T, Soph Cl; Bio A; Chem A; HQn; Sci A.

BARNES, Timothy Lee
Connersville Sr HS; Connersville, IN; Chess C; Drama; Spch C; Sci A; Spch A; Baptist Bible Col; Theology.

BARNES, Timothy Lee
Coon Rapids Sr HS; Coon Rapids, MN (70-650) CYO; Drama; Tres, Hmrm; Tres, SC; Tres, Sr Cl; Tres, Jr Cl; JV, Soccer; Jr Chamber of Com A; Most Out; Psych.

BARNETT, Angela Sue
Baker HS; Baker, LA (15-374) VP, A Cap Choir; BC; Bus C; Pres, FBLA; FTA; InterClub Coun; Math C; Mu Alpha Theta; NHS; Tri-HiY; Secy, Sr Cl; Cl Fav; HCt; Wichita St Col; Dental Hygiene.

BARNETT, Betsey Elgin
Newnan HS; Newnan, GA (2-304) Anchor C; Ann; BC; Chldr; Drama; Hmrm; Lit Ral; Sci C; Secy, SC; Alg A; COM; Citz A; Gov Honor Prog; HCt; Hon Prog; Math A; NEDT; Sal; Sci A; Type A; WW; Nom, US Senate Yth Program; Pres Col Jr Fellow; Dist Math, Sci Sch, Ga Tech; U of Ga; Bus Adm.

BARNETT, Bonnie Sue
Burrell Sr HS; Lower Burrell, PA; Pres, Key C; Alg A; Med Tech.

BARNETT, Cheryl Ann
Nordnoff HS; Ojai, CA (16-350) Fin, AFS; NHS; Swim; Eng A; Nurs.

BARNETT, Daniel L
Atwater HS; Atwater, CA (12-500) Band; Fr C; FBLA; Parl, SC; CSF; Tres, UMYF; Drum Major; Stu o-t Mo; Church Yth Comm; Conf Coun On Yth Ministries; Parl, CASC; U o-t Pacific; Bus Adm.

BARNETT, Debra Kay
Kamiakin HS; Kennewick, WA (10%-319) 4H; Secy, NHS; Orch; Bkbl; JV, Tnns; COM; 4H A; Hon Prog; Yth Fel; Whitworth Col; Phar.

BARNETT, Jeffrey Curtis
S P Waltrip Sr HS; Houston, TX; Tres, Band; Span C; Rptr, Span NHS; Abilene Christian U; Missions.

BARNETT, Jeffrey Paul
Lexington HS; Lexington, AL (15-90) FFA; 4H; SC; Var C; JV, Bkbl; Ftbl; Cl Fav; Pres A; U of N Ala.

BARNETT, Joanne Elise
Northstar Christian Acad; Rochester, NY (2-6) Ed, Ann; Cpt, Chldr; Secy, Chor; Dbte Tm; Drama; Ensm; Hmrm; Co-Ed, Sch P; Var C; Bkbl; Soccer; COM; MLS; Most Out; Sal; Spch A; Swtht; Vlbl.

BARNETT, John Hugh
Lubbock Christian HS; Lubbock, TX (50%-50) Band; 4H; Rptr, Sr Cl; Bsbl; Mgr, Ftbl; Tr; Cl Fav; Abilene Christian U; Agr.

BARNETT, Kimberly Ann
E Jordan HS; E Jordan, MI; Band; Ensm; Ski C; Span C; SC.

BARNETT, Marcus Kerry Jr
Gadsden HS; Anthony, NM; Semi-Fin, BS; Chem C; 4H; NHS; Sci C; Var C; Bkbl; Bkbl; Cr-Ctry; Cpt, Ftbl; Tr; Wrest; 4H A; Hist A; Sci A; Yth Fel.

BARNETT, Mark Stanley
Gadsden HS; Anthony, NM; Parl, A Cap Choir; All Amer Yth; Ann; Band; Parl, Chor; Parl, Drama; Ensm; VP, 4H; Hmrm; Parl, InterClub Coun; NFL; Span C; Tres, Spch C; Parl, SC; Thes; Var C; JV, Ftbl; Wrest; COM; Citz A; Cl Fav; 4H A; Hon Prog; Masque & Gavel A; Most Out; Opt A; Opt Out Tn; Spch A; Yth Fell; Yth Foundation A; Pres, Church Yth; VP, Sub-Dist Church Yth.

BARNETT, Rhonda Lou
Lyon Co HS; Eddyville, KY (10-110) Band; Cpt, Chldr; Ensm; Parl, FHA; MVP, Sftbl; Tnns; Cl Fav; HCt; VP, FHA; Phys Ed, Health, Chldr, A's; Annual Rep; U of Ky; Nurs.

BARNETT, Rita Nan
Hanceville HS; Hanceville, AL (5-103) Chor; FBLA; FTA; GS; NHS; Wallace Comm Col; Acct.

BARNETT, Stephanie Blair
Clear Creek HS; League City, TX (25%-635) Chor; NHS; Tres, Soph Cl; Jr Lieutenant Drill Tm.

BARNETT, Suzanne Simmons
Druid Park Baptist HS; Satsuma, AL; F-Ed, Ann; Cpt, Chldr; S-T, Hmrm; S-T, Jr Cl; Tres, Soph Cl; MVP, Sftbl; Chamber of Comm A; Cl Fav; HCt; Hon Prog.

BARNETT, Suzette Lorraine
Englewood Sr HS; Jacksonville, FL (10%-600) Chor; Fr C; Sch P; Yth Fitness Achv A; Commissioner of Ed A of Hon; Med.

BARNETT, Tim
Lexington HS; Lexington, AL (2-90) FFA; 4H; Pres, Soph Cl; Bsbl; Bkbl; 4H A; HCt; Pianist at Church; U N Ala; Math.

BARNETT, Timothy Andrew
Northeastern HS; Elizabeth City, NC (10%-420) Fr C; 4H; Rptr, Hmrm; Sci C; SC; Bkbl; Co-Cpt, Ftbl; Tr; Alg A; COM; Math A; Pres A; Alg Stu o-t Mo; Boy's C Boy o-t Yr; Pres Phys Fit A; Cty Tbl Tnns Champ; Jr Players; Most Improved, Bkbl; 1st, Oratory Poetry Contest; Hampton Inst; Archt Engr.

BARNETT, Victor Earl
Rufus King HS; Milwaukee, WI; Band; City Conf; Pres, Hmrm; Math C; Var C; Cpt, Bsbl; Mgr, Ftbl; Wrest; Math A; Swtht; Sports As; U W at Madison; Engr.

BARNETTE, Beverly Marjorie
Blanchet HS; Seattle, WA (27-285) Ch, Band; Chor; Community Yth Symph; Cpt, Ensm; FBLA; NHS; Orch; Amer Leg A; COM; Hon Prog; Executive Bus Secy A; Mus A; N Seattle Comm Col; Bus.

BARNETTE, Deborah Michelle
Charles Henderson HS; Troy, AL (2-187) A-Ed, Ann; Band; Pres, BC; Bus C; FBLA; FTA; Fin, Jr Miss Pagent; Rptr, Sch P; Secy A; Ntl Sci Found; Sal; Span A; U of S Ala; Computer Sci.

BARNETTE, Gwendolyn Hannah
Ouachita Parish HS; Monroe, LA; Northeast La U; Nurs.

BARNETTE, Susan Elaine
Pendleton HS; Pendleton, SC (7-132) Ann; BC; Fr C; Sch P; SC; Allied Yth; Best All Around; Miss Sr; Clemson U; Liberal Arts.

BARNETTE, Terri Elaine
N Mecklenburg HS; Huntersville, NC (19-475) Chor; Mgr, Ensm; VP, Fr C; GS; Pres, Hmrm; Model UN; NHS; Pres, World Affairs; Amer Leg A; HCt; Hon Prog; Fr, Annual Staff, Chor, A's; Outst Accompanist; U of NC; Fr.

BARNEWOLT,
Charles Frederick
Carl Sandburg HS; Orland Park, IL (17-775) Bus C; Ed, CYO; City Conf; Tres, Dbte Tm; Fr C; Math C; Mu Alpha Theta; NFL; NHS; Phys C; Ed, Sch P; Pres, Sci C; Spch C; JV, Ftbl; COM; Hon Prog; Journ A; Q&S A; Rotary A; ROTC A; Spch A; St Scholar; Yth Foundation; Rptr, Sch P; WW; Marquette Merit A; Win, Debate Tourn; U of Ill; Pol Sci.

BARNHARDT, Sandra Lynn
Tokay HS; Lodi, CA; A Cap Choir; Span C; Delta Jr Col; Computer Prog.

BARNHART, Brian Arthur
Westboro HS; Westboro, MA (45-216) Demolay; Ski C; Var C; JV, Bkbl; Ftbl; Framingham St Col; Pre-Med.

BARNHART, Carol Ann
Montpelier HS; Montpelier, OH (10-110) Band; BC; Cpt, Chldr; Chor; Ensm; Fr C; 4H; Orch; Pres, Soph Cl; Citz A; Oral Roberts U; Mus.

BARNHART,
Cassondra Elizabeth
Columbia HS; Columbia, MS (14-155) Band; S-T, Chess C; Co-Ch, Drama; Ensm; NHS; Spch C; Pearl River Jr Col; Deaf Ed.

BARNHART, Daniel Edwin
Greencastle-Antrim HS; Chambersburg, PA (100-250) Waynesboro Bus Sch; Acct.

BARNHART, David Bryan
Oak Hill HS; Oak Hill, OH (17-106) BC.

BARNHILL, Carla Denise
Helix HS; La Mesa, CA (10%-312) Hon Prog; Type A; Secy, Jack & Jill C; Hon Soc; Mus A; Phar.

BARNHILL, Christopher Lee
Dallas Christian HS; Dallas, TX (25%-60) A Cap Choir; Chor; SC; Var C; Pres, Soph Cl; Ftbl; Tnns; Okla Christian Col; Bible.

BARNHILL, Kelli Marie
Custer HS; Milwaukee, WI (33%-800) Dbte Tm; Sch P; SC; Sftbl; Swim; Tr; COM; Citz A; JA A; Pres, Fresh Cl; Forensics A; Pub Announcer, Sch Activities; Libra C; Tr & Shot Put A; Church Choir; Northland Col; Bus.

BARNHILL, Mark Walker
Northbrook Sr HS; Houston, TX (185-561) Bsbl; Bkbl; Mgr, Ftbl; Church Sftbl & Tr.

BARNICK, Donna Marie
Jud Pub HS; Jud, ND (2-9) Band; Chldr; Chor; Tres, Soph Cl; Bkbl; MVP, Tr; Hon Prog; Concordia Col.

BARNOT, Rachel Lee
Austintown Fitch HS; Youngstown, OH (1-700) FTA; Ger C; 4H; Hon Men, Bio I Schol Tm; Elem Ed.

BARON, Robert Arthur
New Caney HS; Porter, TX; Band; Chess C; JETS; NHS; All-Dist Band; Academic Bowl Tm; Tex St Solo & Ensm; U of Tex; Engr.

BAROODY, Katherine Jane
St Mary's Acad; Alexandria, VA (10-70) Pres, CYO; Chor; VP, Key C; Outst Mus Theory Stu; WW; Boston Col; Theol.

BARR, Angela Dawn
Newton-Conover HS; Newton, NC (6-200) AFS; VP, Band; BC; Pres, Hmrm; InterAct C; SC; Citz A; Most Out; Band Qn; Eng A; Appalachian St U; Med Tech.

BARR, Brad Joseph
Bishop Ready HS; Columbus, OH (10-150) 4H; Bkbl; Tnns; Sierra C A; Ohio St U; Engr.

BARR, Catherine Elizabeth
Brazoswood HS; Clute, TX (15%-500) Band; NHS; Med Careers C; Brazosport Col; Health Sci.

BARR, Connie Lynne
Langley HS; Langley, WA (10-86) CYO; Cpt, Chldr; Chor; FBLA; FHA; 4H; Hmrm; Span C; Bkbl; Swim; Tr; 4H A; Vlbl; WW; Wash St U; Dental Hygiene.

BARR, Darrel Wayne
Eula HS; Clyde, TX (2-32) Tres, FFA; Pres, SC; MVP, Bkbl; Fin, Tnns; Semi-Fin, Tr; Co-Cpt, Bkbl; Star FFA Chptr Farmer; FFA Schol A; San Angelo St U; Hist.

BARR, David William
Finneytown HS; Cincinnati, OH (30-250) A Cap Choir; Chor; Drama; Madrigal; NHS; Thes; Tr; COM; Citz A; Col of William & Mary; Drama.

BARR, Deborah Jean
W Middlesex HS; W Middlesex, PA (1-168) Chor; FTA; Span C; NEDT; Type A; Ed of Handicapped.

BARR, Eric Floyd
Moorefield HS; Moorefield, WV (2-89) NHS; A-Ed, Sci C; Hon Prog; Journ A; Sal; Type A; Yth Fel; Regional Math Contest; Gifted Prog; Shepherd Col; Secondary Ed.

BARR, Gregory James
Belvidere HS; Belvidere, IL (28-391) 4H; NHS; SC; Var C; Cpt, Bkbl; Cpt, Tnns; Cpt, Tnns; FCA Huddle; Eastern Ill U; Bus.

BARR, Judith Ann
Matoaca HS; Ettrick, VA (12-149) Bus Mgr, Ann; Drama; FBLA; FHA; Key C; NHS; Sch P; Span C; Thes; Var C; JV, Bkbl; Co-Cpt, Sftbl; WW; Va Commonwealth U; Acct.

BARR, Julie Elizabeth
Atlanta HS; Atlanta, TX (10%-200) Band; Ensm; FTA; NHS; A-Ed, Sch P; Secy, Jr Cl; Citz A; Q&S A; Yth Leg; Worthy Advisor, Rainbow Girls; Baylor U; Early Childhood Ed.

BARR, Myrna Yvonne
John Marshall HS; Richmond, VA (111-206) Secy, Chor; Drama; Tri-HiY; Bsbl; Hockey; Bennett Col; Special Ed.

BARR, Nancy Janine
Bardstown HS; Bardstown, KY; Band; Chor; Ensm; Span C; Golf; Type A; Sch Rep, Quad St Chor; Ky Fed of Mus C; Jr Mus C; Sup, Piano Festival Ratings; Asst Pianist & Asst Organist, Chrch; Mus.

BARR, Robert Hiram II
Dewey HS; Dewey, OK (1-92) Band; Demolay; Bsbl; JV, Bkbl; Ftbl; WW; Yth Citz Seminar; Central St U; Mortuary Sci.

BARR, Timothy Allen
Lakewood Sr HS; Lakewood, CA (178-789) A Cap Choir; Chor; Drama; Hon Prog; U of Ariz; Aerospace Engr.

BARRA, Carol Ann
Hall HS; Spring Valley, IL (50%-130) Chldr; Drama; FTA; SC; Var C; Devilette; Ill Valley Comm Col; Occupational Therapy.

BARRAS, Ricky James
Catholic HS; New Iberia, LA; Co-Ch, CYO; K of C;
Key C; Cpt, Ftbl; Hon Prog; K of C A.

BARRAS, Sidney Norbert
Cecilia Sr HS; Cecilia, LA (5-150) BC; Fr C; Tres,
4H; Fin, Lit Ral; NFL; Sch P; Pres, Sci C; Spch C;
SC; Bsbl; Bkbl; Mgr, Ftbl; Tr; Bio A; COM; 4H A;
Hon Prog; Most Out; Sci A; Spch A; Ch, 4-H C;
Altar Boy; Regional & St Sci Fair; U of SW La;
Med.

BARRAZA, Ana Luisa
Hobbs HS; Hobbs, NM; VP, CYO; Chor; SC; Tr;
Co-Cpt, Vlbl; 1st Pl, Essay Winner; Sch Win, Spell-
ing Bee; NM Jr Col; Ath Coach.

BARRAZA, Celia Armida
Hobbs HS; Hobbs, NM (14-500) Secy, CYO; Chor;
FNA; GS; VP, NHS; SC; Alg A; Amer Leg A; Citz
A; Hist A; Math A; Sci A; Vlbl; JA; Eng A; U of
NM; Med.

BARRELL, Cheryl Anne
Hammond HS; Hammond, IN (3-282) Band;
Drama; French NHS; Spch C; God & Country A;
NEDT; Yth Fel; NJHS; Reg Win; Ntl Fr Contest;
Ind U; Med.

BARRENTINE, Patricia Anne
Zephyrhills HS; Zephyrhills, FL (12-230) Band;
CYO; Drama; Bus Mgr, NHS; Sch P; SC; Rep,
Parish Coun; U of S Fla; Ed.

BARRERA, Catherine Jo
Northview HS; Covina, CA (355-475) AFS; Span
C; Kiwanis A; Los Angeles Trade-Tech Col; Mer-
chandise Display.

BARRERAS,
Therese Michele Mary
Chinle HS; Chinle, AZ (1-130) Band; CYO; Chldr;
Dbte Tm; Drama; FHA; Ch, Model UN; VP, NHS;
VP, Ski C; Pres, Span C; VP, SC; Thes; VP, Jr Cl;
JV, Swim; 1st Pl, Arch; 1st Pl, Poetry; Ariz St U.

BARRETO, Marcelino
Francisco Mendoza HS; Isabela, PR; Band; Mus A;
IAU; Mus.

BARRETT, Belinda
Lexington Sr HS; Lexington, NC; Winston Salem
St Col; Bus.

BARRETT, Betty Lynn
Checotah HS; Checotah, OK (3-77) VP, Band;
FHA; NHS; SC; St Hon Soc; Connors St Col;
Home Ec.

BARRETT, Bonnie Marie
Cottage Grove HS; Cottage Grove, OR (3-280)
Chor; Drama; NHS; Thes; Bio A; Home Ec A;
Seattle Pacific U; Elem Ed.

BARRETT, Christie Lea
Williamson HS; Williamson, WV (16-154) GS;
NHS; Phys C; Type A; Sou W Va Comm Col;
Math.

BARRETT, Darrell Andrew
Dothan HS; Dothan, AL; Ftbl; Gordy Hardy Mem
A.

BARRETT, David Dean
Kings Mountain Sr HS; Kings Mountain, NC;
Band; Demolay; Tr; Appalachian St U; Art.

BARRETT, Deborah Elaine
Concord HS; Concord, NC (8-210) Fr C; Math C;
NHS; Sci C; Shorthand A; Appalachain St Col;
Computer Sci.

BARRETT, Debra Ann
Princeton HS; Princeton, WV (79-315) Drama;
Hmrm; Ch, InterAct C; Jr Miss Pagent; SP; SC;
Redemption Singers; Keywanettes; Cripple Chil-
dren's Coun; Mus A; Pep C; Pres Phys Fitness A;
Su-Wams; Fairmont St Col; Phys Therapy.

BARRETT, Donna Lynn
Robert Wood Johnson HS; Gainesville, GA; Band;
BC; Crown & Scepter; Pres, FNA; Hmrm; Hall Sch
of Nurs; Nurs.

BARRETT, Peter Leroy
Campbell HS; Campbell, CA (150-300) A Cap
Choir; Chess C; Chor; Drama; Order/Arrow; Sci C;
Soccer; COM; JA A; Order/Arrow A; Pres A; U of
Wash; Drama.

BARRETT, Robert Mason
James H Hammond Acad; Columbia, SC (25-106)
Band; InterAct C; Mgr, Bkbl; Golf; Citz A; Hon
Prog; Sci A; Civics A; Schol A; Wofford Col.

BARRETT, Robin Anne
Checotah HS; Checotah, OK (16-124) Ann; Band;
FHA; Secy, NHS; SC; Rifle Tm; Connors St Col;
Bus.

BARRICK, Anne Stewart
Joppatowne Jr-Sr HS; Joppatowne, MD (50-254)
AFS; Fr C; FTA; Hmrm; SC; Pres, Soph Cl; JV,
Hockey; Opt Out Tm; Yth Fel; 1st Cl, GSct; La-
Crosse; Coun Del; Coun Prog Comm; JV, Field
Hockey; Pol Sci.

BARRICK, Judy S
Emmanuel Baptist HS; Toledo, OH; Band; Chldr;
Chor; Ensm; Sch P; Tenn Temple Col; Home Ec.

BARRIE, Karol Ann
Doland HS; Doland, SD (27-34) Ann; Chor;
Drama; Fr C; FHA; Mjrte; NFL; Sch P; Sftbl; St
Gym Champ, Uneven Bars; N St Col; Phys Ed.

BARRINGER, Andra Lorraine
Sweet Home HS; Sweet Home, OR; Band; S-T,
FTA; Hmrm; SC; Bkbl; Swim; Tnns; Contra Costa
Col; Med.

BARRINGER, Brent David
Salisbury HS; Salisbury, NC (29-239) AFS; Ch, BS;
Key C; NHS; Span C; Co-Ch, SC; Tres, Var C; Ftbl;
Tr; Fin, Wrest; Hon Prog; Jr Women's C A; U of
NC; Bus Adm.

BARRINGER, Lisa Ellen
Ada Sr HS; Ada, OK (25%-200) Chor; NHS; Span
C; Bkbl; Sftbl; Tnns; Masonic A; MLS; Pres A;
Rotary A; Secy, Drill Tm; Tanti Stu C; Most Tal-
ented; E Central U; Nurs.

BARRIOS, Barry Gilbert
E Chambers HS; Winnie, TX (18-80) Band; BS;
Drama; Fin, Ensm; Rptr, NFL; Spch C; Citz A; Cl
Fav; Hon Prog; Masque & Gavel A; Most Out;
Spch A; 1IL Band A; NFL Rptr.

BARRIOS, Jaime
Dra Maria Cadilla HS; Arecibo, PR (21-429) Bus
C; Commercial C; Dbte Tm; FBLA; VP, Hmrm;
Bsbl; Bkbl; Sftbl; Swim; Cpt, Tr; Hist A; Math A;
Sci A; Tr A; US Air Force Acad; Aeronautical
Engr.

BARRON, Ava LaJuan
Southwest HS; Fort Worth, TX; FHA.

BARRON, Kathryn Ann
Blairsville HS; Blairsville, PA (3-144) Band; Mjrte;
Beauty; HQn; Prom Qn; Co Band; Sch Yrbk; Cl
Couple; Health Professions; Pit Band; Vlbl; U of
Pittsburgh; Nurs.

BARRON, Pamela Jean
James F Byrnes HS; Duncan, SC (53-261) BC; Bus
C; Chor; FBLA; FHA; Lat C; Bkbl; Sftbl; Hon A.

BARRON, Sarah Jane
Spring Branch HS; Houston, TX (5%-575) Chor; Fr
C; JETS; Secy, Mjrte; Math C; Mu Alpha Theta;
NHS; COM; NEDT; Yth Fel; 1st Cl GSct; Tex
A&M U; Engr.

BARRON, Sue Annette
S Point HS; Belmont, NC; BC; Bus C; FBLA; FHA;
InterAct C; InterClub Coun.

BARRON, Vicki Lynn
Obion Co Central HS; Troy, TN (8-185) BC;
Hmrm; NHS; Span C; SC; Rptr, Jr Cl; Pep C; U of
Tenn; Sci.

BARROSO, Elvira
Academia Sagrado Corazon; Santurce, PR (8-92)
Drama; Ch, Hmrm; ARC; SC; Alg A; Bio A; Hon
Prog.

BARROW, Clayton Wayne
Hot Springs HS; Truth Or Consequences, NM
(3-130) Ed, Ann; Pres, Chess C; NHS; Spch C;
Rptr, SC; JV, Bkbl; JV, Ftbl; Golf; Journ A; MLS;
Regent Schol; Spch A; VofDEM; NM St U; Engr.

BARROW, Gwen Sally
S Broward HS; Hollywood, FL; Arch; Chess C;
Chor; FBLA; FHA; NHS; JV, Arch; Ftbl; Hon
Prog; Type A; St Win, Fed of Mus C; Broward
Comm Col; Acct.

BARROW, Jo Ann
Crestview Sr HS; Crestview, FL (15-247) Ed, Ann;
Drama; Pres, Fr C; FTA; U of S Ala; Psych.

BARROW, Jo Anna
Patterson HS; Patterson, LA (15-90) Band; Secy,
BC; Bus Mgr, CYO; Chldr; Ensm; FBLA; Secy,
FHA; 4H; Hmrm; Mjrte; Sch P; Secy, SC; Tnns;
COM; Quad-Hi; Vlbl; Mus A's; LSU; Gov.

BARROW, Kim Jo
River Forest HS; Hobart, IN (30-190).

BARROWS, Victoria Ann
Fernandina Beach HS; Fernandina Beach, FL
(18-217) Chor; Madrigal; WW; Fla St Col; Drama.

BARROWS, Wendy L
Chillicothe HS; Chillicothe, OH; A Cap Choir;
Chor; Secy, Fr C; NHS; Thes; Alt, GS; Art.

BARRY, Escoamed Amanda
Northeastern Acad; New York, NY (10%-50) A
Cap Choir; All Amer Yth; Bus C; Chor; Ensm; Pres,
GS; Math C; Rptr, Ntl Yth Conf; Sci C; VP, SC;
Bkbl; Hockey; MLS; Yth Fel; Yth Leg; Sportsman-
ship A; Oakwood Col; Med.

BARRY, Kay Lynn
Robert E Lee HS; Tyler, TX (180-650) Chem C;
FHA; Drill Tm; TCU.

BARRY, MeLanie Ayden Louise
Smithfield-Selma Sr HS; Smithfield, NC (20-400)
Ann; Band; Chor; Fr C; 4H; Hmrm; NHS; Pol Sci
C; Tres, Jr Cl; U of NC; Child Psych.

BARSCH, Paula Elaine
New Branfels Sr HS; New Braunfels, TX (60-315)
Home Ec A; Walther Lge; Dist Spell; VP, Cross
Lutheran Church; Most Punctual, Royal Bluettes;
VOE-OEA; Sunday Sch Teacher; Kans Wesleyan
Col; Parish Worker.

BARSTOW, Annette Karen
Post Falls HS; Post Falls, ID (6-155) Ann; Drama;
VP, FHA; Sch P; Spch C; Hon Prog; Spch A; N
Idaho Col; Ed.

BARTEL, Gary Warren
Laura Speed Elliott HS; Boonville, MO (5-130)
Chor; NHS; Regent Schol; RF Blankenbaker Mem
Schol; VICA Contest A's; U of Mo; Elec Engr.

BARTEL, Nancy Kay
Herbert Hoover HS; Glendale, CA; Lat C; Secy,
ARC; Jr HS Schol; Top Service A; Nurs.

BARTEL, Scott Bradely
Metamora Twp HS; Metamora, IL (40-250) Ger C;
NHS; VP, SC; Bkbl; Co-Cpt, Ftbl; Tr; Bus.

BARTELS, Cindy Sue
John F Kennedy HS; Bloomington, MN; A Cap
Choir; Chor; Drama; Ger C; Madrigal; Spch C; St
Cloud St Col; Performing Arts.

BARTELS, Mary Lisa
Chadron HS; Chadron, NE (11-81) Band; Dbte
Tm; Drama; Pres, FHA; GS; 4H; NHS; Ntl Yth
Conf; Tres, Span C; Secy, SC; 4H A; Hon Prog; I
Dare You; Kiwanis A; Masonic A; VofDEM;
Chadron St Col; Special Ed.

BARTELS, Rita Jo
Lincoln Ne HS; Lincoln, NE (20-501) A Cap
Choir; Band; Chor; Pres, 4H; SC; Hon Prog; Alt,
Regent's Schol; Concordia Teacher's Col; Special
Ed.

BARTELS, Susan Rae
Chadron HS; Chadron, NE; Band; FHA; 4H; SC;
S-T, Pep C; Drill Tm; Job's Daughters Marshall;
Chadron St Col; Elem Ed.

BARTELS, Timothy John
Jasper HS; Jasper, MN (29-44) Chor; Ensm; FFA;
Var C; Bsbl; Bkbl.

BARTENFELDER, Karen Marie
Elk Grove HS; Elk Grove Village, IL (67-572)
Dbte Tm; Ger C; NFL; NHS; Span C; St Scholar;
VofDEM; Yth Fel; Augustana Col; Med Tech.

BARTER, Sandy Jeanne
Tustin HS; Tustin, CA; Citz A; VofDEM; Mus
Achv; Cal St U; Acct.

BARTFAI, Robert Francis
Notre Dame-Bishop Gibbons HS; Schenectady,
NY (5-160) Tres, CYO; NHS; Rptr, Sch P; Tr;
Journ A; NEDT; Regent Schol; Purdue U; Com-
puter Sci.

BARTH, Anne Marie
James Madison HS; Vienna, VA (80-500) Chor; Drama; NHS; Orch; Pres Clroom, Young Amer; Yth Fitness Achv A; *William and Mary Col; Bio.*

BARTH, Carolyn Martha
McCluer N HS; Florissant, MO (94-760) A Cap Choir; Ensm; Madrigal; NHS; Tnns; Mgr, Wrest; Regent Schol; *NMSU; Med Tech.*

BARTH, Cheryl Joyce
Hughson Union HS; Hughson, CA; Secy, Bus C; Chldr; FHA; Tres, 4H; Ski C; Tres, SC; Swim; CSF; Cl Fav; Bkbl Stat; GAA; *BYU; Secretarial.*

BARTHEL, Kimberly Jean
Franklin HS; Franklin, TN; Bus C; Fr C; 4H; Span C; *Bus.*

BARTHEL, Marguerite Ann
Immaculata HS; Chicago, IL (9-149) Co-Cpt, Chldr; Ger C; Lit Mag; Tres, NHS; F-Ed, Sch P; Bkbl; Fin, Tr; COM; Hon Prog; Journ A; *Loyola U; Nurs.*

BARTHOL, Michael Edward
Melrose HS; Memphis, TN (3-370) Mu Alpha Theta; NHS; Bsbl; Schol; *Southwestern at Memphis; Math.*

BARTHOLOMEW, Carol Ann
Nogales HS; Nogales, AZ; Band; Tres, Chor; Rainbow; *N Ariz U; Mus.*

BARTHOLOMEW, Nancy Elaine
Indian Hill HS; Cincinnati, OH (93-300) Chor; Drama; Yth Fel; *U of Cincinnati; Special Ed.*

BARTIE, Byron Corbett
Fremont HS; Oakland, CA (10-305) VP, SC; COM; Citz A; JA A; Black Belt, Karate; *Bell & Howell Col; Elec.*

BARTLE, Dianna Kae
Amer Christian Acad; Pomona, CA (2-21) Chldr; Chor; HiY; Spch C; SC; Rptr, Soph Cl; Hon Prog; Spch A; *Bob Jones U; Mus.*

BARTLETT, Angela Gay
Hirsch HS; Wichita Falls, TX; A Cap Choir; FTA; Madrigal; JV, Bkbl; Sftbl; Tr; *Arlington Baptist Col.*

BARTLETT, David Lee
Cherryville HS; Cherryville, NC (38-143) Chem C; FTA; Math C; Monogram; Sci C; Tr; HCt; *Cleveland Tech Col; Body & Fender.*

BARTLETT, Elizabeth Anne
Walnut HS; Walnut, MS (6-60) BC; Chor; FHA; *NE Jr Col.*

BARTLETT, Ernest Ancin III
Southside HS; Fort Smith, AR (33%-500) Tnns; Young Life; *Tulane U; Law Sch.*

BARTLETT, James Wade
Ripley HS; Ripley, WV (75-250) VICA A; 1st St Fair, Drawing; *W Va Tech Col; Drafting.*

BARTLETT, Janice Carol
Marysville-Pilchuck HS; Marysville, WA; VP, Chor; Ensm; FBLA; Hmrm; NHS; Pres, Rainbow; Span C; Masonic A; *ECC; Secy.*

BARTLETT, Kimberly Frances
Windsor HS; Windsor, VT (10-90) Chor; Fr C; VP, FBLA; Pres, 4H; Madrigal; Mjrte; VP, S-T, 4 H C; *Bay Path Jr Col; Legal Secy.*

BARTLETT, LaDonna LuAnn
T Wingate Andrews HS; High Point, NC (14-330) Co-Ch, BC; Hmrm; Lit Mag; Monogram; Sci C; SC; Mgr, Bkbl; Sftbl; Hon Prog; Mgr, Vlbl; WW; Pres, Tres, Yth Fel; Civitan Schol; Top 32, Sr Cl; Outst Span Stu; *W Carolina U; Med Tech.*

BARTLETT, Mark Layne
Temple Christian HS; Redford, MI (12-80) A Cap Choir; Bus C; Pres, Ensm; Ed, Sch P; SC; Bsbl; Bkbl; Cpt, Soccer; Sftbl; Fin, Tr; COM; Citz A; Journ A; Yth Leg; MVP, Soccer; Mus A's; *Bob Jones U; Humanities.*

BARTLETT, Rene Dawn
Apple Valley Sr HS; Apple Valley, MN; Tr; Art Asst.

BARTLETT, Sherry Elizabeth
Muncy HS; Muncy, PA (25%-96) Chldr; Tres, Fr C; NHS; *Elem Ed.*

BARTLETT, Steve Bomar
Battle Ground Acad; Franklin, TN (5-98) Lat C; Ftbl; NEDT; Spch A; FCA.

BARTLETT, Sue Ellen
Belton HS; Belton, TX (5-200) Ann; Band; NHS; Mascot; Ftbl Swtht; Outst Soph; *Baylor U; Bus.*

BARTLETT, Susan Jane
Monroe Co HS; Monroeville, AL (3-105) Bus Mgr, Ann; Band; Pres, BC; Chor; Ensm; Jr Miss Pagent; Math A; Sci A; Star Student; *Auburn U; Bio.*

BARTLETT, William Wilson
Willington Acad; Orangeburg, SC (15-30) Key C; Order/Arrow; Secy, Var C; Bsbl; Bkbl; Ftbl; Tnns; Cpt, Tr; HCt; Most Wittiest; Qn of Hearts; *Orangeburg-Calhoun Tech Col; Mech Engr.*

BARTLEY, Brian Jay
Warren Central HS; Indianapolis, IN (63-812) Key C; NHS; Co-Cpt, Golf; Yth Fel; *Ind Central U; Sociology.*

BARTLEY, Charles Cope
Ash Fork HS; Ash Fork, AZ (2-10) VP, Sr Cl; Bsbl; Ariz St Medallion of Merit Schol; *Ariz St U; Engr.*

BARTLEY, Joseph Hubert
Lanphier Edison Complex HS; Springfield, IL; ARC; Cr-Crtry; Order/Arrow A; ARC A; *Lincoln Land Comm Col; Plumbing & Elec.*

BARTLEY, Mae Katherine
Berkeley HS; Moncks Corner, SC (25-341) Ann; BC; FHA; Pres, FTA; Lit Mag; Span C; Bkbl; *U of SC; Broadcasting Journ.*

BARTLEY, Nancy Elizabeth
Lanphier HS; Springfield, IL; ARC; Tr; ARC A; *Lincoln Land Comm Col; Nurs.*

BARTMAN, Julie Ann
Bellflower HS; Bellflower, CA (78-400) Chor; Ensm; Hmrm; SC; *Azuza Pacific Col; Phys Therapy.*

BARTNICKI, Penny Lynn
Permian HS; Odessa, TX (45-668) A Cap Choir; Co-Ed, Ann; Ensm; Jr Miss Pagent; NHS; VP, Span C; Span NHS; Pres, Tri-HiY; Lion A; Pres, Q & S; Hist & Lib, A Cappella Choir; All Region Choir; WW; Span Stu; *Tex A&M U; Wildlife Conservation.*

BARTOL, Richard David
Cedar Cliff HS; Camp Hill, PA; Band; Ensm; VP, Hmrm; Orch; *Lancaster Bible Col; Pastoral Studies.*

BARTOLETT, Deborah Louise
N Penn HS; Lansdale, PA (8-800) Band; Chor; Drama; Hmrm; Madrigal; NHS; Orch; SC; COM; Hon Prog; Yth Fel; NML; Dist, Regional, Bands; WW; *Psych.*

BARTOLETT, Scott Malcolm
N Penn HS; Lansdale, PA; Band; Ensm; Math C; Soccer; Yth Fel; *Math.*

BARTON, Alden Lynn
Southeast HS; Wichita, KS; Chor; Ensm; Bsbl; Bkbl; Sftbl; HR; *Kans Wesleyan Col; Auto Mech.*

BARTON, Alvin Lee
Southeast HS; Wichita, KS; Chor; Bsbl; Bkbl; Sftbl; *Kans Wesleyan Col; Auto Mech.*

BARTON, Celeste Dawn
Oscoda Area HS; Oscoda, MI (23-250) Crown & Scepter; Poet A; Coop Work, Dentist; Leader, GA'S; *Alpena Comm Col; Secy.*

BARTON, Deborah Gaye
High Point Sr HS; Beltsville, MD; Chor; Pres, 4H; Swim; 4H A; *U of Md; Home Ec.*

BARTON, John Thomas
Starkville HS; Starkville, MS; BS; City Conf; Parl, Key C; VP, NHS; Pres, Span C; Pres, SC; Var C; Ftbl; Cl Fav; Hist A; Sr Cl Speaker; FCA; Boy o-t Mo; *Miss St U; Banking & Finance.*

BARTON, Linda Joyce
Llano HS; Llano, TX (50%-77) Ed, Ann; Chor; FHA; FTA; Secy, SC; Poet A; UIL One Act Play; WW; Nom, HQn; Jr Cl Play; *SW Tex St U; Phys Therapy.*

BARTON, Maurice Lamar
T R Miller HS; Brewton, AL (25-95) VP, Sci C; Bkbl; Tnns; *Jefferson Davis Jr Col.*

BARTON, Robin Renee
Mena HS; Mena, AR (8-147) Band; Sci C; *Sci.*

BARTON, Tamara Jo
Jonathan Alder HS; Plain City, OH (9-111) Band; Drama; FTA; 4H; Cpt, Mjrte; NHS; Sch Achieve Tm; VP, Span C; Y-Tns; VP, Sr Cl; Amer Leg A; WW; 1st Runnerup, FBLA Qn; *General Motor Inst; Bus.*

BARTON, Timothy Lee
Page HS; Page, AZ (11-120) Chess C; Chor; Sci C; Alg A; Math A; PA; *Ariz St U; Engr.*

BARTOSZ, Theresa Rose
Sacred Heart Acad; Salem, OR (2-48) F-Ed, Ann; Chem C; Fr C; VP, Hmrm; NHS; F-Ed, Sch P; VP, SC; Alg A; COM; Citz A; Elk A; Hon Prog; Pres A; Rotary A; Spch A; Star Student; Yth Foundation; *Santa Clara Col; Psych.*

BARTZ, Renee Janell
University Prep HS; Mineral Ridge, OH; Chldr; Chor; Sch P; Bsbl; Bkbl; Sftbl; Vlbl.

BARTZ, Stephen James
Iroquois Central HS; Elms, NY (10-350) NHS; Cr-Ctry; Bausch & Lomb A; COM; Hon Prog; Lion A; NMF; NMS; Ntl Sci Found; Regent Schol; Eagle Progress A, BSA; *SUNY at Buffalo; Engr.*

BARWICK, Cynthia Jane
The Danes Sch; New Bern, NC (1-5) Ann; Chem C; Chor; Lat C; Rainbow; Sch P; Mgr, Sftbl; Swim; COM; Yth Fel; MVP, Sftbl; Demolay Swtht; Rainbow A; Outst Stu o-t Yr; *Campbell Col; Sci.*

BARWICK, James Douglas
Wilcox HS; Rochelle, GA (8-116) BC; Chem C; Lit Ral; Math C; Sch P; Sci C; Span C; COM; Hon Prog; Span A; *Middle Ga Col; Biol.*

BASDEN, Debra Lynn
Pleasant Grove HS; Pleasant Grove, AL (7-150) Chem C; NHS; *U of Montevallo; Spch Pathology.*

BASDEN, Susan Denise
Pleasant Grove HS; Pleasant Grove, AL (3-145) Band; NHS; Span C; *U of Montevallo.*

BASKELAND, Wendy Lou
Holstein HS; Holstein, IA (22-65) Ann; Band; Cpt, Chldr; Chor; GS; Sch P; SC; Band A; Pep C A; Chldr A; *Ellsworth Col; Secretarial.*

BASKERVILLE, Donald Lloyd
Humboldt HS; Humboldt, TN; Chor; Bkbl; Phys Ed A; Stu o-t Yr; *St Vo-tech Bus Sch; Bus.*

BASKIN, Carol Lynn
Rio Mesa HS; Oxnard, CA (10-362) Pres, SC; Pres, Jr Cl; Pres, Soph Cl; VP, Swim; Tr; Jr Chamber of Com A; ARC A; Swtht.

BASKIN, James Mark
Craigmont HS; Memphis, TN (10-285) BS; Inter-Club Coun; Pres, Lat C; Mu Alpha Theta; Parl, NHS; Pres, SC; Bsbl; Bkbl; Soccer; Alg A; Amer Leg A; Bio A; Chem A; Sci A; 2nd BS; Archery; Church Bkbl and Bsbl; *Med.*

BASKIN, Marie Annette
Rio Mesa HS; Oxnard, CA (5-301) Pres, Chor; Cpt, FBLA; Cpt, Ntl Yth Conf; Secy; SC; VP, Sr Cl; Pres, Jr Cl; Co-Cpt, Bsbl; Semi-Fin, Swim; Jr Chamber of Com A; MLS; HR; Mus A; *Pepperdine U.*

BASL, Danette Susan
Regis HS; Stayton, OR (4-60) Chem C; Chor; Drama; 4H; Bkbl; DARGCA; Hon Prog; Sacristan; Sci A; Spch A.

BASS, Antoine Arnold
Crenshaw HS; Los Angeles, CA; *South West Col.*

BASS, Brenda Nell
New Brockton HS; New Brockton, AL (5%-50) F-Ed, Ann; Secy, BC; Drama; FBLA; FHA; Sci C; Spch C; SC; Beauty; HCt; *Enterprise St Jr Col.*

BASS, Debbie Ann
Valentine HS; Valentine, NE (5-78) Ann; Band; Cpt, Chldr; Chor; Drama; FHA; FTA; Pres, 4H; Co-Cpt, Mjrte; Sch P; Var C; Tr; Beauty; Bio A; 4H A; HCt; Masonic A; Sci A; Spch A; Yth Fel; Vlbl; Job's Daughters; *Fashion Merchandising.*

BASS, Deborah Ann
Valentine HS; Valentine, NE; Ann; Band; Cpt, Chldr; Chor; Drama; FHA; FTA; Pres, 4H; Co-Cpt, Mjrte; Sch P; Var C; Tr; Beauty; Bio A; 4H A; Hon Prog; Masonic A; Sci A; Spch A; Yth Fel; Hon Qn, Job's Daughters; Vlbl; Cand, Coronation; Fashion Merchandising.

BASS, Debra Lynn
Cape Fear HS; Fayetteville, NC (13-365) BC; Span C; DARGCA; Span A; HR; Scholastic Excellence; Campbell Col; Elem Ed.

BASS, Judi Ann
John W Hallahan HS; Philadelphia, PA (146-404) Ch, CYO; Sodality; Mgr, Sftbl; La Salle U; Theology.

BASS, Ronda Kay
W Mecklenburg HS; Charlotte, NC; 4H; InterAct C; NHS; Sftbl; COM; 4H A; Fla Intl U; Air Travel.

BASS, Sara Adrena
Central HS; Muncie, IN; Band; Cpt, Bkbl; Cpt, Tr; JA A; Sch Service A; 'V' Ltr; Home Ec.

BASS, Terry Lynn
Muskogee HS; Muskogee, OK (10%-45) Band; Math C; Ski C; Swim; God A Country A; Mus As; Jazz Band; Stage Band; Symph A Orch; Johnson Bible Col; Math.

BASS, William Bretford
Sanderson HS; Raleigh, NC (190-580) Ger C; Order/Arrow; ARC; Wrest; Yth Fel; Moderator, Yth Cabinet; 1st Pl, Ntl Math Exam; St Andrew's Presbyterian Col; Pre-Med.

BASSETT, Alice Kay
Morton Jr-Sr HS; Morton, WA (3-48) NHS.

BASSETT, Douglas Gene
Calvary Christian Acad; Midland, MI; Band; Chor; Soccer; Faith Baptist Bible Col; Bible.

BASSETT, John Leonard
Burnsville Sr HS; Burnsville, MN (180-765) Band; Ed, Lit Mag; Span C; Engr.

BASSETT, Kurt Donn
Wilmot HS; Wilmot, SD (1-29) Band; BS; Chor; VP, FFA; Secy, 4H; NHS; Pres, SC; Pres, Var C; Pres, Jr Cl; Mgr, Ftbl; Cpt, Tr; Amer Leg A; DARGCA; 4H A; NMS; Star Student; MVP, Tr; SD St U; Agronomy.

BASSETT, Thomas Edward
Norfolk Cath HS; Norfolk, VA (10%-156) Bus C; CYO; Chor; Dbte Tm; Amer Leg A; Amer Leg Orator A; JA A; Opt A; Spch A; U of Tex; Drama.

BASSETT, Yolanda Faye
Pershing HS; Detroit, MI; FNA; Hon Prog; Med C; Wayne St U; Med.

BASSO, Diana Joan
Interlochen Arts Acad; Interlochen, MI (5-165) A Cap Choir; Band; Chor; Tres, Drama; Math C; Orch; Tres, Span C; SC; Arch; COM; Hon Prog; Badminton; Schol, Interlochen; Win, Concerto; Solo Sr Recital; Hon Hall Resident; Eastman Sch of Mus; Applied Mus.

BAST, Kenneth Lyman
Shenendehowa HS; Clifton Park, NY (5%-685) Key C; NHS; Order/Arrow; Var C; JV, Soccer; Co-Cpt, Wrest; Hon Prog; Order/Arrow A; Yth Fel; Eagle Sct; Bus Adm.

BASTA, Erin Lynn
Skyline HS; Salt Lake City, UT; S-T, Ger C; NHS; Hon Prog; Wings Service C; Outst Candystriper A; U of Utah; Bus.

BASTA, Laura Lee
Hinsdale Township HS; Hinsdale, IL (82%-600) A Cap Choir; Span C; Var C; Hon Prog; Duke U; Lib Arts.

BASTARACHE, Helene
College De Sainte-Anne; La Pocatiere, CANADA (2-29) CYO; Spch A; Vlbl; U Laval; Mus.

BASTIN, Deana Marie
Burnside HS; Burnside, KY (1-70) BC; Alg A; Soph o-t Yr.

BATAILLON, Marie Terese
Lourdes HS; Nebraska City, NE (4-29) Band; Chor; Tres, Math C; Span C; SC; Tr; Vlbl; U of Nebr; Sociology.

BATALIAN, Raffi
Watertown HS; Watertown, MA; Drama; Orch; Library A; Gold Medal Art A; Motion Pictures.

BATCHELOR, Ann Marie
Milford HS; Milford, MI (30-385) Drama; NHS; Span C; JV, Tnns; Hon Prog; Ferris St Col; Bus.

BATEASTE, Ronald Renard
Amite Co Attendance Ctr; Gloster, MS (6-40) BC; Tres, FFA; Secy, Lit Mag; Secy, SC; Rptr, Sr Cl; Ftbl; COM; Citz A; Type A; Southwest Jr Col; Acct.

BATEMAN, Janeen Theresa
Rosary Acad; Sparkill, NY (1-70) Ed, Ann; NHS; Secy, SC; NEDT; Notre Dame Col; Hist.

BATEMAN, Linda Jean
Parsippany Christian HS; Parsippany, NJ; Secy, Band; Chor; Sch P; SC; 'A' Avg, Safety Patrol, A's; Lib, SC, Reading, A's; NE Bible Col; Mus.

BATEMAN, Monte Gene
Yukon HS; Yukon, OK (50-386) Band; Chess C; Sci C; Eagle Sct; Air Force Acad.

BATEMAN, Ronald Scott
Starkville HS; Starkville, MS; Chem C; Bsbl; Ftbl; Miss St U; Bus.

BATEMAN, Terri Lynne
Nanih Waiya HS; Louisville, MS (10-33) F-Ed, Ann; Ensm; FHA; Var C; Bkbl; Miss St U; Banking.

BATEMAN, Willie Dallas Jr
Amite Co Attendance Center; Gloster, MS; FFA; USM; Elec.

BATES, Ava Leann
Fountain Lake HS; Hot Springs, AR; BC; FHA; Bkbl; COM; Citz A; DARGCA; Ark HS Rodeo Assn; Champion Govt Tyer; Champion, Break Away Roper; Ark St U-Bebee.

BATES, Belinda Faye
Continued Education Project; St Louis, MO (10-46).

BATES, Christopher Paul
Adrian HS; Adrian, MI; A Cap Choir; Chor; Sci C; Ski C; JV, Bsbl; W Mich Col; Mus.

BATES, Clyde
Chicago Voc HS; Chicago, IL; Cr-Ctry; Ftbl; Sftbl; JV, Tr; Cl Offices; Grambling Col; Machine Drafting.

BATES, Davis
Lake Clifton HS; Baltimore, MD (10%-250) Chor; NHS; SC; Tr; Radio C; Northeastern U; Pol Sci.

BATES, Dean Allan
Central HS; San Angelo, TX (50-800) Band; Fin, Ensm; Order/Arrow; Ftbl; Tex A&M U; Engr.

BATES, Elizabeth A
Redlands Sr HS; Redlands, CA (10%-850) Chor; Dbte Tm; Drama; Ensm; Madrigal; Ch, Model UN; Co-Ed, Sch P; Amer Leg A; COM; Hon Prog; Journ A; NMS; Vocal Schol; Most Valuable, Madrigal; Soroptomist's A; Hon Girls; Wayland Baptist Col; Vocal Mus.

BATES, Freddie Lee
Sumner HS; St Louis, MO (8-400) Chess C; NHS; Tres, Sr Cl; Hon Prog; Forest Park Col; Bus Adm.

BATES, Janet Lynn
Decatur HS; Decatur, AL (68-295) Chor; Ensm; FBLA; Hmrm; Lat C; NHS; Pres A; Girls Sextet; Vlbl; WW; Ala All-St Chor; U of Ala; Music.

BATES, Janet Marie
Amador Valley HS; Pleasanton, CA (33%-400) Chldr; Hmrm; SC; Soccer.

BATES, Laurel Kay
Wyanet Comm HS; Wyanet, IL (4-25) Secy, Band; Cpt, Chldr; Ensm; NHS; Thes; 4 H A; Spch A.

BATES, Linda Kay
Second Ward HS; Gloster, LA (3-35) Scholastic Achievement; PA; Lib A; Sou U; Eng.

BATES, Lisa Dawn
Warren Central HS; Indianapolis, IN (170-968) Chor; Sci C; SC; Med Explorers; Hospital Auxilary; WW; Patriotism, Drama, A's; Solo-Ensm; Med.

BATES, Lorrin Guy
Iroquois Central HS; Elma, NY (150-360) Band; JV, Bkbl; JV, Ftbl; NYSSMA Solo A; Pres, Church Yth Group; Yth Congress; Hi-Cth, Tres, Westrn NY Conf Yth Co.

BATES, Marcus Wayne
Prairiland HS; Pattonville, TX (12-80) Parl, FFA; FTA; Bsbl; Cpt, Ftbl; Tr; Greenhand, Chapter Farmer, FFA; Colo Stu; Phys Ed.

BATES, Matthew David
Ardmore HS; Ardmore, OK (7-285) Band; NHS; Bkbl; Bio A; Rotary A; Eng, Band, A's; Oral Roberts U; Pre-Med.

BATES, Patrice Elaine
Menlo Atherton HS; Atherton, CA (8-32) Cpt, Chldr; Chor; FBLA; FTA; Ntl Teachers Coun; Rptr, Sch P; Secy, Soph Cl; JV, Sftbl; MVP, Tr; Cl Fav; HCt; JA A; MLS; San Francisco St Col; Early Childhood Ed.

BATES, Paul Louis
Menlo-Atherton HS; Menlo-Atherton, CA; A Cap Choir; Band; Ntl Yth Conf; Ed, Sch P; Var C; H of F; Journ A; Kiwanis A; Lion A; Most Out; Cpt, MVP, Bsbl; Silver Seal A; Cpt, MVP, Ftbl; Comm Serv A; Cpt, MVP, Tr; Golden Key A; U of Colo; Bus.

BATES, Paulette Jean
Weedsport Central Sch; Weedsport, NY (2-120) S-T, Band; Pres, Chor; Ensm; Fr C; NHS; Ntl Yth Conf; Orch; Most Out; PTA A; Yth Fel.

BATES, Samuel Linley
McCluer North HS; Florissant, MO (122-788) Band; Pres, SC; Bkbl; Ftbl; MLS; Harding Col; Phar.

BATES, Todd Stuart
Southfield Christian Sch; Southfield, MI; Chor; Drama; Bsbl; Soccer; Yth Fel; U of Mich; Clergy.

BATES, Vanessa
Lindblom Tech HS; Chicago, IL (220-428) U of Ill; Bus Adm.

BATESON, Deborah Sue
Lakota HS; Kansas, OH (10-136) Chor; Ensm; NHS; Mount Vernon Nazarene Col; Bus.

BATH, Janet Kay
Big Valley Jr-Sr HS; Bieber, CA (2-26) 4H; Ski C; Spch C; Pres, SC; Cpt, Bkbl; Ftbl; Sftbl; Fin, Tr; CSF; Cl Fav; HQn; HCt; Type A; MVP, Bkbl; Vlbl; Eng A; Jr Prom Qn.

BATHKE, Barbara Alice
Port Washington HS; Port Washington, WI; Band; Chldr; Chor; Ensm; Orch; Sch P; Mus A; Alt Wisc HS Hon Band and Choir; Mus.

BATHKE, Brett Charles
Hartford Union HS; Hartford, WI; 4H; JV, Ftbl; Tnns; Colo St U; Architecture.

BATHKE, Todd Allen
Hartford Union HS; Hartford, WI; Drama; Hmrm; Cpt, Bsbl; Ftbl; Tnns; Tr; COM; Citz A; Cl Fav; I Dare You; Most Out; ARC A; Archt Drafting.

BATSON, Barry Clark
Morgan Park HS; Chicago, IL; All Amer Yth; Ch, Chor; Phys Achv A; Chicago St U; Eng.

BATSON, Cathy Ann
Brookhaven Acad; Brookhaven, MS; Band; Secy, BC; Cpt, Chldr; F-T, FHA; Math C; Rainbow; VP, Y-Tns; JV, Bkbl; B Crocker A; HCt; Miss Col; Art.

BATSON, Donald Kevin
Travelers Rest HS; Travelers Rest, SC (5-280) Chor; Ensm; Mod Mus Mas; NHS; SC; COM; Gov Honor Prog; Hon Prog; NMF; All St Chor; Furman U; Church Mus.

BATSON, Lori Anne
Lake Wales Sr HS; Lake Wales, FL; FHA; NHS; Polk Comm Col.

BATSON, Pamela Lynne
Aledo HS; Aledo, IL (10%-117) Pres, AFS; Band; VP, FNA; Secy, 4H; 4H A; NMS; Type A; Monmouth Col; Nurs.

BATT, Brian Christopher
Bishop Carroll HS; Wichita, KS (16-211) CYO; Var C; Bsbl; Ftbl; Tr; Hon Prog; St Scholar; Wichita St Col; Engr.

BATTAGLIA, John Joseph
St Joseph o-t Palisades HS; W New York, NJ (15-225) CYO; Bsbl; Soccer; COM; Hon Prog; NEDT; WW; Rutger's U; Microbio.

BATTEE, Sharon Denise
Summer HS; St Louis, MO; A Cap Choir; Chor; Mjrte; NHS; Beauty; God & Country A; MLS; Most Out; Ntl Achv Schol; ROTC A; Type A; Yth Fel; PA; *Airline Stewardess.*

BATTERTON, Denise Nanette
North Co R-I HS; Desloge, MO (22-246) Band; Cpt, Chldr; Chor; Drama; Fr C; FBLA; VP, FHA; Secy, FNA; 4H; Pres, Hmrm; NHS; Sch P; Rptr, Sci C; SC; Var C; Hon Prog; Pres A; FHA Swtht Qn; *U of Mo; Acct.*

BATTIE, Ringo E
Marshall Islands HS; Majuro, MARSHALL IS-LANDS (12-103) Hon Prog; *E Ariz Col; Pre-Law.*

BATTIGE, David Scott
Manistee HS; Manistee, MI (8-186) Tres, NHS; Stu Rep, Co United Fund; *Mich St U; Engr.*

BATTLE, Barbara Jean
Rocky Mount Sr HS; Rocky Mount, NC; Band; *A&T U; Mus.*

BATTLE, Dwight Samuel
John Hay HS; Cleveland, OH; Alg A; Bio A; COM; Citz A; Attitude A; Hon A; *Computer Programer.*

BATTLE, Joseph Matthew
Russell HS; Hurtsboro, AL (7-56) Chem C; Chor; Drama; VP, FFA; FTA; VP, 4H; Sch P; Up Bound; VP, Sr Cl; Tres, Jr Cl; Co-Cpt, Bsbl; Bkbl; MVP, Tr; Citz A; Elk A; Gov Honor Prog; 4H A; HKg; MLS; ROTC A; Spch A; Yth Fel; Yth Foundation; Yth Foundation A; Yth Leg; *Ala St U; Pol Sci.*

BATTLE, Lillie Belinda
Russell HS; Hurtsboro, AL; Drama; FHA; 4H; NHS; Sch P; Sci C; COM; Citz A; 4H A; Most Out; ROTC A; Swtht; *Ala A&M U; Math.*

BATTLE, Lisa Lynn
Mac Arthur HS; Irving, TX; FHA; Hmrm; SC; *U of Tex; Ed.*

BATTLE, Robbie Suzanne
Nacogdoches HS; Nacogdoches, TX (57-350) Ann; FHA; NHS; Co-Ed, Sch P; Journ A; Home-making A; *Stephen F Austin Col; Journ.*

BATTLE, Scott Lee
Nacogdoches HS; Nacogdoches, TX (7-286) NHS; COM; Hon Prog; Opt A; *Stephen F Austin St U; Engr.*

BATTLE, Sidney Thomas
Pacelli HS; Columbus, GA (58-85) Bethune-Cookman Col; Bus.

BATTLE, Wayne
Jackson HS; Jackson, GA; VP, Fr C; FFA; Bkbl; Ftbl.

BATTLES, Jerome
Rufus King HS; Milwaukee, WI; Bkbl; Ftbl; Tr; Sport As; *UWM; Hist.*

BATTLES, Shelley
Essex Co Voc Tech HS; Newark, NJ; Dbte Tm; Tr; COM; *Interior Decorator.*

BATTLESON, Carol Anne
Wallace HS; Wallace, ID (35-105) Ann; Bus C; Drama; Rainbow; Bkbl; Tr; Elks Roundup Pageant; Pres, Drill Tm; *Columbia Basin Col; Secretarial.*

BATTON, James Howard
Red Springs Sr HS; Red Springs, NC (3-120) Ann; *Archt.*

BATTS, Cheryl Lynn
Carver HS; Columbus, GA (25%-280) Band; *Co-lumbus Col.*

BATTS, Timothy Gay
E Ascension Acad; Gonzales, LA (1-21) Lit Ral; Spch C; Pres, SC; Pres, Sr Cl; Bsbl; Bkbl; MVP, Ftbl; Math A; Spch A; *SE La U; Law.*

BATTY, Heather Diane
Tehachapi HS; Tehachapi, CA (5-128) AFS; Secy, Rainbow; CSF; Elk A; Hon Prog; VFW A; Yth Fel; Tn o-t Yr; Rainbow Proficiency Cert; Piano Audi-tions; *Calif St Col; Phys Ther.*

BATZE, Lisa Marie
Riverdale Joint Union HS; Riverdale, CA (9-140) CYO; NHS; Sch Achieve Tm; Cpt, Swim; Cpt, Tnns; CSF; Citz A; Most Out; *Fresno City Col; Anatomy.*

BATZEL, Daniel Austin
Scranton Central HS; Scranton, PA (13%-500) Hmrm; Span C; SC; Wrest; COM; Hon Prog; Gifted Stu Prog; *Pre-Med.*

BAUCHER, Julye Lynn
Celina Sr HS; Celina, OH (1-275) A Cap Choir; Band; Chor; Pres, FBLA; FTA; Lat C; Tres, NHS; Rainbow; Cpt, Bkbl; JV, Tnns; Hon Prog; Val; Schol Tm; WW; 2nd St, Acct; GAA; GSct; Vlbl; *Findlay Col; Acct.*

BAUCOM, Susan Elizabeth
S Point HS; Belmont, NC; Band; PA.

BAUCUM, John Robert
Gaffney Sr HS; Gaffney, SC; Drama; Sci C; *U of SC; Phys Sci.*

BAUER, Carla Rebecca
Hanson Mem HS; Franklin, LA (6-60) Ann; Fin, Lit Ral; NHS; Bio A; Sci A; Bookkeeping A; Torch of Knowledge A; 1st, St Ral, 3rd Dist Ral, Book-keep.

BAUER, Darlene Hobbs
Lake Braddock Secondary HS; Burke, VA (70-650) French NHS; NHS; Ntl Fed of Mus Cs; *Interior Designer.*

BAUER, Deborah Jean
Ashley HS; Ashley, ND (33%-43) Band; Chldr; Chor; Tres, Drama; Fin, Ensm; Spch C; SC; Var C; Bkbl; Tr; Hon Prog; Star Student; Pres A Phys Fit-ness; Top Rating St Mus Competition; *ND St U; Med.*

BAUER, Elaine Marie
Neshaminy Langhorne HS; Langhorne, PA (100-688) Band; Chor; FNA; Rainbow; Concert Choir; Concert Band; WW Among Mus Stu in Amer HS; Scholastic A; *Elizabethtown Col; Mus Therapy.*

BAUER, Jane Alice
Little Wolf HS; Manawa, WI (23-78) Drama; Ed, Sch P; VP, Span C; SC; Secy, Soph Cl; Sftbl; HCt; Prom Ct; Forensics A; Sr Cl Play; *Stevens Point Col; Communications.*

BAUER, Keith Charles
Durand HS; Durand, WI (33-141) Order/Arrow; ARC; Var C; Bkbl; Ftbl; Tr; Eagle Sct; *U of Minn; Phar.*

BAUER, Kenneth Lee
Windom Area HS; Windom, MN (60-140) Chor; Ensm; Pres, 4H; Orch; Tnns; Wrest; 4H A; Supe-rior Rating, Orch & Choir; *Pillsbury Col; Art & Mus.*

BAUER, Matthew Harlan
Sooner HS; Bartlesville, OK (7-280) Co-Ed, Ann; BS; NHS; Secy, Order/Arrow; F-Ed, Sch P; Pres, Sci C; SC; Elk A; Hist A; ROTC A; NROTC Schol; Outst Sct, BSA; Okla Soc Profess Engr School; Phil-lips Petro Co Schol; *U of Okla; Mech Engr.*

BAUER, Nancy Elizabeth
Lenora HS; Lenora, KS (5-25) Band; Cpt, Chldr; NHS; MVP, Bkbl; MVP, Tr; HQn; MVP, Chldr; Cpt, Bkbl; *Colby Comm Col; Elem Ed.*

BAUER, Paul William
Bay HS; Bay Village, OH (8-371) Band; NHS; Swim; NML; *Tex Christian U.*

BAUER, Paula Carol
Grand Rapids HS; Grand Rapids, MN (70-402) A Cap Choir; Band; Chor; 4H; Madrigal; COM; 4H A; Yth Fel; *Itasca Comm Col; Optometric Asst.*

BAUER, Sheri Lynette
Durand HS; Durand, WI; Chor; Dbte Tm; Fr C; NFL; Pres, NHS; Pres, Sodality; Secy, Soph Cl; Bkbl; Tnns; HCt; Most Out; Spch A; Pope Pius XII A; Lutheran Home's School; *Viterbo Col; Nurs.*

BAUERNFEIND, John Walter
Ripon Sr HS; Ripon, WI (10-175) S-T, Ger C; Math C; Var C; Mgr, Bsbl; Mgr, Bkbl; COM; Math A; *U of Wisc; Phar.*

BAUERSFELD, Brooke Alison
El Camino Real HS; Woodland Hills, CA (170-1076) All Amer Yth; Chldr; Chor; Secy, Hmrm; Ski C; SC; VP, Sr Cl; CSF; HCt; Most Out; *Occidental Col; Bio.*

BAUGH, Cynthia King
Decatur HS; Decatur, AL (25%-300) Secy, Fr C; Hmrm; Mu Alpha Theta; SC; Var C; Secy, Jr Cl; Tnns; Swtht; WW; 2nd Pl, Fr Fair A; Pres, Jr Altar Guild.

BAUGH, Janet Louise
Litchfield Sr HS; Litchfield, IL (38-132) Chor; HCt; GAA; PA A; 300t C A; Friendliest; Swing Choir; 1st & 2nd St A, GAA; Sch Plays; Ftbl Statis-tician.

BAUGH, John Wesley
Fairfield HS; Fairfield, AL (25%-180) Ann; Band; Sch P; COM; Citz A; *Auburn U; Math.*

BAUGHMAN, Barbara Jean
Hightstown HS; Hightstown, NJ (56-253) FBLA; NHS; Bus Mgr, Sch P; Mgr, Cr-Ctry; Mgr, Tr; *New England Col; Foreign Lang.*

BAUGHMAN, Belinda Leann
Spruce Creek HS; Daytona Beach, FL; Chor; FHA; Bsbl Batgirl; Chor A; *Daytona Beach Col; Lib Arts.*

BAUGHMAN, Gail Ann
Modesto HS; Modesto, CA; Chldr; Fr C; Ntl Yth Conf; VP, Jr Cl; 4H A; Pres A; Gym; *Modesto Jr Col; Health Occupations.*

BAUGHMAN, Gary William
Modesto HS; Modesto, CA (1-400) Pres, Band; Fin, BS; Ensm; VP, Key C; Madrigal; Pres, Math C; Pres, SC; Var C; Ftbl; Tnns; Amer Leg A; Bank Of Amer A; Bausch & Lomb A; CSF; Cl Fav; Math A; *UC Davis; Engr.*

BAUGHMAN, Laura Elizabeth
Hartford HS; Hartford, WI (25%-600) Chor; Ski C; Span C; Sftbl; Solo & Ensm; *Carthage Col; Special Ed.*

BAUGHMAN, Mary Ellyn
Farmerville HS; Farmerville, LA (5-157) F-Ed, Ann; Band; Ensm; FHA; Pres, 4H; Hmrm; Fin, Jr Miss Pagent; Sch Achieve Tm; SC; Var C; Bkbl; Sftbl; Beauty; Cl Fav; 4H A; Hist A; HQn; HCt; Hon Prog; JA A; Swtht; Yth Fel; Yth Foundation; 4-H Short Course A; Tr Meet Court; Best Dressed; *NE La U; Med.*

BAUGHN, Aerojean Robin
Charles E Ellis HS; Newtown Square, PA; Ed, Ann; Secy, Sr Cl; Bkbl; JV, Hockey; Prom Court; *U of Pittsburgh; Communications.*

BAUGUESS, Jenene Carol
North Wilkes HS; Hays, NC; Secy, Band; BC; Cpt, Chldr; FHA; Hmrm; Secy, InterClub Coun; Sch P; SC; Tr; Bus.

BAULT, Larry Dean
Cloverdale HS; Cloverdale, IN; Band; Chor; Drama; Bkbl; Golf; *Ind U; Mus.*

BAUM, Marcia Diane
Paint Valley HS; Bainbridge, OH (4-90) VP, Band; Chor; Ensm; Secy, 4H; Lat C; NHS; Sci C; Amer Leg A; Pep C; DAC A; *Nurs.*

BAUMAN, Beverly Helene
Arcadia HS; Arcadia, CA (50-900) Chldr; Ger C; NHS; Orch; SC; VP, Jr Cl; CSF; Hon Prog; Kiowas; *U of Calif; Med.*

BAUMAN, James Edward
Colo Springs Christian HS; Colorado Springs, CO (7-12) Band; Chor; Cpt, Bkbl; Sftbl; Bkbl; HCt.

BAUMAN, Ken David
Foley HS; Foley, MN (33%-175) Chor; Var C; Cr-Ctry; Ftbl; Co-Cpt, Tr; Wrest.

BAUMAN, Roger William
Kerkhoven HS; Kerkhoven, MN (25-50) Chor; FFA; 4H; Tres, Soph Cl; Ftbl; Wrest; *Willmar Vo-tech Col; Carpentry.*

BAUMAN, Ruth Marie
Merrill Sr HS; Merrill, WI; A Cap Choir; Ann; Chor; Ensm; Mjrte; Span C; Tr; *Concordia Col; Elem Ed.*

BAUMAN, Tracey Lea
E Knox HS; Howard, OH (9-53) Band; Chor; Drama; GS; Rptr, Hmrm; VP, NHS; Span C; SC; COM; Journ A; Most Out; Q&S A; Edmont Wilson A; Inservice A; News Ed, Sch P; *Ohio U; Special Ed.*

BAUMANN, Christopher Drew
Pampa HS; Pampa, TX (87-308) Band; *W Tex St U; Computer Information Systems.*

BAUMANN, Eddie Elton
Illinois Valley HS; Cave Junction, OR (20-77) Pres, Chor; Bsbl; Bkbl; Ftbl; *Mus.*

BAUMANN, Elisabeth Karin
Aviation HS; Redondo Beach, CA; Pres A; *Bus.*

BAUMANN, Rodney M
Ashley HS; Ashley, ND (5-40) Band; Ch, Dbte Tm; Bsbl; Bkbl; Ftbl; Co-Cpt, Tr; BScts; Lab Band; Modern Choir; *Mary Col.*

BAUMBERGER, Donna Kay
Chester Area HS; Chester, SD (2-40) Ann; CYO; Cpt, Chldr; Drama; NHS; ARC; Ed, Sch P; Var C; Cpt, Bkbl; Sftbl; Swim; Tr; HCt; Hon Prog; Journ A; Sal; *Presentation Col; Nurs.*

BAUMGARDNER, Elizabeth Ann
Delphos Jefferson HS; Delphos, OH (9-91) Co-Ed, Ann; Pres, Band; Chldr; VP, Fr C; VP, NHS; Sci C; Mgr, Bkbl; Tr; Chor Lib; *Ohio St U; Archt.*

BAUMGARDNER, James Edward
Indianapolis Sch for the Deaf; Indianapolis, IN (37-42) Cpt, Bkbl; Tr; *TVI; Voc.*

BAUMGARDNER, Rebecca Lynn
Delphos Jefferson Sr HS; Delphos, OH (4-90) Band; Chor; Fr C; GS; NHS.

BAUMGART, David John
Simi Valley HS; Simi Valley, CA (10-840) Hmrm; NHS; JV, Swim; CSF; Math A; *UCLA; Math.*

BAUMGARTE, Sherry Lynn
Freeburg Comm HS; Freeburg, IL (3-114) VP, Band; FTA; Model UN; NHS; Secy, Sci C; Var C; Arch; Bausch & Lomb A; COM; HCt; Sal; Sci A; St Scholar; Yth Fel; Vlbl; Schol Athlete; Ill Col Schol; Arion Mus A; Navy Sci A; Pres, Ecology C; Stage Band; Excellence Proficiency A; *Botany.*

BAUMHOWER, Kathy Lynn
Northside HS; Samantha, AL; Chldr; Chor; Hmrm; Span C; SC; Beauty; Cl Fav; HCt; Swtht; Vlbl; *Anderson Col; Bus Adm.*

BAUNE, Rick Donald
William Kelley HS; Silver Bay, MN (2-140) CYO; Chor; NHS; Sci C; SC; Var C; Bkbl; Ftbl; Tr; Bio A; COM; HCt; Sci A; *Chem.*

BAUNE, Steven Joseph
William Kelley HS; Silver Bay, MN (5-155) CYO; Chor; Ensm; NHS; Pres, Sci C; SC; Var C; Tnns; COM; HCt; Most Out; Sci A; Star Student; Curling; Morehead St U Cum Laude Schol; Minn Jr Acad of Sci Del; Reserve Mining Co Schol; *Moorhead St U; Dentistry.*

BAUR, Julie Dawn
Carlsbad HS; Carlsbad, CA (37-403) Chldr; Chor; Hon Prog; JA A.

BAUSCH, Frank Alexander
Lancaster Sr HS; Lancaster, WI (1-151) JV, Bsbl; JV, Bkbl; JV, Ftbl; Tr; HCt; Math A; *UW-MADISON; Acct.*

BAUSERMAN, Patricia Lynn
Patrick Henry HS; Roanoke, VA (25-600) Hmrm; Lat C; NHS; Gov Honor Prog; Hon Prog; NEDT; Yth Fel; Yth Choir; *U of Va; Pre-Med.*

BAUZA, Rosario Quinones
Academia Mira Sra Providencia; Rio Piedras, PR (11-58) A Cap Choir; Ann; Band; CYO; Chldr; Chor; Hmrm; Rptr, Sch P; SC; COM; Cl Fav; Hon Prog; JA A; Conduct A; Jr Cath Daughters of Amer; *U of Puerto Rico; Bus Adm.*

BAVENDER, Robert Gregory
Florence Twp Mem HS; Florence, NJ (9-140) BC; Hmrm; Math C; COM; Math A; *Engr.*

BAXLEY, Carrie Kasandra
Sandusky HS; Sandusky, OH; All Amer Yth; Band; JETS; Mjrte; Ntl Yth Conf; ARC; Tr; JA A; Most Out; Athletic A.

BAXLEY, Rachel Kaye
Vidalia HS; Vidalia, GA; Tri-HiY; *Phys Therapy.*

BAXLEY, Samuel Wesley
Cottonwood HS; Cottonwood, AL; Band; BC; FBLA; Key C; Sci C; *Jacksonville St U; Law Enforcement.*

BAXTER, Barbara Ann
Springfield HS; Bergholz, OH (26-94) A Cap Choir; BC; Chem C; Chor; Drama; Pres, FTA; GS; Tres, Span C; SC; Arch; VP, FTA; Co-Ch, Span C; *Kent St U; Primary Ed.*

BAXTER, Carmen Marlene
Jenkins HS; Millen, GA (5-100) BC; Rptr, FHA; 4H; Hmrm; Sch P; SC; Ch, Tri-HiY; VP, Jr Cl; Tres, Soph Cl; Tr; COM; Rotary A; Bookkeeping A; *Ga Southern Col; Med Tech.*

BAXTER, Craig Stephen
Rider HS; Wichita Falls, TX; SC; Ftbl; Tr; Cl Fav; Church HS Choir; All-Conf Tm; HR; FCA; Soph o-t Yr, Ftbl Dist; 1st Tm Running Back; *Tex Tech U; Vet Med.*

BAXTER, Diana Ray
Hemet HS; Hemet, CA (79-486) Drama; FBLA; NHS; Spch C; CSF; St Scholar; *Humboldt St Col; Drama.*

BAXTER, Donald Franklin
King George HS; King George, VA (17-160) Band; BS; FBLA; SC; Bsbl; Bkbl; Ftbl; Tr; Citz A; Cl Fav; Acct A; *VPI; Acct.*

BAXTER, Helen Marie
Girard HS; Girard, PA (5-160) Band; Chor; GS; 4H; Hmrm; Cpt, Mjrte; Rainbow; Ed, Sch P; Ski C; VP, SC; Grand Immortality, Rainbow Girls; *U of Pittsburg; Nurs.*

BAXTER, Karen Ruth
Reynolds HS; Greenville, PA (4-212) Secy, 4H; Pres, Lat C; NHS; A-Ed, Sch P; Pres, SC; Pres, Thes; COM; NEDT; *Penn St U; Human Development.*

BAXTER, Mary Beth
Olathe HS; Olathe, KS; Band; Dbte Tm; 4H; NFL; S-T, NHS; Tres, SC; JV, Bkbl; Citz A; 4H A; Spch A; Type A; *Nurs.*

BAXTER, Patricia Diane
Wichita HS S; Wichita, KS; Chor; Ensm; VP, Hmrm; V-Ch, SC; Pres, Jr Cl; Hon Prog; Journ A; Church Mus & Art A's; *Friends U; Secy Sci.*

BAXTER, Roosevelt
Concord HS; Concord, NC (130-229) Monogram; Span C; Cpt, Bsbl.

BAXTER, Thomas Francis
Headland HS; Headland, AL (13-90) Ed, Ann; BS; Rptr, FBLA; Key C; NHS; Ftbl; Cl Fav; God & Country A; *Auburn U; Archt.*

BAXTER, Vicky Lynn
Laurel Co HS; London, KY (50%-400) Band; FHA; 4H; Y-Tns; HCt; *Cumberland Col.*

BAY, Evemarie
Nordhoff HS; Ojai, CA (21-339) Band; Chor; Drama; Ensm; Secy, Ger C; Ch, 4H; NHS; Swim; COM; 4H A; Opt A; Spch A; Jr Yr, Exchange Stu in Germany; Yth For Undrstnding; Concert Band; Amer Quarter Horse Assn; Pianist Church & Sch Functions; *Mus.*

BAYCORA, Ibrahim
Eastside HS; Paterson, NJ (7-519) Chess C; Math C; NHS; Cpt, Soccer; Tnns; COM; Hon Prog; MVP, Soccer; *Boston U; Pre-Med.*

BAYCROFT, Lita Marie
Grand Trunk HS; Evansburg, CANADA (2-71) Dbte Tm; Drama; Fr C; Ski C; Spch C; Pres, SC; COM; Odd Fellow Fin; Spch A; *Fr.*

BAYER, Jodelle Jaye
Nathan Hale HS; West Allis, WI (134-431) Ski C; Cpt, Cr-Ctry; Cpt, Tr; Racing Tm; *Mt Mary Col; Art Therapy.*

BAYES, Bruce Alan
Russell HS; Russell, KY (120-250) BS; Chor; Co-Cpt, Ftbl; Tnns; Tr; JA A; *Morehead St U; Acct.*

BAYLER, David Allen
Larkin HS; Elgin, IL (15-700) Fr C; JV, Tr; Yth Fel; Pres, Yth Fellowship; Church Sch Teacher; Recreation Comm.

BAYLES, Janet Lisa
Arkadelphia HS; Arkadelphia, AR (7-169) Chor; Pres, Fr C; VP, NHS; A-Ed, Sch P; Journ A; Key C Swtht; Home Ec A; *U of Ark; Psych.*

BAYLES, Jill Marie
Arkadelphia Sr HS; Arkadelphia, AR; Ann; Fr C; FHA; SC; Thes; Pres, Jr Cl; *Ouachita Baptist U; Journ.*

BAYLESS, Becky Lynn
Nashville Comm HS; Nashville, IL (18-160) A-Ed, Ann; Band; Drama; Rptr, Mod Mus Mas; NHS; *E Ill U.*

BAYLESS, Robin Tanner
Carnegie HS; Carnegie, OK (3-85) Chem C; Math C; NHS; Pres, Span C; VP, SC; Bkbl; Ftbl; Tr; Alg A; Bio A; Chem A; Math A; Span A; *Okla U; Pre-Dental.*

BAYLESS, Stephanie Jo
Keswick Christian HS; St Petersburg, FL (5%-19) Ensm; *Dental Hygiene.*

BAYLIES, Candy Lee
Ausabe Valley Central HS; Clintonville, NY (300-758) Chor; Drama; Up Bound; Tr.

BAYLIES, Kathleen Victoria
Au Sable Valley Central HS; Clintonville, NY (3-150) Band; Rptr, Bus C; Drama; Rptr, FBLA; NHS; Rptr, Sch P; Up Bound; Mgr, Bkbl; Soccer; Tnns; Tr; COM; 4H A; Hon Prog; Type A; Vof-DEM; *Communications.*

BAYLOG, Jamie Lynn
Kelvyn Park HS; Chicago, IL (3-528) Pres, Chor; Drama; Tres, Hmrm; Pres, Madrigal; SC; Bio A; COM; Hist A; Hon Prog; Math A; Sci A; Ch, Peer Counseling Prog; Co-Cpt, Vlbl; Asst Pianist, All City Chor; *Psych.*

BAYLOR, Floyd
West Side HS; Gary, IN (300-1050) Chor; Lat C; Boxing; *Lincoln U; Law.*

BAYNARD, Brenna Baynard
University HS; San Diego, CA (21-374) CYO; Chor; NHS; Hon Prog; Ldr, Leadership Qualities; *U Sand Diego; Bio.*

BAYNARD, Brenna Elaine
University HS; San Diego, CA (21-374) Chor; Hon Prog; Ldrship A; *U of San Diego; Bio Sci.*

BAYNE, Mitsuko
Kubasaki HS; Okinawa, JAPAN (18-271) Hmrm; Mu Alpha Theta; NHS; Co-Ed, Sch P; SC; Pres, Soph Cl; Bkbl; Cl Fav; Hist A; HCt; Hon Prog; Journ A; MLS; PA; *U of Denver; Pre-Law.*

BAYNE, Tammie Jaynean
Waynesboro Central HS; Waynesboro, MS (25%-130) SC; Var C; VP, Soph Cl; Bkbl; Tr; Amer Leg A; Cl Fav; HCt; Best All Around Stu.

BAYS, Bryan Keith
Riverdale HS; Ft Myers, FL (61-368) Bio A; Christian C; HR; PA; *Edison Comm Col; Broadcasting.*

BAZE, Debra Sue
Alton Sr HS; Alton, IL (357-850) Beauty; Opt Out Tn; Yth Fel; *Public Relations.*

BAZEN, Lois Anne
D H Conley HS; Greenville, NC (59-280) Band; Secy, BC; Chldr; FHA; Journ A; ROTC A; Church Swtht; Church Cross A; 3rd Pl Metric Poster; 1st Pl Metric Estimation.

BAZIK, Carolyn Marie
Marian HS; Tamaqua, PA (12-173) Band; CYO; Chor; Orch; Sch P; Sodality; Sftbl; COM; Chamber of Comm A; Hon Prog; Varsity Ltrs; Pres, Yth Parc; Yth Corps; *Kutztown Col; Special Ed.*

BAZILE, Deondra Marie
Covington HS; Covington, LA; *Grambling Col; Nurs.*

BAZINET, Philip Elmer
Tuscaloosa HS; Tuscaloosa, AL (20-600) Cpt, Band; Ensm; Hmrm; Mu Alpha Theta; Orch; SC; Cl Fav; Most Out; Yth Fel; Civitan C; Most Talented Boy, Sr Cl; Drum Major; *U of Ala; Aerospace Engr.*

BAZLEY, Reginald Dennis
George Washington HS; Los Angeles, CA (36-550) Bus C; Hmrm; Ntl Yth Conf; Bank Of Amer A; Citz A; Yth Fel; Toastmaster; Attendance A; Bank of Amer Cert of Achv; Principal's List; Cert of Accomplishment; *UC Berkley; Bus Adm.*

BAZZELL, Kevin DeWight
Pojoaque HS; Santa Fe, NM; Band; BS; Chess C; Math C; NHS; VP, Jr Cl; Alg A; Bio A; Cl Fav; Hist A; Math A; *UCLA; Elec Engr.*

BAZZY, Cindy Layne
St John Lutheran HS; Ocala, FL; Rptr, Hmrm; NHS; Secy, SC; Bkbl; *Berrington Col; Ecology.*

BEACH, Amanda Mae
Ionia HS; Ionia, MI; 4H; NHS; Citz A; 4H A.

BEACH, Bob Bernard
Greenwood HS; Springfield, MO (1-30) BS; Model UN; Pres, SC; Pres, Soph Cl; Co-Cpt, Bkbl; Ftbl; Golf; COM; Kiwanis A; Val; Yth Fel; VP, SC; Soph Pilgram Speedy Collins A; HR; Sports Ltrs; *Baylor U; Law.*

BEACH, Gloria Marie
Las Plumas HS; Oroville, CA (26-246) Secy, FFA; Semi-Fin, GS; Pres, SC; Bank Of Amer A; Citz A; Spch A; Pres, Fresh Cl; Grange; RISE; Organ Secy, SC; Publ Secy, SC; CASC, Oroville Yth Found, Pres; Pres, Chrch Yth Grp; Parl Proc Tm; *Chapmen Col; Govt.*

BEACH, John Ernest Winfield
John Handley HS; Winchester, VA (10-275) Ann; NHS; Arch; Bsbl; Tr; Wrest; Bio A; Chem A; Drafting A; *U of Va; Med.*

BEACH, Lowrain
Howard HS; Georgetown, SC; Chor; 4H; VP, Hmrm; SC; HR.

BEACH, Mishell Denise
Howard Voc HS; Georgetown, SC; Secy, Hmrm; HR; *Morris Col; Bus Adm.*

BEACH, Neil Douglas Jr
North St Acad; Hickory, NC (1-12) Chor; Drama; Fr C; Order/Arrow; Bkbl; Soccer; Sftbl; COM; God A Country A; Order/Arrow A; Rotary A; Eagle Sct; *Carolina Col; Law.*

BEACH, Teresa Lee
Ashton HS; Ashton, IL (16-42) Ann; Band; Chldr; Chor; Secy, FFA; Pres, FHA; Secy, 4H; Key C; Pres, SC; Tr; 4H A; Hon Prog; I Dare You; Swtht; Best Personality; Most Individual; *Moody Bible Inst; Christian Ed.*

BEACH, Terry Lee
Greenland HS; Greenland, AR (2-45) Ann; Pres, Hmrm; Sch P; Bkbl; Cpt, Ftbl; Alg A; Cl Fav; *Ark U; Sci.*

BEACHEM, Laurie Dione
Sawyer Pub Sch; Sawyer, ND (25%-28) A-Ed, Ann; Band; Chor; Type A; Vlbl.

BEACHUM, Lisa Jean
Hart HS; Hart, MI; *Mich St U; Phys Ed.*

BEACHY, Kenton Jay
Eastern Mennonite HS; Harrisonburg, VA; Chor; Fr C; SC; Bkbl.

BEACOM, Patrice Marie
St Mary's Acad; Englewood, CO (11-60) CYO; Cpt, Chldr; Chor; Community Yth Symph; Lat C; Lit Mag; VP, NHS; Ski C; Prom Qn; Backpacking; WW; Photography Ed, Yrbk; Vlbl; *U of Colo; Spch Pathology.*

BEAHM, Charlene Ann
Norview Sr HS; Norfolk, VA; Chor; NHS; MVP, Tnns; God & Country A; Hon Prog; I Dare You; Masonic A; Yth Fel; Yth Foundation; Chaplain, SCA; *Photography.*

BEAL, Eric David
Pine View HS; Sarasota, FL (9-41) Band; Key C; Mgr, Bkbl; Ftbl; Alg A; COM; Spch A; Mus As; Swim As; DAR Cert of Appreciation; Cert of 98%, NEDT; *Baylor U; Med.*

BEAL, James Edward Jr
duPont Manual HS; Louisville, KY (90-520) Chldr; Fr C; Hmrm; SC; Pres, Up Bound; COM; Cl Fav; Hon Prog; Most Out; PTA A; Yth Fel; Yth Leg; Mental Wizard Contest; *W Ky U; Pre-Theology.*

BEAL, Jeremy Lawrence
Booker HS; Sarasota, FL; Band; Chess C; Drama; Hmrm; Orch; Rptr, Sch P; Span C; SC; Bkbl; Soccer; Sftbl; HCt; Ntl Fed of Mus C; Atlanta Boys Choir; *Manatee Jr Col; Aviation.*

BEAL, Jo Ann
Tuscola HS; Waynesville, NC (10%-320) A Cap Choir; Band; Chor; Fr C; InterAct C; Chamber Singers; Co-Cpt, Flag Corps; VP, Ecology C; Humanities C; Asst Director Drama A; *UNC-Chapel Hill; Sociology.*

BEAL, Madeleine Marie
Huntington HS; Huntington, NY (2-612) Chor; Math C; NHS; Regent Schol; Sal; NY St Soc Professional Engr A; Ntl Merit Commendation; *NY Inst of Tech; Mech Engr.*

BEAL, Rose Ann Marie
Sandy Union HS; Sandy, OR (11-180) Chor; FBLA; NHS; FBLA Dist Skills Contest; 5th Pl Acct; *Mt Hood Comm Col; Adm Secy.*

BEAL, Steve Scott
Lexington HS; Lexington, OH (91-285) Cr-Ctry; Tr; Wrest; Yth Fel; *Bus.*

BEALE, James Guy
Norfolk Collegiate HS; Norfolk, VA (25-41) Chess C; Hmrm; Key C; SC; VP, Jr Cl; Soccer; Tr; Yth Fel; *U of Richmond; Bus.*

BEALE, Maria Rosa
Academia Maria Reina; Rio Piedras, PR; Drama; Fr C; Math C; NHS; Sch P; Spch C; Var C; COM; First Hons; *LSU; Commercial Art.*

BEALE, Peggy Sue
Russellville HS; Russellville, AL (29-155) Ann; Secy, FBLA; FHA; 4H; Mu Alpha Theta; NHS; SC; HCt; Yth Fel; WW Friendliest; All A's; Pres, Delta Theta Chi Soroity; Jr Civitan Ntl Traffic Safety C; *U of N Ala; Bus.*

BEALING, John Richard
Daniel M Therrell HS; Atlanta, GA (30-238) Drama; Ger C; Cpt, Cr-Ctry; Cpt, Tr.

BEALL, Cheri Fay
Dublin HS; Dublin, GA (20-200) Ann; Pres, Tri-HiY; Most Out; Secy, Ch, Tri-Hi-Y; WW; *Ga Sou Col; Elem Ed.*

BEALL, John Bone
Robert E Lee HS; Tyler, TX (300-625) Ann; Chem C; Ger C; Sch P; Thes; Tnns; Tr; *Stephen F Austin St Col; Forestry.*

BEALL, Martin D
Miami Coral Park HS; Miami, FL (300-800) Chor; Dbte Tm; SC; COM; Citz A; Opt A; Spch A.

BEALL, Vicki Leigh
Jefferson HS; Jefferson, GA (2-115) A-Ed, Ann; Bus Mgr, BC; Chldr; Drama; Fr C; 4H; Tres, Hmrm; Lit Mag; Sch P; Sci C; Span C; SC; COM; Gov Honor Prog; NEDT; Scholasic Ltr; Pres Coll ledge Jr Fel A; HR.

BEALS, Brynn Rebecca
Lake Oswego HS; Lake Oswego, OR (1%-267) Chor; Fr C; NHS; Piano Recognition Recital.

BEALS, Dale Wesley
Coon Rapids Sr HS; Coon Rapids, MN (260-654) Key C; Ftbl; Mgr, Hockey; Mgr, Tr; ROTC A; Navy; Elec.

BEAM, David Alan
B Reed Henderson Sr HS; W Chester, PA (10-508) Hist.

BEAM, Gary Paul
Coronado HS; El Paso, TX (32-650) NHS; SC; Bsbl; JV, Bkbl; Ftbl; JV, Tr; DARGCA; Opt A; Pres, VP, Church Yth Group; All St Baptist Yth Choir; City Rep, Yth Coun; *Engr.*

BEAM, Herbie Lee
Kings Mountain Sr HS; Kings Mountain, NC; Band; BC; Fr C; Hmrm; Golf; *Wake Forest U; Math.*

BEAM, Jody Elizabeth
Cherryville Sr HS; Cherryville, NC (40-150) Band; Chem C; FBLA; Mjrte; Sci C; Bkbl; Soccer; Sftbl; Swim; Beauty; NEDT; Ntl Art Found; Miss Sch Spirit; Acteen A; *Gaston Col; Bus Adm.*

BEAM, Sandra Carlette
Burns Sr HS; Lawndale, NC; Ann; BC; Cpt, Hmrm; Key C; Sch P; SC; Swim; Citz A; MLS; Type A; Yth Fel; *Appalachian St U; Elem Ed.*

BEAM, Shirlene Elaine
Whitehouse HS; Whitehouse, TX (5-106) Band; Mjrte; NHS; Top 10; *Tex A&M U; Acct.*

BEAMAN, Kimberly Elaine
Tarboro Sr HS; Tarboro, NC (10%-250) Chor; Ensm; Fr C; Secy, FHA; Secy, FTA; Hmrm; Lit Mag; Secy, NHS; Sci C; SC; *U of NC; Mus.*

BEAMON, Kevin Maurice
Maplewood HS; Nashville, TN (20%-450) Band; Up Bound; Tnns; JV, Wrest; *Fisk U; Mus.*

BEAMS, Bradly Dee
Findlay HS; Findlay, OH (5-580) Semi-Fin, BS; Cum Laude Soc; Hmrm; Lit Mag; NHS; Pres, Sci C; SC; Cr-Ctry; Ftbl; Tr; Wrest; Bio A; COM; Coun of Teach A; DARGCA; H of F; Hon Prog; Math A; Order/Arrow A; Pres A; Sci A; Summa Cum Laude; Pres, Med Careers C; Bicycle C; Most Outst Bio Stu; Exchange C Yth o-t Mo; Most Outst Jr; *Ohio Northern U; Phar.*

BEAN, Caryl Louise
Fremont Christian HS; Fremont, CA; Chor; Bsbl; Bkbl; Tr; CSF; HR; *Oral Roberts U; Med.*

BEAN, Diana Naomi
Walton Central Sch; Walton, NY (17-145) Band; Chor; Ensm; NHS; Orch; Var C; Co-Cpt, Hockey; Regent Schol; Mgr, Gym; Colorguard; *Kent St U; Journ.*

BEAN, Martha Lee
Robert H Goddard HS; Roswell, NM (35-305) Ann; NHS; Rainbow; Span C; Span NHS; Bkbl; Swim; JV, Tr; Drum Major; *Cottey Col; Mus Ed.*

BEAN, Michael Ray
Whitehouse HS; Whitehouse, TX (3-99) BC; NHS; Mgr, Bkbl; Mgr, Ftbl; Mgr, Tr; Bio A; Chem A; Hist A; MLS; NMF; NHS; Rotary A; Sci A; Val; Span A; *Rice U; Law.*

BEAN, Tim Dillon
Santa Rosa HS; Santa Rosa, CA (70-375) Band; NHS; Ski C; Tnns; CSF; Pres, New Life Singers; *Calif Polytech Col; Acct.*

BEAN, Valerie Dawn
E Mecklenburg HS; Charlotte, NC (10%-650) InterClub Coun; Sci C; SC; Civinettes; *Elem Ed.*

BEANE, John Christopher
Midland HS; Midland, TX; Co-Cpt, Ftbl.

BEARD, Cheryl Juanita
Acad of Richmond Co; Augusta, GA (15-285) Chor; Span C; Rensselaer A; Essay A; *Fisk U; Med.*

BEARD, Cynthia Anita
Crockett HS; Crockett, TX (5-107) A-Ed, Ann; Band; Pres, Bus C; Ensm; Cpt, Mjrte; NHS; Sch Achieve Tm; SC; VP, Jr Cl; S-T, Soph Cl; Secy, Bus C; Band Coun; Stage Band; Tres, Frsh Cl; Yrbk Stf A; Bnd Swtht; Bndsmn o-t Yr; Al Reg Bnd; FFA Swt; Drum Major; AAA All Dist Band; *Tyler Jr Col; Bus Adm.*

BEARD, Deloris Marie
St Matthew HS; Melrose, LA (9-47) Pres, Sr Cl; Type A; *Northwestern St U; Sec Adm.*

BEARD, John Cullen
Evangelical Christian Sch; Memphis, TN; Chor; Fr C; Order/Arrow; Bsbl; JV, Bkbl; Cr-Ctry; JV, Ftbl; Tr; Order/Arrow A.

BEARD, John Herndon
Owensboro HS; Owensboro, KY (10%-454) Band; Chor; Ensm; Ger C; Hmrm; InterAct C; Tres, NHS; Spch C; SC; Mus As; 1st Pl, Ger Contest; *Wabash Col; Hist.*

BEARD, Kathi Jean
Wilburton Pub HS; Wilburton, OK; Chor; Ensm; FTA; 4H; Spch C; Spch A; Yth Fel; Pres, Yth Fellowship.

BEARD, Lisa Michelle
W H Adamson HS; Dallas, TX; JV, Chldr; Fr C; FHA; *N Tex St; Hist.*

BEARD, Sandra J
Uniontown Area Sr HS; Uniontown, PA; Band; Fr C; Pres, NHS; Sci C; Var C; Bkbl; Sftbl; Tnns.

BEARD, Stacy Anne
Cottage Grove HS; Cottage Grove, OR (43-300) Band; Sftbl; Gym; Secy, Yth Against Dystrophy C; *U of Oreg; Forestry.*

BEARDEN, Patricia Jane
John Overton HS; Nashville, TN (10%-500) BC; FHA; SC; COM; NEDT; *Middle Tenn St U; Med.*

43

BEARDEN, Richard Alan
Robert E Lee HS; Tyler, TX (10%-700) Drama; Ger C; VP, SC; Thes; VP, Jr Cl; Co-Cpt, Ftbl; Swim; Cl Fav; Hon Prog; Best Actor, Dist; All Star Cast, St UIL; Ntl Mus Tchrs Guild Critics Circle; *Sou Methodist U; Law.*

BEARDEN, Theresa Inez
Edwin G Foreman HS; Chicago, IL (47-489) Ed, Ann; Pres, FNA; Pres, FTA; Key C; ARC; Span C; Hon Prog; Journ A; *Lee Col; Elem Ed.*

BEARDSLEE, Dana
All Saints Cathedral Sch; St Thomas, VI (3-18) F-Ed, Ann; Tres, Sr Cl; Phy A; Sci A; *Yale U; Psych.*

BEARDSLEY, Lisa Margaret
Leilehua HS; Wahiawa, HI (100-450) Fr C; Multi-Cultural C; Jazz Dance Group; Pres, St Church Yth; *U of Hawaii; Outdoor Ed.*

BEARERS, Wanda Ann
Mt Ida HS; Mt Ida, AR (8-40) Band; BC; Chldr; Chor; Drama; FHA; Bkbl; Sftbl; Swim; Alg A; COM; Band All Region; Most Improved Band Stu; 7 Solo & Ensemble Metals.

BEARFIELD, Karen Ann
Rancho HS; N Las Vegas, NV (11-576) CYO; Key C; SC; Citz A; Fleischman Schol; *Med.*

BEASLEY, Annette Gayle
Bellevue Sr HS; Bellevue, NE (285-800) Band; Sup Ratng, Plattsmouth Marchng Band; Sup Rating, Flute Quartette; Nebr Marching Band; Grand Island Marching Band; *Concordia Teacher's Col; Social Work.*

BEASLEY, Cynthia Ione
Eldorado HS; Eldorado, IL (20-105) FNA; Span C; *SE Ill Col; Nurs.*

BEASLEY, Donna Jean
Metter HS; Metter, GA (5%-150) Band; S-T, BC; Parl, FHA; 4H; Lit Ral; Cpt, Sch Achieve Tm; Tres, Tri-HiY; Bkbl; DARGCA; 4H A; Hon Prog; MLS; *Math.*

BEASLEY, Eric Wendell
Mitchell HS; Memphis, TN (45-239) Band; Chor; Math C; Sci C; Cl Fav; Young Adult Choir; *Christian Brothers Col; Elec Engr.*

BEASLEY, Henry Dean
Harlem HS; Harlem, GA (7-150) Chor; Drama; 4H; Hmrm; Co-Ed, Lit Mag; Model UN; Rptr, SC; Pres, Sr Cl; Pres, Jr Cl; COM; Citz A; Cl Fav; DARGCA; Gov Honor Prog; 4H A; Hist A; Hon Prog; I Dare You; MLS; Most Out; Sch Service A; Chor A; *Augusta Col; Hist.*

BEASLEY, Jody Alan
Winter Haven HS; Winter Haven, FL (45-641) Pres, Band; Fin, BS; Pres, Ensm; Hmrm; InterClub Coun; NHS; Ed, Sch P; Sci C; SC; Bsbl; Bkbl; Cr-Ctry; Sftbl; Tr; Amer Leg A; COM; Citz A; DARGCA; Hon Prog; Most Out; Opt A; Yth Fel; J P Sousa Band A; HS Band A; All-Amer Band; *U of Fla; Chem Engr.*

BEASLEY, Karen Frances
Claxton HS; Claxton, GA (25%-110) Band; Bus C; Tres, FBLA; 4H; Mjrte; SC; JV, Bkbl; Alg A; COM; Gov Honor Prog; Hon Prog; WW; *Ga Sou U; Bus.*

BEASLEY, Kevin Guy
Loocootee Comm HS; Loogootee, IN (15-114) VP, 4H; Span C; Cr-Ctry; Tr; *Purdue U; Engr.*

BEASLEY, Kirk James
LaConner HS; LaConner, WA (1-51) Pres, Chem C; Chess C; Fin, Dbte Tm; Hmrm; JETS; Math C; NHS; Pres, Phys C; SC; St Stu Congress; MVP, Bsbl; Bkbl; Ftbl; Swim; Amer Leg Orator A; Hon Prog; Math A; Spch A; Val; Yth Leg; ASB Tres; *U of Wash; Engr.*

BEASLEY, Mark Andrew
Saddleback HS; Santa Ana, CA; Cr-Ctry; Tr; Hon Prog.

BEASLEY, Marla Laree
Shawnee Mission Northwest HS; Shawnee, KS (30-900) Chldr; Chor; NHS; Sftbl; HR; Hon Math A; *Kans U; Acct.*

BEASLEY, Michael Anthony
George Washington HS; Los Angeles, CA; Band; Swim.

BEASLEY, Michael Dame
Metter HS; Metter, GA; Pres, FFA; Sci C; COM; DARGCA; Hon Prog; Kiwanis A.

BEASLEY, Susan Kimberly
St Mary's Acad; Alexandria, VA; Ann; Chor; Drama; Math C; Mu Alpha Theta; VP, Span NHS; Soccer; Hon Prog; NEDT; Type A; Eng A; Span A; Mus Appreciation A; *U of Va; Television Broadcasting.*

BEASLEY, Tonya Zanne
Mckenzie HS; McKenzie, TN (1-79) F-Ed, Ann; Band; VP, BC; FHA; Orch; Sci C; MVP, Sftbl; Hon Prog; MLS; Val; Drum Major; Tn-Ager o-t Wk; *U of Tenn; Computer Sci.*

BEASLEY, William Anthony
S View Sr HS; Hope Mills, NC (10%-700) Band; BC; *Mars Hill Col; Ministry.*

BEASON, Richard Eugene Jr
Oak Harbor HS; Oak Harbor, WA (31-369) Fin, BS; Chor; Hmrm; NHS; Span C; VP, SC; Bsbl; JV, Bkbl; Swim; Hon Prog; St Industrial Arts A; Runnerup, 4th of July King; *Phoenix Inst; Archt.*

BEASON, Sherri Ann
Wister HS; Wister, OK; Chor; FHA; NHS; Bkbl; Sftbl; Tnns; COM; 4H A; *Carl Albert Jr Col.*

BEASON, Teresa Suzanne
James F Byrnes HS; Duncan, SC (30-260) Band; BC; Chor; Fr C; Hmrm; Rainbow; Sch P; Span C; Mus Appreciation A; Worthy Advisor, Rainbow Girls; *Spartanburg Methodist Col; Nurs.*

BEATHARD, Philip Scott
London HS; London, OH (8-98) CYO; VP, FFA; Rptr, 4H; Hmrm; NHS; A-Ed, Sch P; SC; Pres, Sr Cl; Mgr, Ftbl; Tnns; JV, Wrest; Alg A; Kiwanis A; *Ohio St Col; Agr Engr.*

BEATTIE, Ezra Authur
Kingsbury HS; Memphis, TN (5-31) Var C; Bsbl; Ftbl; Tr; FCA; *Law.*

BEATTIE, Hubert Lee Jr
Lafayette HS; St Joseph, MO (90-250) St Stu Congress; Bkbl; St Bkbl; *Bus Adm.*

BEATTIE, Louise Elizabeth
Westfield HS; Westfield, MA; All Amer Yth; Band; Chor; Drama; Fr C; FHA; Rainbow; Var C; Tr; Hon Prog; *Psych.*

BEATTY, Andrea Lynn
W Charlotte Sr HS; Charlotte, NC; Orch; *Johnson C Smith Col; Bus Adm.*

BEATTY, Cathy Jean
Western HS; Louisville, KY (125-400) Chor; Ensm; VP, Hmrm; Sftbl; God & Country A; Ntl Cath Mus Ed Asn; Yth Fel; Sch Mus A; *Cambellsville Col; Mus.*

BEATTY, Guy Matthew
Reynolds HS; Troutdale, OR (42-289) Cpt, Band; BS; Community Yth Symph; Cpt, Hmrm; Orch; Pres, SC; Tnns; Tr; *Portland St Col; Aviation Tech.*

BEATTY, Hugh Brian
Compton Sr HS; Compton, CA (1-800) *Pepperdine U; Chem.*

BEATTY, Karen Ann
Tri-City HS; Buffalo, IL (9-54) VP, FTA; Span C; Cpt, Tr; HCt; Hon Prog; Cpt & MVP, Vlbl; *Eastern U; Occupational Therapy.*

BEATTY, Kathryn Susan
St Margaret's-McTernan Sch; Waterbury, CT (5-34) Chor; Drama; Fr C; WW; 1st Cl Sct; HS Schol.

BEATTY, Mary Rachel
Temple Christian Sch; Rockville, MD; Ann; Chor; Tres, SC; Pres A; *Bible.*

BEATTY, Richard Allen
Wallkill HS; Wallkill, NY; Chor; Tr; WSBC News; Tn C; *Tech.*

BEATTY, Stephen Andrew
Benson HS; Omaha, NE (10%-413) Band; BS; Orch; Sch P; Tnns; Drum Major; Advertising Mgr, Sch P; WW.

BEATTY, Steven Scott
Bradley Bourbonnais Comm HS; Bradley, IL (30-420) Ger C; JV, Cr-Ctry; Wrest; Church Board; Pres, Yth Fel; *Olivet Nazarene Col; Law.*

BEATY, Deborah Kay
Burlington Comm HS; Burlington, IA (129-475) Pres, Var C; Bkbl; Tr; Yth Fel; *Southeastern Comm Col; Social Sci.*

BEATY, Miriam Leigh
Vestavia Hills HS; Vestavia, AL (70%-300) Ann; Semi-Fin, Chldr; Chor; Ensm; Thes; Citz A; BASIC; VP, Jr Mus C.

BEATY, Stacey Annette
Terrell Acad; Dawson, GA (2-58) Cpt, Chldr; FTA; VP, Hmrm; NHS; Secy, Tri-HiY.

BEAUCHAMP, Sonja Gail
Springville HS; Springville, AL; Band; Chldr; FHA; 4H; Pres, Hmrm; Rainbow; SC; Var C; VP, Soph Cl; Cpt, Bkbl; Tr; Cl Fav; Yth Fel; Beta C; MVP, Bkbl; All Co Bkbl; All Co, Bkbl; *Jacksonville St Col; Phys Ed.*

BEAUDETTE, John Bernard
Wm J Woodham HS; Pensacola, FL (8-530) Band; Ensm; Fr, Amer Gov, A's; *Pensacola Jr Col; Computer Sci.*

BEAUDOIN, Alain Joseph
Alexander Galt Regional HS; Lennoxville, CANADA (25-539) City Conf; Bsbl; Bkbl; Hockey; Sftbl; Tr; COM; Hon Prog; Math A; Sci A; Fr A; *U of Mass; Sci.*

BEAUFORD, Donny Curtis
Woodham HS; Pensacola, FL; Ann; Rptr, Chldr; Rptr, FBLA; Mgr, Bkbl; Art A; *Morehouse Col; Art.*

BEAUFORT, Helen Denorise
Williamsburg HS; Andrews, SC (4-75) Drama; 4H; Rptr, Sch P; Bkbl; 4H A; Hist A; Hon Prog; Clothing Demonstration; 4-H A; *U of SC; Nurs.*

BEAUREGARD, Daniel Edward
John Marshall Fundamental HS; Pasadena, CA; Key C; Bsbl; *UCLA; Broadcasting.*

BEAUXIS, Donna Kay
Leesville Sr HS; Leesville, LA; Secy, FHA; FTA; 4H; *LSU; Med.*

BEAVER, Diann Sue
S Page Comm HS; College Springs, IA (5-40) Band; Chor; Tres, FHA; S-T, Y-Tns; Secy, Jr Cl; Bkbl; Sftbl; Tr; Spch A; Ch, FHA; Ch, Y-Tns.

BEAVER, Lucina
Broken Arrow HS; Broken Arrow, OK (15-462) Ann; Cpt, Chldr; Hmrm; NHS; Ski C; SC; Tres, Sr Cl; VP, Soph Cl; Sftbl; Citz A; Cl Fav; HQn; Hon Prog; Masonic A; *Okla St U; Bus.*

BEAVER, Newton Herbert
Deerborne Sch; Coral Gables, FL (14-75) VP, BC; InterClub Coun; Secy, Key C; NHS; Pres, SC; VP, Sr Cl; Tres, Jr Cl; Mgr, Bkbl; Chamber of Comm A; Pres A; Star Student; Most Spirited Sr; Service A; Bkbl V Ltr; *The Citadel; Acct.*

BEAVER, Scarlett Rhonada
Nw Cabarrus HS; Concord, NC (10-260) Band; JV, Chldr; Tres, 4H; Pres, Hmrm; InterClub Coun; Co-Cpt, Mjrte; SC; Bkbl; Sftbl; Swim; Citz A; 4H A; HCt; Pres A; Horseshow Trophies; Walk-A-Thon; Piano, Dance, Stu; *Nurs.*

BEAVERS, Becky Ann
Terre Haute N Vigo HS; Terre Haute, IN (15-567) Band; Chor; Hmrm; InterAct C; Pres, InterClub Coun; NHS; VP, Y-Tns; Swim; Gov Honor Prog; HCt; Hon Prog; St Scholar; Pom Pom Corp; Princess, Cotillion C; Bsbl Bat Grl; 1st Alt, Trust Schol; Wrest Mat Maid; Soph, Jr & Sr Sen; Pres, Church Yth Fel; *DePauw U; Med.*

BEAVERS, Charris Denise
Herndon HS; Herndon, VA; Chor; FBLA; Ger C.

BEAVERS, John Eric
Putnam City HS; Okla City, OK (10%-900) Hmrm; Mu Alpha Theta; NHS; SC; Mgr, Bkbl; Hon Prog; Eng Schol A; *Pre-Med.*

BEAVERS, Kathleen Lynn
Holyoke HS; Holyoke, CO (4-58) Band; Chor; Semi-Fin, GS; Secy, 4H; NHS; Pres, Rainbow; Var C; Bkbl; Sftbl; Tr; Alg A; Hon Prog; Sci A; Type A; Yth Fel; Rainbow Grand Off; *Colo St U; Acct.*

BEAVERS, Wanda Ann
Mt Ida HS; Mt Ida, AR (8-40) Band; BC; Chldr; Chor; Drama; Ensm; FHA; Bkbl; Sftbl; Swim; Alg A; COM; All Reg, Solo & Ensm Medals, Band; Most Improved Trophy, Band.

BEAVERT, Deborah Annette
Bledsoe Co HS; Pikeville, TN (4-91) Secy, BC;
FHA; 4H; NHS; ARC; Bkbl; Beauty; Cl Fav; 4H A;
Hon Prog; VICA A; Home Ec A; Top Ten; *Middle
Tenn St U; Pre-Law.*

BEAVON, Camille Sue
Martins Ferry HS; Martins Ferry, OH (12-200)
Band; Chem C; FTA; NHS; Sch P; Span C; Y-Tns;
Pres, Jr Cl; Bkbl; Tres, Church Yth Fel; Girls Ath
C; Prom Committee; YWCA; *Nurs.*

BEAZELL, Michael Lester
Charleroi Area HS; Charleroi, PA; Sch P; SC; Var
C; Pres, Soph Cl; Cpt, Bkbl; Co-Cpt, Soccer; JV, Tr;
Bethany Col; Bio.

BEAZLEY, Rebecca
Jefferson Davis HS; Montgomery, AL (86-742)
Ensm; Lat C; Mu Alpha Theta; ARC; S-T, Y-Tns;
Yth Fel; Young Life Campaigns; McDowell Mus C;
Secy & Social Ch, Yth Coun; Pres & Mission Ac-
tion Ldr, Acteens; *Auburn U; Nurs.*

BECERRA, Maria Guadalupe
Memorial HS; San Antonio, TX (2-300) Pres, Bus
C; FBLA; Pres, FTA; NHS; Secy, Sci C; Span
NHS; Pres A; Type A; World Geography A; Span
A; *St Marys U; Pre-Phar.*

BECHARD, Michele Marie
Clyde HS; Clyde, KS (10-32) Band; Cpt, Chldr;
Chor; Drama; Ensm; Sch P; Thes; Co-Cpt, Tr;
COM; HCt; Type A; Vlbl; Tr Ltr, Schol, A's; *Cloud
Co Comm Jr Col; Bus.*

BECHDOLT, Sharon Marie
Celina Sr HS; Celina, OH (15-278) Ann; Pres,
CYO; Chor; S-T, Drama; Fr C; Ger C; NHS; SC;
S-T, Thes; Hon Prog; Vlbl; *Miami U at Ohio.*

BECHT, Carol Lynn
John Carroll HS; Ft Pierce, FL (17-107) Anchor C;
Ann; Band; Co-Cpt, Chldr; Chor; Tres, Drama; 4H;
NHS; Thes; Var C; Bkbl; Cr-Ctry; Tr; COM; HCt;
Hon Prog; Math A; NEDT; Most Dramatic; Mus
Schol; *U of Fla; Nurs.*

BECHT, Kimberly Ann
Marion HS; Lebanon, KY (25-324) Ann; Band;
CYO; FHA; NHS; Tres, Span C; S-T, SC; Pres,
Soph Cl; HQn; Hon Prog; *Lexington Tech Inst;
Acct.*

BECHTEL, Douglas Allen
Ephrata Sr HS; Ephrata, PA (9-287) Band; Orch;
Order/Arrow; Soccer; COM; God & Country A;
Ntl Hon Men, Schol Arts; *Graphic Design.*

BECHTEL, Patricia Lynn
Robert E Lee HS; Montgomery, AL (1-704)
Hmrm; Lat C; Math C; VP, Mu Alpha Theta; Sci C;
Alg A; Amer Leg A; Citz A; Math A; Ntl Sci
Found; NEDT; ROTC A; Sci A; *Auburn U; Engr.*

BECHTHOLD, Lori Jane
Washington HS; Fremont, CA (10%-350) Cr-Ctry;
Tr; *LABC.*

BECHTOL, E Kathleen
Coshocton HS; Coshocton, OH (25%-250) A-Ed,
Ann; Band; Ensm; Pres, FNA; Pres, 4H; NHS;
ARC; VP, Span C; Citz A; 4H A; I Dare You; ARC
A; Sci A; Spch A; VofDEM; St Band Contest; St
Board of Ed A; Ldrship A; *Ohio U; Med.*

BECHTOLD, Robyn Joyce
Wallace Sr HS; Wallace, ID (2-102) Ann; Math C;
NHS; Rainbow; Span C; JV, Bkbl; Sal; Vlbl; *U of
Idaho; Forestry.*

BECK, Andrea Kay
Watertown HS; Watertown, WI (96-355) Chor;
Secy, Drama; Ger C; GS; Hmrm; Co-Ed, Sch P;
SC; Thes; Mgr, Ftbl; Swim; Mgr, Tr; Mus A's;
Drama Cert; *U of Wis; Special Ed.*

BECK, Betty Ann
Warren Central HS; Bowling Green, KY; Bus C;
Chor; FHA; Most Out; Outst Young Lady, Church;
W Ky U; Art Ed.

BECK, Bobbi Ann
Apollo Ridge HS; Apollo, PA; Chor; FTA; Rainbow; Sch P; Tnns; *PITT; Psych.*

BECK, Catherine Renee
Muncie Northside HS; Muncie, IN (4-256) Band;
Chor; Community Yth Symph; Ensm; Fr C; S-T,
FHA; GS; Math C; NHS; Orch; S-T, Phys C; Sci C;
SC; Sftbl; B Crocker A; COM; Kiwanis A; NMF;
NMS; Rotary A; Summa Cum Laude; Yth Fel; Yth
Del, General Assembly; Eng A; Fr A; Purdue Cert
of Recognition; *Purdue U; Computer Sci.*

BECK, Debra Jean
Colchester Jr And Sr HS; Colchester, IL (2-52)
Ann; Chor; Ensm; Math C; NHS; Span C;
DARGCA; Sal; *Western Ill U; Special Ed.*

BECK, Diane Roselyn
Ottawa HS; Ottawa, KS (10%-250) A Cap Choir;
Chor; Drama; NHS; Math A; NEDT; St Mus Festi-
val; Concert Choir; *Elem Ed.*

BECK, Donald Wayne
Tyler HS; Tyler, MN (22-54) Ann; Band; Chor;
Ensm; Var C; Tres, Sr Cl; Bkbl; Co-Cpt, Ftbl; Co-
Cpt, Golf; Tr; COM; HCt; Med Schol; Ath A
Schol; Ath Mem Schol; Lit A; *U of Minn; Med
Tech.*

BECK, Donna Jean
Sheyenne River Acad; Harvey, ND; A Cap Choir;
Chor; NHS; Rptr, Sch P; S-T, SC; Bkbl; Ftbl; Sftbl;
Pres A; Ldr, Religious Organization; Cl Rep, Stu
Assn; *Walla Walla Col; Nurs.*

BECK, Elizabeth Ann
Santa Fe HS; Alachua, FL; BC; Span C; Tnns;
NEDT; *Teaching.*

BECK, Gail Lynn
Wheaton HS; Wheaton, MO (2-36) Chor; SC; Var
C; Rptr, Jr Cl; Bkbl; Sftbl; Tr; HCt; Hon Prog; Type
A; All Conf, All Dist, All St, Bkbl; Ath o-t Wk.

BECK, Heidi Margaret
Valley Forge HS; Parma Heights, OH (175-838)
Chor; Drama; Ger C; Ski C; HR; Sch Service A;
Hiram Col; Bio.

BECK, Janet Lynn
Buffalo HS; Buffalo, OK (5-47) Ch, Chldr; Chor;
FHA; Secy, SC; Bkbl; Tr; Beauty; Cl Fav; HCt; Hon
Soc; Miss Buffalo; Best Dressed; *Okla St U; Nurs.*

BECK, Janis Charlene
Tyler HS; Tyler, MN (20-44) Band; JV, Chldr;
Chor; Ensm; Madrigal; Var C; Golf; Band As;
Choir As; Pep C; Luther League.

BECK, Jennifer Aileen
Temple Christian Sch; Redford, MI (2-69) Chldr;
Chor; Ensm; FTA; Sci C; Tres, Jr Cl; Alg A; Amer
Leg A; COM; Citz A; Math A; Pres A; Sci A; Type
A; HR; PA; *Math.*

BECK, Julie Anne
Carmichaels Area HS; Carmichaels, PA (4-83)
Band; VP, NHS; Span C; DARGCA; *Duquesne U;
Nurs.*

BECK, Kathleene Sue
Dallastown HS; Dallastown, PA; Sch P; Band Col-
orguard; Ecology C; AFS C; Vlbl; *York Col; Med
Secy.*

BECK, Kathryn Ann
Wethersfield HS; Wethersfield, CT (20-450) Band;
Ski C; JV, Swim; Williams Col Bk A; Outing C;
Sunday Sch Tchr; Jr Marine Guide; Jr Marine
Guide; *Math.*

BECK, Kathy Sue
Dallastown HS; Dallastown, PA; Sch P; Colorguard; Ecology C; AFS; Vlbl; *York Col; Med Secy.*

BECK, Mark Steven
Lutheran HS N; St Louis, MO (36-165) Hmrm;
Pres, NHS; SC; JV, Tnns; Ntl Sci Found; Best
Dressed; *Tulane U; Acct.*

BECK, Melody Gay
Bella Vista HS; Fair Oaks, CA (11-600) Span C;
Chem A; Campus Life; Secy, Church Yth Group;
Insight; Rally C; Pres, Rptr, Yth Assn; *Biol.*

BECK, Michelle Antoinette
Valley Central HS; Montgomery, NY (15-319)
CYO; Fr C; French NHS; Pres, 4H; Amer Leg A;
COM; 4H A; Jr Ldrship; Hon A; *Lang.*

BECK, Patricia Lynn
Pascagoula HS; Pascagoula, MS (20-625) BC; VP,
Chor; FHA; NHS; Span C; Spch C; Citz A; Eng,
Span, Chor, A's; *U of S Ala; Pre-Med.*

BECK, Portia Lynn
Madisonville N Hopkins HS; Madisonville, KY
(20%-370) BC; Ed, Sch P; Pres, SC; Citz A; Hon
Prog; MLS; NEDT; VP, Art C; Secy, Tns Who
Care; 1st & 2nd Pl, Woman's C Art Con; *W Ky U;
Journ.*

BECK, Randall Alan
W Forsyth Sr HS; Clemmons, NC (95-504) Key C;
Order/Arrow; JV, Bkbl; COM; Church Choir;
Pres, Church Yth Fel; *Dentistry.*

BECK, Richard Eugene Jr
William Penn HS; York, PA (275-700) Pres A.

BECK, Steven Craig
W Branch HS; Beloit, OH; Chor; FHA; 4H; Hmrm;
Lat C; SC; Var C; Bkbl; Tnns; Cl Fav; 4H A; Cl
Clown; *Malone Col.*

BECK, Steven David
Will Rogers HS; Tulsa, OK (1-537) Band; BS;
Chem C; Pres, Hmrm; VP, Math C; Pres, NHS;
Span C; Thes; Bausch & Lomb A; Masonic A;
NMS; Rensselaer A; Val; *Rice U; Chem Engr.*

BECK, Teresa Kay
Sylva-Webster HS; Sylva, NC (14-160) Ann; Band;
Rptr, BC; Chem C; 4H; Hmrm; Phys C; Ed, Sch P;
Span C; SC; Alg A; B Crocker A; Chem A; Math A;
Span A; Most Stu; WW; *W Carolina U; Eng.*

BECKER, Carlton William
Chaminade Col Prep Sch; St Louis, MO (1-117)
Ed, Ann; Lit Mag; Secy, NHS; Sch P; Alg A; Bio A;
Chem A; Curator A; Hist A; Hon Prog; Math A;
NMF; NMS; NEDT; Sci A; Type A; Val; *Yale U;
Psych.*

BECKER, Carol Marie
Cedarburg HS; Cedarburg, WI (12-360) Chor;
Swing Choir; Pres, Luther League; Chapel Choir;
Spring Mus; *U of Wis; Math.*

BECKER, Debora Lynn
Fort Lupton HS; Fort Lupton, CO (3-95) Band;
Chldr; Chor; Pres, FTA; GS; 4H; Fin, Jr Miss Pa-
gent; Tres, NHS; Span C; Bkbl; Tr; COM; 4H A;
Hon Prog; Yth Fel; Stu o-t Mo; WW; Ft Lupton Jr
Miss; Candidate, Harvest Fair Qn; HR; *U of Colo;
Bilingual Ed.*

BECKER, Debra Rene
Zillah HS; Zillah, WA (2-65) Chor; Secy, FFA;
NHS; Secy, SC; Tres, Var C; 4H A; Masonic A;
MLS; *Wash St U; Soil & Agronomy.*

BECKER, Donald Joseph
Central Jersey Christian Sch; Asbury Park, NJ;
Chess C; Dbte Tm; Pres, SC; Ger C; Co-Cpt, Bsbl;
Co-Cpt, Bkbl; Co-Cpt, Soccer; Mkg; HCt; Hon
Prog; Math A; NMS; Sci A; Jr Sci Symp; Best
Dressed; USMA Invitational Workshop; DAHSS;
MVP, Soccer; Most Ath A; *Gordon Col; Math.*

BECKER, Elaine Ruth
Wautoma HS; Wautoma, WI (50%-156) Band;
Chor; Drama; Thes; Cpt, Bkbl; Tr; Tr A's; *Arts.*

BECKER, Linda Sue
Mount Vernon Sr HS; Mount Vernon, IN; Band;
Mjrte; SC; Yth Fel; 1st Cl GSct; God & Comm A;
Jr Civitan C; Bstr C.

BECKER, Linda Sue
Fort Lupton HS; Fort Lupton, CO (10-150) Band;
Chldr; Tres, 4H; COM; 4H A; Yth Fel; Band Ltrs;
Beautician.

BECKER, Mark David
Thomas Edison HS; San Antonio, TX; Stu Coun
Rep.

BECKER, Mary Kay
Monroe Sr HS; Monroe, WI (43-255) A-Ed, Ann;
Chor; Tres, FHA; A-Ed, Sch P; COM; Rptr, FHA;
Deaconess Hospital; Nurs.

BECKER, Roselyn Juanita
St John HS; Ennis, TX (2-34) Chor; Secy, NHS;
Bkbl; Bio A; Sal; WW.

BECKER, Steven Duane
Greenview HS; Greenview, IL (4-27) Band; Rptr,
FFA; Pres, 4H; NHS; Pres, SC; Tres, Jr Cl; 4H A;
Kiwanis A; NEDT; *Lincoln Land Comm Col; Agr.*

BECKER, Susan Marie
Foothill HS; Pleasanton, CA (58-390) Band; CYO;
Chldr; Tres, Jr Cl; Hon Prog; Gym Tm; Sup Spirit
A; HR; Outst Service to Sch A; Stu o-t Mo; *Law.*

45

BECKER, Thomas Gunther
Glenbard E HS; Lombard, IL; Community Yth Symph; Orch; Swim; Amer Leg A; Math A; Sci A; High HR.

BECKER, Timothy Gerard
Eden Valley-Watkins HS; Eden Valley, MN (15%-130) NHS; Ski C; Wrest; U of Minn; Computer Sci.

BECKETT, Keith Allen
Sullivan HS; Sullivan, MO (66-199).

BECKHAM, Charlene
Center HS; Center, TX (2-142) Ann; Pres, NHS; Rainbow; Pres, SC; Chem A; Sal; Sci A; U of Tex; Phar.

BECKHAM, Lisa Marie
Bayou Acad; Boyle, MS; Rptr, Ann; BC; Rptr, Sch P; Var C; Mgr, Bkbl; Mgr, Tnns; Mgr, Tr; Amer Leg A; Citz A; Yth Fel.

BECKING, Tina Michelle
Bad Axe HS; Bad Axe, MI; NHS; Secy, Soph Cl; Bkbl; Med.

BECKLEY, Toni Evette
Akron E HS; Akron, OH (16-360) NHS; Vlbl; Girls Assembly, Eastern Star; UNCI Development; U of Akron; Secy Sci.

BECKMAN, Angela Jean
Reynolds HS; Greenville, PA (1-212) Co-Ed, Ann; Bus C; Chor; FBLA; NHS; Span C; Pres Clroom.

BECKMAN, Bradley James
Dassel-Cokato HS; Cokato, MN (25-119) Chor; Madrigal; SC; Bkbl; Ftbl; Tr; Cand, HKg; Gustavus Adolphus Col.

BECKMAN, John Charles
Dassel-Cokato HS; Cokato, MN; Band; Chor; Madrigal; SC; JV, Bsbl; Co-Cpt, Bkbl; Ftbl; Hist.

BECKMAN, Wanda Mae
Lenora HS; Lenora, KS (1-15) Band; S-T, Soph Cl.

BECKMANN, Laurie Ann
Harry A Burke HS; Omaha, NE (137-793) Rptr, Sch P; Tr; Kearney St Col.

BECKMEYER, Karen Lynn
Willowbrook HS; Villa Park, IL (142-789) Bkbl; Core Ldr, Church Yth Group; HR Merits; Data Processing-Key Punch Contest A.

BECKNER, Deanna Kaye
Amarillo HS; Amarillo, TX; Chor; Ensm; Thes; Mgr, Tr; Church Choir; Sojourner; River Ministry; Bus Ministry; W Tex St U; Nurs.

BECKNER, Janice Lynn
Roseville HS; Roseville, MI; Chor.

BECKNER, Jeanie Cleona
Jefferson HS; Jefferson, IA (34-122) S-T, FHA; Var C; Golf; Tr; U of N Iowa; Special Ed.

BECKOM, Lugenie Faith
S Hills HS; Pittsburgh, PA (128-520) Band; Chor; Drama; NHS; Orch; SC; Hon Prog; Most Out; Yth Fel; Vandalism Contr Unit Brd of Pub Ed; Indiana U of Penn; Psych.

BECKS, Elaine Denise
George Washington HS; Denver, CO; Chldr; Chor; Drama; Gym; Bowl Tm.

BECKSTEAD, Richard L
Bonneville HS; Ogden, UT; Band; FBLA; Ski C; Weber Col; Natural Resources.

BECKSTEAD, Riley M
Bonneville HS; Ogden, UT; Band; Tr; Gold 'B' A; Weber St Col; Forestry.

BECKWITH, Nancy Anne
Palisade HS; Palisade, CO (1-69) Chor; Pres, NHS; SC; Tres, Var C; Cpt, Bkbl; Sftbl; Amer Leg A; DARGCA; HQn; HCt; Kiwanis A; Lion A; Math A; Opt Out Tn; Val; Cpt & MVP, Vlbl; MVP, Bkbl; U of Northern Colo; Phys Ed.

BECOATE, Theodosia Francant
Burke HS; Charleston, SC (42-210) Food Service; Norfolk St Col; Special Ed.

BECTON, Elizabeth Ann
Hunter Huss HS; Gastonia, NC (9-465) Band; BC; Drama; Fr C; Rainbow; Thes; Alg A; Hon Prog; Jr Marshal; Sorth, DeMolay Chpt; Mars Hill Pres Schol; Mars Hill Mus Dept Schol; Mars Hill Col; Mus Ed.

BECTON, John Henry
W Carteret HS; Morehead City, NC; Bsbl; Bkbl; NC Central Col; Computer Data.

BEDDINGFIELD, Scott Howard
Baker HS; Baker, LA (2-374) BS; InterClub Coun; Mu Alpha Theta; Pres, NHS; Tnns; Cl Fav; LSU; Chem Engr.

BEDENBAUGH, Kathy
Cooper City HS; Ft Lauderdale, FL (10%-825) Band; Bus C; Hmrm; COM; JA A; Gym; All Star, All Co Band; Sportsmanship A; Pres Phys Fitness A; Journ.

BEDFORD, Steven Charles
St Joseph's Regional HS; Lowell, MA; Tres, Hmrm; Order/Arrow; SC; Tres, Soph Cl; Johnson and Wales Col; Culinary Arts.

BEDINGFIELD, Charisse
Columbus HS; Columbus, GA (10%-435) Ed, Ann; Chor; Ensm; Hmrm; InterClub Coun; NHS; COM; Chem A; Cl Fav; Gov Honor Prog; Hon Prog; Q&S A; Secy, Jr Civitan; Columbus Col; Opthalmology.

BEDNAREK, Theresa Ann
Waupun HS; Waupun, WI; Chor.

BEDNARZ, Philip John
Wilson HS; Wilson, TX (1-25) VP, Band; BS; VP, CYO; VP, FFA; Secy, Jr Cl; Bkbl; Ftbl; Tr; Alg A; Bio A; Hist A; Math A; Sci A; Tex Tech U; Phar.

BEDRICK, Brooke
The Brear Ley Sch; New York, NY (3-57) Chor; Dbte Tm; Drama; Ensm; Hmrm; Lit Mag; Orch; SC; Harvard U; Law.

BEDROSIAN, Ruth Ann
W Aurora Sr HS; Aurora, IL (99-631) A Cap Choir; Chldr; Chor; NHS; Gym; Sun Sch Teacher; Purdue U; Social Sci.

BEDSON, Lance Wade
Fairchance Georges HS; Uniontown, PA (35-153) Drama; FBLA; Pres, Hmrm; Pres, Sr Cl; Bsbl; Wrest; U of Maryland; Bus Adm.

BEDWELL, Mary Anne
New Bern Sr HS; New Bern, NC (3-597) Cpt, Chldr; Fr C; Pres, FHA; Ed, Sch P; SC; Secy, Y-Tns; Tnns; COM; Hon Prog; Journ A; NEDT; Sci A; Home Ec A; Textiles & Merchandising.

BEDWELL, Susan Leanne
Sarasota HS; Sarasota, FL; Tnns; COM; Type A; Secretarial.

BEEBE, Mark Alan
Venice HS; Venice, FL (49-388) BS; Hmrm; Secy, Key C; SC; Co-Cpt, Var C; Ftbl; Co-Cpt, Tr; Bio A; COM; Elk A; U of Fla; Dentistry.

BEEBE, Michael Phillip
Washington HS; Kansas City, KS (199-500) Ftbl; Swim; Tr; Cpt, Wrest; Yth Fel.

BEEBE, Monica Beth
Maranatha HS; Arcadia, CA (53-70) A Cap Choir; Chor; Drama; Thes; CSF; U of Sou Calif; Child Development.

BEEBE, Rory Marty
Fort Sr HS; Fort Atkinson, WI (90-250) Demolay; Key C; Order/Arrow; Secy, Var C; Cpt, Bsbl; Mgr, Bkbl; Ftbl; Wrest; Lakeland Col; Theology.

BEECH, Wayne Edward
Daviess Co HS; Owensboro, KY; Outst Stu, Gen Shop & Elec; 2nd Pl, Sci Fair; U of Ky; Elec.

BEECHING, Mark Richard
Lowell Sr HS; Lowell, IN (40-240) Swim; Art Guild; Industrial Arts A; Art A; Drafting.

BEEKMAN, Amy Lynn
Spruce Creek Sr HS; Port Orange, FL; BC; Key C; Lit Mag; Swim; Berry Col.

BEELER, Lana Kay
Knoxville Central HS; Knoxville, TN (103-371) Chor; Mjrte; Hon Prog; Yth Fel; Yth Ldr; U of Tenn; BA.

BEELER, Linda Marie
Central HS; Knoxville, TN; Chor; SC; VP, Soph Cl; Bkbl; Sftbl; Tr; St Decathalon Champion; FCA; E Tenn St U; Dental Hygiene.

BEELER, Nina Marie
Lawrence HS; Lawrence, KS (30-668) Chor; GS; Hmrm; Tr; Hon Prog; Kans U; Phar.

BEEMAN, Doug
Jennings Co HS; N Vernon, IN; Demolay; FFA; Ftbl; Sci A; Chaplain, DeMolay.

BEEMAN, Paul Avery
Jennings Co HS; N Vernon, IN; Demolay; FFA; Ftbl; Wrest.

BEEMAN, Randy Ray
Brownsville Area HS; Brownsville, PA (50-303) Chor; Drama; NHS; Span C; Spch C; Bkbl; Q&S A; Waynesburg Col; Acct.

BEEMAN, Wendy Ellen
Keith Hall HS; Lowell, MA (24-96) Hmrm; Ski C; SC; Bus Mgr, Bkbl; Tr; MLS; Sci A; Amer Legion Auxilary; Ch, Sports Committee; Math.

BEEN, Beth Ann
Pickens HS; Pickens, WV (3-15) Chldr; Drama; Secy, 4H; NHS; Tres, SC; Bkbl; 4H A; Davidson Col; Med.

BEENE, Debra Lynn
Mexia HS; Mexia, TX (12-50) Drama; FHA; Span C; Yth Fel.

BEENE, Eric Charles
Argo Comm HS; Argo, IL (284-566) Sch P; Ftbl; Tr; Wrest; Cl Fav; DARGCA; Grambling Col; Photography.

BEENER, Judi Ann
Staples HS; Staples, MN (10-150) Ann; Secy, Bus C; Secy, FHA; Ski C; Spch C; Tnns; Tr; COM; Spch A; Alexandria Voc-Tech Col; Legal Secy.

BEER, Angela Rochelle
Hooker HS; Hooker, OK (4-45) Ann; Chor; Ensm; Pres, Jr Cl; Bkbl; Tr; Type A; Offensive Player o-t Yr, Bkbl; Bulldog A, Bkbl.

BEERMANN, Della Gwen
Rochelle Township HS; Rochelle, IL (60-350) Pres, AFS; Band; JV, Bkbl; Tnns; Jazz Band; Pep Band; Loyalty Day Essay Contest; Conf Band; Mus Camp Schol.

BEERS, Cynthia Ann
Central HS; Martinsburg, PA; Pres, Rainbow.

BEERS, Julie Grace
Reading Mem HS; Reading, MA (40%-444) AFS; Drama; A-Ed, Lit Mag; Crisco A; Communications.

BEERS, Richard Townsend
All Saints Cathedral Sch; St Thomas, VI (4-18) Math C; SC; Bkbl; Bio A; NMS; Photo C; 3rd Pl, Essay Contest; Advertising Ed, Photo Ed, Yearbook; Layout Comm, Yearbook; Elec Engr.

BEERS, Sue Ellen
Trotwood-Madison Sr HS; Trotwood, OH (2-350) NHS; ARC; Hon Prog; NEDT; Sal; Full Col Schol; Stu Ombudsman Prog; U of Dayton; Elec Engr.

BEERY, Kathleen Ann
Lancaster HS; Lancaster, OH (319-546) Band; Pres, 4H; Mjrte; Orch; 4H A; Ohio U.

BEERY, Nancy Susan
Lancaster HS; Lancaster, OH (5%-600) A Cap Choir; Band; Chor; Drama; Rptr, 4H; SC; Secy, Soph Cl.

BEES, Robin Eileen
NE Sr HS; Pasadena, MD (3-30) Job's Daughters; Towson St Col; Foreign Lang.

BEESLEY, Kari Lee
Southgate HS; Southgate, MI; Band; Ensm; Band Schol; Nurs.

BEESON, Jan Paige
John D Bassett HS; Bassett, VA (15%-210) Chor; Ensm; Fr C; Swim; Tnns; Region, All Co, Choir; Prom Ch; Win, Girl's Solo; Eng A; Yth Secy; Emmanuel Col; Sci.

BEESON, Timothy Joe
E Davidson HS; Thomasville, NC (20%-150) Monogram; Sch P; JV, Bkbl; Ftbl; Golf; Journ A; Pep C; Wake Forest U; Bus.

BEEZLEY, Karen Lee
St Joseph Sr HS; St Joseph, MI (125-365) Ger C.

BEEZLEY, Sharon Dee
St Joseph Sr HS; St Joseph, MI (150-350) Ger C; F-Ed, Sch P; Hon Men for Lenox Crystal; Lake Mich Col; Nurs.

BEFFA, Georganna Gail
New Bloomfield R III HS; New Bloomfield, MO (25%-45) Cpt, Chldr; Chor; Sch P; Sci C; SC; Bkbl; Sftbl; DARGCA; HQn; HCt; Pres, Pep C; Ltr C.

BEGAY, Cecelia
Chinle HS; Chinle, AZ (10-150) CYO; FFA; Secy, NHS; Span C; Pres, Sr Cl; Tres, Jr Cl; Bkbl; Sftbl; Secy, GAA; Cpt, Vlbl; *Phoenix Col; Ed.*

BEGGS, Lisa Lynn
Southland HS; Arbyrd, MO (3-38) Drama; FHA; FTA; NHS; Bio A; Hon Prog; Sci A; Eng, Psych, Lit, A's; Pres, Lib C; *Ark St U; Social Work.*

BEGGS, Robin Joy
Center Sr HS; Kansas City, MO (39-407) A Cap Choir; Band; Chor; Drama; NFL; NHS; Spch A; Oratory A; *SW Baptist Col; Religion.*

BEHAN, Judith
Bishop Byrne HS; Memphis, TN (3-198) Chess C; Fr C; Ed, Lit Mag; Tres, Math C; Tres, Mu Alpha Theta; Math A-Ed, Sch P; SC; Cr-Ctry; Tr; Alg A; COM; H of F; Math A; MLS; NEDT; ARC A; VofDEM; WW; DAHSS; *U of Ark Fayetteville; Architecture.*

BEHM, Mark Charles
Phoenixville Area HS; Phoenixville, PA (5-281) Secy, Key C; NHS; Var C; Tnns; Amer Leg A; Hon Prog; *PAJHS Achv A; Pre-Med.*

BEHNER, Colleen Kay
S Bend Jr Acad; S Bend, IN; Ann; Chor; Dbte Tm; Rptr, Sch P; Cpt, Ftbl; 4H A; JA A; Val; Church Yth Organization; Yth Song-leader, Church; *Andrews U; Hair Styling.*

BEHNKE, Donald Harold
W Allegheny HS; Imperial, PA (10-250) Chor; Pres, Fr C; Tres, NHS; Var C; Golf; COM; Yth Fel; Vars Ltr; *Carnegie-Mellon Col; Chem Engr.*

BEHNKE, Kathleen Ann
Wethersfield HS; Kewanee, IL (5-90) AFS; Co-Ed, Ann; Band; Fr C; Band A, Yrbk A; Tres, St Paul's Walther League; *U of Ill; Math.*

BEHNKEN, Joel
Kountze HS; Kountze, TX; Chem C; FFA; Hmrm; Math C; NHS; Sci C; Chem A; Math A; Cl Offices; *Tex A&M U; Engr.*

BEHR, Thomas Robert
South Plainfield HS; S Plainfield, NJ (154-356) Hmrm; SC; Var C; Co-Cpt, Bsbl; Bkbl; Ftbl; Cpt, Bowl; *Eastern Ill U; Acct.*

BEHRENDS, Ranae Sue
New Hartford Community HS; New Hartford, IA (1-41) Band; Chor; Ensm; NHS; Mgr, Bkbl; Tr; *U of Northern Iowa; Acct.*

BEHRENS, Bobbie Jo
Brown HS; Sturgis, SD (51-220) Band; Chldr; Dbte Tm; VP, FBLA; Hmrm; Rptr, Pol Sci C; Secy, Ski C; SC; Var C; Pres, Jr Cl; Cr-Ctry; Golf; Sftbl; COM; Cl Fav; Type A; Favorite Underclass Girl; Parl A; Pres, SD St Fbla; *Cottey Col; Law.*

BEHRENS, Jean Marie
Treynor Comm HS; Treynor, IA (3-48) Band; Chor; FHA; 4H; 4H A; Sci A.

BEHRENS, Kurt William
Hastings Sr HS; Hastings, MN (25-350) Chess C; Cr-Ctry; Sci A.

BEHRENS, Lorrey Ann
Richwoods HS; Peoria, IL (206-600) Bus C; Chor; Swim; JA A; *Ill Central U; Bus.*

BEHRING, Robin Renee
Enid HS; Enid, OK; Rainbow; Span C; NJHS; Okla Jr Hon Soc; *Okla St U; Engr.*

BEICHEL, Vicki Lisa
SW HS; St Louis, MO; Chor; Ensm; FHA; Madrigal; Orch; Rptr, Sch P; Sci C; Hon Prog; *U of Mo; Bio.*

BEIDLER, Craig Donald
River Falls Sr HS; River Falls, WI (1-185) NHS; Sch P; Var C; Hockey; Co-Cpt, Tnns; NMF; *UW-RIVER Falls; Physics.*

BEIDLER, Michael Lee
Freedom HS; Bethlehem, PA (205-521) A Cap Choir; Chor; Hmrm; ARC; Semi-Fin, Swim; Mus A; *Pa St U; Civil Engr.*

BEIER, Bernadette
Bishop Luers HS; Fort Wayne, IN (32-237) Mgr, Ftbl; Tr; Hon Prog; *Forestry.*

BEIERSCHMITT, Lynn Marie
Cleveland HS; Cleveland, TN (15%-255) Band; CYO; Co-Cpt, Mjrte; Secy, SC; Tri-HiY; JV, Bkbl; HCt; *Middle Tenn St U; Law.*

BEIGHTON, Sally Bonita
Sheboygan Falls HS; Sheboygan Falls, WI (33%-165) Sch P; Span C; Sftbl; Mgr, Tr; Pom Pon Bar & Pin; Yth Tutor; Forensics A; Journ Pin; *Elec.*

BEIHOLD, Janice Joan
Bellmont HS; Decatur, IN (20%-251) Band; HR; Church Choir; PA; VP, Tres, MYF; Church Quiz Tm; MYF Conventions; *Taylor U.*

BEILER, Judith Ann
Clark HS; Las Vegas, NV (387-781) S-T, Chor; Ski C; Yth Fel; Snow Qn; Yth Fel; *Col of Idaho; Ed.*

BEILER, Scott Alan
Gwynn Park HS; Brandywine, MD; Band; Chor; Ensm; Tr; Mus, Tr, A's; *U of Md; Mus.*

BEINKE, Marty Ann
Deer Park HS; Cincinnati, OH (3-215) City Conf; GS; NHS; SC; Pres, Sr Cl; Pres, Jr Cl; Pres, Soph Cl; Bkbl; Rptr, Ftbl; JV, Hockey; Sftbl; Tr; COM; Hon Prog; Cpt, Vlbl; Red's Straight A Tickets; Pres, Girls Ath Assn; WW Foreign Lang; GAA 3yr A; *U of Cincinnati; Engr.*

BEIO, Adele Edgar
Marshall Islands HS; Majuro, MARSHALL IS-LANDS (16-103) Hon Prog; Star Student; *Dentistry.*

BEIRIGER, Judy Irene
Queen of Peace HS; Burbank, IL (1-360) Ed, Ann; Fr C; Tres, NHS; COM; Chem A; NMF; NEDT; Phy A; St Scholar; Val; Pres, Photography C; General Service A; *Northwestern U; Engr.*

BEISEL, Larry Dale
Perry HS; Perry, OK (1-130) FTA; NHS; JV, Bsbl; Ftbl; JV, Wrest; Masonic A; *Hist.*

BEISEL, Sandra Joan
Salina HS S; Salina, KS (1-331) Band; Chor; Ensm; KMEA District Hon Band; *Mus.*

BEITEL, Linda Nadine
Englewood HS; Englewood, CO (22-360) Ann; Chor; Madrigal; NHS; Q&S A; Fr A; Oil Company Grant; Win, Baptist Conf Solo Contest; Jr Hon Escort, Graduation; *U of N Colo; Eng.*

BEJA, Wendy Ann
Kelly HS; Chicago, IL (26-625) Ch, Hmrm; Rptr, Sch P; Journ A; *DePaul U; Journ.*

BEJARANO, Edward
Goddard HS; Roswell, NM; Band; Ger C.

BELANGER, Daniel
College De Ste Anne De La Pocatiere; La Pocatiere, CANADA (2-29) Pres, Hmrm; SC; Cpt, Bsbl; Hockey.

BELCHER, Carmella Faith
Welch HS; Welch, WV (33%-180) F-Ed, Ann; Chldr; Q&S A; Yth Fel; *Marshall U; Fr.*

BELCHER, David Wayne
Germantown HS; Germantown, TN (2-475) Ed, Ann; BC; Chem C; Chor; Key C; Phys C; Sci C; Span C; Bkbl; Alg A; Bio A; COM; Cl Fav; 4H A; MLS; Opt Out Tn; *Memphis St U; Engr.*

BELCHER, Dewayne Walker
Athens HS; Athens, AL (25-250) Math C; Pres, Sr Cl; Bkbl; Cr-Ctry; Tr; Cl Fav; HCt; FCA.

BELCHER, Mark Steven
Joppatowne HS; Joppa, MD (10%-400) Chor; NHS; Pres, Var C; Ftbl; Tnns; All-Co Ftbl; Stu o-t Month; Most Outst Jr; *Western Md Col; Hist.*

BELCHER, Pamela Jo
F T Wills HS; Smyrna, GA; Band; Chor; Secy, 4H; Bkbl; Sftbl; COM; HCt; Sci A; Jr Civitans.

BELCHER, Peggy Ann
Tehachapi HS; Tehachagi, CA (10%-130) Ann; Band; Chor; Fr C; VP, FHA; Hmrm; Model UN; Pres, Rainbow; Bkbl; CSF; COM; Win, Yth Fel; Ntl Piano Guild Audition; Grand Cross; *UOP; Mus.*

BELCHER, Robert Wesley
Dinwiddie Sr HS; Dinwiddie, VA (1-350) FBLA; Pres, FFA; InterClub Coun; NHS; Pres, Span C; Bkbl; Tnns; COM; DARGCA; Hon Prog; Ntl Conf Chr & Jews; Sci A; Type A; Yth Fel; Asst Degree, FBLA; Forestry Judging A, FFA; Home Improvement A, FFA; *Old Dominion U; Civil Engr.*

BELCHER, William Robert
Madison Acad HS; Huntsville, AL (8-43) BC; Chem C; Math C; Monogram; NHS; Var C; Ftbl; Alg A; COM; Chem A; Citz A; Hon Prog; Math A; MLS; Sci A; Star Student; Type A; *UA; Chem.*

BELDEN, Lori Ann
St Elmo HS; St Elmo, IL (3-50) S-T, Band; Chldr; Chor; Ensm; Fr C; NHS; Mgr, Tr; COM; Citz A; 4H A; HCt; Hon Prog; Cpt, Vlbl; Band A; Piano Camp School; *SIU Edwardsville; Nurs.*

BELDEN, Ronda Lynn
Thurston HS; Springfield, OR (5-255) Bus C; Hmrm; NHS; Hockey; Gov Honor Prog; Type A; *U of Oreg; Acct.*

BELEW, Lee Ann
Rose Bud HS; Rose Bud, AR (2-29) Co-Ed, Ann; Secy, BC; Tres, FHA; NHS; Co-Ed, Sch P; Cpt, Bkbl; Sftbl; Fin, Tr; Citz A; HCt; Hon Prog; MLS; Sal; MVP, Bkbl; Eng A; *U of Central Ark; Journ.*

BELFIELD, Tammy Carol
York Acad; Shacklefords, VA (3-43) BC; Chor; Lat NHS; NFL; Secy, Jr Cl; Hockey; Tnns; HCt; Hon Prog; Magna Cum Laude; Math A; Sci A; Headmaster's, Eng, A's; *Amer Bus & Fashion Inst; Fashion Design.*

BELICA, Marina Elena
Briarcliff HS; Briarcliff Manor, NY (1-127) A Cap Choir; Chor; Drama; Ensm; F-Ed, Lit Mag; Madrigal; NHS; Orch; Tres, SC; COM; Chamber of Comm A; Citz A; DARGCA; Hon Prog; Regent Schol; Val; All-St Orch; All-Eastern Orch; *Yale U; Mus.*

BELISARIO, Phillip Dean
Edward H White HS; Jacksonville, FL (411-749) Chor; Drama; Choral A; *Fla Jr Col; Mus.*

BELK, Deborah Sue
Independence HS; Charlotte, NC (93-600) NHS; Piano A; *U of NC.*

BELK, Valerie Sue
Ethel HS; Ethel, MS; *Hinds Jr Col; Elem Ed.*

BELKNAP, Jim Kennedy
Middle Park HS; Granby, CO (6-78) Ann; Hmrm; Ski C; SC; *Colo St U; Vet.*

BELKNAP, Mark Lee
Odessa HS; Odessa, TX; A Cap Choir; Ensm; NHS; JV, Ftbl; Mgr, Tr; Hist A; All Region Choir; No 1 Rating, UIL Solo Ensm Contest.

BELKNAP, Shirley Marie
Columbus W HS; Columbus, OH (1-581) Ed, Ann; Cpt, Band; Community Yth Symph; Drama; Ch, Hmrm; InterClub Coun; VP, Lat C; Math C; VP, NHS; Cpt, Orch; Rainbow; Sch Achieve Tm; A-Ed, Sch P; SC; Sftbl; COM; Hon Prog; Kiwanis A; Math A; Most Out; Phy A; St Scholar; Val; NML; Ohio St U Fresh School; Exchange Stu; *Ohio St U; Bio Med Engr.*

BELL, Adelbert Joseph
Driscoll HS; Addison, IL (16-144) NHS; VP, SC; Wrest; COM; NMS; St Scholar; *Ill Inst of Tech; Engr.*

BELL, Andrea Kay
Glendale HS; Springfield, MO; Bkbl; Mortarboard; Span Relay A; Yth Observ, John Calvin Union Presb; *Kans U; Archt.*

BELL, Andrea Louise
Marian A Peterson HS; Sunnyvale, CA (10%-485) Drama; Span C; Cpt, Sftbl; CSF; NMF; *Whitman Col; Lib Arts.*

BELL, Andrew Clyde
Plainfield HS; Plainfield, IN (70-297) Band; SC; Ftbl; Tr; FCA; WW; *LSU; Elec Engr.*

BELL, Beverly Ellen
Monroe Area Comprehensive HS; Monroe, GA (1-275) BC; Fr C; Hi-Y; B Crocker A; Piano Stu; Church Choir; Stage Mgr, 'Hello Dolly'; *Agnes Scott Col; Mus.*

BELL, Brenda Jeannette
Mission HS; Mission, TX (35-357) Band; Chor; Math C; Spch C; Parl, SC; Pres, Y-Tns; Beauty; Citz A; H of F; Lion A; Rotary A; Yth Fel; Cotillion C; *Tex A&M U; Acct.*

BELL, Cecilia
E Orange HS; E Orange, NJ (40%-600) S-T, Chor; FNA; Pres, Hmrm; Citz A; Hon Prog; Lat A; *Sociology.*

BELL, Cheryl Annette
N Wilkes HS; Hays, NC (65-135) FBLA; FHA; *Wilkes Comm Col; Child Care.*

BELL, Christine Naomi
Crenshaw HS; Los Angeles, CA; Citz A; Hon Prog; Church Chor & Drama; *Data Processing.*

BELL, Clayton Brian
S Kitsap HS; Port Orchard, WA; JV, Cr-Ctry; JV, Tr; *Pepperdine U.*

BELL, Darryl Alexander
Northwest HS; St Louis, MO (4-728) Band; Hon Prog.

BELL, David Edward
Weld Central HS; Keenesburg, CO (18-100) Band; BS; FFA; NHS; SC; VP, Var C; MVP, Ftbl; Tr.

BELL, Deanna Leigh
Rossville HS; Rossville, GA (24-212) Cpt, Bkbl; MVP, Bkbl; Bkbl Schol; *Covenant Col; Ed.*

BELL, Douglas A
Carmichaels Area HS; Carmichaels, PA (4-83) Band; Semi-Fin, Chess C; Tres, NHS; Co-Ed, Sch P; Span C; SC; Golf; Tnns; Amer Leg A; HCt; Lion A; *Penn St; Journ.*

BELL, Gloria Jean
Crenshaw HS; Los Angeles, CA; Tnns; Citz A; Church Chor & Drama; Service C; *Legal Secy.*

BELL, Hattie L
Alexander HS; Starkville, MS (30-59) Y-Tns; *Miss St U; Bus.*

BELL, Henry Brandt Jr
Columbus Unified HS; Columbus, KS (8-104) Secy, FFA; Pres, NHS; Bkbl; Ftbl; Tr; Amer Leg A; DARGCA; H of F; Pres A; St Scholar; FFA; Empire Dist Hon Stu Conf; *Northeastern Okla A&M.*

BELL, Hiram Jardain
Robert E Lee HS; Montgomery, AL; Hmrm; Inter-Club Coun; Pres, Spch C; SC; Tnns; Spch A; *U of Ala; Ministry.*

BELL, James Alton
W T White HS; Dallas, TX (300-750) Spch C; Spch A; Type A; Trainer, Ftbl, Soccer & Tr; FCA; Tex A&M Trainer Schol; *Tex A&M U; Phys Ed.*

BELL, James Ernest
Exeter HS; Exeter, NE (3-40) Band; Math C; NHS; Bkbl; Ftbl; Tr; Amer Leg A; Order/Arrow A; Regent Schol; David Schol; *U of Nebr; Physics.*

BELL, Janice LaRose
Reidsville Sr HS; Reidsville, NC (5%-375) JV, Chldr; Tres, FHA; *UNC-Chapel Hill; Phys Theraphy.*

BELL, Jeffrey Alan
Malbar HS; Mansfield, OH (87-252) Bkbl; Tr; Yth Fel; Pres, Yth Fel.

BELL, Jeffrey Harold
Oak Hills HS; Cincinnati, OH (288-795) Ski C; JV, Ftbl; Jr Achv; *Bio Chem.*

BELL, Joel Thomas
Blackwell HS; Blackwell, OK (50-200) Ann; Band; Chor; Pres, Drama; Ensm; Sch P; VP, Spch C; Thes; Mgr, Tr; MLS; Drum Major; Best Actor; *Central St U; Mus.*

BELL, Julie Ann
Saint Ursula Acad; Toledo, OH; Semi-Fin, All Amer Y; Arch; Secy, Bus C; Chess C; Secy, Chor; Drama; Semi-Fin, Hmrm; Arch; Bsbl; Fin, Bkbl; Soccer; Sftbl; Tnns; Tr; Cl Fav; Most Out; Tn- ager o-t Month Safety Guard A; *Toledo U; Psych.*

BELL, Julie Lynn
Moultrie Sr HS; Moultrie, GA (30-337) A Cap Choir; Anchor C; Ann; Ch, BC; Chor; Ensm; Hmrm; SC; Tri-HiY; Bkbl; Cl Fav; Coun of Teach A; Hon Prog; Keywanettes; Sr Teacher's Plaque; The Serenaders; Church Choir; Best Actress A; Avion A; Sprtsmnshp A, St Tr-Hi-Y Tourn; *U of Ga; Mus.*

BELL, Karen Sue
Charlestown HS; Charlestown, IN (26-200) Band; Chor; Ensm; FBLA; Span C; Spch C; Var C; Cr-Ctry; Swim; Hon Prog; Opt A; Spch A; *Bus.*

BELL, Karl Irvin
Frederick Douglass HS; Atlanta, GA (45-343) NHS; Cpt, Bsbl; Cpt, Bkbl; ROTC A.

BELL, Kerry Lee
Miami Killian Sr HS; Miami, FL (62-1100) Drama; Cum Laude; Art Hon Soc; *U of Fla; Psych.*

BELL, Larry Leon
M B Smiley HS; Houston, TX (33-400) Ensm; Tres, Fr C; NHS; Span C; COM; Citz A; Hon Prog; Drum Major, Band; Span Band, A's; Solo & Ensm Band Medals; Dist & Regional Band; *U of Houston; Mus.*

BELL, Laurel Lynne
*Douglas Mac*arthur HS;* Saginaw, MI (10%-375) 4H; Orch; Ski C; JV, Tnns; Tr; 4H A; Hon Prog; Secy, Yth Fel; Wilderness Survival Course; *Colo St U; Vet Med.*

BELL, Leigh Ann
Pulaski Acad; Little Rock, AR (7-62) BC; Hon Prog.

BELL, Luana Lea
Wichita E HS; Wichita, KS; Span C; Hist A.

BELL, Martinez
Murray Wright HS; Detroit, MI;

BELL, Martinez Valarie
Murray Wright HS; Detroit, MI;

BELL, Martinez Vessia
Murray Wright HS; Detroit, MI;

BELL, Mary Ann
Coshocton HS; Coshocton, OH (24-214) Chem C; Chess C; Parl, 4H; NHS; Span C; B Crocker A; COM; Hon Prog; NEDT; St Scholar; Swim Timer; Edmont Achv A; *Ohio U; Art.*

BELL, Mary Lucy
Lower Richland HS; Hopkins, SC (23-501) Co-Ed, Ann; BC; ARC; Journ A; Yth Fel.

BELL, Melinda Marie
Susquehanna Comm HS; Susquehanna, PA; Band; Chldr; Chor; SC; *Broome Comm Col; Dental Hygienist.*

BELL, Pamela Jean
Temple Heights Christian HS; Tampa, FL; Drama; HR; *Liberty Bible Col; Home Ec.*

BELL, Pamela Sue
Tabernacle Baptist Sch; Va Beach, VA; Chldr; Chor; Sch P; Spch C; Y-Tns; Alg A; 4H A; Yth Fel; Pro-tns; *Bob Jones U; Christian Service.*

BELL, Perry Lee
Morton HS; Morton, TX; Band; FTA; Parl, SC; Cpt, Tnns; Drum Major; John Philip Sousa A; All St Band; *Tex Tech U; Med.*

BELL, Rebecca Lynn
Lynden Baines Johnson HS; Austin, TX (15-330) Math C; Mu Alpha Theta; NHS; Sci C; Secy, Span C; SC; Tr; COM; Math A; Most Out; Opt Out Tn; PTA A; Yth Fel; PTSA; Young Life; Drill Tm; *U of Tex at Austin; Sci.*

BELL, Rebecca Lynne
Skyline HS; Dallas, TX; FHA; FTA; 4H; ARC; ARC A; *Sou Methodist U; Bus Adm.*

BELL, Rita Lynne
Smithfield-Selma HS; Smithfield, NC (9-355) Ann; Band; Chor; Fr C; Hmrm; Pres, NHS; Sci C; SC; *U of NC; Phys Therapy.*

BELL, Robin Louise
Bradley-Bourbonnais Comm HS; Bradley, IL (34-420).

BELL, Ronald Alexander Jr
Starmount HS; Boonville, NC (27-166) Band; Tres, Mu Alpha Theta; Cr-Ctry; JV, Ftbl; Cpt, Tnns; Wrest; *NC St U; US Army.*

BELL, Russell Loy
Hopewell HS; Hopewell, VA (90-480) Fr C; JV, Bkbl; *Entertainment.*

BELL, Sandra Ellen
Bronx HS of Sci; New York, NY (50%-36) A Cap Choir; Band; Orch; Bio A; COM; Citz A; Hist A; Hon Prog; K of C A; Sci A; *Columbia U; Med.*

BELL, Stanley Alonzo
Northside HS; Memphis, TN (49-476) Band; Bus C; Drama; Ensm; FBLA; Hmrm; Lat C; Lit Mag; Orch; ARC; Spch C; SC; Thes; COM; Citz A; Cl Fav; ROTC A; Spch A; Star Student; Intramural Statistician's A; *U of Tenn at Martin; Comm.*

BELL, Susan Denise
Quitman HS; Quitman, AR (1-43) Ed, Ann; Secy, BC; Cpt, Chldr; Secy, Dbte Tm; Secy, Drama; Secy, FHA; GS; Secy, 4H; Semi-Fin, Jr Miss Pa; Rptr, SC; Rptr, Jr Cl; Bkbl; Cl Fav; 4H A; HQn; WW; Jr Miss QHS; 2nd Runner-Up, Miss Cleburne Co; Home Ec A; Chldr Spirit A.

BELL, Susan Louise
Wapakoneta Sr HS; Wapakoneta, OH (7-335) Band; Chor; Fr C; 4H; NHS; Sch Achieve Tm; Y-Tns; NEDT; *Albion Col; Social Sci.*

BELL, Susan Lynn
Belle Plaine HS; Belle Plaine, KS; Band; Secy, FFA; Span C; COM; St Scholar; Dist Band; *Bus.*

BELL, Tammy Lee
Nevada Union HS; Grass Valley, CA; A Cap Choir; Chor; Ensm; Madrigal; Thes; Most Out; *Sacramento St U; Mus.*

BELL, Terri Jo
Van Buren HS; Van Buren, AR (32-209) Ann; Chldr; GS; Fin, Jr Miss Pagent; NHS; Sch P; SC; Beauty; Cl Fav; HCt; WW.

BELL, Tina Louise
Sou Sr HS; Dudley, NC (44-388) AFS; Ann; Tres, FHA; Pres, FTA; NHS; Span C; Secy, SC; Hon Prog; Page, Gen Assembly; WW; *Mt Olive Col; Elem Ed.*

BELL, Valerie Marie
E Atlanta HS; Atlanta, GA (8-142) F-Ed, Ann; Band; BC; Hmrm; Tres, SC; Tnns; B Crocker A; HCt; Miss Ga Tn Pageant; *Navy; Communications.*

BELL, Wallace Wendell
Gumberry HS; Gumberry, NC (18-97) A-Ed, Ann; FFA; Bkbl; PE Highest Grade A; *A&T St U; Industrial Technology.*

BELLAMY, Brenda Jane
Citrus HS; Inverness, FL (18-250) Chldr; Drama; Fr C; Ed, Sch P; MVP, Tnns; Cl Fav; H of F; Kiwanettes; Outst Fr Stu A; WW; WW Among Amer HS Chldrs; *Fla Sou Col; Secondary Ed.*

BELLANI, Kenneth Edwin
St Peters Prep HS; Jersey City, NJ (13-250) NHS; A-Ed, Sch P; Ch, SC; Bkbl; Golf; Hon Prog; Lat Hon Medals; WW; Ch, Jr Prom; Ch, Social Comm; *Holy Cross Col; Pre-Law.*

BELLARD, Paul Barnes
Church Point HS; Church Point, LA (5-104) BS; VP, CYO; FFA; Hmrm; Lit Ral; VP, NHS; Ftbl; 1st St FFA Elec Mech Contest; *Spartan Sch of Aeronautics; Aeronautics.*

BELLAVANCE, Linda Sylvie
Alexander Galt Regional HS; Lennoxville, CANADA (21-539) Hon Prog; Secy.

BELLE, Charmagne Denise
Oakland Tech HS; Oakland, CA (20-450) Pres, Chor; VP, NHS; SC; CSF; Hon Prog; MLS; Pres A; St Scholar; *U o-t Pacific; Phar.*

BELLES, Gordon Lyle
Zillah HS; Zillah, WA (2-54) BC; Chess C; Chor; Drama; 4H; Pres, NHS; Masonic A; Math A; MLS; NMF; Sal; Win, Ntl Bible Quiz Tm; *Wash St U; Mech Engr.*

BELLEW, Carol Denise
Appalachian HS; Oneonta, AL (5-38) Ann; BC; 4H; Sch P; 4H A; WW; *Lee Col; Mus.*

BELLIFORD, William LerMont
John Overton HS; Nashville, TN (87-425) Band; Chess C; MVP, Bkbl; Cpt, Bkbl; *Aquinas Jr Col; Bio.*

BELLINGER, Cynthia Ann
Granite City HS S; Granite City, IL (321-650) Chor; Drama; Vocal A; *Lewis and Clark Comm Col; Dental Hygiene.*

BELLINGHAUSEN, Danette Kathleen
MacArthur HS; San Antonio, TX (15%-590) Secy, A Cap Choir; Pres, BC; CYO; Chor; Madrigal; Span C; Span NHS; Rptr, SC; COM; NEDT; Dance Tm; Span C Cert; COM Choir; 3 Div 1 Med, Chor UIL Contest; San Antonio Sr Cotillion; Secy, Yth Rel Prog; Joske's Tn Brd; *San Antonio Col.*

BELLINGHAUSEN, Joan Marie
Montrose R-14 Pub HS; Montrose, MO (1-26) CYO; Pres, 4H; NHS; Alg A; 4H A; Math A; Yth Foundation; *U of Mo-Columbia; Bus.*

BELLO, Joseph Mario
St Peters Prep HS; Jersey City, NJ (18-260) Ch, SC; JV, Hockey; Hon Prog; Italian A; Dance Comm; *Cornell U; Sci.*

BELLON, Rhonda Lee
Wayne Comm HS; Corydon, IA (7-65) Band; Chor; FBLA; FHA; Pres, 4H; NHS; JV, Bkbl; Sftbl; COM; 4H A; Type A; Yth Fel; *Grandview Col; Nurs.*

BELLON, Tammy Renee
Sam Houston HS; Lake Charles, LA (13-142) BC; FBLA; Secy, FHA; Lit Ral; Math C; Mu Alpha Theta; NHS; F-Ed, Sch P; SC; Bkbl; Mgr, Tr; DARGCA; Phi Beta Kappa; Yth Leg; Pep Sq; Bicen C; Church Choir; Church Yth Coun; Beta NHS; 3rd Pl, Parish Lit Ral, Home Ec; 5th Pl, St Lit Ral, Home Ec; *McNeese St U; Med Tech.*

BELLOWS, Judith Kelley
Lancaster HS; Lancaster, VA (35-200) F-Ed, Ann; Chor; Ed, Lit Mag; Cpt, Mjrte; Ed, Sch P; Sci C; Span C; Var C; Semi-Fin, Tr; Pep C; Sch Play; *NC Wesleyan Col; Behavoral Sci.*

BELLOWS, Timothy Culver
Lancaster HS; Lancaster, VA (20-200) Band; Chess C; Ensm; Orch; Sci C; COM.

BELONGER, Steven Lee
Belvidere HS; Belvidere, IL (100-363) Span NHS; Tr; VP, FCA; *Northern Ill U; Bus Adm.*

BELOTE, Bonnie
Greater Atlanta Christian HS; Norcross, GA (5-67) A Cap Choir; Tres, Drama; Ensm; NHS; COM; Citz A; Cl Fav; HCt; Magna Cum Laude; Type A; Tres, Yth Fel; WW; Most Talented; *Piedmont Hospital Sch of Nurs; Nurs.*

BELOTE, Robert Edwards
Shenandoah Valley Acad; New Market, VA; *Cleveland St Col; Commercial Art.*

BELT, Dawn Evette
Kenwood HS; Chicago, IL (65-332) Ski C; SC; Mgr, Sftbl; Tr; COM; H of F; Mod Dance; Pres, Pep C; Principal's HR; Amer Cancer Soc Schol; *U of Ill; Biochem.*

BELT, Vanessa Lynne
Lyon Co HS; Eddyville, KY (1-70) Ann; BC; Rptr, FHA; 4H; Alg A; Hon Prog; Val; Acct A; Tr; Chapter, St, FHA Degrees; Murray Math Tourn; *Murray St U; Acct.*

BELTINCK, Teresa Anne
Sacred Heart Acad; Mt Pleasant, MI (4-50) F-Ed, Ann; Chor; Drama; NHS; SC; Pres, Jr Cl; VP, Soph Cl; Bkbl; Sftbl; Mgr, Tr; COM; Hon Prog; Acad A; Freedom Found Essay Contest; *Central Mich U; Acct.*

BELTON, Dwight Clayton
Castlemont HS; Oakland, CA; *San Francisco St Col; Pol Sci.*

BELVA, David Guynn
Newport HS; Newport, AR (23-250) Lat C; Bsbl; Ftbl; Tr; Citz A; Sci A; All A & B A; *U of Ark; Math.*

BELYEU, Teresa Lee
Douglass HS; Douglass, TX (2-8) Chldr; FHA; Hmrm; Co-Ed, Lit Mag; SC; Co-Cpt, Bkbl; B Crocker A; COM; Journ A; *Stephen F Austin Col; Journ.*

BELZ, Ronald Lee
Simley Sr HS; Inver Grove Heights, MN (53-274) Chess C; NHS; Ski C; Var C; Cr-Ctry; Soccer; Tr; *Inver Hills Comm Col; Art.*

BELZER, Ricky Joe
Linn Co R-1 HS; Browning, MO (10-40) Ch, Band; Ch, Ensm; Rptr, 4H; SC; Var C; Pres, Soph Cl; Bkbl; Cr-Ctry; Sftbl; Tr; 4H A; HKg; Interlochen Ntl Mus; Spch A; *NE Mo St U; Phys Ed.*

BEMBENEK, Alan Roger
Dominican HS; Milwaukee, WI (1-225) Ann; BS; CYO; Drama; Hmrm; NHS; Bus Mgr, Sch P; Amer Leg A; COM; Math A; Pres, Art C; *Marquette Col; Law.*

BEMENT, Steve Richard
Highline HS; Seattle, WA; Band; Fin, City Conf; NHS; Soccer; COM; Service to Sch Trophy; Job Interview 'Vica' 1st Pl.

BEMER, Terrie Sue
Valley Forge HS; Parma Hgts, OH (172-881) A Cap Choir; Band; Chor; Fr C; Orch; SC; Y-Tns; COM; Citz A; Hon Prog; Spch A; Yth Fel; Fr A; *Bowling Green Col; Bus.*

BEMIS, Brenda Sue
Quincy Sr HS II; Quincy, IL; NHS; SAA A.

BEMIS, Naomi Jean
Aledo HS; Aledo, IL (5-135) Band; Ensm; Bkbl; Sftbl; GAA; *Engr.*

BEN, Nancy Cheryl
Tahlequah Sr HS; Tahlequah, OK; A Cap Choir; Chldr; Chem C; Chor; Drama; Ensm; FTA; Hmrm; SC; Sftbl; Hist A; HQn; Swtht.

BENALLY, Marilyn Louise
Chinle HS; Chinle, AZ (11-130) Ann; Arch; Drama; FHA; NHS; F-Ed, Sch P; Rptr, SC; Thes; Arch; Bkbl; *Mesa Comm Col; Ed.*

BENAUIDES, Mary Ellen
Johnston HS; Austin, TX (29-210) NHS; Span C; Hon Prog; Clerical A; Baptist Yth Organization; VP, VOE; *Austin Comm Col; Bus.*

BENBOW, Jeff Lee
Newport Harbor HS; Newport Beach, CA; Var C; Soccer; Tr; *Pepperdine U; Hist.*

BENCH, Cynthia Joy
Alsea HS; Alsea, OR (2-22) Ann; Chor; Drama; Fin, FHA; NHS; Rptr, Sch P; Span C; FHA A; Hon Soc; HR; *Oreg Col of Ed; Eng.*

BENCIVENGO, Jean
St Augustine Acad; Lakewood, OH (34-122) VP, CYO; SC; VP, Soph Cl; Bkbl; Mgr, Sftbl; Wmn Accts for Schol Achv in Acct; *Cleveland St U; Acct.*

BENCIVENGO, Raymond
St Ignatius HS; Cleveland, OH (75-326) VP, CYO; Chem C; Chess C; Hmrm; Lit Mag; Math C; Sch P; Sci C; Co-Cpt, Bkbl; Ftbl; Golf; Co-Cpt, Sftbl; Alg A; COM; Chem A; Cl Fav; MLS; Sci A; Coin C; Bowl; *U of Cincinnati; Engr.*

BENCZKOWSKI, Ronald James
John F Kennedy HS; Cheektowaga, NY (2-250) Ed, Ann; Hmrm; NHS; Var C; Pres, Jr Cl; NHS; Cpt, Tr; Hon Prog; NEDT; JFK Jr o-t Yr; 3-Yr Hon Cert; Curriculum Coun; *Engr.*

BENDA, A Michele
Auburn HS; Auburn, NY; Orch; CC, MVP, Gym; Word of Life Bible Inst.

BENDALL, Alice Louise
Grand Blanc HS; Grand Blanc, MI; Chor; VP, Ger C; Tr; *Concordia Lutheran Col; Religion.*

BENDEL, Melody Ann
Greeley HS; Greeley, CO; Bus C; Chor; Drama; Fr C; FBLA; Madrigal; Spch C; Thes; Home Ec A; Theatre A; Hon Spartan; Mus A; *Mus.*

BENDEL, Susan Jean
Downers Grove N HS; Downers Grove, IL (76-555) A Cap Choir; NHS; Bkbl; Sftbl; Co-Cpt, MVP, Vlbl; Tres, Church Yth Group; Off Ed C; FCA; *N Ill U; Acct.*

BENDER, Cynthia Louise
Citrus HS; Inverness, FL (1-250) Co-Ed, Ann; Cpt, Chldr; GS; NHS; Span C; Tres, Soph Cl; Tr; Amer Leg A; H of F; HCt; MLS; Kiwanettes; Miss CHS; WW; Chldr o-t Yr; WW Among Amer HS Chldr; *Mercer U; Pre-Med.*

BENDER, Dell Lee
Ulysses HS; Ulysses, KS (10%-110) Band; Chor; Ensm; Ger C; Madrigal; NHS; Bkbl; Ftbl; Golf; *Baker U; Mass Communications.*

BENDER, Janet Lyn
McCluer N HS; Florissant, MO (8-760) NHS; Top 10 Fresh; *U of Mo; Home Ec.*

BENDER, Jerry Lee
Belvidere HS; Belvidere, IL; Ftbl; Tr; Wrest.

BENDER, Joseph
Lakewood HS; Lakewood, OH (70-800) Math A; Phy A; Calculus & Trigonometry A's; *Miami U; Math.*

BENDER, Linda Jean
Pennsauken HS; Pennsauken, NJ (150-535) Chldr; Chor; Fr C; Ch, Hmrm; Jr Miss Pagent; Cpt, Mjrte; Sch P; Ch, SC; Bsbl; Beauty; COM; God & Country A; HCt; Lion A; Most Out; Yth Fel; Sr Prom Qn; Jr Prom Ct; 3rd Runner-Up, Miss Camden Co; Feature Twirler; *Brandywine Col; Fashion Merchandising.*

BENDER, Melanie Jean
George Washington Sr HS; Cedar Rapids, IA (57-505) Band; Pres, Ger C; Pres, Hmrm; NHS; SC; Hon Prog; St Scholar; *Iowa St U; Bio.*

BENDER, Peter Charles
McHenry HS; McHenry, IL; A Cap Choir; Band; Chor; Dbte Tm; Pres, Drama; Tres, 4H; Madrigal; Spch C; 4H A; Kiwanis A; MLS; Spch A; Hugh O'Brien Ldrship, A; Ntl Sch Choral, A.

BENDER, Susan Elizabeth
Regis HS; Stayton, OR (1-61) Drama; NHS; Cr-Ctry; Tr; COM; *Oreg St U; Biol.*

BENDER, Terry Anthony
Mooresville HS; Mooresville, IN; Band; Orch; Acolytes; *Naval Acad; Navigation.*

BENDER, Thomas Michael
Sullivan Central HS; Kingsport, TN (8%-360) Band; NHS; Order/Arrow; Swim; God & Country A; *Chem.*

BENDURE, Daphne Lynn
Liberty Sr HS; Liberty, MO; Band; Essay A; *Maple Woods Col; Secy.*

BENDYNA, Nanette
John W Hallahan Cath Girls HS; Philadelphia, PA (9-431) NHS; F-Ed, Sch P; Span C; Span NHS; Tres, World Affairs; COM; Hon Prog; Sacristan; VFW A; Eng A; Span A; *Temple U; Journ.*

BENEDICT, Claudia Bea
Battle Mountain HS; Eagle Vail, CO (9-68) Ed, Ann; Band; Arch; Tr; Co-Ed, Ann; Tres & Pres, DECA; *U of Northern Colo; Special Ed.*

BENEDICT, Jeffrey James
Weld Central HS; Keensburg, CO (22-105) Band; BS; Bus C; Drama; Ensm; FBLA; F-Ed, Sch P; Spch C; Co-Cpt, Cr-Ctry; Tr; COM; Hon Prog; Spch A; Art C; Pres, Church Yth Group; Stage & Pep Bnds; Stu Dir, Sch Play; Excel, St Solo & Ensm; Writings Published, Inkwell Magazi; *Social Work.*

BENEDICT, Pamela Sue
Will Rogers HS; Tulsa, OK; Chor; Ensm.

BENEDICT, Patricia Ann
Will Rogers HS; Tulsa, OK (44-520) Chor; Fr C; NHS; ARC; Thes; Hon Prog; JA A; Academic Achv A; *Phillips U; Elem Special Ed.*

BENEDICT, Sandra Jane
Hill HS; Winston-Salem, NC; Rptr, Sch P; Cert of Recogn, Merit A, Art; Gold Key, Art; *Police Sci.*

BENEFIEL, Ann C
Lawrenceville HS; Lawrenceville, IL (8-173) Chem C; NHS; Phys C; Span C; Fr C; Pres, Jr Cl; Daughter of WW II Veteran Schol; *U of Ill; Pre-Med.*

BENEFIEL, Lisa Michele
Winnetonka HS; Kansas City, MO (25%-500) Chldr; FTA; Ger C.

BENEFIELD, Jonathan David
Hernando HS; Brooksville, FL (13-300) BS; NHS; Pres, Span C; Tnns; Sr Cl Play; Quiz Tm; *U of S Fla; Chem.*

BENESCH, Deborah Elizabeth
Grand Trunk HS; Evansburg, CANADA (3-71) Secy, SC; COM.

BENETTI, Mary Elizabeth
Belmond Community HS; Belmond, IA; Ann; Band; CYO; Chldr; Chor; Ensm; Pres, FHA; GS; Hmrm; NHS; SC; VP, Thes; John Philip Sousa Band A; *Iowa St U.*

BENFIELD, Carolyn Anita
Cherryville Sr HS; Cherryville, NC (15-126) Chor; FBLA; Math C; Sci C; *Gaston Col; Nurs.*

BENFIELD, James Gregory
Harding HS; Charlotte, NC; Sci C; ROTC A; *Pepperdine U; Law.*

BENFORD, Burnae Elaine
Clovis HS; Clovis, NM (80-546) Band; Bus C; Pres, Hmrm; Up Bound; Band Qn; All St Band; Tn o-t Wk; *NM St U; Bus Adm.*

BENGE, Martha Anne
Grand Prairie HS; Grand Prairie, TX (11-40) A Cap Choir; *N Tex St U; Mus.*

BENING, Paul Scott
Clarence Central HS; Clarence, NY (20-396) Drama; Thes; Var C; Bkbl; MVP, Ftbl; Tnns; Ftbl, All Conf; HS All Star Ftbl; *St Lawrence U; Chem.*

BENINTENDI, Elisa Ann
Webb City HS; Webb City, MO (19-183) Co-Cpt, Chldr; Dbte Tm; NFL; Co-Ed, Sch P; COM; Hon Prog; Spch A; *U of Ark; Archt.*

BENITEZ, Noemi
Central HS; Santurce, PR; Fr C; Math A; Sci A; High Hon A; Eng A; Home Ec A; *University of PR; Sci.*

BENITEZ, Zoraida Guadalupe
Consuelo Escalona Sch; Carolina, PR (4-38) CYO; Chor; ARC; Swim; Tnns; COM; Hon Prog; Opt A; *U of PR; Biochem.*

BENJAMIN, Debbie Lynn
Centralia HS; Centralia, IL (87-350) Chldr; Chem C; Dbte Tm; 4H; NHS; Sch P; Sci C; Span C; Sftbl; Swim; Tnns; Tr; Alg A; Bio A; Chem A; Hist A; Hon Prog; Pres A; Sci A; St Scholar; Yth Fel; Most Comical; *St Louis Christian Col; Christain Evangelism.*

BENJAMIN, Eileen Ruth
Capitol City Baptist Sch; Lansing, MI (2-6) Co-Ed, Ann; Chor; Drama; NHS; Sch P; Tres, Sr Cl; HQn; Sal; Yth Fel; S-T, Yth Fel; *Baptist Bible Col; Elem Ed.*

BENJAMIN, Jeannie Lynn
Hutchinson HS; Hutchinson, MN (5-221) Fin, AFS; Chor; FFA; 4H; NHS; Orch; Rptr, Sch P; Thes; Swim; Tr; Dorian Orch; Summer AFS Exchange Stu.

BENKERT, Kathleen Marie
Monroe HS; Monroe, WI (18-250) A Cap Choir; Secy, AFS; Band; Chor; Dbte Tm; Fr C; Ed, Lit Mag; Model UN; Sch C; Spch A; *U of Wis; Journ.*

BENNETT, Alice Faye
Marion HS; Marion, IN; Bus C; Chor; Ensm; Swim; COM; Spch A; Job's Daughters; OEA A; Easter Pageant; Spch Tm; *Fort Wayne International Col; Bus.*

BENNETT, Antoinette
Brainerd HS; Chattanooga, TN (3-200) Bus C; Y-Tns; *Middle Tenn St U; Bus Adm.*

BENNETT, Bradley Eugene
Sterling HS; Sterling, KS; Band; Chor; Ensm; SC; JV, Ftbl; JV, Tnns; *K-St U; Drama.*

BENNETT, Carol Faye
Adlai E Stevenson HS; Bronx, NY (17-822) Chess C; Hmrm; InterAct C; InterClub Coun; NHS; Sch Achieve Tm; F-Ed, Sch P; Ski C; SC; Bkbl; Alg A; COM; Chem A; Citz A; Hon Prog; *Bus Mgmt.*

BENNETT, Charles Franklin
Oxon Hill Sr HS; Oxon Hill, MD (5%-560) Hmrm; Sci C; Sci A; Puppet Ministry; Yth Committee; ROTC; *Sci.*

BENNETT, Christopher Anthony
Northview HS; Covina, CA; A Cap Choir; Chor; S-T, Drama; Madrigal; S-T, Thes; Bank Of Amer A; *UCLA; Mus.*

BENNETT, Craig Alan
Gaffney Sr HS; Gaffney, SC (20%-500) BC; Chem C; Fr C; Hmrm; Sci C; Cpt, Tnns; Senate; FCA Huddle C; *Auburn U; Law.*

BENNETT, Craig Steven
Windom Area HS; Windom, MN (88-135) Band; FFA; Var C; Cpt, Ftbl; Tr; *NW Bible Col; Bible.*

BENNETT, Cynthia Jannette
Eupora HS; Eupora, MS; Ann; Co-Cpt, Chldr; Chor; VP, FHA; FTA; Pres, 4H; Sch P; Tres, SC; 4H A; I Dare You; Type A; Farm Bureau Qn, Fin; 4-H Danforth A; Co 4-Her o-t Yr; *U of Miss; Interior Design.*

BENNETT, David William
Tucker HS; Tucker, GA (10%-500) JV, Bsbl; JV, Bkbl; *U of Tenn; Bus Adm.*

BENNETT, Dawn Denise
Pattonville Sr HS; Bridgeton, MO (1%-1000) ARC; COM; Hon Prog; Cert Outst Achv in Fr; *Nutrition.*

BENNETT, Dee Ann
E Aurora HS; Aurora, IL (13-526) A Cap Choir; Drama; Hmrm; NHS; VP, Spch C; SC; VP, Thes; Swim; Tr; COM; Spch A; Vlbl; *Bible Stu.*

BENNETT, Diana Lynn
Central HS; Grand Junction, CO; Ski C; SC; COM; Type A; Job's Daughters; *Secy.*

BENNETT, Don Jeffrey
Clay HS; Oregon, OH (1-350) Band; BC; BS; Chem C; Secy, Chess C; Drama; Fr C; Hmrm; Math C; NHS; Orch; Order/Arrow; Phys C; Sci C; SC; VP, Soph Cl; Hon Prog; Math A; Order/Arrow A; Eagle Sct A.

BENNETT, Elizabeth Owen
Gulf HS; New Port Richey, FL; FHA; Var C; Cr-Ctry.

BENNETT, Ethel Ann
Largo Sr HS; Upper Marlboro, MD; Mgr, Soccer; Mgr, Sftbl; TOFS Cadette; Gym Prog; Church Choir; Church Yth Prog; *Travel.*

BENNETT, Forrest Charles
Battle Creek Central HS; Battle Creek, MI (33%-539) Hmrm; SC; Up Bound; Cpt, Bsbl; Ftbl; Sftbl; Swim; Tnns; Tr; Wrest; God & Country A; Most Out; Eagle Sct; Campus Life Pageant Escort; Best Ath of Cl; *Kellogg Comm Col; Psych.*

BENNETT, Grace Elizabeth
Hammond HS; Hammond, LA (1-298) BC; Fin, Lit Ral; Secy, Rainbow; Secy, SC; Secy, Soph Cl; Spch A; Demolay Swtht; *Eng.*

BENNETT, Jefferson Kane
Weatherford HS; Weatherford, TX (139-252) Demolay; Ensm; Pres, FTA; Lat C; NFL; Spch C; SC; Var C; Pres, Sr Cl; Pres, Jr Cl; Ftbl; Citz A; Cl Fav; HCt; Opt A; Mr WHS; *Baylor U; Biol.*

BENNETT, Jeffrey Lee
S Gwinnett HS; Snellville, GA (10-30) Band; Orch; MLS; *U of Ga; Drama.*

BENNETT, Jennifer Lee
Meridian HS; Meridian, TX (10-23) BC; FHA; JV, Bkbl; Tnns; Tr.

BENNETT, Joan Yvonne
Danbury HS; Danbury, CT (112-826) Drama; Golf; Tnns; Alg A; Cl Fav; *Pepperdine U.*

BENNETT, Kathleen Marie
Auburn HS; Auburn, NY (10-600) Chor; Hmrm; NHS; Sftbl; NYSMA A; *Geneseo Col; Sci.*

BENNETT, Laurie J
W Springfield HS; Springfield, VA; Lat C; Lat NHS; NHS; Span C; *William and Mary Col.*

BENNETT, Linda Dawn
Cedar Falls HS; Cedar Falls, IA; Chor; Drama; Thes; Y-Tns; *UNI; Drama.*

BENNETT, Lowell Jacob
John Muir HS; Pasadena, CA (42-520) Span C; SC; Bkbl; CSF; Ntl Achv Schol; NMS; *Stanford U.*

BENNETT, Margaret Lynn
Miami HS; Miami, OK; Band; CYO; FHA; InterClub Coun; Math C; Orch; Spch C; Thes; *NE Okla A&M U; Nurs.*

BENNETT, Martha Dell
S R Butler HS; Huntsville, AL (10-635) NHS; Type A; Top 25 Sr Cl; AMTA Outst Mus A, Priv Mus Stu; *Murray St U; Mus.*

BENNETT, Melissia Darlene
Franklin Co HS; Carnesville, GA; Band; Chor; Fr C; FHA; *Saint Mary's Col; Nurs.*

BENNETT, Mildred Eugenia
Tishomingo HS; Tishomingo, MS (3-33) Band; BC; Cpt, Chldr; Chor; FHA; 4H; Rptr, Sr Cl; Sftbl; Tr; Alg A; 4H A; HQn; Type A; Hon Stu; *NE Miss Jr Col; Secy Sci.*

BENNETT, Oren Glenn
Vineland HS; Vineland, NJ; Mgr, Band; Orch; ARC; ARC A; *Art.*

BENNETT, Patricia Ruth
Palatka S HS; Palatka, FL; Fr C; FBLA; FHA; Tri-HiY; Civinettes.

BENNETT, Paula
Williamston HS; Williamston, NC (56-185) Key C; Monogram; SC; MVP, Bkbl; Cpt, Tr; Most Out; Cpt, Bkbl; Bkbl, Tr, A's; *Recreation.*

BENNETT, Philip Allen
Quilcene HS; Quilcene, WA (1-30) SC; JV, Bkbl; *Wash St U; Wildlife Mgr.*

BENNETT, Regina Ann
Clinton HS; Clinton, NC (24-185) Cpt, Chldr; FHA; Spch C; S-T, SC; HQn; *NC Central Col; Acct.*

BENNETT, Renee Michelle
Covert HS; Covert, MI (2-40) Chldr; FHA; Mjrte; Tres, NHS; Tr; Sal; Swtht; *Ferris St Col; Med.*

BENNETT, Richard David
Eastside HS; Taylors, SC (40-290) A-Ed, Ann; Band; Tres, BC; Drama; Pres, Hmrm; A-Ed, Lit Mag; NHS; Ed, Sch P; St Stu Congress; SC; Pres, Jr Cl; Journ A; Q&S A; Chamber Choir; *Samford U; Religion.*

BENNETT, Robert Alan
Wellston HS; Wellston, OH (25-130) Co-Ed, Ann; Chor; Ensm; Pres, 4H; Rptr, Sch P; Sci C; 4H A; VP, Yth Fel; *Rio Grande Comm Col; Social Work.*

BENNETT, Robert Neil
Winston Churchill HS; San Antonio, TX (19-864) Band; Ensm; NHS; COM; Hon Prog; NEDT; Eng A; All Dist Band; *Baylor U; Religion.*

BENNETT, Ronald Lee
Washington HS; Kansas City, KS; Band; Royal Ambassadors; *Truck Driving.*

BENNETT, Roy Farris
Uvalde HS; Uvalde, TX; Band; FFA; Opt Out Tn; *SW Tex Jr Col; Agr.*

BENNETT, Sandra Corene
Darby Township HS; Glenolden, PA (37-107) SC; Bkbl; Hockey; COM; *Del Co Comm Col; Bus.*

BENNETT, Sarah Jane
Dan River HS; Ringgold, VA (21-238) BC; Fr C; GS; Secy, SC; Pres, Tri-HiY; WW; *Danville Comm Col; Spch Therapy.*

BENNETT, Sarah Tresa
Lanier HS; Jackson, MS; Fr C; Sch P; Thes; Q&S; Asst Sports Ed, Journ C; YWA-YMA; *Eng Lit.*

BENNETT, Shari Lynn
Columbia HS; Columbia, PA (18-109) Band; Chor; GS; Math C; NHS; Orch; Span C; SC; JV, Tnns; *Penn St U at York; Elem Ed.*

BENNETT, Sheri Lyn
Sterling HS; Sterling, KS (9-49) Band; Chldr; FHA; Secy, Sr Cl; Secy, Jr Cl; Co-Cpt, Bkbl; Sftbl; Tr; HQn; HCt; *Kan St U; Bus.*

BENNETT, Stephanie Michelle
Darby Township HS; Glenolden, PA; Mgr, Bkbl; Hockey; *Secretarial.*

BENNETT, Susan Elizabeth
Henrico HS; Richmond, VA (50%-300) Pres, A Cap Choir; Chor; Ch, Hmrm; Pres, Madrigal; SC; Y-Tns; JA A; MVP, Choir; All Region, All St, Chor; Stu Director, Ensm; *J Sargeant Reynolds Comm Col.*

BENNETT, Susan Graves
Gainesville HS; Gainesville, FL (16-463) Mu Alpha Theta; NHS; Span C; Span NHS; Crisco C; 4H A; Keyettes; FCA; *U of Fla; Bio.*

BENNETT, Susan Marie
Destrehan HS; Destrehan, LA (14-166) VP, BC; Bus C; HCt; Principal's A; *U of SW La; Pre-Dentistry.*

BENNETT, Vanessa Almetta
William Penn HS; Philadelphia, PA; CYO; Secy,
Chor; Sftbl; Citz A; Hist A; Math A; Sci A; PA;
Reading A.

BENNETT, Vanessa Renee
Cedar Falls HS; Cedar Falls, IA (10%-491) Bus C;
Chor; Ger C; Sftbl; COM; JA A; 2nd, Solo Comp;
U of Nor Iowa; Journ.

BENNETT, Vicki Jane
Madison Acad HS; Huntsville, AL (5-51) F-Ed,
Ann; BC; Math C; Monogram; NHS; F-Ed, Sch P;
Var C; Mgr, Bsbl; Mgr, Bkbl; Beauty; COM; Cl
Fav; Hist A; Hon Prog; Sci A; Star Student; Jr
Civitan C; Bible A; *UA; Med.*

BENNETT, William Charles
Ellet Sr HS; Akron, OH (83-425) Drama; Hmrm;
NFL; ARC; Secy, SC; Thes; COM; Yth Fel; Sr
Phys Ed Asst; Mgr, Bowl; Church Off Worker; *Be-thany Col; Relegious Trng.*

BENNEWITZ, Hugh Leo
Burnsville Sr HS; Burnsville, MN (10%-800) Sch P;
Co-Cpt, Swim; Water Polo; Prom Committee; *U of
Minn; Art.*

BENNEY, Michael Jay
Hazelwood E HS; St Louis, MO (64-460) NHS;
Pres, Sr Cl; Bsbl; Cpt, Bkbl; Yth Fel.

BENNING, Pearl Lee
Alameda HS; Lakewood, CO; Band.

BENNINGFIELD, Nancy Ann
W Ottawa HS; Holland, MI (110-305) Chldr; Tr;
Yth for Understanding Exch Stu; Dutch Dancing;
Horizon C; *Grand Valley St Col; Lib Arts.*

BENOIT, Ginger Lynn
Mosley HS; Panama City, FL (50-500) FHA; Pres,
4H; Hmrm; SC; 4H A; Keyettes; *Gulfcoast Comm
Col; Recreation.*

BENOIT, Malinda
Melville HS; Melville, LA; Secy, BC; Chldr; FHA;
Semi-Fin, Lit Ral; NHS; Bkbl; Sftbl; Alg A; Spch A;
La Col.

BENOIT, Marvin Grant
Nederland HS; Nederland, TX (46-480) Pres,
CYO; Pres, Key C; Math C; VP, NHS; JV, Bsbl; JV,
Ftbl; COM; Sci A; *Tex A&M U.*

BENOLKEN, Ann Louise
Tomball HS; Tomball, TX (2-138) Rptr, Band;
CYO; FTA; 4H; Secy, NHS; COM; Eng A.

BENSEMA, David James
Harold L Richards HS; Oak Lawn, IL (18-745)
Band; Fr C; Mu Alpha Theta; Pres, NHS; Co-Ed,
Sch P; MVP, Cr-Ctry; Tr; Citz A; Hon Prog; Math
A; NMF; St Scholar; Cpt, Cr-Ctry; Hon Men, Eng
Tchrs Writing Comp; *Pre-Med.*

BENSEND, Kari Lee
Richardson HS; Richardson, TX (168-949) Bkbl;
Tr; MVP, All District, Bkbl; All Tournament, Bkbl;
U of Okla; Phys Ed.

BENSINGER, Brooke Paula
Garden Spot HS; New Holland, PA (14-283) NHS;
Co-Cpt, Bkbl; Hockey; Sftbl; Yth Fel; Girls Ldr C;
Social Work.

BENSINGER, Janine Renee
Garden Spot HS; New Holland, PA (87-283) Band;
Cpt, Chldr; Chor; Ensm; Tres, 4H; Orch; Bkbl;
Hockey; Swim; 4H A; *Lancaster General Hospital;
Nurs.*

BENSLEY, Brett Dean
Westfield HS; Westfield, IL (3-16) Ann; Band;
Secy, FFA; NHS; JV, Bkbl; JV, Tr; *E III U; Pre-Engr.*

BENSLEY, James Robert
Medina Sr HS; Medina, NY (6-175) A Cap Choir;
Chor; K of C; NHS; Sch P; Ski C; Var C; Soccer;
Cpt, Tnns; COM; Citz A; Hon Prog; NEDT; Re-gent Schol; ROTC A; Creative Writing A; All
League, Tnns; PA; *U of Mo; Civil Engr.*

BENSON, Alice Barbara
Eastside HS; Paterson, NJ (5-519) Ed, Ann; Chess
A; Hmrm; Secy, Math C; Tnns; NHS; Sci C; Pres,
SC; COM; Hon Prog; Horsebackriding C; Pres, 'Z'
C; Century Iii Ldr, Service, A's; Pride o-t Faculty
A; *Douglass Col; Chem.*

BENSON, Barbara Carol
Shabbona HS; Shabbona, IL (15-54) Band; Chor; Fr
C; VP, FHA; GAA As.

BENSON, Barbara Elizabeth
Mercy HS; Albany, NY (22-108) Chldr; Chor;
Drama; Fr C; Hmrm; InterAct C; Lit Ral; NHS; Ski
C; SC; Hon Prog; *SUNY at Cortland; Elem Ed.*

BENSON, Brian Wesley
Bradley Co Central HS; Cleveland, TN; Band; BC;
Fr C; FTA; Span C; Thes; *U of Tenn.*

BENSON, Carol Fay
Broken Arrow HS; Broke Arrow, OK (50-600)
Band; NHS; Symph; Pres Church Yth Coun; *Bay-lor; Mus.*

BENSON, Cheryl Annette
Dallas Christian HS; Mesquite, TX (35-54) Tres, A
Cap Choir; Ann; Chldr; Drama; Secy, FHA; Sci C;
Spch C; SC; HCt; Homemaking A; *Harding Col.*

BENSON, Debra Kathryn
Union Co HS; Morganfield, KY (40-370) Fr C;
Spell Bee A; Story Writing A; *Henderson Comm
Col; Med.*

BENSON, Erica Dawn
Darby Township HS; Sharon Hill, PA; Chor; NHS;
SC; Mgr, Bkbl; Hockey; Spch A; *Duquesne U; Bus
Adm.*

BENSON, Kate Sophia
Lake Braddock Secondary Sch; Burke, VA
(40%-671) Chor; Bkbl; Sftbl; Pres A; Drill Tm; Hor-sebackriding, Bowl, Pep, C'S; Vlbl; Skiing A; *Au-gustana Col; Lib Arts.*

BENSON, Kristine Carol
Crystal Lake HS; Crystal Lake, IL (80-608) Chor;
Secy, 4H; JETS; Span C; Tres, SC; 4H A; NHS;
Span NHS; *Sou Ill U; Paralegal Trng.*

BENSON, Leslie Karen
Dana Hills HS; Dana Point, CA; Hmrm; Math C;
MVP, Swim; Citz A; Hon Prog; Drill Tm; *U of
Calif; Med.*

BENSON, Linda Jo
Boca Ciege HS; St Petersburg, FL; InterAct C;
DECA.

BENSON, Mark William
Richardson HS; Richardson, TX (4-1000) Hmrm;
JETS; Lat C; Lit Mag; Math C; Mu Alpha Theta;
NHS; F-Ed, Sch P; Sci C; Hon Prog; JA A; WW;
Miss Tnage Amer Pageant; *Rice U; Elec Engr.*

BENSON, Robbin Michelle
Cass HS; Cassville, GA (10%-189) FHA; Hmrm;
Math C; Sci C; SC; Tri-HiY; Bkbl; Sr Superlative;
Jacksonville St U.

BENSON, Ruth Adele
Bear Creek HS; Lakewood, CO (33-441) Band;
Cpt, Chldr; NHS; Hon Prog; *Calif St U; Nurs.*

BENSON, Steven Daniel
Stoughton Sr HS; Stoughton, WI (75-303) Band;
Chess C; Lit Mag; Ski C; Var C; Cr-Ctry; Tr; Madi-son Newspaper Schol; Sports Ltr; *Trinity Col.*

BENSON, Steven Edward
Van Nuys HS; Van Nuys, CA (15%-450) Band;
Ensm; Hmrm; NHS; Orch; Sci C; JV, Tnns; Alg A;
CSF; Chem A; Citz A; Hon Prog; Math A; Sci A;
Physics.

BENSON, Tammi Ann
Central HS; Crookston, MN (2%-182) Band; Chor;
Dbte Tm; Secy, Drama; NFL; Orch; Rptr, Sch P;
Spch C; Thes; COM; Spch A; VP, Ntl Med Explor-ers; Hon Stu; Spch, Forensics A; Camp Fire Girls
A; *Med.*

BENSON, Timothy Andrew
Winchester HS; Winchester, MA (40-440) Span C;
Engr.

BENTLAGE, Louise Ann
Owego Free Acad; Owego, NY (75-350) Pres,
AFS; Chor; Drama; Co-Cpt, Mjrte; Rotary A; Ch,
AFS; Secy, Yth Fel; *Nurs.*

BENTLEY, Connie Daneil
Denison HS; Denison, TX (5%-384) FHA; Tres,
NHS; Y-Tns; Pres, Sr Cl; Bio A; Yth Fel; Drill Tm;
VP, United Service C; Ntl HS Bio Hon Soc; Best
Leader Girl, Sr Cl; Nom, GS; *Grayson Co Col; Bio.*

BENTLEY, John Edward
Southside HS; Southside, AL (40-183) Tres, Band;
HiY; Hmrm; Parl, SC; Bsbl; MLS; Most Out; *Gads-den St Jr Col.*

BENTLEY, Lee Allison
W A Berry HS; Birmingham, AL (15%-285) An-chor C; Band; Lat C; NHS; Bkbl; *Auburn U; Off
Adm.*

BENTLEY, Randall Blair
Dyersburg HS; Dyersburg, TN (1-250) Pres, Mu
Alpha Theta; NHS; Var C; Bkbl; Cr-Ctry; Tnns; Tr;
Amer Leg A; Hist A; Hon Prog; *US Air Force
Acad; Intelligence.*

BENTLEY, Shawn Mitchel
Pleasant Valley HS; Chico, CA (33-216) Hmrm;
Var C; Bsbl; Fin, Tr; MVP, Cpt, Bkbl; MVP, Co-Cpt, Ftbl; Easter King; Tr, Record Holder; *U Calif
at LA; Ath.*

BENTLEY, Steven
Central HS; Evansville, IN (25-30).

BENTON, Carol Lynn
Jenkins Co HS; Millen, GA (1-100) Co-Ed, Ann;
Pres, BC; F-Ed, Sch P; Sci C; SC; Secy, Tri-HiY;
Bausch & Lomb A; COM; Hist A; Math A; Phy A;
Rotary A; Star Student; Val; *U of Ga; Ed.*

BENTON, Colette Janine
Kenwood HS; Chicago, IL (30-400) Cpt, Chldr;
VP, Ger C; NHS; Orch; SC; COM; Hon Prog;
Oberlin Col; Psychobio.

BENTON, Daniel R
Washington HS; Cedar Rapids, IA (1-509) Band;
Ed, Lat C; NHS; Order/Arrow; Swim; God &
Country A; Order/Arrow A; St Scholar; Val; Yth
Fel; *U of Iowa; Pre-Med.*

BENTON, David Lee
Milo Adventist Acad; Days Creek, OR (5-66) Ann;
Band; Chor; Phys C; A-Ed, Sch P; Co-Cpt, Ftbl;
Hon Prog; *Union Col.*

BENTON, Denise Kay
Washington HS; Cedar Rapids, IA (104-509) A
Cap Choir; Secy, Ger C; Hmrm; Secy, Sci C; Parl,
SC; Mgr, Swim; JV, Tr; Yth Fel; VP, Aquatic Arts;
EIL Ambassador to Germany; *Colo St U; Forestry.*

BENTON, Jimmie Lee Jr
Morton HS; Morton, WA (25-38) A Cap Choir;
Band; Chor; Pres, Demolay; Drama; Ensm; Hmrm;
Spch C; Pres, SC; Var C; Cpt, Ftbl; Cpt, Tr; COM;
Elk A; Lion A; Masonic A; NEDT; All NW Choir;
W Wash St Col; Archt.

BENTON, John Temple III
W A Berry HS; Birmingham, AL; A Cap Choir;
Chor; Ensm; InterAct C; Lat C; Order/Arrow;
ARC; Thes; Var C; Ftbl; Order/Arrow A; *Auburn
U; Psych.*

BENTON, Randy Alan
Marcus Comm Sch; Marcus, IA (8-64) Band; Chor;
Ensm; Madrigal; Span C; Yth Fel; All St, NW Iowa,
Bands; NW Iowa Chor; Span Schol.

BENTON, Rebecca Kay
Hannah-Pamplico HS; Pamplico, SC (5-125) Ann;
Pres, NHS; Bkbl Statistician; VP, Bus Driver C; *U
of SC; Bus Adm.*

BENTON, Susan Estelle
Bethune HS; Bethune, SC (7-49) A-Ed, Sch P; SC;
Bkbl; Sftbl; VP, Beta C; Pres, Fr C; Block 'B' C;
Mars Hill Col; Med Tech.

BENTZ, Clinton John
Regis HS; Stayton, OR (11-56) A Cap Choir; Chor;
NHS; SC; Var C; Bkbl; JV, Ftbl; Cpt, Tr; B Crocker
A; COM; Chamber of Comm A; Hon Prog; NMF;
VP, Cr-Ctry; Future 1st Citizens; *Portland U; Pre-Law.*

BENTZ, Jay Denton
Homewood-Flossmoor HS; Flossmoor, IL
(150-930) A Cap Choir; Drama; *Purdue U; Agr.*

BENTZEL, James Wilson II
W York Area Sr HS; York, PA (20%-248) Band;
Pres, Mod Mus Mas; Order/Arrow; Tr; *Pa St U;
Elec Engr.*

BENTZINGER, David
Kirkwood HS; Kirkwood, MO (10%-400) Ger C;
Purdue U; Engr.

BENZEL, Kimberly Jo
Lincoln HS; Roseville, CA (11-150) Hon Stu A.

BEOHLER, Bradley Anard
Ulysses HS; Ulysses, KS; Band; BS; Ensm; NHS; Ftbl; Swim; Tnns.

BEOHLER, Douglas John
Ulysses HS; Ulysses, KS (13-103) Band; BS; VP, NHS; Var C; Co-Cpt, Bkbl; Co-Cpt, Ftbl; Tr; St Scholar; Engr.

BEQUETTE, Bryon Kent
Mankato E HS; Mankato, MN (30-300) Hmrm; Co-Cpt, Bsbl; Co-Cpt, Bkbl; Cr-Ctry; Mankato St U; Acct.

BERAUD, Sallie Clara
Lafayette HS; Lafayette, LA (25%-540) Dbte Tm; Fr C; Ed, Lit Mag; NFL; Pres, Rainbow; Sch P; Spch C; COM; Oral Roberts U.

BERBANO, Neil Nabua
Hampton Comm HS; Hampton, IA (15-110) A Cap Choir; Bsbl; Bkbl; Sftbl; Tnns; Pres, Yth Fel; Iowa Methodist Med Center; Med Tech.

BERBANO, Orville Nabua
Hampton Comm HS; Hampton, IA (8-130) A Cap Choir; S-T, 4H; Bsbl; Bkbl; Sftbl; 4H A; JA A; Yth Fel; Iowa Methodist Med Center; Med.

BERBERICH, Linda Frances
Lady Smith HS; Ladysmith, VA (12-100) Tres, BC; Cpt, Chldr; Rptr, FBLA; FHA; FTA; 4H; Hmrm; Monogram; SC; Var C; JV, Bkbl; Sftbl.

BERG, Cindy Anne
Rogers Sr HS; Michigan City, IN; A Cap Choir; Band; Drama; Ski C; SC; Tnns; HCt; Ntl Fed of Mus; Ntl Guild of Piano; Nisbova; Ind U.

BERG, Cynthia Rae
Malcolm HS; Malcolm, NE (4-27) Ann; Bus C; Chldr; Chem C; Chor; Commercial C; Drama; Ensm; Semi-Fin, GS; Pres, 4H; Key C; NHS; Sch P; Var C; Bsbl; Cpt, Bkbl; Cpt, Sftbl; Tr; COM; Gov Honor Prog; 4H A; Hon Prog; Pres A; Spch A; VP, Secy, Tres, 4 H C; Mgr, Bkbl; Bible Sch Teacher; Mgr, Vlbl; Rep, Gov's Safety Coun; Church Pianist & Organist; U of Nebr; Elem Ed.

BERG, DaNaye Janette
Cardinal Stritch HS; Oregon, OH (34-189) VP, FBLA; Sftbl; Hon Prog; Home Ec A; Bus.

BERG, David Michael
Waukesha S HS; Waukesha, WI (1-715) Drama; Fr C; French HS; Math C; Mu Alpha Theta; VP, NHS; COM; Elk A; Hon Prog; Math A; NMF; NMS; Val; Fr A; Mus As; St Olaf Col; Math.

BERG, Deborah Jane
Tiverton HS; Tiverton, RI (12-200) NHS; Brow Book A; U of RI; Conservation.

BERG, Kathryn Joanne
Pine Island HS; Pine Island, MN (9-74) Bkbl; Sftbl; HCt; Hon Prog; Miss Pine Island; DECA; Ntl Fin & St Win, Free Enterprse Pr; Rochester Comm Col; Vet Med.

BERG, Kevin Kenneth
Granite Hills HS; El Cajon, CA (80-450) Tnns; U of Minn.

BERG, Robert Charles
Edw Clark HS; Las Vegas, NV; Bus Mgr, Band; BS; Chem C; Order/Arrow; Chem A; Order/Arrow A; Drum Major; Eagle Sct; Archt.

BERGAMO, Edwin Charles
Sacred Heart HS; Vineland, NJ; Chldr; Fr C; NHS; Pres, SC; Pres, Jr Cl; Pres, Soph Cl; Mgr, Bkbl; Amer Leg A; Rutgers U; Agr.

BERGAN, Jill Lynn
Parkrose Sr HS; Portland, OR (20%-450) Drama; Rptr, Rptr; Ski C; Span C; JV, Bkbl; Bassist Inst; Interior Design.

BERGELAND, Andrea Elaine
Duluth Central HS; Duluth, MN; A Cap Choir; Band; Chldr; Chor; GS; Hmrm; Secy, Model UN; NHS; Ski C; Pres, SC; Swim; Tnns; Tr; Amer Leg A; HCt; MLS; Skiing Tm.

BERGEN, Tom Carl
Harbor HS; Santa Cruz, CA (20%-275) Key C; Ski C; Var C; Co-Cpt, Ftbl; Tr; COM; Aeronautical Engr.

BERGENDAHL, Charles Richard
Harlingen HS; Harlingen, TX (60-650) A Cap Choir; Band; Chor; Ensm; NHS; Orch; COM; US Air Force.

BERGER, Carol Cyrene
Cristobal HS; Coco Solo, CANAL ZONE (1-98) Band; FTA; Pres, NHS; Var C; Pres, Sr Cl; Pres, Jr Cl; Bkbl; Golf; Tnns; Elk A; Cpt, Vlbl; GAA; Math.

BERGER, Christine Eleanor
Spring Branch Sr HS; Houston, TX (10-650) S-T, Ger C; Mu Alpha Theta; Sci C; Bkbl; Sftbl; Hist A; Sci A; Eng A; Tex A&M U; Marine Biol.

BERGER, Leslie Ann
Fremont HS; Sunnyvale, CA (1-620) CYO; Dbte Tm; Secy, Ger C; NFL; NHS; Sch Achieve Tm; Spch C; Secy, SC; Bus Mgr, Soph Cl; Bkbl; MVP, Tnns; CSF; Hon Prog; Spch A; Cascaids Service C; Co-Cpt, Gym; Christmas Ball Court; Sci.

BERGER, Paula Denise
Marietta Sr HS; Marietta, OH; Mgr, Band; Lat C; NHS; Olivet Col; Nurs.

BERGER, Randy
Cherry Hill HS W; Cherry Hill, NJ (53-800) Band; Hmrm; SC; JV, Ftbl; Tr; COM; Art As; Design.

BERGER, Richard Hunt
Canarsie HS; Brooklyn, NY (5-945) Chess C; Cpt, Math C; NHS; Orch; A-Ed, Sch P; Alg A; COM; Elk A; Hon Prog; Math A; Ntl Sci Found; Regent Schol; Sci A; HR, Math Assn of Amer Exam; NYC Math Tm; Cornell U; Math.

BERGER, Scott Bruce
Hillel Acad of Pittsburgh; Pittsburgh, PA (3-20) Ann; Band; Chem C; Chess C; Chor; Dbte Tm; Drama; Fr C; Math C; Ch, Sci C; Pres, SC; Cpt, Sftbl; Cpt, Swim; Tnns; Alg A; Bio A; COM; Cl Fav; Hon Prog; Math A; Most Out; PTA A; Phy A; ARC A; Sci A; Carnegie Mellon U; Life Sci.

BERGER, Sharon Kay
Fremont Ross HS; Fremont, OH (4-493) Ann; Band; Tres, FTA; JV, Bkbl; Amer Leg A; Bowling Green U; Pub Relations.

BERGER, Susan Jane
Field HS; Mogadore, OH; Bus C; FHA; Thes; Y-Tns; Prom Comm; Evangel Col; Bus.

BERGER, Teresa Lynn
New Braunfels HS; New Braunfels, TX; F-Ed, Ann; Band; Rptr, Fr C; FTA; NHS; Sci C; Sodality; Journ A; Type A; Pres, Young Republicans; Theta Epsilon Nu; Duchess, Co Fair; U of Tex; Fashion Design.

BERGER, Theodore James
Nutley HS; Nutley, NJ; Ger C; Math C; Order/Arrow; JV, Wrest; Alg A; Amer Leg A; Citz A; Elk A; Math A; Order/Arrow A; Eagle Sct.

BERGER, Vicky Sharon
Crenshaw HS; Los Angeles, CA; MVP, Bkbl; COM; Calif St U; Sociology.

BERGERON, Ralph John II
St Joseph HS; Jeanerette, LA (3-30) CYO; City Conf; Pres, 4H; Lit Ral; NHS; Pres, SC; Parl, Jr Cl; Tnns; Tr; COM; DARGCA; 4H A; Hist A; NEDT; Sci A; Spch A; WOW, Amer Hist, Local Women's C; Civics A; U of Southwestern La; Agr.

BERGESON, Rebekah Ruth
Rib Lake HS; Rib Lake, WI (50%-65) AFS; Bus Mgr, Ann; Band; Chor; Var C; Mgr, Bkbl; VP, Christian Yth Fel; Swing Choir; Photography C; Mgr, Vlbl; St & Dist Mus Festival; Bethel Col.

BERGEY, Kathy Renee
Mabel-Canton HS; Mabel, MN (6-52) A Cap Choir; Co-Ed, Ann; Band; Chor; Ensm; Parl, FHA; Spch C; Rptr, Jr Cl; Rptr, Soph Cl; Bkbl; COM; Hon Prog; Pres & Tres, SC; Vlbl; Hon Band; Phi Beta Mu; Elem Ed.

BERGEY, Kenneth Couter
Thomas McKean HS; Wilmington, DE (50-310) A Cap Choir; Chor; Drama; Order/Arrow; ARC; Ftbl; JV, Tr; JV, Wrest; Order/Arrow A; Yth Fel; Eagle Sct; Order of St John; Embry-Riddle Aeronautical U; Engr.

BERGFIELD, Amy Kay
Arcola HS; Arcola, IL (6-77) AFS; Chor; Secy, Drama; FTA; GS; NHS; Sch Achieve Tm; Span C; Scholar; Yth Fel; Miss Arcola; Pres, GAA; Co-Cpt, Vlbl; Greenville Free Methodist Col; Psych.

BERGGREN, Ellen Mary
Cary-Grove Comm HS; Cary, IL (1-349) Chor; FBLA; Var C; Tr; U of Ill; Landscape Archt.

BERGGREN, Jane Marie
Orono Sr HS; Long Lake, MN (2-200) Ann; FHA; Lit Mag; NHS; COM; Hon Prog; Sal; Bethel Col; Home Ec.

BERGIN, Jacqi Elaine
Grants HS; Grants, NM; Band; Yth Fel; Tn o-t Mo; All Dist Hon Band; Jr NHS.

BERGLAND, Kristina Marie
Winona Sr HS; Winona, MN; Drama; Secy, Orch; Pol Sci C; Sci C; Ski C; Span C; VP, SC; Var C; VP, Jr Cl; Tnns; Yth Leg; Augsburg Col; Communications.

BERGLAR, Peter Francis
Chaminade Col Prep; St Louis, MO (1-120) CYO; NHS; Cr-Ctry; Tr; Alg A; Bio A; COM; Hist A; Hon Prog; Math A; Ntl Sci Symposium; NEDT; Sci A; Type A; Chem Engr.

BERGLUND, Kristie Dalby
Salina Central HS; Salina, KS; Dbte Tm; NFL; SC; JV, Tnns; VP, Tn Republicans; U of Kans; Law.

BERGLUND, Randy Scott
Denfeld HS; Duluth, MN; DARGCA; God & Country A; Hon Prog; Gun C; Mech A; Oak Hills Col; General.

BERGMAN, Brian Lee
Bennington Pub Sch; Bennington, NE; Chor; Sch P; SC; Pres, Var C; Cpt, Bkbl; Co-Cpt, Ftbl; Tr; HKg; Ath o-t Yr; Midland Lutheran Col.

BERGMAN, Carren Elizabeth
Superior Sr HS; Superior, WI (52-514) Band; Chor; City Conf; Drama; Ensm; Hmrm; Ntl Yth Conf; SC; Tr; COM; Hon Prog; Pres A; Yth Fel; Twirler; Job's Daughters; Mus Contest As; St Scholastica Col; Elem Ed.

BERGMAN, Cheryl Lee
Maine W HS; Des Plaines, IL (10%-800) Hmrm; NHS; Ski C; Bio A; Chem A; Hon Prog; Sci A; Type A; Wittenberg Col; Sci.

BERGMAN, Cynthia Lea
Oconomowoc Sr HS; Oconomowoc, WI (52-700) NHS; Span C; Branch of Service; Bus.

BERGMAN, Daniel West
Superior Sr HS; Superior, WI; Band; Chor; Drama; Ensm; Co-Ch, Hmrm; Rptr, Sch P; SC; Ftbl; Hockey; Swim; Tr; COM; Hon Prog.

BERGMAN, Dave John
Quincy Notre Dame HS; Quincy, IL (22-140) Chor; Ger C; Hmrm; NHS; SC; Pres, Sr Cl; Pres, Jr Cl; Pres, Soph Cl; Soccer; Wrest; Hon Prog; John Woods Comm Col; Ornamental Horticulture.

BERGMAN, Drew William
N Penn HS; Lansdale, PA (160-892) Band; Community Yth Symph; Drama; Orch; God & Country A; Drexel U; Bus.

BERGMAN, Marilee Sue
Bennington HS; Bennington, NE; Band; Chor; Drama; 4H; Mjrte; SC; Var C; Bkbl; Sftbl; COM.

BERGMAN, Roxanne Irene
Burroughs HS; Ridgecrest, CA (20%-499) AFS; Band; Westmont Col; Med.

BERGMAN, Tamara Jo
Belle Vernon Area HS; Belle Vernon, PA (30-380) Band; Fr C; Tres, FBLA; Sftbl; Med Tech.

BERGMAN, Terry Dee
Taylor Center Baptist Acad; Taylor, MI; Rptr, Sch P; Pres, SC; Pres, Var C; Pres, Soph Cl; Arch; Bsbl; Bkbl; Ftbl; Soccer; Sftbl; Tr; MLS; Pres A; Star Student; Swtht.

BERGMANN, Cynthia Jo
Auburn Sr HS; Auburn, NE (1-98) Band; Chldr; FHA; GS; NHS; Span C; SC; Var C; Mgr, Bkbl; HQn; Regent Schol; Val; HR; U of Nebr; Special Ed.

BERGNER, Lori Louise
Oregon HS; Oregon, IL (20-150) Chor; Madrigal; Thes; Awana Hon A; *Computer Sci.*

BERGNER, Robert Dale
Texhoma HS; Texhoma, OK (9-30) Ann; Band; FFA; 4H; *Panhandle St Col; Animal Sci.*

BERGQUIST, David Allen
Hinsdale HS Central; Hinsdale, IL (126-453) Lat C; Orch; Order/Arrow; Swim; Order/Arrow A; *Bio.*

BERGSTRAND, Lori Esther
Jamestown HS; Jamestown, NY (10-525) A Cap Choir; Secy, Band; Hmrm; NHS; Secy, Sch P; Ski C; SC; Cr-Ctry; MLS; Opt A; Yth Fel; Hist Essay A; *Gustavus Aldolphus Col; Nurs.*

BERGSTRESSER, Cliff Parke
Easton Area HS; Easton, PA (100-700) Ntl Yth Conf; JV, Ftbl; Yth Fel; Pres, Yth Fel; Sunday Sch, Bible Sch, Teacher.

BERGSTROM, Cynthia Ann
David Douglas HS; Portland, OR (35-530) NHS; SC; Christian Yth Fel Schol; Hon Fresh Schol; *Bethel Col; Art Ed.*

BERGSTROM, DeAnn Joy
Thomas Jefferson HS; Bloomington, MN; Band; *Normandale Jr Col; Teacher.*

BERGSTROM, Deborah Marie
Morton HS; Morton, IL (173-329) 4H; 4H A; Pres A; *Ill Central U; Art.*

BERGSTROM, Donna Lynn
Wethersfield HS; Wethersfield, CT; Hmrm; Ski C; Outdoors C; *U of RI; Dental Hygiene.*

BERGSTROM, Eric Victor IV
W F Davidson HS; Mobile, AL (16-560) NHS; Sci C; Var C; JV, Bkbl; Ftbl; Hon Prog; NEDT; Yth Fel; Strengthening Church Comm; Church Yth Couns; *Engr.*

BERK, Robert Edward
Marist HS; Chicago, IL (107-370) Drama; Ill St Schol; *U of Ill; Liberal Arts.*

BERK, Thomas Edward
Quigley S HS; Chicago, IL (25-200) Drama; Lat C; Ski C; JV, Soccer; JV, Tnns; COM, Art; *Quincy Col; Law.*

BERKAS, Duane Robert
Roosevelt HS; Minneapolis, MN (87%-600) Bkbl; Co-Cpt, Cr-Ctry; Tr; *U of Minn; Pol Sci.*

BERKEMEYER, Terry Lynn
Las Vegas HS; Las Vegas, NV (16-380) Ann; City Conf; NHS; SC; COM; NEDT; Yth Directors A; *Grand Canyon Col; Behavioral Study.*

BERKEY, Beverly Ann
Spring Woods HS; Houston, TX (10%-500) Drama; VP, Fr C; Hist A; JA A; Math A; Spch A; Good Sportsmanship League; President's Phys Fitness A; VP, Hosp Jr Vol; Med Careers C; Methodist Yth Organization; *Southwestern U; Vet.*

BERKHEISER, Karen Lea
Blue Mountain Sr HS; Schuylkill Haven, PA (63-259) Chor; Fr C; Mu Alpha Theta; Tri-HiY; Sftbl; Yth Fel; *U of Pittsburgh; Oral Hygiene.*

BERKHOUSE, Jeffrey Joseph
Robert E Lee HS; Tyler, TX (130-634) A-Ed, Sch P; Spch C; Var C; Bkbl; Ftbl; Tnns; Tr; Yth Fel; Comm Ch, Moore Brotherhood Assn; Comm Organ, Drug Abuse Control; *Stephen F Austin Col; Pol Sci.*

BERKMAN, David Alan
Memorial Sr HS; Houston, TX (25%-675) A Cap Choir; Chor; SC; Soccer; Balfour A; Poet A; Sci A; Art A; *Austin Col; Bus.*

BERKOMPAS, Daryl Clark
Holland HS; Holland, MI (35-280) VP, Band; Chor; NHS; Mgr, Bkbl; JV, Ftbl; All St Hon Choir; All St, Mus Camp; Dist Yth Coun; BSct; *W Mich U; Aviation.*

BERKOMPAS, Duane Carl
Holland HS; Holland, MI (12-270) BS; Drama; NHS; Order/Arrow; SC; Var C; Pres, Sr Col; JV, Bsbl; Ftbl; Tr; JV, Wrest; God & Country A; Harvard Book A; Hon Prog; *Albion Col; Pre-Med.*

BERKOSKY, Barbara Ann
Riverside HS; Taylor, PA (10-195) FTA; NHS; SC; *U of Scranton; Computer Sci.*

BERLAGE, Teresa Ann
Cristobal HS; Coco-Solo, CANAL ZONE (5-130) Band; Chldr; 4H; Bkbl; Sftbl; Tr; Hon Prog; Pres A.

BERLIN, John Mark
Central HS; Memphis, TN (20%-125) Band; Fr C; Yth Organization; Church Bkbl; *Memphis St U; Mus.*

BERMAN, Edye Marsha
Hillel Acad of Pittsburgh; Pittsburgh, PA (4-15) Fr C; NHS; Y-Tns; Bkbl; Sal; Schol A; VP, Religious Zionist Yth Organ; *Bus Adm.*

BERMAN, Karlene
Wethersfield HS; Wethersfield, CT (50%-449) AFS; Band; Chor; Drama; Fr C; Ski C; Mgr, Hockey; Travel, Photo, C'S; Gym Tm; Church Choir; Rep, Pilgrim Fel; *Lyndon St Col; Mus.*

BERMEL, Christy Lynn
Lindbergh HS; St Louis, MO (50%-1000) A Cap Choir; Chor; Ensm; Sch P; Cl Fav; Journ A; *Southwest Mo St U; Special Ed.*

BERMEL, Curtis Lee
Lindbergh HS; St Louis, MO (5%-1000) Band; Pres, Demolay; JETS; NHS; JV, Wrest; COM; Hon Prog; Masonic A; DeMolay Rep; Past Master Councilor; DeMolay o-t Mo; Principle's List; *U of Okla; Mech Engr.*

BERMUDEZ, Maria Luisa
Maria Reina Acad; Rio Piedras, PR (10-58) CYO; Chor; Drama; Model UN; Pres, NHS; Span C; Secy, Jr Cl; Secy, Soph Cl; COM; Hon Prog; *U of Puerto Rico.*

BERMUDEZ, Paul O
R L Turner HS; Carrollton, TX; Chor; Drama; *Bob Jones U; Pastorial.*

BERNABE, John A
Melodyland HS; Anaheim, CA (2-30) Band; NHS; CSF; Citz A; *Calif Tech Col; Elec.*

BERNARD, Martin Kenneth
Antioch HS; Antioch, CA (25-600) NHS; Bkbl; Cr-Ctry; CSA Schol; *Calif Polytech U; Elec Engr.*

BERNARD, Melissa Mary
Bishop Watterson HS; Columbus, OH (64-254) Chor; Ger C; Rptr, Sch P; Span C; MVP, Bkbl; Fin, Hockey; Co-Cpt, Sftbl; WW; *Ohio St U; Pre-Law.*

BERNARD, Renee Marie
Maplewood Jr Sr HS; Johnson, OH (11-102) BC; Chldr; Chor; Drama; Lat C; NHS; Bio A; COM; Magna Cum Laude; *Youngstown St U; Nurs.*

BERNARD, Renee Marie
Maplewood Jr Sr HS; Mecca, OH (10%-110) BC; Chor; Drama; Lat C; NHS; Sci A; *Youngstown U; Nurs.*

BERNARDO, Ricardo
Amer Military Acad; Guaynabo, PR (4-68) Pres, Ann; Band; A-Ed, Sch P; SC; UN Council; Tres, Soph Cl; COM; Chem A; Hist A; Lion A; Academic Star; Conduct A; Attendance A; Military Sci A; *Tulane U; Bus.*

BERNAT, June Elizabeth
Cumberland Valley HS; Mechanicsburg, PA (14-605) Co-Ed, Lit Mag; NHS; F-Ed, Sch P; Thes; COM; *Bard Col; Creative Writing.*

BERNATH, Nancy Joyce
Maple Shade Jr Sr HS; Maple Shade, NJ (7-241) Band; Hmrm; Lit Mag; Cpt, Mjrte; Math C; NHS; Ski C; WW; *U of Nev; Computer Sci.*

BERNBECK, Terri Lynn
Stanton Comm Sch; Stanton, NE; A-Ed, Ann; S-T, Band; Chor; Drama; Ger C; NHS; Pres, Jr Cl.

BERNECKER, Mark Douglas
William Allen HS; Allentown, PA (162-752) Demolay; Drama; Hmrm; Key C; Sch P; SC; World Affairs C; Hon Prog; Masonic A; *Penn St U; Law Enforcement.*

BERNER, Debra Kay
Switzerland Co Jr-Sr HS; Vevay, IN (1-137) Band; VP, 4H; Span C; JV, Bkbl; Tr; Alg A; 4H A; Sci A; Span A; HR; *Ball St U; Sci.*

BERNETT, Mark Richard
Quincy Sr HS II; Quincy, IL (1-780) Span C; Span NHS; Golf; COM; NEDT; Yth Fel; SAA A; NHS.

BERNHAGEN, Luann Lynn
Hutchinson HS; Hutchinson, MN (16-210) AFS; Chor; NHS; F-Ed, Sch P; Thes; Sftbl; Hon Piano Concert; *U of Minn; Math.*

BERNHARDT, Dolores Marie
John W Hallahan HS; Philadelphia, PA (11-431) Co-Ed, Ann; Bus C; Tres, CYO; Math C; NFL; NHS; Sodality; Span C; Spch C; Mgr, Bkbl; Hon Prog; Spch A; Ath Assn; Glee C; Vlbl; Presidential Clrm; *E Stroudsburg St Col; Math.*

BERNHARDT, Lee William
Clintonville Sr HS; Clintonville, WI (18-196) Math C; NHS; Mgr, Cr-Ctry; Tnns; Mgr, Wrest; Aviation C; Stu o-t Wk; *U of Wis; Mech Engr.*

BERNHARDT, Lynette Lee
Park City HS; Park City, MT (1-17) Ann; Band; Chldr; Pres, Chor; Drama; SC; Tres, NHS; Ed, Sch P; Secy, SC; Pres, Jr Cl; Cpt, Bkbl; Sftbl; Tr; Alg A; Amer Leg A; COM; DARGCA; HQn; I Dare You; Journ A; Math A; NEDT; Type A; Val; *Mont St U; Mus.*

BERNHARDT, Mark Timothy
Barrington Consolidates HS; Barrington, IL (118-650) HiY; VP, Y-Tns; COM; Cert of Excel, Northern Il Tech Shw; Favorable Consideration, ITT Tech; *William Rainey Harper Col; Archt.*

BERNHARDT, Robin Leanette
Lomega HS; Omega, OK (1-18) Ann; Chldr; S-T, FFA; Tres, 4H; Hmrm; SC; Rptr, Jr Cl; Bkbl; Sftbl; 4H A; Hist A; HCt; Math A; Spch A; Okla Hon Soc; FFA Star Greenhand; St Fair 4-H Sewing A; St FHA Spch A; *Okla St U; Child Therapist.*

BERNHARDT, Steven Jay
Clintonville Sr HS; Clintonville, WI (10%-200) Tres, Ger C; NHS; Var C; JV, Tnns; Yth Fel; Hon Reading; Math League.

BERNIER, AnnMarie
Marquette HS; Marquette, MI (250-400) S-T, Lib C; *N Mich U; Data Processing.*

BERNS, Michele Marie
Central of Clifton HS; Clifton, IL (2-126) A Cap Choir; F-Ed, Ann; VP, Band; Chor; Ensm; Madrigal; Math C; Pres, NFL; NHS; Pres, Span C; Pres, Spch C; SC; VP, Thes; Tres, Sr Cl; COM; Hon Prog; Magna Cum Laude; Sal; St Scholar; Roper Found School; Interntl Assn of Machinists School; *Olivet Nazarene Col; Nurs.*

BERNSTEIN, Elizabeth Ann
El Camino Real HS; Woodland Hills, CA (19-1095) French NHS; Pres, 4H; SC; CSF; Hist A; Poet A; Gym; Commended Stu; *Stanford U; Sci.*

BERNZEN, Joseph Michael
Quincy Notre Dame HS; Quincy, IL (16-143) Band; Chor; Ger C; Secy, Key C; NHS; Order/Arrow; Kiwanis A; Eagle Sct; Ill Summer Yth Mus Camp School; Ad Altare Dei; WW; *Creighton U; Bio.*

BEROSIK, Becky Lynne
Flathead HS; Kalispell, MT; A Cap Choir; Drama; Sftbl; Tr; JA A; ARC A; Sci A; S C; PA; Phys Fitness A; *Psych.*

BERQUIST, Gretchen Kay
Batavia Sr HS; Batavia, NY; Chor; Var C; Sftbl; Swim; COM; Babe Ruth Sportsmanship A; GAA; Vlbl Tm; YMCA Most Outst Swim A; Regent's Diploma; *Houghton Col; Phys Ed.*

BERQUIST, Ruth Alice
Chateaugay Central Sch; Chateaugay, NY (7-56) VP, Bus C; Chor; Parl; NHS; Sci A; Yth Fel; *St U of NY; Gen.*

BERREY, Genia Diane
Melbourne HS; Melbourne, FL; FHA; Pres, Yth For Christ; *Fla Inst of Tech; Math.*

BERRIEN, John Paul
Hopewell Valley Central HS; Pennington, NJ (86-302) Chor; SC; Thes; Pres, Bible C; Choir; Cpt, Word of Life C; Jerseymen C; Word of Life C School; Corporal, Boy's Brigade; *Liberty Baptist Col; Pastoral Stu.*

BERRINGER, Mark Douglas
Rocky Grove HS; Franklin, PA (3-140) NHS; Eng A.

BERRIOS, Ana Maria
Antilles HS; Fort Buchanan, PR (9-124) NHS; Sci C; Secy, SC; Soccer; *U of Tampa; Med.*

BERROTERAN, Lucia
Irvin HS; El Paso, TX (25%-545) Parl, A Cap Choir; Co-Ed, Ann; Band; CYO; Parl, Chor; Ensm; Hmrm; Sci C; Mgr, Bkbl; Sftbl; Tr; COM; Citz A; Hon Prog; Interlochen Ntl Mus; Sci A; Type A; Rep, Camera C; Sing Out El Paso; God's Young People; Vlbl; Bkbl A; CCD Teacher & Board; Tr A; CCD Histor; Sftb A; Attend A; *UT-El Paso; Bus Adm.*

BERRY, Bernadette
Jeannette Sr HS; Jeannette, PA (42-198) AFS; FBLA; *Bus Adm.*

BERRY, Brenda Kay
Grace King HS; Metairie, LA; Pres, Hmrm; Inter-Club Coun; VP, SC; Cl Fav; Swtht; VP, SASC; Ntl Assn of SC; Sou Assn of SC; Wrkshps, Confs & Conv Thru-Out St; *LSU; Bus.*

BERRY, Chandra Arnise
Woodrow Wilson HS; Washington, DC; ARC; Co-Cpt, Sftbl; Tnns; ARC A; Schol, HR; *Sweet Briar Col; Med.*

BERRY, Charles Eugene
Canton Acad; Canton, MS (4-100) BC; Ch, CYO; 4H; Sci C; JV, Ftbl; Alg A; Bio A; COM; Hist A; Highest Acad Avg As, Eng, Hist; *US Navy; Nuclear Power.*

BERRY, Deborah Jean
Elizabethton HS; Elizabethton, TN (1-230) Band; Hmrm; NHS; Parl, SC; Tnns; Math A; Phy A; Sci A; Val; Eng A; *E Tenn St U; Math.*

BERRY, Karel Anne
Denison Sr HS; Denison, TX (97%-446) Fr C; FTA; VP, Y-Tns; Hon Prog; Service C; Drill Tm; Jr NHS; Ntl HS Biol Hon Soc; *N Tex St U; Psych.*

BERRY, Karin Denise
Plainview HS; Plainview, TX (5-400) A Cap Choir; Tres, Band; Chldr; Parl, Hmrm; Madrigal; NHS; SC; Tr; Bio A; Hon Prog; Math A; NMS; Rotary A; Spch A; Yth Fel; Cpt, Flag Corps; All Region & All Area Band; All Region & All Area Choir; *Mus.*

BERRY, Kendra Joyce
Lodi HS; Lodi, CA; *Point Loma Nazarene Col; Psych.*

BERRY, Kristi Lyn
Canadian HS; Canadian, TX (13-58) Ensm; Pres, FHA; FTA; NHS; Var C; VP, Jr Cl; Co-Cpt, Bkbl; Tr; Hon Prog; Sgt at Arms, Sr Cl; MVP, Bkbl; Ath A; *Baylor U; Phys Therapy.*

BERRY, Laura Ann
Tift Co HS; Tifton, GA; Chor; *Abraham Baldwin Col; Secretarial Sci.*

BERRY, Laura Kaye
Mira Loma HS; Sacramento, CA (250-300) Ann; S-T, Ger C; NHS; Sch P; Bio A; CSF; Hon Prog; Bacteriology A; Sci Fair A; *U of Calif; Bio.*

BERRY, Leigh Ann
Lufkin HS; Lufkin, TX (20-520) A Cap Choir; Secy, Drama; Co-Ed, Lit Mag; NHS; Secy, Thes; Citz A; Hon Prog; NEDT; Eng A; All St Choir; *Baylor U.*

BERRY, Linda Kay
Rye Cove HS; Clinchport, VA (5-76) BC; Co-Cpt, Chldr; Chor; Secy, FBLA; FHA; 4H; Co-Cpt, Bkbl; Tr; Chem A; 4H A; Pres A; *Mountain Empire Comm Col; Ed.*

BERRY, Marcy L
Texhoma HS; Texhoma, OK (3-28) Chldr; Tres, NHS; Pres, Rainbow; Co-Ed, Sch P; Var C; Bkbl; Tr; Bio A; Masonic A; Outst Yth A; *Wayland Baptist Col; Dentistry.*

BERRY, Melissa Ann
Largo Sr HS; Upper Marlboro, MD (20%-500) Chor; VP, Ger C; NHS; ARC; Rptr, Sch P; Mgr, Wrest; NML; *U of Md; Early Childhood Ed.*

BERRY, Merrilee Ann
Colerain HS; Cincinnati, OH; Band; Pres 1st Pl; Bible Bowl; Usherette; Church Yth Group; *Bus.*

BERRY, Michael Waitsell
South Gwinnett HS; Snellville, GA (1-296) Secy, BC; Cpt, Dbte Tm; Fr C; FBLA; NFL; Secy, Span C; COM; Math A; Spch A; Debate Spch As; Fin, Tm Trophy Debate; Fin, St Extemporaneous Spch; *Med.*

BERRY, Nina Paulette
Compton Sr HS; Compton, CA (53-800) Pol Sci C; Sci C; Sci A; Gov A; *U of Calif; Pol Sci.*

BERRY, Paul Arthur
Imlay City HS; Imlay City, MI; Band; SC; Var C; Pres, Soph Cl; Cpt, Bkbl; JV, Golf; JV, Tr; Fin, Wrest; Pres, Lutheran Church League; *U of Mich; Engr.*

BERRY, Raymond
Dublin HS; Dublin, GA (32-199) COM; ROTC A; Yth Fel; *U of San Diego; Computers.*

BERRY, Robert Dean
Texhoma HS; Texhoma, OK (10-30) FFA; 4H; NHS; Cr-Ctry; Ftbl; Tr; Cl Fav; Math A; Voc Agr A; *Okla St Tech Col; Diesel Mech.*

BERRY, Sandy Gail
Lafayette HS; Lafayette, LA; Span C; Bkbl; Soccer; Sftbl; Swim; Tr; Yth Fel; Life Saving.

BERRY, Shannon Lea
Texhoma HS; Texhoma, OK; A Cap Choir; Chor; Rainbow; Bkbl; Tr; *Okla St U; Journ.*

BERRY, Tina Marie
Dublin HS; Dublin, GA (73-165) Chor; Cl Fav; DARGCA; God & Country A; Yth Fel; Yth Leg; *Saint Mary's Col; Acct.*

BERRY, Valerie Sue
New Philadelphia Sr HS; New Philadelphia, OH (33%-325) Bus C; FBLA; ARC; Span C; Pres, Church Yth Group; *Kent St U; Data Processing.*

BERRY, William Howard
Will C Crawford HS; San Diego, CA (96-578) Ger C; Key C; Graduation With Acad Distinction; *Oreg St U; Wildlife Sci.*

BERRYMAN, Otelia
John Marshall HS; Richmond, VA; FHA; *Cosmetology.*

BERTHA, Brian George
Dominican HS; Whitefish Bay, WI (15-170) NHS; Var C; Cr-Ctry; Hon Prog; Explorers; WW; Tr Medals; Sr Lifesaving; *UW-Madison; Med.*

BERTHOLD, Mary Elizabeth
Central Valley Pub Sch; Buxton, ND (8-32) Drama; FHA; Sci A.

BERTONI, Joanne Marie
MacDuffie Sch for Girls; Springfield, MA; Chor; Rptr, Sch P; JV, Tnns; Jr Extension; Meg Farwell Schol A.

BERTRAM, Laura Lynne
Clinton Co HS; Albany, KY (10%-107) BC; Chldr; FHA; FTA; Hmrm; Math C; SC; VP, Jr Cl; Sftbl; Tr; Cl Fav; Swtht; FFA Qn; *Somerset Comm Col; Nurs.*

BERTRAM, Lee R
Syosset HS; Syosset, NY (436-711) Bkbl; Yth Fel; Lacrosse; Yth Del, Church St Conf.

BERTRAND, Franchette
E Chambers HS; Winnie, TX (16-79) Rptr, Ann; Drama; Ensm; NFL; NHS; Spch C; Bkbl; Tnns; Spch A; *Lon Morris Jr Col; Ed.*

BESALSKI, Carolyn Elaine
Buchholz HS; Gainesville, FL (99-400) Hmrm; Span C; SC.

BESETTE, Karen Lynn
Albany HS; Albany, CA (2%-175) Mgr, Band; Chor; Drama; Pres, Fr C; Thes; CSF; Hon Prog; NMS; Star Student; *Simpson Col.*

BESLER, Elizabeth
Passaic HS; Passaic, NJ; Chor; FBLA; Span C; Cr-Ctry; Tr; Yth Fel; Drama C A; Lib Helper Cert; Candystriper Medal A; *Social Worker.*

BESS, Jill Corrine
Dos Pueblos HS; Goleta, CA (10%-600) A Cap Choir; JV, Chldr; Pres, Drama; Thes; H of F; Hist A; HCt; *U of Redlands.*

BESS, Juana Jean
Pacific HS; Langlois, OR (4-60) Ann; Rptr, Bus C; Ensm; Rptr, FBLA; Semi-Fin, GS; NHS; F-Ed, Sch P; Span C; COM; Shorthand A; *W Baptist Col; Counseling.*

BESS, Karen Louise
Parkway W Sr HS; Ballwin, MO (25-600) Secy, A Cap Choir; Chldr; Chor; Ensm; FBLA; Hmrm; NHS; SC; Hon Prog; Journ A; Most Out; Q&S A; God & Community A; 1st Cl, GSct; *Tex Christian U; Bus.*

BESSENT, Alice Anne
Grants Pass HS; Grants Pass, OR; A Cap Choir; Drama; Ensm; Semi-Fin, GS; NHS; COM; Cl Fav.

BESSENT, Laura Lisa
Salisbury HS; Salisbury, NC (20-161) AFS; Chor; Community Yth Symph; Ensm; Fr C; Madrigal; Pres, Orch; SC; Hon Prog; Orch Hons; Chor Hons; Church Choir; Best All Around Piano Stu; *Catawba Col; Mus Ed.*

BESSETTE, Anne Louise
Lyman Mem HS; Lebanon, CT (3-96) Fr C; Fr A.

BESSETTE, Michael David
Corona Sr HS; Corona, CA; Secy, Key C; Bkbl; Ftbl; Tr; Most Artistic; *Art.*

BEST, Brenda Annette
Gumberry HS; Gumberry, NC (1-97) BC; 4H; COM; Citz A; 4H A; Val; *NC Central U; Acct.*

BEST, David Keith
Valdosta HS; Valdosta, GA (25%-400) BC; Dbte Tm; Drama; FBLA; Spch C; COM; Math A; Outst Jr, Art.

BEST, Debra Elaine
Hammond Tech Voc HS; Hammond, IN (4-283) Cpt, Mjrte; Secy, NHS; Tnns; Eng A; Pleasing Personality A; Best Behaved A; Semi-Fin, HQn Nomination.

BEST, Patti Sue
Nederland HS; Nederland, TX; FTA; Church Princess of Yth; Pres, Secy, Church Yth Coun; Ch, Revival; *E Tex Baptist Col; Religion.*

BEST, Paula Rene
T R Miller HS; Brewton, AL (2-115) Chldr; FHA; FTA; NHS; A-Ed, Sch P; *Phar.*

BEST, Ruetta Gloria
William M Raines HS; Jacksonville, FL (97-417) A Cap Choir; Bus C; Chor; Ensm; Fr C; Sftbl; Citz A; I Dare You; Most Out; Star Student; *Morris Brown Col; Mus.*

BEST, Wanda
Martin Luther King HS; Philadelphia, PA (2-690) Fr C; Rptr, Hmrm; NHS; Secy, Y-Tns; COM; Citz A; Hist A; Hon Prog; Most Out; Amer Federation of Teachers, A; Foreign Lang, Bicen Schol, A's; *Pa St U; Psych.*

BESTE, Ian Robert
Piner HS; Santa Rosa, CA; Key C; Co-Ed, Lit Mag; CSF; *U of Calif; Sci.*

BETHANY, Barbara Lenette
Beaumont HS; St Louis, MO (89-400) *Forest Park Comm Col; Register Nurs.*

BETHANY, James Richard
Venus HS; Venus, TX (2-11) Sch P; Sci C; Pres, Jr Cl; Bkbl; Co-Cpt, Ftbl; Semi-Fin, Tnns; Tr; Chem A; Sci A; 'A' HR; Bookkeeping A; Best All Around Boy; Hon Men, Ftbl; *E Tex St U; Acct.*

BETHANY, Sharon Ann
Beaumont HS; St Louis, MO (206-400) *Lincoln U.*

BETHEA, Michele Renee
Uniondale HS; Uniondale, NY; Chor; Sch P; Swim; Ntl Fraternity of Mus; Modeling Sch; *Hofstra U; Journ.*

BETHEA, William Floyd
Dillon HS; Dillon, SC; Key C; Var C; JV, Ftbl; Golf; Tr; *Clemson U; Forest Mgr.*

BETHEL, Charles Michel
Theodore Roosevelt HS; Bronx, NY; Rptr, Sch P; Bkbl; Math A; Sci A; *Leman Col; Sci.*

BETHEL, Neville Anthony
Theodore Roosevelt HS; Bronx, NY; Band; *Pepperdine Col; Mus.*

BETHER, Charles Jeffrey
Fallbrook Union HS; Fallbrook, CA (2%-450) Madrigal; Golf; CSF; Outst Jr Madrigal; *Oral Roberts U; Bus.*

BETHUNE, Gary Lee
Pearland HS; Pearland, TX (108-340) InterClub Coun; Pol Sci C; Cr-Ctry; Ftbl; Tr; Sch Beau; *Baylor U; Law.*

BETHUNE, Wanda Marie
N Fulton HS; Atlanta, GA (20-180) Band; BC; Hmrm; Hon Prog; Top 10%, Cl; Semi-Fin, Gov Hon's Prog; *Pre-Dentistry.*

BETSCH, Karen Kay
Arapahoe HS; Littleton, CO; 4H; Ski C; *Greenville Col; Phys Ed.*

BETTENHAUSEN, Kay Laura
Centralia Boone Co HS; Centralia, MO (20-120) Chor; Ensm; Pres, 4H; COM; 4H A; Co 4-H Medals; 2nd, St Poetry Contest.

BETTERS, Michael Bryon
Rolling Meadows HS; Rolling Meadows, IL (139-664) Band; Chor; Order/Arrow; Ftbl; Tnns; COM; Opt Out Tn; Order/Arrow A; Eagle Sct; *Sci.*

BETTIN, Mary Elizabeth
Downers Grove S HS; Downers Grove, IL (16-770) Ski C; Tr; Schol Arts A's; *N Ill U; Nurs.*

BETTS, Darla Sue
Le Mars Comm HS; Le Mars, IA; Band; Chor; Orch; Bsbl; Bkbl; Sftbl; Swim; Tr; Yth Fel; Pres, Yth Fel; All St Orch; I Rating, St Mus Contest.

BETTS, David Michael
John Glenn HS; New Concord, OH (25%-180) Ch, FFA; 4H; Lat C; Ftbl; 4H A.

BETTS, Richard L
Greater Latrobe HS; Latrobe, PA (50-560) Secy, Band; Chor; Ensm; NHS; COM; Hon Prog; Kiwanis A; NMF; Sch Organist; Band A; Most Outst Stu, Vocal Dept; *U of Pittsburgh at Johnstown; Engr.*

BETTS, Richard Lee
Greater Latrobe Sr HS; Latrobe, PA (87-518) Secy, Band; Chor; NMS; *U of Pittsburgh; Engr.*

BETTS, Rita Irene
LeMars Comm HS; LeMars, IA (1-216) Band; Dbte Tm; NFL; COM; 1st Chair, NW Iowa Hon Band.

BETTS, Sharon Denice
Lincoln Park HS; Ft Pierce, FL; *U of S Fla; Secy.*

BETTS, Tina Monique
Sumter HS; Sumter, SC; Chldr; Chor; Drama; VP, Hmrm; Lat C; Lat NHS; Tres, NHS; SC; Tnns; Hon Prog; ROTC A; Drama A; *Air Force Acad; Med.*

BETZ, Jana Mary
Pass Christian HS; Pass Christian, MS (25%-110) Band; Tres, BC; Secy, Span C; SC; Type A; Pres, Span C; St Solo & Ensm-Duet Med & Solo Med; *Miss Gulf Coast Jr Col; Bus.*

BETZEN, Betty Josephine
Bishop Carroll HS; Wichita, KS (9-211) CYO; Span C; Hon Prog; Regent Schol; St Scholar; BEOG; *Marymount Col; Nurs.*

BEUKELMAN, Brenda Ann
Sunset HS; Beaverton, OR; Chldr; Chor; 4H; Rptr, Sch P; Ski C; SC; Cl Fav; 4H A; HCt; Gym; *Oreg St U; Nurs.*

BEURY, Walton Venable
New Albany HS; New Albany, IN; Chor; Hmrm; Pres, Lat C; Order/Arrow; Swim.

BEUSCH, Glenda Jean
Stevens HS; Rapid City, SD (235-456) Bsbl; Bkbl; Ntl Col of Bus; *Real Estate Agent.*

BEUST, David Craig
Manhattan HS; Manhattan, KS (117-425) Band; Chor; S-T, HiY; Order/Arrow; Sch P; Cr-Ctry; Tr; JV, Wrest; JA A; Order/Arrow A; Rptr, Yth Fel; *Kans St U; Radio-tV Broadcasting.*

BEUSTER, Teri Lynn
Lincoln Northeast HS; Lincoln, NE (80-502) Chor; Math C; Sftbl; *Concordia Teachers Col; Ed.*

BEVACQUA, David Alan
Glen Oak HS; North Canton, OH (347-708) Chess C; Bsbl; Ftbl; Sftbl; Swim; Wrest; Citz A; *US Army; Intelligence.*

BEVAN, Susan Louise
Brunswick HS; Brunswick, GA (1-386) Ann; Band; Tres, Drama; Hmrm; Lit Mag; Rptr, Sch P; COM; 4H A; Hon Prog; Pres A; *U of Ga; Vet Sci.*

BEVEL, Gregory Haynes
Robert E Lee HS; Midland, TX; Band; *Baylor U; Bus.*

BEVER, Ruth Ann
Parkwood HS; Joplin, MO; Chldr; Chor; 4H; Co-Cpt, Bkbl; Cl Fav; 4H A; Yth Fel; *Social Work.*

BEVERIDGE, Janice Eleanor
Ewing HS; Trenton, NJ; A Cap Choir; Cpt, Chldr; Ensm; Pres, Hmrm; SC; Keywanettes; *Phys Therapy.*

BEVERIDGE, Robert Paul
Moscow Sr HS; Moscow, ID (19-230) AFS; Ski C; Span C; COM; Math A; Phy A; Sci A; *Calif Inst of Tech; Physics.*

BEVERLY, Craig Alonza
Jessis Jones HS; Houston, TX (15-400) Bsbl; Cpt, Ftbl; Swim; Tr; ARC A; MVP, Ftbl; BSct; 3rd, Cty Wide Tr Mt, Life Grd Cert; *U of Houston; MD.*

BEVERLY, Karen Diane
Sam Houston HS; Arlington, TX (123-536) Fr C; Parl, FHA; Rptr, Sch P; Sci C; Sftbl; Tnns; COM; Citz A; Hon Prog; B&PW A; *Tarrant Co Jr Col; Med Secy.*

BEVERLY, Lorna
Chester HS; Chester, PA; Hockey; Tnns; Tr; HR; Essay Contest; *Widner Col; Nurs.*

BEVERLY, Lorraine
Chester HS; Chester, PA; Band; Pres, SC; Sftbl; Swim; Tnns; Hist A; Sci A; Essay A; *Med.*

BEVERLY, Patti Harris
York Comp HS; York, SC (1-261) BC; Fr C; Eng A; *Mary Baldwin U.*

BEVERLY, Vanessa Anita
Biloxi Sr HS; Biloxi, MS (30%-510) Rptr, Ann; FHA; Rptr, Sch P; Span NHS; SC; Mgr, Bkbl; Sftbl; Tr; COM; Citz A; Afro-Amer Beauty; Span NHS; Mock HQn; Secy, Afro Amer C; Outst Sr Phys Ed; Pres, Yth Organ; Les Petites C; Sunday Sch Teacher; *Miss Gulf Coast Jr Col; Nurs.*

BEVERS, Beth Annette
Burkeville HS; Burkeville, TX (4-36) Drama; FHA; Spch C; JV, Tr; NEDT; Spch A; Sch Hon Soc.

BEVIS, Bradley Paul
Mt Vernon Township HS; Mt Vernon, IL (130-400) Span C; Bkbl; Co-Cpt, Ftbl; Tr; HCt; *E Ill U; Phys Ed.*

BEVIS, Leslie Jane
Taylor HS; North Bend, OH (50%-225) JV, Chldr; Secy, Chor; Secy, Ensm; Rptr, Hmrm; SC; *Theatre Arts.*

BEVIS, Melody Ann
Parkview HS; Lilburn, GA; Ch, BC; Chldr; Fr C; Hmrm; Fin, Jr Miss Pagent; Secy, SC; MVP, Tnns; COM; Hon Prog; Most Out; *Pepperdine U; Med.*

BEWLEY, Glenn Nelson
Greeneville HS; Greeneville, TN (13-193) A-Ed, Ann; Chess C; Hmrm; VP, Math C; NHS; Sch P; Thes; Math A; Geom A; Highest Cl Score, ACT; Pres, Photography C; Schol Camp; *Rochester Inst of Tech; Professional Photography.*

BEWLEY, James Tyler
Fair Play HS; Fair Play, MO (5-22) Co-Ed, Ann; Band; Chor; VP, FFA; Co-Ed, Sch P; Var C; Bsbl; Co-Cpt, Bkbl; HCt; Sci A; *Sch of Ozarks; Vet.*

BEYER, Carol Rose
Molalla Union HS; Molalla, OR (1-174) Ann; CYO; Rptr, Sch P; SC; VP, Soph Cl; Tr; Amer Leg A; Chem A; Gov Honor Prog; Hon Prog; Type A; May Day Court; ASB 1st VP; High-Q C; CVC Secy; Girl o-t Month; Most Studious; *Oreg St U; Bio.*

BEYER, Lori Lee
Lubbock Christian HS; Lubbock, TX (1-54) Bus Mgr, Band; Chor; Co-Ch, Dbte Tm; GS; Pres, 4H; VP, NFL; NHS; A-Ed, Sch P; Spch C; Secy, Jr Cl; COM; Citz A; DARGCA; 4H A; Hon Prog; Opt A; Spch A; VFW Orator Win; VofDEM; Bicentennial Yth Debates; *Lubbock Christian Col; Ed.*

BEYER, Nancy Fae
Belmond Comm HS; Belmond, IA (20-81) Ann; Band; Ensm; FHA; Pres, 4H; Span C; JV, Golf; 4H A; Yth Fel; *Mankato St U; Med Tech.*

BEYER, Thomas Reinhardt
Hitchcock Pub HS; Hitchcock, SD (6-22) A Cap Choir; Band; Chor; Ensm; Orch; Sch P; Var C; Bkbl; Ftbl; Sftbl; Swim; Tnns; Type A; Tres, Church Yth; *Augustana Col.*

BEYER, Yvonne Elaine
Plymouth Canton HS; Plymouth, MI; Chor; Hmrm; Madrigal; *E Mich Col; Elem Ed.*

BIALAS, Mitzi Dawn
Parkston Pub Sch; Darkston, SD (23-99) MVP, Band; Chem C; MVP, Chor; Ensm; FHA; Ger C; NHS; Golf; Type A; *Madison Dakota St U; Med Records.*

BIANCHETTA, Margaret Maria
Rosati-Kain HS; St Louis, MO; Band; CYO; Chor; Ensm; Tnns; *Sci.*

BIANCO, Joseph Anthony
William Kelley HS; Silver Bay, MN; Fin, AFS; Band; Chem C; Drama; Ensm; VP, Monogram; NHS; Sci C; VP, SC; Pres, Sr Cl; Pres, Jr Cl; Pres, Soph Cl; Bkbl; Cr-Ctry; Ftbl; Tr; Bio A; Chem A; HCt; Sci A; VofDEM; Interntl Sci Fair Runner- up; Navy Sci A; AFS Summer Exchange Schol; 1st Pl, St Tr Meet; *Med.*

BIAR, Beth Michelle
Nederland HS; Nederland, TX (1-480) Chor; Ensm; Fr C; S-T, Math C; NHS; Alg A; COM; Chamber of Comm A; Math A; Type A; Choral A; Phys Ed A; UIL Piano; Regional Choir; Area Choir Alt; Tres, Secy, VP, Lutheran Yth Lge; UIL Vocal Solo; *Mus Therapy.*

BIAS, Jackie Gail
Ceredo-Kenova HS; Kenova, WV (10%-120) Band; Chldr; FHA; Mu Alpha Theta; SC; Var C; *Marshall U.*

BIBBEE, Robert Boyd
Martin Co HS; Stuart, FL (108-500) Co-Ch, BC; BS; Key C; Bsbl; Amer Leg A; COM; Jr Civitans; WW; *FSU; Marketing.*

BIBBS, Lionel
Alexander HS; Starkville, MS (1-59) Fr C; Bus Mgr, Jr Cl; Pres, Soph Cl; Ftbl; Hon Prog; Ntl Sci Found; *Miss U; Bus.*

BICANIC, Carel Lynn
Waukegan E HS; Waukegan, IL (61-629) Pres, Bkbl; Pres, Arts C; Extracurricular A; Pres, Vlbl; High Achv A; High Hr A; *Med.*

BICHAN, Lynette Kay
Patrick Henry HS; Hamler, OH (6-90) A Cap Choir; Band; Chor; NHS; Orch; Amer Leg A; VofDEM; Yth Fel; WW; WW in Mus; Best of Show-Art; *Bowling Green St U; Acct.*

BICHEL, Scott Bradley
St Charles HS; St Charles, MO (32-543) Band; Key C; NHS; Orch; Golf; *U of Mo; Engr.*

BICK, Nancy Ann
St Ignatius HS; St Ignatius, MT (5-60) Band; 4H; A-Ed, Sch P; Tres, Soph Cl; JV, Bkbl; Tr; NEDT; *Mont St U.*

BICK, Susan Lynn
Farnam Pub HS; Farnam, NE (2-14) Ann; Band; Cpt, Chldr; Chor; 4H; Tr; 4H A; Type A; Yth Fel; Vlbl; Piano A; Vlbl All Around A; *Wesleyan U; Bus.*

BICKEL, Daniel Lavern
Adna HS; Adna, WA (5-24) Band; Fr C; NHS; SC; Var C; Pres, Jr Cl; Bsbl; Bkbl; Ftbl; HCt; Hon Prog; Pres, Stu Body; *Wash St U; Engr.*

BICKFORD, Cheri Luane
Central HS; Providence, RI; Chor; COM; Citz A; Schol A; *Secy.*

BICKFORD, Steven Joseph
Goodrich HS; Goodrich, TX (2-30) BC; FFA; Span C; Bsbl; JV, Swim; JV, Tr; *U of Tex; Elec.*

BICKLEY, Lisa Jo
Charlottesville HS; Charlottesville, VA (45-369) A Cap Choir; Co-Cpt, Chldr; Chor; Secy, Drama; Fr C; FHA; Hmrm; Lat C; Madrigal; NHS; Sci C; Sodality; Tr; Beauty; HCt; Pres A; *Mary Washington Col; Special Ed.*

BICKMEYER, Diane Lynn
Hermann Sr HS; Hermann, MO (13-125) Band; Chor; Ensm; Sftbl; Yth Fel; Tumbling Tm; Secy, Candystriper; Flag Corps; *Nurs.*

BICKSLER, Meggan Elaine
Arcadia HS; Arcadia, CA (20%-860) Secy, A Cap Choir; NHS; *Cal Poly-Pomona; Home Ec.*

BIDDISON, Mark Allen
Glenbrook HS; Northbrook, IL (20%-600) Band; Chor; Drama; Orch; COM; Most Out; Cert of Appreciation; Rifle Trophies & Medals; *Mus.*

BIDDLE, Bartram Scott
William R Boone HS; Orlando, FL (183-599) Var C; Co-Cpt, Ftbl; Cpt, Soccer; Cpt, Wrest; Alg A; Ntl Conf Chr & Jews; Yth Fel; Tres, FCA; Fin Co Wrest; Young Life; Hustler A, Wrest; MVP, Wrest; Semi-Fin, Dist Wrest; *Phys Ed.*

BIDLACK, Myra Lynne
Montpelier HS; Montpelier, OH; Band; Chldr; Chor; FHA; NHS; SC; Bkbl; Most Out; Outst Sr.

BIDNER, Jennifer Lee
Bellflower Township HS; Bellflower, IL (4-14) Band; Chor; S-T, Fr C; S-T, FHA; Sci C; Tr; Citz A; Type A; PA; *Bradley U.*

BIDWELL, Gregory Neal
Washington HS; Kansas City, KS (20%-600) Chess C; Hmrm; A-Ed, Sch P; SC; Church & Campus; Ottawa Alumni; *Ottawa U; Broadcasting.*

BIDWELL, Jonathan Lantz
Damascus HS; Damascus, MD; Chor; Bsbl; Yth Fel; BSct; Church Camps; *Md U; Photography.*

BIEBER, Denise Michelle
Wells-Easton HS; Wells, MN (9-104) Ed, Ann; Band; Drama; Ensm; 4H; Rptr, Sch P; Secy, SC; Bkbl; Tnns; 3rd, Dist Declam; Mus Contest A; *Mankato St U; Med Tech.*

BIEBER, Joel Dean
Tabernacle Baptist Sch; Va Beach, VA (3-28) F-Ed, Ann; Band; Chor; Dbte Tm; Drama; Hmrm; VP, NFL; F-Ed, Sch P; Spch C; Var C; VP, Jr Cl; Co-Cpt, Bkbl; Soccer; Sftbl; COM; Hon Prog; Spch A; Yth Fel; Preacher Boys C; Highest Proteen; HR; Principals HR; *Bible.*

BIEDERMAN, Linda Ruth
Renville HS; Renville, MN (11-44) AFS; A-Ed, Ann; Pres, Band; Chor; Ensm; FHA; FTA; Ger C; Madrigal; Pres, Mjrte; Sch P; Spch C; Var C; Hon Prog; Spch A; Yth Fel; SDAHSS; *Westmar Col; Mus.*

BIEDERMANN, Melba Diane
Western HS; Baltimore, MD (56-790) NHS; COM; *W Md Col; Special Ed.*

BIEL, Daniel Jay
Java HS; Java, SD (7-15) Ann; VP, Band; Chor; Drama; Ensm; Hmrm; Pres, Monogram; Sch P; VP, SC; Var C; Pres, Sr Cl; Pres, Soph Cl; Bsbl; Co-Cpt, Bkbl; Co-Cpt, Ftbl; Cpt, Tr; HCt; Most Out; Type A; Yth Fel; All St Ftbl; WW; *Bus Adm.*

BIEL, Roberta Lynn
Java Pub HS; Java, SD (4-17) Band; Chldr; Drama; Ensm; 4H; Rptr, Sch P; Tres, Jr Cl; Secy, Soph Cl; Journ A; Type A; Secy, Yth Fel.

BIEL, Vanessa Ione
Java Pub Sch; Java, SD (5-13) Ann; Band; Chor; Drama; Ensm; Sch P; Var C; Mgr, Bkbl; Mgr, Ftbl; Sftbl; Type A; Mus A; Band A.

BIELA, Susan Mary
Theodore Roosevelt HS; San Antonio, TX (4-793) Band; Ensm; Ger C; Pres, Hmrm; Key C; Math C; Mu Alpha Theta; NHS; COM; Citz A; Math A; NEDT; Church Chor; Band Medal; Chaplain, Mu Alpha Theta; Hon Social Stu C; Slide Rule Trophies; *St Mary's U; Elec.*

BIELBY, Vicki Lynn
Pocatello HS; Pocatello, ID (133-500) Band; Bus C; Bus Mgr, Sch P; Thes; Sr Princess; Wilderness C; Sch Senator; Job's Daughters; Q&S; *Idaho St U; Bus.*

BIELEMA, Ross Raymond
Fulton HS; Fulton, IL (10%-125) Ann; Chor; F-Ed, Sch P; Span C; Hon Prog; St Scholar; WW; NRA; *Sauk Valley Col; Journ.*

BIEN, Deborah Jean
Durand HS; Durand, WI (28-250) Band; Bus C; CYO; Chor; Community Yth Symph; Fin, Ensm; Fr C; Secy, 4H; A-Ed, Sch P; Sodality; Pres, SC; Soccer; Sftbl; Swim; Tnns; Sanctuary Soc; St Ensm A; 1st Ensm A; *Bus.*

BIENVENU, Dudley Louis
Belmont Acad; Opelousas, LA (4-44) CYO; VP, Key C; Cpt, Golf; MVP, Golf; S-T, Serteen; Individual St Champion, Golf; Serteen A; Key C Cert.

BIER, Thomas Matthew
Wilton-Lynde Borough Co-Op HS; Wilton, NH (5-55) Chess C; NHS; Rptr, Sch P.

BIERER, Debora Ellen
Uniontown Area Sr HS; Uniontown, PA (16-435) Band; NHS; Semi-Fin, Gov's Sch for Arts; *Alderson-Broaddus Col; Mus.*

BIERER, Rebecca Ann
Uniontown Sr HS; Uniontown, PA; Band; FNA; Sci C; Ski C.

BIERLEIN, Kimberly Kay
Arthur Hill HS; Saginaw, MI (309-683) Tres, Bus C; Chor; Drama; Hmrm; Thes; Q&S A; Merit Roll; Co-Op o-t Mo; *Concordia Lutheran Col.*

BIERLEY, Terri Sue
Rogers HS; Toledo, OH; Ger C; Hon Prog; JA A; Bowling Green U; Art.

BIERMAN, Greg Micheal
Dieterich HS; Dieterich, IL (3-42) CYO; FFA; Cr-Ctry; Tr; *Eastern Col; Math.*

BIERMAN, Lisa Michelle
Belvidere HS; Belvidere, IL (8-470) A Cap Choir; F-Ed, Ann; Drama; Ensm; Sch P; SC; Thes; VP, Jr Cl; Sftbl; Tnns; Amer Leg A; DAR Essay A; *Journ.*

BIERNACKI, Laurie Sandra
John F Kennedy HS; Seattle, WA (11-318) A Cap Choir; Band; Ger C; ARC; Ski C; Bsbl; Bkbl; Soccer; Sftbl; Swim; COM; Citz A; Hon Prog; ARC A; Val; Bell Choir; W Seattle Fed Womens C Mus Schol; *U of Wash; Mus.*

BIERNACKI, Ted James
Hoehne HS; Hoehne, CO (2-35) Dbte Tm; NHS; COM; Spch A; Type A; *U of N Colo; Law.*

BIERWIRTH, Jill Suzanne
Mauldin HS; Mauldin, SC (7-225) Chor; Ensm; NHS; Hon Prog; *Furman U; Ancient Hist.*

BIETH, Bonnie Lee
Holy Cross HS; Marine City, MI (21-54) Chor.

BIFFORD, Ricky P
Altheimer HS; Altheimer, AR; Ed, Ann; Pres, SC; Bio A; COM; Citz A; Cl Fav; MLS; Most Out; *U of Ark; Philosophy.*

BIFFORD, Ricky Parneil
Altheimer HS; Altheimer, AR; Ed, Ann; Chor; Pres, SC; Bio A; COM; Citz A; Hist A; MLS; Most Out; *UAPB; Philosophy.*

BIGBY, Terry Dee
Tahlequah Sr HS; Tahlequah, OK; Key C; Ftbl; Hist A; *Okla U.*

BIGELOW, Jill Vernal
Grants Pass HS; Grants Pass, OR; Band; Drama; Span C; Honored Qn, Job's Daughters; *U of Oreg; Journ.*

BIGELOW, Richard Charles
Batavia HS; Batavia, IL (3-224) Band; Lat C; Math C; Orch; Golf; Hon Prog; Math A; St Lat Contest; Dist Mus; *U of Ill; Bus.*

BIGELOW, Shelley Renee
Mona Shores HS; Muskegon, MI (87-475) 4H A; *Calvin Col; Ed.*

BIGGE, Sunshine Brooke
Mena HS; Mena, AR; Co-Cpt, Chldr; FHA; S-T, 4H; Sci C; Bkbl; Tnns; MVP, Tr; 4H A; Pres A; PA, Sun Sch; Ballet, Dance As; *Home Ec.*

BIGGERS, Kathy Lynn
New Braunfels HS; New Braunfels, TX; Band; Ensm; FHA; FTA; Pres, 4H; Fin, Jr Miss Pageant; Sci C; Span C; Bkbl; Amer Leg A; Elk A; 4H A; Kiwanis A; Dist Pres, St Secy, 4-H C; Unity C; Dist Hon Men, Bkbl; All St Vlbl; *N Tex St U; Bus.*

BIGGERSTAFF, Janice Christine
Mountain Heritage HS; Burnsville, NC (1-190) BC; FHA; Hmrm; Ch, Math C; Model UN; Monogram; NHS; Co-Cpt, Bkbl; Alg A; Chem A; Gov Honor Prog; Gr Marshal; Hist A; NHS; Hon Prog; Math A; Secy, Western Dist, NC Beta C; MVP, Bkbl; Beta A; Eng A; Sch Bkbl A; *Appalachian St U; Elem Ed.*

BIGGINS, Brian Bernard
Belvidere HS; Belvidere, IL (35-375) Ger C; Ski C; SC; Var C; Ftbl; Tr; Beauty; *Ill St U; Sci.*

BIGGS, Cindy Lou
Henderson Co Sr HS; Henderson, KY (10%-550) NHS; SC; Bkbl; Church Sftbl; Cotillion C; *Ky Wesleyan Col; Elem Ed.*

BIGGS, Jill Marie
Murphysboro HS; Murphysboro, IL; A Cap Choir; Chor; Ensm; Madrigal; ARC; SC; Tr; Hon Prog; Piano Accompanist, Ensm; Sch Mus; Chor Contest As; *Sou Ill U; Mus.*

BIGGS, Matthew William
Lincoln SE HS; Lincoln, NE; Sci C; *U of Nebr; Engr.*

BIGHAM, Cathy Kay
Union HS; Union Grove, WI (10-249) AFS; Drama; Fr C; NHS; Mgr, Tr; Gym; *U of Wis-La Crosse; Teaching Phys Ed.*

BIGHAM, LuCindia Lu
Edmond Mem HS; Edmond, OK (5%-550) NHS; Pep C; Fin, Art Contest; St Hon Soc; Schol to Amer Seminar; Tres, Art C; Semi-Fin, Best All Around; *Okla Christian Col; Acct.*

BIGHAM, Reginald Alan
Trezevant HS; Trezevant, TN (20%-44) Ann; VP, BC; FFA; 4H; Sci C; Tres, Sr Cl; Bsbl; *Tenn St U; Animal Sci.*

BIGLEY, Scott Arthur
Grove City HS; Grove City, PA (100-250) Band; Chor; Ensm; Hmrm; Key C; Monogram; Orch; Semi-Fin, Spch C; Thes; Co-Cpt, Bkbl; Spch A; VFW Orator Win; VofDEM; Yth Fel; Church Usher; Yth Sunday Speaker; *Law Enforcement.*

BIHARY, Brenda Lee
Fairport Harding HS; Fairport Harbor, OH (20-56) Tres, Band; Chor; Drama; Fr C; Hmrm; Mjrte; Span C; Sftbl; COM; Schol C A; GAA; *Nurs.*

BIJEAUX, Lennett Paul
St Martinville Sr HS; Saint Martinville, LA (10-20) A Cap Choir; VP, CYO; Dbte Tm; Fr C; 4H; VP, Sodality; Bsbl; Ftbl; Sftbl; God & Country A; 4H A; Opt A; Sacristan; Sanctuary Soc; *Mus.*

BIKACSAN, Sharon Jeanette
New Brighton Area HS; New Brighton, PA (1-250) F-Ed, Ann; Band; Drama; Hmrm; NHS; Sch Achieve Tm; SC; Tres, Tri-HiY; Tr; COM; Hon Prog; St Scholar; Yth Fel; 4th Pl, Dist Comp, Fr; *Penn St U; Special Ed.*

BIKKI, Leslie Kornel
Palisade HS; Palisade, CO (30-70) Ann; Band; Var C; Ftbl; Wrest; Opt A; Eagle Sct; *Navy.*

BILBRUCK, Kimberly Ann
Calhoun HS; Calhoun, MO; Ann; Chldr; Ed, Sch P; SC; VP, Sr Cl; VP, Jr Cl; Bkbl; Sftbl; Tr; Amer Leg A; B Crocker A; Cl Fav; Hon Prog; I Dare You; Math A; Regent Schol; Sal; Tailoring A; Miss CHS; *Central Mo St U; Phys Ed.*

BILDERBACK, Sandra Lynn
Terre Haute Vigo HS; Terre Haute, IN (200-676) Band; 4H; Span C; Y-Tns; 4H A; Hon Prog; Band A; *Ind St U; Nurs.*

BILHORN, Delores Ann
Stonington HS; Pawcatuck, CT (16-241) AFS; Band; Ensm; NHS; Var C; JV, Bkbl; Tnns; HCt; Hon Prog; Pres A; Yth Fel; Yth Assn Ldrship Training; *Trinity Col; Secondary Ed.*

BILHORN, Doris Ellen
Stonington HS; Pawcatuck, CT (6-241) A Cap Choir; AFS; Band; Chor; Ensm; NHS; Var C; JV, Bkbl; Tnns; Hon Prog; Pres A; Yth Fel; Yth Assn Ldrship Training; *Trinity Col; Secondary Ed.*

BILITER, Kenneth Neal
Phelps HS; Phelps, KY (1-72) Var C; Cpt, Bsbl; Bkbl; Cpt, Ftbl; Golf; MLS; Val; *U of Ky; Mining.*

BILLADEAU, James Robert
Momence HS; Momence, IL (35-160) Math C; Rptr, Sch P; JV, Ftbl; Co-Cpt, Golf; Tnns; HCt; *Ill St U; Acct.*

BILLEK, JoAnne Marie
Rhinelander HS; Rhinelander, WI (1-400) A Cap Choir; Ann; Chldr; Chor; Drama; Ens m; Fr C; Semi-Fin, GS; Hmrm; Madrigal; NHS; A-Ed, Sch P; Ski C; VP, Span C; Spch C; SC; Thes; Tr; COM; Magna Cum Laude; Spch A; Graduate As Jr; Forensics A; *Eau Claire U; Pre-Law.*

BILLERMAN, Ann Gerri
Coldwater HS; Coldwater, OH; Band; CYO; Chor; Drama; K of C A; *Miami Valley Hospital Sch of Nurs; Nurs.*

BILLESBACH, Bruce Alan
Blair HS; Blair, NE (9-300) A Cap Choir; Ann; Band; Tres, Bus C; Chem C; Chor; Drama; Fr C; Tres, FBLA; Math C; Orch; Phys C; Sci C; SC; Thes; Bsbl; Bkbl; Ftbl; Swim; Tnns; Beauty; Citz A; Cl Fav; MLS; Most Out; Pres A; Spch A; Best All Around Looking Guy; *UCLA; Acting.*

BILLINGS, Arthur Brian
Passaic HS; Passaic, NJ; Span C; Pres, Soph Cl; Cl Fav; VFW A; Yth Leg; *Mich U; Med.*

BILLINGS, Cheryl Lynn
Pontiac N HS; Pontiac, MI; Chldr; Pres, Ger C; Span C; Pres, Jr Cl; Hon Prog; *St Olaf Lutheran Col; Law Enforcement.*

BILLINGS, Eric-Andrew Justin
Martin Luther HS; NY, NY (40-117) Band; CYO; Drama; Orch; ARC; Ed, Sch P; Bsbl; JV, Bkbl; Soccer; Sftbl; Swim; *Ariz St U; Ath.*

BILLINGS, Kurt Myron
Montevideo Sr HS; Montevideo, MN (60-159) Band; VP, Hmrm; Spch C; Var C; Ftbl; Tr; Player o-t Wk, Best Back, Ftbl A's; Hon Men, Conf Ftbl; *U of Minn; Spch.*

BILLINGSLEY, Donna Lynne
Ste Genevieve Sr HS; Ste Genevieve, MO (28-170) FHA; HR; Lib C; Gypsy Schol C; Lib Service A; *U of Mo; Journ.*

BILLINGSLEY, James Mark
Sidney Lanier HS; Austin, TX (64-480) Pres, A Cap Choir; Key C; Lat C; Madrigal; NHS; Spch C; SC; Cr-Ctry; Tr; Beauty; Cl Fav; Opt Out Tn; Rotary A; All St Choir; UIL Solo & Ensm; William Lendell Rushing A; Hon Graduate; *Abilene Christian U; Theology.*

BILLINGSLEY, Laura Elizabeth
Spring HS; Spring, TX (54-500) Lat C; Lat NHS; NHS; Span C; NEDT; Cum Laude; *Tex A&M U; Acct.*

BILLINGSLEY, Shaune Elise
C B Glenn HS; Birmingham, AL; VP, Band; Tres, Hmrm; Tres, NHS; Tres, SC; *Talladega Col; Child Psych.*

BILLINGSLY, Kathryn Geneva
Tallapoosa Acad; Dadeville, AL (5-34) A Cap Choir; Ann; BC; Chor; Dbte Tm; Hmrm; Semi-Fin, Jr Miss Pa; Spch C; SC; VP, Soph Cl; Cl Fav; Journ A; Spch A; *Birmingham-Sou Col; Pre-Med.*

BILLINGTON, Tamera Kay
Adair Co R-II HS; Brashear, MO; 4H; Thes; Dist Contest; Academic As.

BILLS, Nancy Annette
Paris HS; Paris, TX (10%-313) Secy, FHA; FTA; NHS; Span C; Tri-HiY; Hon Prog; Drill Tm; *Tex A&M U; Vet Sci.*

BILLUPS, Carla Marie
Tokay HS; Lodi, CA; Ger C; Phys Fitness A; *Humbult Col; Forestry.*

BILLUPS, Gregory Eugene
Timberline HS; Weippe, ID (3-88) Chor; Drama; Hmrm; NHS; Co-Ed, Sch P; SC; Thes; Pres, Soph Cl; JV, Bkbl; Ftbl; Tr; Citz A; HCt; *Bus.*

BILLUPS, Laura Marie
Skyline HS; Dallas, TX (25-720) Citz A; Dental Asst A; *Tex Tech U; Dental.*

BILLUPS, Marilyn Constella
King And Queen Central HS; King & Queen CH, VA (25%-71) Bus C; Chor; FBLA; 4H; Jr Miss Pagent; Math C; NHS; Sci C; Span C; Tres, Jr Cl; Alg A; Bio A; COM; 4H A; Math A; Sci A; Type A; Norfolk St Col; Elem Ed.

BILLY, Mark Leo
Chaney HS; Youngstown, OH; CYO; Co-Ed, Sch P; Bkbl; Golf.

BILYCIA, Petrina Ann
Terryville HS; Terryville, CT (10-150) Tnns; Hon Prog; *U of Conn; Nurs.*

BINDE, Scott Cornell
Divide Co HS; Crosby, ND (3-51) A Cap Choir; Chor; Dbte Tm; Ensm; Math C; Sci C; COM; Ntl Sci Found; Sci A; Star Student; VofDEM; Win, Sci Fair; Win, ND 'Know Your St' A; Bookkeeping, Mus, Constitution, A's.

BINDEMANN, Diana Sue
Hannibal HS; Hannibal, MO (1-326) Band; Fr C; Pres A; Sci A.

BINEGAR, William Glen
Bismarck HS; Bismarck, ND (18-435) Hmrm; NHS; Ntl Yth Conf; Bkbl; Ftbl; HCt; Hon Prog; Yth Fel; *Jamestown Col; Dentistry.*

BINFORD, Hilde Marga
Albuquerque Acad; Albuquerque, NM (30%-90) A Cap Choir; Bus Mgr, Band; Ch, Chor; Community Yth Symph; Pres, Dbte Tm; Mus; Drama; Ensm; Ger C; Madrigal; Math C; Orch; A-Ed, Sch P; Sci C; Pres, Spch C; Bkbl; Mgr, Ftbl; Superior, Violin; *Smith Col; Mus.*

BINGAMAN, Bradley Charles
Middleburg Joint HS; Middleburg, PA; Key C; Bsbl; Co-Cpt, Bkbl; Co-Cpt, Soccer; HR; Bkbl League All Star Tm; WW; Prom Court; Male Ath A; Lead Scorer, Bkbl Tm; Soccer League All Star Tm.

BINGEMAN, Kirk Howard
Iroquois Central HS; Elma, NY (25-355) Band; Key C; Model UN; NHS; Sci A; VP, JA; Rifle; Engr.

BINGHAM, Carolyn Marie
Vicksburg HS; Vicksburg, MS (12-244) Cpt, Chldr; GS; Math C; NHS; Pres, SC; Pres, Soph Cl; Bkbl; Sftbl; Crisco A; H of F; HCt; Miss VHS; *Jackson St U; Med.*

BINGHAM, Mary Elizabeth
Vicksburg HS; Vicksburg, MS (9-245) Tres, AFS; F-Ed, Ann; Lat C; Math C; NHS; Mgr, Bkbl; Mgr, Tr; *Delta St U; Math.*

BINGHAM, Sandy L
Sycamore HS; Cincinnati, OH (100-425) Type A; Gym; Shorthand A.

BINGLER, Brenda Sue
Charlottesville HS; Charlottesville, VA; Cpt, Sftbl; Hist A; Bkbl A; *Piedmont Va Comm Col; Phys Therapy.*

BINION, Dava Marie
Lindblom Tech HS; Chicago, IL (52-779) A Cap Choir; Pres, Hmrm; NHS; Ntl Yth Conf; Bkbl; Most Out; *Phys Therapy.*

BINION, Jacqueline
Taylor Center HS; Taylor, MI (65-500) Chor; FHA; Ftbl; Sftbl; Tr; JA A; *Calif St Col; Law.*

BINKARD, Brenda Sue
Senath Hornersville HS; Senath, MO; Chor; FHA.

BINKERD, Greg Edward
Maconaquah; Bunkerhill, IN (40-250) Chor; Bsbl; Bkbl; JV, Golf; Yth Fel; Pres, BYF; *Ind Bus Col; Bus Adm.*

BINKLEY, David Lee
R Nelson Snider HS; Fort Wayne, IN (140-568) Chor; Rptr, FBLA; Lat C; SC; Citz A; Hist A; BSct; Cpt, Harvester Quiz Tm; All Star, Intramural Bkbl; *Fort Wayne Bible Col; Christian Ed.*

BINKLEY, Randal Kent
Millard HS; Omaha, NE (30-450) Rptr, Ann; Rptr, Lit Mag; F-Ed, Sch P; SC; Ftbl; Soccer; Tnns; Hon Prog; Journ A; Q&S A; Spch A; Yth Fel; Pres, St CYF Cabinet; *Biola Col; Christian Ed.*

BIONDOLILLO, Cynthia Ann
York Sr HS; Retsof, NY (4-85) AFS; Band; CYO; Drama; Fr C; FTA; Secy, 4H; Hmrm; NHS; Orch; Ski C; Secy, SC; Soccer; Sftbl; Swim; 4H A; Hon Prog; Pres A.

BIRAM, James Darrell
Henderson Co Sr HS; Henderson, KY; Ann; Band; Thes; *Oral Roberts U; Theology.*

BIRCH, Baxter Keith
Central Private Sch; Baker, LA (8-53) Ftbl; Tr; HS Bus Symp; Alpha Theta Psi; *LSU; Engr.*

BIRCH, Deborah June
Wheeling Park HS; Wheeling, WV; A Cap Choir; Chldr; Chor; Pres, Drama; Fin, Jr Miss Pagent; NFL; NHS; Ski C; Secy, Thes; Y-Tns; Tr; Beauty; Spch A; Yth Fel; Young Amer Traveling Theater Co; Dance A; 2nd, St Best Actress; All-St Chor; Choreography A; Best Actress A; *Denison U; Dance & Theater.*

BIRCH, Julia Dale
Valley Forge Acad; Amite, LA; Chldr; Lit Ral; SC; Bkbl; Sftbl; HCt; *U of La.*

BIRCH, Lisa
Sky View HS; Smithfield, UT (3-622) Semi-Fin, Chldr; Chor; FHA; Citz A; Type A; *Ricks Col; Secy.*

BIRCH, Wayne Eric
William Tennent Sr HS; Warminster, PA (251-1017) Band; 4H; Math C; 4H A; ROTC A; *Penn St U; Elec Engr.*

BIRCHMORE, Antoinette
Robert A Taft HS; Cincinnati, OH (2-200) VP, Chem C; Pres, Hmrm; Fin, Jr Miss Pagent; Secy, NHS; Sch Achieve Tm; Rptr, Sch P; SC; Pres, Y-Tns; COM; Citz A; Hist A; HCt; Hon Prog; JA A; Most Out; Ntl Achv Schol; Sci A; Span A; Cincinnati Enquirer A; *Mich St U; Med.*

BIRD, Carrie Jeanne
Henry Sibley Sr HS; W St Paul, MN (39-541) Band; NHS; Swim; Pres A; *Sci.*

BIRD, Edythe Paris
Westminster Sch; Atlanta, GA (1-91) Chor; Cum Laude Soc; Fr C; NHS; Co-Ch, Sr Cl; Ch, Jr Cl; Ch, Soph Cl; Alg A; Bio A; COM; Chem A; Hist A; Math A; Most Out; NMF; Star Student; Val; Yth Fel; Mgr, Gym; *Duke U; Math.*

BIRD, Greg Alan
Alvin HS; Alvin, TX (2-464) Math C; Order/Arrow; Var C; Ftbl; COM; God & Country A; Math A; Most Out; NEDT; Order/Arrow A; Spch A; Yth Fel; Eagle Sct; Pres, Explorer Post; *Tex A&M U; Marine Engr.*

BIRD, Kelly Jo
Cottage Grove HS; Cottage Grove, OR (164-225).

BIRDINE, Eric Paxton
Rufus King HS; Milwaukee, WI; AFS; Rptr, Ann; Drama; Parl, FBLA; Hmrm; Span C; Forensic A; Ann A; *Carroll Col; Drama.*

BIRDWELL, Rebecca Ann
Seneca Valley HS; Germantown, MD (20%-350) Hmrm; 3rd Home Arts in Co Fair; Home Arts Hon Men; Drawing Hon Men HS Stu; *Montgomery Col; Art.*

BIRES, Jill Michelle
New Berlin HS; New Berlin, WI (51-315) AFS; Tres, Drama; Fr C; Spch C; Thes; Wis Forensic Drama Contest; St Solo & Ensm Contest; *U of Wis; Home Ec.*

BIRK, Donna Jean
North Co HS; Desloge, MO (15-188) 4H; NHS; Span C; *SE Mo St U; Sociology.*

BIRKEL, Becky Ann
Burris Laboratory Sch; Muncie, IN (4-72) Chor; Drama; Madrigal; Rptr, Sch P; *U of Nebr; Journ.*

BIRKELAND, Melissa Ann
Luverne Jr Sr HS; Luverne, MN (9-132) Ann; Dbte Tm; Fr C; GS; Hmrm; NFL; Ed, Sch P; Span C; Spch C; Bkbl; Tr; Amer Leg A; COM; Hon Prog; Journ A; Pres A; Spch A; Star Student; Track A; Dist Cpt A; Vlbl; Piano & Organ A; Hon Ntl Guild; *Briar Cliff Col; Journ.*

BIRKENEDER, Robert Allen
Batavia HS; Batavia, IL; Chor; Ensm; Hmrm; Pres, NHS; Span C; SC; Pres, Jr Cl; Tres, Soph Cl; Bkbl; Hon Prog; St Scholar; St Span Contest; *Augustana Col; Sci.*

BIRKENKAMP, Lynn A
Litchfield HS; Litchfield, IL (1-170) GS; NHS; S-T, Span C; *U of Ill.*

BIRKEY, Deborah Lynn
Olympia HS; Stanford, IL (8-250) Chldr; Chor; Ger C; SC; HCt; Hon Prog; NEDT; 1st, IHSA Mus Contest; *Sci.*

BIRKEY, John Edward Jr
Wellington Sr HS; Wellington, TX (14-68) BC; Parl, FFA; 4H; Key C; Order/Arrow; Ftbl; 4H A; Order/Arrow A; Secy, FFA; Farm Bureau Citz Seminar; Eagle Sct; *Tex A&M U; Elec.*

BIRMAN, Kimberly Sue
Springboro HS; Springboro, OH (29-169) Cpt, Chldr; Pres, Chor; NHS; Sftbl; HCt; WW; *Miami U; Secy Sci.*

BIRNEY, Gary Lynn
Copeland HS; Copeland, KS (5-10) Spch C; SC; Mgr, Bkbl; Hist A; *Bus.*

BIRR, Mary Claire
Horicon HS; Horicon, WI (20-110) VP, Band; Chess C; Ensm; Ger C; NHS; Elk A; Opt Out Tn; Drum & Bugle Corp; Hon Girl; Mus A's; *Moraine Park Tech Inst; Secy Sci.*

BISEL, Deborah Jean
Okeene Pub HS; Okeene, OK; Ann; Band; Chor; FHA; Jr Miss Pagent; Rainbow; Rptr, Jr Cl; S-T, Soph Cl; Bkbl; *Nurs.*

BISH, Eldon David
Giltner Pub HS; Giltner, NE (1-16) Chor; Rptr, Sch P; Var C; Bsbl; Bkbl; Ftbl; Tr; COM; Hon Prog; Spch A; Yth Fel; All Conf Ftbl, Hon Men; HR; PA; *Hastings Col; Bus Adm.*

BISHARI, Colleen Shizuka
Regular Baptist HS; Martinez, CA (20-30) Chldr; Chor; Ensm; Span C; Type A; Ntl Piano Playing Auditions Win; *Faith Baptist Bible Col; Missionary-Nurs.*

BISHIR, John Robert
Lake Highlands HS; Dallas, TX; Band; Fr C; Order/Arrow; Order/Arrow A; Sr Patrol Ldr, BSct; MYF; *Chem.*

BISHOP, Beverly Rose
Glasgow HS; Glasgow, KY; Band; Fr C; Mjrte; Sch P; Sci C; Span C; Tres, Sr Cl; JA A; *W Ky U; Dental Hygiene.*

BISHOP, Brenda Faye
Terrell Co HS; Dawson, GA (10%-112) Ann; BC; FHA; Hmrm; SC; HQn; Home Ec, Drama, A's; *Valdosta St Col; Bus.*

BISHOP, Carol Louise
Thomas Jefferson HS; Louisville, KY; Hmrm; SC; Tr; *Harvard U; Law.*

BISHOP, Carrie Louise
Glendale HS; Springfield, MO (10%-400) F-Ed, Sch P; Journ A; Vlbl; Drum and Bugle Corps; *U of Mo; Journ.*

BISHOP, Charles Eugene
St Regis Falls Central HS; St Regis Falls, NY (32-40) SC; Bsbl; Bkbl; Ftbl; Hockey; Soccer; Sftbl; Swim; Social Stu A.

BISHOP, Donald R
N Beach HS; Moclips, WA (3-50) Rptr, Band; Chess C; Key C; VP, NHS; Rptr, Sch P; Ski C; Pres, SC; Pres, Jr Cl; Bkbl; Co-Cpt, Cr-Ctry; Tr; H of F; HKg; JA A; Masonic A; MLS; Cpt, Cr-Ctry; *Ed.*

BISHOP, Donald Richard
N Beach HS; Moclips, WA (4-50) Band; Chess C; Key C; Monogram; VP, NHS; Sch P; Ski C; Pres, Sr Cl; Pres, Jr Cl; Bkbl; Cpt, Cr-Ctry; Tr; H of F; HKg; Masonic A; MLS; *Ed.*

BISHOP, Donna Lynne
Chapman HS; Inmar, SC (53-188) GS; Secy, Hmrm; Rptr, Sch P; SC; Secy, Sr Cl; Tres, Jr Cl; Secy, Soph Cl; Sftbl; Beauty; *Columbia Col; Elem Ed.*

BISHOP, Donna Marie
Carroll HS; Monroe, LA (20%-200) Fr C; Tnns; Hon Prog; *Pepperdine U; Home Ec.*

BISHOP, Elizabeth Arline
Hampton HS; Hampton, VA (34-500) Chor; Secy, Fr C; Hmrm; Tres, Key C; Math C; Secy, NHS; Ski C; SC; S-T, Lib C; Dickinson Schol A; WW; *James Madison U; Lib Sci.*

BISHOP, Jaime Allen
Waynesboro Area Sr HS; Waynesboro, PA (157-366) Band; Chor; Ensm; Orch; Order/Arrow; God & Country A; Eagle; *Shepherd Col; Mus.*

BISHOP, Jennifer Delane
Franklin HS; Franklin, TN (43-419) BC; Crown & Scepter; Fr C; Hmrm; NHS; Tr; *Lambuth Col; Interior Design.*

BISHOP, John Arthur
Canyonville Bible Acad; Canyonville, OR (2-37) Chor; Hmrm; Mgr, Bkbl; Cr-Ctry; Bio A; Citz A; Chaplain, Soph & Jr Cl; Geography A; *Oral Roberts U; Med.*

BISHOP, Juan Don
Libbey HS; Toledo, OH; Chess C; Chor; Bsbl; Ftbl; Wrest; H of F; Ftbl A; *Pepperdine U; Mus.*

BISHOP, Karen Lynn
S Hills HS; Covina, CA; Ann; Pres, Chor; Ski C; COM; Q&S A; Hospitality Ch, Yth Fel; Candystriper; Girls Service C; Vocal Group; *UCLA; Nurs.*

BISHOP, Kelvin Lee
Boling HS; Boling, TX (13-65) Chess C; Bus Mgr, Drama; Hmrm; JETS; Bus Mgr, Spch C; Thes; Ftbl; Tnns; Spch A; All Star Cast, One-Act Play; *Tex A&M U; Elec Engr.*

BISHOP, Leigh Ann
Barboursville HS; Barboursville, WV (7-400) Band; Mu Alpha Theta; NHS; Span C; Tr; *Special Ed.*

BISHOP, Leonard Ray
Capitol Hill HS; Oklahoma City, OK (5-262) BS; Pres, Chor; Hmrm; Mu Alpha Theta; NHS; SC; Pres, Sr Cl; Amer Leg A; Balfour A; Chamber of Comm A; Citz A; Rotary A; Pres, Yth for Christ; Morning Inspiration; Art C; University Schol; Amer Assn Yth Bowl Conf Schol; *U of Okla; Engr.*

BISHOP, Mark Weston
Glenwood HS; Glenwood, WA (1-9) BS; Chess C; Demolay; NHS; Bsbl; Mgr, Bkbl; Hon Prog.

BISHOP, Paul Eric
Normal Comm HS; Normal, IL (1-508) Tres, Ger C; Ntl Guard Jr Rifle Tm; Ger, Industrial Arts, A's; *U of Ill; Engr.*

BISHOP, Paula Jean
N Beach HS; Moclips, WA (3-60) Band; Chor; FHA; VFW A; VofDEM; *U of Wash; Psych.*

BISHOP, Rick Allen
Cleveland HS; Cleveland, OK; Secy, Sci C; Cpt, Ftbl; Tr; Cpt, Wrest; HKg; HCt; Most Outst Athlete; *Okla St U; Animal Husbandry.*

BISHOP, Robert Grady Jr
Vestavia Hills HS; Birmingham, AL; Bsbl; JV, Bkbl; Ftbl; *U of Ala; Dentistry.*

BISHOP, Robin Rebecca
N Gwinnett HS; Suwanee, GA (15%-120) Parl, BC; Secy, Drama; FHA; SC; Thes; Var C; Pres, Soph Cl; Bkbl; Sftbl; Hist A; *Gainesville Jr Col; Ed.*

BISHOP, Sheryl Ann
Eisenhower HS; Yakima, WA; Bus C; Chor; FBLA; *W Coast Bible Col; Secretarial.*

BISHOP, Tammy Ann
Baker HS; Baker, LA (37-374) Band; BC; *LSU; Med.*

BISHOP, Tammy Earline
N Beach HS; Moclips, WA (1-69) F-Ed, Ann; Chor; NHS; Rptr, Sch P; Ski C; S-T, SC; Tres, Jr Cl; S-T, Soph Cl; Bkbl; Swim; Tnns; Tr; Masonic A; MLS; Inspirational A, Tnns; *Central Wash St Col; Math.*

BISHOP, Thomas Alan Jr
Sherwood HS; Sandy Spring, MD (5-250) Ensm; Hmrm; InterClub Coun; NFL; Pres, NHS; VP, SC; Var C; Pres, Soph Cl; Cpt, Bkbl; Cpt, Ftbl; Amer Leg A; COM; Citz A; DARGCA; MLS; PTA A; ROTC A; Sal; Star Student; Christian Ldrship Conf Grant; Prom Kg; *US Naval Acad; Engr.*

BISHOP, Thomas Patrick
Cartersville HS; Cartersville, GA (1-134) Band; BC; VP, HiY; Mu Alpha Theta; Secy, Sch P; Sci C; COM; Gov Honor Prog; Yth Leg; *Emory U; Pre-Law.*

BISHOP, Timothy Edward
Normal Comm HS; Normal, IL (1-503) Ger C; NHS; Val; Fin, Alumni Distinguished Schol; Semi-Fin, Aid As for Lutheran Sch; *Ill St U; Chem.*

BISSEN, Charlene Bernice
Fort Pierce Central HS; Fort Pierce, FL (6-584) BC; Pres, NHS; F-Ed, Sch P; Pres, Span NHS; Var C; Tnns; Hon Prog; Journ A; Church Handbell Choir; Pres, MYF; Exchange C Stu o-t Mo; Keyettes; Bookkeeping A; *Stetson U; Eng.*

BISSEY, Donna Jo
Tuscola Comm HS; Tuscola, IL (2-123) VP, Band; NHS; Sch Achieve Tm; Thes; COM; Cl Fav; Hon Prog; Sal; All-St Band; Chor Accompanist; *Millikin U; Mus.*

BISSEY, Phyllis Lee
Friendly HS; Oton Hill, MD; Band; Ensm; Tnns; Yth Fel; *U of Tex; Bus.*

BITANGA, Melissa Bernadette
Maryknoll HS; Honolulu, HI (1-110) Drama; Hmrm; NHS; Rptr, Sch P; Spch C; Thes; Bio A; COM; Most Out; NEDT; Spch A; VofDEM; Span A; Eng A; Hon Cadet; Miss Tn-Age Honolulu; *U of Puget Sound; Eng.*

BITHER, Thomas Paul
Edgewood HS; W Covina, CA (17-438) Cpt, Band; S-T, Ger C; Thes; CSF; COM; VFW A; Principals HR; Most Improved Actor; Best Adv Actor; *Pepperdine U; Ger.*

BITNER, Janet Gayle
Crockett HS; Crockett, TX (2-110) Band; Drama; Ensm; Lat C; Span C; Sci A; Lat A; *U of Tex; Phar.*

BITTERS, Michael Edward
Daviess Co HS; Owensboro, KY (48-320) Bsbl; Bkbl; JV, Cr-Ctry; H of F; Bsbl, Bkbl, Cr-Ctry, Ltrs; *Murray St Col; Bus Mgr.*

BITTING, Robert Louis
Towson Sr HS; Towson, MD; Order/Arrow; JV, Cr-Ctry; Order/Arrow A; Star Sct.

BIVEN, Jacyra Jo
Pike HS; Indianapolis, IN (104-267) Bus C; FBLA; JA A; Vlbl; Ill Wesleyan U Schol; *Ball St U; Bus.*

BIVENS, Lisa Rae
Payette HS; Payette, ID (10%-165) Band; Ensm; Pres, 4H; Mjrte; Ski C; 4H A; JV, Gym; NIKE; Stage Band; Flag Twirler; Sw Ldr, Pep C; 4-H Win, Trip to Poland; Farm Bureau Talent Find; *Linfield Col.*

BIVIN, Roscoe Stuart
Apollo HS; Owensboro, KY (33%-390) Band; BC; Ensm; Fr C; Band Spirit A; Sup Ensm A; Sup Solo A; *U of Evansville; Lang.*

BIXLER, Stephanie Michele
Waynoka HS; Waynoka, OK; Ann; Band; FHA; Pres, 4H; Tres, Hmrm; NHS; 4H A; *NW Okla St Col; Mus.*

BIZZELL, Beverly Gail
Comstock HS; Comstock, MI; Chor; Span C; COM; Hon Prog; Yth Fel; Pres, Church Yth Choir; Asst Secy, Sunday Sch; Jr Usher; Yrbk Staff; *Western Mich U; Bus Adm.*

BIZZELL, Cathy Susan
Reidsville Sr HS; Reidsville, NC (5-344) FBLA; FHA; SC.

BIZZELL, Larry Wesley Jr
First Assembly Christian Sch; Memphis, TN (10%-33) Hmrm; Sch P; SC; Cpt, Bkbl; Cpt, Cr-Ctry; Cpt, Ftbl; Chamber of Comm A; Cl Fav; H of F; Hon Prog; Magna Cum Laude; Pres A; Yth Fel; *U of Tenn, Knoxville; Sci.*

BIZZELL, Ralph Deloss Jr
Charles Page HS; Sand Springs, OK (50%-330) Chess C; Yth Fel; Co-Ch, Royal Ranger; Firehouse Gang; Radio C; Vol, Hissom Mem Center; *Tulsa Jr Col; Elec.*

BJELLAND, Carol LeAnn
Albert Lea Sr HS; Albert Lea, MN (2-585) S-T, Band; Pres, Fr C; Lit Mag; Orch; Hon Prog; Big 9 Select Band; *Macalester Col; Law.*

BJERKE, Mary Cathryn
Hatton Pub Sch; Hatton, ND (1-31) Chor; Drama; Tres, FHA; GS; 4H; Mjrte; Spch C; Pres, Sr Cl; Secy, Jr Cl; Secy, Soph Cl; 4H A; HCt; I Dare You; Spch A; Val; Dean A; Pom Pon Girl; *Concordia Col; Social Work.*

BJERSTEDT, Carol Lynn
Central HS; LaCrosse, WI (71-535).

BJOKNE, Joanne Rose
Souris Pub HS; Souris, ND (1-7) Band; Chor; Ensm; GS; 4H; Sch P; Secy, Sr Cl; Secy, Jr Cl; Pres, Soph Cl; B Crocker A; Citz A; Hon Prog; Val; Constitution A; *Seattle LBI Col; Social Work.*

BJORKLUN, Julie Ann
Haxtun HS; Haxtun, CO (19-27) Band; Chor; FHA; Pres, 4H; *LSU; Psych.*

BJORKLUND, Brenda Lee
Mankato W HS; Mankato, MN (250-295) Band; Bus C; Chor; Secy, FHA; Span C; *Mankato Voc Col; Secretarial.*

BJORKLUND, Carrie Janine
Glendora HS; Glendora, CA; Drama; Ger C; Lit Mag; Thes; *Citrus Jr Col; Med Sci.*

BJORKLUND, Cindy Annette
A Crawford Mosley HS; Lynn Haven, FL; FBLA; Hmrm; VP, Keyette C; Keyette o-t Yr; *Gulf Coast Comm Col; Secretarial Sci.*

BJORNSTAD, Jay William
McVille Pub Sch; McVille, ND (2-24) Ann; Band; BS; Pres, CYO; Chor; Ensm; Pres, Sr Cl; Pres, Jr Cl; Co-Cpt, Ftbl; *U of ND; Aviation.*

BLACK, Bruce Lee
Highland HS; Highland, IN (19-518).

BLACK, Charles David
Weir HS; Weir, MS (4-53) *Miss St U; Sci.*

BLACK, Charles Ernest Jr
Bennettsville HS; Bennettsville, SC (16-199) BS; VP, SC; Mgr, Bsbl; Ftbl; Hist A; Yth Fel; Chief, Order o-t Arrow; Eagle Sct; WW; *The Citadel; Engr.*

BLACK, Cheryl Adele
Ashbrook HS; Gastonia, NC (150-600) Hmrm; Rainbow; SC; Jr Heart Board; Prog Ch, Yth Ministry; Tres, Civinettes; *U of NC; Bus Adm.*

BLACK, Christopher Franklin
Raleigh Egypt HS; Memphis, TN (50%-293) Pres, Chess C; Fr C; Key C; *Tenn Temple Col; Bible.*

BLACK, Crystal Lee
Maranacook Comm HS; Readfield, ME; Chor; Sftbl; *Commercial Art.*

BLACK, David Henry
Iroquois Central HS; Elma, NY (5-358) Chor; Drama; Swim; Kitty Acting A; Starring Roles, Plays; *Sci.*

BLACK, David J
Heritage Christian Sch; Indianapolis, IN (3-38) Band; 4H; Lit Mag; NHS; Bkbl; 4H A; Hon Prog; Sch Hon Soc; Band A; *Wabash Col; Pre-Med.*

BLACK, Deborah Louise
North Side HS; Fort Worth, TX (11-222) Ann; Band; Pres, FBLA; Lit Mag; NHS; SC; COM; Most Out; Yth Fel; Tres, FBLA; Lieut, Drill Tm; *U of Tex at Arlington; Journ.*

BLACK, Donna
Edmondson Sr HS; Baltimore, MD (4-19) Ger C; Citz A; Star Student; Type A; Pom Pon; Church Yth Choir; *U of Md; Law.*

BLACK, Dorothy Pamela
Glenvar HS; Salem, VA (36-250) Chldr; Fr C; Lat C; Monogram; NHS; Sftbl; Tr; Ntl Conf Chr & Jews; Keyette C; *David Libscomb Col; Med.*

BLACK, Douglas Kirk
Moore HS; Louisville, KY (15-275) BC; Cpt, Dbte Tm; Pres, Demolay; Hmrm; JETS; Key C; Math C; NHS; Order/Arrow; Phys C; SC; Co-Ch, Jr Cl; Bsbl; JV, Ftbl; Citz A; Cl Fav; Masonic A; Math A; Order/Arrow A; Phy A; ROTC A; *U of Louisville; Law.*

BLACK, Gary C
Iroquois Central HS; Elma, NY (101-304) Ftbl; Wrest.

BLACK, George Howard
Grove HS; Grove, OK; BC; Chor; Ftbl; Tr.

BLACK, Gloria Jewelene
Etowah HS; Attalla, AL; BC.

BLACK, Gregory William
Peoria HS; Peoria, IL (25-600) Band; Dbte Tm; NHS; Orch; Golf; Outst Speaker, Forensics Inst; *Bradley U; Pre-Law.*

BLACK, Jeffrey Allen
Mena HS; Mena, AR (5-150) Band; Rptr, NHS; All St Band; St Hon Recital, Piano; Paderewski A, Piano; Page, Ark St Legislature; *U of Ark; Phar.*

BLACK, Katherine Lynn
Palestine HS; Palestine, TX (5%-300) Chem C; Chor; Dist, Region, Choir; *Stephen F Austin Col; Eng.*

BLACK, Kathy Gay
Miss Baptist HS; Jackson, MS; Ann; Chldr; Chor; Ensm; VP, Hmrm; Jr Miss Pagent; Beauty; HCt; Yth Fel; *Miss Col; Religious Ed.*

BLACK, Kathy Marie
Westminster HS; Westminster, SC; *Anderson Col; Off Procedures.*

BLACK, Kenneth Lee Jr
Hixson HS; Hixson, TN (100-403) Band; NHS; Order/Arrow; Span C; MVP, Bsbl; Bkbl; Hon Prog; ARC A; Star Student; Yth Fel; Eagle Sct; Ntl Rifle Assn; Camp Archery Assn; *U of Tenn; Forestry.*

BLACK, Lamar A
Richland HS; Fort Worth, TX; VP, Band; Lat C; NHS; Parl, Spch C; Hon Prog; Magna Cum Laude; Spch A; *U of Tex; Bus.*

BLACK, Lucille Irene
Liberty Jr-Sr HS; Liberty, PA (20%-64) Co-Cpt, Chldr; Pres, FHA; Ger C; SC; Bkbl; *Penn St U; Bus Adm.*

BLACK, Marsha Jean
Northridge HS; Middlebury, IN; Band; Yth Coun.

BLACK, Nancy Dora
Mount Ida HS; Mount Ida, AR (5-36) Ann; BC; VP, FHA; Hmrm; Lit Mag; F-Ed, Sch P; Bkbl; Tr; Hon Prog; WW; *Bell & Howell Sch; Technician.*

BLACK, Patricia Ann
New Haven HS; New Haven, IN (73-250) Chor; ROTC A; *Ft Wayne Bible Col; Christian Ed.*

BLACK, Rhonda Joy
Carbondale Comm HS; Carbondale, IL (35-326) A Cap Choir; VP, Chor; Ensm; Fr C; FHA; 4H; Madrigal; NHS; Rptr, Sch P; Spch C; SC; Thes; COM; Citz A; 4H A; Hon Prog; Most Out; Spch A; St Scholar; Yth Fel; *Sou Ill U; Mus.*

BLACK, Robert Michael
Oregon City HS; Oregon City, OR; Bkbl; *Pepperdine U; Pre-Med.*

BLACK, Robert William
Iroquois Central HS; Elma, NY (48-335) Ann; Drama; Tres, Key C; Pres, Model UN; NHS; Order/Arrow; Sch P; SC; Thes; JV, Ftbl; JV, Wrest; COM; NMS; Order/Arrow A; Regent Schol; ROTC A; Water Show; Gym; Eagle Sct; Pep C; S-T, Yth Against Cancer Committee; Vlbl; *Pa St U; Bus Mgr.*

BLACK, Shannon Ravee
Fox Sr HS; Arnold, MO (2%-600) Band; Chldr; Cpt, Dbte Tm; Drama; Hmrm; NFL; NHS; Cpt, Spch C; Thes; Hon Prog; Spch A; VofDEM; *Notre Dame U; Criminal Law.*

BLACK, Sheldon F
Richland HS; Richland Hills, TX; Pres, Band; Tr; Band Spirit A; UIL Band Medals; *ITA; Computer.*

BLACK, Sheryl Lynn
Sudan HS; Sudan, TX (1-33) Ed, Ann; Pres, Band; Ensm; FHA; Pres, FTA; Pres, NHS; VP, Sr Cl; Pres, Jr Cl; Secy, Soph Cl; Bkbl; Mgr, Tr; Alg A; B Crocker A; Hist A; Journ A; NMS; Star Student; Type A; Val; All Region Band; *Tex Tech U; Engr.*

BLACK, Tim Ray
Lake City HS; Lake City, TN; SC; *U of Tenn.*

BLACKARD, Tammy J
Arapahoe Sr HS; Littleton, CO (13-619) City Conf; FBLA; Tnns; Amer Leg A; COM; *Colo St U; Home Ec.*

BLACKBURN, Barbara Jonell
Bible Baptist HS; Savannah, GA (10-52) Ed, Ann; ARC; HCt; Hon Prog; ARC A; *Armstrong St Col; Phar.*

BLACKBURN, D Jean
Morton HS; Morton, MS; BC; Cpt, Chldr; Var C; Co-Cpt, Bkbl; Sftbl; Tnns; Beauty; Cl Fav; Activities A; Commerce A; *Miss St U; Acct.*

BLACKBURN, Debbie Lynn
Milo Adventist Acad; Days Creek, OR (7-66) Bus Mgr, Band; VP, Sr Cl; *Walla Walla Col; Nurs.*

BLACKBURN, Debbie Sue
Virgie HS; Virgie, KY (9-112) Co-Ed, Ann; BC; FTA; Ger C; Spch C; HCt; Sr Superlative; *Eastern Ky U; Psych.*

BLACKBURN, Donna Marie
Twin Lakes HS; W Palm Beach, FL (5%-500) NHS; Art C; Top 5%; Stu Aid, Art; Geom A; Art & Penmanship A; *South-Eastern Bible Col; Eng.*

BLACKBURN, Glinda Beth
Bethel Christian HS; Ruston, LA (5-12) Ann; MVP, Chldr; Semi-Fin, Lit Ral; S-T, Jr Cl; Sftbl; Tr; Citz A; Journ A; Poet A; PA; March of Dimes Walk- a- thon; Most Sch Spirit; *La Tech U.*

BLACKBURN, Ira Joseph II
Wetumka HS; Wetumka, OK (16-42) Pres, Chor; Drama; Rptr, FFA; VP, 4H; Rptr, Key C; Spch C; Bsbl; Ftbl; Citz A; 4H A; Heart Fund; Page, House of Rep; *Okla St U; Archt.*

BLACKBURN, Julie Ann
Pflugerville HS; Pflugerville, TX (5-76) BC; Co-Cpt, Dbte Tm; VP, Drama; FHA; NHS; Span C; VP, Spch C; Pres, SC; Tres, Sr Cl; Bkbl; Tr; DARGCA; Bkbl As; Span As; Tr As; *Tex Wesleyan U; Psych.*

BLACKBURN, Kamuran
Robert E Lee HS; Jacksonville, FL; Secy, Band; Sftbl; Citz A; Hist A; Math A; Sci A; S-T, MYF; Eng A; *Auburn U; Vet.*

BLACKBURN, Kenneth Neil
Lockport Township HS; Lockport, IL (80-650) Mgr, Cr-Ctry; Swim; ROTC A; Outst Cadet, Ldrship A, AFROTC; Acad Achv, AFROTC; *Lewis Col; AFROTC.*

BLACKBURN, Randy Craig
E Aurora HS; Aurora, IL (184-800) A Cap Choir; Chor; Ski C; Rugby; *Anderson Col; Religion.*

BLACKBURN, Raymond
Burch HS; Delbarton, WV (2-60) BC; Var C; Mgr, Bsbl; Mgr, Bkbl; Mgr, Ftbl; Hon Prog; Sci A; *Sou WV Comm Col; Phys Therapist.*

BLACKBURN, Ruth Eileen
Greensburg Salem Sr HS; Greensburg, PA (1-433) AFS; Band; Chor; Ensm; Fr C; Hmrm; NFL; NHS; Orch; Ski C; SC; Thes; VP, Sr Cl; VP, Jr Cl; VP, Soph Cl; Tnns; COM; Hon Prog; Pres A; St Scholar; Yth Fel; Anne P Ziskind Schol A; Co Chor; Best Musician; Co Band; Dist Band; *U of Penn; Pol Sci.*

BLACKBURN, Terry Lee
Keokuk Sr HS; Keokuk, IA; Fr C; SAA A; F-Ed, Publisher, Explorer Post; *Eng.*

BLACKBURN, Vance Gerald
Baker HS; Mobile, AL (10-175) NHS; Bkbl; Co-Cpt, Ftbl; *Chem.*

BLACKER, John David
Monterey HS; Lubbock, TX (10%-800) Tres, HiY; NHS; Outst Stu; *Tex Tech U; Archt.*

BLACKFORD, Debra Lynn
Northglenn Sr HS; Northglenn, CO (1-805) Chor; Ensm; Pres, NHS; S-T, SC; Tr; *Bradley U; Med.*

BLACKINGTON, Deborah Marie
Westmont Hilltop Sr HS; Johnstown, PA; Band; Ski C; Span C.

BLACKKETTER, Donald Merl
Bozeman Sr HS; Bozeman, MT (158-374) A Cap Choir; 4H; Var C; 4-H C A; *Okla Christian U; Engr.*

BLACKKETTER, Gail Ellen
Trezevant HS; Trezevant, TN; BC; Pres, Bus C; FHA; Pres, 4H; *Murray St U; Acct.*

BLACKKETTER, Neal Edwin
Shamrock HS; Shamrock, TX (7-50) Pres, Band; Chem C; FBLA; Mu Alpha Theta; NHS; Fin, Spch C; Golf; *McMurray Col; Bio.*

BLACKLEY, Sherise Lynnette
Davidson HS; Mobile, AL; A Cap Choir; Chor; Ensm; Fr C; FTA; Madrigal; Ntl Achv Schol; All St Chor; *Sou Miss U; Mus.*

BLACKMAN, Susan Read
Albemarle HS; Charlottesville, VA (12-700) Secy,
NHS; Tres, Span C; NEDT; Sch, District, St, Span
As; *U of Va; Nurs.*

BLACKMER, John Hardin
Niskayuna HS; Schenectady, NY (20%-450)
Hmrm; Key C; Bsbl; JV, Ftbl; COM; NMS; Yth
Fel; Photographer, Sch P; Photo Soc; Schol Pho-
tography Schol; Cpt, Ski Tm; George Naples Piano
Competition; *Syracuse U; Mgt.*

BLACKMER, John Harold
Mahar Regional HS; Orange, MA; NHS; Mahar
Fish & Game C; Off, N Orange Grange.

BLACKMON, Allan Russell
Hattiesburg HS; Hattiesburg, MS; Span C; Eagle
Sct; *U of Sou Miss; Bus Adm.*

BLACKMON, Ava Michelle
SW HS; Fort Worth, TX; Secy, FHA; Tr; *Bus.*

BLACKMON, Billie Teresa
Barnwell HS; Barnwell, SC (9-154) F-Ed, Ann; BC;
NHS; *Col of Charleston; Psych.*

BLACKMON, Edward Lee
Russell HS; Hurtsboro, AL; Chem C; Rptr, FFA;
4H; Math C; NHS; Sci C; Bkbl; 4H A; *Ala St U.*

BLACKMON, Jacquelyn Malette
Miami Northwestern Sr HS; Miami, FL (25-400)
Math C; NHS; SC; Tres, Sr Cl; COM; Hon Prog;
Statistician, Tr; Eng A; Hon Cord Top 30; *Barry
Col; Nurs.*

BLACKMON, Julie Marie
Sidney Lanier HS; Montgomery, AL; Ann; Math
C; Co-Ed, Yrbk; Secy Church Yth Coun; Stu Ac-
tion For Ed; *Auburn U; Bus Adm.*

BLACKMON, Kevin Todd
Holly Springs HS; Holly Springs, MS (59-168)
Ann; Band; Bus C; FBLA; Hmrm; NHS; Sch P; SC;
Beauty; Cl Fav; HCt; Yth Fel; *Southern U; Bus Ed.*

BLACKMON, Michele Kay
Uniontown Area HS; Uniontown, PA; F-Ed, Ann;
Chor; Fr C; NHS; Sci C; Ski C; WW; *Murray St
Col; Marketing.*

BLACKMORE, Terry Gale
Hazelwood W Sr HS; Florissant, MO (300-380)
Chess C; Chor; Ensm; Var C; Mgr, Bsbl; Mgr, Bkbl;
Mgr, Ftbl; Sftbl; Mgr, Tr; Tres, Church Yth; BSct.

BLACKPORT, Teresa Lou
Goshen HS; Goshen, IN (56-268) F-Ed, Ann;
Band; NHS; S-T, Span C; Bkbl; Sftbl; Secy, Sun-
shine; Co- ch, Cheerblock.

**BLACKSHEAR,
Michael Thomas**
Smithfield HS; Smithfield, VA; BS; FFA; COM;
Bio.

BLACKSHER, Mark Edwin
G C Scarborough Jr-Sr HS; Houston, TX (30-320)
Pres, Fr C; French NHS; FTA; NHS; Hon Prog;
Outst Fr Stu; *U of Tex; Acct.*

BLACKSON, Catherine
Sterling HS; Somerdale, NJ; Band; Chor; Phys C;
Mgr, Bkbl; God & Country A; Ntl Achv Schol; Yth
Fel; *Camden Co Col; Probation Off.*

BLACKSON, David
Sterling HS; Somerdale, NJ; *Culinary Inst of Amer;
Cook.*

BLACKSTONE, Kelly Karlene
Superior HS; Superior, NE (33%-84) Chor; Tres,
FFA; FHA; Secy, 4H; Var C; 4H A; Yth Fel; Pres,
VP, Rptr, 4-H C; Spelling Reading, FFA, A's; *UN
Sch of Tech Agr; Vet Tech.*

BLACKSTONE, Sherri Lynn
Superior HS; Superior, NE (10-82) Chor; VP,
FHA; Secy, 4H; Var C; Y-Tns; 4H A; Yth Fel; Rptr,
4-H C; 1st Pl, Co Spelling & Elks Amer; 2nd Pl,
DAR Hist Essay; 2nd Pl, FHA Dist Spch.

BLACKWELL, Amelia Louise
South Hills HS; Pittsburgh, PA; Fr C; Pres A; Outst
Achv A; *Nurs.*

BLACKWELL, Angella Camille
South Hills HS; Pittsburgh, PA; Fr C; Pres A; Outst
Achv A.

BLACKWELL, Cynthia Anne
Joelton HS; Joelton, TN; Band; BC; Rptr, Sch P;
Mgr, Bkbl; Miss Talent.

BLACKWELL, Donna Lynn
G A R HS; Wilkes-Barre, PA (5-198) NHS; Type
A; Mgr, Vlbl; *Bus.*

BLACKWELL, Elizabeth Lea
Splendora HS; Splendora, TX (1-95) Band; CYO;
Secy, Drama; FHA; FTA; NHS; Sch P; Pres, Span
C; Secy, SC; Math A; Sci A; Val; *Tex A&M U; Bio.*

BLACKWELL, James Leslie
Sussex Central HS; Sussex, VA (2-200) Ann; Band;
BC; Ensm; HiY; Sci C; Span C; Tri-HiY; Sci A; Sch
& Ftbl Photo; Spn Outs Achiev A; Outst Achieve-
ment, Geom A; Social Sci C, Outst Achievement
A; Wind Ensm Outst Achievement A; *Va Poly-
technic Inst; Engr.*

BLACKWELL, Johanna Carroll
Scott Preparatory Sch; Opelika, AL (5%-25) Pres,
BC; JV, Chldr; Tnns; Tr; Beauty; COM; Cl Fav;
HCt; Hon Prog; 1st, Runner-Up, Ala US Tn; Miss
Congeniality; Ntl Fin, US Tn; *Auburn U; Phar.*

BLACKWELL, Lee Antonio
Springfield Se HS; Springfield, IL (61-557) Band;
Ensm; Hmrm; Sch P; VP, SC; Bsbl; Bkbl; Cpt, Ftbl;
Tr; Citz A; Most Out; Opt A; Spch A; Yth Founda-
tion; MVP, Ftbl; Hugh O'Brien A; Jazz Band &
Ensm A; VP, YPD; PA A; VP, Dir Jr Choir; HR A;
VP, Jr Usher Board; *Law.*

BLACKWELL, Lisa Kay
E Hills HS; Ft Worth, TX (100-400) Chor; Secy,
Ensm; Tnns; *Tex Weslyan Col; Bus.*

BLACKWELL, Nina Lynn
Sanford Acad; Sanford, MS (2-12) Rptr, BC; Chldr;
Chor; Sch P; Bkbl; Beauty; Cl Fav; *U of Sou Miss;
Pub Relations.*

BLACKWELL, Robin Lynn
Naylor HS; Naylor, MO (10-29) Ann; BC; FFA;
FTA; Sch P; Bsbl; Bkbl; Hist A; HCt; *Three Rivers
Jr Col; Bus Adm.*

BLACKWELL, Sandra Christine
Springfield S HS; Springfield, OH; Band; Chor;
Ensm; SC; Principal's Coun; VP, Executive Board;
Lib C; *Wright St U; Nurs.*

BLACKWELL, Shirley Ann
Whitehouse HS; Whitehouse, TX (6-106) Band;
FHA; FTA; NHS; Homemaking A; *Tyler Jr Col.*

BLACKWELL, Wade Edward
Pattonville Sr HS; Maryland Heights, MO (30-890)
Ger C; NHS; *U of Mo; Engr.*

BLACKWOOD, Carla Lee
Heritage Christian Sch; Indianapolis, IN (9-38) F-
Ed, Ann; Chor; Lit Mag; Var C; Bkbl; Tr; COM;
Hon Prog; *Ind U; Nurs.*

BLACKWOOD, Edwin A H
Heritage Christian HS; Indianapolis, IN (8-65) Fr
C; Bus Mgr, Sch P; Var C; Soccer; Tr; Amer Leg
Orator A; Hon Prog; Journ A; Spch A; Asb Mgr,
Sch P; Most Improved, Soccer; WW; Top 5%
PSAT-NMSQT; *Butler Col.*

BLACKWOOD, Jane Marie
Aldridge Campus HS; Beloit, WI (26-660) Orch;
Rainbow; Journ A; Sci A; Rainbow Merit As; Schol
Letter; *Blackhawk Tech; Acct.*

BLADE, Geneva
Booker T Washington HS; Shreveport, LA
(222-258) Vlbl.

BLADES, Ronnie Edward
Crescent HS; Crescent, OK (9-50) Chem A; Math
A; Sci A; Yth Fel; *OST; Industrial Elec.*

**BLADES JOHNSON,
Keith Anthony**
Poughkeepsie HS; Poughkeepsie, NY; A Cap Choir;
Ftbl; Tr; Sch Monitor, Media, Sports, Certs; *Tex
Tech Col; Elect.*

BLADOW, Kris Dianne
Fargo HS; Fargo, ND; Band; Rptr, Sch P; *U of ND;
Nurs.*

BLADOWSKI, Maria Lynn
St Louise de Marillac HS; Northfield, IL (22-222)
NHS; St Scholar; WW; Art A; *St Mary's Col; Lib-
eral Arts.*

BLAGG, Howard Davis
Memorial HS; Tulsa, OK (3%-550) VP, Hmrm;
Key C; NHS; Span C; Mgr, Ftbl; JV, Golf; Citz A;
JA A; Sci A; Soph Board; *Okla St U; Computer
Tech.*

BLAINE, Allyson Rush
Myers Park HS; Charlotte, NC (15-500) Chor;
Drama; Ensm; VP, Lat C; Math C; Mu Alpha
Theta; NHS; VP, Thes; *Math.*

BLAINE, Dawn Lynnette
Cedar Cliff HS; Camp Hill, PA (100-499) *NE
Christian Jr Col; Ed.*

BLAINE, Douglas Conrad
Lewis C Obourn HS; E Rochester, NY (2-168)
Chor; Drama; Hmrm; VP, NHS; Ed, Sch P; Ski C;
Alg A; COM; Hon Prog; Math A; NMS; Ntl Sci
Found; Regent Schol; Sal; *Lehigh U; Engr.*

BLAINE, John Delbert
Glendale Acad; Glendale, CA (53-60) Band; VP,
SC; Parl, Sr Cl; Bsbl; Bkbl; Ftbl; Soccer; Tr; Secy, Sr
Cl; *Loma Linda U at La Sierra; Pre-Dentistry.*

BLAIR, Blanche Marie
Harry Doss HS; Louisville, KY; Math A; Sci A;
Type A; Human Relations; Shot Put; Most Excel
Stu; *U of Louisville; Bus Adm.*

BLAIR, Brenda Ann
Estherville HS; Estherville, IA; Band; Chor; Pres,
FHA; Pres, 4H; *Iowa St U; Home Ec.*

**BLAIR,
Cornelius Osborne Southern**
Suffolk HS; Suffolk, VA (5-150) Bio A; *Math.*

BLAIR, Frances Shawn
Albuquerque HS; Albuquerque, NM; Chor; Ensm;
Rainbow; Y-Tns; Golf; Mus A; Ltr, Golf; 4th Pl, St
Golf; *Ariz St U; Sociology.*

BLAIR, Geraldine Cornelia
McKinley HS; Washington, DC; Rptr, Sch P; Band;
Mgr, Jr Cl; WW in Voc & Tech Sch in Amer; *Calif
Col of Arts & Crafts; Photography.*

BLAIR, James Edward
Valley Union HS; Elfrida, AZ (16-40) Band; JV,
Bkbl; Ftbl; *Grand Canyon Col; Art.*

BLAIR, Jeffrey Dale
Sidney Lanier HS; Montgomery, AL; Chor; Wrest;
Spch A; *Bible.*

BLAIR, Jeffrey Darren
Jupiter Christian Sch; Jupiter, FL; Orch; Order/
Arrow; Bsbl; Bkbl; Soccer.

BLAIR, Jennifer Lynne
Paonia HS; Paonia, CO (1-80) A Cap Choir; Band;
Dbte Tm; Drama; Ensm; Fin, GS; NHS; Pres,
Rainbow; F-Ed, Sch P; Spch C; S-T, Thes; Secy, Jr
Cl; Amer Leg A; Citz A; Masonic A; Spch A; VFW
Orator Win; VofDEM; *U of Northern Colo; Elem
Ed.*

BLAIR, Kimberly Ann
Crawfordsville HS; Crawfordsville, IN (40-213)
Ann; FHA; FNA; FTA; 4H; Lit Mag; NFL; ARC;
Rptr, Sch P; SC; Spch C; Var C; Mgr, Bsbl; Mgr,
Bkbl; JV, Tr; COM; 4H A; Hon Prog; Poet A; ARC
A; Spch A; Vlbl; Scorer, Wrest; WW; *Ivy Tech Col;
Med Asst.*

BLAIR, Lisa Dorene
W Charlotte HS; Charlotte, NC; Fr C; *Pediatrics.*

BLAIR, Mary Christine
Camdenton R III HS; Camdenton, MO (18-180)
Band; Chor; Dbte Tm; Ensm; FTA; GS; NHS;
Rainbow; Span C; SC; VP, Sr Cl; JV, Sftbl; Amer
Leg A; HCt; Yth Fel; All Star, Sftbl; Vlbl; *Drury U;
Elem Ed.*

BLAIR, Matthew Jack
Camdenton HS; Camdenton, MO; Band; Chor;
Rptr, Sch P; Bsbl; *Drury U; Computer Operator.*

BLAIR, Melody Davette
Muncie Southside HS; Muncie, IN (1-315) Band;
Chor; 4H; COM; Citz A; ROTC A; OEA; Candys-
triper; *Ball St U; Bus.*

BLAIR, Nancy Lawrence
Suffolk HS; Suffolk, VA (4-118) F-Ed, Ann; Band;
Drama; InterClub Coun; Lat C; NHS; Thes; Pres,
Tri-HiY; Chem A; *William & Mary Col; Pol Sci.*

BLAIR, Nola Belle
Wheaton HS; Wheaton, MN (2-80) Band; Chor;
Drama; Ensm; FHA; Madrigal; Sch P; SC; Pres, Jr
Cl; 4H A; Vlbl; St & Region Mus Contest Medals;
Best Supporting Actress; *U of Minn; Art.*

BLAIR, Richard Bruce
George Washington HS; Denver, CO (2-750) Fr C; NHS; Math A; NMF; Regent Schol; *U of Colo.*

BLAIR, Timothy Flynn
Amarillo HS; Amarillo, TX (100-750) Band; Chor; Ensm; Orch; Life Sct; Church Choir; *Tex Tech Col; Bus.*

BLAISE, Opal Karen
Leesburg HS; Leesburg, FL (11-298) AFS; F-Ed, Ann; Chor; Drama; Hmrm; InterClub Coun; Lat C; NHS; Sch P; SC; Pres, Sr Cl; Tres, Jr Cl; Bsbl; Amer Leg A; COM; Cl Fav; Hon Prog; Math A; NML; Jr Ambassador to Colombia; Pres Clrm; Pres Schol of Excel; *Miss U for Women; Pol Sci.*

BLAKE, Barbara Ann
Jones Commercial HS; Chicago, IL (151-457) A Cap Choir; Chldr; FBLA; Cpt, Bsbl; Cl Fav; Hon Prog; Posture Contest; Grooming A.

BLAKE, Carl David
Post Falls HS; Post Falls, ID; Band; Ensm; 4H; 4H A; WW.

BLAKE, Carolyn Sandra
Penncrest HS; Media, PA (30-450) Band; Ensm; Mu Alpha Theta; NHS; JV, Sftbl; Bausch & Lomb A; Hon Prog; 1st Cl GSct; *U of Vt; Biol.*

BLAKE, Charles Edgar
St Peter's Prep HS; Jersey City, NJ (170-250) Pres, Hmrm; SC; Cpt, Ftbl; JV, Tr; NEDT; HS All-Amer Ftbl; 5th Qtr C; 1st Tm All-Conf; *Rutgers U; Bio.*

BLAKE, Charlotte Gail
Banks HS; Birmingham, AL (5-312) Drama; Hmrm; Math C; Mu Alpha Theta; NHS; Sch P; Thes; Sftbl; COM; Hon Prog; NEDT; Excel Prog; Executive HS Intern Prog; *Pre-Law.*

BLAKE, Cynthia Rae
Ainsworth HS; Flint, MI (25-270) A Cap Choir; Secy, Band; JV, Chldr; Secy, Chor; Drama; Hmrm; Madrigal; ARC; SC; Pres, Y-Tns; Tr; PA; Tutoring A; *Harding Col; Nurs.*

BLAKE, Deborah Ann
South Hills HS; Pittsburgh, PA (18-557) Lat C; NHS; Hon Prog; WW; *Median Sch; Med Secy.*

BLAKE, Janine Marcia
NW HS; St Louis, MO (100-450) A Cap Choir; Band; Bus C; Chor; FBLA; Hmrm; Mjrte; SC; Cpt, Sftbl; Swim; Tnns; JA A; Masonic A; Pres A; Type A; Yth Fel; Frontiers C; SOUL; *Spelman Col.*

BLAKE, Jovita Lyann
John F Kennedy HS; Cleveland, OH; Chor; Merit Roll; *Secy.*

BLAKE, Paul Calvin
Dewitt Clinton HS; New York, NY (4-32) Soccer; COM; Citz A; Star Student; Art A; Design A; Arista Group, DWC HS; Pathfinder C; *Oakwood Col; Theology.*

BLAKE, Randall Harris
Vanguard HS; Waco, TX (5%-22) Fr C; JETS; Order/Arrow; SC; Thes; Bio A; Hon Prog; Order/Arrow A; Eagle Sct; *Austin Col; Bio.*

BLAKE, Reynard Nathaniel
HS of Charleston; Charleston, SC; Band; BC; FTA; Pres, Hmrm; InterClub Coun; Ch, Key C; Orch; Pres, Span C; SC; Pres, Soph Cl; Bsbl; Bio A; COM; Citz A; Hist A; Hon Prog; I Dare You; Interlochen Ntl Mus; Kiwanis A; MLS; Most Out; Ntl Cath Mus Ed Asn; Ntl Sci Found; Opt A; Opt Out Tn; PTA A; Pres A; Sci A; Star Student; VofDEM; Yth Fel; Yth Leg; *Yale U; Law.*

BLAKE, Robert Charles
Inglewood HS; Inglewood, CA (3%-450) Ann; Model UN; Var C; Bsbl; Mgr, Ftbl; Tr; CSF; Citz A; Hon Prog; Most Out; St Scholar; All Acad, Higdon Mem Schol, A's; Basic Ed Opportunity Grant; *UCLA; Bus Marketing.*

BLAKE, Tamara Lyn
Denair HS; Denair, CA; *Stanislaus St Col; Psych.*

BLAKELEY, Nanci Lynn
E Hills HS; Ft Worth, TX (1-565) FHA; Ger C.

BLAKELY, Ann Elizabeth
La Canada HS; La Canada, CA (10%-395) A Cap Choir; Chor; Rptr, Hmrm; SC; CSF; Yth Fel; *USC; Performing Arts.*

BLAKELY, Ann Shell
Searcy HS; Searcy, AR (6-174) Ann; BC; Drama; Fr C; GS; Pres, NHS; Sch P; S-T, SC; Thes; Amer Leg A; DARGCA; HCt; Swtht; PEO A; Rptr, Jr Beethoven C; Best Actress A; WW; Co-Cpt, Drill Tm; *Hendrix Col; Fr.*

BLAKESLEE, Beth Agnes
Nova HS; Ft Lauderdale, FL (164-466) Chor; Drama; Most Dedicated; *Col of Boca Raton; Theatre.*

BLAKEY, Judith Anne
Pleasure Ridge Park HS; Louisville, KY; Chor; Hon Prog; Human Relations A; Valueable Service A; *Eastern Ky U; Mus.*

BLAKEY, Kenneth E
Pleasure Ridge Park HS; Louisville, KY; Bkbl; Tr; *Appalachian St U; Decorating.*

BLAKEY, Sidney Paul
Dothan HS; Dothan, AL (200-632) ROTC A; VP, Explorer Post; ROTC Drill Tm; ROTC Color Guard; Church PA; *George C Wallace Col; Anthropology.*

BLAKLEY, Catherine Lee
Woodward HS; Woodward, OK (4-177) Chor; Ensm; Pres, 4H; Hmrm; Key C; SC; Var C; Bkbl; Citz A; 4H A; H of F; I Dare You; Kiwanis A; Sci A; Bus A; Lib A; Home Ec A; *Southwestern Okla St U; Acct.*

BLAKLEY, L Yvonne
Livingston HS; Livingston, TX (33%-234) Band; Chor; Ensm; 4H; Jr Miss Pagent; Mjrte; Y-Tns; Beauty; 4H A; 1st Pl, Flute Duet Medal; Miss GMA; 1st, Piano Solo Med; Jr Ms GMA A; DAR Essay Contest; Sunday Sch PA; 4-H Dress Rev Plq A, Food Shw Plq; *Stephen F Austin St U; Mus.*

BLAKLEY, Linda Susan
Live Oak HS; Morgan Hill, CA (18-404) Cpt, Chldr; FBLA; Hmrm; NHS; Rainbow; Bkbl; Social Ch, Sr Cl; WW; *Gavilan Jr Col; Nurs.*

BLAKNEY, Brenda Gale
Burnsville HS; Burnsville, MS (3-46) F-Ed, Ann; BC; FHA; Hmrm; F-Ed, Sch P; Tres, Jr Cl; Secy, Soph Cl; Beauty; Cl Fav; HCt.

BLAKNEY, Catherine Ann
S Hadley HS; South Hadley, MA (3-280) Chor; French NHS; Pres, NHS; Soccer; Rensselaer A; Teachers Physics A; *Mount Holyoke Col; Bio.*

BLAKNEY, Cecil Kenneth
R S Caldwell HS; Columbus, MS; A Cap Choir; VP, Arch; Band; Chess C; Chor; Demolay; Hmrm; SC; Arch; Bsbl; Bkbl; COM; Most Out; ROTC A; Spch A; VofDEM; VBS Teachers A.

BLAKNEY, Vicki Lynn
Burnsville HS; Burnsville, MS (1-46) Ann; VP, Band; BC; FHA; 4H; Mjrte; Sch P; Tres, SC; Beauty; Band A; Attendance A; HR; Pep C; *North East Jr Col; Data Processing.*

BLALOCK, Micah D Ross
Abernathy HS; Abernathy, TX; Drama; FFA; FTA; NHS; Sci C; Pres, SC; Pres, Soph Cl; Bkbl; Ftbl; Golf; *Sci.*

BLALOCK, Pamela Denise
N L Roth HS; Dayton, OH; Chldr; Mjrte; Tr; Star Student; Attendance A.

BLALOCK, Tamara Jonelle
Ulysses HS; Ulysses, KS (10-105) Band; Chor; Ensm; FBLA; Bus Mgr, FHA; Madrigal; Spch C; Var C; Ch, Y-Tns; Secy, Sr Cl; Bkbl; Co-Cpt, Golf; B Crocker A; God & Country A; Spch A; St Scholar; Kans Hon Stu; *Colby Comm Col; Radio Broadcasting.*

BLAN, Charlotte Anne
Owensboro HS; Owensboro, KY (20%-500).

BLANCETT, Brenda Ann
Vicksburg HS; Vicksburg, MI; Band; *Kalamazoo Valley Comm Col; Bus.*

BLANCHARD, Betty Ann
John Ehret HS; Marrero, LA (17-480) Lit Ral; NHS; Ntl Merit Commended Stu; *U of New Orleans; Marine Bio.*

BLANCHARD, Douglas Alan
N Central HS; Manly, IA; A Cap Choir; Band; Wrest; *Iowa St Col; Agr.*

BLANCHARD, Linda Kay
George C Marshall HS; Falls Church, VA (1-459) Community Yth Symph; Pres, Ger C; Co-Cpt, Math C; Mod Mus Mas; VP, NHS; Orch; Gov Honor Prog; Hon Prog; Math A; MLS; Val; Yth Fel; WW; Teach, Mentally Retarded; Orch A; *William and Mary Col; Chem.*

BLANCHARD, Moliy Van Korb
Wahconah Regional HS; Dalton, MA (40-280) Secy, Chor; Hmrm; SC; Mgr, Soccer; Tr; HCt; Bell & Yth Choirs, Church; HS Play; Piano.

BLANCHARD, Norman James
St Martin Sr HS; St Martinville, LA (2-32) *St Mary's Col; Tech.*

BLANCHARD, Thomas Andrew
Mendenhall Attendance Center; Mendenhall, MS (4-65) BC; Hmrm; Math C; Mu Alpha Theta; Order/Arrow; Bus Mgr, Sch P; Pres, SC; Pres, Sr Cl; Pres, Jr Cl; Bkbl; Tr; Type A; Most Intelligent; Schol A; *US Military Acad; Physics.*

BLANCHARD, Timothy Paul
Nathan Hale HS; Tulsa, OK (70-650) Band; Pres, 4H; Pres, Lat C; NHS; Swim; Citz A; 4H A; *Law.*

BLANCHAT, Lisa Annette
Bishop Carroll HS; Wichita, KS (25-211) NHS; St Scholar; KNC Schol; *Kans Newman Col; Ed.*

BLANCHETTE, Claire Rena
St Dominic Regional HS; Lewiston, ME (2-105) CYO; Fr C; JV, Tnns; COM; NEDT; Sci A; Type A; Future Medics of Amer; Med.

BLANCHETTE, Gisele Margaret
Saint Dominic Regional HS; Lewiston, ME (1-76) Chor; Secy, Fr C; Secy, FTA; Secy, NHS; F-Ed, Sch P; Pres, Sodality; Bio A; COM; Chem A; Elk A; Hon Prog; Sci A; Type A; Val; WW; NHS A; Extra-Curricular Activities A; *Salve Regina Col; Special Ed.*

BLANCHETTE, Kevin Roland
Momence HS; Momence, IL (6-150) Chess C; Drama; 4H; Math C; NHS; Sch P; Span C; S-T, Spch C; SC; Thes; Var C; Tres, Soph Cl; Bsbl; Ftbl; COM; Citz A; 4H A; Hon Prog; Journ A; Math A; Q&S A; Spch A; *U of Ill; Aeronautical Engr.*

BLANCHFIELD, Bonnie Beth
Mercy HS; Albany, NY (3-108) CYO; Chldr; Drama; Hmrm; InterAct C; Fin, Jr Miss Pagent; NHS; SC; Pres, Sr Cl; JV, Sftbl; Hon Prog; NEDT; Art A; Art-Ed, Yrbk; *Siena Col; Acct.*

BLANCKEN, Russell H
Flagler HS; Flagler, CO; Pres, FFA; Tres, FHA; Pres, 4H; Pres, SC; Pres, Jr Cl; S-T, Soph Cl; Bkbl; Co-Cpt, Ftbl; Tr; Coun of Teach A; 4H A; HKg; Most Out; Sci A; Spch A; Ldrship A; 1st St, Parl Procedure; All St Ftbl Champs; Star Farmer, FFA; Voc-Agr A; *McPherson Col; Agr Ed.*

BLANCO, Katherine Ruth
Northview HS; Covina, CA; Tres, CYO; Ski C; Tres, SC; *Mt San Antonio Col; Nurs.*

BLANCO, Magda
Miguel Melendez Munoz; Bayamon, PR (7-220) FHA; FTA; Math C; ARC; Sch P; Sci C; Citz A; Phy A; Sci A; *U of Puerto Rico; Bilingual Secy.*

BLAND, Brenda Sherill
Sparks HS; Sparks, NV (3-375) GS; NHS; Ed, Sch P; S-T, Span C; Journ A; ROTC A; *U of Nev; Journ.*

BLAND, Caroline
Jones Co HS; Gray, GA; FHA; 4H; Math C; NHS; Sci C; Bkbl; 4H A; *Bio.*

BLAND, Darlene
Covington HS; Covington, TN (85-220) *U of Tenn at Martin; Secy.*

BLAND, James Walter
The Lovett Sch; Atlanta, GA (20-144) Dbte Tm; Drama; Ger C; Parl, Lat C; NFL; NHS; Spch C; Tres, SC; Cr-Ctry; Tnns; Tr; NEDT; Spch A; Councilman at Large; Debate, Lat, A's; *Yale U; Law.*

BLAND, Jeffry Allen
Fulton HS; Fulton, IL (5-150) Band; Bkbl; Co-Cpt, Ftbl; Tr; Ftbl, Tr, Bkbl, Ltrs.

BLAND, Joy Ellen
Van-Far R-I HS; Vandalia, MO (25-65) Band; Chor; Ensm; Fr C; FHA; Key C; 4H A; GAA; Church Choir; Church Quartet; Elec A; Church Asst Organist; Home Ec A; Church Librarian; *LPN Sch of Nurs; Nurs.*

BLAND, Judy Lynne
W Craven HS; Vanceboro, NC (10%-212) Bus Mgr, Band; Community Yth Symph; Hmrm; Mjrte; NHS; Sci C; Span C; VP, SC; Pres, Soph Cl; 1st Run-Up, Hugh O'Brien Yth Found; *U of NC; Acct.*

BLAND, Leslie Ruth
Captain Shreve HS; Shreveport, LA; *LSU; Eng.*

BLAND, Robert Earl Jr
John T Hoggard HS; Wilmington, NC; Pres, Demolay; Hmrm; InterClub Coun; Key C; ARC; Mgr, Bkbl; Ftbl; Mgr, Soccer; Tr; Citz A; Masonic A; Opt A; Spch A; Yth Fel; *Duke U; Pre-Med.*

BLAND, Roxanne Li Ane
Duke Ellington Sch o-t Arts; Washington, DC; Band; Orch; Supt of Pub Sch Hon; WW; *Architecture.*

BLANDFORD, LuAnn
Burrell Sr HS; Lower Burrell, PA (82-350) Co-Cpt, Chldr; Chor; Fin, Jr Miss Pagent; Mjrte; Span C; SC; Sftbl; Co-Cpt, Tr; Amer Leg A; Hon Prog; Pres, Jr NHS; Spirit of Jr Miss, A; Yth Fitness Achv, A; *U of Pittsburgh; Engr.*

BLANEY, Darlyn
St Vincent Acad; Newark, NJ (2-70) Pres, Hmrm; SC; Pres, Soph Cl; *Special Ed.*

BLANEY, James Michael
Hobart Sr HS; Hobart, IN (7-396) AFS; Drama; Ger C; Madrigal; NHS; Parl, SC; Thes; JV, Cr-Ctry; JV, Tr; JV, Wrest; Hon Men, Ntl Merit; AFS Exchange, Belgium; WW, HS Foreign Lang; *Ind U; Med.*

BLANK, Christine Sue
Buckhorn HS; Buckhorn, KY (2-41) BC; Chor; FHA; Ger A; *Rosedale Bible Inst; Bible.*

BLANK, Richard Brian
MacArthur HS; San Antonio, TX (40-610) Lat C; NHS; Ftbl; All City, All Dist, Ftbl; Outst Lineman A; *Tex A&M U; Mech Engr.*

BLANK, Rosita Fern
Buckhorn HS; Buckhorn, KY (1-36) Co-Ed, Ann; Pres, BC; FHA; VP, Sr Cl; Citz A; Type A; Val; Eng A; *Berea Col; Ed.*

BLANKENSHIP, Brad Edwin
Warren Co Sr HS; McMinnville, TN (1-416) BS; Pres, HiY; Pres, InterAct C; InterClub Coun; NHS; Sci C; Ftbl; Tnns; Amer Leg Orator A; VFW Orator Win; VofDEM; WW; Scottish Rites Win; Caney Fork Essay Win; Jr Marshal; *David Lipscomb Col; Med.*

BLANKENSHIP, Cindy Renee
Parkway N Sr HS; St Louis, MO (83-545).

BLANKENSHIP, Cynthia Renee
Parkway N Sr HS; St Louis, MO (85-500) Yth Fel; *Phar.*

BLANKENSHIP, Henri Jay
Rustburg HS; Rustburg, VA (10%-450) Fr C; NHS; Var C; Ftbl; *VPI; Sci.*

BLANKENSHIP, Jamie Regina
Wonderview HS; Hattieville, AR (10%-44) Secy, FHA; Pres, Soph Cl; Bkbl; Beauty; HCt; Sci A; *Harding Col.*

BLANKENSHIP, Karen Ann
Citrus HS; Inverness, FL (12-250) NHS; Span C; WW; *Central Florida Comm Col; Nurs.*

BLANKENSHIP, Kent Steven
Blair HS; Hattiesburg, MS (10%-385) BS; Monogram; Bsbl; Co-Cpt, Ftbl; Tr; SC Senator; Pres, FCA; *Pearl River Jr Col; Bus.*

BLANKENSHIP, Kimberly Joan
Charles D Owen HS; Swannanoa, NC (8-267) Band; Drama; Fr C; Bus Mgr, Sch P; NEDT; Pres, Yth Coun.

BLANKENSHIP, Lori Lou
Morton Jr-Sr HS; Morton, WA (5-38) A Cap Choir; Band; Chor; Ensm; FHA; Hmrm; NHS; VP, Span C; SC; Cpt, Bkbl; Sftbl; *Centralia Col; Phys Ed.*

BLANKENSHIP, Lucinda Jane
Seymour HS; Seymour, MO (10-78) VP, BC; Co-Cpt, Chldr; Chor; Drama; FHA; Sftbl; Tr; Worthy Assoc Adv, Rainbow Girls; Crest Qn; *Marketing.*

BLANKENSHIP, Nancy Elizabeth
Shamrock HS; Decatur, GA (68-306) BC; Chor; NHS; Span C; Bkbl; *DeKalb Col; Secy.*

BLANKENSHIP, Rebecca Brooks
Benjamin Russell HS; Alexander City, AL (20-200) S-T, FTA; NHS; Tri-HiY; Yth Leg; *Auburn U; Child Care.*

BLANKENSHIP, Regina Fay
Garden HS; Oakwood, VA (5-68) BC; Chor; Drama; VP, FHA; FTA; NHS; SC; Secy, Soph Cl; Sftbl; B Crocker A; COM; Hist A; Home Ec A.

BLANKENSHIP, Ronald Keith
Cherokee HS; Cherokee, NC (2-55) Ann; VP, BC; BS; Monogram; VP, SC; Bsbl; Ftbl; Wrest; Amer Leg A; Cl Fav; Hist A; MLS; Sal; Mr Brave; *Western Carolina U; Bus Adm.*

BLANKENSHIP, Sandra Gail
Monroe Co HS; Monroeville, AL (10%-110) A-Ed, Ann; Band; BC; Chor; Drama; Ensm; FTA; Fin, Jr Miss Pagent; A-Ed, Sch P; Swim; Best Dramatist A; *Huntingdon Col; Mus.*

BLANKENSHIP, Teresa Diane
Rustburg HS; Lynchburg, VA (10%-400) Ann; Band; JV, Chldr; *Art.*

BLANKINSHIP, Tami Leigh
George Washington HS; Charleston, WV (178-356) Band; Bkbl; 1st Cl GSct A; *Georgetown Col; Phys Ed.*

BLANLOT, Larry Leon
Hartshorne HS; Hartshorne, OK; Secy, FFA; NHS; SC; Ftbl; Driver Ed Pin; Industrial Arts, A; Agr Poultry Products, A; *E Okla St U; Carpentry.*

BLANSON, Vincent P
Carroll HS; Monroe, LA (3%-205) Pres, Hmrm; InterAct C; Secy, Math C; VP, NHS; Pres, Phys C; Pres, SC; Mgr, Bsbl; Mgr, Ftbl; Chem A; Cl Fav; Hon Prog; Math A; MLS; Ntl Achv Schol; Pres A; YES A; Sch Essay Win; Stu o-t Yr; Stu o-t Mo; *LSU; Pre-Law.*

BLANTON, Amy Laura
Burns Sr HS; Lawndale, NC; VP, Health Careers C; Health Careers C Schol; *Cleveland Tech Col; Nurs.*

BLANTON, Barbara Renee
E Rutherford HS; Forest City, NC (2-351) Hmrm; Span C; SC; COM; Gov Honor Prog; Hist A; Math A; MLS; Sci A; Art As; *Sou Sem; Art.*

BLANTON, Billy David
Tivy HS; Kerrville, TX (10%-235) Bus C; Dbte Tm; Key C; Lit Ral; NFL; Order/Arrow; Var C; Pres, Soph Cl; Bsbl; Bkbl; Cpt, Ftbl; Sftbl; God & Country A; Pres A; ARC A; Spch A; Star Student; Yth Fel; *Tex A&M U; Bus.*

BLANTON, Christopher Robin
Burns Sr HS; Lawndale, NC; Band; *Engr.*

BLANTON, Laura Lee
Independence HS; Independence, MS (15%-106) Bus Mgr, Ann; BC; Bus C; Chldr; Drama; FBLA; FHA; Spch C; Bkbl; God & Country A; Yth Fel; *Northwest Col; Bus.*

BLANTON, Michael Eugene
Moultrie Sr HS; Moultrie, GA (3-356) Band; Secy, Chess C; Ensm; Hmrm; Monogram; Orch; Sci C; Span C; SC; Golf; *Valdosta St U; Mus.*

BLANTON, Rhonda Faye
Jules E Mastbaum Voc Tech HS; Philadelphia, PA; Chor; JV, Tnns; Alg A; COM; Citz A; Hist A; Math A; Type A; Vlbl; Lib A; Off Aide; Art Aide; Badminton; HR; Eng A; Nurs Aide.

BLANTON, Shirley Denise
E Rutherford HS; Forest City, NC (60-250) Fr C; Hmrm; SC; Art C; Jr Civitans A; Secy Jr Civinettes; Leo C; Jr-Sr Planning Comm; *Appalachian Col; Hist.*

BLANTON, Willie Louis
Mastbaum Voc-Tec HS; Philadelphia, PA; Tr; Alg A; Bio A; COM; Citz A; JA A.

BLASCO, Jo Ellen
Bishop McDevitt HS; Harrisburg, PA (3-5) Cr-Ctry; *Social Work.*

BLASEG, Judy Kay
Miller HS; Miller, SD (29-90) AFS; F-Ed, Ann; Band; Chldr; Drama; FHA; FTA; Ger C; GS; VP, 4H; Mjrte; Rptr, Sch P; Golf; 4H A; Spch A; *SD St U; Mass Communications.*

BLASING, Jeanne Marie
Freeport Sr HS; Freeport, IL (45-513) Ntl Yth Conf; Freshman Schol; *Goshen Col; Nurs.*

BLASIUS, James Christian
N Olmsted Sr HS; N Olmsted, OH (50-696) Band; BS; Demolay; NHS; Orch; Band A.

BLASKE, Emma Maria
Saint Augustine Acad; Lakewood, OH; Chor; Bkbl.

BLASKO, Kevin Joseph
Riverhead HS; Riverhead, NY (69-240) Key C; Co-Cpt, Bsbl; JV, Bkbl; Co-Cpt, Ftbl; Rptr, VICA; *Cortland Col; Recreation Adm.*

BLASKOWSKI, Julie Ann
Wausau E HS; Wausau, WI; *Bus.*

BLASS, Duane Eugene
Choctaw HS; Choctaw, OK (50%-300) Bsbl; Bkbl; FCA; *Central St U; Phys Ed.*

BLATTNER, Deborah Ann
Christian Life Acad; Mc Keesport, PA (1-3) Ann; Chor; SC; Val; Church Yth Pres; Bible Quiz Tm; Yth Singing Group; *Evangel Col; Learning Disabilities.*

BLAUCH, Christina Mae
Frankfort HS; Ridgeley, WV (10%-151) Chor; FTA; NHS; Tnns; Sch Service A; Ch, Fel Christian Stu; *Potomac St Col; Math.*

BLAUS, Linda Kay
Hickory Sr HS; Sharon, PA (6-255) NHS; Span NHS; Tr; Church Chor; *Carnegie-Mellon U; Archt.*

BLAXTON, Marvin Ernest
Yukon HS; Yukon, OK; FFA; FFA Chpt Farmer A; *Okla St U; Agr.*

BLAYLOCK, Patrick Anthony
Northside HS; Fort Smith, AR; BS; Var C; Ftbl; Tr; All St, Ftbl; 1st Tm, All Area, Ftbl; *Acct.*

BLAYLOCK, Ronald Steven
R L Turner HS; Carrollton, TX (16-850) Band; NHS; Orch; Hon Prog; *Tex A&M U; Vet Med.*

BLAYLOCK, William E
Crestview Sr HS; Crestview, FL (1-300) Band; FTA; Hmrm; Secy, Key C; Orch; Hon Prog; *U of Fla; Med.*

BLAZEK, Joan Elizabeth
Immanuel Christian Sch; Ridgecrest, CA (1-2) Chldr; Chor; Sch P; Secy, SC; *Working with the Deaf.*

BLAZEK, Kim Patricia
Middle River Comm HS; Middle River, MN; Band; Tres, CYO; Chldr; Chor; 4H; NHS; Sch P; Pres, Soph Cl; Bkbl; Sftbl; Fin, Tr; HCt; Type A; Phys Fitness A; Most Improved, Bkbl; St Participant, Tr.

BLAZENIAK, Anita Alice
Kelly HS; Chicago, IL (26-611) Eng A; Mus A; Kelly Hon Soc; *Bradley U; Nurs.*

BLECHA, Gregory John
Herbert Hoover HS; San Diego, CA (44-489) Chem C; Key C; NHS; Phys C; ARC; Swim; JV, Wrest; CSF; Chem A; Citz A; Hist A; Math A; Gold Medal of Achv; *U of San Diego; Lit.*

BLEDSOE, Jetaune Garlette
George Wythe HS; Richmond, VA; Band; Drama; Sch P; Hockey; Tr; Citz A; Ath Hon's & A's; *Howard U; Journ.*

BLEDSOE, Michael Anthony
Tilden HS; Chicago, IL (58-408) Bsbl; Ftbl; Hon Prog; *Northern Ill U.*

BLEDSOE, Nolda Daionese
George Wythe HS; Richmond, VA (100-270) Pres, Bus C; Dbte Tm; Pres, FBLA; Secy, FHA; VP, FTA; Hmrm; Rptr, Sch P; SC; VP, FHA; Outst FBLA Member; FHA Bookclub A; *Va Union U; Acct.*

BLEDSOE, Steve Ashley
Huntsville HS; Huntsville, AL (70-440) Chem C; Chess C; Chor; Phys C; Ftbl; Soccer; Tnns; Tr; COM; *Auburn U; Engr.*

BLEDSOE, Wanda LeNelle
Duncanville HS; Duncanville, TX (68-630) Chor; Ensm; Lit Mag; SC; *Baylor U; Vocal Mus Ed.*

BLEEKER, Jolie Renee
Washburn HS; Minneapolis, MN (125-390) Band; Hmrm; Sftbl; Church Chor; Young Life C; Semi-Fin, Friendship Qn; *Psych.*

BLEER, Sandra Dawn
Asher HS; Asher, OK (1-32) VP, FHA; Secy, 4H; Cpt, Bkbl; Sftbl; HQn; Sal; *Northern Okla Jr Col.*

BLEIL, Cindy Jeanne
E Lansing HS; East Lansing, MI (3-400) JV, Chldr; Chor; Ensm; Orch; Y-Tns; Most Out; Mich Sch Band and Dist; Chrch Mus Fest; Solo & Ensm; Principal Dancer, Spring Musical; No 1 Rating On Solo Violin; *Mus.*

BLENKNER, Carol Ann
Perry Hall Sr HS; Baltimore, MD (5%-650) AFS; NHS; SC; Pres Schol; *Loyola Col; Chem.*

BLESI, Cheryl Nadine
Park Center HS; Brooklyn Park, MN; Chldr; Swim; Tnns; Job's Daughters; Gym; *U of Minn.*

BLESING, Jana Kay
Llano HS; Llano, TX (1-100) Rptr, Band; Ensm; FFA; NHS; VP, Jr Cl; Tr; Band A's; *Lubbock Christian Col; Acct.*

BLESSEN, Douglas Bryan
Amarillo HS; Amarillo, TX; Hmrm; VP, Orch; Span C; COM; Yth Fel; *Baylor U; Engr.*

BLEVINS, Dee Ann
Yucca Valley HS; Yucca Valley, CA (10-212) Rptr, Sch P; Yth Group; Best of Art Show; Awana Chums; Awana Shipmates; Gym Sch Ltr; Ldr, Awana Chums; All-Sch Play Ltr; Church Choir; *Chapman Col; Art.*

BLEVINS, Glenda E
Henderson Sr HS; W Chester, PA (5-508) *Nurs.*

BLEVINS, Melinda Kae
St Charles HS; St Charles, IL (58-548).

BLEVINS, Pamela Leigh
Giles HS; Pearisburg, VA (30-200) Band; Bus C; FBLA; FHA; NHS; Span C.

BLEVINS, Rebecca Jo
Daniel Boone HS; Jonesboro, TN; Chldr; 4H; VP, Span C; *U of Tenn; Vet Med.*

BLIZZARD, Wendee Pauline
St Mary's Jr Col; Raleigh, NC (14-103) BC; Chor; Fr C; NHS; Young Democrats; Young Republicans; *U of NC; Phar.*

BLOCH, Carl Allen
Chapel Hill Acad; Eden Prairie, MN (2-12) Chor; Community Yth Symph; Cpt, Dbte Tm; Ensm; Ger C; Ski C; Pres, SC; Bkbl; Co-Cpt, Ftbl; Cpt, Sftbl; Tr; Best Mus, Violin, ACE Ntl Conv A; *Mus.*

BLOCH, Jeffrey William
SW HS; Kansas City, MO (5-474) Band; BS; Co-Cpt, Dbte Tm; Drama; Ensm; Fr C; Pres, NFL; NHS; Amer Leg Orator A; Hon Prog; Opt A; Spch A; VofDEM; Asst Drum Major; *NW Mo U; Journ.*

BLOCHER, Jill Elizabeth
Klein HS; Spring, TX (46-400) MVP, Band; Tres, Fr C; Orch; COM; ARC A; Superior Ratings, Solo & Ensm; *N Tex St U.*

BLOCHER, Steven Albert
Lexington Sr HS; Lexington, NE (30-134) Chor; FFA; Monogram; Secy, Sr Cl; Bsbl; Co-Cpt, Bkbl; Co-Cpt, Ftbl; JV, Golf; Tr; COM; Yth Fel; HR; Anthropology A; *U of Nebr; Bus.*

BLOCK, Barbara Ann
Shawnee HS; Louisville, KY; Hmrm; Sftbl; Tnns; *Nurs.*

BLOCK, Robin Renee
Broadview Acad; La Fox, IL (50%-77) Chldr; Chor; Ch, Dbte Tm; Ski C; Arch; Bkbl; Ftbl; Golf; Sftbl; Swim; Cl Mascot; Girls C; *Andrews U; Elem Ed.*

BLOCK, Todd Philip
Hibbing HS; Hibbing, MN (25%-425) Band; Drama; Thes; Curling; *U of Minn; Vet.*

BLOCKER, Pamela Gail
McArthur HS; Hollywood, FL; Bus C; FBLA; Pres A; St Champ, Yth Choir; Home Bible Stu A; *Piedmont Tech Col; Bus.*

BLOCKER, Riddick Richard
Conway HS; Conway, SC; Chor; Hmrm; SC.

BLOCTON, Evangeline Marie
Washington HS; Pensacola, FL (90-350) Pres, FHA; SC; Y-Tns; JA A; Most Out; ROTC A; Pres, JA Bank; Diversified Cooperative Trng Prog; Sch Schol; Swtht, FHA; *Pensacola Jr Col; Acct.*

BLOESING, Steven Carl
Fletcher Sr HS; Neptune Beach, FL; Key C; *Ga Tech; Elec.*

BLOKZYL, Donna Ruth
Bainbridge Guilford Central Sch; Bainbridge, NY (24-101) Arch; Arch; Art As; *Computer Programming.*

BLOM, Kevin Dean
Edgerton Pub HS; Edgerton, MN (5%-16) BS; NHS; Sch P; SC; Var C; VP, Soph Cl; Bkbl; COM; Hon Prog; Yth Fel; Pres, Yth Fel.

BLOM, Sherlyn Beth
Chandler-Lake Wilson Pub HS; Chandler, MN (1-34) Band; Chor; Drama; Ensm; SC; Tr; Secy, Reformed Church Yth Fel; *Northwestern Col.*

BLOMBERG, Michael George
Prentice HS; Prentice, WI (25-70) BS; Chor; Bkbl; Ftbl; *U of Wis-River Falls; Agr.*

BLOME, Jane Marie
Adairsville HS; Adairsville, GA; Ann; Band; Dbte Tm; FHA; 4H; Sch P; Sci C; Band A's; *Springfield Col; Law.*

BLOMGREN, Michael R
Stillman Valley HS; Stillman Valley, IL (10-102) Pres, AFS; Rptr, Ann; Band; BS; Drama; Pres, NHS; Rptr, Sch P; Spch C; SC; Mgr, Ftbl; Wrest; Amer Leg A; COM; Q&S A; St Scholar; Mayor, Stillman Valley; *Northern Ill U; Pol Sci.*

BLOMGREN, Susan Lois
Westview Sr HS; Braham, MN (25%-100) Band; Secy, Chor; Ensm; Y-Tns; COM; ARC A; Pom Pon Girls; St Ensm Fin; Vlbl; Band A; Choir A; *Cosmetology.*

BLOMQUIST, Christopher Wayne
Flint Southwestern HS; Flint, MI; NHS; Swim; Tnns; Yth Fel; *Math.*

BLOMQUIST, Kristen Ann
Bellevue Sr HS; Bellevue, WA; Fr C; Hmrm; SC; *Whitworth Col; Psych.*

BLONDE, Holly Hilda
Gurdon S Hubbard HS; Chicago, IL (20-436) Band; FTA; Hmrm; NHS; Rptr, Sch P; Span C; SC; Hon Prog; PTA A; Yth Foundation A; *N Ill U; Special Ed.*

BLONDEL, Monique Angele
Los Fresnos HS; Los Fresnos, TX (5-110) Band; NHS; Sci C; John Philip Sousa A; Cotillion C; Band Swtht; March of Dimes Schol; All Region Band; FNA Schol; UIL Region St A Solo Contest; *U of Tex at Arlington; Nurs.*

BLONIARZ, Darlene Ann
Foreman HS; Chicago, IL (2-373) Bus C; NHS; Hon Prog; Journ A; Sal; Pres, Hostess C.

BLOODWORTH, Beverly Ann
Newberry Jr-Sr HS; Newberry, FL (2-96) Band; BC; Pres, SC; Bio A; Sal; Ldrship A; *U of Fla; Phar.*

BLOOM, Barbara Jean
Farmington Sr HS; Farmington, MO (60-260) Pres, A Cap Choir; A-Ed, Ann; Tres, Bus C; Chor; Drama; Ensm; Madrigal; Swtht; Mus A; *Mineral Area Col.*

BLOOM, Christine Grace
Harbor HS; Ashtabula, OH (74-161) AFS; Cpt, Band; Pres, FTA; SC; Thes; VP, Sr Women; SDAHSS; WW; *Thiel Col; Ed.*

BLOOM, David Aaron
Anderson Union HS; Anderson, CA (45-420) Span C; SC; Tnns; CSF; DARGCA; *U of Minn; Archt.*

BLOOM, Robert Kenneth
Cumberland Valley HS; Mechanicsburg, PA (1-627) Community Yth Symph; Lat C; NHS; Orch; NEDT; *Dartmouth Col; Pre-Med.*

BLOOMQUIST, Mary Elena
Ashland Sr HS; Ashland, WI; A Cap Choir; AFS.

BLOOMQUIST, Michael James
Columbus Comm HS; Columbus, IA (11-67) Band; Chor; FFA; Pres, 4H; Sch P; SC; Bsbl; Ftbl; 4H A; FFA Soil & Water Mgr A.

BLOOMQUIST, Nelda Dean
Douglas HS; Douglas, AZ (7-320) AFS; Band; Ensm; NFL; Pres, Rainbow; Tr; Masonic A; Sci A; All Regional Band; *Baylor U; Psychiatry.*

BLOSSER, Ruth Ann
Goshen HS; Goshen, IN (5-253) Chor; Ensm; NHS; Vlbl; St Mus Auditions; *Fort Wayne Bible Col; Elem Ed.*

BLOSSER, Steven Wesley
Buckingham Co HS; Buckingham, VA (5%-140) Dbte Tm; NHS; NHS A; *VPI; Forestry.*

BLOUNT, Bill
Leroy HS; Leroy, AL (6-70) Ann; BC; BS; FFA; 4H; Bsbl; Bkbl; Cpt, Ftbl; *U of S Ala; Engr.*

BLOUNT, James Marvin
S R Butler HS; Huntsville, AL (25%-650) A Cap Choir; Hmrm; Key C; ARC; SC; Ftbl; Tr; Wrest; *U of Ala; Med.*

BLOUNT, Jeffrey Edward
Smithfield HS; Smithfield, VA (6-140) Ann; Band; BC; BS; Chess C; Math C; Co-Ed, Sch P; Span C; SC; Var C; Bsbl; Bkbl; Ftbl; Hon Prog; *Va Commonwealth U; Mass Communications.*

BLOUNT, John Christopher
F T Wills HS; Smyrna, GA; Ann; Hmrm; Secy, Key C; Var C; Pres, Jr Cl; JV, Bsbl; Bkbl; Cr-Ctry; Tr; Cl Fav; Coun of Teach A; FCA C; *Truett McConnel Col; Ministry.*

BLOUNT, Lee III
Christian Brothers Col HS; St Louis, MO (62-129) Chor; Co-Cpt, Tnns; Elk A; Journ A; *Saint Louis U; Religion.*

BLOW, Laura Lillian
Christian Acad; Waverly, NY; Orch; *Ed.*

BLOWERS, Brian Keith
Tenino HS; Tenino, WA (17-56) Chess C; Chor; FFA; SC; Rptr, Sr Cl; Bsbl; Bkbl; Cl Fav; Hon Prog; JA A; Masonic A; Most Out; *Centralia Comm Col; Carpentry.*

BLOYS, James Benjamin
Kailua HS; Kailua, HI (45-668) Ch, NHS; Bkbl; Ftbl; Outst Industrial Arts Stu; Hon-Men, St Industrial Arts Fair; *Industrial Arts.*

BLUE, Randy Lee
McClellan HS; Little Rock, AR; Band; Lit Safari; *U of Ark; Sci.*

BLUEBAUM, Robert Michael
Hardaway HS; Columbus, GA; Key C; Lat C; NHS; Var C; Cpt, Bsbl; Bkbl; Ftbl; Most Out; *Auburn U; Pre-Med.*

BLUEBOND, Sheri Ann
El Camino Real HS; Woodland Hills, CA; Drama; NHS; Thes; Mgr, Ftbl; Mgr, Tr; CSF; Citz A; Hist A; Hon Prog; Section Ldr, Chor; Outst Conquistador A; NCTE Essay Contest Fin; *Pre-Law.*

BLUE JACKET, David Scott
Central Cath HS; Denver, CO (10-150) Drama; Hmrm; Key C; NFL; NHS; Spch C; Secy, SC; Soph Cl; COM; Opt A; Spch A; VofDEM; HR; St Spch Tourn Cert; Outst Academic Achv Cert; Cast, All Sch Musical; *Saint Thomas Sem; Theology.*

BLUHM, Carilyn Ellen
Delavan HS; Delavan, IL (50%-65) Var C; Bkbl; Sftbl; Tr; Vlbl; *Elem Ed.*

BLUHM, Dana Jo
Parkview HS; Little Rock, AR (45-500) Secy, BC; Hmrm; Mjrte; Mu Alpha Theta; NHS; Secy, Span C; SC; Y-Tns; Tres, Sr Cl; Citz A; Hon Prog; *Baylor U; Computer Sci.*

BLUHM, Garry Frederick
Medina Sr HS; Medina, NY (103-178) Chess C; Chor; Sch P; Mgr, Bsbl; JV, Ftbl; JV, Wrest; *Monroe Comm Col; Bus Mgt.*

BLUM, Craig Lee
Victory Christian Sch; Sacramento, CA (6-21) Rptr, Ann; Band; Chor; Drama; Rptr, Sch P; Pres, SC; VP, Sr Cl; Pres, Jr Cl; Bsbl; Bkbl; Ftbl; Sftbl; Tr; Phys Ed A; *Pepperdine U; Sociology.*

63

BLUM, Nanette Christine
HS of Art and Design; New York, NY (65-504) Chldr; Hmrm; NHS; SC; Hon Prog; Excel in Art A; Arts Hmns Soc; Sch of Art League Schol A; 3rd Pl, Design Contest; Fashion Inst of Tech; Draping.

BLUME, Brenda Sue
Jeffersom Comm HS; Jefferson, IA (7-124) AFS; Ann; Chor; Fr C; NHS; Hon Prog; St Scholar; S-T, Lutheran Yth for Christ; Morningside Col; Bus.

BLUMENSCHEID, Richard Charles
Westfield HS; Westfield, NJ; Band; Ensm; Order/ Arrow; Amer Leg A; Order/Arrow A; Yth Fel; Eagle Sct; Civil Engr.

BLUMENSCHEID, Robert Andrew
Westfield Sr HS; Westfield, NJ (200-600) Band; Lat C; Orch; Order/Arrow; Span C; Order/Arrow A; Eagle Sct; NML; Lehigh Col; Engr.

BLUMENSCHEIN, Suzanne Katherine
Friscoll HS; Addison, IL (4-144) Co-Ed; Ann; Chor; Drama; Lit Mag; Tres, NHS; Hon Prog; St Scholar; Family Ldr of Tomorrow; Found Alumni Distin Schol, Il St U; Ill St U; Marketing.

BLUMENTHAL, Thomas William
South Hills HS; Covina, CA (43-394) AFS; Chem C; Pres, Ger C; InterClub Coun; Order/Arrow; Sci C; SC; Var C; JV, Ftbl; MVP, Tnns; CSF; COM; Order/Arrow A; Rotary A; Eagle Sct; Hiking C; Pres, Yth Conf; Coun, Fel Christian Yth Camp; Acolyte; Claremont Mens Col; Econ.

BLUMER, Frederick Tanner
Thornwell HS; Clinton,SC (1-20) Co-Ed, Ann; BC; Chem C; Chor; VP, Fr C; Hmrm; Monogram; Order/Arrow; Pres, Ski C; Pres, SC; Var C; Pres, Jr Cl; Bkbl; Ftbl; Cpt, Tnns; Tr; Chem A; Gov Honor Prog; MLS; Order/Arrow A; Sci A; Star Student; St Scholar; Val; Yth Fel; Eagle Sct; Gov Yth Advisory Coun; Best All Around; Most Sch Spirit; Col of Charleston; Chem.

BLUMER, Katherine Julia
Thornwell HS; Clinton, SC; Ann; VP, BC; Chldr; Fr C; Secy, Jr Cl; Bkbl; Tnns; HCt; Yth Fel; Presbyterian Jr Fel; Newberry Schol; WW; Converse Col; Psych.

BLUMHANDT, Wayde Russell
Leola HS; Leola, SD (1-43) Pres, Band; BS; Pres, Chor; NHS; Rptr, Sch P; Pres, SC; Pres, Jr Cl; Bsbl; Co-Cpt, Bkbl; Co-Cpt, Ftbl; Sftbl; Tr; HKg; Hon Prog; Math A; Type A; Val; Hons Choir; All-St Chor; Mt Marty Col; Med.

BLUNK, Steven Donald
N Kansas City HS; N Kansas City, MO (3-460) A Cap Choir; Ensm; Madrigal; Tr; Central Mo St U; Mus.

BLUNT, Donna Lynn
Tishomingo HS; Tishomingo, MS; Ann; Secy, FBLA; FHA; Page, House of Rep; Miss Personality; VP, Lib C.

BLY, Denise Monique
Alma J Brown Lab HS; Grambling, LA (10%-60) Band; Drama; FTA; Rptr, 4H; Lit Ral; NHS; Secy, Sci C; Pres, SC; Mgr, Bkbl; Beauty; Bio A; 4H A; HCt; Ntl Sci Found; Sci A; Spch A; Swtht; Outst Jr Ldrs A; Sewing As; Art As; Mus As; Parson Sch of Art; Fashion Designer.

BLY, Eska Roderick
Alma J Brown Lab HS; Grambling, LA (8-52) Chor; Pres, 4H; Key C; NHS; Order/Arrow; VP, Sci C; Parl, SC; Pres, Sr Cl; Co-Cpt, Ftbl; COM; Cl Fav; 4H A; Hist A; Hon Prog; JA A; Ntl Sci Found; Order/Arrow A; Sci A; MVP, All Dist, Ftbl; Brown U; Pre-Med.

BLYDEN, Carla Denise
Montclair HS; Montclair, NJ (95-485) Hmrm; Fin, Jr Miss Pagent; SC; Tr; COM; U of Pittsburg; Phys Therapy.

BLYTHE, Barbara Jean
Asher HS; Asher, OK (5%-29) Chldr; FBLA; Pres, FHA; Sch P; Secy, Sr Cl; Bkbl; Cl Fav; Hist A; Math A; MLS; St Gregory Jr Col; Bus Ed.

BLYTHE, Kathryn Ann
Sherman HS; Sherman, TX; Chor; Span C; Cpt, Sftbl; Tnns; FCA; Trophies, Tourn, A's; Asst Gym Coach, Austin Col; Sftbl Trophies; All Dist, All St, Vlbl; Baylor U; Ath.

BLYTHE, Michael Rollin
Griffith HS; Griffith, IN (80-350) Hmrm; NHS; SC; Secy, Var C; Pres, Sr Cl; VP, Jr Cl; Ch, Soph Cl; Co-Cpt, Ftbl; MVP, Tr; Amer Leg A; HCt; Best Personality; Friendliest; Prom Court; Ind U; Bus Adm.

BLYTHE, Randy Kevin
Lincoln HS; Stockton, CA (79-500) Bsbl; Bkbl; Ftbl; Golf; Tnns; Sftbl.

BOALS, Phyllis Kay
Medina HS; Medina, TN; BC; FHA; Bkbl; U of Tenn; Engr.

BOAN, James Frederick
Jordan Voc HS; Columbus, GA (39-280) Pres, Chor; Hmrm; Key C; Ch, Model UN; Bus Mgr, NHS; Order/Arrow; Pres, Span C; SC; Var C; Pres, Soph Cl; MVP, Ftbl; COM; NEDT; Order/Arrow A; Cpt, Ftbl; Brian Piccolo Bst Def Lineman, A; U of Ga; Marketing.

BOAND, Lynn Carol
McKinney HS; McKinney, TX (2%-250) Band; FHA; FTA; Lat C; Pres, NHS; Spch C; SC; Rotary A; UIL Band & Spelling A's; Hanover Col.

BOARDLEY, Sicily Grace
Brandywine HS; Wilmington, DE; Chor; Alg A; Citz A; Hon Prog; Pa St U; Pre-Med.

BOASE, Kerry Dean
M B Smiley HS; Houston, TX (8-461) NHS; Sci C; Bsbl; Ftbl; Tr.

BOATMAN, Beth Ellen
New Albany HS; New Albany, IN (50%-350) Band; COM.

BOATRIGHT, Sharon Denise
Windsor Forest HS; Savannah, GA; FHA; Ger C; Bio A; Citz A; Sci A; Savannah St Col; Home Ec.

BOATWRIGHT, Gregory Wayne
Batesburg-Leesville HS; Batesburg, SC (2-175) Ch, A Cap Choir; Cpt, Band; BC; BS; Chem C; Cpt, Chor; Ch, Ensm; Ch, Madrigal; Pres, Mod Mus Mas; NHS; ARC; Sci C; S-T, SC; Sftbl; Tnns; COM; Gr Marshal; Hon Prog; MLS; Most Out; Star Student; St Scholar; Yth Fel; Yth Leg; WW; All St Hon Chors; All St Band; Semi Fin, Bob Jones Piano Contest; Bob Jones U; Mus.

BOATWRIGHT, Thad Gully
York Comp HS; York, SC (4-240) Drama; Fr C; VP, FFA; NHS; Sci C; Spch C; Var C; Wrest; Spch A; Jr Marshal; PC Jr Fel; Newberry Schol; FFA Star Greenhand; N Greenville Col; Soil Conservation.

BOBAK, Kimberly Ann
Rossford HS; Rossford, OH (21-180) Tres, CYO; Chldr; Chor; A-Ed, Sch P; Tres, SC; Michael J Owens Tech Col; Health.

BOBBITT, Lisa Louise
John Graham Sr HS; Warrenton, NC (2-152) Co-Ed, Ann; Fr C; Hmrm; Monogram; NHS; SC; Mgr, Bkbl; Chem A; Gov Honor Prog; Hon Prog; Math A; Eng A; Fr A; UNC-Greensboro; Computor Sci.

BOBBITT, Sherri Lynn
Eastern Hills HS; Fort Worth, TX (94-450) Cum Laude Soc; Secy, FHA; Hmrm; Span C; St Fin C Spch Contest; 2nd Pl Area Bus Contest; Tex Christian U; Special Ed.

BOBBITT, Vicky
Vidalia HS; Vidalia, GA; Chldr; VP, Chor; Thes; Ch, Tri-HiY; Beauty.

BOBEK, Kathryn Kaye
Valentine HS; Valentine, NE; Chor; 4H; 4H A; Vlbl; Schol A.

BOBEK, Tana Charlene
Valentine HS; Valentine, NE (23-89) Chor; Dbte Tm; 4H; F-Ed, Sch P; 4H A; Vlbl; Therapist.

BOBEREK, Danielle Rae
Independence HS; Independence, OH; AFS; Band; Orch; JA A; Pres, Pep C; Cr- ctry Scorer; Cuyahoga Comm Col; Respiratory Therapy.

BOBICH, Thomas John
Mary Star o-t Sea HS; San Pedro, CA (1-86) Chess C; InterAct C; InterClub Coun; Pres, Math C; NHS; Ed, Sch P; Sci C; Span C; Pres, SC; Var C; Bsbl; Ftbl; Alg A; Bank Of Amer A; CSF; COM; Hist A; Hon Prog; Lion A; MLS; Most Out; NMF; NMS; NEDT; Val; Principal's A; WW; Ntl Merit Win; Loyola-Marymount U; Bus Adm.

BOBO, Robert Edward
Splendora HS; Splendora, TX (10-87) FFA; NHS; MVP, Bsbl; Bkbl; Cpt, Ftbl; Golf; Semi-Fin, Tr; Cl Fav; PTA A; Most Ath; Best All Around; Friendliest; Sam Houston St U; Radio Broadcast.

BOBO, Teresa Ann
Collinsville HS; Collinsville, AL (14-56) Ann; BC; Cpt, Chldr; Chor; Secy, SC; Tres, Jr Cl; Off, FHA; Gadsden St Jr Col; Early Childhood Ed.

BOBO, Terri Lee
Queen City HS; Queen City, TX (10-44) VP, Band; Cpt, Chldr; FHA; Hmrm; Cpt, Mjrte; NHS; Sch P; S-T, SC; Bkbl; Cl Fav; HCt; Drum Major; Band Swtht; Texarkana Comm Col; Journ.

BOBROWSKI, Daniel
John S Fine Sr HS; Nanticoke, PA (8-347) Chess C; Rptr, Sch P; SC; Amer Leg A; Bio A; Lion A; NEDT; Med.

BOBST, Cindy Lou
Wheelersburg HS; Wheelersburg, OH (50-128) Band; Chor; FHA; Mjrte; A-Ed, Sch P; Bkbl; Tr; HQn; Yth Fel; Morehead U; Bus.

BOCA, Barbara Jean
Geo Washington HS; Chicago, IL (11-556) Chor; FNA; Lat C; NHS; SC; Hon Prog; Lion A; Miss East Side; HR Cert; Alpha C; North Park Col; Nurs.

BOCCHETTO, Philip Gerard
Notre Dame-Bishop Gibbons HS; Schenectady, NY (13-160) NHS; Co-Cpt, Bkbl; Ftbl; Hon Prog; Boston Col; Med.

BOCHOW, Carl Evans
Robert E Lee HS; Tyler, TX (10%-624) Chem C; NHS; Span C; Hon Prog; U of Tex; Chem Engr.

BOCHTE, Jill M
Naperville N HS; Naperville, IL (25%-650) JV, Tr; Vlbl; U of Ill; Phys Ed.

BOCHY, Mark H
Melbourne HS; Melbourne, FL; Key C; Bsbl; Bio A; Semi-Fin, Bio A; U of Fla; Med.

BOCK, Darla Jac
Mangum HS; Mangum, OK (3-68) Chldr; Chor; FHA; VP, 4H; NHS; SC; Bkbl; Tr; 4H A; Hist A; HCt; St Hon Soc; Miss Greer Co 1976; 4-H H of Fame; 4-H Swtht; OSU; Home Ec.

BOCK, Elizabeth Anna
LeRoy HS; Leroy, IL (65%-95) AFS; Tres, Band; Chor; Ensm; FHA; VP, 4H; Hmrm; Bus Mgr, Wrest; 4H A; 2nd Yr Band; 2nd Yr Chor; Madrigal; Cpt, Wrestlerette; Cincinnati Bible Col; Mus.

BOCK, James Michael
Rolling Meadows HS; Rolling Meadows, IL (28-680) NHS; Ski C; Cr-Ctry; Tnns; COM; NMS; Northwestern U; Pre-Med.

BOCKHOLD, Joyce A
Quincy Notre Dame HS; Quincy, IL (18-143) Bus Mgr, Bus C; Chor; Fr C; NHS; COM; Acct A.

BOCKHORST, Paula Marie
Cleveland HS; St Louis, MO (33%-400) Chor; FHA.

BOCOCK, Susan Lynn
Wheelersburg HS; Wheelersburg, OH (1-186) Band; Chldr; Chor; 4H; Pres, Lat C; Swim; COM; NEDT; Miami U of Ohio; Ed.

BODE, Christopher Thomas
St Joseph's o-t Palisades HS; W New York, NJ (4-289) Chess C; Span NHS; Bkbl; Hist A; Hon Prog; MLS; NEDT.

BODEN, Brenda Diane
Manchester HS; Manchester, OH (6-81) Ann; Tres, NHS; Span C; Cl Fav; Most Out; Swtht; Bus.

BODENSCHATZ, Robert Blake
Hempfield Area Sr HS; Greensburg, PA (50-805) A Cap Choir; Band; Chor; Demolay; NHS; Orch; Ski C; Alt, NROTC A; Penn St U; Engr.

BODEY, Tonya Sue
Urbana HS; Uvbana, OH (21-214) VP, Band; Secy, Fr C; S-T, 4H; Math C; NHS; Secy, Span C; World Affairs Inst; *Olivet Nazarene Col; Nurs.*

BODIFORD, Deborah Suzanne
Marvell HS; Marvell, AR (1-151) Band; BC; Rptr, FBLA; SC; Hon Prog; Math A; Civics A; *U of Ark; Law.*

BODIFORD, Gary Lee
Marvell HS; Marvell, AR (1-118) BC; SC; JV, Bkbl; Alg A; Bio A; Citz A; Hist A; Math A; Type A; Eng, Psych, A's; *Med.*

BODLE, Carol Esther
Piner HS; Santa Rosa, CA (20%-400) GS; 4H; Hmrm; Ed, Sch P; SC; 4H A; Young Life; Secy, Stu Body; Ldr, Jr High Life; *U Santa Barbara; Health Sci.*

BODMER, Melody Ann
Hazelwood E HS; St Louis, MO (120-490) Band; Yth Fel; Marian A; Ltr, Concert Band; 2nd & 3rd Pl, Job's Daugh Art Cont; *Sci.*

BODOFF, Miriam Joy
Hillel HS; Lawrence, NY; Chor; Dbte Tm; Drama; Ensm; Fr C; Secy, SC; Tnns; COM; Citz A; Hon Prog; NEDT; Poet A; Val; Dance; Synagogue Yth Ldrship A; Vlbl; Principal's List; Eng-Ed, Yrbk; Ntl Bible Contest; Mus Sch A; *Barnard Col; Mus Therapy.*

BOE, Gerald Frederick
El Camino HS; Oceanside, CA (29-420) Chor; Community Yth Symph; Orch; MIP, Orch; Church Orch; Col Comm Orch; All-St Hon Orch; *Whittier Col; Instrumental Mus.*

BOECHER, Stephanie Ann
Upper Scioto Valley HS; McGuffey, OH; Ann; JV, Chldr; Secy, 4H; Secy, SC; Tres, Jr Cl; VP, Soph Cl; JV, Bkbl; Tr; COM; Cl Fav; 4H A; HCt; *Ohio St U; Elem Ed.*

BOECKER, Garnette
Judson HS; Converse, TX (20-650) Band; Ensm; NHS; Leo C; *N Texas St U; Mus.*

BOECKMAN, Brenda Susan
Okeene HS; Okeene, OK; CYO; FFA; S-T, Soph Cl; Bkbl; Masonic A.

BOECKMAN, Chris J
Okeene HS; Okeene, OK; CYO; VP, FFA; NHS.

BOEDIGHEIMER, Lonida Marie
Regis HS; Stayton, OR (1-56) Bus C; Chldr; Chem C; Drama; Hmrm; Lit Mag; Math C; VP, NHS; Ski C; Span C; SC; Cpt, Sftbl; JV, Tr; Alg A; COM; Chem A; Hon Prog; Math A; WW; Eng A; *Oreg St U; Phar.*

BOEHLER, Michael Keith
Ballard HS; Butler, MO (2-13) Band; CYO; S-T, 4H; Pres, SC; Pres, Var C; Tres, Sr Cl; VP, Jr Cl; Tres, Soph Cl; Bkbl; Bkbl; DARGCA; Math A; Regent Schol; Sal; Sci A; *Central Mo St U; Pre-Engr.*

BOEHM, Daniel Leslie
Wade Hampton HS; Greenville, SC (50%-478) Math C; VP, Order/Arrow; Life Sct; *Clemson U; Computer Sci.*

BOEKE, Thomas Charles
Coldwater HS; Coldwater, OH (12-173) Ann; Chor; Pres, Drama; Ger C; NHS; SC; Thes; VP, Soph Cl; Bsbl; Ftbl; Tr; Elk A; Ch, Columbian Squires; Prom Court; *U of Cincinnati; Phar.*

BOEKER, Judith Kay
Metamora Township HS; Metamora, IL (12-239) Secy, AFS; Co-Ed, Ann; Chor; Drama; Hmrm; Rptr, Sch P; SC; Amer Leg A; COM; Yth Fel; Pom-Pon Sq; *Journ.*

BOELDT, Julie Christine
McHenry HS W; McHenry, IL (63-633) Chor; Madrigal; Mod Mus Mas; GAA; Secy, Yth Group; Choirs; Organist, Children's Choir; *N Ill U; Bus.*

BOELTER, Cheryl Anita
Simon Gratz HS; Philadelphia, PA (9-450) FTA; Hmrm; InterAct C; Sci C; Var C; Bsbl; Bkbl; Sftbl; Swim; Tnns; Co-Cpt, Bowl; Gym Ltrs; WW; Cpt, Gym; CAT A; Bowl A; *Penn St U; Computer Sci.*

BOENIG, James William
Judson HS; Converse, TX (15-430) Band; Dbte Tm; Ensm; Tres, FFA; Pres, 4H; Hmrm; NHS; COM; 4H A; Spch A; FFA Chpt Farmer; *Tex A&M U; Agronomy.*

BOENIG, Jo Ann
Woodsboro HS; Woodsboro, TX (12-42) Ed, Ann; Rptr, Band; Drama; Ensm; Secy, FHA; FTA; 4H; Hmrm; Sch P; SC; Mgr, Bkbl; 4H A; Church Choir; Mgr, Vlbl; SC A; Bell Choir; One Act Play A; Tres, Campfire; Ch Safety; 1st Pl Win, St Industrial Arts; *Tex Lutheran Col; Elem Ed.*

BOERE, Lisa Diane
Tyee HS; Seattle, WA (60-250) JV, Chldr; Chor; H of F; Alt, Hmrm Rep; Hiliners; DECA; *Highline Jr Col; Air Transp.*

BOERGER, Ronald Paul
Highlands HS; San Antonio, TX (10-594) Ch, Band; Ensm; JETS; Lat C; VP, Math C; VP, Mu Alpha Theta; NHS; Orch; Sci C; SC; Alg A; COM; Hon Prog; Math A; NMF; NMS; Phy A; Pres A; Sci A; NSPE Schol Fin; All-Area Orch; UIL As Win; *Trinity U; Computing And Information.*

BOESCH, Josette Susan
Lincoln Sr HS; Sioux Falls, SD (10%-450) Band; Dbte Tm; Ger C; NFL; Pres, Sci C; St Stu Congress; Bio A; COM; Most Out; Poet A; Pres A; ARC A; Sci A; Spch A; Gov, GS; 2nd Pl, Naval Sci A; Pres, SD Jr Acad of Sci; Cert of Excel, SD Sci & Engr Fair; 2nd Pl, St Original Oratory; *U of SD; Med.*

BOESCH, Robert Richard
St Peters Prep Sch; Jersey City, NJ (45-275) Pres, Band; A-Ed, Sch P; SC; S-T, Sr Cl; S-T, Jr Cl; S-T, Soph Cl; Hon Prog; Journ A; PTA A; US Marines Musician; *Stevens Inst of Tech; Chem.*

BOETTCHER, Gregory Allen
Merrill Sr HS; Merrill, WI (25-325) Band; Ger C; Sch P; Ski C; Var C; JV, Bkbl; Co-Cpt, Cr-Ctry; Mgr, Ftbl; Tr; *U of Wis Eau Claire; Bus Admin.*

BOETTCHER, Linda Ruth
Lincoln HS; Park Falls, WI;

BOETTNER, William Paul
Cleveland HS; Cleveland, TN (25%-293) CYO; Span C; Swim; Tr; *Elec.*

BOEVER, Bernadette Mary
Estherville HS; Estherville, IA (50-186) Bus C; CYO; Chor; VP, Hmrm; SC; Pres, Var C; Co-Cpt, Bkbl; Golf; Sftbl; Tr; COM; HQn; Most Out.

BOEYE, Cynthia Ellen
Rock Island HS; Rock Island, IL (2-560) AFS; Cpt, Chldr; VP, Chor; Secy, Fr C; Secy, NHS; Ski C; SC; Var C; Secy, Sr Cl; VP, Jr Cl; VP, Soph Cl; JV, Bkbl; Amer Leg A; COM; Sal; High Hons; *Lawrence Col; Psych.*

BOGAN, Cheryl Ann
Colonel Crawford HS; N Robinson, OH (1-156) Ann; Band; Chor; Ensm; Fr C; FTA; NHS; Sch P; COM; VFW A; Yth Fel; All Dist Band.

BOGAN, Dallas Bernard
Manassas HS; Memphis, TN (20-168) Chor; Ensm; VP, Hmrm; SC; Co-Cpt, Bsbl; Co-Cpt, Ftbl; Cpt, Tnns; Hon Prog; Most Out; ROTC A; W Tenn Chorus; Ath A; Ind A A; W Tenn Solo & Ensm; *Fisk U; Mus.*

BOGAN, J David
Sabino HS; Tucson, AZ (20%-364) Chor; Dbte Tm; Ensm; 4H; Spch C; Thes; Wrest; Fin, 4-H C A; Fin, JA A; Fin, Spch A; Debate A; *Pacific Christian Col; Mus.*

BOGANS, Paris Desiree
DuPont Park S D A Sch; Washington, DC; Chldr; Chor; Dbte Tm; Drama; Secy, Hmrm; Bkbl; *Oakwood Col; Dietician.*

BOGART, Arlene Hall
Meridian HS; Meridian, TX (10%-36) Chor; FFA; FHA; A-Ed, Sch P; Sftbl; Tr; Spch A; Secy, Jr Hist C; Co-cpt, Vlbl; *SW Tex St U; Food And Nutrition.*

BOGART, William Russell
Robert E Lee HS; Tyler, TX (5%-600) Pres, Band; Community Yth Symph; NHS; Ed, Sch P; SC; Amer Leg A; Hon Prog; *SMU; Finance.*

BOGE, Marcia Ann
Grand Junction HS; Grand Junction, CO (75-400) Band; FHA; 4H; Orch; Sci C; Var C; COM; 4H A; Pres A; Sci A; Yth Fel; Job's Daughters; Gym; Band A; *U of N Colo; Ed.*

BOGER, Debra Ann
Nw Sr HS; Rock Hill, SC (5-249) Chldr; City Conf; Pres, Hmrm; Pres, InterClub Coun; Pres, Jr Cl; Hon Prog; Yth Fel; Yth Leg; All Area Vlbl; *U of SC; Engr.*

BOGER, Donna Beth
Wade Hampton HS; Greenville, SC; Band; Mjrte; Mod Mus Mas; Span C; MVP, Bkbl; Swim; Tnns; Interlochen Ntl Mus; Yth Fel; Mus Medals; *Mars Hill Col; Mus.*

BOGER, Eric Eugene
Martin Co HS; Stuart, FL (30-500) BC; Order/Arrow; SC; VP, Sr Cl; JV, Bsbl; Co-Cpt, Cr-Ctry; Co-Cpt, Tr; Chem A; *US Naval Acad; Engr.*

BOGER, John William
Charles H Roth HS; Henrietta, NY (26-250) Hmrm; NHS; Order/Arrow; Rptr, Sch P; Ski C; SC; Pres, Var C; Ftbl; Soccer; Wrest; God & Country A; H of F; Most Out; Lacrosse; Ldrship A; Eagle Sct; *Washington & Lee U; Sci.*

BOGGS, Billy Russell
Kress HS; Kress, TX (20-31) BS; FHA; Pres, Sr Cl; VP, Jr Cl; Parl, Soph Cl; Ftbl; Cpt, Tnns; MLS; Pres A; *Texas Tech; Mass Communications.*

BOGGS, Cheryl Kaye
St Albans HS; St Albans, WV (6-550) AFS; Secy, Anchor C; Ann; Drama; Hmrm; Lat C; Math C; Ch, Model UN; Mu Alpha Theta; NHS; Pres, Rainbow; Rptr, Sch P; Ch, SC; Tri-HiY; UN Council; COM; Hon Prog; JA A; Jr Ntl Achv A; *Salem Col; Pub Adm.*

BOGGS, Debra Jo
Pleasure Ridge Park HS; Louisville, KY (34-315) Chldr; FFA; Hmrm; Y-Tns; Bkbl; Sftbl; Tnns; Beauty; Cl Fav; HCt; Spch A; Star Student; Yth Fel; WW; Star Greenhand; Most Considerate; St Champ, Horticulture Demon Con; *E Ky U; Ornamental Horticulture.*

BOGGS, Etta Jean
Stivers Patterson Co-Op HS; Dayton, OH; Chor; Rptr, Hmrm; Sch Achieve Tm; SC; Pres, Bsbl; Pres, Sftbl; COM; Hist A; Math A; Most Out; Poet A; Sci A; Type A; Vlbl; PA A; Reading A; Mus A; *Med.*

BOGGS, Wanda Jean
Spencer HS; Columbus, GA; FTA; Span C; Fin, Miss Ga Tn; Home Ec A; Co Cpt, Drill Tm; Ecology A; Phys Fitness A; *Morehouse Col; Stenographer.*

BOGGUS, Tamara Kyle
Pickens HS; Jasper, GA (2-110) Secy, Band; Secy, BC; Chor; Drama; Pres, Ensm; FHA; FTA; 4H; Span C; Var C; Sftbl; Tnns; COM; Gov Honor Prog; Most Out; Sal; *Jacksonville St U; Mus.*

BOGLE, Carla Jenine
E Prairie HS; E Prairie, MO; A Cap Choir; Stu o-t Mo; Cpt, Flag Corps; WW; *Bus.*

BOGLE, Hope List
Windom Area HS; Windom, MN; Chor; Sftbl; Yth Fel; Gym St Tour; All Around Girl Gym; *Mankato U.*

BOGLE, Jack Marcus
Lewisville HS; Lewisville, TX (7-365) MVP, Band; Ensm; 4H; Math C; Mu Alpha Theta; NHS; Bkbl; All-St Band; St Outst Soloist; *U of Tex at Austin; Chem Engr.*

BOGLE, James Louis
Bayshore HS; Bradenton, FL (10%-38) *Manatee Jr Col; Yth Ministry.*

BOGOSIAN, Joanne
Haverford HS; Havertown, PA; InterAct C; Mjrte; Sftbl; Yth Fel; Talent Show; Ch, Yth Fel; Bowl C; Ed, Yrbk; *Boston U; Lib Arts.*

BOGUCKI, Barbara Anne
Acad of St Aloysius; Jersey City, NJ (10-!04) Math C; NHS; VP, SC; Hon Prog; NEDT; Ed, Yrbk; WW; DAHSS; *Cook Col; Pre-Vet.*

BOHANNON, Brenda Sue
Tulsa Central HS; Tulsa, OK; Band.

BOHANNON, Donna Kay
Ritenour Sr HS; Overland, MO (9-826) Tres, A Cap Choir; Secy, Band; Chldr; Cpt, Mjrte; NHS; Orch; COM; Hon Prog; John Philip Sousa Band A; *William Jewell Col; Mus.*

BOHL, Annette Marie
Bishop Ryan HS; Minot, ND (3-106) Chor; Drama; Sci A; Pom Pon; Reading A; *Minot St U; Mus.*

BOHLENDER, Peggy Marie
Velva Pub Sch; Velva, ND; Bus Mgr, Ann; Secy, Band; FHA; Sci C; *Trinity Bible Inst; Clerical.*

BOHLER, Christopher Lee
Batavia HS; Batavia, IL; Math C; NHS; SC; Co-Cpt, Wrest; Alg A; Hon Prog; Math A; St Scholar; Span Contest; *Monmouth Col; Physics.*

BOHLING, Joyce Eileen
Johnson-Brock HS; Johnson, NE (1-36) Ann; Chor; NHS; Secy, Soph Cl; Mgr, Bkbl; Regent Schol; Val; Tres, Pep C; Win, Schol Ltr; *Midland Lutheran Col; Bus Adm.*

BOHLMANN, Denise Miriam
Valparaiso HS; Valparaiso, IN (9-450) Chor; Drama; NHS; Bkbl; Bio A; Spch A; Vlbl; Glee C A; Fred Waring Camp Schol; *Ind U.*

BOHM, Karen Lynn
Wichita HS Heights; Wichita, KS (75-478) Ann; Chor; Ensm; Rptr, Sch P; *Exceptional Ed.*

BOHN, James Wilford
Crockett HS; Crockett, TX (12-108) Band; Pres, FTA; SC; Bsbl; JV, Bkbl; Ftbl; *Sam Houston St U; Criminology.*

BOHN, Kathy Sue
Waynesboro Area Sr HS; Waynesboro, PA (20%-375) Band; FTA; B Crocker A; Secy, TKP Sorority; 1st Cl Sct; *Elizabethtown Col; Early Childhood Development.*

BOHN, Steven G
Garner-Hayfield Comm HS; Garner, IA (14-68) Band; Order/Arrow; ARC; Var C; Cpt, Bsbl; Cpt, Ftbl; Tr; Cpt, Wrest; God & Country A; Most Out; Order/Arrow A; ARC A; Yth Fel; MVP, Wrest; Eagle Sct Assn; Scuba Diver Cert; *Iowa St U; Biol Sci.*

BOHNE, Nancy Joy
Harold L Richards HS; Oak Lawn, IL (52-645) Drama; FTA; NHS; Span C; Thes; Girl's C; *Moraine Valley Comm Col; Bus.*

BOHNER, Janet Louise
Sheldon Unit District 5 HS; Sheldon, IL (12-24) Sch P; VP, Lib C.

BOHNSACK, Eric Allen
Freeport Sr HS; Freeport, IL (31-558) Bsbl; Bkbl; Ftbl; *U of Ill; Communications.*

BOHY, Denise Lorraine
Bellevue HS; Bellevue, IA (3-66) Co-Ed, Ann; Band; Chor; Ensm; FHA; 4H; Model UN; NHS; Rainbow; Rptr, Sch P; Span C; Spch C; Tr; Amer Leg Orator A; B Crocker A; 4H A; Spch A; Val; Yth Fel; Outst Sr; *U of N Iowa; Eng.*

BOICE, Vickie Audrey
Bluefield HS; Bluefield, WV (71-400) Chldr; Secy, Drama; Fr C; NFL; Spch C; Secy, Thes; Y-Tns; HCt; Hon Prog; Nebr Eng Hons; *Oral Roberts U; Phys.*

BOIRA, Maria Mercedes
Academia Sagrado Corazon; Santurce, PR (9-65) Madrigal; ARC; Rptr, Sch P; Alg A; Sci A; Humanidades A; Stu o-t Month; *Universidad de Barcelona; Biological Sci.*

BOIS, Matthew Scott
Elk Grove HS; Elk Grove Village, IL (145-620) A Cap Choir; Band; Chem C; Chor; Cum Laude Soc; Drama; Ensm; Lat C; Madrigal; NFL; Ski C; Spch C; Thes; Soccer; *Harper Col; Psych.*

BOKENHAGEN, Alan Jesse
Schafer HS; Southgate, MI (50%-350) All Amer Yth; Fr C; Spch C; Y-Tns; Ftbl; I Dare You; Yth Fel; Ldr of Yth Group; Apothegm Mus Group; ARBA Rep of BYF; *Detroit Bible Col; Bible.*

BOKROS, Sandra Jean
Struthers HS; Struthers, OH (20-275) Chldr; Drama; Lat C; NHS; ARC; Spch C; Mgr, Tr; HCt; Hon Prog; Cpt, Gym; *U of SC; Psych.*

BOLAND, Carol Rose
Helena HS; Helena, MT (1-275) Band; Bus C; Ger C; Hmrm; NHS; SC; Val; *U of Mont; Bus Adm.*

BOLANDER, Rebekah Sue
David H Hickman HS; Columbia, MO (11-567) A Cap Choir; Ann; Chor; Fr C; Madrigal; NHS; ARC; Sch P; Pres, Secy, United Methodist Yth; Council On Ministries; Admin Board, Wilkes Blvd UMC; *U of Mo Columbia; Ed.*

BOLBY, Suzanne Elaine
Greater Latrobe HS; Latrobe, PA (15-540) Rptr, Sch P; Sci C; Health Careers C; Ed, Pub Relations Staff; *Westmoreland Cty Comm Col.*

BOLDEN, Arvin Ross
DuSable HS; Chicago, IL (37-300) SC; Industrial Arts A; *Bradley U; Chem.*

BOLDEN, Clyde Nickerson
Shortridge HS; Indianapolis, IN; Secy, Ann; Sch P; Bus Mgr, SC; Cr-Ctry; JV, Tr; F-Ed, Ann; Geom A; *Ball St U; Archt.*

BOLDEN, Cynthia Ann
Stone HS; Wiggins, MS; Band; Chor; FHA; 4H; Y-Tns; Bsbl; Bkbl; Sftbl; Tr; Citz A; 4H A; Best Stu; *Gulfcoast Jr Col.*

BOLDEN, Phyllis
Calumet HS; Chicago, IL; Chor; Drama; Fr C; SC; Hon Prog; Principal Schol; *U of Ill; Med Research.*

BOLDIG, Elizabeth Anne
Summerville HS; Summerville, SC (10%-550) Band; Chor; Secy, Drama; Ger C; NHS; Sch P; NEDT; Pres, Church Yth; Jr Marshal; Church Choir; *Miami U of Ohio; Bus.*

BOLDING, Lisa Renee
Judsonia HS; Judsonia, AR (8-54) A-Ed, Ann; VP, BC; Co-Cpt, Chldr; Chor; FBLA; Rptr, FHA; Tr; Home Ec A; *Harding Col; Home Ec.*

BOLDING, Susan Kay
Judsonia HS; Judsonia, AR (6-35) Ann; BC; Chor; S-T, Drama; FBLA; FHA; Secy, SC; Bkbl; Sftbl; Tr; Beauty; HQn; Miss JHS; Hon Graduate; HR; *Harding Col.*

BOLDT, Joan Elaine
Immanuel HS; Reedley, CA (2-83) CSF; Vlbl; *Reedley Col; Homemaking.*

BOLDT, Mary Jean
Carrollton HS; Saginaw, MI (5-150) Band; Chor; Dbte Tm; Drama; Tres, Mod Mus Mas; NHS; Orch; Sci C; SC; Thes; Mgr, Vlbl; Tres, Church Yth Group; Valparaiso U Schol; *Valparaiso U; Nurs.*

BOLDT, Sherry Lynn
Shawnee Mission W HS; Overland Park, KS (206-620) AFS; Band; Hmrm; Mjrte; SC; Sftbl; Swim; COM; Pres A; Drum Major; Yth Rep, Co Health Advisory Board; *U of Kans; Nurs.*

BOLEN, David Paul
DeSoto HS; DeSoto, TX; Drama; Ger C; Pres, SC; Ftbl; WW; *Baylor U; Pre-Law.*

BOLEN, Michael Taylor
Whitney HS; Whitney, TX (15-70) Co-Cpt, Dbte Tm; Drama; FFA; FHA; Secy, Hmrm; NFL; Spch C; Ftbl; Tnns; COM; Cl Fav; Hon Prog; Spch A; 2nd, St FFA Ldrship Contest; FFA Pub Speaking; 2nd, Regional & Dist UIL Debate; Quarter Fin, St; *N Tex St U; Pol Sci.*

BOLEN, Timothy Richard
Two Harbors HS; Two Harbors, MN (100-220) Chor; COM; Duluth Area Voc-Tech Sch; Car Sales.

BOLES, Beth Amanda
Starmount HS; Boonville, NC (7-204) Ann; FHA; FTA; SC; Sftbl; Tnns; *Wake Forest Col; Law.*

BOLES, Jeff Ray
Bellaire HS; Bellaire, TX (10%-800) Band; Chess C; Hon Prog; Outst, Phys Ed; *Tex A&M Col; Vet Med.*

BOLES, Terri Lynnett
Savannah HS; Savannah, GA (7%-421) BC; Chem C; Chor; Fr C; Lat C; NHS; Phys C; Hist A; Hon Prog; Math A; Sci A; *Clark Col; Computer Prog.*

BOLEY, Darren Rendell
Etowah HS; Attalla, AL; Bsbl; Bkbl.

BOLEY, Kathy Ann
Orrville HS; Orrville, OH; Chor; JA A; Yth Fel; Tres, JA; Hon Camper; *Johnson Bible Col; Bible.*

BOLEY, William Wesley
Adrian HS; Adrian, MI (33%-380) Hmrm; JV, Bsbl; MVP, Sftbl; Tr; Citz A; Kiwanis A; Yth Fel; Amer Stu C; MYF; Sports As; *Bus.*

BOLGER, Cecilia Graham
Country Day Sch o-t Sacred Heart; Philadelphia, PA (1-10) A-Ed, Ann; Chor; Hmrm; NHS; Secy, SC; Bkbl; Hockey; COM; Hist A; Sacristan; Sci A; Good Sportsmanship A; *Ed.*

BOLGER, Eric W
Tartan Sr HS; Oakdale, MN (40-420) Drama; Co-Ed, Sch P; Ski C; Ftbl; Co-Cpt, Tr; ROTC A; *U of Calif; Oceanography.*

BOLHA, Doreen Ann
Struthers HS; Struthers, OH (13-275) FNA; NHS; *Youngstown St U; Med Asst.*

BOLIEAU, Renee Marie
Acad o-t Holy Family; Baltic, CT (4-40) Chldr; Chor; Drama; Tres, SC; Tr; *St Hyacinthe; Vet Med.*

BOLIN, Deborah Ann
Wade Hampton Acad; Orangeburg, SC (13-68) Chor; Fr C; Lat C; Bus Mgr, Sch P; Sci C; Bkbl; Sftbl; Beauty; NEDT; Member, Pep C; *Col of Charleston; Med.*

BOLIN, Tim Lee
Paradise HS; Paradise, CA (100-250) Rptr, Hmrm; Cpt, Bkbl; Ftbl; JV, Golf; Tr; All League Ftbl.

BOLINGER, Beverly Lynn
Alisal HS; Salinas, CA; AFS; Chldr; Hmrm; Ski C; Sftbl; Tnns; CSF; Gym; GAA; *UCSB; Med.*

BOLINGER, Bradley Robert
McConnellsburg HS; McConnellsburg, PA (20%-93) Chor; Fr C; Ch, Hmrm; Rptr, Sch P; SC; Var C; VP, Soph Cl; Co-Cpt, Bkbl; Cr-Ctry; JV, Soccer; Tr; MLS; *Shippensburg St Col; Adm of Justice.*

BOLINGER, James Michael
Alisal HS; Salinas, CA (250-300) A Cap Choir; Rptr, Band; Hmrm; JV, Tnns; Alg A; CSF; Math A; Program Director, Ed Radio Station; *Monterey Penn Col; Elec.*

BOLINSKY, Catherine Suzanne
Marian HS; Tamaqua, PA (18-153) Hmrm; NHS; SC; Mgr, Bsbl; Bkbl; Hockey; COM; Hon Prog; *Scranton U; Med.*

BOLKA, Barbara Sue
Ashland HS; Ashland, WI (2-210) AFS; Band; Hmrm; NHS; SC; Bkbl; Vlbl; Sftbl League; NHS, Band, A's; Prom Court; *Northland Col; Elem Ed.*

BOLKA, Donna Marie
John S Fine HS; Nanticoke, PA (2-347) ARC; SC; Bkbl; Hockey; Sftbl; NEDT; *Nurs.*

BOLL, Claudia Marie
Oak Creek HS; Oak Creek, WI (8-431) Dbte Tm; Drama; NFL; Spch A; Debate As; Pom Pon Sq; *Drama.*

BOLLENBACHER, Amy Joann
Bellmont HS; Decatur, IN (15-310) Chor; Ensm; Fr C; COM; 4H A; Hon Prog; Most Out; Yth Fel; St & Local NISBOVA Mus Contest; Swing Choir Accompanist Medal; Loyal Service Organist A; Fred Meyer's Keyboard Comp Fin Med; *Mus.*

BOLLER, Susan Marie
W Seneca E Sr HS; W Seneca, NY (75-502) Secy, AFS; Hmrm; NHS; Span C; COM; Math A; Appreciation A; *Elim Bible Col; Theology.*

BOLLING, George Richard Jr
Fayette Co HS; Fayette, AL (18-130) Band; Math C; NHS; Sci C; Span C; Bsbl; Bkbl; Ftbl; Golf; Tnns; Ushers, 'F', C'S; *Auburn U; Phar.*

BOLLING, Laurie Grea
N Clayton Sr HS; College Park, GA; Chor; Drama; Sftbl; Swim; Tr; COM; Civitan C; HR; Runner-Up VICA, Skill Contest Nurs; *Pre-Med.*

BOLLING, Leigh Anne
Fayette Co HS; Fayette, AL (5-140) Chldr; NHS; F-Ed, Sch P; Span C; Var C; Span A; *Auburn U; Elem Ed.*

BOLLING, Robert Stephen
Hazlewood HS; Town Creek, AL (2-50) Bus Mgr,
Ann; Tres, BC; Chem C; FFA; FHA; 4H; Hmrm;
F-Ed, Sch P; Pres, Sci C; Phys C; F-Ed, Sch P; Ftbl;
Bio A; Chem A; Cl Fav; Coun of Teach A; 4H A;
MLS; Sci A; Spch A; Type A; Sci Fair Win; *U of N
Ala; Finance.*

BOLLINGBERG, Del Mari
Courtenay Pub HS; Courtenay, ND (1-8) A Cap
Choir; Co-Ed, Ann; Band; Chldr; Secy, Chor;
Drama; Ensm; Sch P; Tres, Soph Cl; Bkbl; Sftbl;
Hon Prog; *Moorhead St Col; Social Work.*

BOLLINGER, Deborah Lin
POAHS; Philipsburg, PA (20-240) Ann; Fr C;
Tnns; Hist A; MLS; Yth Fel; Fr A; Homemaking A;
Philipsburg St General Hospital; Nurs.

BOLLINGER, Joel Robert
Lumberton Sr HS; Lumberton, NC; NHS; Tnns.

BOLLINGER, Kenney Ray
Bethel Baptist Sch; Memphis, TN (2-26) Demolay;
Draughons Col; Acct.

BOLLINGER, Terry Lee
Hayfork HS; Hayfork, CA (15-65) A Cap Choir;
Dbte Tm; Drama; Pres, FBLA; FFA; Madrigal; SC;
JV, Bkbl; JV, Tr; VofDEM; All St Hon Choir;
Leader, Christ Ambassadors; *Bethany Bible Col;
Mus.*

BOLLS, Linda Denise
Belgrade HS; Belgrade, MT (10%-75) A Cap Choir;
FBLA; VP, 4H; Span C; Swim; Tnns; 4H A; Dist
Win, Ntl Piano Playing Aud; *Harding Col; Bio.*

BOLSTER, Kimberly
Neshaminy-Langhorne HS; Langhorne, PA
(56-735) Chor; Hmrm; VP, NHS; Rptr, Sch P; Ski
C; St Stu Congress; SC; World Affairs C; Pres, Jr
Cl; Bkbl; Tnns; Amer Leg A; *U of Ky; International
Relations.*

BOLTON, Clifton Kent
Nederland HS; Nederland, TX (60-463) AFS;
Tres, CYO; Dbte Tm; Parl, Drama; Key C; NFL;
Spch C; SC; Thes; Co-Cpt, Ftbl; Swim; Archt
Drafting A; *Tulane U; Archt.*

BOLTON, Deanna Rae
Wheelersburg HS; Wheelersburg, OH (60-180)
Band; Chldr; Chor; Lat C; Tr; Yth Fel; JCL; Chldr
A; GAA; Pep C; Schol A; *U of Ky; Phys Therapy.*

BOLTON, Paula Marie
Grand Co HS; Moab, UT; Band; Chor; Drama;
FBLA; S-T, FHA; Tr; Beauty; Lion A; ARC A;
Type A; *Northwest Col; Christian Ed.*

BOLTON, Selwyn Milton
Munford HS; Munford, AL; BC; Drama; 4H; SC;
Ftbl; 4H A; Kiwanis A; *Jacksonville St U.*

BOLTON, Susan Carol
Niwot HS; Longmont, CO; Semi-Fin, GS; Hmrm;
Ski C; SC; JV, Ftbl; Sftbl; Drill Tm; *CSU; General.*

BOLTON, Susan Hazel
Weville HS; Monroe, LA (33%-200) Chor; Tnns;
Tnns As; 2nd, Solo Festival; Hon Choir; *Centenary
Col; Mus.*

BOLTON, Valinda Ann
Westbury HS; Houston, TX (66-614) Anchor C;
Dbte Tm; FHA; Mjrte; Secy, NFL; NHS; *Baylor U;
Oral Communications.*

BOLZ, Bradly Steven
Camdenton R-3 HS; Camdenton, MO (33%-214)
Band; Chem C; Ensm; 4H; Math C; Mod Mus Mas;
NHS; Sci C; Var C; Bsbl; Wrest; Lions C St Band; *U
of Mo; Vet Med.*

BOMAN, Gary Maurice
Topeka HS; Topeka, KS; Hmrm; Bsbl; Ftbl.

BOMBERGER, Elam Douglas
Eastern Mennonite HS; Harrisonburg, VA (1-88)
Chor; Fr C; Pres, NHS; Rptr, Sch P; SC; Pres, Jr Cl;
Cr-Ctry; JV, Soccer; Tr; COM; NMS; *Goshen Col;
Mus.*

BONACCI, Charleen Rita
Central HS; Omaha, NE (25%-514) Chor; Drama;
Fr C; FTA; Ger C; Mgr, Bsbl; Mgr, Bkbl; Yth Fel;
Girls Wrest Aux; *Hasting Col; Teaching.*

BONADIE, Daune Sylvia
Wintrop Jr HS; Brooklyn, NY; *Syracuse U; Social
Studies.*

BONADIE, Robert Errol
Wintrop Jr HS; Brooklyn, NY; *Hunter Col; Math.*

BONAPARTE, Ruth Lydia
Lincoln HS; Portland, OR (1-250) Chor; Commu-
nity Yth Symph; Ntl Yth Conf; Orch; ARC; VP,
SC; Jr Cl; Tres, Soph Cl; Bkbl; Ftbl; JV, Soccer;
Sftbl; Swim; Tnns; COM; Hon Prog; Interlochen
Ntl Mus; Math A; Most Out; Rotary A; Spch A;
Ntl Math Test; Pep C; Russian C; Korchinska A;
LINE, Jr Girls; Harp A; Secy, Fresh Cl; Young
Amer A; Girl's League; *Sweet Briar Col; Law.*

BONAR, Carol Jean
Brooke HS; Wellsburg, WV (70-478) Ed, Ann;
Band; Chor; Drama; Fr C; Secy, Hmrm; Madrigal;
Mjrte; NHS; Ski C; Thes; Tri-HiY; Swim; Tr; *W Va
U; Mus Ed.*

BONAR, Gregg Alan
Shadyside HS; Shadyside, OH; BS; Chor; HiY;
NHS; Pres, Jr Cl; Ftbl; Tr; Amer Leg A; Church Jr
Deacon; Cl Graduating Marshal.

BONARDI, Darlene Rose
Secaucus HS; Secaucus, NJ (7-164) NHS; SC;
Sftbl; Cpt, Tnns; Hon Prog; Tri-Co A, Sftbl; Tnns
A; *Seton Hall U.*

BOND, Amy Laverne
Santa Rosa HS; Santa Rosa, CA; FBLA; FFA; Key
C; FFA Schol; Acad Excel, A's; *Biola Col; Psych.*

BOND, Beverly Browning
Woodford Co HS; Versailles, KY (59-245) Ann;
Chor; Fr C; Hmrm; Sch P; Golf; Yth Fel; Bkbl
Statistician; Pep C; Hon Choir; Copy Ed, Yrbk; *W
Ky U; Bus Adm.*

BOND, Carol Donna
Northwood HS; Shreveport, LA (33%-180) A Cap
Choir; Chor; NHS; SC; Sftbl; Hon Prog; Chaplain,
SC; Superior, Chor Mus Festival; *La Col; Mus.*

BOND, Cheryl Denise
Lake Highlands HS; Dallas, TX (375-701) S-T, A
Cap Choir; Tres, Drama; Hmrm; Thes; Y-Tns; Phys
Fitness A; *Richland Jr Col; Spch & Hearing Ther-
apy.*

BOND, Denise Renee
Columbia Adventist Acad; Battle Ground, WA
(8-66) A Cap Choir; Band; Chor; Cum Laude Soc;
Ensm; Ed, Sch P; VP, SC; Co-Cpt, Bsbl; Cpt, Bkbl;
Semi-Fin, Golf; Semi-Fin, Tnns; Hon Prog; Journ
A; Most Out; ARC A; Star Student; *Pacific Union
Col; Med Secy.*

BOND, Edythe Elaine
Clairemont HS; San Diego, CA (5-700) Pres,
Drama; Madrigal; NHS; Pol Sci C; COM; Hon
Prog; 100% Life Membership, CSF; Top School;
Dept Hon As; Best Sr Actress; *San Diego St U;
Psych.*

BOND, Erik Lyons
St Louis Ctry Day Sch; St Louis, MO (40%-60)
Hmrm; Model UN; Pres, SC; UN Council; Co-Cpt,
Ftbl; NMF; NMS; Yth Foundation; MVP, Ftbl;
Disciplinary Committee; *Brown U; Med.*

BOND, LaShonna Joevette
Los Angeles HS; Los Angeles, CA; Chldr; Hmrm;
Jr Miss Pagent; Bsbl; Beauty; B Crocker A; I Dare
You; Swtht; *UCLA; Law.*

BOND, Lauren Elaine
Elbert Co Comp HS; Elberton, GA (8-412) Anchor
C; Ann; Secy, BC; Chldr; Secy, Fr C; Rptr, Hmrm;
Math C; NHS; SC; World Affairs C; Secy, Soph Cl;
Bkbl; Coun of Teach A; NEDT.

BOND, Lynette Lorraine
Bertie Sr HS; Windsor, NC (1-340) Ed, Ann; BC;
Tres, Fr C; Sci C; SC; Gov Honor Prog; Hon Prog;
Bus Drivers C; WW; *Howard U; Chem.*

BOND, Marion Sue
Amarillo HS; Amarillo, TX (10%-650) A Cap
Choir; AFS; Chldr; Chor; Hmrm; Cl Fav; Kiwanis
A; Ken C; *Tex A&M U; Pre-Med.*

BOND, Travis
Englewood HS; Chicago, IL; Ensm; Phy A.

BONDS, Cynthia Darlene
Gadsden HS; Gadsden, AL (200-325) Band; FTA;
Gadsden St Jr Col.

BONDS, Denise Juanita
Holy Family HS; Birmingham, AL (6-35) Band;
Tres, Fr C; Rptr, Hmrm; SC; *U of Ala; Obstetrics.*

**BONDURANT,
Edward Bradford**
Mountain Brook HS; Mountain Brook, AL
(62-375) Band; NHS; Orch; Rptr, Sch P; Hon Prog;
Auburn U; Archt.

BONDURANT, Randall Joseph
Mountain Brook HS; Mountain Brook, AL; Span
C; Ftbl; Var Ltr, Ftbl; *Harding Col; Vet Med.*

BONE, James Dale
Frankfort HS; Ridgeley, WV (5-151) NHS; Var C;
Co-Cpt, Cr-Ctry; Mgr, Ftbl; COM; Math Tm; WW;
Potomac St Col; Computers.

BONE, Kimberly Jean
Mayfield HS; Mayfield, KY (12-156) VP, Band;
BC; Rptr, Soph Cl; Cl Fav; *W Ky St U; Chem.*

BONE, Pamela Kay
Wellston HS; Wellston, OK (5-51) A Cap Choir;
F-Ed, Ann; Band; Chor; Drama; Ensm; Pres, FHA;
4H; Rptr, Sch P; Sci C; SC; Y-Tns; Sftbl; Amer Leg
A; COM; Citz A; Journ A; JA A; Mus A; Superin-
tendents HR; Candidate, Sch Swtht; *Bus.*

BONEBRIGHT, Cecil Everett
Kelly Walsh HS; Casper, WY (100-400) Drama;
Thes; Math A; Bowl A; Funny Person A; *Ntl Col of
Bus; Higher Acct.*

BONETTI, Edward Paul
Warwick Veterans Mem HS; Warwick, RI (30-371)
French NHS; Ger C; NHS; JV, Bsbl; Tr; Hon Prog;
St Schol; *U of RI; Engr.*

BONEY, Marsherry
Cooley HS; Detroit, MI (2-30) Citz A; *U of Detroit; Bus.*

BONGIOVANNI, Peter Joseph
Mayfield HS; Mayfield Heights, OH (15-570)
Band; NHS; Ski C; NMS; Principal's List; *Kenyon
Col; Med.*

BONGOAT, Caroline Laurence
Muskogee HS; Muskogee, OK; AFS; Chor; Drama;
Fr C; Ger C; SC; MVP, Swim; St Champ, St Re-
cord, Swim; Yth For Understanding, Foreign Exc;
Mus.

BONILLA, Primo Steve
Whittier Christian HS; Whittier, CA; A Cap Choir;
Band; Chess C; Chor; Drama; Orch; Cpt, Bsbl; Cpt,
Bkbl; Cpt, Ftbl; Sftbl; Wrest; Gifted Children Prog.

BONILLA, Sheryll Dean
Maryknoll HS; Honolulu, HI (4-115) Pres, Drama;
Pres, Math C; NHS; Rptr, Sch P; Pres, Spch C;
Math A; NEDT; Sci A; Spch A; Yng Men's Inst
Bicentennial Essay A; Grnd Priz, Pearl Harbor Bi-
cent Cont.

BONINE, Lee Allison
McCluer N HS; Florissant, MO (32-792) Band;
Yth Foundation; Pep Band; Candystriper; *Baylor
U; Law.*

BONK, John M
Central Jersey Christian HS; Asbury Park, NJ (4-7)
Bus Mgr, Ann; Chor; VP, Fr C; Hmrm; Sch P; Span
C; SC; Tres, Sr Cl; Tres, Jr Cl; Tnns; Hon Prog;
Math A; Spiritual Growth A; *The Kings Col; Journ.*

BONKER, Dwayne Eugene
Albia Community HS; Albia, IA (27-172) Band;
Ensm; Cpt, Bkbl; Hon Bands; Mus Contest; HR;
Air Force.

BONNELL, Melanie D
Flora Township HS; Flora, IL (68-154) Chor; Fr C;
Pres, Hmrm; Pres, Y-Tns; Vlbl; *Sou Ill U; Law.*

BONNELL, William Charles
Los Angeles Baptist HS; Sepulveda, CA (35-82)
Septumvir, Chess C.

BONNER, Craig
Princeton HS; Sharonville, OH (280-750) Bkbl;
Ftbl; *U of Cincinnati; Archt.*

BONNER, Cynthia Vanessa
Sussex Central HS; Sussex, VA (8-186) Ann; Pres,
BC; Co-Cpt, Chldr; Hmrm; Span C; SC; Pres, Sr Cl;
Citz A; HCt; *Howard U; Phys Therapy.*

BONNER, James Lincoln
Alma J Brown HS; Grambling, LA (10-52) All Amer Yth; Co-Cpt, Band; Chem C; Chor; Drama; FBLA; FTA; VP, 4H; Lit Ral; Orch; VP, Sci C; SC; Var C; Bsbl; Ftbl; Soccer; Sftbl; Swim; Tnns; Beauty; Bio A; COM; Chem A; 4H A; Hist A; Math A; Most Out; NEDT; Order/Arrow A; Sci A; Yth Fel; Cpt, MVP, Bkbl; Grambling Col; Biol.

BONNER, Kathryn Elizabeth
Haddonfield Mem HS; Haddonfield, NJ (46-232) Hmrm; Span C; Var C; JV, Bkbl; Hockey; JV, Sftbl.

BONNER, Marcia Kay
Waynesboro Central HS; Waynesboro, MS (25%-99) Ann; BC; Drama; S-T, Ger C; Pres, SC; Y-Tns; Cl Fav; HCt; WW; Jones Co Jr Col.

BONNER, Michael Allen
Pasadena HS; Pasadena, TX (7-572) A Cap Choir; Chor; Ensm; InterAct C; Key C; Madrigal; Math C; Mu Alpha Theta; NHS; Span C; Bsbl; JV, Bkbl; Ftbl; Sftbl; FCA; Acad Excel A; Sounds of Salutation; Sports As; UIL Choir, Spch As.

BONNET, Margie Dawn
Leander HS; Leander, TX (15%-140) Secy, Band; FHA; Mjrte; NHS; Span C; Tnns; COM; HCt; Hon Prog; Type A; Band Swtht Nom; HR; Stage Band; Sam Houston St U; Elem Ed.

BONNEVIE, Theresa Annette
Livermore Falls HS; Livermore Falls, ME (12-94) CYO; Commercial C; Fr C; FHA; Hmrm; SC; Hockey; Tr; Husson Col; Executive Secy.

BONNEY, Deborah Lynne
Butler Area Sr HS; Butler, PA; Band; Butler Co Comm Col; Acct.

BONO, Cheryl Ann
Guthrie HS; Guthrie, OK (7-190) Chor; Ensm; Madrigal; NHS; Span C; Citz A; Outst Eng A; Tri St Mus A; Dist Mus A.

BONO, Richard Wayne
South Shelby HS; Shelbina, MO (5-99) CYO; Sch P; Var C; Pres, Soph Cl; Ftbl; NEDT; Sentinel FFA; Schol A; Art A; U of Mo at Columbia; Law.

BONSALL, Laurie Margaret
Dunlap Comm Sch; Dunlap, IA (7-58) Ann; Band; Chor; Fr C; Madrigal; NHS; ARC; Sch P; Bkbl; Swim; Band A; Chor A; Swim A; NHS A; Iowa St U; Acct.

BONURA, Denise Marie
St Charles Borromeo HS; Destrehan, LA (10%-82) BC; CYO; Chldr; Chor; Hmrm; Key C; SC; COM; Southeastern La U; Phys Therapy.

BOOE, Laura Jean
Alamosa HS; Alamosa, CO (9-200) Rptr, 4H; JV, Bkbl; Adams St Col; Phys Therapy.

BOOHER, Diana Joy
Sacred Heart Acad; Springfield, IL; Drama; Sodality; B Crocker A; NMS; NEDT; St Scholar; Yth Fel; Sup, Ill St Lat Contest; Ill Wesleyan U; Fine Arts.

BOOK, Cynthia Mae
Belle Plaine HS; Belle Plaine, KS (3-68) Ed, Ann; Band; Chor; Ensm; Rptr, FHA; Madrigal; Mjrte; Rainbow; Co-Ed, Sch P; Tr; Sch A; TS; Sch St Hon Stu; WW; Mus A's; SW Kans Col; Mus Ed.

BOOK, Stella Marie
Block HS; Jonesville, LA (9-90) Fr C; Lit Ral; Tr; Mu Sigma Hon Soc; Northeast La U; Med.

BOOKER, Angela Renae
King William HS; King William, VA (10-85) Cpt, Chldr; Chor; Drama; FFA; GS; 4H; Hmrm; Semi-Fin, Jr Miss Pa; F-Ed, Lit Mag; A-Ed, Sch P; Sci C; Secy, SC; Co-Cpt, Bkbl; Mgr, Tr; 4H A; H of F; HQn; MLS; Q&S A; WW; Sch Merit A; Miss Personality, Jr Miss Pageant; Va Commonwealth U; Early Childhood Ed.

BOOKER, Beverly Ann
Plainfield HS; Plainfield, NJ (10%-490) Ann; Mgr, Band; NHS; Pres, Jr Cl; Parl, Band; PTS; Principal's Advisory Committee; Tuskegee Inst; Vet Med.

BOOKER, Diedra Divon
Lanier Jr HS; Houston, TX; Chldr; Madrigal; NHS; Citz A; Lib Serv; Service A Chor; Mus Lib.

BOOKER, Dorothy Elizabeth
Kashmere Sr HS; Houston, TX (5-480) Tres, A Cap Choir; Tres, Chor; Drama; Ensm; Fr C; Thes; COM; ROTC A; Mus.

BOOKER, Grace Paulette
Kashmere Sr HS; Houston, TX; Fr C; Hmrm; NHS; Span C; SC; Citz A; U of N Iowa; Psych.

BOOKER, Jennie Lee
McKinley Sr HS; Washington, DC; Band; Hmrm; SC; Up Bound; JA A; Citz A; Law.

BOOKER, Julia Ann
St Albans HS; St Albans, WV; Chor; JV, Bkbl; MVP, Tr; COM; Gov Honor Prog; Most Out; Yth Fel; W Va St U.

BOOKER, Kelly Kaye
Heritage HS; Littleton, CO; Band; Chor; Pepperdine U; Mus.

BOOKER, Kenneth Charles
Douglass HS; Memphis, TN; ARC; Var C; Bsbl; Ftbl; Sftbl; Tr; ROTC A; Ath A; Stu o-t Month; Ldrship A; Dartmouth Col; Chem Engr.

BOOKER, Kenneth Lane
Flint Nw HS; Flint, MI (70-380) Ferris St Col; Phar.

BOOKER, Mark Edward
Poughkeepsie HS; Poughkeepsie, NY; A Cap Choir; CYO; Up Bound; Cpt, Ftbl; Tnns; Alg A; Math A; Sci A; Church Choir; Monitor; MVP, Ftbl; Disc Jockey C; General Achievement Ftbl & Tr As; PA; Vassar Col; Bus Adm.

BOOKER, Ollie LaVern
David Starr Jordan HS; Los Angeles, CA (93-384) Chor; Dbte Tm; Ensm; Hmrm; Jr Miss Pagent; Orch; SC; Var C; Tr; Hon Prog; PTA A; Chor A; Principal's HR; Calif St U; Elem Ed.

BOOKER, Shouneille Denise
S Oak Cliff HS; Dallas, TX; Cpt, Tr; Prairie View Col; Phys Ed.

BOOKER, Vanessa Denise
McKinley Sr HS; Washington, DC; Co-Cpt, Band; Citz A; Val; Scholastic A; Attendance A; UCLA; Drama.

BOOKHARD, Evelyn Pearl
Richmond Hill HS; Richmond Hill, NY; Secy, All Amer Yth; Chor; Cpt, Math C; Swim; Tr; Queens Col; Archt.

BOOKS, Elmer L
Annville-Cleona HS; Annville, PA (70-160) Var C; Bsbl; Cpt, Bkbl; Tr; MVP, Bkbl; Shepherd Col; Acct.

BOOMGARDEN, Brian Lee
Forreston HS; Forreston, IL (6-74) Ger C; NHS; Ftbl; Tr; COM; HCt; Highland Comm Col; Law Enforcement.

BOOMSMA, Lisa Marie
Hitchcock HS; Hitchcock, SD (3-21) Band; Ensm; FHA; Var C; VP, Soph Cl; Bkbl; Sftbl; Tr; All Conf, All St, Bkbl; 1st, Conf Shotput; Northern Col; Coaching.

BOONE, Daniel Allan
Spring Woods Sr HS; Houston, TX (10%-510) JETS; Math C; Mu Alpha Theta; Hon Prog; Texas A&M U; Aerospace Engr.

BOONE, Gwendolyn
Gumberry HS; Gumberry, NC; Ann; Chor; Fr C; FHA; Tres, Jr Cl; Sftbl; King's Col; Acct.

BOONE, Jodie Lynn
Luverne HS; Luverne, MN (13-140) A Cap Choir; Band; S-T, Chor; Ensm; FHA; FTA; Madrigal; NHS; Rptr, Sch P; Span C; SC; Bkbl; Tr; Hon Prog; Pres A; Ensm A's; Dorian Band Festival; Augustana Band Festival; Morningside Col; Nurs.

BOONE, Linda Marie
Highland HS; Ewing, MO (5-130) Band; Drama; Ensm; Pres, 4H; NHS; Cpt, Sch Achieve Tm; VP, Sci C; Bkbl; Beauty; Bio A; COM; Chem A; 4H A; Regent Schol; Sci A; Spch A; Psych, Art, Pep, C'S; All Conf Band; Secy, GScts; VP, Media Center Assn; GSct, Art, A's; NE Mo St U; Botany.

BOONE, Nancy Darlene
Timken Sr HS; Canton, OH; A Cap Choir; Band; Dbte Tm; Drama; Lat C; ARC; Ski C; Spch C; Mgr, Tr; Bio A; Citz A; Hon Prog; ARC A; Sci A; Yth Fel; Booster C; Bowl A; Candlelight Yth Corps; Med Explorers; Schol A; Case Western Reserve U; Bio-Chem.

BOONE, Rebecca Rowena
Mary Brantley Smiley HS; Houston, TX (5-461) NHS; Bio A; COM; Hist A; Sci A; Eng A.

BOONE, Sheri Lynn
Atlanta HS; Atlanta, TX; Ann; Ensm; A-Ed, Sch P; DARGCA; Journ A; Q&S A; Rptr, DECA; Outst Art Stu; N Tex St U; Commercial Art.

BOORSE, Richard Charles
N Penn Sr HS; Lansdale, PA (100-900) Hmrm; Co-Ch, Ski C; Tr; Lafayette Col; Pre-Med.

BOOS, Dana Marie
Bedford Sr HS; Temperance, MI (1-530) Fr C; Ski C.

BOOTES, Deborah Mae
Wilburton HS; Wilburton, OK (15%-62) Bus C; Chor; Secy, FBLA; FHA; GS; 4H; NHS; Rptr, Sr Cl; Rptr, Jr Cl; Hon Prog; Eastern OSC; RN.

BOOTH, Catalina Faye
Baker HS; Baker, LA (3-374) BC; Secy, FTA; GS; Mu Alpha Theta; Secy, NHS; Rptr, Tri-HiY; Mu Sigma; VP, Pepsters; Jr Cabinet; Sch Historian; LSU; Commercial Art.

BOOTH, Charlotte Lorraine
Tuscaloosa HS; Tuscaloosa, AL; Anchor C; Chldr; VP, Fr C; FHA; Lat C; SC; Pres, Tri-HiY; Sftbl; Cl Fav; Yth Leg; U of Ala.

BOOTH, Daniel Todd
Moon Sr HS; Coraopolis, PA (54-442) Band; Ensm; Ger C; Order/Arrow; COM; Hon Prog; Order/Arrow A; Top 5% Ntl Merit; Pre-Law.

BOOTH, Emilyn Janice
Santa Fe HS; Alachua, FL; Band; BC; Sftbl; Citz A; Lee Col; Med Tech.

BOOTH, Gwendolyn Childs
Fupora HS; Eupora, MS (10%-84) Ann; Secy, Band; Pres, BC; Pres, Chor; Pres, FTA; Rptr, Hmrm; Mjrte; F-Ed, Sch P; Rptr, SC; Pres, Sr Cl; S-T, Jr Cl; COM; Miss St U; Mus Ed.

BOOTH, James Philip
Lakeland Sr HS; Lakeland, FL (20%-1200) Band; Community Yth Symph; Ensm; Orch; Amer Leg A; Hon Prog; Most Out; All St Band; Central Fla Select Symph Band; District Solo, Ensm As; All Co Hons Band; USF; Hist.

BOOTH, Jean Ann
Whitney HS; Whitney, TX; Chor; Tres, FHA; S-T, Span C; Bio A; Drill Tm.

BOOTH, Jerry Dwayne
Burges HS; El Paso, TX (249-900) A Cap Choir; Chor; Dbte Tm; Drama; Ensm; Madrigal; Wrest; Pres, Church Yth; Tex Tech U; Forestry.

BOOTH, Judith Kathleen
Jackson Central Merry HS; Jackson, TN (29-489) Chldr; ARC; Y-Tns; SW Col at Memphis; Med.

BOOTH, Kathyrn Anne
Farwell HS; Farwell, TX (15-44) All Amer Yth; Band; FHA; Cpt, Bkbl; Fin, Golf; MVP, Tr; Beauty; HCt; Most Out; Type A; Yth Fel; MVP, Bkbl; Fin, Tr; All-Amer HS Bkbl; Wayland Baptist Col; Phys Ed.

BOOTH, Marie Ann
Christoval HS; Christoval, TX; VP, BC; Fin, Dbte Tm; NHS; Spch C; SC; Bkbl; Tr; MLS; Val; WW; 1st Dist Persuasive Speaking; Hon Men, Dist Sci Fair; HR; Angelo St Col.

BOOTH, Michael Leland
Fort Lauderdale HS; Fort Lauderdale, FL (5%-500) Band; NHS; Cr-Ctry; Tr.

BOOTH, Nina Rochelle
Pleasure Ridge Park HS; Louisville, KY (10-29) BC; Fr C; FBLA; Ger C; GS; Hmrm; Ed, Sch P; Ed, SC; Secy, St Cl; Journ A; JA A; Fin, Ky Ntl Teenager Pageant; Mo On Sch Calendar; WW; U of Ky; Acct.

BOOTH, Sharon Lee
Tecumseh HS; New Carlisle, OH (50-400) AFS; Chor; Drama; Span C; Teacher.

BOOTH, Shelby Jane
Northside HS; Roanoke, VA (25%-500) Fr C; 4H; *Interior Design.*

BOOTH, Stephanie Anquinetta
Humboldt HS; Humboldt, TN (33%-190) Band; BC; Chldr; Chor; Mjrte; *U of Tenn; Modeling.*

BOOTH, William Thomas
Dilley HS; Dilley, TX (3-40) Ann; FFA; NHS; Sch P; Span C; Var C; Bkbl; JV, Ftbl; MVP, Tnns; Tr; MYF; *Texas U; Bus.*

BOOTHE, Cynthia Denise
San Bernardino HS; San Bernardino, CA; Chor; FTA; Bkbl; Sftbl; Kiwanis A; Swan's Debutante; *Cosmetology.*

BOOTHE, Erwin Arevine
Wheaton HS; Wheaton, MO (3-34) FFA; SC; Bkbl; Cr-Ctry; Tr; Spch A; FFA Greenhand A; FFA Chptr Farmer A; Tr A; *U of Mo; Engr.*

BOOTHE, James Edward
San Bernardino HS; San Bernardino, CA (56-400) Chor; SC; Y-Tns; Bsbl; Bkbl; Tr; *San Diego St Col; Ed.*

BOOTHE, Judy LaRue
Hazen HS; Hazen, AR (18-45) FBLA; FFA; Pres, FHA; F-Ed, Sch P; VP, FHA; Asst Ed, Sch P; Co Miss Fluffy Rice; Miss Congeniality Qn; *Miss U for Women; Journ.*

BOOTHE, Kathryn Elaine
Lincoln Jr-Sr HS; Milwaukee, WI (20-24) A Cap Choir; Chor; Rptr, Hmrm; COM; Citz A; Attendance A; *Health.*

BOOZER, Faith Ann
Concord Sr HS; Concord, NC; AFS; VP, Chor; *NC St U; Interior Decorating.*

BOPPE, Terri Lee
John Handley HS; Winchester, VA (85-275) Anchor C; Chor; Hmrm; SC; Secy, Jr Cl; Secy, Soph Cl; *Madison U; Eng.*

BORBON, Peggy Sue
Arroyo HS; Elmonte, CA; Chor; Model UN; Rainbow; Bsbl; Bkbl; Sftbl; Citz A; Hon Prog; MLS; Most Out; Yth Fel; Yth Leg.

BORCHELT, Mark David
Solon HS; Solon, OH (3-300) Ensm; VP, Math C; Secy, Mod Mus Mas; Mu Alpha Theta; NHS; Orch; Cr-Ctry; Tr; Hon Prog; Math A; Eagle Sct; *Wittenberg U; Pre-Med.*

BORCHERDING,
Dennis Delbert
Guttenberg Comm HS; Guttenberg, IA (2-89).

BORCHERS, Amy Lynne
Spring Lake HS; Spring Lake, MI (55-185) Tr; *Western U; Math.*

BORCHERS, Mark Eugene
Holstein Comm HS; Holstein, IA (12-48) Bus Mgr, Ann; Band; Chor; 4H; Madrigal; Bkbl; Ftbl; Tr; 4H A; Math A; MLS; Most Out; WW; *Iowa St U; Agr.*

BORDAS, Theresa Anne
W Springfield HS; Springfield, VA; Bus C; Ch, CYO; Tres, FBLA; FHA; Soccer; Tnns; *Northern Va Comm Col; Human Services.*

BORDELON, Laurie Ann
Thoreau HS; Thoreau, NM; Ann; CYO; NHS; Sci C; Sci A; Eng A; *Eng.*

BORDEN, Sara Elizabeth
Fort Stockton HS; Ft Stockton, TX; Band; Ensm; JV, Tr; Hon Prog; S-T, Yth Fel; 1st Div, St Solo & Ensm; *Trinity U; Mus.*

BORDERS, Katherine Almeda
Jacksonville Episcopal HS; Jacksonville, FL (37-120) Ann; Chor; Drama; Ensm; Lat C; Tres, Thes; Var C; Mgr, Wrest; Magna Cum Laude; Pep C; Hosts & Hostesses; Dist Lat Contest; *Stetson U; Psych.*

BORDERS, Mary Jane
Holy Rosary Acad; Louisville, KY (2-86) Band; Chor; Drama; Fr C; Hmrm; NFL; SC; Hon Prog; JA A; Ntl HS A for Excellence; HR; Secy, JA; *Western Ky U; Humanities.*

BORDLEE, Stephen John
Ozark Adventist Acad; Gentry, AR (15-74) Band; Chor; Ensm; Bkbl; Tnns; *Southwestern Adventist Col; Bio.*

BORDMAN, Stephanie Eileen
Moreau HS; Hayward, CA (15-383) Band; NHS; *U of Arizona at Tucson; Nurs.*

BORDSEN, Kari Lee
Sutter HS; Sutter, CA (3-111) Bus Mgr, Ann; Parl, FHA; Sci C; Ski C; Span C; Pres, Soph Cl; Hockey.

BORDSON, Gayla Chris
Monta Vista HS; Cupertino, CA (15-500) Band; Chor; Dbte Tm; Drama; Fr C; Sch Achieve Tm; Spch C; Tres, SC; CSF; COM; Citz A; Spch A; Most Outst Mus.

BORELLI, Christine Mary Ann
Citrus HS; Inverness, FL (11-250) Secy, NHS; Span C; Sftbl; WW; Outst Span Stu; *Bus Adm.*

BOREN, Carolyn Joy
Warren Co Sr HS; McMinnville, TN (1-25) Sftbl; Ping-Pong A; Sch Rep, Co Algebra Contest; *David Lipscomb Col; Algebra.*

BOREN, James Worthington
W A Berry HS; Birmingham, AL (10%-360) Hmrm; Key C; NHS; Bsbl; Co-Cpt, Ftbl; Hon Prog; Sci A; *U of Ala; Ed.*

BORGER, Brenda Carolyn
Freeburg Comm HS; Freeburg, IL (8-120) FTA; NHS; Sci C; Var C; Arch; Tr; Mgr, Vlbl; Ecology C; Ath School; *Ariz St U; Health Sci.*

BORGER, Debra Lynn
Abraham Lincoln HS; Council Bluffs, IA (30-290).

BORGER, Mark Wayne
Rocky Grove HS; Franklin, PA (66%-140) Hmrm; NHS; Co-Ed, Sch P; Ski C; Var C; Bsbl; Golf; Tnns; Math A; Yth Fel; *Allegheny Col; Math.*

BORGER, Mary Jane
St Henry Sch; St Henry, OH (20-89) Band; Secy, CYO; FHA; FTA; Math C; NHS; Sch P; Amer Leg A; Scholastic Achv As; Amer Hist, Biol & Amer Govt; *Wright St U.*

BORGER, Robert Elden
Luther Burbank HS; Sacramento, CA; AFS; Demolay; CSF; *Engr Archt.*

BORGES, Evan Christopher
Robinson HS; San Juan, PR (4-47) Hist A; NEDT; *Stanford U; Bus Adm.*

BORGES, Josue E
Miguel Melendez Munoz; Bayamon, PR; FFA; ARC; Sch P; Sci C; Tres, Span C; Span NHS; SC; Fin, Bsbl; Fin, Bkbl; Semi-Fin, Sftbl; COM; Cl Fav; Hist A; NMF; Sci A; Eng A; *Mayaguez Tech Col; Engr.*

BORGHI, Christine
Dwight-Englewood Sch; Englewood, NJ; Chor; Girls Phys Ed A; Ath Assn; Choral C; Gym Ath As; Dnce Wrkshp; Sprng Musc; Ntl Fed of Mus Festivals Certs; Bell Chor; Dnce Comp; Fencing Tm; *Theatre Arts.*

BORGMAN, Elizabeth Ann
Clear Lake Comm HS; Clear Lake, IA; Band; Lat C; Tri-HiY; Tr; *N Iowa Area Comm Col; Med Asst.*

BORGMAN, Patricia Dawn
Northgate HS; Walnut Creek, CA (85-425) Bank of Amer A; Hon Prog; Art School; Fin, Miss Walnut Creek Pageant; *U of Calif; Liberal Arts.*

BORGNA, Lori Donna
Notre Dame HS; Salinas, CA (25-101) CYO; Chor; Secy, 4H; Model UN; NHS; A-Ed, Sch P; Ski C; Span C; St Stu Congress; SC; 4H A; Hon Prog; Ntl Achv Schol; *Santa Barbara Col; Phar.*

BORGSCHATZ, Dawn Jean
Wanamingo Public HS; Wanamingo, MN (25%-42) Band; Chldr; Chor; Drama; Ensm; FHA; Secy, 4H; NHS; Secy, SC; Pres, Jr Cl; Tr; 4H A; HCt; Pres A; Type A; Tr A; 4-H As; *Mus.*

BORGSTADT, Janet Lea
Hillcrest HS; Springfield, MO (15-316) Chldr; Chor; Parl, FHA; 4H; Pres, Hmrm; Lat C; SC; VP, Jr Cl; VP, Soph Cl; Sftbl; Hon Prog; *Oral Roberts U; Special Ed.*

BORGSTADT, Ted Randal
Hillcrest HS; Springfield, MO; Key C; ARC; SC; Pres, Soph Cl; Cpt, Bkbl; JV, Ftbl; Tr; PTSA; Stu Against Multiple Sclerosis.

BORIACK, Mike Paul
Westbury Sr HS; Houston, TX; *Tex A&M U; Marketing.*

BORIACK, Steven Matthew
Westbury Sr HS; Houston, TX (210-614) Mu Alpha Theta; Order/Arrow; Order/Arrow A; Eagle Sct A; *Tex A&M U; Environmental Design.*

BORING, Betsy Jo
Katella HS; Anaheim, CA; Chor; Fr C; InterAct C; NHS; Arch; Chor A; *Calif St U; Teaching.*

BORK, Robin Marie
Medford Sr HS; Medford, OR (15%-704) Fr C; Most Out; Gym; FCA; *Oreg St U; Sci.*

BORKLAND, Jay Allen
Dover HS; Dover, NH (5%-520) Band; Chess C; Chor; Drama; Math C; Mu Alpha Theta; Span C; Soccer; Tr; Hon Prog; Math A; MLS; Yth Fel; Band A; *Earth Sci.*

BORLAND, Matthew Wayne
Butler RV HS; Butler, MO; Pres, AFS; Pres, Band; BS; Chor; FBLA; 4H; Co-Ed, Sch P; Pres, Span C; Pres, SC; Bkbl; Ftbl; Wrest; *Central Mo St U; Eng.*

BORLAND, Raymond Neill
N Shore HS; W Palm Beach, FL (3-353) NHS; Span C; Alg A; COM.

BORM, Donna Lee
Red Hook HS; Red Hook, NY (50%-125) AFS; Band; Chor; Golf; Mus A; *Journ.*

BORMAN, Kathryn Dorothy
N Quincy HS; Quincy, MA (90-400) Secy, Band; FNA; *Boston St Col; Nurs.*

BORMANN, Gwynne Ellen
Springfield HS; Springfield, IL (27-448) Fr C; NHS; Hockey; Pres A; Pom Pon Girl; Sen School, Eng A; Superintendant's A, Phys Ed; *Harding Col; Nurs.*

BORMANN, Michele Lynne
Kasson Mantorville HS; Kasson, MN (33%-100) Band; Chor; Ensm; FHA; Tr; COM; SC; Methodist Yth Organization; VP & Pres, Pom Pom Girl.

BORMUTH, Crystal Lee
Ravenna HS; Ravenna, OH (38-415) Band; Chor; Span C; Alg A; Hon Prog; Secy, Theta Rho.

BORMUTH, Shelley Jean
Greeley Central HS; Greeley, CO (59-366) JV, Chldr; FHA; Var C; Tr; Gym.

BORN, Dean Dale
Yankton Sr HS; Yankton, SD; Band; BS; SC; Var C; Tres, Jr Cl; Ftbl; Tr; JV, Wrest; Yth Fel; *Sci.*

BORNE, Allen Helwick
De La Salle HS; New Orleans, LA (75-250) Chess C; Chor; Model UN; NHS; ARC; JV, Ftbl; Tr; Wrest; Pres, Explorers; Ship 23; *Sou Missionary Col; Bus.*

BORNMANN, Carol Ann
St Charles HS; St Charles, MO (8-646) NHS; SC; MVP, Bkbl; Sftbl; Mgr, Tnns; JV Vlbl; *Phys Ed.*

BORON, Neil Joseph
Kenmore Sr HS; Buffalo, NY (100-800) Fr C; Var C; Bkbl; Cpt, Ftbl; Citz A; Journ A; MLS; Poet A; Pres A; Yth Fel; Spelling Bee, Fin; Essay A; *Syracuse U; Journ.*

BORONIEC, Robert Joseph
St Hedwig HS; Detroit, MI (1-71) CYO; NHS; Hist A; Opt A; Spch A; VFW A; Auto Mech A; *U of Mich at Dearborn; Engr.*

BOROWIEC, Catherine Michi
Woodrow Wilson HS; Levittown, PA (4-518) Math C; JV, Hockey; Hon Prog; JA A; Type A; Fr A; *Philadelphia Col of Bible; Elem Ed.*

BORRE, Guy Russell
Beloit Mem HS; Beloit, WI (200-593) Mgr, Tr; *Whitewater Col; Elec.*

BORRE, Mary Ellen
Richmond Burton Comm HS; Richmond, IL (4-79) Band; Chor; SC; Amer Leg A; Pres Phys Fitness A; Mus Camp School; *U of Ind; Mus.*

BORREN, Kathryn Dianne
David Lipscomb HS; Nashville, TN (43-119) NHS; *Belmont Col; Nurs.*

BORRERO, Carmen Lydia
Adolfo Grana Rivera HS; Penuelas, PR (3-336) GS; ARC; Span C; COM; Cl Fav; Hist A; Lion A; Espanish A; *Cath U; Sci.*

BORRERO, Fraticelli Milagros
Adolfo Grana Rivera HS; Penuelas, PR (5-263) CYO; Pres, FHA; Tres, GS; Pres, Hmrm; VP, ARC; Pres, Sch P; SC; COM; Hon Prog; Lion A; *Recinto Universitario Mayaguez; Sci.*

BORS, Pamela Ann
Edison HS; Edison, NJ; Hon Prog; Ger Ntl Hon Hoc.

BORST, Lorrie Ann
Palmer HS; Colorado Springs, CO; Band; Chor; Madrigal; Outst Soprano; *Adams St Col; Mus.*

BORTZ, Karen Kay
Napoleon HS; Napoleon, OH (6-270) Sch Achieve Tm; COM; NHS; *Journ.*

BORUP, Brenda Jo
Saranac Comm HS; Saranac, MI (26-81) Band; Chor; FHA; 4H; NHS; SC; World Affairs C; Mgr, Sftbl; 4H A; VP, Service C; *Western Mich Col; Med.*

BOS, Andrew Richard
Bath HS; Bath, MI (2-120) SC; Bsbl; Bkbl; Golf; COM; Math A; Sal; *Pre-Law.*

BOS, Katherine Diane
Lincoln Sr HS; Sioux Falls, SD; Chor; 4H; 4H A; Candy Striping A; *St Olaf Col; Sci.*

BOS, Kathy Diane
Lincoln Sr HS; Sioux Falls, SD; Chor; 4H; 4H A; 50 Hr Candystriper A; *St Olaf Col; Sci.*

BOSCH, Kristi Fay
Havre HS; Haure, MT (50%-132) Band; Pres, 4H; InterAct C; Ski C; Bkbl; Co-Cpt, Swim; Tr; 4H A; Most Out; Star Student; MVP, Swim; *Valparaiso U; Phys Ed.*

BOSECKER, Brian Timothy
Harrisburg HS; Harrisburg, IL (4-210) Pres, Hmrm; Secy, Key C; SC; Var C; Bsbl; Bkbl; Ftbl; Tr; Soccer C; *SE Jr Col; Mining Engr.*

BOSKO, Rebecca Lynne
Butler Area Sr HS; Butler, PA (117-1000) AFS; Fr C; Sci C; Ski C; Tr; COM; JA A; WW; Secy, Yth Assn For Retarded Citizen; *Recreation.*

BOSMA, Rodney Dale
Lutheran S HS; Affton, MO (45-180) Drama; Bkbl; JV, Ftbl; JA A; Art Contest; Pres, Yth Group; *Hope Col; Art.*

BOSS, Brian Philip
Grissom HS; Huntsville, AL; Key C; JV, Bkbl; Art A; *Auburn U.*

BOSS, Debra Ann
Lebanon Union HS; Lebanon, OR; *Air Traffic Communications.*

BOSS, Eric Christopher
Newport Harbor HS; Newport Beach, CA (150-650) Band; Ski C; Var C; JV, Wrest; DARGCA; MVP, Cpt, Gym; Church Sr Executive Coun; Police A; 'Best Physical Fit'; *Orange Coast Col; Bio.*

BOSSE, Lee Ann
Dover HS; Dover, NH; Fr C; Math C; Mu Alpha Theta; NHS; Secy, Jr Cl; Bkbl; Hockey; Tnns; *U of NH; Math.*

BOSSELL, Susan Lillian
Bridgeport HS; Bridgeport, OH (18-108) Band; FHA; GS; Lat C; NHS; Sch P; Sci C; VP, Sr Cl; VP, Jr Cl; Cpt, Bkbl; H of F; Hist A; HCt; NEDT; Cpt, Vlbl; Phys Ed A; *Ohio U; Phys Therapy.*

BOSSERMAN, Candice Delight
Argos HS; Argos, IN (12-80) Band; JV, Chldr; Ensm; NHS; SC; Pres, Soph Cl; Sftbl; Tr; HCt; Hon Prog; Pres A; Vlbl; 1st, St Ensm Contest; VP, Sunshine C; *Manchester Col.*

BOSSERMAN, Damon Kurt
Argos Comm Sch; Argos, IN (29-78) VP, Soph Cl; Tr; HCt.

BOSSERT, Michael Wayne
Richmond Sr HS; Richmond, IN; Alg A; Yth Foundation; *Air Force; Elec Engr.*

BOSSI, Karen Marie
Windber Area HS; Windber, PA (25%-133) FBLA; NHS; Rptr, Sch P; *Md Med Secy Sch; Med Secy.*

BOST, Warren Pinckney
Myers Park HS; Charlotte, NC (250-600) Chor; Ensm; *Biol.*

BOSTER, Penny Sue
Low Point-Washburn HS; Washburn, IL (9-59) Secy, AFS; Band; Chor; Ensm; 4H; NHS; Rptr, Sch P; Secy, SC; VP, Jr Cl; Bkbl; Cr-Ctry; Sftbl; Tr; COM; Cl Fav; 4H A; Hon Prog; WW; AFS Schol; Top 10; *E Ill U; Phys Ed.*

BOSTIC, Randall A
Flathead HS; Kalispell, MT; VP, Band; Var C; Bsbl; Bkbl; Sftbl; Drum Major.

BOSTIC, Ronald Gene
Flathead HS; Kalispell, MT; Band; Bsbl; Bkbl; Ftbl; Sftbl.

BOSTICK, Bryan Lynn
Meadowdale HS; Dayton, OH (20-156) Band; Tres, SC; Co-Cpt, Bsbl; Bkbl; Ftbl; Sftbl; COM; Citz A; Pres A; Spch A; Type A; PA.

BOSTICK, Christine Leigh
El Paso HS; El Paso, TX; Band.

BOSTICK, Helen Christene
Miami Spring Sr HS; Miami Spring, FL (110-740) Bus C; Cum Laude Soc; Ensm; S-T, FHA; HiY; JETS; Cl Fav; Delta Sigma Theta A; Hon Prog; Opt A; Spch A; *Miami Dade U; Fashion Buyer.*

BOSTJANCIC, Jean Ann
Ridgewood Baptist Acad; Joliet, IL (3-17) Chor; Hon Prog; Yth Foundation; Yth Leg; Cpt, Vlbl; *Bradley U; Art.*

BOSTOCK, Lella Denice
Nettie Lee Roth; Dayton, OH; Chor; Distributive Ed A; Journ A; Mus A; Attendance A.

BOSTON, Brenda Faye
Washington HS; E Chicago, IN (83-300) Drama; FNA; Jr Miss Pagent; NHS; Orch; Beauty; 4H A; Powder Puff Ftbl; Top Twenty A; Orch A; *Bryan Professional Inst; Paramed Mgr.*

BOSTON, Charlotte Georgianna
Western Sr HS; Baltimore, MD; Chor; Drama; Secy, Fr C; NHS; COM; Citz A; Sal; *Morgan St U; Art.*

BOSTON, John William
West HS; Sioux City, IA (14-287) Chor; Var C; Wrest; Hon Prog; Top 5% of Cl; HR; High Q Bowl Schol; *Morningside HS; Math.*

BOSTON, Karen Ann
Grandview Heights HS; Grandview, OH (6-140) Ann; Chldr; Drama; FHA; GS; Hmrm; NHS; ARC; Ed, Sch P; Ski C; Span C; SC; Thes; Tres, Sr Cl; Secy, Soph Cl; Hockey; JV, Tnns; JV, Tr; B Crocker A; Citz A; Hon Prog; Pres A; Outst Sr; *Ohio St U; Agr.*

BOSTON, Laura Lee
O D Wyatt HS; Ft Worth, TX (29-434) A Cap Choir; Drama; SC; Hist A; Magna Cum Laude; Sci A; OEA Off; GS Nom; *Abilene Christian U; Bus.*

BOSTON, Nancy Ruth
West HS; Sioux City, IA (10%-269) Band; Fr C; JV, Tr; Hon Prog; *Oral Roberts U; Elem Ed.*

BOSTROM, Lori Denise
John Marshall Sr HS; Rochester, MN (33%-635) Band; Ski C; *Nurs.*

BOSWELL, Alice Ann
Geneva HS; Geneva, AL (25%-95) Ann; Tres, BC; Chldr; Chem C; Drama; Fr C; FHA; FTA; GS; Hmrm; InterClub Coun; Math C; Ed, Sch P; Sci C; SC; Var C; Citz A; DARGCA; Prs, Yth As for Retarded Children; *U of Ala; Law.*

BOSWELL, Arthur Jennings Jr
Lee-Davis HS; Mechanicsville, VA (10%-500) BC; Chess C; Span C; Gifted-Talent List; *Va Tech Col; Engr.*

BOSWELL, Dottie Denise
Rockwell HS; Rockdale, TX (10-120) Band; Ensm; Fin, Lit Ral; NHS; Co-Ed, Sch P; Type A; Outst Bandsmen; UIL Literary A; 1st Division UIL Ensm; *Tex A&M U; Acct.*

BOSWELL, Kathleen Ellen
Hobart Sr HS; Hobart, IN (97-463) Cpt, Chldr; Secy, Chor; *Eckerd Col; Bus.*

BOSWELL, Lisa Kay
Jennings Co HS; N Vernon, IN (29-432) 4H; Rainbow; Span C; Tr; Ntl Achv Schol; Bus A; *Ball St U; Math Ed.*

BOSWELL, Lynette
N Miami HS; Denver, IN; Band; Chor; Ensm; FHA; Mod Mus Mas; Drum & Rifle Corp; *Bus.*

BOSWELL, Reid Thomas
Ridgeview HS; Atlanta, GA (10-250) BC; NHS; JV, Ftbl; COM; Hon Prog; Opt Out Tn; Presbyterian Col Jr Fel; *Wheaton Col; Pre-Med.*

BOSWELL, Robert McWhorter
Thomson HS; Thomson, GA (4-280) Tres, BC; Drama; InterAct C; VP, SC; Tres, Jr Cl; Ftbl; Golf; COM; Pres, Col Jr Fellow.

BOSWELL, Stuart Eric
Cass Tech HS; Detroit, MI (300-832) Bsbl.

BOSWELL, William Hugh
N Miami HS; Denver, IN (19-124) Secy, FFA; S-T, 4H; Yth For Understanding; *Purdue U; Agr.*

BOSWORTH, Beth Deanna
Rochester Area HS; Rochester, PA (69-180) A Cap Choir; Bus C; Chor; Drama; FHA; Span C; Y-Tns; Drill Tm; Church Pianist; Sch Choir Accompanist; *Roberts Weslyan U; Bus.*

BOSWORTH, Bethany Dawn
McGavock HS; Nashville, TN; Band; BC; Chor; Secy, Dbte Tm; Fr C; Hmrm; Madrigal; ARC; Ed, Sch P; Secy, SC; Hon Prog; Journ A; *Samford U; Vocal Mus.*

BOSWORTH, Cathy Lynne
Westfield Central Sch; Westfield, NY; S-T, Band; Chldr; Chor; Hmrm; Cpt, Swim; MVP, Swim.

BOTELER, Diane Louise
Riverwood HS; Atlanta, GA (1-260) VP, Band; BC; Chor; Ensm; Fr C; French NHS; Hmrm; Mu Alpha Theta; Ski C; SC; Bkbl; JV, Tnns; COM; Hon Prog; Pilot C A; *Duke U; Pre-Med.*

BOTELHO, Sidney Hayward Jr
E Providence HS; E Providence, RI (232-650) JV, Ftbl; Yth Fel.

BOTHWELL, Jackie Lynn
Conroe HS; Conroe, TX (242-900) A Cap Choir; Math C; Span C; Drill Tm; Secy, Yth for Christ; Secy, Yth Coun; *Sam Houston St U; Elem Ed.*

BOTKIN, Lindy Dell
Fowler HS; Fowler, CO (11-55) Chldr; Chor; Secy, Drama; Jr Miss Pagent; NFL; NHS; Secy, Spch C; Thes; JV, Bkbl; NEDT; Spch A; Yth Fel; *Hastings Col; Eng Ed.*

BOTSFORD, Pamela Jo
Crestview Sr HS; Crestview, FL (10%-214) Chldr; FTA.

BOTT, Theresa Lynn
Alamosa HS; Alamosa, CO (31-200) Band; CYO; Drama; FBLA; Pres, FHA; Pres, 4H; Mjrte; Sch P; Ski C; JV, Bkbl; Swim; Fin, Tr; DARGCA; 4H A; Type A; *Adams St U; Bus.*

BOTTERBUSCH, Heidi Ann
Helena HS; Helena, MT (30-350) Chor; Span C; *Pacific Lutheran U; Psych.*

BOTTICELLI, Joyce Ann
Old Forge HS; Old Forge, PA; Tres, Band; Drama; FTA; NHS; Ski C; JV, Bkbl; Sftbl; Hon Prog; WW.

BOTTNER, Donna Rae
Gulf Comprehensive HS; New Port Richey, FL; Chor; Drama; Ger C; Soccer; Hon Prog; *U of S Fla; Ger.*

BOTTNER, Sheryl Lynne
Gulf Comprehensive HS; New Port Richey, FL (33%-250) Drama; Fr C; Tr; COM; Achv A, Fr; *St Petersburg Jr Col; Fr.*

BOTTOM, Phyllis Marie
Asher HS; Asher, OK (5%-29) FBLA; FHA; Sch P; Var C; Tres, Sr Cl; Secy, Soph Cl; Bkbl; COM; Type A; *Employment.*

BOTTOM, Rose Michele
Washington Co HS; Springfield, KY; Band; Chor; FHA; Bsbl; Tnns; Sci A; Rptr, Human Relations; Pep C; *E Ky U.*

BOTTONE, Caroline Reynolds
Oceanside Sr HS; Oceanside, NY (33%-950) Chor; Sch P; Yth Fel; Starve in For Farmers; Go-Getters; Sr HS Bible Study; Explorers; Adult Bible Study; Sports Night; *Law.*

BOTTORFF, Sally Anne
Twentynine Palms HS; Twentynine Palms, CA; Chldr; Chor; Secy, 4H; Rptr, Hmrm; SC; Religion.

BOTTORFF, Shari Lynne
Huguenot HS; Richmond, VA (6-254) VP, FBLA; NHS; Type A; Ath As; Spelling As; Shorthand A; Va Commonwealth U; Legal Secy.

BOTWINSKI, Steven Joseph
Kelly HS; Chicago, IL (7-375) Ed, Ann; Chor; NHS; Ed, Sch P; Bio A; COM; Journ A; Q&S A; Sci A; St Louis Col of Phar; Phar.

BOUCHARD, Amy Louise
Sacred Heart HS; Kingston, MA (10-54) Chor; 4H; Hmrm; Ed, Sch P; Tres, SC; COM; Hon Prog; Q&S A; Liturgical C; St Anselms Col; Criminal Justice.

BOUCHER, David Lane
Queen City HS; Queen City, TX; NHS; Sci C; Span C; Ftbl.

BOUCHER, Gregg William
Miami Killian Sr HS; Miami, FL; Band; Hmrm; MVP, Golf; Semi-Fin, Swim.

BOUCIER, Sharon Elaine
Pacific HS; San Bernardino, CA (6-550) A Cap Choir; Chor; Ensm; NHS; Ch, SC; Swim; CSF; COM; Citz A; Masonic A; Most Out; Ch, Job's Daughters; Girl's C; Christian C; Pacific Christian Col; Early Childhood Ed.

BOUDINOT, Neil R
Northmor HS; Galion, OH (5-94) Band; BS; Chor; Drama; Key C; VP, NHS; Var C; Pres, Soph Cl; Ftbl; Sftbl; Wrest; Amer Leg A; MLS; Yth Fel; Ashland Col; Chem.

BOUDMAN, Cindee Lea
Bloomsburg Sr HS; Bloomsburg, PA (1-225) Band; S-T, Drama; Hmrm; SC; JV, Tr; Hon Prog; Yth Fel; DAR Cert of A, Outst Work; 3rd Pl Relay, Jr Olympics; Christian Stu Course Diploma; Lehigh U; Pre-Med.

BOUDREAUX, Annette Cecelia
St Joseph HS; Jeanerette, LA (2-19) Ann; 4H; Fin, Lit Ral; Band; Tnns; Alg A; COM; Math A; NEDT; Sci A; Sch Spirit A; Eng A; Fr A; Religion A; U of Southwestern La; Ed.

BOUDREAUX, Kim Alison
St John HS; Plaquemine, LA (1-64) Tres, Fr C; Semi-Fin, Lit Ral; Pres, Mu Alpha Theta; Pres, NHS; VP, Sci C; Secy, Soph Cl; Mgr, Bkbl; Mgr, Sftbl; Alg A; Bio A; Chem A; NEDT; Phy A; Val; S Central Bell Sci A; LSU; Chem Engr.

BOUDREAUX, Mary Beth
St Joseph HS; Jeanerette, LA (2-28) Lit Ral; NHS; Tnns; COM; HCt; Math A; NEDT; Eng A; U of Southwestern La.

BOUDREAUX, Renee Antoinette
St Martinville Sr HS; St Martinville, LA (7-VP, FBLA; FHA; 4H; HCt; YACA Chpt Pres & St Prog Ch; Best Dressed; COE Prog; Inst of Cosmetology; Hair Designing.

BOUDREY, Regina Lenore
South HS; Youngstown, OH (5-30) FHA; COM; Cl Fav; Youngstown St U; Social Worker.

BOUGES, Kathy
Seward Park HS; New York, NY (3-700) Orch; VP, Sr Cl; Hist A; Hon Prog; VP, Law Explorers; Bowery Jr Adv; U of Buffalo; Law.

BOUGHAN, Judy Lynne
Trotwood Madison Sr HS; Trotwood, OH; Band; Cpt, Chldr; Drama; NHS; Orch; Sch P; Bkbl; Sftbl; Tr; Cl Fav; HCt; JA A; Most Out; Spch A; Yth Fel; Pres Fitness A; Sch-Ath A; Pol Sci.

BOUGIE, Diane Elaine
Acad o-t Holy Family; Baltic, CT (1-29) Chor; VP, Hmrm; NHS; Rivier Col; Acct.

BOUGIE, Theresa Flora
Acad o-t Holy Family; Baltic, CT (1-23) Chor; NHS; Pres, SC; MLS; Sci A; Type A; Ed.

BOUIE, Patricia Ann
Joliet Central HS; Joliet, IL (136-569) Bkbl; JV Vlbl; Joliet Jr Col; Math.

BOUILLE, Joyce Patricia
Secaucus HS; Secaucus, NJ (114-164) SC; Montclair St Col; Elem Ed.

BOULANGER, Marc Gerard
Lafayette Sr HS; Lafayette, LA (25%-600) Band; Pres, FBLA; Opt A; Bowl Tm; Cert Scuba Diver; Gen.

BOULDIN, Yvonne Catherine
Walnut Hills HS; Cincinnati, OH (50%-500) Chess C; Yth Fel; Eagles Ath Service A; Miami U; Bus Adm.

BOULET, Martin
College De Ste Anne De La Pocatiere; La Pocatiere, CANAD (3-30) Pres, 4H; Lit Mag; Phys C; 4H A; Math A; Type A; Adm.

BOULT, Henry Bernard
San Carlos HS; San Carlos, CA; A Cap Choir; Drama; San Mateo Jr Col; Mus.

BOULTINGHOUSE, David Wayne
La Poynor HS; Poynor, TX (2-38) Bsbl; Wrest; Sal; Tex U at Austin; Chem Engr.

BOULWARE, Kim Marie
Kuemper HS; Carroll, IA (20%-252) CYO; Dbte Tm; 4H; Spch C; COM; 4H A; Spch A; Marian A; Ntl Essay A; Litergy A; Creighton Col; Law.

BOULWARE, Tamera Lee
Kuemper HS; Carroll, IA (53-282) A Cap Choir; CYO; Chor; Ensm; Pres, 4H; Madrigal; Orch; Span C; Spch C; 4H A; Spch A; Marian A; Mus A; Essay A; Buena Vista Col; Mus.

BOUNDS, Johnnie Marie
Cotton Plant HS; Cotton Plant, AR (7-23) Co-Ed, Ann; Pres, BC; Drama; FBLA; FHA; H of F; Ark St U; Acct.

BOUNDS, Paula Jean
Mexico HS; Mexico, MO (15%-300) Chor; Fr C; Hmrm; NHS; SC; Citz A; Regent Schol; Kiwanis Schol; Central Mo St U; Clothing & Textiles.

BOURDEAU, James Arwin
St Louis Park Sr HS; St Louis Park, MN; Chor; Soccer; General.

BOURDETTE, Frances Lynn
Independence HS; Independence, MS (5%-72) Ann; Band; Pres, BC; Co-Cpt, Chldr; Chor; FBLA; FHA; Pres, 4H; Phys C; Span C; COM; 4H A; Most Popular; Church Pianist; 3rd Pl, Sci-Math Tourney; U of Miss; Med Tech.

BOUREK, Joyce Ellen
Wisner-Pilger Jr-Sr HS; Wisner, NE (7-68) Band; FBLA; FHA; NHS; Math A; NE Tech Comm Col; Bus.

BOURELLE, Marvin George
Kiser HS; Dayton, OH (1-250) K of C; Math C; NHS; Sch P; Var C; Pres, Jr Cl; Bsbl; Ftbl; Tnns; Wrest; COM; Hon Prog; K of C A; Math A; Opt A; Sci A; Spch A; Ntl Math of Amer Hon & Sup Achv As; Lang A; MAA Math Contest As; Math A; Spelling Champ; Sci A; Ohio St U; Vet.

BOURGEOIS, Mitchell John
Leesville HS; Leesville, LA (34-262) Sci C; SC; Var C; Bsbl; Ftbl; COM; Star Student; Small Engines A; NE La U; Gen.

BOURGEOIS, Myra Ann
Lutcher HS; Lutcher, LA (4-208) VP, BC; FHA; 4H; Hmrm; Semi-Fin, Lit Ral; Math C; VP, Sci C; VP, SC; Beauty; 4H A; HCt; Swtht; Batgirl Medal; Rifle Corp Swtht; Freeport Schol; Nicholls St U; Med Technology.

BOURGEOIS, Stephanie Elizabeth
Patterson HS; Patterson, LA (60-80) CYO; FBLA; Pres, Pep Squad; 1st Cl GSct; Nicholls Col; Bus.

BOURLAND, Richard Gerard
Bishop Amat Mem HS; La Puente, CA (28-363) JV, Dbte Tm; NHS; Span C; SC; Tres, Sr Cl; JV, Cr-Ctry; Co-Cpt, Hockey; Tr; VFW A; Loyola Marymount Col; Pre-Denistry.

BOURLAND, Steven Paul
Enid HS; Enid, OK; Band; Chor; Fr C; Secy, Hmrm; Orch; Ftbl; Tnns; Wrest; COM; Citz A; DARGCA; ARC A; Okla Hon Soc; Okla St U; Ministry.

BOURNE, Carlton Russell Jr
Winyah HS; Georgetown, SC (30-300) Ed, Sch P; Pres, SC; Ftbl; Amer Leg A; Hon Prog; Yth Fel; Clemson U; Bus.

BOURNE, Robert Clark
Screven Co HS; Sylvania, GA (3-250) Rptr, NHS; Bsbl; Bkbl; Ftbl; Golf; Presbyterian Col Jr Achv A; Ga COM; Communications Engr.

BOURQUE, Jennifer
Nederland HS; Nederland, TX (44-480) AFS; Band; CYO; Fr C; NHS; Parish Board; CYO Dio Rep; Sunday Sch Teacher; Vac Bible Sch Teacher; Lamar Tech Col; Secondary Ed.

BOURQUE, Kevin Michael
James Island HS; Charleston, SC (27-165) Chor; Mu Alpha Theta; NHS; Co-Ed, Sch P; Pres, SC; Journ A; NMF; NMS; U of Md; Phys.

BOURQUE, Laura
Nederland HS; Nederland, TX (15-470) AFS; VP, CYO; Pres, Fr C; French NHS; NHS; Tr; Hon Prog; Phy A; Fr A; Phys Ed A; Lamar U; Pre-Vet Med.

BOURQUE, Lucretia Ann
St Martinville Sr HS; St Martinville, LA; CYO; FHA; 4H; NHS; Co-Cpt, Sftbl; Tr; Gov Honor Prog; 4H A; JA A; Pres A; Vlbl; Art A; LSU; Commercial Arts.

BOURQUE, Luke
St Martin Acad; St Martinville, LA (25-55) CYO; 4H; Bsbl; Ftbl; Sftbl; 4H A; Yth Art Coun; Guitar C; Mitchell Welding Sch; Welding & Woodwork.

BOURQUE, Steve Gardiner
Kelly HS; Beaumont, TX (15-85) NHS; Tr; Hist A; Hon Prog; U of Tex; Law.

BOUTTE, Denise Marie
Foothill HS; Pleasanton, CA; Band; CYO; Hon Prog; Ed.

BOUTTE, Sharon Marie
Kerkhoven HS; Columbus, GA; CYO; Sftbl; SC St Col; Bus Mgt.

BOUTTE, Tony Lane
Morgan City HS; Morgan City, LA (11-285) A Cap Choir; Cpt, Band; Chor; Community Yth Symph; Lit Ral; Madrigal; NHS; Thes; Gov Honor Prog; H of F; Hon Prog; Math A; NEDT; All St Band; Outst Camper; Outst Mus; Pres, Mu Sigma; La Tech U; Mus.

BOUTTE', Denise Marie
Foothill HS; Pleasanton, CA; Band; CYO; ARC; Sch P; Hon Prog; Ed.

BOUWENS, Randal Owen
Piper HS; Sunrise, FL (50%-546) Band; Community Yth Symph; Ensm; Span C; Band A; All St Band; Sup Rating As Stu Conductor; Fla Jr Col; Mus Ed.

BOUYACK, James Edward
Clyde Sr HS; Clyde, OH (2-202) A Cap Choir; Band; FFA; FTA; Secy, 4H; NHS; Pres, Jr Cl; Amer Leg A; 4H A; H of F; I Dare You; Sal; Summa Cum Laude; Inspirational; Band; Ohio St U; Engr.

BOWDEN, Craig Philip
Oakton HS; Vienna, VA (200-600) Band; Chor; Order/Arrow; COM; Order/Arrow A; Yth Fel; Hist Trails A, BSct; Recreation Director; Bible Sch; Church Sftbl.

BOWDEN, Cynthia Anita
Lake Clifton Sr HS; Baltimore, MD (10%-350) Hmrm; NHS; F-Ed, Sch P; Pres, Soph Cl; Cpt, Bkbl; Amer Leg A; COM; Hist A; Journ A; PTA A; Villa Julie Col; Bus-Legal Secy.

BOWDEN, John Bradley
Hopewell HS; Aliquippa, PA; Ann; Band; Ger C; Sci C; Soccer; Elec Engr.

BOWDEN, Larry Donald Jr
Salisbury HS; Salisbury, NC (45-285) AFS; Band; Fr C; Key C; Hon Prog; NC Yth Comm, LCA; All-St Band; Wake Forest Col; Med.

BOWDEN, Misty M
Eastern Hills HS; Ft Worth, TX (50%-800) A Cap Choir; Rainbow; Swtht; OEA A; TCU; Mus.

BOWDEN, Pamela Darlene
Dudley Sr HS; Greensboro, NC; FBLA; Hmrm; SC; JA A; Nurs.

BOWDEN, Rick Bryant
Central HS; San Angelo, TX (50%-700) Parl, A Cap Choir; Parl, Chor; Drama; Ensm; Madrigal; ARC; Thes; Bkbl; Tnns; COM; Citz A; ARC A; Pres, A Cappella Choir; Pres, Chor; All St, All Area Chors; Bible Bowl Tm; Sweepstakes, Choir; *Abilene Christian U; Bible.*

BOWDLE, Donald Keven
Cleveland HS; Cleveland, TN (5%-200) Ed, Ann; Co-Cpt, Band; Chor; Pres, Drama; Ensm; VP, Key C; NHS; SC; Thes; Hist A; Hon Prog; Top 5, Jr Cl; *Lee Col; Bio.*

BOWDRE, Laurie Anita
Skyline HS; Dallas, TX (200-900) FHA; FTA; Hmrm; Span C; SC; Y-Tns; Delta Sigma Theta A; ARC A; Mayor's A; Principal's Adv Committee; *Pepperdine U; Foreign Lang.*

BOWDRE, LeNora Vernesia
Skyline HS; Dallas, TX (117-890) F-Ed, Ann; Chor; NHS; ARC; S-T, SC; Y-Tns; Fin, Sr Cl; Pres, Jr Cl; Fin, Soph Cl; Cl Fav; HCt; Hon Prog; MLS; Cpt, Bowl; Swtht, Bowl C; *Baylor U; Law.*

BOWDRING, Nancy
St Mary's Acad; Alexandria, VA (7-70) JV, Chldr; Chor; S-T, French NHS; Pres, Key C; Math C; Mu Alpha Theta; NHS; Co-Cpt, Swim; Tr; COM; NEDT; MVP, Swim; Outst Mus Theory A; Female Athlete o-t Yr; *Fr.*

BOWE, Beverly Jo
29 Palms HS; Twentynine Palms, CA; Chor; *Col of Desert; Nurs.*

BOWEN, April Rena
Geronimo HS; Geronimo, OK (10%-25) Cpt, Chldr; Drama; Tres, Jr Cl; Rptr, Soph Cl; HQn; HR; Learn & Live Cert; Eng, Shorthand, A's; *Oscar Rose Col; Dental Hygienest.*

BOWEN, Barbara Elaine
Plymouth Whitemarsh HS; Plymouth Meeting, PA (25-656) Band; Chor; Span C; Lieutenant, Marching Band; Chrch Coun For Exceptional Persons; *Millersville St Col; Special Ed.*

BOWEN, Beverly Ann
Fort Myers HS; Fort Myers, FL (60-440) Chor; Drama; Ensm; Madrigal; VP, Rainbow; Tres, Sci C; Thes; All St Chor; Miami Hon Choir; *Elem Ed.*

BOWEN, Brenda
Statesboro HS; Statesboro, GA (8-375) Band; Ensm; Mjrte; Gov Honor Prog; Yth Fel; *U of Ga; Math.*

BOWEN, James Madison
Dodge Co HS; Eastman, GA (20-200) Ann; FBLA; FFA; 4H; HiY; Hmrm; Pres, SC; Var C; Bsbl; MVP, Ftbl; Tr; Citz A; Cl Fav; 4H A; Sr Superlative; Outst Sr A; PA A; *Troy St U; Phys Ed.*

BOWEN, Janet Rochelle
Wayne Co HS; Jesup, GA; BC; Chldr; Hmrm; VP, SC; Sftbl; Gym Tm; *Lee Col; Bus.*

BOWEN, John Franklin
Estill HS; Estill, SC (25%-100) Math C; Var C; Ftbl; Tnns; COM; *U of SC; Geology.*

BOWEN, Kimberly Dawn
Man Sr HS; Man, WV (25-180) Band; NHS; Span C; Type A; *Radiology.*

BOWEN, Linda Jean
Portage Central HS; Portage, MI (175-365) *KVCC; Acct.*

BOWEN, Lucius S
Lew Wallace HS; Gary, IN; F-Ed, Span C; Ftbl; *Valparaiso Col; Law.*

BOWEN, Rodney Joseph
St Augustine HS; New Orleans, LA (15-150) Pres, CYO; Cpt, Bkbl; Tr; MVP, Bkbl; *U of Houston; Engr.*

BOWEN, Sharon Lorraine
Montrose HS; Montrose, CO (125-350) Chor; Dbte Tm; Drama; Ensm; Fr C; FHA; 4H; Ntl Yth Conf; Sph C; Thes; ROTC A; Spch A; VFW A; VofDEM; Yth Fel; Drill Tm; Pres, St Yth Fel; Stage Mgr, Thespians; *Anderson Col; Spch.*

BOWEN, Shelley Celeste
Classical HS; Springfield, MA (45-508) Drama; Hmrm; A-Ed, Lit Mag; Hon Prog; Yrbk; Cum Laude; *Simmons Col; Communications.*

BOWEN, Shelly Ann
Fairland HS; Fairland, OK (2-37) Pres, Band; Chldr; Chor; FHA; NHS; Rainbow; Bkbl; Sftbl; HCt; Okla Hon Soc.

BOWEN, Suzanne
Bertie Sr HS; Windsor, NC; Band; Sci C; Outst Work, Props & Scenery; *E Carolina U; Nurs.*

BOWENS, Bobbie LaDoris
Woodside HS; Woodside, CA (250-600) Chldr; Var C; Co-Ch, World Affairs; Citz A; Cl Fav; DARGCA; God & Country A; Yth Fel; Powderpuff Ftbl; Human Relations C; *UCLA; Phys Sci.*

BOWENS, Christopher Arnez
Southside HS; Greenville, SC (15-260) CYO; NHS; Bkbl; Tr; Hon Prog; *Clemson U; Bio.*

BOWENS, Christopher Canell
J E Brown HS; Atlanta, GA (13-365) BC; Pres, Hmrm; Math C; Ntl Teachers Coun; COM; Hon Prog; Math A; Sci A; Best Attendance; Acad Excel; *Ga St U; Law.*

BOWER, David Alan
Fort Madison Sr HS; Fort Madison, IA; Chor; Rptr, Sch P; VP, Span C; Mgr, Bkbl; COM; Church Bus Ministry Special A; *U of Iowa; Secondary Ed.*

BOWER, Donna Louise
Will C Crawford HS; San Diego, CA (250-576) Ensm; Yth Fel; Choir Spirit A; *Mesa Jr Col.*

BOWER, Lisa Lynne
Quincy Sr HS; Quincy, IL (68-785) A Cap Choir; Chor; Drama; Madrigal; Span NHS; SC; Thes; Amer Leg A; Ntl Achv Schol; Major Chor A; Minor Band A; Major Theatre A; *NW Ill U; Mus.*

BOWER, Wendell Loren
Muncy HS; Muncy, PA; Bkbl; Ftbl; Tnns; *Pa St U; Bus Mgr.*

BOWERLY, Laura Jean
McNary HS; Salem, OR; Ger C; Rptr, Hmrm; Rptr, SC; Tres, Thes; Beauty; Math A; MLS; Best Cast Member A; Drama A; Best Puppeteer A; *Linfield Col; Dental Hygiene.*

BOWERS, Cindy Alene
Newton Falls HS; Newton Falls, OH (28-170) Band; GS; Mjrte; Sci C; Span C; *Criminology.*

BOWERS, David Alan
Normandy HS; St Louis, MO (80-502) Band; Hmrm; Order/Arrow; SC; JV, Tnns; God & Country A; Order/Arrow A; Yth Fel; Eagle Sct; Funniest; *U of Mo.*

BOWERS, Diane Louise
Winchester-Thurston HS; Pittsburg, PA (14-58) AFS; Chor; Drama; Rptr, Sch P; COM; Yth Fel; Vlbl.

BOWERS, Donna Lynne
Lincoln Co R-II HS; Elsberry, MO (25%-48) Band; Chldr; Chor; FHA; NHS; F-Ed, Sch P; Sci C; Rptr, Bsbl; Rptr, Bkbl; Rptr, Cr-Ctry; Rptr, Tnns; Rptr, Tr; COM; HCt; Pres A; Yth Fel; Rptr, Vlbl; Sports Ed, Elsberry Democratic; Sports Ed, Sch Paper; Journ Contest; *SE Mo St U; Athletic Training & Special Ed.*

BOWERS, Jesse Eric
Pisgah Sr HS; Canton, NC (40-350) Band; *Warren Wilson Col.*

BOWERS, John Don
Oppenheim Ephratah HS; St Johnsville, NY (8-39) NHS; Bsbl; Bkbl; Soccer; Regent Schol; *Mowhawk Valley Col; Elec.*

BOWERS, Joyce Louise
Marshall HS; Marshall, MN (5-256) Dbte Tm; Fr C; NFL; Spch C; Spch A; *St Olaf Col; Psych.*

BOWERS, Kathy Faye
Mascoutah Comm HS; Mascoutah, IL; Chor; 4H; MVP, Swim; Swim, Lib, Tr Meet, Chor, A's.

BOWERS, Kelly Jo
Marion Harding HS; Marion, OH; Ann; 4H; Lit Mag; Sch P; 4H A; Jr Ldr, 4-H C; *Airline Sch; Airline Stewardess.*

BOWERS, Kim Theodore
Warren Central HS; Indianapolis, IN; Band; SC; Var C; JV, Bkbl; Ftbl; Tr; COM; Hon Prog; Pres A; FCA; Bus.

BOWERS, Marc
E Central HS; Tulsa, OK (229-663) Chem C; Ger C; Co-Ed, Lit Mag; Mu Alpha Theta; NHS; Pres, Sr Cl; Mgr, Bkbl; Ftbl; Wrest; COM; H of F; Art Schol; *Okla Christian Col; Pre-Med.*

BOWERS, Mary Beth
Atlantic HS; Delray Beach, FL (33%-725) Chor; Drama; Ensm; Madrigal; NFL; NHS; ARC; Sch P; SC; Thes; Cpt, Tnns; Beauty; COM; Citz A; God & Country A; Most Out; ARC A; Type A; PA; Mus Roles; Runner-Up, Miss Atlantic; Sports Events Rptr, Radio Prog; *Blue Mountain Col; Journ.*

BOWERS, Pamela Sue
Lake Braddock Secondary Sch; Burke, VA (157-550) Band; NHS; Ski C; Hockey; Del, Ntl Lutheran Convocation; *VPI; Bus Ed.*

BOWERS, Patricia Lynn
Travelers Rest HS; Travelers Rest, SC (29-196) Band; Chor; Drama; Hmrm; Pres, Hmrm; NHS; SC; Beauty; HCt; 1st Lt, 1st Sargent, Band; *Greenville Tech Col; Secy Sci.*

BOWERS, Rojanne
Circleville HS; Circleville, OH (60-207) AFS; 4H; Hmrm; SC; Co-Cpt, Swim; Tnns; *Ohio U; Sociology.*

BOWERS, Rose Ann
Stephens Co HS; Toccoa, GA; A Cap Choir; Chor; Crown & Scepter; Ensm; FHA; GS; 4H; Hmrm; InterAct C; Jr Miss Pagent; NHS; SC; Secy, Tri-HiY; Cl Fav; Swtht; *Mus.*

BOWERS, Shirley Anne
El Monte HS; El Monte, CA (5%-300) A Cap Choir; Chor; Sci C; CSF; Hon Prog; Laurels Girls Hon C; Christian Lions A; Backpacking C; Stu Director; *Physics.*

BOWERS, Stewart Vandiver
Monroe Area Comprehensive HS; Monroe, GA (7-198) Band; BC; Ensm; Pres, 4H; Hmrm; Inter-Club Coun; Pres, Key C; Rptr, Sch P; Sci C; Pres, SC; VP, Soph Cl; COM; Citz A; 4H A; Hon Prog; I Dare You; Math A; Sci A; *Math.*

BOWERS, Susie Ann
Second Ward HS; Gloster, LA (1-46) *Northwestern St U; Nurs.*

BOWERS, Teresa Lynn
Stephens Co HS; Toccoa, GA; A Cap Choir; Ann; BC; Chor; Crown & Scepter; FHA; 4H; NHS; Tri-HiY; JV, Bkbl.

BOWERSOX, Keith Allen
Liberty HS; Bedford, VA (110-253) Ftbl; Tr; Wrest; Math A; *Central Va Comm Col; Hotel Mgt.*

BOWERSOX, Valerie Jean
Belleville HS; Belleville, KS (6-85) Band; Chor; Drama; Ensm; FHA; Fin, GS; 4H; Fin, ACT; *Manhattan Christian Col; Computer Sci.*

BOWKER, Kyle Lane
Whitehouse HS; Whitehouse, TX (1-106) Band; NHS; Pres, Soph Cl; Golf; Eng, Fr, A's; *U of Tex; Bus Mgr.*

BOWKER, Muriel Jean
Alexander Galt Regional HS; Lennoxville, CANADA (3-477) Chor; 4H; Hmrm; ISCF; Home Ec A; HR.

BOWLBY, Darryl Mark
Putnam City W HS; Oklahoma City, OK (200-700) Demolay; Span C; SC; Thes; Tnns; Journ A; Outst DeMolay; Sons of Liberty; Ed, Demolay Newsletter; *Okla U; Pol Sci.*

BOWLER, Curtis Keith
Sentinel HS; Missoula, MT; Ski C; Bkbl; V Ltrs.

BOWLER, Mary Alice
Richmond Sr HS; Rockingham, NC (7%-850) BC; S-T, Chor; Hmrm; SC; COM; Hon Prog; Star Student; Yth Fel; *Mus.*

BOWLES, John Kevin
Kearsley HS; Flint, MI (25-320) Band; NHS; Var C; JV, Bsbl; Bkbl; Cpt, Ftbl; Alg A; COM; Cl Fav; Hkg; Hon Prog; Math A; Most Out; Most Outst Ath; Most Outst Math Stu; *Jackson St; Med.*

BOWLES, Lisa Gail
Robert E Lee HS; Montgomery, AL; Fr C; SC; Tres, Art C; Stu Ldr; Ltr A; *U of Ala; Dentist.*

BOWLES, Susan Wall
Plant City HS; Plant City, FL (5%-600) NHS; Top 5%; Nom, Calendar Girl; Tns For Christ C; Sci Dept Stu Asst; Most Outst Stu Asst A.

BOWLIN, John Samuel II
Ashville HS; Ashville, AL; BC; FFA; VP, 4H; Hmrm; SC; Eagle Sct; 4-H Ldrship, Achv & Pub Speak As; US Naval Acad.

BOWLINE, Joanna Key
Newbury Park HS; Newbury Park, CA (10-609) Ed, Sch P; Pres, Sr Cl; CSF; Journ A; Win, Art Contests; Calif St U; Journ.

BOWLING, Clyde Russell
Western Grove HS; Western Grove, AR (3-27) Bsbl; Mgr, Bkbl; N Ark Comm Col.

BOWLING, Ruby Jean
Buckhorn HS; Buckhorn, KY (2-36) F-Ed, Ann; BC; Chor; Pres, FHA; 4H; A-Ed, Sch P; Secy, Sr Cl; VP, Jr Cl; VP, Soph Cl; Sftbl; Crisco A; 4H A; HCt; Sal; La Salle U; Interior Decoration.

BOWLS, Kimberly Ann
Redlands HS; Redlands, CA; Ch, Chldr; Ski C; Pres A; Gym Tm; WW; Hon Girl; Calif Poly-Tech St U; Archt.

BOWLWARE, Carl Steven
Moore HS; Moore, OK (10%-700) Lat C; Order/ Arrow; Var C; JV, Bsbl; Bkbl; Order/Arrow A; Yth Fel; Church Choir; Pres, CYF; Central St U; Sci.

BOWMAKER, Diana Beth
Tottenville HS; Staten Island, NY (135-1191) A Cap Choir; Band; Ch, Chor, Drama; Pres, Hmrm; Madrigal; ARC; Ski C; Pres, SC; Pres, Jr Cl; Pres, Soph Cl; ARC A; Excellent Citations; Katherine Von Bora A; Lutheran GSct A; Special Ed.

BOWMAKER, Donna Jean
Tottenville HS; Staten Island, NY (177-1191) A Cap Choir; Band; Ch, Chor; Drama; Pres, Hmrm; Madrigal; ARC; Ski C; Pres, SC; Pres, Jr Cl; Citz A; ARC A; Excellent Citations; Katherine Von Bora A; Lutheran GSct A; Med.

BOWMAN, Brian Elliot
Mt Vernon HS; Mt Vernon, OH (150-413) Band; Chor; Drama; Ensm; Ftbl; Soccer; Tr; Muskingum Col; Biol.

BOWMAN, Carlton Eugene
Bell Voc HS; Washington, DC; Ftbl; Outst Wood Working; Hampton Col; Elec Engnr.

BOWMAN, Danette Mae
Mount Airy Sr HS; Mount Airy, NC (25-190) Chem C; Secy, FNA; Monogram; Span C; Sftbl; Vlbl; Soil & Water Conservation; Bkbl A; Surry Comm Col; Registered Nurse.

BOWMAN, Donna Joyce
Wilbur D Mills HS; Little Rock, AR (30-390) Band; BC; FHA; SC; Y-Tns; Bkbl; Tr; Hist A; All Region Band; Church Yth Coun; Band Drum Major; Yth Coun Guidance; Lib C; Choir A; Acteens Qn-Scepter; Safety Coun; Star Camper ; PA; Baylor-U of Ark; Psych.

BOWMAN, Gregory Michael
Little Miami HS; Morrow, OH (1-200) A Cap Choir; BS; Chor; Drama; Hmrm; NHS; Span C; Span A; Drama A; Ky Christian Col; Ministry.

BOWMAN, Jacqueline Kim
Twin Lakes HS; Monticello, IN; Dbte Tm; Drama; NFL; Sci C; Spch C; Bio A; COM; Spch A; Yth Fel; Essay A; Vet Sci.

BOWMAN, Jenny Brant
Greater Latrobe HS; Latrobe, PA (17-518) AFS; NHS; Sci C; Ski C; Var C; Secy, Soph Cl; Tnns; Co-Cpt, Tr; COM; Q&S A; U of Va; Chem.

BOWMAN, Karen Marie
Flint Northern HS; Flint, MI (2%-600) Band; Secy, Fr C; NHS; Ski C; Cpt, Swim; COM; Hon Prog; Secy, GSct Troop; Ed, MSU Conf Newspaper; Semi-Fin, Mich St Comp Schol Prog; Mich St U; Vet Med.

BOWMAN, Kelly Ann
Boyd Co HS; Ashland, KY (10-450) BC; Bus C; FBLA; GS; Pres, Hmrm; Sch P; Span C; Cr-Ctry; Tr; Alg A; COM; Cl Fav; Journ A; Math A; St Champ, Mile Relay; Piano Mus A; Phys Ed A; Tr A's; U of Ky; Nurs.

BOWMAN, Linda Luezene
Cherokee HS; Cherokee, NC; FHA; PA; Gardener Web Col; Secy.

BOWMAN, Marlyce Lynn
Kerkhoven HS; Kerkhoven, MN (5-50) Band; Chor; FHA; Secy, 4H; Sch P; Soph Cl; Tr; Vlbl; Willman Area Voc-Tech Inst; LPN.

BOWMAN, Mary Lee
Southwestern HS; Detroit, MI; Chor; NHS; Type A; Shorthand A; Recordkeeping A; Spelling A; U of Detroit; Bus.

BOWMAN, Melanie Dawn
Paris HS; Paris, TX (15-325) Chldr; Pres, Chor; Ensm; FTA; Key C; VP, Soph Cl; Phys Ed.

BOWMAN, Melvin
Estill HS; Estill, SC (25%-100) BC.

BOWMAN, Michael L
Baker HS; Columbus, GA (3%-200) Sci C; Biol.

BOWMAN, Michael Wayne
Pleasant Grove HS; Pleasant Grove, AL (4-150) Secy, Chem C; NHS; Secy, Phys C; Most Out; U of Ala; Elec Engnr.

BOWMAN, Mitch Dee
Lawton HS; Lawton, OK (11-567) BS; Commercial C; Key C; NHS; Golf; Lamba Alpha Lamba; Institutional Schol; Ntl Schol; Cameron Col; Chem.

BOWMAN, Samuel Todd
Englewood HS; Jacksonville, FL (25-500) Hmrm; Soccer.

BOWMAN, Scott Carter
Mason City Sr HS; Mason City, IA (26-466) Chor; Tnns; I Ratings, St Vocal Mus Contest; Iowa St U; Engr.

BOWMAN, Sherri Lynn
Rockford Sr HS; Rockford, MI (90-350) Chor; Drama; NHS; Moody Bible Inst; Mus.

BOWSER, Charlotte Willette
New Brunswick HS; New Brunswick, NJ (30-236) NHS; Ryder Col; Acct.

BOWSER, Debie Joy
Santa Barbara HS; Santa Barbara, CA; A Cap Choir.

BOWSER, Debra Janice
Burkeville HS; Burkeville, TX (2-36) Ann; Chor; Drama; VP, FHA; Math C; Sci C; Spch C; Secy, SC; Tres, Soph Cl; Bkbl; Tnns; Tr; COM; Oxford U; Chem.

BOWSER, Douglas Moore
Winter Park HS; Winter Park, FL (298-934) Band; Chor; Hmrm; NFL; Orch; ARC; Span C; SC; COM; Hon Prog; Yth Fel; Presbyterian Col; Sociology.

BOWSER, Helen Louise
Granville HS; Granville, OH (6-142) Fr C; Tres, InterClub Coun; Span C; Y-Tns; Mgr, Bkbl; 4th Pl St, Ntl Fr Test; 1st Pl, St Schol Achv Test; Middleburg Col; Foreign Lang.

BOWSER, Yvette Denise
John F Kennedy HS; Silver Spring, MD (2-400) A-Ed, Ann; Community Yth Symph; Lat C; Orch; COM; Hon Prog; Young Life; Black Caucus; Pep C; Interntl C; Bio.

BOWSHER, Debora Lynn
Lawrence Central HS; Indianapolis, IN; Chldr; Commercial C; 4H; SC; Swim; 4H A; Chldr, Swim, A's; Butler U; TV & Broadcasting.

BOX, Amanda Jean
Natchitoches Central HS; Natchitoches, LA (14-240) Ann; Fr C; FBLA; Mjrte; I Dare You; Math A; Most Out; Q&S A; Sci A; Northwestern U; Special Ed.

BOX, Barry Glenn
Whitney HS; Whitney, TX (1-45) Pres, BC; Chess C; Co-Ch, Dbte Tm; Pres, FFA; NFL; Co-Cpt, Ftbl; Alg A; Hist A; Lion A; MLS; PTA A; Val; Yth Fel; Mr; Whitney HS Health A; Agr Stu A; All-Dist Ftbl Plaque; West Point; Engr.

BOXER, Jodi Wendy
Harrison HS; Harrison, NY (19-287) Chor; Drama; Ensm; Fr C; FTA; Lit Mag; NHS; Hon Prog; Regent Schol.

BOXILL, John Hammond
East Columbus HS; Columbus, OH; Chor; Ensm; VP, SC; Harvard U; Law.

BOYADJIAN, Jack H
Paramus HS; Paramus, NJ (40-585) Chess C; Dbte Tm; Hmrm; NHS; Co-Ed, Sch P; VP, SC; Var C; JV, Ftbl; Hon Prog; MLS; Yth Leg; U of Penn; Bus Adm.

BOYCE, Judy Carol
South Side HS; Memphis, TN (10%-320) Chldr; Math C; Mu Alpha Theta; NHS; Secy, Span C; Washington U; Computer Sci.

BOYCE, Marc Alan
Wichita SE HS; Wichita, KS; Cpt, Bkbl; JV, Ftbl; Coffeyville Juco Col; Elec Engnr.

BOYCE, Wanda Jean
Covington HS; Covington, TN (50-212) A Cap Choir; Chor; FHA; Shelby St Comm Col; Acct.

BOYD, Arnetta Sue
Amanda-Clearcreek HS; Amanda, OH (9-112) Band; Fr C; FNA; Mjrte; NHS; Rainbow; ARC; Secy, Sci C; Parl, SC; Sftbl; COM; Hon Prog; Sci A; Yth Fel; Outst Fr A; Columbus Tech Inst; Nurs.

BOYD, Bradley Duncan
Battle Mountain HS; Minturn-Vail, CO (5-68) N Tex St U; Drama.

BOYD, Calvin Ray
Alexander HS; Starkville, MS (3-28) Bkbl; Ftbl; Miss St U; Math.

BOYD, Carol Lynette
Washington HS; Washington, NC; Chldr; Chor; FHA; Span C; Span NHS; Hist A; Phys Ed A; Home Ec A; Lib A; Law.

BOYD, Cassandra Marie
Joseph S Clark HS; New Orleans, LA (6-36) Chldr; Chor; Mod Mus Mas; Span C; COM; Citz A; Hon Prog; Sci A; Xavier Col; Med Technology.

BOYD, Cecilia June
Loris HS; Loris, SC (10%-189) F-Ed, Ann; F-Ed, Sch P; SC; JV, Bkbl; UNC; Psych.

BOYD, Charles Wesley
Hickory Sr HS; Hermitage, PA (10-286) A Cap Choir; Chor; Drama; Pres, Hmrm; NHS; Span C; Pres, Var C; Ftbl; Tr; Chamber of Comm A; Yth Fel; Eagle Sct; SPAN; Dickinson Col; Law.

BOYD, Charlotte Ann
Sherman E Burroughs HS; Ridgecrest, CA (10-500) Tres, A Cap Choir; Chldr; Tres, Chor; Dbte Tm; Drama; Ensm; Madrigal; NFL; NHS; Spch C; SC; Thes; VP, Soph Cl; Tr; CSF; COM; Hon Prog; Spch A; VFW Orator Win; VofDEM; USC; Mus.

BOYD, Cheryl Elizabeth
St Joseph-Ogden HS; St Joseph, IL (23-100) Co-Ed, Ann; Chor; Ensm; HCt; Hon Prog; Yth Fel; Co-Cpt, Pom Pon Sq; Campus Life; Parkland Jr Col; Nurs.

BOYD, Deborah Ann
Tylertown HS; Tylertown, MS; BC; Ensm; Fr C; FBLA; Spch C; Ntl Sci Symposium; U of Sou Miss; Elem Ed.

BOYD, Debra Regina
Loris HS; Loris, SC (2-123) F-Ed, Ann; FHA; GS; 4H; Secy, NHS; VP, Sci C; VP, Sr Cl; Co-Ch, Jr Cl; Pres, Soph Cl; HCt; Hon Prog; Most Out; Chief Marshal; WW; VP of Records, Allied Yth; Newberry Summer Schol; Col of Charleston.

BOYD, Diana Lynn
Williamsville S HS; Williamsville, NY (100-313) 4H; Ski C; GAA; Houghton Col; Christian Ed.

BOYD, Donna Renee
Bloom Trail HS; Chicago Heights, IL; Cl Fav; HQn; Hon Prog; Sal; President's Phys Fitness A; Ill St U; Acct.

BOYD, Emily Ann
Big Spring HS; Big Spring, TX (10%-400) A Cap Choir; Chor; Ensm; NHS; Pres, Rainbow; Tri-HiY; Ntl Sci Symposium; Pres, FCA; Rainbow's Grand Cross; Cpt, Vlbl; WW; Coaches Vlbl A; Baylor U; Nurs.

BOYD, Eric Evan
Deer Park HS; Cincinnati, OH (8-210) Band; BS; Chor; Drama; Rptr, Lit Mag; Model UN; NHS; Orch; Rptr, Sch P; Sci C; Pres, SC; Thes; UN Council; World Affairs C; Amer Leg A; COM; Citz A; Hon Prog; Magna Cum Laude; Rotary A; Yth Fel; Most Talented; Exchange C A; Drum Major; *Northwestern U; Pre-Law.*

BOYD, Foy William III
Midland HS; Midland, TX (110-515) JETS; Key C; Order/Arrow; VP, SC; Var C; Ftbl; Tr; Order/Arrow A; Rotary A; Pres, EYC; Escort, Jr Coun Swtht; Explorers; Yth Appreciation Wk; SITCA; Eagle Sct; *Tex Tech U; Dental.*

BOYD, Gary John
N Royalton HS; N Royalton, OH (79-238) Demolay; 4H; JV, Ftbl; JV, Tr; *U of Hawaii; Marine Bio.*

BOYD, Gernell
Garfield Sr HS; Hamilton, OH; Ftbl; Tr; Wrest; Cl Fav; H of F; Tr A's; *U of Fla; Elec.*

BOYD, Jacqueline R
Northwest HS; St Louis, MO; COM; *Wash U; Anesthesiologist.*

BOYD, John Harold
Colo HS; Colo City, TX (1-126) Secy, Span C; JV, Tnns; Amer Leg A; *Tex Tech U; Archt.*

BOYD, Joni Lynn
Red Bank HS; Chattanooga, TN (5-349) Semi-Fin, GS; Lat C; NHS; Bkbl; Tr; Alg A; Amer Leg A; COM; Math A; Yth Fel; Hon Soc; *U of Tenn; Phys Therapy.*

BOYD, Katherine Louise
Melbourne HS; Melbourne, FL (50%-630) Band; JV, Chldr; Fr C; Superior Flute, Dist Band; Excel Flute, Ntl Fed of Mus C; *Math.*

BOYD, Keith Douglas
Eastern Hills HS; Fort Worth, TX (7-500) Ftbl; Tnns; Opt A; Star Student; Sch Top 2%; Metal Working A; *Sci.*

BOYD, Kent Arnold
F O Alexander HS; Starkville, MS (10-59) SC; Bsbl; Bkbl; Cpt, Ftbl; *Miss St U; Bus Adm.*

BOYD, Kyle Charles
Norman HS; Norman, OK (98-662) Tres, Chor; Ensm; Pres, Ger C; NHS; Order/Arrow; Sci C; JV, Tnns; COM; Chem A; Order/Arrow A; YFU Exchange Prog; *Austin Col; Bio Chem.*

BOYD, Laura Elaine
S Dade HS; Homestead, FL; Band; Crown & Scepter; Hmrm; Swim; Sup, Piano Festival; Sup, Piano Guild; *Nurs.*

BOYD, Linwood G
Williamston HS; Williamston, NC (51-180) Band; VP, Demolay; Key C; Monogram; Order/Arrow; Tnns; COM; *E Carolina Col; Bus.*

BOYD, Lisa Kathryn
Warren Co Sr HS; McMinnville, TN (165-387) FHA; 4H; Modern Foreign Lang C; Lat C; Creative Writing C; GScts; *David Lipscomb Col.*

BOYD, Lori Jo
Lincoln NE HS; Lincoln, NE (84-479) *SE Comm Col; Commercial Art.*

BOYD, Madonna Lynn
W Craven HS; Vanceboro, NC; Ann; FHA; 4H; Hmrm; NHS; Sch P; Sci C; Span C; Cpt, Drill Tm; Secy, Jr Civitan; Eng A; *E Carolina U; Bus.*

BOYD, Marian Kay
Van-Far HS; Vandalia, MO; Ann; Band; Q&S A; PA.

BOYD, Marie Annette
Van-Far Sr HS; Vandalia, MO (9-62) Band; Drama; Sch P; Spch C; Sci C; Journ A; Q&S A; WW; PA; *Culver-Stockton Col.*

BOYD, Mark Alan
Deer Park HS; Cincinnati, OH (14-210) Band; Chor; Tres, Drama; Model UN; NHS; Orch; Rptr, Sch P; Pres, Sci C; Secy, SC; Tres, Thes; UN Council; World Affairs C; COM; Citz A; Hon Prog; Lion A; Rotary A; Yth Fel; Comm Theatre; Asst, Fr Lab; Choir; Drum Major; Tres, Yth Group; Chrck Mus Comm; St Comp Ldrship; *Case Western Reserve U; Bio Med Engr.*

BOYD, Mary Beth
Williamston HS; Williamston, NC (20-220) Band; Fr C; FHA; Hmrm; Key C; Monogram; SC; Tnns; Yth Fel; *U of NC; Communications.*

BOYD, Phyllis Jo
Lincoln HS; Dallas, TX (10%-200) FTA; Tres, Hmrm; Key C; Math C; NHS; Rptr, Sch P; Sci C; Span C; Cl Fav; MLS; Type A; Span, Mus, Eng, NHS, A's; *N Tex St U; Pub Relations.*

BOYD, Rebecca Lynn
Princeton HS; Cincinnati, OH (200-570) A Cap Choir; Chor; Drama; Secy, FBLA; Type A; Yth Fel; Vikettes; *Ind St U; Bus.*

BOYD, Rhonda Kay
Clay Center Pub Sch; Clay Center, NE (6-32) Ann; Band; Chldr; Chor; Drama; NHS; VP, Y-Tns; Vlbl.

BOYD, Rhonda Lynn
Allen Jay HS; High Point, NC; Band; BC; Chldr; Chor; FHA; Monogram; COM; *NC St U; DVM.*

BOYD, Robert Wade
Victory Christian Acad; Jacksonville, FL (10%-100) Chess C; NHS; Span C; Bkbl; Ftbl; Bible C; *Arlington Baptist Col; Ministry.*

BOYD, Roger Dean
Pottsville Area HS; Pottsville, PA (80-360) Lat C; WW; *Penn St U; Bus Adm.*

BOYD, Scott Joseph
Marine Military Acad; Harlingen, TX (3-37) Band; Dbte Tm; Drama; Ensm; Orch; Bsbl; NEDT; Pres A; ROTC A; Rifle Tm; Superint List Solo & Ensm As; *Annapolis Naval Acad; Elec.*

BOYD, Tammy Jenae
Cleveland HS; Cleveland, TN; A Cap Choir; Band; Chor; Dbte Tm; Drama; Ensm; Fr C; Secy, FHA; FTA; Orch; Spch P; Spch C; Sftbl; Ensm A; Choir A; *Lee Col; Psych.*

BOYD, Terrance Gene
Stanley HS; Stanley, ND (30-57) Chor; Drama; FFA; Var C; Bsbl; Bkbl; Cr-Ctry; Ftbl; Tr; *Whapton Sch of Sci; Automobile Mech.*

BOYD, Yolanda Dorothy
St Mary Acad; New Orleans, LA (13-18) *Xavier Col; Commercial Art.*

BOYDSTON, Christie Anne
NW Classen HS; Oklahoma City, OK (5%-425) Mu Alpha Theta; Pres, NHS; Tnns; Rensselaer A; GS Alt; *Okla St U; Marine Bio.*

BOYDSTUN, Kristine Kay
Lynbrook HS; Cupertino, CA (104-620) CSF; Church Elder.

BOYEA, Elizabeth Ann
Permian HS; Odessa, TX (19-796) NHS; Hon Prog; Art A; VP, GSct; *Math.*

BOYER, Becky Lou
Maysville HS; Maysville, OK (10-40) Chor; FHA; Cl Fav; Talent As; *Home Ec.*

BOYER, Charles Edward
Wyoming Valley HS; Kingston, PA; Band; Chor; Rptr, Sch P; SC; VP, Var C; Bsbl; Cpt, Bkbl; Cr-Ctry; Ftbl; Co-Cpt, Tr; Citz A; ARC A; Spch A; Pres, Tr C; Dist Champ, Winter Tr; Sch Mus; Carpenter Engr School; All Stars, Bsbl; *Wilkes Col; Engr.*

BOYER, Cindy Dawnn
Temple Baptist Acad; Denver, CO; Co-Ed, Ann; Chldr; Chor; Ensm; NHS; VP, SC; HQn; Christian Character; *Tenn Temple; Religious Ed.*

BOYER, David Glenn
Northern Chester Co Tech Sch; Pheonixville, PA (10-192) Hon Prog.

BOYER, Debra Ann
Marian HS; Hometown, PA (58-175) Bus C; Chor; Hon Prog; Pres, Marian Yth Corp; Girl o-t Mo; Future Nurs C; Color Guard; V Ltr; *McCanns Sch of Bus; Secy.*

BOYER, Garry Dee
Horseheads HS; Horseheads, NY (60-600) All Amer Yth; JETS; Span C; Var C; JV, Soccer; Tr; Hon Prog; Pres A; Yth Fel; *Econ.*

BOYER, James William
Beaverton HS; Beaverton, OR (239-552) Feature Cartoonist; Window Decorat; 1st Decorat & Dsgn VW Wagon Cont; 1st Pl, Poster Contest; Illustrated Sermons; *Commercial Art.*

BOYER, Janice Ann
John F Kennedy Sr HS; Bloomington, MN (97-723) Chor; Drama; Madrigal; Tres, Ski C; Swim; JA A; Regional Voice; Job's Daughters; Pres, Tres, Secy, Explorers; *Computer System Analysis.*

BOYER, Joanne Marie
Oppenheim-Ephratah HS; St Johnsville, NY (46-49) Chldr; Chor; Fr C; Soccer; Vlbl; *Foulton Montgomery Comm Col.*

BOYER, June Rebecca
York Suburban Sr HS; York, PA (85-287) Band; Chor; Drama; Var C; Tnns; COM; JA A; Pres A; Yth Ed Assn; *USC Dickinson; Corporate Law.*

BOYER, Meg Ramage
Elston Sr HS; Michigan City, IN (114-370) Co-Ed, Ann; VP, Chor; Hmrm; Ski C; SC; Secy, Sr Cl; HCt; *Ball St U; Ed.*

BOYER, Patricia Kay
Bellevue Sr HS; Bellevue, OH (61-300) Pres, 4H; 4H A; Vlbl; Attitude A; Exchange Stu.

BOYES, Renee Jean
Kennedy Sr HS; Bloomington, MN; Chor; Ger C; Hmrm; Madrigal; Orch; ARC; Spch A; Tres, JA; Cpt, Camp Fire Girls; Stu o-t Month; Trch Bearer, Cooking & Perform Arts; *Mus.*

BOYETT, Phyllis Ann
Reidsville HS; Reidsville, GA; Sci C; SC; Bkbl.

BOYETTE, Pamela Yvette
John F Kennedy HS; Suffolk, VA (10%-281) FBLA; NHS; Bkbl; Co-Cpt, Tr; Hon Prog; Cert of Hon; MVP, Tr; Sch Monitor Trophies; *Social Work.*

BOYETTE, Rodney Glenn
Hopewell HS; Hopewell, VA (4-385) BC; Hmrm; Key C; Monogram; NHS; Span C; Bsbl; JV, Bkbl; Co-Cpt, Cr-Ctry; JV, Ftbl; Tr; Opt A; *U of Richmond; Math.*

BOYKIN, Alisa Tijuan
Clinton HS; Clinton, NC; Band; BC; Chor; Monogram; Choral A; *St Augustines Col; Mus.*

BOYKIN, Dana Leigh
Irwin Co HS; Ocilla, GA (25%-119) Ann; 4H; Tri-HiY; Var C; Bkbl; Tr; Hustler A; *Valdosta St Col; Phys Ed.*

BOYKIN, Deborah Elizabeth
W Guilford HS; Greensboro, NC (60-210) Span C; Alg A; Health Careers; *U of NC; Nurs.*

BOYKIN, Jesse James
Clinton HS; Clinton, NC (17-200) Chor; Span C; Ftbl; Citz A; Cl Fav; PA; Pres, Hist C; *US Army; Adm.*

BOYKIN, Rodney Dale
Ironton HS; Ironton, OH; Sci C; Span C; Bsbl; Bkbl; Ftbl; Tnns; Tr; Sci A.

BOYKIN, Susan Kay
Harlingen HS; Harlingen, TX (100-750) Chem C; Cpt, Mjrte; Math C; Rptr, Sch P; Span C; SC; Cl Fav; Kiwanis A; Yth Fel; Yth Foundation; *Tex Tech U; Bus.*

BOYKO, Denise Ann
Stanton Pub HS; Stanton, ND (3-18) Ann; Chldr; Chor; Pres, Drama; Model UN; Co-Ed, Sch P; SC; Co-Cpt, Bkbl; Golf; Tr; Cl Fav; Hon Prog; I Dare You; Most Outst; Yth Fel; Ath o-t Yr; Best Df Best Reb Best Fr Th Bkbl; *Dickinson St Col; Psych.*

BOYKO, Mary Ellen
Riverside HS; Taylor, PA (3-194) Chldr; FTA; NHS; Hon Prog; NEDT; *Muhlenberg Col; Sci.*

BOYLE, Annetta Marie
Humansville HS; Humansville, MO (2-37) Band; Chor; FFA; FHA; JV, Bkbl; Type A; Sch Play; JV, Vlbl; Shorthand & Creative Writing; *SMSU; Photography.*

BOYLE, Dennis Jay
Nathan Hale HS; Tulsa, OK (400-640) Band; Chess C; Chor; Orch; Sch Achieve Tm; Bsbl; Ftbl; Wrest; Yth Worship; Midshipman, Navy Sea Cadet; *Okla Christian Col; Ministry.*

BOYLE, Elizabeth Ann
Good Counsel HS; Newark, NJ (2-77) Hmrm; NHS; Ed, Sch P; SC; Hon Prog; NEDT; Folk Group; Yrbk Staff; *Clara Maass Col; Nurs.*

BOYLE, Hugh Michael
Mt St Michael Acad; Bronx New York, NY (90-364) Ch, CYO; Drama; Thes; Mgr, Bsbl; Mgr, Hockey; COM; *God & Country A;* Sacristan.

BOYLE, Irvin Robert
Nether Providence HS; Wallingford, PA (4-276) Secy, Band; Chor; NHS; Tres, Orch; Order/Arrow; Hon Prog; NMS; Order/Arrow A; Gypsy Orch; US Arch Congress; Carnival Orch; All St, District Bands; Math Tm.

BOYLE, Judith Ann
Moreau HS; Hayward, CA (27-402) Drama; Hon Prog; *Math.*

BOYLE, Kathleen Erin
Marian Cath HS; Tamaqua, PA (7-153) Cpt, Dbte Tm; VP, NFL; NHS; Rptr, Sch P; Hon Prog; NEDT; Spch A; Yth Foundation; Debate A; Candystriper; Yth Corps; *Penn St U; Chem.*

BOYLE, Kim Maria
Benjamin Franklin HS; New Orleans, LA (30%-186) Band; Secy, SC; Tnns; Citz A; Hist A; Math A; Sci A; Spch A; Superior, LMEA A; Excel, City-Wide Spelling Test; HR A; Off Asst; *Pol Sci.*

BOYLE, Seamos
St Peters Prep Sch; Jersey City, NJ (2-270) CYO; Cpt, Dbte Tm; Co-Ed, Lit Mag; NHS; Elk A; NMF; NEDT; Sal; *Harvard U; Govt.*

BOYLE, Sherry Alison
Prince Edward Acad; Farmville, VA; Pres, Soph Cl; Cpt, Bkbl; Pep C; SCA; Best Offense, Defense, Bkbl; *Zoological Research.*

BOYLE, Stephen Christopher
Sacred Heart HS; Vineland, NJ; CYO; Bkbl; *Rutgers U; Acct.*

BOYLE, Tom Wilson
Western HS; Las Vegas, NV (10%-750) A Cap Choir; NHS; Ski C; Var C; Cr-Ctry; Soccer; Tr; Tnns; COM; Yth Fel; Cr-Ctry, 500 Mile A; Art As.

BOYLES, Bob L Jr
Crosby HS; Crosby, TX; Ann; FFA; NHS; Cpt, Ftbl; Tr; Amer Leg A; Schol A; *U of Tex; Bus Adm.*

BOYLES, Kimberly Luette
Castle Park HS; Chula Vista, CA (20-426) A Cap Choir; Secy, CYO; JV, Chldr; Pres, Chor; Ensm; Hmrm; InterClub Coun; NFL; F-Ed, Sch P; Pres, Spch C; Semi-Fin, SC; Mgr, Bkbl; Mgr, Swim; CSF; COM; Citz A; Hon Prog; Most Out; Rotary A; Spch A; MVP, Chor; Eng A; *Occidental Col; Interior Design.*

BOYNTON, Paul Andrew
Seneca Valley HS; Gaithersburg, MD; Math C; Mgr, Bsbl; Mgr, Ftbl; Pres, Explorers; Pres, Church Yth; Math Tm; Outst Ftbl Achv, A's.

BOYST, Elizabeth Wells
Franklin Regional HS; Murrysville, PA (5%-325) AFS; Ann; Ski C; Yth Fel; Dist Yth Coun; Schol A; Excel, Piano; *Duke U; Child Psych.*

BOYTAR, Tanja Kaye
Chardon HS; Chardon, OH (20-263) Band; Secy, Drama; Ensm; VP, Mod Mus Mas; NHS; Pres, Rainbow; SC; Thes; HCt; Yth Fel; Linda Madaras Schol; Bkbl, St Cert; Hon Thespians; Sunday Sch Teacher; *Ohio St Col; Pre-Law.*

BOYTAR, Thomas Kelly
Chardon HS; Chardon, OH; Band; Ftbl; *Bus.*

BOYTER, Kelle Tlaine
Sulphur HS; Sulphur, LA (33%-430) A Cap Choir; Chor; FHA; Bank Of Amer A; *God & Country A;* Yth Fel; Yth Foundation; *La Col; Acct.*

BOYUM, Mary Erna
Minnehaha Acad; Minneapolis, MN (10%-120) A Cap Choir; Community Yth Symph; Ger C; NHS; MVP, Orch; Tr; Drama & Singing Group.

BOZARTH, Allen Dean
Eula HS; Clyde, TX (2-28) FFA; SC; Bkbl; JV, Tnns; *Tex A&M U; Med.*

BOZARTH, Jeffrey Allen
Southport HS; Indianapolis, IN (138-482) Demolay; Sftbl.

BOZZA, Craig A
Aquinas HS; Rochester, NY; Band; Chor; Bkbl; Ntl Cath Mus Ed Asn.

BOZZA, Craig Alexander
Aquinas Inst; Rochester, NY (106-186) Band; Chor; Bkbl; Ftbl; Sftbl; Ntl Cath Mus Ed Asn; ROTC; Church Folk Group; *Hobart Col; Communications.*

BRAACK, David Allen Jr
R L Turner HS; Dallas, TX; Orch; Order/Arrow; Wrest; *Engr.*

BRAASCH, Kenneth Wayne
Oshkosh W HS; Oshkosh, WI; Band; Ensm; 4H; Orch; Bus Mgr, Sch P; Hon Prog; *Mus Ed.*

BRAATEN, David Scott
Putnam City HS; Oklahoma City, OK (25%-1000) Band; Bus C; FBLA; Pol Sci C; Ski C; Arch; Bsbl; Sftbl; Swim; Wrest; *Okla St U; Bus.*

BRABEC, Bradford Allen
Geneva HS; Geneva, NE (11-44) Ann; Band; Chor; Ger C; Madrigal; NHS; VP, Jr Cl; Golf; Journ A; Type A; Newspaper Carrier A's; *Optometry.*

BRABHAM, Joseph Ronald
S Broward HS; Hollywood, FL (15-360) BS; Model UN; NHS; Hon Prog; Type A; *Broward Comm Col; Liberal Arts.*

BRACAMONTES, John Robert
Granite City HS N; Granite City, IL (91-419) Var C; Cr-Ctry; Tr; Pres & Tres, Yth Group; Coun of Ministries; Adm Board; *Sci.*

BRACE, Linda Marie
Santa Rita HS; Tucson, AZ (35-600) Band; Chor; Community Yth Symph; Ensm; NHS; Orch; Pres, Y-Tns; WW; All St Chor; Excel, St Solo Fest; *Los Angeles Baptist Col; Mus.*

BRACHER, Lisa Beth Margit
S P Waltrip Sr HS; Houston, TX (1-630) Ed, Ann; Pres, Fr C; French NHS; Key C; VP, NHS; Co-Cpt, Tnns; Journ A; Most Out; NMS; NEDT; Q&S A; Rotary A; Yth Foundation A; Hon School; *Augustana Col; Bus.*

BRACHTENBACH, Marie
West HS; Iowa City, IA (99-347) Band; CYO; Drama; Sch P; Geography A; *U of Iowa; Lib Arts.*

BRACK, Lisa Michelle
Saint Bonaventure HS; Ventura, CA; JV, Chldr; SC; Sftbl; Alg A; Cl Fav; Yth Fel; Pres, Fresh Cl; *Nurs.*

BRACKBILL, William Harold
J M Tate HS; Gonzalez, FL (50-800) InterClub Coun; NHS; Soccer; NEDT; *U of Fla; Hotel-Restaurant Mgt.*

BRACKEN, Cynthia Decelle
Clinton HS; Clinton, MS; Chldr; SC; Var C; Y-Tns; Secy, Jr Cl; Bkbl; Cl Fav; HQn; HCt; Miss Clinton HS; FCA; Friendliest; Secy, DECA C; Peer Coun; *U of Sou Miss; Psych.*

BRACKEN, Pamela
Putnam City HS; Okla City, OK (13-850) Fr C; Hmrm; NHS; Sci C; SC; V-Ch, World Affairs; C; Fr A; Girl Popularity; *Wheaton Col; Christian Counseling.*

BRACKENBURY, David Wayne
Northwest HS; Omaha, NE; Order/Arrow; JV, Swim; Hon Prog; Order/Arrow A; Rotary A; *U of NE at Lincoln; Architecture.*

BRACKENS, Tami Michelle
Skyline HS; Dallas, TX (25%-950) Hmrm; S-T, Jr Cl; *U of Houston; Aviation.*

BRACKER, Mary Jane
Abraham Lincoln HS; Council Bluffs, IA (25%-450) Chor; Span C; *Med.*

BRACKER, William Charles
Abraham Lincoln HS; Council Bluffs, IA (25%-425) Pres, Dbte Tm; Fr C; Order/Arrow; Spch C; SC; Swim; Hon Prog; Order/Arrow A; Spch A; Eagle Sct; *Pre-Law.*

BRACKETT, Janana Lea
Nathan Hale HS; Tulsa, OK (332-677) Band; FBLA; *Tulsa Jr Col; Bus.*

BRACKETT, Rebecca Ann
Bokchito HS; Bokchito, OK (1-21) Chor; Tres, FHA; Rptr, 4H; Math C; Sch Achieve Tm; SC; Var C; VP, Sr Cl; Cpt, Bkbl; Beauty; Citz A; 4H A; HCt; Hon Prog; Math A; MLS; Val; Homemaking A; Eng A; Co, Bkbl All-Star; St Hon Soc; *Southeastern Okla St U; Med.*

BRACKETT, Sandra Kay
Eufaula HS; Eufaula, OK; Ann; Chldr; Chor; VP, Span C; VP, Sr Cl; Rptr, Jr Cl; Rptr, Soph Cl; HQn; *NE Okla St U; Psych.*

BRACKETT, Susan Mary
Seekonk HS; Seekonk, MA (10-224) Drama; FTA; Math C; NHS; Spch C; Tnns; Hon Prog; *Dartmouth Col; Med.*

BRACKETT, Vicki Lyn
E Hardin HS; Glendale, KY (2-183) F-Ed; Ann; Rptr, BC; FHA; Pres, FTA; Math C; Tres, Jr Cl; Sal; *Elizabethtown Comm Col.*

BRACKIN, Barry Joe
Hazlewood HS; Town Creek, AL (10%-60) F-Ed, Ann; BC; FFA; Sci C; 4H A; WW.

BRACKOB, Elise Marie
Southfield HS; Southfield, MI; Band; Chor; Ski C; Span C; Co-Cpt, Bsbl; Tr; Hon Prog; Pres, MYF; Phys Ed; Foreign Lang A; *Mich St U.*

BRADBURY, Guy Barton
Patterson Sch; Lenoir, NC (4-21) Rptr, Ann; Secy, Demolay; Order/Arrow; Span C; Bsbl; Ftbl; Swim; *Campbell Col; Govt.*

BRADBURY, Jill Suzanne
Medina HS; Medina, TN (1-23) F-Ed, Ann; Pres, BC; FHA; Secy, SC; Var C; VP, Jr Cl; Secy, Soph Cl; Bkbl; Val; Most Intellectual; *Union U; Math.*

BRADDOCK, Cheryl Patrice
Walnut HS; Walnut, MS (10-55) Ann; FHA; Bkbl; Tr; HCt; Church Worker; Pep C; Sch Play; *NE Miss Jr Col; Nurs.*

BRADDOCK, Freddie Lee
Saginaw HS; Saginaw, MI; Chor; Hmrm; Pres, Sch Achieve Tm; SC; Bkbl; COM; Citz A; JA A; Ntl Achv Schol; Type A; Yth Fel; *Mich St U; Bus Adm.*

BRADDY, Donna Marie
Floresville HS; Floresville, TX; Band; Band Solo and Ensm Contest Medal.

BRADEL, Deborah Ann
Kelly HS; Chicago, IL (5-325) Tres, Math C; NHS; Hon Prog; Sci A; St Scholar; *DePaul U; Acct.*

BRADEN, Barry Matthew
Cottage Grove HS; Cottage Grove, OR (14-300) VP, AFS; Band; BS; Drama; Hmrm; Rptr, NHS; Tres, SC; Thes; Cr-Ctry; Bio A; Sci A; *Oreg St U; Elec Engr.*

BRADEN, Charles Richard
Bradleyville HS; Bradleyville, MO (5-20) BC; Chor; Drama; 4H; SC; Bsbl; Bkbl; Sftbl; Tr; Wrest; 4H A; HCt; Essay Contest Merit A; 4-H A's; Sch o-t Ozarks; *Agr.*

BRADEN, Pamela Ruth
Webster Co HS; Dixon, KY (3-115) Band; Secy, Sr Cl; Mgr, Bkbl; *Murray St Col; Park & Recreation.*

BRADEY, Naomi Dale
Landrum HS; Landrum, SC (10%-55) Ann; BC; Chor; VP, FHA; Rptr, Sr Cl; Rptr, Jr Cl; Bkbl; Hist A; WW; *Newberry Col; Psych.*

BRADFIELD, Laura Sue
Berkley HS; Berkley, MI; Band; COM.

BRADFIELD, Marcus Eugene
Lindblom Tech HS; Chicago, IL (325-750) Band; CYO; ARC; Bsbl; JV, Bkbl; Ftbl; JV, Sftbl; JV, Swim; COM; ARC A; Band, Ftbl & Penmanship A's; *Math.*

BRADFORD, Bronwyn Elise
Putnam City HS; Oklahoma City, OK; Commercial C; SC.

BRADFORD, Cheri Louise
Cartersville HS; Cartersville, GA; Band; Ensm; Fr C; *U of Ga; Vet Med.*

BRADFORD, DeDra Elaine
Central HS; Fayetteville, TN;

BRADFORD, Deidra Annette
Carver HS; Winston-Salem, NC (57-760) Band; Mjrte; SC; Bkbl; Mgr, Tr; COM; JA A; Span Diploma of Merit; Span Drama Cert; Band Ldrship Cert; Drum Mjrte Cert; *UNC-CH; Acct.*

BRADFORD, Ethan Robert
Mt Vernon HS; Mt Vernon, WA (6-300) Pres, Chess C; Ger C; NHS; Soccer; B Crocker A; COM; JA A; NMF; Sci A; Stu Trip, Ger; Hi-Q Tm; *Stanford U; Astronomy.*

BRADFORD, Gloria Elizabeth
Paul Laurence Dunbar HS; Baltimore, MD; Hon Soc; *Coppin St Col; Nurs.*

BRADFORD, Hershal David II
Auburn HS; Auburn, AL (10-251) Chor; Fr C; Mu Alpha Theta; Ftbl; Golf; Fr A; Eng A.

BRADFORD, Mark Lyndon
Jena HS; Jena, LA; Band; VP, Drama; All Dist Band; Superior Band Ensm; Super, Solo & Sight Read Pianist; *La Col; Ministry of Mus & Yth.*

BRADFORD, Nancy Elaine
E Ridge HS; Chattanooga, TN (104-250) Chor; Tri-HiY; Y-Tns; Tnns; *Cleveland St Comm Col; Bus.*

BRADFORD, Tari Tarnette
Huntington HS; Shreveport, LA; Chor; 4H; Tr; COM; Citz A; HCt; 3rd Runner-Up, Miss Zino; JV Swtht; Harvest Qn; *Sou U; Engr.*

BRADFORD, Willie Durant Jr
Bennettsville HS; Bennettsville, SC (39-190) Cert Building Construction; *Chesterfield Tech Col; Bus Adm.*

BRADFUTE, Terry Quinne
Morristown-Hamblen HS W; Morristown, TN (10%-375) BC; Chor; Ensm; Fr C; Madrigal; Tr; *Baylor U; Lib Arts.*

BRADHAM, Carol Gay
Calvary Christian Acad; Ridgeland, SC (2-2) Ed, Ann; Mgr, Chldr; Ensm; Pres, Hmrm; Sftbl; Citz A; HCt; Hon Prog; WW, Mus; Ntl ACE Sch Conv A; *Pensacola Christian Col; Elem Ed.*

BRADLEY, Barbara Ann
Burke HS; Charleston, SC (16-201) F-Ed, Ann; Secy, Drama; VP, Hmrm; Secy, Sr Cl; WW; *U of SC; Med.*

BRADLEY, Carlotta Lynda
Philadelphia HS For Girls; Philadelphia, PA (96-450) Orch; *Theatre Arts.*

BRADLEY, David Wayne
R L Turner HS; Carrollton, TX (231-843) Chor; Drama; NFL; Top 5%, NMS; *U of Okla; Pol Sci.*

BRADLEY, Denise Annetta
Thomas Jefferson Prep Col; St Louis, MO (3-7) Chor; Fr C; COM; *Detroit U; Engr.*

BRADLEY, Donna Kay
Gaffney Sr HS; Gaffney, SC; Chldr; Fr C; VP, Hmrm; F-Ed, Sch P; Sci C; SC; Cl Fav; Sci A; Yth Fel.

BRADLEY, Edward Bryan
El Dorado HS; El Dorado, AR (10%-472) NHS; Ftbl; *U of Ark; Elec.*

BRADLEY, Elisabeth Dianne
Brethren Christian Sch; Osceola, IN (5%-23) Chor; Fr C; ARC; Yth Fel; Semi- fin, Voice of Democracy; *Grace Col.*

BRADLEY, Evelyn
Williamsburg HS; Andrews, SC; HCt; *Columbia U; Secy.*

BRADLEY, Harold Allen Jr
Canyon HS; Anaheim, CA (2%-550) A Cap Choir; BS; Drama; Ftbl; Tr; *Theology.*

BRADLEY, Heather Lynn
Chardon HS; Chardon, OH (25-220) Ann; Secy, Chor; FHA; 4H; Mod Mus Mas; NHS; *Bowling Green St U; Elem Ed.*

BRADLEY, James Authur
W End HS; Birmingham, AL (85-200) Pres, Band; Drama; SC; Thes; COM; Cl Fav; HCt; Hon Prog; Trouble Shooting, Band Achv, A's; Mr Band; *Ala St U; Art Ed.*

BRADLEY, James Haraway
Grace St Luke's Episcopal HS; Memphis, TN (8-16) Chess C; Lat C; Math C; Phys C; Sci C; Var C; Cpt, Bsbl; Bkbl; Co-Cpt, Soccer; Tr; Hon Prog; *Christian Brothers Col; Hist.*

BRADLEY, Jaynie Robyn
Clinton Sr HS; Clinton, TN (25%-200) Chor; Ensm; NHS; Rainbow; Sftbl; Type A; Eng A; Glee C A; *Cumberland Col; Hist.*

BRADLEY, John Clinton
Wakulla HS; Crawfordville, FL; NHS; Stu A; YCC Outst Performance A; *FSU; Hist.*

BRADLEY, Kim Leslie
Watchung Hills Regional HS; Warren, NJ (136-472) Co-Cpt, Chldr; Hmrm; Ski C; JV, Hockey; *Douglass Col; Nurs.*

BRADLEY, Lea Rachelle
East HS; Cleveland, OH (9-534) Chor; Citz A; Hon Prog; *Dyke Col; Secy Sci.*

BRADLEY, Lori Ann
Lanesboro HS; Lanesboro, MN (5-32) Ann; Band; Chor; Ensm; Pres, FHA; Model UN; VP, Jr Cl; Golf; Vlbl; Dist Band As; Dist Chor A; *Fine & Applied Arts.*

BRADLEY, Lynne Louise
Sturgis HS; Sturgis, MI (57-286) Chor; Ensm; 4H A.

BRADLEY, Marrill Lynn
Mumford HS; Detroit, MI (34-500) Chor; Dbte Tm; Hmrm; Rptr, Sch P; Sci C; Span C; Span NHS; Y-Tns; Tnns; Tr; Beauty; Hon Prog; JA A; Swtht; Cl Pretty Smile; *Wayne St Col; Pre-Med.*

BRADLEY, Ruth Lynne
Bloomfield Sr HS; Bloomfield, NJ (83-651) Band; Pres, Hmrm; Mjrte; SC; Tnns; Twirler; Church Singing Group; Pep C; Stu Govt Assn; Off, Yth Group; *Christian Elem Ed.*

BRADLEY, Sharla J'Nell
Shamrock HS; Shamrock, TX (25-50) Band; FHA; Secy, Rainbow; *Amarillo Jr Col; Interior Design.*

BRADLEY, Shrese
East HS; Cleveland, OH (3-479) Chor; ARC; Up Bound; Bio A; Hon Prog; Merit, Spelling Contest; *Case Western Reserve U; Acct.*

BRADLEY, Stefanie Richelle
Grimsley HS; Greensboro, NC; Band; Hmrm; SC; Pres, Soph Cl; Sftbl; Yth Fel; WW Greensboro Yth; Jr Marshal; Jr Jaycettes; Church Activities; *U of Ga; Special Ed.*

BRADOW, Gretchen Alethea
Colonel White HS; Dayton, OH (1-201) Drama; Fr C; Hmrm; Lat C; NHS; SC; COM; Gov Honor Prog; Hon Prog; Math A; NMF; NMS; NEDT; Summa Cum Laude; Val; Treas, JA; Fin, Miss JA; Hochwalt A; Fin, Earthwatch; *Bryn Mawr Col; Chem.*

BRADRICK, Linda Diane
Parkway HS; Rockford, OH (8-89) Band; Chor; Drama; Ensm; Lat C; SC; Bkbl; Tr; Pres, Pep C; Best Actress; GAA; *Anderson Col; Eng.*

BRADSHAW, Carol Jean
DeSoto Sr HS; De Soto, MO (30%-270) Band; Drama; Ensm; FBLA; NHS; Rotary A; Type A; Cpt, Pom Pons; *Jefferson Col; Bus.*

BRADSHAW, Christi Kay
Chatsworth HS; Chatsworth, CA (250-1050) A Cap Choir; Chor; Ensm; Hmrm; Secy, NHS; S-T, SC; Tr; COM; Hon Prog; Concert Choir Ltr; *Pepperdine U; Mus.*

BRADSHAW, Constance Sue
Lakeview HS; Battle Creek, MI; VP, Fr C; NHS; *Albion Col; Bus.*

BRADSHAW, Earl Edward
Spruce Creek HS; Port Orange, FL; Chess C; Community Yth Symph; VP, Drama; Fr C; NHS; Orch; Schol Tm; *Mus.*

BRADSHAW, Janet Ann
Sky View HS; Smithfield, UT (7-611) FHA; Secy, Jr Cl; Bausch & Lomb A; Citz A; LDS Seminary Coun; Acad A; *Utah St U.*

BRADSHAW, Jeffrey Lynn
S Decatur HS; Greensburg, IN (12-110) Pres, FFA; Key C; SC; *Purdue U; Agr.*

BRADSHAW, Jill
Oppenheim-Ephratah Central Sch; St Johnsville, NY (2-39) Chldr; NHS; SC; Var C; Soccer; Sftbl; Tr; Sal; *Fulton-Montgomery C C; Bus Adm.*

BRADSHAW, Lisa DeFrost
Kennedy HS; Atlanta, GA; MVP, Band; Chldr; Chor; Drama.

BRADSHAW, Lisa Louise
Muskogee HS; Muskogee, OK (35-717) Cpt, Chldr; Fr C; SC; HQn; Yth Fel; Gym; Dance; All Sch Musical; Pelphic Literary Soc; *Bradly U; Bus.*

BRADSHAW, Phyllis Thomasine
Suffolk HS; Suffolk, VA (1-118) GS; Secy, Lat C; Monogram; NHS; Ch, Tri-HiY; Bkbl; Sftbl; Bio A; Val; Semi- fin, Miss Ntl Tn; *Louise Obici Nurs Sch; Med Missions.*

BRADSHAW, Robin Elizabeth
Jessamine Co HS; Nicholasville, KY; Ann; BC; VP, Fr C; 4H; Bsbl; Home Ec A; *U of Ky; Dentistry.*

BRADSHAW, Sunda Jeanette
Liberty HS; Liberty, IL (11-46) Cpt, Chldr; FHA; NHS; Sci C; Var C; Secy, Sr Cl; Tr; HQn; Hon Prog; Pres, Pep C; WW; FHA A's; Hist, Songldr, GAA; REA Pageant.

BRADSHER, Royce Duane
Pampa Sr HS; Pampa, TX; Band.

BRADSTREET, Bonnie Kay
Washington HS; Cherokee, IA (13-157) Chor; Rainbow; Stu for Ed Services; *Augustana Col; Teacher of Deaf.*

BRADSTREET, Steven Jay
Addison Comm Sch; Addison, MI (8-110) Band; BS; Ensm; Lit Mag; SC; Pres, Var C; Bsbl; Bkbl; Co-Cpt, Ftbl; Sftbl; Tr; HCt.

BRADWIN, Susan Catherine
Avon HS; Avon, MA (8-90) Lit Mag; VP, NHS; Pres, Sr Cl; Tres, Soph Cl; Mgr, Bsbl; Co-Cpt, Bkbl; *Salem St Col; Nurs.*

BRADY, Ann Marie Lousie
Havre HS; Havre, MT; CYO; Hmrm; InterAct C; Sodality; JV, Bkbl; Tr; God & Country A; 4H A; Marian A; 1st Cl GSct; *Mont St U; Computor Prog.*

BRADY, Benita Carol
Walter Hines Page HS; Greensboro, NC (10%-650) Chor; Ensm; Fin, Jr Miss Pagent; Key C; Lit Mag; NHS; MVP, Orch; VP, Span NHS; WW, Greensboro Yth; Eng Hon Prog; 'Most Talented', Sr Cl; Euterpe Schol; Mus Cert of Merit; KS Reynolds Schol; Mst Outst, Orch; *U of NC at Greensboro; Applied Mus.*

BRADY, Christina Lynne
G A R HS; Wilkes-Barre, PA (4-186) Drama; NHS; Orch; Type A; *Bus.*

BRADY, Daphne Marian
Saint Cecilia Acad; Nashville, TN; Ann; Chor; Pres, Fr C; Mu Alpha Theta; NHS; JA A; Ntl Achv Schol; NEDT; Treas, Yth Coun; AFROTC Schol; WW; *Tenn St U; Pre-Med.*

BRADY, David Allan
Springfield Local HS; Petersburg, OH (20%-150) HiY; NHS; Span C; Ftbl; Tr; *Zoology.*

BRADY, Donna Marie
Boulder HS; Boulder, CO; Hockey.

BRADY, Joseph Patrick
Deerborne Sr HS; Coral Gables, FL (8-75) BC; Chess C; NHS; *Dade Jr Col; Law.*

BRADY, Michael Floyd
Anacortes HS; Anacortes, WA; Ann; VP, HiY; Key C; Model UN; Order/Arrow; Ftbl; JV, Tnns; *W Wash St U; Law.*

BRADY, Patrick Charles
Maple Shade HS; Maple Shade, NJ (10%-235) Band; Key C; NHS; JV, Bkbl; JV, Tr; Alg A; *Drexel U; Chem Engr.*

BRADY, Phillip John
Carrollton HS; Saginaw, MI (15-165) Drama; NHS; Order/Arrow; Order/Arrow A; Yth Fel; Eagle Sct; *Purdue U; Agr.*

BRADY, Scott Russell
Orange Glen HS; Escondido, CA; JV, Golf; COM.

BRADY, Sherry Lynn
Thompson HS; Alabaster, AL (5%-255) A Cap Choir; Band; BC; Chor; NHS; COM; Type A; *U of Ala; Communications.*

BRADY, Vivian Mary
John W Hallahan Cath Girls HS; Philadelphia, PA (5-431) Fr C; Model UN; NFL; NHS; Orch; Rptr, Sch P; Secy, World Affairs; Hist A; Hon Prog; K of C A; Mus A; Nom, Principal's Sch-St Joseph's Co; *St Joseph's Col; Interntl Relations.*

BRAECKEL, Denise Elizabeth
Springfield Catholic HS; Springfield, MO (26-63) JV, Chldr; Drama; Rptr, Sch P; Spch C; SC; Thes; Hon Prog; JA A; Drama A; *SW Mo St U; Bus.*

BRAFFORD, Lori Lynn
Morgan HS; McConnelsville, OH (24-261) Band; Fr C; FHA; Mjrte; Math C; NHS; Sftbl; COM; Hon Prog; Bkbl Statistician; Stu C; *Nurs.*

BRAGAGNOLO, Bruno
Weber HS; Chicago, IL (19-218) Fr C; Math C; COM; Hon Prog; Math A; Sci A; St Scholar; Marine Phys Achv A; Outst A, Jr Acad of Sci; *U of Ill; Aviation.*

BRAGAGNOLO, Robert
Weber HS; Chicago, IL (21-242) Fr C; Hon Prog; NEDT; HR; *U of Ill; Phar.*

BRAGG, Kim Ann
Shaler Area HS; Glenshaw, PA; CYO; Hmrm; Bkbl; Sftbl; Hon Prog; Yth Fel; Ath A; *Pitt Col; Phys Therapy.*

BRAGG, Pamela Camille
Miami Norland Sr HS; Miami, FL (22-526) Band; Tres, Mod Mus Mas; Tres, Mu Alpha Theta; NFL; NHS; Hon Prog; Social Stu Forum; Sub Debs; Yth Choir Accompanist; PSAT Commended Stu; *Broward Comm Col; Acct.*

BRAGG, Patricia Ann
Louisville HS; Louisville, MS; Chem C; Chor; FHA; Spch C; Sftbl; Cl Fav; *Miss Valley St U; Bus Adm.*

BRAGG, Robert Lawrence
El Camino Real HS; Woodland Hills, CA (10-1000) BS; Pres, Ger C; Co-Ch, Hmrm; Co-Ch, Model UN; F-Ed, Sch P; Co-Cpt, Ftbl; CSF; Hist A; Hon Prog; *USF; Pre-Med.*

BRAKE, Kristal Kay
James Buchanan HS; Mercersburg, PA (2-259) AFS; Band; Chor; Drama; Ensm; 4H; NHS; 4H A; Art C; Mus A; *Engr.*

BRAKEL, Pamela Kaye
Hurdsfield Pub HS; Hurdsfield, ND; Ann; Chldr; Chor; 4H; Sch P; Arch; Sftbl; Tr; Type A; *Legal Secy.*

BRAKEL, Timothy Duane
Castle HS; Newburgh, IN (35-342) Band; Cpt, Ensm; NHS; Sftbl; God & Country A; VP, Campus Life; Eagle Sct; All St Band; Mus A's; *Marion Col; Mus.*

BRAMALL, Richard Lee
Arlington HS; Arlington, TX (100-550) Parl, FFA; FFA Horticulture A; *E Tex Bible Col; Mus.*

BRAMALL, Russell James
Arlington HS; Arlington, TX (150-527) FFA; Outst Co-Op Agr Stu o-t Yr; Horticulture A; *Tarrant Co Jr Col; Horticulture.*

BRAMAN, Staci Lou
University HS; Spokane, WA; *Fashion Design.*

BRAME, Deborah Elaine
Lindblom Tech HS; Chicago, IL (92-498) Chess C; Hmrm; Math C; Span C; COM; Citz A; Hon Prog; JA A; Yth Fel; WW; *Bradley U; Acct.*

BRAMER, Debra Louise
Hannibal HS; Hannibal, NY; Pres, 4H; NHS; F-Ed, Sch P; Bkbl; Soccer; 4H A; JA A; Math A; *Airline Stewardess.*

BRAMER, Janet Sue
Big Bay de Noc HS; Cooks, MI;

BRAMLETT, Daryl Lewis
Tates Creek Sr HS; Lexington, KY; Ensm; Lat C; *Georgetown Baptist Col.*

BRAMLETT, Nancy Catherine
The Bolles Sch; Jacksonville, FL (14-156) Chem C; Chor; Fr C; VP, Lat C; NHS; VP, Thes; VP, Jr Cl; Tnns; HCt; Hon Prog; Yth Fel; Pres, Civinettes; Camp Counselor; *Vanderbilt U; Math.*

BRAMMER, Sandra Lynn
Burroughs HS; Ridgecrest, CA; Chor; Ensm; Var C; Cr-Ctry; Tr; Sports Schol A.

BRAMSTEDT, Paula Dee
Carrollton HS; Saginaw, MI (4-160) Dbte Tm; Drama; VP, NHS; A-Ed, Sch P; Sci C; Span C; Pres, SC; Co-Cpt, Tr; HQn; HCt; Vlbl; *Valparaiso U; Engr.*

BRANAN, Debra Jane
Air Acad HS; Colorado Springs, CO (112-398) Ed, Ann; Rainbow.

BRANAN, Gregory Knight
Churchland HS; Portsmouth, VA (15-280) Ann; Chess C; Hmrm; Lat C; Sch P; Cr-Ctry; Tr; Gr Marshal; HCt; Hon Prog; 2nd Prize Hermitage A; City Art Show; 3rd Prize, Seawell Art Show; Able & Ambitious Summer Program; *Hampden-Sydney Col; Engr.*

BRANAS, Linda Jean
Old Forge HS; Old Forge, PA; Drama; FTA; NHS; Bkbl; Sftbl; Hon Prog; Pres A; Bkbl Scoring Title, HS All Amer; *U of Scranton; Med Tech.*

BRANCATO, Elizabeth Ann
Norwich Free Acad; Norwich, CT (9-749) Chor; Fr C; NHS; Sch P; SC; Hon Prog; *Special Ed.*

BRANCATO, James Peter
Norwich Free Acad; Norwich, CT (20-716) Band; Drama; NHS; Hon Prog; Secy, Marching & Dance Bands; *Journ.*

BRANCH, Andre Joseph
HS of Music and Art; New York, NY (239-517) FTA; Hmrm; Up Bound; Hon Prog; Yth Fel; Ch, Yth Coun; Director, Life Ministries; *The Kings Col; Biblical Stu.*

BRANCH, Gary Lee
Meadowdale HS; Dayton, OH (156-342) JV, Bsbl; JV, Ftbl; Tr; Wrest; *Ala A&M; Communication.*

BRANCH, Gary Wayne
Blue Ridge HS; Blue Ridge, TX (2-30) Co-Ed, Ann; VP, BC; BS; Chor; Dbte Tm; FFA; Sch Achieve Tm; Pres, Jr Cl; Bkbl; Ftbl; Tnns; Tr; Cl Fav; MLS; Interscholastic League; UIL 1-Act Play, Dist Best Actor; FFA Rodeo; HS Theater Workshop; *US Air Force Acad; Aeronomics.*

BRANCH, Keith
North Comm HS; Minneapolis, MN (60-100) Kiwanis A; *Howard U; Archt.*

BRANCH, Michael Gerald
San Pedro HS; San Pedro, CA (90-1000) All Amer Yth; Hmrm; InterClub Coun; Amer Leg A; CSF; Hon Prog; Opt A; JV Vlbl; *Pepperdine U; Psych.*

BRANCH, Roberta Jean
Seaside HS; Seaside, CA; Most Outst Stu.

BRANCH, Robin Gail
King William HS; King William, VA; Ann; VP, BC; JV, Chldr; Drama; Secy, Fr C; Hmrm; Ed, Lit Mag; A-Ed, Sch P; Secy, Span C; Tr; COM; Q&S A; Va Coop Yth Tour; *Johnston-Willis Nurs Sch; Nurs.*

BRANCH, Vivian Grace
Greenville Christian Acad; Greenville, NC; Ann; Cpt, Chldr; Chor; FHA; Ath C; *Pitt Tech Inst; Nurs.*

BRANCHE, Richard R
St Paul's HS; Garden City, NY (7-40) Band; Chess C; Fr C; Pres, Span C; Var C; Co-Cpt, Bkbl; Co-Cpt, Soccer; *Wesleyan Col; Bio.*

BRAND, Sandy Ann
Yosemite Union HS; Oakhurst, CA (10%-98) CYO; FHA; 4H; Rptr, Sch P; Ski C; Var C; Mgr, Bsbl; MVP, Bkbl; JV, Sftbl; MVP, Tr; Citz A; 4H A; Swtht; Cpt, Bkbl; Cpt, MVP, Vlbl; Sr Swtht; *Fresno City Col; Phys Ed.*

BRAND, Valerie Jeanne
Girard HS; Girard, PA (25-170) Band; Chor; NHS; Ski C; Pa Gov Sch for the Arts; Carnegie-Mellon U Hon Band; Dist-Regional Band-1st Chair; Dist & Regional, St, All & Chor; *Carnegie-Mellon U; Mus.*

BRANDEMIHL, William Charles
Broadview Acad; La Fox, IL; *Andrews Col; Elec Engr.*

BRANDENBERG, Gregory Alan
Lexington Sr HS; Lexington, NE (3-133) Rptr, Sch P; Tres, Var C; Co-Cpt, Ftbl; MVP, Ftbl; Alt, Regents Schol; WW; David Schol; *U of Nebr; Pre-Med.*

BRANDENSTEIN, Gaye Estelle
Ingraham HS; Seattle, WA (1-480) Tr; *U of Wash; Vet Med.*

BRANDER, Raymond Wayne
Two Harbors HS; Two Harbors, MN; NHS; Spch C; Tr; *U of Minn-Duluth; Data Processing.*

BRANDES, Mark Alan
Larkin HS; Elgin, IL (140-700) Band; Order/ Arrow; *Purdue U; Computer Sci.*

BRANDON, Cheryl Denise
Pike HS; Indianapolis, IN (57-307) Community Yth Symph; NHS; Orch; *Ball St U; Spch Pathology.*

BRANDON, Christine Leigh
Huntington HS; Huntington, NY (15-750) Drama; Hist A; Hon Prog; Gym Tm; Ntl Jr Hon Soc; Eng A; Fire Prevention A; DAR Poetry A; *Saint Mary's Col; Sci.*

BRANDON, Elesha LaNelle
Clarendon HS; Clarendon, TX (4-45) Band; Pres, Chor; Drama; Ensm; Secy, FHA; FTA; Math C; NHS; Spch C; Citz A; Cl Fav; Journ A; Spch A; Yth Fel; Bookkeeping & Geom A's; Regional Fin, Persuasive Spch; VP, Yth for Christ; *Hardin-Simmons U; Sociology.*

BRANDON, Janna Edithe
Clarendon HS; Clarendon, TX; Band; NHS; Spch C; Phys Sci; Hghst Rank Grl, Jr HS Pres Caor A; Hardin Simmons Col; Wild Life.

BRANDON, Kim Annette
Muscle Shoals HS; Muscle Shoals, AL; Band; ARC; SC; *Auburn U; Vet Med.*

BRANDON, Mark Edward
Robt E Lee HS; San Antonio, TX (80-585) NHS; Tnns; COM; NEDT; Optimist Oratorical Contest; 3rd, Zone Tn Bible Quiz; *UTSA; Hist.*

BRANDT, Bethany Denise
Kearsley HS; Flint, MI (2-377) Band; NFL; Spch C; Dietitian.

BRANDT, Carol Diane
Ulysses HS; Ulysses, KS (1-125) Band; Chor; Ensm; VP, NHS; Ch, Y-Tns; JV, Golf; *U of Kans; Med Sci.*

BRANDT, Cheryl Ann
Ruskin Pub Sch; Ruskin, NE (50%-10) Chor; S-T, Soph Cl; Tres, Pep C; Triple Trio; Mgr, Vlbl; *Art.*

BRANDT, Cynthia Ellen
Sterling HS; Sterling, CO (34-365) Band; Ensm; Pres, FHA; Tres, Rainbow; Geometry A; Colo St Mus As; ETTA Cert; VP, Tres, FHA; *Northeastern Jr Col; Psych.*

BRANDT, Jeffrey Mark
Haddonfield Mem HS; Haddonfield, NJ (100-243) CYO; HiY; K of C; Cr-Ctry; Cpt, Hockey; Co-Cpt, Sftbl; Tr; Boy Camper o-t Wk, Summer Yth Conf; *Kings Col; Yth Ministry.*

BRANDT, Jerome Frederick
Richwoods HS; Peoria, IL (38-463) Band; NHS; St Scholar; *Valparaisa U; Engr.*

BRANDT, Jon D
Steubenville HS; Steubenville, OH (91-278) Key C; VP, Lat C; Order/Arrow; SC; Ftbl; Wrest; Alt, BS; *Miami U of Ohio; Bus Adm.*

BRANDT, Laurie Jean
Valmeyer HS; Valmeyer, IL (2-36) Secy, Chor; Ensm; FBLA; Secy, FFA; Pres, 4H; Math C; Tres, NHS; Sch P; Pres, SC; Pres, Soph Cl; Sftbl; MVP, Tr; Amer Leg A; Citz A; HCt; I Dare You; Math A; MLS; Sal; Swtht; SC A; Vocal A; Agr A; Outst Sr Stu; *Belleville Area Col; Acct.*

BRANDT, Susan Elizabeth
Theodore Roosevelt HS; Wyandotte, MI (20-510) Bus Mgr, Ann; Chor; NHS; Tnns; Hon Prog; Future Secy's of Amer; Co-Ed, Yrbk; Shorthand A; *U of Mich; Bus.*

BRANDT, Tammy Celeste
New Braunfels Sr HS; New Braunfels, TX (20-320) Band; FTA; Ger C; Pres A; *SW Tex St U; Pre-Sch Teacher.*

BRANDT, Zoe Ann
Richwoods HS; Peoria, IL (9-530) Chor; Dbte Tm; Rptr, Sch P; Sftbl; Vlbl; *Med.*

BRANDYBERRY, Lisa Caryl
McKinley Sr HS; Canton, OH; Drama; Y-Tns; Swim; *Special Ed.*

BRANEY, David Micheal
Leuzinger HS; Lawndale, CA (130-200) Chess C; Chor; Tres, SC; Bsbl; JV, Bkbl; Ftbl; Golf; Pacific Christian Col; Theology.

BRANHAM, Cyanna Kay
Bryan Adams HS; Dallas, TX (10%-790) F-Ed, Ann; Band; Secy, NHS; Pres, Span C; Citz A; Hist A; Hon Prog; Type A; Bible A; Ed.

BRANHAM, Donald Edwin
Camdenton Sr HS; Camdenton, MO; Band; Ensm; Math C; Model UN; SC.

BRANHAM, Frederick
Virgie HS; Virgie, KY (10-100) BC; Chess C; Rptr, Spch C; U of Ky; Mining Tech.

BRANHAM, Robert James
Park Center Sr HS; Brooklyn Park, MN; Ski C; Pres, SC; Soccer; Swim; Tnns; U of Minn; Psych.

BRANNAN, Beth Ellen
Smithfield-Selma HS; Smithfield, NC (77-355) Ann; Band; Chor; Fr C; FHA; Hmrm; Key C; SC; Secy, Jr Cl; HCt; Type A; Vlbl; Salem Col; Econ.

BRANNAN, George Wyatt Jr
Smithfield-Selma Sr HS; Smithfield, NC (25%-473) Band; Chess C; Order/Arrow; Sci C; God & Country A; Studio Sound Engr.

BRANNEN, Nancy Jane
Oswego HS; Oswego, KS; Chor; Drama; FHA; Span C; Spch C; COM; Citz A; Hon Prog; WW; Pittsburg St U; Cosmetology.

BRANNON, James Norman
Cleburne HS; Cleburne, TX (99-270) Pres, FFA; S-T, Key C; NHS; SC; Ski C; Pres, SC; Co-Cpt, Var C; Bsbl; Bkbl; Cpt, Ftbl; Tr; Cl Fav; Hon Prog; Pres A; Howard Payne U; Coaching.

BRANNON, Joseph Bradford
Southeast Sr HS; Greensboro, NC (15-436) Sci C; Sci A; Elec C; Ch, Amateur Radio Post; Television Post; MIT; Sci.

BRANNON, Melody Jaynette
Milo Adventist Acad; Days Creek, OR (3-50).

BRANOM, Dana Rhea
Skyline HS; Dallas, TX; Chldr; Bkbl; Sftbl; Swim; Tr; Young Life; FCA; Tex Tech; Phys Med.

BRANSCOM, Patricia Sue
Fairfield HS; Arlington, KS (10%-42) Band; Chldr; Chor; Ensm; Co-Ch, Y-Tns; S-T, Soph Cl; Type A; Yth Fel; JV Vlbl; Secy, Pep C; Hutch Jr Col; Nurs.

BRANSCOME, Joni Lynn
Sheffield HS; Sheffield, AL (14-192) Band; Inter-Act C; Span C; Tres, Tri-HiY; Drum Major; Church Pianist; Foreign Lang C; Writing of Lit.

BRANSOM, Lori Carol
Clovis HS; Clovis, NM; Cpt, Chldr; FHA; Type A; Off Ed Assn; Abilene Christian U; Home Ec.

BRANSON, Ruth Marie
Summit HS; Summit, NJ (25%-310) AFS; Band; Hmrm; Orch; Cpt, Hockey; COM; Bio.

BRANSON, Susan Elizabeth
Uniontown Area Sr HS; Uniontown, PA (1-435) NHS; Alg A; Hist A; Schol Pin; Uniontown Sch of Nurs; Nurs.

BRANSTETTER, Randall Gene
Sunbright HS; Sunbright, TN (4-63) Ed, Ann; Pres, BC; FFA; Pres, 4H; Order/Arrow; Rptr, Sch P; FFA A; U of Tenn.

BRANT, Cynthia Ann
Westmont Hilltop HS; Johnstown, PA (1-211) Band; Co-Cpt, Ntl Yth Conf; Orch; Bob Jones U.

BRANT, Dale Eric
Edison HS; Huntington Beach, CA (65-850) A Cap Choir; Chor; Parl, Dbte Tm; NFL; Spch C; CSF; St Scholar; Cal-Tech; Aerodynamic Engr.

BRANT, Viki Loretta
Crestview Sr HS; Crestview, FL (10-250) Anchor C; Band; Ensm; FTA; Cpt, Mjrte; COM; Chamber of Comm A; All Sports A; Miss Mjrte of Fla; Fla St U; Dentistry.

BRANTHOOVER,
Kimberly Diane
Loudon HS; Loudon, TN (1-125) Chor; NHS; Sci C; VP, SC; Bkbl; Tnns; Balfour A; Cl Fav; Hist A; Val; Del, Wash Workshops Congress Sem; U of Tenn; Law.

BRANTHOOVER, Mary Ellen
Fairport Harding HS; Fairport Harbor, OH (4-60) Ed, Ann; Secy, Band; GS; NHS; VP, SC; Y-Tns; HQn; HCt; MLS; Bowling Green St U; Nurs.

BRANTLEY, Charles Palma
Permian HS; Odessa, TX; Tex Tech U; Pre-Med.

BRANTLEY, Duncan Gooding
Woodberry Forest Sch; Woodberry Forest, VA (40-105) Ed, Ann; Ger C; Ftbl; Tnns; Tr; Yth Fel; LaCrosse; Camera C; Service Committee; Orientation Committee; U of NC; Bus.

BRANTLEY, Karen Faye
Washington Co HS; Sandersville, GA (10%-248) Chldr; Drama; Hmrm; Secy, InterAct C; Tres, Jr Cl; Miss Drama; Secy, SOE C; Church Yth Choir; Solo Musicals; Middle Ga Col; Stenography.

BRANTLEY, Patricia Ann
Estill HS; Estill, SC; NHS; Sftbl; Upsala Col; Bus Ed.

BRANTLEY, Rhonda Pearl
Ethel HS; Ethel, MS; BC; Chldr; FHA; Sci C; Bkbl; Type A; Holmes Jr Col; Computer Sci.

BRANTLEY, Robert John
W Milford Township HS; W Milford, NJ (57-334) A-Ed, Ann; Semi-Fin, BS; Hmrm; NHS; ARC; Ski C; SC; Soccer; Citz A; ARC A; Lehigh U; Acct.

BRANTLEY, Thomas Harold Jr
Moultrie HS; Moultrie, GA (15-420) BC; Chor; Pres, Dbte Tm; Key C; Math C; NFL; NHS; Sci C; Var C; Ftbl; Sftbl; Tnns; Tr; COM; Gov Honor Prog; Hon Prog; Auburn U; Pre-Law.

BRANUM, Gene Dale
Robert E Lee HS; Tyler, TX (10-685) Chem C; Lat C; Rptr, Lit Mag; SC; Var C; Bsbl; Ftbl; Tr; Citz A; Hon Prog; Civitan A; Tex A&M U; Med.

BRANZ, Janet Marie
Odell HS; Odell, IL (3-31) Chor; Drama; Ensm; Secy, FHA; Thes; Var C; Pres, Sr Cl; HCt; Hon Prog; St Scholar; Consumers Ed A; Outst Choir Stu; Best Actress.

BRASE, Nancy Jayne
Detroit Lakes HS; Detroit Lakes, MN (50-277) AFS; Band; Span C; Pres A; Band A; Moorhead St U; General.

BRASEL, Gregory Micheal
Greece Olympia HS; Rochester, NY; Band; CYO; Ensm; Rptr, Sch P; Sci C; US Military Acad; Engr.

BRASEL, Jeffry Lynn
Effingham HS; Effingham, IL (20-200) VP, Sr Cl; Bsbl; Bkbl; Ftbl; McKendree Col; Acct.

BRASEL, Michell Louise
Greece Olympia HS; Rochester, NY; Chor; Drama; Marching Band; Explorers Nurs Post; Nurs Home Vol; Hart Sch of Practical Nurs; Nurs.

BRASEL, Michelle Louise
Greece Olympia HS; Rochester, NY; Chor; Explorers; Marching Band; Vol, Nurs Home; Hart Sch of Practical Nurs; Nurs.

BRASGALLA, Stephen Thomas
Plantation HS; Plantation, FL; Band; Chor; Ensm; MYF; U of Fla; Vet Med.

BRASHAW, Gaye Lee
Bay City Central HS; Bay City, MI (10%-625) Mjrte; Swim; Citizenship C; Usher's C; Olivet Nazarene Col; Home Ec.

BRASHEAR, Jeannie Ann
Oregon Howell R 3; Koshkonong, MO (3-25) Bus Mgr, Ann; Cpt, Chldr; Chor; VP, FHA; Rptr, Sch P; Cl Fav; HQn.

BRASHEAR, Kimberly Dawn
McDonald Co HS; Anderson, MO (5-199) Band; Chor; FTA; Tres, NHS; VP, Var C; MVP, Bkbl; Sftbl; Alg A; Hon Prog; Sch o-t Ozarks; Acct.

BRASHEAR, Vicky Lynn
N Mesquite HS; Mesquite, TX (121-500) Eastfield Col; Hist.

BRASHEARS, Jon Gregory
Mt Vernon R5 Sch; Mt Vernon, MO; Band; Golf; Southwest Mo St U; Acct.

BRASHER, Linda Carol
Fayette Co HS; Fayette, AL; Band; Rptr, FBLA; FHA; FTA; Math C; Sci C; Beauty; FFA Swtht; All St Band; Auburn U; X-Ray Tech.

BRASHER, Pamela Jean
Fayette Co HS; Fayette, AL; Band; Chor; FBLA; 4H; Math C; Sci C; Span C; 4H A; Attendance A; Biol.

BRASHERS, Donna Denease
Kalamazoo Central HS; Kalamazoo, MI; FNA; God & Country A; ARC A; Yth Fel; Kal Valley Comm Col; Nurs.

BRASWELL, Daniel Edwin
Headland HS; Headland, AL; 4H; Ch, Hmrm; Order/Arrow; Thes; Ftbl; Order/Arrow A; Eagle Sct.

BRASWELL, Douglas Wayne
Clyde A Erwin HS; Asheville, NC (33-217) Fr C; Key C; SC; Var C; MVP, Bkbl; Ftbl; Golf; Tr; Most Ath A; DECA A.

BRASWELL, Gregory Spencer
Smithfield-Selma Sr HS; Smithfield, NC (115-375) Band; Chess C; Key C; Order/Arrow; JV, Bkbl; Bkbl; Ftbl; Tr; COM; Citz A; God & Country A; Order/Arrow A; ARC A.

BRASWELL, John Kilgo
Irmo HS; Irmo, SC (80-458) BC; Key C; Span C; SC; Ftbl; COM; Clemson Col; Dental.

BRASWELL, Karen Lois
Montgomery Co Joint Voc HS; Clayton, OH (4-25) Cpt, Chldr; Chor; Fin, Ensm; Pres, ARC; Tr; St Champs, Bible Quiz; Hon Star Ministries; HR; SW Assembly of God Bible Col; Mus.

BRASWELL, Martha Annette
Rocky Mount Sr HS; Rocky Mount, NC (5-599) 1st Pl, Jr Women's C Art Contest; U of NC; Art.

BRASWELL, Paulda Christine
Weir HS; Weir, MS (3-50) Band; Pres, BC; Chor; Ensm; Secy, FHA; Jr Miss Pagent; Ed, Sch P; Secy, SC; Crisco A; H of F; HCt; Math A; Swtht; Miss WHS; William Carey Col; Sci.

BRATCHER, Jill Annette
McMinnville Sr HS; McMinnville, OR (4-225) AFS; Ann; Key C; Orch; Sch P; Sftbl; St Scholar; Type A; Ntl Merit Commendation; Bus A; Ntl Bus Hon Soc; Mus A; Secy, VP, DECA; Wells Col; Mus.

BRATCHER, Marla Jeanine
Maysville HS; Maysville, OK (5-40) F-Ed, Ann; FHA; Sch P; Pres, Jr Cl; Tres, Soph Cl; Cpt, Bkbl; Alg A; Hon Prog; Kiwanis A; Math A; Sci A; Type A; E Central St U; Bus.

BRATLIEN, Glenda Gaye
Columbus Pub Sch; Columbus, ND; Ann; Band; S-T, Chor; Ensm; Fin, GS; 4H; Madrigal; Rptr, Sch P; Var C; Secy, Jr Cl; Bkbl; Tr; Amer Leg A; 4H A; Hon Prog; Mus.

BRATRUD, Dan Halvor
N Central HS; Manly, IA (32-64) A Cap Choir; Chor; Pres, 4H; Madrigal; Var C; Wrest; 4H A; Gold Tassel; Albert Lea Vo-tech Sch; Diesel Mech.

BRATSCHUN, Thomas Donald
Lyons Township HS; W Springs, IL (60-1220) JV, Soccer; JV, Tnns; Hon Prog; HR; U of Ill; Biol Sci.

BRATTIN, Kathy
Wheaton R-III HS; Wheaton, MO (10-31) Bus Mgr, Ann; Band; Chldr; Chor; Pres, FHA; NHS; Secy, SC; Sftbl; Tr; Cl Fav; HQn; Type A; HR; SW Mo St U; Teacher.

BRATTLOF, Randy Wayne
Lake Highland HS; Dallas, TX; Key C; Fin, Sr Cl; Semi-Fin, Jr Cl; Bsbl; Ftbl; Cl Fav; Yth Fel; Mr LHHS; Pres, FCA; Soph o-t Yr; Bus.

BRATTON, A Luann
Stamps HS; Stamps, AR; Ann; BC; FHA; NHS; B Crocker A; Hist A; Hon Prog; Type A; Hist, FBLA; Secy, Gen Co- op Ed; Ouachita Baptist U; Eng.

BRATTON, Audrey Pamela
St Mary's Col; Raleigh, NC (7-103) Secy, Chor; Secy, Ensm; ARC; SC; Swim; COM; Hon Prog; NEDT; WW; U of NC; Phar.

BRATTON, Cynthia Lynne
Rock Hill HS; Rock Hill, SC; BC; Chor.

BRATTON, Deborah Ann
Norview Sr HS; Norfolk, VA (25%-900) Band; Mjrte.

BRATTON, Norma Jean
York Comp HS; York, SC (10-240) Band; Secy, FBLA; NHS; Span C; Spch C; Acct A; Jr Marshal; WW; *Kings Col; Secretarial Sci.*

BRATTON, Steve Michael
Lawrence HS; Lawrence, KS; Band; Secy, Chess C; Chor; Community Yth Symph; VP, Drama; Ensm; Orch; Co-Ed, Sch P; Tnns; Alg A; COM; Hon Prog; Math A; Ntl Achv Schol; Sci A; Type A; Yth Fel; Alt, Hmrm Rep; Bowl; Alt, SC; Mus A; Drama A; *Kans U; Mus.*

BRAUCHER, Cynthia Gail
Cedar Shoals HS; Athens, GA (87-380) F-Ed, Ann; Ger C; Hmrm; MVP, Swim; Most Ath; *U of Ga; Phys Ed.*

BRAUER, Sharill Joyce
Guilford HS; Rockford, IL (235-713) A Cap Choir; Drama; Sftbl; *Bethel Col; Pre-Sch Ed.*

BRAUGHT, John Richard
W Mid-High Sch; Norman, OK; Band; Chor; Ch, Ensm; Orch; Span C; JV, Bkbl; Sftbl; JV, Tnns; COM; Citz A; Hon Prog; Math A; Most Out; *Okla U; Law.*

BRAUHN, Cindy May
Tacoma Baptist Sch; Tacoma, WA; Band; Chor; Sftbl; Bookkeeping A.

BRAUN, Corey Wayne
Grand Haven HS; Grand Haven, MI (50-500) NHS; Bsbl; Cpt, Bkbl; Cpt, Ftbl; *Law.*

BRAUN, Karen Le
Watertown Sr HS; Watertown, WI (2-300) AFS; Dbte Tm; Ski C; Local Paper Vol A; *U of Wis-Madison; Nurs.*

BRAUN, Ricky Dean
Crestview Sr HS; Crestview, FL (10%-265) CYO.

BRAUN, Steven Joseph
Warren Hills Regional Sr HS; Washington, NJ (10%-351) Band; Chess C; Ensm; Ger C; Orch; Rptr, Sch P; God & Country A; Hon Prog; Co Spelling Champ; 2nd Pl, St Spelling; All Co Band; *Journ.*

BRAUNBERGER, Lori Lin
Cottage Grove HS; Cottage Grove, OR (26-240) A Cap Choir; AFS; Chor; Drama; Ensm; NHS; Thes; COM; Citz A; Type A; Outst Vocal Mus Stu A; *U of Oreg; Mus Ed.*

BRAUND, Sharon Marie
St Mary's Acad; Alexandria, VA; Band; Secy, Bus C; CYO; Chor; Ensm; Key C; Soccer; Swim; JV, Tr; COM; Most Out; Pres A; *U of Va; Med.*

BRAUNER, Clark David
Dugway HS; Dugway, UT (4-40) Model UN; NHS; SC; Pres, Sr Cl; VP, Jr Cl; Bkbl; Co-Cpt, Ftbl; Tnns; Ntl Merit Commended Stu; *U of Utah; Psych.*

BRAUNESREITHER, Russell Jay
Francis Howell HS; St Charles, MO (3%-500) Band; Chem C; Mod Mus Mas; NHS; Hand Bell Choir; '1' Rating, St Mus Contest; Med C; *U of Mo; Med.*

BRAUNS, Timothy Alan
Crystal Lake Comm HS; Crystal Lake, IL (37-460) Dbte Tm; NFL; Hon Prog; Kiwanis A; NMF; Spch A; *NW U; Geol.*

BRAUSE, Barbara Jo
Buckeye Central HS; New Washington, OH (4-92) Secy, FFA; FHA; Pres, 4H; NHS; SC; Sftbl; Amer Leg A; Citz A; 4H A; Sci A; Spch A; Co-Cpt, Bowl; Runner-Up, Miss FHA; Ldrship A; *Horticulture.*

BRAVIN, Douglas Allen
Parkway N Sr HS; Creve Coeur, MO (60-500) Band; Lat C; NHS; Ski C; *Commercial Art-Design.*

BRAVO, Norman Dennis
Bell HS; Bell, CA (32-480) Band; BS; Dbte Tm; Ensm; Hmrm; Ch, InterClub Coun; VP, Key C; NFL; NHS; Order/Arrow; Spch C; Ch, SC; CSF; Cl Fav; Hon Prog; MLS; Order/Arrow A; Spch A; Pres, SC; Presidential Clrm; Eagle Sct; *Point Loma Col; Pre-Med.*

BRAWDERS, Wendy Sue
Jefferson Sr HS; Jefferson, WI (30%-218) A Cap Choir; Chor; FHA; *Sch of Radiologic Tech; Madison General Hospital.*

BRAWLEY, Rebecca Ann
Mooresville HS; Mooresville, NC (2-175) Ann; BC; Cpt, Chldr; Fr C; Tres, FHA; Monogram; SC; Secy, Jr Cl; COM; Yth Fel; Bridge C; Church Pianist; Chor Accompanist; Jr Marshal; Accompanist, Dist Vocal Contest; *U of NC; Mus.*

BRAWNER, Charlotte Sue
Saint Jo HS; Saint Jo, TX (3-21) Ann; Dbte Tm; Drama; VP, FHA; Cpt, Mjrte; VP, NHS; Bkbl; Fin, Tnns; Fin, Tr; H of F; HCt; Pres, Drum Major; Ldrship A; Miss Saint Jo HS; Most Ath; Eng A; *Tarleton St U; Physical Education.*

BRAXTON, Felicia Delene
Lincoln HS; Tacoma, WA; Chldr; Service A.

BRAXTON, Leslie Davis
Lincoln HS; Tacoma, WA; Ftbl.

BRAY, Bruce Weyman
Stephens Co HS; Toccoa, GA (10%-275) A Cap Choir; HiY; Bsbl; Bkbl; Ftbl; *Clemson U; Acct.*

BRAY, Charles Eugene
Whitehouse HS; Whitehouse, TX (5-99) Tres, BC; NHS; VP, St Stu Congress; Bsbl; Best Dressed; Top 10; *Tex A&M U; Petroleum Engr.*

BRAY, Cynthia Sue
Sterling HS; Sterling, KS (1-50) Band; Chldr; Chor; Ensm; FHA; Madrigal; SC; Tres, Soph Cl; Pres, Keyettes; Director, Yth Choir; GSct Sr Aide; Cand, Cub Royalty; GSct Sr Aide; Cand, Cub Royalty; *Kansas Wesleyan Col; Nurs.*

BRAY, Emily Hope
Leavenworth Sr HS; Leavenworth, KS (34-400) CYO; Tres, Chor; Dbte Tm; NFL; NHS; SC; COM; Gov Honor Prog; OWC Grant; *Kansas U; Engr.*

BRAY, Grace Marie
E Detroit HS; E Detroit, MI; Dbte Tm; Runner-Up, Miss March of Dimes; *Mich St U; Bio.*

BRAY, James Wellborn III
Dalton HS; Dalton, GA; Chor; Bkbl; Golf; *Dalton Jr Col.*

BRAY, Judith Eileen
Hanford HS; Richland, WA; Swing Choir; Concert Choir; Church Soloist; *PLU; Nurs.*

BRAY, Susan Elizabeth
Reidsville Sr HS; Reidsville, NC (5%-375) Drama; Tres, Fr C; Tnns; NEDT; United Cerebal Palsy Spel Bee Champ; *Wake Forest U.*

BRAY, Tammie Kim
South HS; Springfield, OH; Band; Chor; NFL; Span C; Spch C; Spch A; Drill Tm; Star & Chevron A; *Bowling Green St U; Phar.*

BRAYMEN, Russell William
Shenandoah HS; Shenandoah, IA (18-100) BS; Fr C; VP, FFA; Tres, NHS; *Farm.*

BRAZEE, Marcia Lynne
Pender HS; Pender, NE (12-69) Ann; Band; Chldr; Chor; Drama; FHA; 4H; Madrigal; Spch C; 4H A; Spch A; *Mus.*

BRAZIEL, Marten Leigh
Wilcox Co HS; Rochelle, GA (1-97) Ed, Ann; BC; Chor; Dbte Tm; Drama; Ensm; FBLA; 4H; Hmrm; Ed, Lit Mag; Sch P; SC; Alg A; Bio A; COM; Chem A; Cl Fav; DARGCA; Gov Honor Prog; Gr Marshal; Hist A; HCt; Hon Prog; Math A; Star Student; Type A; Val; Yth Leg; Span, Eng, A's; *Mus.*

BRAZLE, Vaughn Keith
Jack Yates Sr HS; Houston, TX; FHA; Sci C; COM; Hist A; Hon Prog; Math A; Sci A; Eng A; Phys Ed A; *Electronics.*

BRDLIK, Lindsay Millon
D U Fletcher Sr HS; Neptune Beach, FL (60-550) F-Ed, Ann; Drama; Fr C; Hmrm; InterAct C; Jr Miss Pagent; NHS; SC; Cr-Ctry; Mgr, Soccer; Tr; COM; Swtht; Chaplain, Anchor C; *U of Fla; Communications.*

BREAULT, Richard Todd
Stratford HS; Stratford, CT (34-401) Pres, Ski C; Var C; Swim; Tnns; Board of Benevolence; Part-Time Job; PF Yth Group; Conn VCC Conf; Varsity Ltr; Board of Ushers; Highest Hon; Alt Del, Church Coun; *Worcester Poly-Tech Col; Pre-Med.*

BREAUX, Denise Ann
St Joseph HS; Jeanerette, LA (1-28) Chldr; VP, 4H; Lit Ral; NHS; VP, SC; Secy, Jr Cl; Secy, Soph Cl; Tnns; Alg A; COM; 4H A; Hist A; HCt; Math A; Religion A; Eng A; *U of Southwestern La; Ed.*

BREAUX, Michele Marie
Cleveland HS; Cleveland, TN (5-220) VP, Anchor C; Band; CYO; VP, Fr C; SC; JV, Tnns; COM; Hon Prog; Math A; Fr A; All St Jr Band Clinic; Mus A; Eng A; Presidential Phys Fitness A; *U of Tenn; Computer Sci.*

BREAZEALE, Ronald Edward
Ill Valley HS; Cave Junction, OR (50-80) Band; Wrest.

BRECH, Brad Louis
Secaucus HS; Secaucus, NJ (9-185) Band; Fin, BS; Chess C; Key C; Order/Arrow; Ftbl; Tr; JV, Wrest; Order/Arrow A; *Air Force Acad; Engr.*

BRECHBUHLER, James Brian
Canton S HS; Canton, OH (15-269) Pres, Band; BS; NHS; Pres, Orch; Order/Arrow; SC; Tr; God & Country A; Hon Prog; Order/Arrow A; Yth Fel; Eagle Sct; Sch Exec Board; Pres, Church Yth Group; Pres, Sunday Sch Cl; Sound Systems Coordinator, Church; *Ohio St U; Agr Sci.*

BRECHT, Julie Ann
Holdrege HS; Holdrege, NE (10%-120) Band; Chor; SC; Bkbl; Sftbl; Hon Prog; Type A; Shorthand A; 2nd Yr Schol Pin; VP & Pres A, Pep C; *Computer Prog.*

BRECHT, Tammy Lee
Saint Mary's HS; Stockton, CA (31-256) CYO; Chor; Dbte Tm; Drama; NFL; NHS; Span C; Spch C; Thes; CSF; Hon Prog; NEDT; Poet A; Sci A; Spch A; Star Student; Fall & Spring Plays; Citizenship C; GAA; Writing A; SDAHSS; Pep C; *Sci.*

BRECKHEIMER, David John
Hilbert Pub HS; Hilbert, WI; Key C; Ftbl.

BRECKWOLDT, Edward Jean
Baker HS; Baker, LA (3-425) Band; BC; CYO; Key C; Opt A; Eagle Sct A; *LSU; Engr.*

BREDEHOFT, Terry Edward
Flagler Pub HS; Flagler, CO (3-14) BS; NHS; Var C; Bkbl; Ftbl; Tr; HCt; NEDT; Type A; *Adams St Col.*

BREDEN, Lois Ellen
Phoenixville Area HS; Phoenixville, PA; Tr; Pep C.

BREDEWEG, Lori Gail
Churchill HS; Livowia, MI; Band; Chldr; Chor; Pres A; 1st, Piano, St Solo & Ensm; 1st, Concer Choir Competition; *Taylor U; Mus.*

BREDLOW, Sheryl Deann
Anoka Sr HS; Anoka, MN (115-926) Orch; *X-Ray Tech.*

BREECE, Carol Beth
Claremore HS; Claremore, OK (54-217) FBLA; COM; *Okla Baptist U; Religion.*

BREEDEN, Montie Rea
Charlottesville HS; Charlottesville, VA (25-400) Math C; Sci C; Span C; SC; *U of Va; Archt.*

BREEDEN, Vicky Lynn
Willian Monroe HS; Stanardsville, VA (33%-78) Ann; BC; FHA; Hmrm; SC; JV, Bkbl; HCt; Hist, FBLA; Gifted Stu; Miss Monroe Pagent; *Bus.*

BREEDING, Neal Hampton
Riverdale Pub HS; Riverdale, ND (25%-21) Chor; Var C; VP, Jr Cl; Tres, Soph Cl; Cpt, Bkbl; *Jamestown Col; Sci.*

BREEDLOVE, Cyndee Olwen
N Gwinnett HS; Suwanee, GA (10%-120) BC; FBLA; FHA; Span C; Secy, SC; Bkbl; COM; Hon Prog; *Gainesville Jr Col.*

BREEDLOVE, Janita June
Seymour HS; Seymour, MO (50%-75) VP, FFA; Wittiest Person, Sr Cl; FHA Hon; *Sch o-t Ozarks; Child Development.*

BREEDLOVE, Laura Margaret
Mercy HS; Albany, NY (5-115) CYO; Drama; Fr C; NHS; NEDT; High HR.

BREELAND, Donna Glynn
Jackson Prep Sch; Jackson, MS (8-186) Ann; Chor; Ensm; Lit Ral; Lit Mag; Mu Alpha Theta; NHS; Ntl Yth Conf; Sch P; Sci C; COM; Hon Prog; Math A; Sci A; Three Gold Cups Jr Mus Festival; Eng A; Three Academic Excellence A; Activities Ltr; Morning Watch Society; *Belhaven Col; Spch Therapy.*

BREEMES, Kristin Jane
Stevens HS; Rapid City, SD (64-436) Chor; Cum Laude Soc; Hmrm; Ski C; Sftbl; Tr; COM; *SD St U; Med Tech.*

BREEN, Catherine Marie
Brooke HS; Wellsburg, WV (99-500) CYO; FNA; Secy, Hmrm; Lat C; SC; Tr; Grapple Gals; Bkbl Babes; Candystripers; *Col of Steubenville; Bus Adm.*

BREEN, Frances Marie
Adirondack Central HS; Boonville, NY (13-156) Chldr; Chor; Fr C; Hmrm; NHS; Rainbow; Tres, SC; Soccer; Tnns; Tr; Girls Ensm; Pres A Ath; *LeMoyne Col; Psych.*

BREEN, James Joseph
Don Bosco Tech HS; Boston, MA (3-222) CYO; VP, Drama; VP, Hmrm; NHS; SC; Hon Prog; *Pre-Med.*

BREEN, Janet Ann
Augusta HS; Augusta, KS; JV, Chldr; Chor; Drama; Hmrm; Monogram; NFL; SC; Thes; VP, Y-Tns; Mgr, Bkbl; JV, Tnns; Vlbl; *Kans St U; Communications.*

BREESE, David Scott
Nishayung HS; Schenectady, NY (40%-300) A Cap Choir; Band; Chess C; Chor; Ensm; JETS; NHS; Orch; Span C; COM; Hon Prog; Regent Schol; NML of Commend; Chrch Yth Choir; Young Performer's Showcase A; NYSSMA Sol Comp A; Prs; Chrch Bras; Explorer Scting; Church Yth Group; *Northwestern U; Physics.*

BREEZE, John Franklin
Montgomery Co HS; Mt Sterling, KY (25%-220) F-Ed, Ann; Band; BS; Chor; Hify; Hmrm; Co-Cpt, Bsbl; Co-Cpt, Bkbl; Co-Cpt, Ftbl; Citz A; HCt; Most Out; Yth Fel; SC Rep; VP FCA; Church Deacon; Phys Ed A; *Morehead Col; Phys Ed.*

BREGEL, Barry Dean
Boulevard Baptist Sch; Burleson, TX (1-9) Drama; Sch P; JV, Bkbl; JV, Ftbl; JV, Sftbl; COM; HCt; Hon Prog; MLS; Most Studious; *Tex A&M U; Math.*

BREHENEY, Sean Michael
St Peters Prep Sch; Jersey City, NJ (50-250) CYO; Drama; Hmrm; SC; Hon Prog; NEDT; Sacristan; Spch A; DAR Hist Essay; Fr A; Serra C Essay A; Outst Dramatist; *St Peter's Col; Theology.*

BREHM, Anne Marie
Bishop Watterson HS; Columbus, OH (50-265) Span C; *Ohio St U; Pub Recreation.*

BREHM, Christine Karen
Guilderland Central HS; Guilderland Center, NY (25-550) Crown & Scepter; NHS; Sftbl; Bio A; Hist A; Math A; Yth Fel; Eng A; *Rochester Inst of Tech; Computer Sci.*

BREHM, Peter Ralph
Clear Creek HS; League City, Chem C; Ger C; JETS; Model UN; NHS; Order/Arrow; Order/Arrow A; *U of Houston; Chem Engr.*

BREHMER, John Wilson
Hillcrest HS; New York City, NY; Sci C; Golf; Pres, Church Yth Fel; Photographer, Sch Paper.

BREIDINGER, Tim Dale
Clay Central Comm HS; Royal, IA (6-33) SC; Bsbl; Ftbl; Tr; B Avg A.

BREIG, Janice Katheryn
Old Forge HS; Old Forge, PA (24-121) FTA; Rptr, Sch P; Ski C; *Marywood Col; Dietician.*

BREIHAN, Luanne Marie
Lancaster Sr HS; Lancaster, WI (8-131) Co-Ch, AFS; Ann; Band; Chldr; Chor; Rptr, 4H; Fin, Jr Miss Pagent; Madrigal; Ch, Model UN; NHS; Orch; Sch P; Span C; JV, Golf; 4H A; Spch A; WW; *Viterbo Col; Mus.*

BREINER, Joyce Karen
Cumberland Valley HS; Mechanicsburg, PA (40-585) VP, Ger C; NHS; NEDT; Yth Fel; *Aeronautics.*

BREINIG, Cheryl Lynn
Marshalltown Sr HS; Marshalltown, IA (82-448) Chor; Mgr, Cr-Ctry; Mgr, Tr; Pres, Church Yth; *Marshalltown Comm Col; Pre-Nurs.*

BREISCH, Elizabeth Ann
N Penn HS; Lansdale, PA (16-900) Chldr; Community Yth Symph; Hmrm; Orch; Swim; Hon Prog; Leader's C; Swim Ltr; Most Promising Fresh, A; Distinguished HR; Sportsmanship, Ger Merit, A's; *Computer Sci.*

BREITE, Douglas Curt
Lutheran HS N; St Louis, MO (10%-130) Chor; Hmrm; SC; Ftbl; JV, Tnns; *Law.*

BREKHUS, Michael Arthur
Soap Lake Jr Sr HS; Soaplake, WA; Band; FBLA; Hmrm; NHS; F-Ed, Sch P; VP, SC; Var C; JV, Bkbl; Ftbl; Tr; Cpt, Wrest; Citz A; HCt; Most Out; Pres Phys Fitness A; *Literature.*

BREKKE, Steven Dennis
Strandquist HS; Strandquist, MN (2-17) Tres, CYO; 4H; Var C; Bsbl; Bkbl; Golf; Swim; All Conf, Northern Lights Conf; *U of ND; Law.*

BRELAND, Pamela May
Neshoba Central HS; Philadelphia, MS (30-137) Band; BC; Chor; Drama; FHA; 4H; Sci C; Hon Prog; DECA C.

BREMER, Michael Patrick
University of San Diego HS; San Diego, CA (10-315) Drama; Co-Ch, Hmrm; NHS; CSF; Journ A; Most Out; *UCLA; Drama.*

BREMER, Sharon Kay
New Haven HS; New Haven, IN (42-288) Band; Pres, Y-Tns; Hon Prog; Type A; OEA Executive; Secy, Off Ed Assn; OEA Diplomat; OEA Stateswoman; Lutheran Yth for Christ; OEA Ambassador; *Indiana-Purdue U; Bus Ed.*

BRENAN, Sue Anne
Warren Area HS; Warren, PA (10%-435) A Cap Choir; Band; VP, Drama; Orch; Span C; Tnns; Yth Fel; Jr Ntl Hon Soc; Jr Philomel; Sch Silver 'B' A; Church Bell Choir; Stage Band; *Allegheny Col; Mus.*

BRENDELL, Janna Kaye
Pisgah Sr HS; Canton, NC (125-349) Band; Pres, Chem C; Chor; FHA; 4H; Tres, Lat C; 4H A; Mus A; Rotary A; All St Chor, Outst 4-H'Er; *Mars Hill Col; Mus Ed.*

BRENDLI, Diann Christel
Rosary HS; Aurora, IL (1-79) Bus C; *Bradley U; Acct.*

BRENEMAN, Deanna Lynn
Van Far Sr HS; Vandalia, MO; Band; Chldr; Chor; Ensm; Madrigal; NHS.

BRENEMAN, Larry Joe
Laurelwood HS; Memphis, TN (6-19) Band; BC; SC; Bkbl; Cl Fav; HCt; *UT Martin Col; Phys Ed.*

BRENNAN, Bruce Robert
N Quincy HS; Quincy, MA (130-450) Ski C; Bkbl; Golf; Soccer; Tnns; Bio A; Sci A; *U of Maine; Chem Engr.*

BRENNAN, Elizabeth Ann
N Harford Sr HS; Pylesville, MD (25%-330) Span C; Off, Job's Daughters; Art Guild; Vlbl; *Art.*

BRENNAN, Mark Wesley
Reading Mem HS; Reading, MA (33%-420) Band; Co-Ch, Hmrm; Orch; Secy, Ski C; Mgr, Soccer; Wrest; God & Country A; Spch A; Yth Fel; Eagle Sct; Water Ski C; *UNH; Wildlife Mgt.*

BRENNAN, Scott William
Trinity Sch; New York, NY (20-90) Lit Mag; ARC; Swim; ARC A; Sanctuary Soc; Yth Fel.

BRENNAN, Sheila Anne
Secaucus HS; Secaucus, NJ (26-164) CYO; Chor; Rptr, Sch P; Sci C; Alt Del, Douglass Col Citznshp Inst; *Montclair St Col; Eng.*

BRENNDOERFER, Hannelore Ruth
Niles N HS; Skokie, IL (100-360) CYO; Ski C; Soccer; Swim; COM; Hon Prog; White Hon; Ger Hon Stu; *Western Ill Col; Interior Design.*

BRENNEIS, Susan Roberta
Miami Springs Sr HS; Miami Springs, FL (1-816) Anchor C; Drama; Lit Ral; Mu Alpha Theta; VP, NHS; VP, Span NHS; Secy, SC; Thes; DARGCA; Hon Prog; Most Out; Val; Accompanist, Chor; Sup A, Fla All St Solo Contest; Concertmistress, Miami Yth Symph; *Oberlin Col; Mus.*

BRENNEISE, Kathryn Ann
Milo Adventist Acad; Days Creek, OR (6-67) *Walla Walla Col; Bus Acct.*

BRENNEMAN, Anne Joy
E L Bowsher HS; Toledo, OH (29-472) Chor; Ensm; Secy, Ger C; Madrigal; NHS; Hon Prog; HR; OMEA Solo A; All City Choir; *Olivet Col; Psych.*

BRENNER, Brenda Lee
Dexter HS; Dexter, KS; Band; Chldr; Chor; FHA; 4H; SC; Bkbl; 4H A; Spch A; Vlbl; Stuco Rep; Chldr A; *Dental Asst.*

BRENNER, Carol Ann
Highland HS; Ewing, MO; CYO; NHS; Sci C; Bio A; Hon Prog; Soph Pilgrimage; *NE Mo St U.*

BRENNER, Jill Rae
North Sr HS; No St Paul, MN (150-500) Var C; Y-Tns; Sftbl; HQn; Type A; Vlbl; *Stout U; Special Ed.*

BRENNFLECK, Kevin Herbert
Dearborn HS; Dearborn, MI; JV, Tnns; Mgr, Tr; Wrest; Hon Prog; Pres A; *Taylor U.*

BRENNO, Karen Ann
Columbus HS; Columbus, ND; Band; Chldr; Chor; VP, Soph Cl; Bkbl; Sftbl; Tr.

BRENT, Deborah Ann
McKinley Sr HS; Baton Rouge, LA (10-250) Pres, CYO; Math C; Mu Alpha Theta; NHS; ARC; *Southwestern U; Acct.*

BRENT, Lisa Kaye
Lanier HS; Jackson, MS (25%-299) Rptr, Sch P; Tr; Citz A; Crisco A; Hon Prog; NJHS; Ltr Tk; Schol; Proficiency in Spelling.

BRENTANO, Steve Thomas
University HS; San Diego, CA (2-311) Rptr, Ann; Math C; NHS; Rptr, Sch P; JV, Bsbl; JV, Ftbl; Hon Prog; *U of Calif; Chem.*

BRENTLINGER, Christopher Lee
University Sch of Nashville; Nashville, TN (10-65) BC; Drama; Lat C; Math C; Rptr, Sch P; SC; Alg A; Math A; NEDT; *Law.*

BRENTON, Patricia Elaine
Westminster HS; Westminster, CA; Var C; Hockey; Tr; CSF; JV Vlbl; *Goldenwest Col; Art.*

BRESETTE, James Lemke
Citrus HS; Inverness, FL (7-250) Band; VP, Chess C; Drama; Hmrm; NHS; Ed, Sch P; Amer Leg A; B Crocker A; ROTC A; VFW A; *Pre-Law.*

BRESHEARS, David Dale
Los Alamos HS; Los Alamos, NM (25%-400) Band; *Bio.*

BRESLIN, David S
Hightstown HS; Hightstown, NJ (17-309) BS; Ed, Sch P; JV, Bkbl; JV, Soccer; 1st Prize, St Hist Fair; *Sci.*

BRETL, Tracy Lynn
Port Washington HS; Port Washington, WI (10-265) Dbte Tm; Math C; NHS; Rptr, Sch P; Math A; Sci A; Spch A; Pom Pom Squad; Choreography Sch; Forensics Musical; *U of Wisc; Med Tech.*

BRETL, Troy Robert
Port Washington HS; Port Washington, WI (49-265) Band; Chor; Demolay; Ensm; FBLA; NHS; Sch P; Ftbl; Golf; Spch A; Forensics; Farewell Address; Sch Musicals; Summer Musical; *U of Wisc-Washington Co; Mass Communication.*

BRETT, Lawrence Gerard
Father Judge HS; Philadelphia, PA (3-630) Pres, CYO; Chldr; Fr C; Pres, NHS; Rptr, Sch P; Pres, SC; Cr-Ctry; Tr; NMF; NEDT; Distinguished Stu A; Rotary Tomorrow's Leader's Conf; *Georgetown U; Government.*

BRETT, Rebecca Lynn
Switzerland Co Jr-Sr HS; Vevay, IN (8-108) Ed;
Ann; Rptr, Band; VP, FHA; NHS; Poet A; Vof-
DEM; *Purdue U; Acct.*

BRETTMANN, Barie Blain
Auburn HS; Auburn, NE (1-100) Band; BS; VP,
Math C; NHS; Span C; SC; JV, Bkbl; Ftbl; Math A;
U of Nebr; Civil Engr.

BRETZMAN, William Charles
Milford Township HS; Milford, IL; Band; Chor;
4H; Madrigal; Order/Arrow; Bsbl; JV, Bkbl; JV,
Ftbl; JV, Golf; God & Country A; 4H A; Order/
Arrow A; *Danvill Jr Col.*

BREUER, Dale Francis
Estherville HS; Estherville, IA; A Cap Choir; Chor;
Drama; Hmrm; Madrigal; Tres, Thes; Var C; Mgr,
Bsbl; Bkbl; Ftbl; Tnns; Tr; COM; *Iowa Lakes
Comm Col; Bus.*

BREUNIG, Janet Lee
Eastern HS; Middletown, KY (150-288) A Cap
Choir; Chor; Ch, Hmrm; S-T, ARC; SC; Cpt, Bkbl;
Cpt, Ftbl; Cpt, Sftbl; ARC A; MVP, Sftbl; Powder
Puff Ftbl; MVP, Ftbl; Ldrship A; Drama A; Choir
A; Bkbl A.

BREVITZ, Elizabeth Edyne
Lakeview HS; Battle Creek, MI; NHS; Sch Achieve
Tm; Bausch & Lomb A; COM; NMF; NMS; Ntl
Sci Found; St Board of Ed School; *Mich St U.*

BREWER, Cynthia Kay
Spring Woods HS; Houston, TX (180-510) Chor;
Sftbl; Pres A; *Houston Baptist U; Phys Ed.*

BREWER, Darryl Wayne
Paul L Dunbar HS; Fort Worth, TX (10-275) A
Cap Choir; Band; Ensm; Hmrm; NHS; Orch; SC;
Ftbl; Tr; Yth Fel; Parl, Yth Fel; *U of Calif at Berke-
ley; Instrumental Mus.*

BREWER, Edwin Blaine
Wayne Co HS; Jesup, GA; Band; PA.

BREWER, Faye Marie
Ogemaw Heights HS; W Branch, MI; Band; Tr; 1st
Cl, GSct; Tr Tm; Band A.

BREWER, James Evans
Killeen HS; Killeen, TX; Cpt, Ftbl; Tr; Opt A; Pres
A; Spch A; Loc & Dist Off, Estrn Strs Yth Frat; *U
of Tex, Austin; Computers.*

BREWER, Michael Wayne
Jenks HS; Jenks, OK (10-300) Band; Ensm; NHS;
Sci C; Hon Prog; Vlbl; Instrumental Mus As;
Okla St U; Engr.

BREWER, Renee Darlene
Clinton HS; Clinton, MS; BC; Bkbl; Sftbl; *Hinds
Col; Computer Sci.*

BREWER, Rick Allen
Skyline HS; Dallas, TX; Hon Prog; *Math.*

BREWER, Susanna
Pickens HS; Pickens, WV (2-15) Co-Ed, Ann; Cpt,
Chldr; Pres A; NHS; Secy; Secy, Sci C; VP, SC;
Pres, Sr Cl; Bkbl; Cl Fav; I Dare You; MLS; Regent
Schol; Sal; *W Va U; Agr.*

BREWER, Terrell Clyde
A L Brown HS; Kannapolis, NC;

BREWER, Theresa Annette
Foley HS; Foley, AL (25%-250) AFS; Dbte Tm;
FHA; Hist A; 1st Pl Oil Painting, Co Fair; *Harding
Christian Col; Hist.*

BREWER, Truman Ward
Minor HS; Birmingham, AL (150-475) Chor; 4H;
Cpt, Bkbl; Cpt, Ftbl; Yth Fel.

BREWER, Vicki Lynn
Peyton HS; Peyton, CO (2-12) Ann; Chor; FHA;
Ger C; NHS; F-Ed, Sch P; Secy, SC; S-T, Sr Cl;
S-T, Jr Cl; Secy, Soph Cl; Bio A; HQn; Sal; *Western
St U; Elem Ed.*

BREWSTER, Barbara Jenine
Lyman Mem HS; Lebanon, CT; Band; CYO; Chor;
Ch, Drama; Sftbl; COM; Badminton; Marion
Medal; Sign o-t Star; Sign o-t Arrow; *Art.*

BREWSTER, Marcie Lyn
Whitehaven HS; Memphis, TN (5-225) Ann; Secy,
BC; Chor; Pres, Fr C; FTA; InterClub Coun; S-T,
Mu Alpha Theta; Sch P; Pres, Tri-HiY; MVP,
Tnns; H of F; HCt; Hon Prog; MLS; *U of Colo;
International Relations.*

BREWSTER, Mark Joseph
Mt Carmel HS; Mt Carmel, IL (80-170) Key C;
Golf; Best Dressed; *U of Evansville; Bus.*

BREWTON, Cynthia Valdean
Claxton HS; Claxton, GA (25%-110) Ann; FBLA;
FHA; *S Ga Col; Secretarial.*

BREWTON, John Carrol Jr
Wayne Co HS; Jesup, GA (75-352) 4H; Hmrm;
Phys C; Sci C; Ftbl; Tnns; Citz A; 4H A; WW;
Middle Ga Col; Elec Engr.

BREWTON, Randolph Greely
S H Blair HS; Hattiesburg, MS (5%-430) BS; VP,
InterAct C; A-Ed, Lit Mag; SC; Pres, Sr Cl; HCt;
Art A; Pres, MYF; Pres, Meistersingers; *U of Sou
Miss.*

BREY, Clare D
Tottenville HS; Staten Island, NY (3-1192) Ensm;
Pres, NHS; Orch; *Eng.*

BREYES, Leopoldo Gerardo
St Augustine HS; Laredo, TX; Ann; BS; NHS; WW
Nom; *Laredo Jr Col; Law Enforcement.*

BRIANO, Kimberly Marie
Covina HS; Covina, CA (3-368) Drama; Model
UN; Ski C; SC; JV, Swim; CSF; COM; Hon Prog;
NEDT; Girl's League; Badminton; *U o-t Pacific;
Phar.*

BRICKER, Arlene Louise
Cottage Grove HS; Cottage Grove, OR; Sch P;
Swim; Tr; Outst Ath A.

BRICKER, Brenda Ruth
Cumberland Valley HS; Mechanicsburg, PA
(22-605) Band; NHS; Ski C; Hockey; Tr; NEDT;
Dickinson Col; Law.

BRICKER, Dale Eugene
Fairchance Georges Sr HS; Fairchance, PA;

BRICKER, Greg Allen
Clark Co R-I HS; Kahoka, MO (1-92) CYO; Chor;
Drama; NHS; Order/Arrow; Span C; Pres, SC;
Thes; Mgr, Bkbl; JV, Cr-Ctry; Golf; Alg A; God &
Country A; Math A; Order/Arrow A; Pres A; ARC
A; Val; Span A; Eagle Sct; Freedom Forum; *Notre
Dame Col; Nucleur Research.*

BRICKER, Kenneth Raymond
Grosse Pointe N HS; Grosse Pointe, MI; Yth Fel;
Ping Pong C; *Elec.*

BRICKLE, Susan Elizabeth
Tift Co HS; Tifton, GA (8-400) A Cap Choir; BC;
Hmrm; Var C; Bkbl; Tnns; COM; Hon Prog;
Emory U; Med.

BRICKMAN, Kathleen Marie
Mansfield Christian HS; Mansfield, OH (3-48)
Chldr; Chor; Ensm; NHS; St Stu Congress; SC;
Bkbl; Alg A; Eng A; Geom A; *Anderson Col.*

BRICKSON, Herbert Orion
De La Salle HS; New Orleans, LA; Key C; Swim;
Hon Prog; Most Improved Swimmer; *Math.*

BRIDDLE, Mary Kay
Quincy Notre Dame HS; Quincy, IL (5-140) Chor;
Ensm; NHS; VP, Span C; Spch C; SC; Secy, Sr Cl;
Cpt, Tnns; Hon Prog; NEDT; MVP, Tnns; SAA A;
NHS Schol; 1st Pl, Doubles Dist Tnns; 1st Pl, St
Mus Contest Solo; U of Ill Mus Camp School;
Quincy Col; Mus.

BRIDEAU, Andrea Lee
Oakmont Regional HS; S Ashburnham, MA
(9-153) Chor; Span C; Hockey; JV, Tnns; Jr-Sr
Prom Princess C.

**BRIDGEFORTH,
Anthony Dwayne**
W End HS; Birmingham, AL (125-399) Band; City
Conf; Ensm; HiY; Orch; Pres, SC; Thes; HCt; JA
A; Jr Chamber of Com A; Most Out; Yth Fel; Yth
Leg; WW; *U of Ala; Pre-Law.*

BRIDGEFORTH, Lillita Irene
John Marshall HS; Indianapolis, IN (34-250) A
Cap Choir; Chor; FBLA; ARC; Gov Honor Prog;
JA A; *Purdue U; Hist.*

BRIDGEMAN, Sharon Faye
Dinwiddie HS; Dinwiddie, VA (15-376) A Cap
Choir; Chor; Ensm; Hmrm; NHS; Cpt, Sftbl; HCt;
Ring Qn; Homecoming Princess.

**BRIDGES,
Andrea Beatrice Teresa**
San Bernardino HS; San Bernardino, CA; Band;
FHA; Cr-Ctry; Tr; COM; Citz A; Cert of Recogni-
tion; *U of Sou Calif; Secy.*

BRIDGES, Angela Marie
Burns Sr HS; Lawndale, NC; JV, Bkbl; Sftbl; Health
Occupations C; FCA; Pres, Yth Training Union;
Acteens; Choir; Outreach Ldr, Sunday Sch Cl.

BRIDGES, Clay Forrester
SW Georgia Acad; Damascus, GA (9-26) BC; BS;
Chor; Pres, Dbte Tm; Drama; Ensm; Fr C; 4H;
HiY; Hmrm; InterClub Coun; Lit Ral; Math C; Cpt,
Sch Achieve Tm; Sch P; Sci C; Spch C; SC; Thes;
Ftbl; Tr; Cl Fav; DARGCA; Gr Marshal; Most
Out; Sci A; Spch A; Boy's Solo; Best All Around;
Y-C Rep; Presbyterian Jr Fellowship; *N Ga Col;
Pre-Law.*

BRIDGES, Cynthia Elaine
Unity HS; Chicago, IL (18-121) Chor; Drama;
Pres, 4H; Span C; Bkbl; COM; 4H A; Hon Prog;
Yth Fel; Mus A; Attendance A; Lib A; Drama A;
Bradley U; Mus.

BRIDGES, Dennis O
Leo HS; Leo, IN (71-100) Bsbl; Ftbl; Hockey;
Swim; Tnns; Pres A; *Purdue U.*

BRIDGES, Donna Faye
Burns Sr HS; Lawndale, NC; Fr C; Sch P; Journ A;
Poet A; Yth Foundation A; Yth Leg; *Bus.*

BRIDGES, Jackie Louise
Linville HS; Linville, LA (3-18) F-Ed, Ann; VP,
FHA; 4H; Lit Ral; SC; S-T, Sr Cl; S-T, Jr Cl; Rptr,
Soph Cl; Bkbl; Cl Fav; Off o-t Yr; Yam A; *Bastrop
Voc Tec Sch; Nurs.*

BRIDGES, Jody Kay
Landmark Christian Sch; Cincinnati, OH (1-36)
Ann; Band; COM; Hon Prog; Val; *Cedarville Chris-
tian Col.*

BRIDGES, Roy Stephen
G W Carver HS; Birmingham, AL (14-237) FBLA;
HiY; NHS; Bsbl; COM; Yth Leg; *Tuskegee Inst;
Acct.*

BRIDGES, Sondra Michelle
Fairley HS; Memphis, TN (50-320) Chldr; Cpt,
Mjrte; Tr; HQn; *U of Tenn; Phys Therapy.*

BRIDGES, Velma
Murray Wright Sr HS; Detroit, MI; Chldr; FHA;
ARC; Sch P; Span NHS; Up Bound; Alg A; Citz A;
JV Vlbl; *U of Mich; Med.*

BRIDGES, Walter Clyde
San Bernardino HS; San Bernardino, CA; Var C;
Cpt, Cr-Ctry; Ftbl; Cpt, Tr; Ath o-t Yr; *Cal-Poly-
Pomona Col; Phys Ed.*

BRIDINGER, Deborah Carol
Bath HS; Lima, OH (1-225) Ann; Chor; Secy, Fr C;
4H; MVP, Swim; Ntl Sci Symposium; MIP, Gym;
Sci.

BRIDINGER, Kathryn Elizabeth
Bath Sr HS; Lima, OH (1-220) A Cap Choir; F-Ed,
Ann; Fr C; FHA; Tres, NHS; Secy, Sci C; Spch C;
Thes; DARGCA; PTA A; Sci A; Val; YFU Ex-
change Stu; Wittenberg U, Hon A; *Wittenberg U;
Ed.*

BRIDWELL, Jennie Lila
Carlsbad Sr HS; Carlsbad, NM; Chor; Fr C; Alg A;
Carsbad Branch Col; Herpatology.

BRIDWELL, Paula Margaret
Bayside HS; Virginia Beach, VA (8-550) Anchor C;
Chor; S-T, FHA; 4H; Hmrm; InterClub Coun; Lit
Mag; Ch, Model UN; NHS; Pol Sci C; Secy; Sci C;
Secy, Ski C; Bio A; COM; JA A; NMF; Summa
Cum Laude; Disciples of Christ Merit Schol;
Lynchburg Col; Med Tech.

BRIDWELL, Ronnie Lynn
R L Paschal HS; Ft Worth, TX (50%-750) Sci C;
Mgr, Bkbl; Industrial Arts A.

BRIEL, John Benjamin
Premontre HS; Green Bay, WI (60-150) Soccer; Tr;
ROTC A; Pres, Explorers; *U of Hawaii at Manoa;
Bus.*

BRIER, Lori Ann
Yough Sr HS; Herminie, PA (10%-380) Band;
CYO; Chor; Sch P; Span C; Secy, Soph Cl; NEDT;
Yrbk Photographer; Colorguard; *Med.*

81

BRIESE, Allan George
Post Falls HS; Post Falls, ID; VP, 4H; Ftbl; Tr; Wrest.

BRIESE, Patricia Ann
White Salmon Christian Sch; White Salmon, WA; Ann; Chor; Ensm; Girls League C; 2nd Pl Win, St Essay; Nurs.

BRIETZKE, Cynthia Dale
Ne Metropolitan Regional Voc Sch; Wakefield, MA; A Cap Choir; Chor; JV, Bkbl; Hockey; JV, Sftbl.

BRIGANTIC, Robert Mark
St Peters Prep Sch; Jersey City, NJ (2-200) Drama; Ch, SC; Alg A; Hon Prog; NEDT; Span A; Bus.

BRIGGINS, Gloria Jean
Wendell Phillips HS; Chicago, IL; City Conf; Drama; NHS; Swim; Hon Prog; Ntl Achv Schol; Yth Leg; U of Ill; Acct.

BRIGGS, Carl
Sol C Johnson HS; Savannah, GA; Span C; Pres, Sr Cl; Tr; MLS; Tuskegee Inst; Chem Engr.

BRIGGS, Charles Whitford
Putnum Co Sr HS; Cookeville, TN (80-400) Fr C; Order/Arrow; Tnns; Life A, Scts; Tenn Tech Col; Sci.

BRIGGS, Danny Brian
Paris HS; Paris, TX; Chor; Secy, Key C; Madrigal; Span C; Golf; All-Dist, All Region Golf; FCA; Texas A&M U; Bio.

BRIGGS, Jill Kerrill
Almont HS; Almont, MI (6-110) Band; 4H; NHS; Sch P; Ski C; VP, Span C; Var C; MVP, Bkbl; JV, Golf; JV, Tr; Citz A; 4H A; NEDT; JV, Vlbl; Bronze, Silver & Gold Schol As; Mich Tech U; Engr.

BRIGGS, Jola Jean
Proctor HS; Proctor, MN (3-244) A Cap Choir; Chor; Ensm; FHA; Math A; 4 Seal Diploma; Yth Temp Counc; Cystic Fibrosis Bike- a- thon Vol A; Math.

BRIGGS, Karen Sue
S Stokes HS; Walnut Cove, NC (11-360) Band; BC; VP, Lat C; Mu Alpha Theta; NHS; SC; Bkbl; Vlbl; UNC; Pre-Med.

BRIGGS, Robert Scott
Lumberton HS; Lumberton, TX (2-128) Pres, Fr C; Hmrm; Tres, Key C; Pres, NHS; Phys C; SC; Pres, Y-Tns; Bkbl; Ftbl; Tr; H of F; Hist A; Sal; Semi-Fin, Tr Regional Meet; Geometry A; Bookkeep A; Eng A; Lamar U; Elec Engr.

BRIGGS, Susan Kay
Frederic HS; Frederic, WI (3-80) Chldr; Chor; Secy, FHA; Semi-Fin, GS; Co-Ed, Sch P; VP, SC; Semi-Fin, Tr; Amer Leg Orator A; COM; Type A; Civic Oration A; Tr As; Conservation A; St Croix Valley All Conf A; Social Work.

BRIGGS, Terri Kay
Bethel HS; Hampton, VA (92-516) Acteens; Drama C; VP, Tidewater Dance Theatre; Yth Choir; Rep, Yth Action; Durham Technical Inst; Optics.

BRIGGS, Wendy Gail
Columbia HS; W Columbia, TX; AFS; Band; Mjrte; Secy, SC; VP, Jr Cl; VP, Soph Cl; Rep, Church Yth Coun; Dental Tech.

BRIGHAM, Debbie Miles
The Concept Sch; Westtown, PA; Chor; Drama; Ensm; Lit Mag; Ski C; I Dare You; Most Out; Val; Hollins Col; Eng.

BRIGHAM, Melissa Ann
Horton Watkins HS; Ladue, MO (33%-450) Drama; Semi-Fin, GS; Swim; Swim Ltr Cert; AAU Meet As; Commercial Arts.

BRIGHT, Allyson Michelle
Wyoming HS; Wyoming, OH; Bkbl; JV, Sftbl; Tr; All Star Bkbl; GAA; Spirit Sq; Babson Col; Mgt.

BRIGHT, Benjamin Fulcher
Gladewater HS; Gladewater, TX (25%-175) Dbte Tm; Drama; Tres, FTA; Hmrm; NHS; ARC; SC; Tnns; Hon Prog; Spch A; Yth Fel; Speech A; Coun On Ministries; Kilgore Jr Col; Med.

BRIGHT, Darryl Glenn
High Point Central HS; High Point, NC; Chess C; Hmrm; Tr; Guildford Tech Inst; Mech.

BRIGHT, Jacqueline Chequetta
Burke HS; Charleston, SC; NHS; NEDT; UNC at Chapel Hill; Radiology.

BRIGHT, James Edward
Liberty Central HS; Liberty, NY (45-130) Chess C; ARC; Pres, Sci C; COM; NEDT; Regent Schol; Cpt, First Aid Tm; Delhiage Tech Col; Engr.

BRIGHT, Joyce Fay
Hillsdale HS; Jeromesville, OH (1-99) Chor; NHS; Alg A; Chem A; Hon Prog; MLS; Yth Fel; Tri-Ed, Yrbk; Bluffton Col; Math.

BRIGHT, Karen Lynette
Hillsboro HS; Nashville, TN; Drama; FHA; 4H; Lat C; ARC; Span C; ARC A; Tennessee St U; Psych.

BRIGHT, Lynn Denise
Alexandar Hamilton HS; Los Angeles, CA; Ed, Sch P; Hon Prog; Journ A; Yth Fel; Adv Stu A; Homecoming A; Church A; Los Angeles Valley Col; Sociology.

BRIGHT, Paulette Andromedia
Spring Brook Sr HS; Silver Spring, MD; Drama; Belmont Col.

BRIGHT, Susan Marie
Belton HS; Belton, TX (25-200) Tres, CYO; Dbte Tm; NHS; Tnns.

BRIGHT, Theresa Ann
Belton HS; Belton, TX (4-196) Bus Mgr, Ann; Pres, CYO; JV, Chldr; NHS; JV, Tr; Fin, Bus A; Semi-Fin, Typing A; Fin, Algebra A; Fin, Hon Prog; Fin, Math A; Mary Hardin Col; Bus Ed.

BRIGHTBILL, Leanna Dawn
Central Dauphin Sr HS; Harrisburg, PA; Chor; Sci C; Garden C; Yth Fel; Solar Energy.

BRIGHTBILL, Lucinda Gay
Cedar Cliff HS; Camp Hill, PA (160-526) Band; Chor; Pres, Hmrm; Tres, Lat C; Orch; Ski C; SC; Tnns; Millersville St Col; Early Childhood Ed.

BRIGHTLY, Constance Emily
Wykeham Rise HS; Washington, CT (7-26) Chor; Rptr, Lit Mag; Pres, SC; Pres, Sr Cl; Swim; Tnns; HR; Headmasters Hon; Mus.

BRIGMAN, Lisa Lorraine
Nw Cabarrus HS; Concord, NC (1-200) Tres, BC; Pres, Fr C; FTA; Secy, Hmrm; DARGCA; Gr Marshal; MLS; Val; Outst Sr; Schol Achv A; U of NC; Early Childhood Ed.

BRIGNAC, Cheryl Ann
Destrehan HS; Destrehan, LA (4-166) Pres, Band; BC; Pres, Bus C; Fin, GS; Fin, Ntl Yth Conf; SC; JA A; Band A; Bus.

BRILEY, Sharon Elaine
Blanchard HS; Blanchard, OK; A Cap Choir; F-Ed, Ann; BC; Chor; Dbte Tm; Drama; Ensm; FHA; 4H; Madrigal; Math C; NHS; F-Ed, Sch P; Span C; SC; Pres, Sr Cl; Bkbl; Sftbl; COM; Gov Honor Prog; 4H A; Hon Prog; Journ A; Magna Cum Laude; Math A; St Scholar; Yth Fel; Yth Foundation A; Secy, Sergeant of Arms, Pep C; Home Ec A; U of Okla; Bus.

BRIM, Jerry Ray
Snyder HS; Snyder, TX (89-195) Chor; FFA; Livestock Judg, Chptr Farmer, A's; Tex Tech U; Pre-Vet.

BRIMER, Sherry Renee
Alton-Wood River HS; Wood River, IL; Chor; FHA; Lewis & Clark Col; Secy.

BRIMM, Martha Sue
Anna-Jonesboro Comm HS; Anna, IL (10-150) F-Ed, Ann; FTA; Span C; Shawnee Col.

BRINDA, William David
Westminister Christian Acad; Huntsville, AL (1-7) Ann; Chor; Ensm; Fr C; Bkbl; Golf; Soccer; Sftbl; Tnns; Tr; Sal; Sci A; Covenant Col; Engr.

BRINDLEY, Elsa L
Beachwood HS; Beachwood, OH (33%-200) Ann; Tres, Ecology C; Bowling Green Col; Special Ed.

BRINDLEY, Joan P
Beachwood HS; Beachwood, OH; SC; JV, Bkbl; U of Cinncinati; Nurs.

BRINDLEY, Joan Pell
Beachwood HS; Beachwood, OH; SC; JV, Bkbl; Swim; Ecology C; OCLUS; Cincinnati Col; Nurs.

BRINEGAR, Melinda Sue
Moulton-Udell HS; Moulton, IA (4-47) A Cap Choir; Band; Chldr; Chor; Drama; Madrigal; Mjrte; Tres, Sr Cl; Mgr, Bkbl; Tr; Type A; Prom Qn; Indian Hills Comm Col; Acct.

BRINGER, Becky Louise
Highland HS; Ewing, MO (11-130) Chor; FBLA; FHA; Patrica Stephens Col; Fashion & Design.

BRINKER, Gregory Charles
Ralston Sr HS; Ralston, NE (16-329) AFS; Chor; Ensm; Madrigal; NHS; Hon Prog; Nebr All-St Chor; Swing Choir; Sch Musical; U of Nebr-Omaha; Bus Adm.

BRINKERHOFF, Donna Marie
Paris HS; Paris, IL (66-219) Band; Chor; Sch P; Span C; SC; B Crocker A; 4H A; Parl, Rptr, S-T, 4-H C; Ill St U; Acct.

BRINKHAUS, Diane Elizabeth
Belmont Acad; Opelousas, LA (4-29) CYO; GS; Cpt, Bkbl; Sftbl; Amer Leg A; Cl Fav; Elk A; Pres A; MVP, Dist Bkbl; Best Personality; Keywanettes; Most Courteous; Pres, Serteen C; Most Ath; Northeast St U; Phar.

BRINKLEY, Elizabeth Marcelle
Treadwell HS; Memphis, TN; Band; Secy, Chem C; Drama; Hmrm; NHS; Rainbow; SC; Thes; VP, Jr Cl; Spch A; Band Qn; Law.

BRINKMAN, Chris David
Mt Blue HS; Farmington, ME; BS; MVP, Bkbl; Ftbl; Tr; Amer Leg A; Elk A; Yth Fel; All-Star Bkbl Tms.

BRINKMAN, Deborah Ann
East HS; Madison, WI; City Cirriculam Comm, Govt Day; Vet.

BRINKMAN, Jan Adrianna
Mount Blue HS; Farmington, ME; Sch P; SC; Bkbl; Tr; Bio A; Sci A; Yth Fel; JV Field Hockey; Hon Men, All-St Girl's Bkbl Tm; Mem Tr & Field Games; St Girls Tr Meet.

BRINKMAN, Julie Marie
Estherville HS; Estherville, IA (35-170) Briar Cliff Col; Special Ed.

BRINKMAN, P Buckley
Edgewood HS; Madison, WI (85-749) Band; Ensm; Hmrm; Math C; Orch; Tres, SC; Var C; Bsbl; Chem A; Hon Prog; Opt A; Wis St Journ Young Achv; 6th Pl, Wis St Econ Test; St Assem Citation; Bus Adm.

BRINLEE, Kelly Dianne
Permian HS; Odessa, TX (263-658) Band; Puppet Group; Stu Missionary; Office Asst; Odessa Col; Ed.

BRINSKY, David Ward
Luther Burbank HS; Sacramento, CA (12-614) AFS; Order/Arrow; Span C; CSF; God & Country A; Order/Arrow A.

BRINTON, Henry Griffith
Bowie Sr HS; Bowie, MD (5-840) Band; NHS; Ski C; St Stu Congress; SC; Pres, Jr Cl; Bio A; Hon Prog; K of C A; Sci A; Superintendent's, Eng, A's.

BRINTON, Marianne Elizabeth
Central Bucks HS; Doylestown, PA (58-513) Drama; Hon Prog; Sunday Sch Teacher; Yth Group; Vacation Bible Sch Teacher; Weschester Col; Elem Ed.

BRIONES, Juan Jr
Mem HS; San Antonio, TX (20-300) Bus C; Chor; Drama; Rptr, FTA; Hmrm; NHS; F-Ed, Sch P; Pres, Span C; Span NHS; VP, SC; Cl Most Spirited; Dist, Stu o-t Month; Boston U; Business Mgt.

BRISBANE, Kathleen Sue
Frontier Central HS; Hamburg, NY; Co-Ed, Ann; Band; Chor; Dbte Tm; Drama; Ensm; VP, Model UN; NHS; Sch P; Secy, Soph Cl; 1st Cl GSct; Mus C; Water Ballet; Radio C; Comm Band; SE Kans Choir; Human Rel Com; Bicen Essay Contest; Tutoring; II Rating, Solo Comp; Hartwick Col; Mus Ed.

BRISCO, Ruth Annette
Patten Acad of Christian Ed; Oakland, CA (5-13) Chor; Cpt, Dbte Tm; Ensm; Orch; Rptr, Sch P; Pres, SC; Citz A; Hon Prog; Patten Bible Col; Bible.

BRISCOE, Daphne Yvette
S Park HS; Beaumont, TX (34-170) FHA; FTA; HiY; ARC; Tres, Sci C; Tri-HiY; Arch; Bkbl; Sftbl; Tnns; ARC A; *Lamar U; Med Lib.*

BRISCOE, John Gilbert
Sherman HS; Sherman, TX (10%-400) BS; Lat C; Mu Alpha Theta; NHS; SC; Bus Mgr, Sr Cl; Ftbl; Tr; Cl Fav; Ftbl & Tr Trnr; *Austin Col; Pre-Med.*

BRISON, Diana Lee
Ahrens HS; Louisville, KY; Parl, Bus C; Chor; Hmrm; Fin, Jr Miss Pagent; NHS; SC; Tr; HCt; Hon Prog; Teacher's Aid A; DECA Comp A; *U of Louisville; Commercial Arts.*

BRISSON, Marsha Candice
Myers Park HS; Charlotte, NC (61-546) BC; Fr C; Tres, Hmrm; InterClub Coun; Pres, Y-Tns; *U of NC; Marine Bio.*

BRISTER, Divia Jane
Briarfield Acad; Lake Providence, LA (20-40) Ann; 4H; Sch P; Span C; Bkbl; Tr; Choir; *La Tech U; Elem Ed.*

BRISTOL, Annette Patricia
Hughes HS; Cincinnati, OH; Secy, Band; Chldr; Secy, Chor; Ch, Hmrm; NHS; Secy, SC; Secy, Sftbl; Tnns; DARGCA; Gov Honor Prog; Hmemg Prin; Miss Sweet Sixteen; Rep, Girl's Wk; Pep C; 'A' HR; *Cincinnati Tech Col; Bus Adm.*

BRISTOL, John Earl
Oregon City Sr HS; Oregon City, OR (21-400) NHS; JV, Ftbl; *Clackamas Comm Col; Auto Mechanics.*

BRISTOL, Susan Ruth
Essex Junction Educational Center; Essex Junction, VT; A Cap Choir; Bus Mgr, Bus C; Chor; 4H; Mgr, Wrest; Citz A; 4H A; JA A; Pres, Secy, Tres, Church Yth; Rptr, Bus C; *Johnson St Col; Childhood Ed.*

BRISTOW, Alesa Mynett
Madison Acad HS; Huntsville, AL (3-51) BC; Monogram; NHS; Var C; Tres, Jr Cl; COM; Hon Prog; NEDT; Star Student; Vlbl; Eng A; Home Ec A; Bible A; *Freed-Hardeman Col; Bus.*

BRISTOW, Dorothy Yvonne
Mayo HS; Darlington, SC (45-113) Chldr; Chor; Drama; FHA; Hmrm; SC; HCt; Star Student; Allston Courtesy A; Lib Service; Chldr A; *Denmark Tech Col; Cosmetology.*

BRISTOW, Karen Anne
Parkway HS; Bossier City, LA (69-334) Band; Bus C; FBLA; Rptr, Art C; CODAC; Flag Line Camp Outst As; Sup, Flag Line Contest; *La Tech Univ; Business Admin.*

BRITSCH, Stephen Eugene
Rogers HS; Toledo, OH (40%-749) Band; Ger C; Orch; Soccer; Mus A; VP, Church Yth Group; *Toledo U; Med.*

BRITT, Beverly Faye
Newton-Conover HS; Newton, NC; BC; FHA; Span C; Flag Corps; PA A.

BRITT, Joan
Ahoskie HS; Ahoskie, NC; ARC; Tnns; ARC A; Yth Fel; Tres, Lib C; Tres, Hist C; *NC Central U; Bus Adm.*

BRITT, Lyle Elaine
Lafayette Sr HS; Lexington, KY; BC; FBLA; Mu Alpha Theta; Span C; Span NHS; Swim; Spch A; Type A; Creative Writing A; *Murray St Col; Bus.*

BRITT, Rodney Stephen
E Prairie HS; E Prairie, MO (12-96) Band; BS; Chor; NHS; Orch; Sci C; Secy, Span C; Ftbl; Tr; Presidential School; *SE Mo U.*

BRITT, Sheila Joretta
Newton-Conover HS; Newton, NC (19-200) AFS; BC; Chldr; Pres, FHA; Span C; COM; NEDT; Yth Fel.

BRITT, William T
Enid HS; Enid, OK (43-537) Band; Dbte Tm; Fr C; HiY; NFL; NHS; Order/Arrow; Thes; Amer Leg Orator A; VFW Orator Win; VofDEM; *Westminster Col; Pre-Law.*

BRITTAIN, Hazel Rhonda
Sangre De Christo Christian Sch; Canon City, CO; Cpt, Chldr; Chor; Bsbl; Ftbl; COM; HCt; Val; Highest GPA; Most Work Completed A; *Baptist Bible Col; Elem Ed.*

BRITTEN, Barbara Leona
Abbotsford Jr Secondary Sch; Abbotsford, CAN-ADA; Chldr; Ski C; Hockey; Hon Prog.

BRITTINGHAM, Lisa Whiteside
The Christian Acad; Chester, PA; AFS; Fr C; Sftbl; MIP, Sftbl; *Journ.*

BRITTON, Lisa Doreen
Shelbyville Central HS; Shelbyville, TN (16-235) Chor; FHA; NHS; Span C; Tri-HiY; Hon Prog; Car Winner, Highest 6 Wk Avg; *Middle Tenn St U; Sociology.*

BRITTON, Vanessa Lynn
Boulevard Baptist Sch; Burleson, TX (4-5) Band; FHA; FTA; Sci C; Bkbl; Tr; COM; *Acct.*

BRIZENDINE, Elizabeth Laverne
King William HS; King William, VA; Ed, Ann; Co-Ed, Lit Mag; COM; Gov Honor Prog; Journ A; Q&S A; *Richmond Mem Hospital Sch of Nurs; Nurs.*

BROACH, Nancy Elizabeth
Monroe Area Comprehensive HS; Monroe, GA (28-170) Anchor C; A-Ed, Ann; FTA; Hmrm; SC; Pep C; *U of Ga; Nurs.*

BROADBENT, Erin Kaye
Camp Verde HS; Camp Verde, AZ (7-56) Ann; Band; Chor; Drama; Rptr, 4H; Rptr, Sch P; Secy, Sr Cl; Bkbl; Sftbl; Tr; 4H A; Poet A; Type A; Interntl Fel Inc; Ltrwomen; Vlbl; Pep C; President's Phys Fitness A; MYF; HERO; *Environmental Health Tech.*

BROADBENT, Lori Gay
Leedey HS; Leedey, OK (3-15) A Cap Choir; Co-Ed, Ann; Chor; Ensm; Rptr, FHA; Sch P; Pres, Jr Cl; COM; Miss LHS; *Southwestern Okla St U; Bus.*

BROADDUS, Eva Patricia
King William HS; King William, VA; COM; HCt; *Bus Adm.*

BROADWATER, Colleen Kelley
Koshkonong HS; Koshkonong, MO; Ann; Chor; Ed, Sch P; B Crocker A; I Dare You; Journ A; Type A; Val; Home Ec A; Mus A; *Southwest Mo St U; Home Ec.*

BROADWAY, Barbara Ann
South Side HS; Counce, TN; BC; Cpt, Chldr; Rptr, FHA; Sci A; *U of N Ala; Social Work.*

BROADY, Marvetta Rose
Dunbar Sr HS; Fort Worth, TX (10-250) Band; Fr C; Tnns; Sci A; Fr, Band, A's; *Law.*

BROADY, Michael Lee
Brazil HS; Brazil, IN (15-192) Cum Laude Soc; NHS; Bsbl; Cpt, Bkbl; MVP, Tnns; WW; *Ind U; Bus.*

BROBST, John Lawrence
Freeport Sr HS; Freeport, IL; Ftbl; JV, Tr; *Automobile Repair.*

BROCK, Angela Carole
N Hall HS; Gainesville, GA (12-194) Band; BC; Chor; Gov Honor Prog; Hon Prog; All St Chor; Hon Graduate; WW; *Bus.*

BROCK, Anna Maria
Northside HS; Atlanta, GA; FHA; Home Ec A; *Ga St U; Nurs.*

BROCK, Brenda Gaye
Captain Shreve HS; Shreveport, LA; Chldr; Drama; GS; InterAct C; NHS; F-Ed, Sch P; Swim; Tr; HCt; Astra C; *Journ.*

BROCK, Brenda Kay
Parkway HS; Bossier City, LA (130-300) Band; Y-Tns; Beauty; Home Ec C; Adventures C; *La Tech U; Bus Adm.*

BROCK, Carolyn Ann
Trinity Christian HS; Chattanooga, TN (2-12) COM; Type A; Piano A; PA; *Tenn Temple U; Secretarial.*

BROCK, Debra Jean
Fulda HS; Fulda, MN; Chor; FHA; VP, NHS; Yth Fel; Church Choir; VP, Off Ed Assn; VP, OEA Pin; *Worthington Comm Col; Secy.*

BROCK, Elizabeth Jean
Cumberland Valley HS; Mechanicsburg, PA (8-650) Chldr; Hmrm; NHS; Ski C; Var C; Swim; Tr; COM; Coun of Teach A; NEDT; *Bucknell Col; Bus Mgr.*

BROCK, Jan Loree
Laurel Co HS; London, KY (19-360) BC; Hmrm; Lat C; Mu Alpha Theta; Sci C; Math A; Ntl Achv Schol; *Georgetown Col; Psych.*

BROCK, Kimberly Elaine
Pendleton HS; Pendleton, SC (15-133) F-Ed, Ann; Pres, Hmrm; SC; *Clemson U; Ed.*

BROCK, Leslie Marie
Monterey HS; Lubbock, TX; Tri-HiY; *Psych.*

BROCK, Mark Allen
Live Oak HS; Morgan Hill, CA (60-500) Band; 4H; Hmrm; Orch; Var C; JV, Bkbl; JV, Ftbl; Tr; JV, Wrest; 4H A; Sports A's; *Gauilan Jr Col; Archt.*

BROCK, Mary Wendy
Cape Fear Acad; Wilmington, NC (4-18) Chess C; Pres, Hmrm; Secy, SC; Secy, Jr Cl; Pres, Soph Cl; MVP, Bkbl; Sftbl; Pres A; Sci A; MVP, Vlbl; MVP, All Tourn Bkbl; Highest % Freethrows; All Conf; *U of NC; Phys Ed.*

BROCK, Rhonda Lynne
Bob Jones HS; Madison, AL (10%-114) BC; Chor; Tnns; Gym; *U of Ala; Ecology.*

BROCK, Rhonda Rebecca
Palmetto HS; Palmetto, GA (18-106) Ann; Band; Drama; Pres, FBLA; Hmrm; Cpt, Mjrte; SC; Beauty; HCt; Miss FBLA; *Middle Ga Col; Bus.*

BROCK, Thomas Gene
Will C Crawford HS; San Diego, CA (5-550) BS; Mgr, Tr; Hon Prog; Yth Fel; B of A Cert; WW; HR; *U of Calif; Med.*

BROCK, Willie James
Northwest HS; St Louis, MO (5-433) Hon Prog; VICA; *Parks Col; Airframe & Powerplants.*

BROCKENBOROUGH, Van
Main Line Day Sch; Haverford, PA (3-11) Chor; Bsbl; *Art.*

BROCKER, Daniel Martin
Valley Central HS; Montgomery, NY; BC; CYO; Chor; Hmrm; ARC; Rptr, Sch P; SC; *Daemen Col; Phys Therapy.*

BROCKETT, Delwin Thomas
Charleroi Area HS; Charleroi, PA (6%-260) Rptr, Sch P; Ski C; SC; Swim; Tnns; Tr; *Bio-Chem.*

BROCKIE, Kay Michelle
NW HS; Jackson, MI (1-320) Band; Chor; City Conf; Drama; Ensm; Semi-Fin, Jr Miss Pa; Pres, NHS; Tres, Phys C; Span C; SC; VP, Sr Cl; Jr Cl; Soph Cl; Golf; Alg A; Citz A; Gr Marshal; Hon Prog; Lion A; NMS; ARC A; St Scholar; Val; Red Cross Instructor; Swim Instructor; GSct o-t Yr; Semi-Fin, Mich Math Prize Comp; *Adrian Col; Bus Mgt.*

BROCKINGTON, Gloria Ann
Albany HS; Albany, NY (176-495) Chor; Arch; Bkbl; Swim; *Branell Col; Fashion Merchandising.*

BROCKISH, Margie Frances
Fairview HS; Boulder, CO (33%-760) COM; Citz A; 1st Cl, GSct; Church Yth Group; Jr Mus C; GSA A; CCD Teacher; Foreign Lang A; Moderator, Jr H Retreats; *Ed.*

BROCKMAN, Nancy Ann
Hershey HS; Hershey, PA (149-266) Band; V-Ch, Ski C; Mgr, Bkbl; Mgr, Cr-Ctry; Tr; *Pa St U; Law Enforcement.*

BROCKMEYER, Beth Louise
George Washington Sr HS; Cedar Rapids, IA (50-550) Pres, Band; Chor; NHS; Orch; Bkbl; Alg A; Hon Prog; NMF; St Scholar; *U of Northern Iowa; Mus.*

BROCKMEYER, Sandra Fay
Wibaux Co HS; Wibaux, MT (7-26) Ann; Chldr; Chor; Drama; Tres, 4H; NFL; Mgr, Tr; 4H A; Poet A; Type A; Miss Eastern Mont Schol Pageant; Pres, Active Christian Tns; Sunday Sch Teacher; *Dickinson St Col; Secondary Ed.*

BROCKSCHMIDT, Debra Ann
Monett HS; Monett, MO (1-106) Dbte Tm; FTA; GS; Pres, NFL; Pres, NHS; Cpt, Sch Achieve Tm; Sch P; Rptr, Span C; St Stu Congress; Parl, SC; Secy, Jr Cl; VP, Soph Cl; Alg A; Amer Leg A; Curator A; Math A; MIS; NMF; NMS; Regent Schol; Val; Yth Leg; Pershing School; *Northeast Mo St U; Math.*

BROCKWAY, Brian Robert
Belvidere HS; Belvidere, IL (31-368) Band; A-Ed, Sch P; Golf; B Crocker A; JC Mem A; *Augustana Col; Religion.*

BROCKWAY, Paul Frederick
N Crawford HS; Gays Mills, WI; Band; Chor; Madrigal; Order/Arrow; Bkbl.

BRODERS, Lorraine Kay
Lincoln Southeast HS; Lincoln, NE (13-524) Chor; COM; Hon Prog; Yth Leg; Pep C; *U of Nebr; Bus Adm.*

BRODIE, Bob Jamie
Maranatha HS; Arcadia, CA (18-60) Secy, Var C; JV, Bkbl; Ftbl; Tr; *Pepperdine U; Bio.*

BRODIEN, Brenda Sue
Northeast HS; Fort Lauderdale, FL (50%-600) Anchor C; Band; Bus C; Ensm; FBLA; Hmrm; InterClub Coun; Secy, SC; Ftbl; Sftbl; COM; Most Dependable; DECA; Pres, Pep C; Radio Correspondent; Hist, Grapplers Fideal; *Trevecca Nazarene Col; Ed.*

BRODIN, John Per
E Rockford HS; Rockford, IL (97-756) A Cap Choir; Orch; ARC; Sch P; Ski C; SC; Pres, Soph Cl; Co-Cpt, Ftbl; Soccer; Sftbl; Wrest.

BRODLAND, Jan Katherine
Winthrop HS; Winthrop, MN (23-68) A Cap Choir; Ann; Band; Chor; Drama; Cpt, Ensm; FHA; Madrigal; Rptr, Sch P; Swim; Mus Ensm; Choir; *Mankato St Col; Nurs.*

BRODY, Adrienne Ann
Hebrew Acad of Nassau Co; Uniondale, NY; Co-Cpt, Chldr; Chor; Drama; NHS; F-Ed, Sch P; Hon Prog; PTA A; Hebrew HR; Eng Ed, Yrbk.

BRODY, Sharon Jeanne
W Chester Henderson HS; W Chester, PA (20-506) Ann; Span C; Sftbl; Hon Prog; Gym; *Communications.*

BROEKER, Laura Ann
Tonawanda Sr HS; Tonawanda, NY (30-420) Anchor C; Arch; Band; Semi-Fin, NHS; Span C; COM; JA A; Pres, Luther League; Co & St Band Competition.

BROERING, Christine
Switzerland Co Jr Sr HS; Vevay, IN (1-96) Secy, 4H; NHS; Sci C; Alg A; Bio A; 4H A; Fr, Lang, A's.

BROERING, Linda Lee
Switzerland Co HS; Vevay, IN (11-108) 4H; Poet A; Fr A.

BROERS, LeAnn Elaine
Auburn HS; Auburn, NE; Band; Chor; FHA; Alt, Auxiliary Schol; Band Participation A; *Beatrice Col; Nurs.*

BROGDON, Kimberly Ann
Tascosa HS; Amarillo, TX; Ann; Bus C; Chor; Drama; FHA; Ch, Hmrm; NHS; Sch P; Span C; Hon Prog; Pres A; Miss GMA; Secy-Tres, St GMA; *Amarillo Col; Social Work.*

BROGDON, Patrick Scott
The Baylor Sch for Boys; Chattanooga, TN; Order/Arrow; JV, Soccer; Tr; Yth Fel; BSct; *U of Tenn; Archt.*

BROGLEY, Nancy Kaye
Eastern Hills HS; Fort Worth, TX (60-475) Co-Cpt, Band; Ensm; Tri-HiY; Tr; *U of Tex; Bus.*

BROHAN, Frances Diane
Wood River HS; Hailey, ID (2-62) CYO; Drama; Fr C; Pres, Ger C; GS; 4H; Hmrm; Pres, NHS; F-Ed, Sch P; Ski C; SC; Thes; Tr; Citz A; 4H A; Sal; Spch A; VP, Ger C; *International Relations.*

BROHAWN, Mark Stephen
Daviess Co HS; Owensboro, KY (18-316) Chess C; VP, Sci C; VP, Bsbl; Bkbl; Ftbl; JV, Tr; Sci A; *U of Ky; Elec Engr.*

BROHN, Belinda Ann
Ridgway Area HS; Ridgway, PA; Chor; Fr C; SC; Thes; God & Country A; 1st Cl Sct; 'My Amer Contest' Dist Win; *Yale U; Art.*

BROKENSHIRE, Ronald Allan
Clearwater HS; Clearwater, FL (10%-1200) BS; Span C; Span NHS; Ftbl; Hon Prog; Opt A; Sci A; *Aeronautical Engr.*

BROLUND, John Samuel
Murphy HS; Mobile, AL (10-620) F-Ed, Ann; Secy, Key C; VP, NHS; Bsbl; Bkbl; Cl Fav; Hon Prog; NEDT; *Engr.*

BROMANDER, Roger William
Ulen-Hitterdal HS; Ulen, MN (8-45) Band; FFA; 4H; NHS; Sch P; JV, Bkbl; 4H A; Hon Prog; Math A; Spch A; *Concordia Col; Bus Adm.*

BRONECKE, David Bryan
Thornton Fractional S HS; Lansing, IL (355-609) Chor; Tr; Concert Choir; Sunday Sch Teacher; *Bradley U; Engr.*

BRONK, Patricia Rose
Cotter HS; Winona, MN (39-96) Ann; Pres, Band; Chor; Ensm; Rptr, Hmrm; Orch; Sodality; Bkbl; Tr; COM; Pres A; Sch Spirit A; Ltrs & Medals, Tr, Bkbl & Band.

BRONKEMA, Greg Scott
Greenville HS; Greenville, MI (60-300) Hmrm; SC; Var C; Cr-Ctry; *Draftmans.*

BRONNENBERG, Rebecca Sue
Walter P Memorial Chrysler HS; New Castle, IN (96-378) Band; Tres, Chor; Madrigal; NFL; Pres, SC; Thes; Tnns; Spch A; Outst Sr A, Chor; *Ball St U; Spch Pathology and Audiology.*

BRONNER, Ellery Carlton
Delta-Private HS; Newtown, PA (10-12) JV, Bkbl; *Pittsburgh Inst of Mortuary; Mortician.*

BRONSON, Anne Joyce
Hinsdale Township HS Central; Hinsdale, IL (1-691) Band; NHS; Orch; Ski C; SC; Tr; Hon Prog.

BRONSON, Laurie Anne
Jackson HS; Birmingham, AL (25-430) Chor; Drama; Order/Arrow; Thes; Pres, Soph Cl; Mgr, Bkbl; Mgr, Ftbl; Tnns; Spch A; *Jackson Comm Col; Med.*

BRONSON, Stephen William
Jackson HS; Jackson, MI (20%-425) Chess C; Pres, Hmrm; NHS; JV, Tnns; *Med.*

BROOKE, Anita Patricia
Weed HS; Weed, CA (16-53) Band; Chor; Secy, FHA; Secy, 4H; Madrigal; Monogram; Ed, Sch P; SC; S-T, Sr Cl; 4H A; Pres, United Presbyterian Yth; Statist, Tr; News Ed, St Grange Yth; Gen Mills Family Ldr of Tomorrow A; Grange Insurance Assn Schol; *Cal Poly San Luis Obispo; Home Ec.*

BROOKE, Kathleen Marie
Cincinnati Christian HS; Fairfield, OH (5-42) Chor; Ensm; Bkbl; Sftbl; Stu Director, Drama C; Church Choir; Fin, Ntl Scholastic Art Show; Vlbl; Organization Ed, Yrbk; Sch Choir; Sch Play; *Cincinnati Bible Col; Ed.*

BROOKENS, Cheryl Lynn
Taylorville Sr HS; Taylorville, IL (22-240) Chor; Fr C; Hmrm; NHS; Opt Out Tn; Pres A; Prom Court; Pres, Office Occupations C; Pep C; GAA; *Teaching.*

BROOKES, Linda Jane
Marathon Central HS; Marathon, NY (6-81) Band; Chor; Fr C; Pres, 4H; Secy, NHS; Soccer; B Crocker A; Hist A; NEDT; Rotary Exchange Stu; Intern, Co Leg; DAR Hist A; *Social Sci.*

BROOKHART, Kathy Diane
Newport HS; Newport, PA (1-89) Band; Chor; GS; Math C; Tres, Mod Mus Mas; Pres, NHS; Span C; Co-Cpt, Bkbl; Co-Cpt, Sftbl; Bausch & Lomb A; Lion A; MLS; Val; Gen Mills Family Ldr of Tomorrow A; *Shippensburg St Col; Religion.*

BROOKHART, Michael Ellis
Cumberland Valley HS; Mechanicsburg, PA (5-675) Band; Pari, Demolay; Ger C; Math C; NHS; JV, Bkbl; Ftbl; Tr; Chem A; NEDT; *US Air Force Acad; Nuclear Engr.*

BROOKHOUSE, Kelly J
H H Dow HS; Midland, MI (46-420) NHS; Golf; JV, Sftbl; *Central Mich U; Psych.*

BROOKINS, Bertha Mae
Hancock Central HS; Sparta, GA; FBLA; 4H; Up Bound; Hist A; *Barbizon Sch; Modeling.*

BROOKINS, Lamar Anthony
Providence HS; New Lenox, IL; Ann; Band; CYO; Chor; Drama; Orch; Bsbl; Bkbl; Sftbl; Citz A; Spch A; Art A; *Judson Col; Psych.*

BROOKOVER, Phillip Jay
W Muskingum HS; Zanesville, OH; Key C; Sci C; Tr; Amer Leg A; JA A; Pres, JA; *Ohio Inst of Tech; Elec.*

BROOKS, Aaron Douglas
Ouachita Parish HS; Monroe, LA (25-500) Lat NHS; Lit Ral; Spch C; Mgr, Bsbl; Mgr, Bkbl; JV, Golf; Alg A; COM; DARGCA; Sci A; *U of Tex; Law.*

BROOKS, Amy Michele
Gen William Mitchell HS; Colorado Springs, CO (31-733) Sftbl; Hon Prog; Yth Fel; *U of Wy; Teaching.*

BROOKS, Andrew David
Starmount HS; Boonville, NC (1-204) Ed, Ann; Pres, Drama; FFA; FTA; Ger C; Sch P; SC; Tnns; Gov Honor Prog; *UNC; Bio.*

BROOKS, Anton Kenneth
Springfield HS; New York, NY; Alg A; Bio A; COM; Sci A; Star Student.

BROOKS, Barbara Ellen
St Patrick's HS; Roxbury, MA (2-67) CYO; Hmrm; VP, NHS; Ski C; SC; Pres, Sr Cl; Alg A; B Crocker A; COM; Hon Prog; Sal; Psych A; Eng A; *Boston Col; Eng.*

BROOKS, Barrington DeVeaux
Granby Sr HS; Norfolk, VA (38-350) Chor; VP, Hmrm; Lat C; Madrigal; NHS; Order/Arrow; SC; Pres, Sr Cl; Pres, Soph Cl; Tr; H of F; HKg; Lion A; Opt A; WW; Mus Stu; NCIE Mus Camp Schol; Elk's Stu o-t Mo; *Morehouse Col; Pol Sci.*

BROOKS, Becky Ann
Paris HS; Paris, TX (33%-400) A Cap Choir; Band; Chor; FHA; Bkbl; Sftbl; Swim; ARC A; *Mus.*

BROOKS, Bonnie Lynn
Minor HS; Birmingham, AL (75-378) A Cap Choir; Chor; Outst Choir Stu; Band Board; Travel C; Girl's Choir; *Auburn U; Law.*

BROOKS, Brenda Ann
Harris Co HS; Hamilton, GA (27-201) Ann; BC; Chor; FHA; Lit Mag; Sch P; PA; *Clark Col; Pre-Law.*

BROOKS, Brenda Michelle
Paoli HS; Paoli, OK; FBLA; VP, SC; Alg A; Journ A; Type A; St Hon Soc; *Okmulgee St Tech Col; Data Processing.*

BROOKS, Carolyn R
Carroll HS; Monroe, LA; Band; 4H; SC; Eng A; Math A; *Sweet Briar Col; Phys Therapy.*

BROOKS, Cathy Annette
Orange HS; Hillsborough, NC (105-306) Chor; 4H; Rptr, Hmrm; Monogram; Cpt, Bkbl; Sftbl; Cl Fav; 4H A; MLS; Most Out; Type A; Most Improved; Most Dedicated; *Chowan Col; Phys Ed.*

BROOKS, Cecilia
Miami Springs Sr HS; Miami, FL; Tres, Fr C; Tres, SC; Amer Leg A; COM; Citz A; Cl Fav; Kiwanis A; Opt A; Spch A; Candado C; VP, Foreign Lang Hon Soc; Phys Fitness A; *Miami Dade Comm Col; Sci.*

BROOKS, Dandrea Lynne
John Tyler HS; Tyler, TX; Band; Secy, FHA; Hmrm; Sci C; SC; COM; Citz A; Hon Prog; Sci A; Sci A.

BROOKS, Dave Harlen
Quincy Sr HS; Quincy, IL (257-800) Chor; Drama; Ensm; Madrigal; Span C; Tr; *Law.*

BROOKS, David Charles
Andrew J Terrell HS; Blanchard, OK; A Cap Choir; F-Ed, Ann; BC; Chem C; Chor; Ensm; Hmrm; Math C; NHS; Sch P; Sci C; Span C; Pres, SC; Var C; S-T, Jr Cl; VP, Soph Cl; Co-Cpt, Bsbl; MVP, Bkbl; Co-Cpt, Ftbl; COM; Citz A; Cl Fav; Gov Honor Prog; Hist A; HCl; Hon Prog; Journ A; Math A; Star Student; Summa Cum Laude; Swtht; Yth Fel; Pep C Beau; Schol, Indust Arts, Bookkeep, A's; *U of Okla.*

BROOKS, David Harry
Lansing East HS; Lansing, MI (77-595) Chess C; NHS; Sch P; Yth Fel; Hon Soc; Hon Men, Short Story in City Comp; *Math.*

BROOKS, David Lee
Goodlettsville HS; Goodlettsville, TN (6-159)
Ann; BS; Hmrm; InterClub Coun; NHS; Pres, Span
C; SC; Pres, Soph Cl; Cpt, Bkbl; Tr; COM; Citz A;
Cl Fav; HKg; HCt; NEDT; Tn o-t Mo; Best All
Around; *Middle Tenn St U; Bus.*

BROOKS, Denise Bobbie
Asbury Park HS; Asbury Park, NJ (6-268) NHS;
Varsity Schol; Omega Psi Phi Frat Scroll of Hon;
Greensboro Col; Commercial Art.

BROOKS, Edsel Carl Jr
Eaton HS; Eaton, OH (30-155) A Cap Choir; Band;
Chor; Parl; Drama; Ensm; HiY; 4H A; Spec A,
Drama C; Concert Choir A; Varsity Band Letter;
Miami U; Communications.

BROOKS, Elizabeth Grant
W Guilford HS; Greensboro, NC (50-200) Band;
Drama; Var C; JV, Bkbl; Tnns; Tr; *Hist.*

BROOKS, Gayle Ann
Clarksville HS; Clarksville, TX; S-T, Drama; Pres,
FHA; VP, FTA; NHS; Span C; Secy, SC; Pres,
Soph Cl; *Paris Jr Col; Art and Creative Writing.*

BROOKS, George Clifford Jr
Danville HS; Danville, IL (120-732) JV, Ftbl; Tr;
Wrest; Amer Leg A; COM; Hon Prog; Most Out;
Air Force Acad; Dental.

BROOKS, Gerry Steven
Baker Sr HS; Baker, LA (16-374) BC; Secy, HiY;
Math C; NHS; Var C; Ftbl; *LSU; Mech Engr.*

BROOKS, Gregory Richard
Marion Harding HS; Marion, OH (101-446) Pres,
Demolay; Fr C; FTA; Hmrm; Ch, Y-Tns; JV, Bsbl;
JV, Bkbl; Sftbl; COM; Masonic A; WW; Past Mas-
ter Coun Meterious Serv A; *Ohio St U; Acct.*

BROOKS, Harold Edward
Brentwood HS; Brentwood, MO (1-126) Band; BS;
Pres, Chem C; Pres, Chess C; Model UN; NHS;
Span C; Pres, SC; S-T, Thes; Var C; Mgr, Bkbl; Cpt,
Cr-Ctry; Tr; NMF; Val; Fin, Pres Schol; Semi-Fin,
Telluride As Summer Prog; *William Jewell Col.*

BROOKS, Jane Carroll
Lincoln HS; Ellwood City, PA (80-275) Fin, AFS;
Fr C; 4H; Pres, Rainbow; A-Ed, Sch P; Sci C; Cr-
Ctry; Tr; Future Physician's; Explorer's; Art C;
Sound Crew; *Grove City Col; Bio.*

BROOKS, Jodene Gay
Enka HS; Enka, NC (19-350) Drama; Ch, FHA;
Span C; Span NHS; Alg A; Acteens Ntl Adv Panel;
Yth Coun; *Primary Ed.*

BROOKS, John Wesley
Morton W HS; Berwyn, IL (400-800) Bkbl; Swim;
MVP, Church Bkbl; Awana Ldr; Camp Ldr; Camp
Life-Guard; *Morton Jr Col; Law Enforcement.*

BROOKS, Judy Kaye
Arts Magnet HS; Dallas, TX; Drama; Hon Prog;
Tex Tech U; Drama.

BROOKS, Judy Leslie
Steinmetz HS; Chicago, IL (275-730) Bus C;
FBLA; ARC; Span C; Alg A; Most Out; *Andrew
Col; Bus.*

BROOKS, Julie Joy
Belaire HS; Baton Rouge, LA (62-400) A Cap
Choir; Band; Chor; Tres, Fr C; Pres, Rainbow;
ARC; Sci C; Alg A; Fr, Symph Band; Concert
Band, A's; Attached Units Band A; *LSU; Acct.*

BROOKS, Katherine Sophie
Saint Paul Acad and Summit Sch; St Paul, MN
(23-68) Cpt, Chldr; Chor; Co-Cpt, Sftbl; Tnns;
NEDT; 1st Pl Region, Ntl Fr Contest; 90%, Ntl
Ger Contest; *Smith Col; Fr.*

BROOKS, Keith Wayne
Southside HS; Gadsden, AL (20%-120) Drama;
FBLA; Sci C; Thes; Var C; Bkbl; Cr-Ctry; Ftbl; Tr;
COM; Hist A; Yth Fel; *Gadsden St Col; Computer
Sci.*

BROOKS, Linda Ann
Harris Co HS; Hamilton, GA (30-201) Ann; Chor;
FHA; Sci C; PA; *Clark Col; Drama.*

BROOKS, Linda Kay
LaPorte HS; LaPorte, TX (14-351) Drama; NHS;
COM; Sci A; WW; Placed, Dist Vocal Solo; *Oral
Roberts U; Pre-Med.*

BROOKS, Lori Anne
Maplewood HS; Nashville, TN; *Data Processing.*

BROOKS, Marianne Kaye
Anacortes HS; Anacortes, WA (20-200) A Cap
Choir; Band; Chldr; S-T, Chor; Dbte Tm; Ensm;
Hmrm; Madrigal; Parl, Model UN; NHS; Ch,
ARC; Cpt, Sch Achieve Tm; SC; Ch, UN Council;
Var C; Bkbl; Tnns; COM; Citz A; Cl Fav; H of F;
Hon Prog; Most Out; VofDEM; Pres, Felicians;
Dist Yth Choir; WW; *Sou Calif Bible Col; Pol Sci.*

BROOKS, Marilyn Lee
Anacortes HS; Anacortes, WA (25-200) Rptr,
Ann; Tres, Band; Ensm; Hmrm; Model UN; NHS;
Orch; Span C; Bus Mgr, SC; Bkbl; JV, Golf; Tnns;
Tr; H of F; Most Out; *Green River Comm Col;
Recreation.*

BROOKS, Mark Anthony
Acad of Math And Sci; St Louis, MO (3-50) Band;
Chor; A-Ed, Sch P; COM; Citz A; Cert, Ntl Guild
of Piano Teachers; Yth Choir; *U of Missouri; Mus.*

BROOKS, Maynard B
Carter G Woodson HS; Tullahassee, OK (3-29) Bus
C; Math C; NHS; Bsbl; Citz A; HCt; Math A; MLS;
Type A.

BROOKS, Monica Ann
Westlake HS; Westlake, LA (10-35) Ann; Chem C;
FHA; HiY; Semi-Fin, Lit Ral; Tri-HiY; COM; Citz
A; Annual A; Camp Fire Girls; Spell A; Read A;
Mus A; *U of SW La; Microbiology.*

BROOKS, Patricia Ann
St Elizabeth HS; Pittsburgh, PA; All Amer Yth;
Hmrm; SC; Mgr, Bsbl; *Wilma Boyde Col; Airline
Hostess.*

BROOKS, Randy
Blanchard HS; Blanchard, OK;

BROOKS, Richard Leonard
North Natchez Adams HS; Natchez, MS (8-230)
Ann; Band; BC; NHS; Pres, SC; Pres, Sr Cl; Amer
Leg A; Bio A; COM; Chem A; Cl Fav; Sci A; *Tex
Sou U; Bus.*

BROOKS, Ricky
St Benedict's HS; Newark, NJ (15-30) Band; Chor;
Drama; Orch; Cr-Ctry; Tr; *NC St U; Mus.*

BROOKS, Robert
Westbury HS; Westbury, NY; MVP, Chor; Drama;
Phys C; Var C; Arch; Cpt, Cr-Ctry; Cpt, Ftbl; Cpt,
Swim; Tr; Wrest; Cl Fav; Kiwanis A; Most Out;
MVP, Cr Ctry; Cl Singer; Outst Phys Ed A; *Oak-
wood Col; Mus.*

BROOKS, Robert Paul
N Gwinnett HS; Suwanee, GA (10%-120) 4H; Var
C; Co-Cpt, Ftbl; Chem A; 4H A; All-Co Ftbl Tm;
Berry Col.

BROOKS, Roberto Luis
Eastern HS; Washington, DC; NHS; Tr; Smith-
sonian Jr Associate Fel; *Maryland Inst of Art; Illustration Art.*

BROOKS, Sharon Rose
Norwalk HS; Norwalk, OH; Ann; Band; Chor; VP,
Drama; NHS; Orch; Rptr, Sch P; SC; VP, Thes; JV,
Bkbl; Tr; Best Actress; Best Female Performer;
Best Thespian; Best One-Act; *Butler U; Drama.*

BROOKS, Sheri Jean
Buena HS; Sierra Vista, AZ (32-480) Band; Hmrm;
NHS; Tres, Span NHS; *Ariz St U; Bus.*

BROOKS, Stephanie
Arts HS; Newark, NJ (60-160) Bus Mgr, Band;
Rptr, Hmrm; Band Ltr; *Fla St U; Foreign Lang.*

BROOKS, Steven David
Lincoln Sr HS; Sioux Falls, SD (25%-500) Chor;
JV, Sftbl; JV, Tr; Hon Prog; JA A; Sci A; *U of Iowa;
Med.*

BROOKS, Steven William
Xenia HS; Xenia, OH; NHS A; Attendance A;
Wright St Col; Bio.

BROOKS, Tara Wynne
Thomas Jefferson HS; Louisville, KY; BC; Hmrm;
SC; Hon Prog; *U of Ky; Law.*

BROOKS, Tawnee Jo
Helena Sr HS; Helena, MT (75-325) Chldr; Hmrm;
S-T, SC; JV, Bkbl; Cpt, Sftbl; Tr; *Phys Ed.*

BROOKS, Theresa Rene
Jerean Bowman HS; Canyon Country, CA; 4H;
ARC; Ski C; *U of Calif at Santa Barbara; Art.*

BROOKS, Tina Louise
Prince George HS; Prince George, VA (20-350)
Secy, A Cap Choir; Ann; Bus C; Secy, Chor; Dbte
Tm; Ger C; Hmrm; Co-Ed, Sch P; Sci C; DECA
Ldrship A; *Richard Bland Col; Theology.*

BROOKS, Vielca Maritza
Paraiso Jr Sr HS; Paraiso, CANAL ZONE; Chor;
FTA; Hmrm; BC, Sch P; Swim; COM; HQn; Type
A; Sch Qn; Mus Cert; GAA.

BROOKS, Wanda Gail
Aynor HS; Aynor, SC (5%-85) BC; Rptr, FHA; 4H;
Ed, Sch P; Sci C; *McCloud's Hospital; X-Ray Tech.*

BROOKS, Warren Barrett
Granby HS; Norfolk, VA; Bsbl; Cr-Ctry; Ftbl; Tr;
Norfolk St; Sociology.

BROOKS, William Henry
Laurel Co HS; London, KY (60-400) Band; BC; Fr
C; 4H; Mu Alpha Theta; F-Ed, Sch P; Sci C; Tnns;
Alg A; 4H A; *U of Ky.*

BROOKS, William Michael
Mathiston HS; Mathiston, MS (1-35) VP, BC; VP,
FFA; Pres, Jr Cl; Pres, Soph Cl; Cpt, Ftbl; Tr; Cl
Fav; Hist A; HCt; Hon Prog; Most Popular; Hon
Men Ftbl; *Miss St U; Civil Engr.*

BROOKSHIRE, Kathy Lynn
Pisgah Sr HS; Canton, NC (2-320) Chldr; Pres,
French NHS; Monogram; NHS; Secy, Soph Cl; Tr;
COM; Cl Fav; Gr Marshal; Church Chor; Math
Tm; FCA; Church Yth Coun; VP, Jr Civitan C; Pep
C; Executive Coun, SC; Vlbl; Presidential Clrm;
Nom, Morehead Sh; *U of NC at Chapel Hill;
Psych.*

BROOKSHIRE, Sharon J
Dobyns-Bennett HS; Kingsport, TN (25%-500)
Secy, CYO; Lat C; SC; Ftbl; Opt Out Tn; *U of
Tenn.*

BROOME, Brenda Lorene
Ashbrook Sr HS; Gastonia, NC (2-567) Ann; BC;
Hmrm; NHS; Span C; SC; Hist A; Math A; Span A;
Graduation Marshal; Outst Achv, Eng & Sci; *U of
NC; Journ.*

BROOME, James Brian
Homewood HS; Birmingham, AL; Band; V-Ch,
Chor; Ensm; Co-Ed, Lit Mag; Chaplain, SC; WW;
Top 10 Outst Band Member; Superior, Solo &
Ensm A's.

BROOME, Robbin Perry
J L Mann HS; Greenville, SC; Chor; Drama; Ensm;
HiY; VP, Hmrm; SC; Var C; Bsbl; JV, Bkbl; JV,
Ftbl; Wrest; *U of Ga; Phys Ed.*

BROOME, Steven Ronnie
Pepperell HS; Lindale, GA; FFA; Ftbl; JV, Wrest;
Floyd Jr Col; Elec.

BROOMFIELD, Allen Ray
Melbourne HS; Melbourne, FL; Pres, A Cap Choir;
Band; Mgr, Bkbl; Citz A; God & Country A; H of F;
Hist A; Ntl Achv Schol; BSct; *Sci.*

BROSEKER, Mary Ann
Lake Clifton Sr HS; Baltimore, MD (10%-500)
NHS; Alg A; Scholastic A; Eng A; Span A; Arch-
ery A; *Towson St U; Early Child Development.*

BROSELL, Deborah Ann
Eagle Rock HS; Los Angelas, CA (111-397) Ann;
Chor; Hmrm; Cpt, Mjrte; Job's Daughters; *Fashion
Inst; Interior Design.*

BROSKEY, Eileen Mae
Laurel Highlands Sr HS; Uniontown, PA; VP,
Hmrm; Ski C; *Bethany Col; Bus Adm.*

BROSMEN, Mark Allen
B Dwenger HS; Ft Wayne, IN (6-254) NHS; Or-
der/Arrow; Ski C; SC; Thes; Tres, Sr Cl; Cpt, Cr-
Ctry; Tr; COM; Chamber of Comm A; Hon Prog;
Order/Arrow A; Phy A; Christian Ldrship A;
Drama A; *Purdue U; Engr.*

BROST, Shirley Pauline
Brown HS; Sturgis, SD (1-34) Dbte Tm; Drama;
FTA; Hmrm; NFL; NHS; Rptr, Sch P; Pres, Span
C; SC; Thes; Gov Safety Coun; DAR Patriot; WW;
USD; Law.

BROSTMEYER, Peggy Lee
Pinckneyville Comm HS; Pinckneyville, IL
(30-130) Ann; Band; Chldr; Drama; Mjrte; Sci C;
Span C; Spch C; Var C; Cpt, Vlbl; WW; *Eastern Ill
U; Phys Ed.*

BROTHERS, Dave Harry
Bridgeport HS; Bridgeport, OH (5%-126) Secy,
Span C; Ftbl; Wrest; Art C; Art A; *Ed.*

BROTHERS, Pamala Suzanne
Moreau HS; Hayward, CA; Ed, Ann; Fr C; Hon
Prog; Journ A; *U of Oreg; Journ.*

BROTHERTON, Matthew Kent
Highland HS; Ewing, MO; Band; Drama; Ensm;
Columbia U; Civil Engr.

BROUGH, Annette Christine
Lyons Township HS; LaGrange, IL (269-1200)
Band; GS; ARC; Swim; NEDT; ARC A; Synchro-
nized Swim Show; *Bradley Col; Nurs.*

BROUGH, Lorilea Gay
Tex City HS; Texas City, TX (25-425) Band; *Stephen F Austin Col; Bus Ed.*

BROUGHER, Glenda Kay
Rockwood Area HS; Rockwood, PA; Band; Chor;
Sch P.

BROUGHTON, Barry Melborne
Bishop McDevitt HS; Wyncote, PA (226-420)
Ftbl; *N Carolina Central Col; Psych.*

BROUGHTON, Linda Lee
Duncanville HS; Duncanville, TX (26-486) FTA;
Ch, Lit Mag; *Abilene Christian U; Pre-Vet.*

BROUK, Gregory Carl
Althoff Cath HS; Belleville, IL (3-285) CYO; Lat
C; NHS; Rptr, Sch P; COM; Hon Prog; St Scholar;
WW; *St Louis U; Acct.*

BROUSSARD, Donna Marie
M B Smiley HS; Houston, TX (2-461) Secy, FBLA;
NHS; Sci C; Alg A; Beauty; Bio A; Cl Fav; Sci A;
Eng A; *Bus.*

BROUSSARD, Frankie Ann
E Ascension Acad; Gonzales, LA (4-21) Co-Ed,
Ann; Pres, FBLA; Lit Ral; VP, SC; VP, Sr Cl; Cl
Fav; HCt; Most Versatile.

BROUSSARD, Willa Jo
Radford HS; Honolulu, HI (200-400) *U of Fla;
Phar.*

BROUWER, Estelle Maye
Tyler HS; Tyler, MN (2-54) Rptr, Ann; Band;
Chor; Ensm; Fin, Jr Miss Pagent; Madrigal; Ed,
Sch P; VP, SC; COM; Journ A; NML; Schol Achv
A; Local & Co Jr Miss; Mus A's; *Augsburg Col;
Mus.*

BROVONT, Barbara Jean
David Starr Jordan HS; Long Beach, CA; *Biola
Col; Secy.*

BROW, Constance Marie
Robert E Lee HS; Montgomery, AL (83-706) Secy,
Anchor C; A-Ed, Ann; Band; Chor; Hmrm; Secy,
Lat C; NHS; Sch P; St Stu Congress; Secy, SC;
Tri-HiY; ROTC A; Yth Leg; *Auburn U; Pre-Law.*

BROW, John Alan
Robert E Lee HS; Montgomery, AL; VP, Lat C;
Order/Arrow; Ed, Sch P; Amer Leg A; Bio A;
COM; Citz A; Journ A; Order/Arrow A; ROTC A;
Lifeguard BSA; NJHS; *US Air Force Acad; Aero-
nautics.*

BROWDER, Carolyn Marie
A E Stevenson HS; Bronx, NY; Chor; NHS; Sci C;
Cpt, Sftbl; Hon Prog; *Theatrical Arts.*

BROWER, Darla Sue
Kathleen HS; Lakeland, FL; Chor; Key C; Span C;
Trevecca Nazarene Col.

BROWER, Karla Joy
Zeeland HS; Zeeland, MI (13-180) All Amer Yth;
Chor; NHS; Co-Cpt, Bkbl; Golf; Sftbl; Hon Prog;
Ath o-t Yr A; *Pine Rest Sch of Nurs; LPN.*

BROWER, Patti Ann
Lakeland Sr HS; Lakeland, FL (116-800) Hmrm;
Lat C; SC; Sftbl; Amer Leg A; K of C A; Keyettes;
U of S Fla; Special Ed.

BROWER, Susan Lee
Riverdale Joint Union HS; Riverdale, CA
(10%-140) Band; Most Out; *UCLA; Mus.*

BROWN, A C Jr
Van Buren HS; Van Buren, AR (8-187) Tres, BS;
Mu Alpha Theta; NHS; Pres, SC; Pres, Soph Cl;
Ftbl; FCA; Mr VBHS; Head Usher at Baccalau-
reate; *U of Ark; Elec Eng.*

BROWN, Aaron Frank
Franklin HS; Somerset, NJ; Chor; Pres, Ensm; Ntl
Yth Conf; Tnns; *Manhattan Sch of Mus; Mus.*

BROWN, Alan Michael
Whitman-Hanson Regional HS; Whitman, MA
(23-328) Band; Chess C; Chor; Drama; NHS; Or-
der/Arrow; COM; Order/Arrow A; Eagle A; *U of
Mass; Pre-Vet Med.*

BROWN, Albert L
Oakhaven HS; Memphis, TN; Hmrm; NHS; JV,
Ftbl; JA A; Sftbl Coach; HR A; Church Bsbl;
Church Bkbl Coach; DECA A.

BROWN, Albert Wendell
Haworth HS; Kokomo, IN (25%-500) Rptr, Ann;
Fr C; Hmrm; SC; Husky Legion; Human Relations;
Q & S; *General Motors Inst; Industrial Mgt.*

BROWN, Alice Francis
Niskayuna HS; Schenectady, NY (10%-480) Pres,
NHS; Orch; Tr; Stage Band; Foreign Lang Hon
Soc; Symph Band; Cr-Ctry Ski Tm; Cr-Ctry Tr;
Bio.

BROWN, Alissa Lea
Whitehouse HS; Whitehouse, TX (8-99) Ann;
Band; Pres, BC; Secy, FHA; Secy, FTA; Cpt, Mjrte;
NHS; Bkbl; Tr; Rotary A; Top 10; *Tyler Jr Col;
Secy.*

BROWN, Angie Lynn
Bowden HS; Bowden, GA (5%-150) BC; Sftbl;
Tnns; *U of Ga; Mus.*

BROWN, Ann Elizabeth
Fort Lupton HS; Fort Lupton, CO (13-95) A-Ed,
Ann; Tres, FBLA; NHS; WW; Swedish C Qn; Fin,
Miss TSS Atlante; Prom Candidate; *Mesa Col; Bus.*

BROWN, Ann Elizabeth
Cumberland Valley HS; Mechanicsburg, PA
(9-585) Fr C; Co-Ed, Lit Mag; NHS; Thes; Bausch
& Lomb A; NEDT; NML; *VPI; Bio-Chem.*

BROWN, Annette
Nanih Waiya HS; Louisville, MS (5-37) F-Ed, Ann;
BC; FBLA; Sci C; SC; Cl Fav; *Jackson St U; Bus
Adm.*

BROWN, Archie Melvin
Colerain Sr HS; Cincinnati, OH (12%-660) Chor;
Ensm; Fr C; Bkbl; Sftbl; All Star, Bible Bowl; *Mi-
ami of Ohio U; Bus Marketing.*

BROWN, Audrey Melva
Red Bank HS; Chattanooga, TN; ARC; Span C;
Drama.

BROWN, Berdell
York Comp HS; York, SC (9-272) Band; FTA;
NHS; Marshal; *Winthrop Col.*

BROWN, Beth Ann
John Glenn HS; New Concord, OH (10-190) Chor;
Ensm; NHS; VP, Span C; Secy, Y-Tns; Eng A's;
Ohio N U; Social Sci.

BROWN, Beverly Ann
Lincoln HS; Dallas, TX; Band; Pres, Hmrm; Pres,
Math C; NHS; ARC; Pres, Sci C; Ch, SC; Pres,
Y-Tns; *N Tex St U; Med.*

BROWN, Bill
Lee HS; Midland, TX (93-632) Key C; NHS; Tnns;
Baylor U; Church Recreation.

BROWN, Bradley J
Allen Cons HS; Allen, NE (4-27) Chess C; Chor;
Dbte Tm; FFA; NFL; NHS; Spch C; Var C; Ftbl;
Tr; B Crocker A; Hon Prog; Magna Cum Laude;
NMF; NMS; *Wichita St U; Computer Sci.*

BROWN, Brenda Jo
Norview HS; Norfolk, VA (130-601) Band; Chor;
Hmrm; Orch; SC; Citz A; *Va St U; Special Ed.*

BROWN, Bruce Alexander
Lancaster HS; Lancaster, VA (95-165) Band; Chess
C; Community Yth Symph; Orch; Span C; COM; H
of F; WW; *Shenandoah Conservatory; Mus Ed.*

BROWN, Bruce Anthony
N Chicago HS; N Chicago, IL (68-255) Hmrm; SC;
VP, Var C; Cpt, Bsbl; Bkbl; Co-Cpt, Ftbl; COM;
Citz A; Cl Fav; HKg; Hon Prog; JA A; Most Out;
Star Student; Swtht; MVP, Ftbl & Bsbl; HR; All Co
& All Conf, Bsbl; St Legislative Schol; Military
Achv A; *Ill St U; Bus Adm.*

BROWN, Bruce R
N Central HS; Morrowville, KS (7-27) Band; Chor;
Community Yth Symph; Ensm; VP, FFA; NHS;
SC; JV, Bkbl; Tr; COM; FCA; Livestock FFA; FFA
Star Farmer; 2nd Pl Dist Star Farmer; Agr Mech.

BROWN, Candy Lynell
Tamalpais HS; Mill Valley, CA (51-360) Chor; Fin,
GS; NHS; Cpt, Bsbl; Soccer; Swim; Tnns; Amer
Leg A; CSF; Delta Sigma Theta A; *U of Calif; Child
Psych.*

BROWN, Carl Lee
Spotsylvania Sr HS; Spotsylvania, VA (14-450)
Band; Ensm; Fr C; Math C; NHS; Orch; Gov
Honor Prog; Outst Band; Region Band; *Va Com-
monwealth U; Psych.*

BROWN, Carmella Josephine
Harrisburg HS; Harrisburg, PA (25-500) Ann;
NHS; Hon Prog; Kiwanis A; Amer Bus Women
Schol A; May Day Ct; Kappa Omega Chapter
Schol A; Presbyterian Synod Minority Schol; *Bea-
ver Col; Bio.*

BROWN, Carol Joan
Mercy HS; Albany, NY (3-115) Drama; Lat C;
NEDT; *Sci.*

BROWN, Carol Louise
Bishop Watterson HS; Columbus, OH; Drama;
NHS; Tr; Field Hockey Ltr; Tr Plaque; *Ohio St U;
Arts and Sci.*

BROWN, Carolyn Ann
Carolina HS; Greenville, SC; Rptr, Sch P; Y-Tns;
Secy, Soph Cl; PA; Tres, Black Culture C; Secy,
Yth C; Secy, Usher Board; *Greenville Tec; Acct.*

BROWN, Carrie Sue
Richarson HS; Richardson, TX (19-954) Fr C;
NHS; VP, Span NHS; NMF; WW; *Baylor U; Eng.*

BROWN, Catherine Kaye
Captain Shreve HS; Shreveport, LA (60-550) NHS;
ARC; Sftbl; Corporal-Librarian; Band; Outst Chris-
tine Yth; Valentine Swtht Qn; *Eng.*

BROWN, Cedric LaValle
West Side Sr HS; Gary, IN (300-700) Var C; Cpt,
Ftbl; Cpt, Golf; ROTC A; Cpt, Rifle Tm; All City
Ftbl; Outst ROTC Cadet; *Ind St U; Phys Ed.*

BROWN, Charles Dickard
Lake Highlands HS; Dallas, TX; Chor; Drama;
Hon Prog; Math A; Hon Choir; *Tex Tech U; Engr.*

BROWN, Cheryl Anne
Natchitoches Central HS; Natchitoches, LA
(40-312) Chor; Drama; Rptr, Spch C; Bkbl; Sftbl;
Swim; *Interior Design.*

BROWN, Cheryl Denise
Francis Scott Key HS; Union Bridge, MD (20-241)
Chldr; Chor; Hmrm; Sci C; JV, Hockey; Gym; Can-
dystriper; Harney Fire Qn; *Liberty Baptist Col;
Nurs.*

BROWN, Cheryl Denise
Alfred E Beach HS; Savannah, GA (25%-250)
FBLA; Lat C; Pres A; Yth Fel; Gym; Eng Cert; Yth
Swtht; *Cosmetology.*

BROWN, Cheryl Jean
McDonogh 35 HS; New Orleans, LA; Chor.

BROWN, Cheryl Lynn
Valley HS; Sanders, AZ; Rptr, FFA; Secy, Soph Cl;
Bkbl; Tr; *NAU.*

BROWN, Cheryl Lynn
Anderson HS; Anderson, IN (167-512) Band;
Chor; FHA; Mjrte; Co-Ed, Sch P; Y-Tns; Journ A;
Q&S A; Band Medals; *Anderson Col; Pre-Law.*

BROWN, Christina Marie
Fountain Lake HS; Hot Springs, AR; Bus Mgr,
Ann; FHA; Fin, GS; Hmrm; Sch P; SC; Cpt, Tnns;
Amer Leg A; Type A; *Phys Ed.*

BROWN, Christine M
Sou Local HS; Salineville, OH; Bus C; Chor; Commercial C; Dbte Tm; SC; Amer Leg A.

BROWN, Cindy Ann
Albia Comm HS; Albia, IA (17-130) Chldr; Chor;
FHA; 4H; Pep C; Church Yth Choir; VP, Yth Fel;
Bkbl Statistician; Mat Maid; *Elem Ed.*

BROWN, Cindy Lynne
Western Hills HS; Ft Worth, TX (59-606) Chldr;
Hmrm; NHS; Swim; Diving; Gym; Sch Achv &
Improv in Social Stu; *TCU; Bus.*

BROWN, Clifton Arnold
Pershing HS; Houston, TX (5-525) Chor; Span C; Ftbl; VP, Yth Fel; *U of Houston.*

BROWN, Clinton Dean
Belle Vernon Area HS; Belle Vernon, PA (120-340) Rifle C; BSct; *US Marines; Aviation Tech.*

BROWN, Corey Lyndon
DeKalb HS; DeKalb, IL (25%-375) Band; Span C; Gym; *NIU at DeKalb.*

BROWN, Corwin Keith
Soldan HS; St Louis, MO; Cr-Ctry; Tr; Chem A; Citz A; Attendance A; *Archt.*

BROWN, Craig Russell
Bellmont HS; Decatur, IN (11-251) BS; Drama; NHS; Span C; Spch C; Pres, Sr Cl; JV, Ftbl; Swim; *Math.*

BROWN, Curtis Leroy
East HS; Cleveland, OH; Ch, SC; Ch, Cr-Ctry; Most Out; *Fla Inst of Tech; Aviation.*

BROWN, Cynthia Leigh
Se Whitfield HS; Dalton, GA (10-244) Anchor C; Band; NHS; VP, Tri-HiY; Hist A; Hon Prog; NEDT; Co-Cpt, Flag Corps; Pres, Co-Ed Y; Woodsmen o-t World, Read, Eng, A's; *Phys Therapy.*

BROWN, Cynthia Maye
Pinole Valley HS; Pinole, CA; NHS; Alg A; Citz A; Hon Prog; Math A; Span A; *Contra Costa Jr Col.*

BROWN, Dan Thomas
Lancaster HS; Lancaster, VA (6-145) Band; BS; VP, FFA; 4H; NHS; VP, Span C; Schol, Leadership As, FFA; Greenhand, Chapter Pins, FFA; *William and Mary Col; Bio.*

BROWN, Dana Lynn
Campbell Co HS; LaFollette, TN; Cpt, Chor; HCt; Pep C.

BROWN, Danette Cecilia
Belle Vernon Area HS; Belle Vernon, PA; Ann; Band; FBLA; Sftbl; *Ind St Col; Spch Therapy.*

BROWN, Daniel Arthur
Pittsburg Sr HS; Pittsburg, KS; Band; Ensm; 4H; Ftbl; Math A; Pres, Luther League; *Pittsburg St U; Ophthamalogy.*

BROWN, Daphne Ann
Kinkaid HS; Houston, TX; Chldr; Pres, Chor; Drama; FTA; Pres, Hmrm; NHS; St Stu Congress; Bkbl; Sftbl; Tr; Amer Leg A; Chem A; Coun of Teach A; Hon Prog; NEDT; ARC A; Type A; PA; Mus A; Art A; Ntl Jr Hon Soc.

BROWN, Darcy Lynne
Amory HS; Amory, MS; Ann; Band; Fr C; FBLA; Hmrm; Rptr, Sch P; Sci C; SC; Thes; Bkbl; *Ole Miss.*

BROWN, Darrell Keith
Northeastern HS; Detroit, MI; Chess C; Sch P; Hon Prog; Med C; *Wayne St U; Med.*

BROWN, David
Lake Park HS; Roselle, IL (170-650) Sci C; Bsbl; Ftbl; Swim; Tr; Wrest; Hon Prog; Poetry C; Ath A; Yth Ministry A; *Northern Ill U; Elec.*

BROWN, David
S Shore HS; Chicago, IL (150-450) COM; Hon Prog; HR; *Elec Eng.*

BROWN, David B
Wapello Comm HS; Wapello, IA (7-68) NHS; Order/Arrow; Sci C; Var C; Bsbl; Co-Cpt, Bkbl; JV, Tr; God & Country A; Order/Arrow A; Grinnel Col Schol; All Conf Bkbl Tm; Prom Kg Cand; 1st Tm-Bkbl; Iowa Daily Press HR; KBUR Radio; Ann Gary Hall Mem Bkbl A; *Grinnell Col; Botany.*

BROWN, David Billings
Skyline HS; Salt Lake City, UT; Chor; Sch P; Cr-Ctry; Tr; *U of Utah; Dentistry.*

BROWN, David Elliott
Springfield N HS; Springfield, OH; Lat C; JV, Wrest; *Cedarville Col; Bible.*

BROWN, David Eugene
A Crawford Mosley HS; Panama City, FL (60-550) BC; JV, Wrest; Sci A; *Fla Inst of Tech; Oceanographic Engr.*

BROWN, David Freeman
Crockett HS; Crockett, TX (4-150) Ftbl; *U of Tex; Engr.*

BROWN, David Wayne
Markoma Bible Acad; Tahlequah, OK (7-22) Ann; Chor; Cl Fav; Shorthand A; *John Brown U; Linguistics.*

BROWN, David Wayne
J W Sexton HS; Lansing, MI (48-479) MVP, Bkbl; Ftbl; Sftbl; Op Bently A; *Pol Sci.*

BROWN, Dawn Sharmaine
Paul G Blazer HS; Ashland, KY (200-357) Chor; Hmrm; SC; ROTC A; JA; *Ashland Comm Col; Secy.*

BROWN, Debbie Ann
La Porte HS; La Porte, TX (50%-325) BC; InterAct C; NHS; Hist A; Hon Prog; Eng A; WW Merit A; *Stephen F Austin U; Ed.*

BROWN, Debbie Beatrice
South HS; Denver, CO; Spirit Day Qn; *Tailoring.*

BROWN, Debbie Ruth
Metter HS; Metter, GA (20-120) Band; FBLA; FHA; 4H; Bible St As; *Middle Ga Col; Vet.*

BROWN, Deborah
Charles Lincoln Harper HS; Atlanta, GA; Pres, Chor; SC; Alg A; COM; Hon Prog; ROTC A; WW, Mus Stu; Mus Trophy; *Computer Tech.*

BROWN, Deborah Diane
Hillside HS; Durham, NC; Band; Fr C; FHA; Tres, Hmrm; SC; Y-Tns; Opt A; Band A; Home Ec A; PE A; *Johnson C Smith U; Special Ed.*

BROWN, Deborah Lynn
Pflugerville HS; Pflugerville, TX (5-75) BC; Chor; FHA; NHS; *Abilene Christian U; Child Development.*

BROWN, Debra Faye
Permian HS; Odessa, TX (171-668) Band; *Lubbock Christian Col; Elem Ed.*

BROWN, Deirdre
Henry Ford HS; Detroit, MI (24-458) Chldr; NHS; SC; Ch, Sr Cl; COM; Hon Prog; MLS; Sch Service A; Focus Hope; *Mich St U; Bio.*

BROWN, Demetrius Lynn
Alma J Brown Jr HS; Grambling, LA; Band; Drama; FBLA; FHA; FTA; *Grambling St U.*

BROWN, Denise June
Nichols HS; Buffalo, NY; Orch; Tnns; Yth Fel; Headmaster's A; St Piano Win, Usher's Assn; *Northwestern U; Mus.*

BROWN, Diana L
Ogallala Sr HS; Ogallala, NE (53-118) Chldr; Drama; Hmrm; Thes; VP, Sr Cl; Pres, Jr Cl; Pres, Soph Cl; Beauty; HQn; HCt; Qn, Jobs Daughters; *Kearney St Col; Acct.*

BROWN, Diane
Jackson HS; Jackson, LA; SC; Rptr, FBLA; Sci C; Type A; Sci A; Math A; Alg A; *LSU; Bus.*

BROWN, Diane Joyce
Apollo HS; Glendale, AZ; *Pepperdine U; Social Work.*

BROWN, Diane Lynne
Ogallala Sr HS; Ogallala, NE; Fin, Chldr; Drama; Rptr, Hmrm; Rainbow; Span C; Thes; VP, Sr Cl; Pres, Jr Cl; Pres, Soph Cl; JV, Bkbl; JV, Tr; Beauty; HQn; Type A; Qn, Job's Daughters; *Kearney St U; Bus Adm.*

BROWN, Diesta Sheri
Seattle Christian HS; Seattle, WA (10-38) JV, Chldr; Chor; Rptr, Sch P; SC; Pres, Soph Cl; Soccer; Sftbl; Friendship Princess; S-T, Girls C; Tres, Yth Group.

BROWN, Donald Craig
Kalamazoo S D A Acad; Kalamazoo, MI (2-8) MVP, Bkbl; Fin, Cr-Ctry; Fin, Ftbl; Fin, Hockey; Cpt, Sftbl; Swim; Tnns; Fin, Tr; Type A; *Andrews U; Radiology.*

BROWN, Donna Lea
Oakhaven HS; Memphis, TN; Chldr; Chor; Mod Mus Mas; Co-Cpt, Bkbl; Sftbl; HCt; Hist, Modern Mus Masters C; Sports A; Lib A; Swing Choir; *Memphis St U; Lib.*

BROWN, Donna Marie
Liberty HS; Liberty, PA (20%-64) Band; Chor; Ger C; 4H; SC; 4H A; Math A; *Messiah Col; Mus Ed.*

BROWN, Donna Marie
Overbrook School for the Blind; Philadelphia, PA; Band; Chldr; Chor; SC; Citz A; Type A; Sch Ath A; *Phys Ed.*

BROWN, Donna Patricia
Tyner HS; Chattanooga, TN (30-261) BC; Co-Ed, Chldr; S-T, Chor; Rptr, Drama; Semi-Fin, GS; Madrigal; NHS; F-Ed, Sch P; Pres, SC; Secy, Sr Cl; Tres, Jr Cl; Bkbl; Mgr, Tr; Sigma Phi Omega; Best All-Round; Christmas Qn; Calendar Girl; *U of Tenn.*

BROWN, Douglas Newten
Paisley HS; Winston-Salem, NC (26-400) Lat C; Ski C; Ftbl; Yth Fel; *UNC Chapel Hill; Med.*

BROWN, Douglas Warren
Morristown-Hamblen HS E; Morristown, TN (30-259) Pres, BC; Chess C; Hmrm; Lat C; Thes; Swim; Tnns; Bausch & Lomb A; JA A; *Carson-Newman Col; Elem Ed.*

BROWN, E Ray
Berea HS; Greenville, SC; JA A; *Mus.*

BROWN, Eileen Ruth
Rogers Sr HS; Michigan City, IN (137-531) A Cap Choir; JV, Chldr; Chor; Community Yth Symph; Drama; Madrigal; Orch; Span C; SC; Tr; COM; Gym; Fin, Tri-Kappa Schol A; Area & St Mus A's; *Ind U; Mus.*

BROWN, Elaine Marie
Springfield Southeast HS; Springfield, IL; MVP, Chldr; NHS; Prom Ct; Golden Laurel A; *Lincoln Land Comm; Bus.*

BROWN, Elizabeth Ann
Diamond Hill-Jarvis HS; Ft Worth, TX (1-240) Tnns; *NTSU; Drama.*

BROWN, Elizabeth Gayle
Briarfield Acad; Lake Providence, LA (1-49) Co-Ed, Ann; VP, BC; S-T, CYO; Pres, Fr C; GS; 4H; Hmrm; Lit Ral; NHS; S-T, SC; Cpt, Bkbl; Sftbl; Swim; Tnns; COM; Magna Cum Laude; Val; MVP, Bkbl; WW; *LSU; Law.*

BROWN, Ella Denise
Oakdale HS; Oakdale, LA; Chldr; NHS; Beauty; *Sou U; Bus Adm.*

BROWN, Emily Lena
Great Bridge HS; Chesapeake, VA (59-385) Band; Pres, 4H; 4H A; Pres, NAACP Yth Coun; *Norfolk St Col; Occupational Therapy.*

BROWN, Esther Ruth
Oppenheim Ephratah Central Sch; St Johnsville, NY (14-38) Band; FBLA.

BROWN, Eva Marie
Valley HS; Pine Grove, WV (5-67) Tres, Band; Cpt, Chldr; Tres, Dbte Tm; Sci C; SC; Secy, Thes; Var C; COM; Cl Fav; Hist A; Sci A; Drum Mjrte; Co Stu Adv Board; Know Your St Govt Day Alt; Jr Cl Play; Del, St SC Convention; *Fairmont St Col; Secretarial.*

BROWN, Frank Edward
Waterproof HS; Waterproof, LA (4-60) BC; Ftbl.

BROWN, Frankie Loretta
Osceola HS; Kissimmee, FL (25%-300) Band; Chor; Drama; VP, FFA; Hmrm; Mjrte; SC; Thes; Swim; Baton A; *Valencia Col; Law.*

BROWN, Gabriel James
Century HS; Bismarck, ND (25%-300) FFA; Spch A; Yth Leg.

BROWN, George Washington
Adlai E Stevenson HS; Bronx, NY; Sch P; Soccer; COM; Hon Prog; PA; *Med.*

BROWN, Gina Lynn
Bradford HS; Starke, FL (26-325) NHS; HCt; *St Johns River Jr Col; Bus.*

BROWN, Glenda Alice
Reidsville Sr HS; Reidsville, NC (5%-375) Band; NEDT; *Wake Forest U; Psych.*

BROWN, Gwendolyn Denise
Bennett HS; Buffalo, NY (18-319) Bus C; NHS; Tr; Yth Fel; *Northwood Inst; Acct.*

BROWN, Helene Marguerite
Inglewood HS; Inglewood, CA; CYO; Fr C; Span C; CSF; Citz A; Hon Prog; *U of Calif; Bus Adm.*

BROWN, Henry Fredrick
Wilcox Co HS; Rochelle, GA (10-97) Band; BC; 4H; Pres, Span C; COM; 4H A; Hon Prog.

BROWN, Holli Kay
Colton HS; Colton, CA (5%-300) Band; Orch; Hon Prog; *Cal-St San Bernardino; Acct.*

BROWN, Jacinta Grace
Erasmus Hall HS; Brooklyn, NY; Chldr; ARC; *La Gaurdia Col; Lib Arts.*

BROWN, Jacqueline Elaine
Hughes HS; Cincinnati, OH (59-460) VP, Bus C; Chor; NHS; Sch P; VP, Sr Cl; Sftbl; Swim; Tr; COM; Citz A; Hon Prog; JA A; Most Out; Star Student; St Scholar; WW; *Computer Programming.*

BROWN, James Newton Jr
Fairview HS; Ashland, KY; Pres, Fr C; NHS; Pres, Jr Cl; Ftbl; Tr; JA A; Sci A; *Phys Sci.*

BROWN, James Ornett
Washington HS; Milwaukee, WI; A Cap Choir; BS; Ftbl; Tr; Citz A; Hon Prog; Mus Hon; City Mus A's; Carthage Schol A; *Carthage Col; Bus Adm.*

BROWN, Jan
Siloam Springs HS; Siloam Springs, AR (20-140) BC; Ftbl; Bkbl; Sftbl; Bkbl A; Newspaper Calendar Girl; *Phys Therapy.*

BROWN, Jane Yvonne
University City Sr HS; University City, MO (30-526) Band; Ensm; Bkbl; Tnns; *Med.*

BROWN, Janell
Corry Area HS; Corry, PA (127-252) Hmrm; Rainbow; Sch P; SC; Pres, Tri-HiY; *Thiel Col; Nurs.*

BROWN, Janice Ann
Surry Co HS; Surry, VA; Band; Bus C; Chor; FHA; Hmrm; Math C; Span C; Alg A; Bio A; Math A; Sci A; *Pediatrics.*

BROWN, Jeannine Louise
Germantown Friends Sch; Philadelphia, PA (24-80) Chor; Drama; Bsbl; Co-Cpt, Bkbl; Pres, Church Yth Group; Rep, Black Stu Union; *Modern Lang.*

BROWN, Jeffrey Carl
Blue Mountain HS; Schuylkill Haven, PA; A Cap Choir; Band; Chor; Ensm; VP, 4H; Hmrm; Rptr, Sch P; VP, SC; Thes; Dist & Regional Chor; *W Chester St Col; Mus Ed.*

BROWN, Jeffrey Scott
Bridgeton HS; Bridgeton, NJ (3-718) Chem C; Orch; F-Ed, Sch P; Var C; Soccer; Hon Prog; Rotary A; Sci A; *Haverford Col; Physics.*

BROWN, Jennifer Ann
Lancaster Sr HS; Lancaster, WI (13-139) AFS; Band; Chor; FFA; 4H; Math C; Orch; Golf; Hon Prog; Yth Fel; Rep, St Safety Conf; Hon Band; *Bio.*

BROWN, Jennifer Yvonne
Thomas Jefferson HS; Brooklyn, NY; NHS; Alg A; Math A; Acct A; *Secretarial Sci.*

BROWN, Jerry Allen
Grand Ridge HS; Grand Ridge, FL; Chor; FFA; FTA; Bsbl; Bkbl; Sftbl; Citz A; Hon Prog; *Chipola Jr Col.*

BROWN, Jerry Glenn
Artesia HS; Artesia, NM (57-223) BS; Chor; Demolay; Hmrm; Sch P; Ski C; SC; Var C; Co-Cpt, Bsbl; Bkbl; Co-Cpt, Ftbl; Citz A; Cl Fav; DARGCA; Lion A.

BROWN, Jewel Denise
Alfred E Beach HS; Savannah, GA (30-400) Band; Span C; Mgr, Bkbl; Alg A; COM; Yth Fel; Band Medal A; *Fisk U; Dentistry.*

BROWN, Joan Amy
Oconomowoc Sr HS; Oconomowoc, WI (19-250) Fr C; Orch.

BROWN, Joan Lea
Clintondale HS; Mt Clemens, MI (98-333) Attendance A.

BROWN, Jose Luis
Cathedral HS; Boston, MA (2-96) NHS; Rptr, Sch P; Span C; Ftbl; COM; Schol A; Academic Excellence; *U of Mass; Econ.*

BROWN, Joseph D
Sooner HS; Bartlesville, OK (20-280) NHS; ARC; Y-Tns; ROTC A; St Scholar; Civil Air Patrol Schol; *Bethany Nazarene Col; Physics.*

BROWN, Joseph Winchester
Princeton HS; Princeton, NJ (50%-250) Rptr, Sch P; SC; JV, Soccer; JV, Tnns; *Vanderbilt U; Eng.*

BROWN, Joyce Luvell
Proviso E HS; Maywood, IL; Chor; Ensm; Tr; HCt; *Triton Col; Court Rptr.*

BROWN, Juanita
Comm Preparatory Acad; Erie, PA; Co-Ed, Ann; Chor; COM; Hon Prog.

BROWN, Judy Caroline
Alcee Fortier HS; New Orleans, LA (18-274) Secy, Bus C; Pres, FBLA; NHS; SC; Hon Prog; Most Intelligent; Stu Coun; *U of NO; Registered Nurse.*

BROWN, Julia Lynn
Kewanna HS; Kewanna, IN; Dean's List.

BROWN, Julie Lynn
Menomonie Sr HS; Menomomie, WI (40-225) FHA; 4H; Sch P; Employee o-t Yr; 1st Pl, Marketing Math Trophy; *Eau Claire Tech Inst; Marketing.*

BROWN, Karen Ann
Plano Sr HS; Plano, TX (88-1100) VP, Fr C; FCA; Vlbl; *N Colo Col; Acct.*

BROWN, Karen Cynthia
Clarkstown HS N; New City, NY; Band; Chor; NHS.

BROWN, Karen Delores
North HS; Nashville, TN; Band; Chldr; Secy, Hmrm; Hon Prog; *Psych.*

BROWN, Karen Kathy
Stevenson HS; Stevenson, AL (4-100) BC; FHA.

BROWN, Karl Bell
Manheim Township HS; Neffsville, PA (25%-450) Chess C; Tnns; Yth Fel; Co Co-Champ, Chess; *Eng.*

BROWN, Kathryn Grace
Burnt Hills-Ballston Lake HS; Burnt Hills, NY (58-400) Ch, Band; Chor; Community Yth Symph; Ch, Ensm; Orch; COM; MLS; Regent Schol; Ntl Hon Band; All-St Jazz Ensm; NY St Mus Camp; No-East Yth Orch; Albany Symph Concert Soloist Win; Jr ETUDE; All-Eastern Concert Band; *The St U Col at Potsdam; Mus Ed.*

BROWN, Kathy Ann
Pampa Sr HS; Pampa, TX (51-326) Band; Bus C; Pres, Hmrm; SC; Bus; *W Tex St U; Bus.*

BROWN, Kathy Jean
Gloucester HS; Gloucester, VA (4-200) AFS; BC; S-T, Chess C; GS; Hmrm; Ch, Lit Mag; Sch P; COM; Cl Fav; Hist A; Hon Prog; Journ A; NMF; All St Chor; Top 10%, Cl; Stu Director, Selected Chor; Distinguished Amer Mus Stu; *Carson-Newman Col; Eng.*

BROWN, Kay Doreen
Allen Jay HS; High Point, NC; Chor; FHA; Most Out; *Voice.*

BROWN, Kelly Marie
Glendale HS; Springfield, MO; Chldr; Chor; Sftbl; Tr; *U Mo-Columbia; Vet Sci.*

BROWN, Kenneth
George Henry Corliss HS; Chicago, IL (67-219) Sci A; Beta Boule A; Top Ten A; Sanatation Dist A; Superintendents A; *Parks Col of Aero Tech; Aviation.*

BROWN, Kenneth Dean
Central HS; St Joseph, MO (140-455) Var C; Cpt, Bkbl; Journ A; Q&S A; Regent Schol; *Phys Ed.*

BROWN, Kevin Bruce
Southport HS; Indianapolis, IN (75-501) Hmrm; Ftbl; JV, Tr; Yth Fel; *Ind U.*

BROWN, Kevin Wayne
Caro HS; Caro, MI (29-220) JV, Ftbl; Yth Fel; *Mich St U; Vet Med.*

BROWN, Kimberly Ann
Chelsea HS; Chelsea, MI (4-217) Ann; Pres, Band; Dbte Tm; Fr C; Mjrte; Fin, NFL; Pres, NHS; Amer Leg A; COM; Citz A; Cl Fav; MLS; Drum Mjrte; Dist Win, Bicentennial Yth Debates; Cert of Recog, St Comp Schol Prog; *U of Mich; Med.*

BROWN, Kimberly Elizabeth
St Albans HS; St Albans, WV (60-540) Secy, Anchor C; GS; NHS; Tres, SC; Tr; Mgr, Wrest; *Fairmont St Col; Pub Service Tech.*

BROWN, Kristi Sue
Pine Grove Area HS; Pine Grove, PA (4-150) Co-Ed, Ann; Arch; Band; Chor; Ensm; NHS; Tri-HiY; Var C; Tres, Jr Cl; Arch; Bkbl; JA A; NEDT; Pres A; *Cornell U; Archt.*

BROWN, Larry Ann
Robert E Lee HS; Midland, TX (10%-700) FTA; Hmrm; NHS; SC; JV, Bkbl; *Abilene Christian U; Elem Ed.*

BROWN, Laura Mae
Percy L Julian HS; Chicago, IL (4-1000) NHS; *Med.*

BROWN, Laurie Ann
San Jacinto HS; San Jacinto, CA; Fr C; FTA; Secy, Rainbow.

BROWN, Lea Ann
Carbondale Comm HS; Carbondale, IL (6-326) NHS; Ed, Sch P; Journ A; Most Out; St Scholar; *Sou Ill U; Med.*

BROWN, Lena Anntoinette
San Bernardino HS; San Bernardino, CA (33%-400) AFS; CYO; Co-Cpt, Chldr; Secy, Fr C; Hmrm; SC; Pres, Jr Cl; HCt; K of C A; Math A; NMS; Christmas Princess; Religion, Fr, Eng, A's; *UCLA; Liberal Arts.*

BROWN, Leslie Ray
Layette HS; St Joseph, MO (120-302) Chess C; JV, Bsbl; JV, Bkbl; JV, Ftbl; JV, Tr.

BROWN, Linda Ann
W Charlotte HS; Charlotte, NC (95-625) A-Ed, Ann; Band; Secy, Fr C; InterAct C; InterClub Coun; Sch P; Pres, IA; V-P, Yth Missionaries; Jr Choir; *UNC Chapel Hill; Journ.*

BROWN, Linda Renee
Surry Co HS; Elberon, VA (10-54) Chor; Secy, FHA; 4H; Secy, Hmrm; Span C; Bio A; 4H A; HCt; Type A; Rptr, Yth Department; *Va Union U; Pol Sci.*

BROWN, Linn Ellen
Del Rio HS; Del Rio, TX (6-450) Secy, 4H; NHS; ARC; SC; 4H A; Sci A; Lt, Drill Tm; *San Marcos U.*

BROWN, Lisa Ann
Portageville HS; Portageville, MO (4-76) S-T, Fr C; FBLA; FHA; FNA; Tres, NHS; DARGCA; Best Personality; Fourth in Cl of 76; *Southeast Mo St Col; Acct.*

BROWN, Lisa Ann
Our Lady of Good Counsel HS; Newark, NJ (3-84) Drama; NHS; F-Ed, Sch P; SC; COM; *Seton Hall Col; Law.*

BROWN, Lisa Marion
Savannah HS; Savannah, GA (17-392) Secy, BC; Chldr; Chem C; Hmrm; InterClub Coun; Pres, Lat C; Tres, NHS; Phys C; COM; Hon Prog; Most Out; Pres, Sun Sch; Nom, WW; Booster C; Outst Sr; Outst Chldr; *Armstrong St Col; Arts & Crafts.*

BROWN, Lori Ann
Gilmer HS; Gilmer, TX (35-100) Band; Drama; VP, FHA; FTA; Spch C; Spch A; *La Col; Social Worker.*

BROWN, Lori Kathleen
Yosemite Union HS; Oakhurst, CA (10-96) Drama; Pres, FHA; Pres, 4H; Span C; Bkbl; Soccer; Sftbl; Tr; CSF; COM; Citz A; Star Student; VFW A; *Santa Barbara St Col; Lib Sci.*

BROWN, Lovie Marie
Alma J Brown Laboratory HS; Grambling, LA; Tres, Band; Tres, FTA; Tres, 4H; Rptr, NHS; S-T, Sci C; Up Bound; VP, Jr Cl; Secy, Soph Cl; Bkbl; Sftbl; Alg A; 4H A; Hon Prog; Math A; Sci A; Swtht; Band A; GScts; Bible Schol; *Grambling St U; Marketing.*

BROWN, LuAnn
Clover Park HS; Tacoma, WA (25%-500) A Cap Choir; Chor; Ensm; Orch; Kiwanis A; *E Tex Baptist Col; Mus.*

BROWN, Lucretia Ann
Bogue Chitto HS; Bogue Chitto, MS (2-60) BC; FHA; Rptr, Hmrm; Rptr, Sch P; *U of Sou Miss; Mus.*

BROWN, Lynn Renee
Starmount HS; Boonville, NC (10%-211) Chor; FHA; VP, Soph Cl; Tnns; Gov Honor Prog; Scorekeeper, Bsbl; Statistician, Bkbl; *Med.*

BROWN, Lynne Ann
Leominster HS; Leominster, MA (10-449) Band; Fr C; NHS; Orch; Tnns; Yth Fel; Fr Prize; *Wheelock Col; Early Childhood Ed.*

BROWN, Lynne Rae
Carbondale Comm HS; Carbondale, IL (26-330) A-Ed, Sch P; COM; Journ A; Pres A; *Sou Ill U; Communications.*

BROWN, Marcus Anthony
Welch HS; Welch, WV; Up Bound; Bkbl; Tr; COM; JA A; *Elec.*

BROWN, Marilyn Rolanda
Lincoln HS; Dallas, TX; Bus C; FHA; Hmrm; Key C; Math C; NHS; ARC; Sci C; Span C; Alg A; Eng, Homemaking, A's; *Tex Women's U; Nurs.*

BROWN, Mark Edward
Caprock HS; Amarillo, TX (10-350) Bus C; Lat C; NHS; JV, Wrest; Magna Cum Laude; Dist DECA Win; St DECA Win; Ntl DECA Participation; *Amarillo Col; Social Sci.*

BROWN, Mark Edward
Stoneville HS; Stoneville, NC; FFA; Var C; Pres, Sr Cl; Co-Cpt, Ftbl; MVP, Golf.

BROWN, Mark Louis
Sacred Heart HS; Klamath Falls, OR (1-54) VP, NHS; Tres, SC; Bkbl; Amer Leg A; Hon Prog; Math A; NMS; NEDT; Type A; Environmental Sci A; Eng A; *Pepperdine U; Computer Sci.*

BROWN, Mark Paul
Howe Military HS; Howe, IN (6-39) A Cap Choir; Ann; Band; Community Yth Symph; Dbte Tm; Drama; Ger C; Model UN; NHS; Orch; Sch P; Spch C; Thes; Var C; Bsbl; Alg A; COM; Chem A; Hon Prog; Math A; NEDT; Opt A; Spch A; *U of Mich; Econ.*

BROWN, Marsheila Lynnette
NW Classen HS; Okla City, OK; Pres, Hmrm; NHS; Tr; Cl Fav; Most Out; *Kans U; Lab Tech.*

BROWN, Martha Lea
Wapello Comm HS; Wapello, IA (7-62) Band; Chor; VP, FHA; SC; Mgr, Bkbl; Golf.

BROWN, Mary Ann
Wapello Comm Col; Wapello, IA (5-62) Band; Chor; FHA; SC; Var C; Bkbl; Golf; Tr.

BROWN, Mary Ella
Eastern Guilford HS; Gibsonville, NC (12-164) Drama; Fr C; French NHS; GS; Pres, NHS; Sci C; COM; Interntl C; Jr Marshal; *U of NC; Phar.*

BROWN, Mary Eloise
Logan Sr HS; Logan, UT (10%-285) A-Ed, Ann; FHA; VP, NHS; Hon Prog; *U of Utah; Hist.*

BROWN, Matthew Richard
King HS; Tampa, FL; *Movie-Making.*

BROWN, Melissa Ann
Leavenworth Sr HS; Leavenworth, KS (57-400) CYO; 4H; COM; Citz A; *Phar.*

BROWN, Melody Elizabeth
Wilcox Co HS; Rochelle, GA (3-116) Parl, BC; Chem C; FBLA; Lit Ral; Lit Mag; Math C; Sci C; Span C; SC; COM; Hon Prog; Eng A & Cert; *Mercer U; Biol.*

BROWN, Michael Blazek
Ridgeview HS; Atlanta, GA (8-230) BC; FBLA; Lat C; COM; Hon Prog; *US Air Force Acad; Sci.*

BROWN, Michael O'Neal
Carroll HS; Monroe, LA; A Cap Choir; Chor; Fr C; Pres, Hmrm; InterAct C; JETS; *Sou U; Engr.*

BROWN, Michael Robert
Hot Springs Co HS; Thermopolis, WY (4-100) Band; BS; Drama; Ensm; Pres, NFL; NHS; Pres, Thes; Golf; Tnns; Amer Leg A; DARGCA; Odd Fellow Fin; Spch A; VFW A; Odd Fellows Win; *Colo St; Bus Mgt.*

BROWN, Mitzi Darlene
Man HS; Man, WV (5-180) GS; Hmrm; NHS; SC; HCt; DECA C.

BROWN, Monica Anita
Soldan HS; St Louis, MO (31-696) Mjrte; Drill Tm A; HR A; *Bus.*

BROWN, Myla Sue
Clay Co HS; Manchester, KY (1-200) VP, BC; Ed, Sch P; Sci C; SC; Alg A; Hist A; Math A; Val; Eng A; *U of Ky; Optometry.*

BROWN, Myra Ronether
Monroe HS; Albany, GA (10%-300) Band; Demolay; Drama; GS; 4H; Madrigal; Mjrte; St Stu Congress; SC; JV, Bkbl; COM; 4H A; *Spellman Col; Spch.*

BROWN, Nadja Sue
Forbush HS; E Bend, NC (40-200) Band; BC; Ensm; VP, Fr C; Hmrm; VP, NHS; SC; Gov Honor Prog; HCt; *Mus.*

BROWN, Nancy Jane
Lyons Township HS; La Grange, IL (75-1100) Chor; Ensm; Lit Mag; Sftbl; Hon Prog; NEDT; Ch, Girl's C Coun; Vlbl; *Math.*

BROWN, Nancy Jane
Sooner HS; Bartlesville, OK (8-289) A-Ed, Ann; SC; Tr; S-T, Jr Civitan C-Okla-Kans Dist; HR; Girls Service C; St Hon Soc; *Okla St U; Advertising.*

BROWN, Nelson Edward
Winyah HS; Georgetown, SC; Hmrm; Ftbl; Civitan C; *U of SC; Law Enforcement.*

BROWN, Nick A
Hope HS; Hope, AR (27-250) Band; Co-Ch, BC; Ch, Ensm; FTA; COM; Hon Prog; Most Out; Drum Major; *Ouachita Baptist Col; Elec Engr.*

BROWN, Pamela Ann
Emsley A Laney HS; Wilmington, NC; Band; Chldr; ARC; *Early Childhood Ed.*

BROWN, Patricia G
Miami Northwestern Sr HS; Miami, FL (6-358) Secy, FTA; InterAct C; Math C; Alg A; COM; Citz A; Math A; Type A; *Principal's HR; Acct.*

BROWN, Patrick Eugene
Norwalk HS; Norwalk, OH (6-240) BS; Demolay; Pres, NHS; Co-Cpt, Ftbl; Co-Cpt, Wrest; COM; DARGCA; Hon Prog; Yth Leg; MVP, Wrest; WW; *Miami U; Math.*

BROWN, Paul Wilfred III
Westboro HS; Westboro, MA (150-250) Demolay; Lit Mag; Var C; Cr-Ctry; Tr; *Criminal Justice.*

BROWN, Paula Ann
Marion HS; Marion, IN (33%-400) Chor; Drama; Lat C; Lat NHS; NHS; Rainbow; Sci C; Thes; Tres, Jr Cl; Tres, Soph Cl; JV, Tnns; Hon Prog; Masonic A; Type A; Yth Fel; Miss Jobs Daughter of Ind; Top 10 Thespian; *Ind U; Pediatrics Nurs.*

BROWN, Paula Anne
Douglass Sr HS; Baltimore, MD (5%-400) Hmrm; Conduct A; Highest Avg A; *Morgan St Col; Bus Adm.*

BROWN, Perry Maurice
Holly Grove HS; Holly Grove, AR (3-70) Ann; BC; Chem C; FFA; Phys C; Sci C; Chem A; MLS; Phy A; Sal; Type A; FFA A; Acct A; Govt A; *U of Ark at Pine Bluff; Elec Engr.*

BROWN, Peter Eugene
San Bernardino HS; San Bernardino, CA; CYO; Cpt, Bkbl; MVP, Ftbl; Tr; Amer Leg A; Cl Fav; Star Student; Swtht; MVP, Bkbl; *U of Sou Calif; Sports.*

BROWN, Phillip Lee
Bryan Adams HS; Dallas, TX; Band; Ger C; All City Band A; *U of Tex; Law.*

BROWN, Phyllis Mae
Battle Ground HS; Battle Ground, WA (86-402) Chor; FFA; FHA; 4H; Hon Prog; Nom, Homecoming Ct; *Clark Col; Landscape Archt.*

BROWN, Rachel Anna
Oppenheim Ephratah Central Sch; St Johnsville, NY (2-50) AFS; Band; Alg A; *Ed.*

BROWN, Randy L
Glen Oak HS; Canton, OH (2-709) Chldr; NHS; F-Ed, Sch P; Mgr, Tr; Schol Athlete A; Varsity Letter; *Miami U; Secondary Ed.*

BROWN, Ray Logan Jr
Temple Christian Sch; Rockville, MD; Ann; Chor; Ensm; Pres, SC; Math A; 1st Pl, Md St Mus Teachers Assn; Md As of Christ Sch Fine Arts Fest.

BROWN, Reginald Thomas
Lexington Sr HS; Lexington, NC; Rprtr, Chess C; MVP, Chor; Pres, Drama; Ensm; Hmrm; Monogram; Sci C; Pres, Soph Cl; Bsbl; Co-Cpt, Bkbl; JV, Ftbl; Sftbl; Citz A; Hon Prog; Pres A; *U of NC; Law.*

BROWN, Rene Michelle
Castlemont HS; Oakland, CA; Hmrm; Model UN; NHS; A-Ed, Sch P; SC; Tres, Jr Cl; Bus Mgr, Soph Cl; B Crocker A; CSF; COM; Citz A; Hon Prog; Sci A; Type A; Big Sisters; *Santa Clara Col; Early Childhood Development.*

BROWN, Renita Sonya
Highlands HS; N Highlands, CA (35-300) Drama; Secy, Fr C; Orch; Pres, Y-Tns; Bsbl; MVP, Tnns; JA A; Most Out; Schol; Outst Tnns A; CSR; Best Female Orch Player; Academic A; *CSU-Sacramento; Phys Therapy.*

BROWN, Richard
Hammond Tech Voc HS; Hammond, IN; Chor; Yth Fel; Pres, Yth Fel; Ind St Police Career Camp; Peer Helping Prog; *De Paul U; Mus.*

BROWN, Richard Bruce
Wheaton HS; Wheaton, MD; Drama; Hmrm; Monogram; SC; Thes; Mgr, Ftbl; Mgr, Wrest; God & Country A; Order/Arrow A; Yth Fel; Yth Foundation; Patrol Ldr, BSct.

BROWN, Richard Duane
Hope HS; Hope, AR (14-200) Chor; Span C; Ftbl; *U of Central Ark; Bus.*

BROWN, Richard Edward III
Gloucester HS; Gloucester, VA (200-400) Chor; FFA; JV, Ftbl; Math A; Campus Life; *Acct.*

BROWN, Richard L
Oakhall Private Sch; Gainesville, FL (12-29) Ann; Drama; *Law.*

BROWN, Richard Wayne
Highlands HS; San Antonio, TX (4-600) Community Yth Symph; Ensm; JETS; Parl, Math C; Mu Alpha Theta; NHS; Sci C; Golf; COM; Hon Prog; Math A; Ntl Sci Found; NEDT; Opt A; Sci A; St VP, Lat C; Concertmaster, Orch; NMS Commended; All St Yth Symph; *Tulane U; Biochem.*

BROWN, Rick Alan
San Angelo Central HS; San Angelo, TX; JV, Tnns; Opt Out Tn; Spch A; 1st Pl, Bible Bowl; *Abilene Christian Col; Bible.*

BROWN, Robert Darrell
Edgewood Sr HS; Ashtabula, OH (80-216) InterClub Coun; Rptr, Sch P; Sci C; Journ A; Audio Visual C; Pres, Camera C; *Bowling Green St U; Visual Communications.*

BROWN, Robert Lee
Mammoth Spring HS; Mammoth Spring, AR (2-45) Tres, Dbte Tm; FFA; Sci C; Bsbl; Bkbl; A; COM; Hon Prog; Math A; Star Greenhand; *Ark St U; Agr.*

BROWN, Robert Lewis III
Skyline HS; Dallas, TX (50%-1700) Pres, Band; Dbte Tm; Spch A; *Fisk U; Pre-Med.*

BROWN, Robert Scott
San Angelo Central HS; San Angelo, TX; Cpt, Tnns; Lion A; Spch A; 2nd Pl, District Tnns Doubles; WW; *Abilene Christian U.*

BROWN, Robin Marlene
Natchitoches Central HS; Natchitoches, LA (50-260) Arch; FBLA; FHA; Arch; Bkbl; Sftbl; Swim; *Northwestern St U; Computer Prog.*

BROWN, Rod Alan
Jonathan Alder HS; Plain City, OH; Band; Fr C; HiY; Math A; Band A; *Mus.*

BROWN, Rosalyn Marie
Captain Shreve HS; Shreveport, LA; Band; Drama; Octagon C.

BROWN, Rosaria Jessie
N Quincy HS; N Quincy, MA (42-463) Chor; Drama; Fr C; French NHS; Lit Mag; Sch P; Hon Prog; Yth Fel; Hon Men, Annual Art Assn Contest; MFA Prog; Internship Prog; Tn Qn, Tn Winter Carnival; *Mount Ida Jr Col; Fashion Illustration.*

BROWN, Roy Neil
Sublette HS; Sublette, KS (3-43) Band; Dbte Tm; SC; S-T, Var C; Pres, Jr Cl; Bkbl; Ftbl; Hon Prog; Sal; *Wichita St U; Pre-Med.*

BROWN, Russell Kenneth
Inglewood HS; Inglewood, CA; SC; Var C; Bsbl; Cpt, Bkbl; COM; Citz A; PTA A; *Bus.*

BROWN, Ruth A
Pleasant Valley HS; Pleasant Valley, IA (50-206) A Cap Choir; Chor; Madrigal; Sftbl; Vlbl.

BROWN, Sally Leona
Lexington Sr HS; Lexington, NE (14-123) Dbte Tm; Rptr, Sch P; Spch C; Sftbl; Hon Prog; Spch A; Yth Fel; *Kearney St Col; Law.*

BROWN, Sandra Kaye
Carver HS; Birmingham, AL (19-237) Chor; Drama; Thes; *Dramatics.*

BROWN, Sandra Lorraine
Winnfield Sr HS; Winnfield, LA (46-115) Chldr; FBLA; FHA; FTA; 4H; Hmrm; Spch C; SC; Var C; MVP, Bkbl; Beauty; Cl Fav; MVP, Dist Bkbl; *U of Houston; Speech Ed.*

BROWN, Sharon Kay
East Central HS; Hurley, MS (14-115) BC; Bus C; FBLA; FHA; 4H; Sch P; Sci C; Cpt, Sftbl; Sci A; *Miss Gulf Coast Jr Col; Acct.*

BROWN, Sharon Lynn
Nordonia HS; Macedonia, OH (10%-500) Band; Drama; Hmrm; Sch Achieve Tm; Co-Ch, Church Yth Chor; U For Yng Amer; Fr Achv A; Tres, 1st Cl, GSct; Superior, Dist Solo & Ensm.

BROWN, Sharon Lynne
Arts HS; Newark, NJ (55-165) Yth Fel; Hon Chor; Color Guards; Mus A; *Kean Col; Pol Sci.*

BROWN, Sharon May
Holyoke HS; Holyoke, CO (23-57) Ann; Band; Chor; Secy, FBLA; FHA; Rptr, FTA; VP, 4H; Sch P; SC; 4H A; Masonic A; Type A; MYF; Piano Accompanist; Select Choir; Flag Corp; Twirler; *Legal Secy.*

BROWN, Sharon Ruth
Humbold HS; Humboldt, TN; Chor; FHA; 4H; Tr; *W Tenn Bus Col.*

BROWN, Sheila Elaine
Howe HS; Howe, OK (1-17) A-Ed, Ann; FHA; SC; Hon Prog; *OSU; Ed.*

BROWN, Shelia Gail
Ironton HS; Ironton, OH; Band; Chor; VP, Commercial C; Tres, FNA; 4H; Hmrm; Sci C; JA A; Sci A; *Columbus Tech Inst; Nurs.*

BROWN, Shirley Ann
McClellan HS; Little Rock, AR; Chor; Sftbl; *U of Central Ark; Nurs.*

BROWN, Shirley Marie
Colo HS; Colo City, TX (3-95) Ann; NHS; SC; *San Angelo St Col; Acct.*

BROWN, Sonja Vanetta
N Nashville HS; Nashville, TN; A Cap Choir; A-Ed, Ann; Band; Chor; VP, Hmrm; Sch P; VP, SC; Golf; Co-E, Annual; *U of Tenn; Bus.*

BROWN, Sonyia Vermell
Walbrook Sr HS; Baltimore, MD (30-480) COM; Yth Fel; Pep Sq; Secy, Jr Usher Board; Distinguished Roll; Mass Choir; Pres Yng Peop Chor; Yng Peop Bible; Secy, Young Peoples Dept; *Catonsville Comm Col; Data Processing Technology.*

BROWN, Stacey Clay
Quartz Hill HS; Quartz Hill, CA; Band; Fr C; Secy, Key C; Ski C; Var C; MVP, Ftbl; MVP, Hockey; MVP, Tr; *Boston U; Engr of Oceangraphy.*

BROWN, Stacy Elaine
Irving HS; Irving, TX (200-662) Secy, Chldr; Lat C; Swim; Yth Fel; Yth Foundation; *U of Tex at Arlington; Nurs.*

BROWN, Stephanie
Spartanburg Sr HS; Spartanburg, SC (10%-900) BC; NHS; SC; *Duke U; Med.*

BROWN, Stephanie Michelle
Oakland Tech HS; Oakland, CA (50-650) SC; Swim; Tr; Hon Prog; Spelling, Traffic, A's; *U of Calif; Bus.*

BROWN, Steven Albert
Aurora HS; Aurora, OH (15%-187) Ftbl; Tr; Ind Arts A; *Valparaiso U; Mech Engr.*

BROWN, Steven Edward
Holt HS; Holt, MI (25-373) Band; VP, Span C; JV, Tr; God & Country A; Green Belt, Taekwon Do; Solo & Ensm, Attendance, A's; Schol Achv, A; *Mich St U; Law.*

BROWN, Susan Elizabeth
Adrian HS; Adrian, MI (5%-400) Hmrm; NHS; Ski C; SC; Var C; Swim; Hon Prog; Foreign Stu; Prom Ch; Co Yth Convention; Secy, Sub-Debs; Methodist Yth; Syncronized Swim.

BROWN, Suzanne Ruth
Washington HS; Kansas City, KS (75-595) Lit Mag; Tr; COM; Hist A; Sci A; Type A; Yth Fel; Yth Leg; Pep C; HR A; Attendance A; Shorthand A; Bus Mach A; Church Choir; *Kansas City Comm Col; Early Childhood Ed.*

BROWN, Tamar Elizabeth
Palmdale HS; Palmdale, CA (50-300) Ski C; Mgr, Wrest; Citz A; *Azusa Pacific Col; Bus.*

BROWN, Tara Elizabeth
Regina HS; Norwood, OH (15-120) CYO; Fr C; Ch, Hmrm; Model UN; V-Ch, ARC; St Stu Congress; Tres, SC; UN Council; Sftbl; H of F; Hon Prog; ARC A; Tres, Stu Sen; MDA; OASC; *Stanford U; Law.*

BROWN, Teresa
Claxton HS; Claxton, GA (25%-116) Chldr; Hmrm; SC; Tr.

BROWN, Teresa Kaye
Centerville HS; Centerville, OH; Chldr; Chor; Soccer; Yth Fel; Ntl Federation of Mus C; *Bus Adm.*

BROWN, Teri S
Cotter HS; Winona, MN (55-99) Bus C; CYO; Chor; ARC; Sodality; Thes; Sftbl; Hon Prog; ARC A.

BROWN, Theresa Jayne
Athens HS; Athens, AL (25-262) FBLA; FHA; Math C; Parl, Sci C; Var C; Cpt, Bkbl; Cpt, Sftbl; Tnns; MVP, Bkbl; Tres, Phi Delta Sorority; MVP, Sftbl; Cpt, Vlbl; Bowl; *Acct.*

BROWN, Theresa Lynn
Sullivan Central HS; Blountville, TN (35-400) F-Ed, Ann; BC; CYO; NHS; Span C; COM; Art A; *Tenn Tech Inst; Wildlife Mgr.*

BROWN, Thlytha
Buckhorn HS; Buckhorn, KY (5-36) Chor; Eng A; *Cumberland Col.*

BROWN, Thomas Lawrence Jr
Dixie Co HS; Cross City, FL (50-127) FFA; *Marine Archt.*

BROWN, Thurman Anthony
Cainhoy HS; Huger, SC (2-62) Chess C; Chor; FFA; 4H; NHS; Span C; JV, Bkbl.

BROWN, Tim Dennis
Logan HS; Logan, UT (250-300) Chem C; Chess C; Ger C; Phys C; Sci C; Soccer; Swim; Bio A; Sci A; *Utah St U; Med.*

BROWN, Timothy Charles
Starmount HS; Boonville, NC (15-204) Ger C; VP, SC; Mgr, Bkbl; Mgr, Ftbl; Tnns; Math A.

BROWN, Timothy Glenn
Kingsway Regional HS; Swedesboro, NJ (13-165) Pres, FFA; NHS.

BROWN, Timothy William
Rockford E Sr HS; Rockford, IL (28-725) Band; Orch; Conductor's A, Mus; *U of Ill; Bus.*

BROWN, Tina Leigh
Bradford Co HS; Starke, FL (20-325) NHS; *St Johns River Jr Col; Elem Ed.*

BROWN, Todd Allan
Coleman HS; Coleman, TX; Ann; FFA; Lat C; Lat NHS; JV, Bkbl; DARGCA; Hist A; WW in Foreign Lang A; Eng As; Lat A; Geom A.

BROWN, Tricia Ann
Zuni HS; Zuni, NM (3-62) Ann; Cpt, Chldr; GS; NHS; Sch P; Rptr, SC; Secy, Jr Cl; Pres, Soph Cl; Bkbl; MVP, Tr; DARGCA; Elk A; HQn; Rotary A; *TVI of Albuquerque; Animal Sci.*

BROWN, Velda Vivette
Carver Area HS; Chicago, IL; FTA; Hmrm; ARC; *UALR; Law.*

BROWN, Velma Deloise
Berkeley Sr HS; Berkeley, MO (99-278) FNA; Hmrm; SC; Arch; Bkbl; Sftbl; Swim; Type A; Shorthand, Driver's Ed, A's; Inst of Black Stu; *Florissant Valley Col; Nurs.*

BROWN, Velvet Ann
Sam Houston HS; Arlington, TX; FHA; FTA; Ger C; NHS; COM; Hon Prog; *Computer Processing.*

BROWN, Venandee Lay
Hueytown HS; Hueytown, AL (10%-416) VP, Soph Cl; Tnns; COM; 4H A; PA A.

BROWN, Venessa Ann
Berkeley Sr HS; Berkeley, MO; FHA; FNA; Hmrm; ARC; Sch P; St Stu Congress; SC; Var C; Tr; MLS; Most Out; Type A; Yth Fel; Vlbl; FCA; Bus.

BROWN, Vernice Castle
Independence Sr HS; Charlotte, NC (338-641) Tres, FTA; JA A; *Mars Hill Col; Elem Ed.*

BROWN, Vickie Verna
Screven Co HS; Sylvania, GA; Band; Chor; Hmrm; SC; Excel Medals, Solo & Ensm Festival.

BROWN, Victor
Jordan HS; Los Angeles, CA; Chess C; Sftbl; Tr; ROTC A; Yth Foundation; *Sci.*

BROWN, Virginia Mae
Alexander Central HS; Taylorsville, NC (40%-385) Band; Drama; Ensm; Mgr, Bkbl; *Vet Med.*

BROWN, Vivian Lea
Appalachian HS; Oneonta, AL (10-38) Band; Chor; Community Yth Symph; Drama; Ensm; FHA; 4H; Hmrm; InterAct C; Orch; Fin, St Stu Congress; SC; Tres, Soph Cl; CSF; 4H A; Hon Prog; NMS; PTA A; Spch A; Calif St Hon Band; Calif Solo & Ensm; *Lee Col; Mus Ed.*

BROWN, Walter Monroe Jr
W Side HS; Newark, NJ (16-280) NHS; Schol Ath; HR; *Rutgers Col; Archt Engr.*

BROWN, Walter Roger
Stony Brook Sch; Stony Brook, NY (40-80) SC; Var C; Ftbl; Tr; Wrest; *Morehouse Col; Bus Adm.*

BROWN, Warren Jeffrey
Lancaster HS; Lancaster, VA (4-170) Cpt, Band; Drama; Fr C; 4H; Hmrm; Sci C; St Stu Congress; Tres, SC; Tr.

BROWN, William
Fayette Ware HS; Somerville, TN; *Military Sci.*

BROWN, William Fredrick
Plymouth HS; Plymouth, NC (50-200) Band; Math C; Monogram; Span C; Var C; Mgr, Ftbl; Tnns; COM; Yth Fel; Secy & Sgt, Plymouth Police Expl C; *NC St U; Bus.*

BROWNE, Andrew Orlando
Paraiso Jr Sr HS; Paraiso, CANAL ZONE; Band; Hmrm; JV, Bkbl; Band A; *Rochester Col; Med.*

BROWNE, Barbara Glenn
Hoopeston-E Lynn HS; Hoopeston, IL (25-130) Band; Chor; Drama; Fr C; Sch P; Spch C; Thes; Var C; Mgr, Bkbl; Swim; Tr; *Bradley U; Nurs.*

BROWNE, Deborah Jean
Doherty HS; Colorado Springs, CO (15%-450) Band; NHS; Orch; Ski C; Tres, Var C; Tr; Hon Prog; Most Out; Gym; *Med.*

BROWNE, Jewell Anne
Capitol Christian Acad; Upper Marlboro, MD; Chor; Drama; ARC; Sch P; Sci C; Span C; SC; VP, Soph Cl; Sftbl; Tr; COM; ARC A; PA; Tr A; *Acct.*

BROWNE, Sandra Lynn
Doherty HS; Colorado Springs, CO (40-200) Band; Chor; Ski C; Swim; Tnns; *Photography.*

BROWNE, Veronica Diane
Boro Hall Acad; Brooklyn, NY (2-17) DA Citz A; Service A; Schol As; *Kingsborough Col; Phys Therapy.*

BROWNELL, Gary Ray
Allen Consolidated Sch; Allen, NE (4%-35) Band; BS; Chor; Secy, FFA; Hmrm; Semi-Fin, NHS; Spch C; SC; JV, Bsbl; JV, Bkbl; Ftbl; Tr; FFA St Agronmy Tm; Chapter Farmer, FFA; Greenhand A, FFA; *NE Tech Comm Col; Auto Mech.*

BROWNELL, Pam Ann
Allen Consolidated Sch; Allen, NE (5-29) Ann; Band; JV, Chldr; Chor; Ensm; FHA; Sch P; Var C; Rptr, Soph Cl; Bkbl; Cpt, Sftbl; Tr; Spch A; Type A; Band A; Chor; Bkbl A; FHA A; *U of Nebr; Commercial Work.*

BROWNING, Cathleen Jane
Mason City HS; Mason City, IA (7-483) Ann; World Affairs C; St Scholar; *Iowa St U; Applied Art.*

BROWNING, Karen Elaine
Plainview HS; Plainview, TX (150-391) GS; Hmrm; Pres, Rainbow; Secy, SC; Dale Carneigie Special Achv A; OEA; Acteens, Qn with Septer; Pres, Med Careers; C of C Stu o-t Mo; *Baylor U; Bus Mgt.*

BROWNING, Karen Lea
Houston Co HS; Erin, TN (15%-65) Ed, Ann; VP, 4H; Rptr, Sch P; Mgr, Bkbl; Cl Fav; Yth Fel; WW; *Cumberland Col of Tenn; Acct.*

BROWNING, Linda Kay
Wheeler Co HS; Alamo, GA (1-50) Ed, Ann; BC; Dbte Tm; VP, NHS; Pres, Tri-HiY; Alg A; COM; Hist A; MLS; *S Ga Col; Journ.*

BROWNING, Lisa Annette
Marion Co HS; Lebanon, KY (30-298) Ed, Ann; FHA; Fin, Jr Miss Pagent; NHS; S-T, Spch C; Var C; Citz A; Gym; *U of Ky; Special Ed.*

BROWNING, Lisa Dawn
W Memphis HS; W Memphis, AR (22%-394) Band; Bus C; Ensm; FHA; Hmrm; Lat C; Sch P; Tres, Sci C; SC; Citz A; Cl Fav; Hon Prog; Yth Fel; Pres, Cake Decorating C; Church Yth Choir; Band Schol; Eng, Home Ec, Band, A's.

BROWNING, Marvin Tim
Rocky Mount Sr HS; Rocky Mount, NC (5-510) Band; Ensm; Sftbl; Band Service A.

BROWNING, Pamela Sue
Man HS; Man, WV (25-180).

BROWNING, Philip Stancil
W Alamance HS; Elon College, NC (75-300) Chess C; Lit Mag; Span C; *David Liscomb Col.*

BROWNING, Robert Sidney
N Mesquite HS; Mesquite, TX (243-452) A Cap Choir; Lat C; Pres, Orch; ROTC A; Off, ROTC; All St Choir; *Hardin-Simmons U; Mus.*

BROWNING, Teresa Ruth
Stephens Co HS; Toccoa, GA; Anchor C; NHS; VP, Tri-HiY; HR; *U of Ga; Spch Pathology.*

BROWNING, William Wesley
Westview HS; Kankakee, IL (67-227) Chor; Drama; Madrigal; Thes; Tres, Soph Cl; Fine Arts Letter; Del, Il Yth Comm; Conf Coun, Yth Ministries; District Pres, UMYF; District Coun, Ministries; *N Central Col; Theology.*

BROWNLEE, Alicia Renice
Banning HS; Banning, CA; *UCR.*

BROWNLEE, Andrew Jerome
Banning HS; Banning, CA (69-160) Ftbl; AAYA; *Cal Poly; Mech.*

BROWNLEE, Kenneth Edward
Springville HS; Springville, AL; All Amer Yth; Chem C; Chess C; Chor; Pres, FFA; FTA; Pres, Hmrm; NHS; Spch C; Var C; Pres, Sr Cl; VP, Jr Cl; Bkbl; Cpt, Ftbl; Tnns; Most Out; Ntl Conf Chr & Jews; PTA A; Yth Fel; *Jacksonville State; PE.*

BROWNLEE, Robert Ellis
Westmont Hilltop HS; Johnstown, PA; Band; Chess C; Ensm; Mem Band A.

BROWNS, Rose Marie
Payette HS; Payette, ID (15-110) Ann; Bus C; Hmrm; Yth Leg; Pres, Job's Daughters; Drill Tm; NIKE; *Ottowa U; Acct.*

BROWNSELL, Susann Valerie
Town of Webb Sch; Old Forge, NY (3-54) Chor; Fr C; GS; Mgr, Bkbl; Cr-Ctry; Regent Schol; Yth Fel; Fr A; *N Co Comm Col; Bus Adm.*

BROWNSON, Laura Gen
Montclair Col Prep Sch; Van Nuys, CA; Span C; Secy, Jr Cl; Alg A; HQn; Hon Prog; *Dental Hygiene.*

BROXTON, Andrea
New Brockton HS; New Brockton, AL (10-60) BC; JV, Chldr; Drama; FBLA; FHA; 4H; Spch C; VP, SC; Hon Prog; *Ringling Col; Art.*

BROYLES, David Eugene
Narrows HS; Norrows, VA (7-111) *Maryville Col; Bachelor of Arts.*

BROYLES, Janis Gay
Lawrence HS; Lawrence, KS (93-530) Cpt, Chldr; GS; Hmrm; SC; Sftbl; Tr; HQn; Co- cpt, Chldr; *U of Kans; Elem Ed.*

BROYLES, Marilyn Kay
Hale Pub R-1 HS; Hale, MO (33%-16) Chor; Ensm; Pres, 4H; NFL; Var C; Bkbl; Sftbl; Beauty; COM; 4H A; Type A.

BROZ, Debra Ann
Paint Rock Ind HS; Paint Rock, TX (4-12) Ed, Ann; BC; Chldr; Pres, FHA; S-T, 4H; NHS; Tres, SC; Pres, Soph Cl; Cpt, Bkbl; Cl Fav; 4H A; HQn.

BRUBAKER, Denise Lynne
Ridgway Area HS; Ridgway, PA (10-207) A-Ed, Ann; Band; Fr C; Var C; God & Country A; MVP, Gym; *Clarion Col; Sci.*

BRUBAKER, Ruth
Nogales HS; Nogales, AZ (12-241) Band; Cpt, Chldr; GS; Pres, Model UN; VP, NHS; Semi-Fin, Ntl Teache; ARCCoun; Rptr, Sch P; Sci C; Pres, SC; Tres, Jr Cl; Chem A; Citz A; Hon Prog; Ntl Conf Chr & Jews; Sci A; VofDEM; Secy, Mat Maid; Prom Court; Eng A; Gym; Zont A Girl; Ability Courts; *U of Ariz; Spch Pathology.*

BRUBAKER, Steve Eric
Garden Spot HS; New Holland, PA (30-292) Band; Tnns; *Math.*

BRUCE, Cynthia Ann
Glendale HS; Springfield, MO (20-415) AFS; Band; Chor; Drama; Ensm; Sftbl; Tr; COM; Elk A; Hist A; Hon Prog; Eng A; Cert of Schol Achv; *Mus.*

BRUCE, George Andrew
Hubbard HS; Hubbard, OH (10%-360) VP, A Cap Choir; AFS; Band; Chor; Lat C; Tres, SC; Thes; Hon Prog; Hon Men, St Schol Achv Tests; *Med.*

BRUCE, Gerald Kevin
Littleton HS; Littleton, CO (25-550) Band; Cpt, Cr-Ctry; Tr; JV, Wrest; Alg A; *Denver U; Computer Sci.*

BRUCE, Julie Ann
Broadmoor HS; Baton Rouge, LA; Chor; Tres, 4H; ARC; VP, Y-Tns; Sftbl; 4H A; ARC A; Bible Quiz Tm; Secy; *Southwestern Bible Col.*

BRUCE, Mike W
Hopkinsville HS; Hopkinsville, KY; FFA; Pres, 4H; Parl, Key C; SC; Ftbl; Citz A; 4H A; Spch A; FFA A; Co- op A; Weightlifting A; *Murray Col; Agr.*

BRUCE, Robert Edward
Lee's Summit Sr HS; Lee's Summit, MO (77-489) Hmrm; NHS; Bsbl; JV, Bkbl; Ftbl; JV, Golf; Amer Leg A; Opt A; Opt Out Tn; Tres, FCA; *Kans U; Pre-Med.*

BRUCE, Robert Hall
Allen HS; Allen, TX (8-65) Order / Arrow; Spch C; Tr; Order / Arrow A; Hon Tr; *US Military Acad; Engr.*

BRUCE, Sandra Nelson
Hopkinsville HS; Hopkinsville, KY (52-300) FHA; Hmrm; Rainbow; Tnns; Spch A; WW; *Hopkinsville Comm Col.*

BRUCE, Steve Alan
Santa Monica HS; Santa Monica, CA; Band; Chor; Ski C; Sftbl; Swim; *Santa Monica Col; Mus.*

BRUCOLI, Vicki Jean
Hubbard HS; Hubbard, OH (75-335) VP, A Cap Choir; AFS; Band; Chor; Lat C; Span C; VP, SC; Secy, Thes; Tri-HiY; Golf; Type A; Shorthand Speed A; 3rd Pl Typing, Yngstwn Col of Bus; *Findlay Col; Legal Secy.*

BRUDI, Lisa Ann
Mark Morris HS; Longview, WA; Chor; NHS; Orch; Ski C; Mgr, Tr; Type A; GSct Wider Opportunity; *Secy.*

BRUDOS, Daniel Timothy
Schalmont HS; Schenectady, NY (33%-240) Chor; Drama; Sr Patrol Adr, BScts; *Bio.*

BRUECHERT, Beverly Ann
W Linn HS; W Linn, OR (5%-300) Ann; Band; Chor; Ensm; 4H; NHS; Secy, Rainbow; SC; Soccer; COM; 4H A; Powderpuff Ftbl; Spelling, Sewing, Mus, A's; Most Friendly; *U of GSct Calif; Mus.*

BRUEGGEMAN, Clay Dwayne
Roxana HS; E Alton, IL (139-251) Var C; Bsbl; Ftbl; Wrest.

BRUEN, Helynne Eileen
St Mary's Regional HS; Lynn, MA (11-117) Chor; Drama; Hmrm; NHS; Sch P; Sci C; Co-Cpt, Bkbl; Co-Cpt, Hockey; Co-Cpt, Sftbl; Alg A; Bio A; Math A; Sci A; Miss Lynn HS; Theilhard de Chardin, Eng, Fr, A's; *Colby Col.*

BRUENER, Cindy Diane
Lake Placid HS; Lake Placid, FL (6-160) Band; Bus Mgr, CYO; VP, 4H; Key C; NHS; SC; 4H A; Pres A; Secy, 4 H C; *Sci.*

BRUENING, Brian James
Goddard HS; Roswell, NM (1-310) Pres, Chor; Pres, Demolay; Pres, Ensm; Hmrm; NHS; Sci C; Ski C; SC; Rotary A; Type A; Val; Yth Fel; Outst Chor Boy; Hon Stu; *UNM; Sci.*

BRUENING, Jill Elaine
Edgewood Sr HS; Ashtabula, OH (15-235) AFS; Secy, Chor; Drama; Fr C; NHS; Rptr, Sch P; Thes; Y-Tns; Bkbl; COM; Citz A; Gym; Pres, Yth Fellowship; *Asbury Col; Phys Ed.*

BRUESKE, Stephen Layton
Southwest Sr HS; Minneapolis, MN; Band; JV, Bsbl; JV, Bkbl.

BRUESS, Richard Dean
Heidelberg American HS; Heidelberg, GERMANY (2-170) NHS; Bsbl; Bkbl; Alg A; Math A; *U of Idaho; Vet Med.*

BRUESS, Tracy Kay
Heidelberg American HS; Heidelberg, GERMANY; InterClub Coun; VP, Lat C; Alg A; Cum Laude A; Acad As; Jr Classical League; Lat Grammar, Lat Verse; *Denver U; Pre-Med.*

BRUESSEL, Bradley Walter
Bowman HS; Canyon Country, CA; *Agr.*

BRUINS, Janese Lynn
West Ottawa HS; Holland, MI (1-395) Band; JV, Dbte Tm; Ensm; 4H; Tr; COM; Coun of Teach A; 4H A; JV, Vlbl; St Win for Art in Tn Talents; Ntl Comp Span o-t Am As of Tchrs; *Lee Col.*

BRUINSMA, Eugene Richard
Castlewood Independent HS; Castlewood, SD (7-23) Ann; Semi-Fin, BS; VP, Sr Cl; VP, Soph Cl; Bsbl; Bkbl; Ftbl; Tr; HCt; Pres A; WW; *SD St U.*

BRUM, Cathleen Anne
Dublin HS; Dublin, CA; F-Ed, Ann; Chldr; 4H; SC; Bank Of Amer A; Cl Fav; Swtht; Co-Ch, Sr Ball; Amer Cancer Soc; Blood Drive Committee; Jr Prom Committee; *Chabot Col; Art.*

BRUMBACK, Robin Coe
Clarke Co HS; Berryville, VA (1-101) Pres, FHA; GS; Pres, 4H; VP, Lat C; Rptr, NHS; F-Ed, Sch P; Pres, Tri-HiY; Pres, Jr Cl; Citz A; DARGCA; 4H A; Hist A; I Dare You; Most Out; Pres A; Val; Qn, 4-H; WW; *Va Polytechnic Inst; Home Ec.*

BRUMBELOE, Sharon Doreen
Pleasant Grove HS; Pleasant Grove, AL (2-145) Band; FTA; Fin, Jr Miss Pagent; NHS; Beauty; COM; Citz A; Coun of Teach A; Hon Prog; Most Out; NEDT; Star Student; AMTA A; *Judson Col; Ed.*

BRUMETT, Thomas Owen
MacArthur HS; Irving, TX; Order / Arrow; Cr-Ctry; Tr; Life Sct.

BRUMLEY, Amanda Sue
Stranahan HS; Fort Lauderdale, FL (14-475) Anchor C; Band; Hmrm; NHS; SC; Top 5%; SC Girl o-t Yr; *Baylor U.*

BRUMLEY, Billy Joe
Lawrence HS; Lawrence, KS (264-668) Dbte Tm; Bsbl; Ftbl; Debate Tm Shawnee-Mission E Jr Div; *Kans U; Bus.*

BRUMLEY, Janet Denise
Olathe HS; Olathe, KS; Journ A; Yth Fel; Cpt, Yth For Christ C; Ntl Guild A; Runner Up, YFC Qn.

BRUMLIC, Mark William
Shawano HS; Shawano, WI; Ski C; Var C; Mgr, Ftbl; Tnns; Wrest.

BRUMM, Diana Lynn
Olympus HS; Salt Lake City, UT (10-400) Band; Ensm; Tres, Fr C; NHS; COM; Hist A; Hon Prog; *Utah St U; Math.*

BRUMM, Michele Ann
Olympus HS; Salt Lake City, UT; Band; Chor; Hon Prog; Secy, Lutheran Yth.

BRUMMA, Sheryl Ann
Xenia HS; Xenia, OH; Academic A; Scholastic A.

BRUMMETT, Donena
Sahvaro HS; Tucson, AZ; Tnns; Varsity Ltr, Tnns; Med.

BRUMMETT, Timothy Ray
Raymore-Peculiar HS; Peculiar, MO (33%-146) Chor; NHS; MVP, Bkbl; Regent Schol; Bkbl Hons; 1st Tm, All Conf, All District; *Central Methodist Col; Psych.*

BRUMMITT, Cynthia Lynn
Foothills Christian Heritage Sch; Montrose, CO (1-9) Ann; Chldr; Chor; Drama; S-T, NHS; Rptr, Sch P; VP, SC; Tr; Citz A; God & Country A; Hist A; Journ A; Swtht; Type A; Shorthand A; Essay A.

BRUMMITT, Joseph Franklin
Foothills Christian Heritage Sch; Montrose, CO (1-5) F-Ed, Ann; Chor; Drama; FBLA; FFA; Rptr, NHS; Sch P; Spch C; Pres, SC; S-T, Var C; Pres, Sr Cl; VP, Jr Cl; Bsbl; Cpt, Bkbl; Cpt, Ftbl; Tr; Alg A; Citz A; God & Country A; HCt; Most Out; Spch A; Type A; Val; Shorthand A; *Baptist Bible Col; Theology.*

BRUMMOND, Greg Allen
Clay Center Pub HS; Clay Center, NE (6-33) Ann; Band; Chor; NHS; VP, SC; Var C; Pres, Jr Cl; Bsbl; Bkbl; Ftbl; Hist A; Pres A; Yth Fel; Bkbl & Ftbl Varsity Ltrs; *U of Nebr; Engr.*

BRUMOND, Greg Allen
Clay Center Pub HS; Clay Center, NE (6-32) Band; Chor; Drama; NHS; VP, SC; Var C; Pres, Jr Cl; Bsbl; Bkbl; Ftbl; Hist A; Pres A; Yth Fel; HR; Var Ltr, Ftbl & Bkbl; *U of Nebr; Engr.*

BRUMOND, Laurel Lee
Clay Center Pub HS; Clay Center, NE (10-32) Ann; Band; Drama; NHS; Y-Tns; Sftbl; Tr; HQn; Yth Fel; All Amer Vlbl; *Acct.*

BRUNDEEN, Laura Faye
Alta Comm Sch; Alta, IA (10%-68) Co-Ed, Ann; Band; Ensm; Orch; Sch P; JV, Bkbl; Sftbl; Vlbl; Stu Director, Play; *Nurs.*

BRUNE, Barbara Alice
Palm Springs HS; Palm Springs, CA (11-550) FFA; Masonic A; Job's Daughters; Tres, Church Yth Group; FFA Cert; Ceramic A of Excellence; *Botany.*

BRUNER, Everett Lynor
John Marshall HS; Oklahoma City, OK (11-80) 4H; NHS; SC; Drafting A; *Central St U; Med.*

BRUNER, Paula Joan
Ladysmith-Hawkins HS; Ladysmith, WI (11-134) Ann; Band; FHA; NHS; VP, Sr Cl; VP, Jr Cl; Co-Cpt, Bkbl; Tr; Hon Prog.

BRUNER, Wanda Gail
Cottonwood HS; Cottonwood, AL (10-65) Band; JV, Chldr; FHA; 4H; Sci C; Sci A; Type A; *Troy St U; Children's Ed.*

BRUNETTI, Anthony Joseph
Milford HS; Milford, MI; Dbte Tm; Model UN; Sci A; *Oakland Comm Col; Computer Tech.*

BRUNGARDT, Julia Michelle
A A Stagg Sr HS; Stockton, CA; Co-Ed, Lit Mag; A-Ed, Sch P; *Delta Col; Psych.*

BRUNING, Burton Lewis
Wesleyan Acad; Guaynabo, PR (9-29) NHS; Ftbl; JV, Tr; Wrest; *Med.*

BRUNKER, Steven Adam
Strongsville Sr HS; Strongsville, OH (32-474) Band; NHS; Phys C; COM; Fin, Fr Declaration Contest; *Elec Engr.*

BRUNNER, Belinda Kay
Flatonia HS; Flatonia, TX (2-38) Co-Ed, Ann; Band; Dbte Tm; VP, FHA; Mjrte; Rptr, Sch P; B Crocker A; WW; *Sam Houston St U.*

BRUNNER, Linda Jean
Iver C Ranum HS; Westminster, CO; Band; Chor; Fr C; Soccer; Sftbl; Tr; COM; Citz A; Cl Fav; A of Distinction; *Mus.*

BRUNNER, Scott Davis
Clear Creek HS; League City, TX (1-450) BS; VP, Drama; Pres, NHS; Order/Arrow; Ski C; Thes; Golf; Swim; DARGCA; Val; St Water Polo Championship Tm; Best Actor; DAR Bicen Essay Cont Win, Hon Men; *U of Calif at Irvine; Biological Sci.*

BRUNO, James Joseph
Toms River HS S; Toms River, NJ; Fr C; 4H; Model UN; JV, Soccer; JV, Tr; Pres A; Yth Fel; BSct; Walk for Mankind; Ch, Traffic Directory.

BRUNO, Julie Lee
Warren Area HS; Warren, PA (10%-435) Mjrte; Sch P; Span C; MLS; Most Out; Ntl Jr Hon Soc; *Med Tech.*

BRUNS, Angela Devon
Freedom HS; Morganton, NC (9-500) A Cap Choir; Ed, Ann; Chor; Ger C; NHS; HCt; *U of NC; Mus.*

BRUNS, Jon
St Charles HS; St Charles, MO (27-381) Hockey; Citz A.

BRUNS, Kristi Jean
Brookings HS; Brookings, SD (39-213) VP, 4H; Orch; Citz A; 4H A; Young Artist A; Candystriper A; President's Phys Fitness A; *SD St U; Nurs.*

BRUNS, Richard A
Elder HS; Cincinnati, OH (200-400) Wrest; JA A; VP, JA; CCD, Sr Williams; *UC at Ocas; Elec Engr.*

BRUNSON, Antoinette Jeanne
Lafayette HS; Brooklyn, NY; Chor; Drama; ARC; Var C; Bkbl; Tnns; Alg A; Hist A; Math A; Type A; *Acct.*

BRUNSON, Christina Annette
Duke Ellington Sch of the Arts; Washington, DC (36-147) A Cap Choir; Ed, Ann; Co-Ch, Chor; Cpt, Hmrm; Ed, Lit Mag; Ch, Madrigal; Ed, Sch P; Tres, SC; Sftbl; JA A; NMF; Jr Executive A, JA; Semi-Fin, Tres o-t Yr, JA; Fin, Ntl Merit Achv Outst Black Stu; *The Cath U of Amer; Vocal Mus.*

BRUNSON, Joan Lynn
Benson Union HS; Benson, AZ (18-83) Ann; Band; VP, FHA; Cpt, Mjrte; Sch P; JV, Bkbl; Yth Fel; Pres, Yth Fel; *Grand Canyon Col; Training & Development.*

BRUNSON, Rhonda Kay
Spring Vale Acad; Owosso, MI; Ann; Band; Chor; 4H; NHS; ARC; Mgr, Bkbl; Tnns; Tr; Citz A; 4H A; Hon Prog; Sci A; *Social Worker.*

BRUNSON, Vanessa LaDiedra
William H Taft HS; Bronx, NY; Hmrm; SC; Mgr, Sftbl; COM; Director of Communications, SC; SC A; *Syracuse U; Marketing Mgt.*

BRUNSWICK, Donna Michelle
William M Baines HS; Jacksonville, FL; Band; Fin, Jr Miss Pagent; Cpt, Mjrte; SC; Up Bound; Miss William M Raines; Miss Congeniality; Most Talented; *Fla A&M U; Drama.*

BRUNSWIG, Althea Rose
Haigler HS; Haigler, NE (1-11) Chldr; Chor; Drama; Ensm; FHA; 4H; Mgr, Bkbl; Alg A; Bio A; Cl Fav; Hon Prog; Math A; Type A; Vlbl; Mus A; *Bethany Col; Bus.*

BRUSE, Robbin Michele
Brown HS; Sturgis, SD; Hmrm; SC; *Bridal Coun.*

BRUSH, Anne Louise
Fort Hunt HS; Alexandria, VA (93-446) Chor; Drama; Ger C; Lit Mag; Hockey; Pres, Sr High Church Fel; Ger Hon Soc; *VPI; Elem Ed.*

BRUSS, Clarice Renee
Crystal City HS; Crystal City, MO (2-92) Ann; VP, Band; Dbte Tm; Ensm; Hmrm; Tres, NHS; Sch P; S-T, Span C; VP, SC; HCt; Math A; Most Out; Sal; Cpt, Pom Pon; Parent-Teacher A; Jeffo Col Salutorian Schol; Rotary Stu o-t Mo; Mus C A; *Central Methodist Col; Math.*

BRUSSEE, Laura Lee
Sheridan HS; Thornville, OH (22-188) Band; Chor; 4H; NHS; Var C; Bkbl; Sftbl; Tr; *Eastern Ky U; Acct.*

BRUTON, Coary Lynn
Palmer HS; Palmer, TX (7-40) Drama; FFA; Bsbl; Ftbl; Tr; Hist A.

BRUX, Kristina Mary
Kaukauna HS; Kaukauna, WI (61-364) Pres, Band; Drama; Ensm; Pres, FNA; Orch; Spch A; Mus As; Vol o-t Yr; Stu o-t Month; *Marquette U; Nurs.*

BRYAN, Charles Alan
Wayne Co Day Sch; Goldsboro, NC (1-33) NHS; SC; Pres, Jr Cl; Bsbl; Bkbl; MVP, Ftbl; COM; Gr Marshal; NEDT; Opt A; Yth Fel; Math Tm.

BRYAN, Christi Lynn
Boyd Co HS; Ashland, KY; Band; BC; Pres, FBLA; Jr Miss Pagent; Mjrte; Ntl Teachers Coun; Sch P; Span C; SC; Marshall U Schol; Mjrte, E Ky U; *E Ky U.*

BRYAN, Clay Tod
Renville Pub HS; Renville, MN (33-45) Arch; Chor; FFA; Ger C; Pres, Hmrm; VP, SC; Var C; Pres, Soph Cl; Arch; Sftbl; Fin, Tr; Fin, Wrest; COM; Pres A; Star Student; Semi-Fin, Wrest; 4th, St Jr Olympics; Dist, Regional, Wrest; Stu o-t Mo; *Willmar Voc Col; Tech Drafting.*

BRYAN, Elizabeth Jayne
Walker HS; Jasper, AL (10%-300) Band; Chor; Drama; Ensm; FHA; InterAct C; Pres, Soph Cl; HCt; Hon Prog; *U of Montevallo; Mus.*

BRYAN, Francine
Savannah HS; Savannah, GA (30-100) Chor; FHA; 4H; SC; Chapter, Jr, St Degrees, FHA; *Savannah St Col; Special Ed.*

BRYAN, Greg Sherman
Cashmere HS; Cashmere, WA; FFA; Ftbl; JV, Golf; JV, Wrest; FFA A's.

BRYAN, Harry Woodward Jr
Walker HS; Jasper, AL (150-300) Band; VP, 4H; MVP, Bsbl; Bkbl; 4H A; *Walker Jr Col; Landscaping.*

BRYAN, John Michael
Foley HS; Foley, AL (30-250) Chor; Ensm; Opt Out Tn; Huntingdon Schol A; 1st Pl, Kiwanis Talent Show; *Huntingdon Col; Mus.*

BRYAN, Karen Dawn
Starmount HS; Boonville, NC (7-151) FHA; Lit Mag; NHS; Secy, Span C; Gr Marshal; Nom, Morehead Schol; Nom, Peace Col Schol; Pep C; Health Careers C; GAA; *UNC; Med Tech.*

BRYAN, Kathy Denise
Celina Sr HS; Celina, OH (25-275) A Cap Choir; Chor; Ensm; FBLA; FTA; Tres, Ger C; Pres, 4H; Secy, NHS; Tr; 4H A; Type A; Vlbl; Shorthand, Acct, A's.

BRYAN, Kim Denise
White Salmon Christian Sch; White Salmon, WA; Cpt, Vlbl; Miss Ath; *Judson Baptist Col.*

BRYAN, Leslie Jane
Winter Haven HS; Winter Haven, FL; Ger C; NHS; SC; Beauty; DARGCA; Tn Board; Sr GSct; Bicycle Court; Ballet Schol; Cpt, Co-Cpt, Drill Tm; *U of NC; Lang.*

BRYAN, Lori Anne
Longmont HS; Longmont, CO; Band; Secy, 4H; 4H A; Earth C; FCA; *Colo St U; Med.*

BRYAN, Mary Linda
Wall HS; Wall, TX (6-42) Band; Chor; FHA; Math C; Secy, NHS; Rainbow; JV, Bkbl; Tr; Type A; All Star Cast; WW; *Drama.*

BRYAN, Nancy Ann
Glenwood HS; Phenix City, AL (10%-75) Band; BC; Chor; Hmrm; Mjrte; SC; Cl Fav; HCt; Hon Prog; Schol A; *Auburn U; Lab Tech.*

BRYAN, Pamela Sue
E L Bowsher HS; Toledo, OH (29-472) Bus C; Hon Prog; Bstr C; Pres, Acteens; Yth Coun; *Bus.*

BRYAN, Silvia Lea
Garfield HS; Akron, OH (13-500) Community Yth Symph; NHS; Orch; Most Out; VofDEM; Ldrship of Tomorrow A; *U of Akron; Mus.*

BRYAN, Tamara Leigh
W Craven HS; Vanceboro, NC (5-160) Drama; Hmrm; F-Ed, Lit Mag; Monogram; NHS; Tres, Sci C; Span C; SC; Tnns; MVP, Tr; Span A; Jr Civitan C; Bronze Med, 220 Yd Dash Conf Meet; *NC St U; Pulp & Paper Tech.*

BRYAN, Vicki Lynn
E L Bowsher HS; Toledo, OH (160-405) FHA; Pres, Acteens; Pres, Yth Coun; DECA; *U of Montevallo; Social Work.*

BRYANT, Alita Marie
Merced HS N; Merced, CA; Spch A; Yth Fel; Calif Baptist St Yth Conv; *Linfield HS; Dietary Sci.*

BRYANT, Allen Sidney
Cairo HS; Cairo, GA (13-250) Tres, BC; 4H; HiY; InterAct C; SC; Tri-HiY; Bsbl; Bkbl; JV, Ftbl; COM; Citz A; 4H A; Hon Prog; MLS; Most Out; Sci A; Yth Fel; Asst Superintendent, Church Sch; Church Usher; Scholastic HR; Finance & Budget Comm, Church; Dance Capades; Yth o-t Yr; *U of Ga; Psychiatric Med.*

BRYANT, Amy Marie
Groves HS; Garden City, GA (21-215) Secy, Anchor C; Ann; BC; CYO; Chor; Ensm; Hmrm; Math C; NHS; Pres, Sci C; Pres, SC; COM; K of C A; NEDT; *U of Ga; Med.*

BRYANT, Brandon Ray
W Rome HS; Rome, GA; Var C; Wrest.

BRYANT, Brigitte Venita
Jefferson HS; Tampa, FL (20%-650) JV, Chldr; *Fla St U; Med Tech.*

BRYANT, D Gordon Jr
Cedar Hill HS; Cedar Hill, TX (5-90) NHS; JV, Ftbl; Golf; 1st, JV Slide Rule; *E Tex St U; Computers.*

BRYANT, Darell Anthony
Kingsbury HS; Memphis, TN; Ann; Fr C; Inter-Club Coun; Lit Ral; Spch C; SC; Thes; Jr NHS; *Memphis St U; Theatre Arts.*

BRYANT, David Andrew
Granite City HS S; Granite City, IL; Band; 4H; Eagle Sct; 1st Pl, Band Contest As.

BRYANT, Dennis Jay
Moulton-Udell Comm Sch; Moulton, IA (15%-45) Chor; Rptr, FFA; VP, 4H; NHS; Co-Ed, Sch P; Co-Cpt, Wrest; 4H A; Type A; Yth Fel; WW; FFA Pub Speaking Gold; Dekalb A, Outst Stu; *Lincoln Tech Inst; Mech.*

BRYANT, Earnest Jr
Middleton HS; Charleston, SC (86-295) 4H; Bsbl; Math A; Yth Fel; *Spartanburg Methodist Col; Elec Engr.*

BRYANT, Gary Alvin
Tabernacle Baptist Sch; Va Beach, VA (3-13) Ed, Ann; Chor; Drama; Spch C; Var C; Pres, Sr Cl; VP, Jr Cl; VP, Soph Cl; Cpt, Bkbl; Soccer; Sftbl; Tr; COM; Spch A; Yrbk & Bkbl Achv A's; *Bob Jones U; Ed Adm.*

BRYANT, George Thompson
Spartanburg HS; Spartanburg, SC (75-900) Chess C; 700 Schol; *Wofford Col; Bio-Chem Research.*

BRYANT, Gerald Cass
McClymonds HS; Oakland, CA; Pres, Band; VP, Bus C; Pres, City Conf; Community Yth Symph; Drama; Pres, FBLA; Pres, Hmrm; Pres, InterClub Coun; Bus Mgr, Lit Mag; Pres, Orch; Pres, Pol Sci C; Pres, SC; Thes; Var C; Cr-Ctry; Ftbl; Cpt, Golf; Tr; *UC at Davis; Law.*

BRYANT, Gregory Alan
Lutheran HS S; St Louis, MO (26-158) A Cap Choir; Ed, Ann; Chor; NHS; Rptr, Sch P; Ftbl; Tr; Journ A; Pres, Fresh Cl; Pres, Yth Group; *Journ.*

BRYANT, Jeffrey Martin
McMinn Co HS; Athens, TN (4-94) Band; Chor; Hmrm; Order/Arrow; SC; God & Country A; Opt A; Pres A; Jr NHS; Pres, Fresh Cl; Eagle Sct; Pres, Pep C; *U of Tenn; Engr.*

BRYANT, Jennifer Elizabeth
Kentridge HS; Kent, WA (25%-500) Orch; Mgr, Tr; Musical; Sun Sch Teacher; Yth Rep, Ed Board Comm; Girls Hon; *U of Wash; Marine Bio.*

BRYANT, Joy Lynne
Fountain Lake HS; Hot Springs, AR; Ann; BC; Drama; FHA; VP, 4H; Thes; Bkbl; 4H A; Library A; FHA A; *Criminology.*

BRYANT, Karen Diane
Rufus King HS; Milwaukee, WI; Fr C; Hmrm; JETS; Math C; NHS; Secy, Y-Tns; COM; JA A; Math A; Most Out; Most Intellectual; *Ill Inst of Tech; Mech Engr.*

BRYANT, Karla Jean
Eastmont Sr HS; E Wenatchee, WA (20%-250) Ann; Hmrm; NHS; SC; JV, Tnns; Tr; Hon Prog; Pres A; Secy, Pep C; Girl o-t Mo; Drill Tm; Sr Ball Qn; Sports Ltrs; Girls League; Gym; *Wenatchee Valley Jr Col; Child Development.*

BRYANT, Kathi Dean
Woodland Hills Baptist Acad; Jackson, MS (50%-55) Ann; Drama; Sch P; Bkbl; Ftbl; Beauty; Yth Fel; Drill Tm A; Miss Miss Tn Pageant; Co-Cpt, Drill Tm; HR; Fashion Tn Board; WW.

BRYANT, Kimberly Lynn
T R Miller HS; Brewton, AL (27-101) Band; Chess C; FBLA; FHA; FTA; A-Ed, Lit Mag; Math C; A-Ed, Sch P; Pres, Sci C; Tnns; 4H A; *Auburn U; Engr.*

BRYANT, Lee Ann
Lord Botetourt HS; Daleville, VA (20%-173) A Cap Choir; F-Ed, Ann; Band; VP, Chor; Ensm; FBLA; 4H; Key C; Tr; Mus A; *Va Western Comm Col; Nurs.*

BRYANT, Lisa Camille
Walnut Hills HS; Cincinnati, OH; A Cap Choir; Chor; Fr C; Hmrm; Lat C; SC; Bkbl; Hon Prog; Columnist & Rptr, Yth Paper; VAST Tutor; Art, Schol, A's; HR; 1st Pl, Singing Group in St; *International Stu.*

BRYANT, Lori Anne
Lyons Township HS; LaGrange, IL (90%-1300) AFS; Community Yth Symph; Math C; NHS; Orch; Mgr, Bkbl; Swim; NMS; St Scholar; *Augustana Col; Special Ed.*

BRYANT, Lynette Angela
Alain Leroy Locke HS; Los Angeles, CA; Pres, FTA; GS; Lit Mag; NHS; Span C; *Trade Tech Col; Bus.*

BRYANT, Marsha Carol
Germantown HS; Germantown, TN (20-500) BC; Chem C; Fr C; GS; Hmrm; Rptr, Lit Mag; Math C; NHS; Sch P; SC; Fr A; WW; *U of Tenn; Church Organ.*

BRYANT, Michael Douglas
Lord Botetourt HS; Daleville, VA; All Amer Yth; Var C; Bsbl; Ftbl; All Metro, Ftbl; *Emory & Henry Col; Ath.*

BRYANT, Mills Robert
Southampton Acad; Courtland, VA (2-35) Ann; BC; Lit Mag; NFL; Co-Ed, Sch P; Span C; Var C; VP, Soph Cl; Bkbl; Mgr, Ftbl; COM; Citz A; Hon Prog; Sal; Yth Fel; Coun on Ministries; Forensics A; *Col of William & Mary; Law.*

BRYANT, Noralee
Washington HS; Kansas City, KS (85-595) Band; 4H; NHS; Cpt, Swim; 4H A; Yth Fitness Achv; *Kansas U; Recreation.*

BRYANT, Pamela Sue
Smackover HS; Smackover, AR (15-70) Band; Bus C; Drama; FBLA; FHA; FTA; Co-Cpt, Mjrte; Ed, Sch P; VP, Spch C; VP, Sr Cl; VP, Jr Cl; Tres, Soph Cl; Cl Fav; Journ A; Q&S A; ARC A; Fin, Beauty Pageant; Miss Congeniality; 1st Lt, Band; Most Talented; *Respiratory Therapy.*

BRYANT, Patricia Ann
Homer L Ferguson HS; Newport News, VA (3-500) AFS; Community Yth Symph; Ensm; Fr C; Hmrm; Parl, Key C; VP, NHS; Orch; VP, Sci C; Bio A; Chem A; Gov Honor Prog; Hon Prog; Lion A; Phy A; Sci A; VofDEM; WW; St Symph Orch; All St Symph Orch; Va Jr Acad of Sci; *Rice U; Math.*

BRYANT, Paula Nianne
Liberty Christian Sch; Durham, NC (3-9) Ann; Chor; Ensm; *Free Will Baptist Bible Col; Christian Ed.*

BRYANT, Randall Gordon
Cristobal HS; Coco Solo, CANAL ZONE; Ed, Ann; Chor; VP, Drama; Key C; NHS; Ed, Sch P; Span C; Pres, SC; Bkbl; Ftbl; Tr; Hon Prog; Book Quiz; *USC; Pre-Med.*

BRYANT, Rebecca Anne
Mountain Brook HS; Mountain Brook, AL; Chor; FHA; S-T, Lat C; Sci C; Pres, Secy & Chaplin, MYF; Adm Board; Del, N Ala UM Conf; Yth Coun; Med Explorer Post; Emmanuel Singers; *Sweet Briar Col; Psych.*

BRYANT, Robert Steven
Benton Sr HS; Benton, AR (30-350) Chor; Hmrm; Ftbl; Kiwanis A; Yth Fel; Yth Outreach Director; Yth Choir A's; Nom Committee.

BRYANT, Sharon Yvette
Windsor Forest HS; Savannah, GA; Band; Ger C; Hmrm; Bkbl; COM; Citz A; *Child Therapy.*

BRYANT, Shelia Elaine
McCurtain HS; McCurtain, OK (3-14) Chldr; 4H; Pres, Hmrm; NHS; SC; Pres, Sr Cl; VP, Jr Cl; Bkbl; Sftbl; Tr; 4H A; Hon Prog; Masonic A; Sal; WW; Pres Phys Fitness A; *Bus.*

BRYANT, Stephen Ralph
Dillon HS; Dillon, SC (8-33) Chor; Lat C; Var C; JV, Ftbl; Tnns; JV, Tr; Pres A; *Furman U; Wildlife & Forestry Cons.*

BRYANT, Sylvia Diane
E Atlanta HS; Atlanta, GA (10-142) Secy, Band; Secy, BC; Secy, FBLA; Hmrm; NHS; Span C; Hon Prog; Great Young Amer; Outst, Band; *Mercer U; Bus Ed.*

BRYANT, Terance G
Asbury Park HS; Asbury Park, NJ; Ger C; *Yale U; Law.*

BRYANT, Theresa Yolande
Merced Union HS; Merced, CA; Drama; JA A; Drama A; *San Francisco City Col; Journ.*

BRYANT, Thomas Earle
Berea HS; Greenville, SC (30-175) Bkbl; Ftbl; Tr; Math A; Pres A; *Furman Col; Acct.*

BRYANT, Thomas Edward
Elbert Co Comprehensive HS; Elberton, GA (1-262) A-Ed, Ann; Cpt, Band; VP, BC; VP, Fr C; Pres, HiY; Pres, Hmrm; VP, Math C; VP, Mod Mus Mas; VP, Mu Alpha Theta; Rptr, NHS; Pol Sci C; VP, Span C; Span NHS; St Stu Congress; SC; Rptr, Jr Cl; Alg A; Bio A; COM; Cl Fav; DARGCA; Gov Honor Prog; Hon Prog; Math A; NEDT; ROTC A; Sci A; Yth Leg; All St, Band Chor; Pres Classroom For Young Amer; John P Sousa, MVP, Bandsman; *U of Ga; Mus.*

BRYANT, Timothy
St Andrew Parish HS; Charleston, SC (50%-250) Chor; Soccer; Tr; Yth Fel; Jr Art Show; *Claflin Col; Commercial Arts.*

BRYCE, Craig Ridgeley
Howard D Woodson Sr HS; Washington, DC (20-600) *Howard U; Archt Drawing.*

BRYCE, Diane
Pima HS; Pima, AZ (1-39) Cpt, Chldr; FHA; Fin, GS; Hmrm; Model UN; Pres, NHS; F-Ed, Sch P; SC; Pres, Soph Cl; Sftbl; Co-Cpt, Tnns; COM; Cl Fav; Elk A; HCt; Hon Prog; MLS; Most Out; Val; MVP, Tnns & Vlbl; Cpt, Vlbl; *Phoenix Col; Dental Hygiene.*

BRYCE, Kevin Marshall
Brethren HS; Paramount, CA (21-88) A Cap Choir; Ensm; SC; Ftbl; Soccer; CSF; COM; Elk A; Hist A; *Long Beach City Col.*

BRYCE, Linda Beth
Pima Pub HS; Pima, AZ; JV, Chldr; Chor; FHA; Hmrm; SC; Mgr, Sftbl; Tnns; Math A; Sal; Sci A; Vlbl; Eng A; SC; *Eastern Ariz Col; Nurs.*

BRYCE, Rebecca J
Princeton HS; Princeton, NJ; Chor; Orch; SC; Pres, Yth Fellowship; Elder, Church; *Animal Sci.*

BRYMER, Charles Stephen
Van Buren Co HS; Spencer, TN; Rptr, BC; FFA; 4H; Mgr, Bkbl; Most Courteous; Most Studious; *Tenn Tech Tech U; Math.*

BRYMER, Lee Anne
Parkway Central Sr HS; Chesterfield, MO (40%-470) VP, Chor; Drama; GS; Madrigal; Yth Fel; Drill Tm; Ch, Govt Bond Campaign; *Baylor U.*

BRYNOFF, Steven Judon
Gateway HS; Aurora, CO (42-420) Lat C; Mu Alpha Theta; NHS; ARC; Elk A; *U of Colo; Sci.*

BRYSON, Myra Lee
Melville HS; Melville, LA (10-38) Rptr, BC; Co-Ch, Chldr; Co-Ch, SC; Tres, Sr Cl; Sftbl; COM; HQn; Sci A; Type A; *LSU; Home Ec.*

BRYSON, Shannon Anne
Richardson HS; Richardson, TX; AFS; Fr C; Tri-HiY; Hon Prog; 15th, Ntl Fr Exam; 1st Cooking; Guild Comp As; *La Sorbonne Col; Lang.*

BUBACH, Russell Leonard
Maddock Pub Sch; Maddock, ND (1-23) Band; SC; Var C; Bsbl; Cpt, Bkbl; Ftbl; Golf; Tr; NMS; Bkbl As; Tr A; *Jamestown Col; Bus.*

BUBIN, Jeffrey Patrick
Clearwater HS; Clearwater, FL; Demolay; Rptr, Sch P; Soccer; *U of Fla.*

BUCCI, Daniel
South Hills Catholic HS; Pittsburgh, PA (9-175) CYO; COM; Citz A; Hist A; Hon Prog; NEDT; *Duquesne U; Acct.*

BUCCINO, Barbara Jean
Copiague Sr HS; Copiague, NY (160-399) Chor; Hmrm; Sch P; SC; Hist A; Spch A; Type A; Hist, VICA; Soc Stu Off Asst; 2nd Pl, Parl Procedure Comp; Sr Play Sr Orphans Party; 2nd Pl, Beauty Culture Comp; *Bradley U; Social Worker.*

BUCHANAN, Ann
R H Watkins HS; Laurel, MS; DECA; *Jackson St U; Bus Adm.*

BUCHANAN, Berniece Jane
Jesup Comm HS; Jesup, IA (11-89) Ed, Ann; VP, Band; FHA; 4H; Hmrm; Mjrte; SC; Bkbl; WW; *Iowa St U; Child Development.*

BUCHANAN, Don Lamar Jr
Coronado HS; Lubbock, TX (158-604) Hon Graduate; Cpt, Rocker Tm; Color Guard; *Tex Tech; Elec Engr.*

BUCHANAN, Douglas Evan
Iroquois HS; Louisville, KY (202-466) Hmrm; F-Ed, Sch P; SC; Ftbl; Soccer; Sftbl; HCt; Rptr, Sch P; *Pol Sci.*

BUCHANAN, George Jr
Rayne HS; Rayne, LA; Band; Ensm; Bkbl; Sftbl; Swim; Superior & Excel A's; Mus; *U of SW La; Med.*

BUCHANAN, Jana Beth
Spearman HS; Spearman, TX; Ann; Band; FHA; FTA; Span C; Var C; Golf; Yth Fel; FCA; *Tex Tech U; Math.*

BUCHANAN, Janet Jonel
Saline HS; Saline, MI; Chor; Community Yth Symph; FHA; FTA; Jr Miss Pageant; Orch; Ski C; Sftbl; Wrestlerette; Voc Ward; *Washan Jr Col; Child Care.*

BUCHANAN, Jeff James
Centerville HS; Dayton, OH; Band; Ensm.

BUCHANAN, Lisa Gaye
Danville HS; Danville, IL; Chor; Tnns.

BUCHANAN, Michael Neal
McGavock HS; Donelson, TN (120-840) Band; BC; BS; Community Yth Symph; S-T, Lat C; NHS; Yth Fel; Blair Acad Mus Schol; *U of Tenn at Knox.*

BUCHANAN, Nancy Elizabeth
Bluestone Sr HS; Skipwith, VA (84-235) Ann; Band; Fr C; Hmrm; Co-Cpt, Mjrte; Monogram; Amer Cancer Sco; *Southside Comm Col.*

BUCHANAN, Neil Harold
Maumee HS; Maumee, OH (1-360) A-Ed, Ann; BS; VP, Dbte Tm; VP, Fr C; VP, NFL; NHS; COM; Harvard Book A; Hon Prog; Math A; NMF; NMS; Sci A; Spch A; Val; Exchange C A; Social Stu A; Fr A; *Vassar Col; Econ.*

BUCHANAN, Paula Kay
Reynolds HS; Greenville, PA (7-207) Chor; Drama; 4H; Thes; 4H A; Gym; *Slippery Rock Col; Bus.*

BUCHANAN, Phillip Lee
Shawnee HS; Shawnee, OK (100-300) Pres, CYO; Span C; Var C; Cpt, Cr-Ctry; Cpt, Tr; Masonic A; Yth Fel; MVP, Cr-Ctry & Tr; *Seminole Jr Col.*

BUCHBERGER, Kurt Joseph
Kaukauna HS; Kaukauna, WI (200-450).

BUCHECK, Delaine Annett
Cardinal Newman HS; W Palm Beach, FL; Pres, CYO; ARC; Math A; ARC A; Drama A; *Hist.*

BUCHELE, Paul Scott
Breckinridge Co HS; Harned, KY (1-200) Band; Fr C; Pres, Math C; Pres, Mu Alpha Theta; Pres, NHS; Sci C; COM; H of F; Hon Prog; Star Student; VP, Math C; HR; WW; *U of Ky; Civil Engr.*

BUCHER, Allyson Ann
Hamburg Sr HS; Hamburg, NY; Band; Chor; FNA; Lat C; Madrigal; NHS; Orch; Tnns; DARGCA; *Alfred U; Nurs.*

BUCHER, Amy Sue
Astoria HS; Astoria, IL; Band; NHS; Span C; Sftbl; Spoon River Jr Col; Acct.

BUCHER, Mark K
Lower Dauphin HS; Hummelstown, PA; Chor; VP, FFA; ROTC A; Superintendents A; FFA Citz; Chor A.

BUCHHEIM, Cathy Jean
Wolsey HS; Wolsey, SD (5-29) Ann; Rptr, FHA; Ger C; Sch P; VP, SC; Bkbl.

BUCHHEIM, Pamela Raye
Chester Area HS; Chester, SD (8-40) Chor; Drama; Mjrte; NHS; Tr; Alt, GS; Pres, VP, Yth C.

BUCHHEIT, Marion Anthony
Regis HS; Stayton, OR (3-60) Pres, 4H; NHS; JV, Bsbl; Ftbl; Tr; *Sci.*

BUCHHOLZ, Dawn Renae
Albert City-Truesdale Comm Sch; Albert City, IA (21-45) Co-Ed, Ann; Band; Drama; Pres, 4H; Spch C; Mgr, Bkbl; Citz A; Spch A; Ldrship A; *NW Col; Elem Ed.*

BUCHL, Stephanie Joan
Rock Lake Pub HS; Rock Lake, ND (2-24) Ed, Ann; Band; CYO; Chor; Drama; Ensm; Pres, 4H; Hmrm; Pres, NHS; Rptr, Sch P; S-T, SC; Co-Ch, Jr Cl; Secy, Soph Cl; Cpt, Bkbl; MVP, Tr; Sal; FHA Ct; *ND St U; Vet Sci.*

BUCHMANN, Tina Lavern
Riverdale HS; Riverdale, ND; Lib A; Pres, Church League; *Wapaton Col.*

BUCHOLZ, Larry
Rock Lake HS; Rock Lake, ND (10%-19) A-Ed, Ann; NHS; SC; Var C; Bsbl; Bkbl; Tr.

BUCHOLZ, Wesley John
Clintonville Sr HS; Clintonville, WI (33%-185) Band; NHS; Var C; Bsbl; JV, Bkbl; Cr-Ctry; Golf; Pres A; Yth Fel; *Fox Valley Tech Col; Acct.*

BUCK, Betsy Dolores
Portsmouth Christian HS; Portsmouth, VA (3-9) Ann; Cpt, Chldr; Chor; VP, Var C; Bkbl; Sftbl; COM; *Old Dominion U; Nurs.*

BUCK, Cheryl Lynn
Eufaula HS; Eufaula, OK; NHS; Var C; Bkbl; Tr; *E Central U; Bus.*

BUCK, Debra Lea
Portland Christian HS; Portland, OR (10-58) NHS; Star Student; *Oral Roberts U; Christian Ed.*

BUCK, Diane Kay
Mid-County Jr-Sr HS; Varna, IL; Band; Chor; Ensm; FHA.

BUCK, Evelyn Mildred
Liberty Central HS; Liberty, NY (40%-134) Mgr, Chldr; Chor; Bkbl; Soccer; Cpt, Tr; VofDEM; MVP, Tr; Pres, Getting It Together C; Art As; Ivan Richard Mem A; *SUNY at Oneonta; Bus Mgt.*

BUCK, Jenny
Vicksburg HS; Vicksburg, MS (4-250) A Cap Choir; AFS; Chldr; Chor; Tres, Drama; Ensm; GS; Key C; Lat C; NHS; Tres, SC; Bkbl; Tnns; Alg A; H of F; Most Versatile; Actress, Sch Mus; Sportsmanship A; Tnns; All Big Eight, Bkbl.

BUCK, John Bloodworth
Columbus HS; Columbus, GA; InterClub Coun; Pres, Math C; Ch, Model UN; Pres, Mu Alpha Theta; Pres, NHS; Ed, Sch P; Sci C; COM; Gov Honor Prog; JA A; Math A; Star Student; *U o-t S; Pol Sci.*

BUCK, Joni Jay
Junius H Rose HS; Greenville, NC (12-429) Anchor C; Ensm; Fr C; Fin, GS; Secy, Hmrm; Key C; Co-Ed, Lit Mag; Madrigal; NHS; Gr Marshal; HCt; Q&S A; WW; Distinguished Schol A; *St Andrews Presbyterian Col; Eng.*

BUCK, Kermit Alan
Eufaula HS; Eufaula, OK (10%-113).

BUCK, Lori Lee
Spencer HS; Spencer, IA (40-210) NHS; F-Ed, Sch P; Secy, Span C; Q&S A; Type A; Thespians; Candystriper; Sunday Sch Teacher; *St Lukes Sch of Nurs; Nurs.*

BUCK, Renae Jay
Ashley HS; Ashley, NC (12-43) A-Ed, Ann; Chor; VP, FHA; Sci C; VP, Jr Cl; Pres, Soph Cl; *Bismarck Jr Col; Bus.*

BUCK, Tamera Ruth
Portland Christian HS; Portland, OR; Band; *Eugene Bible Col; Christian Ed.*

BUCK, Tami Ruth
Evergreen HS; Vancouver, WA (20-48) Band; *Eugene Bible Col; Christian Ed.*

BUCKEY, Cheryl Ann
Ashtabula Harbor HS; Ashtabula, OH (11-187) AFS; Chor; Fr C; Pres, Math C; Pres, Sci C; Hon Prog; *Kent St U; Secy.*

BUCKHAM, Connie Rae
Wallace Sr HS; Wallace, ID (36-106) Bus Mgr, Ann; Chem C; Chor; Drama; FHA; FNA; Pres, Rainbow; ARC; Sch P; Ski C; Spch C; Bsbl; Tr; Pres A; ARC A; Pres, VICA; CIM A; Girl o-t Term; *N Idaho Col; Nurs.*

BUCKHOLT, Christine Ann
Charleroi Area HS; Charleroi, PA; *Robert Morris Col; Legal Secy.*

BUCKINGHAM, Bret Jeffery
John F Kennedy HS; Bloomington, MN (200-700) Yth Fel; *U of Minn; Sci.*

BUCKINGHAM, Dale Eugene
Parma Sr HS; Parma, OH (340-1009) Ski C; Var C; MVP, Cr-Ctry; MVP, Tr; *Bowling Green Col.*

BUCKINGHAM, Gary Allen
Eldorado HS; Albuquerque, NM (1-744) NHS; Secy, Span NHS; Lion A; NMF; NMS; Val; NJHS; *U of NM; Phys.*

BUCKINGHAM, Nancy Ann
Forest Ridge HS; Bellevue, WA (3-53) GS; NHS; SC; Pres, Jr Cl; Math A; *Brown U; Pol Sci.*

BUCKLER, Mary Anne
Marion Co HS; Lebanon, KY (15-298) CYO; Cpt, Chldr; FHA; 4H; Fin, Jr Miss Pagent; NHS; SC; Var C; Citz A; HCt; Most Talented; Sewing, Yth Fitness, A's; WW; *Sullivan Bus Col; Legal Secy.*

BUCKLER, Raymond Neil
Hebrew Acad HS; Yonkers, NY (2-16) Co-Cpt, Chess C; Co-Cpt, Math C; Co-Ed, Sch P; Bkbl; Tr; *Harvard U; Law.*

BUCKLES, Bryan Kieth
Acadiana HS; Lafayette, LA (10%-600) Band; Dbte Tm; NFL; Hon Prog; Opt A; *LSU; Pre-Law.*

BUCKLES, Kristi Rachelle
Stratford HS; Dallas, TX (30-65) FHA; Lat C; SC; JV, Bkbl; JV, Tnns; Superior, Jr Pianist Guild.

BUCKLES, Patty Kaye
Gordon HS; Gordon, NE (20-77) Ann; Band; Ch, Bus C; Chor; Drama; Ch, FBLA; FTA; Sch P; Ski C; Ch, SC; VP, Var C; VP, Soph Cl; MVP, Bsbl; Tnns; COM; Citz A; Most Out; Swtht; *Chadron St Col; Bio.*

BUCKLES, Samuel Brian
Sullivan Cent HS; Kingsport, TN (3-395) Band; BC; NHS; Order/Arrow; Span C; SC; MLS; Order/Arrow A; Eagle Sct; *Tenn Tech U; Chem Engr.*

BUCKLES, Steven Mark
Benton HS; St Joseph, MO (13-260) Chem C; City Conf; Hmrm; NHS; Sci C; Amer Leg A; Citz A; ROTC A; Outst Schol A's; ROTC A's; *Methodist Med Center; Radiological Tech.*

BUCKLEY, Carol Ann
Mercy HS; Albany, NY (2-115) Chldr; Chor; Fr C; Hmrm; NHS; Bio A; COM; Hon Prog; NEDT; Departmental Fr A; HS Schol; WW; *Law.*

BUCKLEY, David James
Western Beaver Jr Sr HS; Industry, PA (20%-163) Chor; NHS; SC; Bkbl; Ftbl; Tr; *Engr.*

BUCKLEY, Heidi Ann
Lyman HS; Lyman, WY (3-40) Chldr; Pres, Chor; Drama; VP, FHA; Tres, GS; Secy, 4H; Math C; SC; Bkbl; Tr; Alg A; Amer Leg A; 4H A; Hon Prog; I Dare You; Math A; MLS; Most Out; Phy A; Sci A; 4-HC A; Vice-Ch, St Fair Coun; Ntl 4-H C Congress; Top Dist Fair Sci A; *Nurs.*

BUCKLEY, John Thomas
Northgate HS; Walnut Creek, CA (25-500) JV, Bkbl; CSF; *U of Calif; Law.*

BUCKLEY, Michael Allen
David Anderson HS; Lisbon, OH (1-119) BS; Fr C; NHS; Sci C; JV, Bkbl; JV, Tr; Amer Leg A; Hist A; Hon Prog; Pres, Audio Visual; *Engr.*

BUCKLEY, Peter Louis
Point Pleasant Boro HS; Point Pleasant Boro, NJ; Soccer; PBA Hon A; Coun A.

BUCKLEY, Renata
Humboldt HS; Humboldt, TN; A Cap Choir; Chem C; Pres, Chor; Ensm; Ntl Yth Conf; PTA A; Sci A; Phys Ed, Mus, A's; *U of Tenn; Nurs.*

BUCKLEY, Sheri Cathleen
Franklin HS; Franklin, OH (12-273) Chor; Ensm; Secy, FTA; NHS; Tres, Sr Cl; Lion A; Swtht; WW; *Anderson Col; Hist Ed.*

BUCKMAN, Belinda Lee
Holy Rosary Acad; Louisville, KY (2-93) NHS; Pres, SC; Co-Cpt, Bkbl; Hockey; Tnns; Tr; Citz A; H of F; *U of Ky; Sci.*

BUCKNELL, Guy Greenslade II
Charles City HS; Charles City, IA (20%-250) Span C; Wrest; Pres, VP, S-T, Church Yth Fel; *Letourneau Col; Engr.*

BUCKNER, Benetia Sequendia
Central HS; Florence, AL (20-150) BC; Co-Ch, Chldr; FBLA; Cpt, 4H; Co-Cpt, Hmrm; SC; Tr; Fav; 4H A; Circuit Court Clerk, Gov Day; Mr & Mrs Central HS Court; *U of N Ala; Sci.*

BUCKNER, Brian Thomas
Daniel Boone HS; Jonesboro, TN (60-275) BC; Drama; 4H; Sci C; SC; Var C; Cr-Ctry; Tr; Bausch & Lomb A; All Conf, Tr; *Milligan Col; Bus Adm.*

BUCKNER, Ricky Lynn
Springville HS; Springville, AL (33%-30) Cpt, Band; Ed, BC; Pres, Community Yth; Drama; FFA; S-T, 4H; Pres, Hmrm; Rptr, Sch P; SC; Sftbl; Mgr, Tr; 4H A; Hon Prog; Spch A; Star Student; Yth Fel; Yth Leg; Yth Outst Choir Member; Drum Mjr; Livestock Judger; PA; *Jaxsonville St U; Mus.*

BUCKNER, Terri J
Papillion Sr HS; Papillion, NE (309-366) Chldr; FBLA; Span C; Modeling.

BUCY, Diane Carol
Arts Magnet HS; Dallas, TX (10%-50) Chor; Fr C; Hmrm; Tres, NHS; SC; Secy, Sr Cl; Bkbl; Sftbl; Tres, Drill Tm; Pres, Church Choir; *N Tex St U; Mus.*

BUDD, James Arnold
Stissing Mountain Jr-Sr HS; Pine Plains, NY; Pres, Chess C; Chor; Var C; Cpt, Bsbl; Cpt, Bkbl; Ftbl; MVP, Bsbl & Bkbl.

BUDD, Robin
Columbia HS; Richland, WA (15%-500) Ger C; Ski C; Arch; Swim; NMS; Ntl Guild Mus A; *U of Wash; Engr.*

BUDDE, Susan Geralyn
Central Comm HS; Breese, IL (7-157) Secy, CYO; Drama; Fr C; Mjrte; Math C; Alg A; Hon Prog; Math A; Most Out; Rptr, V-Ch, VP & Pres, FHA; Eng A; Seamtress A; *Kaskaskia Col; Home Ec.*

BUDEK, Marita Louise
Goodman-Armstrong HS; Goodman, WI (1-25) Bus Mgr, Ann; Bus Mgr, Band; Cpt, Chldr; Ed, Ensm; VP, NHS; NHS; Rptr, S-T, SC; Alg A; HCt; NMS; Sci A; 1st, St Band A; *U of Wis; Math.*

BUDENHOLZER, Theresa Ann
Holbrook HS; Holbrook, AZ (15-150) CYO; Cpt, Chldr; FHA; FTA; SC; Thes; Pres, Sr Cl; VP, Jr Cl; Pres, Soph Cl; MVP, Tr; Elk A; HQn; MVP, Vlbl & Gym; Outst Girl Ath A; Col Gen Resident Schol; Paulsell Mem Schol; Delta Kappa Gamma Schol; *U of Ariz; Ed.*

BUDENZ, Donald Lyle
Central Bucks W Sr HS; Doylestown, PA (1-520) Ann; Chor; Demolay; Drama; Ch, Hmrm; Madrigal; SC; Ftbl; Amer Leg A; Rotary A; Ordained Church Yth Deacon; Sch Bible C; *Oberlin Col; Psych.*

BUDKE, James William
Immaculata HS; Leavenworth, KS; A Cap Choir; Chor; *Pittsburg St U; Air-Conditioning.*

BUDZIAK, Judith Antoinette
Thomas Kelly HS; Chicago, IL (16-476) Secy, Chor; Drama; NHS; Secy, Sr Cl; Hon Prog; NEDT; St Scholar; *North Park Col; Law.*

BUECHLER, Daniel Eugene
United Comm HS; Boone, IA (5-41) Ann; Band; Pres, Chor; Pres, FFA; Pres, 4H; Madrigal; NHS; A-Ed, Sch P; Spch C; Pres, SC; Pres, Jr Cl; VP, Soph Cl; Tr; 4H A; Spch A; FFA A's; *Iowa St U; Agr Bus.*

BUEIOW, Colleen Rose
Hilbert HS; Hilbert, WI (5-80) Bkbl; Tr; Pres A.

BUEKER, Joyce Elaine
Midway HS; Waco, TX (25%-180) S-T, Chor; Ensm; Rptr, FTA; Secy, Mu Alpha Theta; NHS; Tres, Span C; JV, Bkbl; Tr; Beauty; Citz A; Type A; VP, Pep Squad; Silver & Gold Medals, Voice; Kiwanis Citizenship Seminar; Choirmus; *U of Houston; Psych.*

BUENING, Janet Marie
Coldwater HS; Coldwater, OH (6-169) Ann; Rptr, Band; Chem C; Chor; Drama; Ger C; Mjrte; NHS; Sch P; Bkbl; Swim; Tr; Amer Leg A; Hist A; Governor's Traffic Safety Comm; Vlbl; Pres YAC Girls; Church Choir; Church Commentator; CCD Teacher; *Wright St U; Sci.*

BUENTING, Jeffrey David
Rantoul Twp HS; Rantoul, IL; Bsbl; JV, Bkbl; Bus.

BUESCHER, Scott Alan
Chester HS; Chester, IL (14-98) Band; Sci C; Var C; Bkbl; Ftbl; Tr; Ladies C Schol, Band Camp; *SE Mo St U; Nurs.*

BUESCHER, Thomas Neil
Chester HS; Chester, IL (1-99) F-Ed, Ann; VP, Band; NHS; Sci C; Pres, SC; Var C; Pres, Sr Cl; Pres, Jr Cl; JV, Bkbl; Cr-Ctry; JV, Ftbl; Tr; Bausch & Lomb A; COM; DARGCA; Gr Marshal; Hon Prog; Journ A; Math A; MLS; NMS; Sci A; St Scholar; Val; Ned Carlton Schol; Sou Ill Soc of Achv; *Princeton U; Bio.*

BUETOW, Alexander Valentin
Battle Mountain HS; Minturn, CO (10-68) Ann; Bus C; CYO; VP, Chess C; Fin, FBLA; Model UN; Phys C; Sci C; Var C; Co-Cpt, Bkbl; Co-Cpt, Ftbl; Hockey; Soccer; Swim; Co-Cpt, Tr; COM; MVP, Bkbl; *U of Colo; Engr.*

BUETTNER, Jeff James
Holdrege HS; Holdrege, NE; CYO; JV, Bsbl; JV, Bkbl; JV, Ftbl; Type A; FCA.

BUFF, Leanne Denise
Hazen HS; Renton, WA (33%-476) Band; Co-Cpt, Bkbl; Sftbl.

BUFFINGTON, Barbara Kay
Valley HS; Albuquerque, NM; Lit Mag; Semi-Fin, Sftbl; Semi-Fin, Swim; Semi-Fin, Tnns; *Ft Collins Col; Marine Bio.*

BUFFINGTON, Pamela Sue
Valley HS; Albuquerque, NM (31-590) Band; Pres, Drama; Co-Ed, Lit Mag; Pres, NHS; Ski C; Spch C; Span NHS; Thes; COM; Hon Prog; Ntl Achv Schol; Mus A; *Colo St U; Vet Med.*

BUFFINGTON, Vickie Jean
Perry HS; Perry, OK (37-88) Ann; Band; Bus C; FHA; 4H; ARC; SC; Bkbl; Tr; Masonic A; Guthrie Scottish Rite A; *Central St U; Elem Ed.*

BUFFORD, Gloria Marie
Centennial HS; Compton, CA; *Seattle U; Nurs.*

BUFKIN, Emma Melissa
Miami Coral Park Sr HS; Miami, FL (23-662) InterClub Coun; Mu Alpha Theta; NHS; Outstude Ltr; Pres, Ger Hon Soc; Bar & Star; Social Stu Hon; WW; Secy, Sci Hon Soc; Eng Hon Soc; *Baylor U; Nurs.*

BUGAJ, Barry Michael
St Mary's Prep; Orchard Lake, MI (4-32) CYO; Tres, Jr Cl; Bsbl; Bkbl; Ftbl; Golf; Alg A; Hon Prog; Magna Cum Laude; Math A; Sci A.

BUGELLI, Linda
University HS; San Diego, CA (13-315) Hmrm; NHS; Sch Achieve Tm; VP, SC; Mgr, Bkbl; CSF; COM; Hon Prog; Pep C; Badminton; *Bus Mgr.*

BUGG, Edward Douglas Jr
Park View Sr HS; South Hill, VA (20-150) Dbte Tm; Drama; Fr C; NFL; Tres, SC; VP, Soph Cl; Bsbl; Bkbl; Ftbl; Tnns; Alg A; Math A; Poet A; Sci A; Sch A; James Madison U; Engr.*

BUGGS, Philip John
Cass Tech HS; Detroit, MI; VP, Chor; FTA; Orch; Bsbl; Sftbl; *W Mich U; Aerospace Engr.*

BUGH, Andrew Edward
L C Anderson HS; Austin, TX (25%-600) Order/Arrow; COM; Archt Drafting A's; Game Mgr.

BUGH, Tim Charles
Anderson HS; Austin, TX; VP, Chor; COM; *Baylor U; Mus.*

BUGHMAN, Jan Louise
Keokuk Sr HS; Keokuk, IA (24-206) Band; Chor; Secy, NHS; Rainbow; SAA; HR; *Southeastern Comm Col; Ed.*

BUHN, David William
Sweet Home HS; Sweet Home, OR (23-250) Chess C; Key C; NHS; Swim; *Oreg Inst of Tech; Elec Engr.*

BUHR, Rodney Ray
Armstrong HS; Armstrong, IL (7-45) SC; Bsbl; Co-Cpt, Bkbl; Sftbl; HCt; *Ill St U; Bus Adm.*

BUHRER, Debra Lynn
Casa Grande HS; Petaluma, CA (13%-280) Type A; Shorthand A; Word Processing Cert of Achv; *Capernwray Bible Sch; Bible.*

BUHRKE, Mark Allen
LeRoy HS; LeRoy, IL; AFS; Chor; Madrigal; Spch C; Data Processing.

BUHRO, Donald Martin
Belleville HS; Belleville, MI (122-600) Cpt, Tr; JV, Wrest; MVP, Co-Cpt, Cr Ctry; *Eastern Mich U.*

BUIE, Linda Faye
Mullins HS; Mullins, SC (8-209) Band; FHA; 4H; Hmrm; 4H A; Modeling 0280000797c; *Carson Newman Col; Religion.*

BUIKEMA, Randall Allan
Fulton HS; Fulton, IL (50-120) Tres, AFS; Tres, Fr C; Thes; Golf; Tnns; Spch A; *Central Col; Bio.*

BUINING, Bonnie Jean
Irondale Sr HS; New Brighton, MN; A Cap Choir; Span C; VP, Church Yth Group; Young Life; *Calvin Col; Forestry.*

BUISCH, Edward Arthur
Romulus Central Sch; Romulus, NY (2-70) VP, Band; Chess C; NHS; Tres, SC; S-T, Var C; Bkbl; Ftbl; *Baptist Bible Col of Pa; Bible.*

BUKOWICH, Luanne Elizabeth
Lawrence HS; Lawrence, KS (14-530) Chor; Lit Ral; Hon Prog; Lawrence Ed Assn Schol; Pep C; Stu for Action for Ed; *York Col; Elem Ed.*

BULL, James Ray Jr
Sparks HS; Sparks, NV (44-290) Rptr, Sch P; Sci C; Tres, SC; Hockey; JV, Tnns; Mgr, Wrest; Math A; NML; WW; *Willamette U; Broadcasting-Computer Sci.*

BULL, Julie Anne
Gaylord Pub HS; Gaylord, MN (33%-78) A Cap Choir; Band; Ensm; Mod Mus Mas; Span C; Golf; COM; Golf, Mus, Danceline, A's; *Med Tech.*

BULL, Ricky Lynn
Mangum HS; Mangum, OK (1-64) NHS; Bsbl; Cpt, Bkbl; Bio A; Val; All St Bkbl; *Central St U; Bus.*

BULLARD, Angelia Marie
Ballard HS; Louisville, KY; Cpt, Swim; Tnns; *U of Louisville; Nurs.*

BULLARD, Carol Joyce
Bishop Dunne HS; Dallas, TX (39-180) Band; Ensm; Rainbow; Horizon C; Yth Coun; All Region Band; All St Band.

BULLARD, Carolyn Dianne
Southwest McEvoy B HS; Macon, GA (25-466) BC; 4H; Hmrm; ARC; Span C; SC; Cl Fav; *Macon Jr Col; Bus.*

BULLARD, Christy Anne
DeSoto HS; De Soto, TX (70-300) FHA; Yth Fel.

BULLARD, Cindy Jean
Panora-Linden Comm HS; Panora, IA (1-53) Chor; Drama; NHS; Thes; Mgr, Bkbl; Mgr, Tr; Val; *Des-Moines Area Comm Col; Retail Marketing.*

BULLARD, Jesse Franklin III
W Columbus HS; Cerro Gordo, NC (24-211) Fr C; Jr Beta C; Lib C; Pep C; *E Carolina U; Bio.*

BULLARD, Melanie Celeste
Ravenscroft HS; Raleigh, NC; Monogram; ARC; Span C; Var C; Bkbl; Soccer; Mgr, Swim; *NC St U; Sociology.*

BULLARD, Nell Garrell
Salisbury HS; Salisbury, NC (1-283) AFS; Ann;
Semi-Fin, Chldr; Chor; Ensm; Fr C; Hmrm; SC;
Hon Prog; 1st Cl, GSct; Guidance Coun Staff.

BULLARD, Pamela Denise
Pickwick Southside HS; Counce, TN (4-34) BC;
FHA; 4H; Hist A; Hon Prog; Eng A; *NE Miss Jr
Col; Physics.*

BULLARD, Patricia Ann
Tuscola Sr HS; Waynesville, NC (3-312) Band;
Chor; Fr C; Tr; Cert, Tr; *Western Carolina U.*

BULLARD, Terry Lynn
Burnsville HS; Burnsville, MS; Ann; BC; SC; Rptr,
Soph Cl; MVP, Bsbl; Bkbl; Ftbl; Tr; Cl Fav; HCt;
Miss St U; Hist.

BULLARD, Theresa Lagail
Kashmere Sr HS; Houston, TX; Bus C; Drama; SC;
JA A; Most Out; HR; Spch & Drama Tourn; NJHS;
UIL One Act Play Contest; Booster C; Upward
Bound; JA; Secy, Usher's No II; *Drama.*

BULLARD, Wendell
Hillside HS; Durham, NC; *Fayetteville St Col.*

BULLEY, Laurie Lee
The HS of Commerce; Springfield, MA (60-425)
Chldr; Chor; Hmrm; Madrigal; SC; Soccer; Drill
Tm; Cl Vocalist; *U of Mass; Mus.*

BULLMAN, William Randall
Franklin Jr-Sr HS; Franklin, PA (2-280) NHS; Var
C; Ftbl; Tr; MLS; *U of Pa; Elec Engr.*

BULLOCH, Donna Kay
Marshall HS; Marshall, TX (100-470) A Cap
Choir; Chldr; Chor; Ensm; FTA; VP, Hmrm; Semi-
Fin, Jr Miss Pa; Madrigal; Co-Cpt, Mjrte; SC; Yth
Fel; Drill Tm Off; Hon Men, Talent Show; *E Tex
Baptist Col; Mus.*

**BULLOCK,
Cornelius Edwards Jr**
Lumberton Sr HS; Lumberton, NC (3-350) BC; Lat
C; Ch, NHS; A-Ed, Sch P; Sci C; Span C; SC; Golf;
Swim; Fin, Lat A; Fin, Hist A; Fin, Sci A; Fin, Spch
A; *Wake Forest U; Math.*

BULLOCK, Debra Ann
Brooke HS; Wellsburg, WV (122-483) Chldr; Secy,
Hmrm; Span C; Secy, Jr Cl; Tnns; Tr; Cl Fav; HCt;
Spch A; Most Spirited; *Ohio Valley Hospital Sch of
Nurs; Nurs.*

BULLOCK, Harold Edward
Bogue Chitto HS; Bogue Chitto, MS (1-32) A-Ed,
Ann; BC; Bus C; Chess C; VP, Dbte Tm; VP,
Drama; FBLA; Pres, FFA; F-Ed, Sch P; SC; Pres,
Jr Cl; JV, Bkbl; Ftbl; MLS; Star Student; Val; *U of
Sou Miss; Computer Technology.*

BULLOCK, Kenneth Lee
Eastern Vocational-Tech HS; Baltimore, MD
(10%-300) Order/Arrow; Tnns; God & Country A;
Order/Arrow A; Eagle Sct; *U of Md; Forestry.*

BULLOCK, Melissa Arlene
Blenk HS; Gretna, LA (10-120) Chor; Madrigal; B
Crocker A; Sci A; Yth Fel; Pres, Secy, Church Fel;
SE La U; Nurs.

BULLOCK, Myrtis Susan
Westbury HS; Houston, TX (1-614) Rptr, Anchor
C; Chor; Hmrm; Secy, Lat C; Mjrte; Secy, NHS;
Beauty; Magna Cum Laude; Spch A; Summa Cum
Laude; Drum Major, Rebellettes; *Baylor U; Pol Sci.*

BULLOCK, Patricia Kay
Milano HS; Milano, TX; Ann; Chldr; Chor; FFA;
VP, FHA; NHS; Tres, SC; Amer Leg A; Beauty; Cl
Fav; Spch A; Val; Most Dependable; Homemaking
A; Dist Piano Guild; FFA Swtht; *Sam Houston
Col; Sociology.*

BULLOCK, Sandra Rae
Alvin HS; Alvin, TX (133-360) Band; Ensm; Secy,
Fr C; NEDT; Yth Fel; VP, District Yth Coun; *Bus.*

BULLOCK, Sheree Sue
Baker HS; Baker, LA (4-425) Secy, A Cap Choir;
BC; InterClub Coun; Ed, Lit Mag; Madrigal; Tri-
HiY; Cl Fav; Type A; *Southeastern La U; Mus.*

BULLOCK, Steven David
John F Hodge; St James, MO (11-130) Band; Chor;
Ensm; Fr C; *Boston Conservatory; Mus.*

BULLOCK, Teri Lynn
Lincoln Northeast HS; Lincoln, NE (27-504)
Band; Chldr; GS; NHS; Orch; Var C; Co-Cpt, Bkbl;
Sftbl; Tr; NMS; Vlbl; Fin, May Qn; Gifted Stu;
Commended Stu; *Nebr Wesleyan U; Pre-Law.*

BULLS, Derrick Charles
Waukegan West HS; Waukegan, IL (120-550) Fin,
BS; City Conf; Ger C; Hmrm; Pres, SC; JV, Bkbl;
Citz A; Hon Prog; MLS; Ntl Sci Found; *U of Mi-
ami; Biomed Engr.*

BULLUCK, Teresa Susan
Rocky Mount Sr HS; Rocky Mount, NC; Ed, Ann;
Chldr; Hmrm; SC; HCt; Yth for Easter Seals; S-T,
Phalanx C; Yth Coun; Bicentennial Comm; *Appa-
lachian St U; Psych.*

BULTMAN, Darrell Henry
Elkhart HS; Elkhart, KS; Band; Chor; Tres, 4H;
Tres, Span C; Pres, Soph Cl; Bsbl; Ftbl; Alg A; Sci
A; HR; Schol Test.

BUMGARDNER, Bradley Clay
Rosedale HS; Rosedale, IN (16-69) Model UN;
NHS; Pres, Sr Cl; VP, Soph Cl; Bsbl; Bkbl; Pres
Classroom; Christmas Dance King; *Ind St U.*

BUMGUARDNER, Matt Worth
Eldorado HS; Eldorado, TX (1-41) Dbte Tm; FFA;
VP, 4H; NHS; Tr; B Crocker A; 4H A; NMF;
NEDT; Pres A; St Scholar; Val; Gold Star; *Tex
A&M U; Geophysics.*

BUMPUS, Jeff Lee
Centerburg HS; Centerburg, OH (3-82) Semi-Fin,
BS; Tres, NHS; Ed, Sch P; Span C; SC; Var C; Bsbl;
Co-Cpt, Bkbl; Co-Cpt, Ftbl; Tr; Rotary A; 1st Tm
All-St Ftbl; *David Libscomb Col; Bus Adm.*

BUNCH, Donnelle Lorraine
Marysville-Pilchuck HS; Marysville, WA;

BUNCH, Jenise Lynn
Suda E Butler HS; Louisville, KY (1-331) BC;
Chor; FFA; NHS; DARGCA; Pres A; Val; FFA; *U
of Louisville; Acct.*

BUNCH, John Mark
Robert E Lee HS; Midland, TX (7-610) NHS; Bkbl;
Elk A; Hon Prog; Conoco Schol; Academic A; *Tex
A&M U; Petroleum Engr.*

BUNCH, Kathryn Renee
Springfield Cath HS; Springfield, MO (15%-61)
Band; Chor; Fr C; Hmrm; Orch; Sch P; Pres, Span
C; SC; AMS Spelling Test; Sunday Sch Teacher;
Methodist Missions Project Tour; *SMSU; Eng.*

BUNCH, Kirk Paul
Othello HS; Othello, WA (10-250) Chor; Drama;
Ski C; Fin, Spch C; SC; Pres, Soph Cl; Ftbl; Citz A;
Pres A; Sci A; Spch A; Ath A; *Pacific Lutheran U;
Med.*

BUNCH, Mark Keith
Othello HS; Othello, WA (3-150) Chor; Drama;
NHS; Ski C; Spch C; Pres, SC; Hon Prog; NMF; *U
of Wash; Gen Sci.*

BUNCH, Mark Steven
Winyah HS; Georgetown, SC (200-627) Ann;
Band; Ensm; Orch; Drama; Var C; Order/Arrow; Sch P; Bkbl; Tr;
God & Country A; Order/Arrow A; *Citadel Col;
Photographer.*

BUNCH, Maurice Paul
John A Holmes HS; Edenton, NC (6-125) F-Ed,
Ann; Chess C; Cpt, Chor; FFA; Mod Mus Mas;
Monogram; NHS; Mgr, Bkbl; Ftbl; MVP, Tnns;
PA; Nom, BS; *U of NC; Bus Adm.*

BUNCH, Rebecca Lynn
Brainerd HS; Chattanooga, TN (2-438) Secy, BC;
Cpt, Chldr; FBLA; Pres, FTA; Cpt, Mjrte; NHS;
S-T, Spch C; VP, SC; Y-Tns; Secy, Jr Cl; Pres, Soph
Cl; Bkbl; Cpt, Sftbl; Tr; Cl Fav; HCt; Hon Prog;
NMF; Spch A; Star Student; Swtht; *Norte Dame
U; Child Devolopment.*

BUNCH, Sandra Joanne
Naperville Central HS; Naperville, IL (99-420)
Band; Cpt, Chldr; Chor; Orch; Tres, Span C; Spch
C; St Stu Congress; Reading A; *U of Ark; Child
Psychiatry.*

BUNCH, Teresa Elaine
S Grand Prairie HS; Grand Prairie, TX (11-410)
Rptr, A Cap Choir; Drama; FTA; Madrigal; NHS;
Hon Prog; Type A; All Festival Choir; UIL St Vo-
cal Comp; Lead in 'Follies'; *N Tex St U; Ed.*

BUNCH, Wanda Carol
John A Holmes HS; Edenton, NC (2-184) FHA;
Sci C; Tnns; Math A; *U of NC at Chapel Hill.*

BUNCHE, Cynthia Anne
Hernando HS; Brooksville, FL (1500-3000) Band;
Chor; FFA; 4H; Tr; *Fla A&M U; Psych.*

BUNCK, Julie M
Horton HS; Horton, KS (6-60) VP, Band; VP,
CYO; Chor; Ensm; Secy, FHA; Pres, 4H; NHS;
SC; VP, Jr Cl; Bkbl; Tr; Pres, Pep C; Dist Conv; All
League Bkbl; *St Mary's Col.*

BUNDE, Lori Sue
Wallace HS; Wallace, ID; JV, Chldr; Drama; Lat C;
VP, Mjrte; Ski C; Sftbl; Tr; Spch A; Drill Pin; Mi-
nerettes; Vlbl; Cpt, Rifle Squad; *U of Idaho; Forestry.*

BUNG, Susan Mae
Fairhope HS; Fairhope, AL; Band; Ensm; Key C;
Interlochen Ntl Mus; Swtht; Hospital Auxilary;
Band Librarian; Ntl Piano Guild; All-St Comp.

BUNKE, Susan Shirley
Greenfield HS; Greenfield, WI (10-400) Chor;
Swim; *St Olaf Col; Chem.*

BUNKER, David Allan
Sam Rayburn HS; Pasadena, TX (25-588) Chess C;
NHS; *Rice U; Engr.*

BUNKER, Robert Wayne
Sam Rayburn HS; Pasadena, TX; Bsbl; Bkbl; Ftbl;
Tnns; Tr; Bible Quiz Tm; *San Jacinto Jr Col.*

BUNKOFSKE, Raymond James
N U HS; Cedar Falls, IA (6-63) Ann; Chor; Com-
munity Yth Symph; Drama; Madrigal; Orch; Span
C; Thes; Swim; Rotary A; *Carleton Col; Math.*

BUNN, Gina Allyson
Bessemer Acad; Bessemer, AL (40-52) A Cap
Choir; Chor; Leo, Pep, C'S.

BUNN, Jeff Scott
Orangeburg-Wilkinson HS; Orangeburg, SC
(25%-500) Fr C; Order/Arrow; Order/Arrow A;
Yth Choir; Strengthening Church Comm; *U of SC;
Phar.*

BUNN, Tammy Jeannine
Fayetteville Terry Sanford HS; Fayetteville, NC
(1-400) Ed, Ann; BC; Drama; Fr C; Mjrte; Math C;
Mu Alpha Theta; NHS; Gov Honor Prog; Hon
Prog; Flag Girl; Schol A; Highest Avg; *U of NC;
Bus Adm.*

BUNSTER, Jackie Miriam
Lake Braddock Secondary HS; Burke, VA; Chor;
Drama; Ski C; Secy, Spch C; Spch A; Forensic's
Ltr; *George Mason U; Eng.*

BUNT, Richard Scott
Corning Painted Post W HS; Painted Post, NY
(25%-400) Ftbl.

BUNTER, Rebecca Jane
Santa Cruz HS; Santa Cruz, CA (35-200) A Cap
Choir; AFS; Community Yth Symph; Drama;
Ensm; Madrigal; Orch; ARC; Rptr, Sch P; Cr-Ctry;
Tr; CSF; Secy, Ldr C; Department Mus Hon; VP,
GAA; All St Hon Orch; Co Hon Orch; *U o-t Pa-
cific; Biol.*

BUNTING, Denise Ann
Dallas Christian HS; Dallas, TX; FHA; Hmrm; VP,
Soph Cl; Bkbl; Vlbl; Eng A; *Harding Col.*

BUNTON, Matthew Donald
Lamar HS; Lamar, MO (5-81) Chem C; Pres, FFA;
Pres, 4H; Key C; Pres, Math C; Phys C; Sci C; Tr;
Alg A; COM; 4H A; I Dare You; Math A; 2nd Pl,
St Crops Tm; St Farm Mechanics; *UMC; Agr.*

BUNTROCK, Cindy Sue
Merrill Sr HS; Merrill, WI; Chor; Hmrm; SC; JV,
Tr; Secy, Church Yth Group; *N Central Tech Inst,
Secy.*

BUNYARD, Cindy Anne
Plano Sr HS; Plano, TX (365-800) Ann; Sch P; Sci
A; Yth Leg; Cpt, Vlbl; *Stephen F Austin Col; Home
Ec.*

BURBA, Cynthia Louise
Willows HS; Willows, CA (3-130) Band; Ch, FHA;
Orch; Sftbl; Bank Of Amer A; CSF; 1st Cl GSct;
Okla Bus Col; Acct.

BURBA, Deborah Elaine
Hart Co HS; Munfordville, KY (7-150) F-Ed, Ann; BC; NHS; F-Ed, Sch P; *Ky Baptist Sch of Nurs; Nurs.*

BURBA, Robert Carl
Wellington HS; Wellington, TX (3-46) Band; Tres, BC; Math A; Spch A; Regional Fin, Poetry; Regional Qualifier, Number Sense; *W Tex St U; Math.*

BURCH, Angela Janine
Monterey HS; Lubbock, TX; Tri-HiY; Hon Prog; Type A; *Tex Tech U.*

BURCH, Charles
Romulus HS; Romulus, MI (2-400) NHS; Ntl Yth Conf; Ed, Sch P; SC; Pres, Var C; JV, Bkbl; Co-Cpt, Ftbl; Tr; COM; NMS; Attendance A; Sports A; Peer Counseling; *U of Mich; Acct.*

BURCH, Douglas Eugene
St Ignatius HS; Chicago, IL (95-199) Chor; Dbte Tm; Hmrm; SC; Bsbl; Bkbl; Cr-Ctry; Ftbl; Sftbl; Tnns; Tr; COM; *U of Ill; Pre-Law.*

BURCH, Irene Renee
Carver HS; Memphis, TN (10-342) Chem C; Chor; Math C; Phys C; Sci C; Sftbl; Sanctuary Soc; Yth Fel; *Wash U; Bio.*

BURCH, Karen Sue
Licking R8 HS; Licking, MO (30-73) Fr C; FHA; REA Win; *Southwest Baptist Col; Bus Adm.*

BURCH, Kathy Marie
Flathead HS; Kalispell, MT (53-450) AFS; Ger C; NHS; Span C; COM; *U of Puget Sound; Foreign Lang.*

BURCH, Mary Sibet
Beaufort Acad; Beaufort, SC (5-42) F-Ed, Ann; Hmrm; NHS; Tres, SC; Secy, Jr Cl; Hon Prog; Val; Yth Fel; *Clemson U; Bio.*

BURCH, Pamela Kaye
Los Alamitos HS; Los Alamitos, CA; Drama; Fr C; Math A; *NW Nazarene Col; Theatre Arts.*

BURCH, Richard Duane
Stanley HS; Stanley, LA (1-16) Dbte Tm; Tres, FFA; Sch P; SC; Pres, Sr Cl; Pres, Jr Cl; Pres, Soph Cl; Bsbl; MVP, Bkbl; Cl Fav; MLS; Most Ath; All-St, All-Dist & All-Amer; *Phys Ed.*

BURCH, Shelia Renee
Carver HS; Memphis, TN (50-318) Band; Hmrm; Orch; Span C; Band A; *Tex Sou U; Psych.*

BURCH, Vaughn Scott
Quartz Hill HS; Quartz Hill, CA; Ftbl; *Azusa Pacific Col; Mus.*

BURCHAK, Craig B
David Douglas HS; Portland, OR (33%-530) Band; Ski C; MVP, Ski Tm; Eagle Sct; *Mt Hood Comm Col; Bus Ed.*

BURCHAM, Timothy Nolan
Phil Campbell HS; Phil Campbell, AL (3-95) FFA; FTA; Parl, NHS; Var C; JV, Bkbl; Ftbl; *Auburn U; Bio-Chem.*

BURCHAM, Tina Carol
Stonewall Jackson HS; Charleston, WV; NFL; Spch C; Beauty; Spch A; VofDEM; Hist, Drama C; Most Talented; Art A; Best Actress; *W Va U; Drama.*

BURCHELL, Randall Lawrence
York Suburban Sr HS; York, PA (68-285) Bsbl; Bkbl; Co-Cpt, Wrest; Amer Leg A; Wrest A; Bsbl A; *Penn St U; Med.*

BURCHETT, Stacy Wade
Kalama HS; Kalama, WA (9-60) Ann; Pres, Band; Pres, Chor; JV, Bkbl; Ftbl; JA A; Marine Corps Outst Musician; *Northwest Col; Missions.*

BURCHETTE, Lona Rae
Hanes HS; Winston-Salem, NC; Chldr; Hmrm; SC; Bkbl; Sftbl; Beauty; HQn; GSct A; PA; Drama A; *Nurs.*

BURCHFIELD, Mark Ronald
Strasburg HS; Strasburg, CO (4-26) Pres, 4H; NHS; Pres, Jr Cl; Ftbl; Wrest; 4H A; HKg; MLS; *Colo St U; Agr.*

BURCHYETT, David Todd
Pattonville HS; Maryland Hts, MO (300-775) Bsbl; Bkbl; Citz A; WW; Prom Court; *Florasant Valley Comm Col; Communcations.*

BURCICKI, James Michael
G A R Mem HS; Wilkes-Barre, PA (13-179) Pres, NHS; *Army; Elec Engr.*

BURCKHALTER, Julie Reel
Aiken HS; Aiken, SC (70-645) Pres, Hmrm; Span C; Span NHS; SC; Type A; *Clemson U; Elem Ed.*

BURD, Holly Jill
Burrell Sr HS; Lower Burrell, PA (33%-310) AFS; Span C; Alg A; COM; Math A; Ntl Baton & Drum Champs.

BURDA, Michael Christopher
Jesuit HS; Shreveport, LA (1-97) BS; Chess C; Cpt, Dbte Tm; Drama; Key C; Lat C; Fin, Lit Ral; Math C; Pres, NFL; Rptr, Sch P; Pres, Spch C; Tres, SC; Pres, Jr Cl; Soccer; B Crocker A; Bio A; Chem A; Math A; NMF; NMS; NEDT; Pres A; Sci A; Spch A; Val; Yth Leg; Lat A; Theology A; *Harvard U; Environmental Engr.*

BURDEN, Charles William
Grace Baptist HS; Decatur, AL (2-10) Band; Math C; NHS; Pres, Sci C; Pres, Span C; Pres, Sr Cl; Pres, Soph Cl; Bkbl; COM; Cl Fav; Hist A; *U of Ala; Chem.*

BURDEN, Kenneth
Far Rockaway HS; Far Rockaway, NY; All Amer Yth; Bkbl; God & Country A.

BURDETT, Becky Ann
Downers Grove S HS; Downers Grove, IL (92-917) NHS; Beauty; COM; Tres, Yth Fel; Sunday Sch Teacher; Artist, Sch P; Rptr, Yrbk; Painter, Bicentennial Mural; Hon Art A; YMCA Art Instructor; *Amer Acad of Art; Art.*

BURDETT, Kathleen Melanie
Pleasanton HS; Pleasanton, TX (4-161) Band; Ensm; FHA; Fin, Jr Miss Pagent; Math C; NHS; Sci C; Span C; Beauty; Hon Prog; Accreditation Mgt Tm; Jaycee Miss Atascosa; Foreign Lang A; *U of Tex; Physics.*

BURDETT, Lauren Kaye
Cuyahoga Valley Christian Acad; Cuyahoga Falls, OH (8-32) Ann; Drama; Fr C; 4H; ARC; Ski C; Spch C; Tri-HiY; Secy, Soph Cl; Social Ch, Jr Cl; Gen Mills Family Ldr of Tomorrow A; *Wheaton Col; Art.*

BURDETTE, Brooks Roy
Hogansville HS; Hogansville, GA (1-78) Ann; Band; S-T, BC; Pres, Chess C; Key C; Span C; SC; Mgr, Bsbl; Alg A; Bio A; Hist A; NEDT; Math Tm; Southwestern Col Math Meet; Tri-Co HS Chess Champion.

BURDETTE, Ila Leola
Hogansville HS; Hogansville, GA (1-77) Ed, Ann; Band; S-T, BC; Rptr, FTA; F-Ed, Sch P; Pres, Span C; SC; Alg A; Bio A; COM; Gov Honor Prog; Hist A; Math A; NMF; NEDT; Phy A; Sci A; Spch A; Star Student; Type A; Val; Presidential Schol; Ga St STAR Stu; *Agnes Scott Col; Math.*

BURDETTE, Jackie Sue
Gulf Comp HS; New Port Richey, FL; Chor; Social Stu C; *Eckerd Col; Coun.*

BURDETTE, Martha Alice
Venice HS; Venice, FL (30-355) A Cap Choir; A-Ed, Ann; Secy, Chor; Ensm; Hmrm; Madrigal; NHS; F-Ed, Sch P; Swim; Tnns; Pres A; Spch A; VofDEM; *SE Bible Col; Nurs.*

BURDICK, Anthony Hood
Hillcrest HS; Memphis, TN; Band; Sch P; VP, SC; Thes; Swim; ROTC A; *Eng.*

BURDICK, Brian Harry
Wilcox HS; Santa Clara, CA (50-370) Ger C; Soccer; Tr; *W Valley Jr Col; Mech.*

BURDICK, Connie Louise
Susquehanna Comm HS; Susquehanna, PA (11-115) Chor; Drama; Ski C; Type A; WW.

BURDICK, David Douglas
Shenandoah Valley Acad; New Market, VA; BC; Chor; Mu Alpha Theta; WW; *Columbia Union Col; Theology.*

BURDICK, Ellen Marie
Edgerton HS; Edgerton, WI; Chldr; Fr C.

BURDINE, Pamela Dawn
Vanguard HS; Ocala, FL (5-350) Dbte Tm; Pres, FBLA; VP, Lit Mag; Lit Ral; Mu Alpha Theta; NHS; Rainbow; Rptr, Sch P; SC; Hist A; Journ A; Opt A; Sci A; Ed, Lit Magazine; *Central Fla Comm Col; Nurs.*

BURDINE, Tracy Lynn
Eufaula HS; Eufaula, OK (1-98) Band; Ensm; 4H; NHS; Sch P; Rptr, Span C; SC; Hon Prog; Val; Most Industrious; Schol, Ltr, A's; Band Cert; *E Central U; Elem Ed.*

BURELL, Gary Lynn
Pathway Day Sch; Savannah, GA (2-15) SC; Bsbl; Bkbl; Ftbl; Tr; COM; *Bus Adm.*

BURESS, Donna Lynn
Rosedale HS; Rosedale, IN (4-60) Band; Chor; Dbte Tm; VP, 4H; Pres, Model UN; NHS; Secy, Pol Sci C; UN Council; Sftbl; 4H A; Hon Prog; Pres Classroom; *St Mary o-t Woods Col; Secondary Ed.*

BURFORD, Darrell Earl
Fredrick Douglass HS; Atlanta, GA (71-343) CYO; Chor; Dbte Tm; Drama; Pres, Hmrm; Madrigal; Pres, Model UN; NHS; Ch, Pol Sci C; Pres, Sci C; Co-Ch, SC; Ch, UN Council; Up Bound; Co-Ch, World Affairs; Pres, Sr Cl; MVP, Bkbl; Cpt, Cr-Ctry; MVP, Tnns; MVP, Tr; Bio A; COM; Cl Fav; Gov Honor Prog; Hon Prog; JA A; MLS; Ntl Sci Found; Pres A; ROTC A; Sci A; Yth Foundation; Yth Leg; Pres A; VICA; *Morehouse Col; Bio.*

BURFORD, Glenva Sue
Piner HS; Santa Rosa, CA; Chor; 4H; Bkbl; Sftbl; JV, Swim; Tnns; Christian A; Swim A; *Secy.*

BURFORD, Jan
Pleasant Valley Sr HS; Chico, CA (40-400) Chess C; Key C; Order/Arrow; JV, Cr-Ctry; JV, Wrest; Sci A; *Cal Tech; Mech Engr.*

BURFORD, Marlinda Rochelle
Maplewood HS; Nashville, TN; VP, Lat C; NHS; SC; Ntl Honor Guild; Off Worker; Cert of Recognition, Med Col; *U of Tenn; Sociology.*

BURFORD, Patrice Elaine
Nitro HS; Nitro, WV; Chldr; FBLA; FTA; 4H; NHS; 4H A; Masonic A; *Marshall U.*

BURFORD, Randal Lee
Independence HS; Independence, MS (10%-118) BC; FBLA; Mgr, Bkbl; Mgr, Ftbl; Schol Cert; *Miss St U; Sci.*

BURFORD, Scott Daniel
Hardaway HS; Columbus, GA (10%-700) InterAct C; Key C; Lat C; Order/Arrow; Var C; VP, Soph Cl; Bkbl; Ftbl; COM; Citz A; PTA A; Sci A; *Auburn U; Med.*

BURG, Laura Anne
Stamps HS; Stamps, AR (5-70) A-Ed, Ann; Bus C; Tres, Chem C; FBLA; Math C; Mu Alpha Theta; NHS; Tres, Sci C; Rptr, Jr Cl; Hist A; *Stephen F Austin Col; Law.*

BURGAMY, Kenny David
S W HS; Macon, GA; Bsbl; Math A; Frater Sodalis; Reading A; *U of Ga; Communications.*

BURGBACHER, Andrea
Syosset HS; Syosset, NY; Band; Chldr; Chor; 4H; Hmrm; Tr.

BURGE, Teresa Louise
Jacksonville HS; Jacksonville, AR (4-514) Secy, A Cap Choir; BC; Pres, FTA; InterClub Coun; Madrigal; Tres, NHS.

BURGE, Vickie Lynn
Robeson Ctry Day Sch; Red Springs, NC (1-20) Co-Ed, Ann; BC; 4H; Hmrm; Pres, Lat C; Ed, Lit Mag; Ed, Sch P; VP, Sci C; Span C; SC; Bkbl; MVP, Tnns; COM; 4H A; Sci A; *Marshall; May Court Rep; Wake Forest U; Biol.*

BURGEN, Jacqueline Denise
Clements HS; Athens, AL (10-47) Ed, Ann; VP, BC; A-Ed, Sch P; HCt; MLS; Schol Bowl; Miss CHS; Vlbl Scorekeeper; Tres, Pep C; *Auburn U; Vet.*

BURGENER, Gail Marie
Sparks HS; Sparks, NV (20-290) Ann; Pres, CYO; Chldr; FBLA; Fin, GS; Ed, Lit Mag; NHS; Ntl Yth Conf; Rptr, Sch P; VP, Ski C; Span C; Secy, SC; Var C; Y-Tns; Pres, Soph Cl; Sftbl; Tnns; Tr; HQn; Hon Prog; Opt A; *U of Nev; Acct.*

BURGENER, Patricia Rose
Wonderview HS; Hattieville, AR (3-33) FHA; Sftbl; Citz A; Hist A; Sci A.

BURGER, David James
John F Kennedy HS; Tumon, GUAM; Bkbl; Golf; Alg A; Math A; Type A; *U of Calif; Marine Bio.*

BURGER, Marsha Lynn
Anderson HS; Cincinnati, OH (135-415) Ann; S-T, Chor; VP, Ensm; Sch P; Sftbl; JA A; Sci A; GAA; JA; *Ohio U; Arch.*

BURGER, Naomi Jeanette
Centerville HS; Centerville, IA (14-160) Chldr; Chor; Pres, Fr C; 4H; Hmrm; Model UN; Secy, NHS; Pres, SC; Pres, Jr Cl; COM; 4H A; All-St Mus Camp Schol; *Foreign Lang.*

BURGESON, Donna Rae
Maple Grove Jr-Sr HS; Bemus Point, NY (33%-92) AFS; Band; Chor; Drama; 4H; S-T, Yth Fel; *Jamestown Bus Col; Med Secy.*

BURGESS, Debra Ann
Berkeley HS; Berkeley, CA (20%-750) VP, St Stu Congress; VP, SC; HCt; *San Francisco St U; Elem Ed.*

BURGESS, James Michael
Altamont HS; Birmingham, AL (9-40) Math C; Cpt, Bsbl; Cpt, Bkbl; Math A; Henry Neal A; *Acct.*

BURGESS, Kenneth Raymond
Warwick Veterans Mem HS; Warwick, RI (41-371) Var C; Pres, Soph Cl; Cpt, Bkbl; Cpt, Ftbl; St Scholar; Most Respected; Dennis Bianco A; Edmund J Jusczyk A; *Coast Guard Acad.*

BURGESS, Laura Jean
Beaver Local HS; Lisbon, OH (58-225) Ann; Fr C; Math C; Tnns, JV-Tns; Band; JV, Tr; Hon Prog; Swtht; Eng Hons; Office Workers; Flag Corps; GAA; *Kent St U; Secondary Ed.*

BURGESS, Peggy Lee
Spotsylvania Sr HS; Spotsylvania, VA (27-425) FFA; FHA; 4H; Sci C; Span C; Sftbl; 4H A; Type A; Acteens Crown & Scepter; *Va Intermont Col; Biol.*

BURGESS, Reuben Bernard
Fulton HS; Knoxville, TN; Up Bound; *Carson-Newman Col; Religion.*

BURGESS, Robert H
Science Hill HS; Johnson City, TN (40-410) BC; JETS; F-Ed, Sch P; Tr; Pres, JA; Schol A; ETEAC; 1st, Appalachian Dist Fair; VISCA; Achv A, AIIE; Schol A, U of Tenn Alumni Assn; *U of Tenn-Knoxville; Civil Engr.*

BURGESS, Tamela Gay
Meadowbrook HS; Richmond, VA (2-350) Band; Secy, Lat C; Lit Mag; Straight 'A' HR; *U of Va; Med.*

BURGESS, Teri Lynn
Mayfair HS; Lakewood, CA (3-400) Ann; Chldr; NHS; ARC; Ski C; 1st Cl GSct; *Calif St Col; Psych.*

BURGETT, Scott Richard
Grand Blanc HS; Grand Blanc, MI (10%-800) Ger C; JV, Bkbl; Co-Cpt, Golf; Tr; Alg A; Math A; Sci A; Yth Fel; Yth Leg; Ldr, Church Yth Group; Church Yth Choir; *U of Mich; Engr.*

BURGH, Patricia JoAnne
Wilton HS; Wilton, CT (18-420) F-Ed, Ann; Tres, FNA; NHS; St Scholar; Shorthand A's; *Houghton Col; Writing.*

BURGHER, Lawrence Bruce
Hoquiam HS; Hoquiam, WA; Ger C; Tr; *U of Wash; Lang.*

BURGHER, Matthew Allan
Hoquiam HS; Hoquiam, WA; Band.

BURGOON, Deborah Ann
Cumberland Valley HS; Mechanicsburg, PA (15-605) Band; NHS; Orch; Rainbow; NEDT; *U of Pa; Vet Med.*

BURGOON, Teddi Marie
Statesboro HS; Statesboro, GA (5%-300) All Amer Yth; Cpt, Band; Secy, BC; Model UN; NHS; Orch; Span C; COM; Gov Honor Prog; All St Band; Eng Comp; All St Stage Band; *U of Ga; Mus.*

BURGREEN, Joyce Lorene
Flemington HS; Flemington, WV (12-47) Drama; VP, Fr C; FTA; NHS; Var C; Co-Cpt, Bkbl; Citz A; Phys Ed; Prom Qn; Best Girl Ath.

BURGSTAHLER, Carol Jean
Eisenhower HS; Hopkins, MN (10-450) A Cap Choir; Chor; Co-Cpt, Bkbl; Sftbl; Co-Cpt, Vlbl; NML; *U of Minn; Ed.*

BURHANS, Kathy Sue
Lakeview HS; Battle Creek, MI (33%-400) Fr C; NHS; Swim; *U of Ariz; Art.*

BURHANS, Michael Scott
Lakeview HS; Battle Creek, MI (40-420) Band; Ensm; Fr C; Hmrm; VP, Ski C; Var C; JV, Ftbl; Swim; JV, Tr; *Albion Col; Pre-Med.*

BURIFF, Brian John
Red Bluff Union HS; Red Bluff, CA (1-430) Band; Chor; Pres, 4H; Amer Leg A; Amer Leg Orator A; Bank Of Amer A; CSF; 4H A; Spch A; VFW A; VFW Orator Win; VofDEM; *Anderson Col; Ministry.*

BURIFF, Kathleen Ann
Red Bluff Union HS; Red Bluff, CA (30-353) Band; Chor; Ensm; 4H; Bank Of Amer A; CSF; CSF Sealbearer Schol; John Philip Sousa Band A; *Warner Pacific Col; Bus.*

BURK, Carolyn Ann
Northbrook Sr HS; Houston, TX; NHS; Cr-Ctry; Sftbl; Tr; Chaplain, FCA; *Okla Baptist U.*

BURK, Gaye Lynn
Imperial HS; Imperial, CA; F-Ed, Ann; Fr C; NHS; CSF; 4H A; Hist A; Journ A; Type A; Fr A; Publications A.

BURK, Lisa Ann
Garner Hayfield HS; Garner, IA (45-70) Band; Chor; Ensm; FHA; Spch C; Mgr, Bkbl; Tr; Pep C; Swing Choir; Statistician, Bkbl; *NIACC; Nurs.*

BURK, Pamela Sue
Switzerland Co HS; Vevay, IN (10-108) Fr C; Tres, NHS; Hist A; MLS; Sci A; *DePauw U; Med Tech.*

BURKARD, Jeanette Karen
Chester Area HS; Chester, SD (7-40) FHA; NHS; Sch P; Tr; *Nettleton Col; Private Secy.*

BURKE, Amy Dawn
Central HS; Martinsburg, PA; Band; Chor; Rainbow; Span C; Var C; Sftbl; Tr; COM; Hon Prog; Yth Fel; *Phys Therapy.*

BURKE, Carrie Ann
Victory Christian HS; Carmichael, CA (2-15) A Cap Choir; Chor; Ensm; Swim; *Biola Col; Christian Ed.*

BURKE, Cassandra Diane
Burleson HS; Burleson, TX; Band; 4H; Sch P; *Tarrant Co Jr Col; Journ.*

BURKE, Catherine Marie
Acad of Mount Saint Ursula; Bronx, NY (50-155) CYO; Chor; Drama; Y-Tns; Sftbl; Hon Prog; Co-Cpt, Bowl; Vlbl; *Pace U; Nurs.*

BURKE, Christopher Gerard
Scotia-Glenville HS; Scotia, NY (11-372) Lit Mag; NHS; VP, Order/Arrow; Ski C; Hon Prog; NMS; NEDT; Order/Arrow A; Mayflower Compact A; Social Stu Explorer Excellence A; Comm Service A; *Harvard U; Bus.*

BURKE, Elizabeth Lou
Wapato Sr HS; Wapato, WA (4-156) A Cap Choir; Band; Chldr; Chor; City Conf; GS; Secy, NHS; Rainbow; Sch P; Tr; Amer Leg A; COM; Citz A; Cl Fav; Coun of Teach A; DARGCA; HQn; Hon Prog; JA A; Masonic A; Century III Leaders; Fiscus Mem A; Amer Rev Bicentennial A; 1st Pl, St Amer Heritage Essay; *Yakima Valley Col; Allied Health Sci.*

BURKE, Jim Paul
Montclair HS; Van Nuys, CA; JV, Ftbl; Hist A; *Col U at Boulder.*

BURKE, Kathy
Petoskey HS; Petoskey, MI; AFS; Band; Bus C; Dbte Tm; Ntl Yth Conf; Orch; VP, Ski C; Tri-HiY; Bkbl; Hon Prog; NMF; Type A; Acct A; Shorthand A; *Northern Mich U; Bus.*

BURKE, Kimberly Jane
Doane Stuart Sch; Albany, NY (25%-39) Drama; Sch P; SC; Var C; Soccer; *Siena Col; Acct.*

BURKE, Lucille Newsome
Virgie HS; Virgie, KY; BC; FTA; Sch P; Citz A.

BURKE, Maxine Marlyn
Springfield Gardens HS; New York, NY (42-759) Chor; NHS; COM; Hon Prog; *Baruch Col; Acct.*

BURKE, Michael Anthony
Plant City HS; Plant City, FL (40-850) Demolay; NHS; Span C; Amer Leg A; *U of Fla; Chem.*

BURKE, Patrick William
Wakulla HS; Crawfordville, FL; NHS; SC; Tres, Jr Cl; Ftbl; Tr; Wrest; Fin, Pres A.

BURKE, Rusty Dale
Whitmer HS; Toledo, OH (200-1000) A Cap Choir; Chor; Ensm; Ch, Hmrm; Span C; SC; Sftbl; Co-Cpt, Wrest; *Elec.*

BURKE, Sandra
Cape Fear Sr HS; Fayetteville, NC (56-444) Ann; Chor; FHA; Hmrm; Sci C; Sftbl; Math A; Yth Fel; Yth Foundation; Bible Quiz; *Morehouse Col; Register Nurs.*

BURKE, Shannon Colleen
McMinnville HS; McMinnville, OR (3-250) Chor; SC; Bkbl; Sftbl; JV, Tnns; Vlbl.

BURKE, Sharon Kay
Douglas MacArthur HS; San Antonio, TX (139-610) A Cap Choir; Chor; FTA; COM; Miss FTA, Dist; WW; Mus A; Semi-Fin, Ms Tnage San Antonio; *Wayland Baptist Col; Ed.*

BURKE, Shelly Renea
Everman HS; Everman, TX; Hmrm; Sci C; SC; Tr; Sci A; Keywanettes; VP, FCA; JV, Vlbl; Presidential Phys Fitness; *Bethany Nazarene Col; Phys Ed.*

BURKE, Sherri Lu
Gordon HS; Gordon, NE (5-75) Band; CYO; Chldr; Chor; FBLA; FTA; 4H; NHS; Sch P; SC; Tr; 4H A; Hon Prog; Most Out; Spelling A; Pep C A; Sports Qn Alt.

BURKE, Stephen Francis
Don Bosco Tech HS; Boston, MA (15-222) Mgr, Drama; SC; Tr; COM; Hon Prog; *Lowell Col; Engr.*

BURKE, Susan Elizabeth
West HS; Knoxville, TN (46-250) Chor; Drama; Madrigal; VP, Y-Tns; Ftbl; Sftbl; Jr NHS; Vlbl; WW; *U of Tenn; Human Services.*

BURKEE, Cynthia Lou
Whitney Point Sr HS; Whitney Point, NY (3-160) Band; Chess C; Chor; Fr C; Pres, 4H; InterAct C; NHS; COM; 4H A; Regent Schol; Outst Tn Young Woman; NML; *St U of NY; Biol Sci.*

BURKEEN, Rhonda Yvette
Central HS; Columbia, TN (50-376) Bus C; FBLA; FHA; 4H; VP, Hmrm; *Columbia St Comm Col; Elem Ed.*

BURKERT, Cynthia Lynn
John F Kennedy Sr HS; New Orleans, LA (10%-400) Tnns, Band; Lat C; Hon Prog; *McCloskey A; Med Tech.*

BURKETT, Kelly Suzette
Arvin HS; Arvin, CA; Chldr; Chor; Ensm; NHS; ARC; Ski C; SC; Swim; Citz A; HCt; *Point Loma Col; Social Sci.*

BURKHALTER, Christine Elizabeth
Glenwood Springs HS; Glenwood Springs, CO (4-140) Math C; NHS; SC; VP, Fr C; Jr Cl; Secy, Soph Cl; Kiwanis A; GSct; Stu o-t Mo; Attd, Jr Sr Prom; Inter Relations C; Pep C; MVP, Vlbl; *Fort Lewis Col; Acct.*

BURKHALTER, Laurel Ann
Broadmoor HS; Baton Rouge, LA (230-438) Christ's Ambassadors; Yth Choir; Yth Coun; CA Swtht; VP, Young Women's Ministries; Puppet Ministries; *N Tex St Col; Commercial Srt.*

BURKHARDT, Carole Marie
Morrisville HS; Morrisville, PA (4-123) Band; Chor; Pres, InterAct C; Madrigal; VP, NHS; ARC; SC; Swim; COM; WW; PSED Chor; Co Mus Festival; Stu o-t Yr, Exchange C; *Moravian Col; Med Tech.*

BURKHARDT, Cheryll Renee
Jamestown Sr HS; Jamestown, ND (150-300) Community Yth Symph; Drama; Ensm; Secy, Fr C; Pres, 4H; Pres, Orch; All St Orch; St Mus Festival; NW U Summer Sch of Mus; *Concordia Col; Lang.*

BURKHARDT, Daniel Ray
Albuquerque HS; Albuqueque, NM; *NMSU; Wildlife Bio.*

BURKHARDT, Laurie Jo
Davenport Central HS; Davenport, IA (33%-500) A Cap Choir; Dbte Tm; NFL; Spch C; Mgr, Sftbl; JA A; Yth Fel; Yth Leg; Lit Book Staff; *Religion.*

BURKHARDT, Pamela Kaye
Jamestown Sr HS; Jamestown, ND; A Cap Choir; Secy, Ger C; NHS; *Concordia Col; Ger.*

BURKHART, Margaret Susan
Central Davidson HS; Lexington, NC (6-161) Lit Mag; VP, NHS; Sch P; MLS; Church Bkbl & Sftbl; Tres, Yth Fel; Jr Marshal; Secy, Sundy Sch Dept; Pres, Q&S; Bible Sch & Day Cmp Tcr; Pres, Jr Civinettes; *Elon Col; Elem Ed.*

BURKHOLDER, Amy Jean
Patrick Henry HS; Roanoke, VA (50-200) FHA; Span C; Tr; *Sou Sem Col; Equitation.*

BURKIN, Brenda Lee
MacDuffie Sch for Girls; Springfield, MA; Drama; Lit Mag; Rptr, Sch P; Ski C; S-T, Soph Cl; JV, Tnns; Photography C.

BURKLE, Leigh Ann
Martins Ferry HS; Martins Ferry, OH (95-246) Ann; Band; Hmrm; ARC; Span C; Y-Tns; ARC A; Yth Fel; Band A.

BURKLOW, Lisa Jan
Providence HS; Providence, KY; MVP, Band; BC; Chldr; Chor; Drama; FHA; Sci C; Art A; *Western Ky U; Art Teacher.*

BURKS, Flora Angela
Welch HS; Welch, WV (57-152) Chor; COM; *Fairmont St Col; Early Childhood Ed.*

BURKS, Geoffrey Stuart
Giles Co HS; Pulaski, TN (10-186) Band; BC; BS; Drama; Chem A; Math A; *Vanderbuilt U; Astronomy.*

BURKS, Jana Frances
Justin F Kimball HS; Dallas, TX (1-500) Pres, FBLA; VP, NHS; Span NHS; Hon Prog; Type A; Drill Tm; 1st Pl, Co Bus Career Dev Prog; Pres, Girl's FCA; 4th Pl, St FBLA Conf; *Dallas Baptist Col; Bus.*

BURKS, Janet Lynne
Hemet HS; Hemet, CA; Band; Community Yth Symph; Ch, Ensm; Mgr, Bkbl; Soccer; Mgr, Sftbl; Mgr, Tr; COM; Hon Prog; Pres A; Type A; Phys Ed Ltr; *Med.*

BURKS, Lorrie Kaye
Madison HS; San Diego, CA (150-929) Drama; Point Loma Col; *Psych.*

BURKS, Sherri Lynne
Cairo HS; Cairo, GA (2 5%-250) Ed, Ann; Band; Tres, BC; FBLA; Pres, InterAct C; Tnns; Alg A; COM; Gov Honor Prog; Hon Prog; Math A; Landscaping C; Lab-Stage Band; Solo & Ensm; Presbyterian Col A; *Mercer Col; Bus.*

BURKY, Alvin John
Pickens HS; Pickens, WV (2-15) 4H; NHS; Bkbl; 4H A.

BURLEIGH, Carolyn Alice
Acad o-t Sacred Heart; Grand Coteau, LA (15-50) Bkbl; Sftbl; NEDT; Yth Fel; *USL; Bio.*

BURLESON, Cheryl Anne
Ringgold HS; Ringgold, GA; Ann; BC; Cpt, Chldr; FBLA; Hmrm; Ntl Yth Conf; SC; Mgr, Bkbl; Mgr, Ftbl; Sftbl; COM; Hon Prog; Star Student; Type A; Yth Fel; *Dalton Jr Col; Phys Therapy.*

BURLESON, Lisa Carol
Ringgold HS; Ringgold, GA (1-229) Ed, Ann; Band; Pres, BC; Hmrm; SC; VP, Sr Cl; VP, Jr Cl; VP, Soph Cl; COM; Cl Fav; Gov Honor Prog; HQm; Val; *Dalton Jr Col; Phar.*

BURLESON, Scott
The Donoho Sch; Anniston, AL (2-45) Drama; VP, Key C; Lat C; Lit Mag; Math C; Mu Alpha Theta; Sci C; Thes; God & Country A; NEDT; Yth Fel; *Jacksonville St U; Pre-Med.*

BURLINGAME, I Jay
Galion Sr HS; Galion, OH (80-275) Pres, Order/ Arrow; Ed, Sch P; Span C; Pres, Thes; Var C; Mgr, Bsbl; Swim; Order/Arrow A; *U of Fla; Marine Bio.*

BURLISON, Jana Kaye
Putnam City W HS; Oklahoma City, OK (79-603) Band; Chem C; FBLA; FHA; JETS; Lat C; Lat NHS; Math C; Mu Alpha Theta; NHS; Sci C; Hon Prog; Dean's Hon Schol; *Okla St U; Interior Design.*

BURMAN, Jennifer Lydia
Saline HS; Saline, MI; VP, FHA; VP, 4H; Pres A; Yth Fel; *Secretarial.*

BURMESTER, Mary Beth
Pender Pub HS; Pender, NE (13-43) Ann; Band; Chor; FHA; VP, 4H; Var C; Tr; 4H A; Athlete o-t Yr; WW; *Nebr Methodist Hospital Sch of Nur; Nurs.*

BURNAM, Kleanor Elaine
Bowling Green Sr HS; Bowling Green, KY (20-40) Bus C; Co-Cpt, Chldr; Chor; FBLA; Key C; Ntl Yth Conf; Span C; Tri-HiY; Chamber of Comm A; *Fisk U; Psychiatrist.*

BURNAT, Elizabeth Ingram
Buckley Sch; Sherman Oaks, CA (10-63) Ann; Chess C; Chor; Drama; Sch P; JV, Bkbl; Alg A; Citz A; Hist A; Math A; NEDT; Sci A; Lat A; Fr A; Eng A; *UCLA; Pediatrician.*

BURNETT, Carolyn
Sheridan Sr HS; Sheridan, AR; Parl, BC; Chor; Ensm; Madrigal; NHS; Rptr, Thes; COM; Citz A; NEDT; Com, Preliminary Decl Fr II; *Ouachita Col; Drama.*

BURNETT, Carolyn Yvette
Northeast HS; Philadelphia, PA; Chor; Key C; SC; Swim; Tnns; *Drew U; Stenography.*

BURNETT, Cathy Marie
Coon Rapids HS; Coon Rapids, MN (10-728) CYO; NHS; F-Ed, Sch P; Chem A; *St Thomas Col; Eng.*

BURNETT, Duane Arthur
Corsicana HS; Corsicana, TX (2-279) A Cap Choir; Band; Rptr, NHS; Order/Arrow; Tnns; COM; Citz A; Opt Out Tn; Order/Arrow A; Sal; Yth Fel; WW; Eagle Sct; *Baylor U; Math.*

BURNETT, Frederick Tarhan
Wichita Falls HS; Wichita Falls, TX (40-390) JV, Bsbl; Ftbl; MLS.

BURNETT, Gary DeWayne
Thompson HS; Alabaster, AL; *Troy St U; Aviation.*

BURNETT, Jill Suzanne
Kingston HS; Kingston, NY (5-800) French NHS; Mjrte; 4H A; Hon Prog; Kiwanis A; Colorguard; Fr, Eng, Health Highest Avg, A's; *The King's Col; Bible.*

BURNETT, Jonathan Paul
Frayser HS; Memphis, TN (96-156) Drama; Ger C; NFL; Sci C; Spch C; SC; *Elec.*

BURNETT, Leah Ellen
Clearwater HS; Clearwater, FL (19-850) Tres, Key C; NHS; SC; Fin, Earthwatch Schol; Comm Ldrship Prog; President's Ntl Prayer Breakfast; *Clemson U; Zoology.*

BURNETT, Lynda Kaye
Windsor Forest HS; Savannah, GA (2-330) Pres, Anchor C; F-Ed, Ann; BC; NHS; Span C; Alg A; Bio A; COM; Chem A; Hist A; Math A; NMF; NMS; Opt A; Sal; Sci A; Summa Cum Laude; Chor Accompanist; Superintendent's A; Ga Tech Distinguished Sci Schol; *Mars Hill Col; Church Mus.*

BURNETT, Mark Paul
Santa Monica HS; Santa Monica, CA (5%-300) Band; Chess C; Dbte Tm; NHS; Star Sct.

BURNETT, Michael Wayne
Chillicothe HS; Chillicothe, TX (3-38) FFA; Mgr, Bkbl; Mgr, Ftbl; Tr; FFA Chapter Ldrship A; *Tex Tech U; Elec.*

BURNETT, Patricia Jean
James F Byrnes HS; Duncan, SC (56-380) Band; Chor; Ensm; VP, Hmrm; *Furman U; Mus.*

BURNETT, Phil Wayne
Bethel Christian HS; Garden Grove, CA; Chor; Dbte Tm; Drama; Ensm; Spch C; SC; Bkbl; Ftbl; Semi-Fin, Tr; Mr Personality; *Fullerton Jr Col; Social Sci.*

BURNETT, Robyn Kay
Bunker R-3 HS; Bunker, MO (3-32) BC; Chor; FHA; Amer Leg A; Bio A; Curator A; Regional Off, FHA; Family Living A; Chor A; Health A; Most Enthusiactic Pep C Member; Personal Culture A; *U of Mo at Columbia.*

BURNETT, Scott Alan
Kingston HS; Kingston, NY (40%-700) Band; Ed, Lit Mag; Semi-Fin, Sftbl; Regent Schol; Art A's; Outst Lit A; *Nyack Missionary Col; Mus.*

BURNETT, Valerie Jan
Central HS; Kirtland, NM (8-91) Band; NHS; *NMSU at San Juan; Secretarial.*

BURNETT, Wayde Darrell
Western HS; Las Vegas, NV; Tres, Demolay; Bus Mgr, Sch P; Sftbl; God & Country A; Q&S A; Ldrship Correspondence Course; Pastor Seeking Comm; Yth Alt; *Bus Mgt.*

BURNETTE, Greg Curtis
Norcross HS; Norcross, GA (10%-240) Span C; COM; Hon Prog; NMF; *Mercer U; Elec.*

BURNETTE, Michael Winston
N B Broughton HS; Raleigh, NC (120-483) Band; Chor; Pres, Demolay; Ensm; Lat C; Order/Arrow; Ftbl; Sftbl; Chevalier; Eagle Sct; *NC St U; Chem Engr.*

BURNETTE, Sharon Lee
Holy Rosary Acad; Louisville, KY (2-89) Ann; Chor; Drama; GS; F-Ed, Sch P; Spch C; COM; 4H A; Hon Prog; NEDT; Spch A; *Western Ky U HS Jr Schol Prog; Pre-Med.*

BURNEY, Stephen Alexander
Clinton HS; Clinton, MS (25%-300) FBLA; *Hinds Jr Col; Health Related.*

BURNEY, Valerie Elaine
Provine HS; Jackson, MS; Band; Co-Cpt, Chldr; Tres, Chor; NHS; Rptr, Sch P; Cl Fav; Math A; Q&S A; Star Student; Vlbl; Jr Hist Soc; Cert of Attendence; Leadership Cert; *Morris Brown Col; Sociology.*

BURNHAM, Beth Marie
Chico Sr HS; Chico, CA; *Lit.*

BURNHAM, Erin Merle
Sierra Joint Union HS; Tollhouse, CA (6-306) GS; Math C; Monogram; Pres, NHS; SC; Swim; Math A; Rep, CSF; *U of Calif; Math.*

BURNHAM, Jeffery Lynn
St Johns HS; St Johns, MI (30-290) Var C; Bsbl; *Acct.*

BURNHAM, Keith Garland
Jena HS; Jena, LA (7-165) BS; FFA; Pres, Key C; NHS.

BURNHAM, Margaret Sina
Argyll Episcopal Acad; North Hollywood, CA; Ed, Ann; Chor; VP, SC; Bible C; Span C; Tres, Sal, S-T, Church Yth Group; *U of So Calif; Pre-Med.*

BURNHEIMER, Grace Alice
Minford HS; Minford, OH (1-115) VP, NHS; Citz A; I Dare You; Lion A; Most Out; Ed, Church Yth Newspaper; Most Stu; Pres, Bible C; Word of Life Schol; Secy, Art C; Span Schol Tm; Secy, Word of Life C; *Holzer Med Center Sch of Nurs; Nurs.*

BURNLEY, Susan L
Ayer HS; Ayer, MA (1-255) A Cap Choir; GS; Secy, Mu Alpha Theta; Tres, NHS; Pres, Rainbow; Bus Mgr, Sch P; SC; Hon Prog; MTA Merit A; Grand Cross of Color A; Attendance A; All 'A'S' A; *Brandeis Col; Med.*

BURNS, Agnes Ruth
Caldwell HS; Caldwell, TX; Drama; FHA; Sci C; VP, SC; Thes; Cl Fav; Spch A; *Sam Houston U; Hist.*

BURNS, Alisa Ann
Lake Braddock Secondary HS; Burke, VA (145-671) Chor; ARC; Span NHS; Mgr, Swim; *VPI; Hist.*

BURNS, Barbara Jeanne
Port Huron Central HS; Port Huron, MI (2-200) A Cap Choir; Band; Drama; Ensm; Hmrm; Madrigal; NHS; SC; COM; Hon Prog; Most Out; Opt A; Spch A; VFW Orator Win; VofDEM; *Olivet Col; Eng.*

BURNS, Brenda June
Norwood HS; Norwood, OH (25%-326) Co-Ed, Ann; Chor; Ensm; HCt; Girls Glee C; Yth-A-Rama Tn Talent Comp A; Bus Mgr, The Silhouettes; Top 5-Solo, Tns Invlv Reg Comp.

BURNS, Brian Dale
Cooper HS; Abilene, TX (25%-589) FTA; VICA; *Abilene Christian U; Secondary Ed.*

BURNS, Charles Eubank
Linsly Military Inst; Wheeling, WV (15-67) Thes; Var C; Bsbl; JV, Ftbl; Mgr, Wrest; Hon Prog; NMS; Best Drilled Cadet A; Fin, Declamation Contest; *Oral Roberts U; Chem.*

BURNS, Charles Hunt
White Oak HS; Jacksonville, NC (7-250) CYO; Drama; Key C; NHS; Bus Mgr, Sch P; Ftbl; Alg A; Hist A; Journ A; *E Carolina U; Social Sci.*

BURNS, Christopher James
White Oak HS; Jacksonville, NC (3-300) Chess C; Fr C; Math C; Sci C; JV, Bsbl; JV, Ftbl; Alg A; Hist A; Sci A; Fr A; *U of NC; Law.*

BURNS, Debby Denise
Wayne HS; Dayton, OH; Cpt, Chldr; Secy, Chor; Hmrm; SC; Gym; Missionette Qn; *Evangel Col; Phys Ed.*

BURNS, Denise Anne
Springboro HS; Springboro, OH (12-174) Band; Chor; Ensm; Secy, 4H; NHS; 4H A; Musician o-t Yr; Cpt, Flag Corp; 1st Chair, Flute & Piccolo; Pres, Yth Fel; *Cumberland Col; Mus.*

BURNS, Denise Lynn
Old Mill Sr HS; Glen Burnie, MD (25-490) Chor; Drama; Ensm; Mod Mus Mas; NHS; SC; VP, Thes; COM; MLS; Actress o-t Yr A, Thespian; Most Talented; Hon Thespian; Semi-Fin, Citizenship A; *Towson St U; Art.*

BURNS, Donald Lee
Henryetta HS; Henryetta, OK (25-100) Band; BS; Secy, Key C; NHS; *Georgetown U; Foreign Services.*

BURNS, Doris Jean
York Comp HS; York, SC (9-272) FTA; Co-Ch, Hmrm; NHS; Ntl Yth Conf; Span C; Tnns; Gr Marshal; Hon Prog; Jr Cl Steering Comm; *Clemson Col; Elem Ed.*

BURNS, Fredrick
O D Wyatt HS; Fort Worth, TX; Bus C; Ftbl; COM; Citz A; ARC A; Green Cross for Safety; A of Merit; Tex Readers C; Phys Fitness A; *SMU; Acct.*

BURNS, James Franklin
Lakeview Acad; Gainesville, GA (3-24) Ann; Pres, BC; Drama; Pres, Key C; VP, SC; Bsbl; Bkbl; Soccer; Tnns; Citz A; Kiwanis A; Math A; Opt A; Secy, Beta C; VP, S-T, Key C; Soccer A; *Pre Med.*

BURNS, Jennie Sue
Naylor HS; Naylor, MO (4-29) BC; Chldr; FHA.

BURNS, Joyce Ann
Jackson Mem HS; Jackson, NJ (75-389) Hmrm; Model UN; SC; Ftbl; Sftbl; Hon Prog; WW; Acad A; *St John's U; Acct.*

BURNS, Linda Joyce
Cooley Sr HS; Detroit, MI (2-630) FTA; Hmrm; NHS; SC; JV, Hockey; Fin, Sftbl; Tr; Alg A; Citz A; Hon Prog; JA A; Math A; Sci A; Acct A; Academic A; *Wayne St U; Acct.*

BURNS, Linda Lee
Pattonville Sr HS; Bridgeton, MO (468-820) Bus C; Chor; FBLA; 4H; Hmrm; Spch C; SC; Sftbl; Swim; Tnns; Tr; Citz A; 4H A; Hon Prog; Sci A; Spch A; GAA; Singing A's; *Gateway Col; Mus.*

BURNS, Lisa Ann
Hillsboro HS; Hillsboro, OH (12-28) MVP, Bkbl; Bkbl Schol; *Ohio U; Phys Ed.*

BURNS, Lori Ellen
Cherry Hill HS E; Cherry Hill, NJ; Hockey; Tr; *Phys Therapist.*

BURNS, Lynn Michelle
Paradise HS; Paradise, CA (32-350) Madrigal; Mus.

BURNS, Malinda Shepard
Bledsoe Co HS; Pikeville, TN (11-91) Ann; Band; BC; FHA; Mjrte; NHS; Amer Leg A; Cl Fav; HCt; Hon Prog; Swtht; Band A; FFA Swtht; *U of Tenn at Knoxville; Elem Ed.*

BURNS, Mark Edward
W Allegheny HS; Imperial, PA; Var C; Cpt, Wrest; Yth Fel; Wrest A; *Mach.*

BURNS, Marvin Ray
Thomas Car Howe HS; Indianapolis, IN; Chem C; Chess C; Chor; Fr C; Math C; Order/Arrow; Pres, Sci C; Bsbl; Swim; Wrest; Alg A; Chem A; Citz A; ROTC A; Sci A; *Computers.*

BURNS, Melodie Lynne
Hart Co HS; Hartwell, GA; BC; FBLA; Pres, FTA; 4H; Sci C; Cpt, Tri-HiY; Cpt, FTA; VP & Ch, FHA.

BURNS, Michael Frances
Tottenville HS; New York, NY (740-1191) Wrest; Service; Air Sea Rescue.

BURNS, Pamela Deniese
Central HS; Little Rock, AR; Chldr; COM; Citz A; *U of Ark; Acct.*

BURNS, Pamela Denise
North HS; Nashville, TN; A Cap Choir; Chor; FHA; Hist A; Math A; Sci A; Mus; Econ; Gym; *Fla A&M; Hist.*

BURNS, Patricia Lynne
29 Palms HS; 29 Palms, CA; CYO; Lit Mag; Swim; COM; Journ A; Swim A; *Col o-t Desert.*

BURNS, Penny Eileen
Bogue Chitto HS; Bogue Chitto, MS (4-60) BC.

BURNS, Rhonda Kay
Belleville Township HS W; Belleville, IL (1-850) Chor; Drama; Secy, Ger C; Hmrm; SC; Tr; Sci A; S-T, Church Yth Fel; Pep C; Hist C; DAR Outst Hist Stu A.

BURNS, Sheryl Lynn
Pathway Day Sch; Savannah, GA (3-18) BC; Chor; Drama; Pres, Hmrm; Co-Ed, Sch P; VP, SC; COM; HCt; GSct Cooking A; *Armstrong St Col.*

BURNSIDE, Christy Colleen
Chantilly HS; Chantilly, VA; Drama; FBLA; NHS; Thes; Mgr, Swim; Tnns; Tr; COM; Hon Prog; Math A; Yth Fel; HR; Jr NHS.

BUROCK, Lori Jean
Niagara Wheatfield HS; Sanborn, NY; Sch P; Bkbl; Tr; *Brant and Stranton Col; Interior Decoration.*

BUROW, Randall Rueben
Albert City-Truesdale HS; Albert City, IA (6-45) Ann; Band; Chor; Ensm; Bsbl; Ftbl; Golf; *Iowa St U; Bus Adm.*

BURPO, Mark Vernon
Sooner HS; Bartlesville, OK (4-290) Band; BS; Chor; Drama; Pres, NHS; SC; VP, Jr Cl; Amer Leg A; Elk A; Kiwanis A; *U of Okla; Architecture.*

BURR, David Lynn
Bowman HS; Wadesboro, NC; Chess C; Order/ Arrow; Bsbl; VP, Basic Water Safety C; BSct Citz A.

BURR, Richard L
Apollo HS; Simi Valley, CA (3-90) Ann; Chess C; Commercial C; Dbte Tm; Pres, Drama; FBLA; Hmrm; Mod Mus Mas; Ski C; VP, SC; Var C; VP, Sr Cl; Citz A; Cl Fav; Elk A; MLS; Yth Fel; Magic Talent A; *Moorpark Col; Dramatic Arts.*

BURR, Vickie Lorraine
Central Baptist Sch; Hampton, VA (3-12) Chldr; Chor; 4H; Rptr, Sch P; Tres, SC; Pres, Jr Cl; H of F; HCt; Type A; Yrbk, Mus, HR, Cert's; *Bus Adm.*

BURRACK, Frederick William
Stockton HS; Stockton, IL (16-98) A Cap Choir; Tres, AFS; Rptr, Ann; Band; Bus C; Fin, Chldr; Chor; Bus Mgr, Drama; Ensm; FBLA; Ch, FTA; Pres, 4H; Madrigal; Rptr, Sch P; Thes; Swim; Tr; God & Country A; 4H A; I Dare You; Lion A; Spch A; All St Choir; All Star Jazz Band; Band, Arion, A's; *Wartburg Col; Mus Performance.*

BURRAGE, Greg Prentiss
Nanih Waiya HS; Louisville, MS (2-33) BS; FFA; JV, Ftbl; Cl Fav; Sal; *Miss St U; Engr.*

BURRAGE, Krista Dawn
Concord HS; Concord, NC (35-231) Band; Fr C; FTA; Flaggirl; *U of NC at Charlotte; Ed.*

BURRAGE, Martha Lou
Antlers HS; Antlers, OK (8-100) Band; FHA; GS; Pres, 4H; Cpt, Mjrte; Sci C; COM; Citz A; Gov Honor Prog; Journ A; Swtht; Type A; 4H A; Okla Hon Soc; Top Ten Best Dressed Girls in St; *Okla St U; Interior Design.*

BURRELL, Alice Annette
Monticello HS; Monticello, MS; VP, Band; BC; JV, Chldr; S-T, Hmrm; Pres, SC; VP, Jr Cl; S-T, Soph Cl; Bkbl; JV, Tr; Cl Fav; Most Out; WW; Sup Rating, Drum Mjrte, St Ban Con; *Miss St U.*

BURRELL, Debbie Jinice
Temple Booth HS; Des Moines, IA; Chess C; Chor; Hmrm; Span C; Y-Tns; *AIB; Keypunch.*

BURRELL, Edith Roberta
John Bartram HS; Philadelphia, PA (89-900) Chor; Drama; Secy, SC; Secy, Sr Cl; COM; *Pierce Jr Col; Legal Secy.*

BURRELL, Kenneth Sterling
Enka HS; Asheville, NC; Band; Chor; Co-Ch, Hmrm; Bsbl; Ftbl; 1st, 2nd, 3rd Pl A's; Co & St Baptist Tr Meet; *Embry-Riddle Aeronautical U; Pilot Trng.*

BURRELL, Pamela Kathleen
Simon Gratz HS; Philadelphia, PA; FTA; Type A; Gym Tm; *Data Processing.*

BURRELL, Robert Edward
St Francis De Sales HS; Columbus, OH (167-215) Order/Arrow; Bkbl; Co-Cpt, Ftbl; Co-Cpt, Tr; Order/Arrow A; Ftbl Schol; *Salem Col; Acct.*

BURRESS, Julie Lynn
Booneville HS; Booneville, MS (1-98) Anchor C; BC; Math C; Sci C; Spch C; Cpt, Bkbl; Cpt, Tnns; Bio A; Chem A; Citz A; H of F; MLS; Phy A; Sci A; Spch A; Star Student; Val; Eng A; Bus Law A; Women's C A; *Miss St U; Aerospace Engr.*

BURRESS, Pamela Lynn
Pisgah Sr HS; Canton, NC (50-320) Ann; Tres, FTA; Mgr, Bkbl; NHS; Health Careers C; *Haywood Tech Inst; Nurs.*

BURRESS, Robert Derek
Pisgah Sr HS; Canton, NC (25%-350) Tres, Span C; Span NHS; Asst Pub Address Announ & Spotter; *Data Processing.*

BURRIER, Dawn Evelyn
N Central HS; Manly, IA (17-63) Band; Chldr; Chor; 4H; Sci C; SC; Bkbl; Sftbl; Mgr, Tr; Amer Leg A.

BURRIS, Brent
Whiteface HS; Whiteface, TX (1-24) Pres, FFA; Pres, Sr Cl; Pres, Soph Cl; Cpt, Bkbl; Cpt, Ftbl; Tr; Amer Leg A; COM; Cl Fav; All-Dist Ftbl; FFA Lone Star Farmer; *S Plains Col; Law Enforcement.*

BURRIS, Carolyn Heather
Woodlake HS; Woodlake, CA (78-130) Rptr, FHA.

BURRIS, Cynthia Ann
Muskogee HS; Muskogee, OK (10-700) AFS; Band; Chor; Secy, Fr C; FHA; Lat C; Rptr, Lit Mag; NHS; Sci C; SC; Bkbl; Tr; Beauty; Opt A; Yth Fel; Swtht, Jr Civitan; Jr Advisory Board; Okla Hon Soc; Miss Musk St Fair Qn; *Okla U; Dermatology.*

BURRIS, Gayla Kathryn
Yukon HS; Yukon, OK (35%-322) Chor; VP, FHA; Fin, GS; Pres, 4H; Spch C; Citz A; 4H A; Sub-Dist Pres, FHA; Co Press, 4-H; St 4-H Congress; Ntl Jr Horticulture Assn; St Horticulture Judging Tm; *Okla St U; Home Ec.*

BURRIS, Jeffrey Dayel
John Glenn HS; New Concord, OH (10-175) Var C; Bsbl; JV, Bkbl; Cr-Ctry; H of F; Pres A; Med.*

BURRIS, Laura Elizabeth
Green Forest HS; Green Forest, AR (3-70) Band; Secy, BC; Ensm; FHA; Ed, Sch P; Beauty; HQm; *Evangel Col; Mus.*

BURRIS, Lynda Carole
Muskogee HS; Muskogee, OK (15-575) Secy, AFS; Band; Secy, Chor; Ensm; Fr C; GS; Tres, Hmrm; Fin, Jr Miss Pageant; Lit Ral; NHS; Span C; Thes; Beauty; COM; Gov Honor Prog; HCt; Hon Prog; Lion A; Opt A; Opt Out Tn; Summa Cum Laude; Swtht; Yth Fel; VP, Jr Civitan C; Mus Qn Court; 1st Runner Up, Okla Jr Miss; Drill Tm Showstopper; *Hist.*

BURRIS, Melodee Hope
Woodlake Union HS; Woodlake, CA (3-132) Ed;
Ann; Fr C; Rptr, FHA; Hmrm; Rptr, Sch P; Span C;
Secy, SC; Bank Of Amer A; CSF; DARGCA; Best
Personality; *Lib Arts.*

BURRISS, Clifton Albert
Rogers HS; Toledo, OH; Band; COM; Brass Choir;
Mus.

BURROUGHS, Janna Renee
Waco HS; Waco, TX (25%-250) Ed, Ann; Band;
Chor; Hmrm; Key C; NFL; Span C; SC; Thes; Cpt,
Bkbl; HCt; Journ A; Q&S A; Yth Leg; Bkbl Ltr;
All-Tourn Tms; Vlbl; All-Dist Hon Men Bkbl; Pres,
Girl's Service League; *Baylor U; Nurs.*

BURROUGHS, Jayne Allison
Reseda HS; Reseda, CA; NHS; Ski C; Hon Prog;
Val; Vlbl; *Ohio St U; Vet Sci.*

BURROUGHS, Linda Deniece
DeQuoin HS; Du Quoin, IL (1-170) Band; Rptr,
Sch P; Alg A; COM; Citz A; Hist A; Journ A;
Rotary A; Church Yth Choir; Ldr, Pre- sch Choir;
Phys Fitness, 1st Aid, A's; Sch Hon Soc.

BURROUGHS, Rixie Lee
C Leon King HS; Tampa, FL (12-619) BS; Hmrm;
InterAct C; NHS; A-Ed, Sch P; Ch, SC; Tres, Sr Cl;
Mgr, Bkbl; COM; Citz A; Hon Prog; Journ A; PTA
A; Q&S A; Sanctuary Soc; Summa Cum Laude;
Yth Fel; Hon Stu; WW; Church Missions Board St
Conf; *Toccoa Falls Col; Christian Communications.*

BURROUGHS, Timothy Eugene
Friendship Christian Sch; Lebanon, TN; VP,
Hmrm; VP, Sr Cl; Pres, Jr Cl; Tres, Soph Cl; MVP,
Bsbl; Cpt, Bkbl; Cpt, FtbI; Ltr, FHav; HKg; HR; Head-
master's List; MVP, Bkbl; MVP, FtbI; Mr FCS;
Hon Men, All Dist Bkbl; *Cumberland Col; Acct.*

BURROUS, Elaine Kay
N Miami HS; Denver, IN (5-124) Band; VP, Chor;
Semi-Fin, GS; Mjrte; Pres, Mod Mus Mas; Pres,
NHS; Sci C.

BURROW, Adam Lee Jr
E Saint Louis Sr HS; E St Louis, IL (230-824) Chor;
Ensm; Cr-Ctry; Mgr, Soccer; Tr; Most Out; Pres A;
PA; Most Co-Operative; YEWO A; Military A;
Army; Elec.

BURROW, Alice Lee
East Side Sr HS; E Saint Louis, IL; Chor; PA; *Bradley U.*

BURROW, Deborah Jean
Union Springs Acad; Union Springs, NY (4-24)
Band; Chor; Rptr, Sch P; SC; Tres, Jr Cl; S-T, Soph
Cl; Arch; Bsbl; Co-Cpt, Bkbl; Ftbl; Golf; Cpt,
Hockey; Soccer; Co-Cpt, Sftbl; Swim; Tnns; Tr;
WW; Gym A; *Sou Missionary Col; Nurs.*

BURROW, Elie Lee
E St Louis Sr HS; E St Louis, IL (100-800) Chor;
Cr-Ctry; Tr.

BURROW, Judith Dianne
Little Rock Parkview HS; Little Rock, AR; Dbte
Tm; FBLA; Pres, Rainbow; Sci C; Span C; Spch C;
Spch A; *Briar Cliff Col; Spch.*

BURROW, Shirley Lee
East Side Sr HS; E St Louis, IL (110-1033) Chor;
NHS; PA; Best Secy; *Ill St U; Fashion Designing.*

BURROWS, Burges Edwin
Warren Acad; Warrenton, NC (2-27) Bus Mgr,
Ann; BC; Drama; Tres, Fr C; Hmrm; Monogram;
VP, SC; Bkbl; Ftbl; *NC St U; Bus.*

BURROWS, Jean Elaine
Lawrence HS; Lawrence, KS; Band; Lat C; JA A;
VP, JA; *U of Kans; Bus.*

BURROWS, Kevin
N Shore HS; W Palm Beach, FL (72-336) A Cap
Choir; Chor; Drama; Ensm; InterClub Coun; Key
C; Madrigal; SC; COM; Most Out; Rptr, Newspa-
per; Stu Conductor A; Human Relations Tm; Pro-
jectionist C; Fin, St Mus Con; WW; Best All
Around Boy; *Bethune Cookman Col; Mus.*

BURROWS, Laura Melissa
Warren Acad; Warrenton, NC; Ann; Cpt, Chldr;
Chor; Drama; Fr C; Ed, Sch P; Var C; Pres, Jr Cl;
Golf; Swim; Tnns; Beauty; HCt; Type A; *Meredith
Col; Elem Ed.*

BURRUS, Bonnie Jean
Rumson-Fairhaven Regional HS; Rumson, NJ
(20%-300) A-Ed, Lit Mag; Madrigal; NHS; *Psych.*

BURRUS, Byron Franklin
Montgomery Bell Acad; Nashville, TN (40-78)
Ann; Bus C; Lit Mag; Tr; Aux Lat; Hist A; Jr
Chamber of Com A; NEDT; Metals, Dist Meet; 1-2
Inch Off Sch Long Jump Record; *Vanderbilt U;
Hist.*

BURRUS, Dan Swan
Tupelo HS; Tupelo, MS (10%-350) A Cap Choir;
BC; Chor; Ftbl; Golf; COM; HCt; *Vanderbilt U;
Med.*

BURRUS, Debra Jean
Immanuel HS; Reedley, CA (1-92) Chldr; NHS;
Ski C; Tnns; CSF; Pep C; JV, Vlbl; *Nurs.*

BURRUS, George Roger
Montgomery Bell Acad; Nashville, TN (11-88)
Chess C; Sch P; Bkbl; Soccer; Tnns; Alg A; NEDT;
Fr A; *U of NC at Chapel Hill; Med.*

BURRUS, Jan Lovelace
Pisgah HS; Canton, NC; Band; Rptr, Sch P; Hand-
bell Choir; Accompanist, Church Choir; *U of NC;
Sci.*

BURRUS, Kate
Hillsboro HS; Nashville, TN; Lat C; SC; Secy, Soph
Cl; Bkbl; Tnns; Vlbl Tm.

BURRUS, Louie Eugene
Columbus HS; Columbus, GA (20%-400) FBLA;
Data Processing.

BURSELL, Brian George
Cascade Sr HS; Everett, WA (47-408) Pres, Chess
C; NHS; Nom, USMA; *U of Wash; Physics.*

BURSET, Carlos Manuel
Nuestra Senora de la Providencia; Rio Piedras, PR
(1-32) CYO; ARC; Rptr, Sch P; SC; COM; Cl Fav;
Vlbl; Conduct A; *Vet.*

BURSET, Luis Rafael
Academia Ntra Sra Providencia; Rio Piedras, PR
(6-58) Bus C; CYO; Chor; Drama; Math C; ARC;
Co-Ed, Sch P; Sci C; Span C; Spch C; Tnns; Tr; Bio
A; *U of Notre Dame; Industrial Mgt.*

BURSEY, Vincent Michael
Baker HS; Columbus, GA; Band; *Morehouse Col;
Bus.*

BURST, Barbara Joan
Half Hollow Hills HS W; Dix Hills, NY
(20%-2000) Co-Ed, Ann; NHS; Hockey; Hon Prog;
Yth Fel; *US Air Force Acad; Mus.*

BURT, Barbara Ann
Dallas Christian HS; Dallas, TX (3-55) A Cap
Choir; Ann; Chor; Drama; FHA; Spch C; Tnns;
HCt; Spch A; *Harding Col; Bus.*

BURT, Charlotte Ann
Bay City High HS; Bay City, TX; Rptr, Soph Cl; Drill
Tm; *Tex A&M U.*

BURT, Cynthia Marie
East HS; Buffalo, NY (3-25) Chldr; Sch P; COM;
HR; *Bryant & Stratton Col; Bus.*

BURT, John Collier
Glendale HS; Glendale, CA (300-600) JV, Ftbl;
UCLA; Archt.

BURT, Susan May
Franklin Regional Sr HS; Murrysville, PA (60-325)
AFS; Chor; Ski C; Cr-Ctry; Swim; Tr; Pres A; Fin,
AFS; Suzy Kayak A; *Sociology.*

BURT, Terry Sue
Robert E Lee HS; Tyler, TX (47-660) NHS; *Tyler
Jr Col; Art.*

BURT, William John
Arlington HS; Arlington Heights, IL (150-600) A
Cap Choir; Chor; Ensm; NHS; Mgr, Bkbl; JV,
Tnns; Mgr, Wrest; *William Rainey Harper Col.*

BURTON, Anita Denise
Vandalia Christian Sch; Greensboro, NC (1-13)
Math C; Monogram; Sci C; Mgr, Bkbl; Mgr, Soc-
cer; Mgr, Sftbl; COM; Star Student; *Pensacola
Christian Col; Elem Ed.*

BURTON, Carol Elizabeth
Vandalia Christian Sch; Greensboro, NC (1-14)
Co-Ed, Ann; Co-Cpt, Chldr; Chem C; Chor; Math
C; Monogram; Sch P; Span C; Var C; Secy, Sr Cl;
Gr Marshal; Magna Cum Laude; Val; Christian
Ldrship Schol; *Liberty Col; Acct.*

BURTON, Carolyn Janet
W A Berry HS; Birmingham, AL (25%-400) Ch,
AFS; Band; Community Yth Symph; All St Band;
Choir; Tenn Hon Band; Excel A, Lat; Acteens; *U of
Ala; Mus Ed.*

BURTON, Cheryl May
Lourdes HS; Chicago, IL (66-280) Chor; Drama;
COM; Hon Prog; *Bradley U; Religion.*

BURTON, David Reed
Loch Raven Sr HS; Towson, MD (20%-460) Band;
Ch, BS; Pres, Bus C; Chess C; Hmrm; Tres, Pol Sci
C; SC; Tres, Sr Cl; Ftbl; Swim; Pres, PROVE In-
vestment Co, Bus C; Precinct Ch, Bus C; Tres,
Young Republicans, Pol Sci C; NML; *U of Chi-
cago; Econ.*

BURTON, Diana Lindsey
Highlands Sr HS; Natrona Heights, PA (10-493)
Lit Mag; NHS; Span C; SC; Pres, Jr Cl; Bkbl; COM;
Hon Prog; NEDT; Yth Fel; 1st Cl GSct; *Geneva
Col; Psych.*

BURTON, Eric Dwayne
Paint Branch HS; Burtonsville, MD; *Tri State Col;
Law.*

BURTON, John Thomas
Robert E Lee HS; Tyler, TX (10%-700) A Cap
Choir; Band; City Conf; Ensm; Lit Mag; Madrigal;
NHS; ARC; SC; Sftbl; Swim; Tnns; COM; Citz A;
Hon Prog; NEDT; Opt A; ARC A; Yth Fel; Yth
Leg; Drum Major; Pres Clroom; *Baylor U; Bus
Adm.*

BURTON, Kevin Roy
Polytech HS; Sun Valley, CA; Co-Cpt, Bkbl; Ftbl;
UCLA; Police Sci.

BURTON, Kim Lauree
Cokeville HS; Cokeville, WY (1-12) Ann; Band;
Chldr; Chor; Pres, FHA; NHS; S-T, SC; S-T, Sr Cl;
S-T, Jr Cl; Rptr, Soph Cl; Hon Prog; Journ A; Type
A; *Utah St U; Special Ed.*

BURTON, Melvin
Lockland HS; Lockland, OH (4-60) Ann; BS; Pres,
NHS; Rptr, Sch P; Span C; SC; Pres, Jr Cl; Pres,
Soph Cl; Cpt, Bkbl; Tnns; COM; Citz A; WW; *Law.*

BURTON, Michael Charles
Sr Butler HS; Huntsville, AL; Drama; Rptr, Sch P;
Thes; Journ A; Art Publ; The New Renaissance; *U
of Ala at Tuscaloosa; Journ.*

BURTON, Paula Renee
Ruston HS; Ruston, LA (99-250) Chor; FBLA;
COM; Citz A; Marcher o-t Yr; Stu Teacher Day;
Cpt, Drill Tm; Keywanettes; *La Tech U; Elem Ed.*

BURTON, Sandra Jo
York Central HS; Retsof, NY; Chldr; GS; NHS;
Co-Ed, Sch P; Ski C; Secy, Sr Cl; Secy, Jr Cl; Secy,
Soph Cl; Soccer; Beauty; Regent Schol; Most Valu-
able Chldr; Jr Prom Qn; WW; *Saint Bonaventure
U; Journ.*

BURTON, Teresa Gaye
Lafayette Sr HS; Lexington, KY; Span NHS; SC;
Elem Ed.

BURTON, Valerie Lynn
Calhoun HS; Calhoun, GA (7-231) Ed, Ann; Band;
Co-Cpt, Chldr; Chor; Fr C; Hmrm; Fin, Jr Miss
Pagent; Math C; NHS; Orch; Tri-HiY; COM;
Journ A; Most Out; Q&S A; 2nd Pl, Region Liter-
ary, Piano; Talent, Schol A; Acad Letter; *U of
Tenn; Mus.*

BURTRUM, Tamala Susan
Miami HS; Miami, OK (10%-240) Bus C; FBLA;
Semi-Fin, GS; NHS; Hon Prog; Pres, Church Yth
Group; Teacher's Aide; *NEO A&M Col; Bus.*

BURUM, Amby Lynn
Milo Adventist Acad; Days Creek, OR; *Pacific Union Col; Registered Nurs.*

BURWELL, Bianca DeHaas
J E B Stuart HS; Falls Church, VA (24-429) Tres,
Fr C; FHA; French NHS; Lit Mag; Yth Founda-
tion; Jr HS Stu School Medal; Tutoring; Cert of A,
Stu Cooperative Assn; Drill Tm; Westminster
Choir; Keyettes.

BURY, Michele Ann
Martin Co HS; Stuart, FL (25-500) Secy, FBLA; InterClub Coun; NHS; Sci A; Civinettes; WW; Palm Beach Jr Col; Dental Hygiene.

BURY, Trude Ann
Glenbrook HS; Glenview, IL (29-597) Chor; NHS; JV, Bkbl; JV, Sftbl; Phy A; Foreign Lang A; Western Ill U; Acct.

BURYLO, Alice Anne
Holy Cross HS; Marine City, MI (2-41) Chor; 4H; NHS; Ski C; Mich St U; Animal Sci.

BURZYCK, Deborah Ann
Clarkston Sr HS; Clarkston, MI (33%-350) Band; Pres, 4H; Tnns; 4H A; 1st Cl, GSct; Mich St U; Vet.

BUSACKER, William E
Little Falls Central HS; Little Falls, NY; Bkbl; Ftbl; Golf; Tr; Fin, Regent's Schol; Honors Seminar; Wash Workshop; Siena Col; Pre-Law.

BUSBEE, Peggy Irene
Crestview Sr HS; Crestview, FL (22-270).

BUSBOOM, Anita Carol
Rantoul Township HS; Rantoul, IL; Chor; Span C; Cpt, Golf; Parkland Col; Child Development.

BUSBOOM, Donna Lynn
Rantoul HS; Rantoul, IL (70-390) Band; Chor; 4H; Lat C; Orch; IMEA, Dist St; Mus Schol; U of Ill; Mus Ed.

BUSBY, Cassie Lou
Nederland HS; Nederland, TX (14-462) Pres, InterClub Coun; NHS; VP, SC; Tnns; Magna Cum Laude; Spch A; HR; Humane Soc; Lamar U; Vet Med.

BUSCH, Andrea Faye
Milan HS; Milan, MI; Band; Fr C; Rptr, Sch P; Swim; Washtenaw Comm Col; Psych.

BUSCH, Melody Ann
Bishop Carroll HS; Wichita, KS (28-211) CYO; NFL; Secy, NHS; SC; Pres, Sr Cl; HQn; Hon Prog; Radio Broadcasting.

BUSCHBACH, James William
Oak Lawn Comm HS; Oak Lawn, IL (188-790) A Cap Choir; Ger C; Tnns; Church Chor; Off; Yth Fel; Valparaiso U; Bus Adm.

BUSCHE, Dale Robert
Penn Hills HS; Pittsburgh, PA (70-1250) Ger C.

BUSCHER, Tamia Marie
Anamosa HS; Anamosa, IA (3-150) Co-Ed, Ann; Secy, NHS; Hon Prog; Pres, Lib Organ; Patricia Stevens Career Col; Exec Secy.

BUSE, Joseph Daniel
Gordon HS; Gordon, TX (2-18) BC; FFA; Pres, 4H; VP, Hmrm; VP, Soph Cl; Bsbl; Bkbl; Cr-Ctry; Ftbl; Tr; Citz A; Cl Fav; Hon Prog; Math A; Sal; Yth Fel.

BUSH, Barbara Ann
John F Kennedy HS; Richmond, VA (5-309) Cpt, Chldr; Fr C; Math C; Mu Alpha Theta; Pres, NHS; SC; VP, Sr Cl; Cpt, Tr; Hon Prog; Math A; MLS; Swtht; MVP, Tr; Math.

BUSH, Carrie Francis
Magnolia HS; Anaheim, CA (25-450) Ensm; InterClub Coun; NHS; Span C; SC; JV, Tr; CSF; Pres, Pep C.

BUSH, Catherine Jane
Abbeville HS; Abbeville, LA; BC; Community Yth Symph; Drama; HiY; Orch; COM; Rifle Girl; Band; Superior, Piano Festivals; Band A; Accompanist, Stage Band.

BUSH, Charles M
Highland Park HS; Highland Park, MI; Band; Chor; ARC; Cpt, Bkbl; Ftbl; Swim; Tnns; Citz A; Hon Prog; Opt A; U of Mich; Communication.

BUSH, Cheryl Ann
Johnstown-Monroe HS; Johnstown, OH (15-145) Chor; VP, FTA; 4H; Math C; NHS; Span C; Ftbl; Alg A; Citz A; Yth Fel; Span A; Off Asst; Co Spelling A; Composition A; Ohio U Athens; Ed.

BUSH, Christopher Perry
Silsbee HS; Silsbee, TX; Fr C; JETS; Key C; Math C; SC; Pres, Jr Cl; JV, Bkbl; JV, Tr; Bkbl, Tr, Ltrs.

BUSH, Colleen Marie
Susquehanna Comm HS; Susquehanna, PA (10-110) Band; Chor; Drama; 4H; Rainbow; 4H A; Phys Therapy.

BUSH, Danielle Ena
West Side HS; Newark, NJ; NHS; Citz A; Med.

BUSH, Denise Lou
Madison Heights HS; Anderson, IN (32-375) Chor; Fr C; Hmrm; NHS; JV, Tnns; Bus.

BUSH, Diahann Yvonne
Metro HS; St Louis, MO (15%-35) Band; Drama; Mjrte; Sch P; Y-Tns; Bsbl; Tnns; Cl Fav; Hon Prog; Math A; Sci A; Secy, JA; Amer U; Eng.

BUSH, Georgette
West Side HS; Newark, NJ (40-280) FNA; Citz A; Hon Prog; Harriman Col; Fashion Designing.

BUSH, Hobert
South Vigo HS; Terre Haute, IN (18%-590) Math C; NHS; Bkbl; Cr-Ctry; Purdue U; Elec Engr.

BUSH, Howard Kennedy Jr
Burrell Sr HS; Lower Burrell, PA (210-350) Band; Order/Arrow; Order/Arrow A; Eagle Sct; JA; Leo, Astronomy, C'S; Pa St U; Ed.

BUSH, Jacqueline Denise
Mattie T Blount HS; Prichard, AL; Tres, Chor; Pres, FHA; Hon Prog; U of Sou Calif; Journ.

BUSH, Jocelyn Phillippa
Shaker Heights HS; Shaker Heights, OH (169-516) Chess C; Hmrm; SC; Ntl Achv Schol; Tres, Church Yth Group; Cpt, MVP, Vlbl; Fla A&M U; Mgt.

BUSH, Jocklyn Virginia
Manuel Arts HS; Los Angeles, CA (67-431) Co-Cpt, Chldr; Hmrm; Span C; Parl, SC; Bsbl; Northridge Col; Law.

BUSH, Kevin Roy
Zanesville HS; Zanesville, OH; F-Ed, Ann; Band; Community Yth Symph; Ensm; 4H; Hmrm; Orch; F-Ed, Sch P; Pres, Sci C; SC; Bkbl; Ftbl; Tr; Hon Prog; Math A; Sci A; Yth Fel; Joe Berg Math & Sci Seminar; 3 5 C; Marine Fitness A; Quiz Tm; U of Cincinnati; Archt.

BUSH, Linda Faye
Northeastern HS; Detroit, MI; Sch P; Tres, SC; Citz A; H of F; Hist A; Hon Prog; Journ A; JA A; Math A; Poet A; Sci A.

BUSH, Linda Joy
McCurtain HS; McCurtain, OK (1-14) GS; Secy, 4H; Secy, Hmrm; NHS; Secy, Jr Cl; Bkbl; Sftbl; 4H A; Pres Phys Fitness A; WW; Eastern Okla St Col.

BUSH, Linda Kay
Effingham HS; Effingham, IL (41-201) Band; Chldr; Sftbl; Tnns; Tr; St Scholar; Lakeland Jr Col; Elem Ed.

BUSH, Lorrie Eilene
York Acad; Shacklefords, VA; Ann; Tres, BC; Chor; Lat C; Sch P; Bkbl; Hon Prog; Old Dominion Col; Nurs.

BUSH, Luke Hunter
Echols Co HS; Statenville, GA (6-40) VP, BC; FBLA; Secy, FFA; FTA; VP, 4H; InterClub Coun; Tres, SC; Pres, Jr Cl; VP, Soph Cl; Cpt, Bkbl; Tr; Cl Fav; 4H A.

BUSH, Michael Clinton
Orange Glen HS; Escondido, CA (140-500) Secy, Order/Arrow; ARC; Bsbl; Cr-Ctry; Soccer; Tr; Order/Arrow A; Eagle Sct; Scribe & Sr Patrol Ldr; Jr Asst Sct Master; Prs, Church Yth; Jr Ldr, Acorn Trng; Order o-t Arrow Ordeal Tm; Palomar Jr Col; Hist.

BUSH, Pamela Kay
Trenton HS; Trenton, FL (5-43) Band; Secy, FBLA; Secy, FHA; Cpt, Mjrte; Pres, SC; Bkbl; HCt; I Dare You; Type A; Most Dependable; Campbell Col; Bus Adm.

BUSH, Perry Jonathan
John Muir HS; Pasadena, CA (20%-600) Band; Ch, InterAct C; Model UN; Rptr, Sch P; CSF; Poet A; Ch, Conservation C; CSF Seal Bearer; Whitman Col.

BUSH, Tammy Lynn
Robert E Lee HS; Montgomery, AL (320-649) Ann; Band; Chor; Drama; FHA; Thes; Band Ltr; Auburn U; Social Work.

BUSHAW, Michael Charles
Columbus HS; Columbus, GA; Pres, CYO; Chess C; Drama; InterClub Coun; Math C; Mu Alpha Theta; NHS; Sci C; Thes; Amer Leg A; COM; Citz A; Gov Honor Prog; Hon Prog; JA A; Math A; VofDEM; Ldrship A; NML; Outst Young Amer A; U of Ga; Med.

BUSHMAN, Tamara Jean
Anderson Union HS; Anderson, CA; A Cap Choir; Band; Chor; Ensm; 4H; Rptr, Hmrm; Madrigal; Tres, Rainbow; Mgr, Tr; Western Baptist Bible Col; Elem Mus Teacher.

BUSHNELL, Connie Elaine
Shawnee Mission NW HS; Shawnee, KS;

BUSHNELL, Lisa Geneane
Shawnee Mission Northwest Sr HS; Shawnee Mission, KS; Back Packing C.

BUSHNELL, Mary Maxine
Washington Sr HS; Cedar Rapids, IA (101-533) Band; Chor; Ed, Lit Mag; Orch; SC; Spch A; Mus As; Church Adult Choir; Yth Fel; Yth Coun; Cpt, Vlbl; Merit A; Prod-Dir, Lang Arts Video Broadcast; VP, Church Yth Coun; Sci.

BUSIC, Kenneth Albert
Woodham HS; Pensacola, FL (19-530) BC; CYO; Mu Alpha Theta; NHS; Span C; Math A; Pensacola Jr Col; Sci.

BUSKE, Bryan John
Pewaukee HS; Pewaukee, WI (46-138) A Cap Choir; Co-Ed, Ann; Chor; SC; Mgr, Bkbl; Ftbl; Hon Prog; 2nd Pl, Mus Contest; Ldr, Church Yth Group; Hotel-Restaurant Mgt.

BUSKEY, James Douglas
Fayettville-Manlius Sr HS; Manlius, NY; Band; Chor; Ensm; Hmrm; Orch; Var C; Bkbl; Cpt, Cr-Ctry; Ftbl; Soccer; Tnns; Cpt, Tr; Math A; Yth Fel; MVP, Cr Ctry, Tr; Athletic As; All Co, Cr Ctry; All Co, Tr; SUNY; Acct.

BUSKIRK, Paul Raymond
Derby Sr HS; Derby, KS (6-425) Band; Dbte Tm; Math C; NFL; Orch; Spch C; St Stu Congress; COM; Sci A; Spch A; Type A; Optimist Oratorical Contest Win; Outst Band Director's A; Physics.

BUSNELLI, Domenic
Secaucus HS; Secaucus, NJ (20-200) JV, Tr; Princeton U; Math.

BUSS, Jimmy De
Ventura HS; Ventura, CA (75-200) COM; God & Country A; BSct; Pres, Church Yth.

BUSS, Joanne Rose
Perkins Co HS; Grant, NE (1-36) Band; Chor; Dbte Tm; Drama; Ensm; Pres, FFA; Pres, 4H; Spch C; S-T, Jr Cl; JV, Bkbl; Tr; Citz A; 4H A; Hon Prog; Lion A; Yth Fel; Mgr, Vlbl; Eng A; U of Nebr; Biol.

BUSS, Victoria Elaine
Northeast HS; St Petersburg, FL (33%-600) Ann; VP, Span C; Sftbl; COM; Vlbl; Botany.

BUSSARD, Jill Carmen
Spring Lake HS; Spring Lake, MI (2-180) Band; GS; NHS; Sch P; Secy, Jr Cl; Tnns; Interlochen Scho; Mich St U; Bus.

BUSSARD, Jiselle Diane
Spring Lake HS; Spring Lake, MI (4-170) Band; Chldr; NHS; Secy, Sr Cl; Secy, Jr Cl; Secy, Soph Cl; HCt; Mich St U; Bus Ed.

BUSSE, Tamara Sue
Ladysmith-Hawkins HS; Ladysmith, WI (35-130) Band; Chor; Ensm; Orch; Arch; Bkbl; Sftbl; Swim; Tnns; Tr; NEDT; Pep C; Bkbl, Tr, A's; GAA; Vlbl; Jazz Ensm.

BUSSE, Timothy William
Alexander Ramsey Sr HS; St Paul, MN; Drama; Span C; Swim; Yth Fel; Yth Foundation; U of Minn; Commercial Art.

BUSSEY, Bret Alan
Marion Co HS; Guin, AL (3-57) BC; Var C; Bsbl; Bkbl; Ftbl; Candidate, Hugh O'Brien Yth Found; Auburn U; Bus Adm.

BUSSEY, Buck Ray
Marion Co HS; Guin, AL (2-42) Band; Pres, BC; BS; Drama; FFA; 4H; Var C; VP, Jr Cl; Pres, Soph Cl; Bsbl; Ftbl; COM; Cl Fav; 4H A; Sal; Yth Fel; Hugh O'Brian Yth Sem; Auburn U; Vet Med.

BUSSEY, Joey Xavier
T W Josey HS; Augusta, GA (130-234) Bus C; SC; Bsbl; Bkbl; Swim; Tnns; PTA A; *Morehouse Col; Acct.*

BUSSEY, John Paul
Citronelle HS; Citronelle, AL (28-174) Chess C; Opt A; Yth Coun; *U of S Ala.*

BUSSEY, Tina Marie
Harding HS; Marion, OH; A Cap Choir; Cpt, Band; Chor; Drama; Cpt, Ensm; Hmrm; Orch; ARC; Rptr, Sch P; Bkbl; Tnns; Gov Honor Prog; Interlochen Ntl Mus; *Ohio Weslyan Col; Mus.*

BUSSKOHL, Lynn Charles
Midwest HS; Midwest, WY; Ann; Drama; FFA; 4H; Bsbl; Bkbl; Ftbl; Sftbl; Tr; Wrest; 4H A; *Journ A.*

BUSTAMANTE, Patricia Milo
Deming HS; Deming, NM; Band; Pres, CYO; Bkbl; *Lamson Bus Col; Bookkeeping.*

BUSTETTER, Hilda Arlene
Springfield S HS; Springfield, OH; Drama; Math C; NHS; Span C; Thes; Up Bound; COM; Citz A; *Wittenberg U.*

BUSWELL, Shelley Lynn
Winona Sr HS; Winona, MN (65-479) Chor; Mjrte; NHS; Y-Tns; Yth Fel; *Lowthian Sch; Fashion Merchandising.*

BUTAKOW, Alexander
Petersburg HS; Petersburg, VA; Lat C; Lat NHS; Aux Lat; Sci A.

BUTCHER, Angela Lynn
Dallas Christian HS; Mesquite, TX; A Cap Choir; Ann; JV, Chldr; FHA; NHS; SC; Hist A; HCt; *Abilene Christian U; Interior Art & Design.*

BUTCHER, Angela Lynne
Dallas Christian HS; Dallas, TX (3-43) A Cap Choir; Ann; Cpt, Chldr; FHA; Lit Ral; Tres, NHS; SC; Hist A; HCt; *Abilene Christian U.*

BUTCHER, Janice Anne
Baker HS; Baker, LA; A Cap Choir; BC; CYO; Fr C; FBLA; *La Tech U; Med.*

BUTCHER, Karen Ann
Bellmont HS; Decatur, IN (1-300) Sci C; Span C; Mgr, Tr; *Sci.*

BUTCHMA, James Theodore
Greater New York Acad; Woodside, NY (8-72) Ann; Chor; NHS; Sci C; Ski C; Sftbl; Alg A; Hist A; I Dare You; Pres, Stu Assn; Stu Govt A; Yrbk Photographer; Eng A; *Andrews U; Mass Media.*

BUTED, Rolando Respicio
Jolani HS; Honolulu, HI (24-148) Chor; Cum Laude Soc; Pres, Ger C; St Stu Congress; Co-Ch, SC; Co-Cpt, Bkbl; Dennis Omchi A; Father Bray A; *U of Hawaii; Engr.*

BUTENSHON, Karol Sue
Hemet HS; Hemet, CA (5-500) A Cap Choir; Chor; Madrigal; CSF; DARGCA; Most Out; Pres A; Pianist, Jazz Band; Top Stu Schol A; Church Pianist; Flag & Banner Tm; Church Choir; *Math.*

BUTERBAUGH, Dana Marie
Waynesboro Area Sr HS; Waynesboro, PA (10-380) Cpt, Band; Chor; Ensm; Pres, FTA; NHS; Secy, SC; Amer Leg A; Most Musical; LIU Stu Forum; *Elizabethtown Col; Secondary Ed.*

BUTERBAUGH, Jodi Ann
Winfield HS; Winfield, KS (16-187) AFS; Community Yth Symph; Dbte Tm; Secy, GS; NFL; NHS; Orch; SC; VP, Var C; Bkbl; Tnns; Amer Leg A; Citz A; HCt; Hon Prog; Pres, FCA; Girls Nation; *Wichita St U; Pol Sci.*

BUTHMANN, Peter Edward
W Essex HS; N Caldwell, NJ; *Acct.*

BUTIKOFER, Julie Ann
Valley HS; Elgin, IA (3-70) Chor; S-T, SC; HCt; *Area I at Calmer; Nurs.*

BUTKOVICH, Bruce Joseph
Calumet HS; Calumet, MI (9-150) Pres, NHS; SC; VP, Jr Cl; Band; Fresh Cl Pres; *U of Mich; Med.*

BUTLER, Anna Michelle
Harlan HS; Harlan, KY; *U of Ky; Social Work.*

BUTLER, Anne Marie
Los Banos HS; Los Banos, CA; A Cap Choir; VP, AFS; VP, Chess C; Math C; Sci C; Span C; Pres, Jr Cl; Jr Girls Leadership; Soph Cl Coun; Sr Cl Coun; Calif Schol Fed; *Briar Cliff Col; Therapy.*

BUTLER, Annette Elaine
Beach HS; Savannah, GA; Chor; 4H; Sftbl; Tr; Mus A; Patrol A; *Savannah St Col; Bus Secy.*

BUTLER, Barbara Jeanne
Pinole Valley HS; Pinole, CA (120-430) Yth Fel; Sr Choir; Pres, Church Yth; *Heald Bus Col; Acct.*

BUTLER, Bernadette
Will Rogers HS; Tulsa, OK; Model UN; Swim; B Crocker A; *Models of Tulsa; Modeling.*

BUTLER, Carl
Jackson HS; Jackson, LA; F-Ed, Ann; Rptr, BC; Pres, Bus C; Pres, FBLA; Math C; Sci C; Pres, SC; Bio A; *La Tech U; Engr.*

BUTLER, Carolyn Sue
Wheaton HS; Wheaton, MO (1-31) Band; FHA; Pres, 4H; S-T, NHS; SC; Sftbl; Tr; Citz A; 4H A; Sal; Type A; Spelling A; Bookkeeping A; *Bus.*

BUTLER, Catherine Lee
Essex Junction Ed Center; Essex Junction, VT; Drama; Ski C; Span C; Yth Fel; JA; *Dance.*

BUTLER, Cathleen Elizabeth
Jane Addams HS; Bronx, NY; Chldr; Chor; Orch; Bkbl; Sftbl; Swim; Tr; Citz A; Cl Fav; Most Out; *Nurs.*

BUTLER, Cheryl Renee
Douglass HS; Oklahoma City, OK (50%-230) Tres, Band; Chor; Dbte Tm; FHA; Hmrm; NHS; Orch; ARC; Sch P; SC; Tnns; Hon Prog; Mus, HR, Gym, Certs; *Langston U; Ed.*

BUTLER, Craig Jerome
Manual Arts HS; Los Angeles, CA; Span C; ROTC A; Type A; Eng A; Counselor HR; *Cal Poly U-Pomona; Archt Drafting.*

BUTLER, Dana Leroy
Southwest HS; St Louis, MO (50-600) *Archt.*

BUTLER, David Allen
Twentynine Palms HS; Twentynine Palms, CA (7-186) CYO; VP, InterAct C; SC; Var C; VP, Sr Cl; Pres, Jr Cl; VP, Soph Cl; Bkbl; Cpt, Ftbl; Cpt, Tr; Wrest; Cl Fav; Most Out; Home Ec A; *Mirmar Jr Col; Criminal Justice.*

BUTLER, David Brenton
Batavia HS; Batavia, IL (1-211) Band; Lat C; Cr-Ctry; COM; Hon Prog; Mus A; Lat A; *Math.*

BUTLER, Diane Marie
Esperanza HS; Anaheim, CA; Art Talent; *Point Loma Col; Forestry.*

BUTLER, Donna Olivia
Ware Shoals HS; Ware Shoals, SC (10-104) Ann; Band; Cpt, Chldr; Fr C; Tres, NHS; SC; Assoc VP, Sr Cl; Miss Christmas Seal; Campaign Rep; *Clemson U; Elem Ed.*

BUTLER, Ellen McCrea
Ridgefield HS; Ridgefield, CT; Band; Chor; Drama; Hmrm; Orch; SC; Golf; Sftbl; Swim; Tnns; Tr; *Psych.*

BUTLER, Francis Oscar
Oakdale HS; Oakdale, LA; Bus Mgr, Ann; Ch, Band; VP, FFA; Ch, Hmrm; Pres, Key C; Lat NHS; NHS; Spch C; SC; Ch, Jr Cl; Golf; Swim; Tr; Cl Fav; Hon Prog; Chief Photographer; Ann A; *La Col; Law.*

BUTLER, Gwendolen Sue
Bellmont HS; Decatur, IN (20%-250) Band; 4H A; *Depaw U; Mus.*

BUTLER, James Allen
Ellet HS; Akron, OH; Ftbl.

BUTLER, James Hughes Jr
Battle Ground Acad; Franklin, TN (28-64) Chldr; Hmrm; Key C; F-Ed, Sch P; Span C; SC; Var C; Ftbl; Tr; Stu Director of Bank; *Southwestern U A T Memphis; Liberal Arts.*

BUTLER, Jannette Sue
Cottage Grove HS; Cottage Grove, OR (30-240) JV, Chldr; VP, Chor; Hmrm; SC; Pres, Soph Cl; Co-Cpt, Swim; Tr; COM; Fin, Homecoming Court; Outst Ath; Outst Sch Spirit; *Bus Adm.*

BUTLER, Jed Dana
Marion Co HS; Guin, AL (5-43) Ann; Band; VP, BC; BS; MVP, Drama; Rptr, FFA; 4H; Rptr, Sch P; Rptr, Sr Cl; Rptr, Jr Cl; Cr-Ctry; Tr; COM; Citz A; Cl Fav; 4H A; NEDT; *Auburn U; Psych.*

BUTLER, Jo Lynne
Troy HS; Fullerton, CA; Val; *Point Loma Col; Home Ec.*

BUTLER, Joseph James
Valentine HS; Valentine, NE (20-83) Band; Order / Arrow; Var C; Ftbl; Tr; Wrest; Order / Arrow A.

BUTLER, Judy Ann
Bucyrus HS; Bucyrus, OH (36-200) FHA; FTA; COM; FHA Degree As.

BUTLER, Leanna Joy
Marian Co HS; Guin, AL (17-60) Band; Drama; FHA; 4H; Sch P; Jr Cl; Soph Cl; Tr; 4H A; JA A; Bronze Metal, Band; Solo Ensm Medalist; Co Hon Band; 1st Chair, Concert Band; *Samford U; Mus Ed.*

BUTLER, Leigh Karen
Frederick HS; Frederick, OK; Band; FFA; FHA; Math C; NHS; Best Band Field Marcher; *OSU; Dentistry.*

BUTLER, Lisa Lynne
Ouachita Parish HS; Monroe, LA (10%-350) *Northeast La U; Acct.*

BUTLER, Lois Michelle
Cass Tech HS; Detroit, MI; Ger C; Hmrm; Secy, SC; COM; Citz A; Magna Cum Laude; Math A; Pep C; Pre-Med C; HR; *U of Mich; Med.*

BUTLER, Melinda Ann
Southwood HS; Shreveport, LA; *La Tech; Fashion.*

BUTLER, Michele Denise
Havana HS; Havana, FL; NHS; Secy, Jr Cl; Spelling A; Phys Fitness A; Span A; PA; *U of Fla; Communications.*

BUTLER, Rebecca Eleanor
W J Woodham HS; Pensacola, FL (2-530) A Cap Choir; Mgr, Ann; Chess C; Chor; InterClub Coun; Ch, Lit Mag; Math C; Mu Alpha Theta; NHS; Pres, Span C; Span NHS; SC; Sr Cl; Bkbl; Bio A; DARGCA; Hist A; Hon Prog; Most Out; NEDT; Sal; Sci A; Star Student; Theias; Pep C; Regional, St & Ntl Piano A's; Hist C; Span, Amer Writers, Eng, A's; *U of S Ala; Pre-Med.*

BUTLER, Robert Nicholas
Bartow Sr HS; Bartow, FL (2-275) InterClub Coun; VP, Key C; Lat C; Pres, NHS; Cr-Ctry; Tr; NMS; Star Student; High Q Tm; Brain Bowl Tm; Hons Car; Sr Hall of Fame; *Wake Forest U; Med.*

BUTLER, Rosemary Elaine
Tift Co HS; Tifton, GA; Mgr, Band; Chor; *U of Ga; Vet Med.*

BUTLER, Sharon Ann
Tallulah Acad; Tallulah, LA; Band; FHA; 4H; Mjrte; Ftbl; Tr; HQn; HCt; Lifeguard; Outst, Field; St High Jump Champ, Tr; Fin, United Tnager Pageant; Outst, Tr; *Little Rock Sch of Fashion; Modeling.*

BUTLER, Tami Beth
Odessa HS; Odessa, TX (20-800) Band; SC; Jr NHS.

BUTLER, Tammy Gaye
Marion HS; Guin, AL; Secy, Band; BC; Tres, FHA; 4H; Rptr, Sch P; SC; Rptr, Band; Miss VICA; Most Stu; Lieutenant, Rifle Corp; WW; Hist & Recr Ldr, FHA; Stu Lib; VP, VICA; Best Personality; *U of N Ala; Math Ed.*

BUTLER, Trina Jane
Meadowbrook HS; Byesville, OH (9-165) FHA; NHS; Cl Fav; Hist A; Type A; WW; Shorthnd A; Secy, Christ Ambas; Home Ec A; Pres, Missionettes; Future Homemaker Fin; Hon Banquet; Co-teacher, DAISIES; *Central Bible Col; Religious Ed.*

BUTLER, Woody
Goose Creek HS; Goose Creek, SC; BC.

BUTLER, Zella Nicholas
Grant Co HS; Dry Ridge, KY (1-129) Drama; Model UN; NHS; Tri-HiY; VP, Sr Cl; S-T, Jr Cl; Alg A; Bio A; Chem A; DARGCA; Hist A; Spch A; Type A; Val; Presidential Schol; Most Intelligent; *Eastern Ky U; Med Technology.*

BUTTERFIELD, Scott Hamilton
Glen Ridge HS; Glen Ridge, NJ (40-250) Spch C; Var C; Y-Tns; Bkbl; Cr-Ctry; Tr; Hon Prog; Men's Choir, Church; Nom, Church Hon Boy; Best Effort Tr Trophy; Outst Pioneer; *Purdue U; Forestry.*

BUTTNER, Douglas Chapin
E Henderson HS; Flat Rock, NC (40%-213) Band; Drama; InterAct C; InterClub Coun; Key C; Sch P; SC; Mgr, Bkbl; HKg; Pres, Serteen A; Schol A; *UNC; Communications.*

BUTTON, Nancy Lee
Mason City HS; Mason City, IA (33%-459) Sci C; Bkbl; Golf; Sftbl; Tnns.

BUTTRICK, John Andrew
Miami S Ridge Sr HS; Miami, FL; Band; Sci A.

BUTTROSS, Cynthia Marie
Canton Acad; Canton, MS (3-80) Ann; Band; VP, BC; Tres, CYO; Chor; 4H; Hmrm; VP, NHS; Sci C; VP, Span C; SC; Tres, Y-Tns; VP, Soph Cl; JV, Tr; Chamber of Comm A; Cl Fav; HCt; Band Rifle; Eng A; VP, Dixie Deb Social C; GSct; *Sci.*

BUTTS, Harriet Patricia
Martin Luther King HS; Philadelphia, PA (3-697) Math C; Mgr, Tnns; Hon Prog; Foreign Language A; *Calif St Col; Med Technology.*

BUTTS, James Timothy
John Foster Dulles HS; Stafford, TX (140-700) Band; Ensm; *Abilene Christian U; Psych.*

BUTTS, JoLynn
Lely HS; Naples, FL (10-300) Chor; Ensm; Madrigal; NHS; Sci C; Hon Prog; Most Out; St Scholar; All-St Choir; Summer Schol; *U of S Fla; Natural Sci.*

BUTTS, Micheal Dean
Fairview HS; Boulder, CO (200-350) Order/ Arrow; Bible Stu C; *U of Colo.*

BUTTS, Sandra Kay
Coffee HS; Douglas, GA (3-320) Ed, Ann; Secy, BC; FHA; Semi-Fin, GS; Math C; Sch Achieve Tm; Tr; Crisco A; Hon Prog; *S Ga Col; Acct.*

BUTZ, Denise Elizabeth
Northmont Sr HS; Clayton, OH (2%-500) Chor; Sch Achieve Tm; Rptr, Sch P; Swim; Cpt, Tnns; Mgr, Tr; COM; Hon Prog; Most Out; Tnns Ltr; Trustees Academic Schol; Most Improv A, Tnns; Acad Excel A; Sup Gold Cup, Piano Solo & Concerts; Ntl Fed of Mus Prog Piano A; *Heidelburg Col; Bio.*

BUUS, Cynthia Jean
Denfeld HS; Duluth, MN (151-400) Ann; Chor; Hmrm; Swim; Tnns; Tr; HCt; Social Director Power Board C; Girls C; Lib Cadet; Graduation Usher; *U Minn at Duluth; Phy Ed.*

BUXO, Luis Rafael
Colegio Espiritu Santo; Hato Rey, PR (20-96) Ann; Chess C; Math C; Tres, NHS; Pres, SC; Bsbl; Bkbl; COM; Hon Prog; *Reinseleer Polytechnic Inst; Mech Engr.*

BUXTON, Dale Maughan
Sky View HS; Smithfield, UT (11-611) Eagle Sct; *Utah St U.*

BUXTON, LaVeta
Baker HS; Baker, LA (24-374) Band; BC; Tri-HiY; *LSU; Nurs.*

BUXTON, Sid L
Stanton Pub HS; Stanton, NE (3-46) SC; Var C; Bkbl; Ftbl.

BUXTON, Sondra Rebecca
New Augusta HS; New Augusta, MS (10-42) BC; Chldr; Rptr, FBLA; Rptr, FHA; FTA; NHS; Rptr, Sci C; Secy, Span C; Up Bound; Bkbl; Sftbl; *Jones Co Jr Col; Med Tech.*

BUXTON, Vicki Lynn
Limestone Comm HS; Bartonville, IL (45-470) Fr C; Usherette; *Fine & Applied Arts.*

BUXTON, Virginia Pauline
Vancleave HS; Vancleave, MS (14-90) Band; Chor; Drama; Ensm; FHA; FNA; Jr Miss Pagent; NHS; Spch C; Thes; Cpt, Bkbl; Beauty; MLS; Most Spch; Sci A; Spch A; Star Student; VofDEM; Most Reliable; Miss Home Ec; Neatest; Miss Alto; *U of Sou Miss; Nurs.*

BUZARD, Barbara Caryl
Manheim Township HS; Lancaster, PA (40-400) Band; Chor; Hmrm; Ski C; Mgr, Tr; COM; Stu Train, Bkbl, Ftbl, Hockey, Sftb; *Rochester Inst of Tech; Design.*

BUZBEE, Terrence Anthony
St Bede Acad; Peru, IL (50-130) BS; Var C; Cpt, Cr-Ctry; Tr; Gov Honor Prog; Hist A; NEDT; MVP, Cr; Ctry *Armed Services-Army; Law Enforcement.*

BUZZANCO, James Paul
Tech Mem HS Y-Session; Erie, PA (40-400).

BUZZARD, Linda Jeannette
Perryton HS; Perryton, TX (45-150) Band; Rainbow; Tr; Citz A; *Freeman Jr Col; Secy.*

BUZZELL, Paul Francis
Don Bosco Tech HS; Boston, MA (13-211) CYO; NHS; Secy, SC; Secy, Jr Cl; Ftbl; Tr; Hon Prog; NEDT; Art A.

BUZZERIO, Marianna
St Joseph o-t Palisades HS; W New York, NJ (6-225) Chor; VP, NHS; Span NHS; Cpt, Cr-Ctry; Hon Prog; *Stevens Inst of Tech; Chem Engr.*

BUZZY, Alice Mary
St Elizabeth HS; Pittsburgh, PA (39-101) Chor; Ch, Drama; Ski C; Mgr, Sftbl; Alg A; Cl Fav; Star Student; Swtht; Nom, Dorothy Lombardi Schol Fund; *Mercyhurst Col; Home Ec.*

BYARLAY, Jean Ann
Osborne HS; Osborne, KS (4-52) Ann; Band; Chor; FHA; Secy, 4H; NHS; Bkbl; Tr; 4H A; Hon Prog; St Scholar; Type A; *Kans St U; Ed.*

BYARS, Cynthia Kaye
Hobbs HS; Hobbs, NM (42-490) A Cap Choir; F-Ed, Ann; Ensm; NHS; Hon Prog; All St Choir; Super Rating, Solo & Ensm Fest; *Okla St U; Acct.*

BYARS, Karen Stephanie
Lutheran HS; New Orleans, LA (5-48) Bkbl; NEDT; Rptr, Newspaper C.

BYBEE, Leslie Jean
Canyon HS; Canyon, TX; Drama; FHA; Church & Social Ministries; Vol, Home for Aged; Works with Interntl Exchange Stu; *Social Work.*

BYER, Kathy Lynn
Sullivan Central HS; Blountville, TN (10-448) BC; Lat C; Lat NHS; NHS; Bio A; COM; Hon Prog; Summa Cum Laude; *E Tenn St U; Med Tech.*

BYER, Mark Olin
Blaine Sr HS; Blaine, MN (262-734) Ann; Sch P; COM; *Anoka-Ramsey Comm Col; Conservation.*

BYERLEY, John David
Fort Scott Sr HS; Fort Scott, KS (50%-154) BS; Dbte Tm; NFL; NHS; Span C; Bsbl; Bkbl; Yth Fel; *U of Ks; Bus.*

BYERLY, Stephanie Renea
Burkeville HS; Burkeville, TX (4-46) Chor; Var C; Bkbl; JV, Tnns; Hon Prog; Vlbl.

BYERLY, Wendy Hudson
Leon HS; Tallahassee, FL (49-500) Anchor C; Chldr; Drama; NHS; Tnns; *U of NC at Chapel Hill; Bus.*

BYERS, Frank Dale
Boardman HS; Boardman, OH; Chess C; Math C; Ch, Yth Fel; Pres, VP Marketing, JA; *Youngstown St Col; Bus Adm.*

BYERS, Jennifer Ellen
Centennial HS; Champaign, IL; Span NHS; Election Board; Asst Swim Tm; *Parkland Jr Col; Foreign Lang.*

BYERS, Kathleen Ann
Sprague HS; Salem, OR (160-362) CYO; Yth Fel.

BYERS, Kathryn Elaine
Centenial HS; Champaign, IL (95-300) *Parkland Col; Interior Design.*

BYERS, Steven John
Nevada HS; Nevada, MO (10-163) AFS; A-Ed, Ann; BS; Demolay; Secy, FTA; Lat C; VP, NHS; Span C; VP, SC; Thes; Var C; Cpt, Cr-Ctry; Tr; MVP, Wrest; Amer Leg A; COM; Cl Fav; Hist A; Journ A; Math A; Regent Schol; ROTC A; *SW Mo St U; Eng.*

BYHAM, Barbara Jo
T R Miller HS; Brewton, AL (21-95) Chess C; Chor; FHA; Ch, FTA; Co-Ed, Lit Mag; Ed, Sch P; Span C; B Crocker A; Spch A; Yth Fel; Yth Leg; *Judson Col; Eng.*

BYINGTON, Marjorie Marie
Geronimo HS; Geronimo, OK (1-31) Ed, Ann; Drama; 4H; NHS; ARC; Sch P; Pres, Span C; Span NHS; SC; Bkbl; COM; Gov Honor Prog; 4H A; HCt; MLS; Val; VFW A; VofDEM; VP, Secy, Span C; St HS Hon Soc; Schol Medal & A; WW; *Cameron U; Med.*

BYL, Michael J
Spring Lake HS; Spring Lake, MI (50-200) Band; Orch; VP, SC; Cpt, Bkbl; Co-Cpt, Ftbl; Tr; *U of Mich; Acct.*

BYLER, Ronald Lee
Star Spencer HS; Spencer, OK; A Cap Choir; Band; Chor; Key C; Sch P; Lt Gov; Key C; Outst Vocal Stu; *Central St U; Mus.*

BYNES, Delise
Notre Dame HS; Staten Island, NY; Chor; Bsbl; Bkbl; Sftbl; Tr; COM; Cl Fav; YMCA Yth o-t Yr; Art, Tr & Field, Sportsmanship, A's; *U of Social Sci; Law.*

BYNOE, Christine Veronica
Adlai E Stevenson HS; Bronx, NY (28-822) Anchor C; Chem C; City Conf; Dbte Tm; Hmrm; InterClub Coun; Lit Mag; Model UN; NHS; Sch Achieve Tm; SC; Tr; Alg A; COM; Citz A; Hon Prog; Ntl Sci Symposium; Regent Schol; *Pace U; Nurs.*

BYNUM, Della
S Dade Sr HS; Florida City, FL; *U of Miami; Nurs.*

BYNUM, JaCinta Lajuan
Chapel Hill Sr HS; Chapel Hill, NC (178-410) Chldr; COM; *Howard U; Engr.*

BYNUM, James Jordan
Northside HS; Atlanta, GA (38-281) BC; Pres, Fr C; French NHS; Tres, Lat C; Lat NHS; Lit Mag; Model UN; Co-Ed, Sch P; Ftbl; Cpt, Soccer; Hist A; Hon Prog; Journ A; MVP, Soccer; *U of NC at Chapel Hill; Urban Planning.*

BYNUM, Katrina Denise
Williamsburg HS; Andrews, SC (5-105) Drama; FHA; 4H; Alg A; Eng A; *SC St U; Bus.*

BYNUM, Louise Lanius
Wilson Hall HS; Sumter, SC (9-56) Lat C; NHS; Secy, Jr Cl; Hist A; Sci A; Scorekeeper, Bkbl; Daughter's of Amer Colonists; Hist A; *Salem Col; Bio.*

BYNUM, Roxie Anne
Warren HS; Warren, AR (10%-140) Co-Cpt, Chldr; Chor; FHA; GS; Sch P; Amer Leg A; Yth Fel; *Ouachita Baptist U; Phys Ed.*

BYRAM, George Wayne
Haynesville HS; Haynesville, LA (5-53) Band; Bus C; VP, FBLA; FFA; 4H; Hmrm; Pres, NHS; SC; Cpt, Bkbl; Ftbl; Tr; Amer Leg A; NMS; *La Tech U; Med.*

BYRAM, Jeffrey Hunter
Haynesville HS; Haynesville, LA (6-83) Band; FFA; 4H; Bsbl; Bkbl; Ftbl; Swim; *La Tech U; Med.*

BYRAM, Kimberly Sue
Russell County HS; Russell Springs, KY (20-160) Co-Ed, Sch P; Rptr, Jr Cl; Rptr, Soph Cl; Cpt, Bkbl; Golf; Sftbl; Tr; Cl Fav; *Somerset Col; Phys Therapy.*

BYRD, Armenthia Elease
Therrell HS; Atlanta, GA (55-459) Drama; FHA; Walkathon; *Math.*

BYRD, Barbara Ann
Greenville HS; Greenville, AL (50-196) BC; S-T, FBLA; *Lurlean B Wallace St Jr Col; Bus.*

BYRD, Barbara Diane
Suffolk HS; Suffolk, VA; A-Ed, Ann; VP, Band; Chor; VP, FHA; GS; VP, NHS; ARC; Tres, SC; Secy, Sr Cl; Secy, Jr Cl; Tnns; Chamber of Comm A; HCt; Math A; Yth Fel; *Va Commonwealth U; Med Tech.*

BYRD, Charles Roy
Edgewood Acad; Elmore, AL (10-23) Bus Mgr, Ann; Hmrm; Rptr, Sch P; SC; VP, Cl Fav; Wrest; Amer Leg Orator A; Cl Fav; Order/Arrow A; WW; *Livingston U; Gen Stu.*

BYRD, Christopher Allen
E Mecklenburg HS; Charlotte, NC (51-550) Band; Lat C; Math C; JV, Bsbl; *U of NC; Math.*

BYRD, Debbie Elaine
Alexandria Sr HS; Alexandria, LA (20-350) Fr C; FHA; French Club; *La Tech U; Sociology.*

BYRD, Dora Suzette
Oakdale HS; Oakdale, LA; FHA; NHS; *Bus.*

BYRD, Ellen Rosina
Jessamine Co HS; Nicholasville, KY; BC; Chor; *Georgetown U; Modeling.*

BYRD, Erica Jeanine
Rocky Mount Sr HS; Rocky Mount, NC; Band; Rptr, Hmrm; SC; Pres, Yth Fellowship; Human Relation Explorer Post; *Psych.*

BYRD, Holly Shawn
Imperial HS; Imperial, CA (1-125) A Cap Choir; A-Ed, Ann; Chldr; Semi-Fin, Jr Miss Pa; Co-Ed, Lit Mag; Rptr, Spch C; Pres, SC; Var C; Secy, Sr Cl; Secy, Jr Cl; Secy, Soph Cl; Amer Leg A; CSF; Citz A; Cl Fav; DARGCA; MLS; Type A; Val; Secy of St, GS; Evangelism Tm; Vlbl; Best Personality; Comm Involvement Comm; Sunday Sch Teacher.

BYRD, Jaime Alice
Edward White Sr HS; Jacksonville, FL; Bus C; Secy, Drama; Ensm; Semi-Fin, Jr Miss Pa; Secy, Thes; Type A; 2nd Runnerup, HS Pageant; Bus Ed, Eng, A's; Fin, Miss Ntl Tnager Pageant; *Sanford U; Mus.*

BYRD, Jim Bob
Eldorado HS; Eldorado, TX (3-40) Band; Dbte Tm; Drama; Ensm; Pres, Math C; NHS; Var C; Bkbl; JV, Ftbl; Tnns; Journ A; Math A; NEDT; Sal; Spch A; NML; Pres, Treas, Spch C; WW; WW Mus Stu in Amer HS; Drum Major; *Baylor U.*

BYRD, Linda Diane
Days Creek HS; Days Creek, OR (4-18) Chor; Pres, NHS; SC; Sftbl; Tr; HCt; Ntl Choir Director A; *Sou Oreg St U; Nurs.*

BYRD, Mary Margaret
Jackson Prep Sch; Jackson, MS (91-178) A Cap Choir; Chor; Ensm; Yth Fel; Voice Schol; Miss Fed of Women's Mus Schol; Church Singing Group; Miss Opera Assn; *Samford U; Voice.*

BYRD, Merry Lynn
Tivy HS; Kerrville, TX (5%-241) Ger C; InterAct C; SC; Tnns; NMS; Rotary A; FCA; Principal's Tm; *Eng.*

BYRD, Michael Anthony
McClymonds HS; Oakland, CA; Hmrm; Lit Mag; NHS; Sch P; Sci C; Span C; SC; Var C; Fin, Tnns; COM; Citz A; Hon Prog; ROTC A; Star Student; Co-Cpt & Fin, Riflery; Riflery A; Cadet of Quarter A; Ath A; Military Sci Test A; Sup Cadet A; *UCLA; Med Sci.*

BYRD, Michael Craig
Archbishop Carroll HS; Washington, DC (78-160) Chor; Hmrm; Rptr, SC; Bsbl; Bkbl; Ftbl; Citz A; Ntl Conf Chr & Jews; Swim A; Pres, CYF; Mus A; *Johnson C Smith U; Computer Sci.*

BYRD, Nancy Lynn
Smithfield-Selma HS; Smithfield, NC (1-400) Ann; Chor; Fr C; GS; Hmrm; Math C; NHS; SC; COM; Chem A; Gr Marshal; VP, Pep C; _Sct; Church Adm Board; Pres, UMYF; Handbell Choir; VP, Flora Canady Mus C; NCMTA St Piano Contest.

BYRD, Preston Carl
Clarendon HS; Clarendon, TX (10%-62) FFA; FTA; NHS; Order/Arrow; Ftbl; Tr; Hist A; Health A; *Hardin-Simmons U; Psych.*

BYRD, Rodney Allen
Hernando HS; Brooksville, FL (147-400) Var C; Bkbl; Ftbl; Tr; Most Out; *Fla A&M U; Bus Adm.*

BYRD, Saconda Venita
Charlotte HS; Rochester, NY; Cpt, Bkbl; JA A; MLS; *MCC; Nurs.*

BYRD, Sandra Gaye
Raytown Sr HS; Raytown, MO (5%-30) Chldr; Chor; Sci C; Spch C; SC; Y-Tns; Swim; Citz A; Best Dressed A; Cream o-t Crop A; Phy Fitness A; Poise A; *UMKC; Nurs.*

BYRD, Sandra Jean
Paxon Sr HS; Jacksonville, FL; Band; VP, Civinettes; Band Ltr; Alumni Assn; *Fla Jr Col.*

BYRD, Sara Lou
Freedom HS; Morganton, NC (30-450) AFS; BC; Chldr; Hmrm; Ski C; COM; Acad Achv A; Cert, Newspaper Staff; Appalachian St U, Enrichment Prog; Nom, Cullowee Enrichment Prog; *U of NC; Bus.*

BYRD, Sharon Anita
Hernando HS; Brooksville, FL; Band; Chor; Elk A; WW; *U of Fla; Law.*

BYRD, Susan Ann
Southern HS; Durham, NC (9-311) NHS; VFW Essay Contest; HR; *Watts Sch of Nurs; Registered Nurs.*

BYRD, Teresa Diane
S Iredell HS; Barium Springs, NC; FHA; Math C.

BYRD, Terri Lynn
Clarendon HS; Clarendon, TX (4-42) Co-Ed, Ann; Chor; Drama; VP, FTA; NHS; COM; Hon Prog; Yth Fel; Pres, Acteens; FTA A; WW; *Hardin-Simmons U; Sociology.*

BYRD, Tony Charles
Patrick Henry HS; Glade Spring, VA; Var C; Bsbl; Bkbl; Sftbl; HCt; *Va Tech Col; Construction Mgr.*

BYRNE, Bernie Bernard
Custer Co HS; Westcliffe, CO (2-21) Drama; Tres, InterAct C; NHS; Rptr, Sch P; Ski C; SC; Pres, Jr Cl; Mgr, Bkbl; Mgr, Ftbl; Tr; Alg A; HCt; Math A; *Bus.*

BYRNE, Julie Elizabeth
Acad of Our Lady of Mercy; Milford, CT (3-88) Lit Mag; F-Ed, Sch P; Hon Prog; NEDT; Eng A; *Albertus Magnus Col; Archt.*

BYRNE, Lisa Michelle
Livingston HS; Livingston, TX (4-175) Band; Drama; VP, FHA; GS; NHS; Span C; Spch C; Thes; *Stephen F Austin Col; Secondary Ed.*

BYRNE, Loretta Marlene
Arlington HS; Arlington Heights, IL (15-578) Chor; Cum Laude Soc; Mod Mus Mas; NHS; Hon Prog; Summa Cum Laude; *Ind U; Mus.*

BYRNE, Michael Wade
Livingston HS; Livingston, TX (8-175) Chor; Madrigal; NHS; Bsbl; Ftbl.

BYRNE, Rich
Walter Johnson HS; Bethesda, MD; A Cap Choir; AFS; Band; Chor; Community Yth Symph; Drama; Ensm; Madrigal; Orch; Thes; BSct; James Randolph Mem A; *Mus.*

BYRNES, Kathleen Jean
Holy Cross HS; Riverside, NJ (6-378) Drama; Semi-Fin, GS; NHS; Thes; Cpt, Tr; Hon Prog; *Psych.*

BYROM, Eric Von
Monterey HS; Monterey, CA (5-50) Dbte Tm; NHS; VP, Sr Cl; Cpt, Bsbl; Cpt, Ftbl; Cl Fav; Hon Prog; Most Out; MVP, Bsbl & Ftbl; *Long Beach St U; Criminology.*

BYROM, Margaret Elaine
Heritage Baptist Sch; Sand Springs, OK (1-3) Chldr; Secy, SC; Bkbl; Sftbl; *Tulsa Jr Col; Acct.*

BYRON, Joy Bernadette
Boro Hall Acad; Brooklyn, NY (1-18) Schol As; *CUNY; Ba.*

BYRUM, Gail Singletary
John A Holmes HS; Edenton, NC (20-184) Chor; Secy, FHA; Secy, Hmrm; Tnns; Yth Fel; Stu Govt A; Bio C; Cl Off; Tn Democrats; *Peace Col; Elem Ed.*

BYRUM, Karin Lynn
Robert Rogers HS; Toledo, OH; Chor; Sftbl; *Med.*

BYRUM, Pady Bart
McCurtain HS; McCurtain, OK (1-11) Pres, Jr Cl; Bsbl; Bkbl; Hist A; HKg; Phys Fitness; PA, 11 Yrs; *NEOSU; CPA.*

BYTWERK, Scott Edward
Spring Lake HS; Spring Lake, MI (20-120) Model UN; MVP, Swim; *Kalamazoo Col; Pre-Law.*

BYWATER, Diane Bernice
Dublin HS; Dublin, CA; GS; Hmrm; Model UN; SC; Tr; B Crocker A; CSF; Chem A; Type A; Principal's HR.

C

CABALLERO, Mario Luis
McAllen HS; McAllen, TX (17-751) Co-Ch, Chor; Ger C; Secy, Key C; Math C; Mu Alpha Theta; VP, NHS; COM; *Tex A&M U; Engr.*

CABALLERO, Mercedes
Notre Dame HS; Caguas, PR (2-136) Ann; CYO; Chem C; Chor; Drama; GS; 4H; Hmrm; Spch C; SC; MVP, Var C; Sftbl; Swim; COM; Cl Fav; Hon Prog; Sci A; Spch A; MVP, Vlbl; Sch Hons; Ath A; *Marymount Col of Va; Secretarial Sci.*

CABALLERO, Ramon Luis
Colegio San Antonio Abad; Humacao, PR (1-86) Var C; Cr-Ctry; Cpt, Swim; Tr; Math A; *Johns Hopkins U; Med.*

CABALLEROS, J Adrian
Robert H Goddard HS; Roswell, NM; Band; Bkbl; Ftbl; Yth Fel; *U of NM; Aeronautics.*

CABANAW, Cheryl Ann
Sooner HS; Bartlesville, OK; Co-Ch, AFS; Band; Co-Cpt, Mjrte; NHS; COM; Hon Prog; Yth Fel; Shorthand A; Demolay Swtht; Pres, Candystriper; Pres, Da Capo Mus C; St Parl, Okla Fed of Mus C; *Okla St U; Acct.*

CABANELLAS, Marilyn Ivette
Jose de Diego HS; Mayaguez, PR (5-276) Chem C; Drama; GS; Hmrm; Phys C; ARC; Pres, Sch Achieve Tm; Sci C; Span C; SC; Bio A; COM; Hon Prog; JA A; Magna Cum Laude; Most Out; Swtht; *U of Puerto Rico at Mayaguez; Botany.*

CABANISS, Teresa Annette
York Comprehensive HS; York, SC (20-200) FBLA; Secy, FHA; JA A; Jr Marshall; *York Tech Col; Secy.*

CABE, Arnold Edward
Pisgah Sr HS; Canton, NC; Health Careers; Off Maintenance C.

CABE, Deborah Ann
Berrien Co HS; Nashville, GA; Rptr, Band; BC; Rptr, Ensm; Tri-HiY; Most Out; Chaplain, Tri-Hi-Y; *U of Ga; Mus Therapy.*

CABELL, Debrah Ann
Marion Co HS; Lebanon, KY (26-298) Drama; FHA; Pres, FTA; Fin, Jr Miss Pagent; NHS; Spch C; SC; Thes; MLS; Spch A; *E Ky U; Surgical Tech.*

CABELL, Guy Neville
Albia Community HS; Albia, IA (11-148) Chess C; Demolay; Math C; Sch Achieve Tm; Span C; COM; Math A; St Scholar; U of Iowa Schol A; U of Iowa Engr Sch A; UDC Schol; *U of Iowa; Engr.*

CABILLOT, Jean Marie
Duluth E Sr HS; Duluth, MN; Chor; Dbte Tm; Lit Mag; Spch C; Swim.

CABLE, Kenna Lea
McKinley HS; Canton, OH; Ann; Drama; Hmrm; Y-Tns; COM; Citz A; ARC A; DGW A, Schol; *Math.*

CABRERA, Filemon Tecson
John F Kennedy HS; Tumon, GUAM (10-511) Band; CYO; Chess C; Chor; Math C; NHS; St Stu Congress; Tnns; Alg A; COM; Math A; Most Out; Sacristan; Sci A; Yth Leg; Newscarrier o-t Yr; 2nd Pl, Sci Fair; 1st Pl, Math; Newscarrier o-t Mo; Hon Band; *San Jose St U; Mech Engr.*

CABRERA, Lourdes
Juan Jose Osuna HS; Hato Rey, PR (2-101) A Cap Choir; CYO; Chldr; Chor; FHA; FTA; Lit Ral; ARC; Sch P; Span C; Swim; Hist A; JA A; ARC A; *U of Cayey; Occupational Therapy.*

CABRERO, Nancy Esther
HS of Mus And Art; New York, NY; Chor; City Conf; Drama; Ch, Span C; Arch; Cpt, Sftbl; Swim; Beauty; COM; Citz A; Hon Prog; Star Student; Vocal Mus A; Mus Achv A; Outst Chor Achv; Sewing Achv Cert; *Marymount Col; Sociology.*

CACERES, Mercedes
Our Lady of Good Counsel HS; Newark, NJ (9-76) CYO; Chess C; Lat C; Co-Ed, Sch P; Rptr, Span C; Citz A; *Newark Col; Med.*

CADAVONA, Belia Magaoay
Maui HS; Kahului Maui, HI; FBLA; FNA; Pres,
Span C; MVP, Swim; MVP, Tnns; Miss Sampa-
guita; *U of San Francisco; Nurs.*

CADDELL, Debra Ann
New Braunfels HS; New Braunfels, TX (94-290)
Ann; Band; Fr C; FTA; Sci C; Tnns; Yth Fel; Tnns
A; *Colo St U; Phys Ed.*

CADDELL, Serena Lynn
Spackenkill HS; Poughkeepsie, NY (33%-250)
Band; Jazz Band; Ch, Episcopalian Yth C; Art Hob-
bie; Lifeguard & Instructor, Swim.

CADE, Beverly Marie
Rufus King HS; Milwaukee, WI (150-225) Inter-
Urban Health Career Cert; *Psych.*

CADE, Cheryl Angela
Bakersfield HS; Bakersfield, CA; *Bakersfield Col;
Bus Ed.*

CADE, Christopher Gerald
Bakersfield HS; Bakersfield, CA (71-470) Chor;
Ensm; Yth Fel; *Cal St U at Long Beach; Civil Engr.*

CADE, Jeff Glenn
Robert E Lee HS; Tyler, TX (33%-800) Chem C;
VP, FFA; VP, 4H; Mgr, Ftbl; Sftbl; 4H A; Hon
Service Organization; 2nd Hgh Point, Ntl Yth
House Cong; *Abilene Christian U; Bus.*

CADMAN, Kendelyn Anne
Penncrest HS; Media, PA (150-450) Camper in
Leadership Training; *Letourneau Col; Camping &
Rec Adm.*

CADMAN, Linda Rae
Penncrest HS; Media, PA (59-450) Yth Fel; *Forestry.*

CADMUS, Raymond Jay
Saugerties HS; Saugerties, NY (20%-250) Band;
Chor; Sch P; Soccer; Tr; Wrest; Hon Prog; *Broad-
casting.*

CADOGAN, John Kevin
Don Bosco Tech HS; Boston, MA (7-211) CYO;
BSct.

CADWELL, Amy Lynette
Mayfield Sr HS; Mayfield Hts, OH (199-520) A
Cap Choir; Chor; Secy, Drama; Model UN; Ski C;
Spch C; Thes; Yth Fel; *Miami U of Ohio; Bus.*

CADWELL, Ann Louise
Columbia HS; Decatur, GA (3-327) VP, BC; Com-
munity Yth Symph; InterClub Coun; Math C;
Model UN; Mu Alpha Theta; NHS; Orch; SC;
Sftbl; COM; Gov Honor Prog; Hon Prog; Gym;
Schol As; Violin A; Flag Corp; VP, Church Yth
Coun; *Law.*

CADWELL, Jeanette Diane
Thomas Jefferson HS; Pittsburgh, PA (5-420) A
Cap Choir; Chor; Hon Prog; Math A; Pres, Church
Choir; Yth Coun; Sr High Fellowship; Deacon,
Church.

CADWELL, Nancy Louise
Pymatuning Valley HS; Andover, OH (1-106)
Drama; Rptr, Sch P; Thes; Amer Leg A; I Dare
You; Math A; MLS; NMF; NMS; Spch A; Val;
VofDEM; Yth Fel; WW; Actress o-t Evening; Span
A; Govt A; *Geneva Col; Life Support Technology.*

CADY, Susan G
E Providence Sr HS; E Providence, RI; Ed, Ann;
Chor; Mgr, Drama; Fr C; Rptr, Sch P; Tnns; Citz A;
JA A; Kiwanis A; PTA A; S-T, Bowl Tm; Portu-
guese C; Rptr, PTSA; *URI; Nurs.*

CAESAR, Karen Denise
Percy L Julian HS; Chicago, IL (13-280) Secy, Bus
C; Chor; Secy, FBLA; SC; VP, Jr Cl; Cpt, Tr; Most
Out; Regent Schol; Yth Fel; Mgr, Tr; Usher Board;
Church Bus C; *Wartburg Col; Bus Adm.*

CAESAR, Linda Fay
Carroll HS; Monroe, LA; Fr C; Hmrm; SC; *Sou U;
General Stu.*

CAESAR, Lori Ione
Percy L Julian HS; Chicago, IL (10%-610) Band;
Bus C; FBLA; Hmrm; Math C; SC; Tr; Citz A; Hon
Prog; Most Out; Sci A; Jr Usher Board; Fashion
Career C; GAA; Essay A; *Med.*

CAFAZZO, Carmel Jean
Rham HS; Hebron, CT (45-181) Chldr; Chor;
Drama; Fr C; FBLA; FHA; Rptr, Sch P; Ski C;
Bsbl; Hist A; Hon Prog; Math A; *Mitchell Col;
Marine Bio.*

CAFFEY, Vivian Jewel
Central HS; San Angelo, TX (13-671) A Cap Choir;
NHS; Hon Prog; Opt A; Chorale Girl o-t Yr; *Abi-
lene Christian U; Elem Ed.*

CAGE, James William
Central HS; Phoenix, AZ (2-500) Ger C; NHS;
Order/Arrow; Sci C; SC; COM; Math A; NMF;
NMS; Opt Out Tn; Order/Arrow A; Sal; Sci A;
Eagle Sct; *Occidental Col; Sci.*

CAGE, Melanie Jean
Eastmoor HS; Columbus, OH; Chldr; Hmrm; SC;
Massey Jr Col; Fashion Design.

CAGER, Carol Denise
Nichols Senn HS; Chicago, IL; CYO; Secy, Chor;
Hmrm; ARC; SC; Bkbl; Swim; Tr; *Robert Morse
Col; Bus Adm.*

CAGER, Mattie Arlett
Nicholas Senn HS; Chicago, IL; Chldr; Chor;
FBLA; Math C; Mod Mus Mas; ARC; Bsbl; Bkbl;
Soccer; Sftbl; Beauty; COM; Cl Fav; Math A; Most
Out; Poet A; Swtht; *Harry S Truman Col; Bus.*

CAGLE, Lawana Jan
Cass HS; Cassville, GA (10%-200) BC; Chldr;
FBLA; Sci C; Secy, Jr Cl; Sftbl; COM; Chem A;
HCt; Superlative Sr; *Marietta-Cobb Voc Sch; Acct.*

CAGNOLATTI, Lisa Dianne
Inglewood HS; Inglewood, CA; Band; JV, Chldr; Fr
C; Hmrm; Model UN; SC; S-T, Soph Cl; CSF; HCt;
NEDT; MVP, Vlbl.

CAHILL, Lyle Duane
Ord HS; Ord, NE (3-96) Pres, FFA; Tres, 4H;
NHS; Sci C; Hon Prog; Union Pacific Schol; FFA
St Farmer; *Bob Jones U; Pre-Med.*

CAHILL, Mary Rita
Dedham HS; Dedham, MA (37-528) *St Mary's
Col-Ind; Journ.*

CAHOON, Melissa Ann
Scranton Central HS; Scranton, PA (33%-358)
Band; Tres, Fr C; NHS; Orch; First Cl, GSct; *Key-
stone Jr Col; Med Secy.*

CAIN, Becky Lynn
New Bloomfield R-III HS; New Bloomfield, MO
(1-34) Co-Ed, Ann; Band; Cpt, Chldr; Chor; Secy,
Fr C; NHS; Rptr, Sch P; Var C; Sftbl; Tr; COM;
HCt; Kiwanis A; DAR Hist A; *Lincoln U; Bus.*

CAIN, Beverly Diane
Amphitheater HS; Tucson, AZ (314-384).

CAIN, Candy Diane
Burges HS; El Paso, TX (10%-693) A Cap Choir;
Co-Cpt, Chldr; Chor; Ensm; 4H; Hmrm; InterClub
Coun; NHS; SC; Fin, Soph Cl; Bkbl; Swim; Tr;
COM; Citz A; Pres A; *Rice U; Pre-Med.*

CAIN, Cindy Carol
Bridgeton Sr HS; Bridgeton, NJ; Chess C; 4H; S-T,
Hmrm; Up Bound; JV, Hockey; JV, Tr; Citz A; Cl
Fav; God & Country A; Masonic A; Most Out; Pres
A; ARC A; Star Student; St Scholar; Yth Fel; WA,
Rainbow Girl.

CAIN, Danna Beth
Kirkwood HS; Kirkwood, MO (158-597) JV,
Chldr; F-Ed, Sch P; Tri-HiY; HCt; Pom Pon Girl;
KU; Journ.

CAIN, David Trent
Virden HS; Virden, IL (20-90) Band; JV, Bkbl;
NMS; *W III U; Math.*

CAIN, Gayle Rena
Pasadena HS; Pasadena, TX; Band; FHA; FTA;
Hmrm; JETS; SC; Bkbl; Cr-Ctry; Sftbl; MVP, Tr;
Most Out.

CAIN, Gina Louise
Santa Fe HS; High Springs-Alachua, FL; Ann;
Secy, BC; Chldr; FFA; 4H; Hmrm; SC; Var C; Pres,
Soph Cl; COM; HCt; Essay A; *U of Fla; Phar.*

CAIN, Katherine Ann
Dunedin HS; Dunedin, FL;

CAIN, Linda Sue
Madison HS; Richmond, KY; Ann; BC; Drama; Fr
C; Hmrm; Sch P; Spch C; Alg A; Bio A; Hist A;
Math A; Opt A; Sci A; Type A; Off Practice; *East-
ern Ky U; Nurs.*

CAIN, Mary Bridget
Notre Dame-Bishop Gibbons HS; Schenectady,
NY; *Sci.*

CAIN, Steven Franklin
A C Jones HS; Beeville, TX (120-200) Var C; Ftbl;
Tr; 300 C A; All Dist Ftbl; *Bee Co Col; Data Proc-
essing.*

CAIN, Susan Andrea
Ware Shoals HS; Ware Shoals, SC; Pres, BC; Chldr;
S-T, Fr C; Secy, Sci C; S-T, SC; Bkbl; *U of SC; Phys
Ed.*

CAIN, Susan Dale
High Point Central HS; High Point, NC (53-400)
BC; Chor; Crisco A; *Watts Hospital Sch of Nurs;
Nurs.*

CAIN, Timothy Mark
Cincinnati Christian HS; Cincinnati, OH (13-22)
A-Ed, Ann; Chor; Drama; Ed, Sch P; Journ A;
Scholastics Art Exhibit; *Anderson Col; Art.*

CAINES, Heather Erica
Stuyvesant HS; New York, NY; Band; French
NHS; NHS; Orch; COM; Sal; Sci A; *The Juilliard
Sch; Mus.*

CAIRE, Shannon Theresa
Bishop Conaty Mem HS; Los Angeles, CA; CYO;
Drama; ARC; Rptr, Sch P; COM; Citz A; Cl Fav;
Cert of Appreciation; *Calif St U; Photography.*

CAKEBREAD, Timothy Gregg
Forest Lake Sr HS; Forest Lake, MN (175-505) A
Cap Choir; Band; Chor; Drama; Ensm; Madrigal;
Soccer; Comm Mus Group; *Mus.*

CALABRESE, Kevin Joe
Sooner HS; Bartlesville, OK (90-280) Band; BS;
VP, FHA; Key C; NHS; Var C; Cpt, Ftbl; Sftbl;
Wrest; HCt; *Okla St U; Acct.*

CALAME, Michael Eugene
Pendleton HS; Pendleton, OR; Arch; Tnns; *Blue
Mtn Comm Col.*

CALAME, Pamela Juanell
Wortham HS; Wortham, TX (5-20) BC; Rptr,
Hmrm; Jr Miss Pagent; Mjrte; Var C; Rptr, Soph
Cl; Bkbl; Sftbl; Tr; Cl Fav; Pianist, FHA; *Mission-
ary.*

CALAWAY, Angela Raylene
Magnolia HS; Anaheim, CA (30-475) F-Ed, Ann;
Dbte Tm; NHS; Tr; Most Out; Spch A; Mgr, Drill
Tm; Drama Achv; *Pub Relations.*

CALCAVECCHIA, Mark John
N Shore HS; W Palm Beach, FL (47-336) Band;
FBLA; Var C; Cpt, Golf; *Wake Forest Col; Acct.*

CALCOTE, James Hugh
Monticello HS; Monticello, MS; FFA; Bible C;
Journ C; *Copiah-Lincoln Jr Col; Elec.*

CALDCLEUGH, Lisa Anne
Aldine Sr HS; Houston, TX (200-565) Drama;
Tres, FTA; Ch, Hmrm; SC; Mgr, Bkbl; Amer Leg
A; COM; Cl Fav; Swtht; *Abilene Christian U;
Psych.*

CALDER, Jay Scott
New Palestine HS; New Palestine, IN; A Cap
Choir; Chor; Madrigal; JV, Bsbl; Tnns; Yth Fel;
Ball St U; Social Stu.

CALDERWOOD, Thomas James
Benson Polytechnic HS; Portland, OR (20-400)
Chess C; Math C; NHS; Math A; Ntl Merit Schol
Commended Stu; WW; *Calif Inst of Tech; Astron-
omy.*

CALDWELL, Amy Maria
Geneva HS; Geneva, AL (10%-88) BC; Chldr; VP,
Drama; S-T, Fr C; FHA; FTA; Pres, 4H; Hmrm;
InterClub Coun; Math C; Sci C; SC; Var C; Sftbl;
4H A; Hon Prog; Spch A; Christmas Ct; Church
Board; Alt, Methodist Conf; Coun On Ministries;
St Civil Defense Dept Diploma; *U of Ala in Bir-
mingham; Med.*

CALDWELL, Andrea Peresa
Crenshaw HS; Los Angeles, CA; Drama; *Engr.*

CALDWELL, Brian Lee
Denison HS; Denison, TX (10%-400) NHS; Order/ Arrow; Co-Cpt, Bkbl; God & Country A; Hon Prog; FCA; United Service C; Grayson Co Col.

CALDWELL, Carolyn Francesca
Manuel Dominguez HS; Compton, CA; Long Beach Col; Teacher.

CALDWELL, Catherine Laura
Newton Conover HS; Newton, NC (25-200) Rptr, AFS; F-Ed, Ann; Var C; Bkbl; HCt; JA A; NEDT; AFS Schol; PA; Hon Stu A; U of North Carolina; Dental Hygiene.

CALDWELL, Cynthia Dianne
Goodlettsville HS; Goodlettsville, TN (4-159) FTA; Hmrm; St Stu Congress; Secy, SC; Tnns; Hon Prog; Math A; NEDT; Tn o-t Mo; Fr A; HR; Samford U; Math.

CALDWELL, David William
Ridgeview HS; Atlanta, GA (70-225) Band; A-Ed, Sch P; SC; God & Country A; Yth Fel; Eagle Sct; Ed, Church Newspaper; Pres, Church Yth Div; Sou Methodist U.

CALDWELL, Donna Carol
Geronimo HS; Geronimo, OK (10%-29) A Cap Choir; Cpt, Chldr; Chor; Ensm; FHA; Secy, 4H; Pres, Math C; Parl, NHS; VP, SC; Rptr, Soph Cl; Sftbl; Tr; Cl Fav; HCt; Principal's A; Yrbk Photographer; Cameron Col.

CALDWELL, Elizabeth Louise
Ridgway Area HS; Ridgway, PA; Cpt, Band; Chor; FTA; NHS; Rainbow; Sch P; Type A; Asst-Ed, Yrbk; Cpt, Band Rifles; Social Work.

CALDWELL, Ernestine Lothell
Man HS; Man, WV (18-180) Bus C; Chldr; Commercial C; FNA; FTA; Hmrm; NHS; Bkbl; Math A; Vlbl; Chldr, Phys Ed, A's; Most Ath.

CALDWELL, Felicia
Clara Barton HS; Ny, NY (100-250) A Cap Choir; Band; Mgr, Chor; Dbte Tm; Math C; Sch P; Span C; COM; Citz A; Journ A; Hematology.

CALDWELL, Fred Fischer
Del Rio HS; Del Rio, TX (21-500) Ann; SC; Ftbl; Golf; All Dist Ftbl; Oceanography.

CALDWELL, Gail Ann
Lewisville HS; Lewisville, TX (5-355) Hmrm; Math C; NHS; SC; N Tex St U; Bus.

CALDWELL, Glenn Wayne
Abilene HS; Abilene, TX; Chess C; Bsbl; Bkbl; Cpt, Ftbl; Sftbl; Cpt, Tnns; ARC A; Tnns A; Abilene Christian U; Bible.

CALDWELL, Jan Kevin
Mullens HS; Mullens, WV (8-110) Var C; Bkbl; Ftbl; Tr.

CALDWELL, Jean Elizabeth
Niles McKinley HS; Niles, OH (112-423) A Cap Choir; AFS; FTA; Youngstown St U; Bus.

CALDWELL, Joe Dan
Thayer HS; Thayer, MO (25-50) Band; FFA; Bkbl; JV, Ftbl; Engr.

CALDWELL, John Franklin
Newnan HS; Newnan, GA (45-309) A Cap Choir; Ann; Band; Chor; Lit Ral; David Lipscomb Col; Anthropology.

CALDWELL, John Gregory
Alcoa HS; Alcoa, TN (30-110) AFS; BC; Chor; Drama; Key C; S-T, Math C; S-T, Mu Alpha Theta; NHS; Span C; Var C; Ftbl; JV, Tnns; U of Tenn; Engr.

CALDWELL, Mark Anthony
Dominguez Sr HS; Compton, CA; Co-Cpt, Tnns; Long Beach St Col; Air Sci.

CALDWELL, Mary Margaret
Ridgway HS; Ridgway, PA (20-159) Ann; Band; Chor; Rainbow; Span C; Math A; Philipsburg Nurs Sch; Nurs.

CALDWELL, Melanie Kim
Douglas Co Comprehensive HS; Douglasville, GA (2-340) Band; BC; Parl, FHA; Hmrm; NHS; SC; Beauty; COM; Hon Prog; Sci A; NMF.

CALDWELL, Patricia Ann
Fountain Lake HS; Hot Springs, AR (4-55) Chor; Drama; Rptr, Sch P; Thes; M,+, Bkbl; Secy.

CALDWELL, Roderick Eric
Clara Barton HS; Brooklyn, NY; Bkbl; Swim; COM; Math A; Sci A; Swtht; St John's U; Med.

CALDWELL, Rodney Ray
Industry HS; Industry, IL (4-30) Band; Chor; Drama; Fr C; Bkbl; Ftbl; Yth Fel; W Ill U; Agr.

CALDWELL, Stephen Browder
New Kent HS; New Kent, VA (5-80) BC; Math C; Bsbl; Co-Cpt, Ftbl; Cpt, Soccer; Citz A; HCt; James Madison U; Phys Ed.

CALDWELL, Sue Ann
Industry HS; Industry, IL (2-33) Band; Chldr; Chor; Drama; Fr C; Pres, Sci C; SC; Bkbl; Golf; Tr; HCt; Hon Prog; Most Out; Sal; St Scholar; Schol Achv, Chldr, A's; W Ill U; Acct.

CALDWELL, William Keith
Mullens HS; Mullens, WV; BC; HiY; SC; Tres, Soph Cl; Bkbl; Ftbl; Sci A.

CALE, Cheri Ann
Parkersburg South HS; Parkersburg, WV; Chor; JETS; Rptr, Sch P; Yth Fel; DECA C; Lib A; Poetry Hon; Parkersburg Comm Col; Law Enforcement.

CALE, Robert Jeffery
Buffalo Gap HS; Swoope, VA (50-180) Band; 4H; Hmrm; NFL; Sci C; Var C; Bkbl; JV, Cr-Ctry; Golf; Tnns; JV, Tr; Most Out; Champ, Bkbl; Fin, Sci A; Fin, Homecoming Court; Bridgewater Col; Phys Ed.

CALEGA, Virginia Catherine
Saint Benedit Acad; Pittsburgh, PA (1-60) Pres, NFL; NHS; Secy, Sr Cl; Pres, Jr Cl; Secy, Soph Cl; Hon Prog; NEDT; Spch A; SAR Good Citz A; Sci.

CALFEE, Peggy Ann
Central-Hower HS; Akron, OH; A Cap Choir; Chor; Drama; Madrigal; NFL; Sch P; St Runnerup, Ntl Forensics League; Mus.

CALHOUN, Bonnie Rebecca
Terra Alta HS; Terra Alta, WV; Chem C; GS; NHS; Var C; Bkbl; Amer Leg A; B Crocker A; I Dare You; Val; VFW A; VP, VICA; Glenville St Col; Phys Ed.

CALHOUN, Carolyn Joy
Shenandoah Valley Acad; New Market, VA; Ed, Ann; Sou Missionary Col; Nurs.

CALHOUN, Debra Ann
Allen HS; Robeline, LA (3-37) Band; Bus C; Pres, FBLA; 4H; Hmrm; Math C; Secy, SC; Pres, Soph Cl; 4H A; HQn; HCt; Hon Prog; Val; Sou U; Engr.

CALHOUN, John Kevin
Maralapan HS; Englishtown, NJ (2-333) Chor; Dbte Tm; Drama; Lit Mag; Madrigal; Math C; Secy, NHS; F-Ed, Sch P; Thes; Bio A; Hist A; HCt; NMF; NMS; Sal; Ger A; Shield & Key; Yale U; Physics.

CALHOUN, Joseph Lee
Swain Co HS; Bryson City, NC (20-130) Chess C; Fr C; Monogram; Mgr, Bsbl; Mgr, Bkbl; MVP, Ftbl; Mgr o-t Yr; US Coast Guard Acad; Brick Laying.

CALHOUN, Pamela Kaye
Southside HS; Counce, TN (5-26) Rptr, BC; Ch, FHA; SC; Rptr, Jr Cl; Bkbl; U of N Ala; Nurs.

CALHOUN, Phyllis Denyse
Allen HS; Robeline, LA (3-37) Secy, A Cap Choir; Secy, Band; Pres, Bus C; Pres, FBLA; Secy, Hmrm; Sci C; Rptr, SC; 4H A; HCt; Hon Prog; Sal; Cleanup Poster A; Sou U; Engr.

CALHOUN, Timothy Blaine
Saint James Sch; Saint James, MD (4-26) Band; Orch; Drama; Ftbl; Soccer; Order/Arrow A; VPI; Forest Resource Mgr.

CALHOUN, Vicki Elizabeth
Plano Sr HS; Plano, TX (54-850) Chor; Ensm; FBLA; FHA; NHS; Span C; Tex Tech Col; Bus.

CALKINS, Karen Ann
Hannibal Central Sch; Hannibal, NY; AFS; Band; Ensm; NHS; Soccer; 4H A; Math A; Sci A; Math.

CALL, Cecilia Marie
Orofino Sch; Orofino, ID; Pres, CYO; Ski C; Alt, GS; Col of Saint Benedict; Phys Therapy.

CALL, Christine Elizabeth
George Washington HS; Chicago, IL (44-556) Chldr; Hmrm; Lat C; Mu Alpha Theta; SC; Hon Prog.

CALL, Michael Lee
Isu Laboratory Sch; Terre Haute, IN (2-65) Band; BS; Community Yth Symph; Math C; NHS; Order/Arrow; Ch, SC; COM; Kiwanis A; NMF; NMS; NEDT; Sal; Sci A; St Scholar; Outst Sr Bandsman; Ntl Soc of Profes Engr School Win; Rose-Hulman Inst of Tech; Ch Engr.

CALL, Sally Ann
Huntsville HS; Huntsville, AL (15-465) VP, Anchor C; Secy, Chem C; Hmrm; NHS; ARC; Span C; SC; Chem A; Cpt, Gym; Home Ec A; Auburn U; Chem.

CALLAGHAN, Anne Teresa
Carmel HS; Carmel, NY (1-320) Chldr; Drama; Math C; Pres, NHS; Sch P; Var C; Cpt, Hockey; Tr; Hon Prog; PTA A; Regent Schol; Val; N B Harrison A; Superintendant Schol; U of Rochester; Humanities.

CALLAHAN, Bernesia
Marion-Franklin HS; Columbus, OH (99-325) Secy, Band; Tres, Chor; Span NHS; Tr; Chaplain, Sr Cl; Delta Sigma Theta; Vlbl; Modeling A; Ohio All Star Band; All City Band; Bowling Green St U; Deaf Ed.

CALLAHAN, Daryl John
Austin Central HS; Austin, MN (25%-2200) Band; Chor; VP, Hmrm; SC; Bsbl; JV, Bkbl; Ftbl; Sftbl; JV, Tr; HCt.

CALLAHAN, George Edwin
Norman HS; Norman, OK (184-704) BS; 4H; Key C; Ski C; VP, Span C; JV, Bkbl; JV, Ftbl; MVP, Tnns; Amer Leg A; Sr Cl Santa Claus; Okla U.

CALLAHAN, Janet Lynn
Mary Brantly Smiley HS; Houston, TX (8-400) A Cap Choir; FTA; Math C; Mu Alpha Theta; NHS; Pres, Sci C; Alg A; Bio A; Chem A; Sci A; Homemaking Medal; Fr A; U of Houston; Phar.

CALLAHAN, Lori Mae
Chillicothe HS; Chillicothe, OH (1-400) S-T, Band; Dbte Tm; Bus Mgr, Drama; Math C; NFL; Pres, NHS; Pres, Rainbow; Pres, Span C; SC; Thes; Amer Leg A; Bio A; Chem A; Hist A; Journ A; Math A; Sci A; Spch A; Val; Soroptomist Schol; Rainbow Schol; Miami U; Chem Engr.

CALLAHAN, Maretta Dawn
Rhinebeck Central HS; Rhinebeck, NY (12-110) Co-Cpt, Chldr; Hmrm; Secy, SC; Secy, Sr Cl; Cpt, Hockey; Cpt, Sftbl; Cand, Qn of Hearts; The Berkley Sch; Bi-Lingual Secy.

CALLAHAN, Russell Robert
Austin HS; Austin, MN (20-537) Band; Chldr; Chor; Hmrm; NHS; Spch C; Pres, SC; Ftbl; COM; Hist A; HCt; Hon Prog; Kiwanis A; Yth Fel; Amer Yth in Concert; Austin Comm Col; Nurs.

CALLAHAN, Tracy Jonell
Meadowbrook HS; Byesville, OH; Pres, 4H; Sci C; Cr-Ctry; Sftbl; Tr; 4H A; ARC A; Sci A; Ohio St U; Law.

CALLAWAY, Andrea Charneal
Mumford HS; Detroit, MI; Secy, Fr C; NHS; Ed, Sch P; Citz A; Hon Prog; 2nd Pl Medal, Decathelon; Pediactrics.

CALLAWAY, Annette
Waller HS; Waller, TX (26-84) Pres, Band; Ensm; Pres, FHA; SC; Pres, Sr Cl; Mgr, Bkbl; HCt; Pres A; Type A; Girl o-t Yr; Prairie View A&M Col; Home Ec.

CALLAWAY, Kenneth Hugh
N B Forrest HS; Jacksonville, FL; FJC; Elec.

CALLAWAY, Susan Gail
E Rome HS; Rome, GA; Band; Chldr; Drama; Ch, Fr C; Hmrm; Math C; NHS; SC; Gov Honor Prog; Phys Therapy.

CALLEJA, Grisel
Our Lady of Good Counsel HS; Newark, NJ (2-65) Drama; NHS; Ed, Sch P; Span C; COM; U of Miami; Lang.

CALLEJA, Maribel
Our Lady of Good Counsel HS; Newark, NJ (10-84) NHS; Ntl Jr Hon Soc; Candystriping A; U of Miami; Dentistry.

CALLIES, Donna Lea
Beaver Dam Sr HS; Beaver Dam, WI (112-331) Band; Hmrm; Ski C; Pres, Var C; JV, Bkbl; Sftbl; Co-Cpt, Swim; Tr; Pres A; ARC A; UW-LaCrosse; Hist.

CALLIES, Laurie Jo
Lutheran HS E; Harper Woods, MI (20-150) A Cap Choir; Ger C; NHS; Bkbl; Sftbl; Tr; Concordia Col; Ed.

CALLIGY, Nancy Catharine
St Joseph's o-t Palisades HS; W New York, NJ (53-225) A Cap Choir; CYO; Chor; Drama; NHS; Sch P; Span NHS; SC; Swim; Hon Prog; WW; Duquesne U.

CALLIHAN, William Keith
W Carter HS; Olive Hill, KY (10%-154) Band; Parl, BC; Dbte Tm; Drama; Pres, FBLA; 4H; Spch C; VP, Jr Cl; Pres, Soph Cl; COM; Cl Fav; 4H A; Hon Prog; Most Out; Sci A; Spch A; 1st, FBLA Parliamentary Procedure; Written Exam, FBLA Region; High Score, Parliamentary Procedure; Conservation Essay A; Morehead St U; Spch And Drama.

CALLO, Murvyn Rodriguez
Jackson HS; Jackson, LA (5%-92) Ann; BC; Dbte Tm; Fr C; FBLA; Hmrm; Lit Ral; Ed, Sch P; Sci C; SC; LSU; Pre-Law.

CALLOBRE, Anthony Rene
Christopher Columbus HS; Miami, FL (10-200) NHS; Span NHS; Bkbl; Ftbl; Hon Prog; Span A; Ad Altare Del; Harvard U; Lib Arts.

CALLOWAY, Gloria Jean
Clarke Central HS; Athens, GA (9-276) BC; Chor; FHA; Tres, NHS; Pres, SC; Pres, Sr Cl; DARGCA; Gr Marshal; Opt A; VofDEM; Most Involved; WW; Tuskegee Inst; Bus Adm.

CALLOWAY, Renita Lynn
Northwest HS; St Louis, MO (85-652) Bus C; Hon Prog.

CALLUM, Jean Rachel
Interlochen Arts Acad; Interlochen, MI (3-165) Band; Ensm; Orch; Schol, Interlochen Arts Acad; Schol, Ntl Mus Camp; Sr Hon Stu; Northwestern U; Mus.

CALOBRISI, Robert James
Don Bosco Tech HS; Boston, MA (5-249) NHS; Tr; Hon Prog; NE Col; Elec Engr.

CALVERT, Julie Ann
Western HS; Buda, IL (10-55) Ann; Band; Chldr; Drama; FHA; Pres, 4H; NHS; Var C; Tnns; 4H A; HCt; Vlbl; Ill St U; Bus.

CALVERT, Laura Rebecca
Hannibal Sr HS; Hannibal, MO (120-337) Band; Chldr; FTA; 4H; Hmrm; Span C; Central Mo St U; Social Sci.

CALVERT, Marsha Lynn
Lawrenceville HS; Lawrenceville, IL (3-164) Chem C; FHA; Co-Ch, NHS; Sci C; VP, Span C; Hon Prog; St Scholar; Yth Fel; WW; Olney Central Col; Med Tech.

CALVERT, Nancy Jane
Gilmer HS; Gilmer, TX (6-127) FTA; Math C; NHS; Sr Cl; Bus Mgr, Jr Cl; MLS; Rptr, Voc off Ed; Schol A; Stephen F Austin St U; Phys Therapy.

CALVERT, Stephan George
Franklin HS; Franklin, OH (25-289) Fr C; Math C; Sci C; Var C; Bkbl; Golf; Tnns; COM; Cl Fav; HCt; Swtht; Yth Fel; Ohio Sch of Tech; Elec.

CALVERT, Thomas Wayne
Northwest HS; House Springs, MO (85-462) A Cap Choir; Band; Chor; Ensm; Madrigal; Orch; SC; Var C; Bsbl; Co-Cpt, Bkbl; Tr; Co Conf; William Jewell Col; Mus.

CALVILLO, Jeffrey Clyde
Paradise HS; Paradise, CA (50-233) Chor; JV, Bkbl; Tnns.

CALVIN, Bruce Donald
Bridgewater-Raynham Reg HS; Bridgewater, MA; Chor; Drama; SC; Photo, Yr Book; Photo C; TV Crew; Graham Jr Col; TV & Radio Elec.

CALVIN, Elizabeth Marta
Claremont HS; Claremont, CA; AFS; Drama; 4H; Rptr, Sch P; Span C; SC; Thes; Poet A; Whitworth Col; Psych.

CALVIN, Jeffrey Dean
E Alton Wood River Comm HS; Wood River, IL (2-320) Band; Model UN; VP, SC; Bkbl; Ftbl; Tnns; Hon Prog; K of C A; U of Ill; Engr.

CALVIN, Lari Lynn
Rock Bridge Sr HS; Columbia, MO (20-250) Secy, 4H; NHS; Rotary A; U of Mo; Vet Med.

CALVIN, Regina Gail
Arkansas City HS; Arkansas City, AR (1-9) A Cap Choir; Ed, Ann; Secy, 4H; Hmrm; NHS; Pres, SC; Bkbl; Sftbl; Tnns; Most Out; Home Ec As; U Central Ark; Elem Ed.

CALVIN, Roger Alan
Milwaukee Tech HS; Milwaukee, WI (35-800) Hmrm; Rptr, Sch P; SC; Mr Tech; 5th Pl, Mr Wis HS; Sch Service A; U of Wis; Med.

CALVO, John Salas
John F Kennedy HS; Tumon, GUAM (46-511) Co-Ed, Ann; City Conf; Fr C; Hmrm; NHS; St Stu Congress; SC; Tres, Sr Cl; Cr-Ctry; Dance Troupe; San Jose St U; Engr.

CALVO, Rafael Adolfo
Verdugo Hills HS; Tujunga, CA (40-525) Pres, Hmrm; Ski C; VP, SC; MVP, Gym; Occidental Col; Pol Sci.

CAMACHO, Bernard Sablan
George Washington Sr HS; Mangilao, GUAM; Band; VP, 4H; NHS; Citz A; 4H A; MLS; Most Out; Type A; Sct o-t Yr; Bus.

CAMBRE, Carleen Ann
Destrehan HS; Destrehan, LA (7-169) Ann; Rptr, BC; Chldr; Rptr, FBLA; Hmrm; Key C; ARC C; Eng, Religion, A's; LSU; Biol.

CAMBRE, Patricia Ann
French HS; Beaumont, TX (1-440) Bus Mgr, Ann; Fr C; NHS; Stephen F Austin Col; Sci.

CAMBRIA, Robert Anthony
Roselle Cath HS; Roselle, NJ (1-170) CYO; Drama; NHS; Pres, SC; Soccer; NEDT; Holy Cross Col; Bio.

CAMBRIDGE, Karen Lynne
Hastings Sr HS; Hastings, NE (25%-260) F-Ed, Ann; Chor; Hmrm; SC; Y-Tns; HCt; Job's Daughters; YWCA Board; Ed.

CAMBRON, Bonnie Ellen
Washington Co HS; Springfield, KY (3-167) A-Ed, Ann; Band; BC; Ensm; FTA; Hmrm; Rptr, SC; Sftbl; Chem A; Gr Marshal; Hist A; Sci A; Sup, KMEA Solo Festival; All-Dist Bands; All-St Band; Ky Wesleyan Col; Med Technology.

CAMBRON, Gwendolyn Marie
Washington Co HS; Springfield, KY (1-186) Band; BC; Tr; Sup, KMEA Solo Festival; All-Dist Band; U of Ky; Med.

CAMERON, Amna Page
Benhaven HS; Olivia, NC; F-Ed, Ann; Band; Pres, BC; Chldr; Chor; FHA; Rptr, Hmrm; Monogram; F-Ed, Sch P; Tres, Span C; SC; Tres, Soph Cl; Sftbl; Alg A; Math A; Vlbl; Marshall; Eng, Lib, A's; U of NC; Phar.

CAMERON, Cindy Lu
Western Hills HS; Ft Worth, TX (30-600) Ensm; Fr C; FHA; NHS; Pres, Rainbow; ARC; SC; Hon Prog; PWA of Rainbow; Tex Tech U; Psych.

CAMERON, Denise Louise
Palmer HS; Colorado Springs, CO; A Cap Choir; Chldr; Chor; FBLA; Mgr, Bkbl; Tnns.

CAMERON, Duncan Allan
David Anderson HS; Lisbon, OH (13-115) Co-Ed, Ann; BS; Fr C; NHS; Sci C; Bio A; Journ A; NMF; Art C; Tn o-t Mo; Art A; Carnegie-Mellon U; Design.

CAMERON, Ivonne E
Dra Maria Cadilla de Martinez HS; Arecibo, PR (44-429) Secy, FBLA; Tres, FHA; ARC; Bio A; Hist A; Jr Chamber of Com A; Sci A; U of Puerto Rico; Med Technology.

CAMERON, Leon Bernard III
Wellsboro Area Sr HS; Wellsboro, PA (33%-235) A Cap Choir; Band; Cpt, CYO; Chor; Community Yth Symph; Drama; Ensm; Fr C; Hmrm; Co-Ch, Lit Mag; Model UN; Orch; SC; Thes; Cpt, Ftbl; Spch A; VFW A; VofDEM; St Bonnaventure U; Journ.

CAMERON, Louise Ann
Sanderson HS; Raleigh, NC (100-610) A-Ed, Ann; Fr C; Hmrm; Key C; Bkbl; Service A; Appalachian St U; Lib Sci.

CAMERON, Mark Alan
Floresville HS; Floresville, TX (64-160) FFA; Cr-Ctry; Tex A&M U; ROTC.

CAMERON, Melodie Dawn
Council HS; Council, ID; Drama; Secy, NHS; Span C; Var C; Cpt, Bkbl; Citz A; 4H A; Sports Ltrs; Col of Idaho; Sci.

CAMERON, Rita Rose
Lake Placid HS; Lake Placid, FL; Band; 4H; Key C; Mjrte; NHS; Tnns; DARGCA; Pres A; Chaplain, Cath Yth; Dentistry.

CAMERON, Robert Roy
Lake Placid HS; Lake Placid, FL (6-132) Ann; Band; VP, CYO; Ch, InterAct C; NHS; Tnns; B Crocker A; Dist Rep, Interact; US Air Force Acad; Engr.

CAMERON, Scott Evans
Burrell Sr HS; Lower Burrell, PA; Chem C; Fr C; COM; JA A; NEDT; ARC A; Yth Fel; Aeronautical Engr.

CAMERON, Scott Steven
West HS; Billings, MT; Bsbl; Bkbl; Cr-Ctry; Ftbl; Sftbl; Swim; Tnns; Tr; Bozeman Col; Bus.

CAMERON, Veronica Lee
St Jean Baptiste HS; New York, NY (25-120) CYO; Fresh HR; Yrbk Staff; Rutgers U; Sociology.

CAMILLE, Kimberly Sue
Williamsville HS; Williamsville, IL (6-88) CYO; Chor; Drama; Fin, Ensm; FTA; Lat C; NHS; SC; Cpt, Bkbl; Sftbl; Tr; COM; Hon Prog; Ntl Achv Schol; Tr A; Mus A; Bradley U; Ed.

CAMILLERI, Marijane
On o-t Rosary Acad; Amityville, NY (1-85) Chor; NHS; Ed, Sch P; Tres, SC; COM; Hist A; Hon Prog; Journ A; NEDT; Phi Beta Kappa; Viking Stu Project Participant; QR A Schol; Paragon Qil A; Nom, US Cong US Merchant Marine; Special Ed Prog Outst Cert; Eng.

CAMMAROTA, Cynthia Ann
Sacred Heart HS; Vineland, NJ (6-59) NHS; Sci C; Sftbl; Tnns; Rutgers Col; Biological Sci.

CAMP, Deborah Jean
Bloom Trail HS; Chicago Heights, IL; Pres, Lat C; Ski C; SC; Hon Prog; Badminton; Augustana Col; Nurs.

CAMP, Dorothy Frances
Marion Acad; Ocala, FL; Ed, Ann; Chess C; Chor; Drama; VP, Hmrm; NHS; Co-Ed, Sch P; Span C; VP, SC; Bkbl; MVP, Sftbl; Alg A; Bio A; Chem A; Cl Fav; Hist A; Hon Prog; I Dare You; Journ A; Math A; Opt A; Opt Out Tn; Sci A; Star Student; Val; Mrs Sr; Best Personality; Most Intelligent A; Troy St U; Math.

CAMP, Ella Francis
Bloom Trail HS; Chicago Heights, IL (323-1107) Pres, A Cap Choir; VP, Drama; Pres, Thes; Elmhurst Col; Sci.

CAMP, Karen Sue
Leominster HS; Leominster, MA; Band; Chor; Fr C; Hon Prog; Methodist Yth Organization; Bradford Col; Human Sci.

CAMP, Mary Beth
Leominster HS; Leominster, MA; Chor; JV, Bkbl; Methodist Yth Organization; Nurs.

CAMP, Scarlett Joy
Adairsville HS; Adairsville, GA (4-115) Cpt, Band; Dbte Tm; Fr C; VP, FHA; Fin, Jr Miss Pagent; Sci C; SC; Co-Cpt, Var C; Co-Cpt, Bkbl; Beauty; Missionary.

CAMP, Steven Neal
Harlem HS; Harlem, GA (60-240) FFA; InterAct C; Bsbl; Bkbl; Abraham Baldwin Agr Col; Forestry.

CAMP, Valerie Yvonne
Newnan HS; Newnan, GA; Span C; Alg A; COM; Span A; Acct.

CAMPA, Robert G
Memorial HS; San Antonio, TX (17-300) VICA; St Phillips Col; Auto Mech.

CAMPAGNA, Anthony Charles
Colonie Central HS; Albany, NY (17-726) Band; Ensm; Key C; NHS; Orch; SC; JV, Soccer; COM; Elk A; Hon Prog; Regent Schol; Vlbl; Siena Col; Pre-Med.

CAMPAGNARI, Kenneth David
Tidewater Christian Acad; Norfolk, VA (2-4) Chess C; Orch; Ed, Sch P; SC; Hon Prog; Jr Army Navy Guild Organization; Med.

CAMPANELLA, Kathryn Jean
St Joseph HS; Hammonton, NJ (1-67) Bus C; Drama; Secy, Hmrm; NFL; NHS; Sci C; Bkbl; Hockey; Hon Prog; NEDT; Principal's List; Notre Dame U; Pre-Med.

CAMPANELLA, Mary Beth
St Joseph HS; Hammonton, NJ (3-49) Chor; Pres, Drama; FTA; Jr Miss Pageant; NFL; NHS; Pres, Spch C; Co-Cpt, Hockey; Tr; COM; Hon Prog; NEDT; NMS Commendation; WW; Principal's List; Villanova U; Acct.

CAMPBELL, Alice Earl
Moss Point HS; Moss Point, MS (12-381) NHS; Secy, Sci C; Hon Prog; Phy A; U of Sou Miss; Nurs.

CAMPBELL, Andrea Gayle
Franklin HS; Franklin, OH (8-287) Chor; Ensm; Tres, Fr C; VP, FTA; NHS; Secy, Sr Cl; COM; Lion A; MLS; Yth Fel; Outst Fr Stu; Sweetest; Anderson Col; Fr.

CAMPBELL, Andrew MacKinnon
Andover HS; Andover, MA (100-500) A Cap Choir; AFS; Band; Chor; Drama; Ensm; Tres, Lat C; Madrigal; Orch; JV, Bkbl; Hon Prog; Yth Fel; Dist Chor; St Over; Most Mus; Keene St U; Mus.

CAMPBELL, Andrew Michael IV
Bassick HS; Bridgeport, CT (2-280) Band; Sci C; Span C; Bsbl; Bkbl; Ftbl; Chem A; Hon Prog; Star Student; News Writer; U of Wis; Med.

CAMPBELL, Annette Lynn
Vian HS; Vian, OK (15-85) Band; FHA; Pres, Hmrm; Mjrte; Pres, Jr Cl; Span C; Jr Cl Outst Musician; Okmolgee St Tech; Data Processing.

CAMPBELL, Avona Rose
Warth Co HS; Grant City, MO; Ann; Bus C; Chor; FBLA; FHA; Sch P; Span C; Spch C; Journ A; NWMSU; Bus.

CAMPBELL, Bonnie Lou
Simley Sr HS; Inver Grove Heights, MN (4-276) A Cap Choir; NFL; NHS; Rptr, Sch P; Spch C; VP, Thes; Bkbl; Cr-Crty; Co-Cpt, Tr; Spch A; Coaches A; AAL All Col Schol; St Olaf Col; Chem.

CAMPBELL, Carol Louise
Dunlap HS; Dunlap, IL (10-104) AFS; Chor; Drama; FBLA; GS; Lit Mag; Sch P; Pres, Span C; Spch C; VP, SC; DARGCA; Heart of Ill Pageant; Ill Central Col; Journ.

CAMPBELL, Carole Lynn
Southwestern HS; Flint, MI (70-514) Band; Mjrte; Beauty; Hon Prog; WW; U of Mich; Bus Adm.

CAMPBELL, Charles Robert
Arkadelphia HS; Arkadelphia, AR (71-158) Band; BS; Chess C; JV, Ftbl; Golf; U of Ark; Ed.

CAMPBELL, Christopher Lee
Bethel Baptist Sch; Memphis, TN (5-16) Chor; Ensm; Bkbl; COM; Most Out; D L Moody A; Liberty Baptist Col; Mus.

CAMPBELL, Clay Murray
Eastside HS; Gainesville, FL (5%-208) Chess C; Drama; Hmrm; Key C; Order/Arrow; SC; Var C; Pres, Sr Cl; Pres, Jr Cl; Cpt, Bkbl; Cr-Crty; Cpt, Ftbl; Swim; Tr; COM; God & Country A; NEDT; Order/Arrow A; Yth Fel; Eagle Sct; Bicentennial Comm; Citz Adv Coun; 14th World Jamboree; Principals Adv Coun; Civitan Citizenship A; Boise St U.

CAMPBELL, Craig Frederick
Chester HS; Chester, IL (14-98) Chor; Spch C; Var C; Ftbl; Tr; JV, Wrest; Hist A; Hon Prog; Southeast Mo St U; Hist.

CAMPBELL, Cynthia Lynne
Santa Fe Trail Jr HS; Olathe, KS; Chor; Bsbl; Bkbl; Cr-Crty; Ftbl; Golf; Soccer; Sftbl; Swim; Yth Fel; Deaf Minstry; Yth Outreach; Yth For Christ; Yth Retreats; Oral Roberts U; Handicapped Children.

CAMPBELL, Cynthia Marlene
Donora Sr HS; Donora, PA (3-200) Cpt, Mjrte; Yth Fel; Phoenix Col; Nurs.

CAMPBELL, Darren Deon
Edgewood HS; Edgewood, TX (10-70) VP, Band; Ensm; Orch; Span C; Var C; Tnns; Fin, Most Outst; Fin, Highest Hon at UIL; Hon Stu; N Tex Hon Band; N Tex St U; Mus.

CAMPBELL, Devonie Ann
Lake Wales Sr HS; Lake Wales, FL (12-360) Band; Hmrm; NHS; SC; Hon Prog; VP, Beacon C; Fashion Merchandising.

CAMPBELL, Diana Kay
Humansville HS; Humansville, MO (2-29) Bus Mgr, Ann; Cpt, Chldr; Chor; Tres, FHA; Co-Ed, Sch P; SC; VP, Sr Cl; Sftbl; Cl Fav; HCt; Regent Schol; Sal; Type A; Outst Home Ec Stu; Shorthand A; Sftbl A; Semi-Fin, Miss Hnmansville Pageant; Librarian A; SMSU; Home Ec.

CAMPBELL, Diane Marie
N Crawford HS; Gays Mills, WI (3-85) Band; Chor; 4H; Secy, Math C; NHS; VP, Jr Cl; JV, Bkbl; 4H A; HCt; NEDT; Pres A; Evangel Col; Med Tech.

CAMPBELL, Donna Jean
Humansville R-4 HS; Humansville, MO (4-40) JV, Chldr; Chor; FHA; Miss Merry Christmas; Acteens; VLBL; Pres, Fresh Cl; Secy & Song Ldr, Children's Yth Chr.

CAMPBELL, Dwayne Kevin
Pinckneyville Comm HS; Pinckneyville, IL (40-161) Band; Ensm; NHS; Span C; Southeast Mo St U.

CAMPBELL, Elizabeth Lynn
Greenport HS; Greenport, NY (10-80) Chor; A-Ed, Sch P; Span C; Art C; Mathletes; Med Explorers; Med.

CAMPBELL, Eric Wayne
Cottage Grove HS; Cottage Grove, OR (29-225) Hmrm; NHS; Var C; MVP, Ftbl; Tr.

CAMPBELL, Florence Weed
George Wythe HS; Wytheville, VA (25-125) Parl, Mu Alpha Theta; NHS; Sci C; Bkbl; Tnns; Yth Fel; Stu o-t Wk; Tres, Keyette C; Goucher Col; Psych.

CAMPBELL, Gladys Marie
Belton-Honea Path HS; Belton, SC; Bkbl.

CAMPBELL, Gregory Lance
Seventy-First HS; Fayetteville, NC (40%-749) MVP, Tr; N Car Central Col; Mil Sci.

CAMPBELL, Hollie Jean
Cooper City HS; Cooper City, FL (50-800) Bus Mgr, Lit Mag; NHS; Cpt, Sftbl; Hon Prog; Vlbl; Ntl Wildlife & Conservation Sch; U of Fla; Law.

CAMPBELL, James Lloyd
Yukon HS; Yukon, OK; Band; Ensm; Fr C; Co-Cpt, Soccer; Sci A; Jr Asst Sct-Master, BSct; Eagle Sct; Mile Swim; Central St U; Mus.

CAMPBELL, Jeffrey Paul
Central Union HS; El Centro, CA (20%-400) Band; Chor; Key C; NHS; Var C; Cpt, Bsbl; Bkbl; Ftbl; Co-Cpt, Soccer; Sou Calif Col; Ministry.

CAMPBELL, Jerry Sue
Linn Co R-I HS; Browning, MO; Co-Cpt, Chldr; GS; S-T, 4H; Rptr, Sch P; VP, SC; Var C; Tres, Sr Cl; Pres, Jr Cl; Sftbl; Alg A; DARGCA; S-T, SC; Acct, Geom, A's; NE Mo St U; Bus.

CAMPBELL, John Mark
Sevier Co HS; Sevierville, TN (10%-310) Band; BC; VP, Fr C; Ftbl; Elec.

CAMPBELL, John Michael
Northeast HS; Oakland Park, FL (26-600) Parl, Fr C; Hmrm; InterClub Coun; Mu Alpha Theta; NHS; Ftbl; Elk A; NEDT; Drum Major; WW; U of Fla; Bus Adm.

CAMPBELL, Karen Anne
University HS; San Diego, CA (1-315) Ann; CYO; Sci C; Tr; CSF; Hon Prog; Most Out; Med Explorers; Badminton; U of Calif; Pre-Med.

CAMPBELL, Karen Kaye
Hobart Sr HS; Hobart, IN (33%-400) A Cap Choir; Chldr; Drama; VP, Madrigal; Var C; Bkbl; Hon Prog; Sch Plays; Fed Women's C; 1st, Talent Ral; 1st, Mus Festival; 1st, NISBOVA; Lincoln Christian Col; Mus.

CAMPBELL, Karen Lynn
Shoreham-Wading River HS; Shoreham, NY (14-60) Band; Secy, Chor; JV, Sftbl; Sr Cl Committee; JV Vlbl; NYSSMA Vocal A; Stetson U; Psych.

CAMPBELL, Karen Lynn
Abbeville HS; Abbeville, SC (25-170) Ann; BC; Chess C; Tres, Chor; Span C; Tres, Jr Cl; JV, Bkbl; Sftbl; Beauty; Clemson U; Bio.

CAMPBELL, Kathryn Anne
Norman HS; Norman, OK; Band; Secy, Key C; Bus Mgr, Sch P; Parl, Span C; SC; Mgr, Wrest; Faculty, Sunday Sch; Jr NHS; Hostess, Interntl Stu; Okla St U.

CAMPBELL, Kelly Jane
W Mid Hi Sch; Norman, OK; Pres, Band; SC; Faculty, Sunday Sch; Hostess, Interntl Stu.

CAMPBELL, Kerri Lynn
LaConner HS; LaConner, WA; Ann; FHA; NHS; Rptr, Sch P; Span C; Mgr, Bkbl; Semi-Fin, Tr; EWSC; Math.

CAMPBELL, Kevin Allen
Oak Ridge Acad; Oak Ridge, NC (3-30) A Cap Choir; Chor; Fr C; Monogram; Spch C; Var C; ROTC A; Marksmanship Medal; Law Enforcement.

CAMPBELL, Kevin Lyn
Dothan HS; Dothan, AL; Band; Chldr; Ensm; FHA; Mjrte; Span C; Math A; St, Church Choir; Bus.

CAMPBELL, Kirk Martin
LaConner HS; LaConner, WA (4-52) VP, Chem C; Mgr, Drama; Bus Mgr, Math C; NHS; Tres, Phys C; VP, Ski C; Tres, Span C; Alg A; Ftbl Ltrs; Drama A; Wash St U; Agr.

CAMPBELL, Laurie Ann
Reynolds HS; Greenville, PA (109-183) FNA; Lat C; Rainbow; Tri-HiY; Tnns; Bkbl.

CAMPBELL, Lisa Faye
Regina HS; Norwood, OH; Bus Mgr, Ann; Mgr, CYO; NHS; Co-Cpt, Bkbl; Sftbl; Bio A; COM; H of F; PTA A; Sci A; Festival Chrm; Yth Rep, Parish Coun; Xavier U; Nurs.

CAMPBELL, Lynn Karen
Northeast HS; Oakland Park, FL (9-543) Co-Cpt, Chldr; Chor; Fr C; SC; HCt; Hon Prog; Hugh O'Brien Yth Found; JV Chldr Ltr; Social Sci.

CAMPBELL, Mark Alan
Guymon HS; Guymon, OK (10%-160) Pres, FFA; NHS; Bkbl; Pres, Local MYF; Pres, W Zone MYF; Pres, Woodward Dist MYF; Okla St U; Agr.

CAMPBELL, Mark Harrison
Wachusett Regional HS; Holden, MA; FFA; Bkbl; Cpt, Soccer; Tr; COM; Citz A; PTA A; Fife & Drum Corps; Jr Choir; Oceanography.

CAMPBELL, Martha Miles
George Wythe HS; Wytheville, VA (9-135) GS; Math C; Mu Alpha Theta; Rptr, NHS; Pres, Sci C; SC; Co-Cpt, Bkbl; Tnns; Cl Fav; Yth Fel; SCA Leadership, School; Hollins Col.

CAMPBELL, Martin Frederick
Notre Dame-Bishop Gibbons HS; Schenectady, NY (9-161) NHS; Bsbl; Bkbl; Cpt, Cr-Crty; Tr; COM; Hon Prog; NEDT; Sacristan; Psych.

CAMPBELL, Mary Catherine
Plymouth Salem HS; Plymouth, MI (25%-500) 4H; NHS; Swim; Yth Fel; Church Choir; Bell Choir; Eng, Home Ec, Weaving, Soc Stu, A's; Alma Col; Elem Ed.

CAMPBELL, Mary Elizabeth
Yorktown Sr HS; Arlington, VA; Ed.

CAMPBELL, Mary Frances
Mullens HS; Mullens, WV (2-105) BC; CYO; Chldr; Tres, FBLA; FHA; HiY; Hmrm; interClub Coun; NHS; A-Ed, Sch P; Tres, Jr Cl; Tnns; Alg A; Sal; Type A; W Va U; Phar.

CAMPBELL, Melody Ruth
Garfield Sr HS; Hamilton, OH (12-445) Chor; Drama; Ensm; Ch, Hmrm; Lit Mag; NHS; ARC; Sch Achieve Tm; F-Ed, Sch P; Sci C; Span C; SC; Tr; COM; Hon Prog; Journ A; ARC A; Sci A; Type A; Mus A; U of Cincinnati; Nurs.

CAMPBELL, Milika Rochell
Carolina HS; Greenville, SC; Chor; FBLA; FHA; Balfour A; COM; Gr Marshal; MLS; Most Out; Ntl Achv Schol; NMF; Sal; Val; *USC; Acct.*

CAMPBELL, Murle Dean Jr
Lansing Baptist HS; Lansing, MI; Band; Chor; Ensm; SC; Bkbl; Soccer; Wrest; ROTC A; Mus A; *Ministry of Mus.*

CAMPBELL, Nancy Lynn
Andrew Lewis HS; Salem, VA; Chor; FBLA; Y-Tns; *Va W Comm Col; Data Processing.*

CAMPBELL, Patricia Elena
John Marshall HS; San Antonio, TX; VP, Fr C; Lat C; Mu Alpha Theta; Span C; Bio A; COM; Hon Prog; Eng A; Lat A; Fr A; *Rice U; Lang.*

CAMPBELL, Paul Douglas
Buckhorn HS; Buckhorn, KY (3-41) BC; Chor; 4H; S-T, Jr Cl; Mgr, Bkbl; 4H A; Lion A; PTA A; Sci A; Spch A; 4-H Coun; Cert & Trophy, Sci Fair; Secy, Sunday Sch; PA; Sunday Sch Teacher; Outst 4-Her; Garden A; *Eastern Col; Acct.*

CAMPBELL, Paula Ann
Pineville HS; Pineville, LA (10%-248) Ann; Secy, Chor; InterAct C; NHS; *LSU; Nurs.*

CAMPBELL, Phillip Jay
Pendleton HS; Pendleton, SC; A Cap Choir; Arch; Band; Chor; FFA; 4H; Sci C; Arch; Bsbl; Bkbl; Ftbl; Swim; Tnns; 4H A; Fin, 4-H C A.

CAMPBELL, Regina Donnette
Rufus King HS; Milwaukee, WI; Chldr; Dbte Tm; Parl, Drama; Rptr, FBLA; Pres, Hmrm; Ch, Mjrte; NFL; Sch P; Sci C; Tres, SC; JA A; Schol Service A; Comm Service A; Reading Merit A; Ldrship Service A; *Sou Calif U; Pub Relations.*

CAMPBELL, Reginald Isaiah
Carolina HS; Greenville, SC; Band; Chor; Balfour A; COM; Gr Marshal; MLS; Most Out; Ntl Achv Schol; NMF; Sal; Val; *Drama.*

CAMPBELL, Reginald Neal
Oswego HS; Oswego, IL (20-352) Band; Bsbl; Bkbl; Ftbl; Hon Prog; Interlochen Ntl Mus; Sports A; *Morehouse Col; Law.*

CAMPBELL, Russell Shelby
Hoisington HS; Hoisington, KS (8-82) Band; Ensm; Order/Arrow; Pres, Soph Cl; Bsbl; JV, Bkbl; JV, Ftbl; Golf; Tr; Eagle Sct; 60; Merit Badges *Eng.*

CAMPBELL, Sharon Darlene
Chester HS; Chester, PA (23-673) Home Ec, Math, A's; *Pierce Jr Col; Secy.*

CAMPBELL, Sherilyn Kay
Snyder HS; Snyder, TX (7-252) Chor; Ensm; Madrigal; NFL; Thes; Top Ten; *Tex Tech U.*

CAMPBELL, Sherry Ann
Wingfield HS; Jackson, MS (15-283) Chor; NHS; Span C; COM; Hon Prog; Spch A; Yth Fel; WW; *Miss Col; Nurs.*

CAMPBELL, Stephen Rodger
Goodrich HS; Goodrich, TX (5-25) VP, BC; Secy, FFA; Cpt, Bsbl; Cpt, Bkbl; Cpt, Ftbl; All Dist, Bkbl; Most Athletic; *Brigham Young U; Psych.*

CAMPBELL, Susan Elaine
McCluer N HS; Florissant, MO (325-730) Chor; Drama; Hmrm; Madrigal; Pres, Rainbow; Rptr, Sch P; SC; Thes; Mgr, Wrest; Journ A; HR; *SW Mo St U; Bus Adm.*

CAMPBELL, Susan Jean
Crestview Sr HS; Crestview, FL; Anchor C; Band; Tres, BC; *Oglethorpe Col; Sociology.*

CAMPBELL, Terri Deanette
Putnam City HS; Oklahoma City, OK (75-850) Fr C; Math C; Mu Alpha Theta; Ed, Sch P; SC; Journ A; Yth Fel; Engr C; Future Journ of Amer; *Baylor U; Bus.*

CAMPBELL, Terri Lynn
Amador HS; Pleasanton, CA; Bkbl; Soccer; MVP, Sftbl; Swim; *Chabot Col; Counseling.*

CAMPBELL, Thomas Ross
Meridian HS; Meridian, TX; Pres, BC; FFA; Ftbl; 1st, Livestock Judging; Citizen o-t Mo; *Tex A&M U; Vet.*

CAMPBELL, Tina Colette
La Farge HS; LaFarge, WI (5-25) A Cap Choir; Ann; Band; Chor; Drama; Ensm; Pres, FHA; Madrigal; Pol Sci C; Sch P; Secy, Soph Cl; Sftbl.

CAMPBELL, Tina Marie
Troy HS; Troy, KS (3-38) Ann; Band; Sch P; JV, Bkbl; JV, Tr; COM; Sci A; PA; *Med Tech.*

CAMPBELL, Vanesia Jene
W Orange HS; Orange, TX (65-243) Tr; *N Tex St U; Bus.*

CAMPBELL, Vicki Lyn
Lamar HS; Lamar, MO (5-83) NHS; Most Out; Regent Schol; Acct A; Top 10, Cl; *Ozark Bible Col; Christian Ed.*

CAMPBELL, William Marshall
Woodrow Wilson HS; Dallas, TX (5%-300) Band; Span C; *Baylor U; Bus.*

CAMPBELL, William Russell
Harlem HS; Harlem, GA; InterAct C; F-Ed, Sch P; Bsbl; MVP, Ftbl; Cl Fav; Yth Fel; *S Ga Col; Phys Ed.*

CAMPBELL, Yolanda Pertrice
Miami Killian HS; Miami, FL; Chor; *Bethune Cookman Col; Secy.*

CAMPEAS, David E
Hightstown HS; Hightstown, NJ (17-309) Ed, Sch P; Cr-Ctry; Tr; Hist A; 1st Prize, St Hist Fair; *Rutgers U; Law.*

CAMPER, Roderick Bruce
James River HS; Buchanan, VA (10-120) BS; Chess C; NHS; Pres, Span C; COM; *Va Western Comm Col; Acct.*

CAMPING, Donna Joy
Amer Heritage Christian Sch; Hayward, CA; Ensm; S-T, Hmrm; S-T, SC; Bank Of Amer A; CSF; DARGCA; HCt; Most Out; Val; *Reformed Bible Col.*

CAMPNEY, David James
Spencer Comm HS; Spencer, IA; Band; Drama; Co-Ed, Sch P; Span C; Thes; JV, Ftbl; JV, Wrest; Yth Fel; *Iowa St U; Elec Engr.*

CAMPO, Diane Kathryn
Hillsdale HS; San Mateo, CA (98-441) Chldr; Ski C; JV, Ftbl; Golf; Hockey; GAA; Sch Rep, Campus After Dark; *Pepperdine U; Bus.*

CAMPORA, Douglas L
Martin Co HS; Stuart, FL (86-500) Band; Key C; Golf; Chem A; Golf Letter; Band Letter; *U of Fla; Pharmacy.*

CAMPOS, Eleanor Batangan
John F Kennedy HS; Tumon, GUAM (10-511) Band; VP, FNA; Hmrm; NHS; Pep Band A; HR; Eng A; Hon Band A; *U of Hawaii; Ed.*

CAMPOS, Lori Lynn
Chino HS; Chino, CA; Bkbl; Confrence Valentine Qn; *U of Calif at Riverside; Special Ed.*

CAMPOS, Martinez Diana
Colegio La Merced; Hato Rey, PR (2-108) Chldr; Chor; Drama; Fr C; FHA; Alg A; Bio A; COM; Chem A; Hist A; Hon Prog; Math A; Span A; Phy A; Sal; Sci A; Drama A; 9th Grade Hon Graduate; Month's Stu; Span A; Eng A; *Med.*

CAMUS, Patrick Paul
St Elizabeth HS; Pittsburgh, PA (9-101) Tres, Chess C; Drama; Phys C; Ski C; Hockey; Alg A; COM; Hon Prog; Math A; Ntl Sci Found; NEDT; Vlbl; *U of Pittsburgh; Engr.*

CAMUSO, Lawrence Michael
San Jose HS; San Jose, CA (3-308) BS; Pres, FBLA; Hmrm; Fin, NFL; Spch C; Tres, SC; CSF; Opt A; Spch A; *San Jose St Col; Industrial Design.*

CANADA, Lisa K
Dyer Co HS; Newbern, TN; NHS; *Dyersburg St Comm Col.*

CANADAY, Jennifer Renell
Hillside HS; Durham, NC (10-150) JV, Chldr; Chor; SC; Sftbl; Yth Fel; Attendance A; Phys Fitness A; *U of NC-CHAPEL Hill; Math.*

CANADY, Curtis Wayne
Vandalia Christian Sch; Greensboro, NC (1-14) Ann; Rptr, Sch P; Span C; *UNC at Chapel Hill; Acct.*

CANADY, Dorothy Jean
Peach Co HS; Fort Valley, GA (4-200) Ann; BC; Lit Mag; Sch P; COM; Ntl Achv Schol; AKA Cert; *U of Ga; Pre-Med.*

CANADY, Vanessa Lorraine
Ballou Sr HS; Washington, DC; Secy, Hmrm; Citz A; Hist A; *Med.*

CANALES, Armando Rene
Berkner HS; Richardson, TX (40-400) Key C; NHS; Orch; SC; Cr-Ctry; JV, Tr; Pres, Jr NHS; FCA; *Elec Engr.*

CANCEL, Harry
Luis Munoz Rivera HS; Lajas, PR (50-170) Chess C; Most Out; *Colegio Antillano; Enfermeria.*

CANCEL, Roxana Moraima
Academia Discipulos de Cristo; Bayamon, PR (20-122) A Cap Choir; Ann; VP, Bus C; CYO; Chldr; Chem C; Chess C; Chor; Dbte Tm; Drama; Tres, FHA; GS; Hmrm; Lat C; A-Ed, Lit Mag; Math C; NHS; ARC; Sch Achieve Tm; JV, Bkbl; Sftbl; Swim; Tnns; Alg A; Amer Leg A; Beauty; Bio A; COM; Chem A; Cl Fav; Hist A; JA A; Math A; Pres A; Sci A; Spch A; Star Student; *U of Puerto Rico; Med.*

CANDANOZA, Rose Ann
Springdale HS; Springdale, AR; A Cap Choir; Band; Pres, CYO; Chor; Dbte Tm; Hmrm; Spch C; SC; Drill Tm; *U of Ark; Mus Ed.*

CANDELARIA, Antonio
Dr Pedro Perea Fajardo Voc HS; Mayaguez, PR; Hon Stu; *Bradford Col; Elec Engr.*

CANDELARIA, Criss Eugene
Round Valley HS; Springerville, AZ (4-95) VP, CYO; NHS; Ski C; Pres, Var C; Bkbl; Ftbl; Cpt, Tr; Bio A; Eagle Sct; *N Ariz U; Hist.*

CANDELARIA, Isaac
Voc HS; Mayaguez, PR; CYO; Dbte Tm; A-Ed, Sch P; Assistance A; *CAAM; Computers.*

CANDELARIA, Myrna
Greater New York Acad; Woodside, NY (6-73) Ed, Ann; NHS; Chem A; Type A; Eng A; *Atlantic Union Col; Philosophy.*

CANDELL, Gregory Lloyd
Santa Monica HS; Santa Monica, CA; City Conf; Drama; JV, Bkbl; Ftbl; Tr; Citz A; Hon Prog; Most Out; Rotary A; Star Student; Outst Ath; Outst Schol; VP, Church Yth; *UCLA; Med.*

CANDLE, Kelon
Marshall Islands HS; Majuro, MARSHALL ISLANDS (20-103) Star Student; *E Ariz Col; Secy.*

CANDLE, Scott Richard
Ellet HS; Akron, OH (275-388) Ftbl; Tr; Tr Ltrs; Ftbl Ltrs; *Akron U.*

**CANDLER,
Catherine MacGregor**
Woodward Acad; College Park, GA; Chldr; Chor; Drama; Hmrm; InterAct C; JV, Tr; Semi Fin, Dorothy Schol A; *Amer Fashion Col of Switzerland; Fashion.*

CANDLER, Robert Victor
Central HS; Knoxville, TN (4-400) Pres, BC; Fr C; Key C; NHS; Sch P; Pres, Sci C; Tnns; Bio A; *U of Tenn; Optometry.*

CANESSA, Becky Anne
Amador Valley HS; Pleasanton, CA (81-391) CYO; GS; Hmrm; F-Ed, Sch P; Thes; Var C; Swim; Vlbl; Stu o-t Mon; Amer Business Women Schol; Vol Service, Cert of Achv; *CSU Fresno; Phys Therapy.*

CANFIELD, Bradley Rhea
St Joseph-Ogden HS; St Joseph, IL (18-90) Band; Ger C; Cr-Ctry; Ftbl; Tr; *Architecture.*

CANFIELD, Gary D
Hobbs HS; Hobbs, NM; A Cap Choir; Chor; Ensm; FTA; JV, Tnns; Pres, Church Yth Coun; *NM Jr Col; Acct.*

CANFIELD, Laura June
NW HS; Omaha, NE (75-500) Ann; Chldr; Chor; Dbte Tm; Drama; Hmrm; Math C; NFL; Sch P; Thes; Swim; Beauty; 4H A; Math A; *Psych.*

CANINE, Amy Caroline
Newberry HS; Newberry, SC (1-228) BC; Fr C; GS; InterAct C; Rptr, Sch P; SC; Pres, Jr Cl; MVP, Tnns; Gov Honor Prog; NEDT; Furman Schol; PC Schol; Newberry Summer Schol; Gov's Advisory Coun; *Duke U; Marine Bio.*

CANIVEZ, Gary Lynn
Lake of The Woods HS; Baudette, MN (33-78) CYO; Chor; NHS; Bsbl; Ftbl; JV, Hockey; U of ND; General.

CANIZARO, Dianne Marie
Bishop Byrne HS; Memphis, TN (50-191) Fr C; SC; Pres, Sr Cl; Bkbl; 1st Cl GSct; Attendance As; Miss St U; Elem Ed.

CANN, Claudia Marie
Notre Dame HS; Clarksburg, WV (3-52) Ann; Chor; Drama; Rptr, FBLA; FHA; Pres, FTA; GS; Pres, Hmrm; Math C; NHS; Ntl Teachers Coun; Sci C; SC; UN Council; VP, Soph Cl; Swim; Cl Fav; Math A; Odd Fellow Fin; Sci A; W Va U; Law.

CANN, Wendy Patricia
Oregon HS; Oregon, IL (6-139) AFS; Bus Mgr, Ann; Fr C; VP, Jr Cl; Secy, Soph Cl; Pom Pon Squad; Phy Therapy.

CANNADAY, Thomas Duane
Largo Sr HS; Largo, FL; Band; St Petersburg Jr Col; Mus.

CANNING, John Michael
Fremont HS; Sunnyvale, CA (7-618) Dbte Tm; Hmrm; Pres, Math C; NFL; NHS; Pres, SC; Thes; Tres, Soph Cl; Tr; CSF; HCt; Hon Prog; Math A; Sci A; Spch A; Soph Sci A; Dist Math A; Cl Service A.

CANNIZZO, Paul Anthony
St Joseph o-t Palisades HS; W New York, NJ (14-225) Ann; Co-Ch, CYO; NHS; Span NHS; Amer Leg A; Hon Prog; NEDT; WW; US Air Force Acad; Engr.

CANNOCK, Hillary Jean
Monroe-Woodbury Central HS; Central Valley, NY; Band; Vlbl; Span A.

CANNON, Alisa Charlene
John Ehret HS; Marrero, LA (61-480) FHA; Hmrm; Secy, Sch P; Sci C; Pres, SC; Cl Fav; Vof-DEM; WW; VP, Rptr, SC; U of Southwestern La; Ed.

CANNON, Christopher David
Washburn HS; Minneapolis, MN (40-500) Chem C; Hmrm; NHS; SC; Bkbl; Ftbl; Amer Leg A; Citz A; Coun of Teach A; HCt; Hon Prog; Ntl Achv Schol; Ntl Conf Chr & Jews; NMS; U of Minn; Pre-Med.

CANNON, Imogene Ursula
Pass Christian HS; Pass Christian, MS (25%-110) Band; BC; Co-Cpt, Chldr; FHA; Pres, Hmrm; SC; Bkbl; Tr; WW; DAHSS; Xavier U; Pol Sci.

CANNON, Jerry Lance
Alton Sr HS; Alton, IL (45%-700) Bsbl; Ranken Tech Inst; Archt Design.

CANNON, Katherine Jean
Stephen F Austin HS; Austin, TX (50%-406) CYO; Mjrte; Span C; Pres, Scts Exploring; Bus.

CANNON, Kevin Andrew
Washburn HS; Minneapolis, MN; Ski C; SC; Cpt, Ftbl; Tr; MLS; Opt A; Pres A.

CANNON, Lisa Carole
Lyon Co HS; Eddyville, KY (1-110) Band; BC; Cpt, Chldr; Secy, Chor; Rptr, FHA; 4H; Type A; Outst Jr Degree; Chapter Degree; Del, St 4-H Older Yth Conf Wash; Murray St U; Bio.

CANNON, Louise Ann
W Monroe HS; West Monroe, LA (33%-496) Northeast U; Elem Ed.

CANNON, Todd Michael
Orofino HS; Orofino, ID (4-97) BS; Key C; Pres, NHS; A-Ed, Sch P; SC; Var C; Pres, Soph Cl; Bsbl; Bkbl; JV, Ftbl; Golf; B Crocker A; God & Country A; Hon Prog; Odd Fellow Fin; Q&S A; Yth Fel; Yth Leg; Sr Cl Rep; UN Tour Del; Eagle Sct; Engr.

CANNON, Valerie Lynn
Kingstree Sr HS; Kingstree, SC (13-199) CYO; U of SC; Med.

CANNON, Verna Lynn
F O Alexander HS; Starkville, MS (10-59) Chldr; Up Bound; Y-Tns; Secy, Jr Cl; Secy, Soph Cl; Cpt, Bkbl; Sftbl; Tr; Hon Prog; Tr A; Miss St U; Secy.

CANON, Kerri Diane
W Middlesex Area HS; W Middlesex, PA (10-147) S-T, 4H; NHS; Span C; Span NHS; B Crocker A; Agr Tech Inst; Dairy Production.

CANOVA, Kathleen Marie
Parsippany Christian HS; Parsippany, NJ; Arch; Lit Mag; Span C; Computers.

CANRIGHT, Faith Louise
Markoma Bible Acad; Tahlequah, OK; Co-Ed, Ann; Chor; Fr C; JV, Sftbl; Hon Prog; Most Out; Yth Fel; 'A' HR A; 'A' HR A.

CANTERBURY, Karen Lynn
Wallace HS; Wallace, ID (45-100) Band; Pres, 4H; Lat C; 4H A; Med.

CANTERBURY, Kendel Lee
Leland HS; San Jose, CA; A Cap Choir; Chor; Fr C; Pres, 4H; Ch, Hmrm; ARC; SC; 4H A; Sem-Fin, VICA; Silver Medalist, St Olympics; Med Asst; Reg Win, Make It Yourself Wth Wool; Evergreen Valley Col; Med.

CANTLEY, Kenneth Eric
Ritenour Sr HS; St Louis, MO (48-850) VP, NHS; Wrest; Amer Leg A; RA Ntl Service Aid.

CANTOLI, Donna Marie
St Joseph's HS; W New York, NJ (89-232) CYO; Drama; Tres, SC; Tres, Jr Cl; Mgr, Bsbl; COM; Woods Sch; Secy.

CANTRELL, James Allen
Central HS; Thomasville, GA; Pres, Chess C; HiY; Order/Arrow; Sci C; Bkbl; Swim; Tnns; Pres' C; Eagle Sct; Berry Col; Acct.

CANTRELL, Jim Dale
Warrensburg HS; Warrensburg, MO; Band; Sci C; Ftbl; Opt Out Tn; Order of Mic-O-Say; Pheonix Inst of Tech; Auto Mechanics.

CANTRELL, Jodi Marie
Ventura Sr HS; Ventura, CA; Ventura Col.

CANTRELL, Lisa Dawn
Boyd Co HS; Ashland, KY (60-325) A Cap Choir; Ann; Band; Chor; VP, FHA; FTA; GS; Jr Miss Pagent; Mjrte; Span C; All St Piano Ensm; SDAHSS; WW, Mus; Ashland Comm Col; Bus.

CANTRELL, Lori Carol
Warren Co Sr HS; McMinnville, TN (25%-400) FHA; InterAct C; Sci C; TOEC; Middle Tenn St U; Bus.

CANTRELL, Paul Stephen
Cumberland Valley HS; Mechanicsburg, PA (200-605) Pres, A Cap Choir; Hmrm; Key C; Var C; Arch; Ftbl; Tnns; Cpt, Gym; Harding Col; Bible.

CANTRELL, Rhonda Jo
Fayette Co HS; Fayett, AL; A Cap Choir; Band; Chor; Ensm; 4H; Hmrm; Pres, Math C; Mu Alpha Theta; NHS; Rptr, Sch P; Tres, Span C; SC; All St Band; Mu Alpha Theta A; Brewer St Jr Col; Journ.

CANTRELLE, Mary Virginia
Our Lady of Fatima HS; Lafayette, LA; CYO; Fr C; Math C; Mu Alpha Theta; VP, NHS; F-Ed, Sch P; SC; VP, Jr Cl; Beauty; COM; Hon Prog; Ntl Achv Schol; Swth; U of Southwestern La; Psych.

CANTRIL, Richard Nelson
Gordon HS; Gordon, NE (10-71) Band; Pres, CYO; Pres, NHS; Cpt, Bkbl; Golf; Elk A; I Dare You; Sports Kg; Modern Problems A; Outst Bkbl Athlete; Outst Golf Athlete; Chadron St Col; Ed.

CANTWELL, Kelly Alice
Frederick HS; Frederick, SD (18-30) CYO; Swtht; Candidate, Snow Qn; N St Col; Elem Ed.

CANTY, Beverly Clare
Lake Co HS; Leadville, CO; A Cap Choir; Chor; Thes; Cr-Ctry; Swim; Tnns; Tr; Colo Col; Mus.

CANTY, Cheryl Fertessa
Jones Co HS; Gray, GA (10%-190) Fr C; FBLA; FHA; 4H; Hmrm; Math C; NHS; F-Ed, Sch P; Secy, SC; UN Council; COM; 4H A; Math A; Poet A; Pres A; Type A; Col Schol; Mus Cert; Best All Around, Cotillion Ball; WW; Howard U; Nurs.

CANTY, Mary Magdaline
Myrtle Beach HS; Myrtle Beach, SC (24-249) Ann; Chldr; Chor; Ensm; Sch P; SC; Var C; Mgr, Bkbl; Cpt, Tr; COM; Key C Calendar; Lib C; Civinettes; Pres, Fresh Cl; Pep C; Jr Steward; Exec Coun; Band Comm, Jr-Sr Prom; Unity C; Pres, Jr Usher Board; Presbyterian Col; Coun.

CANUPP, Laura Marie
T L Hanna HS; Anderson, SC (7-350) Chess C; Monogram; NHS; Tnns; WW; Commencement Marshal; Presbyterian Col; Elem Ed.

CANVIN, Elisa Maxine
Northwest HS; Jackson, MI (25%-250) A Cap Choir; Chor; 4H; JA A; Jackson Jr Col; Med Tech.

CAPARELLA, Florence
Canarsie HS; Brooklyn, NY (1-945) Pres, NHS; Amer Leg A; COM; Gov Honor Prog; Hon Prog; Regent Schol; Val; Brooklyn Col; Chem.

CAPE, Stanley Darrell
Banks Co HS; Homer, GA; Parl, 4H; Odd Fellow Fin.

CAPEHART, Gayla Elaine
Mount Miguel HS; Spring Valley, CA (17-493) Ensm; Orch; Band A; CSF; Band Lib; Top Bus Stu A; Outst, Bus Eng; San Diego Col of Bus; Court Rptr.

CAPEHART, Mel Roy
Cibola HS; Albuquerque, NM; 3 Weeks Bio Med Course at NM Tech.

CAPEK, Jo Ann
Milligan HS; Milligan, NE (4-12) Ann; Band; Chor; GS; Co-Ed, Sch P; Tres, Sr Cl; Tres, Jr Cl; Tres, Soph Cl; Cpt, Bkbl; Mgr, Tr; B Crocker A; COM; Type A; Cpt, Vlbl; Pres, VP, Secy, 4-H C; Tres & Rptr, 4-H C; U of Nebraska; Pre Physician's Assistant.

CAPEK, Susan Lynn
Centennial HS; Pueblo, CO (48-350) Band; Chor; Fr C; NHS; Ski C; COM; Spirit C; Pres, Job's Daughters; Pom Pom Girls; FCA.

CAPELL, Barbara Lee
Litchfield HS; Litchfield, CT (28-150) 4H; Span NHS; 4H A; NEDT; Pres, Yth Fellowship.

CAPELLA, Claire Marie
John W Hallahan HS; Philadelphia, PA (12-431) CYO; NHS; ARC; Sci C; Bkbl; Cpt, Sftbl; Hon Prog; Ath Schol A; W Chester St Col; Phys Ed.

CAPELLA, Jasmin
Our Lady of Good Counsel HS; Newark, NJ (5-76) CYO; COM; Cl Fav; Hist A; Hon Prog; Most Out; Sci A; Health Careers C; Attendance A; Good Conduct A; Eng A; Seton Hall U; Pre-Med.

CAPELLA, Leida
Kubasaki HS; Okinawa, JAPAN (8-421) ARC; COM; Eckerd Col; Nurs.

CAPEN, Robert Durward
Ticonderoga HS; Ticonderoga, NY; Band; Chor; Sch P; Houghton Col; Mus.

CAPENER, Brent Allen
Payette HS; Payette, ID (14-103) Rptr, Ann; BS; Chess C; FFA; InterClub Coun; JETS; Key C; Tres, NHS; Sci C; Span C; Tnns; Cl Fav; ROTC A; Yth Leg; U of Idaho; Engr.

CAPERS, Deborah Yvette
Middleton HS; Charleston, SC; Tr; Jr Beta C.

CAPERS, Gwendolyn Jeanette
Burke HS; Charleston, SC (11-210) Band; Drama; FNA; Hmrm; Sch P; Cl Fav; HCt; Swtht; Heart Fund A; 1st Alt, Trophy, Sch Qn; WW; Talladega Col; Nurs.

CAPERS, Joseph Wilbert
Alma J Brown Lab HS; Grambling, LA (7-70) Band; NHS; Sci C; Bkbl; Hon Prog; Math A; Sci A; All Star Tm; Bkbl; Ldrship Trng Sch; Bus Mgt.

CAPITOL, Rajene
Marshall Island HS; Majuro, MARSHALL IS-LANDS; Hon Prog; Star Student.

CAPLES, William Griffin Jr
Ne Sr HS; N Little Rock, AR (79-453) Band; Mu Alpha Theta; VICA; Superior, Ensm; Band Ltr.

CAPORICCI, Stella Lynn
Ross S Sterling HS; Houston, TX; JETS; Mu Alpha Theta; NHS; Sci C; Span C; Span NHS; Drill Tm; Pres, Med Careers C; Houston Baptist Col; Nurs.

CAPP, Gregory
Lead Hill HS; Lead Hill, AR (5-21) Pres, FBLA; Sch P; Consumer Ed A.

CAPP, John Phillip Jr
Trinity Christian HS; Chattanooga, TN (20%-14) Pres, SC; Pres, Soph Cl; Ftbl; Sftbl; Sci A; Aeronautics.

CAPP, Timothy Wayne
Zion Benton Township HS; Zion, IL (50-600)
Band; Ger C; NHS; Ski C; MVP, Cr-Ctry; Soccer;
Tr; Co-Cpt, Cr Ctry; *Math.*

CAPPA, Donna Ann
F W Springstead HS; Spring Hill, FL (5-150) Ann;
Chor; Drama; Hmrm; Sch P; Ski C; SC; Hon Prog;
Psychoanalysis.

CAPPEL, Eric Carl
Weatherford HS; Weatherford, TX (19-252) Band;
Dbte Tm; NHS; Order/Arrow; MVP, Tnns; Hon
Prog; Order/Arrow A; *U of Tex; Phys Ed.*

**CAPPELLONI,
Mary Ann Elizabeth**
Bishop Klonowski HS; Scranton, PA (7-105) Dbte
Tm; Drama; NFL; NHS; Spch C; COM; NEDT;
Spch A; WW; *Marywood Col; Ed.*

CAPPER, Sharon Lee
Central Dauphin HS; Harrisburg, PA (40%-472)
NHS; Yth Fel; Co-Ed, Sch Yrbk.

CAPPS, Bonnie Sue
Ensley HS; Birmingham, AL; Secy, FHA; ROTC
A.

CAPPS, Dale Everett
Walhalla Sr HS; Walhalla, SC (10%-175) Band;
Math C; Band Block 'W'; PA; Mus A, St of SC;
Clemson U; Bus Mgt.

CAPPS, Darlene Sheril
Bethel HS; Hampton, VA (15-541) Drama; FBLA;
Hmrm; Jr Miss Pagent; Secy, Span C; SC; Beauty;
COM; Cooperative Office Ed; Pastor, Yth Wk;
Outst Chorale Stu; Highest Hons; *Thomas Nelson
Comm Col; Secretarial Sci.*

CAPPS, Dianna
Sunbright HS; Sunbright, TN (10-66) Chldr; FHA;
4H; Bkbl; Miss Soph; *Middle Tenn Col; Nurs.*

CAPPS, Freida Luretta
Bethel Christian HS; Ruston, LA (2-14) F-Ed,
Ann; Bkbl; Sftbl; Amer Leg A; Citz A; Hon Prog;
MLS; Sal; *Northeast LA U; Elem Ed.*

CAPPS, Julie Ann
J M Tate HS; Gonzalez, FL (29-545) Cpt, Band;
BC; Hon Prog; *Livingston Col; Acct.*

CAPPS, Tammie Rene
Berea HS; Greenville, SC (15-180) A Cap Choir;
Band; Chor; Ensm; Ch, Hmrm; ARC; All St Choir;
Colorguard; *Med.*

CAPUTO, John Joseph
Reseda HS; Reseda, CA (1-750) Amer Leg A; Hist
A; Hon Prog; Math A; Sci A; Span Lang; Phys
Fitness, A's; *UCLA; Med.*

CARABALLO, Edwin
Dr Pila HS; Ponce, PR (20-688) Math C; NHS; Ch,
Sr Cl; COM; Hon Prog; Lion A; *Mayaguez Col;
Chem Engr.*

CARABALLO, Marysol
Yauco HS; Yauco, PR; Commercial C; *Bradley U;
Comercial Adm.*

CARABELLO, Karen Marie
Jefferson Area Local HS; Jefferson, OH (20-207)
CYO; Chor; Fr C; FTA; Tres, 4H; Lat C; NHS; Bus
Mgr, Sch P; Span C; 4H A; *Hiram Col; Psych.*

CARAMBOT, Daniel
Miguel Melendez Munoz; Bayamon, PR (8-220) A
Cap Choir; Arch; Band; CYO; Chem C; Chor; Dbte
Tm; Fr C; Math C; Phys C; Sci C; Span C; SC; Var
C; Arch; Bkbl; Bkbl; Ftbl; Sftbl; Swim; COM; Math
A; Sci A; Art A; Social Stu A; Assistance A; Eng A;
Inter-Amer U; Commercial Adm.

CARASTRO, Joyce Elsie
Neshaminy Maple Point HS; Langhorne, PA
(9-400) Chor; Hmrm; NHS; Rptr, Sch P; Chairperson, Jr & Sr Prom; WW; Color Guard; Sch Mus &
Plays; *Pa St U; Nurs.*

**CARAVETTE,
Eugene Christopher**
Carl Sandburg HS; Orland Park, IL (7-932) CYO;
Chor; Rptr, Drama; Pres, 4H; Math C; Mu Alpha
Theta; Parl, NHS; Sci C; Span C; Pres, SC; Tres, Jr
Cl; Tres, Soph Cl; Cpt, Soccer; Amer Leg A; COM;
4H A; Hon Prog; Math A; Q&S A; Spch A; News
Ed, Sch P; Outst, 4-H; High Achv Commendation;
4-H St Project Honor; 4-H 'A' Rating, St Fair.

CARBAUGH, Carrie Anna
McConnellsburg HS; McConnellsburg, PA
(20%-90) Band; Chor; Ensm; Secy, FNA; Rptr, Sch
P; Span C; SC; Var C; Hockey; *Hagerstown Jr Col;
Nurs.*

CARBONARA, Richard Lee
Laurel Highlands Sr HS; Uniontown, PA (17-419)
Chess C; Amer Leg A; Span A; *Bethany Col; In-
strumental Mus.*

CARBONARA, Therese Marie
Immaculata HS; Chicago, IL (14-150) CYO; Pres,
Hmrm; Mod Mus Mas; NHS; Sch P; Span C; Span
NHS; VP, SC; Var C; VP, Sr Cl; MVP, Bkbl; Sftbl;
Hon Prog; *Loyola U; Acct.*

CARBONE, Nelanne Jane
Acad of Saint Aloysius; Jersey City, NJ (13-104)
VP, Bus C; Math C; NHS; ARC; WW; *Seton Hall
Col; Nurs.*

CARBONE, Thomas Dom
St Joseph's HS; Camden, NJ; Ger C; NHS; Pol Sci
C; Pres, SC; VP, Jr Cl; Bsbl; Cpt, Wrest; B Crocker
A; Hon Prog; Best All Around; *Bus Mgt.*

CARBY, Bobbi Jo
Daviess Co HS; Owensboro, KY (39-316) Ann; VP,
BC; Bio A; Shorthand A; *W Ky U; Phys Ed.*

CARD, Joyce Yvonne
MacKenzie HS; Detroit, MI (12-352) NHS; Yth
Fel; Blue & Grey Hon C; JA; *Oakland U; Law
Enforcement.*

CARD, Lecia Darlene
Ensley HS; Birmingham, AL; Chor; Ensm; Secy,
Hmrm; Y-Tns; Soccer; Type A.

CARD, Patty Ellen
Rutledge HS; Rutledge, TN (57-152) Chem C;
Chor; FHA; Span C; Mgr, Tr; Wittiest; Pep C; Tres,
Bible C; Prom Comm; *U of Tenn; Journ.*

CARDA, Teresa Lynn
Tripp HS; Tripp, SD (2-35) Chor; FHA; Pres, NHS;
Pres, Jr Cl; Bkbl; *U of SD at Springfield; Acct.*

CARDEN, Donna Renee
Tuscola HS; Waynesville, NC (10%-300) Chor;
Ensm; Fr C; Madrigal; Superior, NC Vocal Solo
Comp; Accompanist, Concert Choir; Soloist, FBC
Yth Choir; *Mars Hill Col; Mus.*

CARDEN, Stanley Neil
Wayne Co HS; Jesup, GA (10%-400) Ann; BC;
NHS; JV, Bsbl; *Ga Tech; Chem Engr.*

CARDEN, Tanya Diane
Clinton Sr HS; Clinton, TN; NHS; *U of Tenn;
Computer Sci.*

CARDENAS, Kelly Jeannine
Wilton Christian Sch; Wilton, CA; Chor; Ensm;
Sewing A; Choir A; Quartet A; *Horse Breeding &
Raising.*

CARDER, Kenneth R
East HS; Akron, OH (35-407) Chor; Drama; Ensm;
Span C; Thes; Cr-Ctry; Citz A; Hon Prog; Pres, Yth
Group; Board Member; PA.

CARDIELLE, Peter Guy John
St Peters Prep HS; Jersey City, NJ (17-250) Chor;
Drama; Hmrm; Ski C; SC; Tnns; Gym; *George-
town U; Bio.*

CARDIN, Jane Laura
Acad o-t Holy Family; Baltic, CT (1-45) Chor; SC;
Tr; *Art.*

CARDIS, Audrey Fay
Akron-Fairgrove HS; Fairgrove, MI (20%-80) 4H;
Sci C; Span C; Tr; 4H A; Dist Art A; *Ferris Col;
Med.*

CARDONA, Antonio
Francisco Mendoza HS; Isabela, PR; Chess C; Dbte
Tm; Drama; Fr C; Lit Mag; Math C; Sci C; Tr;
COM; Hist A; Math A; Most Out; Sci A; Spch A;
Movie A; *MIT; Engr.*

CARDONA, Armando Alberto
Colegio San Antonio; Rio Piedras, PR (4-103) Hon
Prog; NEDT.

CARDONA, Ralph Luis
Academia Sagrado Corazon; Santurce, PR (2-65)
Drama; Lit Ral; Lit Mag; Madrigal; Model UN;
VP, NFL; Pres, NHS; ARC; Sch P; Span C; Spch C;
SC; Var C; Bsbl; Cpt, Bkbl; Tr; Alg A; Bio A; COM;
Chem A; Hist A; Hon Prog; Math A; Most Out; Sci
A; Spch A; MVP A; *NCSU; Computer Sci.*

CARDOSO, Gloria Lucille
Tabernacle Christian Acad; San Diego, CA; Bsbl;
Sftbl; Tr; Citz A; MLS; *Apostolic Bible Col; Chris-
tain Ed.*

CARDOSO, Naomi Otillia
Tabernacle Christian Acad; San Diego, CA (6-7)
Cpt, Chldr; FHA; Bsbl; Sftbl; Tnns; Co-Cpt, Tr;
Spch A; *Oral Roberts U; Computer Sci.*

CARDOZA, Lavinia
Luis Munoz Marin HS; Cabo Rojo, PR (7-200)
Commercial C; FBLA; FHA; Sci C; Span C; *Re-
cinto Universitario Mayaguez; Secretaria.*

CARDWELL, Molly Louise
Cottage Grove HS; Cottage Grove, OR (6-240)
NHS; MVP, Bkbl; Sftbl; Tnns; Tr; *U of Oreg; Phys
Ed.*

CARDWELL, Sonya Ann
Kensington HS; Buffalo, NY (164-330) 4H; HiY;
Span C; JV, Cr-Ctry; Hockey; 4H A; Yth Fel;
Sports Ed; Pres, Baptist Yth Fel; HR; Jr Director,
Church Nursery; Merit Roll; Bicentennial Float
Comm; *Medaille Col; Human Services.*

CAREW, Jorge Miguel
Rainbow City Jr-Sr HS; Rainbow City, CANAL
ZONE; Band; Dbte Tm; Sch P; Pres, Sr Cl; Tr;
Chem A; Math A; Phy A; Sci A; *NY Comm Col;
Law.*

CAREW, Kimberly Jo
Waggener HS; Louisville, KY (40-300) Co-Ed,
Ann; BC; Pres, Chor; Hmrm; ARC; Sftbl; Hon
Prog; Q&S A; St Mus Ensm A; *U of Ky; Phys
Therapy.*

CAREW, Ruth Ann
Little Wolf HS; Manawa, WI (7-72) Ann; Band;
Fin, Bus C; CYO; Drama; 4H; NFL; NHS; Bkbl;
Soccer; Tr; COM; Citz A; Hon Prog; ROTC A;
Type A; Schol A; Welding A; Sheet Metal As;
Drafting A; *Platterville U; Industrial.*

CAREY, Curtis Devern
N Kansas City HS; N Kansas City, MO (20%-415)
Pres, Key C; *Elec.*

CAREY, Debbie Ann
Oelwein Sr HS; Oelwein, IA; Tnns; Bicentennial A;
Iowa St U; Home Ec.

CAREY, Debra Ann
Oelwein Comm HS; Oelwein, IA; Bicentennial A;
Bartlesville Wesleyan Col; Home Ec.

CAREY, John A Jr
Wellston HS; Wellston, OH (25-120) Ann; Rptr,
4H; Lat C; Rptr, Sch P; 4H A; Rotary A; Yth Fel;
Ohio U; Communications.

CAREY, Loriann Beth
Neshaminy Langhorne HS; Langhorne, PA
(200-715) A Cap Choir; Band; Drama; Pres A;
Bucks Comm Col; Mus.

CAREY, Lucia Marie
Old Forge HS; Old Forge, PA (23-121) Chor;
NHS; Pres, Sodality; *Wilkes Col; Nurs.*

CAREY, Matthew James
Grinnell HS; Grinnell, IA; Band; Key C; Bsbl; Bkbl;
Cr-Ctry; Tnns; FCA.

CAREY, Monica
McDonogh 35 Sr HS; New Orleans, LA; Chor;
Rptr, Sch P; Mixed Chor A; *U of New Orleans; Bus
Adm.*

CAREY, Rebecca Lee
Antelope Valley HS; Lancaster, CA; *Azusa Pacific
Col.*

CAREY, Steven Lane
Oelwein Comm HS; Oelwein, IA (10%-190) Chor;
Madrigal; NHS; SC; Var C; JV, Golf; Hon Prog;
Bartlesville Wesleyan Col; Acct.

CARGAL, Rebecca Marinelle
Corydon Central HS; Corydon, IN (17-203) Chor;
Orch; *Covenant Foundation Col; Mus.*

CARGILL, Renee Deneen
Faith Baptist HS; Canoga Park, CA (5-25) JV,
Chldr; VP, Soph Cl; Sch A; Sunday Sch Bus
Worker; Sunday Sch Pianist; CYF Missionary
Secy; Sch First Aid Helper; *Hyles-Anderson Col;
Elem Ed.*

CARIS, James Scott
Start HS; Toledo, OH (49-400) Pres, Band; NHS; Orch; Marching & Jazz Bands A's; U of Toledo; Engr.

CARITHERS, Carol Denise
Westside HS; Anderson, SC (3%-400) Band; VP, BC; Ensm; Sci C; Alg A; COM; Citz A; Math A; Most Out; Pres A; ARC A; Sci A; Jr Great Books Achv A; Ecolgy A; Stu Librarian; Eng A; Drama A; Vanderbilt U; Med Field.

CARL, Gary Stephen
Northern Chester Co Tech Sch; Phoenixville, PA (10%-132) Bsbl; JV, Wrest; Penn St U; Chem.

CARLAND, June Adelia
Hendersonville HS; Hendersonville, NC (1-172) Band; Drama; Ensm; Fr C; FHA; NHS; Orch; Alg A; Bio A; COM; Gr Marshal; 4H A; H of F; Hon Prog; Math A; NMF; Summa Cum Laude; Val; First Chair, All-St Band; WW; First Chair of Amer A; Brevard Mus Center Schol.

CARLBERG, Kathleen Ann
Falconer Central HS; Falconer, NY (14-143) Band; GS; Hmrm; Secy, NHS; Orch; SC; JV, Bkbl; Tr; Jamestown Comm Col; Dental Hygenist.

CARLE, Heidemarie
LaFayette HS; La Fayette, NY (9-140) Chor; NHS; SC; Le Moyne Col Psych.

CARLETON, Betty Claire
Union HS; Union, MS (10%-50) Band; BC; Cpt, Chldr; Chor; Hmrm; Sch P; SC; Var C; Tr; Beauty; Cl Fav; HCt; Yth Fel; WW; U of Miss; Fashion Merchandizing.

CARLEY, Laura Louise
Michigan Center HS; Michigan Center, MI (15%-176) Band; Chldr; S-T, Drama; Ensm; Hmrm; NHS; Var C; Hon Prog; Jackson Comm Col; Elem Ed.

CARLIN, Kimberly Joyce
Clark Co R-1 HS; Kahoka, MO (3-95) NHS; Cpt, Sch Achieve Tm; Pres, Span C; VP, Span C; NJHS; Hannibal-La Grange Col; Ed.

CARLISLE, Charles Bryan
Thomasville HS; Thomasville, AL (10%-105) BC; Chor; Drama; FFA; Span C; Bsbl; Bkbl; Ftbl; U of Ala; Engr.

CARLISLE, Lane Stuart
Trinity Heights Christian Acad; Shreveport, LA; BS; Pres, 4H; Key C; Lit Ral; Math C; Mu Alpha Theta; NHS; Sch P; Pres, SC; Var C; Bkbl; Pres, Yth Fel; Top 10 Sr; Most Dependable; La Tech Col; Mech Engr.

CARLISLE, Robbie Nell
Temple Heights Christian Sch; Tampa, FL (3-54) Band; Chess C; FTA; 4H; NHS; Span C; Bus Mgr, Span NHS; Cpt, Bkbl; Sftbl; COM; 4H A; Girl's Varsity Sports; Phys Ed.

CARLO, Dave Allen
Pueblo S HS; Pueblo, CO; Chor; Lat C; JV, Cr-Ctry; JV, Tr; COM; Colo U; Pre-Med.

CARLOCK, Patricia Ann
Soldan HS; St Louis, MO (137-481) Central Mo St U; Nurs.

CARLOCK, Shawn Renee
Warren Central HS; Indianapolis, IN (10%-800) Band; VP, 4H; Citz A; 4H A; Hon Prog; JA A; VP, Church Yth; Bowl & Vlbl Tms; Band A; Bowl Trophies.

CARLOS, Darlene Nunes
Amador Valley HS; Pleasanton, CA (33-410) CYO; French NHS; Cr-Ctry; Tr; CSF; COM; Fashion Inst; Fashion Design.

CARLOS, Maria Theresa
Holgate HS; Holgate, OH (16-72) Band; Secy, FHA; GS; Pres, 4H; NHS; Sch P; Sci C; Pres, Span C; JV, Bkbl; Tr; Span A; Saint Francis Col; Nurs.

CARLQUIST, Scott Lyman
New London-Spicer HS; New London, MN (1-120) Chor; Madrigal; SC; Bkbl; Tr; NRECA Yth Tour; Math.

CARLSEN, Jandi Janee
Redmond HS; Redmond, OR (20%-221) AFS; 4H; NHS; Pres, Span C; 4H A.

CARLSON, Ann Marie
Glenbard W HS; Glen Ellyn, IL; CYO; Chor; Mt Sanario Col; Ed.

CARLSON, Beth Ann
Denfeld HS; Duluth, MN (1-400) Chor; Orch; Badminton; UMD.

CARLSON, Carin Marie
East HS; Rockford, IL; Chor; Pres A; Rock Valley Col; Dental Hygiene.

CARLSON, Carla Joy
Mission San Jose HS; Fremont, CA (33%-460) Chor; FBLA; Soccer; JV, Tnns; Tr; JA A; GAA; Jr Achv; Western Baptist Bible Col; Bus.

CARLSON, Carol Elizabeth
Clinton HS; Clinton, IA (75-585) Acct.

CARLSON, Cheryl Jean
Washburn HS; Washburn, ND (3-20) Ann; GS; 4H; Sci C; Secy, Soph Cl; Bkbl; 4H A; Type A; Jr Cl Play; Ntl Federation of Mus C; Bismarck Jr Col; Bus Adm.

CARLSON, Craig Harlan
Morrow Sr HS; Morrow, GA (30%-450) Co-Cpt, Ftbl; Tr; Hon Prog; Yth Fel; FCA; Hist.

CARLSON, Cynthia
Othello HS; Othello, WA (12-175) NHS; Sch P; Tnns; Sci A; Type A; U & I Sugar A; Wash St U; Nurs.

CARLSON, Dale Duane
Wells-Easton HS; Wells, MN (6-100) Band; BS; Drama; Ensm; Bsbl; Co-Cpt, Bkbl; Cr-Ctry; Gustavus Adolphus Col; Pre-Phar.

CARLSON, David Gilbert
Orange HS; Pepper Pike, OH; Band; Ntl Yth Conf; Hon Prog; Spch A; YTF; Tres, Yth Fel.

CARLSON, David Paul
Ephrata HS; Ephrata, PA; Band; Chor; Orch; Yth Fel; Hon Prog; Band Director's A; Yth & Sr Choir, Church; Concert Band; Lebanon Valley Col; Mus.

CARLSON, Deborah Ruth
Kelvyn Park HS; Chicago, IL (18-275) Chor; Ger C; Hmrm; Key C; Co-Cpt, Mjrte; Parl, NHS; Alg A; Beauty; COM; VofDEM; Northeastern U; Special Ed.

CARLSON, Denise Kay
Los Alamitos HS; Los Alamitos, CA; Band; NHS; CSF.

CARLSON, Diana Sue
Alexander Ramsey HS; Roseville, MN; Vlbl; Bethel Col; Mus.

CARLSON, Eddie
Carver HS; Montgomery, AL; Secy, Key C; Sci C; Var C; Bsbl; Bkbl; Ftbl; Golf; Tr; Cl Fav; HCt; Young Life; Social Ch, Span C; Nom, Jimmy Hitchcock A; Auburn U.

CARLSON, Elizabeth Ann
Two Harbors HS; Two Harbors, MN (22-179) AFS; Drama; Fr C; NHS; Thes; Fr A; Candystriper A; Med.

CARLSON, Eric Henry
Memorial HS; Cedar Grove, NJ (40-202) Cpt, Arch; Pres, Chess C; Ger C; Tres, Order/Arrow; Cpt, Arch; JV, Cr-Ctry; Tr; Amer Leg A; Order/Arrow A; Pres A; VFW A; Eagle Sct; UPSALA Col; Hist.

CARLSON, Eric Reinhold
Newton N HS; Newtonville, MA (51-840) Demolay; Co-Ch, Hmrm; Tnns; Citz A; DeMolay Rep; Sr Acolyte; Conn Col; Bio.

CARLSON, Gayle Marie
Wibaux Co HS; Wibaux, MT (1-28) Co-Ed, Ann; Band; Chldr; Chor; Pres, Drama; Pres, 4H; NFL; Rptr, Sch P; SC; S-T, Var C; Tres, Sr Cl; Pres, Soph Cl; JV, Bkbl; Cpt, Sftbl; Tr; 4H A; HCt; ARC A; Type A; VofDEM; Shorthand A; Forensics A; WW; Bus.

CARLSON, Gregory John
Mount Vernon HS; Mt Vernon, WA; Band; Order/Arrow; JV, Bkbl; Ftbl; Tr; Bausch & Lomb A; Order/Arrow A; Eagle Sct; Skagit Valley Col; Bio.

CARLSON, James Donald
Woodbury Central HS; Moville, IA (4-59) VP, Jr Cl; Bsbl; Bkbl; Ftbl; Iowa St U; Engr.

CARLSON, James Lowell
S Clay Comm Sch; Gillett Grove, IA (4-26) Rptr, FFA; 4H; A-Ed, Sch P; Spch C; Secy, SC; VP, Jr Cl; Pres, Soph Cl; Bsbl; Co-Cpt, Bkbl; Ftbl; Tr; 4H A; HCt; Hon Prog; Journ A; Spch A; Iowa St U; Sci.

CARLSON, Kathryn Marie
Erskine Pub HS; Erskine, MN (7-20) All Amer Yth; Ann; Band; Chldr; Chem C; Chor; Drama; Ensm; Jr Miss Pagent; Rptr, Sch P; Var C; Pres, Jr Cl; MVP, Bkbl; Tr; 4H A; Pres A; Spch A; True Grit, Vlbl; St Lukes Col; Nurs.

CARLSON, Kelly Lynn
Lyons Pub HS; Lyons, NE (7-33) Band; CYO; Chldr; Chor; FHA; Pres, 4H; Rptr, Sch P; Sftbl; Tr; U of Nebr at Lincoln; Elem Ed.

CARLSON, Lauren Therese
Los Alamos HS; Los Alamos, NM (15%-459) Drama; Ensm; Orch; Ski C; Sftbl; Pre-Sch Church Teacher; Piano Teacher; NJHS.

CARLSON, Linda Loann
Ingraham HS; Seattle, WA (25%-430) Sr Torch; Top Ten Home Ec; Seattle Pacific U; Ed.

CARLSON, Linda Sue
Los Alamitos HS; Los Alamitos, CA; Band; NHS; CSF; Hon Prog; Yth Fel; Yth Leg.

CARLSON, Loretta Jane
Hibbing HS; Hibbing, MN (158-432) Chor; World Affairs C; 'H' Pin; Art Cert; Hibbing Area Voc Tech Inst; Apparel Arts.

CARLSON, Marilov Christine
Dulaney Sr HS; Cockeysville, MD (1-633) A Cap Choir; NHS; COM; Hon Prog; Phoenix Choir; Vlbl; Schol A; Lib Arts.

CARLSON, Mark Dougles
Watertown HS; Watertown, CT (35-251) Swim.

CARLSON, Mark Richard
Elk Grove HS; Elk Grove Village, IL (34-599) Community Yth Symph; Drama; NFL; NHS; Orch; Spch C; Thes; Ftbl; Math.

CARLSON, Mary Ann
Hinsdale Central HS; Hinsdale, IL (75%-691) Chor; Ski C; Candystriper; Dean's List; Nurs.

CARLSON, Mary Elizabeth
El Cerrito HS; El Cerrito, CA (11-518) Dbte Tm; Ger C; Hmrm; Ch, InterClub Coun; NFL; SC; Parl, Jr Cl; Parl, Soph Cl; Bank Of Amer A; CSF; DARGCA; NMF; NMS; Spch A; Soroptimist A; Stanford U.

CARLSON, Mary Ellen
Roosevelt HS; Minneapolis, MN; Cpt, Chldr; Chor; Beautician.

CARLSON, Mary Josephine
Timberline HS; Weippe, ID (2-47) Ann; Band; CYO; Pres, Chldr; Drama; FHA; NHS; F-Ed, Sch P; Ski C; SC; Bkbl; Ftbl; Swim; Tr; Elk A; 4H A; HCt; Sal; Yth Leg; Pres & Tres, 4-H C; Carroll Col; Nurs.

CARLSON, Mary Louise
Prosser Sr HS; Prosser, WA (10-123) NHS; Sci C; GAA; Vlbl; Top Ten; Statistician, Girls Bkbl; U of Wash; Bio.

CARLSON, Mary Susan
Gaylord Pub HS; Gaylord, MN (2-88) Band; Chor; Drama; Ensm; FHA; Mod Mus Mas; B Crocker A; Sal; Yth Fel; Mus o-t Yr; Gustavus Adolphus Col; Mus.

CARLSON, Michael David
John Hersey HS; Arlington Heights, IL (239-554) Band; HS Mus Comp Festival.

CARLSON, Mona Kay
Wells-Easton Pub Sch; Wells, MN (2-90) S-T, A Cap Choir; Band; Chor; Drama; Ensm; FHA; Sch P; Secy, SC; Golf; Tnns; Amer Leg A; St Sup Band Solo A; St Sup Ensm A.

CARLSON, Nancy Jo
Holdrege Sr HS; Holdrege, NE (1-125) GS; Sch P; Spch C; Pres, Thes; JV, Bkbl; Sftbl; Tr; COM; Spch A; Type A; JV, Vlbl.

CARLSON, Scott Harold
Temple City HS; Temple City, CA (5%-425) NHS; CSF; Pres, Amateur Radio C; Passadena City Col; Bus.

CARPENTER, Mary Beth
Grace Baptsit HS; Decatur, AL; Chor; 4H; Soccer; U of Ala; Ed.

CARPENTER, Mary Cathryn
Abbotsford Sr HS; Abbotsford, WI (6-68) AFS; Rptr, Ann; Band; CYO; Cpt, Chldr; Drama; NHS; Rptr, Sch P; Var C; Tr; Hon Prog; Sr Lifeguard; JV Vlbl; U of Wis; Archeology.

CARPENTER, Mary Denise
N Mecklenburg HS; Charlotte, NC (16-430) Secy, Ensm; GS; VP, NHS; Span C; U of NC; Med.

CARPENTER, Michael John
Whiteland Comm HS; Whiteland, IN (45-200) Var C; Bsbl; Bkbl; Ftbl; Cpt, Tnns; Ind Arts.

CARPENTER, Michael Keith
N Mecklenburg HS; Huntersville, NC (108-430) Band; BS; Chor; Pres, Ensm; FHA; Key C; Ski C; Span C; Sftbl; Cpt, Swim; NC St U; Engr.

CARPENTER, Michael Leon
Hattiesburg HS Blair Center; Hattiesburg, MS; Band; Key C; Lat C; COM; U of Sou Miss; Math.

CARPENTER, Millie Jan
Lafayette HS; Lafayette, LA (7%-600) F-Ed, Ann; Band; Dbte Tm; FTA; NFL; Secy, NHS; Rainbow; Hospital Aide; WW; LA & Ntl, Miss Tnager Pageant; Agnes Scott Col; Sci.

CARPENTER, Nancy Lynn
McMinnville HS; McMinnville, OR (77-225) Bus C; Chor; FTA; Pres, Key C; NHS; Var C; Tnns; Citz A; Pres, Grls Lge; Judge, Bicycle Ct; Rotana C Schol; GSct Camp Staff; VP, Church Yth Group; Judge, Bicycle Ct; Sou Oreg St U; Bus Adm.

CARPENTER, Randy Dwain
Saginaw HS; Saginaw, MI; Band; NHS; VP, SC; Var C; Bsbl; Ftbl; Cpt, Swim; Hon Prog; Pres A; Engr.

CARPENTER, Rebecca Ann
Ahrens HS; Louisville, KY; Chor; Tres, FBLA; Hmrm; NHS; Cpt, Bkbl; COM; U of Louisville; Bus.

CARPENTER, Sheila Denise
Martin Co HS; Stuart, FL (96-500) Ch, Chor; Pres, FBLA; Amer Leg A; Pres A; WW; Miss FBLA; 1st, 2nd Pl, Talent Win; 3rd Pl, Miss FBLA; Outst Mus Stu; Oral Roberts U.

CARPENTER, Susan Kae
Everett HS; Maryville, TN (2-300) Tres, AFS; Cpt, Dbte Tm; Drama; Pres, NFL; NHS; Tres, Span C; Spch C; St Stu Congress; Hist A; Sal; Spch A; Vof-DEM; Span A; Eng A; Vassar U; Law.

CARPER, Joan Elizabeth
John H Reagan HS; Austin, TX (10%-460) A-Ed, Ann; Chor; Hmrm; Rptr, Sch P; Journ A; Dist Yth Coun; Secy, Church Yth Coun; Drill Tm; Trustee Schol A; Journ.

CARPER, Michael Alan
Quincy Sr HS; Quincy, IL (204-732) Chor; Ger C; NHS; Var C; MVP, Cr-Ctry; Tr; COM; Citz A; Most Out; Cpt, All Amer, Cross Ctry; Liberty Baptist Col; Mus.

CARPER, Timothy Paul
Louisville Sr HS; Louisville, OH (50%-381) Band; Pres, 4H; Tr; 4H A; Yth Fel.

CARR, Amy Logan
Ballston Spa HS; Ballston Spa, NY (2-260) Ann; Drama; Hmrm; NHS; SC; Pres, Sr Cl; Beauty; COM; 4H A; I Dare You; Math A; Regent Schol; Sal; Spch A; Pres, 4-H Co Tn Coun; Tres, Health Careers C; Fin, US Mod Pageant; Miss Personality, US Mod Pageant; Skidmore Col; Fine Arts.

CARR, Brendan Gerard
Don Bosco Tech HS; Boston, MA (11-211) Band; CYO; Bkbl; Sftbl; 1st & 2nd Hon's; Mus.

CARR, Brian Alan
Mullens HS; Mullens, WV; BC; HiY; Hmrm; SC; JV, Ftbl; Tnns; Wrest.

CARR, Chantina Marshall
Texas Sr HS; Texarkana, TX; Band; FHA; Span C; Alg A; Chem A; Cl Fav; Coun of Teach A; 4H A; HQn; JA A; Math A; MLS; Most Out; PTA A; Phy A; Sci A; Spch A; Swtht; Type A; N Tex St U; Secy.

CARR, Cynthia Renee
Northwest HS; St Louis, MO (15-433) NHS; SC; Secy, Sr Cl; Amer U; Fr.

CARR, David J
Goshen HS; Goshen, IN (22-269) Pres, Demolay; VP, Drama; NFL; NHS; Pres, Spch C; SC; VP, Thes; JV, Cr-Ctry; Golf; COM; NMF; NMS; Spch A; Stu Rotarian; Degree of Distinct, Forensic League; Amer Hist.

CARR, Debra Lynn
Williams HS; Montgomery, AL (4-18) Tres, BC; Cl Fav.

CARR, Elizabeth Ann
Winyah HS; Georgetown, SC (30-170) Hmrm; NHS; SC; HCt; Semi-Fin, Miss Winyah Pageant; Vlbl; Secy, Civinettes; S-T, Meth Yth Fel; Clemson U; Pol Sci.

CARR, John Andrew
Smith Station HS; Smith, AL; BC; Key C; Mu Alpha Theta; 4H A; Auburn U; Forestry.

CARR, Joy Marie
Hardaway HS; Columbus, GA (15%-462) FHA; Hon Prog; Columbus Col; Early Childhood Ed.

CARR, Judith Elaine
W Columbus HS; Cerro Gordo, NC (5-180) F-Ed, Ann; BC; VP, Fr C; FHA; Pres, Hmrm; Hon Prog; Marshal; Pres, Church Yth Coun; Golden Star Nom; Health A; WW; Yth Food Win, Strawberry Festival; Meredith Col; Social Sci.

CARR, Julie Ellen
John I Leonard HS; Lake Worth, FL (25-588) Tres, Chor; Community Yth Symph; Ensm; Madrigal; NHS; Span C; Sci A; U of Miami Hon Choir; All St Chor; Church Bible Quiz Tm; Solo Cont Reg Church Tn Talent; Math.

CARR, Lauren
Churchill HS; San Antonio, TX (372-824) Anchor C; Sftbl; Dance Tm; Baylor U.

CARR, Leslie Lind
Nordhoff HS; Ojai, CA; 4H; CSF; Eng Academic Ltr.

CARR, Linda Gayle
Reeds Spring HS; Reeds Spring, MO (16-75) Ed, Ann; BC; FHA; 4H; Hmrm; Span C; Rptr, SC; Secy, Sr Cl; COM; Opt A; Miss Merry Christmas; Journ.

CARR, Margaret Jane
W Branch Area HS; Morrisdale, PA (3-160) Band; Chldr; Chor; Drama; FNA; NHS; Spch C; Var C; Bkbl; Tr; Hon Prog; PTA A; Pres A; Pre-Med.

CARR, Michael Scott
Douglas HS; Douglas, AZ; AFS; Band; Fr C; Sch P; JV, Tr; Mgr, Wrest.

CARR, Pamela Jane
Powell Valley HS; Speedwell, TN; Ann; BC; Bus C; Fr C; FHA; 4H; Sch P; Cl Fav; 4H A; HCt; Swtht; Sr Merit, 1st Aid, A's; E Tenn St U.

CARR, Randall Dean
Goddard HS; Goddard, KS (22-190) Band; Ensm; Wrest; Sci A; Med.

CARR, Robin
Norcross HS; Norcross, GA (20%-182) Ann; FHA.

CARR, Sandra Lynn
Winston Churchill HS; San Antonio, TX (127-843) Cpt, Dance Tm; Baylor U.

CARR, Susan Lynn
Goddard HS; Goddard, KS (4-165) Band; Ensm; 4H; NHS; Orch; COM; 4H A; Hon Prog; Lion A; Sci A; Abilene Christian U; Med.

CARR, Tim Dale
Maysville HS; Maysville, OK (5-37) S-T, FFA; NHS; Pres, Jr Cl; Bio A; Cl Fav; HCt; Masonic A.

CARR, Vincent Louis
Humboldt HS; Humboldt, TN; VICA; Bkbl, Chor, A's; X Ray Tech.

CARR, William Richard Jr
Bellflower HS; Bellflower, CA (112-382) Band; Ensm; Key C; Ski C; JV, Tnns; Kiwanis A; Sports-Ed, Ann; Principal's HR; Mus.

CARRA, Jeffrey Brian
Caney Valley HS; Caney, KS (6-70) Secy, AFS; Ann; Band; VP, Chem C; Pres, Chess C; Community Yth Symph; Dbte Tm; Drama; Ensm; Ch, Hmrm; Ch, InterClub Coun; Model UN; Orch; Order/Arrow; S-T, Phys C; ARC; Sch Achieve Tm; Sch P; Pres, Sci C; Bsbl; Mgr, Bkbl; Mgr, Ftbl; COM; God & Country A; Hon Prog; Order/Arrow A; Spch A; Eagle Sct; St Forensics Competition; Regional Mus Festival; Rep, Interntl Sct Jamboree; Ed.

CARRA, Linda Marie
Caney Valley HS; Caney, KS (10%-70) FBLA; FHA; Bio A; Math A; Principal's HR; Gen Bus, Eng, A's; Coffeyville Comm Jr Col; Aerospace Tech.

CARRASQUILLO, Casiano Yolanda
Colegio Santa Rita; Bayamon, PR (5-33) NHS; JA A; U of Puerto Rico; Administracion Comercial.

CARRASQUILLO, Maria De Lourdes
Notre Dame HS; Caguas, PR (9-136) Ann; Chem C; Chor; Dbte Tm; Drama; S-T, Hmrm; NHS; Sci C; Swim; Alg A; Bio A; COM; Cl Fav; Hist A; Hon Prog; Math A; Most Out; Law.

CARRASQUILLO, Wanda Ivelisse
Manuela Toro HS; Caguas, PR (15-436) CYO; Tres, Drama; 4H; Secy, Hmrm; Ch, ARC; Beauty; COM; U of Puerto Rico; Med.

CARRAWAY, Jeffrey Miller
Saint Andrews Parish HS; Charleston, SC (12-256) Ann; Key C; Mu Alpha Theta; NHS; Col of Charleston.

CARREL, John David
Rogers HS; Wyoming, MI (100-300) NHS; Var C; Co-Cpt, Bsbl; Bkbl; Ftbl; Wrest; Amer Leg A; Yth Coun; Grand Rapids Jr Col; Drafting.

CARRELL, Emily Jean
Bellaire HS; Bellaire, TX (40%-800) Chor; FHA; NHS; Pres, S-T, Christian Stu Union; Drill Tm Flag Corps; Booster C; Abilene Christian U; Ed.

CARRELL, Nancy Elaine
Bellaire Sr HS; Bellaire, TX; Chor; NHS; ARC; Tres, Span C; SC; Christian Stu Union; Drill Squad; Booster C; Bible Bowl; Abilene Christian Col; Bus.

CARRERA, Lloyd Christian
Hillsborough HS; Tampa, FL; Band; ARC; Swim; Tnns; COM; Med Explorers; Band Ltr; Paramedic; Health Occupation Ed; Certs, Medals, A'S, Band; Med.

CARRERA, Miriam
Kensington HS; Philadelphia, PA; Pediatric Nurse.

CARRICO, Ellen Elizabeth
Interlake HS; Bellevue, WA (10%-500) Chor; NHS; COM; Vlbl; Exec Board, Sr Hi Yth Group; Health Sci.

CARRICO, Kathy Ann
Scecina HS; Indianapolis, IN (67-188) CYO; Ind U; Computer Sci.

CARRIER, Chris Alan
Guttenberg HS; Guttenberg, IA (6-89) Sci C; Bsbl; Luther Col; Math.

CARRIER, Chuck H
Greenfield-Central HS; Greenfield, IN; Ftbl; Tr; Wrest; Conservation.

CARRIER, Karen Ann
Union Co HS; Morganfield, KY; Pres, Chor; FHA; 4H; Mgr, Bkbl; Outst Member, FHA; Chor A; Jr & Chapter Degrees; FHA; Murry St U.

CARRIER, LeAnn
Plainwell HS; Plainwell, MI (106-220) Band; Ensm; Hmrm; Spch C; Bkbl; Type A; MSBOA; Proficiency III; All St Hons Band; Western Mich U; Mus Ed.

CARRIER, Richard Warren
Reynolds HS; Greenville, PA (3-183) Chor; Span C; Order/Arrow A; Eagle Sct A; Thiel Col; Acct.

CARRIGAN, Gregory Kent
N Gaston HS; Dallas, NC (40-210) Monogram; Span C; SC; Golf.

115

CARRILLO, Catherine Marie
Bakersfield HS; Bakersfield, CA (33%-450) Drama; NHS; Thes; CSF; *Calif St U; Span.*

CARRILLO, Connie Carole
Bakersfield HS; Bakersfield, CA (33%-500) Type A; JV, Vlbl; Modern Dance; *Cal St U; Bus.*

CARRILLO, Juanita Chapa
Hobart HS; Hobart, OK (25-52) Band; Ch, Bus C; FBLA; Rptr, FHA; 4H; Secy, SC; Shorthand A; Vocalist A; *Evangelism.*

CARRINGTON, Bianca Darice
George Mason HS; Falls Church, VA (84-147) JV, Chldr; Chor; Community Yth Symph; Drama; FBLA; FTA; Orch; SC; Pres A; Chldr; Debutante; *Va St; Special Ed.*

CARRINGTON, Felicia Jo
Tift Co HS; Tifton, GA (33%-500) Band; Tres, Drama; Ch, FHA; FTA; GS; InterClub Coun; VP, FHA; Pres, Phi Zeta Gamma Sorority; Color Guard; Episcopal Young Churchmen Comm; *Valdosta St Col; Pub Relations.*

CARRINGTON, Kevin Juan
George Mason Jr Sr HS; Falls Church, VA; Fr C; French NHS; Key C; Monogram; Order/Arrow; Secy, SC; Var C; Pres, Soph Cl; Bsbl; Cr-Ctry; Tr; Order/Arrow A; Pres A; Light & Sound Crew; Most Improved, Tr.

CARRION, Migdalia
Dr Pila HS; Ponce, PR (4-688) Lion A; Peers Counselor; *Universidad Catolica; Commerical Adm.*

CARROCCIO, Elizabeth Ann
Gulf Comprehensive HS; New Port Richey, FL; Chor; Sch P; S-T, Span C; HR; Categorically Speaking; Secy, Yth Coun; 2 Rating, Dist Solo; *Legal Asst.*

CARROLL, Carla Annette
Walnut Comm HS; Walnut, IA (1-23) Band; Chor; Ensm; Pres, FHA; Secy, FHA; GS; Pres, 4H; Fin, Mjrte; Math C; NHS; Rainbow; Sch P; Sci C; S-T, SC; Var C; Pres, Soph Cl; Bkbl; Sftbl; COM; Citz A; 4H A; Math A; Mus Carnival Qn; Rep, Rainbow Grand; *Pharmacy.*

CARROLL, Cathy Sue
Shawnee Mission NW HS; Shawnee, KS; A Cap Choir; AFS; Chor; COM; *U of Kans; Psych.*

CARROLL, Charles Neal
McCullough-Conroe HS; Conroe, TX; Chess Merit A; *U of Houston; Elec.*

CARROLL, David Brian
W Carter Co HS; Olive Hill, KY; FBLA; Bsbl; JV, Bkbl; Cr-Ctry; Ftbl; Alg A; Conservation Essay A; *Morehead St U.*

CARROLL, David Michael
Prairie du Chien Sr HS; Prairie du Chien, WI (12-145) Band; Fin, Ensm; Lat NHS; NHS; 1st St Mus Festival, Piano; *U of Milwaukee; Mus.*

CARROLL, Dawn Marie
Greenfield HS; Greenfield, WI (36-416) Co-Ed, Ann; Chldr; Ski C; Co Ch, Prom; GAA; Water Ballet; Dancer, Leader, Sch Play; *U of Wisc; Elem Ed.*

CARROLL, Dean Evan
South Shelby HS; Shelbina, MO (15-100) Ann; Band; Pres, Chor; Ensm; FFA; 4H; Madrigal; SC; Pres, Jr Cl; 4H A; FFA St Chor, Soloist; St Farmer Degree; WW-MUS; WW; *Northeast Mo St U; Fine Arts.*

CARROLL, Debra Jean
Sooner HS; Bartlesville, OK (12-291) CYO; Lat C; S-T, NHS; Tnns; Elk A; *Social Stu.*

CARROLL, Debra Lynee
Conroe HS; Conroe, TX (25%-850) Bus C; FHA; Hmrm; MVP, Bsbl; Hon Prog; Type A; St Fin, VOE; OEA; Pol Sci Schol; *U of Houston; Bus Law.*

CARROLL, Dora Myles
York Comp HS; York, SC (1-261) Fr C; FTA; Ch, Hmrm; Rptr, Sch P; SC; COM; Cl Fav; HCt; *Winthrop Col; Bus.*

CARROLL, Eleanor Jane
Watauga HS; Boone, NC (6-300) Cpt, Chldr; Chor; Ensm; Fr C; Pres, FTA; Hmrm; NHS; Secy, SC; DARGCA; Gr Marshal; Hon Prog; Win, Jr Miss Pageant; Sch Schol; BPW Career Girl; Fr A; Selection All-St Chor; *UNC-Greensboro; Mus.*

CARROLL, Fannie Margaret
Fort Yukon HS; Fort Yukon, AK; Spch C; Up Bound; *U of Alaska; Acct.*

CARROLL, Fred Van
Glencliff HS; Nashville, TN; Order/Arrow; VP, SC; Bsbl; Citz A; God & Country A; Yth Fel; *Middle Tenn St U; Mass Communcations.*

CARROLL, Gary Lynn
Wylie HS; Wylie, TX (25%-100) Dbte Tm; NHS; Spch C; Chem A; Sci A; Spch A; *U of Tex at Arlington; Aerospace Engr.*

CARROLL, Glen Eugene
Benson HS; Omaha, NE; Band.

CARROLL, Gwen Allison
O'Neill Pub HS; O'Neill, NE; Band; Var C; VP, Soph Cl; Bkbl; Sftbl; Yth Fel; Frolics Attendent.

CARROLL, James Franklin
Vermilion HS; Vermilion, OH (5-220) Dbte Tm; NHS; Var C; Bsbl; Ftbl; Bausch & Lomb A; Hon Prog; NEDT; Yth Fel; *Cedarville Col; Med.*

CARROLL, Janice Kathleen
St Joseph's Notre Dame HS; Alameda, CA (2-55) A Cap Choir; Chor; Drama; Fr C; GS; NHS; Pres, SC; Pres, Sr Cl; CSF; NEDT; Poet A; Fr A; Span A; Choral A; US Hist A; *U of Calif at Santa Barbara; Eng.*

CARROLL, Jodi Ann
Bellevue Sr HS; Bellevue, OH (2-260) Band; Chor; NHS; DARGCA; Sal; Sch Schol Tm; Secy, Sunday Sch; Asst Bus Mgr, Yrbk; GAA; Church Choir; Pres, Yth Fel.

CARROLL, John Robert
Campbell Co Comprehensive HS; Jacksboro, TN (25%-322) BC; Ch, InterAct C; SC; Var C; Secy, Jr Cl; Bkbl; Golf; Most Handsome; Tn Board; Prom Comm; Best Attitude A, Bkbl; *Lincoln Mem U.*

CARROLL, John Steven
Our Lady of Fatima HS; Lafayette, LA; Key C; VP, Sr Cl; Ftbl; Sftbl.

CARROLL, Julia Theresa
Franklin HS; Franklin, VA (20-125) Band; Chor; Fin, Ensm; Secy, 4H; Span C; Rptr, Tri-HiY; Swim; Chamber of Comm A; 4H A; JA A; Lion A; Agribus & Achv A; *VPI; Vet Sci.*

CARROLL, Katharine Anne
Franklin HS; Franklin, VA (5-125) Tres, Band; Chor; Rptr, 4H; Monogram; VP, NHS; Span C; Tri-HiY; Swim; COM; 4H A; Tres, Horse C; First Cl GSct; *VPI & SU; Med.*

CARROLL, Kathleen Edith
Moreno Valley HS; Sunnymead, CA (25-300) Band; Ger C; Madrigal; NHS; Tres, SC; Pres, Thes; Secy, Soph Cl; CSF; Math A; Gym; *UCSD; Marine Bio.*

CARROLL, Keith Thomas
Mentor HS; Mentor, OH (385-850) Band; Ski C; Mgr, Bkbl; JV, Soccer; Yth Fel; *Lakeland Comm Col; Forestry.*

CARROLL, Kelli Ann
Melbourne HS; Melbourne, FL; Band; CYO; SC; Tr; Ntl Sci Found; *Fla St U; Psych.*

CARROLL, Lisl Ann
Hillsboro Sr HS; Hillsboro, OR (30-650) Chor; Ensm; 4H; NHS; Bkbl; Tr; Bio A; COM; Pres Phys Fitness A for 5 Yrs; *Southern Oreg St; Bus Adm.*

CARROLL, Llane G
Carter Co HS; Ekalaka, MT (3-26) Band; Pres, 4H; Rptr, Sch P; Bkbl; Ftbl; Tr; 4H A; NEDT; Top Hand A, St Yth Range Camp; 1st Pl, Yth Range Forum.

CARROLL, Lori Jean
Balaton Pub HS; Balaton, MN (4-32) Band; Chor; Ensm; FHA; GS; Bkbl; Sftbl; Mgr, Tr; Hon Prog; Pres A; Dist Bkbl Champs; *Elem Ed.*

CARROLL, Lunda Jo
Fayette Co HS; Fayette, AL; Band; Chor; FBLA; Mjrte; Math C; Sch P; Sci C; Span C; *Miss St U; Bio.*

CARROLL, Mark Francis
Archmere Acad; Claymont, DE; Drama; Fr C; Pres, French NHS; Pres, NHS; Sch P; Bkbl; Cr-Ctry; Cpt, Soccer; Tr; Amer Leg A; Hon Prog; Val; Eng A; 4th & 5th in St, Fr As; *Dartmouth Col.*

CARROLL, Pennie DeAnn
Bend Sr HS; Bend, OR; Band; Chor; Yth Senate Church Group; Sunday Sch Teacher; *Northwest Bible Col; Bible Studies.*

CARROLL, Regina Ann
Russell HS; Russell, KY; Monogram; MVP, Var C; Bkbl; Sftbl; Tr; Yth Fel; Ky HS All-St Bkbl; *Dental Hygiene.*

CARROLL, Timothy William
Quincy Notre Dame HS; Quincy, IL (21-140) Pres, Band; CYO; Chor; Ger C; *John Wood Comm Col; Bus.*

CARRUTH, Paul Kevin
Pampa Sr HS; Pampa, TX (62-326) PSU Schol; 1st, Drafting, PSU; 3rd, St Drafting, VICA; *Okla U; Archt.*

CARRUTHERS, Carolyn Marie
Chester Area HS; Chester, SD (5-32) Band; Chor; 4H; Rptr, Sch P.

CARRUTHERS, Shirley Kay
Parma HS; Parma, OH (320-1009) Chor; Lat C; Math A; God & Comm; GSct; Vol Hospital; Alt, Interntl Opportunity; *Akron U; Nurs.*

CARRUTHERS, Thomas Dixon
Grimsley HS; Greensboro, NC (25%-500) Pres, Fr C; Key C; Bkbl; VP, Church Yth; Church Board; Young Lawyers; *Amer U; Pol Sci.*

CARSON, Adriene L
Woodside HS; Woodside, CA (140-477) CSF; Comm Mus Sch; Girls for God; Agape; Sunday Sch Pianist; Tutoring C; The Emporium Teenboard; *Bus Adm.*

CARSON, Brent James
Brookings HS; Brookings, SD (50-213) A Cap Choir; Band; Chor; Ensm; Madrigal; Orch; Order/Arrow; Order/Arrow A; Eagle Sct; SD All-St Hon Choir; *SDSU; Mus.*

CARSON, Carmen Lynn
Northeastern HS; Detroit, MI; Citz A; H of F; Hon Prog; Journ A; JA A; Type A; Decathlon.

CARSON, Cathleen Jane
Wellsboro Sr HS; Wellsboro, PA (10%-230) VP, Band; Chor; Ensm; NHS; HCt; Maple Festival Qn Cand; Dist Band; *Alderson-Broaddus Col; Mus.*

CARSON, Claudette Ann
Alvernia HS; Chicago, IL (35-230) Hmrm; NHS; COM; Hon Prog; Yrbk Ed; Church Liturgy Tm; *Harper Col; Mus.*

CARSON, Daniel Worth
Miami Palmetto Sr HS; Miami, FL (200-1150) Chor; City Conf; S-T, Ger C; Ntl Yth Conf; Swim; COM; Hon Prog; Yth Fel; Dade Co Vol; Pres Prayr Brkfst Cong Invitation; *Gardner-Webb Col; Psych.*

CARSON, David Eugene
Wis Acad; Columbus, WI (30-63) Band; Chor; Tres, Fr C; JV, Bkbl; 1st Pl, Wisconsian Contest; *Andrews U; Bus Adm.*

CARSON, Donna Jean
Altoona Area HS; Altoona, PA (40%-989) Chor; NFL; Pres, Spch C; Bkbl; Spch A; *Wilma Boyd Career Sch; Airline and Travel.*

CARSON, Gregory Ezekiel
T L Hanna HS; Anderson, SC; BC; Pres, Hmrm; Key C; Lat C; Co-Ed, Sch P; Yth Fel; *U of SC; Law.*

CARSON, James Hubert
Waynesboro Area Sr HS; Waynesboro, PA (1-450) Chor; Order/Arrow; Var C; Ftbl; JV, Wrest; Alg A; Amer Leg A; MLS; Unsung Hero Ftbl A; *Gen Sci.*

CARSON, Kathryn Ann
Melodyland Christian HS; Anaheim, CA (3-40) Band; Chor; Ensm; NHS; Amer Leg A; Citz A; Yth Fel; *Sou Calif U; Lang Arts.*

CARSON, Kim Carson
James Island HS; Charleston, SC; Cpt, Chldr; Chor; Hmrm; SC; Y-Tns; Bkbl; HQn; Co-Cpt, Chldr; *Palmer Col; Bus.*

CARSON, Mary Kay
Titusville HS; Titusville, PA (17-269) Band; Chor; Ensm; Orch.

CARSON, Ronald Charles
Lowell HS; Whittier, CA; Order/Arrow; JV, Bkbl; JV, Tr; Yth Fel; Out Reach Comm; Lay Witness; *Forestry.*

CARSON, Scarlett Rae
Scott HS; Huntsville, TN (1-145) Band; Chor; Mjrte; Rainbow; Secy, Soph Cl; Mgr, Sftbl; Swim; *Tenn Tech U; Math.*

CARSON, Terry Henry
Springfield N HS; Springfield, OH (133-370) Chor; Drama; Hmrm; Ch, InterClub Coun; Ski C; Thes; Var C; VP, Sr Cl; Ftbl; Star Student; *U of Cincinnati; Acct.*

CARSON, Valerie Hall
Tara HS; Baton Rouge, LA (15-361) Tres, Band; Secy, Chess C; Drama; Ensm; Hmrm; Lat C; Mu Alpha Theta; NHS; Orch; Spch C; SC; Swim; Magna Cum Laude; Sci A; Pres, Jr Beta C; All-Parish Band; Eng A; All-Star Marching Band; Band A; Econ A; DAHSS; WW; *La Tech Col.*

CARSON, Vincent Dean
Mineral Wells HS; Mineral Wells, TX (6-250) BS; Chem C; Hmrm; Parl, Key C; Pres, Lat C; Math C; NHS; Sci C; SC; Bkbl; Golf; NMS; Sci A; Lat A; *Bio.*

CARSTENS, Renee Jolene
Norfolk Sr Hr; Norfolk, NE (54-298) Bus C; Chor; GS; Pres, 4H; Amer Leg A; Citz A; 4H A; Vlbl; *U of Nebr at Omaha; Med Tech.*

CARSTENSEN, Linda Jo
Jefferson Comm HS; Jefferson, IA (39-122) Tres, FHA; Pres, 4H; Tr; 4H A; Type A; *Iowa Central Comm Col; Child Development.*

CARSTENSEN, Rhonda Diane
Coupeville Jr-Sr HS; Coupeville, WA; Band; Chor; Ger C; NHS; SC; Var C; Secy, Soph Cl; HCt; Hon Prog; Yth Fel; Yth Foundation.

CARSTENSEN, Roxanna Lee
Coupeville Jr-Sr HS; Coupeville, WA; Chor; Yth Fel; Yth Foundation; *Bus Adm.*

CARSTENSEN, Scott Allen
Spencer HS; Spencer, IA (40-215) Band; Chor; Arch; Bsbl; Ftbl; Golf; Sftbl; Type A; Yth Fel; Band A; *Morningside Col; Mus.*

CARTEE, Laura Ailene
Gulport HS; Gulfport, MS (20%-210) Hmrm; Citz A; Hon Prog; Type A; Pres, Acteens; Choir; Folk Group; Jr Civitans; *Pediatrics.*

CARTER, Andrea Dawn
J M Tate HS; Gonzalez, FL; FHA; VP, NHS; Guidance Asst; A & B HR; *U of W Fla; Nurs.*

CARTER, Areatha Marie
Cecilian Acad; Philadelphia, PA; World Affairs C; Y-Tns; Hon Prog; *Ohio St U; Psych.*

CARTER, Barbara Louise
Quartz Hill HS; Lancaster, CA (329-400) AFS; Bus Mgr, Ann; Fr C; Model UN; Tnns; ARC A; Semi-Fin, Presbyterian Schol; *Long Beach St Col; Sociology.*

CARTER, Beth Renee
E Mecklenburg HS; Charlotte, NC; JV, Chldr; Chor; Fr C; Hmrm; Orch; Thes; Sftbl; Citz A; Swtht; Mus As; UMYF; Pres, Yth Coun; Secy, Coun of Ministries; *U of NC; Voice.*

CARTER, Billie Marian
Frederick Douglass HS; Atlanta, GA (47-343) CYO; Secy, FBLA; NHS; F-Ed, Sch P; COM; HCt; *Georgetown U; Acct.*

CARTER, Carla Maria
Northwest HS; St Louis, MO (6-728) *St Louis U; Secy.*

CARTER, Charles Aaron
Provine HS; Jackson, MS; *Westminster Col; Mus.*

CARTER, Cheree Arletta
Skyline HS; Dallas, TX; FHA; NHS; *N Tex St U; Psych.*

CARTER, Christine Mary
Stevenson HS; Livonia, MI; CYO; Dbte Tm; Ski C; Spch A; *U of Mich; Law.*

CARTER, Claudia Irene
Lord Botetourt HS; Daleville, VA (8-230) Band; Fr C; 4H; Hmrm; Ntl Yth Conf; Var C; Bkbl; Sftbl; Swim; Tnns; 4H A; Vlbl; All District, Band; Athletic Letter; Pres Patch; *Bridgewater Col; Foreign Lang.*

CARTER, Colleen Jean
Plantation HS; Plantation, FL (80-516) Chldr; Chor; Ensm; Ed, Sch P; Tr; Journ A; Lion A; Q&S A; Yth Fel; *Goucher Col; Journ.*

CARTER, Cynthia Maria
Starmount HS; Boonville, NC (14-151) Ann; VP, Drama; FHA; FTA; NHS; Gov Honor Prog; Soc Stu C; GAA; Health Careers C; Exchangettes; Miss DECA; Pep C; Win, Job Interview; DECA; Hospital Vol, Hon Cert; *Winsalm Col; Fashion Merch.*

CARTER, Debbie Lynn
Ft Pierce Central HS; Fort Pierce, FL (11-700) Mu Alpha Theta; NHS; SC; Pres, Jr Cl; Star Student; Pres, Ecology C; Bi-Racial Comm; *Indian River Comm Col; Computer Sci.*

CARTER, Deborah Ann
Owego Free Acad; Owego, NY (20%-396) AFS; Band; Sch P; Span C; Tr; Alg A; 4H A; Yth Fel; *Computer Sci.*

CARTER, Debra LaFaye
St Peters HS; New Brunswick, NJ (3-12) Pres, Chor; FHA; SC; Qn, Pastor's Aid; *Pepperdine U; Law.*

CARTER, Debra Louise
Patten Acad of Christian Ed; Oakland, CA (1-14) A Cap Choir; Chor; Drama; Ensm; Orch; Co-Ed, Sch P; VP, SC; VP, Jr Cl; Secy, Soph Cl; Bkbl; Tnns; Citz A; *Patten Bible Col; Mus.*

CARTER, Debrah Janice
Carroll HS; Monroe, LA (10%-205) Pres, Chor; Drama; Ensm; FBLA; NHS; Spch C; Hon Prog; Sing A; Mixed Ensm A; *La Tech U; Executive Secy.*

CARTER, Deloris Ann
F W Ballou HS; Washington, DC; Community Yth Symph; Mjrte; Bkbl; Swim; Tnns; Citz A; *Morgan Col; Psych.*

CARTER, Dorothy Jean
Miramar HS; Miramar, FL (80-491) Band; Ensm; Fr C; Secy, FBLA; Key C; Orch; SDAHSS; DECA.

CARTER, Elizabeth Marie
Indian Springs Acad; Jackson, GA; Ann; Co-Cpt, Chldr; Sftbl; HCt; *Gordon Jr Col.*

CARTER, Fred Jr
Leo HS; Chicago, IL (9-140) Hmrm; NHS; Rptr, Sch P; SC; Var C; Bsbl; Co-Cpt, Bkbl; HCt; Hon Prog; Q&S A; *Bus Adm.*

CARTER, Gerald Leburn
Lancaster HS; Lancaster County, VA; Chess C; Chor; FFA; Bkbl; *Bus.*

CARTER, Greta Lisa
Alma J Brown HS; Grambling, LA; Co-Ch, Chldr; Drama; FTA; Fin, Lit Ral; Secy, NHS; Secy, SC; Bio A; Hist A; Math A; Sci A; Swtht; Type A; Span, Chldr, Eng, Lit Rally, A's; *Psych.*

CARTER, Jackie Sue
Jefferson HS; Jefferson, OR (3-45) Chldr; Chor; FBLA; NHS; H of F; St Scholar; Prom Qn; *Chemekata Comm Col; Fr lang.*

CARTER, James Edward
St Johns CDS HS; Orange Park, FL (2-18) Pres, Lat C; Lat NHS; Ed, Lit Mag; Soccer; Tr; Hon Prog; Poet A; Q&S A; *Duke U; Lib Arts.*

CARTER, James Stuart
Holliston HS; Holliston, MA (20%-268) Drama.

CARTER, Jane Ann
Eastbrook HS; Marion, IN (34-200) Chem C; Pres, Hmrm; Span C; SC; Var C; VP, Jr Cl; Fin, Sftbl; Fin, Tr; Citz A; Cl Fav; HCt; Spch A; Swtht; Type A; Yth Fel; Yth Foundation; *Taylor U; Elem Ed.*

CARTER, John Edward
Menchville HS; Newport News, VA (35-680) Chess C; Pres, Dbte Tm; Order/Arrow; JV, Bsbl; JV, Bkbl; JV, Soccer; Sci A; Jr NHS.

CARTER, John Roe
Huntsville HS; Huntsville, AL (10%-500) Chem C; Chess C; Dbte Tm; Lit Mag; Wrest; Spch A; Dist & St Piano Teachers Guild A; *Clemson U; Elec Engr.*

CARTER, Jon Thomas
Chappell HS; Chappell, NE (25%-32) Band; Tres, FFA; 4H; NHS; JV, Bkbl; Ftbl; Tr; 4H A; I Dare You; *U of Nebr; Agr.*

CARTER, Joyce Lynn
Teays Valley HS; Ashville, OH; Yth Fel; Secy, Bible C; *Franklin U; Social Work.*

CARTER, Jullie Faye
Goodrich HS; Goodrich, TX (5-15) Ann; Chldr; Chor; VP, FHA; MVP, Bkbl; All Dist, Bkbl; Most Ath; All Tourn, Bkbl; *Sam Houston St U; Phys Ed.*

CARTER, Karen Faye
Littlefield HS; Littlefield, TX (5-77) Pres, Band; Ensm; FTA; 4H; Cpt, Mjrte; NHS; ARC; Sch Achieve Tm; Var C; Cpt, Bkbl; Swim; MVP, Tnns; MVP, Tr; COM; Citz A; 4H A; Hist A; Hon Prog; Interlochen Ntl Mus; JA A; Lion A; Ntl Achv Schol; Star Student; Yth Fel; John Philip Sousa A; Woodmen o-t World; Schol; Lions C Qn; *Tex Tech U; Phys Ed.*

CARTER, Kathleen Vanessa
Burke HS; Charleston, SC (80-205) Cpt, Band; Secy, FBLA; Secy, Hmrm; Sch P; SC; Outst Cpt, Flag Grls & Color Guard; *St Augustine Col; Bus Adm.*

CARTER, Kelly Lea
Parkview HS; Little Rock, AR (50%-500) BC; NHS; Rainbow; Y-Tns; DARGCA; Yth Fel; *Hendrix Col; Med.*

CARTER, Kenneth Eugene III
R L Turner HS; Carrollton, TX (50-949) Dbte Tm; Drama; 4H; Hmrm; Lit Mag; NFL; Sch P; Spch C; SC; JV, Tnns; Hon Prog; Rotary A; Spch A; Most Individual; Fin, Most Involved; NFL Degree of Distinction; *Tex A&M U; Bus Adm.*

CARTER, Kenneth Lamar
Breckinridge Co HS; Harned, KY (20-207) Sci C; *Western Ky U; Forestry.*

CARTER, Kent Robert
Carson HS; Carson City, NV (1-400) VP, Band; Ensm; NHS; Order/Arrow; *Elec Engr.*

CARTER, Kerry Scott
Thompson HS; Alabaster, AL (10%-250) Band; VP, BC; Hmrm; VP, Soph Cl; Ftbl; Cl Fav; Hon Prog; Most Out; Sci A; *U of Ala; Law.*

CARTER, Kevin Edward
St Peters Prep HS; Jersey City, NJ (43-269) CYO; Rptr, Sch P; Var C; Mgr, Bsbl; Mgr, Hockey; Cpt, Soccer; Amer Leg A; COM; MVP, Soccer; *St Peter's Col; Acct.*

CARTER, Lela Sue
Douglas Byrd Sr HS; Fayetteville, NC (5-400) BC; InterClub Coun; Pres, SC; Pres, Tri-HiY; Gr Marshal; Morehead Nom; *U of NC; Phys Therapy.*

CARTER, Leon
Overbrook HS; Philadelphia, PA; Bkbl.

CARTER, Leslie Ann
Yuma HS; Yuma, AZ (200-541) Anchor C; Band; Pres, Chldr; 4H; Rainbow; Var C; Golf; Tnns; Tr; *Pacific Christian Col; Sociology.*

CARTER, Mary Kathryn
Troy HS; Troy, KS; Band; Chor; Ensm; 4H; NHS; Alg A; Citz A; Hon Prog; Mus A; Pres, Kayettes; Kayette A; *Mo Western St Col; Med.*

CARTER, Melvin Louis Jr
Northeast HS; N Little Rock, AR; Band; Demolay; Rptr, Sch P.

CARTER, Michael Stennis
Weatherford HS; Weatherford, TX (9-252) Ensm; NHS; Ntl Yth Conf; Phys C; Sch Achieve Tm; Cpt, Ftbl; Golf; Hon Prog; Lion A; Opt A; Opt Out Tn; Yth Fel; MVP, Ftbl; Young Tex A; WW; All Dist Ftbl; *Tex A&M U; Archt.*

CARTER, Myra Sharon
Echols Co HS; Statenville, GA (1-42) Bus Mgr, Ann; BC; Chldr; FBLA; FHA; Secy, 4H; InterClub Coun; Fin, Jr Miss Pagent; Secy, SC; Secy, Jr Cl; Bkbl; Alg A; Bio A; Citz A; Cl Fav; Math A; Most Out; Sci A; Home Ec A; *Valdosta St Col.*

CARTER, Nancy Ann
Desoto HS; DeSoto, TX (70-240) FHA; Rainbow; Span C; Drill Tm, Sociology; A's; Bus Off Ed C; Gov Clerk; *Tex Tech U; Bus Adm.*

CARTER, Nancy Lynn
Palmdale HS; Palmdale, CA; Chldr; Mgr, Wrest; *Orange Coast Col; Dental Asst.*

CARTER, Nina Elizabeth
Welch HS; Welch, WV (57-129) Chor; FBLA; 4H; Tri-HiY; Tr; Bus.

CARTER, Osborne Charles III
Highpoint HS; Beltsville, MD (33%-750) A Cap Choir; Band; BS; Chem C; Chor; Community Yth Symph; Dbte Tm; Drama; Co-Ch, Hmrm; Math C; Ntl Yth Conf; ARC; Sch Achieve Tm; Sci C; SC; Up Bound; Bsbl; Bkbl; Cr-Ctry; Ftbl; Soccer; Sftbl; Swim; Tnns; Tr; COM; Chem A; Cl Fav; I Dare You; Most Out; ROTC A; Sci A; Best Dressed; Tr, Cr-Ctry, A's; Judo; *Ala Lutheran Col; Theology.*

CARTER, Pamela Kay
Tahlequah Sr HS; Tahlequah, OK; Chldr; Tres, 4H; Var C; Bkbl; Tr; Cl Fav; 4H A; HQn; Sal; Dairy Princess; *NE Okla St U; Ed.*

CARTER, Pamela Lynn
W Forsyth Sr HS; Clemmons, NC (1-487) Dbte Tm; NHS; Span C; Gr Marshal; Hon Prog; Math A; Commended Stu Ntl Merit; Ixthous C; Eng A; Morehead Nom; Hi IQ Tm; Span A; Secy, Sunday Sch Cl; Gov Sch Nom; Hist, NHS; Grl Ser C; *Wake Forest U; Math.*

CARTER, Patricia Ann
Clarke Central HS; Athens, GA; A Cap Choir; Co-Cpt, Band; BC; Chor; Hmrm; Beauty; HCt; Mus Sorority; *U of Ga; Mus.*

CARTER, Paula Jane
Dalton HS; Dalton, GA (5-352) Band; NHS; Span C; Tres, Tri-HiY; COM; Citz A; Type A; Rob Hess Mem A.

CARTER, Pier Anglia
S H Rider HS; Wichita Falls, TX (57-451) Mu Alpha Theta; NHS; Cpt, Drill Tm; Princess, Drill Tm; AAUW Schol; *Midwestern St U; Merchandising.*

CARTER, Randy Bryan
Woodham HS; Pensacola, FL (12-530) Anchor C; Ger C; Math C; Mu Alpha Theta; NHS; NEDT; Cl Geog A; *U of S Ala; Optometry.*

CARTER, Ray Frances
Forest Glen HS; Suffolk, VA (85-140) Drama; FBLA; FNA; Pres, 4H; InterAct C; Monogram; ARC; Var C; Cpt, Bkbl; MVP, Sftbl; COM; Chamber of Comm A; Citz A; 4H A; ARC A; *Vet Med.*

CARTER, Rhonda Gail
Andrew Jackson HS; Jacksonville, FL;

CARTER, Rickey Steven
Echols Co HS; Statenville, GA (1-40) Pres, BC; Rptr, FFA; 4H; InterClub Coun; Tres, SC; Tres, Soph Cl; Bkbl; Tr; Alg A; COM; Citz A; 4H A; Hist A; Most Out; Sci A; Outst A, Bkbl; Star Green Hand; Farm Mech A; Livestock Product A; 3rd Pl, St Sci Fair; Star Chptr Farmer; *Valdosta St Col; Law.*

CARTER, Robin Renee
Robert E Lee HS; Jacksonville, FL; Chor; Drama; Fr C; Hmrm; InterClub Coun; Jr Miss Pagent; Pres, SC; Beauty; Citz A; Cl Fav; HQn; HCt; Most Out; Swtht; Yth Fel; Historian; Tr-Hi Y; Girl o-t Month; Sch Service A; Outst Graduate; Tr Cl Fashion Show Coordinator; Most Dependable; *Fla St U; Interior Design.*

CARTER, Ronald Lee
Oak Ridge HS; Orlando, FL (10%-1100) Math C; NHS; Sci C; Span C; Var C; Soccer; COM; Math A; ROTC A; Sci A; Outst, St Span Contest; *Military Acad; Engr.*

CARTER, Rose Ellen
Palatka S HS; Palatka, FL (31-285) Band; Co-Ch, BC; Chor; Jr Miss Pagent; Span C; Var C; Sftbl; COM; Parl, Rptr, Civinettes; Eng A; *St Johns River Jr Col.*

CARTER, Russell Weldon
Central Baptist HS; Newport News, VA (5-14) Pres, SC; Bkbl; Cpt, Ftbl; Sftbl; H of F; ROTC A; Phys Ed A; DAR Hist A; *Tenn Temple U; Secondary Ed.*

CARTER, Sandra Lee
Wakulla HS; Crawfordville, FL; *FSU; Nurs.*

CARTER, Sarah Elizabeth
East HS; Pueblo, CO (45-489) Ger C; Ski C; Gym.

CARTER, Sharon Renae
Riverside Sr HS; Milwaukee, WI (50%-200) A Cap Choir; Chor; Pres, Drama; Hmrm; Madrigal; Sch P; Delta Sigma Theta A; God & Country A; H of F; Hon Prog; MLS; Most Out; Ntl Achv Schol; Phi Beta Kappa; Pres A; *Mt Mary Col; Fashion Merch.*

CARTER, Shelby Ann
Thomson HS; Thomson, GA (5%-350) Band; BC; VP, FHA; 4H; 4H A; Sci A; St 4-H Key, Band, A's; *Sci.*

CARTER, Sherry Ann
Quitman HS; Quitman, MS (15-134) BC; Chor; S-T, FBLA; Ch, FHA; Co-Ch, FTA; Cpt, Hmrm; VP, Spch C; SC; Pres, Jr Cl; Sftbl; COM; Type A; Encounter; *Ms Valley St U; Bus Ed.*

CARTER, Sherry Dawn
Lowndes HS; Valdosta, GA; Bio A.

CARTER, Steven Allan
Breckinridge Co HS; Harned, KY (20%-205) VP, Chor; Hmrm; Tres, Sci C; VP, Var C; Co-Cpt, Ftbl; Tr; Cl Fav; H of F; Yth Fel; Best Personality; *Western Ky U; Bio.*

CARTER, Steven Lowell
Charles Henderson HS; Troy, AL (5%-180) Band; VP, BC; Tres, Dbte Tm; Pres, FFA; Parl, InterAct C; NFL; NHS; VP, Sci C; Tnns; Hon Prog; Ntl Sci Found; Sci A; Spch A; 1st Pl Tm, St Debate; St Farmer, Co Pub Speaker, FFA; St Off Candidate, FFA; *U of Ala; Lab Med.*

CARTER, Teresa Ann
Miami Killian Jr HS; Miami, FL; Church Orientation; Vacation Bible Sch; *Morehouse Col; Drama.*

CARTER, William Glenn
Owego Free Acad; Owego, NY (10%-350) AFS; Band; Chor; Hmrm; NHS; Orch; Order/Arrow; Co-Ed, Sch P; Span C; SC; VP, Jr Cl; Ftbl; Order/Arrow A; Yth Fel; Eagle Sct; Elmira Col Key.

CARTER, William Joseph
Riverview Gardens HS; St Louis, MO; Band; Chess C; Var C; Ftbl; Mgr, Wrest; COM; *U of Mo; Law Enforcement.*

CARTER, William Randal
London HS; London, OH (6-165) Hmrm; SC; JV, Bkbl; Cr-Ctry; Tr; *Miami U of Ohio; Bus.*

CARTER, Yolanda Elaine
Clifford J Scott HS; E Orange, NJ (10%-250) Pres, A Cap Choir; Chor; Ensm; Hmrm; Madrigal; Sch P; SC; Tnns; Citz A; JA A; Math A; *Howard U; Law.*

CARTHORNE, Richard Calvin
Ballou Sr HS; Washington, DC; Var C; Bsbl; JV, Ftbl; *Westminister Col; Archt.*

CARTHORNE, Victor Bryon
Ballou Sr HS; Washington, DC; JV, Ftbl; Tr; *Westminster Col; Elec.*

CARTLIDGE, Lana Lea
Corsicana HS; Corsicana, TX (1-270) Chldr; Hmrm; VP, NHS; Rptr, SC; COM; Citz A; Hist A; Hon Prog; Lion A; MLS; NEDT; Opt A; Opt Out Tn; Val; Van Cliburn-Allison Schol; NHS Outst Soph; 3rd St UIL Shorthand Comp; Commended Stu, NMS; *Baylor U; Mus.*

CARTMILL, Jane Anne
Athens HS; The Plains, OH (33%-250) Band; Chor; Ensm; FHA; FNA; FTA; Sch P; Span C; Sftbl; Swim; COM; Journ A; Bible Bowl A; Bowling A; Sftbl A; Cert of Achv; *Ky Christian Col; Journ.*

CARTNER, Jamye Mechelle
N Gaston HS; Dallas, NC; Band; Pres, Drama; Hmrm; Key C; Orch; Bkbl; DARGCA; HR; Outst Member, All St, Band A's; 1st Chair of Amer, Band; *Bowman-Gray Col; Med.*

CARTRIGHT, Jeffery Dean
Plymouth HS; Plymouth, IN; A Cap Choir; Chess C; Chor; Ensm; ARC; Var C; JV, Bkbl; Ftbl; *Ozark Bible Col; Christian Ed.*

CARTWRIGHT, Anthony Doane
Camden HS; Camden, NC (14-126) Ftbl; *Elizabeth City St U; Teaching.*

CARTWRIGHT, Barbara Theland
N Central HS; Indianapolis, IN (800-1227) CYO; Community Yth Symph; Ensm; Hmrm; Orch; SC; ROTC A; Choir A; Yth Orch A; Church Sch A; *Tenn St U; Pre-Law.*

CARTWRIGHT, Greg Alan
Sooner HS; Bartlesville, OK (4-291) Band; FBLA; NHS; Span C; Golf; Hist A; Hon Prog; St Scholar; Adams GC Outst Jr Golfer; U Schol, Okla St U; 1st-Econ, FBLA St Ldrship Conf; Okla St Bowl Proprietors Schol A; *Okla St U; Econ.*

CARTWRIGHT, James Daniel
J M Tate HS; Gonzalez, FL (7-537) A Cap Choir; Pres, BC; Chor; Ensm; Fr C; Hmrm; InterClub Coun; F-Ed, Sch P; Bio A; COM; Citz A; Hist A; Hon Prog; Most Out; Opt A; Opt Out Tn; Sci A; Spch A; Yth Fel; Pres, Yth Fel; Beta Rho Sorority Boy o-t Yr; WW; *Huntingdon Col; Pre-Med.*

CARTWRIGHT, Lesley Irene
Arsenal Tech HS; Indianapolis, IN; Rensselaer A.

CARTWRIGHT, Mark Allen
Maud HS; Maud, OK; Ann; Band; BC; Chess C; Model UN; Order/Arrow; Pres, SC; Bsbl; Bkbl; Cpt, Ftbl; Tr; Citz A; Cl Fav; H of F; Hist A; VP, Tres, SC; *Southwestern Okla U; Med.*

CARTY, John Patrick
Don Bosco Tech HS; Boston, MA (17-253) Dbte Tm; Drama; NHS; SC; Sftbl; COM; K of C A; NMF; NMS; NEDT; WW; *MIT; Elec Engr.*

CARUSO, Peggy Ann
N Plainfield HS; N Plainfield, NJ (25%-300) Rptr, Chldr; Chor; Hmrm; Co-Ed, Sch P; SC; Co-Cpt, Sftbl; Yth Fel; Model Congress; NJ Bicen Yth Constitutional Conv; *Pol Sci.*

CARUTHERS, Lori Ann
Emerson Sr HS; Gary, IN (4-222) CYO; Co-Cpt, Chldr; GS; Secy, NHS; VP, Jr Cl; Alg A; Citz A; HQn; Type A; Shorthand A; *Ball St U; Ed.*

CARVER, Curtis Glynn
Claiborne Acad; Haynesville, LA (20%-30) Co-Cpt, Band; 4H; Lit Kal; 4H A; *La Tech U; Vet Sci.*

CARVER, Edward Lee
NW HS; Indianapolis, IN; Fr C; Drama.

CARVER, Kathy Lynn
Harrison HS; Colorado Springs, CO (50-429) FBLA; NHS; *Central Col; Med Secy.*

CARVER, Kimberley Ann
Greenwood HS; Greenwood, SC (32-550) BC; Drama; Fr C; NHS; Fr A; *U of SC; Nurs.*

CARVER, Kirk Langston
Clinton HS; Clinton, MS; Bsbl; Ftbl; Jr Superlative; *Hinds Jr Col; Elec Trades.*

CARVER, Lorene
Eldorado HS; Albuquerque, NM (1-814) Chor; GS; Hmrm; NHS; Span C; Span NHS; St Stu Congress; SC; MVP, Bkbl; Sftbl; Citz A; Hon Prog; Q&S A; Sci A; Keyettes; Soroptimist Yth Citizenship A; BYU Trustee's A; Ntl Guild Mus Teacher Win; *Brigham Young U; Elem Ed.*

CARVER, Theresa Dawn
New Bern Sr HS; New Bern, NC (30-550) JV, Chldr; Chor; FBLA; Rainbow; Sci C; Span C; Tr; Hon Prog; NEDT; Yth Fel; Lib A; Pagette; *UNC; Pharmacy.*

CARVER, William Carnell III
NW HS; Indianapolis, IN (146-700) Chess C; Cpt, Bkbl; ROTC A; *Purdue U; Humanities.*

CARY, Kathleen Louise
Corvallis HS; Corvallis, OR (9-300) Band; Chor; Ensm; NHS; Tres, Yth Fel; *Bus Mgt.*

CARY, Kimberly Lee
Whitmer Sr HS; Toledo, OH; Chor; Hmrm; SC; Bkbl; COM; Yth Fel; Asst Song Ldr; Asst Secy, Church; March of Dimes.

CARY, Linda Darlene
King HS; Tampa, FL (16-619) Key C; Secy, NHS; HCt; Hon Prog; Vlbl; *Lee Col; Chem.*

CARY, Marissa Simone
Eau Claire HS; Columbia, SC (29-359) Drama; Hmrm; NHS; Spch C; Secy, SC; Bkbl; JA A; Spch A; *Atlanta U; Law.*

CARY, Ronnie Ray
Bovina HS; Bovina, TX; Band; Rptr, FFA; SC; Var C; Bsbl; Co-Cpt, Bkbl; Ftbl; Golf; Tnns; Tr; COM; HCt; Most Out; Yth Foundation; Hustler A; Win, Pitch, Hit & Throw; Age A; All Dist Bkbl; Most Admired; Hon Men, Ftbl Quarterback; *Texas Tech; Phys Ed.*

CASABONA, Marlen
Eastern Christian HS; N Haledon, NJ; Chor; *Secretarial.*

CASADO, Maria Presentacion
Nuestra Senora de la Providencia; Rio Piedras, PR (6-32) A Cap Choir; Bus C; CYO; Drama; Tres, Jr Cl; COM; Co-Cpt, Vlbl; Conduct A; *Med.*

CASADO, Zenaida Irene
Academia Maria Reina; Rio Piedras, PR; CYO; Chor; Fr C; NHS; Hon Prog; *Med Tech.*

CASADY, Tracy Lorraine
Albia HS; Albia, IA; Chor; Mgr, Sftbl; Pep C; *AIB; Secy.*

CASALE, Michael Angelo
Power Mem Acad; New York, NY; F-Ed, Lit Mag; NHS; F-Ed, Sch P; Bkbl; Tnns; Tr; COM; Hon Prog; *Phar.*

CASARES, Helias
Hughson Union HS; Hughson, CA (6-140) Dbte Tm; Spch C; SC; Tr; Wrest; CSF; Spch A; Pres, VICA; Rotary Yth Ldrship Conf; *Oreg St U; Elec Engr.*

CASCIANA, Rosa Del Carmen
St Augustine Acad; Lakewood, OH; *Dyke Col; Bus.*

CASE, Anna Sue
Paris HS; Paris, AR; Parl, SC; Health A; PA A.

CASE, Brenda Lee
Crockett HS; Crockett, TX (11-120) FBLA; FHA; Pres, Hmrm; NHS; Cpt, Bkbl; Sftbl; Tr; *Tyler Jr Col; Bus.*

CASE, Charlotte Kathleen
Hobbs HS; Hobbs, NM (5-600) Chor; Ensm; Rainbow; SC; Amer Leg A; COM; Citz A; DARGCA; God & Country A; Hon Prog; MLS; Yth Foundation; 1st Cl GSct; *Mus Therapy.*

CASE, Cheryl E
Greeley Central HS; Greeley, CO (87-316) 4H; Cl Fav; HQn; HCt; DECA; *Clothing Design.*

CASE, Cheryl Rose
Wellesley Sr HS; Wellesley, MA; Community Yth Symph; Ensm; Hmrm; VP, Orch; COM; Citz A; Fr A; Eng A.

CASE, Diane Marie
Lancaster Sr HS; Lancaster, WI (6-139) Fin, AFS; Ann; Band; Chldr; Chor; Ensm; Secy, 4H; Hmrm; Model UN; NHS; SC; JV, Bkbl; 4H A; Spch A; AFS Trip Schol; *Mil Sch of Engr; Chem Engr.*

CASE, Douglas William
Neshannock HS; New Castle, PA (41-145) Band; Drama; Math C; Orch; Order/Arrow; VP, Sci C; JV, Tr; Bio A; Hon Prog; Order/Arrow A; Spch A; Yth Fel; Eagle A; *Penn St U; Horticulture.*

CASE, Harry Edgar Jr
Kelly Walsh HS; Casper, WY (108-411) Drama; ARC; Cpt, Bsbl; Cpt, Swim; Cpt, Tr; ARC A; Sci A; Mus A; Bible Quiz; *Jamestown Col; Law.*

CASE, Polly Jean
Candor Central HS; Candor, NY (13-120) Band; Ensm; NHS; JV, Cr-Ctry; Mgr, Sftbl.

CASE, Roslieb D
Easton Area HS; Easton, PA; *Comm Col; Secy.*

CASE, Ruby Jewell
Western Grove HS; Western Grove, AR; Bkbl.

CASE, Thomas Edwin
George Washington HS; Philadelphia, PA; Co-Ed, Sch P; String Band; All Philadelphia Boys Choir.

CASE, Thomas Gilbert
Fayetteville Manlius Sr HS; Manlius, NY (300-450) Co-Ed, Soccer; Pres A; Eagle Sct; 1st Tm, All Amer Soccer; WW; *Syracuse U; Lib Arts.*

CASE, Tracy Adele
Madeira HS; Madeira, OH (10-209) AFS; Hmrm; Span C; SC; Swim; Alg A; Bio A; COM; Citz A; Hon Prog; Math A; Sci A; Type A; PA; Ath A; *U of Cincinnati; Special Ed.*

CASELLA, Judith Katherine
Los Banos HS; Los Banos, CA; S-T, Sci C; SC; Tnns; Cpt, Pomnerette; *Speech Therapy.*

CASELLI, Caron Terese
Foreman HS; Chicago, IL (5-363) Drama; Key C; NHS; Tr; COM; Hon Prog; Math A; Sr Play; Co-cpt, Bowl; 3rd Pl, City Doubles Bowl.

CASELMAN, Karen Kay
Fayetteville Sr HS; Fayetteville, AR (66-352) A Cap Choir; NFL; *Pepperdine U; Nurs.*

CASEMENT, Kim Marie
Medina Sr HS; Medina, NY (19-184) A Cap Choir; Drama; Hmrm; SC; Type A; WW; *Genessee Comm Col; Bus.*

CASEY, J Lyndon
Whiteland Comm HS; Whiteland, IN (21-196) Band; Fr C; FFA; NHS; Var C; Cr-Ctry; JV, Ftbl; JV, Tr; Wrest; WW; *ITT Tech Inst; Elec Engr.*

CASEY, Kevin Eugene
Tyner HS; Chattanooga, TN (23-261) BC; Key C; NHS; Var C; Ftbl; Soccer; Citz A; Most Dependable; Christmas Court; *US Air Force Acad; Engr.*

CASEY, Mary Ann
Rosati-Kain HS; St Louis, MO (45-95) S-T, CYO; Chor; Hmrm; SC; Tres, Sr Cl; Pres, Soph Cl; Tr; Citz A; Schol Art A's; Merit Schol, Art; *Maryville Col; Art.*

CASEY, Michael Andrew
Nolan HS; Fort Worth, TX (100-200) A Cap Choir; Band; Chor; Demolay; Drama; Ensm; Fr C; Madrigal; Orch; Thes; Swim; Hospital Vol Work A; *S Tex Wesleyan Col; Theology.*

CASEY, Michael Edward
Chaminade Col Prep; St Louis, MO (7-118) NHS; Bsbl; Co-Cpt, Bkbl; Co-Cpt, Ftbl; Amer Leg A; Bio A; Chem A; Hist A; Hon Prog; Math A; Sci A; Star Student; *Notre Dame Col; Engr.*

CASEY, Peggy Anne
George Washington Carver HS; Montgomery, AL (47-400) Ann; Sci C; VP, Span C; Tri-HiY; WW; Pres, Spirit C; Pepster o-t Week; Secy, Yth Choir; *U of Ala; Pre-Med.*

CASEY, Timothy Patrick
Destrehan HS; Destrehan, LA (1-300) *LSU; Elec Engr.*

CASEY, Vernida Renee
Saginaw HS; Saginaw, MI (32-380) Co-Cpt, Chldr; Chor; SC; Var C; Sr Cl; Most Out; Type A; *Central Mich U; Dietitics.*

CASEY, Vicki Lynn
Amer Christian Acad; Pomona, CA (3-21) Chldr; Chor; Co-Ed, Sch P; Spch C; SC; Tres, Sr Cl; Tres, Jr Cl; Tres, Soph Cl; Sftbl; Bio A; Citz A; HCt; Hon Prog; ARC A; Sci A; Vlbl; Bible A; Most Outst PE A; PA; *Cal Poly; Elem Ed.*

CASH, Cathy Ellen
Southwood HS; Shreveport, LA (55%-550) Chor; Hmrm; COM; *U of La; Mus.*

CASH, Chet David
Flint Sw HS; Flint, MI; Chor; Bkbl; Tr; *Jackson St Col; Journ.*

CASH, Diane
Second Ward HS; Gloster, LA; Bus C; Tres, FBLA; FHA; Sci C; Bkbl; Sftbl; *Sou U.*

CASH, Donald Wayne
Herbert Hoover HS; San Diego, CA (6-489) Key C; Swim; JV, Wrest; CSF; *Calif Polytech Inst; Engr.*

CASH, Donna Kay
Chase HS; Forest City, NC (10-160) Ann; BC; Cpt, Chldr; Chor; Pres, FHA; FTA; Secy, Hmrm; VP, Key C; Secy, Monogram; Secy, SC; Secy, SC; Tr; COM; HCt; Swtht; *U of NC; Psych.*

CASH, Peggy Sue
Brookfield E HS; Brookfield, WI (268-521) Chldr; Hmrm; SC; Sftbl; Tr; VP, VP, Yth Fel; Jr Prom Ct; Honored Qn; Job's Daughters; *Steven's Point Col; Spch Therapy.*

CASH, Rhonda Lynne
S D Lee Sr HS; Columbus, MS (4-209) A Cap Choir; Band; Chor; Ensm; S-T, Fr C; NHS; Sch Achieve Tm; Chamber of Comm A; Hon Prog; NMS; Star Student; WW; *Harding Col; Med.*

CASH, Susan Harriett
Gaffney Sr HS; Gaffney, SC; Q&S A; Photography Ed, Sch P; Pep C; Bible C; Photography C; *Clemson U; Parks & Recreation Adm.*

CASHION, Kevin Michael
Broad Run HS; Ashburn, VA (33%-400) Band; Drama; Orch; Drama A; *Arts.*

CASO, Lisa Ann
John F Kennedy HS; Tumon, GUAM (35-511) Chldr; Hmrm; NHS; HCt; *Airline Stewardess.*

CASON, Deborah Ann
Victory Christian HS; Carlsbad, CA (11-27) Chldr; ARC; Sch P; Bsbl; Sftbl; Trophys, Baton Twirling; Outst Art A; Girl o-t Yr, Girls C; Chldr A; Hallmark Design Contest A; *Mira Costa Col; Art.*

CASON, Sheila Marie
Fairview Alpha HS; Coushatta, LA (1-21) F-Ed, Ann; Rptr, FHA; 4H; Fin, Lit Ral; Var C; Bkbl; Alg A; Beauty; Cl Fav; 4H A; HCt; Math A; St Scholar; Swtht; *Northwestern St U; Radiologic Technology.*

CASON, Vicki Elaine
Tift Co HS; Tifton, GA; A Cap Choir; Chor; Ensm; 4H; Span C; 4H A; Type A; Yth Camp Qn; 1st Pl Dist, Vocal Ensm; *SE Bible Col; Bus.*

CASPAR, Jeffrey Harvey
Jackson HS; Jackson, MI (89-433) Hmrm; Spch C; SC; VP, Soph Cl; JV, Bsbl; Golf; Swim; H of F; Hon Prog; Spch A; Cum Laude; *Bus.*

CASPER, Kathleen Ann
Bridgeton Sr HS; Bridgeton, NJ (352-718) Drama; Fr C; Yth Fel; Pres, GSct; VP, MIHI; SAS; *Stockton St Col; Criminal Justice.*

CASPER, Paul Vincent
John Marshall HS; San Antonio, TX; Drama; Order/Arrow; Ski C; JV, Ftbl; Wrest; FCA; Eagle Sct; Distin Rifle Marksmanship A, NRA; *U of Tex; Geo.*

CASPER, Steven Arthur
Pleasant Plains HS; Pleasant Plains, IL (60-88) Band; Chor; St Tn Talent; IFMC Piano Contests; *Lincolnland Comm Col; Acct.*

CASPERS, Linda Sue
Johnson-Brock HS; Johnson, NE (33%-24) Ann; Chor; S-T, 4H; JV, Bkbl; Tr; COM; 4H A; Spch A; Win, Church Camp; 4-H Camp A; Pep C; Citiz Sem.

CASPERSON, Tina Mary
Freeburg Comm HS; Freeburg, IL (7-120) Co-Ed, Ann; Band; Chldr; Model UN; NHS; Secy, SC; Thes; Var C; Swim; HCt; St Scholar; Swim Tm Coach's A; WW; *U of Ill; Pre-Journ.*

CASSADA, Alan Brian
Nansemond-Suffolk Acad; Suffolk, VA (11-83) BC; BS; Key C; Monogram; Bsbl; Bkbl; Mgr, Ftbl.

CASSADY, George Howard
Logan HS; Logan, OH; All Amer Yth; CYO; Var C; Co-Cpt, Wrest; Wrest A's.

CASSEL, David Allen
Weatherford HS; Weatherford, OK; Band; Pres, 4H; Spch C; Bsbl; JV, Bkbl; Ftbl; Wrest; 4H A; H of F; I Dare You; Kiwanis A; *Okla St U.*

CASSELL, Carrie May
Longmont Sr HS; Longmont, CO (12-630) AFS; Ann; Band; Ger C; 4H; Orch; Co-Ed, Sch P; Tres, SC; MYF; St Solo & Ensm Contest; Ski C; Citizenship Shortcourse; Line Off, Rainbow Girls; Mus Camp Schol; Boulder Co Coun.

CASSELL, Kellie Ann
Mechanicsburg Sr HS; Mechanicsburg, PA (86-389) Chor; JV, Hockey.

CASSELS, Thomas
Joliet W HS; Joliet, IL (125-470) Bkbl; MVP, Ftbl; Tnns; HKg; Most Out; *Joliet Jr Col; Bus.*

CASSESE, Dominique I
Qn o-t Rosary Acad; Amityville, NY (4-85) NHS; Hon Prog; WW; *St Bonaventure U; Med Technology.*

CASSETTY, Deborah Lee
J W Robinson Secondary Sch; Fairfax, VA (30-530) F-Ed, Ann; Chor; InterAct C; Key C; Mu Alpha Theta; NHS; SC; COM; DARGCA; Drill Tm; *Old Dominion U; Dental Hygiene.*

CASSIDY, Kathleen Marie
John W Hallahan Cath Girls HS; Philadelphia, PA (19-431) CYO; Chldr; NHS; Sci C; Pres, SC; Pres, Sr Cl; Ftbl; Sftbl; Hon Prog; K of C A; Ntl Sci Symposium; Sci A; *St Joseph's Col; Psych.*

CASSIDY, Thomas James
Fridley Grace HS; Fridley, MN; Bsbl; Mgr, Bkbl; Ftbl; HKg; Hon Men, Ftbl; Most Friendly; *St Thomas Col; Bus Adm.*

CASSISA, Yvonne Marie
Cabrini HS; New Orleans, LA (1-115) Fin, Jr Miss Pagent; Alg A; COM; Hon Prog; Most Out; Val; *Tulane U; Art.*

CASSON, Leonard Walter
Gulf Comprehensive HS; New Port Richey, FL (4-367) BS; Pres, Key C; Pres, NHS; SC; MLS; Drum Major; Fla All Star Marching Band; *Vanderbilt U; Civil Engr.*

CASSTEVENS, Nancy Gail
Starmount HS; Boonville, NC (20-204) Band; Fr C; FHA; FTA; Bkbl; Tnns; *Wake Forest Col; Mus.*

CAST, Laura Karen
Sharpstown HS; Houston, TX (299-684) Parl, VICA; 3rd Pl, St VICA Contest; *Tex A&M U; Nurs.*

CASTEEL, Jerri Lynn
Jones Co HS; Gray, GA (20%-191) F-Ed, Ann; Drama; FHA; Hmrm; Semi-Fin, Jr Miss Pa; Co-Ed, Sch P; Span C; SC; Bio A; Church Sftbl Tm; *Ga SW Col; Nurs.*

CASTELLANOS, Janie Belinda
San Marcos HS; San Marcos, CA (49-249) Ann; Chor; Fr C; FHA; SC; Tr; CSF; COM; Citz A; Drill Tm; Asst Sunday Sch Teacher; *Med.*

CASTELLANOZ, Maria Teresa
Liberty Union HS; Brentwood, CA (67-250) AFS; Chor; Fr C; Mus A; Fr A; *San Jose St U; Nurs.*

**CASTELLAR,
Lina De Los Angeles**
Adolfo Grana HS; Penuelas, PR (4-263) Drama; FHA; 4H; COM; Poet A; Val; *Cath U; Sci.*

CASTELLI, Carol Jean
Frontenac HS; Frontenac, KS (10%-45) FHA; DARGCA; Hon Prog; Pres, Pep C; Q & S; *Pittsburg St U; Bus.*

CASTELLO, Carol Jane
Southside HS; Elmira, NY (5-450) Secy, Lat C; Hist A.

CASTELLO, Randy Roxanne
Moorcroft HS; Moorcroft, WY; Band; CYO; Chldr; VP, FTA; GS; 4H; Rptr, NHS; SC; Pres, Sr Cl; Bkbl; Alg A; COM; Chamber of Comm A; Cl Fav; 4H A; Math A; NMS; Phy A; Sci A; Spch A; Type A; VofDEM; Vlbl; *Bus.*

CASTILAW, Iris Elayne
Brookhaven Acad; Brookhaven, MS; *U of Sou Miss; Counselor.*

CASTILLO, Ileana Lucila
Sunnyside HS; Tucson, AZ; *U of Ariz; Archt.*

CASTILLO, Luis Bechtel
Stranahan Sr HS; Fort Lauderdale, FL (2-465) Band; VP, InterClub Coun; Bus Mgr, Key C; Pres, NHS; COM; Chamber of Comm A; Sal; Star Student; *Biscayne Col; Bus Adm.*

CASTILLO, Suzy Ester
Ralls HS; Ralls, TX (25-62) Secy, CYO; Ch, FHA; FTA; Sci C; Span C; SC; *W Tex St U; Secondary Ed.*

CASTILLO, Yolanda
Los Altos HS; Hacienda Heights, CA (129-600) GS; Hmrm; NHS; St Stu Congress; SC; *Calif St U; Computer Prog.*

CASTLE, Jane Elizabeth
Lebanon HS; Lebanon, VA (40-172) Ed, Ann; Pres, Band; JV, Chldr; FTA; 4H; Model UN; Sch P; Span C; SC; Tri-HiY; 4H A; Band Director A; Wash Workshop Sem; All Reg, St Bicentennial, Bands; *Appalachian St U; Early Childhood Ed.*

CASTLE, Janet Gayle
James River HS; Buchanan, VA (1-115) Co-Cpt, Chldr; InterClub Coun; Jr Miss Pagent; NHS; Pres, Span C; COM; Val; *Radford Col; Journ.*

CASTLE, Kathy Ann
Marion Harding HS; Marion, OH (226-573) AFS; *Ohio St U; Elem Ed.*

CASTLE, Kevin Blaine
Marion HS; Marion, IN (30%-750) Band; Chor; Ensm; Madrigal; Tr; 1st, Tr Tm; Band Medal; 1st Pl Tm, Pony League; *Marion Col; Religion.*

CASTLE, Phillip Micheal
Strasburg HS; Strasburg, CO (1-34) Co-Ed, Ann; Band; BS; Chess C; Dbte Tm; Fr C; Pres, NHS; F-Ed, Sch P; Spch C; Mgr, Bkbl; Mgr, Ftbl; Tr; Q&S A; Regent Schol; ROTC A; Spch A; Val; Hon Band; Band A; *Colo St U; Computer Sci.*

CASTLE, Terrie Ann
Clinton Co HS; Albany, KY (9-107) Band; Pres, BC; Chldr; Chor; Parl, FHA; FTA; 4H; Hmrm; Secy, Math C; Sch P; Sci C; SC; Var C; Mgr, Bkbl; Tr; Cl Fav; 4H A; HCt; Spch A; *Western Ky U; Nurs.*

**CASTLEBERRY,
Marlene Mondell**
Eldorado HS; Las Vegas, NV; Chldr; 4H; Tr; *Law.*

CASTLEBERRY, Richard Allan
Papillion-LaVista HS; Papillion, NE (25-350) NHS; ARC; Span C; SC; Var C; Ftbl; Tr; Citz A; Yth Fel; Christmas Royalty; *U of Nebr; Sci.*

CASTO, Janet Marie
Pickens HS; Pickens, WV (3-16) Co-Ed, Ann; Arch; Cpt, Chldr; 4H; NHS; Bkbl; Cl Fav; 4H A; Type A.

CASTONGUAY, Claire
College St Anne De La Pocatiere; La Pocatiere, CANADA (3-31) Swim; Tnns; *Geger Ste-Foy; Technique Radiologie.*

CASTONGUAY, Denis
Col De Ste Anne De La Pocatiere; La Pocatiere, CANADA (3-31) CYO; *CEGEP de La Pocatiere; Hist.*

CASTRO, Cynthia Lee
Tabernacle Christian Acad; San Diego, CA (4-8) All Amer Yth; Drama; Cpt, Sftbl; Cpt, Swim; Swtht.

CASTRO, Daniel Ray
John Marshall HS; San Antonio, TX; Mgr, Bkbl; Tr; *Baylor U; Math.*

CASTRO, Jose J
Colegio Universitario Corazon; San Juan, PR (3-25) Drama; Tres, Hmrm; Tres, Order/Arrow; COM; Citz A; Hist A; Magna Cum Laude; Spch A; Eagle Sct BSA; YMCA As; Psych A; Eng & Span As; 50 Miler A; Historical Trails A; *Universidad de Puerto Rico; Natural Sci.*

CASTRO, Minerva
Antonio S Pedreira HS; Moca, PR (6-38) FHA; Span C; Tnns; COM; *Colegio Mayaguez; Nurs.*

CASTRO, Wanda Maria
Jose de Diego HS; Mayaguez, PR; Chldr; Phys C; SC; Alg A; COM; Magna Cum Laude; Phy A; Span A.

CASTRODAD, Aslin Carmen
Notre Dame HS; Caguas, PR (20-136) A Cap Choir; Chldr; Chem C; Chor; Dbte Tm; VP, Hmrm; Math C; NHS; Phys C; Sci C; Swim; Alg A; Bio A; COM; Chem A; Cl Fav; Hist A; Hon Prog; Math A; MLS; Most Out; Opt A; Opt Out Tm; Phy A; Sci A; Star Student; Swtht; Girl Sct; VP, Cath Daughters of Amer; Span A; Jr o-t Yr; *Med.*

CASTRONOVO, Josephine
Canarsie HS; Brooklyn, NY (2-945) FTA; Hmrm; Secy, NHS; COM; Citz A; Gov Honor Prog; Hon Prog; Math A; Most Out; FHA A; Quill & Scroll; Sal; Star Student; Italian As; *Brooklyn Col; Humanities.*

CASWELL, Deborah May
William Tennent HS; Warminster, PA (18-980) NHS; St Stu Congress; COM; *U of Nev; Renewable Resources.*

CASWELL, Debra Ruth
McNeil HS; McNeil, AR (3-33) BC; Bus C; 4H; S-T, Hmrm; Math C; Sci C; Spch C; S-T, Soph Cl; Alg A; COM; Cl Fav; HCt; Sci A; Eng A; *Sou Ark U; Nurs.*

CASWELL, Terri Anne
Grove HS; Grove, OK (5-143) Band; BC; FHA; NHS; Bkbl; Tr; HCt; Most Out; ARC A; Star Student; HR; Superintendent's HR.

CATALANATTO, Ann Michel
John Ehret HS; Marrero, LA (17-562) BC; CYO; Semi-Fin, GS; 4H; Semi-Fin, Jr Miss Pa; Fin, Lit Ral; Tres, NHS; Ed, Sch P; SC; Tres, Jr Cl; Beauty; 4H A; Hist A; Hon Prog; Ral A; Scholastic A; *U of Southwestern La; Law.*

CATALANATTO, Karen Renee
John Ehret HS; Marrero, LA (4%) CYO; Semi-Fin, GS; Hmrm; Fin, Jr Miss Pagent; Semi-Fin, Lit Ral; SC; Beauty; 4H A; Hist A; Journ A; Ral A; *Art.*

CATALANO, Jim Louis
Pinole Valley HS; Pinole, CA; ARC; JV, Tr; Wrest; Young Life; Night Life; *San Jose St Col; Elec Bus.*

CATALANO, Sally Elizabeth
St Joseph's o-t Palisades HS; W New York, NJ (6-232) Drama; A-Ed, Lit Mag; NHS; Rptr, Sch P; Span NHS; SC; Swim; Hon Prog; NEDT; Hist C; *Rutgers U; Engr.*

CATALDO, Judith Kathleen
Acad o-t Holy Names; Tampa, FL (13-68) Pres, CYO; Chor; InterClub Coun; NHS; Sch P; Span C; Span NHS; Outst Piano Stu A; Sup Performance Ability Schol; *New England Conservatory of Mus; Piano.*

CATALON, Prescylynn Suzette
Glendale Adventist Acad; Glendale, CA (10%-65) Drama; Pres, Spch C; Co-Ed, Bkbl; Lion A; Spch A; *Loma Linda U at La Sierra; Eng.*

CATANZARO, Annette Jean
Riverview Sr HS; Oakmont, PA (17-173) Chor; NHS; Co-Ed, Sch P; Color Guard; Chamber Singers; *Art Inst of Pittsburgh; Interior Design.*

CATANZARO, Ellen Marie
University San Diego HS; San Diego, CA (16-311) Ann; Cum Laude Soc; Hmrm; InterClub Coun; Model UN; NHS; Ed, Sch P; Tnns; CSF; *Point Loma Col; Nurs.*

CATANZARO, Salvatore
Marist Prep HS; Penndel, PA (1-21) CYO; Chor; Drama; Pres, Jr Cl; VP, Soph Cl; Hockey; Alg A; Bio A; Hist A; Hon Prog; Journ A; K of C A; Math A; NEDT; Phy A; Sci A; Theology A; Eng A; Social Stu A; Spelling Bee A; *U of Penn.*

CATCHINGS, Darlene
Westbury HS; Westbury, NY; FBLA; Secy, Pathfinder C; *Oakwood Col; Theology.*

CATE, David Edgar
Trinity Christian HS; Chattanooga, TN (4-14) Sci C; SC; MLS; Sci A; *Tenn Temple Col; Sci.*

CATE, Marla Ann
Burroughs HS; Ridgecrest, CA; *Oral Robert's U; Child Development.*

CATE, Nancy Irene
Trinity Christian HS; Chattanooga, TN (2-12) COM; PA; *Secretarial Sci.*

CATE, Sheree Sue
Maryville HS; Maryville, TN; Co-Cpt, Chldr; FHA; Hmrm; Lat C; SC; HCt; WW; *U of Tenn; Lib Arts.*

CATE, William Norris
Jonesboro HS; Jonesboro, AR (8%-400) A Cap Choir; Band; BC; Chor; Dbte Tm; Ensm; Lit Mag; Mod Mus Mas; Orch; Sch P; Spch C; Radio-tV Announcing A; *Ark St U; Radio-television.*

CATES, Lisa Ann
Webster Co HS; Dixon, KY; Rptr, Bus C; Co-Cpt, Chldr; Chor; FHA; 4H; Hmrm; Sch P; Sftbl; Tr; 4H A; HCt; JA A; PTA A; Spch A; FHA A; Jr Degree, Chapter Degree; Chldr A; DECA A.

CATES, Sherry Annette
Red Springs HS; Red Springs, NC (5-150) BC; Rptr, FTA; Golf; Journ A; Marshal; *U of NC; Computer Sci.*

CATES, Stacie Lynn
Cushing HS; Cushing, OK (10-120) Ch, Band; Chor; FHA; S-T, Key C; Co-Ch, Mjrte; NHS; Pres, Rainbow; Citz A; *E Central U; Mus.*

CATES, Teresa Yvonne
Bradford HS; Bradford, TN (3-35) BC; FHA; 4H; Bkbl; Most Improved Guard, Bkbl; *Union U.*

CATHER, Cosette Yvonne
Penn View Bible Inst; Penns Creek, PA; Chor; Tres, Span C; Soccer; Sftbl; MVP, Swim; Type A.

CATHEY, Charles Edward Jr
Pisgah Sr HS; Canton, NC; Ann; Demolay; Most Patriotic A.

CATLETT, Donna Camille
Little Rock Central HS; Little Rock, AR (11-543) Tres, A Cap Choir; BC; Co-Cpt, Chldr; Drama; S-T, Hmrm; Jr Miss Pagent; Mu Alpha Theta; NHS; Span C; Spch C; Y-Tns; Sftbl; Swim; Tnns; DARGCA; H of F; Hon Prog; NEDT; WW; Span II Declamation Contest Win; *Ouachita Baptist U; Chem.*

CATLETT, Warren Cameron
Central HS; Woodstock, VA (10%-175) Semi-Fin, BS; InterAct C; NHS; Var C; Bkbl; JV, Ftbl; Amer Leg A; *Va Tech; Bus Adm.*

CATLIN, Janice Kay
Oxford HS; Oxford, KS (1-37) JV, Chldr; Chor; Co-Cpt, Bkbl; Sftbl; Tr; Alg A; Math A; Pep C; Chldr A; Vlbl; Kayettes; Kayette Board; Pep C.

CATLIN, Jeanice Fay
Oxford HS; Oxford, KS (4-45) Ann; Band; Chldr; Chor; NHS; Sch P; SC; Bkbl; Sftbl; Tr; HQn; Pres, Tn Town; JV, Vlbl; PA A; Pres, Pep C; Mus A; Kayette Board; Kayette; Pep C A; Hon Soc; *Bryan Inst; Med Asst.*

CATLIN, Michael Kevin
Paoli HS; Paoli, OK (5-17) Band; 4H; VP, Hmrm; NHS; Pres, SC; VP, Sr Cl; Secy, Jr Cl; Pres, Soph Cl; Bkbl; Ftbl; *Okla U.*

CATON, Scott Brenon
E J Wilson HS; Spencerport, NY (1%-380) Band; BS; Drama; Ensm; Math C; Model UN; NHS; Sch P; JV, Swim; COM; Citz A; Hon Prog; NMS; *Dartmouth Col; Med.*

CATRON, Lee Ann Bristow
Daviess Co HS; Owensboro, KY (11-320) Band; BC; Community Yth Symph; Ensm; Hmrm; Orch; SC; Chem A.

CATT, Cynthia Lynn
Coshocton HS; Coshocton, OH; Band; Chor; Ensm; ARC; Span C; ARC A; Sci A; VP, GSct; Rating I, II, I; St Band Contest; Ohio Mus Ed As, Ratings I, II, I.

CATURIA, Colleen Michelle
Payson HS; Payson, AR (2-108) Ed, Ann; Secy, Band; Bus Mgr, Chldr; Secy, Chor; Drama; Ensm; FHA; Fin, GS; Madrigal; NHS; SC; Var C; Beauty; Chamber of Comm A; Gov Honor Prog; HCt; Fin, McDonald's All-Amer Band; Miss Arizona Tn Ldrship A; Miss Tn Qn USA; *Mus.*

CAUDELL, Connie LaRosa
Wister HS; Wister, OK (10%-34) Chldr; FHA; 4H; Sci C; Bkbl; Sftbl; 4H A; HCt; Val; Superintendent's HR; *Carl Albert Jr Col; Bookkeeping.*

CAUDELL, Melinda Jean
Miami Springs Sr HS; Miami Springs, FL; Drama; Tres, FHA; Thes; *Miami Dade Col; Social Work.*

CAUDILL, Anita Delaine
Grove HS; Grove, OK (24-99) Band; Co-Cpt, Chldr; Chor; FBLA; Pres, FHA; SC; Ch, Sr Cl; Ch, Jr Cl; VP, Soph Cl; Bkbl; MVP, Sftbl; COM; Most Out; Type A; WW; *John Brown U; Sociology.*

CAUDILL, Dan Paul
Ross Sr HS; Hamilton, OH (100-182) A Cap Choir; VP, Band; Chor; Drama; Ensm; FTA; VP, Orch; Sch P; Spch C; Thes; Fin, JA Talent Contest; *Miami U; Mus.*

CAUDILL, Karen Lynn
Taylor HS; North Bend, OH; Band; Chldr; Hmrm; Mjrte; ARC; SC; Masonic A; Cpt, Drill Tm; Stu Aid; Honored Qn, Job's Daughters; Rose Prom, Jr Princess; Fin, Drill Tm Contest; *Eastern Ky U; Bus.*

CAUDILL, Linda Faye
Reading HS; Reading, MI (10-90) Band; Chor; SC; *U of Mich; Ed.*

CAUDILL, Lynn
Tates Creek Sr HS; Lexington, KY (125-350) Chor; Sftbl; *Georgetown Col; Law.*

CAUDILLO, Robert
Ennis HS; Ennis, TX (10%-250) Band; BS; Drama; FTA; Hmrm; JETS; NHS; Span C; Spch C; SC; Thes; COM; Spch A; Pres, TARS; March-Of-Dimes A; Eng A; Thespian Hon Bar; One-Act Play; *Southwest Tex St U; Bilingual Teacher.*

CAUDLE, Judith Anne
Treadwell HS; Memphis, TN (10-172) Chldr; Chem C; Rptr, Hmrm; Fin, Jr Miss Pagent; Lat C; NHS; Secy, SC; Golf; H of F; HQn; Hon Prog; Type A; *U of Tenn; Pre-Law.*

CAUDLE, Karen Denise
W Forsyth Sr HS; Clemmons, NC (97-487) AFS; ARC; Span C; Spch A; VofDEM; Yth Fel; Girls Service C; Yth Church Pianist; GSct 1st Cl; Span A; HR; Band Flagtwirler; VP, Church Yth Fel; *High Point Col; Phys Therapy.*

CAUDLE, Leslie Renee
John F Kennedy HS; Winston-Salem, NC; Band; Drama; SC; Yth Fel; GSct; Flagtwirler; Secy, Church Yth Fel; *High Point Col; Psych.*

CAUDLE, Ruth Ann
Atlanta HS; Atlanta, TX (10%-166) Bus Mgr, Ann; Band; Bus C; Ensm; Fr C; FHA; Secy, FTA; GS; Secy, NHS; Sci C; SC; Secy, Sr Cl; Q&S A; *Ouachita Baptist U; Lib Sci.*

CAUDLE, Troy Nathan
Mt Ida HS; Mt Ida, AR (1-43) Band; BC; BS; FFA; NHS; Rptr, Soph Cl; Bsbl; Ftbl; Tr; Val; *U of Ark; Engr.*

CAUGHEY, Carol Ruth
Richland Sr HS; Gibsonia, PA (1-284) Band; Lat C; Lat NHS; NFL; NHS; Co-Ed, Sch P; World Affairs C; Sftbl; Hon Prog; Val; Statistician, Bkbl & Vlbl; Penn St Schol Participant; *Penn St U; Bio.*

CAULFIELD, Ellen Sonita
Fairfield HS; Fairfield, AL (10%-168) COM; Hon A; *Miles Col; Acct.*

CAULFIELD, Joseph Francis
St Joseph's HS; Camden, NJ (1-111) Pres, CYO; Pres, Chess C; Drama; Ger C; NFL; NHS; Sci C; Hon Prog; Spch A; Ger Hon A; Theology A; Regional Film Lib A; *Phys Sci.*

CAULKINS, Donald Ray
Merritt Island HS; Merritt Island, FL (285-687) Chem C; Chor; Bkbl; Tr; Mission Tms, Columbia, Guatemala; Mission Tm, Alaska.

CAULLEY, Christopher Joseph
St Mary's Prep Sch; Orchard Lake, MI (4-36) Chldr; Dbte Tm; Spch C; SC; Ftbl; Tr; First Hon; Oratorical Fin; *Mich Col; Law.*

CAULTON, Warren Louis
Tech HS; Springfield, MA (2-348) Chor; Math C; NHS; Pres, Sci C; Soccer; Sftbl; Tr; Bausch & Lomb A; JA A; NMS; Phy A; Summa Cum Laude; NHS; 3rd Mass St Sci Fair; 1st Mass St Industrial Fair; *Rensselaer Poly Inst; Elec Engr.*

CAUSBIE, Roberta Jean
Weatherford HS; Weatherford, TX (29-252) CYO; FFA; NHS; Span C; *Horticulture.*

CAUSEY, Wanda Gail
Southwest HS; Macon, GA; Camera C; PA; Eng A; 1st Pl, Bake Off; *Child Care.*

CAUSEY, Wyndel Elizabeth
Pascagoula HS; Pascagoula, MS (20%-750) Band; Secy, BC; Fr C; Mjrte; Secy, SC; COM; *U of Sou Miss.*

CAUSSYN, Julie Geralyn
Center HS; Center, ND (5-40) Band; S-T, CYO; Chldr; Chor; FHA; Secy, Ger C; Rptr, Sch P; SC; Bkbl; Sftbl; Tr; Secy, Ger C; *NDSU; Sociology.*

CAUTHEN, Cramer Randolph
First Baptist Church Sch; Charleston, SC (5%-60) Band; Chess C; Rptr, Chor; Drama; Hmrm; Ed, Lit Mag; NHS; Order/Arrow; A-Ed, Sch P; SC; Bkbl; Citz A; DARGCA; God & Country A; NEDT; Order/Arrow A; *Furman U; Eng.*

CAUTHEN, David Thomas
Bayshore HS; Bradenton, FL; HiY; Co-Cpt, Bkbl; Co-Cpt, Cr-Ctry; Opt Out Tn; Pres, DECA; *Treuecca Nazarene Col; Theology.*

CAUTHEN, Phillip Jordan
Andrew Jackson HS; Kershaw, SC (6-170) F-Ed, Ann; Band; Chess C; Drama; Fr C; French NHS; 4H; NHS; Orch; Rptr, Sch P; Secy, Sci C; Spch C; Mgr, Bkbl; God & Country A; Hon Prog; Acad Schol; *Erskine Col; Bio.*

CAVALLARO, Jeanette Marie
Kingsway Regional HS; Swedesboro, NJ; NHS.

CAVALLARO, Virginia Elizabeth
Wakulla HS; Crawfordville, FL; Band; Secy, 4H; Fin, Hmrm; ARC; Pres, SC; Bkbl; Golf; Hockey; Swim; ARC A; Yth Fel; VP, Rptr, SC; Semi-Fin, 4-H A; Fin, HCt; *FSU; Recreational Therapy.*

CAVALLERO, Gina Mary
Lake Placid HS; Lake Placid, NY (27-90) Cpt, Chldr; ARC; Cpt, Bkbl; Cpt, Sftbl; Cpt, Field Hockey; Cpt, Vlbl; Pres, Fish & Game C; Candystriper; Fish & Game C Rifle Tm; *St Mary's Sch of Nurs; Nurs.*

CAVANAUGH, Joni Lee
Gila Bend HS; Gila Bend, AZ (5-52) Chor; GS; NHS; VP, SC; Var C; Pres, Jr Cl; Bk[-1]; Tr; HCt; Type A.

CAVAZOS, Araceli Yvette
Mission HS; Mission, TX (158-365) Rptr, Bus C; Span C; H of F; St Parl Procedure; *Pan American Col; Bus.*

CAVAZOS, Catherine Elizabeth
Oliver Wendell Holmes HS; San Antonio, TX (225-600) Band; CYO; Ensm; FHA; Span C; SC; Bsbl; Bkbl; Ftbl; Sftbl; 3rd CYO Qn Contest; *San Antonio Col; Bus Adm.*

CAVE, Albert Sidney
Beaufort Acad; Beaufort, SC (1-38) Band; Chor; NHS; Hon Prog; Ntl Merit Commendation; *Clemson U; Elec Engr.*

CAVE, Cynthia Renee
Central HS; Waterloo, IA (15%-310) NHS; Hon Prog; DECA C.

CAVE, Diana Ladoris
Springfield Southeast HS; Springfield, IL (149-402) Chor; JA A; Explorer C; JA; *Springfield Sch of LPN; Nurs.*

CAVE, Laura Lee
Rocky Mount Sr HS; Rocky Mount, NC; S-T, Chor; Drama; Ensm; Arch; Swim; Tr.

CAVELL, Nancy Louise
Our Lady of Fatima HS; Lafayette, LA; A Cap Choir; Ann; BC; CYO; Chor; Ensm; 4H; Math C; Mu Alpha Theta; Pres, NHS; Pol Sci C; Ed, Sch P; SC; World Affairs C; Mgr, Bkbl; COM; 4H A; NEDT; Swtht; Cpt, Vlbl; Scholastic Let; WW; Solo & Ensm Festival Medals; All Tourney Vlbl.

CAVEN, Jay Robert
Borah HS; Boise, ID (1-600) Span NHS; Var C; Ftbl; Tnns; Cl Fav; Yth Fel; Bus.

CAVER, Lawrence Hardy Jr
Atlanta HS; Atlanta, TX (30-175) Demolay; Phys C; Rptr, Sch P; Sci C; Ftbl; Tr; *Baylor U; Phar.*

CAVIN, William Pinckney Jr
Spartanburg HS; Spartanburg, SC; Orch; Sci C; Sftbl; Swim; Tr; JA; Converse Col Yth Orch; Acolyte; MYF; Church Choir; *Wofford Col; Radio & TV.*

CAVITT, Jennifer Kaye
Morton HS; Morton, TX (13-56) Bus Mgr, Ann; Chldr; FTA; NHS; SC; JV, Bkbl; Tr; Cl Fav; Ed, Annual; *Acct.*

CAWKINS, Kathryn JoAnn
Parkview HS; Orfordville, WI; AFS; Band; Lit Mag; NHS.

CAWLEY, John Ben
Eldorado HS; Eldorado, TX (11-45) Secy, FFA; 4H; VP, SC; Var C; Ftbl; Tr; 4H A; *Tex A&M U; Animal Sci.*

CAWLEY, Kathleen
South Plainfield HS; S Plainfield, NJ (66-380) Rptr, Ann; Hmrm; Tres, SC; Secy, Soph Cl; Mgr, Bkbl; Pres, SC; *Nurs.*

CAWOOD, Michael David
Peterson HS; Sunnyvale, CA (35-492) Band; VP, Ger C; Order/Arrow; Co-Cpt, Soccer; Swim; CSF; Eagle Sct.

CAWTHON, James Walter Jr
Franklin Co HS; Carnesville, GA; FFA; Bsbl; *N Ga Col; Elec Engr.*

CAWTHON, Jeri Denise
Polo HS; Polo, MO (30%-34) A Cap Choir; Pres, Band; Chor; Ensm; FHA; Pres, 4H; Pres, Hmrm; Pres, Jr Cl; Bsbl; Bkbl; Sftbl; Swim; Citz A; 4H A; JA A; Type A; Band As; GSct A.

CAWTHON, Melissa Amanda
Franklin Co HS; Carnesville, GA; Band; Chor; FHA; Tri-HiY; *N Ga Col; Mus.*

CAWTHORN, Robert John
Garner Sr HS; Garner, NC (1-450) BC; BS; Chess C; Alg A; Hon Prog; *Med.*

CAYTON, Robert Francis
Sutter Union HS; Sutter, CA (3-95) Band; BS; Pres, Monogram; Pres, Sci C; Pres, Sr Cl; VP, Jr Cl; Co-Cpt, Ftbl; CSF; *Air Force Acad; Engr.*

CAYTON, Roger Harold
Upper Scioto Valley HS; McGuffey, OH (1-81) BC; Chem C; Chor; 4H; Math C; NHS; Sci C; Span C; Var C; Bsbl; JV, Bkbl; Cr-Ctry; Alg A; Bio A; Chem A; 4H A; Math A; Sci A; Chem Bowl St Champs; *Med.*

CAZARES, Leonard Lopez
William B Travis HS; Austin, TX (14-306) CYO; Fr C; NHS; Med Careers C; *Santa Fe Col; Priesthood.*

CEBELAK, Kandy L
Oscoda Area HS; Oscoda, MI (26-260) Ed, Ann; Band; Dbte Tm; Drama; 4H; Mod Mus Mas; Rainbow; Secy, SC; Thes; Secy, Sr Cl; Secy, Jr Cl; B Crocker A; Spch A; Grand Officer, Rainbow; Keyette C; *Bethel Col; Social Work.*

CEBRUN, Eva Marie
Phillis Wheatley HS; Houston, TX; Type A; Yth Fel; *Prairie View Col; Nurs.*

CECIL, Lee Anne
Holy Rosary Acad; Louisville, KY (3-116) S-T, ARC; Span C; Sftbl; *Med.*

CEDILLO, Rosa Linda
Ralls HS; Ralls, TX; Pres, CYO; Span C; Parish Coun; *W Tex St U; Secy.*

CELENZA, Donna Jean
Landmark Christian Sch; Cincinnati, OH; A-Ed, Ann; JV, Chldr; Chor; Ensm; Pres, Hmrm; Super Cabin '75; Walkathon.

CENANCE, Debra Ann
Joseph S Clark Sr HS; New Orleans, LA; A Cap Choir; All Amer Yth; CYO; FBLA; JA A; Sci A; Yth Foundation A; *Xavier U; Bus Ed.*

CENTANNI, Gina Anne
Cath Central HS; Troy, NY; Co-Ed, Ann; Chor; Hmrm; K of C A.

CEPEDA, Harry A
Academia Santa Monica; Santurce, PR (5-53) Co-Ed, Ann; Chor; Pres, Drama; Model UN; NHS; Ed, Sch P; VP, Spch C; SC; Tnns; Spch A; *Ga Tech U; Chem Engr.*

CEPEDA, Robert
Dinuba Joint Union HS; Dinuba, CA (7-153) Pres, FFA; Tres, Key C; A-Ed, Sch P; CSF; Rotary A; B of A Plaque Win, Voc Arts; St Farmer Degree; *Reedly Col; Ag-Bus.*

CERALDI, Christopher Michael
Abbeville HS; Abbeville, SC (16%-130) Cpt, Band; BS; Bsbl; Most Out; Palmetto BS; *The Citadel; Pre-Med.*

CERBUS, Gregory Eugene
Wayne HS; Dayton, OH (100-750) Ftbl; Wrest; Jr NHS.

CERCONE, Donna Marie
Notre Dame-Bishop Gibbons HS; Schenectady, NY (36-166) Chor; Drama; Parl, Model UN; NHS; Journ A; *King's Col; Communications.*

CERDA, Arturo Jaime
Harlingen HS; Harlingen, TX (100-800) A Cap Choir; Band; Chor; Ensm; NHS; COM; Hist A; *Tex A&I Col; Mus.*

CEROSALETTI, Karen Marie
Charlotte Valley Central Sch; Davenport, NY (1-44) Band; MVP, Chldr; Chor; Ensm; 4H; Model UN; NHS; Pres, Span C; Secy, SC; Alg A; Bio A; 4H A; Hist A; Math A; Sci A; NYS Summer Mus Sch; Eng, Span, Mus, A's; *Med Tech.*

CERRATO, Cynthia Carol
Arkadelphia HS; Arkadelphia, AR; Chldr; Chor; Fr C; FHA; Hmrm; Sci C; SC; *Henderson St U.*

CERULLA, Fred A
Theodore Roosevelt HS; Wyandotte, MI (10%-465) NHS; Var C; Cr-Ctry; Cpt, Tr; Yth Fel; Underclassmen o-t Yr A; *Mich St U; Criminal Justice.*

CERUTTI, Linda Marie
Oakville Sr HS; St Louis, MO (27-436) CYO; FTA; NHS; Span C; *U of Mo; Special Ed.*

CERWIN, Todd Robert
Burlington HS; Burlington, WI (15-400) Band; Dbte Tm; Drama; NHS; Ski C; Pres, SC; Var C; Golf; NMS; Band Section Ldr; WW, Mus Stu; *U of Wis-Madison; Pre-Med.*

CESSNA, Celeste Janet
Reynolds HS; Greenville, PA (6-207) Band; Chor; Math C; Span C; Sftbl; Drill Tm; *Psych.*

CESSNA, Ellen Ann
Middletown HS; Middletown, OH; Band; Orch; Rainbow.

CETO, Johnny Richard
Providence Christian HS; Riverview, FL (4-9) Var C; Bsbl; Bkbl; Cpt, Ftbl; COM; HCt; Ftbl Schol; *Evangel Col; Bus Adm.*

CETO, Tammy Lynn
Providence Christian Sch; Riverview, FL (4-28) Chldr; HCt; Yth Fel; Best Personality; HR.

CHADEK, Lori Jean
Prague HS; Prague, NE; Ann; Chldr; Chor; GS; VP, Jr Cl; Tr; HCt; Hon Prog.

CHADSEY, Barry Bryson
Catoosa HS; Catoosa, OK (15-184) ARC; A-Ed, Sch P; Pres, Sci C; SC; JV, Ftbl; JV, Swim; JV, Wrest; Bio A; Citz A; Journ A; ARC A; Sci A; Type A; Jr Sci Acad; Okla Hon Soc; Principal's HR; *U of Okla; Bio-Med.*

CHADWELL, Vanessa Ann
Seymour HS; Seymour, MO (1-60) Tres, Band; Pres, BC; Ensm; Parl, FHA; Rainbow; SC; Alg A; Bio A; Chem A; Citz A; Hist A; HCt; Math A; Type A; Val; Secy, Beta C; Feature Twirler; 1st Run-Up, Miss Merry Christmas; Most Stu; Art, Fr, Mus, Eng, A's; Best All Around; *U of Mo; Engr.*

CHADWICK, Cindy Marie
LaCenter HS; LaCenter, WA (3-57) A Cap Choir; Band; JV, Chldr; FHA; S-T, 4H; NHS; Tres, SC; 4H A; HCt.

CHADWICK, Mellany Ann
Robert E Lee HS; Tyler, TX (250-600) Chor; FHA; Hmrm; SC; Tnns; Chor A; *Tex Eastern U; Dental Hygiene.*

CHADWICK, Sandra Kay
Leesville HS; Leesville, LA (50-300) FHA; JV, Bsbl; Bkbl; Sftbl; Lib C; Home Ec A; *Vet Med.*

CHADWICK, Wanda Jean
Battle Mountain HS; Minturn, CO (7-60) A-Ed, Ann; Secy, Band; Chldr; Chor; Drama; Ensm; FHA; Mjrte; Model UN; VP, SC; Var C; Pres, Soph Cl.

CHAFFEE, Bradley John
Clear Lake Comm HS; Clear Lake, IA; VP, Sr Cl; MVP, Ftbl; MLS; Cpt, All Conf, Ftbl; *Central Col; Bus Adm.*

CHAFFEE, Brian Joseph
Clear Lake HS; Clearlake, IA (20%-175) Band; Pres, Jr Cl; Ftbl; Tr; Wrest; Hon Prog; *U of Mont; Biological Sci.*

CHAFFEE, Laura S
Midwest City HS; Midwest, OK; Dbte Tm; Drama; Hmrm; Tres, NFL; Spch C; SC; Opt A; Spch A; VFW A; VofDEM; Outst Novice Debator; *Okla City U; Law.*

CHAFFEE, Lisa Carol
Dewey HS; Dewey, OK (12-85) Band; FHA; *Okla St U; Elem Ed.*

CHAFFEE, Randall Lee
Capitol City Baptist Sch; Lansing, MI (1-5) Ann; Bkbl; Cr-Ctry; Cpt, Soccer; Tr; Wrest; Yth Fel; *Engr.*

CHAFFIN, Janet Leah
Crescent City Jr-Sr HS; Crescent City, FL; Band; BC; Secy, InterAct C; InterClub Coun; SC; Elk A; Hist A; HCt; Sal; Soph, VS Jr Coun; Nom, Hugh O'Brien Ldrship Seminar; Miss Congeniality FFA Swtht Conte; Woodman o-t World Amer Hist A; *St Johns River Comm Col; Therapy.*

CHAFFIN, John Allison
Southland HS; Southland, TX (3-9) Ann; NHS; Sch P; Bkbl; Co-Cpt, Ftbl; *Angelo St U.*

CHAFFIN, Mark Wynn
Upperman HS; Baxter, TN; Band; BC; Chess C; Co-Ch, Dbte Tm; Drama; Tres, Fr C; VP, FFA; Pres, 4H; Math C; NFL; Phys C; Ed, Sch P; Sci C; Spch C; Pres, Jr Cl; Tnns; Alg A; Amer Leg Orator A; 4H A; I Dare You; Spch A; VofDEM; 1st, St 4-H Public Spkr; 1st, Dist Debate; 2nd, St FFA A; 1st, Dist Sci Fair; *Auburn U; Archt.*

CHAFFIN, Martha Rouchelle
Thomas Jefferson Acad; Natchez, MS; A-Ed, Ann; SC; Amer Leg A; Beauty; Sci A; *Geology.*

CHAFFIN, Sherry Lynne
Loop HS ISD; Loop, TX (3-18) Co-Ed, Ann; Band; Pres, FHA; 4H; S-T, Jr Cl; Bkbl; 4H A; Pres A; Yth Fel; Band Drum Major; VP, Area FHA; *Wayland Baptist Col; Social Worker.*

CHAFIN, David Leigh
Vandalia Christian Sch; Greensboro, NC (2-14) Monogram; Span C; Bkbl; *UNC at G; Engr.*

CHAIDEZ, Debra Lynn
Sunset HS; Hayward, CA; Chldr; Co-Cpt, Sftbl; HQn; Type A; Yth Fel; Co-Cpt, Vlbl; *Azusa Pacific Col; Psych.*

CHAIN, Tony Steven
Sanford Acad; Sanford, MS (33%-11) BC; 4H; Bkbl; Ftbl; Tr; 4H A; HCt; *LSU; Med.*

CHALK, Linda Kaye
Berkeley Sr HS; Berkeley, MO; Chor; NHS; Tr Ltr; Mus Pins; *Psych.*

CHALK, Mary Beth
Abilene HS; Abilene, TX (65-500) Bus Mgr, Band; Ensm; Hmrm; Orch; Tri-HiY; COM; Hon Prog; Most Out; All Area Band; Win, St Piano Comp; Win, Ntl Piano Guild Diploma; 1st Division, St UIL Solo; *Abilene Christian U; Bus.*

CHALKER, Debbie Ann
Harlem HS; Harlem, GA (6-150) Ann; Pres, FBLA; COM; FSA; Augusta Col Cert of Achv; FBLA Schol; Shorthand A; NSA Schol Fin; Sr Academic Ltr; *Augusta Area Tech Sch; Executive Secretarial.*

CHALKLEY, Milton DeRohan
Suffolk HS; Suffolk, VA (8-150) Lat C; NHS; Bkbl; A; Math A; *William And Mary Col; Sci.*

CHALMERS, Charles Christopher
Columbus HS; Columbus, GA; Key C; SC; HCt; *U of Ala; Dentist.*

CHAMBERLAIN, Diane E
Ganesha HS; Pomona, CA (10-400) Chor; Drama; Lat C; Madrigal; NHS; CSF; *Pacific Christain Col; Psych.*

CHAMBERLAIN, Faith Annette
Thomas A Edison HS; Elmira Heights, NY (101-140) Band; Bus C; Chor; FBLA; *Elmira Bus Inst; Legal Secy.*

CHAMBERLAIN, Jay Douglas
Montgomery HS; Santa Rosa, CA (102-700) Chor; Hmrm; NHS; Bkbl; Ftbl; CSF; NEDT; *Berkeley Col; Sci.*

CHAMBERLAIN, Jeffrey Stewart
Largo Sr HS; Upper Marlboro, MD; Tres, Chor; Drama; Ensm; Hmrm; Math C; NHS; Order/ Arrow; Sch P; Pres, Sci C; VP, Thes; Bio A; Hon Prog; Co Chorale; St Chor; Drama A; *U of Md; Ed.*

CHAMBERLAIN, Lisa Colette
Indian River HS; Chesapeake, VA; *Norfolk St Col; Early Childhood Ed.*

CHAMBERLAIN, Ross Watson
Glenbrook N HS; Northbrook, IL (206-714) Key C; VP, Var C; Cpt, Swim; Tr; MVP, Swim; Ordained Church Deacon; *Vanderbilt U; Bus Adm.*

CHAMBERLAIN, Sandra Dee
Chrysler HS; New Castle, IN (10%-400) Lat C; Co-Ed, Sch P; Thes; Pianist, Jazz Band; *Brigham Young U; Journ.*

CHAMBERLAIN, Scott Edward
William Penn Sr HS; York, PA (12-693) Band; Orch; Order/ Arrow; JV, Tnns; Eagle Sct; World Conservation A; *NJHS; Penn St U; Engr.*

CHAMBERLAIN, Valeri Anne
Western Hills HS; Fort Worth, TX (1-600) CYO; FHA; NHS; Span C; Val; *Baylor U; Bus.*

CHAMBERLIN, Sandra Louise
Wasco Co Union HS; Maupin, OR (1-40) MVP, Band; Chor; 4H; NHS; Bkbl; Tr; NEDT; Type A; MVP, Vlbl; John Philips Sousa A; *George Fox Col; Mus.*

CHAMBERS, April Reine
Jena HS; Jena, LA (15-145) Ann; Cpt, Chldr; FBLA; FHA; Secy, FTA; 4H; NHS; Sch P; S-T, SC; Lit Ral; HCt; Hon Prog; NMS; GS Alt; VP, Fresh Cl; *Spch and Hearing Therapy.*

CHAMBERS, Bradley Stephen
Centralia HS; Centralia, IL (3-364) Pres, Hmrm; Co-Ch, Key C; NHS; Span C; SC; Soph Cl; Cpt, Bsbl; MVP, Bkbl; Co-Cpt, Ftbl; JV, Tr; Citz A; DARGCA; Hon Prog; St Scholar; WW; *E Ill U; Bus Adm.*

CHAMBERS, Cheryl Ann
Franklin HS; Franklin, OH (32-289) Band; Chor; Hmrm; SC; JA A; Church Ensm; SC A; Teacher Secy A; Off Asst A; Publications Asst A.

CHAMBERS, Cindy Louise
Mississippi Baptist HS; Jackson, MS (10-45) A Cap Choir; Chor; A-Ed, Sch P; Bkbl; COM; Hist A; Hon Prog; Type A; Yth Fel; Yth Leg; Chor A; Woodmen o-t World Hist A; *Hinds Jr Col; Acct.*

CHAMBERS, David Bruce
Bridgeport HS; Bridgeport, OH (7-121) Secy, Span C; Bkbl; Ftbl; Tr.

CHAMBERS, David Freeman
Central HS; Knoxville, TN (38-322) Ann; BC; BS; Chor; Ensm; Lat C; NHS; Opt A; Spch A; *U of Tenn; Law.*

CHAMBERS, Helen Renee
Westwood HS; Memphis, TN (10-202) Chor; Hmrm; Lit Mag; Math C; NHS; Co-Ed, Sch P; Sci C; SC; ROTC A; Span A; *Christian Brothers Col; Bus.*

CHAMBERS, James Kent
Natrona Co HS; Casper, WY (242-569) A Cap Choir; Band; Chor; Commercial C; Ensm; Secy, 4H; Order/Arrow; Var C; Bsbl; Mgr, Ftbl; Tr; MVP, Wrest; COM; 4H A; Most Out; *Casper Col; Engr.*

CHAMBERS, Kelly Ann
Arlington Heights HS; Fort Worth, TX (35-492) GS; Lat C; Co-Ed, Lit Mag; VP, NHS; Rptr, Sch P; Secy, SC; Journ A; Miss AHHS; *SW U; Pol Sci.*

CHAMBERS, Laura Lea
Newman Smith HS; Carrollton, TX (8-322) Ann; Hmrm; Secy, Math C; Fl Arts; Sch P; Pres, Span C; Secy, SC; JV, Bkbl; JV, Soccer; JV, Tr; COM; Hon Prog; Most Out; Sci A; Cpt, Vlbl; *Rice U; Math.*

CHAMBERS, Louis McMillan
Putnam City HS; Oklahoma City, OK (5%-900) Fin, BS; Secy, NHS; Span C; JV, Bkbl; Amer Leg A; Gov Honor Prog; St Scholar; FCA; *Med.*

CHAMBERS, Meshell
Waynesboro Central HS; Waynesboro, MS (25%-99) *Jones Jr Col; Nurs.*

CHAMBERS, Michael Joel
Tuscaloosa HS; Tuscaloosa, AL; Hmrm; InterAct C; Lat C; Var C; Cpt, Ftbl; God & Country A; Yth Fel; *U of Ala; Med Tech.*

CHAMBERS, Michael Thaddeus
Midwestern Christian Acad; Chicago, IL; A Cap Choir; Drama; *Mus.*

CHAMBERS, Patricia Renee
Fairfax HS; Los Angeles, CA (200-800) A Cap Choir; Chor; Drama; Secy, Hmrm; Madrigal; NHS; Ed, Sch P; Thes; COM; Journ A; Q&S A; Hon Tutor A; TV Broadcasting Cert; *Pepperdine U; Pol Sci.*

CHAMBERS, Rhonda Lynn
Bethel Baptist Sch; Memphis, TN (2-20) Chldr; Chor; Ensm; Type A; *Tri-St Baptist Col; Psych.*

CHAMBERS, Sandra Anne
Booker T Washington HS; Norfolk, VA (50%-500) S-T, Band; FBLA; Parl, Key C; Orch; Span C; Pres, SC; Beauty; Cl Fav; H of F; HCt; JA A; Ntl Conf Chr & Jews; *Saint Agustine's Col; Special Ed.*

CHAMBERS, Tanya Lynn
Paw Creek Christian Acad; Paw Creek, NC (10-26) Chor; Drama; Co-Ed, Sch P; Alg A; Hist A; *Nurs.*

CHAMBERS, Theresa Darlene
Paw Creek Christian Acad; Paw Creek, NC (2-10) F-Ed, Ann; Chor; Pres, SC; Var C; Bkbl; Sftbl; Alg A; Hist A; MLS; Sal; *Lee Col; Elem Ed.*

CHAMBERS, Timothy Wayne
Cottage Grove HS; Cottage Grove, OR (93-250) Band; Pres, Demolay; JV, Golf; Swim; HCt; *Aviation.*

CHAMBLEE, Felix Keith
Ahoskie HS; Ahoskie, NC (37-255) FHA; SC; Var C; Bkbl; Ftbl; *Elizabeth City St U; Bus Adm.*

CHAMBLEE, John Schettler
Dalton HS; Dalton, GA (17-245) NHS; Order/Arrow; SC; Ftbl; Co-Cpt, Swim; Elk A; Rob Hess A; *U of Tenn; Pol Sci.*

CHAMBLEE, Wanda Lynn
T L Hanna HS; Anderson, SC (10%-300) Band; Bus C; FTA; Lit Mag; Interntl Relations C; *Anderson Col; Elem Ed.*

CHAMBLESS, Teresa Renea
Crestview Sr HS; Crestview, FL (1-257) Anchor C; Band; BC; Drama; Jr Miss Pagent; F-Ed, Sch P; Sr Section Ed, Ann; Co Hon Stu; Pride Explosion Spch Win; *Shorter Col; Drama.*

CHAMBLIN, Jennifer Jo
Lee's Summit Sr HS; Lee's Summit, MO (100-491) A Cap Choir; Band; Jr Miss Pagent; NHS; Orch; Sftbl; Beauty; Opt A.

CHAMBON, Gregory Edward
Raytown South HS; Raytown, MO (1-615) Band; BS; Hmrm; Pres, NHS; Sci C; SC; Thes; Var C; JV, Bkbl; Tr; Math A; SC A; Centurions; Eagle Sct; Med Exploring; Industrial Arts A; *U of Mo in Kansas City; Med.*

CHAMMOUT, Mike Omar
Luther Burbank HS; Sacramento, CA (40-780) AFS; Chess C; Ensm; Fr C; Orch; Ski C; SC; Tnns; CSF; COM; Hist A; Pres, Pep Band; *UC-DAVIS; Civil Engr.*

CHAMNESS, James Alan
Holland HS; Holland, MI; BS; Chor; Ger C; Hmrm; Model UN; NHS; Orch; Order/Arrow; SC; Cr-Ctry; JV, Ftbl; JV, Tr; I Dare You; Val.

CHAMNESS, Rebecca Elizabeth
Washington HS; Washington, NC (17-300) Chldr; Hmrm; Secy, InterAct C; Monogram; NHS; F-Ed, Sch P; Pres, Span C; Pres, Span HS; Parl, SC; HCt; Hon Prog; Type A; Yth Fel; *Tex Christian U; Bus Adm.*

CHAMNESS, Shannon Lee
Sylmar HS; Sylmar, CA (50-1000) Ger C; Hmrm; Tnns; Lettered, Tnns; Sch Hist A Trophies; Bowl Trophy Sch Tm; *Valley Col; Acct.*

CHAMNESS, William Scott
Holland HS; Holland, MI; Chor; Orch; SC; JV, Ftbl; Tr; Drama A.

CHAMORRO, Ruben
Colegio San Conrado HS; Ponce, PR; NHS; Semi-Fin, Tnns; COM; High Cl Hon; *Universidad Catolica; Sci.*

CHAMPAGNE, Wayne Andrew II
Hahnville HS; Boutte, LA (5-75) Band; Secy, CYO.

CHAMPANOIS, Dawn Marie
Tecumseh HS; Tecumseh, MI (10%-350) Chldr; NHS; COM; Gym.

CHAMPANY, Wendy E
Lyman HS; Lebanon, CT (12-100) CYO; Secy, Mjrte; Hon Prog; Photographer, Sch P; *Eastern Conn U; Nursery.*

CHAMPINE, Kimberly Ann
L'Ance Cruse HS; Mt Clemens, MI; A Cap Choir; Chor; NHS; Hon Prog; Metro Yth Chor; VIP C; Homemaking A; Candystriper; *Nurs.*

CHAMPION, Christopher Todd
Iroquois Central HS; Elma, NY; Band; Bsbl; Cpt, Bkbl; Ftbl; Math A; Sci A; Yth Fel; Boys C; *St U Col at Buffalo; Communications.*

CHAMPION, Mickey Raedean
Houston HS; Houston, MS (10%-105) Pres, Anchor C; Ann; BC; Hmrm; SC; Bkbl; Tr; HCt; Star Student; Most Intelligent; Cutest; *Miss St U; General Bus.*

CHAMPION, Sonya Elaine
Kings Mountain Sr HS; Kings Mountain, NC; FTA; *Appalachian St Teachers Col; Ed.*

CHAMPION, Wanda Sue
Jupiter Christian Sch; Jupiter, FL (1-25) Chor; Bkbl; Sftbl; Citz A; Hon Prog.

CHAMPLIN, Orin Raymond
Helena Sr HS; Helena, MT; Ann; Fin, Chess C; Fin, Chor; Fin, Ensm; Orch; Sch P; Span C; Spch C; COM; Starlighters; Chess Champ, Sch.

CHAN, Aileen Renee
Belmont HS; Los Angeles, CA; Ann; Chldr; Chor; GS; Hmrm; InterClub Coun; NHS; ARC; Ch, Sodality; SC; Thes; Sftbl; Tnns; Tr; CSF; COM; Citz A; Hon Prog; Yth Fel; PA; Yth Fitness, Fr, Bowl, A's; *U of Sou Calif; Phys Therapy.*

CHAN, Dennis Kiman
Lutheran HS; Portland, OR (22-65) Drama; *Southwestern Baptist Bible Col; Foreign Missions.*

CHANCE, Diane Marie
Northside HS; Lafayette, LA; FTA; Secy, Mu Alpha Theta; SC; HCt; *NW La U; Nurs.*

CHANCE, Roger Stephen
John F Kennedy HS; Denver, CO (186-550) Spch C; JV, Bkbl; Mgr, Ftbl; Tr; Sch High Jump Recordholder, Tr; All City, Tr; *Wheaton Col; Creative Writing.*

CHANCE, Stanley John
Denair HS; Denair, CA (2-69) AFS; VP, Band; Chem C; Secy, FFA; Math C; Span C; Var C; VP, Jr Cl; Ftbl; Tr; JV, Wrest; CSF; COM; HKg; Math A; Span A; *Calif Polytech St U; Agr Bus.*

CHANCE, Thomas Stuart
Our Lady of Fatima HS; Lafayette, LA (11-70) BC; CYO; Dbte Tm; Pres, Key C; Parl, Math C; Mu Alpha Theta; NFL; Ed, Sch P; Span C; SC; Pres, Sr Cl; VP, Soph Cl; Cr-Ctry; JV, Ftbl; Tr; Citz A; DARGCA; Hist A; Hon Prog; Math A; MLS; Ntl Sci Found; Opt A; Hardest Worker A; WW; *LSU; Elec Engr.*

CHANCELLOR, Karen Elizabeth
Overton HS; Memphis, TN (15-370) Key C; Mu Alpha Theta; NHS; Alg A; Math A; *Memphis St U; Math.*

CHANCELLOR, Kim LaDawn
Red Oak HS; Red Oak, TX (4-86) Ensm; Madrigal; NHS; Span C; *U of Tex; Mus.*

CHANCELLOR, Sharon Carol
Thomasville HS; Thomasville, AL; Ann; Band; Chor; Ensm; Secy, Fr C; FHA; Mjrte; Sch P; S-T, Y-Tns; Bkbl; Swim; COM; Hon Prog; Yth Fel; Mus A; Spelling A; *Mobile Col; Design.*

CHANCEY, Susan Lyn
James A Shanks HS; Quincy, FL (5-335) Chldr; NHS; COM; Hon Prog; MLS; Cl Prophet; Ntl HS A for Excellence; *U of Fla; Law.*

CHANDLER, Cathryn Anne
Northfield Jr-Sr HS; Northfield, VT; Chor; Drama; Rptr, FHA; NHS; Var C; JV, Bkbl; Mgr, Hockey; JV, Sftbl; Yth Fel; Gym; *Med.*

CHANDLER, Cecelia Angela
Hamilton Jr HS; Washington, DC; Chor; Hmrm; SC; Ntl Achv Schol; ROTC A; Young Adult Chor; *Howard U; Mortuary Sci.*

CHANDLER, Cindy Lou
Eufaula HS; Eufaula, OK (1-93) Chor; Ensm; Bkbl; HCt; Best All Around; Candidate, Yrbk Qn.

CHANDLER, Elaine Leslie
Reading Mem HS; Reading, MA; Rainbow; JV, Cr-Ctry; JV, Tr; Yth Fel; Pres, MYF.

CHANDLER, Gail Elizabeth
Robert E Lee Sr HS; Houston, TX (50%-625) Chor; Ensm; Secy, FHA; JV Vlbl; *Baylor U; Special Ed.*

CHANDLER, James Thomas
Northfield Jr-Sr HS; Northfield, VT (8-86) A Cap Choir; Chor; Drama; VP, Fr C; Thes; SC; JV, Soccer; JV, Wrest; Co-Cpt, Rifle Tm; Photographer, Yrbk; *Aviation.*

CHANDLER, Janet Lynn
Hannibal Sr HS; Hannibal, MO (42-293) Band; Pres, Rainbow; Span C; Yth Fel; WW; *U of Mo at Kansas City; Med.*

CHANDLER, Karen
Shelton HS; Shelton, CT (78-432) NHS; Hon Prog; Type A; Ushers Guild; Shorthand A; *Katharine Gibbs Col; Executive Secy.*

CHANDLER, Karen Lynn
W P Davidson HS; Mobile, AL (100-500) Chem C; Chor; Hmrm; Span C; *U of S Ala; Social Work.*

CHANDLER, Kathy P
Oswego Comm HS; Oswego, IL (1-337) Chor; Ensm; FNA; Math C; S-T, NHS; VP, Pol Sci C; Alg A; Gr Marshal; Math A; Swing Choir; VP, Social Stu C; Health Occupations C; Art A; *Gustavus Adolphus Col; Nurs.*

CHANDLER, Leland Ackerman
Lafayette HS; Ellisville, MO; NHS; Cr-Ctry; Tnns; COM; *U of Mo; Nuclear Engr.*

CHANDLER, Michael Curtis
Aiken HS; Aiken, SC (100-700) Chess C; Ger C; Order/Arrow; Sci C; Tnns; Hiking C; Eagle Sct; *Ga Tech; Nuclear Engr.*

CHANDLER, Monica Lynn
Canton S HS; Canton, OH (8-300) Dbte Tm; Drama; FTA; Hmrm; Lit Mag; VP, Math C; NFL; NHS; VP, Sci C; Spch C; SC; Thes; Tri-HiY; Mgr, Bkbl; COM; NEDT; Spch A; VFW Orator Win; Yale Book A; *Ohio St U; Chem Engr.*

CHANDLER, Nedra Renee
United Township HS; E Moline, IL (25-792) 4H; Tr; *Black Hawk Col; Bus.*

CHANDLER, Polly Alane
Greater Atlanta Christian Sch; Norcross, GA (33%-103) Chor; Drama; PA; *David Lipscomb Col; Secy Work.*

CHANDLER, Regina Marie
Notre Dame HS; Portsmouth, OH; Ann; Chor; 4H; Lat C; Sch P; Sci C; Span C; Bsbl; Bkbl; Ftbl; Soccer; Sftbl; Swim; Tnns; Tr; Beauty; 4H A; HCt; Most Out; Sci A; Vica Qn Court; *Dental Hygiene.*

CHANDLER, Sandra Denise
Scott HS; Toledo, OH;

CHANDLER, Wardell Bennet Jr
Scott HS; Toledo, OH; Band; Chor; Bsbl; Bkbl; Ftbl; Wrest; Interlochen Ntl Mus; Yale Book A; Yth Fel; Yth Foundation A; *ITT; Elec.*

CHANEY, Cathy Michelle
J C Murphy HS; Atlanta, GA (32-240) Chldr; Chor; Dbte Tm; Drama; Parl, FHA; Sci C; Ed, SC; Cl Fav; Swtht; Attendance A; Most Talented; HERO A; Art A; *Tenn St U; Phys Ed.*

CHANEY, Deborah Ann
Preble Shawnee HS; Camden, OH (2-175) FNA; Tres, FTA; NHS; Pres, Span C; Span NHS; COM; Yth Fel; 7th Pl, Dist Schol Test; Co Del, World's Affairs Inst; *Miami U; Nurs.*

CHANEY, Joella Lynn
Glendal HS; Springfield, MO; Anchor C; Band; Fr C; Vol, Mercy Villa; Teacher, Children Dept; Motorboard Hon C; *Southwest Mo St U; Computers.*

CHANEY, Kim Sue
Celina Sr HS; Celina, OH (8-275) Band; Chor; Lat C; Cpt, Mjrte; NHS; Bkbl; Bio A; COM; Hon Prog; Cl Rep, Lutheran Yth; Church Choir; Church Usher; Lutheran Brotherhood Schol; Pres Schol; *Capital U; Nurs.*

CHANEY, Margo Eileen
Lakeside HS; Atlanta, GA (16-350) Pres, Band; VP, BC; Model UN; NHS; COM; *SW Col; Eng.*

CHANEY, Mark Anthony
Hobart HS; Hobart, OK; Var C; JV, Bsbl; Bkbl; Ftbl; Tr; Hon Prog; *Oral Roberts U.*

CHANEY, Tammy
Union HS; Union, MS (10%-60) Ann; BC; Drama; FHA; JV, Bkbl; *Miss St U; Bus.*

CHANEY, Tammy Kaye
Terre Haute S Vigo HS; Terre Haute, IN (59-574) Band; Rptr, 4H; Mjrte; Y-Tns; Tr; *Ind St U; Home Ec.*

CHANEY, William Thomas
Walnut Hills HS; Cincinnati, OH (150-300) AFS; Band; Chess C; Drama; Pres, Ensm; Fr C; Orch; Co-Cpt, Bsbl; Fin, Bkbl; COM; Citz A; Cl Fav; St Champs, Bkbl; *Howard U; Med.*

CHANG, Edna Yin Ping
Lowell HS; San Francisco, CA; Tnns; COM; Chinese C; Yth Fel C; Ntl Fr Contest; Vlbl; *San Francisco City Col; Bus.*

CHANG, Kyong-Mi
Kubasaki HS; Okinawa, JAPAN (8-421) Ann; Fr C; Math A; Art A; Chinese C; Vlbl C; *Stephens Col; Art.*

CHANG, Linda Meng-Yee
Belmont HS; Los Angeles, CA; Fin, Chldr; Chor; GS; NFL; NHS; ARC; Sodality; Spch C; Var C; Bkbl; Fin, Sftbl; Tnns; CSF; COM; Citz A; Hon Prog; Spch A; Chinese Lang Composition.

CHANG, Robert Yee Sang
Lowell HS; San Francisco, CA; *U of Calif at Berkeley.*

CHANNETTE, Dorothy Charlene
Jeanerette Sr HS; Jeanerette, LA; Chldr; Chor; 4H; Bkbl; Sftbl; 4H A; Most Out; *Sou U; Special Ed.*

CHAPA, Sylvia Margaret
Community HS; Houston, TX (10%-98) Pres, FBLA; NHS; Rptr, Sch P; VP, SC; Parl, Sr Cl; COM; Most Out; Sci A; *Sam Houston U; Computer Sci.*

CHAPIN, A Foy
Weldon Valley Sch; Weldona, CO (4-12) Band; BS; Pres, FFA; Pres, 4H; NHS; Pres, SC; Pres, Jr Cl; Co-Cpt, Bkbl; Co-Cpt, Ftbl; 4H A; MLS; Spch A; Yth Fel; Prom Attendant; *Colo St U; Animal Sci.*

CHAPIN, Jacqueline Little
Claremont HS; Claremont, CA; Tr; CSF; *Med.*

CHAPIN, Linda Louise
New Town HS; New Town, ND (4-70) A Cap Choir; Band; Chem C; Chess C; Chor; Dbte Tm; Ensm; FHA; Ger C; Pres, 4H; Mjrte; Math C; Ch, Sci C; SC; Cpt, Bkbl; Bio A; 4H A; Hon Prog; Sci A; Star Student; Dist Sci Fair A; Fight Smoking Contest; *U of ND; Nurs.*

CHAPLIN, Owen Chris
Savannah HS; Savannah, GA (25%-500) FBLA; Order/Arrow; Arch; JV, Bkbl; Bkbl; JV, Ftbl; Swim; JV, Tr; COM; Most Out; Order/Arrow A; ROTC A; ROTC; Highest 10%, A's; *Ga Sou Col.*

CHAPMAN, Alexandra
Kailua HS; Kailua, HI (3-570) Fr C; S-T, Lat C; NHS; VP, SG; Sr GSct; S-T, Jr Classical League; *Purdue U; Vet Med.*

CHAPMAN, Angela Christine
Chadsey HS; Detroit, MI; Citz A; *Detroit Col of Bus; Bus.*

CHAPMAN, Aubrey Eubric
John F Kennedy HS; NY, NY; Chor; *Math.*

CHAPMAN, Belinda Ann
Waynesboro Central HS; Waynesboro, MS (25%-119) FHA; Sch P; Y-Tns; *Jones Jr Col; Bus.*

CHAPMAN, Billie Joyce
Woodmont HS; Piedmont, SC; BC; Chor; Drama; FHA; Hmrm; Sch P; Journ A; Math A; Most Out; Sci A; Tec Schol; *Greenville Tec Col; Nurs.*

CHAPMAN, Charles Eric
Cedar Hill HS; Cedar Hill, TX (20-85) SC; Bkbl; Cpt, Ftbl; Tnns; Hon Men, All Dist Bkbl; Hon Men, Ftbl; Regional Qualifier, Tr & Tnns; *Tex A&M U; Bus Adm.*

CHAPMAN, Christine Carlotta
John F Kennedy HS; Bronx, NY (67-1159) Chor; VP, Key C; Hon Prog; Sci A; *Long Island U; Math.*

CHAPMAN, Christopher Carl
Ballard HS; Louisville, KY; BC; Chor; Ensm; Cr-Ctry; JV, Ftbl; Tr; Hon Prog; 3rd Pl St, Amer Hist; *U of NC; Lib Arts.*

CHAPMAN, Claire Elizabeth
Lansing Eastern HS; Lansing, MI (25-503) A Cap Choir; Band; Chor; Dbte Tm; Fr C; Hmrm; Lat C; Madrigal; NHS; COM; Sup Rating, Ntl Fed of Mus C Piano; *Mich St U; Musical Therapy.*

CHAPMAN, Clarence Edward
Etowah HS; Attalla, AL (6-35) *Jacksonville St U; Mech Engr.*

CHAPMAN, Darla Joy
Cedar Springs HS; Cedar Springs, MI; 4H; Hmrm; Tres, St Stu Congress; Rptr, SC; Tres, Sr Cl; Secy, Soph Cl; Camp Contest; *Western Mich Col; Special Ed.*

CHAPMAN, David Kent
Texhoma HS; Texhoma, OK (5-23) Band; Mgr, Ftbl; Masonic A; Band Ltr; *Tulsa U; Computer Sci.*

CHAPMAN, David Mark
Austin HS; Decatur, AL; *Art.*

CHAPMAN, Davis Howard
Sylva-Webster HS; Sylva, NC; Band; Chor; Demolay; Ensm; Math C; Ski C; Span C; Alg A; Math A; *Mus.*

CHAPMAN, Elizabeth Anne
John Handley HS; Winchester, VA (25-253) Fr C; Hmrm; Hmrm; Lit Mag; Monogram; NHS; Sci C; Tr; Swtht; Co-Cpt, Gym; *Radford Col; Phys Therapy.*

CHAPMAN, Francis Lloyd
Wayne Co HS; Jesup, GA (15%-350) A-Ed, Ann; Band; Hmrm.

CHAPMAN, Gary Lynn
Eminence HS; Eminence, IN (1-51) BS; Chor; Drama; VP, 4H; Lat C; NHS; F-Ed, Sch P; S-T, Var C; Rptr, Sr Cl; Rptr, Jr Cl; Pres, Soph Cl; Bkbl; Cr-Ctry; Tr; Amer Leg A; Bausch & Lomb A; Chem A; 4H A; Math A; MLS; Sci A; St Scholar; Val; *Purdue U; Agr Ec.*

CHAPMAN, Gena Marie
Chadsey HS; Detroit, MI (11-350) Chor; NHS; Citz A; *Mich St U; Computer Sci.*

CHAPMAN, George Wesley
Vidalia HS; Vidalia, GA (22-200) Co-Cpt, Band; Chor; Bus Mgr, Drama; Ch, HiY; Pres, Key C; Thes; Yth City Govt; *U of Ga.*

CHAPMAN, Lonas Bedford
Central HS; Knoxville, TN; NHS.

CHAPMAN, Penny
Smithfield HS; Smithfield, VA (20-175) Ann; Drama; FBLA; Pres, FNA; 4H; Hmrm; Math C; ARC; Ed, Sch P; Thes; Pres, Sr Cl; 4H A; HCt; Hon Prog; ARC A; Ntl Thespian Soc; *Longwood Col; Spch Therapy.*

CHAPMAN, Sheldon Walter
Dr Karnehm Lowell, MA (110-635) Hmrm; SC; Ftbl; Sci A; Yth Fel; *NE U; Chem Engr.*

CHAPMAN, Susan Marie
Fairmont Heights HS; Washinton, DC (5%-400) NHS; SC; Type A; Secy, Bible C; Stu Faculty Senate; Exec Comm, Sr Cl; Vlbl; *Georgetown Col; Elem Ed.*

CHAPMAN, TaJuanna Dora
Monroe HS; Albany, GA (15-265) Band; Chem C; Drama; Hmrm; COM; Hon Prog; Oral Roberts U; Psych.

CHAPMAN, Vickie Lee
Austin HS; Decatur, AL (23-373) Parl, FBLA; Secy, FHA; Math C; Mu Alpha Theta; NHS; F-Ed, Sch P; NEDT; Parl Procedures A; *Calhoun Comm Col; Bus Adm.*

CHAPPEL, Deborah Sue
Upper St Clair HS; Pittsburgh, PA; *Art Inst of Pittsburgh; Interior Design.*

CHAPPELL, Cynthia Joan
Washington Int HS; Honolulu, HI (10-35) Band; Hon Prog; Pres A; Spch A; Mus A; Sch Ltr; Tr Ribbons; Social Stu A; *U of Alberta; Sci.*

CHAPPELL, Debbie Susan
Franklin Co HS; Carnesville, GA; Band; Chor; Fr C; FHA; *Saint Mary's Col; Nurs.*

CHAPPELL, Karen Renee
S Choctaw Acad; Toxey, AL (4-26) Ann; BC; Chldr; Chor; NHS; Secy, SC; Secy, Jr Cl; Alg A; Cl Fav; Hist A; MLS; Most Out.

CHAPPELL, Lisa Lee
England Acad; England, AR (25%-26) Chldr; Chor; Jr Miss Pagent; Span C; Bkbl; Sftbl; Swim; Cl Fav; HCt; Church Comm Activities; *U of Central Ark; Eng.*

CHAPPLE, Jerry Don Jr
W Memphis Christian Sch; W Memphis, AR (5-30) Pres, Hmrm; Fin, Bsbl; Semi-Fin, Bkbl; Fin, Ftbl; Tr; Citz A; Cl Fav; Sci A; Bible A; *Harding Col; Math.*

CHARBONNEAU, Arlene Ann
Kelly HS; Chicago, IL (4-611) SC; COM; Citz A; Hon Prog; MLS; Most Out; Lib Aide; Lamplighter; Kelly Hon Soc; Schol A; *Loyola Col; Med.*

CHARLES, Allen Glenn
Spring Valley Acad; Centerville, OH (20-42) Chor; Ensm; Arch; Bsbl; Hockey; Soccer; Sftbl; 2nd Pl, Drama Reading; 2nd Pl, Comedy Skit.

CHARLES, Brad Frederick
Watonga HS; Watonga, OK (5%-80) Chor; Hmrm; Key C; NHS; Bkbl; Ftbl; Tr; Bio A; Hist A; Hon Prog; Pres A; Yth Fel; FCA; Eng A; Art A; *Calif Inst Tech; Aerospace Engr.*

CHARLES, Daryl
Beaumont HS; St Louis, MO; A Cap Choir; Band; Sci C; *Eckerd Col; Math.*

CHARLES, Jacqueline Stephanie
Erasmus Hall HS; Brooklyn, NY (6-35) CYO; Chldr; Math C; Ftbl; Sftbl; *Olivet Col; Nurs.*

CHARLES, Michael William
Science HS; Newark, NJ; Chess C; Drama; Key C; Lat C; Orch; Span C; Bsbl; Cpt, Bkbl; Ftbl; Cpt, Sftbl; Cpt, Swim; Citz A; Cl Fav; JA A; Math A; MLS; Most Out; PTA A; Pres A; Star Student; Swtht; Yth Fel; Best Dancer; Cl Comedian; Most Ath; Best Actor; *UCLA; Biochem.*

CHARLES, Robert Wesley
Walnut Hills HS; Cincinnati, OH; JV, Bkbl; Ftbl; Tr; Hon Prog; *U of Sou Calif; Pre-Law.*

CHARLESWORTH,
Connie Lynn
Glendale HS; Springfield, MO (200-600) Anchor C; Band; Chldr; Chor; Bkbl; Sftbl; Swim; *Baylor U; Spch Therapist.*

CHARLTON, Elizabeth Nan
Fairmont Sr HS; Fairmont, WV; Band; Chor; Ensm; Key C; Secy, Lat C; Pres, Lat NHS; Madrigal; Mjrte; *WV U.*

CHARLTON, Martha Ann
Homewood HS; Homewood, AL (10%-280) A Cap Choir; Cpt, Band; Chor; Drama; Ensm; Parl, Fr C; French NHS; Math C; Mu Alpha Theta; Thes; Math A; NEDT; St Win, Ala Mus Teachers Assn; Solo & Ensm Medals.

CHARLTON, Sally Ann
Riverside-Brookfield HS; Riverside, IL (53-460) Arch; Fr C; NHS; ARC; Arch; St Scholar; Tres, Media Services C; *Triton Col; Acct.*

CHARNOCK, Roger Clay
Brunswick HS; Brunswick, GA (27-365) Span C; Ftbl; ROTC A; FCA; Scabbard & Blade C, ROTC; *Brunswick Jr Col; Criminology.*

CHARONIS, David M
Belpre HS; Belpre, OH (3-180) Band; CYO; Chor; Pres, Ensm; Lat C; Madrigal; Orch; Order/Arrow; Sch Achieve Tm; SC; JV, Bsbl; JV, Bkbl; Co-Cpt, Sftbl; MVP, Swim; COM; God & Country A; Hist A; Order/Arrow A; Pres A; Spch A; Drm Mjr; US Mar Corps Phys Fit A; Jr Classical Leg; Life Sct; Jazz Band; Woodmn o-t Wrld Hist A; Pep Band; Amer Guild of Organists; *Pre-Law.*

CHARTER, Margie Nell
Spencer HS; Columbus, GA; VP, Chor; NHS; Mus A; *Columbus Col; Nurs.*

CHASE, Barbara Ann
Oviedo HS; Oviedo, FL (69-200) Pres & Rptr, FBLA; Pep C; Bible C; SG; *Seminole Comm Col; Bus.*

CHASE, Carol Annette
Mart HS; Mart, TX; Chor; FHA; Tnns.

CHASE, Cynthia Ann
Billings W HS; Billings, MT; A-Ed, Ann; Lat C; Journ A; Yth Fel; Girls Service C; Lit C; *Mont St U; Nurs.*

CHASE, Cynthia Lee
Charles H Roth HS; Henrietta, NY (143-200) Pres, 4H; 4H A; Co Polo Tm; *RIT; Photography.*

CHASE, June Rene
McKinley HS; Washington, DC; Fr C; Mjrte; NHS; Alg A; Sal; Sci A; *Howard U.*

CHASE, Lorraine
Continued Ed Project; St Louis, MO; FBLA; Mjrte.

CHASE, Terri Lee
Nordonia HS; Macedonia, OH (13-439) S-T, Band; Drama; Ensm; COM; Citz A; Math A; Sci A; Young Life; Attendance A; Presbyterian Yth Assn; Band A; Eng A; *Hiram Col; Ed.*

CHASON, Margaret Claire
Brookwood Sch; Thomasville, GA (8-30) BC; JV, Chldr; Hmrm; F-Ed, Sch P; Tri-HiY; Pres, Soph Cl; Yth Fel.

CHASON, Willard Brian
Brookwood Sch; Thomasville, GA (8-25) VP, Chess C; F-Ed, Sch P; Sci C; Bsbl; Tnns; Acad Bowl Tm; Evaluation Committee; *Mercer U; Law.*

CHASTAIN, Joetta Kay
Fair Play HS; Fair Play, MO (3-29) VP, FHA; VP, 4H; Type A; Miss FHA o-t Yr; 2nd Pl, REA Contest; 4-H Exchange Member; 4-H As & Medals.

CHASTAIN, Joy Elizabeth
Roseburg HS; Roseburg, OR (2-500) Band; GS; NHS; JV, Bkbl; Cr-Ctry; Tr; Bio A; Most Inspirational; Girl o-t Mo; *Oreg St U; Phys Ed.*

CHASTAIN, Manuela Ingeborg
Karlsruhe Amer HS; Karlsruhe, GERMANY; Ger C; NHS; Hon Soc A.

CHASTAIN, Steven Douglas
Belton HS; Belton, MO (33%-350) JV, Tnns; Industrial Arts A's; *Ga Tech; Archt.*

CHATHAM, Caren Michele
Hattiesburg HS; Hattiesburg, MS (20-500) Secy, Hmrm; Lat C; Ed, Sch P; SC; Y-Tns; Pres, ICH C; VP, Deb C.

CHATMAN, Pamela Lisa
Northwest HS; St Louis, MO (13-433) FBLA; NHS; Tnns; *Elec Engr.*

CHATMAN, Wonda
Humfeg HS; Nashville, TN; *MTSU; P D A Nears.*

CHATMON, Yvonne Delores
Douglass HS; Memphis, TN (3-150) Pres, FHA; VP, VICA; Eng A; *Methodist Hospital Sch of Nurs; Nurs.*

CHATTIN, Norma Anne
Lancaster HS; Lancaster, VA; Pres, AFS; Band; Chess C; Dbte Tm; Drama; Fr C; Hmrm; Lit Mag; Mjrte; Sci C; SC; Sci A; Pres, Church Yth; Debate, Mjrte, A's; Nature Camp; *Va Commonwealth U; Journ.*

CHATTO, Carl Leroy
Rockland Dist HS; Rockland, ME (10%-197) Band; Dbte Tm; Ensm; NFL; *Acct.*

CHAVERS, Michele
Cardinal McCloskey Mem HS; Albany, NY (15%-150) Chldr; Drama; Fr C; FBLA; Hmrm; SC; Citz A; WW; *Col of Saint Rose; Bus Adm.*

CHAVES, Sonia I
Colegio San Antonio; Isabela, PR (1-33) CYO; Chor; Tres, Hmrm; Span C; SC; COM; Hon Prog; Pres A; Tres A; *U of Puerto Rico; Phar.*

CHAVEZ, Bryan Edward
Valley HS; Sanders, AZ; CYO; Dbte Tm; Drama; FFA; Model UN; Spch C; Pres, Jr Cl; Co-Cpt, Bkbl; Co-Cpt, Ftbl; *NAU; P E.*

CHAVEZ, Debbie Elizabeth
Round Valley HS; Springerville, AZ (23-95) Pres, CYO; Chldr; Chem C; Chor; Secy, Drama; FHA; 4H; Hmrm; InterAct C; Span C; Rptr, SC; Secy, Soph Cl; MVP, Tr; 4H A; Pres A; Swtht; Prom Qn; All Region Solo & Ensm; Silver Medal, Solo; Talent Show Trophy; *N Ariz U; Secy.*

CHAVEZ, Gloria Maria
Gridley Union HS; Gridley, CA (20-116) CYO; Cpt, Chldr; FNA; Ski C; Span C; S-T, SC; S-T, Sr Cl; VP, Jr Cl; Cpt, Ftbl; Hockey; Tr; Cl Fav; HCt; Hon Prog; Most Out; Pres, S-T, Cpt, Drill Tm; Older Girls Conf; Stu o-t Mo; Secy, Stu Sports Advisory Coun; Vlbl; Modern Dance Production.

CHAVEZ, Janet Christine
Antioch HS; Antioch, CA; A Cap Choir; Band; FBLA; Orch; Tnns; Most Improved; High Schol Achv; U o-t Pacific.

CHAVEZ, Lorraine Lucille
Round Valley HS; Springerville, AZ; VP, CYO; Chldr; FHA; 4H; Phys C; Sch P; Ski C; Span C; Secy, SC; Tres, Soph Cl; Sftbl; Tnns; Tr; Cl Fav; 4H A; MLS; Type A; Yth Fel; Chor A; *Northern Ariz U.*

CHAVEZ, Manuel
Estancia HS; Estancia, NM (5-46) Ed, Ann; Pres, Arch; BS; Pres, Drama; Pres, 4H; NHS; Tres, Sci C; Tres, Span C; Tres, SC; Ch, Sr Cl; Ch, Jr Cl; Tres, Soph Cl; Amer Leg A; Bio A; 4H A; Lib, Drama, Span, Shorthand, A's; *E NM U; Acct.*

CHAVEZ, Michael Emerson
Marine Military Acad; Harlingen, TX (2-57) Ftbl; Swim; Hon Prog; NEDT; *Naval Acad at Annapolis; Math.*

CHAVIS, Alisa Shelley
Eastside HS; Paterson, NJ (11-519) S-T, Band; Drama; Secy, Jr Cl; Secy, Soph Cl; B Crocker A; COM; *Fordham U; Psych.*

CHAVIS, Debra Faye
Eastern Guilford HS; Gibsonville, NC (15-164) Chor; Pres, Drama; Ensm; Pres, FBLA; NHS; Span C; Span NHS; All St Chor A; *U of NC; Acct.*

CHAVOUS, Janelle Melina
Dixie Co HS; Cross City, FL (4-160) BC; Hmrm; Tnns; 4H A; *Mars Hill Col.*

CHEAPE, Michael Douglas
Waialwa HS; Waialua, HI (33%-200) Fr C; Spch C; Tnns; Lion A; Spch A.

CHEASLEY, Linda Jo
Newark HS; Newark, DE (31-389) NHS; NMS; *U of Del; Chem.*

CHEATHAM, Julia Marie
Broken Arrow HS; Broken Arrow, OK; Bkbl.

CHEATHAM, Thomas Eugene
F T Wills HS; Smyrna, GA; Band; Pres, BC; Math C; NHS; Bsbl; Sci A; Gov's Hons Nom; Ntl Sci Found A; All Star Tm, Colt League; Yth in Gov; Bsbl All Stars; *Math.*

CHEEK, Craig Michael
S R Butler HS; Huntsville, AL (20%-600) Chem C; Chess C; Span C; Semi-Fin, Wrest; Math A; Spch A; Yth Fel; Most Outst, Wrest; *U of Ala at Tuskaloosa; Bus Adm.*

CHEEK, David Wayne
Druid Hills HS; Atlanta, GA (57-184) Band; Pres, Chor; Ensm; Orch; Tres, Order/Arrow; Span C; Arch; COM; God & Country A; Order/Arrow A; Yth o-t Yr; *Mercer U; Law.*

CHEEK, Richard Stephen
Chillicothe HS; Chillicothe, TX; Pres, FFA; Pres, Sr Cl; VP, Jr Cl; Pres, Soph Cl; Ftbl; Tr; COM; Citz A; Cl Fav; Star Chapter Farmer; St Lone Star Farmer; Beef Proficiency; Agr Dept A.

CHEEK, Stephen Randal
Briarfield Acad; Lake Providence, LA (1-60) Ann; BC; Semi-Fin, Lit Ral; UN Council; Hist, Lib C; Cl Off; Ftbl Statistician; *Ne La U.*

CHEEK, Tomah Jean
Alma HS; Alma, MI; Tres, FHA; Bkbl; *Johnson Bible Col; Christian Ed.*

CHEEKS, Patricia Ann
Turner Ashby HS; Dayton, VA (45-260) A Cap Choir; JV, Chldr; 4H; Hmrm; NHS; Rptr, Sch P; Sci C; SC; Rptr, Var C; Tr; I Dare You; Pres A; Tres, Church Group; Stu Adv Coun; *Bridgewater Col; Nurs.*

CHEESEBORO,
Anthony Quentin
Hillcrest HS; Dalzell, SC (10%-381) Dbte Tm; Sci C; *Morehouse Col; Sci.*

CHEESMAN, Mark William
Carmel HS; Carmel, IN (31-589) CYO; Chess C; JETS; K of C; Sch Achieve Tm; Sci C; Mgr, Bsbl; JV, Ftbl; JV, Tr; God & Country A; Math A; NEDT; NML; Eagle Sct; *Purdue U; Chem Engr.*

CHELETTE, Delores
Bayou Chicot HS; Bayou Chicot, LA (12-29) Ann; FHA; 4H; Bkbl; *T H Harris Vo-tech Col; Data Processor.*

CHELICH, Martin Joseph
Hobart HS; Hobart, IN (80-406) Band; Ftbl; Tr; *Ind U.*

CHELSTROM, John Karl
Johnson HS; St Paul, MN; Sftbl; Swim; Tnns; Tr; Wrest; *Math.*

CHEMBLES, Clothdia Joyce
Booker T Washington HS; Shreveport, LA (26-288) Secy, Drama; Var C; ROTC A; *Computer Operator.*

CHEMINI, Linda Jane
Holliston HS; Holliston, MA (10%-250) Chor; Secy, Drama; Hmrm; NHS; Pres, Rainbow; Mgr, Bkbl; Acad A's; All Star Casts, Drama Competition; *Phys Therapy.*

CHEN, Catherine Tze-Yung
Ingraham HS; Seattle, WA (7-489) Chor; Community Yth Symph; Ensm; Hist A; Hon Prog; *U of Wash; Applied Math.*

CHEN, Gigi Anna
Hunter College HS; Manhattan, NY (10%-249) Ski C; Tnns; COM; NMF; PTA A; Sci A; *U of Pa; Bio.*

CHEN, Iva
Montebello HS; Montebello, CA (80-626) Band; Community Yth Symph; Orch; Phys C; CSF; Opt A; Phy A; PA A; Commendation Ltrs; Cert Typing; *Med.*

CHEN, Jackie
John F Kennedy HS; Tumon, GUAM; NHS; *U of Minn; Ed.*

CHENEY, Lisa Ann
Eureka HS; Eureka, IL (2-130) A Cap Choir; Band; Chor; Ensm; 4H; Hmrm; Madrigal; NHS; SC; VP, Jr Cl; MVP, Sftbl; MVP, Swim; Hon Prog; Ntl Achv Schol; Stu Coun Cert of Service; *Ill Wesleyan U; Mus.*

CHENOWETH, Gary J
Grand Prairie HS; Grand Prairie, TX; Chor; Ftbl; *Baylor U; Sci.*

CHERCHIAN, Arpie Jane
Fairfax HS; Los Angeles, CA; Qn, Missionettes; Mission Bay Marathon; *Christian Col.*

CHEREWKA, Mark
Riverside Jr-Sr HS; Taylor, PA (14-193) NHS; Bkbl; Ftbl; Tr; COM; Hon Prog; Accelerated Cl; WW; *Penn St U; Pre-Med.*

CHERNIN, Elizabeth Mary
Ft Myers HS; Ft Myers, FL (33%-440) Drama; Hmrm; Lat C; Mgr, Swim; Vet Med Explorers; Span A; *Vet Med.*

CHERNOFF, Lee Joseph
Richfield HS; Waco, TX (10%-350) Bus Mgr, Lat C; Tnns; *U of Tex; Optometry.*

CHERRA, Joseph Francis
Riverside Jr Sr HS; Taylor, PA (5-190) Band; CYO; NHS; Span C; JV, Bsbl; Chem A; *Math.*

CHERRY, Ada Elizabeth
Bertie Sr HS; Windsor, NC (8-340) Chor; Pres, Drama; Fr C; VP, FBLA; InterClub Coun; Ed, Sch P; Tres, SC; Delta Sigma Theta A; Hist A; Hon Prog; NEDT; Spch A; Bus Drivers C; Win, WOW Hist A; WW; *U of NC at Chapel Hill; Psych.*

CHERRY, Deirdre Glennette
Danbury HS; Danbury, CT (121-2500) Hmrm; Hon Prog; Type A; *Med.*

CHERRY, Jeanie Grace
Eisenhower HS; Yakima, WA (40-550) Chem C; Ger C; ARC; Ski C; Bkbl; Young Life; Cpt, Quizz Tm; Fin Modeling Cert; *Point Loma Col; Nurs.*

CHERRY, Mark Lee
Eisenhower HS; Yakima, WA (400-500) Band; Bkbl; All Valley Bkbl; *Point Loma Col; Pre-Med.*

CHERRY, Ronald Delno
Bertie Sr HS; Windsor, NC (2-340) BC; Drama; FBLA; FTA; Sci C; Bus Drivers C; WW; First Pl, St Conv Data Processing; *NC St U; Engr.*

CHESHIRE, Kenneth Lawrence
Wakulla HS; Crawfordville, FL; Band; Chor; Drama; Orch; Pres, Thes; WW; *Fla Sou Col; Mus.*

CHESLOCK, Terri Renea
Fairmont Sr HS; Fairmont, WV (19-264) Band; Chor; Ensm; Hmrm; Mjrte; SC; Keyette; *Fairmont St Col; Secy.*

CHESLOCK, Twyla
Fairmont Sr HS; Fairmont, WV (13-240) Band; Chor; Ensm; GS; InterClub Coun; Madrigal; Cpt, Mjrte; NHS; SC; Coun of Teach A; Kiwanis A; Pres A; Star Student; Pres, Keywanette C; Winter Formal Qn; *Fairmont St Col; Nurs.*

CHESNES, Albert A
Palm Beach Gardens HS; Palm Beach Gardens, FL; Wrest.

CHESNEY, Barbara Ann
Horace Maynard HS; Maynardville, TN; BC; Chor; FHA; 4H; Rptr, SC; *Nurs.*

CHESNEY, Susan Marie
Sunbright HS; Sunbright, TN (7-63) Co-Ed, Ann; Band; BC; Chor; FHA; 4H; F-Ed, Sch P; Rptr, Sci C; B Crocker A; 4H A; MLS; Most Studious; *U of Tenn; Biol.*

CHESNUT, John Wesley
E Clinton HS; Lees Creek, OH (13-131) Band; Chess C; Chor; Dbte Tm; Yth Fel; *Cincinnati Bible Seminary; Ministry.*

CHESNUTT, Patsy Lynn
Harlingen HS; Harlingen, TX (5-650) A Cap Choir; Co-Ed, Ann; Band; Chor; Ensm; Hmrm; Key C; Madrigal; NHS; SC; Bkbl; Semi-Fin, Tnns; COM; Yth Fel; Eng A; All Region Choir, Band; 2nd Pl, District Talent Show; Exchange Stu, Germany; *Baylor U; Mus Theory.*

CHESSER, Bruce Wayne
Choctaw HS; Choctaw, OK (11-250) Bio A; Citz A; Sci A; *Bio.*

CHESSER, Lori Alice
Robert E Lee Sr HS; Jacksonville, FL; A Cap Choir; Chor; Ensm; FHA; Hmrm; Madrigal; SC; Tri-HiY; Parl, Sr Cl; *Teaching.*

CHESSON, Curtis Earl
Plymouth HS; Plymouth, NC (2-30) Jr Cl; Sftbl; MVP, Wrest; Wrest A; Bible Sch A.

CHESSON, Doug Mark
Williamston HS; Williamston, NC (13-200) Band; Pres, Demolay; Fr C; Hmrm; VP, Key C; Monogram; NHS; SC; Pres, Jr Cl; JV, Ftbl; Tnns; Jr-Sr Waiter; *U of NC; Bus.*

CHEST, Carl Martin
Shawnee HS; Louisville, KY; NHS; SC; Ftbl; Most Outst Art Stu; *Art.*

CHESTANG, Edwin Kelley
McIntosh HS; McIntosh, AL (4-90) Ann; Co-Ch, Chor; Rptr, FFA; 4H; NHS; F-Ed, Sch P; SC; 4H A; Hon Prog; Spch A; *Mobile Col.*

CHESTER, Daniel
Carroll HS; Fort Wayne, IN (179-259) Chldr; Ch, Hmrm; Ski C; Span C; SC; Bkbl; Tr; *USC; Law.*

CHESTNUT, LaVerne Inez
East HS; Buffalo, NY (9-330) Chldr; VP, NHS; SC; COM; Hon Prog; Regent Schol; St Scholar; *Buffalo St Col; Computer Tech.*

CHETTLEBURGH, Shari Diane
Forest Hills Central HS; Grand Rapids, MI (25-300) Band; Ensm; Math A; Pep C; Bowl Tm; *Northern Mich U; Psych.*

CHEUNG, Joseph Bong
John F Kennedy HS; Sacramento, CA; *Calif Polytech U; Archt.*

CHEVAKO, Jane Ann
Dominican HS; Whitefish Bay, WI (4-176) NHS; Span C; Bkbl; Sftbl; Tr; Bio A; Chem A; Hon Prog; Math A; Phy A; Poet A; Sci A; Vlbl; Span A; WW; *UW-Milwaukee; Med.*

CHEVALIER, Richard Lee
Western Hills HS; Ft Worth, TX; Math C; Order/ Arrow; Soccer; *U of Tex; Computer Sci.*

CHEVALLIER, Darlene Renee
West HS; Knoxville, TN (13-240) Drama; Fr C; FHA; InterAct C; NHS; *Tenn Tech U; Spec Ed.*

CHEVOYA, Renee Alyce
Arroyo Grande HS; Arroyo Grande, CA (66-450) A Cap Choir; Chor; Ensm; St Scholar; Lib, A Cappella Choir; GAA; S-T, Christian C; Vocal Mus A; *Fresno Pacific Col; Mus.*

CHEVRON, Sally Jo
Hood River Valley HS; Hood River, OR (25%-260) Co-Ed, Ann; Band; 4H; Bsbl; Sftbl; 4H A; Drill Tm A; *Acct.*

CHEW, Thelma Ann
St Matthew HS; Melrose, LA; Bus C; FBLA; Alg A; Hon Prog; Chldr A; *Grambling St U; Law Enforcement.*

CHIARIELLO, Tami Lee
Vista HS; Vista, CA; NHS; ARC; A-Ed, Sch P; Bkbl; CSF; COM; Citz A; Hon Prog; Math A; ARC A; Yth Fel; Eng A; PA A; Academic Excellence; Timothy A; Ntl Span Exam; *LABC.*

CHICHESTER, Douglas Curt
Charlotte Valley Central Sch; Davenport, NY (6-41) Pres, NHS; VP, Var C; VP, Sr Cl; Soccer; Tr; *St U of NY; Sci.*

CHICHESTER, Nanette Sue
Potsdam Central HS; Potsdam, NY (5-200) Chor; NHS; Sch P; Cr-Ctry; Co-Cpt, Tr; Regent Schol; Talented Jrs Prog; Span A; *Nazareth Col of Rochester; Span.*

CHICK, Philip Gregory
St Thomas Aquinas HS; Louisville, OH (30-188) Band; Hmrm; Lat C; Ski C; Hon Prog; Ad Altare Dei; Pope Pius XII; *Bus.*

CHIFFIN, David John
Santa Anna HS; Santa Anna, TX; Ann; BC; Parl, Bus C; Drama; Sci C; Cr-Ctry; Ftbl; Golf; Tr; Chamber of Comm A; Citz A; Lion A; Sal; *Cisco Jr Col.*

CHILCOAT, Judith Ellen
Stanton Comm Sch; Stanton, NE (6-54) Ed, Ann; Pres, Band; Chor; Community Yth Symph; Drama; FHA; VP, Ger C; Ed, Sch P; Cpt, Jr Cl; Tr; B Crocker A; Ntl Merit Schol Commended Stu; *Doane Col.*

CHILDERS, Charles Scott
Gaffney Sr HS; Gaffney, SC (10-500) BC; SC; Cpt, Ftbl; Tr; Gr Marshal; *Clemson Col; Archt.*

CHILDERS, David Wayne
S Iredell HS; Statesville, NC (15-230) Co-Ed, Ann; BC; Chess C; Chor; Dbte Tm; Ensm; Fr C; Key C; Academic A; Outdoors C; NC Forestry Camp; Pres, Yth Group; Hon Schol Western Carolina; *Western Carolina Col; Hist.*

CHILDERS, Kevin Allen
Sweet Home HS; Sweet Home, OR (60-220) Band; Chess C; Drama; Order/Arrow; Wrest; *Phys Sci.*

CHILDERS,
 Morna Alyssa Luisa
Interlochen Arts Acad; Interlochen, MI (5-106) Cpt, Chor; Ch, Hmrm; Secy, SC; COM; Schol Art A; *Rice U; Engr.*

CHILDERS, Patrice Marcia
Lake Clifton Sr HS; Baltimore, MD (10%-600) JETS; NHS; Orch; Alg A; Bio A; COM; Hist A; Hon Prog; Math A; Sci A; PA; Eng A.

CHILDERS, Paula Carole
York Comp HS; York, SC (15-240) Chldr; Drama; FBLA; InterClub Coun; Rptr, NHS; Sci C; Pres, Span C; Var C; Beauty; Jr Marshal; WW; *Winthrop Col; Psych.*

CHILDERS, Sara Frances
Gaffney Sr HS; Gaffney, SC; BC; Fr C; Bkbl; Sftbl; Citz A; Yth Fel; Pep C; *Clemson U.*

CHILDERS, Tammy Denise
York Comp HS; York, SC (23-240) Drama; Secy, FBLA; Ch, Hmrm; VP, Span C; SC; Cl Fav; HCt; *Winthrop Col; Secretarial.*

CHILDRESS, Brenda Kay
E Central HS; Tulsa, OK (130-600) Band; Span C; *Bethany Nazarene Col; Occupational Therapy.*

CHILDRESS, Cathryn
J O Johnson HS; Huntsville, AL (250-600) A Cap Choir; Chor; Drama; FHA; Span C; Creative Writing, Vocal Solo, A's; *U of Ala; Hist.*

CHILDRESS, Michael Ray
Hazlewood HS; Town Creek, AL (10-37) Rptr, Ann; Band; BC; Drama; Sch P; Bsbl; JV, Bkbl; Individual & Ensm Mus Medals; Beta C Cert, Band A's; Outst Girl, Jr NHS; *Lubbock Christian Col; Bus.*

CHILDRESS, Pamela Denise
Levelland HS; Levelland, TX (5%-200) Co-Ed, Ann; Pres, Band; Chess C; Ensm; FHA; Hmrm; Mjrte; NHS; SC; Bkbl; Tr; COM; Type A; Drum Major; Outst Little Sister; Stu Christian Assn; Band A's; Outst Girl, Jr NHS; *Lubbock Christian Col; Bus.*

CHILDRESS, Penny Kay
W Ottawa HS; Holland, MI; HR; *Art.*

CHILDRESS, Venice
Charles B Glenn HS; Birmingham, AL; *Med.*

CHILDREY, Cynthia Ann
Halifax Co Sr HS; S Boston, VA; Chor; GS; Pres, Hmrm; Mod Mus Mas; Secy, NHS; NEDT.

CHILDS, Cory Jonathan
Southeast HS; Wichita, KS; Order/Arrow; Ftbl; Order/Arrow; Coin C; Sr Patrol Ldr; *Harding Col; Bus.*

CHILDS, Danny
Randolph Co Comprehensive HS; Cuthbert, GA; A Cap Choir; FFA; 4H; Parl, Tri-HiY; Cpt, Ftbl; Most Outst, Choir; Vocation A; Royal Ambassador A; *Drafting.*

CHILDS, Derrick Edward
E St Louis Sr HS; E St Louis, IL (76-1036) Bsbl; Co-Cpt, Ftbl; COM; Math A; Most Out; *U of Ind; Industrial Arts.*

CHILDS, Janice Elaine
Pepperell HS; Lindale, GA; Cpt, Chldr; FHA; Hmrm; NHS; Rainbow; SC; Tres, Jr Cl; Tres, Soph Cl; Cl Fav; 4H A; Hon Prog; Most Out; ARC A; Most Spirited; Top 10%.

CHILDS, Nanette Louise
August Marfin HS; New York City, NY (33%-700) Chor; ARC; Sci C; ARC A; Church Commendation; Vlbl; *Houghton Col; Pre-Med.*

CHILDS, Patricia Ruth
Edward Tilden HS; Chicago, IL (14-408) Chldr; Chor.

CHILDS, Ruth Ann
Wilcox Co HS; Rochelle, GA (2-97) Ann; Pres, BC; FBLA; Lit Ral; Sch P; Span C; SC; Parl, Soph Cl; COM; Gr Marshal; HCt; Hon Prog; Yth Leg.

CHILES, Vicky Ruth
Lee's Summit Sr HS; Lees Summit, MO (124-514) A Cap Choir; Band; Chor; Ensm; Fr C; Orch; Y-Tns; Sftbl; Citz A; Outst Y-Tn; 1 Rating, Mus Contest; *Mo W St Col; Mus.*

CHILLE, Joseph Francis
St Joseph Parochial HS; Hammonton, NJ (3-48) Chess C; Chor; Drama; FTA; Parl, Hmrm; NHS; SC; Parl, Jr Cl; VP, Soph Cl; Mgr, Bkbl; Hist A; Hon Prog; Mgr, Stage Crew; Pres, Photography C; Principal's List; WW; *Rutgers U; Theatrical Production.*

CHILSON, Becky Lou
Shenandoah Valley Acad; New Market, VA; Drama; *Sou Missionary Col; Secy.*

CHILTON, Laurie Raye
Hemet HS; Hemet, CA; Band; Drama; FFA; Orch; Arch; *Taft Jr Col; Agr.*

CHILTON, Patricia Kay
Edgewood HS; W Covina, CA (56-441) CSF; Worth Adv, Rainbow Girls; Grand Cross of Color; Grand Page; *Calif St Polytech U; Ed.*

CHIN, Edwin T
Avon HS; Avon, MA (19-98) Fr C; Soccer; *U of NH; Agr Engr.*

CHIN, Noreen Sue
Skyline HS; Oakland, CA; Ann; Orch; SC; CSF; *Hayward St U; Arts.*

CHIN, Peggy
Sutter HS; Sutter, CA (9-165) Band; Sci C; Span C; JV, Hockey; CSF; Hon Prog; Band A; *UOP; Phar.*

CHIN, Silvia S
Newport HS; Bellevue, WA (50-400) Orch; Co- ch, Yth Fel; Special Aides Service C; *U of Wash; Med.*

CHIN, Teresa Sue
Skyline HS; Oakland, CA; InterClub Coun; Orch; SC; Pres, Jr Cl; CSF; MLS; Gym.

CHING, Catherine Taka
Kailua HS; Kailua, HI (63-570) Chldr; HiY; Secy, Sr Cl; Tres, Soph Cl; HQn; HCt; Most Out; Sgt at Arms, Jr Cl; Soph Most Spirited Trophy.

CHINN, Adrienne Mary
Alexander Galt Regional HS; Lennoxville, CANADA (18-539) CYO; Drama; ARC; Ch, SC; Hon Prog; Home Ec A; Hostesses; Prom Comm; Stu Quiz Show; Travel C; *Champlain Col.*

CHINN, Annette Elizabeth
James Monroe HS; Fredericksburg, VA (33-159) Fr C; FTA; Lat C; NHS; Sftbl; Swim; Hon Prog; Tn Coun; *Radford St Col; Lib Sci.*

CHINN, Elizabeth Kay
South Shelby HS; Shebina, MO (2-101) Chor; Ensm; Hmrm; Madrigal; NHS; SC; Secy, Sr Cl; Hon Prog; MLS; Regent Schol; Sal; *Northeast Mo Teachers Assn Schol; Northeast Mo St U; Pol Sci.*

CHINN, Karen Susan
Westchester HS; Los Angeles, CA (25-590) A Cap Choir; GS; CSF; Hon Prog; Journ A; Ntl Sci Found; Spch A; Gold Seal Bearer; *U of Sou Calif; Math.*

CHIODO, Vincent Michael
Madonna HS; Weirton, WV (8-112) Ann; BS; CYO; Drama; Pres, 4H; VP, InterAct C; Bus Mgr, Lit Mag; Pres, Math C; Pres, NHS; Rptr, Sch P; Sci C; SC; Thes; Amer Leg A; Chem A; 4H A; Hon Prog; Sci A; WW; Reader's Digest Ldrship A; Statist & Announcer, Bkbl & Ftbl; *W Va U; Chem.*

CHIODRAS, Ronald Scot
Downers Grove N HS; Downers Grove, IL (82-515) Band; Chess C; Drama; Swim; *Col of Du-Page; Bus.*

CHIPMAN, Terri Lynn
Kalamazoo Central HS; Kalamazoo, MI (112-517) ARC; Mgr, Bkbl; Citz A; ARC A; Yth Fel; Pres, Sr HS UMYF; Ed Commission; Chrch Yth Coordin; Appalachia Serv; Adm Board; Ch, Yth Coun; Co On Minist; Chrch Rep Hunger Sem; *Concordia Lutheran Col; Special Ed.*

CHISHOLM, Ellis
Arts HS; Newark, NJ; Band; Ensm; Orch; COM; Yth Fel; BSct; Tutor.

CHISHOLM, Rosena
Arts HS; Newark, NJ (2-165) Community Yth Symph; Ensm; Hmrm; NHS; Orch; SC; Secy, Var C; Sftbl; Delta Sigma Theta A; Hon Prog; MLS; Sal; *Monmouth Col; Elec Engr.*

CHISM, Roger Harrell
S Pontotoc HS; Pontotoc, MS (10-90) Pres, BC; BS; Bsbl; Bkbl; Ftbl; Citz A; *Itawamba Jr Col; Bio.*

CHISM, William Bradford
Tonica Inst of Learning; Tunica, MS (1-30) BC; Chem C; Hmrm; Lat C; Pres, SC; Var C; Pres, Soph Cl; Bkbl; Ftbl; COM; Cl Fav; Hist A; Hon Prog; 3rd in St, Eng, 3rd in Dist, Math; MPSA.

CHITTMAN, Carolyn Elaine
Shenandoah Valley Acad; New Market, VA; A Cap Choir; NHS; Ftbl; Soccer; Cpt, Sftbl; COM; Pres A; *Columbia Union Col; Phys Therapy.*

CHITWOOD, Joy Elaine
Ben Davis HS; Indianapolis, IN (510-870) Drama; 4H; Hmrm; Span C; Spch C; SC; Swim; Tr; Citz A; 4H A; Spch A; Type A; *Milligan Col; Dentistry.*

CHIU, Christi Lee
Robert A Millikan HS; Long Beach, CA; Lat C; Pres A; JV, Badminton.

CHIU, George M J
John F Kennedy HS; Agana, GUAM; Bkbl; Japanese C; Chinese C; *U of Mich; Law.*

CHIU, Lori Mai
Robert A Millikan HS; Long Beach, CA; Pres A; Special Ed.

CHO, Eric Choonik
Fremont HS; Fremont, IA (2-25) Band; Industrial Arts A; Piano Contest; Eng A; Art A; *Oral Robert U; Engr.*

CHO, Helen Mihae
Masters HS; Dobbs Ferry, NY (30-75) Chor; InterClub Coun; Bkbl; Swim; Journ A; Art As; *Princeton U; Hist.*

CHO, Hyun
Glen Rock HS; Glen Rock, NJ (25%-200) Chess C; Math C; Phys C; JV, Soccer; JV, Wrest; Bicycle C; Bio Tm; Jr NHS; Marine Phys Achv A; *Cornel U; Sci.*

CHO, Kwang Yun
George Washington HS; Denver, CO; *Colo U of Boulder; Econ.*

CHO, Tchan Hee
John F Kennedy HS; Bronx, NY; NHS; *Columbia U; Med.*

CHOAT, Daniel Lynn
Cedar Rapids HS; Cedar Rapids, NE; Chor; Rptr, 4H; Bsbl; JV, Bkbl; Ftbl; 4H A; *U of Nebr-Lincoln; Agr.*

CHOATE, Ada Louise
Panhandle HS; Panhandle, TX (50%-61) FHA; Bkbl; Tr; Home Ec A; *St Philip's Comm Col; Phys Therapy Asst.*

CHOATE, Daniel Louis
Leto HS; Tampa, FL; Band; NHS; Ftbl; Tr.

CHOATE, Teri Beth
Slaton HS; Slaton, TX; Band; FHA; *Vernon Jr Col; Bus.*

CHOATE, Wesley Ray
Anna-Jonesboro HS; Anna, IL (9-160) Ann; Pres, Key C; Pres, Soph Cl; Bsbl; Bkbl; Ftbl; JV, Tr; Amer Leg A; HCt; MLS.

CHOCHOLOUSEK, Sandra Lynn
Gregory Ind Sch; Gregory, SD (25%-61) Band; Ensm; Orch; Amer Leg A; Hon Prog; Q&S A; All St Band; I Ratings; Piano Contest; *Augustana Col; Mus.*

CHODOR, Vince Rocco
Kelly HS; Chicago, IL (12-476) NHS; Span NHS; Bsbl; JV, Ftbl; Bkbl; *Bradley U; Bus Adm.*

CHOE, Anne Hanna
Chester HS; Chester, PA; Cpt, Chor; Ed, Ensm; Math C; Tres, Tnns; Tres, Tr; I Dare You; MLS; Art A; *Widener Col; Biol.*

CHOFFEL, Mary Lou
Cochranton Jr Sr HS; Cochranton, PA (69-100) Band; Chor.

CHOI, Hye Kyong
George Washington Sr HS; Denver, CO; Chor; NHS; Phar.

CHOI, Kihwa
Luther Burbank Jr HS; Los Angeles, CA;

CHOI, Kisook
Franklin HS; Los Angeles, CA; *Glendale Col; Nurs.*

CHOI, Kwan Hong
Palisades Park Jr-Sr HS; Palisades Park, NJ (7%-160) Math C; NHS; Tnns; *Rutgers Col; Bio.*

CHOI, Michael Jin
The Buckley Sch; Sherman Oaks, CA; *Yale Col.*

CHOICE, Charles Jr
Newark HS; Newark, OH (300-600) Var C; Cpt, Bkbl; Tr; *Mt Vernon of Nazarene Col; Bus Adm.*

CHOICE, Myrtle Deanna
Newark Sr HS; Newark, OH; All Amer Yth; Band; Chor; Secy, City Conf; Fin, GS; 4H; Hmrm; InterClub Coun; K of C; Span C; Cpt, Var C; VP, Y-Tns; MVP, Bsbl; Cpt, Bkbl; Sftbl; Co-Cpt, Tr; COM; Cl Fav; Most Out; Yth Fel; Yth Foundation; Secy, Y-Tns; Yth Qn; HS All-Amer; MVP, Varsity C; Cpt, Vlbl; St Champion, Long Jump; Fresh Found; *Ohio State University; Physical Education.*

CHOKAN, Jeannine Therese
St Joseph Acad; Cleveland, OH (10%-280) Band; Secy, CYO; Hmrm; NHS; ARC; Sci C; Ski C; Bsbl; Bkbl; COM; JA A; Sci A; 1st Cl, Sr, Marian A, GScts; *St Mary's Col; Sci.*

CHOMIAK, Robert Thomas
Uniontown Area Sr HS; Uniontown, PA; Ger C; Key C; Math C; Bsbl; Chamber of Comm A.

CHOMNUK, Nina Louise
Pottstown Sr HS; Pottstown, PA (50-282) Cpt, Band; Chor; Drama; Lit Mag; Madrigal; Ski C; Span C; SC; Thes; Hon Prog; JA A; Yth Fel; *Hood Col; Pol Sci.*

CHONG, Jodi Lehualani
Kailua HS; Kailua, HI; Chldr; Chor; HCt; *U of Hawaii; Travel Industry.*

CHONG, Tim Ting
Roosevelt HS; Seattle, WA (119-415) Chor; COM; Mus.*

CHOPSON, Mark Kevin
Terre Haute S Vigo HS; Terre Haute, IN (174-625) Bsbl; Bkbl; Cr-Ctry; Tnns; COM; H of F; *ISU; Journ.*

CHOUINARD, Johanne Linda
Alexander Galt Regional HS; Lennoxville, CANADA (9-539) Hon Prog; Type A; Mus; *Sci.*

CHOUINARD, Marie Noelle
College De Ste Anne De La Pocatiere; La Pocatiere, CANADA (1-31) *Ste-Anne-La-Pocatiere; Sci Sante.*

CHOUINARD, Valerie Kay
Lincoln Co HS; Winfield, MO; FBLA; Operational Data Processing A.

CHOW, Diane
Hiram W Johnson Sr HS; Sacramento, CA (6-809) Hmrm; InterClub Coun; Secy, Math C; NHS; Sci C; CSF; Asian Culture C; Pres, Kiwanettes; *U of Calif; Ed.*

CHOW, Mark Alan
Archbold HS; Archbold, OH (40-135) Chor; Hon Prog; HR; Span A.

CHOW, Teresa Ann
Archbold HS; Archbold, OH (44-141) Chor; FHA; 4H; Thes; *Taylor U; Dietetics.*

CHOW, Yen-Lu
Kubasaki HS; Okinawa, JAPAN (4-271) Pres, Mu Alpha Theta; NHS; Tnns; Alg A; Fr A; Analysis A; Calculus A; *Engr.*

CHRISMAN, Karen Sue
Centennial HS; Pueblo, CO (78-352) Lit Mag; Y-Tns; S-T, Bsbl; Tr; COM; Citz A; JA A; ARC A; Spirit C; Ath Ltr A; Cert of Hon; Phys Fitness A; Service A, Block C; *Sociology.*

CHRISMAN, Paula Joyce
Eastern Hills HS; Fort Worth, TX; A Cap Choir; Bkbl; Tr; Citz A; JV, Vlbl; *Tex Weslen Col.*

CHRISMER, Cynthia Lou
Wapakoneta Sr HS; Wapakoneta, OH (55-358) Chor; Rainbow; Sch P; Span C; Sftbl; *Bowling Green Stu; Art.*

CHRIST, Jana Lynn
Grand Junction Central HS; Grand Junction, CO (250-320) Chor; NHS; JV, Tnns; COM; Outst Schol Achv; *NW Nazarene Col; Mus.*

CHRISTEN, Christine Elisabeth
Oakland-Craig Pub Sch; Oakland, NE (30-47) Ann; Chldr; Chor; Dbte Tm; Drama; FHA; Spch C; SC; Secy, Sr Cl; COM; Hon Prog; Pres A; Spch A; 1st Cl GSct; Superior Rating, Vocal Soloist; VP, G Sct Coun Steering Comm; *Midland Lutheran Col; Journ.*

CHRISTEN, Daniel James
Bishop Ryan HS; Minot, ND (10-77) BS; Pres, Key C; NHS; Mgr, Ftbl; MVP, Wrest; HCt; Hon Prog; *Minot St Col; Bus.*

CHRISTENBERRY, Cindy Lou
Red Lion Area Sr HS; Red Lion, PA; FHA; NHS.

CHRISTENBURY, Donna Gail
Harding HS; Charlotte, NC (10%-340) Band; NHS; Secy, Sci C; Span C; Bio A; Citz A.

CHRISTENSEN, Amy Louise
Robert E Lee HS; Baytown, TX (5-411) Pres, AFS; Secy, Anchor C; Pres, Fr C; French NHS; Hmrm; InterClub Coun; NHS; Co-Cpt, Swim; Cl Fav; Magna Cum Laude; NMF; WW; NCTE Writing A; 1st Dist Ready-Writing; *Rice U; Pre-Law.*

CHRISTENSEN, Brian Keith
Hayfield Secondary Sch; Alexandria, VA (22-465) FBLA; Order/Arrow; Wrest; B Crocker A; *Brigham Young U; Engr.*

CHRISTENSEN, Cheryl Janette
W Waterloo HS; Waterloo, IA (10%-500) Band; Chor; Fr C.

CHRISTENSEN, Chris
Glenbrook HS N; Northbrook, IL (79-714) Chor; Mgr, Soccer; Hon Prog; Most Out; GSct Sign o-t Arrow; GSct Sign o-t Star; *U of Iowa; Psych.*

CHRISTENSEN, Dean Douglas
N Clackamas Christian Sch; Oregon City, OR; A Cap Choir; Chor; Drama; Hmrm; Pres, Jr Cl; Bkbl; Cpt, Soccer; Outst Choir Member; *Mus.*

CHRISTENSEN, Eileen Fae
Sooner HS; Bartlesville, OK (10-280) Drama; FBLA; NHS; Rep, Energy Awareness Sym; *Central St.*

CHRISTENSEN, Gary James
Normal Comm HS; Normal, IL; *ISU; Math.*

CHRISTENSEN, Glenn David
Normandy HS; Parma, OH (25%-630) Band; Ensm; Orch; JV, Ftbl; Bsbl League; Church Bkbl; HR; Service A.

CHRISTENSEN, Jerome Joseph
Herscher HS; Herscher, IL (42-215) Band; VP, 4H; JV, Ftbl; Wrest; 4H A; *U of Ill; Wrest Coach.*

CHRISTENSEN, Karen Lynn
Woodway HS; Edmonds, WA; Bus C; Community Yth Symph; Drama; Hmrm; NHS; Orch; Ski C; VP, SC; Mgr, Bsbl; Sftbl; COM; Hon Prog; JA A; Kiwanis A; PTA A; Poet A; Yth Fel; Yth Leg; Secy, SC.

CHRISTENSEN, Linda Sue
John Marshall HS; Indianapolis, IN (49-425) Drama; NHS; SC; Co-Cpt, Bkbl; Sftbl; MVP, Tnns; Hon Prog; Co-Cpt, Vlbl; *Wishard Mem Hosp; Nurs.*

CHRISTENSEN, Lisa Anne
Ojai Valley Sch; Ojai, CA; Soccer; Bio A; *Briarcliff Col; Sci.*

CHRISTENSEN, Lisa Marie
La Canada HS; La Canada, CA (50-500) Ski C; Cpt, Soccer; Swim; CSF; *U of Calif at Santa Barbara; Fashion Design.*

CHRISTENSEN, Lori Anne
Minden HS; Minden, NE (2-97) Band; Chor; FHA; Sftbl; Yth Fel; Vlbl; Gold Laurel.

CHRISTENSEN, Mark Alan
Lodgepole HS; Lodgepole, NE (3-16) Band; Fin, BS; Chor; Ensm; Pres, 4H; Orch; Pres, Jr Cl; Pres, Soph Cl; Bkbl; Co-Cpt, Ftbl; 4H A; Hon Prog; NMS; Regent Schol; Yth Fel; Pres, Fresh Cl; Union Pacific, ROTC, Schol's; Pres, Church Yth; Pres, 'L' C; *02800003.*

CHRISTENSEN, Marlene Kay
Bushnell Pub Sch; Bushnell, NE (1-8) Chldr; Tres, Chor; Ensm; Pres, 4H; Monogram; Ed, Sch P; S-T, SC; Var C; Y-Tns; VP, Soph Cl; Cpt, Bkbl; Tr; COM; Citz A; Hon Prog; Jr Chamber of Com A; Lion A; Poet A; Yth Fel; WW; Role, Sch Play; Cpt, Vlbl; *Doane Col.*

CHRISTENSEN, Melissa Joy
Lynnville-Sully HS; Sully, IA (20-75) Co-Ed, Ann; Band; Sch P; Mgr, Bkbl; Sftbl; HCt; *DesMoines Area Comm Col; Acct.*

CHRISTENSEN, Pamela Kay
Palmyra HS; Palmyra, WI (2-73) Ann; Band; Chor; Drama; 4H; NHS; Sch P; SC; COM; 4H A; Hon Prog; Math A; Sal; Sci A; John Philips Sousa A; *U of Whitewater; Bio.*

CHRISTENSEN, Paulette Kay
Elk Horn-Kimballton Comm HS; Elk Horn, IA (2-32) Band; Chldr; Drama; Mjrte; NHS; Pres, SC; Pres, Sr Cl; Sal; St Scholar; Type A; Campus Ldr; Dane of Fame; John Philip Sousa A; Al-Am Bnd A; Iowa St U Recogn; US Collegiate Wind Band; *Iowa St U; Elem Ed.*

CHRISTENSEN, Richard Carl
Glendale HS; Glendale, CA (350-596) A Cap Choir; Band; Orch; JV, Swim; Drum Major; Water Polo; 1st Pl, United Spirit Assn; 1st Pl, Kiwanis C Parade.

CHRISTENSEN, Robert Louis
Rogers Sr HS; Michigan City, IN (110-545) A Cap Choir; Cpt, CYO; Pres, Chor; Secy, Commercial C; Drama; Madrigal; JV, Tnns; Chem A; JA A; Gold & Silver Medal, Vocal Comp; Church Yth Organization; *Purdue U; Arts & Sci.*

CHRISTENSEN, Terri Lyn
Minden Pub HS; Minden, NE (27-90) Band; Chor; FHA; Spch C; Thes; Purple Laurel; *U of Nebr; Mus.*

CHRISTENSEN, Todd Allen
Gregory Pub HS; Gregory, SD (12-53) Band; BS; Chor; Tr; *Law Enforcement.*

CHRISTENSON, Ann Claire
Forrest City HS; Forrest City, AR (26-358) BC; Math C; Ed, Sch P; Pres A; Yth Fel; *U of Ark; Bus.*

CHRISTENSON, Dawn Sheila
Winona Sr HS; Winona, MN (40-558) Chor; VP, Soph Cl; Vlbl; Skiing; DeMolay Swtht; *Art.*

CHRISTENSON, Kay Renee
Hastings Sr HS; Hastings, MN (64-467) AFS; Chor; *Augsburg Col; Sociology.*

CHRISTIAENS, Marlene Clara
Willibrord Cath HS; Chicago, IL (2-79) Cpt, Chldr; Secy, Fr C; French NHS; Hmrm; Math C; NHS; Pres, Sci C; SC; Soccer; Tnns; Alg A; COM; Chem A; Hon Prog; Math A; Sal; Sci A; St Scholar; WW; *U of Ill; Math.*

CHRISTIAENS, Pat Joseph
North Toole County HS; Sunburst, MT (6-35) Band; BS; CYO; Pres, Hmrm; Math C; Secy, Monogram; NHS; Sci C; Pres, SC; Secy, Var C; Pres, Jr Cl; Bkbl; MVP, Ftbl; Sftbl; Amer Leg A; NEDT; Top 10% NEDT; *Carroll Col; Optometry.*

CHRISTIAN, Angela Ruth
Booker T Washington HS; Atlanta, GA (12-345) Ann; Secy, Band; CYO; Secy, Model UN; NHS; Ch, SC; UN Council; VP, Soph Cl; COM; Chem A; Hon Prog; Ntl Sci Found; NEDT; Sci A; St A, Russian; *Sci.*

CHRISTIAN, Ann Carol
Darlington Sch; Rome, GA (15%-121) Band; Cpt, Chldr; Math C; SC; Tri-HiY; Sftbl; Swim; Explorers; *Shorter Col.*

CHRISTIAN, Ann Coraly
James Monroe HS; Bronx, NY; FTA; Citz A; *Pace Col; Nurs.*

CHRISTIAN, Bruce Edward
Farmington HS; Farmington, MI; Tr; *Oakland Comm Col; Police Adm.*

CHRISTIAN, Charles Irving
Northeastern HS; Detroit, MI (2-203) NHS; Cpt, Bkbl; Cpt, Ftbl; Tr; Citz A; Cl Fav; H of F; All City Bkbl & Ftbl; *U of Mich; Comm Art.*

CHRISTIAN, Colleen June
Claremont HS; Claremont, CA (11-424) AFS; Ch, Chldr; Fin, GS; Tres, Key C; Orch; Sci C; Tnns; CSF; Gen Mills A; *UCLA; Biochem.*

CHRISTIAN, David Chandler
Anniston HS; Anniston, AL (20-400) Ed, Ann; VP, BC; Chor; Secy, HiY; VP, SC; Swim; Tnns; Alg A; Bio A; COM; DARGCA; Math A; MLS; NEDT; Opt A; Yth Fel; Yth Leg; Statesmanship A; *Auburn U; Archt.*

CHRISTIAN, David Curtis
R-I N Callaway HS; Kingdom City, MO (15-73) Ann; Chor; Drama; Fr C; FFA; Spch C; Pres, SC; Tres, Var C; Bkbl; Co-Cpt, Ftbl; Tr; Citz A; MVP, Ftbl; Sch Sportsmanship A; Christmas Dance Kg; WW; *NE Mo St U at Kirksville; Law Enforcement.*

CHRISTIAN, David Dale
Man HS; Man, WV (10-180) Rptr, Ann; Band; Pres, Chess C; Drama; Ensm; VP, InterAct C; NHS; ARC; Sci C; Span C; Thes; Var C; Co-Cpt, Tnns; COM; Cl Fav; Hist A; MLS; VofDEM; Yth Fel; All Area, All Co, Band; Best Mus, Photography, A's; *W Va U; Biol.*

CHRISTIAN, Dennis Jay
Hubbard HS; Hubbard, TX; FFA; COM.

CHRISTIAN, Ellen Kincaid
Gladewater HS; Gladewater, TX (10%-180) Ann; Dbte Tm; Drama; VP, Fr C; VP, FHA; FTA; Lit Mag; Fin, NFL; Spch C; Thes; Secy, Jr Cl; Secy, Soph Cl; Golf; Tnns; Tr; Poet A; Spch A; *Tex A&M U; Animal Psych.*

CHRISTIAN, Gwenda Gay
Oak Hill HS; Oak Hill, OH (11-100) Band; Cpt, Chldr; Chor; S-T, Lat C; NHS; Co-Ed, Sch P; Pres, Tri-HiY; Var C; DARGCA; Val; 4th of July Qn Court; *Ohio St U; Phar.*

CHRISTIAN, Lisa Michelle
E Ridge HS; E Ridge, TN (31-300) Ann; Secy, BC; Tres, Chor; Madrigal; NHS; SC; Thes; VP, Tri-HiY; ROTC A; ETEA Chor; *Nurs.*

CHRISTIAN, Philip Riley
Mendel Cath Prep HS; Chicago, IL (2-75) CYO; Pres, Chldr; Chem C; Pres, Chess C; Cpt, Dbte Tm; Pres, Fr C; Hmrm; K of C; Key C; Pres, NHS; Rptr, Sch P; Sci C; Ski C; Secy, SC; Tr; COM; Hon Prog; Sal; WW; *Howard U; Pre-Med.*

CHRISTIAN, Samuel Jr
Christopher Columbus HS; Bronx, NY; Drama; SC; COM; Hist A; Sci A; Fr Merit, Span Merit, A's; Fr Conf Cert; *Julliards Sch of Mus; Drama.*

CHRISTIAN, Sandra Kaye
Battiest HS; Battiest, OK (2-24) Co-Ed, Ann; VP, Chor; Ensm; FHA; NHS; Up Bound; Pres, Sr Cl; B Crocker A; Gr Marshal; Swtht; Best Dressed Sr; Cl Swtht; 1st Runner-Up, Yrbk Qn; Co-Head Librarian; *Tulsa U.*

CHRISTIAN, Steven Anthony
Anniston HS; Anniston, AL (5-380) A Cap Choir; A-Ed, Ann; Band; BC; Chor; Drama; Pres, HiY; Hmrm; VP, Key C; Bus Mgr, Sch P; Pres, SC; Tnns; COM; Citz A; MLS; NEDT; Opt A; Q&S A; Sci A; Spch A; Yth Leg; Outst Statesman; Yth Legislature Del, Ntl Affairs; *U of Ala; Law.*

CHRISTIANS, Beth Ann
Mt Morris HS; Mt Morris, IL (19-72) Chldr; VP, 4H; SC; Tnns; Tr; 4H A; Hist A; Hon Prog; Yth Fel; Shorthand A; *Robert Morris Col; Legal Secy.*

CHRISTIANSEN, Beth Anne
Stoughton HS; Stoughton, WI (5%-220) Band; Span C; Swim; Yth Fel; WSMA Mus A; Swim A; Awana As; *Moody Bible Inst; Mus.*

CHRISTIANSEN, Birgit Ann
Douglas HS; Douglas, AZ (6-400) Dbte Tm; S-T, 4H; Sch Achieve Tm; F-Ed, Sch P; 4H A; Journ A; Q&S A; *Nurs.*

CHRISTIANSEN, Dale Jay
Regis HS; Stayton, OR (1-60) Chor; VP, NHS; Var C; JV, Bsbl; Ftbl; Math A.

CHRISTIANSEN, Dean Alan
Stoughton Sr HS; Stoughton, WI (12-232) Band; BS; Pres, Ger C; NHS; Sci C; SC; Var C; Pres, Sr Cl; Wrest; Amer Leg A; Hon Prog; John Philip Sousa Band A; WSMA Mus A; *Miami U; Marine Bio.*

CHRISTIANSEN, Nancy Marie
Washington HS; Portland, OR (15-190) A Cap Choir; NHS; Alg A; COM; Citz A; 4H A; Hon Prog; Math A; Church Ensm; Commendable Attendance A.

CHRISTIANSEN, Peggy Jean
Douglas HS; Douglas, AZ (1-336) Chor; Pres, 4H; F-Ed, Lit Mag; Pres, NHS; Pres, ARC; Ed, Sch P; Tres, SC; InterClub Coun; 4H A; MLS; Regent Schol; Spch A; Type A; Val; Alt, GS; NML; Yth Del, Church Gen Assembly; *Trinity U; Foreign Lang.*

CHRISTIANSEN, Richard Brent
Omaha S HS; Omaha, NE; Ger C; Lat C; Sci C; JV, Wrest; COM; Nebr JCL Convention; *U of Nebr; Med.*

CHRISTIANSON, Debra Lynn
Cambridge HS; Cambridge, WI; Pres, FHA; Rptr, Sch P; Type A; *Evangel Col; Special Ed.*

CHRISTIANSON, Susan Marie
Cambridge HS; Cambridge, WI (26-67) Pres, FHA; Bio A; Hist A; Secy, FHA; Pres, 'Y' C; Spade A; Eng A of Merit; Psych Merit A; *Evangel Col; Teaching.*

CHRISTIE, Judy Lynn
James Madison HS; Vienna, VA (55-483) Chldr; Pres, FBLA; Hmrm; NHS; Sftbl; HCt; Type A; Bus Adm; Outst Bus Stu; Outst FBLA Member; Runner-Up, Miss Madison Pageant; 3rd Pl, Reg Clerk-Typist Event; *Radford Col; Bus Adm.*

CHRISTIE, Vivian Suzanne
Marion HS; Marion, IL; Citz A; Lion A; *Home Ec.*

CHRISTMAN, Jan
Neville HS; Monroe, LA (13-158) Community Yth Symph; Ch, InterClub Coun; Rptr, Lat C; Tres, NHS; Pres, Orch; Hist A; Hon Prog; Summa Cum Laude; E L Neville Schol; Jr Tigerette; Chancellor's A; Monroe Symph; Pep Sq; *Auburn U; Elem Ed.*

CHRISTMAN,
Patricia Margaret
Bishop Luers HS; Ft Wayne, IN (23-213) Chor; Hon Prog; JA A; 1st Pl, Nisbova, Solo; 1st Pl, St Solo Contest; *St Mary's Col; Mus.*

CHRISTMAN, Teresa Elizabeth
Clintonville HS; Clintonville, WI (11-200) AFS; Dbte Tm; Drama; Ensm; Tres, Fr C; GS; Pres, 4H; Math C; NFL; NHS; Bsbl; 4H A; Hon Prog; Journ A; Spch A; Type A; Flag Twirling; Pep C.

CHRISTMAS, Harriett Jeanette
Cary Sr HS; Cary, NC; Ger C; *Wayne Comm Col; Dental Asst.*

CHRISTMON, Horace Jay Jr
Kashmere Sr HS; Houston, TX; Chor; Var C; Ftbl; Tr; Art, Ftbl, A's; JV Trophy; *Tex A&M U; Bus Adm.*

CHRISTMON, Horace Jr
Kashmere Sr HS; Houston, TX; Pres, Chor; Drama; Hmrm; NHS; Sch P; Span C; Hist A; ROTC A; Yth Fel; ROTC Swtht; Cl Rep; Sergeant, Drill Tm; Most Versatile; *Howard U; Med.*

CHRISTNER, William Franklin
Abilene HS; Abilene, KS; BS; Rptr, Sch P; JV, Bkbl; Ftbl; Tr; *Kansas St; Bus.*

CHRISTOFORATOS, Stamatia
Brooklyn Tech HS; Brooklyn, NY (15-2000) Math A; Sal; Sci A; Prog Committee; *Math.*

CHRISTOPH, Lila Rae
LaCrosse HS; La Crosse, IN (2-52) Chor; NHS; WW in Ind HS Foreign Lang; *Purdue N Central U; Acct.*

CHRISTOPHE, Mary Madeline
St Matthew HS; Melrose, LA; Ann; Band; CYO; Pres, FHA; VP, 4H; Sftbl; Alg A; Beauty; 4H A; Hon Prog; Sci A; Spch A; VP, Jr Daughters; *Northwestern St U.*

CHRISTOPHER,
Gayle Kathleen
N Miami HS; Miami, FL; Denver, IN; Chor; Drama; Ger C; Var C; Bkbl; Sftbl; Tr; *Sci.*

CHRISTOPHER, Jimma
Canyon HS; Canyon, TX (100-300) Pres, FHA; FTA; Hmrm; SC; Bkbl; *Lubbock Christian Col; Elem Ed.*

CHRISTOPHER, Kim Sabrina
Menchville HS; Newport News, VA (33%-750) VP, Chor; Secy, FTA; Hmrm; SC; Bsbl; Tr; COM; Citz A; Yth Fel; *Va Commonwealth U; Computer Sci.*

CHRISTOPHER, Lauren Ann
Weedsport Central HS; Weedsport, NY (1-86) Ed, Ann; Band; Chor; Ensm; Fr C; NHS; Ski C; Hockey; JV, Tr; COM; Cl Fav; NEDT; Regent Schol; Rensselaer A; Type A; Val; Yth Fel; Arion A; *MIT; Elec Engr.*

CHRISTOPHER, Lynn Marie
Fort Hill HS; Cumberland, MD; Cpt, Chldr; Tri-HiY; Secy, Sr Cl; Secy, Jr Cl; Tnns; Citz A; Sparkle A; Shorthand A; HR.

CHRISTOPHER RALPH,
Christopher R
Gloversville HS; Gloversville, NY; Soccer; Wrest; Pres, VP, Yth Fel; Yth Camp Counselor; Coach, Yth Soccer League; *Central Col; Yth Work.*

CHRISTOPHERSON,
Jon Bryce
William J Brown HS; Sturgis, SD (35-198) BS; FTA; NHS; Sci C; Ski C; SC; Math A; NMS; Stu o-t Mo; *Cal Tech; Elec Engr.*

CHRISTY, Annette Louise
Jamestown Sr HS; Jamestown, ND (100-300) Band; Ensm; Ger C; Orch; ARC; Golf; Mgr, Tr; Sci A; *Blind Ed.*

CHRISTY, Herbert Lynn
Jones HS; Lynnville, TN; FFA; SC.

CHRISTY, Peggy Jo
Lawrenceville HS; Lawrenceville, IL (35-176) Cpt, Chldr; Chem C; FNA; VP, Jr Cl.

CHRONISTER, Bettye June
Palestine HS; Palestine, TX; *A&M U.*

CHRONISTER, Mark Quintin
Chapman HS; Chapman, KS (30%-175) Tres, 4H; Wrest; 4H A; Spch A; Art A's; St 4-H Conf; Mid-Amer Sq Commissioner; Presbyterian Church Ruling Elder; *Kans St U; Art.*

CHROSTEK, Richard John
St Joseph's HS; Camden, NJ (2-78) CYO; Ger C; Math C; NHS; Pol Sci C; Tres, Sr Cl; Bsbl; JV, Bkbl; Wrest; Hon Prog; MLS; *Med Technology.*

CHROUCH, Laura Daane
Wyoming HS; Cincinnati, OH (57-215) AFS; Secy, Band; Chor; Drama; NHS; Orch; Ski C; Span NHS; Wrestlerette; Spirit Sq; Sup Mus As; Excellent Mus A; *Oral Roberts U; Eng.*

CHRYSLER, Mark Alan
Creston HS; Grand Rapids, MI; Dbte Tm; Spch C; Bsbl; Ftbl; Sftbl; Tr.

CHRYSSOVERGES,
Joseph Earl
St Charles Borromeo HS; Destrahan, LA (2-79) BC; Sci C; COM; Hon Prog; Math A; *U of New Orleans; Engr.*

CHRZ, Donna Rose
Perry HS; Perry, OK (4-88) CYO; FHA; NHS; Regent Schol; *Okla St U; Engr.*

CHUBB, Susan Kay
Valentine HS; Valentine, NE (14-78) Band; Chldr; FTA; Rptr, Sch P; Tr; HCt; Yth Fel; GSct; Valentine Coronation Court.

CHUDOMELKA, John Florian
Ozark HS; Ozark, MO; FFA; Tr; *SW Mo St U; Bus.*

CHUDZINSKI, Monica B
St Joseph's HS; Camden, NJ (12-76) Chor; Fr C; NHS; Sftbl; Q&S A; Sftbl Varsity Ltr.

CHUE, Ben M
Lowell HS; San Francisco, CA (5%-2600) COM; Chem A; Bridge C; *U of Calif-Berkeley; Chem.*

CHUI, Annie Wing-Lun
Burbank Sr HS; Burbank, CA (1-595) CSF; Drill Tm; People-To-People HS Ambassador; Comm Service; *U of Sou Calif; Teacher Ed.*

CHULAY, Maudie Darrell
Westridge Sch for Girls; Pasadena, CA (16-50) A Cap Choir; Chldr; Chor; S-T, Drama; Fr C; Lit Mag; ARC; VP, Soph Cl; Soccer; COM; Pres, Stu Activities; Cl Fav Personality; *UCLA; Art.*

CHUMLEY, Rebecca Louise
Powell Valley HS; Speedwell, TN; Secy, Band; BC; FHA; Mu Alpha Theta; Sch P; Tri-HiY; JA A; Lincoln Mem U; *Acct.*

CHUN, Angela Lyn
Roosevelt HS; Honolulu, HI (63-591) Marketing VP, JA; Mandarin C; Mus Schol; Shorthand A; *U of Hawaii; Bus.*

CHUNG, Christina H
Mather HS; Chicago, IL; Swim; Tnns; Tr; Alg A; Hon Prog; ARC A; Type A; Yth Fel.

CHUNG, Deborah Michelle
Newbury Park Adventist Acad; Newbury Park, CA; Co-Ed, Ann; S-T, Chor; Tres, GS; Rptr, Sch P; Ski C; VP, SC; Parl, Sr Cl; Pres, Jr Cl; Tres, Soph Cl; Alg A; COM; Pres A; Val; *Pacific Union Col; Nurs.*

CHUNG, Henry
Eastchester HS; Eastchester, NY (20-280) AFS; Ski C; Bkbl; Tnns; *Stanford U; Bus Mgt.*

CHUNG, Jung Soo
Franklin HS; Los Angeles, CA (470-700) Wrest; *UCLA; Judo.*

CHUNG, Michael Zachary
Tift Co HS; Tifton, GA (20%-400) Band; Key C; NHS; Ski C; SC; Var C; Tnns; Hon Prog; Swtht; All Dist Band; *U of Ga; Dentistry.*

CHUNG, Sheri Deann
Linda Vista Jr Acad; Oxnard, CA (3-13) Chor; Bsbl; Bkbl; Soccer; Sftbl; Tnns; Tr; *Pacific Union Col; Dietetics.*

CHURA, Richard Peter
Danbury Twp HS; Lakeside, OH (20-80) CYO; NHS; Sci C; Var C; VP, Jr Cl; Mgr, Ftbl; Hon Prog; Sci A.

CHURCH, David Allen
Wheaton Comm HS N; Wheaton, IL (36-330) Chor; NHS; Var C; Co-Cpt, Soccer; Tnns; Citz A; Hon Prog; Cpt, FCA; Gym; All Sectional, Soccer; *Wheaton Col; Hist.*

CHURCH, Joey Lyn
Sweet Home Union HS; Sweet Home, OR (77-177) Ftbl; Tr; Welding Class A; *Welding.*

CHURCH, Kathlene Grace
Fremont HS; Fremont, IN (20-63) Band; Chor; Pres, FHA; Tres, 4H; NHS; COM; 4H A; Type A; Yth Fel; Secy, FHA; WW; Home Ec A; *Fort Wayne Bible Col; Missionary Nurs.*

CHURCH, Sandra Christine
Monroe Union HS; Monroe, OR (4-42) Chldr; Sch P; Tres, Soph Cl; Bkbl; Tr; Most Outst Ath o-t Yr; *Oreg St U; Phys Ed.*

CHURCHILL, Angela Ann
Parkview HS; Little Rock, AR; Pres, AFS; BC; Chor; Lat C; NHS; Yth Foundation A; *Baylor U; Religion.*

CHURCHILL, Annette Denise
Bret Harts HS; Angels Camp, CA; AFS; GSct.

CHURCHILL, Jane Marie
Kalani HS; Honolulu, HI; Ann; Band; Ger C; Tres, Lat C; Span C; Spch C; Arch; Bkbl; Tr; COM; Citz A; Kiwanis A; Spch A; Co-Cpt, Vlbl; *Kapiolani Comm Col; Television Engr.*

CHURCHILL, Karen Kay
Parkview HS; Little Rock, AR (25%-450) VP, AFS; BC; Community Yth Symph; FBLA; Ger C; Orch; Sci C; All St Orch; *Baylor U.*

CHURCHILL, Mary Sue
Breckinridge Co HS; Harned, KY (2%-200) Secy, Chor; FBLA; Secy, FTA; Pres, Math C; Mu Alpha Theta; Secy, NHS; Sch Achieve Tm; SC; Secy, Jr Cl; Cpt, Tnns; H of F; HQn; Hon Prog; NMS; Yth Fel; *U of Ky; Social Work.*

CHURCHWARD, Gloria Jean
James Madison HS; Milwaukee, WI (100-850) Band; Hon Prog; Off Ed C; Numerals; Timothy Trophy; Ltr; Hon Trophy; 3 Chevrons; Meritorious Trophy; 2 Gold Stars; *Baptist Bible Col; Elem Ed.*

CHURCHWELL, Bircendia Antonyce
Jack Yates Sr HS; Houston, TX; Tres, Band; NHS; Ntl Yth Conf; Secy, Sci C; SC; Amer Leg A; COM; Citz A; Hon Prog; Yth Fel; Sch Service A; Hmrm Swtht; Land Use Contest Grand Win; League of Women Voters.

CHURCHWELL, Jerrilyn Kay
Carl Junction HS; Carl Junction, MO (23-124) AFS; Tres, Chor; Drama; Fr C; FHA; Co-Ed, Sch P; Spch C; Thes; Golf; Sftbl; Tr; Fr A; *Stephens Col; Journ.*

CIAMPA, Margherita Gelsomina
Monsignor Ryan Mem HS; Dorchester, MA; City Conf; Hmrm; Lit Ral; Rptr, Sch P; Span C; SC; Secy, Sr Cl; Pres, Jr Cl; Hon Prog; *Boston Col; Law.*

CIANCI, Constance Ina
Broomfield HS; Broomfield, CO; Chldr; Fr C; FHA; Hmrm; Sch P; SC; Yth Fel; *Fla Bible Col; Med Aide.*

CIANCI, Sandy Louise
Broomfield HS; Broomfield, CO; Co-Cpt, Chldr; Rptr, Sch P; Tres, SC; HQn; Pacesetter; WW.

CIANCIMINO, Kenneth Matthew
Montclair HS; Montclair, NJ; Arch; Rptr, Sch P; SC; Arch; Bsbl; Cpt, Hockey; Co-Cpt, Sftbl; COM; Pres A; MVP, Hockey; HR; *Yale U; Law.*

CICHON, Mark Eugene
St Patrick HS; Chicago, IL (34-342) Pres, Chor; NHS; Rptr, Sch P; Ch, SC; Hon Prog; St Scholar; *Loyola U; Bio.*

CIECHALSKI, Steve Anthony
S Park HS; Library, PA (3-180) NHS; Bkbl; Tnns; Hon Prog; MLS; NEDT; *Pitt Col.*

CIEPLINSKI, Cindee Lynn
N B Forrest HS; Jacksonville, FL (210-547) 4H; Hmrm; Var C; Sftbl; Swim; Tr; Secy, MHFM; SC, Swim, Sftbl, Tr, A's; *Fla Jr Col; Nurs.*

CIFREDO, Mary Esther
Academia Discipulos de Cristo; Bayamon, PR (10-122) A Cap Choir; All Amer Yth; CYO; Chldr; Chor; Dbte Tm; Demolay; Ensm; 4H; Tres, Hmrm; K of C; Mjrte; Math C; NHS; Sci C; Swim; Tnns; Alg A; Beauty; COM; K of C A; Lion A; Math A; ARC A; Sci A; Fidelity A; *Universidad de Puerto Rico; Med Technology.*

CIGOL, Brian Alan
Passaic Valley HS; Little Falls, NJ (50%-250) Ger C; JV, Soccer.

CIKO, Anna
St Aloysius HS; Jersey City, NJ (1-110) Co-Ed, Ann; NHS; Math A; Val; 1st Hons; *St Peter's Col; Acct.*

CILLEY, John Harper
Newton Conover HS; Newton, NC (23-235) Band; BC; Ensm; InterAct C; Order/Arrow; Secy, Span C; Pres, Soph Cl; Swim; God & Country A; Hon Prog; NEDT; Order/Arrow A; Yth Fel; Jr Asst Sct-Master; Foreign Exchange Stu, S Australia; *Duke U; Pre-Law.*

CIMINO, Michael Stephan
Palma HS; Salinas, CA; *Santa Clara Col.*

CIMINO, Terri Marie
Notre Dame HS; Salinas, CA; *San Jose St Col; Interior Designer.*

CIMMERER, Mark Willian
Eastern HS; Lansing, MI (4%-550) NHS; Order/Arrow; Co-Cpt, Swim; *Michigan St U; Pre-Med.*

CINDERELLA, Joseph Alan
Eastside HS; Paterson, NJ (1-850) VP, Chess C; Drama; Hmrm; Pres, Math C; VP, Sci C; SC; Mgr, Tnns; COM; Yth Foundation; Sci & Humanities Sem; *Boston U; Med.*

CINICOLA, Frederick Allen
Marian HS; Tamaqua, PA (60-177) CYO; Hmrm; Order/Arrow; SC; Ftbl; Ftbl Coaches A; Varsity Ltrs; *Bio.*

CINK, Melane Carol
Frank Scott Bunnell HS; Stratford, CT (29-460) FNA; Ch, Hmrm; NHS; Rptr, Sch P; Ski C; Tres, Span C; Span NHS; Ch, SC; Swim; Hon Prog; St Scholar; Ch, Ath Assn Yth for Easter Seals; Sr Hon Soc; *U of Conn; Nurs.*

CINK, Melanie Carol
Frank Scott Bunnell HS; Stratford, CT (29-460) FNA; Co-Ch, Hmrm; NHS; Ski C; Span C; Span NHS; Co-Ch, SC; Sch P; Swim; Gov Honor Prog; Hon Prog; Sr Hon Soc; *U of Ct; Nurs.*

CINTRON, Kevin Luis
Seward Park HS; New York, NY; MVP, Soccer; Tr; Bio A; Sci A; Yth o-t Yr; Attendance A; *New Paltz U; Lib Arts.*

CINTRON, Luis Ramon
Jose de Diego HS; Mayaguez, PR (4-276) FBLA; Magna Cum Laude; C de Becarios; Merit As; Adv Eng Group; Adv Math Group; *UPR at Mayaguez; Chem Engr.*

CINTRON, Margarita
William Howard Taft HS; New York, NY; Chor; Dbte Tm; Drama; Sch P; Span C; Tnns; COM; Social C; *Bronx Comm Col; Sci.*

CIOCCHETTI, Rhonda Lee
Niwot HS; Longmont, CO (17-308) Chldr; Secy, FFA; Semi-Fin, GS; Hmrm; Tres, NHS; SC; Cl Fav; 4H A; VP, Rodeo C; Secy & Pres, 4-H C; Zonta C Girl of Month; Alfonso De Rigles Schol; *Colo St U; Animal Sci.*

CIOFFI, Teri Lynn Judith
St Joseph o-t Palisades HS; W New York, NJ (7-225) Hmrm; Secy, NHS; Rainbow; Sch P; Span NHS; Hon Prog; HR; *Montclair St Col; Psych.*

CIPAN, Marilynn
South HS; Willoughby, OH (73-496) Hist.

CIPRIANI, Joyce Ann
John S Fine HS; Nanticoke, PA (7-347) Amer Leg A; NEDT.

CIRAR, Stephanie Anne
Hartshorne HS; Hartshorne, OK (5-60) Pres, Band; Chor; Drama; Pres, FHA; 4H; NHS; Sch P; SC; Citz A; DARGCA; Band A; Band Qn; Home Ec A; *U of Okla.*

CISSEL, Julia Ellen
Skyline HS; Idaho Falls, ID (1-300) Bus Mgr, Ger C; Math C; NHS; Var C; Cr-Ctry; Swim; Rotary A; Attendance A; Ger A; *U of Chicago; Sci.*

CIZA, John Joseph
Fairfield HS; Fairfield, AL (10%-184) BC; Ftbl; *U of Ala; Computer Sci.*

CLAAR, Connie Marie
Natrona Co HS; Casper, WY; Band; Orch; Yth Fel; *Casper Col; Home Ec.*

CLACKS, Carolyn
Northwest HS; St Louis, MO (23-399) NHS; HCt; Cpt, Drill Tm; Pep C; WW; *U of Mo; Pre-Med.*

CLADY, Ronda Jo
Buckeye Central HS; New Washington, OH; Ann; Band; 4H; Sch P; Span C; Span NHS; 4H A; Type A; Cpt, Bowl.

CLAIBORN, Sally Sue
Schlagle HS; Kansas City, KS;

CLAIBORNE, Kirk Kennard
Johnnycake Jr HS; Baltimore, MD (69-330) Chess C; Chor; Fr C; *Harvard U; Law.*

CLAIR, Cheryl Ann
Archbold HS; Archbold, OH (19-141) A Cap Choir; Band; Chor; GS; Mjrte; Span C; *Bowling Green St U; Special Ed.*

CLAIR, Ira Arthur
Hi-Lel Acad of Pittsburgh; Pittsburgh, PA (1-9) Pres, Fr C; Math C; SC; Ftbl; Cpt, Soccer; COM; Sal; Outst Jr Stu; Talmud A; Outst Achv in Hebrew; Excellence in Eng Stu; *Carnegie-Mellon U; Archt.*

CLAMPIT, Robert Edward Jr
Carmel HS For Boys; Mundelein, IL (30-225) Ger C; Wrest; *US Naval Acad; Hist.*

CLANAHAN, Kevin Lee
Andrews HS; Andrews, TX (4-149) Fr C; VP, InterAct C; Pres, InterClub Coun; SC; Tr; Citz A; Hon Prog; Co-Cpt, MVP, Ftbl; Academic A, 4 Yrs; *Tex A&M U; Engr.*

CLANCY, David Michael
Bowling Green HS; Franklinton, LA (10-30) A-Ed, Ann; Chor; 4H; Sch P; SC; Bsbl; Bkbl; Ftbl; Tr; Cl Fav; 4H A; Pres A; Sci A; Yth Fel; BSct; Royal Ambassadors; *NE Col; Bus.*

CLANCY, Erin Marie
St Mary's Acad; Alexandria, VA; Drama; Key C; SC; Pres, Soph Cl; Hon Prog; Magna Cum Laude; Pres A; Summa Cum Laude; *Ed.*

CLANCY, Kathleen Gerette
St Mary's Acad; Alexandria, VA (10%-100) Drama; Math C; Tres, SC; Bkbl; Sftbl; Hon Prog; Magna Cum Laude; Summa Cum Laude.

CLANTON, Gregory Cope
Robert E Lee HS; Midland, TX (33%-625) Band; Bus C; Dbte Tm; Hmrm; Lit Mag; Tres, Order/Arrow; COM; Citz A; God & Country A; Opt A; Q&S A; *Tex Tech U; Acct.*

CLANTON, Pamela Elizabeth
Daviston HS; Daviston, AL; VP, BC; Chldr; Pres, Sr Cl; Beauty; Cl Fav; 4H A; HQn; HCt; *Respiratory Therapist.*

CLANTON, Teresa Ann
E E Smith Sr HS; Fayetteville, NC (15-300) Ensm; Pres, Hmrm; NHS; Secy, Span C; SC; Tri-HiY; Psych A; Span A; Miss EE Smith; *UNC; Pharmacy.*

CLAPP, Sally Beth
New Providence HS; New Providence, NJ (41-291) Home Ec.

CLAPPER, Jodi Ann
Wethersfield HS; Kewanee, IL (25-100) Band; FBLA; *Black Hawk E Col; Bus.*

CLAPPER, Margaret Jane
Red Lion Area HS; Red Lion, PA (30-450) Band; Mod Mus Mas; Sch P; Most Out; Yth Fel; Yth Leg; Ntl Guild of Piano Auditions; *Susquehanna U; Mus Ed.*

CLARDY, Grady Eugene
Hitchcock HS; Hitchcock, TX (51-150) Chem C; Chess C; Ger C; JV, Bsbl; JV, Ftbl.

CLARDY, Kent Karl
Andrew J Terrell HS; Blanchard, OK; A Cap Choir; Ann; Tres, BC; Chor; 4H; Hmrm; Madrigal; NHS; Sch P; SC; Var C; Bsbl; Bkbl; Ftbl; COM; Cl Fav; Gov Honor Prog; 4H A; HCt; Hon Prog; Journ A; Magna Cum Laude; Math A; Most Out; Sci A; Star Student; St Scholar; Yth Fel; Ftbl, SC, Young Lion, A's; Ch, Float Committee; Beau, Pep C.

CLARDY, Lewis Fred
Palmetto HS; Williamston, SC (75-144) Ftbl; Tr; *Greenville Co Tech; Industrial Elec.*

CLARK, Alfretta Diane
Fremont HS; Oakland, CA; Chor; Dbte Tm; FHA; Secy, FNA; Hmrm; Sch P; Span C; Secy, SC; Secy, Jr Cl; St & Ntl Congress; *Cal St Hayward; Law.*

CLARK, Andrew Leo
Turner HS; Kansas City, KS (210-320) Mgr, Bkbl; Mgr, Ftbl; Pittsburg Col; Industrial Tech.

CLARK, Bernice Delores
Darby Township Jr-Sr HS; Glenoden, PA (26-110) Hmrm; Widener Col; Nurs.

CLARK, Blair
Ojai Valley Sch; Ojai, CA (4-24) Pitzer Col; Psych.

CLARK, Brent Duane
Kearsley HS; Flint, MI; Band; Order/Arrow; JA A; U of Mich; Bus Adm.

CLARK, Brian Stuart
Argos Comm Sch; Argos, IN (23-88) Band; Fin, Ensm; Pres, FFA; FTA; Pres, 4H; Bkbl; Co-Cpt, Cr-Ctry; Soccer; Tr; 4H A; HKg; MVP, Cr-Ctry; Tres, FFA; Fin, Tr; Bethal Col; Bus Mgt.

CLARK, Byron Standish II
Apollo HS; Owensboro, KY (3-320) Band; BC; Ensm; Math C; Order/Arrow; Sftbl; Hon Prog; Order/Arrow A; WW; Bell Lab Tour; Western Ky U Jr Schol; U of Ky; Engr.

CLARK, Carol Ann
Grandview Heights HS; Columbus, OH (44-129) Chor; Ensm; FTA; Ski C; JV, Hockey; Drill Tm; Church Choir; Usher; Tres, Coed C.

CLARK, Carol Lynn
Clinton Comm Sch; Clinton, MI (8-106) Chor; Drama; NHS; Rptr, Sch P; Var C; JV, Bkbl; JV, Golf; Mgr, Sftbl; Most Out; Yth Fel; Sunshine Choir; Olivet Col; Mus.

CLARK, Carol Yvette
Holy Family HS; Birmingham, AL (1-41) Band; VP, Fr C; Sch P; MLS; VP, Yth JCCEO; Miss Booster; Fr A; PE A; UA; Pre-Dentistry.

CLARK, Carole Yoshie
Dugway HS; Dugway, UT (6-50) Chor; Drama; Ger C; Hmrm; Model UN; Sci C; Span C; SC; Pres, Var C; Bkbl; Tnns; Tr; WW; Vlbl; USC; Med.

CLARK, Charles Edward Jr
Carver Sr HS; Montgomery, AL; Band; Chor; Drama; Ensm; InterAct C; Span C; Thes; Ftbl; JV, Tr.

CLARK, Cheryl Lee
Centralia HS; Centralia, IL; Orch; Span C.

CLARK, Cheryl Lynn
Kentridge HS; Kent, WA (60-620) Band; Fr C; NHS; Hon Prog; Med Technology.

CLARK, Christine Annette
Moline Sr HS; Moline, IL (150-800) Sci C; Span C; Tnns; Lutheran Hosp Sch of Radiology; Radiology.

CLARK, Cindy Marie
Woodbridge Sr HS; Woodbridge, VA;

CLARK, Connie Michelle
Bennett HS; Martin, SD (3-54) Ed, Ann; S-T, Band; Pres, Chor; Ensm; VP, FHA; Semi-Fin, GS; 4H; Madrigal; NHS; Sch P; HCt; Type A; Eng A; Span A; Dakota Weslyan U; Youth Agency Adm.

CLARK, Connie Pearl
Holly Springs HS; Holly Springs, MS (5-157) Chor; Drama; FBLA; Pres, FHA; NHS; Alg A; Math A; FHA A; Drama A; Vol A; Miss U For Women; Med Technology.

CLARK, Cynthia Ann
Patrician Acad; Butler, AL; F-Ed, Ann; Secy, BC; Chldr; Ensm; VP, Hmrm; NHS; VP, Soph Cl; Golf; Sftbl; Tnns; Beauty; Ntl Achv Schol; U of Ala; Ed.

CLARK, Cynthia Elaine
East Ridge HS; East Ridge, TN (15-270) Ann; Band; BC; Chldr; Chor; Drama; 4H; Hmrm; Span C; Var C; Citz A; 4H A; Hist A; Math A; Pres A; ARC A; Spch A; Star Student; Yth Fel; Art C; Chldr A; Essay A; Civitan C; Mus A; Art A; Phys Ed A; U of Va; Law.

CLARK, Dale Andrew
Ashtabula Harbor HS; Ashtabula, OH; JV, Bkbl; Ftbl; Alg A; Math A; Marine Corps Ntl Yth Fit Prog; Ohio St U; Math.

CLARK, Dana Jane
Royal Oak HS; Covina, CA (27%-310) Thes; Dance Tm; Calif Polytech Inst; Drama.

CLARK, Darlean
W S Creecy HS; Rich Square, NC (5-42) Bus Mgr, BC; VP, Chor; Hon Prog; Math A; Bookkeeping, Beta, A's; Roanoke Chowan Tech Inst; Early Child Care.

CLARK, Darryl Stephen
Leon HS; Tallahassee, FL (150-450) BC; Chor; Madrigal; Ftbl; Tr; Citz A; Math A; Outst Mus A; Barber Shop Quartet A; Fla St U; Mus.

CLARK, David Edward
Carmel HS; Carmel, NY (15-400) A Cap Choir; Band; Chor; NHS; Orch; Golf; Hon Prog; Eastman Sch of Mus; Mus.

CLARK, David Joseph
St Mary's Regional HS; Lynn, MA (7-117) BS; Drama; Pres, NHS; F-Ed, Sch P; Pres, Sr Cl; Cpt, Cr-Ctry; Co-Cpt, Tr; Bio A; God & Country A; Harvard Book A; Hist A; MLS; Bowdoin Col; Hist.

CLARK, Deborah Lee
Ygnacio Valley HS; Concord, CA (20%-431) Band; Auxiliary March Grp; Rally Girl; Secy, Jazz Band; Wind Ensm; UOP; Therapy.

CLARK, Debra Lee
New Bedford HS; New Bedford, MA; AFS; NHS; Swtht; Dartmouth Col; Creative Writing.

CLARK, Dennis Ray
Denair HS; Denair, CA (7-49) AFS; Ann; NHS; Sch P; CSF; COM; Journ A; Bookkeeping, Amer Gov, A's; Lib Merit; W Valley Col; Bus.

CLARK, Donald Lawrence
Hamilton HS; Memphis, TN (91-425) Drama; Spch C; Golf; COM; Gov Honor Prog; JA A; PTA A; Spch A; Outst Comm Leadership; U Tenn; Engr.

CLARK, Donyell Felice
Nolan HS; Ft Worth, TX (10%-200) Chor; Bio A; Hon Prog.

CLARK, Douglas Lynn
Archbold Area Sch; Archbold, OH (105-140) A Cap Choir; Chor; VP, SC; Pres, Jr Cl; MVP, Ftbl; Tr; Wrest; Ed.

CLARK, Elizabeth
McCluer N HS; Florissant, MO; Chor; NHS; Tr; Recognition Cert; Practicum 77; Hospital Vol Service; Florissant Valley Comm Col; Bus.

CLARK, Elizabeth Archer
Princeton HS; Princeton, NJ; A Cap Choir; Chor; Drama; Fr C; Hmrm; Madrigal; Rptr, Sch P; Ski C; SC; JV, Tnns; JV, Tr; Hon Prog; LaCrosse.

CLARK, Ellesa Clark
Crescent HS; Port Angeles, WA (6-18) NHS; Tres, Sr Cl; Tres, Jr Cl; Vlbl; Western Wash St Col; Ed.

CLARK, George Barnes
Hall HS; Little Rock, AR; Pol Sci C; VP, Hist C; Military Sci.

CLARK, George Edwards
Bremerhaven American HS; Bremerhaven, GERMANY (5-31) Chess C; Drama; InterClub Coun; Co-Ed, Lit Mag; NHS; SC; VP, Soph Cl; Cr-Ctry; Ftbl; Tr; Alg A; COM; Hist A; Math A; NMS; Cl Offices; Briar Cliff Col; Law.

CLARK, James Hamel
Greensboro Day Sch; Greensboro, NC (18-66) Lit Mag; Order/Arrow; Bus Mgr, Sch P; Bkbl; Golf; Bio A; COM; Citz A; Sci A; Eagle Sct A; HR Recognition; Wake Forest U; Bus Mgr.

CLARK, James Irving III
Jamaica HS; New York, NY (113-1330) Pres, Band; Chess C; Ch, Chor; Ch, Ensm; Hmrm; NHS; Ntl Yth Conf; Orch; Sch Achieve Tm; Var C; Bkbl; Sftbl; Tr; COM; Citz A; Hon Prog; JA A; Math A; PTA A; Yth Fel; Art A; Creative Arts Hon Soc; Cpt, AAA; Columbia U; Bus.

CLARK, Jane Katherine
Park Center Sr HS; Brooklyn Park, MN (98%-630) A Cap Choir; Band; Drama; Fr C; Fin, GS; Hmrm; Mjrte; NHS; Spch C; Amer Leg A; COM; H of F; Hon Prog; Spch A; Vocal A; St 1-Act Play A; Spch.

CLARK, Janice Louise
Ayer Jr HS; Ayer, MA (42-215) NHS; Tres, Sr Cl; Tres, Jr Cl; Tres, Soph Cl; Hockey; NAACP Merit Achv A; Burdett Col; Secy.

CLARK, Janice Lynn
Tecumseh HS; Tecumseh, OK (33%-100) FHA; FTA; A-Ed, Sch P; COM; HCt; Journ A; Swtht; Type A; Yth Fel; Secy, Pep C; Wrest Mat Maid; Arch Bearer; Asst Ed, Bus Mgr, Yrbk; E Central U; Spec Ed.

CLARK, Jeffery Alexander
Freedom HS; Morganton, NC (70-1700) Pres, FFA; Hmrm; SC; Board of Trustees, Interact C; NC St Col; Horticulture.

CLARK, Jeffrey Floyd
Cedar Cliff HS; Camp Hill, PA (3-530) Fr C; NHS; JV, Tr; Hon Prog; Yth Fel; Carnegie Mellon U; Engr.

CLARK, Jeffrey Lynn
Portersville Christian HS; Portersville, PA (33%-16) Ed, Ann; MVP, Bkbl; Anderson Col; Communication Arts.

CLARK, Jefrey Marshall
Greenville HS; Greeneville, TN (31-197) Lat C; Order/Arrow; Ftbl; Golf; Tnns; Eagle Sct; Outst Sct A; People to People Prg; Tenn Tech U; Pre-Phar.

CLARK, Jenifer Jo
Marion Co HS; Lebanon, KY (5-324) Band; Chldr; Chor; Drama; FHA; Hmrm; NHS; Span C; SC; Var C; Gym; Jr Home Ec A; Recreation.

CLARK, Jenny Lynne
W Morgan HS; Trinity, AL (10%-59) Ann; Band; BC; JA A; Eng A; HR.

CLARK, Jerome
Charles B Glenn HS; Birmingham, AL (1-114) Pres, Band; Math C; Secy, NHS; COM; Hon Prog; I Dare You; MLS; Val; Band Ltr; Engr.

CLARK, Jim Michael
Carlmont HS; Belmont, CA; Var C; MVP, Bkbl; H of F; All Nor-Cal, All League; Skyline Col; Sociology.

CLARK, Joanne
Thomas Jefferson HS; Denver, CO (232-625) Hmrm; ARC; Sch P; Span C; Okla Baptist U; Theology.

CLARK, Joseph Patrick
Archmere Acad; Claymont, DE (7-77) Pres, CYO; NHS; Span NHS; SC; Pres, Sr Cl; Cpt, Ftbl; Cpt, Tr; Wrest; Amer Leg A; COM; Hon Prog; ROTC A; Ftbl All-Amer; Ftbl Coach; Ath o-t Yr, Ftbl; Ursinus Col Pres School; U of Rochester Alumni Reg Schol; Princeton U; Bio.

CLARK, Judith Elaine
Dan River HS; Ringgold, VA (12-250) BC; FBLA; FHA; Tri-HiY; VP, DECA; DECA Stu o-t Yr.

CLARK, Karen Denise
Beth Haven Christian Sch; Louisville, KY (35-90) Drama; Most Out; Pres A; Yth Fel; Teacher Aide; U of Louisville; Home-Ec.

CLARK, Karen Lee
Cottage Grove HS; Cottage Grove, OR (6-220) Pres, AFS; Band; Pres, NHS; Tres, SC; Thes; Sftbl; Math A; Calif St U; Marine Biol.

CLARK, Kathleen DeAnn
Parsons Sr HS; Parsons, KS (3-201) Chor; Dbte Tm; Drama; NFL; NHS; Spch A; VofDEM; Kans Wesleyan Col; Law.

CLARK, Kathy Anne
Fayetteville HS; Fayetteville, AR; FBLA; U of Ark; Bus.

CLARK, Keith Russell
DeLand HS; DeLand, FL (20%-600) Rptr, Sch P; U of Fla; Bus.

CLARK, Kenna Elaine
Anamosa HS; Anamosa, IA (36-105) Band; Var C; Cpt, Bkbl; Tr; Iowa St U; Art.

CLARK, Kenneth Alan
Western Hills HS; Ft Worth, TX (32-650) Ann; Band; JV, Bsbl; Wrest; VP, Russian C; 'A' HR Cards A; Stephen F Austin U; Forestry.

CLARK, Kerry Dayton
Antioch HS; Antioch, TN (7-400) Band; BC; Hmrm; Pres, Lat C; NFL; NHS; Sch P; SC; VP, Jr Cl; Tres, Jr Cl; Band Off; St Stu Congress; Middle Tenn St U; Pol Sci.

CLARK, Kevin Dean
Alton Sr HS; Alton, IL (100-820) Band; Chor; Ensm; Madrigal; Orch; COM; Chor A; Advanced Soph Chor; Sound Operator, 'Katnips'; Sch Pit Orch; Audio Engr.

CLARK, Kimberlee Ann
Lansing E HS; Lansing, MI (350-489) F-Ed, Sch P; Ski C; Pres, Jr Cl; Pres, Soph Cl; Citz A; MLS; Mgr, Vlbl; Service A; Lansing Comm Col; X-Ray Tech.

CLARK, Kimberly Lynne
Freedom Sr HS; Morganton, NC (124-498) Lat C; NHS; Lat A; Appalachian St U; Classical Lang.

CLARK, Laurie Ann
Williamston HS; Williamston, MI; Chor; Pres, 4H; NHS; Ski C; Var C; Cpt, Bkbl; Sftbl; 4H A; Pres A; Sci A; MVP, Bkbl; Mich St U; Vet Med.

CLARK, Lawana
Burkeville HS; Burkeville, TX (1-46) FHA; SC; Tres, Soph Cl; Cpt, Bkbl; Tnns; Tr; Cl Fav; NEDT; Vlbl.

CLARK, Lee Ann
Bronson HS; Bronson, MI (1-156) Tres, A Cap Choir; Band; FTA; Ger C; NHS; Thes; Tnns; WW; Co Bar Assn; Fine Arts Camp Interntl Band; Dist, St, Instrum, Voc, Solo, Ensm; Win, Essay Contest; Taylor U; Elem Ed.

CLARK, Lianne Marie
Panora-Linden Comm HS; Panora, IA (3-40) Cpt, Chldr; Chor; NHS; Thes; Drill Tm; Iowa St U; Applied Art.

CLARK, Linda Maria
Western HS; Detroit, MI (13-263) Tres, FBLA; Ntl Teachers Coun; Detroit Col of Bus; Executive Secy.

CLARK, Linda Marie
Maud HS; Maud, OK (3-50) VP, Band; BC; Co-Ch, Model UN; Rainbow; Sch Achieve Tm; SC; Hon Prog; Most Out; Sal; Eng A; Stu in Service Prog A; Acct.

CLARK, Lorraine Kay
New Bloomfield R-III HS; New Bloomfield, MO (5-35) Ann; Pres, Band; Chor; Fr C; NHS; Rptr, Sch P; SC; VP, Var C; VP, Jr Cl; VP, Soph Cl; Cpt, Bkbl; Cpt, Sftbl; Tr; HCt; Most Out; MVP, Bkbl; U of Mo at Columbia; Agr.

CLARK, Lowell Anne
Watertown HS; Watertown, CT (20%-600) Secy, Chor; Hmrm; Madrigal; Sch P; Hockey; COM; Hon Prog; Miss Amer Talent A; U of Conn; Elem Mus Ed.

CLARK, Lynda Carol
Etowah HS; Ahalla, AL (50%-300) Ann; FBLA; Pres, Hmrm; Sch P; Pres, Tri-HiY; Cl Fav; Journ A; Pres A; Tri Hi Y A; Sch Paper A; Gadsden St Jr Col; Social Worker.

CLARK, Lynda Gayle
Bartow Sr HS; Bartow, FL; Anchor C; Ed, Ann; Drama; FHA; Hmrm; NHS; Rptr, Sch P; Spch C; SC; Swim; B Crocker A; Citz A; Hon Prog; MLS; ARC A; 1st Cl, GSct; Calendar Girl; Poetry A; WW; DAHSS; Furman U; Eng.

CLARK, Margaret Ann
Second Ward HS; Gloster, LA; FBLA; Secy, FHA; Pres, Hmrm; Pres, Jr Cl; Hon Prog; Sou U; Bus.

CLARK, Margaret Katherine
Avondale HS; Avondale Estates, GA (5-300) Anchor C; Band; Lat C; NHS; Med.

CLARK, Mark Howard
Lakeside HS; Hot Springs, AR (10-151) AFS; BC; Chor; Drama; Rptr, Fr C; Madrigal; NHS; Sch P; Tres, Tri-HiY; Tr; Hon Prog; Rotary A; WW; U of Ark; Geol.

CLARK, Mark Robert
Fairfield Comm HS; Fairfield, IL (4-153) Pres, Band; BS; Ensm; VP, Math C; Pres, NHS; Span C; Amer Leg A; COM; Star Student; Most Talented; Elk's Schol; U of Ill; Gen.

CLARK, Martha Vaughn
Union HS; Union, SC;

CLARK, Mary Margaret
Monroe HS; Monroe, NC (36-156) AFS; BC; Drama; NHS; Tres, SC; Yth Fel; WW; Appalachian St Col; Computer Sci.

CLARK, Michael Dwane
Sidney HS; Sidney, TX (6-15) Ed, Ann; Rptr, FFA; FHA; Cl Fav; WW; Tex St Tech Inst; Machinest.

CLARK, Nancy Jo
Oakland Comm HS; Oakland, IA (27-46) Ann; Band; Chor; Ensm; Pres, Fr C; FNA; Rptr, Sch P; Bkbl; Sftbl; Tr; WW; Hon Band; Little All-St; Pres, CYF; Jennie Edmundson Sch of Nurs; Nurs.

CLARK, Nancy Lynne
North HS; Sioux City, IA (10%-400) A-Ed, Ann; Band; Chor; French NHS; Hmrm; Fin, Jr Miss Pagent; Pres, Rainbow; Sch P; SC; Bkbl; Tnns; Hon Prog; Masonic A; Swtht; Grand Cross of Colors A; Piano, Clarinet As; Nurs.

CLARK, Pamela Alys
Newton Comm HS; Newton, IL; Band; Bus C; Chor; Ensm; 4H; Hmrm; Madrigal; 4H A; Hon Prog; Math A; NEDT; Type A; Piano, Vocal, Fr Horn, Medals; Simplicity Sewing A; E Ill U; Mus.

CLARK, Pamela Ann
Cleveland HS; Cleveland, TN; Anchor C; Band; Chor; Spch C; Mgr, Bkbl; COM; Hon Prog; Pres A; Art A; U of Tenn; Lab Tech.

CLARK, Pamela Lynn
Columbus E HS; Columbus, OH; Band; Dbte Tm; Fin, GS; NFL; NHS; Span C; Span NHS; Mgr, Sftbl; Sci A in Botany; Morehouse Col; Med Lab Tech.

CLARK, Patricia Ann
W S Creecy HS; Rich Square, NC (10-42) FHA; Hmrm; SC; Sftbl; COM; Type A.

CLARK, Patricia Cassandra
N Charleston HS; N Charleston, SC (98-133) Pres, Band; Chor; Columbia Commercial Col; Med Secy.

CLARK, Pricilla Joyce
Wheeler Co HS; Alamo, GA (2-89) BC; FHA; NHS; Sci C; Augusta Med Col; Nurs.

CLARK, Rebecca Grace
Tigard Sr HS; Tigard, OR; Secy, Chor; VP, 4H; Rotary A; Gym; Portland Comm Col; Nurs.

CLARK, Renee Therese
Jamaica HS; New York, NY; Band; Chldr; Chor; Hmrm; Bsbl; Bkbl; Ftbl; Sftbl; Swim; Tr; Handball; Merits Soc A; John P McMullian Achv A; Child Psych.

CLARK, Rhonda Lea
Warwick HS; Newport News, VA (10-484) AFS; 4H; NFL; Secy, Tnns; Sci A; Old Dominion U; Phys Therapy.

CLARK, Richard Lee
Lyons Twp HS; W Springs, IL (33-1240) Chess C; Citz A; DARGCA; NEDT; Sal; U of Ill; Computer Sci.

CLARK, Rubylene
Denton HS; Denton, TX; Band; SC; Band A; NTSU; Communications.

CLARK, Ruth Darlene
George P Butler HS; Augusta, GA (57-414) Chor; FBLA; FHA; Augusta Col; Secy Sci.

CLARK, S Lewis
Northeast HS; North Little Rock, AR; Fin, All Amer Yth; Band; Chor; Ensm; Fin, All Amer Hall of Fame; Drum Major; All St Band; U of Ark; Mus.

CLARK, Sally Ann
Franklin Co HS; Frankfort, KY (20-500) BC; JV, Chldr; Chor; Ensm; Fr C; Hmrm; Span C; SC; Sftbl; Alg A; COM; Citz A; 4H A; Hon Prog; Math A; Hon Girl Campr, Christian Serv Camp.

CLARK, Scott Elton
Washington HS; Kansas City, KS; A Cap Choir; Band; Chor; FTA; Golf; Grade of 2 in St Mus Contest; Kansas U; Mus.

CLARK, Shelley Ann
Grand Haven HS; Grand Haven, MI (50-500) NHS; Cr-Ctry; Soccer; Tr; Tr Hon's; Ferris St Col; Archt.

CLARK, Sheryl Elizabeth
North HS; Minneapolis, MN (80-461) Ch, All Amer Yth; Chldr; Drama; As; Yth Fel; 3rd, City Gym; Polarettes Ltr; B-HR; Ausburg Col; Animal Behavior.

CLARK, Sondra Carol
Cache HS; Cache, OK; Rptr, Band; BC; VP, FHA; 4H; NHS; 4H A; Masonic A; PTA A; Sci A; Outst Fresh, Band; Top 10, Band; SW Okla Hon Band; Okla St U; Vet Sci.

CLARK, Stanley Dale Jr
Bolton HS; Alexandria, LA (5%-300) Band; Chess C; Chor; Ger C; NHS; Tres, Soph Cl; Soccer; St Lit Ral; MIT; Engr.

CLARK, Steven Thomas
Mitchell HS; Colorado Springs, CO (4-682) Band; Drama; Ensm; Fr C; 4H; NHS; Order/Arrow; Order/Arrow A; Computer Sci.

CLARK, Susan Elaine
S Charleston HS; S Charleston, WV (240-340) Chor; FHA; Explorers Assn; W Va U; Phys Therapy.

CLARK, Susan Elizabeth
Ottawa Hills HS; Grand Rapids, MI (53-540) A Cap Choir; Ensm; ARC; ARC A; Central Mich U.

CLARK, Teresa Lynn
Newark Valley HS; Newark Valley, NY (6-108) Band; Ger C; Secy, NHS; A-Ed, Sch P; 4H A; Regent Schol; St U of NY; Math.

CLARK, Timothy Earl
Breckinridge Co HS; Harned, KY (23-200) Co-Ed, Ann; FBLA; Math C; VP, NHS; Sci C; Var C; Pres, Sr Cl; VP, Jr Cl; JV, Bkbl; Co-Cpt, Ftbl; Wrest; Cl Fav; H of F; Rotary A; MVP, Ftbl; US Air Force Acad; Pilot.

CLARK, Tony Stewart
Wayne Co HS; Jesup, GA; Hmrm; Rptr, Sch P; Bsbl; Sftbl; Citz A; Morehouse Col; Phys Ed.

CLARK, Valarie Genice
Ahoskie HS; Ahoskie, NC (39-211) Ed, Ann; Chldr; Drama; Jr Miss Pagent; Bus Mgr, Sch P; Secy, Var C; S-T, Y-Tns; Secy, Sr Cl; 4H A; E Carolina U; Anesthesiology.

CLARK, Vid L
Sahuarita HS; Sahuarita, AZ (48-145) Chor; Model UN; Tres, Pol Sci C; Sci C; SC; Mgr, Bkbl; Most Out; Pres, Riot C; Tres, Yth Fel; Mesa Comm Col; Ed.

CLARK, Voletta Gay
Warren Central HS; Bowling Green, KY (25-160) Chor; FBLA; FHA; 4H; 4H A; Hon Prog; ARC A; Most Outst, Eng; Piano A; CO-ED Correspondent; Homemaking A; Western Ky U; Nurs.

CLARK, William Roger
Meridian HS; Meridian, TX; BC; Tres, FFA; VP, 4H; Rptr, Sch P; Bkbl; JV, Ftbl; Baylor U; Phar.

CLARKE, Angela Marie
Maggie Lena Walker HS; Richmond, VA (102-300) FBLA; Secy, Hmrm; Lit Mag; Sch P; SC; COM; Swtht; Yth Fel; Vlbl Tm; Gym Tm; Ch, Sr Comm; Fashion Inst of New York; Fashion Modeling.

CLARKE, Christina Irene
Manhattan Sr HS; Manhattan, KS; Drama; Fr C; Thes; Poet A; Secy, Explorer Post; Kans St U.

CLARKE, Christine Inez
Huguenot HS; Richmond, VA; Chldr; FBLA; Hmrm; NHS; Pol Sci C; Tr; H of F; Hon Prog; Math A; Superintendent's Sch F-T Gifted; Va Commonwealth U; Acct.

CLARKE, Deborah Sue
Lansdowne Sr HS; Baltimore, MD (50-500) Chor; FBLA; Bkbl.

CLARKE, Elaine Angella
Frank H Morrell HS; Irvington, NJ (231-520) Secy, FNA; Sftbl; Swim; Fairleigh Dickinson Col; Nurs.

CLARKE, Jeffrey Brian
Wachusett Regional HS; Holden, MA (50-500) Ski C; Tres, SC; Tr; Entertainment.

CLARKE, Karen Jean
Wessington HS; Wessington, SD (1-14) Ed, Ann; Band; Pres, Bus C; Chldr; Chor; Dbte Tm; Drama; Pres, FBLA; GS; Mjrte; Pres, NFL; NHS; Rptr, Sch P; SC; Thes; Amer Leg A; Beauty; Citz A; DARGCA; HQn; Hon Prog; Journ A; Q&S A; Spch A; Type A; Val; Yth Fel; Northern St Col; Elem Ed.

CLELAND, Christie Lynn
R B Stall HS; Charleston Heights, SC (11-213) Bus C; FBLA; FTA; Hmrm; NHS; Span C; SC; *Baptist Col; Bus Adm.*

CLELLAND, Kimberly Ann
Mannington HS; Mannington, WV (2-110) Chldr; Pres, Fr C; GS; Hmrm; NHS; Ed, Sch P; Tres, Sr Cl; Journ A; Q&S A; Sal; Type A; Woodmen o-t World Hist A; Schol A; Prom C; Shorthand A; Jostens A; *Fairmont St Col; Elem Ed.*

CLEM, Jackie Ann
Gettys D Broome HS; Spartanburg, SC; Chor; Drama; Tres, FHA; Lat C; *U of SC-SPARTANBURG; Nurs.*

CLEM, Karen Sue
Theodore Roosevelt HS; San Antonio, TX (60-694) Band; Ensm; FBLA; NHS; Rptr, Sch P; *U of Tex at San Antonio; Executive Secy.*

CLEM, Kathleen Louise
Theodore Roosevelt HS; San Antonio, TX (40-900) VP; Band; Ensm; FTA; Math C; Mu Alpha Theta; VP, NHS; Math A; MLS; *U of Tex at San Antonio; Teaching.*

CLEMENGER, Sue B
Whitefish HS; Whitefish, MT (10-160) AFS; Band; Thes; Alg A; COM; 4H A; Math A; NMS; Sci A; *U of Mont; Math.*

CLEMENS, Deanna Lisa
Hobart Sr HS; Hobart, IN; Pres, Chor; Ensm; Mgr, Tr; Hon Prog; *Lincoln Christian Col; Sociology.*

CLEMENT, Karen Diana
Briarfield Acad; Lake Providence, LA (2-49) Band; Tres, BC; Chor; Fr C; 4H; Lit Ral; Sci C; S-T, Soph Cl; Mgr, Bkbl; Tr; COM; 4H A; Hon Prog; I Dare You; Sal; Yth Church Choir; One Way C; *La Tech U; Ed.*

CLEMENT, Marianne
Dover HS; Dover, NH (2-400) Math C; Mu Alpha Theta; NHS; Co-Cpt, Bkbl; Co-Cpt, Hockey; Sftbl; Tr; God & Country A; Hon Prog; Math A; *U of NH.*

CLEMENT, Patty Gaye
Henderson Co Sr HS; Henderson, KY; Co-Ed, Ann; Chor; Hmrm; Secy, Lat C; NHS; Span C; SC; Hon Prog; Sci A; Tres, Church Yth Group; *Henderson Comm Col; Lab Tech.*

CLEMENTS, Betsy Ann
Amory HS; Amory, MS (10%-130) Ann; FBLA; Pres, NHS; Sch P; Pres, Span C; Pres, Thes; VP, Y-Tns; Mgr, Bkbl; Amer Leg A; DARGCA; Hon Prog; Rotary A; Sci A; Pres Phys Fitness; PA; *Ole Miss; Phys Therapy.*

CLEMENTS, Christine Renee
Center Grove HS; Greenwood, IN (10%-315) Fr C; 4H; Math C; SC; Tres, Soph Cl; Sftbl; Tr; Booster C; US Vlbl Assn Tm; Christian Yth Fel; Ntl Sunshine Soc; Lassie League Sftbl; Most Improved, Vlbl; *Purdue U; Vet Med.*

CLEMENTS, Debra Lynn
Plant City Sr HS; Plant City, FL; Chor; Hmrm; Citz A; PA.

CLEMENTS, Jesse Andrew
Evergreen Park Comm HS; Evergreen Park, IL (29-432) MVP, Chess C; Math C; NHS; Var C; JV, Cr-Ctry; Swim; JV, Tr; Hon Prog; Water Polo; Nom, Research A; Fin, Bausch & Lomb Sci A; *Northwestern U; Pre-Law.*

CLEMENTS, Karen Lee
Sacred Heart HS; Kingston, MA (3-54) JV, Chldr; Chor; Key C; NHS; VP, Sr Cl; JV, Bkbl; Fr A; Elmira Col A; Yrbk Staff; *Col o-t Holy Cross; Liberal Arts.*

CLEMENTS, Keith William
Englewood Christian HS; Independence, MO; Chor; Yth Fel; *U of Mo; Eng.*

CLEMENTS, Mark Forrest
St Dominic Regional HS; Lewiston, ME; Drama; JV, Bsbl; JA A; Type A.

CLEMENTS, Nathan Tillman
Claiborne Acad; Haynesville, LA (6-41) Chem C; Lit Ral; Yth Fel; Yth Foundation; Lisa Rally; VP, Fresh Cl; *LSU; Vet Med.*

CLEMENTS, Renee Elaine
Aquinas HS; Southgate, MI (10-250) Pres, A Cap Choir; Chor; Dbte Tm; NHS; Rptr, Sch P; Bkbl; Yth Fel; *U of Mich; Psych.*

CLEMENTS, Timothy Ray
Nottoway Sr HS; Crewe, VA (30-300) Chem C; Sci C; Span C; Ftbl; Tr; *Va Tech; Sci.*

CLEMENTSON, Lori Ann
Sooner HS; Bartlesville, OK (2-291) Band; NHS; Tnns; *U of Okla; Med.*

CLEMMER, Brenda Louise
Milburn HS; Milburn, OK (4%-22) VP, 4H; NHS; Bkbl; Sftbl; 4H A; JA A; Val; All Tourn Tm A; *Murray St U; Phys Ed.*

CLEMMER, Juliana Gail
Milburn HS; Milburn, OK; Cpt, Chldr; Secy, 4H; NHS; Secy, SC; Secy, Sr Cl; JV, Bkbl; Gov Honor Prog; 4H A; Hon Prog; Math A; Sal; Yth Fel; Rptr, 4-H C; *Murray St Col; Math.*

CLEMMER, Misty Rae
Shamrock HS; Shamrock, TX (1-50) Band; VP, FHA; NHS; Mgr, Bkbl; Tnns; WW, Soph; *Math.*

CLEMMONS, Clara Louise
Marion HS; Marion, IN; *Nurs.*

CLEMMONS, Ernest Jay
Lawrence HS; Lawrence, KS (750-1000) A Cap Choir; Arch; Tnns.

CLEMMONS, Sonya Renee
W Carteret HS; Morehead City, NC (40%-250) Band; Chldr; Hmrm; Cpt, Mjrte; Span C; SC; Tr; HCt; Most Out; Head Mjrte A; *Norfolk St Col; Bus Adm.*

CLEMONS, Arnetta Kay
Bishop Dunne HS; Dallas, TX (37-154) Chor; Vol Prog; HR; *U of Tex at Arlington; Pre-Law.*

CLEMONS, Carlton L
George Washington HS; Los Angeles, CA; Fr C; Cpt, Bkbl; Cpt, Tr; Spch A; Ntl Fr Contest; *Archt.*

CLEMONS, Curtis
Northeastern HS; Detroit, MI; InterAct C; Cr-Ctry; Citz A; Cl Fav; Hon Prog; Math A.

CLEMONS, Deborah Faith
Hernando HS; Brooksville, FL; VP, Anchor C; Band; Span C; Beauty; COM; Cl Fav; Pres A; Yth Fel; Yth Leg; *Asbury Col; Med.*

CLEMONS, Mark A
Raytown HS; Raytown, MO (10%-500) NHS; Mgr, Bkbl; Co-Cpt, Ftbl; Wrest; Spch A; Eagle Sct; Warrior, Tribe Mic-O-Say.

CLEMONS, Michael Gene
Raytown HS; Raytown, MO (16-500) Band; NHS; Ftbl; Tr; Co-Cpt, Wrest; God & Country A; Pres A; Regent Schol; Sci A; Outst Fresh Ftbl Player; Industrial Arts A; John Strohm Schol A; Eagle Sct; *Southwest Mo St; Cons And Wildlife Mgt.*

CLEMONS, Michele LeeAnn
Cooper HS; Abilene, TX (25%-500) Band; Ensm; Secy, Hmrm; Tri-HiY; Beauty; COM; Lion A; Gym; UIL A's; Girl o-t Mo; *Abilene Christian U; Phys Ed.*

CLEMSON, Gail Louise
Hershey Sr HS; Hershey, PA (50%-390) All Amer Yth; Sch P; JV, Bkbl; JV, Hockey; Sftbl; 100 Hr Pin, Hospital Vol; Vlbl C; *Harrisburg Area Comm Col; Bookkeeping.*

CLENDANIEL, Mary Kathryn
Caesar Rodney Sr HS; Camden Wyoming, DE (27-394) Bus C; FHA; NHS; Orch; Loc & St A, VICA C; John Wesley A; 1st Run-Up, Outst Sr Girl, Church; St Ldrship Conf.

CLENDENEN, Kimberly Jo
East HS; Pueblo, CO; Band; Chor; 4H; 4H A; Yth Fel; Candystriper; Church Nursery Attendant; *Nurs.*

CLENDENON, Cynthia Jean
Heritage Christian Sch; Indianapolis, IN (5-38) Lit Mag; Co-Ed, Sch P; Var C; Tres, Sr Cl; Bkbl; Hockey; Tr; COM; Hon Prog; Journ A; Heritage Hon Soc; Sports Ed; *Butler U; Sci.*

CLETO, Paciencia Clarissa
Orofino HS; Orofino, ID (20%-120) F-Ed, Ann; Chldr; VP, Chor; Fr C; 4H; Bkbl; 4H A; All Around Yth, Horse Show; *Wash St U; Equestrian Courses.*

CLEVELAND, Bobby Glenn
Union HS; Union, MS (12-48) BC; Pres, Sci C; Ftbl; COM; Art A; *E Central Jr Col; Archt.*

CLEVELAND, Bryan Robert
Deerborne Sch; Coral Gables, FL (1-100) Dbte Tm; Drama; Key C; NHS; Pres, SC; Bkbl; Hon Prog; WW; *Harvard Col; Law.*

CLEVELAND, Charles Kevin
Stamps HS; Stamps, AR (33-65) FFA; Ftbl; Tr; Cl Fav; Rptr, VICA.

CLEVELAND, Chris Orrin
Hart Co HS; Hartwell, GA (25%-290) Bus C; VP, 4H; Tres, Key C; Math C; NHS; Sci C; COM; Citz A; 4H A; Hist A; I Dare You; JA A; Opt Out Tn; Ntl 4-H Health Win; St Key A; St Master 4-H C; Distinguished Ldrship A; *Ga Sou Col; Agr.*

CLEVELAND, Elizabeth Kay
Wm J Brown HS; Sturgis, SD (42-196) Band; Chldr; Dbte Tm; FTA; Hmrm; Jr Miss Pagent; NFL; NHS; Ski C; SC; Spch A; VFW A; VofDEM; Yth Fel; Pres, Yth Fel; St Legislative Page; Miss Personality, Miss Tn SD; *Black Hills St Col; Elem Ed.*

CLEVELAND, Elizabeth Windsor
Petaluma HS; Petaluma, CA (18-270) A Cap Choir; Bus C; Chldr; Chor; Pres, Cum Laude Soc; Dbte Tm; Pres, Drama; Pres, Fr C; FBLA; Rptr, Hmrm; Co-Ed, Sch P; Secy, SC; Thes; Beauty; CSF; Hon Prog; Spch A; VofDEM; *Sweet Briar Col; Dramatic Arts.*

CLEVELAND, Gerald Alan
Pleasant Grove HS; Pleasant Grove, AL (33-180) Ftbl; Tnns; *Auburn U; Forestry.*

CLEVELAND, Karen Lianne
Plainview HS; Plainview, TX (92-550) A Cap Choir; Span C; Tres, Jr Cl; JV, Tnns; *Baylor U; Pol Sci.*

CLEVELAND, Melodie Anise
Walnut Ridge HS; Columbus, OH (10%-180) Band; Chor; Ensm; Span C; *Captial Col; Child Ed.*

CLEVELAND, Robert Bruce
Sturgis HS; Sturgis, SD; Band; BS; Hmrm; Ski C; SC; Var C; Golf; COM; VFW A; *U of SD; Med.*

CLEVELAND, Sara Nell
Shelbyville Central HS; Shelbyville, TN (48-325) Chor; Drama; InterAct C; Up Bound; *Phys Therapy.*

CLEVELAND, Tammie Renea
Stamps HS; Stamps, AR (4-60) Bus Mgr, Ann; Chldr; FBLA; FHA; Mu Alpha Theta; NHS; Sch P; Secy, Sci C; Bkbl; Tr; Beauty; COM; Cl Fav; Med Tech.*

CLEVENGER, Brenda Joan
John Glenn HS; New Concord, OH (48-160) Pres, Band; Chor; Ensm; FNA; Lat C; Pres, Orch; Y-Tns; Arion A, Band; *Capital U; Nurs.*

CLEVENGER, Charles Van
Mound Westonka HS; Mound, MN (1-275) Band; Dbte Tm; Ensm; Sch P; Pres, Sci C; Span C; Bausch & Lomb A; MLS; Ntl Sci Symposium; Sci A; Fin, Interntl Sci Fair; St Piano A's; St Page; *U of Minn; Med.*

CLEVENGER, J Todd
Central HS; Camp Point, IL; Sci C; Sci A; *Elec.*

CLEVERINGA, Ruth Eileen
Luverne Jr-Sr HS; Luverne, MN (74%-138) Chor; FHA; Bkbl; *Willmar Vocation Tech Inst; Med Secy.*

CLIATT, Hazel Irelle
W Laurens Sr HS; Dublin, GA; *Mus.*

CLIBURN, Brad Randall
Florence HS; Florence, MS (54-180) Chess C; VP, FFA; Sci C; Bsbl; Co-Cpt, Bkbl; Cl Fav; Bible C; Stu Adv; All St Bsbl; Stu Govt; Mr Florence HS; Campus Life; Most Ath; Sportsmanship A; Best All Around; *Hinds Jr Col; Health.*

CLIBURN, James Harlin Jr
Plant City Sr HS; Plant City, FL (355-600) Band; Church Orch; Band A.

CLICK, Cheryl Lynn
Portsmouth E HS; Portsmouth, OH (25-85) Chor; 4H; Lat C; HCt; *Home Ec.*

CLIFFORD, Debra Diane
Dan River HS; Ringgold, VA (13-238) Ann; BC; Chor; Drama; Span C; Tri-HiY; Jr Marshal; Averett Col; Special Ed.

CLIFFORD, James Edward
West Haven HS; W Haven, CT (14-600) BS; Pres, CYO; Fr C; French NHS; Hmrm; NHS; Ski C; SC; Bkbl; Cr-Ctry; Soccer; Tr; Citz A; H of F; Rotary A; Sch Spirit A; Ten Outst Sr; Georgetown U; Amer Stu.

CLIFFORD, Paul Christopher
Loyola HS; Towson, MD (4-134) Co-Ed, Ann; Hmrm; NHS; Order/Arrow; Ed, Sch P; SC; Mgr, Ftbl; Mgr, Swim; COM; NEDT; Order/Arrow A; Cpt, Frisbee Tm; NML; Math; Math.

CLIFFORD, Pauline May
George Washington Sr HS; Mangilao, GUAM; Pres, NHS; Rptr, Sch P; Alg A; Citz A; Val; Top Ten; 4 0 A; U of Colo; Journ.

CLIFFORD, Rhonda Patricia
Wallbrook Sr HS; Baltimore, MD; Tr; HR; City Wide Gym; UMBC; Sci.

CLIFFORD, Sandra Marquerita
Western HS; Baltimore, MD; Band; Chldr; Chor; Drama; Hmrm; Mjrte; ARC; Secy, Sr Cl; Secy, Jr Cl; Tres, Soph Cl; JV, Bkbl; JV, Sftbl; JV, Tnns; JV, Tr; Beauty; Cl Fav; Yth Fel; Gym A; Miss Poly A; U of Md; Journ.

CLIFT, Randell Warren
Fountain Central HS; Veedersburg, IN (10-135) Band; BS; Ensm; Lat C; NHS; Var C; Bsbl; Tnns; Wrest; COM; H of F; Ind U; Radio & TV Communication.

CLIFTON, Carolyn Rae
Englewood Sr HS; Jacksonville, FL; A Cap Choir; Band; Chor; Ensm; Hmrm; SC; Swim; Jacksonville U; Mus Ed.

CLIFTON, Charles Randall
McGavock HS; Nashville, TN; BC; NHS; Y-Tns; Bkbl; Ftbl; Sftbl; Sci A; Archt.

CLIFTON, Dee Ann
Skyline HS; Dallas, TX; Chor; FHA; Sch P; SC; Bkbl; Tnns; Hon Prog; Vlbl; Drill Tm; Stephen F Austin St U; Eng.

CLIFTON, Marta Gay
Frederick HS; Frederick, OK (8-57) Ann; Chor; Hmrm; NHS; Ed, Sch P; SC; Bkbl; Swim; Coun of Teach A; GS Alt; WW; Pres, Sorority; Okla St U; Journ.

CLIFTON, Patricia A
Maria Regina Diocesan HS; Uniondale, NY; Chor; Drama; Ensm; Ger C; Ntl Yth Conf; Secy, Y-Tns; Bkbl; Sftbl; MLS; Most Outt; Sci A; Coronary Surgeon.

CLIFTON, Shelley Marie
Yukon HS; Yukon, OK; Chor; Drama; Ensm; FHA; FBLA; Tnns; St Vocal A; Bethany Nazarene Col.

CLIFTON, Susan Marie
Live Oak HS; Morgan Hill, CA (153-369) Chldr; Pres, FHA; Hmrm; InterClub Coun; Orch; Sch P; Ftbl; Crisco A; FHA Hero, Medals & Trophy; John Brown U; Home Ec.

CLINCO, Karen Dorothy
Bayside HS; Bayside, NY (137-1138) COM; Arista Soc; Stenotype Inst; Ct Rptr.

CLINE, Alvadine Lili
Fairbury HS; Fairbury, NE (11-126) Band; Chor; 4H; Span C; Elk A; Hon Prog; WW; U of Nebr; Horticulture.

CLINE, Angela Buie
Lenoir HS; Lenoir, NC (14-110) Fin, AFS; Band; Chess C; Chor; VP, Drama; FHA; Lit Mag; Ski C; Span C; Thes; WW; Warren Wilson Col; Drama.

CLINE, Donna Nell
Hall HS; Little Rock, AR; FBLA; HR; Central Baptist Col; Elem Ed.

CLINE, Frank Atwill
Del Norte Co HS; Del Norte Co, CA (15-279) NHS; Order/Arrow; S-T, Var C; Mgr, Bsbl; Mgr, Bkbl; Ftbl; Mgr, Wrest; Yth Fel; Mgr o-t Yr; Co o-t Redwoods; Civil Engr.

CLINE, Gregory E
S Point HS; Belmont, NC (50%-211) Ann; Band; Chor; Drama; Span C; Tri-HiY; Jr Marshal; Averett Col; Museology.

CLINE, Janelle Gay
Cottage Grove HS; Cottage Grove, OR (33%-260) Tres, A Cap Choir; A-Ed, Ann; Thes; Pres, United Methodist Yth; The Col of Idaho; Mus.

CLINE, Jo Anne
Fairfield HS; Fairfield, OH (83-650) Chor; NHS; Span C; Type A.

CLINE, Linda Sue
Kubasaki HS; Okinawa, JAPAN (3-271) Ann.

CLINE, Michael Dewey
Gadsden HS; Gadsden, AL (41-351) A Cap Choir; Pres, Band; Chor; Ensm; FTA; InterClub Coun; NHS; Orch; Pres, SC; Tnns; COM; Citz A; Cl Fav; Hon Prog; MLS; Most Out; PTA A; Pres, A Star Student; Yth Fel; Gadsden St Jr Col; Pre-Law.

CLINE, Ralph Dalton Jr
N Gaston Sr HS; Dallas, NC (3-250) Pres, Band; VP, BC; Pres, Hmrm; InterClub Coun; VP, Span C; SC; Chem A; 1st Chair of Amer; Span A; U of NC; Chem.

CLINE, Robert Wayne
Wintersville HS; Wintersville, OH; Bethany Col; Sci.

CLINE, Sandra Leah
NW Sr HS; Hyattsville, MD (200-600) Hmrm; SC; Var C; Cpt, Sftbl; PG Comm Col; Bus.

CLINE, Sandy Jean
Cottage Grove HS; Cottage Grove, OR (18-260) NHS; Bkbl; JV, Tr; Vlbl; Stewardess.

CLINE, Timothy Ray
Huntington HS; Huntington, WV; Chor; ARC; SC; Mgr, Ftbl; Wrest; Gifted & Talented; Journ.

CLINESMITH, Frederick Clinton
Waco HS; Waco, TX (25%-350) Dbte Tm; Drama; Hmrm; Span C; Spch C; SC; Thes; Cpt, Golf; COM; Baylor U; Pol Sci.

CLINTON, Deena Gail
Lindale HS; Lindale, TX; A Cap Choir; Ed, Ann; Co-Cpt, Chldr; Drama; Math C; Ed, Sch P; Spch C; Var C; Tnns; Tr; Cl Fav; Coronation Duchess; St Fair Chldr Championship; NCA; Tyler Jr Col.

CLINTON, Gregory Wayne
Durham HS; Durham, NC; A Cap Choir; BS; Chldr; Chor; Pres, Hmrm; InterClub Coun; Madrigal; Pres, Math C; Span C; Spch C; Tres, Jr Cl; Pres, SC; Pres, Jr Cl; VP, Soph Cl; Cr-Ctry; JV, Ftbl; Tr; Math A; TH Clagget A; Convention Del, NCASC; Pol Sci.

CLINTON, James D
Ellenville Central HS; Ellenville, NY (40%-125) ARC; Span C; Var C; Ftbl; Tr; Wrest; NEDT; Yth Fel; 2nd Tm All UCAL; Ftbl; Fla Inst of Tech; Oceanography.

CLIPLEF, Tad Alan
Montevideo Sr HS; Montevideo, MN (20-160) Pres, Band; Ensm; Orch; SC; Swim; Tnns; All St Orch; U of Minn; Pre-Med.

CLIPNER, Patricia Ann
Neshaminy Langhorne HS; Langhorne, PA (105-750) A Cap Choir; S-T, Band; Chor; Drama; Hmrm; Cpt, Mjrte; Rainbow; Cl Fav; MLS; Most Out; Opt Out Tn.

CLISTER, Mary Beth
Tri Co Christian HS; Mechanicsburg, PA; Chess C; Chor; Fin, Crown & Scepter; Dbte Tm; Drama; 4H; Sch P; Span C; Bkbl; Sftbl; Tnns; Tr; Fin, Spelling A; Med Asst.

CLODFELTER, Jennifer Ellen
Edwards Co Sr HS; Albion, IL (1-110) Drama; FHA; FNA; 4H; Sch P; 4H A; Spch A; Bradley U; Computer Prog.

CLOESSNER, Russell Wade
Bellaire HS; Bellaire, TX (10%-720) Pres, Chess C; Fr C; Pres, Ger C; SC; Alg A; Hist A; Hon Prog; NEDT; PTA A; NJHS; Ntl Piano Guild; Whitlock Mus Theory Medals; Rice U; Sci.

CLONINGER, Patrick Caswell
North State Acad; Hickory, NC (2-12) Band; Chor; Drama; Fr C; God & Country A; Eagle Sct; Drama A; Museology.

CLOSE, Anne Therese
Carl Sandburg HS; Orland Park, IL (160-840) A-Ed, Ann; Band; Fr C; NHS; Tres, SC; Mgr, Cr-Ctry; Mgr, Tr; St Scholar; WW; HR; U of Ill; Lib Arts.

CLOSE, Buncie Elizabeth
Parkview HS; Springfield, MO (15%-400) Band; Ensm; Span C; Bkbl; Tnns; Nurs.

CLOTFELTER, Susan Katherine
Grinnell Comm HS; Grinnell, IA; A Cap Choir; Band; Ensm; Ger C; NHS; Orch; NMS; All St Band; Grinnell Col Orch; Grinnell Col Collegium Musieum; U of Iowa; Mus.

CLOUATRE, Joan Renee
Roxana HS; Roxana, IL (10%-300) Band; Olivet Nazarene Col; Med.

CLOUD, Eric Scott
Hollywood HS; Hollywood, CA (3-700) Band; Chor; Tres, Key C; Church Asst Organist; Soloist & Accomp, Sch & Comm Events; Westminster Choir Col; Mus.

CLOUD, Joanne Phyllis
Rule HS; Rule, TX (1-20) BC; Chldr; Chor; VP, FHA; Pres, 4H; Ed, Sch P; S-T, Jr Cl; Rptr, Soph Cl; Bkbl; Tnns; Tr; Cl Fav; 4H A; Church Organist; Sch Accreditation Goals Comm; Ann Qn Ct; Hon Men, All Dist Bkbl; UIL Regional Qualifier.

CLOUD, Michael Lynn
Samuel F B Morse HS; San Diego, CA (1-465) Chor; Model UN; Var C; Bkbl; Citz A; Hist A; PTA A; Val; Point Loma Col; Pol Sci.

CLOUSE, James Edward
Somerset HS; Somerset, KY (5-206) Pres, Hmrm; Bsbl; JV, Bkbl; HCt; Hon Prog; Pres, Fresh Cl.

CLOUSE, James Scott
Owensboro Cath HS; Owensboro, KY; CYO; Drama; 4H; Hmrm; Mod Mus Mas; Spch C; Arch; Bkbl; Swim; Tnns; Art A; Racing A; Brecia Col; Art.

CLOUSE, Jeanne E
Hollywood Professional HS; Hollywood, CA (2-40) Pres, Community Yth; NHSph; Bank Of Amer A; COM; NEDT; Paris Conservatory; Violin & Piano.

CLOUSE, Kathryn Louise
Alto HS; Alto, TX (10-29) Band; Chldr; FHA; 4H; A-Ed, Sch P; Bkbl; JV, Sftbl; Tr; I Dare You; Yth Fel; Hist C Schol; Lon Morris Jr Col; Elem Ed.

CLOUTIER, Marie Cecile
St Dominic Regional HS; Lewiston, ME (2-108) CYO; Chor; Fr C; NHS; Rptr, Sch P; Ski C; Y-Tns; JV, Tnns; NEDT; Phy A; Sci A; Future Medics of Amer; Pres, GScts; Med.

CLOUZET, Patricia Elizabeth
Glendale Acad; Glendale, CA; A Cap Choir; Chor; Secy, Span C; Pacific Union Col; Languages.

CLOVER, Susan Renee
Ardmore HS; Ardmore, OK (40-282) Chor; FTA; NHS; OSU; Bus.

CLOWER, Iroma Christine
Cotton Center HS; Cotton Center, TX (5-18) Ann; Dbte Tm; FHA; Secy, FTA; Wayland Baptist Col; Elem Ed.

CLOWERS, Emmanuel
Frederick Douglass HS; Atlanta, GA; Bsbl; Bkbl; Soccer; Tnns; Wrest; MLS; Star Student.

CLUBB, Bobbie Lynn
Chester F Awalt HS; Mountain View, CA; Chldr; Chor; Drama; Rptr, Hmrm; SC; Secy, Sr Cl; Ftbl; Swim; HCt; Swtht; Peer Counciling; Helping Handicapped; De Anza Jr Col; Occupational Therapy.

CLUBB, Elizabeth Anne
Notre Dame HS; Clarksburg, WV (8-63) Dbte Tm; Drama; Fr C; FBLA; FTA; Ger C; Lat C; Math C; NFL; NHS; Tres, ARC; Sci C; Span C; Spch C; Cpt, Tnns; Spch A; Pres, Tnns, Mus C; 1st Pl, St Ntl Woolsewing; Win, Co Tnns Tournaments; Semi Fin, St Tnns Tournament; North Western U; Medicine.

CLUBB, Jeffrey Allan
Sigourney Comm HS; Sigourney, IA (100-130) Chess C; FFA; Ed, Sch P; Var C; VP, Sr Cl; Co-Cpt, Ftbl; Cpt, Wrest; HCt; Yth Fel; All St Hon Men, Ftbl; St Qualifier, Wrest; Waldorf Col; Bio.

CLUBINE, Deborah Jo
Caney Valley HS; Caney, KS (9-66) Bus Mgr, Ann; Ensm; Pres, FFA; Pres, 4H; VP, NHS; Span C; SC; Bkbl; 4H A; St Scholar; WW; Kans St U; Agr.

CLUBINE, Donna Jill
Caney Valley Jr-Sr HS; Caney, KS (10%-70) Drama; FHA; Tres, 4H; JV, Bkbl; 4H A; Phys Therapy.

CLUCKEY, Mary Sue
Clay Sr HS; Oregon, OH; Band; Chor; FNA; 4H; Hmrm; Mjrte; Sch P; Sftbl; Tr; 4H A; Hon Prog; Sci A; Mus A; Yth Larc A; Band A; Phys Fitness A; Toledo U; Med.

CLUGSTON, Janette Gay
Pittsburg HS; Pittsburg, KS; A Cap Choir; Chor; Ensm; Span C; Golf; Alg A; Bio A; COM; Math A; Social Sci.

CLUNK, Marlene May
Riverview HS; Sarasota, FL (10%-635) Band; Nurs.

CLUPEPPER, Katherine Naomi
Huntsville HS; Huntsville, AL (32-500) Anchor C; Chem C; InterClub Coun; NHS; Rptr, Sch P; Tres, Jr Cl; B Crocker A; Maryville Col; Religion.

CLUSKEY, David Brent
Brimfield Unit Dist 309 HS; Brimfield, IL (12-63) Bus C; FFA; Chapter Farmer; Ill Central Col; Agr.

CLUSS, Constance Adair
Uniontown Area Sr HS; Uniontown, PA (11-450) Arch; Band; Chor; Dbte Tm; Drama; Tres, FTA; Pres, Hmrm; Math C; NFL; Tres, NHS; Pres, Phys C; Co-Ed, Sch P; Sci C; Ski C; Span C; SC; U of Va; Chem.

CLUTE, Cindy Jane
Rock Hill HS; Rock Hill, SC (3-450) Chor; NHS; Secy, Sci C; Span C; B Crocker A; Hon Prog; NMF; Jr & Sr Marshal; Furman, Burroughs, Schol; WW; Furman U; Biol.

CLUTTER, Cherri Lynn
Obion Co Central HS; Troy, TN (21-185) BC; Tres, Chor; Rptr, FBLA; FHA; U of Tenn; Nurs.

CLUTTER, Sara Jane
Pueblo Central HS; Pueblo, CO (9-627) Model UN; Monogram; Secy, NHS; ARC; Ski C; Mgr, Swim; B Crocker A; God & Country A; Hon Prog; Regent Schol; Jr Escort; Hon's Inst, Engr; U of Colo; Nurs.

CLYDE, Laura Ann
Robbinsdale Sr HS; Robbinsdale, MN; A Cap Choir; Band; Mjrte; Hon Prog; OEA; Augsburg Col; Para Legal.

COACHMAN, Marcia Elaine
Woodlawn Prog-Wakefield Sr HS; Arlington, VA (116-457) NC Central Col; Sociology.

COAD, Daniel Warren
Waukegan W HS; Waukegan, IL (3-387) Pres, Band; BS; Ensm; Ger C; Math C; Pres, NHS; Amer Leg A; Citz A; Hon Prog; Math A; Order/Arrow A; ROTC A; Yth Fel; King of Turnabout; Outst Sr Bandsman; Marine Phys Fitness A; Col of Lake Co; Math.

COADES, Wanda Denise
Chester HS; Chester, PA;

COADY, Kimberly Ann
N Shore HS; W Palm Beach, FL (8-336) Chess C; Fr C; Secy, FBLA; Hmrm; Alg A; Bio A; Fr As; Geo A; Eng A; FAU; Acct.

COADY, Tracy Ellen
Bayshore Methodist Christian Sch; Tampa, FL (1-13) Bus Mgr, Ann; Chldr; Hmrm; Ed, Sch P; SC; Happiest Girl; Hillsborough Comm Col; Math.

COAST, Michael Ray
Sooner HS; Bartlesville, OK (25-280) Key C; NHS; Cpt, Ftbl; Cpt, Tr; Bio A; Kiwanis A; Ftbl, Blue Chip List; Ftbl, All-St & All-Dist; Tr, Blue Chip List; Shot Put St Champ; Ou Signee, Ftbl; Okla U; Construction Engr.

COATES, Jeffrey S
Carman Sr HS; Flint, MI; A Cap Choir; Chess C; Chor; Order/Arrow; Co-Cpt, Hockey; Cpt, Soccer; Hon Prog; Order/Arrow A; Eagle Sct; U of Mich; Law.

COATES, Jennifer Lee
Hillcrest Lutheran Acad; Fergus Falls, MN (2-63) A Cap Choir; Ann; JV, Chldr; NHS; COM; Chamber of Comm A; Hon Prog; Val; Girl's Dorm Council; Foreign Mission Comm; Vern Watson Mem Schol; Fergus Falls Comm Col; Art.

COATES, Nicholas Edwin
Abilene HS; Abilene, TX (25%-550) A Cap Choir; Ann; Chldr; Chor; HiY; Hmrm; Key C; Lit Mag; JV, Bkbl; Sftbl; COM; Cl Fav; Lion A; Most Out; Opt A; Opt Out Tn; Abilene Christian U; Bible.

COATES, Robert Lane
Mascoutah Comm HS; Mascoutah, IL (78-300) Chess C; Var C; JV, Bkbl; Cr-Ctry; JV, Ftbl; Swim; Tnns; Tr; JV, Wrest; Spch A; Christian Ath C; Conf Tr A; Miss AF Comm Col; Elec Tech.

COATES, Susan Marie
Mio Au Sable HS; Mio, MI (4-49) Band; Chor; GS; Pres, NHS; Pres, Sr Cl; Tres, Soph Cl; Bkbl; Sftbl; 4H A; HCt; Journ A; Pres A; 'Freddie A', Sculpture; Musical Leads; WW; Fine Arts.

COATNEY, Russell Eric
Glenwood Comm HS; Glenwood, IA (7-135) Co-Ed, Ann; Band; BS; NHS; SC; Bsbl; Co-Cpt, Bkbl; Ftbl; Tr; Pres A; MVP, Bkbl; Iowa St U; Med.

COATS, Barbara Jean
Mt Carroll HS; Mt Carroll, IL (1-54) Cpt, Chldr; FHA; 4H; NHS; SC; Co-Cpt, Bkbl; Tr; COM; DARGCA; HQn; HCt; Math A; Spch A; Type A; Val; St Schol; WW; Eng A; Outst SC Member A; Augustana Col.

COATS, Cathy Lane
Nacogdoches HS; Nacogdoches, TX (6-295) Pres, FHA; InterClub Coun; Secy, NHS; Sci C; Span C; SC; Secy, Sr Cl; Hist A; HCt; Hon Prog; Type A; Eng A; Span A; Homemaking A; Stephen F Austin U; Med Technology.

COATS, Debora Lynn
Springfield HS; Springfield, LA (2-59) Band; BC; FBLA; 4H; Lit Ral; Secy, Jr Cl; Hist A; Sal; Southeastern La Col; Sci.

COATS, Randal Wayne
Tampa Bay Voc-Tech HS; Tampa, FL; Chor; Span C; Y-Tns; Citz A; Bible Quiz A.

COATSWORTH, Cindy Joan
Pueblo HS; Tucson, AZ (5-400) Tres, Chldr; GS; Hmrm; Model UN; NHS; ARC; Secy, SC; VP, Var C; Y-Tns; Amer Leg A; COM; Citz A; Crisco A; HCt; Opt A; Opt Out Tn; Rotary A; Type A; S-T, Ben Franklin C; Fin, Miss Ntl Teenage Pageant; Outst Printer; Achv Nom.

COBB, Alisa Ann
Eastern Guilford HS; Gibsonville, NC (10-177) Band; U of NC Mus.

COBB, Betty Gail
W Monroe HS; W Monroe, LA (78-603) Ed, Bus C; Chor; NHS; Sftbl; Hist A; La Col.

COBB, Brian O Riley
Lamar HS; Arlington, TX (184-475) Band; Hmrm; Lat C; Ch, SC; VP, Sr Cl; Ch, Jr Cl; Ch, Soph Cl; Bkbl; Semi-Fin, Tr; Cl Fav; Most Out; Yth Leg; Mr LHS; MVP, Cpt, Ftbl; Soph Favorite; Jr Favorite; Ftbl Ltr; UTA; Bus.

COBB, Cathy
Canton Acad; Canton, MS; BC; VP, CYO; Spch C; Y-Tns; Type A; Home Ec A; Holmes Jr Col; Home Ec.

COBB, Charles Howard
Red Bank HS; Red Bank, TN (12-360) Band; Lat C; Order/Arrow; Sch P; SC; Order/Arrow A; Stage Crew; U of Tenn; Dentistry.

COBB, Helen Ramona
Early HS; Blakely, GA; Chor; Span C; Sftbl; Tnns; Hist A; Art C; Albany Area Vo-tech Col; Computer Sci.

COBB, James Edward
Harlingen HS; Harlingen, TX; 4H; VP, Key C; Ftbl; U of Tex; Wildlife.

COBB, James Stewart
Alcoa HS; Alcoa, TN (5-100) Math C; Order/Arrow; Span C; Tnns; Order/Arrow A; U of Tenn.

COBB, Joyce Ann
Rye Cove HS; Clinchport, VA; BC; Chldr; Drama; FBLA; 4H; NHS; Spch C; MECC; Bus.

COBB, Kathleen Mae
Stevens HS; Rapid City, SD (179-415) Band; JV, Chldr; FHA; Rainbow; Black Hills St Col; Secy.

COBB, Kelly Ann
Canton Acad; Canton, MS; Ann; Band; BC; Pres, CYO; Y-Tns; Tres, Soph Cl; Sftbl; COM; Cl Fav; HCt; Holmes Jr Col.

COBB, Kevin Lee
Starmount HS; Boonville, NC (10%-211) Drama; Ger C; JV, Ftbl; Gov Honor Prog.

COBB, Lisa Adryelle
Riverside Jr-Sr HS; Taylor, PA (42-189) Chor; Drama; Lit Mag; VP, Rainbow; Amer Leg A; Elk A; PTA A; WW, Mus Stu; St Gov's Sch o-t Arts; Eng.

COBB, Mary Louise
Sherman E Burroughs HS; Ridgecrest, CA (57-370) AFS; Key C; VP, SC; Bank Of Amer A; Elk A; Hon Prog; Fin, 'Girls Town Project'; LIFE Bible Col; Special Ed.

COBB, Melissa Ellen
Washington Irving HS; Clarksburg, WV; Band; Scorekeeper, Bkbl; W Va U; Spch.

COBB, Patricia Anne
Martin Luther King Sr HS; Detroit, MI; Wayne St Col; Computer Programming.

COBB, Robert Harrison
Clinton Sr HS; Clinton, TN (200-400) Band; NHS.

COBB, Shirley Ree
Midwood HS; Brooklyn, NY;

COBB, Silas Jr
Cass Tech HS; Detroit, MI (90-850) Band; Chor; Drama; Math C; Ed, Sch P; Sci C; Pres, SC; COM; Citz A; Cl Fav; Hon Prog; Journ A; St Scholar; Pres, Afro-Amer C; Attendance A; U of Mich; Broadcasting.

COBB, Thomas Yardley
Charlotte Latin HS; Charlotte, NC (20-56) Chor; Ensm; Key C; Pres, Monogram; NHS; Ski C; Tres, SC; Thes; Co-Cpt, Bkbl; Cpt, Ftbl; Yth Foundation; Yth Leg; All St Chor; Sr Sportsmanship A; US Military Acad; Civil Engr.

COBB, William Dowell Jr
Arapahoe HS; Littleton, CO (7-587) Ed, Sch P; Ftbl; Tr; NMF; U of Denver; Social Science.

COBBLE, Dean Patrick
Hobart Sr HS; Hobart, IN (1-450) Ger C; SC; JV, Bkbl; JV, Ftbl; Tr; Most Out; Law.

COBBLER, George Edmund
John D Bassett HS; Bassett, VA; 4H.

COBBS, Stephen Hall
Sherman HS; Sherman, TX (34-404) A Cap Choir; Lat C; NHS; Pres, SC; Thes; VP, Jr Cl; NEDT; Rotary A; 3rd Pl, St Eng Oration; 1st Pl, PTA Cultural Arts Contest; Austin Col; Communication Arts.

COBERLEY, Douglas Brian
S P Waltrip HS; Houston, TX (360-650) Band; Chem C; Demolay; Drama; Hmrm; Lat C; ARC; Spch C; Thes; Ntl Thesbian Soc; Special A; All-Star Tech; Excellence Diving; U of Houston; Natural Sci.

COBERN, Vickilee
Paint Rock HS; Paint Rock, TX (2-10) Secy, BC; Parl, FHA; Fin, GS; 4H; Secy, SC; Bkbl; Fin, Tr; Citz A; Cl Fav; 4H A; Lion A; St Champion, Discus; AAU-NJO 4th Pl Discus; Tex Tech U.

COBURN, Melvin Lee
Southwestern HS; Flint, MI; 4H; Bsbl; Bkbl; Sftbl; Swim; Tr; 4H A; MCC; Ministry.

COBURN, Robert Scott
Air Acad HS; Colo Springs, CO (20%-500) CYO; Ski C; Span C; Ftbl; Tr; Wrest; COM; Skiing Medals; Air Force Acad; Aviation.

COBURN, Susan Marie
Huntsville HS; Huntsville, AL (161-500) Ann; FHA; Hmrm; InterAct C; SC; *Calhoun Jr Col; Acct.*

COBURN, Tina Denice
Canton HS; Canton, TX (10-101) Ann; FHA; JV, Bkbl; Sftbl; COM; Hon Prog; Type A; *Tyler Jr Col; Bus.*

COBY, Keith Allen
Richmond Sr HS; Richmond, IN; *ITT Tech Col; Elec.*

COCEK, Anna Marie
West HS; West, TX (12-114) F-Ed, Ann; Band; CYO; FHA; Secy, FTA; NHS; JV, Bkbl; Tr; HCt; *MCC; Sociology.*

COCHELL, Lenette Rae
Cottage Grove HS; Cottage Grove, OR (15-300).

COCHRAN, Allison Kelly
Haynesville HS; Haynesville, LA (3-61) Band; Pres, FHA; Hmrm; Lit Ral; Mjrte; NHS; SC; St Tres, FHA; WW.

COCHRAN, Billye Jean
Keyes HS; Keyes, OK (1-20) Band; Secy, NHS; Bkbl; Tr; Alg A; Cl Fav; H of F; Type A; Woody Nunn Mem; Fighting Heart, Girls Bkbl & Tr; *Panhandle St U; Computer Programing.*

COCHRAN, Bonnie May
Butler HS; Butler, MO (1-90) Co-Ed, Ann; Fr C; NHS; Hist A; Val; Fr A; *SW Mo St U.*

COCHRAN, Brenda Lea
Benton HS; St Joseph, MO (103-259) Pres, Art C; Pep C; JA; PTSA Honorable Men for Art; All Sch Play-Scenic Artist A; *Mo Western St; Art.*

COCHRAN, Cindy Kay
Santa Ana HS; Santa Ana, CA (1-500) NHS; SC; VP, Soph Cl; Amer Leg A; CSF; Yth Fel; *Whitworth Col; Elem Ed.*

COCHRAN, Jack Edward
Franklin HS; Franklin, PA (6-270) Ger C; SC; Achv A; *Carnegie-Mellon Col; Engr.*

COCHRAN, James Jerold
Highland HS; Salt Lake City, UT; Fr C; Cpt, Cr-Ctry; Ftbl; Tr; SB A; *Westminister Col; Bio.*

COCHRAN, Jill Jarmaine
St Francis De Sales HS; Columbus, OH (20-200) Fr C; Hmrm; SC; Sftbl; COM; Hon Prog; Most Out; Yth Fel; Missions C; Drill Tm; Vlbl; Schol Achv A; *Kent St U; Med.*

COCHRAN, Joni Renae
Wilmington Sr HS; Wilmington, OH (65-390) Orch; Sftbl; Tr; COM; 4H A; Yth Fel; Band Marching A; Gym A; Tr A; *Ohio St U; Executive Secy.*

COCHRAN, Keiron Cavell
Wooddale HS; Memphis, TN; Chor; Ftbl; Tr; *Middle Tenn St Col; Math.*

COCHRAN, Kendrick Parker
Foley HS; Foley, AL; Pres, Hmrm; Key C; NHS; Span C; SC; Tnns; Tr; Spch A; 1st, Math Sci Fair; 2nd, Talent Show; *U of Montevallo; Pre-Dentistry.*

COCHRAN, Linda
Ne HS; Oakland Park, FL (51-607) Anchor C; Band; Secy, Chor; Fr C; Hmrm; InterClub Coun; Cpt, Mjrte; NHS; SC; Pres A; VP, Secy, Yth Coun; *Berry Col; Math.*

COCHRAN, Marie Antionette
Ocean Springs HS; Ocean Springs, MS (70-315) Ann; Drama; FHA; Model UN; Y-Tns; Bkbl; Mgr, Tr; Pep Squad; Ms Tn Pageant; Modeling Sch; May Qn Pageant; Tn Board; Afro-Amer C; *U of Ala; Med.*

COCHRAN, Michael Alan
London HS; London, OH (1-91) Tres, NHS; Co-Cpt, Bkbl; Tr; Chem A; Kiwanis A; Alt, BS; *Wittenberg Col; Bio.*

COCHRAN, Mike I
Eleanor Roosevelt Sr HS; Greenbelt, MD (20%-300) Band; Pres, Chor; Ensm; Ger C; Madrigal; Orch; Sftbl; Tnns; Hon Prog; *Liberty Baptist Col; Mus Performance.*

COCHRAN, Monette Jeanne
Highline HS; Seattle, WA (26-400) AFS; Band; NHS; Folk Dance Group; Girls C Cabinet; *U of Wash; Health Sci.*

COCHRAN, Patti Lynn
Milby Sr HS; Houston, TX; VP, French NHS; Mu Alpha Theta; NHS; COM; Eng Hon Soc; Bowl C.

COCHRAN, Rhonda Sue
Man HS; Man, WV (15-180).

COCHRAN, Steve Andrew
Grimsley Sr HS; Greensboro, NC (15%-350) Span C; Bkbl; *Lenoir-Rhyne Col; Bus.*

COCHRAN, Terri Lynn
Cass HS; Cassville, GA (15-190) Cpt, Chldr; S-T, Fr C; Rptr, FBLA; FHA; Jr Miss Pagent; S-T, Math C; Sci C; Rptr, Tri-HiY; JA A; Sci A; MVP, Chldr; WW; Shorthand A; *Marietta Cobb Col; Cosmetology.*

COCHRAN, Twila Kaye
Herrin HS; Herrin, IL (15-200) *Sou Ill U; Engr.*

COCHRAN, Vincent Cosmo
Wooddale Sr HS; Memphis, TN (107-332) Co-Cpt, Chor; FHA; Hmrm; Mod Mus Mas; VP, SC; Cpt, Bkbl; Cpt, Ftbl; Cpt, Tr; COM; Citz A; H of F; JA A; Most Out; Opt A; MVP, Ftbl; *U of Minnesota; Insurance.*

COCHRELL, Darice Jacqueta
Hazelwood Central HS; Florissant, MO (67-837) FBLA; NHS; SC; Bkbl; Tr; Spch A; *Ohio St U; Bus Adm.*

COCKERHAM, Judy Kay
Winnfield Sr HS; Winnfield, LA; Anchor C; Tres, Band; BC; FTA; Lit Ral; Mjrte; Spch C; Secy, SC; HCt; *LSU; Law.*

COCKERHAM, Kathy Sue
Alma J Brown HS; Grambling, LA; Drama; *Grambling St U; Bus Adm.*

COCKERILL, Daniel Timothy
Asheboro HS; Asheboro, NC (15-334) VP, Church Yth; *Central Wesleyan Col; Elec.*

COCKFIELD, Janice
Lake City HS; Lake City, SC (10%-235) BC; Pres, FBLA; Pres, Hmrm; Secy, SC; Pres, Sr Cl; Tres, Jr Cl; Pres, Soph Cl; Cl Fav; Hon Prog; Beta Cert; Hon Jr, Top 10% Cl; *SU St Col; Acct.*

COCKLIN, Julie
Nw Classen HS; Oklahoma City, OK; Key C; Var C; Secy, Soph Cl; Swim; Tr; Hon Prog; Pep C; *Okla St U; Forestry.*

COCKLIN, Julie Catherine
Northwest Classen HS; Okla City, OK; Key C; Var C; Secy, Soph Cl; Swim; Tr; Yth Fel; *Okla St Col; Forestry.*

COCKRELL, Debra Annette
Woodlawn Sr HS; Baltimore, MD (50%-660) *Comm Col of Baltimore; Nurs.*

COCKRELL, Donald Lee
Saluda HS; Saluda, SC; Co-Ed, Ann; Band; BC; Chor; Order/Arrow; Hist A; Order/Arrow A; Sci A; Eagle Sct; Asst Church Organist; All St, All Reg, All Star, Band; *Furman U; Mus.*

COCKRELL, John Edward
George Washington HS; Denver, CO; Chor; Commercial C; JV, Bsbl; Wrest; ROTC A.

COCKRELL, Katrina Marie
Livingston HS; Livingston, AL (7-166) FHA; 4H; Mjrte; World Affairs C; Chem A; 4H A; Hon Prog; Sci A; Spch A; *U of Ala; Communications.*

COCKRELL, Keith Wayne
Woodlawn Sr HS; Baltimore, MD (300-600) *Food Service.*

COCKRUM, Nancy Jean
Lebanon Union HS; Lebanon, OR; Chor; Mgr, Bkbl; Beauty; Social Ch, Bible C; Spiritual Ch, Octegon C; *Albany Col of Beauty; Cosmotology.*

COCO, Jean Lee
Jennings HS; Jennings, LA; Band; VP, BC; JV, Chldr; Mjrte; Sch P; Pres, Soph Cl; Tr; Cl Fav; Yth Fel; Rifle Corp; Yth Recognition; Chaplain, SC; Band Coun; Sr Lifesaving; Coach's A, Tr; *LSU; Wildlife Bio.*

CODAY, Tammy Irene
Wetumka Jr-Sr HS; Wetumka, OK (1-53) Chor; FHA; NHS; Sch P; Alg A; COM; Sal; Home Ec, Eng, Reading, A's; *E Central U.*

CODDING, Roger Alan
Lyman Mem HS; Lebanon, CT (5-78) CYO; Hon Prog; Type A; Asst Secy, Audio Visual C; PA; *Elec.*

CODDINGTON, Julie Theresa
Highland HS; Albuquerque, NM (1-725) Chor; FHA; NHS; Flag Corps; Drug Alert Prog Cert; Lit C; Fine Arts C; Inlow Yth Camp Vol Counselor; Drug Coun; *Valdosta St Col; Math.*

CODOPONY, Oscar Thomas
Cache HS; Cache, OK (10-46) BC; NHS; Var C; Pres, Sr Cl; Bsbl; Bkbl; Cpt, Ftbl; Citz A; Masonic A; MLS; *U of Okla; Engr.*

CODR, David Jean
Prague HS; Prague, NE (6-19) Band; Drama; Pres, FFA; Tres, Hmrm; NHS; Pres, Var C; Tres, Sr Cl; Pres, Soph Cl; Bkbl; Ftbl; Tr; Hon Prog; MLS; John Philip Sousa A; FFA Merit, Home Improvement; *U of Nebr; Pre-Med.*

COE, Guy William
Jesuit Col Prep HS; Sacramento, CA (41-157) Band; Pres, BS; InterAct C; A-Ed, Sch P; SC; Ftbl; Tr; Wrest; CSF; COM; Gov Honor Prog; Hon Prog; Chief Justice, Stu Court; Off, Boys-Girls Nation; Soroptomist Schol Win; WW; St Rep, JA A's; *Stanford U; Law.*

COE, Rhonda Jeanne
Camden Central HS; Camden, NY (50-250) Var C; JV, Bkbl; Semi-Fin, Tnns; Secy, Yth Fel; *Home Ec.*

COE, Robert Allen
Penncrest HS; Media, PA (2-463) BS; Pres, Mu Alpha Theta; NHS; JV, Bkbl; Soccer; Math A; Ntl Sci Found; Win, Dist Lat Contest; *Johns Hopkins U; Pre-Med.*

COE, Roderick Erwin
Camden Central HS; Camden, NY (89-200) Band; Chor; Orch; Sci C; Math A; Yth Fel; *Herkimer Co Comm Col; Mortuary Sci.*

COEN, Mary Grace
Bishop Carroll HS; Wichita, KS (6-211) Cpt, Chldr; VP, Fr C; GS; Tres, NHS; Var C; VP, Sr Cl; Ntl Conf Chr & Jews; St Scholar; Amer Leg Girl's Nation; Ch, Stu-Faculty Sen; *Bio.*

COEYMAN, Joette Louise
Red Lion Area Sr HS; Red Lion, PA (10-500) Band; Ensm; Yth Fel; *Ind U of Penn; Math.*

COFFEY, Barbara Lisa
Cristobal Jr HS; Coco Solo, CANAL ZONE; Band; Drama; FTA; Hmrm; Rptr, Sch P; Secy, SC; Thes; Tr; COM; ARC A; Spch A; *Vet Med.*

COFFEY, Brent Alvin
Orleans HS; Orleans, NE (12-30) Band; Bsbl; Cpt, Bkbl; Cpt, Ftbl; Golf; Tr; HKg; *US Army.*

COFFEY, Bruce Jay
Orleans Pub Sch; Orleans, NE (3-30) Pres, Band; NHS; VP, SC; VP, Sr Cl; Tres, Jr Cl; Bkbl; *U of Nebr; Bus Adm.*

COFFEY, David Alan
Deer Park HS; Cincinnati, OH (60-200) Band; SC; Pres, Soph Cl; Cr-Ctry; Tr; COM; *U of Ind; Optometry.*

COFFEY, Deborah Lynn
Hereford HS; Hereford, TX (44-295).

COFFEY, Lisa Gail
Banning HS; Wilmington, CA; Chor; Bsbl; Bkbl; Ftbl; Sftbl; Swim; Tnns; *Harbor Col; Bus.*

COFFEY, Ronald Bruce
Williamsburg HS; Williamsburg, KY; Bkbl; MVP, Golf; *Cumberland Col; Art.*

COFFEY, Teresa Jane
Shawnee Mission W HS; Overland Park, KS (73-592) Ger C; Co-Cpt, Bkbl; Tr; Vlbl; *Emporia St U; Phys Ed.*

COFFEY, Theresa Ann
Ellenville Central HS; Ellenville, NY; Dbte Tm; Fr C; Pres, 4H; Up Bound; COM; Crisco A; 4H A; Hon Prog; Most Out; Eng A; Basic Law; *Berkeley Sch; Fashion Merchandising.*

COFFEY, Virginia Ann
Ne HS; N Little Rock, AR (25%-450) Bus C; Drama; FBLA; Span C; COM; Hon Prog; Piano & Organ Stu; *Central Baptist Col; Law.*

COFFIELD, Georgia Diane
Jewett-Scio HS; Scio, OH (3-16) Chaplain, VICA; Reg Bronze A, Voc Indust C of Amer; Secy, Yth Group, Sunday Sch Tchr; *Bible Col.*

COFFIN, Barbara Ellen
Bay HS; Bay Village, OH (30-371) Rptr, Ann; NHS; Ski C; Ntl Sci Found; NEDT; Ntl Merit Commendation; *Harvard U; Biol.*

COFFIN, Linda Lee
Westfield HS; Westfield, MA (10%-500) Band; Chor; Ensm; Ger C; Hmrm; Madrigal; NHS; Pres, Rainbow; SC; Mus Helper, Young Life; Dist Chor; W Mass Jazz Ensm Champs; Band Music Camp Schol; Nom, Bronze Tablet; *Barrington Col; Mus Ed.*

COFFMAN, Constance Sue
Madisonville N Hopkins HS; Madisonville, KY (17-296) F-Ed, Ann; BC; Ensm; Model UN; Orch; Pres, Rainbow; F-Ed, Sch P; SC; Tres, Thes; Pres, Tri-HiY; Mgr, Bsbl; Mgr, Bkbl; Sftbl; Hon Prog; NEDT; Spch A; Yth Leg; Cum Laude; Outst Spch Stu; Outst Ky Statesman; *USC.*

COFFMAN, Dana Kay
McCluer Sr HS; Florissant, MO; A Cap Choir; Chor; Ensm; Madrigal; Rptr, Sch P; Bio A; Type A; Gym; Vlbl.

COFFMAN, Jeanne
Arkansas HS; Texarkana, AR; Chldr; Chor; Fr C; Pres, InterClub Coun; SC; Y-Tns; Sweetest Girl; *Ouachita Baptist U; Elem Ed.*

COFFMAN, Lisa Lee
Gilmer Co HS; Glenville, WV (34-94) Band; Chor; Drama; VP, 4H; Fin, Jr Miss Pageant; Co-Cpt, Mjrte; Pres, Rainbow; SC; Var C; Bkbl; Tr; WW; *W Va U; Dental Hygiene.*

COFFMAN, Marc Craig
Bowman HS; Canyon Country, CA; Pres, Y-Tns; Ftbl; Cpt, Bowl Tm; *COC; Real Estate.*

COFIELD, Karen Elaine
Langley HS; McLean, VA (5%-600) Bus C; FBLA; NHS; Span NHS; *Tulane U; Math.*

COGAR, John Lawson
St Albans HS; St Albans, WV (10%-500) Drama; VP, Hmrm; Lat C; Math C; Mu Alpha Theta; SC; Bkbl; Swim; Tr; Math A; *U of Cincinnati; Archt.*

COGBURN,
Elizabeth Georganna
Pisgah HS; Canton, NC (4-349) Chor; Secy, Fr C; FHA; French NHS; NHS; Citz A; Hist A; Poet A; Sci A; *UNC of Greensboro.*

COGBURN, Jana Leigh
Yuma HS; Yuma, CO (1-72) Secy, FBLA; Lat C; Secy, Thes; Bkbl; Cl Fav; Pres, FCA; *U of N Colo; Elem Ed.*

COGER, Susan Elizabeth
Daviston HS; Daviston, AL; Secy, Ann; Secy, BC; VP, 4H; Phys C; Bkbl; Beauty; 4H A; Swtht; *Ed.*

COGGAN, Jeffrey Robert
Kirkwood HS; Kirkwood, MO (20-600) Order/ Arrow; Jr, Sch P; Co-Cpt, Bkbl; Co-Cpt, Ftbl; Hon Prog; Order/Arrow A; Eagle Rank; *Vet Med.*

COGGAN, Kelly Ann
Kirkwood HS; Kirkwood, MO (30-600) A-Ed, Sch P; SC; Tri-HiY; Citz A; HCt; Hon Prog; *U of Tulsa; Psych.*

COGGESHALL, Greg Scott
Mount Vernon Acad; Mount Vernon, OH; Band; Ensm; NHS; Hon Prog; *Columbia Union Col; Ed.*

COGGIN, David Wayne
Newnan HS; Newnan, GA (5-400) BC; BS; Drama; Hmrm; Semi-Fin, Lit Ral; Sci C; Span C; Span NHS; SC; COM; Gov Honor Prog; Kiwanis A; Math A; NMS; *Auburn U; Engr.*

COGGIN, Lisa Marie
Forest Hill HS; Jackson, MS (56-272) A Cap Choir; BC; Bkbl; Friendliest Girl, Sr Cl; *Hinds Jr Col; Nurs.*

COGGIN, Murl Redus Jr
Chipley HS; Chipley, FL; Tres, Key C; NHS; Pres, Jr Cl; Ftbl; Tr; *U of Fla; Civil Engr.*

COGGIN, Oliver Burgess
Fairfield HS; Fairfield, AL (10%-184) Band; BC; Chor; Drama; *Med.*

COHELEY, J Lynn
Cedar Bluff HS; Cedar Bluff, AL (4-35) Ed, Ann; Pres, BC; Cpt, Chldr; Chor; VP, FHA; Hmrm; Math C; Sch P; SC; Tres, Sr Cl; Pres, Soph Cl; Sftbl; Tnns; Citz A; 4H A; HCt; Hon Prog; *Computer Technology.*

COHEN, Daniel O'Neal
Hillcrest HS; Simpsonville, SC; Band; 4H; 4H A; *Morehouse Col; Drafting.*

COHEN, Judith Myrna
Eastside HS; Paterson, NJ (10%-650) FBLA; Hmrm; Horsemanship, Zonta, C'S; Hon Achv Cert; FBLA St Hon's Cert; *Sawyer Sch; Bus.*

COHEN, Marion Charles
Skyline HS; Dallas, TX; Bus C; Key C; Order/ Arrow; Ftbl; Swim; Tr; ROTC A; Swim A; Tr A; Arch A; *U of Tex; Bus Adm.*

COHEN, Robert Allen
Lakewood HS; St Petersburg, FL (63-650) Span C; Var C; Bsbl; Golf; Swim; Pres A; Yth Fel; *U of Fla; Pre-Law.*

COHN, Harry Edward
John F Kennedy HS; Richmond, VA (7-309) Drama; Ftbl; Cpt, Tnns; WW; *U Va; Architecture.*

COHNS, Sandra Kay
Hamilton HS; Memphis, TN; Chor; Math C; Mod Mus Mas; St Stu Congress; Bkbl; Hist A; Math A; MLS; Sci A; Beethoven C; Glee C; All St C; *Mus.*

COHOL, William Alan
Liberty HS; Youngstown, OH (25%-200) AFS; Chem C; Ger C; Bsbl; Ftbl; Tr; COM; Citz A; Math A; Yth Fel; *Ohio St U; Archt.*

COKER, Karen Elizabeth
Warren Acad Inc; Warrenton, NC (16-32) Chor; Drama; Fr C; Sch P; Sftbl; *Raleigh Sch of Data Processing; Computers.*

COKER, Melody Suzanne
Edgewood HS; Edgewood, TX;

COKER, Susan Renee
Spring Sr HS N; Spring, TX (20%-800) Mu Alpha Theta; NHS; Span C; Swim; COM; *U of Tex; Bus Mgt.*

COKER, Terry Andrew
Burkburnett HS; Burkburnett, TX (19-268) NHS; Thes; Golf; Hon Prog; Eng A; Drivers Ed A; World Geography A; *Midwestern St U; Acct.*

COLAHAN, Alexandra Elizabeth
York Central Sch; Retsof, NY (15-85) Hmrm; Sch P; Ski C; Parl, SC; JV, Hockey; Mgr, Soccer; Citz A; *St John's U; Med.*

COLANTRO, Sheila Irene
Salinas HS; Salinas, CA; Chor; NHS; Sch P; Sftbl; *Bethesda Bible Col; Religion.*

COLARELLI, Cylinda Lee
Tascosa HS; Amarillo, TX (162-475) Chor; Semi-Fin, Demolay; Ch, Hmrm; Span C; SC; Y-Tns; Tr; COM; Schol Art A; Phys Ed A; *Bauder Col; Interior Design.*

COLAW, David Emerson
Walnut Hills HS; Cincinnati, OH (33%-937) Band; Arch; Bsbl; Bkbl; Ftbl; Sftbl; Tnns; Yth Fel; Pres, Yth Fel.

COLBATH, Carol Marie
Traverse City Sr HS; Traverse City, MI (221-768) SC; Tr; Alg A; Bio A; Citz A; Math A; Sci A; VP, Pep C; Gym; Bronze Pin Schol A; *N Mich Col; Sci.*

COLBERT, Deborah Jane
Acad HS; Erie, PA (8-30) Chldr; Chor; HCt; Exchange Stu; *Morehouse Col; Bus.*

COLBERT, Kim Gynelle
Glenn HS; Birmingham, AL (1-126) Ann; Band; Pres, Hmrm; NHS; Sch P; VP, SC; Secy, Jr Cl; Bio A; Sci A; *Pa St U; Med.*

COLBERT, Sharon Gwenell
Calumet HS; Chicago, IL; *Math.*

COLBORN, Holli Sharlane
Fletcher Sr HS; Neptune Beach, FL (7%-620) Ann; Hmrm; NHS; Span C; SC; *U of S Fla; Med.*

COLBRY, Sheila Renee
Alma HS; Alma, MI (34-264) Secy, 4H; NHS; Ski C; Span C; *San Fernando Valley Col.*

COLBURN, Kelli Ann
Garland HS; Garland, TX; A Cap Choir; Drama; Drill Tm; St Poetry Soc A; Talespinner's Story League A; Civitan C Essay A.

COLCLASURE, Connie Delores
Hazen HS; Hazen, AR; BC; S-T, Chor; FBLA; Pres, FHA; GS; Madrigal; Tres, Sci C; Pres, SC; Secy, Jr Cl; HCt; Type A; Character A; 1st Runner-Up, Miss Hazen; Miss Congeniality; *Ouachita Baptist U; Mus.*

COLCORD, Carol Lynn
Lakeside HS; Decatur, GA (99-429) COM; *Nurs.*

COLCOTT, Thomas Hutson
Dallas Christian HS; Dallas, TX (2-55) NHS; Sci C; VP, Span C; Tres, Sr Cl; Math A; Sci A; *Engr.*

COLDEWEY, Sharon Lynne
Colo HS; Colo City, TX (4-126) Band; Mjrte; Math C; SC; Bkbl; Tnns; Star Student; Shorthand A.

COLDREN, John Franklin
W-Platte R-II HS; Weston, MO (3-84) Chor; Sci C; Bkbl; Mgr, Ftbl; COM; *US Air Force Acad; Aeronautics.*

COLE, Allison Ann
Central HS; Davenport, IA (30-650) A Cap Choir; Cpt, Chldr; Chor; Ensm; Madrigal; ARC; SC; Swim; Hon Prog; St Singing Contest A; Presidential Phys Fitness A; *Iowa St U; Engr.*

COLE, Bradley Allen
Douglas MacArthur HS; San Antonio, TX (25%-600) Band; NEDT; *Math.*

COLE, Brenda Sue
Tallapoosa Acad; Dadeville, AL (5-34) Band; BC; 4H; Span C; Span NHS; Tri-HiY; Yth Leg.

COLE, Carolyn Ann
Buena HS; Sierra Vista, AZ (75-435) Semi-Fin, InterClub; Hmrm; NHS; Var C; Cr-Ctry; Cpt, Tr; Amer Leg A; COM; Elk A; Most Out; Pres A; Sci A; MVP, Tr; *UCLA; PE.*

COLE, Charlotte Patricia
Wade Hampton HS; Greenville, SC; Chor; *Psych.*

COLE, Cheri Sabrina
Leavenworth HS; Leavenworth, KS (41-375) Ann; Chor; Semi-Fin, Jr Miss Pa; Tres, NHS; ARC; Span C; Alg A; Hon Prog; Math A; NEDT; Sci A; St Scholar; 1st Cl GSct; Pres Clrm; Jr Miss Congeniality; Pres, Yth o-t Chapel; *U of Kans; Pre-Med.*

COLE, Cheryl Danette
Cass HS; Cassville, GA (10%-190) Co-Cpt, Band; VP, BC; Chem C; Ensm; Tres, FBLA; Math C; Phys C; Sci C; Span C; COM; Chem A; Hist A; Type A; All St, Dist, Band; VVP, Band; *U of Fla; Mus.*

COLE, Christine Elizabeth
Moore HS; Moore, OK (33-844) JV, Chldr; FBLA; Fin, GS; Hmrm; NHS; SC.

COLE, Colleen Mary
Westminster Sr HS; Westminster, MD (50%-585) Ch, CYO; Chor; Drama; Thes; Bkbl; Sftbl; JA A; Yrbk; Flag Corp; Vlbl; Bowl; *Towson St Col; Theater Arts.*

COLE, Dana Mark
St Mark's Sch; Southborough, MA; Cpt, Soccer; Tnns; Camp Coun; Vol, Sch Store; *Phys Ed.*

COLE, Darlene Annette
Switzerland Jr-Sr HS; Vevay, IN; Band; Chor; Pres, 4H; Secy, NHS; Alg A; 4H A; Type A.

COLE, Denny William
E Prairie HS; E Prairie, MO (42-103) *SE St U.*

COLE, Edgar Allen II
Kubasaki HS; Okinawa, JAPAN (13-271) Tres, Band; VP, Ger C; Hmrm; NHS; SC; NMS; VP, Tns for Christ; Outst Stu, Eng; *Ouachitah U; Pol Sci.*

COLE, Frederick Martin
John Marshall HS; Rochester, MN (30-564) AFS; Secy, Chor; Secy, Dbte Tm; Drama; Ger C; NHS; Pres, Sci C; Ski C; Cr-Ctry; Ntl Merit Ltr of Commendation; St Legislature Page; *St Olaf Col; Mus.*

COLE, Gino Bruce
Lincoln HS; Jersey City, NJ (14-273) NHS; SC; *Rutgers U.*

COLE, Henry Olen
Schlagle HS; Kansas City, KS; Bkbl; Tr; COM; Art A; *Art.*

COLE, Jacklyn Elaine
Artesia HS; Artesia, NM; Sch P; SC; Var C; MVP, Bkbl; Sftbl; Tr; HCt; Vlbl; *NM St U; Ed.*

COLE, Jeanne Marie
Daviess Co HS; Owensboro, KY (3-316) F-Ed, Ann; VP, Band; BC; Tres, Pol Sci C; Bio A; Chem A; DARGCA; Hon Prog; MLS; NMS; Mus A's; *Hanover Col; Pol Sci.*

COLE, John Michael
Grove City Joint HS; Grove City, PA (12-230) Band; Chor; Pres, Math C; Monogram; Pres, NHS; Orch; Thes; Mgr, Bkbl; Tnns; Mgr, Tr; Hon Prog; NMS; *Lehigh U; Elec Engr.*

COLE, Karen Lisa
Indian Springs Baptist Sch; Eight-Mile, AL (1-3) Ensm; Star Student; Mus A; Social Stu A; *Liberty Baptist Col; Mus.*

COLE, Korvin Nash
Clintondal HS; Mt Clemens, MI (60-333) Band; 4H; Hmrm; NHS; SC; VP, Soph Cl; Bkbl; Swim; 4H A; PA; *Bus Adm.*

COLE, Linda Faye
Millville Sr HS; Millville, NJ; COM; *Executive Secy.*

COLE, Linda Gale
Sunbright HS; Sunbright, TN (6-63) Cpt, Band; Chldr; Chor; FHA; Tres, Sr Cl; Bkbl; Wittiest.

COLE, Maura Aileen
Texhoma HS; Texhoma, OK (5-20) Chor; Ensm; NHS; Tr; Citz A; Masonic A; Pres A; *Panhandle St Col; Bus.*

COLE, Melani
Cashmere HS; Cashmere, WA; Dbte Tm; Pres, FHA; 4H; Type A; Yth Fel; Distrib Ed C of Amer Con, 1st Reg; *Wenatchee Valley Col; Advertising.*

COLE, Michael Dale
Ulysses HS; Ulysses, KS; Band; Ensm; NHS; SC; JV, Bkbl; Ftbl; Tr.

COLE, Michael Lewis
Treadwell HS; Memphis, TN; DECA; *Shelby St Comm Col; Bus Adm.*

COLE, Nancy Ellen
El Camino Real HS; Woodland Hills, CA (38-1094) CSF; Hist A; Hon Prog; Gold Seal Bearer; Ephebian; Vol, Crippled Children's Soc; Ladies Service C; *UC at Santa Barbara.*

COLE, Regina Yvonne
Bloom Trail HS; Chicago Heights, IL (43-337) B Crocker A; Q&S A; Ima Eyvette's Debutante; *N Ill U; Journ.*

COLE, Richard Heilman
W Middlesex HS; W Middlesex, PA (9-158) Band; BS; Chor; Hmrm; Span C; Span NHS; Golf; All Amer Yth Choir; *Math.*

COLE, Ricky John
Los Lunas HS; Los Lunas, NM (4-230) BS; Chess C; Dbte Tm; Drama; NFL; NHS; Pres, Spch C; JV, Ftbl; Spch A; Lib A; Social Stu A; *Oral Roberts U; Theology.*

COLE, Robert Ridgeway
Holbrook HS; Holbrook, AZ (39-140) Bus C; CYO; Chem C; FBLA; Math C; Sci C; Bsbl; Sftbl; Tr; *N Ariz U; Mech Engr.*

COLE, Rueben Lawrence
Rufus King HS; Milwaukee, WI; City Conf; Cpt, Bkbl; JV, Cr-Ctry; Sci A; Most Improved, BB; Phys Fitness A; *Spokane Col; Sci.*

COLE, Shirley Bee
Texhoma HS; Texhoma, OK; Band; Chor; NHS; Rptr, Sch P; *Wayland Baptist Col; Acct.*

COLE, Susan Ellen
Hellgate HS; Missoula, MT (38-583) Tres, A Cap Choir; Band; Chor; Drama; Fin, GS; Hmrm; SC; Cr-Ctry; Citz A; HCt; Hon Prog; Tres, Service C; *Sci.*

COLE, Terri Lynn
Frederick HS; Frederick, OK; A-Ed, Ann; Chor; SC; *Okla St U; Bus.*

COLE, Valerie Teresa
Westminster Sr HS; Westminster, MD; Bus Mgr, Ann; CYO; Chor; GS; NHS; Thes; Q&S A; Schol Ltr A; WW; *St Joes Hosp Sch of Nurs; Nurs.*

COLEBANK, Wendy Renee
Antioch HS; Antioch, TN (5-392) VP, Ensm; NHS; *Blue Mountain Col; Bus Ed.*

COLELLA, Donna Lee
Cherry Hill HS; Cherry Hill, NJ (64%-650) Chldr; Pres, Chor; FHA; Hockey; Type A; Yth Fel; *Covenant Col; Ed.*

COLEMAN, Amy Gail
Mountainburg HS; Mountainburg, AR (1-45) Ann; Co-Cpt, Chldr; Pres, FHA; GS; Rptr, NHS; Sch P; Pres, SC; Bkbl; Sftbl; HQn; HCt; *Ouachita Baptist U.*

COLEMAN, Barry Lee
Triway HS; Wooster, OH (125-181) Band; Chor; FTA; 4H; 4H A; *Ohio St U; Mus.*

COLEMAN, Beverly Alexis
Chester HS; Chester, PA (45-673) Ann; Dbte Tm; World Affairs C; Hist A; DAR Excel in Hist A; WW; *U of Pittsburgh; Law.*

COLEMAN, Bobby Lynn II
Conroe HS; Conroe, TX (50-935) NHS; Span C; Bsbl; Ftbl; *Tex A&M U; Bus.*

COLEMAN, Brian Oliver
Willibrord Cath HS; Chicago, IL (7-91) Pres, Chess C; Fr C; French NHS; Rptr, 4H; Key C; Math C; Monogram; Pres, NHS; Sci C; S-T, SC; Cpt, Bkbl; Tnns; Bio A; COM; Citz A; 4H A; Kiwanis A; Math A; Pres A; ARC A; Sal; Sci A; Spch A; MVP, Bkbl; Mayor Daley Schol; Del, Ntl 4-H Conf; *Knox Col; Pre-Dentistry.*

COLEMAN, Carole Sue
Midwest HS; Midwest, WY (1-23) Chldr; Math C; NHS; Ski C; Var C; MVP, Bkbl; MVP, Tr; Most Out; Type A; Val; MVP, Vlbl; *Central Wyom Col; Engr.*

COLEMAN, Carolyn Jane
Southside HS; Fort Smith, AR (38-430) CYO; Drama; NHS; Span C; Thes; COM; *U of Ark; Nurs.*

COLEMAN, Carolyn Marie
Lawrence HS; Lawrence, KS (93-650) Co-Cpt, Chldr; Bkbl; Tr; Citz A; MLS; *Kans U; Social Working.*

COLEMAN, Cheryl Lynn
Huntington HS; Shreveport, LA; V-Ch, Chem C; Chor; Fr C; Semi-Fin, GS; 4H; Hmrm; Fin, Lit Ral; Math C; Mu Alpha Theta; NHS; Phys C; Y-Tns; Tnns; Tr; Alg A; Bio A; COM; Hon Prog; Math A; Sci A; Star Student; 'Z' C; Dance Tm; WW; *Sou U; Engr.*

COLEMAN, Clarissa Elizabeth
Notre Dame Acad; Toledo, OH (42-138) Chor; Mod Mus Mas; Span C; JA A; K of C A; VP, Mus C; Pres, Yth Fel; Pres, Afro C; Sales VP, JA; Sales VP, JA; VP, Law Explorers; *Tuskegee Inst; Engr.*

COLEMAN, Clifford Michael
Eisenhower HS; Washington, MI (300-600) Pres, CYO; Ski C; *Oakland U; Health.*

COLEMAN, D Mark
W Waterloo HS; Waterloo, IA; Band; Span C; Bsbl; Swim; Tnns; *Auto Mech.*

COLEMAN, David Albert
Bellflower HS; Bellflower, CA (64-450) Chor; Ensm; FCA; *Baptist Bible Col; Mus.*

COLEMAN, Debra Ellen
Hutsonville HS; Hutsonville, IL (4-44) Band; Chor; Drama; VP, FHA; NHS; Hon Prog; Home Ec A; *Lincoln Trail Col; Gen.*

COLEMAN, Dorla Elaine
Saginaw HS; Saginaw, MI; Chor; Hmrm; SC; Citz A; Hon Prog; Attendance A; *Mich St U; Engr.*

COLEMAN, Evelyn Jonetta
Saginaw HS; Saginaw, MI; Chor; Drama; *Delta Jr Col; Sci.*

COLEMAN, Fred Charles
Cogville HS; Coqville, OR (33%-130) 4H; Order/ Arrow; ARC; JV, Ftbl; JV, Golf; JV, Wrest; COM; Citz A; Order/Arrow A; ARC A; Eagle Sct; *NNC.*

COLEMAN, George Mason
Fredrick Douglass HS; Atlanta, GA; Band; Bus Mgr, CYO; Tr; Hon Prog; Most Out; ROTC A; Yth Fel; Best Mem, CYO; Cert of Commendation; 3rd Pl Ribbon; *Florida St U; Child Care.*

COLEMAN, James Douglas
Atkinson W Holt HS; Atkinson, NE (20-80) A Cap Choir; Chor; Drama; Order/Arrow; SC; Bkbl; Ftbl; Golf; Tr; Order/Arrow A; Spch A; WW; All St; *U of Nebr; Mus.*

COLEMAN, Janice Patricia
Martin Luther King HS; Philadelphia, PA (250-698) Dbte Tm; Sci C; Bus Mgr, SC; MVP, Tnns; *Phys Therapy.*

COLEMAN, Jeffrey Lee
Drewry Mason HS; Ridgeway, VA; Wrest.

COLEMAN, John Perry
Robert E Lee HS; Tyler, TX; FFA; Church Chor.

COLEMAN, Jon Tallie
Greenville HS; Greenville, IL (8-191) Band; Mod Mus Mas; NHS.

COLEMAN, Kathleen Marian
La Sierra HS; Carmichael, CA (15%-500) Ed, Ann; Band; Chldr; Chor; Drama; Ensm; Sch P; Bkbl; Vlbl; Victory Baking A; *Biola Col; Psych.*

COLEMAN, Kenneth
Ripley HS; Ripley, TN (20%-260) Ann; VP, Hmrm; Var C; Cpt, Bkbl; Annual Photographer; *Union U; Photography.*

COLEMAN, Kevin Dean
Coronado HS; Colorado Springs, CO (63-331) VP, Chor; Madrigal; Bsbl; MVP, Tnns; Civitan Essay Contest; All City HS Hon Choir; *Colo St U; Forestry.*

COLEMAN, Laverne
J R Masterman Lab And Dem Sch; Philadelphia, PA; Drama; VP, Hmrm; SC; Bkbl; Citz A.

COLEMAN, Lisa Faith
Compton HS; Compton, CA (20%-850) Sci C; Span C; Y-Tns; CSF; Citz A; Hist A; Hon Prog.

COLEMAN, Loretta Ann
Kashmere Sr HS; Houston, TX (92-617) *Prairie View Col; Elem Ed.*

COLEMAN, Mark Christopheor
John T Haggard HS; Wilmington, NC; Band; Bkbl; Sftbl; 2nd HR; *NC St U; Forestry.*

COLEMAN, Michael Edward
Columbia HS; Richland, WA (40-275) Span C; SC; Bsbl; Bkbl; Ftbl; Wrest; Hon Prog; *Wash St U.*

COLEMAN, Nathaniel Allen
Lindblom HS; Chicago, IL (231-497) A Cap Choir; Band; VP, CYO; Chess C; Sci C; Bkbl; Tr; Spch A; *Morehouse Col; Bus Adm.*

COLEMAN, Neresa Lynette
Lumberton Sr HS; Lumberton, NC (168-300) Band; Chldr; Chor; Drama; Parl, French NHS; Secy, Hmrm; Parl, Lat C; Rptr, Sch P; Sci C; Span C; Acteens; VP, Sub-Jr; Tres, Pep C; Gym C; *NC Sch o-t Arts; Dancing.*

COLEMAN, Patricia Ann
Northeast Sr HS; Pasadena, MD (30-632) VP, Chor; Fr C; Rptr, Hmrm; NHS; Pres, Thes; Tres, Soph Cl; COM; Hon Prog; Best Actress; *Towson St U; Drama.*

COLEMAN, Patsy Lynn
Millard HS; Pikeville, KY (9-91) Bus C; Fr C; 4H; NHS; ARC; Sch P; Sftbl; Swim; 4H A; Hon Prog; Journ A; PTA A; ARC A; Type A; *Pikeville Col; Bus.*

COLEMAN, Pauline Elizabeth
Pershing HS; Detroit, MI (30-400) Bus C; NHS; *U of Mich; Bus.*

COLEMAN, Randy Winfred
Antioch HS; Nashville, TN (70-500) Sci Aide; *Middle Tenn St U; Aerospace.*

COLEMAN, Reginald Lynn
McClymonds Sr HS; Oakland, CA; Drama; Fr C; FBLA; Hmrm; Ed, Sch P; St Stu Congress; SC; Mgr, Tnns; Hon Prog; Semi-Fin, Tnns; Block 'M'; Development Prog, UC-BERKELEY; Tnns Medal; Marcus A Foster Inst Comm; *UC at Davis; Biological Sci.*

COLEMAN, Rhonda Renee
McGavock HS; Nashville, TN (513-940) BC; Chor; *Fisk U; Bus Mgt.*

COLEMAN, Rhonda Stacy
McGavock HS; Nashville, TN (10-820) Co-Ed, Ann; BC; Chldr; Ensm; Hmrm; Cpt, Orch; ARC; Co-Ed, Sch P; SC; Alg A; COM; Coun of Teach A; Hon Prog; Math A; Most Out; Sci A; HR; Eng A; Soc Stu A; Miss Home Ec; *Vanderbilt U; Law.*

COLEMAN, Rita Denise
B T Washington HS; Atlanta, GA (4-345) Ed, Ann; Secy, Hmrm; Pres, Lit Mag; NHS; VP, SC; Bus Mgr, Jr Cl; COM; Gov Honor Prog; Hon Prog; Math A; Most Out; NMS; NEDT; Type A; *Harvard U; Law.*

COLEMAN, Samuel Melville
Greensburg Salem Sr HS; Greensburg, PA (30-450) Band; Chor; Demolay; Ensm; Ger C; Hmrm; Orch; SC; Pres, Soph Cl; Golf; Tr; Citz A; Outst Bandsman; *U of Pittsburgh; Pre-Dental.*

COLEMAN, Sharon Denise
Woodlawn HS; Shreveport, LA (60-429) Chor; NHS; Sftbl; Tnns; PA; Ldrship Study Course; Camper's A; *Sou U; Elem Ed.*

COLEMAN, Stanley Edward
Millville Sr HS; Millville, NJ (149-537) Semi-Fin, BS; JV, Bsbl; JV, Ftbl; Bio A; Gov Honor Prog; *UCLA; Archt.*

COLEMAN, Stephen David
La Sierra HS; Carmichael, CA (5-500) JV, Bkbl; JV, Ftbl; Tr; CSF; Hon Prog; Sci A; *U of Calif; Sci.*

COLEMAN, Suzanne Faye
Weir HS; Weir, MS (1-50) A-Ed, Ann; V-Ch, BC; Chldr; Chor; Ensm; FHA; Jr Miss Pagent; Pres, SC; Secy, Jr Cl; Swim; Tnns; Beauty; Bio A; DARGCA; H of F; Hist A; Math A; MLS; Most Out; Sci A; Yth Leg; Sextet; Beta C A; *Miss U For Women; Fashion Merchandising.*

COLEMAN, Suzette
Virgie HS; Virgie, KY (1-150) BC; Chess C; FTA; 4H; Secy, Hmrm; Sci C; Mgr, Bkbl; Sftbl; 4H A; Sci A; Type A; Val; Spelling Bee A; Hon A.

COLEMAN, Sydna Renell
Jesse H Jones HS; Houston, TX (4-347) VP, FHA; Mu Alpha Theta; Pres, NHS; Sci C; Fin, Amer Leg A; Secy, Future Med Careers; *U of Houston; Pre-Med.*

COLEMAN, Sylvia Ann
Medina HS; Medina, TN (2-23) Co-Ed, Ann; BC; Co-Cpt, Chldr; Pres, FHA; Pres, SC; Var C; MLS; Sal; Most Popular; Best Dressed; Miss MHS; *Middle Tenn St U; Biol.*

COLEN, Thomas LaMar
Emerson HS; Emerson, AR (2-30) FFA; 4H; Hmrm; Sch P; Span C; SC; Bkbl; Tr; 4H A; Span A; Most Stu; *Henderson St U; Mech Engr.*

COLES, Harold Andre
Lawrence Central HS; Lawrence, IN (203-746) Ftbl; Tr; Sports Ltrs; *Anderson Col; Psych.*

COLES, Mark Randall
Westfield Sr HS; Westfield, NJ (116-675) A Cap Choir; Chor; Bsbl; JV, Cr-Ctry; NMS; *Math.*

COLES, Robert Darnell
Salem HS; Salem, NJ; Bkbl; Ftbl; Tr; *Elec.*

COLES, Sherie Renee
Donora Sr HS; Donora, PA (60%-499) Secy, Chor; Drama; Ensm; Mjrte; Rainbow; Spch C; *Ind U; Psych.*

COLESON, William Bruce
Madisonville N Hopkins HS; Madisonville, KY (33%-425) A Cap Choir; Band; VP, Chess C; Chor; VP, Drama; Ensm; Hmrm; Orch; Bkbl; Sftbl; COM; Citz A; Instrumental Solo A; All St, Chor; *Murray St U; Mus.*

COLFLESH, Tina Marie
Rockwood Area HS; Rockwood, PA (20-116) Fr C; Ger C; Explorers C; *Nurs.*

COLGAN, Cindy Rose
Holdrege HS; Holdrege, NE (23-135) Ann; Band; CYO; Chldr; Chor; FBLA; 4H; Sch P; Thes; Y-Tns; Sftbl; COM; Cl Fav; 4H A; HCt; Type A; Mus A; *U of Nebr; Mus.*

COLGAN, David Paul
Reynolds HS; Greenville, PA (12-212) Chor; Hmrm; Sci C; Span C; Rptr, Thes; Var C; Mgr, Cr-Ctry; Citz A; Elk A; Silver Palm Eagle; Wildlife Conservation A; VICA Comp A; NRA Marksman A.

COLGAN, Debra Renae
Canby Pub HS; Canby, MN (15-120) Band; Chor; Drama; Ensm; Spch C; Spch A; VofDEM; Flute Solo A; St Hon Band; Drama Ltr; General Activity Ltr; *U of Minn St Paul; Lib Sci.*

COLGAN, Marilyn Sue
Brimfield HS; Brimfield, IL (3-66) Ann; Chor; Pres, Drama; Fr C; FHA; NHS; Span C; *Fr.*

COLITZ, Frank J Jr
Crystal River HS; Crystal River, FL; Ann; BC; Rptr, Sch P; Span C; Span NHS; Chamber of Comm A; Citz A; Rotary A; Star Student; Type A; Val; Sch Photographer Span A; *Central Fla Comm Col; Engr.*

COLL, Eric Jon
Roswell HS; Roswell, NM (2%-462) A Cap Choir; Chor; Ensm; Pres, NHS; Ski C; Bkbl; COM; Math A; Most Out; NEDT; Sci A; Outst Choral; Schol A; Page, NM House of Rep; All St Mus Clinic; *Oral Roberts U; Vet.*

COLLADO, Harold
Luis Munoz Rivera HS; Lajas, PR (5-175) Hmrm; NHS; ARC; Co-Ed, Sch P; Alg A; Amer Leg A; COM; Cl Fav; Hist A; Hon Prog; *Recinto U de Mayaguez; Anthropology.*

COLLAR, Kathryn Marie
Little Wolf HS; Manawa, WI (24-83) Chor; Var C; Sftbl; Pres A; ARC A; Vlbl; Snowfest Qn Contest; GAA; Pep C; YARC; *Appleton Tech; Practical Nurs.*

COLLAR, Katie Marie
Little Wolf HS; Manawa, WI (24-88) Chor; ARC; Var C; Sftbl; Tr; Citz A; Pep C; Vlbl; Cand, Snofest Qn; GAA; *Appleton Tech Sch; Practical Nurs.*

COLLAZO, Antonio E
Academia Sagrado Corazon; Santurce, PR (5-92) CYO; Chor; VP, Drama; Hmrm; NHS; Order/ Arrow; ARC; SC; Bsbl; Alg A; COM; Hon Prog; Sanctuary Soc; Damascos Yth Movement; Scenography-Director; Drama-VP; *Bradford Col; Architecture.*

COLLAZO, Armando Baez
Jose de Diego HS; Mayaguez, PR (6-276) Pres, Hmrm; Sci C; SC; Ftbl; Sftbl; Tr; Magna Cum Laude; Most Out; Eng A; *U of Puerto Rico at Mayaguez; Med.*

COLLAZO, Gilberto H
Weslevan Acad; Guayhabo, PR; A Cap Choir; Bus Mgr, Ann; Chor; Model UN; NHS; A-Ed, Sch P; Tres, Sr Cl; Tres, Jr Cl; Val; *U of Puerto Rico; Med.*

COLLAZO, Jose
Cardinal Spellman HS; Bronx, NY; Band; Pres, CYO; Chess C; Orch; Bsbl; Swim; COM; Citz A; Pres A; Yth Leg; Second Hon; Band Ltr; *NYU; Pol Sci.*

COLLAZO, Louise Susan
St Joseph's HS; W New York, NJ (21-225) Drama; NHS; Span NHS; NMS; NEDT; Cl Mus; *Duquesne U; Journ.*

COLLAZO, Margarita Rosa
Academia Maria Reina; Rio Piedras, PR; CYO; Chor; NHS; Hon Prog; *U of Puerto Rico; Med Tech.*

COLLEN, Janice Marie
Ralph C Mahar Regional HS; Orange, MA (8-166) F-Ed, Ann; Band; Key C; NHS; Co-Ed, Sch P; SC; Tnns; All Dist Band; Excel in Art A; Most Artistic; *Sch o-t Worcester Art Museum; Art.*

COLLETT, Marsha Jo
Riverview Gardens Sr HS; St Louis, MO (83-709) Pres, FHA; FTA; NHS; WW; Top 15%; Mo Sch Col Relations; *NE Mo St Col; Bilingual Ed.*

COLLEY, Alfred Wayne
Greenup Co HS; Greenup, KY (200-400) Chor; 4H; Sftbl; 4H A; Hon Prog; Attendance A.

COLLEY, Fred Peter
Crestview Christian Acad; O'Fallon, MO; Ensm; Sftbl; Tr; Yth Fel; Yth Leg; School Quiz Tm; *Mid-America Nazarene Col.*

COLLIER, Cindy Ann
Sylacauga HS; Sylacauga, AL (18-160) Band; FBLA; Jr Miss Pagent; Cpt, Mjrte; NHS; Beauty; Rep, Jr Cl; Sr Cl Beauty; WW; Most Typical Stu; Sr Scholastic Soc; *Huntingdon Col; Mus.*

COLLIER, Clay Allen
Pine Forest HS; Fayetteville, NC (30%-450) Pres, BC; Lit Mag; Co-Ed, Sch P; Span C; Parl, SC; Bsbl; Bkbl; Cr-Ctry; Journ A; *U of NC; Journ.*

COLLIER, Crystal
Kenwood HS; Chicago, IL; Chor; Drama; Secy, FBLA; Modern Dance Tm; *Olive Hardy Col; Bus Ed.*

COLLIER, Helen Marie
Elston Sr HS; Michigan City, IN; Pres, CYO; JV, Chldr; Fin, Jr Miss Pagent; Sftbl; Beauty; Citz A; Cl Fav; HQn; Most Out; Phy A; Spch A; Star Student; Swtht; Type A; *Terre Haute Col; Modeling.*

COLLIER, Horace Alphonso
Chester HS; Chester, PA; Band; Chess C; Chor; Drama; Hmrm; *Mus.*

COLLIER, Katherine Beth
New Braunfels HS; New Braunfels, TX (16-250) Band; Ensm; FTA; JETS; Math C; Mu Alpha Theta; NHS; Sci C; Tr; Amer Leg A; NEDT; *Tex Tech U; Engr.*

COLLIER, Kathryn Ann
Clintonville Sr HS; Clintonville, U; Cpt, Chldr; NHS; SC; Var C; Co-Cpt, Bkbl; JV, Tr; HCt; Hon Prog; Pres A; Rotary A; Vlbl; Gym; Art A; *U of Wis; Art.*

COLLIER, Kerry Lee
Winnfield Sr HS; Winnfield, LA (5-122) VP, Anchor C; Ann; Band; Secy, BC; Secy, Chldr; Fr C; FBLA; FHA; VP, FTA; GS; 4H; Fin, Jr Miss Pagent; Lit Ral; Mjrte; SC; Mgr, Bkbl; Beauty; Cl Fav; HCt; Hon Prog; Ad Staff; Feature Twirler; WW; Superior Stu Prog; *LSU; Med.*

COLLIER, Lelia Anne
Warsaw Comm HS; Warsaw, IN; Chor; Dbte Tm; NFL; Ski C; Tr; DARGCA; Hon Prog; Opt A; Tri Kappa Hon A; *Wash U; Hist.*

COLLIER, Mark David
Port St Joe HS; Port St Joe, FL; HKg; VICA; *Gulf Coast Comm Col; Bus.*

COLLIER, Mark Edward
Belton HS; Belton, TX; FFA; 4H; MVP, Bsbl; Ftbl; Tr; Tres, FCA; *Tex Tech U.*

COLLIER, Mark Steven
Pine Forest HS; Fayetteville, NC (4-250) Pres, BC; Ger C; Key C; Co-Ed, Sch P; SC; Bsbl; Ftbl; *Wake Forest U; Med Field.*

COLLIER, Pamela Jill
Del Oro HS; Loomis, CA (75-396) *Nurs.*

COLLIER, Paul Stephen
Owosso Sr HS; Owosso, MI (55-404) Pres, A Cap Choir; Chor; Drama; Ensm; Madrigal; NHS; Cr-Ctry; Tr; *Oral Roberts U; Mus.*

COLLIER, Robert Wayne
Bloom Township HS; Chicago Heights, IL (3-1152) Math C; NHS; Bio A; Hon Prog; NHS A; Cand, NCTE A in Writing; *Purdue U; Engr.*

COLLIER, Sharon Denise
Chattanooga HS; Chattanooga, TN (15-30) Drama; Lat C; SC; Tr; *U of Tenn at Knoxville; Social Work.*

COLLIER, Tamra Jean
Crystal City HS; Crystal City, MO (27-95) Band; NHS; COM; Outst Home Ec Stu; Comm Teachers Assn Schol; *Columbia Col; Fashion Design.*

COLLIER, Tina
Starkville HS; Starkville, MS; Chldr; VP, FBLA; FTA; Sch P; SC; Y-Tns; Sftbl; Tr; Cl Fav; HCt; Sr Cl Rep; Outst, Tr; All-Star Chldr; *Jackson St U; Bus Ed.*

COLLIER, Tracy Sue
Del Norte HS; Albuquerque, NM; Chor; City Conf; Hmrm; Rainbow; SC; COM; Masonic A; PTA A; ARC A; Type A; Yth Fel; Pres, Yth Coun; CCYM Rep for Church; *U of NM; Law.*

COLLIER, William Patrick
Del Norte HS; Albuquerque, NM; A Cap Choir; Chor; City Conf; Dbte Tm; Pres, Demolay; Drama; Ensm; Lat C; Lat NHS; Madrigal; NFL; Ntl Yth Conf; Spch C; Thes; Bsbl; Ftbl; Sftbl; Wrest; Aux Lat; COM; Masonic A; PTA A; ARC A; Spch A; Yth Fel; Homecoming Emcee; Conf Yth Coun Rep; Demolay A; Meritorious Service A; Tres, Yth Coun; *U of NM-Albuquerque; Industrial Mfg.*

COLLINS, Alfred Charles
W End HS; Birmingham, AL (20-200) Bus C; Chess C; Drama; Thes; Cl Fav; MLS; *Tenn St Col; Pol Sci.*

COLLINS, Alphonso
East St Louis Lincoln Sr HS; E St Louis, IL (2-409) Tres, Chess C; Drama; Ger C; Hmrm; NHS; Spch C; Pres, SC; Pres, Sr Cl; Tres, Jr Cl; VP, Soph Cl; Alg A; Citz A; Cl Fav; Elk A; Hon Prog; Math A; MLS; Most Out; Opt A; Sal; Spch A; Pres NAACP; Stu Adv, St Board of Ed; *Northwestern U; Pre-Med.*

COLLINS, Amelia Lynn
Palmetto HS; Miami, FL (20%-1075) Chor; Yth Fel; Concert Choir; Pres, Yth Assn for Retarded Citz; Church Drama; *Rolling Col; Bus.*

COLLINS, Barbara Diane
Mathews HS; Vienna, OH (13-160) Ann; Pres, Bus C; FTA; Tres, Span C; Y-Tns; Bkbl Scorekeeper; *Youngstown St U; Math Ed.*

COLLINS, Brenda Lea
Sheldon HS; Sheldon, MO (1-14) Ann; Ensm; Secy, FHA; S-T, NHS; Sch P; S-T, SC; Secy, Sr Cl; Alg A; Bio A; Sci A; *Kans St of Pittsburg; Teaching.*

COLLINS, Carol Ann
Qn o-t Rosary Acad; Amityville, NY (20-70) CYO; Hmrm; NHS; VP, SC; Cpt, Bkbl; Sftbl; Vlbl; Pub Relations Comm; Ldrs C; Badminton; *St Johns U; Communication Arts.*

COLLINS, Catherine Anne
Halifax Co Sr HS; S Boston, VA (14-588) A Cap Choir; Ann; Co-Cpt, Chldr; Chor; VP, Drama; Mod Mus Mas; NHS; Rptr, Sch P; Tres, Span C; Alt, GS; WW, Mus; WW, Chldrs; Asst Ed, Co Ed, Sch P; WW; All Region & All St Choirs; Jr Marshall; *Westhampton Col; Journ.*

COLLINS, Charlotte Irene
Springdale HS; Springdale, AR; Chor; Rptr, FHA; Secy, FHA.

COLLINS, Cheryl Ann
Nordonia HS; Macedonia, OH (175-439) Ski C; SC; Tr; Horseback Riding; Art A; *Art.*

COLLINS, Cheryl Lynn
Oliver Wendell Holmes HS; San Antonio, TX (90-600) Cum Laude Soc; Dbte Tm; Drama; Pres, Lat C; NFL; Spch C; Parl, SC; PTA A; Spch A; Latin-Mythology, Roman Life; *Baylor U; Law.*

COLLINS, Chris Ann
Ringgold Monongahela Div; Monongahela, PA (99-367) A Cap Choir; Bus C; Chor; FBLA; Mjrte; Ski C; Tr.

COLLINS, Chris Vette
Mary Brantley Smiley HS; Houston, TX (15-400) Co-Ed, Ann; Chess C; Drama; FTA; Hmrm; Math C; Mu Alpha Theta; NHS; Sci C; SC; Thes; Tres, Jr Cl; Tr; Bio A; COM; Citz A; Asst-Ed, Annual; Rptr, Sch P; Eng A; VP, Creative Writing C; Press C; *Baylor U; Biol.*

COLLINS, Connie Gean
Stevenson HS; Livonia, MI; Chor; Orch; Sch P; Sftbl; Pep C; Yth Comm; Walk-A-Thon A; Dist 1 Fest Orch A; Church Choir; C-Ch, Rock-A-Thon; Pianist; Vacation Bible Sch Teacher; *Eastern Mich U; Social Work.*

COLLINS, Cornelia Marie
Oak Ridge Acad; Oak Ridge, NC (5-30) Chor; Monogram; Sch P; Cpt, Bkbl; Sftbl; MVP, Tnns; ROTC A; Morehead Nom; Outst Ath; Adv Chor; *U of N Carolina; Psych.*

COLLINS, Cynthia Joanne
Princess Anne HS; Virginia Beach, VA (10%-650) Band; Phys Fitness A; *Old Dominion U; Primary Ed.*

COLLINS, Deborah Elaine
Gadsden HS; Gadsden, AL (3-301) Band; Hmrm; Math C; NHS; Span C; Colorguard; Most Stu; *U of Ala; Chem.*

COLLINS, Debra Ann
Greenville Sr HS; Greenville, PA (26-201) Ann; VP, Band; S-T, Span C; Tri-HiY; *Pres Hos Sch of Radiology; Radiologic Tech.*

COLLINS, Dennis Keith
Belton Sr HS; Belton, MO (145-300) Bsbl; Wrest; Bus.

COLLINS, Doris Jean
Dunbar HS; Chicago, IL (64-512) Ann; Secy, Chor; NHS; COM; Citz A; Off Aide; Secy, Pastor's Choir; Pres & Secy, Jr Usher Board; Secy, Jr Usher Board; Sunday Sch & BTU Teacher; *Ntl Col of Ed; Special Ed.*

COLLINS, Doris Mae
Hardee Co Sr HS; Wauchula, FL (15-264) Band; Rptr, FHA; NHS; Fla Ntl Tn Pageant; Tn C; Soph Server; Yth Choir; *Journ.*

COLLINS, Douglas R
Orleans HS; Orleans, NE; VP, Band; BS; Chor; 4H; NHS; Ski C; Pres, SC; Bkbl; Ftbl; Tr; Elk A; 4H A; HCt; Hon Prog; I Dare You; All-Conf, Ftbl & Bkbl; Stu Member, St Ed Advisory Coun; *U of Nebr; Agr.*

COLLINS, Eddie B
Vanden HS; Travis AFB, CA (3-150) Hmrm; SC; JV, Tr; Hon Prog; *Fort Wayne Bible Col; Christian Ed.*

COLLINS, George Bryan Jr
Wilkes Central HS; N Wilkesboro, NC (5%-292) Chess C; InterAct C; NHS; SC; Pres, Sr Cl; Pres, Soph Cl; JV, Bkbl; Cr-Ctry; HCt; Hon Prog; NEDT; *Wake Forest U; Bus Adm.*

COLLINS, Ginger Lynn
Wichita W HS; Wichita, KS (50%-250) A Cap Choir; Chor; Mgr, Cr-Ctry; Mgr, Tr; Opt Out Tn; Yth Fel; Outst, Church Yth Convention; *Gulf Coast Bible Col; Yth Ldr.*

COLLINS, Herbert Davis Jr
St Augustine HS; New Orleans, LA (18-32) Ftbl; Tr; Most Out; *LSU; Geol.*

COLLINS, Jeffrey Todd
MacArthur HS; Irving, TX (33%-500) Band; NHS; Bkbl; *SMU; Med.*

COLLINS, John Russell
Niwot HS; Longmont, CO (27-311) Chor; Dbte Tm; Wrest; Bio A; Chem A; Lab Asst, Aide, Sci Dept; *US Army.*

COLLINS, John William
Wilbur Wright HS; Dayton, OH (20-250) BS; Tres, Hmrm; Order/Arrow; Var C; JV, Bkbl; Ftbl; Ushers C; Pres, Yth Fel; JA; Ntl Eagle Sct Assn; Locker Sq; *Sci.*

COLLINS, Juanita Faye
HS For Health Professions; Houston, TX (98-139) Chess C; Drama; Hmrm; K of C, NFL; A-Ed, Sch P; Spch C; Sftbl; Tnns; COM; Citz A; Cl Fav; Sci A; *UT Maritine Col; Marine Phar.*

COLLINS, Judith Kay
Springfield Sr HS; Springfield, OR; A Cap Choir; Ann; Band; Chor; Fin, Jr Miss Pagent; NHS; Sch P; Swim; Cpt, Dance Tm; Gym; St Fin, Eagles A; *LCC; Elem Ed.*

COLLINS, Judith Lynn
Hazelwood E HS; St Louis, MO (118-520) Chor; Mjrte; Hon Prog; Yth Fel; Candystriper.

COLLINS, Kendra Lee
James Ford Rhodes HS; Cleveland, OH; Pres, Bus C; ARC; Y-Tns; Bsbl; COM; Citz A; Hon Prog; Drill Tm; Ed, Church Paper; Gym Ldr C.

COLLINS, Lawrence Turner
Glendale HS; Springfield, MO; *Humanities.*

COLLINS, LeRoy Wight
Woodmere Acad; Woodmere, NY (4-52) Band; Chor; Drama; Fr C; Rptr, Sch Achieve Tm; Ntl Achv Schol; Regent Schol; WW; *Harvard U; Journ.*

COLLINS, Lisa Jan
Westminster Christian Sch; Gadsden, AL; BC; Hmrm; Tri-HiY; COM; Hon Prog; Yth Fel; *Auburn U; Marketing.*

COLLINS, Lorinda Ruth
Forest Park Sr HS; Forest Park, GA; A Cap Choir; Band; Chor; HiY; 1st Pl, Ntl Flag Corps; *Clayton Jr Col; Art.*

COLLINS, Mark Alan
Atlanta HS; Atlanta, LA (1-40) Rptr, FFA; FTA; Alg A; *La Tech U; Engr.*

COLLINS, Mary Jo
Block HS; Jonesville, LA; Chor; Community Yth Symph; Drama; 4H; Spch C; Var C; Bkbl; Sftbl; COM; Cl Fav; Hon Prog; *Sou U; Secy.*

COLLINS, Melanie Lynn
Philadelphia HS; Philadelphia, MS (2-70) BC; 4H; Hon Prog; *Miss U for Women; Sociology.*

COLLINS, Melba Joyce
Rosedale HS; Rosedale, MS; Rptr, Ann; BC; Drama; Parl, FBLA; NHS; Rptr, Sch P; Sci C; *U of Miss; Acct.*

COLLINS, Melissa Ann
Sycamore HS; Cincinnati, OH (10%-480) Ann; Band; Community Yth Symph; Pres, Fr C; NHS; Rptr, Sch P; Thes; S-T, Fr C; *Vanderbilt U; Bus Mgr.*

COLLINS, Michael Jerome
McCluer Sr HS; Florissant, MO (3-680) Chor; Hmrm; Madrigal; Sch P; Mgr, Bkbl; Soccer; JV, Wrest; JA A; Pres A; VP & Tres, Church Yth Group; Tres, JA; Hon Stu; *Mo at Columbia; Journ.*

COLLINS, Michelle Denise
Northwestern HS; Flint, MI; Cpt, Chldr; Math C; NHS; Hon Prog; Math A; *U of Mich; Med Sci.*

COLLINS, Nathaniel Perryman
Robert E Lee HS; Houston, TX (1-650) InterClub Coun; Key C; Pres, NHS; F-Ed, Sch P; Cpt, Bkbl; Journ A; Math A; Q&S A; MVP, Bkbl; Fin, Math A; Fin, Q&S.

COLLINS, Norma Jan
N Hall HS; Gainesville, GA; Co-Cpt, Band; FBLA; Hmrm; *Nurs.*

COLLINS, Penny Ann
Atlanta HS; Atlanta, LA; Ann; Cpt, Chldr; Chor; Tres, FHA; FTA; Hmrm; Lit Ral; Yth Fel; Hist, FHA; Hist, SC; Semi-Fin, St Bar Assn Essay Cont; Project LET; Win, Grambling St U Poetry Contest; *La Tech U; Art.*

COLLINS, Regina Marie
Big Bay de Noc HS; Cooks, MI; Ed, Ann; Drama; 4H; Alg A; Bausch & Lomb A; Bio A; 4H A; Hon Prog; Spch A; Bus Mgr, Annual; *N Mich U; Nurs.*

COLLINS, Richard Ellison
Sky View HS; Smithfield, UT (8-611) Ger C; Pres, Hmrm; Order/Arrow; Var C; JV, Bsbl; Ftbl; COM; Citz A; God & Country A; Schol A; Eagle Sct; *Utah St U; Engr.*

COLLINS, Robert Benjamen
Barnwell HS; Barnwell, SC (40%-150) Pres, Band; Ensm; COM; Pres A; *U of SC; Mus.*

COLLINS, Robert Dale
Jordan HS; Long Beach, CA; Lion A; VP, VICA; Lions CA; *Long Beach City Trade Sch; Elec.*

COLLINS, Robin Rolanda
Booker T Washington HS; Atlanta, GA (9-365) VP, Band; Drama; Fr C; Pres, Hmrm; NHS; SC; COM; HCt; Hon Prog; St Scholar.

COLLINS, Sara Lucille
Oglethorpe Co HS; Lexington, GA (4-104) F-Ed, Ann; Secy, BC; Dbte Tm; Key C; Lit Mag; Co-Ch, Sci C; VP, SC; Beauty; Citz A; Cl Fav; 4H A; H of F; HCt; Hon Prog; Journ A; MLS; Most Out; Ntl Achv Schol; VP, St 4-H C; WW; Ldrship As; Miss Black & Gold; Most Intellectual; *U of Ga; Eng.*

COLLINS, Sharon Elizabeth
Sharkey-Issaquena Acad; Rolling Fork, MS (3-29) Co-Ed, Ann; BC; 4H; Math C; Mu Alpha Theta; NHS; Sch P; Y-Tns; Mgr, Bkbl; COM; Cl Fav; 4H A; PA; *Miss St U; Acct.*

COLLINS, Sheri Lee
Lane Tech HS; Chicago, IL (181-1200) Chldr; Orch; SC; Hon Prog; Church Chor & Sftbl; Pres, Leo's C; Campus Life; Gym; *Wheaton Col; Phys Ed.*

COLLINS, Sherry Lynn
Man Sr HS; Man, WV (11-180) FNA; GS; V-Ch, Hmrm; NHS; Sch P; Span C; Eng A; *Med Lab Tech.*

COLLINS, Stephen Thomas
Atlanta HS; Atlanta, LA (2-29) Ann; FBLA; FFA; Parl, FTA; Semi-Fin, Lit Ral; Pres, Sci C; SC; Bsbl; Mgr, Bkbl; Sftbl; Masonic A; Math A; MLS; Ntl Sci Found; Sal; *La Col; Math.*

COLLINS, Tamarah Joy
Hartshorne HS; Hartshorne, OK (4-60) Ed, Ann; Chldr; Drama; Secy, FHA; Semi-Fin, GS; NHS; Sch P; Spch C; Thes; Bio A; COM; Gov Honor Prog; Hon Prog; Journ A; Math A; Spch A; OSU Alumni A; Citizenship Seminar; SE Okla U; Criminology.

COLLINS, Teresa Elane
Parker HS; Greenville, SC (1-335) Chor; Hmrm; Clemson U; Nurs.

COLLINS, Teryl Denise
Weed HS; Weed, CA (9-58) Secy, Band; VP, Chor; Sch P; Pres, Ski C; Sftbl; Tr; Amer Leg A; Hon Prog; Journ A; Spch A; Vlbl; Humbolt Col; Psych.

COLLINS, Thomas Earl
West Side HS; Newark, NJ (8-525) JV, Band; NHS; Cpt, Bkbl; Cr-Ctry; Tr; Citz A; ARC A; Schol Ath; U of Mich.

COLLUM, Janelle Gay
Caroline HS; Bowling Green, VA (1-250) Fr C; NHS; Citz A; Hist A; Math A; Type A; Fr, Geom, A's; Yth Coun; Nurs.

COLLUM, John Wright
Bowling Green Sr HS; Bowling Green, VA (10%-198) 4H; Span C; Citz A; 4H A; Spch A; Yth Fel; Span A.

COLLVER, Bobbi Jean
Parkview HS; Springfield, MO; Chor; Drama; Fr C; 4H; Ski C; Sftbl; JV, Tr; Evangel Col.

COLOGNE, Steven John
University HS; San Diego, CA (33-311) CYO; Chem C; 4H; Math C; NHS; Ntl Yth Conf; Ed, Sch P; Ski C; Cpt, Golf; Amer Leg A; CSF; COM; Cl Fav; Hon Prog; Journ A; MLS; Most Out; Star Student; U of Sou Calif; Bus Adm.

COLOMBO, Larry Anthony
Hartland HS; Hartland, MI (30-180) NHS; Wrest; Western Mich U; Printing.

COLOMER, Vanessa de Lourdes
Colegio San Antonio Abad; Humacao, PR (15-72) Chem C; Pres, Hmrm; Lit Ral; Math C; NHS; Spch C; SC; Tres, Sr Cl; COM; Chem A; Cl Fav; Hon Prog; Journ A; Math A; ARC A; Spch A; Swtht; Home Ec A; Emmanuel Col; Med Technology.

COLON, Ada Elena
Dr Pila HS; Ponce, PR (6-688) A Cap Choir; CYO; Chem C; Dbte Tm; Ensm; FHA; Hmrm; Madrigal; NHS; Sch P; Span C; Swim; Beauty; COM; Citz A; Cl Fav; H of F; Hon Prog; Ntl Cath Mus Ed Asn; Yth Fel; U of PR; Psych.

COLON, Cecilia
Eastside HS; Paterson, NJ; A Cap Choir; Chor; Drama; Ensm; Madrigal; Mod Mus Mas; Orch; Montclair St Col; Law.

COLON, Griselle
Dr Pila HS; Ponce, PR (10%-688) A Cap Choir; Chem C; Chor; Drama; Ensm; FHA; Hmrm; Madrigal; Sch Achieve Tm; Sch P; Span C; SC; COM; Citz A; Cl Fav; H of F; Hon Prog; Ntl Cath Mus Ed Asn; Yth Fel; Boston U; Occupational Therapy.

COLON, Luis Alberto
Eastside HS; Paterson, NJ; FFA; FTA; 4H; ARC; Bsbl; Cpt, Bkbl; Cr-Ctry; Sftbl; Tr; COM; 4H A; Hon Prog; Montclair St Col.

COLON, Madelyn
Eastside HS; Paterson, NJ (24-519) SC; Aspira C; HR; Upsala U; Sociology.

COLON, Marcos Antonio
Centro Oportunidad Educativas B HS; Guaynabo, PR; CYO; COM; Eng Essay A; U of Puerto Rico; Med.

COLON, Maria Lina
Colegio Puertorriqueno de Ninas; Caparra Heights, PR (1-48) Chor; NHS; COM; Chem A; Hon Prog; Val; Conduct A; First & Second Hons; Yrbk Staff; Newcomb Col of Tulane U; Sci.

COLON, Marjorie Lyzzette
Juan Jose Osuna HS; Hato Rey, PR; Pres, Chem C; FHA; Pres, ARC; Sci C; Span C; Bio A; COM; Hist A; Math A; ARC A; Sci A; Span As; Art A; U of Cayey; Sci.

COLON, Rosa Elvira
Antilles HS; Fort Buchanan, PR (5%-135) Hon Prog; Type A; Keyettes; Conservatory of Mus; Phar.

COLON, Victor M
Academia San Jorge; Santurce, PR (7-75) CYO; InterAct C; NHS; U of Puerto Rico at Mayaguez; Engr.

COLONREXACH, Judith I
Consuelo Escalona Private Sch; Carolina, PR (15-28) Chor; ARC; Spch C; Sftbl; Tnns; COM; Loyalty A; Cl Hon; U of PR; Occupational Therapy.

COLSON, Cindy Lou
Alliance HS; Alliance, NE (1-150) S-T, Chor; Secy, SC; Y-Tns; Bio A; Hist A; Art A; All Star Chor; Concordia Teacher's Col;.

COLSON, Lee Wayne
Blue Valley HS; Randolph, KS (2-18) 4H; Secy, Jr Cl; 4H A; Math A; ARC A; Type A; Kans St U; Math.

COLSTON, Andrea Willnette
Woodham HS; Pensacola, FL; Chldr; Chor; GS; HiY; ARC; Ed.

COLSTON, Arnita Jean
Havana HS; Havana, FL (4-124) VP, Hmrm; NHS; SC; Journ A; Fla A&M U; Nurs.

COLSTON, Brian Keith
Adairsville HS; Adairsville, GA; Secy, FFA; Bsbl; Ftbl; Sftbl; Tr.

COLSTON, Carl Antony
William J Woodham HS; Pensacola, FL (230-700) Band; Order/Arrow; Span C; Hon Prog; JA A; Swtht; Fiction A; Span A; Pensacola Jr Col; Law.

COLTER, Curtis Herman
Crockett HS; Crockett, TX (6-140) FFA; FHA; Bkbl; Ftbl; Tr; TSU; Child Care Director.

COLTHARP, Glenn Perry
Pittsburg HS; Pittsburg, KS (52-181) Pres, Band; Chess C; Demolay; Ensm; FTA; Hmrm; SC; Pittsburg St U; Elem Ed.

COLTON, Carl G
E Syracuse-Minoa HS; East Syracuse, NY (7-500) NHS; Soccer; Tnns; Wrest; Johns Hopkins U; Med.

COLTON, Charles James
E Syracuse-Minoa Central HS; E Syracuse, NY (2-520) Band; NHS; Bkbl; Tr; Hon Prog; Art, Social Stu, Math, A's; US Naval Acad.

COLTON, Karen Marie
Jacksonville HS; Jacksonville, IL (1-313) Band; Pres, Fr C; French NHS; NHS; Bkbl; Sftbl; Hon Prog; St Scholar; Val; Co Cpt, Vlbl; Augustana Col; Math.

COLTON, Nancy Jean
Jacksonville HS; Jacksonville, IL; Band; Fr C; French NHS; NHS; Bkbl; Sftbl; Vlbl; Oral Roberts U; Bus.

COLTRAIN, Jill Renee
Williamston HS; Williamston, NC (23-179) Ed, Ann; Chldr; Fin, Demolay; Drama; FBLA; Key C; Monogram; Tres, NHS; SC; Mgr, Bsbl; Bkbl; Hon Prog; Meredith Col; Math.

COLTRAIN, Robert Scott
Fern Creek HS; Louisville, KY (25-290) BC; ROTC A.

COLUBRIALE, Toni
St James HS; Carney's Point, NJ (32-72) Chor; Hmrm; SC; Var C; Hockey; Amer Leg A; God & Country A; HCt; Peirce Jr Col; Fashion Merchandising.

COLUMBIA, Michael Ray
Brethren Christian HS; Orange, IN (5%-26) Ann; Band; Chess C; Chor; Drama; Ensm; Fr C; Hmrm; SC; Nisbova Contest; Notre Dame U; Pol Sci.

COLUMBUS, Nanette Lynn
John F Kennedy HS; Denver, CO (350-553) Chor; 4H; Madrigal; ARC; SC; DARGCA; Ldrship A; Oral Roberts U; Sociology.

COLVIG, Dorothy Gail
Henrica HS; Richmond, VA (50%-342) Band; Chor; Ensm; Ger C; Hmrm; Co-Cpt, Mjrte; Y-Tns; Tr.

COLVIN, Ben Allen
Muncie Central HS; Muncie, IN (13-300) Band; Drama; 4H; Madrigal; NHS; Span C; SC; Thes; VP, Soph C; Tnns; COM; 4H A; Hon Prog; Kiwanis A; 1st, St Instrumental Contest; Exchange C Academic Hon; Theatre.

COLWELL, Kent Alan
Alliance HS; Alliance, NE (17-147) VP, Band; Chor; Ger C; SC; Thes; Var C; Pres, Jr Cl; Bkbl; Ftbl; Tr; Hon Men, Western Conf, Ftbl.

COMARDO, Margaret Lucia
York Central Sch; Retsof, NY (12-95) AFS; Ann; Band; Chor; Drama; Madrigal; NHS; Sch P; SC; Hon Prog; Nazareth Col of Roch; Theatre Arts.

COMBELLICK, Linda Marie
Heritage HS; Littleton, CO (43-479) A Cap Choir; Chor; Drama; Hon Prog; Outst Choir Stu; Director's A, Drama; Best Actress; U of Wash.

COMBEST, Becky Louise
E Ascension Acad; Gonzales, LA; 4H; Lit Ral; Sch P; SC; Bkbl; 4H A; LSU; Dentistry.

COMBS, Allen Dale
W Memphis Christian HS; W Memphis, AR; BS; Bsbl; Cpt, Bkbl; Cpt, Ftbl; Tr; HCt; Harding Col; Med.

COMBS, Kathy Sue
Zanesville HS; Zanesville, OH (60-325) Band; 4H; ARC; Mgr, Tr; 4H A; ARC A; Yth Fel; Sun Sch Teacher; Ohio U; Nurs.

COMBS, Mark Dewayne
Temple Christian Sch; Jacksonville, FL; Bsbl; JV, Bkbl; COM; Bsbl Trophies; Bkbl Trophy; 2nd Pl, Sermon Trophy; Arlington Baptist Col; Bible.

COMBS, Melanie Dianne
El Camino Real HS; Woodland Hills, CA (25-1095) SC; Secy, Sr Cl; Secy, Soph Cl; DARGCA; HCt; MVP, Drill Tm; Spelling A; Candy Striper; Girls League; Job's Daughters; Best Over All, Drill Tm; Stanford U; Ed.

COMBS, Mike Alan
E Clinton HS; Lees Creek, OH (21-136) Pres, Band; Chess C; Ensm; Pres, NHS; Band Directors A; Kent St Col; Archt.

COMBS, Ricky Eugene
John F Kennedy HS; Richmond, CA (17-306) JV, Tnns; CSF; COM; St Scholar; Secy, BSct; U of Calif; Dentistry.

COMBS, Roberta Dorothy
Alvernia HS; Chicago, IL (25%-240) S-T, Hmrm; Rptr, Sch P; Hon Qn, Job's Daughters; Tres, GSct; Board, NSCC; CYF; NE III Col; Liberal Arts.

COMBS, Steven Ray
Cloverleaf Sr HS; Lodi, OH (128-269) Chor; Drama; Ensm; FTA; NFL; Spch C; Thes; Mgr, Cr-Ctry; Tr; Best Male Thespian; All St Yth Choir.

COMBS, Timothy Ray
W Memphis Christian Sch; W Memphis, AR; Hmrm; Bsbl; Bkbl; Ftbl; Tr; Cl Fav; HCt; Harding Col; Bible.

COMCHOC, Rosanne Carol
Cumberland Valley HS; Mechanicsburg, PA (29-564) Co-Cpt, Chldr; Math C; NHS; Most Sch Spirit; Shippensburg Col; Math.

COMEAU, Michael Charles
Don Bosco Tech HS; Boston, MA (1-211) CYO; Pres, Hmrm; Tres, NHS; Tres, SC; Mgr, Hockey; Hon Prog; NEDT.

COMEAUX, Betsy Marie
Our Lady of Fatima HS; Lafayette, LA; VP, BC; Chldr; Fr C; Math C; Ed, Sch P; SC; Bkbl; Cpt, Ftbl; Co-Cpt, Sftbl; Cl Fav; HQn; Hon Prog; Cpt, Flag Ftbl; High PSAT Math Score; Beta C Swtht; Ch, Liturgical Comm; USL.

COMEAUX, Lisa Ann
John B Ehret HS; Marrero, LA (12-550) Tres, CYO; Chor; Lit Ral; Math C; Mu Alpha Theta; NHS; Sftbl; Tr; Hist A; Hon Prog; PTA A; Sci A; Prep Quiz Bowl; Tulane U; Law.

COMELLA, Anthony Charles
Lane Tech HS; Chicago, IL (100-1205) Bsbl; Bkbl; Cpt, Sftbl; Semi-Fin, Tr; Hon Prog; Awana Hon A; Taylor Col; Bus.

COMER, Deborah Arie
East HS; Columbus, OH (19-350) Graduate, Art Instruction Sch; Columbus Col of Art & Design; Commerical Art.

COMER, Sharon Elaine
Brethren HS; Paramount, CA (20-102) A Cap Choir; Ntl Yth Conf; JV, Sftbl; Drill Tm; Point Loma Col.

COMING, Joan Marie
Magnificat HS; Rocky River, OH (10%-130) CYO; Hmrm; NHS; Rptr, Sch P; SC; Bkbl; Secy, Tr; Sci A; Spch A; HS Schol; Tr A's; *U of Ky; Bio.*

COMING, Mark Andrew
St Edward HS; Lakewood, OH (75-400) CYO; Ger C; Lit Mag; Order/Arrow; COM; Hon Prog; Order/Arrow A; Spch A; Eagle Sct; Ad Altare Dei; *Borremeo Col; Theology.*

COMITO, Melanie Ann
Kuemper HS; Carroll, IA (1-280) Chor; Fr C; Hmrm; Monogram; SC; Pres, Jr Cl; Cr-Ctry; Tr; Sci A; *Iowa St U; Math.*

COMLEY, Alma Ruth
Lafayette HS; Lexington, KY (33%-600) Lat C; Hon Prog; Yth Fel; *Dentistry.*

COMMANDER, Amelia Jean
Decatur HS; Decatur, AL (91-291) FBLA; FHA; FTA; Span C; *U of Ala; Marketing.*

COMMONS, Kathleen Sue
Boca Ciega HS; St Petersburg, FL (123-533) Bus C; Chor; Ensm; Fr C; FBLA; Tres, Hmrm; Co-Ed, Sch P; 1st Pl, FBLA Contest; HR; Camper o-t Week; PA; *Pensacola Christian Col; Pre-Sch Ed.*

COMPARIN, Cynthia Jane
Eastern Hills HS; Fort Worth, TX (110-487) Cum Laude Soc; Ch, Hmrm; Sftbl; *U of Tex; Social Work.*

COMPSTON, Jill Ann
Walnut Hills HS; Cincinnati, OH; Band; Chor; Bkbl; Sftbl; COM; Citz A; Yth Fel; Comm On Missions.

COMPTON, Carin Ann
Dupont Sr HS; Hermitage, TN (36-300) BC; NHS; *Tenn Tech U; Interior Design.*

COMPTON, Charles Curtis
Rich S HS; Richton Park, IL; Hon Prog; Type A; *Moody Bible Inst; Aviation.*

COMPTON, Cinthia Lyn
Wylie E Groves HS; Birmingham, MI (10%-700) Chor; Drama; Ensm; Hmrm; ARC; JV, Bkbl; Sftbl; Tnns; COM; ARC A.

COMPTON, Kelsie Maurice
John D Bassett HS; Bassett, VA (10%-150) All Amer Yth; AFS; Band; BS; 4H; Hmrm; Math C; Monogram; NHS; Order/Arrow; JV, Bkbl; Co-Cpt, Ftbl; Co-Cpt, Wrest; MVP, Ftbl; Yth o-t Mo; Full Ftbl Schol; *VPI; Engr.*

CONAR, Stephen Clark
McMinn Co HS; Athens, TN; HiY; Hmrm; Tres, Order/Arrow; Span C; St Stu Congress; Golf; Tnns; Order/Arrow A; Pres A; Yth Leg; *U of Tenn; Law.*

CONARD, Jeffrey Dean
Hilltop HS; Chula Vista, CA (5%-600) Secy, Hmrm; Var C; Ftbl; Wrest; CSF; Citz A; Hon Prog; Best Manners; *Engr.*

CONARD, Torrence Lynn
Warren HS; Monmouth, IL (1-70) Band; Chor; Cpt, Dbte Tm; Ensm; Ftbl/FFA; Hmrm; Math C; Sci C; SC; Secy, Var C; Pres, Soph Cl; Bsbl; Bkbl; Ftbl; Cpt, Sftbl; Swim; Tnns; Tr; Wrest; COM; Citz A; Gr Marshal; Hct; Hon Prog; Yth Fel; Yth Leg; *Western Ill U; Math.*

CONARROE, Pam Clark
Groveton HS; Groveton, TX (4-54) BC; FHA; Span C; Rptr, SC; Secy, Jr Cl; Bkbl.

CONAWAY, Johnnie Mae
Wheeler Co HS; Alamo, GA (9-50) Rptr, BC; Pres, Bus C; Pres, FBLA; Pres, FFA; Pres, NHS; SC; Var C; Secy, Jr Cl; Bkbl; HQn; HCt; Most Dependable Stu; WW; 2nd, St Pub Spch; *Armstrong St Col; Nurs.*

CONAWAY, Patty Jean
Emmaus HS; Emmaus, PA (300-492) *Asbury Col; Sociology.*

CONCA, Kenneth Louis
Warwick Vets HS; Warwick, RI (5-400) French NHS; Math C; Hist A; Hon Prog; Math A; NMS; Marshal Robertson A; *NJHS; WW; Sci.*

CONCEPCION, Marissa
Juan Jose Osuna HS; Hato Rey, PR (4-150) CYO; Dbte Tm; FHA; Math C; ARC; Span C; COM; Hon Prog; Math A; Rensselaer A; Star Student; *U of Puerto Rico; Exec Secy.*

CONCKLIN, Craig West
Hinsdale Central HS; Hinsdale, IL (50%-650) Var C; Soccer; Young Life; Ltrman; *Denver U; Bus.*

CONDIE, Christopher James
Skyline HS; Salt Lake City, UT (47-675) Chor; ARC; Tnns; COM; Citz A; Sci A; Eagle Sct; Sr Patrol Ldr; Pres, Deacon's Quorum; *U of Utah; Med.*

CONDRA, Anita Delores
F T Wills HS; Smyrna, GA (25%-300) Secy, BC; Co-Cpt, Chldr; NHS.

CONDRA, Melanie Gaye
SW Miami HS; Miami, FL; Chor; Ensm; Hmrm; NHS; SC; Citz A; Hon Prog; Most Out; Yth Fel.

CONDRA, Nina Yvonne
Andrews HS; Andrews, TX; Parl, Bus C; Rptr, 4H; NHS; Rainbow; Shorthand; Social Stu C; *Secy.*

CONDRON, Lynn
Peoria Central HS; Peoria, IL; Chldr; Chor; Sftbl; Yth Fel; Campus Life.

CONE, Michael Bruce
Brandon HS; Ortonville, MI (36-170) Pres, Band; NHS; Rptr, Sch P; Pres, Jr Cl; VP, Soph Cl; Ftbl; JV, Wrest; Citz A; Q&S A; Most Outgoing; Govt A; Social Stu A; Best Bandsman; *Northern Mich U; Pre-Med.*

CONE, Rosemary
New Caney HS; Porter, TX (25%-225) FHA; Hmrm; NHS; Rainbow; Tres, SC; Type A; Historian, Lt & Cpt, Drill Tm; *Stephen F Austin St U; Ed.*

CONE, Stephen Hart
St Andrew's Parish HS; Charleston, SC (16-264) Tres, Mu Alpha Theta; NHS; Gov Honor Prog; Gr Marshal; Presbyterian Col Jr School; WW; *Furman U; Engr.*

CONEENY, Christine Marie
Penns Grove HS; Penns Grove, NJ (28-230) Chldr; Secy, Lat C; SC; Hockey; *U of Del; Bio.*

CONEY, Chandra Yvonne
Gibbs Sr HS; St Petersburg, FL (23-383) Ger C; Lit Mag; Secy, NHS; Ed, Sch P; SC; Cl Fav; NMS; Ger A; Social Stu A; Eng A; Air Force ROTC Schol; *Purdue U; Chem.*

CONGDON, Joyce Ann
Piqua Central HS; Piqua, OH (1-420) Fr C; Acomodadore; 'Top 100' Stu.

CONGER, Lynn Marie
Albuquerque HS; Albuquerque, NM (1-620) AFS; Drama; Ensm; NHS; *San Diego St U; Pol Sci.*

CONGER, Steven Marshall
Glenbrook S HS; Glenview, IL (300-629) Dbte Tm; Hmrm; NFL; God & Country A; Spch A; Yth Fel; Forensic A; Debate A's; *N Ill U; Pol Sci.*

CONGER, Susan Frances
Summit HS; Summit, NJ (39-360) Chor; Orch; Tr; Colorguard; Pres, Tres, Church Yth; NML; *Eng.*

CONINE, Karla
Skyline HS; Dallas, TX; FHA; ARC; *Baylor U; Ed.*

CONKEY, Joel Robert
Douglas HS; Douglas, AZ (10%-310) Chor; Ensm; Ftbl; *Point Lama Nazarene Col; Acct.*

CONKLING, Marsha Lynn
Lincoln HS; Lincoln, NE; A Cap Choir; Chor; Madrigal; Sch P; Hon Prog; Dist Yth Coun; Pres, Church Yth; Church Pianist; *Mid-America Nazarene Col; Mus.*

CONKWRIGHT, Joy Elizabeth
Breckinridge Co HS; Harned, KY (3%-200) F-Ed, Ann; FBLA; FTA; Math C; Mu Alpha Theta; NHS; Rainbow; Sch Achieve Tm; VP, Span C; Span NHS; Secy, SC; Var C; Mgr, Bkbl; Tnns; COM; H of F; Hon Prog; Star Student; WW; HR; Hist C; FBLA A; Span A; *U of Ky; Hist.*

CONLEE, Kerry Layne
Bath Co HS; Owingsville, KY (38-136) Band; BS; 4H; Tr; Citz A; Yth Fel; Best Dressed, Sr Cl; *Eastern Ky U; Pre-Law.*

CONLEN, Tracey Ann
Catholic Central HS; Troy, NY (50%-350) *Special Ed.*

CONLEY, Darrell Lynn
Cotton Plant HS; Cotton Plant, AR (3-35) Drama; FBLA; Pres, 4H; NHS; Pres, Soph Cl; Bkbl; Tr; Alg A; Citz A; Cl Fav; 4H A; Sci A; Tr A; Bkbl A; *Data Processing.*

CONLEY, Evelyn Joy
James I ONeill HS; Highland Falls, NY (17-230) Band; Community Yth Symph; Drama; Ensm; ARC; SC; Mgr, Soccer; Hon Prog; Methodist Yth G; Pres, Yth Group; Leo C; Sunday Sch Teacher; GSct; GSct Citz Conf; Schol Excel A; *Phys Therapy.*

CONLEY, Jacqueline Marie
Notre Dame HS; Shreveport, LA (9-31) Pres, AFS; Fin, NHS; Pres, ARC; Sodality; Pres, Soph Cl; Sftbl; Citz A; Cl Fav; 4H A; HQn; Masonic A; ARC A; *Prairie View Col; Data Processing.*

CONLEY, Jonathan Joe
Fairborn Baker HS; Fairborn, OH (106-377) VP, FBLA; HR; FBLA A; *Central St Col; Broadcasting.*

CONLEY, Karen Marie
Cass Tech HS; Detroit, MI (30%-800) Bus Mgr, Ann; Fr C; SC; Citz A; Q&S A; Yth Fel; *Mercy Col of Detroit; Bus.*

CONLEY, Kevin Christopher
Liggett Sch; Grosse Pointe Woods, MI (1-75) Chor; Cum Laude Soc; Drama; Fr C; French NHS; Lat C; Span C; Pres, SC; Var C; Ftbl; Tr; COM; Star Student; Summa Cum Laude; First, St Fr Contest; First, St Span Contest; Best Actor; *Harvard U; Eng.*

CONLEY, Lisa Montez
Kashmere Sr HS; Houston, TX; Band; Chldr; FNA; Hmrm; Orch; Spch A; VP, Good Listenes C; *San Jancinto Jr Col; Nurs.*

CONLEY, Marta Joanne
Cleveland HS; Reseda, CA; SC; Bkbl; Co-Cpt, Sftbl; MVP, Sftbl; *Pierce Jr Col; Phys Ed.*

CONLEY, Regina
Fairborn Baker HS; Fairborn, OH; FBLA; Outst Stu Aid; FBLA A; *Sinclair Comm Col; Bus.*

CONLEY, Sharon Lee
Wilburton HS; Wilburton, OK (15-62) Chldr; Secy, FTA; Bkbl; Alg A; St Scholar; Secy & Rptr, FFA; St NHS; Jr Cl Qn; *Eastern Okla St U; Acct.*

CONLEY, Sheila Christine
Terrell Acad; Dawson, GA (2-40) NHS; Tri-HiY; Presbyterian Col Jr Fellow; *Albany Jr Col; Math.*

CONLEY, Yvonne Victoria
Cy-Fair HS; Cypress, TX (230-620) Swim; All-St Hons Drafting; *Abilene Christian U; Drafting.*

CONLIN, Patricia Mary
Kings Park HS; Kings Park, NY; CYO; Cpt, Chldr; Chor; Hmrm; Sch P; Bkbl; Hockey; Sftbl; B Crocker A; Pres A; *Fashion.*

CONN, Anthony Pinckney
Monticello HS; Monticello, MS; BC; FFA; Hmrm; Tnns; HCt; *U of Sou Miss; Acct.*

CONN, Sara Ann
Orleans Pub HS; Orleans, NE (1-31) Co-Ed, Ann; Band; Chldr; Chor; VP, Dbte Tm; Secy, 4H; NHS; COM; Hon Prog; Spch A; Type A; Mgr, Vlbl; WW; Outst, Band; 1st Pl, Amer Lit, Inter-High Day; *Kans Wesleyan Col; Sci.*

CONN, Steve Ray
Dupont Manual HS; Louisville, KY; Demolay; Ensm; *United Elec Inst; Elec.*

CONNA, David Russell
Westborough HS; Westborough, MA (30-242) Chess C; JV, Cr-Ctry; JV, Tr; *Ecology.*

CONNALLY, Sally Love
Heritage Sch; Newnan, GA (1-14) A-Ed, Ann; Co-Cpt, Chldr; VP, Fr C; 4H; Secy, InterAct C; Ed, Lit Mag; Pres, SC; Bsbl; Soccer; Tnns; Elk A; Gov Honor Prog; Hon Prog; NEDT; Tres, SC; Pres Clrm For Young Amer; *Law.*

CONNAUGHTON, James Laurence
Loyola HS; Towson, MD (1-180) CYO; Chor; Drama; Lat C; NFL; Order/Arrow; ARC; Spch C; Thes; JV, Cr-Ctry; Soccer; Swim; Tnns; JV, Tr; COM; NEDT; Opt A; Order/Arrow A; Spch A; *Natural Sci.*

143

CONNAUGHTON, Jeffrey Joseph
Huntsville HS; Huntsville, AL (8-500) Secy, Chem C; InterClub Coun; Math C; Mu Alpha Theta; NHS; Pres, Phys C; Golf; *U of Pa; Econ.*

CONNEALLY, Mary Helen
Gordon HS; Gordon, NE (37-72) Ann; Band; CYO; Chor; VP, Drama; Pres, FTA; 4H; Hmrm; ARC; SC; VP, Thes; Var C; Bkbl; Tr; HCt; Vlbl; Hon Choir; Prom Ct; *Regis Col; House Design.*

CONNELL, Alison Ruth
Wyoming HS; Cincinnati, OH (45-200) Ger C; Sci C; Tri-HiY; Hockey; Semi- fin, St Gov Art Show; *Miami U.*

CONNELL, John Doyle
Everett HS; Lansing, MI (348-500) All Amer Yth; Ensm; Var C; Ftbl; MVP, Wrest; HKg; HCt; Cpt, All Amer, St Champ, Wrest; 1000% A.

CONNELL, Mary Kathryn
Sam Rayburn HS; Pasadena, TX; Band; BC; JETS; Math C; Mu Alpha Theta; Tr; Math A; Acad Excel A; *U of Tex; Archt.*

CONNELLY, Edwin Ray
Hope HS; Hope, AR (26-235) BC; Ch, Key C; Math C; Mu Alpha Theta; NHS; Span C; SC; Bsbl; Ftbl; Tr; *Ouachita Col; Bio.*

CONNELLY, Lisa Renee
Wachusett Regional HS; Holden, MA (164-511) Band; Chldr; Chess C; Chor; Drama; COM; Elk A; Hon Prog; Green Cross Safety, Hon Thrift, A's; Order o-t Battered Boot; *Simmons Col; Communications.*

CONNER, Barry Noble
Stonewall Jackson HS; Charleston, WV (40-275) A Cap Choir; Chess C; Chor; Ensm; Lat C; Madrigal; Math C; Mu Alpha Theta; Swim; Tnns; Math A; *W Va Weslyan Col; Math.*

CONNER, Carol Ann
Vidalia HS; Vidalia, GA; VP, BC; Cpt, Chldr; Fin, Model UN; VP, Tri-HiY; Alg A; Bio A; COM; Gov Honor Prog; Hist A; Hon Prog; Math A; NEDT; Opt A; Yth Leg; Participant, Y-C Beauty Pageant; Woman's C Stu o-t Month; Presbyterian Col Jr Fel A; Indian Star.

CONNER, Cynthia Jean
Montrose Pub Sch; Montrose, MO; *SW Baptist Col; Ed.*

CONNER, Gary David
Stafford HS; Stafford, VA (20-526) VP, Fr C; Hmrm; Pres, Key C; NHS; *Va Tech U; Physics.*

CONNER, Julie Jolene
Belle Plaine HS; Belle Plaine, KS; Chor; F-Ed, Sch P; HCt; *Butler Co Comm Col; Child Care.*

CONNER, Laura Lynn
Central HS; Knoxville, TN (10-350) BC; Fr C; NHS; Cpt, Bkbl; COM; Citz A; PTA A; Pres, UMYF; Art C; Fr II A; Entry Mid-South Art A P Eng; *International Relations.*

CONNER, Lodie Dee
Fairpark HS; Shreveport, LA; *Gramble St Col.*

CONNER, Nadeen Margie
Jesup W Scott HS; Toledo, OH (35-354) VP, Chor; Math C; NHS; SC; Up Bound; Hon Prog; Math A; Acad Achv A; 2nd Pl, Eng Contest; *U of Toledo; Special Ed.*

CONNER, Nancy Verlon
Briarwood HS; East Point, GA (3-160) Pres, BC; Chor; FTA; Madrigal; Orch; Span C; Sftbl; COM; Hon Prog; All St Choir; All St Orch; Talented & Gifted Prog; Highest Scholastic Achv A; *Mercer U; Piano.*

CONNER, Nathan
Jesup W Scott HS; Toledo, OH; Chor; Commercial C; Hmrm; Up Bound; Acad Achv A; *Columbus Col of Art; Commerical Arts.*

CONNER, Richard Clayton
DuVal Sr HS; Lanham, MD; NHS; Ed, Sch P; Q&S A; *U of Md; Tech Writing.*

CONNER, Robert Glenn
St Bede Acad; Peru, IL (12-101) Chor; Bsbl; Bkbl; Ftbl; Tr; COM; Hist A; Hon Prog; Math A; Pres A; Sci A; Church Lector; Altar Boy; Fin, Young Columbus A; *U of Ill.*

CONNER, Steven Howard
Tuscola Comm Unit HS; Tuscola, IL (36-115) Drama; Fr C; Spch C; Pres, Thes; Var C; Bkbl; Cr-Ctry; Tr; Cl Fav; Spch A; Yth Fel; Pres, Church Yth Group; Theatre Promise; Church Deacon; Homecoming Master of Ceremonies; Church Outst Yth; *Ill St U; Bus.*

CONNER, Tina Ann
Sesser-Valier Comm HS; Sesser, IL (15-47) Thes; Fr & Lib A's; WW; Church Singer.

CONNICK, Megan
El Cerrito HS; El Cerrito, CA (1-500) NFL; Orch; Sci C; Swim; Bank Of Amer A; CSF; NMF; *Mount Holyoke Col; Bio Sci.*

CONNIGAN, Francis James
All Hallows HS; Bronx, NY; *Manhattan Col; Math.*

CONNOLLY, Judith Elaine
Harding HS; Charlotte, NC; A Cap Choir; Ann; Chor; Drama; NHS; ARC; Sci C; Span C; Secy Church Yth Coun; Sci Cert; Crown & Scepter; *NC St U; Ed.*

CONNOLLY, Kathleen Susan
Dwight D Eisenhower HS; Rialto, CA (120-761) FNA; Secy, SC; Citz A; Outst Teacher Asst; *San Bernardino Valley Col; Nurs.*

CONNOLLY, Margaret Irene
Jacksonville Sr HS; Jacksonville, NC (19-402) F-Ed, Ann; Cpt, Chldr; Sch P; Pres, Span C; Bkbl; Graduation Marshal; Candystriper; Vlbl; Extraordinary Min Eucharist; HR; Poetry Contest Win; Poetry Contest Win; *Journ.*

CONNOR, Cheryl Lynn
Riverside HS; Taylor, PA (4-196) Chor; Pres, FTA; Ger C; NHS; SC; Hon Prog; NEDT; *Liberal Arts.*

CONNOR, Christine Eileen
Grandview Heights HS; Grandview Heights, OH (7-129) Chor; Drama; Thes; Wrest; Q&S A; Yth Fel; A-Ed, Yrbk; Treas, Coed C; Usher; *Nurs.*

CONNOR, Douglas Robert
Southern Wayne Sr HS; Mount Olive, NC; Order/ Arrow; Sci C; Ftbl; Tnns; *Guilford Col; Bio.*

CONNOR, James Wallace
Riverside Jr-Sr HS; Taylor, PA (6-186) Ger C; Hmrm; NHS; Rptr, Sch P; Co-Cpt, Bsbl; Ftbl; Chem A; NEDT; *Pre-Med.*

CONNOR, Lee Ann
Fuquay-Varina Sr HS; Fuquay-Varina, NC; BC; Lat C; *Atlantic Christian Col.*

CONNOR, Sharon Lee
Riverside Jr-Sr HS; Taylor, PA (28-187) Chor; FNA; NHS; *Nurs.*

CONNOR, Suzanne Elaine
Southern Wayne Sr HS; Dudley, NC (20-400) AFS; Ann; Rptr, SC; Pres, Sr Cl; Nom, Hugh O'Brien Ldrship Seminar; HR; *Meredith Col; Eng.*

CONNORS, Marypat
Cath Central HS; Troy, NY (50-325) Chor; VP, Ger C; Hmrm; NHS; Rptr, Sch P; SC; Hon Prog; K of C A; *Col of St Rose; Elem Ed.*

CONOVER, Brooks William
Cleburne HS; Cleburne, TX (1-310) BS; Dbte Tm; VP, Demolay; Drama; HiY; Key C; Lit Mag; NFL; NHS; Pres, Span C; Pres, Spch C; Thes; Bio A; Chem A; DARGCA; Hist A; Sci A; Span, Jr Grammar, A's; *Baylor U; Law.*

CONOVER, James Michael
Pennsauken HS; Pennsauken, NJ (496-535) Pres, A Cap Choir; Pres, Chor; ARC; SC; Ftbl; Swim; Tr; Cl Flirt; *Trenton St Col; Industrial Arts.*

CONRAD, Alan James
Jasper HS; Jasper, MN (22-44) Chor; Ensm; Rptr, FFA; FFA Sheep Mgt & Crop Mgt A's; *Pipestone Vo Tech Col; Farm Operation.*

CONRAD, Anne Marie
Lawrence HS; Lawrence, KS (75-500) A Cap Choir; Chor; Community Yth Symph; Ger C; Orch; Church Ldrship Schol; *Bethany Col; Math.*

CONRAD, Annette Karen
Duke Ellington Arts HS; Washington, DC (3-147) Ensm; Hmrm; NHS; Rptr, Sch P; Sftbl; COM; Citz A; Hon Prog; Sci A; Women Bar Assn A; Trigonometry A; Hon Men, Anatomy-Physiology; *MIT; Elec Engr.*

CONRAD, Barbara Lynne
Springfield Sr HS; Springfield, PA (15-440) A-Ed, Ann; Fr C; Ger C; Ed, Lit Mag; NHS; Rptr, Sch P; COM; Hist A; Yth Fel; WW; Scott's Hi-Q; Pioneer Girls Guide; Westinghouse Family Schol; *Wake Forest U; Communications.*

CONRAD, James Robert
Colegio San Antonio Abad; Humacao, PR (3-72) A Cap Choir; Chem C; VP, NHS; Tres, Var C; VP, Sr Cl; Ftbl; Tr; Wrest; Semi-Fin, Chem A; *U of Fla; Aerospace Engr.*

CONRAD, Kay Marie
Roy C Start HS; Toledo, OH; Band; Chldr; Community Yth Symph; NHS; Rptr, Orch; Alg A; Math A; Super & Excel, Dist Solo Mus Cont; *Heidelberg Col; Elem Ed.*

CONRAD, Lawrence Allan
Terre Haute S Vigo HS; Terre Haute, IN (125-625) *Religion.*

CONRAD, Linda Susan
DeSales HS; Geneva, NY (10-54) Secy, Sr Cl; Secy, Soph Cl; *SUNY at Geneseo; Special Ed.*

CONRAD, Merri Lynne
Allen Jay HS; High Point, NC; Band; BC; Monogram; Bkbl; MVP, Sftbl; Vlbl; *U of NC; Math.*

CONRAD, Shelley Kaye
E Central HS; Tulsa, OK; Chor; NHS; Span C.

CONRATH, Arenda Lee
Herrin HS; Herrin, IL; *Sou Ill U; Bus.*

CONREY, Calvin Frank
Wm J Woodham HS; Pensacola, FL (17-530) Band; Hmrm; NHS; Orch; SC; NEDT; Sewanee Excel A; *U of Tenn; Elec Engr.*

CONROY, Michael Joseph
Don Bosco Tech HS; Boston, MA (9-222) BS; Chess C, K of C; Var C; Cr-Ctry; Tr; COM; Hon Prog; NEDT; Spch A; *Springfield Tech Col; Elec.*

CONROY, Michael Wayne
Pearl City Comm HS; Pearl City, IL (26-63) Band; Mgr, Bkbl; Mgr, Ftbl; JV, Golf; Golf, Most Improved Player; *Highland Comm Col; Automotive Mech.*

CONROY, Patricia Michelle
Pearl City Comm HS; Pearl City, IL (4-54) Band; Chldr; FTA; NHS; Tres, SC; Pres, Soph Cl; 4H A; HCt; *Highland Comm Col.*

CONRY, Dolores Patricia
Our Lady of Good Counsel HS; Newark, NJ (2-84) Ski C; Hon Prog; *Nurs.*

CONSOLE, Pennie Lynn
Canyonville Bible Acad; Canyonville, OR (1-37) Ed, Ann; Chor; Pres, Sr Cl; Tr; Bio A; COM; HCt; Hon Prog; Bible, Eng, A's; *Pre Law.*

CONSTANT, Bryant
Kirkwood HS; Kirkwood, MO; *U of Mo Columbia; Med.*

CONSTANTINE, Theodore John
Glenbrook N HS; Northbrook, IL; Band; *Loyola Dental Sch; Dentistry.*

CONSUEGRA, Lois Marla
Greater New York Acad; Woodside, NY; Chor; NHS; Ed, Sch P; Bkbl; Sftbl; Bio A; Chem A; Citz A; JA A; Eng A; Fine Arts A; Geom A; Mus A; *Sou Missionary Col; Nurs.*

CONTENTO, Anna Marie
Notre Dame HS; Clarksburg, WV (1-52) Ed, Ann; Dbte Tm; Drama; FBLA; FTA; GS; Lat C; Lat NHS; NHS; Bkbl; Tr; Cl Fav; Hist A; Hon Prog; NEDT; Sci A; Spch A; Val; *W Va U; Pre-Med.*

CONTIJOCH, Joseph
St Joseph's o-t Palisades HS; W New York, NJ (33-289) Fr C; Rptr, Sch P; World Affairs C; COM; Hon Prog; NEDT; 1st Hon A; *Rutgers Col; Bio.*

CONTRERAS, Maria Cuevas
McClymonds Sr HS; Oakland, CA; A Cap Choir; Hmrm; NHS; Span C; SC; Up Bound; B Crocker A; CSF; Citz A; Crisco A; Math A; Sci A; Type A; *Cal St U at Hayward; Bus Adm.*

CONTRERAS, Mary Alice
Hiram W Johnson HS; Sacramento, CA (113-500) Hmrm; Sci C; Pres, Span C; Tribe; Executive HS Internship; Tres, Church Sr High & Col Age; *Warner Pacific Col.*

CONTRERAS, Norka Gilda
Pass Christian HS; Pass Christian, MS (25%-110) Secy, BC; Chor; Drama; FHA; Tres, SC; Jr Miss Contestant Talent Win; Sup Ratings, Voice-Regional Comp; Span A; Amer HS A For Excellence; Century III Ldrship A; *MSU; Elec Engr.*

CONVILLE, Mark Brian
Schuylkill Haven HS; Schuylkill Haven, PA (60-120) Band; Orch; Var C; Cr-Ctry; Tr.

CONWAY, Carol Ann
Cony HS; Augusta, ME; *Thomas Col; Acct.*

CONWAY, Joy Suzette
Tarrant HS; Tarrant, AL (10-154) Band; FBLA; FHA; SC; COM; Hon Band Bars; Solo & Ensm A's.

CONWAY, Karen Renee
Patrick Henery Sr HS; San Diego, CA; Chor; Secy, Drama; Sftbl; Tnns; Tr; St Stephen's Choir Qn; Regional Jr Ch; *Oral Roberts U; Pre-Med.*

CONWAY, Katherine Irma
White Mt Regional HS; Whitefield, NH (13-120) Band; 4H; NHS; SC; Secy, Jr Cl; Bkbl; Cr-Ctry; Co-Cpt, Hockey; Tr; 4H A; *UNH; Occupational Therapy.*

CONWAY, Kathleen Marie
Aledo HS; Aledo, IL (8-120) AFS; Band; Pres, CYO; Chldr; Chor; FHA; FTA; F-Ed, Sch P; *St Ambrose Col; Acct.*

CONWAY, Pamela Susan
Sidney Lanier HS; Montgomery, AL (130-467) Bus C; FBLA; FHA; Bkbl; *Auburn U; Social Work.*

CONWAY, Robert Alan
Bridgeport HS; Bridgeport, OH (1-121) Band; Drama; NHS; Span C; Tnns; *Cincinnati U; Elec Engr.*

CONWAY, Robin Allen
Yosemite Union HS; Oakhurst, CA (1-100) Chor; Dbte Tm; Ger C; Pres, 4H; Hmrm; VP, Math C; Tr; Alg A; Bio A; CSF; COM; Citz A; 4H A; Hist A; Hon Prog; Journ A; Math A; Pres A; Sci A; Type A; Val; VFW A; Gemco Schol; *Col of Idaho; Biol.*

CONWAY, Sheryl Lynn
Northview HS; Covina, CA; CYO; Chldr.

CONWILL, Douglas Alan
Tupelo HS; Tupelo, MS (39-359) Band; Community Yth Symph; Fr C; Key C; COM; Band A; Distinguished Mus Cert; Accompanist Chor; MMEA Band Clinic; Mid-South Hon Band; *U of Sou Miss; Instrumental Mus.*

CONYBEARE,
Bruce Chadwick Jr
Lake Mich Cath HS; St Joseph, MI (15-100) Chess C; Ski C; JV, Golf; Tnns; *U of Mich; Law.*

CONYERS, Derek Alan
Henry Ford HS; Detroit, MI; Bsbl; Bkbl; Ftbl; *U of Mich; Bus.*

COODY, Karen Lynn
Bastrop HS; Bastrop, LA (25-314) Band; Mjrte; Ch, Model UN; Tnns; NHS; Orch; Sch P; SC; UN Council; NEDT; *NE La U; Phar.*

COOEY, Dorothy Alice
St James HS; Montgomery, AL (5-43) Anchor C; BC; Fr C; NHS; Tri-HiY; COM; NEDT; Sci A; Eng, Schol, A's; *Med.*

COOK, Annette Susan
Meeker HS; Meeker, CO (8-54) Ann; Band; Chor; FBLA; NHS; Cr-Ctry; Tr; 4H A; Delta Cappa Gamma A; *Mesa Col; Child Care.*

COOK, Barbara Antoinette
Polytechnic HS; Fort Worth, TX (33-300) FHA; Vlbl Jacket; *Tarrent Co Jr Col; Acct.*

COOK, Barbie Gayle
Nathan Hale HS; Tulsa, OK (100-750) Cpt, Dbte Tm; Secy, Drama; Hmrm; Secy, Thes; Pres, NFL; NHS; Pres, Spch C; Tr; COM; VofDEM; *Spch.*

COOK, Betty Jane
W Bridgewater HS; W Bridgewater, MA (9-140) Ed, Ann; Band; Chor; Dbte Tm; Drama; NHS; Ed, Sch P; Thes; Q&S A; *Bridgewater St Col; Communication Disorders.*

COOK, Beverly Ann
Montrose R 14; Montrose, MO (4-26) CYO; Secy, NHS; Home Ec A; Family Living; Outst Bus Stu; *Central Mo St U; Secretarial Work.*

COOK, Brian Donald
Greeley Central HS; Greeley, CO (75-373) Band; Ensm; Ger C; Key C; Orch; Ski C; Ftbl; Eagle Sct; *Colo Col; Bus.*

COOK, Carolee
LaConner HS; LaConner, WA (4-50) Band; Chor; Drama; NHS; ARC; Ski C; Mgr, Bkbl; Sftbl; MVP, Swim; Tr.

COOK, Charles Richard
Rossville HS; Rossville, GA (13-212) VP, BC; Hmrm; Key C; S-T, SC; Tres, Jr Cl; Bsbl; Mgr, Bkbl; Alg A; COM; Kiwanis A; Math A; Sci A; Star Student; Yth Fel; WW; *U of Ga; Acct.*

COOK, Cheryl Lynn
Springfield HS; Springfield, LA (15-53) BC; FFA; Sftbl; Phys Ed A; *Southeastern U; Computer Sci.*

COOK, Christopher Allen
Greeley Central HS; Greeley, CO (55-319) Chem C; Ensm; S-T, Key C; Orch; Order/Arrow; Phys C; Ski C; Span C; Cr-Ctry; Cpt, Swim; FCA; Eagle Sct; Top Ten, St Swim A; *Sou Methodist U; Chem Engr.*

COOK, Cynthia
Eli Whitney V H S; Brooklyn, NY; *Med.*

COOK, David Len
Broadview Acad; LaFox, IL; Chor; VP, Ski C; *Pacific Union Col; Nurs.*

COOK, Debra Lynn
Langley HS; McLean, VA (10%-550) MYF; Pioneer Girls C; Tn Rep, Counc On Ministries; Adm Board; Yth Coun; Life Danced, Fund Raisng Talent Shw.

COOK, Diane Elaine
Douglas HS; Douglas, AZ (82-290) Bkbl; Sftbl; Gym; Bkbl A; *Cochise Col; Phys Therapy.*

COOK, Edith Corrine
Sharwood HS; Sandy Spring, MD; Chor; SC; Cr-Ctry; Cpt, Tr; Mus A; Record in Tr; *Towson St Col.*

COOK, Edwin Dee Jr
Nathan Hale HS; Tulsa, OK; Order/Arrow; Order/Arrow A; *Okla Christian Col; Horticulture Tech.*

COOK, Elizabeth Ann
Jefferson City HS; Jefferson City, MO (50-570) Band; Drama; NHS; Sup, Church Mus Festival; Sup, NEDT Test; *Okla Baptist U; Learning Disabilities Teacher.*

COOK, Greg Scott
Burbank HS; Burbank, CA (19%-580) Secy, Order/Arrow; Cpt, Swim; Kiwanis A; Order/Arrow A; Fin & MVP, Swim; Cpt & MVP, Water Polo; Metal Shop Voc Stu o-t Yr; Eagle Sct; *UC at Santa Barbara; Bus.*

COOK, James Edmund
Denbigh HS; Newport News, VA; 4H; NHS; Bsbl; Cpt, Bkbl; Ftbl; Citz A; 4H A; Pres A.

COOK, James Robert
St Edward HS; Lakewood, OH (73-292) CYO; Bkbl; Soccer; Wrest; Bio A; Hon Prog; JA A; Type A; Explorer; *Northland Col; Biol.*

COOK, Jane Karen
Cuyahoga Valley Christian Acad; Cuyahoga Falls, OH (1-31) Cpt, Chldr; Chor; Drama; Ensm; Ed, Sch P; SC; Co-Ch, Sr Cl; Alg A; Citz A; Hist A; HQn; HCt; Journ A; Math A; NEDT; Yth Fel; WW; Eng A; *Wheaton Col.*

COOK, Janet Lynn
Cuyahoga Valley Christian Acad; Cuyahoga Falls, OH (2-65) Rptr, Sch P; Ski C; HCt; Math A; NEDT; Sci A; St Scholar; Eng A; Fr A.

COOK, Janet Marie
Montrose Pub HS; Montrose, MO (5-26) Chor; VP, Hmrm; VP, NHS; VP, Jr Cl; Sftbl; 4H A; Hist A; HCt; Math A; Sci A; St Mus A; *Central Mo St U; Eng.*

COOK, Janice Lee
Blackstone Milliue HS; Blackstone, MA; Chldr; Drama; ARC; Sch P; Y-Tns; Golf; Swim; Beauty; Cl Fav; Semi-Fin, Jr Prom; Co-Cpt, Gym; Sunday Sch Teacher; Vlbl; Bicycling; *Rhode Island Col; Art Therapy.*

COOK, Jennifer Kaye
Clarkrange HS; Clarkrange, TN (12-51) Ed, Ann; BC; Chem C; Drama; FHA; 4H; Sch P; Pres, Sci C; Spch C; Cpt, Var C; VP, Sr Cl; Cpt, Bkbl; Bio A; Citz A; Jr, Chapter & St Degrees, FHA; All Conf, All Reg, All Dist, Bkbl; *Tenn Tech U; Bus.*

COOK, Jill Ilene
St Johns HS; St Johns, MI (55-339) Pres, 4H; NHS; 4H A; Ushers C; FCA; Gym.

COOK, John Thomas
Rossville Comp HS; Rossville, GA (16-225) VP, Band; BC; Pres, FTA; Hmrm; Key C; NHS; SC; Tres, Jr Cl; Alg A; Bio A; COM; Hon Prog; Math A; NEDT; Sci A; Dist Band; SC A; *U of Ga; Pre-Law.*

COOK, Karen Lynn
Campbell HS; Campbell, CA; Drama; Ger C; NHS; Ski C; SC; Pres, Fresh Cl; *International Bible Col; Christian Counseling.*

COOK, Karen Maureen
Washington HS; Tacoma, WA (118-302) Band; Chor; Drama; Ensm; Tr; Hiking C; Secy, Pep C; Girl's C; Mgr, Vlbl; *Pacific Lutheran U; Mus.*

COOK, Karen Michelle
South Sr HS; Columbus, OH; Chldr; Chor; Ensm; Hmrm; Tnns; COM; Citz A; Most Outst; Opt A; Yth Fel; MVP, Co-Cpt, Tr; *Psych.*

COOK, Karen Yvonne
Springfield HS; Springfield, LA; FHA; Sftbl; *Southeastern U.*

COOK, Kathy Merle
Crockett HS; Crockett, TX (6-106) Band; NHS; Health A; Industrial Cooperative Training A; Dist & St VICA Win; Dist Band; *Angelina Col.*

COOK, Kenneth James
Del Campo HS; Fair Oaks, CA (50-500) CSF.

COOK, Kenneth Reynard
Carolina HS; Greenville, SC; Band; Hmrm; Spch C; Bkbl; Tr; Cl Fav; Band A; *SC St Col.*

COOK, Kenneth Samuel
Gloucester HS; Gloucester, VA; Band; VP, BC; Lit Mag; NFL; DARGCA; NMF; NMS; *Fisk U; Psych.*

COOK, Kimberly Dawne
Nw Cabarrus HS; Concord, NC (40-205) A-Ed, Ann; Fr C; 4H; VP, Hmrm; Monogram; SC; Cpt, Tnns; Opt A; Swtht; Outst Sr; Friendliest; Pres, Q & S; *U of NC; Bus.*

COOK, Kimberly Ruth
Mumford HS; Detroit, MI; Chor; Commercial C; NHS; Hon Prog; Type A; Mumford Modern Dance Group; *Phys Ed.*

COOK, Kip D
Kewanna HS; Kewanna, IN (4-17) Ann; Band; Drama; Fr C; A-Ed, Sch P; Sci C; SC; Bsbl; Bkbl; Cr-Ctry; *Manchester Col; Radio & TV Communications.*

COOK, Larry Glenn
River Road HS; Amarillo, TX; Pres, Drama; FFA; Cpt, Ftbl; Spch A; *U of Tex; Ftbl.*

COOK, Laurie Ann
N Clayton Sr HS; College Park, GA; HR; *Clayton Jr Col; Nurs.*

COOK, Lisa Kay
St Johns HS; St Johns, MI (10%-383) Chor; 4H; HCt; Alumni Schol; *Great Lakes Bible Col; Mus.*

COOK, Lori Ann
Antelope Valley HS; Lancaster, CA (152-654) Chldr; Hmrm; SC; Jr Prom Court; Choir; Z C; Girls Service C.

COOK, Lynette Rene
Herrin HS; Herrin, IL (3%-206) Band; Chor; NHS; GSct First Cl; *U of Miami; Art.*

COOK, Margaret Evelyn
J M Morehead Sr HS; Eden, NC; Chor; Pres, Drama; Math C; NHS; ARC; Sci C; Span C; ARC A; *Duke U.*

COOK, Mark Alan
George Washington Sr HS; Cedar Rapids, IA (200-500) Order/Arrow A; Yth Fel.

COOK, Mary Lynne
Tech Mem HS; Erie, PA; Hmrm; Pres, Protestant Yth Organization; *Bethal Hospital of Nurs; Nurs.*

COOK, Michael Lee
Whiteland HS; Whiteland, IN (80-210) Golf; MVP, Tnns; *Conservation of Wild Life.*

COOK, Mitzi Ellen
Pflugerville HS; Pflugerville, TX (10%-103) Ann; Ger C; NHS; Spch C; Alg A; Hon Prog; *A&M U; Math.*

COOK, Nicquelina Una
Holy Family HS; Birmingham, AL (5-41) Band; CYO; Chldr; Swim; Most Ath; PE A; Chldr Ltr; Vlbl A; *Grady Col; Rn.*

COOK, Pamela Gail
River Road HS; Amarillo, TX; Chldr; Chor; FFA; Rptr, 4H; Rptr, Sch P; JV, Bkbl; Tnns; *Tex Tech U; Agr.*

COOK, Pamela Kay Hunt
Rising Star HS; Rising Star, TX (2-13) VP, FHA; 4H; Sch P; SC; Secy, Soph Cl; Bkbl; Tr; Cl Fav; Most Ath; Miss Rising Star HS.

COOK, Peter Bernard
Minsdale Central HS; Hinsdale, IL (80%-720) Chess C; Orch; Bsbl; *U of Ill; Med.*

COOK, Richard Earl
Ensley HS; Birmingham, AL (25-430) Chor; Drama; Order/Arrow; Thes; Pres, Soph Cl; Mgr, Bkbl; Mgr, Ftbl; Tnns; Spch A; *Jefferson St Jr Col; Radio & TV Broadcasting.*

COOK, Richard Scott
Mountain Brook HS; Birmingham, AL (250-375) JV, Ftbl; *Auburn U; Archt.*

COOK, Richard William
Montrose HS; Montrose, MO (6-26) Ann; Band; CYO; Chor; NHS; Span C; Chem A; Cl Fav; Mus A; *Mus.*

COOK, Robin Beth
Sunset HS; Beaverton, OR (1-510) Community Yth Symph; Orch; SC; VP, Jr Cl; JV, Tnns; Opt A; Type A; Gold Cup A, Piano; Fin, St Solo Contest-Violin; *Lewis and Clark Col; Mus.*

COOK, Robin LaVerne
Notre Dame Acad; Washington, DC (15%-86) Band; Chor; Drama; Hmrm; Lat C; Mjrte; Math C; NHS; Orch; Alg A; COM; Chem A; Citz A; Math A; Mus, Lat, A's; *Dayton U; Math.*

COOK, Ronald
East HS; Columbus, OH (45-220) MVP, Golf; Hampton Inst; *Psych.*

COOK, Sally Jo
Gull Lake HS; Richland, MI (10%-250) Band; Bus C; Sci C; JV, Tnns; FCA; Bible C; Vlbl; *Forestry.*

COOK, Sheri Leigh
Bridgeport HS; Bridgeport, OH (2-126) Band; Chor; Ensm; Lat C; SC; VP, Y-Tns; Pres, Y-Tns; Schol Tm; Pomerette; Secy, Fresh Cl; Church Choir Accompanist; *Capital Col; Nurs.*

COOK, Shirley Susan
Santa Monica HS; Santa Monica, CA (15%-1200).

COOK, Stacy Lynn
Columbine Sr HS; Littleton, CO; Band; Bus C; Barnes Bus Col; *Secy.*

COOK, Stanley Leo
Rochester Comm HS; Rochester, IL (10-105) Band; Chem C; Ger C; NHS; Sci C; Var C; Bsbl; Bkbl; MVP, Cr-Ctry; Tr; Bio A; Chem A; Hon Prog; Most Out; St Scholar; WW; MV Male Ath; Millikin U; *Med.*

COOK, Stephanie Diane
Pittsburg HS; Pittsburg, KS; Secy, A Cap Choir; Band; Type A; *Pittsburg St U.*

COOK, Stephen Allen
Rancho Cordova HS; Rohnert Park, CA; Fr C; Spch C; SC; Tnns; Mgr, Tr; Spch A; *Chico St U; Broadcast Communication Arts.*

COOK, Stephen Preston
Cache HS; Cache, OK; Band; BC; Pres, 4H; NHS; St Stu Congress; JV, Bsbl; JV, Bkbl; JV, Ftbl; JV, Swim; JV, Tr; Citz A; 4H A; H of F; JA A; Masonic A; Spch A; Band Contests; Amer Royal A; Sci Fairs; Top 10, Band; *US Air Force Acad; Astronaut.*

COOK, Susan Graham
Cleveland Heights HS; Cleveland Heights, OH (10%-800) Band; Orch; SC; Hon Prog; *Biological Sci.*

COOK, Tawiana Lynn
Eastmoor Sr HS; Columbus, OH (50%-500) ARC; COM; ARC A; Pres, Yth Fellowship; *Columbus Tech; Nurs.*

COOK, Timothy Harold
Goose Creek HS; Goose Creek, SC (10%-350) Bus Mgr, Ann; Pol Sci C; Ed, Sch P; Span C; Var C; JV, Bkbl; MVP, Tr; COM; Hist A; Hon Prog; Yth for Christ Intern; FCA; *Col of Charleston; Pol Sci.*

COOK, Timothy Kevin
Thomas A Edison HS; Tulsa, OK (245-483) Ftbl; Swim; Eagle Sct; Pres, United Methodist Yth; *Okla St U; Bus Mgt.*

COOK, Beth Elaine
Ft Myers HS; Fort Myers, FL (33%-380) Math C; Rainbow; Tnns; Pres, GSct; Outst Bus A; Outst Shorthand A; Outst Ath A; *Fla Atlantic U; Marine Bio.*

COOKE, Camille Lydia
St Angela Hall Acad; Brooklyn, NY (5-90) NHS; Secy, ARC; Alg A; COM; Chem A; Hon Prog; Math A; ARC A; JV Math League; Cpt, Bowl Tm; Acad Achv Citation; *Hofstra U; Law.*

COOKE, Davis Lee
Alexander Central HS; Taylorsville, NC (10%-385) A Cap Choir; Ann; Band; BC; Ensm; Fr C; Hmrm; Ed, Sch P; Sci C; SC; Sci A; Val; Newspaper A; HR; Schol A.

COOKE, Dawn Eileen
Fort Myers HS; Ft Myers, FL (33%-300) Rainbow; Yth Fel; *Nurs.*

COOKE, Jeffrey Lloyd
Borah Sr HS; Boise, ID (435-500) Hmrm; Spch C; Bsbl; Cr-Ctry; Tr; Yth Leg; *NW Nazarene Col; Religious Ed.*

COOKE, Kathy Lu
Rockdale HS; Rockdale, TX; Chldr; Chor; FTA; Tnns; Fresh Eng A; *Tyler Jr Col; Photography.*

COOKE, Martha Ruffin
Dobyns Bennett HS; Kingsport, TN; Chor; Community Yth Symph; Orch; Pep C; Church Choir; Yth Group; Jr Achv; Church Choir; Symph Orch; Sch String Quartet; *Sweet Briar Col; Mus.*

COOKE, Michael Charles
Marysville Pilchuck HS; Marysville, WA; *U of Puget Sound; Herpetology-Zoology.*

COOKE, Paige Kimball
Ferndale Union HS; Ferndale, CA (11-73) CYO; Chor; Span C; CSF; Church & Comm Choirs; *Mills Col; Eng.*

COOKE, Richard Preston
Smithfield-Selma Sr HS; Smithfield, NC (13-330) Ed, Ann; Band; BS; Chor; Ensm; Hmrm; NHS; Order/Arrow; ARC; SC; Pres, Sr Cl; Amer Leg A; Most Out; Yth Foundation; Eagle Sct; Morehead Schol Semi-Fin; A G Glenn Schol; *U of NC at Chapel Hill; Med.*

COOKE, Ruby Jane
Horace Maynard HS; Maynardville, TN; BC; Sci C; 1st Pl, Sr Bio Div, Sci Fair; 1st, Bio Col Sci Day Exam; Outst Sch Bio Stu; Service A; Christian Life A; *Zoology.*

COOLEY, Debra Arlene
Clara HS; Clara, MS (2-55) Ann; Pres, BC; Chor; Rptr, SC; COM; H of F; HCt; Sal; Pres, Lib C; Geography A; Most Dependable; Drivers A; *Jones Co Jr Col; Secy.*

COOLEY, Faith Sharon
Penn View Bible Inst; Penns Creek, PA; Band; Chor; Ensm; 1st Stu, Acad; *Nurs.*

COOLEY, Janet Ruth
King's Acad; W Palm Beach, FL (5-61) Chldr; Chor; Pres, Hmrm; Pres, NHS; Citz A; HCt; Hon Prog; VofDEM; Most Sch Spirit A; Most Inspirational Christian; Swtht Banquet Attendant.

COOLEY, Jeffrey John
Canyon HS; Anaheim, CA; A Cap Choir; Drama; Ensm; Swim; COM; Hon Prog; Sci A; Lettered in Mus; *Pacific Christian Col; Yth and Mus Ministry.*

COOLEY, Jerry Jean Jr
Merryville HS; Merryville, LA (12-50) VP, Fr C; Tres, Key C; Bsbl; Bkbl; Cpt, Ftbl; Most Handsome; All Star Ftbl; Acad A; *NE La U; Bio.*

COOLEY, Jill Diane
Smithtown HS E; St James, NY (99%-650) Band; Chor; NHS; Chor Pianist; All Conf Band; All St Orch; Church Organist; *Mus.*

COOLEY, Joseph Edwin
Arkadelphia HS; Arkadelphia, AR (38-180) Band; Order/Arrow; Bsbl; Swim; Tnns; Order/Arrow A; *Ouachita Col; Vet Med.*

COOLEY, Kathleen Suzette
New Smyrna Beach Sr HS; New Smyrna Beach, FL (1-420) Drama; NHS; Tres, Span C; Cpt, Cr-Ctry; Golf; Hon Prog; Cpt, Vlbl; Fla Found of Future Scientist; *U of Fla; Sci.*

COOLEY, Sharon Teresa
Lake Clifton Sr HS; Baltimore, MD (10-40) Chor; Tres, NHS; Co-Ed, Sch P; SC; Tnns; Alg A; Bio A; Hon Prog; JA A; Math A; Eng A; Gym A; *Morgan St U; Bus Adm.*

COOLEY, Timothy Jack
E Beauregard HS; DeRidder, LA (2-50) BC; FFA; Lit Ral; Bsbl; MVP, Bkbl; Sftbl; *McNeese St U; Acct.*

COOMBS, Kenneth Scott
Byram Hills HS; Armonk, NY (53-185) Band; JV, Bsbl; JV, Ftbl; JV, Soccer; Regent Schol; *Lehigh U; Elec Engr.*

COOMBS, Scott Edward
The Master's Sch; Simsbury, CT (2-16) Co-Cpt, Bsbl; Fr A; *Carpentry.*

COON, Connie Lynn
McColl HS; McColl, SC; Ann; FHA.

COON, Nancy Louise
Brethren HS; Paramount, CA (17-98) A Cap Choir; Chor; Ensm; CSF; Spch A; Drill Tm; Off, Sunday Sch; Future Teacher; Preachey, Missionary C; 1st Pl, WACS Piano Festival; *Elem Ed.*

COON, Patricia Linda
Washington HS; Fremont, CA; Drama; 4H; Tr; 4H A; *Counselor.*

COONC, Melody May
LaConner HS; LaConner, WA (2-56) Chor; 4H; Hmrm; NHS; ARC; Ski C; SC; Var C; Bkbl; Sftbl; Swim.

COONEY, Colleen Mary
Immaculata HS; Chicago, IL (16-157) NHS; Sci C; Sodality; Span C; Citz A; Hon Prog; Kiwanis A; St Scholar; *Creighton U; Med.*

COONEY, John Alan
Indianapolis Baptist HS; Indianapolis, IN (1-100) A-Ed, Ann; Rptr, Sch P; Mgr, Bkbl; Mgr, Cr-Ctry; Mgr, Tr; Alg A; Amer Leg A; Bio A; Math A; Sci A; *Purdue U; Elec.*

COONEY, Mary Margaret
Sacred Heart HS; Kingston, MA (1-54) Band; Chldr; Chess C; Chor; Drama; Pres, Key C; Pres, NHS; Sch P; Sodality; Pres, Soph Cl; Arch; Bkbl; Hockey; Sftbl; Tnns; Bausch & Lomb A; Co-Ed, Yrbk; Piano; *Holy Cross Col; Pre-Med.*

COONS, Chet David
Paris HS; Paris, KY (9-73) BC; Tres, CYO; VP, Lat C; Order/Arrow; Sch P; SC; Pres, Jr Cl; VP, Soph Cl; Ftbl; Tnns; Tr; Pres, Fresh Cl; *Archt.*

COONS, Eric Fay
Lyons Jr-Sr HS; Lyons, NY; Order/Arrow; JV, Ftbl; God & Country A; Order/Arrow A; Most Artistic; *Conservation.*

COONS, Michelle Rene
Cherokee HS; Cherokee, NC (5-53) Band; Mu Alpha Theta; *SW Tech Inst; Radio Broadcasting.*

COOPER, Anne Kyle
Alamosa HS; Alamosa, CO (21-186) A-Ed, Ann; Chldr; Chor; NHS; Sch P; Thes; *U of Ariz; Nurs.*

COOPER, Anne Melinda
Tigard HS; Tigard, OR (63-350) A-Ed, Ann; Hmrm; InterClub Coun; Lit Mag; Mjrte; NFL; NHS; Spch C; Dance Tm; *U of Oreg; Bus.*

COOPER, Annellen
Washington Irving HS; New York City, NY (61-641) Chor; Swim; Hist A; Yth Fel; Hon Hist; Hon Eng; Biology Sq; Mus A; *Howard U; Nurs.*

COOPER, Antoinette
Miami Edison Sr HS; Miami, FL; Tres, Chldr; Fashion Inst of Tech; *Fashion Design.*

COOPER, Barbara Diane
Evart Pub HS; Evart, MI (33%-85) NHS; *Bob Jones U; Off Adm.*

COOPER, Betsy Young
Menchville HS; Newport News, VA (5-563) Fr C; Lit Mag; NHS; Sci C; Secy, Geog C; WW; *Longwood Col; Early Childhood Ed.*

COOPER, Brian Paul
Jefferson Davis HS; Montgomery, AL (168-742) Chor; Ensm; Key C; I Dare You; Math A; *Auburn U; Engr.*

COOPER, Bruce Dean
Eastside HS; Taylors, SC (32-350) Mgr, Bsbl; Ftbl; Amer Leg A; FCA; Sportsmanship A, Ftbl; *Anderson Col; Bus.*

COOPER, Candee Catherine
El Dorado Springs HS; El Dorado Springs, MO (31-103) Drama; Fr C; FHA; Spch C; Bkbl; Sftbl; Tr; Spch A; Yth Fel; Cpt, Co-Cpt, Chldr; Cand, Miss Merry Christmas; *Stephens Col; Fashion Buyer.*

COOPER, Catherine Elaine
Arapahoe HS; Littleton, CO (50%-650).

COOPER, Cathy Lyn
Los Altos HS; Hacienda Hgts, CA (25-612) Swim; CSF; Hon Prog; Drill Tm; *Humbolt St Col; Sci.*

COOPER, Charles Allen
W Carter HS; Olive Hill, KY (10%-155) Co-Ed, Ann; Rptr, FBLA; Pres, 4H; Mgr, Bsbl; Mgr, Bkbl; Mgr, Ftbl; Mgr, Tr; 4H A; 4-H A of Excellence; *U of Ky; Hist.*

COOPER, Cheryl Jean
Arapahoe HS; Littleton, CO (50%-645) A Cap Choir; Chor; Hmrm; Madrigal; SC; *Baylor U; Bus.*

COOPER, Cheryl Lynn
Crockett HS; Crockett, TX (10-140) Ch, FHA; Phys Ed A.

COOPER, Cynthia Diane
Wayne Co HS; Jesup, GA; Chldr; Chor; FBLA; FHA; 4H; Span C; Secy, Tri-HiY; Bsbl; Cl Fav; *Brunswick Jr Col.*

COOPER, Debbie Kay
North Iredell HS; Olin, NC (5%-250) AFS; Dbte Tm; Pres, InterAct; Model UN; NFL; Spch C; UN Council; Hist A; Journ A; Spch A; *Freed-Hardeman Col; Bus Adm.*

COOPER, Diane Ida
John S Fine HS; Nanticoke, PA (5-300) FHA; FTA; 4H; Tres, Key C; 4H A; Spch A; *Pa St U; Math.*

COOPER, Doris Marie
Leesville HS; Leesville, LA; Chor; 4H; Sftbl; Spelling A; *U of Sou La; Modeling.*

COOPER, Dorothy Louise
Kensington HS; Philadelphia, PA (40%-200) Cpt, Sftbl; *Temple U; Phys Ed.*

COOPER, Elizabeth Faye
Heritage Christian Acad; Ravenswood, WV (3-58) Ann; Band; Chldr; Chor; Dbte Tm; Ensm; Orch; Span C; SC; Sftbl; Vlbl; *Liberty Baptist Col; Elem Ed.*

COOPER, Felix Alexander
Bayside HS; Bayside, NY; Orch; Tr; Pres, Yth Organization VP, JA; Traveling Trio; Mus A; Fin, COM; *Tex Lutheran U; Religion.*

COOPER, Gena Elaine
Frederick Douglass HS; Atlanta, GA (21-418) Secy, Hmrm; NHS; COM; N Starette Drill Tm; *U of Ga; Journ.*

COOPER, Gwendolyn Denise
Lanier HS; Jackson, MS (25%-309) Chldr; Chor; Fr C; S-T, Hmrm; Semi-Fin, Jr Miss Pa; Lit Mag; NHS; Hist A; HCt; Quill & Scroll; Ed, Newspaper; *Penn St U; Child Psych.*

COOPER, Iris Charlene
Sussex Central HS; Sussex, VA (20-186) Band; Dbte Tm; Drama; HiY; Hmrm; Pol Sci C; Sch P; Sci C; Bkbl; Sftbl; Tr; COM; HCt; Sci A.

COOPER, Jean
Charleston HS; Charleston, IL (10-279) Band; Chor; Madrigal; NHS; VP, Orch; Sch P; Pres, SC; Hon Prog; St Scholar; Most Civic Minded; *E Ill U; Elem Ed.*

COOPER, Jeffrey Glenn
Carroll HS; Dayton, OH (24-351) JETS; Math C; NHS; Var C; Ftbl; Bio A; Hon Prog; Sci A; Torch HR; Special Sci A; Eng & Sci As; Dist & St Sci Fair Day; *U of Oreg; Med.*

COOPER, Jennifer Ellen
George C Marshall HS; Falls Church, VA (1-470) F-Ed, Ann; JV, Chldr; Dbte Tm; Key C; NHS; Ski C; Secy, Span NHS; SC; Secy, Jr Cl; Tr; Gov Honor Prog; Journ A; Most Out; Q&S A; Val; Jr NHS; Best Personality; *Col of William and Mary; Modern Lang.*

COOPER, Jennifer Melissa
Scott Preparatory Sch; Opelika, AL (10%-26) Pres, Anchor C; F-Ed, Ann; VP, BC; VP, SC; Pres, Jr Cl; Bkbl; Cl Fav; NEDT; VofDEM; GSct; Phys Ed A; *Auburn U; Bus Adm.*

COOPER, JoAnn Ellen
Highlands HS; Natrona Heights, PA; Chor; COM; Hon Prog; NEDT; Ntl Jr Hon Soc; 1st Cl GSct.

COOPER, John Thomas
Wayne Co HS; Monticello, KY (15-180) Ann; FFA; 4H; Hmrm; Key C; SC; Ftbl; Cl Fav; 4H A; Mr Soph; *U of Ky; Agr.*

COOPER, Karen Elizabeth
Levelland HS; Levelland, TX (10%-200) A Cap Choir; Band; Ger C; NHS; WW; NML; *Baylor U; Pre-Med.*

COOPER, Karen Jo
Troy HS; Troy, TX (8-49) Band; BC; Secy, FHA; Rptr, FTA; Ch, 4H; Spch C; JV, Bkbl; Tr; COM; 4H A.

COOPER, Kathy M
Huntington Park HS; Huntington Park, CA (1-700) F-Ed, Ann; Chor; Fin, GS; Alg A; CSF; Hon Prog; JA A; Lion A; Spch A; Yth Fel; YGAD; Job's Daughters; Jr Statesmen of America; Flag Tm; *USC; Law.*

COOPER, Kendra Elaine
Chester Co HS; Henderson, TN (2-124) VP, Commercial C; FHA; 4H; Secy, Math C; Ed, Sch P; Sci C; S-T, Jr Cl; Alg A; COM; Citz A; Cl Fav; Elk A; H of F; HCt; I Dare You; MLS; NEDT; Sal; Summa Cum Laude; 100 Dollar C; Pep C; WW; Alt, GS; Hon C; Most Versatile; Geom A; W E Montgomery A; St FHA Chor; Bookbacker's A; Most Intellectual; *Lambrith Col; Art.*

COOPER, Kerry Duane
Blytheville HS; Blytheville, AR; Chor; Demolay; ARC; JV, Bkbl; Mgr, Ftbl; JV, Tr; Valentine Ct, Kg; Best Stu; Wood Working Shop A; *Mech Engr.*

COOPER, Kevin Leo
Glenbard W HS; Glen Ellyn, IL (250-500) Tres, A Cap Choir; Pres, CYO; Chor; Spch C; Thes; Var C; Cr-Ctry; Tr; Sports Ltrs; *W Ill U; Mass Communications.*

COOPER, Kim D
Theodore Roosevelt HS; Bronx, NY (136-199) Band; Tr; *Hunter Col; Nurs.*

COOPER, Kimberly Dawn
Abilene HS; Abilene, TX (30-550) Band; FHA; Pres, Hmrm; NHS; Orch; SC; Miss Tn Amer Pageant; Champ, Bible Bowl; WW; *Abilene Christian U; Sci.*

COOPER, Lawrence Neal
Thomas Jefferson HS; Richmond, VA (6-300) A Cap Choir; Band; Drama; Pres, Hmrm; Key C; Madrigal; Orch; Span C; SC; Thes; VP, Soph Cl; Tnns; Bio A; COM; Chem A; Hon Prog; Sci A; Omega Psi Phi Talent Hunt; Superior, Mus Guild; Region Band; *Mus.*

COOPER, Linda Ann
Sunbright HS; Sunbright, TN (10-66) FHA; 4H; Sch P; Sci C; Cl Fav; HCt; *U of Tenn; Spch.*

COOPER, Lisa Jayne
Warren Co Sr HS; McMinnville, TN (25%-400) Chldr; Chor; FHA; FTA; 4H; Tri-HiY; Bkbl; Sftbl; Demoiselle Sorority; Best Defensive Player, Jr Pro; Hist.

COOPER, Lisanne
Palatka Central HS; Palatka, FL (29-150) Chor; FBLA; COM; Shorthand C; *St Johns River Comm Col; Gen.*

COOPER, Lynn Elaine
Jackson HS; Jackson, MI; Chor; Drama; Fr C.

COOPER, Maria Lee
Holy Rosary Acad; Louisville, KY (4-116) Ann; ARC; Span C; NEDT; ARC A; *Health.*

COOPER, Mariane Louise
Lourdes HS; Nebraska City, NE (2-30) Bus Mgr, Ann; Secy, Band; Chor; Ensm; Pres, Mu Alpha Theta; NHS; VP, Span C; Tr; Hon Prog; *Benedictine Col; Mus Ed.*

COOPER, Patricia Loretta
John Bartram HS; Philadelphia, PA (139-600) Chor; Ch, Hmrm; World Affairs C; Cr-Ctry; Hon Prog; Sci A; *Comm Col of Philadelphia; Nurs.*

COOPER, Pauline Sue
C E Byrd HS; Shreveport, LA (97-400) Cpt, Band; 4H; ARC; Tres, SC; B Crocker A; Crisco A; ROTC A; *Sou U; Sociology.*

COOPER, Penny Arlon
Central Valley HS; Buxton, ND; Co-Ed, Ann; Chor; FHA; GS; 4H; Madrigal; Tres, Mod Mus Mas; A-Ed, Sch P; Rptr, Sr Cl; Tres, Jr Cl; 4H A; Spch A; *NDSU.*

COOPER, Randall Eugene
Aledo HS; Aledo, IL (1-117) Co-Ed, Ann; Band; BS; Pres, Chor; Ensm; FTA; Key C; Pres, SC; Var C; Tr; Citz A; St Scholar; Val; SAR A; All-St Choir; *Augustana Col; Pre-Law.*

COOPER, Reuben Jr
Miami Edison Sr HS; Miami, FL (53-335) Cpt, Band; Community Yth Symph; Ensm; Orch; Cpt, Bsbl; Co-Cpt, Ftbl; Tr; COM; Citz A; Kiwanis A; Pres A; Swtht; Unsung Hero; John F Kennedy, John P Sousa, A's; Silver Knight, A; *FAMU; Mus.*

COOPER, Sandra Ann
Jenkins Co HS; Millen, GA (3-100) Band; Tres, BC; Chldr; Pres, Chor; Hmrm; Rptr, Sci C; SC; Ch, Tri-HiY; Bkbl; COM; Rotary A; Music A.

COOPER, Sharon Lynn
Paso Robles HS; Paso Robles, CA (11-204) AFS; Tres, Lat C; NHS; Sci C; CSF; WW; *Concordia Lutheran Col; Ed.*

COOPER, Silas Berry III
Abbeville HS; Abbeville, LA; BC; BS; Drama; Fr C; FBLA; Hmrm; Pres, Key C; Fin, Lit Ral; NHS; Sch P; Tres, SC; Pres, Thes; Pres, Sr Cl; Pres, Jr Cl; Cr-Ctry; Tr; H of F; Hon Prog; Journ A; MLS; Spch A; Best Actor; Best Supporting Actor; *Tulane U; Law.*

COOPER, Stephanie Tracy
Normandy Sr HS; St Louis, MO; Hmrm; Normandy Valiant; Drill Tm Colorguard; Orch A; Sr GSct; *Bauder Col; Interior Decorating.*

COOPER, Steven Craig
Sylva-Webster HS; Sylva, NC; Demolay; Monogram; Ski C; Span C; Var C; Cpt, Golf; I Dare You; Masonic A; *Bus.*

COOPER, Sue Ellen
Laurel Valley Jr Sr HS; New Florence, PA (12-126) AFS; Band; Chor; FHA; NFL; NHS; SC; Tnns; Hon Prog; Spch A; *Med.*

COOPER, Tammy Renee
Livingston Central HS; Burna, KY; Band; Chldr; Chor; 4H; Secy, HiY; Rptr, Soph Cl; Sftbl; HCt; Swtht; Cpt, Co-Cpt, Drill Tm; GSct; Girls in Action; *Paducah Comm Col; Nurs.*

COOPER, Terry Lamon
Alma J Brown HS; Grambling, LA (9-52) Band; Rptr, FTA; NHS; Sci C; SC; Alg A; Cl Fav; Hon Prog; PE A; Band A; *Grambling St U; Data Processing.*

COOPER, Thomas Wesley
Greenwood HS; Midland, TX (7-14) Ann; Band; Drama; Spch C; SC; Bsbl; Tr; Opt A; Spch A; UIL 1-Act Play; Preacher; 'Cream o-t Crop'; 1st Pl, Band Ensm; *Lubbock Christian Col; Bible.*

COOPER, Tina Joyce
Chester HS; Chester, PA (37-673) Chor; Hmrm; Hockey; Acct A; *Pierce Jr Col; Legal Secy.*

COOPER, Tommie Gay
Waynesboro Central HS; Waynesboro, MS (25%-99) BC; Drama; Ger C; Fin, Jr Miss Pagent; A-Ed, Sch P; Rptr, SC; Rptr, Y-Tns; Rptr, Soph Cl; *U of Miss; Law.*

COOPWOOD, Ray Anthony
Douglass HS; Memphis, TN; NHS; Span C; Bkbl; HCt; ROTC A; Stu o-t Month; *Memphis St U; Architecture.*

COPA, Kimberly Marie
St Louise de Marillac HS; Northfield, IL (8-222) Ann; Chor; NHS; Ed, Sch P; Amer Leg A; Hon Prog; St Scholar; Lead, Plays; Choraleers; Liturgy Committee; *NW U; Law.*

COPAUS, Marvin Allen
Lubbock Co HS; Lubbock, TX (29-301) A Cap Choir; Band; Chor; Ensm; NHS; Orch; COM; All Region Band & Orch; All Region, All Area, Choir; *Tex Tech U; Mus.*

COPE, Cindy Lynn
S Bay Bible Baptist HS; Gardena, CA; Ann; Citz A; *Special Ed.*

COPE, Donna Jayne
Potomac Sr HS; Oxon Hill, MD; *Marine Bio.*

COPE, Julaine Ann
Alexander Hamilton HS; Milwaukee, WI (81-820) Chor; Hmrm; COM; Hon Prog; Col Schol; *Alverno Col; Psych.*

COPE, Linda Jean
Hamilton HS; Milwaukee, WI; Yth Fel; *Physch.*

COPE, Margaret Parham
Abraham Lincoln Sr HS; Bloomington, MN (2-574) AFS; Band; Drama; Ensm; NHS; Orch; A-Ed, Sch P; Spch C; Journ A; Spch A; Fr A; Church Yth Group; Mus A; Drama A; Sup Rating, St Solo & Ensm, Flute; Camp Fire Girls A; *Carleton Col; Med.*

COPE, Thomas Lynn
Warren Co Sr HS; McMinnville, TN; Chem C; Lat C; ARC; Sci C; Tri-HiY; Golf; Sftbl; *MTSU; Bus.*

COPELAND, Cathy Ann
Hermitage HS; Hermitage, AR (10-56) BC; Chldr; Chor; Pres, Fr C; VP, FHA; Pres, 4H; Semi-Fin, Jr Miss Pa; Pres, Math C; MVP, Bkbl; B Crocker A; HCt; Most Out; Swtht; All-Star Bkbl Player; WW in Bkbl; *U of Monticello.*

COPELAND, Cecilia Machelle
Savannah HS; Savannah, GA; BC; Chor; Drama; Ensm; Secy, Fr C; VP, 4H; Span C; SC; 4H A; *Savannah St Col; Secy Sci.*

COPELAND, Christine Annette
Trenton HS; Trenton, FL (4-80) Band; BC; Cpt, Chldr; FHA; Mjrte; Pres, SC; Bkbl; Tr; Alg A; COM; Math A; Historian, FBLA; Geom A; Eng A; *Lake City Comm Col; Court Rptr.*

COPELAND, Darrel Glenn
S Grand Prairie HS; Grand Prairie, TX; Math C; NHS; JV, Bsbl; JV, Bkbl; Hon Prog; *Northwestern U; Engr.*

COPELAND, Gary Wayne
Newberry Jr-Sr HS; Newberry, FL (10%-137) Ann; Band; Hmrm; JV, Bkbl; JV, Ftbl; Math A; Sci A; Yth Leg; PA; Poster Contest; 1st Pl, Sci Exhibit; Reading Achv A; *U of Fla; Med.*

COPELAND, Jon Bradley
John F Hodge HS; St James, MO (1-106) BS; Chor; Fr C; Tres, FFA; Mod Mus Mas; Sci C; Pres, SC; Bkbl; Tr; Curator A; Hist A; I Dare You; MLS; NMS; Val; *U of Mo; Pre-Vet.*

COPELAND, Joseph Edward
Mooresville HS; Mooresville, IN (16-340) Var C; Pres, Soph Cl; JV, Bkbl; JV, Ftbl; Tr; Jr NHS; *Ind Central U; Law Enforcement.*

COPELAND, Kenneth Wayne
Webster Groves HS; Webster Groves, MO (25-350) A-Ed, Ann; BS; Chess C; Pres, Math C; Tnns; Hon Prog; *U of Mo; Elec Engr.*

COPELAND, Margaret Jean
Arkadelphia Sr HS; Arkadelphia, AR; Band; Chor; Ensm; FHA; Hmrm; SC; Band Schol; Solo & Ensm Medals; Region Band; Pres, Church Yth; *Henderson St U; Special Ed.*

COPELAND, Pamela Denise
Lanphier HS; Springfield, IL; Chor; Cpt, Golf; Cpt, Sftbl; Interlochen Ntl Mus; ARC A; *Nurs Asst.*

COPELAND, Regina Kay
Trenton HS; Trenton, FL (5-90) Band; BC; Cpt, Chldr; Ensm; Tres, FHA; 4H; Hmrm; S-T, Soph Cl; Tr; Amer Leg A; HCt; Math A; Sci A; St Pres, FHA; Eng A; Straight 'A' A; Home Ec A.

COPELAND, Sandra Dean
Martin Co HS; Stuart, FL (125-675) Cert of Appreciation, Hospital; Friendliest Girl; *Indian River Comm Col; Med.*

COPELAND, Thomas Vane Jr
Levelland HS; Levelland, TX (29-200) Pres, Chor; NHS; Ftbl; Pres, FCA; VP, Stu Christian Assn; NMST Commended Stu; *Texas A&M U.*

COPENNY, Peggy Rebecca
Dublin HS; Dublin, GA; Band; Chldr; FHA; Hmrm; Jr Miss Pagent; Pres, Soph Cl; Tr; HCt; Yth Fel; *Ga Col; Nurs.*

COPLAND, Michael Aaron
Bellingham HS; Bellingham, WA (5%-320) A Cap Choir; Band; CYO; Chor; Community Yth Symph; NHS; Orch; JV, Wrest; Hon Prog; 1st Pl, Barbershop Quartet; Church Yth Coun; Hon Orch; *Wash St U; Mus Ed.*

COPLEN, Lisa Gale
Wendell Phillips HS; Chicago, IL (15-310) Ann; NHS; Sch P; *Ill St U; Special Ed.*

COPLEY, Amy Evelyn
Aiken HS; Aiken, SC (5-600) Ann; Band; Pres, Fr C; Mu Alpha Theta; NHS; Alg A; COM; District, All St Bands; Gov's Schol; Fr A; *Clemson U; Chem Engr.*

COPLEY, Peggy John
Aiken HS; Aiken, SC; Band; Ger C; Mu Alpha Theta; NHS; COM; SC All St, Central, Region Bands; Ger A; *U of SC; Mus.*

COPOUS, Kimberley Kaye
Taylor Center HS; Taylor, MI (29-470) NHS; *Special Ed.*

COPPAGE, Selina Marie
Lowndes HS; Valdosta, GA (25-450) Anchor C; BC; JV, Chldr; Chor; Drama; Pres, Hmrm; SC; Thes; Tri-HiY; Beauty; Lowndes High Swing Choir; Outst Bible Stu; Ping Pong; *Freed-Hardeman Col; Teaching.*

COPPALA, Mark Harril
St Albans HS; St Albans, WV (20-450) Band; Chess C; Ensm; Span C; Span NHS; COM; *Sci.*

COPPEDGE, Jana Lea
Tahlequah HS; Tahlequah, OK (25%-300) Band; Chor; FTA; NHS; COM; Sci A; Band A; Mus A; *Okla Christian Col; Mus.*

COPPELLUCCI, Dick
Hoehne HS; Hoehne, CO; Sch P; SC; Alg A; Poet A; Spch A.

COPPER, Kimberly Ann
Newton HS; Newton, IL (40-200) Band; 4H; NHS; Tr; *U of I; Vet Med.*

COPPESS, Audrey Eileen
Brookville HS; Brookville, OH (19-125) Ann; S-T, Band; Sch P; WW, Mus Stu; WW, HS Stu; Shorthand A; HR; *Sch of Beauty Culture; Cosmotology.*

COPPINGER, Paul Mac
Eula HS; Clyde, TX (1-28) Ann; FFA; SC; Bkbl; JV, Tnns; *Baylor U; Med.*

COPPLE, Bret Stanley
Centralia HS; Centralia, IL (12-250) Fr C; NHS; COM; Hon Prog; St Scholar; *Sou Ill U; Industrial Design.*

CORAZZA, James Neil
Sunset HS; Beaverton, OR (35-502) Pres, Chess C; Pres, Dbte Tm; Model UN; NFL; Order/Arrow; Sch P; Pres, Span C; Pres, Spch C; SC; Elk A; Odd Fellow Fin; Order/Arrow A; Spch A; Nom, BS; 1st, St Extemporaneous Speaking; 21st, Ntl Dbte Tourn; *U of Calif; Pol Sci.*

CORBALIS, Hugh Stephen
Independence HS; San Jose, CA (10%-900) F-Ed, Ann; Chess C; Ch, Drama; Co-Ch, Hmrm; NHS; Sch P; Span C; Bsbl; Bkbl; Ftbl; Tnns; CSF; Opt Out Tn; *U of Calif-Berkeley; Archt.*

CORBEIL, David Robert
E Detroit HS; E Detroit, MI (10%-973) Band; Ensm; Var C; Bsbl; Bkbl; Ftbl; COM; Hon Prog; Runner-Up, Stu of Yr; Fin, Sportsman o-t Yr.

CORBEIL, Stephen Edward
E Detroit HS; Detroit, MI (10%-980) Pres, Band; Ensm; Var C; Bsbl; Bkbl; Ftbl; Co-Cpt, Tr; COM; Hon Prog; Most Out; Star Student; Stu o-t Yr; Fin, Sportsman of Yr.

CORBETT, James Abram
Hunter Huss HS; Gastonia, NC (60-495) Band; BC; Chor; Ensm; Orch; Span C; Bsbl; Bkbl; Sftbl; Hon Prog; All St Band; *U of NC; Bus.*

CORBETT, Jefferson Morris
Eau Claire HS; Columbia, SC (13-359) Chess C; NHS; *U of SC; Pre-Med.*

CORBETT, Raymond Daniel Jr
Samuel Clemens HS; Schertz, TX (5-328) BS; NHS; Cpt, Bsbl; Cpt, Ftbl; Most Out; Sci A; FCA; Most Ath; HS All Amer Ftbl; WW; *Tex A&M U; Engr.*

CORBETT, Stanley Wyatt
Echols Co HS; Statenville, GA (4-38) Pres, BC; Pres, FFA; Pres, 4H; InterAct C; InterClub Coun; SC; 4H A; MLS; Sci A; *Abraham Baldwin Agr Col; Agr & Ind Equip Tech.*

CORBETT, Von Alan
Aldine HS; Houston, TX (69-537) Tres, Lat C; Lit Mag; Tnns; Hon Prog; Cum Laude; *Tex A&M U; Pre-Dental.*

CORBIN, Cynthia Deborah
Clovis HS; Clovis, NM (70-532) FHA; Pres, Hmrm; *E NM U; Acct.*

CORBIN, Deborah Karen
Mehlville HS; St Louis, MO (250-500) Chor; FHA; MCA; Cpt, Bus Ministry; Evangelism Dynamics; *Central Bible Col; Mus.*

CORBIN, Glenn Eugene
Milburn HS; Milburn, OK (1-20) 4H; NHS; F-Ed, Sch P; Spch C; Pres, Jr Cl; Cpt, Bkbl; Cl Fav; Gov Honor Prog; Hon Prog; Journ A; Val; Yth Fel; Yth Foundation; MVP, Bkbl; Eng, Civics, Spelling, A's; *Med.*

CORBIN, Sheila Nadine
N Co Sr HS; Desloge, MO (20-188) Bus C; Chor; Drama; FBLA; VP, FHA; Thes; Co-Cpt, Tnns; Top 10%; *SE Mo St U; Nurs.*

CORBITT, Daniel Robert
Duncanville HS; Duncanville, TX (3-450) Band; Ensm; Ger C; A-Ed, Lit Mag; Tnns; Alg A; Chem A; Math A; NMF; NMS; Drum Major; *Abilene Christian U; Religion.*

CORCHADO, Nancy
Adlai E Stevenson HS; Bronx, NY; Mjrte; Hon Prog.

CORDARO, Mimi Delores
Ft Pierce Central HS; Ft Pierce, FL; Band; BC; Lat C; Lat NHS; NHS; Citz A; DARGCA; Hon Prog; Sal; Win, Optimist Orator; WW; Win, DAR Essay; *Jackson Mem Sch of Nurs; Nurs.*

CORDELL, Melanie Anne
Benton HS; Benton, AR (50-190) Chor; Math C; NHS; Scc C; Tnns; *U of Central Ark; Nurs.*

CORDERO, Carlos Alberto
Academia Ntra Sra Providencia; Rio Piedras, PR (13-58) Bus C; Chem C; Chess C; Dbte Tm; Drama; Fr C; InterClub Coun; Lat C; Lit Ral; Math C; Sci C; Span C; Spch C; Secy, Sr Cl; Tnns; Tr; JV, Wrest; COM; Chem A; Hon Prog; Spch A; *Bus Adm.*

CORDERO, Diana Milagros
Antonio S Pedreira HS; Moca, PR (3-49) CYO; FHA; 4H; ARC; Span C; SC; Sftbl; Alg A; COM; Cl Fav; Math A; High Hon A; *Recinto Universitario de Mayaguez; Sci.*

CORDERO, Minerva
Miguel Melendez Munoz; Bayamon, PR (1-220) Pres, Ann; Band; Secy, CYO; Chldr; Chem C; Chor; Pres, Commercial C; Pres, Cum Laude Soc; Pres, Drama; Secy, FFA; Tres, FHA; Pres, FTA; Hmrm; Pres, Math C; Orch; VP, Phys C; Pres, ARC; Ed, Sch P; Sci C; Cpt, Bkbl; Alg A; Amer Leg Orator A; Beauty; Bio A; COM; Chem A; Citz A; Cl Fav; Coun of Teach A; Hist A; Hon Prog; JA A; Magna Cum Laude; Math A; Opt A; Phy A; Poet A; Pres A; ARC A; Sci A; Spch A; Star Student; Summa Cum Laude; Essay A; *U of Puerto Rico; Math.*

CORDERO, Yolanda
Francisco Mendoza HS; Isabela, PR; Band; Hmrm; Alg A; Chem A; Hon Prog; Art A; Mus A; CAAM; Med.

CORDES, Deborah Deaun
Mason HS; Mason, TX (2-70) Band; Ensm; Pres, FHA; NHS; Sch Achieve Tm; Bkbl; Hon Prog; Magna Cum Laude; Sal; Concordia Col.

CORDES, Scott Alan
Wanamingo Pub HS; Wanamingo, MN (3-41) Band; Secy, FFA; Tres, 4H; SC; JV, Bkbl; Ftbl; FFA Dairy Judging Tm; Agr.

CORDLE, Jill Regina
Truman HS; Independence, MO (10-663) Ensm; GS; NHS; VP, Orch; Pres, Thes; Citz A; Tres, Church Yth; Lieutenant, Drill Tm; Eng.

CORE, Leslie Joann
Pawhuska HS; Pawhuska, OK (9-125) Band; Mu Alpha Theta; NHS; Bkbl; Golf; U of Okla; Med.

CORELL, Charles Calvin
Washington HS; Cedar Rapids, IA (83-533) Order/ Arrow; Iowa St U; Bio.

CORENO, Judy Ann
St Augustine Acad; Cleveland, OH (50%-124) CYO; Communication Arts Cl A; Hospital Vol; Ohio Sch of Broadcast Technique; Broadcasting.

COREY, Barbara Leslie
Lansdowne Aldan HS; Lansdowne, PA (14-275) CYO; Chor; Hmrm; ARC; SC; UN Council; Bkbl; Hockey; Odd Fellow Fin; Yth Fel; La Crosse; Harcum Jr Col; Med Secy.

COREY, Cynthia Leigh
Westminster Christian Sch; Miami, FL (23-112) Hmrm; Key C; NHS; VP, SC; Cpt, Tr; COM; NEDT; Swtht; MVP, Tr; Yth For Christ Movie Tm; Christian Singing Group; Girls Service C; Auburn U; Bus Adm.

CORKLE, George Patrick
N Park HS; Walden, CO (2-24) Pres, FBLA; FFA; NHS; SC; VP, Jr Cl; Co-Cpt, Bkbl; Co-Cpt, Ftbl; WW.

CORLEW, Rebecca Suzanne
Edgewood Sr HS; Ashtabula, OH (100-300) AFS; Band; Chor; FTA; Pres, 4H; Span C; Y-Tns; Citz A; 4H A; Ed.

CORLEY, Brenda
Whitehouse HS; Whitehouse, TX (11-99) Rptr, Band; BC; Parl, FHA; NHS; Hist, FTA; 1st Div, Band Solo & Ensm Contests; Tyler Jr Col; Elem Ed.

CORLEY, Carla Lynn
Loara HS; Anaheim, CA; Ann; FNA; Ski C; Span C; Pres, Y-Tns; Arch; Bkbl; Sftbl; Swim; Tnns; Pres A; Job's Daughters; Biola Col; Nurs.

CORLEY, Emery Layton
Rowan Center HS; Hattiesburg, MS (5%-500) Ann; Band; Order/Arrow; COM; U of Sou Miss; Sci.

CORLEY, Mark Andrew
Castleberry HS; Fort Worth, TX (2-231) Band; Chor; Hist A; Hon Prog; Kiwanis A; Howard Payne Col; Eng.

CORLEY, Steven Bryan
Freedom HS; Morganton, NC (4-430) AFS; Band; BC; Dbte Tm; VP, Ger C; Hmrm; Key C; NFL; NHS; Order/Arrow; Ed, Sch P; SC; Cr-Ctry; JV, Ftbl; Tr; God & Country A; Gov Honor Prog; Gr Marshal; Opt A; Order/Arrow A; Spch A; Yth Fel; Yth Leg; Optimist Orator; Outst Ger I Stu; 5th Debate Tm Gatlinburg Invitation; City Planning.

CORLISS, Keith Ronald
Oak Grove Lutheran HS; Fargo, ND (5-45) A Cap Choir; BS; Chor; Madrigal; NHS; SC; Tres, Jr Cl; Bkbl; Cr-Ctry; MVP, Tr; Mont St U; Bio.

CORMIER, David S
LaGrange HS; Lake Charles, LA (25-150) Band; Chor; Tres, Yth Art Coun of Amer; McNesse St U; Art.

CORN, Cecil Edward Jr
Edneyville HS; Edneyville, NC (12-90) A Cap Choir; Ann; Secy, Key C; Sftbl; Sch Service A; Eng A; Textile Summer Prog; NC St U; Textiles.

CORNACCHIA, Daniel Joseph
Geneva HS; Geneva, NY; Band; Chess C; Chor; SC; Swim; Tr.

CORNELISON, Melissa Doris
Sparks HS; Sparks, NV (11-380) Drama; FTA; Ed, Lit Mag; NHS; Span C; 1st Atl, GS; Pep C; Fla Col; Law.

CORNELIUS, Beth Joleen
Perkins Co HS; Grant, NE (2-36) Band; Chldr; Chor; Dbte Tm; Ensm; Secy, FFA; FHA; Pres, 4H; Pres, Rainbow; SC; VP, Jr Cl; Mgr, Bkbl; Mgr, Tr; 4H A; Hon Prog; Yth Fel; Mgr, Vlbl; U of Nebr; Med.

CORNELIUS, Georgia Elizabeth
Leander HS; Leander, TX (13-120) Cpt, Chldr; FHA; FTA; Hmrm; NHS; Bus Mgr, Sch P; SC; Runner-Up, Beauty; Ath Support A; Homemaking Schol; WW; Southwestern U; Elem Ed.

CORNELIUS, Linda Anne
Kirkwood HS; Kirkwood, MO (27-590) AFS; Band; Pres, Tri-HiY; COM; Pres, Girls Pep C; Christmas Qn; Hon Schol, DePauw U; Gold 'K' A; Best Citizen A; DePauw; Eng.

CORNELIUS, Steven Merle
Leaf River HS; Leaf River, IL (10-45) VP, FFA; Var C; Co-Cpt, Bsbl; Cpt, Bkbl; Cr-Ctry; Ftbl; MVP, Bkbl; Rock Valley Col; Agr.

CORNELIUS, Thomas Glendell
Northwest HS; St Louis, MO (68-315) SC; Tr; WW; St Louis U; Pre-Law.

CORNELIUS, Tina Ann
W Hills HS; Fort Worth, TX (1-615) Ann; Hmrm; ARC; Span C; SC; Tri-HiY; Hon Prog; Yth Fel; Jr NHS; Church Bkbl; Pres, Yth Group; Austin Col; Ed.

CORNELIUS, Valerie Ann
Leaf River HS; Leaf River, IL (50%-51) Arch; Band; Chor; FHA; FTA; 4H; Sch P; Cpt, Arch; Bsbl; Bkbl; Soccer; Sftbl; Highland Comm Col; Nurs.

CORNELL, Jeanne M
Willows HS; Willows, CA (7-130).

CORNELL, Kimberly Carol
Frankford HS; Philadelphia, PA; Chldr; Tr; Citz A; Hon Prog; Med Tech.

CORNELL, Tammy Denise
Allison HS; Allison, TX (4-10) Tres, Sr Cl; Co-Cpt, Bkbl; Most Ath; All Tourn; All Dist, Bkbl; Frank Phillips Col; Phys Ed.

CORNETT, Andrea Gail
Seven Hills HS; Cincinnati, OH (27-75) Ann; Chor; Dbte Tm; Lit Mag; The Amer U; Gov.

CORNETT, Duane Douglas
Wilkes Central HS; Wilkesboro, NC (130-247) Band; FFA; Span C; Swim; Tr; Wrest; Yth Fel; Brevard Col; Sales and Marketing.

CORNETT, Janet Gay
L C Anderson HS; Austin, TX (20%-550) A Cap Choir; Tres, Chor; Ensm; Madrigal; Interlochen Ntl Mus; All St Choir; Superior, UIL Solo; Baylor U; Mus.

CORNETT, Laurel Elizabeth
Clay Co HS; Manchester, KY (11-210) BC; VP, FHA; Pres, 4H; F-Ed, Sch P; B Crocker A; 4H A; E Ky U; Elem Ed.

CORNFORTH, Kathy Sue
Prior Lake Senior High; Prior Lake, MN (60-207) Ann; Chldr; Chor; Fr C; Ger C; Hmrm; NHS; Co-Ed, Sch P; Pres, SC; Tnns; COM; Spch A; Yth Fel; Vlbl; Fin, Spch Conf; Miss Minn Ntl Tm; Miss Photogenic; Yth Rep, Pastor Parish Relations; All City Choir; Stewardess.

CORNIA, Lynn C
Cokeville HS; Cokeville, WY (2-12) Band; NHS; Cpt, Bkbl; Ftbl; Type A; U of Wyo; Agr Engr.

CORNING, Annette Louise
Homewood-Flossmoor HS; Flossmoor, IL (49-884) Band; Chor; Ensm; COM; Citz A; Hon Prog; Mus A; Math.

CORNISH, Elisa Christina
Golden St HS; Golden, CO (152-420) Chem C; Chor; Drama; NHS; Hon Prog; Tex Sou U; Pol Sci.

CORNISH, Helena Elaine
Golden St HS; Golden, CO (152-420) Pres, Chor; Drama; NHS; Ntl Yth Conf; Pres, SC; Thes; Pres, Soph Cl; MVP, Tnns; Hon Prog; Tex Sou U; Elec Engr.

CORNISH, Vicky Lynn
Van Buren HS; Keosauqua, IA; Band; Chldr; Chor; FHA; Rptr, FTA; Secy, 4H; Rainbow; Sch P; Var C; Sftbl; Tr; 4H A; Type A; Worthy Advisor, Rainbow Girls; Indian Hills-Ottumwa Col; Clerical.

CORNS, Richard Evan
Copley HS; Copley, OH (60-320) Chor; Order/ Arrow; ARC; Var C; Soccer; Semi-Fin, Swim; Tr; Wrest; Eagle Sct; Sr Patrol Ldr; Swim Ltr & 2 HS Records; Col of William And Mary; Econ.

CORNS, Tamara Jo
Man HS; Man, WV (21-180) Band; Bus C; Secy, Hmrm; Key C; Mjrte; Interlochen Ntl Mus; Kiwanis A; Type A; Yth Fel; Band, Bookkeeping, Shorthand, A's; W Va U; Acct.

CORNS, Wilma Sue
Bucyrus Sr HS; Bucyrus, OH (12-200) Pres, FHA; Secy, FTA; 4H; Sch P; Tri-HiY; Amer Leg A; COM; 4H A; Pres, Interntl C; Dist Historian, FHA; Jr Degree, FHA.

CORNWALL, Elizabeth Turner
Wethersfield HS; Wethersfield, CT; HiY; Arch; Bkbl; Swim; Tnns; 4H A; Church Choir; Pilgrim Fel; Ski Tm.

CORNWELL, Gloria Annette
Aiken HS; Cincinnati, OH; Hmrm; Lat C; SC; COM; Ball St U; Bus Adm.

CORNWELL, Michael Lewis
York Comp HS; York, SC (22-240) BS; NHS; SC; Var C; Bsbl; Ftbl; HCt; WW; Bsbl A; Ftbl Player of Week; VP, Bus Drivers C; York Tech Col; Engr.

CORNWELL, Steve Douglas
Montclair HS; Montclair, CA; Biola Col; Pastor.

CORONA, Ardith Rachel
Modesto HS; Modesto, CA (21-276) Chor; Semi-Fin, GS; Pres, Key C; Orch; Ski C; CSF; Midland Lutheran Col; Nurs.

CORPENING, Crystal Dannette
Lenoir HS; Lenoir, NC (12-100) All Amer Yth; Ann; Band; Bus C; Chem C; Chor; Community Yth Symph; Ensm; FBLA; FHA; 4H; Hmrm; InterClub Coun; Jr Miss Pagent; Math C; Ntl Yth Conf; Sch P; SC; World Affairs C; Bsbl; Tnns; Beauty; COM; Citz A; Cl Fav; Nom, WW; All St Band; Most Valuable, FHA; Winston Salem St U; Early Childhood Ed.

CORPENING, Dawn Michelle
Lenoir HS; Lenoir, NC; A-Ed, Ann; VP, Band; Cpt, Chldr; Community Yth Symph; Ensm; FHA; 4H; A-Ed, Sch P; SC; Cpt, Bsbl; Cpt, Bkbl; Sftbl; Tnns; Beauty; COM; Citz A; Cl Fav; DARGCA; Pres A; U of NC; Journ.

CORR, Andrew Reade
Gloucester HS; Gloucester, VA (5%-280) AFS; VP, BC; Chess C; Hmrm; InterAct C; InterClub Coun; Madrigal; Parl, SC; Var C; Bkbl; Co-Cpt, Tnns; Alg A; Spch A; VPI; Engr.

CORRELL, Jamie Alexander
Reynolds HS; Winston-Salem, NC (300-900) Dbte Tm; Key C; Lat C; Order/Arrow; ARC; World Affairs C; Bsbl; Ftbl; Soccer; Tr; Citz A; Hist A; ARC A; Yth Fel; HR; Coach, Soccer Tm; Counselor, Camp Ridgecrest; Ed, Church Newspaper; UNC-Chapel Hill; Hist.

CORRELL, Loreea Lynn
Adair Co R II HS; Brashear, MO (2-15) Ed, Ann; Chor; Secy, NHS; Secy, SC; Var C; Tres, Jr Cl; JV, Bkbl; Mgr, Sftbl; Tr; Alg A; HCt; PTA A; Spch A; VofDEM; WW; Yrbk Qn; U of Mo at Rolla; Computer Sci.

CORRELL, Rhonda Lynne
United Township HS; E Moline, IL (20-798) Chor; Drama; Ensm; Secy, 4H; Span C; Secy, SC; Secy, Soph Cl; Tnns; Tr; Amer Leg A; Hon Prog; Most Out; Merit, Best Sprtsmnship, Serv, A's.

CORRELL, Valerie Lou
Western Hill HS; Cincinnati, OH; Drama; Lat C; Rainbow; SC; Tn Board; Horse Drill Tm; VICA; Raymond Walters Col; Dental Hygiene.

CORRETORE, Janet Marie
H W Schroeder Sr HS; Webster, NY (3-325) Band; Chor; FEng; Ger C; NHS; Pres, Soph Cl; Hockey; Bio A; Math A; Yth Fel; Ger Hon Soc; Outst, Ger; Art A; Pres, Yth Fel; Elem Ed.

CORRIGAN, William Michael
Chaminade Col Prep; St Louis, MO (9-118) NHS; F-Ed, Sch P; VP, SC; JV, Bkbl; Ftbl; JV, Tr; Alg A; Bio A; Chem A; Hist A; Hon Prog; Opt A; Dress Code Comm; Head, Sr Gift Comm; Plumber Essay Contest Win; *St Mary's U; Pre-Law.*

CORRIN, Michael Ellis
The Bolles Sch; Jacksonville, FL (20-156) BC; Drama; NHS; Tres, Order/Arrow; Rptr, Sch P; Span C; VP, SC; Var C; Bsbl; Wrest; Chem A; Hon Prog; Order/Arrow A; Tres, SC; Eagle Sct; WW; Prog Director, FCA; Headmasters A; Sgt of Arms, Soph Cl; Dean's List; Jacksonville Yth Adv Coun; Dist Ser; *N Carolina St U; Engr.*

CORRIPIO, Nancy
Academia Sagrado Corazon; Santurce, PR (3-90) ARC; Sci C; Math A; Phy A; Geography A; Span A; Eng A; Conduct A; *St Mary's Dominican Col; Med.*

CORRY, Jill Alice
Melbourne HS; Melbourne, FL (15%-800) SC; Pres A; Keyettes; VP, Jr Achv; EYC; *Interior Design.*

CORSER, Carol Ann
L A Webber HS; Lyndonville, NY (9-65) Band; VP, 4H; NHS; Pres, Var C; Bkbl; MVP, Soccer; Cpt, Sftbl; COM; 4H A; Yth Fel; Vlbl; *Houghton Col; Math.*

CORSON, Mike Dale
Leeton R-X HS; Leeton, MO; Var C; Bsbl; Co-Cpt, Bkbl; Cr-Ctry; Tr; Hon Prog; *Central Mo St U; Auto Mech.*

CORTES, Margarita
Dra Maria Cadilla de Martinez HS; Arecibo, PR (64-636) Pres, Hmrm; ARC; COM; H of F; Most Out; Hon Achievement Medals; *University of Rio Piedras; Executive Secy.*

CORTES, Norma Veronica
Notre Dame HS; Salinas, CA; CYO; NHS; Sch P; Span C.

CORTES, Rosa A
Francisco Mendoza HS; Isabela, PR; CYO; Hmrm; Bio A; COM; Interlochen Ntl Mus; Magna Cum Laude; *U of PR; Med.*

CORTEZ, Cristela
Harlingen HS; Harlingen, TX (85-627) Bus Mgr, Ann; CYO; Cpt, Chldr; VP, FHA; Pres, SC; Tres, Soph Cl; Tnns; Tr; Cl Fav; HCt; Q&S A; VP, SC; Col Schol; Bus A; Shorthand A; CYO Swtht; *Tex Southmost Col; Bus Ed.*

CORTEZ, Louise Bernadette
Hahnville HS; Boutte, LA (129-384) A Cap Choir; BC; Tres, CYO; Chor; Ensm; FHA; Sci C; Sftbl; Hon Prog; Most Out; Most Outst CYO Girl; English A; DARYC A; Numerous Spelling A; *Nicholls St U; Mus Therapist.*

CORUM, Rhonda Renee
Horace Maynard HS; Maynardville, TN (8-127) BC; Co-Cpt, Chldr; FHA; FNA; 4H; NHS; Sci C; B Crocker A; COM; 4H A; HQn; WW; Sport's Qn; *Fort Sanders Sch of Nurs; Nurs.*

CORY, Donna Lorrine
Sylmar HS; Sylmar, CA (86-648) AFS; Chor; VP, FHA; 4H; Hmrm; SC; DARGCA; GAC Girl o-t Yr; *Home Ec.*

CORYELL, Lisa Winther
Hazel Ave Christian HS; Fair Oaks, CA (1-7) Ann; Co-Cpt, Chldr; Chor; Hmrm; Rainbow; VP, SC; Sftbl; Citz A; HCt; Val; *Trinity Sch o-t Bible; Theology.*

CORZINE, Carlo Wayne
Highland HS; Anderson, IN (17-280) Ch, BS; City Conf; Pres, Hmrm; NHS; Ntl Yth Conf; Span C; Pres, SC; VP, Var C; Parl, Sr Cl; VP, Jr Cl; VP, Soph Cl; Bsbl; JV, Bkbl; MVP, Ftbl; Sftbl; Co-Cpt, Tr; Wrest; Amer Leg A; Chamber of Comm A; Hist A; HKg; Masque & Gavel A; Most Out; Yth Fel; Stu o-t Mo; *Anderson Col; Bus.*

CORZINE, Guy Kent
Assumption Jr-Sr HS; Assumption, IL (10%-56) Band; FFA; Y-Tns; Bsbl; JV, Bkbl; Yth Fel; *General Motors Inst; Engr.*

CORZINE, James Clayton
Dongola HS; Dongola, IL (4-23) Band; BC; Sci C; Family Ldrship A; *Shawnee Jr Col; Pre-Law.*

CORZINE, Mark Lewis
Dongola Unit HS; Dongola, IL (5-23) BC; Chor; Pres, FFA; Pres, Sr Cl; VP, Jr Cl; VP, Soph Cl; Bsbl; MVP, Bkbl; HCt; All Amer Ath; FFA A; *Shawnee Jr Col; Farm Agr.*

COSBY, Jennifer Elise
Eastside HS; Taylors, SC (23-271) Pres, A Cap Choir; Ensm; VP, Hmrm; NHS; S-T, Sr Cl; Beauty; Cl Fav; HCt; Hon Prog; *Samford U; Mus.*

COSBY, Ruth May
Emmerich Manual HS; Indianapolis, IN (54-425) JV, Chldr; Hmrm; Alg A; Bio A; Hist A; Hon Prog; Math A; Chldr, Phys Ed, A's; League of Hon; *Sch of Practical Nurs; Nurs.*

COSBY, Terris Ray
Horace Maynard HS; Maynardville, TN (2-127) Ed, Ann; Pres, BC; Rptr, 4H; Var C; Bkbl; 4H A; Most Courteous; *U of Tenn; Aerospace Engr.*

COSCIA, Arlene Kay
Hillsborough HS; Tampa, FL; FHA; Pres, Hmrm; Sftbl; *Sweet Briar Col; Legal Secy.*

COSENS, Julie Rose
Jayhawk Linn HS; Mound City, KS (1-48) Ed, Ann; Band; CYO; Drama; VP, FHA; Semi-Fin, GS; Pres, 4H; Co-Cpt, Mjrte; A-Ed, Sch P; Spch C; SC; Tres, Jr Cl; Sftbl; Tr; Amer Leg A; 4H A; HCt; Journ A; Spch A; Type A; HR; *Kans St Col; Spch.*

COSENS, Kim Jay
Spirit Lake Comm HS; Spirit Lake, IA (44-130) Band; Chor; Drama; Ensm; Madrigal; Mod Mus Mas; Order/Arrow; Span C; Spch C; Thes; COM; Piano A; *USD; Mus.*

COSEY, Dawn Ann
James H Bowen HS; Chicago, IL (194-487) SC; *Bradley U; Nurs.*

COSLOP, Francis Marino
Sacred Heart HS; Vineland, NJ (2-56) Chess C; Drama; Fr C; NHS; Sch P; Span C; Thes; Hon Prog; NEDT; Sal; Yrbk Staff; Accelerated Stu; *U of Penn; Fine Arts.*

COSNER, Miles Douglas
N E HS; Springfield, OH (69-351) Chor; Ensm; NHS; Var C; Bkbl; Ftbl; Tr; HCt; Yth Fel; Prom King; *Evangel Col; Phys Ed.*

COSNER, Tina Louise
Carmel HS; Carmel, NY; A Cap Choir; Chor; Drama; Yth Fel; Home Ec, Twirling, A's; *Psych.*

COSPER, Michael Allan
Woodway HS; Edmonds, WA (162-370) Drama; Ger C; Phys C; Var C; Cr-Ctry; Tr; Varsity Ltr; *U of Wash; Bus.*

COSPER, Wendy Sue
Woodway Sr HS; Edmonds, WA (12-423) A Cap Choir; Chldr; Chor; Ensm; Ger C; Hmrm; NHS; Y-Tns; Hon Prog; *U of Wash; Law.*

COSSABOON, Pamela Dawn
N Penn HS; Lansdale, PA (15%-850) SC; Mgr, Sftbl; Swim; Yth Fel; Sumner Diving A; *Phys Therapy.*

COSSU, Sergio Fabian
St Joseph's o-t Palisades HS; W New York, NJ (8-289) Chess C; Fr C; French NHS; Sch P; JV, Tr; Hon Prog; Hon Cert; *Med.*

COST, Robert William
Fairlawn HS; Sidney, OH (7-40) A Cap Choir; Band; Chem C; Chess C; Chor; Var C; Community Yth Symph; Drama; Ensm; Secy, FFA; FTA; Ger C; Pres, 4H; Lit Mag; Orch; Phys C; Bsbl; Bkbl; Cr-Ctry; Swim; Tr; COM; 4H A; Hon Prog; Yth Fel; Coaches A; FFA St Band; All Co Band; Jr Fair Board; *Ohio Northern U; Psych.*

COSTA, Domenic
Mary Star HS; San Pedro, CA (8-94) InterAct C; NHS; Span C; VP, SC; Var C; JV, Bsbl; Ftbl; CSF; Chem A; Hon Prog; Serra C Essay Contest A; *Harbor Col; General.*

COSTANZA, Donna Lee
John Ehret HS; Marrero, LA (10-474) NHS; Hon Prog; Poet A; *U of New Orleans; Eng.*

COSTAS, Janet Elizabeth
Moline Sr HS; Moline, IL; Band; Church Sftbl.

COSTAS, Judson Paul
Moline Sr HS; Moline, IL (82-831) NHS; Bkbl; Cr-Ctry; Mgr, Ftbl; Sftbl; Tr; *U of Ill; Engr.*

COSTELLO, Patrick Thomas
Coon Rapids Sr HS; Coon Rapids, MN (60-650) CYO; Pres, Hmrm; VP, NHS; Pres, SC; Var C; Pres, Jr Cl; Pres, Soph Cl; Cpt, Hockey; JV, Soccer; Tnns; HCt; Yth Fel; Most Improved, Hockey; Open Sch Adv Committee; Lay Curriculum Committee; *St Johns U; Law.*

COSTEPHENS, Alton Jess
S Albany HS; Albany, OR (100-250) JV, Ftbl; JV, Wrest.

COSTIN, Brenda Kay
Worth Co HS; Grant City, MO (12-54) Band; Bus C; Chldr; FHA; FTA; 4H; Mjrte; Rainbow; SC; S-T, Var C; Bkbl; Golf; Sftbl; Tr; HCt; Best Dressed; Rainbow Grand Cross of Colors; *NW Missouri St U; Bus.*

COSTIN, Felicity Anne
Kent Sch; Kent, CT (3-55) Ed, Sch P; NMS; NEDT; Earthwatch Sci School; Poetry A; Lib Proctor, Top Ten; Canoe C; Ctry Skiing C; *Wellesley Col; Bio.*

COSTIN, Norman Joseph
St Mary's Regional HS; Lynn, MA (2-117) All Amer Yth; CYO; NHS; SC; Bsbl; MVP, Ftbl; Swim; Wrest; Tr; Alg A; Bio A; Hon Prog; Math A; Sci A; Star Student; Swtht; Co- cpt, Tr; *Psych.*

COSTIN, Opal Denett
Worth Co R III HS; Grant City, MO (12-54) Band; Bus C; Ensm; FTA; 4H; Mjrte; NHS; Rainbow; Var C; Bkbl; Golf; Sftbl; Tr; *NW Mo St U; Mus.*

COSTIN, Sandra Rae
Oconto HS; Oconto, NE (2-6) Band; Fin, GS; VP, 4H; Sch P; Sftbl; Mgr, Tr; Bio A; *Curtis Vo-tech Col; Vet Technology.*

COSTNER, Charmaine
Silsbee HS; Silsbee, TX (115-230) Band; Fr C; FHA; FTA; Fin, Jr Miss Pagent; Rainbow; Beauty; Poet A; Sci A; *Lamar U; Ed.*

COSTNER, Jean Herren
Mountain Brook HS; Birmingham, AL; A Cap Choir; AFS; Pres, Chor; Crown & Scepter; Ensm; Ger C; InterClub Coun; Fin, Jr Miss Pagent; Pres, Mod Mus Mas; Sch P; Spch C; Secy, Thes; Var C; Cr-Ctry; Sftbl; Swim; Tr; Beauty; Hon Prog; JA A; Yth Fel; Most Talented; Jr Miss Schol; Superior, St Voice Competition; *Birmingham-Sou Col; Voice.*

COSTNER, Joy Lisa
Conway HS; Conway, SC; Fr C; Hmrm; Type A; *Psych.*

COSTNER, Susan Lynn
Mountain Brook HS; Birmingham, AL (20%-300) A Cap Choir; VP, Chor; Cpt, Drama; Ensm; Ch, Hmrm; Lat C; Mod Mus Mas; Thes; Sftbl; Service, Bike, Art, CS; Gym; Cpt, Yth Coun; Acteens; Day Camp Counselor; *Judson Col; Elem Ed.*

COSTON, Steven Randy
Herbert Henry Dow HS; Midland, MI; Band; *Elec.*

COTA, Diane Marie
Terre Haute S Vigo HS; Terre Haute, IN (54-509) A Cap Choir; Pres, CYO; Chor; Pres, Drama; Ensm; InterClub Coun; Madrigal; Model UN; NFL; NHS; Ed, Sch P; Pres, Spch C; VP, SC; UN Council; Y-Tns; Swim; Amer Leg Orator A; COM; Journ A; Most Out; Opt A; Spch A; Best Actress A; Outst Speaker; *Ind St U; Lang.*

COTE, Catherine Marie
Glenbard W HS; Glen Ellyn, IL; AFS; Mu Alpha Theta; COM; Hon Prog.

COTHRAN, Juanita Victoria
Covington HS; Covington, TN (39-228) BC; Dbte Tm; Secy, Drama; FHA; NHS; Miss FHA Fin; Art A; *Art.*

COTNER, Cecilia Lynn
Putnam City HS; Oklahoma City, OK (130-850) Span C; Cooperative Off Ed A; Achv Schol; *Okla Baptist U; Math.*

COTNER, Kathryn Eileen
Warrior Run Sr HS; Turbotville, PA (21-191) All Amer Yth; Secy, FNA; Co-Ed, Sch P; Tres, SC; Tri-HiY; Var C; Hockey; Tr; Christmas Court Young Amer; *Robert Packer Sch of Nurs; Nurs.*

COTT, Kathleen Marie
Clay Center Comm HS; Clay Center, KS (2-128) Band; Secy, FHA; GS; Pres, 4H; Sch P; S-T, SC; Secy, Sr Cl; JV, Tr; Chamber of Comm A; DARGCA; 4H A; St Scholar; Co Farm Bureau Jr; Bicentennial Courier to Sweden; *Kans St U; Interior Design.*

COTT, Robert James
Clay Center Comm HS; Clay Center, KS (10-135) Band; Pres, 4H; Cr-Ctry; Tr; 4H A; *Kans St U; Agr.*

COTTEN, Deborah Lucille
Miller Co R III HS; Tuscumbia, MO (3-27) Band; Chor; Rptr, Sch P; WW; *Secy Sci.*

COTTEN, Mary Dee
Ole Main HS; N Little Rock, AR (10%-450) Band; Chem C; Ger C; Math C; Mu Alpha Theta; NHS; COM; Citz A; Hon Prog; Ntl Achv Schol; *U of Ark at Fayetteville; Special Ed.*

COTTEN, Ruby Marie
John Bartram HS; Philadelphia, PA (461-900) Ed, Ann; Hmrm; SC; Var C; World Affairs C; Mgr, Bkbl; Tnns; Journ A; *Cheyney St Col; Ed.*

COTTEN, Stacey Alan
Carbondale Comm HS; Carbondale, IL (25-250) Band; Demolay; Mgr, Bkbl; DARGCA; Hist A; Yth Fel; *SE Mo Col; Hist.*

COTTER, Abby Gail
Lake City HS; Lake City, TN (3-132) BC; Drama; 4H; Co-Ch, Hmrm; Span C; SC; Pres, Jr Cl; Bkbl; Sftbl; FCA; Pep C; Cpt, Vlbl; Eng A; *Hiwassee Col; Med.*

COTTER, Elizabeth Ann
Bishop Watterson HS; Columbus, OH (50%-247) CYO; Chor; Cum Laude Soc; Tres, Lat C; Lit Mag; Bkbl; Cr-Ctry; Cpt, Hockey; Sftbl; Cpt, Tr; COM; Magna Cum Laude; *Ohio St U; Dental Hygiene.*

COTTER, Helen Kay
Mountain View HS; Mtn View, AR; Cpt, Chldr; Pres, FHA; Hmrm; Span C; Spch C; SC; Math A; PA; *Fashions.*

COTTER, MaryElla Christine
Brewster Pub Sch; Brewster, MN (5-26) Band; Chor; Drama; Pres, FHA; GS; 4H; Pres, Mjrte; NHS; Ed, Sch P; Spch C; Tres, Soph Cl; Bkbl; Tr; 4H A; Spch A; Marian Medal; Vlbl; Dist VP, FHA; *Col of St Benedict; Home Ec.*

COTTER, Teresa Annette
New Brockton HS; New Brockton, AL (5%-75) BC; FBLA; Parl, FHA; Rptr, 4H; S-T, Soph Cl; 4H A; *Enterprise St Jr Col; Secretarial.*

COTTERILL, Suzanne Lynn
Niagara Wheatfield Sr HS; Sanborn, NY;

COTTERMAN, Ronald Lee
Sarasota HS; Sarasota, FL (1-617) FBLA; Hmrm; Tres, Key C; A-Ed, Lit Mag; NHS; SC; JV, Swim; COM; MLS; Val; Sr Cl Officer; *U of Fla; Elec Engr.*

COTTET, Brenda Lynn
Chittenango HS; Chittenango, NY; FHA; NHS; Span C; BYF; Guild 0280003239c; *Elem Ed.*

COTTIER, Amy Elizabeth
Maumee HS; Maumee, OH; Chldr; Drama; Fr C; Ski C; SC; Y-Tns; Tres, Jr Cl; Tres, Soph Cl; Tr; Hon Prog; *Journ.*

COTTINGHAM, Kelly Jane
Odessa HS; Odessa, TX (10%-800) A Cap Choir; Ch, Hmrm; Tres, NHS; SC; Var C; Fin, Tr; MVP & Fin, Gym; Fin, Pres A; Semi-Fin, Amer Leg A; Fin, Citz A; AAU St Champ, Gym; Sem-Fin, Opt A; All-St Gym Tm; Fin, Most Outst.

COTTINGHAM, Sandra Lee
Cloverdale HS; Cloverdale, IN (1-70) Band; JV, Chldr; Chor; Fr C; Mjrte; NHS; Sci C; Pres, Thes; Bkbl; Tr; Alg A; Bio A; DARGCA; Hon Prog; Math A; NMF; NMS; Spch A; Val; Vlbl; St GAA A; Hon Thespian; Most Versatile; *Ind U; Bio Sci.*

COTTLE, Jana Sue
Moran HS; Moran, TX (1-5) Co-Ed, Ann; Ch, Chldr; Pres, FHA; 4H; Bkbl; Tnns; Tr; Citz A; Cl Fav; DARGCA; 4H A; Hon Prog; Math A; Sci A; Val; *Cisco Jr Col; Agr.*

COTTO, Lesbia E
Fernando Suros Chaves HS; Barceloneta, PR; Band; Pres, FHA; Tres, Hmrm; COM; Lion A; Magna Cum Laude; Peer Counselor; *Univ of Puerto Rico; Med Technology.*

COTTO, Rafael
Manuela Toro HS; Caguas, PR; *U of Puerto Rico; Engr.*

COTTON, Eric Mathew
Henderson Sr HS; W Chester, PA (14-509) JV, Tr; Hon Prog; *Sci.*

COTTON, Joanne
Troup HS; LaGrange, GA (10%-175) BC; Bus C; FBLA; Pres, FHA; VP, HiY; InterClub Coun; Beauty; Bio A; Cl Fav; H of F; HCt; Hon Prog; Most Out; Yth Leg; *Southeastern Acad; Reservationist.*

COTTON, Laura Carol
Wingfield HS; Jackson, MS (20%-250) NHS; Pres, Yth Fel; Drill Tm; Choir; *Hinds Jr Col; Phys Therapy.*

COTTON, Marcia Ann
Polo HS; Orient, SD (2-11) Bus Mgr, Ann; Chor; Drama; Co-Ed, Sch P; VP, SC; Tres, Var C; Pres, Sr Cl; MVP, Bkbl; MVP, Cr-Ctry; MVP, Tr; HCt; Journ A; Sal; *Ntl Col of Bus; Airline & Travel Career.*

COTTON, Michael
East HS; Columbus, OH; COM; MLS; Opt A; Sci A; *Ohio St Col; Med.*

COTTON, Robert Williams
New Bern Sr HS; New Bern, NC; Band; Order/ Arrow; Order/Arrow A.

COTTON, Vanessa Latrice
W Fulton HS; Atlanta, GA; Chldr; Fr C; Sci C; Spch C; COM; ROTC A; Yth Fel; *Barber Scotia Col; Pre-Nurs.*

COTTRELL, Bryan Douglas
Therrell HS; Atlanta, GA; Cpt, Bsbl; MVP, Ftbl; Fin, Tr; Most Out; *Fla A&M U; Physical Education.*

COTTRELL, Kevin Ray
Midview HS; Grafton, OH; Sch P; Bsbl; Bkbl; Journ.

COTTRELL, Lisa Lyles
Red Springs HS; Red Springs, NC (1-130) VP, BC; Cpt, Chldr; FTA; Secy, Soph Cl; Pres, FHA; Gov Honor Prog; HCt; Type A; Yth Fel; Chief Marshall; *U of NC; Bus Adm.*

COTTRELL, Russell Warren
Colerain HS; Cincinnati, OH (65-650) Band; Chess C; Chor; Ensm; Math C; Span NHS; Hon Prog; Math A; Sci A; *U of Cincinnati; Physics.*

COTTRELL, Tracy Kim
Andrew J Terrell HS; Blanchard, OK; A Cap Choir; F-Ed, Ann; BC; Chor; Dbte Tm; Drama; Ensm; FHA; 4H; Hmrm; JETS; Madrigal; Math C; NHS; F-Ed, Sch P; Var C; Co-Cpt, Bkbl; Co-Cpt, Sftbl; Tr; Alg A; COM; Gov Honor Prog; 4H A; HCt; Hon Prog; Journ A; Math A; St Scholar; Summa Cum Laude; Drafting A; Rptr, Pep C; Ch, Float Committee.

COTTRILL, Rebecca Kay
University HS; Morgantown, WV (2-150) Chldr; VP, Soph Cl; Bkbl; MVP, Tr.

COUCH, Betty Jane
Rosedale HS; Rosedale, IN; Band; Chldr; Mjrte; NHS; Rptr, Sr Cl; Pres, Jr Cl; Tres, Soph Cl; Bkbl; Tr; HCt; Christmas Qn; Prom Jr Attendant; *Ind U; Life Sci.*

COUCH, Paula Jean
Laurel Highlands Sr HS; Uniontown, PA (156-428) Band; FBLA; PA A.

COUCH, Thomas Howard
Ware Shoals HS; Ware Shoals, SC (3-100) BC; VP, Fr C; Pres, NHS; Pres, Sci C; SC; Var C; Bsbl; Ftbl; Tr; Chamber of Comm A; Cl Fav; Hon Prog; ROTC A; Star Student; Sr Standout; *US Air Force Acad; Engr.*

COUCH, Timothy Roberts
Huntington HS; Huntington, NY (20-600) AFS; Drama; Order/Arrow; Thes; Amer Leg A; COM; Citz A; Lion A; MLS; Most Out; Order/Arrow A; Ad Altare Dei.

COUGHLIN, Richard Barry
Franklin Acad; Malone, NY; Cpt, Band; BS; Fr C; Hmrm; Sch P; Var C; Cpt, Ftbl; Swim; COM; Most Out; Pres A; *Paul Smiths Col; Hotel Mgt.*

COULSON, Boyd Allen
Superior Sr HS; Superior, WI; Band; *U of Wis; Airline-Airport Mgr.*

COULSON, Marcia Renee
Superior Sr HS; Superior, WI; Chor; Drama; Orch; Ski C; Spch C; Tr; COM; Spch A; Tres, Yth Group; Win, Optimist Spch; Jr HS Service A; *Med.*

COULSON, William Russell
Cedar Cliff HS; Camp Hill, PA (33%-500) Demolay; JV, Wrest; Fire Dept; *Cabinetmaking.*

COULTAS, Peter Leon
Havana HS; Havana, FL; Bus Mgr, Ann; Pres, FFA; NHS; Rptr, SC; VP, Soph Cl; Hist A; Eng A; Phys Fitness A; *Sci.*

COULTER, Carolyn Sue
Danville HS; Danville, KY (50-221) Anchor C; Hmrm; Span C; SC; HCt; Bus Mgr, Pep C; *Morehead U; Special Ed.*

COULTER, Cheryl Lynn
Ysleta HS; El Paso, TX; Band; JV, Chldr; Co-Ch, Mjrte; JV, NHS; SC; Cpt, Tr; Math A; Most Out; MV Band Fresh; Asst Drum Major; *Mus.*

COULTER, John Frederick
Cleburne HS; Cleburne, TX (1-250) Band; VP, Chess C; Lat C; Order/Arrow; Co-Ed, Sch P; Alg A; Hon Prog; Math A; Order/Arrow A; Pres A; Eagle Sct; *Sou Methodist U; Law.*

COULTER, Seth Baker
Norman HS; Crossett, AR (8-250) Pres, BC; Key C; Span C; SC; Bkbl; Ftbl; Tr.

COUNCELLER, Larry
Cumberland Valley Christian Sch; Chambersburg, PA (4-12) Ed, Ann; Band; Chor; Drama; Ensm; JV, Bkbl; JV, Cr-Ctry; COM; Cpt, Church Bus; Cl Chaplain; AWANA Leader; *Tenn Temple Sch; Evangelist.*

COUNT, Paul James
Muncie Central HS; Muncie, IN (40-256) Sch P; Var C; Cr-Ctry; Tr; COM; HCt; Journ A; Math A; Q&S A; *Ball St U; Bus.*

COUNTER, Sarah Jane
Oliver Wolcott Reg Voc-Tech HS; Torrington, CT (113-160) Chor; JV, Cr-Ctry; JV, Tr; *Nurs.*

COURAND, Marie Celeste
Douglas MacArthur HS; San Antonio, TX (15%-610) CYO; FTA; Span C; Span NHS; GSct Marion Medal; Summer Ecology Course Schol; *Tex A&M U; Bio Environmental Sci.*

COURNEYA, Paul Curtis
Minneapolis Lutheran HS; Minneapolis, MN; Ski C; Sftbl; Tnns; Industrial Arts A; *Golden Valley Lutheran Col; Law Enforcement.*

COURNOYER, Michael John
Newman HS; Wausau, WI (1-134) Cpt, Ftbl; Hmrm; Ski C; Var C; Co-Cpt, Ftbl; Bausch & Lomb A; Math A; Val; *Col of St Thomas; Med.*

COURNOYER, Richard George
Newman HS; Wausau, WI; Bsbl; Ftbl.

COURSE, Cheryl Diane
Lakewood Sr HS; Lakewood, CA; AFS; Cpt, Bkbl; *Grace Col; Psych.*

COURSE, Steven Howard
Lakewood Sr HS; Lakewood, CA; Drama; Secy, Ensm; Madrigal; Thes; COM; *Calif St U; Mus.*

COURTNEY, Bradford Jay
Whitefish Bay HS; Milwaukee, WI (130-315) BS; Chor; Order/Arrow; SC; Pres, Sr Cl; Ftbl; Wrest; Eagle Sct; Prom Court; Ltrman C; Yth Coun; *Tex Christian U; Bus Adm.*

COURTNEY, Cynthia Ann
Silsbee HS; Silsbee, TX; Fr C; Hmrm; Math C; Rainbow; ARC; Rptr, Sch P; SC; Secy, Jr Cl; Golf; Yth Coun; Leo C; Mgr, Tigerettes Drill Tm; Miss Satsuma Run-Up, Ann-Yrbk, A.

COURTNEY, David Howard
Acalanes HS; Lafayette, CA (19-343) AFS; A-Ed, Ann; Model UN; Mu Alpha Theta; NHS; Span C; SC; World Affairs C; Cr-Ctry; Tr; Bank Of Amer A; CSF; Elk A; NMF; Gemco Found A; Outst Liberal Arts Stu; Outst Social Stu Stu; *Dartmouth Col; Econ.*

COURTNEY, Judy Lenora
Broadmoor HS; Baton Rouge, LA (300-552) Ann; Drama; Fr C; Lat C; Rptr, Sch P; MVP, Sftbl; Amer Leg A; Journ A; Q&S A; Sftbl Cert's & Trophies; Mus A; *SE La U; Journ.*

COURTNEY, Larry Allen
Franklin Central HS; Indianapolis, IN (70-250) Tr; *Bus.*

COURTNEY, Richard Owen
Marion Independent HS; Marion, IA; Band; Chor; COM; Sci A; Pres, Amer Legion Rifle C; *U of Iowa; Computer Sci.*

COURTNEY, Robbin Marie
Monticello HS; Monticello, MS; F-Ed, Ann; Band; BC; Ensm; GS; Cpt, Mjrte; Tnns; B Crocker A; WW; *Acct.*

COURTNEY, Robert Francis
Maple Shade HS; Maple Shade, NJ (9-241) CYO; Key C; NHS; Soccer; Hon Prog; *Drexel U; Mech Engr.*

COURTNEY, Vanessa Eileen
Pflugerville HS; Pflugerville, TX; BC; Drama; FHA; Rptr, Ger C; VP, 4H; Rptr, Sch P; SC; Mgr, Bkbl; Mgr, Tr; 4H A; Bible A; 4-H Fair A; Co Dress Revue A; *Lubbock Christian Col; Pharmacy.*

COURTON, Anne Michele
Sweet Home Sr MS; Amherst, NY; Drama; SC; Ntl Federation of Mus C; *Law.*

COURTRIGHT, Carla Allyne
Moore HS; Moore, OK; Band; Tres, NHS; Span C; COM; Type A; Sch Mus.

COURTRIGHT, Laura Janyne
Moore HS; Moore, OK; Ch, NHS; Span C; Alg A; Masonic A; Type A.

COURTRIGHT, Leslie Leigh
O H Cooper HS; Abilene, TX (50%-580) A Cap Choir; Secy, Hmrm; NFL; Sci C; Spch C; Bio A; Amer Soc, Microbio; Win, Sci Fair Sweepstakes; Most Outst, US Air Force, Microbi; AAUW; *Abilene Christian Col; Bio.*

COURTRIGHT, Linda Kay
Wichita Heights HS; Wichita, KS; Band; Orch; Sch P; Hon Prog; Ntl Federation of Stu of Ger; *Special Ed.*

COURTY, Carole Leslie
Acad o-t Holy Names; Tampa, FL; Ed, Ann; Hmrm; InterClub Coun; Lat C; Lat NHS; NHS; Span NHS; SC; Hon Prog; *U of Fla; Journ.*

COUSER, Terri Beth
Peebles HS; Peebles, OH (2-109) Band; Chor; Drama; VP, FHA; A-Ed, Sch P; B Crocker A; H of F; Hon Prog; Sal; Spch A; Drum Mjrte; Most Talented, Sr Cl; *Sou St U; Secondary Ed.*

COUSSOULIS, Helen Alice
St Augustine HS; Laredo, TX; Drama; NHS; Secy, SC; NEDT; WW; *Tex A&M U; Psych.*

COUTURE, Irene Faye
Clyde HS; Clyde, KS (6-34) Band; Chor; Drama; Ensm; Fin, GS; Madrigal; Mjrte, Pres; SC; Thes; Parl, Sr Cl; Tres, Jr Cl; Rptr, Soph Cl; COM; Citz A; Hon Prog; Spch A; St Scholar; Type A; VFW A; Pep C; St Mus, Drama, A's; Secy, Kayettes; GAA; Vlbl.

COVE, Christopher Jack
Auburn HS; Auburn, NY (15-650) Chor; NHS; ARC; Ski C; Mgr, Bkbl; *Pre-Med.*

COVER, Brant Bricker II
Andover HS; Andover, MA; Band; *Elem Ed.*

COVEY, Lisa Renee
Kentwood HS; Grand Rapids, MI; Ski C; Swim; Gym.

COVINGTON, Debra DeFane
E Aurora HS; Aurora, IL (100-420) Mgr, Tr; Black Stu Assn; Secy, Ebonairs; *Miss Valley St Col.*

COVINGTON, Debra Louise
Reidsville Sr HS; Reidsville, NC (33-344) Lit Mag; NHS; Span C; Pres, Sr Cl; *U of NC at Greensboro;; Nurs.*

COVINGTON, Donna Jo
Perry Meridian HS; Indianapolis, IN (142-546) GS; Hon Prog.

COVINGTON, Dorcas Ann
Duncanville HS; Duncanville, TX; Band; Span C; SC; *Stephen F Austin Col; Foreign Lang.*

COVINGTON, Patricia Ann
Carver HS; Memphis, TN; F-Ed, Ann; NHS; Hon Prog; Sci A; Charmettes; *Memphis St U; Nurs.*

COVINGTON, Ramon Christopher
Christian Fenger HS; Chicago, IL (8-510) *Ill Inst of Tech; Bus Mgt.*

COVINGTON, Sheron Lynn
W Charlotte HS; Charlotte, NC (213-594) Ann; Cpt, Mjrte; Span C; Pres, Sr Cl; Citz A; Most Out; Interact; Civinettes; Project Aires; Order o-t Lion; *Spellman Col; Television Broadcasting.*

COVINGTON, William Dwayne
Brookhaven Acad; Brookhaven, MS; *Copiah-Lincoln Col; Agr.*

COVINGTON, William Sydney
Western Hills HS; Fort Worth, TX (1-600) Tr; Sea Cadet, Navy League; *US Naval Acad; Oceanography.*

COWAN, April La Gina
Big Sandy HS; Big Sandy, TX (3-50) Pres, Band; Chldr; FHA; Tres, NHS; Secy, Jr Cl; Secy, Soph Cl; Cl Fav; Most Intellectual; *Ambassador Col; Mus.*

COWAN, Cindy Sue
Tupelo HS; Tupelo, MS (10%-300) A Cap Choir; Anchor C; Chor; Ensm; Fr C; Madrigal; NHS; *Miss St U; Med Technology.*

COWAN, Joyce Aileen
Kentridge Sr HS; Kent, WA (10%-500) Band; VP, 4H; NHS; SC; Outst Math Stu; *U of Wash; Law.*

COWAN, Kenneth Samuel
Chattanooga Valley Comprehensive Hs; Flintstone, GA (45-120) A Cap Choir; Band; Chor; Pres, Ensm; Fr C; FBLA; Pres, Hmrm; Tres, Key C; Orch; Sch P; Mgr, Bsbl; Bkbl; JV, Ftbl; Most Out; *Jacksonville St U; Mus.*

COWAN, Mary Catherine
S Mecklenburg HS; Pineville, NC (33%-750) Chor; Drama; Ensm; Mjrte; Bkbl; Sftbl; Beauty; Miss S Meck; Carrousel Princess; Best All Around, Choral Mus A; *Appalachian St U; Eng.*

COWAN, Patricia Renea
E St Louis Sr HS; E St Louis, IL (15-1001) Chor; Ch, Dbte Tm; Rptr, Hmrm; Ed, Sch P; St Stu Congress; VP, SC; COM; Cl Fav; Hist A; HCt; Hon Prog; Sci A; VofDEM; Yth Fel; Jr Choir Pres; HR; *Ill St U; Social Worker.*

COWAN, Wanda Lue
Robert E Lee HS; San Antonio, TX (50-627) A Cap Choir; *Dallas Christian Col; Elem Ed.*

COWAN, William David
Hopkins Eisenhower Sr HS; Hopkins, MN (34-409) JV, Cr-Ctry; Wrest; *Bible.*

COWAND, John Wesley III
New Hanover HS; Wilmington, NC; Band; *E Carolina U; Mus.*

COWARD, Elizabeth Frances
Sylva-Webster HS; Sylva, NC (5-168) Ann; Band; Chldr; Chem C; Drama; FHA; F-Ed, Sch P; Ski C; Span C; Secy, Soph Cl; Bkbl; Hon Prog; Pres A; Jr Marshall; *U of NC; Journ.*

COWART, Charles Francis
Herschel V Jenkins HS; Savannah, GA (2-350) Ann; Pres, BC; VP, NHS; Cpt, Bsbl; Tr; COM; Math A; NEDT; Rensselaer A; Sci A; Presbyterian Col Jr Fel; King Col Fel; Erskine Col Hon Schol; *Erskine Col; Chem.*

COWART, Dennis Keith
Vancleave Consolidated HS; Ocean Springs, MS (3-105) BC; Sci C; VP, Jr Cl; Swim; Tr; Amer Leg A; Bio A; Hist A; VFW A; Dbte C; Most Dependable; Yth Ldrship A; Most Patriotic; Geom A; Outst Yth A; Eng A; *Miss St U; Archt.*

COWART, Donald Edward
W Monroe HS; W Monroe, LA; ARC; *Med.*

COWART, Janice Lyneve
Reidsville HS; Reidsville, GA (30-150) A-Ed, Ann; FHA; 4H; JV, Bkbl; 4H A; *Swainsboro Vo-tech Col; Bus Adm.*

COWART, Kenneth Coleman
Vancleave Cons HS; Ocean Springs, MS (10-124) Band; BC; Ensm; Hmrm; Sci C; SC; Alg A; Amer Leg A; Page, House of Reps; Youth Choir; *Miss St U; Sci.*

COWART, Melinda
Arlington HS; Indianapolis, IN (10-350) A Cap Choir; Chldr; Chor; Ensm; Fr C; Hmrm; Madrigal; NHS; Orch; SC; Hist A; Most Out; Type A; Swing Choir; Eng A; Fr A; *Oral Roberts U; Art.*

COWDERY, Todd Shawl
Durham Acad; Durham, NC (3-70) AFS; F-Ed, Ann; Chor; Drama; Math C; SC; Pres, Soph Cl; Soccer; Tr; COM; Hist A; Hon Prog; Yth Fel; *Davidson Col; Med.*

COWELL, Colleen
Duncanville HS; Duncanville, TX; Secy, Chor; FHA; Ger C; COM; Hon Prog; Drill Tm A; Bible Credit A; *Tex Tech U; Dental Hygiene.*

COWELL, Janet Lynn
Northwood HS; Northwood, OH (3-60) A Cap Choir; Ann; Secy, Band; Cpt, Chldr; Drama; Ensm; Semi-Fin, GS; NHS; Secy, SC; COM; Citz A; Hon Prog; Math A; Sci A; Rep, Jr C; *Bowling Green St U.*

COWELL, Joseph Michael Jr
Notre Dame-Bishop Gibbons HS; Schenectady, NY (22-160) CYO; Drama; JV, Cr-Ctry; JV, Tr; WW; *Boston Col; Acct.*

COWEN, Sarah Cantrell
Williamston HS; Williamston, NC; Band; Tres, FHA; Key C; Tres, NHS.

COWGILL, Ann M
Winchester HS; Winchester, MA; *Williams Col; Philosophy.*

COWGILL, Simone Lynn
Riverview HS; Sarasota, FL; Band; Span C; *Med.*

COWHER, Susan Adair
L E Dieruff HS; Allentown, PA (15-633) Band; Chor; Drama; Hmrm; NHS; Orch; Sch P; Drama; SC; COM; Coun of Teach A; Hon Prog; Ch, Church Yth Coun; Orch A; *Secy.*

COWTHRAN, Jeanette
Second Ward HS; Gloster, LA (7-46) *Grambling St U; Special Ed.*

COX, Allyson Jean
Brewer HS; Brewer, ME (15-300) Band; Chor; Ensm; NHS; Orch; Pres, Rainbow; Amer Leg A; Beauty; COM; Citz A; VofDEM; Yth Fel; All St Mus, St Solo, Festivals; *Boston Conservaty of Mus; Mus Ed.*

COX, Angela Ruth
Wm Monroe HS; Stanardsville, VA (33%-129) F-Ed, Ann; Chor; Drama; Rptr, FTA; Pres, 4H; NFL; F-Ed, Sch P; Sci C; 4H A; Interpreter For Deaf; Rptr, Co Newspaper; *Mary Baldwin Col; Eng.*

COX, Anthony Glen
Maud HS; Maud, OK (5-58) BC; Parl, FFA; Model UN; Bsbl; Bkbl; Ftbl; HCt; *Okla St U; Agr.*

COX, Ballard Phillmore
Jasper HS; Jasper, IN (15-300) BC; Bsbl; Cr-Ctry; Ftbl; Swim; Wrest; Alt, BS; Church Lay Ldr; Interntl Affairs Seminar; Yth Adv Coun; Yth Center Board of Directors; *Naval Air Sci.*

COX, Bertram Eldred
Hamilton HS; Memphis, TN; Lat C; Lat NHS; NHS; SC; Alg A; COM; Hon Prog; Math A; MLS; *Humanities.*

COX, Bobby
Rufus King HS; Milwaukee, WI; NHS; Cpt, Bkbl; Attendance A; Sports A; *UWM; Computer Operator.*

COX, Brownley Franklin
Sussex Central HS; Sussex, VA (6-186) BC; BS; VP, FFA; Bsbl; COM; *Va Polytechnic Inst; Engr.*

COX, Carla Jeannette
Canyonville Bible Acad; Canyonville, OR (1-21) Band; JV, Chldr; Chor; Drama; Pres, Sr Cl; Secy, Jr Cl; VP, Soph Cl; Bkbl; Mgr, Tr; Bio A; Hist A; Type A; Bible A; Med.

COX, Carla Lynn
Harry Doss HS; Louisville, KY (45-350) Band; Pres, Drama; *Eastern Ky U; Industrial Arts.*

COX, Carla Rae
El Dorado HS; El Dorado, AR; Chor; Pres, Hmrm; Madrigal; VP, Soph Cl; HCt; *Math.*

COX, Carol Janet
St Marys Acad; New Orleans, LA (2-21) Chor; Fr C; Hmrm; Sch P; Span C; MVP, Cr-Ctry; MVP, Tr; *Med.*

COX, Catherine Lynn
Middle Park HS; Granby, CO (15-76) Ann; Chldr; Pres, Sr Cl; VP, Jr Cl; Bkbl; Sftbl; Tr; Vlbl; *U of Colo; Pre-Med.*

COX, Charlene Lynn
Whitewater HS; Whitewater, MT (1-14) Ann; Chldr; Drama; NHS; Sch P; S-T, SC; Bkbl; *Billings Bus Col; Acct.*

COX, Charles Patrick
Bryan HS; Bryan, OH (51-325) Lat C; Co-Cpt, Bkbl; Ftbl; Sftbl; Tr Announcer; *Ashland Col; US Hist.*

COX, Connie Annita
Ahrens HS; Louisville, KY; Rptr, Bus C; Chor; Rptr, Sch P; Sci C; COM; Service A; DECA A; *U of Louisville; Law.*

COX, Connie Beth
Kennewick HS; Kennewick, WA (115-300) Secy, A Cap Choir; Chor; Ensm; Rptr, SC; Pres, Soph Cl; Yth Fel; Fin, Beauty; Fin, Cl Fav; *Cottey Col; Social Worker.*

COX, Darlene Louise
Bellevue Sr HS; Bellevue, NE (191-800) ARC; ARC A; Sci A; *U of Nebr; Nurs.*

COX, Darrell Eugene
Yorktown HS; Arlington, VA; Madrigal; NHS; VP, Jr Cl; JV, Bsbl; JV, Ftbl; Tri-M.

COX, David Layton
Middle Park HS; Granby, CO (4-70) Band; Ed, Sch P; Ski C; VP, Soph Cl; Ftbl; Graduation Escort; Hon Band; Essay A; *Colo Sch of Mines; Geophysics.*

COX, Debbie Marie
Monticello HS; Monticello, MS; Band; BC; S-T, FHA; GS; Hmrm; Sch P; SC; Var C; Bkbl; Tnns; Crisco A; *William Carey Col; Nurs.*

COX, Debra Jean
Wade Hampton HS; Greenville, SC (63-473) Band; Drama; Secy, Hmrm; Cpt, Mjrte; NHS; Secy, Span C; Secy, Span NHS; Cpt, Bkbl; Tr; COM; Hon Prog; Spch A; Outst Command, Furman U Rifle Camp; *Clemson U; Acct.*

COX, Ellen Clarice
Snyder HS; Snyder, TX; Secy, FTA; Rainbow; Citz A; Choir A; *W Tex St U; Dental Sci.*

COX, Jean Ann
Rhinebeck Central HS; Rhinebeck, NY (8-120) AFS; S-T, Band; Chor; Ensm; NHS; Sch P; Span C; Hon Prog; Backgammon C; Mgr, Jazz Band; *Math.*

COX, Jeff Allen
Pacific HS; San Leandro, CA (16-317) Band; Chor; Ensm; Orch; Bsbl; *Arizona St U; Mus.*

COX, Jeffrey Wayne
Centrl HS; Flint, MI; Cpt, Bsbl; Var A; *Mich Christian Col.*

COX, Jermaine
Taylor Alderdice HS; Pittsburgh, PA (30-700) Secy, Bus C; Span C; Alg A; MLS; Type A; Yth Fel; *Wayne St U; Bus Adm.*

COX, John Samuel
NE HS; Ft Lauderdale, FL (222-568) Chess C; Chor; Spch C; Tnns; VofDEM; *Lincoln Christian Col; Ministry.*

COX, Karen Louise
Allen Jay HS; High Point, NC (12-100) Band; BC; *Cabarrus Nurs Sch; Nurs.*

COX, Kathy
Sidney Lanier HS; Austin, TX (124-475) Bus C; Hmrm; JETS; SC; JV, Cr-Ctry; Golf; Tr; Math A; *U of Tex at Austin; Elec Engr.*

COX, Kenneth Ervan
Lasalle Sr HS; Niagara Falls, NY (26-525) Ann; Bus C; Fr C; Math C; NHS; Var C; Ftbl; Tr; Hon Prog; NMS; *U of Sou Calif; Bus Adm.*

COX, Kimberly Sue
William Chrisman HS; Independence, MO (15%-488) A Cap Choir; Band; Chor; Ensm; Hmrm; Orch; ARC; Var C; JV, Bkbl; Sftbl; Citz A; Hon Prog; Most Out; Spch A; Vlbl; Cream o-t Crop; *Oral Roberts U; Humanities.*

COX, Lester Gene
Bryan Adams HS; Dallas, TX (50%-750) Band; BS; Ensm; Orch; Order/Arrow; God & Country A.

COX, Linda Marie
Fairland HS; Fairland, OK (10%-47) Band; FHA; VP, 4H; NHS; Phys C; MVP, Bkbl; 4H A; Hist A; Sal; *NE Okla A&M Col; Ed.*

COX, Lori Ann
Van-Far HS; Vandalia, MO; A Cap Choir; Sci C; Hist A; Sci A; Schol, Creative Writing, A's; *Edinburgh U; Scottish Hist Stu.*

COX, Lori Beth
Geneva HS; Geneva, IL (30-230) Band; Chor; Community Yth Symph; Ensm; Fr C; Tres, 4H; Orch; Span C; Tr; COM; 4H A; Hon Prog; Opt A; Yth Fel; Mus A's; *Mus.*

COX, Lynn Elaine
Taloga HS; Taloga, OK (4-13) Secy, A Cap Choir; Ann; Cpt, Chldr; Chor; Drama; Ensm; Fr C; FHA; 4H; Fin, Jr Miss Pagent; NHS; Sch P; Spch C; SC; Rptr, Sr Cl; Bkbl; Swim; Tnns; Tr; B Crocker A; Cl Fav; Hon Prog; MLS; Yth Fel; Miss Dewey Co; Fin, NW St U; *SW Okla St Col; Mus.*

COX, Marion Elizabeth
Myers Park HS; Charlotte, NC (61-546) BC; Fr C; Ski C; Tnns; COM; HCt; Girls Ambassador Civinettes; Pres, Church Yth Fel; *Salem Col; Special Ed.*

COX, Martha Jane
Belmond HS; Belmond, IA (7-82) AFS; Ann; Band; Chor; Drama; Ensm; FHA; Hmrm; Madrigal; NHS; SC; Thes; B Crocker A; COM; Thespian A; Ntl Merit Commendation; *U of Northern Iowa; Bio.*

COX, Mary Kathleen
Rhinebeck Central HS; Rhinebeck, NY (5-130) AFS; Chor; Pres, 4H; Hmrm; Pres, Lat C; NHS; Sch P; NEDT; Backgammon C; Cpt, Gym; Church Yth Group; Yrbk; Quiz Bowl.

COX, Nola Gaye
Daniel Boon HS; Jonesboro, TN; Cpt, Band; Chor; Drama; Orch; Sci C; Civinette; Drum Mjrte; Christian Action; *Milligan Col; Beautician.*

COX, Patricia Ann
Muskogee HS; Muskogee, OK; Chldr; Chor; Ensm; Sci C; SC; COM; Yth Fel; Sci Contest; Vocal Mus Contest; Piano Contest As; US Air Force Sci A; *Okla City U; Psych.*

COX, Patricia Ann
Bixby HS; Bixby, OK; A-Ed, Ann; Band; Chor; S-T, Drama; Hmrm; ARC; SC.

COX, Randall Joe
Mississinewa HS; Gas City, IN (22-275) Ann; Drama; Fr C; Thes; DECA.

COX, Randall Shelton
Abingdon HS; Abingdon, IL (8-140) Pres, Soph Cl; Bkbl; Golf; HCt; Church Choir; Jr Deacon; Church; Outst Stu o-t Mo; *Biol.*

COX, Robbie Calista
Carver HS; Montgomery, AL; Co-Ed, Ann; Pres, Chor; Crown & Scepter; Pres, 4H; Hmrm; Span C; SC; COM; 4H A; Spch A; Star Student; Span A; *Judson Col; Elem Ed.*

COX, Robert Allen
Mississinewa HS; Gas City, IN (36-235) BS; Drama; Fr C; Thes.

COX, Robert Michael
S Choctaw Acad; Toxey, AL (4-26) MLS; PA.

COX, Robin Ann
Harry Doss HS; Louisville, KY (26-325) Band; BC; Drama; Ensm; FTA; NHS; Rainbow; Hon Prog; Math A; Phi Beta Kappa; Yth Fel; *Acct.*

COX, Sandra
Oakland Tech HS; Oakland, CA; Chldr; NHS; Cpt, Bkbl; Cpt, Sftbl; Co-Cpt, Tr; Citz A; Delta Sigma Theta A; Hon Prog; Most Out; Opt A; Opt Out Tn; Phi Beta Kappa; Pres A; MVP, Vlbl; *UCLA; Nurs.*

COX, Scott Raymond
W Albany HS; Albany, OR (25-300) Band; Chess C; Chor; 4H; Co-Ch, Key C; NHS; Var C; Tr; Rotary A; *Seattle Pacific U; Ed.*

COX, Sharron Leslie
Texas City HS; Texas City, TX; AFS; Tres, Fr C; Lit Mag; NHS; Thes; MVP, Swim; Hist A; NEDT; VP, FCA; WW; *Tex A&M U; Liberal Arts.*

COX, Sherri Renee
Del City HS; Del City, OK (10-67) A-Ed, Ann; NHS; Sch P; Span C; Col Schol; *Central St U; Special Ed.*

COX, Steve Carl
Daleville HS; Daleville, IN (55-75) Band; SC; Bsbl; Tr.

COX, Suzanne Gay
Roy J Wasson HS; Colo Springs, CO (20-560) F-Ed, Ann; Band; Community Yth Symph; NHS; ARC; Swim; Tr; Hon Prog; *Colo St U; Med Tech.*

COX, Terry Gay
Spring Woods Sr HS; Houston, TX (25%-450) Pres, Chor; Drama; NFL; VP, SC; Thes; Spch A; *Auburn U; Drama.*

COX, Thomas Earl
Hall HS; Little Rock, AR (15-415) Cum Laude Soc; Math C; Mu Alpha Theta; VP, NHS; Sci C; Cpt, Cr-Ctry; Tr; NMF; *John Hopkins U; Pre-Med.*

COX, Troy Douglas
Meridian HS; Meridian, TX; Co-Ed, Ann; Band; BC; Ensm; 4H; NHS; SC; Bkbl; Ftbl; Tnns; Tr; COM; Cl Fav; Gov Honor Prog; 4H A; Masonic A; Sal; *Baylor U; Acct.*

COX, Wendy Jo
Metamora Township HS; Metamora, IL (47-210) AFS; Chldr; Drama; NHS; Ski C; Span C; VP, Sr Cl; Pres, Jr Cl; Pres, Soph Cl; Amer Leg A; HCt; Type A; *Ill St U; Ed.*

COX, William Earl
Toulminville HS; Mobile, AL; Bus C; Alg A; Hon Prog; *Ga Tech; Engr.*

COXEN, John Stephen
Morgantown HS; Morgantown, WV (15%-500) A Cap Choir; Chess C; Chor; Madrigal; Span C; *W Va U; Phys Sci.*

COXSON, Sharon Kay
Joseph Badger HS; Kinsman, OH (11-120) BC; Chldr; Chor; Ensm; Hmrm; NHS; SC; Tr; COM; Cl Fav; Hon Prog; Most Dependable; Col Hon's Admission With Schol; *Malone Col; Special Ed.*

COXSON, Tamera Renee
Forest Park HS; Baltimore, MD (2-300) Chor; NHS; Secy, COM; Hon Prog; Golden Pass; Mixed Choir A; *Howard U; Dentistry.*

COY, Ardena Jayne
Denby HS; Detroit, MI; Pres, Hmrm; SC; Swim; Yth Fel; *Ohio St U; Computer Programmer.*

COY, Dean Bernard
Manatee HS; Bradenton, FL (15-700) Span NHS; JV, Bkbl; JV, Cr-Ctry; JV, Tr; Hon Prog; *Theology.*

COYKENDALL, Andra Lynn
Edison HS; Stockton, CA (35-450) Band; Chldr; Semi-Fin, GS; Hmrm; Semi-Fin, Jr Miss Pa; NHSt; SC; CSF; Citz A; Swtht; Gym; *Delta Jr Col.*

COYKENDALL, Ann Louise
Fallbrook HS; Fallbrook, CA; NHS; Var C; Bkbl; Co-Cpt, Hockey; Sftbl; Swim; CSF; WW; 2nd Tm, CIF Field Hockey; All Prep Athlete; *U o-t Pacific; Phys Ed.*

COYKENDALL, Kent Ramon
Edison HS; Stockton, CA (5%-550) Band; Ski C; SC; JV, Bsbl; Co-Cpt, Ftbl; Citz A; Hon Prog; Achv, Hon A; *Delta Jr Col; Law.*

COYLE, Patricia Ann
Brimfield HS; Brimfield, IL (9-55) Band; Chldr; FHA; NHS; *Ill Central Col; Bus.*

COYLE, Richard Eugene
Brimfield HS; Brimfield, IL (7-64) FFA; NHS; Jr Cl; Pres, Soph Cl; Bsbl; *U of Ill; Agronomy.*

COYLE, Richard Michael
Manasquan HS; Manasquan, NJ; A Cap Choir; Chor; Drama; Tres, Ger C; NHS; SC; Thes; Pres, Soph Cl; JV, Soccer; JV, Tr; Hon Prog; Journ A; Kiwanis A; Board of Ed A; Kiwanis Hon Soc; Ldrship Trng Camp; *Penn St U; Psych.*

COZART, Russell Earl
Dyer Co HS; Newbern, TN (20-120) Band; Chor; Fr C; Lat C; NHS; VP, DECA; Brass Player o-t Yr; *Dyersburg St Col.*

COZBY, Ceci Ann
Waco HS; Waco, TX (7-201) Band; Ger C; NHS; Pres, Rainbow; Cr-Ctry; COM; Hon Prog; *U of Tex; Mech Engr.*

COZIAHR, Thomas Alan
Thomas Jefferson HS; Council Bluffs, IA (8-498) NHS; Order/Arrow; SC; Cr-Ctry; JV, Golf; Tr; Wrest; Order/Arrow A; Pres A; Eagle Sct; *Iowa St U; Engr.*

COZMA, Valerie Lynn
Santa Rosa HS; Santa Rosa, CA (20-330) NHS; Bkbl; JV, Cr-Ctry; Sftbl; Bank of Amer A; Vlbl; Christian C; *Calif Col of Arts and Crafts; Fine Arts.*

CRABB, Cheryl Adell
Duncan V Fletcher HS; Neptune Beach, FL; VP, OMEGA; *Fla Jr Col; Nurs.*

CRABB, Elizabeth Ann
Richardson HS; Richardson, TX (24-954) AFS; Drama; Hmrm; Lat C; NFL; NHS; Secy, Span C; Spch C; Span NHS; SC; Thes; Swim; Hon Prog; JA A; Opt A; Spch A; Outst Span Stu; *Acct.*

CRABTREE, Bonnie Marie
James Bowie HS; Arlington, TX (20%-375) Pres, AFS; Chor; Ensm; NHS; *Hardin-Simmons Col; Bus.*

CRABTREE, Carl Eugene
Odessa R-7 HS; Odessa, MO (69-139) Band; Ensm; Secy, FFA; St Farmer Degree, FFA; Band A; Area A, Livestock Production; Sr HR; *Agr.*

CRABTREE, Debra Kay
Oak Hill HS; Oak Hill, OH; Chor; Fr C; Secy, FHA; Secy, Hmrm; Tri-HiY; Tr; HCt; Vlbl; *Rio Grande Col; Phys Ed.*

CRABTREE, Julia Kay
Shawnee Mission S HS; Overland Park, KS (25-775) A Cap Choir; Dbte Tm; Ensm; NFL; NHS; SC; Pres, Jr Cl; Hon Prog; NHS School Pin; *Olivet Nazarene Col.*

CRABTREE, Paul Thomas
Heidelberg American HS; Heidelberg, GERMANY; Dbte Tm; Model UN; NHS; Bsbl; Ftbl; JV, Swim; COM; Hon Prog; Yth Organization; *Ariz St U; Archt.*

CRACE, Cheryl Ann
Charlestown HS; Charlestown, IN (38-174) Band; Bus C; FHA; Tnns; Piano Solo, ISMA; *Ind U; Bus.*

CRADDOCK, Kathy Miranda
North Union HS; Richwood, OH (32-110) JV, Chldr; Chor; NHS; Span C; Tr; Type A; Yth Fel; VP, Future Secy of America; *Tenn Temple Col; Secondary Ed.*

CRAFT, Charlene Ellen
David Douglas HS; Portland, OR (5%-532) AFS; Ger C; NHS; Var C; Bkbl; Tnns; Amer Leg A; COM; Hon Prog; PTA A; St Scholar; Silver Medal, Ntl Explorer; Olympics, Tnns; *Oreg St U; Chem Engr.*

CRAFT, Donna Loulena
Pine Plains Central Sch; Pine Plains, NY; A Cap Choir; VP, 4H; NHS; Rptr, Sch P; NJHS; Teaches Sunday Sch; Very Active Church; *Columbia Mem Sch of Nur; Nurs.*

CRAFT, Jeanne Anne
Assumption Jr-Sr HS; Assumption, IL (4-34) Band; Chor; Drama; 4H; Secy, NHS; Ed, Sch P; SC; Secy, Thes; Var C; Pres, Sr Cl; Tres, Jr Cl; Tnns; Tr; B Crocker A; DARGCA; Journ A; Pres A; St Scholar; Co-Cpt, Vlbl; WW; Prep Tr & Field, Ath o-t Yr; 'Best Thespian' A; *Sou Ill U at Edwardsville; Bus Adm.*

CRAFT, Kenneth Earl
McMain Sr HS; New Orleans, LA (5-95) Hmrm; NHS; SC; MVP, Bsbl; MVP, Bkbl; COM; HCt; Most Out; *Delgado Jr Col; X-Ray Tech.*

CRAFT, Pamela Christine
Warwick HS; Newport News, VA (83-413) A Cap Choir; Chor; Ensm; Madrigal; Bus Mgr, Sch P; Yth Fel; Outst Art Stu; Outst Choral Singer; *Radford Col; Art Ed.*

CRAFT, Robert Earl
Florence HS; Florence, MS; BC; FFA; Sch P; Bsbl.

CRAFT, Tera Lynn
Villa Park HS; Orange, CA; Yth Fel; *Golden W Col; Graphic Design.*

CRAFT, William Kenneth II
Northside HS; Roanoke, VA (211-414) Band; VP, Drama; VP, Lat C; Order/Arrow; VP, Thes; JV, Ftbl; COM; Eagle Sct with Bronze Palm; Best Thespian; *US Navy; Radioman.*

CRAFTER, Jacqueline Louise
Raye HS; Youngstown, OH; Chldr; Key C; Span C; SC; Bkbl; *Youngstown St U; Nurs.*

CRAFTON, Ethelyn Dabney
Blytheville HS; Blytheville, AR (100-300) Ann; JV, Chldr; Sch P; Pres A; Gym.

CRAFTON, Laura Kay
Madisonville N Hopkins HS; Madisonville, KY (1-297) A Cap Choir; Tres, BC; Chor; Drama; Ensm; Hmrm; Pres, Rainbow; Tri-HiY; Gr Marshal; Hon Prog; NEDT; Type A; Val; Eng A; Spell As; *Transylvania U; Med.*

CRAGG, Jeffrey Todd
Fountain Lake HS; Hot Springs, AR; Ann; VP, BC; VP, SC; Ftbl; Ntl Sci Symposium; *U of Ark at Little Rock; Bus Mgt.*

CRAGGS, Robert William
Taylorville Sr HS; Taylorville, IL (1-300) Band; Pres, CYO; Dbte Tm; Fr C; Pres, Key C; NHS; Bsbl; JV, Bkbl; Mgr, Ftbl; Golf; Tr; Citz A; Sci A; Yth Fel; 1st Pl, Trumpet Solo; Fin, St Jaycee Tr; Discip of Christ; Yth Coun; Regional Yth Commission; Pony League Bsbl All Star; *U of Ill; Law.*

CRAGLE, Matthew Bruce
Blacksburg HS; Blacksburg, VA; Order/Arrow; Order/Arrow A; Yth Fel; Stage Crew; *VPI; Nuclear Engr.*

CRAGLE, Steve Paul
Hudson HS; Hudson, IA (4-70) Chor; JV, Bsbl; JV, Bkbl; JV, Ftbl; Tr; Spch A; Yth Fel; St Mus, Division I; 1st Pl, Original Oratory, St Spch; *Mus.*

CRAGO, Bill Graham
Arlington Baptist HS; Randelstown, MD; Bsbl; Bkbl; *Bob Jones U; Bible.*

CRAIG, Brad Steven
Wichita Collegiate HS; Wichita, KS; Chor; ARC; JV, Bkbl; Ftbl; Tr; ARC A; *Harding Col; Acct.*

CRAIG, Colleen Annette
Naperville Central HS; Naperville, IL; Secy, Sch P; Yth Fel.

CRAIG, Cynthia Sue
Whitmer HS; Toledo, OH (33%-991) A Cap Choir; Arch; Chor; FHA; Hmrm; SC.

CRAIG, Dan Robert
Starkville Acad; Starkville, MS (8-50) BC; Pres, NHS; SC; Bsbl; Co-Cpt, Bkbl; Ftbl; Tr; Amer Leg A; Cl Fav; HCt; Math A; Sci A; Outst Fresh.

CRAIG, Debora LaChalle
Northeastern HS; Detroit, MI; Band; Math A; *Wayne St U.*

CRAIG, Gina Elizabeth
Ahoskie HS; Ahoskie, NC (56-243) Band; Rptr, FHA; InterClub Coun; Mjrte; S-T, SC; Var C; S-T, Jr Cl; Bkbl; Swim; Pres, FHA; Band A; St Rptr, Dist Pres, FHA; *Bennett Col; Biol.*

CRAIG, James Randall
Sooner HS; Bartlesville, OK (15-280) Pres, Chor; Key C; Pres, NHS; Bsbl; Bkbl; Ftbl; Kiwanis A; Masonic A; *Okla St U; Computer Sci.*

CRAIG, James Russell
Waukegan W HS; Waukegan, IL (26-450) Band; Ski C; Amer Leg A; Audio-Visual Work; Pep Band; Aquarist C; *UMYF; U of Ill; Bus.*

CRAIG, Jean Ann
Peru HS; Peru, IN (60-234) Chor; Mod Mus Mas; Pres, Rainbow; Mgr, Vlbl; *Ind U; Math.*

CRAIG, Julienne Rose
Hughson Union HS; Hughson, CA; Chldr; Dbte Tm; Drama; Rptr, FFA; FHA; GS; Pres, 4H; NFL; VP, Ski C; Spch C; Rptr, SC; Var C; Pres, Jr Cl; Rptr, Soph Cl; Ftbl; Sftbl; Co-Cpt, Tnns; Tr; Citz A; 4H A; Lion A; Pres A; MVP, Vlbl; Horse Show As; Lambs & Pigs As; *San Luis Obispo Col; Animal Sci.*

CRAIG, Kelli Rae
Marysville-Pilchuck HS; Marysville, WA (15-500) Chor; Dbte Tm; Ensm; GS; Tres, 4H; Hmrm; NHS; Rptr, Sch P; Span C; Spch C; SC; JV, Tr; VofDEM; WW; Semi-Fin, Voice of Democracy; Semi-Fin, Amer Legion A; Fin, Beauty; Fin, 4-H C A; *Wash St U; Eng.*

CRAIG, Martha Faye
Orangeburg-Wilkinson HS; Orangeburg, SC (20-600) Ann; Fr C; Lat C; NHS; SC; COM; Interlochen Ntl Mus; Yth Fel; Page, US Senate; Yth Choir; Yth Coun; Yth Del, General Assembly; Tres, Yth Fellowship; *Mary Baldwin Col; Pol Sci.*

CRAIG, Patricia Susan
Weir HS; Weir, MS (2-50) BC; F-Ed, Sch P; Bio A; COM; Cl Fav; Sci A; *U of Miss; Foreign Lang.*

CRAIG, Pearlie Mae
B T Washington HS; Shreveport, LA; Chem C; Fr C; FHA; 4H; Hmrm; Sch P; Alg A; Bio A; Cl Fav; 4H A; Hon Prog; Yth Fel; *Law.*

CRAIG, Robert Marc
Sparta HS; Sparta, IL (25-160) Band; Pres, 4H; NHS; Orch; Golf; Tnns; 4H A; I Dare You; Yth Fel; IFEC Trip; Citizenship Short Course; Church Usher; VP, VICA; *Agr.*

CRAIG, Ruby Addell
Westchester HS; Los Angeles, CA; Chor; Orch; Interlochen Ntl Mus; *Los Angeles City Col; Mus.*

CRAIG, Susan Louise
Miami Palmetto Sr HS; Miami, FL (25%-800) Band; Pres, 4H; 4H A; Yth Leg; Grand Champ, FL Fair Homemaking; Foley Foods A; *Cumberland Col; Early Childhood Ed.*

CRAIG, Thomas Lewis
Purcell HS; Cincinnati, OH (12-171) Ftbl; Tr; Math A; WW; *Case Western Reserve U; Pre-Med.*

CRAIG, Vincent
C L Harper HS; Atlanta, GA; Bkbl; Hist A; Hon Prog.

CRAIN, Bruce Grieg
Northfield Jr Sr HS; Northfield, VT (15-100) Band; Fr C; Order/Arrow; Var C; Hockey; Soccer; Order/Arrow A; Yth Fel; Eagle Sct; Alt, BS; *Bus Mgt.*

CRAKER, Constance Aye
Corry Area HS; Corry, PA; Co-Cpt, Chldr; Chor; Ger C; Hmrm; Pres, Rainbow; SC; Pres, Tri-HiY; Sftbl; Swim; Tr; Sci A; Vlbl; *Nurs.*

CRAMER, Ann Maurine
Webster Groves HS; Webster Groves, MO (113-470) Band; Ensm; Orch; Sftbl; God & Country A; Phi Beta Mu; Outst Ability Band A; *Eastern Ill U; Mus.*

CRAMER, Gale Marie
Gainesville HS; Gainesville, GA (54-200) Secy, Chor; FHA; Hmrm; Madrigal; Rainbow; Span C; Chamber of Comm A; WW; Best Soprano; Best Span Stu; *U of Ariz; Mus Ed.*

CRAMER, Kurtis C
Glasco HS; Glasco, KS (7-28) VP, Band; Ger C; Pres, SC; VP, Soph Cl; Bkbl; Ftbl; Tr; St Scholar; Yth Fel; Yth Leg; Lead, Jr & Sr Cl Plays; Page, St Legislature; Intr-Ntl Christian Yth Exchange; *Kans St U; Humanities.*

CRAMER, Lori Jean
Greenview HS; Greenview, IL (3-27) Chor; FHA; FTA; VP, 4H; NHS; Sch P; Secy, Sr Cl; Amer Leg A; 4H A; All Amer Prom Ct; *MacMurray Col; Bus.*

CRAMER, Mishelle Barbara
Imlay City HS; Imlay City, MI; SC; Piano Accompianist, Chor; JV, Vlbl; Attendance A; *Data Processing.*

CRAMER, R Neil
Rancho HS; Las Vegas, NV (116-524) Chor; Order/Arrow; Ski C; God & Country A; Order/Arrow A; Eagle Sct; Brotherhood; *U of Nev at Las Vegas.*

CRAMER, Richard William II
Fremont Christian Acad; Syracuse, NY (1-3) Band; Chor; Drama; Ed, Sch P; Pres, Sc; Pres, Sr Cl; Cpt, Bkbl; Co-Cpt, Ftbl; Co-Cpt, Sftbl; Cpt, Bible Quiz Tm; Pres, Church Yth Group; MVP, Ftbl; Academic Excellence A; 1st Pl, NY St Pub Speaking; *Baptist Bible Col; Theology.*

CRAMER, William Orvis
Mathews-Fowler-Vienna HS; Vienna, OH (72-113) Chess C; Sch P; Bkbl; Ftbl; Tr; Citz A; *Liberty Baptist Col; Econ.*

CRAMTON, Angela Carol
Lynchburg-Clay HS; Lynchburg, OH (6-108) Co-Ed, Ann; Pres, Band; Chor; Drama; Ensm; Orch; Sch Achieve Tm; Span C; Spch C; SC; Alg A; COM; Most Out; Type A; VofDEM; Ldrship Committee; Schol A; HR; St Mus Contest, Young Republicans; *Ohio St U; Nurs.*

CRANDALL, Cory Adam
East Sr HS; Duluth, MN; Band; *Minn Bus U; Court Reporting.*

CRANDALL, Kelly Rae
Crestview Christian Acad; O'Fallon, MO (1-3) Ed, Ann; Band; Drama; Orch; Pres, SC; Table Tnns; 1st Pl, St Table Tnns; 1st Pl, Pace Bowl; 1st Pl, Poetry; *Olivet Nazarene Col; Nurs.*

CRANDOL, William Lonnie
MacKenzie HS; Detroit, MI (5-352) NHS; *Lawrence Inst; Elec.*

CRANDON, Cynthia Lucille
Semco Comm HS; Gilman, IA (4-34) FTA; GS; Tres, 4H; M W Alsip Math & Sci A; Resident Schol A; *U of Northern Iowa; Math.*

CRANE, Annette
Lincoln HS; Dallas, TX (2-100) FHA; Most Out; *SMU.*

CRANE, Darryl Kenneth
Conecuh Co HS; Castleberry, AL (1-32) BC; Rptr, Jr Cl; Ftbl; Tr; Outst Stu A, Sou Pine; Christian Ldrship Trophy; *Jefferson Davis Jr Col; Elec Tech.*

CRANE, Jane Blair
Duncan U Fletcher Sr HS; Jacksonville Beach, FL; Ger C; Semi-Fin, GS; Tnns; Hon Prog; Tres, Church Yth Group; Tres, Delta; Astra; *Chapel Hill Col; Special Ed.*

CRANE, Michael Bruce
Norman HS; Norman, OK (140-633) Pres, A Cap Choir; Band; Ensm; Orch; SC; *Okla U; Mus Ed.*

CRANFORD, Gregory Sherrill
Newton-Conover HS; Newton, NC (13-191) AFS; BC; BS; Dbte Tm; InterAct C; InterClub Coun; Secy, Key C; Pol Sci C; F-Ed, Sch P; Ed, Span C; St Stu Congress; Pres, Soph Cl; Tr; Beauty; Chamber of Comm A; NEDT; Pres, Stu Govt; VP, SB; Pres, Church Yth; *U of NC-Chapel Hill; Pol Sci.*

CRANFORD, Lori Ann
Towers HS; Decatur, GA; Fr C; Yth Fel; *DeKalb Jr Col; Nurs.*

CRANFORD, Mark
Farmerville HS; Farmerville, LA; 4H; Ftbl; *La Tech U; Bus.*

CRANFORD, Shelley
San Angelo Central HS; San Angelo, TX (25%-684) A Cap Choir; Ch, Tri-HiY; Tres, Soph Cl; Most Out; Opt A; Rotary A; Rotarian A; *Abilene Christian U.*

CRANILLO, Arthur
Bellflower HS; Bellflower, CA (98-385) Chor; Ensm; Hmrm; Var C; Cpt, Ftbl; Tr; Type A; Mr Spirit of Sr Cl; *Baptist Bible Col; Missionary.*

CRANKSHAW, Steven Dale
Redwood Christian HS; Castro Valley, CA; Fr C; Pres, Hmrm; Pres, Soph Cl; Tr; Yth Fitness A; *Northrup U; Aeronautics.*

CRASKE, Walter Donald III
Dallas HS; Dallas, OR (18-190) Band; Dbte Tm; Hmrm; NHS; Rptr, Sch P; S-T, Span C; Spch C; SC; Var C; Cpt, Bsbl; Magna Cum Laude; MLS; Rotary A; Spch A; St Scholar; *U of Utah; Med.*

CRASS, Kevin Arlen
Pine Bluff HS; Pine Bluff, AR (106-592) BS; Pres, Key C; NHS; Var C; Cpt, Bkbl; HCt; Rotary A; *Ouachita Baptist U; Hist.*

CRATER, Elneeta Ann
Burkburnett HS; Burkburnett, TX (17-286) NHS; Yth for Christ C; Home Ec A; 3rd Pl, Painting, Sch Lit Issue; *Midwestern St U.*

CRATER, Juanita Lea
Burkburnett HS; Burkburnett, TX (16-286) NHS; Alg A; Yth for Christ C; Geom A; *Midwestern St U.*

CRATTIC, Elena Kimberly
Sacramento HS; Sacramento, CA; Tres, AFS; Drama; InterClub Coun; Rptr, Sch P; SC; Pres, Y-Tns; Pres, Soph Cl; JV, Bkbl; *Amer River Col; Bus.*

CRAUN, John Richard
Madison Grant HS; Fairmount, IN (2-220) Chor; SC; Bsbl; JV, Bkbl; Ftbl; *Math.*

CRAVEN, Carol Lynne
John Ehert HS; Marrero, LA; 4H; Hmrm; MVP, Glee C; *William Carey Col; Sci.*

CRAVEN, Heidi Marie
Cooper Sr HS; New Hope, MN (10%-740) NHS; MVP, Vlbl.

CRAVEN, Patrick Thomas
Moeller HS; Cincinnati, OH (120-290) Bus Mgr, Ann; Pres, CYO; Lat C; Order/Arrow; Pres, Pol Sci C; ARC; JV, Tr; Citz A; Eagle Sct; Ad Altare Dei A; Pope Pius XII A; *Communications.*

CRAVENS, Joyce Lynell
Russell County HS; Russell Springs, KY (21-150) Ann; S-T, Band; Sch P; Golf; Cl Fav; Hon Prog; WW; All Dist Sr Band; Spirit C; Outst Bnd Mem; Ky Solo & Ensm Cont; Outst Camper, Band Camp; All Dist Jr Band; *Somerset Comm Col; Med Lab Tech.*

CRAWFORD, Barbara Carol
Goodlettsville HS; Goodlettsville, TN; Ann; Chor; Pres, Fr C; FTA; GS; InterClub Coun; NHS; Sci C; VP, SC; COM; H of F; NEDT; Fr A; Econ A; Tn o-t-Month; Eng A; *Religion.*

CRAWFORD, Brenda Lee
East HS; Columbus, OH; *Acct.*

CRAWFORD, Catherine Renee
Southfield HS; Southfield, MI; Chor; Dbte Tm; Drama; FTA; Pres, Hmrm; Thes; Bsbl; Bkbl; MVP, Soccer; Alg A; COM; Citz A; Hon Prog; Math A; ROTC A; Star Student; *U of Mich; Psych.*

CRAWFORD, Cedric Ronald
John F Kennedy HS; Cleveland, OH; Chess C; Dbte Tm; COM; Citz A; DARGCA; Stage Crew A; PA; *Civil Law.*

CRAWFORD, Clarice Lavonne
Glenn HS; Birmingham, AL (17-115) Ann; Band; Secy, FBLA; Band Ltr; *U of Ala; Bus Adm.*

CRAWFORD, Cynthia Ann
Maries Co R-1 HS; Vienna, MO (8-70) Ann; Bus C; Chor; Drama; Parl, FBLA; Pres, FHA; FTA; Spch C; Var C; Secy, Sr Cl; Mgr, Bkbl; Tr; B Crocker A; COM; Regent Schol; Type A; 4th St Parl Procedure Tm; Top Ten Sr Cl; Most Outst FHA As.

CRAWFORD, Cynthia Lea
Thayer Sr HS; Thayer, MO (25%-60) Ann; Band; Chldr; Chor; Ensm; Tres, Jr Cl; Tres, Soph Cl; Sftbl; Citz A; Pres A; Miss Merry Christmas; Eng A; Soph Pilgrimage; *Clerical.*

CRAWFORD, David Wayne
John Adams HS; Cleveland, OH (6-30) Demolay; *Cuyahoga Comm Col; Teaching.*

CRAWFORD, Dean Clint
Chanute HS; Chunute, KS (10%-180) Pres, Chess C; Dbte Tm; Drama; Lit Mag; Order/Arrow; Span C; VP, SC; Sftbl; Order/Arrow A; Star Student.

CRAWFORD, Diane
Crenshaw HS; Los Angeles, CA; Up Bound; Tnns; *Court Rptr.*

CRAWFORD, Donna Lou
New Bloomfield HS; New Bloomfield, MO; Chor; Sch P; JV, Bkbl; JV, Sftbl; Citz A; 4H A; *Kirksville Col; Legal Secy.*

CRAWFORD, Jane A
Warsaw Comm HS; Warsaw, IN (29-412) Pres, Band; All St Band; *Taylor U; Nurs.*

CRAWFORD, Janet Lynn
Sylmar HS; Sylmar, CA; Ensm; Hmrm; *Cal Luthern Col; Med.*

CRAWFORD, Jessica Allison
St Stephen Acad; St Stephen, SC (1-22) Co-Ed, Ann; BC; Chor; Pres, Hmrm; Fin, Jr Miss Pagent; Tres, Jr Cl; Pres, Soph Cl; Co-Cpt, Bkbl; Beauty; *Med Tech.*

CRAWFORD, Jonathan Mark
Biggs HS; Biggs, CA (2-47) Band; Span C; SC; Pres, Jr Cl; Bkbl; Tr; Bank Of Amer A; CSF; Cl Fav; MLS; *Butte Col; Bus Adm.*

CRAWFORD, Kim Anne
Clarke Comm HS; Osceola, IA (2-109) AFS; Band; Cpt, Chldr; NHS; SC; Sftbl; Tnns; HCt; Needs Assessment Comm; Co Fair Princess; *Amer Inst of Bus; Court Rptr.*

CRAWFORD, Krista Jean
Greenland HS; Greenland, AR (2-44) Co-Cpt, Chldr; Fr C; FHA; Hmrm; VP, SC; Var C; Sftbl; Tr; Bio A; Cl Fav; Hist A; HCt; PTA A; Sci A; Type A; Fr, Eng, Geog, Phys Ed, A's.

CRAWFORD, Lee Andrew
Rebecca Comer HS; Eufaula, AL (5-40) F-Ed, Ann; FFA; Secy, SC; Pres, Bkbl; *Tuskegee Inst; Elec Engr.*

CRAWFORD, Linda Faye
Mount Olive HS; Seale, AL; Chldr; 4H; NHS; 4H A; *Pol Sci.*

CRAWFORD, Lori Lynn
Prosser HS; Prosser, WA; Chldr; Drama; FFA; 4H A; Spch A; *Eastern Wash St Col; Phys Ed.*

CRAWFORD, Lou Ann
Los Alamos HS; Los Alamos, NM (33%-420) Chor; Secy, Drama; Ensm; Pol Sci C; Ski C; Thes; Alt, GS; *Pacific U; Journ.*

CRAWFORD, Michael David
Maud HS; Maud, OK (1-32) Pres, BC; Dbte Tm; FBLA; Model UN; NHS; F-Ed, Sch P; Pres, SC; Pres, Soph Cl; Bsbl; Bkbl; Cpt, Ftbl; Tr; Alg A; Bio A; Chem A; Hist A; HCt; Math A; Most Out; Phy A; Sci A; Spch A; Star Student; Val; Ntl Math Exam; Model UN A; *Seminole Jr Col; Engr.*

CRAWFORD, Michael Edward
Williamsburg City Sch; Williamsburg, KY; Chor; Bsbl; JV, Bkbl; JV, Ftbl; Church Worker; *U of Ky; Sci.*

CRAWFORD, Nancy Jean
Pinckneyville Comm HS; Pinckneyville, IL (7-161) Band; Chor; Drama; Fr C; FHA; NHS; Spch C; Hon Prog; Most Out; Yth Fel; *U of Ill; Elem Ed.*

CRAWFORD, Nilha Lynne
Charles Henderson HS; Troy, AL (15%-200) Ann; BC; Chor; Drama; Ensm; FTA; Hmrm; Co-Ed, Sch P; Pres, Span C; Journ A; Span A; Quill & Scroll; Voice As; VP, Bro & Sis in Christ C; *Asbury Col; Voice.*

CRAWFORD, Patricia Ann
Crenshaw HS; Los Angeles, CA (41-37) VP, FHA; Up Bound; Tnns; *Trade Tech Col; Fashion Designer.*

CRAWFORD, Patricia Ellen
Grace Baptist HS; Decatur, AL (2-10) Ed, Ann; Band; Chldr; Chor; Ensm; Math C; Tres, NHS; Ed, Sch P; Span C; Tres, Sr Cl; Tres, Jr Cl; Tres, Soph Cl; Cl Fav; Hist A; HCt; Sci A; Vlbl; WW; Outst Achv, Hist; Most Dependable; Assn of Distinguished Young Amer.

CRAWFORD, Patricia Lea
Maynard Evans Sr HS; Orlando, FL; Chor; Ensm; Tr; Yth Coun, Church; Secy, DECA; Torch Soc; Pres, Cooperative, Home Ec C; Kgs Daughters.

CRAWFORD, Robert
John Adams HS; Cleveland, OH (3-37) *Baldwin Wallace Col; Mus.*

CRAWFORD, Ruthanne Joyce
Chanute Sr HS; Chanute, KS (10%-220) Chess C; Span C; JV, Bkbl; Sftbl; JV, Tnns; Tr; Pres A; Star Student; Clothing Cert of A.

CRAWFORD, Stephen Floyd
John Adams HS; Cleveland, OH; *Cleveland St U; Mus.*

CRAWFORD, Stephen James
Ponca City HS; Ponca City, OK; Dbte Tm; Drama; 4H; NFL; Orch; Span C; Spch C; Thes; Bkbl; Swim; Tnns; Cl Fav; Spch A; Amer Soc of Christian Magicians; Interntl Brotherhood of Magicians; *Drama.*

CRAWFORD, Wanda Samthiea
Union HS; Union, NJ (300-700) A Cap Choir; Band; Chldr; Chor; Hmrm; Sftbl.

CRAWFORD, William Scott
Riverview HS; Sarasota, FL (94-664) Band; Key C; JV, Ftbl; U of Fla; Mech Engr.

CRAWL, Margarette Marie
Troup HS; LaGrange, GA (15-177) F-Ed, Ann; Chldr; FBLA; Ch, HiY; Lit Mag; Sch P; Tres, SC; Cl Fav; Hon Prog; Sr Service A; Chldr A; La-Grange Col; Pre-Law.

CRAWLEY, April Deadrene
Woodlawn Sr HS; Baltimore, MD; Chor; UCLA; Mus.

CRAWLEY, Leroy
Marvell HS; Marvell, AR (5-118) BC; Chor; Orch; SC; Pres, Jr Cl; JV, Bkbl; Most Out; U of Ark; Computer Prog.

CRAWLEY, Lisa Ann
Chase HS; Forest City, NC (7-160) BC; FHA; Secy, Lat C; Lat NHS; Monogram; COM; DARGCA; Appalachian St U; Elem Ed.

CRAWLEY, Ricky Alonzo
Great Bridge HS; Chesapeake, VA (130-518) Co-Cpt, Band; Tr; 1st Chair, Regional Band; 1st Pl Drum Major, Band Day; Tr V Ltr; E Carolina U; Mus.

CRAWLEY, Sara Beth
West Mid HS; Norman, OK; Co-Ed, Ann; NHS; Span C; 3rd Pl, Span A; 1st Cl, GSct.

CRAWN, Kitty Ann
Twin Lakes HS; Monticello, IN (32-219) Band; FHA; 4H; 4H A; Home Ec Tailoring A; Purdue U; Home Ec.

CRAYCRAFT, Barbara Ellen
Culver Comm HS; Culver, IN (12-100) Band; Drama; S-T, Fr C; Pres, FHA; FTA; Rptr, NHS; A-Ed, Sch P; Thes; Tr; Pres A; Mat Maid, Wrest; Mus A's; Bus.

CRAYCRAFT, Dorothy Jean
Culver Comm HS; Culver, IN (50%-150) Parl, FHA; 4H; Mjrte; Span C; Mgr, Wrest; Dist Off, FHA; Ind U; Bus.

CRAYCRAFT, Mark Thomas
Montgomery Co HS; Mt Sterling, KY (10-290) A Cap Choir; BS; Chor; VP, FFA; Hmrm; Madrigal; Math C; Mu Alpha Theta; NHS; SC; Bkbl; Cr-Ctry; Sftbl; Hist A; Sci A; Spch A; Jr Improvement, FFA; Hist.

CREACH, Ronald Dwane
Ritenour Sr HS; Overland, MO; Chor; Drama; Spch C; Choir, Drama, Church; Preach; Mo Baptist Col.

CREASY, Denise Elaine
Pottstown Sr HS; Pottstown, PA (48-285) Band; COM; Hon Prog; JV Lacrosse.

CREASY, Jane Ellen
Groveton HS; Groveton, TX (3-44) F-Ed, Ann; Tres, Band; Chldr; Chor; FHA; Pres, 4H; Hmrm; SC; Bkbl; Sftbl; Tr; Bio A; Citz A; 4H A; Lion A; Swtht; Yth Fel; WW; Nom, Regional NTL All Star Chldr; Sam Houston St U; Phys Ed.

CREECH, Anita Faye
Smithfield-Selma Sr HS; Smithfield, NC (25-473) Ann; Chor; V-Ch, FHA; V-Ch, Pol Sci C; Cpt, Sftbl; S-T, NJHS; Bsbl Stat Ath A; Opti-Mrs C; Jaycee's Outst Tnager; SSS Marshal; UNC-Chapel Hill; Elem Ed.

CREECH, Barry Lynn
Smithfield Selma Sr HS; Smithfield, NC (2-457) Band; God & Country A; Sergeant- at- arms, Soph Cl; Eagle Sct.

CREECH, Rebecca Lillian
Liberty Christian Sch; Durham, NC (1-9) Ed, Ann; Chldr; Chor; Hmrm; Citz A; dir Basketball; Sch Achv A; Christian Character A; Free Will Baptist Bible Col; Eng.

CREECY, Deirdre Faye
Gordon HS; Atlanta, GA (10-220) Secy, Chldr; Chor; Dbte Tm; Drama; Math C; NHS; ARC; Sci C; SC; COM; Citz A; HCt; Hon Prog; Most Out; ARC A; Yth Fel; Talent, Bowl, Chor, NHS, A's; Spelman Col; Social Sci.

CREED, Dawn Grace
S Haven HS; S Haven, KS (4-22) Ann; Band; Chor; Ensm; FHA; Lit Mag; Madrigal; Mjrte; A-Ed, Sch P; Spch C; Pres, Y-Tns; Tr; HCt; Co-Cpt, Vlbl; WW; Schol Win; SW Col; Phys Therapy.

CREEDON, Richard Daniel
Don Bosco Tech HS; Boston, MA (2-222) Rptr, Sch P; Hon Prog; Framingham St Col; Liberal Arts.

CREEK, Teresa Lynne
Benton Co R-I HS; Cole Camp, MO (3-56) A Cap Choir; F-Ed, Ann; Band; Chldr; VP, Chor; GS; Madrigal; F-Ed, Sch P; Secy, SC; VP, Var C; VP, Sr Cl; Sftbl; HQn; Swtht; Vlbl; HR; U of Mo; Nurs.

CREEKMORE, Donna Faye
Green Forest HS; Green Forest, AR; FHA; Co-Ed, Sch P; S-T, Soph Cl; Bkbl As; PA Cert; Bkbl A, Best Free Throw; 5th Pl, Dist Tr Meet; John Brown U; Phys Ed.

CREEKMORE, Raymond Lee Jr
Acme-Delco HS; Delco, NC (18-92) Rptr, FBLA; Monogram; Order/Arrow; Ftbl; God & Country A; Hist A; Order/Arrow A; Eagle Sct; Appointed Page; Campbell Col; Law.

CREEKMUR, Suzanne
Lyon Co HS; Eddyville, KY (7-77) Ann; Secy, Band; BC; Secy, Chor; VP, FHA; 4H; Sch P; Sftbl; Outst, Mus; Chor A; Top 12; Murray St U; Special Ed.

CREEL, Bobby Ray
Groves HS; Garden City, GA; Band; Chess C; 4H; Hmrm; Sci C; Var C; Ftbl; Porterville Col; Phys Ed Teacher.

CREEL, Doug William
Mt Vernon Township HS; Mt Vernon, IL; Span C; Bsbl; Bkbl; Kiwanis A; Opt A; Bkbl A; Bsbl A.

CREEL, Terry Glen
Winnfield Sr HS; Winnfield, LA (3-122) Parl, BC; FBLA; VP, FFA; Rptr, FTA; 4H; Lit Ral; Spch C; Pres, SC; NE La U; Phar.

CREELY, Charlotte Nell
Copiah-Lincoln HS; Wesson, MS (2-45) Ann; NHS; Ed, Sch P; VP, Y-Tns; Pres, Sr Cl; MVP, Bkbl; Sftbl; Tr; HCt; Hon Prog; I Dare You; Lion A; Math A; Sal; Sci A; Spch A; Copiah-Lincoln JC; Math.

CREESY, Ann Elizabeth
Mainland Sr HS; Daytona Beach, FL (68-430) Band; Off Ed.

CREGEEN, Scott Douglas
Belvidere Sr HS; Belvidere, IL (36-390) Band; Ski C; SC; Var C; VP, Jr Cl; Golf; Tnns; DARGCA; Acct.

CREGER, Melanie Lynn
Crookston Central HS; Crookston, MN; Chor; Drama; Secy, FHA; Orch; Spch C; Hon Prog; Spch A; Yth Fel; School Achv A; Secy, Jr Vol; Drill Tm; Brainerd Comm Col.

CRENSHAW, Eldredge Bryan III
Elbert Co Comprehensive HS; Elberton, GA (5%-350) F-Ed, Ann; Band; BC; Ensm; Semi-Fin, Lit Ral; Mu Alpha Theta; NHS; Sch P; Alg A; Bio A; COM; Gov Honor Prog; Journ A; Math A; NEDT; Ga Tech; Bio-Chem.

CRENSHAW, Frances Jane
Bishop Byrne HS; Memphis, TN (32-187) Ann; CYO; Sci C; Span C; Mgr, Sftbl; Tr; Vlbl; Memphis St U; Special Ed.

CRENSHAW, Lynda Lee
Ky Ctry Day Sch; Louisville, KY (15-65) Ann; VP, Chor; Co-Ch, Hmrm; Lat C; Cpt, Mjrte; Ch, ARC; Sftbl; COM; Hon Prog; Secy, Pep C; Sch Letter, Mjrte; Statistician Letter; U of Ky; Secondary Ed.

CRENSHAW, Michael Charmont
Martin Luther King Acad; Gary, IN (11-25) Chor; SC; COM; Citz A.

CRENSHAW, Thomas Bedford III
Spartanburg Day Sch; Spartanburg, SC; Dbte Tm; Bsbl; Ftbl; Soccer; Tnns; Palmetto Ath Conf Championship; Hist A; Eng A; Nominee, Ntl Tchrs Creative Writng; The Citadel.

CRESCIO, Mary Joan
Randolph HS; Randolph, WI (2-55) AFS; Band; Chldr; Chor; Ensm; Mjrte; NHS; VP, Soph Cl; Bkbl; Tr; Hon Prog; U of Wisc; Phys Ed.

CRESPIN, Andrea Yvonne
Rio Grande HS; Albuquerque, NM (50-1000) Band; Chor; COM; Hon Prog; Yth Fel; Yth Leg; Teachers Aid A.

CRESPO, Ana
Dr P Perea Fajardo Voc HS; Mayaguez, PR; Hon Stu.

CRESPO, Ricardo
Voc HS; Mayaguez, PR; CYO; Dbte Tm; Drama; COM; Eng A; Spelling A; Assistance A; CAAM; Computers.

CRESS, Tina Louise
Carl Junction HS; Carl Junction, MO (10-130) Math C; NHS; Sci C; Span C; JV, Bkbl; Golf; Chem A; Span A; Mo Sou St Col; Math.

CRESTON, Daniel Joseph
Edgewood HS; Pittsburgh, PA (15-90) NHS; A-Ed, Sch P; Span C; Var C; Golf; COM; Hon Prog; Grove City Col; Bus Adm.

CRESTON, Linda Marie
Edgewood HS; Pittsburgh, PA (4-83) Drama; Rptr, Sch P; Ski C; Span C; Y-Tns; Tres, Soph Cl; Mgr, Bkbl; COM; Hon Prog; NEDT.

CREW, Philip Allan
New Hope-Solebury HS; New Hope, PA; 4H; SC; Soccer; 4H A; NEDT; Spelling A; Attendance A.

CREWS, Annette
Kalamazoo Central HS; Kalamazoo, MI; Band; Chor; Ensm; Ski C; Span C; Secy, Yth Fel; UCLA; Law.

CREWS, Denise Michelle
Bartow Sr HS; Bartow, FL (11-300) JV, Chldr; Tres, Drama; Secy, Fr C; FHA; NHS; Pres, Rainbow; Hon Prog; Phys Fitness A; Fr Declamation Red Ribbons; Polk Comm Col; Foreign Lang.

CREWS, Donna Patricia
Montclair Kimberley Acad; Montclair, NJ (45-99) Chldr; Chor; Drama; Fr C; Ski C; S-T, Sr Cl; S-T, Soph Cl; JV, Vlbl; Mgr, Lacrosse; Mount Holyoke Col; Fr.

CREWSE, Dennis Lee
Arlington HS; Riverside, CA; Chess C; Dbte Tm; Spch C; Spch A; Calif Baptist Col; Religion.

CRIBB, Sheri Lynn
E Campus HS; Waukegan, IL (50-450) A Cap Choir; Community Yth Symph; Secy, FTA; Mod Mus Mas; NHS; VP, Orch; Ski C; JV, Bkbl; Sftbl; JV, Swim; Tr; HCt; Vlbl; WW; Mus Performance As; Nth Ath Schol Soc of Secondary Sch; La Crosse Col; Mus.

CRIBBS, Delilah Rhea
Mount Clemens HS; Mount Clemens, MI; Chldr; Orch; Tr; Mich Christian Col; Nurs.

CRIBBS, Karen Sue
Lenox Comm HS; Lenox, IA (10-40) Ann; Chor; Drama; Bkbl; Cr-Ctry.

CRICK, Joy Lynne
Los Altos HS; Los Altos, CA; Band; Hmrm; Kiwanis A; Fin, Kiwanis A; Secy, Church Yth Group; Young Life; Church Schol; Foothill Jr Col.

CRICK, Steven Edward
Truman HS; Independence, MO (120-650) Chess C; Hmrm; NFL; Span NHS; Pres, Thes; Eagle Sct; Avila Col; Drama.

CRIDER, Frances Marie
Acad o-t Holy Family; Baltic, CT (2-22) Chor; 4H; Hmrm; NHS; SC; Pres, Jr Cl; Secy, Soph Cl; Bkbl; Sftbl; Tr; Type A; VofDEM; Fr A; Lat A; Mus A; WW; Eastern Conn St Col; Psych.

CRIDER, Jennifer Anne
Martinsville HS; Martinsville, VA (83-281) Band; Pres, FBLA; FHA; Span C; Norfolk St Col; Acct.

CRIDER, Katherine Hope
Edisto HS; Cordova, SC (35-85) Ed, Ann; Pres, FTA; GS; Lit Mag; Bus Mgr, Sch P; SC; HQn; Spch A; VofDEM; Most Dependable; Col of Charleston; Phys Therapy.

CRIE, Bonnie Ann
Nyack HS; Nyack, NY; Drama; Fr C; French NHS; Armed Services; Bio.

CRIHFIELD, Karen Sue
Ravenna HS; Ravenna, OH (12%-425) Chor; JV, Bkbl; Schol A; Church Tn Choir; Kent St U; X-Ray Tech.

CRIM, Marjorie Lillian
Weedsport Jr Sr HS; Wordsport, NY (9-86) Tres, Fr C; Sch P; Type A; Eastern Star; *Houghton Col; Bus Adm.*

CRIMM, Cynthia Jane
Eastern HS; Louisville, KY (54-288) Secy, BC; Chldr; Chor; Madrigal; Spch C; Thes; I Dare You; *Georgetown U; Home Ec.*

CRIPE, Lisa Anne
N Montgomery HS; Crawfordsville, IN (1-225) Band; 4H; NHS; Rainbow; Span C; JV, Swim; WW; *Purdue U; Engr.*

CRIPPS, Jerry Lynn
Tri Jr And Sr HS; Straughn, IN; Semi-Fin, BS; NHS; SC; VP, Jr Cl; Bsbl; Bkbl; MVP, Ftbl; Hon Prog; Sci A; Drafting A; *Ball St U; Architecture.*

CRISLER, Jeffrey Dale
Plano Sr HS; Plano, TX (275-850) Chess C; Hmrm; Math C; Sci C; JV, Soccer; JV, Sftbl; *N Tex St U; Pre-Dentistry.*

CRISLIP, Timothy William
Clairton HS; Clairton, PA (4-169) Chess C; Span C; *Pittsburgh U; Elec Engr.*

CRISMAN, Joni Ellen
Grand Junction HS; Grand Junction, CO; Band; Cr-Ctry; Tr; Job's Daughters; *Mesa Col.*

CRISOSTOMO, Timothy Alan
John F Kennedy Sr HS; Tumon, GUAM; Val; Band A; Best Dressed; Prom Kg; *MIT; Computers.*

CRISP, Denise Katherine
Shadyside HS; Shadyside, OH; Chor; Y-Tns; Bkbl; *Belmount Tech Col; Nurs.*

CRISP, Donna Kaye
Briarcrest Baptist HS; Memphis, TN (75-324) Ann; Bus C; FBLA; Lat C; Mu Alpha Theta; ARC; Sci C; Opt Out Tn; ARC A; *Memphis St U.*

CRISP, Gordon William
Briarcrest Baptist HS; Memphis, TN (85-352) Order/Arrow; Sci C; Tr; Order/Arrow A; *U of Tenn Knoxville; Architecture.*

CRISP, Michelle Marie
Holdrege HS; Holdrege, NE (37-129) Co-Ed, Ann; Chor; Pres, 4H; A-Ed, Sch P; Thes; Ch, Y-Tns; Lead, Sch Mus; *Hastings Col; Psych.*

CRISSMAN, James Virgil
Allen Jay HS; High Point, NC; Ann; VP, Fr C; Monogram; Sch P; Pres, Jr Cl; Bkbl; Civitan A; *Lees-McRae Col; Bus.*

CRISSMAN, Linda Rae
Burrell Sr HS; Lower Burrell, PA; AFS; Chor; Hmrm; Key C; NHS; Orch; Sch P; SC; Tnns; Alg A; COM; Hon Prog; NEDT; Pres A.

CRIST, David Kerry
Bedford Area HS; Bedford, PA (36-251) VP, Band; Chor; Ensm; Tnns; Dist Band; *Engr.*

CRIST, Desiree Kay
Bedford Area HS; Bedford, PA (79-240) Band; Bkbl; Tnns; *Slippery Rock St Col; Health Sci.*

CRIST, Keith Dewayne
Dos Pueblos HS; Goleta, CA; Ftbl; JV, Tr; COM; JV Ltr; *UC Santa Barbara; Police Sci.*

CRIST, Laura Virginia
Cumberland Valley Sr HS; Mechanicsburg, PA (2-650) NHS; Rainbow; Ski C; Type A; *U of Md; Med.*

CRIST, Mark Owen
Fremont Ross HS; Fremont, OH (3-526) BS; Pres, Chess C; Model UN; NHS; Rptr, Sch P; SC; VP, Sr Cl; Alg A; COM; JA A; Math A; WW; Chess Champion; *Miami U; Math.*

CRIST, Mary Catharine
Van Buren Comm HS; Keosauqua, IA; AFS; Band; FTA; Rainbow; Var C; Bkbl; Sftbl; Masonic A; *U of N Iowa; Elem Ed.*

CRIST, Norman Eugene
Englewood Christian Sch; Independence, MO; Band; Chor; Drama; Rptr, Sch P; Pres, Sr Cl; Bsbl; MVP, Bkbl; COM; HKg; Cpt, Vlbl; Band A; *Civil Engr.*

CRITCHFIELD, Bobbi Jo
Westmont Hilltop Sr HS; Johnstown, PA (40-211) Band; Chldr; Chor; Mjrte; Ski C; Golf; Hon Prog; *Rollins Col; Bio.*

CRITER, DuWayne Donald
Chilton HS; Chilton, WI (15-150) Band; BS; FFA; Bsbl; Bkbl; Ftbl; Tr; *Kenosha-Gateway Tech Inst; Broadcasting.*

CRITER, Phyllis Mary
Chilton HS; Chilton, WI (12-140) AFS; Band; VP, CYO; JV, Chldr; Rainbow; Rptr, Sch P; VP, Sodality; Span C; COM; Hon Prog; Sacristan; Type A; Pep C; Band Medal; Church Lector; Yth Assn For Retarded Citizens; Bike Hike, Chldr, Pom Pon, A's; *Phys Therapy.*

CRITES, F David
Carbondale Comm HS; Carbondale, IL; Demolay; Ch, Order/Arrow; God & Country A; Hon Prog; Order/Arrow A; Yth Fel; Eagle Sct; *Math.*

CRITES, Jean Ann
Jackson HS; Jackson, MO (22-205) VP, Band; Chor; Ensm; Madrigal; NHS; Orch; Var C; Tres, Jr Cl; Tr; Stage Band; St Mus Contest; Big Sister Prog; MFA Schol; Phi Beta Mu Mus A; *SE Mo St U.*

CRITTENDEN, Cheryl Denise
Merced HS N Campus; Merced, CA (10-600) FHA; 4H; Rptr, Hmrm; Fr Jr Miss Pagent; Key C; SC; Cpt, Bkbl; Cpt, Ftbl; Cpt, Sftbl; Co-Cpt, Tnns; VP, St John's Dist Assn; Secy, Ntl Yth Convention; Miss Black Merced; *Linfield Col; Pol Sci.*

CRITTENDEN, Frazelma Denise
Rebecca Comer HS; Eutaula, AL (1-64) Pres, Ann; Cpt, Chldr; Chor; Tres, FHA; 4H; Hmrm; Pres, SC; Tr; 4H A; Hist A; HQn; Hon Prog; Sci A; Spch A; VFW Orator Win; VofDEM; Yth Fel; Cpt, Vlbl; Pres, Stu Advisory; Eng A; *Tauedega Col; Acct.*

CRITTENDEN, Gina Kay
E Central HS; Tulsa, OK; JV, Chldr; Chor; Hmrm; ARC; Var C; Hon Prog; Spch A; Principal's HR; Yth Choir, Secy; Gym As; Soph Board; *Oral Roberts U; Med.*

CRITTENDEN, James Ottis
West HS; Minneapolis, MN (33%-250) *DeVry Inst; Elec.*

CRITTENDEN, Lorri June
Western Hills HS; Fort Worth, TX (1-675) Young Life; 'A' Hon Stu; *Tex Christian U; Psych.*

CRITTENDEN, Robin Lynn
E Central HS; Tulsa, OK; JV, Chldr; Hmrm; ARC; SC; Masonic A; Sci A; Church Choir; Church Off; Gym A; Principals HR; *ORU; Law.*

CRITTENDEN, Steven Scott
McHenry W HS; Mc Henry, IL (29-485) BS; Chess C; Chor; VP, Dbte Tm; Drama; NHS; Pres, Sci C; St Scholar; WW; 3rd, St Sci Fair; *Bradley Col; Philosophy.*

CROCKER, Cynthia Jean
McKenzie HS; McKenzie, TN (27-89) FHA; Hmrm; Sci C; *U of Martin; Bus Ed.*

CROCKER, Elizabeth Ann
Monroe Union HS; Monroe, OR (9-43) Ed, Sch P; Bkbl; Type A; *Linn-Benton Comm Col; Acct.*

CROCKER, Kevin Andrew
Staples HS; Staples, MN (24-150) A Cap Choir; Band; Semi-Fin, BS; Madrigal; Ski C; SC; Co-Cpt, Cr-Ctry; Co-Cpt, Tr; *St Cloud St Col; Industrial Arts.*

CROCKER, Mary Kathryn
Rainier HS; Rainier, OR (4-115) Chor; Ensm; NHS; JV, Tr; Alg A; COM; Math A; Star Student; Type A; Bsbl & Bkbl Statistician.

CROCKER, Norman Lloyd
Cuyahoga Valley Christian Acad; Akron, OH (1-65) Rptr, Sch P; JV, Bkbl; Soccer; Tr; Alg A; Bio A; *Houghton Col; Med.*

CROCKER, Tanya Marie
Overbrook HS; Philadelphia, PA (100-850) Orch; Outst Instrumentalist; *Temple U; Mus Ed.*

CROCKER, Thomas Lynn
Trezevant HS; Trezevant, TN (3-42) Ed, Ann; BC; BS; Bus C; Secy, FFA; Order/Arrow; Sci C; Mgr, Bkbl; Sftbl; Alg A; Amer Leg A; 4H A; MLS; Most Out; Order/Arrow A; Yth Fel; *Union U; Pre-Med.*

CROCKER, Victoria Ann
Plant City Sr HS; Plant City, FL (33%-700) *U of Fla; Art.*

CROCKETT, Carrie
Pima HS; Pima, AZ (1-35) Band; JV, Chldr; Chor; FHA; Hmrm; Sch P; SC; Mgr, Bsbl; Sftbl; Math A; Sci A; Cpt, Vlbl; Eng A; Hon Stu; *Eastern Ariz Col; Nurs.*

CROCKETT, Daphne Christine
Maple Shade HS; Maple Shade, NJ (10%-230) VP, Band; Drama; Hmrm; Key C; NHS; SC; Var C; JV, Bkbl; Co-Cpt, Hockey; Sftbl; *Math.*

CROCKETT, Donna Lisa
Reuben McCall Sr HS; Tallulah, LA (15-120) A Cap Choir; Co-Ed, Ann; Drama; MVP, Ensm; FBLA; FHA; 4H; Madrigal; ARC; Co-Ed, Sch P; SC; Cl Fav; 4H A; HCt; Hon Prog; Yth Fel; Most Talented; Acad Tm A; *Sou La U; Early Childhood Development.*

CROCKETT, Donna Sheri
Reuben McCall Sr HS; Tallulah, LA (8-122) A Cap Choir; Ed, Ann; Bus C; Chor; Drama; Pres, Ensm; FBLA; Secy, FHA; 4H; Secy, Lit Ral; Madrigal; ARC; Ed, Sch P; COM; Citz A; Cl Fav; 4H A; Hon Prog; Journ A; MLS; Yth Fel; Lib C; Pafa C; Singing Group; *Sou U; Spec Ed.*

CROCKETT, Mary Katherine
Colo HS; Colo City, TX (1-95) Ann; VP, Band; FHA; Lit Mag; NHS; Span C; SC; VP, Jr Cl; Amer Leg A; NMS; Val; Most Acad; *Tex Tech U.*

CROCKETT, Mynan Hardy
Harlingen HS; Harlingen, TX (17-700) Dbte Tm; Hmrm; Key C; Tres, Model Cl; Swim; Cl Fav; HCt; Sci A; Vlbl; Art Assn; Stu PTA; Cl Exec Coun; *Tex A&M U; Med.*

CROCKETT, Phillip Barnard
Lincoln HS; Dallas, TX (25%-269) Cr-Ctry; Ftbl; Tr; Alg A; *SW Tex St U; Pub Adm.*

CROCKETT, Rhonda
Pima Pub Sch; Pima, AZ (1-35) Ann; Band; Pres, Dbte Tm; NHS; Tnns; Val; Hon Stu; Eng A; AIA Solo Mus Festival; *Eastern Ariz Col; Mus.*

CROCKETT, Shirley Elizabeth
Independence HS; Independence, MS (15%-72) BC; Pres, FHA; MVP, Bkbl; Tr; *NWJC.*

CROFCHECK, Sandra Ann
Uniontown Area HS; Uniontown, PA; Chldr; Secy, FNA; VP, Hmrm; NHS; Sci C; SC; Span C; Alg A; Hon Prog; Pres A; WW; Candy Striper; Semi-Fin, Miss Tnage Amer; Best Acrobat o-t Yr; Fin, Daffadil Qn; *Uniontown Hospital Sch of Nurs; Nurs.*

CROFFORD, Mark Donald
Spencerport HS; Spencerport, NY (5%-350) Band; NHS; Jazz Band; Top Zone, Dist, Reg, Intr Bible Qz; *Eastern Nazarene Col; Bus Adm.*

CROFT, Sandra Lynn
Terry Parker HS; Jacksonville, FL (50%-675) IXOYC; *Baptist Bible Col; Elem Ed.*

CROFT, Stephanie Joanne
Rio Americano HS; Sacramento, CA (10-400) A Cap Choir; Ger C; InterClub Coun; NHS; SC; Sftbl; CSF; Powder Puff Ftbl; Pres, SC; Church Choir; Phys Fitness A; Chrch Yth Grp; Rio Amer Spirit Soc; Del, Lutheran Yth Conventions; *Calif Lutheran Col; Pol Sci.*

CROFT, Susan Elizabeth
Park View HS; South Hill, VA; BC; Sftbl; Math A; Fr, Eng, A's; *Va Commonwealth U; Dental Hygiene.*

CROFT, Teresa Lynn
Lancaster Sr HS; Lancaster, WI (1-135) Ch, AFS; Ann; Band; CYO; Co-Ch, Chor; Ensm; VP, 4H; Key C; Math C; NHS; Orch; Sch P; Bkbl; Sftbl; Tr; 4H A; Pres A; Val; St Bkbl Champs; Co Pork Qn; Alt, GS; Outst Girl, Grant Co A; 4th, Conf Tr; St Mus A; 2nd, St Vlbl; Forensics Contest; *Platteville; Accounting.*

CROFTON, Deborah Ann
George Washington HS; San Francisco, CA; Hmrm; Citz A; I Dare You; Star Student; *Humbolt Col; Child Psych.*

CROMER, Jon Tracy
Kingman HS; Kingman, KS; FFA; Mgr, Ftbl.

CROMER, Susan Lynette
Skyline HS; Pratt, KS (15-20) Ann; Cpt, Chldr; Chor; Rptr, Sch P; Cl Fav; HQn; HCt.

CROMPTON, Jennifer Jean
Horseheads Sr HS; Horseheads, NY (20%-579) Chor; Fr C; Tr; Regent Schol; St U of NY; Nurs.

CROMWELL, Peggy Lynn
Searcy HS; Searcy, AR; BC; Drama; Pres, FTA; GS; Thes; Bkbl; Sftbl; Spch A; Vlbl; U of Central Ark; Hist.

CROMWELL, Twila Marie
New Bern Sr HS; New Bern, NC (13-436) F-Ed, Ann; Fr C; Math C; NHS; Sci C; NEDT; Fr A; Academic Excellence A; Commencement Marshal; U of NC; Fashion Merchandising.

CROMWELL, Yvette Dawn
Brooklyn Tech HS; Brooklyn, NY;

CRON, Mary Kay
W Jefferson HS; W Jefferson, OH; Band; CYO; Fr C; Y-Tns; COM; Cl Fav; Type A; PA; Shorthand, Calculator, A's; St Off Ed Assn, A.

CRON, Thomas Wayne
W Jefferson HS; W Jefferson, OH (10-120) Hmrm; NHS; Var C; Bsbl; Bkbl; Mgr, Ftbl; COM; Type A.

CRONE, Dana Ellen
Frankfort HS; Ridgeley, WV (10%-149) FTA; VP, 4H; Var C; Bkbl; Phys Ed.

CRONE, David Jennings
Warren Area HS; Warren, PA (33%-500) Arch; Band; Orch; Arch; Golf; Swim; Tnns; Citz A; Hon Prog; Yth Fel; Talent Show; U of Pittsburgh; Optometry.

CRONE, Michael John
Warren Area HS; Warren, PA (33%-450) Band; Ensm; Hmrm; Orch; Order/Arrow; JV, Ftbl; Tr; Citz A; God & Country A; Hon Prog; Order/Arrow A; Yth Fel; Penn St U; Forestry.

CRONK, Beverly Jane
Mason City HS; Mason City, IA; Chor; Y-Tns; Bkbl; Tr; COM; Citz A; PA; Sgn o-t Arrow & Sgn o-t Str; G Sct; Westmar Col; Social Work.

CRONK, Laura Louise
McMinnville HS; McMinnville, OR (18-229) AFS; Chldr; Chor; Drama; NHS; Rainbow; Sci C; SC; Thes; Tr; HCt; Eastern Oreg St Col; Zoology.

CROOK, Becky Ann
Milford Township HS; Milford, IL (13-59) Ed, Ann; Chor; 4H; Sch P; Milligan Col; Teaching.

CROOK, Caroline Susan
Oak Ridge Acad; Oak Ridge, NC (4-30) Ann; Chldr; Chor; Ensm; Monogram; Var C; Sftbl; Tnns; HCt; Salem Col; Ed.

CROOK, Donald Paul
Bridgeport HS; Bridgeport, OH (10%-126) Math A.

CROOK, Harold David
Mossyrock HS; Mossyrock, WA (5%-34) Band; Chess C; Fr C; FFA; NHS; Co-Ed, Sch P; VP, Sci C; Bus Mgr, SC; Var C; Pres, Jr Cl; JV, Bkbl; Ftbl; COM; NEDT; Maltromak Sch o-t Bible; Religion.

CROOK, James Eugene Jr
Central HS; Pageland, SC; 4H; Monogram; Bsbl; Ftbl; Sftbl.

CROOK, Janet Ellen
Cleveland Heights HS; Cleveland Heights, OH; A Cap Choir; Madrigal; Hockey; Ashland Col.

CROOK, Meleta Anne
Star Valley HS; Afton, WY (9-150) Band; Pres, 4H; NHS; ARC; Bkbl; Sftbl; Tr; COM; 4H A; ARC A; Type A; Vlbl; Ricks Col; Nurs.

CROOK, Mickie May
Doland HS; Doland, SD (1-34) Chldr; Chor; Drama; Fr C; Pres, FHA; Pres, FNA; Semi-Fin, GS; Jr Miss Pagent; Monogram; Ed, Sch P; Var C; Sftbl; Tr; Amer Leg A; B Crocker A; Citz A; Hon Prog; Journ A; Most Out; NMS; Spch A; Type A; Yth Fel; 1st Runner-Up, Snow Qn; Swtht Candidate; St Gym Champ, Uneven Bars; Outst FHA.

CROOK, Pamela Lee
Terry Sanford Sr HS; Fayetteville, NC (10%-460) Chor; Drama; ARC; S-T, Span C; SC; Tri-HiY; Swim; Tnns; Hon Prog; Yth Fel; Yth Leg; U of NC-Wilmington; Eng.

CROOK, Tom Eugene
Milford HS; Milford, IL (9-60) Chor; FFA; Order/Arrow; Sci C; SC; Cpt, Bsbl; Bkbl; Co-Cpt, Ftbl; Soccer; Sftbl; Swim; JV, Tr; Wrest; Citz A; God & Country A; HCt; Journ A; MLS; Spch A; Ill Wesleyan Col; Biol.

CROOK, Tracey Rachelle
Capital HS; Boise, ID (70-593) Chor; Drama; Christian C; NW Nazarene Col; Primary Ed.

CROOKS, Sheila Kay
Washington HS; Kansas City, KS (20%-800) Band; COM; Type A; Pres, BYF; Pres, GSct; 1st Cl Citz A; Ottawa Col; Math.

CROOM, Catherine Belinda
Del Rio HS; Del Rio, TX (1-475) Lat C; NHS; U of Tex; Psych.

CROOM, Robert Evan
Del Rio HS; Del Rio, TX (5-750) Rice U; Tech.

CROOM, Trula Gail
Bolton HS; Alexandria, LA (10-270) Bus C; Tres, FBLA; Lit Ral; NHS; Hon Prog; Q&S A; LSU; Phar.

CROSBY, Debbie Waydeen
Fairland HS; Fairland, OK (6-31) Band; Pres, FBLA; FHA; Jr Miss Pagent; Mjrte; Secy, Sr Cl; Secy, Jr Cl; Beauty; HCt; Ann Qn; NEO A&M U; Bus.

CROSBY, James Edward
Metter HS; Metter, GA; Band; FFA; DARGCA; 1st Drummer, Band.

CROSBY, Jeffrey Henry
Allendale Acad; Allendale, SC (3-19) Ann; BC; Chor; Sch P; Clemson U; Math.

CROSBY, Jerry Robin
Las Plumas HS; Oroville, CA (111-280) Ftbl; Wrest; Point Loma Col; Gen.

CROSBY, Kimberly Joyce
Niceville HS; Niceville, FL (200-417) Ann; Thes; Yth Fel; Church Chor & Sftbl; Church Yth Coun & Puppet Ministry; Okaloosa-Walton Jr Col; Social Work.

CROSBY, Larry Wayne
Bogue Chitto HS; Bogue Chitto, MS (3-32) BC; Secy, FFA; Var C; Cpt, Ftbl.

CROSBY, Michael Kevin
Canton Acad; Canton, MS (15-70) BS; CYO; 4H; Sci C; SC; Tres, Soph Cl; Bsbl; Bkbl; Ftbl; Swim; 4H A; Miss St U; Archt.

CROSBY, Mickey Eugene
Simpson Co Acad; Mendenhall, MS; Sch Achieve Tm; Pres, Soph Cl; Bkbl; Ftbl; Cl Fav; Best Offensive Lineman, Ftbl; All Conf, Ftbl; U of Miss; Med.

CROSBY, Toni Laletha
MacKenzie HS; Detroit, MI (25-352) NHS; U of Detroit.

CROSIO, Denise Mary
St Joseph's o-t Palisades HS; W New York, NJ (14-232) Ed, Lit Mag; NHS; Span NHS; COM; Hon Prog; Bio Sci.

CROSLAND, David Patrick
Peachtree HS; Chamblee, GA (11-250) Cpt, Band; BC; Dbte Tm; Ensm; Ger C; NHS; Orch; COM; Gov Honor Prog; ROTC A; Solo & Ensm A's; All St Band; Davidson Col Schol; Band A's; Duke U; Chem.

CROSLAND, Mills Edwin
Richard J Reynolds Sr HS; Winston-Salem, NC (15-800) Hmrm; Key C; Lat C; Lat NHS; Math C; Pres, NHS; Tres, SC; Cr-Ctry; Tr; Bio A; COM; God & Country A; Gr Marshal; Hon Prog; Order/Arrow A; Sci A; Bio.

CROSS, Ada B
Tilden HS; Chicago, IL; Tnns; MLS; Most Out; Ntl Achv Schol; Type A.

CROSS, Brenda Diane
Amarillo HS; Amarillo, TX (110-625) A Cap Choir; Chor; Ensm; Madrigal; Y-Tns; Adv Coun, FCA; Cap & Gown Comm; Sandettes; Secy, Church Yth Choir; Secy, Yth Coun; Amarillo Col; Mus Therapy.

CROSS, Carl Edward
Boone HS; Boone, IA (30-136) Chor; Demolay; Drama; Rptr, Sch P; Span C; Thes; Mgr, Ftbl; Ftbl Ltrs; CIC Conf Champ; Vocal Mus Ltr; DMACC; Emergency Med Tech.

CROSS, Carla Beth
W Morgan HS; Trinity, AL (10%-63) Tres, BC; FHA; Secy, Span C; Beauty; HCt; Type A; Bookkeeping A; Home Ec A; Miss W Morgan; Draughons Bus Col; Secretarial Sci.

CROSS, Charlotte Fay
Westview Jr Sr HS; Topeka, IN;

CROSS, Cynthia L
Salem Acad; Salem, OR (18-75) Pres, Yth Group; Ed, Church Paper; Writer o-t Yr A; George Fox Col; Acct.

CROSS, David Thomas
Whitmer HS; Toledo, OH (33%-1021) JV, Ftbl; Tr; JV, Wrest; Yth Fel; Religion.

CROSS, Dawn Lee
Jefferson Davis HS; Montgomery, AL (105-742) BC; Math C; Tri-HiY; Art C; CYF Pres; Art As; St Yth Coun; Dist Pres, Church; Auburn U; Art.

CROSS, Diana
Dusable HS; Chicago, IL (128-300) Chldr; SC; Tnns; Curator A; Most Out; Ntl Achv Schol; Outst Stu, Archt & Interior Design; UCLA; Archt.

CROSS, Gordon Lyle
Tuscola HS; Tuscola, IL (14-118) Band; BS; Fr C; NHS; Sch Achieve Tm; Sci C; SC; Var C; Cpt, Bsbl; Cpt, Ftbl; Cpt, Golf; Cpt, Tr; Amer Leg A; Cl Fav; HCt; MLS; U of Ill; Pre-Den.

CROSS, Jane Ellen
Claremont HS; Claremont, CA (74-482) AFS; Sci C; Span C; Y-Tns; JV, Bkbl; JV, Tr; CSF; JV, Field Hockey; JV, Vlbl; Badminton; UC Santa Cruz; Ed.

CROSS, Joy Ellen
Darby-Colwyn Sr HS; Darby, PA; All Amer Yth; Band; Co-Cpt, Mjrte; Washington Bible Col; Secy.

CROSS, Judith Geralyn
Robichaud HS; Dearborn Hts, MI (21-183) Pres, Drama; Secy, SC; Tres, Y-Tns; Hon A, Acad; Art A; Modern Dance A; Manicuring Diploma; Mich St U; Pre-Med.

CROSS, Julie Ann
Westview Jr-Sr HS; Topeka, IN (9-87) NHS; Ft Wayne International Bus Col; Secy.

CROSS, Kay Laurie
Choctawhatchee HS; Fort Walton Beach, FL (300-610) Chor; Yth Fel; Yth Coun; Puppet Ministry; Cosmotology.

CROSS, Leslie Carin
Glenwood HS; Phenix City, AL; Band; BC; Chor; Mjrte; Sci A; All St Band; Auburn U; Psych.

CROSS, Michael Wayne
Esenihower HS; Lawton, OK; ROTC A; Camron Col; Mus.

CROSS, Pamela Denise
Mabank HS; Mabank, TX (10-96) Chldr; Rptr, Drama; FHA; 4H; Spch C; Rptr, Thes; 4H A; Navarro Col; X-Ray Tech.

CROSS, Pauline Linda
S Miami Sr HS; Miami, FL; Chldr; Chor; FTA; Hmrm; Sch P; COM; Cl Fav; Hist A; Fla St U; Elem Ed.

CROSS, Ralph Ray
Douglass HS; Memphis, TN; Band; Pres, Chess C; Dbte Tm; Bus Mgr, Lat C; Pres, Math C; Pres, NHS; Pres, Phys C; SC; Var C; Ftbl; Alg A; COM; HCt; Hon Prog; Math A; Most Out; ROTC A; Memphis St U; Engr.

CROSS, Reggie Lamar
Nettie Lee Roth HS; Dayton, OH; Citz A; God & Country A; Yth Fel; Social Work.

CROSS, Shirley Ann
Spencer HS; Spencer, IA; Chldr; Chor; Drama; Hmrm; Span C; Spch C; SC; Thes; Golf; Spch A; Comm Theatre Schol; Outst Actress A; Dramatic Arts.

CROSS, Steven James
Whitmer HS; Toledo, OH (521-974) Var C; Ftbl; Tr; Yth Fel; Defiance Col; Lib Arts.

CROSSEN, David James
Boulder HS; Boulder, CO (350-700) CYO; Arch; Swim; Machine Shop.

CROSSER, Brenda Lee
Iowa Falls Sr HS; Iowa Falls, IA (3-142) Chor; Dbte Tm; Ger C; Spch C; Poet A; Spch A; Sunday Sch Teacher; Published Poems, Lit Mags; Hon Men, Poetry Assn; Anderson Col; Ed.

CROSSLEY, John Henry
Canton Pub HS; Canton, MS (4-216) Pres, Hmrm; NHS; Sci C; Var C; Bus Mgr, Jr Cl; Tr; COM; Chamber of Comm A; Hist A; Math A; Phi Beta Kappa; ROTC A; U of Sou Miss; Fine Arts.

CROSSLEY, Susan Dianne
Central Dauphin E HS; Harrisburg, PA (54-358) Ann; Tres, FBLA; Jr Civic C; Secy.

CROTHERS, Colleen Mary
Marquette Sr HS; Marquette, MI; Ger C; COM; 4H A; Most Out; Law.

CROTHERS, Kenneth David
Chippewa Valley HS; Mt Clemens, MI (25-400) A Cap Choir; Chess C; Chor; Ski C; Var C; Mgr, Wrest; Law Enforcement.

CROTS, Wayne Allen
Summerfield HS; Petersburg, MI (20-120) Band; NHS; Tres, Soph Cl; Hon Prog; Bob Jones U; Drafting.

CROTTY, Cathy Lynn
Valley HS; Lucasville, OH (1-102) Band; Co-Ch, Chor; Ensm; FTA; 4H; Sch Achieve Tm; Alg A; COM; 4H A; Math A; Rptr, Lib; Morehead Band C; OMEA A; All City Band; Yth Sci Conf; Pep Band; VP, Bible C; U of Cincinnati; Chem Engr.

CROUCH, Arthur Weir
Peach Co HS; Fort Valley, GA (4-180) F-Ed, Ann; BC; Chem C; Dbte Tm; 4H; HiY; S-T, Key C; Math C; Tnns; COM; Citz A; Cl Fav; Gov Honor Prog; 4H A; I Dare You; Math A; Poet A; Hon Graduate; U of Ga; Geology.

CROUCH, Gary Wayne
DeSoto HS; De Soto, TX (21-250) F-Ed, Ann; S-T, NHS; Ed, Sch P; Band; Journ A; Baylor U; Bus.

CROUCH, Jean Shelfer
Girls' Prep Sch; Chattanooga, TN (45-90) Ann; Drama; Sch P; JV, Tnns; Visual Applied Arts.

CROUCH, Wanda Kay
Pelion HS; Pelion, SC; Ann; Fr C; FBLA; S-T, FHA; S-T, SC; U of SC; Acct.

CROUCHER, Carol Lee
Oceanside HS; Oceanside, NY (15%-850) Chldr; Hmrm; Rptr, Sch P; JV, Bkbl; Jr NHS; Vlbl; JV Gym; Sunday Sch Tchr; Win CYO Talent Sh; Dance Teacher; Girls Sports Night; Cl Rep, Girl's Ldr Corps; Adelphi Col; Dance.

CROUSE, Thelma Sue
John S Fine Sr HS; Nanticoke, PA (13-297) Chor; FHA; VP, Key C; Rptr, Sch P; SC; COM; K of C A; St Lukes Hospital; Nurs.

CROW, Ashley Diane
Mountain Brook HS; Mountain Brook, AL (20%-300) Fin, AFS; Ann; Band; Drama; Fr C; Sch P; 2nd VP, Church Yth Fel; Social Ch & Chaplain, Sorority; WW; Most Helpful, Sorority; U of Ala; International Relations.

CROW, Billy Jack
Geronimo HS; Geronimo, OK (2-31) Drama; Pres, FFA; 4H; SC; Bkbl; Amer Leg A; COM; Citz A; 4H A; Hist A; HKg; Sal; VP, Rptr, FFA; Drama, FFA, A's; St HS Hon Soc; St Farmer; Cameron Col; Vet.

CROW, Brent Lee
Geronimo HS; Geronimo, OK (10%-25) Drama; VP, FFA; SC; Var C; Bkbl; COM; Gr Marshal; HCt; WW; WW; FFA Chapter, Civics, A's; Live & Learn, A; Cameron U; Agr.

CROW, Catherine Rose
Covina HS; Covina, CA (13-415) CYO; Drama; NHS; Ch, SC; Secy, Thes; Parl, Soph Cl; CSF; COM; K of C A; Poet A; Yth Leg; Girl o-t Mo.

CROW, Daryl Eugene
A C Davis HS; Yakima, WA; Band; Math C; Var C; Bsbl; Bkbl; Cr-Ctry; Yakima Valley Comm Col.

CROW, David Alan
Arkoma HS; Arkoma, OK (10-38) SC; Bsbl; Ftbl; Best Sportsmanship A.

CROW, David Scott
Forest Hills N HS; Grand Rapids, MI; Var C; Bkbl; JV, Ftbl; Tr; Wrest; Med.

CROW, Dencie Jean
Ross S Sterling HS; Baytown, TX (95-550) Pres, Chor; Drama; Hmrm; Jr Miss Pagent; Ed, Sch P; Rptr, SC; Cl Fav; HCt; Jr Diretor, Keyettes; Cpt, Drill Tm; Shorthand A; Lee Col; Bus.

CROW, Leslie Lee
Loara HS; Anaheim, CA (33%-660) A Cap Choir; Band; Cpt, Chldr; Chor; Drama; Pres, Ensm; Fin, Jr Miss Pagent; NHS; SC; Tri-HiY; Y-Tns; Secy, Soph Cl; Beauty; Cl Fav; HCt; Drill Tm; Hardin-Simmons U.

CROW, Randall Alvin
Scotland HS; Scotland, AR (1-20) Pres, Chess C; Math C; SC; Pres, Jr Cl; Bsbl; Bkbl.

CROW, Ronald Warren
Grimsley Sr HS; Greensboro, NC (10%-500) Chor; VP, City Conf; Fr C; Pres, Hmrm; Ed, Lit Mag; NHS; SC; Mgr, Tr; COM; Citz A; Hon Prog; Opt A; Opt Out Tn; GYC Merit Medal; GYC Activities Medal; WW, Greensboro Yth; U of NC-CHAPEL Hill; Pre-Med.

CROW, Sharrie Suzanne
Loara HS; Anaheim, CA (1-600) A Cap Choir; Band; Chldr; Chor; Ensm; Tres, HiY; Lat C; NHS; Ski C; SC; Y-Tns; Bkbl; Tnns; Amer Leg A; CSF; COM; Cl Fav; Flag Twirler; MGM; Miss Ldrship; Mentally Gifted Minor; Baylor U.

CROW, Toni Marie
Van-Far Sr HS; Vandalia, MO (12-64) Band; FHA; SC; Pres, Jr Cl; Gem City Bus Col; Data Processing.

CROWDER, Angela Rosita
Fulton HS; Atlanta, GA (4-150) BC; Cpt, Chldr; Drama; FTA; Pres, Hmrm; NHS; SC; Tres, Jr Cl; Tres, Soph Cl; B Crocker A; Bio A; COM; Hon Prog; I Dare You; MLS; Sci A; Spch A; Claude S Benette A; PA; Beta C A; Spelman Col; Bio.

CROWDER, David Wayne
Maryville HS; Maryville, TN (25%-100) Hmrm; Lat C; Ski C; Var C; Ftbl; Swim; Tnns; Tr; U of Tenn; Sci.

CROWDER, Donna Maria
North Mecklenburg HS; Huntersville, NC (179-430) NC Central U; Early Childhood Ed.

CROWDER, Felecia Germaine
Fulton HS; Atlanta, GA (10%-140) Secy, Band; Ensm; Pres, Hmrm; Orch; VP, Sci C; Gov Honor Prog; Hist A; HCt; Hon Prog; WSB Hon Band A; Xavier U of LA; Phar.

CROWDER, Jacqueline
Jones Commercial HS; Chicago, IL; Fin, Bkbl; Hon A; PA A; Cert of Proficiency; Pepperdine U; Engr.

CROWDER, James Robert
Denham Springs HS; Denham Springs, LA (4-260) Key C; Lit Ral; NHS; Rptr, Sci C; Tr; WW; Chem Rally; Tr Ltr; LSU; Chem Engr.

CROWDER, John David
Montery HS; Lubbock, TX; A Cap Choir; Co-Ch, Madrigal; Spch C; Ftbl; Yth Fel; Ntl Rifle Assn A; Wheaton Col.

CROWDER, Mary Thelma
Halifax Sr HS; S Boston, VA (3-550) Band; Drama; Pres, Lat C; Mod Mus Mas; NHS; SC; Secy, Tri-HiY; Swim; Mgr, Tnns; COM; God & Country A; Vlbl; Duke U.

CROWDER, Todd Allen
Alliance HS; Alliance, NE (13-150) Semi-Fin, BS; Ger C; VP, SC; VP, Var C; Pres, Soph Cl; Bsbl; Bkbl; Ftbl; Tr.

CROWE, Dorinda Diane
Franklinton HS; Franklinton, LA (7-130) A Cap Choir; Ed, Ann; Rptr, BC; Chor; Ensm; FBLA; Lit Ral; Ed, Sch P; Pres, SC; Cl Fav; HQn; HCt; Sci A; Swtht; Drill Tm; Solo & Ensm A; WW; LSU; Elem Ed.

CROWE, Gaylen Rae
Nazarene Sch of Roseburg; Roseburg, OR; Ed, Ann; Co-Ed, Sch P; Journ.

CROWE, Joquetta Juanice
Hamill Road Christian Sch; Hixson, TN (3-9) Ann; Band; BC; Tres, Bus C; Co-Cpt, Chldr; Chor; Ensm; Secy, NHS; Tres, Sch P; Bkbl; Cpt, Sftbl; Tr; HCt; Pres A; Swtht; Yth Fel; Vlbl; Calendar Girl; Most Ath; Runnerup, Soccer Qn, Miss HRCS; U of Tenn; Phar.

CROWE, Karen Elizabeth
Gainesville HS; Gainesville, GA (20-250) BC; Hist A; Hon Prog; PA; Superior Work As; Gainesville Jr Col; Med Secy.

CROWE, Mary Elizabeth
Cashmere HS; Cashmere, WA (21-93) Band; Chor; Drama; Mjrte; Ch, Soph Cl; Mgr, Tr; PA, Sunday Sch; Kinman Bus Col; Bus.

CROWE, Mayson Keith
Sullivan Central HS; Blountville, TN (70-450) BC; Pres, Span C; SC; ARC; Tr; Citz A; Cl Fav; Math A; ARC A; Black Belt, Karate; Eagle Sct; U of Tenn; Aerospace.

CROWELL, Brian Lee
Robert E Lee HS; Midland, TX (20%-600) NHS; SC; Co-Cpt, Ftbl; Ftbl A; Tex A&M U; Engr.

CROWELL, Lisa Anne
University HS; San Diego, CA (33-311) Co-Cpt, Chldr; Cum Laude Soc; CSF; HCt; Magna Cum Laude; San Diego St U; Nurs.

CROWELL, Michelle Marie
Harbor Springs HS; Harbor Springs, MI (20-85) Chor; 4H; Yth Poll Amer; 'A' HR; Midwestern Baptist Col; Secy Courses.

CROWELL, Thomas Martin
Irvington HS; Fremont, CA (10-1000) Chess C; Chor; Math C; JV, Tnns; CSF; Math A; Math Contest; Cal-Poly Inst; Ornamental Horticulture.

CROWGEY, Eric Wayne
George Wythe HS; Wytheville, VA (40-130) Secy, FFA; 4H; Sci C; Tres, Jr Cl; Tr; FFA Federation Pres; FFA A's; Wytheville Comm Col; Dairy Sci.

CROWHURST, Marie Louise
Sutter Union HS; Sutter City, CA (10-98) A Cap Choir; Ann; Band; Chldr; Chess C; Chor; Community Yth Symph; Drama; Fin, GS; NHS; A-Ed, Sch P; Sci C; Ski C; VP, Span C; Secy, SC; Rptr, Sr Cl; Pres, Jr Cl; VP, Soph Cl; Mgr, Bsbl; Mgr, Bkbl; Cpt, Hockey; Mgr, Tr; Amer Leg A; COM; Cl Fav; UC at Berkeley; Law.

CROWL, Joann Michelle
Columbiana HS; Columbiana, OH;

CROWLEY, Chris Anthony
Arcadia HS; Arcadia, CA (75-350) A Cap Choir; Cr-Ctry; Swim; Cr-Ctry A; Bus.

CROWLEY, Chris Mark
Conroe HS; Conroe, TX; NHS; U of Hou; Elec Engr.

CROWLEY, Karen Lorraine
Eastwood HS; El Paso, TX (33%-800) Band; Pres, FHA; El Paso Tech Center; Med Receptionist.

CROWLEY, Mark Jonathan
Maryvale Sr HS; Cheektowaga, NY (3-550) Band; Tres, Ensm; NHS; Orch; COM; Hon Cert, Ntl Fr Contest; St U of NY; Fr.

CROWLEY, Rae Cene
Corsicana HS; Corsicana, TX; A Cap Choir; Chor; Golf; Citz A; All Dist Choir; Friendliest Girl; Baylor U; Mus Ed.

CROWLEY, Richard Benson III
Notre Dame HS; Clarksburg, WV (5-55) Band; Mgr, Tr; Marshall U; Mus.

CROWLEY, Samuel Corbet
Lafayette HS; St Joseph, MO (10-350) Mgr, Drama; Mo W St Col.

CROWLEY, Scott Robert
Cedar Falls HS; Cedar Falls, IA; Hmrm; SC; Swim.

CROWNOVER, Sharon Lynne
Huntsville HS; Huntsville, AL; Anchor C; ARC A; Yth Fel; Genesis A; U of Ala; Med.

CROWSON, Melanie Ann
Monroe Union HS; Monroe, OR (2-57) Mgr, Bkbl; JV, Tr; Alg A; Sci A; Social Sci A; Pres, Girl's League; Merrit-Davis Bus Col; Acct.

159

CROWSON, Prima Donna Pearl
Bethel Christian Sch; Ruston, LA (10%-15) Co-Ed, Ann; Chldr; 4H; Jr Miss Pagent; Fin, Lit Ral; Rptr, SC; S-T, Jr Cl; VP, Soph Cl; Bkbl; Sftbl; Tr; COM; Citz A; HCt; Math A; Yth Fel; Miss BCHS; Most Improved, Most Schol, Bkbl; All Dist, Bkbl; *La Tech U; Data Processing.*

CROZIER, Patricia Lee
E Sr HS; W Chester, PA (40-500) Band; NHS; Orch; ARC; F-Ed, Sch P; VP, Soph Cl; Leo C; Law Explorers; Young Life; *Grove City Col; Bus Adm.*

CRUDGE, Jacqueline Sue
Attica HS; Attica, IN (1-98) Band; Chldr; Fr C; 4H; NHS; Y-Tns; Bkbl; JV, Tnns; Tr; Hon Prog; WW; Tnns A; *Purdue U; Geol.*

CRUICKSHANK, Cynthia Dale
Northfield Jr-Sr HS; Northfield, VT (1-93) Band; Chor; NHS; Orch; Var C; Mgr, Bkbl; Mgr, Sftbl; Hon Prog; *Norwich U; Engr.*

CRUICKSHANK, Elizabeth Leigh
N Kingstown Sr HS; N Kingstown, RI (20%-524) Chor; VP, 4H; NHS; 4H A; *U of RI; Ed.*

CRUICKSHANK, Susan Lee
Cashmere HS; Cashmere, WA (20%-80) Band; Chldr; GS; NHS; Rainbow; Secy, SC; Tnns; JA A; Masonic A; *Secy.*

CRUICKSHANKS, Fay Miriam
Milton HS; Milton, MA; Band; Ensm; Church Bkbl; Schol, Summer Yth Mus Camp.

CRUM, Diane Elizabeth
Edgewood HS; Trenton, OH; Ger C; Candystriper; *Secy.*

CRUM, Donna Melisa
Pascagoula HS; Pascagoula, MS (5%-454) BC; Chor; Ensm; FBLA; Pres, Hmrm; Hon Prog; WW; *Jones Co Jr Col; Mus.*

CRUM, Lynette Ann
Williamston HS; Williamston, MI; Band; Sch P; Ski C; Tnns; Beauty; Citz A; DARGCA; God & Country A; H of F; Hist A; Hon Prog; MLS; Most Out; Ntl Achv Schol; St Scholar; Top Stu, Cl; *Mich St U; Journ.*

CRUM, Robert Lee
Geurnsey Cath Central HS; Cambridge, OH (10-32) Chor; Bsbl; Co-Cpt, Bkbl; *Notre Dame U; Mech Engr.*

CRUMB, Martha Nell
Trinity Episcopal HS; Richmond, VA (5-96) A Cap Choir; Ann; Chor; NHS; Span NHS; SC; Tres, Sr Cl; Tres, Jr Cl; Secy, Soph Cl; Hon Prog; NEDT; T Brady Saunders Hon Schol; Sword & Shield Soc; *Lynchburg Col.*

CRUME, Deborah D
Days Creek HS; Days Creek, OR (2-18) Chldr; NHS; Pres, SC; Var C; Bkbl; Tr; DARGCA; HCt; Sal; Ntl Chor A; *Home Ec.*

CRUMLEY, Cathy
David Crockett HS; Jonesboro, TN (10-278) Co-Ed, Ann; Co-Cpt, Arch; Chor; Ensm; GS; Hmrm; SC; Bkbl; Sftbl; Mgr, Tr; Journ A; Vlbl; Bstr C A; Bkbl A; Civinette o-t Yr; Jr Civitan Gov; *Journ.*

CRUMLEY, Stephen Lee
Robert E Lee HS; San Antonio, TX (333-585) Band; *Tex A&M U; Vet Med.*

CRUMLEY, Tyra Dee
Anderson HS; Austin, TX (20%-600) Band; Chor; FHA; FTA; Tres, Hmrm; SC; Tri-HiY; *Tex Christian U; Guidance.*

CRUMLEY, Victoria Linn
Acad o-t Holy Family; Baltic, CT (2-26) Chor; Drama; NHS; Pres, Jr Cl; JV, Bkbl; Tr; *Oceanography.*

CRUMP, James Shaw Jr
John Shaw HS; Mobile, AL (15-360) Key C; NHS; Bsbl; Bkbl; Tr; COM; NEDT; Yth Fel; Pres Clrm; *Auburn U; Phar.*

CRUMP, John Hunter
Starkville HS; Starkville, MS (4%-250) Chem C; Parl, FBLA; Key C; NHS; Bsbl; Co-Cpt, Ftbl; Sftbl; Tr; Piano Guild As; Church Yth Coun; *Miss St U; Bus Adm.*

CRUMP, Megan Louise
Mitchell HS; Memphis, TN (28-228) Ann; Hmrm; Math C; Sci C; Type A; Attendance A; *Engr.*

CRUMPACKER, Carol Louise
Hillsboro HS; Nashville, TN (10-280) Anchor C; Band; Hmrm; Ntl Teachers Coun; Orch; SC; Tr; Fin, Sci A; *Southwestern A T Memphis.*

CRUMPACKER, Denise Eloise
Homestead Sr HS; Fort Wayne, IN (50-252) Rptr, Ann; COM; Cheerblock; *Ozark Col; Journ.*

CRUMPLER, Priscella Ann
Treutten HS; Soperton, GA (4-77) Band; BC; Cpt, Mjrte; Sch P; Sci C; Beauty; Gov Honor Prog; NBTA Trophies; *W Ga Col.*

CRUMPLER, Tamara Lynn
Sulphur HS; Sulphur, LA (25%-600) BC; Chldr; FTA; Lit Ral; Mu Alpha Theta; Beauty; COM; Cl Fav; *McNeese St U; Acct.*

CRUMPTON, Deborah Ann
Pleasant Grove HS; Pleasant Grove, AL (1-145) Band; Chem C; NHS; Span C; NEDT; *Judson Col; Phar.*

CRUMPTON, Kimberly Kay
W J Woodham HS; Pensacola, FL (27-530) NHS; NEDT; DECA; Tres, Service C; *Pensacola Jr Col; Biol Ed.*

CRUMRINE, David Clayton
Clarke Central HS; Athens, GA; Sch P; Span C; Gov Honor Prog; *Cornell U; Vet Med.*

CRUMRINE, James Lee
Olathe HS; Olathe, KS (45-500) BS; Chor; Community Yth Symph; Dbte Tm; Demolay; Drama; Ensm; Madrigal; VP, NFL; NHS; Orch; Spch C; St Stu Congress; SC; Tres, Sr Cl; COM; Hon Prog; Opt A; Spch A; Yth Leg; Champ, NFL District Debate; St Debate; I Ratings, St Mus Festival; *Pre-Law.*

CRUSE, Barbara Sue
Paonia HS; Paonia, CO (6-71) Ann; Dbte Tm; NHS; Ed, Sch P; Spch C; Thes; Citz A; Coun of Teach A; Journ A; *Mesa Col; Acct.*

CRUSE, James Arthur
Niagara-Wheatfield HS; Niagara Falls, NY (100-450) JA A; Sales C; *Acct.*

CRUSE, Rhonda Eloise
Central HS; St Joseph, MO (80-455) F-Ed, Ann; Chor; NHS; Hon Prog; Journ A; JA A; Q&S A; *U of Mo-Columbia; Bus Adm.*

CRUTCHER, Marshall Craig
Tower Hill HS; Tower Hill, IL (1-32) Sci C; Var C; Bsbl; JV, Bkbl; Type A; Pres, Fresh Cl; Crafts C; United Methodist Yth Fel.

CRUTCHER, Melanie Kay
Princeton HS; Sharonville, OH (140-570) Lat C; Lat NHS; NHS; Bkbl; Tr; Awards Banquet; *Bowling Green St U; Pre-Med.*

CRUTCHFIELD, Debra Lynn
Chilhowie HS; Chilhowie, VA; Pres, BC; FHA; 4H; InterClub Coun; Secy, SC; Church Valentine Qn; Best Personality; Best Citizen; *Tenn Temple Col; Bus.*

CRUTCHFIELD, Lisa
Choctaw HS; Choctaw, OK (5%-300) FHA; Key C; NHS; Co-Cpt, Bkbl; Sftbl; Alg A; Cl Fav; Hist A; Masonic A; Sci A; Type A; Yrbk Qn; Pres, Pep C; *Okla St U; Early Childhood Development.*

CRUZ, Alicia Reyes
George Washington Sr HS; Mangilao, GUAM; NHS; Pres, SC; Tres, Soph Cl; Mgr, Soccer; Span A; *U of Guam; Secondary Ed.*

CRUZ, Anthony
Jose de Diego HS; Mayaguez, PR; Chem C; ARC; Sci C; Span C; Swim; Bio A; Magna Cum Laude; Secy, Conquistadores; Cadettes Medicos; Premio Eningles; Defensa Civil; Buceo, SCUDA; Premio Especial En Ciencias Ambien.

CRUZ, Christie Lynn
Wesleyan Acad; Guaynabo, PR (7-29) Secy, Hmrm; NHS; Secy, Sr Cl; Bkbl; MVP, Sftbl; Tr; Sports Ltrs; *Special Ed.*

CRUZ, David
Eastwood HS; El Paso, TX (25-1000) Band; NHS; Ftbl; Sci A; 1st Pl, Trans-Pecos Sci Fair; Amer Meteorology Soc Special A; Marine Tech A; US Naval Inst A; *Tex A&M U; Meteorology.*

CRUZ, Edwin Geraldo
Miguel Melendez Munoz; Bayamon, PR; Bsbl; Semi-Fin, Bkbl; Tr; Alg A; COM; Hist A; Hon Prog; Math A; Sci A; Star Student; Eng A.

CRUZ, Elizabeth
Eastside HS; Paterson, NJ (27-519) Drama; Ensm; Hmrm; Lat C; Sch Achieve Tm; Ed, Sch P; SC; Thes; Citz A; Hon Prog; Journ A; Ntl Achv Schol; *Douglas Col; Eng.*

CRUZ, Eric Daniel
Consuelo Escalona Private Sch; Carolina, PR (1-38) CYO; Pres, Hmrm; ARC; SC; Bkbl; COM; Hon Prog; Math A; Summa Cum Laude; Faculty A; Loyalty A; *Agri y Artes Mecanicas; Veterinaria.*

CRUZ, Geraldine
San Bernardino HS; San Bernardino, CA; A-Ed, Ann; Tres, CYO; S-T, NFL; COM; Spch A; *Valley Col; Med.*

CRUZ, Ivonne
Academia Discipolos de Cristo; Bayamon, PR (10-122) Pres, 4H; Pres, Hmrm; Pol Sci C; Secy, Sr Cl; Secy, Jr Cl; Secy, Soph Cl; COM; Cl Fav; *U of Wis at Madison; Interntl Relations.*

CRUZ, Juan Jose
Lola Rodriguez de Tio; San German, PR (9-277) CYO; Sci C; Pres, Span C; Math A; Summa Cum Laude; *Recinto Univ de Mayaguez; Med.*

CRUZ, Liliana
Academia Ntra Sra Providencia; Rio Piedras, PR (4-58) VP, CYO; Chldr; Chor; Drama; Pres, FHA; Hmrm; Math C; ARC; Ed, Sch P; Sci C; Spch C; Secy, SC; Tr; COM; Hon Prog; JA A; Sal; Spch A; Sports As; CDA As; Poetry A; FHA A; *Saint Mary's Dominican Col.*

CRUZ, Madeline
Jose de Diego HS; Mayaguez, PR (1-276) Phys C; Magna Cum Laude; Pres, Adv Eng C; *U of Puerto Rico at Mayaguez; Phar.*

CRUZ, Marvin Patrick
Leesville HS; Leesville, LA (50-200) Band; Secy, CYO; Ensm; Hmrm; SC; *Northeast La U; Mus.*

CRUZ, Nora Liz
Dra Maria Cadilla de Martinez HS; Arecibo, PR (66-429) CYO; Chor; FHA; FTA; Secy, Hmrm; Sci C; COM; Hist A; Math A; Sci A; *Universidad de Puerto Rico; Ed.*

CRUZ, Nydia Enid
Miguel Melendez Munoz; Bayamon, PR (4-220) Chor; FFA; Secy, FHA; FTA; 4H; ARC; Sci C; St Stu Congress; Tnns; COM; Cl Fav; Hon Prog; NMS; Star Student; *Univ Puerto Rico-Rio Piedras; Bachillerato en Ciencias Soc.*

CRUZ, Rafael Angel
Notre Dame HS; Caguas, PR (1-136) Pres, Chem C; Drama; Pres, JETS; Pres, NHS; Tres, Jr Cl; Bsbl; Bkbl; Tr; Alg A; COM; Chem A; Most Out; Ntl Sci Found; Phy A; *Sci.*

CRUZ, Raymond Candaso
George Washington HS; Mangilao, GUAM; Chess C; NHS; *MIT; Engr.*

CRUZ, Reina Matilde
Centro Oportunidad Educativas B HS; Guaynabo, PR; *Colegio Regional at Bayamon; Acct.*

CRUZ, Rene Gerardo
Academia San Jorge; Santurce, PR (9-75) Order/ Arrow; SC; Pres, Sr Cl; Hon Prog; *Auburn U; Architecture.*

CRUZ, Simone Lee
Leesville HS; Leesville, LA (35-350) Pres, CYO; 4H; Hmrm; InterClub Coun; SC; Flag Lgt, Band; Cpt, Flag Corp; *Northeast La U; Law Enforcement.*

CRUZ, Sonia Helene
Notre Dame HS; Caguas, PR (24-128) Drama; NHS; Rptr, Sch P; Hon A; Excelencia A; *Lang.*

CRUZAN, Russell Thomas
Edison Sr HS; San Antonio, TX (10-700) Drama; Rptr, Order/Arrow; Thes; COM; Hon Prog; Most Out; Order/Arrow A; ROTC A; Spch A; Eagle Sct; Outst Newscarrier; Military Proficiency Ribbon, ROTC; Acad Achv A, Cadet o-t Mo, ROTC; *St Mary's U; Law.*

CRUZE, Kevin Hill
Rutledge HS; Rutledge, TN (10-150) Band; FFA; Pres, 4H; Soph Cl; Mgr, Bkbl; Mgr, Tr; Alg A; 4H A; Bkbl Photographer; FFA Schol A; *U of Ariz; Law.*

CRUZEN, Linda Louise
Mt Whitney HS; Visalia, CA (3%-500) Chor; Ensm; Key C; CSF; *Santa Barbara U; Spch Pathology.*

CRYER, Susan June
Thomas S Wootton HS; Rockville, MD (10%-380) AFS; Chor; Hmrm; Fin, NHS; Rptr, Sch P; Fin, Span NHS; JV, Tr; NEDT; Church Ensm; Tres, Pep C; *Wheaton Col; Christian Ed.*

CRYSLER, Jeffrey Donald
Lafayette Central HS; La Fayette, NY (25-110) All Amer Yth; FFA; Pres, 4H; Hmrm; ARC; Co-Ed, Sch P; Co-Cpt, Bsbl; Wrest; Citz A; Cl Fav; 4H A; Opt A; ARC A; Yth Fel; Yth Foundation; *Morrisville Col; Agr.*

CSELLAK, Laura Ann
Forest Hill HS; W Palm Beach, FL (10-430) A Cap Choir; Secy, Chor; Dbte Tm; Ensm; Semi-Fin, GS; 4H; Madrigal; NFL; NHS; Secy, Sr Cl; COM; DARGCA; Hon Prog; Math A; MLS; Pres, Yth for Christ; Drill Tm; Nom, Girl's Nation; Choral A; Historian, Keyettes; Exchange C A; Sgt at Arms, Span NHS; *Muhlenberg Lutheran Col; Pol Sci.*

CSELLAK, Linda Marie
Forest Hill HS; W Palm Beach, FL (1-450) Hmrm; Pres, Key C; Secy, Lat C; NHS; Sch P; Tres, Span NHS; Secy, Sr Cl; Secy, Jr Cl; Secy, Soph Cl; COM; Math A; Star Student; Most Intellectual, Jr Cl; *Math.*

CUBIE, Sallie Rankin
Mount Vernon HS; Mount Vernon, OH (25%-407) MVP, Chldr; Fr C; Secy, Mod Mus Mas; Sftbl; Tr; Hon Prog; Sci A; Secy, Jr Beethoven C; Mus, Eng, A's; Spelling Champ; Cabin Qn, Church Camp; *E Nazarene Col; Eng Lit.*

CUBINE, Carla Gail
Bible Baptist Christian Sch; Wichita Falls, TX; Chor; S-T, SC; *Arlington Baptist Col; Mus.*

CUCCHIARA, Francene
St Joseph Acad; McSherrystown, PA (1-14) Co-Cpt, Chldr; Chor; Rptr, Sch P; SC; VP, Soph Cl; Hon Prog; *Art.*

CUCCHIARA, Laura Bernice
St Joseph Acad; McSherrystown, PA (2-15) Chor; Rptr, Sch P; JV, Bkbl; Hon Prog; Vlbl; *Ocean Engr.*

CUDA, Tanya Laine
Liberty Jr-Sr HS; Liberty, PA (1-61) Band; Co-Cpt, Chldr; Chor; Ensm; VP, Ger C; Ed, Sch P; Tnns; Math A; Most Out; *Boston U; Journ.*

CUDNEY, Catherine Claire
Winston Churchill; Potomac, MD (1-585) Hmrm; Key C; Tres, Span C; SC; Cr-Ctry; Tr; COM; Hon Prog; Yth Fel; *Science.*

CUDWORTH, Melissa Clo
Englewood Christian HS; Independence, MO; Chor; Hmrm; Pol Sci C; Span C; *Rheama Col; Religion.*

CUELHO, Deborah Ann
Riverdale HS; Riverdale, CA; FFA; 4H; *Fresno St U; Bus Mgt.*

CUEN, Patricia Marie
Castle Park HS; Chula Vista, CA (30-425) Hmrm; St Stu Congress; CSF; Drill Tm; Squire of Pep; *San Diego Col of Bus; Bus.*

CUEVAS, Angel
Dra M Cadilla HS; Arecibo, PR (60-636) Bsbl; Bkbl.

CUEVAS, Carmen Delia
Luis Munoz Marin HS; Cabo Rojo, PR (10-200) Chor; FBLA; FHA; Sch P; COM; Art A; *Bilingual Executive Sec.*

CUEVAS, Patricia
Diamond Hill-Jarvis HS; Ft Worth, TX (6-171) Band; CYO; *TCJC; Elem Ed.*

CUEVAS, Tammy Lee
Hancock N Central HS; Pass Christian, MS (8-90) Band; BC; S-T, CYO; Chldr; FHA; 4H; Mjrte; Tr; Beauty; Cl Fav; HCt; Wendell Ladner Mem Bowl Qn; *Architecture.*

CUGINI, Crissa Ann
Forest Ridge Sch; Bellevue, WA; A Cap Choir; Chor; Cum Laude Soc; Lit Mag; NHS; Pres, Var C; JV, Bkbl; Hon Prog; Math A; NEDT; Rensselaer A; MVP, Vlbl; Ntl Fr Contest.

CULBERSON, Donna Kay
R L Turner HS; Carrollton, TX; A Cap Choir; Chor; Ensm; Madrigal; SC; Coun of Teach A; Hon Prog; Outst Chor Mus; All Region Choir; Solo & Ensm UIL Medals; *Mus.*

CULBERSON, Jeffery Lynn
Poway HS; Poway, CA; Arch; Apathy A; *Mus.*

CULBERSON, Steven Seals
Goodwater HS; Goodwater, AL (4-38) Ann; Band; BC; Chor; Ch, FFA; FNA; FTA; 4H; Math C; Phys C; Pres, Sr Cl; Arch; Bsbl; JV, Bkbl; Co-Cpt, Ftbl; Sftbl; 4H A; Varsity Ltr, Ftbl; *Alex City St Jr Col; Bus.*

CULBERT, Imelda Sara
Andover HS; Andover, MA (210-510) Band; Chor; Dbte Tm; Drama; Hmrm; Mjrte; Sch P; Bkbl; Cpt, Soccer; Tr; Mgr, Gym; Faculty A; Foods A; Sch Newspaper A; Dbte A; *Mass St Col; Psych.*

CULBERTSON, Carol Anne
W Bloomfield HS; W Bloomfield, MI; InterClub Coun; Ed, Sch P; SC; Var C; Ed, Jr Cl; Bkbl; Sftbl; Tnns; CSF; COM; Journ A; Rotary A; *Journ.*

CULBERTSON, Cynthia Kay
Leeton HS; Leeton, MO (1-21) Cpt, Chldr; Chor; Ensm; Rptr, FHA; Secy, 4H; Co-Ed, Sch P; Co-Ed, Sci C; VP, SC; Pres, Sr Cl; VP, Jr Cl; Rptr, Soph Cl; Sftbl; Spch A; Val; *Central Mo St U.*

CULBERTSON, Jean Kay
Delavan HS; Delavan, IL (4-63) Band; Chor; Drama; 4H; VP, Jr Cl; VP, Soph Cl; Bkbl; Sftbl; Tr; 4H A; Hon Prog; Cpt, Vlbl; Yrbk; *Phys Ed.*

CULBERTSON, Richard Maron
Lucy Coffin Ragsdale HS; Greensboro, NC (73-385) BC; *Psych.*

CULBERTSON, Terry Lee
Colo HS; Colo City, TX (6-95) All Amer Yth; Band; 4H; Tres, NHS; Sch P; Bkbl; JV, Golf; Tnns; Nuclear Sci Symposium, U of Tex; *Angelo St U; Chem.*

CULBREATH, Arnold Marcus
Aiken Sr HS; Cincinnati, OH; Band; Soccer; *Bradley U; Drafting.*

CULBREATH, Martha Sheila
Chester HS; Chester, PA (5-673) Ann; NHS; Up Bound; *Widener Col; Engr.*

CULBREATH, Randall Lee
Towering Oaks Baptist HS; Memphis, TN; Band; Demolay; Drama; Fr C; Lat C; Orch; Order/Arrow; Sch P; God & Country A; Eagle Sct; *Memphis St U; Agr.*

CULBREATH, Totsy Thescia Carol
Towering Oaks Baptist HS; Memphis, TN; Chldr; Chor; Drama; Orch; S-T, Jr Cl; Yth Fel; Key C; Swtht; Demolay Swtht; *Memphis St U; Sociology.*

CULBRETH, Helen Carol
Smithfield-Selma Sr HS; Smithfield, NC (10-355) Ann; GS; NHS; Span C; *E Carolina U; Math.*

CULHANE, Joseph Raymond III
Marin Cath HS; Kentfield, CA (40-156) CYO; Chess C; Chor; Fr C; NHS; Rptr, Sch P; Ski C; Hockey; Soccer; Hon Prog; *U of Calif; Psych.*

CULLEN, Catherine Ann
Southside HS; Fort Smith, AR (29-430) NHS; *U of Ark; Acct.*

CULLEN, David Alan
John Marshall HS; Milwaukee, WI (300-700) Chess C; Math C; Sftbl; Tr; Hon Prog; Math A; Sci A; Yth Fel; Commission on Missions; *U of Wis; Pol Sci.*

CULLEN, David Allan
Two Harbors HS; Two Harbors, MN (25-174) Band; Chor; NHS; Rptr, Sch P; Spch C; *Med.*

CULLEN, David Allen
John Marshall HS; Milwaukee, WI (300-698) Chess C; Math C; Sftbl; Tr; Hon Prog; JA A; Math A; Sci A; Yth Fel; Commission on Missions; Sftbl All-Star; *U of Wis at Madison; Pol Sci.*

CULLEY, Katie E
Hillsboro HS; Nashville, TN; A Cap Choir; Band; BC; Drama; Fr C; Hmrm; Ed, Sch P; NEDT; Drama A; *Anthropology.*

CULLINAN, Margaret Eileen
St Pius X HS; Pottstown, PA; Chor; A-Ed, Sch P; Span C; COM; Hon Prog; Type A; Lion's Interntl Exchange Stu; *Guynedd-Mercy Col; Nurs.*

CULLINS, Kimberly Marie
Queen City HS; Queen City, TX; Ann; Chldr; FHA; NHS; Sch P; Sci C; Tres, Soph Cl; Bkbl; Cl Fav; HCt.

CULLISON, Gary Wayne
Shawnee HS; Shawnee, OK (7-375) FTA; Ger C; Orch; Pres, Royal Ambassadors; Orch A; Hnd Bell Chr; Childrens Chrch Pian; St Win, Elks Essay Contest; All-St Orch; Ok Hist A; 4 0 Avg A; *Okla Baptist U; Hist.*

CULP, Christopher Mark
Baylor HS; Chattanooga, TN (7-70) AFS; Ann; Chess C; Lit Mag; Rptr, Sch P; VP, Span C; VP, Span NHS; Soccer; Tr; *Emory U; Med.*

CULP, Janice Sue
Lewis Cass Jr Sr HS; Walton, IN (75-150) Ann; Ger C; Math C; A-Ed, Sch P; Bkbl; Pep C; *Wrights Beauty Col; Beauty Operator.*

CULP, Scott Daryl
Campbell-Tintah HS; Campbell, MN (10-41) FFA; Tr; Acct A's; *Moorhead Area Vo-tech Col; Elec.*

CULPAN, Susan G
Henry Hudson Reg HS; Highlands, NJ (40-120) Band; Cpt, Chldr; Chor; Hmrm; Mjrte; SC; Bkbl; Sftbl; Pres A; Type A; Honorable Mention Shore Conf Bkbl; Hon Men, Shore Conf Bkbl; *Brookdale Comm Col; Phys Ed.*

CULPEPPER, Anglie LaVon
Compton Sr HS; Compton, CA (25%-850) FHA; Hmrm; Sch P; Sci C; Span C; SC; CSF; Citz A; Journ A; *San Diego St Col; Psych.*

CULPEPPER, Bethna Gay
Warren Central HS; Vicksburg, MS (2-340) Band; Dbte Tm; Hmrm; Secy, Lat C; Mu Alpha Theta; Rptr, NHS; SC; DARGCA; Hist A; MLS; NMS; Yth Fel; Page, Miss Legislature; *MSU; Pre-Law.*

CULPEPPER, Celeste Renee
Sharkey-Issaquena Acad; Rolling Fork, MS (20-30) Ann; Band; Chor; Sch P; SC; Y-Tns; Citz A; HCt; Bandsmen A; *MSU; Ed.*

CULPEPPER, Charles Brian
Fountain Lake HS; Hot Springs, AR (3-42) BC; BS; Tres, Sr Cl; Co-Cpt, Bkbl; Math A; HCt; MLS; Mr FLHS; Most Outst Sr; All Dist Bkbl; Highest % Field Goal Shooter; *United Elec Inst; Elec.*

CULPEPPER, Darlene Annette
New Caney HS; Porter, TX; Band; Drama; Ensm; Rptr, 4H; JETS; Lit Ral; NFL; NHS; Spch C; Thes; 4H A; Hon Prog; Sci A; Spch A; VofDEM; St Solo & Ensm; UIL Ready Writing; *Sam Houston U; Elem Ed.*

CULPEPPER, Kim Elizabeth
McLean HS; McLean, VA (147-408) Chldr; Jr Miss Pagent; Swim; Mgr, Tr; Mgr, Wrest; HCt; Hon Prog; JV, Gym; Mgr, Rugby; Heather A; *N Va Comm Col; Psych.*

CULPEPPER, Nan Victoria
Marshall Sr HS; Marshall, TX (25-450) Rptr, A Cap Choir; FTA; Mod Mus Mas; NHS; Tnns; *Stephen F Austin St U; Dentistry.*

CULPEPPER, Patricia Ann
Warren HS; Warren, AR (28-144) A Cap Choir; Band; Chor; Ensm; All-Regional Choir 8th Position; Most Impressive 1st Yr Band Member; 1st & 3rd, 1st All-Region Jr Bans; *Ouachita Baptist U; Math.*

CULPEPPER, Sherry Lynn
Denison Sr HS; Denison, TX (70-375) Drama; FHA; FTA; HiY; Hmrm; InterClub Coun; Key C; Rainbow; Span C; Spch C; SC; Y-Tns; Cpt, Sftbl; Cl Fav; HCt; Swtht; Friendliest; Miss Congeniality; Off, Drill Tm; VP, Church Yth; *Tex Christian U; Interior Design.*

CULPEPPER, Terrance Mark
Fountain Lake HS; Hot Springs, AR;

CULVER, Joan Ann
Benton Sr HS; Benton, AR; Cl Fav; Kiwanis A; Yth Fel; 1st Lieutenant, Drill Tm; *Nurs.*

CULVERSON, Marilyn Kay
S Gwinnett HS; Snellville, GA; *Dekalb Tech Col; Art.*

CUMBERLAND, Lisa Ann
Glasgow HS; Glasgow, KY (15%-140) A Cap Choir; Band; BC; Pres, Chor; Pres, FHA; Madrigal; ARC; SC; Tres, Tri-HiY; Citz A; Yth Fel; Handbell Choir; Choir A; PA A; Yng Singers; Tres & Sec UMYF; St & Ntl Handbell Festival; Jr Degree, Chapter Degree, FHA; *U of Ky; Phar.*

CUMBERWORTH, Shannon Lynn
Eaton Rapids Sr HS; Eaton Rapids, MI (11-243) Chor; 4H; NHS; Y-Tns; 4H A; Hon Prog; MBSA Schol; A-B HR; PA; *Lansing Bus U; Legal Secy.*

CUMBIE, James Claude
Apalachicola HS; Apalachicola, FL (1-60) BC; BS; Chess C; Pres, 4H; Hmrm; InterAct C; InterClub Coun; St Stu Congress; Pres, Jr Cl; Citz A; 4H A; I Dare You; Parl, Rptr; Stu Coun; Jayce Qz Bowl; Sch Spelling Bee Champ; Fin, 4-H Statewide Congress; Pres, 4-H Dist 2; Am Leg, Rep, BS; *U of Fla; Law.*

CUMMELIN, Barbara Rosann
John F Kennedy HS; Bloomington, MN (80-600) F-Ed, Ann; Chor; NHS; JV, Tnns; Journ A; *Normandale Jr Col; Lib Arts.*

CUMMER, Nancy Louise
Lutheran HS W; Detroit, MI (1-160) NHS; Co-Cpt, Bkbl; Sftbl; Tr; Val; Phi Beta Kappa Cert of Commend; *Northern Mich U; Nurs.*

CUMMING, Alan Lee
St Edward Pub Sch; St Edward, NE (33%-26) Chor; Parl, FFA 4H; Bkbl.

CUMMING, Scott Dean
St Edward Pub Sch; St Edward, NE (3-30) Ann; Chor; Drama; Rptr, FFA; Pres, 4H; SC; Thes; Pres, Jr Cl; COM; 4H A; Hon Prog; Swtht; Hon Band; *Bus Adm.*

CUMMING, William Thompson
Cleveland Heights HS; Cleveland Heights, OH (1-860) Band; Orch; Hon Prog; NMS; Phi Beta Kappa; All St Orch; Sergeant, Band; Cpt, Stage Crew; Yth Rep, Church Cabinet; *Oberlin Col; Pre-Med.*

CUMMINGS, Brian Joseph
Quincy Notre Dame HS; Quincy, IL; Band; Chor; NHS; Order/Arrow; Order/Arrow A; *Quincy Col; Mus.*

CUMMINGS, Daniel Scott
Harry Hill HS; Lansing, MI (2%-400) Band; Chem C; NHS; Var C; Bsbl; Co-Cpt, Bkbl; Co-Cpt, Ftbl; Amer Leg A; Citz A; Hist A; Sci A; Hinman A; Eng A; Band Director's A; *Wheaton Col; Med.*

CUMMINGS, Jennifer Ann
Central HS; Thomasville, GA; FHA; Tri-HiY.

CUMMINGS, Karen Denise
Central HS; Thomasville, GA; Co-Cpt, Band; Hmrm; Tri-HiY; Stu o-t Month.

CUMMINGS, Kevin Allen
Benson Polytech HS; Portland, OH (20-375) NHS; Yth Fel; Church Bus Ministry; Sunday Sch Teacher; Ldr, Yth Group; Ldr, Yth Group; Campus Crusade for Christ; *Oreg St U; Civil Engr.*

CUMMINGS, Kimberlyn Sheryl
Jefferson HS; Portland, OR; Tres, Church Yth Group; Zoo Vol; Cert of Achv; *Judson Col; Bus.*

CUMMINGS, Marcus Eldridge
San Diego HS; San Diego, CA; Bsbl; Ftbl; Swim; Tr; Wrest; Citz A; Boys C; Men Action Group; Yth Choir; *UCLA.*

CUMMINGS, Randy Bruce
Buffalo Sr HS; Buffalo, MN (33%-220) Band; Ski C; VP, SC; Var C; Co-Cpt, Ftbl; Tr; Wrest; H of F; HCt; Yth Fel; *St Scholastica Col; Phys Therapy.*

CUMMINGS, Sheena Ann
Middleton HS; Caldwell, ID (16-90) Band; Chor; FHA; NHS; Sch P; Secy, SC; Type A; VofDEM; Gym; Hon Choir; Choir A; *Northwestern Col; Mass Communications.*

CUMMINS, Cristi Sue
Putnam City W HS; Oklahoma City, OK (29-650) Chldr; Fin, GS; Lat C; NHS; SC; Mu Alpha Theta; Alg A; Cl Fav; Spch A; Ventriloquist; Gym; Outst Contribution, Pep C; Most Loveable Girl; *UCLA; Psych.*

CUMMINS, Debbie Lenise
Grossmont HS; La Mesa, CA; A Cap Choir; Chor; Drama; Ski C; Pres A; Lib A; *Fashion Inst; Merchandising.*

CUMMINS, Deborah Lynn
Robert E Lee HS; Tyler, TX (20%-624) A Cap Choir; NHS; COM; Hist A; *Tyler Jr Col; Voice.*

CUMMINS, James R
Kosciusko HS; Kosciusko, MS (10-110) Ftbl; Math A.

CUMMINS, Margie Sue
Kosciusko HS; Kosciusko, MS (25%-125) Ann; *Miss St U; Bus Ed.*

CUMMINS, Myra Jan
Colonial Hills Christian HS; East Point, GA (20-45) Band; Chor; *Maranatha Col; Ed.*

CUMMINS, Paul Frederick
Balboa HS; San Francisco, CA (5%-400) Pres, Hmrm; SC; Pres, Sr Cl; CSF; Hon Prog; Phi Beta Sigma A; One Hundred Buccaneers; Church Yth Choir; Yth Assn; *UC Berkeley; Archt Engr.*

CUMMINS, Peter Scott
Ballard HS; Seattle, WA (75-493) Chor; Ger C; NHS; Order/Arrow; A-Ed, Sch P; Ski C; SC; Cr-Ctry; Cpt, Soccer; God & Country A; Hon Prog; Order/Arrow A; Sal; Eagle Sct; Stu o-t Mo; *Pacific Lutheran U; Bus Adm.*

CUMMINS, Susan
DeSoto HS; W Helena, AR (15-48) Band; BC; Chor; Drama; Sch P; Sci C; *Hendrix Col; Elem Ed.*

CUNDIFF, Carolyn Denise
Bel Air Sr HS; Bel Air, MD; *Towson St U; Fine Art.*

CUNEGIN, Patricia Marie
Roosevelt HS; Gary, IN; Chor; NHS; Y-Tns; Citz A; Hon Prog; *Ind U; Bus Mgt.*

CUNNINGHAM, Anne Marie
Lawrence Central HS; Indianapolis, IN; Hmrm; SC; Tri-HiY; Tr; Pres, Yth Fel; Flag-Rifle Corps; Unitedspirit C; Tr Chldr, Essay & Religious A's; *Ind U; Elem Ed.*

CUNNINGHAM, Carol Ann
S Central Jr-Sr HS; Elizabeth, IN (2-67) Chor; Fr C; Bus Mgr, FHA; GS; Pres, 4H; Mu Alpha Theta; NHS; Bus Mgr, Jr Cl; Alg A; Bio A; DARGCA; 4H A; Hist A; Math A; Sci A; Eng A; Home Ec A; Chor A; St Police Career Camp; Top 3 Schol Achv; PA A; *Ind U; Govt Service.*

CUNNINGHAM, Cynthia Gail
Harding Acad; Memphis, TN; FHA; Key C; Math C; Sci C; SC; Tr; Cl Fav; HCt; *Biol.*

CUNNINGHAM, Don Ray
North HS; Bakersfield, CA (10-400) VP, Band; Semi-Fin, Dbte Tm; VP, Key C; Model UN; Ski C; Cpt, Tnns; CSF; Citz A; Hon Prog; Kiwanis A; MVP, Tnns; *Wash St U; Med.*

CUNNINGHAM, Donald Ray
North HS; Bakersfield, CA (29-500) VP, Band; Dbte Tm; VP, Key C; Model UN; NFL; Ski C; MVP, Tnns; CSF; Spch A; Mus As; *Wash St U; Vet Mech.*

CUNNINGHAM, Frank E
Reseda HS; Reseda, CA; Chess C; Bkbl; Tnns; CSF; *U of Calif; Math.*

CUNNINGHAM, George Gould III
Fairfield Sr HS; Fairfield, OH; Band; Chor; Drama; Ensm; Mod Mus Mas; Thes; Sftbl; *Hocking Col; Engr Design.*

CUNNINGHAM, James Glen
W Middlesex HS; W Middlesex, PA; Band; Span C; Bsbl; Ftbl; HCt; *US Air Force Acad.*

CUNNINGHAM, James Richard Jr
Leo HS; Grabill, IN (4-107) Chor; Sci C; Cr-Ctry; Tr; Tri Kappa A; *Purdue U; Biol.*

CUNNINGHAM, James Woodruff
Kiskiminetas Springs Sch; Saltsburg, PA (14-40) Chor; Spch C; Var C; JV, Bsbl; JV, Ftbl; Mgr, Wrest; Current Events A; *Journ.*

CUNNINGHAM, Jamie Ann
Uniontown Area Sr HS; Uniontown, PA; Chldr; Secy, Fr C; VP, Hmrm; NHS; S-T, Jr Cl; Chamber of Comm A; Jr-Ed, Yrbk; Stu o-t Month, Exchange C; *U of Pittsburgh; Law.*

CUNNINGHAM, Jana Tracy
Adlai E Stevenson HS; New York, NY; Mgr, Band; Chess C; V-Ch, Dbte Tm; Pres, Drama; FTA; Math C; Ed, Sch P; Sci C; MVP, Bsbl; Bkbl; Ftbl; Soccer; Alg A; COM; Citz A; Cl Fav; Gov Honor Prog; Hon Prog; I Dare You; Journ A; Math A; MLS; Most Out; Opt A.

CUNNINGHAM, Jay Allen
Kewanna HS; Kewanna, IN (1-17) Band; Pres, Fr C; Order/Arrow; Mgr, Bkbl; Cr-Ctry; Golf; Bio A; God & Country A; Order/Arrow A; Lib C; Audio C; *Interntl Bus Col; Bus.*

CUNNINGHAM, Jeffrey Alan
Sissonville HS; Charleston, WV (1-195) Band; Fr C; Pres, Hmrm; Mu Alpha Theta; Tres, SC; Bkbl; Wrest; Alg A; Math A; MLS; Fr A; *Brigham Young U; Math.*

CUNNINGHAM, Laurie Ann
Richland Sr HS; Gibsonia, PA; Hmrm; Rptr, Sch P; SC; Bkbl Statistician; Teacher's Aide; Guidance Off Worker; Hospital Vol; *Bus Mgr.*

CUNNINGHAM, Lisa Dawn
Ripley HS; Ripley, WV (7-253) Ann; VP, FHA; NHS; JV, Bkbl; Vlbl C; GAA Special A; *Marshall U; Home Ec.*

CUNNINGHAM, Loretta Marie
York Comm HS; Elmhurst, IL; *Tricoci's Sch of Cosmetology; Cosmetology.*

CUNNINGHAM, Mark Thomas
Spearman HS; Spearman, TX (3-84) Band; NHS; Span C; SC; Co-Cpt, Bkbl; Cpt, Ftbl; Tnns; Bio A; HCt; Math A; *US Air Force Acad; Elec Engr.*

CUNNINGHAM, Nawon Shernice
Continue Ed Project; St Louis, MO; Co-Cpt, Band; Citz A; *Forest Park Col; Nurs.*

CUNNINGHAM, Neshanta Denise
C L Harper HS; Atlanta, GA; VP, Hmrm; Jr Miss Pageant; Span C; SC; Bio A; COM; HCt; Math A; Sci A; Cpt, Flag Girl Sq; *U of Mich; Bus.*

CUNNINGHAM, Pamela Faye
Trigg Co HS; Cadiz, KY (10-140) BC; Drama; NFL; Spch C; Alg A; 4H A; Math A; *Mus.*

CUNNINGHAM, Pamela Gail
Porter HS; Maryville, TN (6-70) BC; Co-Ch, Bus C; FHA; 4H; Math C; VP, Span C; COM; 4H A; HCt; *William and Mary Col; Hist.*

CUNNINGHAM, Patrick Allison
Gordon HS; Gordon, TX (33%-17) Tres, FFA; Ftbl; Tr; Program Comm, MYF; *Tex Tech U; Paramedics.*

CUNNINGHAM, Ralph Lee
Hickory HS; Hickory, NC (62-315) Band; BS; Ed, Sch P; Bsbl; Bkbl; Ftbl; Tr; Wrest; Q&S A; *U of Nev at Las Vegas; Hotel Adm.*

CUNNINGHAM, Raymond Thomas
Sam Houston HS; Arlington, TX (50-570) Pres, Chess C; NHS; Sci C; Span C; JV, Golf; Hon Prog; *Tex Tech U; Chem.*

CUNNINGHAM, Sandra Kay
East HS; Corning, NY (20-280) A Cap Choir; Bus Mgr, Band; Cpt, Chldr; Chor; Community Yth Symph; Tres, Drama; Ensm; Hmrm; Semi-Fin, Jr Miss Pa; Madrigal; Orch; Ski C; Var C; Beauty; Citz A; Hon Prog; Outst Mus Stu; Stu Coun A; Orch A; *Fashion.*

CUNNINGHAM, Sophia Ruth
John Bowne HS; Flushing, NY; Chor; Drama; *Morehouse Col; Elem Ed.*

CUNNINGHAM, Tara LeAnne
North HS; Bakersfield, CA (10-400) A-Ed, Ann; VP, 4H; Ski C; CSF; 4H A; Rptr, S-T, 4-H C; Secy, Jr Symph Assn; Modern Dance C; *Calif Polytech Inst; Spch Therapy.*

CUNNINGHAM, Terri Jo
Owensboro Sr HS; Owensboro, KY (15%-500) Pres, Band; Chor; Community Yth Symph; Pres, Hmrm; Lat C; Orch; SC; COM; Math A; Most Out; Type A; *U of Ky; Mus.*

CUNNINGHAM, Terrie Lynn
Springfield Southeast HS; Springfield, IL (109-557) Ntl Yth Conf; Tn Resolved in Progress; NAACP; Secy, Bapteens; *Bradley U; Computers.*

CUNNINGHAM, Vickie Elizabeth
Dobyns-Bennett HS; Kingsport, TN; Band; Mgr, Bkbl; Tr; Pres, Yth Fel; *Hist.*

CUNO, Michael Lee
New Bloomfield R III HS; New Bloomfield, MO; Chor; Pres, SC; Citz A; Soph Pilgrimage.

CUNY, Mark Wesley
Papillion HS; Papillion, NE; Span C; Hon Prog; *U of Nebr.*

CUPP, Deborah Denise
Awalt HS; Mountain View, CA (60-350) Chor; CSF; Hon Prog; Toastmistress C; *Columbia Christian Col; Ed.*

CUPP, Richard Lee Jr
Chester F Awalt HS; Mountain View, CA (11-300) Rptr, Sch P; Spch C; JV, Soccer; *Columbia Christian Col; Journ.*

CURD, Steven Elliott
Fort Osage HS; Independence, MO (16-323) Band; Cpt, Ensm; VP, Math C; Model UN; NHS; Sci C; H of F; Math A; MLS; PTA A; Pres A; Regent Schol; US Rep, Interntl Sk Olymp Holland; *William Jewell Col; Computer Sci.*

CURDY, Katrina Marie
Benjamin Franklin HS; Los Angeles, CA; Secy, Band; CYO; Community Yth Symph; Marian Medal; Mus A; *USC; Mus Performance.*

CURETON, Janet Elice
W Charlotte Sr HS; Charlotte, NC (250-600) A Cap Choir; Band; Chor; Drama; Ensm; Hmrm; ARC; Sch P; Span C; SC; *Gardner-Webb Col; Psych.*

CURETON, Yvette Rose
Overbrook HS; Philadelphia, PA; Sch P; Sftbl; Hon Prog; NMF; *Pre-Med.*

CURFMAN, Kevin Thomas
Oakville HS; Oakville, WA (3-30) Ann; Tres, Chess C; Pres, FFA; VP, Math C; NHS; F-Ed, Sch P; Pres, Sr Cl; JA A; St Sentinel, FFA; St Farmer Degree, FFA; 3rd Pl, St Poultry Production; *Wash St U; Farm Mgt.*

CURINGTON, Donna Lynn
Kickapoo HS; Springfield, MO (158-300) A Cap Choir; Band; Chor; FHA; Hmrm; Madrigal; SC; Swim; Tr.

CURINTON, Karen
HS of Mus & Art; New York, NY (130-525) Band; Chor; City Conf; Drama; FTA; Hmrm; Rptr, Lit Mag; Sch Achieve Tm; Rptr, Sch P; SC; Secy, Sr Cl; Beauty; COM; Citz A; Hon Prog; Math A; Spelling A; *Bennett Col; Fashion Designer.*

CURIS, George John
Polytech Prep Ctry Day Sch; Brooklyn, NY (19-72) JV, Bsbl; Soccer; Tr; Tutor; Bank School; Dean's List; Best Offense, Soccer A; *NY U; Acct.*

CURLEE, Camille
Colo HS; Colo City, TX (8-95) A Cap Choir; Ann; Rptr, Band; Bus C; Chor; Ensm; FBLA; NHS; Tres, Sr Cl; *Tex Tech U; Dental Tech.*

CURLEW, Douglas James
Temple Christian Sch; Detroit, MI (23-70) Cr-Ctry; Tr.

CURLEY, August Onorato
Southwest HS; Atlanta, GA (35-189) Cpt, Bsbl; Bkbl; Cpt, Ftbl; COM; HCt; Hon Prog; Most Out; ROTC A; MVD, McDonald's Ftbl; Rookie o-t Yr, Bsbl; Prep Ftbl HR; Pitched HS 1st No Hitter; *U of Sou Calif; Engr.*

CURLEY, Lorenzo
Valley HS; Sanders, AZ; Hmrm; InterClub Coun; Model UN; SC; Var C; Bsbl; Cpt, Bkbl; Fin, Cr-Ctry; Cpt, Ftbl; Tr; Cl Fav; HKg; *Brigham Young U; Pre-Law.*

CURLEY, Stephen Charles
Parkdale Sr HS; Riverdale, MD (10%-850) Band; Orch; Hockey; Sftbl; Jazz Band; *Md U; Pre-Med.*

CUROTT, Kelly Sue
Bridgeport HS; Bridgeport, OH; Band; Chldr; Pres, Drama; FNA; Mjrte; Span C; SC; Thes; Y-Tns; Type A.

CURRIE, David Glenn
Myers Park HS; Charlotte, NC (100-500) Band; BC; Chess C; Order/Arrow; Span C; Order/Arrow A; DECA; *U of NC at Charlotte; Law.*

CURRIE, Don Howard Jr
W Memphis Christian Sch; W Memphis, AR (3-30) Bkbl; Ftbl; Tr; Citz A; Hist A; Sci A; Bible A.

CURRIE, Jacqueline Barbara
Zillah HS; Zillah, WA (5-60) Ann; BC; Chem C; Chess C; FHA; Math C; Sci C; Tres, SC; Masonic A; Math A; *Eastern Wash St Col; Math.*

CURRIE, Linda Faye
Dudley HS; Greensboro, NC; Hmrm; Tr; Dudley Dance Company; Jr Jaycettes; Jr Missionary; Tres, Jr Usher Board; Pres, Yth Dept-Church Jr Missionar; *A&T St U in NC; Bus.*

CURRIE, Mark Richard
El Camino Real HS; Woodland Hills, CA (414-1095) Chldr; MVP, Bkbl; Tr; Cpt, Bkbl; *Pierce-Biola Col; Ed.*

CURRIE, Sonja Anita
Coolidge Sr HS; Washington, DC; Fr C; Citz A; Sci A; Jr Hon Soc; *Eng.*

CURRIER, Cynthia R
Concord Christian Sch; Concord, NH; Co-Cpt, Chldr; Dbte Tm; VP, 4H; SC; Swim; Pres, 4-H C; Eng A; *Philadelphia Col of Bible; Bible.*

CURRIER, Michael Alahn
Roy HS; Roy, UT (175-450) Ch, BS; Cpt, Dbte Tm; Drama; Ger C; COM; Spch As; VP, Lutheran Yth; *Weber St Col.*

CURRIER, Paul Charles
Fruita Monument HS; Fruita, CO (20-203) Chor; Dbte Tm; Drama; Hmrm; Sci C; Ski C; Pres, Sr Cl; Bsbl; JV, Bkbl; Opt A; Rotary A; *Colo St U; Agr Engr.*

CURRINGTON, Lynda Cheryl
Harlan HS; Harlan, KY; BC; Rptr, Up Bound; Bkbl; Shorthand A; Best Achv, Upward Bound; *W Ky U; Med Tech.*

CURRY, Adeana Lynn
Bob Jones HS; Madison, AL (10%-140) BC; NHS; Sch Achieve Tm; VP, SC; Mgr, Bkbl; Tnns; Bio A; Most Out; *U of Ala at Tuscaloosa; Journ.*

CURRY, Amelia Jane
Westminster Christian Acad; Huntsville, AL (2-6) Chldr; Chor; Drama; Ensm; ARC; Rptr, Sch P; Secy, SC; Hon Prog; Vlbl; *John Brown U; Broadcasting.*

CURRY, Beverly Diane
Herrin HS; Herrin, IL (9-251) Chor; NHS; *John A Logan Col; Acct.*

CURRY, Brenda L
Catalina HS; Tucson, AZ (160-495) Co-Cpt, Bible Quiz Tm; *Bus.*

CURRY, Debbie Sue
Hemet HS; Hemet, CA (1-500) AFS; Chor; CSF; *Biola Col.*

CURRY, Denise Louse
Broad Ripple HS; Indianapolis, IN (25-474) Ger C; Amer Leg A; Hist A; ROTC A; *Purdue U; Eng.*

CURRY, Jaynie Zoanna
David Crockett HS; Austin, TX (33%-650) Span C; Acteens; Church Yth Coun; Church Valentine Swtht; Drill Tm; Explorers; *Baylor U; Sociology.*

CURRY, Jennie Joyce
Las Cruces HS; Las Cruces, NM (10%-900) A Cap Choir; Chor; Ensm; FNA; 4H; Key C; NHS; ARC; Church Fel Yth; Church Choir; *NM St U; Nurs.*

CURRY, Katherine Ann
Campolindo HS; Moraga, CA (108-386) Pres, CYO; ARC; Cpt, Swim; CSF; Young Life; GSct Ldr; Church Deacon; MVP, Swim; *Calif Polytech St U; Social Sci.*

CURRY, Kelly Jo
Abbeville HS; Abbeville, LA; Chor; FNA; *USL.*

CURRY, Marilyn Lynette
Grand Ridge HS; Grand Ridge, FL (5-49) BC; *Chipola Jr Col; Psych.*

CURRY, Nealda Diane
Herbert H Lehman HS; New York, NY (87-834) Orch; *Data Processing.*

CURRY, Sherry Lynn
Abbeville HS; Abbeville, LA (5-254) Band; BC; Academic A; Flag Corps; *Northeastern U; Phar.*

CURRY, Valerie Eve
Miami Christian HS; Miami, FL; Chor; COM; Fel.

CURRY, Yolanda Lee
Franklin Co HS; Frankfort, KY; Drama; Pres, FHA; Ger C; Secy, 4H; Span C; 4H A; WW; *Murray St U; Home Ec.*

CURTI, Martha Elena
Port Huron Northern HS; Port Huron, MI; A Cap Choir; Ensm; NHS; SC; Bkbl; Tr; HCt; *St Clair Co Comm Col; Special Ed.*

CURTIS, Beckie Lynn
Lake of the Woods HS; Baudette, MN (34-87) Chldr; Chor; Fr C; NHS; Secy, Jr Cl; Secy, Soph Cl; Mgr, Hockey; Sftbl; Tr; Ltr Win C; VP, Curling; Vlbl; Most Improved Vlbl A; *ND St U; Interior Decorating.*

CURTIS, Beverley Gail
Russellville HS; Russellville, AL; F-Ed, Ann; Band; Chor; FHA; Math C; Mu Alpha Theta; F-Ed, Sch P; Sci C; Span C; Journ A; *U of N Ala; Social Work.*

CURTIS, Blanche Denice
Booker T Washington HS; Norfolk, VA (10-28) Chor; *Norfolk St Col; Math.*

CURTIS, Brian Kendell
Missian HS; San Francisco, CA; Co-Cpt, Drama; Co-Cpt, Bkbl; *City Col; Bio Sci.*

CURTIS, David Blaine
Manchester HS; Manchester, OH (1-84) A Cap Choir; Band; Chess C; Chor; Drama; Ensm; Fr C; Madrigal; NHS; Sch Achieve Tm; Pres, Sr Cl; COM; I Dare You; Math A; MLS; Most Out; Sci A; Val; Choir A; *Western Ky U; Pre-Med.*

CURTIS, James Alan
Greater Latrobe HS; Latrobe, PA (70-591) Pres, Chor; Hmrm; SC; Var C; VP, Soph C; Swim; Amer Leg A; Citz A; Cl Fav; *Lehigh U; Bus.*

CURTIS, Joann
Southside HS; Memphis, TN (10%-370) Band; Secy, Bus C; Secy, Chor; Secy, Hmrm; NHS; Fin, Spch C; Secy, SC; Secy, Jr Cl; Secy, Soph Cl; HCt; Hon Prog; Spch A; Progress, SC; Trophies; Effort & Proficiency A; Most Versatile; *Memphis St U; Bus.*

CURTIS, Jonathan Clay
Charles Henderson High; Troy, AL; Band; Chem C; Bkbl; *Auburn U; Sound Engr.*

CURTIS, Kathy
Center HS; Center, TX (10-200) Ann; Rptr, Band; Chor; Ensm; FHA; Math C; SC; Cl Fav; Math A; Type A; Mus School; Band A; *Tyler Jr Col; Phar.*

CURTIS, Kathy Ann
Eisenhower HS; Utica, MI (5%-600) Band; CYO; Community Yth Symph; Ger C; Orch; Dist & St Solo-Ensm Competition.

CURTIS, Linda Jane
Calhoun HS; Calhoun, GA (10%-250) Bus C; Chor; Fr C; FBLA; NHS; Tri-HiY; Gold Cert, Bus Machine Operation; *Coosa Valley Tech Col; Med Off Asst.*

CURTIS, Lorie Jayne
Alexander Galt Regional HS; Lennoxville, CAN-ADA (8-477) Hmrm; ARC; Rptr, Sch P; SC; Hon Prog.

CURTIS, Lorraine Ann Marie
Frank H Morrell HS; Irvington, NJ (241-520) Chor; FNA; Star Student; *Bloomfield Col; Bus.*

CURTIS, Mary Elizabeth
Harper Creek HS; Battle Creek, MI (20-262) Co-Ed, Ann; Chor; Bsbl; Mgr, Bkbl; *Kellogg Comm Col.*

CURTIS, Mary Teresa
Forest Ridges Sch; Bellevue, WA;

CURTIS, Nancy Ann
Center HS; Center, TX (14-147) Ed, Ann; Secy, Band; Chor; Ensm; Secy, FHA; NHS; A-Ed, Sch P; SC; Cl Fav; Journ A; Rotary A; Type A; Mus A; Band A; *Tyler Jr Col; Nurs.*

CURTIS, Robert Freeman
Sumter HS; Sumter, SC (25%-850) Ann; Drama; Tres, Hmrm; Key C; F-Ed, Sch P; S-T, Span C; Yth Chairman, March of Dimes; *USC at Columbia.*

CURTIS, Sandra Faye
South Side HS; Memphis, TN (10%-370) Band; JV, Chldr; Spch C; Pres, Soph Cl; Tr; Spch A; All Around, Acad, Ath; *Memphis St U; Optometry.*

CURTIS, Sharron Kelly
St Mary's Acad; Alexandria, VA (9-83) Ann; Pres, Chor; Community Yth Symph; Jr Miss Pagent; Model UN; Tres, NHS; Math A; Talent Show Win; Best Delegation, Mod UN; *Col of William & Mary; Pre-Med.*

CURTIS, Steven Donnell
Ahrens HS; Louisville, KY; MVP, Band; Hmrm; Pres, NHS; Cpt, Bkbl; Cr-Ctry; Tnns.

CURTIS, Terri M
Alamosa HS; Alamosa, CO (1-156) Chldr; Secy, FHA; NHS; Hist A; Math A; Sci A; Semi- fin, Gym; *Colo St U; Math.*

CURTIS, Therisa Karen
Clinton HS; Clinton, MS; Chor; FBLA; FHA; 4H; Sci C; Secy, Y-Tns; Sftbl; 3rd Pl, Prepared Spch, VICA; *Activity Aide, Elderly.*

CURTISS, Carole Sue
Pendleton Heights HS; Pendleton, IN; BC; Chor; Swim; Mus A; *Ball St U; Nurs.*

CURTO, Jeffrey Nicholls
Lyons Township HS; LaGrange, IL (90%-1250) Ed, Ann; NHS; Spch C; NEDT; Q&S A; St Scholar; Co-E, Annual; Ntl Schol Photography A's; WW; *Ill Wesleyan U.*

CURTSINGER, Beverly Ann
Owensboro Cath HS; Owensboro, KY (15-236) A Cap Choir; CYO; Chor; Drama; 4H; Hmrm; Thes; Swim; COM; Citz A; DARGCA; 4H A; HCt; Hon Prog; Most Out; Opt A; Spch A; Swtht; Pep C A; Chor A; *Brescia Col; Acct.*

CUSACK, Michael Francis
St Thomas Episcopal HS; Houston, TX (10-48) Chor; Drama; Lat C; Tnns; DARGCA; NEDT; Bagpipes A; Best Amateur Piper; *Med.*

CUSHING, Charla Gwynn
Leesville HS; Leesville, LA (2-296) Band; Tres, BC; FTA; Hmrm; Lit Ral; Mjrte; Math C; SC; *N La St U; Sci.*

CUSHMAN, John Chandler
B Reed Henderson Sr HS; W Chester, PA (11-507) Hmrm; SC; Hon Prog; Gym; *Eng.*

CUSTALOW, Bryson Scott
King William HS; King William, VA (20-115) Cpt, Chldr; Co-Ch, Chor; Hmrm; VP, Jr Cl; Mgr, Tr; Chldr A; *St Augustine's Col; Special Ed.*

CUSTER, Cindy Faye
Musselman HS; Bunker Hill, WV (15-92) Band; VP, Chor; Jr Miss Pagent; F-Ed, Mjrte; Beauty; 4H A; Hon Prog; Talent, Jr Miss, A's; Civitan Qn; Fin, Charm Revue; *Hagerstown Jr Col; Law Enforcement.*

CUSTER, Jerri Ann
Cleveland HS; Cleveland, OK; Band; Fr C; Ch, FHA; DECA Swtht; Fr, DECA, A's; *Ozark Bible Col; Mus.*

CUTBIRTH, Monta Gwen
Silsbee HS; Silsbee, TX; Chess C; FHA; FTA; JETS; NHS; Rainbow; Ed, Sch P; Tres, Span C; Spch C; Tres, SC; Tnns; Beauty; Journ A; Magna Cum Laude; Sal; Cpt, Drill Tm; Eng A; *LSU; Pre-Dentistry.*

CUTCHIN, Stephen Gary
Loyola HS; Towson, MD (10-134) Fr C; Hmrm; NHS; SC; *Engr.*

CUTLER, Cathy Lynn
Putnam City HS; Oklahoma City, OK (519-850) Hmrm; SC; Yth Fel; VICA; Pep C; *Paul's Beauty Col; Cosmetology.*

CUTLER, Donna Renea
Hudson HS; Lufkin, TX; Band; Crown & Scepter; FFA; Mjrte; Swtht; Spring Festival Court; *Tex A&M U; Vocational Agr.*

CUTLER, Kevin Joseph
Tift Co HS; Tifton, GA; InterAct C; Ftbl.

CUTLER, Theodore Mark
Spring Lake HS; Spring Lake, MI (22-196) Band; BS; Demolay; Model UN; NHS; Order/Arrow; Ski C; Tr; Alg A; COM; Math A; NMS; Eagle Sct; *U of Mich; Aero-Space Engr.*

CUTLIFF, Kimberly Sue
Yorkwood HS; Monmouth, IL; Chor; Ensm; FHA; Pres, FTA; Hmrm; NHS; Span C; Citz A; Tres, Pom Pon; Dean's List; HR; Mus Ltr; *Lincoln Christian Col; Ed.*

CUTRER, Colette Ann
Pascagoula; Pascagoula, MS (1-452) Co-Ed, Ann; BC; Pres, Lat C; SC; H of F; Val; Lat A; *Miss Col; Pre-Med.*

CUTRIGHT, James Kurt
Chillicothe HS; Chillicothe, OH (1-400) Band; Dbte Tm; NFL; Pres, NHS; Orch; Amer Leg A; Bio A; Spch A; MENSA; Adelphi Wine Soc; *Ohio St U; Med.*

CUTRONA, Peter Daniel
Whittier HS; Whittier, CA; Bkbl; Senators; *Calif St U at Fullerton; Bus.*

CUTTER, Bonnie Ann
Switzerland HS; Vevay, IN (2-100) Band; Chor; Secy, Drama; Fr C; VP, 4H; Secy, Mod Mus Mas; NHS; SC; Alg A; COM; 4H A; PTA A; ARC A; *Mus.*

CUTTINO, Anita Faye
Mullins Sr HS; Mullins, SC (75%-230) Band; Chor; 4H.

CUTTS, Laurie Ann
Bedford HS; Temperance, MI (10%-468) Bus C; Chor; FBLA; NHS; *Andrews Barber Col; Hair Stylist.*

CUTTS, Tim DeWitt
Weir HS; Weir, MS (5-53).

CVITANOVICH, Susan Elizabeth
Greenville HS; Greenville, TX (25-325) Band; CYO; FTA; 4H; Mjrte; Math C; NHS; Rptr, Span C; Parl, Tri-HiY; Soccer; Altrusa C Secy; UIL Twirling A; Span C A; Academic Excellent A; Soccer Qn; *Tex Tech U; Engr.*

CWIKLA, Nancy Jean
Middle River Comm HS; Middle River, MN (5-34) Band; Drama; GS; Ed, Sch P; SC; Pres, Jr Cl; Bkbl; Sftbl; HCt; Star Student; Type A; Vlbl; Best Defensive Player, Bkbl; *Northland Comm Col; Elem Ed.*

CYPHERT, Janet Marie
Bishop Carroll HS; Wichita, KS (3-211) Fr C; Model UN; Sci C; *Marymount of Salina; Nurs.*

CYR, Jayne Ann
Livermore Falls HS; Livermore Falls, ME (6-94) Co-Ed, Ann; Fr C; Parl, FHA; Math C; Pres, SC; S-T, Var C; Bkbl; Co-Cpt, Hockey; Mgr, Sftbl; Tr; Bio A; Winter Carnival Qn.

CYR, Karen Louise
Richmond HS; Richmond, CA (12-225) Band; NHS; CSF; Citz A; St Scholar; Type A; *Simpson Col; Ed.*

CYRIER, Rosalie
Foreman HS; Chicago, IL (9-373) FTA; Key C; Mjrte; Mu Alpha Theta; Pres, NHS; Span C; Hon Prog; St Scholar; HR Pins; *Ntl Col of Ed; Special Ed.*

CYRS, David Maurice
Newman HS; Wausau, WI (21-136) Ann; Fr C; Hmrm; Rptr, Lit Mag; NHS; Ski C; Tres, Var C; Bsbl; Co-Cpt, Ftbl; Golf; Hon Prog; Rotary A; *St Thomas Col; Bus.*

CYRUS, Teresa Carolyn
Appomattox Co HS; Appomattox, VA (5-207) Ed, Ann; Pres, FHA; GS; NHS; SC; Var C; Cpt, Tr; Amer Leg Orator A; Citz A; DARGCA; Hon Prog; Spch A; Honorary FHA Member; *James Madison U; Communications.*

CZAKO, Andrew Robert Jr
Plainville HS; Plainville, CT; *Mech.*

CZAPLA, Colleen
Vincent Massey HS; Windsor, CANADA; Math C; Tres, SC; Acct Contest A; *Bus.*

CZARAPATA, Renee Denise
Greenfield HS; Greenfield, WI (44-465) A Cap Choir; Band; Chor; Mjrte; Mus Festival A's; *St Olaf Col; Sociology.*

CZECH, Connie Kay
Fort Atkinson Sr HS; Fort Atkinson, WI (85-230) Pep C; Redskins; Co-Ldr, Tops; *Cosmetology.*

CZELUSNIAK, Katherine Ann
Windham HS; Willimantic, CT (17-330) AFS; GS; Tres, Mjrte; Secy, Mu Alpha Theta; NHS; SC; Bus A; *U of Conn; Math.*

CZERWINSKI, Terry Lee
Philipsburg-Osceola Area HS; Philipsburg, PA (105-250) Ch, Drama; FHA; Co-Cpt, Mjrte; Pres, Rainbow; F-Ed, Sch P; Arch; Sftbl; Tnns; *Philipsburg Sch of Nurs; Nurs.*

CZESHINSKI, Mark A
Wausau W HS; Wausau, WI; Arch; Ftbl; Golf; Cpt, Soccer; Sftbl; Tnns; Tr.

CZULEWICZ, Carrie Ann
Community Preparatory Acad; Erie, PA (1-13) Secy, Ann; Span C; COM; Hon Prog; Cpt, Bowl; Vet Asst.

D

D'AGATA, Michael Charles
Halifax Co Sr HS; S Boston, VA (36-580) CYO; Fr C; Hmrm; JV, Bkbl; WW; DAHSS; *Hampden-Sydney Col; Law.*

D'ALESSIO, Dina C
Our Lady of Good Counsel HS; Newark, NJ (7-77) Cpt, Chldr; Chem C; Drama; Parl, Hmrm; Pres, NHS; Rptr, Sch P; S-T, SC; S-T, Soph Cl; Sftbl; Hon Prog; Pres A; *Fashion Inst of Tech; Fashion Merchandising.*

D'AMBOLA, Cheryl Lynn
Cave Spring HS; Roanoke, VA (66-489) Chor; Pres, FHA; FTA; Span C; SC; Hon Prog; *Carson-Newman Col; Psych.*

D'AMICO, Nancy Dorothy
Alief Hastings HS; Alief, TX (1-435) NHS; VP, Span C; Alg A; Bio A; Sci A; Val; Best Actress, UIL All Star Cast; *Houston Baptist U; Law.*

D'AMOUR, Marie Jeanne
The MacDuffie Sch; Springfield, MA (2-48) Chor; VP, Drama; Key C; Lit Mag; Math C; Rptr, Sch P; VP, Jr Cl; Bkbl; Tnns; Citz A; NEDT; *Dartmouth Col; Med.*

D'ANDREA, Mary Ellen
Rosary Acad; Sparkill, NY (2-79) Ed, Ann; Secy, CYO; Chor; Drama; Ensm; NHS; Rptr, Sch P; Hist A; Hon Prog; Sal; Type A; Amer Home Sewing Contest; Art A; Cardinal Spellman Yth A; Span A; Outst Service, Glee C A; Eng A; *Fordham U; Liberal Arts.*

D'AURIA, Elisa Ann
W Haven HS; W Haven, CT; Swim.

D'URSO, Mark Anthony
Reynolds HS; Greenville, PA (14-212) FTA; Lat C; Math C; NHS; Sci C; Var C; Pres, Sr Cl; Pres, Jr Cl; Pres, Soph Cl; Mgr, Ftbl; HCt; Pres Clroom for Young Amer; *Penn St U; Vocational Cordinator.*

DAAM, Ben Mark
Portage Central HS; Portage, MI; Band; Sch P; *Kalamazoo Valley Comm Col; Construction.*

DABEL, Elizabeth Ann
Star Valley HS; Afton, WY (3-105) Chor; Ensm; Fr C; Madrigal; Secy, NHS; Orch; Sch P; Hon Prog; *Brigham Young U; Mus.*

DABELOW, Bonnie Susan
Elk Grove HS; Elk Grove Village, IL; Arch; Band; MVP, Chor; Ensm; Orch; Semi-Fin, Arch; COM; Band A's; Band Clinic; St Arch Semi- fin; *Mus.*

DaCOSTA, Patrick Anthony
Eastside HS; Paterson, NJ (6-519) Ed, Ann; BS; Hmrm; Key C; NHS; Ed, Sch P; SC; Tr; Amer Leg A; COM; Hon Prog; JA A; Most Out; St Scholar; Elmira Key A; WW; *Princeton U; Engr.*

DADE, Charles Michael
DuVal HS; Lanham, MD (25-600) Chor; Ensm; JV, Soccer; Eng A; Jr Hon Soc; HR.

DADE, Patricia Annette
Pecos HS; Pecos, TX (120-240) Rptr, Sch P; Tr; Pres, Church Chor; *Angelo St U; Data Processing.*

DADEKIAN, Susan Elizabeth
Northern Highlands Regional HS; Allendale, NJ (15-381) Tres, APS; Chor; Lit Mag; Math C; NHS; Pol Sci C; Chem A; Hon Prog; Magna Cum Laude; Math A; Phy A; *Bucknell U; Bus.*

DADO, Steven Floyd
Turner HS; Kansas City, KS; Band; Ensm; Orch; *Recording Engr.*

DAEHLER, Nancy Lynn
Mt Whitney HS; Visalia, CA (9-428) Pres, Fr C; CSF; *U of Calif; Fr.*

DAGANAAR, Mark Leslie
Ralston HS; Ralston, NE (99-296) Co-Ed, Ann; 4H; Thes; COM; Citz A; 4H A; Journ A; Partial Tuition to Ldrshp Workshop; *SD St Col; Hist.*

DAGGETT, Esther Ann
Wilson Central HS; Wilson, NY (20-140) Ann; Fr C; JV, Tnns; Citz A; JA A; Lion A; Sci A; Vlbl; Ntl Fr Contest; Eng A; *Pol Sci.*

DAGGETT, Karyl Sue
Melvin Comm HS; Melvin, IA (1-19) Ed, Ann; Band; Chor; Pres, 4H; Secy P; Tres, SC; VP, Sr Cl; Pres, Soph Cl; Mgr, Bkbl; Golf; Sftbl; Tr; 4H A; Hon Prog; Sch A; St Scholar; Type A; Val; NML; *U of Iowa; Liberal Arts.*

DAGIT, Molly Genette
Crestwood HS; Cresco, IA (59-150) Co-Ed, Ann; Band; *Grace Col o-t Bible; Nurs.*

DAGIT, Molly Gennette
Crestwood HS; Cresco, IA (59-150) Co-Ed, Ann; Band; Journ A; Q&S A; *Grace Col of Bible; Nurs.*

DAGNAN, Susan Melinda
R B Stall HS; Chas Hghts, SC (33%-219) Bus C; FBLA; FHA; FTA; Hmrm; Span C; SC; Sftbl; Sftbl A's; *Col of Charleston; Bus.*

DAHL, Arden Bruce
Oscoda Area HS; Oscoda, MI (4-250) Band; Ensm; Hmrm; NHS; Order/Arrow; SC; Var C; Bsbl; Co-Cpt, Bkbl; Cr-Ctry; COM; Order/Arrow A; Eagle Sct; *Air Force Acad; Engr.*

DAHL, Carolyn Marie
N Kansas City HS; Kansas City, MO; Chor; Tnns; People to People; *Columbia Col; Travel Adm.*

DAHL, Diane Kimberly
Moorhead Sr HS; Moorhead, MN; Community Yth Symph; Ensm; Orch; Citz A; St Piano Hon Concerts; *St Olaf Col.*

DAHL, Donald Ramsey
Fargo S HS; Fargo, ND (30%-850) A Cap Choir; Band; Chor; Drama; Ensm; Madrigal; Orch; Thes; Mgr, Bkbl; Mgr, Ftbl; Bkbl Ltr; Sunday Sch Teacher; Church Usher; Growth Ch, Church Yth Group; *Moorhead St U; Mus.*

DAHL, James Ernest
Viroqua Sr HS; Viroqua, WI; Bkbl; Tnns; Yth Fel; *U of Wis; Acct.*

DAHL, Jeffrey Allen
Aledo HS; Aledo, IL (8-117) BS; Chor; Key C; Tres, SC; Var C; Pres, Soph Cl; Ftbl; Golf; St Scholar; *U of Ill; Elec Engr.*

DAHL, Todd Keven
Albert Lea Sr HS; Albert Lea, MN (125-597) Sch P; Var C; Ftbl; Cpt, Hockey; Tr; Q&S A; *Air Force Acad; Civil Engr.*

DAHLBERG, Richard Peter
Lebanon Union HS; Lebanon, OR (1-316) Band; Chor; Ensm; FBLA; VP, InterClub Coun; Math C; VP, NHS; JV, Tnns; Val; Pres, Bible C; 1st Cl Sct; Sr Band A; WW; 2nd Pl Jr Band A; *Sou Calif Col; Math.*

DAHLEM, Jerome Anthony
Many HS; Many, LA (6-100) Lit Ral; NHS; Pres, Sr Cl; Tnns; MLS; NMF; *La Tech U; Chem Engr.*

DAHLEN, Andrew Oliver
Mabel-Canton HS; Mabel, MN (15-50) Ann; Band; BS; VP, Chor; Parl, FFA; Pres, 4H; NHS; Sch P; Spch C; Var C; Pres, Jr Cl; Bsbl; Co-Cpt, Bkbl; Co-Cpt, Ftbl; 4H A; HCt; Hon Prog; Spch A; MVP, Bkbl; Hon Band; Hon Choir; *Math.*

DAHLEN, Andy Oliver
Mabel-Canton HS; Mabel, MN (16-50) Ann; Band; BS; Chor; Ensm; Rptr, FFA; Pres, 4H; Semi-Fin, Hmrm; Madrigal; NHS; Sch P; Var C; Pres, Jr Cl; Bsbl; Co-Cpt, Bkbl; Co-Cpt, Ftbl; HCt; MVP, Bkbl; Hon Stu; *ND U; Med.*

DAHLEN, Martha Jane
Mabel-Canton HS; Mabel, MN (10-60) Band; Tres, Chor; Ensm; FHA; Pres, 4H; Sch P; Spch C; Var C; Co-Cpt, Bkbl; MVP, Tr; 4H A; Spch A; Vlbl; *Phys Ed.*

DAHLER, David Mark
Bishop Byrne HS; Memphis, TN (60-191) NEDT; Opt A; *Memphis St U; Bus.*

DAHLGREN, Dean Emmett
Theodore Roosevelt HS; Minneapolis, MN (40-605) Tres, A Cap Choir; Chor; Drama; Hmrm; NHS; Rptr, Sch P; Co-Cpt, Swim; Most Out; Co-Ch, Homecoming; Co-Ch, Sr Banquet; Lead, Sr Cl Play; *U of Minn.*

DAHLGREN, Tami Garland
Stafford Sr HS; Falmouth, VA; Band; Chor; 4H; Sch P; COM; *James Madison U.*

DAHLGREN, Teresa Lee
N Platte HS; N Platte, NE; Band; Chor; 4H; Lat C; Tri-HiY; Tr; *U of Nebr; Nurs.*

DAHLKE, Jamie Sue
Wausau Comm HS; Wausau, WI (15-136) Chldr; Chor; NHS; Hon Prog; Type A; Pep C; Peppermint Court; WW.

DAHLKE, Vicki Jean
Westfield HS; Westfield, WI (3-130) NFL; NHS; Secy, Span C; Span NHS; COM; Spch A; Type A; Sch Play; GAA; Alt, GS; Pres, Lutheran Yth Group; Radio Group; *U of Wis-Madison; Home Ec.*

DAHLMAN, Rita Sue
Mt Vernon HS; Mt Vernon, MO (21-98) Chor; Ensm; SC; VP, Jr Cl; Sftbl.

DAHLQUIST, Kimberly Louise
Mission Viejo HS; Mission Viejo, CA (10%-250) Chor; Hmrm; Span C; SC; Bkbl; Church Yth Committee; *UCLA; Med.*

DAHLSTRAND, John Henry
Strong Vincent HS; Erie, PA (90-360) Hmrm; SC; Bkbl; Ftbl; Sftbl; Tr; Lion A; Yth Fel; All-City Ftbl; *Penn St; La.*

DAHLSTROM, Marcus Larry
Stevens HS; Rapid City, SD (100-450) Band; BS; Chor; Orch; A-Ed, Sch P; Ski C; Pres, SC; Jr Cl; Pres, Soph Cl; Bsbl; Ftbl; Amer Leg A; Citz A; Journ A; Q&S A.

DAHMER, Lizabeth Jo
Luther HS N; Chicago, IL (23-310) A Cap Choir; Rptr, Sch P; Span C; *Augustana U; Journ.*

DAHMS, Kelly Sue
Ravenna HS; Ravenna, MI; Band; Chldr; SC; Tres, Soph Cl; Tr; *Western Mich U; Ed.*

DAHMS, Thomas Michael
Ravenna HS; Ravenna, MI; Hmrm; NHS; SC; Ftbl; Tr.

DAIDA, Jason Masao
Maui HS; Kahului, HI (2-299) Tres, NFL; Tres, NHS; St Stu Congress; 4H A; Most Out; Sci A; Spch A; NML; Critics Circle; *U of Sou Calif; Engr.*

DAIGLE, Deborah Lee
John B Ehret HS; Marrero, LA (2-550) CYO; Lit Ral; Math C; Mu Alpha Theta; Tres, NHS; Sftbl; Tr; Bio A; Hist A; Hon Prog; Math A; PTA A; Sci A; Prep Quiz Tm; Span A; Eng A; *LSU at Baton Rouge; Vet Med.*

DAIGLE, Gail Marie
Cecilia Sr HS; Cecilia, LA (11-122) BC; Secy, Fr C; VP, FFA; *Spencer Bus Col; Bus.*

DAIL, Robert John
Foothill Christian HS; N Highlands, CA; Bkbl.

DAILEY, Brenda Kay
Middletown HS; Middletown, OH (20%-500) Sch P; SC; I Dare You; Off Practice A; *Miami Jacobs Col; Bus.*

DAILEY, Robert Gerard
St Patrick's HS; N Platte, NE (3-35) Drama; Parl, FBLA; VP, 4H; Key C; NHS; Spch C; Pres, Soph Cl; JV, Bkbl; Bio A; 4H A; *U of Nebr, Lincoln; Vet Sci.*

DAILY, Monte Dane
Van Buren HS; Van Buren, AR (35-235) Band; Math C; Mu Alpha Theta; *U of Ark; Engr.*

DAIN, Sandra Leigh
Stow HS; Stow, OH; Secy, Rainbow; SC; Rainbow Grand Cross of Color.

DAINTY, Jane Renee
Alleghany Co HS; Covington, VA (100-250) Ann; Span C; Pres, Yth Group; Church Choir; Acolyte; *Dabney S Lancaster Comm Col; Radio Communications.*

DAJER, Carmen Lucia
Academia Maria Reina; Rio Piedras, PR; CYO; VP, Drama; Fr C; French NHS; InterAct C; Pres, NFL; NHS; Sch P; COM; Hon Prog; NEDT; Spch A; PA; *Yale U.*

DAKE, Rory Jay
Orleans HS; Orleans, NE (1-27) Ann; Band; 4H; NHS; Var C; Secy, Jr Cl; Mgr, Bkbl; Mgr, Ftbl; Golf; 4H A; Lion A; Trustee Achv A; Special Ability in Mus School, Col; *Doane Col; Pre-Engr.*

DALBERG, Cynthia Lou
Struthers HS; Struthers, OH (4-320) JV, Chldr; Chor; NHS; Span C; Y-Tns; COM; Chem A; NEDT; PTA A; *Youngstown St Col; Sci.*

DALBERG, Pamela Faye
Bend Sr HS; Bend, OR (1-550) Chor; Ensm; Alg A; Sci A; Val; All Northwest Choir; CBA Yth Coun; VP, Jr Hi Girls Baptist Assn; *Judson Baptist Col; Mus.*

DALBEY, Lori Lynn
Alliance HS; Alliance, NE (47-148) JV, Chldr; Chor; VP, 4H; Orch; Co-Ch, Y-Tns; JV, Bkbl; Mgr, Tr; 4H A; Job's Daughters; *Kearney St Col; Ed.*

DALBO, Mary Ann Alexandra
Riverside Jr-Sr HS; Taylor, PA (15-190) FNA; Lit Mag; NHS; Span C; Hon Prog; *Wilkes Col; Nurs.*

DALE, Charla Rene
Broken Bow HS; Broken Bow, OK (10%-135) VP, Chor; Drama; Ensm; Ch, FHA; NHS; Sch P; VP, Jr Cl; Hist A; Hon Prog; Secy, Chor; GS Alt; *E Central St U; Med.*

DALE, David Arthur
Lubbock Monterey HS; Lubbock, TX; HiY; Citz A; *Tex Tech U; Forestry.*

DALE, Debra Mae
Midwest City HS; Midwest City, OK (6-560) Bus C; Bus Mgr, FHA; French NHS; S-T, Ger C; Hmrm; Key C; NHS; Sch P; Ch, SC; Mgr, Bkbl; MVP, Tnns; Alg A; B Crocker A; HCt; Kiwanis A; Young Life; Bus & Professional Girl o-t Mo; Stu o-t Mo; *Okla St U; Engr.*

DALE, Donna Annette
Booker T Washington HS; Atlanta, GA (10%-326) COM; Yth Fel; *W Ga St Col; Special Ed.*

DALE, Morris Russell
Mitchell HS; Memphis, TN (19-241) Ch, Hmrm; Parl, SC; JV, Tr; COM; Cl Fav; Hon Prog; ROTC A; Best Draftsman; *Naval Col; Advanced Elec Engr.*

DALE, Rhonda Kay
Morman Trail Sch; Humeston, IA (11-46) Chor; FHA; Golf.

DALESSIO, Theresa Marie
Cardinal Newman HS; W Palm Beach, FL (52-277) VP, CYO; Chldr; Hmrm; Tres, NHS; SC; Sftbl; Alg A; JA A; *Palm Beach Jr Col; Nurs.*

DALEY, Julie Marie
Portage Central HS; Portage, MI; Band; Chor; Fr C; Hmrm; Orch; ARC; SC; Swim; Citz A; Pres A; *Kalamazoo Valley Comm Col.*

DALEY, Rebecca Ruth
Corinth Christian Acad; Johnson, OH; Band; Pres, Chor; Pres, Hmrm; Bkbl; Val; *Central Bible Col; Missions.*

DALIN, Dallas Vern
Stevens HS; Rapid City, SD; Order/Arrow; God & Country A; Yth Fel; Eagle A; *Elec.*

DALIN, Wendy Ann
Winthrop HS; Winthrop, MN (6-68) Ann; Band; Chor; Drama; Semi-Fin, Ensm; Secy, FHA; NHS; Sch P; S-T, Sr Cl; S-T, Jr Cl; Mus Ltr; Dance Line; *Gustavus Adolphus Col; Nurs.*

DALKE, Kellee Marie
Cascade Union HS; Turner, OR (14-190) Tres, Drama; Secy, FFA; Ch, Hmrm; Tres, NHS; ARC; SC; Tres, Jr Cl; Bkbl; Tr; *Seattle Pacific Col; Human Sci.*

DALLAL, Saaid
Crestview Sr HS; Crestview, FL; MVP, Wrest; COM; PA; *OWJC; Engr.*

DALLAS, Thomas Walton
Callaway HS; Jackson, MS (63-450) A Cap Choir; Chess C; Chor; Math C; Mu Alpha Theta; Order/ Arrow; VP, SC; Bsbl; Ftbl; Hon Prog; Math A; Most Out; *Miss St U; Pre-Law.*

DALLAS, Willie III
Laurel Park HS; Martinsville, VA; Cpt, Bsbl; Cpt, Bkbl; Cpt, Cr-Ctry; Cpt, Tr; God & Country A; Journ A; *Ferrum Col; Hist.*

DALLMAN, Kevin Scott
Hamilton HS; Sussex, WI (20%-425) Mgr, Bkbl; JV, Ftbl; JV, Tr.

DALLMANN, Becky Lynn
Downers Grove S HS; Downers Grove, IL (175-700) Tr; Gym; Drill Tm; *Col of Dupage; Phys Therapy.*

DALLMANN, Patricia Elizabeth
Mercy HS; Albany, NY (1-135) Rptr, Sch P; NEDT; Sci A; A-Ed, Sch Paper; Fr A; Eng A; *Bradford Col; Journ.*

DALRYMPLE, Leslie Ray
Dolores HS; Dove Creek, CO (2-29) Band; Chor; NHS; Bsbl; Cpt, Bkbl; Elk A; *Fort Lewis Col; Ed.*

DALRYMPLE, Mary Ellen
Hernando HS; Brooksville, FL (11-412) Anchor C; FHA; NHS; Math A; Home Ec Outst Jr Plaque; PA; Powder-Puff Ftbl; Sewing A's Co Par; Brd of Dir, Anchor C; Pres Yth Fel; Outst Anchor Member; *Tailor.*

DALTON, George Bartlett
Sequoia Union HS; Redwood City, CA (5%-525) Band; Drama; Pres, Hmrm; Mentally Gifted Minor; *Stanford U; Elec.*

DALTON, Larry Lee
Henryville HS; Henryville, IN; Band; Pres, NHS; Bkbl; Cr-Ctry; Tr; Alg A; Amer Leg A; Bio A; Hist A; Math A.

DALTON, Robert Glenn
Cabrillo HS; Lompoc, CA (100-434) *Industrial.*

DALTON, Sarah Constance
Upperman HS; Baxter, TN; Bus Mgr, Ann; BC; Dbte Tm; Drama; Secy, Fr C; FHA; Pres, 4H; Secy, NFL; Co-Ed, Sch P; Secy, Spch C; Thes; Amer Leg A; Beauty; 4H A; MLS; Q&S A; VofDEM; Co-Ed, Annual; Home Ec A; *Tenn Tech U; Home Ec.*

DALTON, Sheryl Dee
Amos P Godby HS; Tallahassee, FL (19-326) Bus Mgr, Ann; Secy, FBLA; Secy, NHS; Chem A; Q&S A; Co-Ed, Ann; *Fla St U; Bus.*

DALTON, Teresa Fay
Towering Oaks Baptist HS; Memphis, TN; Chor; Drama; Ensm; Fr C; FTA; Mod Mus Mas; NHS; Spch C; Var C; MVP, Bkbl; Cpt, Sftbl; Citz A; Hon Prog; Cpt, Vlbl Tm; W Tenn Chorus; Chaplain, SC; Cpt, Bkbl.

DALUGA, Josephine Marie
Heidelberg American HS; Heidelberg, GERMANY (8-173) A Cap Choir; Band; VP, CYO; Drama; Hmrm; NHS; Sch P; SC; Cr-Ctry; COM; ROTC A; Cl Offices; *Cornell U; Pre-Med.*

DALY, Andy James
Post Falls HS; Post Falls, ID; *Idaho St Col; Broadcasting.*

DALY, Denise Catherine
University HS; San Diego, CA (3-311) Ch, CYO; NHS; Sch P; SC; Hon Prog; Most Out.

DALY, Kathleen Ann
University of San Diego HS; San Diego, CA (11-311) Cum Laude Soc; Tres, Sr Cl; Hon Prog; *Grossmont Col.*

DALY, Margaret Adell
Our Lady of Fatima HS; Lafayette, LA (10%-67) F-Ed, Ann; BC; Fr C; Hmrm; Lit Ral; Pres, Math C; NHS; ARC; F-Ed, Sch P; SC; Secy, Sr Cl; VP, Soph Cl; Bkbl; Sftbl; H of F; Hon Prog; NEDT; Swtht; Dist Gov, Mu Alpha Theta; Pep Sq; Cpt, Flag Ftbl; Scholastic Ltrs; Sr Cl Hrdst Wrker; NLU Dancr of Wk; Dance Tm; Foreign Lang Festival; *U of Southwestern La; Nurs.*

DALZIEL, Janet Faye
East HS; Waterloo, IA (51-315) Secy, A Cap Choir; Chor; Fr C; NHS; Ski C; Hon Prog; Mus Contest; Mus Festival; Choir Secy; *Hawkeye Tech Col; Nurs.*

DAMBERG, Suzanne Stephanie
Henry Sibley Sr HS; W St Paul, MN; Chldr; Hmrm; Orch; Pres A; Yth Fel; Piano Exam Level Five; Piano Theory Level Three; *Liberal Arts; Sci.*

DAMERON, Magdalene Louise
W Carter HS; Olive Hill, KY (1-189) BC; FBLA; Up Bound; Mgr, Bkbl; Citz A; Sci A; Val; VFW A; Yth Fel; Conservation Essay A; Army Sci A; Academic Bkbl A; *Western Ky U; Mus.*

DAMERON, Reginald
Alain Leroy Locke HS; Los Angeles, CA (5-658) Band; Key C; Span C; Pres, SC; Hon Prog; MLS; *Bio.*

DAMIAN, Teresita Anderson
George Washington Sr HS; Mangilao, GUAM; Chor; S-T, NHS; SC; COM; Type A; *Sec Ed.*

DAMIANI, Hollis Marie
Northgate HS; Walnut Creek, CA (30-425) AFS; 4H; Model UN; Pres, Span C; CSF; Hon Prog; NML; *U of Calif; Vet Med.*

DAMIANI, Mary Alice
Maple Shade HS; Maple Shade, NJ (1-241) Chldr; Hmrm; Pres, NHS; SC; Var C; JV, Bkbl; Sftbl; Citz A; MLS; Win, Bulletin Essay Contest; *Rutgers U; Med Tech.*

DAMIANO, Linda Mary
Old Forge HS; Old Forge, PA (10-121) Commercial C; NHS.

DAMMAR, Cheryl Lynn
Park Center Sr HS; Brooklyn Park, MN (25-600) Band; Drama; Semi-Fin, GS; NHS; Ed, Sch P; Spch C; Secy, SC; H of F; Hon Prog; Journ A; Spch A; *Eng.*

DAMON, Cheron Shermayne
Rehoboth Christian HS; Rehoboth, NM (7-23) Ann; Cpt, Chldr; Chor; Ensm; Spch C; Secy, SC; *Calvin Col; Pre-Med.*

DAMON, Mark Elliot
Harrison-Chilhowee Baptist Acad; Seymour, TN (6-46) BC; BS; Chor; Madrigal; Sci C; Pres, SC; Bsbl; Mgr, Ftbl; Soccer; Amer Leg Orator A; Bio A; Chem A; Type A; Driver Ed A; WW; *Wake Forest U; Med.*

DAMON, Mary Ann
Fremont HS; Sunnyvale, CA (1-572) Dbte Tm; Drama; Fin, Jr Miss Pagent; NHS; Ski C; Spch C; SC; Thes; Tr; CSF; Opt A; Spch A; Badminton; Most Outst Art Stu; Most Outst Eng Jr; *UCLA; Med.*

DAMRON, Cherie Paulette
Person Sr HS; Roxboro, NC (5-477) A Cap Choir; Chor; Jr Miss Pagent; Monogram; NHS; Span C; Tri-HiY; Golf; Swim; Tnns; Tr; Hon Prog; Drill Tm; Accompanist, Concert Choir; Hand Bell Choir; Sr Pres, UMYF; *E Carolina U; Mus.*

DAMRON, Ronnie Eugene
Virgie HS; Virgie, KY (1-120) BC; Pres, Chem C; Cpt, Bkbl; Tr; COM; Citz A; 4H A; H of F; Hon Prog; Most Out; Type A; *Pikeville Col; Math.*

DAMRON, Scott
N Ridgeville HS; N Ridgeville, OH (4-302) NHS; Ski C; Tr; COM; Math A.

DAMSCHRODER, Linda Odelle
Benton-Carroll-Salem HS; Oak Harbor, OH (25-185) Band; 4H; NHS; Span C; Thes; Tr; Hon Prog; Yth Fel; WW; JV Vlbl; Herbie A; Best Supporting Actress; *Ohio U; Lit.*

DAMSCHRODER, Roger William
Benton-Carroll-Salem HS; Oak Harbor, OH (90-200) Band; Yth Fel; Church Ushers; Church Litergists; *Bus.*

DANAHER, Marguerite Veronica
Gloucester Cath HS; Gloucester City, NJ (7-158) Chor; FNA; NHS; Hockey; Sftbl; Hospital Jr Vol A; *Our Lady of Lourdes Col; Nurs.*

DANCE, Charles Gregory
Humboldt HS; Humboldt, TN; Up Bound; MVP, Bkbl; *Tenn St U; Phys Ed.*

DANCE, John Claiborne
Tidewater Acad; Wakefield, VA (18-65) NHS; JV, Bsbl; JV, Bkbl; JV, Ftbl; *Col of William & Mary; Pol Sci.*

DANCE, Rick Wayne
Daniel Boone HS; Jonesboro, TN (114-280) Chem C; 4H; Pres, Key C; Monogram; Sci C; Tres, SC; Var C; Pres, Soph Cl; Cpt, Bsbl; Co-Cpt, Ftbl; Tr; HCt; All ULC, Ftbl; *Walters St; Agr.*

DANCE, Sara Lyn
Snake River HS; Moreland, ID (12-127) Ensm; Co-Ch, FHA; 4H; Fin, Jr Miss Pagent; NHS; S-T, Ski C; COM; Hon Prog; Summa Cum Laude; *Brigham Young U; Internatl Relations.*

DANCY, Joyce Elaine
Lincoln Comm HS; Lincoln, IL; *Lincoln Christian Col.*

DANDY, Gregg Erwin
Sioux Rapids Comm Sch; Sioux Rapids, IA (5-21) Pres, Soph Cl; Bsbl; Bkbl; Ftbl; Tr; *U of N Iowa; Bus.*

DANE, Shirley Katherine
Indian River HS; Frankford, DE (10-254) Band; JV, Chldr; Ensm; Fr C; Ch, Hmrm; Orch; SC; Secy, Soph Cl; Semi-Fin, Tnns; COM; Hist A; ARC A; PA; A Avg A; Gym Ribbons; HR; *U of Del; Psychiatrist.*

DANEHART, Brenda Kay
Wheeling Park HS; Wheeling, WV (59-700) Chor; Drama; Ensm; Hmrm; NFL; NHS; Ed, Sch P; Spch C; SC; HCt; Journ A; Spch A; Quill & Scroll; WW; *W Va U; Drama.*

DANFORD, Bobbi Lee
New Brockton HS; New Brockton, AL (10%-75) Ann; BC; Drama; FBLA; Parl, FHA; Spch C; SC; Hon Prog; *Alabama U; Computer Sci.*

DANGERFIELD, Charles Dawes
Wakefield HS; Arlington, VA (50%-400) Tnns; Baptist Traing Union Off; *Recreation.*

DANGERFIELD, Michael
George Henry Corliss HS; Chicago, IL (17-215) *Chicago St U; Elec Engr.*

DANGERFIELD, Steven Gregory
James Island HS; Charleston, SC; BC; Fr C; NHS; Bsbl; Ftbl; COM.

DANIEL, Aaron Duane
John F Kennedy Sr HS; Sacramento, CA (150-673) Chor; FBLA; Ger C; Ftbl; Citz A; Jack & Jill of Amer; Best Stu, Ger; NAACP Yth Coun; Outst Usher; 1st Pl Tm, Bowling Assn; Best Stu, Vocal Mus; *Sacramento City Col; Denistry.*

DANIEL, Collette Yvonne
Ponderosa HS; Shingle Springs, CA (10-420) Bkbl; Swim; Tnns; CSF; Span A; *Bio Sci.*

166

DANIEL, Du Valle Mechalle
J O Johnson HS; Huntsville, AL (10-500) Hmrm; Math C; Mu Alpha Theta; NHS; Pres, Span C; SC; Mgr, Tr; Dance Tm; *Vasser Col; Journ.*

DANIEL, Frederick Gilbert Jr
M B Smiley HS; Houston, TX (17-400) Fr C; Math C; Mu Alpha Theta; NHS; Tnns; Magna Cum Laude; Eng A; WW; *Houston Baptist Col; Pol Sci.*

DANIEL, Jeffrey Lynn
Moore HS; Moore, OK; Band; Ger C; NHS; Orch; Outst, Band; *SW Okla St U; Mus.*

DANIEL, Kelly Ann
Alexander Hamilton HS; Los Angeles, CA (10%-500) Secy, SC; Hon Prog; *UC at Santa Barbara; Sociology.*

DANIEL, Leslie Jewel
Spring HS; Spring, TX (80-490) Lit Mag; NHS; Var C; Mgr, Bkbl; Tr; Art A; *U of Houston; Ed.*

DANIEL, Linda Ruth
Smithfield-Selma Sr HS; Smithfield, NC (4-355) Co-Ed, Ann; Band; Fr C; Hmrm; NHS; Orch; Sch Achieve Tm; Pres, Jr Cl; *NC St U; Pre Vet.*

DANIEL, Linda Sue
Ottaw HS; Ottawa, KS (30%-200) Drama; Pres, FHA; Gym; Presidential Phys Fitness A.

DANIEL, Marilyn Renee
Westside HS; Anderson, SC (50-305) Band; BC; Hmrm; NHS; Win, St Tn Talent; Runner Up; Ntl Tn Talent Comp; *Lee Col; Psych.*

DANIEL, Martishia
E Ridge HS; Chattanooga, TN (37-289) BC; Cpt, Chldr; FHA; Hmrm; NHS; Thes; Co-Cpt, Tnns; Amer Leg A; *U of Tenn at Knoxville; Home Ec.*

DANIEL, Paula
Edgewood Reg Sr HS; Atco, NJ; Bus C; Chor; Interlochen Ntl Mus; *Morehouse Col; Bus.*

DANIEL, Robert Allen
Heritage Christian Sch; Indianapolis, IN (2-61) Rptr, Ann; Ger C; A-Ed, Sch P; Mgr, Bkbl; Mgr, Soccer; NMS; *West Point Acad; Chem Engr.*

DANIEL, Roy Wallace
Independence HS; Independence, MS (15%-72) BC; FFA; Pres, Spch C; Bsbl; Cpt, Bkbl; Ftbl; Tr; Cl Fav; H of F; *Miss Valley St U; Phys Ed.*

DANIEL, Sara Jane
Powell HS; Powell, TN; Band; Drama; VP, Hmrm; Mjrte; Sci C; SC; Bkbl; Sftbl; Church Yth Choir.

DANIEL, Sharon Velicia
Booker T Washington HS; Atlanta, GA (16-345) Chor; Ensm; FHA; Hmrm; Mjrte; NHS; COM; JA A; Span A; *Howard U; Dentistry.*

DANIEL, Sondra Elaine
Haworth HS; Kokomo, IN; Fr C; FHA; Hmrm; *Indiana St U; Journ.*

DANIEL, Steven Anthony
Harry S Truman HS; Bronx, NY (480-750) Band; CYO; Y-Tns; Bsbl; Bkbl; Golf; Tr; Cl Fav; MLS; *Nathaniel Hawthorne Col; Phys Ed.*

DANIEL, Teresa Lynn
Johnson Central HS; Paintsville, KY (1-217) BC; Chor; Fr C; Pres, FHA; 4H; Hmrm; Thes; SC; Parl, Soph Cl; Hist A; Hon Prog; I Dare You; Math A; Val; Jr Chpt & St Homemaker Degree; WW; *Prestonsburg Comm Col; Acct.*

DANIELEY, Jane Elizabeth
Western Alamance HS; Elon College, NC (2-240) Chor; Fr C; FTA; Pres, Hmrm; NHS; DARGCA; Hon Prog; Magna Cum Laude; MLS; Sal; VP, Exchangettes; Exchange C, Yth o-t Mo; Jr Marshal; St Andrews Sci Schol; *Wake Forest U.*

DANIELL, Dewitt Woodruff
Enka HS; Enka, NC (120-260) Drama; Secy, NFL; SC; Ftbl; Tr; Ftbl & Tr Ltrs; *Tex Christian U; Hist.*

DANIELS, Barbara Fay
Brandon Sr HS; Brandon, FL (150-950) A Cap Choir; Band; Chor; Ensm; COM; Piano Guild; Children's Bible Mission HR; Band Contest A; *Trinity Bible Col; Teaching.*

DANIELS, Cheryl Denise
Columbus HS; Columbus, GA; CYO; JV, Chldr; FHA; Hmrm; NHS; VP, Jr Cl; *Clark Col; Bio.*

DANIELS, Christine Grace
Mayo HS; Rochester, MN (365-411) A Cap Choir; Chem C; Chor; Drama; ARC; Swim; 1st Cl GSct; *Recreational Therapy.*

DANIELS, Cynthia Kay
Brandon Sr HS; Brandon, FL (7-854) Band; BC; Orch; Rainbow; Stage Band; Sup Solo, St Contest; Band Ltr; Orch Ltr; Sup, Ntl Piano Play Chldrns Bib Mis; *Trinity Bible Col; Mus Ed.*

DANIELS, David Paul
San Georgonio HS; San Bernardino, CA (3%-640) Community Yth Symph; InterClub Coun; Pres, NHS; Tres, SC; Var C; MVP, Cr-Ctry; MVP, Tr; CSF; Principal's A; Runner Up Ken Hubbs A; All Amer, Tr & Field; All Amer, Cr-Ctry; *UC at Irvine; Safety Engr.*

DANIELS, DeLinda Gale
George Washington HS; Denver, CO; Band; NHS; Med.

DANIELS, Della Margot
Soldan HS; St Louis, MO (167-600) Chor; Y-Tns; I Dare You; Lion A; ROTC A; Spch A; Yth Fel; Distributive Ed; *Home Ec.*

DANIELS, Denise Monica
Northwest HS; St Louis, MO (7-433) Chor; Math C; NHS; SC; Hon Prog; JA A; MLS; *U of Mo; Nurs.*

DANIELS, Franklin Bennett
The McCallie Sch; Chattanooga, TN (55-115) Ftbl; Wrest; *Vanderbilt U; Psych.*

DANIELS, Jacklyn Ann
Science Hill HS; Johnson City, TN; Chldr; Chor; Cr-Ctry; Tnns; *E Tenn St U; Special Ed.*

DANIELS, Janet Gayle
Kountze HS; Kountze, TX (2-92) Ed, Ann; Band; Bus C; Ensm; Tres, FHA; Rptr, FTA; Hmrm; Cpt, Mjrte; Math C; Orch; Sci C; SC; H of F; Type A; WW; YHT Little Sister; *Lamar U; Health.*

DANIELS, Jean Doreen
Montclair HS; Montclair, NJ; Mjrte; ARC; Future Physicians C; *Oral Roberts U; Med.*

DANIELS, Jerome Henry
S Park HS; Buffalo, NY (50%-780) JV, Bkbl; Tr; *Sci.*

DANIELS, Karen Gayle
Norte Del Rio HS; Sacramento, CA; Band; MVP, Bkbl; Cpt, Sftbl; Most Out; *Art.*

DANIELS, Linda Alberta
Southside Jr HS; Buffalo, NY (3-30) Chldr; Sch P; Span C; COM; Gym A; *NY St U; Sci.*

DANIELS, Linda Jean
Round Lake Sr HS; Round Lake Beach, IL (31-377) Hon Prog; Quizzing A's; *Bob Jones U; Child Care.*

DANIELS, Lisa Gaye
Colegio La Merced; Hato Rey, PR (1-108) Drama; Var C; Secy, Jr Cl; Alg A; Bio A; COM; Citz A; Hist A; Math A; Most Out; Phy A; Sci A; Swtht; Val; Exchange C A; Span A; Eng A; *Med.*

DANIELS, Randle Curtis
Western Hills HS; Fort Worth, TX (77-616) Hmrm; SC; JV, Bsbl; JV, Ftbl; Cl Fav.

DANIELS, Ronald Roy
Wasatch HS; Heber City, UT (17-134) A Cap Choir; Band; BS; Chor; Dbte Tm; Drama; Model UN; Orch; Tres, SC; Secy, Var C; Ftbl; Tr; Wrest; 3rd, St Wrest; *Snow Col; Pol Sci.*

DANIELS, Terry Wayne
Hillsborough HS; Tampa, FL (75-640) Band; Chor; Mu Alpha Theta; NHS; *Fla St U; Acct.*

DANIELS, Tim Leon
Highland HS; Albuquerque, NM; Band; Chor; Ger C; Orch; JA A; Bowl Tm.

DANIELS, Vinnie Rolean
Hamilton Co HS; Jasper, FL (2-139) Parl, BC; Tres, 4H; Tr; Hist A; Math A; *Fla A&M U.*

DANIELSON, Donita Dawn
Janesville HS; Janesville, IA (11-36) Bus Mgr, Ann; FBLA; GS; NHS; Sch P; Citz A; Spch A; Stu Teacher; *U of N Iowa; Bus Mgt.*

DANIELSON, Kenneth Wright
Christian HS; El Cajon, CA (10%-120) Band; Dbte Tm; Rptr, Sch P; Pres, SC; Thes; Cpt, Cr-Ctry; JV, Ftbl; Tr; CSF; NMS; Spch A; DAR Nom; Sunday Sch Off; Most Spiritual Ldr; WW; WW; Laurels For Ldrs; *Bob Jones U; Religion.*

DANKA, Judith Ann
Nehsaminy Maple Point HS; Langhorne, PA (14-413) CYO; Chldr; NHS; Bkbl; JV, Hockey; Sftbl; Hon Prog; *Phys Therapy.*

DANKENBRING,
Barbara Bunting
Norwalk HS; Norwalk, CT (1-557) Band; Hon Prog; Church Organist; *Math.*

DANKER, Susan Kay
Dryden Jr HS; Dryden, NY (10%-225) Band; Span C; Yth Fel; Tutor; Phys Ed A; *Phys Therapy.*

DANLEY, Karen Ann
East Central HS; Hurley, MS (7-115) Pres, FBLA; VP, FHA; Sci C; Tres, Sr Cl; *Acct.*

DANLEY, Steven Andrew
Katella HS; Anaheim, CA (4-641) NHS; SC; Var C; Pres, Jr Cl; Bkbl; Ftbl; Amer Leg A; CSF; HCt; Mayor, Yth in Gov Day; Driver Ed A.

DANLEY, Sylvia Michelle
DuPont Park S D A Sch; Washington, DC; Band; Chldr; Chor; Dbte Tm; Span C; VP, Soph Cl; Type A; Mus A.

DANN, Lisa Marie
Goddard HS; Roswell, NM (4-310) F-Ed, Ann; VP, Band; GS; NHS; Sch P; S-T, Span C; Span NHS; Citz A; Most Out; Type A; *Tex Christian U; Bus.*

DANNEHL, William B
Lexington Sr HS; Lexington, NE (1-140) All Amer Yth; Ann; Chor; 4H; NHS; Pres, Sr Cl; Pres, Jr Cl; Bsbl; Bkbl; MVP, Ftbl; Tr; COM; HKg; NMS; Outst Stu; Eng A; *Augustana Col.*

DANNER, Wendella
Franklin HS; Franklin, OH; Rainbow; Church Ensm; Church Bkbl; YMCA Bkbl; *Math.*

DANNI, Eileen Elizabeth
Arapahoe HS; Littleton, CO (45-700) Band; Chor; Key C; JV, Tnns; Hon Prog; Swtht; Key C Swtht; All St Choir; *Colo U; Med Tech.*

DANSBY, Shelia Renee
M B Smiley HS; Houston, TX (14-400) A Cap Choir; FTA; Hmrm; Math C; Mu Alpha Theta; NHS; Tres, Sci C; SC; Bio A; COM; Sci A; FSA Swtht; *U of Houston; Phys Therapy.*

DANTZLER,
Jonathan Christopher
German Twp HS; Mc Clellandtown, PA (3-350) Band; NHS; Orch; *U of Pittsburgh; Med.*

DANTZLER, Marilyn Louise
German Twp Sr HS; Uniontown, PA (40%-125) Band; Mjrte; Stage Band; *Calif St Col; Biochem.*

DANTZLER, Raymond Todd
Winter Haven HS; Winter Haven, FL (115-630) Ed, Ann; BS; Key C; VP, Jr Cl; Tnns; HCt; Yth Fel; *U of Fla.*

DANZEY, Byron Arnold
Bay HS; Panama City, FL (30-400) Pres, Chor; Ensm; NHS; Outst Christian Boy; All St Choir; *Gulf Coast Comm Col.*

DAQUILA, Peter Anthony
St Peters Prep HS; Jersey City, NJ (26-275) Pres, Hmrm; NHS; Sch P; SC; Pres, Sr Cl; Hon Prog; *St Peter's Prep Col; Acct.*

DARBY, Jennifer Jo
Lexington Sr HS; Lexington, NE (13-133) Ann; Chldr; Chor; Sci C; Var C; Alg A; HCt; Hon Prog; Math A; Type A; Cpt, Drill Tm; Vlbl; United Way Girl; Top 10 Fin, Miss Drill Tm Compet; *Nebr U; Foreign Lang.*

DARBY, William Wade
W Morgan HS; Trinity, AL (10%-63) Band; BC; Math C; COM; WW; HR; Most Participating Jr; *Calhoun Comm Col; Bus.*

DARDAR, Virginia Gail
Lafourche HS; Galliano, LA (15-318) ROTC A; Pres, Christ Ambassadors; 1st Pl, Eng Fair; *Southwestern A-G Col; Ministry.*

DARDEN, Arthur Keene
Battle Ground Acad; Franklin, TN (5-76) Chem C; Lat C; Lat NHS; Math C; NHS; JV, Tr; NEDT; St Math Contest; *Auburn U; Phar.*

DARDEN, Kimberly Denise
W Forsyth Sr HS; Clemmons, NC (22-504) AFS; Chor; Drama; Hmrm; Span C; St Stu Congress; SC; Sftbl; Hon Prog; VP, Yth Fel; GSct; *U of NC; Psych.*

DARE, Frances Virginia
Los Alamos HS; Los Alamos, NM (10%-440) Band; Bus C; Chor; Commercial C; Drama; NHS; Pol Sci C; Ski C; Type A; Yth Leg; Ger A; CEA Regional & St, Spch & Typ As; *Journ.*

DARE, John Dale
Fremont Christian HS; Fremont, CA; Drama; VP, SC; Var C; MVP, Soccer; Cpt, Wrest; Cl Fav; MVP, Wrest; *Yth Pastor.*

DARGAVELL, James Wesley
Madison HS; Richmond, KY; Pres, 4H; Sci C; Spch C; Bkbl; 4H A; *Eastern Ky U; Sci.*

DARGITZ, Diane Marie
Pittsburg HS; Pittsburg, KS; Fr C; Mgr, Tr; Hon Prog; Yth Fel; Fr A; *Kans St U; Vet Med.*

DARIEN, Glinton Roy Jr
Leto Comprehensive HS; Tampa, FL; Chess C; Key C; JV, Wrest; *U of Fla; Med.*

DARLEY, Diane Lynn
Patrick Henry HS; San Diego, CA (113-1173) NHS; Ski C; MVP, Tnns; CSF; Yth Fel; Campus Life; Fin, Sewing Olympics; *San Diego St Col; Fashion Merchandising.*

DARLING, Eric Evan
Marysville-Pilchuck HS; Marysville, WA (20-426) Ann; BS; Ger C; Hmrm; InterClub Coun; Ed, Lit Mag; VP, NHS; Rptr, Sch P; Sci C; Ski C; SC; Var C; Swim; JV, Tr; JA A; Masonic A; *Wash St U; Commercial Art.*

DARLING, Margaret Marie
Midwest HS; Midwest, WY (1-23) Ann; Co-Cpt, Chldr; Drama; Pres, Hmrm; Sch P; SC; Var C; Cpt, Bsbl; Bkbl; Tr; Type A; Vlbl; Hon Stu.

DARLING, Renee Nanette
Santa Monica HS; Santa Monica, CA; Chor; Madrigal; Swim; Citz A; Hon Prog; Kiwanis A; ARC A; Type A; Semi-Fin, Tnns; Kiwanis Hon Men; Most Improved Soph, Swim Trophy; Achv A; Mixed Chor; Viking Chorale; HR; Ocean League Finals.

DARLING, Susan Jean
Hannibal Central Sch; Hannibal, NY; Band; Pres, NHS; Secy, Soph Cl.

DARNALL, Ann Louise
Hanson Mem HS; Franklin, LA (3-70) Dbte Tm; 4H; Fin, Lit Ral; NFL; Swim; COM; 4H A; NEDT; Spch A; Torch A; Eng A; Rally A; *La St U; Law.*

DARNALL, Christine Alice
Hanson Mem HS; Franklin, LA (9-65) Dbte Tm; Tres, 4H; Lit Ral; NFL; NHS; Swim; Tnns; COM; 4H A; NEDT; Spch A; Torch A; Fr A; *LSU; Sci.*

DARNALL, John Palmer IV
Mountain Brook HS; Mountain Brook, AL; Demolay; S-T, Key C; Lat C; Order/Arrow; Bsbl; Soccer; Order/Arrow A; *Vanderbilt U; Med.*

DARNELL, David Mark
University of San Diego HS; San Diego, CA (15-311) Chess C; Cum Laude Soc; Bus Mgr, Drama; InterClub Coun; Model UN; NHS; Thes; Mgr, Swim; CSF; COM; Summa Cum Laude; Tres, Drama C; Best Supporting Actress; *U of Calif; Psych.*

DARNELL, Joseph Edward
Cody HS; Detroit, MI (6-35) Drama; Ensm; Ftbl; Ftbl Ltr; Dramatic A; *Morehouse Col; Archt Tech.*

DARR, Howard Melbern
Erie Acad; Erie, PA (25-201) Hmrm; VP, ARC; Co-Ch, SC; Var C; Tr; *Westminster Col; Ed.*

DARR, Lisa Kim
Imperial Unified HS; Imperial, CA; Ann; Band; Ensm; 4H; Co-Cpt, Mjrte; Rainbow; Span C; Spch C; Var C; Mgr, Bsbl; Mgr, Wrest; Cl Fav; 4H A; HCt; *Bus.*

DARRAH, Sherri Elizabeth
Yorkwood HS; Monmouth, IL (10-60) Band; Chor; FHA; Madrigal; Secy, NHS; Span C; Bkbl; Tr; Amer Leg A; Citz A; Co-Cpt, Pom Pon Girl; Vlbl; *Carl Sandburg Col; Nurs.*

DARRELL, Barton David
Daviess Co HS; Owensboro, KY; Bsbl; Bkbl; Yth Leg; Young Hist.

DARRELL, Kim Elyse
Maple Shade HS; Maple Shade, NJ (11-241) Ed, Ann; Hmrm; NHS; Ski C; SC; Secy, Sr Cl; Sftbl; Jr & Sr Plays; Pep C; *Burlington Co Col; Para-Legal.*

DARRELL, Lynn Marie
Highlands Intermediate HS; Notrona Heights, PA; AFS; Band; Orch; Tr; COM; Hon Prog; 1st Cl GSct; *Penn St Main Campus; Mus.*

DARROW, Susan Carol
Highland HS; Bakersfield, CA; Chor; Ski C; Tr; CSF; COM; Citz A; Tn C; Pres, Yth Group; *Pacific Christian Col; Psych.*

DARTT, Pamela Sue
Columbus HS; Columbus, WI (15-141) AFS; Chor; Madrigal; NHS; Pres, Ski C; Var C; Kiwanis A; Cpt, Vlbl; Miss Columbus; *UW Eau Claire; Special Ed.*

DARUS, Heidi Carol
James Ford Rhodes HS; Cleveland, OH (61-486) A Cap Choir; AFS; Chess C; Chor; Pres, French NHS; Secy, FTA; Ch, SC; Y-Tns; Citz A; Hon Prog; Fr A; *Ohio Wesleyan U; Psych.*

DARWELL, Andrew Walter
Kelly HS; Chicago, IL (19-486) Math C; Model UN; Pres, Order/Arrow; Span NHS; Hon Prog; Math A; Order/Arrow A; Ald Swinarski Yth A; *Loyola Col; Acct.*

DASBURG, Albert Scott
Central Jersey Christian Sch; Asbury Park, NJ (2-3) Chess C; Chor; Ensm; Tres, Fr C; SC; JV, Bsbl; JV, Bkbl; JV, Soccer; HCt; *US Coast Guard Acad; Marine Sci.*

DASCOLI, Luwona Aileen
Coventry HS; Akron, OH (44-196) Band; Rptr, Sch P; Hon Prog; *Wittenburg U; Religion.*

DASH, Grace Neomia
Crenshaw HS; Los Angeles, CA (1-1100) Mu Alpha Theta; NHS; Jr Cl; JV, Bkbl; Amer Leg A; CSF; *U of Southern Calif.*

DASHER, Greg Joeseph
Leo HS; Chicago, IL (5-152) Span C; Bsbl; Bkbl; Hon Prog; *DePaul U; World Hist.*

DASHER, Kathryn Gay
Prospect HS; Mount Prospect, IL; Tres, Chor; NFL; NHS; Rptr, Sch P; Spch C; Arch; Spch A; All St Chor; *Abilene Christian U; Psych.*

DATCHER, Victor Glenn
Mergenthaler Voc-Tech HS; Baltimore, MD (15%-670) Band; Drama.

DATI, Deborah Jo
Dominican HS; White Fish Bay, WI (39-225) Ann; NFL; NHS; COM; Spch A; Art A; St Forensics; *Marquette Col; Human Relations.*

DAUGHENBAUGH, Cynthia Kay
Charleston HS; Charleston, IL (5-250) Chor; NHS; SC; Secy, Jr Cl; Hon Prog; Yth Fel; Most Studious; *Ill Wesleyan U.*

DAUGHERTY, Craig Brion
Charles D Owen HS; Swannanoa, NC (80-267) BS; 4H; Hmrm; JV, Bsbl; JV, Bkbl; COM; Outst Sun Sch Stu; PA; A&B HR; Sports As.

DAUGHERTY, Darlene Kay
Poway HS; Poway, CA (32-438) Ch, Band; Community Yth Symph; Hmrm; Orch; Laurel Chain; *San Diego St U; Law.*

DAUGHERTY, Gerald Edward
Dunbar HS; Dayton, OH (5-185) Hmrm; NHS; Sci C; Alg A; COM; Citz A; Cl Fav; Hon Prog; Math A; Sci A; Swtht; WW; SPEEDY Prog; *Morehouse Col; Mech Engr.*

DAUGHERTY, Gloria Denise
Marion Co HS; Lebanon, KY (6-324) Ann; CYO; Cpt, Chldr; Tres, FHA; Hmrm; NHS; SC; Hon Prog; Pres, Art C; Eng A; *Lexington Tech Inst; Acct.*

DAUGHERTY, Keith J
Monroe Union HS; Monroe, OR (2-43) Var C; Bsbl; Bkbl; Ftbl; Sargeant at Arms, Sr Cl; 1st Tm, All League Ftbl & Bsbl; *Oreg St U; Phar.*

DAUGHERTY, Nancy Jean
Renville Pub Sch; Renville, MN (17-45) Band; Chor; FHA; Mjrte; Bkbl; Sftbl; Swim; Tnns; *Alexandria Col; Nurs.*

DAUGHERTY, Paul Francis
Tuscarawas Central Cath HS; New Philadelphia, OH (2-64) Chem C; Key C; Math C; NHS; SC; Pres, Jr Cl; Cpt, Bkbl; Golf; Tr; Alg A; Bio A; COM; Chem A; Hist A; Hon Prog; Math A; MLS; Most Out; Phy A; Type A; MVP, Bkbl; Dover Exchange C; *Ohio N U; Nuclear Engr.*

DAUGHERTY, Richard Alan
Chardon HS; Chardon, OH (62-249) Pres, 4H; NHS; Ftbl; Tr; Wrest; Citz A; 4H A; Hon Prog; Most Out; Jr Fair King; Citz Course; 4-H Congress; Gold Medal, Public Speak & Ldrship; *Agr Tech Inst; Livestock Production.*

DAUGHERTY, Richard Steve
Western Hills HS; Cincinnati, OH; *Anderson Ind Col; Art.*

DAUGHERTY, Robert Wayne
Switzerland HS; Vevay, IN (2-137) Golf.

DAUGHERTY, Ronald Darrell
Early Co HS; Blakely, GA (10%-219) A Cap Choir; BS; Chor; Ensm; Secy, FFA; Madrigal; Bsbl; Bkbl; JV, Ftbl; Wrest; COM; Spch A; *U of Ga; Fish & Game Bio.*

DAUGHERTY, Ronnette Earlene
Mt Zion HS; Mt Zion, IL (40-225) AFS; Ann; Drama; Rptr, 4H; Sch P; Spch C; JV, Tr; COM; 4H A; Hon Prog; Journ A; PTA A; Bkbl; Cr-Ctry & Tr Statistician; S-T, Yth Fel; Young Democrats; Explorers C; *Communications.*

DAUGHERTY, Thomas Wilcox
Wellsboro Area Sr HS; Wellsboro, PA (33%-216) Order/Arrow; Order/Arrow A; Yth Fel; Torch A; Photo A; Schol Arts A; Life Sct; *Rochester Col; Photography.*

DAUGHERTY, Tom Charles
Yerba Buena HS; San Jose, CA; Var C; Ftbl; Soccer; Tr; Wrest; Citz A; Pres A; Ath As.

DAUGHTREY, Bethanne
Suffolk HS; Suffolk, VA (3-120) Drama; VP, Lat C; NHS; ARC; SC; Thes; Bio A; Outst, Piano; *U of Va; Law.*

DAUGHTREY, Vicki Lynn
Paris HS; Paris, TX (2-263) Secy, Band; Pres, FTA; Ger C; NHS; Tri-HiY; Most Out; Opt Out Tn; Sal; FCA; Best All Around Girl; Keywanette C; Tn Adv Board; Cpt, Flag Corps; *Tex Christian U; Acct.*

DAUGHTRY, Vicki Carlyn
James Madison Sr HS; San Diego, CA (45-1060) Chor; Ensm; Pres, VP, Church Missions Organ; *Point Loma Col.*

DAULEY, Annette Marie
Whitney Point Sr HS; Whitney Point, NY (12-150) Band; CYO; Chldr; Pres, FTA; Pres, 4H; Hmrm; Secy, NHS; SC; COM; 4H A; HCt; *Elem Ed.*

DAULYS, Loretta Salome
Maria HS; Chicago, IL (27-364) Chor; Drama; Fr C; Hmrm; SC; Thes; Tr; COM; Kiwanis A; Schoenstadt A; IABA Mus A; Geneva Mus A; *U of Ill-Urbana; Psych.*

DAULYS, Vitas Kazys
St Ignatius Col Prep Sch; Chicago, IL (10-218) CYO; Amer Leg A; COM; God & Country A; NEDT; Mus Trophies; IABA Mus Contest; Geneva Mus Contest; Essay Contest Trophy; *Loyola Col; Physics.*

DAUM, Marilyn Susan
Lindbergh HS; St Louis, MO (1-901) Chor; 4H; NHS; Span C; Sftbl; Curator A; Yth Fel; Yth Leg; Span A; Singer Sewing A; *U of Mo-Rolla; Computer Sci.*

DAUPHIN, Kathryn Millard
Thomasville HS; Thomasville, AL; Band; Chldr; Chor; Community Yth Symph; Drama; Ensm; VP, Fr C; FHA; Key C; Beauty; COM; Yth Fel; *U of Ala; Psych.*

DAUPHINE, Millie Melba
Cecelia Sr HS; Cecelia, LA; VP, Band; BC; 4H; Jr Miss Pagent; Cpt, Mjrte; Cpt, Sftbl; Swim; Beauty; 4H A; Hon Prog; ARC A; *U of Southwestern La; Commerce.*

DAUTERMAN, Crystal Kay
Fostoria HS; Fostoria, OH; Band; Chor; Ensm; FHA; ARC; Span C; Y-Tns; Hon Prog; Band As; *Eckerd Col; Nurs.*

DAUTERMANN, Kim Allen
Parkview HS; Orfordville, WI (25-180) Pres, 4H; COM; 4H A.

DaVALT, Brian Harold
Beaver Dam HS; Beaver Dam, WI (78-307) Band; Semi-Fin, BS; Ensm; 4H; Hmrm; JV, Golf; Type A; Church Orch; WW; *Mus.*

DAVANZO, Marian Melinda
Cardinal Mooney HS; Youngstown, OH (50-343) Band; Drama; Math C; NHS; Orch; ARC; Span C; Best Bandsman; *Youngstown St U; Mus Ed.*

DAVENPORT, Angela Elaine
St Bernard HS; Playa del Rey, CA; CYO; Hon Prog; *UCLA; Psych.*

DAVENPORT, Anthony
Montclair HS; Montclair, NJ (50%-545) Mgr, CYO; Chor; Drama; Bus Mgr, Ensm; Hmrm; SC; Ftbl; Tnns; Mgr, Tr; COM; Cl Fav; Spch A; Yth Fel; Founders A; *Boston U; Pol Sci.*

DAVENPORT, Cheryl Louise
Martin Luther HS; Maspeth, NY; Chor; Tr; Yth Fel; Sunday Sch Merit List; *Morgan Col; Psych.*

DAVENPORT, Connie Jean
Orleans HS; Orleans, NE (15-30) Chor; 4H; JV, Golf.

DAVENPORT, Jacqueline Louise
Carroll HS; Monroe, LA (12-205) Chor; Drama; FHA; Co-Cpt, Mjrte; SC; B Crocker A; Hon Prog; Mjrte A; Singing A; *Robinson Bus Col; Acct.*

DAVENPORT, Leigh Ann
Stamford HS; Stamford, TX (4-68) Co-Ed, Ann; Band; Chldr; S-T, FHA; Lat NHS; Tres, NHS; Pres, SC; Thes; Tnns; Cl Fav; HQn; Sr Most Rep; Best Actress, Dist; Win, Region Ready Writing; Outst Stu; *Tex A&M U; Journ.*

DAVENPORT, Tamela Ann
Antelope Valley HS; Lancaster, CA; Chor; CSF; Drill Tm.

DAVENPORT, Tami Lu
Findlay Sr HS; Findlay, OH (15%-700) Tr; Pepper C; Explorers; Explorers; *Legal Secy.*

DAVERSA, Sandra J
Bishop Gibbons HS; Schenectady, NY (22-161) NHS; JA A; K of C A; Type A; *Siena Col; Acct.*

DAVID, Andrew Kaleel
Columbia HS; Decatur, GA (1-350) BC; Key C; SC; MVP, Soccer; Gov Honor Prog; Hon Prog; Interntl Lang C; *Med.*

DAVID, Camille
Goddard HS; Roswell, NM; A Cap Choir; Chor; Ensm; NHS; Span C; Span NHS; Beauty; Most Out; Jolliest Couple A; Service A; Swtht, Chor; Octagon C; Pres, Yth Group; All St Choir; *Tex Tech U; Phys Theraphy.*

DAVID, Donald
Church Point HS; Church Point, LA (11-125) A Cap Choir; BC; Pres, CYO; Chor; Dbte Tm; Ch, FFA; FHA; K of C; NHS; Spch C; Pres, Jr Cl; Pres, Soph Cl; Pres A; Spch A; *Agr Engr.*

DAVID, Donald Gilbert Jr
Columbia HS; Decatur, GA (23-360) Ann; BC; Drama; Hmrm; Key C; Model UN; Span C; SC; Soccer; U of Ga; Pre Med.

DAVIDS, Susan Elizabeth
S Garland HS; Garland, TX (50-660) VP, FHA; Mu Alpha Theta; WW; *U of Tex; Bus.*

DAVIDSON, Anita Doreen
Summit HS; Frisco, CO; Chor; Drama; S-T, FHA; Sch P.

DAVIDSON, Candace
Aptos HS; Aptus, CA (40-300) Chor; 4H; Ski C; Y-Tns; Swim; Tr; CSF; COM; Cl Fav; 4H A; Hist A; Swim A's; Co Fair A's; HR; Sewing A; *Biola Col; Special Ed.*

DAVIDSON, Cindy Ann
Springfield HS; Springfield, IL (102-509) Chor; Drama; Ger C; COM; Pres A; *Nurs.*

DAVIDSON, Dana Marie
Piper HS; Sunrise, FL; A Cap Choir; Band; Chor; Ensm; S-T, 4H; Orch; 4H A; *Warren Wilson Col.*

DAVIDSON, Donna Joy
William Penn HS; Philadelphia, PA; Mjrte; Tnns; Citz A; Spch A; Perfect Punctuality; Candystriper; *Comm Col; X-Ray Tech.*

DAVIDSON, Gregory Lee
Maddock Pub Sch; Maddock, ND (4-28) Tres, Band; Pres, FFA; Secy, 4H; Secy, Var C; Pres, Jr Cl; Secy, Soph Cl; Bsbl; Cpt, Bkbl; Pres, Golf; Tr; Bio A; Chem A; 4H A; Hist A; HKg; Type A; Shop A; Ag A; St FFA Pub Speaking Win; All-Conf Bkbl; *ND St U; Architecture.*

DAVIDSON, Jeffery Thomas
Broad Ripple HS; Indianapolis, IN; Chor; Art C; Art A's; *Art.*

DAVIDSON, Jill Kerri
Wachusett Regional HS; Holden, MA (92-530) A Cap Choir; Cpt, Chldr; Pres, Chor; Drama; Hmrm; Madrigal; Rptr, Sch P; VP, SC; Cpt, Sftbl; *Hartt Sch of Mus; Mus.*

DAVIDSON, John Carl
Baker HS; Baker, LA (10%-351) BC; HiY; Ftbl; Mu Signia; Pres, FCA; *LSU; Law.*

DAVIDSON, Kent Joel
Stanton Comm Sch; Stanton, NE (6-45) Bus Mgr, Ann; Mgr, Band; Chor; Community Yth Symph; Drama; Ch, FFA; Pres, 4H; NHS; Rptr, Sch P; Wrest; 4H A; Hon Prog; Band A; FFA Proficiency A; *Agr.*

DAVIDSON, Kimberly Anne
Scotia-Glenville Sr HS; Scotia, NY; CYO; Chor; Drama; Hmrm; SC; JV, Hockey; Hon Prog; JV, Vlbl; 1st Cl, GSct; *Cornell U; Vet Med.*

DAVIDSON, Kirsten Heidi
Wachusett Regional HS; Holden, MA (44-519) FHA; VP, NHS; *Upsala Col; Sociology.*

DAVIDSON, Lorri Ann
Englewood Christian Sch; Independence, MO; Chldr; Chor; Drama; Semi-Fin, Jr Miss Pa; A-Ed, Lit Mag; NHS; Co-Ed, Sch P; Pres, SC; Pres, Jr Cl; COM; Citz A; HQn; Journ A; Math A; Sal; Spch A; Yth Fel; Miss Photogenic, Miss Mo Ntl Tn; *Math.*

DAVIDSON, Marjorie Alice
Queen City HS; Queen City, TX (5-44) Ed, Ann; VP, Band; Ensm; FHA; NHS; Co-Ed, Sch P; SC; Mgr, Bkbl; Mgr, Tr; Band Swtht; WW; Historian, FHA; Band Medal Win; *Texarkana Comm Col; Law.*

DAVIDSON, Mark Allen
Austintown Fitch HS; Youngston, OH (128-650) NHS; JA A; Rptr, Italian C; VP, JA; S-T, Yth Fel; WW; *Youngstown St U; Computer Programming.*

DAVIDSON, Mary Helen
Gilmer HS; Gilmer, TX (33%-200) Band; Parl, FHA; Mjrte; Span C; Spch C; SC; Golf; Regional Golf Tourn; *Baylor U; Sci.*

DAVIDSON, Michael Joseph
Meridian HS; Meridian, TX; SC; FFA; Pres, Hmrm; Pres, Jr Cl; Bkbl; Ftbl; Fin, Tr; COM; Math A; *Baylor U; Math.*

DAVIDSON, Patricia Gay
Muenster Pub Sch; Muenster, TX (1-25) Ed, Ann; Rptr, Band; Ensm; Pres, FHA; Pres, 4H; Cpt, Mjrte; VP, NHS; Sci C; Rptr, Span C; Secy, SC; VP, Sr Cl; Tres, Jr Cl; 4H A; Church Choir; Most Outst; MYF; Most Talented; Busy Bee; *Texas Tech; Journalism.*

DAVIDSON, Penny Joy
Eisenhower HS; Decatur, IL; Pres, Chor; *Nurs.*

DAVIDSON, Ramona Gale
Patrick Henry HS; Glade Spring, VA;

DAVIDSON, William Harrison III
Parkview HS; Springfield, MO (33%-400) Order/Arrow; ARC; Order/Arrow A; ARC A; Tres, VICA; Church Bkbl; Hockey, Sftbl & Swim; Eagle Sct; Camp Counselor; *SW Mo St U; Computer Sci.*

DAVIE, Laura Elizabeth
Dunlap Comm HS; Dunlap, IA (20-60) Band; JV, Chldr; Chor; FHA; 4H; Madrigal; SC; Secy, Jr Cl; MVP, Swim; HCt; *Iowa W Comm Col; Nurs.*

DAVIES, Beth
Barnesville HS; Barnesville, OH (14-110) Ann; Band; Chor; Fr C; FTA; 4H; Sch P; SC; Ch, Y-Tns; Bkbl; Mgr, Tr; Mgr, Wrest; Journ A; *Mt Carmel Sch of Nurs; Nurs.*

DAVIES, Candace L
Northgate HS; Walnut Creek, CA (26-427) Tnns; CSF; Hon Prog; *U of Calif; Math.*

DAVIES, Darcia Lou
Lancaster Sr HS; Lancaster, WI (16-131) Band; Chor; Ensm; GS; 4H; Mjrte; VP, NHS; Orch; Sch P; VP, Sr Cl; Tres, Jr Cl; Tres, Soph Cl; Co-Cpt, Bkbl; Tr; 4H A; Pres A; Most Improved, BB; DAHSS; *UW-LACROSSE; Bus.*

DAVIES, Frank Wesley
Mt Brook HS; Mt Brook, AL (33%-400) Demolay; Lat C; Order/Arrow; Co-Cpt, Soccer; Order/Arrow A; A-B HR; Yth Rep, Church Retreat; Great Son Camp; Parish Yth Comm; MVP Church Bkbl; Membership, Care Comm; *Auburn U; Engr.*

DAVIES, Janet Lindsay
King Goerge HS; King George, VA (17-160) Chldr; Drama; 4H; Hmrm; NHS; Tres, Thes; Co-Cpt, Hockey; Tr; Citz A; 4-Star Thes A; *J Sergeant Reynolds Col; Med Records Tech.*

DAVIES, Jill Annette
Grand Blanc HS; Grand Blanc, MI; Tnns; Thespian Apprentice; Best Director; Most Believable Performance; NAC Service A; *Broadcasting.*

DAVIES, Kenna Jo
Monterey HS; Lubbock, TX (20%-690) Band; VP, FHA; NHS; Tri-HiY; Hon Prog; *Tex Tech U; Psych.*

DAVIES, Luellen Lee
W Forest HS; Tionesta, PA (3-20) Chor; Ensm; Span C; GSct.

DAVILA, Elyda
Thomas A Edison HS; San Antonio, TX; Tres, A Cap Choir; CYO; Chor; Dist Choir A; Dist Solo Silver Medal; *SAC; Mus.*

DAVILA, Rosa Matilde
Colegio San Conrado HS; Ponce, PR (1-49) VP, NHS; COM; Hon Prog; *Recinto Universitario Mayaguez; Ciencias Naturales.*

DAVILA, Samuel R
Southwest HS; San Antonio, TX; Pres, Band; Chess C; Dbte Tm; Ensm; Ftbl; JV, Tr; Citz A; Most Out; Mr Sports, Yth Camp; Pres, Church Yth; All City Band; *Col Coach.*

DAVIS, Aaron Clay
Friendly HS; Oxon Hill, MD; *U of Md; Art.*

DAVIS, Althea Lynette
Bryan Adams HS; Dallas, TX; NHS; Spch C; Band A; Jazz Dance A; *Pepperdine U; Acct.*

DAVIS, Alvin Kendell
Nether Providence HS; Wallinsford, PA (200-277) SC; Bkbl; Ftbl; Tr; *U of Pittsburgh; Econ.*

DAVIS, Angela Laketta
Asbury Park HS; Asbury Park, NJ; Drama; Ger C; Delta Sigma Theta A; HR; Pub Address A.

DAVIS, Angela Louise
Lindblom Tech HS; Chicago, IL (237-433) A Cap Choir; Chor; Hmrm; VP, Lat C; Lit Mag; Madrigal; SC; UN Council; COM; Ntl Achv Schol; NEDT; PA; Golden Eagle A; *Southern U Baton Rouge La; Bio.*

DAVIS, Anthony Lyvoughn
St Joseph HS; Cleveland, OH; Band; Co-Ch, Order/Arrow; ARC; Ski C; Var C; Cr-Ctry; Ftbl; Tr; Citz A; Journ A; Order/Arrow A; *Ohio N U; Phar.*

DAVIS, Bambi Lynn
Daviess Co HS; Owensboro, KY (67-390) Band; BC; Drama; Fr C; *Nurs.*

DAVIS, Barbara Jean
Niagara Falls HS; Niagara Falls, NY; A Cap Choir; Chldr; Chor; Most Out; *Miami Dade Col.*

DAVIS, Barbara Jean
Crestview Sr HS; Crestview, FL (10%-257) Drama; Fr C; ROTC A; Spch A; Comm A; Bronze Legion of Valor A; Editorial Ed, Sch P; *Sociology.*

DAVIS, Barbara Lynn
Sallisaw HS; Sallisaw, OK; Chor; Ensm; Pol Sci C; Sci C; Chor A; STP C.

DAVIS, Barbetta Allean
E Aurora Sr HS; Aurora, IL (43-676) A Cap Choir; Band; Chldr; Chor; City Conf; Community Yth Symph; Ensm; Hmrm; NHS; SC; Up Bound; Bsbl; HCt; Star Student; Church Choir Director; VP, Black Stu Assn; *N Ill U; Math.*

DAVIS, Barry Rodgers
The Carolina Acad; Lake City, SC (1-20) Ann; Secy, BC; Chor; Cum Laude Soc; NHS; Sch P; SC; Var C; Bsbl; Cpt, Bkbl; MVP, Ftbl; Golf; Swim; Tnns; Gr Marshal; H of F; Hist A; Hon Prog; JA A; Most Out; Ntl Achv Schol; Summa Cum Laude; Val; Yth Fel; WW; PC Fel; Order of Bobcat; Cand, Gov Sch; *Clemson U; Med.*

DAVIS, Benny Warren
Englewood HS; Jacksonville, FL (10%-500) Chor; Ensm; SC; Ftbl; Tnns; Hon Prog; *Pre-Med.*

DAVIS, Benny Warren Jr
Englewood HS; Jacksonville, FL (10%-500) Ensm; SC; Ftbl; Tnns; *Med.*

DAVIS, Bernadette Gertrude
Lake Clifton Sr HS; Baltimore, MD (10%-350) Hmrm; NHS; JV, Bkbl; Bio A; Hist A; Math A; Sci A; *UMBC; Nurs.*

DAVIS, Betty Lea
Hattiesburg HS Rowan Center; Hattiesburg, MS (5%-500) Ann; Mu Alpha Theta; Rainbow; Pres, SC; Y-Tns; *U of Sou Miss; Med.*

DAVIS, Bill
Butler HS; Butler, MO (2-90) Pres, FFA; NHS; Chem A; Hon Prog; *U of Nebr; Agr.*

DAVIS, Bradford Allen
Princeton HS; Princeton, NJ; Chor; Co-Cpt, Soccer; Deacon; Yth Fellowship; Choir; Cabinet, Nassau Presb Yth Felwshp; *Forestry.*

DAVIS, Bradford J
Bend Sr HS; Bend, OR (15%-486) NHS; ARC; Ftbl; COM; MLS; Most Out; Order/Arrow A; ARC A; Eagle Sct; *NW Bible Col; Bible Theology.*

DAVIS, Brenda Gayle
Edward H White HS; Jacksonville, FL (28-646) Chor; Drama; Hmrm; NHS; Span C; Spch C; SC; Bio A; Coun of Teach A; Hist A; Spch A; Col, Johnson, Schol's; Woman's C; *Jacksonville U; Eng.*

DAVIS, Brenda Sue
Ottumwa HS; Ottumwa, IA (70-590) Band; Chor; Drama; Ensm; Madrigal; Bkbl; Sftbl; PTA A; Type A; Secy, Christian Yth Fel; Books For Brotherhood A; *Phys Therapy.*

DAVIS, Bryant Dale
Sherman E Burroughs HS; Ridgecrest, CA (5-750) Band; Dbte Tm; NFL; Order/Arrow; ARC; SC; Kiwanis A; Yth Foundation A; Eagle Sct; Ch, Ecology; *San Francisco St Col; Pol Sci.*

DAVIS, Carla Susanne
Bethel Baptist Christian HS; Memphis, TN (2-20) Chldr; Ensm; Cl Fav; HQn; HCt; Type A; Bible A; Most Talented; Friendliest; Miss Bethel; *Tri-State Baptist Col; Piano Ed.*

DAVIS, Carol Ann
John F Kennedy Sr HS; New Orleans, LA; BC; NHS; Hon Prog; Most Out; Type A; Yth Fel; *Engr.*

DAVIS, Carol Beth
DeSoto Sr HS; De Soto, KS; Chldr; Chor; NHS; *Olivet Col.*

DAVIS, Carol Jean
Morrow Sr HS; Morrow, GA; Chor; FHA; *Clark Col; Mus.*

DAVIS, Carol Leonora
Beaufort Acad; Beaufort, SC (4-38) F-Ed, Ann; Fr C; NHS; A-Ed, Sch P; Var C; Mgr, Bkbl; Hon Prog; May Day Court; Presbyterian Col Fel; *Converse Col; Bus.*

DAVIS, Carolyn Berniece
Hammond Christian Acad; Griffith, IN (3-20) A Cap Choir; Band; Chldr; Chor; Ensm; Orch; Sch P; Cl Fav; HCt; Pres A.

DAVIS, Carolyn Sue
Dan River HS; Ringgold, VA (100-222) BC; Chess C; FBLA; Rptr, FHA; Hmrm; Sch P; SC; Bkbl; Sftbl; HCt; *Danville Comm Col; Stenography.*

DAVIS, Catherine Elissa
Crestview Sr HS; Crestview, FL (30-252) Anchor C; Band; Chldr; FTA; Fin, GS; Hmrm; SC; Tnns; Pres A; Comm of Ed A of Merit & of Excel.

DAVIS, Charles Alvin
Hunter Huss HS; Gastonia, NC (5%-700) Band; BC; Tnns; *Physics.*

DAVIS, Charles Christopher
Alto HS; Alto, TX (4-50) Dbte Tm; Drama; Fr C; FFA; Hmrm; NHS; Sci C; Spch C; Golf; Tr; Cl Fav; Hon Prog; Sci A; Yth Fel; *Stephen F Austin St Col.*

DAVIS, Charles Kenneth
Tipton HS; Tipton, OK (2-38) VP, Band; Ensm; Rptr, FFA; 4H; Math C; Alg A; Amer Leg A; Citz A; 4H A; Hist A; HCt; Hon Prog; Math A; Sal; Spch A; St Scholar; Alt, BS; WW; Okla Hon Soc; *Okla Christian Col; Math.*

DAVIS, Charlotte Quinnette
Hinton HS; Hinton, WV (30-150) Band; Drama; Fr C; Pres, 4H; Hmrm; Jr Miss Pagent; Lat C; Mjrte; Math C; 4H A; WW Hist C; *Nurs.*

DAVIS, Cherie Renee
Palo Duro HS; Amarillo, TX (114-445) VP, Band; Chldr; Drama; Secy, FHA; Hmrm; Lat C; SC; Y-Tns; VP, Soph Cl; Tr; Tr Qn; SC Fav; Smiler, Soph Cl Fav, Runner- up; Vlbl.

DAVIS, Cheryl Lynn
Herbert Hoover HS; San Diego, CA (122-400) Band; Chldr; Drama; 4H; Spch C; SC; VP, Jr Cl; AFS; BS; Cl Fav; Pres A; Spch A; Star Student; Bible Memory Verse A; Jr Best Vocalist; Oretorical Contest; Spiritual Growth & Development A; *U of Calif; Eng.*

DAVIS, Christopher Allen
Daviess Co HS; Owensboro, KY (21-306) Pres, Chess C; Order/Arrow; Amer Leg A; B Crocker A; God & Country A; Opt A; Order/Arrow A; Eagle Sct; Fin, Preacher Boy Contest; Pres, Sr High Church Yth Group; Church Yth A; *Johnson Bible Col; Religion.*

DAVIS, Christopher George
Webster Groves HS; Webster Groves, MO (17-500) AFS; Drama; Lit Mag; Math C; NHS; Order/Arrow; Phys C; Arch; Bkbl; Golf; Sftbl; Tnns; COM; DARGCA; God & Country A; Hon Prog; Order/Arrow A; Rotary A; Yth Foundation; Eagle Sct; Sr Service A; *Rice U; Math.*

DAVIS, Christopher Lynn
Lompoc Sr HS; Lompoc, CA (56-467) CSF; Yth Fel; *U of Calif; Environmental Engr.*

DAVIS, Cindra Dee
Palo Duro HS; Amarillo, TX; Chor; Secy, FBLA; Cl Fav; HCt; Type A; All Star Acad Achv A; Young Life.

DAVIS, Cynthia Dianne
Greencastle-Antrim Sr HS; Greencastle, PA (12-243) Band; Chor; Ensm; Lat C; Madrigal; *Lancaster Gen Hospital Sch of Nurs; Nurs.*

DAVIS, Dana Sue
MacArthur HS; Irving, TX; Rptr, Hmrm; NHS; F-Ed, Sch P; VP, SC; Secy, Soph Cl; Swim; Citz A; Cl Fav; Hon Prog; Most Out; Yth Fel; Civic Ballet; Cpt, Drill Tm; Stu Adv Committee; Outst Dancer & Marcher, Drill Tm S; *Tex Christian U; Performing Arts.*

DAVIS, Darcell
John Charles Fremont HS; Los Angeles, CA (141-550) Chor; Sch P; SC; Citz A; Most Out; Cert Accomplishment, Ed Aide Train; *Southland Med Col; Med Terminology.*

DAVIS, David Jordan
Slaton HS; Slaton, TX (10-120) Band; BS; Dbte Tm; FTA; NHS; Span C; Hon Prog; *Tex Tech U; Archt.*

DAVIS, David William
Wayne Comm HS; Corydon, IA (4-80) Band; Chor; SC; Thes; JV, Bkbl; Ftbl; Tr; *Forestry.*

DAVIS, Dawn Ann
Washington Comm HS; Washington, IL (72-384) Chor; Co-Ed, Sch P; Mgr, Bkbl; MVP, Sftbl; Yth Fel.

DAVIS, Debbie
Wasatch HS; Heber City, UT (4-155) Chldr; SC; Sftbl; Tr; Hon Prog; Vlbl; Accompanist, A Cappella Choir; *Brigham Young U; Eng.*

DAVIS, Debbie Lynn
John Overton HS; Nashville, TN; Chor; NHS; Pres, Sci C; Span C; *Med Field.*

DAVIS, Debbie Wynell
Jackson Central Merry HS; Jackson, TN; MVP, Bsbl; MVP, Bkbl; Hon Prog.

DAVIS, Debby A
Westminster Christian HS; Miami, FL (18-102) Band; Chor; Ensm; Monogram; NHS; Orch; ARC; Co-Cpt, Tr; *Gardner-Webb Col; Nurs.*

DAVIS, Deborah Diane
Grace Christian HS; Prattville, AL (6-11) Ann; Tres, Sch P; Attendance, Art, A's; *Auburn U; Art.*

DAVIS, Deborah Elaine
Chester HS; Chester, PA; Rptr, Sch P; COM; Citz A; Kiwanis A; Sci A; Spch A; Yth Foundation A; Jr NHS; HR; Foreign Lang A; *Med.*

DAVIS, Deborah Ellen
Westminster HS; Westminster, MD (10%-500) NHS; Scholastic Ltr; *The King's Col; Fr.*

DAVIS, Deborah Renee
Beaumont-Charlton-Pollard HS; Beaumont, TX (5%-1000) Tri-HiY; VP, Vocational Off Ed; Drill Tm; *Lamar Col; Registered Nurse.*

DAVIS, Debra Jan
Oak Hill HS; Oak Hill, OH (5-115) Band; BC; Chldr; Chor; 4H; Lat C; Mjrte; NHS; Sch Achieve Tm; Sch P; Tri-HiY; Tr; 4H A; Swtht; Hon 'O'; Hon Stars; *Portsmouth Interstate Bus Col; Secretarial Work.*

DAVIS, Debra Jean
Celina HS; Celina, TN (1-66) Secy, FTA; Math C; NHS; F-Ed, Sch P; Sci C; Balfour A; Eng A; Bus Ed A; *Tenn Tech U; Special Ed.*

DAVIS, Dennis Wayne
Roosevelt HS; Dallas, TX (25%-1000) Y-Tns; Bsbl; Ftbl; Soccer; Swim; Citz A; God & Country A; Order/Arrow A; Yth Foundation A; Sr Patrol Ldr, BSct; Amer Cancer Soc; Most Outst, Bsbl; Church Service A; Woodshop A; *Dental Tech.*

DAVIS, Donald Edward
Lumberton Sr HS; Lumberton, NC (22-260) Pres, Band; Chor; Parl, FBLA; NHS; Orch; Sci C; Span C; COM; Hist A; Hon Prog; Outst Sr; WW; *Pembroke St U; Pol Sci.*

DAVIS, Donna Elaine
Orangeburg-Wilkinson HS; Orangeburg, SC (5%-439) Pres, 4H; COM; 4H A; Hon Prog; *Orangeburg Calhoun Tech Col; Radiologic Tech.*

DAVIS, Donna Eleanor
Castlewood Ind Sch; Castlewood, SD (7-22) F-Ed, Ann; Band; Dbte Tm; Drama; Parl, FHA; 4H; Mjrte; Sch P; VP, SC; MVP, Bkbl; Co-Cpt, Tr; Mgr, Bkbl; *Dakota St Col; Elem Ed.*

DAVIS, Donna Faye
The Heritage Sch; Newnan, GA (4-13) Chldr; Drama; Fr C; Pres, InterAct C; VP, SC; JV, Bkbl; JV, Soccer; JV, Sftbl; JV, Tr; Secy, Tres, SC; Fr A; *Elem Ed.*

DAVIS, Donna Jean
Richland HS; Ft Worth, TX; FHA; Ger C; Bus Mgr, Sch P; Secy, Hist C; *N Tex St U; Med Tech.*

DAVIS, Donna Lynn
Splendora HS; Splendora, TX (12-86) FBLA; FHA; FTA; Tres, NHS; Sch P; Beauty; HQn; HCt; Pres A; Vlbl; Best All-Around; WW; *Southwestern A-G Col; Christian Ed.*

DAVIS, Dora Lynne
Harrison HS; Colorado Springs, CO (20-450) Pres, FHA; Hmrm; *U of Colo; Sci.*

DAVIS, Edna Delores
Gumberry HS; Gumberry, NC (4-100) BC; Chldr; Chor; Drama; FHA; VP, 4H; I Dare You; JA A; *U of NC; Acct.*

DAVIS, Elaine
Orange HS; Orange, NJ; Chor; COM; MLS; Most Out; Star Student; Yth Fel; Mus A; *Seton Hall U; Bus.*

DAVIS, Elise Lawton
Hammond Acad; Columbia, SC (20-90) Drama; Fr C; ARC; Sch P; Thes; Hon Prog; NEDT; Pres A.

DAVIS, Elizabeth Anne
Ruskin HS; Kansas City, MO; FHA; NHS; Span C; JV, Tnns; *Central Mo St Col; Acct.*

DAVIS, Elizabeth Willene
Briarfield Acad; Lake Providence, LA (12-49) Ensm; 4H; Lit Ral; Sch P; Span C; 2nd Pl, Span Lit Rally; *La Polytechnical U; Bus Mgt.*

DAVIS, Eloise Ann
E J Wilson HS; Spencerport, NY (5%-348) A Cap Choir; Chor; VP, Drama; Hmrm; Math C; Model UN; A-Ed, Sch P; SC; Tnns; 1st Cl GSct; God & Comm A; GSct Coun & Board of Directors; Vlbl; 'V' Sports Ltr.

DAVIS, Elsie
Russell HS; Hurtsboro, AL (8-57) Chor; Drama; FTA; 4H; Tres, NHS; Tres, Sr Cl; 4H A; Hon Prog; ROTC A; Superior Cadet; *Selma U; Pre-Med.*

DAVIS, Emily Ruth
Willow Glen HS; San Jose, CA (20%-300) Ed, Ann; Chldr; VP, Chor; GS; NFL; NHS; SC; Tnns; Bio A; CSF; Hon Prog; Spch A; Ed, Church Paper; JV, Vlbl; Spch Win, Baptist General Conf; *Bethel Col; Spch.*

DAVIS, Emma
Orange HS; Orange, NJ; Chor; Hmrm; SC; COM; MLS; Most Out; Star Student; Yth Fel; Mus A; *Seton Hall U; Bus.*

DAVIS, Ernest Tobias
Christian Acad; Chester, PA (15-31) Chor; Drama; Ger C; Rptr, Sch P; VP, SC; Pres, Soph Cl; Pres, Tr; Amer Leg A; COM; Cl Fav; Hon Prog; Spch A; *Pa St U; Med.*

DAVIS, Ervin Bernard
Saginaw HS; Saginaw, MI (16-400) Chor; Amer Leg A; COM; Citz A; Type A; Creativity A; *Central Mich U; Pre-Nurs.*

DAVIS, Eula Paulette
Eastside HS; Paterson, NJ (10%-615) Band; NHS; SC; HR Bronze Pin; *Cornell U; Pre-Med.*

DAVIS, Evelyn
Orange HS; Orange, NJ; Tres, Chor; Hmrm; SC; Secy, Soph Cl; COM; MLS; Most Out; Star Student; Yth Fel; Mus A; *Seton Hall U; Bus.*

DAVIS, Felecia Lynn
Music and Art HS; New York, NY; Chor; Pres, Hmrm; Fin, Jr Miss Pagent; SC; Tr; 1st Run-Up, Ms Talented Tn A, Schol; *Westminister Choir Col; Performance.*

DAVIS, Frieda Gail
Mackenzie HS; Detroit, MI; NHS; *Bishop Col; Nurs.*

DAVIS, Gary Lynn
South Side HS; Counce, TN (11-26) BC; FFA; *U of Tenn; Park And Recreation Adm.*

DAVIS, Gary Marsh
Lumberton Sr HS; Lumberton, NC (50-259) VP, Chem C; Fr C; Hmrm; Key C; Lat C; Order/Arrow; SC; Cpt, Tnns; God & Country A; MVP, Tnns; VP, MYF; Eagle Sct; *Pembroke Col.*

DAVIS, Gary Ray
Burkburnett HS; Burkburnett, TX (40-268) Band; Ensm; Rptr, 4H; NHS; 4H A; Pres, Yth for Christ; *Oral Roberts U.*

DAVIS, Gayla Elaine
James W Robinson Secondary Sch; Fairfax, VA (212-501) Chor; Ed, Sch P; Yth Fel; Yth Engaged in Service; Yth Staff for Cont Event; *George Mason U; Special Ed.*

DAVIS, Gayla Sue
Green Forest HS; Green Forest, AR (3-65) BC; Sci C; Most Out; Geography, Eng, A's.

DAVIS, George Preston Jr
Ayden-Grifton HS; Grifton, NC (2-206) Rptr, Ann; Chem C; Fr C; Key C; Math C; Monogram; NHS; Ntl Yth Conf; Phys C; Sci C; Span C; Bsbl; Ftbl; Golf; Wrest; Gr Marshal; Nom, Morehead Schol; Appointee, US Naval Acad; Gov Century Yth Conf; Nom, Stuart Schol; *US Naval Acad; Chem.*

DAVIS, George Washington III
Trent Acad of Basic Ed; New Bern, NC (1-5) Hmrm; Pres, SC; Pres, Sr Cl; Bsbl; MVP, Bkbl; Golf; Cl Fav; Gr Marshal; HCt; MLS; Most Out; Val; Yth Fel; Sportsmanship A; Chief Marshal; Nom, Wm R Hearst A; *Washington & Lee U; Pre-Med.*

DAVIS, Gertrude Denise
Holy Family HS; Birmingham, AL (2-35) Fr C; Pres, NHS; SC; Bio A; 1st Runner Up, Miss Sr; Miss Booster; Adv Math A; HR A; *Xavier U; Phar.*

DAVIS, Gregory Earl
Kathleen Sr HS; Lakeland, FL; Amer Leg A; JA A; Yth Fel; Pres, JA; *Bethany Col; Math.*

DAVIS, Gregory Hill
Suffolk HS; Suffolk, VA (13-118) A-Ed, Ann; Drama; InterAct C; NHS; VP, Thes; Tres, Soph Cl; Co-Cpt, Ftbl; Tr; *U of Va; Law.*

DAVIS, Helane Elizabeth
Thornridge HS; Dolton, IL (10%-500) Chor; NFL; NHS; Span C; Spch C; Span NHS; COM; Kiwanis A; Spch A; Pep C Service A; *Northwestern U; Hist.*

DAVIS, Inajo Theresa
Hathaway Brown Sch; Shaker Heights, OH (20%-50) AFS; Chor; Ensm; Ed, Sch P; JV, Hockey; Yth Rptr, Channel 5 News; 1st Prize, Oral Hist Contest; *Northwestern U; Journ.*

DAVIS, Irene Geneva
Cecilian Acad; Philadelphia, PA; CYO; Fr C; Lat C; Sci C; World Affairs C; Hon Prog; NEDT; AFNA; Classical Soc A, Lat Competition; *Law.*

DAVIS, Ivory
Russell HS; Hurtsboro, AL; Chem C; Secy, FFA; VP, 4H; Lit Mag; Sci C; Bkbl; ROTC A; PE A; PA; Reading A.

DAVIS, Jacqueline Renee
Compton Sr HS; Compton, CA (1-30) Co-Cpt, Chldr; Cpt, Ftbl; Cl Fav; Swtht; Chimmettes and Squires; *USC; Nurs.*

DAVIS, James Werner
Hollywood Professional Sch; Hollywood, CA; Fr C; VP, Soph Cl; Fin, Swim; Fin, Tnns; ARC A; Law Enforcement Explorers; Jr Life Guard; Top Handler Dog A; *Pepperdine Col; Law.*

DAVIS, Jana Lynn
Wayne Comm HS; Corydon, IA (2-62) Band; Co-Cpt, Chldr; Tres, Chor; FHA; Secy, FTA; VP, 4H; Mjrte; NHS; Span C; Parl, SC; Bkbl; Golf; Sftbl; Tr; COM; 4H A; HCt; Math A; Yth Fel; *NE Mo St U.*

DAVIS, Jannafer Rose
Independence HS; Independence, MS (15%-106) Ann; FBLA; VP, FHA; 4H; Sch P; Tres, Soph Cl; COM; New Testament A; Water Safety Cert; *Southwestern Christan Col; Home Ec.*

DAVIS, Jayme Ruth
Union HS; Tulsa, OK (10-181) Band; Chor; Dbte Tm; Fr C; NHS; Citz A; Fr A; Geography A; *Tulsa Jr Col; Nurs.*

DAVIS, Jeanne Adele
S Charleston HS; S Charleston, WV (5%-250) Chor; Span NHS; *Psych.*

DAVIS, Jeffrey Alan
El Camino Real HS; Woodland Hills, CA; FBLA; Hmrm; F-Ed, Sch P; Var C; Bsbl; Bkbl; Ldr o-t Future; All-League Bkbl; *U of Oreg; Communications.*

DAVIS, Jeffrey Allen
S Willibrord Cath HS; Chicago, IL (9-82) Mgr, Band; Chor; Ch, Math C; NHS; Rptr, Sch P; Co-Cpt, Tnns; *Ill Inst of Tech; Elec Engr.*

DAVIS, Jeffrey Allen
Zion-Benton Township HS; Zion, IL (100-465) Chor; NHS; VP, Soph Cl; Cpt, Bkbl; Tr; MVP, Bkbl; Stu o-t Mo; Prom Court; Most Dependable; *Knox Col; Psych.*

DAVIS, Jeffrey Arnold
McArthur HS; Hollywood, FL (247-446) Tnns; *Broward Comm Col; Lib Arts.*

DAVIS, Jeffrey Brian
S Albany HS; Albany, OR (53-242) A Cap Choir; Band; Drama; Ensm; Madrigal; Mod Mus Mas; *Seattle Pacific U; Church Mus.*

DAVIS, John Gregory
Irondale HS; New Brighton, MN; Chor; Drama; NHS; Outst Choir Stu; *Archt.*

DAVIS, John Mark
Hart Co HS; Hartwell, GA; Band; Academic Achv; Band Achv; *U of Ga; Hist.*

DAVIS, John Roger
Newton Falls HS; Newton Falls, OH (22-200) Band; Sch P; Span C; Superior, Solo, Ensm; Inter Cl Plays.

DAVIS, John Thornton
Willow Glen HS; San Jose, CA; Commercial C; Drama; Tnns; COM; St Scholar; Director's A; Art Scholastic A; *Foothill Col; Drama.*

DAVIS, Jolene Rae
Ottumwa HS; Ottumwa, IA (50%-467) Mgr, Tr; COM; Type A; Yth Fel; *Heights Col; Acct.*

DAVIS, Jonathan Earle
Wachusett Regional HS; Holden, MA (9-525) Fr C; Math C; Sci C; MVP, Bsbl; Hon Prog; Math A; MLS; Sci A; Yth Fel; Chocksett A; Best Dressed; Pres, VP, Sr High Fel; *Dartmouth Col; Bus.*

DAVIS, Jonathan Ernest
Hopewell Valley Central HS; Pennington, NJ (16-280) Chess C; Math C; NHS; Phys C; *Sci.*

DAVIS, Joy Lynn
Manchester HS; Manchester, OH (5-96) Band; Chem C; Chor; Ensm; 4H; Lit Mag; NHS; Rainbow; Span C; Pres, Jr Cl; Cl Fav; 4H A; Most Out; Most Intelligent; *Nurs.*

DAVIS, Karen Grace
Bishop Union HS; Bishop, CA (40%-220) F-Ed, Ann; Chor; 4H; Jr Miss Pagent; Pres, Rainbow; Ski C; SC; Y-Tns; Swim; 4H A; Lion A; Masonic A; Spch A; Demolay Swtht; Rainbow Girls-Grand Cross; *Whitworth Col; Occupational Therapy.*

DAVIS, Katheryn Lucille
Worthington HS; Worthington, OH (323-596) Band; 4H; Rotary A; Yth Fel; Drill Tm; *Ohio St U; Home Ec.*

DAVIS, Kathlyn Lynett
Justin F Kimball HS; Dallas, TX; Hmrm; ARC; Y-Tns; JV, Bkbl; Yth Fel; Mus & Ath A's; *Mountain View Col; Bus.*

DAVIS, Kathy A
Mt Juliet HS; Mt Juliet, TN (42-265) Ann; Drama; Pres, Fr C; FHA; Key C; NHS; Sci C; Pres, Art C; WW; Stu Schol, Amer Abroad; *U of Tenn; Fashion Merchandising.*

DAVIS, Kathy Ann
Bay City Central HS; Bay City, MI (39-516) A Cap Choir; Chor; *Data Processing.*

DAVIS, Kathy Devon
Corliss HS; Chicago, IL (20-760) Drama; NHS; SC; COM; Citz A; Hon Prog; MLS; Type A; Teacher Aid Asst; *Bradley Col; Computer Prog.*

DAVIS, Kathy Marie
Sumter HS; Sumter, SC (298-753) Chor; Lat C; ARC; Rptr, Sch P; Sci C; Hon Prog; Yth Fel; Pres, Yth As For Retarded Citizens; *USC; Special Ed.*

DAVIS, Keith Robert
Susquehanna Comm HS; Susquehanna, PA (3-110) SC; JV, Bsbl; JV, Bkbl; Co-Cpt, Ftbl; *Phar.*

DAVIS, Kenneth Tyrone
Robert Lindblom Tech HS; Chicago, IL (96-601) Chess C; Sci C; Swim; Tnns; COM; Hon Prog; *Knox Col; Med.*

DAVIS, Kent Reid
John A Rowland HS; Rowland Hts, CA; Secy, Order/Arrow; God & Country A; Auto-Diesel Mech.

DAVIS, Kerry Lane
Hot Springs HS; Truth Or Consequences, NM (1-110) BS; NHS; Span C; SC; Co-Cpt, Bkbl; Co-Cpt, Ftbl; Tr; Amer Leg Orator A; Cl Fav; HCt; Magna Cum Laude; Math A; Val; Yth Fel; Yth Leg; Top Ten Scorers St, Bkbl; Cpt, FCA; District, Ftbl, Bkbl; Art As; 1st Piano Talent Shows; *NM St U; Math.*

DAVIS, Kevin
J E Burke HS; Dorchester, MA; Drama; Pres, Hmrm; Rptr, Sch P; Ch, SC; Cr-Ctry; Tr; Wrest; Ldrship A; Pol Discovery A; *Boston U; Elec.*

DAVIS, Kevin Don
Lee HS; Midland, TX; A Cap Choir; Co-Ed, Ann; Rptr, NHS; VP, SC; God & Country A; Yth Fel; Sharpshooters A, Ntl Rifle Assn; *Abilene Christian U; Bible.*

DAVIS, Kimberly Ann
Princeton HS; Cincinnati, OH (23-570) Band; VP, FBLA; Hmrm; NFL; NHS; COM; Delta Sigma Theta A; ROTC A; Yth Fel; Pres Schol; Top Acct Stu; *Xavier U; Acct.*

DAVIS, Kirk Fulton
Midland HS; Midland, TX; A Cap Choir; Most Out; All Area, All Region, Choirs; *Lubbock Christian Col; Mus.*

DAVIS, Kita Wilmette Twana
Maplewood HS; Nashville, TN; Chor; FHA; *Middle Tenn St U; Journ.*

DAVIS, L S
Jim Hill HS; Jackson, MS; Chess C; Pres, Chor; HiY; Pres, Hmrm; Order/Arrow; Phys C; Up Bound; Ftbl; Tr; Citz A; Cl Fav; Order/Arrow A; Phys Ed A; *Sales.*

DAVIS, LaVaugn Mae
Saegertown HS; Saegertown, PA (32-119) FHA; Mjrte; Sch Pr; Pres, Church Yth Fellowship; Pres, Phys Fitness A; *Sharon Nurs Sch; Nurs.*

DAVIS, Laura Ann
Park Hill Sr HS; Kansas City, MO (30-522) Chor; Drama; Orch; Thes; God & Country A; ARC A; *U of Mo; Drama.*

DAVIS, Laura Lynn
Lakeview HS; Battle Creek, MI (24-413) NHS; Rptr, Sch P; Span C; Spch C; Golf; Q&S A; *Adrian Col; Pol Sci.*

DAVIS, Lea Annette
J L Mann HS; Greenville, SC; Rainbow; ARC.

DAVIS, Lee Edsel
Trinity Heights Christian Acad; Shreveport, LA (10%-65) Rptr, SC; VP, Jr Cl; Bsbl; Bkbl; Golf; Soccer; Sftbl; Swim; Tnns; Tr; *LSU-Shreveport; Marketing.*

DAVIS, Leisa Denise
NW Classen HS; Okla City, OK (56-460) Co-Ed, Ann; Lat C; NHS; Hon Prog; *SW Okla St U; Phar.*

DAVIS, Lettie Ann
Princeton HS; Cincinnati, OH; NFL; SC; Thes; Princeton Drill Tm; Tres, Princeton Interacial C; Secy, Michelangelo Art Soc; VP, Mt Zion Yth Organization; *U of Cinti; Industrial Design.*

DAVIS, Linda Kay
Staunton River HS; Moneta, VA (3-164) Co-Ed, Ann; BC; Fr C; COM; Geom A; Gifted Stu Prog.

DAVIS, Linda Kristine
Lawrence Central HS; Indianapolis, IN (55-744) NHS; Spch C; ROTC A; Spch A; *SD St U; Computer Sci.*

DAVIS, Lisa Anne
Houston HS; Houston, MO; A Cap Choir; Band; Chor; Drama; Ensm; Mod Mus Mas; Spch C; Beauty; Spch A; 1st Pl, St Duet; Pep C, Art Fair, Hon's; Top World Geog A; *Colo St U; Journ.*

DAVIS, Lisa Diane
Hall HS; Little Rock, AR; FBLA; NHS; Span C; FBLA A; ACT Schol; *Ouachita Baptist U.*

DAVIS, Lisa Elizabeth
Cedar Bluff HS; Cedar Bluff, AL; BC; FHA; Pres, Hmrm; Math C; Pres, Soph Cl; Cl Fav; Vlbl; Highest Avg; Most Dilegence.

DAVIS, Lloyd Holmes
Spruce Creek Sr HS; Port Orange, FL (150-500) Ann; Order/Arrow; Sftbl; *Daytona Beach Comm Col.*

DAVIS, Loretta Kay
Big Walnut HS; Sunbury, OH (129-216) A Cap Choir; Cpt, Ensm; Pres, FBLA; Sch P; Span C; Ensm Contest A; Ensm A; Choir A; *Bus.*

DAVIS, Lynnette Carlene
McArthur HS; Hollywood, FL (95-701) Sftbl; St Champs, Sftbl League.

DAVIS, Marcia
Crestview Sr HS; Crestview, FL (8-247) Pres, Anchor C; Pres, BC; GS; F-Ed, Sch P; Tnns; *Troy St U; Pre-Law.*

DAVIS, Margaret Catherine
Leaksville HS; Leaksville, MS; Ann; VP, Band; Secy, BC; 4H; Jr Miss Pagent; Sch P; VP, Jr Cl; Beauty; DARGCA; 4H A; Most Out; *Jones Co Jr Col; Med.*

DAVIS, Margaret Julia
Tuscola Sr HS; Waynesville, NC; Secy, A Cap Choir; Band; Chor; InterAct C; Secy, Madrigal; All St Band; Solo & Ensm; *Mus Ed.*

DAVIS, Margaret Lynn
Clearwater HS; Clearwater, FL (328-850) Band; Chor; Ensm; 4H; Lat C; Ski C; Var C; MVP, Bkbl; Hockey; Sftbl; Tr; *Baylor U; Social Work.*

DAVIS, Margaret Magdalene
Gumberry HS; Gumberry, NC (9-97) BC; Chor; Fr C; Pres, SC; *NC St U; Pol Sci.*

DAVIS, Margaret Padgett
Central HS; Little Rock, AR (59-565) AFS; BC; Sci C; Span C; VP, Y-Tns; Hon Prog; NEDT; *Southwestern U; Sociology.*

DAVIS, Mark Alan
Skyline HS; Dallas, TX (33%-1100) Band; NHS.

DAVIS, Mark Leslie
Superior HS; Superior, NE (10%-85) Chor; Demolay; VP, Yth Fel; *Hastings Col; Sci.*

DAVIS, Martin Dale
Simi Valley HS; Simi Valley, CA (207-675) Band; Air Force; Mech.

DAVIS, Mary Carol
Rossville Comp HS; Rossville, GA (2-225) Band; BC; Tres, FTA; Cpt, Mjrte; Y-Tns; VP, Jr Cl; COM; Gov Honor Prog; Math A; NEDT; Type A; *Ga Inst of Technology; Elec Engr.*

DAVIS, Mary Christine
Humboldt HS; Humboldt, TN; *Tenn St U; Nurs.*

DAVIS, Mary Lynn
Pembroke Sr HS; Pembroke, NC (18-200) BC; FBLA; FHA; Span C; COM; Journ A; Writing A; Span A; Most Studious; *UNC-Chapel; Sociology.*

DAVIS, Michael Dwane
Cass HS; Cassville, GA (10%-195) Pres, BC; BS; Secy, Chem C; Fr C; Hmrm; VP, Math C; Secy, Phys C; Secy, Sci C; SC; Co-Cpt, Tr; COM; Chem A; HCt; Type A; Cpt, MVP, Cr-Ctry; Tr Reg Champ A; St Tr A; Cpt, MVP, Wrest; Cr-Ctry St A; *West Point Military Acad; Sci.*

DAVIS, Michael Dwight
Quartz Hill HS; Quartz Hill, CA (15-450) Chess C; Ger C; 4H; Math C; CSF; Citz A; *Biola Col; Aviation.*

DAVIS, Michael Foster
Traverse City HS; Traverse City, MI (80-750) NHS; Order/Arrow; Var C; Bkbl; Golf; Order/Arrow A; Eagle Sct; 4th Pl Golf LMAC; *Ferris St Col; Bus.*

DAVIS, Michael Keith
Columbia HS; Decatur, GA (31-301) VP, Band; Orch; Hon Prog; International Lang C; Gov's Hons Prog Nom; Outst Mus A, Jazz Festival; *Mus.*

DAVIS, Miranda Claseal
Strawberry Mansion HS; Philadelphia, PA (20-192) Hon Prog; MLS; PA, Eng, A's; Motivation Prog; *Ind U of Pa; Biol.*

DAVIS, Miriam H
Middleburg HS; Middleburg, PA (19-127) Band; Chess C; Drama; Hmrm; Var C; Bkbl; Hockey; Sftbl; COM; *Pa St U; Recreation & Parks.*

DAVIS, Nancy Jean
Hermitage HS; Hermitage, AR (4-57) Ann; Chor; FHA; Sftbl; Balfour A; Hist A; Lib A; Hon Cert; *UAM; Elem Ed.*

DAVIS, Nancy Lynn
Huntsville HS; Huntsville, AL (50-500) Pres, Anchor C; Tres, Chem C; Hmrm; InterClub Coun; NHS; Phys C; SC; *Huntingdon Col; Vet Med.*

DAVIS, Nolan Ray
Hunter Huss HS; Gastonia, NC (5%-700) Band; BC; Tnns; *Computers.*

DAVIS, Pamela Ann
Brown Deer HS; Brown Deer, WI (43-275) AFS; Ann; Chldr; SC; Pres, Sr Cl; Sftbl; MVP, Tnns; *U of Wis; Nurs.*

DAVIS, Pamela Claudette
Hicks HS; Hicks, LA; Ann; Rptr, Chor; FHA; 4H; Lit Ral; COM; 4H A; Sal; Eng A; Outst Mus; Hon Choir; *La Col; Mus.*

DAVIS, Pamela Evelyn
St Joseph's Notre Dame HS; Alameda, CA (10-55) Ch, Ann; Tres, Bus C; NHS; Fr A; Shorthand A; PA, 1st & 2nd Hons; *UC-BERKELEY; Bus Adm.*

DAVIS, Pamela Sue
Warren Western Reserve HS; Warren, OH (19-493) A Cap Choir; Chor; Drama; Ensm; Ger C; NHS; Var C; Cpt, Bkbl; Co-Cpt, Golf; Soccer; Co-Cpt, Sftbl; Tnns; Alg A; COM; Citz A; Hon Prog; GAA; Secy, Pep Squad; Nom, GS; *Radiology.*

DAVIS, Patricia
Swifton HS; Swifton, AR (4-28) Band; FBLA; Pres, FHA; Up Bound; Beauty; Most Courteous; Friendliest; *Bradley U; Home Ec.*

DAVIS, Patricia Leigh
Canoga Park HS; Canoga Park, CA; Chor; *Cal St U at Northridge; Law Enforcement.*

DAVIS, Patricia Louise
N Kingstown Sr HS; N Kingstown, RI (21-350) Band; Co-Cpt, Chldr; Chor; Cum Laude Soc; Hmrm; Madrigal; NHS; Pres, Sr Cl; JV, Bkbl; Cr-Ctry; Tr; Pres A; HR; Highest Scholastic Achv; Arion A; Top 6% PSATS; NH HR; *Brown U; Pre-Med.*

DAVIS, Patricia Marie
Hillsboro Sr HS; Hillsboro, OR (20%-700) CYO; Chldr; Fr C; Pres, 4H; NHS; 4H A; Hon Prog; *Portland Comm Col; Home Ec.*

DAVIS, Paula Sue
York HS; York, NE (63-156) Band; Chor; Ger C; 4H; SC; Y-Tns; Cand, Prom Duchess; VICA; Hon Qn, Job's Daughters; *Nebr Wesleyan Col.*

DAVIS, Phyllis Jean
Hueneme HS; Oxnard, CA (294-485) Drama; Hmrm; Ftbl; Tr; Vlbl; Spec Ed; *Oxnard Col; Spec Ed.*

DAVIS, R Elaine
Jenkins Co HS; Millen, GA (8-100) BC; Chor; F-Ed, Sch P; Sci C; Secy, Tri-HiY; Beauty; Rotary A; Yth Leg; *Ga Southern Col; Elem Ed.*

DAVIS, Raymond Allen
S Hills HS; Pittsburgh, PA; Band; Tnns; HR; *Med.*

DAVIS, Rebecca Annette
Sheffield HS; Sheffield, AL (3-225) Ann; Dbte Tm; Lat C; SC; Sch Achieve Tm; Tr; HCt; *U of Ala; Nurs.*

DAVIS, Regina Ann
Lincoln Square Acad; New York, NY (2-20) Dbte Tm; Drama; Ch, Hmrm; Lit Mag; F-Ed, Sch P; Span C; VP, SC; Ch, Jr Cl; VP, Soph Cl; Alg A; COM; Cl Fav; Math A; NEDT; Sal; *Bus Mgt.*

DAVIS, Reginald
Altheimer HS; Altheimer, AR; VP, Drama; Math C; Bkbl; Alg A; Bio A; Chem A; *U of Ark; Engr.*

DAVIS, Reginald D
Troup HS; LaGrange, GA (9-25) BC; NHS; Ftbl; Citz A; Hon Prog; *U of Ga; Hist.*

DAVIS, Renee Denise
E Atlanta HS; Atlanta, GA (12-142) Fr C; VP, Hmrm; Cpt, Var C; VP, Sr Cl; Cpt, Bkbl; Tnns; COM; Essay A; *DeKalb Col; Bus Ed.*

DAVIS, Rhea Denise
Bishop Union HS; Bishop, CA (40%-250) Bus Mgr, Ann; Chldr; Chor; 4H; VP, Rainbow; Spch C; Secy, SC; Y-Tns; Swim; Amer Leg A; Citz A; 4H A; Lion A; Spch A; VofDEM; Demolay Swtht; Best Sense of Humor; *Med Lab Tech.*

DAVIS, Rhon Lauren
Chanute HS; Chanute, KS; Chess C; Sftbl; Yth Fel; *Ottawa U; Religion.*

DAVIS, Rhonda Kaye
Macon R 1 HS; Macon, MO (12-126) Ann; Chor; Drama; GS; NHS; Yth Pianist; *NE Mo St U; Eng.*

DAVIS, Richard Dean
Phillips HS; Phillips, TX (6-41) A Cap Choir; Chor; Semi-Fin, Dbte Tm; Madrigal; Order/Arrow; Pres, SC; Bkbl; Ftbl; Semi-Fin, Tnns; Amer Leg A; Elk A; MLS; Order/Arrow A; Rotary A; Spch A; Eagle Sct; Dist Win, Dbte; Gen Mills Family Ldr of Tomorrow; *Baylor U; Pol Sci.*

DAVIS, Richard Jerome
Westside Sr HS; Gary, IN; Fr C; Orch; Special Achv School; Orch Cert; *Purdue U; Bus Adm.*

DAVIS, Robert Charles
Jim Hill HS; Jackson, MS; Chess C; HiY; Ftbl; Order/Arrow A; Phys Ed A.

DAVIS, Robert Clyde
Lodgepole HS; Lodgepole, NE (6-18) Sch P; Bsbl; Cpt, Bkbl; Cpt, Ftbl; Tr; COM.

DAVIS, Robert Jonathan
N Springs HS; Atlanta, GA (90-156) Chor; Drama; Ensm; *Berry Col; Mus.*

DAVIS, Robin Ann
Rapid City Stevens HS; Rapid City, SD (300-456) A Cap Choir; Band; Chor; FBLA; FHA; 4H; Orch; 4H A; *Black Hills St Col; Ed.*

DAVIS, Roger Craig
Lindblom HS; Chicago, IL (72-780) Chess C; JV, Ftbl; Bowl; *Ind U; Engr.*

DAVIS, Ronald Redd
Durham Acad; Durham, NC (15-46) Ann; Rptr, Sch P; VP, SC; Bkbl; Cr-Crtry; NMS; Yth Fel; WW; Sr Mid-Term Rep; *Davidson Col; Pre-Med.*

DAVIS, Ronda Gail
William Monroe HS; Stanardsville, VA (30-90) Band; BC; Drama; FBLA; 4H; Lit Mag; Bkbl; Tr; COM; Type A; Karate; Gifted Stu Prog; All Regional Band; *U of Va; Sci.*

DAVIS, Rosemary
Carroll HS; Monroe, LA; Fr C; Hmrm; Cl Fav; HCt; Hon Prog; *Sou U.*

DAVIS, Sandra Lorraine
Cedar Falls HS; Cedar Falls, IA (112-461) Chldr; Chor; Drama; GS; Rainbow; Ch, SC; DARGCA; Co-Ed, Yrbk; *U of N Iowa; Elem Ed.*

DAVIS, Sara Kathryn
James A Shanks HS; Quincy, FL (10%-300) Ann; Pres, 4H; Hmrm; NHS; VP, Span C; St Stu Congress; SC; COM; Citz A; 4H A; Hon Prog; I Dare You; Most Out; Ntl Sci Found; Sci A; Spch A; Yth Leg; Jr Ldr Comm C; Pres, Co Coun; Dancing Stu; Gym Instructor.

DAVIS, Scott Francis
Bishop Watterson HS; Columbus, OH (25-250) CYO; Chor; Lat C; Wrest; NEDT; *Ohio St U; Law.*

DAVIS, Scott Joseph
New Haven HS; New Haven, IN (231-305) Sch P; Mgr, Ftbl; JV, Tr; JV, Wrest; Journ A; *Ind U; Engr.*

DAVIS, Sharon Deneise
Jackson Solomon Abrams HS; Bessemer, AL (6-100) S-T, Hmrm; A-Ed, Sch P; Pres, Sci C; VP, VICA; *U of Ala; Nurs.*

DAVIS, Sharon Elizabeth
Alfred E Beach HS; Savannah, GA; Rptr, Anchor C; Rptr, Sch P; Sci C; Span C; Gov Honor Prog; NEDT; Outst Ldrship A; HR; Outst Achv, Span; *Armstrong St Col; Para-Legal Work.*

DAVIS, Sharon Kay
Ainsworth HS; Flint, MI; A Cap Choir; Madrigal; Soccer; Tr; Yth Pres.

DAVIS, Sheila Lea
Ritenour HS; St Louis, MO (311-961) Hmrm; SC; Home Ec.

DAVIS, Sherbery Joy
Baker HS; Columbus, GA; FHA; Hmrm; JA A; Spelling B A; *Tuskegee Inst; Secretarial.*

DAVIS, Sherry Lynne
Garden HS; Oakwood, VA; Chor; Tres, 4H; NHS; GAA; Club Coordinating Comm; Nominating Comm; *Clinch Valley Col; Nurs.*

DAVIS, Sheryl Althea
Science HS; Newark, NJ; Bkbl; Sftbl; Vlbl; Future Physicians C; *Col of Med & Dentistry of NJ; Med.*

DAVIS, Sophia Yvett
C E Byrd HS; Shreveport, LA; Band; Chem C; Secy, 4H; Mjrte; SAC; ARC; Bkbl; 4H A; JA A; MLS; Band; Jr Med League; Best Dressed; *LSU; Pre-Law.*

DAVIS, Stacy Richard
Newnan HS; Newnan, GA; Demolay; Citz A; *Elec.*

DAVIS, Stephen Lee
Dixon R-I HS; Dixon, MO (10-75) 4H; Math C; JV, Bsbl; Co-Cpt, Bkbl; JV, Golf; Alg A; 4H A; HCt; Math A; 97%, SCAT; Hghst St Score, Navy Nuclear Test; *Westminster Col.*

DAVIS, Stephen Mark
West HS; Green Bay, WI (170-430) Order/Arrow; ARC; Mgr, Bkbl; JV, Ftbl; JV, Tnns; Order/Arrow A; *U of Wis; Natural Resources.*

DAVIS, Steve Anthoney
Wayne Co HS; Jesup, GA (20%-360) A Cap Choir; Ann; Chor; Dbte Tm; FBLA; FFA; Parl, 4H; HiY; Hmrm; Mgr, Bsbl; Ftbl; Co-Cpt, Soccer; Sftbl; 4H A; PTA A; ROTC A; Yth Fel; MVP, Bsbl; *Brewton-Parker Col; Mus.*

DAVIS, Steve Bobby
Clovis HS; Clovis, NM (200-450) Pres, A Cap Choir; JV, Tnns; *Okla Christian Col; Acct.*

DAVIS, Steven Earl
Sandia HS; Albuquerque, NM (23-708) Soccer; Sftbl; Tr; Baylor U Academic Schol; *Baylor U; Pre-Med.*

DAVIS, Sue Evelyn
Denham Springs HS; Denham Springs, LA (25%-300) Band; Chor; FHA; NHS; Sci C; Sftbl; Dist Hon Band; Lib C; *Southeastern La U; Ecology.*

DAVIS, Susan Elizabeth
Traverse City HS; Traverse City, MI (41-776) 4H; Orch; Bkbl; Tr; 4H A; NEDT; Art A.

DAVIS, Susan Patricia
Mt Carmel HS; Poway, CA; Chor; Tnns; Candystriper; *Medical Secy.*

DAVIS, Tammy Claudette
South Rowan Sr HS; China Grove, NC (30-283) Anchor C; Pres, Bus C; FFA; Pres, FHA; Hmrm; NHS; SC; Beauty; Hon Prog; Type A; VP, Bus C; Miss Merry Christmas Court; *Bus.*

DAVIS, Tammy Jo
Hazlewood HS; Town Creek, AL (7-53) Ann; Band; BC; Drama; FHA; 4H; Math C; Sci C; Spch C; Alg A; 4H A; Math A; Acteens Schol; *Pepperdine U; Sci.*

DAVIS, Tammy Marie
Enterprise HS; Brookhaven, MS; FBLA; FHA; 4H; Pres, Hmrm; Co-Cpt, Mjrte; NHS; Alg A; Cl Fav; Hon Prog; Shorthand A; Mjrte A; Sensible Soph.

DAVIS, Tammy Sue
Crowley HS; Crowley, TX (50-206) Chor; Tres, FHA.

DAVIS, Tammy Sue
Lumberton Sr HS; Lumberton, NC (150-270) A-Ed, Ann; Chem C; Hmrm; Lat C; Co-Ed, Sch P; Span C; SC; Mgr, Cr-Crtry; Mgr, Tr; *Louisburg Col; Journ.*

DAVIS, Teresa Darlene
Lourdes Co HS; Valdosta, GA (10-30) Bus C; Chor; Drama; FBLA; FHA; Rainbow; Sch P; Tres, Thes; *Secretarial.*

DAVIS, Teresa Dean
South Side HS; Counce, TN (7-34) Ann; FHA; Tres, Soph Cl; *NE Jr Col; Social Work.*

DAVIS, Teresa Diann
Russell HS; Hurtsboro, AL (3-58) VP, Chem C; FHA; 4H; Lit Mag; Rptr, NHS; VP, Sci C; Pres, SC; COM; Citz A; Elk A; 4H A; ROTC A; Sci A; Spch A; Eng A; *Ala A&M U; Special Ed.*

DAVIS, Terri Lyn
Neville HS; Monroe, LA (10%-200) Fr C; Hmrm; NHS; SC; Hon Prog; Fr A; Dance Tm; *NE La U; General.*

DAVIS, Terri Lynn
Alain Leroy Locke HS; Los Angeles, CA (11-575) Chor; NHS; Fin, Sch P; Fin, Bkbl; Fin, Tr; Hon Prog; Gifted Stu; *USC; Bus Adm.*

DAVIS, Terry Ann
Permian HS; Odessa, TX (35-739) Co-Cpt, Band; Chor; Community Yth Symph; Ensm; FHA; NHS; Orch; Tri-HiY; Sftbl; Swim; COM; Citz A; Hon Prog; Lion A; Swtht; Yth Fel; Symph Deb; S-T, Church Group; All Region Band; UIL Solo & Ensm A; *Tex Tech U; Chem.*

DAVIS, Terry Edward
Canfield HS; Canfield, OH (127-251) Drama; 4H; Mgr, Ftbl; MVP, Ftbl; *Malone Col; Religion.*

DAVIS, Thomas Ervin
John Handley HS; Winchester, VA (38-284) Band; Chor; Ensm; Pres, Hmrm; Key C; Cpt, SC; VP, Soph Cl; Mgr, Ftbl; Hockey; Soccer; Sftbl; HCt; Outst Mus A; Sr Cl Prophet; All Regional Band; *Madison Col; Mus Ed.*

DAVIS, Thomas Melton
Suffolk HS; Suffolk, VA (7-150) Band; Drama; Parl, Key C; Lat C; NHS; Bsbl; *VPI; Engr.*

DAVIS, Timothy Alan
Beavercreek HS; Xenia, OH (60-800) Chess C; SC; Var C; Bkbl; JV, Ftbl; JV, Soccer; Sftbl; Cpt, Tnns; COM; Most Out; Opt A; Spch A; VFW A; Tn Trophy; Shooting Trophy; Jr Fin, News Carrier; 3 Yr Carrier; *Phys Ed.*

DAVIS, Timothy Scott
James F Byrnes HS; Duncan, SC (23-280) Band; BC; Chor; Rptr, Sch P; *Anderson Jr Col; Mus.*

DAVIS, Tony
Autaugaville HS; Autaugaville, AL (3-60) Pres, BC; BS; Pres, SC; I Dare You; MLS; Drum Major.

DAVIS, Tony Anthony
Forest Park HS; Cincinnati, OH (33%-350) Chor; Bkbl; *Cumberland Col; Acct.*

DAVIS, Tracy Ann
Dover HS; Dover, OH (90-278) Ed, Ann; Swim; Yth Fel; *Ohio Northern Col; Pre-Law.*

DAVIS, Tracy Kay
Marion HS; Marion, IN (43-700) Chldr; Fr C; Orch; Tnns; Superior Mus A; Model UN; *Bus.*

DAVIS, Twila Ree
Lubbock Christian HS; Lubbock, TX (20-51) A Cap Choir; Chor; Ensm; Mus A; *Lubbock Christian Col; Mus.*

DAVIS, Vanessa Alberta
Aquinas Dominican HS; Chicago, IL (29-177) Chldr; Ch, Hmrm; SC; Beauty; COM; Hon Prog; GSct C; *Pepperdine U; Pol Sci.*

DAVIS, Vanessa Elaine
Lincolnton Sr HS; Lincolnton, NC (90-250) Co-Ed, Ann; Chor; Pres, Fr C; FTA; 4H; Lit Mag; Ntl Teachers Coun; Sch P; Secy, Sci C; Secy, SC; Journ A; Q&S A; Sci A; SC; Sch Service, A's; *Brevard Col; Pre-Law.*

DAVIS, Verlene Clare
Safford HS; Safford, AZ (8-198) FBLA; NHS; Hon Prog; Rotary A; Carlotta Pace A; Pepsi-Cola Bottling Schol; *Eastern Ariz Col; Bus.*

DAVIS, Veronica
Kirkman Tech HS; Chattanooga, TN (5-25) *Erlanger Nurs Sch; Sci.*

DAVIS, Vicki Delphine
East HS; Columbus, OH (11-350) DECA C; *U of Tenn; Interior Design.*

DAVIS, Walter Abram
Rufus King HS; Milwaukee, WI;

DAVIS, Wanda Kaye
Lincoln HS; Dallas, TX (3%-185) Ed, Ann; Band; Pres, Hmrm; VP, Key C; Math C; Model UN; NHS; Sci C; Secy, SC; Rptr, Sr Cl; COM; Cl Fav; Math A; Q&S A; Bkbl Swtht; *Real-Estate.*

DAVIS, Wanda Lynette
Lew Wallace HS; Gary, IN (173-490) Helen Redd Schol Prog; Pres, Yth Choir; Yth Forum; Secy, Yth Usher Board; Yng Peoples Dept, Missionary Soc; *Purdue-Calumet Col; Computer Tech.*

DAVIS, Wayne Richard
Morris Hills Regional HS; Rockaway, NJ (95-350) A Cap Choir; Pres, Band; Chor; Ski C; JV, Tr; Drum Major; All St Chor; St N Region Chor; *SUNY-COBLESKILL; Nursery Mgt.*

DAVIS, William Brent
Allegany HS; Cumberland, MD (10-300) AFS; Chess C; Demolay; Drama; NHS; Span C; NEDT; *VPI; Engr.*

DAVIS, Wilma Diane
Texas City HS; Texas City, TX (25%-500) Thes; Opt A; WW; Pres, Tx As of Health Occup Stu; *Baylor U; Occupational Therapy.*

DAVISON, Dale Alan
Southeast Nebraska Consolidated HS; Stella, NE (2-32) Band; BS; Pres, Chor; Drama; Ensm; Secy, FFA; Math C; NHS; Sci C; Spch C; Var C; Pres, Jr Cl; Ftbl; Tr; Hon Prog; Math A; Sci A; Spch A; Star Student; Sci Fair A; FFA A; *U of Nebr; Engr.*

DAVISON, Kay DeAnn
Columbus Sr HS; Columbus, NE (16-295) A-Ed, Ann; Band; Chor; Pres, 4H; Orch; Thes; *Psych.*

DAVISSON, Cindy Sue
Monte Vista HS; Spring Valley, CA (50%-558) AFS; Chor; JV, Tnns; Sr HR; *San Diego Col of Bus; Court Rptr.*

DAVISSON, Thomas Andrew
Gilmer Co HS; Glenville, WV (35-122) JV, Bkbl; Co-Cpt, Golf; *Glenville St Col; Bus.*

DAW, Phillip Wayne
Midland HS; Midland, TX; Band; Chor; Hon Prog; *Pol Sci.*

DAWES, Janise B
Adlai E Stevenson HS; Bronx, NY (446-788) Chor; Mod Mus Mas; *AVC; Child Psych.*

DAWKINS, Cathy Lynne
Richmond Sr HS; Rockingham, NC; Band; Drama; FHA; *Richmond Tech Inst; Bus Adm.*

DAWS, Bonnie Jean
Sheffield HS; Memphis, TN (6-142) Band; Hmrm; Mod Mus Mas; Rptr, NHS; Co-Ed, Sch P; SC; Rptr, Thes; Quill & Scroll; Lib C; WW; Court of Lord & Lady Sheffield; Best Flute A; *Memphis St U.*

DAWS, Rebecca Lynn
Dillon HS; Dillon, SC (2%-309) Band; BC; Chor; Ensm; 4H; Lat C; Orch; Hist A; Regional & Dist Band Clinic; Excel A; *Acct.*

DAWS, Susan Marie
Michigan Pub Sch; Michigan, ND (1-29) Ed, Ann; Secy, Band; Chor; Ensm; GS; Pres, 4H; B Crocker A; 4H A; MLS; Sci A; Val; Pres, Secy & Parl, FHA; *ND St U; Home Ec.*

DAWSON, Cynthia Lois
Queensbury HS; Glens Falls, NY (5%-279) Chldr; Drama; NHS; Co-Ed, Sch P; Pres, Span C; Hon Prog; Nom, Best Supporting Actress; *Middlebury Col; Sociology.*

DAWSON, Diana Lynn
Atlanta HS; Atlanta, TX (15-190) Chldr; Ensm; Rptr, FTA; Rainbow; Sch P; Rptr, Sci C; Journ A; Q&S A; *E Tex St U; Secondary Ed.*

DAWSON, Edward
Willibrord Cath HS; Chicago, IL (4-90) Chess C; Math C; Monogram; VP, NHS; VP, Sci C; Pres, Span C; VP, Span NHS; SC; Bsbl; Mgr, Bkbl; Tnns; COM; Cl Fav; Hon Prog; Math A; Phy A; Sci A; St Scholar; *Harvard U; Govt.*

DAWSON, Gary Lee
Richland HS; Fort Worth, TX (112-568) Sci C; Drafting A; 1st Pl, Tx Soc of Prof Engr; *Tex Christian U; Chem.*

DAWSON, Karen Lynne
Southwest HS; Macon, GA (10%-750) Parl, AFS; BC; FHA; Hmrm; VP, InterClub Coun; ARC; VP, Sr Cl; Secy, Jr Cl; Tres, Soph Cl; COM; Cl Fav; Hon Prog; Q&S A; Sci A; Yth Leg; VP, Ch & S-T, SC; LaSertoma; 1st Cl GSct; *Bus Mgt.*

DAWSON, Mary Ann
Col Crawford HS; N Robinson, OH (4-110) Ann; Secy, FHA; NHS; Tr; MLS; *Columbus Bus Col; Fashion Merchandising.*

DAWSON, Patti Ann
Eufaula HS; Eufaula, OK (10%-100) 4H; NHS; Var C; Cpt, Bkbl; Tr; Val; *E St Col; Med Bus.*

DAWSON, Rhonda Rahnae
Valhalla HS; El Cajon, CA; Ann; Chor; Dbte Tm; Drama; Y-Tns; Bkbl; Amer Leg A; CSF; Most Out; PTA A.

DAWSON, Sarah Anne
Nathaniel Narbonne HS; Harbor City, CA (125-900) Yth Fel; *Phar.*

DAWSON, Terena Gay
Southland HS; Arbyrd, MO (4-38) FHA; FTA; NHS; Bio A; Crisco A; Sci A; Type A; Psych, Lib, Occupations, PA, A's; *Cotton Boll Voc-Tech Sch; Bus.*

DAY, Amy Denise
Starmount HS; Boonville, NC (10%-211) Chor; Cpt, Hmrm; Bkbl; Sftbl; Tnns.

DAY, Benjamin Lee
J J Pearce HS; Richardson, TX (185-650) SC; Bkbl; Mgr, Ftbl; Citz A; DARGCA; *Tex Wesleyan Col; Med.*

DAY, Charles Robert
Sheffield HS; Memphis, TN (55-142) Ann; Pres, InterClub Coun; Sch P; Span C; Pres, SC; Var C; Bsbl; Cl Fav; H of F; Honorary Shelby Co Court Squire; Lord Sheffield; WW at Sheffield; WW; Mr Cool; SC Rep o-t Yr; *US Air Force Acad.*

DAY, Cynthia Lou
East Central HS; Hurley, MS (8-115) Band; Secy, Bus C; Co-Cpt, Chldr; FBLA; FHA; Sci C; SC; Beauty; Cl Fav; HQn; HCt; Miss Congeniality; VP, PTSA.

DAY, Don Richard Jr
Mt Whitney HS; Visalia, CA (86-428) Lat C; Math C; *Calif St U; Computer Sci.*

DAY, Elizabeth Ann
Oakwood Jr-Sr HS; Dayton, OH; Band; Chor; Thes; Yth Fel; *U of Ariz; Geology.*

DAY, James Edward
Centralia HS; Centralia, WA; SC; Bsbl; Tr; *Air Force Acad; Sci.*

DAY, Keith Allan
MacArthur HS; San Antonio, TX (50%-610) Mgr, Ftbl; Mgr, Tr; FCA; Ath Schol; *Ranger Jr Col; Agr.*

DAY, Kelly Martha
Jamestown HS; Washington, DC; F-Ed, Ann; Co-Cpt, Chldr; Chess C; Chor; Dbte Tm; NHS; Ed, Sch P; Span C; Spch C; Pres, SC; VP, Soph Cl; Swim; COM; Citz A; Hon Prog; MVP, Stu Coun; Highest Cl Avg, Lat A; Busiest, Soph Cl; US Senate Page.

DAY, Kevin Layne
Glendale HS; Springfield, MO; A Cap Choir; Band; Chess C; VP, Drama; Ensm; Madrigal; Orch; VP, Thes; Bsbl; Sftbl; COM; Hon Prog; *SW Baptist Col; Mus.*

DAY, Kyle Wayne
Mt Carmel HS; Mt Carmel, IL (54-190) Chess C; Secy, Key C; Order/Arrow; Bkbl; Kiwanis A; Order/Arrow A; Eagle Sct; *Vincennes U; Graphic Arts.*

DAY, Leslie Annette
N Mesquite HS; Mesquite, TX (37-452) Chor; FTA; Math C; NHS; Span C; Sftbl; 2nd Pl, Dist Slide Rule; *Stephen F Austin St U; Ed.*

DAY, Marsha June
Tex Sr HS; Texarkana, TX (20-430) FBLA; FTA; Ger C; NHS; Art A; 1st Pl, Ger Spell, Archt; 2nd Pl, Ger Map; *Texarkana Col; Fine Arts.*

DAY, Michael James
Brunswick HS; Brunswick, GA (100-429) Cpt, Dbte Tm; FBLA; Var C; Ftbl; God & Country A; Hon Prog; FCA; *Law.*

DAY, Patricia Ann
Marvell HS; Marvell, AR (10-120) FHA; Ger C; Sci A; Ger C A; *U of Ark; Acct.*

DAY, Richard Roy
St Augustine HS; St Augustine, FL; Drama; InterClub Coun; NHS; *Fla St U; Engr.*

DAY, Sandra Jean
Marion HS; Marion, LA (3-30) Rptr, FHA; GS; Rptr, 4H; Lit Ral; ARC; VP, SC; Bkbl; Sftbl; 4H A; ARC A; Yth Fel; *La Col; Bus.*

DAY, Sue Ellen
Ottumwa HS; Ottumwa, IA (125-497) Chor; Drama; Ensm; Rptr, 4H; Key C; Madrigal; Thes; Tr; Amer Leg A; Beauty; COM; 4H A; 1st Runner-Up, Jr Miss Pageant; All-St Mus As; Drama A; 4-H Fair Ribbons; *Ottumwa Heights Col; Mus.*

DAY, Susan Gayle
Sacred Heart Acad; Salem, OR; Chldr; Drama; Pres, Hmrm; NHS; Rptr, Sch P; Pres, Sr Cl; Pres, Jr Cl; Tnns; Elk A; Opt A; Soph & Sr Cl Princess; *Fashion Merchandising.*

DAY, Tanya Jo
Mt Carmel HS; Mt Carmel, IL (85-190) FHA; GAA; Teambackers.

DAY, Teri Lee
Abingdon Sr HS; Abingdon, IL (59-107) Chor; VP, FHA; Pep C; Cpt, Bowling; GAA; Chor Letter; *Carl Sandburg Col; Child Care.*

DAY, Theresa Lou
Laurel Co HS; London, KY; FBLA; FFA; 4H; InterAct C.

DAY, Tina Geneva
Aiken HS; Aiken, SC (42-640) A-Ed, Ann; NHS; Span C; COM; Yth Fel; NHS Cert; *U of SC Aiken; Early Childhood Ed.*

DAYE, Jenifer Nadallie
Gilbert's Sch; Brooklyn, NY (1-35) Co-Cpt, Chldr; Mjrte; Pres, SC; Pres, Sr Cl; Co-Cpt, Tr; COM; Citz A; Service A; *Manhattanville Col; Med.*

DAYE, Lissa Anne
Watauga HS; Boone, NC; Band; FTA; Orch; Superior, St Solo & Ensm; All St Band.

DAYTON, Kathy Lynn
Frankfort HS; Ridgeley, WV (10%-139) Chldr; Chor; NHS; Hist A; *Potomac St Col; Psych.*

DAZEY, Andrea Mae
Sullivan HS; Sullivan, MO (31-203) Vlbl; *Ed.*

DEACON, Catherine Major
Liberty HS; Bedford, VA (8-267) Pres, BC; Chldr; S-T, 4H; Hmrm; JETS; Secy, Lat C; Lat NHS; Math C; Sci C; Tri-HiY; Tres, Sr Cl; Tres, Soph Cl; HQn; DAR Essay Contest Win; *Madison Col; Library Science.*

DEAGAN, Scot Douglas
Westview HS; Kankakee, IL (33%-210) All Amer Yth; Community Yth Symph; Hmrm; Orch; ARC; SC; Pres, Var C; Secy, Sr Cl; Cpt, Swim; MVP, Swim; WW; Prom Court; *Eastern Ill U.*

DEAGLE, Susan Carol
Highland HS; Pocatello, ID (35-500) Ger C; Pres, 4H; Secy, Hmrm; NHS; Bus Mgr, Sch P; Thes; Tr; 4H A; JA A; Semi Fin, VP Highest St Office; *Bus.*

DEAHL, Charles Raymond Jr
Butler Area Sr HS; Butler, PA (200-1100) Band; Ski C; Hockey; Sftbl; *Butler CC Col; Bus Mgt.*

DEAHL, Evelyn Alice
Butler Intermediate HS; Butler, PA (20%-1100) AFS; Band; Chor; Ensm; Orch; Ski C; COM.

DEAHL, Timothy Paul
Charleston HS; Charleston, WV (10%-350) Band; NHS; Orch; Hon Prog; Jeffersonian A; *W Va U; Med.*

DEAKIN, Anne Elizabeth
Newnan HS; Newnan, GA (49-452) Band; BC; Chldr; Chor; Span C; Sftbl; Swim; Civinettes; Secy, Church Yth.

DEAKINS, James Scott
R E Lee HS; Tyler, TX (10%-750) Drama; Key C; SC; Tnns; Del, Ntl Sci Fair; Best Personality; *Law.*

DEAKINS, Lori Ann
Belton Sr HS; Belton, MO (82-336) FHA; NHS; Span C; Sftbl; HR; NHS A; *Maplewoods Comm Col; Animal Tech.*

DEAL, Dana Eileen
Sunset HS; Dallas, TX (12-350) A-Ed, Ann; Drama; Hmrm; Secy, Lat C; Secy, NHS; Thes; Hon Prog; Math A; PTA A; Q&S A; DeMolay Swtht; Sch Swtht Nom; Cpt, Drill Tm; *Tex Tech U; Engr.*

DEAL, Daniel Joel
Gull Lake HS; Richland, MI; Band; JV, Bkbl; Tnns; Pres A; FCA; MIP, Tnns; Auto C; Bible C; YMCA Bsbl.

DEAL, James Edmond
Statesboro HS; Statesboro, GA (35-300) Band; Ensm; Model UN; *Ga Sou Col; Mus.*

DEAL, James Lee
Hickory HS; Hickory, NC (120-400) Lit Mag; Sci C; Jr Human Relations Coun; Humanities Prog; *Western Carolina U; Hist.*

DEAL, Jeffrey Lee
Brazil HS; Brazil, IN (17-175) Band; NHS; Golf; Yth Fel.

DEAL, Victoria Elaine
Roy C Start HS; Toledo, OH; Band; Chor; VP, Orch; Superior Rating Band Contest; Excellent Rating Band Contest; *Toledo U; Elem Ed.*

DEAMUES, Valerie Jeaneen
W End HS; Birmingham, AL (31-273) Ed, Ann;
Dbte Tm; Secy, Drama; Sci C; SC; Secy, Thes;
COM; Journ A; JA A; Winter Sports Princess; *U of Ala; Dentistry.*

DEAN, Allen Thomas
Ida HS; Ida, MI (4-146) Band; NHS; Cr-Ctry; Tr;
NEDT; Coach's A; *Mich Tech U; Elec Engr.*

DEAN, Barbara Ann
Lebanon Sr HS; Lebanon, IN (85-250) Band; Pres,
4H; Rainbow; Span C; Mgr, Bkbl; Mgr, Tr; *Ball St U; Nurs.*

DEAN, Catherine Shawen
E Mecklenburg HS; Charlotte, NC (85-600) A Cap
Choir; Ensm; Hmrm; Span C; SC; Tres, Sr Cl;
Beauty; Nom, Carrousel Princess; Musicals; Civi-
nette Board Mem; Friendliest; All Co Choir; St
Choral Clinic; Piano A'S; Chrch Spec Ed Mus Dir;
Appalachain St Col; Ed.

DEAN, David Arnold
Connersville Sr HS; Connersville, IN (535-665)
Hyles-Anderson Col; Pastor.

DEAN, Deanna Beth
Glasco HS; Glasco, KS (10-28) F-Ed, Ann; Band;
FHA; F-Ed, Sch P; VP, Ch & Secy, Y-Teens; Hon
Men, St Clothing School Test; *Meramec JC; Interior Decorating.*

DEAN, Deborah Gail
Copian-Lincoln HS; Wesson, MS (4-46) Ann; VP,
FBLA; Y-Tns; Hon Prog; Homemaking A; *Co-Lin Col; General.*

DEAN, Elese
Velma Jackson HS; Camden, MS (10-27) FHA;
Hmrm; SC; Citz A; Hist A; Hon Prog; Math A;
Hon Soc A; Eng A; *Lansing Comm Col; Eng.*

DEAN, Gloria Jean
Toulminville HS; Mobile, AL (12-273) Band; VP,
FTA; InterClub Coun; Mjrte; Tres, SC; Most Out;
2nd VP, Stu Action for Ed; *Ala St U; Early Childhood Ed.*

DEAN, Jack Osbon Jr
Washington Ave Ch Sch; Greenville, SC (3-12) BC;
Bsbl; Golf; Tr; Sci A; *Furman Col; Med.*

DEAN, James Tyler
Jena HS; Jena, LA; FFA; Key C; Bsbl; FFA Dairy
Judging Tm; *U of SW La; Law Enforcement.*

DEAN, Ken L
Cascade Sr HS; Everett, WA (5%-500) Band; Chor;
Community Yth Symph; NHS; Orch; Span C; Hon
Prog; Lion A; Yth Fel; Everett Lions; *Western Wash St Col.*

DEAN, Kimberly Anne
S R Butler HS; Huntsville, AL; Bkbl; Sftbl; Tnns;
Oral Roberts U; Phys Ed.

DEAN, Leah Lisa
Warren Co Sr HS; McMinnville, TN (25%-300)
FHA; GS; NHS; Ed, Sch P; Journ A; Q & S; Rptr,
TOEC; *Middle Tenn St U; Bus.*

DEAN, Linda Joyce
Wilmer-Hutchins HS; Hutchins, TX; Chor; FHA;
Hmrm; NHS.

DEAN, Linda Kay
Ravenswood HS; Ravenswood, WV (52-201)
Band; FBLA; Hon Prog; Pom Pom Tm; GAA;
Mount Vernon Nazarene Col; Bus.

DEAN, Margaret Ellen
Carmel HS; Carmel, NY (10%-400) Band; NHS;
Tres, Sr Cl; Cpt, Hockey; Peer Ldrship; *Bus Adm.*

DEAN, Patrice Annette
E Alton-Wood River Comm HS; Wood River, IL
(21-315) A Cap Choir; Band; Chor; Ensm; FHA;
GS; Hmrm; Secy, NFL; NHS; Spch C; SC; Secy,
Thes; Pres A; Spch A; 21st Pl, St Ensm; *Evangel Col; Communications.*

DEAN, Richard Alan
DeSmet Jesuit HS; St Louis, MO (25-200) CYO;
Order/Arrow; JV, Golf; JV, Hockey; JV, Soccer;
Order/Arrow A; Pres A; Eagle Sct.

DEAN, Scott Edward
Northminster Presbyterian Church Hs; Peoria, IL
(29-463) Band; NHS; S-T, Order/Arrow; Var C;
Cpt, Cr-Ctry; Tr; God & Country A; Hon Prog;
Church Orch; Sch Jazz Board; Pres, Church Yth
Group; *U of Ill; Pre-Med.*

DeANDA, Bryan Charles
Derby Sr HS; Derby, KS (25%-175) Band; VP, Bus
C; Dbte Tm; Span C; Bsbl; Ftbl; JV, Golf; Soccer;
JA A; Jr NHS; *Kans St U; Archt.*

DeANGELIS, Debra Lynn
Seekonk HS; Seekonk, MA (13-224) Drama; Fr C;
FTA; NHS; Ski C; Span NHS; Tnns; Hon Prog; Jr
Prom Ct; *Providence Col; Bio.*

DEARDORFF, Heather Kathleen
Hughson Union HS; Hughson, CA; Band; Pres,
FFA; Pres, 4H; Lit Mag; Sch P; Secy, Sci C; Ski C;
Thes; Sftbl; Bank Of Amer A; CSF; 4H A; Spch A;
U of Redlands; Communications.

DEAREN, Sandra Jean
Eastern HS; Middletown, KY (144-228) Fr C; JV,
Bkbl; Golf; Eagle Prin Ct; *Western Ky U; Secy Adm.*

DEAREN, Tamie Denise
Texas City HS; Texas City, TX (1-440) Band; Fr C;
Tres, Thes; Opt Out Tn; PTA A; Sci A;
Morning Watch; Straight A A; Ntl Merit Com-
mended Stu; Moody Hon Schol; Band Swthl; *Bay-
lor U; Dentistry.*

DEARMAN, Janet LaVerne
Tupelo HS; Tupelo, MS; *Harding Col; Secy Training.*

DEARMON, Kathy A
Clarkrange HS; Clarkrange, TN; BC; FHA; Sci C;
Spch C; Bkbl.

DEARMON, Pamela Dionne
Jena HS; Jena, LA; Band; Drama; FTA; Lit Ral;
SC; Stage Band; Band A; Sup Rating, Piano Festi-
val; All Dist Band; *La Col.*

DEATON, Beverly Lynne
Ensley HS; Birmingham, AL (20%-300) Secy,
Math C; Reach Out; Bus & Off Ed; A, A-B HR;
Comm Vol Service A; *Psych.*

DEATON, David Addis
Tishomingo HS; Tishomingo, MS (7-33) BC; FFA;
Bsbl; Bkbl; Ftbl; Hist A.

DEATON, David Hugo
Hickory HS; Hickory, NC (35-350) AFS; Band;
VP, Fr C; Key C; Math C; Tres, NHS; Sci C; MVP,
Swim; Tnns; Rotary A; Ntl Merit Commended Stu;
NC Gov's Sch; *Haverford Col; Bio.*

DEATON, Donna Marlene
Willits HS; Willits, CA; AFS; Tr; Span A; Nurs
Aide A; *Pacific Union Col; Nurs.*

DEATON, Joseph Charles
Loyola HS; Towson, MD (1-134) Bus Mgr, Ann;
Chem C; Order/Arrow; JV, Wrest; COM; NEDT;
Order/Arrow A; *Purdue U; Chem.*

DEATON, Michael Adam
Campbell HS; Fairburn, GA (3-124) Mgr, Band;
BC; Key C; Math C; Ch, Model UN; Mu Alpha
Theta; NHS; Order/Arrow; Span C; Span NHS;
Ftbl; Wrest; COM; Elk A; Math A; NEDT; Math
Tm; Parl, Jr Civitan C; *Middle Ga Col; Audio-
Visual Communications.*

DEATRICK, Teresa Christine
Clark Co HS; Kahoka, MO (10-92) FHA; NHS;
Art C.

DEAVER, Lori Marie
Notre Dame HS; Salinas, CA; Gym; Modern
Dance; *Gavilan Col.*

DEAVERS, Denson Bennett
Sumrall Attendance Center HS; Sumrall, MS
(14-57) Ann; BC; Chem C; FFA; Phys C; Sci C;
Spch C; Tres, SC; Bkbl; Ftbl; Tr; Citz A; H of F; I
Dare You; Ath A; Ath Schol; *Miss Col; Eng.*

DeBAKKER, Andre Albert
Altoona Area HS; Altoona, PA (20%-1000) Ski C;
Ftbl; *Penn St U; Engr.*

DeBAKKER, Audrey W
Altoona Area HS; Altoona, PA (20%-1000) Ski C;
Tnns; *Bucknell Col.*

DeBARROS, Michael John
San Marin HS; Novato, CA (10-250) CYO; Span
C; Bkbl; Tr; CSF; Hon Prog; St Scholar; Tres, The
Calif Wind Children; *U of Santa Clara; Humanities.*

DeBATES, Estelle Christine
Jasper HS; Jasper, MN (5-50) Band; CYO; Chor;
Drama; Ensm; Rptr, FHA; 4H; Pres, Jr Col; Mgr, Tr;
COM; *SD St U; Pol Sci.*

DeBAUCHE, Rhonda Elaine
Allison HS; Allison, TX (2-10) Co-Ed, Ann; Secy,
FFA; Pres, FHA; Secy, Sr Cl; Co-Cpt, Bkbl; Sftbl;
Tnns; Cl Fav; Sal; Swtht; Best All Around; Miss
Allison; *Bauder Fashion Col; Interior Decorating.*

DEBBAN, Dawn Marie
Holdrege Sr HS; Holdrege, NE (33%-125) JV,
Chldr; SC; Swim; Tr; Type A; Campus Life; Vlbl; *U of Nebr.*

DeBEAUX, Donald Wayne
Crestview Sr HS; Crestview, FL (62-260) Drama;
Westminster Col; Vet.

DeBEAUX, John Edward Jr
Crestview Sr HS; Crestview, FL (36-260) ROTC A;
Sci A; Excel A; *Westminster Col; Med.*

DeBEER, David Paul
Morrison HS; Morrison, IL (7-152) Pres, Chess C;
FTA; NHS; SC; Pres, Sr Cl; Bausch & Lomb A;
NMF; St Scholar; *Swarthmore Col; Sci.*

DeBELLIS, Vittorio
St Josephs o-t Palisades; W New York, NJ (16-232)
Tres, Hmrm; Rptr, Sch P; Sci C; Span NHS; Hon
Prog; NEDT; Pres, Hist C; Bowl; *Stevens Tech Col; Eng.*

DeBERG, Kim Raine
Loyalton HS; Loyalton, CA (33%-45) Ann; Drama;
FBLA; 4H; Pres A; Secy, Drill Tm; Sch Photogra-
pher; *Chico St Col; Bio.*

DeBERRY, Cynthia
Jame B Dudley HS; Greensboro, NC (25-516)
Hmrm; Sch P; Thes; Y-Tns; Gr Marshal.

DeBERRY, Denise
Welch HS; Welch, WV (34-164) Chldr; Tri-HiY;
Bkbl; Tr; COM; HCt; Yth Leg; *W Va U; Engr.*

DeBIES, Valerie Yvonne
Granger High And El Camino Real HS; Granger,
UT (367-1095) Dbte Tm; Drama; FHA; 4H; Inter-
Act C; Semi-Fin, Jr Miss Pa; Sch P; Ski C; Tnns; Tr;
1st Pl, Sewing, NAACP Contest; Highest Sch Sewing Hon; *The Fashion Inst of Desgn & Merch; Design & Merchandising.*

DeBLECOURT, Karen Sue
Timothy Christian HS; Elmhurst, IL (38-94) Band;
JV, Tnns; Tr; JV Vlbl; *Calvin Col; Med.*

DeBLOCK, Dale Byron Jr
Temple Heights Christian Sch; Temple Terrace, FL
(45-90) Chor; Bsbl; Sftbl; Cpt, Tnns; Wrest; Bio A;
MLS; Sci A; Bsbl & Tnns Trophies; Secy, VP, Pres,
Royal Ambassadors; *U of S Fla; Bus Adm.*

DeBLOCK, Gail Kimberly
Temple Heights Christian Sch; Tampa, FL (4-90)
Chldr; Chor; NHS; Beauty; Bio A; COM; Sci A;
Mission Support-Acteens; HR; Bell Choir; Puppet
Ministry; *Bob Jones U; Bus Adm.*

DeBLOCK, John David
High Point Regional HS; Sussex, NJ (36-214) A
Cap Choir; Chor; Hmrm; SC; Thes; Pres, Jr Cl;
Mgr, Bkbl; Golf; Amer Legion Citz A; *Meteorol-
ogy.*

DeBLOIS, Kim Rose
Canby Pub HS; Canby, MN (6-126) Pres, AFS; Ed,
Ann; Band; FHA; SC; Var C; Mgr, Bkbl; Amer
Abroad Stu; *Southwest St U; Phys Therapy.*

De BOER, Marcia Ann
Ogilvie HS; Ogilvie, MN (15-60) Chor; SC; Dance
Line; *X-Ray Tech.*

de BOER, Mirte
Northgate HS; Walnut Creek, CA (46-428) Band;
Hmrm; SC; Cr-Ctry; MVP, Sftbl; CSF; Tres, Sr
Service Organization.

DeBOIS, Lisa Marie
Dover Sr HS; Dover, OH (135-266) CYO; Chldr;
Span C; Tri-HiY; *Kent St U; Acct.*

**DEBOLES,
Eugene Rueben Dolph**
Penncrest HS; Media, PA; Hmrm; SC; Bkbl; JV,
Ftbl; Tr; Amer Leg A; Most Out; *Fla U; Law.*

DeBORD, John Douglas
Bolton HS; Alexandria, LA; Drama; FFA; Fin, Lit
Ral; *Tex A&M U; Agr.*

DeBRUIN, Darlene Mary
Kaukauna HS; Kaukauna, WI (63-364) Band; Tres, 4H; Co-Cpt, Spch C; Bsbl; 4H A; Journ A; Spch A; VFW A; VofDEM; GAA; St Forensic As; HR; *U of Wis-Stevens Point; Bus Ed.*

de BRUM, Philomena
Marshall Islands HS; Majuro, MARSHALL ISLANDS (26-103) Hon Prog; Most Out; Star Student; *South Bay Col of Bus; Bus Secy.*

DeBRUYN, Gayle Lorraine
East Kentwood HS; Kentwood, MI (50-500) Band; NHS; GSct Board of Directors; Pep Band; Yth Choir; Flag Corps; Church Orch; Handbell Choir; PA; 1st Cl GSct; Radio Broadcast C; Schol Achv; *Central Mich Col; Interior Design.*

DEBS, Nelly
Academia Sagrado Corazon; Santurce, PR (2-90) ARC; Sci C; Span C; SC; Alg A; Phy A; Type A; Eng A; Span A; Geography A; Conduct A; *St Mary's Dominican Col; Med.*

DEBUS, Christi Arlene
Atherton HS; Burton, MI (4-147) Drama; Mjrte; NHS; ARC; Pres, Sci C; Pres, SC; Var C; MVP, Bkbl; MVP, Sftbl; Co-Cpt, Tr; DARGCA; Opt A; Opt Out Tn; Pres A; Regent Schol; Spch A; VofDEM; Drama A; *U of Mich; Bus Adm.*

DEC, Thomas Walter
Auburn HS; Auburn, NY (44-600) Band; Math C; Orch; Sch P; SC; COM; Hon Prog; *Siena Col; Math.*

DeCAGNA, Robert
Vailsburg HS; Newark, NJ (10-300) Ed, Ann; Band; City Conf; Drama; Hmrm; Lit Mag; NHS; Orch; Ed, Sch P; SC; Pres, Sr Cl; Pres, Jr Cl; COM; JA A; *NYU; Communications.*

De CARDENAS, Lourdes Margarita
Colegio Espiritu Santo; Hato Rey, PR (1-96) Dbte Tm; Drama; Math C; ARC; Rptr, Sch P; Spch C; Secy, SC; VP, Var C; Bkbl; Sftbl; Swim; Cpt, Tr; COM; Hon Prog; Most Out; ARC A; Spch A; *U of Pa; Biochem.*

DeCARLO, Patricia Celesta
Morgan Gardner Bulkeley HS; Hartford, CT (2-310) GS; Tres, Hmrm; NHS; Span C; Span NHS; SC; Co-Ch, Sr Cl; Swim; Cpt, Tnns; DARGCA; St Scholar; *U of Conn; Span.*

DeCARO, Mark Arthur
Harriton HS; Rosemont, PA (49-276) *Spring Garden Col; Building Construction Engr.*

DeCARR, Danny Carl
St Regis Falls Central HS; St Regis Falls, NY (10-30) Chem C; Chor; Fr C; Math C; Phys C; Rptr, Sch P; Tres, Jr Cl; COM; Cl Fav; MLS; Most Out; Star Student; Swtht; *Paul Smith's Col; Hotel-Restaurant Mgr.*

DECHALUS, Henry Philip
Jamaica HS; Jamaica, NY; Band; NHS; Bkbl; Swim; *Bradley U; Psych.*

DECK, Deborah Ann
Cedar Crest HS; Lebanon, PA; Bus C; Chldr; Drama; FBLA; Mjrte; Pres, ARC; Beauty; 4H A; ARC A; Spch A; Gym C; Sunday Sch Teacher; Tap Dancing; *Vo-tech Nurs Sch; Nurs.*

DECKARD, Amy Beth
Eldorado HS; Eldorado, IL (25-127).

DECKARD, Mark Alan
Eldorado HS; El Dorado, IL (55-103) Band; Drama; Citz A; *Elec.*

DECKER, Carolyn Anne
Rio Americano HS; Sacramento, CA; A Cap Choir; Chor; Madrigal; Yth Fel; WW; Miss Tn Amer Pageant; Church Touring-Singing Group; *Amer River Jr Col; Fashion Design.*

DECKER, Dianna Lynne
Forestville Central HS; Forestville, NY (10-82) Band; NHS; Rptr, Sch P; Regent Schol; Span Medal.

DECKER, Elaine Susan
Deposit Central HS; Deposit, NY (3-89) JV, Chldr; Chor; Drama; Tres, NHS; Secy, Sr Cl; Secy, Jr Cl; Rptr, Cr-Ctry; Rptr, Hockey; Rensselaer A; Alt, Regent's Schol; Med Mem A; Commerce A; Health Prize; Co Med Schol; *Rensselaer Poly Inst; Bio.*

DECKER, Gay Valerie
Eastwood HS; El Paso, TX; Ger C; Tr; *U of Tex; Ed.*

DECKER, Lori Jean
Sigourney HS; Sigourney, IA (53-116) Chldr; Mjrte; Rainbow; Var C; Yth Fel; *Bus Col; Bus.*

DECKER, Ronda Jo
Everett HS; Lansing, MI (15-500) NHS; Ski C; Tnns; MIP Tnns A; *Mich St U; Dentistry.*

DECKER, Susan Nelle
Breckinridge Co HS; Harned, KY (8-200) Band; FBLA; 4H; Rainbow; Span C; Art C; All Dist Band; Sup Rating, Brass Choir; Morehead Clinic Band; *Eastern Ky U; Bus Adm.*

DeCLUE, Girtha Gwen
SW HS; St Louis, MO (75-496) St Scholar.

DeCLUE, Penny Sue
Mehlville Sr HS; St Louis, MO; *Ed.*

DeCLUE, Rosanna E
Del Rio HS; Del Rio, TX (250-600) *SW Tex St U; Criminal Law.*

DeCRACKER, Merilynn
McKinley Sr HS; Canton, OH (11-662) Chess C; NHS; Span C; Span NHS; Hon Prog; *SE Bible Col; Missions.*

DECUIR, Gary Martin
Serra HS; Gardena, CA (10-41) CYO; Drama; JV, Cr-Ctry; JV, Ftbl; JV, Tr; Religion A; Drama A; Sports A; *Pepperdine U; Drama.*

DEDERMAN, Douglas Alan
Lincoln E HS; Lincoln, NE (4-503) Band; HiY; Var C; Bsbl; Ftbl; JV, Golf; Sftbl; Wrest; Fresh Engr Schol; HR; Outst Newspaper & Sr Carrier; *U of Nebr; Civil Engr.*

DEDMAN, William Griswold
The Baylor Sch; Chattanooga, TN (12-110) Ann; Bus C; Secy, Chess C; Dbte Tm; VP, Demolay; Drama; Lat C; F-Ed, Lit Mag; Model UN; Sch P; JV, Bsbl; MVP, Bkbl; Sftbl; Hon Prog; NMF; NMS; ARC A; Yth Fel; Drama A; Ed, DeMolay Paper; Off, Tn Republicans; De Molay R D A & Oratory; *Lib Arts.*

de DUBOVAY, Mark Porter
Pius X HS; Downey, CA; Band; Chor; Drama; Tres, HiY; Sci C; CSF; NEDT; PTA A; Val; HR; Yth Advisor, YMCA; YMCA Camp Counselor; Yth Advisor, Church Council On Min; *U of S Calif; Med.*

DEEDS, Deborah Ann
Uniontown HS; Uniontown, PA; Usherettes.

DEEKENS, Mary Maynard
St Mary's Col; Raleigh, NC (16-103) Chor; Fr C; ARC; Rptr, Sch P; Hon Prog; Yth Fel; Tn-Age Republicans; Young Republicans; Sch Fr Play.

DEER, Shannon Kay
Fort Osage HS; Independence, MO; Span C; Span NHS; 4H A; Pres, Methodist Yth Organization; NJHS; *Teaching.*

DEERE, Vickie Lynn
Antelope Valley HS; Lancaster, CA; HiY.

DEES, Audrey Marie
Christopher Columbus HS; New York City, NY (479-798).

DEES, Jessie Robert
Harlem HS; Harlem, GA (40-150) FFA; Parl, InterAct C; Bsbl; *Ga Sou Col; Sociology.*

DEES, Lisa LeAnne
Gainesville HS; Gainesville, TX (20%-250) Band; Chor; FHA; Rainbow; Health C; *Baylor U; Vet.*

DEES, Michael Fredrick
O'Fallon Township HS; O'Fallon, IL (103-352) Bkbl; Ftbl; Golf; Tnns; Pres, Royal Ambassadors.

DEETS, Mark Donald
E Liverpool HS; E Liverpool, OH (72-320) BS; Demolay; Secy, Key C; Sch P; Pres, Span C; SC; Thes; Pres, Sr Cl; *Bethany Col; Religion.*

DeFILIPPO, Robert Lewis
Wellsboro Area Sr HS; Wellsboro, PA (33%-200) Pres, Band; Ensm; Hmrm; Ski C; Var C; Pres, Soph Cl; JV, Bkbl; Ftbl; Tr; John Philip Sousa C; Shop A; Phys Fitness A; *Penn St U; Bus Adm.*

DeFILIPPO, Vicki Jane
Thomas A Edison HS; Elmira Heights, NY; Chor; Dbte Tm; Drama; Ensm; Secy, Soph Cl; *Nurs.*

DeFOOR, Deborah Lynne
Stephens Co HS; Toccoa, GA (4-254) VP, FTA; Mgr, Mjrte; Tri-HiY; Acteens; Del, Yth Assembly.

DeFOOR, Laura Ann
Stonington HS; Stonington, IL (15-40) Pres, Arch; Band; Cpt, Chldr; Drama; Mjrte; Hmrm; Rainbow; Pres, Arch; Sftbl; Tnns; MVP, Tr; Cl Fav; 4H A; HCt; PTA A; Tr A; *Central Bible Col.*

DeFORD, Mary Elizabeth
Coon Rapids Sr HS; Coon Rapids, MN; Band; CYO; Sch P.

DeFOREST, Craig Allen
Washington HS; Cherokee, IA (30%-170) Band; Var C; Bkbl; Ftbl; Tnns; Tr.

DeFOREST, Douglas Alan
Beaverton HS; Beaverton, OR (200-600) A Cap Choir; Band; Orch; Order/Arrow; Sch P; Opt Out Tn; Order/Arrow A; Stage Band; *Portland Comm Col; Bus.*

DeFOREST, James Edward
Beaverton HS; Beaverton, OR; Ger C; Order/Arrow; Soccer; Tr; Order/Arrow A; Eagle Sct.

DEGAN, Joe Craig
Duncan Sr HS; Duncan, OK; Drama; FFA; *US Marines; Aviation Elec.*

DEGENER, Debra Ann
Sparta HS; Sparta, IL; Band; 4H; Mjrte; Sci C; *Murray St U; Social Work.*

DeGEORGE, Patricia Ann
John F Kennedy Sr HS; New Orleans, LA (1-368) Fin, Jr Miss Pagent; Lit Ral; Mu Alpha Theta; NHS; Sci C; Pres, Span NHS; Secy, Tri-HiY; Alg A; Bausch & Lomb A; Bio A; COM; Hon Prog; Math A; Pres A; Sci A; Val; S Central Bell A; McCloskey A; Miss Congen A & Sch A, No Jr Ms Pag; *U of New Orleans; Sci.*

DEGGES, Pamela Joy
Whispering Hills Christian Acad; Nashville, TN (5-20) F-Ed, Ann; Co-Cpt, Chldr; Chor; VP, Jr Cl; HCt; Superlatives; Carnival Qn.

DEGHI, Patricia Ann
Providence HS; Burbank, CA (1-75) A-Ed, Ann; Chldr; Drama; Fr C; Monogram; NHS; Span C; Var C; Sftbl; CSF; Citz A; Hon Prog; St Scholar; *U of S Calif; Foreign Languages.*

DEGNER, Reginel Max
Palo Verde HS; Tucson, AZ (120-592) Band; K of C; Swim; Eagle Sct; Grand Canyon A; *Pepperdine U; Law.*

DEGONIA, Karen Sue
Maplewood-Richmond Heights HS; Maplewood, MO (17-220) Fr C; Sftbl; *SE Mo St Col; Elem Ed.*

De GRAAF, George Lawrence
Addison Trail HS; Addison, IL (6-600) Band; NHS; PTA A; *Covenant Col; Math.*

DeGRADO, Timothy Richard
Paradise HS; Paradise, CA (7-233) Chor; SC; JV, Bkbl; JV, Cr-Ctry; Tnns; Bio A; CSF; Hon Prog; Math A; *Stanford U; Engr.*

DeGRAW, Pamela Lee
Red Bluff HS; Red Bluff, CA (206-350) Chor; 4H; Span C; *Shasta & Chico Col; Home Ec Teacher.*

DeGROOTE, Karen S
Mascoutah Comm HS; Mascoutah, IL (64-288) FHA; Acteens; Church Yth Choir; Secy, Churcy Yth Cl.

DeGROOTE, Karen Suzanne
Mascoutah Comm HS; Mascoutah, IL (64-288) FHA; Acteens; Church Yth Choir.

DeGROOTE, LeaAnn Kay
Mascoutah HS; Mascoutah, IL (94-314) Acteens; Church Yth Choir.

DeGROSS, Timothy Carl
Marysville-Pilchuck HS; Marysville, WA (2%-425) Hmrm; Key C; NHS; Order/Arrow; SC; JV, Ftbl; Tr; Wrest; *U of Wash.*

DeHAAN, Douglas Gene
Pella Comm HS; Pella, IA (50-100) Band; FFA; 4H; *Bible.*

DeHART, Ruth Elisabeth
Cupertino HS; Cupertino, CA (84-609) Bus C; FBLA; Hmrm; SC; Bkbl; Ftbl; *Seattle Pacific Col; Bus.*

DEHN, Gary Allen
Ottawa Sr HS; Ottawa, KS (16-203) Band; BS; NHS; Bkbl; Hon Prog; *U of Kans; Bio.*

DeHOFF, Betty Jane
Boardman HS; Boardman, OH (55-627) Chor; Fr C; Tres, 4H; Hmrm; Spch C; SC; Y-Tns; Bkbl; Sftbl; 4H A; Pres A; Lib Asst; Bstr C; Stage Crew; Alt, Rotary Exchange; *Youngstown St U; Nurs.*

DEHOSIER, Karen Lynn
Lincoln Park HS; Lincoln Park, MI (18-620) A Cap Choir; Chor; Drama; Ensm; Fr C; Fin, GS; Hmrm; NHS; SC; Hon Prog; Journ A; Most Out; NMS; Swim As; Creative Art As; Acting As; Yth o-t Mo; *Eastern Mich U; Occupational Therapy.*

DEICHMANN, Ellen Marie
Watertown Sr HS; Watertown, CT (60-300) Band; Rainbow; Hockey; Hon Prog; *U of Connecticut; Bio.*

DEIHL, Sharon Janet
Arlington HS; Arlington Heights, IL; Co-Cpt, Band; Dbte Tm; Fr C; NFL; NHS; Orch; Sci C; Swim; Magna Cum Laude; Spch A; Summa Cum Laude; Modern Mus Masters; Hon Pin; Foreign Lang A; *Northland Col; Environmental Sci.*

DEISLER, Richard Lee
Coldwater HS; Coldwater, MI; Band; Chor; Drama; Model UN; NHS; Rptr, Sch P; SC; NFL; Bsbl; Bkbl; Cr-Ctry; Tr; Alg A; Bio A; Citz A; Hist A; Hon Prog; Math A; Rotary A; Spch A; Drama A; Church Y Pres; *Marion Col.*

DEISSLER, Harriett Edna
Woodham HS; Pensacola, FL (25-530) Ger C; Lat C; Parl, NHS; JV, Bkbl; Tnns; Hist A; Poet A; Pres A; Eng A; Pres, Med Explorer Post; *Lycoming Col.*

DEITS, Jeanne Marie
Corona Sr HS; Corona, CA (56-583) Cpt, Chldr; InterClub Coun; Semi-Fin, Jr Miss Pa; gent; Special Recogn A, Ca Jr Miss Prog; *U of Calif at Irvine; Dance.*

DEITZ, Brian Howard
East HS; Salt Lake City, UT; Co-Ch, Ensm; Model UN; Semi-Fin, Tnns; Type A; *U of Utah; Bus.*

DeJARNETTE, Gregory Lee
Lincoln Comm HS; Lincoln, IL (60-282) Band; 4H; Lat C; NHS; Tnns; Wrest; St Scholar; *U of Ill; Gen.*

DeJONG, John Jesse
Cedar Falls HS; Cedar Falls, IA (40-465) Band; Ger C; COM; Kiwanis A; *Iowa St U.*

DeJONG, Nanette Tracy
Vermillion HS; Vermillion, SD; A Cap Choir; Band; Chor; Community Yth Symph; Ensm; 4H; Madrigal; Orch; Tnns; All St Bands & Orch; Superior, Mus Contests; *Mus.*

DeJONG, Steven Allen
Iroquois HS; Iroquois, SD (1-32) Var C; Bkbl; Ftbl; Tr; *NF St U; Architecture.*

DeKEYZER, Brenda Louise
St Joseph HS; Jeanerette, LA (2-29) Chldr; GS; 4H; Fin, Lit Ral; Lit Mag; NHS; Sch P; B Crocker A; COM; NEDT; 1st, Eng, Dist Ral; 2nd, Eng, St Ral; Eng A; *Loyola U; Communications.*

DEKKER, Jane Elizabeth
Mt Miguel HS; Spring Valley, CA (43-500) Chor; Ensm; Vlbl; Most Outst, Church; *Westmont Col; Mus.*

DEKKER, Kent Alan
Craigmont HS; Memphis, TN (150-250) *Evangel Col; Engr.*

DEKKER, Nelly Ann
Zillah HS; Zillah, WA; JV, Chldr; Chem C; Ensm; Pres, FHA; FNA; VP, 4H; Math C; NHS; Sci C; Spch C; SC; Tr; COM; 4H A; Masonic A; Chldr Ltr; *Calvin Col; Special Ed.*

DEKKER, Paul Gregory
Mt Miguel HS; San Diego, CA (25%-1000) A Cap Choir; Chor; Spch C; Var C; Ftbl; Wrest; Odd Fellow Fin; Spch A.

De LA GARZA, Ma Francisca Penny
St Augustine Sch; Laredo, TX (11-67) Chess C; Drama; NHS; Spch C; Bkbl; Drama A; *St Thomas U; Computer Sci.*

DeLANCEY, Patricia Jo
Marion HS; Marion, IA (11-220) A Cap Choir; Chor; Semi-Fin, NHS; Spch C; Spch A; Yth Fel; *Psych.*

DELANEY, Allen Edward
Queen Anne Episcopal Sch; Upper Marlboro, MD; Drama; F-Ed, Sch P; Bsbl; JV, Soccer; MVP, Swim; *Fla Technological U; Elec Engr.*

DELANEY, Diana Marie
Effingham HS; Effingham, IL (20%-178) Band; Ensm; Pres, Fr C; Literary A; Mus Contest; *E Ill U; Mus.*

DELANEY, Glenda Ann
Burke HS; Charleston, SC (5-205) Pres, Hmrm; VP, NHS; Math A; WW; Eng A; *Va Union U; Math.*

DELANEY, Kenneth Ronald
N Hills and A W Beattie Tech HS; Pittsburgh, PA (20%-800) Hmrm; NHS; Order/Arrow; Bsbl; Moderator, Yth Fel; Buhl Planetarium Sci Fair; *Hutchinson Area Voc Tech Inst; Non-Destructive Testing.*

DELANEY, Lisa Ann
Harris-Lake Park HS; Lake Park, IA (11-44) A Cap Choir; Ann; Band; Chor; Ensm; FHA; Madrigal; ARC; Tres, SC; Pres, Jr Cl; Swim; Tnns; ARC A; Band & Chor Ltrs; *Mus.*

DELANEY, Tim E
St Ignatius HS; St Ignatius, MT (6-32) BS; NHS; S-T, Var C; Pres, Jr Cl; Bkbl; Ftbl; Tr; Type A; *Mont St U; Ed.*

DELANEY, William Gerard
Hicksville HS; Hicksville, NY; ARC; Sacristan; Life Sct; *Nassau Comm Col; Bus.*

DeLANGE, Tracy Lynn
Cedar Falls HS; Cedar Falls, IA; Band; JV, Bkbl; Young Life.

DELANOY, Brian George
Fullerton Union HS; Fullerton, CA (51-376) Band; VP, Key C; Orch; Ski C; VP, Sr Cl; Bkbl; Cr-Ctry; Tr; CSF; ARC A; *U of Calif.*

DELANOY, Darlene Ann
Fullerton Union HS; Fullerton, CA; Chldr; Pres, Hmrm; NHS; Ed, Sch P; Ski C; Secy, SC; S-T, Y-Tns; Tnns; COM; Citz A; Cl Fav; JA A; MLS; Most Out; Pres A; Rotary A; Spch A; Dance Company.

DELAO, Jeffrey Lane
Memorial HS; San Antonio, TX (6-300) A Cap Choir; Band; Chor; Ensm; Madrigal; NHS; Band Drum Major; UIL Mus A; *Berkley Sch of Mus; Mus.*

De LA O, Maria Yolanda
Estancia HS; Estancia, NM (25%-46) JV, Bkbl; E NM U.

de la PENA, Cynthia Ann
St Joseph-Notre Dame HS; Alameda, CA (8-56) NHS; Secy, Sci C; Span C; Citz A; Sewing A; *Chabot Col; Merchandizing.*

de la PENA, Teresa Lynn
St Joseph's Notre Dame HS; Alameda, CA (6-72) NHS; Hon Prog; *Chabot Jr Col; Data Processing.*

DELAPLANE, Sandra Lee
Beverly Hills HS; Beverly Hills, CA (33%-600) JV, Chldr; Drama; ARC; Tr; COM; Hon Prog; ARC A; Piano A; *USC.*

DeLaROCHE, Douglas A
Camden HS; Camden, NY (66-210) Drama; SC; Pres, Var C; Bkbl; Cpt, Cr-Ctry; Cpt, Tr; DARGCA; Most Out; MVP, Cr-Ctry & Tr; Most Friendly; Sch Tr Records; *Mohawk Valley Comm Col; Human Services.*

De La RUE, Richard Joseph
New Caney HS; Porter, TX; FFA; Hmrm; NHS; SC; Ftbl; Sftbl; MVP, Tnns; COM; Cl Fav; Hon Prog; Eng A; *Tex A&M U; Oceanography.*

DELASHAW, Don Alan
Lee Acad; Clarksdale, MS (10-80) Band; Mgr, Bkbl; Tnns; *U of Ala.*

DE lA TORRE, Maria Ines
Luis Munoz Marin HS; Cabo Rojo, PR (5-200) Band; Chldr; Chem C; Chor; City Conf; Dbte Tm; Drama; Ensm; Pres, FHA; Pres, Hmrm; InterAct C; Lit Ral; Lit Mag; Math C; Sci C; Span C; Spch C; Secy, SC; Amer Leg Orator A; Bio A; COM; Chem A; Hist A; Hon Prog; Masonic A; Math A; Sci A; *CAAM; Med Technology.*

DeLAUGHTER, Cassandra Ann
Miami Jackson Sr HS; Miami, FL; Band; Chldr; Citz A; Pres A; 100% Attendance; Chldr Ltrs; *Nurs.*

DeLAUGHTER, Tony
Miami Jackson Sr HS; Miami, FL; Cpt, Var C; Bkbl; Cpt, Ftbl; Tr; Citz A; Most Out; Pres A; MVP, Bkbl & Ftbl; Sports Ltrs; *Tulane U; Bus Mgr.*

DeLAURIER, Gregory Alan
Central-Lanier B HS; Macon, GA (16-232) BC; 4H; Model UN; UN Council; Y-Tns; Sftbl; Gov Honor Prog; 1st Pl, St Conservation A; *Mercer U; Med.*

DeLAY, Bradley Douglas
Ringgold HS; Ringgold, GA (1%-214) BC; Chess C; Pres, 4H; InterAct C; Pres, Key C; Span C; SC; Pres, Sr Cl; Tres, Jr Cl; JV, Wrest; COM; Gl Fav; Gov Honor Prog; 4H A; H of F; Hon Prog; I Dare You; MLS; Sci A; Val; Sup SC Rep; *Ga Inst of Tech; Pre-Med.*

DELAY, Nancy Lorraine
Franklin HS; Franklin, IL (4-40) JV, Chldr; FFA; 4H; VP, NHS; S-T, Span C; Mgr, Tr; Type A; GAA; Vlbl; IAC; Lib C; *Ill Wesleyan U; Art.*

DELBAUGH, William Scott
Selinsgrove Area HS; Selinsgrove, PA (30-240) Hmrm; Math C; SC; Math A; Stu Coun; *NE Christian Col; Archt.*

DELBERT, Stephanie Lynn
Philo HS; Philo, OH; Chldr; Chor; Secy, Span C; COM; Hon Prog; Most Out; *Ohio U; Nurs.*

DELEMEESTER, Gregory
St Charles HS; St Charles, MI (13-140) SC; St Scholar; High Hons; *Michigan St U.*

DELER, Ingrid Eulalia
L D Brandeis HS; New York, NY (250-1000) A Cap Choir; Chldr; Chor; VP, Drama; HiY; Tnns; Hon Prog; Gym; Hospital Vol A; *Religion.*

DELER, Rosa Valentina
Louis D Brandeis HS; New York, NY (5%-800) Cpt, Chldr; Chor; VP, Drama; Y-Tns; Hon Prog; Vol A; Clrm Activities; *Yale U; Law.*

DelFRATE, John Henry
Albuquerque HS; Albuquerque, NM (50-450) Chor; NHS; F-Ed, Sch P; Sci C; Span C; Bsbl; Journ A; Phy A; ARC A; Regent Schol; Sci A; Erda's ALO A; *U of NM; Mech Engr.*

DelFRATE, Renzo Joseph
Albuquerque HS; Albuquerque, NM (15-800) CYO; Chor; NHS; Sci A; Dept of Transportation & FAA A; *U of NM; Elec.*

DELGADO, Antonio Nascimento
E Providence HS; E Providence, RI (100-500) CYO; Drama; NHS; ARC; Var C; Bsbl; Cpt, Bkbl; Sftbl; Wrest; COM; Cl Fav; Hon Prog; Sci A; Yth Fel; MVP, Bkbl; Sports A; Ldrship A; *Law.*

DELGADO, Asdrubal A
Jose de Diego HS; Mayaguez, PR; Tres, Phys C; Bsbl; Sftbl; COM; Magna Cum Laude.

DELGADO, Digna Maria
Juan Jose Osuna HS; Hato Rey, PR (5-150) Chldr; Drama; Fr C; Parl, FHA; ARC; Sch P; Bkbl; Swim; COM; Hon Prog; Lion A; MLS; VP, Explorers BSA; Pres, GSct; Vlbl; *U of Puerto Rico; Sci.*

DELGADO, Elizabeth Kay
Burleson HS; Burleson, TX; Cpt, Chldr; Tr; *Tex Christian U; Commercial Art.*

DELGADO, Luis Gregorio
Consuelo Escalona HS; Carolina, PR (1-30) Bkbl; COM; Loyalty A; *U of PR at Mayaguez; Engr.*

DELGADO, Marta Maria
Our Lady of Good Counsel HS; Newark, NJ (1-84) Chor; NFL; Math A; Pres A; Co 4-H Coun; WW; Co 4-H Qn; SCAB; Cpt, Pom Pon Sq; Pres, Lib C; Church Choir; *Brown Mackie Bus Col; Secretarial.*

DELIGANIS, Teina Louise
J W Nixon HS; Laredo, TX (24-537) GS; Hmrm; Secy, NHS; Span NHS; Ch, SC; Tres, Sr Cl; COM; Citz A; Cl Fav; DARGCA; H of F; MLS; Most Out; Pres A; *St Edward's U; Pol Sci.*

DeLISA, Barbara JeanAnn
Mother McAuley HS; Chicago, IL (20-481) Chor; NHS; Pres, Orch; SC; NEDT; St Scholar; Yth Foundation A; U of Chgo Schol; WW; *U of Chicago; Sci.*

DeLISLE, Susanne Marie Leilani
Whitney HS; Whitney, TX (8%-43) BC; FHA; Pres, Span C; Tnns; Tr; Pres, VP & S-T, Rainbow Girls; Reading A; PA; Grand Cross of Colors; *Hill Jr Col; Elem Ed.*

DELK, Lisa Ann
East HS; Buffalo, NY; Secy, Chor; ARC; Sftbl; Swim; Beauty; God & Country A; H of F; Math A; ARC A; Star Student; VofDEM; Yth Fel; *Canisus Col; Math.*

DELK, Rollie Dale
Tift Co HS; Tifton, GA; Hmrm; InterAct C; Span C; Parl, Tri-HiY; Mgr, Bkbl; Tr; Wrest; Cl Fav; HCt; Chaplain, Band; Friendliest; *Abraham Baldwin Agr Col; Bus Adm.*

DELL, Chris Alan
Freeport HS; Freeport, IL (40-516) Chor; Drama; Ensm; SC; Thes; MLS; Spch A; St Chorus; Best Thespian; Mus Dept Hon; *Harding Col; Mus.*

DELLA TORRE, Signe Andrea
Colegio Puertorriqueno de Ninas; Caparra Heights, PR (6-48) Math C; NHS; Co-Ed, Sch P; Sci C; Var C; Bkbl; Swim; *Loyola U; Communications.*

DELLETT, Lesa Jo
La Crosse HS; La Crosse, KS (11-50) Band; Chldr; FHA; 4H; Orch; SC; Secy, Sr Cl; Bus Mgr, Jr Cl; Type A; WW; WW Among HS Chldr; Shorthand A; *Kans St U at Fort Hayes; Bus.*

DELLINGER, Andy Hugh
Lumberton Sr HS; Lumberton, NC (50-250) Band; Lat C; *NC St U; Bus.*

DELLINGER, Donald Jr
Gaffney Sr HS; Gaffney, SC; Chess C; Bsbl; Bkbl; S-T, Royal Ambassadors; *Spartanburg Tech Col; Air Con & Refrig.*

DELLINGER, Evelyn Lee
Cherryville Sr HS; Cherryville, NC (25-126) Chor; Drama; Fr C; FHA; FTA; InterAct C; NHS; *Mars Hill Col; Social Work.*

DELLINGER, Robert Donald Jr
Cherryville Sr HS; Cherryville, NC (43-143) Band; FFA; *Cleveland Tech Inst; Automobile Body Repair.*

DELLINGER, Theresa Marie
Gaffney Sr HS; Gaffney, SC; BC; Fr C; Hmrm; Cpt, Sftbl; Pres, Acteens; *Ed.*

DELMONICO, Barbara Jean
Archbishop Grace HS; Fridley, MN (69-226) Band; Hmrm; Span C; SC; Cpt, Bkbl; Cpt, Cr-Ctry; Sftbl; Tr; HCt; Cl Friendliest; Candidate, HQn; *St Catherine's Col; Sociology.*

DeLOACH, Charles Ray
W Monroe HS; W Monroe, LA (15%-461) Chor; Drama; Pres, Key C; NHS; Span C; VP, Thes; Hon Prog; Most Out; Sci A; Spch A; Best Supporting Actor; *La Tech U; Engr.*

DeLOACH, Joe Alexander
Daniel Boone HS; Jonesboro, TN (1-300) BC; Chess C; Fr C; 4H; NHS; Sci C; VP, Span C; Golf; 4H A; Kiwanis A; NMF; Val; *E Tenn St U.*

DeLOACH, Kathleen Joy
W Memphis Sr HS; W Memphis, AR; Band; FHA; Hmrm; *Practical Nurs.*

DeLOACH, Scott Allan
Papillion-LaVista HS; Papillion, NE (19-363) Band; JV, Bsbl; JV, Bkbl; JV, Ftbl; *U of Nebr Lincoln; Elect Engr.*

DELOATCH, Lillian Delois
Gumberry HS; Gumberry, NC (6-97) Pres, BC; Chor; Drama; Secy, FTA; FHA; Hmrm; SC; Secy, Jr Cl; Secy, Soph Cl; *U of NC at Chapel Hill; Med Technology.*

DELOATCH, Linett
Gumberry HS; Gumberry, NC (1-110) Co-Cpt, Chldr; Fr C; FHA; Co-Ed, Sch P; SC; Alg A; Citz A; Cl Fav; HCt; Math A; Most Out; Sal; Yth Fel; Chor C Cert; *NCU; Econ.*

DELOATCH, Sharon Adams
W S Creecy HS; Rich Square, NC (9-42) Drama; Secy, SC; Y-Tns; Bkbl; *A & T St U; Phys Ed.*

DeLOERA, Elida
Loraine HS; Loraine, TX; Band; Chldr; FHA; Secy, FTA; NHS; Secy, SC; VP, Soph Cl; Bkbl; Tr; HCt; *W Tex Col; Secy.*

DeLONE, Katherine Ann
Country Day Sch o-t Sacred Heart; Overbrook, PA; Drama; NHS; F-Ed, Sch P; Pres, Bkbl; Hockey; Hon Prog; Coach's A, Bkbl; Good Sportsmanship A; *Pa St U; Art.*

DeLONG, Diane Phyllis
Westview Sr HS; Braham, MN;

DeLORD, Craig Allen
Nederland HS; Nederland, TX (16-484) CYO; Fr C; NHS; VP, SC; JV, Bsbl; JV, Bkbl; Ftbl; Hon Prog; *U of Tex; Pre-Med.*

DELORME, Jeffrey Lee
Thomas A Edison HS; Elmira Heights, NY (10-150) Band; NHS; Orch; Var C; Ftbl; Tr; Wrest; Amer Leg A; Chem A; Rotary A; Sci A; VFW Orator Win; Yth Fel; Win, NOW Essay; Life Sct; Hist C; Yth Co; *Sociology.*

DeLOTTO, Mark Simon
Tampa Cath HS; Tampa, FL (35-306) Hmrm; Key C; Semi-Fin, SC; Soccer; Hist A; HR; Principal's List; *U of S Fla; Bus.*

DELPH, Charles Brian
James Wood HS; Winchester, VA; Chor; Drama; NHS; Thes; *Dance.*

DELPHIN, Bernice Isabel
St Matthew HS; Melrose, LA (3-44) A Cap Choir; CYO; Chldr; Chor; Hmrm; Pres, Jr Cl; Alg A; Beauty; Citz A; Cl Fav; HCt; Hon Prog; Civics A; *NSU.*

DELPHIN, Julie Ann
St Matthew HS; Melrose, LA (5-45) Ann; Band; CYO; FHA; 4H; VP, Soph Cl; 4H A; Hon Prog; Sci A; Spch A; Eng A; PE A; Gen Bus A.

Del RE, Angie
Modesto HS; Modesto, CA (16-276) Chldr; InterAct C; Lit Ral; COM; Citz A; PA; *Modesto Jr Col; Bus.*

del RIO, Eddy Manuel
Palm Beach Gardens HS; Palm Beach Gardens, FL (39-466) A Cap Choir; Chor; Ensm; NHS; Bsbl; JV, Bkbl; Most Talented; Citz A; WW; Most Inspirational Christian A; *Juilliard Sch; Piano.*

Del ROSARIO, Alex Velasco
Northeastern HS; Detroit, MI; *U of Mich; Med.*

Del TORO, Yolanda
Lola Rodriguez de Tio; San German, PR (13-350) Band; FHA; ARC; Sci C; Span C; Sftbl; Bkbl; COM; Hon Prog; Interlochen Ntl Mus; Phy A; Rotary A; Sci A; Summa Cum Laude; *U of Puerto Rico at Mayaguez; Med.*

DeLUCA, Dawn Veronica
Barringer HS; Newark, NJ (24-500) Chess C; NHS; Eng A; Councilman Carrino A; Ephraim Eisenberg A; *Cook Col; Acct.*

DeLUCA, Peter Francis
St Peters Prep HS; Jersey City, NJ (15-260) CYO; NHS; Sch P; Tres, Jr Cl; Hockey; Amer Leg A; Hon Prog; Summa Cum Laude; Italian A; *St Peter's Col; Biochem.*

DeLUCE, Ciara Lynn
Linton Intermediate HS; Pittsburgh, PA; Span C; *Nurs.*

DeLUCIA, Jon Gregory
Las Cruces HS; Las Cruces, NM (10%-600) Band; Chor; Key C; NHS; Tnns; *Bowdoin Col; Math.*

DeLUDE, Terese Gigi
Cleveland HS; Cleveland, TN; BC; Pres, CYO; Chor; Fr C; COM; Citz A; Pres, Art C; Art A; Win, Civitan C Essay Contest; *Bellmount Abbey; Theology.*

del VALLE, Jose Ignacio
S Florida Military Acad; Miami, FL (5-40) Drama; Span C; Sr Cl; Fin, Soccer; Star Student; Bowl; Span A; Eng A; *Miami-Dade Comm Col; Med Sci.*

del VALLE, Maria Milagros
Our Lady of Pilar HS; Rio Piedras, PR (20%-166) Secy, CYO; VP, Chem C; Hmrm; Lit Ral; Ch, NHS; Pres, Sci C; Span C; COM; Hist A; Merit Achievement.

DelVALLE, Milagros
Adlai E Stevenson HS; Bronx, NY; *Psych.*

DELWICHE, Jeffrey Scott
Eisenhower HS; Hopkins, MN (11-445) Order/Arrow; ARC; Cr-Ctry; JV, Soccer; JV, Tnns; Tr; God & Country A; Hon Prog; Order/Arrow A; Pres A; Eagle Sct; *U of Minn; Oceanography.*

DEMANCHYK, Linda Ann
Shelton HS; Shelton, CT; COM; Type A; Span A; Amer Bible Soc A; *Acct.*

DEMANDANTE, Godfred Niepes Jr
John F Kennedy HS; Tumon, GUAM; Chess C; NHS; JV, Cr-Ctry; Span A; *Physics.*

DeMARIA, Domenick Don
Midview HS; Grafton, OH (112-286) Span C; Tnns; *Taylor U; Missionary Aviation.*

DEMAS, Ellen Ann
Woodrow Wilson HS; Portland, OR; ARC; Pres, SC; Citz A; Pres, Fresh Cl; Judiciary Comm; Historian, Soph Cl; Pres, GOYA; SB Exec Coun; Med Explorer Post; Assemblies Comm; Maids of Athens; *Pre-Med.*

DEMAS, LouAnn
Kashmere HS; Houston, TX (10-35) Bus C; Chor; French NHS; ARC; Y-Tns; Bsbl; God & Country A; Gov Honor Prog; Most Out; Ntl Conf Chr & Jews; PTA A; ARC A; Yth Fel; Yth Leg.

DEMBEK, Renata Maria
Driscoll HS; Addison, IL (19-144) Chldr; Tnns.

DeMEESTER, Andrea Lynn
Bensalem Sr HS; Cornwells Hgts, PA (15-700) Chldr; Drama; Fr C; Hmrm; NHS; Miss Pa Hemisphere Beauty Pageant; *Nurs.*

DeMELLO, Celeste Day
Piedmont Hills HS; San Jose, CA; CYO; Drama; Span C; Swim; Tr; Coaches A; *San Jose St U.*

de MIER, Maria Isabel
Antilles HS; San Juan, PR (5%-135) SC; Pres, Soph Cl; Mgr, Bkbl; Swim; Hon Prog; Co-Cpt, Drill Tm; Vlbl; *Interntl Relations.*

DeMILT, Kevin Stacy
Thomas Blackwell Barlett HS; Bartlett, TN; Key C; Bsbl; Co-Cpt, Ftbl; Tr; Wrest; Eng A; Sports A; *Engr.*

DEMING, Mark William
Genoa-Kingston HS; Genoa, IL (56-132) Pres, Band; Chor; Pres, Drama; Ensm; FFA; Madrigal; Co-Ed, Sch P; SC; Thes; HCt; Hon Prog; Most Out; Yth Fel; Jazz Band; WW Music; Stu; Arian A; MYF Yth Fel; Outst Sr Musician; Church Choir; Outst Jazz Bnd; *SIU; Recreation.*

DEMING, Richard Wayne
Abbotsford HS; Abbotsford, WI; Band; Bsbl; JV, Ftbl; Wrest.

DeMINT, Michael Ray
Westran HS; Huntsville, MO (26-43) Secy, FFA; Var C; Bsbl; Bkbl; Cpt, Ftbl; HCt; *Moberly Jr Col.*

DeMIRJIAN, Timothy Haig
Penncrest HS; Lima, PA (251-432) Co-Cpt, Bsbl; Church Choir; Ch, Christian Yth Fel Comm; *Drexel U; Bus Adm.*

DEMLOW, Julie Lynn
Ernest W Seaholm HS; Birmingham, MI (50-600) Band; Chldr; Fr C; Model UN; NFL; NHS; Orch; Swim; Ntl Sci Found; Comm Symph; Mus Solo-Ensm A's; Rookie o-t Yr; *Ithaca Col; Communications.*

DEMMER, Rick Lynn
A C Davis HS; Yakima, WA (28-490) VP, Dbte Tm; NFL; NHS; Order/Arrow; Co-Ed, Sch P; Spch C; Journ A; Opt A; Spch A; Ntl Merit Commendation; Q & S Soc; Commencement Spkr; Photo C; Eagle Sct; Sct Exchng Prog, Norway; NFL Degree of Distinction; *Wash St U; Chem.*

DEMMING, Lori Ann
Ephrata Sr HS; Ephrata, PA (40-250) F-Ed, Ann; Band; FBLA; Co-Cpt, Mjrte; Type A; Yth Fel; WW; WW, Mus Stu; Thompson Inst; Med Secy.

DEMOLEAS, Kyra
St Andrew Acad; Beechhurst, NY (2-10) Chess C; ARC; Swim; Tnns; Math A; ARC A; Yth Fel; St John's U; Acct.

de MONCH, Michael David
Marine Military Acad; Harlingen, TX; Ann; Band; UCLA; Elec Engr.

DEMOND, JoJean Ann
Heritage HS; Monroeville, IN (14-200) A Cap Choir; Chor; Ensm; Tres, Fr C; Ntl Yth Conf; Swim; Tr; Bio A; Hon Prog; Most Out; Pres A; Type A; Yth Fel; Co-Cpt Quiz Tm; Sct A; Ft Wayne Bible Col; Elem Ed.

De MOSS, Jim Roberts
Elida HS; Elida, OH (30-160) Pres, Band; Chor; S-T, 4H; Lat C; Spch C; Co-Cpt, Bkbl; Cpt, Ftbl; JV, Tr; Cpt, Wrest; COM; 4H A; Pres A; Yth; Jr Choir Director, Church; 1st Trumpet, Band; Ohio St U; Law.

DeMOSS, Richard James
Temple Christian HS; Detroit, MI; Band; BS; Dbte Tm; Drama; Ensm; Sch P; Spch C; Var C; VP, Jr Cl; Bsbl; Bkbl; Cpt, Soccer; COM; Citz A; Spch A; MVP, All League, All St, Soccer; All League, All Tourn, Bkbl.

DeMOSS, Robert Lee III
River Oaks Sch; Monroe, LA (5-50) Band; Community Yth Symph; Fr C; Lit Ral; Span C; II Pl, District Fr; III Pl, St Fr; Oral Roberts U; Foreign Lang.

DE MOSS, Robert Lee II
St Frederick HS; Monroe, LA (1-53) Ann; BS; Chor; Fr C; Lit Ral; NHS; Pres, SC; Cl Fav; Hon Prog; MLS; NEDT; Sal; Spch A; Yth Fel; Rep, Jr Cl; Pres, District Yth Tm; Most Intellectual; Most Dependable; All St Chor; Centenary Col of La; Christian Ed.

DeMOSS, Ruth Eleanor
Melvin-Sibley HS; Melvin, IL (9-33) Band; Ensm; FHA; Pol Sci C; Ill Commercial Col; Off Practice.

DeMOTT, Kelli
Center Grove HS; Greenwood, IN (2-238) Chor; Drama; Pres, 4H; Secy, NHS; Thes; DARGCA; 4H A; Sal; Yth Fel; Franklin Col; Art.

DEMOUGES, Scena Renee
Albert G Lane HS; Chicago, IL (400-1100) Band; Chess C; Rptr, Hmrm; SC; Mgr, Bsbl; Cpt, Bkbl; Mgr, Sftbl; COM; Spch A; GAA; Sun Sch As; Oral Roberts U; Drafting.

DEMPS, Roderick Glenn
Central Cath HS; Melbourne, FL (30-77) MVP, Ftbl; MVP, Tr; Most Out; Cpt, Ftbl, Tr; All Central, All St, Ftbl; All Space Coast, Ftbl; All St, Tr; Tenn Tech U.

DEMPSEY, Charles Terry
Cook HS; Adel, GA; VP, Chess C; Chor; Pres, Hmrm; Sci C; Golf.

DEMPSEY, Christopher Daniel
Middleton HS; Middleton, ID (31-90) VP, FFA; Key C; NHS; SC; Ch, Var C; Rptr, Sr Cl; Bus Mgr, Jr Cl; Bsbl; Co-Cpt, Ftbl; MVP, Ftbl; All Area, All Conf Defen Tm, Ftbl; Eastern Wash St Col; Journ.

DEMPSEY, Dochia Ann
Winnfield HS; Winnfield, LA; Anchor C; BC; FBLA; FTA; Lit Ral; VP, NHS; Ch, Spch C; SC; Cl Fav; Spch A; Win, Pub Speaking; Super Ratng, Semi-Fin, Forensic Trn; U of SW La; Anesthesiology.

DEMPSEY, Donald Jack
Englewood HS; Englewood, CO (2-366) Chess C; NHS; Tres, Span C; Spch C; St Stu Congress; Pres, SC; Var C; Tnns; Citz A; Hon Prog; Rotary A; Sci A; Del, Civitan Yth Sem; Campus Life Ldrship Conf; Alt Del, Church Ntl Yth Congress; Tex Christian U; Bus Adm.

DEMPSEY, Ellice Ann
Pinckneyville Comm HS; Pinckneyville, IL (53-133) Chor; FHA; Span C; WW; Rend Lake Col; Nurs.

DEMPSEY, James Irvin
Rocky Mount Sr HS; Rocky Mount, NC; Howard U; Journ.

DEMPSEY, Timothy Lee
Beech Hill HS; Pulaski, TN (1-26) BC; COM; Cl Fav; Hist A; Hon Prog; Win, Co US Senate Yth Prog; Vanderbilt U; Bus Law.

DEMPSEY, Timothy Peter
Willows HS; Willows, CA (2-130) CYO; Pres, SC; VP, Jr Cl; Tres, Soph Cl; Bsbl; Bkbl; Ftbl; CSF; HCt; Hon Prog; Math A; Sal; Santa Clara Col; Math.

DEMPSTER, Robert Charles
Morgan Park HS; Chicago, IL (60-560) Band; Mu Alpha Theta; NHS; Var C; Co-Cpt, Golf; Wrest; Hon Prog; U of Ill; Engr.

DEMT, Joannie
Sumner HS; St Louis, MO; Drama; Pres, Hmrm; Harris Teacher's Col; Phys Ed.

DeMUNDO, Melinda Louise
Notre Dame HS; Clarksburg, WV (4-55) Ann; Drama; Pres, 4H; Lat C; ARC; Bio A; 4H A; Pep C; W Va U; Med.

DENARD, Robert Ray
Springdale HS; Springdale, AR (40-438) Chem A; Phy A; U of Ark; Acct.

DeNEUI, Donna Lynn
Loup City HS; Loup City, NE (15-78) Chor; FHA; Rptr, Sch P; Pres, Church Yth; Omaha Methodist Col; Nurs.

DENHAM, Valerie Jo
Lee Co HS; Leesburg, GA (24-120) Ann; Pres, FHA; Hmrm; SC; Tri-HiY; COM; Cl Fav; MLS; Q&S A; Albany Jr Col; Secretarial Sci.

DENHART, Mark Charles
Fairmont HS; Kettering, OH (125-499) Bsbl; Co-Cpt, Bkbl; MVP, Bkbl; All Star Bkbl; Ohio Wesleyan U; Hist.

DENISON, Joy Lynn
Vernon HS; Vernon, TX (50%-125) Fr C; Thes; Mgr, Bkbl; Drill Tm; Spch Tm; Novice Spch Tm; Tex Tech U; Sociology.

DENISON, William Clinton
Spruce Creek Sr HS; Port Orange, FL (30-430) Band; BC; Mod Mus Mas; NHS; Cpt, Swim; Cl Fav; NEDT; Spch A; VofDEM; Auburn U; Pre-Med.

DENIZ, Mary Ann
Gridley Union HS; Gridley, CA (52-186) Secy, CYO; Chldr; Drama; Sch P; Bkbl; Sftbl; Butte Col; Fashion Designing.

DENMAN, Carol Lynn
Raytown HS; Raytown, MO (25%-624) Fr C; Sci.

DENMARK, Gary Wayne
Hoke Smith HS; Atlanta, GA (3-293) Band; Chess C; Tres, Soph Cl; Outst Mus A; Math.

DENMARK, James Austin
Tuscola HS; Waynesville, NC (30-300) Chess C; Hmrm; Lat C; Sci C; SC; Bkbl; Cr-Ctry; Soccer; Tr; Hon Prog; Opt A; ARC A; Sci A; Yth Fel; U of NC; Med.

DENMON, Donna Lynn
Robert L Osborne HS; Marietta, GA (10%-483) Band; BC; Ensm; Rptr, Hmrm; Orch; SC; COM; Most Out; President's Phys Fitness A; Stage Band; Hon & Dist Band; Secy, Church Yth Coun; Secy, Church Yth Choir; Dental Asst.

DENMON, Michael Alan
R L Osborne HS; Marietta, GA (10%-400) Band; BC; Tnns; All St Band; Cobb Co Hon Band; Berry Col; Mus.

DENNARD, Margaret Leslie
Fernandina Beach Sr HS; Fernandina Beach, FL; City Conf; Rainbow; Pres, Soph Cl; Sftbl; Little Women; Vlbl; Messenger, Fla St Legislature.

DENNEN, Bobbie Madison
Cambridge HS; Cambridge, OH; Hon Band A; Ohio St U; Mus.

DENNEY, Barry Dean
Prague HS; Prague, OK; Fr C; FFA; Ed, Sch P; Cpt, Ftbl; Tr; Amer Leg A; Citz A; Lion A; All Dist Half-back; Okla St U; Agronomy.

DENNEY, Carolyn Marie
Elmhurst HS; Ft Wayne, IN (139-456) Band; Orch; Yth Fel; Band Schol; NISBOVA, 2 Ensm, 3 Solo; Great Lakes Bible Col; Ed.

DENNEY, Douglas Dale
Seymour HS; Seymour, MO (25%-60) A-Ed, Ann; BC; Pres, Chor; Drama; A-Ed, Sch P; Pres, SC; Pres, Jr Cl; Pres, Soph Cl; Chor; Drama; SW Mo St U; Bus Mgt.

DENNING, William Kirk
Smithfield Selma Sr HS; Smithfield, NC (20%-410) Band; BS; Key C; Order/Arrow A; Yth Fel; Country A; Order/Arrow A; Yth Fel; Eagle Sct; Wake Forest U.

DENNIS, Allen Johnson
Augusta Prep Sch; Augusta, GA (40%-45) A Cap Choir; Ann; Dbte Tm; Key C; Lit Mag; SC; Co-Ch, Jr Cl; Tr; Hist A; Hon Prog; Hist.

DENNIS, Anne Harvey
Lake Taylor HS; Norfolk, VA (27-504) Ann; Bus C; Fr C; FBLA; Hmrm; Key C; NHS; SC; Va Polytechic Inst; Psych.

DENNIS, Carolyn Virginia
Ravenswood High; Ravenswood, WV (33%-210) Tr; Mt Vernon Nazarene College; Accounting.

DENNIS, David Glenn
Nederland HS; Nederland, TX; Band; Ensm; Order/Arrow A; JV, Bsbl.

DENNIS, Deanna Lynn
Walla Walla HS; Walla Walla, WA (20-530) Hmrm; VP, Sci C; COM; Girls League; Girl's Tri-St; Young Life; Church Yth Organization; Northwest Nazarene Col; Social Work.

DENNIS, Denise Rochelle
Geo Henry Corliss HS; Chicago, IL (5-238) Chor; Drama; FTA; Ch, Hmrm; VP, NHS; Ski C; Span C; Ch, SC; Tr; COM; Citz A; Hon Prog; Most Out; Drama A; Span A; DePaul U; Law.

DENNIS, Donald Eugene Jr
Lake Highlands HS; Dallas, TX (2-715) Math C; Pres, Mu Alpha Theta; NHS; VP, Phys C; Span C; Cr-Ctry; Tr; Gr Marshal; Math A; MLS; NMF; Phy A; Rensselaer A; Rotary A; Sal; WW; A of Excellence; Rice U; Chem Engr.

DENNIS, Doreen LaMar
Highland HS; Bakersfield, CA (4-362) InterClub Coun; Tres, Ski C; Tnns; CSF; COM; Oral Roberts U; Acct.

DENNIS, Doreen LaMar
Canyon Del Oro HS; Tucson, AZ (1-365) NHS; Ski C; Bausch & Lomb A; NMS; Val; Outst HS Jr A, U of Ariz; U of Puget Sound; Occupational Therapy.

DENNIS, Elizabeth Ann
Ashley Hall HS; Charleston, SC (5-65) F-Ed, Ann; Fr C; Lit Mag; Y-Tns; Bkbl; Hon Prog; S-T, Art C; Furman Schol; Jr Hon Marshal; Furman U; Hist.

DENNIS, Jennifer Rhea
HS for Performing and Visual Arts; Houston, TX (9-173) AFS; COM; Math A; NML; Col Women's C Schol; U of Tex; Bus.

DENNIS, Keith Alan
University City HS; University City, MO; Hon Prog; Sports Letter.

DENNIS, Kimberly Ann
Middletown HS; Middletown, OH (11-610) Chor; Community Yth Symph; Ensm; Fin, GS; NHS; Orch; Span NHS; Hon Prog; Journ A; Yth Fel; Pres, Yth Fel; Miami U.

DENNIS, Mark Kevin
Hale R-I Pub HS; Hale, MO (2-20) Band; Chor; Ensm; Madrigal; SC; Var C; Bsbl; Co-Cpt, Bkbl; Sftbl; Tr; Type A; Soph Pilgramage; St House of Rep, Honorary Page; Engr.

DENNIS, Michael Foster
Stratford HS; Houston, TX (40%-450) Band; Order/Arrow A; Soccer; God & Country A; Order/Arrow A; U of Tex; Engr.

DENNIS, Paul Kevin
Central HS of Clifton; Clifton, IL (30-146) Chor; FTA; Madrigal; SC; Pres, Thes; Var C; Pres, Yth; Cpt, Cr-Ctry; Tr; Mus Camp Schol; Philadelphia Col of Bible; Social Work.

DENNIS, Paul Olin
Newnan HS; Newnan, GA; Arch; Pres, 4H; Arch; Sftbl; Citz A; 4H A; JA A; Kiwanis A; Pres A; PA; NRA Rifle C Hons; *Carson Newman Col; Religion.*

DENNIS, Tina Marie
Gladewater HS; Gladewater, TX (25%-161) Band; Rptr, Chldr; Chor; FHA; NHS; ARC; Span C; Spch C; *Ambassador Col.*

DENNIS, Vicki Lynn
Alief Hastings HS; Alief, TX; Ann; Rptr, Sch P; Christian Stu Union; *U of Houston; Ed.*

DENNIS, Zoe Anne
Passaic Valley Regional HS; Little Falls, NJ (1-476) Drama; Var C; Mgr, Wrest; Amer Leg A; Cl Fav; PTA A; S-T, Church Yth Fel; Church Sch Teacher; Campus Life.

DENNLER, Peggy Ellen
LeMars Comm HS; LeMars, IA (16-204) Band; FHA; FTA; 4H; NHS; B Crocker A; Citz A; 4H A; NMS; St Scholar; Band Medals; Delta Epsilon Phi; Resident Schol A; *U of Northern Iowa; Elem Ed.*

DENNSTAEDT, Jeffrey Viet
Lake Clifton Sr HS; Baltimore, MD (10%-600) Chem C; VP, Dbte Tm; Pres, Math C; Span NHS; Bio A; COM; Hist A; Hon Prog; Math A; NMS; Sci A; Phys Ed A; *MIT; Math.*

DENNY, Julie Anne
Sacred Heart Acad; Louisville, KY; S-T, Hmrm; Secy, Span C; Hon Prog; Comm Awareness Comm; Yth Group; Religious Ed Dept, Church; Parish Yth Group; *U of Ky; Horticulture.*

DENNY, Thomas Patterson
West HS; Phoenix, AZ (26-588) Band; Ger C; NHS; Orch; *Engr.*

DeNOON, James Robert
Thomas Carr Howe HS; Indianapolis, IN (120-460) Band; Orch; Quiz Tm; Ntl Eagle Sct Assn; Hist C; Eagle Sct A; Firecraft; Pat Ldr, Eg; Sct Bicen Cel; Stge Bnd Wrld Jambre; Crossroads of Amer Sct Band; *Ind Col; Pol Sci.*

DENSEL, Meg
Wayne Valley HS; Wayne, NJ (45-525) AFS; Bus C; Secy, Chor; Commercial C; VP, FNA; 4H; Hmrm; F-Ed, Lit Mag; NHS; A-Ed, Sch P; Pres, Span C; Span NHS; SC; Mgr, Bsbl; COM; Citz A; 4H A; Hon Prog; Most Valuable, Zonta C; *William Paterson Col; Nurs.*

DENSON, Donna
Booneville HS; Booneville, MS (2-100) Pres, Anchor C; Ann; BC; FHA; Math C; Sci C; Span C; Tnns; Chem A; Citz A; H of F; Hon Prog; Math A; Sal; Span A; Service A; *NE Miss Jr Col; Phar.*

DENT, Carmen Michele
Hammond HS; Hammond, IN (132-289).

DENT, Cheryl Lynn
West HS; Columbus, OH (21-581) NHS; ARC; PTA A; ARC A; Rotary A; *Ohio St U; Elem Ed.*

DENT, Susan Margaret
Thomas Downey HS; Modesto, CA; AFS; Ger C; Tres, 4H; Orch; Tr; Amer Leg A; CSF; *UC at Davis; Vet Med.*

DENT, Wanda J
Se HS; Detroit, MI (2-58) *Morehouse Col; Bus Adm.*

DENTON, Cynthia Lawrence
Goodlettsville HS; Goodlettsville, TN (20%-190) Chor; Secy, Fr C; Hmrm; InterClub Coun; ARC; SC; Sftbl; Tnns; Hon Prog; Office Worker; *Vanderbilt U; Math.*

DENTON, James Arthur
Lompoc Sr HS; Lompoc, CA (1-500) AFS; Hmrm; SC; Var C; Pres, Soph Cl; Soccer; Swim; CSF; Citz A; Elk A; Hon Prog; Yth Fel; Waterpolo; Eng Achv A; Cultural Arts A; Allan Hancock Col Math; *UC at San Diego; Nuclear Chem.*

DENTON, James Manley Jr
Vestavia Hills HS; Vestavia Hills, AL; Ftbl; Tr; Citz A; FCA; *U of Tex; Med.*

DENTON, Joel Lynn
Tyner HS; Chattanooga, TN (54-261) Co-Cpt, Band; BC; Chor; Drama; Ensm; Madrigal; Cl Fav; *U of Tenn; Mus.*

DENTON, Kelly Sue
Calhoun HS; Calhoun, MO (4-13) Ann; Chor; Sch P; SC; Crafts A; *CMSU in Warrensburg; Data Processing.*

DENTON, Pamela Jane
Southeast HS; Oklahoma City, OK; Rptr, Sch P; Span C; SC; Sftbl; COM; Citz A; Church Bus Driver; Jr High Dept; Party-Ch, Sr High Dept; GS As; GSct; Cooking A; Church Song Director.

DENTON, Thomas Paul
Lompoc Sr HS; Lompoc, CA (10-400) AFS; BS; SC; Pres, Var C; VP, Sr Cl; Cpt, Swim; Amer Leg A; Bank Of Amer A; Cl Fav; Elk A; Sci A; Swtht; MVP, Swim; Cpt & MVP, Water Polo; *UCSD; Pre-Dental.*

DENTON, Walter Malcolm Jr
Oak Ridge HS; Orlando, FL (25%-1100) Ger C; Lit Mag; NHS; Bsbl; Bkbl; Ftbl; Sftbl; Swim; Tr; Sport Trophies; Church Choir & Drama; *Baptist Col; Christian Ath.*

DEO, Rita Kaurr
Hollywood Professional Sch; Los Angeles, CA (5-35) Band; Ed, Bus C; Dbte Tm; Drama; Fin, FHA; French NHS; NHS; Pres, Pol Sci C; St Stu Congress; SC; Thes; Bank Of Amer A; COM; Citz A; 4H A; Hon Prog; JA A; Ntl Achv Schol; Opt A; *USC; Law.*

De PALMA, Mark Gabriel
St Joseph HS; Hammonton, NJ (1-67) Ftbl; Hon Prog; Principal's List; *U S Coast Guard Acad; Elec Engr.*

De PASTINA, David
Loyola HS; Towson, MD (5-134) CYO; Chldr; Hmrm; Ed, Lit Ral; NHS; ROTC A; *Loyola Col; Pre-Med.*

DEPEW, Nancy Ann
W Haven HS; West Haven, CT (15%-650) Ann; Bus C; Chem C; Fr C; Hmrm; Math C; Phys C; Ski C; SC; Arch; Hockey; Hon Prog; Type A; *Simmons Col; Phys Therapy.*

DePEW, Pamela Dawn
Cumberland HS; Crossville, TN (25-300) Chor; FBLA; 4H; Ntl Yth Conf; ARC; Bkbl; Swim; Tnns; Bio A; ARC A; Spch A; Yth Fel; Tres, Candy Stripers; Christian Stu Union; Voc Coop Prog; *Carson Newman Col; Elem.*

DePIETRO, Jamie Rene
Providence HS; Providence, RI (10-57) Band; BC; Chldr; Drama; FHA; NHS; Sci C; Golf; Tr; Hon Prog; Tr, Beta C, Stu, Hon's; Schol Pin.

De PINTO, Joseph
St Joseph's o-t Palisades HS; W New York, NJ (38-232) CYO; Hmrm; NHS; Rptr, Sch P; Mgr, Ftbl; Hon Prog.

DEPOLO, David Alan
Northgate HS; Walnut Creek, CA (95-425) Band; Swim; Tnns; Most Improved, Swim; Rallies Commissioner; *U of Calif; Biol.*

DEPPERT, Karen Lynn
Lutheran HS W; Rocky River, OH (24-100) Dbte Tm; Hmrm; NHS; Orch; Rptr, Sch P; Secy, SC; VP, Jr Cl; Secy, Soph Cl; Sftbl; Tr; NHS; Cpt, Vlbl; Drill Tm; VP, GAA; Ch, Drill Tm Try- outs; *Dyke Bus Col; Secy Studies.*

DEPPONG, Lori Ann
Imlay City HS; Imlay City, MI; Band; Span C; Hon Prog; Luther League; Band A; Server; Cl Secy; PA A; Secy.

DePROSPO, Michael
St Anthony's HS; Smithtown, NY (50-200) Tres, Band; Chor; Orch; Fin, Tr; Hon Prog; *Acct.*

DePUE, Lisa Elizabeth
Gwinn HS; Gwinn, MI; NHS; DECA; 1st, Advertising, DECA Reg Comp; *Abilene Christian U; Foreign Lang.*

DEPUTY, Cynthia Cay
Fort Stockton HS; Fort Stockton, TX; All Amer Yth; 4H; Jr Miss Pagent; Rainbow; Spch C; Cpt, Swim; Most Out; MVP, Swim; *San Marcos Col.*

DER, James Joe Jr
Alhambra HS; Alhambra, CA (85-784) Dbte Tm; Drama; Ger C; NFL; JV, Tnns; CSF; Chem A; Hon Prog; NMS; Spch A; Explorers; VP, Med Explorers; *UCLA; Bio.*

de RAAD, Mark Pieter
South Pasadena HS; South Pasadena, CA (24-330) Band; Fin, BS; Key C; Pres, SC; Pres, Jr Cl; Bkbl; Soccer; Amer Leg A; CSF; Citz A; Elk A; HCt; *Claremont Men's Col; Bus.*

DeRAMUS, DeAnn
Glen A Wilson HS; Hacienda Heights, CA (5%-500) Bus Mgr, Ann; Model UN; Var C; JV, Tnns; CSF; *Fashion Inst Design & Merch; Fashion Merchandising.*

DeRAMUS, Patricia Diane
Thornton Township HS; Harvey, IL; Bus.

DERBY, Joseph Thomas
Center Sr HS; Kansas City, MO (72-395) A Cap Choir; Chor; Pres, SC; Jazz Band; Art Show Gold Key A; Art Camp Schol A; Original Theme & Composition Bnd, A; *Central Mo St Col; Mus.*

DERISE, Angelle Marie
St Joseph HS; Jeanerette, LA (1-30) Semi-Fin, GS; Secy, 4H; Lit Ral; Lit Mag; VP, NHS; MVP, Bkbl; MVP, Tnns; Alg A; COM; Chem A; Math A; Cpt, Bkbl; Cpt, Tnns; *U of Sou La; Bus Adm.*

DERIVAN, Colleen Anne
Waupun Sr HS; Waupun, WI (22-300) Tres, AFS; F-Ed, Ann; Tres, Chor; FBLA; GS; NHS; SC; VP, Jr Cl; HQn; Prom Court; Pep C; Prom-Pom; Rep, Co Gov Day; GAA; *U of Wis; Nurs.*

DERK, Karen Louise
Downingtown Sr HS; Downingtown, PA (100-600) Hmrm; Span C; SC; Fin, Tr; Hon Prog; Wrestling Belles; Tutored C; Outst Merit, SC & SB; *Psych.*

DERKSEN, Ellen Diane
Thornwood HS; South Holland, IL (306-1050) AFS; Drama; GS; Lit Mag; Semi-Fin, NFL; Co-Ed, Sch P; Fin, Spch C; Thes; Spch A; St Spch Fin; St Reader's Theatre Fin; *Ill St U; Special Ed.*

deROCHEMONT, Katherine Mae
Rockland Dist HS; Rockland, ME; AFS; Band; Chor; Drama; Fr C; FTA; GS; NHS; ARC; Coun of Teach A; Yth Fel; NMS; Sea Coast Mus Festival; Central Maine Symphonic Wind Ensm; RDHS Stage Band; *U of Maine; Secondary Ed.*

deROCHEMONT, Susan Elizabeth
Rockland Dist HS; Rockland, ME; A Cap Choir; Secy, AFS; Band; Chor; Drama; Thes; Coun of Teach A; *Eng.*

DEROMEDIS, David Lonnie
Cokeville HS; Cokeville, WY; Band; Pres, Soph Cl; Bkbl; Ftbl; Tr.

DERR, Elinor Lynn
Winn Acad; Winnfield, LA (1-18) Ann; Ensm; Lit Ral; Pres, Rainbow; A-Ed, Sch P; Co-Cpt, Bkbl; Sftbl; Cl Fav; MLS; Most Intelligent; WW; *La Tech U; Computer Sci.*

DERRITT, Edwina Alicia
Bowen HS; Chicago, IL (300-567) Chor; FNA; Rptr, Hmrm; ARC; Bkbl; Sftbl; Swim; COM; Citz A; JA A; Attendance A; *Okla St U; Sci.*

DERUITER, William Harry
N Shore HS; W Palm Beach, FL (21-266) NHS; Var C; Bsbl; Bkbl; Alg A; Human Relations.

De SANTIS, Kathleen
Maple Shade HS; Maple Shade, NJ (11-241) F-Ed, Ann; NHS; Tres, Sr Cl; LaCrosse; Pep C; *Bryn Mawr Sch of Nurs; Nurs.*

DeSANTIS, Victor Joseph
Loyola HS; Towson, MD; CYO; Hmrm; NHS; A-Ed, Sch P; SC; Cpt, Cr-Ctry; Tr; Hon Prog; NEDT; Part, Johns Hopkins Verb Gifted Yth; *Yale U; Law.*

DeSHAZO, Julie Ann
Dewey HS; Dewey, OK; Band; VP, Math C; Span C; Y-Tns; Sftbl; HCt; *Ozark Bible Col; Bible.*

DESHER, Drew Philip
Gloucester Cath HS; Gloucester City, NJ (17-180) NHS; Cr-Ctry; Co-Cpt, Tr; Wrest; *Drexel U; Engr.*

DeSHIELDS, Virginia Ann
Fayette Ware N HS; Somerville, TN (48-295) Chor; FBLA; FHA; FTA; S-T, Hmrm; Pres, SC; *Memphis St Col; Secy.*

DeSHON, Kathy Clair
Macon R I HS; Macon, MO; Chor; Drama.

DESILET, Dean William
Two Harbors HS; Two Harbors, MN; Chor; Madrigal; SC; JV, Bkbl; Ftbl; Amer Leg A; *U of Minn; Ministry.*

DeSIMONE, Joseph Michael
Don Bosco Tech HS; Boston, MA (10-222) CYO; NHS; VP, SC; Cr-Ctry; Tr; COM; Hon Prog; *Tufts Col; Dental Field.*

DESKINS, Tamara Susan
Bluefield HS; Bluefield, WV (26-330) A Cap Choir; Co-Ed, Ann; VP, Fr C; Pres, Hmrm; Secy, NHS; V-Ch, SC; VP, Sr Cl; Secy, Jr Cl; HCt; Hon Prog; Q&S A; Laurel Leaves; Most Outgoing; Second Miler; *Lenoir Rhyne Col; Nurs.*

DESLATTE, Dawn Marie
W End Acad; Franklin, LA; Arch; Chor; Fr C; Hmrm; Fin, Jr Miss Pagent; SC; Var C; Arch; Bkbl; Sftbl; Swim; Tnns; Tr; Alg A; Beauty; Citz A; HCt; Math A; Opt A; Opt Out Tn; Yth Fel; Ath A; *USL; Med.*

DESMARAIS, Diane Lyn
Gulf Comprehensive HS; New Port Richey, FL (5-300) Ann; Band; Hmrm; NHS; Sch P; SC; COM; Hon Prog; Math A; Most Out; WW; 4 0 Grade A; 100% PA; *Pasco Hernando Col; Nurs.*

DESMOND, Michael A
Eli Whitney Voc HS; Brooklyn, NY; Band; Sch Achieve Tm; Co-Cpt, Tnns; Bio A; COM; Hist A; Hon Prog; Math A; Sci A; Phys Ed, Gym, A's; Fin, Mr Whitney; *Calif Inst of Tech; Elec.*

DESMOND, Robert Paul
Santa Barbara HS; Santa Barbara, CA; A Cap Choir; Band; Chor; Ensm; Orch; Stu Conductor, Band, Orch; *San Diego St U; Mus Ed.*

DeSPAIN, Raymond Earl
Pleasanton HS; Pleasanton, TX (15-160) Band; Fr C; FTA; Math C; Ch, NHS; Span C; SC; Var C; Pres, Soph Cl; Bsbl; Cpt, Bkbl; Cpt, Ftbl; Tr; COM; Citz A; Opt A; Spch A; Star Student; Swtht; Yth Fel; *Sam Houston St U; Coaching.*

DESPER, Michael Bryce
Crossville Comm HS; Crossville, IL (6-28) BC; Thes; Var C; Bsbl; Bkbl; Tr; Best Defensive Player, Bkbl.

DeSTEFANO, Ned Matthias
Oak Ridge Acad; Oak Ridge, NC (9-30) Chor; Sch P; Sci C; Citz A; *Washington and Lee U; Bio.*

DeSWART, Marilyn Trena
Tillamook HS; Tillamook, OR (5-175) F-Ed, Ann; Band; Pres, FBLA; Secy, 4H; Hmrm; InterClub Coun; S-T, NHS; Pres, Rainbow; SC; Secy, Thes; Bkbl; Tr; Chem A; Citz A; 4H A; Type A; Professional Business Women's A; *Oreg St U; Bus Adm.*

DETCHON, Paula Rae
Marlington HS; Alliance, OH (35-317) Band; Drama; Ensm; Orch; Sch Achieve Tm; Span C; Span NHS; Sftbl; Swim; COM; Citz A; Cl Fav; Hon Prog; MLS; Most Out; Star Student; Swtht; Yth Fel; PA A; Ensm Solo Contest Medal; Trophy, May Day Derby Walk.

DETERDING, Terri Denise
Granite City HS S; Granite City, IL (69-656) Ann; Chldr; Tri-HiY; Q&S A; Gym Tm.

DETERS, Kathryn Therese
Quincy Notre Dame HS; Quincy, IL (3-143) JV, Chldr; Chor; Fr C; 4H; Hmrm; NHS; SC; VP, Soph Cl; Hon Prog; Most Out; NEDT; St Scholar; Yth Foundation A; Jaycee's A; SAA As; WW; *Quincy Col.*

DETERS, Kathy Anne
Flanagan Unit 4 HS; Flanagan, IL (9-50) Band; Chor; Pres, Drama; Ensm; 4H; Madrigal; Mjrte; NHS; Arch; Tr; St Scholar; Type A; *Ill Wesleyan U; Mus.*

DETERS, Mary Elizabeth
Highland HS; Ewing, MO; Chor; FHA; NHS; Sci C; Amer Leg A.

DETERS, Patricia Ann
Highland HS; Ewing, MO (1-130) FHA; NHS; Sci C; Hon Prog; Regent Schol; Type A; Val; Art C; WW; Soph Pilgrimage; Acad Bowl; *NE Mo St U; Bus.*

DETLOFF, Karen Marie
Brooten HS; Brooten, MN (13-63) A Cap Choir; Chldr; Chor; Drama; Ensm; Spch C; Spch A; Vocal Solo A; Schol A; *St Cloud Vo-tech; Computer Programming.*

DETOY, Lauri Rachelle
Poway HS; Poway, CA; Band; Cpt, Chldr; FBLA; HCt; *San Diego St Col; Elem Ed.*

DETTMAN, James Lincoln
Sturgis HS; Sturgis, MI (25-265) Key C; Lat C; NHS; JV, Cr-Ctry; JV, Tr; NMS; Semi-Fin, Mich Math Comp; *Albion Col; Engr.*

DETTMER, Scott Alan
Wayne HS; Ft Wayne, IN (103-346) Hmrm; Rptr, Sch P; JV, Golf; MVP, Hockey; COM; Journ A; ARC A; Photographer, Sch Paper; Water Ski Tm; *Photo Journ.*

DETWEILER, Karen Ruth
Langley HS; McLean, VA (1-500) VP, Chor; Drama; Ger C; Madrigal; Parl, Model UN; NHS; World Affairs C; Gov Honor Prog; Hon Prog; Human Relations Committee; Colonial Dames of Va A; Ger Excel A; Regional & All Co, Chor; *Pol Sci.*

DETWEILER, Lawrence John
Manatee HS; Bradenton, FL (39-517) JV, Bsbl; *Wheaton Col; Christian Ed.*

DETWILER, Jay Eldon
Triad HS; N Lewisburg, OH (9-96) Pres, 4H; Var C; Ftbl; Cpt, Golf; Co-Cpt, Tr; 4H A; *Ohio St U; Med.*

DETWILER, Sally Lucille
Schuylkill Haven Area HS; Schuylkill Haven, PA (50-115) Band; Co-Cpt, Chldr; Chor; Hmrm; Sci C; Pres, SC; VP, Jr Cl; Tr; WW; Ath o-t Yr, Prep Tr & Field; *Kean College of NJ; Occupational Therapy.*

DEUBEL, Theresa Marie
Notre Dame-Bishop Gibbons HS; Schenectady, NY (16-161) Rptr, Ann; Chor; NHS; Rptr, Sch P; Ski C; SC; Cpt, Bkbl; Cpt, Sftbl; NEDT; Cpt, Vlbl; Bowl; Gym; Fin, JC Outst Woman o-t Yr; Eng A; Ath o-t Wk, Vlbl; *Col of St Rose; Elem Ed.*

DEURLOO, Kathleen Lucille
Montabella HS; Edmore, MI (2-107) Co-Ed, Ann; Band; Chldr; Chess C; Chor; Drama; Ensm; VP, Math C; Pres, NHS; Sch P; Ski C; Tres, Span C; Band; Span A; WW; St Cert of Recognition; *Ferris St Col; Legal Asst.*

DEUTSCHENDORF, Terri Ann
Eisenhower HS; Lawton, OK (81-610) Chor; Ensm; FHA; NHS; Tr; Hon Prog; Teachers Aide; Gym; *Cameron U; Phys Ed.*

DeVANE, Gloria Inez
Lenoir HS; Lenoir, NC (20-113) Ann; Chldr; Hmrm; Lit Mag; Monogram; NHS; Ski C; Span C; Bkbl; Sftbl; *Howard U; Pre-Law.*

DeVANNO, Elizabeth Susan
Acad o-t Holy Family; Baltic, CT; Chldr; Chor; Sch P; SC; Pres, Sr Cl; VP, Soph Cl; Bsbl; Bkbl; Tr; Type A; *Inst of Fashion; Fashion Merchandising.*

DeVANTIER, Brian Elton
Niagara Wheatfield Sr HS; Sanborn, NY (40-420) Ger C; Eng A; PA; *Niagara U; Acct.*

DeVANTIER, Kent Robert
Niagara Wheatfield HS; Sanborn, NY (150-560) Bkbl; Ftbl; Tr; *Bus.*

DeVAUGHN, Lorris Tresbee
Frank H Morrell HS; Irvington, NJ; Chor.

DEVAUL, Kathleen Rita
Wheeling Park HS; Wheeling, WV (51-660) Anchor C; Fr C; FBLA; Ski C; Var C; Y-Tns; Bkbl; Tr; Hon Prog; Yth Fel; Tres, GSct; 3rd Pl in St Tr Meet; Semi-Fin, St Bkbl; *Shepherd Col; Park Adm.*

DEVAUL, Marlene Ruth
Wheeling Park HS; Wheeling, WV; Y-Tns; Yth Fel; GSct, Patrol Ldr; UM Womens W Va Conf; MYF; Hospital Vol.

DeVAULT, Tim Francis
Colo Springs Sch; Colorado Springs, CO (2-21) Math C; Span C; SC; Bsbl; Bkbl; Cpt, Cr-Ctry; Soccer; Tr; Math A; Sci A; Eng A.

DeVAULT, William Keith
Lee Acad; Clarksdale, MS; Ftbl; Soil & Water Conservation Essay; *MIT; Metallurgical.*

DEVEREAUX, Ellen Jean
St Mary's HS; Lynn, MA (12-117) CYO; ARC; Ski C; Sftbl; Tnns; Alg A; Hist A; Math A; Miss Lynn HS; *U of NH; Parks & Recreation.*

DeVERNA, Daniel David
Nassau Christian Acad; Yulee, FL (3-7) Ann; Rptr, Sch P; Bkbl; Ftbl; Most Intelligent; *Baptist Bible Col; Mus.*

DeVERNA, Jonathan Wayne
Nassau Christian Acad; Yulee, FL (2-15) Bkbl; Ftbl; Christian Testimony; Most Dependable; *Liberty Baptist Col; Math.*

DEVILLE, Timothy Casey
Ville Platte HS; Ville Platte, LA (1-102) VP, BC; CYO; 4H; Lit Ral; Co-Ed, Sch P; Bausch & Lomb A; Chem A; 4H A; Math A; Sci A; Star Student; Val; Social Sci A; *Northeast La; Pre-Phar.*

DEVINE, Loren Donald
Forest Lake Sr HS; Forest Lake, MN (108-447) A Cap Choir; Band; Chor; Drama; Pres, 4H; Hmrm; Madrigal; Ski C; SC; JV, Ftbl; Tr; 4H A; Superior, St Vocal Mus Contest; *Dunwoody Inst; Archt Drafting.*

DeVITA, Nadine Marie
Salpointe Cath HS; Tucson, AZ (110-200) CYO; Chor; VP, Y-Tns; DECA; Tuition Asst; DECA St Contestant A; *U of Ariz; Bus.*

DEVITA, Nadine Marie
Salpointe HS; Tucson, AZ (132-200) Chor; FBLA; VP, Y-Tns; *U of Ariz; Marketing.*

DEVITT, Ivan Neil III
Spring Woods HS; Houston, TX; A Cap Choir; Ftbl; *Tex A&M U.*

DeVOLIN, Jeannette Lorraine
Fabens HS; Fabens, TX (6-89) Band; Chldr; Chor; FHA; FTA; NHS; Rainbow; Pres, Sci C; SC; Mgr, Bsbl; Mgr, Bkbl; Mgr, Ftbl; Mgr, Tr; Beauty; HQn; Swtht; *Tex Tech U; Home Ec.*

DeVOLIN, Lorianne
Fabens HS; Fabens, TX; Band; Chldr; 4H; NHS; Rainbow; SC; Bkbl; Tnns; All Dist, All Regional, Vlbl; *Sul Ross Col; Bus.*

DEVORE, Angie Doris
Nederland HS; Nederland, TX (1-463) AFS; FHA; FTA; NHS; Alg A; COM; Hon Prog; Rotary A; Eng A; 'A' HR; Mus Critic Circle A; Highest Soph Acad Average; Acad Ltr; NCTE Achv A; UIL Comp; Highest Sr Schol A; Mus Hon Stu; *Lamar U; Math.*

DeVORE, Debra Patricia
Frankfort HS; Ridgeley, WV (10%-149) Band; Cpt, Chldr; Chor; FHA; FTA; 4H; NHS; Ftbl; Vlbl; Tm; Hon Guard; Secy, Yth Fel; *W Va U; Med.*

DEVORE, Denicia Kay
Oxford HS; Oxford, KS (12-42) Band; Chor; Ensm; Madrigal; COM.

DEVORE, Helen Marie
Central Valley HS; Central Valley, CA (9-240) Bus C; Pres, FBLA; VP, FHA; Secy, Sr Cl; Mgr, Ftbl; Bank Of Amer A; CSF; Hon Prog; Outst Service A, Ftbl Mgr; Hikers C; *Puget Sound Col o-t Bible; Christian Ed.*

DeVORE, Laurie Ann
Gates-Chili HS; Rochester, NY; Chor; S-T, Y-Tns; Citz A; Hon Stu; Safety Patrol; *Med.*

DeVRIES, Barbara G
Holland HS; Holland, MI (25%-400) Ger C; Rptr, Sch P; Cl Offices; *Calvin Col; Spec Ed.*

DeVRIES, Daren Donald
Edinburg Comm Dist 4 HS; Edinburg, IL (10-60) *Grace Bible Col; Sci.*

DeVRIES, Kathleen Marie
N B Forrest Sr HS; Jacksonville, FL (8-575) Anchor C; Band; Hmrm; NHS; Sci C; SC; Kiwanis A; *U of Fla; Nurs.*

DeVRIES, Mary Beth
Grundy Center Comm HS; Grundy Center, IA (50%-84) Ann; Cpt, Bkbl; HCt; Hon Prog; MVP, Bkbl; Jo Theilan Bkbl A.

DeVRIES, Paul Lee
Luverne, MN (28-129) Chor; Ftbl; Golf; Tr; COM; Pres A; Activities A; *Bus.*

DEVRIES, Richard Jay
Hillcrest HS; Springfield, MO (10%-380) Band; Hmrm; SC; VP, Soph Cl; Bkbl; Tr; Alg A; Math A; *Evangel Col; Phys Ed.*

De VRIES, Robert Donald
Thornwood HS; South Holland, IL (199-1016) *Northern Ill U; Industrial Ed.*

DeVRIES, Sheila Ann
Ackley-Geneva Comm Sch; Ackley, IA (23-63) Co-Ed, Ann; Band; Chor; 4H; Tr; B Crocker A; 4H A; *Hawkeye Inst of Tech; Bus Off.*

DeVROU, David Scott
Thornapple-Kellogg HS; Middleville, MI; Demolay; VP, Ski C; JV, Bsbl; JV, Golf; Swim; HCt; *Hope Col; Bus Adm.*

DEW, David William
United Township HS; E Moline, IL (7-600) Chor; Community Yth Symph; Drama; NHS; Var C; Ftbl; Tr; COM; Chamber of Comm A; Hon Prog; Rotary A; Yth Fel; Ftbl Hon's; 4th St, Drama; Service A; *Bradley U; Engr.*

DEW, L Michelle
Ulysses HS; Ulysses, KS (3-126) Chldr; 4H; Secy, NHS; SC; Y-Tns; Tres, Soph Cl; Bkbl; Tnns; 4H A; Yth Fel; *Brigham Young U; Interior Decoration.*

DEW, Pamela Jean
Oconomowoc Sr HS; Oconomowoc, WI; Band; Drama; NFL; ARC; Span C; Spch A; MVP, Church Bsbl; *Drama.*

DEWAR, James Craik
Westmont Hilltop Sr HS; Johnstown, PA (3-208) Chor; Drama; Hmrm; Key C; NHS; VP, Ski C; Ftbl; Hon Prog; Med Explorers; Penn Wood Player; Scholastic A; Most Valuable Actor; *Pre-Med.*

DEWAR, Sandra Gale
Apex HS; Apex, NC; Lat C; Hon Camper; *E Carolina U; Med.*

DeWATER, Janet Louise
Bellevue Sr HS; Bellevue, WA (120-486) Ed, Ann; Band; Fr C; NHS; Swim; Tr; *U of Wash; Nurs.*

DEWBERRY, Dwayne Edward
Poteau HS; Poteau, OK; Key C; Bkbl; Tr; Bio A; Chem A; Coun of Teach A; Kiwanis A; MLS; Ntl Sci Found; *Tex Tech U; Sci.*

DEWBERRY, Sherry Lynn
Gretna Sr HS; Gretna, VA (130-262) FHA; 4H; Span C; *Photography.*

DeWEES, Steven Kelly
Permian HS; Odessa, TX (33%-678) Chldr; City Conf; Pres, Demolay; Hmrm; Pres, Lat C; Order/Arrow; ARC; VP, SC; Sftbl; JV, Tnns; Aux Lat; Most Out; Opt A; Order/Arrow A; Muscular Dystrophy Vol Worker; *Odessa Col; Phys Therapy.*

DeWEESE, Dorothy Mae
Licking R-8 HS; Licking, MO; Ann; Band; Chor; Ensm; Acct A; Band, Chor, Ltrs; *SW Baptist Col; Acct.*

DeWEESE, Robert Eugene
Evertt HS; Lansing, MI; Band; *Mich St U; Full Time Christain.*

DeWITT, Douglas Alan
Woodlan HS; Woodburn, IN (70-141) Mgr, Bkbl; Intramurals; PA; Sportsman C; *Ivy Tech; Drafting.*

DeWITT, Jeffrey Scott
Fairfield Comm HS; Fairfield, IL (8-194) Pres, 4H; Monogram; Cr-Ctry; Tr; Wrest; Amer Leg A; 4H A; Sportsmanship A; *Wabash Valley Col; Conservation.*

DEWITZ, Barbara Ann
Springfield HS; Springfield, OR (20-300) Band; Pres, Ger C; NHS; ARC; Tr; *U of Oreg; Pre-Med.*

DEWOODY, Lisa Lynn
Tahlequah HS; Tahlequah, OK (5%-285) Ed, Ann; S-T, Band; Cpt, Chldr; Pres, FHA; GS; Math C; NHS; Rainbow; Tres, SC; *Okla St U; Ophthalmologist.*

DEYARMOND, Connie Joy Ann
DeKalb HS; DeKalb, IL; Ann; Band; Chor; 4H; Orch; ARC; Span C; MVP, Arch; MVP, Golf; MVP, Sftbl; MVP, Swim; Cl Fav; 4H A; Hon Prog; Interlochen Ntl Mus; Ntl Achv Schol; Spch A; *Creative Writing.*

DEYKES, Allison Lee
N Pocono HS; Moscow, PA (17-235) Chldr; Lit Mag; NHS; Span C; Tnns; Tr; Women's C Sewing & Art Contest; *Art.*

DEYOE, William Howard
Shawnee HS; Louisville, KY; Arch; FTA; HiY; Hmrm; Bsbl; *Law.*

DeYOUNG, Debbie May
Ottawa Hills HS; Grand Rapids, MI; ARC; Nature Trail Guide; Secy, Church Group.

DeYOUNG, James Ennis
Calvary Christian Sch; Glens Falls, NY; Fr C; VP, SC; Var C; Bsbl; Cpt, Bkbl; Cpt, Soccer; Co-Cpt, Tnns; Cl Fav; HCt; Sportsmanship A; *Tenn Temple Col.*

DeYOUNG, Ruth
E Central HS; San Antonio, TX (5-304) A Cap Choir; Chor; Drama; FHA; Lat C; Madrigal; NHS; Co-Cpt, Tnns; COM; VofDEM; *Southwestern U; Sociology.*

DEZELSKY, Joan Loree
Mona Shores HS; Muskegon, MI (57-447) A Cap Choir; Chor; Drama; Fr C; *Carthage Col; Ed.*

DEZIEL, Sheila Marie
Brady HS; W St Paul, MN (2-150) Pres, Fr C; Cpt, Mjrte; NHS; Rptr, Sch P; Thes; HCt; Hon Prog; Journ A; Sal; Service A; *U of Wis at Riverfalls.*

DHUYVETTER, Barbara Anastasia
Noonan HS; Noonan, ND (1-20) Ed, Ann; Band; CYO; Chor; Ensm; GS; Secy, 4H; Phys C; Rptr, Sch P; Pres, Jr Cl; Co-Cpt, Bkbl; Sftbl; Tr; 4H A; Hon Prog; Val; *UND; Med Tech.*

DIAL, Deidra Lynn
Groveton HS; Groveton, TX (5-46) Bus Mgr, Ann; BC; Chor; FHA; Secy, Hmrm; Lit Ral; SC; Bkbl; Cl Fav; Val; Rptr, Hmrm; Candidate, H Qn; St Beta C Convention Talent Show; Win, Alg, Bkkepng, Eng, Sch Fair; 1st Pl Homemaking; *Angelina Col; Secy Stu.*

DIAMOND, Christine Ann
Franklin Sr HS; Franklin, LA; Ann; Chor; VP, Fr C; FBLA; 4H; Jr Miss Pagent; Pres, NHS; COM; 4H A; Church Yth Group; Jr Miss Spirit A; Young Life; Talent Show Trophy; Sheriff's Tm Sftbl; WW; Excel, Fr Rally; *Spencer's Bus Col; Bus.*

DIAMOND, Comilla Faye
Boyd Co HS; Cannonsburg, KY;

DIAMOND, Edgar Wallace Jr
W Craven HS; Vanceboro, NC (10%-213) BC; FBLA; Monogram; NHS; Order/Arrow; Span C; SC; Pres, Jr Cl; Bsbl; Ftbl; Co-Cpt, Wrest; Order/Arrow A; Driver's Ed A; Eagle Sct A.

DIAMOND, Joan Marie
Hannibal Central HS; Hannibal, NY (10-100) Chor; NHS; Ed, Sch P; Soccer; Tnns.

DIAMOND, Thomas Neil
Washington HS; Washington, PA (70-194) Var C; VP, Sr Cl; Pres, Soph Cl; Cpt, Cr-Ctry; Co-Cpt, Wrest; Amer Leg A; MVP, Wrest; MVP, Cr Ctry; *Clarion St Col; Ed.*

DIAZ, Alice
St Cecilia HS; Kearny, NJ (1-50) Chor; Drama; Pres, Hmrm; Co-Ed, Lit Mag; NHS; Ed, Sch P; Ski C; Span C; VP, Jr Cl; Hon Prog; Opt A; St Peter's Col Summer Schol; George Washington U Engr Medal; *Seton Hall U; Ed.*

DIAZ, Florentino
Central HS; Santurce, PR; Bus C; MVP, Chor; InterAct C; Orch; COM; *Yale U; Drama.*

DIAZ, Frank Alex Jr
Holy Trinity HS; Chicago, IL (14-175) Pres, NHS; Ed, Sch P; Mgr, Bkbl; Man o-t Yr; High Hons; *Marquette U; Journ.*

DIAZ, Gilda V
Academia Maria Reina; Rio Piedras, PR; VP, CYO; Fr C; NHS; Sch P; Pres, Spch C; COM; Hon Prog.

DIAZ, Jesus Manuel
Manuela Toro HS; Caguas, PR; CYO; Tres, Chor; Orch; Hon Prog; Mus A; *U of Puerto Rico; Architecture.*

DIAZ, Lilian Yolanda
Manuela Toro HS; Caguas, PR; CYO; *U of Puerto Rico; Natural Sci.*

DIAZ, Martha Kathleen
Aquinas HS; San Bernardino, CA; CYO; Drama; NHS; Amer Leg A; Bio A; COM; Citz A; Coun of Teach A; Hon Prog; Sci A; Drama A; CCD Teaching Cert's; *Ed.*

DIAZ, Orlando
Juan Jose Osuna HS; Hato Rey, PR (6-150) Pres, CYO; Dbte Tm; FBLA; Pres, 4H; Pres, Phys C; Pol Sci C; ARC; Pres, Span C; Bsbl; Bkbl; Sftbl; Tr; Alg A; Bio A; COM; Cl Fav; God & Country A; 4H A; H of F; Hist A; Lion A; Opt A; Pres A; Sci A; Star Student; *U of Puerto Rico; Engr.*

DIAZ, Paula Marie
Montgomery HS; San Diego, CA (73-492) Ann; Drama; Orch; ARC; Amer Leg A; CSF; Drill Tm; Counselor's Aide; Tr Helper; WW; *U of Calif; Ed.*

DIAZ, Phyllis Anne
Huntington Park HS; Huntington Park, CA (4%-700) A Cap Choir; FTA; Hmrm; SC; CSF; Yth Fel; Yth Foundation; Police Essay; *UCLA; Social Stu.*

DIAZ, Ricardo
Amer Military Acad; Guaynabo, PR; Pres, Sch P; MIT; Computer Prog.

DIAZ, Tami Ellen
Monongahela Valley Cath HS; Monongahela, PA (10-100) Co-Ed, Ann; Band; Chldr; Chor; Community Yth Symph; Fr C; FBLA; Hmrm; Phys C; F-Ed, Sch P; Sci C; SC; Bkbl; Hon Prog; Sci A; Acct, Art, A's; *U of Pittsburgh; Engr.*

DIBLE, Kimberly Kay
Carey HS; Carey, OH (2-110) Chor; GS; Pres, Span C; Pres, Y-Tns; Tres, Soph Cl; Sci A; VP, GAA; Vlbl; FTA Schol A; *Kent St U; Teaching.*

DICAPO, Joslyn
Melville HS; Melville, LA; Ann; BC; FBLA; Lit Ral; Alg A; Bio A; Math A; Type A; Shorthand A.

DICE, Pamela Gail
Fairchance Georges Sr HS; Uniontown, PA (40-135) Secy, Chldr; Chor; FNA; NHS; Span C; Bkbl; NEDT; Yth Fel; Art A; Pres, Yth Fel; *Jameson Mem Col; Nurs.*

DICE, Paula Gay
Fairchance-Georges Sr HS; Uniontown, PA (40-135) Tres, Chldr; Chor; Bkbl; S-T, Yth Fel; Art A.

DiCIOCCIO, Cindy
Struthers HS; Struthers, OH (8-275) Ann; Chldr; Drama; Secy, Lat C; NHS; Thes; NEDT; Eng A, St Schol Test; *Ohio St U; Phys Ther.*

DICK, Alanea Marie
Frankfort HS; Ridgeley, WV (5-151) Chor; NHS; Co-Ed, Sch P; Alg A; B Crocker A; Bio A; Chem A; Hist A; HCt; Journ A; MLS; Sci A; VofDEM; Amer Chem Soc; *The Amer U; Bio.*

DICK, Betty Diane
E Gaston HS; Mt Holly, NC; JV, Chldr; Ger C; Hmrm; Cpt, Mjrte; Monogram; Sch P; FBLA; Bkbl; Tr; Comm Chor; Acad Col Schol; *Brevard Col; Phys Therapy.*

DICK, Jennifer Beth
Richfield HS; Waco, TX (50%-326) Lat C; ARC; Drill Tm; *Tex Tech U; Marketing.*

DICK, Lori Ellen
Coral Gables Sr HS; Miami, FL; Chor; Drama; FTA; Thes; Jr Mental Health C; VP, Productions C; *Miami-Dade Col; Social Work.*

DICK, Mary Lisa
Sparks HS; Reno, NV (5-290) VP, Drama; NFL; NHS; Thes; COM; Masque & Gavel A; Spch A; *Sou Oreg St Col; Performing Arts.*

DICKEN, Robin Rnee
Logan Sr HS; Logan, OH; Band; Rainbow; Swim; Yth Fel; Pep Band; HR; Past Worthy Advisor, Rainbow Girls; Pep C; Jayteens.

DICKENS, Laura Margaret
W A Berry HS; Birmingham, AL (33%-400) Lat C; Yth Fel; *Agnes Scott Col.*

DICKENS, Ross Norman
W A Berry HS; Birmingham, AL (90%-400) Chor; City Conf; Lat C; Ntl Yth Conf; JV, Bkbl; Cr-Ctry; Tr; Cl Fav; Most Out; Lat Schol A; *Davidson Col; Religion.*

DICKERSON, Diana P
Trigg Co HS; Cadiz, KY (25%-150) Cpt, Band; S-T, Drama; 4H; NFL; Spch C; Sftbl; 4H A; The Director's A; *Bio.*

DICKERSON, Kathleen
Nederland HS; Nederland, TX (36-485) AFS; Band; Fr C; Mjrte; NHS; Cpt, Drill Tm; VP, Yth Coun; St & Ntl Drill Tm Champs; St Solo & Ensm; 2nd Runnerup, Comm Pageant; *Oral Roberts U; Engr.*

DICKERSON, Kathy Diane
Briarfield Acad; Lake Providence, LA; Ensm; Secy, 4H; Sch P; Span C; Y-Tns; Sftbl; Swim; Tr; 4H A; *Northeast U; Elem Ed.*

DICKERSON, Kenneth Eugene
Oswego HS; Oswego, KS (2-35) Band; BS; NHS; SC; MVP, Bkbl; MVP, Ftbl; MVP, Tr; Hon Prog; MLS; Most Out; NEDT; Rotary A; Sal; St Scholar; *Bryan Inst; Computer Programming.*

DICKERSON, Kenneth Thomas
Crystal Lake Comm HS; Crystal Lake, IL (38-550) Ann; Ger C; Math C; NHS; Amer Leg A; COM; Hon Prog; JA A; St Scholar; Navy ROTC Schol; WW; *NW U; Engr.*

DICKERSON, Patricia Diane
Reidsville Sr HS; Reidsville, NC (13-344) Math C; Span C; Co-Ch, Jr-Sr Prom; NCSU Engr Prog; *NC St U; Engr.*

DICKERSON, Randy Clay
Union HS; Union, MS (10%-57) VP, Band; Chor; Sch P; Tres, Sci C; Stu Conductor; All St Band; Outst Mus; 1st Chair Player; *U of Sou Miss; Mus.*

DICKERSON, Tammy Annette
McComb HS; McComb, MS (24-234) Chor; Tres, NHS; Ed, Sch P; VP, Span C; SC; Span A; DECA A; *Southwest Jr Col; Counseling.*

DICKERSON, Willene
Fort Pierce Central HS; Fort Pierce, FL; *Secy.*

DICKERT, Steven Grady
Wade Hampton HS; Greenville, SC (176-383) Chldr; Co-Ch, Hmrm; *Greenville Tech Inst; Archt.*

DICKEY, Dennis Michael
Marine Military Acad; Harlingen, TX; Drama; ARC; Spch C; Thes; Ftbl; Co-Cpt, Swim; COM; Pres A; ARC A; ROTC A; Hardest Worker & Most Improv, Swim; *US Naval Acad.*

DICKEY, Dianna Darlene
Weatherford HS; Weatherford, TX (74-250) FBLA; Fha; VP, SC; Bkbl; Tnns; HQn; Opt A; FFA Chapter, Dist FFA, Swtht; Rep, Melon Vine; *Weatherford Col; Bus.*

DICKEY, Janet Matilda
Hazlewood HS; Town Creek, AL; BC; Chldr; FHA; 4H; Sch P; 4H A; Stu o-t Mo; *Calhoun Jr Col; Teaching.*

DICKEY, Lori Beth
Rosedale HS; Rosedale, IN (5-66) VP, Band; Chor; GS; Pres, 4H; NHS; Tres, Sr Cl; Bkbl; 4H A; I Dare You; Ntl Sch Chor A; *Ind St U; Elem Ed.*

DICKEY, Mamie Patricia R
Eastside HS; Paterson, NJ; Chor; Pres, Drama; Tres, Ensm; Hmrm; SC; Thes; Co-Ch, Y-Tns; Sch Safety Patrol; YWCA Cert; *Rutgers U; Voice.*

DICKEY, Neal Curtis
Churchill Co HS; Fallon, NV (42-201) Tres, Band; BS; NHS; Var C; Cpt, Ftbl; Soccer; Wrest; COM; PTA A; Sci A; *Phoenix Inst of Tech; Archt.*

DICKEY, Roxanna Marie
Gulf Comprehensive HS; New Port Richey, FL; Band; FHA; 4H; Hmrm; Jr Miss Pagent; Sch P; Beauty; COM; 4H A; Powderpuff Ftbl; Fin, Miss Ntl Tn; Band A's; Gym; *Miami International Arts Col; Fashion Merchandising.*

DICKEY, Sandra Ann
Lamar HS; Lamar, MO (73-101) AFS; Chor; Opt A; Lib A; Chor A.

DICKEY, Tamera Jane
Berkeley Sr HS; Berkeley, MO (20-270) Ann; Chor; Drama; Ensm; NHS; SC; Var C; VP, Soph Cl; Pom Pons; Gym; *Harding Christian Col; Nurs.*

DICKIE, Claire Llewellyn
St Mary's Col; Raleigh, NC (8-103) Ann; BC; Co-Cpt, Dbte Tm; Secy, Fr C; Lat C; Tres, Monogram; NHS; SC; Cpt, Bkbl; Sftbl; HCt; MVP, Bkbl; Ballet Jazz Dance Group; S-T, Scottish Dance Group; The Beacon Honorary Soc; *Pol Sci.*

DICKINSON, Cathy Dorris
Salem HS; Salem, IN; Lat C; Rainbow; Secy, Tri-HiY; Tr; Secy, GAA; Job's Daughters; *Cambellsville Col; Mus.*

DICKINSON, Curtis Joel
Hill HS; Lansing, MI (110-385) Pres, Sr Cl; Ftbl; Tnns; Cpt, Wrest; HCt; U of Mich Hon Trophy A; Mich St Schol; *Anderson Col; Law.*

DICKINSON, Debra Kay
Bridgman HS; Bridgman, MI; Chor; Ger C; 4H; Sch P; Bkbl; Sftbl; Church Handbells; Bkbl Sportsmanship A; *Andrews U; Floristry.*

DICKINSON, Debra Lynn
St Michael's Central HS; Chicago, IL (3-126) Var C; Phys Ed A; Health A; *Northwestern U; Art.*

DICKINSON, Dolores Jean
West HS; Iowa City, IA (19-320) Chor; Dbte Tm; Drama; Madrigal; NFL; Pres, Thes; JV, Bkbl; JV, Golf; Amer Leg Orator A; NMS; Opt A; Parish Coun; Swing Choir; *Mount Holyoke Col; Mus.*

DICKINSON, Edson Dietrich
Robert E Lee HS; Jacksonville, FL (18-485) Co-Cpt, Band; Chor; Lat C; Madrigal; NHS; Amer Leg A; God & Country A; Sci A; Summa Cum Laude; Most Talented; Solo-Ensm, A; Louis Armstrong Jazz, A; *Fla Jr Col; Mus.*

DICKINSON, Frederick Richard
Lebanon HS; Lebanon, IN (10-272) Band; Semi-Fin, Ensm; Fr C; Key C; ARC; Var C; Swim; Fr As; Outst Fr Stu.

DICKINSON, James Richard
Clio HS; Clio, MI; Bkbl; Ftbl; Tr.

DICKINSON, Jeni Lynn
Lebanon Sr HS; Lebanon, IN (17-240) Pres, Chor; Fr C; GS; S-T, NHS; Span C; SC; VP, Jr Cl; COM; Hon Prog; St Scholar; Prom Qn; Outst Span V Stu; *Ind U; Foreign Lang.*

DICKINSON, Jerard Spencer
Arts HS; Newark, NJ (30-165) F-Ed, Ann; VP, Drama; Hmrm; SC; Up Bound; Tres, Var C; Co-Cpt, Cr-Ctry; Swim; Tr; YMCA, TWA Art, A's; PUSH Cultural Achv, Art & Mus, A; *Bus.*

DICKINSON, John Rox
Monroe Area Comph HS; Monroe, GA; BS; Hmrm; Key C; SC; Mgr, Ftbl; Tr; JV, Wrest; Attendence A; Art A; *Augusta Med Col; Paramedical.*

DICKINSON, Karen LeAnn
Putnam City W HS; Bethany, OK (169-630) Span C; Span NHS; COM; Citz A; Sunday Sch Teacher; Bus Ministry; Impact Tm; Hospital Visitation Vol; Yth Choir; VP, Lifeliners; Yth Ensm; Ntl Tn Talent Win; *Okla City Southwestern Col; Sociology.*

DICKINSON, Lisa Ann
Mount Anthony Union HS; Bennington, VT; Chor; Dbte Tm; Drama; Ch, Model UN; NFL; Sch P; Secy, SC; UN Council; Hon Prog; Spch A; Gov A, VT Coun On World Affairs; *McGill U; Pol Sci.*

DICKINSON, Paul Warren
Valley Central HS; Walden, NY (4-20) Ann; French NHS; SC; *New Paltz St U; Ed.*

DICKINSON, Tamara Sue
Linda Vista Acad; Oxnard, CA (4-14) A Cap Choir; Ann; Band; Chor; Ensm; Hmrm; Bsbl; Cpt, Soccer; Hon Prog; VP, SA; MV Soc; Looking, Mus, A's; *La Sierra Col; Med.*

DICKINSON, Thomas Wheeler
Robert E Lee Acad; Bishopville, SC (2-70) Ed, Ann; VP, BC; Chor; Lat C; Madrigal; Var C; JV, Bkbl; Tnns; Citz A; Gov Honor Prog; Gr Marshal; MLS; NHS; Ch, District Yth Comm; Church Organist, Pianist; Win, St Conservation Schol; *Clemson U; Pre Pharmacy.*

DICKMAN, Susan Elaine
Memorial HS; St Marys, OH (10-220) Ann; Chor; VP, FHA; GS; Pres, 4H; InterClub Coun; NHS; World Affairs C; Y-Tns; Tr; 4H A; Yth Fel; Co Fashion Board; Jr Fair Board; Co & Dist Off, FHA; *Ohio St U; Phys Therapy.*

DICKS, Dwayne Edward
Patterson Cooperative HS; Dayton, OH (35-850) Sch Achieve Tm; JV, Bsbl; Cpt, Bkbl; Fin, Cr-Ctry; Co-Cpt, Ftbl; Bio A; COM; Citz A; Cl Fav; Hist A; Hon Prog; MLS; Most Out; Opt A; Opt Out Tn; Spch A; Star Student; Swtht; Type A; Yth Fel; Win, Spelling Bee; *Sinclair U; Acct.*

DICKSON, Angela Denise
W Charlotte Sr HS; Charlotte, NC (218-640) A-Ed, Ann; Ensm; Hmrm; InterClub Coun; SC; Pres, Jr Cl; HQn; HCt; *Howard U; Child Psych.*

DICKSON, Barbara Jo
Tecumseh HS; New Carlisle, OH (76-368) AFS; Chor; Drama; NHS; Span C; Thes; WW; *Eng.*

DICKSON, Carol Lynn
Washington Co HS; Sandersville, GA (5%-288) BC; Drama; COM; Math A; Span A; Acad Excellence A; Drama A; Home Ec A.

DICKSON, Christine Beth
Powell HS; Powell, TN; BC; Drama; FHA; Y-Tns; COM; Drill Tm; *Airline Stewardess.*

DICKSON, Dannes Dell
Cross Plains HS; Cross Plains, TX (1-25) Ed, Ann; Band; Chldr; Drama; Pres, FHA; Pres, NHS; Pres, SC; Pres, Jr Cl; Tres, Soph Cl; Mgr, Bkbl; JV, Tnns; Hist A; HQn; Val; Val; Miss CPHS; Highest Ranking Soph; WW; *Stenographic Inst of Texas; Court Reporting.*

DICKSON, Dave DuWayne
Campbell HS; Campbell, CA (15%-200) NHS; JV, Ftbl; CSF; Yth Fel; *San Diego St Col; Photography.*

DICKSON, Debbie Celeste
Bellflower HS; Bellflower, CA; Tnns; CSF; Type A; Service C; *Sou Calif Col.*

DICKSON, Edna Pearl
Covington HS; Covington, TN; FHA; Rptr, Hmrm; MLS.

DICKSON, Elizabeth Louann
Columbus HS; Columbus, GA (½-435) Chor; Ensm; Hmrm; SC; COM; Gov Honor Prog; Hon Prog; Jr Civitan; All St Chor; *Auburn U; Textiles.*

DICKSON, Jody Blair
Richland Sr HS; Gibsonia, PA (50-269) AFS; Chldr; Chor; Drama; Hmrm; Span C; SC; Cpt, Swim; Tnns; Tr; Most Out; Most Outst Swimmer; *Westminster Col; Communications.*

DICKSON, June Elizabeth
Fountain Lake HS; Hot Springs, AR; Bus Mgr, Ann; BC; VP, FHA; Tnns.

DICKSON, Karen Lynn
Berea HS; Greenville, SC; FHA; *Greenville Tech Col; Bus Adm.*

DICKSON, Kevin Scott
Lubbock Christian HS; Lubbock, TX; Band; Bsbl; Ftbl; Tr; Pres, Church Yth; Outst Agr Stu; *Tex Tech U; Criminology.*

DICKSON, Kirby Byron
Lincoln HS; Stockton, CA; A Cap Choir; Chor; Ensm; Madrigal; Bsbl; Ftbl; Tr; *Mus.*

DICKSON, Mark Edwin
Towering Oaks Baptist Sch; Memphis, TN; Band; Fr C; *Math.*

DICKSON, Paula June
Petersburg HS; Petersburg, VA (5%-600) A-Ed, Ann; Secy, Chess C; Chor; Hmrm; NHS; SC; Hon Prog; Math A; Sci A; Ntl Guild A; *Mars Hill Col; Mus.*

DICUS, Bonnie Lynne
N Shore HS; W Palm Beach, FL (39-266) Cpt, Chldr; InterClub Coun; Orch; Co-Ch, SC; Pres, Jr Cl; HQn; HCt; Superior, St Orch; *Nurs.*

DIDDAMS, Stan S
Gallup HS; Gallup, NM (3-500) Band; BS; Pres, NHS; Span C; SC; Hon Prog; *Wheaton Col; Bus.*

DIDDAMS, Stanley Scott
Gallup HS; Gallup, NM (1-550) Band; NHS; Span C; JV, Wrest; Hon Prog; Superior As, NM Fed Mus C; *Wheaton Col; Bus & Commerce.*

183

DIDDAMS, Steven Paul
Gallup HS; Gallup, NM (78-870) Band; Fin, Dbte
Tm; Key C; Rptr, Lat C; Lat NHS; Spch A; *Wheaton Col; Pre Med.*

DIDIER, August Grant
Thomas Pub HS; Thomas, OK (1-38) Band; FFA;
NHS; Bkbl; Ftbl; Tr; Val; Rodeo Tm; Most Congenial.

DIDLICK, Gail Jeanne
Princeton HS; Cincinnati, OH (118-501) Band;
Ensm; Russian C; Russian Dancer; *Ohio St U; Agr.*

DiDONATO, Yvette Marie
Valley Central HS; Montgomery, NY; CYO; Chor;
Orange Co Comm Col; Secy.

DIEBOLD, John William
Spring Valley Sr HS; Spring Valley, NY (20-512)
Secy, Dbte Tm; Pres, Ger C; Lit Mag; Math C;
NHS; Ch, Orch; Ch, Order/Arrow; Ed, Sch P;
Spch C; Parl, SC; Parl, Sr Cl; Parl, Jr Cl; Amer Leg
A; COM; Math A; Order/Arrow A; Regent Schol;
Spch A; NML; WW; NYSSMA Solo; 'Above &
Beyond' A, Service; *Harvard Col; Pol Sci.*

DIECE, Rebecca J
Webb HS; Reedsburg, WI (1-209) Chem C; Ch, Fr
C; VP, FHA; GS; 4H; Math C; Amer Leg A; COM;
Math A; NEDT; Val; Vlbl; *U of Wis; Industrial
Engr.*

**DIEFFENWIERTH,
Mary Katherine**
St Augustine HS; St Augustine, FL (10%-500) Ed,
Ann; Band; Rainbow; Tres, Soph Cl; Swim; Tnns;
Asbury Col; Deaf Ed.

DIEHL, Ann Marie
Sacred Heart Acad; Salem, OR (10%-55) CYO;
Chor; Mus Schol A.

DIEHL, Beverly Ann
Aledo HS; Aledo, IL (10%-135) Chor; SC; Pres,
Soph Cl; Amer Leg A; Pres Phys Fitness A.

DIEHL, Deborah Louise
Waynesboro HS; Waynesboro, VA (40%-260)
Chldr; Pres, Chor; Fr C; Hmrm; VP, Key C; Var C;
Madison Col; Elem Ed.

DIEHL, Timothy Vaughn
New Lothrop HS; New Lothrop, MI (8-110)
Drama; NFL; Sch P; Span C; Spch C; SC; Arch;
Golf; Swim; COM; Spch A; VFW A; VFW Orator
Win; VofDEM; Yth Fel; Weight-Lifting Tm; Hon
Stu A; *Olivet Nazarene Col; Med.*

DIEKELMAN, Dawn Lynn
Freeport Sr HS; Freeport, IL (5%-550) Band; Chor;
Dbte Tm; Ensm; Span C; Tr; 1st Pl, St Solo; 1st
Chair, Band; Straight A HR; UCC Camp Committee; *Wheaton Col; Sci.*

DIEKHOFF, Susan Marie
Eisenhower HS; Rialto, CA; Chor; JV, Bkbl; JV,
Sftbl; Citz A; Math A; Type A; Yth Fel; *Valley Jr
Col; Gen.*

DIELSCHNEIDER, Gae Nanette
B C L Comm HS; Conrad, IA (10-60) Band; Chor;
Drama; Ensm; GS; Secy, 4H; Madrigal; Rptr, Sch
P; Thes; Mgr, Bkbl; Cr-Ctry; Tr; Amer Leg A; 4H
A; HCt; Spch A; *U of Northern Iowa; Spch Therapy.*

DIELSCHNEIDER, Jill Annette
B C L Comm HS; Conrad, IA (1-60) Ann; Band;
Chor; Drama; Ensm; Rptr, 4H; NHS; Secy, SC;
S-T, Thes; Secy, Sr Cl; Mgr, Bkbl; Cr-Ctry; Tr; 4H
A; *NIACC; Mech Design Tech.*

DIELSCHNEIDER, Lia Lorette
B-C-L HS; Conrad, IA (6-58) Band; Chor; Drama;
Ensm; 4H; NHS; Thes; Co-Cpt, Bkbl; Cr-Ctry; Tr;
U of Northern Iowa; Elem Ed.

DIELTZ, Mary Elizabeth
Jasper HS; Jasper, MN (1-42) Band; Cpt, Chldr;
Chor; Ensm; FHA; Var C; Tr; COM; Var, Vlbl; *Bio.*

DIEM, Daniel James
Carsonville-Pt Sanilac HS; Carsonville, MI (5-67)
Ed, Ann; Band; NHS; ARC; Sch P; Sci C; Ski C;
Pres, Sr Cl; Pres, Jr Cl; Pres, Soph Cl; Journ A;
MLS; Summa Cum Laude; Most Contributing; Sr
Activity A; Math Assn of Amer A; Betty Crocker
Family Ldr of Tmrw A; *Mich St U; Forestry.*

DIEMER, Judith Ann
Secaucus HS; Secaucus, NJ (2-187) Chem C; Chor;
GS; Hmrm; Co-Ed, Sch P; Sci C; SC; S-T, Jr Cl;
Tres, Soph Cl; Sftbl; Tnns; Amer Leg A; Hon Prog;
Journ A; Sci A; Hunting & Fishing, Strategy, C'S;
Cpt, Bowl; Essay Win, Women's C; Pres, Yth Fel;
Secondary Ed.

DIENER, Kay Ann
Hilbert HS; Hilbert, WI (2-66) Ann; GS; NHS;
MVP, Tr; Sal; Prom Ct; Swtht Hop Ct.

DIENST, Charles Sedgwick
Campolindo HS; Moraga, CA (15%-350) Soccer;
Hon Soc.

DIERBERGER, Linda Sue
Columbus Sr HS; Columbus, NE (10-294) Band;
Chor; Ensm; Span C; Swim; Gym; *Platte Tech
Comm Col; Math.*

DIERKES, Terrence Eugene
Central Comm HS; Breese, IL (6-157) CYO; Pres,
SC; JV, Bsbl; St Scholar; *U of Ill; Vet Med.*

DIERKS, Darla Jeanette
John Overton HS; Nashville, TN (33%-475) Chor;
FHA; NHS; Sci C; Span C; *Freed Hardeman Col;
Acct.*

DIETER, David Allen
Batavia HS; Batavia, IL (7-211) Math C; *Math.*

DIETERT, Carey Scott
New Braunfels HS; New Braunfels, TX (9-280)
Ann; VP, Band; VP, Chor; Drama; Ger C; Pres,
InterClub Coun; Madrigal; NFL; NHS; Order/
Arrow; Pres, Span C; Spch C; Pres, SC; Thes;
COM; Cl Fav; Elk A; Hon Prog; MLS; NMS;
NEDT; Order/Arrow A; VFW Orator Win; Vof-
DEM; Yth Fel; *U of Tex; Dramatic Arts.*

DIETRICH, Betty Carmen
Jackson Mem HS; Jackson, NJ; JV, Tr.

DIETRICH, Kandy Kay
Clear Lake HS; Clear Lake, WI (14-72) Band;
Chor; Ensm; FHA; Math C; Sci C; Co-Cpt, Bkbl;
Solo-Ensm A's; 1st Pl, Dist Vocal Solo; *Malone
Col; Nurs.*

DIETRICH, Karen Scott
Waynesboro Are Sr HS; Waynesboro, PA (1-356)
Chor; Pres, Drama; NHS; ARC; NMS Commendation; *Hood Col; Psych.*

DIETRICH, Linda Jean
Butler Sr HS; Butler, PA; *Butler Comm Col; Secy.*

DIETRICH, Lorie Jean
Barrington HS; Barrington, IL; A Cap Choir; Ensm;
Madrigal; Jr Ldr; Ch, Yth Sunday Sch Committee;
Mus.

DIETRICH, Patty Diane
Stratford HS; Stratford, TX (10-52) Band; Chldr;
FHA; 4H; Secy, Soph Cl; Bkbl; Golf; Tr; HCt;
FCA; Schol Hon, 3 Yrs; *Tex Tech U; Vet.*

DIETRICH, Penny Sue
Effingham HS; Effingham, IL; Ann; Fr C; Spch C;
McKendree Col.

DIETRICH, Stephen John
Marian HS; Tamaqua, PA (1-178) Chor; Hmrm;
Pres, NHS; Co-Ed, Sch P; SC; Bkbl; Amer Leg A;
COM; DARGCA; Hon Prog; NEDT; Pres A; Val;
PA St U, Notre Dame, Centen, Sch; *Scranton U;
Pre-Med.*

DIETSCHE, Patricia Jean
Hauppauge HS; Hauppauge, NY (150-600) A-Ed,
Ann; Chor; NHS; GScts; Yrbk Ltr; Lit Mag Publication; *Special Ed.*

DIETTERICH, Karin Elizabeth
Naperville N HS; Naperville, IL (33-469) Band;
Spch C; Thes; JV, Bkbl; Tr; Sci A; Publicity Ch,
German C; Tr Medals; Eng A; DAR A; *Brown U;
Marine Bio.*

DIETZ, Robin Lynn
Wade Hampton HS; Greenville, SC (50-378) A
Cap Choir; Chor; NHS; Span C; Span NHS; Cpt,
Bkbl; Amer Leg A; Vlbl; *Greenville Tech; Paralegal.*

DIETZEL, David John
St Paul's Sch; Garden City, NY (5-36) Cum Laude
Soc; Var C; Cpt, Cr-Ctry; Swim; Tr; Hon Prog; Yth
Fel; Hon Soc; *Phar.*

DIETZEL, Kathy Diann
Winnfield Sr HS; Winnfield, LA (2-12) Pres, Anchor C; Ed, Ann; VP, BC; Fr C; FBLA; FHA; Rptr,
FTA; Lit Ral; Rptr, SC; Mgr, Bkbl; Beauty; Cl Fav;
Hon Prog; Sal; Fin, Miss FHA; Pres, Church Yth;
Ad Staff; WW; *NE La U; Counseling.*

DIFFERDING, Dawn Marie
Lisbon HS; Lisbon, ND (15-70) Band; Chor; Ensm;
Kiwanis A; Spirit A's; *ND St Sch of Sci; Nurs.*

DIFFOOT, Nanette
Luis Munoz Marin HS; Cabo Rojo, PR (3-150)
Secy, Hmrm; Pres, ARC; SC; COM; Hon Prog;
ARC A; *Recinto Universitario de Mayaguez; Med.*

**DiFRANCESCA,
Salvatore Thomas III**
Niceville Sr HS; Valpariso, FL (125-408) Hmrm;
InterClub Coun; Sch P; SC; Pres, Karate C;
Okoloosa-Walton Jr Col; Elec.

DIGGS, Kay Elaine
Hendersonville Sr HS; Hendersonville, TN
(50%-550) Sci A; Stu Director, Spring Play; *Vol St
Col; Health.*

DIGGS, Sharon Denise
Forest Park HS; Baltimore, MD (20-300) FNA;
Ed, Lit Mag; Hon Prog; *Nurs.*

DIGIAMBATTISTA, Gail
Philadelphia HS For Girls; Philadelphia, PA
(100-450) Church Choir; Gym A; Church Yth
Coun; HR; *Oral Roberts U; Secy Sci.*

DiGILIO, William Francis
Glenbrook S HS; Glenview, IL; Ski C; Hockey;
Sftbl; Tnns; Bio A; Hon Prog; Lang A; *Med.*

DIGIROLAMO, Deena Lee
Destrehan HS; Destrehan, LA; BC; Chldr; Secy,
FTA; Sftbl; Vlbl; Fr A.

DIGMON, George Gregory
Autauga Co HS; Prattville, AL; *Dentistry.*

DIGNUM, Michele Anne
Notre Dame-Bishop Gibbons HS; Schenectady,
NY (24-161) Chldr; NHS; Hon Prog; NEDT; Adm
Mgr Soc Trophy; Model Congress; WW; Gregg
Steno & Typing A's; *Siena Col; Acct.*

DiGREGORIO, Robert Scott
Penns Grove HS; Penns Grove, NJ (41-230) NHS;
Ch, SC; Var C; Co-Cpt, Bsbl; Ftbl; Spch A; VofDEM; *U of Delaware; Agr.*

DILE, James Michael
Central Jr HS; Chambersburg, PA (5-300) Band;
Chor; Ger C; Orch; Amer Leg A; *W Chester Col;
Mus.*

DILES, Richard Michael
Jonath Alder HS; Plain City, OH (5-119) Band; BS;
Chess C; Chor; Drama; Fr C; FTA; Secy, 4H; HiY;
Pres, NHS; Sch Achieve Tm; Bus Mgr, Sch P; Span
C; Pres, Jr Cl; Golf; Amer Leg A; Citz A; Cl Fav;
Journ A; Q&S A; *Ripon Col; Law.*

DILIBERT, Ann Karla
Gurdon Hubbard; Chicago, FL (22-449) Mu Alpha
Theta; NHS; Var C; Bkbl; COM; Hon Prog; Ntl
Achv Schol; Vlbl; Pres, Church Luther League; *U
of Ill.*

DILL, Carolyn Marie
W T Woodson HS; Fairfax, VA (33%-500) Band;
Chor; Ensm; Lat C; Orch; Yth Fel; VP, Church Yth
Coun; 1st Chair, Bnd; Va All Reg Bnd; Church
Choir Librarian; Sch Band Librarian; *Philadelphia
Musical Acad; Church Mus.*

DILL, Cynthia Lee
Sou Wayne Sr HS; Dudley, NC (27-388) BC; FHA;
NHS; Span C; *Wayne Comm Col; Nurs.*

DILL, David Jordan
Del Mar HS; San Jose, CA; Semi-Fin, Tr.

DILL, Elizabeth Ann
Sou Wayne Sr HS; Dudley, NC (4-400) Band; BC;
Fr C; COM; Hist A; NEDT; Lat & Eng A's; *Hist.*

DILL, Laura Lynn
Gaffney HS; Gaffney, SC (10%-350) A-Ed, Ann;
BC; Chor; SC; Tres, Soph Cl; COM; Most Out; Pep
C; Ch, Citz o-t Mo; *U of SC; Archt.*

DILL, Marlys Yvonne
Mott Lincoln HS; Mott, ND; Ann; Band; Orch; Sci
C; Mgr, Bkbl; Sci A; Band A; *Jamestown Col; Nurs.*

DILLA, Ann Marie
Alvernia HS; Chicago, IL (1-194) NHS; Pres, Jr Cl; *Sci.*

DILLARD, Jon Eliot
Passaic Valley Regional HS; Little Falls, NJ; Order/Arrow; Tr; Order/Arrow A; Yth Fel; Eagle Sct; Brotherhood A; *US Air Force Acad; Math.*

DILLARD, Kenneth Alan
Bethel Sr HS; Spanaway, WA; Hmrm; JV, Ftbl; JV, Tr; Ath A.

DILLARD, Stephen Bryant
Booker T Washington Sr HS; Pensacola, FL (150-400) Bkbl; COM; Citz A; HCt; Star Student; Bkbl A; Mus A; *Fla St U; Law.*

DILLARD, Twyla Kay
Dothan HS; Dothan, AL (5-525) Lit Mag; NHS; Span C; Hon Prog; Val; Most Intellectual; *Troy St U; Elem Ed.*

DILLARD, Ty Walter
Campbell HS; Fairburn, GA; 4H; Hmrm; Lat C; Var C; Ftbl; Wrest; JA A; Pres A; *Ga St U.*

DILLER, Cathy Joann
Coldwater HS; Coldwater, OH; CYO; Chor; FHA; K of C A; *Ohio St Beauty Acad; Beautician.*

DILLER, Julia Ann
St Elmo Community HS; St Elmo, IL (11-50) Ed, Ann; Band; Chor; Ensm; Fr C; NHS; Pres, SC; Tr; Hon Prog; Yth Fel; Secy, Lib C; Women's C Schol, Mus Camp; Pres, MYF; *Med.*

DILLINGER, Susan Dawn
Thomson HS; Thomson, GA (10%-250) BC; Secy, Drama; FTA; Lit Ral; Span C; COM; Citz A; Gov Honor Prog; Hon Prog; Outst Span Stu; *Presbyterian Col; Ed.*

DILLINGHAM, Mark Allen
Hopewell HS; Hopewell, VA; BC; NHS; *U of Richmond; Bus Adm.*

DILLINGHAM, Mark Dean
Hartley Comm HS; Hartley, IA (17-172) Ann; Band; Ensm; Tres, FFA; NHS; VP, SC; Var C; VP, Sr Cl; Pres, Soph Cl; Bsbl; Bkbl; Ftbl; Golf; JV, Tr; Alg A; COM; HCt; Hon Prog; Yth Fel; WW; *Iowa St U; Agr.*

DILLON, Alice Elizabeth
Henley HS; Klamath Falls, OR (15-155) Parl, Band; Community Yth Symph; Drama; Pres, 4H; Parl, NHS; 4H A; Swtht; Type A; Drama A; *U of Idaho; Horticulture.*

DILLON, Anne Marie
Bemidji HS; Bemidji, MN (150-300) Fin, Office Proc.

DILLON, Karen Lynn
Corona Sr HS; Corona, CA; 4H; CSF; COM; 4H A; Math A; Rotary A; Drill Tm; Pantherettes Service C; *Pepperdine U; Accountant.*

DILLON,
Kendrick Vann Crawford
Vestavia Hills HS; Vestavia Hills, AL (20%-302) Fr C; Pres, Hmrm; InterAct C; VP, Sr Cl; Pres, Yth Fel; *Auburn U; Archt.*

DILLON, Lisa
Newbury Park HS; Newbury Park, CA (9-636) NHS; Ski C; SC; Tnns; CSF; Hon Prog; MLS; *U o-t Pacific; Phar.*

DILLON, Margaret Michele
Tallulah Acad; Tallulah, LA (3-30) Ann; Chldr; Parl, FHA; 4H; Semi-Fin, Lit Ral; Tres, NHS; Alg A; Beauty; HCt; WW; Home Ec, Bookkeeping, A's; *La Tech U; Bus.*

DILLON, Mark Charles
Bemidji HS; Bemidji, MN (100-400) Co-Cpt, Bsbl; *Westpoint Navel Col; Elec.*

DILLON, Mary Marshall
Monroe HS; Monroe, NC (5-158) AFS; Ed, Ann; Pres, Fr C; GS; Hmrm; VP, InterClub Coun; Monogram; NHS; SC; Secy, Sr Cl; Tnns; Beauty; HCt; Marshal; Pres, Jr Civitan; Morehead Nom; Miss St; *UNC-Chapel Hill; Bus.*

DILLON, Michael Donn
Roosevelt Sr HS; Minneapolis, MN (27-603) Band; Ensm; NHS; ROTC A; Distin Mus A; Marching Band; Concert Band; Stage Band, Ger Band; Augsburg Col Sch; Alt, ROTC A; Minn St School Grant; *Augsburg Col; Aeronautical Engr.*

DILLON, Nelda Elaine
Butler HS; Huntsville, AL; Band; Tres, Christ Ambassadors; GSct; Explorers; *U of Ala; Mus.*

DILLON, Patricia Anne
Batavia Sr HS; Batavia, IL; Ensm; VP, Hmrm; Math C; NHS; Orch; SC; Alg A; Hon Prog; Math A; Pres, Off Ed; Jv, Vlbl; Off Ed Contest; *Northern Ill U; Acct.*

DILWORTH, Lee Craig
Greater Atlanta Christian Sch; Norcross, GA (6-102) Chor; Drama; SC; Bkbl; JV, Tnns; Citz A; Hist A; Math A; Sci A; Cpt, Religious Emphasis C; Bible A.

DILWORTH, Randolph Mason
McMullen Co HS; Tilden, TX (5-6) Drama; Tres, FFA; 4H; NHS; VP, SC; Pres, Sr Cl; Pres, Jr Cl; Mgr, Bkbl; Tnns; Tr; COM; 4H A; WW; *Tex A&M U; Agr Econ.*

DILWORTH, Rose Ann
Wendell Phillips HS; Chicago, IL; Dbte Tm; Hmrm; ARC; SC; Up Bound; COM; GSct A; *Sou Ill U; Nurs.*

DiMARCO, Marino Edward
St Edward HS; Lakewood, OH (260-367) CYO; Bsbl; MVP, Ftbl; *Cleveland St Col; Law.*

DIMERY, Martin Eric
Byrnes HS; Duncan, SC (35-200) Band; Chem C; Pres, Hmrm; Sci C; Span C; SC; Bsbl; Bkbl; Cl Fav; I Dare You; Pres A; Swtht; Yth Fel; Yth Foundation; Art C; Wittiest; *U of SC.*

DI MILIA, Carol Lynn
Tottenville HS; Staten Island, NY (14-1058) Key C; NHS; Hon Prog; Regent Schol; Italian C A; *SUNY at Stony Brook; Pre-Dental.*

DIMINICH, Doris
Greater Ny Acad; Woodside, NY (7-73) A Cap Choir; Chor; V-Ch, Dbte Tm; Ch, Hmrm; NHS; Rptr, Sch P; Ski C; SC; Bkbl; Sftbl; Citz A; *Andrews U; Elem Ed.*

DIMINUCO, Steven Lewis
Warren Travis White HS; Dallas, TX; Ger C; HiY; Citz A; Young Life; FCA; Med Careers C; *U of Tex; Communications.*

DIMITRATOS, Olga
St Joseph's Notre Dame HS; Alameda, CA (12-55) Chor; Fr C; NHS; Sci C; CSF; Hon Prog; Math A; Eng A; Religion A; *U of San Francisco; Med Technology.*

DIMMITT, Alice Mae
South Shelby HS; Shelbina, MO (13-100) Band; Secy, CYO; Chor; FHA; NHS; SC; VP, Soph Cl; Cpt, Bkbl; Tr; Citz A; 4H A; Pres, Ltrwomen; Most Ath A; Schol Cert; Top 15% Cert; Most Courtesy A; Tr A; *Blessing's Nurs Sch; Nurs.*

DIMON, Scott Brian
Garden Spot HS; New Holland, PA (5%-300) NHS; Co-Ch, SC; Var C; Bsbl; Bkbl; Cr-Ctry; *Communications.*

DIMOND, Stephanie Rosemonde
St Mary's Acad; Alexandria, VA; Ann; CYO; French NHS; Tres, Key C; ARC; Soccer; Tr; Alg A; Hist A; Hon Prog; NEDT; Pres A; Geom A; Chor A; Fr A; *Vet Med.*

DiNATALE, Jean Annette
New Providence HS; New Providence, NJ (196-328) Band; Ski C; SC; Presbyterian Yth Organization; Color Guard; *Special Ed.*

DINELLI, Deborah Lynn
Niles East HS; Skokie, IL (100-571) Badminton; Outst Ldrship A; Prom Ct; Vlbl; All Dist Band; Candystriping A; *Carthage Col; Mus.*

DINENNA, Debra Ann
W Philadelphia Girls HS; Philadelphia, PA (3-354) NHS; Alg A; Bio A; Math A; Fr A; Lat A; *Thomas Jefferson Col; Lab Technology.*

DINGEY, Deanna Lynne
Zanesville HS; Zanesville, OH; Band; Fin, Mjrte; Orch; Span C; Ntl Essay A; Ntl Poetry A.

DINGLE, James Stephen
Wm J Woodham HS; Pensacola, FL (6-530) Band; Community Yth Symph; Ensm; Pres, Math C; Pres, Mu Alpha Theta; VP, NHS; Orch; Cpt, Sch Achieve Tm; SC; Alg A; B Crocker A; COM; Chamber of Comm A; Hon Prog; Math A; NMF; NMS; NEDT; Opt A; Star Student; Boy o-t Mo; Geog o-t Yr; *U of Fla; Pol Sci.*

DINGWERTH, Carol Lynn
James Bowie HS; Arlington, TX (14-286) Ger C; Hmrm; Pres, InterAct C; NHS; SC; Hon Prog; Opt A; Spirit C; Best Actress A; Vlbl; N Tex Dist Texanne o-t Mo; Sunshine A; *Biola Col; Elem Ed.*

DINKEL, Douglas Parker
Truman HS; Independence, MO (15%-480) CYO; Chem C; Cr-Ctry; Co-Cpt, Wrest; *Med.*

DINKELA, Angela Beth
Orchard Farm HS; St Charles, MO; Band; Drama; Ensm; NHS; Mgr, Tr.

DINKINS, Donna Marie
Simon Gratz HS; Philadelphia, PA; Chor; Rptr, Sch P; Hon Prog; MLS; Phy A; Type A; Best Rptr; Outst Player; *Bever St Col; Pre-Law.*

DINNDORF, Kathleen Mary
Lake of the Woods HS; Baudette, MN (10-84) Ann; Band; CYO; Cpt, Chldr; Chor; Fr C; NHS; Spch C; Tr; HCt; *Col of Saint Benedict; Fr.*

DINNING, Lora Kaye
R J Reynolds HS; Winston-Salem, NC; Fr C; Yth Fel; Girl's Coun; *Math.*

DINSMORE, Lloyd Creighton
Xenia HS; Xenia, OH (85-503) Band; Chess C; NHS; Span C; JV, Bkbl; Tnns; PALS A; *U of Cincinnati; Graphic Design.*

DINWIDDIE, Deirdre Patrice
Arlington HS; Indianapolis, IN (53-490) JA A.

DiPIETRO, F Angela
U S Grant HS; Portland, OR (25%-425) Orch; JA A; *Portland St U; Nurs.*

DIPPOLITO, Michael Allen
Byram Hills HS; Armonk, NY (20-184) SC; Hon Prog; Regent Schol; *Rice U; Chem.*

DIRCK, Marilyn Fay
Humansville HS; Humansville, MO; F-Ed, Ann; Chor; A-Ed, Sch P; S-T, Jr Cl; S-T, Soph Cl; MVP, Bkbl; Sftbl; HiJm; HCt; Type A; Jr Personality; Select Choir; Tm Mascot; Bkbl Statistician; Outst Homec Stu; Shorthand A; VP & Pres, Homec C; *SMSU; Elem Ed.*

DIRCKY, Devin Louise
LaCanada HS; La Canada, CA; Drama; Ger C; CSF; Drill Tm.

DIRENG, Elizabeth Lynne
Fitchburg HS; Fitchburg, MA (10-400) AFS; Band; Community Yth Symph; Secy, Drama; Ensm; French NHS; Sch P; Secy, SC; Beauty; Bio A; COM; DARGCA; NMS; Sci A; VofDEM; WW; Ntl Coun Tchrs Eng Wrtng Achv Ntl; *Smith Col; Fine Arts.*

DIRKSON, Beverly Lorraine
Simon Gratz Sr HS; Philadelphia, PA (22-450) Band; FTA; Math C; Tres, NHS; Orch; Citz A; Civic League; Nom, Schol; Meritorius Schol; *Penn St U; Engr.*

DI SANTO, Mary Ellen
Clintonville Sr HS; Clintonville, WI; Chor; Parl, FHA; S-T, 4H; 1st Pl, 4-H Play.

DISHMON, Vivian Lynnell
Killeen HS; Killeen, TX;

DISHONG, Margie Lou
Ravenna HS; Ravenna, OH (25-298) Chor; Fr C; Secy, Hmrm; NHS; Hon Prog; Schol Achv Test For Fr; Tn Choir; Vestor, Church Yth Group; *Kent St U; Nurs.*

DISHONG, Patricia Ann
Patrick Henry HS; San Diego, CA; Chor; Ntl Hon Stu; *Grossmont Col; Child Development.*

DISKE, Laurie Ann
Sauk Prairie HS; Prairie Du Sac, WI (20-260) Secy, Band; Pres, Drama; Ensm; Tres, 4H; Mod Mus Mas; NFL; Orch; Spch C; SC; Sftbl; 4H A; JA A; Most Out; Spch A; VFW A; VofDEM; Yth Fel; *Med.*

185

DISMORE, Carol Ann
Quincy Sr HS I; Quincy, IL (400-800) Band; Tres, Bus C; 4H; Span C; DECA; *Sou Ill U; Bus.*

DISMUKE, Norma Lee
Ritenour HS; St Louis, MO; Chldr; Chor; Drama; Ensm; Sch P; Sftbl; Acteen A's.

DISMUKE, Renee Marie
Ritenour HS; St Louis, MO (17%-730) Ann; Chor; Drama; Ensm; Type A; Coun, Summer Camp; Pianist, Jr Choir; Acteen As; *Mo Baptist Col.*

DISNEY, Paul Ray III
Southwest Miami Sr HS; Miami, FL (175-800) Band; Var C; Cr-Ctry; Ftbl; Tr; *Armed Forces Acad; Elec Communications.*

DISQUE, Renee Gayle
Salina Central HS; Salina, KS; Chor; Pep C; Lib Worker; ALYAG; HR; Sch Play; *Marymount Col; Secretarial.*

DISS, Lucy Margaret
St Mary's Acad; Englewood, CO (10-57) CYO; Chldr; Drama; Pres, Lat C; Co-Ed, Lit Mag; NHS; Co-Ed, Sch P; Pres, SC; JV, Bkbl; Sftbl; Journ A; VFW A; VFW Orator Win; Rptr & F-Ed, Sch Paper; Secy, SC; Fresh Service A; Prom Court; WW; Century III Ldrs of Amer; *U of Denver; Mass Comm.*

DISSER, Gail Diane
John F Hodge HS; St James, MO; Fr C; Pres A; Health A; *Allied Arts.*

DISTASIO, Anthony Raymond
John S Fine Sr HS; Nanticoke, PA (3-350) Ftbl; Tr.

DISTOR, Jocelynn A
Pacific HS; San Leandro, CA; InterAct C; Sci C; CSF; Hon Prog; Sci A; Presidential A, Span A; Falcon A; *UC Berkley; Ecology.*

DITTERLINE, Gary Wayne
Hot Springs HS; Truth Or Consequences, NM (10%-80) A Cap Choir; Chor; Demolay; Drama; Ensm; JV, Bsbl; JV, Bkbl; JV, Golf; Swim; Tnns; COM; Citz A; Yth Fel; All-St Mixed Chor.

DITTMER, Christine Ruth
Vines HS; Plano, TX; NHS; Span C; St George Assn A; *U of Tex; Bus.*

DITTMER, Jeffrey Scott
Capitol City Baptist Sch; Lansing, MI (3-8) Bus Mgr, Ann; Chor; Drama; Hmrm; NHS; Bkbl; Cr-Ctry; Soccer; Tr; Wrest; Sci A; Semi-Fin, H Ct; VP, Yth Fel; Social Stu A.

DITTO, Angela Ann
Herrin HS; Herrin, IL (20%-206) CYO; FHA; HCt; *John A Logan Col; Stenographer.*

DITTRICH, Denise Ellen
Keene HS; Keene, NH (60-500) Band; Drama; Lat C; *Roger Williams Col; Amer Hist.*

DITTUS, Timothy Roy
Glen Ullin HS; Glen Ullin, ND (4-46) Ann; Band; BS; Chor; Parl, Sci C; Mgr, Bkbl; Mgr, Ftbl; Chem A; Valedictorian; *Jamestown Col; Bus Adm.*

DITZER, Rebecca May
Union Co HS; Morganfield, KY (18-213) Band; Fr C; Jr Miss Pagent; NHS; Bkbl; Hon Prog; Jr Miss, Congeniality; Bkbl A's; *Pre-Vet.*

DITZER, Stephen Wayne
Union Co HS; Morganfield, KY; Band; Span C; MVP, Cr-Ctry; Ftbl; Tr.

DiVALL, Frank LeRoy III
Arkansas City HS; Arkansas City, KS (45-230) BS; CYO; Chem C; Secy, Demolay; HiY; JETS; Math C; Sci C; Tnns; Mgr, Wrest; I Dare You; VofDEM; Yth Leg; Wrest A; *Kan St U; Engr.*

DiVALL, Phil Thomas
Arkansas City HS; Arkansas City, KS (15-250) Rptr, BS; Cpt, Chem C; Pres, Demolay; Fr C; Rptr, HiY; VP, Sci C; SC; Mgr, Bkbl; Sftbl; Mgr, Tr; *Kans St U; Recreation.*

DIVELEY, Karen Sue
Highland HS; Highland, KS (10%-35) Band; Chor; Ensm; Tr; COM; Type A; Yth Fel; Band A; Pep C; *Highland Jr Col; Acct.*

DIVEN, Robert Sherwood
Las Cruces HS; Las Cruces, NM; A Cap Choir; Chor; Drama; Ger C; A-Ed, Lit Mag; Thes; Spch A; Daniel A; Outst Soloist, St Ensm Festival; *Christian Heritage Col; Ministry.*

DIVINCENZO, Frank Anthony
Oak Lawn Comm HS; Oak Lawn, IL (45-750) St Fin, Quiz Tm; St Fin, Piano Comp; *Ill Inst of Tech; Computer Sci.*

DIXON, Albert Elmore
Harry E Davis Jr HS; Cleveland, OH (3-39) Chor; NHS; Ftbl; Sftbl; Tnns; Tr; Alg A; Bio A; Citz A; JA A; Math A; Type A; *Cleveland St U; Acct.*

DIXON, Amelia Norene
Fairley HS; Memphis, TN (1-300) Ed, Ann; Pres, Band; Pres, Hmrm; Math C; NHS; Sci C; Pres, Span C; Span NHS; COM; Cl Fav; Most Out; Ntl Achv Schol; Val; Yth Fel; Tnager o-t Week; Eng A; Foreign Lang A; Young Amer A; *Howard U; Pol Sci.*

DIXON, Anna Webster
Walter Hines Page Sr HS; Greensboro, NC (15%-600) French NHS; Ski C; Bkbl; Hockey; Sftbl; Tnns; Pres, Episcopal Young Churchmen; Greensboro Yth Coun; Civinettes; Pep C; *U of NC; Bio.*

DIXON, Arne William
Bothell HS; Bothell, WA (1-410) Band; Fin, BS; Ensm; Hmrm; NHS; Sch P; Pres, Sr Cl; VP, Jr Cl; VP, Soph Cl; Cpt, Soccer; Elk A; JA A; Val; Drum Major; Jr Prom Hk g; ASB A; All Amer H of Fame Band Hon; 1st Pl Wash Industrial Arts Conf.

DIXON, Barbara Jeanne
Elmhurst HS; Fort Wayne, IN; Rptr, Hmrm; SC; Tr; COM; Citz A; HR.

DIXON, Billy D Jr
Macedonia HS; Moncks Corner, SC (6-90) BC; Fr C; Hmrm; Co-Ed, Sch P; SC; Pres, Jr Cl; *Trident Tech Col; Engr.*

DIXON, Bobby Roy Jr
Vidalia HS; Vidalia, GA (25%-150) Parl, HiY; Hmrm; Key C; JV, Bkbl; Ftbl; HCt; Yth Fel; *Math.*

DIXON, Carolyn Evaughn
West HS; Salt Lake City, UT; Hon Prog; *Westminster Col; Journ.*

DIXON, Connie Sue
Huffman HS; Birmingham, AL; Bus Mgr, Bus C; Chor; Bus Mgr, FBLA; FTA; Pres, Hmrm; ARC; Sci C; SC; Tri-HiY; COM; Secy, Yth Coun; Agape C.

DIXON, Cynthia Renee
Burns HS; Fallston, NC; BC; Chldr; Drama; Fr C; SC; HCt; Opt A; Fr A; Writing Achv A; *UNC C; Med.*

DIXON, Dacia
Dunbar Voc HS; Chicago, IL (3-500) All Amer Yth; VP, Band; Chor; Hmrm; NHS; Orch; ARC; Sch Achieve Tm; Bkbl; Sftbl; Tnns; Alg A; COM; Citz A; Cl Fav; Hon Prog; JA A; Math A; Most Out; NMS; Star Student; *U of Wis-Madison; Occupational Therapy.*

DIXON, Daryl
Frederick Douglass HS; Atlanta, GA (25-341) Chor; Pres, Hmrm; Madrigal; Bus Mgr, Orch; Pres, Sr Cl; COM; Cl Fav; Gov Honor Prog; Hon Prog; MLS; *Morehouse Col; Mus.*

DIXON, Delicia Jan
Whitehouse HS; Whitehouse, TX (12-99) BC; FHA; St Stu Congress; Hist A; MLS; Homemaking A; Top 10; *Tyler Jr Col; Math.*

DIXON, Dolores Ann
Vanguard HS; Ocala, FL (15-350) Band; NHS; *Fla St U; Med.*

DIXON, Donnie Wayne
Texas City HS; Texas City, TX; A Cap Choir; Chor; Drama; Ensm; NHS; SC; JV, Bsbl; Bkbl; JV, Ftbl; Golf; Cl Fav; FCA.

DIXON, Douglas Barry
Steubenville; Steubenville, OH; Band; Hmrm; Sch P; VP, Span C; SC; *Acct.*

DIXON, Douglas Ray
Elk City HS; Elk City, OK (11-132) Dbte Tm; Drama; Hmrm; Span C; Spch C; Bio A; Citz A; Gov Honor Prog; Hist A; Hon Prog; St Scholar; Lib A; HR; St Hon Soc; Acad & Ldrshp Sch, Nowestern Ok U; *Northwestern Okla St U; Psych.*

DIXON, Edna Marie
Trotwood Madison Sr HS; Dayton, OH; PA, Sunday Sch; Sunday Sch Teacher; Founder, Yth Usher Board; VP, Secy, Yth Ushers; Yth Choir; *Cosmetology.*

DIXON, Felecia Ann
Iroquois HS; Louisville, KY; Ed, Ann; Band; Chldr; Chor; Ensm; Secy, SC; Tr; COM; Cl Fav; HCt; MLS; Sci A; *Murray St U; Acad.*

DIXON, George Matthew
Carrollton HS; Carrollton, GA (17%-200) Band; Ensm; Tnns; HR; *Aviation.*

DIXON, Jennifer Gail
Western Hills HS; Fort Worth, TX (55-604) CYO; FHA; Sftbl; *Weatherford Jr Col; Bus.*

DIXON, Johanna Hayes
Lafayette HS; Lafayette, LA; Bus C; Fr C; NHS; NEDT; Church Bkbl; City League Ftbl & Sftbl; Off, Church Yth.

DIXON, John Randall
Waynesboro HS; Waynesboro, VA (51-253) BC; Lat C; Yth Fel; Art Guild; Art A; *VPI; Mineralology.*

DIXON, Joyce Teresa
Inglewood HS; Inglewood, CA; Chor; Hmrm; Span C; Cpt, Bkbl; Cpt, Sftbl; Citz A; Math A; Most Out; PTA A; Cpt, MIP, Most Dedicated, Vlbl; Cpt, Most Inspirational, Sftbl; *San Diego St Col; Sociology.*

DIXON, Karen Anne
Lincoln HS; Stockton, CA (58-468) Drama; Fr C; NFL; ARC; Spch C; SC; Secy, Thes; CSF; COM; Hon Prog; Spch A; Rally Comm; Secy and Future Pres, Church Yth; *Nurs.*

DIXON, Kimberly Kay
Highland HS; Ewing, MO (6-130) Secy, Chor; Drama; FHA; Hmrm, 4H; Madrigal; NHS; Pres, Sci C; Bio A; 4H A; Sci A; Rptr, 4-H C; Mus A; WW; S-T, Sci C; Pres, Psych C; Pep C; *Baptist Bible Col; Mus Ed.*

DIXON, Lori Leta
Campolindo HS; Moraga, CA; Chor; A-Ed, Commercial C; HiY; Ch, Hmrm; Arch; Bkbl; Sftbl; Swim; Tnns; Tr; ARC A; Horsemanship A; *Calif Polytech U; Mech Engr.*

DIXON, Louie Myron
D H Conley HS; Greenville, NC (22-270) BC; Hmrm; NHS; Order/Arrow; VP, Sci C; SC; Bsbl; Bkbl; Sci A; *E Carolina U; Sci.*

DIXON, Marian Clorine
Southside HS; Greenville, SC; Chor; Secy, Hmrm; Bkbl; Hockey; Sftbl; Tr; Cl Fav; JA A; Art School; Attendance A; *Rudledge Col; Secy Work.*

DIXON, Mark Sherwood
Searcy HS; Searcy, AR; Pres, Key C; SC; Bkbl; Ftbl; *U of Ark; Phys Therapist.*

DIXON, Martha Corinne
Thornwell HS; Clinton, SC; Ann; BC; Fr C; VP, FHA; Hmrm; Model UN; Var C; Bkbl; Sftbl; Tnns; Gov Honor Prog; NEDT; Yth Fel; Presbyterian Col Jr Fel; Newberry Col Summer Schol; *Marine Biol.*

DIXON, Mary Clair
Carrollton HS; Carrollton, GA; Band; BC; Pres, FTA; Ed, Lit Mag; NHS; COM; Gov Honor Prog; NMF; *W Ga Col.*

DIXON, Mary Gilmore
Walter Hines Page Sr HS; Greensboro, NC; Ann; Ski C; Mgr, Bkbl; Hockey; Sftbl; JA A; Treas, JA; Episcopal Yth Churchmen; Civinettes; Intl C; *U of NC at Chapel Hill.*

DIXON, Michael George
J H Rose HS; Greenville, NC (75-370) Monogram; NHS; Order/Arrow; *UNC-Greensboro; Sci.*

DIXON, Michael Henry
Burns HS; Lawndale, NC; VP, Key C; Bsbl; JV, Bkbl; JV, Ftbl; HCt.

DIXON, Patsy Ann
Kemper Acad; DeKalb, MS; Ed, Ann; BC; Chor; Drama; Fin, Jr Miss Pagent; Arch; Bkbl; Cpt, Sftbl; Tnns; Tr; HCt; Math A; Sci A; Shorthand, Art, A's; Miss Kemper Acad; *Miss St U; Secy Sci.*

DIXON, Paula
West Side Sr HS; Newark, NJ (10%-385) Pres, Band; Chem C; Hmrm; Tres, NHS; Orch; VP, Span C; Up Bound; Swim; Tnns; COM; Citz A; Interlochen Ntl Mus; Most Out; Pres A; *Fisk U; Pre-Med.*

DIXON, Rebecca Ann
J H Rose Sr HS; Greenville, NC (1-425) Anchor C; Ed, Ann; Chldr; Monogram; Span C; Tr; *Meredith Col; Pol Sci.*

DIXON, Robert Anthony
Trenton Central HS; Trenton, NJ (44-728) All Amer Yth; Band; Drama; K of C; Lit Mag; Orch; F-Ed, Sch P; Cpt, Cr-Ctry; Cpt, Tr; Citz A; MLS; Star Student; *Morehouse Col; Mass Communications.*

DIXON, Robert Emory Jr
Dodge Co HS; Eastman, GA (10%-210) F-Ed, Ann; Pres, Chor; VP, HiY; Sch P; Span C; SC; Var C; JV, Bkbl; Ftbl; Tr; Cl Fav; Hist A; Sr Superlative; Marshal Schol; Creative Writing A; *Andrew Col; Eng.*

DIXON, Robin Elizabeth
Cross Keys HS; Atlanta, GA (27-240) A Cap Choir; Fin, All Amer Yth; F-Ed, Ann; Band; BC; Chor; Drama; Ensm; Fr C; French NHS; SC; Mgr, Soccer; Citz A; Cl Fav; Gov Honor Prog; Hon Prog; Most Out; Yth Fel; *Wesleyan Col; Church Mus.*

DIXON, Susan Elizabeth
Rockville Comm HS; Rockville, IN (16-83) Tres, Band; Chor; Ensm; FHA; Lat C; NHS; Rainbow; Sci C; Secy, Sr Cl; Tres, Soph Cl; Swim; Most Out; St Scholar; Yth Fel; Semi-Fin, Co Fair Qn; FCA; Tary Acad Sailing Camp; God & Comm A; Amer Yth Symph Band; *Oral Roberts U; Elem Ed.*

DIXON, Tamra Joyce
Palmer HS; Palmer, TX (1-28) Chldr; Dbte Tm; S-T, FHA; Ed, Sch P; SC; Tres, Jr Cl; Tres, Soph Cl; Bkbl; Tr; Alg A; Citz A; Vlbl; WW; HR A; Drama A; 1st Dist UIL Sliderule; *Tex A&M U; Computing Sci.*

DIXON, Ted David
E Ascension Acad; Gonzales, LA; Bsbl; *Westmar Col; Chem.*

DIXON, Theda Ann
Middletown HS; Middletown, OH; F-Ed, Ann; Band; Fr C; Sch P; JA A; Top 10% A; *Engr.*

DIXON, William Rand
Ontario Christian HS; Ontario, CA (8-70) BS; Chor; Hmrm; SC; Bsbl; JV, Ftbl; Co-Cpt, Soccer; Amer Leg A; CSF; Homecoming MC; Sr Marshal; *Pre-Law.*

DIXSON, JoAnne Alma
Marcus HS; Marcus, IA (6-48) NHS; Span C; Pres, SC; Pres, Sr Cl; Sftbl; Mgr, Wrest; Rotary A; Yth Fel; FCA; *U of N Iowa; Spch Pathology.*

DLUZNIEWSKI, Diane Theresa
John W Hallahan Cath Girls HS; Philadelphia, PA (4-431) NFL; NHS; Co-Ed, Sch P; Secy, Span C; Alg A; Type A; Liturgy C; Span A; *Episcopal Hospital; Nurs.*

DMYTROW, Bruce William
St Joseph's o-t Palisades HS; W New York, NJ (15-232) Ann; Drama; NHS; Sci C; Span NHS; SC; Swim; Amer Leg A; H of F; Hon Prog; Hist C; Hon Achv, Art; *Boston Col; Pre-Med.*

DOAK, Dara Kathleen
Guthrie HS; Guthrie, OK (1-186) Chor; FBLA; NHS; Sch Achieve Tm; Span C; Spch C; H of F; Hon Prog; Math A; Regent Schol; Val; *Wartburg Col; Span.*

DOAK, Deidre Jane
Wheeler Co HS; Alamo, GA (1-79) Cpt, Band; BC; Drama; Fr C; NHS; Spch C; Tri-HiY; Tr; COM; Gov Honor Prog; Leadership A.

DOAN, Richard Lucas
Barnesville HS; Barnesville, OH (8-12) BS; HiY; Sch Achieve Tm; VP, Var C; VP, Jr Cl; Bkbl; Co-Cpt, Ftbl; Tr; Bio A; *Ohio St U; Psych.*

DOBBERSTEIN, Julie Faye
Balaton HS; Balaton, MN (4-30) VP, Band; VP, Chor; Pres, FHA; Cpt, Mjrte; Spch C; SC; Bkbl; Tr; COM; HCt; MLS; Spch A; Type A; Mus A; Ath A; Vlbl; *McKennan Hospital; Radiologic Tech.*

DOBBINS, Anderson Levi Jr
Purcell HS; Cincinnati, OH (33%-220) Chess C; Cum Laude Soc; Bsbl; Ftbl; Hon Prog; Math A; Archt.

DOBBINS, Claire Ellen
John Thomas Hoggard Sr HS; Wilmington, NC (228-600) Fr C; Swim; Careers C; Aeronautics C; Med Explorers C; Scuba Diving C; *U of NC; Fr.*

DOBBINS, Debra Ann
Johnston City HS; Johnston City, IL (3-90) Chor; Drama; Lat C; Math C; Secy, NHS; Sch P; Sci C; SC; Thes; Pres, Soph Cl; Lion A; MLS; St Scholar; *John A Logan Jr Col; Psych.*

DOBBINS, Joan Leslie
Jamaica HS; Jamaica, NY (269-1160) Hmrm; ARC; Swim; COM; ARC A; Yth Fel; *Hunter Col; Geology.*

DOBBINS, John Kevin
Johnston City HS; Johnston City, IL; Math C; NHS; Sci C; Amer Leg A; Hist A; Lion A; Sci A; Eng A; *Sou Ill U; Arch.*

DOBBINS, Kim Yvette
High Point HS; Beltsville, MD (20%-773) CYO; ARC; Bkbl; Sftbl; Tr; COM; Citz A; Hon Prog; Yth Fel; Bible Sch Cert; Vol, Area Sci Fair; *U of Md; Bio.*

DOBBINS, Linda Arlene
Walnut Hills HS; Cincinnati, OH (20%-400) CYO; Chor; Tr; *Case Western Reserve U; Med.*

DOBBINS, Robert Wayne
Starmount HS; Boonville, NC (15-151) Chess C; Pres, Chor; Ensm; Math C; Mu Alpha Theta; NHS; SC; JV, Ftbl; VICA; *NC St U; Math.*

DOBBINS, Rodney James
Purcell HS; Cincinnati, OH (15%-220) Band; Chess C; Chor; Ntl Jr Hon Soc; *U of Cincinnati; Engr.*

DOBBINS, Sharon Yvonne
Skyline HS; Oakland, CA; FNA; ARC; Cpt, Bsbl; Cpt, Bkbl; Cpt, Sftbl; Cpt, Tnns; Citz A; Cl Fav; Most Out; Swtht; *Montford Ntl; Registered Nurse.*

DOBBINS, Stephanie Annette
Oakland HS; Oakland, CA; Drama; Orch; Citz A; Cl Fav; Swtht; *Law.*

DOBBINS, William Curtis II
Pearl HS; Nashville, TN; BC; Chor; Pres, Hmrm; Sch Achieve Tm; SC; COM; Cl Fav; Yth Fel; Mus, Attendance, A's.

DOBBS, Janice Marie
Pacifica HS; Garden Grove, CA (36-652) A Cap Choir; Ch, Band; Ger C; CSF; Band Service A; *Long Beach St U; Ed Psych.*

DOBBS, Jerry Ellis
Pleasant Grove HS; Pleasant Grove, AL (1-150) Band; NHS; Sci A; Tn Code A; *Birmingham Sou Col; Med.*

DOBBS, Linda Sue
Pacifica HS; Garden Grove, CA; Band; Ger C; Hmrm; NHS; CSF; Hon Prog; Sci A; MVP, Gym; *Long Beach St Col; Med.*

DOBBS, Samuel George
Fort Payne HS; Fort Payne, AL (6-117) Pres, BC; Chess C; Hmrm; Key C; NHS; Order/Arrow; Pres, Sci C; SC; JV, Ftbl; NEDT; Order/Arrow A; ARC A; *U of Ala; Sci.*

DOBBS, Victoria Lynne
Denbigh HS; Newport News, VA (93-439) Bus Mgr, Ann; Chldr; Chor; Drama; FBLA; 4H; Ch, Hmrm; NFL; ARC; Sci C; Span C; Secy, SC; Thes; Bkbl; Sftbl; Tr; COM; ARC A; Keyettes; WW; Presidential Chrm For Young Amer; George Washington U Schol; Mary Washington Schol; *Mary Washington Col; Interntl Relations.*

DOBELL, Terry Lynn
Colerain Sr HS; Cincinnati, OH (65-664) Chor; Ger C; 4H; NHS; Rainbow; SC; Citz A; Sci A; *Christ Hospital Sch of Nurs; Nurs.*

DOBERER, Kim Yvonne
Clay Co Comm HS; Clay Center, KS (20-126) F-Ed, Sch P; Journ A; *Manhattan Voc Tech Sch; Practical Nurs.*

DOBERNECK, Donna Lee
Notre Dame Bishop Gibbons HS; Schenectady, NY (17-161) Ann; CYO; Chor; Ch, Hmrm; NHS; Sftbl; Regents Scho; Nurs Alt; *Siena Col; Math.*

DOBEY, Lisa Ann
Patrick Henry HS; San Diego, CA (424-1309) Rptr, Chor; Sftbl; COM; Citz A; Yth Fel; Campus Life; Square Dancing; Secy, Yth Fel; *UCLA; Drama.*

DOBIES, Kenneth Francis
Draper HS; Schenectady, NY (50-110) ARC; Tr; *Union Col; Lib Arts.*

DOBOSZ, Mark Joseph
St Mary's Prep; Orchard Lake, MI (2-35) Drama; ARC; Ski C; Secy, Jr Cl; Mgr, Bsbl; Mgr, Bkbl; Mgr, Ftbl; Mgr, Tr; Hon Prog; Sacristan; Lang Oratorical Contest; 1st Hon; *U of Detroit; Bus Adm.*

DOBRES, Catherine Mary
Qn o-t Rosary Acad; Amityville, NY (7-85) Chor; Hmrm; NHS; Parl, Jr Cl; Tnns; COM; Hon Prog; Type A; *Nassau Comm Col; Special Ed.*

DOBRINSKI, Connie Jo
Okeene HS; Okeene, OK (1-45) Band; Chldr; Chor; Secy, FHA; NHS; Rainbow; Bkbl; Chamber of Comm A; Jr Chamber of Com A; VP, St FHA; St HR; Whea-Esta Pageant Qn; *Phillips U; Nurs.*

DOBRUCKI, Renata Maria
Hollywood Professional Sch; Hollywood, CA (4%-20) CYO; Chor; Pres, Soph Cl; Fin, Bsbl; Fin, Bkbl; Fin, Sftbl; Fin, Swim; Cl Fav; Most Out; ARC A; Yth Fel; Eng A; *UCLA; Journ.*

DOBSCHA, Steven Keith
Dublin HS; Dublin, CA (2-400) A Cap Choir; Band; Ensm; Pres, Ger C; Math C; Sci C; SC; JV, Swim; JV, Tnns; CSF; COM; Hon Prog; Math A; Most Out; Most Improved, Band; *Schiller Col; Sci.*

DOBSON, Charles Jr
Bremerhaven American HS; Bremerhaven, GERMANY (3-24) Ann; F-Ed, Lit Mag; NHS; SC; Var C; Tres, Jr Cl; JV, Bkbl; Cr-Ctry; Tnns; Pres A; *Math.*

DOBSON, Peggy Jo
Pendleton HS; Pendleton, SC (9-133) Ed, Ann; BC; VP, Fr C; *U of NC at Chapel Hill; Behavioral Sci.*

DOBSON, Regina Denise
Bremerhaven American HS; Bremerhaven, GERMANY (2-24) Ann; Cpt, Chldr; NHS; F-Ed, Sch P; SC; Pres, Jr Cl; Bkbl; Sftbl; Tr; HCt; Cpt, Vlbl; *Vet Sci.*

DOBSON, Rose Nan
Estill HS; Estill, SC; Bus Mgr, Ann; VP, SC; TAPS C.

DOBSON, Sheila Annette
Murrah HS; Jackson, MS (15-300) Chldr; Chor; SC; Amer Leg A; COM; Citz A; Cl Fav; HCt; Gayfer Girl; *Xavier U; Phar.*

DOCK, Steven Gregory
Jasper HS; Jasper, MN; A Cap Choir; Ann; Chem C; Chor; Drama; Ensm; FFA; 4H; Phys C; Spch C; SC; Pres, Soph Cl; Cl Fav; 4H A; Hon Prog; VBS Teacher; Sunday Church Organist; Sch Accompianist; Ensm A; Pastor's Asst, Rest Homes; *Augustana Col; Hist.*

DOCKENDORF, Susan Elaine
Eden Valley-Watkins HS; Eden Valley, MB (2-102) Band; Ensm; FHA; Mjrte; NHS; COM; Sal; Star Student.

DOCKERY, Sandra Denise
Tuscaloosa HS; Tuscaloosa, AL (17-561) Anchor C; Chldr; Fr C; Mu Alpha Theta; NHS; SC; Cl Fav; HCt; Sci A; Outst Sr; *U of Ala; Med.*

DOCKERY, Tom W Jr
Fayetteville HS; Fayetteville, AR (50-400) InterClub Coun; VP, Key C; NHS; NEDT; Elec Engr.

DOCKHAM, John Mark
Imlay City HS; Imlay City, MI (33%-188) Bsbl; Ftbl; Wrest; Sci.

DOCKTER, Kelly Dean
Hurdsfield HS; Hurdsfield, ND (1-9) Chor; Sch P; SC; Pres, Soph Cl; Bsbl; MVP, Bkbl; Co-Cpt, Sftbl; Tnns; B Crocker A; Math A; MLS; Type A; Val; Yth Fel.

DOCKTER, Lori Jo
Hurdsfield HS; Hurdsfield, ND; Chor; GS; 4H; Arch; Bkbl; Sftbl; Swim; Tr; 4H A; ARC A; *Valley City St Col; Elem Ed.*

DOCKTER, Shelly Jean
Hurdsfield Pub HS; Hurdsfield, ND; Ann; Co-Cpt, Chldr; Chor; 4H; Rptr, Sch P; Pres, Jr Cl; Pres, Soph Cl; Arch; Co-Cpt, Bkbl; Sftbl; Tr; 4H A; Ntl Chldr A.

DOCTOR, Matthew Aaron
South Side HS; Fort Wayne, IN (150-450) Bus C; FBLA; World Affairs C; Type A; Pres, Church Yth Fel; Bowl Tm; *Wartburg Col; Bus.*

DODD, Carol Elizabeth
Campbell HS; Fairburn, GA; Drama; Tres, FBLA; Hmrm; Math C; Mu Alpha Theta; Span C; Span NHS; SC; Tres, Y-Tns; COM; Hon Prog; Cpt, Drill Tm; Span A; *Ga Sou Col; Secy Sci.*

DODD, Constance Denise
Central HS; St Joseph, MO (167-512) Chor; Tri-HiY; Y-Tns; Gov Honor Prog; Hist A; *Mo W Col; Bus Adm.*

DODD, Dale Alan
Wis Acad; Columbus, WI (15-63) Band; Ger C; Cpt, Bsbl; Bkbl; Cpt, Ftbl; Cpt, Sftbl; Fin, Tr; COM; Val; *Andrews U; Law.*

DODD, David Franklin
U Military Sch; Mobile, AL (30-90) Band; Chor; Ensm; Bkbl; Opt A; All St Chor; Superior, St Ensm, Church Chor Comp; *Samford U; Mus.*

DODD, Elizabeth Susan
Adrian Sr HS; Adrian, MI (75-500) A Cap Choir; Band; VP, Fr C; Fin, GS; Ski C; Thes; Tnns; Gym; *Albion Col; Bus.*

DODD, Jeffrey Lynn
Springfield HS; Springfield, IL (2-500) AFS; Drama; Fr C; Sales VP, JA Radio Company; Tres, Church Yth Fel; Quarter Master, BSct; *Sou Ill U; Communications.*

DODD, Jeffrey Lynn
Howe HS; Howe, OK (5-17) Chor; FFA; 4H; COM; Citz A; 4H A; Yth Fel; *Evangel Col.*

DODD, Pamela Ann
Herbert Hoover HS; Clendenin, WV; Drama; FBLA; FTA; VP, Rainbow; *Social Work.*

DODD, Richard Brian
Sooner HS; Bartlesville, OK; Key C; Ski C; Bkbl; Ftbl; *Okla St U; Mech Engr.*

DODD, Tony Ray
Newton Co Comprehensive HS; Covington, GA (10%-438) BC; Secy, InterAct C; Order/Arrow; Ftbl; Order/Arrow A; *U of Ga; Oceanography.*

DODDS, Bonnie Marie
Elisabeth Ann Johnson HS; Mt Morris, MI (10-32) Chor; *Olivet Col; Legal Secy.*

DODDS, Margaret Juanita
Cuyahoga Valley Christian Acad; Cuyahoga Falls, OH (7-31) Co-Cpt, Chldr; Chor; Drama; Ensm; Orch; Rptr, Sch P; Pres, SC; Bkbl; Cpt, Hockey; HCt; Opt A; Ensm A; Orch A; *Cuyahoga Comm Col.*

DODGE, Charles Carlin
Benson HS; Portland, OR (30-370) CYO; Chor; NHS; SC; Y-Tns; JV, Bsbl; Tr; Citz A; Most Out; Pres A; Sci A; *Portland Comm Col; Criminal Justice.*

DODGE, Charles Thomas
Washington-Lee HS; Arlington, VA (75-450) Band; Pres, Demolay; Fr C; Order/Arrow; Ski C; Var C; JV, Bsbl; Wrest; COM; Lion A; Sci A; Yth Fel; *Madison Col; Phys Ed.*

DODGE, Cynthia Elaine
Cy-Fair HS; Cypress, TX (33%-650) Type A.

DODGE, Darla Jean
Wellington HS; Wellington, TX (11-44) Ann; BC; FHA; Secy, SC; Pres, Sr Cl; Secy, Jr Cl; Rptr, Soph Cl; WW; Most Dependable; Sch Photographer; *W Tex St U; Journ.*

DODGE, David Duane
Strasburg HS; Strasburg, CO (3-28) Ann; BS; NHS; Ed, Sch P; Cpt, Bsbl; Bkbl; Ftbl; Journ A; Q&S A; MVP, Bsbl; *U of Ariz; Acct.*

DODGE, Joni Ione
Jamestown HS; Jamestown, NY (53-517) Ed, Ann; Co-Ch, Lat C; NHS; 4H A; *Grove City Col; Med Tech.*

DODGE, Sally Anne
Ralph C Mahan Reg HS; Orange, MA (30-185) Band; Drama; Orch; Mgr, Bkbl; Hockey; Sftbl; Band; Stu o-t Mo; *Bridgewater St Col; Phys Ed.*

DODIER, Grace Marie
Sacred Heart Acad; Salem, OR (5%-55) Ann; Chldr; Ch, City Conf; NHS; Orch; Co-Ed, Sch P; Span C; Pres, Soph Cl; Elk A; Odd Fellow Fin; Opt A; Yth Leg; Grasp; Hugh O'Brien A; *Seattle U; Pol Sci.*

DODILLET, David Ray
Mt Vernon Township HS; Mt Vernon, IL (10%-400) Secy, 4H; Key C; Bkbl; Ftbl; *U of Ill; Journ.*

DODLEY, Traci Lynn
East HS; Columbus, OH; VP, OEA; All 'A'S' A; *Miami U; Bus Adm.*

DODSON, Donald William
Terre Haute S Vigo HS; Terre Haute, IN (1-625) BS; Dbte Tm; VP, Key C; Math C; NFL; Orch; Spch C; Secy, SC; World Affairs C; COM; Citz A; Math A; Opt A; Spch A; *Journ.*

DODSON, Janet M
Cottage Grove HS; Cottage Grove, OR (37-260) Chor; Hmrm; SC; Ch, Bkbl; Tr; *Bus.*

DODSON, Keith David
Lone Tree Comm HS; Lone Tree, IA (3-43) Band; BS; Chor; Tres, FFA; NHS; VP, Jr Cl; Pres, Soph Cl; Bsbl; Bkbl; Yth Fel; *Agr.*

DODSON, Leslie D Aun
Trinity HS; Euless, TX (100-750) A Cap Choir; Ensm; Golf; Executive Cl Coun; Secy, Sport C; Young Life; Outst Girl, Church Camp; *Baylor U; Ed.*

DODSON, Ricky Joe
Elgin HS; Elgin, OK (34-69) BS; FFA; Var C; Cpt, Bsbl; Cpt, Bkbl; Masonic C; Tm Contribution A, Bkbl & Bsbl; Sportsmanship A, Bsbl; Athlete o-t Yr A; *Cameron U; Bus.*

DODSON, Sharon Rose
Benhaven HS; Olivia, NC; Secy, Band; BC; FHA; Tres, FTA; 4H; Hmrm; Span C; SC; Tres, Sr Cl; COM; 4H A; HCt; Eng, FHA, Piano, A's; *Campbell Col; Elem Ed.*

DODSON, Terri Rhonda
Jackson HS; Jackson, GA; Cpt, Chldr; Drama; Tres, Math C; Tres, Tri-HiY; VP, Soph Cl; Sftbl; Tnns; Tr; HQn; HCt; Best All Around A; *Macon Jr Col.*

DODT, Theresa Elizabeth
Manatee HS; Bradenton, FL (27-520) Chor; Drama; Fr C; Madrigal; Thes; Amer Leg A; Dist & HS Win, Piano; Piano Intermediate Concerts Win; Fla St Mus Teachers Assn; *Pre-Med.*

DOE, Denise Sheree
Mount Vernon HS; Alexandria, VA (10%-611) *William and Mary Col; Biol.*

DOEDE, Diane Mae
Chelan HS; Chelan, WA; Co-Ed, Ann; Chor; VP, NHS; Sch P; SC; Tnns; *Palmer Col; Chiropractic Asst.*

DOERFLINGER, Helen Diane
Benton Co R-1 HS; Cole Camp, MO (1-51) A Cap Choir; Ed, Ann; Band; Chor; FTA; GS; Pres, NHS; Ed, Sch P; Rptr, Sr Cl; VP, Jr Cl; Citz A; Hon Prog; Regent Schol; Type A; Val; *Mid-Amer Nazarene Col; Ed.*

DOERING, Donald Wayne
Lutheran S HS; St Louis, MO (50-150) Hmrm; Pres, Sr Cl; VP, Jr Cl; Bsbl; Bkbl; Ftbl; Pres, Church Yth Fel; Hon Men; League Ftbl; *Oceanography.*

DOERR, Deborah
Conroe HS; Conroe, TX (235-1000) Secy, A Cap Choir; Band; Chor; Fr C; 1st Div, Girls Trio Sea Arama Fest; *Mus.*

DOERR, Judy Kay
Bowdle HS; Bowdle, SD (2-32) A-Ed, Ann; VP, Chor; FTA; GS; SC; Parl, Jr Cl; S-T, Soph Cl; Mgr, Bkbl; Alg A; Citz A; Hon Prog; Journ A; MLS; Sal; Chor A; PA; Lib A; *Northern St Col; Eng.*

DOERS, Jesse Thomas
Ripon Sr HS; Ripon, WI (4-171) BS; Chess C; Tres, Math C; NHS; Order/Arrow; Sch P; Var C; Cr-Ctry; MVP, Wrest; Math A; Order/Arrow A; Rotary A; *St John's Col; Pre-Med.*

DOERSCH, Georgeann
Newbury Park HS; Newbury Park, CA (75-636) Secy, AFS; Drama; MVP, Ensm; Ger C; Hmrm; Citz A; Hon Prog; Most Out; MVP, Piano; Pi Mu Mus A; *Moorpark Jr Col; Commercial Art.*

DOGGETT, Donald Douglas
Olympic HS; Charlotte, NC; Chor; Ski C; Bsbl; Bkbl; Ftbl; Hockey; Tr; Wrest; *U of NC; Archt.*

DOGGETT, Timothy Wayne
Centralia HS; Centralia, IL (126-350) *St Louis Christian Col; Missionary.*

DOHLEN, Bradley Kent
Polo Comm HS; Polo, IL (15-100) Chor; Madrigal; NHS; Var C; Pres, Y-Tns; Mgr, Tr; *Sauk Valley Col; Construction.*

DOHM, Barbara Jean
Dowagiac Union HS; Dowagiac, MI (13-315) Band; Bus C; Ensm; 4H; Hmrm; NHS; Ntl Yth Conf; Orch; SC; COM; 4H A; Hon Prog; JA A; Type A; Yth Fel; Summer Band Schol; *Western Mich U; Bus.*

DOHM, Bettie Gene
New Haven HS; New Haven, IN (11-272) Band; Chor; Ensm; InterClub Coun; NFL; Orch; Spch C; Y-Tns; Spch A; S-T, Bible C; Sunday Sch Teacher; Church Yth Group; Band Merit As; St Church Ambassadors in Missions; Bus Min; 1st Instrum Solo Wind Div; *South-Eastern Bible Col; Bible.*

DOHNER, Wendy Sue
Ephrata Sr HS; Ephrata, PA (44-267) F-Ed, Ann; Band; 4H; Hmrm; NHS; SC; JV, Tr; 4H A; Hon Prog; *U of Bridgeport; Dental Hygiene.*

DOIDGE, Diana
Highland HS; Salt Lake City, UT; Chor; DARGCA; ROTC A; Job's Daughters; *U of Utah; Law.*

DOIDGE, Gregory Thomas
Collegiate Sch; Passaic, NJ (3-23) CYO; Hmrm; NHS; Ski C; Bsbl; Co-Cpt, Bkbl; Ftbl; Alg A; Math A; NEDT; Phys Ed A; HR; WW; *NJ Inst of Tech; Chem Engr.*

DOIDGE, William Wayne
Highland HS; Salt Lake City, UT; Sup Cadet, ROTC; Mayor's Stu Adv Coun; Deacon; *U of Utah; Bus.*

DOIRON, Marie Alice
Livermore Falls HS; Livermore Falls, ME (3-104) Band; Chor; FHA; GS; Math C; Tres, NHS; Ski C; Span C; SC; Var C; Cr-Ctry; Hockey; Sftbl; HQn; *U of Maine; Med Tech.*

DOKE, Carol Lynn
Newcastle HS; Newcastle, OK (8-86) Band; Chor; Ensm; FHA; NHS; Hon Prog; Type A; OSU Academic Achv A; *Okla St U; Computer Sci.*

DOLAGARAY, Nilda
Academia Sagrado Corazon; Santurce, PR (4-65) NHS; ARC; SC; Tres, Sr Cl; *U of Puerto Rico; Bio.*

DOLAN, Dan Martin
Eastview HS; Bartlet, IL (9-1000) K of C; *Clown Trade Sch; Clowning.*

DOLAN, David Patrick
Chaminade Col Prep; St Louis, MO (16-118) Hmrm; NHS; ARC; SC; Ftbl; Golf; Soccer; JV, Swim; Tr; Alg A; Bio A; Hist A; Hon Prog; Math A; NEDT; Phy A; ARC A; Sci A; Type A; *Pre-Med.*

DOLAN, Karen Jean
Bolling Meadows HS; Rolling Meadows, IL (1-612) AFS; NHS; Orch; Span C; Span NHS; Tr; Val; Ill St Schol; *U of Ill; Bio.*

DOLAN, Kevin Campbell
St Pius X HS; Atlanta, GA (11-196) Bus Mgr, Ann; Hmrm; NHS; SC; MVP, Ftbl; Co-Cpt, Tnns; Bkbl; Math A; Most Out; Ntl Sci Found; Phy A; Sci A; *Fla Inst of Tech; Marine Bio.*

DOLAN, Timothy John
St Xavier HS; Cincinnati, OH (99-330) Chor; Bsbl; Tr; Wrest; Hon Prog; NEDT; Tnns Schol; *Pepperdine U; Law.*

DOLBINSKI, Steve Joseph
St Marys Central HS; Bismarck, ND; Ann; Chem C; Bus Mgr, Sch Achieve; Sch P; Ski C; Golf; Photography A; *Audio Engr.*

DOLBY, Jeffrey William
Troy HS; Fullerton, CA; Ger C; Order/Arrow; JV, Swim; COM; Order/Arrow A; Eagle Sct; *Fullerton Col; Television Production.*

DOLGENER, Rebecca Leona
Fredericksburg HS; Fredericksburg, TX (8-180) Chor; Hon Prog; PTA A; UIL A; *Schreiner Jr Col; Law.*

DOLIN, Mark Anthony
Scott HS; Madison, WV; Band; Chor; Pres, Drama; Hmrm; Lat C; Thes; Tnns; All Area, All St, Band; *W Va Wesleyan Col; Mus.*

DOLINAR, Christina Mary
S Park HS; Library, PA (2-163) Pres, FNA; NHS; ARC; Var C; Tnns; NEDT; Sal; *Duquesne U; Phar.*

DOLINISH, Ilona Jeanne
Old Forge HS; Old Forge, PA (3-121) Secy, CYO; Chldr; Secy, FHA; Hmrm; NHS; Ski C; SC; Swim; Chem A; Pres A; *U of Scranton; Pre-Med.*

DOLL, Mary Katherine
Napoleon HS; Napoleon, ND (25%-71) A-Ed, Ann; FFA; FHA; Tr; *Mary Col; Social Work.*

DOLL, Virginia Jane
Center Pub HS; Center, ND (17-36) Pres, CYO; Chor; VP, Drama; 4H; Thes; 4H A; Type A; Best Actress; *Mary Col; Nurs.*

DOLLAR, Billy Joe
Palmetto HS; Palmetto, GA (26-126) Drama; Key C; Pres, SC; Thes; Bkbl; Cr-Ctry; Cpt, Ftbl; Tnns; Cpt, Tr; COM; Hon Prog; *US Military Acad; Law.*

DOLLAR, Lisa Jeannette
SW Miami Sr HS; Miami, FL; Hon Prog; Sch Service C; *Miami Dade Col; Psych.*

DOLLAR, Valarie Ann
Morgan City HS; Morgan City, LA (6-350) Band; Chor; 1st Pl, Spelling A.

DOLLAR, William Alan
Tyrone Area HS; Tyrone, PA (20%-240) FBLA; Hmrm; Cr-Ctry; Tr; Kiwanis A; Exchange Stu to England; Pres Classroom for Yng Am Wsh, DC; *Acct.*

DOLLERSCHELL, Miriam Lillian
Litchfield Sr HS; Litchfield, MN; Chor; FHA; Pres, 4H; Sftbl; 4H A; Sftbl A; *Willmar Area Voc Sch; Secretarial.*

DOLLINS, Jack Daniel
Hartshorne HS; Hartshorne, OK (1-65) A-Ed, Ann; BS; Drama; NHS; Sch P; Spch C; Pres, SC; Thes; Cpt, Bsbl; Bkbl; Alg A; COM; MLS; Spch A; Val; Cpt, FCA; *Okla St U.*

DOLLOFF, Mildred Lisa
Provine HS; Jackson, MS (10%-225) Band; BC; Commercial C; Community Yth Symph; Lit Mag; Mu Alpha Theta; NHS; Bkbl; Yth Fel; VP, UMYF; Jr Historical Soc; Secy, Yth Coun; Citz Seminar; Ed, Yth Newspaper; 1st C GScts; Computer Sci Workshop; *Hinds Co Jr Col; Med Tech.*

DOLLOFF, Teresa Mae
Northwood-Kensett HS; Northwood, IA; Chldr; Chor; Drama; Fr C; 4H; Golf; 4H A; *NIACC; Nurs.*

DOLLOFF, Vicki Sue
Ponder HS; Ponder, TX (1-18) FHA; *Cook Co Col; Nurs.*

DOLPH, DeMarise Lorraine
Havre HS; Havre, MT (23-230) Pres, A Cap Choir; Pres, Chor; Ensm; Fr C; GS; Hmrm; NHS; SC; COM; Hist A; Co-Cpt, Pep C; Ntl Mus A; *Carroll Col; Sociology.*

DOLPH, Kurt Allen
Wakefield HS; Wakefield, NE (8-57) Band; Chor; NHS; Orch; SC; Pres, Jr Cl; Ftbl; Co-Cpt, Wrest; Amer Leg A; Hon Prog; Regent Schol; ROTC A; David Schol; *U of Nebr; Engr.*

DOMAN, Deborah Ann
Neshaminy Maple Point HS; Langhorne, PA (12-450) Hmrm; K of C; Ski C; SC.

DOMANGUE, Warren Joseph Jr
W Jefferson HS; Harvey, LA (15%-620) JETS; Bsbl; Tnns; Bio A; COM; Hon Prog; ROTC A; Sci A; Air Force ROTC Ldrship Sch; Nom, US Air Force, Nav & Mil Acads; *Tulane U; Elec Engr.*

DOMBLESKY, Bernard Edward Jr
Southmoreland Sr HS; Alverton, PA (25-269) Chess C; Math C; NHS; Ski C.

DOMBLESKY, Joseph Paul
Southmoreland Sr HS; Alverton, PA (18-291) Fr C; FFA; Arch; Co Spelling Bee Champ; *Penn St U; Agr.*

DOMBROSKY, Adam John
Marian Cath HS; Tamaqua, PA (49-177) Chess C; Order/Arrow; Bsbl; Cpt, Bkbl; Cr-Ctry; *Scranton U; Computer Sci.*

DOMERESE, Sandra Elaine
Kearsley HS; Flint, MI (63-407) A Cap Choir; Band; Pres, Chor; Ensm; NHS; Hon Prog; *Cedarville Col; Bus Adm.*

DOMINICK, Michael Douglas
Washington HS; Massillon, OH (142-505) A Cap Choir; Chor; Span C; *Stark Tech Col; Drafting.*

DOMINIONI, Dennis Neal
Bishop Byrne HS; Memphis, TN (6-183) A-Ed, Ann; Dbte Tm; Hmrm; NHS; Sch P; Alg A; COM; Citz A; NEDT; Opt A; Spch A; Span, Attendance, Conduct, A's; *Memphis St U; Engr.*

DOMINY, Eddie LeNeve
E Laurens HS; Dublin, GA (3-80) Ed, Ann; Pres, BC; VP, FHA; Rptr, Sr Cl; Mgr, Bkbl; B Crocker A; COM; HQn.

DOMINY, Karen Kay
Centerville HS; Centerville, TX (10-40) Ann; S-T, Band; Chldr; Ensm; NHS; Bkbl; Tr; Hon Prog.

DOMINY, Michael D
Superior HS; Superior, NE (22-80) Ann; Key C; Rptr, Sch P; Thes; Var C; Ftbl; Journ A; Q&S A; Kim Squires Mem Art Schol; Scarlet Masque A; *Kearney St U; Lib Arts.*

DOMM, Jason Wayne
Castleberry HS; Fort Worth, TX (10%-230) A Cap Choir; Drama; Hmrm; NHS; A-Ed, Sch P; SC; Thes; Hon Prog; Journ A; Spch A; Yth Fel; Witnessing For Christ; 4th Pl, St Sports Photography; All Star Cast, Contest Play; *Tex A&M U; Journ.*

DOMOKOS, Judith Ann
Thompson HS; Alabaster, AL (1%-240) Chor; Ensm; Hmrm; Model UN; NHS; Orch; Y-Tns; JV, Hockey; Math A; NHS A; A HR A; *Math.*

DOMONKOS, Julie Ann
Kinnelon HS; Kinnelon, NJ; Chor; Span C; Span NHS; Soccer; JV, Tr; High HR.

DONAHAY, Joseph Glynn
Lake Placid HS; Lake Placid, FL (5-165) VP, Band; BS; CYO; Drama; Pres, Key C; VP, NHS; Wrest; Congressional Intern; *U of Fla; Criminology.*

DONAHUE, Connie Marie
Brewster Pub Sch 513; Brewster, MN; Band; Chor; Ensm; FHA; Cpt, Mjrte; Sch P; Spch C; Secy, Sr Cl; Tres, Soph Cl; Bkbl; Hon Prog; Spch A; *Mankato Commercial Col; Med Secy.*

DONAHUE, Karen Elizabeth
Chester HS; Chester, PA (12-673) ARC; Hon Prog.

DONALD, Cassandra Anita
R H Watkins HS; Laurel, MS; FHA; *Jones Co Jr Col; Elem Ed.*

DONALD, Cynthia Marie
Walter L Cohen HS; New Orleans, LA; FBLA; Hmrm; SC; *U of New Orleans; Med Tech.*

DONALD, Paulettee Diane
Medina HS; Medina, TN (1-27) F-Ed, Ann; BC; S-T, Jr Cl; *U of Tenn; Algebra.*

DONALDSON, Deborah Denise
John Adams HS; Cleveland, OH; Chor; Hmrm; NHS; Orch; SC; COM; Citz A; HCt; Hon Prog; Math A; Most Out; *Kent St U; Med.*

DONALDSON, Diane Louise
Cambridge Sr HS; Cambridge, MN (56-276) Band; Chor; Ensm; 4H; Secy, Jr Cl; Cr-Ctry; *Anoka Voc-Tech Inst; Med Secy.*

DONALDSON, Donette Louise
Lenox Comm HS; Lenox, IA (10%-45) Ann; Chor; Drama; Spch C; Yth Fel.

DONALDSON, Doris Felicia
Geneva Comm HS; Geneva, IL (50-202) Chor; Drama; Ensm; FTA; Orch; JV, Tr; Hon Prog; Art.

DONALDSON, Evelyn Devonne
N Mecklenburg HS; Huntersville, NC (190-430) Fr C; FHA; JA A; DECA C; VP, Fashion Merch; Art A; Graphic C; *Barber Scotia Col; Bus Adm.*

DONALDSON, Geraldine
Rayen HS; Youngstown, OH; Key C; SC; Library A; *Youngstown Col; Bus.*

DONALDSON, Janet Susan
Chilhowee Acad; Seymour, TN (2-48) Ed, Ann; VP, BC; GS; SC; Mgr, Bkbl; DARGCA; Hist A; Sal; Health, Bible, A's; Bsbl Scorekeeper; Ftbl Statistician; *Tenn Tech U; Psych.*

DONALDSON, John Gilbert
Calvary Baptist HS; Savannah, GA (13-69) AFS; BC; Drama; Fr C; Sch P; Tnns; COM; DARGCA; Special Faculty Recognition A.

DONALDSON, Megan Joline
Marion HS; Marion, IN (140-700) Drama; Fr C; Forestry.

DONALDSON, Patricia Denise
Geneva Comm HS; Geneva, IL (15-224) Orch; Span C; Art.

DONALDSON, Theo DeLoach
W A Berry HS; Birmingham, AL (13-358) Fr C; French NHS; Key C; NHS; ARC; JV, Ftbl; Hon Prog; ROTC A; Star Student; Sunday Sch Teacher; Church Service Committee; Mitchell A; *Auburn U; Aerospace Engr.*

DONAUGH, DeAnn DeLee
Heath HS; Heath, OH (14-159) F-Ed, Ann; Pres, Band; Pres, Chor; Drama; FNA; Madrigal; Orch; Spch C; Thes; Yth Fel; WW; Otterbein-Wesley Schol; *Otterbein Col; Mus.*

DONAUGH, Deneen
Heath HS; Heath, OH (1-174) Cpt, Chldr; Chor; Drama; Hmrm; Madrigal; Secy, SC; Yth Fel; Vlbl; *Capital U; Phys Therapy.*

DONEGAN, Eileen
James Island HS; Charleston, SC (21-223) Cpt, Chldr; Secy, Fr C; FBLA; Hmrm; Math C; NHS; SC; Hon Prog; Math A; Y-C; 1st Cl Sct; GSct; Pep C; GSct o-t Yr; *Col of Charleston; Computer Technology.*

DONELSON, Kathleen
Silsbee HS; Silsbee, TX (5-260) Band; Dbte Tm; Drama; JETS; Tres, Lat C; NHS; Rainbow; F-Ed, Sch P; Spch C; SC; Thes; Golf; Citz A; Journ A; Opt A; Spch A; GSct; Dogwood Festival Duchess; 2nd, St Feature Writing; Miss Tex United Teenager; Gifted Stu Schol; Twirling Medal; *Tex A&M U; Engr.*

DONEY, Timothy John
Fremont HS; Fremont, MI (9-247) Secy, Band; BS; Dbte Tm; NHS; Span C; Var C; Bsbl; Golf; Interlochen Ntl Mus; Magna Cum Laude; Spch A; Blue Lake Fine Arts Camp Mus A; 1st Cl A, Drum Major Comp; 3rd, St Solo & Ensm; John Philip Sousa A; *U of Mich; Pre-Med.*

DONG, Melissa Jean
C K McClatchy HS; Sacramento, CA (48-515) Tres, Ger C; Hmrm; Math C; Sci C; SC; Tres, Jr Cl; Amer Leg A; Type A; Yth Fel; *Sacramento St Col; Bus.*

DONLEY, Cynthia Jean
Cleveland Heights HS; Cleveland Heights, OH (38-860) A Cap Choir; Chor; Drama; Ensm; Hmrm; Span C; Y-Tns; COM; Citz A; Hon Prog; Yth Fel; Bd of Deacons; Math Adv Placement; *Psych.*

DONLEY, Tammy Jo
Westmont Hilltop HS; Johnstown, PA (40-230) Co-Cpt, Chldr; Chor; NHS; Swim; Hon Prog; WW; *W Va U; Child Psych.*

DONNALLY, David Paul
John I Leonerd HS; Lakeworth, FL (40-400) Chor; Ensm; NHS; Superior, Chor; Lettered, Chor; Outst Service, Chor; *Evangelical Bible Col; Theology.*

DONNAN, Lisi Anne
Highland HS; Salt Lake City, UT (25-450) Chor; Dbte Tm; Fr C; NFL; Spch C; COM; Kiwanis A; *Foreign Relations.*

DONNAN, Robert Mack
Berea HS; Greenville, SC; Chor; Mus.

DONNEAUD, Lisa Marie
Post Falls HS; Post Falls, ID (17-154) Chldr; Hmrm; SC; Tr; Powderpuff; Drill Tm; Most Daring; Prom Qn; Pep C; GAA; N Idaho Col; Nurs.

DONNELLY, James Warren
Lindbergh HS; St Louis, MO (20-1000) NHS; Pre-Med.

DONNELLY, Kevin Terrence
St Bede Acad; Peru, IL (27-130) Fin, JETS; Co-Ch, SC; Ftbl; Co-Cpt, Tnns; Amer Leg A; Sci A; Outst, St Sci Fair; Air Force Sci A; Navy Sci A; Army Sci A; Westinghouse St Talent Search; JETS Engr A; U of Ill; Pre-Med.

DONNELLY, Kim Joanne
Custer HS; Milwaukee, WI; A Cap Choir; Chor; 4H; Ski C; Sftbl; JV, Swim; 4H A.

DONNELLY, Linda Kathleen
Barrington HS; Barrington, IL; Lat C; NHS; Orch.

DONNELLY, Margaret Ann
Beaufort Acad; Beaufort, SC (1-42) Pres, CYO; Tres, NHS; Tres, SC; Pres, Jr Cl; Hon Prog; Headmasters A; Sociology.

DONNELLY, Mary Lou
Jefferson City HS; Jefferson City, MO (125-550) A Cap Choir; AFS; Chor; Drama; ARC; Sch P; SC; Pres, Thes; God & Country A; Drama A; SW Mo St U; Spch Therapy.

DONNELLY, Pamela Maureen
Pearl HS; Nashville, TN; U of Tenn; Nurs.

DONNELLY, Scott John
Rockville HS; Vernon, CT (50-522) FFA; 4H; Col of DuPage; Horticulture.

DONNER, Keith Allen
Morristown HS; Morristown, IN (6-65) Lat C; SC; Var C; Tr; Sci A; Yth Fel; Indiana Central Col; Math.

DONOFRIO, Michelle
Lauralton Hall HS; Milford, CT (6-93) Drama; NHS; Ski C; Co-Cpt, Swim; WW; Amer Interntl Col; Special Ed.

DONOHOE, Susan Nadine
Pineville HS; Pineville, LA (45-239) Bus Mgr, Ann; Band; Fr C; InterClub Coun; Lit Mag; Sch P; Pres, Y-Tns; Co-Cpt, Bkbl; Sftbl; WW; La Tech U; Med Tech.

DONOHUE, Amy Beth
James Madison HS; Milwaukee, WI; Chor; Fr C; Lit Mag; Math C; Ski C; JV, Tr; COM; Citz A; Hon Prog; Sch Service A; U of Wis.

DONOHUE, Kathryn Mary
James Madison HS; Milwaukee, WI (35-875) Fr C; NHS; A-Ed, Sch P; Hon Prog; Q&S A; U of Wis; Journ.

DONOHUE, Malachy Gerard
Chaminade HS; St Louis, MO (3-126) NHS; Pres, SC; MVP, Ftbl; MVP, Tr; Bio A; Hist A; Hon Prog; NEDT; Spch A; Sports-Ed, Sch Paper; Religion A; HR; Brown U; Biological Sci.

DONOVAN, Dawn Marie
Grandview Sr HS; Grandview, MO (45-459) A-Ed, Ann; NHS; A-Ed, Sch P; Pres, SC; Bkbl; Tr; Regent Schol; FCA; Fr C; Photo C; Journ A; Q & S; Sph A; Stu Advisory Board; Vlbl; Augustana Col; Public Relations.

DONOVAN, Kevin Charles
Archmere Acad; Claymont, DE; BS; CYO; NHS; Span NHS; SC; Amer Leg A; St Joseph's Col; Hist.

DONOVAN, Teri Lynn
Ben Davis HS; Indianapolis, IN (10-905) A Cap Choir; Tnns; S-T, FCA; Pres, Soultns; Tres, Omegans; Vlbl; Most Responsible Omegan A; Puts Christ First A; Med.

DONSELAR, Matthew Lee
Spring Lake HS; Spring Lake, MI (106-235) Band; Chor; Madrigal; Sch P; Thes; Bsbl; Mgr, Swim; Band Schol.

DOOLEY, Paula Delia
Susquehanna Comm Sch; Susquehanna, PA; Chor; Drama; Rptr, Sch P; Moravian Col; Pol Sci.

DOOLEY, Teresa Lynn
Hamburg Comm HS; Hamburg, IA (4-34) Ann; Band; Cpt, Chldr; Pres, FHA; Mjrte; NHS; Sch P; VP, SC; Pres, Jr Cl; Pres, Soph Cl; Tr; HQn; Hon Prog; Iowa St U; Med Technology.

DOOLIN, William Ray
Williamsburg City Sch; Williamsburg, KY (10-60) BC; Cpt, Dbte Tm; Drama; Spch C; Ftbl; Spch A; The Col of Idaho; Sci.

DOOLING, Timothy James
Claremont HS; Claremont, CA (33%-441) Key C; Var C; Pres, Sr Cl; Bsbl; HCt; Kiwanis A; Powder Puff Kg; Kg Grub Court; FCA A; U of Calif; Med.

DOOLITTLE,
Charles Edward Jr
Oxnard HS; Oxnard, CA; Bsbl; Bkbl; Cpt, Ftbl; Tr; Coaches A; Ventura Col; Black Stu.

DOOLITTLE, Ronald Scott
W Ottawa HS; Holland, MI (50-327) Order/ Arrow; Bkbl; Tr; Yth Fel; U of Mich; Archt.

DOONAN, Laura Ann
Batavia HS; Batavia, IL (1-224) Band; Ensm; Pres, 4H; Lat C; Math C; Mod Mus Mas; Orch; 4H A; Hon Prog; Math A; St Lat Contest; Acct.

DORASKI, Susan Christine
Mount Mercy Acad; Buffalo, NY (9-217) F-Ed, Ann; NHS; Secy, Sftbl; Hon Prog; Niagara U; Nurs.

DORCHAK, James Michael
Columbus HS; Columbus, GA (10%-367) CYO; Hmrm; InterClub Coun; Pres, Key C; Math C; Mu Alpha Theta; NHS; Span C; Var C; Tres, Jr Cl; Pres, Soph Cl; Bsbl; Ftbl; Hon Prog; Outst Young Amer; U of Ga; Pre-Dentistry.

DORCHAK, John David
Columbus HS; Columbus, GA (10%-367) CYO; Key C; VP, Math C; VP, Mu Alpha Theta; NHS; Span C; VP, Sr Cl; Co-Cpt, Ftbl; Amer Leg A; COM; Hon Prog; Most Out; MVP, Acad A, Ftbl; Outst Young Amer; U of Ga; Pre-Med.

DORE, Teresa Ann
Blanchet HS; Seattle, WA (5-308) Chor; NHS; JV, Sftbl; JV, Tr; Dean's List.

DORES, Graca Maria
MacDuffie Sch for Girls; Springfield, MA; Chor; Lit Mag; Rptr, Sch P; SC.

DOREY, Gary Lee
De Anza HS; Richmond, CA (67-391) AFS; Bus Mgr, Ann; BS; Drama; Fr C; Hmrm; NHS; Sch Achieve Tm; Ed, Sch P; Spch C; SC; Pres, Jr Cl; Cr-Ctry; JV, Ftbl; Golf; Tnns; Tr; Amer Leg A; CSF; COM; Cl Fav; Most Out; Y-Tns; NHS; Sch 'A', Sports C; WW; Pres, Ldrship C; Cert of Achv; Parl, Young Life; Athlete o-t Yr; Stu Sen; Calif St U-Sacramento; Pol Sci.

DORGAN, Darlene Marie
St Mary's Regional HS; Lynn, MA (1-117) Chldr; Hmrm; NHS; Sch P; Tres, SC; Tr; Alg A; Beauty; Bio A; COM; Cl Fav; God & Country A; Hist A; Hon Prog; K of C A; Math A; Sci A; Star Student; Merrimack Col; Pre-Law.

DORIAN, James Peter
Lower Merion HS; Aromore, PA (69-465) Hmrm; Order/Arrow; Span C; JV, Bsbl; Hon Prog; Order/ Arrow A; Type A; Yth Fel; Eagle Sct; Jr Vol A, Hospital; Hon A's; Pa St U; Engr.

DORIAN, Paul Bernard
Lower Merion HS; Ardmore, PA (68-465) Ger C; Order/Arrow; Bsbl; Hon Prog; Order/Arrow A; Yth Fel; Eagle Sct; Jr Vol A, Hospital; HR; Pa St U; Meteorology.

DORMAN, John Eubank
Maine Township HS S; Park Ridge, IL (40%-900) Band; Var C; Ftbl; Tnns; Cpt, Wrest; Hon Prog; MVP, Wrest; Tarkio Col; Bus.

DORMAN, Paul Thompson
Lockport Township HS; Lockport, IL (74-600) Band; Joliet Jr Col; Chem.

DORMAN, Rebecca Jean
Canyon HS; Canyon, TX; Band; French NHS; Band Lib; 1st Chair of Amer; Stephen F Austin St U; Pre-Med.

DORMINEY, Bruce Gresham
Irwin Co HS; Ocilla, GA; BC; Dbte Tm; Thes; Tnns; COM; Hon Prog; U of Ga.

DORN, David Edward
Warren Area HS; Warren, PA (20%-400) Band; NHS; Orch; Span C; COM; Citz A; Hon Prog; Board of Directors, Leo C; Hist C; US Power Squadron A; Church Choir; Hon News Carrier A; Chem Engr.

DORN, Julia May
Millburn HS; Millburn, NJ (33%-345) Chor; Sci C; Jr Vol.

DORN, Mariellen Arlene
Beatrice Sr HS; Beatrice, NE (101-239) Y-Tns; COM; Tres, Secy, Luther League; Sunday Sch Teacher; HR; Shorthand A's.

DORN, Ruth
Millburn HS; Millburn, NJ (10%-345) Co-Ed, Sch P; Sci C; NEDT; Philosophical Soc; Tn Arts Festival; U o-t South.

DORNBRACK, Julie Ann
Merrill Sr HS; Merrill, WI (3-324) A Cap Choir; Ed, Ann; Chor; NFL; COM; Journ A; NMS; Spch A; Pom Pon Girls; Optimist Hon; U of Wis; Bus.

DORNBUSH, Calvin Wayne
Pollock Ind HS; Pollock, SD (1-39) BS; FFA; Secy, 4H; Sci C; Cpt, Sftbl; Bio A; Hon Prog; Type A; VP, Sftbl; Sci Sampler A; Pres, Reform Christian Church Group; SD St U; Sci.

DOROTHY, Connie Jane
Van Buren Comm HS; Keosauqua, IA (16-81) 4H; NHS; F-Ed, Sch P; Var C; VP, Sr Cl; Cpt, Bkbl; Golf; Sftbl; Tr; Amer Leg A; Citz A; Hon Prog; Rotary A; FCA; Indian Hills Comm Col; Counseling.

DORR, Bernadette Wilahmeniah
Philadelphia HS For Girls; Philadelphia, PA; Hmrm; Star Student; Psych.

DORR, David William
Harry A Burke HS; Omaha, NE (190-675) Order/ Arrow; Pres Schol, Wesleyan; Nebr Wesleyan Col; Chem.

DORR, Wendy Susan
Marysville-Pilchuck HS; Marysville, WA (16-390) A Cap Choir; Chor; Ensm; Fin, GS; NHS; Ski C; Span C; Ftbl; JV, Swim; JV, Tr; University of Wash; Med Therapy.

DORRIS, Clay Stephen
Plano Sr HS; Plano, TX; JV, Cr-Ctry; JV, Ftbl; Mgr, Soccer; JV, Tr; Theology.

DORRIS, Renee Lynn
Alan B Shepard HS; Alsip, IL (131-667) Spch C; Northwest Bible Col; Christian Ed.

DORSETT, Jan Anita
Fairfield HS; Fairfield, AL; Band; Secy, BC; Chor; Ensm; Y-Tns; HCt; Samford U; Phar.

DORSEY, Amelia Gaye
Sherman HS; Sherman, TX (1-404) A Cap Choir; Semi-Fin, GS; Lat C; Madrigal; Mu Alpha Theta; Secy, NHS; Tres, Span C; Citz A; Magna Cum Laude; Trustee's Merit Schol; Mus Theory Medals; 2nd Pl, St Jr Classical Lge Conv; Austin Col; Math.

DORSEY, Barbara Ann
Howard Career Center; Wilmington, DE (10%-152) A Cap Choir; Band; Chor; NHS; Ed, Sch P; Up Bound; Bio A; Hist A; Secy, VICA; Howard U; Mass Media.

DORSEY, Daniel Lee
Arlington HS; Riverside, CA; Chor; Drama; Bsbl; Bkbl; Ftbl; Cpt, Tr; UCR at Berkley; Data Processing.

DORSEY, Debra Ann
Weir Attendance Center; Weir, MS (1-54) BC; Chor; Sch P; Alg A; Bio A; COM; Chem A; Hist A; HCt; JA A; Miss St U; Acct.

DORSEY, Sheila Yvette
Pierre Sammuel DuPont HS; Wilmington, De; All Amer Yh; Band; Drama; Ensm; Pres, FTA; Bus Mgr, GS; Hmrm; NHS; Bus Mgr, Sch P; St Stu Congress; SC; Secy, Soph Cl; Amer Leg A; Beauty; Delta Sigma Theta A; HCt; JA A; Yth Fel; Morris Brown Col; Special Ed.

DORSHER, Mary Ann
Marillac HS; Northfield, IL (14-222) Drama; InterClub Coun; Math C; NHS; Orch; Ed, Sch P; COM; Hon Prog; Journ A; SC; Math Tutor A; U of Ill; Econ.

DORSI, Mary Victoria
West Haven HS; W Haven, CT (1-600) Ed, Ann; S-T, CYO; GS; Hmrm; Lit Mag; Pres, NHS; Sci C; Tres, Soph Cl; COM; Citz A; DARGCA; Elk A; H of F; Hist A; Hon Prog; MLS; Most Out; NEDT; PTA A; St Scholar; Val; Yth Foundation; Yth Foundation A; Most Helpful; Tnager o-t Yr; Comm Mental Health Bd; *Wesleyan U; Humanities.*

DORT, Timothy Clare
Guysborough Municipal High; Guysborough, CANADA; Chem C; Leo C; Physics A; *Dalhousie Col.*

DORTCH, Brenda
Ben C Rain HS; Mobile, AL; Bkbl; Sftbl.

DORWORTH, Caroline Adair
Montgomery Blair HS; Silver Spring, MD (33%-450) VP, Jobs Daughters; Alg A; *Human Services.*

DOSAL, Paul Jaime
Hillsborough HS; Tampa, FL (5%-600) Band; Hmrm; Mu Alpha Theta; SC; Golf; Soccer; Wrest; MLS; *Bus Adm.*

DOSBIBER, Dave Alan
Medina Sr HS; Medina, OH; Band; Ch, Hmrm; Key C; Ntl Teachers Coun; MVP, Tnns; Tr; COM; Air Traffic Sch; *Aviation.*

DOSS, David Lee
Monett HS; Monett, MO (50%-128) Bkbl; Ftbl; Tnns; Amer Leg A; Alt, BS; *Woodworking.*

DOSS, David Randolph
Salem Baptist Day Sch; Winston-Salem, NC (1-28) Co-Ed, Ann; Pres, Yth Group; Top Schol A; *U of NC at Chapel Hill; Chem.*

DOSSEY, Mary Jane
Shawnee HS; Shawnee, OK (100-350) FHA.

DOSTAL, Margaret Elise
Eagle Mountain HS; Eagle Mountain, CA (3-50) F-Ed, Ann; Band; FHA; NHS; Bus Mgr, Sch P; SC; Sftbl; CSF; Hist A; HQn; Sr Cl Rep; *Col o-t Desert; Elem Ed.*

DOSTERHOUSE, Dawn Renae
Thornapple Kellogg HS; Middleville, MI; Sftbl; Tnns; *Shiek Col; Cosmetology.*

DOSZAK, Gregory Alan
Providence HS; New Lenox, IL (6-160) Dbte Tm; Var C; Golf; Wrest; Type A; Marine Corp PE Medal; Art A; *Lewis U; Bus Adm.*

DOTRAY, Saundra Lynn
Lincoln-Way Comm HS; New Lenox, IL (200-545) Chor; Ch, Hmrm; Rainbow; Spch C; Secy, Y-Tns; Hon Prog; Spch A; Section Ldr, Chor; *Joliet Jr Col; Special Ed.*

DOTSON, Billy Joe
Woodford Co HS; Versailles, KY; Drama; 4H; InterClub Coun; Pres, Key C; Ch, Order/Arrow; ARC; Span C; Mgr, Bkbl; Mgr, Tr; Mgr, Wrest; Citz A; God & Country A; 4H A; IA A; Kiwanis A; Order/Arrow A; ARC A; Eagle Sct; *Asbury Seminary; Ministry.*

DOTSON, Brian Robert
Enterprise HS; Enterprise, AL (14-396) Fr C; Key C; NHS; JV, Tnns; *Auburn U; Elec Engr.*

DOTSON, David Richard
S R Butler HS; Huntsville, AL; Key C; Order/Arrow; Order/Arrow A; Eagle Sct; *U of Ala; Engr.*

DOTSON, Debra Ann
Northwood Sr HS; Shreveport, LA; Drama; Hmrm; Rptr, Span C; Sftbl; Type A; Yth Fel; VP, Christian Stu Union; Comm Organ for Drug Abuse Control; *Vo Tech Col; Secy.*

DOTSON, Jacqueline Meva
Riverside HS; Milwaukee, WI; Drama; *Clark Col; Drama.*

DOTSON, Jayne
Lake Charles HS; Lake Charles, LA (50-355) Tri-HiY; Citz A; Hon Prog; Yth Fel; DAR Civics, DAR Amer Hist, A's; Yrbk Staff, A; *McNeese St U; Nurs.*

DOTSON, Jeffrey Alan
Groves HS; Garden City, GA (40%-300) Chor; Fr C; Hmrm; SC; Citz A; PA; *Med Col of Ga; Med.*

DOTTLEY, Timothy Alan
La Porte HS; La Porte, TX; A Cap Choir; Chor; Dbte Tm; Ensm; Madrigal; Math C; NHS; Golf; Alg A; Bio A; Math A; Pres A; Sci A; Yth Fel; Distinguished HR; Ensm A; Outst Eng Stu; Outst Singer; *Sci.*

DOTY, Andrew Steven
St Thomas More Sch; Colchester, CT (6-30) Chem C; Chess C; Dbte Tm; Sch P; SC; Cr-Ctry; St Scholar; *Dartmouth Col; Econ.*

DOTY, Debra Jean
Riverdale HS; Ft Myers, FL; Chor; SC; Hon Prog; 1st Pl, Solo Comp; Superior, Vocal Rating; Pres, Marantha C; *Mus.*

DOTY, Heather Dawn
Westbury Sr HS; Houston, TX (70-614) Ann; Chor; Ensm; Hmrm; Madrigal; VP, SC; Beauty; Cl Fav; HCt; Swtht; WW; Choir Off; Ntl Piano Guild; *Okla Baptist Col; Mus.*

DOTY, Kevin Dale
Harlingen HS; Harlingen, TX; Tres, 4H; Key C; Mgr, Bkbl; Mgr, Tr; 4H A; DECA A; *Tex U; Archt.*

DOTY, Kimberly Ann
Cleburne HS; Cleburne, TX (50%-280) A Cap Choir; Chor; FHA; Span C; *Harding Col; Spch Therapy.*

DOTZENROD, Laurie Jean
Wyndmere HS; Wyndmere, ND (11-50) A-Ed, Ann; Band; Chor; Drama; Madrigal; Mjrte; S-T, NHS; Sch P; Spch C; S-T, SC; Dist Pres, FHA; All St Choir; *U of ND; Journ.*

DOUBLIN, Deborah Lynn
Carroll HS; Monroe, LA; F-Ed, Ann; FBLA; Tr; Ath A; *NE La U; Journ.*

DOUCET, Catherine
Church Point HS; Church Point, LA; BC; Rptr, CYO; Pres, FBLA; FHA; NHS; Sch P; Spch A; Service A, CCD; Hon Men, Essay Contest; *USL; Secondary Ed.*

DOUCET, Shane James
St Martin Sr HS; St Martinville, LA; Fr C; 4H; Hmrm; Sch P; 4H A.

DOUCETTE, Carl Joseph
Tignish HS; Tignish, CANADA (2-16) ARC; *Dalhousie Col; Oceanography.*

DOUCETTE, Emily Marie
Duncan MacMillan HS; Sheet Harbour, CANADA (5-24) Chess C; Hmrm; Rptr, Sch P; Bio A; Hist A; Sci A; Acad Excel; *Acadia U; Fr.*

DOUCETTE, Richard Anthony
St Dominic Regional HS; Lewiston, ME (4-78) Secy, CYO; FTA; Tres, Key C; Pres, NHS; Rptr, Sch P; Sodality; COM; Chem A; Hon Prog; Sci A; Type A; WW; Extra-Curricular Activity Trophy; *Cath U of Amer; Bus.*

DOUD, Thomas Myles
Victoria HS; Victoria, TX (16-548) Pres, Key C; VP, NHS; Magna Cum Laude; *SW Col; Med.*

DOUGAN, Stacey Lee
Fremont Pub HS; Fremont, MI (11-247) Community Yth Symph; Madrigal; NHS; Orch; SC; Var C; Pres, Sr Cl; Pres, Jr Cl; Pres, Soph Cl; Bkbl; DARGCA; HCt; Magna Cum Laude; Type A; Ntl Sch Orch Assn A; *Grand Valley St Col; Pub Adm.*

DOUGHERTY, Brenda Kay
Bakersfield R-4 HS; Bakersfield, MO; Pres, 4H; NHS; Rptr, Soph Cl; 4H A; *Secy.*

DOUGHERTY, Catherine Grace
Our Lady of Good Counsel HS; Newark, NJ (12-77) Co-Cpt, Chldr; Drama; Pres, FBLA; Parl, Hmrm; NHS; Rptr, Sch P; Ski C; Pres, SC; Pres, Sr Cl; Pres, Jr Cl; Bkbl; Hon Prog; Type A; *Kean Col; Elem Ed.*

DOUGHERTY, Christine Marie
Tioga Center Christian Sch; Tioga Center, NY (1-8) Ann; Band; Chor; SC; Co-Cpt, Bkbl; Cr-Ctry; Sftbl; Sch Plays; Home Ec A; Most Cooperative; *Social Work.*

DOUGHERTY, Douglas Micheal
El Cerrito HS; El Cerrito, CA (150-520) Model UN; VP, Sr Cl; JV, Soccer; Tnns; *Humboldt St U; Forestry.*

DOUGHERTY, Jennifer Ann
John Jay Sr HS; Hopewell Junction, NY (3-570) A Cap Choir; VP, Band; Chor; Ensm; Lat C; NHS; Orch; Hon Prog; NMS; Harvey Lederstein Mem Schol; All St Conf; Mus Ed Ntl Conf; Saratoga Sch of Orch Stu Schol; *St U of NY; Mus Ed.*

DOUGHERTY, Kenneth Thomas
Killian HS; Miami, FL (7-127) Chor; 4H; Citz A; Hon Prog; Drama A; Hons Choir; Reading A; *Miami Dade Col; Auto-Mech.*

DOUGHERTY, Michelle Ann
Leominster HS; Leominster, MA (55-200) Band; Orch; Tnns; All-Amer Hall of Fame; Band Hon; Mus Appreciation A.

DOUGHTERY, Laura
Odenton HS; Odenton, MD (15-300) A Cap Choir; Chldr; Chess C; Dbte Tm; 4H; HiY; Lat C; Math C; Orch; Bkbl; Cr-Ctry; Sftbl; Swim; Tnns; *Secy.*

DOUGHTY, John Robert Jr
Marina HS; Huntington Beach, CA (57-830) Bsbl; Bkbl; CSF; Yth Fel; Art A; Ntl Jr Hon Soc; *Art.*

DOUGLAS, Alisa Carlyn
Fremont HS; Oakland, CA; *UCLA; Mus.*

DOUGLAS, Anne Elizabeth
Milton Sr HS; Milton, WI (9-188) Fr C; FHA; 4H; Co-Cpt, Math C; NHS; 4H A; Hon Prog; *U-W Rock Col; Math.*

DOUGLAS, Christopher Lynn
Clyde Rural HS; Clyde, KS (5-30) Bsbl; JV, Bkbl; Ftbl; Golf; Sacristan; Type A.

DOUGLAS, Dennis Duane
Huffman HS; Birmingham, AL; Band; Chem C; Hmrm; Golf; Tnns; *U of Ala; Engr.*

DOUGLAS, Donald Ray II
W Mecklenburg HS; Charlotte, NC (5%-352) VP, Band; NHS; Bsbl; Bkbl; Ftbl; Sftbl; Sci A; Yth Fel; Stage Band; Sportsmanship A; Jr Marshall; Page, St House of Rep.

DOUGLAS, Elizabeth Ann
Allegany HS; Cumberland, MD (10-300) Pres, AFS; Drama; NHS; Span NHS; Tri-HiY; NEDT; Citizen of Tomorrow A; *Hist.*

DOUGLAS, Joyce Faye
Quitman HS; Quitman, MS (25%-210) Bus C; Chldr; Rptr, FHA; Secy, 4H; Ch, Hmrm; Spch C; Pres, SC; Secy, Y-Tns; COM; Hon Prog; Most Out; Type A; Most Versatile, News Staff; Encounter; *Miss St U.*

DOUGLAS, Karen Lanelle
John Jay HS; San Antonio, TX (11-622) A-Ed, Ann; Pres, Chor; Fr C; Lit Mag; Madrigal; Mu Alpha Theta; NHS; SC; COM; Hist A; Hon Prog; *Baylor U; Eng.*

DOUGLAS, Kevin James
Marion Harding HS; Marion, OH (360-466) Tres, Bus C; Chor; Demolay; JV, Ftbl; Tr; Wrest; *Ohio St U; Acct.*

DOUGLAS, Margaret Kathryn
Thomson HS; Thomson, GA (10%-300) BC; Chldr; Chor; Drama; FHA; 4H; Span C; Gov Honor Prog; Hist A; ARC A; *U of Ga; Law.*

DOUGLAS, Nita Louise
Briarcrest Baptist HS; Memphis, TN (2-322) GS; Hmrm; VP, Lat C; Mu Alpha Theta; Pres, NHS; Alg A; COM; Cl Fav; H of F; Hon Prog; Math A; MLS; Sal; Summa Cum Laude; Lat A; *Vanderbilt U; Pre-Med.*

DOUGLAS, Pedro Windom
Plainfield HS; Plainfield, NJ (245-434) Chor; Pres, FBLA; BSU; Jr Usher Board; Jr Gent Schol A; Dorcass Schol A; Young Adult Choir; *Trenton St U; Bus Adm.*

DOUGLAS, Randolph Charles
Mount Pleasant HS; San Jose, CA; NHS; Sci C; JV, Soccer; CSF; Sci A; Sci.

DOUGLAS, Stacy Joe
Leakesville HS; Leakesville, MS (10-67) BC; VP, FFA; Pres, SC; Ftbl; Cl Fav; Spch A; Yth Fel; *Jones Co Jr Col; Phys Therapy.*

DOUGLAS, Terry Glen
Kashmere HS; Houston, TX; Band; Curator A; MLS; PTA A; Marching Band; Taxidermy; *NTSU; Elec.*

DOUTHIT, Ann Elizabeth
Westbury HS; Houston, TX (1-700) Chor; Ensm; FHA; Tres, FTA; Mjrte; NHS; DARGCA; Hon Prog; 1st Pl, Houston Piano Tchr's Cont; *Baylor U; Mus.*

DOUTHIT, Gina Diane
Flora HS; Flora, IL (59-159) Band; Chem C; Chor; Ensm; Sch P; *Mus.*

DOUTHIT, James Russell
Swain Co HS; Bryson City, NC (5%-135) Band; Fr C; Secy, 4H; SC; 4H A; *Mus.*

DOUTHIT, Paula Denise
Swain Co HS; Bryson City, NC (3-131) Band; Chldr; Chess C; Fr C; FTA; Monogram; NHS; Sci C; Bkbl; Sftbl; Sci A; *Sweet Briar Col; Math.*

DOUTHITT, Phillip Dean
Frankfort HS; Ridgeley, WV (10%-149) 4H; Mgr, Bkbl; Tnns; 4H A; Hist A; Fr A; *WVU.*

DOVE, Deloris Anne
George Wythe HS; Wytheville, VA (57-160) Pres, Band; Hmrm; Sch P; VP, Sci C; SC; Sftbl; Math A; Jazz Band; All Co Band; Art, Pep, C'S; Chaplain, Lib C; Most Spirit, Sr Activity, A's; Tn Republicans; *Longwood Col; Phar.*

DOVE, James Peter III
Winston Churchill HS; Potomac, MD; Bkbl; Ftbl; Tr.

DOVE, Jeffrey C
East HS; Cheyenne, WY (52-434) Band; Ger C; NHS; *U of Wyoming; Bus Adm.*

DOVE, Robert Michael
N Mecklenburg Sr HS; Huntersville, NC (25-450) Co-Ch, Chor; Key C; NHS; Span C; *U of NC; Earth Sci.*

DOVE, Russell Lloyd
Nucla HS; Nucla, CO; Ski C; Bkbl; Ftbl; MVP, Swim; Alg A; Citz A; Lion A; Math A; *Colo St U; Aeronautics.*

DOVE, Terrance St Clair
William Penn HS; Philadelphia, PA; Citz A; *Temple U; Photographer.*

DOVER, Deborah Jeanne
Western Reserve Acad; Hudson, OH; Pres, Chor; Drama; Ger C; ARC; Rptr, Sch P; Ski C; COM; Citz A; Hon Prog; MLS; Yth Fel; Gym; Director, Church Children's Choir; Top 5%, Ntl Merit Schol Exam; *Journ.*

DOVER, Reta Felicia
York Comp HS; York, SC (13-240) Chldr; FBLA; NHS; Span C; SC; VP, Soph Cl; Type A; Pres, Fresh Cl; Marshal; *Winthrop Col.*

DOVER, Richard Kenneth
Aquinas HS; Augusta, GA (4-120) Drama; Math C; NHS; Order/Arrow; Tr; COM; NMS; NEDT; Eagle Sct; Fresh, Highest Average; *GA Inst of Tech; Chem Engr.*

DOW, Diana Gail
Prosser HS; Prosser, WA (20-140) Cpt, Chldr; FHA; NHS; SC; Cl Fav; 4H A; HQn; Cpt, Gym; Secy, Pres, 4-H C; Most Inspirational; *Wash St U; Phys Ed.*

DOW, Joseph Henry
Classical HS; Springfield, MA (11-508) Pres, Demolay; VP, NHS; JV, Tnns; Kiwanis A; *Wesleyan U.*

DOWBOR, Liza Rene
Decatur Central HS; Indianapolis, IN (68-343) Band; Mgr, Swim; Tr; COM; Kiwanis A; Ath A; *Ind U; Recreational Therapist.*

DOWD, Elizabeth Anne
Rockville HS; Rockville, IN (2-83) Band; Ensm; FHA; GS; 4H; Lat C; NHS; Sci C; Cpt, Swim; B Crocker A; Hon Prog; MLS; Sal; St Scholar; MVP, Swim; Statistician, Bsbl; *Auburn U; Early Childhood Ed.*

DOWD, Kathy Lorraine
Jordan Matthews HS; Siler City, NC (10-180) BC; Fr C; Monogram; Co-Cpt, Bkbl; Sftbl; Hon Prog; *U of NC; Med.*

DOWDLE, John Oliver
Canton Acad; Canton, MS (24-92) Ann; Band; BC; Pres, CYO; NHS; Order/Arrow; Sch P; Sci C; Span C; Pres, SC; VP, Sr Cl; VP, Jr Cl; JV, Ftbl; Cl Fav; HCt; Lion A; Rotary A; Most Dependable; *U of Miss; Bus Adm.*

DOWDY, Alan K
Cheyenne E HS; Cheyenne, WY (53-535) Band; Semi-Fin, BS; NFL; NHS; Spch C; Drum Major; Amer Yth Symph Band; *Hastings Col; Journ.*

DOWDY, Cheryl Anne
N Hall HS; Gainesville, GA (20-250) Ann; Pres, BC; Dbte Tm; Drama; VP, FBLA; Ch, FTA; 4H; Lit Mag; Secy, Math C; ARC; Span C; COM; Chem A; Hist A; Sci A; Eng A; Stu o-t Mo; *N Ga Col; Phar.*

DOWDY, Myles Patrick
Killian HS; Miami, FL (94-1102) Bsbl; Ftbl; Sftbl; Religion.*

DOWDY, Royal Sidney
Miami Christian Sch; Miami, FL; Chem C; Chor; Drama; Journ A; ARC A; Spch A; Poetry A; Royal Ambassador Teacher; Church Yth Coun; Church Pupeteer; Jr Church Teacher; *Vet.*

DOWDY, Sarah Heidi
Cave Spring HS; Roanoke, VA (43-450) Ensm; Fr C; Hmrm; Lat C; NHS; SC; COM; Citz A; DARGCA; Hon Prog; *Furman U.*

DOWELL, James Michael
Hastings HS; Hastings, MN (121-436) Ftbl; *Red Wing Vo-tech; Pipefitting.*

DOWELL, Janice Gwynn
Breckinridge Co HS; Harned, KY (14-200) Ann; Band; Chldr; Chor; FBLA; FTA; 4H; Math C; Mu Alpha Theta; NHS; Sch P; Sci C; Var C; VP, Soph Cl; Sftbl; Tnns; Cl Fav; 4H A; H of F; HCt; *U of Ky; Nurs.*

DOWELL, Jonathan Andrew
Lyons Township HS; Lagrange, IL (200-1150) Chess C; JETS; SC; Ftbl; NEDT; St Scholar; Rugby; Life Badge, BSct; *US Naval Acad; Nuclear Engr.*

DOWELL, Michael Lee
Sooner HS; Bartlesville, OK; Ch, Mural Comm; Outst Art Stu Service A; Concert Choir.

DOWLER, Debra Lea
Tift Co HS; Tifton, GA; Band; *Criminal Law.*

DOWLER, Gayle Fay
Tift Co HS; Tifton, GA; Band; Span C; ASA All Tourn, Ntl Champs; *Berry Col; Phys Ed.*

DOWLESS, Linda Gail
Tar Heel HS; Tar Heel, NC; Ann; BC; FBLA; FFA; FHA; Hmrm; Sci C; Span C; JV, Bkbl; Sci A; Span A; Eng A; FHA A; *UNC-CHAPEL Hill; Med.*

DOWLING, Jeffrey Dean
Ogallala Sr HS; Ogallala, NE (1-125) A Cap Choir; Pres, Band; BS; Chor; Drama; Ensm; Madrigal; Pres, NHS; Thes; Var C; Bkbl; Ftbl; MVP, Golf; Amer Leg A; Chamber of Comm A; Elk A; Hon Prog; Val; *U of Nebr; Phys Therapy.*

DOWLING, Maureen Frances
University HS; San Diego, CA (1-315) Ann; Key C; NHS; Sch Achieve Tm; SC; Tres, Jr Cl; CSF; Hon Prog; *Foreign Lang.*

DOWLING, Sherry Ann
Parkside HS; Jackson, MI (201-392) Chor; Rainbow; Grand Cross, Rainbow Girls; *Jackson Comm Col; Dental Hygiene.*

DOWNER, Vielka Angelica
Rainbow City HS; Rainbow City, CANAL ZONE; Band; Chldr; Secy, Drama; Sci C; SC; JV, Bsbl; JV, Bkbl; JV, Sftbl; Alg A; Spch A; *Med.*

DOWNEY, Brenda Jo
Portage HS; Portage, IN (63-615) Bus C; VP, Chor; Madrigal; NHS; Span C; COM; Citz A; Jr Chamber of Com A; Lion A; Phi Beta Kappa; Pres A; Type A; Schol, Music Sch; *Lincoln Christian Col; Mus.*

DOWNEY, Darla Sue
Portage HS; Portage, IN (1-769) Ed, Ann; Secy, Chor; Dbte Tm; Ensm; NFL; Tr; Alg A; COM; Citz A; Math A; Spch A; Type A; VP, Jr NHS; Spelling, Debate, A's; HR; *Acting.*

DOWNEY, Dee Lynn
Southside HS; Gadsden, AL (20%-140) Chem C; HiY; Math C; NHS; Secy, Sci C; Pres, Vocabulary C; WW; *Auburn U; Phar.*

DOWNEY, Lorraine
Kingsbury HS; Memphis, TN (69-250) Rptr, Bus C; Fr C; Hmrm; SC; COM; ROTC A; Bronze A; *Tenn St U; Police Work.*

DOWNIE, John Edward
Quartz Hill HS; Quartz Hill, CA; Tr; *Aviation.*

DOWNING, Brenda Lynne
Copeland HS; Copeland, KS (1-11) Ann; Band; Cpt, Chldr; Chor; Ensm; Rptr, Sch P; SC; S-T, Sr Cl; Pres, Jr Cl; Pres, Soph Cl; Sftbl; HQn; HCt; Type A; Val; Pres, Keyettes; Drill Tm; *Ft Hays St U; Secy.*

DOWNING, Clifford Dale
Wilburton HS; Wilburton, OK (15-60) Math C; Spch C; Ftbl; HCt; Spch A; Church Dist Yth Coun; Ftbl Ltrman; Ltrman's C; Eagle Sct; Ftbl Defensive Player o-t Wk; *E Okla St U; Pol Sci.*

DOWNING, David Joseph
Pinole Valley HS; Pinole, CA (10-350) NHS; Ski C; Span C; Var C; Ftbl; Co-Cpt, Swim; Bank Of Amer A; JA A; Eagle Sct; Sr Advisory Board; Pres, JA; *U of Calif St Col; Phys Ed.*

DOWNING, Deborah Lynn
Airline HS; Bossier City, LA (41-301) Pres, Forensic C; Debate Tm; Pep Sq; NTL Forensic C; Ch, Y-Tns; Beta C; Ad Staf; Sch Mus; Close Up; Mu Alpha Theta; Pres, MYF; *LSU; Spch & Law.*

DOWNING, Gwendolyn
Dothan HS; Dothan, AL (35-632) Pres, FTA; InterClub Coun; COM; Journ A; Fin, Cert of Merit; Semi Fin, Journ A; *Journ.*

DOWNING, Jefferson
Superior HS; Superior, NE (24-84) Chor; Hmrm; Key C; Monogram; SC; JV, Bkbl; Golf; *Mid-America Nazerene Col; Religion.*

DOWNING, Karen Elaine
Copeland HS; Copeland, KS (4-12) Cpt, Chldr; Chor; Key C; Secy, SC; Pres, Soph Cl; Bkbl; Tr; Type A; Co-Cpt, Drill Tm; Ch, Sch Service Publicity.

DOWNING, Katherine Vay
New Braunfels HS; New Braunfels, TX; Ger C; JV, Bkbl; Yth Fel; Vlbl; *SW Tex St Col; Ed.*

DOWNING, Phyllis Lynette
First Assembly Christian Sch; Memphis, TN; Chldr; Tnns; Tr.

DOWNING, Terri Dawn
South Side HS; Jackson, TN (33%-155) Chldr; City Conf; VP, FHA; FTA; Rptr, Sci C; Bkbl; HCt; Pres A; *Freed-Hardeman Col; Psych.*

DOWNING, Wendy Sue
McCluer HS; Florissant, MO (30-783) Chor; MYF; FCA; *Religion.*

DOWNS, Bob Alan
Anderson HS; Anderson, IN (20-493) Demolay; VP, Hmrm; MVP, Bsbl; Cpt, Bsbl; Babe Ruth Ath o-t Yr; Church Bkbl; Eng A; All 'A' Avg; All 'A' Avg; *Purdue U; Computer Sci.*

DOWNS, David Layne
Robert E Lee HS; Houston, TX; Sci C; *SWTSU; Marine Bio.*

DOWNS, Gary Lee
Anderson HS; Anderson, IN (33%-600).

DOWNS, Jamie Anita
York Comp HS; York, SC (6-272) Band; Ch, Hmrm; NHS; Co-Ch, Hmrm Rep; Marshal; Sr C Steering Comm; *Winthrop Col; Bus Ed.*

DOWNS, Karen Linda
Neshaminy Maple Point HS; Langhorne, PA (3-415) Hmrm; NHS; Hockey; *Phys Therapy.*

DOWNS, Sharon Felecia
Vanguard HS; Ocala, FL; FHA; Tri-HiY; Most Out; Deb, Delta Theta Sigma; Outst Leadership, Church; *FSU; Nurs.*

DOWSING, Eileen Patrice
Holly Springs HS; Holly Springs, MS (23-157) F-Ed, Ann; Band; Chor; Drama; FBLA; Hmrm; NHS; Ntl Yth Conf; Rptr, Sch P; SC; Var C; Pres, Soph Cl; Tr; Alg A; COM; Hon Prog; Math A; Type A; Yth Fel; *Ms St U; Pre-Med.*

DOWTY, Sharon Jolene
N Ft Myers HS; N Ft Myers, FL; Band; Pres, Rainbow; Sci A; Post Expl; Jr Cl Band Rep; Keyettes, Worthy Adv Rainbow Girls; 1st Cl Badge, GSct; Fr C As; Sci Fair As; VP, Yth Group; *Edison Co Col; Med.*

DOYLE, Cindy Linda
Maynard Evans HS; Orlando, FL (35-909) Fr C; NHS; Puppet Ministry; Bus Ministry; Yth Choir; *Nurs.*

DOYLE, Curtis Elvin
Grissom HS; Huntsville, AL (5%-700) Chor; Mu Alpha Theta; NHS; Swim; Tnns; Hon Prog; NEDT; *U of Ala; Engr.*

DOYLE, Debbie Lynne
Clairton HS; Clairton, PA (6-169) Chem C; Chor; Hmrm; Mjrte; Sci C; Ski C; VP, SC; VP, Jr Cl; Tnns; COM; Hon Prog; Math A; Pres A; Yth Fel; Explorers; *Engr.*

DOYLE, Deborah Linda
Las Plumas HS; Oroville, CA (12-279) Chldr; Hmrm; Sch P; Citz A.

DOYLE, Dennis Dean
John H Reagan HS; San Antonio, TX (28-350) Sch Achieve Tm; Co-Cpt, Sftbl; COM; Hon Prog; Yth Fel; Yth Prayer Group; Yth Choir; Baptist Royal Ambassadors; *U of Tex; Bus.*

DOYLE, Donley Bryan
Sam Houston HS; Arlington, TX (250-600) Band; Ensm; *Elec Engr.*

DOYLE, Elois
Wossman HS; Monroe, LA; Sch Achieve Tm; Sch P; Sftbl; MLS; Drill Tm A; *Northeast U; Bus Adm.*

DOYLE, Gerald Walter
Royal HS; Simi, CA (8-964) 4H; Hmrm; NFL; NHS; SC; Bkbl; Cr-Ctry; Tr; Citz A; *US Air Force Acad.*

DOYLE, John Kerry
Buhl HS; Buhl, ID (15-104) Band; Ensm; Key C; Ski C; *Boise St U; Engr.*

DOYLE, Katherine Adele
Las Plumas HS; Oroville, CA (33%-164) Sch P; Tnns; Yth Fel; FCA; *Butte Jr Col; Ed.*

DOYLE, Paula Esther
Ridley Sr HS; Folsom, PA (33%-750) Band; Chor; Hospital Vol; *Art.*

DOYLE, Suzanne Houser
Decatur HS; Decatur, AL (65-435) Band; VP, Bus C; Pres, Fr C; FTA; Secy, Hmrm; Secy, Lat C; Math C; Mu Alpha Theta; NHS; ARC; JA A; *U-o-t South; Nurs.*

DOZIER, Belinda Cornelius
Williamsburg HS; Andrews, SC; Rptr, Ann; 4H; A-Ed, Sch P; *Francis Marion Col; Med Tech.*

DOZIER, Douglas Theodore
Mullins Sr HS; Mullins, SC (10%-300) BC; Tres, Hmrm; Pres, Math C; Tres, SC; Bsbl; Co-Cpt, Ftbl; HCt; Ltrman; *U of Md; Computer Sci.*

DOZIER, Gloria Fredericka
N Shore HS; W Palm Beach, FL (30-336) Hmrm; Key C; Spch C; SC; Alg A; Math A; Spch A; GSct; VP, Pep C; Human Relations; Jr NHS; *Acct.*

DOZIER, Katherine Louise
Thomasville Acad; Thomasville, AL (4-18) Ann; S-T, BC; Co-Cpt, Chldr; Chor; S-T, Hmrm; Beauty; B Crocker A; Cl Fav; HQn; HCt; Yth Fel; *Livingston U; Ed.*

DOZIER, Norene Christina
Dothan HS; Dothan, AL (2-790) Tres, Chor; Lit Ral; COM; Hon Prog; ROTC A; Hist C; *Tuskegee Inst; Fashion Design.*

DOZIER, Perry Micheal
R H Watkins HS; Laurel, MS; Fr C; VP, Hmrm; Bsbl; MVP, Ftbl; Amer Leg A; Citz A; Hon Prog; ROTC A; Art A; Acting A; *Harvard U; Sci.*

DOZIER, Rory Neal
Martin Van Buren HS; Queens Village, NY (330-1065) Chess C; Hmrm; SC; Bsbl; Bkbl; Tr; COM; JA A; Pres A; *SUNY at Buffalo; Engr.*

DOZIER, William Gregory
Stoneville HS; Stoneville, NC (1-75) Chor; Demolay; Fr C; FFA; NHS; SC; Gr Marshal; *U of NC-CHAPEL Hill; Phar.*

DOZIER, William Perry Jr
Harlem HS; Harlem, GA (13-178) Co-Ed, Ann; Drama; Tres, Hmrm; VP, SC; Pres, Jr Cl; Mgr, Bkbl; Tnns; Photographer, Annual; Pres, Church Yth; *Annapolis.*

DRABEK, Gregg Allen
Winner HS; Winner, SD (20-125) Band; Chor; Ensm; Madrigal; Order/Arrow; JV, Bkbl; Mgr, Ftbl; Tr; God & Country A; Order/Arrow A; *Dakota Weslyan Col; Bus.*

DRABING, Drew Evan
Springs Valley HS; French Lick, IN (1-90) Band; BS; CYO; Chess C; Fr C; NHS; Var C; VP, Jr Cl; Pres, Soph Cl; Bkbl; Cpt, Ftbl; Golf; Swim; COM; Cl Fav; MLS; Most Out; Type A; Val; Prom Prince; *Math.*

DRACHENBERG, Brian Earl
Oconomowoc Sr HS; Oconomowoc, WI (33%-220).

DRAGO, James John
Prescott HS; Prescott, AZ (31-432) CYO; Bus Mgr, Drama; Tres, 4H; Bus Mgr, Key C; NHS; Ed, Sch P; VP, Ski C; Var C; Bsbl; Ftbl; Alg A; Bio A; COM; Cl Fav; Elk A; 4H A; Hon Prog; JA A; Math A; Most Out; Sci A; Secy, 4 H C; Elks Schol; *N Ariz U; Engr.*

DRAGOUN, Sandra Lynn
Holdrege Sr HS; Holdrege, NE (19-129) JV, Chldr; Chor; FBLA; Semi-Fin, GS; Sch P; SC; Tr; Vlbl Tm; Nebr Yth Safety Prog; *Creighton U; Law.*

DRAGSETH, Tracy Jo
Central HS; Crookston, MN (23-221) Band; Ensm; *Concordia-Moorhead Col.*

DRAHM, John Marvin
Rockdale HS; Rockdale, TX (50%-150) Chess C; Sch P; Bkbl; Ftbl; Opt A; Dist Bkbl; St Ftbl Champs; Wittiest; Ftbl Schol; *Sam Houston St Col; Law Enforcement.*

DRAIN, Brenda Sue
Bridgeton HS; Bridgeton, NJ (20%-750) Secy, Band; Hmrm; Math A; NEDT; *Math.*

DRAIN, Kenneth Mark
Corsicana HS; Corsicana, TX (51-360) F-Ed, Ann; Tres, BC; Secy, FFA; F-Ed, Sch P; SC; Cpt, Bsbl; JV, Bkbl; Cpt, Ftbl; Tr; Yth Fel; Friendliest Sr; *Tex Tech U; Bus Law.*

DRAIN, Lisa Meg
Richardson HS; Richardson, TX (62-908) Hmrm; NHS; SC; S-T, Tri-HiY; Outst A; MVP, Drill Tm; Key C Swtht; *Tex Tech U; Elem Ed.*

DRAKE, Dana Richard
Ilwaco HS; Ilwaco, WA; Band; Order/Arrow; Ftbl; Tr; Eagle Sct; *Wash St U; Anthropology.*

DRAKE, Diana Lea
Hutchinson HS; Hutchinson, MN (51-229) Ann; Band; Ski C; JV, Bkbl; JV, Golf; 5 & 7 Yr Dance A's; Bronze & Silver Ski Racing Medals; Best Sport Cup.*

DRAKE, Donald Keith
Hobbs HS; Hobbs, NM; Sci C; Golf; Sftbl; Hon Prog; Sci A; Span A; *Baylor U; Bio.*

DRAKE, Dorothy Ann
Carroll HS; Monroe, LA (12-205) FBLA; SC; Hist A; *NE U; Bus Adm.*

DRAKE, Emily Jean
Genoa-Kingston HS; Genoa, IL (15-113) Secy, Band; Chor; Ensm; 4H; NHS; COM; 4H A; Hon Prog; Yth Fel; *Valparaiso U; Nurs.*

DRAKE, James Edward Jr
Anacostia HS; Washington, DC; Sch P; SC; COM; Citz A; NJHS; Academic Achievement A; Audio-Video Stu A; *Rochester Inst of Technology; Graphic Communications.*

DRAKE, Kelly Joanne
Archbold HS; Archbold, OH (25%-150) A Cap Choir; Band; Chor; Drama; 4H; Orch; Swim; *Bowling Green St U; Teaching.*

DRAKE, Kimberly Ann
Firth Norris HS; Firth, NE (3-83) Bus C; CYO; FNA; 4H; NHS; Var C; MVP, Tr; Hon Prog; Pres A; Cpt & MVP, Vlbl; Capital Conf A, Vlbl; *Southeast Comm Col; Dental Asst.*

DRAKE, Margaret Ann
Rockford-Guilford HS; Rockford, IL (60-672) A Cap Choir; Anchor C; Ann; Cpt, Chldr; Chor; Hmrm; Rainbow; Ed, Sch P; SC; Co-Cpt, Sftbl; Tnns; Tr; COM; Citz A; Cl Fav; H of F; Hon Prog; Journ A; MLS; Yth Fel; *Northern Ill U; Psych.*

DRAKE, Philip LaRue
Archbold HS; Archbold, OH (75-150) Ger C; Sch P; Sci C; Ftbl; Wrest; VP, Church Yth Fel; Mr Congeniality; Most Improved, Ftbl; *U of Wyom; Creative Writing.*

DRALLE, Daniel Dwight
Batavia Sr HS; Batavia, IL (7-211) Math C; Golf; Hon Prog; Math A; *Math.*

DRALLE, Susan Lynn
John F Kennedy HS; Tamuning, GUAM (24-511) F-Ed, Ann; NHS; Sci A; Vlbl; Jobs Daughters; *Stewardess.*

DRAPELA, Karen Jean
Sacred Heart Acad; Salem, OR; Chor; Secy, NHS; VP, Span C; Opt A; *Chemeketa Col.*

DRAPER, Cynthia Anne
Daviess Co HS; Owensboro, KY (10-320) Ann; 4H; Golf; H of F; Hon Prog; *Murray St U.*

DRAPER, David Greg
Richland HS; Ft Worth, TX (15-550) Chor; Hmrm; NHS; SC; Bsbl; Sftbl; Tr; *U of Tex at Arlington; Archt.*

DRAPER, David Wayne
Cashmer HS; Cashmere, WA; Band; Chor; Drama; Ensm; Var C; Bsbl; Ftbl; Superior, Snare Drum Solo; *Wenatchee Valley Col; Mus.*

DRAPER, Frank Neal
Carter HS; Strawberry Plains, TN (25%-180) Band; Ensm; Cr-Ctry; Tr; *U of Tenn; Sci.*

DRAPER, Karl Bradley
Richland HS; Ft Worth, TX; Ann; Chor; Drama; Hmrm; VP, SC; Ftbl; Sftbl; Tnns; Tr; Nom, Jr Cl Fav; *U of Tex at Arlington; Elec.*

DRAPER, Marjorie Gail
Horseheads HS; Horseheads, NY (35-600) Band; Chor; NHS; 1st Cl GSct; *Math.*

DRAPER, Martin Alan
Abraham Lincoln HS; Council Bluffs, IA (158-420) Pres, Demolay; Key C; Pres, Order/Arrow; Sci C; Tnns; JV, Wrest; Eagle Sct; Iowa DeMolay St Chaplin; *Iowa St U; Fisheries & Wildlife Bio.*

DRAPER, Robert James
Pima HS; Pima, AZ; Chem C; Fr C; NHS; Rptr, Sch P; Span C; Var C; Bsbl; Ftbl; Chem A; Hon Prog; Sci A; ASU Medallion of Merit A; Duty to God A; Nom, Congressional Schol; WW; *Eastern Ariz; Mining Technology.*

DRAPER, Russell Lamar
Bradley-Bourbonais HS; Bradley, IL (33%-400) Cpt, Ftbl; Tr.

DRASCHER, Ellen Lois
John Adams HS; Ozone Park, NY; JETS; Math C; NHS; Sch P.

DRASKO, Marcia Lynn
Crestview HS; Crestview, FL (10-247) Band; BC; Cpt, Chldr; Drama; Fin, Jr Miss Pagent; Rainbow; VP, SC; Cpt, Bkbl; Cpt, Sftbl; Tr; Beauty; Spch A; Crestview's Jr Miss; Highest Scorer, Bkbl; Scholastic Ath A; Dbte Win; *Brigham Young U; Med.*

DRAUCKER, Lesa Marie
Ogallala HS; Ogallala, NE (10%-176) Band; Dbte Tm; Pres, Ensm; Pres, 4H; Hmrm; ARC; Span C; SC; Var C; Soph Cl; Swim; Mgr, Wrest; COM; 4H A; Hon Prog; Opt A; ARC A; Spch A; Star Student; Type A; Yth Fel; Job's Daughters; 1st, Flute Duet & Quartet; Hon Bell Choir; 1st, Piano Sup Player Over-All; *NE Wesleyan Col; Med.*

DRAUGHON, Christine Mary
Nathan Hale HS; Tulsa, OK (25%-700) Band; Chess C; Dbte Tm; Drama; Lat C; NFL; Spch C; Thes; Y-Tns; Yth Fel; Pres, Episcopal Young Churchmen; VP, Med C; Jr Daughters o-t King; Sunday Sch Teacher; *Rockhurst Col; Theology.*

DRAVES, Catherine Marie
Marshalltown Comm Sr HS; Marshalltown, IA (9-448) A-Ed, Ann; Chor; Ensm; FTA; Ger C; Y-Tns; COM; Chamber of Comm A; Citz A; Gov Honor Prog; Hon Prog; NMF; NMS; Opt A; St Scholar; Yth Fel; Yth Leg; Concertmistress, Orch; All-St Orch; Yth for Understanding; Ames Interntl Orch; Festival Yth Symp; *Iowa St U; Engr.*

DRAVES, Thomas John
Imlay City Comm Sch; Imlay City, MI (15-200) Secy, FFA; Bsbl; Cr-Ctry; JV, Ftbl.

DRAXLER, Nancy Lou
Goodman-Armstrong HS; Goodman, WI (2-29) Band; CYO; Mjrte; NHS; Pres, Soph Cl; Bkbl; *Stevens Point Col; Mus.*

DRAYTON, Antoinette Delores
Sol C Johnson HS; Savannah, GA; SC; Up Bound; Bkbl; Sftbl; Tr; *Norfolk St Col; Acct.*

DRAYTON, Lorenzo Lewis
Martin Co HS; Stuart, FL (190-500) *Mus.*

DRAYTON, Robert Lee
Cainhoy HS; Huger, SC (5-45) Band; FFA; 4H; Math C; NHS; Phys C; St Achieve Tm; Span C; Var C; Bkbl; Math A; *NC A&T Col; ROTC.*

DREAKFORD, Kimberly Ann
Jeannette Sr HS; Jeannette, PA (110-169) Ski C; Co-Cpt, Chldr; *Slippery Lock St Col; Phys Ed.*

DRECHSLER, Walter Michael
Lynnwood Sr HS; Lynnwood, WA (30-400) Hmrm; NHS.

DREESEN, Jeane Lynn
Luverne Jr-Sr HS; Luverne, MN (81-133) Tres, 4H; 4H A; *Pipestone Vo-tech Col; Fashion Merchandising.*

DREGE, Jane Marie
Rugby HS; Rugby, ND; Ann; Chor; Drama; Pres, FHA; Sch P; Spch C; SC; 4H A; Spch A; VP, Church Hi-League; *Communications.*

DREIFKE, Laura Maria
Incarnate Word Acad; St Louis, MO (78-109) All Amer Yth; CYO; Span C; Var C; Co-Cpt, Bkbl; Sftbl; Swim; Tnns; Tr; COM; Sci A; 1st Alt Piano Schol to Rosat; Kain; A for B-Tm Vlbl; Piano A; Swim A; A for Catching Fly Ball; *St Louis U; Pre-Law.*

DREIMAN, Amy Lynn
Groves HS; Birmingham, MI (25%-400) Hmrm; SC; Var C; Bkbl; Soccer; Sftbl; Tnns; NJHS.

DREMEL, Eric Von
Custer County HS; Westcliffe, CO (4-21) Drama; VP, NHS; Ed, Sch P; Span C; Pres, SC; Tres, Soph Cl; Bkbl; Ftbl; Cpt, Tr; Bio A; Elk A; Ntl Stu Coun Conf; All-Conf Ftbl; *Okla U; Bio.*

DRENNEN, James Martin
Waverly HS; Waverly, OH (13-155) Semi-Fin, BS; Pres, Drama; NHS; Sch Achieve Tm; Cpt, Golf; Hon Prog; Yth Fel; Instructor, Jr Golf League; *U of Tenn; Engr.*

DRENNING, Lori Dawn
Waukesha S HS; Waukesha, WI; Chor; Fencing C A; 2nd Pl, WSMA; *Home Ec.*

DRESCHER, Carol Elizabeth
St Albans HS; St Albans, WV (24-496) AFS; Pres, Lat C; Math C; Mu Alpha Theta; Span C; Bkbl; JA A; NMF; WW; Pres, Church Yth; *W Va U; Forestry.*

DRESNER, Diane Dee
Richfield HS; Waco, TX (10%-350) NHS; Rainbow; *Math.*

DRESSEL, Amy Vivian
W Essey Regional HS; N Caldwell, NJ; Chor; Hmrm; SC; Bkbl; COM; Hon Prog; Yth Fel; *Social Behavior.*

DRESSEL, Kathryn Enid
W Essex Sr HS; N Caldwell, NJ (31-460) NHS; Hon Prog; Type A; Yth Fel; Co-Ed, Church Newspaper; *Wheaton Col; Law.*

DRESSEL, Susan Amelia
Briarcliff HS; Atlanta, GA; Chor; Lat C; Kiwanis A; Lion A; Most Out; Secy, Industrial Arts C; Natl Comp, C Swtht; *Ga Tech; Interior Design.*

DRESSER, Donna Jean
Granville HS; Granville, OH (6-126) Drama; Fr C; NHS; F-Ed, Sch P; MVP, Tr; *Rollins Col; Environmental Stu.*

DRESSER, Peter Daniel
Lutheran HS W; Detroit, MI (10-150) A Cap Choir; Chor; Madrigal; NHS; Amer Leg Orator A; Phi Beta Kappa; Best Male Vocalist; *Oral Roberts U; Social Work.*

DRESSLER, Susan Lynn
Kingman HS; Kingman, KS (1-120) Band; JV, Chldr; Ensm; FTA; Span C; Var C; Y-Tns; Tnns; High HR; *U of Kans; Math.*

DREW, Judith Lee
W S Creecy HS; Rich Square, NC (1-42) VP, BC; Chor; Fr C; FHA; Tres, Y-Tns; COM; Val; Miss Atlantic Dist Fair; Lib, Guidance, C'S; Bus Driver; *U of NC; Phar.*

DREW, Marie Patricia
St Mary's HS; Lynn, MA (10-146) Drama; Fr C; NHS; JV, Bkbl; Sftbl; Tnns; Fr, Eng, Drama, A's; Sch Rptr, City Newspaper; *Journ.*

DREW, Paula Geraldine
Sammamish HS; Bellevue, WA (150-550) Chor; Job's Daughters; *U of Wash; Nurs.*

DREWES, Diane Marie
Belvidere HS; Belvidere, IL; Band; Pres, 4H; Tr; 4H A; GAA; Zonta C.

DREWES, Douglas Alan
Rogers HS; Toledo, OH (20-500) Band; BS; City Conf; Community Yth Symph; Ensm; Ger C; NHS; Orch; COM; Hon Prog; Math A; *U of Cincinnati; Engr.*

DREWRY, William Bill
Bishop Byrne HS; Memphis, TN (10-200) Fr C; NHS; Var C; Bkbl; Cr-Ctry; Tr; NEDT; Pres A; Phys Fitness A; Most Improved, Bkbl; *Christian Brothers Col; Engr.*

DREYER, Janine Lynn
Bentworth Sr HS; Bentleyville, PA (33-157) Band; Chor; FHA; Hmrm; Mgr, Bsbl; Campus Life; *Nurs.*

DREYER, Lori Anne
Franklin Road Christina Sch; Murfreesboro, TN (2-15) Bus Mgr, Ann; Chor; Drama; Ensm; Citz A; Hon Prog; Math A; Sal; Sch Spirit A; Miss Franklin Road; Creative Writing; Patriotic Poster A; *Tenn Temple Sch; Secy.*

DREYER, Susan Jean
Lyons Township HS; W Springs, IL (97%-1255) ARC; Tr; Hon Prog; NEDT; Pres A; *U of Ill; Phar.*

DRIEHAUS, Donald Gerard
Elder HS; Cincinnati, OH (50-389) Lat C; NHS; Phys C; SC; Thes; Sftbl; Wrest; Hon Prog; Pres, Yth C; Pol Campaigner; *Xavier U; Urban Stu.*

DRIGGANS, Deborah Ann
Tyner HS; Chattanooga, TN (17-261) Ed, Ann; Rptr, BC; NHS; SC; VP, Tri-HiY; Yrbk A; E Tenn Sr Band Clinic; *Middle Tenn St U; Bus.*

DRIGGERS, Cindy
Skyline Career Development Center; Dallas, TX (150-986) A Cap Choir; Chor; Drama; Ensm; Fr C; Rptr, Hmrm; Madrigal; Sch Achieve Tm; SC; Beauty; Most Out; Ntl Achv Schol; PTA A; Spch A; Swtht; Yth Fel; Life Ldrship; Theory A; Young Life; Sup Rating, Piano; Drill Tm; Lead, Sch Musical; Stu Affiliate; *Phillip U; Mus Therapy.*

DRIGGERS, Karen Ann
Christian Sch; Mesquite, TX (7-43) Cpt, Chldr; FHA; Hmrm; Fin, Most Outst; *Harding Col.*

DRIGGERS, Michael Steven
Vestavia Hills HS; Vestavia Hills, AL; Cr-Ctry; Tr; JV, Wrest; *U of Ala; Elec Engr.*

DRIGGS, James Irwin Jr
Chillicothe HS; Chillicothe, OH (33%-350) Yth Coun; Planning & Survey Comm; City League Athletics; *Pol Sci.*

DRIGGS, Vincent Lee
Cambridge HS; Cambridge, OH (31-282) A Cap Choir; Chor; Drama; Ensm; Secy, Key C; NHS; Thes; Golf; Ohio Key C School; *Miami U; Pre-Med.*

DRINKWATER, Jacqueline
Clay Co HS; Ashland, AL; BC; Chor; Ensm; FBLA; FHA; FTA; 4H; Semi-Fin, Jr Miss Pa; NHSt; Sch Achieve Tm; Sci C; SC; Beauty; COM; 4H A; HCt; VofDEM; Col Schol; *Judson Col; Bus.*

DRINNON, Patricia Lee
Lawrence HS; Lawrence, KS (267-528) Band; 4H; *Kans U; Special Ed.*

DRISKELL, Cynthia Carolyn
Pinckneyville Comm HS; Pinckneyville, IL (71-130) Band; Chor; Drama; Fr C; FHA; Hmrm; Ed, Lit Mag; NHS; Sch P; Spch C; Mgr, Wrest; Hon Prog; NEDT; Spch A; *Reno Lake Col; Beauty Culture.*

DRISKELL, Jane Carol
Iroquois HS; Louisville, KY (4-470) Ed, Ann; Fr C; Hmrm; NHS; Co-Ch, ARC; Rptr, Sch P; Span C; SC; Sftbl; Swim; Tnns; Tr; COM; HCt; Hon Prog; Math A; HCt; Sci A; Principal's List; Pep C; Choir; Service A; Sunday Sch Teacher; Off Aide; United Methodist Choir A; Drill Corps; Puppeteer; *Engr.*

DRISKELL, Kara Lou
Clark Co R-1 HS; Kahoka, MO (4-95) Sci C; Span C; Sci A; Mus A; Tr A; *Vet.*

DRISKILL, Tracy Leigh
Matoaca HS; Ettrick, VA (15-185) Chldr; Chor; Fr C; French NHS; Key C; NHS; VP, SC; Ch, Jr Cl; Citz A; Pres A.

DRIVER, Jan Denise
Carrollton HS; Carrollton, GA (13-173) Bus C; FBLA; Tri-HiY; Shorthand A; Acad Achv Hon's; *W Ga Col; Bus.*

DRIVER, Paul Edward
Robbinsdale Sr HS; Robbinsdale, MN (120-750) NHS; Bsbl; Hockey; JV, Soccer; *Navy; Law.*

DRIVER, Sharon May
Kingsway Regional HS; Swedesboro, NJ; Secy, 4H; NHS; SC; Tres, Jr Cl; Tres, Soph Cl.

DRLIK, Patrick Joseph
Cardinal Stritch HS; Oregon, OH (5-175) JV, Bkbl; Golf; Hon Prog; Quiz Bowl.

DROBNER, Tracie Lynn
Ravena-Coeymans-Selkirk HS; Ravena, NY; FBLA.

DROGE, Nancy Lynn
Irondale HS; New Brighton, MN (82-475) NHS; Bkbl; Type A; Pres, Young Peoples Society, Church; *Dordt Col; Bus Adm.*

DROKE, Pennie Juaneece
Deshler HS; Tuscumbia, AL; Chor; VP, FBLA; Bkbl; *U of N Ala; Mus.*

DROMSKY, Laurie Ann
Bryan Sr HS; Omaha, NE (66-393) Chor; Swim; Tnns; *U of Nebr; Mus.*

DROPPERS, Daren
Bozeman Sr HS; Bozeman, MT (143-385) Lit Mag; Sch P; *Mont St U; Anthropology.*

DROST, Sally Lena
Putnam Co Sr HS; Cookeville, TN; Ann; Chor; Span C; *Tenn Tech U.*

DROZD, John Anthony
St Joseph HS; Camden, NJ (5-76) CYO; Chem C; Ger C; NHS; Phys C; Pol Sci C; ARC; Sci C; JV, Bkbl; Hon Prog; Fresh & JV Bkbl Ltrs; JV Bowl Ltr; *U of Notre Dame; Architecture.*

DRUEN, Veronica Gayle
Hart HS; Munfordville, KY (4-177) BC; Bus C; NHS; VP, Jr Cl; Beauty; COM; Hist A; HQn; HCt; Hon Prog; Raiderette; Tn Who Care; *Western Col.*

DRUM, Jill Dean
Penn Hills HS; Pittsburgh, PA (300-1150) Chor; Hmrm; Sci C; Var C; MVP, Cr-Ctry; MVP, Tr; Tr A; *Pa St U; Bio.*

DRUMMER, Jacqueline
Rosedale HS; Rosedale, MS (1-120) Ann; Secy, BC; Secy, FBLA; Pres, Hmrm; SC; Pres, Jr Cl; Mgr A; Bio A; Chem A; Hist A; Hon Prog; MLS; Sci A; Spch A; Eng A; *Delta St U; Acct.*

DRUMMOND, Ann Melinda
Pawhuska HS; Pawhuska, OK (8-140) Band; Mu Alpha Theta; NHS; Span C; Secy, SC; Tnns; *Trinity Col.*

DRUMMOND, Phillip Jennings
Hanceville HS; Hanceville, AL; Ann; FTA; Math C; NHS; *Elec Engr.*

DRUMMOND, Robert William
Arkadelphia Sr HS; Arkadelphia, AR (28-226) Band; Drama; Fr C; Thes; Stage Band; *Henderson St U; Elec Engr.*

DRUMMOND, Thomas Alan
George Rogers Clark HS; Hammond, IN (25-273) Chem C; Chess C; Fr C; Tnns; Hist A; Hist As; Sch Hist, DAR As; *Ind U; Law.*

DRUMRIGHT, Vicki Lynn
Hillwood HS; Nashville, TN (10%-200) VP, Anchor C; GS; NHS; Span C; Cr-Ctry; Tr; COM; *Middle Tenn St U; Dentistry.*

DRURY, Darcy
Cottage Grove HS; Cottage Grove, OR (1-240) Co-Ed, Ann; Chldr; Chor; FBLA; GS; Hmrm; NHS; SC; Tnns; Tr; COM; Elk A; HCt; Math A; Q&S A; Sci A; Type A; Val; Co- cpt, Gym; Outst Ldrship A; *U of Oreg; Bus Adm.*

DRURY, Derek Dean
Holstein Comm HS; Holstein, IA (23-47) Band; Pres, 4H; Orch; Tres, Sr Cl; VP, Jr Cl; Golf; 4H A; *Iowa St U; Agr Bus.*

DRUVENGA, Aruin Duane
Aplington Comm HS; Aplington, IA (2-45) Band; Chor; Ensm; Bsbl; Bkbl; Cr-Ctry; *U of Northern Iowa; Bus.*

DRYDEN, John David
W Aurora HS; Aurora, IL; Band; Chor; Drama; Bkbl; *Moody Bible Inst; Jewish-Hebrew Stu.*

DRYER, Kymberly Glee
Batavia HS; Batavia, IL; Lit Mag; Span C; Tr; Citz A; Hon Prog; Art C; Play Usherette; *U of Ill; Hist Ed.*

DRYER, Sarah Emily
DeSoto HS; De Soto, TX (11-150) Band; FHA; FTA; 4H; Span C; 4H A; Pres, VOE; Pres, OEA; Drum Major; Extemporaneous Verbal Commun A; *U of Tex; Bus.*

DRYMON, Cara Jo
Sarasota HS; Sarasota, FL; Community Yth Symph; NHS; Orch; COM; Spch A; Gold Key, Orch; *U of Fla; Ed.*

DSURNEY, Allan Richard
Cedar Grove Mem HS; Cedar Grove, NJ; Key C; Bus Mgr, Soccer; Hist C; *Drew U.*

DUBA, Bruce Franklin
Princeton HS; Princeton, NJ; A Cap Choir; BS; Chor; Drama; InterAct C; JV, Soccer; NMS Ltr of Commendation; Tres, Yth Fel; *Mech Engr.*

DUBAY, Leona Katharine
Hickory Sr HS; Hermitage, PA; Chor; Rptr, Lit Mag; NHS; Sci A; Sch P; Span C; Span NHS; Thes; Tres, Tri-HiY; Var C; Mgr, Bkbl; 1st & 2nd A, PSPA Lit A's; Hon Men, Ntl Merit Schol; Publication, The Eng Journ; *Pa St U; Eng.*

DUBBS, Benedict Harold Jr
Pine Grove Area HS; Pine Grove, PA (35-164) Order/Arrow; JV, Bsbl; JV, Bkbl; Citz A; God & Country A; Order/Arrow A; Life A, BSct; *Marine Biol.*

DUBE, Ghislain
College De St Anne De La Pocatiere; La Pocatiere, CANADA (3-29) Lit Mag; Phys C; *Sci.*

DUBE, Roland Leo
St Dominic Regional HS; Lewiston, ME (2-78) FTA; Key C; Secy, Sodality; COM; NEDT; WW; Ed, Jour Sch Page; *U of Maine; Special Ed.*

DUBEROWSKI, Joyce Renee
Lakewood Sr HS; Lakewood, CA; Cpt, Chldr; NHS; Tres, SC; Bkbl; Sftbl; *Long Beach City Col.*

DUBIN, David Maximilian
Hillel HS; Lawrence, NY; Math C; Co-Ed, Sch P; NEDT; Val; Win, Schwide Sci Contest; *Yeshiva U; Med.*

DU BOIS, Dean Alan
Boca Ciega HS; St Petersburg, FL (83-559) Co-Cpt, Chess A; Fr C; Arch; Bsbl; Bkbl; Ftbl; Golf; Hockey; Soccer; Sftbl; Swim; Wrest; *Fla Inst of Tech; Computer Sci.*

DuBOISE, Jamey Ann
Edmond HS; Edmond, OK (20%-652) Band; *Abilene Christian U; Acct.*

DUBOSCQ, Genevieve
Star o-t Sea Acad; San Francisco, CA; Ed, Ann; Chor; Model UN; Sci C; Bank Of Amer A; CSF; Eng A; *Dominican Col; Liberal Arts.*

DuBOSE, Jacqueline Marguerite
Gosnell HS; Blytheville, AR (8-94) BC; Drama; VP, NHS; VP, World Affairs C; B Crocker A; NEDT; ARC A; *Ark St U; Art.*

DuBOSE, Marjorie Marie
Vista HS; Vista, CA; Chor; COM; *Mira Costa Col; Beautician.*

DUBREE, Michael Glenn
Breckinridge Co HS; Harned, KY (15%-200) Chor; Golf; *Bus.*

DuBUQUE, Vincent Micheal
Fremont Christian HS; Fremont, CA (19-28) Band; Orch; Phys C; Pres, Sr Cl; Cpt, Bsbl; Bkbl; Pres A; *Calif St U; Dentistry.*

DUCE, Alisa Yvette
Hilliard Jr-Sr HS; Hilliard, FL (1-74) Ann; Band; VP, BC; Chess C; Ensm; Cpt, Mjrte; Sch P; Span C; Cl Fav; Most Out; Val; VFW A; ITT Rayoneir Schol; *FJC; Computer Sci.*

DUCHAI, Darlene Helen
Hightstown HS; Hightstown, NJ; Fr C; NHS; ARC; Tres, Ski C; SC; Secy, Sr Cl; Bkbl; Mgr, Hockey; Cpt, Sftbl; Amer Leg A; Hon Prog; GAA; *Rutgers Col; Agronomy.*

DUCHARME, Cass Hendley
Plant City HS; Plant City, FL (8-35) Band; Ensm.

DUCHAT, Valerie Elizabeth
Poteau HS; Poteau, OK (33%-140) FHA; 4H; Bkbl; Co-Cpt, Sftbl; 4H A; MLS; GSct; Church Rep, Dist Yth; VP, Sunday Sch Cl; Ch, Yth Coun; Secy, Dist Yth; *Acct.*

DUCHENY, Dale Craig
Orange HS; Orange, CA; Band; Orch; Order/Arrow; Span C; Bsbl; Bkbl; JV, Ftbl; Tr; COM; Coun of Teach; God & Country A; Order/Arrow A; Yth Fel; Eagle Sct A; Top 40 A.

DUCHESNE, Shadi
La Merced HS; Rio Piedras, PR (3-108) Swim; Alg A; Bio A; COM; Hon Prog; Magna Cum Laude; Sal; Summa Cum Laude; Eng A; Espanish A; *U of Puerto Rico; Med.*

DUCKER, Thomas Edwin
Hillcrest HS; Dallas, TX; Lat C; Secy, Order/Arrow; Sci C; Citz A; Hon Prog; Math A; Order/Arrow A; Sci A; NJHS; Sr Patrol Ldr, BScts; Church Jr Deacon.

DUCKETT, Debra Lynn
C K McClatchy HS; Sacramento, CA (112-458) Hmrm; COM; Masonic A; *Calif Baptist Col; Religious Ed.*

DUCKETT, Martin Lee
Plainview HS; Plainview, TX (10-400) A Cap Choir; Chem C; FTA; Hmrm; Co-Ch, Madrigal; Math C; Pres, NHS; Sci C; JV, Tnns; COM; Citz A; Hon Prog; JA A; Math A; Sci A; Yth Fel; Yth Foundation; Yth Leg; *Acct.*

DUCKWORTH, Jerry Wayne
Dongola HS; Dongola, IL (2-23) BC; Sci C; SC; Var C; Tres, Soph Cl; MVP, Bsbl; Bkbl; Cr-Ctry; HCt; Hon Prog; Math A; Sal; *Shawnee Jr Col; Bus Mgr.*

DUCKWORTH, Laura Courtney
Piggott HS; Piggott, AR (3-108) Ann; Band; BC; Rptr, FHA; Mjrte; Sci C; COM; Yth Fel; Alpha C; Mjrte Clinic Hons; *U of Ark; Phar.*

DUCKWORTH, Phil
Brookhaven Acad; Brookhaven, MS; Co-Ed, Ann; BC; Fr C; Order/Arrow; Bsbl; JV, Bkbl; JV, Ftbl; COM; Citz A; Order/Arrow A; Sci A; *Miss St U; Pol Sci.*

DUCKWORTH, Thomas Sterling
Piggott HS; Piggott, AR (12-82) BC; FFA; Math C; Sci C; SC; Co-Cpt, Bkbl; COM; Cl Fav; H of F; General Mills Family Ldrship A; All Dist Bkbl; Bkb Offensive Trophy; Fin, St Golf Champ; *U of Ark; Banking & Finance.*

DuCOTE, Karen Lee
Acadiana HS; Lafayette, LA; Band; Drama; NHS; Hon Prog; Spch A; Runnerup, Miss Tn Lafayette; Best Camper, Piano, A's; *Landscape Design.*

DUCOTE, Mary Beth
Bordelonville HS; Bordelonville, LA (2-25) Secy, Ann; Band; BC; CYO; Cpt, Chldr; Chess C; Dbte Tm; Fr C; FBLA; FHA; GS; 4H; Lit Ral; Cpt, Mjrte; NHS; ARC; Sch P; Sci C; VP, SC; Tnns; Tr; Beauty; Bio A; Cl Fav; 4H A; Hon Prog; ARC A; Sci A; Type A; Band A; Mus A; Mjrte A; *U of Southwestern La; Law Enforcement.*

DUDDLES, Gayle Beth
Napa HS; Napa, CA (3-456) VP, Band; Fr C; Inter-Act C; Fin, Jr Miss Pagent; Key C; Model UN; Mu Alpha Theta; VP, SC; Bank Of Amer A; CSF; COM; DARGCA; NMF; US Yth Senate Prog; *U of Calif; Biol.*

DUDECK, Kathy Diane
Belle Plaine HS; Belle Plaine, KS (29-65) Band; Ensm; FHA; Sch P; Spch C; Hon Prog; Spch A; Yth Fel; I Rating, St Instrumental Contest; *SW Col.*

DUDECK, Michael Matthew
Belle Plaine HS; Belle Plaine, KS (15-77) Bus Mgr, Ann; Band; Pres, Chor; Community Yth Symph; Drama; Ensm; Madrigal; Spch C; COM; Spch A; Yth Fel; Dist Band; St-Wide Orch; *SW Col; Mus.*

DUDEK, Mary Lou
Bremerhaven American HS; Bremerhaven, GERMANY (7-31) Co-Ed, Ann; Cpt, CYO; Cpt, Drama; NHS; SC; Var C; Pres, Sr Cl; Tres, Jr Cl; Pres, Soph Cl; Bkbl; Sftbl; Tnns; COM; HQn; HCt; Athletic As; VP, PTSA; Secy, Tn C; Bowl A; *Bradford Col; Hospital Admin.*

DUDICK, Catherine Jane
Gar Mem HS; Wilkes-Barre, PA (4-186) Secy, Band; Chldr; Chor; Drama; Hmrm; NHS; SC; Bkbl; Tnns; Tr; WW; Co- cpt, Vlbl; Church & Comm Worker; *Med.*

DUDICS, Matt Andrew
Savanna HS; Anaheim, CA (16-586) Ger C; NHS; Co-Ed, Sch P; Sci C; Arch; Ftbl; Hon Prog; NEDT; Sci A; Yth Fel; Ldrship Training; Yth For Understanding; Ger Achv, Co Sci, A's; *UCLA; Med Sci.*

DUDLEY, Angelyn Lee
Scott Preparatory Sch; Opelika, AL; Anchor C; Ann; BC; Cpt, Chldr; Chem C; Ensm; Hmrm; Ntl Yth Conf; SC; Var C; VP, Soph Cl; Bkbl; Beauty; COM; HCt; NEDT; ARC A; Type A; Yth Fel; *Auburn U; Textile Engr.*

DUDLEY, Ben Clayton
Kemper Acad; DeKalb, MS (2-37) Ann; Band; BC; Chor; Bkbl; Ftbl; Tr; Beau; *Miss St U; Agr Engr.*

DUDLEY, Brenda Kay
Van-Far R-1 HS; Vandalia, MO (3-63) Secy, NHS; Bkbl; Tr; Regent Schol; Vlbl; 3rd Runner- up, Outst Art Stu; Hon Men, All Conf Bkbl; *NE Mo St U; Bus.*

DUDLEY, David Gerard
Uniondale HS; Uniondale, NY; Drama; Co-Ch, Hmrm; Bsbl; Tr; Black Stu C; Sunday Sch Teacher; Attendance A; Hon Soc; All Star Bsbl; *Psych.*

DUDLEY, Janice Elizabeth
Smiths Station HS; Smiths, AL (15%-188) BC; FBLA; Pres, FHA; 4H; Sci C; 4H A; *St Vincent Sch of Nurs; Nurs.*

DUDLEY, Lori May
McMinnville HS; McMinnville, OR; Chor; Cpt, Bkbl; Citz A; Cl Fav; Cpt, Vlbl; *Modeling.*

DUDLEY, Mary Elizabeth
Kemper Acad; DeKalb, MS (4-32) Co-Ed, Ann; BC; Bkbl; *Miss St U; Sci.*

DUDLEY, Pamela Louise
Kemper Acad; DeKalb, MS (5-32) A-Ed, Ann; BC; 4H; Bkbl; 4H A; *Miss Col; Med.*

DUDLEY, Penny Lu
Suffolk HS; Suffolk, VA; FFA; VP, Soph Cl; *Ferrum Col; Biol.*

DUDLEY, Sonya Renee
Overbrook HS; Philadelphia, PA (26-832) Band; Community Yth Symph; Ensm; Hmrm; Mjrte; Orch; Bowl Tm; Badminton Tm; Ath A; Service A; *Penn St U; Lib Arts.*

DUDLEY, Teri Lyn
Pleasant Grove HS; Pleasant Grove, AL (11-150) Ensm; Secy, NHS; Tres, Phys C; Span C; Tres, Sr Cl; Bkbl; Beauty; HCt; NEDT; Ch, Dance C; Phys Ed Asst; Pep C; *Girl's Sports Assn; U of Ala; Phys Therapy.*

DUDLEY, Thomas Kirk
Camarillo HS; Camarillo, CA; Bsbl; Bkbl; Ftbl; *Theology.*

DUE, Debra Louise
Lufkin HS; Lufkin, TX (130-520) Secy, A Cap Choir; Chldr; Tres, Drama; Secy, SC; Tres, Thes; Cl Fav; *Baylor U.*

DUEHRING, James Michael
Ripon HS; Ripon, WI (2-170) BS; Ger C; Pres, Math C; NHS; JV, Cr-Ctry; JV, Tr; NMS; Jr Kiwanian; *Carthage Col; Religion.*

DUELL, Kimberly Dawn
Woodlake Union HS; Woodlake, CA (2-132) Fr C; VP, FHA; SC; Tr; Bank Of Amer A; CSF; HCt; MLS; Vlbl.

DUELL, Rebecca Yvonne
Holyoke HS; Holyoke, CO; Band; Chor; Ensm; FHA; Madrigal; Sch P; Span C; Rptr, SC; 4H A; Type A; Pep C; FHA St Entertainment; JV Vlbl; Pres, Yth Group; Tn Missionary; News Essay Win; *Oral Roberts U; Journ.*

DUENAS, Eleanor Florida
John F Kennedy Sr HS; Tumon, GUAM; CYO; Chor; Hmrm; Ntl Yth Conf; Secy, SC; Tres, Soph Cl; Tnns; Hist A; Leadership A; Effort A; Hon Choir; *Morehouse Col.*

DUENAS, Marie Lujan
John F Kennedy HS; Tumon, GUAM (24-511) Drama; NHS; Bsbl; Sftbl; COM; Most Out; Sci A; *Pepperdine U; Teacher.*

DUENO, Sonia Ivette
Francisco Mendoza HS; Isabela, PR; Hmrm; Ed, Sch P; Bkbl; *U of Puerto Rico; Med.*

DUERKSEN, Nona Gay
Ulysses HS; Ulysses, KS (8-100) Band; Ensm; Mjrte; NHS; *Tabor Col; Elem Ed.*

DUERST, Ann Louise
Cottage Grove HS; Cottage Grove, OR (20-201) Dbte Tm; Pres, Drama; Hmrm; NHS; F-Ed, Sch P; Spch C; Pres, Thes; JV, Tnns; Drama A; *U of Oreg.*

DUES, Frank Gerald
Coldwater HS; Coldwater, OH; VP, FFA; *Body Repairman.*

DUES, Pam Jane
Coldwater Exempted Sch; Coldwater, OH (15-168) Chor; 4H; ARC; Span C; Bkbl; 4H A; *Miami Valley Col; Nurs.*

DUFF, Anthony Carl
Arlington HS; Indianapolis, IN (125-250) BS; 4H; Ntl Yth Conf; Bsbl; Ftbl; Wrest; ROTC A; Sportsmanship A; Foreign Leg A; *Armed Force Acad; ROTC Ed.*

DUFF, Donald Glenn
Pleasure Ridge Park HS; Louisville, KY (17-365) Chor; Drama; Ensm; Fr C; Ger C; Hmrm; Lat C; Span C; SC; Bkbl; Ftbl; JV, Tnns; Hon Prog; Sci A; Yth Fel; Chor, Bkbl, A's; *Ky Wesleyan Col; Ministry.*

DUFF, Kevin Omer
Marianapolis Prep Sch; Thompson, CT (2-24) Ann; Chess C; Pres, NHS; Order/Arrow; JV, Bkbl; Cr-Ctry; SC; Soccer; Tnns; COM; NEDT; HS Schol; *US Air Force Acad; Biochem.*

DUFF, Linda Marie
Belton HS; Belton, MO (8-328) Fr C; NHS; COM; NML; *William Jewell Col; Psych.*

DUFF, Robert Lynn
Russell HS; Russell, KY (6-250) Band; Pres, BC; BS; Rptr, Fr C; Hon Prog; Pres, Co-Ed Y; *VPI; Chem Engr.*

DUFF, Rodney James
Belton HS; Belton, MO (100-400) 150 Hr Serv, Sr Candystriper, A's; *Nurs.*

DUFF, Saleta Ann
Levelland HS; Levelland, TX (10-270) Co-Ed, Ann; Band; Rptr, FHA; Sch P; COM; Hist A; *South Plains Col; Math.*

DUFF, Theodis Donnell
High Point Central HS; High Point, NC (286-400) A Cap Choir; Chor; Var C; Bkbl; Cr-Ctry; Tr; FCA; Sch Mascot; VICA; *Elizabeth City St U; Mus.*

DUFF, Tyrone Curtis
Arlington HS; Indianapolis, IN (79-355) Chor; Cpt, Ntl Yth Conf; JV, Tr; COM; Hon Prog; Yth Fel; *Wallace Murry Schol; Mus As; Ind Central U; Ed.*

DUFFEK, Michael Anthony
Valley Regional HS; Deep River, CT (11-140) Pres, Band; BS; Drama; Ensm; Madrigal; NHS; Orch; VP, SC; Hon Prog; St Scholar; NML; Band, Art, A's; *Oberlin Arts & Sci Col; Mus.*

DUFFEY, Carolyn Jo
Montrose Pub Sch; Montrose, MO (4-26) Band; Chor; Ensm; VP, 4H; NHS; Bio A; 4H A; *Central Mo St U; Bio.*

DUFFEY, Christopher Kear
Yankton HS; Yankton, SD; Chor; Dbte Tm; Ensm; Ger C; Order/Arrow; Bsbl; Bkbl; Ftbl; Sftbl; Tr; Order/Arrow A; Spch A; Excel, St HS Mus Assn A; All St Chor; *Physics.*

DUFFEY, Donna Brenda
Lauralton Hall HS; Milford, CT (10-93) Pres, Key C; NHS; ARC; F-Ed, Sch P; Bkbl; Sftbl; NEDT; Type A; *Central Conn St Col; Bus Adm.*

DUFFEY, Van Marcus
Union Hill; Pittsburg, TX (4-16) Pres, BC; Pres, FFA; Sch P; Ann; Fin, Tr; B Crocker A; Cl Fav; MLS; Star Student; Advertising Ed, Sch Paper; MVP, Co-Cpt, Bkbl; Kekalb A; *Kilgore Jr Col; Pre-Vet.*

DUFFIELD, David Eugene
Milo Acad; Days Creek, OR (9-66) A Cap Choir; Tres, BS; Chor; *Walla Walla Col; Pre-Dentistry.*

DUFFIN, Kenneth
E Aurora HS; Aurora, IL; Arch; Tr; *Hinds Co Jr Col; Construction Director.*

DUFFOURCE, Jane Rachael
Grand Isle HS; Grand Isle, LA (3-24) Drama; FBLA; Sch P; Arch; Bkbl; Ftbl; Swim; Citz A; God & Country A; Spch A; Type A; Yth Fel; *Delgado Col; Bus.*

DUFFY, Elizabeth Theresa
John W Hallahan HS; Philadelphia, PA (2-431) Pres, Bus C; CYO; Chor; Fr C; NFL; NHS; Amer Leg A; Hon Prog; K of C A; Ch, Prom Comm; Ath Assn; Ch, Activity Rep; Top Rank A; *La Salle Col; Psych.*

DUFFY, Leslie B
Hightstown HS; Hightstown, NJ (16-309) Drama; Sci C; Span C; JV, Cr-Ctry; Soccer; JV, Sftbl; JV, Tr; Elk A; Hon Prog; Yth Fel; GAA; Amer Involved Doing; One Acts, Make Up; Phys, Make Up; *Allegheny Col; Bio.*

DUFFY, Mary Sheila
Bishop Watterson HS; Columbus, OH (100-240) Lat C; Var C; Bkbl; Hockey; Hon Prog; *U of Dayton; Dental Hygiene.*

DUFFY, Robert Lamar
William J Woodham HS; Pensacola, FL (1-530) Ger C; Math C; Mu Alpha Theta; Pres, NHS; Sch Achieve Tm; Co-Cpt, Ftbl; Bio A; Chem A; Hist A; Hon Prog; Math A; NEDT; Sci A; Val; Brain Brawl All Star Tm; Boy o-t Mo; HS Bowl Tm; *U of S Ala; Chem.*

DUFRENE, Marguerite Candace
Erath HS; Erath, LA (3-77) Tres, BC; Drama; Rptr, Fr C; VP, FBLA; Math C; Rptr, Sci C; COM; Chem A; Sci A; Star Student; Sup, La Mus Teacher's Assn Ral; Sup, Eva Mouton Keyboard Festival; Fin, Reg Sci Fair, 1st, HS Tal Shw; 2nd Pl, Dist Lit Ral Chem; *La Col; Chem.*

DuFRESNE, Gwendolyn June
Ainsworth HS; Flint, MI (78-291) COM; Citz A; Sci A; Yth Fel; Church Yth Coun; *Olivet Nazarene Col; Art.*

DUGAL, Lydia Jo
North Co R-I HS; Desloge, MO (10%-193) Fr C; FTA; NHS; Hon Prog; Top 10% A.

DUGAN, Jimmy Hugh
Frost HS; Frost, TX (2-27) Ann; Secy, FFA; Tres, SC; Bkbl; Ftbl; Tnns; Tr; Cl Fav; FFA Found; Outst Ath; Best Actor, Dist.

DUGAN, Kathy Joyce
Montrose Public HS; Montrose, MO (8-26) Co-Ed, Ann; Chor; Tres, Jr Cl; Cl Fav; HCt; Pres, Pep C; Instrumentalist A; Chorus Officer.

DUGAN, Latangalar Denise
Henry Ford HS; Detroit, MI (60%-249) FTA; Lat C; Span C; SC; Rptr, Secy, Future Lawyers; Church Secy; Tres, Yth Usher Board; Church Choir.

DUGAN, Linda Grace
Heritage Christian Sch; Indianapolis, IN (3-38) Tres, Band; Chor; Ensm; Fr C; GS; Ed, Sch P; Var C; Mgr, Tr; WW; Jv Bkbl Spirit A; Win, Amer Leg Spch Contest; *Ind U; Pre Med.*

DUGAS, Jennifer Lynette
Sulphur HS; Sulphur, LA (164-454) BC; 4H; *McNeese St U; Agri-Bus.*

DUGAS, Marc Jude
St Martinville Sr HS; St Martinville, LA; CYO; Dbte Tm; Fr C; VP, 4H; Bsbl; Ftbl; Religious A; Gov Rally; *U of SW La; Econ.*

DUGDALE, Jonathan Gregory
DeKalb Co HS; Smithville, TN (5-167) Pres, Fr C; FBLA; SC; Bsbl; Ftbl; Alg A; Amer Leg Orator A; Sci A; *Theology.*

DUGGAN, Carol Jane
Heidelberg American HS; Heidelberg, W GERMANY; Chor; NHS; Math A.

DUGGAN, Jean Marie
Foreman HS; Chicago, IL (1-373) CYO; Drama; Tres, FTA; Hmrm; Key C; Co-Ed, Lit Mag; Madrigal; Mu Alpha Theta; NHS; COM; Hon Prog; St Scholar; Val; Sergeant- at- arms, Span C; Service Ltr; HR Pins; *Loyola U; Dentistry.*

DUGGAN, Kathleen Elizabeth
Briarcliff HS; Atlanta, GA (15%-300) BC; Chldr; Fr C; Hmrm; Tres, SC; Mgr, Swim; HCt; Cpt, Drill Tm; Most Impressive Baronette; 1st Runner-Up, Miss BHS Pageant; *Oglethorpe U.*

DUGGER, Denise Marie
Andrew J Terrell HS; Blanchard, OK; F-Ed, Ann; BC; Chor; Drama; Ensm; FHA; Math C; NHS; Ntl Yth Conf; F-Ed, Sch P; Span C; Sftbl; Swim; Tnns; COM; Citz A; Gov Honor Prog; Hon Prog; Magna Cum Laude; Yth Fel; S-T, Pres Clrm; WW; Pep C; DECA A; *Fashion.*

DUGUID, Paula J
Vandercook Lake HS; Jackson, MI (6-102) Secy, Band; Ensm; NHS; Type A.

DUHART, Michael Steven
Bellaire Sr HS; Bellaire, TX; Chor; F-Ed, Lit Mag; JV, Bsbl; Bkbl; Tr; Alg A; Cl Fav; Hist A; Writing A; *Oral Roberts U; Psych.*

DUHE, Cheryl Ann
Destrehan HS; Destrehan, LA (6-200) BC; A-Ed, Sch P; SC; VP, Jr Cl; Cpt, Dance Tm; *Nicholls St U; Bus Adm.*

DUHN, Sandra Joy
Aplington Comm HS; Aplington, IA (50%-46) Band; Chldr; Chor.

DUHON, Karen Denise
Lake Charles HS; Lake Charles, LA; A Cap Choir; Band; Chor; FHA; Tri-HiY; Zeta Phi Beta; *La Tech Col; Rehabilitation.*

DUIS, Kevin Jeffrey
Spencer HS; Spencer, IA; Chess C; Chor; Drama; Spch C; Bsbl; Fin, Drama, Spch, A's; *Concordia Col; Ministry.*

DUKE, Alan Douglas
Pioneer Christian Acad; Whites Creek, TN (4-25) Pres, Chess C; Order/Arrow; Bkbl; Ftbl; *Mus.*

DUKE, Brenda Eileen
Hume Fogg Tech HS; Nashville, TN; *Nashville Tech Col; Food Service.*

DUKE, Bryan Wilkins
Ft Lauderdale HS; Fort Lauderdale, FL; Chor; Dbte Tm; Hmrm; Lat C; Madrigal; NFL; Golf; *Davidson Col; Law.*

DUKE, Jeffrey Franklin
Holyoke HS; Holyoke, CO (21-51) Band; Chor; VP, FBLA; Pol Sci C; Pres, ARC; F-Ed, Sch P; Sci C; SC; JV, Bkbl; COM; Sci A; Select Chor; *Colo St U; Law.*

DUKE, Karen Elizabeth
T R Miller HS; Brewton, AL (7-95) Band; FHA; FTA; Co-Ed, Lit Mag; NHS; Sci C; Dept of Interior A; Spring Hill Col Ntl Alumni A; Fin, Mobile Regional Sci Fair; *Auburn U; Vet Med.*

DUKE, Peggy Darlene
Milford HS; Milford, TX (1-10) BC; Chldr; Drama; FHA; 4H; Bkbl; Tr; HCt; HR; *Sam Houston Col; Beauty Adm.*

DUKE, Ray James
Clovis HS; Clovis, NM (87-546) Band; BS; Parl, FFA; Pres, Hmrm; DARGCA; Weightlifting; Stu Rotarian; Tn of Wk; Eagle Sct; WW; 2nd Pl, FFA St Pub Spc H; *NM St U; Agr Engr.*

DUKE, William Christopher
Moore HS; Louisville, KY (10%-300) Ch, BS; Dbte Tm; NHS; Co-Ed, Sch P; SC; Parl, Jr Cl; Swim; Tnns; COM; Yth Fel; Pres o-t Yr, JA; Outst A, Tnns; *Bus.*

DUKES, Garland Doyce
Allison HS; Allison, TX (5-10) *Clarendon Col; Agr.*

DUKES, Gina Larose
Buena HS; Sierra Vista, AZ (149-495) Co-Cpt, Chldr; Span C; Cr-Ctry; Tr; *Ariz St U; Child Care.*

DUKES, Jennifer Denise
Hoke Smith HS; Atlanta, GA (2-293) Band; SC; HQn; Mus Trophy; *Mus.*

DUKES, Linda Nancy
Hernando HS; Brooksville, FL (30-300) Secy, FFA; Pres, 4H; Span C; Sftbl; COM; 4H A; Most Out; Proficiency A, FFA; *U of Fla; Dairy Sci.*

DUKES, Roxanne
Independence HS; Independence, MS (10%-106) A-Ed, Ann; BC; Chldr; FHA; Bkbl; Beauty; Cl Fav; HQn; HCt; *U of Miss; Art.*

DUKES, Sandra Taye
Anniston HS; Anniston, AL; BC; Cpt, Chldr; 4H; VP, Hmrm; NFL; Bsbl; Bkbl; Cl Fav; Most Athletic; *Gadsden St Tech Inst; Bus Adm.*

DUKES, Sharon Denise
Wayne Co HS; Jesup, GA (10%-360) Ann; BC; Chor; FHA; 4H; HiY; Span C; Bkbl; NEDT; Jr Homemaker Degree; *Ga Sou Col; Nurs.*

DUKESHERER, Rhonda Kay
Benton Harbor HS; Benton Harbor, MI (10%-500) A-Ed, Ann; 4H; Co-Ed, Sch P.

DUKESHERER, Sharon Elaine
Benton Harbor HS; Benton Harbor, MI (33-420) Ed, Ann; Fr C; 4H; NHS; Ski C; SC; COM; 4H A; HCt; Hon Prog; JA A.

DULANEY, Sharon Denee
George Henry Corliss HS; Chicago, IL (8-250) Chor; Math C; NHS; Rptr, Sch P; Span C; Cpt, Bkbl; Tr; Citz A; Hon Prog; Math A; Sci A; Cpt, Vlbl; *Milwaukee Sch of Engr; Elec Engr.*

DULANY, Kenneth Wayne
Midway HS; Waco, TX (10%-257) Lat C; VP, Soph Cl; Bsbl; JV, Ftbl; COM; Citz A.

DULIN, Christopher Duane
Richardson HS; Richardson, TX (250-950) Band; Orch; Church Chor; Church Sftbl; All St Orch; Col Schol; *Sou Methodist U; Mus.*

DULL, Beverly June
Tri-City HS; Buffalo, IL (8-56) Band; Chor; FTA; 4H; A-Ed, Sch P; Pres, SC; 4H A; Hist A; I Dare You; WW; Outst Sr Eng Stu; *Lincoln Land Comm Col; Nurs.*

DULL, Charlotte Louise
Tri-City HS; Buffalo, IL; Band; Chor; VP, FHA; FTA; Sch P; Spch C; Tres, Soph Cl; Mgr, Tr; Spch A; Band Ltr; Tr Ltr; Newspaper A; *Lincoln Rand Col; Nurs.*

DULL, Dennis Downing
E Jackson HS; Jackson, MI (15%-120) Band; Wrest.

DULLUM, Sharyn Louise
Stoughton Sr HS; Stoughton, WI (24-237) Band; Lat C; NHS; Hon Prog; GAA A; Band A; *Madison Area Tech Col; Registered Nurs.*

DUMANTT, Iride Marie
Dra Maria Cadilla de Martinez HS; Arecibo, PR (9-429) Chor; Dbte Tm; VP, FHA; Pres, Hmrm; NHS; Pres, SC; Hon Prog; High Hon Stu; *Arecibo's UPR Regional Col; Med.*

DUMAS, Beverly Anita
Danbury HS; Danbury, CT (266-864) Chldr; Drama; Fr C; French NHS; Hmrm; SC; Bkbl; COM; JA A; MLS; Most Out; Rotary A; Rotary C Exchange Stu, Phillipines; *Morehouse Col; Med.*

DUMAS, Tanya R
W Monroe HS; W Monroe, LA; Anchor C; Band; Dbte Tm; FHA; 4H; InterAct C; Key C; NHS; Rainbow; SC; Y-Tns; Sftbl; COM; Citz A; Cl Fav; DARGCA; 4H A; VFW A; Yth Coun; *NE La U; Therapy.*

DUMKE, Mark Hobart
Lewiston HS; Lewiston, ID (61-500) Ger C; Lit Mag; *NW Nazarene Col; Eng.*

DUMLAO, Dana Ann
George Washington Sr HS; Mangilao, GUAM; NHS; Sch P; VP, Jr Cl; Secy, Soph Cl; Sftbl; Most Out; Sal; Miss GW; *Med.*

DUMMEYER, David Michael
Lindbergh HS; St Louis, MO (1%-1000) Band; Chess C; Community Yth Symph; Ensm; NHS; Orch; Sci C; Tr; Photo C; Symph Band; Col Comm Orch & Symph Band; *U of Ariz; Astrophysics.*

DUMOND, Frank Vincent
Christopher Columbus HS; Miami, FL (10-200) Bus C; JV, Ftbl; Tr; Amer Leg A; Hon Prog; Top Ten; *MIT; Eng.*

DuMONT, Denise
Lamar HS; Houston, TX (211-526) Chor; Hmrm; SC; Pres, Drill Tm; *Stephen F Austin Col; Elem Ed.*

DUMPSON, Donald
Overbrook HS; Philadelphia, PA; A Cap Choir; Chor; Drama; Ensm; Hmrm; Madrigal; Most Out; Star Student; Vocal A; *Wilberforce U; Mus Ed.*

DUMSTORFF, JoAnn Rose
Central Comm HS; Breese, IL (9-157) Chor; Drama; Span C; Amer Leg A; Bio A; Hist A; Shorthand A; Chor A.

DUNAGAN, Dee Ann
Frost HS; Frost, TX (2-15) Ann; Drama; FHA; Cpt, Mjrte; Spch C; Tres, Sr Cl; *Navarro Col; Bus.*

DUNAHAY, Jeffrey Duane
Bath Sr HS; Lima, OH (50%-219) Chor; Drama; SC; Var C; Pres, Sr Cl; Pres, Soph Cl; Ftbl; Tr; Yth Fel.

DUNAWAY, Chandra Vonzetta
Northumberland HS; Heathsville, VA (46-114) Co-Cpt, Chldr; SC; Tres, Sr Cl; Tres, Jr Cl; Citz A; Chldr A; *Rappahannock Comm Col; Bus.*

DUNAWAY, Terry Ann
South Side HS; Jackson, TN; Rptr, BC; 4H; Mu Alpha Theta; Sch P; 4H A.

DUNBAR, Brenda Susan
Harlingen HS; Harlingen, TX (87-650) Band; *E Tex Baptist Col; Elem Ed.*

DUNBAR, Christine Marie
Geneva HS; Geneva, OH; Pres, 4H; JV, Bkbl; MVP, Tr; 4H A; *Coun.*

DUNBAR, Douglas Kent
Holly Grove HS; Holly Grove, AR (1-66) BC; BS; Chem C; Demolay; Hmrm; NHS; Phys C; Sci C; Span C; SC; Bsbl; MVP, Ftbl; Golf; Tr; Wrest; Chem A; Citz A; Hon Prog; Math A; *US Air Force Acad; Engr.*

DUNBAR, Greg Allen
Lower Dauphin Sr HS; Hummelstown, PA; FFA.

DUNBAR, Pamela Ann
John Marshall HS; Oklahoma City, OK; Chldr; Jr Cl; Tres, Soph Cl; Secy, Modern Dance; Pep C; *Okla St U.*

DUNBAR, Rebecca Sally
Geneva HS; Geneva, OH (81-250) Chor; 4H A; VP & S-T, 4-H C; Stu Librarian A; *Kent St U; Ed.*

DUNBAR, Seth Owen
Lower Dauphin Sr HS; Hummelstown, PA; FFA; Order/Arrow; Order/Arrow A; Spch A; Yth Fel.

DUNCAN, Alice Earlene
W Carter HS; Olive Hill, KY; Pres, FHA; Sci C; Co-Ed Correspondent; *Morehead St U; Home Ec.*

DUNCAN, Beatrice
Estill HS; Estill, SC; Ann; Hmrm; Ntl Yth Conf; Sch P; Span C; SC; Bkbl; *USC; Bus Adm.*

DUNCAN, Carol Marie
West-Windsor Plainsboro HS; Princeton Junction, NJ; Chor; SC; Tres, Jr Cl; Bkbl; Hockey; Sftbl; Hon Prog; Yth Fel.

DUNCAN, Cathy Jean
Alma J Brown HS; Grambling, LA (5-40) Drama; Fr C; FTA; 4H; 4H A; Star Student; Yth Fel; *NW U; Acct.*

DUNCAN, Ceresa Gay
Lindbergh HS; Renton, WA; Drama; Hmrm; NHS; Spch C; SC; Thes; Sftbl; Hist A; High Point, Pep Sq; Duet Acting A, Spch Festival; *Wash U; Drama.*

DUNCAN, Charlotte Martin
William H Hall HS; W Hartford, CT (263-512) Chor; Sci C; Jr Citz Dance C; Natural Sci C; Barn Staff & Jr Coun, YMCA; Secy, Church Yth Group; Sunday Sch Teacher; *Animal Sci.*

DUNCAN, Cheryl Lynn
M B Smiley Sr HS; Houston, TX (2-400) FTA; Math C; Mu Alpha Theta; NHS; Sci C; Var C; Cpt, Tr; Alg A; COM; Chem A; Cl Fav; Hon Prog; Math A; Most Out; Sci A; Star Student; Tres, 1st Ladies; Miss Soph; Cpt, MVP, Vlbl; St Fin, Tr; HS All Amer; Gen Bus Medal; Eng Medal; *U of Houston; Pre-Med.*

DUNCAN, Clark William
Unicoi Co HS; Erwin, TN (92-168) All Amer Yth; HiY; Hmrm; Tres, Key C; NHS; Sci C; SC; Tri-HiY; Cpt, Var C; Bsbl; Bkbl; Cpt, Ftbl; Cpt, Tr; WW; E Tenn Back o-t Yr; Ftbl Schol, U of Tenn; All E Tn, All St, All Amer, Ftbl; *U of Tenn; Bus.*

DUNCAN, Connie Lynn
Tylertown HS; Tylertown, MS (40%-160) Band; FBLA; *Math.*

DUNCAN, D Lynn
Fairfield Local HS; Leesburg, OH; NHS; Pres, Sr Cl; COM; 4H A; HQn; Hon Prog; Yth Fel; Best Actress A; Cpt, Drill Tm; Ch, Prom; 4-H Camp Counselor; *Miami U; Psych.*

DUNCAN, Dale Ray
Broken Arrow HS; Broken Arrow, OK; Band; NHS; COM; MLS; *U of Okla; Archt.*

DUNCAN, Daniel Patrick
Alamance Christian Sch; Graham, NC (2-32) Band; Chor; Fr C; Pres, NHS; Bkbl; Soccer; Tr; Bio A; Hon Prog; Math A; Eng A; Jr Marshal.

DUNCAN, David Doyle
Kickapoo HS; Springfield, MO; Key C; JV, Ftbl; Swim; JV, Tr; *William Jewell Col.*

DUNCAN, David Gerald
Bethel Christian Sch; Garden Grove, CA (1-7) A Cap Choir; Ann; Chor; Drama; Ensm; Ger C; Ski C; VP, SC; Var C; Bkbl; Hon Prog; Cpt, MVP, Ftbl; *Mesa Col.*

DUNCAN, David Paul
Tartan Sr HS; Oakdale, MN (99-465) Band; Chor; Drama; Ensm; Bkbl; Co-Cpt, Swim; Tr; COM; Chamber of Comm A; Hon Prog; PTA A; Spch A; Ntl PTA A, Cultural Arts; Superior, Region Trombone; Tex Congress A's; Cultural Arts & Drama Entry; *Pol Sci.*

DUNCAN, David Walter Jr
Myers Park HS; Charlotte, NC (100-350) Band; Chor; Mod Mus Mas; Orch; Ski C; Bsbl; *Appalachian St Col; Mus.*

DUNCAN, Debbie Anne
Troy HS; Troy, KS (7-40) Band; Chor; Ensm; GS; Pres, 4H; Secy, Hmrm; Mjrte; Spch C; Secy, Jr Cl; Secy, Soph Cl; Bsbl; Bkbl; Tr; COM; Citz A; 4H A; PTA A; Spch A; Yth Fel; VP, Kayette; One Act Play; Pep C; Swtht Cand, FFA; 4-H Fair Princess; *Sociology.*

DUNCAN, Deborah Suzanne
Penn Manor HS; Millersville, PA (99-400) Ann; Chor; Ensm; Lit Mag; NHS; Sch P; Tres, JA; Gym; V Ltr; *Clarion St Col; Spch Pathology & Audiology.*

DUNCAN, Debra Diane
Caney Valley HS; Caney, KS (10%-70) CYO; FHA; Sch P; Mgr, Tr; Journ A; *Kans St U; Photo Journ.*

DUNCAN, Deland Roosevelt
N Denver HS; Denver, CO (138-440) Band; Bkbl; Tnns; Tr; *Metro St Col; Recreation Director.*

DUNCAN, Delwyn Lynn
Benton Co R-1 HS; Cole Camp, MO; A Cap Choir; Ann; VP, Band; BS; Chor; Drama; VP, FTA; Pres, SC; Thes; Var C; Co-Cpt, Bsbl; Co-Cpt, Bkbl; Co-Cpt, Cr-Ctry; Amer Leg A; Citz A; HCt; Type A; Ath, Mus, A's; Ed.

DUNCAN, Janice Marie
Holy Family HS; Birmingham, AL (1-35) Co-Cpt, Chldr; Fr C; NHS; Pres, SC; VP, Soph Cl; Alg A; COM; Chem A; DARGCA; HQn; Hon Prog; Math A; Type A; Geom A; Adya WW Chldr; Alg A; Eng A; WW; Fisk U; Spch Therapy.

DUNCAN, Jody Janel
Kokomo HS; Kokomo, IN (30-481) Fr C; Howard U; Law.

DUNCAN, Karen Louise
W Windsor Plainsboro HS; Princeton Jct, NJ; Chor; SC; Var C; Bkbl; JV, Hockey; Sftbl; Hon Prog; Yth Fel.

DUNCAN, Laura Lee
Wyoming HS; Cincinnati, OH (10-215) AFS; Band; Cum Laude Soc; Drama; NHS; Orch; SC; Hon Prog; Magna Cum Laude; WW; Miami U; Home Ec.

DUNCAN, Leslye Andre
Corona del Mar HS; Newport Beach, CA; A Cap Choir; Chor; Ensm; Semi-Fin, Jr Miss Pa; Bkbl; Mgr, Swim; WW; Biola Col; Nurs.

DUNCAN, Lillie Mae
Estill HS; Estill, SC (25%-100) U of SC; Bus.

DUNCAN, Peggy Sue
Forest Lake Sr HS; Forest Lake, MN (300-511) Chor; Rptr, 4H; 4H A.

DUNCAN, Rebecca Ann
Landmark Christian HS; Cincinnati, OH (10-36) Band; Chor; Orch; Yth Fel; Choir; Bible Quiz Tm; Evangelism Explosion; Asbury Col.

DUNCAN, Ronnie Lazard
T R Miller HS; Brewton, AL; Ann; Chess C; Chor; Bkbl; Sftbl; Tnns; Type A; US Air Force; Bus Adm.

DUNCAN, Sharon Minette
Richfield Sr HS; Richfield, MN (10%-800) Drama; Ger C; Spch C; Amer Leg A; Ed.

DUNCAN, Susan Margaret
Arkadelphia Sr HS; Arkadelphia, AR (10%-195) Band; Fr C; GS; Hmrm; Sch P; Rptr, SC; Hist A; Journ A; Fr A; U of Ark; Fr.

DUNCAN, Thomas Charles
Forest Lake Sr HS; Forest Lake, MN (309-496) A Cap Choir; Chor; 4H; 4H A.

DUNCAN, Veronica Lynn
North HS; Denver, CO; HR; Hon C; Bus.

DUNDAS, Steven Lestlie
Thomas Alva Edison Sr HS; Stockton, CA (117-375) Band; Chess C; Secy, Fr C; InterClub Coun; Spch C; JV, Ftbl; Hockey; JV, Tr; ROTC A; V Trnr, Ftbl; San Joquin Delta Col; Hist.

DUNFEE, Connie Lee
Hopewell HS; Aliquippa, PA; Chor; Hmrm; Rainbow; SC; Yth Fel; F-Ed, Yrbk; Scarab Art C; Yth Choir; Med.

DUNGAN, Darla Anita
Ritenour Sr HS; Overland, MO (15%-855) A Cap Choir; NHS; Stu of High Schol Promise A; SE Mo St U; Fashion Merchandizing.

DUNGAN, Joseph Charles
Brimfield HS; Brimfield, IL (4-57) Ed, Ann; Band; Chor; VP, Drama; NHS; VP, SC; Thes; St Scholar; All St Choir; 1st Pl, Vocal & Instrum Mus Cont; Ill St U; Mus.

DUNGAN, Lynda Sue
Baker HS; Baker, LA (30-374) GS; VP, NHS; Tres, Tri-HiY; Jr Cabinet; S-T; Pepsters; Mu Sigma; Southeastern La U; Nurs.

DUNHAM, Boyd Charles
Pawhuska HS; Pawhuska, OK (15-90) NHS; Pres, SC; Bsbl; Co-Cpt, Ftbl; Eagle Sct; Ntl Explorers C; OSU-Stillwater; Geol Engr.

DUNHAM, Gary Herbert
Telstar Regional HS; Bethel, ME (5%-83) Band; Chor; Alg A; Balfour A; Hist A; Math A; Sci A; Highest Cl Avg, Eng; Adirondack Comm Col; Hist.

DUNHAM, Leon Ray
Ilwaco HS; Ilwaco, WA (20-100) Band; Pres, 4H; NHS; Wrest; Foxfire Project, Centrum Found; Biol.

DUNHAM, Melody Sue
Copeland Unified HS; Copeland, KS; Chor; Secy, 4H; Bkbl; Sftbl; Fin, Tr; 4H A.

DUNHAM, Sarah Ann
N Central HS; Indianapolis, IN (239-1255) Chor; Drama; 4H; Hmrm; JETS; NHS; SC; Thes; Bkbl; Sftbl; Most Out; Vlbl; Bsbl, Best Sportsmanship; Secy, St Crew C; GAA; Valparaiso Col; Theology.

DUNHAM, Theodore Adams
Memorial HS; Joplin, MO; A Cap Choir; Chor; Mgr, Ftbl; Mgr, Wrest; God & Country A; Eagle Sct; Computer and Elec Tech.

DUNITHAN, Valerie Jean
Northridge HS; Middleburg, IN (33%-130) GS; Amer Leg A; COM; Bus.

DUNIVAN, Sandra Jean
Jefferson Comm HS; Jefferson, IA (11-122) AFS; Chldr; Chor; 4H; Var C; Tr; 4H A; Type A; U of Northern Iowa; Elem Ed.

DUNKLE, Brenda Diane
Homestead HS; Fort Wayne, IN (60-250) Band; Drama; S-T, 4H; Mjrte; NHS; Rainbow; Bio A; 4H A; Sci A; Sci.

DUNKLEE, Rodney Louis
New Lothrop Area Sch; New Lothrop, MI (7-98) Band; Chor; Dbte Tm; Drama; Ensm; 4H; Madrigal; NFL; Sch P; Ski C; COM; 4H A; PTA A; Sci A; Yth Fel; Comm Choir; Dist Solo & Ensm; Jerry Lewis A; Michigan St U; Engr.

DUNKLEY, Connie Leigh
Person Sr HS; Roxboro, NC (3-399) A Cap Choir; Cpt, Chldr; Chor; Drama; Fr C; Jr Miss Pagent; Monogram; Secy, NHS; SC; Tri-HiY; COM; Gov Honor Prog; HCt; U of NC; Phar.

DUNLAP, Cassandra Adelle
Palo Duro HS; Amarillo, TX (2-400) Dbte Tm; Drama; FHA; Bkbl; Tr; Spch A; 1st Cl GSct; SC; Harvard U; Law.

DUNLAP, Dale Irwin
Cass Tech HS; Detroit, MI (17-836) NHS; Swim; Hon Prog; Math A; Phi Beta Kappa; Yth Fel; Mich Tech U; Mech Engr.

DUNLAP, Lisa Jean
Brookings HS; Brookings, SD (90-209) Chldr; Secy, Chor; Span C; Bkbl; Sftbl; Tr; Gym Tm; Sch Musical; Pres Phy Fitness A; SDSU; Floristry.

DUNLAP, Pamela LeAnn
Kingsbury HS; Memphis, TN (180-232) Chor; Pres, Hmrm; Mod Mus Mas; Rainbow; Spch C; SC; Y-Tns; Bkbl; Sftbl; Swim; ROTC A; Type A; Evangel Col; Bus.

DUNLAP, Paula Ann
Temple Heights Christian Sch; Tampa, FL (3-59) Chess C; Tres, NHS; Secy, Jr Cl; COM; HR; Clearwater Christian Col; Ed.

DUNLAP, Rhonda Jeane
Rock Hill HS; Rock Hill, SC; Fr C; S-T, Hmrm; Y-Tns; Vet.

DUNLAP, Robert Henry Jr
Robert E Lee HS; Baytown, TX (191-400) Dbte Tm; Pres, Drama; Thes; Lee Col; Dramatics.

DUNLAP, Scott Williamson
Bartow Sr HS; Bartow, FL (2%-300) Chess C; Key C; NHS; Sci C; Span C; Span NHS; Golf; Alg A; COM; H of F; Math A; Sci A; Hi-Q Tm; Brain Bowl Tm; High Point Avg Cap; Duke U.

DUNLAP, Vicki Gail
Tahlequah HS; Tahlequah, OK; FBLA; FTA; Math C; NHS; Bkbl; Sftbl; Tnns; Tr.

DUNLEAVY, John Patrick
Bishop Watterson HS; Columbus, OH (75-255) Chor; Drama; Hmrm; Rptr, Sch P; Ftbl; Tr; Cpt, Wrest; COM; NEDT; NML; Ga Tech; Civil Engr.

DUNLOP, Debbie Ann
Jefferson Comm HS; Jefferson, IA (4-122) AFS; Ann; Chor; Fr C; JV, Golf; Type A; Iowa St U; Acct.

DUNMIRE, John Douglas
Harbor HS; Santa Cruz, CA (20-300) VP, Key C; Ski C; Davis Col; Vet.

DUNMIRE, Rechell Layne
Chardon HS; Chardon, OH (50-225) AFS; Cpt, Chldr; S-T, Chor; Drama; 4H; NHS; SC; Co-Cpt, Cr-Ctry; Tr; 4H A; HCt; MVP, Gym; Grove City Col; Bus.

DUNMIRE, Renna Lynn
Chardon HS; Chardon, OH; A Cap Choir; JV, Chldr; Tr; Gym; Outst Fresh, Track; Nurs.

DUNMORE, Gwendolyn Irene
Ballou HS; Washington, DC; FHA; ARC; ARC A; Strayer Col; Bus Adm.

DUNN, Albert Joseph
Sharpsville Area Sr HS; Sharpsville, PA (3-187) Ann; Chor; Ger C; Bkbl; Yth Fel; Asst Director, Vacation Bible Sch; Cl Play; Church Official Board.

DUNN, Bernetta Ann
Hueytown HS; Hueytown, AL; NHS; 4H A; UAB; Nurs.

DUNN, Carla Ann
Henry Grady HS; Atlanta, GA (7-180) A-Ed, Ann; VP, BC; VP, Fr C; VP, FHA; Pres, FTA; Pres, Hmrm; Fin, Jr Miss Pagent; Math C; Mu Alpha Theta; NHS; Phys C; Co-Ed, Sch P; VP, SC; Pres, Var C; Pres, Jr Cl; Beauty; Citz A; Cl Fav; Gov Honor Prog; HCt; Hon Prog; Journ A; Most Out; Q&S A; Swtht; Cpt, Drill Tm; City & St All-Star Drill Tm; Emory at Oxford; Eng.

DUNN, Carolyn Louise
Fair Park HS; Shreveport, LA (33%-300) F-Ed, Ann; Spch C; Hon Prog; ARC A; Type A; PA, 2 Yrs; McNeese St; Bus.

DUNN, Casey A
York Central Sch; Retsof, NY; Drama; Rptr, Sch P; SC; Pres, Soph Cl; Tr; Regent Schol.

DUNN, David Charles
Putnam City HS; Okla City, OK (100-850) Band; Bus C; FBLA; Model UN; NHS; Pol Sci C; F-Ed, Sch P; Ski C; Spch C; World Affairs C; DARGCA; Hist A; Journ A; Spch A; St Scholar; VFW A; VFW Orator Win; VofDEM; Okla St U; Bus.

DUNN, Debbie Jo
Ross S Sterling HS; Baytown, TX; AFS; Band; Jr Rotary Ann's C.

DUNN, Donna Kaye
Antelope Valley HS; Lancaster, CA (20%-800) A Cap Choir; Ensm; Madrigal; Ski C; CSF; Hon Prog; Yth Fel; Bkbl Princess; Hon Choir; Magazine Creative Writing A; Azusa Pacific Col.

DUNN, Frances Norine
Wakulla HS; Crawfordville, FL; Band; Chor; 4H; Orch; Up Bound; 4H A; Fla St U; Law.

DUNN, Gilda Suzette
Alma J Brown Laboratory HS; Grambling, LA; Band; Ensm; 4H; Sci C; Bkbl; Fin, 4-H C A; Semi-Fin, NEDT Cert; Fin, Sci A.

DUNN, Jennifer Ann
Wilkes Central HS; Wilkesboro, NC (44-243) Band; Chor; Secy, InterAct C; Poet A; U of NC; Nurs.

DUNN, John Rees Jr
Cullman HS; Cullman, AL (7-195) AFS; Band; 4H; NHS; Sci C; Span C; Bsbl; Ftbl; Swim; Bio A; COM; 4H A; Sci A; Spch A; Most Improved, Piano; Swim, Span, A's; Trevecca Nazarene Col; Med.

DUNN, John Timothy
Parkview HS; Springfield, MO (10%-400) BS; Dbte Tm; Fr C; FBLA; NFL; Spch C; Var C; Ftbl; JV, Tr; Spch A; Military Acad; Engr.

DUNN, Joni Lynn
Norhtside HS; Vernon, TX (2-8) Co-Ed, Ann; VP, BC; Dbte Tm; Tres, FHA; 4H; Secy, Sr Cl; Secy, Jr Cl; Secy, Soph Cl; Co-Cpt, Bkbl; Tnns; Tr; Cl Fav; HCt; MLS; Sal; Type A; WW in Phys Ed; Best All Around; Scholastic A; Hardin-Simmons Col; Pre-Law.

DUNN, Kathy Sue
Lyon County HS; Eddyville, KY; BC; FHA; Drill Corps; Berea Col; Drafting.

DUNN, Kelly Allen
Newport Harbor HS; Newport Beach, CA (450-1100) Ger C; Ski C; Ftbl; Soccer; Cpt, Tnns; Golden West Col.

DUNN, Kris William
Newport Harbor HS; Newport Beach, CA (40%-700) Var C; Ftbl; Cpt, Soccer; MVP, Tnns; Citz A; Most Spirited; MVP, Soccer; All Tourn; Coaches A; *Cuesta Col; Archt.*

DUNN, Lawrence Douglas
Edison HS; Minneapolis, MN (5-530) MVP, Band; Ger C; Hmrm; Pres, Key C; NFL; NHS; Orch; Co-Cpt, Spch C; COM; H of F; Hon Prog; Kiwanis A; Math A; MLS; Most Out; NMF; Rotary A; ROTC A; Spch A; VFW A; US Marine Corps Quist Musician A; Ntl WW in Mus; Lewis G Cook A; St Spch Contest; Highest Schol A; *U of Minn; Elec Engr.*

DUNN, Lisa Darlene
Milburn HS; Milburn, OK (4%-19) FHA; NHS; Sch P; Bkbl; Sftbl; HQn; Wittiest; Most Popular; *Murray Col; Phys Ed.*

DUNN, Lisa Marie
Mt Rainier HS; Des Moines, WA (85-465) Band; Chem C; Chor; Dbte Tm; Drama; NFL; NHS; COM; Spch A; *Whitworth Col.*

DUNN, Michael Leon
Telstar Regional HS; Bethel, ME (7-75) BS; NHS; Ski C; Var C; Cpt, Bsbl; Co-Cpt, Ftbl; Alg A; Balfour A; Bio A; Chem A; Gr Marshal; Hist A; Hon Prog; Math A; Phy A; Pres A; Sci A; *Navy; Iron Structure.*

DUNN, Nancy Lea
Watkins Glen Central HS; Watkins Glen, NY; A Cap Choir; Band; Mgr, Chldr; Chor; Ensm; Var C; Swim; Tr; WW; *Mus.*

DUNN, Paula Kay
Madison Grant HS; Fairmount, IN (52-205) Chor; Gym; *Marion Col; Dental Hygienest.*

DUNN, Rebecca Anne
Homer L Ferguson HS; Newport News, VA (100-450) A Cap Choir; VP, Drama; Key C; Co-Ed, Lit Mag; NFL; Span C; Job's Daughters; *Va Intermont Col; Communications.*

DUNN, Robert Thomas
Houston HS; Houston, MO (1-120) Band; Dbte Tm; Pres, 4H; Math C; NHS; Ed, Sch P; Sci C; Pres, SC; UN Council; Var C; Pres, Soph Cl; Bkbl; Ftbl; Cpt, Swim; Tr; Curator A; 4H A; HCt; Spch A; Star Student; Val; Debate A's; Tr Hon's; Acad Hon Schol; Alt, MFA Schol; *Westminster Col; Bio.*

DUNN, Rodney Scott
Monterey HS; Lubbock, TX (11-700) NHS; Span C; Cr-Ctry; JV, Ftbl; Tr; Citz A; Cl Fav; DARGCA; JA A; Opt Out Tn; Yth Fel; Tn o-t Mo; Most Acad; *Tex Tech U; Archt.*

DUNN, Roquel Yvette
Green B Trimble Tech HS; Fort Worth, TX; FHA; Hmrm; SC; Parl, OEA; Bstr C; JA; *Tarrant Co Jr Col; Eng.*

DUNN, Susan Laurie
Bethel Baptist Christian Sch; Garden Grove, CA (2-30) Ann; Dbte Tm; Drama; Ensm; Spch C; Thes.

DUNN, Suzanne Gaye
Daviess Co HS; Owensboro, KY; Band; Community Yth Symph; VP, Fr C; Math C; Bio A; *U of Ky; Math.*

DUNNAGAN, Katrina Ruth
Eldorado HS; Albuquerque, NM (418-744) Ger C; Sch P; Co-Cpt, Bkbl; *NM St U; Police Sci.*

DUNNAM, Bill Carl
Jonesboro HS; Jonesboro, AR; Geom A; Rifle Range A; *ASU; Archt.*

DUNNAM, Jerry Keith
Patrick Henry HS; San Diego, CA (675-1100) MVP, Bsbl; MVP, Bkbl; Church Choir; *Mesa Jr Col; Archt Drafting.*

DUNNAM, Robin Jane
New Augusta Educational Center; New Augusta, MS (4-28) Ann; Band; BC; Chldr; FHA; NHS; Sch P; HCt; Lion A; *Belhaven Col; Bus.*

DUNNAM, Roger Eliot
Acadiana HS; Lafayette, LA; Chor; FFA; Var C; Bsbl; JV, Bkbl; Ftbl; *U of Sou La.*

DUNNAVANT, Kay Edith
Fairmont Sr HS; Fairmont, WV (2-235) Pres, Chess C; Chor; Ensm; Fr C; Mu Alpha Theta; Service C; Math Field Day.

DUNNIGAN, Ann Renee
St Marys Central HS; Bismarck, ND (25-172) CYO; Fr C; SC; Tr; *U of ND; Early Childhood Ed.*

DUNNING, Lori Kay
Henry Ford II HS; Sterling Heights, MI (50-460) Chor; Fr C; Wrestleltte; *Grand Valley St Col; Nurs.*

DUNNO, Janet Lynn
Tinora Sr HS; Defiance, OH (6-113) Band; Chldr; Chor; Ensm; 4H; Mjrte; Monogram; NHS; ARC; Sch Achieve Tm; Bkbl; Tr; Math A; ARC A; Sup, Solo & Ensm; OPRC As; 5th Grade Cl Schol; Math.

DUNRUD, Kevin Todd
Lake of the Woods HS; Baudette, MN (20-90) NHS; 4H A; HCt; Curling; *Bemidji Area Voc Col; Auto Mech.*

DUNSE, Ellen Marie
Sauk Prairie HS; Prairie du Sac, WI; Band; 4H; Sftbl; 4H A.

DUNSON, Annie Louise
Jess Lanier HS; Bessemer, AL; Rho Alpha Soc; Ntl Spell Bee A; Poetry Festival Cert; Little Miss Red Ore; *St Vincent Nurs Sch; Med.*

DUNSON, Lillian Denise
Stivers Patterson Cooperative HS; Dayton, OH (50-500) Bus C; Y-Tns; Parl, Jr Cl; COM; Type A; Pep C; Church Choir; Shorthand Theory A; *Bowling Green U; Bus Adm.*

DUNWELL, Nancy Harriet
Pamlico Comm Sch; Washington, NC; Bkbl; Most Unselfish, Bkbl; *Art.*

DUNWOODY, Melinda Gayle
Moberly Sr HS; Moberly, MO (25%-200) Bus C; Secy, Chor; Pres, Fr C; FBLA; Secy, Madrigal; NHS; Secy, SC; Citz A; Swtht; Psych C; Gym; Winter Sports Qn; *SMSU; Psych.*

DUPAS, Mary Jacqueline
Stephe F Austin Sr HS; Houston, TX; 4H A; *U of Houston.*

DUPAY, Michael Dean
Nitro HS; Nitro, WV; BS; Hmrm; NHS; Var C; Bsbl; Bkbl; HCt; Hon Prog; *Marshall U; Gen Stu.*

DUPEE, Edward Antonia
Christian Co HS; Hopkinsville, KY (10-31) Dbte Tm; NFL; Spch C; Cr-Ctry; Tr; Citz A; Eng A; Most Improved; Tr; Merit Badge; *Aviation.*

DUPLECHAN, Lloyd Simon
Antelope Valley HS; Lancaster, CA; Band; Orch; Hon Prog; *Calif St U-Northridge; Mus.*

DUPLESSIS, Connie Marie
Bishop Conaty Mem HS; Los Angeles, CA; *Pepperdine U; Med.*

DUPLESSIS, Trudy Ann
Bishop Conaty HS; Los Angeles, CA; *Rehabilitation.*

DUPRE, Kendra Ann
Lutheran HS; New Orleans, LA (5-38) Ed, Ann; Chor; Hmrm; Bus Mgr, Sch P; SC; JA A; NEDT; *U of New Orleans; Eng Ed.*

DUPREE, Donna Faye
St Matthew HS; Melrose, LA; CYO; FHA; Secy, 4H; Alg A; 4H A; Hon Prog; Spch A; Miss 4-H; *Northwestern U.*

DUPREE, Mark Dale
Conroe HS; Conroe, TX (455-935) Ind Arts C; *Religion.*

DUPREE, Mary Lynn
Fitzgerald HS; Fitzgerald, GA (10-150) Band; BC; Chor; Ensm; 4H; Hmrm; Lit Ral; St Stu Congress; SC; Pres, Tri-HiY.

DUPREE, Michael Loyd
Atlanta HS; Atlanta, TX; Ensm; JETS; Sci C; Mgr, Bkbl; JV, Ftbl; JV, Golf; Mgr, Tr.

DuPREE, Ralph Wadsworth
Bennettsville HS; Bennettsville, SC (30-249) Band; BC; BS; 4H; HiY; Sch P; Sci C; Hon Prog; Sci A; *U of Sci; Ed.*

DUPREE, Ron Dwane
Sparkman HS; Toney, AL (1%-161) A Cap Choir; F-Ed, Ann; Band; BC; Chem C; Chess C; Chor; Cum Laude Soc; Dbte Tm; Ensm; Key C; Ed, Lit Mag; MVP, Math C; NHS; Phys C; ARC; Ed, Sch P; Sci C; Tri-HiY; Bsbl; Bkbl; Golf; Alg A; Bio A; COM; Chem A; Gov Honor Prog; Hist A; Hon Prog; Math A; Ntl Achv Schol; Phi Beta Kappa; Phy A; ROTC A; Sci A; Summa Cum Laude; Cpt, Math C; Army ROTC Schol; Acad Achv A; Yth Pastor A; *U of Ala; Bio.*

DUPREE,
Roussaint L Ouverture
Pine View Sch; Sarasota, FL (32-36) Key C; NFL; Spch C; Var C; Tres, Sr Cl; Ftbl; Opt A; Spch A; *U of Fla; Acct.*

DUPREE, Sandra Diann
Atlanta HS; Atlanta, TX (10-190) Ensm; FTA; GS; NHS; Rainbow; Bus Mgr, Sch P; Sci C; Q&S A; Del, GS; Outst, Eng; *Mus.*

DUPREE, Terry Denice
Gila Bend HS; Gila Bend, AZ (2-37) Chldr; Chor; Pres, NHS; Pres, Rainbow; Secy, SC; Var C; Pres, Jr Cl; Secy, Soph Cl; Tnns; COM; Citz A; Cl Fav; DARGCA; HQn; Most Out; Regent Schol; Rotary A; Type A; WW; *Ariz St U; Lib Arts.*

DuPREE, Yolonda Gail
Bennettsville HS; Bennettsville, SC (11-182) Ann; Band; BC; Tres, Chor; Rptr, Hmrm; Ed, Sch P; SC; Hon Prog; Sci A; WW; *U of SC; Acct.*

DUPUY, Brett Michael
Archbishop Rummel HS; Metairie, LA (17-365) Hmrm; SC; VP, Jr Cl; Tr; Outst Schol Achv Cert.

DUQUE, David Duane
Pueblo S HS; Pueblo, CO (7-540) Band; Chem C; Chor; Hmrm; Key C; Lat C; Math C; NHS; Orch; Order/Arrow; Sci C; SC; Var C; Cr-Ctry; Mgr, Ftbl; Tr; Wrest; Hon Prog; Order/Arrow A; Star Student; Yth Fel; *Baylor U; Med.*

DURA, Paul Andrew
Bound Brook HS; Bound Brook, NJ (1-237) Band; CYO; Chess C; Drama; Tres, Ger C; Rptr, Hmrm; Lit Mag; Math C; Rptr, Sch P; SC; Alg A; Hist A; Hon Prog; Val; Schol A; Instrumental Mus A; *Princeton U; Biochem.*

DURAN, Agatha Frances
Valley HS; Sanders, AZ (10-50) CYO; Cpt, Chldr; Drama; Pres, 4H; Model UN; Spch C; Secy, SC; Cpt, Bkbl; Tr; 4H A; Sports As; Vlbl; *U of A at Tucson.*

DURAN, Cecelia
Baldwin Park HS; Baldwin Park, CA; FBLA; *NW Col; Med Asst.*

DURAN, Diane Irene
Pojoaque HS; Santa Fe, NM (18-87) Pres, Band; Mjrte; Prom Court; Cpt, Drill Tm; *NMTVS; Clerk Steno.*

DURAN, Manuel
Francisco Mendoza HS; Isabela, PR; CYO; Dbte Tm; Math C; ARC; Rptr, Sch P; Bsbl; Sftbl; Alg A; Bio A; Chem A; Hon Prog; Math A; *Col of Agr & Mech Arts; Civil Engr.*

DURAN, Merika Christina
Green Mountain HS; Lakewood, CO (38-446) Hmrm; InterClub Coun; NHS; Spch C; VP, SC; Thes; Pres, Jr Cl; HCt; *Regis Col; Pre-Law.*

DURANCEAU, Diane Lynn
Waukesha S Campus HS; Waukesha, WI; Chor; Drama; *Olivet Nazarene Col; Dietary Tech.*

DURASKI, Rhonda Ann
Smiths Station HS; Smiths, AL; Ed, Ann; BC; GS; Secy, Math C; Mu Alpha Theta; Sci C; Span C; Citz A; Cl Fav; DARGCA; Outst Young Amer; *Huntingdon Col; Journ.*

DURASKI, Russell Turner
Smith Station HS; Smiths, AL; Ann; Parl, Band; BC; Key C; VP, Mu Alpha Theta; Sci C; Sftbl; Swim; Tnns; COM; Outst Ldrship, Band; Cert of Appreciation, Outst Yng Am; *Auburn U; Math.*

DURBIN, Deborah Ann
MacArthur HS; Decatur, IL (33%-450) Church High Tn Yth Board; Soul Search; Soul Seekers; *Pima Co Nurs Sch; Nurs.*

DURBIN, Martin Thomas
Owensboro Cath HS; Owensboro, KY (1-226) CYO; Co-Cpt, Chem C; Fr C; Hmrm; Co-Cpt, Math C; NHS; Co-Cpt, Sci C; SC; Bkbl; Soccer; Tnns; Tr; Alg A; Bio A; Chem A; Hon Prog; Math A; NEDT; Sci A; *U of Ky; Oceanography.*

DURBIN, Susan Marie
Owensboro Cath HS; Owensboro, KY (7-226) CYO; NHS; Alg A; Bio A; COM; Hon Prog; Math A; NEDT; Rensselaer A; *U of Louisville; Biomed Engr.*

DURBON, Angela Starr
Nathan Hale HS; Tulsa, OK (77-677) Fr C; FBLA; Hmrm; NHS; SC; Amer Citizenship Sem Schol; Cooperative Off Ed; *Okla St U; Spch Pathology.*

DURDEN, Marva Lynette
Herbert HS; Beaumont, TX (10%-237) Chor; Cum Laude Soc; Secy, Dbte Tm; Fr C; French NHS; FTA; Hmrm; Math C; NHS; SC; Y-Tns; COM; HCt; Drill Tm; Cum Laude; Top Tn of Amer A; *Incarnate Word Col; Pre-Med.*

DURDEN, Marvin III
Hebert HS; Beaumont, TX (50%-200) FBLA; NHS; Span C; Span NHS; COM; JA A; Acct A; Minority Introd-Engr, U of Houston; *U of Houston; Acct.*

DURDEN, Zelda Denise
George Washington Sr HS; Los Angeles, CA (21-510) Bus Mgr, Ann; Span C; SC; Up Bound; Cpt, Sftbl; Bank Of Amer A; CSF; COM; Hist A; Hon Prog; Math A; Sci A; Yth Fel; JA; Ephebian Soc; Most Intelligent; Drum & Bugle Drill Tm; MVP, Sftbl; Principal's List; Bowl; *U of Calif Berkeley; Chem Engr.*

DUREN, Zachary Kelvin
Danbury HS; Danbury, CT (98-706) Chor; JV, Bsbl; Bkbl; Ftbl; MVP, Bkbl; Art As; Phys Fitness As; *St Mary's Col; Phys Ed.*

DURHAM, Donald Paul
Ft Payne HS; Ft Payne, AL (42-147) FTA; Ch, Key C; SC; Bio A; Pep C; Bookkeeping A; *Navy; Solar Energy.*

DURHAM, Donna Lynn
Laurel Co HS; London, KY; Chldr; Dbte Tm; Drama; FHA; MVP, Tnns; WW.

DURHAM, Gina Lee
Walnut Hills HS; Cincinnati, OH (75-400) Chor; Model UN; Rainbow; *U of Cincinnati; Journ.*

DURHAM, Odessa
Bennett HS; Buffalo, NY (10-28) Tr; *Fashion Designer.*

DURHAM, Terri Lynn
Victory Christian Acad; Jacksonville, FL (10%-100) Band; JV, Chldr; JV, Bkbl; MVP, Sftbl; HCt; *Phys Ed.*

DURKAN, William James
Uniontown Area Sr HS; Uniontown, PA; Pres, Chess C; Fr C; Key C; Math C; NHS; Tres, Phys C; Tres, Sci C; Ski C; Golf; Alg A; Chamber of Comm A; Math A; *Sci.*

DURKIN, Edward Joseph
Adlai E Stevenson HS; Bronx, NY; Chess C; NHS; Bus Mgr, Bsbl; Wrest.

DURKIN, Jane
A E Stevenson HS; Bronx, NY (45-788) Hmrm; SC; Hon Prog; Teacher's Pet; *Buffalo Col; Police Sci.*

DURKIN, Linda Ann
Roxborough HS; Philadelphia, PA (11-430) Drama; Pres, FTA; Mgr, Tnns; Alg A; Math A.

DURKOVIC, Jonathan Todd
Ashtabula HS; Ashtabula, OH (12-260) A Cap Choir; Band; Chor; Drama; Ensm; Hmrm; Lat C; Madrigal; Thes; Chamber of Comm A; Citz A; Fleischman Schol; Kiwanis A; Lion A; Masque & Gavel A; Most Out; Opt A; Pres A; Sanctuary Soc; Yth Fel; *Mus.*

DURR, Saundra Renee
Parkview HS; Springfield, MO (65-398) Bus C; FBLA; FHA; Rptr, Hmrm; *SMSU; Archaeology.*

DURRANCE, Rita Kay
Wakulla HS; Medart, FL; Co-Cpt, Chldr; Tres, NHS; Pres A; WW; Campus Crusade for Christ Rep; Historian, GAA; *Tallahassee Comm Col.*

DURRANCE, Steven Martin
Hardee HS; Wauchula, FL; Key C; Co-Cpt, Ftbl; Golf; Tr; Chaplain, FFA; Bicen Ntl FFA Conf; 2nd, St Meat Judging Tm; Most Improv Gulf; Star Greenhand A; FFA Ldrship; Director, Key C; *Agr.*

DURRER, Elizabeth Ann
William Monroe HS; Stanardsville, VA (5-90) BC; Tres, FTA; Lit Mag; VP, Soph Cl; HCt; Type A; *Mary Washington Col; Pol Sci.*

DURRETT, Janice Kay
Thompson HS; Alabaster, AL (10%-180) BC; Chldr.

DURRWACHTER, Linda Susan
Delhaas HS; Bristol, PA (11-565) Band; FTA; Hon Prog; Secy, Baptist Yth Organization; Church Choir; Fr A; *The King's Col; Elem Ed.*

DURST, David Mark
Helix HS; LaMesa, CA; Pres, Band; Ensm; Grand Mus A; *Grossmont-Christian Col Seminary; Religious Stu.*

DURST, Lewis Craig
Aurora HS; Aurora, WV (10-32) Band; Pres, FFA; 4H; NHS; Sci C; VP, Soph Cl; Co-Cpt, Bkbl; COM; Parl Procedure A; FFA Member o-t Yr; *Potomac St Col; Agr.*

DUSEK, Charles Elijah
Denison Sr HS; Denison, TX (25%-400) Dbte Tm; Order/Arrow; Span C; SC; Ftbl; God & Country A; Order/Arrow A; Spch A; VFW A; VofDEM; Eagle Sct; *Grayson Co Jr Col; Psych.*

DUSEK, William Forrest
Denison Sr HS; Denison, TX (25%-360) Dbte Tm; Hmrm; Order/Arrow; Sci C; SC; God & Country A; Hon Prog; Eagle Sct Bronze Palm; 5th Pl, Interntl Poetry Contest; *Grayson Co Jr Col; Sci.*

DUSENBURY, Anne Elizabeth
Dondero HS; Royal Oak, MI (46-475) F-Ed, Ann; Band; F-Ed, Lit Mag; Model UN; NHS; Orch; VP, Sr Cl; Ftbl; Q&S A; Semi-Fin, Expository Writing A; *Albion Col; Psych.*

DUSHKOFF, Robert Boyne
Mullens HS; Mullens, WV; Ann; BC; BS; Chess C; HiY; Pres, InterClub Coun; NHS; Sci C; VP, Span C; VP, SC; Var C; Mgr, Bkbl; Ftbl; Tnns; Tr; Val; *W Va U; Pre-Med.*

DUSSAULT, Jeffrey Scott
Little Falls Jr-Sr HS; Little Falls, NY (9-131) BS; NHS; Bkbl; Golf; *Mohawk Valley Comm Col; Bus Adm.*

DUSSAULT, Jerry Leon
Little Falls HS; Little Falls, NY (13-131) BS; NHS; JV, Bkbl; Cr-Ctry; Golf; Bausch & Lomb A; COM; NMS; Regent Schol; ROTC A; *Mohawk Valley Comm Col; Engr Sci.*

DUSSAULT, Mary Elizabeth
Little Falls HS; Little Falls, NY (1-135) VP, Band; Fr C; GS; Monogram; VP, NHS; Rptr, Sch P; Pres, Soph Cl; Co-Cpt, Bkbl; Co-Cpt, Sftbl; Cpt, Tnns; Math A; NMF; Regent Schol; Val; Ath o-t Wk; Schol Mag Hon Men, Original Song; *Wellesley Col; Sci.*

DUSTIN, Scott Wayne
Iroquois Central HS; Elma, NY; MVP, Ftbl; Hockey; Tr; Best Defensive Lineman, Ftbl; *Sci.*

DUSTRUD, Christopher James
Park Center HS; Brooklyn Park, MN (62-546) Band; Ensm; NHS; Orch; Ftbl; Tr; Wrest; COM; H of F; Hon Prog; Yth Fel; *Hamline U; Psych.*

DUTKO, Karen Marie
Liberty HS; Youngstown, OH; A Cap Choir; Secy, Chor; Ensm; Fr C; Jr Miss Pagent; Madrigal; ARC; Sch P; ARC A; Yth Fel; Spelling Bee; Ntl Talent Search; *Youngstown St U; Mus.*

DUTRIDGE, Grace Ann
Whitmer HS; Toledo, OH (80-895) FHA; *Owens Tech Col; Food Service.*

DUTTON, Dennis William
Aledo HS; Aledo, IL (10%-145) Ann; Band; Chor; Ensm; Rptr, Sch P; Yth Fel; *Mus.*

DUTTON, Lori Ann
Aurora Central HS; Aurora, CO (63-600) ARC; Sch P; Ski C; SC; Swim; *U of N Colo; Span.*

DUTTON, Marla Kay
Cave-In-Rock HS; Cave- in-Rock, IL (1-40) Spch C; Alg A; Bio A; Hon Prog; NEDT; Spch A; Geom A; Health A; Eng A; *Law.*

DUTTON, Rhonella Michelle
Grace Baptist HS; Decatur, AL (4-26) Ann; Band; FHA; VP, 4H; NHS; Co-Ed, Sch P; Bkbl; 4H A; Secy, 4-H C; Vlbl; *Bus.*

DUTTWEILER, James Frederick
Cedar Shoals HS; Athens, GA (30-350) BC; Chem C; Chess C; Pres, FFA; Golf; ROTC A; *Ga Inst of Tech; Engr.*

DUTWEILER, Jace Jay
Annville-Cleona HS; Annville, PA; SC; Var C; Tr; *Millersville St Col; Industrial Arts.*

DUTY, James Robert
Hull Daisetta HS; Daisetta, TX (8-50) BC; FFA; JETS; Spch C; Pres, SC; Var C; Bkbl; Ftbl; Tr; COM; Spch A; Star Student; *Tex A&M U; Drafting.*

DUVALL, Clarence James Jr
Webster Groves HS; St Louis, MO (104-462) A Cap Choir; Cpt, Bkbl; Best Defensive Player A, Bkbl; *SE Mo St U.*

DuVALL, Denise Ann
Fairfield HS; Fairfield, OH (40-712) Chor; VP, Hmrm; Ch, Mod Mus Mas; Span C; Alg A; Opt A; Spch A; Yth Fel; PA; HS Musical; *U of Cincinnati; Bus.*

DUVALL, Dennis Glen
Cresbard HS; Cresbard, SD (6-32) Semi-Fin, BS; Chor; Cpt, Math C; Var C; Cpt, Bsbl; Bkbl; Tr; Alg A; Amer Leg A; COM; Hist A; Hon Prog; Math A; Star Student; Yth Fel; High Quiz Bowl Schol to Huron Col; *Huron Col; Hist.*

DUVALL, Hazel Paula
Dunbar Sr HS; Washington, DC; Chor; Hmrm; VP, Ntl Yth Conf; Citz A; Cl Fav; Yth Choir; *Amer U; Ed.*

DUVALL, Leslie Ann
Webster Groves Sr HS; Webster Groves, MO; A Cap Choir; Co-Cpt, Chldr; Chor; VP, Drama; Hon Prog; Drama A; *NE Mo St U; Med Records.*

DUVALL, Mary Marie
Rochester HS; Rochester, IL (25-104) A Cap Choir; Chor; NHS; Opt Out Tn; Val; Yth Fel; *Lincoln Land Comm Col; Bus Adm.*

DUVALL, Michael Landon
W Carter Co HS; Olive Hill, KY; FBLA; Bkbl; JA A; *Med.*

DUVALL, Teresa Faye
Shawnee HS; Shawnee, OK;

DUVICK, Geraldine Lynn
Gage Park HS; Chicago, IL (38-728) Band; Drama; Hmrm; Swim; Tnns; COM; Citz A; Hon Prog; Pres A; Sci A; Teachers Aid; Hon C; *Sou Ill U; Bus.*

DUYCK, Lauren Grace
Montgomery HS; San Diego, CA (98-900) Citz A; Schol A; *San Diego St U.*

DUZAN, Rosa Lee
Paris HS; Paris, IL (83-243) Ann; Band; Drama; Rptr, 4H; Lat C; Mgr, Bkbl; Golf; Mgr, Tr; 4H A; Hon Prog; GAA.

DVORAK, Joseph Paul
Cary-Grove HS; Cary, IL (20-326) BS; Pres, Bus C; Pres, FBLA; NHS; Sch P; JV, Cr-Ctry; Ftbl; HCt; Hon Prog; VP & Tres, FBLA; *Northern Ill U; Bus.*

DVORAK, Melissa Jane
S Haven HS; S Haven, KS; Band; Chldr; Chor; Ensm; Secy, FHA; Pres, 4H; Y-Tns; Bkbl; Tr; Cl Fav; 4H A; HQn.

DWORANCZYK, Ann Marie
St Joseph's HS; Camden, NJ (3-96) Fr C; Hmrm; NHS; COM; Hon Prog; Fr A; *Interior Decorating.*

DWYER, Barbara Carol
John Ehret HS; Marrero, LA (21-450) GS; VP, Mu Alpha Theta; NHS; Hon Prog; 3 5 Avg A; *LSU.*

DWYER, Kay Ann
Oxford HS; Oxford, KS (1-44) Band; Chor; Ensm; GS; VP, NHS; S-T, SC; Alg A; Math A; Spch A; Type A; Mus A; *K-St; Home Ec.*

DWYER, Mary Louise
Cecilian Acad; Philadelphia, PA; Lat C; Model
UN; Sci C; VP, World Affairs C.

DWYIER, Gary Lee
Parkview HS; Springfield, MO; A Cap Choir; Pres,
Band; VP, Bus C; Chor; Community Yth Symph;
Ensm; FBLA; Key C; Lit Mag; Madrigal; Math C;
Orch; SC; Tnns; Kiwanis A; Lion A; Rotary A;
Drum Major; Lions Band; 'I' Rating, Mus Festival;
Southwest Mo St U; Mus.

DYBDAHL, Sandra Kay
Pflugerville HS; Pflugerville, TX (10%-103) BC;
Drama; FHA; Span C; Spch C; SC; Var C; Bkbl;
Fin, Tr; Hon Prog; A&M U; Phys Ed.

DYBEVIK, Eric John
Acalanes HS; Lafayette, CA (130-300) A Cap
Choir; Ski C; Bsbl; Ftbl; Wrest; St Olaf Col; Chem.

DYCE, Eric Ward
Ramey HS; Aguadilla, PR (1-20) F-Ed, Ann; NHS;
Tres, Jr Cl; Tres, Soph Cl; Bsbl; JV, Bkbl; JV, Cr-
Ctry; Bio A; COM; NEDT; Eng A; Geom A; Art
A; Span A.

DYCHES, Phyllis Renee
Barnwell HS; Barnwell, SC (10-160) NHS; Pres
HR; Computer Sci.

DYCUS, Brenda Gay
E Alton-Wood River HS; Wood River, IL (11-300)
A Cap Choir; Chldr; Chor; Ensm; NHS; Tr; Amer
Leg A; Psych.

DYE, Beverly Jean
Parkersburg South HS; Parkersburg, WV; ARC;
Sftbl; Tnns; GAA; FSA; DECA C.

DYE, Daniel Peter
A A Stagg HS; Palos Hills, IL (12-512) NHS; Cpt,
Bkbl; Hon Prog; Kiwanis A; PTA A; St Scholar;
MVP, Bkbl; Fresh Schol A; All Conf & All Area
Hon Men, Bkbl; Bkbl Participation A; Ministerial
A; Bethel Col; Communications.

DYE, Donald Wayne Jr
Lanier HS; Austin, TX (60-475) Pres, JETS; NHS;
Trustee A; Tex A&M U; Engr Graphics.

DYE, Kathryn Deanna
Tupelo HS; Tupelo, MS; A Cap Choir; Anchor C;
NHS; Distinctive Acad A; NE Miss Jr Col; Art.

DYE, Lawrence Michael
Erie Comm Unit 1 HS; Erie, IL; Chor; Golf; Yth
Fel; Black Hawk Jr Col; Hist.

DYE, Marcus Duane
Paul Harding HS; Ft Wayne, IN (30-300) A Cap
Choir; Pres, Chess C; Madrigal; NMF; NMS; St
Scholar; Purdue U; Chem Engr.

DYE, Sheila
T Wingate Andrews HS; High Point, NC (52-298)
Co-Ed, Ann; BC; Co-Cpt, Chldr; Dbte Tm; Drama;
Pres, FTA; HiY; Hmrm; Secy, InterClub Coun;
NHS; Ntl Yth Conf; VP, ARC; Rptr, Sch P; Soc C;
Span C; Secy, SC; Secy, Sr Cl; Tr; Super Sr; WW;
UNC; Bio.

DYER, Beth Allison
N Gaston Sr HS; Dallas, NC (25-200) Art C; 2nd
Pl, Ntl Ed Wk Writing Contest; Ltr- girl; U of NC;
Criminal Justice.

DYER, Crystal Dawn
Wyanet Comm HS; Wyanet, IL (3-21) Pres, Band;
Chor; Ensm; NHS; Alg A; DARGCA; Hon Prog;
Bowling; IMEA; Home Ec A; U of Iowa; Phar.

DYER, Deborah Anita
Newton Co Comprehensive HS; Covington, GA
(40%-600) HiY; Med Tech.

DYER, Jack Wesley
Monterey HS; Lubbock, TX; NHS; Orch; Abilene
Christian U; Pre-Med.

DYER, Jean Marie
Montabella HS; Edmore, MI (20%-140) Ski C;
Montcalm Comm Col; Cosmetology.

DYER, Kelly Craig
N Daviess Jr Sr HS; Elnora, IN (27-90) FFA; Pres,
Span C; Bkbl; Pres, Church Yth Group; Pep C; HR;
Agr.

DYER, Lisa Faye
Maine Township HS N; Des Plaines, IL (25%-369)
A Cap Choir; AFS; Chor; Sci A; Yth Fel; Pom-Pon
Sq; HR; Tres, Yth Leg; Sch Musicals; Church Yth
Choir; JV, Badminton; AFS Domestic Stu; Campus
Life; Pre-Sch Tchr's Aide; Augsburg Col; Social
Work.

DYER, Phillip Wayne
Dugway HS; Dugway, UT (1-45) Pres, Model UN;
NHS; SC; Bkbl; Co-Cpt, Ftbl; Golf; MLS; ROTC
A; Val; Sen Yth Prog Win; U of Utah; Law.

DYKEMAN, Jane Marie
Fremont Sr HS; Fremont, NE; Band; Chor; Ensm;
Ger C; Mjrte; Bkbl; Sftbl; COM.

DYKES, Andrew
Terrell Co HS; Dawson, GA (10-112) F-Ed, Sch P;
Fort Valley St Col; Eng.

DYKES, Connie Lorraine
Hamill Road Christian HS; Chattanooga, TN (2-9)
Co-Ed, Ann; BC; Pres, Bus C; Fr C; FHA; Tres,
NHS; Sch Achieve Tm; Secy, Sch P; Sftbl; COM;
HCt; Ntl Achv Schol; Swtht; Yth Fel; Most De-
pendable; MVP, Vlbl; 1st Runnerup, Miss Hamill
Rd; 4th Runnerup, Qn of Hamill Rd; 1st Pl, Sch
Essay & Spelling; Bus Ed.

DYKES, Cynthia Diane
W Jones HS; Laurel, MS (40-300) Band; Chor; Mu
Alpha Theta; Sci C; U of Miss; Anesthesia.

DYKES, F Diane
W Jones HS; Laurel, MS (5-300) BC; Chor; FHA;
Bkbl.

DYKES, Kathy Melissa
Dodge Co HS; Eastman, GA (19-199) Anchor C;
BC; FBLA; FHA; Pres, 4H; Key C; Span C; COM;
Cl Fav; 4H A; I Dare You; JA A; Key A; Middle Ga
Col; Secy.

DYKES, Kimberly Kay
Hanson Mem HS; Franklin, LA (10-45) Chldr;
Chor; NHS; Sftbl; Swim; Yth Fel; Young Life;
GSct; Ntl March of Dimes; Swim Instructor; U of
SW La; Photography.

DYKES, Lisa Jayne
John Ehret HS; Marrero, LA (46-550) Fin, Lit Ral;
Tnns; Amer Leg A; Beauty; Bio A; COM; Hist A;
Sci A; Art C; Media Fair A; Lit A; Art A; LSU;
Fine Arts.

DYKES, Mark William
Highland HS; Pocatello, ID (150-500) Wrest; God
& Country A; Type A; Outst, Drama; U of Oreg;
Psych.

DYKES, Rebecca Lynn
Charles Henderson HS; Troy, AL (10%-170) BC;
Drama; NHS; Span C; Amer Leg A; Troy St U.

DYKES, Sherry Lynne
W Jones HS; Laurel, MS (5%-300) BC; Chor;
Ensm; FHA; Madrigal; Math C; Mu Alpha Theta;
Sftbl; Most Cooperative, Piano; Mus.

DYKHOFF, Kenneth L
Marion HS; Marion, IN (300-900).

DYMOND, Daryl Ann
Dallas Sr HS; Dallas, PA (65-244) Ann; Band;
Chor; Drama; Ensm; Hmrm; Madrigal; Orch; Dist
Choir; GSct; Talent Comp As; All-St Reg Chor;
Bus Mgr, Sch Music; Secy, Christian Endeavor Yth
Soc; WW Among Amer HS Mus Stu; Westminster
Choir Col; Mus Ed.

DYNES, Tom Bernard
Mt Healthy HS; Cincinnati, OH (14-496) BC;
NHS; Span C; Tnns; PTA A; U of Cincinnati;
Chem Engr.

DYRDAHL, Marcie Eileen
Mt Rainier HS; Des Moines, WA; Outst Schol A.

DYSON, Charles Jerome
Bell Voc HS; Washington, DC; VP, CYO; JV, Bkbl;
Cpt, Ftbl; Alg A; Elec Engr.

DYSON, Robyn LaRae
Williamsburg HS; Andrews, SC; Commercial.

DZIOBA, Donna Marie
Waupun HS; Waupun, WI; Span C; Mus Fest A;
Nurs.

DZIUBINSKI, Brian Keith
Bangor HS; Bangor, MI (20%-125) Chor; Pres, Key
C; SC; Pres, Soph Cl; Bkbl; Ftbl; Tr; Ath Ltrs;
Moral Booster A.

E

EACKER, Bradley Russell
Roy J Wasson HS; Colorado Springs, CO (29-512)
A Cap Choir; Chess C; Chor; Community Yth
Symph; Madrigal; Math C; NHS; Orch; Order/
Arrow; Sci C; Hon Prog; Order/Arrow A; Regent
Schol; U of Colo; Elec Engr.

EACKER, Joel Andrew
Wasson Sr HS; Colorado Springs, CO (5-600)
Chess C; Fr C; Orch; Order/Arrow; Soccer; Hon
Prog; Order/Arrow A; Phi Beta Kappa; Air Force
Acad; Sci.

EADES, Sharon Kay
Burbank HS; Burbank, CA; Chldr; Tnns; Hon A,
Drill Tm; CFS; Biola Col; Nurs.

EADES, Thomas Edward
Charles A Lindbergh Sr HS; Kenton, WA
(206-382) Band; Orch; Tres; Yth Fel; BSct of
Amer; Dixieland Band; Band Contest; U of Wash;
Mus.

EADS, Deena Ann
E Aurora HS; Aurora, IL (68-797) A Cap Choir;
Ensm; Span C; Tnns; COM; Span C, Tnns, Chor,
A's.

EADS, Edward John
Neshaminy Maple Point HS; Langhorne, PA
(9-413) Order/Arrow; JV, Bkbl; Soccer; Tr; Hon
Prog; Order/Arrow A; Life Sct; Math.

EADY, Pamela Mechelle
Hobbs HS; Hobbs, NM (6-496) A Cap Choir; Band;
Chor; FTA; Mjrte; Hon Prog; Type A; Worthy
Adv, Rainbow Girl; 1st Cl GSct; NMSU; Ed.

EAGAN, Gail Ann
Forest Park Sr HS; Forest Park, GA (15%-700)
Ann; Band; Pres, BC; Hmrm; Fin, Jr Miss Pagent;
SC; All St Orch; Band Medals; 2nd Pl, Energy
Poster; U of Ga; Pre-Law.

EAGEN, Maribeth Kateri
Bishop Klonowski HS; Scranton, PA; Chess C; V-
Ch, Dbte Tm; Ch, Drama; Lit Mag; Math C; NFL;
Sch P; Ski C; Spch C; Bkbl; Cr-Ctry; Alg A; Hist A;
Hon Prog; Journ A; Math A; Type A; Med.

EAGLESON, Mona Louise
Crossville Comm HS; Crossville, IL (10-43).

EAGLETON, Sheila Denise
Westville HS; Westville, OK; Ann; Co-Cpt, Chldr;
FBLA; FHA; GS; NHS; SC; Bkbl; HQn; VP, FCA.

EAKIN, John Randall
Northside HS; Roanoke, VA (100-420) Band; 4H;
Key C; Orch; Order/Arrow; Rptr, Sch P; Cr-Ctry;
WW; VPI; Computer Sci.

EAKINS, JuJuan
East HS; Cleveland, OH (18%-350) ARC; COM;
Citz A; Bowl; HR; Jr Missionary Soc; Col C; Cleve-
land St U; Financing.

EALING, Beth Ann
Elmhurst HS; Ft Wayne, IN (35-500) Chor; City
Conf; Dbte Tm; Pres, Ensm; Fin, GS; Hmrm; Mod
Mus Mas; NFL; Spch C; SC; Most Out; Ed, Church
Paper; St Vocal Fin; Ind U; Mus.

EALY, Donald Ray
Green Oaks HS; Shreveport, LA (12-214) Math C;
NHS; Math A; ROTC A; Sci A; U of SW La; Com-
puter Prog.

EAMES, Nancy Lee
Holliston HS; Holliston, MA (25-257) Hmrm;
NHS; Span C; SC; Secy, Sr Cl; Mgr, Bkbl;
DARGCA; Ideal Sr Girl; HR; Westfield St Col;
Psych.

EANES, Melissa Gay
Eastern Guilford HS; Gibsonville, NC (10-164) Fr
C; Pres, FHA; French NHS; NHS; Jr Marshal;
UNC; Med.

EARHART, Elaine Marie
Burrell Sr HS; Lower Burrell, PA (20%-300) Ann;
Ger C; Bkbl; Sftbl; NEDT; JA; Ntl Jr Hon Soc Cert
& Pin; Outst, Church Membership Cl; Calif St Col;
Psych.

EARL, Cynthia Shawn
Paint Branch Sr HS; Burtonsville, MD; MVP, Sftbl; MVP, Tr; Bio A; COM; Hon Prog; Sci A; 2nd, Annual Pallotti Relays; *Fisks U; Psych.*

EARL, Helene Jane
Valley HS; Sanders, AZ; Ann; Band; CYO; Chldr; Pres, Model UN; SC; Cl Fav; HCt; *NAU.*

EARL, Marvin Lee
Crestline HS; Crestline, OH (20-150) Ger C; Ftbl; Tr; Sci A; Spch A; *Ohio N Col; Aerospace Engr.*

EARLE, Helen Belinda
Walhalla HS; Walhalla, SC (1-170) Pres, Anchor C; Band; Pres, BC; FTA; Lat C; Lat NHS; Cpt, Mjrte; Math C; Rptr, Sch P; SC; VP, Sr Cl; VP, Jr Cl; Gov Honor Prog; Gr Marshal; Hon Prog; Phi Beta Kappa; Val; Most Intellectual; WOW Achv, Hist; Alpha; Bell Labs A; *Clemson U; Lib Arts.*

EARLE, Sandra Beverly
Churchville-Chili Sr HS; Churchville, NY (35-350) A Cap Choir; JV, Chldr; FTA; Hmrm; NHS; Ski C; Ch, Jr Cl; Choir Lib; *Phar.*

EARLES, Martin Brian
Tulare Western HS; Tulare, CA (31-214) Tres, BS; Model UN; Sci A; Ger A.

EARLEY, Charmaine Diane
Westinghouse HS; Pittsburgh, PA (59-390) Chldr; Chor; FHA; Hmrm; Lat C; Lat NHS; Sci C; SC; Bkbl; Sftbl; Tnns; Bio A; HQn; MVP, Vlbl; *Duquesne Col; Nurs.*

EARLEY, Edward Taylor
Birch Run HS; Birch Run, MI (2-133) Arch; Band; Chess C; Ensm; NFL; NHS; Pres, Sci C; Var C; Bsbl; Bkbl; Ftbl; Bio A; COM; Math A; Phy A; Sal; Sci A; Spch A; Summa Cum Laude; *Mich St U; Med.*

EARLEY, Vonnie Lilaine
Harlingen HS; Harlingen, TX (62-850) A Cap Choir; Chor; Drama; Ensm; FHA; Pres, Hmrm; Rptr, Lit Mag; Madrigal; Bio A; Ntl Fed of Mus C A; Ntl Fraternity of Stu Mus A; *Baylor U; Eng.*

EARLY, Ira Gordon Jr
R J Reynolds Sr HS; Winston-Salem, NC (80-823) Key C; Math C; NHS; SC; JV, Bkbl; Mgr, Soccer; Hon Prog; Math A; *Emory U; Math.*

EARLY, LaVonne Catherine
Valmeyer HS; Valmeyer, IL (3-45) CYO; Chor; Tres, FHA; Rptr, 4H; Math C; NHS; Tres, Jr Cl; Math A; *Edwardsville Col; Acct.*

EARLY, Theresa June
Shamrock HS; Shamrock, TX (5-48) A Cap Choir; Band; FTA; Pres, Lat C; Madrigal; NHS; Rptr, Sch P; Spch C; Bkbl; Mgr, Tr; Hon Prog; Magna Cum Laude; NMS; Century III Ldr Schol; All-Region Band & Choir; WW; *Tex Tech U; Biological Sci.*

EARLY, Wayne Allen
Bishop Union HS; Bishop, CA; Y-Tns; Mgr, Tr; Wrest; Wrest Trophy & Ribbons.

EARLYWINE, Karen Sue
Highland HS; Ewing, MO; Band; FHA; VP, NHS; SC; Tr; Bio A; Hon Prog; Sci C Rep; *Social Work.*

EARNEST, Ruby Lee
Berry HS; Berry, AL; Ann; VP, BC; FHA; VP, Sci C; US Naval Inst A; *Brewer St Jr Col; Math.*

EARP, Anita Jill
Atholton HS; Simpsonville, MD (20%-200) Tres, NHS; Hockey; Sftbl; *Phys Therapy.*

EARP, Stephanie Lee
Central HS; La Crosse, WI; A Cap Choir; Band; Chor; Drama; Span C; COM; Yth Coun; B-1, Mixed Choir; Top 10, Choir; A-1, Solo; C-1, Swing Choir; *U of La Crosse; Nurs.*

EASH, Calvin Dale
Buckhorn HS; Buckhorn, KY (3-36) BC; *Hazard St Voc-Tech Col; Carpentry.*

EASH, Carol Diane
Buckhorn HS; Buckhorn, KY (1-41) BC; Secy, FHA; Pres, Soph Cl; Ger A; *Bus.*

EASH, Mary Lois
Brethren Christian Sch; Osceola, IN (5%-23) Band; Chor; Ensm; Sftbl; Tr; Spch A; VofDEM; Yth Fel; Fin, Spch A; Fin, Voice of Democracy; *Ft Wayne Bible Col; Mus.*

EASLEY, Dianne Camille
Richfield HS; Waco, TX (25%-250) Chor; Mjrte; Drill Tm; *Tex A&M U; Bus.*

EASOM, Susan Elizabeth
Sebastopol Attendance Center; Sebastopol, MS (5%-45) F-Ed, Ann; VP, Band; BC; VP, Drama; Ensm; FHA; Orch; Mgr, Bkbl; Mgr, Tr; Beauty; Hon Prog; Drum Mjrte; Soc Stu, Home Ec, A's; WW; *Miss Col; Phar.*

EASON, Alvita Selecia
Ahoskie HS; Ahoskie, NC (1-227) A-Ed, Ann; Pres, BC; InterClub Coun; SC; Y-Tns; Pres, Sr Cl; Pres, Jr Cl; Gr Marshal; Rotary Summer Intern; AB Duke Fin; *Duke U; Zoology.*

EASON, Angela Renee
Compton Sr HS; Compton, CA (25%-850) CYO; FNA; NHS; Y-Tns; CSF; Hon Prog; Type A; *U of Sou Calif; Nurs.*

EASON, Charles Anthony
N Clayton Sr HS; College Park, GA (14-30) Chor; *Ga St U; Elec Mech.*

EASON, Cheryl Lynn
Claxton HS; Claxton, GA (25%-116) Ann; Chldr; 4H; Sch P; Rptr, Jr Cl; COM; 4H A; Hon Prog; Kiwanis A; Chaplin, SC; 1st Pl, Oral Interpretation; 1st Pl, Dist Piano; *Ga Sou Col; Mus.*

EASON, Doris Marie
Jefferson Township HS; Dayton, OH; Rptr, Sch P; Span C; COM; Journ A; PA A; *U of Cincinnati; Nurs.*

EASON, Katherine
Paul L Dunbar HS; Dayton, OH; Tr; Pres A; Sanctuary Soc; *Ky St U; Dentistry.*

EASON, Kevin Richard
O D Wyatt HS; Fort Worth, TX (12-435) Co-Ed, Ann; Ensm; Pres, FTA; NHS; SC; Hon Prog; Magna Cum Laude; Bible C; People; 1st Runner-Up, Dist Mr FTA; WW; *U of Tex-Arlington; Ed.*

EASON, Marvin
P L Dunbar HS; Dayton, OH; Arch; Commercial C; Dbte Tm; Drama; FFA; FHA; FTA; 4H; Key C; Lit Mag; Monogram; NHS; Var C; Arch; Bkbl; Co-Cpt, Cr-Ctry; Ftbl; Sftbl; Swim; Tnns; Tr; COM; Citz A; JA A; Most Out; PTA A; Pres A; Star Student; Tr A; *Wright St U; Hist.*

EASON, Stephen Bradford
O D Wyatt HS; Ft Worth, TX (1-435) Co-Ed, Ann; Ensm; Tres, FTA; NHS; SC; Hon Prog; Summa Cum Laude; Bible C; People; WW; *U of Tex at Arlington.*

EASON, Tenishelah Yvonne
Groves HS; Garden City, GA; Parl, FHA; Sci A; Spelman Col; *Home Ec.*

EAST, Bobby Molloy
Lyon Co HS; Eddyville, KY (4-98) BC; 4H; Order/ Arrow; VP, Soph Cl; Tnns; *Sanford U; Bio.*

EASTBERG, Susan R
Burke HS; Omaha, NE (1-875) AFS; Fr C; FNA; Parl, SC; Alg A; Bio A; Hon Prog; Opt A; Type A; *Sci.*

EASTBURG, Steven Roger
Cherry Hill HS E; Cherry Hill, NJ (55-865) Band; Ensm; Hmrm; Lat C; NHS; SC; Co-Cpt, Bsbl; Bkbl; Co-Cpt, Soccer; Pres, Church Yth; *US Naval Acad; Engr.*

EASTBURN, Margaret Louise
Bristow HS; Bristow, OK (1-143) Ann; Lat C; NHS; Rainbow; Ed, Sch P; Bio A; COM; Gov Honor Prog; Gr Marshal; I Dare You; Journ A; Masonic A; Vassar Book A; Okla Hon Soc; Principal's HR; *Okla St U; Bus.*

EASTER, Claire Denise
Jefferson Davis HS; Montgomery, AL (234-742) Chor; Tri-HiY; *U of Ala; Fashion Design.*

EASTER, Eula Faye
Emerson HS; Emerson, AR; FHA; 4H; Arch; Bsbl; Bkbl; Ftbl; Sftbl; Tnns; Tr; COM; JA A; Page Cert; *U of Ark; Elem Aide.*

EASTER, Jeff
Mortimer Jordan HS; Morris, AL (5-100) F-Ed, Ann; Pres, Chor; NHS; Pres, Sr Cl; All St Chor; *Dentistry.*

EASTER, Shelly Rene
Bakersfield HS; Bakersfield, CA (23-500) Orch; Amer Leg A; CSF; Modern Dance; Yth Coun; Prayer Cpt; Yth Choir; Bible Quiz Tm; *Central Bible Col; Mus.*

EASTERDAY, Karen Ann
Fort Lupton HS; Fort Lupton, CO (4-100) A-Ed, Ann; Chor; Tres, Fr C; Math C; Secy, NHS; Sci C; Span C; Spch C; Var C; Bkbl; Tr; Alg A; COM; Cl Fav; Hon Prog; MLS; Spch A; Yth Fel; Cand, Prom Qn; *U of Colo; Bus.*

EASTERLING, Connie
Centerville HS; Centerville, TX (25%-39) Band; Secy, Dbte Tm; FFA; 4H; Hmrm; NHS; SC; Var C; Cpt, Bkbl; MVP, Sftbl; COM; 4H A; HCt; Math A; Swtht; *Tex A&M U; Phys Ed.*

EASTERLING, Mary Ann
Aiken Sr HS; Cincinnati, OH; Bus C; Dbte Tm; FHA; Parl, FTA; Ger C; Hmrm; Mgr, Jr Miss Pagent; SC; MVP, Sftbl; Tr; Beauty; Citz A; Most Out; Ath A; Stu Service; A of Honor; *Cincinnati Tech Col; Bus Management.*

EASTERLING, Stephen Edwards
Hattiesburg HS Rowan Center; Hattiesburg, MS (5%-500) VP, Fr C; Rptr, Sch P; *Clemson U; Architecture.*

EASTERLY, Judith Ellen
Lebanon HS; Lebanon, VA; Co-Ed, Ann; Band; Cpt, Chldr; Chor; Drama; GS; 4H; HiY; Ch, Model UN; Monogram; Tres, NHS; Sch P; Span C; Spch C; St Stu Congress; SC; Tri-HiY; Var C; Tnns; HCt; Lion A; Yth Fel; Princess, Jr-Sr Prom; Secy, Model Gen Assm; UN Sem; *Mary Baldwin Col; Phys Therapy.*

EASTERWOOD, Telicia Lee
Bremen HS; Bremen, GA (17-78) Ann; FBLA; 4H; Hmrm; VP, InterClub Coun; Sch P; VP, SC; VP, Jr Cl; Mgr, Bkbl; Cl Fav; Gov Honor Prog; 4H A; Hist A; HCt; Swtht; Pres, Pep C; Merit A; Miss BHS; *Auburn U; Art.*

EASTERWOOD, Wayne Emmett Jr
Del City HS; Del City, OK (10%-682) Chor; Drama; Ensm; Thes; Sftbl; COM; Pres A; Yth Fel; Best Supporting Actor; *Chem.*

EASTGATE, Patti Jo
Larimore HS; Larimore, ND (20%-78) Co-Ed, Ann; Band; Ensm; Tres, FHA; Var C; JV, Bkbl; 4H A; Tres, United Methodist Yth Fel; All-Sch A; Band Ltr; *Mayville St Col; Bus Adm.*

EASTMAN, Ben Robert
Western Hills HS; Fort Worth, TX; Ann; CYO; *Archt.*

EASTMAN, Gale Ellen
Schafer HS; Southgate, MI; Bus C; Ensm; Bsbl; Swim; Type A; 1st Pl, District Spell; Church Choir; Outreach Tm; *Henry Ford Comm Col; Computer Sci.*

EASTMAN, Robin Lynn
Schafer HS; Southgate, MI; Band; Drama; Ensm; Hmrm; SC; Thes; Bsbl; Swim; Alg A; COM; Hist A; Math A; Most Out; Sci A; Type A; Church Choir; Stu Coun As; District, St, Bands; *U of Mich; Nurs.*

EASTMAN, Susan Marie
Rowland HS; Rowland Heights, CA; Secy, Var C; Bkbl; Sftbl; Girls League; Principal's HR; Most Improved, Bkbl; *Pepperdine U; Med.*

EASTOM, Elizabeth Adrienne
Northglenn HS; Northglenn, CO (95-755) A Cap Choir; Band; Chor; Drama; Ensm; NHS; Tres, Church Yth Fel; Coun, Stu Director, Chor; Drama A's; Band & Choir Ltrs.

EASTOM, Lynne Ann
Northglenn Sr HS; Northglenn, CO (46-805) A Cap Choir; Band; Chor; Drama; Mjrte; Yth Fel; Drama A; Band Ltr.

EASTON, Martha Ellen
Andover HS; Andover, MA (22-500) A Cap Choir; Ann; Chldr; Chor; Hmrm; Madrigal; Rptr, Sch P; SC; Tr; Pres A.

EASTWICK, Simon Richard
Bradenton Christian HS; Bradenton, FL (13-26) Ann; Chor; Pres, Drama; A's; SC; Pres, Soph Cl; Bsbl; MVP, Soccer; ARC A; Chapel Committee; *Aviation.*

ECKERT, Kathryn Mary
Argenta-Oreana HS; Argenta, IL (49-104) CYO; Chldr; Chor; Fr C; FHA; Ger C; 4H; K of C; Math C; Pol Sci C; Sci C; Wrest; Millikin U; Eng.

ECKERT, Paula Marie
John F Kennedy HS; Granada Hills, CA; Chor; Hmrm; Rptr, Sch P; Beauty; V Bat Girl; Var Bat Girl; Eng.

ECKHARDT, Alison Lynn
Lutheran HS W; Rocky River, OH (1-106) JV, Chldr; Chor; Drama; SC; COM; Hon Prog; NEDT; Valparaiso U.

ECKHARDT, Patricia Ellen
Alameda HS; Lakewood, CO (10%-630) Key C; Mjrte; NHS; Hist A; Sci A; Nom, Bio A; Nom, Gifted & Talented; Northwestern Comm Col; Sci.

ECKLES, Elizabeth Byrd
Lee-Davis HS; Mechanicsville, VA; Chor; Ensm; Lit Ral; Rptr, Sch P; William & Mary Col; Sci.

ECKLEY, Andrea Beth
James Madison HS; San Diego, CA (18-930) A Cap Choir; AFS; Secy, Band; Cpt, Dbte Tm; Model UN; NFL; NHS; Co-Ed, Sch P; Pres, Spch C; Secy, Soph Cl; Swim; CSF; Hon Prog; Lion A; VFW Orator Win; VofDEM; Yth Fel; Yth Leg; Commencement Speaker; ASB Ball Attendant; LaVerne Col; Law.

ECKLEY, Richard Carl
Norfolk Sr HS; Norfolk, NE (4-28) Evangel Col; Law.

ECKLUND, Lynnette Joy
Ashland-Greenwood Sr HS; Ashland, NE (10-73) Ann; Band; JV, Chldr; Chor; Ensm; Pres, HiY; Y-Tns; JV, Bkbl; JV, Tr; Piano Solo A; Special Ed.

ECKLUND, Mark Edward
Ashland-Greenwood Sr HS; Ashland, NE; Band; Chor; Ensm; Pres, HiY; Sci C; Pres, Y-Tns; JV, Bkbl; Mgr, Ftbl; Co-Cpt, Sftbl; Tr; Wrest; Rockmont Col; Yth Ministries.

ECKMAN, Rufina Lynn
Warwick HS; Lititz, PA (14-279) Band; Chor; Drama; SC; COM; HQn; Hon Prog; Franklin & Marshall Col; Art.

ECKMEDER, Lynn Brittain
Hopewell Valley Central HS; Pennington, NJ (23-280) Fr C; Secy, Hmrm; NHS; Yth Fel.

ECKWALL, Charisse RaNae
L C Anderson HS; Austin, TX (202-525) FHA; FTA; Hon Prog; Yth Fel; Church Choir; 'B' A; SW Tex St U; Primary Ed.

ECTOR, Rickie Dean
Palo Verde HS; Blythe, CA; F-Ed; Ann; Parl, Hmrm; Co-Ed, Sch P; Sci C; Pres, SC; Pres, Var C; Co-Cpt, Bkbl; Cpt, Ftbl; Tr; COM; Citz A; Cl Fav; Coun of Teach A; Journ A; Kiwanis A; Most Out; Pres A; Yth Foundation; Fin, CIF Tr; Outst Defense Bkbl; Schol; Imperial Valley Col; Sociology.

EDA, Stephanie Jane
Spring Woods Sr HS; Houston, TX; AFS; VP, Ger C; Bus Mgr, Lat C; Math C; Mu Alpha Theta; NHS; Lat II A; Texas A&M U; Engr.

EDDINGS, Lynne
Grace Christian HS; Prattville, AL (33%-48) Ann.

EDDINGTON, Mark Edward
Adlai E Stevenson HS; Bronx, NY (15-650) NHS; Var C; Tr; COM; Hist A; Hon Prog; Attendance A; Engr.

EDDINS, Becky Jane
Star Valley HS; Afton, WY (12-96) Co-Ed, Ann; Chor; Drama; Fr C; Fin, GS; 4H; NHS; Rptr, Sch P; Ski C; Band; Hon Prog; Yth Leg; Brigham Young U; Communications.

EDDINS, William Bradford
Fayetteville HS; Fayetteville, AR (150-350) Band; Order/Arrow; Order/Arrow A; Eagle Sct; U of Ark; Bus Adm.

EDDLEMAN, Kenneth Eugene
Livermore HS; Livermore, CA; Cal Poly; Agr.

EDDY, Douglas Paul
Brazosport HS; Freeport, TX (27-304) A Cap Choir; NHS; Mgr, Bsbl; Hist A; Baylor U; Hist.

EDDY, John Daniel
Brandon HS; Ortonville, MI (3%-250) Hmrm; Model UN; NHS; Span C; Var C; Bsbl; Bkbl; Golf; Citz A; Math A; Pres A; Sci A; Foreign Lang A; U of Mich; Phys Sci.

EDDY, Margaret Estelle
Inola HS; Inola, OK (1-94) Spch C; S-T, Jr Cl; Alg A; Bio A; Val; E Tex St U; Elem Ed.

EDEL, Alan David
Oroville HS; Oroville, WA (2-70) Band; Chor; VP, Key C; NHS; Sci C; Jr Cl; Soph Cl; Bkbl; Mgr, Ftbl; Tnns; Air Force Acad; Elec Engr.

EDELMAN, Barbara Jean
Midwest HS; Midwest, WY (8-20) Ann; Chldr; Drama; SC; Thes; Var C; Cpt, Bkbl; COM; Journ A; Masonic A; Casper Col; Secy.

EDELMAN, Diane Denise
Lake Highlands HS; Dallas, TX (7-701) A Cap Choir; AFS; Chor; Drama; Ensm; Fr C; Madrigal; Math C; NHS; Thes; Y-Tns; Hon Prog; Math A; Baylor U; Voice.

EDEN, Anthony DeWayne
Lone Tree Comm HS; Lone Tree, IA (8-44) Band; Chor; Drama; NHS; Secy, Jr Cl; VP, Soph Cl; Bsbl; Bkbl; Yth Fel; Marching, Concert, Bands; Mixed, Boys, Chor; Church Choir; Mixed Quartet; Highest Schol; Ath; Stage, Pep, Bands; St U of Iowa; Amer Hist.

EDEN, Marion Douglas
Lone Tree Comm HS; Lone Tree, IA (8-28) Band; Chor; Drama; Span C; SC; Bsbl; JV, Bkbl; H of F; Yth Fel; Mixed & Boys Chor; Pres, Fresh Cl; Mixed Quartet; Church Choir; Stage, Pep, March & Concert Bands; VP, Yth Fel; St U of Iowa.

EDEN, Russell Allen
Seneca HS; Louisville, KY (2%-300) BC; Hmrm; Math C; Span C; SC; Co-Cpt, Golf; Most Considerate; U of Louisville; Acct.

EDENS, Corey Dodd
Cut Bank HS; Cut Bank, MT (2-100) Ed, Ann; Rptr, Hmrm; Pres, Key C; Pres, NHS; Ski C; SC; Var C; Pres, Soph Cl; Ftbl; Wrest; Yth Fel; U of Mont; Acct.

EDENS, Joyce Ilene
Sooner HS; Bartlesville, OK (24-280) AFS; VP, Band; FBLA; NHS; Pres, Rainbow; Elk A; Kiwanis A; Masonic A; VofDEM; U of Tulsa; Bus.

EDGAR, Laurel Elizabeth
Westminster Christian Acad; Huntsville, AL (1-7) Ed, Ann; Cpt, Chldr; Drama; Hmrm; ARC; Ed, Sch P; SC; Vlbl; Covenant Col; Lib Arts.

EDGAR, Randall David
North Co HS; Desloge, MO (89-190) A Cap Choir; Chor; Dbte Tm; Ensm; S-T, Hmrm; Madrigal; ARC; Var C; Bkbl; Cr-Ctry; Ftbl; Swim; Tr; I Dare You; ARC A; Yrbk Carnation; HR Court; All Dist Chor; Mineral Area Col; Bus.

EDGE, Beverly Diane
Acme-Delco HS; Delco, NC (12-98) Chldr; Fr C; Pres, FBLA; FFA; Pres, FHA; Secy, Lit Mag; Monogram; F-Ed, Sch P; Sci C; SC; Secy, Jr Cl; VP, Soph Cl; Sftbl; HCt; Swtht; Home Ec A; FFA Chpt Farmer; Fayetteville St U; Bio.

EDGE, David Michael
Lompoc Sr HS; Lompoc, CA (24-485) Band; CSF; Citz A; Eng Achv A; UCSB; Math.

EDGE, Joan Elizabeth
Venice HS; Venice, FL (90-380) Band; Chldr; Drama; NHS; Bus Mgr, Sch P; Bio A; COM; Journ A; Scorekeeper, Wrest; Wheaton Col; Voice.

EDGE, Steven C
Crestview Sr HS; Crestview, FL (10%-260) Chess C; Drama; Ftbl; ROTC A; Marion Military Inst; Military.

EDGELL, Deborah Lynn
Breckinridge Co HS; Harned, KY (1-225) Band; Secy, Math C; Mu Alpha Theta; NHS; Rainbow; Rptr, Span C; Bkbl; Murray St U; Nurs.

EDGERTON, Kenneth Bill
Rocky Mount Sr HS; Rocky Mount, NC (21-530) Chldr; Chor; NHS; Order/Arrow; JV, Bkbl; Gr Marshal; NC St U; Engr.

EDGINGTON, Jon Mark
Frontier Central HS; Hamburg, NY (30-520) Ger C; Cpt, Wrest; Pottsdam Col; Bus Adm.

EDGISON, Cheryl Lynne
S Rowan Sr HS; China Grove, NC; Tres, Chor; Drama; Ensm; Pres, Yth Coun; Essay Writing A; Acteens Crown & Scepter; Miss Merry Christmas, Church; Central Piedmont Col; Phys Therapy Asst.

EDIN, Barbara Lisa
Jamestown HS; Jamestown, ND (15-300) A-Ed, Ann; Band; Ensm; Fr C; 4H; Hmrm; NHS; Pres, Orch; Rainbow; SC; Secy, Soph Cl; Crisco A; Elk A; Lion A; Cpt, Pom Pons; Concordia Col; Phys Therapy.

EDINGER, Lynn Ellen
St Joseph HS; St Joseph, MI; Band; Chor; Interlochen Ntl Mus; Flute Schol; Mich St; U of Mich; Mus.

EDLER, Gary Lee
New Haven HS; New Haven, MO (9-40) Band; Chor; Ensm; FTA; NHS; Sch P; Bsbl; JV, Bkbl; Yth Fel; Pres Schol; Most Talented; All Conf Choir; 100% C; SE Mo St U; Phys Ed.

EDLER, Susan Lynn
Deerfield Beach HS; Deerfield Beach, FL (50-670) Drama; NHS; Interntl C; U of Fla; Foreign Lang.

EDLEY, Virginia Ann
St Joseph HS; Jeanerette, LA (4-30) 4H; Lit Ral; Lit Mag; NHS; Rptr, SC; Bsbl; Bkbl; COM; Citz A; Poet A; U of Southwestern La.

EDLING, Sally Ann
Blue Mountain HS; Schuylkill Haven, PA (143-248) Chor; Drama; French NHS; Hmrm; Sch P; SC; Thes; Tri-HiY; Mgr, Tr; God & Country A; 1st Cl GSct; Tres, Church Yth Group; Glee C; Social Work.

EDMINSTER, Sally M
Rainier HS; Rainier, WA (3-42) A Cap Choir; Band; Chem C; Chor; Ensm; FFA; Hmrm; NHS; Sch P; Type A; Vlbl; Bowling; Ellensburg Teachers Col; Home Ec.

EDMINSTER, Susan Lynnette
Rainier HS; Rainier, WA; Ann; Band; Bus C; Chldr; Secy, FFA; Secy, Hmrm; NHS; Sch P; Var C; Secy, Soph Cl; Bkbl; Sftbl; Tr; COM; Cl Fav; Hon Prog; Pep C; St Bowl; Sociology.

EDMOND, Pamelia
Mount Olive HS; Fort Mitchell, AL; Chldr; Chor; FHA; 4H; Sch P; 4H A; Hist A; HCt; Hon Prog; JA A; Most Out; Sci A; Nurs.

EDMOND, Russell Lynn
Concord HS; Concord, NC (34-249) Chor; Inter-Act C; NHS; Ntl Yth Conf; Span C; Type A; UNC-Chapel Hill; Bus.

EDMONDS, Deborah Jean
East Noble HS; Kendallville, IN (42-295) Ger C; 4H; SC; MVP, Bkbl; MVP, Tr; Vlbl; Cole Found Sch; HS All Amer; Outst Female Sr Ath; East Noble Girls Superstar; Prep Tn & Field Ath o-t Yr; Anderson Col; Phys Ed.

EDMONDS, Gary Duane
Dallas Christian HS; Mesquite, TX (25-55) A Cap Choir; Ann; Chem C; Chor; Drama; Ensm; NHS; Sci C; Spch C; Var C; VP, Sr Cl; Bsbl; Ftbl; Cr-Ctry; Cpt, Ftbl; Tr; Cl Fav; U of Tex at Arlington; Bus.

EDMONDS, Howard Cecil
Summerville HS; Summerville, SC; BC; Chor; Ch, Span C; Span NHS; Ch, SC; Alg A; COM; Hon Prog; Hons All St Chor; Med Col of Charleston; Nuclear Tech.

EDMONDS, Terry Linn
Argos HS; Argos, IN (6-69) Band; NHS; Var C; Pres, Sr Cl; Pres, Jr Cl; MVP, Bsbl; Bkbl; Cr-Ctry; Tr; Yth Fel; Principal's 100% C; AIC Rep; Purdue U; Med Tech.

EDMONDSON, Holly Ann
Union HS; Grand Rapids, MI (15%-500) Chor; Ski C; Bsbl; Swim; Diving Tm; Vlbl Tm; Outst Acad Achv; 2nd Pl, St Diving Competition; Ath.

EDMONDSON, Neil Page
Tishomingo HS; Tishomingo, MS (25%-33) Ann; Band; Ensm; 4H; Pres, Sr Cl; VP, Jr Cl; Rptr, Soph Cl; Mgr, Bkbl; Ftbl; Cl Fav; Gov Honor Prog; H of F; MLS; NE Miss Jr Col; Lib Arts.

EDMONSON, Kenneth Ray
Skyline HS; Oakland, CA; Alg A; Citz A; Phy A; Type A; Calif St U at Hayward; Philosophy.

EDMONSON, Virginia Grace
Quincy Sr HS II; Quincy, IL; Chor; Fr C; Soc For Acad Achv; *Gem City Bus Col; Secy.*

EDMUND, Richard Manly Jr
W Columbus HS; Cerro Gordo, NC (5-200) BC; Pres, Hmrm; Pres, Order/Arrow; Pres, Sci C; SC; Co-Cpt, Bkbl; Co-Cpt, Ftbl; Order/Arrow A; Sci A; 'A' A; *U of NC.*

EDMUNDOWICZ, Colette Anne
John S Fine Sr HS; Nanticoke, PA; Band; Chor; Drama; HiY; Mjrte; Model UN; Sch P; SC; Tri-HiY; Var C; COM; Gov Honor Prog; NEDT; *Bucknell U; Biol.*

EDNEY, Tralonia Faye
Little Rock Central HS; Little Rock, AR (82-524) A Cap Choir; Pres, Hmrm; Pres, Sch Hostess C; Sr Banquet Comm; *Central Baptist Col; Elem Ed.*

EDSALL, Elaine Louise
Lowell HS; San Francisco, CA (33%-900) Pres, Hmrm; NHS; CSF; Citz A; Cl Fav; Bridge C; GAA; Dance Comm; *U of Colo; Eng.*

EDSON, Lynn Karon
M B Smiley HS; Houston, TX (13-461) Pres, FHA; Co-Ch, Math C; Co-Ch, Mu Alpha Thet; Tres, NHS; Sci C; COM; Hist A; Sci A; Homemaking A.

EDUARDO, Menichella
Adlai E Stevenson HS; Bronx, NY; Bus C; Chor; Drama; Hmrm; Math C; Span C; Tnns; Alg A; Bio A; COM; Sci A; *Math.*

EDWARDS, Abraham James
Simon Gratz HS; Philadelphia, PA; *Temple U; Pre-Med.*

EDWARDS, Andrew Delwin
Belleville Township HS W; Belleville, IL (15-800) Band; Community Yth Symph; Ger C; NHS; Orch; Pol Sci C; Soccer; All St Orch; Ill Summer Yth Mus Schol; *Biological Engr.*

EDWARDS, Anne Hall
Smithfield-Selma HS; Smithfield, NC (25-350) Band; Chor; Hmrm; Co-Cpt, Mjrte; NHS; Sch P; Span C; HCt; Win, Dist & St Voice, Dist Mus; Sergeant-At-Arms, Sr Cl; *E Carolina U; Bus.*

EDWARDS, Anthony Jerome
Stony Brook Sch; Stony Brook, NY (30-78) Chor; Drama; SC; Var C; JV, Bsbl; Ftbl; Tr; Wrest; Bank Of Amer A; COM; Citz A; Hon Prog; Yth Fel; Christian Service; Stu Chaplain; *Furman U; Religion.*

EDWARDS, Arthur David
Marion C Moore HS; Louisville, KY (103-367) Chor; Drama; MVP, Cr-Ctry; MVP, Tr; Tres, Pres, JA; All Amer, Cr Ctry; All St, Cr Ctry & Tr; Sen Page, St Leg; *Harding Christian Col.*

EDWARDS, Brenda Joyce
Grand Prairie HS; Grand Prairie, TX; *Mountain View Col; Bus.*

EDWARDS, Carolyn Anita
Georgiana HS; Georgiana, AL; Band; Chem C; Drama; GS; Cpt, Mjrte; VP, NHS; Spch C; SC; Amer Leg A; Beauty; Hon Prog; Val; *Ala A&M U; Guidance.*

EDWARDS, Carolyn Anne
Tennyson HS; Hayward, CA (5%-420) Band; Hmrm; SC; *Nurs.*

EDWARDS, Carolyn Pia
Arlington Sr HS; Poughkeepsie, NY (300-600) Jr Prom Qn; *Spelman Col; Computer Sci.*

EDWARDS, Connie Lee
Greenview HS; Greenview, IL (1-27) Ann; Chldr; Chor; GS; NHS; Pres, Soph Cl; Sftbl; COM; Cl Fav; Gr Marshal; NEDT; St Scholar; Span A; *Eastern Ill U; Acct.*

EDWARDS, Cynthia Elaine
Marion-Franklin HS; Columbus, OH (53-360) Band; Fr C; FTA; Orch; ARC; SC; Sftbl; COM; JA A; Spch A; Type A; HR; Little Sisters; Marionettes; *Columbus Tech Inst; Banking & Financing.*

EDWARDS, Cynthia Lafayee
St Helena HS; Greensburg, LA (1-63) Bus C; Chor; FBLA; FTA; Secy, Sci C; Secy, Sr Cl; Cpt, Sftbl; Alg A; Bio A; COM; Cl Fav; HQn; Hon Prog; Type A; Val; Mus A; *Sou U.*

EDWARDS, Danny Ray
Winston Churchill HS; Potomac, MD (20%-576) Bsbl; Cpt, Ftbl; H of F; All Met, All St, All Amer, Ftbl; *Montgomery Col; Archt.*

EDWARDS, Dary Franklin
Shelby Co HS; Columbiana, AL; Tres, BC; Tres, Key C; Sci C; Ftbl; Sci A; Star Student; Outst Eng A; Hon Usher.

EDWARDS, David Russell
Hudson Falls Sr HS; Hudson Falls, NY (156-269) Band; Order/Arrow; Soccer; God & Country A; Eagle Sct; *Adirondack Comm Col; Nurs.*

EDWARDS, David William
Pershing HS; Detroit, MI; Band; Chor; Bkbl; Ftbl.

EDWARDS, Dean Albert
Blue Mountain HS; Orwigsburg, PA; Yth Fel; *Elec.*

EDWARDS, Delores Denise
Alief Hastings HS; Houston, TX (111-435) *SW Col; Bus.*

EDWARDS, Dennis Robert
Stuyvesant HS; New York, NY (30%-600) Band; Community Yth Symph; Ftbl; Wrest; COM; Citz A; DARGCA; Attendance Medal; Mus Medal; *Cornell U; Engr.*

EDWARDS, Doris Aletha
Leaville McCampbell HS; Graniteville, SC (20%-99) Band; BC; JV, Chldr; Fr C; FBLA; Semi-Fin, GS; Sch P; Beauty; HCt; Yth Fel; Most Progress Band Trophy; 1st Run-Up, Qn of Hearts, Aiken Co; *Psych.*

EDWARDS, Doris Elizabeth
Winyan HS; Georgetown, SC;

EDWARDS, Dwayne Ray
Wonderview HS; Morrilton, AR (10%-44) Parl, FFA; Pres, Soph Cl; Bkbl; Cl Fav; HCt; Eng A.

EDWARDS, Earla Ann
Benjamin-N-Cardozo HS; Bayside, NY (179-1010) Chor; Drama; MVP, Hockey; Tr; Type A; Ldrs C; High Jumping A; Vlbl Coach; Humanitarian's A; Steno A; *AUC; Special Ed.*

EDWARDS, Elizabeth Ann
S San Antonio HS; San Antonio, TX (8-360) *U of Tex; Acct.*

EDWARDS, Elsie Elaine
Copiah-Lincoln HS; Wesson, MS (1-39) NHS; Sci C; Y-Tns; Bio A; Hon Prog; Lion A; Val; *Copiah-Lincoln Jr Col; Med Laboratory Technician.*

EDWARDS, Erney Stuart
Colonial HS; Orlando, FL (5%-850) Band; Ger C; Math C; NHS; *Stetson U; Bus Adm.*

EDWARDS, Evelyn Elaine
Melbourne HS; Melbourne, FL; SC; Mgr, Cr-Ctry; Mgr, Tr; Journ A; Pres A; Pep C; Sun Sch A; *Morris Brown Col; Med Tech.*

EDWARDS, Felicia Karey
Central HS; Louisville, KY; VP, FBLA; Hmrm; Pres, Rainbow; ARC; SC; Thes; Sftbl; COM; *U of Louisville; Law.*

EDWARDS, Gloria Jean
Continued Ed Project; St Louis, MO; Pres, Hmrm; Cpt, Bkbl; Phys A.

EDWARDS, Godwin Reynold
Automotive HS; Brooklyn, NY;

EDWARDS, Gordon
Amite Co Attendance Center; Gloster, MS (1-40) BC; FFA; Cpt, Ftbl; Chamber of Comm A; Gov Honor Prog; MLS; Val; *Southwest Ms Jr Col; Industrial Elec.*

EDWARDS, Gregory Alan
Silsbee HS; Silsbee, TX (25-260) Demolay; JETS; Key C; NHS; Span C; Pres, SC; Ftbl; Tnns; Mr Silsbee HS; Twirp Kg; Freedom's Found Sch, Valley Forge; *Tex A&M U; Bus Adm.*

EDWARDS, Gregory Robert
Lenoir HS; Lenoir, NC; Chor; Monogram; Span C; SC; Tr; Wrest; Opt A; Outst Service, Jr Police; Jr Asst Super, Black Yth in Prog; *Hist.*

EDWARDS, James Michael
New Bloomfield R III HS; New Bloomfield, MO; Ann; Band; Chess C; Chor; Mjrte; Sci C; Var C; Bsbl; Bkbl; Cr-Ctry; Amer Leg A; Hist A; Opt A.

EDWARDS, Jeannette
Pasadena HS; Pasadena, CA (496-640) Most Out; Best Vocalist A; *Pasadena City Col; Secy.*

EDWARDS, Jerry Don
Mansfield HS; Mansfield, LA; Order/Arrow; Pres, Sr Cl; Pres, Jr Cl; Tres, Soph Cl; Ftbl; Golf; Cl Fav; Order/Arrow A; *Forestry.*

EDWARDS, Jill Diane
Laurel Highlands Sr HS; Uniontown, PA (2-415) Chldr; Chor; Madrigal; Sci A; Yth Fel.

EDWARDS, John Burkhalter
Claxton HS; Claxton, GA (25%-110) Parl, Chess C; JETS; Rptr, Sch P; Sci C; Y-Tns; Mgr, Bsbl; Ftbl; Sftbl; Mgr, Tr; *S Ga Col; Recreation.*

EDWARDS, John Henry
Williamston HS; Williamston, NC (9-200) Band; BC; Pres, Key C; Monogram; Pres, Soph Cl; Bsbl; Ftbl; Wrest; Chem A; MLS; Pres A; *NC St U; Sci.*

EDWARDS, Julia Lorraine Lord
Telstar Regional HS; Bethel, ME (3-77) Ger C; GS; Balfour A; Bio A; Hon Prog; Most Out; Fr, Ger, A's; *U of Maine; Early Childhood Ed.*

EDWARDS, Karen Kay
Leetonia HS; Leetonia, OH (22-90) A-Ed, Ann; Band; Hmrm; Cpt, Mjrte; NHS; Rainbow; Sch P; Span C; Tri-HiY; Var C; Bsbl; Bkbl; Sftbl; Hon Prog; VFW A; Yth Fel; Carnegie Hero, Bkbl, A's; *U of Pittsburg; Phys Therapy.*

EDWARDS, Kathleen Louise
Blue Valley HS; Randolph, KS (2-23) Ed, Ann; VP, Band; Chor; Ensm; Pres, 4H; SC; Tres, Jr Cl; Orch; Sftbl; Tr; Bio A; DARGCA; 4H A; Sci A; Type A; St VP, FHA; Vlbl; 'A' HR; Kans Interntl Lion's Band; *Kans St U; Nurs.*

EDWARDS, Laura Constance
Scott Preparatory Sch; Opelika, AL (10%-29) Secy, Anchor C; Pres, BC; Co-Cpt, Chldr; Chor; Hmrm; Span C; SC; Var C; S-T, Sr Cl; Cl Fav; Hist A; HCt; Hon Prog; WW; GSct; Jr Civitan; *Sanford U.*

EDWARDS, Linda Joyce
Minden HS; Minden, LA (25%-250) Fr C; FHA; COM; Hon Prog; Most Out; Drill Tm; Darling Pageant; *La Tech U; Computer Sci.*

EDWARDS, Lisa Gayle
Temple Christian Sch; Detroit, MI (1-60) Band; Chor; FTA; Bkbl; Co-Cpt, Sftbl; Fin, Tr; Alg A; A-Ed, Yrbk A; Vlbl; 'A' HR; *Baptist Bible Col; Elem Ed.*

EDWARDS, Lorene Sue
Queen Anne HS; Seattle, WA (14-350) WW; *Seattle Pacific U; Fine Arts.*

EDWARDS, Lorrie Jane
Tabernacle Christian Sch; Greenville, SC (5-18) Band; Chor; VP, SC; Bkbl; Cpt, Sftbl; S-T, SC; WW; Sports Ldrship A; *Bob Jones U.*

EDWARDS, Lynda Lee
Covington HS; Covington, TN; Band; Co-Cpt, Chldr; Drama; Fr C; Semi-Fin, Jr Miss Pa; Lat C; NHS; Rptr, SC; Tnns; Solo & Ensm Band A; Imperial Miss Talent; 1st Pl, Tnns Tourn; *Howard U; Law.*

EDWARDS, Margaret Elaine
Wheaton Central HS; Wheaton, IL; Band; Chor; NHS; Lion A; Stu o-t Yr; Band A; Phys Fitness, Girls Ath, A's; *Wheaton Col; Christian Ed.*

EDWARDS, Marion Louise
H V Jenkins HS; Savannah, GA (18-356) Chor; Sch P; Span C; COM; Gov Honor Prog; Ntl Achv Schol; Star Student; Alt, Quiz Bowl; Beta C A; Savannah Sci Seminar; WW; WW in Foreign Lang; *Armstrong St Col; Engr.*

EDWARDS, Mark Lee
Salem Church Jr HS; Chesterfield County, VA; Dbte Tm; Drama; 4H; Sci C; Bsbl; Sftbl; Tnns; Bio A; 4H A; Co Arts Fair A; Drama; *Virginia Commwelth U; Drama.*

EDWARDS, Michele Ione
Columbus Pub HS; Columbus, ND (4-21) A Cap Choir; Ann; Band; Chor; Drama; Ensm; Fin, GS; Madrigal; ARC; Sch P; Var C; Tres, Jr Cl; Pres, Soph Cl; Bkbl; Sftbl; Tnns; Tr; Amer Leg A; Lion A; PTA A; ARC A; Star Student; Yth Fel; Legion Aux A; Ath C; GAA; *Concordia Col; Mus.*

EDWARDS, Nancy Carolyn
Myers Park HS; Charlotte, NC; Chor; Drama; Span C; MVP, Swim; Hon Prog; Yth Fel; *UNC at Chapel Hill; Eng.*

EDWARDS, Nancy Karol
W J Woodham HS; Pensacola, FL (14-530) FBLA; NHS; Span C; Secy, Soph Cl; *Pensacola Jr Col; Cytology.*

EDWARDS, Nancy Lyn
Winston Churchill HS; Potomac, MD (500-750) Chor; Drama; Hmrm; ARC; Ski C; SC; Hockey; Sftbl; COM; Cl Fav; MLS; ARC A; Mus A's; *Mus.*

EDWARDS, Nathan Earl
Marian HS; Bellaire, TX (60-103) Chess C; Chor; Fr C; Math C; Sci C; Ftbl; Tr; MVP Tr; All-Dist; All-St; *Tex A&T U; Bio.*

EDWARDS, Patty Johnette
Saluda HS; Saluda, SC; BC; *Greenville Tech Col; Pediatric Nurs.*

EDWARDS, Paul Albert
Benjamin N Cardozo HS; Bayside, NY (168-1010) Speedwriting A; Spelling Bee A; *City Col; Engr.*

EDWARDS, R Wayne Jr
Daniel Webster HS; Tulsa, OK (38-287) Semi-Fin, BS; Chess C; Hmrm; Span C; SC; Var C; Bsbl; Golf; COM; Masonic A; Pep C; Golf Ltr; FCA; Church Yth Choir, Pres & Tres; Bowl Coach; *Okla St U; Engr.*

EDWARDS, Rebecca Barker
T L Hanna HS; Anderson, SC; Drama; Lat C; NHS; Rptr, Sch P; Spch C; Tr; Hon Prog; Yth Fel; St Bronze Med, Illus Tri-Cent Book.

EDWARDS, Rhonda Lynn
Perimeter S Christian Acad; Conley, GA (2-26) Cpt, Chldr; F-Ed, Sch P; Ski C; Pres, SC; VP, Soph Cl; Cpt, Bkbl; Sftbl; Cl Fav; Coun of Teach A; H of F; Yth Fel; *Bryan Col; Bus.*

EDWARDS, Robbie Melinda
Rockwood HS; Rockwood, TN; Ann; BC; InterAct C; Math C; Sci C; Lion A; *U of Tenn-Knoxville; Vet Sci.*

EDWARDS, Robert Arthur
Glen Crest Jr HS; Glen Ellyn, IL;

EDWARDS, Robin Starri
Cape Fear Sr HS; Vander, NC; Hmrm; SC; Citz A; Most Out; Med Self-Help A; *Med.*

EDWARDS, Ruth Elaine
Highland HS; Albuquerque, NM (60-725) Ensm; Co-Ed, Sch P; Sci A; Art A's; Dist Bible Quiz; St Sci Fair; Sectional Tn Talent; *Tex A&M U; Animal Sci.*

EDWARDS, Sandra Lea
Albemarle HS; Charlottesville, VA; FHA; Span C; *Sweet Briar Col; Ed.*

EDWARDS, Scott William
Leavenworth Sr HS; Leavenworth, KS; ROTC A; Rifle Tm; Baptist Evening Fel; New Way Singers.

EDWARDS, Sharon Anita
Leto Comprehensive HS; Tampa, FL; *Eckerd Col; Med.*

EDWARDS, Sharon Lynn
Rock Bridge Sr HS; Columbia, MO; FBLA; *Bus.*

EDWARDS, Susan
Wasatch HS; Heber City, UT; A Cap Choir; Chor; FHA; GS; VP, SC; Var C, Jr Cl; JV, Bkbl; Tnns; Mgr, Tr; *Brigham Young U; Home Ec.*

EDWARDS, Susan JoAnne
Litchfield Comm HS; Litchfield, IL (38-155) Span C; *Union University; Nursing.*

EDWARDS, Tammy Darlene
Westfield HS; Westfield, IL (1-19) Chor; 4H; VP, NHS; Span C; VP, SC; Pres, Soph Cl; Bkbl; Sftbl; Tr; HCt; Hon Prog; VP, GAA; *Danville Jr Col; Nurs.*

EDWARDS, Tena Rae
Metropolis Comm HS; Metropolis, IL (1-185) Chor; Drama; Ger C; Secy, 4H; Spch C; Thes; COM; 4H A; NEDT; Spch A; UMYF; Jr Civitan; Vlbl; *Social Work.*

EDWARDS, Timothy Bryant
Interlochen Arts Acad; Interlochen, MI; Ensm; Orch; Soccer; *Eastman Col; Violin.*

EDWARDS, Toni Kay
Metropolis Comm HS; Metropolis, IL (2-185) Chor; Drama; Ger C; Pres, 4H; Spch C; SC; Thes; Bkbl; Sftbl; Tnns; COM; 4H A; NEDT; Spch A; UMYF; Jr Civitan; Vlbl; *Med.*

EDWARDS, Tracy Jean
Leetonia HS; Leetonia, OH; Band; Span C; Tri-HiY; Sftbl; Hon Prog; Yth Fel; Vlbl; PA; *Phys Handicap.*

EDWARDS, Treva Gail
Abilene HS; Abilene, TX; FFA; FHA; COM; *Baptist Bible Col; Bus.*

EDWARDS, Van Blake
Cary Sr HS; Cary, NC (3-475) Ger C; Hmrm; JV, Ftbl; Tr; *NC St U; Architecture.*

EDWARDS, Victoria Ann
N Hollywood HS; N Hollywood, CA (20-700) AFS; Chldr; Chor; Fin, GS; VP, 4H; Ski C; SC; Var C; Swim; CSF; COM; 4H A; Hon Prog; Math A; Type A.

EDWARDS, Voluton George
J H S Hudde; Brooklyn, NY; Math C; Sci C; Spch C; Ftbl; Sftbl; *City Col; Math.*

EDWARDS, William Daniel
Shelby Co HS; Columbiana, AL; BC; FFA; 4H; Pres, Hmrm; Key C; SC; Bsbl; Ftbl; Cl Fav; Jr Civitan Swtht; Lettered in Bsbl.

EDWARDS, William Edwin
Abington Heights Sr HS N Campus; Clarks Summit, PA (29-366) Pres, Band; Chor; Community Yth Symph; Ensm; Madrigal; NHS; Orch; ARC; Hon Prog; Yth Fel; PMEA Reg Bnd & Chor; Crystal Band; Drum Major; Brass Ensm; Pit Orch; Ld Role, HS Musical; Hospital Vol; Pres, Concert Band; Concert Choir; *Communications.*

EDWARDSON, James Leif
Abington HS; Abington, PA (30-867) Band; JETS; NHS; JV, Wrest; *Geneva Col; Industrial Engr.*

EELMA, Karen Lynn
Homestead HS; Cupertino, CA (270-509) Drama; Lit Mag; Spch C; JV, Tr; S-T, Foreign Lang C; Pres, Pep C; Pres, Church Yth Fel; *U of Calif; Bio Sci.*

EFIRD, Andrew Neal
S Mecklenburg HS; Pineville, NC (83%-581) A Cap Choir; Pres, Church Choir; VP Yth Coun; Yth Pastor; *Gardner-Webb Col; Theology.*

EGAN, Christopher Adams
Nyack HS; Nyack, NY; Band; Drama; Rptr, Sch P; Bsbl; *Marist Col; Communication Arts.*

EGAN, Katherine Daly
Nyack HS; Nyack, NY (13-225) Chor; Fr C; French HNS; NHS; Sch P; Dance Company; *Lib Arts.*

EGAN, Mary Susan
W Philadelphia Cath Girls HS; Philadelphia, PA (9-399) Ch; CYO; NHS; Span C; Mgr, Bsbl; *LaSalle Col; Nurs.*

EGAN, Michael Aloysius
St Peters Prep HS; Jersey City, NJ; Ann; Chor; Drama; Hmrm; Lit Mag; ARC; Rptr, Sch P; Ski C; SC; Var C; S-T, Y-Tns; Ftbl; Swim; WW; *Bio.*

EGBERT, Debra Ann
Cokeville HS; Cokeville, WY (1-17) Chor; FHA; Pres, 4H; Co-Ed, Sch P; SC; Bkbl; Citz A; 4H A; SBR, Soph Cl.

EGBERT, Parris Karl
Sky View HS; Smithfield, UT (3-622) JV, Bkbl; Math A.

EGE, Nancy Davis
Center HS; Kansas City, MO (40-412) A Cap Choir; Chor; Drama; Ger C.

EGE, Sharon Kaye
N Miami HS; Denver, IN (7-124) Ann; Band; Secy, Chor; VP, Fr C; Semi-Fin, GS; Mjrte; Mod Mus Mas; NHS; Sci C; Pres, SC; COM; 4H A; Hon Prog; Band Contest; 4-H Judging Hon; Choir Contest.

EGELSTON, Kathi Sue
Middletown HS; Middletown, OH; Band; Chldr; Pres, Fr C; Rainbow; Grnd Cross of Clor, Rainbow Girls; *Miami U; Nurs.*

EGER, Julie Ann
Owensboro Cath HS; Owensboro, KY (16-235) Pres, Chor; Hmrm; Math C; NHS; Sci C; Span NHS; SC; VP, Soph Cl; Tnns; COM; Chem A; JA A; Math A; NEDT; Christian Service A; *Murray St U; Nurs.*

EGERTSON, David Brian
Mission Viejo HS; Mission Viejo, CA (98,-600) HiY; Cpt, Bkbl; Tnns; CSF; MVP, Bkbl; *U of Calif; Computer Sci.*

EGGEMEYER, Tamara Sue
Chester HS; Chester, IL (6-106) Band; FHA; NHS; Sch P; Sftbl; Woman's C Mus Schol; VP, Church Yth Group; Vlbl; *SE Mo St U; Nurs.*

EGGER, Terrence Stone
Justin F Kimball HS; Dallas, TX (15-450) A Cap Choir; Chor; Hon Prog; *U of Tex; Elec Engr.*

EGGERS, Daryl Kevin
Plainfield Jr-Sr HS; Plainfield, IN (2-297) Band; BS; Ger C; Pres, NHS; Var C; Tnns; COM; Chem A; Math A; Phy A; Sal; St Scholar; Geometry A; 3rd Yr Ger A; 4th Yr Ger A; *Rose-Hulman Inst; Chem Engr.*

EGGERS, Karen Lea
Oconomowoc Sr HS; Oconomowoc, WI; Chldr; Chor; Hon Prog; Church Choir; Pianist; Sunday Sch Teacher; *Bus.*

EGGERS, Mary Lorraine
Prescott Sr HS; Prescott, WI; Band; Chor; NHS; Hons Chor; Band, Chor, Solo, Ensm A; *UCLA; Mus.*

EGGERS, Paul Andrew
Watertown Sr HS; Watertown, WI (174-355) Chor; Dbte Tm; Ensm; Ski C; Bkbl; Cr-Ctry; Tnns; Spch A; *U of Wis; Interior Decorating.*

EGGERT, Patricia Lynn
Downers Grove Comm HS N; Downers Grove, IL (30-565) NHS; Sftbl; St Scholar; Co Cpt, Vlbl; WW; *N Ill U; Phys Ed.*

EGGESTEIN, Kay Marie
Arvada W HS; Arvada, CO (320-800) Chor; FHA; Spch C; COM; Hon Prog; Cpt A; Yth Fel; Job's Daughters; Cadette Prog; Drill Tm; Mus A; Accompanist, Chor Groups.

EGGLESTON, Douglas Glenn
Oconto HS; Oconto, NE (1-6) Rptr, Sch P; Sci C; S-T, Jr Cl; VP, Soph Cl; Co-Cpt, Bkbl; Co-Cpt, Ftbl; Tr; Wrest; Hon Prog.

EGGLESTON, Eileen Marie
LeRoy HS; LeRoy, KS (1-27) Band; Chor; Ensm; Pres, 4H; NHS; Var C; Secy, Jr Cl; VP, Soph Cl; Bkbl; Tr; 4H A; St Scholar; Type A; Vlbl; JV Vlbl; WW; Coach & Ath Tr & Field Ath o-t Yr; St Hon Stu; *Kans St U; Vet Med.*

EGGLESTON, Jeffrey Lee
Plano Sr HS; Plano, TX; VP, Bus C; Demolay; Golf; JA A; *Tex Tech U; Bus.*

EGGLESTON, Kelli Dawn
Behl HS; Buhl, ID; Ann; Drama; FHA; Spch C; Job's Daughters; Campfire Ldr; Blue Bird.

EGGLESTON, Willie Alexander
Lake Clifton Sr HS; Baltimore, MD (10%-500) NHS; Tres, Jr Cl; Eng A; *Morgan St U; Acct.*

EGLAND, Susan Kay
Albert Lea Central HS; Albert Lea, MN (83-575) Band; GS; Orch; ARC; SC; Tres, Jr Cl; Swim; Cpt, Tr; Tr & Field Athlete o-t Yr; Gym; Synchronized Swim; *Concordia Col; Med Tech.*

EGLIN, Mary Susan
Riverwood HS; Atlanta, GA (17-255) AFS; F-Ed, Ann; S-T, BC; Chor; Key C; Lat C; Model UN; Mu Alpha Theta; NHS; Hon Prog; Yth Fel; *Davidson Col; Pol Sci.*

EGLY, Carla Jo
Sycamore HS; Sycamore, IL (4-212) Fr C; VP, NHS; Pres, Soph Cl; I Dare You; St Scholar; Hist, Pom Pon Squad; WW; S-T, Church Yth Group; NHS Schol; Essie B Smith Mem Schol; *Wheaton Col.*

EGR, Julie K
Prague Public HS; Prague, NE (3-16) Band; VP, Soph Cl; Swim; Vlbl; *U of Nebr; Dental Hygiene.*

EHLER, Scott Edward
Parkston Pub Sch; Parkston, SD (6-85) Band; Dbte
Tm; Ensm; NFL; Spch C; Golf; Hon Prog; Spch A;
Type A; Debate Ltrs; *Brookings St Col; Journ.*

EHLERT, Anne Thresher
Charles F Brush HS; Lyndhurst, OH (20-700)
Chor; NHS; Ski C; COM; Hon Prog; NML; NHS
A; *U of Mich; Bus.*

EHLY, Thomas Martin
Fremont Sr HS; Fremont, NE (50%-375) Band;
Yth Fel; *Saint Paul Bible Col; General Bible.*

EHRET, Paul Eugene
N Union HS; Richwood, OH (26-120) Band; Tres,
FFA; 4H.

EHRETT, Sheryl Kay
Lutheran HS South; Afton, MO; A Cap Choir;
Chldr; Chor; Drama; NHS; Secy, SC; HCt; Hon
Prog; Vlbl.

EHRETT, Stuart William
Lutheran HS; Afton, MO (1-160) SC; Bsbl; Bkbl;
Ftbl; HCt; HR; Pres, Fresh Cl; HS Clamp, Table
Tn; *Med.*

EHRHARDT, Diane Drew
Arapahoe HS; Littleton, CO (158-660) Tr; Yth Fel;
Southglen Yth Core; Church Yth C; FCA; GSct;
Yth Adv Board; Cadet Sct; Explorers Sct.

EHRHART, Michael Steven
Carver HS; Columbus, GA (10-235) Ann; Chldr;
Pres, Hmrm; Lit Ral; Ed, Lit Mag; Model UN;
Pres, NHS; Ed, Sch P; Pres, Sci C; SC; COM; Hon
Prog; Journ A; Most Out; NMS; Art A; Sail Stu;
WW; Century III Win; *U of Ga; Art.*

EHRLICH, Corinne
Loch Raven Sr HS; Towson, MD (49-476) NHS;
Ski C; SC; Bkbl; Hon Prog; Co Page; Lacrosse;
Rotary Schol; Md Forestry Camp; Cpt, Vlbl;
Goucher Col; Forestry.

EHRMAN, Richard Lee
Hay Springs HS; Hay Springs, NE (1-32) VP,
CYO; Drama; Monogram; NHS; SC; Var C; Bkbl;
Ftbl; Alg A; Amer Leg A; Amer Leg Orator A;
COM; Hist A; Hon Prog; Spch A; VofDEM; *Chadron St Col; Geol.*

EHRMANN, Herbert Max
Benhaven HS; Olivia, NC (1-87) NHS; Order/
Arrow; VP, Sci C; SC; Tr; Alg A; Bio A; COM; Gov
Honor Prog; Hist A; Natl Sci Found; Order/Arrow
A; Sci A; Jr Schol; Marshall; Stu o-t Mo; Eng A; *US
Air Force Acad; Engr.*

EHRNFELDT, Bonnie Jo
Tulpehocken HS; Bernville, PA; Band; Cpt, Chldr;
Chor; Secy, Hmrm; Mjrte; Ntl Yth Conf; VP, SC;
4H A; Mjrte A's; *Radiology.*

EICH, Brian Dean
Mendota Township HS; Mendota, IL (2-254) Fr C;
Math C; NHS; VP, Phys C; Amer Leg A; Lion A;
Math A; *Ill St U; Math.*

EICHEL, David R
MacArthur HS; Decatur, IL; Ensm; ARC; Bsbl; Tr;
Bus.

EICHEL, Judith Renee
E Park Acad; Boody, IL (6-14) Cpt, Chldr; Secy,
SC; Vlbl; VP, Pep C; *Mus.*

EICHENBERG, John Richard
Thomas Jefferson HS; Pittsburgh, PA (60-374) VP,
Chor; Var C; Cpt, Cr-Ctry; Cpt, Tr; *Bucknell Col;
Elec Engr.*

EICHER, Jeffery Dale
Fremont Ross HS; Fremont, OH; Bsbl; JV, Bkbl;
Yth Fel.

EICHER, John Jay
Valparaiso HS; Valparaiso, IN (86-470) Chess C;
4H; JV, Bkbl; Tr; Yth Ldr Inmanuel; Lutheran Yth
Group; Lead Role in Bicentennial Drama; *Mich St
U; Theatrical and Dramatical Art.*

EICHINGER, Brenda Lee
Rapid City Stevens HS; Rapid City, SD (180-415)
Band; Chor; Ensm; FHA; Mgr, Bkbl; Soccer; Mgr
A; Typing A; Sectional Tournament As; *Sioux Falls
Col; Social Work.*

EICHINGER, Karen Elizabeth
Cumberland Valley HS; Mechanicsburg, PA
(3-650) F-Ed, Ann; Hmrm; NHS; SC; Tres, Soph
Cl; JV, Swim; *Penn St U; Acct.*

EICHLING, Sally Jo
Watonga HS; Watonga, OK (1-58) Ann; Cpt,
Chldr; Fr C; VP, FBLA; GS; NHS; Rainbow; SC;
Thes; Secy, Jr Cl; Cpt, Bkbl; Tnns; Chem A; Elk A;
HCt; Masonic A; Math A; Val; Yth Fel; 1977 Pres
Leadership Cl-OU; OSU Achv A; *U of Okla; Phys
Therapy.*

EICHMANN, Catherine Ann
Harrisburg HS; Harrisburg, SD (2-54) Band; Chor;
Community Yth Symph; Ensm; FHA; Orch; Var C;
Bkbl; Sftbl; Co-Cpt, Tr; Pres A; *Bethany Col.*

EICHMANN, Christine Jane
Harrisburg HS; Harrisburg, SD (10-54) Band;
Chor; Community Yth Symph; Parl, FHA; Orch;
Var C; Bkbl; Soccer; Tr; Pres A; Type A.

EICHOLTZ, Timothy Craig
St John Lutheran HS; Ocala, FL (1-29) Hmrm; SC;
Bkbl; Ftbl; Tr; Hon Prog; *Computer Programming.*

EICK, Charlie Mitchell
W Hills HS; Cincinnati, OH; SC; JV, Ftbl; JV, Tr;
Wrest; *Carpentry.*

EIDE, Kaye Marie
Rice Lake HS; Rice Lake, WI (4-259) Ann; Band;
VP, 4H; NHS; VP, Span C; Hon Prog; K of C A;
Rotary A; Fortnightly A; *Carthage Col; Sociology.*

EIDE, Michael Thomas
Rice Lake HS; Rice Lake, WI (10-318) Band; 4H;
JV, Bsbl.

EIDSON, Barry Lee
Central HS; Camp Point, IL (27-85) Pres, 4H;
Hmrm; NHS; SC; Pres, Var C; Co-Cpt, Wrest; 4H
A; NEDT; Pres, Church Yth; MVP, Wrest; *W Ill U;
Agr.*

EIDSON, Debra Jean
Foothill HS; Santa Ana, CA (10%-750) Hmrm;
Redlands Col; Computer Sci.

EIDSON, Kae Ann
Grand Haven HS; Grand Haven, MI; Ann; NHS;
Co-Cpt, Bkbl; Sftbl; Hon Prog; *Central Mich U; Ed.*

EIDSON, Lisa Ann
Scottsboro HS; Scottsboro, AL (50-240) Anchor C;
Band; Sci C; Span C; *Birmingham-Sou Col; Mus.*

EIDSON, Michelle Ann
Mason HS; Tulsa, OK (21-350) AFS; Chem C;
Chor; Drama; 4H; Tres, Lat C; NHS; Sch Achieve
Tm; SC; Bio A; 4H A; Sci A; VofDEM; S-T, Assisteens; Horse Amatuer A; *Stephens Col; Sci.*

EIDSON, Rebecca Ann
Tecumseh Sr HS; Tecumseh, MI; Ann; Drama;
Span C; Pep C; *Mich St U; Nurs.*

EIFERT, Deborah Lee
Waukegan E HS; Waukegan, IL (128-450) A Cap
Choir; Chor; Fr C; FNA; Secy, Thes; *Northern Ill
U; Elem Ed.*

EIFERT, Jennifer Lynn
Waukegan E HS; Waukegan, IL (52-452) Chor;
Span C; SC; Amer Leg A; COM; HCt; NEDT;
Wheaton Col; Ed.

EIKANAS, Lori Lee
Bismarck HS; Bismarck, ND (123-435) Tres,
FBLA; NHS; Var C; Tnns; Worthy Advisor, Rainbow Girls; Grand Cross A; Cpt, S-T, Rifle Tm.

EILAND, Laurie Lynn
Spring Woods Sr HS; Houston, TX (79-510) A Cap
Choir; Chor; Community Yth Symph; Ensm; Fr C;
Jr Miss Pagent; NHS; Orch; Region, Orch, Choir;
Baylor U; Mus.

EILDERTS, Janet Lynn
Aplington Comm Sch; Aplington, IA; Ed, Ann;
Chor; Sch P; HCt; Type A; *Amer Inst of Bus; Acct.*

EISBERG, Alan Bruce
Lincoln Comm HS; Lincoln, IL (42-340) Band;
Span C; Sci A; Mus A; *Computer Tech.*

EISENBURG, Denise Ann
Nyack HS; Nyack, NY;

EISENCOFF, Bonnie Lynn
Nova HS; Davie, FL (265-500) COM; Citz A; Sci
A; *U of Fla; Phys Therapy.*

EISENHOWER, Cynthia Lee
Cumberland Valley Sr HS; Mechanicsburg, PA
(28-640) MVP, Community Yth S; NHSh; MVP,
Orch; Span C; Most Mus; Area Symph Orch; Area
Comm Orch; NML; *Bryn Mawr Col; Modern
Lang.*

EISENMAN, John Robert
Grinnell Comm Sr HS; Grinnell, IA; Key C; NHS;
Var C; Ftbl; Golf; Co-Cpt, Swim; Cornell Col Pres
Schol; *Cornell Col; Bus.*

EISERMAN, Leslie Warren
Maynard Evans HS; Orlando, FL (15-1000) Mu
Alpha Theta; NHS; Cpt, Cr-Ctry; Cpt, Tr; HCt; Ntl
Conf Chr & Jews; Yth Fel; Teacher Advisory
Comm; *U of Fla; Acct.*

EISERT, Douglas Alan
Andrew Jackson HS; Portland, OR (1-250) Co-Ch,
Chor; NHS; Bausch & Lomb A; MVP, Gym; *Lewis
& Clark Col; Sci.*

EISON, Donna Lane
McEachern HS; Marietta, GA; Chor; Drama;
Ensm; Tnns; Tr; S-T, God Sq; GMTA Mus Workshop Schol; Sup & Excellent Ratings, Festival;
Kennesaw Col; Med.

EISSES, Kenneth John
N Kitsap HS; Poulsbo, WA (12-214) Band; FFA;
NHS; Order/Arrow; Var C; Bkbl; Coun of Teach
A; Lion A; Order/Arrow A; Eagle Sct; Principal's
A; All Olympic Tm; Sportsmanship A, Bkbl; *U of
Wash; Civil Engr.*

EISSES, Mark William
N Kitsap HS; Poulsbo, WA; Band; FFA.

EISWERTH, Cynthia Lee
Sunset HS; Beaverton, OR (113-640) Fr C; 4H; 4H
A; *Lewis and Clark Col; Math.*

EITZMANN, Russell Loyal
Johnson-Brock HS; Johnson, NE; Band; BS; Chor;
Var C; Bkbl; Ftbl; Kiwanis A; Farm Bureau Citizenship Sem; All St, Art; *Art.*

EKBLAD, Joy Marie
Grantsburg HS; Grantsburg, WI (2-68) Band;
Chor; FHA; Co-Ed, Sch P; Spch C; Amer Leg A;
Amer Leg Orator A; Hon Prog; Sal; Spch A; Type
A; Yth Fel; Co Honey Qn; WW; Mus Stu; Phys
Fitness A; St Mus A; *Pillsbury Baptist Bible Col;
Bible.*

EKDAHL, Lawrence Wayne
Lueder-Avoca HS; Avoca, TX; Ann; Tres, FFA;
Bkbl; Crop Prod & Star Farmer, FFA As; *Tex Tech
U; Agricultural Engr.*

EKENSTEN, Jodi Lynn
Ashtabula Harbor HS; Ashtabula, OH (32-160)
AFS; Ensm; FTA; 4H; Hmrm; Math C; Sch P; Sci
C; SC; JV, Bkbl; Swim; 4H A; Yth Fel; Sports A;
Centre of Ky; Vet Med.

EKMANIAN, Allison Sarah
Lutheran HS; Burbank, CA (2-69) Chor; Fin, GS;
Co-Ed, Sch P; CSF; Flag Sq; Pep C; Candystriper
Vol.

EKSTRAND, John Robert
Lakeview HS; Columbus, NE (5-76) Chor; Demolay; Madrigal; Var C; JV, Bkbl; Cr-Ctry; Ftbl; Tr;
Math A; Opt A; Pres A; ARC A; Spch A; Tr, Cr-Ctry Ltrs.

EKSTROM, Mark Arlan
San Marcos HS; San Marcos, CA; JV, Bsbl.

ELACQUA, Jamie Lynne
The Doane-Stuart Sch; Albany, NY; Chldr; Cum
Laude Soc; Drama; Fr C; Hmrm; Lit Mag; Sch P;
Ski C; SC; Pres, Jr Cl; VP, Soph Cl; Cpt, Soccer;
Co-Cpt, Sftbl; Hon Prog; Ath As; *Hobart-William
Smith Col; Law.*

ELAM, Curtis Jay
Obion Co Central HS; Troy, TN (2-176) BC; BS;
Hmrm; Pres, NHS; Var C; Bkbl; Ftbl; Tnns; MLS;
Sal; Eagle Sct; Most Versatile; Amer Legion BS; Tn
o-t Wk; Ntl HS A for Excel; WW; *U of Tenn;
Pre-Med.*

ELAM, Gloria Lynne
Maplewood HS; Nashville, TN (1-287) Chor;
Drama; Fr C; InterClub Coun; Lat C; NFL; NHS;
SC; Math A; NEDT; Spch A; *Spelman Col;
Biomed.*

ELAM, Janice Kay
Piggott HS; Piggott, AR (25-78) Ann; Chor; Drama; FHA; Sci C; S-T, Sr Cl; Dist Pres, Lib C; *Bus Mgt.*

ELAM, Jeana Karlene
Willis HS; Willis, TX (10-150) Tres, A Cap Choir; JV, Chldr; Tres, Chor; Ensm; Pres, FTA; Lit Mag; Madrigal; Sch P; VP, SC; VP, Jr Cl; Swtht; Tres, SC; Madrigal A; SC A; Choir A; *Sam Houston U; Mus.*

ELAM, Lynette Lyndell
Richmond Acad; Augusta, GA; Rptr, Bus C; Chor; Dbte Tm; Rptr, FBLA; Hmrm; SC; WW; Cpt, Drill Tm; *Ga Sou Col; Data Processing.*

ELAM, Melody Ann
Western HS; Louisville, KY (63-360) Chor; Drama; Ensm; Ger C; Hmrm; Secy, Mod Mus Mas; Spch C; Pres, Thes; WW, Mus Stu; *U of Ky; Phys Therapy.*

ELAM, Phyllis Marie
Cahawba Christian Acad; Centreville, AL (5-9) Ann; BC; Chldr; Sftbl; WW Friendliest; *Mobile Col; Nurs.*

ELAM, Regina
Sumner HS; St Louis, MO (33-474) Sch P; SC; Hon Prog; Journ A; JA A; Q&S A; Scholastic Soc; Pep Sq; TEAM; *Ga St U; Computer Sci.*

ELAM, Teresa Diana
Pickerington HS; Pickerington, OH (25%-173).

ELBELAU, Itpang
Emmaus HS; Koror, PALAU, WESTERN CAROLINE ISLANDS (4-13) Chem C; Math C; Bsbl; Sftbl; Tnns; Hon Prog.

ELBON, Antari
Marshall Islands HS; Majuro, MARSHALL ISLANDS; Most Out.

ELBY, Nina Lenice
Arcadia HS; Arcadia, CA (24-806) Ch, Hmrm; NHS; CSF; Hon Prog; Girls League; Drill Tm; Badminton; Welfare Comm; Gold Seal Grad; Campus Life; Pres Recogn List; Jr Exchng; Exec Coun, Church; *Pepperdine U.*

ELCHUCK, Cheryl Ann
Bridgeport HS; Bridgeport, OH (1-121) Chldr; Drama; FTA; Fin, GS; NHS; Sch Achieve Tm; Rptr, Sch P; Span C; SC; Thes; Y-Tns; Bio A; Swtht; Phys Ed A; NHS A; Daisy Mae; Chldr A; *Ohio U; Ed.*

ELDAL, Lynda Lee
Thomas Jefferson Sr HS; Bloomington, MN (98-720) NHS; Span C; Swim; *U of Minn; Elem Ed.*

ELDEN, Paul
St Mary's Prep; Orchard Lake, MI; Ski C; Magna Cum Laude; First Hon; *U of Mich; Med.*

ELDER, Barbara Kay
Columbiana HS; Columbiana, OH (31-101) VP, Bus C; NHS; Bkbl; Tr; Vlbl.

ELDER, Brenda Lee
Riverdale HS; Mt Blanchard, OH (65-110) Band; Chor; Pres, 4H; Tres, Hmrm; Sch P; Span C; Var C; Mgr, Bkbl; Tr; Co-Ch, Rptr, 4-H C; Co-Ch, S-T, Yth Fel; Superior, Sci Fair; Sundy Sch Tchr; Co Fair Ribbons; *Nurs.*

ELDER, Bruce Lamar
South HS; Springfield, OH; A Cap Choir; Chor; SC; Cr-Ctry; Mgr, Tr; *Youngstown St Col; Mortuary Sci.*

ELDER, Charlene
Beech Hill HS; Pulaski, TN; Ann; Chor; FHA; 4H; Hmrm; Y-Tns; Sftbl; Cl Fav; 4H A; HCt; *Columbia St Col; Psych.*

ELDER, Debra Lee
Bowling Green HS; Bowling Green, KY (39-378) Secy, A Cap Choir; Secy, Chor; Hmrm; Fin, Jr Miss Pagent; NHS; ARC; SC; Tri-HiY; Fin, Sr Cl; Beauty; Cl Fav; Most Out; Outst Mus Stu; Jr Miss Poise & Appearance; Swtht Ball Cand; *David Lipscomb Col; Sociology.*

ELDER, Edie Mae
J C Harmon HS; Kansas City, KS; Chor; Bus Mgr, Sch P; Span C; COM; Star Student; Drill Tm; *William Jewel Col; Psych.*

ELDER, Iris Anne
Shaler Area HS; Pittsburgh, PA (100-1000) Chor; Fr C; Home Ec A; Cashier o-t Mo; PA; *Bradford Bus Col; Acct.*

ELDER, Jonathan David
N Fla Christian Sch; Tallahassee, FL (6-100) BC; MVP, Soccer; *Wheaton Col; Elec.*

ELDRED, Janet Marie
Los Banos HS; Los Banos, CA (11-208) Band; Chldr; 4H; Swim; Bank of Amer A; CSF; Ldr, CYO; Sons of Italy Schol; Asilmar; Frank Celano Schol; Soroptomist Med Schol; YLI Schol; *Fresno St; Optometry.*

ELDRIDGE, Amy Lou
Potsdam Central HS; Potsdam, NY; Cpt, Chldr; NHS; Ski C; Co-Cpt, Bkbl; Soccer; Tr; Best Attitude, Soccer; *St U of NY; Sociology.*

ELDRIDGE, Jacqueline Susan
W Mecklenburg HS; Charlotte, NC (80-500) Ann; ARC; Span C; *U of NC; Pol Sci.*

ELDRIDGE, Jennifer Joyce
Red Bank HS; Chattanooga, TN (4-336) Hmrm; Secy, Math C; Tres, NHS; Span C; SC; Star Student; MVP, Church Bkbl; Church Sftbl; Jr Miss St Hostess; *Middle Tenn St U; Med Tech.*

ELDRIDGE, Margaret Amy
Terra Linda HS; San Rafael, CA (10%-500) Chess C; Community Yth Symph; VP, Fr C; InterAct C; Orch; Cr-Ctry; CSF; *Mus.*

ELEM, Kimberly Ann
Skyline HS; Dallas, TX (60-891) NHS; Beauty; Drill Tm; Runner-Up, Jr Miss Transportation; SEOG Grant; *Baylor U; Dental Hygiene.*

ELFRINK, Mark Anthony
W Jefferson HS; West Jefferson, OH (65-119) Band; CYO; Chor; Fr C; OEA; HR; Church Choir; Gold Medals; Ltr of Commendation; *Ohio Dominican Col; Religious.*

ELFTMAN, Mary Ann
Southport HS; Southport, IN; Drama; Fr C; VP, Ger C; Secy, 4H; Hmrm; ARC; SC; Secy, Thes; Mgr, Tr; *Ball St U; Social Work.*

ELIAS, Walter III
Matoaca HS; Ettrick, VA (2-149) Ann; Secy, Band; Drama; Fr C; Pres, French NHS; Hmrm; Pres, Key C; NHS; Sci C; SC; Tres, Jr Cl; Pres, Soph Cl; Gov Honor Prog; Ntl Achv Schol; All-Regional Band; WW; WW Among Mus Stu in Amer HS; Math & Sci Center Hon Seminar; *Wake Forest U; Bio.*

ELIASEN, Victoria Ann
Westford Acad; Westford, MA (20-200) Chor; Fr C; Hon Prog; Vol, General Hospital; *Gordon Col; Foreign Lang.*

ELIEZER, Jean Mary
Stafford Sr HS; Falmouth, VA (40%-400) Band; NHS; SC; Band A; *VPI; Biol.*

ELIZER, Grace Lynne
Bells HS; Bells, TN; F-Ed, Ann; Secy, BC; Pres, Fr C; Tres, FHA; GS; Pres, 4H; Co-Ed, Sch P; Pres, Thes; Secy, Jr Cl; Amer Leg Orator A; Beauty; B Crocker A; Cl Fav; 4H A; HCt; Journ A; Sal; Spch A; *Lambuth Col; Spch.*

ELIZONDO, Eloy
Roma HS; Roma, TX (6-130) FFA; Math C; NHS; *A&I U; Acct.*

ELKIN, Roy Thomas III
Woodrow Wilson HS; Beckley, WV (91-576) BS; Thes; Cr-Ctry; Cpt, Tnns; Wrest; *W Va U; Bus.*

ELKINS, Catherine Jill
John T Hoggard HS; Wilmington, NC (3-600) Chor; Span C; Tr; *Vet Med.*

ELKINS, Doug Ray
Arkansas HS; Texarkana, AR (20%-500) Span C; Ftbl; Sftbl; Yth Coun; Straight 'A' C; *Elec.*

ELKINS, James Earl
Bainbridge HS; Bainbridge, GA; Band; FFA; Forestry A.

ELKINS, Jan
Gordon HS; Gordon, TX; BC; Chldr; FHA; SC; Bkbl; Tnns; Tr; Regional Qualifier, Tr; Win, Dist Prose; Candidate, H Qn; *Acct.*

ELKINS, Jodie Lynn
Pike Central HS; Petersburg, IN (25%-250) Band; NHS; Secy, SC; Cpt, Bkbl; Tnns; Tr; HCt; Hon Prog; FCA; Peer Counseling; Vlbl; *Vincennes U; Ed.*

ELKINS, Julia Martin
John T Hoggard HS; Wilmington, NC (25-700) Chor; Ensm; Hmrm; *Fr.*

ELKINS, Kevin Tyrone
Melbourne HS; Melbourne, FL; Band; Var C; Bsbl; Bkbl; Cpt, Ftbl; Sftbl; Tr; Most Out; Star Student; Yth Fel; *Bus Mgt.*

ELKINS, Kimm Lu
York HS; York, NE (15-170) Chldr; Chor; Ger C; 4H; NHS; Rainbow; Var C; VP, Soph Cl; Swim; Tr; COM; 4H A; Type A; Yth Fel; Pom Pom; Vlbl; *Reece Sybil Sch of Beauty; Cosmetology & Hair.*

ELKINS, Rita Jean
Franklin Road Christian Sch; Murfreesboro, TN (2-7) Ann; Chor; Dbte Tm; NHS; Sch P; Bkbl; Sftbl; COM; Citz A; JA A; NMS; *Tenn Temple Col; Elem Ed.*

ELL, Gerald Francis
Chamberlain HS; Grassy Lake, CANADA (1-16) Pres, SC; Co-Cpt, Bkbl; Cpt, Vlbl; *Sou Alberta Inst of Tech; Computer Tech.*

ELLARD, Mary Elizabeth
Jena HS; Jena, LA (11-128) Ed, Ann; Chldr; Drama; FHA; Secy, FTA; GS; Key C; Semi-Fin, Lit Ral; NFL; Rainbow; Ed, Sch P; Spch C; SC; Mgr, Bkbl; Mgr, Sftbl; Amer Leg A; Journ A; Spch A; Swtht; VofDEM; Best Actress; Delta Kappa Gamma Schol; Chancellor's Fresh Hon A; FTA Faculty A; *LSU; Social Stu Ed.*

ELLCESSOR, Mark Alan
Cowan HS; Muncie, IN (2-90) SC; Bsbl; JV, Bkbl; Golf; Alg A; *Purdue U; Engr.*

ELLEDGE, David Louis
Litchfield Sr HS; Litchfield, IL; Chor; Pres, Fr C; NHS; VFW A; Swing Choir; Sch Mus; Children's Theater; WW; *E III U; Acct.*

ELLEDGE, Emmett Scott
Albemarle HS; Charlottesville, VA (32-624) NHS; Order/Arrow; A-Ed, Sch P; Soccer; God & Country A; Order/Arrow A; Yth Fel; Lacrosse; Eagle Sct A's; *U o-t S; Pre-Med.*

ELLEDGE, Kathy Anne
James F Byrnes HS; Duncan, SC; Band; Chldr; FHA; Pres, Hmrm; SC; Beauty; Fin, Miss BHS; SAE; Chldr Ltr; *U of SC; Ed.*

ELLEDGE, Steven James
Superior HS; Superior, NE (41-83) Ftbl; Tr.

ELLENA, Lori Anne
Riverdale HS; Riverdale, CA (1-155) Tres, Jr Cl; Tnns; CSF; Rptr, Gym C; Stu o-t Month; Pep C; Sonora, Yth Conf; JV, Gym; Outst Stu, Math & Foreign Language; Outst Stu, Art & Social Sci; *Fresno St U; Sci.*

ELLENS, Harold Rocklan
Harrison HS; Farmington Hills, MI; A Cap Choir; Band; BS; Chor; Ensm; Ger C; Cpt, Mjrte; SC; Var C; Bkbl; Tr; COM; *Calvin Col; Engr.*

ELLENS, Harold Rocklin
Harrison HS; Farmington Hills, MI; Band; BS; Chor; Ger C; SC; Bkbl; Swim; *Calvin Col.*

ELLENWOOD, Patricia Elain
Papillion-LaVista Sr HS; Papillion, NE (71-449) JV, Bkbl; Sftbl; Church Chor; Vlbl; Qn, Acteens; HR; *Ath.*

ELLER, Cynthia Allyn
Kelly Walsh HS; Casper, WY (1-411) A Cap Choir; NHS; *Evangel Col; Home Ec.*

ELLER, Edward Dean
Moran HS; Moran, TX (1-9) *Tex Tech Col; Math.*

ELLER, Phillip Brooks
Newton-Conover HS; Newton, NC (144-209) Band; Community Yth Symph; Ensm; Orch; NEDT; All-St Band; Mus A; *Berklee Col of Mus.*

ELLER, Ronald Ray
Canyon HS; Canyon, TX (10-345) SC; Bsbl; JV, Ftbl; Chem A; Type A; *Abilene Christian U; Architecture.*

ELLER, Sander Mack
Benita HS; LaVerne, CA (1-273) A Cap Choir; Pres, Chess C; FTA; Hmrm; Madrigal; SC; Bausch & Lomb A; Chem A; NMS; Phy A; *LaVerne Col; Math.*

ELLERBEE, Audrey
Cooley Sr HS; Detroit, MI; *Oakland Comm Col.*

ELLERBUSCH, Linda Kay
Belleville Township HS W; Belleville, IL; Ann; Gym; *Bradley U; Interior Design.*

ELLESON, Linda Sue
W Allis Central HS; West Allis, WI (1-531) Co-Ed, Ann; Band; Community Yth Symph; Ger C; GS; Pres, 4H; Tres, HiY; Hmrm; Math C; NHS; Orch; Cpt, Cr-Ctry; Tr; 4H A; Val; S-T, Handbell Choir; WW; NMS Commended Stu; *N Central Col.*

ELLEVEN, Patricia Louise
Burleson HS; Burleson, TX (10-270) Band; Dbte Tm; Pres, FTA; Lat C; NHS; Magna Cum Laude; Spch A; Cl I Solos; 1st Cl GSct; *Sam Houston St U; Chem.*

ELLIFF, Laura Beth
Harlingen HS; Harlingen, TX (73-600) A Cap Choir; Ann; Chor; Ensm; Madrigal; SC; Q&S A; Keywanettes; All St Choir; Solo, Ensm Medal; WW; *Baylor U; Mus Ed.*

ELLINGSON, Donna Marie
Maddock Pub Sch; Maddock, ND (2-24) Ann; Band; Chldr; Chor; Ensm; FHA; Sch P; Secy, SC; Pres, Soph Cl; Hist A; Type A; Chldr A; Band A; Literature A; Ensm A; *Secy.*

ELLINGSON, Kari Lynn
St Francis HS; St Francis, MN (25-270) Band; Cpt, Chldr; Ensm; GS; 4H; SC; Tr; 4H A; Yth Fel; Stu Life, Crusade for Christ; Superior Ratings, Mus; *Bethel Col; Social Work.*

ELLINGTON, Clarence
Inglewood HS; Inglewood, CA; Spch C; Bsbl; Co-Cpt, Bkbl; Stu o-t Wk; Athlete o-t Wk; *U of Denver; Bus Mgt.*

ELLINGTON, Elizabeth Ann
N Forsyth Sr HS; Winston-Salem, NC (47-672) Secy, Anchor C; Ann; Sch P; Sftbl; Tnns; Q&S A; *Guilford Col; Biol.*

ELLINGTON, Marsha Renee
Washington Co HS; Sandersville, GA; Ann; BC; Drama; Rptr, FHA; 4H; Hmrm; Sch P; SC; 4H A; Drama C Qn; Church Yth Coun; Church Sftbl; *Dentistry.*

ELLINGTON, Mitzi Ellen
Southland HS; Arbyrd, MO (4-44) Drama; Pres, Fr C; Tres, FHA; VP, FTA; Hist A; HCt; Hon Men, Fr; *Memphis St Col; Phys Theat.*

ELLINGWORTH, Kimberly Kay
Morristown Pub Sch; Morristown, MN (10-42) Ann; Chor; Sch P; Secy, Yth Fel; Pep C; Pom Pom Girl; Jr Auxiliary.

ELLINOR, Lisi Ann
Richardson HS; Richardson, TX (30-920) Hmrm; Fin, Jr Miss Pageant; Math C; Mu Alpha Theta; NHS; VP, Ski C; Span C; Pres, Span NHS; Pres, SC; Cpt, Tnns; COM; DARGCA; Hon Prog; Most Out; Rotary A; Spch A; Ntl Merit Commended Stu; *The U of Tex at Austin; Advertising.*

ELLIOTT, Beverley Susan
Edmond Mem HS; Edmond, OK; Co-Ed, Ann; Band; Fr C; NHS; Tri-HiY; Sftbl; Flag Drill Corp Tm; CODA Band; All-St Band; *Okla Christian Col; Bus.*

ELLIOTT, Bruce Darren
Belton HS; Belton, MO; Chor; Madrigal; Bsbl; Spch A; *Southwest Baptist Col; Pastorate.*

ELLIOTT, Carol Joyce
McMinnville HS; McMinnville, OR (7-250) Fin, GS; Key C; NHS; SC; Cr-Ctry; NCTE Achv A; Girl's League Board.

ELLIOTT, Carol Sue
Pineville HS; Pineville, LA (2-323) Co-Ed, Ann; Chor; Tres, Dbte Tm; Lit Ral; NFL; NHS; Spch C; Hon Prog; Spch A; *Baylor U; Ed.*

ELLIOTT, Carolyn Elaine
Lyons Township HS; La Grange, IL (75%-1182) Sch P; NEDT; *Conservation.*

ELLIOTT, Carrie Marie
Highland HS; Albuquerque, NM (125-900) Chor; Fr C; Hmrm; NHS; Rainbow; SC; Tri-HiY; Cr-Ctry; Golf; Swim; Tr; *LSU; Chem.*

ELLIOTT, Cheryl Lynn
Eau Gallie HS; Melbourne, FL; Rptr, Bus C; FBLA; NHS; Star Student; *Bus.*

ELLIOTT, Cynthia Ada
Ashville HS; Ashville, AL; Band; Chor; Secy, FHA; FTA; 4H; 4H A; Miss FHA; Most Courteous; *Gadsden St Jr Col; Home Ec.*

ELLIOTT, David Lee
Anamosa HS; Anamosa, IA (11-149) A Cap Choir; Band; Chor; Drama; Ensm; Madrigal; NEDT.

ELLIOTT, Dennis Craig
Winnfield Sr HS; Winnfield, LA (15-124) FBLA; FFA; FTA; Lit Ral; Spch C; Ftbl; Yth Fel; Project LET; Most Versatile; FFA St Lit Rally Contest; *La Tech U; Petroleum Engr.*

ELLIOTT, Don Edward
Sterling Heights HS; Sterling Heights, MI; A Cap Choir; Cr-Ctry; JV, Ftbl; Tr; ARC A; Athletic As; HR; *U of Mich; Engr.*

ELLIOTT, James David Jr
Wichita E HS; Wichita, KS; Band; Chess C; Ensm; Span C; Cr-Ctry; Tr; JV, Wrest; COM; Hon Prog; Span A Trip; Bible Quiz Tm; Yth Ctz Sch; 3rd, Marching Band; I Rating, ST Mus Festival; Win, Inst ENSM; 2nd, Concert Band; *Wichita St U; Bio Sci.*

ELLIOTT, Joan Therese
Boulder HS; Boulder, CO (20%-600) CYO; COM; Opt A; Boulder Mem Hosp Auxilary Schol; *Colo St U; Occupational Therapy.*

ELLIOTT, Karen Deborah
Reidsville Sr HS; Reidsville, NC (8-344) Rptr, Band; Chldr; Fr C; Hmrm; NHS; Tres, Soph Cl; Mgr, Sftbl; Gr Marshal; Hon Prog; NEDT; *Meredith Col.*

ELLIOTT, Karen Sue
Nashville Comm HS; Nashville, IL (13-166) Secy, A Cap Choir; Tres, Band; Secy, Chor; Ensm; FBLA; Madrigal; Mod Mus Mas; NHS; Spch C; Hon Prog; Type A; Tres, GAA; Co-Cpt, Vlbl; Cpt, JV Vlbl; Pep C.

ELLIOTT, Kent Floyd
Henderson HS; Atlanta, GA (40%-300) *Eckerd Col; Vet.*

ELLIOTT, Kimberly Sue
Fairlawn HS; Sidney, OH (4-33) Co-Ed, Ann; Cpt, Chldr; Chor; Drama; Ensm; Parl, FHA; FTA; Pres, 4H; Secy, NHS; SC; Var C; Bkbl; Tr; 4H A; Most Out; Opt A; Type A; Yth Fel; WW HS Stu; Vlbl; WW, Chldrs; WW, Mus Stu; All St Yth Choir; *Asbury Col; Art.*

ELLIOTT, Laura Ann
Sooner HS; Bartlesville, OK (1-291) AFS; NHS; Span C; Span NHS; Tnns; Hist A; *Okla St U; Sci.*

ELLIOTT, Leslie Carroll
N Central HS; Indianapolis, IN (201-1143) Band; Hmrm; SC; Tnns; Yth Fel; 1st, Band Contest; *Ind U; Sociology.*

ELLIOTT, Lonna Lynn
Haralson Co HS; Tallapoosa, GA (14-142) Bus Mgr, Ann; S-T, Band; Tres, BC; 4H; Rptr, Sch P; COM; Gov Honor Prog; MLS; Rptr, Band; WW; Soc of Mus; *Jacksonville St U; Journ.*

ELLIOTT, Marcus Blake
Spring Valley Acad; Centerville, OH (2-40) Chor; Bkbl; Ftbl; Sftbl; Soph Cl Pastor; Ftbl A; Bkbl A; Scholastic A; *Med.*

ELLIOTT, Marvin L
Elizabethton HS; Elizabethton, TN (1-260) Band; Pres, Chor; Hmrm; NHS; SC; *Milligan Col; Bible.*

ELLIOTT, Patricia Jo
Winona Sr HS; Winona, MN (26-479) FTA; NHS; Span C; *Hamline U; International Relations.*

ELLIOTT, Patricia Joann
Nashville Comm HS; Nashville, IL (12-129) A Cap Choir; Chor; Ensm; NHS; Tres, SC; Hon Prog; GAA; Pom Pon Squad; VP, Pep C; Bio C; Vlbl; *Kaskaskia Col; Secy.*

ELLIOTT, Paula Ann
El Camino Real HS; Woodland Hills, CA (27-1095) A Cap Choir; S-T, Band; Chor; French NHS; Mgr, Tr; CSF; Rptr, Tr; *UCLA.*

ELLIOTT, ReGina Gay
Breckinridge Co HS; Harned, KY (10%-250) Co-Ch, FFA; VP, 4H; 4H A; Spch A; Yth Fel.

ELLIOTT, Rhonda Darlene
Sulphur HS; Sulphur, LA; A Cap Choir; Pres, Chor; 4H; 4H A; Most Outst, Pep Squad; *McNeese St U.*

ELLIOTT, Roswietha
Holly Springs HS; Holly Springs, MS (2-157) Band; FBLA; Hmrm; VP, NHS; Sch P; SC; Bkbl; Alg A; Math A; Sal; Type A; Yth Fel; *U of Miss; Bio.*

ELLIOTT, Rupert Randolph Jr
Berea HS; Greenville, SC (25-261) NHS; Var C; Bsbl; Bkbl; Cr-Ctry; Tnns; PTA A; *Acct.*

ELLIOTT, Sharon Jane
Lakeland Sr HS; Lakeland, FL; *Midway Col.*

ELLIOTT, Theresa Elaine
York Acad; Shacklefords, VA; BC; Chor; FHA; Tri Lingua; Rptr, Athena Soc.

ELLIOTT, Tim Wade
Vienna HS; Vienna, IL (33%-124) Co-Cpt, Bsbl; Bkbl; Bkbl Ltr; *U of Ill; Phys Ed.*

ELLIOTT, Timothy Scott
Newton-Conover HS; Newton, NC (20%-250) Drama; InterAct C; InterClub Coun; Pol Sci C; Co-Ed, Sch P; Span C; SC; JV, Bkbl; Art As; PA; Mr Newton-Conover HS; *Appalachian St U; Commercial Design.*

ELLIOTT, Toni Dawn
Bowman HS; Canyon Country, CA; Drama; Lat C; SC; Secy, Sftbl; Tr; Ath A; *USC; Law.*

ELLIOTT, Victoria Lynn
Flushing HS; Flushing, NY (400-1020) Hmrm; JV, Bkbl; Attendance A; Service A; *Laguardia Comm Col; Occupational Therapy.*

ELLIS, Alan Eugene
Miami Killian HS; Miami, FL (4-1102) Band; Math C; Model UN; Mu Alpha Theta; Sci C; Bio A; Citz A; Summa Cum Laude; Sailing C; Cpt, MVP, Bowl; Span, Graphic Arts, A's; *Duke U; Biomed Engr.*

ELLIS, Ann Elizabeth
Robert E Lee HS; Midland, TX (248-649) Chor; VP, FHA; Ch, GS; Hmrm; Sch P; SC; Tres, Sr Cl; Opt Out Tn; Spch A; Rebelettes; SITCA; *Abilene Christian U; Social Work.*

ELLIS, Anne Farrier
Decatur HS; Decatur, AL (10%-536) Band; Chor; Lat C; Lat NHS; Mu Alpha Theta; NHS; Sci C; Tr; COM; NEDT; *Auburn U; Engr.*

ELLIS, Barbara Lynn
Pickwick South Side HS; Counce, TN (2-35) BC; FHA; 4H; Sal; Bookkeeping A; *W Tenn Bus Col; Acct.*

ELLIS, Barry Dean
Wade Hampton HS; Greenville, SC; A Cap Choir; Chor; Ensm; SC; Ch, Sr Cl; Sr Action Committee; *Mus.*

ELLIS, Carolyn Diane
Charles Lincoln Harper HS; Atlanta, GA (5-259) Band; VP, Drama; Fr C; Tres, Hmrm; Rptr, Lit Mag; Tres, Math C; Model UN; Bus Mgr, NHS; Co-Ed, Sch P; Sci C; SC; Alg A; Bio A; COM; Chem A; Hon Prog; Journ A; Math A; Ntl Achv Schol; Ntl Conf Chr & Jews; NMF; Phy A; Rotary A; Sci A; Spch A; Star Student; Cancer Soc A; Army Cert; *Oakwood Col; Bio.*

ELLIS, Carrie Beth
Niceville HS; Niceville, FL; NHS; *Social Work.*

ELLIS, Celia Eloise
Burkeville HS; Burkeville, TX (8-47) Dbte Tm; Drama; FHA; ARC; Var C; Cr-Ctry; Swim; Tnns; Tr; NMS; ARC A; CAP A 'Mitchell'; *Tex Woman's U; Sci.*

ELLIS, Clifford Lee
Northside HS; Roanoke, VA (100-420) Hmrm; Key C; Order/Arrow; Pres, Sr Cl; MVP, Bkbl; Tr; WW; *Roanoke Col; Pre-Med.*

ELLIS, Darryl Lynn
Grand Ridge HS; Grand Ridge, FL (1-45) BC; Chor; FFA; FTA; Type A; *Miss Col; Law.*

ELLIS, Donna Kay
Ellet HS; Akron, OH; Chor; Tr.

ELLIS, Doris Jean
McAdams HS; McAdams, MS; Ann; Band; Ensm; FFA; FHA; 4H; Secy, Hmrm; VP, Tri-HiY; Beauty; HCt; Hon Prog; Poet A; *Holmes Jr Col; Journ.*

ELLIS, Elizabeth Lynne
H D Woodson Sr HS; Washington, DC (2-400) Chor; Drama; Fr C; Hmrm; Orch; ARC; SC; Bkbl; Sftbl; Tr; Citz A; Math A; Sci A; Type A; Fr; Mus; *Fisk Col; Dance.*

ELLIS, Elizabeth Thorne
Sheboygan Falls HS; Sheboygan Falls, WI (25-150) Ed, Ann; Chldr; Chor; GS; NHS; Var C; Cpt, Sftbl; Q&S.

ELLIS, Gail Maria
McKinley HS; Washington, DC (25%-700) Chor; Hmrm; NHS; Orch; ARC; SC; Citz A; Hist A; Women's Bar Assn A; *U of Los Angeles; Chem.*

ELLIS, Gregory Scott
Santa Monica HS; Santa Monica, CA (9-900) Band; Ensm; Pres, Ger C; Madrigal; NHS; Alg A; Bank Of Amer A; CSF; Kiwanis A; Opt A; Yth Fel; Mildred Montgomery Mem A; George Drake Schol; Charles C Hirt Mem A; United Methodist Women Schol; *CSU Fullerton; Mus Ed.*

ELLIS, Henry Louis
Northeastern HS; Detroit, MI (2-250) NHS; Bkbl; Cr-Ctry; Phi Beta Kappa; *Wayne St U; Engr.*

ELLIS, Jacqueline Ce Vara
Leesville HS; Leesville, LA; Span C; HCt; *LSU; Secy.*

ELLIS, James Barnett
Pittsburg HS; Pittsburg, KS; Pres, Demolay; HiY; Pres, Order/Arrow; Sch P; SC; Tri-HiY; Ftbl; Tr; Balfour A; God & Country A; Order/Arrow A; Eagle Rank; Past Master Couns Meritorious Serv; *Kans St U; Vet Med.*

ELLIS, James Jeffrey
Ripley HS; Ripley, WV; VICA; FFA, Band, A's; *W Va U; Pre-Med.*

ELLIS, Jan C
Van-Far HS; Vandalia, MO (11-64) WW; *NE Mo St U; Bus Adm.*

ELLIS, Jill Diane
Lincoln Comm HS; Lincoln, IL; Orch; Span C; Spch C; Thes; Soccer; Swim; Spch A; Art A's; *U of Hawaii; Marine Bio.*

ELLIS, John Scott
Arlington Heights HS; Fort Worth, TX (272-448) Band; Ensm; Orch; Cr-Ctry; *SMU; Bus Adm.*

ELLIS, Joyce Ann
St Augustine HS; St Augustine, FL (15-390) Co-Ed, Ann; Band; BC; VP, FHA; 4H; NHS; Pres, Rainbow; Sch P; Thes; Swim; *Fla Med & Dental Asst Sch; Med Asst.*

ELLIS, Kimberly Anne
Aiken HS; Cincinnati, OH (2%-600) Chor; Drama; Pres, Ensm; Fr C; Secy, NHS; Bus Mgr, Sch P; SC; Thes; COM; Citz A; Hon Prog; Most Out; Yng Life; Nelson Schwab A; OMEA Vocal Solo & Ensm Contest; Ivy Arch Girl; *Miami U; Bus.*

ELLIS, Lisa Lynn
Arlington HS; Arlington, TX (3-479) Ch, NHS; SC; Hon Prog; Magna Cum Laude; All Dist, All Region, Vlbl; HS All Amer, Vlbl; *Stephen F Austin St U.*

ELLIS, Maria Theresa
Crystal River HS; Crystal River, FL; Sci A; PA A.

ELLIS, Marilyn Denise
Humboldt HS; Humboldt, TN; BC; FHA; Hmrm; PA.

ELLIS, Mary Alice
Greenville HS; Greenville, MS (9-616) Ann; Band; FBLA; Hmrm; Lit Ral; NHS; Alg A; Bio A; COM; Citz A; Crisco A; Hist A; Math A; Sci A; Type A; Yth Leg; Cand, NCTE Achv A, Writing; Fin, District FBLA Comp; *Miss Col; Ed.*

ELLIS, Michael LeRoy
Howard D Woodson Sr HS; Washington, DC; A Cap Choir; Chor; Fr C; NHS; SC; Chamber of Comm A; Citz A; Math A; PTA A; PA; All City Chor Mus Festival; Maxi Arts Gala; *Mus Ed.*

ELLIS, Mitzi Carole
Chickasaw Acad; Van Vleet, MS (1-10) Bus Mgr, Ann; VP, BC; Cpt, Chldr; Fin, Jr Miss Pagent; Beauty; Cl Fav; Hist A; HCt; Math A; Sci A; Star Student; Jr Miss Okolona; Most Intellectual; *U of Miss.*

ELLIS, Nancy L
Struthers HS; Struthers, OH (1-274) F-Ed, Ann; Chor; Ensm; Lat C; NHS; ARC; Bkbl; Tr; Alg A; Amer Leg Orator A; COM; Math A; NEDT; Val; VofDEM; 1st Cl GSct; Eng, Lat, A's; *Ohio U; Math.*

ELLIS, Nancy Lou
Lexington Sr HS; Lexington, NE (6-136) Ann; Band; Chor; Dbte Tm; Drama; FTA; GS; NHS; Sch P; SC; COM; Hon Prog; Creative Writing, Sertoma C, A's; *U of Nebr; Journ.*

ELLIS, Ralph Harold
C L Harper HS; Atlanta, GA; Bkbl; Hon Prog; *Oakwood Col.*

ELLIS, Randall Wayne
Abraham Lincoln HS; Denver, CO (53-780) NHS; Cpt, Var C; Cpt, Soccer; V Sports Ltr; *Colo Sch of Mines; Chem & Petroleum Refining.*

ELLIS, Sharon Kay
Dalton HS; Dalton, GA (109-241) Pres, Anchor C; F-Ed, Ann; Cpt, Chldr; Hmrm; Span C; Bkbl; Tnns; Alpha Delta Kappa Schol; Sr Ser A; Miss DHS; Best All Around; *U of Ga; Fashion Merchandising.*

ELLIS, Shelley Mae
Duncan MacMillan HS; Sheet Harbour, CAN-ADA (3-24) Sch P; Bsbl; Bkbl; Athletic A; *Acadia U; Lang.*

ELLIS, Stephanie June
Wilbur Wright HS; Dayton, OH (5%-300) Ger C; Hmrm; SC; *Alderson-Broaddus Col; Med Sci.*

ELLIS, Valerie Richelle
Sumter HS; Sumter, SC (37-753) Chldr; GS; NHS; SC; Beauty; HCt; WW; Hon Marshal; *Columbia Col; Spch Correction.*

ELLIS, Vep Raymond
Central HS; Thomasville, GA (20%-350) Band; Chor; Ensm; Lit Ral; Bsbl; Ftbl; Tr; Chaplain, Hi-Y; C Swtht; *Coaching.*

ELLISON, Amy Leigh
Ensley HS; Birmingham, AL (15%-365) Drama; Pres, Hmrm; S-T, Lat C; SC; Pres, Jr Cl; Cpt, Soccer; Sftbl; COM; DARGCA; Hon Prog; ROTC A; Yth Foundation; Cpt, Vlbl; *Montevallo U; Psych.*

ELLISON, Arlene
Olney HS; Philadelphia, PA (166-899) A Cap Choir; Band; Drama; Hmrm; Span C; SC; Sftbl; COM; Citz A; JA A; Art, Camping A; March of Dimes Schol; AFNA; *The King's Col; Bio.*

ELLISON, Cynthia
Flint Central HS; Flint, MI (171-407) Y-Tns; NJHS; Career Explores C; Girls Glee C Trophy; Ch, Church Yth Group.

ELLISON, Michael DeAngelous
Rockledge HS; Rockledge, FL;

ELLISON, Pamela Elaine
Bus And Mgt Center; Dallas, TX; FHA; NHS; Sci C; Span C; Hon Prog; *El Centro Col; Data Processing.*

ELLISON, Robert Cofer
Pojoaque HS; Pojoaque, NM; Band; Cpt, Bkbl; Tr; Bio A; COM; Mech Drawing; *U of Ariz; Architecture Drafting.*

ELLISON, Susan Jean
Anadarko HS; Anadarko, OK; Chor; Pres, Ensm; Parl, FHA; Hmrm; VP, NHS; Span C; OSU Academic Achv A; *Med.*

ELLISON, Vickie Renee
Forest Park HS; Cincinnati, OH (22-390) Band; NHS; Span C; Poet A; Co-Cpt & MVP, Vlbl; Michison Annual Giving Schol; *U of Mich; Foreign Lang.*

ELLSTROM, Pamela Denise
Guilford HS; Rockford, IL (115-700) Lat C; *Bethel Col; Nurs.*

ELLSWORTH, Christa Lydine
Manila HS; Manila, UT (1-14) Pres, Chor; Drama; Pres, 4H; Rptr, Sch P; Span C; Pres, SC; Secy, Jr Cl; Mgr, Bkbl; Mgr, Tr; COM; 4H A; Hist A; Swtht; Chor A; Most Dependable; *Snow Col; Elem Ed.*

ELLSWORTH, Cynthia Ann
Belleville HS; Belleville, MI (94-494) A Cap Choir; Chor; Ensm; Madrigal; NHS; *Tenn Temple Col; Elem Ed.*

ELLSWORTH, Diana Joyce
Olathe HS; Olathe, KS (25%-448) Chor; Drama; 4H; Thes; 4H A; Drill Tm.

ELLSWORTH, Tim Robert
Oconomowoc Sr HS; Oconomowoc, WI; Bkbl; Golf; Sftbl; Conservation.

ELLWEIN, Jeffrey James
Riverdale HS; Riverdale, ND (6-30) Band; VP, 4H; SC; Var C; Bkbl; Ftbl; 4H A; *ND St U; Animal Sci.*

ELLYSON, Roberta Louise
Salem Sr HS; Salem, OH; Tres, Bus C; FBLA; Hmrm; Sch P; Spch C; Y-Tns; JV; Tr; *Ct Rptr.*

ELLZEY, Tamara Lynn
Crichton Acad; Mobile, AL; Ann; Chor; City Conf; Ensm; Sch P; Yth Fel; Yth Leg; *U of S Ala; Mus.*

ELMER, George Mitchell
Victoria HS; Victoria, TX (60-548) Cum Laude Soc; Key C; Lit Mag; Bkbl; Best Attitude A, Bkbl; Cum Laude Graduate; *Sam Houston St U; Acct.*

ELMER, Lauren Rose
Victoria HS; Victoria, TX (60-550) Chldr; Hmrm; NHS; SC; *Baylor U; Nurs.*

ELMER, Steven Ronald
Webb HS; Reedsburg, WI (18-200) A-Ed, Ann; Band; Cum Laude Soc; Pres, Ensm; Lat C; Madrigal; NHS; Bkbl; Cr-Ctry; Tr; Magna Cum Laude; NEDT; Forensics; Young Columbus A; 300 Mile C; Vicky Lee Hirsh Schol; Ltrman's C; Math Tm; *U of Wis-Madison; Landscape Archt.*

ELMES, Kristen Ann
Putnam Cath Acad; Putnam, CT; Chess C; Pres, 4H; ARC; Ski C; JV; Bkbl; Sftbl; 4H A.

ELMLINGER, Thomas Joseph
Dobyns-Bennett HS; Kingsport, TN (40-430) BC; Pres, CYO; InterClub Coun; Pres, JETS; Cpt, Cr-Ctry; Tr; NMF; Tn o-t Wk; Marshall Hahn Merit Schol; *VPI; Chem Engr.*

ELMORE, Alan Clark
Houston HS; Houston, MO (21-121) A Cap Choir; Band; Chor; Ensm; FFA; Rptr, 4H; SC; *Sch of The Ozarks; Elec.*

ELMORE, Debora Kay
Frost HS; Frost, TX (1-15) Bus Mgr, Ann; Drama; FHA; Spch C; DARGCA; MLS; *Tex St Tech Inst; Dental Asst.*

ELMORE, Felicia Kathleen
Luther Burbank HS; Sacramento, CA; Band; Chor; Ensm; Madrigal; Orch; Ski C; SC; VP, Jr Cl; Beauty; HCt; Swtht; Lead, Sch Play; Sch Delicate Assembly; *Mus.*

ELMORE, Joanna Lee
Crawfordsville HS; Crawfordsville, IN (110-217) Pres, Rainbow; JV, Bkbl; Tr; Kiwanis A; Masonic A; Pres, Church Yth Group; Most Improved Reserve, Vlbl; Trs, St Grand Rep Ma, Rainbow Girls; *Ind Voc-Tech Sch; Nurs.*

ELMORE, Rebecca Lynn
Jenkins Co HS; Millen, GA (2-100) Co-Ed, Ann; Tres, BC; Chor; Rptr, Sch P; Cpt, Sci C; Cpt, Tri-HiY; COM; Hist A; HCt; Hon Prog; Rotary A; Sal; Swtht; Yth Fel; WW; Eng A; Music A; Woodman o-t World A; *Ga Southern Col; Psych.*

ELMORE, Ruth Elaine
Churchland HS; Portsmouth, VA (73-230) Hmrm; Span C; Tri-HiY; Bkbl; Hockey; HCt; Hon Prog; Rptr, DEC; Art Excellence A; Art Hon Men.

ELMORE, Stephen Lee
Tulare Union HS; Tulare, CA; Band; Tnns; CSF; Church Choir; *Law.*

ELMORE, Wanda Marie
Grace Christian Sch; Blackstone, VA; Cpt, Chldr; Chor; FBLA; Rptr, Sch P; SC; Bio A; Hist A; MLS; Sci A; *Sci.*

ELRIDGE, Anderson Clarence
Deland Sr HS; Deland, FL; Chor; JA A; *Morehouse Col; Mus.*

ELROD, Brian Glenn
Mascoutah HS; Mascoutah, IL (45-303) BC; Drama; Pres, NHS; SC; Pres, Var C; VP, Sr Cl; VP, Jr Cl; VP, Soph Cl; MVP, Ftbl; Co-Cpt, Tr; JV, Wrest; DARGCA; Most Out; Indian o-t Yr; Most Popular; All Metro, All E Side, Linebacker; *Elmherst Col; Engr.*

ELROD, Donna Gail
N Gaston Sr HS; Dallas, NC (8-300) InterClub Coun; Mjrte; Monogram; Span C; Co-Cpt, Bkbl; Cpt, Sftbl; Tr; Alg A; Gr Marshal; Pres A; MVP, Bkbl; Most Improved, Tr; Band, Phys Ed, A's; Qn Regent, Church; *Appalachian St U; Phys Ed.*

ELSEA, Robert Jay
Greenfield-Central HS; Greenfield, IN (1-280) Drama; JV, Bsbl; Ftbl; Swim; Hon Prog; NEDT; Pres A; *Law.*

ELSEA, Tamela Renee
Green City R-1 HS; Green City, MO (15%-45) Band; Ensm; NHS; Secy, Soph Cl; Bkbl; Sftbl; Tr; Alg A; Hon Prog; Math A; Most Out; Historian, FHA; HR A; Labor Day Qn; Health A; Dist Mus Contest; Yth Found; *Med.*

ELSEA, Tammy Renee
Green City R-1 HS; Green City, MO (3-47) Band; Ensm; Secy, Hmrm; NHS; Bkbl; Sftbl; Tr; Alg A; Hon Prog; Math A; Most Out; Hist, FHA; Green Castle Labor Day Qn; Band, Sftbl, Bkbl & Tr Ltrs; I Ratng Dist, II Ratng St Clar Qrt; *Med.*

ELSEN, Carol
Evanston Township HS; Evanston, IL; Lat C; Cr-Ctry; Tr; JV, Vlbl; Vergil Contest As; *Phys Ed.*

ELSER, Brian E
Lakeview HS; Battle Creek, MI; Arch; Hockey; Soccer; Tr; Yth for Understanding; *Marine Bio.*

ELSKEN, Dana Marie
Msgr Nolan HS; Fort Worth, TX (64-190) CYO; VP, Hmrm; SC; Hon Prog; Stu Serv A; 1st Cl GSct; Guitarist, Chrch Instrum Group; Secy, Sr Planning Board, GSct; Pres, Sct Troup; *Child Developement.*

ELSON, Kelly Jeanne
Fort Myers Sr HS; Fort Myers, FL; Chldr; Swim; Pres A; Gym; *Eckerd Col; Phys Ed.*

ELSON, Tao Viet
Willows HS; Willows, CA (7-130) CSF; *Math.*

ELSTON, Dirk Michael
Neshaminy Maple Point HS; Langhorne, PA; Hmrm; Math C; Ch, NHS; Ed, Sch P; SC; Alg A; Amer Leg A; COM; Hon Prog; Math A; NMF; Val; Eng A; Distinguished Stu A; WW; *Pa St U; Med.*

ELSTON, Thomas Frederick
Shades Vly Annex-Resource Lrng Cnt; Birmingham, AL (7-55) Band; NHS; Hon Prog; Yth Fel; Church Choir; *Col of William and Mary; Dentistry.*

ELVIG, Mark Frithjof
Stratford HS; Houston, TX (70-435) Dbte Tm; Ger C; Mu Alpha Theta; NFL; Secy, SC; JV, Bkbl; Tnns; Hon Prog; Yth Fel; *U of Tex at Austin; Pre-Law.*

ELVIN, Caren Sue
Marquette HS; Marquette, KS (3-13) A Cap Choir; Band; Chldr; Chor; Ensm; Spch C; SC; Rptr, Jr Cl; Bkbl; Spch A; Mus A; *Mus.*

ELWELL, Glenn Leslie
Lincoln E HS; Lincoln, NE (50%-476) Band; VP, Chess C; Rep, Mo Synod Luth Yth.

ELWOOD, Betty Jane
Bloomfield HS; N Bloomfield, OH (7-34) A Cap Choir; BC; Chldr; Chor; Sch P; Bkbl; Sftbl; Swim; HCt; Yth Fel.

ELWOOD, Lori Ann
Fremont HS; Fremont, NE; Band; Chor; Ensm; VP, 4H; VP, Sci C; Vlbl; People to People; *Nurs.*

ELY, Ronald Gene
Quakertown Comm Sr HS; Quakertown, PA (1-350) Band; BS; Model UN; NHS; Bkbl; Ftbl; Amer Leg A; Bausch & Lomb A; COM; Phy A; Sci A; Star Student; *Pa St U; Physics.*

EMANUEL, James Mark
N Bend Central HS; N Bend, NE (1-76) F-Ed, Ann; Drama; NHS; Spch C; SC; Pres, Jr Cl; Sci A; Spch A; *Horticulture.*

EMANUEL, Janice Mary
Dover HS; Dover, NH (4-400) Fr C; GS; Lit Mag; Mu Alpha Theta; Pres, NHS; Mgr, Bkbl; Mgr, Ftbl; Mgr, Hockey; Mgr, Tr; Hon Prog; *U of NH; Bio.*

EMBALSADO, Anne Nakandakari
Kubasaki HS; Okinawa, JAPAN (8-355) Cpt, Chldr; NHS; S-T, Var C; Bkbl; Hon Prog; Type A; GAA; Vlbl; *U of Hawaii; Med.*

EMBER, Cynthia Suzanne
El Camino Real HS; Woodland Hills, CA (78-1075) A Cap Choir; Semi-Fin, Chldr; Chor; Secy, Hmrm; Ski C; SC; Pres, Sr Cl; CSF; HCt; Drill Tm; Dance Tm; Most Valuable Sr Cabinet Member; *Cal St U at Northridge; Mus.*

EMBLER, Nancy Jeanne
Ravena Coeymans Selkirk Central HS; Ravena, NY; NHS; *Environment.*

EMBREY, Pamela Denise
Sheffield HS; Memphis, TN (3-142) Cpt, Chldr; Hmrm; Secy, Lat C; Mu Alpha Theta; VP, SC; Sftbl; Alg A; COM; H of F; HCt; Lion A; Magna Cum Laude; Swtht; WW; Govn SW Region, Mu Alpha Theta; Tnager o-t Week; *Baptist Sch of Nurs; Nurs.*

EMBRY, Sheila Gail
Ahrens HS; Louisville, KY; Pres, Bus C; Pres, FBLA; Hmrm; NHS; COM; FBLA Cert of Appreciation; Pa; Jr Cl Serv A; Mod Office Bus A; NHS Cert of Participation; Regional Most Outst Project, FBLA; *Chaffey Comm Col; Bus.*

EMERICH, Brian David
Schuylkill Haven HS; Schuylkill Haven, PA (17-116) Demolay; NHS; S-T, Var C; Bkbl; Ftbl; Co-Cpt, Tr; COM; NEDT; Yth Fel; Spirit A, Tr & Bkbl; *Del Valley Col; Acct.*

EMERICH, Jane Louise
Cedar Crest HS; Lebanon, PA (13-418) Chor; NHS; Tri-HiY; 4H A; Hon Prog; Yth Fel; *Messiah Col; Elem Ed.*

EMERICK, Linda June
Martin Co HS; Stuart, FL (65-500) Band; BC; CYO; 4H; Bkbl; Hockey; Sftbl; Hon Prog; Yth Fel; Civinettes; *Nurs.*

EMERSON, Annette
Skyline HS; Salt Lake City, UT; A Cap Choir; Madrigal; Solo, Symph Orch; Fin, BYU Interntl Comp; Win, Utan Mus Teachers HS Comp; Mus Instructor; *U of Utah; Piano Performance.*

EMERSON, Clinton Louis
Fargo S HS; Fargo, ND; BS; Tnns; Yth Fel; Ntl Ath Schol Soc; 2nd Pl Acct, St Meet; HS Achv A.

EMERSON, Jacqueline Alice
Booker T Washington HS; Tulsa, OK (21-288) Cpt, Chldr; FBLA; NHS; Rptr, Sch P; Parl, SC; Var C; Rptr, Soph Cl; Most Out; Most Spirited; Vlbl; *Langston U; Bus.*

EMERSON, James Matthew
Reeds Spring HS; Reeds Spring, MO (25%-90) Chor; Bkbl; Tr; Hist A.

EMERSON, Janice Rebecca
Washington HS; Tulsa, OK; Ensm; Hmrm; SC; Var C; Ch, Soph Cl; Mgr, Wrest; COM; Hon Prog; Ntl Conf Chr & Jews; Vlbl.

EMERSON, Jean Marie
Apollo HS; Owensboro, KY; Chor; FFA; Ger C; 4H.

EMERSON, Lisa Gail
Apollo HS; Owensboro, KY; FHA; FTA; Ger C; Tr; COM; Most Out; Stu Orientation Committee; Pep C; *U of Ky; Counseling Field.*

EMERSON, Michael James
Green HS; Greensburg, OH (107-345) Chess C; Chor; ARC; SC; JV, Bsbl; JV, Tr; JV, Wrest; Citz A; God & Country A; PTA A; ARC A; Pres, Ntl Eagle Sct Assn; Secy, FCA; Merit Roll; Red Cross Swim Instructor; *Joint Voc Sch; Automotive Mech.*

EMERSON, Nancy Jean
Coldwater HS; Coldwater, KS (2-34) Band; Chor; Ensm; FHA; GS; VP, NHS; Journ A; Sal; Yrbk Staff; Job's Daughters; Pep C; Scholastic A; *Fort Hays St U; Nurs.*

EMERSON, Robin Annette
Hobart HS; Hobart, OK (13-68) Ed, Ann; Cpt, Chldr; FHA; Rainbow; Bkbl; Tr; Yth Fel; *Southwestern St U; Journ.*

EMERT, Sandra Louise
Grant Union HS; Sacramento, CA (2-260) FHA; Fin, GS; Math C; NHS; Pres, Span C; Bio A; CSF; NEDT; Eng A; Span A; *Law.*

EMERY, Allen George
Liberty Christian Sch; Durham, NC; Chor; VP, SC; Bkbl.

EMERY, David Earl
Liberty Christian Sch; Durham, NC (9-20) Ann; Chor; Cpt, Bkbl; Sftbl; Tr.

EMERY, David Eugene
Champion HS; Warren, OH (56-230) NHS; Order/Arrow; God & Country A; Order/Arrow A; Eagle Sct; *Rochester Inst of Tech; Professional Photography.*

EMERY, Dawn Rene
Champion HS; Warren, OH; Band; Chor; ARC; Sch Achieve Tm; Span C; NEDT; Yth Fel.

EMERY, Gina L
Telstar Regional HS; Bethel, ME; Bkbl; Tr.

EMERY, James Lohr
St Thomas Aquinas HS; Louisville, OH (35-185) NHS; ARC; Swim; Hon Prog; *Miami U; Bus Adm.*

EMERY, Susan Diane
Portsmouth Sr HS; Portsmouth, NH (270-460) Pres, 4H; Hockey; 4H A; Yth Fel; NRA; Pres, Explorers; *Law Enforcement.*

EMILY, Katie Olivia
Potosi R-3 HS; Potosi, MO (10-160) A Cap Choir; Ed, Ann; Chor; Ensm; FNA; FTA; Madrigal; NHS; VP, Thes; VP, Sr Cl; VP, Jr Cl; Mo Freedom Forum; *Mineral Area Col; Journ.*

EMMANUEL, Roberta Elsie
Darby Township HS; Glenolden, PA (11-137) Chor; Fr C; Spch C; Spch A; PA; *Journ.*

EMMANUELLI, Mario Federico
Colegio San Antonio Abad; Humacao, PR (12-90) Pres, Hmrm; InterAct C; Sci C; SC; Pres, Jr Cl; Bio A; COM; Most Out; Rotary A; Sci A; Spch A; Interntl Sci Fair; Premio Americo Pomales Lebron; *U of Georgetown; Pol Sci.*

EMMERICH, Susan Ann
Mosinee HS; Mosinee, WI (4-200) Band; Cpt, Chldr; Chor; Drama; GS; Jr Miss Pagent; Madrigal; NHS; Co-Ed, Sch P; Ski C; Var C; Cpt, Bkbl; MVP, Bkbl; Cpt, Vlbl; *U of Wisc; Bus.*

EMMETT, Rick Ronald
Alhambra HS; Alhambra, CA (20-800) Ensm; Bsbl; MVP, Bkbl; Tr; CSF; Citz A; MLS; *Natural Sci.*

EMMETT, Ruth Ann
Perry Meridian Ha; Indianapolis, IN; Chor; Drama; Ensm; Ch, Hmrm; S-T, Span C; SC; Tr; COM.

EMMETT, Teresa Sue
Perry Meridian HS; Indianapolis, IN (55-569) A Cap Choir; Band; Chor; Ensm; NHS; COM; Hon Prog; NMS; PTA A; 'A' HR; *U of Evansville; Mus Therapy.*

EMMONS, Donald Eugene
John F Kennedy HS; Richmond, CA (1-388) Band; Hmrm; Lat C; NFL; Order/Arrow; SC; Cr-Ctry; JV, Swim; MVP, Tr; CSF; Citz A; DARGCA; Pres A; Spch A; Type A.

EMMONS, Jerome Keith II
Okeene HS; Okeene, OK (6-38) Ann; Band; BS; Ensm; Pres, Sci C; *OSU; Med Technology.*

EMMONS, Leslie Elizabeth
Watertown HS; Watertown, CT (28-304) Band; VP, Rainbow; SC; Rainbow Girls Schol; WW; *U of Conn; Liberal Arts.*

211

EMMONS, Myra
Okeene HS; Okeene, OK (2-47) Band; Chor; Ensm; Fin, Jr Miss Pageant; NHS; Ed, Sch P; S-T, Jr Cl; S-T, Soph Cl; Most Out; Outst Soloist at Tri-St; Jr Miss Okeene 1977; Super Ratings, Dist & St Vocal; *Okla St U; Commercial Art.*

EMMONS, Randy Clinton
Trenton HS; Trenton, FL (1-46) Pres, BC; Dbte Tm; Drama; Tres, FBLA; Pres, FFA; Hmrm; Parl, SC; S-T, Jr Cl; S-T, Soph Cl; Bsbl; Ftbl; Sftbl; Wrest; HCt; Math A; Pres A; Star Student; Val; *Agr.*

EMMONS, Scott Everett
Marshall Sr HS; Marshall, MN (7-260) Band; Chor; SC; JV, Ftbl; Swim; *Sci.*

EMNACEN, Maria Theresa
Abbotsford Jr Secondary HS; Abbotsford, CAN-ADA; Co-Cpt, Chldr; Ch, Hmrm; ARC; SC.

EMO, Janet Kay
Freeport Sr HS; Freeport, IL; Community Yth Symph; Ger C; Orch; Bkbl; Tr; Amer Leg A; *Child Psych.*

EMOND, Rosaire
College De Ste Anne De La Pocatiere; La Poca-tiere, CANADA (4-29) CYO; Lit Ral; Phys C; Hockey; *CEGEP-DE La Pocatiere.*

EMPTAGE, Malynda Kaye
Living Word Acad; Okla City, OK; Ed, Ann; NHS; Ed, Sch P; Var C; Secy, Soph Cl; Bkbl; Sftbl; Tr; COM; Rptr, Sch P; Most Creative; Bible, Phys Ed, A's; Most Christlike; *Pepperdine U; Eng.*

EMRY, Rhonda Sue
Belvidere HS; Belvidere, IL (1-374) Band; VP, 4H; NHS; Hockey; *Phar.*

ENABNIT, Jeffrey Arthur
Dewey HS; Dewey, OK (50%-95) Pres, Band; Bsbl; Cpt, Bkbl; Ftbl; Cl Fav; HKg; Okla Senate Page; *Midwest Christian Col.*

ENABNIT, Robyn Rae
Solon HS; Solon, IA (20-86) Chldr; Drama; Span C; Spch C; Pres, SC; JV, Golf; Type A; Pres, Future Secys of Amer.

ENDERLEIN, Steven Eugene
Lincoln HS; Thief River Falls, MN (1-279) Pres, Ger C; SC; Bkbl.

ENDO, Mark Kimihisa
Elcerrito HS; El Cerrito, CA (128-501) Sci C; Vol, Phys Handicapped Sch; MVP, Yth Bkbl League; *U of Calif.*

ENDSLEY, Ricky Dale
Queen City HS; Queen City, TX (9-44) NHS; Sci C; SC; MLS; Sci A; WW; *Texarkana Col; Chem Engr.*

ENFIELD, John David
A Bonnabel HS; Metairie, LA (11-509) BS; Math C; Tres, NHS; Golf; Hon Prog; Yth Fel; Criminol-ogy A; Ntl Champ Academic Games; Hon Grad; *Tulane U; Law.*

ENFINGER, Kim Lynn
Foley HS; Foley, AL (30-200) Fr C; FNA; 4H; Hmrm; InterAct C; ARC; SC; Tnns; 4H A; ARC A; Med Careers; Candy Striper C; Most Talented; *Troy St U; Nurs.*

ENFINGER, Melissa Jaye
Fairhope HS; Fairhope, AL (10%-327) A-Ed, Ann; JV, Chldr; NHS; Beauty; Holmes Jr Board; Cand, Harding Col Citznship Sem; *Troy St U; Park Recre-ation.*

ENFINGER, Melissa Joyce
Fairhope HS; Fairhope, AL (10%-324) A-Ed, Ann; JV, Chldr; NHS; Beauty; Holmes Jr Board; Jr Civi-tan Cand, Harding Col Semnr; *U of Ala; Park Rec-reation.*

ENG, Daniel William
Lowell HS; San Francisco, CA (25-820) JETS; Math C; NHS; CSF; COM; Computer C; Bridge C; *U of Calif; Elec Engr.*

ENG, Judith Leigh
Franklin HS; Seattle, WA (1%-375) Chor; SC; Secy, Sr Cl; Amer Leg A; Hon Prog; Math A; Val; *Claremont Men's Col; Bus.*

ENG, Michael Paul
Wolfson Sr HS; Jacksonville, FL; Dbte Tm; Fr C; Swim; *Hist.*

ENGBRING, Mary
Valmeyer HS; Valmeyer, IL (6-39) CYO; Chldr; Chor; FHA; Math C; NHS; Sch P; Sftbl; HCt; Hon Prog; Pres A; *SIU; General Stu.*

ENGBRING, Susan
Valmeyer HS; Valmeyer, IL (3-43) Band; CYO; Chldr; Chor; FHA; Math C; Orch; Sch P; Sftbl; *U of Va; Archeology.*

ENGEL, Cheryl Denise
Whispering Hills Christian Acad; Nashville, TN (5-20) Chldr; Chor; Span NHS; HCt; *Falls Business Col; Secretarial Work.*

ENGEL, Crystal Joy
Guilford HS; Rockford, IL (50-683) JV, Bkbl; Be-thel Col.

ENGEL, Cynthia Anne
Lutheran HS E; Harper Woods, MI (9-154) A Cap Choir; Band; Mjrte; NHS; Pep C; Instrumental & Vocal A's.

ENGEL, Peter
Arlington Sr HS; Poughkeepsie, NY (300-700) Band; Golf; Soccer; *Acct.*

ENGEL, Tracy Ann
Merrill Sr HS; Merrill, WI (70-375) Chor; 4H; Madrigal; Ski C; COM; Spch A; *Deaf Ed.*

ENGELBART, Linda Louise
Lutheran HS S; St Louis, MO (13-157) Chor; Hmrm; ARC; Bkbl; NMS; *U of Mo.*

ENGELBARTS, Dennis Lee
Lakota HS; Lakota, IA; Sch P; SC; MVP, Bsbl; MVP, Bkbl; MVP, Tr; MLS.

ENGELHARD, David Frost
Glenbrook N HS; Northbrook, IL; St Scholar; Semi-Fin, Gym; Eagle Sct; *Mich St U; Communi-cations.*

ENGELHARDT, Matthew Lynn
Brazos HS; Wallis, TX (50%-70) Band; CYO; Drama; Ensm; Span C; COM; Sci A; Most Im-proved, Band.

ENGELHARDT,
Patrick Anthony
Brazos HS; Wallis, TX (12-38) Parl, Band; Pres, CYO; Drama; COM; Chem A; Mus As; *Wharton Co Jr Col; Chem Engr.*

ENGELHART, Tammy Jo
Frederic HS; Frederic, WI (35-70) Band; Chor; FHA; Var C; Cpt, Bkbl; Cpt, Sftbl; Type A; MVP, All Conf, Bkbl; *Superior Col; Phys Ed.*

ENGELKE, Carolyn Alys
N Shore HS; W Palm Beach, FL (33-266) Bus Mgr, Ann; Key C; Journ A; *Palm Beach Jr Col.*

ENGELSTAD, Mary Beth
St Mary's Central HS; Bismarck, ND; A Cap Choir; Band; Chor; Drama; Fr C; GS; K of C; Madrigal; Math C; Spch C; St Stu Congress; SC; Sftbl; Swim; JV, Tnns; JV, Tr; Interlochen Ntl Mus; Poet A; Swim & Tr A's; *Mus.*

ENGEN, Terrence Alan
Parkview HS; Orfordville, WI (46-150) A Cap Choir; Band; Chess C; Chor; Drama; FFA; Madri-gal; Thes; Bkbl; Doshart Swartz Schol for Boys; *U of Wis Madison; Agr.*

ENGER, Anastasia Caroline
Nerinx Hall HS; Webster Groves, MO (55-98) Orch; Sftbl; Swim; Sr Life Saver; Hon Men, Art Bazaar; *U of Mo; Art.*

ENGER, Mary Elizabeth
Hortonville HS; Hortonville, WI (18-158) Chor; Drama; NHS; Pres, Tnns; *U of Wis-Madison; Ed.*

ENGERMAN, Alphonso
Samuel Gompers HS; New York, NY;

ENGERMAN, Yolanda
Dodge Vocational HS; New York, NY; Chor; FTA; Bkbl; Tnns; Type A; *Secy.*

ENGH, Julie Ann
Larimore HS; Larimore, ND (5%-79) Band; Chor; Ensm; FHA; Span C; Spch C; Secy, Jr Cl; Pep C; *NDSU; Pharmacy.*

ENGLAND, Joseph Brooks
Northwest HS; Rives Junction, MI (110-300) Var C; Ftbl; Sftbl.

ENGLAND, Laura Lynn
Lindbergh HS; St Louis, MO (149-875) NHS; Ntl Cath Mus Ed Asn; 5th Messenger, Job's Daugh-ters; Yth Sunday Speaker; Dancing A; Ntl Mus Guild; *U of Tulsa; Deaf Ed.*

ENGLAND, Pamela Von
Stockton HS; Stockton, MO (1-77) Ann; Chldr; Chor; Ensm; FBLA; FHA; Tres, NHS; Pres, Span C; SC; Pres, Sr Cl; VP, Jr Cl; JV, Sftbl; MLS; Re-gent Schol; Sci A; Val; Ntl Merit Schol Com-mended Stu; Span A, Mus A; Prom Qn; o-t Cedar Co Child Welfare & Adv Cm; Most Admired; *Southwest Mo St U; Span.*

ENGLAND, Richard Bradley
New Smyrna Beach Sr HS; New Smyrna Beach, FL (6-340) NHS; Tres, Sci C; SC; Elk A; Math A; Summa Cum Laude; *U of Fla; Architecture.*

ENGLAND, Sheri Denise
Venus HS; Venus, TX; Chldr; Drama; Sci C; VP, Soph Cl; Bkbl; Cl Fav; Hist A; Hon Prog; Math A; Sci A; Span A; *UTA; Med.*

ENGLAND, Tamra Jean
Wheaton HS; Wheaton, MO (4-31) Ed, Ann; VP, FHA; NHS; Rptr, SC; S-T, Sr Cl; Rptr, Jr Cl; VP, Soph Cl; Sftbl; Type A; Val; Most Popular; Most Fun to Be With; *Crowder Col.*

ENGLAND, Trenton Todd
Kosciusko HS; Kosciusko, MS; Pres, Hmrm; SC; Ftbl; *Miss St U; Elec Engr.*

ENGLANDER, Helaine Frances
Richfield HS; Waco, TX; Citz A; Yth Foundation; Yth Foundation A; Stanley David Levy A; *U of Tex; Fine Arts.*

ENGLE, Deborah Lynn
Northglenn HS; Northglenn, CO (1-805) Band; Chor; Drama; Tres, FHA; Hmrm; NHS; SC; COM; Citz A; Yth Fel; Pres, Church Yth; HR; Stu o-t Mo; Stu Aid; Span A; Foreign Lang Fair; Gym; *Sci.*

ENGLE, Edward Alan
Temple Christian Sch; Reford, MI (3-58) Chess C; Dbte Tm; FTA; Co-Ed, Sch P; SC; Var C; Pres, Sr Cl; Cpt, Cr-Ctry; Co-Cpt, Tr; Alg A; Bio A; COM; Chem A; Citz A; Cl Fav; Hist A; Math A; Most Out; Phy A; Pres A; Sci A; Spch A; MVP, C Ctry; *Baptist Bible Col; Bus.*

ENGLE, John Stephen
Harding HS; St Paul, MN (22-766) Band; NHS; Var C; MVP, Cr-Ctry; Tr; *Conservation.*

ENGLE, Margaret Ann
Western Brown HS; Mt Orab, OH (5-156) Band; Chor; Community Yth Symph; Ensm; Mjrte; VP, NHS; Span C; Cl Fav; MLS; Mus A; *Cincinnati Bible Col; Psych.*

ENGLEHART, Edward G Jr
Varina HS; Richmond, VA; A Cap Choir; Sftbl; COM.

ENGLEMAN, Gary Kirt
Stockton R-1 HS; Stockton, MO; Var C; Bsbl; Co-Cpt, Bkbl; Cl Fav.

ENGLER, Cynthia Denise
Foothill Sr HS; Sacramento, CA; A Cap Choir; Band; Chor; Ensm; Fr C; Lit Ral; NHS; COM; Pres, Job's Daughters; Piano A; TV Talk Show; *Calif Lutheran Col; Bus.*

ENGLER, Jean Anne
Marian HS; Tamaqua, PA (5-173) Ed, Ann; CYO; Fr C; French NHS; Hmrm; NHS; Rptr, Sch P; SC; NEDT; *Villanova U; Pre-Law.*

ENGLER, Robert Michael
Linn-Mar HS; Marion, IA (25-238) Band; Secy, Order/Arrow.

ENGLER, Sally Jo
Belleville Township W HS; Belleville, IL (64-850) Chldr; Drama; Ski C; Span C; Bkbl; Swim; Tnns; Alg A; B Crocker A; Elk A; Yth Fel; Yth Founda-tion A; Jobs Daughters; *Belleville Area Col; Med.*

ENGLISH, Brenda Kay
Parkview HS; Little Rock, AR; BC; FBLA; Y-Tns.

ENGLISH, Cheryl Ann
Timberline HS; Weippe, ID (10-47) Ann; Band; NHS; Bkbl; Tr; Hon Prog; *Lewis & Clark St Col; Nurs.*

ENGLISH, James Roy
Long Co HS; Ludowici, GA; Ann; FFA; HiY; Sci C; Tr.

ENGLISH, Janice Sue
Faith Christian Sch; Quincy, MI; Band; Cpt, Chldr; Ensm; Fr C; Bus Mgr, Sch P; Var C; Tres, Y-Tns; Sftbl; Tr; Sci A; Vlbl; *Marion Col; Nurs.*

ENGLISH, Kathie Darlene
Ocean Springs HS; Ocean Springs, MS (2-250) Ed, Ann; BC; SC; Balfour A; B Crocker A; Citz A; Cl Fav; HCt; MLS; NEDT; Sal; VFW A; Most Ambitious; Hall of Fame; *U of Miss; Journ.*

ENGLISH, Marlanda
Elizabeth Seton HS; Fairburn, GA (44-276) NFL; Orch; Spch C; COM; Citz A; PTA A; Spch A; Piano Teacher; Sunday Sch Teacher; Reading A; Ldrship Workshop; *Bradley U; Engr.*

ENGLISH, Stephanie Camille
Acad of Our Lady; Chicago, IL (42-167) Chor; Madrigal; Sftbl; COM; Hon Prog; Cert of Explorer Health Prog; Hon Men, Fine Arts; Bible Trophies; Cert, Ntl Cath Stu Lib Asst Assn; *U of Ill at Chicago Circle; Phar.*

ENGQUIST, Carol Lynn
Oak Lawn Comm HS; Oak Lawn, IL (33-734) *Moraine Valley Comm Col; Sociology.*

ENGRAM, Leigh Ann
Campbell HS; Fairburn, GA (50-108) Chldr; FBLA; FTA; Lat C; Span C; *Clayton Jr Col; Legal Secy.*

ENGRAM, Maxine Delois
Wheeler Co HS; Alamo, GA (3-79) Pres, FHA; NHS; VP, Sci C; VP, SC; Pres, Jr Cl; Bkbl; Tr; COM; Jr FHA Degree; *Morris Brown Col; Nurs.*

ENGRAM, Melody Kay
M B Smiley HS; Houston, TX (30-400) A-Ed, Ann; Band; Ensm; Hmrm; Mjrte; Math C; Mu Alpha Theta; NHS; Sch P; Sci C; SC; VFW A; Homemaking, UIL Twirling, A's; UIL Flute Ensemble, A; *Harding Col; Law.*

ENGSTROM, Carol Jane
Columbus Pub HS; Columbus, ND (14-21) Band; Chor; Drama; 4H; Sch P; Bsbl; GAA; *Williston Col; Nurs.*

ENIS, Arlie Donald
Bethel HS; Shawnee, OK (15-80) BS; FFA; Econ Judging; *E Okla St Col; Agr.*

ENK, Cynthia Joanne
Normandy Sr HS; St Louis, MO (26-502) A Cap Choir; Co-Ed, Ann; Chor; Ger C; NHS; SC; Pres, Sr Cl; Journ A; Q&S A; God & Comm A.

ENK, Sandra Jill
Normandy Sr HS; St Louis, MO; Band; Chor; Hmrm; SC; Swim.

ENLOE, Roger Dale
Kearny HS; San Diego, CA (135-1129) Ftbl; *San Diego St U; Liberal Arts.*

ENLOE, Stuart Ellington
N Fulton HS; Atlanta, GA (9-20) Fr C; Order/Arrow; Bkbl; God & Country A; *U of Ga.*

ENNIS, Lori Jenene
Auburndale Sr HS; Auburndale, FL (20-335) Anchor C; BC; Tres, Fr C; Ch, Hmrm; A-Ed, Sch P; SC; Bkbl; COM; H of F; HCt; Spch A; Type A; Silver Garland A; *Polk Comm Col; Social Work.*

ENNIS, Nancy Erin
Wm R Boone HS; Orlando, FL (15-602) AFS; Rptr, Ann; BC; Fr C; SC; COM; NMF; NMS; Jr Civitan; *Oral Roberts U; Pre-Dentistry.*

ENOCH, James DunBarton
Westbury Sr HS; Houston, TX; Band; Cr-Ctry; JV, Tr; Hon Prog; NEDT.

ENOCH, Michelle Yvonne
Anacostia Sr HS; Washington, DC; ICEP A; Hon Soc; *SE U; Acct.*

ENRIGHT, Brenda Lea
Hayti HS; Hayti, MO (3-85) Chldr; S-T, Chor; VP, FHA; FTA; Tres, Math C; Secy, NHS; Tres, SC; VP, Tres; Secy, Jr Cl; COM; HCt; Vlbl; Quad St, All Dist, Choirs.

ENRIQUEZ, Lupe
Mission HS; San Fernando, CA; F-Ed, Ann; Hmrm; Math C; Sch Achieve Tm; Sch P; Sci C; SC; Citz A; Cl Fav; Star Student; Swtht; Val; *Bus.*

ENS, Brad Dean
Immanuel HS; Reedley, CA (11-57) Drama; NHS; SC; Pres, Sr Cl; VP, Soph Cl; Bsbl; Cpt, Ftbl; Bank Of Amer A; Rotary A; *Bus.*

ENSER, Jody Lynn
Minnesota Lake HS; Minnesota Lake, MN (8-38) Ann; Band; Chor; S-T, Drama; Tres, FHA; S-T, NHS; F-Ed, Sch P; S-T, SC; Thes; Bkbl; COM; Dist Rating, Mus Contest; *Mankato St U; Home Ec.*

ENSLEY, Daniel Henry
Roy Miller HS; Corpus Christi, TX; Sftbl; Yth Fel; *Tex A&I Col; Engr.*

ENSMINGER, Robin Faye
Ruston HS; Ruston, LA (18-250) Band; Chess C; Dbte Tm; Fr C; Lat Kd; NFL; NHS; Hist A; Opt A; VofDEM; All Dist Band; Sup Rating, Solo, Ensm; Sch Ltr; Principal's List; *La Tech U; Lib Sci.*

ENSOR, Carl Thomas
Patten Acad of Christian Education; Oakland, CA (20%-13) Band; Chor; Community Yth Symph; Fin, Dbte Tm; Ensm; Orch; Rptr, Sch P; Pres, SC; Bsbl; Bkbl; Ftbl; Hockey; Sftbl; Swim; CSF; Citz A; Most Out; WW Mus Stu in Amer HS; *Patten Bible Col; Bible Theology.*

ENSOR, Michele Denise
High Point Sr HS; Beltsville, MD; GS; SC; Sftbl; Tr; Yth Fel; *Bus.*

ENTERLINE, Leslie Carl
James W Robinson Secondary HS; Fairfax, VA; Ed, Ann; Ch, Fr C; Hmrm; Order/Arrow; Span C; Spch C; COM; Citz A; Journ A; Opt A; Order/Arrow A; Spch A; Vol Worker; Phys Handicapped; Yrbk Design; Hon Men, Heart & Lung Assn; *VPI; Pediatrics.*

ENTREKIN, John Manor
Cedar Shoals HS; Athens, GA (1-475) Band; BC; VP, Chess C; Lat C; Math C; Mu Alpha Theta; Sch Achieve Tm; Gov Honor Prog; Math A; Sch Ping-Pong Champ; 3rd Pl Chess; 1 of 4 Best Soph in St On Piano; *Cal Tech; Math.*

ENTZ, Lowell James
Berean Acad; Elbing, KS (2-37) A Cap Choir; Ensm; NHS; Phys C; Sci C; Pres, Sr Cl; Bkbl; JV, Cr-Ctry; Soccer; HCt; Hon Prog; Most Out; Sal; *Grace Col o-t Bible; Bible.*

ENTZMINGER, John Kayln
Skyline Center HS; Dallas, TX; Band; Lat C; Wrest; *Baylor U; Hist.*

ENYART, William Edward
Robert S Rogers HS; Toledo, OH (25%-530) COM; Yth Leg; Pres, VP, Yth Legislature; *Ohio St U; Horticulture.*

ENZOR, Mark Alan
Robert E Lee HS; Montgomery, AL (10%-600) Dbte Tm; NHS; Sci C; JV, Bkbl; JV, Ftbl; COM; Cl Fav; Hon Prog; Math A; Ed Stu Committee, Church; Yth Coun; Church Yth Choir; Cpt, Puppet Tm; Mission Tm; Yth Wk Outst Work A; *Auburn U; Acct.*

EPHRAIM, Foster Albert
Greater N Y Acad; Woodside, NY (20-46) Band; Orch; Ski C; Bsbl; Bkbl; Sftbl; Swim; COM; Citz A; Bible Doctrines; Mus A; *Atlantic Union Col; Med.*

EPHRIAM, Barbara Ann
Pecos HS; Pecos, TX (69-210) Tres, FBLA; Tres, FHA; Tr; *Spch Therapy.*

EPKE, Janet Lucille
Valentine HS; Valentine, NE; Chor; GS; Y-Tns; Masonic A; WW; *Bus.*

EPLEE, Robert Eugene Jr
Whiteville HS; Whiteville, NC (2-190) Rptr, Fr C; VP, Math C; Model UN; NHS; Bausch & Lomb A; NMF; Sal; Yth Fel; Eagle Sct; Drum Major; Presidential Clrm for Young Amer; John Philip Sousa Band A; Gov Sch; *U of NC at Chapel Hill; Physics.*

EPLEY, Joseph Alan
Central Davidson Sr HS; Lexington, NC; Band; Monogram; Orch; Citz A; *Sci.*

EPLEY, Kenneth Eugene
Freedom HS; Morganton, NC (90-430) *W Pied Comm Col; Elec Bus.*

EPLING, Kent Herbert
Gallia Acad HS; Gallipolis, OH; Hmrm; NHS; F-Ed, Sch P; Var C; Bkbl; *Okla St U; Vet Med.*

EPP, Beverly Jane
Sou Dist 1 HS; Wymore, NE (15-60) Tres, Band; 4H; NHS; Span C; VP, SC; Pres, Y-Tns; Bkbl; Sftbl; Tr; HQn; Outst Athlete; *Bryan Mem Nurs Sch; Nurs.*

EPP, Steven Allen
Wymore Sou HS; Wymore, NE (25-70) 4H; Bsbl; Bkbl; Ftbl.

EPPARD, Ruth Ann
Fairmont HS; Fairmont, MN (23-199) A Cap Choir; Chor; Drama; FHA; Ger C; Tnns; Hon Prog; Gym; *Oral Roberts U; Computer Sci.*

EPPELAND, Roy Anton
St James Pub HS; St James, MN; Band; Chor; Ensm; Golf; Swim; *Mus.*

EPPERSON, Dale Eugene Jr
Commerce HS; Commerce, OK (24-75) Band; Chor; 4H; Sch P; Span C; Secy, Soph Cl; Bkbl; Tr; Beauty; Cl Fav; 4H A; Hist A; Hon Prog; Pres A; Coach, Girls Flag Ftbl; VICA Regionals; Sch Carnival Att; Parl, VICA; Ann Attendant; *Heavy Duty Equip Operator.*

EPPERSON, Jana Lynne
Cardnal HS; Eldon, IA (30-100) A Cap Choir; Band; Chor; Drama; Rptr, 4H; Hmrm; SC; Pres, Soph Cl; Tr; 4H A; ARC A; Yth Fel; Y-H St As; Comm Theatre A; Mst Improv Dncr A; Sndv Sch Organst; Art A; Farming Frontier Film; Gun Safety A; 4-H Exchange Stu; *Bus Adm.*

EPPERSON, Robin Darlene
E Ridge HS; Chattanooga, TN; Chldr; Chor; Hmrm; SC; Thes; Bkbl; Amer Leg A; MLS; Pres A; Opti-Miss C; Soph Coun; Ltrettes C; *U of Tenn; Phar.*

EPPERSON, Suzetta
Pulaski Co HS; Somerset, KY; Cpt, Chldr; FHA; Bkbl; *Somerset Comm Col.*

EPPICH, Irel Scott
Sky View HS; Smithfield, UT (16-611) Pres, Band; Community Yth Symph; Drama; Ensm; Orch; Spch C; Tr; Citz A; God & Country A; Schol A; Life Sct; *Brigham Young U; Sci.*

EPPLER, Barry Windfield
Mayme S Waggener HS; Louisville, KY; A Cap Choir; Chor; Ensm; JV, Cr-Ctry; Tr; JV, Wrest; Amer Leg A; Sci A; Spch A; 1st Pl, St Choir Ensm; *Ecological Sci.*

EPPLING, Jean Alvina
S R Butler HS; Huntsville, AL; Anchor C; Fr C; Mu Alpha Theta; Pres, NHS; Hon Prog; Math A; *Peabody Col of Teachers; Special Ed.*

EPPOLITO, Joseph Anthony
Marist Prep; Penndel, PA (1-11) CYO; Chor; ARC; Pres, Sr Cl; Cpt, Bkbl; Amer Leg A; Hist A; Phy A; ARC A; Sci A; Val; Eng A; Math Analysis A; *Drexel U; Human Behavior & Develop.*

EPPS, Alvin Wendell
Westwood HS; Memphis, TN (8-214) Band; Co-Ch, Hmrm; Math C; NHS; VP, Sr Cl; Pres, Soph Cl; Bsbl; Alg A; Cl Fav; HCt; Hon Prog; Math A; All-City Band; Band A; Eng A; *Tenn St U; Elec Engr.*

EPPS, Lee Ernest
Simon Gratz HS; Philadelphia, PA (3-400) Cpt, Chess C; Drama; FTA; Ch, Hmrm; Math C; NHS; Phys C; Pol Sci C; Sch P; Var C; VP, Sr Cl; Cr-Ctry; Ftbl; Tr; COM; Math A; MLS; Most Out; NMF; NMS; Val; Principles A; *Penn St U; Chem Engr.*

EPPS, Sarah Ann
Gumberry HS; Gumberry, NC (10-97) Fr C; *Asheville-Buncombe Col; Data-Processing.*

EPTING, Mitzi Carole
Salisbury HS; Salisbury, NC (1-250) AFS; Ed, Ann; Band; Fr C; GS; Hmrm; NHS; COM; DARGCA; Hon Prog; Journ A; Keywanettes; Co-Chief Marshal; *Animal Sci.*

ERAZO, Jose Angel
Academia Discipulos de Cristo; Bagamon, PR (10-122) MVP, Arch; Pres, Chem C; Pres, Chor; Cum Laude Soc; Drama; Math C; Sci C; Pres, SC; Bus Mgr, Sr Cl; MVP, Arch; Cpt, Bsbl; Fin, Golf; VP, Swim; MVP, Tnns; Alg A; Bio A; COM; Chem A; Cl Fav; Gr Marshal; H of F; Hon Prog; Interlochen Ntl Mus; Magna Cum Laude; Math A; Most Out; Phy A; Sci A; Star Student; Val; *U of Puerto Rico at Mayagez; Chem.*

ERB, Diane Laurie
St Mary's Acad; Englewood, CO (5-58) NHS; Ski C; Hon Prog; WW; Colo St U; Bus.

ERB, Jeff George
Marissa Jr-Sr HS; Marissa, IL (10-85) Band; VP, FFA; NHS; VP, SC; Var C; Bsbl; Bkbl; Amer Leg A.

ERB, Jerri Lee
Davison HS; Davison, MI (35-490) Tres, A Cap Choir; Band; Bus C; Madrigal; NHS; Y-Tns; Tnns; Type A; All St Hon Choir; 1st Pl St, Gen Clerical; 2nd St, BOEC; Shorthand A; Central Mich U; Secy.

ERCK, Karen Stephenson
Charles W Woodward HS; Rockville, MD (33-320) AFS; Co-Ed, Ann; Hmrm; Sch P; SC; Var C; Bkbl; Cpt, Hockey; Tnns; Tr; Hon Prog; Yth Fel; HS All Amer, Field Hockey; Ch, Graduation Comm; VP, Girls Sports Assn; Denison U; Pre-Law.

ERCK, Sharon Gayle
Robert E Lee HS; Midland, TX (349-739) Inter-Club Coun; Bsbl; Pep Squad; High Point Jr; Hon Squad; U of Tex; Elem Ed.

ERDBRUEGGER, Mark R
Webster Groves HS; Webster Groves, MO (58-495) Drama; SC; Golf; JA A; Yth Fel; Acad As; MIP, Hockey; Purdue U; Engr.

ERDLEY, Guy I Jr
Warrior Run HS; Turbotville, PA; Band; Ensm.

ERDMAN, Lynn Carol
Merrill Sr HS; Merrill, WI; A Cap Choir; Pres, AFS; Ann; Chor; Drama; Ensm; Ger C; Hmrm; Madrigal; NFL; Sch Achieve Tm; Sch P; SC; Tnns; UW Madison; Anthropology.

ERDMAN, Nancy Ilene
Haigler HS; Haigler, NE (3-11) Ed, Ann; Arch; Band; Chor; Drama; Secy, 4H; Math C; Phys C; Ed, Sch P; Secy, SC; VP, Jr Cl; VP, Soph Cl; Arch; Bkbl; Sftbl; Tnns; Tr; Alg A; 4H A; HCt; Math A; Vlbl; Home Ec A; Kearney U; Nurs.

ERDMAN, Susan Lynn
Saint Charles HS; St Charles, IL (2-548) Band; Chor; Fr C; Orch; Sftbl; COM; Hon Prog; Pres A; Yth Fel; Vlbl; Accompanist, Mus Contests; Adver Mgr & Prog Layout, Sprng Mus; Sci.

ERDMANN, Cindy Sue
Twin Lakes HS; Monticello, IN (60-290) Rptr, Band; Co-Cpt, Chldr; Pres, 4H; Span C; Swim; 4H A; Mus As; Purdue U; Home Ec.

ERDMANN, Judy Kay
Barneston HS; Barneston, NE (13-18) Ann; Chor; Ed, 4H; JV, Bkbl; Tr; Citz A; 4H A; Yth Fel; Food & Nutrition A; Vlbl; Pep C; Consumer Ed; Home Living; Home Mgt A; Clothing A.

ERDMANN, Michael Lee
Clintonville Sr HS; Clintonville, WI; Sch P; Var C; Bsbl; JV, Bkbl; Ftbl; Pres A.

ERDMANN, Scott Gregory
Clintonville Sr HS; Clintonville, WI; Bsbl; Bkbl; Ftbl; Pres A; Fox Valley Tech Col; Auto Body.

ERDWIN, Karla Kay
Broomfield HS; Broomfield, CO (25%-250) Group Ldr, Awana C; Campus Crusade for Christ; U of Northern Colo; Special Ed.

ERFLE, Carolyn Louise
Rapelje HS; Rapelje, MT (3-10) Ann; Chldr; Chor; Tres, FHA; Hmrm; Sch P; SC; Var C; Bkbl; Tr; Type A.

ERFOURTH, Kenneth F
Kettle Moraine HS; Wales, WI (100-220) Band; Ensm; GS; Cr-Ctry; Tr; Wrest; NMS; Mus.

ERHARDT, Clement Dumont
Loyola HS; Towson, MD; Ed, Ann; Commercial C; Dbte Tm; NFL; NHS; Rptr, Sch P; Pres, Soph Cl; Cr-Ctry; COM; DARGCA; Hon Prog; NEDT; Opt A; Sci A; Spch A; U of Pa; Acct.

ERHARDT, Jalane Elizabeth
Center Pub Sch; Center, ND (1-52) CYO; Chor; VP, FHA; SC; Type A; PA.

ERHARDT, Myron Peter
Center HS; Center, ND (5-45) CYO; Pres, FFA; Ger C; Parl, SC; JV, Bkbl; FFA Star Greenhand.

ERHARDT, Susan Elizabeth
Qn o-t Rosary Acad; Amityville, NY (10-85) Chor; Pres, NHS; SC; Parl, Sr Cl; VP, Jr Cl; Parl, Soph Cl; JV, Swim; COM; Hon Prog; NEDT; Alt, Regents Schol; WW; Bio.

ERICKSEN, Frances G
Chester Area HS; Chester, SD (15-40) Child Psych.

ERICKSON, Andrea Ruth
Elk Point HS; Elk Point, SD; Band; Chldr; Chor; Ensm; Madrigal; Rptr, Sch P; Bkbl; Sftbl; Tr; St Hons Choir; U of SD; Phys Ed.

ERICKSON, Andrew Mark
Muskego HS; Muskego, WI; Chor; Lit Mag; NHS; Span C; SC; JV, Swim; Tnns; PSAT-NMSQT Commended Stu; Carroll Col; Pol Sci.

ERICKSON, Barbara Lynn
Marina HS; Huntington Beach, CA (20%-800) Bank of Amer A; Hon Prog; Spch A; Shorthand Tourn; Golden West Col; Bus.

ERICKSON, Brian Lee
Central HS; Crookston, MN (11-192) Band; Ensm; Math C; Var C; Ftbl; Tnns; Math A.

ERICKSON, Carla Diane
Bemidji Sr HS; Bemidji, MN;

ERICKSON, Christina Linnea
Avon HS; Avon, CT (36-180) Band; Chor; Lit Mag; Rptr, Sch P; Yth Fel; International Affairs Organization; Pres, United Church Yth; Vlbl; Syracuse U; Writing.

ERICKSON, Cindy Marie
Winona Sr HS; Winona, MN (82-479) Band; FBLA; Orch; Bkbl; Type A; Winona St U; Secy.

ERICKSON, Cynthia Ann
Jackson Central Merry HS; Jackson, TN (61-483) BC; Dbte Tm; Drama; VP, Fr C; Lit Mag; NHS; Pres, Pol Sci C; Sch P; Spch C; St Stu Congress; Thes; COM; Hon Prog; Spch A; Yth Leg; Art A; Kans U; Fine Arts.

ERICKSON, Daniel Ty
Cumberland Co HS; Crossville, TN (33%-450) BS; Chor; COM; Win, Scottish Rite Essay; Tenn Tech Col; Bus Ed.

ERICKSON, David Michael
Crescent HS; Joyce, WA (3-31) NHS; Rptr, Sch P; Soph Cl; NEDT.

ERICKSON, Douglas Frank
Columbia River HS; Vancouver, WA; Pres, 4H; Bsbl; Ftbl; Soccer.

ERICKSON, Elaine Marie
Joliet Township E HS; Joliet, IL (1-370) VP, Band; Math C; Pres, NHS; Orch; Tnns; Tr; Alg A; Hon Prog; Math A; MLS; Rotary A; Sci A; Spch A; St Scholar; Val; Drum Major; Exchange C Yth o-t Yr; Yth Orch of Greater Chicago; Badminton; NHS Schol; Cpt, Vlbl; U of Ill-Urbana; Biochem.

ERICKSON, Ellen Rai
Batavia Sr HS; Batavia, IL; Chor; Lat C; Math C; NHS; Span C; Hon Prog; Math A; Lat Contest; Span Contest; Elem Ed.

ERICKSON, Greg John
Balaton HS; Balaton, MN (14-30) Chor; SC; Pres, Soph Cl; Bsbl; Co-Cpt, Bkbl; Co-Cpt, Ftbl; Golf; Sftbl; Tr; Amer Leg A; COM; HCt; Willmar Votech Col; Carpentry.

ERICKSON, JoAnne Ellen
Northwood-Kensett HS; Northwood, IA (20-70) A Cap Choir; Band; Chldr; Chor; Pres, 4H; Bkbl; Golf; 4H A; N Iowa Area Comm Col; Nurs.

ERICKSON, John Olaf
Littleton HS; Littleton, CO; Chor; Pres, Demolay; Span C; SC; JA A; Engr.

ERICKSON, Julie Ann
Ashland HS; Ashland, WI; FFA; SC; Sftbl.

ERICKSON, Karen Evelyn
Dassel-Cokato HS; Cokato, MN (6-132) Chor; FHA; GS; Sch P; Swim; ARC A; Mus Recital A; NW Col; Mus.

ERICKSON, Kathryn Lynn
Southfield HS; Southfield, MI (50-360) Chor; Drama; NHS; Ski C; COM; Citz A; Secy, Yth Organization; Achv A; Artwork A; Poster-Slogan A; Olive Col; Art.

ERICKSON, Keith Jonathan
Moorhead Sr HS; Moorhead, MN (7-605) A Cap Choir; Band; Chor; Pres, Key C; Bsbl; Ftbl; Sal; Val; Mhd High Hon Soc; ND St U; Wildlife Bio.

ERICKSON, Lorri Rei
Batavia HS; Batavia, IL (11-224) Lat C; Math C; Span C; Hon Prog; Math.

ERICKSON, Louise Elizabeth
Grinnell Comm Sr HS; Grinnell, IA (33-205) Co-Cpt, Chldr; Hmrm; NHS; SC; Co-Cpt, Swim; HCt; Top 10 Most Influential Stu; Cornell Col; Recreation.

ERICKSON, Lyle C
Cambridge Sr HS; Cambridge, MN (161-264) 4H; Bsbl; Bkbl; Golden Valley Lutheran Col; Recreational Ldrship.

ERICKSON, Mark Kevin
Marion HS; Marion, IA; Band; Ftbl; JV, Wrest; Yth Fel.

ERICKSON, Marlene Janette
Bradley-Bourbonnais Comm HS; Bradley, IL (51-431) Band; SC; Olivet Nazarene Col.

ERICKSON, Matt Rodney
Columbia River HS; Vancouver, WA; 4H; Bsbl; Ftbl.

ERICKSON, Neal Allen
Carl Sandburg HS; Orland Park, IL (10-969) Band; Ensm; Hmrm; Math C; Mu Alpha Theta; NHS; Y-Tns; Order/Arrow; Bkbl; Alg A; COM; Citz A; Hon Prog; Math A; Order/Arrow A; ARC A.

ERICKSON, Paula Irene
Bemidji Sr HS; Bemidji, MN;

ERICKSON, Paula Lynn
Mott Lincoln HS; Mott, ND (12-52) Ann; Fin, GS; Sci C; Bkbl; Tr; Jamestown Col; Med.

ERICKSON, Ralph Burdette
Kalamazoo Central HS; Kalamazoo, MI; Cr-Ctry; Tr; Ferris St Col; Graphic Arts.

ERICKSON, Richard William
Elk Point HS; Elk Point, SD (25-55) Pres, Band; Chor; Madrigal; Pres, Var C; Bsbl; Cpt, Bkbl; Cpt, Ftbl; Tr; U of SD; Phys Ed.

ERICKSON, Robert Roy
Victoria HS; Victoria, TX (10%-700) NHS; ARC A; Bsbl; JV, Tnns; Citz A; God & Country A; Kiwanis A; Eagle Sct; Brigham Young U; Psych.

ERICKSON, Roger Dean
Clay Center Comm HS; Clay Center, KS (52-135) 4H; Sch P; Bkbl; Ftbl; Tr; HKg; FCA; Cloud Co Jr Col.

ERICKSON, Sheila Kay
Marshall Co Central HS; Newfolden, MN (20-60) Band; Chor; FHA; Pres, 4H; Sch P; Northland Jr Col; Mus.

ERICKSON, Sheryl Sue
Central Lee; Argyle, IA (25%-110) Ann; Band; Chor; FHA; Rainbow; SC; Golf; Swim; Tnns; Pep C; Hons, Band, Chor; Phys Fitness; SW Assemblies of God Col; Christian Ed.

ERICKSON, Steven LeRoy
S St Paul Sr HS; S St Paul, MN; Ski C; Bus Mgr.

ERICKSON, Susan Gail
Coon Rapids Sr HS; Coon Rapids, MN (59-730) CYO; Cpt, Chldr; Chor; Drama; Hmrm; Semi-Fin, Jr Miss Pa; NHS; ARC; Ski C; Secy, SC; Secy, Jr Cl; Cr-Ctry; Swim; Tnns; Tr; Beauty; COM; Hon Prog; JA A; Spch A; Acad HR; Nurs.

ERICKSON, Thomas John
Armstrong HS; Plymouth, MN (25-761) Band; Community Yth Symph; Dbte Tm; Ensm; NFL; Orch; Ski C; Soccer; U of Minn; Med.

ERICKSON, Tod Laurence
Biggs HS; Biggs, CA (2-40) Band; BS; Hmrm; Co-Ed, Sch P; Ski C; Span C; SC; VP, Sr Cl; VP, Jr Cl; MVP, Bkbl; MVP, Ftbl; MVP, Tr; Bank Of Amer A; CSF; COM; HKg; Hon Prog; Math A; Sal; Yth Fel; Co-Cpt, Bkbl, Ftbl & Tr; Block B; Butte Col; Elec Engr.

ERICKSON, Tracey Dean
Bradley-Bourbonnais Comm HS; Bradley, IL; Pres, Var C; Ftbl; Tnns; Olivet Nazarene Col; Engr.

ERICKSON, Wesley Wayne
Cumberland Co HS; Crossville, TN (77-340) Chem C; Fr C; Hmrm; Lit Mag; Var C; Mgr, Bkbl; Poet A; Yth Fel; HR; *Grace Col; Ministerial.*

ERICSON, Cindy Ann
Kuemper HS; Carroll, IA; Chldr; Chor; Monogram; Var C; Sftbl; Tr; *Briar Cliff Col; Phys Ed.*

ERICSON, Karen Elizabeth
Keene HS; Keene, NH (48-430) NML; *Quinnipiac Col; Lab Animal Tech.*

ERICSON, Kris Kay
Westside HS; Omaha, NE (13-794) Lat C; Magna Cum Laude; Summa Cum Laude; *Archeologist.*

ERIKSON, Sherri Beth
W Middlesex Area HS; W Middlesex, PA; A Cap Choir; Band; Tres, Chor; Madrigal; NHS; Orch; *Youngstown St Col; Psych.*

ERK, Stephanie Diane
Ward Melville HS; Setauket, NY (15%-750) Chor; Madrigal; S-T, NHS; Orch; Ski C; *Syracuse U; Environmental Stu.*

ERKMAN, David Charles
Campbell HS; Campbell, CA; NHS; Cpt, Bsbl; Ftbl; Soccer; CSF; *UCLA; Criminology.*

ERLAND, Michael Eric
Goldendale HS; Goldendale, WA (28-80) Rptr, Ann; Chor; Drama; Rptr, Sch P; Span C; Pres, SC; Var C; Pres, Soph Cl; MVP, Tr; H of F; St Tr Champ; *Ed.*

ERLER, Cindy Lou
Calvary Christain Acad; Midland, MI; Cpt, Vlbl; *Grace Bible Col; Phys Ed.*

ERLER, Nancy Irene
Hazelwood E Sr HS; St Louis, MO (76-445) Tres, Band; Ensm; NHS; Orch; Rptr, Sch P; Cpt, Golf; Sci A; *U of Evansville; Med Tech.*

ERNANDEZ, Keith Stewart Jr
Rock Hill HS; Rock Hill, SC (15%-412) BC; Hmrm; Order/Arrow; Span C; JV, Bkbl; God & Country A; Order/Arrow A; Eagle A; *U of SC; Bus Operations.*

ERNEST, Daryl Paul
Brethren Christian HS; Osceola, IN (5%-30) A Cap Choir; Ensm; 4H; SC; Pres, Jr Cl; Bsbl; MVP, Bkbl; Soccer; Tr; *Grace Col; Bible.*

ERNEST, Debbie Lynn
Pendleton Heights HS; Pendleton, IN (50-295) BC; Chor; FHA; Sch P; Q&S A; *Anderson Col; Elem Ed.*

ERNEST, Jacqueline
Knob Noster HS; Knob Noster, MO (33%-129) SC; Tres, Soph Cl; Bkbl; Mgr, Tr; Citz A; Opt Out Tn; Yth Fel; *Central Mo St U; Bus Adm.*

ERNEST, James Abbott
Newburgh Free Acad; Newburgh, NY (85-850) Ann; Band; Drama; Hmrm; Math C; Orch; Order/Arrow; Phys C; SC; Swim; COM; Regent Schol; Yth Fel; Life Sct; *Carnegie Mellon U; Archt.*

ERNEST, Melissa Margaret
Hightstown HS; Hightstown, NJ (1-308) Fr C; Ger C; Math C; Ski C; Var C; Hockey; Tnns; Tnns Sportsmanship A; *Phys Therapy.*

ERNEY, Sue Ellen
Columbia Jr-Sr HS; Columbia, PA (4-143) Band; Fr C; JV, Tnns; *Cosmetology.*

ERNSBERGER, Jackie Irene
LaVille Jr Sr HS; Lakeville, IN; Chor; Fr C; FHA; 4H; Lat C.

ERNST, James Robert
Katella HS; Anaheim, CA (89-560) VP, Chor; VP, Madrigal; JV, Tr; Type A; *Calif St U; Psych.*

ERNST, Jill Norann
Stephen Decatur HS; Decatur, IL (25%-358) A Cap Choir; Chor; Drama; Hmrm; NHS; SC; Pom Pom Sq; Tumbling & Acrobatics; Songsters; Hospital Vol; Church Exec Board; *Nurs.*

ERNSTBERGER, Dianne
Kelly HS; Chicago, IL (16-391) NHS.

ERNY, James Jerome
Greater Latrobe HS; Latrobe, PA (306-554) VP, Jr Cl; Ftbl; Tr; JV, Wrest; V Ltrs, Ftbl & Tr.

ERRECA, Emil Douglas
Los Banos HS; Los Banos, CA; CYO; VP, FBLA; Rptr, Jr Cl; Bsbl; JV, Bkbl; Mgr, Ftbl; Type A.

ERREICH, Deborah Renee
Bruriah HS; Elizabeth, NJ (5-26) Drama; NHS; Sch P; Art C; Dance C; Sch Play Cast; Tutor Comm.

ERSKINE, Linda Elaine
Brazos Port Sr HS; Freeport, TX; Ed, Ann; S-T, SC; Journ A; Admiral, Drill Tm.

ERSKINE, Robin Lee
DeVilbiss HS; Toledo, OH; Bus C; Chor; Hmrm; Span C; HR; Outst Home Ec Stu; *Toledo U; Nurs.*

ERSKINE, Thomas Wilder
Boothbay Region HS; Boothbay Harbor, ME; AFS; Drama; Hmrm; Sch P; SC; Var C; Bsbl; Bkbl; Cr-Ctry; Tnns; Hon Prog; *U of Maine; Teaching of Phys Ed.*

ERST, Victoria Ellen
Frank Scott Bunnell HS; Stratford, CT (104-470) Conn Bus Inst; *Legal Secy.*

ERTS, Elizabeth Ann
Burlington Comm HS; Burlington, IA; Tr; Batgirl; *Southeastern Comm Col; Bus.*

ERTSGAARD, Lori Ann
Wheaton HS; Wheaton, MN (7-81) Ann; Band; Drama; Ensm; Madrigal; Dist & St Band; Dist & St Choir; *Anoka-Ramsey Comm Col; Nurs.*

ERVIN, Betty Lee
Poteau HS; Poteau, OK (10%-120) Chor.

ERVIN, Dean Wilson II
Wilton HS; Wilton, CT (6-362) Dbte Tm; Tnns; Chem A; Pres, Acolytes; *Math.*

ERVIN, Elaine Edwards
N Mecklenburg HS; Huntersville, NC (20-450) Band; NHS; Orch; Span C; Tr; HCt; Civinettes; Cpt, Flag Corps; Jr Marshal; *U of NC.*

ERVIN, James Masico
Whiteville HS; Whiteville, NC (70-250) FFA; Hmrm; Monogram; Var C; Bsbl; Bkbl; Ftbl; Tr; MLS; Ftbl, Bkbl, Bsbl, Tr, A's; *A&T St U; Phys Ed.*

ERVIN, Jayne Miriam
Claremont HS; Claremont, CA (66-550) Chldr; Chor; Var C; CSF; COM; Gym; Sr High Church Yth Group; Fin, Jr Prom Princess; *Ed.*

ERVIN, Kathy Marie
S Miami Sr HS; Miami, FL; Co-Cpt, Chldr; Chor; InterClub Coun; VP, SC; Arch; Bkbl; Soccer; Sftbl; Tnns; Tr; Swtht; *Morehouse Col; Criminology.*

ERVIN, Mary Rachel
Franklin Road Christian Sch; Murfreesboro, TN (1-7) Chor; Stu o-t Yr A; *Tenn Temple Sch; Secondary Ed.*

ERWIN, Charles Breeden
Freedom HS; Morganton, NC (100-450) Hmrm; Pres, Key C; NHS; Ski C; St Stu Congress; Cpt, SC; Ftbl; Tnns; *NC St U; Liberal Arts.*

ERWIN, Czarena Annette
Permian HS; Odessa, TX; Band; FHA; Rptr, 4H; 4H A; All City Band; FHA, Candystriper, A's; *U of Tex; Pol Sci.*

ERWIN, Sharon Elaine
Permian HS; Odessa, TX; Band; Ensm; FHA; All City Band; 1st Pl, Band Ensm; Vlbl; *Baptist Bible Col; Voc Trng.*

ERWIN, Yvette
Duke Ellington Sch o-t Arts; Washington, DC (1-140) Drama; Ensm; NHS; Pres, Sr Cl; Pres, Jr Cl; Hon Prog; Val; Schol A, Georgetown U; Willie J Hardy Ldrship A; Ward 7, DC; *NYU; Drama.*

ESANNASON, Angela Carol
Charlotte Amalie HS; St Thomas, VI; Pres, Hmrm; NHS; F-Ed, Sch P; SC; Bio A; COM; Pres A; Eng A; *Clark Col; Journ.*

ESCH, Christina Geralyn
Sacred Heart Acad; Mt Pleasant, MI (1-50) Chor; Fr C; NHS; Val; VFW A; VofDEM; *Aquinas Col; Photography.*

ESCHBACH, Kris Ann
Tyrone Area HS; Tyrone, PA (10%-220) Cpt, Chldr; Chor; Hmrm; Jr Miss Pagent; Lat C; Rainbow; Ski C; SC; Swim; Magna Cum Laude; Powder Puff Ftbl; *Hospital of U of Pa; Radiologic Tech.*

ESCHLIMAN, Shelli Dawn
Moberly Sr HS; Moberly, MO (28-272) Drama; Thes; Swim; Drama A; *Stephens Col; Writing.*

ESCO, William Earl
Canton Pub HS; Canton, MS (14-222) A-Ed, Ann; Bus C; Fr C; FBLA; NHS; Sci C; Span C; COM; Hon Prog; MLS; ROTC A.

ESCOBAR, Carlos Rafael
Nuestra Senora de la Providencia; Rio Piedras, PR (7-64) Bus C; Pres, CYO; Chor; Drama; NFL; Tr; Wrest; Citz A; Pres A; Pres, SC; Conduct A.

ESCOBAR, Linda
Roma HS; Roma, TX (6-144) NHS; SC; Secy, Jr Cl.

ESHLEMAN, David Lee
Annville-Cleona HS; Annville, PA (25%-183) NHS; Var C; JV, Cr-Ctry; Tr; *Penn St U; Engr.*

ESHLER, William Jay
Barnesville HS; Barnesville, OH; Key C; Sch Achieve Tm; Var C; JV, Ftbl; Tr; Wrest.

ESKANDARIAN, Karen Jean
Souderton Area HS; Souderton, PA (60-400) Pres, Ski C; Secy, SC; Var C; Cpt, Hmrm; JV, Bkbl; Tnns; Yth Fel; Ecology, Girl's Sports, C'S; Ch, Sr Party; Co-Ch, Sr Lounge; V Tnns Ltr; *Widener Col.*

ESKELAND, Stephen Peter
Tottenville HS; Staten Island, NY (17-1191) Community Yth Symph; Ensm; Fr C; Key C; NHS; Co-Ch, Order/Arrow; Amer Leg A; COM; Citz A; God & Country A; Order/Arrow A; Eagle Sct A; *NY U; Dentistry.*

ESKEW, Jenny Marie
Fairmont Sr HS; Fairmont, WV; Band; Chor; Ensm; Hon Prog; All-St Band; All-Area Band; Prom Hostess; All-Co Chor; *W Va Wesleyan Col; Sci.*

ESKEW, Marcia Annette
Del City HS; Del City, OK (1-650) Band; JV, Chldr; Chor; Drama; Rptr, Fr C; NHS; Thes; Most Out; Spch A; Win, Ed Essay; Eng A; Miss Church Yth.

ESKRIDGE, Kathy Rae
Industry HS; Industry, IL (5-33) Band; Chor; Drama; Fr C; 4H; Math C; Ed, Sch P; Sci C; JV, Bkbl; Golf; Sftbl; Tnns; Kiwanis A; *Monmouth Col; Foreign Lang.*

ESMOND, Howard Kirk
Nederland HS; Nederland, TX (10%-475) AFS; Band; CYO; 4H; Key C; Tres, SC; 4H A; Non Parade, Band; Performing Band A; *Tex A&M U; Vet.*

ESOLDI, Patricia Lorraine
Watchung Hills Regional HS; Warren, NJ (90-494) Pres, CYO; Chldr; Hmrm; SC; Bkbl; *Boston Col; Law.*

ESPARZA, Dolores Ann
Foreman HS; Chicago, IL (33-422) Chor; COM; Citz A; Yth Fel; *Circle Col; Acct.*

ESPENSCHEID, Laura Christine
Tabernacle Baptist Sch; Va Beach, VA; Chor; FNA; COM; Citz A; 2nd Pl, ODACS; Attendance A; *Bob Jones U; Med Missionary.*

ESPERSEN, Raymond Michael
Colegio San Conrado HS; Ponce, PR (2-49) Pres, Chess C; Drama; VP, NHS; Pres, SC; COM; Hon Prog; NEDT; Vlbl; NMS Commended Stu; *Boston U; Law.*

ESPESETH, David Eric
Centennial HS; Champaign, IL (25-350) French NHS; NHS; JV, Bkbl; *U of Ill; Archt.*

ESPESETH, Rebecca Louise
Dodgeville HS; Dodgeville, WI (3-131) S-T, Band; Chldr; Tres, FBLA; 4H; NHS; Orch; Spch C; Cpt, Tr; 4H A; Hon Prog; Spch A; Jr Prom Court; *U of Wis; Phys Ed.*

ESPEY, Pamela Rena
Chattanooga HS; Chattanooga, TN; Band; Tres, FHA; *Morehouse Col; Drama.*

ESPINA, Luzien Lopez
Bishop Conaty Mem HS; Los Angeles, CA (1-150) CYO; Drama; GSc; V Miss Pagent; NHS; ARC; Span NHS; Sftbl; CSF; Chem A; Most Out; Vlbl; Rookie o-t Yr; Excellent, US History A; Comm Service Commendation; *USC; Sci.*

ESPLANA, Evangeline Bernardo
John F Kennedy HS; Tumon, GUAM; Pres, Jr Cl; ROTC A; *Sociology.*

ESPOSITO, Kevin Louis
St Peters Prep Sch; Jersey City, NJ (30-252) Band; CYO; Chess C; Chor; Dbte Tm; Drama; Ch, Ensm; Pres, Hmrm; ARC; Sch P; Spch C; Cpt, Hockey; Tnns; COM; Cl Fav; Hon Prog; Magna Cum Laude; Math A; MLS; Most Out; NEDT; Opt A; ARC A; Sacristan; Spch A; Star Student; MVP, Hockey; Eng A; *Pre-Med.*

ESPOSITO, Mark Gerard
Secaucus HS; Secaucus, NJ (20-185) Fin, BS; Chess C; Pres, Key C; Rptr, Sch P; Sci C; Tres, SC; Jr Cl; Soph Cl; Ftbl; Mgr, Tnns; JV, Tr; JV, Wrest; Hon Prog; Kiwanis A; PTA A; Sci A; VP, PTSA; VP, Chef's C; *Law.*

ESPRABENS, Christine Chantal
Inglewood HS; Inglewood, CA; Fr C; CSF; COM; Citz A; Hon Prog.

ESPY, Joy Darlene
East Ridge HS; East Ridge, TN (11-350) BC; Chor; Hmrm; NHS; ARC; Tres, Span C; Thes; Amer Leg A; Hon Prog; NEDT; *U of Tenn; Sci.*

ESPY, Paula Anne
Burlington HS; Burlington, IA (38-492) Band; Bus C; Ensm; Hmrm; Alt, SC; Hi-Steppers; *Bus.*

ESPY, Sara Annette
Gadsden HS; Gadsden, AL (1-400) Secy, FBLA; GS; Hmrm; Math C; Tres, NHS; Sftbl; Tr; Hon Prog; Type A; Val; Sr Notable; *Jacksonville St U; Acct.*

ESQUIVEL, Gustavo Vela
Crystal City HS; Crystal City, TX (1-100) Band; VP, Chess C; FFA; 4H; Math C; Phys C; Alg A; Bio A; Chem A; Phy A; Sci A; Val; *U of Tex at Austin; Med.*

ESRA, Kelly Ann
Mississinewa HS; Gas City, IN (33%-228) F-Ed, Ann; Pres, Chor; Drama; FTA; GS; Tres, NHS; Span C; Thes; Secy, Tri-HiY; Tres, Soph Cl; Most Out.

ESSER, Robert Worth Jr
Huntington HS; Huntington, NY (10%-560) Arch; Chess C; Hmrm; InterAct C; Key C; Math C; NHS; A-Ed, Sch P; Arch; Hon Prog; Rptr, Ed, Sch P; Church Elder; *Engr.*

ESSMANN, Julie Ann
McCluer Sr HS; Florissant, MO (40-776) Band; Chor; NHS; Hon Prog; Pom Pom.

ESSMANN, Robert Floyd
McCluer N Sr HS; Florissant, MO (4-788) Band; NHS; Order/Arrow; Thes; JV, Tr; Order/Arrow A; *US Air Force Acad; Aeronautical Engr.*

ESSMANN, William George
McCluer N HS; Florissant, MO (3-788) Chor; NHS; Order/Arrow; Thes; Co-Cpt, Ftbl; Tr; Wrest; Order/Arrow A; Eagle Sct; *U of Mo-Kansas City; Med.*

ESTABROOK, Tracy Helen
Hobart HS; Hobart, IN (148-399) Cpt, Chldr; Chor; Fr C; Tr; Jr Deaconess; Ltr to Governor.

ESTAL, Jan Marie
Grinnell-Newburg Comm Sr HS; Grinnell, IA (1-200) NHS; SC; JV, Bkbl; Mgr, Tr; NMF; NMS; St Scholar; Val; *Knox Col; Chem.*

ESTANICH, Cynthia Ann
Gilmer Co HS; Glenville, WV (16-94) VP, Chor; Drama; Tr; *Fairmont St Col; Vet Med.*

ESTEP, Barbara Gerry
Cleburne HS; Cleburne, TX (3-230) Band; Chor; Dbte Tm; FHA; Hmrm; Span C; SC; Good Citz A; Bsbl Swtht; *Abilene Christian Col; Social Work.*

ESTEP, Lynne Christine
Stillwater Sr HS; Stillwater, MN (34-647) A Cap Choir; Band; Chor; Madrigal; *Acct.*

ESTEP, Teresa Ann
Tabernacle Baptist Sch; Virginia Beach, VA; Chor; Spch C; *Bob Jones U; Elem Ed.*

ESTEP, William David
Pulaski HS; Somerset, KY (1-225) S-T, Dbte Tm; Pres, NHS; Sch P; Sci C; Secy, SC; Pres, Jr Cl; MLS; NMS; *Pepperdine U; Pol Sci.*

ESTER, Edward Albert
Mount Tahoma Sr HS; Tacoma, WA (20-170) Band; JV, Bsbl; JV, Wrest; Spch A; *Calif Baptist Col; Religion.*

ESTERGARD, Richard Lee
Callaway Pub Sch; Callaway, NE (5-31) BS; Pres, 4H; NHS; Ftbl; 4H A; *Nebr Sch of Tech Agr; Vet Tech.*

ESTERLY, Mark Gilbert
Robbinsdale Sr HS; Robbinsdale, MN; Hmrm; JV, Bsbl; JV, Ftbl.

ESTES, Brad Thomas
Saline HS; Saline, MI (33-200) CYO; Order/ Arrow; Phys C; ARC; Var C; Tres, Y-Tns; Wrest; Order/Arrow A; Phy A; Pres A; Semi-Fin, Jr-Sr Homecoming; Welding A; Wrest Coaches A; Fin, League Wrest; Semi-Fin, St Wrest; *Ferris St U; Phar.*

ESTES, Craig Ross
W Forsyth Sr HS; Clemmons, NC (60-487) Cpt, Band; Ensm; Key C; NHS; Pres, SC; Var C; Bsbl; COM; *NC St U; Med Technology.*

ESTES, Elizabeth Ann
Caney Valley HS; Caney, KS (10%-70) Band; CYO; JV, Chldr; Chor; Drama; FBLA; FFA; FHA; Semi-Fin, GS; Rptr, Sch P; SC; Var C; Bkbl; Golf; Tr; Swtht; HR; Bkbl, Vlbl, Ltrs; Nom, Snowball Qn; Secy.

ESTES, James Wyman Jr
Marion Co HS; Guin, AL (28-45) Var C; Bsbl; Cpt, Bkbl; Ftbl; *NW Ala Jr Col; Bus.*

ESTES, Janet Sue
Mendota Township HS; Mendota, IL (95-203) Band; Span C; COM; Pom Pon Girl; *Data Processing.*

ESTES, Jennifer Joan
Ripley HS; Ripley, TN (10-200) Ann; Band; BC; Chor; 4H; Hmrm; Math C; Sch P; Sci C; Tres, SC; MVP, Var C; MVP, Bkbl; Sftbl; MVP, Tr; Cl Fav; HQn; HCt; Hon Prog; Swtht; Flag Girl; Tr Trophies; Ltrman; Math Tourn; Semi-Fin, Fin, Tr; Alpha Kappa Alpha A's; *Tenn St U; Engr.*

ESTES, Jon Leslee
N Mecklenburg HS; Huntersville, NC (136-428) Band; Ensm; Co-Cpt, Soccer; *Central Piedmont Col.*

ESTES, Tonia Vanessa
Ripley HS; Ripley, TN (7-250) Band; BC; JV, Chldr; Chem C; Drama; Fr C; JV, 4H; Hmrm; Fin, Jr Miss Pagent; Math C; Phys C; Sci C; SC; Var C; Mgr, Bkbl; Sftbl; Tr; Beauty; 4H A; H of F; HQn; HCt; Math A; MLS; Pres, Rossette C; Miss Rice Park; Lead, Sr Play; 'R' C; Outst Sr Band; *Tenn St U; Engr.*

ESTILL, Burnace Dian
Hale R-I HS; Hale, MO (3-28) Ann; Chor; NFL; Regent Schol; Type A; Shorthand A; Courier Schol; Departmental Schol; Combined Adm Schol; *SW Baptist Col; Secretarial Sci.*

ESTILL, Karla Darlene
Hale R-1 Pub HS; Hale, MO; Chldr; Chor; Dbte Tm; Ensm; FHA; 4H; NFL; Mgr, Bkbl; Sftbl; COM; 4H A; Spch A; Type A; Pep C; Health A; NFL A.

ESTILL, Timothy Gordon
Gainesville HS; Gainesville, TX (49-244) Band; Chor; ROTC A; *U of Tex; Military Sci.*

ESTILL, Vicki Lynn
Richland HS; Ft Worth, TX (15%-500) Ger C; NHS; Bkbl; Semi-Fin, Tr; Cpt, Vlbl; *Phys Ed.*

ESTIS, April Arlene
East HS; Columbus, OH; Band; Dbte Tm; Tres, Fr C; Mjrte; NFL; Orch; Ed, Sch P; SC; Hon Prog; 1st Pl Debate A; *Emmerson Col; Communications.*

ESTRADA, Miriam Rosa
Academia Santa Monica; Santurce, PR; Ann; Chor; Hmrm; NHS; SC; *Bus Adm.*

ESTRIDGE, Sabryna Renee
Grace King HS; Metairie, LA (10%-900) Co-Cpt, Chldr; Ger C; Lit Ral; Math C; Swim; Amer Leg A; COM; Citz A; Hon Prog; Icthus C; Ger A; Foreign Lang C; Gold Medal, Jr Olympics; Ger Ntl Soc; Co-Cpt, YMCA Judo Tm; Blue Belt, US Jr Judo Assn; *U of New Orleans; Pre-Law.*

ESTRONZA, Nydia Arely
Lola Rodriguez de Tio; San German, PR (2-350) A Cap Choir; Band; Chor; FHA; 4H; NHS; Sci C; COM; Magna Cum Laude; Star Student; Summa Cum Laude; High Hon; Symbolia; *Recinto Universitario Mayaguez; Bio Chem.*

ETHERIDGE, Karen Denise
French HS; Beaumont, TX; A Cap Choir; Chor; Ensm; NHS; S-T, ARC; COM; Off Asst A; *Lamar U.*

ETHERLY, Linda Gayle
West HS; Salt Lake City, UT; Chor; FBLA; VP, Orch; Tr; JA A; *Cosmotology.*

ETHERTON, Joel Allen
Yucca Valley HS; Yucca Valley, CA (4-212) AFS; Band; Order/Arrow; Sci C; Ftbl; Golf; DARGCA; NEDT; Eagle Sct; *Air Force Acad; Sci Field.*

ETHREDGE, David Leon
Junction City HS; Junction City, AR (6-60) Bus Mgr, Ann; Pres, Band; Ensm; FFA; Rptr, 4H; Ed, Lit Mag; Pres, SC; Pres, Jr Cl; Mgr, Bkbl; JV, Ftbl; Tr; MLS; WW; Mr Dragon Band; *La Tech U; Forestry.*

ETHRIDGE, Craig N
Rogersville HS; Rogersville, TN; Arch; Key C; Order/Arrow; Arch; Bsbl; Eagle Sct; *U of Tenn; Archt.*

ETHRIDGE, Katherine Michelle
Del City HS; Del City, OK (10%-598) Ann; NHS; Secy, Yth for Christ; WW; Schol Off; VP, Church Yth Coun; *Okla U; Nurs.*

ETHRIDGE, Kirk S
Rogersville HS; Rogersville, TN; VP, Arch; Bus Mgr, Order/Arrow; Key C; Ftbl; MVP, Tr; Eagle Sct; Brotherhood, Order o-t Arrow; Kiwanis Player o-t Yr Ftbl; Leadership A; *VPI; Liberal Arts Sci.*

ETIENNE, Gilbert Jude
George Washington Carver Sr HS; New Orleans, LA; *Eckerd Col; Vocalist.*

ETO, Annie Jo
Alexander Hamilton Sr HS; Milwaukee, WI (100-1200) HiY; Swim; Chem A; Math A; Rensselaer A; Yth Fel; *UW Stevens Point; Forestry.*

ETRA, Elizabeth
Hillel HS; Lawrence, NY; Chldr; Drama; NHS; Span C; Span NHS; SC; Bkbl; Swim; Tnns; Tr; Hon Prog; *Brandeis U; Math.*

ETTER, Jamma Yvonne
Paul G Blazer HS; Ashland, KY; Drama; Hmrm; Ed, Sch P; Fin, Spch C; SC; Soph Cl; Co-Cpt, Bsbl; Mgr, Bkbl; Cpt, Sftbl; Cpt, Tr; Citz A; Journ A; Opt A; Spch A; Yth Fel; Spelling A; *Vanderbilt U; Journ.*

ETTER, Nancy Waynell
Lone Oak HS; Paducah, KY (33%-200) A Cap Choir; Band; Cpt, Chldr; Mjrte; Tres, Var C; Swim; Tnns; Homecoming Attendant; *David Lipscomb Col; Bus Adm.*

ETTLIN, Mark Alan
Northgate HS; Walnut Creek, CA; MVP, Wrest; Bank Of Amer A; CSF; *U of Calif.*

ETZOLD, Heidi
Deerborne HS; Coral Gables, FL; NHS; Golden Book A; Hon A Cert; *Miami Dade S Col; Graphic Art.*

EUBANKS, Carol Ellen
Anderson HS; Austin, TX (85-525) BC; Lat C; NHS; Sch P; Sci C; Soccer; Bio A; Hon Prog; Church Choir; Director, Hand Bell Choir; Vol, Hospital; *Baylor U; Med.*

EUBANKS, Dana Dawn
Ringgold HS; Ringgold, GA; Band; BC; JV, Chldr; InterAct C; Var C; Secy, Soph Cl; COM; Cl Fav; HCt; Hon Prog; Star Student; *Dalton Jr Col; Dental Hygiene.*

EUBANKS, Hugh Joseph
N Augusta Sr HS; North Augusta, SC (16-389) BC; Drama; Lit Mag; Math C; Monogram; NHS; Co-Ed, Sch P; Sci C; Hon Prog; Q&S A; Benjamin Metairim Wofford Schol; Augusta Col Cert of Achv; WW; *U of S Carolina; Law.*

EUBANKS, Lavelle Sherice
St Martin de Porres HS; Detroit, MI; Band; *Morehouse Col; Bus Adm.*

EUBANKS, Michael Carl
Central HS; Pageland, SC; Chess C; Var C; Bsbl; Ftbl; Best Lineman Ftbl.

EUBANKS, Rochelle Angela
St Martin DePorres HS; Detroit, MI; Band; *Morehouse Col; Engr.*

EUCHLER, John Charles
Lord Botetourt HS; Daleville, VA (20-164) Ann; Chess C; Semi-Fin, Dbte Tm; Pres, FTA; NFL; NHS; Ch, SC; B Crocker A; St Debate Champion; Parl, Jr Civitan; *George Mason U; Bus Adm.*

EULISS, William Ramsey
Riverview Gardens Sr HS; St Louis, MO (225-749) Var C; Ftbl; Sftbl; Wrest; *Engr.*

EURE, Betty Ann
Woodrow Wilson HS; Portsmouth, VA; JV, Chldr; Pres, Drama; Tres, FBLA; Span C; Spch C; Pres, Thes; Spch A; 1st Pl, Dist Howell-Walker Schol; Tres, Var Chldr; Job's Daughters; 2nd Pl, Sch-Wide Spch Contest; 3rd Pl, Dist Forensics Comp; *Bus.*

EURE, Jeffrey Lane
Blair HS; Hattiesburg, MS; InterAct C; Var C; Bsbl; Ftbl.

EUTZ, Craig
Northwest HS; St Louis, MO (14-652) Band; Fr C; NHS; JV, Cr-Ctry; Tnns; Tr; COM; Citz A; *Mich St U; Biochem.*

EVAN, Mitch Bogan
Springfield Local HS; Petersburg, OH (17-131) BS; FTA; 4H; HiY; NHS; Span C; Ftbl; Tr; I Dare You; *Youngstown St U; Bio.*

EVANS, Alfonso Jackson Jr
Bishop England HS; Charleston, SC (92-195) Bkbl; Ftbl; Tr; *SC St U; Social Studies.*

EVANS, Barbara Mae
Boardman Sr HS; Boardman, OH (155-590) Hmrm; V-Ch, Lat C; SC; Girls Boosters; *Pub Relations.*

EVANS, Betsy Morgan
Woodrow Wilson HS; Beckley, WV (72-510) Chldr; Chor; SC; Thes; Var C; Yth Fel; Yth Leg; Adm Board, United Meth Temple; Pres, Yth Fellowship; *W Va Wesleyan Col; Rehabilitation Coun.*

EVANS, Beverly Ann
Hartshorne HS; Hartshorne, OK (2-60) Chldr; Drama; FHA; NHS; Ntl Yth Conf; Spch C; Rptr, SC; Thes; JV, Bkbl; Bio A; COM; Cl Fav; Gov Honor Prog; Hist A; HCt; Hon Prog; Sal; Sci A; 1st Econ, Cirriculum Contest; WW; *E Okla St U; Gen Bus.*

EVANS, Blair Hugh
Mumford HS; Detroit, MI (21-386) Math C; Sci C; Span C; Arch; Tnns; COM; Citz A; Hon Prog; Math A; NMS; Sci A; SME Drafting A; Detroit News Drafting A; Span Achv A; WW; *MIT; Engr.*

EVANS, Bobby
Edisto HS; Cordova, SC (1-88) Co-Ed, Ann; FTA; GS; Hmrm; Ed, Lit Mag; Pres, NHS; Sch P; SC; Secy, Sr Cl; Pres, Jr Cl; Pres, Soph Cl; Gr Marshal; Hist A; Journ A; JA A; Math A; Opt A; Spch A; VofDEM; Yth Fel; Vlbl; Home Ec A; Furman Schol; Wofford Schol; *Med U of SC; Nurs.*

EVANS, Brenda Johnatta
Curie HS; Chicago, IL;

EVANS, Bruce Roger
Huntington HS; Huntington, WV (1-350) HiY; Pres, Mu Alpha Theta; NHS; Co-Cpt, Wrest; NMF; Val; *Vanderbilt U; Engr.*

EVANS, Charelesa
J Graham Brown HS; Louisville, KY; Ed, Sch P; Tres, Sr Cl; *U of Ky; Pre-Med.*

EVANS, Charles Michael
Hastings HS; Hastings, NE (67-302) Dbte Tm; NFL; Order/Arrow; Sch P; Bicycle Racing; Eagle Sct; *Art.*

EVANS, Connie Yvonne
Hancock Central HS; Sparta, GA; Band; Pres, Dbte Tm; Math C; Co-Cpt, Var C; Co-Cpt, Bkbl; Tr; *Albany Col; Nurs.*

EVANS, Danita Lynette
Stanley HS; Stanley, ND (5%-50) Ann; Chor; Drama; FHA; GS; Jr Miss Pagent; Span C; Spch C; Tres, Jr Cl; Secy, Soph Cl; VofDEM; Yth Fel; Pres, FHA ND 5th Dist; FFA Swtht; Pres, BYF; Yth Ministry; *Sioux Falls Col; Med Tech.*

EVANS, Dara Jo
Cottage Grove HS; Cottage Grove, OR (4-260) A Cap Choir; Ed, Ann; Rptr, Band; Chldr; VP, Chor; Ensm; 4H; Mjrte; Secy, NHS; SC; Var C; Bkbl; Tr; Amer Leg A; Vlbl; *Pacific U; Law.*

EVANS, David Anthony
Norfolk Cath HS; Norfolk, VA (20%-150) Ftbl; Tr; *UCLA; Med.*

EVANS, David Russell Jr
North Co Tech Sch; Florissant, MO (5%-400) Chor; FFA; Order/Arrow; Cr-Ctry; Tr; God & Country A; Order/Arrow A; Star Student; Eagle Sct with 9 Palms; Dekalb A; Yth Pastor; Rep, BSct Jamboree in Oslo Norway; 1st Pl in Horticulture; *Mo Baptist Col; Bible.*

EVANS, David Shipherd
Friendly HS; Oxon Hill, MD (10%-500) Co-Cpt, Cr-Ctry; Tr; Ntl Mus Camp; Eng Handbell Ringers; Sr Yth Orch; *Carleton Col; Pre-Med.*

EVANS, Deanna Jean
Englewood Christian HS; Independence, MO (2-24) Chor; Cpt, Bkbl; Sftbl; Journ A; Bkbl; Vlbl.

EVANS, Debbie Jean
Englewood Christian HS; Independence, MO (1-24) Chor; Ensm; Key C; Ed, Sch P; VP, SC; Cpt, Bkbl; Sftbl; Tnns; Journ A; Type A; Sch Spirit & Hon Stu; Bkbl; Vlbl.

EVANS, Deborah Ann
Kress HS; Kress, TX (3-31) Ed, Ann; Rptr, FHA; Pres, FTA; Bkbl; Tr; B Crocker A; Citz A; MLS; Eng A; Homemaking A; Academic A; UIL-SCI; *Hardin-Simmons U; Med Tech.*

EVANS, Deborah Ann
Immaculata HS; Detroit, MI (16-91) Chor; Dbte Tm; Lat C; Lat NHS; Aux Lat; WW; Semi-fin, Ntl Achv Schol; *Kalamazoo Col; Eng.*

EVANS, Denise Louise
Warwick HS; Newport News, VA; 4H; Sci C; Span C; Alg A; Bio A; 4H A; Hist A; Math A; Campus Life; Hon Soc; *Christopher Newport Co; Handicap Ed.*

EVANS, Diane Louise
Akron E HS; Akron, OH (15-350) Band; Chor; Ensm; NHS; Orch; Thes, Span C; Tres, JA; Pres, Yth Fel; Most Talented; WW; *Akron U; Mus.*

EVANS, Donna Jane
Plant City HS; Plant City, FL (4-585) Band; Ensm; Secy, Model UN; VP, NHS; Hon Prog; Math A; Tampa Times Hon Stu; Sr Eng A; Fresh Hon; Schol Prog; *Polk Comm Col; Secondary Ed.*

EVANS, Elizabeth Ellen
Melodyland HS; Anaheim, CA (1-11) Ann; Chor; Drama; VP, Hmrm; Secy, SC; VP, Sr Cl; HQn; Hon Soc; *Biola Col; Art.*

EVANS, Faith Elaine
Mt Gilead HS; Mount Gilead, OH (30-150) Co-Ch, Bus C; Ch, Drama; Fr C; Sch P; Tr; COM; Cl Fav; 4H A; Hon Prog; GAA; VP, Yth Fel; Human Soc A; Cl Clown; *N Central Tech Col; Retail Management.*

EVANS, Glen Edward
Takoma Acad; Takoma Park, MD; Fr C; Rptr, Sch P; Spch C; Var C; Bsbl; Cpt, Bkbl; *Oakwood Col; Bus Adm.*

EVANS, James Michael
Carterville Comm HS; Carterville, IL; SC; Bsbl; MVP, Bkbl; Ftbl; Sftbl; Most Out; Cpt, Bkbl; Church Yth Coun; *John Logan Jr Col; Auto Mech.*

EVANS, James Noble
Thomas B Doherty HS; Colo Springs, CO (52-425) Band; Chor; NHS; Swim; Hon Prog; Yth Fel; Yth Leg; Hon Caddie; Choir Ltr; *Med.*

EVANS, Janet Renae
Wetumpka HS; Wetumpka, AL (28-205) BC; Secy, Church Yth Choir; Secy, Yth Christian Assn; Pres, Qn, Acteens; *St Margaret's Col; X-Ray Tech.*

EVANS, Jennifer Louise
Columbiana HS; Columbiana, OH (16-105) A Cap Choir; Cpt, Chldr; Chor; Fr C; Madrigal; NHS; Tri-HiY; Prom Qn; *Mount Union Col.*

EVANS, Joan Elaine
F J Reitz HS; Evansville, IN (110-501) Chor; Cum Laude Soc; Citz A; *Tenn Temple Col; Vocal Mus.*

EVANS, Joan Elizabeth
Bryan Adams HS; Dallas, TX; Band; Ensm; Ski C; Tri-HiY; Sftbl; Ntl Conf Chr & Jews; MLS; Yth Fel; Outst Squad; Best of Kind, Woodwind Ensm; *N Tex St U; Visual Art.*

EVANS, John Bridger Jr
Wayne Co HS; Jesup, GA; NHS; Order/Arrow; Order/Arrow A; Eagle Sct; *Ga Sou Col; Engr.*

EVANS, John Eldon
Northwood-Kensett HS; Northwood, IA (10-63) Chor; VP, 4H; VP, Jr Cl; JV, Cr-Ctry; JV, Tr; *Med.*

EVANS, Julie Anne
Middle Park HS; Granby, CO (1-78) Band; Ensm; NHS; Bkbl; Type A; Mgr, Vlbl; *Fort Lewis Col; Computer Prog.*

EVANS, Kathy Journette
N Shore HS; W Palm Beach, FL (49-266) Cpt, Chldr; FBLA; Hmrm; Var C; Sftbl; *FSU; Acct.*

EVANS, Kimberly Sue
Norwin Sr HS; North Huntington, PA (52-712) Ed, Ann; FNA; NHS; *Shadyside Hospital Sch of Nurs; Nurs.*

EVANS, Larry Gene
Western Alamance HS; Burlington, NC (43-305) Ann; Pres, Hmrm; Sch P; Tnns; *UNC-Chapel Hill; Archaeology.*

EVANS, Laurie Ellen
Uniontown Sr HS; Uniontown, PA; Band; VP, Hmrm; NHS; Sch P; Pres, Span C; St Stu Congress; VP, SC; Up Bound; Var C; Pres, Jr Cl; VP, Soph Cl; Bkbl; Citz A; Cl Fav; H of F; Hon Prog; Most Out; *U of Pittsburg; Dentistry.*

EVANS, Letitia Allene
Bishop England HS; Charleston, SC (95-211) Co-Cpt, Chldr; Sftbl; Alt, GS; *U of SC; Biol Sci.*

EVANS, Linda Lee
Ashford Acad; Ashford, AL (15-42) Band; A-Ed, Sch P; *Math.*

EVANS, Linda Loretta
Curie HS; Chicago, IL;

EVANS, Linda Renee
Suncoast HS; Riviera Beach, FL; FBLA; MVP, Sftbl; MVP, Vlbl; Best Hitter, Sftbl; *Palm Beach Jr Col; Bus Adm.*

EVANS, Loretta Ann
Baker HS; Baker, LA; S-T, BC; Mu Alpha Theta; *Bus.*

EVANS, Lynda Diane
Van Horn HS; Indep, MO (50%-360) Chor; Crown & Scepter; Madrigal; Bkbl; Sftbl; Art A; Mus A; *William Jewell Col; Elem Ed.*

EVANS, Mark Anthony
Watson Chapel HS; Pine Bluff, AR (19-225) BC; BS; Secy, Key C; Sftbl; *U of Ark; Agr Engr.*

EVANS, Marva Paulette
North HS; Nashville, TN (1-205) Mgr, Ann; Band; 4H; Pres, NHS; Bkbl; Cr-Ctry; Sftbl; Tr; Alg A; COM; Chem A; HCt; Math A; MLS; Sci A; Type A; Val; *Tenn St U; Elec Engr.*

EVANS, Marvin S Jr
N Nashville HS; Nashville, TN; Band; NHS; Orch; Tr; HCt; *Tenn St U; Elec Engr.*

EVANS, Merry Alissa
W Carter HS; Olive Hill, KY (10%-154) Ann; BC; FBLA; 4H; Co-Ed, Sch P; 4H A; Hon Prog; Math A; Most Out; Type A; PA; Geom A; *Morehead St U; Bus.*

EVANS, Michael Robert
Cumberland Valley HS; Mechanicsburg, PA (31-600) Chess C; Drama; Ger C; Co-Ed, Lit Mag; NHS; Order/Arrow; F-Ed, Sch P; Thes; Order/Arrow A; Rotary A; Spch A; *Bowdoin Col; Eng.*

EVANS, Michelva Rosalia
Rainbow City Jr-Sr HS; Rainbow City, CANAL ZONE; Band; Chldr; Chor; Dbte Tm; SC; Bsbl; Sftbl; Swim; Tnns; Alg A; Hist A; *Canal Zone Col; Med.*

EVANS, Mickie Karen
Pisgah Sr HS; Canton, NC (20%-320) Band; Ensm; Rptr, 4H; Span C; VICA Graphics; Qn Regent, Acteens; *Appalachian St U; Graphic Arts.*

EVANS, Myra Lynn
Laurel Sch; Shaker Hts, OH (40%-44) Key C; Lat C; Sci C; Secy, SC; Cpt, Tnns; Cl Fav; Ntl Achv Schol; Yth Fel; WW; *Yale U; Engr.*

EVANS, Nelda Wydell
Union HS; Union, MS (10%-50) F-Ed, Ann; BC; Chor; Drama; Pres, FHA; Sch P; S-T, Sr Cl; COM; WW; *E Central Jr Col; Journ.*

EVANS, Noel Thomas
Jones Co HS; Gray, GA (10%-250) Sci C.

EVANS, Norma Ruth
Clovis HS; Clovis, NM (80-575) *E NM U; Merchandising.*

EVANS, Pamela Elaine
Lutheran HS E; Cleveland Heights, OH (10-60) Chor; Drama; Ensm; Rptr, Sch P; SC; Bio A; COM; Citz A; Sci A; Type A; Ntl Jr Hon Soc; Yrbk Staff; Choir A; Social Stu A; *Ohio St U; Journ.*

EVANS, Patricia Ann
The Carolina Acad; Lake City, SC (3-19) A Cap Choir; Ed, Ann; BC; Chor; Mgr, Bsbl; Bkbl; HCt; Hon Prog; Yth Fel; Bus Mgr, Annual; Cl Marshal; Pres, Church Yth; Presbyterian Col Jr Fel; Church Adm Board; *Duke U; Computer Sci.*

EVANS, Ramona Lea
Stanley HS; Stanley, ND (10%-70) Ann; Chor; FHA; Pres, BYF; Secy, NW Assn BYF; Yth Ministry; *Sioux Falls Col; Med.*

EVANS, Reginald
Zwolle HS; Zwolle, LA (10-38) Bsbl; Bkbl; Tr; Cl Fav; *Kans Wesleyan U; Bus Mgr.*

EVANS, Rex Angelo
Banning HS; Banning, CA; Band; ARC; Var C; MVP, Bsbl; Co-Cpt, Ftbl; MVP, Tr; COM; Yth Fel; AAYA; Police Explorer; *Fullerton U; Bus.*

EVANS, Ricky Darwin
Sou Wayne HS; Dudley, NC; Sci C; Ftbl; Swim; Art C; VICA C; *Wayne Comm Col; Bus.*

EVANS, Roger Nikita
Dunbar Sr HS; Baltimore, MD (10%-461) VP, Hmrm; NHS; SC; COM; Hon Prog; BSct A & Merit Badge; Cert of Appreciation; *Morgan St U; Elem Ed.*

EVANS, Scott Carlton
Kubasaki HS; Okinawa, JAPAN (10-271) Mu Alpha Theta; Tres, NHS; JV, Bkbl; CSF; Analysis A; 2nd Pl, Foreign Lang Festival; Vlbl; *Wash St U; Engr.*

EVANS, Teresa Ann
Suncoast HS; Riviera Beach, FL (20%-293) VP, FBLA; NHS; Sftbl; Citz A; Spch A; PA; *Madison Col; Art.*

EVANS, Teresa Lee
Centerburg HS; Centerburg, OH (20-75) F-Ed, Ann; Chor; Drama; Rainbow; COM; Yth Fel; Drill Tm; Chor Pianist; *Acct.*

EVANS, Theresa Mallene
Watson Chapel HS; Pine Bluff, AR (10-300) Band; Chldr; Drama; NHS; Y-Tns; Sftbl; COM; Cl Fav; Sci A.

EVANS, Thomas David
Cottage Grove HS; Cottage Grove, OR (65-300) Cpt, Bsbl; Ftbl; Swim; Tr; Wrest; Diving; *Gym; Ed.*

EVANS, Thomas Edward
Elbert Co Comprehensive HS; Elberton, GA; Band; Fr C; Secy, 4H; JV, Ftbl; 4H A; Opt A; ROTC A; Spch A.

EVANS, Tracey Lynn
Central HS; Thomasville, GA; Cpt, Chldr; Tres, InterAct C; Cl Fav; *Fashion Merchandising.*

EVANS, Verlion Vanetta
Halter HS; Wellston, MO (3-110) Hon Prog; Ntl Achv Schol; HR; *Forest Park Col; Natural Sci.*

EVANS, Vickie Lane
Sou Wayne Sr HS; Dudley, NC (50-420) AFS; FBLA; Rptr, FHA; Tres, FTA; Hmrm; SC; FHA A's; Col Schol; *Mt Olive Col; Early Ed.*

EVANS, Wanda Kay
Wheeler Co HS; Alamo, GA (6-50) Ann; Pres, BC; Chor; VP, FBLA; FTA; Fin, GS; 4H; NHS; Pres, Sr Cl; Tres, Jr Cl; COM; Most Out; Type A; *Abraham Baldwin Col; Bus Adm.*

EVE, Alison Gordon
Hauppauge HS; Hauppauge, NY (200-549) Band; Chor; Drama; Ensm; Lit Mag; Orch; Ski C; Tres, Tnns; H of F; Hon Prog; Interlochen Ntl Mus; Poet A; Swtht; Choreographer, 'Bye Bye Birdie'; Tnns Ltr; Ltr & Pin, Eaglettes; Ltr, Pin, Plaque, Key Chain, Mus; Theatre Ltr; *Emory & Henry Col; Mus.*

EVE, Mary Sue
N Augusta Sr HS; N Augusta, SC; A Cap Choir; Rptr, Bus C; Chor; Drama; Ensm; NHS; Sandspur Ct; *U of SC at Aiken; Secretarial Sci.*

EVELER, Dawn Elizabeth
Red Lion Area Sr HS; Red Lion, PA (52-289) Hockey; HR; Varsity Letter; *Elizabethtown Col; Elem Ed.*

EVELETH, Cheryl Dennise
Estherville HS; Estherville, IA; Co-Ed, Ann; Cpt, Chldr; Chor; NHS; Y-Tns; Tr; Tres, VICA; HR; Tr Letter; *U of Northern Iowa; Phys Ed.*

EVENHOUSE, Jeanne Kay
Timothy Christian HS; Elmhurst, IL (3-89) A Cap Choir; Chldr; Chor; NHS; Tnns; COM; Pres A; Fine Arts Vocal A; Marshall; *Calvin Col.*

EVENSEN, Paul Robert
Ripon HS; Ripon, WI (33%-175) AFS; Band; Chor; JV, Dbte Tm; Drama; Ger C; Hmrm; Madrigal; SC; Thes; *Ed.*

EVERETT, Cindra Lynn
Oakridge HS; Orlando, FL; Chor; Pres, Ensm; InterClub Coun; Madrigal; Secy, Sr Cl; Secy, Soph Cl; COM; ARC A; Yth Fel; Yth Rep; Coun On Ministries; Solo Super A, Dist & St Festivals; Coun On Ministries; Fin, Pathfinder Attendant; *U of Miss; Mus Ed.*

EVERETT, Evelyn Rose
Cope Center North HS; Miami, FL; Chess C; Secy, FHA; NHS; Sftbl; Citz A; Sci A; *Miami Dade Comm Col; Dietician.*

EVERETT, Jeffrey Scott
Lincoln Comm HS; Lincoln, IL; Band; Tres, Dbte Tm; Fr C; Orch; Tr; DARGCA; Hist A; Math A; Sci A; Eng A; Principal's A; *Med.*

EVERETT, Keith Alan
Arkadelphia Sr HS; Arkadelphia, AR (10%-205) Band; Chess C; Order/Arrow; *U of Ark; Elec Engr.*

EVERETT, Kerry Edmond
Hilltop HS; Chula Vista, CA; Bsbl; Bkbl; Masonic A; *Point Loma Col.*

EVERETT, Lou Ann
Eminence Consolidated HS; Eminence, IN (1-45) Pres, Band; Fin, GS; NHS; Co-Ed, Sch P; MVP, Bkbl; MVP, Tr; Lead, Sch Play; Amer Leg Mus A; Cpt, Bkbl; Vlbl; Sch Bus A; *Ind Bus Col; Acct.*

EVERETT, Marion Bradley
Thompson HS; Alabaster, AL (1%-250) A Cap Choir; Chor; Ensm; NHS; SC; Var C; Bkbl; Cpt, Ftbl; Tr; COM; Gr Marshal; Hon Prog; Math A; NMS; NEDT; Val; *Auburn U; Dentistry.*

EVERETT, Mildred Denise
MacKenzie HS; Detroit, MI (17-352) NHS; ROTC A; *U of Mich; Law.*

EVERETT, Roslein Marie
Milo Adventist Acad; Days Creek, OR (8-66) Band; *Sou Missionary Col; Pre-Med.*

EVERETT, Stephanie Jane
Hilltop HS; Chula Vista, CA; Chldr; CSF; *Point Loma Col; Bus.*

EVERETT, Susan Marie
Moss Point HS; Moss Point, MS (30-400) Ed, Ann; Chor; Drama; Fr C; Sch P; SC; *Miss Gulf Coast Jr Col; Commercial Arts.*

EVERETT, Timothy Alan
Crawfordsville HS; Crawfordsville, IN (68-217) Chess C; Chor; Dbte Tm; Drama; Madrigal; NFL; Sci C; Eagle Sct; Alt, Navy Acad; Voting Yth Del, Church; *Computer Sci.*

EVERETT, Timothy Ray
Springhill HS; Springhill, LA (7-200) BS; InterClub Coun; NHS; A-Ed, Sch P; Var C; Bkbl; Tnns; Cl Fav; Outst Boy, Tnns; *Quachita Baptist U; Pol Sci.*

EVERHART, Cindy Renee
E Davidson HS; Thomasville, NC (20-135) Dbte Tm; Cpt, Hmrm; Monogram; Rainbow; ARC; Spch C; Bkbl; *East Carolina U; Med Technology.*

EVERHART, Cynthia June
Basehor HS; Basehor, KS; Ann; Sch P; Y-Tns; Bkbl; Cl Fav; HCt; Yth Fel; JV Vlbl; Shorthand Pin; *Kans City Jr Col; Bus.*

EVERHART, Gwen Kaye
El Toro HS; El Toro, CA; AFS; Tres, Rainbow; ROTC A; *Nurs.*

EVERHART, Robin Kay
R B Worthy HS; Saltville, VA (3-72) Ed, Ann; Band; BC; Chldr; Pres, Chor; Ensm; FHA; Mjrte; Sci C; Tri-HiY; Beauty; Yth Fel; Secy, St Yth; UT Hons Band; WW; Regional Choir; Jr Cl Play; *Va Highlands Comm Col; Acct.*

EVERHART, Wendy Sue
Windham HS; Windham, OH (10-83) Pres, Band; Chor; Lit Mag; Madrigal; Span C; Pres, SC; Sftbl; B Crocker A; *Mount Union Col; Mus.*

EVERMANN, Kimberly Ann
Park Center HS; Brooklyn Park, MN (25%-400) AFS; Chor; Ensm; Ger C; Pres, Soph Cl; *Social Work.*

EVERS, Janice Caprice
Caprock HS; Amarillo, TX (10-375) Band; Hmrm; Tres, Lat C; SC; Amer Leg A; VP, MYF; *Amarillo Col; Math.*

EVERS, Layne Alan
St James Sr HS; St James, MN; FFA; Pres, 4H; Mgr, Bkbl; Tr; 4H A.

EVERS, Paul David
Vanguard HS; Ocala, FL (7-350) Anchor C; Math C; Mu Alpha Theta; NHS; Ski C; Span C; Cpt, Ftbl; Most Out; Swtht; All Conf Ftbl; *Computers.*

EVERSOLE, Andrew Kenneth
Ft Jennings HS; Ft Jennings, OH; Band; Chor; Secy, Soph Cl; Golf; Amer Leg A; NEDT; Sci A.

EVERSOLE, Beth Anne
Reading HS; Reading, OH; Chor; Drama; Ensm; Sch P; Thes; Tr; HR; Girls Vocal A; *U of Cincinnati; Bus.*

EVERSOLE, Dana Lynn
Muskogee HS; Muskogee, OK; AFS; Parl, Lat C; Lat NHS; Lit Ral; Ed, Sch P; Sci C; Thes; Hon Prog; Yth Fel; Stu Adv Coun; Jr Civitan; S-T, Yth Group; Okla Hon Soc; *Journ.*

EVERSOLE, David Wayne
Muskogee HS; Muskogee, OK (210-692) Band; Hmrm; SC; Pres, Soph Cl; Bsbl; Opt A; *Okla St U; Mus.*

EVERSON, Ann Berniece
Parkview HS; Orfordville, WI (37-158) AFS; Band; JV, Chldr; Chor; NHS; SC; Tr; Gym; Cpt, Rifle Sq; Prom Ct; *U of Wis Madison; Nurs.*

EVERSON, Ellen Therese
Homewood-Flossmoor HS; Flossmoor, IL (75-931) Band; Ger C; Swim; Bowl C; Pres, CYF; *Northern Ill U; Acct.*

EVERSON, Kristen Denise
Erskine HS; Erskine, MN (2-30) All Amer Yth; Ann; Band; Chor; Hmrm; Madrigal; Sch P; Ensm; Arch; Bkbl; Sftbl; *Concordia Col; Ed.*

EVERSON, Mark Alan
Middle Park Jr Sr HS; Granby, CO (5-72) Bkbl; Sftbl; *U of Minn; Industrial Arts.*

EVERSON, Ronald Dennis Jr
Albany HS; Albany, GA; Chess C; Var C; Bsbl; Gov Honor Prog; Hist A; Journ A; Boy o-t Mo; Essay, Boxing, Trophies; *Eckerd Col; Phys Ed.*

EVETTS, Cynthia Lee
Skyline HS; Dallas, TX; Band; Fin, Chldr; VP, Chor; Ensm; Lat C; Co-Cpt, Mjrte; Secy, ARC; Co-Ed, Sch P; Sftbl; Citz A; Hon Prog; Drum Mjrte; VICA; Pres, Italian C; 1st Pl, VICA Dist & St Commer Art; 1st Cl GSct; Commercial Art.

EWALD, Dawn Elaine
Rockford E HS; Rockford, IL (70-649) Y-Tns; WW; Drama A; Vlbl; Tres, Christian Yth Fel; Pres, Yth Group; Bethel Col; Sociology.

EWAN, Starla Ann
Artesia HS; Artesia, NM; AFS; Band; Bkbl; Tr; Outst Soph Bandsman A; Drum Major A; Lion's Int Band; E NM U; Ed.

EWEN, Mary Ellen
Marillac HS; Northfield, IL (6-197) CYO; Bus Mgr, Sch P; COM; Hon Prog.

EWERS, Kathryn Marie
Kirksville Sr HS; Kirksville, MO (23-228) Chor; City Conf; Drama; FHA; Span C; Cr-Ctry; Yth Adv Coun; Hons Prog, NE Mo St U; Miami U of Ohio; Gen.

EWERT, Charlene Faith
Grace Baptist HS; South Bend, IN (4-14) Chor; Ger C; 4H; SC; Secy, Church Yth Group; Tenn Temple Col; Mus.

EWERT, Jeanine Lenore
Fred Beyer HS; Modesto, CA; Band; Ensm; Rptr, 4H; A-Ed, Sch P; CSF; 4H A; Church Board; VICA; Yth Cabinet; Del, Annual Church Conf; Calif Poly Sch; Archt.

EWING, Brian Paul
Whitehall Mem HS; Whitehall, WI (2-71) Co-Ed, Ann; Fin, BS; Chor; Ensm; Madrigal; Model UN; Monogram; NHS; Spch C; SC; Var C; Mgr, Bkbl; Tr; Amer Leg A; Journ A; Yth Foundation A; Tres, VICA; NCTE Writing A; Piano Schol; All Conf Chor; U of Wis at Platteville; Archt.

EWING, David Dale
Whitehall Mem HS; Whitehall, WI; Band; Chor; Madrigal; NHS; SC.

EWING, Dorothy Jean
Cotton Plant HS; Cotton Plant, AR (2-23) BC; Drama; Fr C; Tres, FBLA; VP, FHA; SC; Bio A; Most Out; Sal; Eng A; Ark St U; Journ.

EWING, Karla Michele
Issaquah HS; Issaquah, WA (73-650) NHS; Orch; Dance, Silver Voice, A's; W Wash St Col; Mus.

EWING, Kevin Gerard
Metro HS; St Louis, MO (16-30) Band; Chor; Drama; Fr C; Swim; JV, Tnns; HR; Highest Avg; Swim Ltr; Howard U; Law.

EWING, Laura Jane
Dulaney Sr HS; Cockeysville, MD; NHS; Citz A; Hon Prog; Pres, Yth Fel; Ballet; Horseback Riding; Med.

EWOLDSEN, Ramona Margarita
Pomona Sr HS; Arvada, CO (71-407) AFS; Band; Chor; InterAct C; Citz A; 1st Cl A, GSct; U of Colo.

EWRY, James Anthony
Celina Sr HS; Celina, OH (16-275) A Cap Choir; Co-Ch, CYO; Drama; Lat C; NHS; Thes; Tr; Wrest; DARGCA; NEDT; Dist Festival Choir; Cl Play; Swing Choir; Mens Chorale; Mus; Wright St U; Pre-Med.

EXCEEN, Robert James
Maryville R-II HS; Maryville, MO (100-185) Chess C; VP, Var C; Ftbl; Tr; Hon Men, Conf Ftbl; Church Trustee & Board Member.

EXLINE, David Eric
Salina HS S; Salina, KS (19-356) Ann; Chor; Ensm; HiY; Hmrm; Madrigal; SC; Pres, Sr Cl; Mgr, Bkbl; Tnns; Mgr, Wrest; Kans St U; Pre-Law.

EXLINE, Kyle Ann
Central HS; Salina, KS (12-350) Dbte Tm; NFL; Span C; VP, SC; Tnns; Hon Prog; Presbyterian Yth Group; Hugh O'Brian Yth Found.

EXUM, Angela
Essex Co-tech Girls Voc Sch; Newark, NJ (20-210) Secy, Hmrm; SC; COM; MLS; Secy, Yth Fel; Mus A; Setan Col; Bus.

EXUM, Marianne
Reidsville Sr HS; Reidsville, NC (1-324) Pres, AFS; Band; GS; Orch; Pres, Span C; NEDT; Sci A; Pep C; Secy, Bible C; Wake Forest U; Biological Sci.

EYINK, Gregory Lawrence
Celina Sr HS; Celina, OH (1-275) CYO; FTA; Lat C; NHS; Alg A; COM; Chamber of Comm A; Chem A; Hon Prog; Math A; NMF; Sci A; Val; Math.

EYINK, Karen Marie
Coldwater HS; Coldwater, OH (12-168) Band; CYO; Ger C; JV, Bkbl; Tr; Pres A; JV, Vlbl; Gym; VP, Young Active Christians; Bowling Green Col; Elem Ed.

EYRES, Rhonda Jane
Muskogee HS; Muskogee, OK (29-658) Pres, AFS; Chor; Ensm; Ger C; Jr Miss Pagent; NHS; Orch; Thes; Y-Tns; Hon Prog; Opt A; Sci A; Okla Hon Soc; Superior Ratings, Dist, St Vocal; Little Theatre; Musicals; Cottey Col; Mus.

EYSTER, Angela Jane
Fremont Ross HS; Fremont, OH; Band; Secy, 4H; InterAct C; JV, Bkbl; Tr; 4H A; Pres, VP, Secy & Rptr, Hi-Y; Cosmotology.

EZELL, Angela Carol
Northwestern HS; Rock Hill, SC; Chor; All St Hon Choir; Furman U; Counseling.

EZELL, Angie
W Jones HS; Laurel, MS; Rptr, FHA; Sci C; SE Baptist Col.

EZELL, Gwendolyn
Shaw HS; East Cleveland, OH (98-450) AFS; Chor; Secy, FNA; SC; Bkbl; Tnns; Citz A; DHO Cert; U of Cincinnati; Nurs.

EZELL, Jeffrey Coleman
Glenwood Sch; Phenix City, AL (6-77) Tres, BC; InterClub Coun; Math C; Var C; Pres, Sr Cl; Tres, Jr Cl; JV, Bkbl; Ftbl; MVP, Tnns; Cl Fav; Cpt, Tnns; Best All-Around; WW; Page, Ala House of Rep; U of Ala; Pre-Law.

EZELL, Sandra
John Adams HS; Cleveland, OH; Bus C; Fr C; Hmrm; Mgr, Mjrte; Citz A; Type A; Cleveland St U; Bus Adm.

EZELL, Sharon Kay
Waynesboro Central HS; Waynesboro, MS (25%-119) Ann; Band; BC; Drama; Mjrte; SC; Y-Tns; Jones Co Jr Col; Photography.

F

FA'APOULI, Siose
El Camino HS; Oceanside, CA; Band; Chor; Y-Tns; Bsbl; JV, Ftbl; Tr; Mira Coasta Col.

FAAIUASO, Rudolph S
Marist Brothers' HS; Pago Pago, AMERICAN SAMOA (5-50) Dbte Tm; Tres, Hmrm; Sch P; Pres, Spch C; JV, Bkbl; Mgr, Ftbl; Alg A; Bio A; Hon Prog; Math A; Sci A; Hastings Col; Med.

FAASUA, Angel M
Vista HS; Vista, CA (12-29) A Cap Choir; All Amer Yth; Chor, Ch, Phys C; SC; Y-Tns; Semi-Fin, Bkbl; Soccer; Sftbl; God & Country A; PTA A; Yth Fel; Yth Foundation A; Yth Leg; Mira Coasta Col; Teacher.

FABBO, Carolee Ann
Old Forge HS; Old Forge, PA; FNA; NHS; Ski C; Chem A; Hon Prog.

FABER, Nancy Evelyn
Delavan-Darien-HS; Delavan, WI (49-180) FBLA; FFA; 4H; Northwestern Col; Agr.

FABIAN, Judith Katherine
Roma HS; Roma, TX (24-130) Band; FFA; FHA; Mjrte; Bio A; Tex A&I U at Kingsville; Phys Therapy.

FABRIS, James Jeffery
Weber HS; Chicago, IL (7-278) Hon Prog; NEDT; Loyola U of Chicago; Bus.

FACEY, Scott Hanson
Citrus HS; Inverness, FL (21-250) Tnns; Liberal Arts.

FACKLER, Joseph Brent
Breckinridge Co HS; Harned, KY (5%-250) Ann; Band; Chor; Ch, FFA; 4H; 4H A; H of F; Hon Prog; Band Comp A; Director's A; Academic Achv A.

FADAL, Robert Edward II
Richfield HS; Waco, TX (25%-400) SC; Ftbl; Baylor U; Med.

FADDEN, Alice Celia
Hannibal Central HS; Hannibal, NY; Band; Chor; GS; VP, Key C; NHS; Tres, Var C; Bkbl; Soccer; Tnns; Regent Schol; Buzzy Grant, Amer, A's; MVP, Vlbl; Phys Therapy.

FAFARD, Lyne
Col De Ste Anne De La Pocatiere; La Pocatiere, CANADA (3-28) VP, CYO; Hmrm; Var C; Cr-Ctry; Swim; Tnns; Wrest; Math A; Spch A; Vlbl; Ski; Fr A; Cegep U; Med.

FAGAN, Kay Frances
Bishop Carroll HS; Wichita, KS (26-211) NHS; Mus A; Vocal Schol; WSU; Wichita St U; Vocal Mus.

FAGAN, Martha Anne
Mount Vernon Christian Acad; Atlanta, GA (1-6) Ann; Pres, BC; Chor; Lit Mag; Ed, Sch P; Span C; Tres, SC; Mgr, Bkbl; DARGCA; Hon Prog; Star Student; Ed, Sch P; Covenant Col; Home Ec.

FAGAN, Terri Lynn
Coatesville Area Sr HS; Coatesville, PA (58-630) A Cap Choir; Band; Tres, Ger C; NHS; Orch; Secy, SC; Hon Prog; Washington & Jefferson Col; Bus.

FAGGART, Paul Scott
Richmond Sr HS; Hamlet, NC (100-480) Sch P; Bsbl; Bkbl; Ftbl; Sci A; Bkbl & Bsbl A's; Knowledge Replaces Fear A; Duke U; Forestry.

FAGGART, Sabrina Lynne
Richmond Sr HS; Rockingham, NC (50-645) Cpt, Chldr; Hmrm; Span C; SC; Bkbl; Sftbl; COM; HCt; Vlbl; Most Outst in Phys Ed; Ath Ltr 3 Sports; Del of UN-Washington Stu Tour.

FAGRELL, Barbara Ann
Niles N HS; Skokie, IL; Band; Orch; JV, Sftbl; JV, Tnns; W Ill U; Bus Ed.

FAHEY, Carolyn Marie
Gilbert HS; Gilbert, MN (13-78) Band; Fin, GS; Thes; Bkbl; Cpt, Tnns; Tr; HCt; Psych.

FAHEY, Mary Michelle
Doane Stuart Sch; Albany, NY; CYO; Chldr; Drama; Lit Mag; Sch P; SC; Regent Schol; Skidmore Col; Eng.

FAHNDRICK, Nancy Lynne
Crestview HS; Columbiana, OH (5%-94) Ann; Band; VP, 4H; Math C; NHS; Ed, Sch P; Sci C; Var C; Bkbl; Tr; 4H A; Tres, Rptr, 4-H C; Vlbl; Psych.

FAHRNEY, Marlene Joyce
Central HS; Grand Junction, CO (6-266) Chor; Ensm; NHS; Thes; Mesa Col; Art.

FAHY, Lorelei Dawn
Dundee Comm HS; Dundee, IL (37-340) Band; Chor; Ger C; Citz A; Gov Honor Prog; Sci A; Champaign Urbana Col; Sci.

FAIN, Cathy Lynn
Dell City HS; Dell City, TX (5-26) Ed, Ann; Drama; FHA; 4H; NHS; Sch P; SC; Co-Cpt, Bkbl; Tr; Cl Fav; Sam Houston U; Health Career.

FAIN, Jeni Lea
River Road HS; Amarillo, TX (30%-150) Band; Chor; Mjrte; Rptr, Sch P.

FAIN, Kevin Lee
Llano HS; Llano, TX (1-105) FFA; 4H; SC; Var C; Bkbl; Ftbl; Tr; NEDT; Sal; Star Student; Win, Conservation Essay; U of Sou Calif; Engr.

FAIN, Kristi Rene
Llano HS; Llano, TX; Band; FFA; FHA; NHS; Cr-Ctry; Tr; FFA Swth; Bkbl Swth; Nom, HQn; WW; U of Tex; Acct.

FAIR, Bryan Keith
East HS; Columbus, OH (10-350) BS; Chess C; Pres, Dbte Tm; Drama; Fr C; VP, NFL; NHS; VP, SC; Tnns; Bio A; Kiwanis A; Rotary A; Spch A; Yth Foundation A; WW; Harvard U; Econ.

FAIR, Eunice Ellen
Victory Christian Acad; Jacksonville, FL; Band; NHS; *U of Ga; Vet Med.*

FAIR, J Daniel
Beth Haven Christian HS; Greenville, MI; Bsbl; Bkbl; Mgr, Ftbl; Cpt, Soccer; Sftbl; Fin, Tr; Wrest; Fin, Wrest; Soccer Ltr; *Tenn Temple Col; Law.*

FAIR, James Lawrence
Inola HS; Inola, OK; Chor; Spch C; *Wayland Baptist Col; Religion.*

FAIR, Ruth Dianne
Beth Haven Christian Sch; Greenville, MI; Band; Chor; NHS; Orch; Span C; COM; WW; *Tenn Temple Col; Med.*

FAIR, Sharon Jane
W Holmes HS; Millersburg, OH (10-200) Band; Lat C; NHS; Sci C; Sftbl; Sci A; *Ohio St U; Pediatrics.*

FAIR, Vickie Rena
East St Louis Sr HS; E St Louis, IL (2-699) Fr C; VP, NHS; Math A; Fr A; Lib Worker A; *Northwestern U; Engr.*

FAIRBAIRN, Timothy Scott
Westmont HS; Campbell, CA (113-423) A Cap Choir; Lit Mag; Madrigal; Var C; Tr; COM; Medals, Ribbons, Tr, High Jumping; *W Valley Jr Col; Elec Engr.*

FAIRBANK, Carolyn
Robinson HS; Santurce, PR (5-45) F-Ed, Ann; Drama; Lit Mag; Tres, Math C; Tres, Mu Alpha Theta; NHS; SC; NEDT; *Psych.*

FAIRBANKS, Amy Jo
Clintondale HS; Mt Clemens, MI (1-400) Band; Sftbl; Sports Ed, Sch P; *Mich St U; Journ.*

FAIRBANKS, Carol Ann
Shelton HS; Shelton, CT; Chor; Drama; Fr C; Fr A; Tres, Fresh Cl; Fr Exchange; *Fr.*

FAIRBANKS, Robert Sumner
Shelton HS; Shelton, CT (135-435) A Cap Choir; BS; Chor; Ger C; Madrigal; Order/Arrow; SC; Ftbl; Tr; Citz A; God & Country A; Eagle Sct; *Central Col; Art.*

FAIRBANKS, William Leonard
Goodrich HS; Goodrich, TX (1-25) Pres, BC; FFA; Bkbl; *Sam Houston St U; Chem.*

FAIRCHILD, Patrick Shawn
Harlingen HS; Harlingen, TX; A Cap Choir; Choir; ROTC; Yth Choir; FFA; *Baylor U; General Arts.*

FAIRCLOTH, Carol Jean
Central Baptist HS; Hampton, VA (7-14) Ann; Chor; Ed, Sch P; Mgr, Sftbl; COM; H of F; *Bob Jones U; Eng.*

FAIRCLOTH, Paul David Jr
S Broward HS; Hollywood, FL; A Cap Choir; Chor; Community Yth Symph; Ensm; Madrigal; NHS; Orch; Rptr, Sch P; Span C; Journ A; Span A; Comm Orch A; *Mus.*

FAIRCLOTH, Phillip Neal
New Bern Sr HS; New Bern, NC (125-502) Bus Mgr, Band; Span C; VP, Bkbl; Mgr, Ftbl; Tr; *NC St U; Acct.*

FAIRCLOTH, Tammy Latrisa
Randolph Sou Sch; Shellman, GA (1-20) S-T, BC; Tri-HiY; Bkbl; Tr; NEDT; Highest Academic Avg; *Eckerd Col; Art.*

FAIRCLOTH, Thomas Curtis Jr
Reidsville Sr HS; Reidsville, NC (37-344) AFS; VP, Key C; NHS; Pres, SC; Ftbl; Tr; *UNC-Chapel Hill; Law.*

FAIRLESS, Cindy June
Litchfield Sr HS; Litchfield, IL; Chor; Fr C; Encore Players; Acteen Qn; *Nurs.*

FAIRLEY, Doris Jayne
Vancleave HS; Vancleave, MS (33-90) Ann; BC; Chem C; Drama; FHA; GS; NHS; Sch P; Sci C; SC; Thes; Bkbl; Cpt, Sftbl; B Crocker A; Bio A; Cl Fav; Hon Prog; MLS; Most Out; Sci A; Most Talented; Miss Jr VHS; Marine Sci A; Miss Alto; *U of Sou Miss; Nurs.*

FAIRROW, Dawn Elaine
Chillicothe HS; Chillicothe, OH; Band; SC; Bsbl; Tr; *Tuskegee Inst; Nurs.*

FAIRROW, Ronald Lee Jr
Whetstone HS; Columbus, OH (11-529) Tr; Win, Poem Contest.

FAIRROW, Susan Ranay
Chillicothe HS; Chillicothe, OH (5-13) *Acct.*

FAISON, Dean
Williamsburg HS; Andrews, SC; GS; Cpt, Bkbl; COM; Ntl Achv Schol; MVP, Bkbl; *Spartanburg Methodist Col; Secretarial Sci.*

FAISON, Sandra Teresa
Windsor Forest HS; Savannah, GA; Chor; Fr C; SC; Piano Guild Founders A; *U of Ga; Commercial Art.*

FAIST, Jill Hope
Alvin HS; Alvin, TX (201-465) Ann; Lit Mag; Rptr, Sch P; Beauty; S-T, Drill Tm; MYF.

FAIT, Carolyn Davidson
Loch Raven Sr HS; Towson, MD (75-425) Drama; NHS; SC; Tres, Jr Cl; *Goucher Col; Pre-Med.*

FAITH, Beth
Holy Ghost HS; Pittsburgh, PA (2-48) NHS; Pres, SC; COM; *Carnegie-Mellon Col; Art.*

FAJER, Elizabeth Joy
Sacred Heart Acad; Salem, OR (10%-55).

FAJKUS, Wesley Delane
Charlotte HS; Charlotte, TX (7-43) Band; Ensm; FFA; VP, 4H; Fin, Bsbl; Fin, Bkbl; JV, Ftbl; Mgr, Tr; Citz A; 4H A; Math A; PTA A.

FALER, Joan Louise
Reynolds HS; Greenville, PA (18-212) Chor; Ger C; Lit Mag; Rptr, Sch P; Secy, Art C; Art A; *Art.*

FALES, Kristie Pearce
Vanguard HS; Ocala, FL (9-350) Band; Mu Alpha Theta; NHS; Rainbow; Span C; Masonic A; Eng, Band, A's; *Bus.*

FALK, Arnold Fredrick
Courtenay Pub Sch; Courtenay, ND (5-7) Sch P; Bkbl; Cpt, Cr-Ctry; Sftbl; Tr; *Valley City St Col; Math.*

FALK, Carol Ann
Holy Rosary Acad; Louisville, KY (2-116) Ann; Span C; VP, Spch C; Secy, SC; 4H A; Opt A; ARC A; Spch A; Hugh O'Brian Yth Found Fin; *U of Louisville; Engr.*

FALK, Marna Marie
Courtenay Pub Sch; Courtenay, ND (3-9) Sch P; SC; Bkbl; Sftbl; Tr; Type A; HR.

FALK, Micheal Duane
Marshall HS; Marshall, TX; Chess C; Chor; Ftbl; *Baylor U; Lawyer.*

FALK, Polly Ann
Jasper HS; Jasper, MN (4-40) Cpt, Chldr; Chor; Drama; FHA; Mjrte; Spch C; Var C; Bkbl; Sftbl; Tr; Pres A; ARC A; All Conf Bkbl; Cpt, Vlbl All Conf.

FALKENSTERN, John Eugene
Concordia Lutheran HS; Fort Wayne, IN (144-226) VP, Ger C; Bkbl; Tr; MVP, Summer Bsbl Tm; *Olivet Col; Acct.*

FALKNOR, Robert Lynn
Litchfield Sr HS; Litchfield, MN (10-183) Co-Ed, Ann; Band; Dbte Tm; Drama; Ger C; Key C; NHS; Sch P; Spch C; Thes; Sal; Spch A; Star Student; *Hamline Col at St Paul; Creative Writing.*

FALKOSKI, Rose Ann
Lead Hill Sch; Lead Hill, AR (1-21) Tres, FBLA; FHA; Ed, Sch P; SC; Bio A; Chem A; Math A; Shorthand A; Eng A; Bus Law A.

FALLENSTEIN, Deborah Ann
Charleroi HS; Charleroi, PA; Hmrm; Bkbl; Sftbl; COM; *Slippery Rock Col; Phys Ed.*

FALLICK, Eric Scott
Neshaminy Maple Point HS; Langhorne, PA (3-400) Chess C; Math C; NHS; Var C; COM; Hon Prog; NMF; Ntl Sci Found; Sci A; *Pa St U; Physics.*

FALLON, Linda Louise
United Township HS; E Moline, IL (285-792) Chor; Secy, 4H; JV, Bkbl; Tr; 4H A; *Western U; Child Psych.*

FALLON, Michael Edward
St Raphael Acad; Pawtucket, RI (6-130) CYO; Pres, NHS; Order/Arrow; ARC; SC; Tres, Sr Cl; Ftbl; Tr; Order/Arrow A; ARC A; Spch A; *Pol Sci.*

FALLS, Mark Steven
Jack Yates Sr HS; Houston, TX (2-420) Chor; NHS; Sci C; Bsbl; Co-Cpt, Ftbl; Alg A; Cl Fav; Elk A; Semi- fin, Algebra A; Fin, Cl Fav; *Mech Engr.*

FALLS, Willa Jean
York Comp HS; York, SC (1-240) Ann; BC; Fr C; 4H; NHS; SC; PC Jr Fel; Newberry School; Marshal; *Winthrop Col; Secretarial Sci.*

FALSTAD, Kristin Leslie
Victoria HS; Victoria, TX (13-800) NHS; Drill Tm; Church Choir; Yth Coun; *Tex A&M U; Engr.*

FALTER, Donna Sue
Maries R-1 HS; Vienna, MO (8-89) S-T, CYO; Chor; FBLA; Pres, FHA; FTA; *Bus.*

FALVEY, Robin Gail
El Segundo HS; El Segundo, CA (7-285) AFS; Fin, GS; Co-Cpt, Mjrte; Span C; Secy, SC; Sftbl; CSF; Span A's; Most Exciting; Pres, Girl's League; Sftbl Ltr; *Spch Pathology & Audiology.*

FALZANO, Marianne
Mercy HS; Albany, NY (12-108) Dbte Tm; Drama; Fr C; InterAct C; Lit Mag; NHS; A-Ed, Sch P; Ski C; NEDT; *Hudson Valley Comm Col; Nurs.*

FALZONE, Angela Marie
Wyoming Valley W HS; Kingston, PA (19-450) Chor; SC; Amer Leg A; God & Country A; Hon Prog; Marion A; *Drew U; Med.*

FANCE, Deborah Annette
Compton HS; Compton, CA (20%-850) *UCLA; Dental Asst.*

FANCHER, Lisa Marie
Mena HS; Mena, AR (3-147) Band; Chor; NHS; Sci C; SC; HCt; Math A; Optimist Oratorical Win; St Hon Recital; *Ark Polytechnic U; Math.*

FANCHER, Teresa Lynn
Trinity Christian HS; Chattanooga, TN (8-14) Chor; S-T, FHA; Hmrm; SC; Most Talented; 1st Pl, TACS; *Mus.*

FANDERCLAI, Tari Lin
Fulton HS; Fulton, IL; Band; Chor; Thes; Faculty Hon A; *Engr.*

FANG, Su Chan
Inglewood HS; Inglewood, CA (19-465) Fr C; Ger C; Math C; Tnns; Alg A; CSF; Citz A; Cl Fav; DARGCA; H of F; HQn; JA A; Math A; MLS; Most Out; Ntl Achv Schol; NMF; Regent Schol; Star Student; St Scholar; *UCLA; Modeling.*

FANKHANEL, Anita Marty
Aldine Sr HS; Houston, TX; A-Ed, Sch P; Thes; COM; Q&S A; *SW Tex St U; Journ.*

FANKHAUSER, Cynthia Sue
Miramar HS; Miramar, FL (25%-550) Band; Chor; Swim; COM; Drill Tm; *Miami Dade Jr Col; Stewardess.*

FANKHAUSER, Jamie Scott
Bern HS; Bern, KS (2-25) Ann; Band; BS; Chor; Madrigal; NHS; Sch P; SC; Var C; Pres, Soph Cl; Bkbl; Ftbl; Amer Leg A; HCt; Yth Fel; *Kans U; Bus.*

FANNIN, Angela Vernice
Harris Co Sr HS; Hamilton, GA; Chldr; FHA; Secy, Var C; *Phys Ed.*

FANNIN, Glenn Scott
St Joseph's o-t Palisades; W New York, NJ (6-289) French NHS; Sch Achieve Tm; Soccer; JV, Tr; Amer Leg A; Hon Prog; NEDT; Val; *Psych.*

FANNING, Charles Donald
First Assembly Christian Sch; Memphis, TN (7-32) Lat C; Ed, Sch P; Bsbl; Bkbl; Cr-Ctry; Tr; *Memphis St U; Med.*

FANNING, Christy Lynn
NW Classen HS; Oklahoma City, OK; Pres, Bus C; Chor; Pres, FBLA; Rptr, Hmrm; SC; Secy, Soph Cl; Citz A; Type A; Bus Girl o-t Mo; *Central St U; Bus.*

FANNING, Cindy Ann
Northwest Classen HS; Oklahoma City, OK (10%-340) FBLA; Ger C; Mu Alpha Theta; Orch; VP, Var C; Bkbl; Sftbl; Tres, Pep C; Badminton; Cpt, Vlbl; Most Valuable Catcher; *Okla State U; Elem Ed.*

FANNING, Jed
Artesia HS; Artesia, NM (10-329) Hmrm; NHS; Ski C; SC; Ftbl; Cl Fav; Spch A; Most Handsome; Twirp King Attendent; *NM St U; Mech Engr.*

FANNY, Marvin Lee Jr
Suffolk HS; Suffolk, VA (2-150) Lat C; NHS; Tres, Span C; SC; Tri-HiY; Bio A; Math A; Sci A; *Eng.*

FANOURAKIS, Catherine
Packer Collegiate Inst; Brooklyn, NY (12-41) Sch P; Span C; Co-Cpt, Bkbl; Sftbl; Hon Prog; Span A; Pres, Yth Group; Sunday Sch Teacher; *Fordham U; Math.*

FANSLAU, Nancy Jane
Kingsway Regional HS; Swedesboro, NJ (20-166) F-Ed, Ann; Chldr; FNA; Hmrm; Jr Miss Pagent; Key C; NHS; ARC; SC; GS; Tr; Beauty; HQn; ARC A; VFW A; Yth Fel.

FANSLER, Edward Randolph
Norfolk Collegiate HS; Norfolk, VA; Chor; Hmrm; Key C; Lat C; Monogram; NHS; Bkbl; Most Outst Stu; *U of Richmond; Dentistry.*

FANSLER, Mary Frances
Fairfield Comm HS; Fairfield, IL (15%-177) A Cap Choir; Band; Chldr; Chor; Ensm; Pres, 4H; Bkbl; Amer Leg A; Citz A; Cl Fav; God & Country A; 4H A; MLS; Val; Yth Fel; Secy, Rptr, 4h C; Outst Yth, Vocal Mus, A's; *E Ill U; Eng.*

FANSLER, Susan Jean
Fairfield Comm HS; Fairfield, IL (21-162) Chor; FHA; Secy, 4H; Secy, NHS; Span C; Citz A; 4H A; Yth Fel; Rptr, 4H C; *Olney Central Col; Med Secy.*

FANT, Julian Earle Jr
Pendleton HS; Pendleton, SC (8-125) BC; Fr C; 4H; Hmrm; InterClub Coun; Ed, Sch P; Var C; Bkbl; Cpt, Ftbl; Golf; 4H A; Journ A; Q&S A; Yth Fel; *Clemson U; Park & Recreation.*

FANTAZIA, Robert Alfred
Orestimba HS; Newman, CA (50-70) Band; Pres, CYO; Mgr, Sftbl; CYO A; *MJC; Bus.*

FANTINI, Carol
Oceanside Sr HS; Oceanside, NY (100-900) Chor; Drama; Tnns; Five Towns Theatrical Workshop; Red Cr Life Saving Cert; Yth Fel; Sunday Sch Teacher; *Performing Arts.*

FAQUIN, Lee Ann
Evangelical Christian Sch; Cordova, TN (4-57) Cpt, Chldr; Chor; NHS; Citz A; HCt; Headmaster's List; *Biola Col; Psych.*

FAQUIN, Lisa Carol
Evangelical Christian Sch; Cordova, TN (8-76) Fr C; Hmrm; SC; Bkbl; Cr-Ctry; Tnns; MVP, Tr; Citz A; HQn; Sci A; Schol A; Vlbl; Ltr C; 100 Mile C; *Med.*

FARABEE, Beverly Renee
Callaway Sr HS; Jackson, MS (30-460) Band; Co-Cpt, Chldr; Mjrte; Rptr, Sch P; SC; Pres, Soph Cl; Bio A; COM; Hon Prog; Spch A; Miss Personality; Chldr o-t Yr; Ldrship & Acad Ltrs; Drill Tm; *Oral Roberts U; Nurs.*

FARAH, Kirklin Wesley
Wheaton N HS; Wheaton, IL; Drama; Bkbl; Ftbl; Tnns; Hon Prog; HR; *Communications.*

FARAHANI, Ahmad
Farmerville HS; Farmerville, LA; NHS; Var C; Bkbl; Ftbl; Tr; Yth Fel; FCA; Soccer C.

FAREK, Gwendolyn Marie
Flatonia HS; Flatonia, TX (7-39) A-Ed, Ann; Cpt, Chldr; FHA; F-Ed, Sch P; Tnns; Cl Fav; HCt; *Blinn Col.*

FARGIS, Marie Dixon
Reidsville Sr HS; Reidsville, NC (5%-375) Band; Ensm; Fr C; Jr Miss Pagent; Mjrte; Math C; *U of NC at Chapel Hill; Math.*

FARGO, Donna Rae
Norwich Free Acad; Norwich, CT; DARGCA; Hist A; Math A.

FARHART, Linda Rose
Stanley HS; Stanley, ND (3-70) Band; Pres, FHA; Tres, 4H; 4H A; Math A; VofDEM; Poetry Published; Star Rating Flute; *U of ND; Special Ed.*

FARINAS, Carlos Alejandro
Colegio San Antonio Abad; Humacao, PR (3-72) Chem C; Drama; Tres, NHS; ARC; Sch P; Tnns; Chem A; 1st Prize, Short Story Span Lit Con; *Johns Hopkins U; Med.*

FARISON, Brian Kent
Walnut Hills HS; Cincinnati, OH (250-500) Soccer; COM; Hon Prog; Var Ltr, Soccer; Hon Mention, Schol Art Show; *Art.*

FARKAS, Gary Louis
Green HS; Greensburg, OH (68-349) Chor; Bkbl; JV, Ftbl; JV, Tr; Hon Prog.

FARKAS, Stephen Joseph
Green HS; Greensburg, OH (38-342) Chor; Ensm; NHS; SC; Var C; Bkbl; Ftbl; Tr; HCt; FCA; All Suburban League, Ftbl.

FARLEY, Adrienne Ann
Claremore HS; Claremore, OK (25-217) Ed, Ann; Band; Ensm; Math C; Mu Alpha Theta; Pres, NHS; Opt Out Tn; WW; HR; PA; St Hon Soc; Eng A; WW, Mus Stu; Jr Quest Off; Jr Opt; Secy, Leo C; Archbearer; Candystrip; Sup Ratng, Solo & Duet Dist Cont; *Okla U.*

FARLEY, Daryl Wayne
E Atlanta HS; Atlanta, GA (6-175) Band; Tr; Pres, Jr Civitan; *Aviation.*

FARLEY, Debra Ann
Los Altos HS; Hacienda Heights, CA; Pres, Yth Fel; *Mt San Antonio Col; Bus.*

FARLEY, Jill Ann
McGavock HS; Nashville, TN (75-950) A Cap Choir; Band; BC; Chor; Ensm; Ger C; Madrigal; NHS; Sch P; Arch; Grace Moore Schol; All St Chor; Departmental A's; *U of Tenn; Chor Conducting.*

FARLEY, Lisa Ann
R L Turner HS; Carrollton, TX (80-800) Ann; VP, Bus C; FBLA; FHA; *Southwestern Col; Life Insurance.*

FARLEY, Patrick Richard
Northwestern Sr HS; Hyattsville, MD (1-650) CYO; Rptr, Sch P; JV, Wrest; Balfour A; NMF; Val; Span A; *U of Md at Col Park; Engr.*

FARLEY, Paula Jean
Cumberland Co HS; Crossville, TN; Chor; Candystriper; DECCAC.

FARLEY, Quinton Alan
Slaton HS; Slaton, TX (5%-95) NHS; Alg A; Hon Prog; ROTC A; Fr, Shorthand A; *Tex Tech U; Pol Sci.*

FARLEY, Timothy Joe
NW Classen HS; Okla City, OK (198-485) Key C; NFL; Rptr, Sch P; Span C; SC; JV, Cr-Ctry; Tr; JA A; Opt A; VP, FCA; VP, JA; *Okla City U; Journ.*

FARLEY, Trudi Jane
Joliet Township HS Central; Joliet, IL (55-521) Secy, Band; Drama; Pres, Fr C; NHS; Orch; Beauty; COM; Ch, Jr Sr Prom; Badminton; Modern Dance; Yth Board; Focus C; Stu Dir; Pres, Yth Group; 1st Pl, St Tn Talent Search; *Joliet Jr Col; Fine Arts.*

FARLING, Mary Jane
Findlay HS; Findlay, OH; Chor; Amer Leg A; LaSertoma Service A; *Ohio St U; Livestock.*

FARLOW, Harold Anthony
New Augusta HS; New Augusta, MS (4-34) Pres, FFA; NHS; MVP, Bsbl; MVP, Bkbl; Cl Fav; H of F; HKg; HCt; *Jones Co Jr Col.*

FARLOW, Theresa Ann
Tallulah Acad; Tallulah, LA (15-29) Chor; FHA; 4H; Spch C; Tr; 4H A; *Northeast La U; Nurs.*

FARM, Tamara Louise
Fairmont Sr HS; Fairmont, MN (170-220) Band; Chor; Tnns; HR; Yth Choir; Luther League; *Nurs.*

FARMER, Ann
San Benito HS; San Benito, TX; Band; FFA; FHA; Keywanettes; GSct; *Sul Ross U; Bet Asst.*

FARMER, Carol Elaine
Welch HS; Welch, WV; FHA; NHS; UN Council; Bkbl; Tr; *Vet.*

FARMER, Carolyn Marie
Red Bank HS; Chattanooga, TN (142-336) Pres, Lat C; Cpt, Mjrte; Span C; Tri-HiY; Yth Fel; HR; *U of Tenn.*

FARMER, Erin Lynn
Pacific Christian Acad; Graton, CA (4-6) Chor; Hon Prog; Most Sincere; *Freed-Hardeman Col; Lib Arts.*

FARMER, Gregg Steven
Windsor Forest HS; Savannah, GA; Bkbl; Sftbl; Math A; Bowl Tm; Art A; *Armstrong St Col; Vet.*

FARMER, Jan
San Benito HS; San Benito, TX; Band; Ensm; FHA; Pres, Jr Cl; Keywanettes; GSct; All Valley, Band; Outst FHA; Medals, Band Solo.

FARMER, Jeanette Marie
Hudson HS; Hudson, NC (18-315) A Cap Choir; BC; Chor; Math C; Mu Alpha Theta; Span C; Span NHS; Opt A; Spch A.

FARMER, John Anderson
Man HS; Man, WV (21-180) Ann; Pres, Band; Chem C; Secy, Chess C; InterAct C; NHS; Sci C; Span C; VP, Span NHS; Golf; Tnns; Cl Fav; VFW A; VFW Orator Win; VofDEM; Yth Fel; Pres, St Baptist Yth Convention; Pres, Baptist Yth Assn; Highest Score A, Golf Tm; Fertilizer A; *W Va U; Pol Sci.*

FARMER, Kelly Faye
Pacific Christian Acad; Graton, CA (3-6) Ann; Chor; Drama; Sch P; Tres, SC; Hon Prog; Most Stu; *Freed-Hardeman Col; Home Ec.*

FARMER, Leslie Ann
West HS; Bakersfield, CA (124-402) Secy, Band; Ensm; Fr C; Model UN; Ntl Yth Conf; SC; VP, Var C; Cpt, Sftbl; Pres A; Tres, Rptr, Band; Work Camp; 1st Cl GSct; WW; *San Jose St U; Phys Therapy.*

FARMER, Lisa Marie
Charlotte Valley Central Sch; Davenport, NY (1-41) JV, Chldr; Secy, Chor; Secy, NHS; Tres, Sch P; Span C; Alg A; Math A; Most Out; Val; *Cobleskill Agr & Tech Col; Nursery Ed.*

FARMER, Lynn Denise
R J Reynolds HS; Winston-Salem, NC; Chldr; ARC; Tres, Soph Cl; ARC A; Elections Committee; Sr Girls Service C; Hon's Art; *U of NC; Med.*

FARMER, Marsha Ann
Summit HS; Frisco, CO (3-93) Chor; FBLA; Pres, NHS; Pres, Pep C; Varsity Letter; Co Cpt, Vlbl; MIP, Vlbl; Stu o-t Wk; *CSU; Bus.*

FARMER, Rebecca Marie
Beloit Jr-Sr HS; Beloit, KS (1-67) Band; Chor; Orch; Sci C; SC; Y-Tns; Cpt, Bkbl; Tnns; Tr; Pres A; VFW A; Vlbl; Sch 880 Yd Run Record Holder; Choral Ensm; 1st Cl GSct; Bkbl All League Tm; *Liberal Arts.*

FARMER, Rosanne
Butler Sr HS; Butler, PA; Chor; Hmrm; Rainbow; SC; Secy, Thes; Pres, Jr Cl; *Ind of Pa; Psych.*

FARMER, Thomas Matthew
Harvard Comm HS; Harvard, IL (30-157) A Cap Choir; Chor; Ensm; Madrigal; Mod Mus Mas; VP, Thes; JV, Golf; COM; 1st, 1st Mus Contest; *Engr.*

FARMER, Walter John
St Regis Falls Central HS; St Regis Falls, NY; Tres, Sr Cl; Bsbl; Bkbl; Photographer, Yrbk; *Canton ATC; Bus Adm.*

FARMWALD, Hal Wesley
Northwood HS; Nappanee, IN (76-182) Drama; Tres, Monogram; Thes; Var C; Bsbl; Bkbl; Lion A; St Scholar; FCA; *Goshen Col.*

FARNDEN, Jacqueline Anne
Mission HS; San Fernando, CA; F-Ed, Ann; Band; Hmrm; Math C; Sch Achieve Tm; Sch P; SC; COM; Citz A; Cl Fav; Star Student; *Vet.*

FARNESI, Gary Anthony
S Philadelphia HS; Philadelphia, PA (50%-900) A Cap Choir; Chor; Drama; Hmrm; SC; Bsbl; Ftbl; Swim; COM; Citz A; VFW A; *U of Pa; Bio.*

FARNSLEY, Arthur Emery
New Albany HS; New Albany, IN (5%-700) Fr C; JV, Ftbl; Star Student; *Eng.*

FARNSWORTH, Bradley Steven
Gilroy HS; Gilroy, CA (3%-400) Chess C; Order/Arrow; God & Country A; Order/Arrow A; Eagle Sct; 7 Yr Piano Stu.

FARNSWORTH, Heidi R
Exeter Township Sr HS; Reading, PA (78-265) Band; Chldr; Chor; Ensm; S-T, Hmrm; Y-Tns; JV, Hockey; Word of Life Singing A; Silver Eagle A; Word of Life Chldr A; Most Enthusiastic; *Messiah Col; Dietetics.*

FAUNCE, Pamela Kay
Muncie Central HS; Muncie, IN (3-416) Chem C; Ger C; Tnns; Tr; Hon Prog; Acolyte A; FCA; Vlbl; *Ball St Col.*

FAUSNAUGH, Michelle Elaine
St Martin HS; Biloxi, MS (5-250) BC; COM; Hon Prog; NEDT; Sci A; St Pres, FHA; Co-Ed Correspondent; St Del, Ntl FHA Conv; *U of Sou Miss; Home Ec Ed.*

FAUSS, David Herman
University Christian HS; Jacksonville, FL (1-71) Band; NHS; *Fla Jr Col; Bus Adm.*

FAUX, Edward Matthew
W Allegheny HS; Imperial, PA; Pres, Chor; Fr C; Ski C; SC; Bsbl; Hon Prog; Drum Major; *Penn St U; Engr.*

FAVOR, Jocelyn Marcia
Dos Pueblos HS; Goleta, CA (20%-660) Band; Chor; Drama; Orch; Co-Cpt, Drill Tm; Handbell Choir; Secy, GAA; Puffets; Semi-Fin, Model Tn Contest.

FAWBUSH, Jeff H
Abingdon HS; Abingdon, IL (25-77) Band; Chldr; Ftbl; Yth Fel; Kappa Delta Chi; Tn Choir; WW; *Elec.*

FEAGANS, DeAnn Elizabeth
Ritenour Sr HS; Overland, MO; *Washington U.*

FEAGIN, Kimberly Lynn
T R Miller H; Brewton, AL (12-98) Pres, FHA; FTA; 4H; Jr Miss Pagent; Lit Mag; NHS; Pres A; Cpt, Rifle Corps; Phys Fitness Achv A; *Jefferson Davis Jr Col; Nurs.*

FEARCE, Dianna Renee
Serra Jr Sr HS; San Diego, CA;

FEARCE, Vanessa Rochelle
Junipero Serra Jr Sr HS; San Diego, CA (50-137) Gym; Pep C; Sec & Tchr, Sundy Sch & Trng Union; *La Verne Col; Law.*

FEARNOW, Kimberly Ann
Crystal Lake Jr HS; Lakeland, FL;

FEARS, Douglas Neil
Etowah HS; Attalla, AL (1-275) BC; FFA; Tr; MLS; Mus; Span A; Pres, Career C; *Birmingham-Sou Col; Mus.*

FEARS, Lilah Claire
Morgan City HS; Morgan City, LA; Band; Hmrm; SC; *LSU; Psych.*

FEARS, Marvin William
Plant City HS; Plant City, FL (155-600) FFA; *Engr.*

FEARS, William A
Jackson HS; Jackson, GA (16-140) HiY; Pres, Key C; NHS; Sch P; Var C; Bsbl; Bkbl; Co-Cpt, Ftbl; Golf; *Gordon Jr Col; Pol Sci.*

FEASTER, Bruce Sullivan
SW Comm HS; Flint, MI (4-27) Band; Orch; Alg A; Citz A; Hon Prog; Math A; Highest Achv, Math Contest; *U of Mich; Law.*

FEASTER, Rodney Lee
Flint Southwestern HS; Flint, MI (70-550) Var C; Cpt, Bkbl; Ftbl; Cpt, Tr; Citz A; Hon Prog; Most Out; Opt A; Spch A; Yth Fel; *U of Mich; Sci.*

FEATHER, Linda Lee
Steel Valley Intermediate HS; Munhall, PA (10%-353) Chor; Drama; Tres, Lat C; Pres, Rainbow; Grand Cross of Color; *Social Work.*

FEATHERSTONE, Neil James III
Fremont HS; Fremont, MI (45-250) NHS; Ski C; Pres, Var C; Cpt, Cr-Crtry; Cpt, Tr; NMS; *Mich U; Ed.*

FEAZELL, Donald Wayne
Saks HS; Anniston, AL; Pres, Chor; Ensm; Pres, Sr Cl; Outst Stu, Chor; *Jacksonville St Col.*

FEBO, Margarita
Colegio San Antonio HS; Rio Piedras, PR; NHS; COM; Hon Prog; *U of Puerto Rico; Secretarial.*

FEBUS, Elizabeth
Miguel Melendez Munoz; Bayamon, PR; Band; CYO; Chldr; Chem C; Chor; Pres, Drama; Secy, FHA; Pres, 4H; Jr Miss Pagent; S-T, Math C; Orch; Phys C; ARC; Span C; Spch C; SC; Alg A; Beauty; Bio A; COM; Chem A; Hist A; Math A; Phy A; ARC A; Sci A; Summa Cum Laude; *U of Puerto Rico; Phar.*

FECHHELM, Linda Marie
Newman HS; Wausau, WI (32-134) Type A; Cert, Ntl Ed Development Tests.

FECK, Suzanne Delores
Jefferson HS; Jefferson, OR (2-85) Ann; Pres, Band; Fin, GS; NHS; Bkbl; Acct A; Pep Band A; *Oreg Col of Ed; Ed.*

FEDDE, John Douglas
Plymouth-Whitemarsh HS; Plymouth Meeting, PA (317-634) Band; Ensm; Pres, Orch; Phys C; MVP, Arch; Best Overall, Band; Order of Anthony Wayne; Cpt, Explorers; *Mountgomery Co Comm Col; Phys Sci.*

FEDDERKE, Sandra Lynn
Steeleville Comm HS; Steeleville, IL (5-56) FHA; SC; Hon Prog; *Concordia Teachers Col; Ed.*

FEDERHOFER, Cheryl Rae
Notre Dame HS; St Louis, MO (60-150) Pres, CYO; ARC; Cpt, Sftbl; HCt; K of C A; *Avila Col; Nurs.*

FEDOR, Colleen Marie
St Joseph's Notre Dame HS; Alameda, CA (7-56) NHS; Ski C; SC; VP, Var C; Bkbl; Cpt, Sftbl; Hon Prog; *San Diego U; Law.*

FEDOR, Richard Donald
St Joseph HS; St Joseph, MI (200-360) Band; Chor; Ensm; COM; Citz A; Kiwanis A; Rotary A; Yth Fel; *Aderson Col; Bus.*

FEE, Carol Jeanine
E Mecklenburg HS; Charlotte, NC (47-707) BC; NHS; 1st Cl, GSct A; *NC St U; Computer Sci.*

FEE, Cynthia Kay
Linn-Mar HS; Marion, IA (5-224) Ann; Band; Ensm; Pres, 4H; Hmrm; NHS; Ed, Sch P; Spch C; SC; Golf; COM; 4H A; Journ A; Q&S A; Spch A; Yth Ldrship; Mayor's Yth Coun; Dist & St SC; Most Improved Player; *Nurs.*

FEEHRER, Kelly Wayne
Cleveland HS; Cleveland, TN; Band; Chor; Community Yth Symph; Ensm; Orch; Mus As; *Bus.*

FEEMSTER, Keith Parnell
Crosby HS; Crosby, TX (32-139) Band; Chess C; FFA; 4H; Sci C; 4H A; Sci A; All-Area Band; *Lee Col; Mus.*

FEES, Russell Eugene
Miller HS; Miller, MO (17-90) Chor; FFA; Bsbl; JV, Bkbl; *Wildlife Conservation.*

FEES, Teresa Elaine
Miller HS; Miller, MO (15-54) S-T, Band; Chor; Ensm; Secy, FHA; Secy, Mod Mus Mas; Pres, Span C; Secy, Jr Cl; Mgr, Bkbl; Sftbl; Citz A; Co-Cpt, JV Vlbl; A of Excellence; *Southwest Baptist Col; Transportation.*

FEESE, Bonnie Sue
Pampa HS; Pampa, TX (73-326) Chldr; Pres, Chor; FHA; Bkbl; Ftbl; Spch A; Girls Powderpuff; *McMurry Col; Bus.*

FEESER, April Diana
McArthur HS; Hollywood, FL (25%-600) Chor; COM; Pres A; Muscular Dystrophy A; Good Penmanship A; *Miami Dade Col; Nurs.*

FEGAN, Jamie Danita
Brimley HS; Brimley, MI (5-47) Chor; FTA; Hon Prog.

FEHLER, Laurie Kay
Lutheran HS; Houston, TX (21-97) Chess C; Chor; Ger C; Hmrm; NHS; ARC; SC; Arch; JV, Bkbl; Sftbl; Swim; Tnns; COM; Hon Prog; NEDT; *Concordia Col; Bus Mgr.*

FEHLHABER, Thomas Frank
Omaha S HS; Omaha, NE (7-660) Lat C; Math C; Alg A; Bio A; COM; Math A; Omaha Echng Cl Soph A Boy's St Alt; *U of Neb at Lincoln; Engr.*

FEHR, Laura Rochelle
Lindberg HS; St Louis, MO (349-1085) Type A; Yth Fel; Pep C; Sr GSct A; God & Comm A; Hospital Vola; *Med.*

FEHSE, Vera Elizabeth
Roth HS; Henrietta, NY (2-225) NHS; SC; Sal; Gregg Shorthand Achv A; Scholastic Ltr; COM, Amer Assn of Teach of German; *Monroe Comm Col; Secretarial Sci.*

FEICHT, Doreen Carol
Toms River HS N; Toms River, NJ (307-701) Drama; 4H; Pres, Thes; Mgr, Bsbl; Mgr, Soccer; 4H A; *Westminster Col; Christian Ed.*

FEICHTNER, Deborah Kay
Buckeye Central HS; New Washington, OH (15-95) FHA; Pres, 4H; Span C; Span NHS; VP, SC; Sftbl; 4H A; Type A; Outst Driver; *Nurs.*

FEICHTNER, Glen David
Buckeye Central HS; New Washington, OH (30-95) Band; VP, FFA; JV, Bsbl; Amer Leg A; COM; Citz A; Sci A; FFA St Farmer Degree; FFA Star Chapter Farmer.

FEIDT, Julie Kay
E Pennsboro Sr HS; Enola, PA (20-240) Band; Chor; Drama; VP, Span C; Tr; Model; Tres, Church Yth; Dancer, Supporting Role, Mus; Craftman Fair A; Miss Congeniality; *Valley Forge Christian Col; Psych.*

FEIERABEND, Susan Gwen
Abraham Lincoln HS; Denver, CO (25%-700) Chor; Ensm; 4H; Hmrm; ARC; SC; Y-Tns; Mgr, Swim; COM; 4H A; Most Out; Opt A; Spch A; Type A; Church Choir; Choir Piano Accomp; St Piano Comp; Pep C; Dance A; *Bus.*

FEIGHT, Steven William
Clyde HS; Clyde, KS (10-45) Fin, BS; SC; Pres, Soph Cl; Ftbl; Tr; Pres A.

FEIL, Lawrence Anthony
Chelan HS; Chelan, WA (5-50) CYO; NHS; SC; Var C; Pres, Jr Cl; Bkbl; Ftbl; Ntl Merit Ltr of Commendation; *U of Wash; Engr.*

FEIMSTER, Mae Lois
N Iredell HS; Olin, NC (7-25) F-Ed, Ann; FHA; Sch P; Sftbl; Cl Swtht; *Modeling.*

FEIMSTER, Tim Morrow
W Iredell HS; Statesville, NC (100-191) Chor; FFA; Sci C; Bsbl; JV, Bkbl; Bio A; Sci A; *Mitchell Comm Col.*

FEINBERG, Brian Elliot
Neshaminy Maple Point HS; Langhorne, PA (9-388) NHS; Rptr, Sch P; *Muhlenberg Col; Med.*

FEISEL, Margie Ann
Stevens HS; Rapid City, SD (8-473) Pres, AFS; Band; Secy, NHS; Orch; Opt Out Tn; Alt, GS; All St Band & Orch; *Oceanography.*

FEIST, Karl Daniel
Bishop Ryan HS; Minot, ND (9-92) NHS; JV, Wrest; Hon Prog; *Minot St Col; Contracting.*

FEIST, Kathy Jean
Bishop Ryan HS; Minot, ND (3-75) A-Ed, Ann; Pres, 4H; Hmrm; K of C; NHS; S-T, SC; Var C; Secy, Jr Cl; Secy, Soph Cl; Co-Cpt, Bkbl; Sftbl; Beauty; COM; Citz A; Cl Fav; Gov Honor Prog; 4H A; HCt; Hon Prog; JA A; K of C A; Most Out; Poet A; Sal; Star Student; Type A; Pom-Pon; Shorthand A; GAA; Ltrwinners; Jack Coughlin, Art, Schol's; *Minot St Col; Bus.*

FEIST, Xavier Joseph
Jeanerette Sr HS; Jeanerette, LA; Tres, CYO; Chor; Cpt, Bsbl; Bkbl; Bio A; Sci A; Type A; Bkbl Trophy; *U of SW La; Executive Secy.*

FEIT, Danny Harold
Hebrew Acad of Nassau Co; Uniondale, NY; Band; Drama; Hmrm; Bkbl; COM; Cert of Hon; Service A; *Yeshiva U.*

FEITSHANS, Alice Lynn
Urbana HS; Urbana, IL; Band; Chor; Drama; NHS; Secy, Span C; Tr; Hon Prog; Type A; *E Ill Col; Gen.*

FELBER, Stacey Adair
Park Center HS; Brooklyn Center, MN (10-719) Chor; A-Ed, Lit Mag; NHS; Rptr, Sch P; Spch C; Spch A; Choir Accompanist A; X-L Cl A; Semi-Fin GS; Vision Support Group; *St Mary's Jr Col; OT Paraprofessional.*

FELCYN, Wendy Ann
Eisenhower HS; Washington, MI (10%-675) Span C; SC; Service Ch, St Kieran's Yth Group; Campfire Ldr; *Oakland U; Ed.*

FELD, Richard Thomas
Chaminade Col Prep; Creve Coeur, MO (5-118) CYO; NHS; Rptr, Sch P; Soccer; Tnns; Alg A; Bio A; Hon Prog; Math A; MLS; Ntl Sci Symposium; NEDT; Sci A; Type A; *U of Mo at Columbia; Chem Engr.*

FELDER, Jessica Annetta
Block HS; Jonesville, LA; Chldr; 4H; Tres, Hmrm; *Sou U; Elem Ed.*

FELDERMAN, Mark Thomas
Bellevue Comm HS; Bellevue, IA (19-67) Ed, Ann; Chor; Pres, Demolay; Drama; Sch P; Span C; Spch C; Var C; Bsbl; Bkbl; Cr-Ctry; Tr; Masonic A; Rep, DeMolay; WW; *Iowa St U; Communications.*

FELDMAN, David N
Woodmere Acad; Woodmere, NY (4-42) Drama; Ed, Sch P; Span C; Thes; Mgr, Bkbl; JV, Soccer; Tr; Hist A; Parl & Secy, SC; Span A; Sch Service Commendation; *Acct.*

FELESKY, Cynthia Linn
W Middlesex Area HS; W Middlesex, PA (20-146) Chldr; Chor; FTA; SC; HCt; Jr Chamber of Com A; SPAN; *Med.*

FELICIANO, Crecensio
Dr P Perea Fajardo HS; Mayaguez, PR;

FELICIANO, Enidza
Adolfo Grana Rivera HS; Penuelas, PR (4-263) Chor; Secy, FFA; FHA; COM; HCt; *Cath U; Lawyer.*

FELICIANO, Marco A
Adolfo Grana Rivera HS; Penuelas, PR (5-342) VP, BS; Tres, 4H; ARC; Bkbl; COM; Hon Prog; Val; *U of Puerto Rico; Math.*

FELICIANO, Marisol
Adolfo Grana Rivera HS; Penuelas, PR (3-336) Drama; Sci C; COM; Hist A; Hon Prog; Math A; Sci A; Span A; *Cath U; Acct.*

FELIU, Astrid
Luis Munoz Rivera HS; Lajas, PR (26-175) Band; BC; Chldr; Chor; Drama; FBLA; 4H; InterAct C; Thes; Beauty; COM; 4H A; Hon Prog; Poet A; *Recinto U de Mayaguez; Phar.*

FELIX, Alice Mae
Waterproof HS; Waterproff, LA (10-59) *NE La U; Clothes & Textiles.*

FELKER, Joseph Allen
Marian HS; Tamaqua, PA (13-153) CYO; NHS; Co-Ed, Sch P; Bkbl; Cr-Ctry; Tr; Hon Prog; NEDT; *Elec.*

FELKNER, Jimmy Oren
Waco HS; Waco, TX (39-226) Chor; Ensm; Madrigal; Span C; Tnns; COM; Hon Prog; District Choir; Gold Medal Vocal Solo, UIL; *McLennan Comm Col; Bus Adm.*

FELLA, Vicky Leigh
Warren Central HS; Indianapolis, IN (227-791) Chor; Swim; Hi-C; FCA; Swim-Maid; *Ky Christian Col; Mus.*

FELLERS, Vonda Dee
Pampa HS; Pampa, TX; Chor; Pres, Rainbow; ARC; Rainbows Grand Cross of Color; *Phys Therapy.*

FELLMAN, Georgia Ann
Churchland HS; Portsmouth, VA (10%-290) AFS; Band; Chess C; Hmrm; Lat C; A-Ed, Sch P; SC; Secy, Y-Tns; Mgr, Bsbl; Lung Assn; Drill Tm; Hon Men, Tidewater Sci Congress; Jr Marshal; *Old Dominion Univ Medical Sch; Medicine-Pediatrics.*

FELLOWS, Douglas Miles
Aquinas HS; San Bernardino, CA; *Cal-Poly Pomona; Sci.*

FELLOWS, Jean Marie
Mabel-Canton HS; Mabel, MN; Band; Chldr; Chor; FHA; COM.

FELPS, Jenni Lynn
Ft Worth Christian HS; Ft Worth, TX; A Cap Choir; A-Ed, Ann; Chor; Sch P; Secy, SC; Cl Fav; Most Out; Pres, Pep C; Most Dependable; Outst, SC; *Harding Christian Col; Ed.*

FELTMAN, Laura Jeaniece
Hart Co HS; Hartwell, GA; VP, Bus C; JV, Chldr; Pres, Chor; VP, FBLA; FHA; Pres, 4H; Tnns; 4H A; *Acct.*

FELTON, Belinda Elaine
Northeastern HS; Detroit, MI (11-206) NHS; *Wayne St U; Pre-Med.*

FELTON, David Dean
Fredonia HS; Fredonia, NY (50%-210) Band; Chor; Ensm; Cr-Ctry; Soccer; Tr.

FELTON, John F
Pasco Sr HS; Pasco, WA (4-323) Band; Ger C; Hmrm; NHS; Order/Arrow; JV, Golf; DARGCA; Hon Prog; JA A; Masonic A; Order/Arrow A; Eagle Sct; *Yale U; Pre-Med.*

FELTS, Charles Douglas
Castleberry HS; Fort Worth, TX (20-216) Pres, Band; Key C; NHS; SC; VP, Sr Cl; Tr; Amer Leg A; Cl Fav; Magna Cum Laude; WW; Mus Stu; John Philip Sousa A; Band Bstr Schol; *Baylor U; Mus.*

FELTS, Tania Kay
Hazen HS; Hazen, AR (2-45) Band; Chor; FHA; Madrigal; Mjrte; Span C; SC; Drum Majorette; Ruth Barret Fox A Schol; Outst Band Member; Win, Co Talent Contest; *U of Central Ark; Eng.*

FELTUS, Bernetha Ducha
Eastridge HS; Kankakee, IL (2-350) Fr C; 4H; Semi-Fin, Jr Miss Pa; Beauty; COM; Opt Out Tn; Vocal Mus A; Cert of Appreciation; *Bradley U; Bus.*

FELTY, Donna Lynne
Mac Arthur HS; San Antonio, TX (50%-610) A Cap Choir; Chor; Tres, FHA; Span NHS; SC; Mus A; *Stephen I Austin U; Sociology.*

FELVER, Gretchen Loncy
Glenwood Springs HS; Glenwood Springs, CO; A Cap Choir; Pres, Chor; S-T, Drama; VP, Rainbow; COM; Citz A; Pres A; Yth Fel; Vocal Mus A; Rainbow Service Bars; GSct Budges; Presidential Phys Fitness A.

FENDER, Daniel Kevin
Robert E Lee HS; Midland, TX (9-20) Co-Cpt, Bkbl; VP, JA; Fin, Spelling A; Fin, Math A; Fin, Sci A; Fin, Bible Reading A; *Abilene Christian U; Acct.*

FENDER, Scott Cameron
Grover Cleveland HS; Reseda, CA (45-600) CSF; Sci A; *Math.*

FENDLEY, Patricia Lee
New Caney HS; Porter, TX (15-218) FHA; NHS; *U of Houston; Acct.*

FENDT, Lawrence Kenneth
Lake Clifton Sr HS; Baltimore, MD (10-315) Ed, Ann; Pres, NHS; Phys C; COM; Math A; Eng A; Hist A; Ed, Yrbk; Fr A; *Morgan St Col; Bio.*

FENICIN, Carolyn Mary
Aquinas HS; Augusta, GA (20%-120) Ann; NHS; ARC; Hon Prog; Top 5%, NMSQT; *Ga Inst of Technology; Engr.*

FENICIN, Nancy Ann
Aquinas HS; Augusta, GA (6-130) Ann; NHS; ARC; Hon Prog; Ntl HS A for Excellence; Ntl Observer Stu Achv A; Ed & Charit Found Trust to Ga Tech; *Ga Inst of Technology; Engr.*

FENITY, Joanne Montine
Hightstown HS; Hightstown, NJ (10-300) AFS; Chor; Fr C; Hmrm; Cr-Ctry; JV, Hockey; Tr; Citz A; Top Sportswoman; Tr; *Secondary Ed.*

FENN, Laura Anne
Eldorado HS; Albuquerque, NM; Fr C; Hmrm; JA A; WW; *U of NM; Acct.*

FENN, Richard Lee
Mountain View Acad; Mountain View, CA; Band; Chldr; Chor; Spch C; FCA; Soccer; Semi-Fin, Tr; *Pacific Union Col; Computer Sci.*

FENNELL, Susan Beth
Chaney HS; Youngstown, OH (25%-300) A Cap Choir; Rptr, Band; Chor; Ensm; Lat C; Orch; ARC; Arch; Sftbl; COM; Citz A; Cl Fav; Poet A; ARC A; Yth Fel; Church Flute Soloist; Bible Sch Asst; Pres, Church Yth Fel; Super, Reg Flute Competition; *Westminster Col; Eng.*

FENNELLY, Kathleen Marie
Saint Joseph's Notre Dame HS; Alameda, CA (2-80) Secy, SC; CSF; Citz A; Hon Prog; NEDT; *Col of Notre Dame-Belmont; Sociology.*

FENNEMA, Cherie Kaye
Holstein Comm Sch; Holstein, IA (25%-50) Chldr; Chor; Rptr, 4H; ARC; Sch P; Bkbl; Sftbl; Tr; COM; 4H A; Journ A; Prom Server; St Sci Fair A's.

FENNER, Thomas Collins
Northgate HS; Walnut Creek, CA; Dbte Tm; Var C; Bsbl; Cpt, Ftbl; CSF; MVP, Ftbl; *Stanford U; Bus.*

FENSKE, Kristen Ann
Homestead HS; Mequon, WI (33%-400) Ger C; Walther League; Harmony C A; Summer Mus Schol; Dist & St Solo En; Jr Yth for Mus Auditions; Ntl Guild Piano Tchrs Auditions; *Mus.*

FENTER, Debbie Ronine
A J Terrell HS; Blanchard, OK; F-Ed, Ann; Chem C; FHA; Model UN; NHS; Sch P; Span C; Mgr, Var C; Mgr, Bkbl; Sftbl; Tr; COM; Citz A; Hist A; Hon Prog; Yth Fel; Yth Leg; Secy of St A; WW; Pep C; *SW St U; Secondary Ed.*

FENTON, Frank Kevin
Freeport Sr HS; Freeport, IL (86-516) Band; Dbte Tm; Rptr, Sch P; Drum Major; Nom, Kiwanis A; *U of S Fla; World Hist.*

FENTON, Kevin Lynn
Duluth HS; Duluth, GA; Var C; JV, Bkbl; Ftbl; Golf; Pres A; *Ath.*

FENTRESS, Brenda Lynn
Joelton HS; Joelton, TN (10%-100) Chor; FHA; 4H; Bkbl; Yth Fel; PA; *Middle Tenn St U; Hist.*

FENTRESS, Lorri Jeneene
Wooddale HS; Memphis, TN; Fr C; Mjrte; Math C; Mu Alpha Theta; Spch C; Alg A; COM; JA A; *U of Sou Calif; Law.*

FENTRESS, Sherry Anne
Joelton HS; Joelton, TN (10%-125) BC; Chldr; FHA; Hmrm; SC; Pres, Soph Cl; Hon Prog; Sci A; Eng A; *AM Airlines Sch; Airline Stewardess.*

FENWICK, Mary Ann
Sacred Heart Acad; Louisville, KY; Dbte Tm; NFL; NHS; Spch C; SC; Tri-HiY; Golf; Swim; COM; Hon Prog; NEDT; 1st, JV St Debate.

FENZ, James Rupert
N Plainfield HS; N Plainfield, NJ; Band; Order/Arrow; Cr-Ctry; Tr; Hon Prog; Yth Fel.

FEQUET, Della Marjorie
Alexander Galt Regional HS; Lennoxville, CANADA (10-477) Hon Prog.

FERALDI, Philip Dean
Pioneer Central HS; Yorkshire, NY (50-250) Band; BS; Pres, CYO; Chor; Drama; Pres, FTA; Key C; Madrigal; Sch P; Span C; VP, SC; VP, Cath Yth; WW; Lead, Sch Mus; Tres, FTA; Co Gov Intern Prog; Lib C; Lead, Sr Cl Play; Hands of Christ; *St U of NY; Pol Sci.*

FERENCE, Stephen Wayne
Bremerhaven American HS; Bremerhaven, GERMANY (9-31) Ftbl; Tr; *Briar Cliff Col; Med.*

FERG, Joanne
Westmont Hilltop Sr Hr; Johnstown, PA; Chor; Ski C; Pres, SC; Sftbl; Mgr, Wrest; *Slippery Rock St Col; Phys Ed.*

FERGERSON, Cheryl Ann
Highlands HS; N Highlands, CA (11-470) Chor; Math C; F-Ed, Sch P; Span C; Tres, Jr Cl; Tnns; CSF; Sal; Outst Achv, Span; Outst Achv, Swing Choir; *UCLA; Business Mgt.*

FERGERSON, Elizabeth Jeanne
Highlands HS; N Highlands, CA; Chor; 4H; Span C; Sftbl; Tnns; *Bus.*

FERGUSON, Brook Alan
Ridgedale HS; Morral, OH (17-98) Band; Chess C; 4H; Span C; Var C; Mgr, Bkbl; Ftbl; Tr; COM; Chem A; 4H A; Sci A; *Ohio St Col; Bus.*

FERGUSON, Bruce Alan
W T Woodson HS; Fairfax, VA (205-561) Band; Orch; Secy-Tres, Sci Fiction Soc; Pres, Church Yth Fel; Band A; *VPI; Physics.*

FERGUSON, Charlotte Marie
Plainfield HS; Plainfield, IL; Band; Math C; Sch P; Span C; Spch C; Ftbl; Band; 8th Grade Phy Fitness A; 8th Grade Journ A; Rife's Women's Sftbl; *Bradley Col; Social Worker.*

FERGUSON, Consolvia Donzetta
Jean Baptist Point DuSable HS; Chicago, IL; SC; Tnns; Type A; SC A; *Ill St U; Phys Ed.*

FERGUSON, Danita Adel
Howell HS; Howell, NJ (25-360) Chldr; NHS; Bio A; Hon Prog; Russian Lang C; Afro-Lat C; Pres, Church Choir; Acad Achv A; Eng A; Russian Lang A; *Howard U; Communications.*

FERGUSON, David Harvey
N Shore HS; W Palm Beach, FL (23-266) Band; Dbte Tm; Hmrm; InterClub Coun; NHS; Pres, SC; COM; DARGCA; WW; Stu o-t Mo; Ntl Achv Commended Stu; *Engr.*

FERGUSON, Dawn Marie
Mount Vernon HS; Alexandria, VA (25%-600) Band; Bkbl; Soccer; Pres A; *Phys Ed.*

FERGUSON, Dean William
Druid Hills HS; Atlanta, GA (1-200) BC; Ger C; Secy, Key C; Model UN; NHS; Pres, SC; Cr-Ctry; Wrest; *Gov Honor Prog; Harvard Book A.*

FERGUSON, Deborah Lorraine
Rockledge HS; Rockledge, FL (50%-333) BC; Tres, Chor; Ensm; FBLA; Semi-Fin, GS; Rptr, Hmrm; Semi-Fin, Jr Miss Pa; Sci C; Amer Leg A; COM; Citz A; Kiwanis A; Most Out; Pres A; Sci A; Spch A; Yth Fel; Chor Qn; Hugh O'Brien Ldrship A; Merit A; Cert of Recognition; *Med.*

FERGUSON, Denise Sue
Ansley Pub Sch; Ansley, NE (2-48) Co-Ed, Ann; Band; Chldr; Chor; Drama; Madrigal; A-Ed, Sch P; SC; Var C; Secy, Soph Cl; Bkbl; Tr; All St Hon Choir; All St, Vlbl; Win, St Fr, Ch C; *Nebr Christian Col.*

FERGUSON, Donald Rhett
Osbourn Park Sr HS; Manassas, VA; Band; Bus C; Order/Arrow; Most Out; Yth Fel; Pres, MYF; *Oral Robberts U; Med Sch.*

FERGUSON, Donna Renee
Centerville HS; Centerville, TX (12-44) FHA; 4H; *Hardin-Simmons U; Elem Ed.*

FERGUSON, Ellen Marie
Eastside HS; Paterson, NJ (10-800) Tr.

FERGUSON, Janese Marie
Immaculata HS; Leavenworth, KS; Band; CYO; Chor; Dbte Tm; Drama; Tres, Ger C; GS; Secy, 4H; Pres, Hmrm; Amer Leg A; COM; 4H A; Hon Prog; Math A; NEDT; *Saint Marys Col; Linguistic.*

FERGUSON, Janet Suzanne
Parkway N Sr HS; Creve Coeur, MO (129-532) Fr C; Swim; Metropolitan Ballet of St Louis; Position Equiv to Elder in Church; *Butler U; Dance.*

FERGUSON, Jeanell
Rufus King HS; Milwaukee, WI; Secy, Hmrm; Sci A; Home Ec Cert; *UWM; Nurs.*

FERGUSON, Jo Ann Sandra
Crenshaw HS; Los Angeles, CA; Tr; *Pepperdine U.*

FERGUSON, Joel Alan
Fayettville HS; Fayetteville, AR (25%-400) Band; Ensm; Order/Arrow; *Pre-Med.*

FERGUSON, Larry Joe
Harrah HS; Harrah, OK (16-122) Chem C; Dbte Tm; Drama; Pres, Fr C; FTA; Spch C; Thes; Tnns; Hon Prog; Pres A; Fr A; *Okla Baptist U; Mus.*

FERGUSON, Larry Rustin
Cleveland HS; Cleveland, OK (2-150) NHS; Sch P; SC; Bkbl; Ftbl; Alg A; Ed, Yth Church Paper; St Hon Soc; Pres, Fresh Cl; Outst, SC; Eng A; *U of Okla; Journ.*

FERGUSON, Laura Rene
Beavercreek HS; Xenia, OH (27-630) A Cap Choir; NHS; Hockey; Hon Prog; St Phys Fitness Tm; *Wright St U; Med.*

FERGUSON, Laverne
St Margaret's HS; Tappahannock, VA; Bkbl; Hockey; Tnns; *Clerical.*

FERGUSON, Leah Ann
Bethany Christian HS; Troy, MI; MVP, Bsbl; Beauty; Citz A; Cl Fav; Qn Candidate; Friendliest; *Free Will Baptist Bible Col; Christian Psych.*

FERGUSON, Leland James
Inglewood HS; Inglewood, CA; HiY; Hmrm; SC; Var C; Bkbl; Mgr, Ftbl; CSF; HCt; JA A; Vlbl; Work Stu Program; Sr Fashion Show; *U of Calif; Pharmacist.*

FERGUSON, Linda Louise
Lubbock Christian HS; Lubbock, TX (3-40) Band; 4H; Orch; Bkbl; DARGCA; Hon 'A' A; NJHS; *Tex Tech Col; Med.*

FERGUSON, Lisa Annette
Fayetteville HS; Fayetteville, AR (25%-400) A Cap Choir; Chor; Mu Alpha Theta.

FERGUSON, Lisa Kaye
Ironton HS; Ironton, OH; Ann; Band; Drama; VP, Fr C; Hmrm; Rainbow; Eddy A; Freshie A; *Oral Roberts U; Nurs.*

FERGUSON, Lisa Lynn
Nathan Hale HS; Tulsa, OK; Pres, 4H; Pres, Church Yth Fel; *William Woods Col; Equestrian Sci.*

FERGUSON, Lisa Marie
Tyee Sr HS; Seattle, WA (20-275) NHS; Span C; SC; Tr; Vlbl; Ftbl Statistician; 1st Cl GSct; Girl's C Cabinet; *E Wash St Col; Dental Hygiene.*

FERGUSON, Lon Harrison
Blairsville Sr HS; Blairsville, PA (25-165) NHS; JV, Wrest; COM; Conservation A; Pres, Yth Fel; Wrest Cert; *Ind U of Penn; Ed.*

FERGUSON, Lori Gay
Cleveland HS; Cleveland, OK (5-90) Ann; Hmrm; NHS; Sch P; SC; VP, Soph Cl; Bkbl; Hist A; Type A; Tres, Pep C; Tres, Yth Fel; Writing, Secy of St A's; Civics, Home Ec, A's; *U of Okla; Journ.*

FERGUSON, Mark Dwain
Gilmer HS; Gilmer, TX (25-120) Co-Ed, Ann; Cpt, BS; Tres, FFA; NHS; Bsbl; Bkbl; Ftbl; Sftbl; Tnns; Tr; Rptr, FFA; Star Elec A; *Elec.*

FERGUSON, Marla Denise
Lubbock Christian HS; Lubbock, TX (11-54) Secy, A Cap Choir; Band; Secy, Chor; GS; NHS; Mgr, Bkbl; Tr; Amer Herritage C; Band Swtht Ct; *Abilene Christian U; Interior Design.*

FERGUSON, Mary Elizabeth
Bentworth Sr HS; Bentleyville, PA (10-160) F-Ed, Ann; Band; VP, Drama; Pres, 4H; NHS; Ski C; *Clarion St Col; Elem Ed.*

FERGUSON, Mary Kathryn
St John Vianney Regional HS; Holmdel, NJ (20-208) Bus Mgr, Ann; Chor; Drama; Fr C; Secy, NHS; ARC; Var C; Swim; COM; Hon Prog; K of C A; Ntl Achv Schol; Cpt, Drill Tm; Gold & White As; Fr As; DAHSS; Varsity Ltrs; *Trinity Col; Lang.*

FERGUSON, Morris Denman
Canton Acad; Canton, MS; 4H; Order/Arrow; Bkbl; Ftbl; HKg; HCt; Order/Arrow A; Rotary A; *Holmes Jr Col; Forestry.*

FERGUSON, Pamela Rosetta
Farwell Area HS; Farwell, MI (37-133) Band; Ensm; 4H; Cpt, Bkbl; Citz A; 4H A; Band Festival; *Mid Mich Comm Col; Social Service.*

FERGUSON, Phyllis Dayle
Dan River HS; Ringgold, VA (20-300) Chess C; VP, FBLA; FHA; Lit Mag; Pres, Monogram; NFL; Sch P; SC; Tres, Sr Cl; Pres, Jr Cl; Pres, Soph Cl; Bkbl; Gr Marshal; Math A; Acct, Spelling, A's; Vlbl; *Danville Comm Col; Acct.*

FERGUSON, Randy Curtis
Tyee Sr HS; Seattle, WA (20%-253) Ftbl; Tr; *U of Wash; Dentistry.*

**FERGUSON,
Thomas Thornton Jr**
S Florence HS; Florence, SC (10%-384) Chor; NHS; Order/Arrow; Span C; Var C; JV, Ftbl; Tr; Hon Prog; Order/Arrow A; ARC A; Yth Fel; FCA; YMCA Vlbl & Karate; City Bsbl Tm; Eagle Sct A; *Francis Marion Col; Bus Adm.*

FERGUSON, William Henry
Grapevine HS; Grapevine, TX; Order/Arrow; Cr-Ctry; Ftbl; Soccer; Tnns; Tr; Order/Arrow A; Eagle Sct.

FERKUL, Erika Maria
Gilbert HS; Gilbert, MN (3-84) Band; Chldr; Chor; Bkbl; Tnns; Interlochen Ntl Mus; *St Scholastica Col; Med.*

FERLAN, Sharon Ann
Molalla Union HS; Molalla, OR (5-174) Pres, CYO; Chor; NHS; Span C; Bkbl; St Scholar; Type A; *Oreg St U; Agr.*

FERNANDEZ, Ana Luisa
Colegio San Antonio Abad; Humacao, PR (2-94) Drama; 4H; Sch P; *Hollins Col; Russian Stu.*

FERNANDEZ, Daneris Gisel
Colegio Espiritu Santo; Rio Piedras, PR (17-96) A-Ed, Ann; Secy, Chess C; Chor; Secy, Drama; Secy, Hmrm; Secy, Math C; Rptr, Sch P; SC; COM; Hon Prog; Tres, Ecology C; *Lafayette Col; Sci.*

FERNANDEZ, Francisco Ruben
Deerborne HS; Coral Gables, FL; BC; Inter-Club Coun; NHS; SC; VP, Soph Cl; Bsbl; Cpt, Bkbl; Golden Book A; *Acct.*

FERNANDEZ, Guadalupe
Adlai E Stevenson HS; Bronx, NY (9-822) Pres, Hmrm; NHS; Sch Achieve Tm; SC; Alg A; COM; Citz A; Gov Honor Prog; Val; Scholastic Achv A; Service A; CCNY Schol; *Manhattan Col; Management.*

FERNANDEZ, Hector Nicolas
Deerborne HS; Coral Gables, FL; BC; Key C; NHS; SC; Tres, Soph Cl; Bsbl; JV, Bkbl; *Med.*

FERNANDEZ, Jacqueline
George Robinson Sch; Santurce, PR (3-48) Band; Chess C; Chor; Drama; Lit Mag; Math C; Pres, NHS; Secy, Span C; NEDT; *Math.*

FERNANDEZ, John
Jose de Diego HS; Mayaguez, PR; Magna Cum Laude.

FERNANDEZ, Maria Eugenia
Our Lady of Pilar HS; Hato Rey, PR (10%-148) Chem C; NHS; Bio A; COM; Hist A; *Boston Col; Special Ed.*

FERNANDEZ, Maria Mercedes
Colegio San Antonio Abad; Humacao, PR (9-72) Chem C; Chor; Drama; 4H; Pres, Hmrm; NHS; ARC; Ed, Sch P; SC; COM; Chem A; Fin, Summer Fair; Phylosophy C; Photography Summer Camp; Qn Cand; Co-Ch, Photo C; Photography As; Pep C; Span Poetry As; *Pace U; Nurs.*

FERNANDEZ, Nancy
Jose de Diego HS; Mayaguez, PR; Dbte Tm; ARC; COM; Magna Cum Laude; Math A; *U of Puerto Rico at Mayaguez; Chem Engr.*

FERNANDEZ, Noel Galvez
John F Kennedy HS; Tumon, GUAM (1-511) Chem C; Chess C; NHS; Tnns; Alg A; Amer Leg A; Citz A; DARGCA; Math A; ROTC A; Sci A; *U of Hawaii; Engr.*

FERNANDEZ, Sophia
Stamford HS; Stamford, TX; Bus C; CYO; Span C; *Abilene Christian U; Ed.*

**FERNANDEZ-DOMENECH,
Luis A**
Colegio San Antonio; Isabela, PR (2-48) Bsbl; Bkbl; Cr-Ctry; Sftbl; Swim; Tr; Alg A; Bio A; COM; Chem A; Cl Fav; Hist A; Hon Prog; Most Out; Phy A; Sci A; Val; Academic General Excellency A; *RUM; Civil Engr.*

FERNANDO, Russell Paul
Nyack HS; Nyack, NY; Chor; Fr C; Tnns; Hon Prog; *Aviation.*

FERNS, Sarah Ruth
Eastern HS; Lansing, MI; Band; Pres, Ski C; Swim; Art A; *Keddall Sch of Design; Advertising.*

FERO, Cynthia Louise
Whitewater HS; Whitewater, WI (11-192) Ann; Chor; Ensm; 4H; Ski C; Var C; Bkbl; Sftbl; Mgr, Tnns; Tr; 4H A; Sports As; Mus As; GAA As; *Whitewater U; Phys Ed.*

FERQUERON, Shawn Louise
Dixie Hollins HS; St Petersburg, FL; Chor; Ensm; Amer Auxiliary A.

FERRAGINA, Gina
Saks HS; Anniston, AL; JV, Chldr; Chor; Ensm; NHS; Parl, Tri-HiY; Secy, Sr Cl; Secy, Jr Cl; Cl Fav; Hon Prog; Pres A; WW; Friendliest; All St Choir; *Jacksonville St U; Sociology.*

FERRALL, Glenn Edwin
Dixie Hollins HS; St Petersburg, FL (1-730) Inter-Club Coun; Pres, Lat C; Mu Alpha Theta; NHS; Order/Arrow; Span C; JV, Ftbl; Amer Leg A; Chem A; Math A; Rensselaer A; Eagle Sct; *U of Fla; Vet Med.*

FERRANTE, Maryann
Weymouth N HS; East Weymouth, MA; Elk A; *Northeaster Col; Medical Records.*

FERRARI, Albert Anthony
Adlai E Stevenson HS; Livonia, MI; Chess C; Ski C; ST Edith Yth Group; Bowl As; Service As; Staff, Summer Day Program; *Lawrence Inst of Tech; Archt.*

FERRARI, Giovanni Bruno
Cristobal HS; Coco Solo, CANAL ZONE (7-130) Bus Mgr, Ann; Band; Chess C; Parl, Demolay; Secy, Fr C; FTA; ARC; Rptr, Sch P; SC; Soccer; *Sci.*

FERRARI, Patricia Kay
Herrin HS; Herrin, IL; F-Ed, Ann; Band; CYO; Chldr; Dbte Tm; Pres, SC; S-T, Sr Cl; Amer Leg A; Citz A; DARGCA; HQn; HCt; Spch A; St Scholar; Gym; Herrin Hon Soc; *Sou Ill U; Law.*

FERRARO, Rosemary
Salisbury-Elk Lick HS; Salisbury, PA (7-45) Band; Secy, Yth Fel; Bkbl Statistician; *Garrett Comm Col; Wildlife Mgt.*

FERREE, Judith Marie
Butler Intermediate HS; Butler, PA; Band; Chor; Ensm; *Phys Therapist.*

FERREE, Pamela Sue
Dallastown Area HS; Dallastown, PA (158-340) AFS; Chor; FNA; Lat C; Lat NHS; *Geneva Col; Elem Ed.*

FERRELL, Albert A
Swan Valley HS; Saginaw, MI; Mgr, Bkbl; Swim; MVP, Bkbl; JA; Var Ltr; *Carpenter Work.*

FERRELL, Belinda Yvonne
Eastern Sr HS; Washington, DC (6-604) NHS; Secy, Span C; COM; Delta Sigma Theta A; Hist A; Hon Prog; JA A; NMS; Yth Fel; Xavier U Acad Schol; Prince Hall Masonic Schol; Woodward Foundation Fellowship; Grace Coleman A; *Xavier U; Pre-Med.*

FERRELL, Billy David
Central HS; Thomasville, GA (30%-300) Ann; FFA; HiY; VP, Key C; Bkbl; Beau o-t Yr; *ABAC; Criminal Justice.*

FERRELL, Cathy
Bullitt Central HS; Shepherdsville, KY (2%-500) A Cap Choir; Chor; Sup Rating, Solo & Ensm; *Freed-Hardeman Col.*

FERRELL, Clifford Ray
Wilmot HS; Wilmot, AR (2-32) HR.

FERRELL, Courtney Delise
Melbourne HS; Melbourne, FL; Chldr; Key C; SC; Dance C; Nom, Hugh O'Brien Leadership A; *Dental Hygiene.*

FERRELL, Diane Louise
Big Spring HS; Big Spring, TX (114-500) Band.

FERRELL, Jean Ann
Englewood Christian Sch; Independence, MO; Rptr, Sch P; Spch C; Pres, SC; Thes; Rotary A; Spch A; Phys Ed & Drama A's; *Longview Jr Col; Bus.*

FERRELL, Jimmie Ruth
Walnut HS; Walnut, MS (10-57) Arch; Chem C; FFA; FHA; 4H; Var C; Co-Cpt, Bkbl; Co-Cpt, Sftbl; Tr; 4H A; JA A; Most Improved, Bkbl; Horsemanship A; *NE Jr Col; Med.*

FERRELL, Lisa Kate
Hobart HS; Hobart, OK; Band; FTA; VP, 4H; NHS; SC; Var C; Bkbl; Sftbl; Tr; 4H A; *Okla St U.*

FERRELL, Mikki Lynne
Daniel Boone HS; Jonesboro, TN (30-235) Band; BC; Secy, Chor; Secy, Fr C; Sci C; Select Chor; Boonettes Drill Tm; Maximum Ordinates Drill Sq; *East Tenn St U; Journ.*

FERRELL, Nancy Elizabeth
Hermitage HS; Hermitage, AR (3-65) Ann; BC; Rptr, FHA; Math C; Sch P; Hist A; Lib A; HR; Graduation Attendant; *U of Ark at Monticello; Pre-Med.*

FERRELL, Robert Stephen
New Braunfels Sr HS; New Braunfels, TX (42-298) Band; Chor; Tres, Ger C; Madrigal; Order/Arrow; Sci C; SC; Amer Leg A; NEDT; Tex All St Choir; *U of Tex; Govt.*

FERRELL, Victoria Michelle
Jones Co HS; Gray, KS (10-200) F-Ed, Ann; Pres, Fr C; Fin, Jr Miss Pagent; NHS; F-Ed, Sch P; SC; Pres, Sr Cl; Bsbl; Bkbl; Beauty; COM; NEDT; PA; Fr C A; FHA A; Tres, Fr C; *Kans Wesleyan U; Merchandising.*

FERRER, Joaquin Jimenez
Miguel Melendez Munoz; Bayamon, PR (1-250) Chem C; Hmrm; Math C; Sch Achieve Tm; Sci C; Pres, SC; Alg A; Bio A; COM; Chem A; Hist A; Math A; Sci A; Star Student; *U of Puerto Rico; Chem.*

FERRER, Luis Rene
Dr Pila HS; Ponce, PR; Chem C; Chess C; Chor; Ensm; Hmrm; ARC; Pres, Sch P; COM; Hon Prog; Sci A; *U of PR; Lang.*

FERRERAS, Zwinda S
Consuelo Escalona Private Sch; Carolina, PR (3-38) Chor; Drama; Hmrm; Model UN; SC; Beauty; COM; Hist A; ROTC A.

FERRERO, Martha Gideon
Northbrook Sr HS; Houston, TX (10%-550) Dbte Tm; Drama; Ensm; VP, NFL; NHS; Span C; Spch C; Thes; Hon Prog; Spch A; Parl, Med Careers C; *Rice U; Environmental Sci.*

FERRI, Dana Suzanne
N Plainfield HS; N Plainfield, NJ (22-270) Secy, Chor; NHS; SC; Pres, Jr Cl; Pres, Soph Cl; Cpt, Hockey.

FERRILL, Mitchell Glenn
Norris HS; Firth, NE (6-115) Fr C; Bkbl; Ftbl; Fr Achv A; *U of Nebr.*

FERRIN, Julie Ardelle
Marshalltown HS; Marshalltown, IA (60-448) Chor; Secy, City Conf; Ensm; FTA; Span C; Spch C; COM; Spch A; Yth Fel; *Marshalltown Comm Col; Elem Ed.*

FERRIN, William Myron
Bend Sr HS; Bend, OR (2-500) Band; Ensm; NHS; Tres, Jr Cl; JV, Bkbl; Ftbl; All District Hon Band; *Math.*

FERRIS, Darlene Lynne
Hannibal Central Sch; Hannibal, NY; Band; Secy, Chor; Ensm; NHS; *Nurs.*

FERRO, Maria Elena
Miller R3 HS; Tuscumbia, MO (5-27) Ann; Cpt, Chldr; Chor; 4H; NHS; ARC; Sch P; Pres, SC; Cpt, Bkbl; Sftbl; Tr; HQn; Ath A's; WW; Col Bus School; *SW Baptist Col; Secy.*

FERRY, Anthony
Greater Latrobe HS; Latrobe, PA (262-591) Pres, Jr Cl.

FERTIG, John Edward Jr
Southern HS; Louisville, KY (2-423) VP, BC; Hmrm; Key C; Math C; Pres, NHS; SC; Bsbl; Mgr, Ftbl; Hon Prog; Kiwanis A; *Engr.*

FESENMYER, Catherine Ann
Dover Sr HS; Dover, OH (45-273) A Cap Choir; CYO; Chor; Ensm; 4H; NHS; Span C; Thes; Swim; 4H A; 1, Vocal Solo Dist Comp; *Mus.*

FESKO, Steven Franklin
Medina Sr HS; Medina, OH (30-400) BS; Key C; NHS; Sci C; Ski C; Co-Cpt, Cr-Ctry; Co-Cpt, Tr; Hon Prog; *U of Cincinnati; Engr.*

FESTER, James Joseph
Bridgman HS; Bridgman, MI (3-80) BS; NHS; Sci C; JV, Bsbl; Amer Leg A; *U of Mich; Engr.*

FETHERLAND, Susan Carol
Fairfield Sr HS; Fairfield, OH (150-700) Chor; Mod Mus Mas; Rainbow; *Cincinnati Bible Col; Religion.*

FETT, Sharla Marie
Rapid City Stevens HS; Rapid City, SD (1-450) Band; Chor; Ensm; Fr C; FHA; 4H; Hmrm; SC; Tr; Hist A; Star Student; Pres Phys Fitness A; *Sioux Falls Col; Bio.*

FETTER, Mark Frederick
Warrior Run HS; Turbotville, PA; Band; Chor; Mgr, Bkbl.

FETTERMAN, Miriam Beth
Treynor Comm HS; Treynor, IA (3-48) F-Ed, Ann; Pres, Band; Pres, Chor; Pres, Drama; Madrigal; Cpt, Mjrte; NHS; ARC; Secy, Sr Cl; Secy, Jr Cl; Secy, Soph Cl; JV, Golf; COM; Citz A; HCt; Hon Prog; Star Student; Outst Actress A; Top 20 Instrumental A; Iowa St Bar Assn Ciz A; Exchng Stu Sch with Yth for Undrs; *Augustana Col; Psych.*

FETZER, Laurie Ellen
Salisbury HS; Allentown, PA (20-188) Cpt, Band; Chor; Mjrte; Model UN; NHS; SC; Sftbl; Hon Prog; Lion A; Yth Fel; *U of Pittsburgh; Nurs.*

FEUCHT, Paul William
Bellaire Sr HS; Bellaire, TX (146-700) Span C; Schol Art A's; Most Attractive Soph; *Med.*

FFOLKES, Annette May
Brooklyn Tech HS; Brooklyn, NY (20%-1000) Chldr; Chor; Ntl Yth Conf; Span C; COM; Math A; ARC A; Sci A; All City Chor Cert; *George Washington U; Bio.*

FIA, Bob Letterman
Marist Brother's HS; Pago Pago, AMERICAN SAMOA (6-50) A-Ed, Ann; Dbte Tm; Hmrm; Rptr, Sch P; Ftbl; Alg A; COM; Hist A; Hon Prog; Math A; Sci A; Spch A; *Jamestown Col; Elec.*

FICEK, Jeffrey W
Parkville Sr HS; Baltimore, MD; JV, Wrest.

FICK, Barbara Jean
Winona Sr HS; Winona, MN (13-525) Chor; Bkbl; Cr-Ctry.

FICK, Robert James
Winona Sr HS; Winona, MN (2-497) NHS; Bkbl; Tr; Pres A; *Winona St U; Chem Engr.*

FICKE, Jolene Marie
Milford Jr Sr HS; Milford, NE (16-60) Co-Ed, Ann; Band; Ensm; FBLA; Pres, 4H; Orch; ARC; SC; S-T, Soph Cl; Sftbl; B Crocker A; 4H A; HQn; HCt; Yth Fel; Tres, Rptr, 4h C; JV Vlbl; Pres, VP, Pep C; Co Feeders & Breeders Qn; *Wesleyan U; Special Ed.*

FICKE, Lori Annette
Milford Jr Sr HS; Milford, NE (17-63) Chor; Secy, 4H; Bkbl; Co-Cpt, Sftbl; Tr; Aksarben Exhibitor Planning Comm; 4-H Coun; 4-H Camp Counselor; Bible Sch Teacher; Sunday Sch Teacher; *Phys Ed.*

FICKER, Raymond Gerard
Saint Viator HS; Arlington Heights, IL (8-243) Order/Arrow; Citz A; Hon Prog; Order/Arrow A; Sacristan; NHS School; Regional Sci A; *Math.*

FIDALGO, Rosanna
Consuelo Escalona Private Sch; Carolina, PR (3-38) CYO; ARC; COM; *Universidad de Puerto Rico; Med.*

FIDDES, Russell Gordon
Temple Christian Sch; Redford, MI (1-57) VP, Chess C; Amer Leg A; Citz A; Hon Prog; Val; Sch Board A; *U of Mich; Engr.*

FIDLER, Christina Maire
Rancho HS; N Las Vegas, NV; Secy, FBLA; Bio A; Citz A; Type A; *UNLV; Bus.*

FIDLER, Diana Jeanne
Rancho HS; N Las Vegas, NV; Pres, FBLA; Citz A; Swtht; *Comm Col; Bus.*

FIDLER, Jane Louise
Pine Grove Area HS; Pine Grove, PA (3-146) Chor; Drama; NHS; VP, SC; Tri-HiY; Var C; Co-Cpt, Bkbl; Amer Leg A; Citz A; DARGCA; MLS; NEDT; Pres A; Rotary A; Pres Clroom for Young Amer; Cl Offices; *Shippensburg St Col; Math.*

FIDLER, Kenneth James
Maple Shade HS; Maple Shade, NJ (10%-235) Key C; NHS; Bkbl; Golf; *Pre-Med.*

FIEBIG, William Alfred
Homestead HS; Mequon, WI (11-431) NHS; Order/Arrow; Ftbl; Tr; Order/Arrow A; Pres A; Ltrman C; Co- cpt, Gym; Eagle Sct; NHS A; *U of Ill; Chem Engr.*

FIEDERER, Jens Bernhard
All Saints Cathedral Sch; St Thomas, VI (1-18) Chess C; Dbte Tm; Math C; Wrest; Bausch & Lomb A; Hist A; Hon Prog; Math A; NMS; Sci A; Lang A; Eng A; *Yale U; Physics.*

FINCH, Kevin Eugene
Oroville Union HS; Oroville, CA (73-283) Chess C; NHS; Industrial Arts.

FINCH, Mary Catherine
Eupora HS; Eupora, MS (10%-84) Chor; FBLA; FHA; HCt; Holmes Jr Col; Secretarial.

FINCH, Sandra Lynn
Maryville HS; Maryville, TN (10%-183) AFS; Band; Semi-Fin, GS; Hmrm; Lat C; Mu Alpha Theta; NHS; Tnns; Aux Lat; NEDT; Cpt, Flag Corps; Girl's Co; Jr & Sr Cl Plays; WW; E Tenn St U; Pre-Phar.

FINCH, Steven Richard
Dow HS; Midland, MI (10%-400) Band; Orch; Order/Arrow; Win, Mi Mus Tchr's As Comp Cont; U of Mich; Mus Composition.

FINCH, Teresa Sue
Mona Shores HS; Muskegon, MI; Drama; Thes; Citz A; Span A.

FINCH, Timmy Wayne
Madison HS; Madison, TN; Bsbl; Bkbl; Ftbl; Sftbl; Swim; Tnns.

FINCH, Tommy William
Madison HS; Madison, TN; Bsbl; Bkbl; Sftbl.

FINCH, Wallyne Laree
L D Bell HS; Hurst, TX; Chor; Drama; Secy, SC; Most Out; VP, Pep C; Soph Cl Coun; Abilene Christian U; Interior Decorating And Design.

FINELLO, Lu Ann Elizabeth
Acad of Saint Aloysius; Jersey City, NJ (2-127) Ann; CYO; Drama; Hmrm; Math C; NHS; Sch P; Ch, SC; Ch, Jr Cl; Hon Prog; K of C A; NEDT; SG; Service A; Pol Sci.

FINGERLIN, Becky Jean
Lutheran HS; Denver, CO (1-128) A Cap Choir; Dbte Tm; Drama; Ger C; Hon Prog; NEDT; Ntl Piano Guild; Metro League Soloist; St John's Winfield Col; Med.

FINK, Allison Elaine
Anderson HS; Austin, TX (13-545) A Cap Choir; Pres, Chor; Madrigal; NHS; SC; Beauty; Cl Fav; Trustee Schol; Baylor U; Nurs.

FINK, Jill Marie
Nw Cabarrus HS; Concord, NC (5-300) Ann; Band; BC; JV, Chldr; FTA; VP, Hmrm; SC; Beauty; 4H A; HCt; Most Out; Opt A; Opt Out Tn; Spch A; Chi-Alpha C; Dist Del, Church Conf; St Senate Page; Del, Elizabethan Shakespearean Fest; NW Cabarrus Hs; Eng.

FINK, Karl John
Lutheran HS; Los Angeles, CA (33%-70) NHS; Bsbl; Bkbl; Alg A; CSF; COM; Citz A; Hon Prog; PTA A; Val; Yth Fel; Yth Leg; Math.

FINK, Melisa Anne
Chamberlain HS; Tampa, FL (65-720) Hmrm; NHS; Span C; SC; Co-Cpt, Swim; Secy, 'Z' C; Swim A's; U of Fla; Journ.

FINK, Terese Geradine
Loyola HS; Mankato, MN (1-72) Chor; Hmrm; Sch P; Fin, Spch C; SC; VP, Soph Cl; Bkbl; Tnns; Cl Fav; HCt; Spch A; Val; Super, Reg & St Mus Competition; St Benedict Col.

FINK, Timothy Christian
Jacksonville Episcopal HS; Jacksonville, FL (21-117) JV, Bsbl; JV, Bkbl; JV, Ftbl; Math A; Crew; Chaplains List; Stu Conductor, Band; Headmaster List; Acad HR; Med.

FINK, W Philip
Park Hill HS; Kansas City, MO (270-450) Ch, Band; Co-Cpt, Chldr; Ch, Ensm; Ch, Orch; SC; Var C; Ftbl; Tr; Regent Schol; Yth Fel; Asst Band Director; I Rating, Dist, St Mus Comp; Mo Western St Col; Instrumental Mus.

FINKBEINER, Julie Ann
Poway HS; Poway, CA; Band; Chldr; Chor; Ger C; Hmrm; Secy, SC; Tr; COM; Type A; Bethany Nazarene Col; Elem Teacher.

FINKBEINER, Sherri Lynne
Capital HS; Boise, ID (15%-500) Band; Chor; Ensm; NHS; Cr-Ctry; Tr; Gym; Northwest Nazarene Col; Nurs.

FINKEL, Martha Ann
MacDuffie Sch; Springfield, MA (4-47) Cum Laude Soc; Ed, Sch P; Sch HR; Salem St Col; Social Work.

FINLEY, Gary Leon
Centralis HS; Centralia, IL; Kaskaskia Jr Col; Elec.

FINLEY, Joan Ann
Notre Dame of Acadia Parish; Crowley, LA (3-99) BC; GS; Lit Ral; SC; Alg A; Amer Leg A; Chem A; Hist A; MLS; NEDT; Sci A; Pres, Rohna C; WW; Co-Cpt, Marching Corps; Most Reliable; Candystriper o-t Yr.

FINLEY, Linda Louise
Clay Co HS; Manchester, KY (2-216) Pres, FHA; Hmrm; Rptr, Sch P; Bio A; Hist A; Eng A; Home Ec A.

FINLEY, Lynn Anne
Ritenour Sr HS; St Louis, MO (16-826) Co-Cpt, Chldr; NHS; Sch P; SC; Curator A; Academic Excellance; William Jewell Col.

FINN, Paul Martin
Don Bosco Tech HS; Boston, MA (10-220) Mgr, Bkbl; Hockey; Sftbl; NHS Cert; Bunker Hill Comm Col; Radiologic Sci.

FINNEGAN, Timothy Robert
Kaukauna HS; Kaukauna, WI (70%-330) CYO; Ski C; Golf; JV, Tnns; Archt.

FINNELL, Michael L
Bremerhaven American HS; Bremerhaven, GERMANY (1-31) Ger C; Lit Mag; NHS; Pres, SC; VP, Jr Cl; Cr-Ctry; Cpt, Tnns; Citz A; MVP, Tnns; Outdoor C; Hastings Col; Environmental Ed.

FINNELL, Teresa Ruth
Sweet Home HS; Sweet Home, OR; Hmrm; Pres, Rainbow; SC; Chamber of Comm A; Masonic A; Grand Cross of Color; Past Worthy Advisor; Wallemate Col; Law.

FINNEMAN, Tonnee Ann
Cascade HS; Everett, WA (25%-550) Band; Pres, Yth of Unity; Most Improved Stu; PA; Everett Comm Col; Ed.

FINNER, Patricia Maire
Mumford HS; Detroit, MI; ARC; Y-Tns; MVP, Bsbl; MVP, Swim; MVP, Tnns; Math A; ARC A; Service A; Hon A; Ath League; Child Psych.

FINNEY, Claude Dennis
Locke HS; Los Angeles, CA; A Cap Choir; CYO; Chor; MVP, Bkbl; Ftbl; Citz A; JA A; MVP A; Bell & Howell Tech Col; Elec.

FINNEY, Darla Lyn
Brandon Sr HS; Brandon, FL (516-813) Secy, DCT; Outst DCT Stu; Recordkeeping Outst Achv; Bus.

FINNEY, Paula Marie
Lakeview HS; Battle Creek, MI; Drama; Lat C; Kellogg Comm Col; Med Asst.

FINOCCHIO, Joseph A
Struthers HS; Struthers, OH (11-275) Pres, Band; Tres, CYO; Drama; Ensm; S-T, FTA; Ch, Lat C; NHS; Orch; ARC; Sci C; COM; Citz A; Cl Fav; Coun of Teach A; Hist A; Hon Prog; Joust A; Magna Cum Laude; Most Out; ARC A; Ohio N U; Phar.

FIOL, Luis Fernando
Consuelo Escalona Private Sch; Carolina, PR (2-38) Bsbl; Bkbl; Ftbl; Swim; Tnns; Tr; COM; Loyalty A; Engr.

FIORE, Charles Anthony
St Joseph's HS; Camden, NJ (13-77) Fr C; NHS; VP, Sr Cl; WW; Rutgers U; Pre-Law.

FIPPINGER, Dale Allen
Robert E Lee HS; Baytown, TX (20%-550) Lat C; Cr-Ctry; Tr; Sci.

FIQUETT, Daffony Jean
Brilliant HS; Brilliant, AL (2-44) Secy, Band; Chldr; Chor; FHA; Tres, SC; Tnns; Alg A; COM; Citz A; Hon Prog; Spch A.

FIQUETT, Dennis Alexander
Woodland Christian HS; Phenix City, AL; Ann; 4H; Tr.

FIRESTONE, Pamela
Southmoreland Sr HS; Alverton, PA (40-272) Ann; Chor; VP, FTA; Math C; NHS; Pres, Rainbow; Sch P; Span C; Tri-HiY; World Affairs C; I Dare You; Calif St Col; Spch Pathology.

FIROS, Patricia Louise
Bellingham HS; Bellingham, WA (75-308) CYO; Fr C; Math C; Bsbl; Bkbl; Sftbl; Tnns; Sci A; Attendence A; Math & Sci.

FIRPI, William Jose
Dra Maria Cadilla HS; Arecibo, PR (75-480) CYO; VP, Hmrm; Magna Cum Laude; University of Puerto Rico Mayaguez; Engr.

FIRRINCIELI, Linda Anne
Eastside HS; Paterson, NJ (4-519) A Cap Choir; Secy, Drama; Secy, NHS; Rutgers Col; Nurs.

FIRTH, Holly Marion
Cedar Shoals HS; Athens, GA (25%-400) Bus C; FBLA; Hon Prog; Ga Sou Col; Early Childhood.

FISACKERLY, Claude Kelso III
Indianola Acad; Indianola, MS (33%-100) BS; Chor; 4H; HiY; Hmrm; Madrigal; Var C; VP, Soph Cl; Ftbl; Tnns; Tr; Cl Fav; 4H A; NEDT; Sci A; Yth Fel; Hon Camper; Amer Legion Boys St A; Miss St U; Agr.

FISCHER, Ann Marie
Cunningham HS; Cunningham, KS (2-21) Ed, Ann; Band; CYO; Chor; VP, SC; Tres, Sr Cl; VP, Jr Cl; Cpt, Bkbl; Tr; HQn; St Scholar; U of Kan; Acct.

FISCHER, Anne Crowe
Durham Acad; Durham, NC (2-70) Chor; S-T, Lat C; Math C; Rptr, Sch P; Sci C; SC; Cr-Ctry; Tr; Sci.

FISCHER, Cynthia Lorraine
Hannibal Sr HS; Hannibal, MO (10-369) Pres, 4H; NHS; VP, Art C; Home Ec A; Helm Art A; Secy, St Jr Quarter Horse Assn; Amer Jr Quarter Horse; Pres Phys Fitness A.

FISCHER, Deborah Suzzanne
Sacred Heart Acad; Salem, OR (1-35) VP, NHS; Rptr, Sch P; SC; Pres, Sr Cl; Val; S-T, NHS; Commercial Bank Jr Board; Co Yth Coun; Secret Coun; Oreg St U; Acct.

FISCHER, Jeffrey Keith
Parkwood HS; Joplin, MO (1-371) A Cap Choir; Drama; Ensm; Ftbl; Tr; Mus Letter A; Fr Cert of Merit; Zoology.

FISCHER, Joel Raymond
Pinole Valley HS; Pinole, CA; U of Calif; Vet.

FISCHER, Lynnette Marie
LeRoy HS; LeRoy, KS (3-27) Ann; Band; Chor; Ensm; Semi-Fin, GS; 4H; NHS; Var C; Tres, Jr Cl; Bkbl; Sftbl; Tr; 4H A; Hon Prog; Type A; Emporia U; Bus.

FISCHER, Margaret Ann
St Mary's Acad; Englewood, CO (9-58) Co-Ed, Anchor C; CYO; Chldr; Chor; Fr C; French NHS; NHS; ARC; Ski C; Var C; Secy, Jr Cl; Hon Prog; ARC A; Vlbl; U of Colo; Pol Sci.

FISCHER, Mark Joseph
Trinity HS; Louisville, KY (11-341) Pres, Bus C; Fr C; Pres, FBLA; Ed, Lit Mag; VP, NHS; Phys C; Pres, Spch C; Var C; Tnns; COM; Hon Prog; JA A; Most Out; Pres A; Spch A; Vanderbilt U; Bus.

FISCHER, Russell Kirk
Lancaster Sr HS; Lancaster, WI (1-151) Band; Ensm; FFA; Orch; Pres A; Spch A; Platteville Col.

FISCHER, Steven Dale
Rapid City Stevens HS; Rapid City, SD (59-472) Fin, BS; Drama; Pres, Ger C; Thes; U of Nebr; Med.

FISCHER, Stuart Charles
Le Mars Comm HS; Le Mars, IA (100-310) JV, Bsbl; Yth Fel; Iowa Wesleyan Col; Hist.

FISCHETTI, Patricia Jane
Suffolk HS; Suffolk, VA (6-118) Ed, Ann; Secy, Drama; Rptr, HiY; Hmrm; InterClub Coun; Lat C; Pres, NHS; SC; Secy, Tri-HiY; Rptr, Tr; Bio A; DARGCA; Madison Col; Communications.

FISCHLER, Lisa Collynn
El Camino Real HS; Woodland Hills, CA; Band; Ensm; Ger C; 4H; NHS; Tnns; Soph Cl; Arch; Bkbl; Soccer; Tnns; CSF; COM; Citz A; 4H A; Hon Prog; Kiwanis A; Math A; MLS; Sci A; Yale U; Foreign Lang.

FISH, Alice Catherine
Mayfield HS; Las Cruces, NM (9-500) FHA; 4H;
NHS; Hon Prog; Pi Beta Phi Angel; *New Mexico St U; Acct.*

FISH, Barbara Darlene
Gallia Acad; Gallipolis, OH (97-230) Band; Chor;
FTA; Sci C; Band, Choir As; *Holzer Sch of Nurs; RN.*

FISH, Bobbie Jean
Ashbrook HS; Gastonia, NC (44-447) Chor;
Hmrm; NHS; SC; Tres, Sr Cl; Sftbl; Type A; Color-
guard; Chaplin, Keyettes; *U of NC at Greensboro; Special Ed.*

FISH, John James
Oak Lawn Comm HS; Oak Lawn, IL (100-700)
Chem C; Order/Arrow; ARC; Order/Arrow A;
ARC A; Eagle Sct; *Edison Jr Col; Engr.*

FISH, Kelly Albert
Princeton HS; Cincinnati, OH (86-690) A Cap
Choir; Ensm; Bsbl; Ftbl; Most Out; Mus Schol; Top
25; *Engr.*

FISH, Rebecca Ann
Rapid City Stevens HS; Rapid City, SD (100-439)
Ger C; 4H; A-Ed, Sch P; Tnns; 4H A; Journ A;
Q&S A; Ntl Merit Schol Commended Stu; *SD Sch
of Mines & Tech; Pre-Law.*

FISHBAUGH, Timothy Jay
Celina Sr HS; Celina, OH (15-275) Band; Lat C;
NHS; Chem A; Hon Prog; Yth Fel; Dist Band;
Wright St U; Sci.

FISHBEIN, Elisa Fay
Hillel HS; Lawrence, NY (3-46) Chldr; Chor; Dbte
Tm; Drama; Ed, Lit Mag; NHS; Rptr, Sch P; Span
C; Span NHS; S-T, SC; COM; Hon Prog; NMS;
Summa Cum Laude; NEDT; *Brandeis U; Sci.*

FISHBURN, Donna Marie
St Elizabeth HS; Pittsburgh, PA (8-101) Drama; Fr
C; Model UN; VP, Soph Cl; Math A; NEDT; WW;
Dorothy Lombardi A Nom.

FISHEL, Barry L
Loch Raven HS; Towson, MD (10%-400) Chor;
NHS; Thes; Cr-Ctry; JV, Tr; Cl Fav; Hon Prog; Yth
Fel; NML; *Bucknell U; Bus Adm.*

FISHELL, Dianne Joy
Van Horn HS; Independence, MO (163-415) Chor;
Yth for Christ C; Citz C; Gold Key.

FISHER, Angela Maria
Holy Family HS; Birmingham, AL (1-41) Fr C;
Hmrm; Secy, NHS; Sch P; SC; Hon Prog; *Samford
U; Law.*

FISHER, Anne Rita
Rosati-Kain HS; St Louis, MO (5-95) NHS; SC;
COM; NMF; Summa Cum Laude; Cert of Recogn,
Mo Sch-Col Rel Comm; *Florida Bible Col; Biblical
Ed.*

FISHER, Billie Rae
Butte Falls HS; Butte Falls, OR; Ed, Sch P; Secy, Jr
Cl; Bkbl; Citz A; DARGCA; Journ A; Sal; Spch A;
Val; VofDEM; *Portland St U; Mus.*

FISHER, Carolyn Jean
Lomega HS; Omega, OK; Pres, Sr Cl; Bkbl; Sftbl;
Phar.

FISHER, Cheryl Lynne
E Henderson HS; Hendersonville, NC (20%-200)
AFS; Band; Chldr; Semi-Fin, GS; InterAct C; Key
C; Monogram; Yth Fel; Dance A; Gym Tm; Pres,
Yth Group; *Duke U; Pre-Med.*

FISHER, Corine Jay
MacDuffie Sch for Girls; Springfield, MA (5-48)
Secy, Chor; Drama; Math C; JV, Bkbl; Hon Prog;
Am As of Tchrs of Fr Ntl Contest; *Yale U; Med.*

FISHER, Dale Patrice
Eastside HS; Taylors, SC; ST, CYO; Chor; FHA;
Greenville Technical Col; Secretarial.

FISHER, David James
Homestead HS; Mequon, WI (111-431) Band;
Community Yth Symph; Lat C; JV, Cr-Ctry; COM;
Hon Prog; St Mus Fest Cert, Athletic Achv; *Bio.*

FISHER, Dennis Ray
Fair Park HS; Shreveport, LA (1-352) MVP, Band;
Rptr, Hmrm; Span C; SC; COM; Citz A; Hon Prog;
Service A, Span; Cert of Hon; *NE La U; Mus Ed.*

FISHER, Diane Elizabeth
Union Co HS; Blairsville, GA (3-104) FBLA; Ed,
Sch P; COM; Hist A; Hon Prog; Phy A; Sci A; Type
A; GMEA & GMTA Mus A; Presbyterian Col Jr
Academic Achv A.

FISHER, Elizabeth Ann
Belton-Honea Path HS; Belton, SC; Band; Acad A;
Clemson U; Biol.

FISHER, Francia Ann
N Mercer R-3 HS; Mercer, MO (4-13) Ed, Ann;
Band; Chldr; Chor; Mjrte; Sch P; S-T, Sr Cl; Pres,
Soph Cl; Bkbl; Sftbl; HCt; WW; *Secy.*

FISHER, Gerald Thomas Jr
Northern HS; Durham, NC (67-469) Order/
Arrow; Citz A; Span Excellence; *NC St U; Engr.*

FISHER, Jeri Lisanne
Chamberlain HS; Tampa, FL (300-1000) Rptr,
FFA; Span C; First Cl GSct; Vo-Ag-Greenhand;
Vo-Ag Chapter Farmer; *Cincinnati Bible Seminary.*

FISHER, John Michael
Plantation HS; Plantation, FL (85-725) Chor; Ftbl;
Pres A; Ch, United Methodist Yth Coun; United
Methodist Fla Conf Yth; *Religion.*

FISHER, Julie Ellen
Whitestation HS; Memphis, TN; A Cap Choir;
Drama; ARC; Ed, Sch P; Pres, Span C; Secy, SC;
Sftbl; Tnns; Bio A; COM; Citz A; H of F; Hon Prog;
Math A; Pres A; Q&S A; Band Lib; Most Stu; HR;
VP, Span C; All W Tenn Band; 1st Cl GSct; Span,
Health, A's; *Math.*

FISHER, Karen Diane
Hagerstown Jr Sr HS; Hagerstown, IN (11-186)
Band; Fr C; Y-Tns; Mgr, Bsbl; Sftbl; Swim; FCA.

FISHER, Karen Lynn
Belton-Honea Path HS; Belton, SC (2-246) Ed,
Ann; BC; Drama; Hmrm; Secy, NHS; SC; Secy, Sr
Cl; S-T, Jr Cl; Tr; Gr Marshal; *Clemson U; Med
Tech.*

FISHER, Karen Yvonne
Lincoln HS; Dallas, TX; Pres, Hmrm; Model UN;
SC; *Spelman Col; Law.*

FISHER, Kathleen Shaun
Mahar Regional HS; Orange, MA (20-198) Band;
Chldr; Chor; Fr C; Hmrm; SC; Sch Comm Rep;
Designed Town Bicentennial Button; *Learning
Disabilities Ed.*

FISHER, Kathryn Ann
Hagerstown Jr-Sr HS; Hagerstown, IN (110-143)
Chor; Span C; Mgr, Swim; Mgr, Vlbl; Pres, Ex-
plorer Post; Devotional Ldr, FCA; Church Coun;
Historian, OEA; Tres, Sct; CIT & Jr Coun, Lu-
theran Hills; *Ball St U; Phys Ed.*

FISHER, Kathryn Elizabeth
Circleville HS; Circleville, OH (1-215) AFS; Ed,
Ann; 4H; NHS; Sch Achieve Tm; Rptr, Sr Cl; Secy,
Soph Cl; Tr; Alg A; JV Vlbl; Annette G Will Mem
A; WW, Lang; *Sci Research.*

FISHER, Kevin Bruce
Sooner HS; Bartlesville, OK (1-280) BS; VP, Lat C;
NHS; Pres, SC; Pres, Jr Cl; Fin, Tnns; Amer Leg A;
Citz A; Elk A; Kiwanis A; Val; Govn Energy Sym-
posium; *U of Okla; Med.*

FISHER, Kimberly Kay
Palatka S HS; Palaka, FL; Parl, Tri-HiY; Bravette.

FISHER, Lee Ann
Cedar Shoals HS; Athens, GA (25%-450) Ger C;
4H; Sigma Delta; Jr Civitans; *U of Ga; Interior
Decoration.*

FISHER, Linda Diane
Philadelphia HS for Girls; Philadelphia, PA; Band;
Westchester St Col; Mus Ed.

FISHER, Linda Sue
Circleville HS; Circleville, OH (1-205) AFS;
Drama; GS; Lit Mag; NHS; Amer Leg A; Citz A;
DARGCA; NMF; Val; Eng Merit Soc; *Miami U;
International Stu.*

FISHER, Lisa Ann
Peoria Central HS; Peoria, IL (30-450) Cpt, Chldr;
Span C; Swim; God & Country A; Jr NHS; Schol
Art A; *Interior Decorating.*

FISHER, Lynda Danell
Del Rio HS; Del Rio, TX; A-Ed, Ann; Band; 4H;
San Angelo St U; Animal Husbandry.

FISHER, Marc Paxton
Musselman HS; Bunker Hill, WV (4-92) A-Ed,
Ann; Band; BS; Chor; Pres, 4H; Hmrm; Mod Mus
Mas; Pres, NHS; Orch; Cr-Ctry; *W Va U; Land-
scape Archt.*

FISHER, Mike Vincent
Lancaster Sr HS; Lancaster, WI (1-151) *Platteville
Col; Sci.*

FISHER, Nicole Suzanne
Gwinn HS; Gwinn, MI (21-186) Ann; Band; Co-
Cpt, Chldr; Chor; Drama; Ensm; Madrigal; NHS;
ARC; Swim; Tnns; Tr; ARC A; HR; Cpt, Drill Tm;
Chem Aide; Vol Service; Most Spirited A; Tnns
Camp, Most Improved A; NHS; Water Ballet &
Swim Aide; *U of Okla; Home Ec.*

FISHER, Pamela Jane
Rocky Mount Sr HS; Rocky Mount, NC (60-560)
Pres, Hmrm; SC; Sftbl; Citz A; Opt A; Church
Choir; Jr Booster C; Pres, Acteens; Jr Merit Phys
Ed A; *E Carolina U; Eng.*

FISHER, Robert Allen
Fayette Co HS; Fayette, AL; 4H; Span C.

FISHER, Robert Van Hyning
Hunterdon Central HS; Flemington, NJ (210-560)
Band; Chor; Community Yth Symph; Drama;
Ensm; Parl, 4H; Orch; Sch P; 4H A; NMS; Yth Fel;
Conductor, Church Choir; SAM Originality A;
Westminster Col; Bus.

FISHER, Ronald Mark
Bethel Tate HS; Bethel, OH; NHS; Cr-Ctry; Tr; *U
of Cincinnati; Banking.*

FISHER, Roxie Lee
Belton Honea Path HS; Honea Path, SC (10%-300)
Ann; BC; Chldr; NHS; COM; *Clemson U.*

FISHER, Sandy Kay
Reeds Spring HS; Reeds Spring, MO (3-75) BC;
Pres, FHA; Span C; VP, Jr Cl; COM; Type A; WW.

FISHER, Shara Lee
Marion Sr HS; Marion, IL; Chldr; Chor; Ensm;
Madrigal; Span C; SC; Cpt, Sftbl; Hon Prog; *Cos-
metology.*

FISHER, Sheila Denise
Paul Laurence Dunbar HS; Baltimore, MD; Pres,
FBLA; FTA; NHS; Secy, SC; *US Army; Bus Adm.*

FISHER, Timothy R
Montpelier HS; Montpelier, OH (30-130) Band;
BS; Bsbl; Bkbl; God & Country A; *Air Force Acad;
Aeronautics.*

FISHER, Willis Gerald III
Loris HS; Loris, SC; Order/Arrow; Spch C; Bsbl;
Ftbl; Mark Clark A; *U of SC; Dentistry.*

FISHPAUGH, Evelyn Jane
Parkville Sr HS; Baltimore, MD; Chor.

FISK, Debbie Ann
Council HS; Council, ID; Pres, Chor; Drama; GS;
Hmrm; Spch C; S-T, SC; Rptr, Bkbl; Rptr, Ftbl;
Swim; Tnns; Tr; Amer Leg A; Phy A; Pres A; Type
A; Yth Fel; Mgr, Bkbl & Ftbl; *U of Idaho; Pub
Relations.*

FISK, Jan Rebecca
Eldorado HS; Albuquerque, NM (145-744) Chldr;
NHS; Ski C; *U of Hawaii; Ed.*

FISK, Jody Lee
King's Acad; West Palm Beach, FL (40%-60) Chor;
Palm Beach Jr Col; Secy.

FISK, Philip John
Richardson HS; Richardson, TX (480-960) Cr-
Ctry; Tr; *Mont St U; Wildlife Mgt.*

FISKE, Joy Louann
Herbert Hoover HS; Glendale, CA; Hmrm; Tres,
ARC; Sch Achieve Tm; Ed, Sch P; Yth Fel; Drill
Tm; *Interior Design.*

FISKE, Thomas Gerald
Herbert Hoover HS; Fresno, CA (17-740) A Cap
Choir; Chor; Secy, Demolay; Madrigal; Order/
Arrow; Thes; CSF; Hon Prog; Masonic A; Math A;
Rotary A; Mus A; *Calif St U; Physics.*

FITCH, Michael Jon
Roseburg Sr HS; Roseburg, OR; Chess C; Cr-Ctry;
Swim; Tr; *Oreg St U; Engr.*

FITE, Gregory Estes
Clearwater HS; Clearwater, FL (20%-1000) Chess C; Yth Fel; Patrol Ldr, BScts; Hon Men, Soc of Mech Engr Contest; Comm Ldrship Prog; Archt.

FITE, Kenneth David
Longmont HS; Longmont, CO (33%-600) Ann; Band; NHS; Orch; Bkbl; JV, Ftbl; JV, Tnns; Pre-Law.

FITE, Sharon Suzanne
Del Oro HS; Loomis, CA; Ger C; HCt; Hon Prog; Oral Roberts U.

FITE, Thomas Isaac
Del Rio HS; Del Rio, TX (40-432) ARC; Ftbl; Tnns; God & Country A; Yth Fel; Eagle Sct; W Tex St U; Phys Ed.

FITHIAN, Michael Humbert
Moreno Valley HS; Sunnymead, CA (210-475) Ann; Drama; FBLA; Hmrm; InterAct C; Madrigal; Thes; Mgr, Ftbl; JV, Swim; Pres, Fresh Cl; Pepperdine U; Christian Ed.

FITHIAN, Sharyn Lane
Moreno Valley HS; Sunnymead, CA (85-367) Band; Drama; Spch C; Thes; COM; Lion A; Flag Chldr; 3 Star Thespian; Calif Baptist Col; Christian Ed.

FITTER, Susan Diane
New Providence HS; New Providence, NJ (120-319) AFS; Yth Fel; VP, Explorer's; Church Choir; Mission Commission; York Col; Retailing.

FITTJE, Denise Marie
Niwot HS; Longmont, CO (34-301) Chor; FBLA; Secy, Pep C; On Going Ambassadors For Christ; Pres, Church Yth; Bus Adm.

FITTRO, Mary Elizabeth
Rustburg HS; Rustburg, VA (20-275) FHA; NHS; Central Va Comm Col; Med Record Tech.

FITTRO, William David
Rustburg HS; Rustburg, VA (50-250) FBLA; Golf; Bsbl Sportsmanship A; Jr Tn Golf Trophy; Lynchburg Col; Elec.

FITTS, Marilyn Elizabeth
Weldon HS; Weldon, NC (4-117) AFS; Ann; Band; Chor; Pres, FBLA; Math C; Pres, NHS; Rainbow; Sci C; SC; Secy, Sr Cl; Co-Cpt, Bkbl; Sftbl; Tr; B Crocker A; MLS; Pres A; Fr As; PA; Sci C; Christmas Qn; NC Central U; Bus Adm.

FITTS, Robert Dale
Pontotoc HS; Pontotoc, MS; Chor; Christian Workers Training Band; RA Cert; Journ.

FITZER, Richard Alan
Luverne Sr HS; Laverne, MN (20-127) A Cap Choir; Ann; Band; Chor; Ensm; Madrigal; Sch P; Bkbl; Ftbl; Cpt, Tr; COM; Hon Prog; Conf High Jump Champ; ND St U; Archt.

FITZGERALD, Althea Lynnette
Cathedral HS; Natchez, MS (2-34) CYO; Chor; Pres, NHS; Span C; Amer Leg A; Hist A; Hon Prog; NEDT; Type A; WW; Tulane U; Pre-Med.

FITZGERALD, Angela Evon
Princeton HS; Sharonville, OH (206-586) Jr Miss Pagent; SC; Drill Tm; Best Attendance; Trackette; Off Helper; Fisk U; Sociology.

FITZGERALD, Brenda Gayle
Goodlettsville HS; Goodlettsville, TN (10%-185) Chldr; FTA; Hmrm; NHS; Span C; SC; Tr; Bio A; COM; Cl Fav; Ntl Sci Symposium; Opt A; Sci A; Spch A; Swtht; Eng, Span, A's; Vanderbilt U; Sci.

FITZGERALD, Cheryl Kim
Joseph Kershaw Acad; Camden, SC (2-30) Pres, BC; Chldr; Drama; Bkbl; Soccer; MVP, Tnns; Sci A; VofDEM; Yth Fel; Furman U; Med.

FITZGERALD, Debthy Lee
Oscoda Area HS; Oscoda, MI; Chldr; Var C; Central Mich U; Acct.

FITZGERALD, Demetrius Jacques
Hamilton HS; Memphis, TN; ARC; Parl, SC; Co-Cpt, Bsbl; MVP, Bkbl; Cr-Ctry; Cpt, Ftbl; COM; Cl Fav; Gov Honor Prog; HCt; ARC A; VP, Noblemen; Best Dressed; Minister of Gospel; Most Ath; Best Personality; Olivet Col; Religion.

FITZGERALD, Donna Lynn
William Tennent HS; Warminster, PA (20%-1000) Band; Chor; Orch; Y-Tns; Bkbl; Hon Prog; Yth Organization; Most Friendliest; Best Sportsmanship; Teaching.

FITZGERALD, Glenda Faye
Wilcox Co HS; Rochelle, GA (10-97) BC; FBLA; Ga SW Col; Math.

FITZGERALD, James Joseph
Pasadena HS; Pasadena, CA; Bsbl; Bkbl; Cpt, Cr-Ctry; Soccer; Tr; Pepperdine U.

FITZGERALD, Kathryn Ann
Forest Park HS; Beaumont, TX (75-500) Chor; Span C; Thes; COM; Family Living Merit; Drama A; Phys Ed Merit; Lamar U; Psych.

FITZGERALD, Mary Ann
Oscoda HS; Oscoda, MI; Chor; Sftbl; Phys Fitness A; Ferris Col; Mus.

FITZGERALD, Melanie
Jenkins HS; Chewelah, WA (45-71) Ann; Band; Y-Tns; H of F; Most Mischievious; Central Col.

FITZGERALD, Russell Wayne
Pioneer Christian Acad; Whites Creek, TN; Bkbl; Bob Jones U; Bus.

FITZGERALD, Sonya Marie
Harlan HS; Harlan, KY (7%-74) A Cap Choir; BC; Chor; Ensm; Ensm A; SE Col.

FITZMAURICE, Anne Marie
Notre Dame-Bishop Gibbons HS; Schenectady, NY; Rptr; Sch P; SC; Bkbl; Mgr, Sftbl; NEDT; Vlbl.

FITZPATRICK, Ben George
David Lipscomb HS; Nashville, TN (1-114) A Cap Choir; Pres, Ann; Band; Chor; Pres, Lat C; NHS; Pres, Sch P; Wrest; Aux Lat; Tenn Vet Yth A; Acad Achv; Auburn U; Elec.

FITZPATRICK, Eileen Mary
Doane Stuart HS; Albany, NY (4-40) Cum Laude Soc; Fr C; Rptr, Sch P; Ski C; SC; Cpt, Bkbl; Soccer; Sftbl; Hon Prog; Fr A; Religion A; Boston Col; Math.

FITZPATRICK, Rosemary Ann
North HS; Akron, OH (197-373) A Cap Choir; Band; Cpt, Chldr; Chor; Drama; Ensm; FTA; Hmrm; Mjrte; ARC; Ed, Sch P; Ski C; Span C; SC; Y-Tns; COM; Citz A; Chldr A; Church Choir A; Loose Leg A; U of Akron; Communication.

FITZPATRICK, Victor Bryan
Harris Co HS; Hamilton, GA (66%-283) Bkbl; Ftbl; Swim; Wrest; Morris Brown Col; Phys Ed.

FITZSIMMONS, Susan
Our Lady of Mercy Acad; Syosset, NY (20-146) Tres, CYO; NHS; COM; Citz A; Pep Squad; NHS; Engr.

FITZTHUM, Lesa Ann
Tonasket HS; Tonasket, WA (4-77) Chldr; Chor; Drama; FHA; Fin, Jr Miss Pagent; NHS; ARC; VP, SC; COM; H of F; Wash St U; Psych.

FIVEASH, Charlene Renee
Claxton HS; Claxton, GA (25%-115) Ann; Chess C; FBLA; FHA; Sch P; Tri-HiY; Jr Cl Homecoming Rep; Bus.

FIXEL, Martha J
Berea HS; Berea, OH (80-593) Chor; Drama; NHS; Thes; RSVP; Academic Achv; Academic Hon; Capital U; Bus.

FIXEL, Rebekah L
Berea HS; Berea, OH; Chor; Drama; Lat C; RSVP; Academic Achv; Legal Secy.

FJERSTAD, Sandie Lynn
Coon Rapids Sr HS; Coon Rapids, MN; Span C; Swim; Alg A; I Dare You; ARC A; Sci A; Type A; Anoka-Ramsey Jr Col; Med.

FLACK, Anita Louise
Flushing HS; New York City, NY (248-1280) Band; Queens Col; Mus.

FLADE, John Willard
N Kingstown Sr HS; N Kingstown, RI (52-290) Pres, Demolay; NHS; Rptr, Sch P; COM; ROTC A; ROTC Drill Tm Commander; Demolay St Suite; US Air Force Acad; Astronautical Engr.

FLAGSTAD, Ruth Marie
Lincoln Sr HS; Sioux Falls, SD; Orch; Sup, Ntl Piano Playing Auditions; Concordia Col; Mus.

FLAHAVIN, Paulette Marie
Richardson HS; Richardson, TX (40-970) Band; NHS; Tri-HiY; Hon Prog; Journ.

FLAHERTY, Kathryn Lou
Zeeland HS; Zeeland, MI (1-170) Band; Semi-Fin, GS; Jr Miss Pagent; NHS; Orch; Cpt, Bkbl; Golf; HCt; Hon Prog; Summa Cum Laude; Val; Dutch Dancer; Vol Coach, Girl's Bkbl; Calvin Col; Math.

FLAHERTY, William Chris
Warren Travis White HS; Dallas, TX; Soccer; VP, Superior St A, VICA; Art.

FLANAGAN, Betti Jean
Findlay Sr HS; Findlay, OH (71-583) Pres, Chor; Pres, Drama; Ensm; Secy, NHS; Orch; Thes; Amer Leg A; Opt Out Tn; Spch A; Horizon C; Oral Roberts U; Mus.

FLANAGAN, Robert Jay
Suffolk HS; Suffolk, VA (9-118) NHS; Tri-HiY; Madison Col; Pre-Med.

FLANAGAN, Terry Lynn
Drewry Mason HS; Ridgeway, VA (2-144) Ann; Pres, BC; Pres, Sr Cl; Ftbl; DARGCA; Sal; Gov's Sch; U of Va; Pre-Med.

FLANARY, Sharon Elizabeth
Anderson HS; Austin, TX (14-680) COM; Hon Prog; Type A; Trustee Schol A; U of Tex; Bus.

FLANEGAN, Diane Rae
Lew Wallace HS; Gary, IN (67-500) JV, Chldr; Hmrm; SC; Tr; HQn; HCt; Math A; Eng A; SC A; Saint Mary's Col; Bus.

FLANIGAN, Kelly Lynn
Belvidere HS; Belvidere, IL (11-420) VP, AFS; Dbte Tm; Tres, GAA; Marine Bio.

FLANIGAN, Thomas Joseph
Holly HS; Holly, MI (1-250) Fr C; Hmrm; NHS; Co-Ed, Sch P; Tres, SC; Bkbl; Cpt, Cr-Ctry; Tr; MLS; Val; U of Mich.

FLANNAGAN, William Marvin Jr
W P Davidson HS; Mobile, AL; Key C; Model UN; Var C; JV, Cr-Ctry; Ftbl; JV, Tr; Cl Fav; Hon Prog; MLS; NEDT; Yth Fel; Bio.

FLANNEL, Cassandra Gail
Forest Brook HS; Houston, TX (25%-480) Pres, Fr C; FTA; Hmrm; JETS; Math C; Mu Alpha Theta; Secy, NHS; SC; B Crocker A; COM; Citz A; Magna Cum Laude; Math A; Fisk U; Pre-Med.

FLANNERY, Gregory Lloyd
Augusta HS; Augusta, KY (2-32) VP, BC; Sci C; Alg A; DARGCA; Hist A; MLS; Rotary A; Sci A; Type A; Sch Play; General Bus A; Consumer Ed A; Morehead St U; Math.

FLANNIGAN, Rebecca Lynn
Ringgold-Monongahela Campus; Monongahela, PA (2-380) A Cap Choir; Chor; Drama; Ensm; Madrigal; NHS; Rptr, Sch P; Ski C; Beauty; Hon Prog; Most Out; Sal; Chopin Piano A; Most Outst Choir Member; Trap Shooting Skill; Penn St; Health Related Field.

FLANNIGAN, Timothy Aaron
Ringgold HS; Donora, PA (5%-150) Arch; NHS; Bsbl; Sftbl; Wrest; Hon Prog; U of Pittsburgh; Conservation.

FLATE, John Michael
N Quincy HS; Quincy, MA (170-463) Pres, Chor; Pres, Hmrm; Sci C; Golf; Co-Cpt, Swim; Tr; COM; Cl Fav; Most Out; Yth Fel; Art A; Art Schol; Mass Col of Art; Design.

FLATER, Douglas Guy
Flambeau HS; Tony, WI (25-85) Chor; FFA; VP, 4H; Y-Tns; Bsbl; Bkbl; Co-Cpt, Ftbl; Bausch & Lomb A; God & Country A; Hon Prog; Sal; St Scholar; Dist I Tech Sch; Wood Tech.

FLATLEY, Nancy Eileen
Kennedy HS; Cedar Rapids, IA (19-539) Drama; Span C; Bkbl.

FLATLEY, Patricia Denise
John F Kennedy Sr HS; Cedar Rapids, IA (108-547) Fr C; JV, Tr; Opt A; Yth Fel; Ken Bell A, Yth Group; Iowa Weslyn Col; Religion.

FLATLEY, Patty Jean
Waupun HS; Waupun, WI; CYO; Chldr; Ski C; Sodality; Span C; JV, Tr; Gym; Sci.

FLATTERY, Cindy Marie
Albia Community HS; Albia, IA (12-150) Band; Chor; Drama; Rptr, Sch P; Golf; Hon Prog; Pres A; Outst Musician; Hon Band A; Vocal Hon; Drama As; Swing Choir As; Bus.

FLAUGHER, Jill Diane
Elmwood HS; Bloomdale, OH (5-144) Co-Ed, Ann; Chldr; Chor; Pres, Ensm; Secy, FTA; VP, 4H; Mod Mus Mas; Tres, NHS; 4H A; Most Out; Vlbl; WW, HS Stu; WW, HS Chldrs; Bowling Green St U; Early Childhood Ed.

FLAVIN, Janet Lee
Eden Prairie HS; Eden Prairie, MN (33%-200) A Cap Choir; Band; Ensm; Bkbl; Sftbl; Church Choir; Band Section Ldr; Lead, Sch Mus; Horse Show A's; Dist Mus Contest.

FLAXINGTON, L Colleen
Antelope Valley HS; Lancaster, CA (65-700) Ger C; Sftbl; CSF; Linguistics.

FLEAGLE, Christine Ruth
Virgil I Grissom HS; Huntsville, AL; Chor; Hmrm; Soccer; Yth Fel; Pres, Phys Fitness A; Auburn U; Visual Arts.

FLECK, Joseph R
A J Terrell HS; Blanchard, OK; Ann; BC; Bus C; Math C; NHS; Sch P; Sci C; Span C; Var C; Co-Cpt, Bsbl; Bkbl; Co-Cpt, Ftbl; Golf; Bio A; COM; Citz A; Cl Fav; Gov Honor Prog; Hon Prog; Journ A; Summa Cum Laude; Yth Fel; Pres, Biol C; St Gregory's Col; Engr.

FLECK, Linda Lee
N Central HS; Indianapolis, IN (26-1230) A Cap Choir; Ensm; NHS; SC; Tr; Dean's Fresh Schol at Purdue; Purdue U.

FLEER, Cathy Anne
Clark Co R-1 HS; Kahoka, MO (2-96) Bus C; Drama; NHS; Pres, Rainbow; Thes; Hon Prog; Northeast Mo St U; Bus.

FLEET, Anica De Neen
Trinity HS; Washington, PA (92-421) Ann; Band; Mjrte; Tr; Pres A; WW; Prom Comm; May Day Damler; Washington & Jefferson Col; Pol Sci.

FLEMING, Carl Nolan III
Montpelier HS; Montpelier, OH (50%-93) Ann; Band; Drama; 4H; Orch; Sci C; Var C; Bkbl; Ftbl; Wrest; God & Country A; 4H A; Yth Fel; Northwest Technology Col; General Sci.

FLEMING, Carol Barton
Northside HS; Roanoke, VA; Spch A.

FLEMING, Charles Earl
Odessa Sr HS; Odessa, TX; A Cap Choir; Band; Ensm; NHS; Pres, Orch; Order/Arrow; Ftbl; Swim; Amer Leg A; Most Out; Opt Out Tn; Order/Arrow A; Tex Tech U; Mus.

FLEMING, David Clifford
Richwoods Comm HS; Peoria, IL (15-520) Band; Order/Arrow; Rptr, Sch P.

FLEMING, Deborah Tonia
Louisville HS; Louisville, GA (5%-140) Ann; VP, Fr C; Fin, Hmrm; Lit Mag; Ed, Sch P; Pres, Soph Cl; JV, Bkbl; COM; Citz A; Gov Honor Prog; HCt; Ntl Sci Found; Academic Achv A; Sci.

FLEMING, Diane Lynn
Putnam City W HS; Oklahoma City, OK (350-600) Tnns; Tr; Yth Fel; Pep C; 1st Pl, Ice Sculpting; Vlbl; VP, Yth Fel; Girls Sports; Bicentennial Symbol A; U Colo; Psych.

FLEMING, Dorothy La Shay
Dothan HS; Dothan, AL (25%-521) FBLA; NHS; Rptr, Sch P; SC; Val; Best All Around; Exchange Ed; S-T, Birancial C; Ala A&M U; Bus.

FLEMING, Julie Page
Webster Co HS; Dixon, KY (8-160) BC; Chor; FHA; 4H; 4H A; PTA A; Sal; Sci A; Eng A; Jr Degree, FHA; Sch Win, Co Run-Up, Conserv Essay; Western Ky U; Journ.

FLEMING, Katharine Sterrett
Kingswood-Oxford HS; W Hartford, CT (25%-128) Chor; Math C; Rptr, Sch P; JV, Hockey; Hon Prog; Shield & Dragon; Choir Cross.

FLEMING, Loris Lorene
Davis Sr HS; Davis, CA (1-476) Band; Chor; Span C; Sftbl; Kiwanis A; Span A.

FLEMING, Louise Catherine
Indian Springs Sch; Helena, AL (50%-50) Fr C; U of Montevallo; Social Sci.

FLEMING, Marshall Alton
Norlina HS; Norlina, NC (10-102) Ann; VP, BC; Chess C; Chor; Tres, Soph Cl; U of NC.

FLEMING, Robin Jo
Greeley Central HS; Greeley, CO (47-320) A Cap Choir; Chor; Thes; Spch A; Ntl Sch Chor A; Outst Pops Choir; Outst Concert Choir.

FLEMING, Sally Ann
Western Hills HS; Fort Worth, TX (1-600) Chor; Community Yth Symph; FTA; Lit Mag; NHS; Orch; COM; DAHSS; Austin Col; Eng.

FLEMING, Sharon Lynn
Franklin HS; Franklin, TN; FHA; 4H; Bkbl; 4H A; OGA A; Cosmetology.

FLEMING, Sharyn Lynne
Andrew Jackson HS; New York, NY (43-537) Chldr; Secy, Chor; Ensm; NHS; SC; Hon Prog; Dance C; Artista C; Northeastern U; Marketing Research.

FLEMING, Teresa Ruth
Grand Blanc HS; Grand Blanc, MI; 4H; 4H A; Yth Fel; Candystriper; Art.

FLEMING, Terry George
Hogansville HS; Hogansville, GA (2-97) Co-Ch, Chess C; FTA; Order/Arrow; SC; Alg A; NEDT; Asbury Col; Religion.

FLEMING, Timothy T
Robert E Lee HS; Tyler, TX (20%-630) Fr C; Key C; NHS; VP, Var C; Bsbl; Bkbl; Cpt, Ftbl; Sftbl; Tr; COM; Hon Prog; NEDT; Opt A; Yth Fel; FCA; All Dist Ftbl; Southwestern U; Acct.

FLEMING, Todd Burk
Robert E Lee HS; Tyler, TX (50%-600) Drama; Key C; Lat C; Pres, SC; Thes; Pres, Jr Cl; Pres, Soph Cl; Ftbl; Cl Fav; Hon Prog; Most Out; Yth Fel; Yth Leg; Church Ftbl & Sftbl; Top Hon, Drama Contest.

FLEMISTER, Myra Colleen
Booker T Washington HS; Atlanta, GA (13-345) Pres, Fr C; Secy, Hmrm; Co-Ch, Model UN; NHS; Ed, Sch P; Parl, Soc C; COM; Chem A; Gov Honor Prog; MLS; Ntl Sci Found; Photographer, Sch P; Cpt, Mgr, Fencing; Miss ROTC; Debutante; Tex Christian U; Chem.

FLEMMING, Damaris Ruth
Columbus E HS; Columbus, IN (102-388) Band; Mt Vernon Nazarene Col; Reading Disabilities.

FLEMMING, Donald Joel
Rhinebeck Central HS; Rhinebeck, NY (7-110) Pres, AFS; Bus Mgr, Ann; Lat C; NHS; Mgr, Bsbl; Tr; Hon Prog; NEDT; Regent Schol; Rptr, Local Paper; Jaycee's OYTM Area & Regional; Caes Lat Week; RPI; Bio.

FLEMMING, Doreen Elizabeth
Columbus E HS; Columbus, IN; Chor; Tr; S-T, Yth Fel; Mount Vernon Nazarene Col.

FLEMMING, Eleanor Marie
Hallahan HS for Girls; Philadelphia, PA (135-404) S-T, CYO; Chldr; Hmrm; Ftbl; Nurs.

FLEMMING, Mara Lynn
Chaska Sr HS; Chaska, MN (19-236) Band; Dbte Tm; FHA; Ger C; 4H; NFL; NHS; Rptr, Sch P; Spch C; JV, Golf; Citz A; 4H A; Spch A; Campfire Girls; Debate A; U of Minn; Ed.

FLEMMING, Thelma Jean
Bell HS; Bell, FL (10-56) Ed, Ann; BC; Chldr; FHA; Tres, Hmrm; SC; Bkbl; Co Essay Contest Win; Lake City Comm Col; Acct.

FLESER, April Michele
El Camino Real HS; Woodland Hills, CA; Semi-Fin, Chldr; Chor; Drama; Semi-Fin, Jr Miss Pa; Orch; ARC; Ski C; Span C; SC; COM; HCt; Drill Tm; Dance Tm; Explorers Pres Assn Recording Secy; Hale A; Red Cross A; UCLA; Sci.

FLESHER, Jeanne Lee
Moore HS; Moore, OK (90-152) Ger C; Rptr, NHS; Tres, Pep C; Church Choir; Pres, Church Yth Group; Co-Ch, Evangelism Committee; Alter Guild; Psych.

FLESHER, Julie Lynn
Moore HS; Moore, OK (77-165) Co-Ch, Ger C; Ch, NHS; Yth Fel; Pres, Pep C; Secy, OHOSO; Alter Guild; Church Choir; U of Okla; Nurs.

FLETCHER, David Bruce
Cabot HS; Cabot, AR (70-234) BS; FBLA; Var C; Pres, Sr Cl; Cpt, Bkbl; Tr; Amer Leg A; Sch WW; All Region & All St Bkbl; Pres, Church Choir; Ouachita Baptist U; Bus Adm.

FLETCHER, Deborah Susan
Manasquan HS; Manasquan, NJ; Madrigal; Tr; Board of Ed A; Bus.

FLETCHER, James Barton
Wichita HS E; Wichita, KS (100-500) Chor; COM; Pres, Church Yth Coun; Wichita St U; Bus.

FLETCHER, Jeri Lynn
Milo Adventist Acad; Days Creek, OR (2-66) Chem C; Chor; NHS; Sch P; Cpt, Bsbl; Cpt, Bkbl; Soccer; Sftbl; Tr; COM; 4H A; Pres A; Sch HR; Theta Tau Alpha; Walla Walla Col; Nurs.

FLETCHER, Kathy Jo
Sumner HS; Sumner, WA (50%-400) Band; Chor; Ensm; Ger C; NHS; Sftbl; Vlbl; PLU; Nurs.

FLETCHER, Lauren Sue
Harrison HS; Farmington Hills, MI (10%-435) Drama; Fr C; Fin, GS; NHS; VP, Thes; Co-Cpt, Pom Pon; Sr Board; Regional Fin, Forensic Tourn; Secy & Organizer, FCA; U of Mich; Pre-Bus.

FLETCHER, Marion Thomas
Andrew Jackson HS; Kershaw, SC (2-185) Chess C; Fr C; NHS; Order/Arrow; Sci C; Sci A; Eagle Sct A; Archt.

FLETCHER, Mary Debra
Van Horn HS; Independence, MO; Chor; Bkbl; Sftbl; Yth Fel; Yth Foundation; Athene Lit Soc; Vlbl Tm; Drill Tm.

FLETCHER, Mitchell Lee
Fulton HS; Fulton, MO (52-201) Chor; Hmrm; SC; Math A; Sci A; Mo U; Conservation.

FLETCHER, Norene
McCracken HS; McCracken, KS (5%-14) Chor; Ed, Sch P; Secy, SC; S-T, Sr Cl; Bio A; Sci A; Health A; Oral Roberts U; Nurs.

FLETCHER, Pamela Jean
Oregon-Howell R-3 Kosh HS; Koshkonong, MO (5-21) Bus Mgr, Ann; Chor; Pres, FHA; 4H; Lit Mag; Rptr, Sch P; COM; Cl Fav; Hist A; Type A; WW; Sch o-t Ozarks; Social.

FLETCHER, Renee Fern
Courtenay Pub Sch; Courtenay, ND (3-9) Chldr; Chor; Bkbl; Sftbl; Tr; Type A; HR.

FLETCHER, Sarah Jane
Beaver Dam Sr HS; Beaver Dam, WI (15%-300) Ann; Band; Chor; Ensm; ARC; Ski C; SC; Var C; Swim; JV, NHS; Masonic A; Sci A; Job's Daughters; Cert Adv Red Cross Life-Saving; Wis Assn A, Med Tech; Wis Soc of Pathologists A; U of Wis; Med Tech.

FLETCHER, Scott Earl
Northwest HS; Omaha, NE (1-700) Golf; Hon Prog; Rotary A; Outst Soph A; Ariz St Col; Math.

FLETCHER, Shannon Gail
Forest Park HS; Beaumont, TX (50%-450) Hmrm; Bkbl; Tr; Chem A; Yth Fel; Cpt, Vlbl; Tex A&M.

FLETCHER, Teresa Elaine
Temple HS; Temple, TX; A Cap Choir; Chor; Span C; SC; Mary Hardin Baylor Col; Pediatrician.

FLEWELLEN, James Franklin
Columbia HS; Decatur, GA (5-279) BC; NHS; Bsbl; Ftbl; Ga Tech.

FLICK, Rocky J
Winfield HS; Winfield, KS (2-211) Fin, AFS; NHS; Bkbl; Ftbl; Swim; Tr; AVL Offensive End; U of Kans; Med.

FLINK, James Duncan
Centralia HS; Centralia, MO (65-118) A Cap Choir; Band; Ensm; Key C; Madrigal; Sci C; Bsbl; JV, Ftbl; JV, Tr; JA A; Conf, Dist, Choirs; NW Mo St U; Commercial Art.

FLINN, Deborah Kay
Parkersburg South HS; Parkersburg, WV (10%-506) DECA; Tres, De Cl; Co-Op; *Parkersburg Comm Col; Acct.*

FLINSPACH, Jennifer L
Franklin HS; Franklin, OH (50%-350).

FLINT, Bonnie Sue
Newfane Central HS; Newfane, NY (71-225) Band; NY St Solo Mus A; *Practical Bible Col; Mus.*

FLINT, Steven Christopher
Mount Saint Joseph HS; Baltimore, MD (59-300) Chor; Dbte Tm; Fr C; Y-Tns; Bsbl; Ftbl; Tr; Yth Fel; *Ed.*

FLIPPEN, Katheryne Denise
Drewry Mason HS; Ridgeway, VA; Chldr; VP, Chor; 4H; Fine Arts C; GAA.

FLIPPER, Richard Alan
Kirkwood HS; Kirkwood, MO; Mgr, Cr-Ctry; Tr; Wrest; Yth Fel; *SW Mo St U; Forestry.*

FLIPPIN, Alan Keith
Northwest Cabarrus HS; Concord, NC (40-150) A Cap Choir; Band; Chor; Ensm; FTA; Tr; Phys Fitness A; Band A; *U of NC; Engr.*

FLIPPO, Novelyn Marie
Caprock HS; Amarillo, TX; Band; VP, Chor; Ensm; FHA; Hmrm; Lat C; Madrigal; Pres, Orch; 1st Alt, All St Choir; Mus As; Qn, Swtht Banquet; Yth For Christ; *WTSU; Mus.*

FLITCRAFT, Carlynn Sue
Springfield Local HS; Petersburg, OH (2-135) Cpt, Chldr; Fr C; Hmrm; NHS; VP, Soph Cl; Bkbl; HCt; Hon Prog; JV, Vlbl; US Army Recruiting Command, Com; *Dental Hygiene.*

FLODMAN, Lynette Ann
Polk Pub HS; Polk, NE (7-19) Band; Secy, Bus C; Chor; Drama; Ensm; FBLA; A-Ed, Sch P; Secy, SC; Bkbl; Sftbl; Tr; Type A; Yth Fel; Bookkeeping A; PA; Twirling A; *Midland Lutheran Col; Med.*

FLOEN, Linda Dale
William M Kelley HS; Silver Bay, MN; NHS; Sch P; Sci C; Var C; MVP, Bkbl; Tr; COM; Hon Prog; Sci A; Vlbl.

FLOHR, David Robert
Ladysmith-Hawkins HS; Ladysmith, WI (50-100) FFA; *Tech Sch; Diesel & Auto Mech.*

FLOHR, Donald Keith
Ladysmith-Hawkins HS; Ladysmith, WI (30-90) FFA; Bkbl; Wrest; *Agr.*

FLOOD, James Robert
Sprague HS; Salem, OR (10%-375) Ch, Hmrm; Co-Ed, Sch P; Co-Ch, SC; Bkbl; Ftbl; Tr; Citz A; Hon Prog; Ch, Elections Comm; *Journ.*

FLORA, David H
National Trail HS; New Paris, OH (35-150) Semi-Fin, BS; Chor; FTA; 4H; Sch P; Rptr, Sci C; Span C; Eng A; *Theatre.*

FLOREK, Pam Elaine
N Beach Jr Sr HS; Moclips, WA; Ann; Chldr; Chor; Sch P; Tr; Journ A; *Nurs.*

FLORENCE, Joan
Arkadelphia HS; Arkadelphia, AR (47-158) Band; Chor; FTA; 4H; Math C; Orch; Sci C; COM; Math A; DAR Page, St Conf; All St Orch; *Henderson St U; Mus.*

FLORENCE, Leslie Grace
Lakeside HS; Atlanta, GA (10%-420) BC; Chor; Orch; Tres, Soph Cl; HR; *Wheaton Col; Math.*

FLORENCE, Mary Kay
Park Hill HS; Parkville, MO; Band; Chldr; Ensm; Jr Deaconess; Church Activities.

FLORES, Edwarda Oneilia
George Washington Sr HS; Agana, GUAM; Chldr; Chor; Ensm; Hmrm; NHS; SC; Beauty; Hon Prog; *U of Colo; Psych.*

FLORES, Elizabeth Pangelinan
Acad of Our Lady of Guam; Agana, GUAM (10-90) NHS; Citz A; Most Out.

FLORES, Horacio Salvador
Roma HS; Roma, TX (4-130) Tres, FFA; NHS; SC; Pres, Sr Cl; MLS; *Tex A&M U; Vet Med.*

FLORES, Jonathan Edward
Baldwin Park HS; Baldwin Park, CA (30%-200) VP, Band; Ensm; Orch; Cpt, Bkbl; Cr-Ctry; *Azusa Pacific Col; Communications.*

FLORES, Norma Delia
Harlingen HS; Harlingen, TX (25%-600) A Cap Choir; Ed, Ann; JETS; VP, SC; Tr; Q&S A; Pre Med C; Fin, Miss Tex United Tn; *Yale U; Med.*

FLORES, Paul Angel
Baldwin Park HS; Baldwin Park, CA (10%-300) Band; Co-Cpt, Bkbl; Outst Frosh, Band; *U of Sou Calif; Bus Adm.*

FLORES, Rebecca
Los Altos HS; Hacienda Heights, CA; Chldr; Drama; Span C; Hon Prog; WW; *Psych.*

FLORES, Sara Esther
Wesleyan Acad; Guaynabo, PR (6-28) Chor; NHS; SC; Bkbl; NEDT; Exchange Stu, Houghton Acad; High Hon; PA; *U of Puerto Rico; Ed.*

FLORES, Teresita Maria
John F Kennedy HS; Tumon, GUAM (24-511) Cpt, Chldr; Hon Prog; Type A; HR; *U of Guam; Ed.*

FLORES, Tina Lorraine
Ventura Sr HS; Ventura, CA (79-545) SC; JV, Bkbl; MVP, Sftbl; CSF; COM; Hon Prog; Val; Yth Fel; Most Improved; Most Inspirational; All-League Tm; *Pepperdine U; Chem.*

FLORESCA, Edgar Zerda
John F Kennedy HS; Tumon, GUAM; A Cap Choir; Chor; Ensm; NHS; Bio A; Citz A.

FLORY, Barbara Jo
Sebring McKinley HS; Sebring, OH (35-85) Chor; Pres, FHA; 4H; HiY; SC; Mgr, Bkbl; *Massillon City Sch of Nurs; Nurs.*

FLORY, Becky Lynn
Brookville HS; Brookville, OH; Drama; 4H; Span C; Bio A; Sci A; Eng A; Candystriper; *Sinclaire Comm Col; Sci.*

FLORY, Marsha Leah
Tinora HS; Defiance, OH (25%-104) A Cap Choir; Chor; Ensm; Most Improved Choir Stu; GAA; *Chicago Art Inst; Commercial Art.*

FLORY, Rebecca Lynn
Brookville HS; Brookville, OH; Drama; 4H; Span C; Bio A; 4H A; Sci A; Candystriper A; Eng A; *Sinclair Comm Col; Sci.*

FLOTH, Martin Allen
Burke HS; Omaha, NE (25%-793) Chor; Var C; JV, Golf; Swim; Rotary A; Yth Fel; Tres, Order of St John; *U of Nebr; Math.*

FLOURNOY, Carolyn Matsue
James Madison HS; San Diego, CA (100-924) Chor; Ensm; NHS; *Mus.*

FLOURNOY, James Allen
Terrel Co HS; Dawson, GA (10%-147) BC.

FLOURNOY, Kevin
Thomas M Cooley HS; Detroit, MI (200-618) ARC A; Tr A; Attendance A; *Mary Grove Col; Hygienist.*

FLOWER, Dorothy Arlene
Osceola HS; Kissimmee, FL (30-375) Chor; Dbte Tm; 4H; Hmrm; Rainbow; Span C; Spch C; SC; Tri-HiY; VP, Jr Cl; Pres A; Spch A; Yth Fel; Camp Fire Girls; Stu Senator; *Med.*

FLOWER, Wesley Andrew
La Porte HS; La Porte, TX; Band; Chor; Ensm; Bsbl; Co-Cpt, Bkbl; Ftbl; Tnns; Mgr, Tr; Pres A; Band Ensm A's; 1st Rank, Royal Ambassadors; *Acct.*

FLOWERS, Alice Emiko
William Monroe HS; Stanardsville, VA; F-Ed, Ann; BC; Chldr; Chor; Ensm; Hmrm; Lit Mag; NHS; SC; Secy, Sr Cl; JV, Swim; Tr; JA A; *Troy St U; Biol.*

FLOWERS, Christella
Northside HS; Memphis, TN; Beauty; Citz A; Ntl Achv Schol; Ntl Sci Found; Ntl Sci Symposium; Sci A; *Pepperdine U; Beauty.*

FLOWERS, Laura Jane
C E Byrd HS; Shreveport, LA; Community Yth Symph; Fr C; Orch; Exchange Stu to Germany; Pep Sq; *Centenary Col; Hist.*

FLOWERS, Margaret Irene
Crawford Co R II HS; Cuba, MO; Chor; *Lee Col.*

FLOWERS, Martyn Lance
Providence HS; New Lenox, IL (127-244) Band; Chor; Ch, Dbte Tm; Drama; Ensm; Hmrm; Sci C; Bsbl; Cpt, Ftbl; Hockey; Swim; Tnns; Wrest; Cl Fav; Sci A; Area 1 Board; Yth Chaplin; *Judson Col; Ministry of Mus.*

FLOWERS, Mary
Compton Sr HS; Compton, CA (37-800) Co-Ed, Sch P; SC; Secy, Sr Cl; CSF; Journ A; Eng A; *LaVerne Col; Pol Sci.*

FLOWERS, Pamela Denise
Portageville HS; Portageville, MO (12-80) Chor; Fr C; FHA; NHS; Hon Prog.

FLOWERS, Pamela Lynn
George Henry Corliss HS; Chicago, IL (13-726) Drama; SC; COM; Hon Prog; Sal; Yth Fel; *Bus Adm.*

FLOWERS, Stacey Jan
Churchill HS; Livonia, MI (25%-675) Chor; Drama; Ensm; Secy, Orch; Span C; Swim; Schol, E Mich Summer Mus Sem; Plymouth Symph Orch; 1st Pl A'S, St Violin Solo Fest; *Stetson Col; Mus.*

FLOWERS, Vanessa Azalean
John F Kennedy HS; Cleveland, OH; Chor; Ensm; Fr C; COM; Citz A; Radio C; Usher C; *Computor Tech.*

FLOYD, Brenda Kay
Brawley Union HS; Brawley, CA (37-341) AFS; Chor; *Grossmont Col; Ed.*

FLOYD, Debbie
Smith HS; Atlanta, GA (6-293) ARC; Cr-Ctry; Soccer; Tr; COM; Math A; *Vet Med.*

FLOYD, Elizabeth Marie
Myrtle Beach HS; Myrtle Beach, SC (40-220) Ann; Drama; Fr C; FTA; Pres, MYF; GSct; Comm Service; Candy Striper; *Columbia Col; Fr.*

FLOYD, Kenneth Eskil
Highline HS; Seattle, WA (110-410) Ftbl; Order / Arrow A.

FLOYD, Kim Allyn
Livermore HS; Livermore, CA (6-300) Band; 4H; COM; MLS; Most Out; St Scholar; *UC at Davis; Vet Med.*

FLOYD, Kimberly Jean
Hazel Park HS; Hazel Park, MI (20-450) VP, Fr C; Rptr, Sch P; VP, Span C; Tr; COM; Pres A; Outst Acad Achv A; Eng Excel A; *Mich St U; Psych.*

FLOYD, Lisa Lynn
Adair Co R II HS; Brashear, MO (1-15) Pres, Band; Chldr; S-T, 4H; Cpt, Mjrte; Sci C; COM; 4H A; Dist Contest; Herff Jones Mus A; Band Cert As; Mus Soloist; *Northeast Mo St U; Math.*

FLOYD, Marsha Ann
Salem HS; Salem, IN (33%-170) FHA; Rptr, Hmrm; Spch C; Tri-HiY; Semi-Fin, Cr-Ctry; Semi-Fin, Tr; *Communication.*

FLOYD, Merdis Leslie
Laurens Dist SS HS; Laurens, SC; Drama; Fr C; FHA; 4H; Powder Puff Ftbl; *Benedict Col; Sociology.*

FLOYD, Nancy Patricia
Havre HS; Havre, MT; Band; Chor; Pres, 4H; Hmrm; InterAct C; Span C; 4H A; Sci A; Sunday Sch Teacher; MYF Coun; 4-H Congress Del; Ed Commission, Church; *Northern Mont Col.*

FLOYD, Noma Ann
El Dorado HS; El Dorado, AR; A Cap Choir; Band; BC; Bus C; Chor; Ensm; FBLA; FHA; NHS; Sch P; COM; Type A; Yth Fel; Yth Foundation; Mus A; *Ouachita Baptist Col; Mus.*

FLOYD, Robin Lynn
Levelland HS; Levelland, TX (75-200) Chor; Drama; FHA; Most Improved Choir; Most Likable Choir; *Abilene Christian U; Ed.*

FLOYD, Sheila Fay
New Site HS; Newsite, MS (6-38) Ann; BC; FHA; *NE Miss Jr Col; Advanced Math.*

FLOYD, Valerie Regina
W Charlotte Sr HS; Charlotte, NC (20-580) Bus C; Chldr; Chor; Drama; FBLA; Span C; *Central Piedmont Comm Col; Bus Adm.*

FLUD, Alisa Diane
Abernathy HS; Abernathy, TX (25-76) Band; Tnns; COM; *Dallas Bible Col; Elem Ed.*

FLUITT, Carol Suzanne
Fredericksburg HS; Fredericksburg, TX (7-168) Band; Parl, 4H; NHS; Chem A; Citz A; 4H A; Hist A; PTA A; Eng A; Soil Conservation A; OEA; TAHOS; *Tex Womans U; Phys Therapy.*

FLUKER, Rameld Darlene
Chicago Voc HS; Chicago, IL (54-1214) A Cap Choir; Chor; Hmrm; Scholastic Hon A; *Mus.*

FLURY, Christopher Alan
Gresham Union HS; Gresham, OR (23-520) Fin, BS; CYO; FFA; 4H; Fin, NHS; Ski C; Swim; COM; Most Out; All-Amer; *Washington St U; Forestry.*

FLY, David Loyd
Ft Scott Sr HS; Ft Scott, KS; SC; Tnns; *Kans U; Archt.*

FLYNN, Anthony Joseph
Langley Jr-Sr HS; Langley, WA (39-78) Band; Pres, CYO; Chor; FFA; 4H; Bsbl; JV, Bkbl; Cr-Ctry; *Gonzaga Col; Journ.*

FLYNN, Deborah Susan
Chester HS; Chester, PA (10%-675).

FLYNN, Elizabeth Louise
Ensley HS; Birmingham, AL; VP, Y-Tns; Hospital Vol A; *Jefferson St Jr Col; Psych.*

FLYNN, John William Jr
Lee HS; Midland, TX; *Midland Col; Law Enforcement.*

FLYNN, Judith
Queen o-t Rosary Acad; Amityville, NY (4-85) Tres, NHS; COM; *Adelphi Col; Bus.*

FLYNN, Julie Ann
St Mary's HS; Lynn, MA (16-117) Ed, Ann; Band; CYO; Chor; Drama; Hmrm; NHS; Span C; Alg A; Bio A; Hist A; Sci A; Eng, Span, A's; *Anna Maria Col; Biol.*

FLYNN, Marra Leah
London HS; London, OH; Fr C; Art C; TriL; *Wittenberg U; Child Psych.*

FLYNN, Martha Elaine
E Hartford HS; E Hartford, CT (1%-425) Band; Hmrm; Lat C; NHS; Hon Prog; Yale Book A; S-T, Pilgrim Yth Fel; Girls Ldr C; *Yale U; Law.*

FLYNN, Sandra Euneta
Douglass HS; Memphis, TN; Chor; Secy, Hmrm; Rainbow; Secy, ARC; SC; Cpt, Bsbl; Cpt, Sftbl; Cpt, Swim; Cpt, Tnns; Citz A; Masonic A; ARC A; ROTC A; PWA, Rainbow Girl; *Memphis St U; Social Work.*

FLYNN, Siobhan Shelagh
Immaculate Conception HS; Elmhurst, IL (20-150) Fr C; S-T, NHS; Rptr, Sch P; Tnns; COM; Citz A; Journ A; Type A; Marian A; Fr A; St Millicent Cert; DAHSS; *Col o-t U of Chicago; Biological Sci.*

FLYNN, Victoria Jane
Deerborne HS; Coral Gables, FL (1-75) BC; Secy, CYO; InterClub Coun; Secy, NHS; Sch P; Secy, SC; Secy, Sr Cl; Co-Cpt, Bkbl; Sftbl; Tr; Bio A; Most Out; Sci A; Val; Vlbl; Golden Book A; WW; Co Sci Fair; *Sou Methodist U; Biol.*

FLYNN, William Edward
E Hartford HS; E Hartford, CT; Band; Yth Fel; *Quinnipiac Col; Computer Sci.*

FLYNT, Deborah Ann
Robert E Lee HS; Midland, TX; Chor; Ensm; Mgr, Bkbl; *Midland Jr Col.*

FOARD, Merwin Edsel
Charlotte Christian Sch; Charlotte, NC (10-23) Chor; Fr C; Pres, Hmrm; Monogram; Tres, SC; Var C; Pres, Soph Cl; Bkbl; Soccer; COM; Knowledge of Bible Tm; Bicentennial Chor; *U of NC; Bus Adm.*

FOCHS, Joseph Gordon
Newman HS; Wausau, WI; Var C; Bsbl; Cpt, Bkbl; JV, Ftbl; *Viterbo Col; Bus Mgr.*

FOCHS, Mary Lynn
Hilbert HS; Hilbert, WI; Secy, AFS; Drama; Co-Cpt, Mjrte; Rptr, Sch P; Pom Pon A; *U of Wis; Phys Therapy.*

FOCHTMANN, Curt William
Wetumpka HS; Wetumpka, AL (2%-215) VP, BC; Drama; Ensm; FFA; FTA; Hmrm; Monogram; VP, Sci C; Pres, Span C; SC; Var C; Bsbl; Mgr, Bkbl; Cpt, Ftbl; Tr; *U of Ala; Law.*

FOCIA, Pamela Jean
Estancia HS; Estancia, NM (4-68) Drama; Parl, FFA; 4H; JV, Bkbl; Tr; 4H A; Type A; FFA A; *NM St U.*

FOCKLER, Robert Mitchell
Memphis University Sch; Memphis, TN (6-94) A-Ed, Ann; Band; Cum Laude Soc; Lit Mag; Pres, Mu Alpha Theta; NHS; Sch P; Hon Prog; Math A; Most Out; NMF; NEDT; Q&S A; Summa Cum Laude; Lit A; Span A; Photography C; *Princeton U; Econ.*

FODDRELL, Betty Ruth
Camden Co HS; St Marys, GA (25-201) Ann; Band; Chldr; Rptr, FBLA; FFA; Hmrm; HCt; Adverting Ed, Ann; Best All Round Sr; Most Dedicated Var Chldr; WW; *Macon Jr Col; Dental Hygiene.*

FOELSCH, Paul Edward
Greenwich Central Sch; Greenwich, NY (7-105) Band; Chess C; Dbte Tm; Co-Ch, FFA; Pres, 4H; NHS; Ed, Sch P; COM; Regent Schol; *Cornell U; Agr.*

FOGARTY, Catherine Ileen
St Mary of the Annunciation HS; E Cambridge, MA (10-69) Chldr; Chor; Dbte Tm; Drama; Fr C; Hmrm; Lit Mag; Sch P; SC; Bkbl; Sftbl; Cl Fav; Hon Prog; Most Out; Most Popular A; *Northeastern U; Criminal Justice.*

FOGARTY, Ellen Rose
Catholic Central HS; Troy, NY (33%-350) CYO; Chldr; Chor; Hmrm; Span C; Mgr, Bsbl; K of C A; *Siena Col; Eng.*

FOGARTY, Gerald Robert
Leo HS; Chicago, IL (9-115) Hmrm; F-Ed, Sch P; SC; Ftbl; Hon Prog; Q&S A; *Law.*

FOGEL, Gregory Paul
Irvin HS; El Paso, TX (25%-525) CYO; Bkbl; Ntl Jr Hon Soc; *Tex A&M U; Constr Mgt.*

FOGEL, Mary Eileen
Irvin HS; El Paso, TX (40%-565) Chor; French NHS; FTA; Lang A; CCD Secy; Church Receptionist; *Tex Woman's U; Occupational Therapy.*

FOGEL, Suzanne Marie
Irvin HS; El Paso, TX (25%-550) CYO; Chor; Span C; 3rd Pl, Foreign Lang Tourn; NJHS; *Special Ed.*

FOGERSON, Candi Michelle
Reseda HS; Reseda, CA (5%-640) Band; Hmrm; InterAct C; CSF; Hon Prog; JA A; Principal's Acad Achv List; Badminton Tm; *Boston U of Engr; Math.*

FOGG, Linda Kathleen
Cumberland Valley Sr HS; Mechanicsburg, PA (15-585) Chor; NHS; S-T, Span C; JV, Swim; Tr; Hon Prog; *Mount Holyoke Col; Marine Biol.*

FOGLE, Kimberly Ann
Ottawa HS; Ottawa, KS (33%-225) Fr C; Rptr, Sch P; SC; Citz A; Yth Fel; Yth Leg; Drill Tm; Pres, Job's Daughters; Outst Schol; *Kans St U; Retail Merchandising.*

FOGLE, Rose Denise
St Vincents Acad; Savannah, GA; Vlbl; *SE Acad; Airline Travel.*

FOGLESONG, Douglas Scott
Stow HS; Stow, OH (3-510) A Cap Choir; Band; Chor; Tres, Fr C; NHS; COM; Hist A; Hon Prog; Star Student; Drum Major; Chor A; Superior, Solo Contest; 1st Chair, St Fair Band; *Akron U; Mus.*

FOGLI, Paul Lawrence
E L Bowsher HS; Toledo, OH (20-400) A Cap Choir; Chor; Cum Laude Soc; Cpt, Dbte Tm; Pres, Drama; Ensm; Hmrm; Lat C; Madrigal; NHS; F-Ed, Sch P; Spch C; Thes; Alg A; COM; Magna Cum Laude; Spch A; Bicentennial A; HR; NEDT Cert; Bowsher Cert of Hon; *Toledo U; Eng.*

FOGLIA, Michael Anthony
Adlai E Stevenson HS; Bronx, NY (62-788) Band; City Conf; Pres, Hmrm; NHS; Up Bound; Var C; Ftbl; Tnns; Cl Musician; Service A; Louie Armstrong A; *Fordham U; Sci.*

FOGLIA, Thomas George
Edgewood HS; Pittsburgh, PA (30-82) Ger C; Rptr, Sch P; Ski C; Span C; Secy, Var C; Bsbl; Mgr, Ftbl; *Xavier U; Acct.*

FOHN, Richard John
LaConner HS; LaConner, WA; Ann; CYO; 4H; Hmrm; NHS; VP, Sci C; SC; Var C; Pres, Soph Cl; JV, Bkbl; Ftbl; COM; Most Out; Val.*

FOISEL, John Wilhelm
Eastlake N HS; Eastlake, OH; Ger C; Ftbl; Tr; *Cleveland St U; Elec Engr.*

FOLEY, Cynthia Louise
Rham Jr-Sr HS; Hebron, CT (10-180) Chor; Drama; Fr C; Fin, GS; Math C; Tres, NHS; Citz A; Hon Prog; Holy Name Soc Schol; Cl '1960' A; Graduation Hon Court; *U of Bridgeport; Dental Hygiene.*

FOLEY, Deborah Sue
Paris HS; Paris, IL (13-235) Co-Ed, Ann; Chldr; Drama; VP, NHS; Tr; HCt; Hon Prog; *Eastern Ill U; Art.*

FOLEY, Diana Kim
Paris HS; Paris, IL (11-250) Band; Chem C; Pres, Chor; Drama; Ensm; Hmrm; Pres, NHS; SC; WW, Mus.*

FOLEY, Ellen Ann
Garfield Heights HS; Garfield Heights, OH; Tr; Spirit C; GAA; *Elem Ed.*

FOLEY, James Joesph
Blair Comm HS; Blair, NE (13-173) CYO; MVP, Chor; Rptr, FFA; 4H; Var C; Ftbl; Tr; Pres A; Spch A; *U of Nebr; Agr.*

FOLEY, James Terry
J D Bassett HS; Bassett, VA; Band; Order/Arrow; 4H A; Eagle Sct; *Va Tech U; Agr.*

FOLEY, John Joseph III
Rham Jr-Sr HS; Hebron, CT (30-225) CYO; Dbte Tm; Drama; Span C; Amer Leg A; Citz A; Hist A; Stu Faculty Senate A; Most Improved, Span A; Woodwork, Drafting, A's; Eng, Industrial Arts, A's; *Archt.*

FOLEY, Leisa Karroll
Lumberton Sr HS; Lumberton, NC; Pres, A Cap Choir; Chldr; Chor; Dbte Tm; Drama; Fr C; VP, Hmrm; Sch P; Pres, Sci C; Var C; Tr; Spch A; Yth Fel; Pep C; All Around Mus & Dance A; Acteens; Little Theater; Talent Show A's; *Mus.*

FOLEY, Peter Martin
Wichita Falls HS; Wichita Falls, TX; Pres, Key C; VP, SC; Tnns; S-T, FCA; *Hardin-Simmons Col; Bus.*

FOLEY, Rosemarie
Lumberton Sr HS; Lumberton, NC; Band; FHA; Mjrte; Sch P; Sci C; Span C; Tri-HiY; *Louisburg Col; Special Ed.*

FOLEY, Valerie Ann
Acad of Our Lady of Mercy; Milford, CT (5-93) Chor; Drama; VP, Fr C; Secy, NHS; NEDT; Outst Jr; Fr A; *Trinity Col; Fr.*

FOLK, Jean Alexander
E Mecklenburg HS; Charlotte, NC (243-587) Fr C; Ch, Hmrm; InterAct C; Co-Ch, SC; *W Carolina Col; Sociology.*

FOLKERTS, Barbara Ann
Allison Bristow Comm HS; Allison, IA (35-54) Chor; Drama; 4H; Spch A; Yth Fel; *Wartburg Col; Mus Therapy.*

FOLKERTS, John Garth
Roxana HS; Roxana, IL (62-223) Ensm; JV, Bsbl; JV, Ftbl; Tr; Citz A; *Belleville Comm Col; Air Conditioning.*

FOLKERTS, Michelle Marie
Rochelle Township HS; Rochelle, IL (32-216) Band; Chor; Community Yth Symph; Orch; Var C; Cpt, Bkbl; Sftbl; Cpt, Tnns; Hon Prog; St Scholar; Yth Fel; Vlbl; Pres, Yth Fel; Art, Army Ath & Schol, A's; *Iowa St U; Phys Ed.*

FOLLEN, Richard James
Brewster HS; Brewster, MN (10-27) Band; Chor; Ensm; Hmrm; Sch P; Var C; Cpt, Bkbl; Ftbl; Sftbl; Tr; HCt; Pres A; All-Conf Ftbl; *South West St U; Bus.*

233

FOLLETT, Kevin Michael
Manhattan HS; Manhattan, KS (1-450) HiY; JV, Cr-Ctry; Tr; Val; Yth Fel; Rep, Yth Fel; BSct; CAR.

FOLLETT, Winifrid Follett
Valley HS; Sanders, AZ; Ann; FFA; Hmrm; Model UN; Tres, Rainbow; SC; Rptr, Jr Cl; Mgr, Bkbl; Mgr, Tr; Masonic A; Acct A; *Eastern Ariz Col.*

FOLLETTE, Debbie Ruth
So Nevada Voc Sch; Las Vegas, NV; Rainbow; Sftbl.

FOLLETTE, John Glen
Valley HS; Las Vegas, NV; Demolay; Wrest.

FOLLETTE, Serene Beth
Abraham Lincoln HS; Denver, CO; Chor; Drama; Ensm; *Houghton Col; Ed.*

FOLMAR, Patrick Lee
Crenshaw Christian Acad; Luverne, AL (1-24) Ann; Math C; NHS; Var C; VP, Sr Cl; Bsbl; Bkbl; Ftbl; Tnns; NEDT; *Davidson Col; Engr.*

FOLSOM, Jim Dean
A C Davis HS; Yakima, WA (10-450) Semi-Fin, Ntl Yth Co; Wrest; Yth Fel; Cpt, Bible Quiz Tm; Lila Miller Schol; *Grace Col & Seminary; Eng & Bible.*

FOLSOM, Merrill Lee
Jackson HS; Jackson, GA; Key C; NHS; SC; Bsbl; Ftbl; Tnns; Tr; Wrest; Co-Ed-Y; *U of Ga; Vet Med.*

FOLSOM, Nancy Louise
Englewood HS; Jacksonville, FL (10%-503) Dbte Tm; NHS; Rainbow; Spch C; Tres, Yth Fel; *Acct.*

FOLTZ, Marla Lynn
E Peoria Comm HS; E Peoria, IL (50-396) Band; Chem C; Chess C; Lat C; NHS; Orch; Rptr, Sch P; *Goshen Col; Pre-Med.*

FOLZ, Marcia Jean
Faith Baptist Sch; Canoga Park, CA; Chldr; ARC; VP, Jr Cl; Bkbl; Sftbl; Tr; COM; Spch A; JV Vlbl; HR; Principal's List; *Law.*

FONCANNON, Cindy Lorraine
Waialua HS; Waialua, HI (25%-170) NHS; Swim; *Pepperdine U; Zoology.*

FONDREN, Ronald Wayne
Jackson Central Merry HS; Jackson, TN (65-535) BC; Hmrm; Lat C; SC; Mgr, Ftbl; *Eckerd Col; Liberal Arts.*

FONDREN, Theresa Kaye
Horace Mann HS; Gary, IN; Mjrte; NHS; Up Bound; Citz A; *Purdue U; Math.*

FONDRY, John Alan
Trinity Christian Sch; Williston, VT (1-1) VP, Chess C; Chor; Dbte Tm; Drama; Sch Achieve Tm; Ski C; Span C; Spch C; VP, SC; Pres, Sr Cl; Cpt, Bkbl; JV, Cr-Ctry; JV, Soccer; JV, Sftbl; JV, Tr; Val; Sch Spirit A; Ath Hons; 1975-76 Athlete of the Yr; *Bob Jones U; Bible.*

FONDY, Stephanie Fondy
Belton HS; Belton, TX (30-250) Lit Ral; Rptr, Sch P; Span C; *Tex A&M U; Elem Ed.*

FONES, Lisa Kay
Atwater HS; Atwater, CA (25%-700) Band; Secy, FNA; ARC; Certified Lay Speaker; Flag Carrier; Pres, Yth Fel; *U Calif at Davis; Laboratory Research.*

FONG, Peying
Ellenville HS; Ellenville, NY (4-135) Cpt, Chldr; Dbte Tm; Drama; Hmrm; Ed, Lit Mag; Math C; NHS; A-Ed, Sch P; Sci C; Span C; SC; Tnns; JV, Tr; Elk A; MLS; NEDT; Regent Schol; *Yale U; Pre-Med.*

FONTENETTE, Rachelle
San Diego Sr HS; San Diego, CA (231-707) Band; Bkbl; MVP, Sftbl; Alg A; COM; Hon Prog; Math A; Ntl Achv Schol; NMS; Opt A; Sci A; Spch A; Star Student; Type A; Co- cpt, Vlbl; Most Improved, Vlbl; *Morehouse Col; Probation Off.*

FONTENOT, Carole Anne
Thomas Jefferson HS; Port Arthur, TX; NHS; *Lamar Col; Secondary Ed.*

FONTENOT, Judy Ann
Baker HS; Baker, LA; Band; BC; *Spencer Draughon Col; Executive Secy.*

FONTENOT, Wendy Faye
Kinder HS; Kinder, LA (15-72) Cpt, Band; VP, 4H; Semi-Fin, InterAct C; SC; Bkbl; Cl Fav; H of F; HCt; Most Out; *La Col; Elem Ed.*

FONTES, Francine Renee
Riverdale Joint Union HS; Riverdale, CA (1-125) FFA; Hmrm; Secy, SC; Most Out; Star Student; Type A; Val; Secy, SB; Star Greenhand; Secy, CSF; Chptr Degree, FFA; Pres, Fresh Cl; Stu o-t Mo; Pep C; Ed, FFA Newsletter; *Calif Polytechnic U.*

FONTES, George Anthony
Riverdale Union HS; Riverdale, CA (1-80) CYO; Rptr, FFA; Hmrm; Sch Achieve Tm; SC; CSF; COM; Chamber of Comm A; Coun of Teach A; Elk A; Sci A; Star Student; Val; Pep C; VP, CSF; FFA Jr Rodeo; FFA Food Drive; Fresno Fair; Small Engine Tm; Banking Quiz; Yth o-t Yr, Rvrdale Chmbr of Comm; *Calif Polytech St U; Industrial Engr.*

FONTES, Philip
Riverdale Joint Union HS; Riverdale, CA; FFA; Hmrm; SC; Cr-Ctry; Tr; CSF; Star Student; Val; Yth Fel; Pres, Fresh Cl; Ch, Homecoming Wk; VP, SB; FFA Del, St Convention; Stu o-t Mo; Jr Play; Photographer, Ann, FFA.

FONVILLE, Debra Marie
Central HS; St Paul, MN; A Cap Choir; Bus C; FBLA; JV, Bkbl; JV, Tnns; God & Country A; JA A; Ntl Conf Chr & Jews; *Dakota Co TVI; Fashion Merchandising.*

FOOTE, Carol Ann
Glenbrook S HS; Glenview, IL (42-597) Band; Dbte Tm; Key C; NHS; Pres, SC; Tres, Jr Cl; Cr-Ctry; JV, Swim; JV, Tr; Hon Prog; Fin, COM; Tribune Schol; *US Air Force Acad; Interntl Affairs.*

FOOTE, Cynthia Denise
Tyner HS; Chattanooga, TN; BC; *Lee Col; Ed Training.*

FOOTE, Kelly Jo
York Central HS; Retsof, NY (6-90) NHS; Ski C; JV, Soccer; Hon Prog; Water Ballet; *Math.*

FOOTE, Robert Martin
Bay HS; Bay Village, OH (181-375) Band; Ensm; Key C; ARC; Yth Fel; 3 Yr Summer Sch Schol; Pres, Church Yth Group; Water Safety Instructor; Pres, Explorer Post; *Ohio St U; Dentistry.*

FOOTE, Ruth Anita
Lafayette HS; Lafayette, LA; Dbte Tm; Fin, GS; Co-Ch, Hmrm; InterClub Coun; Ed, Lit Mag; NFL; Rptr, Sch P; SC; COM; HCt; Poet A; Swtht; Hon Prog; Mr & Missee LHS Court; *Journ.*

FOOTE, William LeFelton
Jim Hill HS; Jackson, MS; Alg A; *Hind Jr Col; Telephone Engr.*

FORBES, Angela Marie
Duke Ellington Sch o t Arts; Washington, DC (8-151) Chor; Drama; Ensm; FBLA; 4H; Hmrm; Sch P; St Stu Congress; SC; COM; Hon Prog; I Dare You; Most Out; Type A; WW; Woodward Found; Eng A; Acad School; *Pace U; Theatre.*

FORBES, Bonita Lucille
Camden Co HS; Camden, NC (27-100) BC; Chem C; Chor; Dbte Tm; Secy, Drama; Secy, 4H; Hmrm; Lit Mag; NHS; Phys C; Bio A; Citz A; Cl Fav; Hon Prog; MLS; *NC Central U; Nurs.*

FORBES, Gloria Yvonne
Woodside HS; Woodside, CA; Chor; Jr Miss Pageant; Lit Mag; SC; Cpt, Bkbl; Cpt, Sftbl; Cpt, Swim; Citz A; Math A; Schol Hon's; Ldrship Abilities A; Peer Tutor; *U of Sou Calif; Med.*

FORBES, M Danelle
Yuma HS; Yuma, CO (5-107) Band; Parl, 4H; *Colorado U; Phar.*

FORBES, Michael Aloysius
Cardinal Dougherty HS; Philadelphia, PA (90-500) CYO; Math C; Ntl Yth Conf; Bkbl; Cr-Ctry; Yth Foundation; Fin, COM; Fin, Hons Prog; *Messiah Col; Math.*

FORBES, Robert Steven
Bayshore HS; Bradenton, FL (7-279) Pres, Band; Chor; NHS; Co-Cpt, Bkbl; Cpt, Tnns; COM; Drum Major; Most Talented; Coaches A, Bkbl; MVP, Tnns.

FORBES, Tommy Lee
Grant HS; Portland, OR; A Cap Choir; Chor; Sch Achieve Tm; COM; Cl Fav; Star Student; Choir; Drum Mjrte; *PCC; Math.*

FORBUS, Leonard Scott
Pacific HS; San Bernardino, CA (40-632) Band; Tres, InterAct C; Orch; Tnns; CSF; COM; Hist A; Calif Found For Ldrship; *Fla A & M Col; Law.*

FORCE, John R
Kennedy Sr HS; Denver, CO (281-520) JV, Tr; *Colo St U; Bus.*

FORCE, Richard Allen
Williamston HS; Williamston, MI (75-150) Band; 4H; Order/Arrow; Var C; JV, Bsbl; Mgr, Bkbl; Cr-Ctry; Mgr, Ftbl; JV, Tnns; 4H A; BSct; *Lansing Comm Col.*

FORCH, Cornell Dion
Proviso E HS; Maywood, IL (139-712) NHS; Ftbl; Hon Prog; Ftbl Ltr; HR; Schol A; *U of Ill; Ath Adm.*

FORD, Alan M
Humboldt HS; Humboldt, KS (23-68) Dbte Tm; Math C; ARC; Var C; Bkbl; Co-Cpt, Ftbl; Tr; Journ A; NEDT; VofDEM; *Pittsburgh St U; Computer Sci.*

FORD, Alison
Little Rock Central HS; Little Rock, AR (58-666) BC; Fr C; FBLA; Mjrte; SC; Y-Tns; COM; Hon Prog; Church Handbell Chor; St Senate Pag; Church Handbell Choir; Drill Tm; Church Yth Choir; Minister of Ed, Yth Wk; *Baylor U; Med.*

FORD, Apryl Arlena
Jefferson Twp Sr HS; Dayton, OH (13-181) Chor; Hmrm; Sch P; SC; Tr; *US Air Force Acad.*

FORD, Betty Ann
N Natchez HS; Natchez, MS; A Cap Choir; Pres, BC; Chor; Lit Mag; Secy, Sr Cl; Secy, Jr Cl; Amer Leg A; COM; Citz A; DARGCA; H of F; MLS; Type A; *U of Miss; Acct.*

FORD, Carole Lynn
Grand Island HS; Grand Island, NY (19-340) AFS; Chor; Ger C; NHS; Bio A; COM; Hon Prog; NEDT; Phy A; Regent Schol; *Valparaiso U; Lang.*

FORD, Cathy Anita
Wilburton HS; Wilburton, OK (15-62) Ann; Pres, Chldr; FHA; FTA; GS; 4H; NHS; Spch C; Rptr, SC; Var C; Bkbl; Amer Leg A; HQn; Masonic A; Spch A; Type A; Val; Yth Fel; *Eastern Okla St Col; Elem Ed.*

FORD, Cylinda Nannette
Weatherford HS; Weatherford, TX (22-252) Secy, FBLA; FTA; NHS; Vlbl; *Weatherford Col; Elem Ed.*

FORD, Diane K
Ulysses HS; Ulysses, KS; Chldr; Ger C; NHS; Y-Tns; Pres, Jr Cl; *Kans U; Occupational Therapy.*

FORD, Fran Alecia
Eastwood HS; El Paso, TX (450-900) Chldr; FHA; SC; Type A; Nom, WW; *U of Tex; Bus Adm.*

FORD, Frederick Jackson
Harlem HS; Harlem, GA (1-150) BC; Drama; VP, Math C; SC; Alg A; COM; Gov Honor Prog; NMF; Drama A; *W Va U; Pre-Med.*

FORD, Gina Fay
Dayton HS; Dayton, TX (5-105) Ann; Secy, Chess C; Pres, FHA; Rptr, FTA; Ch, Hmrm; Pres, NHS; Rptr, Sch P; Sci C; Span C; SC; Cr-Ctry; Golf; Tnns; Tr; Balfour A; DARGCA; Hon Prog; Journ A; Math A; Q & S; Vlbl; WW; Miss Dayton HS; Yth for Christ; Most Versatile; Past Worthy Adv, Rainbow Girls; Pres, MYF; Most Intellectual; *Baylor U; Pre-Law.*

FORD, Glenn Francis
Paraiso Jr Sr HS; Paraiso, CANAL ZONE (6-75) Band; Chor; Hmrm; Sch P; Span C; SC; Bsbl; Ftbl; Soccer; Tnns; Co-Cpt, Tr; COM; H of F; Hist A; Interlochen Ntl Mus; MLS; Most Out; Poet A; ARC A; Sci A; Spch A; *Rutgers Col; Computer Programming.*

FORD, Jack Philip
S Grand Prairie HS; Grand Prairie, TX; A Cap Choir; Rptr, Chor; Dbte Tm; Drama; VP, Ger C; Madrigal; Spch C; Tr; Journ A; Opt A; Opt Out Tn; Bicentennial Musical; 1st Pl, UIL; *Rice U; Physics.*

FORNSHELL, Mark James
Hurdsfield HS; Hurdsfield, ND (1-8) Ann; Chor; Sch P; SC; Pres, Soph Cl; Bsbl; Bkbl; Sftbl; Tnns; Cl Fav; Hon Prog; MLS; Type A; Jamestown Col.

FORREST, Craig William
Mission Viejo HS; Mission Viejo, CA; Cal Poly at San Luis Obispo; Elec.

FORREST, Randal Lee
Conroe HS; Conroe, TX (449-825) Fr C; Sam Houston St Col; Bus Adm.

FORRESTER, Beth Christine
Parkview HS; Springfield, MO (25-409) Lat C; Math C; Bkbl; Sftbl; SW Bible Col; Acct.

FORRESTER, Gena Alexandra
Cal Prep Sch; Encino, CA (4-35) All Amer Yth; Chldr; Chor; Drama; Jr Miss Pageant; Model UN; Orch; Sftbl; MVP, Tr; COM; Citz A; Hon Prog; Journ A; Sal; Cal St Northridge.

FORRESTER, Lisa Rennee
Papillion-LaVista Sr HS; Papillion, NE; GA'S; Foreign Lang C; NCE Sch of Commerce; Fashion Merchandising.

FORRESTER, Michael Lee
Giles Co HS; Pulaski, TN (22-160) BC; BS; Chem C; Fr C; Hmrm; Lat C; Order/Arrow; SC; Bkbl; Ftbl; Tnns; Amer Leg A; Order/Arrow A; Yth Fel; Pres, Church Singing Group; Win, Civitan Essay Contest; Martin Col; Law.

FORRESTER, Thomas Harvel
Giles Co HS; Pulaski, TN (8-150) BC; BS; Chem C; Fr C; Hmrm; Lat C; Order/Arrow; SC; Bkbl; Ftbl; Tnns; Amer Leg A; Order/Arrow A; Yth Fel; Pres, Church Singing Group; Pres, Sunday Sch; U of Tenn; Pre-Law.

FORRESTER, Vicky Lynn
Bridgman HS; Bridgman, MI (50%-106) Chor; Sch P; Sftbl.

FORRISTALL, Ronald Mark
Tulsa Daniel Webster HS; Tulsa, OK (1-243) Hmrm; Tres, Lat C; Model UN; NHS; Pres, Ski C; Var C; Cpt, Ftbl; Cl Fav; HCt; Masonic A; Most Out; Regent Schol; Bus Mgr, FCA; 'Warrior Chief'; NE Okla St U; Pre-Med.

FORRY, Donna Leigh
Manheim Twp HS; Lancaster, PA (15%-400) Band; Orch; JV, Hockey; Swim; Interlochen Ntl Mus; Sr Life Saving; Leaders C; Psych.

FORRY, Keith Raymond
Pine Grove Area HS; Pine Grove, PA (5-140) A Cap Choir; Co-Ed, Ann; BS; Chess C; Chor; Drama; Hmrm; NHS; MLS; NMF; NEDT; Pres Clroom for Young Amer; Stu o-t Month Schuykill Co Chor; Penn St U; Chem.

FORSBERG, Debra Jane
Concordia Acad; St Paul, MN (1-56) Band; NHS; Secy, SC; Bkbl; Cr-Ctry; Tnns; COM; Hon Prog; NEDT; Val; WW; Vlbl; Augsburg Col; Home Ec.

FORSELL, Jim Arnold
Forest Lake HS; Forest Lake, MN; FFA; 4H; Var C; JV, Ftbl; Hockey; Tr; 4H A; Agr.

FORSHEY, John Patrick
Albuquerque HS; Albuquerque, NM (50-700) BS; Chor; Fr C; NHS; Ski C; Soccer; Swim; Outst Chor; Baylor U; Mus.

FORSMAN, Laurie Ann
Groveton HS; Alexandria, VA; Drama; Model UN; Tnns; VICA; George Mason U; Bus Adm.

FORSTER, David Alan
Kearsley HS; Flint, MI (5-450) A Cap Choir; Dbte Tm; NHS; Golf; Tnns; COM; Hon Prog; Spch A; David Lipscomb Col; Math.

FORSTER, Nancy Kaye
Beloit Jr-Sr HS; Beloit, KS (25-70) Band; Chldr; Chor; Parl, FHA; Orch; Ch, Y-Tns; Bkbl; Sftbl; Tr; Eng A; Art A.

FORSTER, Stephen J
Durand HS; Durand, WI (25-136) Fr C; Order/Arrow; Bkbl; Ftbl; God & Country A; Order/Arrow A; Eagle Sct; Pius XII A; Marquette U; Dentistry.

FORT, James Robert
Filer HS; Filer, ID (12-76) Band; Key C; Tr.

FORT, Theresa
Chester HS; Chester, PA (35-673) Band; Bus C; Chor; Ch, FBLA; Mjrte; JV, Bkbl; Hockey; JV, Sftbl; Temple U; Private Secy.

FORT, Thomas Otto
Macedonia HS; Moncks Corner, SC (7-90) BC; Fr C; FTA; Gov Honor Prog; Math A; Lib C; US Navy; Nuclear Power.

FORTE, Mary Katherine
St Mary's Acad; Englewood, CO (4-58) Ed, Ann; Cpt, Chldr; Fr C; French NHS; Hmrm; NHS; Ski C; SC; Var C; Bkbl; Sftbl; Hon Prog; Math A; JV, Vlbl; WW; Miss 'Spirit of 76'; Stanford U; Bio.

FORTENBERRY, Jewel Kay
Bogalusa HS; Bogalusa, LA (30-256) Band; BC; Chor; Drama; Math C; Sch P; Tres, Span C; Bkbl; Cpt, Sftbl; Type A; Northeast Col; Acct.

FORTENBURY, Martha Lucinda
Burns HS; Lawndale, NC (23-250) FBLA; FHA; Rptr, Hmrm; SC; HCt; King's Col; Fashion Merchandising.

FORTIER, Thomas Wayne
Mount Ida HS; Mount Ida, AR (7-35) Band; BS; FFA; Alg A; Hist A; Sci.

FORTNER, Charles Richard
Claremore HS; Claremore, OK (30-290) A Cap Choir; Chor; Drama; Ensm; Madrigal; Balfour A; Elk A; Cpt, A Theory; All-St Choir; All-Dist Choir; Okla Baptist U; Mus.

FORTNER, Leesa Gayle
Eupora HS; Eupora, MS (6-84) F-Ed, Ann; Band; BC; FTA; Cpt, Mjrte; F-Ed, Sch P; John Philip Sousa A; Miss St U; Acct.

FORTNER, Martha Anita
Eupora HS; Eupora, MS (10-84) Band; Delta St U; Phys Therapy.

FORTNER, Peggy Anne
Sylvan Hills HS; N Little Rock, AR; FBLA; FHA; NHS; Sftbl; Yth Fel; Drill Tm; Nurs.

FORTNER, Rachel Kay
Logan Elm HS; Circleville, OH (65-210) Bus C; Secy, 4H; NHS; Ed, Sch P; Span C; Bkbl; Sftbl; Fin, Tr; 4H A; Yth Fel; Bowl C; Valentine Qn; Y-F Pres; HR; Anderson Col; Elem Ed.

FORTNER, Terry Lynn
Sylvan Hills HS; N Little Rock, AR (8-421) A Cap Choir; NHS; Bsbl; Ftbl; Sci A; Yth Fel; Med.

FORTSON, Carolyn Marie
Russell HS; Hurtsboro, AL; A Cap Choir; Fin, FHA; 4H; Secy, Sci C; 4H A; ROTC A; Spch A; Miss FHA A.

FORTUNE, Angela Louise
Parkway N Sr HS; St Louis, MO (150-700) Bsbl; Sftbl; Tr; Florissant Valley Col; Phys Ed Teacher.

FORTUNE, Twila Jeane
John Herbert Phillips HS; Birmingham, AL (20%-300) Chldr; Secy, FBLA; NHS; Citz A; Most Out; WW; Alumni A; U of Ala; Phys Ed.

FORTUNER, Albert Joseph
Saint Rose HS; Carbondale, PA (4-54) Chor; Tres, NHS; Sch Achieve Tm; Ski C; Pres, Jr Cl; JV, Bkbl; JA A; U of Scranton; Computer Sci.

FOSBENNER, Kathe Claire
John W Hallahan HS; Philadelphia, PA (20-432) CYO; Chor; NHS; Pres, Orch; COM; Hon Prog; Ntl Sci Symposium; WW; Holy Family Col; Nurs.

FOSKEY, Thomas Michael
Treutlen Co HS; Soperton, GA (10%-83) A-Ed, Ann; VP, HiY; SC; VP, Sr Cl; MVP, Ftbl; Cpt, Ftbl; Middle Ga Col; Acct.

FOSNAUGH, William Lee
Lancaster HS; Lancaster, OH; Band; Ensm; Orch; Most Out; VP, Paramed Careers C; Band Coun; BSct; Appreciation Cert, Hospital Vol; Male Nurs.

FOSS, Dawn Pamela
Boothbay Region HS; Boothbay Harbor, ME (15-70) Mgr, Chldr; Chor; Hmrm; A-Ed, Sch P; SC; Mgr, Bkbl; Mgr, Ftbl; Hon Prog; Thomas Col; Secy.

FOSS, Jeffrey Scott
Boothbay Region HS; Boothbay Harbor, ME; Var C; Bsbl; Bkbl; Co-Cpt, Ftbl; Best Defensive, Bsbl; Phys Ed.

FOSS, Kimberly Ann
Essex Junction HS; Essex Junction, VT; Span C; SC; Cpt, Swim; JA; Kite Flying A.

FOSTER, Amber Jo
Lee's Summit HS; Lees Summit, MO; Chor; Dbte Tm; Drama; Fin, GS; 4H; NFL; NHS; Ntl Yth Conf; A-Ed, Sch P; MVP, Sftbl; COM; Citz A; 4H A; Journ A; Opt A; Opt Out Tn; Poet A; Sci A; Spch A; Yth Fel; Pres, Yth Group; Painting A.

FOSTER, Benjamin Patrick
Daviess Co HS; Owensboro, KY (11-350) BC; FFA; Key C; NHS; VP, Pol Sci C; SC; COM; Chem A; Cl Fav; H of F; NMS; Ky Wesleyan U; Religion.

FOSTER, Beverly Diane
Woodlawn HS; Shreveport, LA; VP, Rainbow; Special Ed.

FOSTER, Cathy Diane
Reeds Spring HS; Reeds Spring, MO (25%-90) BC; Rptr, SC; Cpt, Bkbl; Tr; Math A; Pres A; Tr Medal; Drury Col; Acct.

FOSTER, Chuck Eric
Glendale HS; Springfield, MO (50%-650) MVP, Sftbl; MVP, Swim; MVP, Tr; Carpenter.

FOSTER, Daniel Haines
Mounds View HS; New Brighton, MN (85-655) Band; NHS; Ski C; Thes; JV, Cr-Ctry; JV, Tr; JV, Wrest; Citz A; Most Talented; Bus.

FOSTER, David Anderson
Woodrow Wilson HS; Portsmouth, VA (3-231) A-Ed, Ann; Drama; Sch Achieve Tm; Thes; Math A; Spch A; Mayor's Yth Advisory; Pres, Young Churchmen; Bio.

FOSTER, David James
Central HS; Omaha, NE; Lat C; Var C; Golf; Swim; Hon Prog.

FOSTER, Debbie Sue
St Joseph-Ogden HS; St Joseph, IL (40-130) Chor; Fr C; Bkbl; HCt; Type A; Milligan Col; Secretarial Sci.

FOSTER, Deborah Ann
Melbourne HS; Melbourne, FL (10%-786) Ger C; NHS; Bio A; COM; Hon Prog; Jr Civitan; Yth For Christ; Dist Band Comp; U of S Fla; Bio.

FOSTER, Delois
Hancock Central HS; Sparta, GA; Chor; FHA; 4H; NHS; Up Bound; NHS Cert; Chor Cert; Journ.

FOSTER, Donna Sue
Washington Co HS; Springfield, KY (10-177) Ann; CYO; Chor; Secy, FBLA; FHA; 4H; Ed, Sch P; Type A; Cand, Farm City Qn; PA; Gregg Shorthand A; Cert of Proficiency; Ltr of Commendations.

FOSTER, Doris Teresa
McCallum HS; Austin, TX (84-280) JV, Band; Chor; Fr C; FHA; Pres, Yth Fel; Gym; Blue Brigade, Dance Tm; Church Choir; U of Tex; Home Ec.

FOSTER, Dorothy Louise
Glasgow HS; Newark, DE (7-450) AFS; Chor; Hockey; Swim; HR; Child Care & Dev.

FOSTER, Eileen Marie
Madras Sr HS; Madras, OR (11-120) A Cap Choir; Band; Hmrm; NHS; Ntl Yth Conf; Span C; SC; Pres, Thes; Var C; JV, Tnns; Citz A; Kiwanis A; Yth Fel; Vlbl; Outst A Cappella Member; St Thespian A-Schol; Soroptomist Schol; Outst Lang Arts A; Willamette U; Theatre.

FOSTER, Frances Elizabeth
Claiborne Acad; Haynesville, LA (5-41) Band; Chem C; VP, Fr C; 4H; Lit Ral; Cpt, Mjrte; Orch; Pres, SC; Bkbl; Sftbl; Cl Fav; NE La U.

FOSTER, Gail Westley
Oak Hills HS; Cincinnati, OH (7-855) Band; Drama; Ger C; Thes; Mgr, Bkbl; Citz A; Principal's A; Cincinnati Bible Seminary.

FOSTER, Gregory Adolph
W Monroe HS; W Monroe, LA; Band; Bkbl; Tr; Sou U; Bus.

FOSTER, Hadley
Robert E Lee HS; San Antonio, TX (30%-550) V-Ch, Order/Arrow; Ftbl; Sftbl; Swim; Tex A&M; Oceanography.

FOWLER, Lloyd Kammy
Forest Park HS; Beaumont, TX (200-500) JV, Ftbl; Sftbl; JV, Tr; Bio HR; *Bio.*

FOWLER, Lucius Sloan III
Wade Hampton HS; Greenville, SC (120-450) Chem C; JV, Ftbl; Hon Prog; Church Summer Mission Worker; *Clemson U.*

FOWLER, Margie
Chester HS; Chester, PA (20%-750) Ed, Sch P; *Goldey Beacom Col; Bus Ed.*

FOWLER, Martha Jane
Marina HS; Huntington Beach, CA; Rptr, Sch P; Span C; Bkbl; Hockey; Sftbl; Nurs; GAA; Vlbl; Mentally Gifted Minor Prog; Pres, Jr Walking Horse Assn; High Point Juvenile Champ Exhibitor; *Golden West Col; Nurs.*

FOWLER, Michael Gregg
King William HS; King William, VA; Ed, Ann; Rptr, BC; Drama; Fr C; 4H; Ed, Lit Mag; Order/Arrow; Bus Mgr, Sch P; Span C; Pres, SC; Mgr, Bkbl; Ftbl; Mgr, Tr; COM; Gov Honor Prog; Hon Prog; Journ A; Order/Arrow A; Q&S A; Spch A; Col Enrichment Prog; *U of Va; Math.*

FOWLER, Neil Robert
Christian Sch of York; York, PA (1-12) Band; Chor; Hmrm; Ntl Yth Conf; Pres, SC; Soccer; WW; *Acct.*

FOWLER, Sally Ross
Beeson Acad; Hattiesburg, MS (20%-40) Ann; BC; Chor; COM; NEDT; WW; Co Cpt, Drill Tm; Best Dressed; Pres, Foreign Lang C; Yth Coun; Spirit; *U of Miss; Pre-Law.*

FOWLER, Sandra Kay
N Gwinnett HS; Suwanee, GA (10%-150) Bkbl; Sftbl; Alg A.

FOWLER, Sandra Lee
Forest Park HS; Beaumont, TX (73-425) Chor; Ger C; NHS; Pres, Orch; ARC; Tnns; COM; Cum Laude Graduate; *U of Tex; Nurs.*

FOWLER, Susan Dianne
McKinney HS; McKinney, TX (12-200) A-Ed, Ann; Drama; FHA; FTA; Lat C; Lat NHS; Ed, Sch P; Span C; Spch C; MLS; Band Lib; Vlbl; Most Dependable; Outst, Band; *Lindenwood Col; Cinematography.*

FOWLER, Wanda Jean
Macomb Sr HS; Macomb, IL (38-226) Chor; NHS; Thes; *Judson Col; Christian Ed.*

FOWLIS, Barbara
John O'Connell HS; San Francisco, CA (16-153) Pres, Hmrm; NHS; SC; Type A; Win, Close Up Contest; *Heald Bus Col; Legal Secy.*

FOWLIS, Connie Marie
Warren W Reserve HS; Warren, OH; Chldr; Chor; Hmrm; Cpt, Tr; Bio A; Citz A; Cl Fav; Hon Prog; *Clark Tech Col; Nurs.*

FOWLIS, Rondalee
Warren W Reserve HS; Warren, OH; Band; Fr C; NHS; Rotary Wheel.

FOX, Andrew Gilbert
DeKalb HS; Waterloo, IN (4-321) CYO; Chem C; Chess C; Ger C; Phys C; Sci C; JV, Ftbl; Golf; Tnns; *Notre Dame U; Nuclear Engr.*

FOX, Bridget Raye
Gainesville HS; Gainesville, TX; A Cap Choir; CYO; Chldr; Chor; Dbte Tm; Drama; FHA; Mod Mus Mas; Span C; Spch C; SC; Bkbl; Soccer; Sftbl; Tnns; 4H A; Poet A; ARC A; Spch A; Vlbl; Campfire Girls; Art A; *Art.*

FOX, Connie Sue
Naperville Central HS; Naperville, IL (220-450) Band; Chor; Ensm; Pres, FNA; ARC; F-Ed, Sch P; COM; Hon Prog; Interlochen Ntl Mus; *W Suburban Col; Nurs.*

FOX, Danaille Pauline
Wyanet Comm HS; Wyanet, IL (1-23) Band; Chldr; NHS; Span C; Spch C; VP, Thes; Alg A; Math A; Spch A; VofDEM; *Northern Illinois Univ; Finance.*

FOX, David Alan
Brush HS; Lyndhurst, OH; Ftbl; Tr; Ath A; *Eckerd Col; Broadcasting.*

FOX, Eben Samuel
Woodmere Acad; Woodmere, NY; Arch; Key C; Co-Ed, Sch P; JV, Soccer; Bio A; COM; Sci A; *Cornell U; Bio.*

FOX, Edward Phelps
Terrell Acad; Dawson, GA (10-55) Chor; Order/Arrow; JV, Ftbl; Tr; Yth Fel; BSct; Church & Bell Choirs.

FOX, Glenn Allen
Milford Township HS; Milford, IL (25-47) Ger C; Bkbl; Ftbl; Golf; Odd Fellow Fin; *Med.*

FOX, Hans James
Defiance HS; Defiance, OH (2-300) A Cap Choir; Drama; NHS; Bkbl; *Nuclear Med.*

FOX, James Gerry
Jamestown HS; Jamestown, NY (112-520) Tres, A Cap Choir; Ann; Tres, Band; Pres, Chor; Community Yth Symph; Drama; Hmrm; Pres, Key C; Madrigal; VP, Orch; Order/Arrow; ARC; Sch P; Span C; SC; Bkbl; Cr-Ctry; Sftbl; Tr; COM; Citz A; Kiwanis A; Most Out; NMS; NEDT; Order/Arrow A; Yth Fel; Top Mus, Sch, Section; Outst Jr, Sr Band; *Edinboro St Col; Mus.*

FOX, James Michael
Glenmora HS; Glenmora, LA (7-32) Tres, FBLA; Hmrm; Lit Ral; NHS; SC; Bsbl; Bkbl; COM; Cl Fav; All Dist Bsbl; World Geog A; *LSU; Phys Ed.*

FOX, Jane Byrne
Elk Valley Christian Sch; Charleston, WV (10-22) Cpt, Chldr; Chor; Span C; Chem A; MLS; FPC Tumbling Tumbliers; *W Va St U; Nurs.*

FOX, Jayne Carol
Midwest City HS; Midwest City, OK (50-550) Fr C; Hmrm; NHS; Tnns; H of F; HCt; Hon Prog; Swtht; Yth Fel; Jr Executive Board, VP, Pep C; Executive Board, Princess, SC; Principal's HR ; Young Life; Graduation Usherette; Okla Hon Soc; *Okla St U; Health.*

FOX, Joanna Lee
Mooresville HS; Mooresville, IN (10-310) VP, 4H; Span C; *Taylor U; Math.*

FOX, Karen Angela
Madison Acad HS; Huntsville, AL (5-43) A Cap Choir; BC; Chor; Dbte Tm; Ensm; Span C; Var C; COM; Hon Prog; Star Student; *Freed-Hardeman Col; Nurs.*

FOX, Kenny Lee
East Waterloo HS; Waterloo, IA; Chess C; Drama; JA A; 1st in Cl, Driver's Ed.

FOX, Linda Sharon
Palo Duro HS; Amarillo, TX (3-445) Chor; FTA; Hmrm; SC; Pres, Soph Cl; Smiler; *U of Tex; Math.*

FOX, Marilyn Kim
Bakersfield R-4 Sch; Bakersfield, MO (3-16) Ann; Band; Chldr; Chor; FHA; VP, NHS; Sch P; SC; VP, Sr Cl; Rptr, Jr Cl; Secy, Soph Cl; Bkbl; Sftbl; Hist A; Drama A; Chldr A; *SMSU.*

FOX, Melinda Sue
Yosemite Union HS; Oakhurst, CA (15-120) Co-Cpt, Chldr; Drama; Hmrm; SC; Lion A; *Calif St U; Public Speaking.*

FOX, Nancy Kathryn
Leesburg HS; Leesburg, FL; A Cap Choir; Band; Sci C; Secy, 'S' C; *Psychiatry.*

FOX, Norman Keaton
Middleton HS; Charleston, SC (21-263) Cpt, Band; BC; Chor; Ensm; NHS; Orch; Tnns; All St, All Regional; Hon, Bands; All St, All Regional, Orch; Superior, Solo & Ensm; *Clemson U; Chem Engr.*

FOX, Rebecca Jane
Montour Sr HS; McKees Rocks, PA (61-439) Band; Drama; NHS; Orch; Ski C; God & Country A; HCt; NEDT; Cpt, Drill Tm; WW; *Westminster Col; Communications.*

FOX, Robert Alan
Riverside HS; Ellwood City, PA (15-230) Ger C; NHS; Alg A; *Geneva Col; Bio.*

FOX, Shelley Carla
Tillamook HS; Tillamook, OR; A Cap Choir; Band; Chor; Ensm; Mod Mus Mas; SC; VP, Soph Cl; Girl o-t Mo; Secy, Med Explorers; Miss Tillamook Hi Princess; Pep C; Oceanaires; Pres, Yth League; *Mount Hood Comm Col; Med.*

FOX, Susan Marie
Lafayette HS; Lexington, KY (33%-700) Band; BC; Mu Alpha Theta; NHS; Orch; *Pol Sci.*

FOX, Susan Michele
Lindenhurst Sr HS; Lindenhurst, NY; *Nassau Comm Col; Lib Arts.*

FOX, Tammi Rayna
Harrah HS; Harrah, OK (1-120) Band; FHA; NHS; Span C; Math A; Off, Booster C.

FOX, Teresa Mae
Tascosa HS; Amarillo, TX (89-486) A Cap Choir; Chor; Pres, Drama; FHA; Madrigal; Cr-Ctry; God & Country A; Most Out; Yth Fel; Yth Leg; All St Chor; Outst Soloist, Solo Competition; Lead, Sch Mus; Semi-Fin, NATS Solo Competition; *N Tex St U; Mus.*

FOX, Thomas Howard
Terrell Acad; Dawson, GA (3-47) Chor; Dbte Tm; Drama; Fr C; Secy, HiY; NHS; Order/Arrow; Var C; Tres, Jr Cl; Co-Cpt, Ftbl; Tr.

FOX, Warner Holly II
San Angelo Central HS; San Angelo, TX; Ger C; Order/Arrow; Var C; Ftbl; Soccer; Cl Fav; HKg; Order/Arrow A; Swtht; Yth Fel; Best Personality; Pres, FCA; *Angelo St U; Bus Mgt.*

FOXWORTH, Henry Eugene Jr
Mullins Sr HS; Mullins, SC; *Florence-Darlington Tech Col; Graphic Arts.*

FOXWORTH, Norma Jean
Geneva HS; Geneva, AL; FTA; Hmrm; SC; 4H A; Spch A; *George C Wallace Col; Nurs.*

FOXWORTH, Royce
Francis T Nicholls HS; New Orleans, LA; *U of New Orleans; Journ.*

FOXX, Sherry Elaine
DeSoto HS; De Soto, KS; Cpt, Chldr; Chor; Mjrte; Sch P; COM; Hon Prog; Type A; *JUCO.*

FOY, Jessica Herren
Tuscola Sr HS; Waynesville, NC (10%-400) Band; Fr C; GS; Hmrm; NHS; Tres, Sci C; SC; Hist A; Most Out; *Wake Forest U; Hist.*

FOY, Joyce Ellen
N Central HS; Indianapolis, IN (39-1300) A Cap Choir; Chor; Hmrm; NHS; SC; Recognition A; Schol Citation; *Greenville Col; Special Ed.*

FOY, Veronica Diane
Plainfield HS; Plainfield, NJ (50-500) Ann; NHS; Secy, ARC; Coun of Teach A; Hon Prog; ARC A; VP, Young Adult Choir; Jr Church Clerk; Sunday Sch Teacher; *Howard U; Med Tech.*

FOY, Vickie
San Juan HS; Blanding, UT (3-89) Pres, FHA; NHS; Citz A; Math A; *Brigham Young U; Nurs.*

FRAATS, Patricia Lynn
Lane Tech HS; Chicago, IL (99-1008) Key C; Tr; St Scholar; Major Art Tr; Newspaper Schol; Bible Quiz All Star Tm; Medal; Soc of Women Engr A; *Moody Bible Inst; Bible Theology.*

FRACTION, Lynette Marie
Washburn HS; Minneapolis, MN (10%-500) *St Catherines Col; Communications.*

FRAHER, Cathleen Mary
Prescott HS; Prescott, AZ (30-496) CYO; Tres, FBLA; Tres, FTA; NHS; Type A; 1st Cl GSct; *N Ariz U; Elem Ed.*

FRAHER, Lynn Ann
Odell Comm HS; Odell, IL (1-31) Ann; CYO; Pres, Fr C; Ed, Sch P; S-T, Var C; Golf; Sftbl; Amer Leg A; Bio A; COM; Citz A; Hist A; Hon Prog; Math A; Sci A; St Scholar; Val; VofDEM; Vlbl; WW; *U of Ill; Acct.*

FRAHER, Therese Mildred
Prescott HS; Prescott, AZ (130-475) CYO; FBLA; *Yavapai Jr Col; Bus.*

FRAHM, Judd Paul
William Kelley HS; Silver Bay, MN (12-161) A Cap Choir; Chor; Drama; Ensm; ARC; Sci C; SC; Thes; Var C; Bsbl; Ftbl; Hockey; Tr; HCt; Sports Ltrs; Lifesaving A; A-HR; Kelley Players A; *U of Minn; Dentistry.*

FRAKES, Michael Bruce
Lanphier HS; Springfield, IL (64-500) Band; Order/Arrow; Bsbl; Order/Arrow A; VP, Church Dist Yth Fel; Regional Champs, Bsbl; BSct A's; *U of Ill; Computer Sci.*

FRALEY, Douglas Jerome
Muskegee HS; Muskogee, OK (130-550) Drama; Fr C; Tres, Hmrm; NFL; Ski C; Spch C; Thes; COM; Citz A; Cl Fav; God & Country A; Hist A; Hon Prog; Most Out; Spch A; Yth Fel; *Oral Roberts U; Law.*

FRALEY, Jana Lee
Jefferson Davis HS; Montgomery, AL (40%-760) FBLA; Tri-HiY; Adult Choir; 4-Part Ensm; VP, Church Yth Group; Tres, Al-NW Fl Christian Yth Fel; *Secretarial.*

FRALEY, Michael Allen
Papillion HS; Papillion, NE (14-357) Ger C; NHS; ARC; JV, Bsbl; JV, Ftbl; NMS; W Point Summer Workshop; HR; *MIT; Nuclear Engr.*

FRALEY, Michelle
Madonna HS; Weirton, WV (4-120) Chldr; FNA; InterAct C; NHS; Tnns; COM; High Sch Yr Avg; *W Va U; Phys Therapy.*

FRALEY, Sandra Lee
Hobbs HS; Hobbs, NM; Band; *NM Jr Col; Nurs.*

FRALEY, Tammy Elaine
Cherryville Sr HS; Cherryville, NC (12-136) Chldr; Ensm; Fr C; FBLA; InterAct C; Math C; Sci C; VP, Art C; Miss Photogenic, NC Tn Qn Pageant.

FRAME, Gail Ruth
Smithtown HS E; St James, NY (75%-300) Band; Chor; Ski C; JV, Sftbl; *Suffolk Comm Col; Liberal Arts.*

FRAMPTON, Peggy Sue
Kingsway Regional HS; Swedesboro, NJ; Cpt, Mjrte; NHS; *Gloucester Co Col; Legal Secy.*

FRANC, Susan Miller
Osceola HS; Kissimmee, FL (50-200) Pres, A Cap Choir; Ann; BC; Chor; Ensm; Key C; Secy, SC; Superior Chor Medal; *Stetson U.*

FRANCE, Debbie Lynne
Acad o-t Holy Names; Tampa, FL (4-68) Ann; CYO; NHS; Span C; Span NHS; SC; Pres, Jr Cl; Pres, Soph Cl; Swim; Hon Prog; Intramural; 'Miss Pride', Swim; *Bucknell U; Liberal Arts.*

FRANCE, Kelley Lynn
Lutheran HS; Burbank, CA (10-84) A-Ed, Ann; VP, SC; CSF; *Brooks Col; Interior Design.*

FRANCE, Kimberley Anne
Wayne HS; Dayton, OH (200-741) Band; NHS; Yth Fel; Church Choir; *U of Nebr; Ecology.*

FRANCIS, Calvin Leon
Sacramento Sr HS; Sacramento, CA (86-482) COM; Citz A; JV Ftbl Ltr; CJSF A; *Consumnes River Col; Bus.*

FRANCIS, Deborah Hart
Bayshore Christian Sch; Tampa, FL (2-24) Hmrm; SC; S-T, Soph Cl; Sftbl; FCA; Vlbl; *Colo Col; Med Tech.*

FRANCIS, Donald James
Harrison HS; Colorado Springs, CO (115-425) Key C; JV, Ftbl; JV, Wrest; JA A; *US Military Col; Bio.*

FRANCIS, Douglas Allen
Gridley Union HS; Gridley, CA (63-164) CYO; FFA; 4H; Sch Achieve Tm; Bkbl; Sftbl; 4H A; Greenhand, Chapter, FFA; St, Qualified Showman, FFA; *Butte Comm Col; Agr.*

FRANCIS, Janet Sheila
Erasmus Hall HS; Brooklyn, NY; Chor; Sch Achieve Tm; Tnns; *Mus.*

FRANCIS, Janice Lee
Van-Far R-1 HS; Vandalia, MO; Chor.

FRANCIS, Jerome Howard
Bethel HS; Hampton, VA; Band; 4H; JV, Bkbl; Ftbl; Tr; *Hampton Inst.*

FRANCIS, Mark David
Davis County Comm HS; Bloomfield, IA (15-140) A Cap Choir; VP, Band; Chor; NHS; Span C; *Ozark Bible Col; Mus.*

FRANCIS, Mark Kevin
Parker Sr HS; Janesville, WI (104-608) A Cap Choir; Band; Chor; Tr; Ath Trnr.

FRANCIS, Oteka Gail
Blanchard HS; Blanchard, OK; F-Ed, Ann; Chem C; Chor; Ensm; FHA; Hmrm; NHS; ARC; Sch P; Sci C; Span C; Tres, SC; Var C; Bkbl; Sftbl; Swim; Tr; COM; Cl Fav; HQn; Hon Prog; ARC A; Secy of St A; Pres, Pep C; WW; Rep, Sr Cl; *Okla U; Fashion Merchandising.*

FRANCIS, Tim John
Bishop Ryan HS; Minot, ND (5-91) BS; NHS; Bkbl; Tr; COM; Most Out; Hardest Worker, Most Improved, Tr; *Minot St U.*

FRANCK, Daniel Paul
Central HS; LaCrosse, WI (150-540) A Cap Choir; Chor; Ensm; Hmrm; SC; COM; Most Out; Pres A; Yth Leg; Artistic A; St Fair Art A; Vocal A; *Oral Roberts U; Bus.*

FRANCKE, Suzanne Frances
Northern Valley Regional HS; Old Tappan, NJ (103-350) A Cap Choir; Chor; *U of Bridgeport; Dental Hygiene.*

FRANCOIS, Demetria Louise
Simmesport HS; Simmesport, LA (1-55) Band; BC; FHA; Lit Ral; Mjrte; Sch Achieve Tm; Sci C; SC; Mgr, Bkbl; Sftbl; Tr; Bank Of Amer A; Coun of Teach A; I Dare You; Masonic A; Math A; Most Out; Sci A; Val; Yth Foundation A; Hon Schol; Corinne Saucier Schol; Patriotism A; Lib A; *Northwestern St U; Math Ed.*

FRANCOIS, Victoria Elizabeth
Nebraska City Lourdes; Nebraska City, NE (3-33) JV, Chldr; Chor; Secy, 4H; Sftbl; Tr; 4H A.

FRANDSEN, Jill Renee
Washington HS; Cherokee, IA (10-122) DARGCA; VP, Art C; Art C A.

FRANDSEN, Karen Elizabeth
SW DeKalb HS; Decatur, GA (50-400) Chor; Drama; Lat C; Rainbow; Sci C; Swim; Alg A; Hist A; Masonic A; ARC A; Yth Fel; Sr Sct; *Med.*

FRANGOS, Niki Dawn
St Mary's Acad; Englewood, CO (1-60) Pres, French NHS; GS; Pres, NHS; Orch; Ski C; VP, SC; Var C; Cpt, Swim; JA A; Dean's A; Swim A; *U of Colo; Law.*

FRANIA, Patricia Ann
Gar Mem HS; Wilkes-Barre, PA; NHS; Type A; Bus.

FRANK, Anthony Alan
Mendota Township HS; Mendota, IL (8-400) Pres, Band; Chor; Pres, 4H; NHS; Bkbl; Sftbl; 4H A; Hon Prog; NMS; *Purdue U; Vet Med.*

FRANK, Bill Richard
Beaver Dam HS; Beaver Dam, WI (20%-300) Chor; Drama; FFA; 4H; NFL; Tr; COM; 4H A; Hon Prog; FFA A's; Tr A's; *Oreg St U; Industrial Ed.*

FRANK, Danette Elaine
Wolsey Pub HS; Wolsey, SD (3-31) Ann; Band; Chldr; Chor; FHA; Ger C; Mjrte; Bkbl; Tr; HQn; Most Out; *Willmar Minn Voc Sch; Med Off Asst.*

FRANK, Debra Ann
Halifax Co Sr HS; South Boston, VA; Drama; FHA; Fin, GS; S-T, Lat C; NHS; ARC; VP, Tri-HiY; Presidential Phys Fitness A; Best Actress A; Lat A; *Vet Sci.*

FRANK, Debra Ann
Melville HS; Melville, LA; Band; BC; Hmrm; SC; Bkbl; *Spencer Col; Bus.*

FRANK, Donna Kay
Wilson Mem HS; Fishersville, VA; Chor; Ensm; Secy, FBLA; NHS; Type A; Spell A; *Blueridge Comm Col; Secy.*

FRANK, J Christopher P
Plymouth HS; Plymouth, NC (81-196) Monogram; Sci C; Span C; Tnns; Ath A; *U of NC; Bus.*

FRANK, Jaffa Vernon
Highland HS; Albuquerque, NM; Chor; Rainbow; Alg A; Bio A.

FRANK, James Richard
Saranac HS; Saranac, MI (20-89) MVP, Band; Arch; *Bob Jones U; Religion.*

FRANK, Janelle Kaye
Wolsey Pub HS; Wolsey, SD (1-27) Ann; Band; Chldr; Chor; Tres, FHA; Ger C; GS; Sch P; VP, Sci C; VP, SC; Pres, Jr Cl; Tres, Soph Cl; Bkbl; Tr; Most Out; Type A.

FRANK, Kari Kay
Spring Lake HS; Spring Lake, MI;

FRANK, Katheryn Marie
Beaver Dam Sr HS; Beaver Dam, WI (35-323) AFS; Chor; Drama; Ger C; 4H; Madrigal; Spch C; 4H A; Hon Prog; Stu o-t Mo; *U of Wis; Social Work.*

FRANK, Kathy Elizabeth
Hershey Sr HS; Hershey, PA (15-230) Cpt, Band; Pres, Chem C; Chor; Secy, FNA; Ger C; SC; Bkbl; Mgr, Swim; Tr; Beauty; Chem A; HCt; I Dare You; Most Out; Sci A; Swtht; Type A; *Med Secy.*

FRANK, Kim Marie
Boulder HS; Boulder, CO (83-517) CYO; Chor; *Colo U; Nurs.*

FRANK, Kimberly Ann
Winona Sr HS; Winona, MN (28-564) Band; Pres, Ger C; NHS; Var C; Bkbl; Co-Cpt, Sftbl; JV, Tnns.

FRANK, Linda Jean
Elk Grove HS; Elk Grove Village, IL (1-572) Ann; A-Ed, Lit Mag; NHS; Span C; SC; Hist A; Hon Prog; Lion A; Q&S A; St Scholar; Val; Pom Pon; Span A's; *Valparaiso U; Elem Ed.*

FRANK, Lisa Sue
Galva HS; Galva, IA; Ann; Band; 4H; SC; Bkbl; Sftbl; Tr; *Iowa Central Comm Col; Bus.*

FRANK, Mary Kristine
Berkeley Sr HS; Berkeley, MO (29-278) Co-Ed, Ann; Band; Drama; VP, FHA; Hmrm; NHS; SC; Cl Fav; *SE Mo St U; Psych.*

FRANK, Rindi Ann
Salisbury HS; Salisbury, NC (15-270) AFS; Band; Fr C; Cpt, Mjrte; Secy, NHS; COM; Hon Prog; *U of NC; Nurs.*

FRANKE, Bruce Walker
Woodlan HS; Woodburn, IN (71-122) Ann; Drama; FFA; Ger C; Lit Mag; NFL; Rptr, Sch P; Spch C; SC; Thes; COM; Journ A; JA A; Spch A; VFW Orator Win; VofDEM; Interntl Thespian Soc; Outst Orator; Ntl Forensics League; *Concordia Col; Eng Ed.*

FRANKE, Rick Alan
Lutheran HS S; St Louis, MO (55-158) Order/Arrow; Cr-Ctry; Soccer; Order/Arrow A; Jr Knight; *Environmental Stu.*

FRANKEL, Alan David
Inglewood HS; Inglewood, CA; Math C; Model UN; Tnns; CSF; NEDT; *UCLA; Math.*

FRANKENFIELD, Bruce Joseph
Parkway W Sr HS; Ballwin, MO; Golf; Wrest; *U of Mo; Engr.*

FRANKENSTEIN, Holly Allison
Bellevue HS; Bellevue, MI (33%-95) Ann; Band; Ski C; Var C; Sftbl; Chamber of Comm A; Art A; Athletics As; *Mich Tech U; Forestry.*

FRANKLIN, Benjamin Donnie
Castle Heights Military Acad; Lebanon, TN (8-45) Ann; Demolay; Fr C; Lat C; Order/Arrow; Var C; Ftbl; Soccer; Tnns; ROTC A; *U of Tenn; Law Enforcement.*

FRANKLIN, Bernard Curtis
Mitchell Prep HS; Philadelphia, PA; Tr; *Wireless Tech Inst; Elec.*

FRANKLIN, Carol Elizabeth
Bishop Byrne HS; Memphis, TN (11-209) Ann; Bus C; CYO; Fr C; FBLA; Math C; Mu Alpha Theta; NHS; Swim; COM; NEDT; *U of Tenn; Acct.*

FRANKLIN, Donna Louise
Jamaica HS; Jamaica, NY (250-1100) Band; Hmrm; SC; *Hunter Col; Phys Therapy.*

FRANKLIN, Evelyn Darlene
Dunbar Sr HS; Baltimore, MD; Chess C; Secy, Chor; FBLA; Hmrm; NHS; SC; Secy, Soph Cl; Swim; NMS; Hon Prog; WW; *Loyola Col; Computer Sci.*

FRANKLIN, Georgia Ann
Indian Springs Acad; Jackson, GA (3-13) Ann; Hmrm; Co-Ed, Sch P; VP, SC; Cpt, Bkbl; Cpt, Sftbl; Cl Fav; Hon Graduate; *Gordon Col; Law.*

FRANKLIN, Hazel Lee
Goodlettsville HS; Goodlettsville, TN (7-159) Ch, FHA; Citz A; Home Ec, Health Ed, A's; Win, Civitan Essay; *David Lipscomb Col; Sociology.*

FRANKLIN, Henry Douglas
Northeastern HS; Detroit, MI; Band; JETS; Ftbl; Citz A; Hon Prog; MLS; Photo C; Schol; *U of Detroit; Engr.*

FRANKLIN, Kenneth Richard
Shawnee HS; Louisville, KY (11-170) Band; Community Yth Symph; Ensm; Hmrm; Pres, NHS; Orch; *U of Ky; Mus Ed.*

FRANKLIN, Lizabeth Lynn
Goodlettsville HS; Goodlettsville, TN (49-159) Span C; SC; Var C; Cpt, Bkbl; Tr; Citz A; H of F; HCt; *Nashville Tech Inst; Bus.*

FRANKLIN, Mary Alice
Anoka Sr HS; Anoka, MN (16-803) Band; VP, Chor; Ensm; Secy, 4H; Mjrte; NHS; Orch; Secy, Sr Cl; COM; 4H A; St 4-H Key, Ford Fund Achv, A's; Camp Counselor, A; *Anoka-Ramsey Jr Col; Eng Lit.*

FRANKLIN, McArthur
Amite Co Attendance Center; Gloster, MS (7-40) Bkbl; Ftbl; Alg A; *Jackson St U; Phys Ed.*

FRANKLIN, Natalie Dawn
Fieldale-Collinsville HS; Collinsville, VA (100-200) Secy, Band; Span C; SC; VP, Soph Cl; HCt; Pres, Pep C; Band A.

FRANKLIN, Patricia Jean
University of San Diego HS; San Diego, CA (14-315) CYO; Drama; Hmrm; InterClub Coun; Ed, Lit Mag; NHS; Ntl Yth Conf; F-Ed, Sch P; St Stu Congress; Thes; VP, Jr Cl; Sftbl; CSF; Journ A; Q&S A; Outst Feature A; *Journ.*

FRANKLIN, Peggy Lynne
McMullen Co HS; Tilden, TX (1-18) Ann; Drama; Secy, 4H; NHS; Secy, Jr Cl; Secy, Soph Cl; Bkbl; Tnns; COM; 4H A; Annual Photographer; WW; *Tex A&M U; Wildlife Mgr.*

FRANKLIN, Ramona Mae
Savannah HS; Savannah, GA; Chor; FHA; *Savannah St Col; Child Development.*

FRANKLIN, Robert Arthur
Dallas Christian HS; Dallas, TX (1-55) NHS; F-Ed, Sch P; Pres, Span C; DARGCA; Hist A; Span A; Eng A; Bible A; Outst Schol A; *Abilene Christian U; Bible.*

FRANKLIN, Rodney Lee
Evergreen HS; Vancouver, WA; Chor; Bsbl; MVP, Bkbl; Ftbl; Swim; Wrest; COM; Most Out; Civil Air Patrol; Teacher Asst; Phys Ed Referee; *USAF; Pilot.*

FRANKLIN, Ruth Ann
Milano HS; Milano, TX; Ann; Band; Ensm; Tres, FHA; Math C; JV, Bkbl; Tr; COM; Citz A; Math A; Yth Fel; *Tex A&M U; Vet.*

FRANKLIN, Tammie Gwyn
Lookeba-Sickles HS; Lookeba, OK; A-Ed, Ann; Rptr, FHA; Rptr, 4H; Spch C; 4H A; Win, VICA; FBLA Data Processing Contest; Civic Oriation A; *Southwestern Okla St Col; Bus Adm.*

FRANKLIN, Terrance Randall
Baker Sr HS; Baker, LA (7-374) All Amer Yth; F-Ed, Ann; Band; VP, BC; HiY; InterClub Coun; Semi-Fin, Lit Ral; VP, Mu Alpha Theta; Rptr, NHS; Pres, SC; Alg A; Bio A; Cl Fav; *Tulane U; Archt.*

FRANKLIN, Troy Lee Jr
Lincoln Sr HS; E St Louis, IL (208-235) Band; Chor; SC; *Bradley U; Bookkeeping.*

FRANKLIN, Vincent Todd
Concord HS; Concord, NC (96-223) Monogram; Cpt, Ftbl; Co-Cpt, Tr; Wrest; Rotary A; WW; *Catawba Col.*

FRANKLUND, Terri Joan
Bismarck HS; Bismarck, ND; FHA; 4H; ARC; 4H A; ARC A; YCL; *Bismarck Jr Col; Secy.*

FRANKS, Bonnie Faye
Hatley HS; Hatley, MS; BC; Chor; Span C; *Itawamba Jr Col; Data Processing.*

FRANKS, Christopher J
Kirkwood HS; Kirkwood, MO (20%-609) Orch; Order/Arrow; Sftbl; Tr; NMS; Order/Arrow A; Computer C; Scuba Cert; *Elec Engr.*

FRANKS, Gary Blake
Permian HS; Odessa, TX (3%-758) NHS; Tnns; Hon Prog; *Texas Tech U; Engr.*

FRANKS, Kenneth Steven
Marion Co HS; Guin, AL (5-62) BC; Drama; FFA; Rptr, Var C; Bsbl; Bkbl.

FRANKS, Paula Diane
Westside HS; Jonesboro, AR (50-100) Chor; FBLA; FHA; Span C; Up Bound; *So Baptist Col; Art.*

FRANKS, Teresa Roxanne
Bridgman HS; Bridgman, MI (29-81) Ann; Band; Sch P; Sftbl; Musicals; WW; Church Yth Group; Vlbl; Instramurals; *Lake Michigan Col; Bus Mgt.*

FRANTZ, Aida E
Tulpehocken HS; Bernville, PA; Band; Chor; Drama; 4H; Mgr, Bkbl; JV, Hockey; Tnns; Jr Co Band; *Computer Tech.*

FRANTZ, Joanne Louise
Wellsboro Sr HS; Wellsboro, PA (22-220) Band; CYO; Chess C; Chor; Drama; Ensm; Pres, Fr C; GS; Model UN; Tres, NHS; SC; Var C; Secy, Jr Cl; Bkbl; Tnns; Tr; *Ind U; Phys Ed.*

FRANTZ, Troy Bret
Lake Highlands HS; Dallas, TX (450-800) Orch; Ftbl; Interlochen Ntl Mus; All St Orch; *Abilene Christian U; Bible Theory.*

FRANZ, Becky Marie
Nevada HS; Nevada, MO (10-176) 4H; Lat C; 4H A; *St Luke's Col; Nurs.*

FRANZ, Kimberly Lynne
Carmel HS; Carmel, NY; Band; Bus C; Chldr; NHS; Alg A; Fr A; *Psych.*

FRANZ, Thomas Raymond
Thomas Jefferson HS; Pittsburgh, PA (1-400) A Cap Choir; Chor; Hmrm; NHS; Sci C; Span C; Bkbl; Alg A; Amer Leg A; COM; Chem A; Citz A; Math A; Ntl Sci Found; Ntl Sci Symposium; Rensselaer A; Sci A; St Scholar; Val; Yth Leg; *Cornell U; Chem Engr.*

FRANZEN, Steven Wayne
E Chambers HS; Winnie, TX (5%-85) FFA; NHS; Span C; VP, Jr Cl; VP, Soph Cl; JV, Bkbl; Ftbl; NEDT; Top 5%, Most Talented; A's; Highest Ranking Freshman; *Tex A&M U; Vet Med.*

FRANZEN, Tamara Ann
Columbus Sr HS; Columbus, NE (36-290) Ed, Ann; Chor; Pres, 4H; 4H A; Q&S A; Lutheran Yth.

FRANZMEIER, Cheryl Lee Grace
Klein HS; Spring, TX (10%-500) NHS; Bkbl; Spch A; *U of Tex; Interior Design.*

FRAPPIER, Kelly Wayne
McHenry Pub HS; McHenry, ND (2-15) Ann; Band; BS; Tres, CYO; Chor; Ensm; Sch P; Pres, SC; Bsbl; Bkbl; Sal; *Valley City St Col; Archt.*

FRAPPIER, Suzette Marie
Cumberland Co HS; Crossville, TN (39-450) St Area Voc-Tech Sch; Bus.

FRARACCIO, Rudolph Michael
Cardinal Mooney HS; Sarasota, FL (30-86) Secy, Chess C; Key C; SC; Bsbl; Bkbl; Ftbl; Hon Prog; *Manatee Jr Col; Bus.*

FRASER, Bryan Dale
Columbus Sr HS; Columbus, NE; Chor; Bsbl; Cpt, Bkbl; Ftbl; Spch A; *U of Nebr; Law.*

FRASER, Cynthia Lynn
Adirondark Central Sch; Booneville, NY (37-160) Gregg A; *Mohawr Valley Comm Col; Secretarial Sci.*

FRASER, Karen Elizabeth
St Mary's Regional HS; Lynn, MA (13-129) Cpt, Chldr; Drama; Hmrm; Sftbl; Swim; Tr; Alg A; Hon Prog; Math A; Sci A; Eng, Phys Ed, Soc Stu, A's.

FRASER, Peggy Lynn
Fletcher Sr HS; Neptune Beach, FL; NHS; Secy, Omega; *Fla Jr Col; Nurs.*

FRASHER, David Richard
St Thomas Aquinas HS; Louisville, OH (10%-198) Ski C; Lit A; *Wooster Col; Computer Sci.*

FRASHER, Martha Sue
Hughes Springs HS; Hughes Springs, TX (35-67) Pres, FHA; Sch P; *Tyler Comm Col; Modern Office Asst.*

FRASIER, Darrell Leigh
Bonds-Wilson HS; N Charleston, SC; Yth Foundation A; *Palmer Col; Criminal Justice.*

FRASIER, Eric Marc
Alexander Hamilton HS; Los Angeles, CA (33%-600) Hon Prog; Q&S A; Co-Cpt, Vlbl; *UC at San Diego; Sci.*

FRASIER, Sharon Yvette
Bonds-Wilson HS; N Charleston, SC (40-170) Band; ARC; Tr; ARC A; *Columbia Col; Early Childhood Ed.*

FRASIER, Vivian Delores
Burke HS; Charleston, SC (9-210) Drama; FNA; Hmrm; NHS; B Crocker A; HCt; *SC St U; Bio.*

FRAY, Nancy Jean
Speedway HS; Speedway, IN (35-200) Band; GSct; St Solo & Ensm.

FRAZE, Mark Eduard
Mission Viejo HS; Mission Viejo, CA (17-600) AFS; Chess C; Dbte Tm; Math C; CSF; Hon Prog; NML; *U of Calif; Computer Sci.*

FRAZEE, Brenda Kay
Laurel Highlands HS; Uniontown, PA (134-416) Band; Secy, Western Pa Dist Yth Group.

FRAZEE, Colette
Jay Co HS; Portland, IN (1-447) NHS; Amer Leg A; Most Out; *Ball St U; Lib.*

FRAZEE, Susan Marie
Lapeer W Sr HS; Lapeer, MI; Art Inc; *Florist.*

FRAZEE, William Stewart
S Plantation HS; Plantation, FL (20-600) A Cap Choir; Band; NHS; Order/Arrow; Hon Prog; NEDT; Eagle Sct; Newpaper Essay Contest Runner-Up; VP-YTH Fel; *Ga Inst of Technology; Energy Engr.*

FRAZER, Douglas William
Branham San Jose HS; San Jose, CA (12-400) Bank of Amer A; CSF; HS Dist Schol; *U of Calif; Atmospheric Sci.*

FRAZER, Lola Jean
Trico HS; Campbell Hill, IL; FHA.

FRAZER, Susan Michelle
Chester HS; Chester, IL (10-90) Band; Chor; Amer Leg A; *Belleville Area Col; Nurs.*

FRAZER, Ted III
Crittenden Co HS; Marion, KY (15-146) Marching & Concert Band; *Sci.*

FRAZIER, Alan Brian
Puckett Attendance Center; Puckett, MS; FFA; 4H; Bsbl; Ftbl; *Clarke Jr Col.*

FRAZIER, Belinda Felicia
St Andrews Parish HS; Charleston, SC; Bkbl; Cpt, Sftbl; Tr; Miss BTU Qn; *Morehouse Col; Med Secy.*

FRAZIER, Ivy LaVerne
Continued Ed Project; St Louis, MO; Hmrm; Sch P; Citz A.

FRAZIER, Janet
Chicago Voc HS; Chicago, IL (113-829) COM; Hon Prog; Yth Fel; Pres, GAA; Stu Faculty Adm Coun; Hostess C; *Wash U in St Louis; Pre-Med.*

FRAZIER, Jeanette
St John's HS; Darlington, SC; Chor; FHA; 4H; *Kings Col; Secretarial Sci.*

FRAZIER, John K Jr
Wheeling Park HS; Wheeling, WV (300-728) A Cap Choir; Ann; Community Yth Symph; HiY; Up Bound; Tr; JA A; Yth Fel; Tres, Power of Yth; Pianist A; Ed Black Stu A; *Marshall U; Bus Mgt.*

FRAZIER, John Scott
Patterson Sch; Lenoir, NC (7-15) Band; Chess C; Key C; Lat C; Order/Arrow; Sch P; SC; JV, Bsbl; JV, Bkbl; Soccer; MVP, Tnns; Order/Arrow A.

FRAZIER, Kelly Gene
Timberline HS; Weippe, ID (4-46) Chem C; Fr C; Tres, 4H; JETS; NHS; SC; Pres, Sr Cl; JV, Bkbl; 4H A; Hon Prog; Yth Leg; *U of Idaho; Elec Engr.*

FRAZIER, Loretta
Bushwick HS; Brooklyn, NY; Chor; Bkbl; Sftbl; *Brooklyn Col; Nurs.*

FRAZIER, Mark William
Thomas Jefferson HS; Pittsburgh, PA (50-400) A
Cap Choir; Band; Chor; NHS; Hon Prog; Yth Fel;
Col of Wooster; Mus.

FRAZIER, Philamesia
Tilden HS; Chicago, IL (12-408) Math C; Sch P;
SC; *U of Chicago Circle; Bus Adm.*

FRAZIER, Rebecca Lynn
Trinity Heights Christian Acad; Shreveport, LA
(10-56) Cpt, Chldr; Lit Ral; Mu Alpha Theta; NFL;
NHS; Sci C; Span C; VP, SC; Beauty; HCt; Opt A;
Ftbl Swtht; Jamboree Qn; Miss Trinity Heights;
Top 10 Sr; Miss La Ntl Teenager; WW, Most Spir-
ited; *LSU; Law Enforcement.*

FRAZIER, Sheryl Kathleen
Albia Comm HS; Albia, IA; Band; FHA; JV, Bkbl;
JV, Golf; JV, Sftbl.

FRAZIER, Shirley Ann
Lake Clifton Sr HS; Baltimore, MD (10%-500) Bus
C; FBLA; Hmrm; NHS; Alg A; Math A; Mus A;
Extra-Curriculum A; *U of SC; Distributive Ed.*

FRAZIER, Stephen Kenneth
Taylorville HS; Taylorville, IL (20-285) Band;
Drama; Fr C; Key C; JV, Bkbl; Tr; Opt A.

FRAZIER, Susan Grace
Taylorville HS; Taylorville, IL (75-250) Band;
FHA; 4H; Span C; 4H A; Ntl Guild Mus A; *Gem
City Bus Col; Acct.*

FRAZIER, Tammy Leigh
Banks HS; Birmingham, AL; Pres, Sftbl; Secy, Lib,
Church Yth Choir; Rep, Church Yth Coun; Tres,
KAB Sorority; Jettet.

FRAZIER, Wilma Arlene
Starmount HS; Boonville, NC (10-151) NHS; Soc
Stu C; VICA; *Agr.*

FRAZIER, Yolanda Kay
Pittsburg HS; Pittsburg, CA; DARGCA; *Oakwood
Col; Home Ec.*

FRAZIER, Yvonne
Williamsburg HS; Andrews, SC (13-59) Pres,
Drama; 4H; Rptr, Sch P.

FREALY, Linda Caroline
Koshkonong HS; Koshkonong, MO (5-19) CYO;
Chor; Secy, Hmrm; SC; Soccer; Sftbl; Hon Prog;
Home Ec A; *Home Ec.*

FREBERG, Mary Sue
Ralston HS; Ralston, NE (26-327) NHS; Type A;
Vlbl; Fr Achv; *Design.*

FRECH, Kimberly Jo
Thomas Carr Howe HS; Indianapolis, IN (10-700)
Band; Chor; FTA; Sunday Sch Teacher; Church
Choir; Christ Ambassadors; 2nd, Chrch Solo-Ensm
Flute Contest.

FRECH, Norman Ronald
Granite City HS N; Granite City, IL (51-363) FTA;
Mu Alpha Theta; NHS; Order/Arrow; Sci C; Span
C; Sftbl; Tnns; Alg A; Hon Prog; Math A; Order/
Arrow A; VP, Yth Group; Chor; New Singing
Group; *Sou Ill U; Math.*

FRED, Chuck Lander
Capital HS; Helena, MT; Hmrm; SC; Var C; Bkbl;
Co-Cpt, Cr-Cptry; Tr; H of F.

FRED, Vicki Linn
Helena Capital HS; Helena, MT (45-350) Hmrm;
Cpt, Mjrte; NHS; Rainbow; SC; Var C; Secy, Sr Cl;
Cpt, Cr-Cptry; Tr; COM; Cl Fav; H of F; HCt; *U of
Mont; Spch Pathology.*

FREDERIC, Cindy Gail
Tishomingo HS; Tishomingo, MS; *North East Col;
PE.*

FREDERICK, Betsy Ann
Roger C Sullivan HS; Chicago, IL (5-300) F-Ed,
Ann; Chor; Fr C; 4H; COM; 4H A; Hist A; Hon
Prog; Pres, Church Yth Group; St Historian; *Knox
Col; Med.*

FREDERICK, Beverly Jean
Tonawanda Sr HS; Tonawanda, NY (82-395) A
Cap Choir; S-T, Band; Chor; Ensm; Ch, Hmrm;
Sftbl; Mgr, Swim; COM; Yth Fel; NY St Mus Com-
petition A; Band Schol; *Cedarville Col; Bible.*

FREDERICK, Carlie Ann
Roosevelt HS; Wyandotte, MI; Band; Chor; Mgr,
Sftbl; COM; Hon Prog; JA A; Mus Schol; Person-
nel Director, JA; St Ensm Festival; Tutor, Eng
Dept; VP, Chrch Yth Grp; Statist, Bkbl; Church
Hospitality Group; *Med.*

FREDERICK, Carol Sue
Hobbs HS; Hobbs, NM (10%-664) Band; Sci C;
Span C; *Sci.*

FREDERICK, Cynthia Gail
Tishomingo HS; Tishomingo, MS (33%-58) Band;
BC; FHA; 4H; S-T, Soph Cl; Cpt, Bkbl; Cpt, Sftbl;
Cl Fav; 4H A; *NE Miss Jr Col.*

FREDERICK, James Wayne
Winnfield Sr HS; Winnfield, LA (6-128) Anchor C;
BC; Pres, CYO; FTA; Ed, Sch P; Spch C; SC; Var
C; Bsbl; Bkbl; All Dist, Bsbl; WW; *La Tech U; Phys
Ed.*

FREDERICK, John Wilson
Nederland HS; Nederland, TX (40-489) CYO; Fr
C; NHS; Order/Arrow; Ftbl; Tr; Amer Leg A; Ntl
Sci Symposium; Order/Arrow A; *Tex A&M U;
Chem.*

FREDERICK, Laurie Ann
Plymouth Whitemarsh HS; Plymouth Meeting, PA
(40%-600) Mjrte; *Secy.*

FREDERICK, Lynn Ellen
Crockett HS; Crockett, TX; Band; *Tex A&M U;
Vet.*

FREDERICK, Nancy Lee
Council Rock HS; Newton, PA (86-690) FBLA;
Sftbl; Charm Course A; *Secy.*

FREDERICK, Patty Lynette
Tishomingo HS; Tishomingo, MS (2-33) Ann; BC;
4H; Cpt, Bkbl; Cpt, Sftbl; H of F; Hon Prog; Sal;
Miss THS; MVP, Bkbl; *NE Miss Jr Col.*

FREDERICK, Sharon Denise
Welch HS; Welch, WV (15-128) Chor; NHS; Drivers A; *Pepperdine U; Social Worker.*

FREDERICK, Sherry Dean
Moore HS; Moore, OK (70-844) Chor; FBLA; Ger
C; Secy, Pep C; Pres, Christian Yth Fel; *Emotion-
ally Disturbed Children.*

FREDERICK, Stephen Michael
Ahrens HS; Louisville, KY (33%-350) Band; Bus C;
Pres, Chess C; FBLA; Hmrm; Church Bkbl; Co-
Cpt, Church Sftbl; PA; Outst, Mus; *Ky Wesleyan
Col; Acct.*

FREDERICKS, Karen Lynn
Arlington Sr HS; Freedom Plains, NY (25%-700)
Band; Chor; Orch; Arch; Swim; Tnns; Yth Fel;
Dutchess Comm Col; Med Tech.

FREDERICKS, Mark Alan
Hartley Comm HS; Hartley, IA (50%-75) Band;
Chor; Ensm; Madrigal; Bkbl; Mgr, Ftbl; Golf; Yth
Fel; *Mo Inst of Tech; Elec.*

FREDERIKSEN, Leann Roe
Mazon Verona Kinsman HS; Mazon, IL (11-55)
Ann; Band; Chldr; Chor; Drama; Ensm; VP, 4H;
Lat C; Sch P; Rptr, Soph Cl; JV, Tr; 4H A; St
Scholar; Jr Classical League; *Ill St U; Art Ed.*

FREDERKING, Douglas Dean
Salina HS S; Salina, KS (41-316) Band; Ensm; Ger
C; *Math.*

FREDERKING, Esther Jane
Salina HS Central; Salina, KS (57-308) Ger C; A-
Ed, Sch P; Q&S A; *Bus.*

FREDERKING, Rhonda Marie
Salina HS-S; Salina, KS (5%-400) Ed, Ann; JV,
Chldr; Chor; Ensm; Pres, 4H; Hmrm; Key C; A-Ed,
Sch P; Sftbl; 4H A; *Special Ed.*

FREDIN, Tamera Jean
Winthrop HS; Winthrop, MN (15-62) Drama;
FHA; NHS; Rptr, Sch P; *St Cloud Beauty Col;
Cosmotology.*

FREDRICK, Cheryl Joan
Hastings Sr HS; Hastings, MN; Ski C; SC; Golf; Tr;
Normandale Col; Dental Hygiene.

FREDRICK, Julie
Irving HS; Irving, TX (50%-590) Secy, Band;
Drama; Span C; Spch C; I-Teens; Young Life; *Abi-
lene Christian U; Fashion Merchandising.*

FREDRICKSON, Lane Marie
Cassadaga Valley HS; Sinclairville, NY (8-137)
Chor; Dbte Tm; Rptr, Sch P; Ski C; Span C; Tr;
Maine Maritime Col; Nautical Sci.

FREDRICKSON, Paula Sue
Luther L Wright HS; Ironwood, MI (5-200) Band;
CYO; Ensm; Orch; Tnns; COM; ARC A; Lutheran
Yth Organization; Craft A; Band A; Bible Quiz;
GSct; Mich Tech U; Sci.

FREDRIKSSON, Jane Lisa
Wachusett Regional HS; Holden, MA (250-500)
Chldr; Chor; HiY; Church Yth Committee; *Acct.*

FREE, Karen Lynett
Powder Valley HS; N Powder, OR (2-12) Band;
Chor; Secy, Jr Cl; Ftbl; Type A; Yth Fel; WW; Jr Cl
Schol; Hon Choir.

FREE, Stanley James
Yorkwood HS; Monmouth, IL (1-60) Band;
Drama; VP, 4H; Tres, NHS; Spch C; SC; Bkbl;
Co-Cpt, Ftbl; Tr; 4H A; I Dare You.

FREE, Steven John
St Francis HS; St Francis, MN (41-165) Drama;
FFA; NFL; Ski C; Spch C; Tnns; Bkbl; Bkbl; Cr-
Ctry; Ftbl; Tnns; Tr; COM; Spch A; Cr Ctry Ski;
Drama A; *N Suburban Hennipen Vo-tec Inst; Agri-
Bus.*

FREEBERG, David Allen
Andress HS; El Paso, TX (10%-677) Band; Order/
Arrow; Citz A; Kiwanis A; Jr NHS; *Tex Tech U;
Med.*

FREEBERG, Julie Kay
Andress HS; El Paso, TX; Band; Citz A; Kiwanis A;
Band Lib; Jr NHS; *Tex Tech U; Special Ed.*

FREEBURG, Jonathan David
Silver Creek HS; San Jose, CA; A Cap Choir; VP,
Band; Chor; Ensm; Ed, Lit Mag; Orch; Pres, Sci C;
Span C; JV, Tnns; Citz A; *Bethel Col; Psych.*

FREEBURG, Kelly Rae
Spencer Sr HS; Spencer, IA (100-186) Model UN;
VP, St Stu Congress; SC; *Iowa Lakes Comm Col;
Nurs.*

FREECHTLE, Sharon Louise
Sutter HS; Sutter City, CA (2-165) Span C.

FREED, Jason Andrew
Crestview HS; Crestview, FL (43-250) Cpt, Var C;
Cpt, Ftbl; Tr; Ftbl A; *Morehouse Col; Law.*

FREED, Joseph Dean
NorthWood HS; Nappanee, IN; A Cap Choir;
Band; Drama; Thes; Tnns; Swing Choir; *Bethel Col;
Med.*

FREED, Mark Ronald
Vincent Massey Secondary Sch; Windsor, CAN-
ADA; *U of Toronto; Law.*

FREEDLAND, Karin Marie
Minnehaha Acad; Minneapolis, MN; Ann; Band;
Chldr; Ski C; *Nurs.*

FREELAND, Lee Ann
Columbia HS; Columbia, PA (3-118) Band; Chor;
NHS; Span C; Mgr, Tnns; I Dare You; *Regional &
Dist Band; Hon Chor; Pa St U; Mgt.*

FREELAND, Ruth Antoinette
William Penn HS; York, PA (200-250) Band;
Hmrm; Y-Tns; Mgr, Tr; HCt; I Dare You; JA A;
Wash Sch for Secy; Secy.

FREELS, Sharon Diane
Sunbright HS; Sunbright, TN (10-65) Band; BC;
Drama; FHA; 4H; Mjrte; Math C; Sch P; Sci C;
Mgr, Bkbl; Beauty; Cl Fav; *Tenn Tech U; X-Ray
Tech.*

FREEMAN, Alice Charlene
Ahoskie HS; Ahoskie, NC; Band; Chldr; Hmrm;
SC; Bkbl; Elk A; Gov Honor Prog; Tr A; GSct A;
NC St U; Med.

FREEMAN, Amy Ruth
Nordonia HS; Macedonia, OH (6-437) Band; Chor;
Drama; Ensm; NHS; Ski C; Thes; Bkbl; Hon Prog;
Drill Tm.

FREEMAN, Angelia Doris
Holly Springs HS; Holly Springs, MS (75%-183)
Ann; Band; GS; Sch P; Span C; SC; Amer Leg A;
Band; *Fisk U; Social Work.*

FREEMAN, Angie Leigh
E Davidson HS; Thomasville, NC (22-160) Bus Mgr, Ann; Cpt, Chldr; Drama; Monogram; SC; Secy, Soph Cl; HCt; Yth Fel; Miss Fresh; Soph Attendant; *Davidson Co Comm Col; Nurs.*

FREEMAN, Christopher William
Gainesville HS; Gainesville, GA; Band; Key C; Order/Arrow; Ski C; Span C; Span NHS; Eagle Sct; Nom, Gov Hon Prog.

FREEMAN, Cynthia Ann
McCluer Acad; Jackson, MS; Band; Chldr; SC; Beauty; Cl Fav; HCt; Pres, Yth Church Choir.

FREEMAN, Cynthia Dean
M B Smiley HS; Houston, TX (11-400) Fr C; NHS; COM; ROTC A; Eng, Data Processing, A's; Wave o-t Yr; *Data Processing.*

FREEMAN, Cynthia Diane
Darlington HS; Rome, GA (25-115) Ann; Band; Co-Cpt, Chldr; Pres, SC; Tri-HiY; MVP, Bkbl; Mgr, Swim; Beauty; Cl Fav; MLS; *NC St U; Fashion Design.*

FREEMAN, Daniel Evan
Merrill Sr HS; Merrill, WI (14-325) Band; Dbte Tm; Ensm; Ger C; NFL; Amer Leg A; Elk A; Most Out; Spch A; Cpt, High Quiz Bowl; *U of Wis-Madison; Mus.*

FREEMAN, Felita Jacquetta
Burke HS; Charleston, SC (26-210) *Colombia Comm Col; Bus Mgt.*

FREEMAN, James Jesse
Bennett HS; Buffalo, NY; SC; JV, Bkbl; Cr-Ctry; Tr; *Morehouse Col; Pre-Med.*

FREEMAN, Jane Elizabeth
Houstonr-1 HS; Houston, MO; Band; *U of Mo at Columbia; Social Work.*

FREEMAN, Kirk Alan
Clay City HS; Clay City, IN (4-86) Pres, Fr C; Pres, HiY; VP, Math C; NHS; Pres, SC; Bsbl; Pres A; Type A; *Ind U; Ed.*

FREEMAN, Lance Patrick
St Joseph-Ogden HS; St Joseph, IL (41-110) Ger C; Monogram; Var C; Pres, Soph Cl; MVP, Bkbl; Cr-Ctry; Ftbl; Tr; Co-cpt, All St, All Conf, Bkbl; *Mont St U; Criminal Justice.*

FREEMAN, Linda Diane
Pascagoula HS; Pascagoula, MS (15%-450) Pres, A Cap Choir; Pres, Chor; Ensm; FHA; Pres, Hmrm; NHS; Span C; Sftbl; COM; Citz A; Lion A; Most Outst Choralier of Yr; Church Pianist; VP, Yth Choir; Historian, Choralier; *William Carey Col; Mus.*

FREEMAN, Marisa Ann
Lake Clifton Sr HS; Baltimore, MD (10%-500) Alg A; Foreign Lang A; *City Col.*

FREEMAN, Martha Macon
Oak Ridge Acad; Oak Ridge, NC (3-30) Ann; Co-Cpt, Chldr; Chor; Drama; Ensm; Ger C; Lat C; Monogram; Var C; VP, Sr Cl; Secy, Jr Cl; VP, Soph Cl; Sftbl; HQn; HCt; Hon Prog; ROTC A; Jr Marshal; *Sweet Briar Col; Vet Med.*

FREEMAN, Nina Claudette
Weatherford HS; Weatherford, TX (21-252) Secy, Drama; Tres, FTA; NHS; VP, Spch C; SC; Secy, Thes; Pres, Stu Task Force; *Trinity U; Psych.*

FREEMAN, Randy Miller
Clayton HS; Clayton, MO (60-170) Band; Bus C; Rptr, Sch P; Var C; Bkbl; Cr-Ctry; Sftbl; Cpt, Tnns; Star Student; Pres, CYF; Pres, Chi Rho; Mock Democratic Conv; *U of Mo; Journ.*

FREEMAN, Rebecca Anne
Bastrop HS; Bastrop, LA (36-300) Bus Mgr, Ann; Band; Chldr; Model UN; NHS; Sch P; Parl, SC; Semi-Fin, Tnns; Amer Leg A; Citz A; HQn; Mu Sigma Hon Soc; *La Tech U; Early Childhood.*

FREEMAN, Richard Eugene
Waynesboro Central HS; Waynesboro, MS (25%-99) Ann; Rptr, BC; Pres, Drama; Ger C; Ftbl; Amer Leg A; NEDT; Star Student; WW; *Jones Co Jr Col.*

FREEMAN, Rilla Lorraine
Perry HS; Pittsburgh, PA; Chor; Drama; Citz A; *Allegenly Comm Col; Executive Secy.*

FREEMAN, Roger Junior
Garfield HS; Garfield, NJ; Cpt, Ftbl.

FREEMAN, Scott Wayne
Hazelwood W Sr HS; Hazelwood, MO (100-500) Ensm; SC; Bkbl; Sftbl; COM; 2nd & 3rd Pl, Sch Art Exhibit.

FREEMAN, Susan Nicole
Arts HS; Newark, NJ (100-200) Chor; Yth Fel; Girls Glee C; *Seton Hall Col; Elem Ed.*

FREEMAN, Tina Janine
Vestaburg Comm Sch; Vestaburg, MI (2-80) Bus Mgr, Ann; Tres, Band; Chldr; NHS; Ski C; Pres, Span C; Secy, Jr Cl; Secy, Soph Cl; Bkbl; Vlbl; Church Elder; Choir; Sun Sch Teacher; *Mich St U; Med.*

FREEMAN, Tyrone Kenneth
Verbum Dei HS; Los Angeles, CA (4-22) CYO; Secy, Soph Cl; *U of Ala; Phys Ed.*

FREEMYER, Patti Neal
Central HS; Helena, AL (8-330) Ann; Cpt, Band; Chess C; Drama; FTA; GS; Hmrm; Cpt, Mjrte; NHS; Pres, Span C; Spch C; Span NHS; Thes; Hon Prog; Kiwanis A; *Ed.*

FREER, Kenneth Richard
Manistee HS; Manistee, MI; Band; Drama; Co-Ed, Sch P; Span C; Thes; Rptr, Sch P; Outst News Carrier; Win, Yng Authors & Illustrators Con; *U of Mich; Med.*

FREER, Rebecca Ione
Manistee HS; Manistee, MI; Band; Cpt, Chldr; Mjrte; Span C; Bsbl; Cl Fav; HCt; Chldr A's; *Central Mich U.*

FREER, William Lawrence
Kearns HS; Kearns, UT; Band; Pres, Chess C; Math C; Sci C; Tr; Sacristan; Pres, United Ministries Yth Coun; Support Comm; Square Dance C; *Math.*

FREESE, Debra Ann
Lancaster Sr HS; Lancaster, WI (8-131) AFS; CYO; FHA; Tres, 4H; NHS; Span C; Pres A; *U of Wis at Whitewater; Bus.*

FREESE, Elaine Marie
Our Lady of Angels HS; St Bernard, OH (20-150) Bus Mgr, Bus C; Commercial C; FBLA; Math C; NHS; Rptr, Sch P; SC; Tr; COM; God & Country A; Hon Prog; Math A; Poet A; Spch A; Type A.

FREESLAND, Francis Michael
Benjamin Franklin HS; Los Angeles, CA (24-600) CYO; Mgr, Bsbl; JV, Ftbl; COM.

FREIBOTH, Sharon Louise
N Kitsap HS; Poulsbo, WA (60-250) Band; Chldr; Chor; Drama; Pres, 4H; Pres, Rainbow; Mgr, Bsbl; Sftbl; Tr; God & Country A; 4H A; I Dare You; Yth Fel; Past Worthy Advisor, Rainbow Girls; *Clover Park Col; Interior Decorator.*

FREIS, Daniel Edward
Buena Park HS; Buena Park, CA; A Cap Choir; Chess C; Chor; Ensm; Madrigal; Order/Arrow; COM; Eagle Sct; *Christ Col.*

FREITAG, Cynthia Ann
Wilson HS; Wilson, TX (2-26) Band; Chor; Community Yth Symph; Ensm; Fin, Lit Ral; JV, Bkbl; Tr; COM.

FREITAS, Ronald John
Los Banos HS; Los Banos, CA; Band; FFA; 4H; Mem o-t Mo, Star Greenhand, FFA; *Calif Polytech Col; Agr Bus.*

FRENCH, Adele Norgress
The Westminster Sch; Atlanta, GA (13-94) Band; Chor; Span C; SC; Bkbl; Sftbl; Tnns; Vlbl; Span A; Academic Excellence; *U of Ga; Elem Ed.*

FRENCH, Danny Ray
Mt Carmel HS; Mt Carmel, IL; *Gulf Coast Bible Col; Christian Ed.*

FRENCH, Donna Kay
Mt Carmel HS; Mt Carmel, IL (91-170) *Gulf Coast Bible Col; Christian Ed.*

FRENCH, Franklin Carl
East HS; Pueblo, CO (150-384) God & Country A; VICA; Pacific Auto Achv A; Church Deacon; *USC; Pre-Vet.*

FRENCH, Joann Marie
Big Sandy HS; Big Sandy, TN; BC; Rptr, FHA; 4H; Bkbl.

FRENCH, Joe Kelly
Lyons Pub Sch; Lyons, NE (20-33) *Wayne St U; Mus.*

FRENCH, Karen Jean
Jamestown HS; Jamestown, NY (60-600) Chor; NHS; Yth Fel; *Acct.*

FRENCH, Laura Elizabeth
Central HS; Thomasville, GA; Band; FBLA; FHA; 4H; Mjrte; Stu o-t Mo; PA; *Valdosta Col; Nurs.*

FRENCH, Laurie Lynn
Belle Vernon Area HS; Belle Vernon, PA; FBLA; Pres, Hmrm; SC; Win, Regional Spelling Contest; Sch Rep, Ntl Secy Assn.

FRENCH, Lisa Cien
Skyline HS; Salt Lake City, UT (38-650) A Cap Choir; Chor; 4H; Hmrm; Madrigal; NHS; Sci A; Type A; Outst Schol Achv; *Brigham Young U.*

FRENCH, Margaret Mary
Westminster HS; Westminster, MD (20%-550) Band; Tres, CYO; Fr C; Key C; COM; *Social Work.*

FRENCH, Michael Patrick
Westminster Sr Hs; Westminster, MD (20-550) Pres, CYO; Fr C; Orch; Mock Pres Election; Eagle o-t Cross; Anthropology C; Church Yth o-t Yr; Co-Cpt, MVP, CYO Bkbl; Ntl CYO A; Outst Member, CYO; *U of Md; Pol Sci.*

FRENCH, Teresa Lynne
Chillicothe HS; Chillicothe, OH (40-390) Fr C; NFL; NHS; Co-Ed, Sch P.

FRENDT, Joel Michael
Village Christian HS; Sun Valley, CA; Hmrm; SC; JV, Bsbl; Bkbl; Ftbl; Sftbl; Tr; CSF; Eagle Sct; *BIOLA Col; Bus Adm.*

FRENG, Lori Ann
Gayville-Violin HS; Gayville, SD (7-21) Chldr; Chor; Ensm; 4H; Rptr, Sch P; Secy, Jr Cl; Bkbl; Tr; 4H A; Type A; *U of SD; Secy.*

FRENSLEY, Susan Annette
Goodlettsville HS; Goodlettsville, TN (14-159) Secy, Band; InterClub Coun; Secy, Lat C; Mjrte; Pres, NFL; NHS; COM; Sci A; Spch A; Degree of Excel; Band Hon Squad; Lat A; *David Lipscomb Col; Pre-Med.*

FRERES, Claire Bernadette
Moreau HS; Hayward, CA (25-404) CYO; Drama; ARC; Bkbl; Hon Prog; Pres, Pantomine C; Essay A; *U of San Francisco; Fine Arts.*

FRERICHS, Kelli Jane
Litchfield Sr HS; Litchfield, IL; Chor; Ensm; 4H; Span C; SC; Sftbl.

FRERICKS, Michael James
William Kelley HS; Silver Bay, MN (6-150) CYO; Pres, Chor; Drama; Ensm; NHS; Sci C; SC; Thes; Pres, Soph Cl; Bkbl; Co-Cpt, Ftbl; Tr; COM; Citz A; HCt; Hon Prog; K of A; MLS; Sci A; St Tr Meet Events Win; 4th St Bkbl; Win, St Tr Meet Tm; *St John's U; Bus Adm.*

FRERICKS, Thomas James
William Kelley HS; Silver Bay, MN (13-150) VP, A Cap Choir; Fin, BS; CYO; Chem C; VP, Chor; Drama; Ensm; NHS; Sch P; Sci C; Var C; Cpt, Bkbl; Ftbl; Tr; COM; Citz A; HCt; Masonic A; MLS; Sci A; *St Johns Col; Journ.*

FRETHEIM, Karla Mae
Stanley HS; Stanley, ND (6-53) Chor; Drama; Secy, FHA; 4H; Sch P; Academic Achv A; *Dickinson St Col; Nurs.*

FRETTOLOSO, Shirlee Filomena
T Wingate Andrews HS; High Point, NC (175-300) Band; FHA; Tres, Key C; Band Letter; Outst, Band; *Meredith Col; Home Ec.*

FRETWELL, Gail Denise
Spruce Creek HS; Port Orange, FL (92-450) Anchor C; Band; Hmrm; NHS; Pres, Span C; Sci A; *Daytona Beach Comm Col.*

FREUDENSPRUNG, Kelly Odell
Columbia HS; W Columbia, TX (25%-299) VP, AFS; Chess C; Dbte Tm; VP, Drama; Parl, Fr C; Order/Arrow; Spch C; Pres, SC; Thes; Pres, Jr Cl; Cl Fav; Lion A; Order/Arrow A; Rotary A; Star Student; Thespian A; Interntl Friendship A; *Brazosport Jr Col; Dentistry.*

FREVERT, Karla Sue
Wayne-Carroll HS; Wayne, NE (25-100) Band; Chor; Sftbl; Mgr, Wrest; COM; Hon Prog; Lion A; Type A; Vlbl; Bible Sch Teacher; Secy, Zone Pres, Walther League; Chrch Organist; Sundy Sch Tchr; 2nd Pl, Co Spelling Test; *Westmar Col; Bus.*

FREY, Keith Warren
Cleveland Heights HS; Cleveland Heights, OH (25-800) JV, Wrest; Hon Prog; Yth Fel; *MIT; Med.*

FREY, Lori Elizabeth
W Monroe HS; W Monroe, LA; Anchor C; Secy, InterAct C; Y-Tns; HCt; Drill Tm; World's Ideal Miss 16 Yr Old; *La Tech U; Fashion Merchandising.*

FREY, Peggy Jo
Wintersville HS; Wintersville, OH; Span C; JV, Bkbl; Stu Athletic Assn; *Ohio U; Amer Hist.*

FREY, Robert Lawrence
Speedway HS; Speedway, IN (32-190) Band; Chor; Ger C; Hmrm; Madrigal; Orch; SC; *Johnson Bible Col.*

FREYER, Kimberlyn Lea
Homestead HS; Mequon, WI (100-431) Band; Chldr; Hmrm; SC; HCt; *Carthage Col; Ed.*

FREYER, Lisa Susan
Montville HS; Oakdale, CT (103-294) Ann; Drama; Ski C; Bowl; *Beautician.*

FREYMILLER, Grace Laurena
Arcola HS; Arcola, IL (1-80) AFS; Band; Span C; Tres, Soph Cl; JV, Vlbl; *Greenville Col; Mus.*

FRIBLEY, Catherine Sue
W P Chrysler HS; New Castle, IN (183-380) Band; Chess C; Chor; Orch; Rainbow; JA; Band Contest As; *Ball St U; Art.*

FRICK, Betty Mae
Sacred Heart Acad; Mt Pleasant, MI (5-50) Ed, Ann; Chor; Dbte Tm; Drama; Ensm; Pres, Lat C; Madrigal; Tres, NHS; Sftbl; COM; Hon Prog; Journ A; Spch A; Vlbl; Lat, Mus, Service, A's; Dist Win, Debate; *Ferris St Col; Dental Hygiene.*

FRICK, Christine Claire
Norwich Free Acad; Norwich, CT (5%-749) Chldr; Chor; Fr C; Hon Prog; Art A; Project Outreach A; *Writing.*

FRICK, Cynthia Louise
Waukegan E HS; Waukegan, IL (58-602) Band; Chor; Ger C; Mod Mus Mas; Orch; Tr; NEDT; Mus Ltr; *U of Ill; Vet Med.*

FRICK, James Edward
Norwich-Free Acad; Norwich, CT (5%-700) A Cap Choir; BS; Chor; MVP, Bkbl; Citz A; Hon Prog; Ger A; BSct A; *Yale U; Politics.*

FRICKE, Mary Ellen
Sparks HS; Sparks, NV (8-290) Bus C; Chldr; FBLA; NHS; CSF; *U of Nev; Computer Sci.*

FRICKEL, Bethene Ann
W Holt HS; Atkinson, NE (9-72) Chor; VP, 4H; Tr; 4H A; Tres, 4-H C.

FRICKS, Ronald Keith
Southaven HS; Southaven, MS (50%-367) Bus C; Bkbl; Sftbl; Tr; *Southwestern Okla U; Aeronautics.*

FRIDAY, Donna Coleen
Central Dauphin HS; Harrisburg, PA (40%-500) SC; VP, Sr Cl; Hist, Modern Mus Masters C; Jr Civic C; *Pa St U; Archt.*

FRIDAY, Tony Tyrell
Patten Acad; Oakland, CA (3-13) Chor; Dbte Tm; Drama; Spch C; Pres, SC; Pres, Sr Cl; Cpt, Ftbl; Cpt, Sftbl; COM; Citz A; Hon Prog; *Patten Bible Col; Ministry.*

FRIEBOLIN, Michael P
Elk Grove HS; Elk Grove Village, IL (76-609) NHS; Hist A; Hon Prog; VFW A; VofDEM; Pres, Yth in Gov; NHS A; *N Ill U; Math.*

FRIEBURG, Carolyn Joy
Saybrook-Arrowsmith HS; Saybrook, IL (5-30) VP, FHA; VP, 4H; Fin, Spch C; 4H A; Spch A; *Lincoln Christian Col; Christian Ed.*

FRIEDEMANN, Beth Ann
Perry HS; Perry, OK (5%-105) Tres, Band; Drama; FHA; VP, FTA; NHS; Golf; Amer Leg A; *Okla St U; Ed.*

FRIEDEMANN, Richard William
Perry HS; Perry, OK; Chem C; NHS; Bsbl; Bkbl; Ftbl; Golf; Tr; Wrest; Hist A; Sports A's; *Okla St U; Agronomy.*

FRIEDLY, Kevin C
Thomas Carr Howe HS; Indianapolis, IN (13-600) Band; Chess C; Chor; Drama; Ensm; Fr C; Pres, NHS; Sci C; Bausch & Lomb A; Sci A; Regional Sci Fair A's; Irvington Mus Stu A; *Purdue U; Physics.*

FRIEDMAN, Todd Alan
Chillicothe HS; Chillicothe, OH; Band.

FRIEDRICH, Lynette Ann
LDF Comm HS; Le Grand, IA (2-46) A Cap Choir; Ann; Band; Chor; Dbte Tm; Drama; Ensm; FHA; Ger C; Madrigal; NFL; Spch C; St Stu Congress; COM; Chamber of Comm A; Sal; St Scholar; Yth Leg; Annual Photographer; Church Vlbl; Fin, AAL Schol; Recognition & Schol A; *Iowa St U; Social Sci.*

FRIEDRICH, Paula Marie
Mercy HS; Red Bluff, CA; Chldr; Chor; Tres, Sr Cl; Co-Cpt, Bkbl; Co-Cpt, Sftbl; 4H A; HCt; Pres A; MVP, Bkbl; *Shasta Col; Bus Adm.*

FRIEDRICHS, Lonna Nan
Ellen McCarter HS; Houston, TX (10%-20) Hmrm; Ch, ARC; Spch C; World Affairs C; Pres, Soph Cl; Swim; Tnns; Beauty; B Crocker A; HQn; ARC A; Spch A; Vet Asst; *Fashion Designing.*

FRIEDRICHSEN, Kirk Edward
Holstein Comm HS; Holstein, IA (25-50) Band; Chor; Ensm; 4H; Madrigal; Spch C; VP, Jr Cl; JV, Tr; Spch A; Stage Band; Luther League; Swing Choir; *ISU; Agr.*

FRIEND, Michael Lawrence
Paul Lawrence Dunbar HS; Fort Worth, TX; BS; Chor; NHS; All City Chor; *Computer Sci.*

FRIEND, Rita Kaye
Fredonia HS; Fredonia, KS; Ann; Chor; Ensm; FHA; Fin, GS; Jr Miss Pagent; Co-Ed, Sch P; SC; Tres, Y-Tns; COM; DARGCA; HCt; Rotary A; Bartlesville Wesleyan Col.

FRIERSON, Kerek Edward
Oakland HS; Murfreesboro, TN; Band; BC; Community Yth Symph; Key C; Lat C; Mu Alpha Theta; Soc Stu A; MIP, Band; Mid St Band, All St Orch; *U of Tenn; Med.*

FRIERSON, Linda Merle
Wade Hampton Acad; Orangeburg, SC (15-75) Ann; F-Ed, Lit Mag; Secy, SC; Cl Fav; DARGCA; HCt; Yth Fel; Distinguished Yth A; *Converse Col; Art.*

FRIERSON, William Robert
Sumter HS; Sumter, SC (58-753) Hmrm; Key C; SC; Bsbl; JV, Bkbl; Ftbl; Pres A; Jr Marshal; WW; *Clemson U; Engr.*

FRIES, Cathy Christina
Reseda HS; Reseda, CA; Drama; Ensm; Hmrm; Madrigal; NHS; Rainbow; SC; Bio A; CSF; COM; Citz A; Hon Prog; Sal; Principal's Academic Achv List; Mus Schol; *UCLA; Eng.*

FRIES, Elizabeth Ann
Fremont HS; Fremont, MI; Tr; Most Studious.

FRIES, John Frederick
Fremont HS; Fremont, MI (98-270) 4H; Fin, NHS; Order/Arrow; Span C; Bsbl; Swim; Tr; NMS; Order/Arrow A; Yth Fel; NESA; Eagle Sct; *Ferris St Col; Automotive.*

FRIESE, Ingrid Maria
Winston Churchill HS; San Antonio, TX (38-800) NHS; Span C; Type A; VOE; Jr Lab A; Shorthand A; Outst Scholastic Achv Recognition; High Hons; St Fin, OEA Steno Comp; Historian, OEA.

FRIESEN, Amy Louise
Manhattan HS; Manhattan, KS (41-431) Chor; Community Yth Symph; Ensm; Ger C; NFL; Orch; Thes; Sftbl; Hon Prog; Yth Fel; Pres, Square Dance C; I Rating, Regional Mus Contest; *Mus.*

FRIESEN, David Wayne
Baymonte Christian HS; Scotts Valley, CA (7-27) Chor; 4H; SC; Pres, Soph Cl; Bsbl; JV, Bkbl; Cr-Ctry; Tr; 4H A; *Biola Col; Seminary.*

FRIESEN, Diane Kay
Palisade HS; Palisade, CO (11-66) Ann; Chor; VP, FBLA; NHS; Span C; SC; Var C; Secy, Sr Cl; Bkbl; Kiwanis A; Lion A; Pres, Pep C; Vlbl; *Mesa Col; Bus.*

FRIESEN, Gary James
Immanuel HS; Reedley, CA (14-60) Bus Mgr, Ann; Chor; Var C; Ftbl; MVP, Tnns; *Le Tourneau Col; Mech Engr.*

FRIESEN, Greg Lee
Immanuel HS; Reedley, CA (10-56) Band; SC; VP, Sr Cl; Pres, Soph Cl; Bkbl; Ftbl; Tnns; *Col of Sequoias; Bus.*

FRIESEN, Kenneth Eugene
Temple Baptist Acad; Denver, CO (8-54) Mgr, Ftbl; Mgr, Sftbl; COM; Citz A; Acad Achv A; *National Technical Sch; Auto-Mech.*

FRIESEN, Tammy Michele
Baymonte Christian HS; Scotts Valley, CA (6-24) Ann; Chldr; Chor; NHS; Tres, Soph Cl; CSF; 4H A; Most Out; Spch A; Ltr Girl; Yrbk Artist; Toastmasters A; Bible A; *Biola Col; Art.*

FRIESNER, Paul Edward
Lancaster HS; Lancaster, OH (200-650) Bus Mgr, Key C; SC; Var C; Bsbl; Bkbl; Ftbl; Swim; Tr; COM; Citz A; MLS; Yth Fel; Yth Leg; VICA; Secy, FCA; *Ohio U; Hist.*

FRIESTAD, Dale Howard
Stillman Valley HS; Stillman Valley, IL (17-103) Drama; NHS; Sch P; Ftbl; Wrest; St Scholar; *US Navy; Nuclear Engr.*

FRIETSCH, Carol Jeanne
E Peoria Comm HS; E Peoria, IL (7-391) CYO; Pres, Ger C; Math C; Secy, NHS; Tres, SC; Tr; Art Schol; *Rockford Col; Art.*

FRILEY, Valerie Ann
Greenon HS; Springfield, OH (50-250) Chldr; Chor; FTA; VP, 4H; NHS; VP, Span C; Pres, Span NHS; 4H A; HCt; WW; *Cedarville Col.*

FRINT, Julia Joy
Belvidere HS; Belvidere, IL (117-357) Band; *Rock Valley Col; Bus.*

FRISBIE, Holly Dean
Cushing HS; Cushing, OK; Band; Chor; Fr C; Spch C; Tnns; Amer Leg A; Sftbl & Bkbl Coach, Yth Center; Twirling Instructor, Yth Center; Pianist, Chor, Church; Yth Chor; Yth Center.

FRISBIE, Kenneth Richard
University HS; Greeley, CO; Band; Var C; Ftbl; Sftbl; Tr; *U of Northern Colo; Phys Ed.*

FRISBIE, Mariann Elizabeth
Bartow HS; Bartow, FL (1-280) Pres, Anchor C; Chem C; FHA; Semi-Fin, GS; Co-Ch, InterClub Cou; Secy, NHS; Rptr, Sch P; Pres, Span C; SC; Secy, Sr Cl; Secy, Jr Cl; Secy, Soph Cl; Hon Prog; NMS; Val; Yth Fel; WW; *Wesleyan Col; Med Tech.*

FRISBIE, Patricia Louise
Cainsville R-I HS; Cainsville, MO (5-15) Ann; Band; Chldr; Chor; Ensm; Fr C; Tres, FHA; Ed, Sch P; VP, Sr Cl; VP, Jr Cl; Secy, Soph Cl; Bkbl; Sftbl; Tr; HQn; Hon Prog; Swtht.

FRISBIE, William Clayton
Butler Sr HS; Butler, MO (42-90) AFS; Band; Semi-Fin, BS; A-Ed, Sch P; Span C; SC; Var C; Pres, Sr Cl; VP, Jr Cl; Ftbl; Tr; Co-Cpt, Wrest; Amer Leg A; Opt A; *Mo U; Eng.*

FRISBY, Cathy Susan
Huntington HS; Huntington, NY (40%-606) Chor; Co-Ch, Hmrm; InterClub Coun; Orch; Special Orch A.

FRISCH, Frank Eugene
Madison HS; Madison, NE; Chor; Sftbl; Tr.

FRISCH, Kathryn Lea
Seguin HS; Sequin, TX (10-350) Band; 4H; VP, SC; Sci.

FRISKE, Richard Wilfred Jr
Ellsworth HS; Ellsworth, MI (6-30) Band; Sch P; Ski C; SC; Pres, Sr Cl; Pres, Jr Cl; Sci A; *Bob Jones U; Bus Adm.*

FRISLID, Janice Ann
Robert H Goddard HS; Roswell, NM (26-310) Ann; Band; Ger C; NHS; SC; Mgr, Bkbl; COM; Band Lib; *NM St U; Home Ec.*

FRITSCH, Lauren Jan
Auburn HS; Auburn, NE (13-109) A Cap Choir; A-Ed, Ann; Band; VP, Chor; 4H; Mjrte; NHS; Sch P; Pres, Soph Cl; Swim; Journ A; Q&S A; ARC A; *Hastings Col; Elem Ed.*

FRITSCH, Michlle Denise
Pell City HS; Pell City, AL (20%-150) Chldr; Drama; Secy, 4H; Jr Miss Pagent; Rptr, Sch P; Spch C; Rptr, SC; Thes; Var C; Cpt, Bsbl; Bkbl; Cpt, Sftbl; Swim; Tnns; Tr; Beauty; Citz A; 4H A; HCt; Hon Prog; Pres A; Spch A; Type A; Yth Fel; SC Rep & Historian, FHA; Bkbl A; SC Rep, Hmrm; Vlbl A; Gym A; Encounter I, FHA; *Jacksonville U; Gym.*

FRITSCHLE, Gail Ann
Newton Comm HS; Newton, IL (46-227) Bus C; FNA; Secy, 4H; NHS; Sci C; Ftbl; Beauty; COM; 4H A; Type A; *E Ill U; Med Tech.*

FRITTS, Susan Lynette
N Haven HS; N Haven, CT (93-450) Ed, Ann; Secy, Band; Chldr; Chor; Mgr, Tr; Usherette; Church Camp Schol; *Concordia Col; Interdisciplinary-Social Work.*

FRITZ, Arthur Louis Jr
Auburn HS; Auburn, NY (10-600) NHS; Ski C; Var C; Ftbl; Math A; Sci A.

FRITZ, Christine Elizabeth
Chaska Sr HS; Chaska, MN (60-250) Band; Chldr; Fr C; Jr Miss Pagent; Ski C; Golf; *St Scholastica Col; Nurs.*

FRITZ, Donna Rose
Rye Cove HS; Clinchport, VA (11-77) Band; BC; Bus C; Co-Cpt, Chldr; Chor; Drama; FBLA; Pres, 4H; Hmrm; Spch C; VP, SC; Sftbl; 4H A; HCt; Eng A; Co Civitan Essay A; *Mtn Empire Comm Col; Respiratory Therapy.*

FRITZ, Steven Eric
Warwick HS; Lititz, PA (50-260) Band; Eagle Sct.

FRITZENSCHAFT, Peter Kurt
Merryville HS; Merryville, LA (2-48) Fr C; Secy, Key C; Lit Ral; Parl, Sci C; Pres, Sr Cl; Bsbl; Co-Cpt, Bkbl; Ftbl; Tr; Cl Fav; Hon Prog; Kiwanis A; Sal; Sci A; VofDEM; *McNeese St U; Mech Engr.*

FRITZLER, Candace Belle
Tigard Sr HS; Tigard, OR; Band; Chor; Community Yth Symph; NHS; Orch; St Solo A; Dist Solo Win, Choir; Prom Court; *Warner Pacific Col; Mus Ed.*

FRITZLER, Julie Marie
Grant HS; Portland, OR (33%-300) SC; Most Spirited; *Warner Pacific Col; Secretarial.*

FRIZ, Alan Paul
McCluer N HS; Florissant, MO (10%-780) Band.

FRIZZELL, Tyler
Pine Crest Sch; Ft Lauderdale, FL (15-135) BC; Cum Laude Soc; Model UN; Cpt, Ftbl; MVP, Golf; *Duke U; Biomed Engr.*

FRNDAK, Philip Alan
General McLane HS; Edinboro, PA (5-210) Var C; Tr; Wrest; COM; *Phys Therapy.*

FROBEL, Melanie Lynn
Hinsdale Central HS; Hinsdale, IL (83-673) Bus C; Ski C; Sftbl.

FROEHLICH, Lori Kay
Nathan Hale HS; West Allis, WI; Hmrm; Ski C; Sftbl; JV, Tr; HQn; Pom Pon Girl; JV Gym; *UW-Eau Claire; Special Ed.*

FROEMMING, Randy James
St Francis HS; St Francis, MN; JV, Bsbl; JV, Bkbl; Ftbl; Marine Phys Fitness A.

FROEMMING, Scott Rian
St Francis HS; St Francis, MN (5-259) Bsbl; Bkbl; Ftbl.

FROESEL, Julie Ann
Kirkwood HS; Kirkwood, MO (11-650) Chor; Fr C; Sch Achieve Tm; Sftbl; Hon Prog; Yth Fel.

FROMAN, Richard Lee Jr
Tracy Joint Union HS; Tracy, CA (58-418) Band; Hmrm; F-Ed, Sch P; SC; Sftbl; CSF; Church Sanctuary & Yth Choir; Yth Puppet Prog; *Med.*

FROMM, Theresa Maria
Wesleyan Acad; Guaynabo, PR (1-32) Chor; NHS; Mgr, Sftbl; NEDT; *Nurs.*

FROSH, Cheryl Mae
Chase Co HS; Imperial, NE; FHA; Var C; Y-Tns; Sftbl; Tr; COM; Order/Arrow A; Type A; Vlbl Ltr; Tr Ltr; Part, St Track Meet; Presidential Phys Fitness; *Kearney Col; Cosmopolitan.*

FROST, Angela Len
Henderson Mill HS; Atlanta, GA (38-429) BC; Bus C; Chldr; FBLA; Cpt, Hmrm; Jr Miss Pagent; Tres, SC; Secy, Jr Cl; Tres, Soph Cl; Gov Honor Prog; Miss Henderson Pageant; Kappa C; Yth & Bell Choirs; Church Benevolent Committee; *Ga St Col; Bus Adm.*

FROST, Betty Jean
Colonel White Sch; Dayton, OH; Chor; FHA; OWA A; *Central St Col; Mus.*

FROST, David Jay
Pennsauken HS; Pennsauken, NJ (12-600) Band; BS; Ensm; NHS; Hon Prog; WW, Mus Stu; *Penn St U; Plant Sci.*

FROST, Dexter Jerome
Burke HS; Charleston, SC; Bkbl; Sftbl; Tnns; COM; Yth Foundation; *Trident Tech Col; Carpentry.*

FROST, Jacquelyn Marie
Durrett HS; Louisville, KY; BC; Secy, Lat C; NHS; Hist A; Prom Committee; SIFT; *E Ky U; Ed.*

FROST, Janet D Ann
Eastland HS; Eastland, TX (2-60) Ed, Ann; Band; Pres, BC; Ensm; FHA; Span C; Journ A; Ntl Sci Symposium; Sal; Scholastic Achv & Citz Schol; *Cisco Jr Col; Pre-Med.*

FROST, Thala Fern
Wheeler Co HS; Alamo, GA (4-89) *Ga Sou Col; Acct.*

FROYD, Robert LaVerne Jr
Lakewood HS; Lakewood, CA (10%-1000) Co-Cpt, Ftbl; Sports Off, City Recreation Prog; *Math.*

FRUEH, Debra Mae
Anamoose Pub HS; Anamoose, ND (7-20) Ann; Band; Chldr; Chor; 4H; Sch P; Sci C; Mgr, Bkbl; 4H A; Hon Prog; *Elem Ed.*

FRUEND, Terri Lynn
Carlyle HS; Carlyle, IL (11-170) Drama; Ch, FBLA; Tres, 4H; Ch, Jr Cl; 4H A; Hon Prog; VofDEM; Yth Leg; Tres, Lutheran Yth For Christ; Gym; *Kaskaskia Jr Col; Bus.*

FRUIN, Paul Arthur
Argenta-Oreana HS; Argenta, IL (125-832) Band; CYO; Hmrm; NHS; SC; Var C; Tres, Soph Cl; Bkbl; Ftbl; Golf; Tnns; *E Ill U; Engr.*

FRUNZI, Anette Marie
Bakersfield R-4 HS; Bakersfield, MO; Chldr; FHA; NHS; *Vet.*

FRY, Becky Jane
Nansemond-Suffolk Acad; Suffolk, VA (8-72) Co-Ed, Ann; Band; BC; JV, Chldr; Drama; Fr C; Semi-Fin, GS; Hmrm; NHS; Rptr, Sch P; Pres, SC; Thes; Tri-HiY; Secy, Y-Tns; COM; Citz A; Hist A; Hon Prog; Most Out; Pres A; Star Student; Art A; Piano A; Gym; *Med.*

FRY, Bryan David
Abraham Lincoln HS; Denver, CO (70-800) Cr-Ctry; Tr; HR; *Colo St U; Engr.*

FRY, Carol Lynette
Princeton HS; Princeton, WV (16-311) A Cap Choir; Band; Tres, 4H; Secy, Span C; 4H A; Kiwanettes; Med C; *Concord Col; Psych.*

FRY, David Joe
Woodlan HS; Woodburn, IN (10-126) Chess C; Pres, 4H; JV, Bkbl; JV, Ftbl; Tr; 4H A; Drafting A; Pastor's A.

FRY, Dawn D Lynn
Floyd Co HS; Floyd, VA (17-160) BC; Chldr; Pres, Fr C; Rainbow; Tri-HiY; Rptr, Jr Cl; HCt; Yth Fel; Gym; Snow Qn Court; Adm Board of Church; *Emory & Henry Col; Psych.*

FRY, Debra Lynn
Groveton HS; Groveton, TX (4-46) Ann; BC; Chldr; Chor; FHA; 4H; F-Ed, Sch P; Span C; Spch C; Mgr, Bkbl; Fin, Tr; Alg A; Bio A; Chem A; 4H A; Hist A; Hon Prog; Math A; Phy A; Poet A; Sci A; Yth Fel; St Beta C; WW; Attendance A; *Sam Houston St U; Special Ed.*

FRY, John Russell III
E Alton-Wood River Comm HS; Wood River, IL (27-320) Hmrm; SC; Thes; JV, Bkbl; Ftbl; Tr; *Math.*

FRY, Julia Lynne
North HS; North St Paul, MN (50-450) Secy, Band; SC; Cr-Ctry; JV, Tr; MVP, Skiing; *St Katherines Col; Journ.*

FRY, Karen Margaret
Abraham Lincoln HS; Denver, CO (55-800) Semi-Fin, GS; Mgr, Tr; Yth Fel; HR.

FRY, Melissa Lassiter
Vicksburg HS; Vicksburg, MS (22-244) AFS; Ann; Chldr; Chor; Drama; Ensm; FBLA; GS; Lat C; Tres, NHS; SC; Bkbl; Tnns; DARGCA; H of F; Most Out; *La St U; Spch Ed.*

FRY, Nancy Lynne
Warwick HS; Lititz, PA (8-273) Band; Chor; Ensm; NHS; Var C; JV, Hockey; Tr; COM; Math A; Sr o-t Month; *Juniata Col; Bio.*

FRY, Sharon Louise
Columbia HS; Columbia, PA (4-109) FNA; Span C; SC; Pres, Sr Cl; Pres, Jr Cl; Tnns; WW; Columbia Bus Women's, Girl o-t Mon; *Franklin & Marshall Col; Math.*

FRY, Susan Lynn
Warwick HS; Lititz, PA (16-275) Band; *Penn St U; Bus Adm.*

FRY, Terri Lynn
Mt Carmel HS; Mt Carmel, IL (50-200) Ann; SC; NEDT; *Wabash Valley Col; Psych.*

FRYE, Debra Sue
Tyrone Area HS; Tyrone, PA (40%-225) Band; Lat C; Rainbow; Bkbl; Grand Cross of Colors; *Philipsburg St Hospital; Registered Nurs.*

FRYE, Deena Louise
Weir Sr HS; Weirton, WV; Band; Ensm; *Nyack Col; Mus.*

FRYE, Jane McGovern
Henry Sibley HS; St Paul, MN; Chor; Drama; Swim; Nurs Home Vol; Jr Curling Assn; *Law.*

FRYE, Lacy B III
Jenkins Co HS; Millen, GA (12-100) Co-Ed, Ann; BC; FFA; Secy, HiY; Tres, Sci C; Pres, SC; COM; Yth Fel; Yth Leg; World Hist A; *U of Ga; Law.*

FRYE, Sarah Elizabeth
Brandon HS; Brandon, MS; Ann; BC; Chldr; SC; Beauty; HCt; *U of Miss; Radiology.*

FRYE, Sue Kelly
Powell Valley HS; Speedwell, TN; BC; Cpt, Chldr; Chor; FHA; Madrigal; NFL; Sch P; Thes; Tri-HiY; Pres, Jr Cl; Secy, Soph Cl; Cl Fav; HCt; Pres A; *E Tenn St Col; Journ.*

FRYE, Timothy McCheyne
Portsmouth Christian HS; Portsmouth, VA (2-6) A-Ed, Ann; Chor; Drama; Span C; Bkbl; Ftbl; Citz A; Hist A; Sal; Sci A; *Old Dominion U; Eng.*

FRYER, Debora Loretta
The Acad of Richmond Co; Augusta, GA; Hmrm; Sch P; Alg A; Hist A; MLS; Opt A; Sci A; Type A; Eng A.

FRYER, Jane Annette
Richfield HS; Waco, TX (19-300) Drama; Rptr, FHA; Hmrm; NHS; Sci C; Cpt, Drill Tm; Dance Schol; Performance A; *Tex Tech U; Biochem.*

FRYMAN, David Lawrence
Westlake HS; Westlake, OH (35-307) Band; Chor; FTA; Orch; Span C; Var C; MVP, Cr-Ctry; Tr; Bio A; Chem A; NEDT; Sci A; *Spring Arbor Col; Med.*

FUCHS, Chris Tina
Lincoln HS; Park Falls, WI (90-120) 4H; 4H A; Hon Prog; Type A; Trees for Tomorrow; Spelling A.

FUCHS, Donna Lynn
Delaware Co Christian Sch; Newtown Square, PA (1-48) Chldr; Secy, Chor; Drama; Mgr, Hockey; Cand, Stu Coun Pres; *Bob Jones U; Cinematography.*

FUCHS, Sara Ann
San Marcos HS; San Marcos, CA (170-326) Band; Public Relations.

FUDGE, Alan Stuart
Glynn Acad; Brunswick, GA; Band; Pres, Order/
Arrow; Eagle Sct; *Aeronautical Engr.*

FUDGE, Cathy Sue
Searcy HS; Searcy, AR (12-174) BC; VP, FBLA;
NHS; Span C; Type A; St Secy, FBLA; Bus Ed A;
Hon Graduate; Jr Auxiliary Schol; *U of Central
Ark; Bus.*

FUDGE, John Steven
Prince George HS; Prince George, VA (5%-400)
BC; Ger C; *Va Military Inst; Math.*

FUEHNE, David Franklin
Mater Dei HS; Breese, IL (25-160) Hmrm; Amer
Leg A; Star Student; Art A.

FUELLER, Leanore Ann
Old Forge HS; Old Forge, PA (14-121) FHA;
NHS; Ski C; Pres, Sodality; VP, Sodality; *Allen-
town Bus Sch; Stenographic.*

FUENTES, Becky
Christoval HS; Christoval, TX (2-11) Ann; BC; VP,
4H; Secy, Hmrm; Secy, SC; Bkbl; Tnns; 4H A;
Angelo St U; Bus.

FUERTE, Anthony
Yolo Jr HS; Newman, CA (17-74) Band; Pres,
CYO; 4H; Tr; 4H A; *Pepperdine U; Vet Med.*

FUGATE, Eric J
Gate City HS; Gate City, VA (3-204) Hmrm; Math
C; NHS; Bkbl.

FUGATE, Pamela Sue
Van Horn HS; Kansas City, MO (139-415) Chor;
Ensm; St A No 1 For Girls Sextet; *Indep Sch of
Hairdressing; Hairdressing.*

FUGLEVAND, Elizabeth Emma
Havre HS; Havre, MT (30-250) F-Ed, Ann; Pres,
Bus C; Pres, CYO; Chldr; Chor; Ensm; Semi-Fin,
GS; NHS; Var C; Swim; *U of Mont; Phys Therapy.*

FUHLBRUCK, Leslie A
Kensington HS; Buffalo, NY; Chldr; Fr C; Hmrm;
SC; Bsbl; Sftbl; Tnns.

FUHLER, Steven Joseph
Brussels Comm HS; Brussels, IL (10-34) Band;
CYO; S-T, FFA; Pres, 4H; Pres, Soph Cl; Citz A;
4H A; I Dare You; JA A.

FUHR, Alice Jane
East Sr HS; Duluth, MN; Chess C; Chor; Pep C;
GScts; Treas, Luther League; *U of Minn; Social
Work.*

FUHRMAN, Jeffrey Eugene
Gates-Chili HS; Rochester, NY (10%-650) Band;
JV, Ftbl; JV, Soccer; JV, Tr; JV, Wrest; Hon Prog;
Most Improved, Soccer; Most Improved, Tr; *Ga
Tech; Arch.*

FUHRMAN, Roger Jimm
Williamsville E HS; Williamsville, NY (35-400)
Band; Chess C; Ensm; Fr C; Co-Ed, Sch P; Var C;
JV, Bsbl; JV, Bkbl; Soccer; *Penn St U; Acct.*

FUJII, Deena Tomiko
Laupahoehoe HS; Laupahoehoe, HI (2-41) F-Ed,
Ann; Secy, FHA; Sci C; Tres, Jr Cl; Pres, Soph Cl.

FUJIKAWA, Richard Masaji
Reseda HS; Reseda, CA (10%-800) InterAct C;
CSF; Hon Prog; *UCLA; Health.*

FUJIMOTO, Dana Emiko
McKinley HS; Honolulu, HI (16-819) HiY; Secy,
NHS; ARC; Sch P; Tri-HiY; VP, Var C; Tnns; Tr;
ARC A; Japanese Lang A; Attendance A; Phys Ed
A; *U of Hawaii; Bus Adm.*

FUJITANI, Jay Masa
H P Baldwin HS; Wailuku, HI (3-300) Cpt, Dbte
Tm; Fr C; VP, NFL; Tres, NHS; Sci C; Pres, Spch
C; VP, SC; VP, Sr Cl; Pres, Soph Cl; Amer Leg A;
Spch A; VofDEM; Cl Speaker; Commended Stu;
UCLA.

FUKUDA, Leimomi Yuki
John F Kennedy HS; Tumon, GUAM; Cpt, Chor;
Math C; Alg A; Bio A; Hist A; Hon Prog; Math A;
Sci A; Stu o-t Mo; Jr NHS; Eng A; Mus A; Art
Medal; PA; *U of Hawaii; Nurs.*

FULAYTER, Steven Bradley
Barrackville HS; Barrackville, NV (1-50) BS; Dbte
Tm; Drama; Fr C; NFL; Pres, NHS; Sci C; Var C;
Bsbl; Bkbl; Tr; Bausch & Lomb A; Elk A; MLS; Phy
A; Q&S A; Spch A; Type A; Val; *Fairmont St Col;
Pol Sci.*

FULBRIGHT, Jeffrey Vance
Clay Co HS; Ashland, AL; Band; BC; Chor; FFA;
4H; Cpt, Bsbl; Ftbl; Sci A; Spch A; Bicentennial
Chor; Distinctive Achv A, Bsbl; 1st Pl, Rifle Tar-
get; *Auburn U; Phar.*

FULCHER, Barbara Ann
Pulaski HS; Somerset, KY; Co-Ed, Ann; Band;
Secy, FHA; Hmrm; F-Ed, Sch P; SC; Tres, Sr Cl;
Miss Brigadier; Miss FHA; FFA Swtht; *Somerset
Comm Col; Bus.*

FULCHER, Candace Joy
Sou Wayne Sr HS; Dudley, NC (57-389) Drama;
Secy, FHA; Sci C; Secy, Span C; SC; Hist C; Col
Work Stu Prog; Bicentennial C; WW; Faculty
Schol; *Mount Olive Col.*

FULCHER, Pamela Jeannine
Eupora HS; Eupora, MS (4-108) BC; Chor; Ensm;
FTA; A-Ed, Sch P; COM; *Miss St U; Math.*

FULFER, Carla Jean
Gordon HS; Gordon, TX; VP, BC; Rptr, FHA;
Amer Leg A; HQn; *Tarleton St U; Nurs.*

FULFORD, Bonita Gail
E Laurens HS; Dublin, GA; Co-Ed, Ann; Secy, BC;
Chldr; Pres, FHA; Pres, Sr Cl; Tnns; Alg A; Bio A;
COM; Hist A; Hon Prog; JA A; MLS; Swtht; *U of
Ga; Home Ec.*

FULGER, Ronald Douglas Jr
Everett HS; Lansing, MI (35-375) A Cap Choir;
Chess C; Drama; Ensm; JV, Cr-Ctry; *Word of Life
Bible Inst; Bible.*

FULGHAM, Keith Alan
Pelham HS; Pelham, AL; Var C; Bsbl; Art C; *U of
Montevallo; Technical Drawings.*

FULGHUM, Edith Amanda
Wilcox Co HS; Rochelle, GA (2-116) Tres, BC;
Tres, Chor; Ch, FBLA; FTA; Hmrm; Ed, Lit Mag;
Span C; SC; Mgr, Bkbl; Gov Honor Prog; Hist A;
Hon Prog; Yth Leg; Span, Eng, Glee C, A's; *Val-
dosta St Col; Mus Ed.*

FULK, Carol Annette
C E Donart HS; Stillwater, OK (10%-350) Chor;
Ensm; Math C; Mu Alpha Theta; Hon Prog; Inter-
lochen Ntl Mus; Top 10% Schol; *Okla St U; Journ.*

FULKERSON, Julene Kay
Franklin Pierce HS; Tacoma, WA; S-T, Chor;
Drama; Semi-Fin, GS; Spch C; JV, Tnns; Citz A;
Spch A; *Social Worker.*

FULKERSON, Richard Keith
Harrisburg HS; Harrisburg, IL; *SE Ill Col; Bus.*

FULKERSON, Wendy Gae
Brownfield HS; Brownfield, TX (7-144) Band;
Ensm; VP, Lat C; S-T, NHS; Opt Out Tn; Drum
Mjtre; Top Ten Schol; Chaplin, SC; WW; Band A;
Tex Tech U; Pre-Nurs.

FULLBRIGHT, Valerie Jane
Cottage Grove HS; Cottage Grove, OR (1-260)
AFS; VP, FFA; 4H; NHS; Pres, SC; Var C; Bkbl;
Cr-Ctry; Tr; 4H A; Math A; Underclman A; Outst,
Schol & Ldrship; Rotary-Ann o-t Mo; *Colo St U;
Vet Med.*

FULLEN, Susan Dianne
Johnstown-Monroe HS; Johnstown, OH (15-134)
Band; Chor; Fr C; FTA; Ftbl; Alg A; Yth Fel; Fr,
Schol Achv, A's; *Amer Hist.*

FULLER, Bobby Michael
Munford HS; Munford, AL;

FULLER, Christine Lynn
Mifflinburg Area HS; Mifflinburg, PA (20%-162)
Band; Fr C; 4H; NHS; SC; 4H A; *Harding Col.*

FULLER, Cynthia Kaye
Second Ward HS; Gloster, LA (1-35) Scholastic
Achievement; PA; Lib A; *Grambling St U; Secre-
tarial Sci.*

FULLER, Dana Jill
Blue Ridge HS; Blue, OK (1-16) Chldr; Secy, Chor; Pres,
FHA; Rptr, Hmrm; NHS; Rptr, SC; Rptr, Jr Cl;
Secy, Soph Cl; Cl Fav; Hist A; Hon Prog; Masonic
A; St HS Hon Soc; *SE Okla St U.*

FULLER, Darlene Vanessa
Second Ward HS; Gloster, LA (3-35) 4H A; Scholastic Achievement; PA; *Grambling Col; Bio.*

FULLER, David Edward
R L Turner HS; Carrollton, TX (70-753) Dbte Tm;
Hmrm; NFL; Tres, SC; Spch A; Most Individual;
Most Involved; *Sou Methodist U; Law.*

FULLER, Denise Julia
Eastern HS; Lansing, MI (250-500) Band; Chor;
JV, Tr; Citz A; Hist A; *Grand Rapids Bible Col.*

FULLER, Diane Kay
Cleveland HS; Cleveland, TN (15%-200) Anchor
C; Ann; Fr C; Lat C; NHS; SC; Co-Cpt, Bkbl; Tnns;
Sci A; *U of Tenn; Health.*

FULLER, Janie Vanessa
Thornridge HS; Dolton, IL (130-825) A Cap Choir;
Ann; Band; Co-Cpt, Chldr; Chor; Ensm; Hmrm;
Orch; SC; COM; Citz A; Val; May Ct Court; Scot-
tish Dance Group; Pep C; 1st Pl Mus A's; *DePaul
U; Psych.*

FULLER, Jeanne Vita
Marian Cath HS; Tamaqua, PA (1-173) A-Ed,
Ann; Chor; Drama; Pres, French NHS; NFL; NHS;
Sch Achieve Tm; Mgr, Hockey; Tr; Hon Prog;
Spch A; Nth HS A For Excellence; WW; *Immacu-
lata Col; Pre-Med.*

FULLER, Jeffrey Maurice
Ringgold HS; Donora, PA; Bus C; Chor; Fr C;
Hmrm; SC; Bkbl; Wrest; *Chelney St Col; Bus
Adm.*

FULLER, Jerry Lynn
Clay Co HS; Ashland, AL (50%-59) Ensm; Pres,
FFA; Hmrm; SC; Pres, Var C; Ftbl; MLS; Yth Fel;
Scottish Rite Schol A; Basic Grant A; *Sou Union U;
Religion.*

FULLER, John Mark
Springfield HS; Springfield, OR (218-266) Chldr;
Chess C; Sch P; Soccer; Swim; Co-Cpt, Wrest;
Most Outst Wrestler; Gym; St All Star Wrest Tm;
U of Pittsburg; Theology.

FULLER, Katherine Gale
Halifax Co Sr HS; South Boston, VA; Band; Lat C;
Pres, Mod Mus Mas; Pres, NHS; Gov Sch F-T
Gifted.

FULLER, Lisa Karen
Trinity Heights Christian Acad; Shreveport, LA;
Lit Ral; Sci C; Pres, Y-Tns; Swim; JA A; Leading
Lady, Play; *NE Col; Spch Therapy.*

FULLER, Meladie June
Greenville Sr HS; Greenville, MI (19-332) Band;
Ensm; Fr C; Tr; NEA Fitness A; Presidential Phys
Fitness A; *Grand Rapids Baptist Bible Col; Teach-
ing.*

FULLER, Melba Lynn
Patrick Henry HS; San Diego, CA (263-1309)
COM; Citz A; God & Country A; Gov Honor Prog;
ARC A; *Oral Roberts U; Dentistry.*

FULLER, Michael Kelley
Graham HS; Bluefield, VA (40-148) Sci C; Cpt, Jr
Rescue Sq; Jr Coun, DeMolay; *Auburn U; Engr.*

FULLER, Monte Ron
Wonderview HS; Hattieville, AR (10%-40) Band;
FFA; Pres, 4H; Bkbl; *Ark Tech U; Parks & Recrea-
tion.*

FULLER, Robert Charles
Seekonk HS; Seekonk, MA (4-224) Fr C; Math C;
NHS; Order/Arrow; JV, Bsbl; *Worcester Poly
Tech; Engr.*

FULLER, Roy Calhoun
The Baylor Sch; Chattanooga, TN (17-75) AFS;
Drama; A-Ed, Lit Mag; JV, Cr-Ctry; Tnns; FCA;
DAR Essay A.

FULLER, Steven Brian
Hales Franciscan HS; Chicago, IL (16-88) Chess C;
Bkbl; Hon Prog; Sci A; *St Johns U; Law.*

FULLER, Susan M
Chaska Sr HS; Chaska, MN (100-232) AFS; Ann;
Fr C; FHA; Pres, 4H; Ski C; Bkbl; Golf; JV Vlbl; Co
Homemaker's Schol; *U of Wis; Home Ec.*

FULLER, Tammie Lynne
Tishomingo HS; Tishomingo, MS (10%-53) Band;
Secy, BC; FHA; 4H; A-Ed, Sch P; S-T, Jr Cl; Pres,
Soph Cl; Sftbl; Alg A; Bio A; 4H A; Hist A; HCt;
Math A; Phy A; Sci A; Type A; VP, Beta C; Most
Dependable Girl; Neatest Girl; WW; Govt A; Hon
Men, GEMS Poetry A; Miss Personality; *North-
east Ms Jr Col.*

FULLER, Tracy Marie
Butler Area Sr HS; Butler, PA (70-990) JV, Chldr; Drama; NHS; Thes; COM; Drama A; Rep, World Affairs Coun; *LaSalle Col; Special Ed.*

FULLER, Vanessa Elise
Dunbar Sr HS; Fort Worth, TX; Band; JV, Chldr; NHS; Hist A; Math A; *U of Houston; Math.*

FULLER, William Goy
Marshalltown Sr HS; Marshalltown, IA; 4H; JV, Cr-Ctry; JV, Tr; Most Dedicated Ath; *Harding Col; Bible.*

FULLERTON, Kelly Dawn
Union HS; Biggsville, IL (10%-95) Band; Chor; Rptr, Drama; Ch, FHA; Madrigal; JV, Tr; *Therapeutic Dietitian.*

FULLERTON, Matthew James
Parishville-Hopkinton Central HS; Parishville, NY; A Cap Choir; Band; CYO; Chor; Span C; Bsbl; Bkbl; 4H A.

FULLERTON, Shawna Jean
Irving HS; Irving, TX (253-590) VP, Chor; Hmrm; Tri-HiY; Choir Swtht; VP, Church Group; I-Tn-R Christian Service; Rep, FHA; *Abilene Christian U; Social Work.*

FULLMER, Walter Bruce
Niles McKinley HS; Niles, OH (59-448) A Cap Choir; Ensm; Madrigal; NHS; Order/Arrow; Ski C; Ftbl; Order/Arrow A; Eagle Sct; *Kent St U; Forestry.*

FULLWOOD, Kathy Lynn
South Side HS; Counce, TN (3-34) Co-Ed, Ann; Tres, BC; Pres, FHA; Mod Mus Mas; Co-Cpt, Var C; VP, Sr Cl; Secy, Jr Cl; Tres, Soph Cl; Bkbl; Miss Southside HS; *NE Miss Jr Col; Mus.*

FULMER, Deborah Ann
McKeesport Sr HS; McKeesport, PA (33%-700) Hmrm; Mjrte; WW.

FULMER, Dixie Anna
Hilliard HS; Hilliard, FL (1-90) Ann; BC; Chem C; Pres, 4H; Hmrm; Sch P; SC; Pres, Jr Cl; Bkbl; Chem A; 4H A; Hist A; Hon Prog; Pres A; VFW Orator Win; VofDEM; Eng A; *Valdosta St Col; Phys Therapy.*

FULMER, Donna Sue
Ole Main HS; N Little Rock, AR (30-350) Band; Chem C; S-T, Hmrm; Sci C; Flag Line; Ch, Band Publicity Committee; *U of Central Ark; Nurs.*

FULMER, James Paul Jr
Tuscaloosa HS; Tuscaloosa, AL (130-500) Chor; Ensm; Hmrm; InterAct C; SC; Var C; Ftbl; *Jacksonville St U; Phys Therapy.*

FULP, Ann Leonard
Central Dvaidson Sr HS; Lexington, NC (8-270) Chor; FTA; Span C; Hon Prog; Vlbl; Qn with Sceptor, Acteens; *Mars Hill Col; Religion.*

FULP, Pamela Kaye
Bluestone Sr HS; Skipwith, VA (9-240) Ann; Tres, BC; Chldr; Fr C; VP, FBLA; Pres, FHA; Monogram; F-Ed, Sch P; SC; COM; Hon Graduate; *Averett Col; Bio.*

FULPER, Rebecca Suzanne
Booneville HS; Booneville, MS (3-104) Anchor C; Pres, Band; Pres, BC; Math C; Sci C; MVP, Tr; Citz A; 4H A; H of F; Hist A; Lion A; Pres A; Type A; Comm Service A; Lion's Band; Most Talented; Band As; *Miss St U; Psych.*

FULTON, Darcey Elizabeth
Broodmoor Sr HS; Baton Rouge, LA (20-517) A Cap Choir; BC; Ensm; Spch C; Alg A; COM; Hon Prog; Choir Trophy; *LSU; Mus.*

FULTON, Deborah K
Wethersfield HS; Wethersfield, CT; Band; Hmrm; SC; Sftbl; Co-Cpt, Swim; COM; Hon Prog; Pres A; Sci.

FULTON, Debra Kay
Cedar Hill HS; Cedar Hill, TX (3-67) Rptr, JETS; VP, NHS; Span C; Rptr, Soph Cl; COM; Citz A; HCt; Journ A; Lion A; Math A; Sci A; Type A; HR; PA; *Baylor U; Computer Sci.*

FULTON, Douglas P
Loup City HS; Loup City, NE (8-70) BS; NHS; Cpt, Ftbl; HKg; Math A; *U of Nebr; Pre-Med.*

FULTON, Gregg Norman
Odessa HS; Odessa, TX; Ch, Ensm; Ch, Madrigal; VP, NHS; SC; JV, Bkbl; JV, Ftbl; JV, Tr; COM; Citz A; Hist A; Section Ldr, A Cappella Choir; PA; Top 10, Choir; All-Region Choir; First Alt, All-Area Choir; HR; Most Outst, All-City Choir; *UCLA; Sci.*

FULTON, Kathleen Bell
Forest Hill HS; W Palm Beach, FL (4-560) VP, Ger C; Fin, GS; SC; Swim; COM.

FULTON, Kevin Thomas
Loup City HS; Loup City, NE (4-78) Pres, FFA; NHS; Bsbl; Ftbl; Wrest; Math A; *Kans St U; Agr.*

FULTON, Lorelie Josephine
Byram HS; Jackson, MS (1-60) Pres, BC; Chor; Ensm; FHA; Hmrm; Lit Mag; Ed, Sch P; Span C; SC; VP, Sr Cl; Tr; Amer Leg A; Beauty; COM; Citz A; Cl Fav; H of F; HCt; Hon Prog; Star Student; Val; Tres, Q & S; *Miss U for Women; Pre-Med.*

FULTON, Ruth Ann
Ben Davis HS; Indianapolis, IN (100-1000) A Cap Choir; Ann; Bus C; Chor; Drama; Hmrm; NHS; SC; Thes; Amer Leg A; *Johnson Bible Col; Bus.*

FULTON, Vonderlear Antoinette
Lake Clifton Sr HS; Baltimore, MD (10%-350) Band; Hmrm; JETS; Ed, Lit Mag; Math C; NHS; A-Ed, Sch P; Cpt, Tnns; Tr; Alg A; COM; Hist A; Hon Prog; Sci A; Gym; Swahili A; Eng A; Phys Ed A; *Hofstra U; Engr.*

FULTZ, Andrea
W Carter HS; Olive Hill, KY; Band; BC; Chldr; Chor; FBLA; Alg A; Math A; Chor A; *Morehead St U; Math.*

FULTZ, Kathaleen Elizabeth
Avondale Sr HS; Auburn Heights, MI; Fr C; Orch; Span C; Citz A; Cl Fav; Hon Prog; JA A; MLS; Most Out; Type A; Child Care, Art, Dancing, A's; Cooking, Camping, Pet Care, A's; Sewing & Needle C, A's; *Ferris Inst; Phar.*

FULTZ, Sheryl Annette
Bakersfield HS; Bakersfield, CA (74-450) Band; S-T, Chor; Fr C; Semi-Fin, GS; InterClub Coun; Semi-Fin, Jr Miss A; Madrigal; SC; Bank Of Amer A; Opt A; Sr Cl Rep; Outst Ldrship; *Calif St Col; Ed.*

FULTZ, Tom
Ontario HS; Mansfield, OH; Var C; MVP, Wrest; Most Out; Most Valuable; Most Pins; Ltr; St Participant A.

FULWIDER, Bryan George
Marina HS; Huntington Beach, CA (50%-1100) Dbte Tm; NFL; Wrest; Lion A; Spch A; Phys Ed A; *Goldenwest Jr Col; Theology.*

FUNCHES, Sharon Denise
Unity HS; Chicago, IL (64-160) Chor; Tres, FBLA; Rptr, Hmrm; Schol Art A; *Ill St U; Acct.*

FUNDELL, Robin Elizabeth
Malden Comm HS; Malden, IL (9-17) Ann; Band; Chldr; Chor; Drama; Fr C; Tres, FHA; Secy, Hmrm; Co-Ed, Sch P; Secy, Sr Cl; Golf; Hon Prog; Type A; Chor A.

**FUNDENBERGER,
Michael Cornelius**
Heritage Christian Sch; Indianapolis, IN (3%-61) Soccer.

FUNDERBURK, Melissa Faye
Daviston HS; Daviston, AL; BC; Rptr, 4H; Cl Fav; *U of Ala; Biol.*

**FUNDERBURKE,
Kimberly Deane**
Douglas Freeman HS; Richmond, VA; FHA; Beauty; Cl Fav; JA A; Yth Fel; *VPI; Home Ec.*

FUNK, James Preston
Ridgewood HS; W Lafayette, OH; Amer Leg A; Pres, Church Yth; Basic Skills Merit A's.

FUNK, John Kent
Lisbon HS; Lisbon, ND (39-89) Dbte Tm; Drama; Pres, FFA; Pres, SC; Thes; HCt; Hon Prog; Spch A; FFA Star Green Hand A; FFA St Farmer A; *NDSU; Agr.*

FUNK, Kevin Knight
Lincoln Comm HS; Lincoln, IL (18-340) Chor; Fr C; 4H; Ed, Sch P; Bsbl; JV, Bkbl; JV, Ftbl; Hon Prog; Yth Fel; *U of Ill; Vet Med.*

FUNK, Pamela Wynne
Paul Harding HS; Fort Wayne, IN (55-293) 4H; *Ind U; Acct.*

FUNK, Thomas Wesley
Lincoln Comm HS; Lincoln, IL (120-282) Fr C; 4H; Hmrm; Mgr, Ftbl; *E Ill U; Pol Sci.*

**FUNKENHAUSER,
Mark Joseph**
Vincent Massey Secondary Sch; Windsor, CANADA; Chem C; Math C; Ski C; Swim; *U of Wester Ontario; Natural Sci.*

FUNKHOUSER, Kathy Jo
Hobart HS; Hobart, OK (4-68) Chldr; FHA; NHS; SC; *Okla Baptist U; Ed.*

FUNSTON, Rick Jay
Post Falls Sr HS; Post Falls, ID; *U of Wash; Archt.*

FUQUA, Vickey Darleen
Crestview HS; Crestview, FL; BC; Bus C; FBLA; Job Interview A; COM Fin; Filing A; Semi-Fin, Typing A; *Secretarial.*

FURBRINGER, John Meigs Hill
The Donoho Sch; Anniston, AL (15-47) Fr C; Key C; Order/Arrow; Sci C; Bkbl; Soccer; HCt; Order/Arrow A; Yth Fel; Eagle Sct; *Vet Med.*

**FURBRINGER,
Paul Herbert Hill**
The Donoho Sch; Anniston, AL (15-42) Chess C; Key C; VP, Mu Alpha Theta; Order/Arrow; Pres, Span C; Bkbl; MVP, Soccer; Order/Arrow A; Yth Fel; Eagle Sct; *Math.*

FURGESON, Cinda Kay
Taylorville Sr HS; Taylorville, IL (36-247) Society For Acad Achv; *E Ill U; Home Ec.*

FURIO, Cynthia Claire
Lee HS; Huntsville, AL (8-300) Band; 4H; Inter-Club Coun; Cpt, Mjrte; NHS; Span C; Beauty; Citz A; Elk A; 4H A; Most Out; Sr Rep, Anchor C; WW; Dunnavant's Tn Board; *Birmingham-Sou Col; Ballet.*

FURLONG, Maureen Patricia
St Joseph's o-t Palisades HS; W New York, NJ (8-225) F-Ed, Ann; CYO; Chor; Drama; NHS; Span NHS; Hon Prog; *Trenton St Col; Eng Ed.*

FURMAN, Michael John
Clay Center HS; Clay Center, NE; Var C; Ftbl; Tr; Wrest; *Central Nebr Tech U; Welding & Mech.*

FURNEY, Dale Allan
Canton S HS; Canton, OH (6-280) Tres, HiY; NHS; Bsbl; Golf; *U of Cincinnati; Engr.*

FURNISH, Ketrina Lynn
Greenup Co HS; Lloyd, KY (26-315) Band; Hmrm; Lat C; SC; Pres, Tri-HiY; Secy, Jr Cl; Pres A; 4-H A; Miss Flame; *Morehead St U; Phys Thearpy.*

FURR, Lori Kathleen
Boron HS; Boron, CA (10-78) Band; Hmrm; NHS; SC; Mgr, Bsbl; Mgr, Bkbl; Amer Leg A; CSF; Fresh Christmas Ball Princess; HR; Yrbk Staff; Pres, 8th Grade; *Fresno St U; Bus.*

FURSE, Tracy Kay
Jayhawk-Linn HS; Mound City, KS (5-48) Pres, Ann; Band; Pres, Drama; Ensm; FHA; GS; Pres, Rainbow; Ed, Sch P; Pres, Spch C; S-T, SC; Var C; Pres, Jr Cl; VP, Soph Cl; Co-Cpt, Bkbl; Tr; HCt; Journ A; Masonic A; Spch A; Type A; Cpt, Vlbl; Pres, Pep C; HR; Courtwarming Court; Yrbk Candidate; Sch Plays; *Kans St Col; Botany.*

FURSE, Trenda Gay
Jayhawk-Linn HS; Mound City, KS (1-51) Ann; Band; Drama; FHA; Rainbow; Rptr, Sch P; S-T, Soph Cl; Bkbl; Vlbl.

FURUTA, Jennifer Satomi
Kailua HS; Kailua, HI (136-556) Hmrm; SC; Secy, Soph Cl; *U of Hawaii.*

FUSICH, Cecelia Claire Anne
St Joseph's Notre Dame HS; Alameda, CA (3-78) NHS; Ski C; Bsbl; Sftbl; Alg A; Bio A; Citz A; Hist A; Hon Prog; NEDT; Spch A; Type A; Vlbl; *UC at Davis; Law.*

FUSON, Amy Jo
Sou Baptist Educational Center HS; Memphis, TN; BC; Lat C; Bkbl; Mgr, Sftbl; Vlbl; Bowl; *U of Tenn; Sci.*

FUSON, Patricia Jean
Shrine Sheffield HS; Memphis, TN; BC; NHS; Memphis St U; Bus.

FUSSELL, Alisa Denean
Mt de Sales HS; Macon, GA (15-120) ARC; Span C; Hon Prog; NEDT; ARC A; Span A; Early Childhood Ed.

FUSSELL, Karen Yvette
Oxnard Union HS; Oxnard, CA; Biol C; Olivet Col; Law.

FUSSELL, Laura Tracy
Lakeland Christian Sch; Lakeland, FL (6-39) Band; Chldr; Chor; Math C; NHS; SC; HR A; Math.

FUSSELL, Mary Elizabeth
Lake Highland Prep Sch; Orlando, FL (10-96) Chldr; Drama; Purdue U; Med.

FUSTIN, Susan Elaine
Bethany HS; Bethany, IL (14-29) Band; FHA; FTA; VP, Sr Cl; MVP, Bkbl; Sftbl; Tr; Lakeland Jr Col; Acct.

FUTATO, Gracann
Riverside Sr HS; Ellwood City, PA; Band; Chor; Ensm; Tri-HiY; Hon Prog; Mus A; Geneva Col.

G

GAAL, Peter John
Calvary Christian Sch; Glens Falls, NY (1-5) Fin, Chess C; Chor; Ensm; Bkbl; Ftbl; Sftbl; MLS; Val; Bob Jones U; Landscaping.

GAAN, Linda Evelyn
Oak Grove HS; San Jose, CA; Ger C; San Jose St Col; Home Ec.

GAAR, Reyna Denise
Castlemont HS; Oakland, CA; Ann; Chor; Hmrm; NHS; SC; CSF; COM; Hon Prog; NMS; Yth Fel; Yth Leg; Pomona Col; Eng.

GABA, James Edwin
Artesia HS; Artesia, NM; Secy, Demolay; Hmrm; NHS; Order/Arrow; SC; Arch; Bsbl; Bkbl; Ftbl; Swim; Hon Prog; Order/Arrow A; Pres A; Sci A; Cpt, Demolay; Ntl Fraternity of Stu Mus; Ftbl & Bkbl Ltrs; Life Sct A; Air Force Acad; Sci.

GABBARD, Kenneth Lewis
Horatio HS; Horatio, AR (8-30) Dbte Tm; VP, FFA; FTA; VP, SC; Var C; Cpt, Bkbl; Co-Cpt, Ftbl; Sftbl; Tr; MVP, Bkbl; Runner Up, Most Handsome; All District, Bkbl; Pastor, Two Churches; Sou Ark U; Reg.

GABBARD, Lisa Ann
Miami Norland Sr HS; Miami, FL (35-525) Tres, Chor; Ensm; Madrigal; Mod Mus Mas; NHS; HQn; Swtht; Type A; Outst Chor Mus Stu; All St Chor Mus A; Fla St U; Mus.

GABBERT, Carolyn Sue
Terre Haute N Vigo HS; Terre Haute, IN (86-656) Secy, Hmrm; Tres, InterClub Coun; Orch; Co-Ch, Y-Tns; Hon Prog; Social Work.

GABEL, Faye Ann
Crystal Lake Comm HS; Crystal Lake, IL (78-585) Fr C; NHS; COM; Hon Prog; Yth Fel; Pensacola Christian Col; Secy.

GABEL, Mary Ellen
Lourdes HS; Chicago, IL (4-263) NHS; Ed, Sch P; COM; Hon Prog; Drama A; Ftbl Ldrship A; Cpt, Girl's Flag Ftbl.

GABLE, Cathy Ann
Hobart Sr HS; Hobart, IN; FHA; NHS; Tr; Crisco A; Span A.

GABLE, Kevin P
Logan HS; Logan, OH (1-310) Rptr, Ann; BS; Chess C; VP, Fr C; Tres, Lat C; NHS; A-Ed, Sch P; Val; TV Quiz Show; Miami U; Chem.

GABLE, Linda Faye
Grand Ridge Sch; Grand Ridge, FL (2-49) BC; 4H; Y-Tns; 4H A; Sal; Type A; Chipola Jr Col; Pre-Med.

GABLER, Keith Allen
Lake Oswego HS; Lake Oswego, OR (116-276) A Cap Choir; Chor; Sci C; Pres A; Ecology C; Rock Creek Comm Col; Building Construction Tech.

GABLER, Mark Louis
Lake Oswego HS; Lake Oswego, OR; Chem C; Hon Prog; Recycling C; U of Oreg; Chem.

GABRIEL, Annette Felicia
Central HS; Louisville, KY; Ann; Drama; ARC; Ftbl; JA A; U of Louisville; Primary Ed.

GABRIEL, Daniel David
Central HS; St Joseph, MO (10%-700) AFS; Chor; Ger C; Pres, HiY; Tr; U of Colo; Law.

GABRIEL, Gretchen Gene
Central HS; St Joseph, MO (1-525) Chem C; Chor; VP, Fr C; NHS; U of Kans.

GABRIEL, Robert Paul
Niles HS; Skokie, IL (25%-550) Chor; Cpt, Cr-Ctry; Co-Cpt, Tr; U of Ill; Sci.

GABRIELSON, Kathy Ann
Luverne HS; Luverne, MN (20-132) Chldr; Chor; Semi-Fin, GS; Amer Leg A; Pres A; Yth Fel; Phys Therapy.

GABRYSZEWSKI, Joseph Paul
Oppenheim Ephratah Central Sch; St Johnsville, NY (1-38) AFS; Fr C; NHS; VP, Jr Cl; JV, Bkbl; Hon Prog; Math A; Union Col; Med Sci.

GACA, Paul Joseph
Hubbard HS; Chicago, IL (206-449) BS; Hmrm; InterClub Coun; ARC; SC; Tres, Var C; Cpt, Ftbl; Tr; Amer Leg A; COM; Citz A; Bradley U.

GADD, Ricky A
Thomas Jefferson HS; Louisville, KY; U of Louisville; Theology.

GADDIS, David Marshall
N Gaston HS; Dallas, NC; Span C; Bsbl; Bkbl; Cr-Ctry; Sftbl; Carolina Col; Law.

GADDY, Jimmy Ray
Waltrip Sr HS; Houston, TX (5%-650) NHS; JV, Bsbl; Chem A; Hist C; Rice U; Marine Bio.

GADDY, Kenneth Clyde
Thomasville Acad; Thomasville, AL (5-17) Bus Mgr, Ann; VP, BC; BS; Pres, Var C; Pres, Sr Cl; Bsbl; Bkbl; Ftbl; Tr; Soph Cl Rep; Acad & Sportsmanship, Ath A's; U of S Ala; Vet Med.

GADSDEN, David Bernard
Charleston HS; Charleston, SC (17-108) BC; Chor; Wrest; Bradford Col; Bus Adm.

GADSDEN, James Solomon
John Overton HS; Nashville, TN (75-365) BS; Chldr; Community Yth Symph; Hmrm; Orch; SC; JA A; Tenn St U; Bus.

GADSEY, Steven Lynn
Glencliff HS; Nashville, TN; Ftbl; Tnns; Tr; Wrest; FCA; Middle Tenn St U; Acct.

GADSON, Irene LaVerne
Savannah HS; Savannah, GA; Drama; FHA; Math C; COM; Hon Prog; JA A; Masonic A; ROTC A; Home Ec A; Hero C; Dist Sci Fair A; PA; HR; Bus.

GADSON, Karen Yvonne
August Martin HS; Queens, NY (40-1004) Band; Chor; Dbte Tm; SC; Var C; Soccer; Bio A; COM; Citz A; Cl Fav; Hon Prog; Math A; Most Out; Poet A; Sci A; Spch A; Mus; Morehouse Col; Law.

GADSON, Shelley Denise
Julia Richman HS; NY, NY; Pres, Chor; Alg A; COM; Hon, Effort, A's; Queensboro Comm Col; Nurs.

GAETANI, John August
Binghamton HS; Binghamton, NY (7-230) NHS; Golf; Tnns; Hon Prog; Regent Schol; Broome Comm Col; Bus Adm.

GAFFEY, Gene P
Huntington HS; Huntington, NY; Band; Pres, InterAct C; Fencing; Bus.

GAFFNER, Patti Jean
Greenville HS; Greenville, IL; AFS; Ann; Band; Chor; Ensm; Rptr, 4H; Parl, Hmrm; Madrigal; Span C; Parl, SC; 4H A; Sal; Church Sftbl; Pres, Secy, 4 H C; Ozark Bible Col.

GAFFNEY, Cynthia Louise
W Mecklenburg HS; Charlotte, NC (5%-352) GS; NHS; VP, Sci C; S-T, Span C; SC; Civinettes; Civitan Conf; Fel of Christian Girls; Jr Marshal; Pep C; Page, NC House of Rep; Schol, Span, A's; Biol.

GAFFNEY, Tina Marcell
W Orange HS; Winter Garden, FL (10%-310) Math C; NHS; Sci C; COM; Most Liked; Baylor U; Health.

GAFFRON, Eric Robert
SW HS; St Louis, MO (13-550) Chess C; Chor; Ger C; Math C; Sci C; Tnns; Alg A; Eagle Sct; HR; Air Force Acad; Elec Engr.

GAGE, Alicia Anne
Dobyns-Bennett HS; Kingsport, TN (77-500) BC; CYO; S-T, Fr C; Lat C; Biol.

GAGE, Cameron George
Central HS; La Crosse, WI; A Cap Choir; Ensm; Ger C; Swim; Skiing; Communications.

GAGE, Earl Raymond
Salem HS; Salem, NJ (27-235) Tres, Band; BS; NHS; Orch; Friends of Animals C; Executive Board, SC; Mus As; Rutgers U; Social Sci.

GAGE, Mark Brendan
Dobyns-Bennett HS; Kingsport, TN; Band; CYO; Ensm; Hmrm; Mgr, Orch; Sftbl; Theology.

GAGE, Myrtie Michele
White Hall HS; Pine Bluff, AR; Chldr; Chor; Pres, SC; Sftbl; Ldrship A; UAPB; PE.

GAGER, Deborah Sue
Heritage HS; Littleton, CO (154-404) Chor; Ensm; Swim; COM; JA A; Close Up Program; Mus As; Tanglewood Equestrian Inst; Breeding & Training Horses.

GAGNE, Lorraine Ann
St Dominic Regional HS; Lewiston, ME (3-98) Sftbl.

GAGNE, Michelle Jeanne
Gloucester HS; Gloucester, MA; Band; Mjrte; Tr; ROTC A; Type A; Academic Hons; Tailoring; Sr Prom Qn; Mount Ida Jr Col; Fashion Merchandising.

GAGNON, Gary W
Dover HS; Dover, NH (33-394) Band; BS; Chor; Drama; Mu Alpha Theta; NHS; Tr; Hon Prog; U of NH; Bio.

GAGNON, Linda Kay
Saint John HS; Ennis, TX (4-34) Ann; NHS; Co-Ed, Sch P; Artist, Sch Paper; Bazaar Qn Cand; Executive Secretarial Sch; Bus.

GAGNON, Pauline
College De Ste Anne De La Pocatiere; La Pocatiere, CANADA (2-32) Vlbl.

GAHL, Steve Wayne
S Beliot HS; S Beloit, IL (30-100) JV, Ftbl; Wrest.

GAIER, Mark Andrew
Cath Central HS; Springfield, OH; Chor; Wrest; Alg A; Sci A; Bus A; Acct.

GAIER, Stephen Francis
London HS; London, OH (3-96) Ed, Ann; BS; Lat C; Lit Mag; Pres, NHS; VP, Sr Cl; Pres, Jr Cl; Chamber of Comm A; Jr Chamber of Com A; Kiwanis A; Sci A; Spch A; VofDEM; Ohio Northern U; Bio.

GAILEY, Carol Lynne
N Quincy HS; Quincy, MA (43-463) Hmrm; NHS; Bkbl; JV, Sftbl; Eastern Nazarene Col.

GAINER, James Alan
Shenandoah Valley Acad; New Market, VA (4-80) Rptr, Ann; Pres, Band; NHS; SC; Fin, Bkbl; Ftbl; Sftbl; COM; NMS; NEDT; Columbia Union Col; Chem.

GAINES, Brett Mitchell
Frederick Douglas HS; Atlanta, GA (8-330) Band; Drama; Hmrm; NHS; Bsbl; Tnns; COM; Atlanta Public Sch Hon A; Georgia Tech; Engr.

GAINES, Brian Anthony
East HS; Buffalo, NY; Co-Cpt, Bsbl; Cpt, Ftbl; Cpt, Swim; Regent Schol; Black Burn Col; Sociology.

GAINES, Carolyn Faye
Humboldt HS; Humboldt, TN; Jackson St Comm Col; Modeling.

GAINES, Jerry Denise
Wade Hampton HS; Greenville, SC (33%-376) FHA; Hmrm; ARC; Span C; SC; Tres, Sr Cl; Tres, Jr Cl; US Senate Page; Sr Superlative; *Erskine Col; Pol Sci.*

GAINES, Kristin Kay
Yankton HS; Yankton, SD (25%-250) Chor; Drama; GS; Pres, Hmrm; NHS; Secy, SC; JV, Bkbl; Swim; Tr; Cpt, Drill Tm.

GAINES, Lisa Creymore
Lancaster HS; Lancaster, VA (1-167) AFS; S-T, Band; JV, Chldr; Fr C; 4H; Hmrm; Sci C; JV, Bkbl; Sftbl; Tr; Bio A; Gov Honor Prog; Phys Ed A; *Sci.*

GAINES, Michael Dean
Humboldt HS; Humboldt, TN; *Jackson St Comm Col; Modeling.*

GAINES, Ruth Lynette
Lancaster HS; Lancaster, VA; F-Ed, Ann; Band; Chldr; Drama; GS; Madrigal; Pres, NHS; Secy, Span C; SC; Pres, Soph Cl; Tr; Pres A; *Madison Col; Math.*

GAITHER, Sharon
Clay Co HS; Ashland, AL; Band; BC; Chor; Ensm; FHA; FTA; Mjrte; Rptr; Sci C; Beauty; HCt; Yth Fel; *Samford U; Child Psych.*

GAKING, Donna Lynn
Kelly HS; Chicago, IL; Bus C; Chor; Community Yth Symph; Drama; Secy, Hmrm; Lit Ral; Tres, Sodality; SC; Citz A; Hon Prog; MLS; Yth Fel.

GALARZA, Brenda
Luis Munoz Rivera HS; Lajas, PR (30-170) Band; Chldr; Chor; Drama; FHA; Mjrte; Arch; Swim; COM; Hon Prog; Poet A; *CAAM; Med Tech.*

GALAS, Cynthia Suzanne
St Bede Acad; Peru, IL (65-140) Band; Rptr, Sch P; Sci A; Sci Fair; *Special Ed.*

GALASSINI, Mary Ann
Marillac HS; Northfield, IL (12-197) Chldr; Chor; Hmrm; NHS; SC; Thes; Swim; *St Mary's Col; Bus.*

GALATOCKY, Susan Christina
Cardinal Stritch HS; Oregon, OH (20-174) Band; CYO; Chor; Ensm; Fr C; Orch; Bkbl; Hon Prog; Type A; Eng A; Mus A; Diploma, Ntl Guild of Piano Tchrs; *St Petersburg Jr Col; Legal Secy.*

GALAZ, Marta Celia
Inglewood HS; Inglewood, CA (20%-325) Chor; Madrigal; Math C; Pres, Rainbow; CSF; Citz A; Hon Prog; NEDT; Stu ct Mo; *UCLA; Bio.*

GALBRAITH, James Albert
Tahlequah HS; Tahlequah, OK (15%-280) Demolay; FTA; NHS; SC; Bkbl; Ftbl; Tr.

GALBRAITH, Neill Norris
Texas City HS; Texas City, TX (33-410) Ann; Tres, Key C; Sch P; SC; Mgr, Bkbl; NEDT; WW; Moody Found Schol; Church Yth Comm; Press C; *U of Tex-Austin; Acct.*

GALBRAITH, Sherri Lynn
Christian Sch; Dallas, TX; A Cap Choir; JV, Chldr; NHS; *Harding Col; Interior Decorating.*

GALBREATH, Beverly Jane
Columbia HS; Richland, WA; Chor; FBLA; Orch; Tn Talent Contest; Secy, Church Yth; *Bethany Bible Col; Mus.*

GALE, Carol Emily
Roxborough HS; Philadelphia, PA (150-395) Tnns; Wrest; Bowl; *Dental Asst.*

GALE, Dana Eileen
Houston HS; Houston, MO (3-124) Chor; Model UN; NHS; Covert A; *Central Christian Col of The Bible; Bible.*

GALE, Kathleen Francis
Holy Rosary Acad; Louisville, KY (17-84) VP, Drama; Secy, FBLA; SC; *U of Louisville; Acct.*

GALE, Melece Louise
Sky View HS; Smithfield, UT (107-573) A Cap Choir; Drama; FHA; InterClub Coun; Key C; Mjrte; Spch C; Secy, SC; COM; Citz A; Sci A; Spch A; 2nd Runnerup, 'Miss Jantzen'; *Utah St U; Elem Ed.*

GALE, Michael Stewart
E Hartford HS; E Hartford, CT (19-360) Tres, Band; CYO; VP, Chess C; Community Yth Symph; Drama; Ensm; Hmrm; JETS; Lit Mag; Madrigal; VP, Math C; NHS; Orch; Pres, Phys C; ARC; Ed, Sch P; VP, Sci C; World Affairs C; Journ A; Q&S A; Sci A; St Scholar; VofDEM; Mus A; Central NW Band; Yth Chorale; Yth in Gov Prog; *U of Conn; Nuclear Physics.*

GALE, Teri Lea
E Hartford HS; E Hartford, CT (15-360) Chor; Drama; Ensm; Fr C; VP, FTA; JETS; VP, Math C; NHS; Co-Ed, Sch P; VP, Sci C; World Affairs C; Q&S A; Drama A; *Social Sci.*

GALEGHER, Claudia Adele
Thompson Pub Sch; Thompson, ND; Ann; Band; Chldr; Chor; Drama; Ensm; GS; 4H; Key C; Sch P; SC; Pres, Jr Cl; Bkbl; 4H A; I Dare You; Spch A; WW; *ND St U; Foods And Human Nutrition.*

GALER, Norman Wayne
Enid HS; Enid, OK (15-530) Dbte Tm; HiY; Hmrm; NFL; NHS; Thes; Tnns; *Med.*

GALIETTI, Patricia Kathleen
Secaucus HS; Secaucus, NJ (1-185) Hon Prog; Co-Cpt, Colorguard; *Math.*

GALINANES, Ingrid Milagros
Academia del Sagrado Corazon; Santurce, PR (1-90) ARC; Sci C; Span C; Alg A; Phy A; Type A; Conduct A; Geography A; Geol A; Span A; Eng A; *Bethany Col; Lang.*

GALLA, Shirley
Kubasaki HS; Okinawa, JAPAN (1-271) S-T, Fr C; Tres, Mu Alpha Theta; Ch, NHS; Pres, GAA; Cpt, Vlbl; GAL; Bus Mgr, Stu Directory; RATO; VP, Vlbl C; *Sac St U.*

GALLAGHER, Ann Colette
St Augustine Acad; Lakewood, OH (12-138) NHS; Secy, SC; Bkbl; First Hons; Service A; Vlbl; *Ursuline Col; Nurs.*

GALLAGHER, Ingrid Marie
Ocean City HS; Ocean City, NJ; Chldr; Pres, 4H; 4H A; Yth Fel; VP, 4-H C; Pres, Church Yth; Candystriper; GSct; Comm Dune Grass Planting; Church Nursery Sch Teacher; *Social Worker.*

GALLAGHER, James Francais
Northside HS; Atlanta, GA (40-275) BC; Sch P; Cr-Ctry; Tr; ROTC A; Yth Fel; Jr Civitan Little League Coach; Young Life; *Ga St U; Journ.*

GALLAGHER, Leslie Madelyn
St Augustine HS; Laredo, TX (2-70) Drama; NHS; Mgr, Bkbl; Tr; Chem A; Hon Prog; MLS; Sal; Gov A; *Tulane U; Architecture.*

GALLAGHER, Marc Allen
Clyde HS; Clyde, KS (1-26) Sch Achieve Tm; Bsbl; MVP, Bkbl; Ftbl; Tr; COM; Hon Prog; Lion A; St Scholar; *Kans St; Acct.*

GALLAGHER, Marie Theresa
St Francis Preparatory HS; Fresh Meadows, NY (2-673) Chor; City Conf; Drama; Hmrm; NHS; Sch Achieve Tm; SC; Y-Tns; Pres, Jr Cl; Amer Leg A; COM; Hon Prog; JA A; Sal; Type A; *Pace U; Bus.*

GALLAGHER, Mark Ivan
Oroville HS; Oroville, CA (14-285) Demolay; NHS; SC; Var C; Pres, Soph Cl; Co-Cpt, Ftbl; JV, Tr; Co-Cpt, Wrest; CSF; Pres A; *Air Force Acad; Aeronautical Engr.*

GALLAGHER, Scott David
Oroville HS; Oroville, CA (42-283) Demolay; NHS; Ftbl; *UCLA; Hist.*

**GALLAGHER,
Sheila Mary Elizabeth**
San Ramon Valley HS; Danville, CA; Ann; CYO; Chor; FNA; 4H; ARC; A-Ed, Sch P; Ski C; Span C; SC; VP, Sr Cl; Cr-Ctry; Tr; CSF; Chamber of Comm A; 4H A; ARC A; Jr Vol; *Chico St U; Nurs.*

GALLAHER, Mary Lou
Obion Co Central HS; Troy, TN; F-Ed, Ann; BC; Chor; Pres, Fr C; FBLA; Secy, NHS; *U of Tenn; Bus.*

GALLEGO, Noel Garrucha
John F Kennedy HS; Tumon, GUAM; VP, Bus C; Chess C; Hmrm; NHS; Secy, Order/Arrow; Rptr, Sch P; Soccer; Order/Arrow A; ROTC A; Yth Leg; Aerospace A; Model Rocketry A; BSA A; PON; Pacific Media A; *Aerospace.*

GALLENI, Donna Louise
Carlmont HS; Belmont, CA; A Cap Choir; Chldr; Nurs.*

GALLETTA, Theresa Gayle
Bible Baptist HS; Savannah, GA (25%-54) Chor; Sftbl; HCt; Hon Prog; *Armstrong St Col; Computer Sci.*

GALLI, Michael Joseph
Tower HS; Warren, MI (75-367) Chor; Bsbl; Ftbl; MVP, Sftbl; Wrest; Pres A; Mary Mala Fouris; Mem A; RBI A; *Central Mich Col; Bus.*

GALLIEN, Cheryl Denice
Cloutierville HS; Cloutierville, LA; Bus C; Chldr; FBLA; Pres, FHA; *NW St U; Special Ed.*

GALLINGER, Bridget Regina
Seaside HS; Seaside, OR (8-94) Chor; Fr C; NHS; SC; Var C; Bkbl; Cr-Ctry; JV, Golf; Tres, GSct; 1st Cl, GSct; Vlbl; Hon Soc Schol; Bus & Professional Women's Schol; *Oreg Col of Ed; Elem Ed.*

GALLION, Franklin Ray Jr
Central Sr HS; Victoria, VA (10-119) Key C; Monogram; Tres, NHS; Span C; SC; Pres, Y-Tns; Alg A; COM; 4H A; Sci A; *Sci.*

GALLMEISTER, Debra Ann
DuQuoin HS; DuQuoin, IL (35-147) Band; VP, Chor; VP, FHA; Circus A; Hon Prog; Swtht Dance Attendant; Band Medals; *John A Logan Col; Cosmetology.*

GALLOGLY, Laura Jean
Lakewood HS; Hebron, OH (41-209) Cpt, Chldr; Chor; Drama; FHA; FTA; Rainbow; Sch P; Y-Tns; Tr; COM; 4H A; Pres A; Sci A; Type A; Yth Fel; Co Talent Show; Sch Talent Show; *Central Ohio Tech Col; Computor Programing.*

GALLOP, Louis Alexander
Camden HS; Camden, NC; 4H; Mgr, Bkbl.

GALLOT, Daphne Elizabeth
Alma J Brown HS; Grambling, LA; Band; Fr C; 4H; NHS; Sci C; SC; Tres, Soph Cl; 4H A; NEDT.

GALLOTTE, Donald Jeffrey
Bellevue HS; Bellevue, WA (33%-500) Ann; Band; NHS; Var C; Bsbl; Ftbl; *Whitworth Col; Phys Ed.*

GALLOWAY, Angela Renee
Keokuk Sr HS; Keokuk, IA (50-260) Band; Chor; Drama; Ensm; Fr C; Hmrm; Spch C; SC; Scholastic Achv A.

GALLOWAY, Bryan Eugene
Millard Sr HS; Omaha, NE (52-417) Dbte Tm; VP, NFL; NHS; *Bethel Col; Bible.*

GALLOWAY, Gregory Bruce
Spruce Creek HS; Port Orange, FL; Anchor C; Chor; Orch; SC; UN Council; Pres, Sr Cl; Pres, Jr Cl; Ftbl; Cpt, Soccer; Swim; Tr; DARGCA; H of F; HCt; Most Out; Yth Leg; Lt, Band; Principal's A; Ensm Accompanist; Mr Spruce Creek; Most Outst, Gym; *Appalachian St U; Pol Sci.*

GALLOWAY, James Allen
Clearwater HS; Clearwater, FL; Band; COM.

GALLOWAY, Jeffrey Lee
Jupiter Christian Sch; Jupiter, FL (6-18) Ann; Band; Chor; Span C; Spch C; Cpt, Bsbl; Cpt, Bkbl; Co-Cpt, Soccer; Tnns; HCt; Hon Prog; Spch A; *Bsbl.*

GALLOWAY, John Anthony
Pendleton HS; Pendleton, SC (17-133) BC; NHS; Sci C; Var C; Cpt, Bkbl; MLS; *Central Wesleyan Col; Bus.*

GALLOWAY, Rene Elizabeth
John Jay HS; San Antonio, TX (200-600) Chldr; Tres, FNA; Tres, ARC; *St Phillips U; Med.*

GALLOWAY, Sherry Jo
Burroughs HS; Ridgecrest, CA; Chor; Drama; *Azusa Pacific Col; Mus.*

GALLOWAY, Veronica Marie
St Martin HS; Biloxi, MS (4%-195) Ann; BC; Bus C; City Conf; Drama; Fr C; Hmrm; F-Ed, Sch P; SC; Var C; Cpt, Bkbl; MVP, Sftbl; MVP, Tr; Cl Fav; Hist A; Hon Prog; Most Out; *Tougaloo Col; Computer Sci.*

GALLOWAY, William U III
Clearwater HS; Clearwater, FL (1-800) Band; Math C; NHS; Orch; Alg A; Hist A; Hon Prog; Math A; Val; *U of Fla; Archt.*

GALLY, Janet Elizabeth
Arvada Sr HS; Arvada, CO; Band; Job's Daughters; *U of Colo; Mus.*

GALOW, Susan
Bay City HS; Bay City, TX; Secy, Bus C; FHA; FTA; VP, Spch C; Rptr, Sr Cl; JV, Bkbl; Golf; Tnns; Beauty; VP, Luther League; VP, DECA C; All Star Cast, Dist Play; *Wharton Jr Col; Sociology.*

GALPHIN, Margaret Annette
John T Hoggard HS; Wilmington, NC (2%-750) 4H; Hmrm; Mgr, Bkbl; Mgr, Cr-Ctry; *E Carolina U; Math.*

GALT, Nicole Suzanne
Tyler Street Christian Acad; Dallas, TX (25%-40) Chldr; Pres, Drama; Rptr, Sch P; Pres, SC; VP, Jr Cl; Beauty; Cl Fav; Lion A; Most Out; Yth Fel; Yth Leg; *SMU; Psych.*

GALUSHA, Gaye Lynn
Monmouth HS; Monmouth, IL (11-157) Band; Secy, Sci C; Span C; Ch, Sci C; *Bradley U.*

GALUSZKA, Laura Lynne
St Hedwig HS; Detroit, MI (4-86) Cpt, Chldr; Span C; VP, Soph Cl; Mgr, Sftbl; Hon Prog; High School Hon A; Special Sci A.

GALUTIA, Teresa Jean
Ottawa Sr HS; Ottawa, KS; Chor; Drama; Ensm; NHS; Spch C; COM; Hon Prog; Spch A; Art A; Musical Productions; Choir; VP, Art C; St Mus Festival Group; VP, Keyettes; Ch, Prom Comm; Pep C; Homcom Com; Pres, Chrch Yth; *Baker U; Art.*

GALVAN, Gerard
Travis HS; Austin, TX; VP, CYO; Span C; *U of Tex; Law.*

GALVAN, Laura
Tilden HS; Chicago, IL (8-408) Bio A; Lib Aid; Jr Career Day; *U of Mexico; Med.*

GALVAN, Leora Ruth
Douglas HS; Douglas, AZ (2-301) AFS; Secy, Chor; Drama; Secy, Ensm; NHS; Thes; Math A; *NW Nazarene Col; Math.*

GALVIN, Sharon Allen
Baldwin Park HS; Baldwin Park, CA; Dbte Tm; Hmrm; Y-Tns; VP, Drill Tm; *Mt San Antonio Col; Bus.*

GALYEAN, Becky Ann
McClellan HS; Little Rock, AR (110-420) Band; BC; Chor; FHA; Flagline; Church Ensm; *Ouachita U.*

GALYEAN, Julie Lynn
Oakville HS; Oakville, WA (2-30) F-Ed, Ann; Band; Chess C; Secy, FFA; VP, FHA; S-T, Math C; NHS; Rptr, Sch P; Span C; Secy, SC; S-T, Sr Cl; Secy, Jr Cl; Secy, Soph Cl; Mgr, Bkbl; Tr; Sal; 1st Chair, Flute; FFA St Band; *Centralia Col; Home Ec.*

GALYEAN, Molly Melissa
Briarfield Acad; Lake Providence, LA; Ann; Tres, BC; Ensm; 4H; NHS; Sch P; Mgr, Bkbl; Tr; 4H A; WW; Lib Service A; *LSU; Merchandising.*

GALYON, Stacy Merle
Carney HS; Carney, OK; Ann; Chldr; FHA; Sch P; VP, Jr Cl; Secy, Soph Cl; Bkbl; Cl Fav; Hist A; HCt; Math A; Type A.

GAMACHE, Richard Edmond
Seekonk HS; Seekonk, MA (1-224) Dbte Tm; Drama; Hmrm; Math C; Pres, NHS; Sch P; SC; Alg A; Bio A; Hon Prog; MLS; Val; Drama A; *MIT; Engr.*

GAMBER, Janine Louise
Northern HS; Flint, MI (350-700) Span C; *Mott Comm Col; Nurs.*

GAMBER, Lori Beth
Tecumseh HS; Tecumseh, MI (37-263) Pres, Chor; FTA; 4H; NHS; Ed, Sch P; Pres, Span C; 4H A; Church Yth Chor; Pres, Luther Lge; Span Award; PA; Modern Dance C; Tuition Grant; Schol, U of Guadalajara; *Hope Col; Sociology.*

GAMBER, Rebecca Lynn
Coronado HS; Colo Springs, CO (9-369) A Cap Choir; Chor; Community Yth Symph; Drama; Madrigal; Pres, NHS; Orch; Hist A; Hon Prog; Pres A; Rotary A; Yth Fel; Advanced Placement Prog; WW; *U of N Colo; Mus Ed.*

GAMBILL, Daniel Lloyd
Paris HS; Paris, TX; Arch; Tres, FFA; HiY; Key C; Span C; Arch; Bsbl; Cpt, Ftbl; Opt A; Rotary A; Pres, FCA; MVP, Ftbl; Parl, FFA; *McMurry Col; Phys Ed.*

GAMBILL, Margaret Bard
Claremont HS; Claremont, CA (33-577) Chor; Ski C; JV, Tnns; CSF; Pres, Ntl Charity League; Cl Rep, Girl's League.

GAMBLE, Arthur Forrest
New Caney HS; Porter, TX (25%-360) Ed, Ann; Band; NHS; Amer Leg A; Journ A; ROTC A; Sci A; *Air Force Acad; Aerospace Engr.*

GAMBLE, Deborah Faye
Williamsburg HS; Andrews, SC;

GAMBLE, Dena Lynn
Slaton HS; Slaton, TX (20-112) Ann; FHA; FTA; Rptr, Sch P; JV, Bkbl; Golf; Journ A; Sci A; Type A; Yth Fel; *Eng.*

GAMBLE, Gail Arlene
Laurel Valley HS; New Florence, PA (1-120) AFS; Band; Chor; NHS; Tres, Jr Cl; Mgr, Bkbl; Drum Mjrte; Church Yth Choir Director; Mgr, Vlbl; Church Choir; *Med.*

GAMBLE, Kimberly Ann
Shawnee HS; Springfield, OH (50%-250) A Cap Choir; Band; Drama; FTA; Lit Mag; Rptr, Sch P; Span C; Thes; COM; Journ A; Yth Fel; Church St Executive Yth Board; Pres, Area Assn Yth.

GAMBLE, Lisa Gay
Mansfield HS; Mansfield, LA (9-99) FBLA; 4H; Jr Miss Pagent; Bsbl; Bkbl; Beauty; Citz A; 4H A; Pep C; Drill Tm; Pres, UMYF; Church Choir; *LSU; Med Records.*

GAMBLE, Mark Jensen
Hart HS; Hart, MI (24-141) BS; Cum Laude Soc; Math C; NHS; Ski C; Pres, Var C; Bsbl; MVP, Bkbl; Co-Cpt, Ftbl; HCt; D E Meyer A; All-Around Best Ath A; Bkbl Trophy; *Mich St U; Ed.*

GAMBLE, Phyllis Ann
Cushing HS; Cushing, TX (1-40) Pres, Band; FHA; NHS; VP, SC; Bkbl; Tr; HCt; Vlbl; WW; *Baylor U; Phys Ed.*

GAMBLE, Ruth Louella
Albion Sr HS; Albion, MI (43-240) Spch C; VP, Y-Tns; Spch A; Greater Albion Schol Fund; *Oakland U; Nurs.*

GAMBLE, Wanda Elaine
Sidney Lanier HS; Montgomery, AL (10-500) Ann; Drama; GS; 4H; Hmrm; InterClub Coun; Math C; NHS; Sci C; Span C; VP, Span NHS; SC; Var C; Pres, Sr Cl; Pres, Soph Cl; Bkbl; Sftbl; MVP, Tr; Amer Leg A; Citz A; Cl Fav; 4H A; HQn; HCt; Hon Prog; Journ A; Kiwanis A; Math A; Most Out; Opt A; Pres A; Q&S A; Sci A; Spch A; Star Student; Vlbl; Most Popular A; BT Washington Schol; UIVA Schol; 2nd & 3rd Pl, Spch Contest; *Sociology.*

GAMBRELL, Alice Kathleen
Westminster HS; Atlanta, GA (33%-100) Hmrm; NHS; F-Ed, Sch P; SC; Type A; *Dartmouth Col; Journ.*

GAMBRELL, Eric Collins
Woodmont HS; Peidmont, SC; Chor; 4H; SC; Var C; Ftbl; Tr; COM; I Dare You; JA A.

GAMBRELL, Preston Lee
duPont Manual HS; Louisville, KY (22-420) Dbte Tm; NHS; Rptr, Sch P; Spch C; Golf; JV, Tr; *Murray St U; Hist.*

GAMBRELL, Sarah Belk
Chapin Sch; New York, NY (33%-36) Ensm; Ski C; Secy, Jr Cl; Soccer; Christian Ed Committee; Pres, Dance C.

GAMELSON, Steven Lee
La Jolla HS; La Jolla, CA; Band; Orch; Mgr, Soccer; CSF; *Point Loma Col; Bus.*

GAMMAGE, Alethea Jean
Crenshaw Christian Acad; Luverne, AL (2-24) Co-Ed, Ann; Math C; Sch P; Tnns; NEDT; S-T, Hon Soc; *Auburn U; Vet Med.*

GAMMAGE, Linda Irene
La Jolla HS; La Jolla, CA (49-500) AFS; Chor; Madrigal; SC; CSF; Hon Prog; Yth Fel; *U of Calif at Berkley; Bus.*

GAMMILL, Patricia Joy
W Point HS; W Point, MS; COM; Hist A; Patriotic Amer Yth; Church Bkbl; Home Ec A; Hon Attendance Certs.

GAMMILL, Vonda Lou
Oak Grove HS; Paragould, AR (1-65) BC; FBLA; FHA; Hmrm; SC; HR; *U of Ark; Communications.*

GAMNES, Joanne Lynn
Cary-Grove HS; Cary, IL (2-336) l nd; Chor; Ensm; Fr C; FBLA; Sch P; Sftbl; Tnns; Hon Prog; MLS; Sal; Vlbl; *U of Ill; Archt.*

GAMPKA, Cynthia Sue
Port Washington HS; Port Washington, WI (21-300) ARC; Span C; Math A; Sci A; Yth Fel; Vlbl; Sewing A; Eng A; *Marian Col of Fond du lac; Nurs.*

GAMPKA, Daniel Kevin
Port Washington HS; Port Washington, WI (26-300) Bkbl; Ftbl; Golf; Tres, UMYF; *Pepperdine U; Jour.*

GANAWAY, Kenny Darnell
Humboldt HS; Humboldt, TN (20%-200) BS; 4H; MVP, Var C; Ftbl; *Navy.*

GANDENBERGER, Lynne Marie
Colerain Sr HS; Cincinnati, OH; VP, Chor; Drama; Ensm; Ger C; Madrigal; Sch Achieve Tm; Var C; Best Actress; Daisy Chain; OMEA Medals.

GANDY, Allison B
Claiborne Acad; Haynesville, LA (4-37) Ed, Ann; Dbte Tm; Semi-Fin, Lit Ral; Secy, NHS; Secy, Spch C; Parl, SC; Secy, Sr Cl; Citz A; DARGCA; Most Intelligent; *La Tech U; Elem Ed.*

GANDY, Donna Kay
Cairo HS; Cairo, GA (10%-300) BC; Pres, FHA; Pres, Tri-HiY; Tr; *Young Harris Jr Col; Social Work.*

GANG, Tammy Lea
Tallmadge HS; Tallmadge, OH; Chor; Drama; Tres, 4H; NFL; Span C; Vol Service A; Chor A; *Mus.*

GANGLUFF, Charles Anthony
Wonderview HS; Hattieville, AR (10%-40) CYO; FFA; VP, 4H; Bsbl; Bkbl; Bio A; 4H A; MLS; Val; Fire Marshal; Farm Safety A; *Ark Tech U.*

GANGLUFF, Linda Rose
Wonderview HS; Hattieville, AR (10%-40) CYO; Chldr; FHA; S-T, 4H; Bkbl; Sftbl.

GANN, Clinton Troy
LaPoyner HS; LaRue, TX (1-46) Ann; FFA; Sci C; Cpt, Bsbl; Bkbl; Tnns; Mgr, Tr; COM; Citz A; Harvard Book A; HCt; Hon Prog; JA A; Sci A; Val; Yale Book A; UIL Sci As; *U of Tex; Med.*

GANN, Donna Kay
Sevier Co HS; Sevierville, TN (10-245) Ch, AFS; Rptr, Ann; Band; BC; Co-Cpt, Chldr; Drama; Ensm; Tres, Fr C; Orch; Y-Tns; Summa Cum Laude; Yth Fel; WW; *U of Tenn; Ed.*

GANN, Gregory Scott
Greenville Sr HS; Greenville, TX; Sch P; VP, Span C; Ftbl; Golf; Good Conduct A; *E Tex St U; Forestry.*

GANN, James Ray
Shawnee Mission South HS; Shawnee Mission, KS (33%-800) Band; *Math.*

GANN, Michael Claude
Wills HS; Smyrna, GA (40-250) Ann; Hmrm; Pres, Key C; SC; Cr-Ctry; Ftbl; *Ga St U; Law.*

GANN, Timmothy Wayne
Thompson HS; Alabaster, AL; Ann; BC; Chor; Ensm; 4H; Ftbl; Cl Fav; Chor A; *Ala U; Marketing.*

GANNON, Maryanne Elizabeth
St Pius X HS; Atlanta, GA (12-183) VP, Chor; Lit Mag; NHS; Hon Prog; Math A; WW; *Agnes Scott Col; Mus.*

GANNON, Robert James
Holdrege HS; Holdrege, NE (10%-160) CYO; Chor; JV, Bkbl; Ftbl; Tr; FCA; HR; *U of Nebr; Math.*

GANNON, Thomas Sean
Chaminade Col Prep; St Louis, MO (62-118) CYO; Co-Cpt, Ftbl; Hockey; *Loyola U at New Orleans; Bus Adm.*

249

GANO, Deanna Lynn
St Joseph HS; St Joseph, MI (33%-350) Chem C; Chor; Drama; Ger C; Var C; Bkbl; Sftbl; God & Country A; *Health Sci.*

GANO, Debra Marie
Saint Joseph HS; Saint Joseph, MI (10-350) Chem C; Chor; Drama; Ger C; Var C; Bkbl; Sftbl; God & Country A; *Med.*

GANONG, Patricia Anne
T Wingate Andrews HS; High Point, NC (14-327) BC; Fr C; French NHS; HCt; Juniorettes; Art A; *Appalachian St U; Elem Ed.*

GANOTE, Lesa Louise
Van Horn HS; Independence, MO; A Cap Choir; Chor; Ensm; Bsbl; Bkbl; Sftbl; Swim; Tres, Drill Tm; Cream o-t Crop; Yth Missionary Work; Yth Choir.

GANOUNG, Regan Jo
Hoisington HS; Hoisington, KS (10-81) Band; Ensm; VP, 4H; Model UN; COM; 4H A; Hon Prog; *Physics.*

GANSKE, Jeffery Lee
Robert E Lee HS; Baytown, TX (25%-534) Band; Key C; NHS; JV, Bsbl; JV, Bkbl; JV, Ftbl.

GANSKIE, Sheryl Lynn
Pacifica HS; Garden Grove, CA; A Cap Choir; Chor; Ensm; Hmrm; NHS; Mod Dance; *Sou Calif Col.*

GANSSLE, Cindy Dawn
St Thomas Pub Sch; St Thomas, ND (3-23) JV, Chldr; Chor; Ensm; 4H; MVP, Bkbl; Type A; *NDSU; Home Ec.*

GANSSLE, Susan Kaye
St Thomas Pub Sch; St Thomas, ND (6-20) Ann; Band; Cpt, Chldr; VP, Chor; Ensm; Secy, 4H; Sch P; SC; Co-Cpt, Bkbl; Beauty; 4H A; Bkbl; Statastician; Mus; Alt GS; *Mayville St Col; Legal Secy.*

GANT, Cynthia Fern
Kempsville HS; Virginia Beach, VA (174-735) *Harding Col; Nurs.*

GANTT, Gena Lee
N Iredell HS; Olin, NC; FBLA; Ch, FFA; Pres, FHA; Ch, Hmrm; Home Ec A; *Chowan Col; Merchandising.*

GANTT, Gheta Vanesser
Conecuh Co HS; Castleberry, AL (2-31) Ann; Band; BC; 4H; Secy, Hmrm; Up Bound; COM; HCt; *U of Ala; Med.*

GANTT, Rosetta
Cainhoy HS; Huger, SC (2-84) Chor; FHA; 4H; NHS; Sci C; Span C; 4H A; Hist A; HCt; Sci A; Type A; Eng A; *Med U; Dentistry.*

GANTT, Sara Lynn
Lincolnton Sr HS; Lincolnton, NC; Band; FBLA; NHS; Sch P; Mgr, Bkbl; God & Country A; Jr NHS; Yrbk A; *U of NC.*

GANTVOORT, Kelly Leann
Alamosa HS; Alamosa, CO (13-196) Band; S-T, 4H; NHS; COM; 4H A; Outst Soph, Band; Demolay Swtht; Hon Bands; Co Qn; *Adams St Col; Vet Sci.*

GANTZ, Mary Robin
Pampa HS; Pampa, TX (52-326) A Cap Choir; Chor; 4H; Mardigal; Span C; Cr-Ctry; Mgr, Tr; 1st Pl Art A, Tri-St Fair; *W Tex St U; Vet Med.*

GANZ, Kevin William
Mendota Township HS; Mendota, IL (72-218) Band; Pres, FFA; Pres, 4H; Bsbl; JV, Ftbl; 4H A; JA A; *Farming.*

GAPPEN, Tamara Lynn
S Plantation HS; Plantation, FL; *Eng.*

GAPPERT, Vonette Joy
Stanton HS; Stanton, ND (1-18) Ed, Ann; VP, Band; Drama; Model UN; Ed, Sch P; Pres, SC; Tres, Soph Cl; Bkbl; Amer Leg Orator A; B Crocker A; Citz A; Journ A; MLS; Spch A; Val; St Spch Fest Star Rating; *U of ND; Pol Sci.*

GARBERMAN, Scott Francis
Maple Shade HS; Maple Shade, NJ (10-235) NHS; Mgr, Bsbl; Amer Leg A; Hon Prog; *Med.*

GARBIN, Jeanine Marie
Girard HS; Girard, IL (2-74) Ann; VP, Chor; Ensm; FHA; Pres, 4H; Jr Miss Pagent; NHS; F-Ed, Sch P; 4H A; Journ A; GAA As; 4-H C As; Sci Fair A; Chorus A; Mus As; *E Ill U.*

GARBUTT, Nancy Anne
Engleside Christian Sch; Alexandria, VA (2-17) Ann; Chldr; Chor; Ensm; VP, Hmrm; VP, Soph Cl; Bsbl; Alg A; Citz A.

GARCIA, Ada Janet
Roma Ind HS; Roma, TX (11-180) NHS; SC; Secy, Soph Cl; COM; Journ A; HR; PA.

GARCIA, Andrew Angel
Covina HS; Covina, CA (190-250) Band; VP, Chess C; Ensm; Sch P; Span C; SC; Var C; Ftbl; Co-Cpt, Wrest; Chem A; Colt o-t Week; Band A's; 1-2-3 Yr A, Ftbl & Wrest; *Azusa Pacific Col; Ed.*

GARCIA, Antonio Jose
Jesuit HS; New Orleans, LA (4-160) Rptr, Ann; Cpt, Band; Ensm; Pres, Hmrm; Lat C; Lit Ral; Math C; Mu Alpha Theta; NHS; Rptr, Sch P; Span C; Pres, Soph Cl; COM; DARGCA; Hon Prog; Ntl Cath Mus Ed Asn; NMF; NEDT; ROTC A; Summa Cum Laude; Cpt, Drum Major; Blue Jay o-t Month; Band Ldrship A; Gold Medal, Mus A; Span Excellence A; *Loyola U; Mus.*

GARCIA, Camille Marie
MacArthur HS; San Antonio, TX; A Cap Choir; Band; CYO; Chor; Drama; *SW Tex U; Mus.*

GARCIA, David
LaConner HS; LaConner, WA (4-50) Bkbl; Ftbl.

GARCIA, Demecio
Voc HS; Mayaguez, PR; Pres, CYO; Dbte Tm; COM; Assistance A; Span A; *CAAM; Elec Engr.*

GARCIA, Edmee
Academia Discipulos de Cristo; Bayamon, PR (10-122) A Cap Choir; Chem C; Chess C; Dbte Tm; Fr C; VP, Hmrm; Math C; Phys C; Pol Sci C; Sci C; Spch C; Fin, Swim; Alg A; Beauty; Bio A; COM; Chem A; Cl Fav; Hist A; Hon Prog; Math A; Phy A; Sci A; Val; *Cornell U; Interntl Relations.*

GARCIA, Elia Maria
McMullen Co HS; Tilden, TX (3-16) Bus Mgr, Ann; NHS; Ed, Sch P; COM; Crisco A; *Tex A&I U; Nurs.*

GARCIA, Gladys Omedi
Roma HS; Roma, TX (9-130) VP, FHA; Hmrm; NHS; *Pan Amer U; Ed.*

GARCIA, Irma L
St Joseph's Notre Dame HS; Alameda, CA (10-55) Fr C; Hmrm; NHS; Phys C; Sci C; Ski C; Span C; Alg A; Bank Of Amer A; Bio A; CSF; COM; Citz A; DARGCA; Hist A; Hon Prog; K of C A; Most Out; Regent Schol; Co-Ed, Yrbk; Yrbk A; John Ellender Fel; Span A; Sewing A; *University of California, Berkeley; Combined Sciences.*

GARCIA, John Todd
Columbus HS; Columbus, GA (5%-350) InterClub Coun; Math C; Model UN; Mu Alpha Theta; Order/Arrow; Var C; Pres, Sr Cl; Ftbl; Soccer; Gov Honor Prog; Hist A; Hon Prog; Order/Arrow A; Speak Up for Young Amer; *U of Ga; Arts.*

GARCIA, Josie Alice
St Augustine HS; Laredo, TX (33%-67) Ann; Chess C; NHS; Bkbl; Opt A; Spch A; WW; *U of Tex; Bus Adm.*

GARCIA, Kimberly Michelle
Natchitoches Central HS; Natchitoches, LA; Chldr; Dbte Tm; Drama; Sci C; Spch C; *NW St U; Ed.*

GARCIA, Laura M
Stamford HS; Stamford, TX (50%-70) CYO; FHA; Span C; Pres, HERO; Homemaking A; Qn of Cath Church.

GARCIA, Linda Patricia
Weed HS; Weed, CA; Bus Mgr, Ann; S-T, HiY; Pres, Mjrte; NHS; Pres, SC; CSF; COM; DARGCA; Hon Prog; Type A; Steno A; *Sacramento St Col; Social Welfare & Corrections.*

GARCIA, Madeline
Juan Jose Osuna HS; Hato Rey, PR (7-101) CYO; Drama; FHA; 4H; Orch; ARC; Span C; Swim; Tnns; Aux Lat; COM; Hist A; Hon Prog; Lion A; Spch A; *Universidad de Puerto Rico; Cienciasnaturales.*

GARCIA, Magdalena Hernandez
John F Kennedy HS; San Antonio, TX (10%-500) Fr C; FHA; Var C; Mgr, Tr; Most Out; Yth Fel; Vlbl; Outst Player, Vlbl Tm; *Med.*

GARCIA, Margaret Rose
Ash Fork HS; Ash Fork, AZ (3-9) Band; Chor; Drama; GS; 4H; Span C; Cpt, Bkbl; *Northern Ariz U; Sci.*

GARCIA, Maria Dolores
Norman Thomas HS; Manhattan, NY; Y-Tns; Bsbl; Sftbl; Bookkeeping A; Arts & Crafts A; VP, Yth Soc; Pres, Missionettes; *Bookkeeping.*

GARCIA, Maria Ramoncita
Battle Mountain HS; Minturn-Vail, CO; Chor; VP, FBLA; Sch P; Span C; SC; Secy, Jr Cl; Arch; Mgr, Ftbl; *Secretarial.*

GARCIA, Maria Victoria
Tracy Joint Union HS; Tracy, CA (27-385) Band; Chldr; Chor; Community Yth Symph; Dbte Tm; Drama; Ensm; 4H; Rptr, Hmrm; Mjrte; Rptr, Orch; Sci C; Span C; Rptr, SC; CSF; Elk A; 4H A; Kiwanis A; Type A; Asilomar Del; Pres, Girl's League; *Bethany Bible Col; Psych.*

GARCIA, Melba Idalia
Colegio San Antonio HS; Isabela, PR; CYO; Chldr; Chor; 4H; Tres, SC; COM; *U of Puerto Rico; Phys Therapy.*

GARCIA, Nigel R
Gladys Porter HS; Brownsville, TX; Ftbl; *Okla U; Hist.*

GARCIA, Orpha Linda
Lamar HS; Houston, TX (20%-600) Drama; Inter-Act C; Secy, Span C; Secy, Span NHS; Thes; Arch; Sftbl; Tnns; Tr; *Pepperdine U.*

GARCIA, Palmira
Roma HS; Roma, TX (1-144) Band; Math C; NHS; Spch C; Tres, SC; Math A; Jr Historian C; HR A; *U of Tex at Austin; Pre-Med.*

GARCIA, Robert Roy
Wesleyan Acad; Guaynabo, PR (8-29) Drama; NHS; Sch P; SC; NEDT; *Wash U of St Louis; Architecture.*

GARCIA, Robert William
Memorial HS; San Antonio, TX (3-300) VP, A Cap Choir; Co-Ed, Ann; Pres, Band; VP, Chor; Ensm; Madrigal; NHS; ARC; Pres, Sci C; Pres, SC; Cl Fav; Hist A; Most Out; Ntl Sci Found; Sci A; Band As; *Harvard U; Scietific Research.*

GARCIA, Sara Nerea
Colegio Nuestra Senora Merced; Hato Rey, PR (4-108) Drama; Var C; Alg A; Bio A; COM; Chem A; Hist A; Math A; Most Out; Phy A; Sci A; Val; Vlbl; Eng A; Span A; *U of Miami; Phar.*

GARCIA, Terry
Bridgeport HS; Bridgeport, TX; *Tex Woman's U; Interior Decoration.*

GARCIA, Thomas George
Warwick Valley HS; Warwick, NY (20-215) Hmrm; NHS; Bkbl; Ftbl; Soccer; Tnns; HCt; Hon Prog; WW; HS All Amer; Sch HR; *U of Ariz; Computer Sci.*

GARCIA, Walterio Rivera
Consuelo Escalona Private Sch; Carolina, PR (1-37) Tres, Hmrm; Model UN; SC; COM; Hon Prog; Semi-Fin, Judo; Span A; Civics A; Loyalty A; *U of PR; Social Sci.*

GARD, Catherine Loree
King's Temple Christian Sch; Seattle, WA; Chor; GS; Hmrm; SC; COM; Hon Prog; Pres A; Yth Fel; *Wash St U; Animal Husbandry.*

GARDENHIRE, Richard Alton
Delsea Regional HS; Franklinville, NJ (7-32) Co-Cpt, Dbte Tm; Bsbl; Bkbl; Co-Cpt, Ftbl; Tr; Track and Field, Ftbl, Bsbl, A's; *U of Sou Calif; Arch.*

GARDINER, Jill Deann
Cortland Jr Sr HS; Cortland, NY (26-280) Ann; Band; Drama; Lit Mag; Orch; Ed, Sch P; Thes; Secy, Yth Fel; Radio Guild; Math Tutor; Sr Cl Committee; *St Lawrence U; Eng.*

GARDNER, Anita Louise
Halter HS; Wellston, MO (1-150) Chldr; Sch P; Secy, Soph Cl; Hon Prog; Math A; MLS; Attendance A; HR; *Bus Off Ed.*

GARDNER, Barbara Ellen
J L Mann HS; Greenville, SC (90-254) Co-Cpt, Chldr; Drama; VP, Hmrm; Ch, Span C; SC; COM; MLS; SC St Rep, Interntl Yth Camp; Precint Officer; Most Witty; Most Friendliest.

GARDNER, Brad
Kickapoo HS; Springfield, MO (5%-288) Ger C; NHS; Rptr, Sch P; SC; Ftbl; *Communications.*

GARDNER, Cynthia Celeste
Kansas City Christian HS; Merriam, KS (3-30) BC; Chldr; Hmrm; SC; Most Out; Sci A; Mus A; *Med.*

GARDNER, Dawn Denee
Miller Co R III HS; Tuscumbia, MO (6-27) Bus Mgr, Ann; Co-Cpt, Chldr; Secy, 4H; NHS; Ed, Sch P; Secy, SC; VP, Jr Cl; Bkbl; Tr; HR; Bicentennial Bell; Carnival Qn; HS Play; *Kans U; Art.*

GARDNER, Debra Linn
W Hills HS; Fort Worth, TX (78-622) Band; Orch; All City Orch & Band; Cl I Solo; *Mus.*

GARDNER, Frances Annette
S San Antonio W Campus HS; San Antonio, TX (25-185) Secy, Drama; FHA; NHS; SC; Pres, Thes; Best Actress, UIL Drama; *Nurs.*

GARDNER, Gary Christopher
Shaker Heights HS; Shaker Heights, OH; A Cap Choir; Chess C; Dbte Tm; JV, Bsbl; JV, Bkbl; Secy, Bow C; *Wheaton Col; Computer Sci.*

GARDNER, James Guy
Lakeville HS; Lakeville, MN (100-194) Ed, Ann; Pres, Demolay; Order/Arrow; A-Ed, Sch P; Skiing; *Engr.*

GARDNER, Jan Maria
Warren Acad Inc; Warrenton, NC (4-32) A-Ed, Ann; Chor; Drama; Tres, Fr C; Pres, Hmrm; Secy, Monogram; Co-Ed, Sch P; Pres, Sr Cl; Tres, Jr Cl; Pres, Soph Cl; Bkbl; MVP, Sftbl; Yth Fel; Marshal; Home Ec A; Mus A; *Meredith Col; Home Ec.*

GARDNER, Jessica Jean
Arendell Parrott Acad; Kinston, NC (3-49) A Cap Choir; Chldr; Chor; Hmrm; NHS; SC; Citz A; Homecoming Princess; *Wake Forest U; Law.*

GARDNER, Kathryn Gladys
Mansfield Christian HS; Mansfield, OH (2-12) Chor; Community Yth Symph; GS; VP, NHS; Orch; Alg A; COM; Hist A; Hon Prog; Math A; Most Out; Hist A; Span A; Eng A; Outst Soph A; Adv Composition; Bible A; Milestones of Freedom A; Shorthand A; NMS Top 5%; *Ohio St U; Genetics.*

GARDNER, Laura Kay
Farnam Pub Sch; Farnam, NE; Ann; Band; Chldr; Chem C; Chor; 4H; Mjrte; Rptr, Sch P; SC; Sftbl; Tr; 4H A; Hon Prog; Pres A; Type A; Yth Fel; JV, Vlbl.

GARDNER, Lisa Marie
W Hills HS; Ft Worth, TX (10%-800) Band; Dbte Tm; Hmrm; Lat C; Lit Mag; NHS; Pres, Rainbow; Ed, Sch P; Swim; Tnns; COM; Citz A; Hon Prog; Journ; *N Tex St U; Eng.*

GARDNER, Luan Kae
Roxana Sr HS; E Alton, IL (45-178) Chldr; Ger C; *McKendree Col; Ed.*

GARDNER, Naomi Jo
Hattiesburg HS Rowan Center; Hattiesburg, MS (5%-500) Ed, Ann; VP, Mgr, Bkbl; Swim; A-B Cert; *U of Sou Miss; Marine Bio.*

GARDNER, Philip Craig
Roxana HS; Roxana, IL (34-328) Chem C; Ger C; Model UN; Var C; Cpt, Bkbl; Golf; JV, Tnns; *McKendree Col; Bus.*

GARDNER, Rebecca Denise
Meridian HS; Meridian, TX; BC; Chldr; FHA; JV, Bkbl; Ftbl Swtht; Sewing A; *San Marcos St Col.*

GARDNER, Richmond Leland
Winchester HS; Winchester, MA; SC; JV, Cr-Ctry; JV, Soccer; Swim; JV, Tr; Gregor Mendel A; *Social Stu.*

GARDNER, Ronald Davison
L Frazier Banks HS; Birmingham, AL (7-325) Band; Chem C; Chor; Drama; Ensm; HiY; Hmrm; Pres, Key C; Lat C; Lat NHS; Math C; Mu Alpha Theta; NHS; Ntl Yth Conf; Orch; Phys C; Sci C; SC; Thes; Bsbl; Bkbl; Sftbl; COM; Citz A; Hon Prog; Math A; NEDT; Secy, Key C; Ed, Bama Bulletin; Executive HS Intern; Excel & Enrichment Stu A's; *U of Ala; Pre-Med.*

GARDNER, Sovella Dean
Emerich Manuel HS; Indianapolis, IN; A Cap Choir; Chldr; Chor; FTA; 4H; Cr-Ctry; Tr; Sunday Sch Teacher o-t Yr; *Ind U; Computer Tech.*

GARDNER, Susan Diane
LaConner HS; LaConner, WA (4-45) Bus Mgr, Ann; Chldr; FHA; NHS; Rainbow; Sch P; Ski C; *U of Wash; Bus Adm.*

GARDNER, Vicki Dianne
Sam Houston HS; Arlington, TX (18-650) AFS; Ann; Chess C; NHS; Sci C; Span C; SC; *Baylor U; Nurs.*

GARETSON, Kerri Kristine
Copeland HS; Copeland, KS (2-11) Ed, Ann; Chor; Ensm; GS; Secy, 4H; Secy, Key C; Sch P; Pres, SC; Pres, Sr Cl; Secy, Jr Cl; Bkbl; Amer Leg A; B Crocker A; Citz A; Crisco A; HCt; Sal; Vlbl; *Fort Hays St U; Home Ec.*

GAREY, Deborah Jean
Williamsburg HS; Andrews, SC (7-75) Drama; Secy, 4H; Bkbl; *Morris Col.*

GAREY, Frederica Elizabeth
McKinley HS; Sebring, OH (29-89) Pres, Band; Chor; Ensm; SC; John Philips Sousa A; *Mount Union Col; Mus Ed.*

GAREY, Marleta Fae
Ulysses HS; Ulysses, KS (5-105) Band; Chor; Ensm; Pres, FBLA; FHA; NHS; Span C; VP, Y-Tns; KU Alumni Hon Stu; *John Brown U; Bus.*

GARGIULO, Peter Jerome
St Peters Prepratory Sch; Jersey City, NJ (34-275) All Amer Yth; NHS; Bkbl; Cpt, Ftbl; COM; Hon Prog; WW; *Lafayette Col; Engr.*

GARIBAY, Ester Cecilia
Pawnee ISD HS; Pawnee, TX (50%-14) F-Ed, Ann; CYO; Parl, FHA; Pres, Jr Cl; Cpt, Bkbl; Ftbl; Tr; Cl Fav; All Dist, High Point Girl, Vlbl; *Tex Women's U; Elem Ed.*

GARLAND, Ann Estelle
Los Angeles Baptist HS; Sepulveda, CA (4-81) Chor; Pres, Soph Cl; Sftbl; CSF; COM; Hmrm; Chaplain, Sr Cl; Chaplain, Girl's Service C; All Star Sftbl; *Biola Col; Nurs.*

GARLAND, Belinda Lee
Estancia HS; Estancia, NM (5-68) FFA; 4H A; FFA A; *NM St U.*

GARLAND, Darcy Roberta
Trigg Co HS; Cadiz, KY (25%-140) Bus Mgr, Band; BC; Bus Mgr, Drama; Ensm; 4H; NFL; Spch C; 4H A; Spch A; NFL Degree of Excel; All Dist Band; 1st Pl, Murray U Workshop; *U of Ky; Law.*

GARLAND, Lee Renee
Daniel Boone HS; Jonesboro, IN (30-250) NHS; SC; Cpt, Ntl Champ Max Ordin Drill Sq; Co-Cpt, Ntl Chmp Boonette Drill Pl; *E Tenn St U; Phys Therapy.*

GARLAND, Phillip Clark
Broken Arrow HS; Broken Arrow, OK; Band; *Okla U; Mus.*

GARLAND, Reaver LaDonna
Covington HS; Covington, TN (5-200) Band; JV, BC; Secy, Fr C; FHA; Semi-Fin, Jr Miss Pa; NHSt; Mgr, Bkbl; *U of Tenn; Elem Ed.*

GARLAND, Rosa Mae
Walnut Ridge HS; Columbus, OH; Chor; Bkbl; Sftbl; Citz A; Hon Prog; Tres, OWE; Best Attendance.

GARLAND, Shelia Yvette
Beaumont HS; St Louis, MO (11-569) CYO; Fr C; Secy, Hmrm; NHS; Sci C; SC; Co-Cpt, Hockey; COM; Citz A; *U of Mo; Chem Engr.*

GARLAND, Susan Marie
Arvada W HS; Arvada, CO (98-730) Chor; NHS; Swim; Tr; Kiwanis A; Yth Fel; Job's Daughters; Pres, Drill Tm; Gym; *W St Col; Ed.*

GARMIRE, Stacy Kay
Archbold HS; Archbold, OH; A Cap Choir; Chldr; 4H; Span C; 4H A; Spch A; Qn, Jr High Sports Tourn; *Work With Disabled Children.*

GARMON, James Wayne
Marion HS; Marion, IN; Chess C; Dbte Tm; Orch; SC; Bkbl; Ftbl; Sftbl; Swim; Tr; COM; Pres, YPD; Gold & Siver Medals, Orch Contest; *Ind St U; Mgt.*

GARMON, Susan Gaye
Lincoln HS; Ellwood City, PA (52-249) Ger C; Rainbow; Y-Tns; NHS; Sci A; *Clarion St Col; Library Sci.*

GARMON, Timothy Alan
Mt Carmel HS; San Diego, CA (100-350) *Math.*

GARNER, Charles Jeffrey
Evangelical Christian Sch; Memphis, TN (4%-54) Chor; Fin, Hmrm; Rptr, Sch P; SC; Bsbl; Bkbl; Cr-Ctry; Golf; Tr; All Conf A, Cr Ctry; Mr Personality; *Baylor U; Bus.*

GARNER, Cheryl Ann
Newnan HS; Newnan, GA; 4H; Hmrm; Swim; Horseback Riding A; Reading A; Horseshow A; *W Ga Col; Horses.*

GARNER, Connie Faye
Jonesboro HS; Jonesboro, AR (76-307) Ann; Chldr; Hmrm; NHS; Beauty; HQn; HCt; Opt Out Tn; Model Fashion Board; Miss Hurricane Pageant; *Ark St U; Bus Mgr.*

GARNER, David Bruce
Henderson Co Sr HS; Henderson, KY (1-600) Chem C; NHS; Bus Mgr, Sch P; Span C; Mgr, Bkbl; Sftbl; *Purdue U; Chem Engr.*

GARNER, Debra Ann
Bridgeport HS; Bridgeport, OH (1-121) Band; Dbte Tm; Drama; Tres, FNA; S-T, FTA; Semi-Fin, GS; Co-Ch, NHS; Orch; Sch Achieve Tm; Sci C; Span C; Spch C; Thes, Pres, Y-Tns; Alg A; Bio A; Hist A; VofDEM; Amer Leg Essay Contest St Win; 2nd, St Eng School Test; 1st Run-Up, Best Spkr Jr Twn Meetng; *Nurs.*

GARNER, Denise Michele
Pius Tenth HS; Downey, CA; *Long Beach St Col; Bio.*

GARNER, Faith Fontanna
Cambridge HS; Cambridge, MA; Up Bound; Sci A; Baptist Yth Fel; Sunday Sch Teacher; Theater Guild; *Boston U; Special Ed.*

GARNER, Golden William II
Norcross HS; Norcross, GA (29-225) Ann; Chem C; Fr C; Hmrm; Sci C; Var C; Bsbl; Cpt, Ftbl; Sftbl; *Ga U.*

GARNER, Jeanne Martheil
Lutcher Stark HS; Orange, TX; All Amer Yth; Chor; MVP, Tnns; Asst Secy, Girls C; Vlbl; Publicity Ch, Church Yth; *Lamar Extension Col; Bus.*

GARNER, Kenneth Leon
Temple HS; Temple, TX (10-20) 1st Pl, Mech Reproduction; *Temple Jr Col; Child Counselor.*

GARNER, Kennie Yvonne
Lutcher Stark HS; Orange, TX; All Amer Yth; Chor; Sci C; Y-Tns; Tnns; Tr; Kiwanis A; Vlbl; Pres, Yth C; Secy, Girl's Auxilary; *Lamar U; Law.*

GARNER, Kim Terese
Danville HS; Danville, AR (5-52) Band; Cpt, Chldr; Chor; VP, FHA; Mjrte; Tres, NHS; Tres, Soph Cl; Bkbl; Sftbl; Tr; Beauty; Cl Fav; HCt; Most Out; *U of Ark; Computer Sci.*

GARNER, Mary Denise
Pike Central HS; Petersburg, IN (200-1000) Chor; Sch P; Sftbl; *Purdue U; Journ.*

GARNER, Mary Fergrieve
Laurel HS; Shaker Heights, OH (11-43) Drama; Fr C; Lit Mag; Rptr, Sch P; SC; VP, Sr Cl; Secy, Jr Cl; Hockey; Hist A; Yth Fel; Board of Trustees, Church; Hospital Vol; *Duke U; Pre-Law.*

GARNER, Sharenn Athena
Ben L Smith HS; Greensboro, NC (5%-499) Lat C; Cpt, Bkbl; Sftbl; *A&T St U; Psych.*

GARNER, Steven James
Fostoria HS; Fostoria, OH (19-200) Band; Demolay; NHS; *Bowling Green St U; Social Sci.*

GARNETT, Kim Donise
Jamaica HS; Jamaica, NY (452-1102) Hmrm; SC; COM; Math A; Pres A; Mus A; *Johnson & Wales Col; Travel and Tourism.*

GARNETT, Libbi Ann
Vernon HS; Vernon, TX (33%-125) Tres, FTA;
Secy, 4H; Span C; Spch C; SC; Secy, Soph Cl;
COM; 4H A; Spch A; Yth Fel; Co-Ch, 4-H Co
Coun; Vlbl; Tex Christian U; Eng.

GARNETT, Lori Ann
Jefferson City HS; Jefferson City, MO (82-550) A
Cap Choir; Band; Chor; Drama; NHS; S-T, SC;
Bkbl; Sftbl; Stu Coun A; SMSU Springfield; Mus.

GARNETT, Vicky Lee
Manchester HS; Richmond, VA (19-325) Band;
Chor; Community Yth Symph; Drama; Fr C;
Hmrm; Lit Ral; Co-Ed, Lit Mag; Madrigal; NHS;
Rptr, SC; Tri-HiY; Q&S A; All Region, All St,
Choirs; Radford Col; Mus.

GARNTO, Patricia Lynn
Lowndes HS; Valdosta, GA (25-435) Ch, Anchor
C; Band; Tres, BC; FHA; Mjrte; Gov Honor Prog;
Hist A; Flag Corps; Explorers; Chaplain, Tri-Hi-Y;
Soph, Jr, Sr, Cl Cabinets; Band Medals; Tift Col;
Math.

GARON, Lise
College De Ste Anne De La Pocatiere; La Pocatiere, CANADA (1-31) Swim; Tnns; Ste-Anne-de-
la-Pocatiere; Sci Sante.

GARR, Joy Ellen
Ottumwa HS; Ottumwa, IA (60-573) S-T, Crown &
Scepter; Amer Leg A; Citz A.

GARRAMONE, Don Edward
Eastside HS; Paterson, NJ (9-850) Drew U; Mech
Engr.

GARRARD, Steve Hardin
Hardin Co Central HS; Savannah, TN (50-250)
Chem C; FFA; FTA; 4H; Hmrm; Lat C; Sci C; SC;
Ftbl; Sftbl; Courteous A; Middle Tenn St U; For-
estry.

GARRASTEGUI, Janette Robles
Dr Pedro Perea Fajardo HS; Mayaguez, PR; COM;
Exc Hon; Drew U; Occupational Technology.

GARRETSON, Laura Jean
All Amer Christian Acad; Hollywood, FL
(33%-36) Band; Chor; Ensm; Var C; Sftbl; Hon
Prog; 2nd Pl A, Vlbl M; 4th Pl, Girls Ensm;
GSct Cadette; Fashion & Desgn As; Wrk Study
Schol; 1st Pl Mus A; 1st P A Memorization; All
American Bible Institute; Bible.

GARRETSON, Randy G
Humansville HS; Humansville, MO; Chor; Tres,
FFA; 4H; JV, Bkbl; COM; 4H A; Opt A; Spch A;
Chapter Farmer; Livestock A; FFA School; U of
Mo; Animal Sci.

GARRETT, Adetrice
George Washington Carver HS; Birmingham, AL
(18-237) Band; Orch; Sch P; Sci C; SC; Secy, Sr Cl;
VP, Soph Cl; Beauty; Hon Prog; Poet A; U of Ala,
Birmingham.

GARRETT, Allyson Elyse
Flint Northern HS; Flint, MI; Co-Cpt, Chldr; Mich
St U; Acct.

GARRETT, Andrea Lynn
Klein HS; Spring, TX (100-720) U of Houston; Art.

GARRETT, Ann Elizabeth
Kinmundy-Alma HS; Kinmundy, IL (8-40) Rptr,
Fr C; Ch, FHA; SC; Tres, Sr Cl; Cl Fav; Swtht;
Type A; Best All Around; Best Personality; WW; E
Ill U; Special Ed.

GARRETT, Cathy Yolanda
Phineas Banning HS; Wilmington, CA; Nurs Prog;
Schol Soc; Health Sci.

GARRETT, Christopher Lee
Steubenville HS; Steubenville, OH; Ger C; Tnns;
Bus.

GARRETT, Columbus
Lincoln HS; Dallas, TX; Bkbl; Tnns.

GARRETT, Cynthia Gail
Hope HS; Hope, AR (10%-200) Band; BC; Chor;
City Conf; FTA; Cpt, Mjrte; Model UN; NHS; F-
Ed, Sch P; Tnns; COM; Journ A; Nike C; Tres, Leo
C; All St Band Hon; Ntl Piano Auditions A;
Ouachita Baptist U; Spch.

GARRETT, Dana Kathryn
Memorial Sr HS; Houston, TX (148-640) Crown &
Scepter; Mjrte; Span NHS; Hon Prog; Shorthand
A; Jr NHS; Fin, Cert of Merit; Fin, Citizenship A;
Baylor U.

GARRETT, Darrell Wayne
Civic Mem HS; Bethalto, IL (128-214) Chor;
Ensm; Bsbl; Bkbl; Sftbl; DE, Art, C'S; Lewis &
Clarke Jr Col; Automotive Design.

GARRETT, Derrick Earl
Westchester HS; Westchester, CA; Band; Ensm;
Orch; Tr; Most Out; Mus & Tr A's; European Invi-
tation, Trombone Mus; U of Sou Calif; Mus.

GARRETT, Ellen
Calvert Adult Education Center; Baltimore, MD
(4-137) Bio A; Hist A; Math A; Comm Col of Baltimore; Nurs.

GARRETT, Grady Hugh
Crestview Sr HS; Crestview, FL; Band; Chess C.

GARRETT, Jason Lee
Northwest HS; Indianapolis, IN (137-491) Co-Cpt,
Bkbl; COM; Hon Prog; Outst Service A; Ind U;
Ministry.

GARRETT, Karen Lynnette
Central Valley HS; Veradale, WA (32-350) Secy, A
Cap Choir; Co-Cpt, Chor; Dbte Tm; Ensm; Lit
Mag; Mjrte; Math C; NFL; Rptr, Sch P; Hon Prog;
Opt A; Fin, Spch A; Fin, Raft Race; Fin, VFW
Orator Win; Fin, Voice of Democracy; Fin, Bowl;
EWSC; Eng Ed.

GARRETT, Kathryn Sue
Moran HS; Moran, TX (2-10) F-Ed, Arch; Chldr;
Secy, FHA; NHS; Bkbl; Tnns; Tr; Cl Fav; Journ A;
Swtht; Yth Fel; Tex Tech U; Art.

GARRETT, Keenan Ray
Maryville R-II HS; Maryville, MO (40-130) A Cap
Choir; Mgr, Band; Chor; Key C; Var C; Ftbl; Tr;
COM; Hon Prog; Most Out; USC; Elec.

GARRETT, Kyle Wayne
Maryville R-II HS; Maryville, MO (33-128) A Cap
Choir; Mgr, Band; Chor; Ensm; VP, Hmrm; Pres,
Key C; NHS; Orch; Sci C; SC; Var C; Bkbl; Tnns;
COM; Hon Prog; Kiwanis A; Band Performance
Schol A; NW Mo St U; Sci.

GARRETT, Laura Jo
Ulysses HS; Ulysses, KS (4-103) Band; Ensm; Pres,
Span C; Bkbl; St Scholar; NGPT HS Diploma; Art
Instruction Sch; Commercial Art.

GARRETT, Linda Diane
Sagina HS; Saginaw, MI; Sftbl; Tr; Most Out; Type
A; Attendance A; Baker Jr Col; Secy.

GARRETT, Lori Ellen
Pendleton HS; Pendleton, SC (10-133) Ed, Ann;
Cpt, Band; BC; Fr C; Pres, Hmrm; Sci C; SC;
Beauty; HCt; Q&S A; WW; Anderson Col; Mus.

GARRETT, Marion Lea
Honesdale HS; Honesdale, PA (40-220) Band;
FHA; Pres, 4H; Hmrm; Span C; Tri-HiY; COM;
4H A; Runner Up, Outst 4-H Girl; St 4-H Demon-
stration Contest; 4 Yr Tn, 4-H Leader; 2nd Pl,
Dairylea Essay; Ind U of Penn; Home Ec.

GARRETT, Mary Lois
Crosby HS; Crosby, TX; Chor; Secy, FHA; Tres,
4H; Hmrm; S-T, NHS; SC; 4H A; Tres, Church Yth
Fel; HR; Bookkeeping.

GARRETT, Matthew Jay
Glenwood Comm HS; Glenwood, IA (1-135) Chor;
NHS; Pres, Jr Cl; Cr-Ctry; JV, Golf; Alg A; Hist A;
Math A; Opt A; Spch A; Mus, Principal, Bus, Golf,
A's; Iowa St U; Math.

GARRETT, Pamela Lynn
Reeds Spring HS; Reeds Spring, MO (14-75) BC;
FHA; COM; Hist A; WW; Tourn of Knowledge;
Pre-Law.

GARRETT, Paul Anson
Jackson HS; Jackson, MI (10%-500) Ger C; Pres,
Hmrm; SC; Var C; Pres, Sr Cl; Swim; Pres A;
Spring Arbor Col; Pre-Law.

GARRETT, Sherry Denise
Carroll Co HS; Carrollton, KY (25%-123) FHA;
NHS; Y-Tns; Alg A; Bio A.

GARRETT, Stephanie Jean
Atwater HS; Atwater, CA (1-434) Dbte Tm; Pres,
Fr C; Spch C; CSF; NEDT; Davis Col; Dietetics.

GARRETT, Sylvia Alfreda
Phineas Banning HS; Wilmington, CA; Bsbl; Sftbl;
Tr; COM; Citz A; Phy A; Drill Tm A; Schol Soc;
Long Beach St Col; Social Stu.

GARRETT, Tamara Lee
Montgomery Co HS; Mt Sterling, KY; Chor; 4H;
Y-Tns; Bkbl; PA; Morehead St U; Ed.

GARRETT, Tim Len
Lubbock HS; Lubbock, TX; VP, A Cap Choir; VP,
Chor; SC; Golf; Most Out.

GARRETT, Virginia Elaine
N Shore HS; W Palm Beach, FL (35-266) Chor;
Drama; InterClub Coun; Tres, NHS; Pres, Span C;
Spch C; Var C; Sftbl; Hon Prog; Vlbl.

GARRETT, Virginia Louise
Shaler Area Sr HS; Glenshaw, PA (40%-968) VP,
Band; Community Yth Symph; Ensm; Hmrm;
Orch; Ski C; Span C; SC; HCt; Mus A; Hons Band;
Westminster Col; Eng.

GARRETTE, Cathy
Patrick Henry HS; Ashland, VA (40%-350) AFS;
Sci C; Tres, Span C; Span NHS; Var C; Tr; COM;
Type A; Yth Fel; Va Poly Inst U.

GARRICK, Amy Ruth
Fairhope HS; Fairhope, AL (20%-250) Band;
Drama; Ensm; Outst Band Stu; Band Coun; All St
Medal; U of Ala; Psych.

GARRIDO, Carmen
Colegio San Antonio; Rio Piedras, PR (2-103)
NHS; COM; NYU; Finance.

GARRINGTON, Patricia Lynn
Gainesville HS; Gainesville, FL (22-463) Band;
Ensm; Mu Alpha Theta; NHS; Span NHS; COM;
Davidson Col; Bio.

GARRIOTT, John Francis II
Westfield-Washington HS; Westfield, IN (25-116)
VP, CYO; JV, Bkbl; Fel, Adult Catholic Yth;
Search Prog; Rep, Rotary C; Rep, Kiwanis C; Ball
St U; Archt.

GARRIS, Dennis Lanatra
Menchville HS; Newport News, VA; Band; NHS;
Interlochen Ntl Mus; MLS; Ntl Cath Mus Ed Asn;
Norfolk St U; Mus.

GARRIS, Sheryl Lynn
Highland HS; Sparta, OH (50%-143) Rainbow; Social Services.

GARRIS, Tanya Lynn
Myrtle Beach HS; Myrtle Beach, SC (20-230)
Drama; Fr C; Hmrm; SC; Tnns; Columbia Col; Art.

GARRISON, Cynthia Gean
Lexington HS; Lexington, MO (8-130) Ensm;
NHS; Orch; ARC; Thes; Tres, Jr Cl; Sftbl; HCt;
Type A; Yth Fel; Soph Pilgrimage; 1st Cl Sr GSct;
St & Dist Mus Contests; People to People Tour;
Freedom Forum; Acct.

GARRISON, Gary Dewayne
Piggott HS; Piggott, AR (20-84) FFA; Order/
Arrow; Sci C; SC; Bsbl; Bkbl; Ftbl; Tr; God &
Country A; Hall of Merit; Most Joyful; Eagle Sct;
Ark Tech U; Pre-Med.

GARRISON, Geoffrey Michael
Ramey HS; Ramey, PR (1-18) Pres, Chess C; VP,
NHS; VP, Sr Cl; Bkbl; Co-Cpt, Cr-Ctry; Bio A;
COM; Math A; Phy A; Type A; MIT; Civil Engr.

GARRISON, Lynne Consuela
Spingarn HS; Washington, DC; Art A.

GARRISON, Robert Earl
Ripley HS; Ripley, TN (3-30) FFA; 4H; Hmrm;
Var C; Bkbl; Tr; 4H A; Tr A.

GARRISON, Thomas Paul
Thomson HS; Thomson, GA (2-280) BC; Drama;
Hmrm; InterAct C; Thes; Ftbl; Golf; COM; Citz A;
Gov Honor Prog; NEDT; Harvard U; Journ.

GARRISON, Vincent Gray
Forbush HS; E Bend, NC; FTA; Monogram; Ftbl;
Tnns; Tr; Yth Coun As.

GARRISON, Wesley Dean
Manzaro HS; Albuquerque, NM (25%-709) Chor;
Semi-Fin, Hmrm; Key C; SC; Mgr, Bkbl; Ftbl;
Wrest; HCt; Young Life; FCA; SW Assemblies of
God Col; Ministry.

GARRITY, Michael James
Honesdale Jr-Sr HS; Honesdale, PA (35-240)
Band; Chess C; *Computer Technology.*

GARROUTTE, Randall Burl
Tahlequah Sr HS; Tahlequah, OK; Arch; FFA;
FTA; Hmrm; Key C; SC; Var C; Arch; Bkbl; Ftbl;
Golf; Wrest.

GARTH, Carolyn Denise
George Washington; Denver, CO (3-750) Chor;
City Conf; FBLA; GS; Mgr, Tr; Yth Fel; Tr A;
Gym A; Head Girl; *Northeastern Jr Col; Bus.*

GARTHER, Colin Claire
Sidney Sr HS; Sidney, MT; CYO; VP, FFA; 3rd Pl,
Dist FFA Mech; St Mech Profiency A; *Mont St U;
Agr.*

GARTLAND, James Gerard
W Alamance HS; Elon College, NC (3-250) NHS;
Span C; Hon Prog.

GARTMAN, Rachel Dianne
Glendale HS; Springfield, MO (25%-500) AFS; Sch
P; Span C; SC; Pub Relations Comm, SC; *Humanities.*

GARTNER, Julie Lynn
Vanguard HS; Ocala, FL (32-350) Fr C; Tres,
FBLA; NHS; SC; Pres, Sr Cl; VP, Jr Cl; Cpt, Swim;
HCt; *S Fla U.*

GARTON, Cindy Sue
Ozark HS; Ozark, MO (20-105) Band; Chor; FHA;
Rptr, Sch P; Spch C; Sftbl; Journ A; *Mo Sou St U;
Journ.*

GARTZKE, Heather Rae
Martin Co HS; Stuart, FL (57-500) Chldr; Chor;
InterAct C; *Journ.*

GARVEY, Dana Ann
Frayser Baptist Sch Inc; Memphis, TN (43-85)
Chldr; Tnns; Bible C; Lib C; *Memphis St U; Lab
Tech.*

GARVEY, Greg Patrick
Frayser Baptist Sch; Memphis, TN; Var C; Golf; *St
Tech Inst; Computer Programming.*

GARVEY, John Francis
Holy Cross HS; Riverside, NJ; Pres, SC; Pres, Soph
Cl; JV, Soccer; Tr; Hon Prog; *Georgetown U; Pol
Sci.*

GARVEY, Mary Kristine
Mercy HS; Albany, NY (1-108) NHS; Ed, Sch P;
Hon Prog; NEDT; Regent School; Spch A; *Syracuse
U.*

GARVIN, Bettye Faye
York Comp HS; York, SC (18-240) Secy, Chor;
Drama; Fr C; NHS; JV, Bkbl; NMS; Wofford
Schol; WW; *Wofford Col; Math.*

GARVIN, Drake Robert
Helix HS; La Mesa, CA (16-450) A Cap Choir; BS;
Chor; Pres, Drama; Ensm; Pres, Lat C; Semi-Fin,
NFL; Semi-Fin, Spch C; SC; MVP, Tnns; JV,
Wrest; CSF; Hon Prog; Odd Fellow Fin; Spch A;
Pres, Yth Group; 'Camper of Week'; Jr Rep,
Church Board; *Theology.*

GARWOOD, Lori Anne
Van Wert HS; Van Wert, OH (75-225) Lat C; Yth
Fel; Jr Classical League; Church Choir & Orch;
Mount Vernon Nazarene Col; Psych.

GARY, Charlene Evonne
Sto-Rox HS; McKees Rocks, PA (129-245) Chor;
Y-Tns; Afro-Amer C; *Pittsburgh Beauty Acad;
Cosmotology.*

GARY, Cheryl Denise
Greenville HS; Greenville, MS (25-560) Band; Bus
C; Lat C; NHS; COM; NEDT; Ecology C; Triplett
Eng A; *Delta St U; Bus.*

GARY, Darla Eileen
Patten Acad of Christian Ed; Oakland, CA (2-13)
A Cap Choir; Band; Chor; Dbte Tm; Drama; Ensm;
Orch; Rptr, Sch P; Citz A; *Patten Bible Col; Ed.*

GARY, Guy Michael
Jefferson HS; Los Angeles, CA (10-750) Chor;
Hmrm; JETS; Spch C; Cpt, Ftbl; Tr; Hon Prog;
Calif St Poly-Pomona; Elec.

GARY, Linda Sue
Bridgeport HS; Bridgeport, OH; Bus Mgr, Ann;
FHA; 4H; NHS; Rptr, Sch P; Secy, Sci C; SC;
Y-Tns; *Wheeling U; RN.*

GARY, Lise Mathis
Rowan HS; Hattiesburg, MS (25%-509) Bus Mgr,
Sch P; VP, Y-Tns; VP, Deb C; Talent As; Art A;
Piano As; Acad A; *U of Sou Miss; Teaching-
Counseling.*

GARY, Louanne
Denison Sr HS; Denison, TX (25%-375) All Amer
Yth; Chor; Drama; FHA; FTA; Hmrm; Key C; Lit
Mag; Ski C; Span C; SC; Thes; Y-Tns; COM; HCt;
Drill Tm; Mus Schol; *Tex Christian U; Drama.*

GARY, Phil Eugene
W Charlotte Sr HS; Charlotte, NC; Parl, Chor;
Parl, Ensm; Hmrm; Key C; ARC; Bkbl; JV, Sftbl;
HR.

GARY, Robin Elaine
Marshall HS; Marshall, MI; Dbte Tm; JV, Bkbl;
MVP, Sftbl; Hon Prog; Yth Fel; *U of Mich; Nurs.*

GARZA, Elizabeth Melanie
Robert E Lee HS; San Antonio, TX (127-515)
AFS; *Occupational Therapy.*

GARZA, Nora B
Chino HS; Chino, CA; Band; 4H; Span C; 4H A;
Zoology.

GARZA, Violeta
Woodrow Wilson HS; Los Angeles, CA; Chor;
CSF; Citz A; 2nd Girl o-t Yr; Outst Achv Cert;
Merit A; HR; *E Los Angeles Col; Bus.*

GARZA, Yolanda Kauikeaulani
Pearl City HS; Pearl City, HI (37-542) InterAct C;
Span C; May Day Qn; Found for Stu Aboard; *U of
Hawaii; Bus.*

Garza₀ORTIZ, Lisa
Owasso HS; Owasso, OK; Band; Chor; Ensm; Span
C; VP, Yth Fel; *ORU; Mus Therapy.*

GASAL, Debra Jean
Jamestown HS; Jamestown, ND (5-300) Rptr,
Ann; Chem C; Chor; Drama; Fr C; Ger C; GS; 4H;
NHS; F-Ed, Sch P; Kiwanis A; 1st Pl St, Know
Your St Contest; WW; *Moorhead St U; Mass Com-
munications.*

GASIEWSKI, Stanley Joseph
Secaucus HS; Secaucus, NJ (1-164) Drama; NHS;
Sci C; Ski C; Tnns; Hon Prog; MLS; Val; Regional
Fin, Yahama Mus Festival; *Seton Hall U; Pre-Law.*

GASKIN, Richard
Denby HS; Detroit, MI; Phy A; ROTC A.

GASKINS, Alretta Joy
St Michael's HS; Los Angeles, CA; Pres, CYO;
Chor; Hmrm; Model UN; NHS; SC; Var C; VP,
Soph Cl; Bkbl; Hist A; Pres A; Spch A; NHS; Vol,
Daniel Freeman Hospital; *Acct.*

GASKINS, Debra Rose
W Craven HS; Vanceboro, NC (10-160) A-Ed,
Ann; Fr C; FBLA; Tres, NHS; Ed, Sch P; Sci C; VP,
DECA C; Jr Marshal; DECA A; Co-Cpt, Drill Tm;
Pres, S-T, G Scts; Bible C; Young Woman o-t Yr A;
Jaycee Outst Tnager A; *Craven Comm Col; Med
Secy.*

GASKINS, Stephen Wayne
Bladenboro HS; Bladenboro, NC (10-100) Pres,
BC; Pres, Chor; Ensm; Fr C; Parl, FFA; Bsbl; Citz
A; Cl Fav; Rotary A; Chor A; Bookkeeping A;
Campbell Col; Trust Mgt.

GASMAN, John David
Mercy HS; Red Bluff, CA (2-30) Ch, Ann; Fin, BS;
CYO; Hmrm; Model UN; VP, SC; Pres, Var C;
Pres, Soph Cl; Bkbl; JV, Ftbl; JV, Tr; CSF; NEDT;
Med.

GASMAN, Margaret Ann
Mercy HS; Red Bluff, CA; Ann; Chor; Semi-Fin,
GS; Model UN; UN Council; Secy, Sr Cl; VP, Jr Cl;
Bkbl; Tr; Amer Leg A; CSF; Hon Prog; *St Mary's
Col; Sci.*

GASPARD, Joel Karine
Hilcrest HS; Jamaica, NY (5-45) *Med.*

GASPARD, Johanne Marjorie
Hillcrest HS; Jamaica, NY (6-45) ESL A; *Bus.*

GASPARIAN, Sonya
Classical HS; Springfield, MA (155-508) A Cap
Choir; Chor; Drama; Citz A; Armenian Church
Yth Group; Secy, Church Choir; Girl's Patrol;
Study A to Armenia; Armenian Sch Staff; *Bay Path
Jr Col; Theater Arts.*

GASQUE, Marianne
Aynor HS; Aynor, SC (15%-85) Tres, BC; Fr C;
Pres, FHA; 4H A; *Lab Technican.*

GASS, Cindy Jo
Morristown-Hamblen HS W; Morristown, TN;
Ann; Band; BC; Hmrm; Span C; SC; Tri-HiY; Math
A; *Carson-Newman Col.*

GASS, Elizabeth Ann
Eufaula HS; Eufaula, OK (5%-113) Chor; VP,
Drama; FHA; NHS.

GASS, Steven Ray
Chillicothe HS; Chillicothe, MO (1-190) Ed, Ann;
Band; Demolay; FBLA; SC; Pres, Sr Cl; VP, Jr Cl;
Bio A; Curator A; DARGCA; K of C A; Lion A;
Type A; Val; Mo Mr FBLA; J P Sousa Band A; *U of
Mo-Columbia; Acct.*

GASSAWAY, Mary Martha
Borger HS; Borger, TX (23-288) FHA; NHS; ARC;
Golf; ARC A; *Translator.*

GASSEL, Lynn Marie
Rosary HS; St Louis, MO (4-385) Band; Secy,
NHS; Hon Prog; I Dare You; Band A; *Sou Ill U at
Edwardsville; Mus Ed.*

GASSER, Gerald Edward Jr
Lutheran HS; New Orleans, LA (3-78) Bkbl.

GASSNER, John Richard
Newman HS; Wausau, WI (11-134) Arch; Fr C;
Hmrm; NHS; Phys C; Arch; Bsbl; Tr; Amer Leg A;
UWMC; Med.

GASSNER, Mary Jean
Newman HS; Wausau, WI; A Cap Choir; Chor;
Drama; S-T, 4H; Span C; Sftbl; 4H A; Interlochen
Ntl Mus; Ntl Cath Mus Ed Asn; Cpt, Vlbl.

GAST, Lizbeth Robin
Worthington HS; Worthington, OH (110-580)
Dbte Tm; NFL; NHS; Cpt, Tnns; COM; Pres A;
Drill Corp; Bsbl C; *Wittenberg U; Bus.*

GAST, Sharon Kay
Monett HS; Monett, MO; Span C; JV, Bkbl; Tr;
HCt; Type A.

GASTINEAU, Wanda Lynn
J J Pearce Sr HS; Richardson, TX; Chor; *Sou Methodist U; Mus.*

GASTON, Douglas Ben
Lexington HS; Lexington, NE (29-134) Band;
Chor; NHS; Sci C; SC; Var C; VP, Soph Cl; Bsbl;
Bkbl; Ftbl; Tr; Hon Prog; Most Out; NMS; FCA;
Agape Singers; *U of Nebr; Med Tech.*

GASTON, Edriel Denise
E Atlanta HS; Atlanta, GA (6-145) Band; BC;
Drama; Rptr, FBLA; Secy, Span C; SC; MVP,
Tnns; COM; Hist A; Hon Prog; MLS; Sigma
Gamma Rho; Eng A; *Tuskegee Inst; Eng.*

GASTON, Gregg Steven
Steubenville HS; Steubenville, OH (4-268) A Cap
Choir; BS; Hmrm; Key C; Sci C; Tres, Span C; SC;
Var C; Wrest; Amer Leg Hist A; *Law.*

GASTON, Laura Lee
Parkwood HS; Joplin, MO (2-375) Chldr; Lit Mag;
Math C; Sch P; Y-Tns; NMS; Social Sci Achv Test
A; *U of NC; Social Sci.*

GASTON, Lillie Diane
Murray-Wright HS; Detroit, MI; Chldr; Cl Fav;
Pre-Law.

GASTON, Maury Douglas
Sylacauga HS; Sylacauga, AL (5-170) Chor;
Drama; JETS; NHS; Order/Arrow; SC; Pres, Sr Cl;
Hon Prog; Yth Fel; Pres, Yth Fel; Outst Sr SC;
Avondale Textile Schol; Eagle Sct; WW; *Auburn
U; Textile Engr.*

GASTON, Steven Ned
Van Buren Comm HS; Keosauqua, IA (30%-90)
Band; Chor; Var C; Wrest; *Math.*

GASTON, Theresa Jean
Ballou Sr HS; Washington, DC; FBLA; *U of DC;
Bus Ed.*

GASUNAS, Geraldine Susan
Immaculate Heart of Mary HS; Westchester, IL;
Co-Cpt, Chldr; Chor; Ger C; Ed, Sch P; SC; COM;
NEDT; Sci A; Val; Marian A; *Loyola U; Dentistry.*

GASWAY, Valarie Etheldra
Ritenour Sr HS; St John's, MO (129-850) A Cap
Choir; NHS; SC; *Stephen's Col; Criminal Justice.*

GATES, JoAnn Marie
Emerson Voc HS; Buffalo, NY; Ann; Chldr; Sch P; Sch Monitor; *ECC-N; Dietitics.*

GATES, Mary Lee
Mt Whitney HS; Visalia, CA (16-500) Chor; Fr C; GS; Hmrm; Key C; CSF; Hon Prog; Math A; Secy, Jr Status For Women; Candystriper; *Mills Col; Nurs.*

GATES, Robin Jo
Alamosa HS; Alamosa, CO (8-150) Band; Chor; Drama; VP, Fr C; FBLA; FHA; Cpt, Mjrte; NHS; Ski C; Spch C; Thes; DARGCA; Band, Choir A's; *Northwest Nazarene Col; Med Tech.*

GATES, Thresa Ann
Goodrich HS; Goodrich, TX (2-25) BC; Chldr; Chor; Pres, FHA; Bkbl; Homemaker o-t Yr.

GATES, Vickie Lynn
Harding HS; Marion, OH (300-466) Bus C; FHA; Cooperative Ed, C; Pres, Young People's Dept; Secy for Sch Guidance Counselor.

GATEWOOD, Autry Elaine
Melrose HS; Memphis, TN (116-340) FHA; Charmettes; JA; Secy, Sunday Sch; Ntl Convention; *Memphis St U; Law.*

GATHAS, Eileen Valerie
Anaheim HS; Anaheim, CA; Ger C; Ski C; Swim; CSF; Hon Prog; GAA Service A; Spirit A, Pep C; Schol A; *U of Calif; Bus.*

GATHERIGHT, Adele Renae
Winnfield Sr HS; Winnfield, LA (13-128) BC; FBLA; FHA; FTA; Lit Ral; SC; HCt; *NW St U; Nurs.*

GATLIN, Rafael Nathan
B T Washington HS; Shreveport, LA (3-851) Drama; Fr C; 4H; Sci C; Bsbl; Sftbl; Tnns; Amer Leg A; Hon Prog; *Central Kansas Col.*

GATLIN, Roxanne
Florence HS; Florence, MS; Band; BC; Fr C; Cpt, Mjrte; Sftbl; Swim; Band A; *Miss St U.*

GATLIN, Troy Lee
Halter HS; St Louis, MO (9-58) Hon Prog; Math A; *Bus Adm.*

GATREL, Deanna M
Naperville N HS; Naperville, IL; Band; NHS; Span C; Hon Prog; Yth Fel.

GATTIS, Marsha Lynn
Frederick HS; Frederick, OK (10%-98) Bus C; Chldr; Chor; Ensm; GS; Hmrm; Math C; Mu Alpha Theta; NHS; Sci C; SC; Var C; Pres, Sr Cl; Bkbl; Amer Leg A; COM; HCt; Hon Prog; Swtht; Yth Fel; Jr Cl Rep, SC; Commencement Usherette; Page, House of Rep; *Okla St U; Bus.*

GATTO, Barbara Lynn
Old Forge HS; Old Forge, PA (15-121) FTA; Hmrm; Ed, Lit Mag; NHS; SC; Hon Prog; Ch, Yrbk Lit Committee; *Keystone Jr Col; Med Secy.*

GATTOZZI, Joseph Walter
Tuscaloosa Sr HS; Tuscaloosa, AL (170-650) Inter-Act C; JV, Ftbl; Tnns; Cl Fav; Chaplain, Inter- act C; *U of Ala; Bus.*

GAUB, Joel Bradley
Olivia Public HS; Olivia, MN (33%-86) Ann; Band; Chor; Drama; Ensm; Madrigal; Mjrte; Sch P; Spch C; SC; Var C; Tr; Co-Cpt, Wrest; Sal; Spch A; FCA; Pop Singers; Treas, Lutheran Yth C; *U of Minn-Morris; Phar.*

GAUDET, Julie Marie
St Mary's Regional HS; Lynn, MA (25-129) Chldr; Sftbl; Tr; Sci A; Chldr, Sftbl, Fr, Gym, A's.

GAUDETTE, Blair William
Tignish Regional HS; Tignish, CANADA;

GAUDETTE, Suzanne
Rock HS; Rock, MI (33%-28) Rptr, Sch P; Mgr, Bkbl; Tr; Art A; *Northwestern Mich Col; Aviation.*

GAUDREAU, Ghislain
College Ste-Anne De La Pocatiere; La Pocatiere, CANADA (1-30) Var C; Golf; Hockey; Tnns; Co Cpt, Vlbl; *Med.*

GAUGER, Karen Loraine
James Madison Sr HS; Milwaukee, WI (427-850) Arch; Swim; Tnns.

GAUGER, Kristie Lynn
James Madison HS; Milwaukee, WI (33%-1100) Arch; Cpt, Mjrte; Ski C; Arch; JV, Tnns; Tr; COM; Citz A; *Marquette U; Legal Profession.*

GAUGHRAN, Lynn
Secaucus HS; Secaucus, NJ (20-165) Co-Cpt, Bkbl; Sftbl; *Montclair St Col.*

GAUGLER, Beth Anne
Brethren Christian Sch; Osceola, IN (5%-30) A Cap Choir; Band; Cpt, Chldr; 4H; Tres, Jr Cl; Tres, Soph Cl; HCt; Co- cpt, Chldr; *Bob Jones U; Home Ec.*

GAULDEN, Felicia Jenine
Alma J Brown HS; Grambling, LA (20-40) Chldr; FHA; 4H; COM; 4H A; Hon Prog; Poet A; Sci A; Secy, Teenlifters; Church Choir; *Grambling St U.*

GAULDEN, Gary Leslie
Eastern Guilford HS; Gibsonville, NC (1-164) Hmrm; Monogram; NHS; VP, Span C; Span NHS; SC; Co-Cpt, Cr-Ctry; Tr; Escort, Homecoming Court; *U of NC; Bus Adm.*

GAULT, Angela Zan
Okolona HS; Okolona, MS (20%-70) Band; Chldr; Mjrte; HCt; Yth Fel; ESAA Comm; *Miss St U.*

GAULT, Gloria Trivette
Gaffney HS; Gaffney, SC; Bus Mgr, Ann; BC; Chldr; Chess C; ARC; Sch P; Span C; Pres, SC; Pres, Sr Cl; VP, Jr Cl; JV, Tnns; Citz A; Yth Fel; *U of Ga; Real Estate.*

GAULT, Wendy Victoria
Carrollton HS; Saginaw, MI (10%-100) Band; Mod Mus Mas; NHS; SC; Mgr, Sftbl; Tr; Citz A; Pres A; Correspond Secy, SC; Pep Band; VP, Mod Mus Masters; Ch, Publicity Committee; Homecoming Committee; *Delta Comm Col; Pub Relations.*

GAUME, David John
Alliance HS; Alliance, OH (10-335) BS; Pres, NHS; Span C; SC; Var C; Tres, Jr Cl; Ftbl; Tr; Wrest; Amer Leg A; Hist A; Hon Prog; Sacristan; Ath Honorary; *U of Akron; Bus.*

GAUNTLETT, Philip VanPelt
Winter Haven HS; Winter Haven, FL (20%-700) *U of Fla; Bus.*

GAUSA, Heidi Ruth
Robert H Goddard HS; Roswell, NM (25%-365) Community Yth Symph; Ensm; NHS; Orch; Span C; COM; Type A; Dist Orch Festival Medals & Cert; *NM St U; Math.*

GAUSE, Joseph Allen
Ripley HS; Ripley, TN; Cpt, Ftbl; *U of Sou Calif.*

GAUSE, Kevin Glenn
Loris HS; Loris, SC; BS; FHA; 4H; Hmrm; Order/ Arrow; Sci C; SC; Var C; Bsbl; Bkbl; Ftbl; Amer Leg A; Boy Ath o-t Month; Boy Stu o-t Month; *USC Coastal Carolina; Phys Ed.*

GAUT, Gwendolyn
William Howard Taft HS; Bronx, NY (5%-1250) NHS; *Journ.*

GAUT, Rebecca Lynn
Tuloso Midway HS; Corpus Christi, TX (26-164) Secy, Chor; FTA; Type A; *Bee Co Col; Gen Bus.*

GAUTHIER, Michael Arthur
St Dominic Regional HS; Lewiston, ME (3-78) Tres, Fr C; VP, NHS; VP, Sodality; *St Anselm's Col; Nurs.*

GAUTHIER, Philip James
Telstar Regional HS; Bethel, ME; Drama; NHS; SC; JV, Bkbl; Cr-Ctry; Tr; Hist A; *Mech.*

GAUTHIER, Roger A Jr
Pine Forest HS; Fayetteville, NC (197-535) Band; Rptr, Drama; Ger C; Rptr, 4H; 4H A; ROTC A; Spch A; Yth Fel; Ntl Win, Creative Writing; 1st Pl, Narrative Presentation; Win, St 4-H Pub Spch; *Emmanuel Col; Religion.*

GAUTHREAUX, Wade Paul
Destrehan HS; Destrehan, LA (5%-200) BC; *U of New Orleans; Math.*

GAUWITZ, Juliann Marie
Prairie Comm HS; Gowrie, IA (28-85) Ann; Band; Chor; FHA; Madrigal; Pres, Mod Mus Mas; NHS; SC; Thes; Spch A; Yth Fel; Pres, Lutheran Yth for Christ; Master Mus A; Thespian o-t Yr A; *Concordia Teachers Col; Mus.*

GAVALES, Ourania Alexander
Brooklyn Tech HS; Brooklyn, NY (4-40) Chldr; Mjrte; Alg A; Chem A; Hist A; Hon Prog; Math A; Sci A; Penmanship, Effort, PA, A's; *Acct.*

GAVIN, Lassie Mae
Wakulla HS; Crawfordville, FL; Lit Mag; Highest Avg, Eng; *FSU; Fashion Merchandising.*

GAWLOCKI, Kathleen Ann
St Mary's Regional HS; Lynn, MA (4-117) CYO; Fr C; Tres, NHS; ARC; Bkbl; Hockey; Swim; Alg A; Beauty; Bio A; COM; Crisco A; God & Country A; Hon Prog; Math A; MLS; Ntl Achv Schol; Sci A; Star Student; *St Anselm's Col; Nurs.*

GAWLOWSKI, David Vincent
Eisenhower HS; Washington, MI (207-524) Tres, CYO; Cr-Ctry; Tr; ACT St A; MIES A; *Lawrence Inst of Tech; Archt.*

GAWTHROP, Keirn Roy
Hobart Sr HS; Hobart, IN (9-404) BS; Pres, Chor; Parl, Drama; Ensm; VP, Ger C; Madrigal; NHS; A-Ed, Sch P; SC; Parl, Thes; Citz A; DARGCA; Hist A; Journ A; Most Out; Mus, Drama, A's; *Ball St U.*

GAWTHROP, Linda Dawn
Fairmont Sr HS; Fairmont, WV (6-226) Chor; Fr C; French NHS; Hmrm; NFL; NHS; Hon Prog; Masque & Gavel A; Spch A; *Cedarville Col; Med Tech.*

GAY, Catherine Elizabeth
Apollo HS; Phoenix, AZ; Y-Tns.

GAY, David Eugene
Homewood-Flossmoor HS; Flossmoor, IL (80-900) VP, Lat C; *Church Recreation.*

GAY, Delores
Carter G Woodson HS; Tullahassee, OK; Chor; FHA; 4H; NHS; Pres, Jr Cl; Co-Cpt, Bkbl; Sftbl; COM; Citz A; 4H A; Hist A; HQn; HCt; Math A; Sci A; Type A.

GAY, Donna Lynn
Williamston HS; Williamston, NC (25-221) Band; Cpt, Chldr; Fr C; Tres, FHA; Key C.

GAY, Holly Trilisa
Ind Presbyterian Sch; Savannah, GA (10%-23) Bus Mgr, Ann; Band; Chor; Drama; VP, Hmrm; Ed, Sch P; Span C; Secy, SC; Bkbl; Sftbl; Beauty.

GAY, Jacqueline Diane
Osceola Sr HS; Kissimmee, FL; Chldr; Chor; Secy, Thes; Tri-HiY; VP, Sr Cl.

GAY, Robert Luther Jr
West York HS; York, PA (78-248) Var C; JV, Cr-Ctry; Tnns; Tr; Co-Cpt, Wrest; All Co, MVP, Wrest; *Juniata Col; Pre-Vet.*

GAY, Sandra Lee
Pontotoc HS; Pontotoc, MS (12-92) Chldr; FBLA; FHA; Span C; Y-Tns; *Nurs.*

GAY, Sharon Lee
Hume-Fogg HS; Nashville, TN (17-225) Ann; Chor; Drama; NHS; ARC; Secy, Sci C; St Semi-Fin & Cl Secy, VICA; *Martin Col; Nurs.*

GAY, Sheila Dawn
Brandon HS; Brandon, FL; Hmrm; Rptr, Sch P; Sftbl; Journ A; ROTC A; Type A; Yth Fel; *Georgia Military Col.*

GAY, Tonya K
Floral HS; Floral, AR (3-17) Ann; FBLA; Pres, FHA; F-Ed, Sch P; SC; Pres, Sr Cl; VP, Jr Cl; Secy, Soph Cl; Bkbl; Sftbl; Citz A; HQn; Journ A; Math A; MLS; Opt A; *U of Central Ark; Journ.*

GAY, Vicki Marie
J C Fremont HS; Los Angeles, CA; *Pepperdine U; Bus.*

GAYAN, Rochelle Elizabeth
Myers Park Sr HS; Charlotte, NC (25-546) Co-Cpt, Band; S-T, Hmrm; Math C; Mu Alpha Theta; NHS; Ski C; Y-Tns; Alg A; Jr Marshal; Schol Art; *UNCC.*

GAYDOS, Lauretta Irene
Kiski Area Sr HS; Vandergrift, PA (45-496) Chem C; Cum Laude Soc; NHS; Ski C; Color Guard; Pep C; Health Careers C; *Grove City Col; Elem Ed.*

GAYDOS, Sandy Sherry
S Park Sr HS; Library, PA (3-180) NHS; Pres, Acct C; Academic Games, Lang Arts.

GAYLE, Anna R
Brooklyn Tech HS; Brooklyn, NY; Chldr; Tr; COM; Spch A; SPARK, Drug Ed Sq; Cafeteria Sq; SOS, Stu Service Organization; Yth Involvement Organization; *Howard U; Communications.*

GAYLEY, Jennifer Anne
Penncrest HS; Media, PA (95-499) A Cap Choir; Chldr; Chor; Madrigal; Hockey; JV, Tnns; Alg A; Math A; Sci A; Ger A; Piano Accompanist A; Vocal A; Most Improved Alto; *Sci.*

GAYLOR, Bruce Wayne
Hillsborough HS; Tampa, FL; FFA; Tnns; Tr; DECA; Bible Quizzer; *Med.*

GAYLOR, Rosalie
Holston HS; Knoxville, TN (8-209) Fr C; FHA; NHS; PTA A; *Carson Newman Col; Religion.*

GAYTEN, Sanchia Margarita
John W Hallahan HS; Philadelphia, PA (16-432) CYO; Math C; Orch; COM; Hon Prog; Span A; Rohm & Hars Schol; *Drexel U; Chem Engr.*

GAYTON, Nell Marie
Wayne Co HS; Jesup, GA; 4H; Soccer; Sftbl; Tnns; *Col of Saint Benedict.*

GAZAWAY, Connie Sue
Tyner HS; Chattanooga, TN (12-273) BC; Chor; VP, Drama; Ensm; NHS; ARC; SC; Tri-HiY; Cl Fav; DARGCA; Star Student; *U of Tenn; Bus.*

GAZAWAY, Gwendalyn Jean
Lynbrook HS; San Jose, CA (53-594) Secy, Bus C; Chor; Secy, FBLA; NHS; CSF; Type A; Ntl Win, Drill Tm; St Bus Development Prog; *Seattle Pacific U; Bus Adm.*

GAZLEY, Cynthia Lorraine
Gladstone HS; Covina, CA (40%-274) Band; Secy, CYO; Pres, FNA; InterClub Coun; VP, Jr Achv; Health Careers A; *Citrus Jr Col; Med.*

GEARHART, Cheryl Louise
Neshaminy Maple Pt HS; Langhorne, PA (7-388) Band; Chor; Hmrm; Cpt, Mjrte; NHS; Math A; Sci A; Yth Fel; Chor Mus, Band, Drum Mjtre, A's; Eng, Sch Service, A's; *Helene Fuld Sch of Nurs; Nurs.*

GEARHART, Sharon Lynn
Castlemont HS; Oakland, CA (1-555) NHS; Bank of Amer A; CSF; Sci A; Val; General Mills Ldrship A; NHS A; Marcus A Foster Achv A; *U of Calif; Pre- med.*

GEARHEART, Gary Martin
Bluefield HS; Bluefield, WV (95-350) Fr C; Inter-Act C; Bsbl; Ftbl; Weightlifting; FCA; Pres, Dist Methodist Yth; UMYF Yth Coun; *W Va U; Phys Ed.*

GEARHEART, Pamela Rae
Bluefield HS; Bluefield, WV (11-350) City Conf; Fr C; GS; NHS; Magna Cum Laude; Second Miler; WW; YSF Educator of WVa; *Roanoke Mem Hospital; X-Ray Tech.*

GEBAUER, Richard Henry Felix III
Marist Brothers' HS; Pago Pago, AMERICAN SAMOA (1-50) Pres, Hmrm; SC; Pres, Soph Cl; Alg A; COM; Hon Prog; Math A; Sci A; Martial Arts; *Pepperdine U; Med.*

GEBBIE, Donald Grant
Bloomfield HS; Bloomfield, NJ (123-679) Band; Chess C; NMF; *Cornell Col; Physics.*

GEBERT, Ned Courtney
Marysville-Pilchuck HS; Marysville, WA (17-340) Ger C; VP, NHS; Var C; Bkbl; Ftbl; Tnns; MLS; ROTC A; Cl Speaker; Graduation; Sch Athlete o-t Yr; *U of Wash; Archt.*

GEBHART, Debbie Darlene
Chula Vista HS; Chula Vista, CA; Drill Tm; *Point Loma Col; Child Development.*

GEBHART, Lucy Ann
Hickman Co HS; Centerville, TN (2-190) A-Ed, Ann; BC; Community Yth Symph; Drama; FHA; Pres, Sci C; Poet A; Soph Sal.

GEBKE, Patricia Ann
Mater Dei HS; Breese, IL (56-166) VP, CYO; Drama; COM; WW; *Kaskaskia Col; Data Processing.*

GEDDIE, David James
Nathan Hale HS; Tulsa, OK (200-680) Mgr, Band; Chem C; Chess C; Ensm; Pres, Hmrm; Ch, Key C; Math C; Mu Alpha Theta; Order/Arrow; Phys C; Span C; SC; Arch; Bsbl; Bkbl; Ftbl; Sftbl; Swim; Tnns; COM; Cl Fav; Most Out; Order/Arrow A; Sci A; Yth Fel; Mus A; BSct A; Eagle Sct; *Okla St U; Engr.*

GEDDLING, Sandra Kay
Moline Sr HS; Moline, IL (101-832) Fr C; NHS; *Black Hawk Col; Bus Adm.*

GEDE, Victor Edward
Granada HS; Livermore, CA (143-560) Band; Ger C; JETS; Order/Arrow; JV, Wrest; *U of Calif; Engr.*

GEE, Susan Grace
Alhambra HS; Alhambra, CA; VP, SC; Tri-HiY; Girl's League.

GEEDING, Jeffrey Charles
National Trail HS; New Paris, OH (20-140) Chem C; Pres, FFA; Mgr, Bkbl; COM; 4H A; Hon Prog; Journ A; Math A; Sci A; Spch A; Yth Fel; Yth Foundation; Yth Leg; Rptr, FFA; St Farmer Degree, A'S; FFA; *Ohio St U; Agr.*

GEENE, Burke Alan
E Greene HS; Eastern Heights, IN (1-84) NHS; SC; S-T, Soph Cl; Mgr, Bkbl; Cr-Ctry; MVP, Golf; Tr; Alg A; COM; Citz A; Geom A; *Ind U; Med.*

GEER, Grant Keith
Granger HS; Granger, UT (20%-560) Dbte Tm; Model UN; NFL; Orch; Rptr, Sch P; Kiwanis A; *NW Christian Col; Pastoral Stu.*

GEER, Rosalie Jean
Brooten HS; Brooten, MN (14-60) Band; Chldr; Spch C; *Evangel Col; Communications.*

GEERLINGS, Todd Robert
Zeeland HS; Zeeland, MI (10-175) BS; Chem C; Dbte Tm; Lat C; Model UN; Phys C; SC; Var C; Pres, Soph Cl; Bkbl; Ftbl; Tr; Hon Prog; MVP, A'S, Bkbl; *Pre-Med.*

GEERTS, Lauri Jo
Thomson HS; Thomson, IL (15-35) Pres, FHA; *Clinton Comm Col; Acct.*

GEERTS, Sue Ann
Fulton HS; Fulton, IL (20-136) Band; FTA; Mgr, Bkbl; MVP, Vlbl; Faculty Hon A; *Math Ed.*

GEESEY, Carol Ann
Montpelier HS; Montpelier, OH (3-93) Ann; Chor; Rptr, Sch P; Amer Yth Symph Band & Chor; *Bowling Green St U; Journ.*

GEESEY, Cathy Jean
Montpelier HS; Montpelier, OH (12-92) Band; Chor; Fr C; Bio A; NMF; Fr A; Academic Achv C; *Ohio St U; Nurs.*

GEESEY, Emily Sue
Montpelier HS; Montpelier, OH (1-120) Band; JV, Chldr; Fr C; VP, Rainbow; Sch Achieve Tm; Swim; Alg A; Vlbl; Yth Fel; *Math.*

GEFFRE, Theresa Rose
Leola HS; Leola, SD; Secy, Band; CYO; Chldr; Secy, Chor; Ensm; Secy, FBLA; Sch P; SC; HQn; I Dare You; Type A.

GEGNER, Julie Ann
Merrill Sr HS; Merrill, WI (20-324) AFS; Ski C; Cr-Ctry; Tr; Opt A; Co-Cpt, Gym; *UW Madison; Sci.*

GEHLBACH, Bruce D
Shawnee Mission NW HS; Shawnee, KS (2-700) VP, Dbte Tm; Pres, FFA; NFL; Tres, NHS; Order/Arrow; F-Ed, Sch P; SC; Tr; Order/Arrow A; Q&S A; Sal; Spch A; NML; *Kans St U; Horticulture.*

GEHLY, Brenda Claire
Derby Sr HS; Deby, KS (50-400) Band; Drama; Fr C; 4H; Cpt, Mjrte; Math C; NHS; Sci C; Bkbl; Cpt, Golf; Co-Cpt, Hockey; MVP, Sftbl; MVP, Tr; Bio A; COM; 4H A; Hon Prog; Math A; Most Out; Yth Fel; *Sterling Col; Bio.*

GEHMAN, Leslie Paul
Lincoln HS; Stockton, CA (50-420) Band; Ensm; Co-Ed, Sch P; Arch; Hon Prog; *U of Calif; Vet Sci.*

GEHRI, Dawn Kathleen
Agoura HS; Agoura, CA (170-471) Chor; Tres, SC; Tres, Jr Cl; JV, Swim; Mgr, Wrest; CSF; JV Waterpolo; *UCLA; Psych.*

GEHRING, Barbara Jane
Lincoln Sr HS; Sioux Falls, SD (87%-683) Band; Ger C; *Oral Roberts U; Nurs.*

GEHRKE, Debbie Ann
Winthrop Comm Sch; Winthrop, MN; Chor; Ensm.

GEHRKE, Marcia Lynn
Little Wolf HS; Manawa, WI (15-83) Band; Cpt, Chldr; Chor; Drama; NFL; ARC; Ski C; SC; Var C; Sftbl; Tr; Citz A; Pres A; ARC A; Vlbl; GAA; Pep C; *Fox Valley Tech Col; Dental Asst.*

GEHRS, Mitzi Jean
Robert E Lee HS; Tyler, TX (72-680) Fr C; FHA; NHS; Rptr, Sch P; Hist A; NEDT; Eng A; U Interschol Win, Extem Writing; *Tex A&M U; Drafting.*

GEHRT, Joanna Dorothy
Topeka HS; Topeka, KS (5%-527) VP, AFS; Band; Hmrm; Span C; SC; S-T, AFS; S-T, VP, Church Yth Fel; Fresh Hon Band; *Bio.*

GEHRTS, Ronda Lee
Irving HS; Irving, TX; Band; Ger C; Pres, Tri-HiY; Soccer; *Alcoa Beauty Sch; Hair Styling.*

GEIGER, Brooks Scott
Easton Area HS; Easton, PA (66-662) Chor; Hon Prog; *Lebanon Valley Col; Actuarial Sci.*

GEIGER, Gail Rae
Ft Lauderdale HS; Fort Lauderdale, FL; Band; Semi-Fin, Chldr; Chor; Ensm; Semi-Fin, Hmrm; Madrigal; Ed, Sch P; SC; *Broward Comm Col; Med.*

GEIGER, Kathleen
Bishop Klonowski HS; Scranton, PA; Chor; NHS; *U of Scranton; Bus.*

GEIGER, Stanley William Jr
Western Hills HS; Cincinnati, OH (6-800) Tres, HiY; Pres, Lat C; Mgr, Soccer; Tr; Alg A; Bio A; Math A; Sci A; WW; *Cincinnati Bible Col.*

GEIGER, Timothy Edward
John F Kennedy HS; Richmond, CA (37-308) Alg A; Math A.

GEIMAN, Gilbert Dee
Astoria HS; Astoria, IL (5-29) Band; NHS; Span C; SC; God & Country A; *Lincoln Christian Col; Religious Teaching.*

GEIS, Barbara Jean
Seward Sr HS; Seward, NE (35-172) Band; CYO; Chldr; Chor; Ensm; FHA; Ger C; VP, 4H; Pres, Hmrm; Ch, SC; Tres, Soph Cl; Sftbl; Tr; Amer Leg A; 4H A; Pres A; Alt, GS; Pep C Cabinet; Band Coun; Grange; St Grange Princess; *Kearney St Col; Psych.*

GEIS, Becky Joan
Seward Sr HS; Seward, NE (17-149) CYO; Chor; FFA; Pres, FHA; VP, 4H; SC; Sftbl; 4H A; Alt, GS; St Grange Princess; Off, Pep C; St Jr Grange Director; *U of Nebr; Agr Ed.*

GEIS, Diana Lynn
Northville HS; Northville, MI (33%-397) Chor; 4H; NHS; *E Mich U; Commercial Art.*

GEIS, Tammie Annette
Putnam City HS; Oklahoma City, OK (11-925) Ger C; *Therapy.*

GEISENDORFER, Lisa Kay
Quincy Notre Dame HS; Quincy, IL (7-161) Band; Chor; NHS; Tnns; COM; NEDT; SAA Cert; *Microbio.*

GEISLER, Vicky Rae
Sangr DeCristo Christian Sch; Canon City, CO; Chldr; Chor; *Baptist Bible Col; Missionary.*

GEISSAL, Marjorie Mertz
Lane Tech HS; Chicago, IL (500-1150) GS; St Scholar; Yth Fel; Secy, Lutheran Yth; *Lake Forest Col; Pol Sci.*

GEISSLER, Grant Howard
Joliet W Township HS; Joliet, IL (5-548) Band; Community Yth Symph; Ger C; VP, NHS; Orch; Var C; Cr-Ctry; Ftbl; Tr; Wrest; Hon Prog; Rotary A; All City Orch; *U of Ill; Biochem.*

GEISSLER, Nancy Jean
North HS; Eau Claire, WI; Co-Ed, Chldr.

GEISTLINGER, Lee William
Glenbrook HS; Glenview, IL (14-600) NHS; Bkbl; Sftbl; Chem A; Hon Prog; Phy A; Sci A; Span Commendation; *Cornell U; Engr.*

GEITHMAN, Glenn Andre
Nathan Hale HS; W Allis, WI; Band; Mgr, Bkbl; Ftbl; Swim; Mgr, Tr; Pep & Jazz Bands; Awana C.

GELDARD, Cynthia Gordon
Chadwick Sch; Palos Verdes Penn, CA (24-46) Chldr; Drama; InterAct C; Var C; Swim; Vol Service A; *Northridge St Col; Special Ed.*

GELINA, Shawne Laurice
Engleside Christian Sch; Alexandria, VA (1-4) A Cap Choir; Chor; Drama; Secy, Hmrm; Secy, SC; JV, Swim; PTA A; Val; *Baptist Bible Col; Elem Ed.*

GELLER, William Eugene
Deerborne HS; Coral Gables, FL (6-75) BC; Tres, Drama; InterClub Coun; Key C; NHS; Bkbl; Cpt, Golf; Alg A; COM; Math A; *Cornell U; Dentistry.*

GEMPP, Brenda Lynn
Baltimore; Balto, MD; A Cap Choir; Hmrm; *Medix Sch; Medical Receptionist.*

GENDRON, Sylvie Carole
Alexander Galt Regional HS; Lennoxville, CANADA (4-439) Swim; Tr; Hon Prog; Jazz; Cycling; Badminton; Jr Home Ec Housing & Design; *Med.*

GENEREUX, Nicole
Col De Ste-Anne De La Pocatiere; La Pocatiere, CANADA (1-28) Ski C; Var C; Bkbl; Cr-Ctry; Swim; Tnns; Fin, Tr; *Ottawa U; Pol Sci.*

GENNETT, Paul Louis
Cottage Grove HS; Cottage Grove, OR (3-240) AFS; NHS; Alg A; Math A; Sci A; Span A; *US Naval Acad; Sci.*

GENNOE, James Samuel Jr
Rossville Comp HS; Rossville, GA (22-212) Bkbl; Cpt, Tnns; Alg A; COM; Gov Honor Prog; Math A; Secy, Jr Exchange C; MVP, Tnns; *UT Chattanooga.*

GENO, Charles Edward
Coronado HS; El Paso, TX (55-642) Pres, Chor; Ensm; Ger C; Madrigal; NHS; Order/Arrow; COM; God & Country A; HCt; Hon Prog; Order/Arrow A; Yth Fel; Eagle Sct Wth Palm; Conf Co Yth Min; Pres, Ythcoun; Jr Asst Sctmaster; All Region, All Area Choir; Ger Ntl Hon Soc; NMS Ltr of Recogn; *Mus.*

GENO, Joel Owen
Central Acad; Macon, MS (10%-65) BC; SC; Var C; Bsbl; Bkbl; MVP, Tnns; Cl Fav; DARGCA; *U of Miss; Phar.*

GENO, Marlon Wayne
Tupelo HS; Tupelo, MS (25%-432) Band; Orch; Bsbl; *Freed-Hardeman Col; Law.*

GENOVESE, Torene Lucia
Herricks Sr HS; New Hyde Park, NY (25%-480) Hmrm; Hon Prog; NMS; *St U at Stony Brook; Oceanography.*

GENRY, Christopher Donald
Indian Springs Sch; Helena, AL (6-45) BC; Chess C; Parl, Chor; 4H; Pres, Hmrm; Sch Achieve Tm; JV, Bkbl; COM; Hon Prog; Most Out; St Scholar; Top 5, Ntl Fr Contest; Best Dressed; *Harding Col; Pre-Med.*

GENTES, James Daniel
Melvin-Sibley HS; Melvin, IL (14-34) Tres, Band; Key C; Sch P; Span C; Bsbl; Bkbl; Ftbl; Golf; Soccer; Sftbl; Swim; Tnns; 4H A; Hist A; Lion A; Type A; *Agr.*

GENTILE, Curtis Alan
Parkway Sr HS; Ballwin, MO (250-600) A Cap Choir; Chor; Fr C; Ftbl; Tr; Wrest; Hon Prog; Yth Fel; *U of Mo-Columbia; Bus.*

GENTRY, Brenda Gale
Dell City HS; Dell City, TX (5-24) Bus Mgr, Ann; VP, NHS; Tres, Sr Cl; Cl Fav; Type A; Homemaking A; *Bus.*

GENTRY, Christopher Owen
Nicolet HS; Glendale, WI (131-505) Band; Ensm; JV, Bsbl; JV, Cr-Ctry; JV, Tnns; Wrest; Wisc Sch Mus As Dist Fest As; *Dennison Col; Lib Arts.*

GENTRY, David Carroll
Mesa Verde HS; Citrus Heights, CA (25%-215) Chor; Sch P; SC; Var C; Cpt, Ftbl; SC; Soccer; JV, Tr; MVP, Bkbl; Summer Missionary; MVP, Soccer; Sunday Sch Teacher; Vol Tutor; *Religion.*

GENTRY, Gary Dwayne
Springbrook HS; Silver Spring, MD (9-700) CYO; Ch, Hmrm; Bkbl; Cpt, Ftbl; Soccer; Swim; Tnns; Tr; Wrest; Most Out; MVP, Best Lineman, Ftbl; DC Yth Ldr; Alumni, All Co, A's; *Bullis Preparatory Col.*

GENTRY, George Wesley III
Person Sr HS; Roxboro, NC (15%-500) Chor; Drama; Key C; Order/Arrow; Ftbl; Golf; God & Country A; *INC; Med.*

GENTRY, Jacqueline Rene
Mission San Jose HS; Fremont, CA (15-495) Band; Hmrm; Math C; SC; CSF; Hon Prog; *UC-Berkeley.*

GENTRY, Jimmy Keith
Mesa Verde HS; Citrus Heights, CA (55%-450) Chor; JV, Soccer.

GENTRY, Lula Ann
Reidsville Sr HS; Reidsville, NC (3-324) AFS; Band; Fr C; Math C; Orch; Gov Honor Prog; NEDT; Yth Fel; *NC St U; Math.*

GENTRY, Margaret Dianne
Hickory HS; Hickory, NC; Band; Math C; Flag Corp; *Appalachian St U; Elem Ed.*

GENTRY, Ralph Earl
Stamps HS; Stamps, AR (1-70) Math C; Mu Alpha Theta; NHS; Ftbl; Amer Leg A; Sci A; T&I A.

GENTRY, Randall Layne
Mt Vernon HS; Mt Vernon, IN; AFS; Chor; Hmrm; Parl, Lat C; SC; VP, Soph Cl; Cpt, Bsbl; Cpt, Ftbl; Wrest; *Oral Roberts U; Med.*

GENTRY, Robert Brent Jr
Grimsley HS; Greensboro, NC (4-29) Co-Cpt, Bkbl; Golf; Yth Fel; Exchange C; Young Life; MVP; *U of NC; Bus.*

GENTRY, Robert Brooks
Person Sr HS; Roxboro, NC (15%-500) Chor; Key C; Order/Arrow; Ftbl; Golf.

GENTRY, Sara Jane
Weston-McEwen HS; Athena, OR (1-39) Band; Chldr; Chor; Parl, Dbte Tm; Ensm; FBLA; Secy, FFA; FHA; Fin, GS; NHS; Ed, Sch P; Secy, Span C; Thes; Var C; Mgr, Bsbl; Journ A; Type A; Vlbl; *Blue Mtn C C; Mus.*

GENTRY, Terri Lynn
McCallum HS; Austin, TX (20%-350) Bus C; FHA; Hmrm; Math C; F-Ed, Sch P; SC; Math A; Type A; Vlbl; VOE Area Fin; *Southwest Tex U; Acct.*

GENTRY, Thomas Mordecai
Jack Yates Sr HS; Houston, TX (13-450) Band; Chem C; Ch, Hmrm; Sci C; Parl, SC; Pres, Sr Cl; Pres, Soph Cl; Ftbl; Exec HS Internship Prog Achv A; *Bus Adm.*

GENTRY, Thomas Scott
Greeley Central HS; Greeley, CO (19-331) Ann; Band; BS; Key C; Order/Arrow; Ski C; SC; Var C; Ftbl; Co-Cpt, Swim; Tr; Order/Arrow A; Eagle Sct; 3-Sport Ltrman; Prom King Cand; WW; *Colo St U.*

GENTZ, Kristy Lynne
Madison HS; Madison, KS (4-28) Ann; Band; Chldr; Chor; Secy, Jr Cl; Bkbl; Sftbl; Tr; Hon Prog; Type A; Kg & Qn Courts; Forensics; FCA; Kayettes; Vlbl; Stage Band; *Phys Ed.*

GENTZLER, Joanne Helen
Littlestown Sr HS; Littlestown, PA (35-160) Ann; Band; Co-Cpt, Mjrte; Ski C; Var C; VP, Sr Cl; Pres, Soph Cl; Hockey; Tr; HCt; WW; *Widence Col.*

GENTZLER, Kenneth Lee II
N Sr HS; Dillsburg, PA (10-184) Ensm; Hmrm; Bsbl; JV, Bkbl; Golf; Cpt, Soccer; Citz A; Hist A; Math A; Most Out; Sci A; Spch A; Principal's Schol, Bible, A's; *Cedarville Col; Acct.*

GENTZLER, Sandra Kay
N Sr HS; Dillsburg, PA (6-199) Ed, Ann; Ensm; Secy, NHS; Amer Leg A; B Crocker A; Citz A; DARGCA; Most Stu; Best All Around; *Baptist Bible Col; Christian Ed.*

GEORG, Marjorie Lynn
Old Mill Sr HS; Glen Burnie, MD (25%-500) Band; Pres, Mod Mus Mas; Oust Instrumental Mus A; *Mus Ed.*

GEORGE, Alice Dewauna
Northeast HS; Meridian, MS (5-125) Anchor C; VP, Fr C; SC; *Meridian Jr Col; Med.*

GEORGE, Angela Veronica
St Raymond Acad; Bronx, NY (33%-93) S-T, Band; CYO; SC; Pres, Jr Cl; Pres, Soph Cl; Band A; *Med.*

GEORGE, Charlene Colette
Saint Elizabeth HS; Pittsburgh, PA (10-110) CYO; Chor; Drama; Lit Mag; Model UN; Sch P; Sci C; Span C; Alg A; Yrbk; Geom A; *Math.*

GEORGE, Cheryl Dawne
Southmoor Baptist HS; Memphis, TN; BC; Bkbl; Sftbl; Tr; *Med.*

GEORGE, David Rex
Monterey HS; Lubbock, TX; VP, SC; Ftbl; Church Sftbl & Yth Coun; Jr NHS; *Tex Tech U; Archt.*

GEORGE, Deborah Edythe
Evander Childs HS; New York, NY (12-766) Sci A; Trigonometry Cert; *Nurs.*

GEORGE, Denise Lorraine
Evander Chiles HS; New York, NY (5-968) Chem A; *Hunter Col; Nurs.*

GEORGE, Kerry Lynn
Nevada Union HS; Grass Valley, CA; Chor; Ensm; 4H; CSF; 4H A; Yth Fel; *Sierra Col; Eng.*

GEORGE, Marilyn Renee
Southmoor Baptist HS; Memphis, TN; Bkbl; Sftbl.

GEORGE, Michael Edward
Clyde HS; Clyde, KS (12-36) BS; SC; Thes; Bsbl; Cpt, Bkbl; Ftbl; Tr; *Kans U; Bus.*

GEORGE, Robert W Jr
Vidalia HS; Vidalia, GA (20-150) Demolay; HiY; Hmrm; Key C; Sch P; Bsbl; Bkbl; HCt; Wittiest; Chaplain, Hi-Y; *Brewton-Parker Col; Bus.*

GEORGE, Roberta Ann
Lowndes HS; Valdosta, GA; Anchor C; Band; CYO; Hmrm; SC; Pres, Tri-HiY; Tres, Jr Cl; Tres, Soph Cl; HQn; *Valdosta St Col; Dentistry.*

GEORGE, Rose Ann
Bells HS; Bells, TN (20-50) Ann; Band; Fr C; FHA; FTA; 4H; ARC; Sch P; Span C; World Affairs C; Journ A; Most Out; Most Dependable; *Freed-Hardeman Col; Elem Ed.*

GEORGE, Rose Ann
Marshall Island HS; Majuro, MARSHALL ISLANDS (2-103) Sftbl; Star Student; *Maui Comm Col; Bus Mgt.*

GEORGE, Sharolyn JoAnn
College View Acad; Lincoln, NE (7-22) Chor; Hmrm; NHS; Ed, Sch P; SC; Bkbl; Cpt, Ftbl; Hon Prog; *Union Col; Social Welfare.*

GEORGE, Timothy Bland
Marion Co HS; Lebanon, KY (18-324) Co-Ch, CYO; Hmrm; NHS; SC; Var C; Pres, Sr Cl; Pres, Jr Cl; Bkbl; Ftbl; MLS; Mr Soph; Mr Jr; Eng, Phys Ed, A's; *U of Ky; Pre-Med.*

GEORGE, Timothy Garth
Norwell HS; Ossian, IN (4-180) Pres, Band; NHS; Hon Prog; Rotary A; Yth Fel; Pres, Yth Fel; John Phillip Sousa A; *Ball St U; Telecommunications.*

GEORGE, Verna Jean
S H Archer HS; Atlanta, GA (3-248) Tres, Hmrm; NHS; Alg A; Bio A; Hist A; Hon Prog; JA A; Math A; Most Out; Sci A; Type A; Eng A; *Duke U; Med.*

GEORGES, Ingrid Loraine
Springfield Gdns HS; New York, NY (81-962) *Air Force.*

GEORGEU, Arthur Gary
St Mary's Regional HS; Lynn, MA (2-117) All Amer Yth; CYO; NHS; SC; Cpt, Bsbl; Cr-Ctry; Ftbl; Cpt, Tr; Alg A; Beauty; Bio A; Hon Prog; Math A; Sci A; Star Student; *Sci.*

GEORGI, Diane Michele
Woodlake HS; Woodlake, CA (4-144) Band; Chem C; FHA; Sci C; Var C; VP, Jr Cl; Tnns; CSF; Crisco A; JV Vlbl; *Pepperdine U; Gen.*

GEORGI, Linda Renee
Elmhurst HS; Fort Wayne, IN (120-456) A Cap Choir; Chor; Fr C; Alg A; COM; Fr, Writer, A's.

GEORGULIS, Annette Helen
Belle Vernon Area HS; Belle Vernon, PA; Chor; FBLA; Hmrm; Ftbl; Church Choir; GSct; Campus Life; Med Interest C; *Ind U of Pa; Journ.*

GEORSKEY, Thomas Allan
Midpark HS; Middleburg Hts, OH (25%-642)
Amer Leg A; COM; *Embry-Riddle Aviation U;*
Aeronautical Sci.

GEPHART, John Dennis
Bonita HS; La Verne, CA (8-270) CSF; *Cal Poly;*
Mech Engr.

GEPHART, Mary Anne
McGregor HS; McGregor, MN (4-66) Band; Chor;
NHS; F-Ed, Sch P; Var C; Bkbl; Tr; Cpt, Vlbl; *U of*
M at Duluth; Acct.

GERACI, Michael Gerard
St Xavier HS; Cincinnati, OH (117-248) Model
UN; UN Council; World Affairs C; CAP; CCD
Teacher; Tutor; Comm Service Course; *U of San*
Diego; Bus Mgt.

GERALD, Marilyn Elois
Loris HS; Loris, SC; A-Ed, Ann; 4H; Hmrm; Sci C;
Cpt, Bkbl; 4H A; VP, Secy & Ch, FHA; Bkbl A;
Phys Fitness A; *USC; Bus.*

GERARD, Martha Jane
Montrose R-14 HS; Montrose, MO; CYO; NHS;
4H A; Sci A.

GERBERS, Jeffrey Robert
Woodlan HS; Woodburn, IN (15-121) BS; Chess C;
HiY; NHS; Cr-Ctry; Tr; Amer Leg A; CYO;
Woodburn Days King; FCA; A of Hon; *Ball St U;*
Archt.

GERDES, Jeff Wayne
Auburn HS; Auburn, NE (10-104) Math C; Sci C;
VP, SC; Var C; VP, Sr Cl; Bsbl; Bkbl; Ftbl; Golf;
Swim; Yth Fel; FCA; *U Nebr; Math.*

GERDES, Jerry D
Auburn HS; Auburn, NE (9-92) Band; VP, Math C;
VP, Sci C; COM; Hon Prog; Mem Schol; Book-
keeping A; *U of Nebr; Engr.*

GERDES, Terry G
Auburn HS; Auburn, NE (20-92) Band; Math C;
Sci C; COM; Hon Prog; Kiwanis A; *CTCC; Diesel.*

GERDIN, JoAnn Elaine
Westview HS; Braham, MN (43-86) A-Ed, Ann;
Pres, 4H; Ed, Sch P; Bkbl; Tr; COM; 4H A; Pres A;
F-Ed, Ann; All-Conf, Vlbl; Most Ath; Photo C;
Most Artistic; Ltrman's C; 4-H Forestry A; MVP,
Vlbl; 4-H Conservation A; *River Falls Col; Phy Ed.*

GEREN, Jean Ann
Wapakoneta Sr HS; Wapakoneta, OH (80-343)
Band; Bus C; Chor; Drama; FNA; VP, FTA; Thes;
Spch A; Yth Fel; Bus Director; MYF; Hospital Vol;
Dance Trophy; Asst Gen Mgr, Video Comm C;
Best Sport, Most Co-Operative, FTA; *Ohio St U*
Lima; Nurs.

GERENA, Luis Ricardo
Academia Ntra Sra Providencia; San Juan, PR
(5-58) A Cap Choir; Band; CYO; Chor; Dbte Tm;
Drama; InterClub Coun; Key C; Orch; Rptr, Sch P;
Sci C; Span C; Spch C; Pres, SC; UN Council; Pres,
Jr Cl; Cpt, Bsbl; JV, Bkbl; Ftbl, Cr-Ctry; Alg A;
COM; Hon Prog; Math A; Ntl Cath Mus Ed Asn;
Pres A; Sci A; Spch A; Star Student; Karate A; Judo
A; Vlbl.

GERHARDT, Clarence William
Iroquois HS; Elma, NY; Rptr, FFA; 4H A; VP &
Tres, 4-H C.

GERHARDT, Gary Leon
Warsaw HS; Warsaw, IL; Tres, FFA; Var C; Co-
Cpt, Bsbl; Co-Cpt, Bkbl; Co-Cpt, Ftbl; Sftbl; HKg;
Yth Fel; All Conf, Ftbl & Bsbl; Hon Men, Jr Yr
Bkbl; *Agr.*

GERHARDT, Nancy Lou
Iroquois Central HS; Elma, NY; Tres, FFA; 4H;
NHS; 4H A; Tres, Church Yth Fel; Rptr, NY Hol-
stein Assn; Amer Agr Found A; St Empire Farmer,
St FFA Assn A; *Agr.*

GERIG, Dawn Michelle
Adams Central HS; Monroe, IN; Ann; Band; Chor;
Ensm; Madrigal; Mjrte; NHS; Span C; Schol A.

GERJETS, Lynette Lea
Proctor Sr HS; Proctor, MN (30-239) Chor; FHA;
Ger C; Co-Cpt, Bkbl; JV, Tr; *Duluth Bus U; Legal*
Office Asst.

GERKE, John Paul
Roger Bacon HS; St Bernard, OH (24-256) Pres,
CYO; ARC; Citz A; HS Schol; Acad Excel A's;
Duns Scotus Seminary; Psych.

GERKE, Nicholas Anton
Otterville Plubic HS; Otterville, MO (6-30) FFA;
Star Green Hand; Swine Production; *Disel Mech.*

GERKE, Paula Anne
Columbia HS; Troutdale, OR (10%-700) A Cap
Choir; Band; CYO; Chor; NHS; Dance Tm; *Oreg*
St U; Mus.

GERKEN, Thomas E
Kodiak Regional Alvetian HS; Kodiak, AK (7-103)
BS; VP, NHS; Tres, Sr Cl; Mgr, Bkbl; Cpt, Golf; Elk
A; Hon Prog; Rotary A; KBEA Schol; *Embry Rid-*
dle Aeronautical U; Aviation Sci.

GERKIN, Amelia Ann
Nitro HS; Nitro, WV; Chor; FBLA; Secy, NHS;
Span C; All Co Choir; *W Va U.*

GERLACH, Ann Marie
Chippewa Falls Sr HS; Chippewa Falls, WI
(10%-400) Thes; JA A; Pres A; DECA; Athena C;
U of Wisc; Home Ec.

GERMAIN, Mariann Camille
Dover HS; Dover, NH; Fr C; NHS; *St Anselm's*
Col; Nurs.

GERMAN, Dawn Richelle
Pascagoula HS; Pascagoula, MS; Pres, Ger C; Rptr,
Sch P; Spch C; SC; WW; *U of Sou Miss; Spch &*
Hearing.

GERMANY, Cheryl Denise
Clear Creek HS; League, TX (1-520) Drama;
Hmrm; Model UN; NHS; Spch C; Secy, Jr Cl; JV,
Bkbl; JV, Tr.

GERMANY, Mary Etta
Waterproof HS; Waterproff, LA (25%-55) BC;
Chor; FBLA; 4H; Mjrte; Bkbl; *Meadow's Draughn*
Bus Col; Computer Prog.

GERMER, Paul Harold
Ottawa HS; Ottawa, KS; Drama; Fr C; Tres, FBLA;
Spch C; JV, Tnns; Opt A; Spch A; *Ottawa U; Bus.*

GERNHARDT, Mark Gordon
Hempfield Sr HS; Greensburg, PA (20-805) Chess
C; Pres, Hmrm; Mu Alpha Theta; Var C; JV, Bkbl;
Cr-Ctry; I Dare You; Yth Fel; Sportsmanship,
Schol-Ath, A's; *Pa St U; Engr.*

GEROLD, Tomee Jo
Red Bank HS; Red Bank, TN (10-200) FBLA;
Hmrm; SC; Var C; Cpt, Bkbl; Sftbl; Tnns; Tr; ARC
A; Vlbl Tm; *Jamestown Col; Probation.*

GERRARD, Tracie Guion
Hattiesburg HS; Hattiesburg, MS; Cpt, Chldr;
Ensm; Key C; SC; Tres, Sr Cl; Sftbl; HQn; Swtht;
Yth Fel; *U of Miss; Bus Adm.*

GERRED, Susan Lea
Quanah HS; Quanah, TX (3-70) FHA; 4H; Math C;
Mu Alpha Theta; VP, NHS; Sch P; SC; MVP, Bkbl;
Tnns; Tr; Chem A; Hist A; Geom A; Epsilon Sigma
Alpha; All Dist Bkbl; Bkbl Schol; *Midwestern St U;*
Math.

GERREGANO, William Anthony
Memphis Preparatory Sch; Memphis, TN; Key C;
Bkbl; Mgr, Ftbl; Citz A; Yth Fel; Current Affairs C;
U of Tenn; Hist.

GERRELS, Tammie Amy
Brainerd Sr HS; Brainerd, MN (145-430) Chor;
Dbte Tm; Spch A; Type A; *Brainerd Comm Col;*
Special Ed.

GERST, Jill Diane
Paris HS; Paris, IL; Ger C; NHS; Orch; Rainbow;
NEDT; *E Ill U; Math.*

GERST, Karen Elaine
Paris HS; Paris, IL (16-270) Band; Cpt, Chldr;
Hmrm; Tres, NHS; Orch; Rainbow; St Stu Con-
gress; NEDT; Yth Fel; *Eastern Ill U; Sci.*

GERTEISEN, Shirley Marie
Daviess Co HS; Owensboro, KY (9-316) F-Ed,
Ann; Tres, BC; Sci C; Chem A; Hon Prog; Phy A;
W Ky U.

GERTSCH, Lynda Kay
Wasatch HS; Heber City, UT (13-105) A Cap
Choir; Band; Semi-Fin, Chldr; Chem C; FHA; GS;
Model UN; Ski C; SC; Bkbl; Tnns; Tr; Amer Leg A;
Friendliest; Hon Stu; *Brigham Young U; Art.*

GERTSON, Ronald B
E Bernard HS; East Bernard, TX (4-60) Band; Co-
Ch, FFA; Hmrm; Math C; Model UN; VP, NHS;
Rptr, Sch P; Sci C; Pres, SC; Ftbl; Tr; DARGCA;
Lion A; Yth Fel; *Tex A&M U; Agr Econ.*

GERTZ, Chris Timothy
Winters HS; Winters, CA; Dbte Tm; FFA; Ski C;
Pres, SC; VP, Soph Cl; Bsbl; Bkbl; Ftbl; CSF; High-
est GPA, FFA A; *UC at Davis; Agr Bus.*

GERVAIS, Lorraine Suzanne
Saint Dominic Regional HS; Lewiston, ME (10-78)
Ed, Ann; CYO; Chor; Ch, Fr C; VP, FNA; NHS;
Ed, Sch P; Sftbl; Bio A; Chem A; Hon Prog; Sci A;
Type A; Yth Leg; Fr Ntl Exam; 1st Pl, St Sci Fair;
Extra-Curricular Activity Trophy; *U of Ct; Phar.*

GERWITZ, LaMerle
Valley HS; Sanders, AZ; Cpt, Drama; Hmrm;
Model UN; SC; Type A.

GESELL, Loren Gene
Crestwood HS; Cresco, IA; Historian, Lib C; VP,
Lutheran Walter League; *Iowa St U; Elec.*

GESSNER, Lynne Ellen
E Brunswick HS; East Brunswick, NJ; Hand in
Hand; Church Yth Group; Fund Raisng Actv; Free
Sprit Clr Gd; Evangelism Comm; Church Folk
Choir; Secy, Christ Memorial.

GEST, Melissa Janine
Rockdale HS; Rockdale, TX (10-150) Band; Chldr;
Chor; NHS; Tres, Jr Cl; Tnns; Homemaking I; S-T,
Handbell Choir; *Baylor U; Mus Ed.*

GETER, Kirk
Trenton HS; Trenton, NJ (10%-700) Semi-Fin,
Bsbl; Co-Cpt, Swim; Amer Leg A; Highest Ranking
Boy; *Howard U; Lib Arts.*

GETER, Todd
Trenton HS; Trenton, NJ (10%-700) Bsbl; Swim;
MVP, Babe Ruth Bsbl League; JF Kennedy A;
Archt.

GETHERS, Jacquetta Latonia
Chicora HS; Charleston, SC; Band; NHS; SC;
Bandsman o-t Yr; *Tenn St U; Bus Adm.*

GETZ, Jackie Lee
Monte Vista HS; Monte Vista, CO (3-120) Band;
Pres, 4H; NHS; Sci C; Ski C; Tr; 4H A; Vlbl; Sci
Fair; *U of N Colo; Med Tech.*

GEVERD, Tina Jo
Columbia Acad; Columbia, MS; Band; Sftbl.

GEYER, Daniel Keefer
McConnellsburg HS; McConnellsburg, PA
(20%-100) Chess C; Chor; Fr C; SC; Var C; Mgr,
Bkbl; Soccer; *Penn St U; Computer Programming.*

GEYER, Karen Lee
Sequoyah HS; Doraville, GA (10-262) Ed, Ann;
Secy, BC; Chor; Ger C; Hmrm; Math C; Model
UN; NHS; SC; Cl Fav; WSB Great Young Amer;
Furman U; Christian Ed.

GEYER, Thomas William
Lutheran HS E; Harper Woods, MI (28-140) Band;
NHS; Sch P; SC; Var C; Pres, Soph Cl; MVP, Bkbl;
Co-Cpt, Ftbl; Tr; MVP, Ftbl; Most Ath Sr Ath A;
Wayne St Col; Finance.

GHERARDINI, Lisa Sue
Carlyle HS; Carlyle, IL (9-132) Band; Drama; 4H;
VP, Jr Cl; Bsbl; HCt; VofDEM; Prom Waitress;
Lead, Sch Play; Batgirl; *SIU Edwardsville Col;*
Med Tech.

GHERNA, Mary Kathryn
Leuzinger HS; Lawndale, CA; CYO; Cpt, Chldr;
GS; InterClub Coun; F-Ed, Sch P; Ski C; SC; Secy,
Sr Cl; Tres, Jr Cl; VP, Soph Cl; Bsbl; Bkbl; Soccer;
Cpt, Sftbl; HCt; Hon Prog; Journ A; JA A; Swtht;
Pres, Fresh Cl; MVP, Sftbl; Vlbl; *UCLA; Psych.*

GHEZZI, Antonio Shiras
George O Robinson HS; Santurce, PR (6-47) NHS;
Pol Sci C; Ftbl; Wrest; COM; Hon Prog; Most Out.

GHOLSON, Kathy Marie
Eubank HS; Eubank, KY; Rptr, FHA; Sftbl; Sci
Fair; Chpt Homemaker; *Somerset Col; Practical*
Nurs.

GHOLSTON, Cassandra Camille
J Graham Brown HS; Louisville, KY;

GHOLSTON, Dawn Cameron
Suda E Butler HS; Louisville, KY; *Photography.*

GHOLSTON, Eric Bernard
Carroll HS; Monroe, LA (2-205) Pres, Hmrm; Phys
C; SC; Pres, Sr Cl; Ftbl; Tr; MLS; Most Out; Pres
A; YES A; Ldrship A; PA; *Alcorn U; Bus Mgmt.*

GHRIST, Jane
Greater Latrobe HS; Latrobe, PA; *Archt.*

GHRIST, Judith Ann
Greater Latrobe HS; Latrobe, PA;

GIACALONE, John Giacomo
Richmond Hill HS; New York, NY (19-576) Pres,
Fr C; K of C; Rptr, Sch P; Pres, Span C; Pres, Span
NHS; Bsbl; Tnns; COM; Hon Prog; Sci A; Spch A;
Arista Hon Soc; Eng Merit, Span Merit, A's; Schol
Achv, A; *Sci.*

GIACCI, Lisa Jo
Norwood Sr HS; Norwood, OH; Bus Mgr, Ann;
Chor; Fr C; Hmrm; NHS; Job's Daughters; Pep C.

GIACOMO, Brenda Leigh
Pinckneyville Comm HS; Pinckneyville, IL
(39-155) FHA; NHS; Span C; Spch C.

**GIAMFORTONE,
Joseph Edward**
Mt Pleasant HS; Mt Pleasant, TX (11-217) Pres,
CYO; Pres, Key C; NHS; Span C; Pres, SC; Pres,
Soph Cl; MVP, Bsbl; Bkbl; Ftbl; JV, Tr; Cl Fav;
Hon Prog; I Dare You; Opt A; *TCU; Pre-Dentistry.*

GIAMONA, Denise
Terra Linda HS; San Rafael, CA; *Dominican Col;
Elem Ed.*

GIANNECCHINI, Mary Ann
Saint Mary's HS; Stockton, CA (5-256) NHS; CSF.

GIANNONE, Lisa Mary
Acad of Our Lady of Mercy; Milford, CT (5-86)
Chor; Drama; ARC; Span C.

GIBB, Ruth Ellen
Union HS; Biggsville, IL; Band; MVP, Chldr; Chor;
Pres, Drama; Pres, NHS; DARGCA; HCt; Spch A;
Western Ill U; Eng.

GIBBAR, Valerie Elaine
Proviso W HS; Hillside, IL (76-900) Band; FHA;
NHS; Ski C; COM; Bronze Schol A; Silver Schol
A; *Baptist Bible Col; Missions.*

GIBBLE, Thomas Scott
Warwick HS; Lititz, PA (117-254) Fin, AFS; F-Ed,
Ann; Tres, Chor; Drama; Ensm; Order/Answer; F-
Ed, Sch P; SC; Order/Arrow A; Rotary Sr o-t Mo;
Eagle Sct A; Sch Mus; *Elizabethtown Col.*

GIBBONS, Chere Michele
Richardson HS; Richardson, TX (387-989) Chor;
Chaplin, Tri-Hi-Y; Tres, Richardson High Girls C;
Baylor U; Math.

GIBBONS, Kathleen Joyce
Niskayuna HS; Schenectady, NY; A Cap Choir;
Band; Chldr; Chor; Drama; Span C; Vet Explorers
Post; Food Ch & Secy, Church Yth Group; Folk
Culture C; Jr Prom Comm; *Mich St U; Vet Med.*

GIBBONS, Phillip B
Granville HS; Granville, OH (5-140) Band; Drama;
Tres, Bkbl; Cr-Ctry; JV, Soccer; Tr; Wrest; COM;
Hon Prog; Math A; NEDT; Ohio Mus Ed Assn;
Ntl Fr Test A; Ohio Tests, Schol Achv, Geo; *Math.*

GIBBONS, Sarah Marie
Ne HS; N Little Rock, AR (21-479) A Cap Choir;
Chor; FBLA; Mu Alpha Theta; NHS; *Harding Col;
Eng.*

GIBBONS, Tamara Marie
Faith Christian Acad; Florissant, MO (7-16) Bus
Mgr, Bus C; Chldr; Secy, Chor; Secy, Drama;
Ensm; Secy, Jr Cl; Vlbl; Secy A; *Tenn Temple Col;
Secy Sci.*

GIBBS, Charles Merrill
Permian HS; Odessa, TX (14-620) BS; Demolay;
JETS; Secy, Math C; NHS; Order/Arrow; Pres, Sci
C; SC; Tr; Amer Leg A; NMS; Eagle Sct; WW;
Rice U; Pre-Med.

GIBBS, Charles Stanley Jr
N Gwinnett HS; Suwanee, GA (15%-150) BC; Key
C; Chem A.

GIBBS, Garry Kent
Quincy HS; Quincy, IL; Tres, Band; Demolay;
Tres, 4H; Hmrm; Span C; SC; NEDT; Organ,
Piano, St Fair; Explorer; Stage Band; Tres, St Mary
Hosp; *Quincy Col; Psych.*

GIBBS, Jeanne Michelle
Powell Valley HS; Speedwell, TN; Secy, BC; FHA;
VP, Mu Alpha Theta; Tri-HiY; *Ga Tech; Archt.*

GIBBS, Julie Claire
Cooper HS; Abilene, TX (50%-550) Chldr; Chor;
Pres, FHA; Hmrm; Tri-HiY; Bkbl; Sftbl; Tr; COM;
Cl Fav; Most Out; Pres A; Swtht; *Abilene Christian
U; Phys Ed.*

GIBBS, Lisa Carolyn
Mattamuskeet HS; Swan Quarter, NC (6-75) Co-
Ed, Ann; Secy, BC; Fr C; Pres, 4H; Secy, Soph Cl;
Tnns; COM; Eng A; *E Carolyn U; Bus.*

GIBBS, Paul Clifford
Crystal River HS; Crystal River, FL (25-250) BC;
CYO; Fr C; Tr; *Central Florida Comm Col.*

GIBBS, Randolph McKinley
Moultrie Sr HS; Moultrie, GA; A Cap Choir; BC;
Chor; Drama; Ensm; Hon Prog; FFA, Star Green-
hand; *Georgia St; Vet Study.*

GIBBS, Robert Daniel
Loganville Jr And Sr HS; Loganville, GA (5%-100)
Drama; 4H; Span C; Pres, SC; Pres, Soph Cl; Ftbl;
Gov Honor Prog; *Young Harris Col; Religion.*

GIBBS, Robin Rue
Powell Valley HS; Speedwell, TN; BC; Tres, Mu
Alpha Theta; Secy, Mu Alpha Theta; *U of Tenn;
Interior Design.*

GIBBS, Ross James
Crystal River HS; Crystal River, FL (7-235) BC;
CYO; Tres, Fr C; InterAct C; Tnns; Mgr, Tr;
ROTC A; Fr A; Knights o-t Altar A; *Central Flor-
ida Comm Col; Elec.*

GIBBS, Sandra Dorthea
Henry Senachwine HS; Henry, IL (2-90) Drama;
Spch C; Var C; Sftbl; Tnns; Spch A.

GIBBS, Sherri Lynn
Martin Luther HS; Maspheth, NY;

GIBBS, Shirley Marie
Washington HS; Washington, NC (2-30) Band;
Chor; Drama; Ensm; FHA; Span NHS; Cpt, Tnns;
Star Student; Type A; Bible Stu A; *Elizabeth City
St U; Bus Adm.*

GIBBS, Stephanie Lyn
The Mac Duffie Sch for Girls; Springfield, MA
(10-13) Ski C; JV LaCrosse.

GIBBS, Theola
NE Acad; Manhattan, NY (2-26) Hon Prog; *Med.*

GIBBS, Timothy Dwayne
W Charlotte Sr HS; Charlotte, NC (47-617) Tres,
FBLA; SC; Gr Marshal; *U of NC; Journ.*

GIBBS, Valerie
Martin Luther HS; Maspeth, NY; Chor; Sftbl.

GIBE, Roberta Jean
Ambassador Christian Acad; Glassboro, NJ (7-18)
Ann; Chor; VP, Sr Cl; Bkbl; Hockey; Cpt, Sftbl;
MVP, Sftbl; Most Ath, Sr Yr; *Phys Ed.*

GIBEAUT, Cathy Jo
Nitro HS; Nitro, WV; Chldr; FBLA; VP, Hmrm;
NHS; Citz A; Type A; *W Va St U.*

GIBLIN, Jack B
Eastern Christian HS; N Haledon, NJ; Chess C;
Audio Visual Aids; Yth Group; Jr First Aid Sq;
Engr.

GIBO, Lauren Kiyomi
Maryknoll HS; Honolulu, HI (12-106) Hmrm;
NHS; Co-Ed, Sch P; Pres, SC; Journ A; NEDT; *U
of Hawaii; Psych.*

GIBOWSKI, Bonnie Jean
Alexander Hamilton Sr HS; Milwaukee, WI
(6-800) CYO; Hmrm; NHS; Span C; SC; Hon Prog;
Math A; Sci A; Span A; Eng A; *Marquette U; Nurs.*

GIBSON, Alice Diane
Pendleton HS; Pendleton, SC (25%-130) Band; Fr
C; Mgr, Bkbl; 4H A; Q&S A; Eng A; Sunday Sch
Teacher; Pom-Pon Squad; Church Yth Choir; HR;
Allied Yth C.

GIBSON, Barbara Lois
Washington Sr HS; Washington, MO (64-180) A
Cap Choir; JV, Chldr; Chor; Ensm; Orch; SC; Up
Bound; JV, Tr; *Sou Ill U; Mus.*

GIBSON, Betty Ann
Howard HS; Georgetown, SC (5-145) Sci C; Bkbl;
Sftbl; *Saint Augustine's Col; Bus Adm.*

GIBSON, Camelia
Nugent Center HS; Benoit, MS; Bio A; Hist A;
HQn; Most Out; *Alcorn St U; Agr Econ.*

GIBSON, Cindy Lynn
Pattonville HS; Maryland Hts, MO (81-820) Ed,
Ann; Chldr; GS; NHS; SC; Tres, Sr Cl; Sftbl; Citz
A; Hon Prog; Journ A; MLS; Q&S A; Sports Ed,
Sch P; Yrbk A; III Ldrshp Contest; Yrbk Layout
Design A; Activities A; *Ark St U; Pub Relations.*

GIBSON, Corrine Darlene
Estancia HS; Estancia, NM (5-67) Chor; 4H; Secy,
NHS; Swtht; Type A; Shorthand A; *U of NM; Secy
Stu.*

GIBSON, Deena Gay
Loop HS; Loop, TX (1-11) Co-Ed, Ann; Band; VP,
BC; Dbte Tm; VP, FHA; Rptr, Jr Cl; Rptr, Soph Cl;
Cpt, Bkbl; Tnns; Tr; Star Student; Val; Band Swtht;
Bkbl Qn; John Philip Sousa A; Farm Bureau Citz
Seminar; *Tex Tech U; Pol Sci.*

GIBSON, Donna Lee
Warwick HS; Newport News, VA (10-500) Span C;
Citz A; St Mus C Gold Cup; Fraternity of Stu Mus,
A; Eng, Span, A's; *U of Va; Phar.*

GIBSON, Donna Marie
S Choctaw Acad; Toxey, AL (3-26) Ann; Chor;
Mjrte; Tres, SC; Secy, Soph Cl; Beauty; Most Sch
Spirited; Best Personality; *Livingston U.*

GIBSON, Dorcas May
E Hills HS; Fort Worth, TX (70-600) VP, Span C;
Mgr, Tr; COM; Citz A; Lion A; *Eng.*

GIBSON, Dwayne Watkins
Meadowbrook HS; Richmond, VA (150-285) F-
Ed, Ann; HiY; Rptr, Hmrm; InterAct C; SC; Co-
Cpt, Bsbl; Co-Cpt, Bkbl; JV, Ftbl; Cpt, Tr; Journ A;
Yth Fel; Fin, Tr; Art A; *Photography.*

GIBSON, Elizabeth Ann
Bartow Sr HS; Bartow, FL (25-250) Anchor C; Ed,
Ann; Cpt, Chldr; Ensm; FHA; Hmrm; InterClub
Coun; Fin, Jr Miss Pagent; Secy, NHS; Sch P; SC;
Pres, Sr Cl; Pres, Jr Cl; Pres, Soph Cl; Swim; Tnns;
Beauty; Citz A; H of F; Interlochen Ntl Mus; Con-
geniality A; Essay A; *Stetson Col.*

GIBSON, Ellen Ruth
Martin Co HS; Stuart, FL (7-500) Hmrm; InterAct
C; NHS; SC; HQn; HCt; Pres A; Sci A; Swtht; Type
A; Yth Fel; Kickoff Qn; *U of Mich; Phys Therapy.*

GIBSON, Gregory Stuart
Jacksonville Sr HS; Jacksonville, NC; Band; CYO;
Fr C; InterClub Coun; Key C; Jr Cl Senator; Nom,
Gov Sch; *Elec Engr.*

GIBSON, Howard Andrew
Collegiate Sch; Passaic, NJ; Chess C; Demolay;
NHS; Bus Mgr, Sch P; SC; Bsbl; Bkbl; Golf; Alg A;
Hist A; Hon Prog; Math A; Yth Fel; *Rutgers; Acct.*

GIBSON, Janice Maria
Howard HS; Georgetown, SC; Band; Drama; VP,
NHS; Hon Soc Cert; *U OfSC; Nurs.*

GIBSON, John Alan
Patrician Acad; Butler, AL (3-40) BC; NHS; VP,
SC; Pres, Soph Cl; *U of Ala; Law.*

GIBSON, John Gilbert
Days Creek HS; Days Creek, OR; Band; Chor;
Rptr, 4H; VP, NHS; VP, SC; Var C; VP, Soph Cl;
Bsbl; Bkbl; Ftbl; *Oreg St U; Air Navigation.*

GIBSON, John Grant
Lovett Sch; Atlanta, GA (12-140) Drama; Key C;
NHS; COM; Hon Prog; NMS; *Duke U; Biochem.*

GIBSON, Kathy Marie
Maumee HS; Maumee, OH; Ed, CYO; Chor; Y-
Tns; Bkbl; Sftbl; Tr; Sci A; Secy, Lutheran Yth
Organization.

GIBSON, Kenneth Winifred Jr
Greenville Sr HS; Greenville, TX (12-335) BS;
NHS; Span C; Cpt, Bkbl; Outst Sr A; *Tex A&M U;
Pre-Dental.*

GIBSON, Kimberly Josephine
Jacksonville Sr HS; Jacksonville, NC (99-495)
CYO; Fr C; Secy, FHA; Jr Miss Pagent; Health
Occupations C; Secy, Med Explorers; *Atlantic
Christian Col; Nurs.*

GIBSON, Kimberly Lynn
Oak Ridge Acad; Oak Ridge, NC (8-30).

GIBSON, Letha Carol
Killeen HS; Killeen, TX; Band; Chor; Spch C; Secy, SC; S-T, Jr Cl; Cl Fav; Spch A; Drill Tm; *Bus Adm.*

GIBSON, Linda Rae
Coronado HS; Colo Springs, CO (17-500) Chor; Madrigal; NHS; Orch; Ski C; Span C; Hon Prog.

GIBSON, Lisa Kay
Port Richmond HS; Staten Island, NY; Chldr; Model UN; Tnns; *Hampton Inst; Modeling.*

GIBSON, Margaret Eileen
Rock Island Sr HS; Rock Island, IL (9-548) Band; Fr C; NHS; Ski C; Spch C; Hon Prog; Spch A; Win, St Oratory; Presidential Clrm Rep in Wash DC; *U of Ill; Engr.*

GIBSON, Mark Sweeney
Colerain Sr HS; Cincinnati, OH (200-750) Var C; Y-Tns; Bsbl; Bkbl; Ftbl; Tnns; VICA; Graphic Communications C; Nom, Jr Boy o-t Yr; *Graphic Communications.*

GIBSON, Mary Eloise
Jackson HS; Jackson, AL; Bus C; FHA; Secy, NHS; *Patrick Henry St Jr Col; Bus Ed.*

GIBSON, Mary Lynn
Viburnum C-4 HS; Viburnum, MO (13-66) Band; Chldr; Pres, Chor; FHA; Sch P; SC.

GIBSON, Michelle Adrian
Regina HS; Cincinnati, OH (35-116) Ann; Pres, CYO; Chldr; Fr C; Bkbl; MLS; Most Out; *Syracuse U; Journ.*

GIBSON, Mike Jerome
Sooner HS; Bartlesville, OK (10%-300) Fr C; Bsbl; Cr-Ctry; Soccer; Tr; St Hon Soc; *U of Okla; Journ.*

GIBSON, Nancy Ellen
S Choctaw Acad; Toxey, AL (2-33) BC; Chldr; NHS; Beauty; Sal; *Livingston U.*

GIBSON, Penny Carol
S Choctaw Acad; Toxey, AL (8-33) Ann; BC; Chor; NHS; Secy, SC; VP, Sr Cl; Secy, Jr Cl; Bkbl; Sftbl; Cl Fav; Hist A; MLS; Best Dressed; Neatest.

GIBSON, Rhonda Ann
Hazelwood E HS; St Louis, MO; A Cap Choir; Ann; Band; Chess C; FHA; Ger C; 4H; Bkbl; Hockey; Sftbl; Secy, Yth Fel; *Eng.*

GIBSON, Richard
Chicora HS; Charleston, SC; ARC; Semi-Fin, SC; MVP, Ftbl; Amer Leg A; Math A; *SC St U; Med.*

GIBSON, Sheila Denise
Jesse H Jones HS; Houston, TX; Hmrm; Secy, Jr Cl; Bkbl; Swim; Tnns; COM; MLS; Most Out; Sci A; Fr A; *Secy.*

GIBSON, Stanley Jay
Pendleton HS; Pendleton, SC (20-110) Tres, FFA; VP, 4H; Co-Cpt, Bkbl; Citz A; Cl Fav; 4H A; Allied Yth; Ntl 4-H Congress; Bus Driver; St 4-H C, A, Star Chapter Farmer, FFA; Ntl FFA Convention; *Clemson U; Agr.*

GIBSON, Tammi Jo
Lancaster Mennonite HS; Lancaster, PA; A Cap Choir; Hockey; *Lancaster Bible Col; Bible.*

GIBSON, Terry Lynn
San Angelo Central HS; San Angelo, TX (20%-800) *Angelo St U; Art.*

GIBSON, Tracy Layne
Perryton HS; Perryton, TX; Bsbl; Bkbl; Ftbl; Golf; *Bethany Nazarene Col; Bus.*

GIBSON, Venita Louise
Bosse HS; Evansville, IN (10-20) Arch; MVP, Bsbl; Bkbl; Tr; COM; Citz A; Pres A; Sci A; *Bloomington Col; Bus.*

GIBSON, Virginia Mae
Matoaca HS; Ettrick, VA (33-148) Band; Secy, Chldr; Fr C; Pres, FHA; 4H; Monogram; SC; Var C; *Hampton Inst; Elem Ed.*

GIBSON, Wanda Elaine
Estill HS; Estill, SC; Chor; FHA; Sch P; Rptr, Soph Cl; *Paine Col; Bus Adm.*

GIBSON, William Scott
Jonesboro HS; Jonesboro, AR (20-430) Ann; FBLA; Ftbl; *U of Ark; Law.*

GIDDENS, Connie Lynn
South Hills HS; Pittsburgh, PA; Chor; *Ind U of Pa; Sociology.*

GIDDINGS, Sarah Delano
Paramus HS; Paramus, NJ; Chor; Dbte Tm; NFL; Sch P; JV, Bkbl; *Hampshire Col; Pol Sci.*

GIEBELHAUS, Cheryl Ann
Kent-Meridian HS; Kent, WA; A Cap Choir; Band; Ensm; NHS.

GIECK, Diane Marie
Waunakee HS; Waunakee, WI (28-148) AFS; Ann; Bus C; 4H; Sftbl; Hon Prog; *Madison Area Tech Col; Printing.*

GIEGOLD, Jane Ellen
Secaucus HS; Secaucus, NJ (52-164) Chor; Sch P; Del, Douglass Col Citizenship.

GIENGER, Jeffery Arthur
Tillamook HS; Tillamook, OR (32-180) Pres, A Cap Choir; Chor; Mod Mus Mas; NHS; Bkbl; Ftbl; Tr; *Linfield Col; Bus.*

GIERE, Amy Louise
Coldwater HS; Coldwater, OH; Band; Pres, CYO; Drama; Span C; SC; Swim; JV, Vlbl; CYO Bkbl; Relig Ed o-t Mentally Handicapped; *Special Ed.*

GIERE, Timothy Eugene
Coldwater HS; Coldwater, OH (33%-170) Ann; Chor; Drama; Ger C; SC; Thes; Bsbl; Tr; Cl Fav; Pres A; Squires; Religion Teacher A; CCD Instructor; Ed Comm; Community Affairs Comm.

GIERHAN, Marcia Lynne
Lakewood HS; Lakewood, CA; Chldr; Chor; NHS; CSF; Principal's HR; *Calif St U; Teacher.*

GIERHAN, Teresa Sue
Lakewood Sr HS; Lakewood, CA; Chldr; Chor; NHS; Bkbl; CSF; Principals HR; *Calif Sch of Tech; Math.*

GIERINGER, Cindy S
Shawnee Mission S HS; Leawood, KS; A Cap Choir; Chor; Ensm; SC; Citz A; *Med.*

GIERMANN, Wayne Carl
Bloomington HS; Bloomington, IL (97-418) JA A; *Ill Central Col; Data Processing.*

GIERTZ, Gregory William
Bellflower HS; Bellflower, IL (5-14) Band; Chor; VP, FFA; Pres, 4H; Sci C; Span C; Var C; Pres, Sr Cl; VP, Jr Cl; Bsbl; Bkbl; Tr; 4H A; *Parkland Col; Agricultural.*

GIES, William Edward Jr
Scott Comm HS; Scott City, KS (27-110) A Cap Choir; Band; Chor; Ensm; SC; Var C; Co-Cpt, Bkbl; Ftbl; Tr; Lion A; Yth Fel; All League Ftbl; Dist Band; I Rating, St Mus; All Star Sr League Bsbl; *Southwestern U; Secondary Ed.*

GIESE, Beth Ann
Suring HS; Suring, WI (23-61) Ann; Band; Chor; Drama; FHA; Madrigal; Ski C; Var C; Cpt, Bkbl; Cpt, Tr; Cl Fav; Most Out; Spch A; MVP, Cpt, Vlbl; Phys Fitness A; St Choir A; Co Pres, Yth As for Retarded Citz; *Northwest Tech Inst; Operating Room Asst.*

GIESE, Jeffrey Warren
Bloomington HS; Bloomington, IL; Fr C; Bsbl; Bkbl; Ftbl; Golf; Cl Fav; *U of Ill.*

GIESENSCHLAG, Russell Lee
Clairemont HS; San Diego, CA (25-682) Drama; Ensm; Madrigal; VP, SC; Thes; Bank Of Amer A; CSF; MLS; *San Diego St U; Theater Arts.*

GIESON, Jill Gay
Hilliard HS; Hilliard, FL (10-76) *U of Columbia; Bus.*

GIEST, Jerry Douglas
Highland HS; Albuquerque, NM (300-700) A Cap Choir; Band; Chess C; Chor; Pres, Demolay; COM; Interlochen Ntl Mus; All St Chor; Up With People; *Mus.*

GIETT, Julie Marea
Parkwood HS; Joplin, MO (15-346) BC; Chor; Drama; NHS; Orch; Rainbow; Thes; NMF; Dist Outst Stu; WW; Mus & Fr A's; *SW Baptist Col; Mus.*

GIFFHORN, Diana Lynne
Tremont HS; Tremont, IL (6-84) Ed, Ann; Band; Chor; FHA; Cpt, Mjrte; Math C; NHS; Spch C; Math A; St Scholar; Yth Fel; TV Tech & Camera Operator; Points Ch, GAA; *Wheaton Col; Elem Ed.*

GIFFIN, John Lawrence
Moreau HS; Hayward, CA (27-310) Dbte Tm; Hmrm; Mu Alpha Theta; NFL; Spch C; Var C; Tr; Wrest; Hon Prog; Ntl Sci Found; Ntl Sci Symposium; Spch A; *Roses-Hulman Inst of Technology; Math.*

GIFFIN, Lisa Joan
Frankfort HS; Ridgeley, WV (10%-139) Band; FHA; 4H; NHS; Secy, Jr Cl.

GIFFORD, Cheryl Lynn
Wayne Comm HS; Corydon, IA (30-75) Chor; Sftbl; Spch A; *Psych.*

GIFFORD, Mary Marchant
N Fulton HS; Atlanta, GA (9-198) BC; Drama; Hmrm; InterClub Coun; Lat C; Co-Ch, Model UN; NHS; Ed, Sch P; SC; VP, Jr Cl; COM; H of F; Hon Prog; Journ A; NMF; Francis C Tucker A; *U of Ga; Art.*

GIGER, Patricia Annette
Weston McEwen HS; Athena, OR (1-41) Ann; Chldr; Drama; FHA; NHS; ARC; Sch P; Span C; SC; Thes; Var C; Sftbl; Tr; Alg A; Math A; Type A; Vlbl; *Blue Mountain Comm Col; Elem Ed.*

GIGER, Sherri Lanelle
Weston-McEwen HS; Athena, OR (3-33) Chor; Secy, FHA; NHS; Pres, Span C; Type A; Best Cl Singer; Most Friendly; *Nurs.*

GIGLIOTTI, Joanne Michelle
Swissvale Area HS; Pittsburgh, PA (10%-150) VP, A Cap Choir; Chldr; Chor; VP, Fr C; A-Ed, Sch P; SC; Y-Tns; Amer Leg A; Sci A; *U of Pittsburgh; Dental Nurs.*

GIKAS, Kathleen Ann
El Camino HS; Woodland Hills, CA; Band; Chldr; Drama; Hmrm; Orch; HCt; *Calif St U at Northridge; Retail Bus.*

GIL, Irene
Sylmar HS; Sylmar, CA; Ensm; Hmrm; SC; *Bus.*

GIL, Lily Louise
Sylmar HS; Sylmar, CA (2-600) Ensm; Hmrm; Ed, Sch P; CSF; COM; Rptr Journ A; *LA Mission Col; Phys Ed.*

GILBAUGH, JoAnn Lynn
Fairmont HS; Fairmont, MN; Band; Chor; Fr C; 4H; Tnns; 4H A; Hon Prog; Yth Fel; Choir Hon Group; *Winona Col; Mus.*

GILBERT, Angela Jean
Red Bank HS; Red Bank, TN (61-363) Chldr; Hmrm; Sci C; Secy, Span C; Secy, SC; Tri-HiY; Tres, Sr Cl; Tres, Jr Cl; Tres, Soph Cl; Sftbl; Yth Fel; *Middle Tenn St U; Bus.*

GILBERT, Barbara Dianne
Ellen McCarter Stewart Sch; Houston, TX (10%-20) Model UN; Spch C; Sr Cl; Val; Skiing.

GILBERT, Carole Lynn
Bremerhaven American HS; Bremerhaven, GERMANY (5%-31) Hmrm; NHS; SC; Hist A; HCt; Type A; Vlbl; Acct A; Eng A; *U of Ga.*

GILBERT, Cindy Jean
Schuylkill Haven HS; Schuylkill Haven, PA (23-116) F-Ed, Ann; Chor; Ger C; Sch P; Mgr, Bkbl; Sftbl; WW; *Point Park Col; Journ.*

GILBERT, Collette Ami
East HS; Denver, CO (190-560) Chess C; Up Bound; *Drew U; Med.*

GILBERT, Darrell William
Mason City HS; Mason City, IA (5%-400) Chor; Bkbl; Tr; Type A; 4 0 GPA As; Presidential Phys Fitness As; Sports Ltr; *Iowa St U; Engr.*

GILBERT, Gerri Lynn
Sullivan Central HS; Blountville, TN (20-525) BC; Chldr; Lat C; Sch P; Var C; Hist A; HQn; HCt; Hon Prog; Best All Around; Candidate, Optimist A; FCA C; Pep C; *U of Tenn; Sci.*

GILBERT, Jean-Marc
Alexander Galt Regional HS; Lennoxville, CANADA (9-477) Cpt, Band; BS; Hon Prog.

GILBERT, Joann Marie
McLoud HS; McLoud, OK (7-85) Band; Chor; FHA; NHS; Span C; Hon Prog.

GILBERT, Karen Lynn
Blacksburg HS; Blacksburg, VA; Chor; Span C.

GILBERT, Karen Sue
Charlottesville HS; Charlottesville, VA; FBLA; FHA; Sodality; *Madison Col; Phys Therapy.*

GILBERT, Lara Ann
Norcross HS; Norcross, GA (7-200) VP, A Cap Choir; Ed, Ann; Cpt, Band; Chor; Drama; Ensm; FTA; GS; HiY; Jr Miss Pagent; Lit Ral; Orch; Sch P; SC; Thes; Secy, Jr Cl; Sftbl; Cl Fav; HCt; Miss NHS; Piano As; Chor As; Demolay Swtht; *U of Ga; Mus Ed.*

GILBERT, Loretta Jo
Doland HS; Doland, SD (6-30) A-Ed, Ann; Band; Chor; Tres, FHA; Rptr, FNA; GS; 4H; Madrigal; Monogram; NFL; Mgr, Tr; Citz A; 4H A; Type A; Co Pork Qn; Outst Fresh A; *SD St U.*

GILBERT, Mary Lynne
Grimsley Sr HS; Greensboro, NC (10%-500) Community Yth Symph; Fr C; NHS; Orch; Bkbl; Sftbl; Yth Fel; Co-Cpt, Vlbl; Pres, MYF; Dist Yth Coun; *UNC Chapel Hill; Computer Sci.*

GILBERT, Robert Frank
Jonathan Dayton Regional HS; Springfield, NJ (59-400) BS; Chor; Drama; Pres, Ger C; Rptr, Sch P; Thes; Bsbl; Cr-Ctry; Hockey; Amer Leg A; WW; *U of Hartford; Mus.*

GILBERT, Sheila Renee
S Choctaw Acad; Toxey, AL (5-33) Ed, Ann; Secy, BC; Cpt, Chldr; Chor; NHS; Pres, Var C; Secy, Sr Cl; Secy, Jr Cl; Secy, Soph Cl; Beauty; Citz A; Cl Fav; HCt; I Dare You; Most Out; Best Dressed; *Livingston U; Fashion Merchandising.*

GILBERT, Steven LeRoy
Flint N HS; Flint, MI (91-628) Parl, Bus C; Hon Prog; JA; *Baker Jr Col; Acct.*

GILBERT, Terri Lynette
Calico Rock HS; Calico Rock, AR (2-33) Ann; Tres, BC; Pres, Chor; Fr C; FBLA; Bio A; *Bus.*

GILBERT, Winston Ivan Keith
Ashland HS; Ashland, AL; FFA; Var C; Ftbl; Sftbl.

GILBERTSON, Christine Jannan
Highland HS; Highland, WI (9-49) Ann; Chldr; Chor; Drama; 4H; Model UN; Ski C; Soph C; Var C; VP, Sr Cl; B Crocker A; 4H A; HCt; JA A; *UW Platteville; Dietetics.*

GILBERTSON, Rodney Lynn
Highland HS; Highland, WI (18-46) Arch; Band; Secy, FFA; NFL; Spch C; Bkbl; Ftbl; Golf; Tnns; Spch A; Solo and Ensm; Prom Ct; Ltr Win, Ftbl; FFA A; SS Teacher; *Oshkosh Col; Psych.*

GILBERTSON, Sonya Rae
River Valley HS; Spring Green, WI (9-175) A Cap Choir; Band; Chor; Ensm; 4H; Madrigal; 4H A; Gym; Outst Mus, Choral Directors, A's; *NW Col; Mus.*

GILBERTSON, Sue Ann
Highland HS; Highland, WI (4-46) Band; Chldr; Chor; Sci C; SC; Sftbl; Swim; HCt; 3 Yrs Solo and Ensm.

GILBRETH, Jimmy Mark
Kubasaki HS; Okinawa, JAPAN (8-355) VP, Chess C; Hmrm; NHS; Pres, Order/Arrow; ARC; SC; COM; Hon Prog; Eagle Sct; Lat A; Elec A; Chain Gang, Ftbl; *Air Force Acad; Med.*

GILCHRIEST, Gail
Silsbee HS; Silsbee, TX (25-350) Fr C; Mgr, Mjrte; Bus Mgr, Sch P; Tnns; *U of Tex; Journ.*

GILCHRIST, David Zenaieda
Bell Voc HS; Washington, DC; Cpt, Chor; Ch, Hmrm; VP, Soph Cl; JV, Bkbl.

GILCHRIST, Scott William
Bellevue Sr HS; Bellevue, NE (281-851) Span C; Ftbl; Tr; Attendant, Sadie Hawkins; Cand, Outst Soph; *U of Nebr; Bus.*

GILDAY, Bonnie Louise
Harlingen HS; Harlingen, TX (235-609) A Cap Choir; Ann; Cpt, Chldr; SC; Bkbl; Tnns; Beauty; Swtht; Yth Fel; HR; Keywanettes; FCA; Fin, Miss Ntl Tn of Amer; Fin, Miss Rebel Days; Nom, DAR Good Citz A; *Tyler Jr Col; Fashion.*

GILDEA, Norma
Seekonk HS; Seekonk, MA (20-224) Tr; *Wheaton Col; Art.*

GILDROY, Doreen Marie
Madame Curie HS; Chicago, IL (27-788) Chor; Drama; Hmrm; Span NHS; Thes; COM; Citz A; Hon Prog; ARC A; Sci A; Gym; Drama A; Pres Phys Fitness A; Pep C; Media Aide; VP, Christian Fire; *Nurs.*

GILES, Barbara Carol
Baker HS; Columbus, GA (12-250) Hmrm; Co-Ed, Sch P; Bsbl; Sftbl; Cl Fav; *Columbus Col; Journ.*

GILES, Beth Anne
Field HS; Mogadore, OH (6-236) Secy, Bus C; NHS; COM; Hon Prog; Type A; Shorthand A; Penmanship A; *Allegheny Wesleyan Col; Ed.*

GILES, Cynthia Darlene
Pendleton HS; Pendleton, SC; BC; Cpt, Chldr; Fr C; 4H; VP, Hmrm; SC; 4H A; Lion A; Fr A; *Clemson U; Pre-Med.*

GILES, Edna LaZetta
Kingstree Sr HS; Kingstree, SC (2-204) SC; Bio A; Hon Prog; *Performing Arts.*

GILES, Gretchen Erika
Wallace HS; Wallace, ID (28-101) Fr C; Ger C; Lat C; Lat NHS; Swim; Tnns; Math A; S-T, VICA; 2 Yrs Span Stu, Mexico; Lat Hon Soc; Most Artistic; *U of Puget Sound; Occupational Therapy.*

GILES, Janis Kay
Oswego Sr HS; Oswego, IL (80-360) Band; 4H; Ski C; Var C; Bkbl; Co-Cpt, Hockey; Sftbl; Tnns; MVP, Hockey; All Conf Bkbl; *U of Ala; Deaf Ed.*

GILES, Jill Ann
Crystal Lake Comm HS; Crystal Lake, IL (73-535) A Cap Choir; S-T, AFS; Arch; Chor; Drama; Ensm; Secy, Fr C; French NHS; Ger C; Hmrm; Madrigal; NHS; Ed, Sch P; Sci C; Ski C; Thes; Arch; Beauty; COM; Citz A; Hon Prog; Journ A; Yth Fel; *U of Colo; International Relations.*

GILES, Karen Marie
Montclair HS; Montclair, NJ; Chldr; Chor; Commercial C; Drama; Hmrm; Jr Miss Pagent; Madrigal; Orch; Sch P; SC; Bkbl; Soccer; Sftbl; Swim; Tr; COM; MLS; Most Out; Yth Fel; Drill Tm; Mat Maids; *Calif St U; Bio.*

GILES, Karen Stacy
San Carlos HS; San Carlos, CA; Cpt, Chldr; S-T, Jr Cl; S-T, Soph Cl; Sftbl; Mgr, Tr.

GILES, Linda Gail
San Carlos HS; San Carlos, CA; ARC; SC; Sftbl; NMS; Church Group; Job's Daughters; *San Diego St U; Bus Adm.*

GILES, Mary Laceada
South Choctaw Academy; Toxey, AL (7-32) Ann; BC; NHS; Best All Around; Rebelette.

GILES, Percy Wesley
Lew Wallace HS; Gary, IN; Band; Bsbl; Cr-Ctry; Citz A; Type A; *Purdue U; Elec Engr.*

GILES, Remonia Lisa
Baker HS; Columbus, GA (10-450) Chor; FHA; 4H; Pres, Hmrm; Math C; ROTC A; Principals List; HR; Drill Tm; *Ga St U; Criminal Justice.*

GILES, Veronica Beatrice
Holy Family HS; Birmingham, AL (1-42) Chldr; Fr C; Hmrm; NHS; Hon Prog; *Tulane U; Mech Engr.*

GILFILLAN, Alisa Ann
York Comp HS; York, SC (7-261) Band; Sci C; Span C; Bkbl; *Math.*

GILFILLAN, Susan
Monte Vista HS; Monte Vista, CO (1-103) Band; NHS; Secy, Sci C; Secy, SC; Tr; Masonic A; NMF; Vlbl.

GILJUM, Paul William
Oakville Sr HS; St Louis, MO (65-504) Co-Ch, CYO; NHS; Order/Arrow; JV, Soccer; JV, Tnns; Order/Arrow A; Eagle Sct; *Research.*

**GILKESON,
Kristen Michelle Hammann**
Neshaminy-Langhorne HS; Langhorne, PA (300-650) Chor; 4H; Pres, InterAct C; Ed, Lit Mag; Sci C; 4H A; Hon Prog; NMS; Sr Coun; Sci Lab Asst; *Eastern Col; Bio.*

GILL, Brenda Ann
Raymond S McLain HS; Tulsa, OK; Hmrm; NHS; Tnns; COM; HCt; MLS; *Nurs.*

GILL, Carl Edwin
Menlo Sch; Menlo Park, CA (40-60) Sci C; JV, Bkbl; JV, Ftbl; JV, Tr; Math A; Sportsmanship A; Gifted Stu Inst; *Chem.*

GILL, Carol Denise
S R Butler HS; Huntsville, AL (5%-567) Ch, Anchor C; FHA; Hmrm; NHS; Sci C; SC; COM; Hist A; Sci A; Swtht; *Auburn U; Bus.*

GILL, David Kent
Panhandle HS; Panhandle, TX (1-59) Band; JV, Bkbl; Tr; Alg A; Journ A; Type A; Piano & Eng A's; *Acct.*

GILL, Deana Rae
Moses Lake HS; Moses Lake, WA (11-314) Band; Chor, Mjrte; NHS; Yth Fel; Jolly Old Chief Supporters; Egles A; *Big Bend Comm Col; Acct.*

GILL, Diana Elizabeth
S Gwinnett HS; Snellville, GA; FHA; JA A; Cpt, Drill Tm.

GILL, Jeffrey Lee
Tift Co HS; Tifton, GA; Tri-HiY; Cpt, Bkbl; MVP, Bkbl; Most Ath; *Abraham Baldwin Agr Col; Bus Adm.*

GILL, John A
Chester HS; Chester, PA (41-673).

GILL, Kathryn Elizabeth
Bartow Sr HS; Bartow, FL (18-300) Anchor C; Drama; Secy, FHA; NHS; F-Ed, Sch P; Hon Prog; Kiwanis A; Yth Fel; Gold Cup, Piano; 1st Cl GSct; WW; *Fla St U; Eng.*

GILL, Kevin Gerald
Imlay City HS; Imlay City, MI (16-167) BS; Pres, Fr C; Pres, NHS; Pres, Sci C; Secy, Var C; VP, Soph Cl; Cpt, Cr-Ctry; Tnns; HCt; MLS; Regent Schol; VofDEM; Regionals Forensics A; *U of Mich; Pre-Med.*

GILL, Michele Amanda
Cambridge-S Dorchester HS; Cambridge, MD (25-240) A Cap Choir; AFS; Chor; Drama; Ensm; Madrigal; NHS; Span C; COM; JA A; Most Out; *Goldey Beacom Col; Bus Adm.*

GILL, Randy Don
McMinnville Sr HS; McMinnville, OR (2-250) Band; Key C; F-Ed, Sch P; SC; Tnns; *Bus.*

GILL, Suzanne Elizabeth
Alhambra HS; Martinez, CA; Band; SC; Tnns; Tr; Rally C; Most Improved; Soph Cl Officer; *San Jose St U; Police Sci.*

GILL, Sylvia Renee
Chinle HS; Chinle, AZ (1-146) Dbte Tm; FHA; Model UN; NHS; Span C; *Pol Sci.*

GILL, Watson Ray
Malvern HS; Malvern, AR; A Cap Choir; Chor; Tres, Hmrm; F-Ed, Sch P; Spch C; *Henderson St Col; Bus.*

GILLAN, Steven George
Hinsdale Central HS; Hinsdale, IL (20-625) Band; Golf; *Bus.*

GILLARD, Cammie Yvonne
Parkwood HS; Joplin, MO; Chor; Ensm; Mus, Gym, A's; *Mo Sou St Col; Law.*

GILLASPY, John Dale
Willows HS; Willows, CA (5-136) Band; Drama; FFA; 4H; CSF; 4H A; VP, CSF; *U of Calif; Sci.*

GILLELAND, Carol Ann
Johnson HS; Gainesville, GA; Span C; *Gainesville Jr Col; Social Stu.*

GILLEN, Colleen Marie
Hannibal Central Sch; Hannibal, NY; Secy, AFS; NHS; VP, Jr Cl; *Biol.*

GILLEN, Esta Leah
Copeland HS; Copeland, KS (3-11) A Cap Choir; Ann; Band; Chldr; Chor; FHA; VP, 4H; A-Ed, Sch P; Co-Cpt, Sftbl; Fin, Tr; COM; 4H A; Math A; Pres A; Type A; *Dodge City Comm Col; Agr.*

GILLENTINE, Angela Dale
Tupelo HS; Tupelo, MS (12-400) Anchor C; Drama; GS; Spch C; St Stu Congress; SC; Thes; JV, Tnns; Cl Fav; God & Comm A; VFW Orator Semi-Fin; Honorary, Gov's Staff; *U of Miss; Pol Sci.*

GILLESPIE, Claire Ellen
Ridley Sr HS; Folsom, PA (368-810) Band; Chor; VP, InterAct C; Ski C; COM; VFW A; Safety Patrol A; Hospital Vol A; *Nurs.*

GILLESPIE, Claire Euen
Ridley HS; Folsom, PA (250-810) Band; VP, Inter-Club Coun; Ski C; Citz A; VFW A; Yth Fel; Church Chor; Safety A; Hospital Vol A; *Nurs.*

GILLESPIE, Darlene
M T Blount HS; Prichard, AL (90-463) Band; Pres, Chor; Tres, Hmrm; Hon Prog; Mardi Gras Qn; *Selma U; Mus.*

GILLESPIE, Georgetta Lyn
Greeneville HS; Greeneville, TN (66-193) F-Ed, Ann; Co-Cpt, Chldr; Sch P; Sftbl; HCt; Most Sch Spirit; *E Tenn St U; Airlines.*

GILLESPIE, John Francis Jr
Chaminade Col Prep; St Louis, MO (16-117) Band; CYO; Chess C; Dbte Tm; Drama; Model UN; NFL; NHS; A-Ed, Sch P; Spch C; Parl, St Stu Congres; Amer Leg Orator A; Bio A; Hist A; Hon Prog; NEDT; Opt A; Sci A; Spch A; Yth Leg; Ntl Merit Commended Stu; Amer Acad of Achievement; Academic Schol; *St Louis U; Pol Sci.*

GILLESPIE, John George III
H M King HS; Kingsville, TX (25%-400) Lat C; Mu Alpha Theta; *Tex A&I; Engr.*

GILLESPIE, Pamela Kay
Batavia HS; Batavia, IL (7-224) Band; Ensm; Math C; Orch; Ed, Sch P; Ski C; Hist A; Hon Prog; Math A; Dist Mus; *U of Ill; Elem Ed.*

GILLESPIE, Rhonda Renee
H M King HS; Kingsville, TX (5%-395) Secy, Band; Mu Alpha Theta; NHS; Orch; Gym; *Howard Payne U; Bus.*

GILLETTE, Charles Eugene
Leland HS; San Jose, CA; Wrest; Academic Achievement A; *San Jose U; Commercial Art.*

GILLETTE, Clayton Arthur
Bellingham HS; Bellingham, WA (100-300) Eagle Sct; Organist; Board of Dir, NW Yth Services; Yth Choir; Adult Choir; *Whitworth Col; Yth Ministry.*

GILLETTE, Scott Kevin
Linesville-Conneaut-Summit HS; Linesville, PA (1-88) Band; Chess C; Chor; Fr C; Hmrm; SC; Bkbl; Cr-Ctry; Soccer; Band Director's A; *Engr.*

GILLEY, Daniel Lee
Mann HS; Davin, WV (29-180) Band; Chess C; Pres, Hmrm; Tnns; Wrest; Bookkeeping A; All Co Band; *W Va U; Bus.*

GILLEY, Dwight Marion
Alexandria Sr HS; Alexandria, LA; Hmrm; SC; *LSU; Engr.*

GILLFILLAN, Dana Chris
Oak Harbor HS; Oak Harbor, OH (10%-200) Rptr, Ann; Band; Tres, 4H; Golf; Bausch & Lomb A; Hon Prog; Photographer, Ann; *Computer Tech.*

GILLHAM, Gregory Vernon
Berkley HS; Berkley, MI (5-550) Band; Dbte Tm; Sci C; Hon Prog; Yth Foundation A; Eagle Sct; *U of Mich; Engr.*

GILLHAM, Karla Dawn
Maysville HS; Maysville, OK (1-40) Chldr; FHA; Pres, NHS; Cpt, Bkbl; Tr; Alg A; COM; Citz A; Cl Fav; Gov Honor Prog; Hist A; HCt; Math A; Sci A; Type A; Superintendent's HR; *Okla U; Ed.*

GILLIAM, Arther L
Arsenal Tech HS; Indianapolis, IN; Bsbl; Mgr, Ftbl; *Woodshop.*

GILLIAM, Donald Lynn
Trezevant HS; Trezevant, TN (20%-41) Ann; BC; Semi-Fin, SS; VP, FFA; Bsbl; Bkbl; FFA A's.

GILLIAM, Geraro Conrad
Eastside HS; Paterson, NJ; Secy, Sci C; Schol Cert; YMCA; Boy's C; *Okla St U; Zoology.*

GILLIAM, James Renley
Pleasant Grove HS; Pleasant Grove, AL (11-140) Chem C; Wrest; *U of Ala; Engr.*

GILLIAM, John Sherman
Sw HS; Patriot, OH (2-50) Parl, BC; 4H; Sch Achieve Tm; Ed, Sch P; VP, Soph Cl; JV, Bkbl; 4H A; Hon Prog; St Scholar; Yth Fel; Cincinnati U Sch, Preparatory Mus; *Oral Roberts U; Mus Theory.*

GILLIAM, Pauline Lois
Wyandanch Mem HS; Wyandanch, NY (42-120) Band; Drama; Lat C; Mod Mus Mas; Span C; *Labortory Inst Tech Col; Fashion Merchandising.*

GILLIAM, Peggy Sue
Walnut Hills HS; Cincinnati, OH (80-420) Cum Laude Soc; Ger C; COM; Hon Prog; NMS; *Transylvania U; Bio.*

GILLIAM, Sheila Joyce
Treadwell HS; Memphis, TN (10-200) Chem C; Lat C; NHS; Bkbl; Golf; Tr; Bio A; COM; Hon Prog; ROTC A; Cpt, Church Sftbl; *Methodist Sch of Nurs; Pediatrics.*

GILLIAM, Susan Lorraine
Boone Comm HS; Boone, IA; Chor; Sch P; Span C; S-T, Yth Fel; Sch Ltr; Q & S.

GILLIAM, Timberley Ruth
Freedom HS; Morganton, NC (17-450) Anchor C; Ann; BC; Fr C; Hmrm; InterAct C; NHS; SC; NMS; Yth Fel; Church Yth Choir; JV, Vlbl; MYF; Jr Cl Coun; *UNC-Chapel Hill; Med.*

GILLIARD, Thomas Junior
Reid Ross Sr HS; Fayetteville, NC (20%-250) Sci C; JV, Ftbl; MVP; Tr; Citz A; Cl Fav; Cpt, Tr; *NC Central Col; Engr.*

GILLIEM, Laurie Ann
Jackson HS; Massillon, OH; Fr C; MVP; Tr; Cpt, Vlbl; Pres Phys Fitness A.

GILLILAND, John Douglas Jr
First Baptist Acad; Dallas, TX (25%-42) Bsbl; Co-Cpt, Bkbl; Co-Cpt, Ftbl; Golf; Tr; Cl Fav; *Baylor U; Law.*

GILLILAND, John Ervin
Mathiston HS; Mathiston, MS; BC; Var C; Ftbl; Cl Fav; *Ms St U; Bus.*

GILLINGHAM, Carol Ann
Albuquerque HS; Albuquerque, NM (21-641) VP, Chor; NHS; Orch; SC; Outst Alto; All-St Choir; *McMurry Col; Bi-Lingual Ed.*

GILLINGHAM, Sara Gail
Albuquerque HS; Albuquerque, NM; Band; Chess C; Ensm; Chor & Band Ltrs; All St Choir.

GILLIS, John Delbert Jr
LaSalle HS; South Bend, IN; 4H; 4H A; Pres, Church Yth Group; *Industrial.*

GILLIS, Lois Elaine
Huron HS; Huron, OH (50-200) Chem C; City Conf; Dbte Tm; Drama; Fr C; Fin, Lit Mag; Madrigal; Math C; Pres, Rainbow; Ed, Sch P; Sci C; Swim; COM; Curator A; Hon Prog; Masonic A; NEDT; Opt A; Poet A; Sanctuary Soc; Sci A; Spch A; Yth Fel; Accompanist, A Cappella Choir; Win, Ntl Speaker's Tour; N Ohio Arts Coun; Wurlitzer A; Bicentennial Courrier Project; *Samford U; Law.*

GILLIS, Mary Anne
Dover HS; Dover, NH (25-396) Pres, Chess C; Ger C; Lat C; Lit Mag; NHS; ARC; Rptr, Sch P; Y-Tns; NMS; *Wellesey Col; Eng.*

GILLIS, Renee Jean
Las Cruces HS; Las Cruces, NM (141-586) Pres, Bus C; FFA; 4H; NHS; COM; Most Out; Pres & Tres, DECA; SW Dist Pres, DECA; Fin, FFA Ornamental Contest; 1st Pl, Fruit & Nut Comp, FFA; *NM St U; Forestry.*

GILLMAN, Catherine Marie
Holy Cross HS; Marine City, MI (1-41) Arch; Hmrm; NHS; Rptr, Sch P; Ski C; SC; Var C; Arch; Bsbl; Bkbl; Sftbl; Swim; COM; Hist A; Hon Prog; Ntl Achv Schol; Opt Out Tn; Religion A; Outst Art A; *Olivet Col; Art.*

GILLQUIST, Patti Lynn
Park Center HS; Brooklyn Park, MN (100-600) Band; Hmrm; SC; Yth Fel; Candystriper A; Pit Orch; Band Mascot; *Mankato St Col; Nurs.*

GILLUM, Laura Lee
LaPorte HS; LaPorte, TX (80-360) NHS; SC; Thes; Cl Fav; Star Student; Cpt & Major; Drill Tm; *San Jacinto Jr Col; Bio.*

GILMARTIN, James Richard
Collinsville HS; Collinsville, OK (11-138) AFS; BC; NHS; Cpt, Bsbl; Cpt, Bkbl; Cpt, Golf; Cpt, Tnns; Cl Fav; Most Out; Star Student; Type A; MVP, Bsbl, Bkbl; Most Athletic; News Player o-t Wk.

GILMER, Elwood Vernon
Smithfield HS; Smithfield, VA (54-157) Ann; Chor; VP, FBLA; 4H; Hmrm; ARC; Ed, Sch P; SC; Var C; Bkbl; Ftbl; VP, VICA; *Columbia Bible Col; Bible.*

GILMER, Margaret Painter
Blacksburg HS; Blacksburg, VA (34-300) Chldr; Chor; Span C; Pep C; HR; *Madison Col; Hist.*

GILMER, Tanya Louise
Shelton HS; Shelton, CT; Band; BC; Cpt, Chldr; Secy, Crown & Scepte; Drama; 4H; Hmrm; Span C; SC; Bkbl; Sftbl; Tr; 4H A; Secy, Keyettes.

GILMER, Venessa Renay
Haralson Co HS; Tallapoosa, GA (7-190).

GILMORE, Daniel Bailey
Sunset HS; Dallas, TX; AFS; Key C; JV, Ftbl; Sftbl; Hon Prog; Pres, Yth Choir; Jr NHS; Yth Coun; Life Leadership; FCA; *Baylor U; Med.*

GILMORE, Irene Frances
Burke HS; Charleston, SC (13-151) Bus Mgr, FBLA; Secy, Hmrm; WW; *Palmer Tech Col; Stenography.*

GILMORE, James Marion Jr
Fairfield HS; Fairfield, AL; Band; BC; Chor; Pres, Key C; Bsbl; JV, Bkbl; COM; Chamber of Comm A; *U of Ala; Law.*

GILMORE, Jeffrey Lloyd
Zion Benton HS; Zion, IL (183-396) Pres, Bus C; Stu o-t Mo; Phys Ed A; *Col of Lake Co.*

GILMORE, John Frances
Reeds Spring HS; Reeds Spring, MO (25%-99) AFS; Math C; Span C; *Law.*

GILMORE, John Marshall
Chaminade-Julienne HS; Dayton, OH; Band; Chor; Fr C; Tr; COM; Citz A; Opt A; Spch A; Radio C; *Law.*

GILMORE, Julie Lynne
Vines HS; Plano, TX (50%-450) Band; FHA; NHS; Orch; Yth Fel; *Elem Ed.*

GILMORE, Katie
Wadley HS; Wadley, GA (13-72) Band; FBLA; Pres, FHA; Mjrte; Hist A; HQn; *Morris Brown Col.*

GILMORE, Kevin Michael
Bedford HS; Temperance, MI (1-475) Chess C; Ger C; NHS; Span C; Golf; Hon Prog; *Pepperdine U; Lib Arts.*

GILMORE, Marie Ann
Carroll HS; Monroe, LA; Fr C; Hmrm; SC; HCt; Hon Prog; *Sou U; General Bus.*

GILMORE, Michi Simore
Fair Park HS; Shreveport, LA; All Amer Yth; Jr Miss Pagent; Pres, Model UN; Rptr, Sch P; SC; Y-Tns; Arch; Tnns; Cl Fav; Coun of Teach A; God & Country A; HQn; I Dare You; Lion A; MLS; ARC A; Swtht; *Central Col.*

GILMORE, Rebecca Jane
Collinsville HS; Collinsville, IL (383-625) Bus C; Hmrm; Co-Cpt, Mjrte; SC; Soccer; Swim; JA A; *Belleville Jr Col; Data Processing.*

GILMORE, Samuel David
Lincoln HS; Dallas, TX; ROTC A; ROTC; *El Centro Col; Archt.*

GILPIN, Bruce Lloyd
Foxborough HS; Foxborough, MA (42-271) Chess C; Hmrm; Order/Arrow; SC; Var C; Bkbl; Ftbl; Tr; Wrest; Eagle Sct; *US Air Force; Elec.*

GILPIN, Gary Franklin
Anoka Sr HS; Anoka, MN (38%-823) Band; Secy, 4H; Orch; Cpt, Ski C; Cpt, Cr-Ctry; Ftbl; Hockey; Tr; Citz A; Cl Fav; God & Country A; Yth Fel; Cr-Ctry Ski C; *Moorhead St U; Agr.*

GILREATH, Nanette Aileen
Concord HS; Concord, CA (85%-450) Hmrm; Rainbow; Y-Tns; JV, Swim; Citz A; Cl Off.

GILREATH, William Russell II
Ashbrook HS; Gastonia, NC (25%-469) A Cap Choir; Pres, Band; Community Yth Symph; Ensm; Key C; Hon Prog; All St Band; Stage Band; Schol, Summer Mus Camp; *U of NC; Mus.*

GILSTRAP, Laura Ann
SW HS; St Louis, MO (37-500) Choir; Hmrm; NHS; SC; Swim; Hon Prog; Comm Recognition A; Top 15%, Cl; Chor A; WW; *Moody College of Bio Sci; Marine Bio.*

GIMENEZ, Steven Jarvis
Lead Hill HS; Lead Hill, AR (4-21) Ann; BS; FBLA; FFA; Secy, Key C; Sch P; Tres, Sr Cl; Tres, Jr Cl; Pres, Soph Cl; Bkbl; MLS; Type A; Lib C; *Ouachita Baptist U; Religion.*

GIMESON, Pam Sue
Orleans Public HS; Orleans, NE (3-30) Dbte Tm; NHS; SC; Hist A; Yth Fel; *Sci.*

GINGRICH, Carter
Everett HS; Alcoa, TN; AFS; Dbte Tm; Rptr, Drama; NFL; Spch C; JV, Bkbl; Soccer; Spch A; *Marine Corps Col; Aviation Tech.*

GINLEY, James Francis
St Ignatius HS; Cleveland, OH (20-267) CYO; NHS; Ftbl; Tr; Wrest; Hon Prog; Booster C; NML; *Bus.*

GINLEY, Michael Patrick
St Ignatius HS; Cleveland, OH (50-282) CYO; Hmrm; SC; Ftbl; COM; *Kenyon Col.*

GINN, David Domrese
Shaker Heights HS; Shaker Heights, OH (50-500) A-Ed, Ann; Hmrm; Rptr, Sch P; Co-Cpt, Soccer; Swim; St Swim Champs.

GINN, Jeffery Byron
Memphis Sr HS; W Memphis, AR (10-590) Bkbl; Co-Cpt, Cr-Ctry; Tr; Eng A; *Ark St U.*

GINN, Lelia Ellen
Newton Co Comprehensive HS; Covington, GA (5-300) BC; Jr Miss Pagent; Key C; Span C; Pres, Tri-HiY; Tr; COM; Gov Honor Prog; Rotary A; Top 10, Sr Cl; Art Merit A; Sr Superlative; WSB Great Young Amer; *U of Ga; Commercial Art.*

GINN, Paul Leland
W Memphis HS; W Memphis, AR (56-350) Pres, Chem C; Pres, Sci C; Bkbl; Cr-Ctry; Tr; PA; *Memphis St U.*

GINN, Sheila Anita
Muscle Shoals HS; Muscle Shoals, AL (10-180) Tres, Anchor C; Math C; Mu Alpha Theta; A-Ed, Sch P; Sci C; Span C; SC; Hon Prog; Math A; Pres A; *U of N Ala; Med.*

GINTZ, Glenn Nicholas
Chippewa Falls Sr HS; Chippewa Falls, WI (1-388) BS; Dbte Tm; Model UN; Span C; SC; Ftbl; Tr; NMS; Val; *USAFA; Engr.*

GIOIA, Samuel William
Sacred Heart Acad; Salem, OR (5-33) Rptr, Ann; Band; Pres, Chess C; Rptr, Sch P; Co-Ch, Sr Cl; Stu Rotarian; *Linfield Col; Communications.*

GIOVANELLI, David Jeremry
St Joseph's HS; N New York, NJ (81-232) CYO; SC; Pres, Jr Cl; Bkbl; Ftbl.

GIOVANETTI, Roberto
Dr Pila HS; Ponce, PR (8-688) A Cap Choir; Chem C; Pres, Chess C; Chor; Pres, Dbte Tm; Drama; Ensm; Hmrm; Lit Mag; Math C; Mod Mus Mas; NHS; ARC; Pres, Sch P; SC; Cpt, Bsbl; Bkbl; Bio A; COM; Citz A; Cl Fav; H of F; Hist A; Hon Prog; MLS; Most Out; Opt A; Star Student; VofDEM; 1st Prize, Sci Fair; Pres, Baptist Yth Organization; *Allegheny Col; Bio.*

GIOVANNIELLO, Josephine Angelina
Canarsie HS; Brooklyn, NY (11-945) Swim; *Psych.*

GIPSON, Catherine Marie
Franklin Co HS; Winchester, TN; Band; CYO; Secy, FHA; Tres, FTA; Most Trustworthy Stu; *Middle Tenn St U; Ed.*

GIPSON, Grady Lee
Florence HS; Florence, MS (10-150) BC; FFA; Cpt, Bsbl; Bkbl; Cpt, Ftbl; Sftbl; Alg A; COM; Hon Prog; Lion A; Math A; Yth Fel; *Hinds Jr Col; Elec.*

GIPSON, Patricia Ann
Holly Springs HS; Holly Springs, MS (75%-183) Ann; Chor; FHA; Hmrm; Up Bound; COM; Citz A; Hon Prog; Math A; Yth Fel; GSct A's; *Rust Col; Law.*

GIPSON, Robin Lee
Winter Haven Sr HS; Winter Haven, FL (25-750) Band; 4H; Lat C; NHS; Phys C; Sci C; Sftbl; Bio A; Type A; *U of Fla; Horticulture.*

GIPSON, Sanquenetta
Jackson S Abrams HS; Bessemer, AL (15-139) Secy, Band; Rptr, Chor; Fr C; Secy, Hmrm; Fin, Jr Miss Pagent; VP, Mjrte; Mod Mus Mas; VP, Soph Cl; Bkbl; Swim; Modeling A; Dancing A; Chor A; Band A; *Morehouse Col; Drama.*

GIPSON, Steve Michael
Portage Central HS; Portage, MI (200-350) Swim; Word of Life C; Most Improved, Swim.

GIPSON, Theresa Ann
Franklin Co HS; Winchester, TN; Band; Secy, CYO; FHA; FTA; *Middle Tenn St U; Ed.*

GIRARD, Frank Albert
La Puente HS; La Puente, CA; CYO; Drama; Thes; *Math.*

GIRARD, Kristina Marie
Battle Ground HS; Battle Ground, WA (1-400) Band; FFA; FHA; Span C; *Writing.*

GIRARDEAU, James Ward Jr
Robert E Lee HS; Baytown, TX (3-450) AFS; Ann; Band; Fin, BS; Lat C; Math C; NHS; MVP, Cr-Ctry; Tr; *Engr.*

GIRBACH, Mary Ann
Saline HS; Saline, MI (20-250) Band; FHA; 4H; NHS; Span C; 4H A; *U of Mich; Elec Engr.*

GIRDNER, Duane Lee
Creighton Comm HS; Creighton, NE (70-95) A Cap Choir; Arch; Chor; Ensm; Madrigal; SC; Bkbl; Ftbl; Pres A; ARC A; Sr Lifesaving A; Karate.

GIRDZIS, Amy Anne
Acad of Our Lady of Mercy; Milford, CT (4-88) CYO; Chldr; Chor; Drama; Fr C; Key C; Ski C; NEDT; DAR Sci A; *Math.*

GIRON, Lorinda Inez
Pojoaque HS; Santa Fe, NM (23-87) Band; Pres, Bus C; VP, 4H; Tres, NHS; SC; 4H A; Type A; Historian, Span C; *NM St U; Bus Adm.*

GISH, Alison Rae
John Adams HS; Ozone Park, NY (42-1076) Ed, Lit Mag; Math C; NHS; Co-Ed, Sch P; Pres, SC; Pres, Sr Cl; Pres, Jr Cl; Alg A; Gov Honor Prog; Hon Prog; Ch, Judean C; Century III Ldrs Sch Win; Eng Medal.

GISH, Michael Stanley
Battle Ground HS; Battle Ground, WA (70-420) NHS; Ed, Sch P; VP, SC; Var C; VP, Jr Cl; Bkbl; JV, Ftbl; Golf; Soccer; Tnns; Citz A; HCt; Hon Prog; *Clark Jr Col; Bus.*

GISH, Stacey Diane
Horton HS; Horton, KS (7-56) A Cap Choir; Band; CYO; Ensm; Fin, GS; Fin, Jr Miss Pagent; Mjrte; Pres A; Marion A; Pres, Keyettes; GSct; 1st Cl A; Cpt, Drill Tm; Parish Coun; *Benedictine Col; Dental Hygenist.*

GISI, Mardell Ann
Leola HS; Leola, SD; CYO; Rptr, FBLA; Rptr, FHA; Type A; St Off, FBLA; FHA Jr, Chapter & St Degrees; Beef Cook-Off; FBLA Asst Degree.

GIST, Gary
Klein HS; Spring, TX; Dbte Tm; Pres, JETS; Math C; Mu Alpha Theta; NFL; NHS; Spch C; Math A; NMF; NMS; Sal; Spch A; *Tex A&M U; Chem Engr.*

GIST, Joyce Darlene
Raymore-Peculiar HS; Peculiar, MO (46-147) Chor; FHA; FTA; Var C; Mgr, Bkbl; Sftbl; *Central Methodist Col; Child Psych.*

GIST, Melanie Lea
Central HS; W Helena, AR (20-360) Band; BC; Mjrte; Span C; Thes; Most Outst Band A; *'Ole Miss'; Sci.*

GITCHELL, Phyllis Pandora
Monache HS; Porterville, CA; Band.

GITTENS, Joseph Augustus Jr
Essex Catholic HS; Newark, NJ (10-35) Chess C; SC; JV, Ftbl; JV, Tr; COM; Hon Prog; Phys Fitness A; Cert of A Ftbl and Tr; *Drew U.*

GITTER, Dwayne
Harry S Truman HS; Bronx, NY (139-637) Chess C; Bsbl; Bkbl; Social Stu A; *Fordham U; Engr.*

GITTMAN, Cynthia Lynn
Dinwiddie Co Sr HS; Dinwiddie, VA (10%-350) Ann; Band; FBLA; FHA; Secy, Span C; Secy, SC; Bkbl; Tnns; COM; Secy, Church Yth Coun; Secy, Alpha Beta Sigma Sorority; Tres, FCA; Bkbl & Tnns Ltr; GAA; Superior, Regional Band Ensm; *Madison Col; Bus.*

GIUNTA, Susan
Huntington HS; Huntington, NY (10%-600) AFS; Band; Secy, Chor; Math C; NHS; Hon Prog; *Math.*

GIVANS, Rachelle Rena
Carol William Hayes HS; Birmingham, AL (10-150) Chem C; FBLA; Ger C; Secy, Hmrm; ARC; Pres, Sci C; Rptr, SC; Rptr, Sr Cl; Secy, Jr Cl; Rptr, Soph Cl; Bsbl; Tnns; Bio A; Chem A; HCt; Hon Prog; JA A; MLS; ARC A; Sci A; WW; Executive Internship Prog; VICA; Ger A; *Sanford U; Secondary Ed.*

GIVEN, Elizabeth Anne
Hightstown HS; Hightstown, NJ (51-253) Pres, FBLA; GS; NHS; Amer Leg A; COM; Hon Prog; Sci A; Type A; Schol Hon's; Special Commendation, GS, A; FBLA Bus Law, A; *Law.*

GIVENS, Brenda Ann
Motley HS; Columbus, MS (8-81) BC; Drama; FHA; Pres, 4H; Sch P; SC; Tri-HiY; Var C; Bkbl; Sftbl; Tr; Cl Fav; HCt; Math A; Eng A; *E Miss Jr Col; Social Sci.*

GIVENS, Jefferson Carr
Jefferson Davis HS; Montgomery, AL; Ann; Band; Ensm; VP, HiY; VP, Hmrm; Key C; Lat C; Co-Ed, Sch P; VP, SC; Tnns; JV, Tr; RA Service A; Pres, Yth Coun; *Auburn U; Mus.*

GIVENS, Jill Leigh
Watonga HS; Watonga, OK (15%-105) Ann; Band; Chldr; FBLA; NHS; *Southwestern Okla St U; Mus.*

GIVENS, Silas Wright
Daviess Co HS; Owensboro, KY (50-316) A Cap Choir; BC; Pres, Pol Sci C; Sci C; Ch, SC; Tnns; Bio A; *Vanderbilt U; Molecular Biol.*

GLAAB, Lyle Christopher
Williams HS; Williams, AZ (4-45) Band; Chess C; NHS; Sci C; Ftbl; Tr; Wrest; *Ariz St U; Archt.*

GLAD, Cynthia Marie
Jamestown HS; Jamestown, NY (50%-600) Band; SC; Swim; Yth Fel; Band A; *JCC; Elem Ed.*

GLADDEN, Diana Marie
Houston HS; Houston, MO; Band; Orch; COM; HR; Top Ten.

GLADDEN, Edgar Lyles
Houston HS; Houston, MO (5-122) Band; Ensm; NHS; Orch; SC; Bkbl; Ftbl; Tr; All Conf Ftbl; *U of Mo.*

GLADFELTER, Ann Elizabeth
Dallastown Area HS; Dallastown, PA (45-450) Lit Mag; Mjrte; Sch P; Var C; Bkbl; Co-Cpt, Vlbl; Yth Fel; *Computer Sci.*

GLADNEY, Vanessa Denise
Olympic Sr HS; Charlotte, NC (282-477) Chor; 4H; ARC; Sch P; Var C; Cr-Ctry; Tr; 4H A; JA A; ARC A; Church 52 C; *NC U at Durham; Journ.*

GLADSON, Jerry Allen
W Craven HS; Vanceboro, NC; FFA; Bsbl; Sportsmanship A; *Craven Comm Col.*

GLADSTONE, Jeff Dwight
Acalanes HS; Lafayette, CA (6-312) Ger C; CSF; Math A; Sci A; Ger A; Straight 'A' A; *UC Davis; Math.*

GLANDORF, Brenda Kay
Williamsburg Comm HS; Williamsburg, IA (5-97) Bus Mgr, Ann; Chor; FHA; NHS; Regent Schol; *Wartburg Col; Elem Ed.*

GLANDT, Marianne Kay
Lyons Township HS; LaGrange, IL (80%-1300) Tres, Jr Achv; Candystriping; *Nurs.*

GLASER, Alan Lawrence
Yough HS; Herminie, PA (15-300) Band; Pres, Chor; NHS; I Dare You; John Philip Sousa A; Choral A; *U of Pittsburgh; Chem.*

GLASER, Bruce William
Normal Comm HS; Normal, IL (214-491) VP, A Cap Choir; Band; Chess C; VP, Chor; Tres, Drama; Ensm; Hmrm; Co-Ch, Madrigal; Orch; Sch P; SC; Thes; Mgr, Bsbl; JV, Soccer; JV, Sftbl; Mgr, Swim; Valparaiso Col; Sacred Mus.

GLASER, Marilyn Agnes
Community HS; Houston, TX (10%-98) Band; InterAct C; NHS; SC; Math A; NEDT; Sci A; Vlbl; Free Style Ice Skating.

GLASGOW, Debra Kay
Southern HS; Durham, NC (50-295) Hmrm; NHS; Civinettes C; WW; NC St U; Sociology.

GLASGOW, Mary Jane
Bad Axe HS; Bad Axe, MI (14-167) Chor; Mjrte; NHS; Sci C; SC; Vlbl; Central Mich U; Lang.

GLASGOW, Wayne Collier
Henderson HS; Atlanta, GA (8-369) Chem C; Key C; Lat C; NHS; Bkbl; Ftbl; COM; DARGCA; Gov Honor Prog; Hon Prog; GA Merit Schol; Academic Bowl Rep; Pres, NHS; VP, Key C; Lat A; Ga Tech; Chem.

GLASPY, Cheryll Armentia
Plainfield HS; Plainfield, NJ (70-720) Band; Chor; Hmrm; Orch; Soph Cl; Tr; Hon Prog; Mus A; Drew U; Sci.

GLASS, Brian Thomas
Wes-Del HS; Gaston, IN (33%-120) Band; 4H; Order/Arrow; Sci C; Bkbl; Ftbl; 4H A; Order/Arrow A.

GLASS, Cecil Jr
Campbell of Fairburn HS; Fairburn, GA (30-120) Model UN; Order/Arrow; Sci C; VP, SC; Cpt, Golf; Tnns; Wrest; Pres, MYF; Pres, Sub District; Ga Tech; Nuclear Engr.

GLASS, Cheryl Ann
Hightstown HS; Hightstown, NJ (34-253) Bus Mgr, Ann; Fr C; NHS; SC; Hon Prog; Sci A; Shield & Key, Fr, A's; Trenton St Col; Bus Adm.

GLASS, Chester Karl
Thomas M Cooley HS; Detroit, MI (87-487) Pres, Bus C; French NHS; Bsbl; Cpt, Ftbl; U of Miami; Elec Engr.

GLASS, Cynthia Rena
Ripley HS; Ripley, TN (60-300) Ann; FHA; 4H; Hmrm; Var C; Mgr, Bkbl; UT-Martin; Bus.

GLASS, Debra Kay
Duncan HS; Duncan, OK (9-310) Band; FNA; NHS; Sci A; Okla Hon Soc; Tulsa Jr Col; Respiratory Therapy.

GLASS, Elizabeth Ann
Campbell HS; Fairburn, GA (10%-169) Band; BC; Lat C; Lat NHS; Golf; COM; Ga Tech; Math.

GLASS, Jeff Allen
Tyner HS; Chattanooga, TN (12-250) Bsbl; Bkbl; Ftbl; Tnns; Wrest; Yth Fel; U of Chattanooga; Computer Analysis.

GLASS, Jeffrey Taylor
Loch Raven Sr HS; Towson, MD (25%-470) Drama; VP, SC; Var C; Ftbl; Best All Around; Johns Hopkins U; Chem.

GLASS, John Brian
Lake Highlands HS; Dallas, TX (108-701) Key C; Hon Prog; Tex A&M U.

GLASS, Joseph Dinson III
Hickory HS; Hickory, NC (12-354) S-T, Key C; Tres, Span C; Cr-Ctry; Ftbl; Tnns; Cl Fav; VP, FCA; Jr Human Relations Coun; Best Blocker, Jr Ftbl Tm; Duke U; Engr.

GLASS, Linda Gail
Newton Co Comp HS; Covington, GA;

GLASS, Terri Lynn
Maranatha Baptist Acad; Watertown, WI (2-32) Band; Chor; S-T, Hmrm; S-T, Soph Cl; MVP, Bkbl; MVP, Sftbl; MVP, Vlbl; Cl Rep, Ntl Acad Meet; Bob Jones U; Mus.

GLASSCOCK, David John
Keokuk Sr HS; Keokuk, IA (1-204) NFL; NHS; Spch A; Southeastern Comm Col; Sci.

GLASSFORD, Brian Thomas
Nathan Hale HS; Tulsa, OK (200-690) AFS; Band; Chess C; Var C; Cpt, Bkbl; Golf; 4H A; Yth Fel; Yth Leg; Cpt & MVP, Sftbl; Okla St U; Wildlife Ecology.

GLASSFORD, Debbie Lee
Mt Juliet HS; Mt Juliet, TN; Fr C; FHA; Elem Ed.

GLASSFORD, Denise Lorrainne
Mt Juliet HS; Mt Juliet, TN; Chor; FHA.

GLASSFORD, Dianne Lynn
Mt Juliet HS; Mt Juliet, TN (25%-270) BC; Chor; FHA; Span C; Spch C.

GLAZE, Phillip Curtis
Clements HS; Athens, AL (1-52) F-Ed, Ann; Tres, BC; Chor; Pres, 4H; Cpt, Sch Achieve Tm; F-Ed, Sch P; Bkbl; Ftbl; Tr; Amer Leg A; Amer Leg Orator A; B Crocker A; Bio A; COM; Cl Fav; 4H A; Hist A; HKg; Journ A; NMS; Val; VFW A; VFW Orator Win; VofDEM; Martin Col Hon Schol; Most Intelligent; Woodmen o-t World, A; Athens St Col Biol, A; Auburn U; Pre-Med.

GLAZE, Teresa Lyn
S Central HS; Elizabeth, IN (20-70) Band; Drama; FHA; S-T, 4H; Mjrte; Tres, Mu Alpha Theta; Tres, Span C; Rptr, Soph Cl; Co-Cpt, Bkbl; Sftbl; Tr; Band A; PA; 4-H Round- up.

GLEASON, Bonnie Jeanne
Alta Loma HS; Alta Loma, CA (58-485) Chor; JV, Swim; Tn Missionary; Jr Church Teacher; Pres, VP, Church Yth Fel; Wheaton Col; Ed.

GLEASON, Edgar Hubert III
Trinity Heights HS; Shreveport, LA (20-65) Band; Var C; Ftbl; Soccer; Tr; FCA.

GLEASON, Jude V
Xavier HS; New York, NY (80-225) Pres, CYO; Lat C; Semi-Fin, NHS; Var C; Bkbl; Ntl Achv Schol; Vassar Col.

GLEASON, Lisa Ann
Lutheran HS; Burbank, CA (10-85) Parl, A Cap Choir; Chor; Ensm; CSF; St Joseph Mercy Sch of Nurs; Nurs.

GLEASON, Margaret Mary
Ennis HS; Ennis, TX (10%-250) Band; Dbte Tm; Drama; Tres, FTA; JETS; NHS; Spch C; Thes; Spch A; Pre-Law.

GLEASON, Mary Fay
Waukegan Christian Sch; Zion, IL; Ann; Lat C; Bio A; COM; Chem A; Hist A; Most Out; Star Student; Awana; Timothy, Meritorious, A's.

GLEDHILL, Nannette Louise
N Kingstown Sr HS; N Kingstown, RI; Yth Fel; U of RI.

GLEGHORN, Vicki Denise
Paris HS; Paris, TX; Chor; Ensm; FTA; Keywanettes.

GLEIN, Susan Elaine
Marysville-Pilchuck HS; Marysville, WA (20-396) Hmrm; Var C; Bkbl; Tnns; Tr; U of Wash; Math.

GLENDENNING, Michele Lynne
Galesburg Sr HS; Galesburg, IL (249-700) Chor; Drama; Pres, 4H; Lat C; Sch P; SC; 4H A; Hon Prog; I Dare You; Spch A; Flag Corps; Ch, Social Comm, Soph Cl; Cand, Soph Attendant, Wntr Formal; Christian Col; Teaching.

GLENN, Bernadine
Wendell Phillips HS; Chicago, IL; Chor; Fin, Crown & Scepter; Hmrm; NHS; Sch P; SC; Journ A; Yth Leg; Executive Secy.

GLENN, Cynthia Joann
Morgan City HS; Morgan City, LA; Band; FBLA; Ch, Rainbow; Nicholls St U; Nurs.

GLENN, Derek
Goodwater HS; Goodwater, AL (5-38) FBLA; FFA; 4H; Cpt, Var C; Cpt, Bkbl; 4H A; Most Studious Sr Cl; MVP, Bkbl; All-Co, Bkbl; Alex City Jr Col; Bus Adm.

GLENN, Dianne Kaye
Hamburg Comm HS; Hamburg, IA (2-37) Ann; Band; VP, FHA; NHS; Pres, Rainbow; Rptr, Sch P; Secy, Jr Cl; Sftbl; Law.

GLENN, Felisa Jo
Lafayette Sr HS; Lexington, KY; BC; Mu Alpha Theta; NHS; Span C; Span NHS; SC; Acct.

GLENN, Julie Katherin
Helena Sr HS; Helena, MT; Ann; Chldr; GS; Hmrm; SC; Cr-Ctry; Tr; U of Missoula; Ed.

GLENN, Karen Elisabeth
Shelby Co HS; Shelbyville, KY; Chor; Span C; Georgetown Col; Art.

GLENN, Karen Jo
Hartshorne HS; Hartshorne, OK (5-81) NHS; Bkbl; Tr; St Hon Soc; E Okla St U; Phys Ther.

GLENN, Kelly Owen
Angola HS; Angola, IN (37-170) Bkbl; Ftbl; Tnns; Yth Fel; Yth Foundation; Yth Leg; Rptr, VICA C; ICE C; Ind Perdue U; Bus.

GLENN, Reginald Gerard
Ripley HS; Ripley, TN;

GLENN, Theresa Ann
Daviston HS; Daviston, AL (1-13) Ann; BC; FBLA; 4H; Span C; Bkbl; Cl Fav; 4H A; U of Ala; Ed.

GLENNON, David Alexander
Harrison HS; Harrison, NY (31-280) Ski C; Cr-Ctry; Golf; Wrest; Bus.

GLENNON, Douglas Ross
Chaminade Col Prep; Creve Coeur, MO (36-128) Ftbl; Co-Cpt, Hockey; Swim; Tr; COM; Cl Fav; Hon Prog; Math A.

GLEYSTEEN, Guy
St James Sch; St James, MD (3-30) Dbte Tm; Lit Ral; Soccer; Cpt, Rugby; Reed Col; Hist.

GLICK, Heidi Ellen
Springfield N HS; Springfield, OH (5-430) Band; Community Yth Symph; Lat C; Orch; SC; US Marines Yth Found Outst Mus A; Oberlin Col.

GLICKLICH, Caren Marlene
Inglewood HS; Inglewood, CA; CSF; COM; Citz A; Hon Prog; UCLA; Med.

GLIDDEN, Kathryn Mearn
Westview HS; Braham, MN; Band; Cpt, Chldr; FHA; SC; Tr; Anolca Ramsey Jr Col.

GLIDDON, Susanne Lynn
Genoa-Kingston HS; Genoa, IL (10-123) S-T, Band; Chor; Drama; Ensm; Fr C; FFA; Madrigal; NHS; Ed, Sch P; Ski C; SC; Thes; Var C; MVP, Bkbl; Sftbl; Hist A; Pres A; Yth Fel; Cpt, Bkbl & Vlbl; Band A; U of Ill; Phys Ed.

GLIDEWELL, Barbara Gail
Burnsville HS; Burnsville, MS; BC; FHA; VP, Soph Cl; Bkbl; Ole Miss; Data Processing.

GLIDEWELL, Frank Armond Jr
Springville HS; Springville, AL (2-70) S-T, Band; BC; Ensm; Pres, 4H; Order/Arrow; A-Ed, Sch P; Bkbl; 4H A; Hist A; I Dare You; Order/Arrow A; Type A; 4-H Citz Trip; U of Ala; Aeronautical Engr.

GLIMPSE, Kelly Elizabeth
El Cajon Valley HS; El Cajon, CA; Campus Life; Scorer, Wrest; Vol; Hospital; Board of Directors, Yth Group; Mat Maid; Grossmont Jr Col; Dental Asst.

GLINKE, Karl Anthony
Eisenhower HS; Washington, MI (130-600) BS; Chem C; Community Yth Symph; Pres, SC; Var C; Pres, Sr Cl; Ftbl; Cpt, Wrest; Amer Leg A; NMS; Yth Leg; Coach, Yth Wrest Tm; Pres, Church Yth Group; Usher; Commentator; U of Mich; Engr.

GLINKE, Tim Joesph
Dwight D Eisenhower HS; Washington, MI; Band; Pres, CYO; Chess C; Drama; SC; Ftbl; Mgr, Wrest; Sci A; Macomb Comm Col; Bus.

GLISSON, Janice Glisson
Northeast HS; St Petersburg, FL; Chor; SC; Sftbl; Swim; Tnns; Hon Prog; Pres A; Mus.

GLISSON, Janice Marie
Northeast HS; St Petersburg, FL; Chor; 4H; Hmrm; Sftbl; Pres A; Mus.

GLISSON, Lisa Renee
Treadwell HS; Memphis, TN (7-172) Chem C; Hmrm; Lat C; Math C; Mu Alpha Theta; Tres, NHS; ARC; Rptr, Sch P; Span C; SC; COM; Union U; Math.

GLISSON, Raymond Harold
McKenzie HS; McKenzie, TN (50-79) Band; FFA; 4H; Lit Mag; Sftbl; Tr.

GLOCKNER, Cynthia Joan
Notre Dame HS; Portsmouth, OH (22-63) Chor; Span C; Tnns; Pep C; Vlbl; HR; *Shawnee St Col; Executive Secy.*

GLODEN, Sheila Kay
Guymon HS; Guymon, OK (50%-185) FFA; Bkbl; Tr; FFA Swtht; *Panhandle St U; Elem Ed.*

GLOGIEWICZ, Jeffrey Stanley
Notre Dame HS; Caguas, PR (35-136) Chess C; Drama; Hmrm; Pres, NHS; Pres, Order/Arrow; Spch C; SC; Pres, Var C; Semi-Fin, Tr; COM; Eagle Sct; Vigil Hon-OA; Academic Excellence A; Spelling Bee, Regional Win; *SUNY; Forestry.*

GLOMB, William Brendle
Brazoswood HS; Clute, TX; A Cap Choir; Pres, Chem C; Chor; Drama; JETS; NHS; Sch P; VP, Span C; Cr-Ctry; Co-Cpt, Soccer; Swim; Tr; Chem A; Opt A; *Duke U; Med.*

GLOSTER, Jonathan Alvin
Eleanor Roosevelt HS; Greenbelt, MD (10%-350) Lat C; NHS; VP, Y-Tns; Bsbl; Tr; COM; Citz A; Hon Prog; Math A; PTA A; Star Student; Yth Fel; Attendance A; Scholastic Ltr; HR; *George Washington U; Elec Engr.*

GLOTH, Paul Daniel
Loyola HS; Towson, MD (1-134) Fr C; NHS; Cpt, Wrest; COM; Hon Prog; NEDT; MVP, Wrest; *William And Mary Col; Pol Sci.*

GLOUDEMAN, Jodi Lee
Beaver Dam Sr HS; Beaver Dam, WI (41-318) Ann; Chldr; Hmrm; Ski C; SC; Var C; JV, Bkbl; Sftbl; Swim; JV, Tr; Hon Prog; Pres A; Spch A.

GLOVER, Beverly Jean
Henry Ford HS; Detroit, MI (271-457) Chor; SC; *Associated Sch Inc; Airlines.*

GLOVER, Bryan Craig
Walnut HS; Walnut, MS (15-55) Secy, FFA; Ed, Sch P; *NE Jr Col; Journ.*

GLOVER, Christie Marie
W A Berry HS; Birmingham, AL; Anchor C; Cpt, Chldr; Crown & Scepter; FHA; SC; Bkbl; 'Powder Puff' Ftbl; *Auburn U; Ed.*

GLOVER, Deborah Renae
W A Berry HS; Birmingham, AL (17-350) Anchor C; Ann; Chor; Crown & Scepter; Parl, FHA; Secy, NHS; Span C; SC; Cr-Ctry; Sftbl; Tr; Hon Prog; Most Dependable; Schol 3 9 Avg A; *U of S Ala; Nurs.*

GLOVER, Evelyn Lemar
West End HS; Birmingham, AL (6-270) Dbte Tm; NHS; Ed, Sch P; Bus Mgr, Span C; Pres, Sr Cl; Journ A; JA A; Most Out; NHS; B'Ham Exchange C, Yth o-t Mon; BTNB Tnage A; UAB Alumni Excel A; *Stillman Col; Pre-Med.*

GLOVER, James Michael
Atlanta HS; Atlanta, TX (10%-220) Demolay; NHS; Sch P; Sci C; Q&S A; Yth Leg; Outst, Eng; HR A; *Tex A&M U; Pre-Med.*

GLOVER, Joy Ellen
Beaufort Acad; Beaufort, SC (4-43) JV, Chldr; Secy, Hmrm; Var C; Bkbl; Sftbl; Tnns; Hon Prog.

GLOVER, Julia Kathleen
Memorial Sr HS; Houston, TX (120-640) Chor; Fr C; JETS; Math C; Mu Alpha Theta; NHS; Mgr, Bkbl; Tnns; Hon Prog; Yth Foundation A; HR; Vlbl; *Mount Holyoke Col; Urban Stu.*

GLOVER, Mary Jane
Arsenal Tech HS; Indianapolis, IN (65-850) FBLA; VP, 4H; Pres, Hmrm; JETS; Semi-Fin, Jr Miss Pa; NHStt; Sch Achieve Tm; Span C; VP, SC; Y-Tns; Bkbl; Alg A; Beauty; COM; Cl Fav; God & Country A; HQn; Hon Prog; JA A; Math A; MLS; Most Out; Ntl Achv Schol; NMS; Star Student; Type A; Yth Fel; Voc A; *Branell Worker Col; Professional Mod.*

GLOVER, Michelle Dena
Milwaukee Tech HS; Milwaukee, WI; Chldr; Chor; Sftbl; *U of Wis at Madison; Psych.*

GLOVER, Rebecca Lynn
Northside HS; Roanoke, VA (60-416) Band; Chor; Span C; Tr; FCA; Tr & Band Ltrs; Selected YCC Employment; Izaac Walton League Employment.

GLOVER, Tammy Renee
Whitehall HS; White Hall, AR (100-350) Chor; MVP, Bkbl; Tr; *U of Ark Monticello; Elem Ed.*

GLOVER, Willie Herbert
Bok HS; Philadelphia, PA; Cpt, A Cap Choir; Cpt, Chor; VP, Ensm; MVP, Ftbl; MVP, Tnns; Tr; Kung Fu Tm; *UCLA; Law.*

GLYNN, Arthur William
Benson Polytechnical HS; Portland, OR; Chor; Ensm; JV, Wrest; *US Navel Acad; Aviation.*

GLYNN, Pam Lynnette
Stevens HS; Rapid City, SD (48-473) Chor; 4H; Hmrm; NHS; Soccer; Tr; *Sioux Falls Col; Eng.*

GLYNN, Pierre David
Lycee Francais De Ny HS; NY, NY (6-70) A Cap Choir; Chor; Ger C; Secy, Cr-Ctry; Fin, Swim; Alg A; Chem A; Math A; Phy A; Regent Schol; Sci A; *Columbia Col; Bio- chem.*

GLYNN, Thomas Patrick
Don Bosco Tech HS; Boston, MA (11-230) CYO; Demolay; Hmrm; Y-Tns; Bsbl; Bkbl; Ftbl; Hockey; Sftbl; COM; Hon Prog; Marine Phys Fitness Test A; *Suffolk U; Criminal Law.*

GMINDER, Esther
Western Alamance HS; Elon College, NC (9-235) Band; NHS; Span C; SC; Citz A; Hon Prog; Yth Fel; MIP, Band; *Elon Col; Psych.*

GMINDER, Joseph
Western Alamance HS; Elon College, NC; Tres, Chess C; Chor; Drama; Ensm; Lat C; Orch; Sgt Major, Band; Nom, Gov's Sch; Pearson Mus Schol; NSOA; *Emmanuel Col; Mus.*

GMINDER, Nathan
W Alamance HS; Elon College, NC (60-232) Band; Community Yth Symph; Drama; Span C; Tnns; Hon Prog; Most Improved Percussionist; Band Cpt; Exchange Stu, Chile; *Mus.*

GO, Carol YukYu
Belmont HS; Los Angeles, CA (10-35) Chor; Pres, Chinese Cultural C; Ladyes; Open House Art A; Coun of C Pres; Drawing Con Win; Chinese Comp As; *Fashion Inst of Design And Merch; Fashion Design.*

GOAD, Darla J
Greenville Sr HS; Greenville, TX (10%-317) Fr C; NHS; Off, Drill Tm; Academic Excellence A; *E Tex St U; Computer Sci.*

GOBLE, Edward Earl
Eisenhower HS; Rialto, CA (5-800) Ann; Hmrm; Cpt, Swim; Bank Of Amer A; CSF; Citz A; Masonic A; Yth Fel; Arts and Crafts A; Top 5 Stu A; Ch, Evangelism Comm; Cpt, Water Polo; Yth Counselor; *Cal St Fullerton; Illustration Yth Ministry.*

GOBROGGE, Shelley Jane
Pinconning Area HS; Pinconning, MI (4-260) Chess C; Pres, 4H; NHS; VP, Church Yth Group; Health Careers C; Young Authors A; *Ferris St Col; Phar.*

GOCHENAUR, Garry Lee
Central Dauphin HS; Harrisburg, PA; NHS; Order/Arrow; Order/Arrow A; Sct o-t Yr; Conservation Camp Outst Stu; *Penn St U; Forestry.*

GOCKE, Carol Rose
Holy Rosary Acad; Louisville, KY (13-96) CYO; VP, Chess C; NHS; Ed, Sch P; SC; Soccer; Sftbl; COM; Citz A; Hon Prog; *Ball St U; Special Ed.*

GOCSIK, Ann Patrice
Cardinal Stritch HS; Oregon, OH (34-175) Secy, Fr C; ARC; SC; JV, Bkbl; Sftbl; Mgr, Tr; Hon Prog; PTA A; Sci A; Spch A; Secy, Pep C; Organist; *Saint Mary's Col; Gov.*

GODBEY, Judy Gwynn
Princeton HS; Cincinnati, OH (210-820) Chor; Bkbl; Sftbl; Citz A; Outst Art Stu; Young Authors; HR; Stu Coun Service.

GODBEY, Susan Elizabeth
Garden HS; Oakwood, VA (1-80) Hmrm; Co-Ch, Model UN; NHS; Span C; VP, SC; Tri-HiY; Pres, Jr Cl; Pres, Soph Cl; Cpt, Bkbl; Tnns; Alg A; Math A; Pres A; Sci A; Ann; A; General Bus A; Gov's Sch; 2nd Pl, Dist Bookkeeping.

GODBY, Bruce Allan
Westfield Washington Sch; Westfield, IN (70-120) CYO; Fr C; Var C; Ftbl; Golf; Co-Cpt, Wrest; All-Conf Wrest A; Wrest A; *US Air Force.*

GODBY, Leah Justine
E Noble HS; Kendallville, IN (50-278) Band; Bus C; Type A; *Denver Baptist Bible Col; Church Ed.*

GODDARD, Lori Ayres
Quabbin Regional HS; Barre, MA (20%-140) Tres, Bus C; Fin, GS; 4H; NHS; Span C; SC; Mgr, Bkbl; Mgr, Sftbl; 4H A; *Bus Adm.*

GODDARD, Shari Lenora
David Douglas HS; Portland, OR (28-530) GS; SC; Sftbl; Girl's Nation; Hon Men, NML; *Bethel Col.*

GODDARD, Terri Ann
Ouray HS; Ouray, CO (2-11) Band; Pres, Chldr; Chor; Elk A; HCt; Hon Band.

GODEHN, Sally Alina
Hendersonville HS; Hendersonville, NC (18-170) A-Ed, Ann; Chldr; Drama; Rptr, Hmrm; Tres, Key C; NHS; Span C; SC; Ch, Stu Elections; FCA; *U of NC; Sociology.*

GODERE, Mike Phalen
Lyman Mem HS; Lebanon, CT (80-100) CYO; Drama; SC; Bkbl; Soccer; Tr; Pres A; Tutor; *NW Col; Park Ranger.*

GODFREY, Cecelia Ann
McColl-Fletcher Mem HS; McColl, SC (10-74) Secy, Ann; Chldr; FHA; Cpt, Mjrte; Monogram; NHS; Bkbl; Sftbl; HCt; *Chesterfield-Marlboro Tech Col; Automotive Tech.*

GODKE, Donald Glen
Kewanee HS; Kewanee, IL; Hon Prog; Opt A; *Morrison Inst of Tech; Drafting.*

GODLEY, Kathryn Leslie
Bradwell Inst; Hinesville, GA (10-300) Pres, BC; FTA; Hmrm; Model UN; Co-Ed, Sch P; Pres, Sci C; SC; Tr; COM; Gov Honor Prog; Journ A; Sci A; *U o-t S; Biol.*

GODLEY, Latonya Diane
Compton Sr HS; Compton, CA (50%-800) Hmrm; Pres, Y-Tns; CSF; Hon Prog; *Calif St U; Nurs.*

GODOY, Steve Micheal
Nazareth Regional HS; Brooklyn, NY (22-288) NHS; SC; Hon Prog; *Pace U; Pre-Law.*

GODSEY, Frederick Gregory
Bristol Tenn HS; Bristol, TN; Lat C; MIV, Golf; *Law.*

GODSEY, Henry Dwayne
Ketron HS; Kingsport, TN (20-144) Ann; BC; Pres, Key C; VP, Sr Cl; Bsbl; Amer Leg A; 100% Bsbl A; All-Conf Bsbl; *U of Tenn; Archt.*

GODSEY, Mark Allen
Tennessee HS; Bristol, TN (132-270) A Cap Choir; All Amer Yth; Chor; Madrigal; MVP, Ftbl; Elk A; Quarterback C A; All St Chor; All Big Six, All Big Nine, Ftbl.

GODSHALL, David Lee
Cumberland Valley Sr HS; Mechanicsburg, PA (26-564) Band; Community Yth Symph; NHS; Orch; COM; NEDT; *Lebanon Valley Col; Mus Performance.*

GODSHALL, Miriam Frances
Pendleton HS; Pendleton, SC (25%-120) A Cap Choir; Chor; Fr C; Outst Piano Perform, Clemson Mus C; *Furman U; Mus.*

GODSHALL, Robin Neil
Toms River HS S; Toms River, NJ (30-440) Band; Model UN; Orch; Wrest; Pres Inaugural Parade; *US Merchant Marine Acad; Naval Engr.*

GODSTON, Peter Phillips
Wethersfield HS; Wethersfield, CT; Band; JV, Ftbl; JV, Tnns; Wrest; NEDT; Pres, Pilgrim Fel; Sunday Sch Teacher; Band Director's A; President's Phys Fitness A.

GODT, Wendy Ann
Traverse City Sr HS; Traverse City, MI; Tr; Balfour A; Type A.

GODWIN, George Hansel III
Decatur HS; Decatur, AL (1-335) Band; Co-Cpt, Chldr; Chor; Secy, Fr C; Pres, Key C; Lat NHS; Mu Alpha Theta; NHS; SC; Var C; Tres, Soph Cl; JV, Bkbl; TC; COM; Hon Prog; Math A; NEDT; Val; Phi Sigma Alpha; Outst Sr; Most Talented; *Auburn U; Pre-Med.*

GODWIN, John Stephens
Decatur HS; Decatur, AL; Fr C; Key C; NHS; Var C; Pres, Soph Cl; Bsbl; Ftbl; COM; Cl Fav; MLS.

GODWIN, Kay Elizabeth
Cairo HS; Cairo, GA; Ann; Band; Ensm; FBLA; 4H; Mjrte; *Valdosta St Col; Elem Ed.*

GODWIN, Lisa Ann
Wayne Co HS; Jesup, GA (15%-405) Ann; Chor; Drama; VP, FHA; Parl, Span C; Thes; Bkbl; Gov Honor Prog; Jr Homemaker; *Brewton Parker Jr Col; Mus.*

GODZIEBA, John
Marist Prep HS; Penndel, PA (1-11) CYO; Drama; ARC; Thes; Ftbl; Cpt; Hockey; Alg A; Chem A; Math A; NEDT; Sal; Sci A; Eng A; Physics A; HR; Social Sci A; *Drexel U; Chem Engr.*

GOEBEL, Robert Howard
Westview Sr HS; Braham, MN (15-110) Ann; Band; Ensm; NHS; Var C; Co-Cpt, Ftbl; Fin, Tr; Cl Fav; HKg; HCt; Band Off; Most Improved, Ftbl; Sno-Daze Court; Superior, Dist & St Mus Contest.

GOEBIG, Marlene Mary
John W Hallahan Cath Girls HS; Philadelphia, PA (21-431) NFL; Secy, NHS; Orch; Rptr, Sch P; Span C; Spch C; World Affairs C; Amer Leg A; Hon Prog; *La Salle Col; Eng.*

GOEDE, Robert George
Lakewood HS; Lakewood, OH (20%-854) *Kent St U; Bus Law.*

GOEHL, Leslie Rana
Maple Point HS; Langhorne, PA (7-413) Hmrm; NHS; Ntl Yth Conf; Ski C; SC; Cr-Ctry; Tnns; Tr; Psych.

GOEHRING, Mary Alice
Forest Hill HS; W Palm Beach, FL (129-417) Key C; Tres, Lat C; Orch; COM; *Nyack Col; Psych.*

GOEKEN, Heidi Sue
Delavan Comm HS; Delavan, IL (7-65) Band; Cpt, Chldr; Chor; Drama; Ensm; Madrigal; VP, SC; Sftbl; Tr; Citz A; Hon Prog; NEDT; Yth Fel; Vlbl; Exchange Stu to Greece; Stu o-t Mo; *Foreign Lang.*

GOERGEN, Anna Maria
Pflugerville HS; Pflugerville, TX (10%-108) BC; Chldr; Drama; FHA; 4H; Span C; Spch C; Tres, Jr Cl; Tres, Soph Cl; Mgr, Bkbl; MVP, Sftbl; Tnns; Tr; Beauty; 4H A; Hon Prog; Spch A; Joske's Tn Board; *Tarleton St Col; Psych.*

GOERINGER, Christine
Riverside Jr-Sr HS; Taylor, PA (16-193) Co-Cpt, Band; Chor; Orch; Span C; JV, Tr; *Keystone Jr Col; Art.*

GOERS, Lynnette Kaye
Gunderson HS; San Jose, CA (10-260) Band; FTA; Pres, Orch; Span C; World Affairs C; Bank Of Amer A; CSF; Advanced Span A; Teacher's Assn Schol; Orch Trophy; Orch A; *West Valley Col; Span.*

GOETTEL, Claudia Gisele
Oppenheim-Ephratah HS; St Johnsville, NY (3-38) NHS; Bkbl; Swim; Tr.

GOETTING, Jay Carl
Steeleville HS; Steeleville, IL (7-45) Ann; NHS; Span C; Pres, Jr Cl; Bsbl; Bkbl; HCt; NEDT; *Phys Therapy.*

GOETTSCH, Ann Rene
Holstein Comm Sch; Holstein, IA (15-62) Band; Semi-Fin, GS; ARC; Ed, Sch P; Citz A; Sci A; Spch A; Yth for Understand, Stu Exchg Japn; *Iowa St U; Home Ec.*

GOETZ, Anita Laraine
Smithfield-Selma Sr HS; Smithfield, NC; Band; NHS; Pol Sci C; Span C; JV, Bkbl; *NC St U; Wildlife Biol.*

GOETZ, Kathy Ann
Bradleyville HS; Bradleyville, MO (2-27) Drama; Fr C; FHA; Math C; *Sch o-t Ozarks.*

GOETZE, David Wil
Gibraltar HS; Fish Creek, WI (1-68) Band; NMS; Major Role, Sch Play; Church Orch; Church Male Choir; *John Brown U; Elec Engr.*

GOFF, Brian Lee
Maryville R-II HS; Maryville, MO (33%-140) Band; Ensm; Sci C; Var C; Ftbl; Tnns; Wrest; Yth Fel; Mic-O-Say; Eagle Sct A.

GOFF, Gale Ann
G A R Mem HS; Wilkes-Barre, PA (7-186) Secy, Band; NHS; Orch; *Phys Therapy.*

GOFF, Kenneth Loyle
Will C Crawford HS; San Diego, CA (311-576) Band; Chor; God & Country A; Most Improved Mus; *San Diego St Col; Mus Ed.*

GOFF, Sylvia Ann
Enterprise HS; Enterprise, MS (3-51) A-Ed, Ann; VP, BC; Tres, FHA; Alg A; Bio A; Crisco A; Hist A; Hon Prog; *The U of Miss; Med.*

GOFFNER, Rory Craignell
Thomas Jefferson HS; Louisville, KY (36-299) BC; Chor; FBLA; Madrigal; All-St Chor; Acct &; WW Among Mus Stu; Voc Bus Stu; *U of Louisville; Acct.*

GOFORTH, Anthony Wayne
Hammond Hills HS; Memphis, TN (1-25) Span C; Hon Prog; *Bible.*

GOFORTH, Terry Lynn
Okeene HS; Okeene, OK (1-38) Band; Chor; FHA; Jr Miss Pagent; Mjrte; Ed, Sch P; Var C; Bkbl; St Hon Soc; *Pre-Med.*

GOGAN, Catherine Mary
Mt Mercy Acad; Buffalo, NY (3-220) Chor; Fin, Jr Miss Pagent; Pres, Math C; NHS; A-Ed, Sch P; Beauty; COM; Hon Prog; NEDT; Regent Schol; *Pre-Med.*

GOGGANS, Patti Lucille
Robert E Lee HS; Montgomery, AL; BC; FHA; VP, Soph Cl; Lt Gov, Jr Civitans; Friendliest; *Auburn U; Home Ec.*

GOIN, Cheryl Faye
Belton HS; Belton, MO (134-350) Crown & Scepter; *Health.*

GOING, Jeffrey Lee
Lyons Pub Sch; Lyons, NE (33%-33) A Cap Choir; Ann; Band; Chor; Tres, FFA; 4H; NHS; Orch; Bkbl; Ftbl; Sci A; FFA Beef Mgt.

GOINGS, Jan Elizabeth
Walnut Hills Col Prep Sch; Cincinnati, OH (20%-450) Chldr; Ensm; Tr; COM; Hon Prog; Yth Fel; Black Cultural Workshop; HR A; Jack & Jill of Amer; Mus A; Vol, Phys Handicapped; Modeling C; *Miami U; Psych.*

GOINS, Brenda Alice
Bradley-Bourbonnias Comm HS; Bourbonnais, IL; Secy, Fr C; Orch; SC; *Olivet Nazarene Col; Law.*

GOINS, Norma Jean
Continued Education Project; St Louis, MO; *Wash U.*

GOINS, Yolonda Kay
Fairland HS; Fairland, OK (1-31) Band; Secy, FHA; 4H; NHS; 4H A; MLS; Val; Most Stu; *NEO A&M Col; Med Secy.*

GOKEE, Charles Jeffrey
Wm H Boone HS; Orlando, FL; Ann; Hmrm; Sch P; Var C; Tr; MVP, Wrest; COM; Yth Fel; VP, FCA; Most Talented; Wittiest; Jr NHS; Karate; Wrest A; *Zoology-Archaeology.*

GOLAY, Evangeline Rose
James Madison HS; Milwaukee, WI (5%-950) Band; Drama; Hmrm; Math C; Span C; SC; JV, Swim; Citz A; Hon Prog; Math A; ARC A; Jr NHS; Secy, Tres, Church Yth; St Bible Quizzing; Service A; *Olivet Nazarene Col; Math.*

GOLD, Lori Louise
Langley HS; McLean, VA (100-550) Drama; Cpt, Karate; Schol Art A; *Math.*

GOLD, Michael Allan
Collegiate HS; Passaic, NJ (1-21) NHS; Co-Ed, Sch P; Bsbl; Alg A; *Pol Sci.*

GOLDAMMER, Jay Paul
Fountain Valley HS; Fountain Valley, CA (150-1183) Soccer; Hon Prog.

GOLDBAUGH, JoAnn
Wheeling Park HS; Wheeling, WV (16-690) Anchor C; S-T, GS; Hmrm; Pres, NHS; Co-Ed, Sch P; SC; Bkbl; Sftbl; Hon Prog; Journ A; Q&S A; Vlbl; Stifel Schol; Know Your St Govt; *W Liberty St Col; Med Technology.*

GOLDBERG, Bruce Elliot
Neshaminy Maple Point HS; Langhorne, PA (21-406) Chor; Co-Cpt, Dbte Tm; NHS; Sci C; COM; NMF; NMS; Fr A; *Haverford Col; Biol.*

GOLDBERG, Heidi Elyse
Canarsie HS; Brooklyn, NY; Chem C; Chor; Pres, Hmrm; Pres, Lit Ral; F-Ed, Lit Mag; Phys C; ARC; A-Ed, Sch P; Alg A; Bio A; COM; Chem A; Citz A; Hist A; Hon Prog; Math A; Phy A; ARC A; Sci A; *6yr Bio-Med-Prog City Col; Med.*

GOLDBETTER, Barbara Joyce
A E Stevenson HS; Bronx, NY (38-788) Band; Chem C; Dbte Tm; InterClub Coun; NHS; Orch; Phys C; SC; Hon Prog; Sci A; Service A; *Hunter Col; Nurs.*

GOLDEN, DeLana Lee
Pendleton Heights HS; Pendleton, IN (19-295) BC; 4H; NHS; Span C; Var C; *Ind U; Acct.*

GOLDEN, Dianne Michelle
Andress HS; El Paso, TX; Chldr; Y-Tns; JV, Tr; Tr A; Chldr A; *U El Paso; Secretarial.*

GOLDEN, Felix Leon
William C Overfelt HS; San Jose, CA; *San Jose State Col.*

GOLDEN, Hugh Brian
SW Central Sch; Jamestown, NY; Ger C; JV, Bsbl; Hon Prog.

GOLDEN, Laurie Gay
Harding Acad of Memphis; Memphis, TN (25%-214) F-Ed, Ann; Chor; Hmrm; NFL; NHS; Eng, Health, Piano, Lib, A's.

GOLDEN, Linda Joanne
Anacostia Sr HS; Washington, DC; Bus C; FBLA; FHA; Hmrm; NHS; ARC; SC; Citz A; PA; *Wash Tech Col; Bus Adm.*

GOLDEN, Michele Andree
Karlsruhe Amer HS; Karlsruhe, GERMANY; CYO; 4H; Hmrm; Secy, Var C; MVP, Bkbl; Soccer; Sftbl; COM; Math A; MVP, Vlbl; *Acct.*

GOLDEN, Randal Louis
Peoria HS; Peoria, IL (10-450) Key C; NHS; Orch; Sch P; SC; Var C; Pres, Soph Cl; JV, Golf; Swim.

GOLDEN, Richard Martin
La Salle Col HS; Philadelphia, PA (10-205) NHS; Rptr, Sch P; COM; Hist A; Hon Prog; NEDT; Type A; Cpt, Bowl C; *Temple U; Acct.*

GOLDEN, Steven Sean
Polo Comm HS; Polo, IL (12-110) Ftbl; Tr; Sci A; Industrial Arts A; *Photography.*

GOLDEN, Susan Lynn
Mathiston HS; Mathiston, MS (3-35) A-Ed, Ann; BC; FHA; NHS; Bus Mgr, Sch P; *Miss St U; Sci.*

GOLDEN, Thaddeus Randell
William C Overfelt HS; San Jose, CA; SC; Co-Cpt, Bsbl; Bkbl; Ftbl; Alg A; *U of Sou Calif; Phys Ed.*

GOLDENBERG, Robin Lee
Vincent Massey Secondary Sch; Windsor, CANADA; Math C; Ontario Schol; *U of Toronto; Law.*

GOLDFUSS, Beth Ann
O'Neill Pub HS; O'Neill, NE (1-83) Ann; Drama; GS; NHS; Rptr, Sch P; Var C; MVP, Vlbl; *X-Ray Tech.*

GOLDING, Martha Lynn
North Mesquite HS; Mesquite, TX; A Cap Choir; Chor; Drill Tm; Blue Brigade; Pacesetter Drill Tm; *Texas A&M St U; Interior Decorating.*

GOLDING, Paul Mark
W Forsyth HS; Clemmons, NC; Bsbl; Bkbl; Ftbl; *Phys Ed.*

GOLDING, Robin Jeannine
Cashmere HS; Cashmere, WA; Chor; Drama; 4H; Yth Fel.

GOLDSMITH, Sherrill Lynn
Carterville Comm HS; Carterville, IL (11-90) Secy, Band; Ensm; Pres, Fr C; Gym; PA; High Hons; 1st, Ensm; *John Logan Jr Col; Bus.*

GOLDSPRING, Lynn Marie
De Anza HS; Richmond, CA (14-450) Chor; NHS; Var C; Sftbl; CSF; COM; Citz A; Hon Prog; Pres A; Judo; Don Quixote A; WW; *Biola Col; Med.*

GOLDSTEIN, Marcy
Hebrew Acad HS; Yonkers, NY (1-16) Cpt, Chess C; A-Ed, Sch P; *Stern Col; Judaic Stu.*

GOLDY, Timmy Lee
Bath Co HS; Owingsville, KY; 4H; Bsbl; JV, Bkbl; Ftbl; Pres A; *Eastern Ky U; Law Enforcement.*

GOLIGHTLY, Dannette Marie
Romulus Sr HS; Romulus, MI (10-390) Band; NHS; JA A.

GOLIGHTLY, Gary Kevin
Bishop Byrne HS; Memphis, TN (19-185) Bsbl; Engr.

GOLIGHTLY, Lynn Bowie
Shaler Area HS; Glenshaw, PA (42-960) AFS; Band; Chor; Fr C; French NHS; Hmrm; NHS; Ski C; SC; Y-Tns; Yth Fel; Secy, Candystripers; Grove City Col; Bus Adm.

GOLINO, Roger Paul
De Anza HS; Hercules, CA; Band; Ftbl; Cogswell Col; Construction.

GOLLAN, Darlene
Ursuline HS; Youngstown, OH (168-400) Special Ed Vol; Bethany Col; Graphic Arts.

GOLLIHUE, Mark A
Oak Hill HS; Oak Hill, OH (8-60) Var C; Bkbl; Cr-Ctry; Tr; HCt; Shawnee St Col; Elec.

GOLOB, Lisa Louise
W Allis Nathan Hale HS; West Allis, WI (85-440) A Cap Choir; Chldr; Chor; Drama; Hmrm; Fin, Jr Miss Pagent; Madrigal; NFL; SC; Thes; St Solo & Ensm Mus Contest Win; Co-Ch, Homecoming; Performing Arts.

GOLTER, Beckie Sue
Longmont Sr HS; Longmont, CO; Co-Cpt, Chldr; NHS; Basic Design A; Colo St U; Art.

GOLTRY, Kimberly Jan
Amer Christian Acad; Pomona, CA (2-21) Band; Chor; Drama; Hmrm; Spch C; SC; Secy, Jr Cl; Sftbl; Bio A; Citz A; HCt; Hon Prog; Spch A; Rep, TV Quiz Show; Pacific Coast Baptist Bible Col; Missions.

GOLWITZER, Tina Ann
Waukegan E HS; Waukegan, IL (100-200) Bus C; FBLA; Rainbow; ARC; COM; Masonic A; Orch A.

GOMER, Richard Henry
Gilroy HS; Gilroy, CA (5%-300) Semi-Fin, BS; Pres, InterAct C; VP, Pol Sci C; A-Ed, Sch P; Ski C; SC; Var C; Sr Cl; Pres, Jr Cl; Bkbl; JV, Cr-Ctry; Amer Leg A; CSF; Hist A; HCt; Hon Prog; ROTC A; Nom, West Point Acad; St Officer, Calif Jr Statesmen; Sch District Mgt Tm; West Point; Pol Sci.

GOMES, Rebecca Lynn
Willows HS; Willows, CA (4-148) VP, FTA; CSF.

GOMES, Susan Lynn
Los Banos HS; Los Banos, CA (33%-277) Band; CYO; Chldr; Pres, 4H; SC; 4H A; HCt.

GOMEZ, Calvin Michael
Louis D Brandeis HS; New York, NY; Chor; SC; Bkbl; Tnns; Attendance A's; Drew U; Pre-Med.

GOMEZ, Ellis Eugenia
Greater New York Acad; Woodside, NY (1-72) A Cap Choir; Ed, Ann; Chor; NHS; Ntl Yth Conf; Sci C; Ski C; SC; Bio A; COM; Chem A; Citz A; Val; Yth Fel; Vlbl Intramurals; Andrews U; Psych.

GOMEZ, Frank
Adlai E Stevenson HS; Bronx, NY (14-788) Anchor C; Band; Lit Mag; NHS; Sch Achieve Tm; COM; Hon Prog; Regent Schol; Sci A; DeVry Tech Inst.

GOMEZ, Gilda
Academia Sagrado Corazon; Santurce, PR (3-90) ARC; Sci C; Phy A; Span A; Eng A; Conduct A.

GOMEZ, John Joseph
Christopher Columbus HS; Miami, FL (12-200) Band; Chess C; JV, Golf; JV, Soccer; Alg A; Hon Prog; Sci A; Dean's List; Top Ten; Wash U; Engr.

GOMEZ, Joyce Amparin
Eastside HS; Paterson, NJ (14-519) Chor; Drama; COM; 'Z'; Horsemanship, C'S; Univ Natl de Pedro Enriquez Urena; Med.

GOMEZ, Juan Carlos
Academia Ntra Sra Providencia; Rio Piedras, PR (4-32) Tres, CYO; Arch; Wrest; COM; Math A; Conduct A; Psych.

GOMEZ, Pylar
Francisco Mendoza HS; Isabela, PR; A Cap Choir; CYO; Chldr; Chor; Dbte Tm; FHA; 4H; Hmrm; NHS; Ntl Yth Conf; Sch P; Span C; Var C; Pres, Jr Cl; Pres, Soph Cl; Bkbl; Co-Cpt, Sftbl; Alg A; Bio A; COM; Chem A; Cl Fav; Gov Honor Prog; Hon Prog; Ntl Cath Mus Ed Asn; Rotary A; Geom A; Col of Agr & Mech Arts; Pol Sci.

GOMEZ, Santiago G
Bay City Central HS; Bay City, MI (412-522) A Cap Choir; CYO; Chor; Commercial C; Span C; SC; Bkbl; MVP, Cr-Ctry; Ftbl; MVP, Tr; Citz A; Star Student; Yth Fel; FCA; Minority Cs; Boys C of Amer; Saginaw Valley St Col; Social Sci.

GOMEZ, Yolanda
Notre Dame HS; Caguas, PR; A Cap Choir; Ann; Band; Chem C; Chor; Dbte Tm; Hmrm; Ch, Inter-Act C; Lit Ral; Math C; ARC; Sch Achieve Tm; SC; Alg A; COM; Journ A; Math A; Rotary A; Spch A; Hon A; Excellence A; Spelling Bee; UPR at Cayey; Med.

GOMIEN, David Michael
Tyner HS; Chattanooga, TN (26-269) BC; Rptr, NHS; F-Ed, Sch P; Hon Prog; U of Tenn; Journ.

GOMKE, Monte Allan
Lancaster Sr HS; Lancaster, WI (5-152) JV, Ftbl; JV, Wrest.

GOMMER, Pamela Jean
Huron Sr HS; Huron, SD (50%-290) Span C; Art.

GONCE, William Allan
Estancia HS; Estancia, NM (2-68) Drama; FFA; 4H; SC; Rptr, Soph Cl; Bio A; 4H A; PTA A; Spch A; Swtht; Type A; OEA, FFA, Amer Horseman; Horse C; A's; Dentistry.

GONDECK, Maureen Sue
Ingleside HS; Ingleside, TX (1-74) Ed, Ann; CYO; Pres, NHS; Tres, SC; I Dare You; MLS; Val; Cpt, Vlbl; Most Dependable; WW; Best All-Around; Tex A&I U; Bus.

GONDER, Annette
Soldan HS; St Louis, MO; A Cap Choir; Chldr; Chor; JA A; BMgr, JA; Peer Coun; Audio Visual; Vacation Bible Sch Teacher; X-Ray Tech.

GONDER, Vannessa
Soldan HS; St Louis, MO (25-500) Band; Tr; JA A; Pres A; Pres, Church Yth Grop; WW; VP, Pep C, Vlbl, Band, Ltrs; St Louis U; Med Tech.

GONGORA, Orfelinda
John Ehret HS; Marrero, LA (15-550) Dbte Tm; NFL; NHS; Hon Prog; Co-Cpt, Flag & Drill Tm; Span A; Academic A; Media Fair A; Scholastic A; UNO; Acct.

GONO, Robert Byron
Thomas Jefferson HS; Dallas, TX (23-422) Chess C; Hmrm; Key C; Math C; NHS; Sch P; Sftbl; COM; Hon Prog; Artist, Sch Paper; Most Creative; Young Designers of Amer; Bob Jones U; Art.

GONYEA, Mark Allen
Flint Southwestern HS; Flint, MI (75-425) Order/ Arrow; JV, Ftbl; ST; Yth Fel; Mich St U; Law Enforcement.

GONZALES, Giselle Joan
Eisenhower HS; Rialto, CA (211-746) AFS; CYO; San Bernadino Valley Col; Social Work.

GONZALES, Karen Suzanne
Del Oro HS; Loomis, CA; Chldr; Cum Laude Soc; Flag Tm; Chldr A; Sierra Jr Col; Bus.

GONZALES, Mary Ann
Pawnee HS; Pawnee, TX (25%-14) Band; CYO; Secy, FHA; S-T, Jr Cl; Bkbl; Ftbl; Tr; Cl Fav; Swtht; Val; Vlbl; Tex Women U; Elem Ed.

GONZALES, Milca
Frankford HS; Philadelphia, PA (54-700) Chess C; Mod Mus Mas; JA A; Penn St U; Spch Pathology.

GONZALEZ, Adrian Gilberto
St Augustine HS; Laredo, TX (16-67) Ann; Chess C; NHS; JV, Bkbl; U of Tex; Architecture.

GONZALEZ, David
Herbert H Lehman HS; Bronx, NY (381-1439) Hmrm; Orch; Order/Arrow; Sch P; MVP, Cr-Ctry; Tr; COM; God & Country A; Order/Arrow A; ARC A; Superstar A; Bronx Boro Champs; Aerospace Engr.

GONZALEZ, David Allen
Fremont Christian HS; Fremont, CA; Chor; Ensm; Hmrm; SC; Bsbl; Soccer.

GONZALEZ, Dinah A
Academia Maria Reina; Rio Piedras, PR; Chor; Drama; Fr C; NHS; COM; Hon Prog; Spell Bee; Modeling; Dancing; Lib Arts.

GONZALEZ, Edward
Evander Child HS; Bronx, NY; Band; Protestant Yth Organization; Broadcasting.

GONZALEZ, Emine
Lakewood HS; Lakewood, NJ (32-300) CYO; Fr C; NHS; Span C; Span NHS; Georgian Ct Col; Bilingual Ed.

GONZALEZ, Erick Roberto
Mission HS; San Fernando, CA; Ann; Hmrm; Sch Achieve Tm; MLS; Star Student; Humboldt Col; Wildlife Mgr.

GONZALEZ, Gilbert
Vineland Sr HS; Vineland, NJ; Span C; Alg A; Ed & Country A; Math A; Yth Fel; NE Christian Col; Acct.

GONZALEZ, Glenda Iriet
Consuelo Escalona Private Sch; Carolina, PR (1-36) NHS; COM; U of PR; Med.

GONZALEZ, Gloria Socorro
Notre Dame HS; Caguas, PR; Sch Achieve Tm; Ed, Sch P; Lib C; Hon A; Excelencia A; U of Puerto Rico; Physics.

GONZALEZ, Gregory Bradford
Skyline HS; Salt Lake City, UT; Pres, Chor; JV, Bkbl; Ftbl; Tr; Amer Leg A; Lion A; Brigham Young U; Bus.

GONZALEZ, Heriberto
Dr Pedro P Fajardo Voc HS; Mayaguez, PR; Hon Stu; Colegio Agricultura; Ingenieria Civil.

GONZALEZ, Ida Luz
Bassick HS; Bridgeport, CT; CYO; Drama; Hmrm; SC; Bkbl; Vlbl.

GONZALEZ, Jose Anibal
William Howard Taft HS; Bronx, NY; Bronx Comm Col; Art.

GONZALEZ, Leticia Marie
Roma HS; Roma, TX (2-180) FHA; NHS; Parl, SC; COM; Journ A; MLS; Most Out; Sci A; Val; HR; Spelling A.

GONZALEZ, Luz Celeste
Wesleyan Acad; Guaynabo, PR (3-32) Chor; Hmrm; NHS; SC; Pres, Sftbl; Hon Prog; Houghton Col; CPA.

GONZALEZ, Manuel
Dra Maria Cadilla de Martinez HS; Arecibo, PR (56-429) Chem C; Phys C; Sci C; JV, Bsbl; JV, Sftbl; Alg A; COM; Cl Fav; Hist A; Hon Prog; Math A; Sci A; Arecibo Regional Col; Med.

GONZALEZ,
Maria De los Angeles
Dra Maria Cadilla HS; Arecibo, PR (65-429) Universidad Interamericana; Psicologia.

GONZALEZ, Mariano Enrique
San Antonio Abad HS; Humacao, PR (2-72) Fin, Chem C; Pres, Hmrm; Lit Mag; ARC; Sci C; SC; Var C; Pres, Sr Cl; JV, Bsbl; Bkbl; Ftbl; Chem A; Hon Prog; Tulane U; Med.

GONZALEZ, Mario
Adlai E Stevenson HS; Bronx, NY (45-814) A Cap Choir; Band; Chor; Var C; Regent Schol; Gym Tm.

GONZALEZ, Maximino Jr
Adlai Stevenson HS; New York City, NY; Band; NHS; Hist A; Hon Prog; Law.

GONZALEZ, Paul Anthony
Wm B Travis HS; Austin, TX; Pres, CYO; VP, Chess C; NHS; Tres, Span C; Pres, SC; Citz A; Pres A; Civitan Schol; Outst CCD Member; St Edwards Col; Hist.

GONZALEZ, Rocio
Academia Ntra Sra Providencia; Rio Piedras, PR (5-58) Co-Ed, Ann; Band; CYO; Chldr; Chor; Dbte Tm; GS; Hmrm; SC; Pres, Sr Cl; Tres, Jr Cl; COM; Hon Prog; JA A; Jr Cath Daughters of Amer; Conduct A; U of Puerto Rico; Social Sci.

266

GONZALEZ, Rosa M
Academia Sagrado Corazon; Santurce, PR (2-65) Hmrm; Pres, Model UN; NHS; Rptr, Sch P; Tres, SC; Tres, Soph Cl; JA A; *U of Puerto Rico; Acct.*

GONZALEZ, Ruth Mary
Herbert H Lehman HS; Bronx, NY; Orch; COM; Hon Prog; Sci A; Eng A; Attendence A; Band A.

GONZALEZ, Sandra Y
Fernando Suria Chaves HS; Barceloneta, PR; Band; CYO; Chldr; Chor; FBLA; Hmrm; Tres, Sch P; COM; Gov Honor Prog; Val; Spelling Bees; *Universidad de Puerto Rico; Bus Adm.*

GONZALEZ, Zaira Magdalena
Lola Rodriguez de Tio; San German, PR (1-350) CYO; FHA; ARC; Sci C; COM; Hon Prog; Magna Cum Laude; Summa Cum Laude; *Recinto Univ Mayaguez; Med.*

GOOCH, Kim Robert
Benton County R 1 HS; Sedalia, MO (17-51) A Cap Choir; BS; Chor; Ensm; SC; Pres, Var C; Pres, Jr Cl; Cpt, Bsbl; Cpt, Bkbl; Cpt, Cr-Ctry; *S Mo St U; Social Work.*

GOOCH, Mary Gail
Treadwell HS; Memphis, TN (8-172) Ed, Ann; VP, Lat C; Math C; Mu Alpha Theta; NHS; SC; Journ A; *Memphis St U; Acct.*

GOOCH, Shelley Jean
Marion HS; Marion, IL; JV, Chldr; FBLA; Sftbl; *E Ill U; Phys Ed.*

GOOCHER, Scott Orin
Trinity Presbyterian HS; Montgomery, AL (9-40) BC; Key C; Pres, Lat C; NHS; Ftbl.

GOOD, Diane Marie
LaVille Jr-Sr HS; Lakeville, IN; Band; Fr C; FHA; 4H; Math C; SC; Pres, Soph Cl; Alg A; NEDT; Lang Arts A; *Manchester Col; Acct.*

GOOD, Donya Jeanne
San Francisco Christian Sch; San Francisco, CA (10%-13) A Cap Choir; Ann; Chor; Ensm; NHS; Ed, Sch P; Hon Prog; Sal; SD All-St Hon Choir; *Point Loma Col; Nurs.*

GOOD, Glenn Ford
Montclair HS; Montclair, NJ (104-500) Fin, BS; Chor; Drama; Hmrm; JETS; Order/Arrow; Pres, SC; Up Bound; Pres, Sr Cl; Pres, Jr Cl; Pres, Soph Cl; MVP, Arch; JV, Wrest; Amer Leg A; COM; Citz A; Cl Fav; Hon Prog; MLS; Most Out; Order/Arrow A; Yth Foundation; Eagle Sct; *Allegheny Col; Archt.*

GOOD, Kathleen Louise
Langley HS; Langley, WA (10-78) Ann; Tres, CYO; Chor; Ensm; FHA; GS; Hmrm; S-T, NHS; Span C; VP, Jr Cl; Masonic A; JV Vlbl; *Gonzaga U.*

GOOD, Lynn Ann
San Ramon Valley HS; Danville, CA (2-350) Chldr; Semi-Fin, GS; SC; Pres, Sr Cl; Secy, Soph Cl; Co-Cpt, Tnns; CSF; DARGCA; MLS; Val; Outst Stu, Outst Eng, A's; *UCLA; Psych.*

GOOD, Mark James
Leo HS; Chicago, IL (8-140) Pres, Hmrm; NHS; Hon Prog; *U of Ill-Chicago; Phar.*

GOOD, Patte Kay
J R Tucker HS; Richmond, VA (50%-500) Ensm; FHA; Hmrm; Jr Miss Pagent; SC; Soccer; NRA Hunter Safety A; Jr Phys Fitness A; *Art.*

GOODALE, Cinda Marie
Chester Area HS; Chester, SD (1-40) Tres, FHA; NHS; SC; Pres, Sr Cl; S-T, Jr Cl; Pres, Soph Cl; HQn; *Presentation Col; Med Lab Tech.*

GOODALL, Desmond Dwayne
Millikan HS; Long Beach, CA; Chess C; *Calif St U; Oceanography.*

GOODALL, Karla Kay
Dearborn HS; Dearborn, MI; Chor; Math C; JV, Hockey; Pres A; *U of Mich.*

GOODAN, Karen Robbyn
W Carter HS; Olive Hill, KY (10-154) Band; Pres, BC; VP, Bus C; Chor; VP, Dbte Tm; FBLA; Secy, FHA; Pres, 4H; Secy, Hmrm; F-Ed, Sch P; Sci C; Var C; Secy, Jr Cl; Secy, Soph Cl; Bio A; Cl Fav; Hon Prog; Math A; Sci A; Val; Parliamentary Procedure A; *Eastern Ky U; Med.*

GOODBREAD, Ramona
Rutherford HS; Panama City, FL (20%-550) Band; BC; FBLA; Rainbow; Pres, Keyettes; Amer Cancer Soc Steering Comm; *Gulf Coast Comm Col; Social Services.*

GOODE, Charlotte Ann
Pontotoc HS; Pontotoc, MS (8-96) Band; FBLA; FHA; *Itawamba Jr Col; Bus Ed.*

GOODE, Dolores Ann
Bells HS; Bells, TN (11-50) Chor; FHA; Rptr, Sch P; *Voc Sch; Bus.*

GOODE, Lynette Louise
Arvada W HS; Arvada, CO (88-750) A Cap Choir; Chldr; Chor; Ensm; NHS; Soccer; HCt; Yth Fel; Job's Daughters; Jr Attendant, Prom Qn; Friendship A; *W St Col; Acct.*

GOODE, Michael
duPont Manual HS; Louisville, KY (89-465) Chor; Dbte Tm; Drama; Parl, FBLA; FTA; Ger C; Hmrm; Lat C; Rptr, Sch P; Spch C; SC; Tr; Most Sch Spirit; 1st Run-Up, Church Spch Contest; *Western Ky U; Spch Therapy.*

GOODE, Victoria Marie
Richardson HS; Richardson, TX (22-908) NHS; God & Country A; *Baylor U; Computer Sci.*

GOODEN, Faye Annette
Plantation HS; Plantation, FL; JV, Chldr; Rptr, Chor; Hmrm; HCt; Semi Fin, Outst Soph; *Benedict Col; Math Instructor.*

GOODIN, Jackie Dale
Mercer R-III Sch; Mercer, MO (2-13) Ann; VP, Sr Cl; Bkbl; Sftbl; Tr; *Comm Col of Air Force; Flight Engr.*

GOODIN, Julie Frances
Marion Co HS; Lebanon, KY (35-298) JV, Chldr; FHA; 4H; Hmrm; NHS; Span C; SC; Var C; Y-Tns; Secy, Sr Cl; VP, Jr Cl; VP, Soph Cl; Bkbl; Sftbl; HCt; Pres A; Mayor's Advisory Committee; WW; *E Ky U; Med Record Tech.*

GOODIN, Sandra Lynn
N Canton Hoover HS; N Canton, OH (48-459) Band; Chor; 4H; SC; JV, Bkbl; 4H A; Yth Fel; Job's Daughters; Color Guard; Candystriper; Bowl; Church Choir; *Kent St U; Med.*

GOODING, David James
Montville Township HS; Montville, NJ; NHS; Cr-Ctry; Tr.

GOODING, Donna Lynn
Dixie Co HS; Cross City, FL; Ann; Co-Cpt, Band; BC; FHA; 4H; Span C; VP, SC; Cl Fav; 4H A; HCt; Rotary A; *Bauder Col; Fashion Merchandising & Model.*

GOODING, Nancy Marie
Spring Lake Jr And Sr HS; Spring Lake, MI (30-190) ARC; *Hackley Sch of Nurs; Nurs.*

GOODLETT, Charlotte Ann
Colo HS; Colo City, TX (7-126) VP, FHA; FTA; SC; JV, Bkbl; Tnns; WW; Top 5; *Angelo St U; Elem Ed.*

GOODLICK, Julie Denise
Heyworth HS; Heyworth, IL (1-65) Ann; Pres, FHA; NHS; Rptr, Sch P; MVP, Spch C; Var C; Bkbl; Mgr, Tr; Spch A; St Scholar; Val; NML; Nom, NCTE Writing; WW; *E Ill U; Spch.*

GOODLOE, Jenifer Arlene
Burges HS; El Paso, TX (33%-630) COM; Citz A; Kiwanis A; *Tex Tech U; Phys Therapy.*

GOODLOE, Stephen Hylton
N Springs HS; Atlanta, GA; Key C; ARC; Ski C; Co-Cpt, Ftbl; Tr; Wrest; Pres A; *U of NC; Bus.*

GOODMAN, Diana Pearl
Tecumseh HS; New Carlisle, OH (20-400) AFS; Drama; F-Ed, Sch P; Span C; WW; Jr NHS; *Wright St Col; Psych.*

GOODMAN, Doris Jean
Northmor HS; Galion, OH; Ann; Chor; Fin, GS; *Ohio St U; Elem Ed.*

GOODMAN, Ginger Kathaleen
Princeton HS; Princeton, TX; Chldr; NHS; SC; Cpt, Bkbl; Journ A; Most Out; Miss PHS; VP, FHA; *Richland JC Col; Bus.*

GOODMAN, Julie Ann
W Marshall HS; State Center, IA (7-65) Ann; Band; Chldr; FBLA; Hmrm; NHS; SC; Sftbl; Co-Cpt, Tnns; Crisco A; Pres A; Yth Fel; *Iowa St U; Industrial Adm.*

GOODMAN, Kathy Sue
Northern U HS; Cedar Falls, IA; Arch; Chem C; Chor; Drama; Arch; Soccer; Sftbl; Swim; *Bartlesville Wesleyan Col; Special Ed.*

GOODMAN, Kenneth Wayne
George Washington Carver HS; Montgomery, AL (1-400) Pres, Chess C; Fr C; French NHS; Math C; Mu Alpha Theta; Pres, NHS; F-Ed, Sch P; COM; Math A; NMF; NEDT; Sci A; Val; *Auburn U; Elec Engr.*

GOODMAN, Michael Dwayne
Breckinridge Co HS; Harned, KY (20-200) Chess C; Math C; Mu Alpha Theta; Span C; JV, Bkbl; JV, Cr-Ctry; Ftbl; Golf; *U of Ky; Civil Engr.*

GOODMAN, William Earl
Brown Deer HS; Brown Deer, WI (10%-275) Ski C; Var C; JV, Bkbl; Ftbl; Cpt, Tr; *Madison-U Wis.*

GOODNIGHT, Stanton Alan
Asher HS; Asher, OK (5%-21) FFA; Var C; Bsbl; Bkbl; Cl Fav; HCt; FFA A; Drivers Ed A; Eng A; *OCG; Pre-Med.*

GOODNIGHT, Walter Duane
Phillips HS; Phillips, TX (3-50) Chor; Drama; NHS; Spch C; JV, Bkbl; Co-Cpt, Ftbl; Golf; Lion A; Sci A; *Baylor U; Law.*

GOODNO, Kari Jo
Mabel-Canton HS; Mabel, MN (5%-57) Band; Ensm; Secy, Soph Cl; COM.

GOODNOW, Paul Steven
East HS; Duluth, MN; Chor; Pres, Hmrm; Bus Mgr, Sch P; Ch, SC; Eagle Sct; *U of Minn; Sci.*

GOODREAU, William Mark
Wellsboro Area Sr HS; Wellsboro, PA; Mgr, Bkbl; Ftbl; Yth Fel; Jr NHS; Red Cross Sr Lifeguard; *LeTourneau Col; Spch.*

GOODRICH, Bibiana Felecia
Our Lady of Peach Acad; San Diego, CA (2-75) CYO; Beauty; St Scholar; Phys Sci A; *San Diego St U; Vet Med.*

GOODRICH, Natalie Marcella
Hillsboro HS; Hillsboro, OH (35-180) Chor; Ensm; Fr C; GS; 4H; Sch P; COM; 4H A; Type A; Jr-Sr Prom Banquet Comm; Ohio Wesleyan Hons Choir; *Miami U; Mus.*

GOODRIDGE, Kenneth Alan
Cradock HS; Portsmouth, VA (10-250) Chess C; Citz A; Hon Prog; PTA A; Yth Choir; Earth Sci A; PA A; Eng A; Industrial Arts A; Phys Ed A; *Old Dominion U.*

GOODRUM, Frederick James II
Sharon HS; Sharon, MA (60%-270) Chor; Dbte Tm; Drama; Sci C; Soccer; Tr.

GOODRUM, Mark Timothy
Madison Co HS; Danielsville, GA; Parl, HiY; Parl, SC; Cpt, Ftbl; Tr; *Phys Ed.*

GOODSEN, Stephanie Genae
St Louis Park Sr HS; St Louis Park, MN; Band; Mjrte; Orch; Tnns; COM; Bible Quiz Tm; Tres, JA; *Normandale Jr Col; Mus.*

GOODSON, David Theodore
Sou Wayne Sr HS; Dudley, NC (9-450) A Cap Choir; VP, Band; VP, BC; Span C; Ftbl; *NC St U; Archt.*

GOODSON, James Jacob
Crestview HS; Crestview, FL; Chor; Drama; Order/Arrow; Bkbl; Ftbl.

GOODSON, Kenneth Stewart
Jefferson HS; Dayton, OH; All Amer Yth; Parl, Bus C; Fr C; FBLA; Var C; Bkbl; Bkbl; Ftbl; COM; Cl Fav; Hon Prog; Sci A; Star Student; High Hons; Completeness A; *U of Cincinnati; Computer Programing Tech.*

GOODSON, Lucretia Renee
Crosby HS; Waterbury, CT (40-495) Chor; Ntl Yth Conf; JV, Sftbl; Hon Prog; *Commerical Art.*

GOODSON, Peggy Ann
Sunbright HS; Sunbright, TN (10-66) BC; FHA; Tres, 4H; Ed, Sch P; 4H A; Spch A; Bicentennial, Baking, A's; *U of Tenn; Interior Design.*

GOODSON, Sandra Rosilyn
Grand Ridge HS; Grand Ridge, FL (3-50) FHA; Q&S A; Sci A; Spch A; Summa Cum Laude; Type A; Attendance A; U of Fla; Vet Med.

GOODSON, Sharon Joyce
Mississippi Baptist HS; Jackson, MS; Chor; Ensm; VP, Hmrm; Sch P; COM; Cl Fav; HCt; Home Ec A; Pres, Jr Civitan C; Church Yth Coun.

GOODWILL, Vincent L
Northeastern HS; Detroit, MI; VP, NHS; Citz A; U of Detroit; Bus.

GOODWIN, Becky Jane
Hobbs HS; Hobbs, NM (52-476) Drama; Ger C; Secy, Sch Achieve Tm; Spch C; Thes; JA A; Poet A; Spch A; Child Psych.

GOODWIN, Deborah Anne
Southern HS; Durham, NC (5-350) Ed, Ann; Ensm; Madrigal; Co-Ed, Sch P; Span C; Mgr, Tr; NEDT; HR; Close-Up Prog; Duke U; Law.

GOODWIN, Donna Beth
Eldorosdo HS; Albuquerque, NM; Chldr; Chor; COM; Citz A; Hon Prog; Kiwanis A; Yth Fel; All St Choir; Eng A; Del, World Methodist Conf; Del, World Methodist Conf, Ireland; Sou Methodist U.

GOODWIN, Elizabeth Stuart
R J Reynolds HS; Winston-Salem, NC (19-800) NHS; Span C; Span NHS; Cr-Ctry; Tnns; Opt A; U of NC; Eng.

GOODWIN, Jeanne Cecile
Herndon HS; Herndon, WV (1-58) Band; Chldr; Chor; Secy, FBLA; FHA; S-T, Hmrm; NHS; Sch P; SC; VP, Tri-HiY; Mgr, Bkbl; Mgr, Sftbl; Alg A; Bio A; Hist A; Type A; Home Ec A; Fr A; Sch Ltr & Symbols; Concord Col; Bus.

GOODWIN, Jeffrey Walter
Holt Senior HS; Holt, MI (30-373) Chor; Dbte Tm; Drama; Ensm; NFL; NHS; Order/Arrow; Outst Choir Member; U of Mich; Geol.

GOODWIN, Kevin Charles
John A Rowland HS; Rowland Hts, CA; Band; Ensm; U of Southern Cal; Dentistry.

GOODWIN, Lester Kendall
Industry HS; Industry, IL (7-33) Drama; Fr C; Sci C; Bkbl; Cpt; Ftbl; Tr; HKg; I Dare You; St Scholar; Yth Fel; W Ill U; Archt.

GOODWIN, Lisa Faye
Wade Hampton HS; Greenville, SC; Chor; Bkbl; Sftbl.

GOODWIN, Marty Keith
Sheridan HS; Sheridan, AR; FFA; Bsbl; Bkbl; Ftbl; Swim; Tr; Tnns; 4H A; HKg; Ltrman's C; Best All Around; Ath o-t Yr; Hon Cert, Tr; U of Ark; Agr.

GOODWIN, Mary Alice
Sacred Heart Acad; Salem, OR (4-48) Ed, Ann; Co-Cpt, Chldr; Fin, Community Yth S; NHSh; Co-Ed, Sch P; Swim; Tnns; COM; Yth Leg; Bus Mgr, Annual; Swtht Ball Princess; Pres, Pep C; U of Notre Dame; Eng.

GOODWIN, Mary Ann
Eisenhower HS; Rialto, CA; Azurettes Service C; San Bdno Valley Col; Early Childhood Ed.

GOODWIN, Mary Margaret
Presbyterian Pan Amer Sch; Kingsville, TX; A Cap Choir; Co-Ed, Ann; Pres, Jr Cl; Bkbl; Hon Prog; Sociology.

GOODWIN, Michael Warren
Daniel M Therrell HS; Atlanta, GA (2-313) Band; BC; Dbte Tm; Drama; FBLA; Ger C; Hmrm; Model UN; Rptr, NHS; Sch P; Pres, Sci C; SC; Tres, Jr Cl; Hon Prog; JA A; ROTC A; Semi-Fin, Sen Yth Prog; Princeton U; Pol Sci.

GOODWIN, Nancy Jean
James Madison HS; Rochester, NY (1-230) Chor; NHS; Soccer; Mgr, Sftbl; Math A; Regent Schol; Sci A; Val; Standard Bearer, UN Pilgrimage; Monroe Comm Col; Acct.

GOODWIN, Robin Renee
Southern HS; Durham, NC; Cpt, Chldr; Span C; Sftbl; Tnns; Tr; Chldr A.

GOODWIN, Scott Allan
Beverly HS; Beverly, MA (107-581) Order/Arrow; Sch P; Bsbl; Ftbl; Eagle Sct; Brian Hubis Sportsmanship A; Brian Hubis Campership A; HR; Colorado St U; Elec Engr.

GOODWIN, Shari Leigh
Terrell Co HS; Dawson, GA (3-200) Ann; BC; Chldr; Pres, Tri-HiY.

GOODWIN, Sheri Ann
Winfield HS; Winfield, KS (10%-218) A Cap Choir; Community Yth Symph; Ensm; 4H; Hmrm; Orch; Sftbl; Tnns; 4H A; Amer Federated Mus A; Mus.

GOODWIN, Susan Juanita
John Hay HS; Cleveland, OH; Cuyahoga Comm Col; Vet.

GOODWINE, Pamela Renee
South HS; Youngstown, OH (1-238) Chldr; Chor; Drama; Hmrm; NHS; Secy, SC; Y-Tns; Bkbl; Tr; Alg A; COM; Hon Prog; JA A; MLS; Most Out; Rotary A; Type A; Val; Sewing, Bus, A's; Outst Stu; NW Col; Acct.

GOODWINE, Phyllis Marie
South HS; Youngstown, OH (8-238) Chess C; Chor; Hmrm; Ed, Sch P; Secy, Spch C; SC; Tr; Bio A; COM; Journ A; Most Out; Spch A; Northwestern U; Communications.

GOODYEAR, Lori Ann
Phillipsburg HS; Phillipsburg, NJ; Drama; Secy, Fr C; SC; Yth Fel; Philadelphia Dist Impact Tm; Hostess C; Psych.

GOOGE, Jim Harold
Booneville HS; Booneville, MS (5-103) Ann; BC; Dbte Tm; 4H; Hmrm; Tres, Lat C; Math C; Sci C; SC; Pres, Sr Cl; Tr; Citz A; 4H A; H of F; HCt; MLS; Northeast Miss Jr Col; Pre-Med.

GOOLSBY, Cheryl Leigh
Los Fresnos HS; Los Fresnos, TX (1-113) FFA; NHS; SC; VP, Sr Cl; Bkbl; Hon Prog; Val; Hi-Ten; Southwost Col; Elem Ed.

GOOLSBY, Linda Louise
Latexo HS; Latexo, TX (3-17) Pres, FHA; SC; JV, Bkbl; COM; Crisco A; HCt; Vlbl; Sam Houston St U; Bus.

GOON, Julie Lynn
Longmont Sr HS; Longmont, CO (9-597) Rptr, AFS; Ann; Fr C; NHS; Rptr, Sch P; Journ A; Math A; Ch, Earth C; Fr A; Span A; Engr.

GOOS, Jane Ann
Treynor Comm HS; Treynor, IA (20-50) Chldr; Golf; Iowa St U; Ed.

GOOSBY, Gary Lee
Murray-Wright HS; Detroit, MI; Lawrence Col; Engr.

GORA, Cynthia Gay
Columbia HS; Maplewood, NJ (61%-669) V-Ch, Hmrm; MVP, Bkbl; Artist, Yth Group; Church Yth Singing Group; Rptr Church Newspaper; Northeastern Bible Col; Christian Ed.

GORBY, Gary Lee
W Branch HS; Beloit, OH (1-235) Pres, Chor; Ensm; Lat C; Pres, NHS; SC; Var C; Pres, Sr Cl; Pres, Jr Cl; Tnns; Amer Leg A; Bio A; Summa Cum Laude; Val; Del, BS; Youngstown St U; Med.

GORBY, Jill Elizabeth
W Branch HS; Beloit, OH (10-220) Chldr; Chor; Var C; Tr; Vlbl.

GORDEN, Cullen Wadsworth
Franklin Learning Center; Philadelphia, PA; SC; Sftbl; Tnns; Tr; Amer Leg A; Pastoral Stu.

GORDEN, LaDonna Kay
Panhandle HS; Panhandle, TX (10-50) A-Ed, Ann; Band; Pres, Chor; FHA; Secy, 4H; Hmrm; NHS; SC; Co-Cpt, Bkbl; Sftbl; Tnns; Tr; 4H A; Showmanship A; Tex A&M U; Phys Therapist.

GORDIN, Anita Louise
Middletown HS; Middletown, OH (236-493) Chor; Drill Tm; Pres, Girl's Assembly; Bowling Green U; Acct.

GORDON, Beth Ann
Calvary Christian Sch; Glens Falls, NY (1-4) Chldr; Chor; Ensm; Span C; Span NHS; SC; Cl Fav; MLS; Vlbl.

GORDON, Carl Ray
Bellflower HS; Bellflower, CA (44-424) Chor; Ensm; Key C; Bsbl.

GORDON, Charles Edward
Charles B Glenn HS; Birmingham, AL; Pres, Hmrm; Sci C; Cl Fav; U of Ala.

GORDON, Cynthia Yvette
Rolling Fork HS; Rolling Fork, MS (1-81) Ed, Ann; Band; Chor; Ensm; FHA; Mjrte; Tres, NHS; A-Ed, Sch P; Pres, SC; Beauty; B Crocker A; Chem A; Spch A; Star Student; Summa Cum Laude; Val; Most Intellectual; Miss Power and Light Schol; Delta St U; Finance.

GORDON, Debbie Lynn
Jesse Stuart HS; Louisville, KY; Lat C; Var C; Hockey; Sftbl; Ky Weslyan Col; Elem Ed.

GORDON, Deborah Ann
Gilmer Co HS; Glenville, WV (15-122) FHA; Secy, 4H; SC; St Polled Hereford Qn; St Poultry Princess; Glenville St Col; Math.

GORDON, Denise Ann
Muskogee HS; Muskogee, OK (55-600) Chess C; Chor; Secy, Ger C; GS; Rainbow; Sch P; Y-Tns; COM; Hon Prog; Opt A; St Essay Contest Win; Bicen Courier to Denmark, YFU; U of Ark.

GORDON, Diana Carol
Madison HS; Richmond, KY; BC; Mjrte; Sci C; COM; 4H A; Opt A; Opt Out Tn; Fr A; Eng A; Home Ec A; Eastern Ky U; Bus.

GORDON, Donald Dennis
Bloom Township HS; Chicago Heights, IL (175-1105) Bkbl; Cpt, Ftbl; E Ill U; Sociology.

GORDON, Douglas Bruce
Salem HS; Salem, OH (1-299) Band; BS; Ger C; Pres, InterAct C; Math C; Mu Alpha Theta; SC; Alg A; Bausch & Lomb A; Jr Chamber of Com A; NMF; Ntl Sci Symposium; Val; Pres, Sing-Out Salem; Case Western Reserve Col; Engr.

GORDON, Glenda Ann
Marion Abramson Sr HS; New Orleans, LA; Drama; Citz A; Math A; Computer Prog.

GORDON, Gregory Eugene
Miami Central HS; Miami, FL; VP, Chess C; Drama; Thes; Swim; Alg A; Math A; Drama A; Eng A; Phys Ed A.

GORDON, Heather Elizabeth
Springfield HS; Springfield, OR (8-347) Band; Chor; Ger C; George Fox Col; Lib Arts.

GORDON, Jack Andrew Jr
Trinity Christian Acad; Jacksonville, FL (7-95) Chor; Dbte Tm; Ger C; Ftbl; Opt A; Spch A; Jacksonville U; Law.

GORDON, Judith Ann
Neptune Sr HS; Neptune, NJ (43-549) Pres, Fr C; Semi-Fin, GS; NHS; Omega Psi Phi A; Schol Ltr; Princeton U; Biochem.

GORDON, Katherine Logan
La Jolla HS; La Jolla, CA (52-500) Chor; Tres, Fr C; Lit Mag; Chem.

GORDON, Kay Lucinda
McConnellsburg HS; McConnellsburg, PA (1-80) Band; Chor; NHS; Sch P; JV, Hockey; Outst Explorer Post Pres; Mason-Dixon Coun; Explorer Rookie o-t Yr; Med Tech.

GORDON, Kimberly Joyce
Frederick Douglass HS; Atlanta, GA (13-347) Band; FBLA; Tres, NHS; F-Ed, Sch P; SC; Rptr, Sr Cl; Tnns; COM; HCt; Journ A; MLS; WSB Great Young Amer; Debutante; Flute Section Ldr, Band; Marching, Honorary Concert, Bands; U of Tenn; Acct.

GORDON, Laurene Marie
Northwood-Kensett HS; Northwood, IA (13-68) Ed, Ann; Chldr; Chor; 4H; Sch P; Tr; N Iowa Area Comm Col; Med Secy.

GORDON, Linda Olga
Eddyville HS; Eddyville, OR (2-17) S-T, Jr Cl; Bkbl; Mgr, Ftbl; Tr; Vlbl; Oreg St U; Phys Ed.

GORDON, Lisa Catherine
Hooper Acad; Hope Hull, AL (5-69) Ann; VP, BC; VP, Chor; Math C; Ed, Sch P; Sci C; SC; Journ A; MLS; Ntl Sch Choral A; Bus A; Pres, FHA; Miss FSA; U of Ala; Early Childhood Development.

GORDON, Lydia Sheree
Wayne Co HS; Jesup, GA; Ann; BC; Chldr; 4H; NHS; SC; Secy, Sr Cl; HCt; NEDT; Stetson U; Piano.

GORDON, Pamela Denise
Crestview Sr HS; Crestview, FL (13-300) Chor; FTA; Hmrm; SC; COM; Type A.

GORDON, Peter Albert
Gaithersburg HS; Gaithersburg, MD (20%-500) Chess C; NHS; COM; *Engr.*

GORDON, Robert Bruce
Big Sandy HS; Big Sandy, TX (10%-44) Band; Chess C; Community Yth Symph; NHS; Sch P; SC; Bkbl; Tr; Wrest; Hist A; Highest GPA; *Ambassador Col.*

GORDON, Scott Brian
Thomas Jefferson HS; Denver, CO; Bus C; Chor; Tnns; *Colo U; Bus.*

GORDON, Sheryl Annette
Memorial HS; Tulsa, OK (76-586) Chor; Ensm; Fr C; Tr; Qn, Tres, Church Yth; Yth Board; Yth Choir; *Okla St U; Archt Engr.*

GORDON, Steve Philip
Everett Jr HS; Lincoln, NE (10%-300) Rptr, Sch P; Bsbl; Swim; Star Sct; HR; Win, Sct Patch Design; SPL, Scts; *Air Force Acad; Aerodynics.*

GORDON, Susan Reilly
Batavia HS; Batavia, IL; Band; Ensm; Sch P; Ski C; SC; Sftbl; Pres A; *Interior Design.*

GORDON, Thomas Chillison
Ironton HS; Ironton, OH (26-220) Sci C; Span C; Cpt, Bkbl; Ftbl; Phy A; Sci A; *Jamestown Col; Chem.*

GORE, Alberta Yvonne
Myrtle Beach HS; Myrtle Beach, SC (50%-250) Band; Chldr; Chor; Ensm; Rptr, Sch P; Yth Fel; Dancing A; Christian Service A; Gym A; Pom Pon A; Chldr A; *Coastal Carolina Col; Secretarial Sci.*

GORE, Elizabeth Marie
W Geauga HS; Chesterland, OH; A Cap Choir; Band; Chor; Hmrm; Orch; SC; VP, Jr Cl; VP, Soph Cl.

GORE, Eric Craig
Savannah HS; Savannah, GA; HR; *Savannah St Col; Communications.*

GORE, Howard Andre
Kinston HS; Kinston, NC; Band; HiY; Mus A; *Drew U; Bus.*

GORE, Julie Lynn
Bellflower HS; Bellflower, CA; Chor; Ensm; B Crocker A; CSF; Hon Prog; Outst Church Tn; *Mus.*

GORE, Louise Ann
Zephyrhills HS; Zephyrhills, FL (7-159) F-Ed, Ann; Cpt, Chldr; Drama; Fr C; FHA; GS; Lit Mag; NHS; A-Ed, Sch P; SC; Tres, Jr Cl; Tres, Soph Cl; Tr; Cl Fav; HCt; Drum Major; Sup Ratng, St Cont, Piano Solo; *Fla St U; Mus.*

GORE, Shelia Ann
Scott HS; Madison, WV; NHS; Bkbl; *W Va U; Ed.*

GORGES, Michael James
Moreau HS; Hayward, CA (23-348) Fr C; Hmrm; Rptr, Sch P; Ski C; JV, Tnns; Hon Prog; *Columbia U; International Relations.*

GORHAM, Denise Michelle
Clearview HS; Lorain, OH (17-109) Band; Bkbl; HR; Merit Roll; *Lorain Comm Col; Television Communications.*

GORIS, Marilyn Anne
Little Wolf HS; Manawa, WI (5-80) Band; Hmrm; Math C; NHS; ARC; Ski C; Span C; VP, SC; Pres, Soph Cl; Mgr, Bsbl; Elk A; Math A; Pres A; ARC A; Pep C; *U of Wis; Psych.*

GORLEY, Rodney Eric
Princeton HS; Cincinnati, OH; Chem C; Fr C; French NHS; Hmrm; NHS; SC; MVP, Bkbl; MVP, Ftbl; Tr; MVP, Wrest; Bio A; HKg; Math A; Most Out; Sci A; Chem A; *Sci.*

GORMAN, Anthony Duane
Halter HS; Weldon, MO (1-58) Band; Bsbl; Cpt, Bkbl; Hon Prog; Val; *Miss Valley St U; Phys Ed.*

GORMAN, Jane Ann
Fulton HS; Knoxville, TN; Anchor C; Co-Cpt, Chldr; NHS; Y-Tns; Secy, Sr Cl; Fin, Tnns; COM; HCt; Pres A; WW; Girl's St Rep; *U of Tenn; Col of Nurs.*

GORMAN, John Courtney
Marion HS; Marion, IN; Swim; Tnns; Yth Fel; Stu Govt; Project Up; *Med.*

GORMAN, John Eugene
St Edwards HS; Lakewood, OH (25%-350) A Cap Choir; CYO; Chor; Drama; Ntl Yth Conf; Span C; Spch C; Fin, Swim; *Borromeo Seminary; Theology.*

GORMAN, Richard Edward
Archmere Acad; Claymont, DE; NHS; Sci C; Ski C; VP, Span C; Span NHS; Tr; Wrest.

GORMAN, Tami Ann
Cottage Grove HS; Cottage Grove, OR (31-300) AFS; F-Ed, Ann; F-Ed, Lit Mag; Rainbow; Secy, SC; Tr; Gym; *Med.*

GORMLEY, Cathy Anne
John A Brashear HS; Pittsburgh, PA; CYO; NHS; Sftbl; Swim; Tnns; Hon Prog; Presidential; Explorer; Sr Life Savings; *U of Pittsburgh; Law.*

GORMLEY, Shauna Marie
Butler HS; Butler, NJ; Var C; Fencing; *Co Col of Morris.*

GOROUCH, Debi Lynn
Arcadia HS; Arcadia, CA (156-806) A Cap Choir; Chor; Hmrm; Key C; Ski C; SC; Sftbl; Swim; Drill Tm; Jr Exchange C; Kindergarten Sunday Sch Teacher; Cpt, Church Ushering Tm; Elem PE Teacher, Visually Handicap; *Cal Poly; Child Development.*

GORTON, Kirk Arthur
Herbert Hoover HS; Glendale, CA; Chor.

GORZELANSKI, Laura Anne
St Mary's Acad; Englewood, CO (3-50) CYO; Chor; Secy, French NHS; Pres, Lat C; NHS; Opt A; Spch A; Star Student; Specialized Musical Organization; *Creighton U; Med.*

GOSET, Cheryl LeAnn
Kingman HS; Kingman, KS (17-117) Band; Chor; Ensm; Madrigal; VP, Sci C; Ch, Y-Tns; Bkbl; Sftbl; Tr; COM; Hon Prog; Yth Leg; FCA; Band Ltr; Choir Ltr; Bowl; Madrigal Medal; Ensm Medal; Vlbl; Pres, BYF.

GOSHA, Tonya LaShon
Hardaway HS; Columbus, GA; Anchor C; Band; Span C; Cert of Schol; Outst Acad; *Med.*

GOSHEA, Hilton
Russell HS; Hurtsboro, AL; Chem C; 4H; Lit Mag; VP, NHS; SC; Hist A; Hon Prog; ROTC A; PA; Eng A; Drivers Ed; *Ala A&M U.*

GOSHEN, Brian William
Central Jersey Christian Sch; Asbury Park, NJ (1-10) Chess C; Fr C; Lit Mag; Bsbl; Bkbl; Soccer; JV, Tnns; MVP, Tr; HCt; Hon Prog; *Hist.*

GOSS, Anita Sheri
Polytechnic HS; Ft Worth, TX; Chldr; 4H; SC; *N Tex St Col; Nurs.*

GOSS, Donna M
Sebastopol HS; Sebastopol, MS (5%-45) Co-Ed, Ann; Band; BC; Co-Ch, Drama; Ensm; FHA; Cpt, Mjrte; Orch; SC; Mgr, Bkbl; HCt; Hon Prog; WW; Civics Cert; *Miss Col.*

GOSS, Gina Liegh
Roxana HS; Roxana, IL (79-230) Band; Chor; Mjrte; SC; *Sou Ill U; Childcare.*

GOSS, Michael Anthany
Poly HS; Ft Worth, TX; *Tarrant Co Jr Col; Bus.*

GOSS, Michael Keith
Cedar Bluff HS; Cedar Bluff, AL (1-30) BC; BS; VP, FFA; VP, 4H; Parl, Math C; Co-Ed, Sch P; Pres, SC; Pres, Sr Cl; VP, Jr Cl; DARGCA; 4H A; MLS; Sci A; Val; *Jacksonville St U.*

GOSS, Mitchell Wayne
Wolfe City HS; Wolfe City, TX (10-145) Ann; BC; FTA; Math C; Rptr, Sch P; Sci C; Bkbl; Tnns; Hon Prog; Sci A; Top Schol A; Church Usher Board; Lib Aid; Teacher Aid; Church Choir; *E Tex St U; Bio.*

GOSS, Rebecca Andrea
Greater Atlanta Christian HS; Norcross, GA; Fr C; Sci C; Bkbl; Citz A; *Harding Col; Law.*

GOSS, Samuel Edward
Colonial Hills Christian HS; E Point, GA (5-30) Ann; Band; BC; NHS; Rptr, Sch P; Pres, Soph Cl; Mgr, Bkbl; Ftbl; Outst Sct; *Ga Tech; Civil Engr.*

GOSSAR, Peg Annette
Providence HS; New Lenox, IL (63-206) Chor; Secy, FTA; Ed, Sch P; Amer Leg A; Journ A; PTA A; 2nd Pl, Sci Fair; *Religious Ed.*

GOSSELIN, Michael Leon
Don Bosco Tech HS; Boston, MA (6-211) CYO; NHS; Cr-Ctry; Cpt, Swim; COM; Holy Name A; *Boston Col; Pre-Med.*

GOSSETT, Garrie Lynne
Central HS; Memphis, TN (87-260) Secy, Chor; Rptr, Sch P; Span C; SC; Yth Fel; Ntl Jr Hon Soc; HS Rptr; SC Rep; *Memphis St U; Comm.*

GOSSETT, Mark Walter
Greenfield Central HS; Greenfield, IN (30-300) BS; Pres, Chor; Pres, Drama; Pres, 4H; Hmrm; Madrigal; Math C; NHS; Order/Arrow; Sci C; SC; Pres, Thes; Var C; Swim; Tnns; 4H A; NEDT; Eagle Sct; Exercise in Knowledge Tm; Independents; Bicentennial Show; *Purdue U; Biochem.*

GOSSETT, Phillip Reginald
Douglass HS; Memphis, TN; Parl, Bus C; Dbte Tm; Bus Mgr, FBLA; Pres, Lat C; Lat NHS; ARC; Var C; Cr-Ctry; Ftbl; Swim; Tr; COM; Citz A; Cl Fav; Hist A; HCt; Hon Prog; JA A; Most Out; ROTC A; Star Student; *Morris Brown Col; Pol Sci.*

GOTH, John Joseph
Montrose R14 HS; Montrose, MO (6-26) Bsbl; Bkbl; Cr-Ctry; COM; Bookkeeping A; General Bus A.

GOTSCHALL, Cindie LeAnn
Hoisington HS; Hoisington, KS (1-90) F-Ed, Ann; Cpt, Chldr; VP, NHS; Tres, Soph Cl; St Scholar; *Kans St Col; Bus.*

GOTSCHALL, Steven Charles
St John Lutheran HS; Ocala, FL (5-25) Band; Chess C; Drama; NHS; *Elec Engr.*

GOTTBERG, Melanie Denise
David Anderson HS; Lisbon, OH (2-120) Band; Chor; Ensm; Fr C; VP, FTA; Semi-Fin, GS; VP, 4H; InterClub Coun; NHS; Sci C; Y-Tns; Sftbl; 4H A; Secy, 4-H C; DAR Essay A; Jazz Band; Comm Yth Choir; JV Vlbl; *Ohio St U; Optometrist.*

GOTTMAN, Dee
Druid Hills HS; Atlanta, GA (48-184) Band; Community Yth Symph; Drama; Ensm; Hmrm; Orch; SC; Mgr, Bsbl; Mgr, Bkbl; Ftbl; Hockey; Tr; Cl Fav; Stu Coun Service A; Yth o-t Yr; Jr Cl Service A; Cpt's A; WW; Most Dependable; Best Lineman As; Faithful Serv A; *Elec Engr.*

GOTTSCH, Kenneth Herbert
Bennington Pub Sch; Bennington, NE (12-42) BS; Chor; Pres, 4H; VP, NHS; Pres, Var C; Bsbl; Bkbl; Ftbl; Tr; 4H A; HCt; Hon Prog; *Midland Col; Math.*

GOTTSCHALK, Douglas Lee
Perry HS; Perry, OK (3%-130) BS; Rptr, FFA; NHS; Ftbl; Tr; JV, Wrest; Citz A; Hist A; *Okla St U; Vet Med.*

GOUDE, Trudy Carol
Western Alamance HS; Elon College, NC (126-250) Tech Inst of Alamance; *Interior Decorating.*

GOUGE, Mary Elizabeth
SW Miami HS; Miami, FL; Drama; FTA; Hmrm; ARC; Swim; Beauty; Most Dep; Drama Cert; Chor Cert, Outst Grades; *Bradley U; Bus Adm.*

GOUGH, Karen Michele
Starmount HS; Boonville, NC (10%-211) Cpt, Chldr; Chor; FHA; SC; Sftbl; Tnns; HCt; *U of NC; Acct.*

GOUGHENOUR, Cynthia Lee
Salem Sr HS; Salem, OH (50%-299) FHA.

GOUIN, Diane Mary
Big Bay de Noc HS; Cooks, MI; Cpt, Chldr; Pres, SC; Bus Mgr, Bkbl; Bus Mgr, Tr; Bausch & Lomb A; Bio A; HCt; *Mich St U; Acct.*

GOULARTE, Joseph Paul
Bellingham HS; Bellingham, WA (30-310) VP, CYO; Chem C; VP, Sci C; Kg A, CYO; *Stanford U; Med.*

GOULD, Benson Robert
Northridge Jr-Sr HS; Whitinsville, MA (15-150) Band; Chess C; Drama; Fr C; NHS; Order/Arrow; Mgr, Bkbl; Cr-Ctry; Tr; Order/Arrow A; Eagle Sct; Ltr of Commendation; Gold Medalist; *Worcester Polytechnic Inst; Chem.*

GOULD, Hal William
St Francisville HS; St Francisville, LA; Band; Rptr, Sch P; Outst Musician; Yth Coun Member; Yth Photographer; *LSU; Journ.*

GOULD, Julie Beth
Humble HS; Humble, TX; FBLA; FHA; VOE; *Bus.*

GOULD, Melissa Lee
La Marque HS; La Marque, TX (22-550) Ed, Ann; Pres, Bus C; Drama; FHA; Hmrm; NHS; Pres, Rainbow; Thes; *Baylor U; Journ.*

GOULD, Michele Marion
Piscataquis Comm HS; Guilford, ME; Chor; FNA; 4H; ARC; GSct; Crusade Choir; Photo C; Clean Up Your Comm Comm; Lib Aid; Church Chor; Church Yth Group; Scorekeeper, Pee Wee Bkbl Tm.

GOULD, Michelle Ilona
E Ridge HS; E Ridge, TN (134-287) Commercial C; Span C; COM; *Chattanooga St Comm Col; Bus Ed.*

GOULD, Rodney Dale
Fairfield Comm HS; Fairfield, IL (25-155) VP, Band; Pres, Chess C; Pres, Dbte Tm; Ensm; Lat C; Monogram; Orch; VP, Pol Sci C; Var C; Bsbl; JV, Bkbl; Mgr, Ftbl; Tnns; COM; Hist A; NEDT; Yth Fel; *Cincinnati Bible Col; Ministry.*

GOULD, Roxanne Eileen
Imlay City HS; Imlay City, MI; Sftbl.

GOULDING, Timothy Scott
Southwestern Central HS; Jamestown, NY (5-189) Ed, Ann; Dbte Tm; NFL; NHS; Order/Arrow; Span C; Mgr, Ftbl; Mgr, Tr; Citz A; Hon Prog; Order/Arrow A; ARC A; Spch A; Alt, Regent's Schol; Fin, ROTC A; Prodeo Et Patria A; *Purdue U; Chem Engr.*

GOULET, Russell William
Clay Sr HS; Oregon, OH (75-393) F-Ed, Ann; Order/Arrow; *Journ.*

GOUR, Richard Emmett
Roy HS; Roy, UT (24-420) AFS; Band; VP, Chess C; Dbte Tm; Key C; NHS; COM; Math A; PTA A; Sci A; Spch A; Yth Leg; VICA; Ger A; VICA Skills Olympics; *U of Utah; Mech Engr.*

GOURDIN, Theodore Gaillard
Williamsburg Acad; Kingstree, SC (1-50) Secy, Key C; NHS; Ed, Sch P; JV, Bkbl; Tnns; Gov Honor Prog; Gr Marshal; Hist A; Journ A; Val; Block WA C; Wofford Sch; PC Schol; Most Intellectual; Newberry Schol; 'A' HR; Woodmen o-t World A; Daughters of Amer Colonists A; *Col of Charleston.*

GOURDINE, Harriet Loretta
James Island HS; Charleston, SC; Chldr; Fr C; Math C; Mu Alpha Theta; Y-Tns; HQn; *U of SC; Bus Adm.*

GOURLEY, Anita Dawn
Southwood HS; Shreveport, LA (23-446) Bus C; Secy, Fr C; French NHS; NHS; SC; Y-Tns; COM; *Secy.*

GOURLEY, Barbara Jean
University HS; San Diego, CA (1-374) Chor; Drama; Secy, 4H; 4H A; Hon Prog; Spch A; *Eng.*

GOUVEIA, Donna Marie
St Joseph's Regional HS; Lowell, MA; *Lowell General Hosp Sch of Nurs; Nurs.*

GOVAN, Arlene Renee
Herbert Hoover HS; San Diego, CA; 4H; Y-Tns; Sftbl; Phy A; *City Col; Beautician.*

GOVAN, Lesila Lynnette
Douglass HS; Memphis, TN; Chor; FHA; ARC; Lit Exposition; Phys Fitness; Daughters o-t Amer Revolution; *Model.*

GOVAN, Ruth
Highland HS; Anderson, IN (165-456) Home Ec A.

GOVE, Alan Paul
St Johns HS; St Johns, MI (10%-365) Band; Bsbl; Bkbl; Tnns; Tn o-t Wk.

GOW, John Hugh Fulton
Bishop Turner HS; Buffalo, NY (9-169) NEDT; Varsity Academic Ltr; *Bryant & Stratton Col; Acct.*

GOWAN, Karen Ann
Trezevant HS; Trezevant, TN; Chldr; Chor; Tres, FHA; Miss THS; *Union U; Elem Ed.*

GOWAN, Ronda Lynn
Three Rivers HS; Three Rivers, MI (32-214) GS; Rotary A; *Olivet Nazarene Col.*

GOWDY, Denise Elaine
Aledo HS; Aledo, IL (13-110) AFS; Band; S-T, Chor; VP, 4H; Bkbl; Tr; 4H A; Jr Historian's St A; Co Essay A, Farm Bureau; *Ill St U; Musical Therapy.*

GOWEN, Pamela Ann
Dover HS; Dover, NH (10-396) Pres, Band; Chor; Drama; Lit Mag; NHS; Pres, Span C; Spch A; All-St Chor; All-Eastern Chor; Original Song, Ntl Schol Writing A; *UNH; Mus.*

GOWER, Julie Ann
Flemington HS; Flemington, WV (2-43) VP, FHA; Citz A; Hist A; W Va Golden Horseshoe; *W Va U; Law.*

GOWER, Linda Michelle
Maysville Sr HS; Maysville, OK (27-40) FHA; Okmulgee St Tech Col; Art.

GOWLAND, Kimbal Lauren
Payette HS; Payette, ID (3-103) BS; Chem C; Secy, FFA; Pres, Ger C; InterClub Coun; Key C; Pres, NHS; Phys C; Sci C; VP, Ski C; Pres, Span C; SC; Var C; Cpt, Golf; COM; Chem A; MLS; Yth Leg; *U of Idaho; Agr Econ.*

GRABER, Kathleen Marie
Mercy HS; Albany, NY (1-115) Ann; Chldr; Drama; Fr C; Lit Mag; NHS; Bio A; Hon Prog; NEDT; HS Schol; Co-Ch, Prom Comm; Eng A; Social Action C; Intercl Play.

GRABLE, Elizabeth Ann
Crestwood HS; Dunwoody, GA; Secy, AFS; BC; Chldr; Secy, FBLA; *Col of William & Mary; Elem Ed.*

GRACE, Nadine Michelle
Miami Northwestern Sr HS; Miami, FL (14-390) Chor; InterClub Coun; Math C; NHS; Citz A; Hon Prog; Math A; Most Out; Sci A; 1st Att Sch Qn; Miss Seventeen; *Bethune Cookman Col; Engr.*

GRACE, Natalie Joetta
T R Miller HS; Brewton, AL; Chor; Fr C; FHA; Secy, 4H; NHS; Y-Tns; Bkbl; Sftbl; Swim; Tnns; Tr; Alg A; Beauty; COM; 4H A; Hist A; Math A; Sci A; Spch A; Type A; Yth Fel; Win, Miss Comm Pageant; *Pepperdine U; Guidance Counselor.*

GRACE, Warren Scott
Hopkinsville HS; Hopkinsville, KY (34-341) BC; Chess C; JV, Ftbl; Mgr, Swim; COM; NEDT; Sci A; NHS; Top 5%, Ntl Merit Schol Test; *Marine Biol.*

GRADDICK, Barbara Lynne
Eau Claire HS; Columbia, SC (13-359) Fr C; NHS; NHS A; *U of SC; Med.*

GRADER, Mark Peter
Norwich Free Acad; Norwich, CT; Band; Hon Prog.

GRADNEY, Cheryl Lynne
Hardin-Jefferson HS; Sour Lake, TX (50-112) Band; Hmrm; SC; COM; Type A; Secy, DEA; Nom, MLS; Area Win, OEA; All Dist Band; Band A; *Lamar U; Bus.*

GRADNEY, Gerald Glenn
Hardin-Jefferson HS; Sour Lake, TX (73-150) Band; Fr C; VICA.

GRADY, Eunice Ray
Wingfield HS; Jackson, MS; *Med.*

GRADY, Gloria Jean
S Garland HS; Garland, TX (156-645) A Cap Choir; Madrigal; ARC; SC; COM; Interlochen Ntl Mus; *Baylor U; Mus.*

GRADY, Jodi Lynn
Tippecanoe HS; Tipp City, OH (5-200) Ed, Ann; Band; Semi-Fin, GS; Mjrte; NHS; Secy, SC; Beauty; COM; HCt; Hon Prog; Lifeguard; Candy Striper; Baton Teacher; Sun Sch Teacher; *U of Cincinnati; Nurs.*

GRADY, Karen Denise
NW HS; St Louis, MO (80-400) S-T, A Cap Choir; Chor; Secy, Hmrm; Mjrte; Cl Fav; *Central St U; Eng.*

GRADY, Maureen Elizabeth
St Mary's Acad; Englewood, CO (6-50) Chldr; Chor; Dbte Tm; Ski C; SC; Bsbl; Sftbl; Tnns; HCt; *Colo St U; Wildlife Bio.*

GRADY, Otis Lee
Crenshaw HS; Los Angeles, CA (50-1200) FFA; K of C; Mgr, Tnns; CSF; K of C A; Future Doctors of Amer; *UCLA; Med.*

GRAEBER, O Mardell
Evergreen HS; Seattle, WA; Chor; Ger C; Hmrm; Bus Mgr, Mjrte; Orch; Rptr, Sch P; SC.

GRAETHER, Anna Noel
Washington HS; Kansas City, KS (22-595) 4H; NHS; Rptr, Sch P; COM; St Scholar; Type A; Art C; Scholastic Art A.

GRAF, Pamela Marie
Maryvale HS; Cheektowaga, NY; Band; Chldr; Chor; Fr C; Hmrm; SC; Bkbl; COM; Star Student; Erie Co Band Recognition; *Occupational Therapy.*

GRAF, Reed Arthur
Wheaton Warrenville HS; Wheaton, IL (35-330) Tres, AFS; Ger C; NHS; Sch P; Thes; Var C; Golf; Soccer; Cpt, Tr; Commencement Spkr; *Knox Col; Math.*

GRAFELMAN, Lyle Ray
Lincoln NE HS; Lincoln, NE (24-531) Band; JV, Bsbl; JV, Bkbl; JV, Tnns; *Bus.*

GRAFF, Bret Matthew
Hickory HS; Hickory, NC (10%-460) BC; Span C; Golf; COM; Church Coun Yth Rep; *U of NC at Chapel Hill; Sci.*

GRAFF, Resa Fay
Bruriah HS; Elizabeth, NJ (4-26) Dbte Tm; NHS; Ch, Charity Comm; Tutor Comm; Mus C.

GRAFFIS, Ardath F
Joliet Central HS; Joliet, IL (8-555) Community Yth Symph; Math C; NHS; Pres, Orch; SC; HCt; Hon Prog; Ntl Sch Orch Assn A; *U of Ill-Urbana; Environmental Sci.*

GRAFFIS, Dale Warren
St Joseph-Ogden HS; St Joseph, IL (8-96) Band; Chor; Monogram; NHS; Ftbl; Tr; Wrest; Hon Prog; St Scholar; Pres, FCA; *Valparaiso U; Civil Engr.*

GRAFFT, Charles David
Carlsbad HS; Carlsbad, CA (40-400) AFS; Ann; Drama; Hmrm; InterClub Coun; Ch, Model UN; NFL; Pres, SC; JV, Tnns; Hon Prog; Most Out; *Stanford U; Pol Sci.*

GRAFFT, Paul Willard
Miramonte HS; Orinda, CA (15%-430) Semi-Fin, BS; Cpt, Chldr; Cpt, Hmrm; InterClub Coun; Ski C; SC; Var C; Bsbl; Cpt, Soccer; CSF; Hon Prog; All League, MVP, Soccer; Rep, Orinda Yth As; Chrch Deacon; Champ, Inter-Sch Conf of Vlbl; Intramurals Director; *UCLA; Bus Adm.*

GRAHAM, Angela Lane
Woodland Christian HS; Phenix City, AL (9-29) BC; Span C; *Chattahoochee Valley Col; Acct.*

GRAHAM, Anquinette Denise
Proviso E HS; Maywood, IL (157-712) Chor; Ski C; *Ball St U; Special Ed.*

GRAHAM, Beverly
Albany Acad for Girls; Albany, NY (15-34) SC; Soccer; Modern Dance Workshop; Yrbk Committee; Most Likely to Do Extra Crdt Wrk A.

GRAHAM, Carol Edna
Bluefield HS; Bluefield, WV (8-310) GS; Lat C; NHS; S-T, Bible C; Tres, Jr Civitan C; Pres, Church Yth; *Concord Col; Phys Therapy.*

GRAHAM, Claudia
Wood River HS; Hailey, ID (5-105) Ed, Ann; Fin, GS; NHS; Pres, Ski C; Span C; VP, SC; Pres, Soph Cl; Bkbl; Tr; Amer Leg A; Citz A; Hon Prog; Pres A; Spch A; *U of Sou Calif; Sci.*

GRAHAM, Clifton Leroy
Sumner HS; St Louis, MO (230-450) Chldr; *Southern Ill U; Mortuary Sci.*

GRAHAM, Curtis Allen
Meadville Area Sr HS; Meadville, PA (150-365) Vlbl; Varsity Ltr.

GRAHAM, Dana Anne
Jefferson City HS; Jefferson City, MO (100-550) Fr C; NHS; Hon Prog; Vlbl; *Lincoln U; Bus.*

GRAHAM, Danette
MacKenzie HS; Detroit, MI (14-352) Chor; FTA; NHS; Soccer; Tnns; Citz A; *Detroit Col of Bus; Secy.*

GRAHAM, Danny Edward
Jonesboro-Hodge HS; Jonesboro, LA (20-175) Ed, Ann; VP, Band; Chess C; Ensm; Hmrm; Orch; SC; VP, Sr Cl; Bsbl; Tnns; Cl Fav; Hon Prog; Masonic A; MLS; Poet A; All Star Band; WW; Cpt, Dope Stop; Future Mus Ldrs of Amer; *La Tech U; Acct.*

GRAHAM, Dawn Elaine
Manhattan HS; Manhattan, KS (2%-490) Community Yth Symph; Co-Ch, Orch; Span C; Thes; Job's Daughters; Kans Author's C; Published Author; *Kans U; Lib Arts.*

GRAHAM, Debora Carol
James B Dudley Sr HS; Greensboro, NC; Band; Ensm; VP, 4H; Hmrm; Mjrte; Span C; SC; Tnns; 4H A; JA A; MLS; ROTC A; Swtht; Church Thespians; Ball Qn; *NC Central U; Pol Sci.*

GRAHAM, Debra Valerie
John F Kennedy HS; Bronx, NY (10%-30) Chldr; Chor; Drama; Math C; MVP, Bkbl; Swim; Tr; Phy A; Tr A.

GRAHAM, Diana Marie
Puyallup HS; Puyallup, WA (200-465) AFS; Band; Drama; *Warner Pacific Col; Psych.*

GRAHAM, Elizabeth Jeanne
Central HS; Newnan, GA (10%-400) Ann; BC; Chldr; Drama; Sci C; Pres, SC; Pres, Soph Cl; Sftbl; Swim; COM; Cl Fav; Most Out; NEDT; Yth Fel; *Sci.*

GRAHAM, Elizabeth Suzanne
Hermitage HS; Hermitage, AR (1-50) BC; Chldr; Chor; FHA; Math C; HCt; Eng A; *Ouachita Baptist U.*

GRAHAM, Eunita Maria
Jenkins HS; Savannah, GA; Chldr; Chor; Drama; Pres A; Drama; Dancing; *Savannah Tech Col; Cosmotology.*

GRAHAM, Geoffrey William
Ballard HS; Louisville, KY (56-339) BC; CYO; Ger C; Hmrm; Tres, Key C; ARC; SC; JV, Wrest; Hon Prog; Sci Symp; Retreat Work; Sr Play, Prom & Activities Comm; Confirmation Teacher; Hospital Vol; *de Pauw U; Pre-Med.*

GRAHAM, Gregory Van
Latexo Isd HS; Latexo, TX (6-16) VP, FFA; VP, Sr Cl; Rptr, Jr Cl; Rptr, Soph Cl; Bsbl; Cpt, Bkbl; Ftbl; Sftbl; Tr; Cl Fav; *Sam Houston St U; Agr.*

GRAHAM, Gwendolyn Tabb
The Auburndale Sch; Cordova, TN (21-42) A-Ed, Ann; Cpt, Chldr; Chor; Drama; Fr C; Sch P; Span C; SC; Hmrm; Beauty; HQn; Spch A; 1st Pl, Talent Contest; Miss Auburndale; Pres, Pep C; Church Yth Service Board.

GRAHAM, Jan
Dodge Co HS; Eastman, GA (25-199) FBLA; Pres, 4H; Hmrm; Key C; Span C; SC; Tr; Citz A; 4H A; Math A; 4-H Key C A & Jr Ldrship A; *Ga Sou Col.*

GRAHAM, Jeffery John
Harrison HS; Colo Springs, CO; Bsbl; Ftbl; Golf; Swim.

GRAHAM, Jill Ann
Wooster HS; Wooster, OH (200-400) Band; Secy, 4H; Hmrm; Orch; SC; Bkbl; Tr; COM; Gym.

GRAHAM, Julie
Union HS; Biggsville, IL; A-Ed, Ann; Band; Chess C; Rptr, Drama; NHS; Bkbl; St Scholar; *Western Ill U; Acct.*

GRAHAM, Karen Sue
S Hamilton HS; Jewell, IA (27-78) Ann; Band; Chor; SC; JV, Bkbl; Tr; *Teaching.*

GRAHAM, Kenneth Ross
Oakton HS; Vienna, VA (194-574) VIP; *Acct.*

GRAHAM, Kevin Lee
College HS; Bartlesville, OK (39-320) Chor; Tres, Demolay; Okla Jr HS Hon Soc; Okla Northeast Dist Hon Choir; *U of Okla; Elec Engr.*

GRAHAM, Laurie Theresa
Secaucus HS; Secaucus, NJ (15-185) CYO; Sch P; Journ A.

GRAHAM, Lisa Gale
Shawsville HS; Shawsville, VA (10-100) Band; *Va Tech Col.*

GRAHAM, Mark John
Norwich Free Acad; Norwich, CT (60%-756) Chess C; Order/Arrow; Pol Sci C; ARC; Citz A; Order/Arrow A; *Maharishi International U; Physics.*

GRAHAM, Michael Turner
North State Acad; Hickory, NC (2-12) Drama; Fr C; NHS; Order/Arrow; Sch P; Bsbl; Cpt, Bkbl; Soccer; Cpt, Sftbl; Cpt, Tr; COM; Citz A; God & Country A; Hon Prog; Order/Arrow A; Pres A; Yth Fel; *U of NC; Dentistry.*

GRAHAM, Norman Percy
Trinity Heights Christian Acad; Shreveport, LA (4-65) Lit Ral; Span C; Bsbl; Ftbl; JV, Golf; JV, Tr; Cl Fav; *La Tech Col; Elec.*

GRAHAM, Pamela Marie
Jane Addams Voc HS; Cleveland, OH (9-259) Pres, Dbte Tm; Secy, FHA; Hmrm; NHS; Secy, ARC; Rptr, Sch P; VP, SC; Y-Tns; Tres, Sftbl; VP, Tnns; Secy, Tr; B Crocker A; COM; Citz A; Hon Prog; JA A; MLS; Rotary A; *Cleveland St U; Child Psych.*

GRAHAM, Rivette Ilene
Highland Park Sr HS; St Paul, MN; Yth Fel; Jr Choir; *St Paul TVI; Bus Adm.*

GRAHAM, Robert Samuel
Jackson Prep Sch; Jackson, MS (130-174) Chor; Ensm; Key C; Lat C; Madrigal; Order/Arrow; Sci C; SC; Pres, Jr Cl; Secy, Soph Cl; MVP, Ftbl; Soccer; Tr; Order/Arrow A; Swtht; Most Handsome; Mr Jr Cl; All Conf, Ftbl; Service A.

GRAHAM, Ross Borsodyi
Bassick HS; Bridgeport, CT (70-300) Band; CYO; Best Singer; *Sacred Heart U; Span.*

GRAHAM, Sheila Opal
Passaic HS; Passaic, NJ (4%-525) Chldr; Drama; FTA; Hmrm; Mjrte; Tr; Pom Pon Sq A; Tr Tm; Sch Talent Show; *Criminal Justice.*

GRAHAM, Suzanne Kay
Newton Falls HS; Newton Falls, OH (25-197) Sci C; Span C; Yth Fel; Job's Daughters; *Med.*

GRAHAM, Virginia Elizabeth
Bay HS; Panama City, FL (33%-400) Anchor C; VP, Band; InterClub Coun; HCt; Valentine Qn Court; Band As; *Fla Col; Spch.*

GRAINGER, Pamela Ann
Leeton HS; Leeton, MO (2-21) NFL; NHS; Pres, Rainbow; Thes; 4H A; Journ A; Sal; Shorthand A; Choreography Hon; Debate Hon; *U of Mo at Columbia; Journ.*

GRALEWICZ, Jason Ernst
Greenfield HS; Greenfield, WI (90-412) Band; Chess C; Drama; NHS; Sci C; *U of Wis; Military Sci.*

GRALEWICZ, Thomas Joseph
Greenfield HS; Greenfield, WI (150-400) Band; *Elec.*

GRAMBERG, Curt Allen
O'Neill Pub HS; O'Neill, NE (10%-90) NHS; Order/Arrow; Bkbl; Ftbl; Order/Arrow A; Eagle Sct; Co-Cpt, FCA.

GRAMLICH, Gregory Forrest
Westminster HS; Westminster, MD (10%-500) CYO; Chor; Bsbl; Bkbl; Sftbl; Tnns; *U of Md; Acct.*

GRAMLING, Janine Patricia
Carroll HS; Ozark, AL (174-296) Band; Bus C; Chor; Coun o-t Arts, Mus A; Fin, Miss Ozark; *Enterprise St Jr Col; Bus.*

GRAMMATICO, Teresa Ann
R L Thomas HS; Webster, NY; Chor; Piano Audition Diploma; *Monroe Comm Col; Bus.*

GRAMS, Pamela Jean
Anoka Sr HS; Anoka, MN; Orch; Secy, Yth Fel; Danceline.

GRAMZA, Mary Beth
Greenfield HS; Greenfield, WI (33%-400) CYO; MATC; *Secretarial.*

GRANDBERRY, Barbara Denise
Covington HS; Covington, TN (6-200) Band; BC; Ensm; Secy, FHA; GS; VP, NHS; VP, SC; VP, Jr Cl; Secy, Soph Cl; Hon Prog; *UT-Martin; Elem Ed.*

GRANDE, Donna Lee
Mount Vernon HS; Alexandria, VA (33%-600) Drama; Fr C; Lit Mag; ARC; Thes; Bowinan A; Marksman A; Mus A; Sr GSct Certs; *U of Ga; Journ.*

GRANDELL, Steve Lawrence
East HS; Duluth, MN; Sch P; *Voc Tech Inst; Commercial Art.*

GRANDERSON, Linda Joyce
Bentonia HS; Bentonia, MS; Chor; FBLA; Rptr, 4H; Sftbl; Amer Leg A; COM; 4H A; *Holmes Jr Col; Secretarial Sci.*

GRANDIN, Albert W
New Hyde Park Mem HS; New Hyde Park, NY (35-389) Fr C; NHS; Order/Arrow; JV, Ftbl; Tr; Hon Prog; Regent Schol; Pres, Audio-Visual C; *Rensselaer Polytech Inst; Aeronautical Engr.*

GRANDIN, John Lewis
New Hyde Park Mem HS; New Hyde Park, NY; Chem C; Hmrm; Order/Arrow; Sci C; SC; Soccer; Hon Prog; Order/Arrow A; PTA A; Sci A; VFW A; Camera C; Audio-Visual C; Outst Service A; *Agr.*

GRANDJEAN, Gayle Marie
Hannibal Central Sch; Hannibal, NY; Chor; Secy, NHS; Pres, Health Careers.

GRANDLIENARD, Paul Jay
Celina Sr HS; Celina, OH; VP, 4H; 4H A; Yth Fel; Church Bkbl; Pres, Church Yth; Church Vlbl; Campus Life.

GRANDMAISON, Nicole
College De Ste Anne De La Pocatiere; La Pocatiere, CANADA (1-32) Tnns; Vlbl; *Med.*

GRANDT, Barbara Ann
McHenry HS W; McHenry, IL (34-600) Band; Chor; Fr C; Lit Mag; Mod Mus Mas; *Bus.*

GRANDT, Tammy Rose
Whitewater HS; Whitewater, WI (10-185) Ann; Chor; Fr C; 4H; Ski C; Var C; Pres, Soph Cl; Sftbl; Tr; 4H A; Type A; Gym; 4-H Okla Exchange; *U of Wisc; Home Ec.*

GRANGER, Billy Jack
Clinton HS; Clinton, IN (15-179) BS; Demolay; Drama; 4H; Tres, Math C; Tres, NHS; Order/Arrow; Sci C; Span C; *Rose-Hulman Inst of Tech; Engr.*

GRANGER, Gail Louise
Maryvale Sr HS; Cheektowaga, NY (21-450) Chor; Drama; Fr C; French NHS; Orch; Rptr, Sch P; COM; *St U of NY; Phys Therapy.*

GRANGER, Gary Steven
Cottonwood High; Cottonwood, AL (10-47) Ann; Cpt, Arch; Band; Pres, FFA; 4H; Tres, Key C; Sci C; SC; VP, Soph Cl; COM; Cl Fav; HCt; FFA Chapter Farmer; CHS WW; Band A; *Engr.*

GRANGER, Jennifer Lynn
Oshkosh N HS; Oshkosh, WI (80-384) Co-Ed, Ann; Band; Chor; Drama; Fr C; Tres, 4H; Key C; Ed, Lit Mag; MVP, NFL; Secy, NHS; SC; 4H A; Hon Prog; Journ A; Most Out; Spch A; St Forensics; *U of Wis; Elem Ed.*

GRANGER, Maria Frances
St Martin Sr HS; St Martinville, LA; Var C; Sftbl; Amer Leg A; *USL; Teaching.*

GRANGER, Melissa Ann
St Martin Sr HS; St Martinville, LA; Var C; Sftbl; *USL; Phys Ed Teacher.*

GRANGER, Rebecca Sue
Lyons Township HS; La Grange, IL (188-1207) Chor; *Augustana Col; Biol.*

GRANGER, Ruth Ann
Maryvale Sr HS; Cheektowaga, NY (114-562) A Cap Choir; AFS; Band; Chor; Orch; Span C; Bkbl; Hockey; GAA; Humanities C; *Erie Comm Col; Med Secy.*

GRANGER, Ruth Elena
Hobbs HS; Hobbs, NM (180-419) Pres, CYO; Secy, Chor; Ensm; FTA; COM; Band; VP, Solo-Ensm; Bsbl Qn; 1st Runner- up, Eagle o-t Cross A; *NM Jr Col; Special Ed.*

GRANGER, Shelby J
Tower Hill Comm HS; Tower Hill, IL (5-23) Chor; Ed, Sch P; Hist A; *Lakeland Comm Col; Sci.*

GRANGER, Zana Lynne
Hillsboro HS; Hillsboro, OH (25%-190) Band; Chor; Drama; Fr C; Pres, 4H; Orch; Tnns; Amer Leg A; COM; 4H A; Hon Prog; God & Comm; 1st Cl GSct.

GRANIS, Joyce Anne
Hiram Johnson Sr HS; Sacramento, CA (222-808) AFS; Band; Bank Of Amer A; CSF; COM; Elk A; Lion A; PTA A; *Sacramento City Col; Aviation.*

GRANROTH, Neal Verner
East HS; Rockford, IL (27-520) Band; Community Yth Symph; NHS; Orch; *Milwaukee Sch of Engr; Computer Technology.*

GRANT, Albert William
Burke HS; Charleston, SC; JV, Ftbl; Tr; *SC St Col; Math.*

GRANT, Anita Louise
Paxon Sr HS; Jacksonville, FL; Hmrm; Cl Fav; HCt; *U of Fla; Bus Adm.*

GRANT, Ann Marie
Fort Hunt HS; Alexandria, VA (1-503) Pres, French NHS; Hmrm; InterClub Coun; NHS; Sch P; SC; Tnns; HCt; Hon Prog; Val; Secy, Jr Civitans; *Col of William and Mary; Arts and Sci.*

GRANT, Becky Lynn
Kountze HS; Kountze, TX; Band; Bus C; CYO; Chem C; Ensm; FBLA; FHA; Secy, FTA; 4H; Hmrm; Jr Miss Pagent; Mjrte; Orch; Sch P; SC; SC; Type A; Twirler, Band, A's; *Lamar U; Phys Therapy.*

GRANT, Clint Alan
Kountze HS; Kountze, TX (6-84) A-Ed, Ann; Band; Pres, CYO; Chem C; Ensm; VP, FFA; 4H; Math C; NHS; Orch; Phys C; Sci C; SC; Pres, Jr Cl; Co-Cpt, Ftbl; COM; Cl Fav; HCt; Hon Prog; Diocese Rep; Section Ldr, Band; *Tex A&M U; Computer Programmer.*

GRANT, Cordie Mae
Chatham HS; Chatham, VA;

GRANT, Darrell Lyne
Clovis HS; Clovis, NM (125-546) Pres, Hmrm; JV, Ftbl; Tr; WW; Tn o-t Wk; *NM St U; Acct.*

GRANT, Dawn Denise
Harrison Central HS; Lyman, MS; BC; Chldr; Jr Miss Pagent; NHS; SC; Pres, Soph Cl; Amer Leg A; Hon Prog; MLS; Win, Jr Miss Pageant; Eng A; Superior A, St Piano; Pres, St DECA; *U of Sou Miss; Marketing.*

GRANT, Elizabeth Moreece
Chattanooga HS; Chattanooga, TN (13-210) Band; BC; Fr C; Lat C; Model UN; ARC; UN Council; COM; Fr A; Lab Band; Marching Band; Most Versatile; Mus A; Yth Hospital Volunteer; Concert Band; *U of Tenn at Chattanooga; Mus.*

GRANT, Felicia Althea
Miami Springs Sr HS; Miami Springs, FL; FBLA; *Miami Dade Comm Col; Court Rptr.*

GRANT, General
Russell HS; Hurtsboro, AL; FFA; 4H; Bsbl; Bkbl; ROTC A; *Ala St Col.*

GRANT, George Henry
Saint Angela Acad; Aiken, SC (10-50) A-Ed, Ann; BS; Chor; Community Yth Symph; Dbte Tm; Demolay; Drama; Fr C; Key C; Pres, Pol Sci C; Pres, SC; Pres, Jr Cl; VP, Soph Cl; Bkbl; Golf; Soccer; Tnns; Tr; COM; Citz A; Hist A; Opt A; Opt Out Tn; Rotary A; Spch A; *Wofford Col; Pre-Law.*

GRANT, Jane Allison
H D Jacobs HS; Algonquin Township, IL (33-190) A Cap Choir; Band; Chor; Rptr, Sch P; SC; Tr; Journ A; Sci A; *Evangel Col; Nurs.*

GRANT, Joanna
Anderson HS; Anderson, IN (82-620) Chor; Community Yth Symph; Ensm; Pres, Hmrm; Lat C; Co-Ch, Lit Mag; Pres, Orch; Tres, SC; Q&S A; Outst Mus A; Tres, Stu Body; *Anderson Col; Pre-Law.*

GRANT, Jon Allen
Lincoln HS; Dallas, TX; Drama; Tnns; Tr; Cl Fav; Spch A; Pol Awareness, Gen Bus, Drama, A's; *Acct.*

GRANT, June Roshelle
Patten Acad of Christian Ed; Oakland, CA (1-11) A Cap Choir; Chem C; Chor; Dbte Tm; Madrigal; Rptr, Sch P; Spch C; VP, SC; VP, Soph Cl; Soccer; Sftbl; Citz A; Silver A A; *Sci.*

GRANT, Marianne Kay
Milo Acad; Days Creek, OR (2-74) Chem C; Cum Laude Soc; Drama; JV, Bkbl; JV, Sftbl; *Union Col; Pre-Med.*

GRANT, Mary Jane
W A Berry HS; Birmingham, AL; AFS; Chor; Drama; Pres, FTA; InterClub Coun; Band Board; Mgr, Vlbl; Badminton; *Jefferson St Jr Col.*

GRANT, Pattie Sue
Chatham HS; Chatham, VA; Bus C; Chor; *Ntl Bus Col; Secy.*

GRANT, Penny Elaine
Hebert HS; Beaumont, TX; Fr C; FTA; Cr-Ctry; Tr; COM; Math A; Sci A; Tr A; Art Cert; JV, Vlbl Tm; Drill Tm; *Lamar U; Special Ed.*

GRANT, Randall Wayne
Valley HS; Eden-Hazelton, ID (25%-50) Order/ Arrow; Var C; Co-Cpt, Bkbl; Co-Cpt, Ftbl; God & Country A; Eagle Sct; *Wash St U; Vet Med.*

GRANT, Regina Rochell
Ben L Smith HS; Greensboro, NC (101-511) Anchor C; InterAct C; Up Bound; Y-Tns; Sftbl; Fin, Miss ULB; Chldr A; *Howard U; Law.*

GRANT, Reginald Alphonso
Windsor Forest HS; Savannah, GA (24-325) Band; BC; Order/Arrow; VP, Pol Sci C; Rptr, Sr Cl; Rptr, Jr Cl; Ntl Merit Commended Stu; *Howard U; Pol Sci.*

GRANT, Sharon Gean
York Central Sch; Retsof, NY; S-T, Band; Chor; Community Yth Symph; Drama; Ensm; FTA; Secy, 4H; NHS; Orch; Ski C; Bkbl; Alt, SC; All-Co Band; Musical; Color Guard.

GRANT, Stephanie
Parkway North Sr HS; Creve Coeur, MO (60-508) *Human Relations.*

GRANT, Surlene Georgette
Crystal Springs Sch; Hillsborough, CA (9-30) Ed, Ann; Chor; HiY; Ed, Sch P; Span C; Pres, Jr Cl; Bkbl; Citz A; Hon Prog; Yth Fel; WW; *NW U; Journ.*

GRANT, Thomas Howard
Allen Jay HS; High Point, NC; Band; JV, Bkbl; JV, Ftbl; Jazz Band A; *UNC-G; Mus.*

GRANT, Tracie Lynn
Cedar Hill HS; Cedar Hill, TX (25%-100) Drama; FHA; Lit Ral; NHS; S-T, Span C; Spch C; Citz A; Lion A; Drill Tm; Pres, Yth Coun; *Baylor U; Nurs.*

GRANT, Walter Kas
Pascagoula HS; Pascagoula, MS (5%-500) Pres, Band; Lat C; NHS; Order/Arrow; JV, Ftbl; NEDT; Order/Arrow A; Sci A; Spch A; Citz A; Eagle Sct; Red Cross Sr Lifesaving; Industrial Arts A; Eng A.

GRANT, Yvonne
Clovis HS; Clovis, NM; Cl Fav; *Eastern NM U; Phys Ed.*

GRANTHAM, Melinda Ann
Silsbee HS; Silsbee, TX (7-260) A Cap Choir; Fr C; French NHS; FTA; JETS; TMEA All-Region Choir; UIL Medalist; Tri-St Medalist; *Ed.*

GRANTZ, Connie Louise
Ephrata HS; Ephrata, PA (117-296) Band; Type A; *Eastern Nazarene Col; Nurs.*

GRAS, Christena Marie
Natrona Co HS; Casper, WY; Chor; Pres, 4H; NFL; Citz A; 4H A; Most Out; *Hastings Col; Home Ec.*

GRASING, Linda Sue
Middletown HS; Middletown, RI (60-250) Chor; Drama; Ensm; NHS; Bkbl; Yth Fel; Christian Singing Group.

GRASMEDER, Mary Margaret
Saint Mary's Acad; Alexandria, VA (9-70) Ann; Ch, CYO; Pres, Chor; VP, Drama; GS; Hmrm; Key C; Lit Mag; SC; COM; NEDT; Opt A; Spch A; WW; *Old Dominion U; Nurs.*

GRASS, Paul Rivers
Lee Acad; Clarksdale, MS (3-87) Ann; Drama; Tres, Mu Alpha Theta; Pres, NHS; Sch P; VP, SC; Pres, Sr Cl; Bkbl; Tnns; God & Country A; MLS; NMF; NMS; *U of Miss; Banking and Finance.*

GRASSEL, Richard Shawn
McGuffey HS; Claysville, PA (80-219) Chor; Tr; Sci A; Yth Fel; Chor Certs; Yth Conference; Musical Play; Campus Life; Church Adm Board; Church Soloist; Spiritual Frontiers; *Bethany Col; Theology.*

GRASSO, Neil Thomas
Paramus HS; Paramus, NJ (10%-560) Order/ Arrow; Pres, SC; Pres, Soph Cl; Ftbl; Order/Arrow A; Life Sct; *Law.*

GRASTY, Dawn Marie
Tuscola HS; Waynesville, NC (10%-426) Band; Ensm; Fr C; InterAct C; COM; All St Band; Solo Choral Comp; 1st Runner Up, District Spell Bee; Certs of Merit; *Mus.*

GRATACOS, Alma Iris
Barringer HS; Newark, NJ (10-475) Pres, Hmrm; A-Ed, Sch P; SC; Citz A; Hist A; Hon Prog; Journ A; Sci A; St Scholar; Val; Cpt, Twirler; *Rutgers U; Dentistry.*

GRATSCH, Linda Mary
Grand Blanc HS; Grand Blanc, MI (8-633) A Cap Choir; NHS; Pres, MYF; Young Life; Ten Ten C; Concern; *U of Mich; Ed.*

GRAU, Judy Lynn
Acadiana HS; Lafayette, LA (10%-400) Band; Fin, Lit Ral; VP, NHS; COM; Hon Prog; *La Col; Acct.*

GRAUL, Kellei Lynne
Daniel Boone HS; Birdsboro, PA (54-182) Chldr; Varsity A; *Elem Ed.*

GRAUNKE, Pamela Anne
Glenbard S HS; Glen Ellyn, IL (2-375) Arch; Band; Chor; Community Yth Symph; Ensm; Hmrm; Math C; Sch P; S-T, Ski C; Span NHS; SC; Arch; Mgr, Bkbl; Alg A; Amer Leg A; COM; Hist A; Hon Prog; MLS; Sci A; Spch A; Director's A, Band; *Harvard U; Psych.*

GRAVELY, Angela Renee
James B Dudley HS; Greensboro, NC (10-360) JV, Chldr; NHS; Span C; Secy, SC; MLS; Sal; Dance Co; Most Stu; Secy, JA; Jr Jaycettes; Best Dressed; *U of NC; Bus.*

GRAVELY, Cynthia Lea
Wade Hampton HS; Greenville, SC (81-370) Ann; Fr C; Secy, Hmrm; Rainbow; Yth Coun; Yth Choir; Handbell Choir; Mission Tour, Grenada; *Greenville Tech Col; Acct.*

GRAVELY, Marcia Andreas
Laurel Park HS; Martinsville, VA (34-183) Bus C; Chor; FBLA; FHA; 4H; Hmrm; Sci C; Span C; Pres, Soph Cl; 4H A; *Psych.*

GRAVES, Barbara Lynn
Grants Pass HS; Grants Pass, OR; Ann; Band; Schol Ntl Photo A; *Brooks Inst; Photography.*

GRAVES, Cyndi Pandora
Pine HS; Franklinton, LA (4-62) Band; Ftbl; FBLA; VP, FHA; Pres, 4H; Lit Ral; Beauty; B Crocker A; COM; 4H A; Hon Prog; I Dare You; JA A; St Scholar; Yth Foundation A; *Southeastern La Col.*

GRAVES, Daniel James III
Sullivan Central HS; Blountville, TN (136-379) VP, Drama; Ger C; Orch; Mgr, Bsbl; JV, Bkbl; God & Country A; *E Tenn St U; Mech Engr.*

GRAVES, Edward Christopher
St Johns Military Acad; Delafield, WI (4-62) A Cap Choir; Band; CYO; Chor; Community Yth Symph; Drama; Ensm; Madrigal; Ski C; Sftbl; Swim; Tr; ROTC A; Star Student; *Northwestern U; Mus.*

GRAVES, Joan Page
John F Kennedy HS; Richmond, VA (1-309) Lat C; Tres, Math C; Mu Alpha Theta; VP, NHS; Ntl Merit Commended; *Va Commonwealth U; Pre-Med.*

GRAVES, Joy Renee
Barrackville HS; Barrackville, WV (1-45) Ed, Ann; Drama; Cpt, Hmrm; Cpt, Mjrte; S-T, NHS; SC; Tres, Y-Tns; VP, Sr Cl; VP, Jr Cl; VP, Soph Cl; Beauty; Swtht; Type A; Quill & Scroll; Camp Horseshoe; Know Your St Govt Day; *Fairmont St Col.*

GRAVES, Kathy Joan
Burkburnett HS; Burkburnett, TX (1-267) Ed, Ann; Band; Secy, FHA; Secy, NHS; SC; Chem A; Phy A; Q&S A; Type A; Val; Eng A; Home Ec A; WW; *Tex Tech U; Archt.*

GRAVES, Kay Maurine
L B Johnson HS; Austin, TX (75-480) A Cap Choir; VP, Chor; Rptr, FHA; Lat C; Madrigal; A-Ed, Sch P; Sftbl; Citz A; Opt A; All Reg, All Area, All Dist, Chor; *U of Tex; Mus.*

GRAVES, Linda Arlyne
Kent-Meridian Sr HS; Kent, WA (7-468) Band; GS; Pres, InterAct C; InterClub Coun; NHS; SC; Mgr, Soccer; Tr; Elk A; Rotary A; *W Wash St Col; Teaching.*

GRAVES, Martha Jean
Fletcher Sr HS; Neptune Beach, FL (242-543) Co-Cpt, Chldr; Chor; Hmrm; InterAct C; ARC; SC; VP, Sr Cl; Swim; Mgr, Wrest; Beauty; HCt; Pres A; Most Improved Swimmer o-t Yr; Calender Girl; *Chipola Jr Col; Med Lab Tech.*

GRAVES, Melanie Arlene
Greenwood HS; Greenwood, SC (75-700) Ed, Ann; Band; BC; Cpt, Chldr; Chor; Drama; Pres, Hmrm; VP, Hmrm; Christian Ldrship A; WW; Colorguard; *Baptist Col of Charleston; Hist.*

GRAVES, Shannon Greene
Ouachita Parish HS; Monroe, LA; FHA; Bkbl; Citz A; *NE U; Special Ed.*

GRAVES, Shirley Ann
Conroe HS; Conroe, TX (335-1231) A Cap Choir; Secy, Chor; Parl, FHA; Span C; Tnns; Alg A; Most Out; *Sam Houston St U; Mus.*

GRAVES, Tracy RaNae
Norfolk Sr HS; Norfolk, NE; Chor; *Tech Sch; Secy.*

GRAVITT, Ramona Lee
Duluth HS; Duluth, GA; Band; 4H; Rainbow; ARC; ARC A; Co-Cpt, Drill Tm; *N Ga Col.*

GRAWE, Deborah Ann
Geronimo HS; Geronimo, OK (10%-29) Span C; Span NHS; Alg A; Math A; Sci A.

GRAWE, Winston Boyd
Dugway HS; Dugway, UT (11-45) Chess C; Drama; Model UN; NHS; Spch C; SC; Mgr, Bkbl; Ftbl; Tr; Valentine Kg; *Brigham Young U; Bus.*

GRAWL, Robert Jr
M B Smiley HS; Houston, TX (1-400) Band; VP, Fr C; Pres, Math C; Pres, Mu Alpha Theta; VP, NHS; Alg A; COM; DARGCA; Hist A; Magna Cum Laude; Math A; NMS; Sci A; Fr, Eng, A's; Good Sportsmanship League; *Austin Col; Pre-Law.*

GRAY, Beth Ilene
Galva Comm Sch; Galva, IA (3-25) Ed, Ann; Band; Secy, Chor; Parl, GS; Pres, 4H; Mgr, Bkbl; Mgr, Sftbl; 4H A; Hon Prog; Type A; Yth Fel; WW; *U of N Iowa; Ed.*

GRAY, Bonnie Ann
Zephyrhills HS; Zephyrhills, FL; Band; Secy, CYO; VP, Drama; Fr C; French NHS; Mjrte; Tr; Citz A; Pres A; Type A; *Nurs.*

GRAY, Bruce William
La Jolla HS; La Jolla, CA (159-494) Hmrm; SC; Sftbl; CSF; Yth Fel; Co-Cpt, All Star Sftbl Tm; Acolyte o-t Yr; Ntl Model Railroad Assn; *U of Calif; Hist.*

GRAY, Cara Sue
Hazelwood Central HS; Florissant, MO (69-1045) Band; NHS; *Ouachita Baptist U; Acct.*

GRAY, Carey Dean
Glenbard W HS; Glen Ellyn, IL (100-481) Ski C; SC; Var C; Cpt, Golf; COM; Hon Prog; Yth Fel; Yth Foundation; MVP, Golf; Stewardship Committee; *Okla St U; Bus.*

GRAY, Cathryn Lee
Bowman HS; Canyon Country, CA; *Col o-t Canyons; Math.*

GRAY, Charles Clifton
Mercersburg Acad; Mercersburg, PA (3-85) Lat C; Math C; Var C; Swim; Water Polo; *U of Va; Law.*

GRAY, Dave Louis
Colorado Springs Christian Sch; Colorado Springs, CO; Chor; Bkbl; Sftbl; Bridge Playing Contest; *U of Va; Math.*

GRAY, David Samuel
Tabernacle Christian Acad; San Diego, CA (2-8) Chess C; Community Yth Symph; Sci C; Pres, SC; Bsbl; Bio A; DARGCA; Ntl Sci Found; *Sci.*

GRAY, Dean Franklin
Lakewood HS; Lakewood, OH (32-900) NHS; Ch, ARC; SC; Citz A; Hon Prog; Yth Fel; Cirriculum Advisory Coun; *Wheaton Col; Pol Sci.*

GRAY, Debbi Kathleen
Andress HS; El Paso, TX (10%-546) Band; Drama; Fr C; Rainbow; Spch C; *Tex A&M U; Zoology.*

GRAY, Deborah Sue
Tipton HS; Tipton, OK (2-46) Ann; Secy, Band; FHA; Okla Hon Soc.

GRAY, Denise Jocelyn
Inglewood HS; Los Angeles, CA (30-650) Chldr; Rptr, Hmrm; Math C; Citz A; Hon Prog; Most Out; Schol A; *Pepperdine U; Med.*

GRAY, Donna Jean
Riverview HS; Sarasota, FL; 4H; InterClub Coun; NFL; NHS; Rainbow; Co-Ed, Sch P; Secy, Sci C; VP, Span C; Spch C; SC; COM; Chem A; 4H A; Journ A; Spch A; WW; *Mercer U; Med.*

GRAY, Harry Lasha
South Side HS; Memphis, TN (85-334) A Cap Choir; Chor; City Conf; Ensm; HiY; Sci C; SC; Bkbl; Ftbl; Cpt, Tnns; Wrest; Hon Prog; ROTC A; Yth Leg; Cpt, MVP, JV Wrest; Stu Director Chor; Ecology C; Asst Supt, Yng People's Sunday Sch; Commissioner of Human Relations,; *Memphis St U; Bus Mgt.*

GRAY, Jane Elizabeth
Russell HS; East Point, GA (18-145) BC; Chor; Orch; Sch P; *Clayton Jr Col; Communications.*

GRAY, Jane Lorraine
David Lipscomb HS; Nashville, TN; Secy, Band; Chor; Dbte Tm; Secy, Hmrm; Math C; Sci C; Span C; Swim; Tr; Beauty; Citz A; Sci A; *David Lipscomb Col; Archeology.*

GRAY, Jennifer Ruth
Niskayuna HS; Niskayuna, NY;

GRAY, John Richard Jr
Brookhaven Acad Inc; Brookhaven, MS (5-32) Ann; BC; Chess C; Key C; Tnns, Sr Cl; Bkbl; Ftbl; Tr; HCt; *Belhaven Col; Marine Zoology.*

GRAY, Jolene Mecenia
Red Bank HS; Red Bank, TN (43-359) Band; BC; Chor; Math C; NHS; ARC; Span C; MVP, Bkbl; Swim; Tr; Yth Fel; Art A; Hon Soc; *U of Tenn at Chatt; Pre-Vet.*

GRAY, Karen Beth
Kenmore HS; Akron, OH; MVP, Sftbl; COM; Yth Fel; God & Comm A.

GRAY, Karen Elizabeth
John A Holmes HS; Edenton, NC (5-145) A-Ed, Ann; Secy, Chor; VP, FHA; VP, Mod Mus Mas; NHS; Sci C; Amer Leg A; Gr Marshal; Spch A; Dist Win, NFMC; *Meredith Col; Mus.*

GRAY, Kathryn
Winter Haven HS; Winter Haven, FL; S-T, AFS; Bus Mgr, Ann; Drama; NHS; ARC; Tnns; DARGCA; Hon Prog; Type A; *Clemson U; Med.*

GRAY, Kathy Lynne
Greenland HS; Greenland, AR (6-44) Band; Rptr, FHA; Rptr, Hmrm; Mjrte; Sch P; Var C; Rptr, Jr Cl; Bkbl; H of F; PTA A; Outst, Band; WW; *Fayetteville Bus Col; Acct.*

GRAY, Keith Earl
Skyline HS; Dallas, TX; A Cap Choir; Ann; Band; FTA; Key C; NHS; Pol Sci C; Span C; SC; Alg A; Bio A; COM; Hon Prog; JA A; Kiwanis A; Sci A; Yth Fel; Yth Foundation A; Marching Band A; Symphonic Band A; Jack & Jill, Inc; Social Sci A; *Sou Methodist U; Law.*

GRAY, Kenneth Orlando
Booker T Washington HS; Shreveport, LA (50-368) Sch Achieve Tm; Sch P; Amer Leg A; COM; Hon Prog; Most Out; ROTC A; Military Ball Kg; Alpha Phi Alpha Cert; Scholastic Excellence; BEOG Grant; *La Tech Col; Photography.*

GRAY, Linda Maria
G W Carver HS; Montgomery, AL (21-400) Band; Chor; Drama; Math C; Mu Alpha Theta; NHS; Sci C; Secy, SC; Cl Fav; Hon Prog; Phi Beta Kappa; *Elec Engr.*

GRAY, Linda Sue
Kenmore HS; Akron, OH; Sftbl; Citz A; JA A; Yth Fel.

GRAY, Lynne
Reading Mem HS; Reading, MA (205-411) Chor; Ski C; Yth Fel; *N Shore Comm Col; Liberal Arts.*

GRAY, Lyvonne Celeste
Hillsboro HS; Nashville, TN (22-280) Pres, FHA; Hmrm; Key C; SC; Secy, Sr Cl; VP, Soph Cl; Sftbl; Citz A; Crisco A; DARGCA; Elk A; HQn; HCt; MVP, Church Bkbl; Sewanee C A; Civinettes; Prom Court; Faculty A; Gym; Best All Around; Key C Swtht; *Furman U; Special Ed.*

GRAY, Margaret Lynn
Chicopee HS; Chicopee, MA (9-398) Co-Ed, Ann; NHS; *Syracuse U; Communications.*

GRAY, Mark Fletcher
Hemet HS; Hemet, CA (10-500) JV, Bsbl; CSF; Rotary A; *Christian Heritage Col; Missionary Aviation.*

GRAY, Melinda Ewing
Central Acad; Macon, MS (20-60) Ann; Chldr; MVP, Bkbl; Sftbl; Tr; Beauty; Cl Fav; HCt; Most Versatile; Wittiest; *Miss St U; Ed.*

GRAY, Michael Albert
Oswego HS; Oswego, IL; Var C; Wrest; *U of Ill; Engr.*

GRAY, Pamela Ann
Whitesboro Sr HS; Marcy, NY (40%-450) A Cap Choir; Band; Chor; Drama; Ch, Hmrm; Ski C; Ch, SC; Yth Fel; Most Prog Achieved, A Cappella Chor; *Keuka Col; Psychiatry.*

GRAY, Patrice M
Bishop Noll Inst; Hammond, IN (100-348) A Cap Choir; Pres, Chor; Ensm; Pres, Hmrm; Madrigal; Pres, Mod Mus Mas; ARC; Y-Tns; Bsbl; Citz A; Interlochen Ntl Mus; Ntl Cath Mus Ed Asn; Most Talented; *Ind U NW; Elem Ed.*

GRAY, Patricia Ann
Auburndale Sr HS; Auburndale, FL (50-320) Sftbl; Math A; Type A; Outst Schol Achv; Phys Ed.

GRAY, Paul Thaxton Jr
Mena HS; Mena, AR (44-175) Band; Sci C; 1st All Region, Band; *Ark Tech U; Mus.*

GRAY, Phebian Cietta
E Rome HS; Rome, GA (35-115) F-Ed, Ann; Chldr; Secy, Chor; Dbte Tm; Drama; Pres, Hmrm; Mjrte; NHS; Co-Ed, Sch P; Pres, SC; World Affairs C; VP, Y-Tns; Pres, Jr Cl; Pres, Soph Cl; Bkbl; Swim; Tnns; Tr; Alg A; Beauty; Cl Fav; HCt; Interlochen Ntl Mus; Math A; Pres A; Spch A; St Scholar; Yth Fel; VP, Chor; Secy, Y-Tns; Stu Affairs; *Albany St Col; Civil Engr.*

GRAY, Richard Alan
Science Hill HS; Johnson City, TN; Lat C; Cr-Ctry; Tr; Tr A's; *Med.*

GRAY, Richard Scott
El Camino Real HS; Woodland Hills, CA (25%-1000) Semi-Fin, BS; FBLA; Var C; Cpt, Bkbl; Cpt, Ftbl; Citz A; Hon Prog; Most Out; MVP, Ftbl; FLA; All League Bkbl & Ftbl; All San Fernando Valley; *Penn St U; Med.*

GRAY, Robert Ernest
John A Holmes HS; Edenton, NC (8-170) Anchor C; Ann; JV, Ftbl.

GRAY, Robert Frederick III
Garinger HS; Charlotte, NC (125-700) Yth Fel; Church Chor; WW; *W Carolina U; Bio.*

GRAY, Sharon Ann
Alexandria Sr HS; Alexandria, LA (3-315) Fr C; French NHS; Semi-Fin, Lit Ral; Secy, Lit Mag; Model UN; Tres, NHS; Y-Tns; Bio A; NEDT; *Baylor U; Pre-Med.*

GRAY, Sharon Beatrice
Calhoun HS; Calhoun, GA (33%-367) Fr C; Rptr, Sch P; Co-Ch, Tri-HiY.

GRAY, Sheila Joyce
Hatley HS; Amory, MS (3-38) Pres, BC; FHA; SC; Cpt, Bkbl; VP, Beta C; HR.

GRAY, Steven Dirk
Artesia HS; Artesia, NM (24-220) Demolay; NHS; Var C; Ftbl; JV, Golf; Math A; Rotary A; Yth Fel; Offensive Player o-t Yr, Ftbl; *Tex Tech U; Engr.*

GRAY, Suzanne Lee
Beaufort Acad; Beaufort, SC (10-38) Ed, Ann; Chldr; Drama; Fr C; Secy, NHS; Pres, SC; Bkbl; *Wofford Col; Acct.*

GRAY, Tara Joy
Winfield HS; Winfield, KS (1-200) Mjrte; NFL; NHS; Var C; Tnns; Hon Prog; ROTC A; Spch A; Mgr, Tnns; Navy Schol; *Okla U; Physics.*

GRAY, Valerie Ann
Davenport HS; Davenport, IA (150-800) A Cap Choir; AFS; Chor; Community Yth Symph; Ensm; Lit Mag; Madrigal; MVP, Orch; Hon Prog; Yth Fel; St Mus Contest A; Church Dist Mus Contest A; *Union U; Nurs.*

GRAY, Veronica Danelle
Plymouth Canton HS; Plymouth, MI; Band; Community Yth Symph; Var C; MVP, Tr; Pianist, Chor; Plymouth Marching & Symph Band.

GRAY, Vicki Marcia
Broad Ripple HS; Indianapolis, IN; Band; JV, Chldr; Ger C; SC; COM; *UCLA; Bus.*

GRAY, Wilma Sue
Clay Co HS; Manchester, KY; Bio A.

GRAYBEAL, Lisa Marie
North Col Hill HS; Cincinnati, OH (15-200) Drama; Ger C; NHS; Co-Ed, Sch P; Beauty; HCt; Journ A; *Northern Ky St U; Journ.*

GRAYSON, Cynthia Renee
Morningside HS; Inglewood, CA; Sftbl; Tnns; Citz A; Math A; *El Camino Jr Col; Bus Adm.*

GRAYSON, Starlene
Alexandria Sr HS; Alexandria, LA; Span C; Y-Tns.

GRAZIER, Shirley Louise
Cheltenham HS; Wyncote, PA (23-550) NHS; Type A; *Allied Health Field.*

GREATHOUSE, Peggy Michelle
Flagler Palm Coast HS; Bunnell, FL; Ann; BC; Tres, FBLA; FHA; Eng A; Sewing A.

GREB, Curtis Ren
Okeene HS; Okeene, OK; Tres, FFA; *Panhandle Col; Agr Ed.*

GREBE, Terri A
Hershey Sr HS; Hershey, PA (1-275) Band; Chor; Community Yth Symph; NHS; Orch; Var C; Tnns; Hist A; Hon Prog; Field Hockey; Dist, Regional & All St Orch; *Pre-Med.*

GREEDE, Linda Carolin
N Shore HS; W Palm Beach, FL; Fr C; Rptr, Sch P; Spch C; SC; Spch A; *Eckerd Col.*

GREELEY, Brad Louis
Wellsboro Sr HS; Wellsboro, PA (2-210) NHS; Tres, Var C; Bsbl; JV, Bkbl; Co-Cpt, Cr-Ctry; Tr; Alg A; Amer Leg A.

GREELEY, Wendy Carol
Portland Christian HS; Portland, OR (30-55) A Cap Choir; Cr-Ctry; *Psych.*

GREEN, Alfreida Germaine
W O Boston HS; Lake Charles, LA; Band; Chldr; *U of Houston; Nurs.*

GREEN, Alice Elizabeth
St Andrews Episcopal HS; St Andrews, TN (1-30) Chor; Drama; Bkbl; Alg A; NEDT; Eng A; Distinguished List; Hon Stu; *Art.*

GREEN, Alicia Jane
Valentine HS; Valentine, NE (7-66) Band; NHS; *Biochem.*

GREEN, Amy Renea
Highland HS; Anderson, IN (256-480) A Cap Choir; Chor; *Dental Asst.*

GREEN, Andre Dezan
Andress HS; El Paso, TX; Arch; Cr-Ctry; Ftbl; Tr; Tr A; Ftbl A; *U of Tex; Elec.*

GREEN, Ann Louise
H V Jenkins HS; Savannah, GA; *Savannah St Col; Textiles.*

GREEN, Barbara
William Penn HS; Philadelphia, PA; *Temple U; Social Worker.*

GREEN, Benjamin Howard IV
Live Oak HS; Morgan Hill, CA (97-364) Bkbl; Ftbl; *Hardin-Simmons U; Math.*

GREEN, Beverly Ruth
South Side HS; Memphis, TN (10%-370) Secy, Drama; Lat C; NFL; ARC; Secy, Spch C; Mgr, Bkbl; COM; ROTC A; Spch A; Home Ec A; *Tenn Med Col; Sci.*

GREEN, Brian Lee
Spring Woods Sr HS; Houston, TX; Band; Chor; Drama; Ensm; NFL; Orch; Spch C; Thes; Cl Fav; All Star Cast, UIL; 1st Pl, HMTA; Lead, Sch Mus; 1st Pl, Sch Talent Show; *Communications.*

GREEN, Cathie Denise
Tupelo HS; Tupelo, MS; BC; Chor; Secy, FHA; Bkbl; Sftbl; Tr.

GREEN, Cheryl Ann
Pampa HS; Pampa, TX (55-326) Bus C; Chor; FHA; Pres, Hmrm; NHS; SC; Yth Fel; Secy, Pres, Christian Yth Fel; Yth Rep, Church Cabinet; *San Angelo St U; Bus.*

GREEN, Constance Enonia
Richard Arnold HS; Savannah, GA (94-140) FHA; SC; *Morris Brown Col; Lab Tech.*

GREEN, Cora Lucile
E Kemper HS; Scooba, MS (2-24) Bus C; Drama; FBLA; Pres, FHA; Pres, Hmrm; Jr Miss Pagent; Math C; NHS; SC; Pres, Sr Cl; Pres, Jr Cl; Pres, Soph Cl; Bkbl; Hist A; Hon Prog; MLS; Sal.

GREEN, Cynthia Mary
Notre Dame Bishop Gibbons HS; Schenectady, NY (7-160) Ann; NHS; Tr; Bio A; Math A; Variety Shows; AAU Swim; *Engr.*

GREEN, Darren Blaine
Christoval HS; Christoval, TX; Ed, Ann; Pres, BC; VP, Sr Cl; Cpt, Bkbl; Co-Cpt, Ftbl; Fin, Tnns; MLS; Sci A; Most Outst; *Angelo St U; Engr.*

GREEN, David Kluttz
Durham Acad; Durham, NC (6-46) Math C; Order/Arrow; Sci C; SC; Soccer; Tr; Alg A; God & Country A; Hist A; Eagle Sct.

GREEN, Dayna Marie
Fairview HS; Boulder, CO (61-720) Co-Ed, Sch P; JA A; Opt A; Candy Striping As; Pep C; Jr Auxillary A; Secy, Mod Explorer; 1st Cover Contest; Hospital Vol; HR; JA Boulder Broadcasting Co; *Biological Sci.*

GREEN, Debra Ann
Charleroi Area HS; Charleroi, PA (40%-240) Chor; Pres, FNA; Rainbow; Sch P; Tres, Ski C; Swim; *Ind U of Pa; Bus Mgt.*

GREEN, Donna Claire
Rowan HS; Hattiesburg, MS (25%-509) A Cap Choir; Pres, 4H; Co-Ed, Lit Mag; Secy, SC; Y-Tns; Bkbl; 4H A; Hon Prog; Harmony Mus C; Eng As; Piano As; Horsemanship As; *U of Miss; Nurs.*

GREEN, Douglas Ray
Washington HS; Kansas City, KS; Dbte Tm; FBLA; NFL; Orch; Order/Arrow; Pres, SC; *Psych.*

GREEN, Eddie
C F Brewer HS; White Settlement, TX; Fr C; Key C; NHS; Camping C; *Tarrant Co Jr Col.*

GREEN, Edmund Delano
Paraiso Jr-Sr HS; Paraiso, CANAL ZONE; Dbte Tm; Hmrm; A-Ed, Sch P; SC; Var C; Bkbl; Soccer; Hist A; Journ A; Shorthand A; Economy A; *Pepperdine U; Bus Law.*

GREEN, Elizabeth Kimberly
Round Rock HS; Round Rock, TX (37-286) A Cap Choir; Band; Madrigal; Span C; Sftbl; *Tex Tech U; Bio.*

GREEN, Elliott Renaldo
East St Louis Lincoln Senior HS; E St Louis, IL (1-409) Band; Chem C; Drama; Fr C; Ger C; 4H; Math C; NHS; Sch Achieve Tm; Sch P; Spch C; Co-Ch, SC; S-T, Sr Cl; Tr; Alg A; Bausch & Lomb A; Bio A; Elk A; Hon Prog; Math A; Most Out; Sci A; Val; Pres, Hist C; *U of Kans; Elec Engr.*

GREEN, Eric William Jr
Burnsville Sr HS; Burnsville, MN (22-750) NHS; Ftbl; Tr; Wrest; Hon Prog; Pres A; Yth Fel; *Med.*

GREEN, Evelyn Marie
Sheffield HS; Memphis, TN (14-142) Band; Chor; Lat C; VP, Mod Mus Mas; Mu Alpha Theta; Rptr, Sch P; ROTC A; Drum Major; Bn Co of ROTC; Brig Co, 4th Brigade; *Memphis St U; Nurs.*

GREEN, Gary James
Andress HS; El Paso, TX (75-650) Arch; Chess C; Chor; Order/Arrow; Arch; Tnns; Wrest; *U of Tex; Forestry.*

GREEN, Gary Raynard
Huntington Park HS; Huntington Park, CA; Hmrm; SC; JV, Bkbl; Yth Fel; House of Reps; Spartan's C; Pres, Pacific Jr Brotherhood; *Southwest Jr Col; Physiology.*

GREEN, Gordie Thomas III
Jesuit HS; Shreveport, LA (5-30) CYO; Demolay; Fr C; Bsbl; Eng A; *La St U; Sci.*

GREEN, Gregory Eugene
Southside HS; Elmira, NY (1-435) Tres, Band; BS; VP, Ensm; VP, Ger C; Hmrm; Lat C; Math C; Model UN; NHS; Ski C; SC; Cr-Ctry; Hon Prog; JA A; Kiwanis A; Lion A; Math A; Regent Schol; Val.

GREEN, Hannah Elizabeth
Gainesville HS; Gainesville, GA; Chor; French NHS; Spelling A; *Med.*

GREEN, Ida Mae
John Hay HS; Cleveland, OH; *Wooster Col; Psych.*

GREEN, James Robert
Mt Carmel Area HS; Mount Carmel, PA (2-212) Dbte Tm; Drama; Fr C; Sci C; JV, Cr-Ctry; Tr; NEDT; *Air Force Acad; Aeronautical Engr.*

GREEN, Jamie Lee
Bernalillo Jr HS; Bernalillo, NM; Chor; Jr NHS; *Baylor U; Mus.*

GREEN, Jane Ann
Alliance HS; Alliance, NE (9-153) A Cap Choir; Band; Chor; Ensm; Madrigal; Rainbow; S-T, Thes; Y-Tns; Hon Prog; Yth Fel; WW; Ger Schol; Semifin, Ntl Presbyterian Schol; *Hastings Col; Eng.*

GREEN, Jane Helene
Andress HS; El Paso, TX (50-350) Band; Orch; ROTC A; Sup Cadet A; *Sul Ross St U; Vet.*

GREEN, Janice Ellen
Whitman Hanson Regional HS; Whitman, MA; Chor; *Baptist Bible Col; Mus.*

GREEN, Jayson Dee
Bernalillo HS; Bernalillo, NM (1%-225) Chess C; NHS; Sci C; Alg A; Bio A; Hist A; Math A; Sci A; Eng, Ava, A's; *Biochem.*

GREEN, Jerry
Ben L Smith HS; Greensboro, NC (200-400) Chor; Drama; Ger C; Lat C; Pol Sci C; Var C; Mgr, Bsbl; Bkbl; Cl Fav; *E Wash St U; Sociology.*

GREEN, John David
Cocalico Sr HS; Denver, PA (18-202) Chor; Drama; FNA; Hmrm; SC; Mgr, Tr; WW in Jr Historians; *Nurs.*

GREEN, John Glover
Hixson HS; Hixson, TN; BC; Demolay; Fr C; FBLA; Hmrm; InterClub Coun; Ski C; Tnns; Cl Fav; MLS; Pres, DECA; 1st Pl, St Comp in DECA; *MTSU; Bus.*

GREEN, Julie Ann
Fountain Valley HS; Fountain Valley, CA (10%-1200) A Cap Choir; Chor; Madrigal; Orch; ARC; Tr; Outst, Vocal Mus; Coronet A; Most Dedicated Player, Tr; Shot Put Champ, St Finals, Tr; *Mus Ed.*

GREEN, Karen Sue
NW HS; Jackson, MI (54-324) Band; Bkbl; *Secy.*

GREEN, Katey Denise
Natchez Adams HS; Natchez, MS (25-269) BC; Chor; Fr C; Lit Mag; COM; Hon Prog; *MUW; Pre-Med.*

GREEN, Kathy Lynn
E Aurora HS; Aurora, IL (14-526) Secy, A Cap Choir; Band; Ger C; NHS; Orch; Secy, Thes; *Wheaton Col; Mus Ed.*

GREEN, Kerry Dean
McGavock HS; Nashville, TN; Band; ARC; ARC A; Good Friends Vol; MTS BOA; *Trevecca Nazarene Col; Mus.*

GREEN, Leo Donald
Bellevue HS; Bellevue, MI; NHS.

GREEN, Lesia Kay
Spring Hill HS; Spring Hill, KS; FHA.

GREEN, Lisa Alane
Granite HS; Salt Lake City, UT; Ski C; Kiwanis A; Pep C; 100% Attendance A; Gym A; Cl Off A; *U of Utah; Kindergartin Ed.*

GREEN, Lisa LaDawn
Pomona Sr HS; Arvada, CO (46-475) Chor; Drama; Secy, 4H; Cpt, NHS; Sch P; Sci C; Thes; 4H A; Opt A; Opt Out Tn; Outst Home Ec; Most Advanced Sewing; MV Mem, NHS; *Colo U; Bus.*

GREEN, Lisa Marie
L W Higgins HS; Marrero, LA (10%-250) Ch, CYO; Secy, Dbte Tm; Drama; Semi-Fin, Jr Miss Pa; Semi-Fin, Lit Ral; Secy, Spch C; Pres, SC; Up Bound; Beauty; Cl Fav; HQn; Hon Prog; Spch A; 1st Runnerup, Ms Black Hist; *Morehouse Col; Psych.*

GREEN, Lonnie Charles
Montgomery HS; San Diego, CA (150-400) Hmrm; VP, InterAct C; InterClub Coun; SC; Var C; Bkbl; Co-Cpt, Ftbl; MVP; Tr; Most Out; Type A; Yth Leg; *U of Sou Calif.*

GREEN, Marian Fountain
Martin Acad; Everetts, NC (1-7) Co-Ed, Ann; Pres, BC; Chor; Pres, Hmrm; Ed, Sch P; MVP, Bkbl; Sftbl; Chem A; Cl Fav; Gr Marshal; Hist A; Hon Prog; Math A; MLS; Most Out; Val; Geom, Eng, Acct, A's; Summer Schol, Meredith Col; *St Mary's Col.*

GREEN, Marilyn Ann
Warrensburg HS; Warrensburg, MO (53-200) Chor; Drama; NHS; Ed, Sch P; Thes; Journ A; Mus Ltr; Secy, Yth Coun; Scholastic Ltr; Secy, Yth Choir; REA Essay Winner; Pres, Secy Associates Acteens; *Central Mo St U; Acct.*

GREEN, Marilyn Gail
North Co R-1 HS; Desloge, MO (10%-200) Band; Bus Mgr, FHA; NHS; Sci C; VofDEM; Top Ten Percent; *Pol Sci.*

GREEN, Marilyn June
Tri-Valley HS; Dresden, OH (51-225) Band; Tres, FTA; Ch, Span C; Mgr, Sftbl; PTA A; Orch Asst; Drill Tm St Champs; Cpt, Drill Tm; Best Dancer; 2 Lt A; *Ohio Northern U; Ed.*

GREEN, Marsha Beth
Belton HS; Belton, TX; Tres, CYO; Hmrm; Rptr, Sch P; Chldr; Cl Fav; F-Ed, Sch Paper; Central Tex Pack & Paddle C; *Tex A&M U; Marine Bio.*

GREEN, Mary Elisabeth
Lansing Baptist HS; Lansing, MI; Band; Cpt, Chldr; SC; Yth Fel; Vlbl; *Missionary.*

GREEN, Melanie Ann
Hardaway HS; Columbus, GA (119-391) Secy, FHA; Pres, JA; March of Dimes Walkathon; Anatomy Teachers Asst; Pres, MYF; Action Prog; Med Explores C; Hosp Careers Prog; Chrch Yth Coun; *Columbus U; Phys Therapy.*

GREEN, Michael Allen
Marshall HS; Marshall, MO (11-250) Band; Hmrm; Ftbl; Swim; Tr; *Drafting.*

GREEN, Michelle Carol
Weequahic HS; Newark, NJ (6-400) Co-Ed, Ann; NHS; Church Chor; Secy, Med Explorers; Push A, Acad Excel; *Rutgers Col; Nurs.*

GREEN, Monica E
Southside Sr HS; Greenville, SC; Ann; CYO; Y-Tns.

GREEN, Pamela Eloise
Southside HS; Elmira, NY (10%-460) Chor; Drama; Model UN; Rptr, Sch P; Span C; JV, Tnns; Hon Prog.

GREEN, Pamela Jean
Carney HS; Carney, OK (1-12) 4H; NHS; Cpt, Bkbl; Bio A; COM; Gov Honor Prog; HQn; MLS; Sci A; *Central St U; Phys Ed.*

GREEN, Pamela Sue
Champion HS; Warren, OH;

GREEN, Paula Sue
Saint Ursula Acad; Toledo, OH; Chldr; City Conf; Fr C; Hmrm; Orch; Pres, Jr Cl; Rptr, Soph Cl; Swim; Tnns; JA A; Jacobson's 'T' A; Cottilion; Internation Festival Inst; *Journ.*

GREEN, Rhoda Fay
Nederland HS; Nederland, TX; F-Ed, Sch P; Mgr, Tr; Mgr, Vlbl; *Auburn U; Math.*

GREEN, Richard Lynn
Wakulla HS; Medart, FL (10%-117) Fin, FBLA; Secy, Sci C; Amer Leg A; Type A; Yth Fel; Cpt, CCC; *Fla St U; Bus.*

GREEN, Rickey James
Amite Co Attendance Center; Gloster, MS (2-40).

GREEN, Robert Mark
Mannington HS; Mannington, WV (5-109) Secy, Chess C; Chor; Pres, NHS; Sci C; Amer Leg A; Hon Prog; MLS; Jr Schol A; Dean's List; Highest Hon A; *Olivet Nazarene Col; Sci.*

GREEN, Rosemary Ann
Moreau HS; Hayward, CA (8-246) Fr C; Rptr, Sch P; COM; Hon Prog; Math A; Sci A; Star Student; High Hon; *Calif Polytechnic St U; Computer Sci.*

GREEN, Sally Elizabeth
El Dorado HS; El Dorado, AR (10%-400) Band; Chor; Cpt, Mjrte; *La Tech U; Mus.*

GREEN, Scott Douglas
St Edward Pub HS; St Edward, NE (2-28) Band; Chor; Pres, Jr Cl; Bsbl; Ftbl; Tr; Wrest; Yth Fel.

GREEN, Sherri Dare
Valleydale Sch Inc; Charlotte, NC (4-12) Chldr; Fr C; Sftbl; Alg A; HCt; Yth Fel; MVP, Vlbl; *Western Carolina U; Ed.*

GREEN, Steven Michael
Shenandoah Valley Acad; New Market, VA;

GREEN, Susan Ruth
Brandon HS; Brandon, FL (10%-800) Band; Chldr; Hmrm; NHS; SC; Service C; Gym; *U of S Fla; Psych.*

GREEN, Suzanne Rae
Washington HS; Fremont, CA; Acteen Qn.

GREEN, Tere Alan
Bethany HS; Bethany, OK (10-60) Chor; Drama; Ensm; Key C; Math C; NHS; MVP, Ftbl; Tr; Citz A; Top 50 Ftbl Players, St; Outst Bass Singer; *Oliver Nazarene Col; Archt.*

GREEN, Teri Lynn
Airline HS; Bossier City, LA (65-301) Band; FHA; FTA; 4H; Mjrte; Y-Tns; 4H A; Flag Corps; Color Guard; VP, UMYF; Helped Organize Chrysalis; *LSU; Sociology.*

GREEN, Terry Dale
McGavock HS; Nashville, TN; Band; Good Friends Vol; MTSBOA; *MTSU; Vet Med.*

GREEN, Terry Rugenia
Lowndes HS; Valdosta, GA; Chor; Span C; Sr Cl Cabinet; Choir; Yth Coun; DECA; Sr Cl Cabinet; Bronze, Gold Medal As, DECA; Valentine Qn; Choir; Yth Coun; *Missionary.*

GREEN, Thomas Lloyd
Valentine HS; Valentine, NE (7-87) Var C; VP, Soph Cl; JV, Bkbl; Ftbl; Tr; COM; NHS; HR; Valentines Day Coronation Court; *U of Nebr; Chiropractic.*

GREEN, Tim Allen
Cowan HS; Muncie, IN (4-90) SC; Bsbl; JV, Bkbl; *Ind U; Med.*

GREEN, Timothy Joel
Manual HS; Peoria, IL (86-318) Bkbl; Cr-Ctry; Tnns; JV, Tr; Campus Life; HS Church Choir; Pres, Christian Endevor; *Moody Bible Inst; Christian Ed.*

GREEN, Timothy Mark
McGavock Sr HS; Nashville, TN; BC; NHS; Bio A; Math A; Fr A; Eng A; *Trevecca Nazarene Col; Religion.*

GREEN, Veronica Benaye
Mart HS; Mart, TX (15-72) Bus C; FHA; Beauty; Most Beautiful; Sch Mascot; *Kindergarden Teacher.*

GREEN, Vicki Lynette
Danville Sr HS; Danville, IL (100-612) Chor; Drama; Ensm; Madrigal; Span C; Y-Tns; Pres A; *U of Ill; Mus.*

GREEN, Wallace Bowie
Walsh Jesuit HS; Stow, OH (20%-215) Swim; Yth Fel; UMYF; Riding; Bowling; Reach Out For Peace; *Stanford U; Acct.*

GREEN, Wendy Areatha
Eastern Sr HS; Washington, DC; *Printing.*

GREEN, William Myron
Wakefield Sr HS; Arlington, VA; A Cap Choir; BS; Chor; Drama; Madrigal; Thes; Jr Cl; Geog Achv, Schol, A's; *Norfolk St Col; Bus.*

GREENAWALT, Jeffrey Craig
West Haven HS; W Haven, CT (34-580) Ftbl; Rifle C; *Engr.*

GREENAWAY, Cindy J
Woodrow Wilson HS; Youngstown, OH (150-350) Bus C.

GREENBERG, Steven Jay
Deerborne HS; Coral Gables, FL (5-75) Tres, BC; Math C; Pres, NHS; Ch, SC; DARGCA; JA A; Math A; Golden Book A; *Drexal U; Acct.*

GREENE, Alan Rustin
Winston Churchill HS; Potomac, MD (15-622) Ed, Ann; Band; Chess C; Chor; Hmrm; NHS; Span C; Pres, SC; COM; Math A; NMF; NEDT; Span Excellence Cert; WW; *Princeton U; Pre-Med.*

GREENE, Alice Ann
John Curtis Christian Sch; New Orleans, LA (10%-100) BC; Chor; Ensm; NHS; Span C; Tri-HiY; Y-Tns; Rptr, Jr Cl; S-T, Soph Cl; Beauty; Hon Prog; Math A; NMS; Sci A; Nom, WW; *Oral Roberts U; Nurs.*

GREENE, Cassandra Juliette
Newark Sr HS; Newark, OH; Chor; Drama; Span C; Tr; Mary Barnes A; *Ohio St U; Bus Adm.*

GREENE, Cynthia Darlene
Akron N HS; Akron, OH (59-377) Citz A; *Akron U; Computer Processing.*

GREENE, Cynthia Lynne
N Augusta Sr HS; N Augusta, SC; Chldr; S-T, SC; Most Out; Sandspurs Court.

GREENE, Donna Lynne
Middletown HS; Middletown, OH; Band; Hmrm; Mjrte; Sch P; Bkbl; Tr; JA A; YMCA; Laymens; NBTA Twirling; *Ohio St U; Child Psychiatry.*

GREENE, Doreen Claudia
Howard HS; Georgetown, SC; Band; Ch, Mjrte; Pres, Sci C; SC; *Biscayne Med Col; Nurs.*

GREENE, Jennifer Anne June
Saint Cecilia's Acad; Nashville, TN (2-87) VP, NHS; SC; Pres, Sr Cl; Alg A; B Crocker A; Hon Prog; *Duquesne U; Engr.*

GREENE, Jennifer Evelyn
Bangor N HS; Bangor, ME (87-408) AFS; Chor; Type A; *Husson Col; Acct.*

GREENE, Jewel Michelle
Gumberry HS; Gumberry, NC; FHA.

GREENE, John Alton
Terrell Acad; Dawson, GA (28-44) 4H; HiY; Ftbl; Pres, Sub-Dist Yth; VP, Church Yth; *Ga SW Col.*

GREENE, John Howard
St John Lutheran HS; Ocala, FL; Chess C; Dbte Tm; Co-Cpt, Bkbl; Ed.

GREENE, Kathryn Lee
Rockdale HS; Rockdale, TX (23-140) Ann; Chem C; Ensm; VP, FHA; FTA; Mjrte; NHS; Ed, Sch P; Tres, Span C; Tnns; COM; Cl Fav; Journ A; Sci A; VofDEM; Band Coun; UIL Band & Twirling; FHA Ldrship; *SE Tex Col; Ed.*

GREENE, Lauratta Leonette
Huntington HS; Shreveport, LA; Band; Chem C; Chor; Fr C; 4H; Mu Alpha Theta; 4H A; Hon Band & Choir; *Sou U; Bus Ed.*

GREENE, Lisa Lavonne
Xenia HS; Xenia, OH; Gym.

GREENE, Maurice Adrain
Wakefield HS; Arlington, VA; Drama; FBLA; Bkbl; Tnns; COM; Citz A; Hon Prog; JA A; Yth Fel; *Md U; Archt.*

GREENE, Melissa Boschian
Nyack HS; Nyack, NY; French NHS; COM; Manhattan Sch of Mus Schol A.

GREENE, Nancy Sue
Central HS District of Westosha; Salem, WI (28-231) Drama; NHS; Ed, Sch P; VP, SC; Var C; Cpt, Vlbl; Co Cpt, Gym; Drama A; *U of Wisc.*

GREENE, Phyllis Arlisa
Forest Park HS; Baltimore, MD (20-300) NHS; UMBC.

GREENE, Sandra Kay
Duval Sr HS; Lanham, MD; Bkbl; Soccer; Sftbl; Tnns; Tr; Elem Ed.

GREENE, Stanlee Parks
Heidelberg American HS; Heidelberg, GERMANY (31-170) Pres, A Cap Choir; Chor; Ensm; Madrigal; Model UN; NHS; Order/Arrow; Pres, SC; VP, Var C; Pres, Jr Cl; Cpt, Ftbl; JV, Tr; NMS; Order/Arrow A; ROTC A; Fin, Stu Coun A; Princeton U; Bus Adm.

GREENE, Sue Ellen
Northside Christian Sch; Charlotte, NC (1-41) Ann; Chor; Ensm; NHS; Type A; NC Christian Arts Assn Essay A; Mus.

GREENE, Taci Grace
Smiths Station HS; Smiths, AL (4-150) Tres, BC; Chldr; FHA; Lit Mag; Math C; Mu Alpha Theta; Secy, Sci C; SC; Swim; Tnns; Cl Fav; Archaeology C; Outst Soph; Co-Cpt, Drill Tm; Outst Young Amer; Coed Correspondent, Magazine; U of Alaska.

GREENE, Teresa Jaye
Narrows HS; Narrows, VA (10-90) Bus Mgr, Ann; Secy, Bus C; FBLA; NHS; Radford Col; Bus Adm.

GREENE, Teresa Regenald
Landrum HS; Landrum, SC; Pres, BC; COM; Gr Marshal; Spartanburg Methodist Col.

GREENE, Theodore Michael
Eureka Sr HS; Eureka, CA (10%-550) Band; Key C; CSF; Math A; Humboldt St U; Math.

GREENFIELD, Lola Marie
Castlewood Ind Sch; Castlewood, SD (7-23) F-Ed, Ann; Band; Co-Cpt, Chldr; Chor; Pres, FHA; Ed, Sch P; SC; Amer Leg A; HCt; Swtht; Cosmotology.

GREENFIELD, Marsha Ranae
Castlewood HS; Castlewood, SD (5-23) Ed, Ann; Band; Cpt, Chldr; Chor; Ensm; Tres, FHA; GS; F-Ed, Sch P; Bkbl; B Crocker A; 4H A; Page, St Legislature; Hon Stu; SD St U; Home Ec.

GREENFIELD, Matthew Brian
DuVal Sr HS; Lanham, MD; Drama; Co-Ed, Lit Mag; Sch P; Liberal Arts.

GREENFIELD, Patty Jo
Castlewood HS; Castlewood, SD (3-23) Ann; Chor; FHA; Semi-Fin, Jr Miss Pa; Rptr, Sch P; Bkbl; Sftbl; Top Salesman A, DECA; Hon Stu; Northwestern Col; Eng.

GREENFIELD, William Charles
Bridgemont HS; San Fransico, CA; Ann; Drama; Rptr, Sch P; Cpt, Bkbl; Math.

GREENHOLT, Wendy Ann
Littlestown Sr HS; Littlestown, PA (10%-161) Chor; FHA; Pres, 4H; Fin, Jr Miss Pagent; NHS; Secy, Spch C; 4H A; I Dare You; Lion A; Opt A; Spch A; Ntl, Flag Carrier, Band; Swing Choir; ORU; Religion.

GREENIA, Roy Charles
Holy Cross HS; Marine City, MI; Chor; K of C; NHS; Order/Arrow; Ski C; Tres, Soph Cl; Bsbl; Bkbl; HCt; Hon Prog; NMS; Spch A; Mich St U; Bus Adm.

GREENLEE, Pamela Elaine
NW HS; St Louis, MO;

GREENLEE, Sandra Warbington
S Choctaw Acad; Toxey, AL (9-31) BC; Mjrte; Meridian Jr Col; Nurs.

GREENLEE, Thomas Damian
Bloomer HS; Bloomer, WI (30-146) Pres, Band; Ensm; Ski C; Hon Prog; 1st Dist & St, Band Solo; U of Wis; Bus.

GREENLEY, Warren Andrew
Northwest HS; Indianapolis, IN; Citz A; Pres A.

GREENLEY, Brian Timothy
Tomahawk HS; Tomahawk, WI (11-187) Chess C; Chor; Dbte Tm; Ger C; Math C; Bsbl; Hon Prog; Math A; Math.

GREENOUGH, Gregg Paul
Chagrin Falls HS; Chagrin Falls, OH (25-230) A Cap Choir; Band; Chor; Drama; Ger C; NHS; Orch; A-Ed, Sch P; VP, Jr Cl; Cpt, Cr-Ctry; Tr; COM; Hon Prog; Most Out; Tr As; Cr-Ctry As; Most Musical A; Bucknell U; Engr.

GREENQUIST, Bradley Wallace
Falls Church HS; Falls Church, VA (149-503) Drama; George Mason U; Drama.

GREENSHEILDS, Jane Ann
Kirkwood HS; Kirkwood, MO; Pres, Fr C; ARC; Tri-HiY; Hon Prog; ARC A; Young Life; UMYF; God & Comm A.

GREENSMITH, Nancy Jane
Riverview HS; Sarasota, FL (1-664) Band; Fr C; Semi-Fin, GS; NHS; Sci C; Tres, Soph Cl; Amer Leg A; Bio A; Chem A; Comm Band; Hist, Key C; Best Girl, Mus; Superior A & Medal, Flute Contest; Fla Sou Col; Nurs.

GREENWAY, Christopher George
Central HS; Springfield, MO; A Cap Choir; Band; Fr C; Model UN; Var C; Pres, Soph Cl; Cpt, Bkbl; Golf; Tnns; Sou Mo St U; TV & Radio Broadcasting.

GREENWELL, Brenda Denise
Science Hill HS; Johnson City, TN (10%-400) A Cap Choir; Chldr; Chor; Hmrm; SC; Sftbl; Citz A; DARGCA; Hon Prog; Cpt, Bible Bowl Tm; Milligan Col.

GREENWELL, Martin George
Chaminade Col Prep; St Louis, MO (2-117) Chess C; Pres, Drama; NFL; VP, NHS; Ch, Order/Arrow; Rptr, Sch P; Spch C; Alg A; Bio A; Chem A; Curator A; Hist A; Hon Prog; Math A; NEDT; Order/Arrow A; Sal; Sci A; Type A; Eagle Sct, Silver Palm; St Mary's U; Bio.

GREENWELL, Teresa Lynn
Ahrens HS; Louisville, KY; NHS; Alg A; Hist A; JCC; Data Processing.

GREENWOOD, David Warren
Notre Dame-Bishop Gibbons HS; Schenectady, NY; NHS; Order/Arrow; Sch P; Ski C; COM; Hist A; Clarkson Col of Tech; Chem Engr.

GREENWOOD, Reva Jeannine
Rochester HS; Rochester, TX (3-20) Ann; Tres, Band; Bus C; Chor; Drama; FHA; Rptr, Hmrm; Mjrte; Bkbl; Sftbl; Tr; Cl Fav; Best All Around; Stenograph Inst of Tex; Secretarial.

GREENWOOD, Roslyn Denise
South HS; Youngstown, OH (15-283) NHS; Cl Fav; HCt; Hon Prog; Most Out; Rotary A; Youngstown St U; Nurs.

GREENWOOD, Roy Allen II
Valencia HS; Placentia, CA (93-322) Fr C; Bsbl.

GREENZWEIGHT, Heather Roxanne
Cleveland HS; Reseda, CA; LA City Col; Dental Asst.

GREENZWEIGHT, Heidi Joanne
Cleveland HS; Reseda, CA;

GREER, Brent Craig
E Detroit HS; E Detroit, MI (25%-900) Dbte Tm; Clemson U; Adm Mgt.

GREER, Carolyn Jane
Gadsden HS; Gadsden, AL (140-319) Chor; FHA; FTA; 4H; Sci C; Swim; VICA, Bible, 'G', C'S; Med Explorers; Swim-a-thon A; Gadsden St Jr Col; Vet Tech.

GREER, Christine Gail
Harding HS; Marion, OH; Ohio St U; Legal Secy.

GREER, Harry Lawrence III
Salisbury Elk-Lick HS; Salisbury, PA (10-45) A Cap Choir; Band; Chor; Pres, Jr Cl; JV, Bkbl; Type A; Erie Bus Col; Acct.

GREER, Jane Everett
Norfolk Acad; Norfolk, VA (11-79) Chor; Cum Laude Soc; Fr C; Sci C; Diving Tm; Church Choir; Speech Fin; VP, Church Yth Fellowship; Randolph-Macon Col.

GREER, Judy Ann
Bauxite HS; Bauxite, AR (16-44) Bus Mgr, Ann; VP, FBLA; VP, FHA; VP, FTA; GS; Sci C; Semi-Fin, Most Outst; Rptr, St FTA; Pres, Lib Staff.

GREER, Martha Annette
Watauga HS; Boone, NC (20%-280) Chldr; Chor; Ensm; FTA; Hmrm; Span NHS; SC; Christmas Court; Mars Hill Col; Psych.

GREER, Mary Jac
Mangum HS; Mangum, OK (23-65) F-Ed; Ann; Pres, FHA; Semi-Fin, GS; 4H; 4H A; Hist A; Cameron Col; Med.

GREER, Robert Eugene Jr
Jackson HS; Massillon, OH (10%-360) A Cap Choir; Ann; Band; Chor; Dbte Tm; Drama; Ensm; NFL; Span C; Spch C; SC; Bkbl; COM; ROTC A; Spch A; VP, Good News C; Cleff C; Sch Musical; Camp Chef Staff; Bob Jones U; Fine Arts.

GREER, Sandra Gail
Apollo HS; Owensboro, KY; Sch P; Pres, Yth Group; Hospital Vol; Nursing Home Vol.

GREER, Valerie Ann
Weedsport Jr-Sr HS; Weedsport, NY (26-80) Band; Cpt, Chldr; Drama; Fr C; Mjrte; Ski C; Var C; Sftbl; Cl Fav; Swtht; Type A; Yth Fel; Cayuga Co Comm Col; Lib Arts.

GREER, William Thomas Jr
Hannibal Central Sch; Hannibal, NY (1-140) Chess C; Math C; NHS; SC; Hon Prog; Sci A; PA; Syracuse U; Math.

GREESON, Brenda Cheryl
Eastern Guilford HS; Gibsonville, NC (10-175) F-Ed, Ann; Fr C; VP, FTA; Monogram; NHS; Sci C; JV, Bkbl; Tr; U of NC; Phys Therapy.

GREESON, Jeffrey Allen
Thomas B Doherty HS; Colorado Springs, CO (19-414) Dbte Tm; NFL; NHS; Ski C; Spch C; Bsbl; JV, Ftbl; COM; Hon Prog; Math A; Sci A; Fr A; General Mills Family Ldr A; Colo St U Hon; Colo St U; Elec Engr.

GREESON, Tamara Ann
Mt Ida HS; Mt Ida, AR (1-36) F-Ed, Ann; Secy, BC; Co-Cpt, Chldr; Tres, FHA; GS; Semi-Fin, Jr Miss Pa; F-Ed, Lit Mag; ARC; Rptr, Sch P; JV, Bkbl; JV, Tr; Amer Leg A; Beauty; COM; 4H A; Hist A; Hon Prog; Math A; Historian; SC; Beta C Qn; Miss Montgomery Co Fair Qn; Hon Camper; Border Jr Miss; U of Ark; Elem Ed.

GREESON, Tammie Rene
Eastern Guilford HS; Gibsonville, NC (1-164) Ann; Fr C; French NHS; Hmrm; Monogram; Tres, NHS; Bkbl; HCt; Fr A; U of NC; Nurs.

GREESON, Tammy Ann
Mount Ida HS; Mount Ida, AR (1-34) F-Ed, Ann; Secy, BC; Co-Cpt, Chldr; Tres, FHA; GS; Pres, 4H; Semi-Fin, Jr Miss Pa; F-Ed, Lit Mag; ARC; SC; JV, Bkbl; JV, Tr; Beauty; COM; SC; Hist A; Hon Prog; Math A; Val; Yth Fel; Hist, SC; Valentine Qn; Miss Montgomery Co; Jr Miss Spirit A; Pres, Executive Yth Committee; U of Ark; Med.

GREEVER, Glenna Sue
Newton Comm HS; Newton, IL (15-189) Band; Bus C; VP, 4H; NHS; Hon Prog; NEDT; Outst Sci Stu; E Ill U; Elem Ed.

GREGA, Jerome Stephen
Marian HS; Tamaqua, PA (20-130) NHS; Sch P; Hon Prog; Sacristan; WW; Penn St U; Engr.

GREGG, Deborah Kay
Daviston HS; Daviston, AL; Secy, BC; U of Ala; Elem Ed.

GREGG, Donald Wayne
Sooner HS; Bartlesville, OK; Band.

GREGOIRE, Lisa Beth
Thompson Pub HS; Thompson, ND (6-28) Ann; Chor; GS; Bkbl; Tr; ND St U.

GREGORIO, Michael
Maple Shade HS; Maple Shade, NJ (10%-235) VP, Key C; Ftbl; Engr.

GREGORY, Bryan Lee
Laurel Valley Jr-Sr HS; New Florence, PA (1-139) AFS; Chor; NHS; Var C; Bkbl; Golf; Hon Prog; B Crocker A; H of F; HKg; HCt; MLS; Val; Adam Eid; Miller A; Case W Reserve U; Computer Engr.

GREGORY, Claude Douglas
Lord Berkeley HS; Moncks Corner, SC (10-18) BS; Sci C; SC; Sr Cl; Soph Cl; Bsbl; Cpt, Bkbl; Amer Leg A; WW; Citadel Col; Civil Engr.

GREGORY, David Martin
Middleton HS; Charleston, SC (10%-360) Band; BC; Chor; Ensm; Madrigal; Bkbl; Sftbl; Alg A

GREGORY, Deborah Jean
Brandon Sr HS; Brandon, FL; 4H; Mgr, Mjrte; Sftbl; Chapel Choir; *Baylor U; Psych.*

GREGORY, James Edward
East HS; Buffalo, NY (20-360) Bus C; Chor; Pres, Dbte Tm; Drama; Pres, Key C; NHS; Var C; Swim; Tnns; Citz A; MLS; Most Out; Yth Fel; *U of NY at Buffalo; Bus Adm.*

GREGORY, Johnie Eileen
Booker T Washington HS; Tulsa, OK (150-300) Masonic A; *Okla U; Journ.*

GREGORY, Jonathan Eric
Buhler HS; Buhler, KS; Band; Ensm; Math A; Engr Drawing As; Mus Contest As; Ch, Evangelism Comm; *Southwest Baptist Col; Mus.*

GREGORY, Linda Allison
Briarcrest B HS; Memphis, TN (188-322) Sodality; Beauty; Citz A; H of F; HQn; Kiwanis A; Pep C; VP, Social C; Guidance C; *Memphis St U; Phys Therapy.*

GREGORY, Martha Robin
Warwick HS; Lititz, PA (34-260) Band; Ensm; FFA; Pres, 4H; Orch; A-Ed, Sch P; SC; 4H A; Most Out; *Penn St U; Agr Ed.*

GREGORY, Pamela Gail
Mabank HS; Mabank, TX (5-96) Ann; Pres, Band; FHA; Cpt, Mjrte; Secy, NHS; Span C; Secy, SC; Rptr, Soph Cl; Golf; Alg A; Bio A; Cl Fav; Eng A; *Interpreter.*

GREGORY, Sheri Lynn
Dilce Combs HS; Jeff, KY; Ann; BC; Chldr; Chor; Drama; Ensm; Hmrm; Rainbow; Rptr, Sch P; Spch C; SC; Beauty; COM; HCt; Hon Prog; Spch A; Co-Pres, Thespians; Drama A's; *Eastern U; Theater Arts.*

GREGORY, Tami Denise
Warrensburg Latham HS; Warrensburg, IL (24-87) AFS; Pres, Chor; Drama; Pres, Madrigal; SC; Tnns; COM; Spch A; Type A; Yth Fel; Shorthand A.

GREGORY, Wendy Cameron
Hamburg Sr HS; Hamburg, NY (15-520) Chldr; VP, Fr C; Hmrm; ARC; SC; VP, Jr Cl; Tnns; Hon Prog; Girls Service C; GAA; *Bucknell Col; Math.*

GREGURIC, Jean Allison
Norwin Sr HS; Irwin, PA (13-756) Band; NHS; Rainbow; Ski C; Span C; COM; Math A; NEDT; Yth Fel; Ntl Merit Ltr Commentation; Yth Leadership Prog; Sch Service A; Yth Fitness Achv A; 1st Cl Sct; *U of Pittsburgh; Math.*

GREIMAN, Jeffrey George
Garner-Hayfield HS; Garner, IA (7-66) Chor; Drama; JETS; Order/Arrow; SC; Var C; JV, Ftbl; Golf; Order/Arrow A; Scholastic A; *US Air Force Acad; Engr.*

GREISE, Mary Frances
Bishop Walsh HS; Cumberland, MD (8-141) NHS; Lion A; ARC A; Comm Involvement Comm; Religion A; Pres, Yth Coun Red Cross; Cath War Veterans Outst Yth o-t Yr; Principal's A; *Frostburg St Col; Acct.*

GREIST, James Eric
Parsippany Christian Sch; Parsippany, NJ; Band; Chor; Drama; Ski C; Cr-Ctry; HR; Ed, Church Newspaper; Church Yth Choral; *Bio-Chem.*

GREMEL, Robert Raymound
Rincon HS; Tucson, AZ; Chor; Mgr, Cr-Ctry; Mgr, Ftbl; Mgr, Tr.

GRENEVICKI, Lisa Marie
G A R Mem HS; Wilkes-Barre, PA; Band; NHS; Orch; Rptr, Sch P; Sftbl; Tr.

GRENIER, Erin Beth
Davison Sr HS; Davison, MI (90-402) Band; Cpt, Chldr; Drama; NHS; Ski C; Sftbl; Hon Prog; Opt A; Spch A; *Butterworth Sch of Nurs; Nurs.*

GRESH, John Prospero
Citurs HS; Inverness, FL (3-250) BS; Tres, CYO; Pres, NHS; Span C; Amer Leg A; H of F; Hon Prog; MLS; WW; Fla St Span Conv; Pep C; Outst Span Stu; *U of Fla; Dentistry.*

GRESHAM, Bob
Centerville HS; Centerville, TX (4-38) Rptr, Ann; Band; FFA; 4H; Order/Arrow; Rptr, Sch P; Arch; Golf; Tnns; Bio A; COM; Chem A; 4H A; FFA A; *Hardin-Simmons U; Geology.*

GRESHAM, Jack Nance
Hamblen HS E; Morristown, TN (90-239) Co-Cpt, Cr-Ctry; Tr; *E Tenn St U; Pre-Law.*

GRESHAM, Kevin Erwin
Richwoods HS; Peoria, IL (123-550) Band; Dbte Tm; Drama; F-Ed, Sch P; Q&S A; Wash Workshops Congressional Sem; Ill Gen Assembly Schol; *Ill St U; Spch Communication.*

GRESS, Nancy Jayne
Qn o-t Rosary Acad; Amityville, NY (1-85) Ed, Ann; Cpt, Chldr; Math C; Mu Alpha Theta; VP, NHS; Sci C; SC; Tres, Soph Cl; Amer Leg A; Hon Prog; Math A; NEDT; Regent Schol; S-T, Folk Group; Ldrs C; *Le Moyne Col; Bio.*

GRETEMAN, Matthew Paul
Kuemper HS; Carroll, IA (4%-260) Lat C; Monogram; JV, Bkbl; Tnns; Citz A; Top 10, Cl; Acct.

GREULICH, Amy Carol
West HS; Minneapolis, MN (1-200) Ger C; VP, Lat C; VP, NHS; Tnns; Phy A; VofDEM; Tnns & Badminton Ltrs; *Bethel Col; Lib Sci.*

GREUNKE, Karen Anne
Bayside Sr HS; Virginia Beach, VA; Chor; Fr C; Madrigal; NHS; Hist A; 2nd Pl, Sch Talent Show; Lion's C Comp; Talent, Dependability & Inter Mus A; *Mus.*

GREVE, Beth Ann
Lancaster HS; Lancaster, OH (100-725) Chldr; FHA; 4H; Hmrm; Span C; SC; COM; 4H A; Yth Fel; Princess, Dairy Goat C; *Vet Med.*

GREVE, Brenda Jo
Lancaster HS; Lancaster, OH (103-603) FHA; FNA; VP, 4H; Span C; Cr-Ctry; Tr; 4H A; Yth Fel; Para Medic Careers; 4-H Qn Contestant; *Phys Therapy.*

GREVING, Loretta Christina
Quincy Sr HS; Quincy, IL (10%-677) Chor; Ensm; Orch; Alt, Church Pianist; Piano Teacher; Ch, Church Talent Rallies; Sch & Church Musicals; Gospel Trio; Jr Church Service; *Lincoln Christian Col; Mus.*

GREVING, Veronica Lynn
Quincy Sr HS I; Quincy, IL (10%-815) Chor; Ensm; Orch; Church Choirs; Church Mus; Gospel Trio; Soph Ch, Chrch Yth Grp Talent Rally; *Sou Ill U; Mus.*

GREWATZ, Stuart Elton
Valley City HS; Valley City, ND (4-154) F-Ed, Ann; Band; BS; NHS; Order/Arrow; Sci C; Cr-Ctry; Tr; JV, Wrest; Hon Prog; Math A; NMS; Order/Arrow A; Eagle Sct A; *Mass Inst Tech; Civil Engr.*

GREWATZ, Vincent Evan
Valley City HS; Valley City, ND (1-178) Dbte Tm; Hmrm; NHS; Pres, Order/Arrow; Sci C; Tres, Span C; St Stu Congress; SC; JV, Tnns; Citz A; Hon Prog; Yth Fel; *Sci.*

GREWE, Christopher Neil
Coshocton HS; Coshocton, OH (3-210) Chess C; Drama; Fr C; Pres, HiY; NHS; Ch, Order/Arrow; Spch C; DARGCA; MLS; NEDT; Sal; Outst Jr Hist & Fr; NCTE Essay Rep; Dist Sci Fair; *Miami U-Ohio; Communications.*

GREWE, Marcia Ann
Cashocton HS; Coshocton, OH (5-250) Ann; Fr C; FTA; Sch P; SC; JV, Tnns; *Bowling Green St U; Fashion Merchandising.*

GRGURICH, Kathleen Kay
McNally HS; Costa Mesa, CA; FFA; *UCI; Psych.*

GRIBBIN, Gene Marie
Parkville Sr HS; Baltimore, MD (10-550) Secy, Band; Lit Mag; NHS; *Loyola U; Med Tech.*

GRICE, Arnitta Jane
Havana HS; Havana, FL (7-124) Band; Cpt, Chldr; Chor; Jr Miss Pagent; Mjrte; SC; Pres, Tri-HiY; Pres, Jr Cl; Bsbl; Beauty; Cl Fav; Hist A; Hon Prog; ROTC A; Spch A; *Fla A&M U; Phar.*

GRICE, Carl Donald
Westwood Comm HS; Sloan, IA (3-70) Chess C; NHS; Bkbl; Ftbl; Tr; *US Air Force Acad; Aviation.*

GRICE, Kevin Myles
Destrehan HS; Destrehan, LA (5%-200) Secy, Key C; Amer Leg A; *Air Force Acad; Aerospace Engr.*

GRICE, Sandra Dale
Harriman HS; Harriman, TN (3-147) BC; Co-Cpt, Bkbl; Sftbl; Tr; HCt; *Roane St Comm Col; Law.*

GRICE, Wanda Letethia
Roosevelt HS; Atlanta, GA; BC; Secy, Chor; Ensm; Sch P; Hon Prog; Chor Qn; *Pepperdine U; Choral Director.*

GRIDER, Patrick Stuart
Waggener HS; St Matthews, KY (2%-320) Sci C; Span C; Co-Cpt, Wrest; COM; Good Conduct A; *Tulane U; Pre-Med.*

GRIDER, Stephen Todd
Moore HS; Okla City, OK; Dbte Tm; FBLA; Hmrm; Model UN; NFL; Spch C; SC; COM; Journ A; PTA A; ARC A; Spch A; Hon Page, St Capitol; 3rd, Fin, Debate; *U of Okla; Finance.*

GRIEBEL, Caroline Sue
Heritage HS; Monroeville, IN (30-180) Rptr, Sch P; VP, Y-Tns; Pres, Jr Cl; Secy, Soph Cl; Journ A; Q&S A; *Phys Therapy.*

GRIEBEL, Robert Wayne
Heritage HS; Monroeville, IN (28-201) Chess C; Rptr, FFA; Rptr, 4H; Ed, Sch P; SC; VP, Sr Cl; VP, Jr Cl; VP, Soph Cl; Golf; 4H A; HCt; Journ A; Q&S A; Vlbl; *Ind U; Pol Sci.*

GRIEBEL, Roger Wayne
Heritage HS; Monroeville, IN (55-200) FFA; VP, 4H; Ed, Sch P; Pres, Sr Cl; HCt; Q&S A; Sch Ping Pong Tourney; Interntl Twins Assn; *Ind U; Journ.*

GRIEME, Kathryn Ann
Springfield HS; Springfield, IL (59-487) Chem C; Chor; Fr C; 4H; Hmrm; Math C; NHS; Y-Tns; Hockey; Pres A; Yth Fel; GAA; Hon Ment, Hockey; Pres, Invite; Choir, Bible Stu, Ldr, Church; *Milligan Col; Engr.*

GRIEPENSTROH, Sandra Kay
Lourdes Central HS; Nebraska City, NE (3-30) Ed, Ann; Chor; Drama; Pres, 4H; Mu Alpha Theta; NHS; Span C; Co-Ch, Spch C; SC; Secy, Sr Cl; Secy, Jr Cl; Citz A; Elk A; 4H A; Hon Prog; I Dare You; Musical; WW; Outst 4-H Achievement; Pep C; Dress Revue, 4-H Service A; JV, Vlbl; 4-H Food & Nutrition A; *Kearney St Col; Eng Ed.*

GRIEPP, Jodi Rae
Sisseton HS; Sisseton, SD; A Cap Choir; Band; Chor; FHA; Sch P; Tr; Type A; *U of Minn; Law.*

GRIES, DeAnne Maris
Regis HS; Stayton, OR (2-61) NHS; Var C; Bkbl; Tr; COM; Hon Prog; Most Out; Sci A; Vlbl; Creativity A; Best Competitior; Most Inspirational; Best Ath; *Oreg Col of Ed; Phys Ed.*

GRIESEMER, Brian Keith
Herscher HS; Herscher, IL (30-200) Var C; Bsbl; Bkbl; Ftbl; Yth Fel; Kg, Christmas Ball; *KCC; Law Enforcement.*

GRIESEMER, Kevin Scot
Herscher HS; Herscher, IL; Var C; Bsbl; Ftbl; *KCC; Engr.*

GRIESHABER, Kim Denise
Antelope Valley HS; Lancaster, CA (46-625) GS; Hmrm; ARC; SC; Pres, Tri-HiY; Hon Prog; Type A; Ch, YMCA Camp Committee; Yth & Gov; Pres, YMCA Adv Ldrs C; Drill Tm; Sr Guide; Stu Relations Committee; Hon Sch; Flag Carriers; Yth o-t Mo; *Antelope Valley Col; Med.*

GRIESHOP, Joseph Michael
Carroll HS; Dayton, OH (119-320) Chor; Key C; Ed, Lit Mag; VP, Jr Cl; Bsbl; Bkbl; Golf; Yth Fel; Drug & Alcohol Committee; Art A's; John Cantenner A; *Law.*

GRIESMER, Stacey Kay
Royal Oak Kimball HS; Royal Oak, MI (134-678) Ensm; Ntl Yth Conf; Mgr, Orch; Thes; Hon Prog; *W Mich U.*

GRIESS, Cynthia Martha
Sutton Pub HS; Sutton, NE (8-59) Chor; FHA; Pres, 4H; NHS; Tr; Citz A; 4H A; *Mary Lanning Nurs Sch; Nurs.*

GRIESS, Timothy Armin
Lincoln Northeast HS; Lincoln, NE (25%-500) Band; Var C; Bsbl; Hon Prog; Ltr Bsbl; Ltr Band; *U of Nebr; Archt.*

GRIFFEN, Amy Kathleen
Hannibal Sr HS; Hannibal, MO; Chor; VP, FBLA; NHS; Type A; FBLA Ntl Conf, Washington DC; 1st Pl, Jr Clerk Typist, Mo FBLA; *Central Methodist Col; Secy Sci.*

GRIFFEY, Melissa Jean
E Ridge HS; East Ridge, TN (94-288) Chor; Choral A; Hospital Vol; Bible Sch Teacher; Church Choir; *Baroness Erlanger Col; Nurs.*

GRIFFIN, Angela Marie
Thomasville HS; Thomasville, GA; Pres, Anchor C; Ann; Band; Secy, BC; Hmrm; Secy, NHS; Secy, Tri-HiY; Sftbl; Most Improved, Band; *Thomas Co Comm Col; Elem Ed.*

GRIFFIN, Anita Jean
Temple Heights Christian HS; Tampa, FL (7-62) Ed, Ann; S-T, Band; S-T, NHS; S-T, Sr Cl; Citz A; MLS; *Business.*

GRIFFIN, Beth Anne
Hannibal Central Sch; Hannibal, NY; VP, 4H; NHS; 4H A; *Nurs.*

GRIFFIN, Bonnie Lynn
Middle Township HS; Cape May Court House, NJ (25-220) A Cap Choir; Ann; Chor; Madrigal; Monogram; ARC; Span C; Mgr, Bsbl; Mgr, Hockey; Yth Fel; Interntl Coral Festival; Sch Mus; *Social Work.*

GRIFFIN, Bradley Michael
Southfield-Lathrup Sr HS; Lathrup Village, MI; Chor; Madrigal; VP, SC; JV, Bkbl; Cpt, Ftbl; Cpt, Tr; Yth Fel; St Fin; Madrigal; Star BSct; FCA; 100% A, All Area, Ftbl; All Conf, Ftbl; Hon Men All Metro Yth, Ftbl; *W Mich U.*

GRIFFIN, Bret Linwood
Columbus HS; Columbus, GA (5%-367) Math C; Mu Alpha Theta; NHS; COM; Citz A; Hon Prog; *Shorter Col; Pre-Med.*

GRIFFIN, Bruce Marshall
E Jordan HS; E Jordan, MI (6-80) Jr Cl Play; *Mich Tech U; Mech Engr.*

GRIFFIN, Carrie Jane
Albens Acad; Athens, GA (10-21) Drama; Fr C; *U of Ga; Arts.*

GRIFFIN, Christopher Shawn
Elizabeth Ann Johnson HS; Mt Morris, MI (58-239) Band; Swim; Art & Wood Carving A.

GRIFFIN, Countis Vernice
Simeon HS; Chicago, IL (13-413) Tres, Chor; Secy, Hmrm; Math C; Pres, NHS; SC; Secy, Jr Cl; Secy, Soph Cl; COM; Citz A; Cl Fav; Hon Prog; Math A; *Computer Sci.*

GRIFFIN, Cynthia Angelinea
Weequahic HS; Newark, NJ (99-350) Ann; Chor; Drama; Ensm; 4H; Lit Mag; Sch P; Bkbl; COM; Cl Fav; Hon Prog; MLS; Spch A; Girls Select Chor; Hon Chor; Human Relations Board; *Essex Co Jr Col; Child Psych.*

GRIFFIN, Dana Lynn
Switzerland Co HS; Vevay, IN (3-150) Bsbl; Hist A; Sci A; Eng A.

GRIFFIN, Deborah Jean
Jamestown HS; Jamestown, NY (75-600) Band; Co-Cpt, Chldr; Chor; SC; Citizen o-t Mo; *Spec Ed.*

GRIFFIN, Debra Ann
Grantie City HS S; Granite City, IL (10-560) Bus C; Cpt, Chldr; Chor; Ensm; Hmrm; Madrigal; Mod Mus Mas; NHS; ARC; Var C; Soccer; Sftbl; Hist A; Hon Prog; ARC A; Type A; FSA; Pep C; Amer Ldrship Stu Group; Ldrship C; Gym; AAU Swim A; Mus A; Bstr C; Phys Fitness A; Chldr A; Social Stu C; Wrest Tourn Qn; *Sou Ill U; Bus Major.*

GRIFFIN, Donna Gail
Osceola HS; Kissimmee, FL (100-300) A Cap Choir; Band; Chldr; Chor; Dbte Tm; Drama; Ensm; Hmrm; Key C; Mjrte; Rainbow; Spch C; SC; Thes; Tri-HiY; Tnns.

GRIFFIN, Dwain Burnett
McNeil HS; McNeil, AR (5-34) Ann; BC; Chem C; Ch, Drama; Sch P; Sci C; Tres, Span C; Pres, Spch C; Rptr, Sr Cl; Pres, Soph Cl; MVP, Bkbl; *Henderson St U; Computer Programming.*

GRIFFIN, Dwayne Edward
Switzerland Co HS; Vevay, IN (1-96) BS; Span C; Tres, Soph Cl; Bsbl; Bkbl; Sftbl; Tr; Amer Leg A; Bkbl, Spelling, A's; *Math.*

GRIFFIN, Elizabeth Ann
T L Hanna HS; Anderson, SC (10-340) BC; Chem C; VP, Drama; Ensm; Fr C; FTA; Lat C; Monogram; NHS; Phys C; Rptr, Sch P; Sci C; Thes; Alg A; Gr Marshal; Hon Prog; Journ A; NEDT; Sci A; Ed, Annual; Thespian A; *Clemson U; Med Tech.*

GRIFFIN, Elizabeth Lisle
Laurel Co HS; London, KY (11-351) Ann; Tres, BC; Pres, FHA; Hmrm; S-T, Lat C; Secy, Mu Alpha Theta; Sci C; Eng A; Teacher's Pet; Play Production A; *Furman U.*

GRIFFIN, Herbert Lee Jr
Oscoda Area HS; Oscoda, MI; Hmrm; NFL; Spch C; SC; Cpt, Bkbl; Ftbl; *Oral Robert U; Psych.*

GRIFFIN, Iris Ramona
A H Parker HS; Birmingham, AL; FBLA; HiY; Tri-HiY; Var C; Co-Cpt, Tr; Pres A; Yth Leg; *U of Ala; Bus Adm.*

GRIFFIN, James Edward
Columbus HS; Columbus, GA (20-350) CYO; Chor; Rptr, FBLA; JV, Ftbl; Wrest.

GRIFFIN, James Edward
Weequahic HS; Newark, NJ (61-425) Ftbl; Wrest; Hist A; Journ A; Filmmaking A; *Phys Ed.*

GRIFFIN, Kathy
Bainbridge HS; Bainbridge, GA; *Thomasville Text Sch; Cosmetology.*

GRIFFIN, Keith Alan
Richardson Sr HS; Richardson, TX (218-954) A Cap Choir; Sftbl; *Baylor U; Bus Adm.*

GRIFFIN, Kenneth Royce
Uniontown Area HS; Uniontown, PA (99-436) Arch; Pres, 4H; Sci C; Ski C; Var C; Ftbl; Tr; NMS; Rifle C; *Penn St U; Agr.*

GRIFFIN, LaVern Jesse Lee Jr
Galileo HS; San Francisco, CA; Chor; Bank Of Amer A; Cl Fav; Crisco A; God & Country A; I Dare You; Masonic A; Pres A; Yth Fel; *City Col; Bus.*

GRIFFIN, Leslie Gay
Rockledge HS; Rockledge, FL; Band; Chor; Key C; Rainbow; ARC; Mgr, Sftbl; Grnd Cross of Color, Rainbow Girls; *Med.*

GRIFFIN, Linda Denette
N Gaston HS; Dallas, NC; Key C; Sftbl; Type A; Co- cpt, Colorguard; *Secy.*

GRIFFIN, Madolin Dell
Tuloso-Midway HS; Corpus Christi, TX; Secy, Chor; FTA; *Del Mar Jr Col; Sociology.*

GRIFFIN, Mark Ellis
Pisgah Sr HS; Canton, NC; Chor; All St Chor; *Haywood Tech Inst; Fish & Wildlife Mgr.*

GRIFFIN, Mitchell Edward
Anderson Union HS; Anderson, CA; A Cap Choir; Chor; City Conf; Ensm; Gr C; Hmrm; Pol Sci C; SC; Y-Tns; *Shasta Col; Police Sci.*

GRIFFIN, Pamela Jo
Burlington Comm HS; Burlington, IA (50%-456) Pres, Rainbow; Pres, MYF; Tres, Sub District Yth Coun; District Yth Coun; Choir; *Garrett Seminary Col; Religion.*

GRIFFIN, Pamela Raenette
John Marshall HS; San Antonio, TX; Span C; Dance Tm; *U of Tex; Nurs.*

GRIFFIN, Pamela Rose
Rochester HS; Rochester, MI; Citz A; *Bus.*

GRIFFIN, Phyllis Lynn
Weatherford HS; Weatherford, TX (10-30) FHA; Horse Riding C; Run-Up, Hgh Point-Horse Riding C; *Special Ed.*

GRIFFIN, Rahno Doreen
North HS; Omaha, NE; A Cap Choir; Chldr; Chor; Madrigal; Ltr, Chldr; Ltr, Mus; *Grace Col of Bible; Mus.*

GRIFFIN, Rebecca Joyce
Brandon HS; Brandon, FL (17?-1000) S-T, Chor; Drama; Ensm; Hmrm; Fin, Jr Miss Pageant; Rainbow; SC; Beauty; COM; Most Out; Sci A; Yth Fel; Pres, Area Mus; WW; VP, Christian Yth Fellowship A; Past Worthy Advisor, Rainbow Girls; Soloist; *U of S Fla; Mus.*

GRIFFIN, Regina
Southside HS; Greenville, SC; A Cap Choir; CYO; Chor; Fin, Jr Miss Pageant; Bkbl; Tr; All-St Chor; *SC St; Mus.*

GRIFFIN, Ruth Ellen
Lake Forest HS; Felton, DE (4-233) Band; Bus C; Drama; Pres, Fr C; Tres, FNA; Hmrm; Rptr, Mgr, Bsbl; COM; Mus A; *Eastern Nazarene Col; Nurs.*

GRIFFIN, Sheila
Bainbridge HS; Bainbridge, GA; FBLA; FHA.

GRIFFIN, Sherrie Felicia
Southwestern HS; Detroit, MI; Bkbl; Tnns; *Mich St U; Teaching.*

GRIFFIN, Thomas Weaver Jr
Hattiesburg HS; Hattiesburg, MS (25%-509) Hmrm; SC; VP, Soph Cl; JV, Bkbl; Tnns; Hon Stu; Young Peoples Choir; Most Courteous; Spirit Ensm; Ftbl Statistician; Yth Coun.

GRIFFIN, Tommie Lynn
Anniston HS; Anniston, AL (13-305) BC; Chor; FBLA; Hmrm; Rptr, NHS; Ed, Sch P; SC; Journ A; Opt A; Q&S A; Spch A; *U of Ala; Eng.*

GRIFFIN, Wanda Itelia
Hillsdale HS; San Mateo, CA; Soccer; BSU; *Bus.*

GRIFFIN, Wendy Ann
Huntington HS; Huntington, NY (40%-650) AFS; Sftbl; Swim; Tr; Presidential Phys Fitness A; Var Ltrs; Girls Ath A; Candystriper A; *Col of New Rochelle; Econ.*

GRIFFIS, Henry Samuel
Dos Pueblos HS; Goleta, CA (1-600) Tres, A Cap Choir; Tres, Madrigal; CSF; Hist A; HCt; NEDT; Entrance Hon's, Col; NML; *Pomona Col; Pre-Law.*

GRIFFITH, Arva Gene
Loomis Pub Sch; Loomis, NE (1-21) Band; NHS; Bkbl; Tr; Bio A; Spch A; Home Ec A; Pres, Pep C; Secy, ACT; Vlbl; *U of Nebr at Omaha; Nurs.*

GRIFFITH, Chris Alan
Logan Elm HS; Circleville, OH; Chor; Demolay; Ensm; Golf; Sftbl; Bus Ministry; Choir; Karate 0280003; *Ohio St U; Aeronautics.*

GRIFFITH, Christopher Alan
Logan Elm HS; Circleville, OH; Chor; Demolay; Ensm; Golf; Sftbl; Chor A; Bus Ministry; Church Chor; Karate C; *Ohio St U; Aeronautics.*

GRIFFITH, Chrystal June
Gull Lake HS; Richland, MI (10%-250) Band; Fr C; 4H; NHS; Sci C; Ski C; Var C; Bkbl; Tr; Bio A; 4H A; Pres A; Type A; FCA; Mgr, Vlbl; St of Mich Special Tribute; *Law.*

GRIFFITH, Jacqualyn June
Weatherford HS; Weatherford, TX (33-252) Chldr; Drama; FTA; Hmrm; Mjrte; NHS; Span C; Var C; Bkbl; Tr; Opt A; Swtht; Phys Ed A; *Stephen F Austin Col; Elem Ed.*

GRIFFITH, Jeffrey Randolph
Vinton Co HS; McArthur, OH; Sch Achieve Tm; Span C; Alg A; COM; St Scholar; *Ohio St U; Law.*

GRIFFITH, Katharine Bontecou
Clearwater HS; Clearwater, FL (50-850) Ann; Drama; VP, Ger C; Hmrm; InterAct C; Key C; Ed, St Ger Newspaper; Ger Schol A; Interntl C; Delta Epsilon Phi; Co Horsemen's Assn; Ad Mgr, Yrbk; Fla Assn of Stu of Ger.

GRIFFITH, Keith Douglas
Sunbright HS; Sunbright, TN (10-65) Band; FFA; 4H; Sci C; Var C; Bsbl; Bkbl; Ftbl; 4H A; Ftbl A.

GRIFFITH, Lynn Ann
Wheaton HS; Wheaton, MN (47-84) Bus C; Chor; FHA; Tr; Yth Fel; *ND St U; Child Development.*

GRIFFITH, Marcia Ann
Hattiesburg HS; Hattiesburg, MS; Band; Drama; Jr Miss Pageant; Pres, Span C; Co Cpt, Flag Corps; Outst Gen Bus Stu A; *U of Sou Miss.*

GRIFFITH, Margaret Jane
Robert E Lee HS; Baytown, TX (25-400) Band; Lat C; Lat NHS; Mjrte; Keywanettes; MYF; *Tex U; Engr.*

GRIFFITH, Mark Shannon
Nathan Hale HS; Tulsa, OK (82%-750) Band; Dbte Tm; Hmrm; ARC; Span C; SC; Bkbl; Sftbl; *Oral Roberts U; Pol Sci.*

GRIFFITH, Mary Elizabeth
Hogansville HS; Hogansville, GA (6-60) Band; Pres, BC; FTA; Gov Honor Prog; Hon Prog; Math A; NEDT; Spch A; *LaGrange Col; Bio.*

GRIFFITH, Patricia Avonda
St Joseph Acad; Mc Sherrystown, PA (5-12) Chldr; Dbte Tm; Drama; Hmrm; Orch; Ed, Sch P; Bkbl; Sftbl; Swim; Hon Prog; Prom Qn; WW; *Widener Col; Bio.*

GRIFFITH, Rebecca Anne
Mount Ida HS; Mount Ida, AR (3-30) Ann; Band; BC; JV, Chldr; FHA; A-Ed, Lit Mag; Rptr, Soph Cl; Most Talented; *Garland Co Comm Col; Nurs.*

GRIFFITH, Roger Wade
Sunbright HS; Sunbright, TN (10-66) Band; BC; FFA; 4H; Bsbl; Bkbl; Ftbl; Ftbl, FFA, A's; *Tenn Tech U; Engr.*

GRIFFITH, Steven Douglas
Van-Cove HS; Cove, AR (3-28) FFA; 4H; SC; Pres, Jr Cl; Pres, Soph Cl; Cpt, Bkbl; Bio A; Hist A; HCt; MLS; Sal; Sci A; Most Helpful; Most Intellectual; Most Talented; *Sou Ark U.*

GRIFFITH, Vena Louise
South Salem HS; Salem, OR; Band; Ensm; FHA; Ger C; Tr; VP, Church Yth Group; *Home Ec.*

GRIFFITH, Vivian JoAnne
Robert E Lee HS; Baytown, TX (20-400) VP, AFS; Band; Secy, Fr C; French NHS; Mjrte; NHS; Tres, Keywanettes; MYF; *Baylor U; International Bus.*

GRIFFITH, Vivian Joanne
Robert E Lee HS; Baytown, TX (9-411) VP, AFS; Band; Secy, Fr C; French NHS; Mjrte; NHS; Magna Cum Laude; Tres, Keywanettes; NHS School Win; *Baylor U; Foreign Service.*

GRIGAR, William James
E Bernard HS; East Bernard, TX (2-60) Chem C; Math C; Model UN; Phys C; Sch P; Sci C; Tr; *Wharton Co Jr Col; Engr.*

GRIGG, Jack Norwood
Winnfield Sr HS; Winnfield, LA (17-143) FBLA; FFA; 4H; Bsbl; Ftbl; Tr; Cl Fav; *La Tech U; Engr.*

GRIGG, Reena Ann
W Mecklenburg HS; Charlotte, NC (10%-353) A-Ed, Ann; Hmrm; NHS; SC; Swim; Civinette; *U of N Carolina; Nurs.*

GRIGGS, Glynn Jordan
Dalton HS; Dalton, GA (50-266) HiY; NHS; Swim; 'Y' C A; *Dalton Jr Col; Bus.*

GRIGGS, Mary Katherine
Langley HS; McLean, VA (58-540) Ed, Ann; Chor; NHS; VP, Span NHS; Tr; *U of Va; Med.*

GRIGGS, Mildred Gladys
Franklin HS; Portland, OR; Chor; Ensm; Bsbl; Bkbl; Tnns; *Sylvania Col; Nurs.*

GRIGLEN, Wayne Herman
C L Harper HS; Atlanta, GA; Band; Chor; NHS; Ftbl; Tr; COM; ROTC A; Yth Fel; *Computer Sci.*

GRIGSBY, Parthena Faye
Skyline HS; Pratt, KS (1-22) Ed, Ann; Band; Chor; Ensm; Secy, 4H; Mjrte; F-Ed, Sch P; SC; VP, Var C; Tres, Sr Cl; Pres, Jr Cl; Bkbl; Citz A; DARGCA; 4H A; H of F; HQn; HCt; Hon Prog; Journ A; MLS; Most Out; Spch A; Type A; Val; Yth Fel; Vlbl; Two St 4-H Stu Congress; 1st Chair Flute, Dist Band; US Collegiate Wind Band; WW; *Okla City U; Mus.*

GRILK, Cynthia Elizabeth
Central HS; Davenport, IA; A Cap Choir; Drama; Ensm; FTA; GS; Hmrm; Jr Miss Pagent; Madrigal; Thes; Raggers Soc; Rep, Adm Board; Pres, Sr High Yth Fel; Rep, Coun On Ministries; Rep, Social Concerns Work Area; *Special Ed.*

GRILLS, Barbara Jane
Bayless Sr HS; St Louis, MO (11-184) Band; FTA; Hmrm; NHS; Sci C; SC; *Luthern Hospital Nurs Sch; Nurs.*

GRIM, Brian Edward
James Bowie HS; Arlington, TX (33%-350) Order/Arrow; JV, Tnns; Order/Arrow A; *UTA; Engr.*

GRIM, Sara Teresa
North Co Sr HS; Desloge, MO; Band; NHS; Bkbl; Hon Prog; Math A; *MAC.*

GRIMBALL, Gilbert Nikita
Burke HS; Charleston, SC (14-201) City Conf; Drama; Pres, Hmrm; Tres, NHS; A-Ed, Sch P; Pres, Sr Cl; Tres, Jr Cl; Tr; COM; Chamber of Comm A; Cl Fav; MLS; Most Out; WW; *U of SC; Special Ed.*

GRIMES, Barbara Anita
Rufus King HS; Milwaukee, WI; CYO; FBLA; *UWM; Med.*

GRIMES, Charlotte Green
Roanoke HS; Robersonville, NC (20-150) Ed, Ann; Band; Fr C; Hmrm; Co-Cpt, Mjrte; Math C; Phys C; Sci C; SC; Secy, Sr Cl; Tnns; HCt; *Meredith Col.*

GRIMES, Deborrah
Broxton HS; Broxton, GA (4-40) Co-Ed, Ann; VP, BC; Chldr; FHA; GS; Hmrm; SC; COM; Cl Fav; HCt; Most Out; *S Ga Col; Med Secy.*

GRIMES, Dianne
Wheeler Co HS; Alamo, GA; BC; FBLA; NHS; *Brewton Parker Col; Secy Sci.*

GRIMES, Elizabeth Anne
The Fayetteville Acad; Fayetteville, NC (4-26) Cpt, Chldr; Rptr, Fr C; Pres, Lat C; Tres, NHS; Ch, Var C; Sftbl; COM; DARGCA; HCt; I Dare You; Kiwanis A; Yth Fel; MVP, Chldr; Rptr, Interntl C; Pres, VP, Keywannettes; Marshal; Planning & Environment Coun; *U of NC at Chapel Hill; Dentistry.*

GRIMES, Katharine Leawanna
La Porte HS; La Porte, TX (7-335) Fr C; NHS; WW; *U of Houston; Eng.*

GRIMES, Kathleen Elizabeth
St Pius X HS; Atlanta, GA (1-196) Ann; Chldr; NHS; MVP, Tnns; COM; HCt; Hon Prog; Math A; Presbyterian Col Jr Fellow; *U of Va; Math.*

GRIMES, Kay Ann
Maysville HS; Maysville, OK (5-40) Ann; Chor; Pres, FHA; Pres, 4H; Pres, NHS; Sch P; VP, SC; Pres, Sr Cl; Cl Fav; 4H A; Hon Prog; I Dare You; MLS; Type A; VP, FHA; Sr Cl Qn; Secy, NHS; Key C Swtht; FHA Swtht; *Central St U; Bus.*

GRIMES, Lisa Jo
Niceville Sr HS; Niceville, FL; Church Yth Choir; Church Puppet Ministry; Yth Adv Coun; Qn A, Acteens; *Bus Adm.*

GRIMES, Rebecca Ann
La Porte HS; La Porte, TX; *U of Houston; Secondary Ed.*

GRIMES, Sandra Lynn
Niceville Sr HS; Niceville, FL (39-408) FHA; Hmrm; NHS; SC; Hon Prog; Qn & Qn With Secptor, Acteen A's; Chrch Choir, Nursery Wrkr & Pup Min; *U of Ala; Cancer Research.*

GRIMES, Sherry Lynn
Sylvan Hills HS; Sherwood, AR (48-421) Pres, Rainbow; Y-Tns.

GRIMES, Sue Anne
Bartow W HS; Bartow, FL (4-300) Secy, Anchor C; Ed, Ann; Co-Cpt, Chldr; Drama; Pres, FHA; GS; Hmrm; NHS; Rptr, Sch P; SC; Tres, Soph Cl; MVP, Tnns; Amer Leg A; Beauty; Citz A; H of F; Yth Fel; WW; *Clemson U; Bus Adm.*

GRIMM, Alisa Arlene
Keystone HS; La Grange, OH (2-140) Chess C; Chor; Drama; S-T, JETS; COM; Mjrte, Drill Tm; Engr.

GRIMM, Douglas Paul
Benton Co R-1 HS; Cole Camp, MO (6-56) NHS; F-Ed, Sch P; SC; Citz A; 4H A; Type A; *U of Mo; Phar.*

GRIMM, Joanne Renee
Hershey HS; Hershey, PA (14-299) Chor; Span NHS; Sunday Sch Teacher; Stu o-t Wk.

GRIMM, Karyn Lee
Stranahan HS; Ft Lauderdale, FL (1-450) Cpt, Band; Tres, InterClub Coun; VP, NHS; SC; Mgr, Swim; Tr; Citz A; DARGCA; Val; Smith Book A; Band Swtht; *Brown U; Med.*

GRIMM, Michelle Lynette
Dover Area HS; Dover, PA (8-280) Band; Chor; Ensm; NHS; Rainbow; Sal; Val; Ntl A, Piano Teachers Guild; Tres, Bible C; Jr Matinee Mus C; Mus.

GRIMMER, William Edward III
Lee Acad; Marianne, AR (15-26) Drama; FFA; NHS; Bsbl; Bkbl; Ftbl; Sftbl; Wrest; Cl Fav; *U of Central Ark; Agr.*

GRIMMETT, Avery Trent
John Adams HS; Cleveland, OH; Band; *Oberlin Col; Mus.*

GRIMMETTE, Debra DeLane
Man HS; Man, WV (30-180) Band; Commercial C; FNA; FTA; Hmrm; NHS; ARC; Hon Prog; Type A; Bookkeeping A; *Marshall U; Elem Ed.*

GRIMSHAW, David N
Danville HS; Danville, IL (7-650) Pres, Band; Chor; Community Yth Symph; Ensm; Hmrm; Madrigal; Orch; Order/Arrow; Sch P; Cr-Ctry; COM; Citz A; Hon Prog; Order/Arrow A; Pres A; All St Band; Eagle Sct.

GRIMSHAW, David Norman
Danville HS; Danville, IL (7-650) Pres, Band; Chor; Community Yth Symph; Drama; Rptr, Hmrm; Madrigal; Orch; Order/Arrow; Bus Mgr, Sch P; Cr-Ctry; COM; Citz A; Hon Prog; Order/Arrow A; Pres A; Rotary A; Eagle Sct; All St Band; Health.

GRIMSHAW, Richard Scott
Spruce Creek HS; Daytona Beach, FL (17-480) Cpt, Band; NHS; Orch; Swim; Hon Prog; Magna Cum Laude; WW; Band; *Daytona Beach Comm Col; Med.*

GRIMSLEY, Patricia Denise
Hardee HS; Wauchula, FL; Band; FBLA; FTA; 4H; Hmrm; Jr Miss Pagent; Cr-Ctry; Tr; *Polk Comm Col; Nurs.*

GRIMSTAD, Pamela Sue
Central HS; Waterloo, IA; JA A.

GRINDLEY, Anne Heather
Wheeling Park HS; Wheeling, WV (21-800) Fr C; 4H; Secy, Y-Tns; Swim; Tnns; COM; Citz A; Hon Prog; *Psych.*

GRINER, Kathryn
Elgin Acad; Elgin, IL (1-28) BC; Cum Laude Soc; Drama; Fr C; French NHS; Lit Mag; NHS; Thes; VP, Jr Cl; Sftbl; MVP, Tnns; HCt; Rotary A; Val; Tnns Osborn A; Most Ath, Jr-Sr Cl; *Wellseley Col; Fr.*

GRINER, Lewis Eugene
Dillard HS; Ft Lauderdale, FL (15-250) Dbte Tm; Sch P; Bsbl; Soccer; Cpt, Swim; *Broward Comm Col; Law Enforcement.*

GRINER, Martha Ellen
Claxton HS; Claxton, GA (25%-110) Bus Mgr, Ann; BC; Drama; Ed, Sch P; Pres, SC; Thes; Tres, Sr Cl; Bkbl; Tnns; Citz A; HQn; Journ A; WW; *Ga Sou Col; Ed.*

GRING, David Carl
Lasalle HS; South Bend, IN (19-465) NHS; Cpt, Bsbl; Wrest; Gov Honor Prog; Kiwanis A; Magna Cum Laude; St Scholar; Yth Fel; Most Improved, Bsbl; Best Ath A; *Valparaiso U; Enviromental.*

GRINNELL, Daniel Lee
Liberty Jr-Sr HS; Liberty, PA (10-60) Ger C; VP, Jr Cl; Bsbl; Cpt, Bkbl; Soccer; Tr; *Penn St U; Engr.*

GRINNELL, Paul David
Waterford Kettering HS; Drayton Plains, MI; JV, Bkbl; Sch Sportsmanship A.

GRINOLDS, Donald Scott
Erskine Pub HS; Erskine, MN (5-20) Band; Chldr; Chor; Drama; 4H; Rptr, Sch P; Pres, SC; VP, Soph Cl; Bkbl; Ftbl; Tr; Hon Choir; Swing Choir; Stage Band.

GRINSTEAD, Cathy Jane
N Augusta Sr HS; N Augusta, SC (73-416) F-Ed, Ann; Cpt, Chldr; Hmrm; InterClub Coun; Fin, Jr Miss Pagent; NHS; VP, SC; Pres, Sr Cl; Bkbl; Pres A; Ldrship A; *Clemson U; Ed.*

GRINTON, Pamela Jean
Starmount HS; Boonville, NC (10%-211) Cpt, Chldr; FHA; Secy, Sftbl; Vlbl; *NC Central Col; Beautician.*

GRISANTI, Becky Lynn
Forestville Central Sch; Forestville, NY; Chor; FHA; 4H; *Jamestown Comm Col; Secy Stu.*

GRISCOM, Carol Ann
Salem HS; Salem, NJ (24-248) Pres, 4H; NHS; Bkbl; Tnns; 4H A; Yth Fel; WW; Rider Col; Bus.

GRISE, Karen Jean
Niles Sr HS; Niles, MI; Band; Hon Prog; Pres A; Yth Fel.

GRISHAM, Sharon Tratina
Daniel Webster HS; Tulsa, OK (35-148) Bus C; VP, FBLA; GS; Hmrm; NHS; Rptr, ARC; Span C; SC; Parl, Sr Cl; Tres, Jr Cl; Secy, Soph Cl; Citz A; JA A; ARC A; Northeastern Okla St U; Elem Ed.

GRISSINGER, Janis Lee
McConnellsburg HS; McConnellsburg, PA (20-84) Co-Ed, Ann; VP, Band; Chldr; Chor; Hmrm; Mjrte; NHS; SC; Var C; Hockey; Elizabethtown Col; Lab Tech.

GRISSOM, Elvis Edward Jr
Malvern HS; Malvern, AR (50-221) Band; BC; BS; Hmrm; Order/Arrow; F-Ed, Sch P; Sci C; SC; Pres, Sr Cl; All St Band; Mr Christ Ambassador; Henderson St U; Instrumental Mus.

GRISSOM, Gordon Ray
Flathead HS; Kalispell, MT (35-650) Band; Fr C; Ftbl; Opt Out Tn; Type A; Northwest Col.

GRISSOM, Janice
Tupelo HS; Tupelo, MS (15%-500) A Cap Choir; Anchor C; Chldr; Chor; Ensm; GS; Madrigal; Thes; Cl Fav; HCt; Yth Fel; God & Comm A; Delta St Hon Choir; Northeast Jr Col; Psych.

GRISSOM, Jeffrey Mark
Bovina HS; Bovina, TX; Drama; 4H; Spch C; Tnns; 1st Pl, Soil & Water Essay Contest; Tex Tech U; Bus Adm.

GRISWOLD, Debra Lee
Clearwater HS; Clearwater, FL (90-1500) Y-Tns; HR; Pep C; Candystriper; Dean's List; Fel Commission; Diocesan Yth Comm; Alter Guild; Pres, Church Yth Group; Sr Acolyte.

GRISWOLD, Kathy Jo
Mtn View HS; Mountain View, AR (10-80) Band; BC; Orch; Secy, Jr Cl; Bkbl; Tr; HCt; Eng A; Med.

GRISWOLD, Margaret Anna
West Wilkes HS; Millers Creek, NC; Band; Lat C; Sci C; Tnns; God & Country A; Sr GSct; NC St U; Vet.

GRISWOLD, Patricia Bryant
Western HS; Alamance Co, NC; Chor; Drama; FHA; Hmrm; SC; Tr; Catawba Col; Social Work.

GRISWOLD, William Maverick
Cumberland Valley HS; Mechanicsburg, PA (15-600) NHS; Rptr, Sch P; NEDT; Brown Col; Art Hist.

GRITSKO, Patricia Ann
John S Fine Sr HS; Nanticoke, PA; Rptr, Ann; FHA; Rptr, Sch P; Tri-HiY; Var C; Tres, Sr Cl; Tres, Jr Cl; Tres, Soph Cl; Bkbl; Cpt, Hockey; COM; NEDT; Spch A; Vlbl; Most Reliable; Most Ambitious; Temple U; Phar.

GRITTON, Richard Kenneth
Madison C-3 HS; Madison, MO (3-27) Band; VP, SC; Var C; Bsbl; Bkbl; Alg A; Citz A; Math A.

GRITTON, Tom Edward
Moline Sr HS; Moline, IL; Ftbl; Fin, Tnns; MVP, Wrest; Hon Prog; FCA; Young Life; Most Improved Tn Player.

GRIZZARD, Max Albert
Columbia HS; Decatur, GA (7-250) Pres, BC; Tres, Math C; Tres, Mu Alpha Theta; NHS; SC; Ftbl; COM; People-To-People HS Stu Ambassador; Communications.

GRIZZELL, Donnethia
Palm Springs HS; Palm Springs, CA; COD; Fashion Design.

GRIZZLE, Patti Joyce
Feds Creek HS; Feds Creek, KY (7-72) Ann; Band; Bus C; Chor; Fr C; 4H; Mjrte; Pres, Tri-HiY; 4H A; HCt; Wittiest Soph; Superlative; Best All Around Jr, Superlative; Most Unforgettable Sr, Superlative.

GROAT, Leslie Kenneth
Cottage Grove HS; Cottage Grove, OR (1-300) Band; Span C; Bsbl; Bkbl; Outst, Ath & Schol; Phys Ed.

GROAT, Scott Alan
Ft Walton Bch HS; Ft Walton Bch, FL (200-610) FNA; InterAct C; Span NHS; Var C; Bsbl; Co-Cpt, Ftbl; Tr; H of F; HCt; Lion A; Pres A; Newpaper A; U of Dayton; Pre-Med.

GROB, Debbie Ann
Lutcher HS; Lutcher, LA; Band; Tres, BC; FHA; Math C; Mu Alpha Theta; Phys C; Sci C; COM; Poet A; Nicholls Col; Med.

GROBE, Steven Edward
Prospect HS; Mt Prospect, IL (12%-810) Band; Community Yth Symph; VP, Fr C; Sup, St in Mus; Puppet Ministry; Hi-League; Mus.

GROCE, Christopher Douglas
Starmount HS; Boonville, NC (21-154) Mu Alpha Theta; Co-Cpt, Bkbl; Tnns; Nom, Morehead Schol; MVP, Bkbl; NC St U; Civil Engr.

GROCE, Jay Michael
Starmount HS; Boonville, NC (27-151) A Cap Choir; Bus Mgr, Chor; Drama; Ensm; Pres, FFA; NHS; SC; Tres, Sr Cl; Tnns; Spch A; VofDEM; Win, FFA Pub Spch; Win, St FFA Quartet; Ch, FFA Parl Procedure Tm; Soc Stu C; VICA; NC St U; Agr.

GROEBNER, James Alan
William A Wirt HS; Gary, IN (20-240) Demolay; NHS; Span C; Bsbl; Soccer; Hon Prog; Ind U Northwest; Bus.

GROEBNER, Jerri Lynn
William A Wirt HS; Gary, IN; Mjrte.

GROENEWEG, Mark Allen
Bay HS; Bay Village, OH (10%-300) Band; Math A; Acad Achievement A; Ohio St U; Engr.

GROENHAGEN, Dawn Marie
Oregon HS; Oregon, IL (50%-135) AFS; GAA; Bowl C.

GROENKE, David William
Cannon Falls HS; Cannon Falls, MN (47-136) Band; FFA; 4H; Bkbl; Ftbl; Tr; U of M at Waseca; Farm Mgt.

GROENKE, JoEllen Louise
Cannon Falls HS; Cannon Falls, MN (20%-145) Band; Rptr, 4H; 4H A; VP, Church Yth Group; Sewing Contest; Designer.

GROETHE, Jo Alice
Elk Point HS; Elk Point, SD (9-66) Chor; Fr C; Tr.

GROETHE, Kimberly Kay
Elk Point Pub HS; Elk Point, SD (25-58) Ann; Bkbl; Sftbl; Mgr, Tr; 4H A; S-T & Rptr, 4-H C; SD St U; Home Ec.

GROETHE, Rhetta Marie
Elk Point HS; Elk Point, SD (4-66) Fr C; Special Ed.

GROFF, Carolyn Louise
Upper Merion Sr HS; King of Prussia, PA (31-580) Band; Hmrm; InterAct C; Hon Prog; NMS; Academic Achv A; LaCrosse Jr-Var; Bio.

GROGAN, Roy J Jr
Weatherford HS; Weatherford, TX (7-252) BS; Dbte Tm; Secy, FTA; Lat C; Lat NHS; Ch, NHS; ARC; Pres, SC; MVP, Golf; Opt A; Young Tex o-t Mo; Duke U; Pol Sci.

GROH, Philip James
Aloha HS; Portland, OR (60-600) Band; Ensm; Orch; Co-Cpt, Bkbl; Cpt, Swim; Tr; Law.

GROLEAU, Florestine Mary
Big Bay de Noc HS; Cooks, MI; Band; Chldr; Chor; Drama; Ensm; Tres, 4H; Key C; VP, Jr Cl; Cpt, Bkbl; Sftbl; Tr; Citz A; 4H A; Band, Choral, A's; N Mich U; Home Ec.

GROLEAU, Sheila Marie
Big Bay de Noc HS; Cooks, MI; Band; Drama; Ensm; Pres, 4H; F-Ed, Sch P; Bkbl; Sftbl; Tr; 4H A; Band A's; Bay De Noc Comm Col; Nurs.

GROMAN, Donna Marie
J W Hallahan HS; Philadelphia, PA (10-431) Ed, Ann; CYO; Hmrm; Math C; NHS; Sci C; Secy, Sodality; Ftbl; Hon Prog; U of Scranton; Physics.

GRONITZ, Gail Ellen
Brown Deer HS; Brown Deer, WI (25%-272) Chess C; Bkbl; Co-Cpt, Sftbl; JV, Tr; Yth Fel; U of Wis; Special Ed.

GRONWICK, Vicki Lee
Maine South HS; Park Ridge, IL (85%-800) Chor; Fr C; Wheaton Col; Special Ed.

GROOME, Susan Fox
Warren Central HS; Vicksburg, MS (30-350) Chor; Hmrm; VP, Lat C; Mu Alpha Theta; Sci C; LSU.

GROOMS, Sharon Elaine
Mims Acad; Harleyville, SC (3-18) Ann; Chldr; NHS; F-Ed, Sch P; Pres, Sr Cl; Pres, Jr Cl; VP, Soph Cl; Hist A; Hon Prog; 2nd Runner-Up, HS Beauty Contest; Woodmen o-t World A.

GROOVER, Cindy Lou
Muskogee HS; Muskogee, OK; Rptr, FBLA; NHS; Ed, Sch P; Hist A; Journ A; MLS; Sci A; Spch A; Yth Fel; Church Yth Choir; Art Schol; Bus Ministry; Top 10%; Ed, Scout; Original Oratory Writing Cert; Regional Sci Fair, 2nd Pl.

GROSCOST, Cynthia Joyce
Deer Lakes HS; Cheswick, PA (52-280) Band; Chor; Fr C; NHS; Colorguard; Secy.

GROSCOST, Pamela Sue
Deer Lakes HS; Cheswick, PA (20%-256) Band; Cpt, Chldr; Gym Coach.

GROSE, Margaret Cary
Vermilion HS; Vermilion, OH; A Cap Choir; Tres, Lat C; Ntl Teachers Coun; Ski C; HCt.

GROSENBACH, Melinda Sue
LeRoy HS; LeRoy, IL (20-95) AFS; Ann; Band; FHA; JV, Bkbl; Mgr, Tr; Flag Corps; Church Paper; Charts; S-T, Yth Group; Cincinnati Bible Col; Bus.

GROSKREUTZ, Joel Kim
Wells-Easton HS; Wells, MN (20-110) Band; Semi-Fin, BS; Fin, Ensm; Pres, FFA; 4H; Bsbl; Co-Cpt, Ftbl; Tnns; Wrest; COM; 4H A; Creed Speaking A; U of Minn; Agr Ed.

GROSS, Barbara Jane
Napoleon HS; Napoleon, ND (28-71) Band; CYO; Chor; Ensm; FHA; Rptr, Sch P; Var C; Bkbl; Sftbl; Mary Col; Phys Ed.

GROSS, Christine Diane
Hickman Mills Sr HS; Kansas City, MO (154-601) Band; Drama; Rainbow; A-Ed, Sch P; Thes; Tnns; COM; Gov Honor Prog; Journ A; Poet A; Journ.

GROSS, John Donald
Robert E Lee HS; Baytown, TX (5%-543) Band; Lat C; Lat NHS; Hist A; Jr Classical League; High Score, Ann HS Math Exam; Naval Acad; Weaponry.

GROSS, John William
Bay HS; Bay Village, OH (10%-375) Ger C; Rptr, Sch P; Bsbl; Bkbl; All Conf Bsbl; Bus Adm.

GROSS, Judy Ann
Arnett HS; Arnett, OK (2-13) Tres, Ann; Band; Pres, Sr Cl; Co-Cpt, Bkbl; Alg A; Citz A; Val; MVP A; Northwestern St Col; Ed.

GROSS, Laurie Ann
Robert H Goddard HS; Roswell, NM (70-310) A Cap Choir; CYO; Chor; Ensm; 4H; Hmrm; Inter-Club Coun; Ski C; Span C; Pres, St Stu Congres; SC; Pres, Sr Cl; Ftbl; Tr; Beauty; COM; Citz A; Most Out; SC Snkbr Mgr; DECA Swtht, Na Deca; Yth Adv Brd; Rotary Forgn Excng Stu; Alt, GS; DECA Girl Stu o-t Yr; Secy, DECA; 2nd Pl, St DECA Conv; Baylor U; Law.

GROSS, Michael Raymond
Marine Military Acad; Harlingen, TX (2-43) Band; NHS; COM; NEDT; ROTC A; Marine Corps League Oratory A; Highest GPA; Tex A&M U; Chem Engr.

GROSS, Rachel Celeste
Windsor Forest HS; Savannah, GA; Up Bound; Ms Young Peo Dept, Church; Savannah St Col; Child Care.

GROSS, Shirley Ann
Tupelo HS; Tupelo, MS (50-359) Anchor C; Ann; Chor; Ensm; Fr C; Madrigal; Foreign Culture League C; Miss St U; Child Development.

GROSS, Suellen Jo
Norwalk HS; Norwalk, OH (15-249) Band; Drama; VP, Fr C; NHS; Orch; Co-Ed, Sch P; Pres, Thes; Hon Prog; Q&S A; Hon Thespian; Best Thespian; Eng Dist Achv; Best Actress A; Siena Heights Col; Theatre Arts.

GROSS, Tamara Mae
Ashley HS; Ashley, ND (50%-40) Ann; Band; Chor; Drama; Ensm; FHA; Sch P; SC; JV, Bkbl; Journ A; Spch A; Pres, Mus C; Pilots A; Mus A; Arion A; Phys Ed A; Drama C Pin; *Moorhead St Col; Early Childhood.*

GROSS, Van Leonard
Ashley HS; Ashley, ND (10-44) Band; Chor; Ensm; Var C; Mgr, Bkbl; Hon Prog; *NDSU; Agr.*

GROSS, Victoria Heidi
Lutheran HS W; Rocky River, OH (8-93) Ann; Band; JV, Chldr; Drama; Hmrm; Orch; Ski C; SC; Bkbl; COM; Hon Prog; GAA; VP, Church Yth Group; Dance Comm; Yth Choir; GAA Trophy; Statistician, Vlbl, Bkbl, Tr; Scorekeeper, Bsbl; *Concordia Ann Arbor Col; Eng.*

GROSSENBACHER, Mark David
Ritenour Sr HS; Overland, MO (10%-800) A Cap Choir; NHS; SC; Ftbl; Royal Ambassador 5th Service Aid A; *Sci.*

GROSSENBACHER, Timothy Jay
Bern HS; Bern, KS (3-25) Co-Ed, Ann; Model UN; NHS; SC; Pres, Sr Cl; Cpt, Bkbl; Tr; Alg A; Bio A; 4H A; Hist A; Math A; Sci A; Type A; Yth Fel; Eng A; *Kans St U; Chem.*

GROSSENBACHER, Wendy Sue
Ritenour Sr HS; Overland, MO (10%-900) Band; Chldr; Orch; Sch P; SC; *Wheaton Col; Mus.*

GROSSMAN, Lisa Jaye
Watchung Hills Reg HS; Warren, NJ (1-472) SC; HR; *U of Del; Psych.*

GROTERS, Douglas J
Zeeland HS; Zeeland, MI (2-180) Lat C; Model UN; NHS; JV, Ftbl; Tnns; Pres, RCYF; Co-Ed, Church Newsletter; *US Naval Acad; Marine Bio.*

GROTH, Alan Stewart
Port Washington HS; Port Washington, WI (83-424) Ftbl.

GROTH, Dale Alan
Viroqua HS; Viroqua, WI (12-146) Band; 4H; Sci C; Var C; Cr-Ctry; Mgr, Wrest; Ntl Sci Found; ARC A; *Val of Wis Stevens Point; Natural Resources.*

GROTH, Ivy Lynn
Mitchell HS; Colo Springs, CO; Band; 4H; Rainbow; ARC; SC; Job's Daughters; *El Paso Comm Col; Social Sci.*

GROTHAUSE, Debora Louise
Ft Jennings HS; Ft Jennings, OH; Tres, Band; Chor; Sch Achieve Tm; Sftbl; Amer Leg A; NEDT; *Toledo U; Med.*

GROTHAUSE, Thomas Barry
Celina HS; Celina, OH (1-275) CYO; Chem C; Chess C; Dbte Tm; Drama; FTA; Key C; Math C; NFL; Ch, NHS; Ch, SC; Chem A; Hon Prog; Val; Yth Fel; *Kenyon Col.*

GROTHE, Annette Kay
Wanamingo HS; Wanamingo, MN (14-40) Band; Chor; Ensm; FHA; Rptr, 4H; Var C; Secy, Jr Cl; Bkbl; Tr; COM; 4H A; Pres A; *Rochester Comm Col; Elem Ed.*

GROTT, Thomas Anthony
Purcell HS; Cincinnati, OH (3-205) Bio A; Math A.

GROVE, Debra Eve
Springfield Local HS; Petersburg, OH (1-175) Fr C; FTA; Mjrte; Tri-HiY; Chem A; Hist C; Pep C; Statistician, Tr; Published, Essay Anthology; *Ohio St U; Pre-Med.*

GROVE, Donna Lee
N Harford HS; Pylesville, MD; Band; Chor; 4H; Madrigal; Sftbl; Swim; 4H A; Chor, Band, A's; *Eckerd Col; Mus.*

GROVE, Duane Michael
Pinedale HS; Pinedale, WY (8-47) Ann; Band; Sci C; Thes; Bkbl; Sci A; Band A; Pres Phys Fitness; *Bus.*

GROVE, John Richard
Jefferson Moore HS; Waco, TX;

GROVE, Robert Douglas Jr
Handley HS; Winchester, VA (25-267) Band; Chor; City Conf; Semi-Fin, Fr C; Hmrm; Key C; Lit Mag; Orch; SC; Co-Ch, Jr Cl; JV, Ftbl; JV, Tr; JV, Wrest; Most Out; Art, Ntl Fr Contest, A's; Cert of Schol Achv; *U of Va; Math.*

GROVE, Rodney Lee
Crown Point HS; Crown Point, IN; *John Brown U.*

GROVE, Todd Wallace
W York Area Sr HS; York, PA (10%-250) Band; Ensm; Madrigal; Mod Mus Mas; Orch; Order/ Arrow; Co-Ed, Sch P; Tres, SC; God & Country A; *Webb Inst; Naval Archt.*

GROVER, Kevin Allan
Janesville Craig HS; Janesville, WI (20%-547) Var C; Bsbl; Yth Fel; Interntl Geog Soc; Babe Ruth Tourn Tm; Amer Legion Bsbl; *Ariz St U; Bus.*

GROVER, Monica Elaine
Model HS; Rome, GA (1-154) BC; Math C; NHS; Sci C; Alg A; Bio A; Gov Honor Prog; Math A; Sci A; Eng, Outst Achv, Top Schol, A's; *Sanford U; Sci.*

GROVER, Ramonia Jean
Killeen HS; Harker Heights, TX (526-856) Secy, Chor; Ftbl; Nurs.

GROVES, Bonnie June
St Ignatius Pub HS; St Ignatius, MT (10-30) Rptr, 4H; Mjrte; VP, NHS; Ed, Sch P; SC; Secy, Sr Cl; Secy, Jr Cl; HQn; Type A; Bus Machine Ltr of Commendation; *U of Mont; Law.*

GROVES, Brenda Kay
Weldon Valley HS; Weldona, CO (3-19) Chldr; Chor; FHA; Semi-Fin, GS; ARC; Sch P; SC; Bkbl; HCt; Most Out; Pres A; *U of Northern Colo; Phys Ed.*

GROVES, Clarence Jerry II
E Orange HS; E Orange, NJ (28-417) A Cap Choir; Chor; Drama; Ensm; Key C; Lat C; Sch Achieve Tm; Spch C; Cr-Ctry; Ftbl; Tr; COM; Hon Prog; Masonic A; Poet A; Spch A; *Morehouse Col; Med.*

GROVES, Donna F
Tuscola HS; Tuscola, IL (28-122) Ann; Chor; Drama; Ensm; Fr C; FHA; FTA; Spch C; COM; Flag Corps; GAA; Tribe; *E Ill U; Elem Ed.*

GROVES, Everett Harris
Tuscola HS; Tuscola, IL (13-118) BS; Drama; NHS; Thes; Hon Prog; *Elec.*

GROVES, Jeffrey Keith
Crook Co HS; Prineville, OR; Band; FFA; Secy, 4H; NHS; VP, Soph Cl; JV, Bsbl; Bkbl; *U of Oreg.*

GROVES, Joseph Kelley
Midwest City HS; Midwest City, OK (25%-560) Band; Drama; Fr C; Hmrm; InterClub Coun; Pol Sci C; ARC; SC; Thes; Regent Schol; Kappa Psi Kappa; *Oscar Rose Jr Col; Journ.*

GROVES, Karen Sue
Greeley Central HS; Greeley, CO (10%-350) Band; Ch, Chldr; Orch; Tres, SC; Soph Cl; Bkbl; Tnns; HCt; Most Out; Pres A; Pres, NJHS.

GROVES, Leslie Ann
Spearman HS; Spearman, TX; Band; Span C; Hist, FHA; Hghst Point Fresh A, Grl o-t Mo; *Home Ec.*

GROVES, Lori Denise
Shelbyville Central HS; Shelbyville, TN (10%-250) Ann; Chor; Fr C; FHA; SC; Keyettes; Ebony C; Statewide Chrch Oratorical Contest; *Tenn St U.*

GROVES, Patti Shawn
Morton HS; Morton, TX (13-56) Ann; Band; FHA; FTA; 4H; NHS; JV, Bkbl; Tnns; Tr; Hon Prog; Jazz Band A; 1st Runner Up, Miss Cochran Co; Piano A; *McMurry Col; Mus.*

GROVES, Thoyia Earline
East HS; Columbus, OH (18-350) *Howard U; Communications.*

GROVES, Verna Carol
Bradley-Bourbonnais Comm HS; Bradley, IL (15-485) Fr C; NHS; SC; Tr; *Olivet Nazarene Col; Ed.*

GROWDEN, Arthur Dee
Antioch HS; Antioch, TN; NHS; *Middle Tenn St Col; Commercial Art.*

GROZIER, Sherilyn Anne
L B Johnson HS; Austin, TX (36-336) NHS; Trustee A; OEA Area Fin; *U of Tex; Ed.*

GRUBB, Alice Lucille
Dawson Bryant HS; Coal Grove, OH (13-130) MVP, Band; Math C; Mu Alpha Theta; Sci C; Cl Fav; Hon Prog; Most Out; Ohio St Fair Band; WW; *Mount Vernon Nazarene Col; Mus.*

GRUBB, Kathy
Greensburg-Salem HS; Greensburg, PA (20-400) AFS; Band; Chor; Ger C; Lit Mag; *Art Inst of Pgh; Commercial Art.*

GRUBB, Randall Alan
N Rowan Sr HS; Spencer, NC (2-200) BS; Pres, Chess C; Hmrm; NHS; Pres, Span C; Pres, Span NHS; Var C; Co-Cpt, Bkbl; Cpt, Ftbl; Cpt, Tr; Hon Prog; WW; Span A; Jr Marshal; MVP Tr; *West Point Military Acad; Civil Engr.*

GRUBBS, Deborah Ann
Hitchcock HS; Hitchcock, TX (3-146) Band; NHS; Bkbl; Tr; VofDEM; Outst, Geom; *Baylor U; Law.*

GRUBBS, Jo Lynn
John Randolph Tucker HS; Richmond, VA (101-345) Band; Hmrm; SC; Y-Tns; *Madison Col; Bus.*

GRUBBS, Karen Eileen
Broad Ripple HS; Indianapolis, IN (21-474) Chldr; Chor; Ger C; COM; Type A.

GRUBBS, Kimberly Elizabeth
Ellet Sr HS; Akron, OH; FHA; ARC; Hon Prog.

GRUBBS, Korene Elaine
Broad Ripple HS; Indianapolis, IN (92-314) Chor; Ger C; COM; HCt; *Vincennes U; Phar.*

GRUBBS, Wayne Kenneth
Broad Ripple HS; Indianapolis, IN (193-475) Band; Bkbl; JV, Ftbl; JV, Tr; *Bradley U; Elec.*

GRUBER, Barbara Ann
Lexington HS; Lexington, MO (1-105) Ensm; NFL; NHS; Orch; Span C; Amer Leg A; COM; Citz A; Curator A; DARGCA; Hist A; Regent Schol; Star Student; Val; BPW Girl o-t Mo; *Central Mo St U; Eng Ed.*

GRUBER, David Paul
Lexington HS; Lexington, MO (5%-128) Band; Fr C; NHS; Orch; Amer Leg A; Citz A; Top 5% PSAT-NMSQT; *U of Mo; Agr Engr.*

GRUBER, Mark John
Hilbert HS; Hilbert, WI; Band; CYO; VP, Key C; Var C; Mgr, Tr; *Fox Valley Tech Inst; Production Agr.*

GRUBER, Michelle Ellen
Apollo HS; Simi Valley, CA; Ed, Sch P; Journ A; Type A; *Moorpark Col; Exotic Animal Training.*

GRUBER, Sheila Dawn
Shenandoah Comm HS; Shenandoah, IA (19-160) Band; Chor; NHS; COM; Yth Fel; *Iowa W Col.*

GRUE, Thomas Andrew
NE Clinton Central Sch; Champlain, NY (8-148) BS; NHS; SC; Tnns; COM; NEDT; Regent Schol; ROTC A; *Cornell U; Pol Sci.*

GRUEBER, Timothy Allen
Carrollton HS; Saginaw, MI; A Cap Choir; Drama; ARC; Thes; JV, Bkbl; JV, Ftbl; COM; ARC A; *Ann Arbor Concordin Col; Teaching.*

GRUEL, Renee Lynne
Milford Mill Sr HS; Baltimore, MD (5%-400) A-Ed, Ann; Chor; Ed, Lit Mag; NHS; Thes; Var C; Mgr, Bkbl; Hockey; Lacrosse; Mus, Service, Hon, Ath, A's; GRA Schol; Faculty Play Schol; *U of Md; Pre-Med.*

GRUENIG, Lynn Adele
Westside HS; Omaha, NE (25%-794) Band; Chor; Fr C; Hmrm; Cr-Ctry; Tnns; Bio A; Hon Prog; Masonic A; Type A; Yth Fel; Outst Performance, Fr; *U of Nebr at Omaho; Bus.*

GRUMBLEY, Marcia Sue
John Marshall HS; Los Angeles, CA (65-800) Hmrm; NHS; Span C; St Stu Congress; HCt; Badminton; Drill Tm; Sr Planning Board; *U of Redlands; Sociology.*

GRUNDEN, Terry Lee
Lebanon Comm HS; Lebanon, IL (3-75) Var C; Cr-Ctry; Fin, Tr; *US Air Force Acad; Astrodynamic Engr.*

GRUNER, Valerie Jo
Cedar Shoals HS; Athens, GA (10%-400) Band; BC; Drama; Ger C; Thes; Gov Honor Prog; Thespian A; AADA; Drama.

GRUNEWALD, Joy Marie
Oconomowoc Sr HS; Oconomowoc, WI (32-249) Ski C; Bkbl; Cosmetology.

GRUNEWALD, Judy Kay
Yukon HS; Yukon, OK (50-257) Chor; Drama; Ensm; Fr C; Pres, FHA; NHS; Mgr, Wrest; Outst Home Ec; Panhandle St U.

GRUNIG, Gail
Sky View HS; Smithfield, UT (3-622) Semi-Fin, Chldr; Chor; FHA; Pres, 4H; Hmrm; Amer Leg A; Citz A; Ed.

GRUPE, Robin M
McNally HS; Costa Mesa, CA; Citz A; OCC.

GRUPP, Lucy Dianne
Boulder HS; Boulder, CO (132-487) JV, Chldr; Spch A; Creative Writing A; Colo St U; Home Ec.

GRUSSING, Terri Linn
George Washington Sr HS; Cedar Rapids, IA (53-533) Ann; Band; Dbte Tm; Drama; Hmrm; Lit Mag; NFL; Orch; Sch P; VP, Sci C; Spch C; SC; Hon Prog; Opt A; Spch A; All St Spch Festival.

GRUVER, Jeffrey Eugene
York Co Vo-tech HS; York, PA (88-553) Band; Elec C; Vica C; Computer Tech.

GRUYTER, Florence P
Menlo Atherton HS; Atherton, CA; San Jose St U; Bus.

GRYMKOSKI, Gale Diane
Waukegan E HS; Waukegan, IL (20%-398) Bus C; Chor; Drama; FBLA; Lit Mag; Sch P; Span C; Thes; Swim; High & Regular Hr's; Culgahoga Col; Dental Hygiene.

GRYPARIS, Christ John
William Fremd HS; Palatine, IL (200-500) Orch; Cr-Ctry; Tr; COM; Hon Prog; Sci A; Type A; Elec A; Orch A; Church of God Yth; Phys Fitness A; Church Chor; Anderson Col.

GRYS, Jeane Luise
Lincoln HS; Wis Rapids, WI (235-720) A Cap Choir; Chor; Community Yth Symph; Drama; Ensm; Ger C; Madrigal; Mod Mus Mas; Orch; JV, Bkbl; Mgr, Tr; COM; Hon Prog; Pres A; Co-cpt, JV Vlbl; U of Minn; Mus.

GRYTDAL, Loretta Anne
Jenkins HS; Chewelah, WA (4-79) Pres, 4H; 4H A; Dairy Princess, Stevens Co; Social Working.

GRZELECKI, Daniel Peter
Notre Dame Bishop Gibbons HS; Schenectady, NY (13-161) Band; CYO; NHS; Orch; Sch P; Sch Mus, Sch Religion, A's; WW; Union Col; Mech Engr.

GRZYBICKI, Sandra Emily
Old Forge HS; Old Forge, PA (6-121) Chldr; NHS; Ski C; VP, Sr Cl; VP, Jr Cl; Chem A; VFW A; Head, Marching Units; U of Pa; Dental Hygiene.

GRZYMSKI, Therese Ann
John S Fine Sr HS; Nanticoke, PA (5-320) Hmrm; Secy, Sodality; Tri-HiY; Amer Leg A; Jeffries Slapikas A; Wilkes Col; Biol.

GUADIANO, Steven P
Memorial HS; San Antonio, TX (19-300) Ann; FTA; NHS; VP, Sci C; SC; Cpt, Bsbl; Cr-Ctry; Ftbl; COM; WW; St Marys U; Med Technology.

GUAJARDO, Irene
Whiteface HS; Whiteface, TX; Band; FHA; JV, Bkbl; Sftbl; Tr; Scholastic Favorite; Solo-Band A; 'A' HR; S Plains Jr Col; Secondary Ed.

GUARANO, Linette Susanne
University HS; San Diego, CA (13-311) Drama; GS; InterClub Coun; Pres, Model UN; NHS; Ed, Sch P; SC; VP, Soph Cl; CSF; COM; Hon Prog; Most Out; Pres, Med Explorers; Pep C; Candystriper; Stanford U; Pre-Med.

GUBBELS, Joyce Marie
Lake o-t Woods HS; Baudette, MN; CYO; Chor; VP, FFA; 4H; NHS; Bkbl; Swim; Nurs.

GUDA, Sheryl Lynne
Asbury Park HS; Asbury Park, NJ (7-289) Secy, Band; Fin, GS; Math C; NHS; SC; Tr; COM; Elk A; Kiwanis A; Ntl Achv Schol; Phy A; Northwestern U; Bio.

GUDDAL, Kari Jonette
Ballard HS; Seattle, WA; Band; Candystriper; Luther League; Pres, Camp Fire; Spades; Norwegian C; Seattle Pacific U; Phys Therapy.

GUDDE, Barbara Kay
Hickman Mills HS; Kansas City, MO (204-487) A Cap Choir; Co-Cpt, Bkbl; Tnns; Ntl Ger Hon Soc A; St Champ, Bkbl; Mo Western Col; Phys Ed.

GUDDE, Marta Ann
Hickman Mills HS; Kansas City, MO; Bkbl; FCA; Girls Ath C; Mgr, Vlbl; St Bkbl A; Nurs.

GUDOWICZ, Mary Jane
Goodman Armstrong HS; Goodman, WI (2-23) Band; Cpt, Chldr; Ensm; Pres, NHS; Co-Ed, Sch P; Tres, Soph Cl; Cpt, Bkbl; HCt; Cpt, Vlbl; U of Wis; Phys Therapy.

GUECO, Edgar Santos
John F Kennedy HS; Tumon, GUAM; NHS; USC; Pol Sci.

GUEDRY, Edgar Paul
Destrehan HS; New Sarpy, LA (4-244) BC; Fr C; Pres, Hmrm; Span C; SC; 4H A; Stu Aid; Effort, Courtesy, Alpha, A's; LSU; Ed.

GUEGLIO, Kimberly Ann
Gridley Union HS; Gridley, CA (40-113) Tres, CYO; Rptr, Sch P; Butte Col; Special Ed.

GUEMAREZ, Blanca Iris
Wesleyan Acad; Guaynabo, PR (3-31) Chor; Tres, Hmrm; Secy, NHS; SC; Cpt, Sftbl; Exchange Stu; Span Literary A; High Hon; U of Puerto Rico; Med.

GUEMPEL, Mary Jo
St Joseph HS; Toms River, NJ (10-182) Key C; NHS; St Scholar; Fr A; Attendance A; Douglass Col; Med.

GUENTHER, Alice Louise
Mossyrock HS; Mossyrock, WA (5%-34) Band; Chor; Fr C; FHA; Pres, NHS; Sci C; JV, Bkbl; Tr; NEDT; Ambassador Col; Biol Sci.

GUENTHER, Joseph Patrick
Chaminade HS; St Louis, MO (25-118) Band; VP, Drama; NHS; Sch P; Alg A; NEDT; U of Mo at Kansas City; Art.

GUENTHER, Sandra Kay
Saline HS; Saline, MI (1-275) Drama; Fr C; FHA; Pres, 4H; NHS; Amer Leg A; 4H A; Hon Prog; Yth Fel; JV Vlbl; Drama A; Computer Sci.

GUENTHNER, Roxanne Lynn
Bismarck Central Sr HS; Bismarck, ND; Chor; Drama; S-T, 4H; Rptr, Sch P; 4H A; Journ A; Spch A; Eng.

GUERNSEY, Linda Maureen
Sanger HS; Sanger, CA (25-521) AFS; Band; 4H; NHS; Rainbow; JV, Tnns; CSF; COM; Citz A; 4H A; Sci.

GUERRA, John Fryar
Roma HS; Roma, TX (9-180) Ann; Band; NHS; Spch C; Rptr, SC; COM; Journ A; Sci A; Spch A; HR; Prose A; Rice U; Pol Sci.

GUERRA, Kelly Maureen
Weed HS; Weed, CA (7-72) Chldr; Sch P; SC; Pres, Jr Cl; HCt; HR; Col of Siskiyous; Bus.

GUERRERO, Doris San Nicolas
George Washington Sr HS; Mangilao, GUAM (30-640) Band; Chldr; Hmrm; NHS; Ntl Yth Conf; HCt; Yth Leg; U of Manoa; Law.

GUERRERO,
Evelyn San Nicolas
George Washington Sr HS; Mangilao, GUAM; Band; VP, CYO; Community Yth Symph; NHS; SC; COM; Psych.

GUERRERO, Francis Joseph
George Washington Sr HS; Mangilao, GUAM (13-640) A Cap Choir; Chor; Ensm; Madrigal; Ch, NHS; SC; Win, Amateur Talent Contest; Mus A; Royal Prince, Prom; Hon Choir; Berklee Sch of Mus; Mus.

GUERRERO, Lola Alicia
John Ehret HS; Marrero, LA (8-470) CYO; S-T, Fr C; Hmrm; Lit Ral; Pres, Math C; S-T, Mu Alpha Theta; NHS; SC; Tres, Sr Cl; Tres, Soph Cl; Hist A; Hon Prog; Math A; U of New Orleans; Bus.

GUERRERO, Margarita S
Colegio Puertorriqueno de Ninas; Caparra Heights, PR (5-61) NHS; Var C; Vlbl; Bus Adm.

GUESMAN, Kelli Jean
Southmoreland Sr HS; Alverton, PA (5-315) Chor; Ensm; Ski C; SC; World Affairs C; Span C; Flag-twirler; Fire Prevention A.

GUESMAN, Kimberly Jo
Southmoreland Sr HS; Alverton, PA (9-272) Ann; Chldr; Chor; FNA; Lat C; Math C; NHS; Rainbow; Tri-HiY; HCt; W Va Wesleyan Col; Nurs.

GUESS, Donald Wayne
Rutledge Acad; Rutledge, GA (12-21) Chess C; Dbte Tm; FFA; Ftbl; Tr; Wrest; Cl Fav; Yth Fel.

GUESS, Lynsey Ann
Dallas Christian HS; Dallas, TX (5-43) A Cap Choir; Harding Christian Col.

GUESS, Mary Crystal
W Mecklenburg HS; Charlotte, NC (20-400) A-Ed, Ann; Chldr; NHS; Span C; Civinettes; Elections Comm; Pres, Pep C; UNC; Med.

GUESS, Sherrie
Eupora HS; Eupora, MS; Ann; Pres, FHA; VP, Hmrm; SC; Var C; Secy, Sr Cl; Cpt, Bkbl; Tr; Most Out; Miss Valley Col; Counciling.

GUEST, Alice Lee
Belton-Honea Path HS; Honea Path, SC (7-315) Band; COM; Clemson U; Psych.

GUEST, Eugene Jr
Bayside HS; Bayside, NY; Bsbl; Bkbl; Mgr, Sftbl; Swim; JA A; NEDT; VP, Church Yth Fel; Queens Boro Comm Col; Lib Arts.

GUETSCHOW, Steven Gene
Dundee Comm HS; Carpentersville, IL (145-292) VP, Var C; Ftbl; All Conf, Ftbl; Elgin Comm Col; Criminal Justice.

GUETTERMAN, Arthur Lee
Oceanside HS; Oceanside, CA (100-200) Co-Cpt, Bsbl; Liberty Baptist Col; Phys Ed.

GUETTERMAN, Robert Lance
Oceanside HS; Oceanside, CA (200-600) Bsbl; JV, Bkbl; Ftbl; Dean, Jr Easter Camp; All Tourn JV Bkbl; Christian Heritage Col; Theology.

GUEVARA, Arnoldo Enrique
Jesuit HS; New Orleans, LA (10-169) Lat C; NHS; Hon Prog; NEDT; Summa Cum Laude; Militry Ordr Foregn War o-t US Med; Tulane U; Pre-Med.

GUEVARA, Roger Carreon
Antonian HS; San Antonio, TX (10%-115) Chess C; Chor; Hmrm; SC; Var C; Cr-Ctry; JV, Ftbl; JV, Soccer; Swim; Tr; NEDT; Yth Fel; Stanford U; Dentistry.

GUEVARA, Victor M
Francisco Mendoza HS; Isabela, PR; Band; CYO; COM; Sci A; Band A; CAAM; Chem Engr.

GUFFEY, Denise Michelle
Swifton HS; Swifton, AR (4-20) BC; FBLA; FHA; Type A; Ark St U; Mus.

GUHIT, Nancy Vida
George Washington Sr HS; Mangilao, GUAM (3-740) Tres, Mjrte; NHS; ARC; SC; Tres, Sr Cl; Achv A; U of Colo.

GUICE, Dorothy Jean
Bullock Co HS; Union Springs, AL (3-145) Chor; Tres, FBLA; 4H; NHS; Bio A; 4H A; Hon Prog; Type A; Auburn U; Bus Adm.

GUICE, James Jeffery
Geraldine HS; Geraldine, AL (20%-67) Ann; BC; 4H; Hmrm; Sci C; SC; Bkbl; Ftbl; NE Ala Jr Col.

GUICE, Wayne Earl
Woodlawn HS; Shreveport, LA; A Cap Choir; Chor; Dbte Tm; Bsbl; Bkbl; Top Tn Amer; Northwestern Col; General Studies.

GUIDER, Robin Lea
Loudon HS; Loudon, TN (34-125) Bus Mgr, Ann; Chor; FHA; Sci C; JV, Bkbl; Lib Aide; Prayer Group; Pep C; Hiwassee Col; Lib Sci.

GUIDRY, Bryan Jude
St Joseph HS; Jeanerette, LA (1-19) 4H; Lit Ral; Bkbl; Tr; Alg A; 4H A; Hist A; Math A; NEDT; Sci A; Fr A; Ral A; *U of Southwestern La; Acct.*

GUIDRY, Craig Michael
St Charles Borromeo HS; Destrehan, LA; VP, BC; BS; VP, CYO; 4H; Hmrm; Key C; Fin, Lit Ral; Sch Achieve Tm; SC; Tres, Sr Cl; VP, Jr Cl; Pres, Soph Cl; Bio A; COM; Hist A; Hon Prog; Math A; NEDT; *U of New Orleans; Acct.*

GUIDRY, Denise Louise
Nederland HS; Nederland, TX (226-463) Ch, CYO; Fr C; VP, FTA; *Lamar U; Bus Adm.*

GUIDRY, Kenneth Joseph
Church Point HS; Church Point, LA; Pres, CYO; Ch, FFA; 4H; Fin, Lit Ral; 4H A; Hist A; St, Dist, Parish, FFA; *NE La U; Hist.*

GUIDRY, Todd James
Lafayette HS; Lafayette, LA (40%-560) USL; Archt.

GUILFORD, Sharene T
Norfolk Cath HS; Norfolk, VA (20%-160) CYO; Monogram; Sftbl; 2nd Pl Trophy, Span Forensics; *Old Dominion U.*

GUILLEN, Luis Gerardo
San Conrado HS; Ponce, PR (4-72) NHS; VP, SC; Swim; Tr; *U de PR; Med.*

GUILLEN, Richard
St Thomas HS; Houston, TX (30-125) A Cap Choir; Pres, CYO; Math C; Span C; Hon Prog; Yth Fel; Yth Leg; *U of Houston; Math.*

GUILLORY, Stanley Kirk
First Baptist Acad; Dallas, TX (25%-25) Sch P; Parl, SC; Pres, Sr Cl; Bsbl; Bkbl; Cpt, Ftbl; All Conf Ftbl, Church; Serve Aid A; *Baylor U; Law.*

GUIMARAES, Omar Frederick
Coon Rapids Sr HS; Coon Rapids, MN (119-654) Co-Ch, CYO; NHS; Rptr, Sch P; SC; Co-Cpt, Soccer; Tr; HKg; Journ A; MVP, Soccer; Friendliest; Hon Graduate; Cr-Ctry Skiing; Most Popular; *University of Minnesota; Photography.*

GUIN, Olga Weiss
Piedmont HS; Monroe, NC (14-250) Tres, Band; Fr C; FHA; 4H; NHS; SC; Beauty; Gov Honor Prog; SC Adv Board; VP, Jr Usher Board; Tres, NJHS; Mini Gov Sch; Miss Piedmont; Asst Secy, Chrch Con; Corresponding Secy, Church Dist; *Morris Brown Col; Acct.*

GUINN, Andrew Lee
Robert E Lee HS; Tyler, TX; Ann; Chem C; Ch, Key C; Order/ Arrow; Span C; St Stu Congress; VP, SC; VP, Sr Cl; JV, Bkbl; JV, Tnns; Hon Prog; *Texas U; Law.*

GUINN, Brian Dean
Grimsley HS; Greensboro, NC (10%-500) Band; Key C; Hon Prog; Yth Fel; *NC St U; Engr.*

GUION, Terry Ann
Roy Miller HS; Corpus Christi, TX (8-412) Chldr; Mu Alpha Theta; NHS; SC; Sr Coun; Booster Girls; *Tex A&I U; Bus.*

GUIST, David J
Oregon HS; Oregon, IL (1-114) Fr C; Pres, NHS; Bsbl; JV, Bkbl; Ftbl; Tr; Hon Prog; Regent Schol; St Scholar; *Luther Col; Bus.*

GULBRANDSEN, Allen Michael
Inglewood HS; Inglewood, CA; Tnns; CSF; Citz A; *UCLA; Oceanography.*

GULICK, Lois Andrea
Joplin HS; Joplin, MT (5-11) Ann; Band; Chldr; Chor; Drama; Var C; Mgr, Bkbl; Ftbl; Golf; Tr; H of F; Hon Prog; Math A; Spch A; VFW A; VofDEM; Chldr A; *Northern Mont Col; Registered Nurs.*

GULINELLO, Margaret Ann
Msgr Ryan Mem HS; Dorchester, MA; Ann; Pres, Sr Cl; Pres, Soph Cl; Sftbl; Swim; Diocesan Art A; *Forsyth Sch; Dental Hygiene.*

GULLEDGE, Ainslie
Mayme S Waggener HS; Louisville, KY (98-400) Chor; Ensm; Hmrm; Rainbow; *Samford U; Psych.*

GULLETTE, Yolanda Giselle
G W Carver Sr HS; New Orleans, LA; Cl Fav; Hist A; Hon Prog; *Dillard U; Special Ed.*

GULLEY, Anna Marie
Carmel HS; Carmel, IN (563-667) Chor; Sch P; *Metropolitian Beauty Acad; Cosmetology.*

GULLY, Raymond Brittian Jr
Kemper Acad; DeKalb, MS (3-37) BC; Hist A; *U of Miss; Engr.*

GUMM, Kimberly Marie
Norwood Sr HS; Norwood, OH;

GUMMELT, William Lee
Victoria HS; Victoria, TX; Pres, Ger C; NHS; Ftbl; Tr; Poet A; AATG Schol A; Ger A; *Stephen F Austin St U; Modern Lang.*

GUMS, Henry L
Norlina HS; Norlina, NC (50-100) Chor; Bsbl; Ftbl; All Conf Ftbl.

GUNDERSON, Deborah Kay
Kulm HS; Kulm, ND (1-32) A Cap Choir; Co-Ed, Ann; Band; Chldr; Chor; Dbte Tm; Drama; Ensm; Semi-Fin, GS; 4H; Lat C; ARC; Ed, Sch P; Sci C; Spch C; Pres, SC; S-T, Var C; Pres, Soph Cl; Cpt, Bkbl; Cr-Ctry; Cpt, Tr; Bio A; Chem A; HCt; Hon Prog; Magna Cum Laude; MLS; Ntl Achv Schol; Pres A; Sal; Sci A; Spch A; *U of ND; Pre-Med.*

GUNDERSON, Gaylene Therese
Central Valley HS; Buxton, ND (5-33) Ann; VP, Band; Cpt, Chldr; Chor; Drama; FFA; Tres, FHA; GS; Secy, Mod Mus Mas; Pres, SC; Sci A; *Area Voc Tech Inst; Secretarial.*

GUNDERSON, Todd Allen
Triangle Lake HS; Blachly, OR (3-13) Band; Ensm; VP, SC; Bkbl; Ftbl; Tr; HCt; Most Inspirational Ath.

GUNDESEN, Joan Louise
Lutheran HS; New Orleans, LA (4-50) Co-Ed, Ann; COM; Hon Prog; Math A.

GUNG, Edna
Philadelphia HS For Girls; Philadelphia, PA; Chor; COM; *Temple U; Surgical Asst.*

GUNGNER, David John
Los Angeles Baptist HS; Sepulveda, CA (5%-120) Bus C; Chem C; Math C; Phys C; Pol Sci C; Sch Achieve Tm; Sci C; World Affairs C; CSF; Hon Prog; *Cal-Tech Col; Physics.*

GUNIA, Linda Sue
Kelly HS; Chicago, IL (9-485) Band; Pres, NHS; Pres, Sr Cl; COM; PTA A; Fr A; *Ill St U; Spec Ed.*

GUNN, Cynthia Faye
York Acad; Shacklefords, VA (8-42) BC; Lat C; VP, Span C; Pres, SC; VP, Jr Cl; MVP, Bkbl; Co-Cpt, Sftbl; *Madison Col; Phys Ed.*

GUNN, Doris Lorraine
Nottoway Sr HS; Nottoway Co, VA (17-225) Drama; Parl, FBLA; 4H; Hmrm; NHS; Sch P; Sci C; Span C; HCt; Kiwanis A; Rotary A; Pep C; DECA Schol; Stu o-t Yr; St Pres, DECA; Lucy C Crawford A; WW; *Madison Col; Marketing.*

GUNN, Earl Jefferson Jr
St Joseph Col Inst; Kenmore, NY (119-195) Band; Parl, Chor; *Morehouse Col; Law.*

GUNN, Julie Beth
Linda Vista Jr Acad; Oxhard, CA (3-15) Ann; Band; Chor; Tres, Hmrm; COM; Hon Prog; *Loma-Linda Col; Pre-Med.*

GUNN, Linda Kaye
Fort Zumwalt Sr HS; O'Fallon, MO (20-541) Chor; COM; Hist A; Shorthand As; PE Ribbons; *Secy.*

GUNN, Nancy Gale
Westover HS; Albany, GA (109-329) A Cap Choir; Ann; Band; Cpt, Chldr; Drama; Mjrte; A-Ed, Sch P; Sodality; Mgr, Sftbl; Swim; Tnns; COM; Band, Mjrte, Ltrs; Mjrte Twirling Trophies; Art A; *Albany Jr Col; Nurs.*

GUNN, Robert Maynard
Milford HS; Milford, TX (1-12) Co-Ed, Ann; BC; VP, FFA; S-T, Sr Cl; Math A; Sci A.

GUNN, Shelly Lynn
Walnut HS; Walnut, MS (10-65) BC; Chldr; VP, Chor; FHA; Lit A; *Secy.*

GUNN, Terry Wayne
Anderson HS; Austin, TX; 2nd Nation, Power Lifting; Weight Lifting, Olymp Lifting, A's; *Tex Tech Col; Phys Ed.*

GUNNELS, James Chenault
Davidson HS; Mobile, AL (30-600) Fr C; Pres, Lat C; Sch Spelling A.

GUNNELS, John Kenneth
Rye HS; Rye, CO (3-65) Pres, A Cap Choir; Band; Pres, Chor; Drama; Ensm; Thes; Tres, Soph Cl; Cr-Ctry; Cpt, Golf; Tr; Wrest; Band A; *Ariz St U; Mus.*

GUNNING, Jane Marie
Belvidere HS; Belvidere, IL (33-374) VP, AFS; Ger C; Secy, Span C; Hockey; *Bradley U; Photojournalist.*

GUNNINK, Jay
Todd Co HS; Mission, SD; Band; Bsbl; Bkbl; Ftbl.

GUNNINK, Jean
Todd Co HS; Mission, SD; Band; Chor.

GUNTER, Brenda Ann
R B Stall HS; Charleston Heights, SC; HCt; *Col of Charleston.*

GUNTER, Dorothy Christeen
Foley HS; Foley, AL (7-250) Secy, AFS; BC; Drama; VP, Fr C; Tres, InterAct C; Lat C; NHS; Opt A; *Huntingdon Col; Social Work.*

GUNTER, Ellen Danielle
Battle Ground HS; Battle Ground, WA (27-400) Band; Dbte Tm; Drama; GS; 4H; Rptr, Sch P; Spch C; Bkbl; Sftbl; Fin, JA A; Hon Schol to NNC in Dbte & Drama; Sr Girl o-t Mo A; *Northwest Nazarene Col; Spch.*

GUNTER, Jacquline Darlene
W Blocton HS; West Blocton, AL (3-67) Anchor C; Band; NHS; Tres, Sr Cl; I Dare You; Most Out; Val; *Birmingham-Sou Col; Math.*

GUNTER, Kathy Lynn
Appomattox Co HS; Appomattox, VA; Bus C; Chor; Drama; FBLA; FFA; 4H; NHS; Sch P; Span C; Type A; *Central Va Comm Col; Bus Mgt.*

GUNTER, Kevin Ashley
Coral Gables Sr HS; Coral Gables, FL; Band; Tres, Hmrm; InterAct C; Tres, SC; COM; Hist A; Sci A; Yth Fel; Yth Leg; Mus A; *Mus.*

GUNTER, Mark David
E Central HS; Tulsa, OK (10%-750) Band; Co-Cpt, Chess C; Ger C; Ftbl; Sftbl; COM; Citz A; Yth Fel; 1st Pl Fishing Tour; Top Bible Quizzer; 2nd, Bowl Tm; 2nd, Regional Bible Quiz; *Bethany Nazarene Col; Data Processing.*

GUNTER, Pamela Rene
M B Smiley HS; Houston, TX (10-461) Bus Mgr, Ann; NHS; Bus Mgr, Sch P; Alg A; Bio A; COM; Citz A; Hist A; Math A; Sci A; Eng A; *U of Houston.*

GUNTER, Richard Neal
Burkeville HS; Burkeville, TX (3-46) Band; Chor; FFA; Math C; NHS; Sci C; Tres, SC; Mgr, Bsbl; COM; Math A; *Stephen F Austin U; Elec Engr.*

GUNTER, Rick Joe
Houston HS; Houston, MO (26-124) NHS; WW; Co-Op Yth Ldrship Conf; *U of Mo Rolla; Civil Engr.*

GUNTER, Sherry Selina
Burkeville HS; Burkeville, TX (4-47) Band; Chor; Drama; FHA; Parl, SC; Hon Prog; *Stephen F Austin Col; Sci.*

GUNTER, Susan Marie
Fairland HS; Fairland, OK; Band; FHA; Rptr, 4H; Bkbl; 4H A; HCt; Masonic A; Drum Mjrte.

GUNTER, Tami Joleen
Arlington HS; Riverside, CA; *Life Bible Col.*

GUNTERT, Conni Lynn
Tokay HS; Lodi, CA; Pres, A Cap Choir; Cpt, Band; S-T, Chor; Ensm; Fr C; Pres, Madrigal; Pres, SC; Alt, GS; WW; Semi-Fin, H-Qn; Fin, Bank of Amer A; Stu Director, Choir Festival; Honorary Rotarian; *Concordia Lutheran Teachers Col; Primary Ed.*

GUNTHER, Alan Lavern
Arnold Pub HS; Arnold, NE (5-34) Band; Drama; FFA; FHA; Soph Cl; Bsbl; Bkbl; Ftbl; Golf; Tr; Woodworking A.

GUNTHER, Jeffrey Phillip
Evanston Township HS; Evanston, IL (40%-1000) SC; COM; Hon Prog; Tres, JA; *Art.*

GUPTON, Christopher
Southwestern HS; Detroit, MI; A Cap Choir; Chor; Ftbl; Most Out; Audio-Visual Outst Voice, Choir; Wayne St U; Tech.

GUPTON, Deborah Faye
Edward Best HS; Louisburg, NC (6-60) BC; Pres, Candystripers; Pres, Needlecraft; Acteens.

GUPTON, Henry Lewis
Battle Ground Acad; Franklin, TN (4-64) Lat C; NHS; Cr-Ctry; Tr; U of Tenn; Vet Med.

GUPTON, Janene
Joelton HS; Joelton, TN (10-126) BC; Ensm; Sftbl; Ntl Piano Playing Auditions; Cert of Recognition, Sci.

GURGANUS, Ira Lynn
Tallasee HS; Tallassee, AL (30-140) Band; Rptr, Sch P; Secy, Ftbl; Math A; NEDT; Hon Band A; Ala Christian Col; Bible.

GURGANUS, Martha Rae
Williamshs; Williamston, NC (11-219) BC; VP, FHA; Yth Fel; Yth Choir; Girls Quartet; Jr Sr Waitress; Bible Sch Teacher; Dentistry.

GURLEY, Chanie Annette
Eastside HS; Paterson, NJ (21-550) Secy, Chor; Drama; Hmrm; Orch; Ed, Sch P; SC; Thes; Secy, Jr Cl; Secy, Soph Cl; Journ A; Rptr, Sch P; Rutgers Col; Journ.

GURLEY, Jack Russell Jr
Homewood HS; Homewood, AL (5-250) Chor; Drama; Cpt, Ensm; Fr C; Hmrm; Math C; Mu Alpha Theta; SC; Thes; JV, Bsbl; JV, Bkbl; Tnns; Cl Fav; NEDT.

GURLEY, Laura Marie
Los Alamos HS; Los Alamos, NM; Band; NHS; Ski C; GSct; Archeology C.

GURLEY, Ted Michael
Eastern Hills HS; Fort Worth, TX (80-500) Ann; Semi-Fin, BS; Demolay; Eagle Sct; Rep, Demolay; U of Tex; Law.

GURNEE, Jeff Dean
Melodyland HS; Anaheim, CA; Bsbl; Bkbl; Ftbl; Tr; Spch A; Ath o-t Wk; Marine Biol.

GURNEY, Janelle Margaret
Hemet HS; Hemet, CA (207-500) Band; Mt San Jacinto Col; Mus.

GURNON, Emily Ann
Tartan Sr HS; Oakdale, MN (8-427) Band; Ensm; NHS; A-Ed, Sch P; Spch C; JV, Tnns; Sci A; Spch A; Star St Mus Contest; Theology.

GURR, Colleen Patrice
Canyon HS; Anaheim, CA (332-519) Band; Chor; Ch, Hmrm; NHS; ARC; Ski C; SC; Var C; Semi-Fin, Sci C; Bkbl; Co-Cpt, Cr-Ctry; Sftbl; Cpt, Swim; Tr; Beauty; CSF; Citz A; Cl Fav; Pres A; ARC A; ASB Associate of Justice; Drill Tm; Clarinet; Secy, GAA; Piano; Brigham Young U; Ed.

GURSKY, Ronald Thomas
Jones Co HS; Gray, GA; BC; Drama; Fr C; Hmrm; Order/Arrow; F-Ed, Sch P; Rptr, Sci C; Cpt, Ftbl; Golf; Citz A; God & Country A; Order/Arrow A; Phy A; Eagle Sct; Pre-Med.

GURULE, James Patrick
Los Lunas HS; Los Lunas, NM (19-230) BS; SC; Bsbl; Bkbl; Ftbl; Tr.

GUSAAS, Beth Marie
Valley City HS; Valley City, ND; A Cap Choir; Chor; Ensm; SC; VP, Pep C; Most Points Achieved, Pep C; Bus.

GUSKE, Kathleen Marie
Hueneme HS; Oxnard, CA (1-510) Community Yth Symph; Hmrm; Orch; SC; CSF; Hon Prog; UCSB; Aquatic Bio.

GUSTAFSON, Ann Marie
Washington HS; Cherokee, IA (25-160) Dbte Tm; VP, 4H; NFL; Orch; JV, Tnns.

GUSTAFSON, Curtis Scott
Harding HS; St Paul, MN (20%-748) Chor; Mankato St Col; Computer Sci.

GUSTAFSON, David Alan
Wachusett Regional HS; Holden, MA; All Star, Church Bkbl; Choir; Yth Comm; Hi League; Archt.

GUSTAFSON, David Bradley
Denfeld Sr HS; Duluth, MN (1-400) Band; Ensm; Model UN; Orch; Order/Arrow; Hon Prog; U of Minn; Math.

GUSTAFSON, David Farrle
Technical HS; St Cloud, MN (18-525) A Cap Choir; Drama; Ger C; Hmrm; JV, Swim; JV, Tnns; Med.

GUSTAFSON, Debbie Kay
Northwest Sr HS; Omaha, NE (16-647) JV, Chldr; Chor; French NHS; Tr; Jr Chamber of Com A; Rotary A; Bethal Col.

GUSTAFSON, Jane Marie
Chetek HS; Chetek, WI (12-105) Pres, Bus C; Chldr; Chor; Pres, FBLA; Hmrm; Madrigal; Model UN; Ed, Sch P; Span C; SC; Var C; JV, Bkbl; Sftbl; Swim; Tr; 4H A; Journ A; Math A; P, VP, 4-H C; NJHS; Vlbl; U Eau Claire; Bus.

GUSTAFSON, Janice Carol
Esko HS; Esko, MN (10-93) AFS; Band; Chor; Semi-Fin, Spch C; Y-Tns; 4H A; Spch A; Math.

GUSTAFSON, Jean Evonne
Faith HS; Faith, SD; Ann; Band; Drama; 4H; Sch P; Mgr, Bkbl; Mgr, Tr; Dakota Weslyan Col; Christian Ed.

GUSTAFSON, Joan Carol
Youngsville HS; Youngsville, PA (6-125) Ed, Ann; Chor; Fr C; Madrigal; Secy, NHS; Tres, Sr Cl; Bkbl; Tr; Cl Fav; Statistician, Tr; Scorekeeper, Bkbl; U of Pittsburgh; Psych.

GUSTAFSON, Joyce Alene
Fairview HS; Fairview, MT (3-36) Band; CYO; JV, Chldr; Chor; Rptr, FHA; Madrigal; Mjrte; Math C; Sci C; S-T, SC; S-T, Jr Cl; Co-Cpt, Bkbl; Sftbl; Swim; Elk A; HQn; I Dare You; JA A; Sci A; Swtht; John Philip Sousa A; Ntl Choral A; Carroll Col; Med Records.

GUSTAFSON, Kevin John
Chetek HS; Chetek, WI (34-100) Chor; Madrigal; Bsbl; Bkbl; JV, Ftbl; Golf; Bio A; COM; Sports A's; U of Wis; Bio.

GUSTAFSON, Lori Jean
McNally HS; Costa Mesa, CA; Band; VP, InterClub Coun; Ski C; Tr; Most Out; Cpt, Vlbl; Pepperdine U; Psych.

GUSTAFSON, Lori Jo
Central HS; Minneapolis, MN (10%-275) AFS; Chldr; Chor; Ensm; Hmrm; Span C; SC; Tr.

GUSTAFSON, Marcia Lee
Tartan Sr HS; St Paul, MN (18-247) Cpt, Band; NHS; Ski C; Bkbl; Tnns; Tr; HCt; Cpt, Gym; Young Life; St Solo Competition Star; Gustavus Col; Phys Ed.

GUSTAFSON, Robert Michael
Zion Benton Township HS; Zion, IL (1%-600) Band; Span C; Tr; Hon Prog; Greenville Col; Span.

GUSTAFSON, Sara Ann
Aurelia Comm Sch; Aurelia, IA (32-63) Co-Ed, Ann; Band; Chor; Fr C; FHA; Sch P; Bkbl; Golf; Tr; Spch A; Type A; Bkbl, Band, Chor, A's; Augustana Col; Nurs.

GUSTAVSON, Paul Arthur
Miller Place Sr HS; Miller Place, NY; Weighttraining; European Stu; Mus A; Essay A; Art A; Art.

GUSTIN, Michael Evan
Calvary Baptist Day Sch; Savannah, GA (38-65) Key C; Mgr, Bkbl; Tnns; Tr.

GUTARRA, Jeanette
Colegio Santa Rita; Bayamon, PR (1-33) Chor; Tres, Sr Cl; Chem A; JA A; U of Puerto Rico; Ciencias Naturales.

GUTENBERGER, Debra Joann
Manila HS; Manila, UT (4-14) Hon Prog; Type A; Rick's Col; Bus.

GUTHA, Nadine Ellen
Fulda HS; Fulda, MN (43-73) Band; Chor; Ensm; FHA; Vocal & Band Dist & Region As; Col Mus Schol; Buena Vista Col; Art.

GUTHMILLER, Lucinda Marie
Wolsey Ind HS; Wolsey, SD (1-31) Ann; Pres, Band; Chor; FHA; Ger C; Ntl Yth Conf; Sch P; S-T, Sci C; Co-Cpt, Bkbl; Tr; Bio A; COM; Hon Prog; MLS; Most Out; Sci A; Type A; Val; Yth Fel; SD All-St Chor; Co-Ch, Easter Seals; Amer Soc for Microbiology; St Sci Fair Win; SD St U; Med Technology.

GUTHRIE, Anne Somers
Largo HS; Largo, FL (10-862) Lat C; NHS; Var C; Cpt, Swim; Elk A; All St, MVP, Swim; U of Mich; Chem Engr.

GUTHRIE, Cindy Lou
Rock Island HS; Rock Island, IL (29-570) NHS; Ski C; Var C; Cr-Ctry; Golf; Tr; Augustana Col; Acct.

GUTHRIE, Darlene Allicia
Pearl Sr HS; Nashville, TN; JV, Chldr; Memphis St; Nurs.

GUTHRIE, Dorothy Jane
Twin Palms HS; Blythe, CA (3-20) Chor; FHA; Palo Verde Jr Col; Bus.

GUTHRIE, Jan Ellen
Shenandoah Comm HS; Shenandoah, IA (15-113) FNA; VP, 4H; NHS; Rptr, Sch P; Span C; Hon Prog; Span A; Iowa W Comm Col; Bus Adm.

GUTHRIE, Kathy Sue
Quail HS; Quail, TX; Ed, Ann; VP, FHA; Secy, Sr Cl; Cpt, Bkbl; Beauty; Citz A; Cl Fav; DARGCA; Hist A; Yth Fel.

GUTHRIE, Patricia Ann
Jonesboro Sr HS; Jonesboro, AR (50%-401) Drama; A-Ed, Sch P; Spch C; ROTC A; Lib Sci; Acteens.

GUTHRIE, Samuel Lester Jr
Palm Cove Beach Sch; Pompano Beach, FL (10%-27) Order/Arrow; Var C; VP, Sr Cl; Cpt, Cr-Ctry; Cpt, Swim; Cl Fav; Pres A; Yth Fel; MVP, Cr-Ctry; MVP, Swim; Eagle Sct; Ath o-t Yr; Pfeiffer Col; Bus Adm.

GUTHRIE, Steven Dale
MacArthur HS; San Antonio, TX (25%-800) Lat C; Co-Cpt, Bkbl; Tr; FCA; Southwestern Okla St U; Phar.

GUTHRIE, Susan Janice
Nathan Hale HS; Tulsa, OK; Ed, Ann; Hillsdale FWB.

GUTIERREZ, Diana
St Augustine HS; Laredo, TX; Drama; Spch C; NEDT; Opt A; Poet A; Rotary A; VFW A; Dance Troupe; Eng A; HR; Best Actress, Drama C As; Best Supporting Actress Drama C As; Columbia U; Astrobiology.

GUTIERREZ, Guillermo Rene
St Augustine HS; Laredo, TX (19-68) Bus Mgr, Drama; Co-Ch, FBLA; Ch, SC; Pres, Sr Cl; Pres, Jr Cl; Tres, Soph Cl; Citz A; Most Out; Sci A; Spch A; WW; U of Tex.

GUTIERREZ, Laura
St Augustine HS; Laredo, TX (7-68) Drama; GS; VP, NHS; Tres, Sr Cl; Tres, Jr Cl; Tres, Soph Cl; Bkbl; NEDT; Spch A; Presidential Clrm For Young Amer; WW; Eng A; Reading A; Columbia Col; Eng.

GUTIERREZ, Lawrence David
Christian Brothers HS; Sacramento, CA (15-147) CYO; Pres, Hmrm; NHS; Tr; Citz A; Hon Prog; Excellent-Eng, Span & Religion As; Bus Achv A; Sacramento City Col.

GUTIERREZ, Peter John
Pioneer HS; Whittier, CA (35-400) JETS; Model UN; ARC; UN Council; Bkbl; JV, Cr-Ctry; CSF; Hon Prog; Westmont Col; Bio.

GUTIERREZ, Rafael Alberto
Lola Rodriguez de Tio; San German, PR (1-350) Band; Order/Arrow; Hon Prog; Col Agr at Mayaguez; Ingenieria Quimica.

GUTIERREZ, Ralph Henry
Junipero Serra HS; Gardena, CA (5%-148) F-Ed, Ann; Band; Math C; Sci C; CSF; Chem A; Citz A; Journ A; Math A; Span Merit Diploma; UCLA; Engr.

GUTIERREZ, Susan Jane
Northern HS; Durham, NC (110-499) Drama; Rainbow; COM; MLS; Civinettes; Church Yth Coun; VP, Health Occupations C; Stu o-t Mo; Church Choir; Guidance Asst; Pres, Fresh Cl; *Nurs.*

GUTIERREZ, Terri Lynne
Pojoaque HS; Santa Fe, NM (27-87) Bus C; Type A.

GUTKNECHT, Ricky Lynn
New Hartford HS; New Hartford, IA (50%-40) Span C.

GUTMAN, Lee Ann
Citrus HS; Inverness, FL (20-250) Fr C; FTA; Orch; Mgr, Bkbl; Hon Prog; NYSSMA; LISF; SCMEA; OFO; *Central Fla Comm Col; Fashion Design.*

GUTSHALL, Ellen Elaina
Butler HS; Butler, MO (13-90) AFS; Band; Secy, Chor; Fr C; Type A; WW; *SW Baptist Col; Mus.*

GUTTMAN, Deborah Lane
Marion-Adams HS; Sheridan, IN (5-80) Pres, Band; Ensm; Tres, 4H; NHS; Secy, Var C; VP, Jr Cl; Co-Cpt, Swim; Tr; 4H A; Tm Mental Attitude, Vlbl A; HQ Job's Daughters; Vlbl; *De-Pauw U; Sci.*

GUTTU, William Frank
Ridgecroft Sch; Ahoskie, NC (50%-22) Ann; Pres, Chor; 4H; VP, Hmrm; Monogram; Sci C; VP, Jr Cl; Bkbl; Tnns; 1st Pl, Tnns Tournament; *E Carolina U; Bus Adm.*

GUTWAKS, Fabio Massimo
Cathederal HS; Springfield, MA; Polish Folk Dancing; Hospital Vol; *Restaurant Mgt.*

GUTY, Joseph Michael
Scotch Plains-Fanwood HS; Scotch Plains, NJ (229-594) Ann; F-Ed, Sch P; Co-Cpt, Cr-Ctry; Tr; Journ A; *Gettysburg Col; Religion.*

GUTZWILLER, Douglas Jerome
Elder HS; Cincinnati, OH (100-480) CYO; K of C; Bkbl; Ftbl; Sftbl; Citz A.

GUY, Barbara Susan
Monticello HS; Monticello, MS; Band; BC; Drama; FHA; Pres, 4H; Sch P; COM; Secy, G Sct; Acteens Qn; Most Dependable; 2nd Pl, Talent Auxilary Comp; Solo & Ensm Band; *Mus.*

GUY, CasSandra Drussilla
George Henry Corliss HS; Chicago, IL; Hmrm; NHS; Sch P; COM; NEDT; *IIT; Computer Sci.*

GUY, Cedric DaRand
W Division HS; Milwaukee, WI; *UWM; Mortician.*

GUY, Cynthia Ann
Ne HS; Fort Lauderdale, FL; Co-Cpt, Chldr; Chor; JV, Drama; Hmrm; Lat C; Span C; Cr-Ctry; Tr; Yth Fel; Yth Leg; Juniorettes Service C; Bat Girl C; *Fla Sou Col; Religion.*

GUY, Dauphine Marie
West Division HS; Milwaukee, WI; Pres, Chor; Drama; Sci C; Hon Prog; JA A; Pres A; Sci A; Yth Fel; Runner-Up, Miss West Pageant; *UWM; Obstetrician.*

GUY, Jean Ann
Red Cloud HS; Red Cloud, NE (9-40) Band; Chor; Secy, Drama; Mjrte; Rainbow; Span C; Pres, SC; Mgr, Wrest; *Nebr Wesleyan Col; Bus.*

GUY, Margaret Elizabeth
West Point HS; West Point, VA (15-47) A-Ed, Ann; Co-Cpt, Chldr; Chor; FBLA; GS; Rptr, Hmrm; Span C; SC; Pres, Jr Cl; Semi-Fin, Tr; Bus Mgr, Annual; *Va Commonwealth U; Merchandising.*

GUY, Shelia Gwen
Nanih Waiya HS; Louisville, MS (4-33) BC; FHA; Secy, Sr Cl; Secy, Jr Cl; Secy, Soph Cl; Cl Fav; Gov Honor Prog; Swtht.

GUYN, Laura Carol
Eastern HS; Louisville, KY; Band; Chldr; Chor; Hmrm; Sch P; Cpt, Swim; Journ A; Chldr A; Ice Skating A; *U of Louisville; Interior Decorating.*

GUYRE, Alice Ann
Port Barre HS; Port Barre, LA (20%-200) Band; Semi-Fin, Ensm; ARC; Pres, Church Yth; Church Yth Coordinator; *U of SW La; Nurs.*

GUYTON, Thonya Delean
Cartersville HS; Cartersville, GA; All Amer Yth; Band; Chor; Crown & Scepter; FHA; Tri-HiY; Type A; Safety C; Off Practice Silver A & Gold Cert; *Bus.*

GUZMAN, Larry Joe
Harlingen HS; Harlingen, TX (126-622) Band; Tres, CYO; Bsbl; Alg A; Sci A; *Tex Southmost Col; Phar.*

GUZMAN, Leah Abastillas
Castle Park HS; Chula Vista, CA (59-425) Hmrm; InterAct C; InterClub Coun; SC; CSF; *San Diego U; Math.*

GUZMAN, Letizia Ann
Gridley Union HS; Gridley, CA (72-116) CYO; *Butte Col.*

GUZMAN, Nydia Ivette
Academia Santa Monica; Santurce, PR; Chess C; Drama; Model UN; NFL; Pres, NHS; Rptr, Sch P; SC; Tnns; COM; Spch A; *U of Puerto Rico.*

GUZY, Carole Ann
Catholic Central HS; Troy, NY (20%-328) Chor; Hmrm; NHS; SC; Hon Prog; *Elem Ed.*

GWALTNEY, Charlene May
Andrew Lewis HS; Salem, VA (55-272) Chor; Tr; Keyettes; 1st C GSct A; Best Bible Stu; TAP Prog; *David Lipscomb Col; Sociology.*

GWALTNEY, Dorothy Stephens
Isle of Wight Acad; Isle of Wight, VA; Ann; Co-Cpt, Chldr; Hmrm; Monogram; Pres, NHS; Rptr, SC; Tnns; HCt; *Lib Arts.*

GWALTNEY, Mary Shepherd
Isle of Wight Acad; Isle of Wight Co, VA (1-50) S-T, Chor; Hmrm; NHS; F-Ed, Sch P; Ruritan A; *Col of William and Mary; Hist.*

GWALTNEY, Tammy Bea
Herrin HS; Herrin, IL (35-200) Secy, Chor; Mjrte; Rptr, Sch P; Span C; *Sou Ill U; Travel Agent.*

GWALTNEY, Wanda Nell
Isle of Wight Acad; Isle of Wight, VA (2-42) Ann; Co-Cpt, Chldr; Secy, Chor; GS; S-T, Monogram; NHS; Pres, SC; MVP, Bkbl; MVP, Sftbl; COM; HCt; Jr Marshal; All Conf Bkbl; HS All Amer; *Va Wesleyan Col; Elem Ed.*

GWIN, Lisa Marina
Wellston HS; Wellston, OK (1-51) A-Ed, Ann; Chldr; Chor; Pres, FBLA; Hmrm; NHS; Ed, Sch P; Secy, SC; Alg A; Bio A; Hist A; Math A; Most Out; Ntl Sci Found; Sci A; Type A; Val; 1st Pl, Sci Fair; 2nd Pl, Regional Sci Fair; 4th Geom, St Inter-Schol Contest; *Okla U; Bus Adm.*

GWIN, Virginia Ann
Hatley HS; Amory, MS (5-38) Ann; BC; Chor; Co-Ed, Sch P; Pres, Span C; HR; *Itawamba Jr Col; Bus Adm.*

GWINN, Casey Edward
San Lorenzo Valley HS; Felton, CA; Band; Chem C; Dbte Tm; Key C; Sch P; Pres, SC; Var C; Bsbl; Cpt, Bkbl; Golf; Tnns; Alg A; MLS; Star Student; *Westmont Col; Pol Sci.*

GWINN, Helen Marie
Gladewater HS; Gladewater, TX (10%-146) Band; Co-Ed, Lit Mag; NHS; Co-Ed, Sch P; Span C; NHS; WW; *Child Therapy.*

GWINN, Jeffrey Peter
St Mary's Prep; Orchard Lake, MI (1-36) Soccer; Sftbl; Summa Cum Laude; Arts & Crafts; Rowing; Highest Hon; *MIT; Bio.*

GWYNN, Michelle Diane
Martin Luther King HS; Philadelphia, PA (63-692) Chor; Fr C; NHS; COM; Service & Dedication A; *Kutztown St Col; Elem Ed.*

GYLLECK, Barbara Faye
Genoa-Kingston HS; Genoa, IL (20-128) Band; Drama; Art A; Methodist Yth Fel; *Art.*

H

HA, Michael Bruce
Hollywood Professional Sch; Hollywood, CA; NHS; VP, SC; Tres, Jr Cl; Bank Of Amer A; Hon Prog; Ntl Sci Found; NEDT; *UCLA; Med.*

HAAG, Cheryl Ann
St Joseph HS; Hammonton, NJ (2-49) Chor; Drama; Pres, Fr C; Sch P; Ski C; Mgr, Bkbl; Mgr, Cr-Ctry; Mgr, Ftbl; Hon Prog; Art C; WW; Principal's List; Homecraft C; Tres, Ecology C; Ed, Yrbk; *Dental Hygiene.*

HAAG, Scott Ray
New Braunfels HS; New Braunfels, TX (108-250) Band; Order/Arrow; Order/Arrow A; Yth Fel; Stage Band; Parl, ICT; Eagle Sct; *Tex A&M U; Law Enforcement.*

HAAGENSON, Gwen Marilyn
Wayzata Sr HS; Wayzata, MN (35-568) Band; NHS; Sup Rating, Regional Band Contest; Summer Missionary; Church Sr HS Yth Group.

HAAR, Frederick Hubbard Jr
Albemarle HS; Charlottesville, VA; Band; Soccer; Tnns; Beauty; All-St Hon Men, Soccer Tm; *Hampden-Sydney Col.*

HAARBERG, David Robert
Chase Co HS; Imperial, NE (15-70) Ann; NHS; Hon Prog; Q&S A; Regent Schol; Secy, Lutheran Yth Organization; *U of Nebr.*

HAARBERG, Joet Kay
Chase HS; Imperial, NE (23-71) Ann; Band; Chor; Ensm; FHA; 4H; Mjrte; Span C; Y-Tns; Golf; *U of Nebr; Pre-Phys Therapy.*

HAAS, Cheryl Denise
Oscoda Area HS; Oscoda, MI (20%-250) NHS; S-T, Keyette C; *Central Mich U; Acct.*

HAAS, David Stewart
Grinnell HS; Grinnell, IA (30-190) BS; Chess C; Chor; Dbte Tm; Ensm; Ger C; Madrigal; Sch P; Spch C; Var C; Co-Cpt, Cr-Ctry; Mgr, Ftbl; Hockey; Tr; Citz A; Spch A; Yth Fel; BSct; Sports A; *Lawerence Col; Humanities.*

HAAS, Gregory Brian
Fruita Monument HS; Fruita, CO; Band; Hmrm; Key C; VP, Ntl Yth Conf; SC; Tr; COM; Citz A; Yth Fel; Yth Leg; *Mesa Col; Forestry.*

HAAS, Lori Diane
Brooke HS; Wellsburg, WV (42-483) Band; Chem C; Drama; GS; Hmrm; Mjrte; Secy, NHS; Rainbow; Ed, Sch P; Ski C; Span C; Spch C; SC; Thes; Tri-HiY; Tres, Sr Cl; Swim; Elk A; Spch A; Vof-DEM; Yth Fel; WW; Jr Town Meeting; Win, Essay Contest; *W Va U; Phar.*

HAAS, Melinda Ann
Pottstown Sr HS; Pottstown, PA (75-200) Band; Rainbow; Ski C.

HAAS, Robert Austin
Watauga HS; Boone, NC (25%-287) Band; Drama; Fr C; FTA; Order/Arrow; Ftbl; Tr; Eagle Sct; Band Ltr & A; Lodge Chief Order o-t Arrow; Church Choir & Yth Group; *UNC-Chapel Hill; Pre-Med.*

HAASE, Carrie Lynne
Lind HS; Lind, WA (1-20) Ann; Band; Chor; GS; Jr Miss Pagent; Pres, NHS; Pres, Jr Cl; Bkbl; Tnns; Most Inspirational, Vlbl, Bkbl; *Pacific Lutheran U; Bio.*

HAASE, Claudia Margaret
Red Hook Central HS; Red Hook, NY; AFS; Band; Chor; Drama; Ger C; Mus A; *Mus.*

HAASE, Lawrence Karl
Red Hook Central Sch; Red Hook, NY (28-176) AFS; Chess C; Ger C; NHS; Var C; Mgr, Bkbl; JV, Cr-Ctry; Tr; Computer Achv A; *Rensselaer Polytechnic Inst; Computer Engr.*

HABEDANK, Karen Ann
Twin Valley Pub HS; Twin Valley, MN; A Cap Choir; Band; Chor; Drama; Ensm; Pres, 4H; Co-Ed, Sch P; Spch C; Cpt, Bkbl; Tr; 4H A; H of F; *Golden Valley Luth Col.*

HABEGGER, Jill Elaine
North Side HS; Fort Wayne, IN (12-501) Ensm; Madrigal; NHS; Span A.

HAGANS, Patrease Antionette
William M Raines HS; Jacksonville, FL; *Morris Brown Col; Marketing.*

HAGAR, Valerie Verlene
Martin Luther King Acad; Gary, IN; Chor; Hmrm; Sch P; Ch, Sci C; SC; *Eng.*

HAGBERG, Cindy Joann
Luverne Pub HS; Luverne, MN (72-130) Chldr; Chor; Ensm; *Bus.*

HAGEBUSCH, Dennis Michael
Cottage Grove HS; Cottage Grove, OR; A Cap Choir; Band; Chor; Thes; *Oreg St U; Mus.*

HAGEDON, Marsha Rae
Ottumwa Sr HS; Ottumwa, IA; Band; Chor; Ensm; Orch; SC; Amer Leg A; Secy, Yth Fel; Jr Choir Pianist; Church Choir; *Mus.*

HAGEMAN, John Robert
Elder HS; Cincinnati, OH (77-442) Tres, CYO; Hmrm; Sftbl; Hon Prog; Sci A; 1st Pl Earth Sci Div, Engr Soc; *Environmental.*

HAGEMAN, Tammi Irene
University HS; San Diego, CA (16-311) Cpt, Chldr; Cum Laude Soc; Key C; NHS; Sch Achieve Tm; Var C; CSF; Hon Prog; Summa Cum Laude; WW; *U of San Diego; Psych.*

HAGEMEIER, Fred Glen
Odell Pub HS; Odell, NE (12-24) Band; Bkbl; *Agr.*

HAGEMEIER, Janice Ruth
Clay Center Pub Sch; Clay Center, NE (7-33) Ann; Band; Chor; GS; Mjrte; NHS; Spch C; Y-Tns; Pres, Soph Cl; Sftbl; Swim; HCt; Hon Prog; *Kearney St Col; Fine Arts.*

HAGEN, Barbara Kay
Jefferson Sr HS; Jefferson, WI (21-209) Band; JV, Chldr; Drama; *U of Wisc.*

HAGEN, Brian Patrick
Parker HS; Janesville, WI (318-650) Swim; Wrest; *Airline Pilot.*

HAGEN, Diane Marie
Jefferson HS; Jefferson, WI (17-200) Band; Chor; NHS; HCt; Hon Prog; I Dare You; Ntl Sch Choral A; *UW-MADISON; Behavioral Disabilities.*

HAGEN, Pamela Dawn
North Central Jr-Sr HS; Manly, IA (6-66) A Cap Choir; Ann; Band; Chor; Ensm; 4H; Madrigal; Cpt, Mjrte; NHS; Mgr, Bkbl; 4H A; *NIACC; Bus.*

HAGENOW, Rebecca Lynne
Wapsie Valley HS; Fairbank, IA (2-87) Chor; Tres, FFA; Pres, 4H; Tr; 4H A; *Iowa St U; Vet Med.*

HAGER, Jill Ann
Lakeland Sr HS; Lakeland, FL (206-790) Band; Lat C; *Bethany Col; Pre-Med.*

HAGER, Karen Gayle
Alamo Heights HS; San Antonio, TX (135-374) Chor; Hmrm; Span C; SC; *Tex Tech Col; Lib Arts.*

HAGERTY, Clare Frances
John W Hallahan HS; Philadelphia, PA (1-403) Secy, CYO; Fr C; Math C; Ch, Orch; Alg A; *Math.*

HAGGAN, Sonya Marie
Pleasantville HS; Pleasantville, NJ; Band; Chldr; Chor; Hmrm; JV, Tnns; Gospel Chor; Photo C; Home Ec, Choir, Dance, A's; *Westminster Col; Mus.*

HAGGARD, Gregory Dale
Seymour HS; Seymour, TN (6-90) BC; Pres, FFA; Key C; Madrigal; Tres, SC; VP, Var C; Bsbl; Bkbl; Ftbl; Opt Out Tn; FFA Ldrship A; Bank Sr High Assoc Board of Dir; *Middle Tenn St U.*

HAGGARD, Kellye Ann
Seymour HS; Seymour, TN (20-120) Pres, FHA; Madrigal; Var C; VP, Soph Cl; Bkbl; Tnns; HQn; Church Sftbl.

HAGGARD, Ken Ray
Ballard Mem HS; Barlow, KY (2-102) A-Ed, Ann; Rptr, BC; BS; FFA; Parl, Span C; Tr; Hist A; NMS; Sal; Spch A; Span As; *Murray St U; Pre-Law.*

HAGGARD, Pamela Ann
Searcy HS; Searcy, AR (10%-245) BC; Chldr; Drama; Pres, Rainbow; SC; Beauty; Masonic A; *Ark St U; Social Sci.*

HAGGEN, Gayle Eileen
N Kitsap Sr HS; Poulsbo, WA (3-268) A Cap Choir; Chor; Drama; Ensm; Orch; JV, Tr; JV Tr, Yth Fitness Achv, A's; *Wash St U; Vet Med.*

HAGGEN, Kathleen Anne
N Kitsap HS; Poulsbo, WA (8-268) Chldr; Hmrm; NHS; Sch P; Span C; SC; JV, Tr; *Whitman Col; Psych.*

HAGGERSTONE, Linda Mary Violet
Alternatives for Individuals HS; Tacoma, WA; Co-Ch, Ann; Ch, Drama; NHS; Sch Achieve Tm; F-Ed, Sch P; Secy, SC; Cl Fav; Hon Prog; Star Student; *St Mary's Col; Anthropology.*

HAGOPIAN, Sonig
Waltham HS; Waltham, MA (10-900) Ger C; Hmrm; Sch P; Tr; COM; Pres, Armenian C; Armenian Yth Found; Jr Page Writer Trophy; *San Diego U; Corporate Law.*

HAGSTROM, Julie Lynn
Campolindo HS; Moraga, CA (20%-450) A Cap Choir; VP, AFS; Hmrm; NHS; SC; CSF; Chamber Choir; Amer Abroad Stu; Amer Indian Exchange Stu; *Col of Idaho; Eng.*

HAGSTROM, Ron Alan
Rochester HS; Rochester, WA (1-120) Demolay; NHS; Var C; Bsbl; JV, Bkbl; Ftbl.

HAGUE, Marjory Alison
Abilene HS; Abilene, KS (5%-125) Band; Dbte Tm; NFL; Orch; ARC; *Phys Therapy.*

HAGWOOD, Theresa
John Bartram HS; Philadelphia, PA; Achv; *Morehouse Col; Secy.*

HAHLEN, Kim Marie
Shawnee Mission NW HS; Shawnee, KS; Band; CYO; *Med.*

HAHN, Cynthia Sue
Auburn HS; Auburn, NE (25%-115) A Cap Choir; Chor; Math C; Pres, Monogram; SC; Secy, Sr Cl; Secy, Jr Cl; Secy, Soph Cl; Co-Cpt, Bkbl; Sftbl; Swim; Tr; All Conf, Hon Men All St, Bkbl; Sch Recordholder, Bkbl & Tr; Sunday Sch Teacher; *Phys Ed.*

HAHN, Ellen L
Hannibal Sr HS; Hannibal, MO (9-299) Secy, Band; Drama; Tres, FTA; NHS; Ed, Sch P; Span C; SC; Q&S A; 1st Chair, Lion's C Band; *Mus.*

HAHN, Michelle
Williamston HS; Williamston, MI (66-154) Chor; JV, Tr; Vlbl; *Mich St U; Psych.*

HAHN, Mitchell Joel
Greenfield HS; Greenfield, WI (100-390) Yth Fel; Stout Inst; Industrial Arts.

HAHN, Sarah Jane
Hannibal Sr HS; Hannibal, MO (1-346) Band; JV, Chldr; FTA; S-T, 4H; Span C; Mahan Lit A; Top 10%; *Math.*

HAIDUK, Kim Joann
Shenendehowa HS; Clifton Park, NY; Chor; COM; MLS; Type A; *Calif St U at Long Beach; Bus Adm.*

HAIG, Sandra Kay
Northgate HS; Walnut Creek, CA (5-428) Model UN; JV, Swim; JV, Tnns; CSF; Hon Prog; *U of Calif; Bus Ed.*

HAIJSMAN, Lori Ann
Encinal HS; Alameda, CA (20%-425) SC; JV, Sftbl; Vlbl; Homemaking Outst Achievement A.

HAIL, Lori Ann
Eunice HS; Eunice, LA (5%-220) Ann; Chldr; Chor; Lit Ral; NHS; Pres, Sci C; Span C; Alg A; Bio A; Hon Prog; Magna Cum Laude; Sci A; Type A; *LSU; Med.*

HAILE, Lydia Lynn
University HS; Baton Rouge, LA (1-62) Band; Ensm; Fr C; FHA; Key C; Lit Ral; Mjrte; NHS; Pres, SC; Citz A; Cl Fav; DARGCA; NEDT; PTA A; Swtht; Val; Outst Fresh Girl; Fr A; *La St U; Nurs.*

HAILEY, Janet Lynn
Halifax Co Sr HS; South Boston, VA (10-557) Ann; Rptr, Fr C; NHS; Co-Ed, Sch P; Tr; Hon Prog; Journ A; *Va Commonwealth U; Mass Communications.*

HAILEY, Robert Bernard
Robert E Lee Sr HS; Jacksonville, FL; Hmrm; Key C; Var C; Y-Tns; Ftbl; Wrest.

HAIN, David Bruce
Las Cruces HS; Las Cruces, NM (2%-600) Chor; Ger C; NHS; Order/Arrow; VP, Jr Cl; JV, Cr-Ctry; JV, Tnns; Hon Prog; People to People; *U of Pa; Pol Sci.*

HAIN, Maryellen Elizabeth
John W Hallahan HS; Philadelphia, PA (80-432) Bus C; VP, CYO; Cpt, Chldr; Sodality; Sftbl; Sci A; Liturgy C; Flag Ftbl.

HAINDS, Timothy Laverne
Union HS; Biggsville, IL (1-80) Ed, Ann; Band; Chor; Secy, FFA; NHS; ARC; HCt; Hon Prog; St Scholar; WW; *Vet Med.*

HAINES, Jeff Daniel
Charles F Brush HS; Lyndhurst, OH (20%-600) Band; Pres, Hmrm; Key C; Orch; VP, SC; Var C; Soccer; JV, Tnns; Citz A; Kiwanis A; MLS; PTA A; Eagle Sct; *Yale U; Law.*

HAINES, Jerryne Remae
Foothill Christian HS; Roseville, CA; Chldr; Chor; Tr.

HAINES, Nancy Marie
Pleasant Valley Sr HS; Chico, CA (50-200) A Cap Choir; Madrigal; *Sacramento St Col; Counselling.*

HAINES, Shirley Jean
Johnson Co HS; Wrightsville, GA (2-123) A-Ed, Ann; Rptr, BC; Chldr; FHA; VP, FTA; Jr Miss Pagent; Alg A; Bio A; Hist A; Type A; Historian, Tri-Hi-Y; FHA Chpt Degree; *U of Ga Merit Win; Ga Sou Col; Psych.*

HAINSEY, Robert Francis
Swissvale Area HS; Pittsburgh, PA (2%-187) CYO; Chess C; Golf; Bio A; Chem A; Hist A; Hon Prog; Math A; Sci A; *Law.*

HAIP, Angelika Maria
Lake Shore HS; St Clair Shores, MI; NHS; Yth Fel; Hospital Jr Vol; *Wayne St U; Nurs.*

HAIR, Dale Robert
Central Dauphin HS; Harrisburg, PA (10%-550) NHS; Order/Arrow; Var C; Cpt, Cr-Ctry; Cpt, Tr; God & Country A; Lion A; Yth Fel; Eagle Sct; *Miami U; Archt.*

HAIR, Jenny Caroline
Bay HS; Panama City, FL (10%-400) VP, Chor; Ensm; Lit Mag; NHS; COM; Tn Action Prog Hall of Fame; Chor Swtht; Q&S Hon Soc; *Gulf Coast Comm Jr Col; Religion.*

HAIR, Mary Jo
Merryville HS; Merryville, LA (8-47) Bus Mgr, Ann; Fr C; FBLA; VP, FHA; Lit Ral; Orch; Co-Ed, Sch P; Rptr, Soph Cl; Type A; VofDEM; Most Courteous; Miss FBLA; *La Col; Elem Ed.*

HAIR, Patti Leigh
Chickasha HS; Chickasha, OK (6-215) Band; Chor; Tres, Drama; S-T, Fr C; Ch, Model UN; Ed, Sch P; SC; Thes; COM; Hon Prog; Spch A; GSct; Art Talent, Thespian, A's; Bible Quizzing; *Bethany Nazarene Col; Math.*

HAIRE, Cynthia Louise
Claxton HS; Claxton, GA (25%-110) Secy, Dbte Tm; FBLA; Hmrm; SC; Rptr, Sr Cl; Pres, Jr Cl; COM; WW; Presbyterian Col Jr Fellow; *U of Ga Merit A; U of Ga; Phar.*

HAIRE, Terri Lynne
Dinwiddie Sr HS; Dinwiddie, VA (11-350) MVP, Band; Fr C; FHA; Secy, NHS; Mgr, Bkbl; Art A; Piano A; Pres, Tres, Yth Fel; Semi-Fin, Coun of Teachers A; *Richard Bland Col; Religion.*

HAIRE, Tony Gregory
Benhaven HS; Olivia, NC; Ann; BC; FTA; Sch P; *E Carolina U; Phar.*

HAIRSINE, Margaret Adelaide
Ursuline Acad; Wilmington, DE (2-48) Chor; VP, NHS; Mgr, Bkbl; Bio A; Chem A; DARGCA; Hon Prog; Math A; NEDT; SAR Good Citz A; Pres, Children of Amer Revolution; Natl Hist, Children of Amer Rev; *Bio.*

HAIRSTON, Conova
Morehead HS; Eden, NC (56-308) Band; Chor; FTA; Hmrm; NHS; Span C; *NC Central U; Bus Adm.*

HAIRSTON, Dorothy Louise
Motley HS; Columbus, MS (10-70) BC; Chldr; F-Ed, Sch P; Sci C; Tri-HiY; Pres, Soph Cl; Arch; Bio A; COM; Hist A; HCt; Pres A; Eng A; Span A; Miss St U; Journ.

HAIRSTON, James H Jr
Welch HS; Welch, WV (33%-141) Var C; Bsbl; Bkbl; Ftbl; Tr.

HAIRSTON, Julie Ann
Smoky Hill HS; Denver, CO (111-490) A Cap Choir; Chldr; Chor; Ski C; VP, SC; VP, Sr Cl; Sftbl; Tnns; Baylor U; Med.

HAIRSTON, Karen Jeannine
Frederick Douglass HS; Atlanta, GA (17-434) Fr C; Math C; NHS; Gov Honor Prog; Tex Christian U; Med.

HAIRSTON, Paul Russell
Smoky Hill HS; Denver, CO (103-350) Chess C; Ger C; Key C; Sch P; Ski C; Ftbl; Golf; Soccer; Sftbl; Tnns; Tr; Baylor U; Bio.

HAIRSTON, Teresa Renee
Chapel Hill Sr HS; Chapel Hill, NC (211-405) Chldr; Chor; Secy, FHA; Hmrm; SC; Y-Tns; COM; HCt; Jr Cl Qn; Sr Cl Qn; Raleigh Sch of Data Processing; Computer Prog.

HAKARI, Heidi Ann
Luther L Wright HS; Ironwood, MI; Chor; VP, Key C; Tr; Northern Mich U; Phys Therapist.

HAKES, David Scott
Hillsboro HS; Hillsboro, OH (11-218) Band; Chess C; Fr C; Hon Prog; Math A; Eng, Band, A's.

HALASEK, Evonne Kay
Russell HS; Russell, KY (14-250) Band; VP, BC; Secy, Fr C; GS; Hmrm; Secy, SC; Tri-HiY; Semi-Fin, Bkbl; Swim; Tr; Hon Prog.

HALBACH, Daniel Gerard
Hilbert HS; Hilbert, WI (3-65) BS; Ger C; NHS; SC; Var C; VP, Soph Cl; Bkbl; Ftbl; Tr.

HALBACH, Lorraine Lila
Chilton HS; Chilton, WI; A Cap Choir; All Amer Yth; CYO; FHA; 4H; ARC; Sch P; Bsbl; Sftbl; Tnns; Tr; 4H A; Yth Fel; Yth Leg; Moraine Park Col; Child Care.

HALBERSMA, Elizabeth Mae
Verdi Pub Sch; Verdi, MN; A Cap Choir; Ann; Band; S-T, Chor; Drama; Secy, 4H; Sch P; SC; Tres, Sr Cl; Sftbl; 4H A; HCt; Spch A; Nettleton Col; Med Secy.

HALBERT, Marva Ann
Crawford Co R-II; Cuba, MO (2-100) Band; Chor; Ensm; GS; NHS; Rainbow; Amer Leg A; HCt; Opt A; Soph Pilgrimage; Vlbl; Pres, Pep C; Ariz St U; Acct.

HALBOTH, Barbara Ann
Mendota HS; Mendota, IL; Band; Secy, FFA; FHA; Secy, 4H; Tr; 4H A; Luther League.

HALBOTH, Henry Wayne
Mendota HS; Mendota, IL (1-218) VP, FFA; Pres, 4H; Math C; NHS; Phys C; Pres, SC; Ftbl; Tr; JV, Wrest; DARGCA; 4H A; HCt; I Dare You; Lion A; St Scholar; Val; DeKalb Agr A; Ill St Farmer; Social Stu A; U of Ill; Agr Ec.

HALBRITTER, Cynthia Ann
Ahrens HS; Louisville, KY; NHS; SC; Alg A; Hist A; HCt; Type A; Western U; Eng.

HALCOMB, Marcia Gayle
Dilce Combs Mem HS; Jeff, KY (10-113) Band; BC; Citz A; VP, Bible C; Cumberland Col; Nurs.

HALDER, Katherine Rose
Aquinas HS; San Bernardino, CA (74-177) Hmrm; St Stu Congress; SC; Pres, Jr Cl; COM; K of C A; Most Out; Opt A; Religion A; Calif Polytech Col; Hist.

HALDORSON, Kent Lee
Tigard HS; Tigard, OR (20-350) Ed, Ann; Dbte Tm; Spch C; Bkbl; Ftbl; MVP, Tr; Alg A; Most Out; Spch A; Yth Fel.

HALE, Cari Dee
Pearland HS; Pearland, TX (45-350) Band; Mjrte; Spch A; Piano A & Trophy; Outst Mus Trophy; Clarinet Solo & Ensm Medal; U of Tex; Dental Hygienics.

HALE, James Allan
Ensley HS; Birmingham, AL; Chor; Pres, Hmrm; Order/Arrow; Bsbl; Ftbl; Friendliest.

HALE, Joyce Lynn
Highland HS; Albuquerque, NM; Chor; Fr C; Key C; HR; Okla U; Bus.

HALE, Margaret Anne
Pineville HS; Pineville, LA (30-230) Band; Chor; COM; La Col; Phar.

HALE, Michael John
Warren Central HS; Indianapolis, IN (300-800) CYO; SC; Swim; Eagle Sct; IUPUI; Communications.

HALE, Robert Earl
Se HS; Springfield, IL (215-515) Community Yth Symph; Ch, Dbte Tm; Orch; Mgr, Bkbl; Ftbl; Sangamon St Col; Psych.

HALE, Robert Wayne
Centralia HS; Centralia, IL; FFA; Arch; Tr; Wrest; U of Evansville; Lab Tech.

HALE, Shannon Layne
Texhoma HS; Texhoma, OK; Band; Secy, 4H; Mjrte; NHS; Rainbow; Bkbl.

HALE, Susan Beth
Scotia-Glenville HS; Scotia, NY (25%-200) Chldr; Chor; Orch; Sftbl; Church Organist; Westminister Choir Col; Organ.

HALE, Terri Jane
Plano Sr HS; Plano, TX (68-850) Band; BC; FHA; Span C; Span C Del, Pan Am Stu Forum Conv; Okla Christian Col; Special Ed.

HALE, Virginia Ann
Prestonsburg HS; Prestonburg, KY (50-150) Tr; U of Ky.

HALE, Walter Alan
Warren Travis White HS; Dallas, TX (389-650) MVP, Bkbl; Tr; Tex A&M Col; Phys Ed.

HALEY, Laurence Parker
Joelton HS; Joelton, TN; Pres, Hmrm; NFL; NHS; VP, SC; Pres, Jr Cl; Ftbl; Wrest; Gov Honor Prog; Yth Leg; Rptr & S-T, Debate Tm; S-T & Pres, FFA; Ldrship Training A; Austin Peay St U; Agr.

HALEY, Victoria Diane
Abilene HS; Abilene, KS (120-160) Y-Tns; Drama A; Hon Qn, Job's Daughters; Church Deacon; Cloud Co Jr Col; Drama.

HALFORD, Della Sandra
Bolton HS; Alexandria, LA (13-270) Drama; Fr C; Pres, FBLA; FNA; NHS; Hon Prog; Type A; Stenography, Spelling, & Off Procedures, A; NW St U; Off Adm.

HALL, Agnes Diane
Cheraw HS; Cheraw, SC; Math A; Sci A; C&M Tech Col; Bus Adm.

HALL, Anita Sue
Sussex Central HS; Sussex, VA (1-200) BC; FBLA; Tres, FHA; Span C; Pres, Jr Cl; Mgr, Bkbl; Mgr, Sftbl; Hist A; Math A; Most Out; Sci A; Type A; Longwood Col; Bus Adm.

HALL, Becky Lynn
Hutchinson HS; Hutchinson, MN (22-229) Band; Sci.

HALL, Belinda Jane
Kirksville Sr HS; Kirksville, MO (20-197) Band; Chor; FHA; Mod Mus Mas; Orch; Sftbl; Tnns; COM; NMSU; Animal Tech.

HALL, Bertha Ann
Virgie HS; Virgie, KY (26-112).

HALL, Beth Ann
Oakdale HS; Oakdale, LA (5-105) CYO; Drama; 4H; NHS; Spch C; 4H A; Hon Prog; Schol Avg A; McNeese Col; Dental Hygiene.

HALL, Blake Curtis
Skyline HS; Dallas, TX; Demolay; NHS; Bsbl; Ftbl; Pres, FCA; WW; 'A' HR; 100% HS Bible; Tex A&M U.

HALL, Bonita Cecilia
Emerson HS; Emerson, AR (14-31) Ann; Chor; FHA; Tres, Hmrm; Span C; SC; Arch; Bkbl; Ftbl; Soccer; Sftbl; Tnns; Tr; Most Courteous; Neatest; Cutest; U of Ark; Interior Decorating.

HALL, Brenda Kay
Mathiston HS; Mathiston, MS (4-35) Ann; BC; VP, FHA; NHS; Sch P; HCt; Clarke Col; Elem Ed.

HALL, Brenda May
Northwest HS; Clarksville, TN (25%-430) Vol, Med Explorer; Austin Peay St U; Nurs.

HALL, Brian K
Dryden Central Jr Sr HS; Dryden, NY (40-150) Ann; Band; Chor; Yth Fel; Band & Choir A's; Bradley U; Math Ed.

HALL, Bryan Keith
Southwest HS; Fort Worth, TX (42%-642) Cr-Ctry; Ftbl; Tr; VP, Russian C; Jr Deacon; Tres, Training Union; Tarleton St Col; Bus.

HALL, Bryan Warren
Plano Sr HS; Plano, TX (57-850) Band; Drama; Hmrm; Math C; Mod Mus Mas; NHS; SC; Thes; Bsbl; Mgr, Soccer; Hon Prog; Singapore Am Com Act Coun Citation; Tex A&M U; Acct.

HALL, Carla Ann
Palo Duro HS; Amarillo, TX (30-260) Secy, FBLA; Hmrm; NHS; SC.

HALL, Carla Celeste
George Henry Corliss HS; Chicago, IL (2-250) Drama; Fr C; Hmrm; NHS; Ski C; St Stu Congress; SC; COM; Citz A; Hon Prog; Pep Sq; Co-Ed, Yrbk Staff; Art Scholastic Achievement A; Eastern U; Bus Adm.

HALL, Carol Raye
Luther HS; Orlando, FL; Band; Chor; Drama; Ensm; Bkbl; Interlochen Ntl Mus; Chor Accompanist; Dist Band; Pianist, Stage Band; Medal, Dist Ensm; St Vocal Assn; Sup, Ntl Fed of Mus C Piano Solo; Marine Sci Research.

HALL, Caroline
Aiken HS; Aiken, SC (107-640) BC; Fr C; GS; Hmrm; Ch, InterAct C; InterClub Coun; Jr Miss Pagent; VP, SC; Mgr, Bkbl; U of SC; Bus Adm.

HALL, Cassandra Marie
Franklin Co HS; Frankfort, KY (220-425) Chor; Drama; Ensm; Parl, FHA; 4H; Sch P; Spch C; Arch; Beauty; Citz A; Yth Fel; Baptist Matching Schol; Service Aid Schol; Murray St U; Home Ec.

HALL, Cathy Ann
George Washington HS; Cedar Rapids, IA (99-509) Band; Chor; Pre-Law.

HALL, Ceceila Merris
Greater New York Acad; Woodside, NY; Chldr; NHS; Sch P; VP, SC; Bkbl; Alg A; Bio A; COM; Chem A; Citz A; Val; Sportswoman o-t Yr; St John's U; Pre-Med.

HALL, Charles William
Breckinridge Co HS; Harned, KY (15%-225) Chess C; Chor; NHS; Sch P; Span C; Span Poetry A; W Ky U; Acct.

HALL, Cheryl Wynne
Northwest HS; Indianapolis, IN; Tres, A Cap Choir; Chldr; Mjrte; JV, Gym; Gym A; Mus A; Wrest A; Ind U; Social Sci.

HALL, Christian David
Summerville HS; Summerville, SC; Order/Arrow; Life Sct; Trident Technical Col; Broadcast Engr.

HALL, Cynthia Denise
Edward H White Sr HS; Jacksonville, FL; A Cap Choir; Chor; Ensm; 4H; Hmrm; SC; COM; Chor Member o-t Yr; Nurs.

HALL, Cynthia Denise
Dayton Fairview HS; Dayton, OH; Miami U; Ed.

HALL, Cynthia Gail
Herndon HS; Herndon, VA (35%-500) Bkbl; Sftbl; Tnns; Beauty; Yth Fel; Jr Festival Mus A; Ntl Piano Playing Auditions; Comm Girls Sftbl Championship; Central Bible Col; Bible.

HALL, Cynthia Henry
Hooper Acad; Hope Hull, AL (12-68) Pres, BC; VP, 4H; Math C; Sci C; Secy, Sr Cl; Cl Fav; 4H A; Service A; Auburn U; Therapy.

HALL, Deborah Kim
Dayton Fairview HS; Dayton, OH; Y-Tns; Cpt, Bkbl; Ohio St U; Med.

HALL, Donald Keith
Brandon HS; Brandon, MS; Pres, Band; BC; Rptr, SC.

HALL, Dudley Glenn
Huntington HS; Shreveport, LA; Golf; Hist A; Hon Prog; Most Out.

HALL, Edward Randall Jr
Winnfield Sr HS; Winnfield, LA; Anchor C; VP, Band; BC; Ensm; FBLA; FTA; 4H; Lit Mal; Secy, Order/Arrow; Spch C; Hon Prog; Gov Prog for Gifted Children; Dist Hon Band; Beau; *La Tech Col; Elec Engr.*

HALL, Edwin Joseph
Lick-Wilmerding HS; San Francisco, CA; Arch; Chess C; Ger C; Math C; Order/Arrow; ARC; Fin, Arch; Fin, Swim; Alg A; God & Country A; Hon Prog; Order/Arrow A; ARC A; Val; Eagle A; Mile Swim; 50 Mile A; *U of Calif at Berkeley; Computer Sci.*

HALL, Elizabeth Ann
Charles A Sprague HS; Salem, OR (12%-360) CYO; Drama; Sch P; Span C; Swim; *U of Oreg; Art Hist.*

HALL, Elizabeth Ann
Virden Comm HS; Virden, IL; Band; Chor; Drama; FHA; Arch; Bkbl; Sftbl; Tr; Poet A; Sci A; Spch A; Art, Sports, A's; Church Run A; Drill Tm; JA; *Lincoln Land Comm Col; Med Tech.*

HALL, Eric Joseph
Cohn HS; Nashville, TN (12-225) Band; Drama; FTA; Pres, InterClub Coun; Pres, NHS; VP, SC; Arch; Ftbl; Tnns; COM; MLS; *Martin Col; Advertising.*

HALL, Eva Eugenia
Huntsville HS; Huntsville, AL (30-550) Pres, FBLA; NHS; *U of Ala; Acct.*

HALL, George Alan
Champion HS; Warren, OH (47-233) Band; Order/Arrow; Bsbl; Ftbl; God & Country A; *Bio.*

HALL, Henry Clive
Graham HS; Bluefield, VA (44-175) Fr C; Sci C; Co-Cpt, Golf; Sup Perform; Ntl Ed Develop Tests; *Oral Roberts U; Archt.*

HALL, Jacqueline Antoinette
Simon Gratz HS; Philadelphia, PA (6-450) Drama; Secy, 4H; Sch P; Most Out; *Villanova U; Nurs.*

HALL, Jeffrey Allen
Batavia HS; Batavia, IL (27-217) Band; Lat C; NHS; Orch; Order/Arrow; SC; Var C; Cpt, Ftbl; Cpt, Wrest; Hon Prog; *Taylor U; Bus Adm.*

HALL, JoAnn Louise
Lake of the Woods HS; Baudette, MN (14-90) Chldr; GS; 4H; NHS; Spch C; SC; Var C; 4H A; HCt; NMS; Spch A.

HALL, Joey Earl
Bell HS; Bell, CA (10%-1000) Band; Ensm; FTA; Math C; Sch P; SC; Var C; Bkbl; Ftbl; Swim; Tr; Alg A; Math A; *Pepperdine U; Math.*

HALL, John Lane
Riverside HS; Greer, SC (2-240) Band; Fr C; Math A; Sci A; Gov Sch; Fr A; *Math.*

HALL, Joy Gina
Mosley HS; Panama City, FL (1-550) Band; Hmrm; Mjrte; Mu Alpha Theta; NHS; SC; *Auburn U; Phar.*

HALL, Julie Ann Lonae
Jamestown HS; Jamestown, ND; Band; Cpt, Chldr; 4H; Hmrm; NHS; Rainbow; Golf; Hon Prog; Gym; Drill Tm; Mus A; *Bus Ed.*

HALL, Julie Lee
Tewksbury Mem HS; Tewksbury, MA (74-460) Rainbow.

HALL, Julius LeRay
Windsor Forest HS; Savannah, GA (25-326) AFS; Band; Cpt, InterClub Coun; A-Ed, Sch P; Pres, SC; Bkbl; Ftbl; Swim; Tnns; Ntl Achv Schol; Yr HR; Sr Superlative; *NW U; Pre-Law.*

HALL, Karen Elizabeth
Forest Park HS; Cincinnati, OH (77-360) SC; World Affairs C; Achv A Banquet; Co-Cpt, Wrestlette; Trackette; *Edgecliff Col; Special Ed.*

HALL, Karen Sue
Eastwood HS; El Paso, TX (40-780) Pres, Band; Chor; Community Yth Symph; Orch; Most Out; All St Band; WW; WW, Mus; *NM St U; Mus.*

HALL, Kathy Rosemarie
St Petersburg Sr HS; St Petersburg, FL (112-402) Ann; Band; ARC; *Nurs.*

HALL, Kevin Dale
Peoria HS; Peoria, IL (185-450) Cr-Ctry; Sftbl; JV, Tnns; Tr; Math A; St Art A; *Ill Central Col; Elec.*

HALL, Kris Kay
Sidney HS; Sidney, MT (16-145) A Cap Choir; AFS; Rptr, Band; CYO; Cpt, Chldr; Rptr, Chor; Ensm; Key C; Madrigal; Orch; Co-Ed, Sch P; Bkbl; HCt; Swtht; *U of Oreg; Mus.*

HALL, Lance Norman
Batavia HS; Batavia, IL; AFS; Band; Drama; Lat C; Math C; NHS; VP, Order/Arrow; Span C; Spch C; Bsbl; Wrest; Alg A; God & Country A; Hon Prog; Math A; Order/Arrow A; Spch A; St Scholar; St Lat Contest; Span Contest; *Northwestern U; Math.*

HALL, Larry
Huntington HS; Shreveport, LA; Chem C; Key C; NHS; Sci C; Ftbl; Golf; JA A; Math A; Most Out; Sci A; Ath A; Most Improved, Bowl; *Prarie View Col; Sports.*

HALL, Leirdre
Crawford HS; San Diego, CA (77-594) Chor; Community Yth Symph; Hon Prog; Type A; *St Col-SD Calif; Bus.*

HALL, Linda Jane
Dilce Combs HS; Jeff, KY (15-86) Ed, Ann; Secy, BC; Sch P; S-T, Sr Cl; Hon Prog; MLS; Most Dependable; *Southeast Comm Col; Human Services Tech.*

HALL, Linda Kay
Northwest HS; Clarksville, TN (25%-430) Church Organist; Voc Tech; *Austin Peay St U; Bus.*

HALL, Lisa Gail
Slaton HS; Slaton, TX (10%-120) Band; FFA; 4H; Bkbl; 4H A; UIL; *Tex Tech U; Dietetics.*

HALL, Lolita Francine
Stephen F Austin HS; Houston, TX; FHA; Sch P; Spch C; COM; Cl Fav; *Nurs.*

HALL, Malissa Lynn
Bartow Sr HS; Bartow, FL; Co-Cpt, Chldr; Drama; Fr C; FHA; Hmrm; NHS; Bus Mgr, Sch P; SC; Mgr, Bkbl; Mgr, Cr-Ctry; Mgr, Ftbl; Mgr, Tr; Beauty; COM; Journ A; *FSU; Pub Relations.*

HALL, Marcia Evon
HS of Music And Art; New York, NY (364-495) Tres, Chor; Ensm; Orch; Sch P; Vol Service A; Eng A's; Mus A's; *Mus.*

HALL, Margaret Ruth
York Comp HS; York, SC (1-272) Band; Fr C; Pres, FTA; InterClub Coun; NHS; A-Ed, Sch P; Co-Cpt, Bkbl; HCt; Eng A; Jr Marshal; *Appalachian St U; Dentistry.*

HALL, Mark Arden
Central HS; Springfield, MO (95-278) Band; BS; Drama; Key C; Model UN; Order/Arrow; Sci C; SC; Thes; God & Country A; JA A; Order/Arrow A; Eagle Sct; HS Dramatics Best Newcomer; HS Outst Stage Mgr; *SW Mo St U; Industrial Arts.*

HALL, Mark Joseph
Parkview HS; Springfield, MO (40-405) ARC A; *Sou Mo St U; Bus.*

HALL, Mark Randall
Calhoun HS; Calhoun, MO (1-12) Ed, Ann; Chor; Rptr, Sch P; Secy, Sr Cl; Tres, Jr Cl; Tres, Soph Cl; Mgr, Bkbl; Mgr, Tr; Alg A; Amer Leg A; Bio A; Chem A; Citz A; Cl Fav; Hist A; Hon Prog; MLS; Opt A; Regent Schol; Val; Rural Elec Cooperative Trip; *Central Mo St U; Eng.*

HALL, Martha Jean
Central Baptist HS; Hampton, VA (9-14) Cpt, Chldr; Chor; Ensm; Rptr, Sch P; Sftbl; H of F; *Special Ed.*

HALL, Mary Ellen
Newman HS; Wausau, WI; Chor; Span C; Sftbl; Tr; Marion A; HS Schol; *NCTI.*

HALL, Maurice Wayne
Huntington HS; Shreveport, LA; BC; Fr C; Var C; Golf; Cl Fav; Yth Fel; WW; Prom Court; FCA; *NW La St U; Bus Mgt.*

HALL, Melinda Sue
Cape Fear HS; Fayetteville, NC (82-390) BC; Secy, Drama; Secy, Lit Mag; Tri-HiY; COM; WW; *Fayetteville Tech Col; Office Tech.*

HALL, Melinda Sue
William Monroe HS; Stanardsville, VA; FBLA.

HALL, Michael Alan
Evans HS; Evans, GA (5%-450) BC; Chem C; Golf; COM; Gov Honor Prog; Hon Prog; MLS; Augusta Col Cert of Achv; *Ga Tech U; Computer Sci.*

HALL, Michael Lynn
Union HS; Roosevelt, UT (2-160) A-Ed, Ann; Bus C; Tres, FBLA; Ger C; NHS; Bausch & Lomb A; COM; Cl Fav; God & Country A; Hon Prog; Sal; Sci A; Type A; High HR A; Acct A; Hardest Worker A; *Brigham Young U.*

HALL, Missy Katherine Jo
St Martin HS; Biloxi, MS (13-186) BC; Chor; Drama; Drama A; Bus & Professional Women A; Most Intellectual; *U of Tulsa; Special Ed.*

HALL, Paul Reed
Ross S Sterling HS; Baytown, TX (225-561) VP, Chor; Key C; JV, Ftbl; *Lee Jr Col; Mus.*

HALL, Paula Kay
Gilmer HS; Gilmer, TX; Band; Chor; VP, FHA; FTA; Bkbl; Sftbl; Campfire Girls A; UIL Marching A; Semi-Fin, GMA Contest; *La Col; Ed.*

HALL, Regan Davis
Dallas Christian HS; Dallas, TX (11-50) A Cap Choir; Drama; Hmrm; NHS; Sci C; Span C; Spch C; SC; Var C; Bkbl; Ftbl; *Harding Col; Bio.*

HALL, Reginald Maurice
Gardena HS; Gardena, CA; Fr C; Pres, SC; Bkbl; Ftbl; Tr; JA A; Yth Fel; Ltrmans C; Black Culture C; Moe-Town Get It Together C; BAC; *Morehouse Col; Law.*

HALL, Richard Denham
McGavock HS; Nashville, TN (212-836) Hmrm; Lat C; SC; MVP, Bkbl; JV, Ftbl; Soccer; *Carson Newman Col; Recreation.*

HALL, Richard William
Groton Central HS; Groton, NY (60-98) Band; Chor; Ftbl; Yth Fel; *Fla St U; Marine Bio.*

HALL, Robert Wayne
Douglas HS; Douglas, AZ (24-250) NHS; Var C; Ftbl; JV, Tr; Alg A; Math A; *Engr.*

HALL, Roberta Carol
Ahrens HS; Louisville, KY; Hmrm; NHS; SC; Secy, Jr Cl; Type A; *Bus.*

HALL, Robyn Diane
Forest Hills HS; Jamaica, NY; Chor; Tr; Phy A; Regent Schol; Type A.

HALL, Rodricka Dupre
Glencliff HS; Nashville, TN; Hmrm; SC; Wrest; *Nashville Tech U; Commercial Art.*

HALL, Ronald Clifton
Hermitage HS; Richmond, VA (200-450) Bsbl; Bkbl; Ftbl; Sftbl; VICA; *Bluefield Col; Theology.*

HALL, Rosalind Marie
Gardena HS; Gardena, CA; Cr-Ctry; Ftbl; Sftbl; Tr; Co-Cpt, Drill Tm; Tr & Field; Phys Fitness A; Phys Fitness A; *Morehouse Col; PE Teacher.*

HALL, Sharon Delores
W End Christian Sch; Tuscaloosa, AL (2-73) BC; Sci C; Bio A; Citz A; Hist A; Outst Service, Jr Beta C Chaplin; Cert of Appreciation, Friedman Lib; Appreciation Cer, Vol Action Cntr; *UA; Med.*

HALL, Shelley Jean
Lee HS; Midland, TX; Lat C; Tr; JA A; Spch A; *Abilene Christian U; Phys Ed.*

HALL, Shirley Joann
Lane Tech HS; Chicago, IL (133-1205) Chor; *Loyola U; Bus.*

HALL, Stephen Wayne
Pasadena HS; Pasadena, TX (1-470) Tres, Fr C; InterAct C; JETS; Mu Alpha Theta; NFL; Pres, NHS; Spch C; Var C; NML; *Northwestern U; Econ.*

HALL, Steve E
Bell HS; Bell, CA; Band; Ensm; FTA; Orch; Rptr, Sch P; SC; Var C; Bkbl; Cr-Ctry; Swim; Tr; *Pepperdine U; Psych.*

HALL, Teresa Lyn
Midland HS; Midland, TX (50-500) Dbte Tm; Fr C; NHS; SC; Poet A; NHS A; *Tex Tech U; Med Lab Tech.*

HALL, Terry Lynn
Clinton HS; Clinton, MS; Bus C; Chor; FBLA; FHA; Fin, Jr Miss Pagent; Y-Tns; Mac- ette; Bicentennial Qn; 2nd, Miss Mississippi Ntl Tn; *Hinds Jr Col; Mentally Handicapped Children.*

HALL, Theatrice Lynette
Gardena HS; Gardena, CA; Secy, Chor; Hist A; *Pepperdine U; Nurs.*

HALL, Theresa Marie
Bishop Ryan HS; Minot, ND (6-92) Rptr, Ann; Band; Ensm; VP, 4H; NHS; Tr; COM; 4H A; Hon Prog; Math A; Sci A; Star Student; Outst Counselor; *U of ND; Mus.*

HALL, Thomas Murphy
Winston Churchill HS; Potomac, MD; Cr-Ctry; Tr; COM; NEDT.

HALL, Timothy Leonard
N Charleston HS; Charleston, SC; Chor; Mus A.

HALL, Tonda B
Greenup Co HS; Greenup, KY (30-260) Type A; Home Ec A; Journalism A; Attendance As; *Morehead Col; Data Processing.*

HALL, Valerie Kaye
Harding HS; Marion, OH (1-582) Chor; 4H; Span C; COM; 4H A; Sci A; Yth Fel.

HALL, Valerie Lynne
Weir Sr HS; Weirton, WV (15-400) VP, Fr C; Secy, NHS; Parl, Fr C; St Runner-Up, Bowl; *WVU; Chem.*

HALL, Vickie Yvette
Niagara Falls Sr HS; Niagara Falls, NY; VP, FBLA; SC; Bkbl; *Psych.*

HALL, Wallace Vann
George Washington HS; Danville, VA (27-569) Dbte Tm; Drama; Lit Mag; NHS; Sci C; Pres, SC; B Crocker A; Gov Honor Prog; NMF; NMS; Opt A; Tres, SC; Century III Ldrs of Tomorrow; *U of Va; Eng.*

HALL, William Elden
Warren Central HS; Indianapolis, IN (3-935) Co-Ch, Band; VP, Lat C; SC; JV, Bsbl; JV, Bkbl; Bio A; COM; Star Student; J P Sousa Band A; Hugh O'Brian Yth A; *Purdue U; Med.*

HALL, Yvette Aline
Dayton Fairview HS; Dayton, OH; Chldr; Hmrm; Y-Tns; *Iowa U; Pre-Law.*

HALLAM, Cheryl Ann
Macon HS; Macon, IL (3-58) Band; BC; FHA; 4H; NHS; Span C; SC; *Ill St U; Acct.*

HALLBERG, Charles John III
Memphis Prep Sch; Memphis, TN (20-100) Bus C; Chess C; Math A; NEDT; *U of Miss; Acct.*

HALLBERG, Kathryn Louise
Charles F Brush HS; Lyndhurst, OH; Tres, AFS; Alg A; COM; *Occupational Therapy.*

HALLBLADE, Gaylene Joy
Thomas Jefferson Sr HS; Bloomington, MN (20%-748) Fin, GS; Hmrm; NHS; ARC; Sftbl; Cpt, Swim; Tnns; Tr; COM; NMF; NMS; ARC A; Gym; 1st, 2nd, Region Swim; Candystriper; St Swim; St Quiz; *U of Minn; Med.*

HALLCROFT, Lori Rae
Memorial HS; Tulsa, OK (250-500) Span C; JA A; Explorers; Pres, JA Bank; *Okla St U; Acct.*

HALLELAND, Linda Jean
S Hamilton HS; Jewell, IA; Ann; Band; Chor; SC; Bkbl; Tr; IA Yth Art Mo; *Secy.*

HALLEMAN, Sherry Lynn
Cedarburg HS; Cedarburg, WI (138-365) FHA; Ger C; 4H; Ski C; JV, Tr; 4H A; *U of Wis; Med.*

HALLENBECK, Melody Sue
Rome Free Acad; Rome, NY (50%-867) Upstate NY Nazarene Tn; Girls Sportsmanship A; Jr NHS; *Alfred St U; Nurs.*

HALLER, Charles Ellsworth Jr
Baltimore Lutheran HS; Baltimore, MD (5-67) F-Ed, Ann; Chor; Drama; Fr C; Ger C; NHS; Ch, ARC; Ed, Sch P; NMS; Civitan Essay; *Johns Hopkins U; Writing.*

HALLER, Pamela Sue
Limestone Comm HS; Bartonville, IL; Bus C; COM; Yth Fel; Pep C; *Ill Central Col; Bus.*

HALLETT, Debra Sue
Charlotte HS; Charlotte, MI (10-303) Band; Ensm; NHS; Orch; Ski C; Fin, SC; Secy, Jr Cl; Fin, Soph Cl; Hon Prog; Math A; Co-Cpt, Secy, GSct; Cadette St; Ch, Prom Committee; Job's Daughters; Pres, Chrch Yth Fl; Prof & 1st Div, St Solo & Ensm; *Olivet Col; Bus Adm.*

HALLFORD, Cathy Renee
John Jay HS; San Antonio, TX (126-639) VP, Church Yth Choir; Church Sftbl; Sunday Sch Teacher; Lifeline C; *US Air Force Reserves; Med Tech.*

HALLIBURTON, Lawrence Gray Jr
Maplewood HS; Nashville, TN (5-420) Co-Ed, Ann; Dbte Tm; Drama; NFL; NHS; ARC; Alg A; COM; Citz A; Hon Prog; Math A; MLS; Spch A; 1st Pl, Forensics; Stu Congress; *Vanderbilt U; Med.*

HALLINAN, James Francis
Oakville Sr HS; St Louis, MO (136-430) CYO; Drama; MVP, Ftbl; Co-Cpt, Golf; Wrest; Outst Stu, Ind Arts; Thespian Troupe; MIP, Golf; *Southeast Mo St U; Ind Arts Ed.*

HALLISEY, William Lane
29 Palms HS; Twenty Nine Palms, CA (2-180) F-Ed, Ann; CYO; Hmrm; NHS; ARC; Span C; SC; Var C; Ch, Y-Tns; Pres, Soph Cl; JV, Ftbl; Co-Cpt, Swim; Alg A; COM; Citz A; Hist A; Hon Prog; Math A; Rotary A; Type A; MVP, Cpt, Golf; *Stanford U; Law.*

HALLMAN, Maxine Angela
Dwight D Eisenhower HS; Washington Township, MI (153-593) Pres, CYO; Chor; Commercial C; Ger C; Fin, GS; Ntl Yth Conf; ARC; Secy, Sch P; Bkbl; JV, Sftbl; COM; Citz A; Hon Prog; Secy, CYF; Ath A's & V Ltr; *Macomb Co Comm Col; Nurs.*

HALLMAN, Thomas Ross
Homewood HS; Homewood, AL (30-200) Band; Key C; Mu Alpha Theta; Order/Arrow; Span C; God & Country A; Order/Arrow A; Eagle Sct; *Auburn U; Archt.*

HALLMARK, Ricky Glenn
Loraine I S D HS; Loraine, TX; Band; FFA; Ftbl; Tnns.

HALLOCK, Judith Ann
N Pocono HS; Moscow, PA (104-231) 4H; Ski C; SC; 4H A; *Bus.*

HALLOWELL, Lorraine Jo
Mound Westonka HS; Mound, MN (3-300) Chldr; Chor; Tres, Ski C; Span C; SC; Tres, Soph Cl; Golf; Pres A.

HALLQUIST, Christine LaVerne
Springfield S HS; Springfield, OH; Chor; Ensm; Hmrm; COM; Hon Prog; St & Chevron A; *Wittenberg U; Math.*

HALLS, Mark Stephen
Chaney HS; Youngstown, OH (135-389) VP, Band; Mus A; C-Pin Academic Merit; *Westminster Col; Mus.*

HALLUM, Vicki Joyce
Glendale HS; Springfield, MO; AFS; F-Ed, Sch P; Span C; SC; JV, Swim; Journ A; *William Jewell Col; Pre-Law.*

HALLY, Frankie Lee
Norte Del Rio HS; Sacramento, CA; *Air Force Acad; Engr.*

HALONE, Beth Ann
Evergreen HS; Vancouver, WA (6-340) AFS; Band; Drama; FHA; 4H; Pres, NHS; SC; DARGCA; 4H A; Hon Prog; Yth Fel; Col School; *Chase Bus Col; Legal Secy.*

HALOUSKA, Sandra Sue
Columbus HS; Columbus, GA (10%-360) NHS; COM; Yth Fel; JA; Allied Med Careers; Tres, Lib C; Fine Arts C; *Wesleyan Col; Amer Stu.*

HALPHEN, Robert Pierre
Catholic HS; New Iberia, LA (2-43) F-Ed, Ann; CYO; Chor; Fin, Lit Ral; VP, Math C; Mu Alpha Theta; Secy, NHS; ARC; SC; Tnns; Hon Prog; Sal; Sci A; Spch A; *U of SW La; Acct.*

HALPIN, Margaret English
Rosarian Acad; W Palm Beach, FL; All Amer Yth; CYO; Chldr; Chor; Drama; Mgr, Hmrm; Spch C; Var C; Bkbl; Sftbl; Swim; Tnns; Tr; COM; Citz A; Hon Prog; Pres A; Star Student; Yth Fel; Private Schol; PA A; Service to Sch A; *U of Conn; Phys Therapy.*

HALSALL, Betty Jane
Alexander Galt Regional HS; Lennoxville, CANADA (13-477) Chor; Pres, 4H; Hmrm; Pres, ARC; SC; Soccer; Hon Prog; MVP, Vlbl.

HALSELL, Keith Lamar
Waynesboro Central HS; Waynesboro, MS (25%-130).

HALSTEAD, Robert Thomas
Scott HS; Madison, WV; Chor; InterAct C; S-T, Var C; Mgr, Bsbl; Mgr, Bkbl; Mgr, Ftbl; Bio A; Cl Fav; Yth Fel; *W Va Inst of Tech; Industrial Arts Ed.*

HALT, David John
Woodrow Wilson HS; Youngstown, OH (51-368) Band; Chess C; Secy, Key C; Pres, Lat C; Orch; Order/Arrow; Rptr, Sch P; Pres, Sr Cl; Ftbl; JA A; VP, Yth Fel; Eagle Sct; *Ohio U; Bus Adm.*

HALTER, Eric David
Thomas Stone HS; Waldorf, MD (20-400) Tres, NHS; MVP, Soccer; Tr; Cpt, Soccer; Ath As; Varsity As; Publication Citations; Merit Scholastic A; Cert of A; Fishing in Md A; *Salisbury St Col; Engr.*

HALTERMAN, Robin Dee
Christian HS; Hopkinsville, KY; Bus C; FBLA; Pres, Hmrm; Mgr, Ftbl; Golf; *Stenography.*

HALTHON, Oliver Bidwell
Pascagoula HS; Pascagoula, MS; Band; Swim; *Jackson Co Jr Col; Industrial Arts.*

HALTHON, Ollie Mary
Pascagoula HS; Pascagoula, MS; Band; GS; Swim; Tr; *Jackson Co Jr Col; Bus Ed.*

HALVERSON, Diane Lee
Ondossagon HS; Ashland, WI (8-58) Band; Chor; FHA; Pres, 4H; Spch C; MVP, Bsbl; MVP, Bkbl; 4H A; Spch A; PA; *Law Enforcement.*

HALVERSON, Peggy Rae
Linn-Mar HS; Marion, IA (50-230) Band; Drama; Golf; 4H A; Hospital Vol; Ch, Vol Board; *St Lukes Sch of Nurs; Pediatric Nurs.*

HALVERSTADT, Adrian Lee
Leetonia HS; Leetonia, OH (50-100) Bsbl; Ftbl; Sftbl; Tr; *Fort Wayne Bible Col; Sociology.*

HAM, Leah Anne
Raytown S HS; Raytown, MO (33%-600) A Cap Choir; Ann; Chor; Drama; Orch; Mgr, Bkbl; Amer Leg A; Citz A; Vlbl; *Central Mo St U; Counselor.*

HAM, Terri Margaret
Sutton Pub HS; Sutton, NE (3-54) Band; Tres, Jr Cl; Secy, Soph Cl; HQn; HCt; Yth Fel; Top 10%; Cpt, Vlbl; Pep C; Phys Fitness As; *Bus Adm.*

HAMANN, Carlton Marvin
Pflugerville HS; Pflugerville, TX (6-76) VP, Band; Ensm; Secy, FFA; Pres, 4H; Math C; NHS; VP, Sr Cl; Mgr, Bkbl; Ftbl; COM; Citz A; 4H A; Hon Prog; I Dare You; Math A; Yth Fel; 4-H Gold Star Boy; All District Band; Sweepstakes Band; Band Favorite; 2nd High, District Land Judging; *Tarleton St U; Agr Engr.*

HAMASAKI, Sara Akemi
Laupahoehoe HS; Laupahoehoe, HI (4-39) Tres, NHS; Cr-Ctry; *Hawaii Comm Col; Secy Sci.*

HAMAY, Cynthia
Bentworth Sr HS; Bentleyville, PA (7-162) F-Ed, Ann; Drama; FNA; NHS; Thes; Var C; Co-Cpt, Bkbl; Sftbl; DARGCA; Sci A; Drum Mjrte; NHS, Yrbk, A's; Most Ath; *Wash Hospital Sch of Nurs; Nurs.*

HAMBERG, Charles Douglas
Southwick HS; Southwick, MA (32-178) A Cap Choir; Band; Ensm; Hmrm; Orch; Spch C; Hockey; COM; John Philip Sousa Mus A; Pres, Dance Band; Part Time Job; *Western New England Col; Bio.*

HAMBRICK, Donald Ray
Ne HS; Springfield, OH (70-300) NHS; VP, Span C; Span NHS; Tres, Var C; Bsbl; Bkbl; MVP, Ftbl; Sftbl; Tr; Wrest; Prom Court; *U of Dayton; Ed.*

HAMBRIGHT, James Douglas
Shelby HS; Shelby, NC (65-340) Drama; Fr C; Phys Ed A; Mus Cert of Merit; *U of SC; Psych.*

HAMEL, Leona Dorene
Alexander Galt Regional HS; Lennoxville, CANADA (7-477) Ger C; Pax; Ger A; HR; *Nurs.*

HAMEL, Nadine Marie
Saint Lucys Priory HS; Glendora, CA; CYO; Chldr; Chor; Hmrm; CSF; COM; Citz A; Teen Hospital Vol; Convalescent Home Vol; Church Stu Coun; *Med.*

HAMEL, Patty Kay
Napoleon HS; Napoleon, ND (5-73) Band; Chor; FHA; GS; NHS; Co-Ed, Sch P; Co-Cpt, Bkbl; Tr; Star Student; Yth Fel; Co-Cpt, Gym; *Mary Col; Nurs.*

HAMER, Mark Evan
Belvidere Sr HS; Belvidere, IL (4-470) A Cap Choir; Band; Ensm; SC; Cpt; Cr-Ctry; Tr; Amer Leg A; COM; DARGCA; God & Country A; Hon Prog; Yth Fel; *U of Ill; Sci.*

HAMERNIK, Julie Kay
Ulen-Hitterdal HS; Ulen, MN (5-31) Band; Chldr; Chor; Dbte Tm; Ensm; VP; 4H; Orch; Bkbl; Sftbl; Tr; Wrest; COM; 4H A; Hon Prog; Math A; Pres A; Spch A; Type A; Vlbl.

HAMILTON, Angela Janeal
Lookeba-Sickles HS; Lookeba, OK; Ann; Chor; Pres, FHA; Pres, 4H; Sci C; Pres, SC; Bkbl; Tr; Amer Leg A; Citz A; Cl Fav; 4H A; I Dare You; Most Out; Spch A; Outst FHA Homemaker o-t Yr; HR; Outst 4-Her; HS Hon Soc; Superintendents; *S Western Okla St U; Home Ec.*

HAMILTON, Anne Elizabeth
Charlottesville HS; Charlottesville, VA; Band; Chor; FBLA; Hmrm; Lat C; NHS; Qn, Acteens; Yth Corps; Cpt, Drill Tm; Handbell Choir; Pres, Yth Coun; *SODA.*

HAMILTON, Brenda Carol
T L Weston HS; Greenville, MS (27-700) Hmrm; Lat C; Tnns; COM; *U of Miss; X-Ray Tech.*

HAMILTON, Brenda Irene
Harrisonville Sr HS; Harrisonville, MO (25-178) Ann; Band; Rptr; FHA; NHS; VP, Span C; COM; Journ A; Regent Schol; Type A; Freedom Forum; Girl o-t Mo; *UMKC; Acct.*

HAMILTON, Catherine Ann
Cleveland HS; Reseda, CA (48-585) F-Ed, Ann; FNA; Hmrm; ARC; Pres, SC; Pres, Var C; Bkbl; Cpt, Tr; Hon Prog; Most Out; Spch A; City Ephebian Soc; Sports A's; Church Bible Study & Yth Groups; City Semi-Fin & Quarter Fin, Tr; Vlbl; Mgr, Wheelchair Bkbl; *Calif St U; Special Ed.*

HAMILTON, Cathy Bea
Florence Twp Mem HS; Florence, NJ (3-120) Chem C; Chor; Tres, FTA; GS; Math C; NHS; Span NHS; Var C; Tres, Jr Cl; Hockey; Sftbl; Citz A; Hist A; Math A; Schol A; *Drew U; Math.*

HAMILTON, Denise Marie
Proviso E HS; Maywood, IL (29-1238) Chldr; Chor; Hmrm; SC; Amer Leg A; Kiwanis A; *Ill St U; Bus Ed.*

HAMILTON, Glenda Marie
Harrisonville Sr HS; Harrisonville, MO (6-178) Ed, Ann; Band; FHA; NHS; Sci C; Span C; COM; Journ A; Math A; Regent Schol; Sci A; Mo Freedom Forum; Girl o-t Mo; Q & S; *U of Mo; Dental Hygiene.*

**HAMILTON,
Gwendolyn Juanita**
Theodore Roosevelt HS; Bronx, NY (251-719) Chor; Hmrm; Up Bound; Bkbl; Swim; Type A; *Specialized Ed.*

HAMILTON, Herbert S
Mayfield HS; Las Cruces, NM; Ann; Sch P; SC; VP, Soph Cl; Tnns; Tr; Cl Fav; Most Out; Spch A; Win, Talent Show; *NMSU; Journ.*

HAMILTON, Ian Neil
McCallie HS; Chattanooga, TN (54-111) Ftbl.

HAMILTON, Irene May
N Kitsap HS; Poulsbo, WA (12-250) Chldr; Chor; Hmrm; NHS; Pres, Rainbow; Ski C; SC; Mgr, Wrest; VofDEM; Demolay Swtht; Sen Page; *U of Wash; Eng.*

HAMILTON, Janet Ellen
Cambridge Acad; Greenwood, SC; Co-Cpt, Chldr; Drama; HCt; Typist, Ann; *Piedmont Tech & Lander Col; Human Services.*

HAMILTON, Janet Lee
Wauconda HS; Wauconda, IL; FHA; 4H; NHS; Ntl Yth Conf; St Sword Drill; *Don Roberts Beauty; Cosmetology.*

HAMILTON, Janet Lynne
Wetumpka HS; Wetumpka, AL; JV, Chldr; Drama; Ensm; VP, FHA; Sch P; Span C; Yth Fel; DECA Competition A; *Auburn U; Interior Decorator.*

HAMILTON, Jeanette
Community HS; Houston, TX (10%-98) VP, Hmrm; SC; Type A; *Pre-Med.*

HAMILTON, Jeffrey Howard
Palestine HS; Palestine, TX (40-235) A Cap Choir; Arch; Chess C; Chor; FFA; Span C; Arch; JV, Bsbl; Bkbl; Sftbl; Tnns; Tr; Grass Judging A; Bible Memory A; *Howard Payne Col; Religion.*

HAMILTON, Jerome Henry
E Alton-Wood River Comm HS; Wood River, IL (32-305) Band; MVP, Ftbl; *Mo Inst of Tech; Elec Engr.*

HAMILTON, Jo Nell
Milburn HS; Milburn, OK (2-20) 4H; SC; VP, Jr Cl; Bkbl; Citz A; 4H A; HQn; Sal; Yth Fel; Yth Foundation A; Best Personality; *Aviation.*

HAMILTON, Joy Anna
Western Alamance HS; Elon College, NC (27-250) Band; Drama; FHA; FTA; NHS; F-Ed, Sch P; Journ A; Yth Fel; All St, Band; *Catawba Col; Social Work.*

HAMILTON, Julia Marie
Bedford Comm HS; Bedford, IA (4-70) AFS; Band; VP, Drama; NHS; Span C; SC; Y-Tns; *U of Nebr Sch of Tech Agr; Vet Technology.*

**HAMILTON,
Katherine Elizabeth**
William Byrd HS; Vinton, VA (56-280) AFS; Chor; Drama; Fr C; Hmrm; *Randolph-Macon Col; Phar.*

HAMILTON, Kathleen Elizabeth
Tuscarawas Central Cath HS; New Philadelphia, OH (25-52) Drama; NHS; Tres, Jr Cl; Mgr, Bkbl; Alg A; COM; Math A; Ch, Prom Committee; Religion A; Pres, Y Yth Ldrs; Art A; JV Vlbl; Sch Spirit A; *Phys Ed.*

HAMILTON, Kathleen Marie
Civic Mem HS; Bethalto, IL (5%-258) Band; Ensm; JA A; Accompanist, Double Sextet; Bowling Sporthead, GAA; *SIU-Edwardsville; Mus.*

HAMILTON, Kenneth Gerald
Sheridan HS; Sheridan, OR; Rptr, Sch P; Spch C; Var C; VP, Soph Cl; JV, Ftbl; Tr; Wrest; Hon Prog; May Day Prince; *Lane Comm Col; Aviation.*

HAMILTON, Laurel Joanne
S Hadley HS; South Hadley, MA (6-301) Band; Secy, Ger C; Hmrm; Ch, NHS; Pres, Rainbow; COM; S-T, Pilgrim Fel; Rainbow Girls A's; Christian Ed Committee; Church Sch Teacher; Church Choir; *Mount Holyoke Col; Fr.*

HAMILTON, Leon Antonio
Biloxi Sr HS; Biloxi, MS (20%-500) Co-Cpt, Ann; BS; Chem C; Chess C; Chor; Dbte Tm; Fr C; Math C; Order/Arrow; Sci C; Spch C; Var C; Bsbl; Bkbl; Cpt, Ftbl; Cpt, Swim; Tnns; Tr; Wrest; Alg A; Balfour A; COM; Delta Sigma Theta A; Hist A; Math A; Order/Arrow A; Pres A; Type A; Best Dressed; St BTU Congress; Hist, Dist BTU & Ss Congress; *Wash U; Med.*

HAMILTON, Linda Kay
Charles Henderson HS; Troy, AL (20-145) Band; BC; Dbte Tm; NFL; NHS; Rptr, Sch P; Span C; Amer Leg A; Amer Leg Orator A; MLS; Q&S A; ROTC A; Spch A; Mus A; *Troy St U; Bus.*

HAMILTON, Lisa Gaye
Buckingham Co HS; Buckingham, VA (36-225) BC; 4H; SC; Secy, Art C.

HAMILTON, Lisha Faye
Grace Baptist HS; Decatur, AL (5%-26) NHS; Sch P; COM; Hist A.

HAMILTON, Lori Lynn
Cleveland HS; Cleveland, OK; HQn.

HAMILTON, Mark Lee
Milburn HS; Milburn, OK (1-23) 4H; Lit Mag; NHS; MVP, Bkbl; Alg A; 4H A; Hist A; Hon Prog; Math A; Most Out; Sci A; Yth Fel; Reading, Lang Arts, A's; *Ath.*

HAMILTON, Mary Helen
Warrior Acad; Eutaw, AL (4-26) Bus Mgr, Ann; BC; Math C; NHS; SC; Tres, Sr Cl; Tres, Jr Cl; Bio A; Chem A; Hon Prog; Sci A; WW; *U of Ala; Med Tech.*

HAMILTON, Mary Kathryn
San Diego HS; San Diego, CA (10%-431) A Cap Choir; Drama; Madrigal; NHS; Sch Achieve Tm; SC; Tnns; CSF; COM; Yth Fel; Gym Tm; Madrigal A; Piano Schol; Most Talented; Drama C; Local Talent Win; Cappella Chor, Madrigal Accompanist; *Point Loma Col; Pre-Med.*

HAMILTON, Mary Lisa
Canyon HS; Anaheim, CA (216-514) Chldr; Ski C; Span C; Bkbl; JV, Hockey; Sftbl; Cpt, Vlbl; *George Fox Col; Law.*

HAMILTON, Mickey Ray
E Alton-Wood River Comm HS; Wood River, IL; Band; Tr; *Lewis & Clark Comm Col; Drafting.*

HAMILTON, Nancy Ellen
Monterey HS; Monterey, CA; Band; Community Yth Symph; Rainbow; Tr; CSF.

HAMILTON, Pamela Ann
Crawford R-II HS; Cuba, MO (4-75) Chor; Ensm; FHA; Pres, FTA; Rainbow; Secy, SC; Var C; Mgr, Sftbl; Tr; HQn; Opt A; President's Phys Fitness A; Historian, NHS; Grand Cr of Color; Drill Tm; *US Air Force; Inventory Mgt.*

HAMILTON, Patricia Ann
Sou Normal HS; Brewton, AL (3-30) Band; FTA; 4H; Rptr, Hmrm; NHS; Up Bound; Bkbl; Sftbl; Alg A; HCt; Math A; Eng, Phys Ed, A's; Outst Hon; *Computer Sci.*

HAMILTON, Regina Ann
Union HS; Leslie, GA (2-63) Pres, SC; Pres, Jr Cl; COM.

HAMILTON, Renee Carmen
La Crosse HS; La Crosse, KS (2-50) Pres, Band; Tres, CYO; Secy, Chor; Dbte Tm; Drama; VP, Fr C; VP, FHA; Mjrte; NFL; Spch C; St Stu Congress; Bus Mgr, SC; Pres, Jr Cl; Secy, Tr; Lion A; Spch A; St Scholar; Type A; VofDEM; Secy, FHA; WW; *Colo Women's Col; Mus.*

HAMILTON, Richard Clark
Summit HS; Summit, NJ (151-361) Sunday Sch Teacher; VP, Church Yth Fel; Church Property Committee; Vol, Child Care Center; *Lebanon Valley Col; Religion.*

HAMILTON, Richard Joe
Cedar Bluff HS; Cedar Bluff, AL; BC; Pres, Math C; A-Ed, Sch P; Cpt, Jr Cl; Ftbl; Sftbl; Tnns; Tr; *Auburn U.*

HAMILTON, Richard Warren
Thornapple Kellogg HS; Middleville, MI (10-170) Band; 4H; Span C; Tnns; COM; *Mich St U; Chem Engr.*

HAMILTON, Rickey Earl
Coronado HS; Lubbock, TX (25%-635) Fr C; Sci C; *LIFE Bible Col; Christian Theology.*

HAMILTON, Robin Louise
Crittenden Co HS; Marion, KY (3-150) VP, BC; Pres, FHA; Secy, GS; Hmrm; VP, SC; Alg A; Amer Leg A; Beauty; Yth Fel; Eng A; Page, Ky Gen Assm; Ky Colonel; Drill Corps; *Dance.*

HAMILTON, Sally Ann
Belle Plaine HS; Belle Plaine, KS (8-65) Chldr; Chor; SC; Tr; Vlbl.

HAMILTON, Sandra Lynn
Hopewell HS; Aliquippa, PA; Ann; Chor; Lat C; Alg A; *Nyack Col; Mus.*

HAMILTON, Shari Lynn
Harrison HS; Harrison, NY (68-285) Mgr, Band; Chor; Bkbl; Tr; Cpt, Color Guard; Vlbl; *Daytona Comm Col; Mental Health Tech.*

HAMILTON, Sharon Jane
Gulf Comprehensive HS; New Port Richey, FL; HR; Campus Life; Yth Choir; 2nd Pl, Essay Contest; Flag Core; Gym C; Asst Dance Teacher; Yth Coun; *Dance.*

HAMILTON, Sheila Ann
F O Alexander HS; Starkville, MS (3-28) Miss St U; Bus.

HAMILTON, Stephen Douglas
Parkview HS; Orfordville, WI (13-158) A Cap Choir; Band; Chor; Sftbl; 4H A; Sgt at Arms, 4-H C; 4-H Co A; Band A; Platteville Col; Broadcasting.

HAMILTON, Susan J
Belle Plaine HS; Belle Plaine, KS (3-75) Ann; S-T, Fr C; St Scholar; St Hon Stu; U of Kans; Biol.

HAMILTON, Tara Elaine
Alameda HS; Alameda, CA (11-379) Fr C; CSF; JA A; Law.

HAMILTON, Teresa Renee
La Porte HS; La Porte, TX (1-384) InterAct C; Model UN; Thes; Hon Prog; Math A; Yth Fel; GSct; U of Tex; Med.

HAMILTON, Terry Hwang
Hobart Sr HS; Hobart, IN (1-400) BS; VP, Fr C; VP, NHS; SC; VP, Sr Cl; Bsbl; JV, Ftbl; Co-Cpt, Wrest; Amer Leg A; Pres A; Val; Purdue U; Civil Engr.

HAMILTON, Terry Wayne
Ahrens HS; Louisville, KY; NHS; Chem.

HAMILTON, Theresa Ann
Fort Pierce Central HS; Fort Pierce, FL; BC; 4H; NHS; Citz A; 4H A; Type A; Interntl Lib of Piano Mus; PA; Sou U of Tampa; Med.

HAMILTON, Virginia Ann
Groveton HS; Groveton, TX (5-53) Band; BC; Drama; FHA; Mjrte; JV, Bkbl; Sftbl; Tr; 4H A; Spch A; Co Del, 4-H C; 4-H Gold Star Girl; WW; FHA Choir; Halloween Qn; Tex A&M U.

HAMLETT, Jeff Lee
Kenston Forest HS; Blackstone, VA (22-35) A-Ed, Ann; Chor; Dbte Tm; Drama; Fr C; NFL; Sch P; Spch C; Mgr, Ftbl; Golf; Tnns; Southside Va Comm Col; Elec Tech.

HAMLETT, Susan
Buffalo Seminary; Buffalo, NY; Drama; Fr C; Hmrm; Ski C; SC; Hockey; Soccer; 1st Cl GSct; Challenge of Promise & Law.

HAMLEY, Lorri Diann
Tioga Center Christian HS; Tioga Center, NY (3-5) Bkbl; Yrbk Comm; Baptist Bible Col.

HAMLIN, David Clifford
Hoover HS; N Canton, OH (195-420) Band; Orch; Tnns; Wrest; Yth Fel; Band A; Tnns A; Wrest A; U of Akron; Acct.

HAMLIN, Janet Lynn
Denbigh HS; Newport News, VA (37-488) Ger C; Mu Alpha Theta; NHS; Rptr; SC; Hockey; Sftbl; Alt, GS; Nurs.

HAMM, Larry Elbert
Lansing Baptist Sch; Lansing, MI (4-8) Band; JV, Bkbl; Soccer.

HAMM, Lisa Marie
Centennial HS; Gresham, OR (162-500) AFS; Rptr, Ann; Rptr, Sch P; SC; Stu Senate Rep; Cert of Appreciation, Elks C; MHCC; Hist.

HAMMACK, Marie Inez
Mtn Brook HS; Mtn Brook, AL; Chess C; Chor; Fr C; ARC; Samford U.

HAMMACK, Susan Blake
Calhoun Co HS; Edison, GA (35%-150) Band; Chor; Drama; FBLA; FTA; 4H; Thes; Var C; Tnns; Tnns Letter; Auburn U; Drama.

HAMMAR, Linda Susan
Rio Mesa HS; Camarillo, CA; Band; Ch, Hmrm; SC; JV, Tr; CSF; Phys Therapy.

HAMMER, Anne Christine
Tartan Sr HS; St Paul, MN; Band; Drama; ARC; Sftbl; Swim; Swim Instructor; Gym.

HAMMER, Kolette Kay
Durand HS; Durand, WI (25%-150) Dbte Tm; S-T, Drama; NFL; Pres, NHS; Sodality; Spch A; Pope Pius XII Medal; Gen Ch, Prom; Viterbo Col; Ed.

HAMMER, Leta Jo
Denison Sr HS; Denison, TX (28-365) Drama; Fr C; NHS; Spch C; Thes; Tr; Hon Prog; Oral Roberts U; Foreign Lang.

HAMMER, Rhonda Louise
Alfred B Maclay HS; Tallahassee, FL (3-22) Anchor C; Chldr; Drama; Span NHS; Sftbl; Hon Prog.

HAMMER, Robin Deniese
Big Sandy HS; Big Sandy, TX (2-50) Rptr; Band; Cpt, Chldr; Ensm; NHS; Sch P; Cpt, Bkbl; Tr; Fin, Talent Contest; Ambassador Col; Eng.

HAMMERBERG, Tamara Maxine
Pacific HS; Langlois, OR (18-45) Ann; Band; FHA; 4H; Bkbl; Tr; Vlbl; U of Oreg; Nurs.

HAMMERMILLER, Carl Ray
Brazos HS; Wallis, TX (25%-39) FFA; Cpt, Ftbl; Sftbl; Mgr, Tr; Lincoln Tech Inst; Automotive Tech.

HAMMERSTROM, James Hart
Mercer Island Sr HS; Mercer Island, WA; Ger C; Order/Arrow; Tr; Wrest; Order/Arrow A; Ski; HR; Moutaineering; Co Champ, Wrest; MIP, Wrest; Sci.

HAMMETT, Eugenia Maye
Santa Rosa HS; Santa Rosa, TX (25%-35) Band; FHA; FTA; NHS; Pres, Sci C; Secy, SC; Bio A; Hon Prog; Ntl Sci Found; Sci A; Rio Grande Valley Mus Hon Soc; Candy Striper; Baylor U; Pre-Med.

HAMMETT, Leisa Ann
Riverside HS; Greer, SC (30-214) Chor; Fr C; VP, Hmrm; Co-Ed, Lit Mag; Rptr, Sch P; Tnns; Art A; Artist, Newspaper & Yrbk; 1st Pl, Essay Contest; U of SC; Art.

HAMMETT, Marcia Ellen
Travelers Rest HS; Travelers Rest, SC (2%-273) Chor; Community Yth Symph; Pres, Hmrm; Mod Mus Mas; VP, NHS; Orch; COM; Gov Honor Prog; Hist A; Hon Prog; NMS; Swtht; Span A; Furman U; Chem.

HAMMETT, Mary Lou
Gettys D Broome HS; Spartanburg, SC (10%-200) Chor; Ensm; Fr C; Span C; Hon Prog; Fr A; N Greenville Jr Col; Elem Ed.

HAMMETT, Randolph Scott Jr
Gaffney Sr HS; Gaffney, SC (25%-450) BC; Sci C; Span C; JV, Bkbl; Golf; Citz A; Jr C Champion, Golf; U of Ala; Engr.

HAMMOCK, Latonya
Jonesboro-Hodge HS; Jonesboro, LA (25-128) Bus C; Chor; 4H; Jr Cl.

HAMMOND, Chris Aaron
Oak Hill HS; Oakhill, OH; Band; Sch P; Sci C; Sci A; Spirit C; Rio Grande Col.

HAMMOND, Edith Maude
Tehachapi HS; Tehachapi, CA (7-128) AFS; GS; Semi-Fin, Jr Miss Pa; Bank Of Amer A; B Crocker A; CSF; Yth Fel; UCLA; Med.

HAMMOND, Edith Van Keuren
N Fulton HS; Atlanta, GA (7-180) Band; BC; Pres, Fr C; InterClub Coun; Model UN; NHS; Secy, SC; COM; DARGCA; H of F; Exchange C Yth o-t Mo; Cpt, Drill Tm; Davidson Col; Pol Sci.

HAMMOND, Emma Frances
Seward Park HS; New York, NY; Math A; ARC A; Yth Fel; Math; Home Ec A; Eng A; LIU; Acct.

HAMMOND, Frances Ann
Spencer Pub HS; Spencer, WI (18-59) Secy, Drama; Ed, Sch P; Beauty; Journ A; Masque & Gavel A; Q&S A; Bauble A; Cl Spkr at Graduation; U of Wis; Bus.

HAMMOND, Gary Edward
Greencastle HS; Greencastle, IN (53-187) Chor; Drama; Fr C; 4H; Key C; ARC; Spch C; Thes; Swim; Franklin Col; Bio.

HAMMOND, George Arthur
Brooten-Pub HS; Brooten, MN;

HAMMOND, Jeffery Lee
Abilene HS; Abilene, TX; Band; Ger C; Order/Arrow; Air Force Acad.

HAMMOND, John Joseph
New Hope-Solebury HS; New Hope, PA; Bsbl; Bkbl; Soccer; NEDT; Attendance A; Sci.

HAMMOND, Kelly Marie
Leaf River HS; Leaf River, IL; Band; Chor; Yth Fel.

HAMMOND, Kimberley Gail
Plainfield Jr-Sr HS; Plainfield, IN (23-290) Chor; FHA; Fin, Jr Miss Pagent; NHS; Ed, Sch P; SC; Tres, Sr Cl; Sftbl; Mgr, Swim; Tnns; Mgr, Tr; Elk A; Hon Prog; Ball St U; Special Ed.

HAMMOND, Lisa Mary
Weedsport Central HS; Weedsport, NY (43-105) Chor; Fr C; FHA; Yth Fel; PA.

HAMMOND, Rebecca Eileen
Springwoods Sr HS; Houston, TX; Band; Chor; JETS; Math C; Mu Alpha Theta; Span C; Hon Prog; Eng A; Texas A&M U; Marine Bio.

HAMMOND, Remie Oliver Jr
Stranahan HS; Ft Lauderdale, FL (10%-480) Band; Chor; ARC; Cpt, Bsbl; Cpt, Ftbl; Sftbl; Bank Of Amer A; Cl Fav; Yth Fel; VP A; Broward Comm Col; Acct.

HAMMOND, Retha Mae
Seward Park HS; New York, NY (770-1148) Band; Chldr; Chor; Orch; ARC; Bsbl; Bkbl; Swim; Tnns; Tr; Citz A; Math A; ARC A; Sci A; Type A; Yth Fel; Home Ec, Art, Gym, Attendence, A's; NY City U; Sci.

HAMMOND, Schanetta Denee
Notre Dame HS; San Jose, CA; Band; Chldr; NHS; Ed, Sch P; SC; MVP, Swim; MVP, Tr; De Anza Col; Acct.

HAMMOND, Sharon Kay
Columbia Acad; Columbia, MS (11-57) Ann; Drama; FHA; Sci C; Bkbl; U of Sou Miss; Lab Tech.

HAMMOND, William Brian
Landmark Christian HS; Cincinnati, OH (3-36) Chor; Rptr, Sch P; Liberty Baptist Col; Pol Sci.

HAMMONDS, Billy Mark
Broadmoor HS; Baton Rouge, LA (33%-450) Band; Ensm; Span C; Tr; Hon Prog; St Fin, Dodge, Driver's Excellence; Industrial Arts C; Puppetteer; LSU; Dentistry.

HAMMONDS, David Lee
Essex Co Voc-Tech HS; Newark, NJ (10%-69) SC; Var C; Bkbl; Citz A; HR; Bkbl Ltrman; Stu Faculty; Lyons Inst; Elec.

HAMMONDS, Thomas Anton
Regular Baptist HS; Martinez, CA (10-63) Band; Chor; Ensm; Span C; Bsbl; Co-Cpt, Bkbl; Soccer; Citz A; Hon Stu; LA Baptist Col; Teacher Ed.

HAMMONDS, Vanessa Gail
George Washington Carver Sr HS; Houston, TX (10%-229) FHA; Mjrte; Pres, Soph Cl; Bkbl; Sftbl; Tr; Bio A; PA; Homemaking A; Computer Programming.

HAMMONS, James Edward Jr
Crockett HS; Crockett, TX (9-120) Band; Pres, Bus C; NHS; Bio A; Hon Prog; Phy A; Tex St Tech Inst; Nuclear Sci.

HAMNER, Mary Claire
Jesse O Sanderson HS; Raleigh, NC; Drama; Fr C.

HAMPE, Anne Maria
Algonac HS; Algonac, MI (75-310) Mjrte; Type A; FOE C; MSBA School; NHS School; Mt Clemens Bus Sch; Secy.

HAMPSHIRE, Sheri Lynn
James Monroe HS; Portland, OR (1-125) Semi-Fin, GS; Secy, NHS; ARC; VP, SC; Tnns; Vlbl; VP, Diplomats; Bus.

HAMPTON, Anita Gail
Murray Co HS; Chatsworth, GA; BC; Pres, 4H; Bkbl; Sftbl; Tomlinson Col; Christian Ed.

HAMPTON, Beverly Jean
McMinnville Sr HS; McMinnville, OR (18-230) Chor; Kiwanis A; VP, Ntl Bus Hon Soc; Portland Comm Col; Bus Adm.

HAMPTON, Bridgett Jane
Skyview Baptist Acad; Memphis, TN (35-91) Chor; Drama; FTA; Sci C; Var C; Bkbl; Sftbl; Tr; Sportsmanship A; Vlbl; Wittiest; Ath for Christ C; Memphis St U; Phys Ed.

HAMPTON, Clayton Lee
Pearl HS; Nashville, TN (12-215) CYO; Pres, Hmrm; Span C; SC; Sftbl; Bible C; Free Will Baptist Bible Col; Hist.

HAMPTON, Frank Livingston
Hart Co HS; Hartwell, GA (5%-200) Co-Cpt, Band; Ch, BC; Ch, Sci C; Co-Cpt, Golf; COM; Cl Fav; Gov Honor Prog; Gr Marshal; Hon Prog; Kiwanis A; Sci A; Type A; Social Stu A; *Mercer U; Pre-Med.*

HAMPTON, Jeanna Lea
Farmington HS; Farmington, MO (44-259) Band; Bus C; Drama; Fr C; Hon Prog; *Mineral Area Col; Bus.*

HAMPTON, Johnna Marie
Hart Co HS; Hartwell, GA (5%-300) Ann; BC; Fr C; FBLA; FHA; VP, Hmrm; Sci C; SC; COM; Hist A; Ldrship A; Outst Stu; *Child Psych.*

HAMPTON, Kent Burdett
Sunset HS; Portland, OR; A Cap Choir; Band; JV, Ftbl; *U of Oreg.*

HAMPTON, Laura Ann
Pearl HS; Nashville, TN (5-200) Bus Mgr, Ann; BC; Tres, Bus C; Lat C; Math C; NHS; Alg A; COM; Math A; Summa Cum Laude; Bible C; Lat As; *Free Will Baptist Bible Col; Elem Ed.*

HAMPTON, Mary Ann
Litchfield Sr HS; Litchfield, IL (43-155) Chor.

HAMPTON, Phyllis Denise
W Morgan HS; Trinity, AL (5-63) F-Ed, Ann; BC; FHA; Hmrm; Span C; SC; Pres, Sr Cl; Tres, Soph Cl; COM; Cl Fav; Hist A; Home WW; Eng A; Woodmen o-t World; HR; *Vanderbilt U; Journ.*

HAMPTON, Robert Theodore
Gaffney Sr HS; Gaffney, SC (1-350) Band; BC; Hmrm; Span C; NMS; *Clemson U; Elec Engr.*

HAMPTON, Ronnie Dwane
Northside HS; Muncie, IN; Bkbl; Cr-Ctry; Tr; Huntington Col; Bus Adm.

HAMPTON, Sheila Rose
Virgie HS; Virgie, KY; Band; BC; FTA; 4H; Sch P; Bkbl; Bus.

HAMPTON, Steven Andrew
Eastern Local HS; Macon, OH (3-100) Fr C; Pres, FTA; NHS; Sch Achieve Tm; Sch P; Math A; MLS; Sci A; Co Spelling Win; Merit Trophy; Cl Historian; *U of Cincinnati; Med.*

HAMPTON, Steven Ray
Mt Vernon Twp HS; Mt Vernon, IL; Band; Chor.

HAMPTON, Susan Elizabeth
Lemuel A Penn Center HS; Washington, DC; Chldr; *Howard U; Architecture.*

HAMPTON, Terry Jim
Chillicothe HS; Chillicothe, TX (1-22) Bus C; Chem C; Chor; Drama; VP, FFA; 4H; Ed, Sch P; SC; Ftbl; Co-Cpt, Golf; Tenn; B Crocker A; 4H A; Journ A; Math A; Spch A; Val; FFA Area IV Off; City Sports Ed; *Tarleton St U; Agr Bus.*

HAMPTON, Valerie
University City Sr HS; University City, MO (12-526) HR; *Theatre Arts.*

HAMRE, Jacqueline Anne
E Sr HS; Duluth, MN (80-500) Orch; *U of Minn; Psych.*

HAMRE, Marcia Gail
Erskine Pub HS; Erskine, MN; Ann; Band; Chldr; Chor; Drama; Ensm; S-T, NHS; Sch P; Spch C; Pres, Jr Cl; Bkbl; HCt; Spch A; Artist o-t Yr A; *ND St U.*

HAMRE, Susan Kay
Erskine Pub Sch; Erskine, MN (2-22) Band; Chldr; Chor; Ensm; NHS; Sch P; Spch C; SC; Pres, Soph Cl; Bkbl; Spch A; Vlbl.

HAMRICK, C Lawana
Petaluma Sr HS; Petaluma, CA (66-360) Chor; 4H; Sch P; Span C; COM; Journ A; Principal's Ltr; *Cal Christian Col; Eng.*

HAMRICK, Janice Lorraine
Chester HS; Chester, PA; Chor; *Pierce Junior Col; Stenography.*

HAMRICK, Judith Anne
Cuyahoga Valley Christian Acad; Cuyahoga Falls, OH (3-31) Band; Chor; Bkbl; *Nyack Col; Ed.*

HAMRICK, Susan Priscilla
S Point HS; Belmont, NC (150-240) *Central Piedmont Comm Col; Human Services.*

HAMRICK, Wyndell W Jr
Vienna HS; Vienna, GA (20%-125) Band; Drama; Fr C; FFA; 4H; SC; H of F; Most Out; *Ga Tech; Mech Engr.*

HAN, Connie Boyun
Broomfield HS; Broomfield, CO (50%-358) Chor; Cpt, Bkbl; Hon Prog; *Colo U; Med.*

HANAMI, Eddie Toru
Reseda HS; Reseda, CA (61-700) Chess C; Math C; Orch; Sch Achieve Tm; Sci C; CSF; Hon Prog; Spch A; Hon Stu A, Japanese Sch; BSct Medals; Private Band; *U of Sou Calif; Sci.*

HANAWALT, Jenny Lu
Ysleta HS; El Paso, TX (19-620) Rptr, A Cap Choir; Chldr; Rptr, Chor; Ensm; Rptr, FFA; Lat C; Madrigal; NHS; COM; Citz A; Kiwanis A; Ntl FFA Chor; Gym Tm; WW; *Tex Tech U; Phys Ed.*

HANBURY, Lucy Levering
Norfolk Collegiate HS; Norfolk, VA (25%-125) Chor; Drama; Fr C; ARC; Bkbl; Hockey; Sftbl; COM; Yth Fel; Pres, Yth Fellowship; VP, Church Organization; *Mary Baldwin Col; Psych.*

HANCE, Andrea Lynn
Hubbard HS; Hubbard, TX (6-36) Pres, FHA; FTA; Secy, NHS; Mgr, Bsbl; COM; Citz A; WW; Lt, Drill Tm; Homemaking A; *Aladdin Beauty Col; Cosmetology.*

HANCHETT, Ivy Danita
Robinson Sch; Santurce, PR (2-38) Math C; Mu Alpha Theta; NHS; Bausch & Lomb A; NEDT; *Sci.*

HANCOCK, Alison Lee
Tuscola HS; Tuscola, IL (8-118) Pres, Band; Chor; Dbte Tm; Fr C; NHS; Sch Achieve Tm; Sci C; Secy, Spch C; S-T, SC; Thes; B Crocker A; Cl Fav; Gr Marshal; St Scholar; WW Among HS Musicians; *U of Ill; Pre-Law.*

HANCOCK, David Scott
Herbert W Schroeder HS; Webster, NY; Band; Ensm; Var C; Cr-Ctry; Tr; Alg A; Hist A; MLS; Sci A; Bible Quiz Tm; Span A; Explorers.

HANCOCK, Joey Scott
Tex City HS; Texas City, TX; BS; NHS; JV, Bkbl; Ftbl; Tr; Cl Fav; NEDT; *Tex U; Architecture.*

HANCOCK, Johnny Stewart
Madison Acad HS; Huntsville, AL (9-43) BC; Monogram; NHS; Var C; Cpt, Bkbl; JV, Ftbl; COM; HKg; HCt; Hon Prog; Star Student.

HANCOCK, Laura Anne
Acad of St Aloysius; Jersey City, NJ (3-127) Drama; Fr C; Ger C; Hmrm; Lat C; NHS; Span C; SC; Alg A; Chem A; Hist A; Hon Prog; Math A; MLS; NEDT; Sal; Fr A; Religion A; Eng A; *Sci.*

HANCOCK, Leslie Ann
Eastern HS; Middletown, KY (40%-293) Chor; Ensm; Ger C; Bkbl; Soccer; Sftbl; Swim; Highest Choir Hon's; *Georgetown Col; Mus.*

HANCOCK, Paul Russell
Monterey HS; Lubbock, TX; Pres, Chor; Madrigal; NHS; Sci C; VP, SC; JV, Cr-Ctry; Ftbl; JV, Tr; DARGCA; Opt A; Runner-Up, Eagle o-t Yr; Outst Choir Member; Star Sct; 2nd Pl, Optimist Oratorical Contest; *Abilene Christian U; Pre-Med.*

HANCOCK, Phyllis Marie
Bentonia HS; Bentonia, MS; Co-Cpt, Chldr; Dbte Tm; Drama; Pres, FBLA; Rptr, Sch P; Bkbl; Sftbl; Swtht; *Holmes Jr Col; Bus Adm.*

HANCOCK, Ramona Kay
Stillman Valley HS; Stillman Valley, IL (5-117) Chor; Fr C; FHA; GS; 4H; NHS; Span C; 4H A; 1st Cl GSct; Acad A's; Church Deaconess; *Med Tech.*

HANCOCK, Randall Lane
John Glenn HS; Westland, MI (21-750) NHS; Magna Cum Laude; Phi Beta Kappa; PSAT-NMSQT, Ltr of Commendation; *U of Mich; Engr.*

HANCOCK, Reenie
Wilcox Co HS; Rochelle, GA (3-97) Ann; Band; BC; Chldr; FBLA; Secy, FHA; 4H; Type A; Acct Cert; Modeling Sch Diploma; Bus.

HANCOCK, Russell Bret
Carterville HS; Carterville, IL (20%-120) Fr C; 4H; Var C; Bkbl; Ftbl; Golf; JV, Tr; Wrest; 4H A; *Sou Ill U; Acct.*

HANCOCK, Sherry Dawn
E Carteret HS; Beaufort, NC; Band; Chldr; Chor; 4H; Hmrm; SC; Tr; Gr Marshal; Spch A.

HANCOCK, Steve Daryl
Woodway HS; Edmonds, WA; Ann; Var C; Cpt, Soccer; COM; Honorable Men All Conf for Soccer; *Edmonds Comm Col.*

HANCOCK, Tamara
Pima Pub Sch; Pima, AZ (2-45) Co-Ed, Ann; FHA; Semi-Fin, GS; Model UN; NHS; VP, SC; Bio A; Hon Prog; Type A; Val; Band A; *Ariz St U; Home Ec.*

HANCOCK, Tonya Lynn
Stillman Valley HS; Stillman Valley, IL (60-130) FHA; FTA; 1st Cl GSct.

HANCOCK, William Brent
Mtn View HS; Mountain View, OK (4-31) VP, FFA; Sch Achieve Tm; SC; Bkbl; Ftbl; Cpt, Golf; COM; Hist A; HCt; Rotary A; St Scholar; Pres, Church Yth; Sch Judging Tms; Soph & Jr Cl Rep, SC; Conservation A; Top 10% Co Hon A; *Okla St U; Vet Med.*

HANCOCK, William Kevin
DuPont Sr HS; Hermitage, TN; *UT at Knoxville; Parks and Recreation.*

HANCOCK, Winton Allan
H W Schroeder HS; Webster, NY (120-290) Band; Span NHS; Var C; Cr-Ctry; Tr; Hist A; Regent Schol; Archt Tech.

HANCOX, Claire Neale
Stafford Sr HS; Stafford Co, VA; Pres, Fr C; Lang.

HAND, Joseph Eugene Jr
Winnfield Sr HS; Winnfield, LA; Parl, BC; Dbte Tm; FBLA; Secy, FFA; Fin, Lit Ral; Sch P; SC; Star Greenhand; FFA Schol; *La Tech Col; Agr.*

HAND, Paul Chris
Dauphin Co Voc-Tech Sch; Harrisburg, PA; Band; Chor; JV, Wrest; Pres, VICA; St Game & Fish Comm Conservation A; *Williamsport Area Comm Col; Machine Trades.*

HANDANYAN, Donna Rose
Seekonk HS; Seekonk, MA (2-224) Hmrm; Math C; NHS; Swim; Yrbk Layout Ed; Swim Coach's A; Most Intelligent; Ntl Merit Schol; Hon Men; *Special Ed.*

HANDFIELD, Laurie Ann
John W Provine HS; Jackson, MS (11-200) F-Ed, Ann; CYO; Chldr; Lat C; Lit Mag; Mu Alpha Theta; VP, NHS; Ed, Sch P; VP, SC; Tri-HiY; Beauty; Citz A; H of F; Hon Prog; Journ A; Ntl Achv Schol; Yth Fel; Church Choir; Cpt, Rifle Corp; VP, PTSA; Ed, Church Paper; Sch Prod; Yth Co; Top 20 Schol A; Puppetteers; Pres, Church Fel; *Miss Col; Art Ed.*

HANDKE, Raymond Herman Jr
Guttenberg Comm HS; Guttenberg, IA (11-90) Math C; Phys C; Rptr, Sch P; Sci C; Bkbl; Nom, WW.

HANDLAN, Patricia Ann
Parkersburg HS; Parkersburg, WV; Co-Cpt, Bkbl; Chruch Yth Group; GAA; Stu Exchange Service; *W Va U; Animal Sci.*

HANDLEY, Allan Dwain
Spring Woods Sr HS; Houston, TX (25%-600) A Cap Choir; Chor; NHS; Interlochen Ntl Mus; Yth Fel; Co-Ed, Church Paper; Tres, Church Yth Coun; Region Choir; Nom, Outst Soph; *Tex A&M U.*

HANDLEY, Rod Eugene
Eastmont HS; E Wenatchee, WA (4-300) Chor; NHS; SC; Var C; Bkbl; Ftbl; Tr; DARGCA; JA A; Masonic A; Hist Ed.

HANDLEY, Tina Marie
American HS; Fremont, CA (5%-565) Band; Ensm; Fr C; Pres, Hmrm; Orch; Crisco A; *Pepperdine U; Mus.*

HANDLIN, Christina Dawn
Paul Harding HS; Fort Wayne, IN (11-283) Ski C; Commercial Art.

HANDRAHAN, Nadine Agnes
Tignish Regional HS; Tignish, CANADA; Tres, CYO; S-T, ARC; SC; Bkbl; Hockey; COM; Most Out.

HANDY, Charles Louis
John H Francis Polytech HS; Sun Valley, CA; Band; Orch; *Calif St U; Archt Drafting.*

HANDY, Jeffrey Dalton
Belfry HS; Belfry, KY (92-202) Band; Ch, Fr C; VP, Hmrm; Order/Arrow; Pres, Yth Fel; All Co, Stage, Bands; BSct; Prom, Band, Committees; WW.

HANDY, Molly Ruth
Appomattox Co HS; Appomattox, VA (5-239) Drama; 4H; Hmrm; Lat C; Span C; Tri-HiY; Spch A; *Sweet Briar Col; Math.*

HANE, David Robb
Drummond Pub Sch; Drummond, OK (1-21) A-Ed, Ann; Chor; Ensm; Secy, FFA; Order/Arrow; VP, SC; Rptr, Sr Cl; Pres, Jr Cl; VP, Soph Cl; Bkbl; Gov Honor Prog; Masonic A; NEDT; Phy A; NML; *Bethany Nazarene Col.*

HANEL, Lisa Kathryn
Ashtabula HS; Ashtabula, OH (11-221) AFS; Bus Mgr, Band; CYO; FTA; NHS; All Co Band A; *Suomi Col; Dental Hygiene.*

HANELINE, Barbara Ann
Kearsley HS; Flint, MI (70-350) A Cap Choir; Ensm; Sftbl; Hon Prog; *Huntington Col.*

HANELT, Patricia Meta
Crystal Lake Comm HS; Crystal Lake, IL (32-585) Chor; Ger C; NHS; Hon Prog; *Med.*

HANES, Lawrence Edward
Springbrook HS; Silver Spring, MD; Wrest.

HANEY, April Annette
Columbia Comm HS; Columbia, IL (18-127) Band; Church Chor; Secy, GSct; Vlbl; *Belleville Area Col; Social Working.*

HANEY, April Renee
Temple City HS; Temple City, CA (20%-440) Chldr; Chor; Drama; Cr-Ctry; COM; Most Out; Secy, HS Choir; Pres, Christian Girl's C; Sanctuary Choir; *Sou Calif Col; Mus.*

HANEY, Cindy Lee
W Carter HS; Olive Hill, KY (5%-125) FBLA; Sch P; *Morehead Col; Computer Tech.*

HANEY, HelenMarie Elizabeth
Holy Cross HS; Riverside, NJ (6-350) Ed, Ann; Chor; Dbte Tm; Fr C; Hmrm; NHS; Sodality; SC; Mgr, Tr; Hist A; Hon Prog; VFW A; Masque & Lance; HR; Musicals; Villanova Schol; *Villanova U; Bus Adm.*

HANFORD, Brad
Kenmore E Sr HS; Tonawanda, NY (15%-775) AFS; Chor; NHS; Ski C; Var C; Ftbl; Hon Prog; *St U of NY; Phar.*

HANGER, Nancy Wright
Westminster Sch; Atlanta, GA (7-100) Chldr; Chor; Cum Laude Soc; Tres, Ensm; InterAct C; NHS; Span C; Secy, Jr Cl; Bio A; Chem A; Math A; Pres A; *Sweet Briar Col.*

HANKE, Barbara Lynn
Altamont HS; Altamont, UT (5-39) Ed, Ann; Chldr; Chor; Dbte Tm; Drama; FHA; GS; SC; Amer Leg Orator A; COM; Hist A; HCt; Sci A.

HANKIN, Jennifer Deanne
Monte Vista Acad; Spring Valley, CA; Yth Fel; Pub Ch, Girls League; Phys Ed A; Acad HR; *Powers Sch of Modeling; Modeling.*

HANKIN, Karen Elaine
Monte Vista HS; Spring Valley, CA; Chor; FHA; GS; Span C; SC; Bkbl; Cpt, Ftbl; Cpt, Sftbl; Phy A; Yth Fel; Span A; Statistician; Soccer; *Southwestern Col.*

HANKINS, Anthony Bruce
Oil Trough HS; Oil Trough, AR (3-30) FFA; FTA; Rptr, 4H; Mgr, Bkbl; 4H A; MLS; Sal; Sci A; Service A; *Harding Col.*

HANKINS, Bruce
Oil Trough HS; Oil Trough, AR (4-30) FFA; FTA; Rptr, 4H; Mgr, Bkbl; 4H A; MLS; Sal; Sci A; *Harding Col; Law.*

HANKINS, Buddy Ross
Anna-Jonesboro Comm HS; Anna, IL (60-168) *Shawnee Col; Welding.*

HANKINS, Curtis Elijah Jr
Wenatchee HS; Wenatchee, WA; A Cap Choir; Band; Chor; Community Yth Symph; Ensm; Hmrm; Orch; SC; COM; Most Out; *Mus Ed.*

HANKINS, Daniel Keith
Monterey HS; Lubbock, TX; Dbte Tm; 1st Pl Debate, Tex Tech U; Ldrship of Stu Life; *Notre Dame U; Law.*

HANKINS, Donna Joyce
Marion Co HS; Guin, AL; FHA; Bkbl; Sftbl; Tr; Cl Fav.

HANKINS, Joan Lynelle
Stanton Pub HS; Stanton, NE (4-45) Band; Chor; FHA; Pres, 4H; Ch, Jr Cl; COM; Citz A; 4H A; I Dare You; MLS; Most Out; Spch A; VofDEM; Pep C; Hon Band; Win, Women's C Mus Contest; 3rd St Alt, Hugh O'Brien Yth Semnar; 4-H Exchange Stu; *Wayne St Col; Mus.*

HANKINS, Lydia Kay
Northern HS; Owings, MD (4-300) Chor; Drama; Pres, NHS; Phase IV; Co Ed Correspondent, SG; Top 5%, HR; Qn with Sceptor, Acteens at Chrch.

HANKINS, Shelaine
Saginaw HS; Saginaw, MI; *Saginaw Valley St Col; Bus.*

HANKINS, Vicki Jo
Dawson Bryant HS; Coal Grove, OH (11-98) Band; GS; Co-Cpt, Mjrte; NHS; 2nd Pl, Sr Math; WW; *Ohio U; Secretarial.*

HANKINSON, Angela Sharlayne
Westside HS; Augusta, GA; BC; Fr C; FHA; Hmrm; Sci C; SC; COM; HCt; Hon Prog; Most Out; Sci A.

HANKS, Alan Ethan
Rapid City Stevens HS; Rapid City, SD (197-486) A Cap Choir; Hmrm; Ski C; SC; JV, Bkbl; JV, Ftbl; JV, Tr; Yth Foundation; Yth Leg; Pres, Yth Fel; *Northern St Col; Social Work.*

HANKS, Beth
Colo HS; Colo City, TX (9-95) Band; Ensm; FBLA; FHA; Mjrte; NHS; Rainbow; *Angelo St U; Bus.*

HANKS, Kenneth Gary
Strasburg HS; Strasburg, CO; BS; Chess C; Chor; Drama; NHS; Pres, SC; Pres, Jr Cl; Pres, Soph Cl; Bkbl; Ftbl; Tr; Wrest; Math A; Best Actor; *CSU; Vet-Med.*

HANKS, Rita Mae
Bethany HS; Reidsville, NC; Anchor C; FHA; Semi-Fin, Jr Miss Pa; Monogram; Sch P; Co- cpt, Vlbl.

HANKS, William Franklin III
Holston HS; Knoxville, TN (33%-200) BS; Chor; Key C; Monogram; Span C; Var C; VP, Sr Cl; VP, Jr Cl; Bsbl; Co-Cpt, Bkbl; Pres, Yth Fel; *Radio-tV.*

HANLEY, Fredia Ann
Booker T Washington Sr HS; Tulsa, OK (75-450) Band; SC; S-T, Soph Cl.

HANLEY, Kelly Anne
Bremerhaven American HS; Bremerhaven, GERMANY (1-24) Ann; Band; Co-Cpt, Chldr; Hmrm; Madrigal; NHS; F-Ed, Sch P; SC; VP, Jr Cl; Mgr, Bkbl; Tnns; Citz A; HCt; *Forestry.*

HANLON, Hal Norris
Hannibal Central Sch; Hannibal, NY; Band; BS; Chor; Math C; Rptr, NHS; Pres, Var C; Ftbl; Tr; Amer Leg A; *SUNY at Oswego; Industrial Arts.*

HANN, Davida Lynette
Saint Joseph Acad; Columbus, OH (6-16) Chor; Fr C; Secy, Hmrm; ARC A; F-Ed, Sch P; Secy, Jr Cl; Bkbl; Soccer; ARC A; Vlbl; *Ohio U; Psych.*

HANNA, Amy Lou
Lincoln HS; Ellwood City, PA; Span C; *Secy.*

HANNA, Anita Fay
Meridian HS; Meridian, TX; BC; Parl, FHA; Tres, Jr Cl; Bkbl; Tr; HCt; Type A; Secy, FHA; Ldr, Drill Tm; Co Soil & Water Conser Dist Essay; Fresh Rptr; *Baylor U; Phar.*

HANNA, Cindy Lynn
W T White HS; Dallas, TX (200-658) Secy, Bus C; Chor; Y-Tns; Pep Squad; Cum Laude.

HANNA, Garry Odell
Hannah Pamplico HS; Pamplico, SC; Ann; Cpt, Band; Drama; Ensm; NHS; Orch; Secy, Sci C; COM; Sci A; *Newberry Col; Mus.*

HANNA, Jodi Renee
Bethel Christian HS; Garden Grove, CA; A Cap Choir; Ann; Cpt, Chldr; Chor; Drama; Ensm; HiY; Madrigal; NHS; Tri-HiY; Bkbl; JV, Hockey; JV, Sftbl; Citz A; Cl Fav; Hist A; Most Out; Phys Ed A; Span A; Hon Stu; *San Diego St U; Bus.*

HANNA, Karen Sue
Lincoln HS; Ellwood City, PA (35-252) Ann; Ger C; 4H; Math C; Y-Tns; Sftbl; Hon Prog; NEDT; Achv A's; *Phys Therapy.*

HANNA, Lonnie Daryl
East Central HS; Hurley, MS (15-115) *U of Miss; Elec.*

HANNA, Micheal David
W Holmes HS; Millersburg, OH (15%-240) Band; Pres, 4H; HiY; Span C; Pres, Var C; Cpt, Ftbl; Cpt, Tr; *Hist.*

HANNA, Richard Mckim
Miller Sch; Miller School, VA (1-10) ARC; Ftbl; Wrest; MLS; ARC A; ROTC A; Star Student.

HANNA, Sue Ellen
Ouachita Parish HS; Monroe, LA (3-350) A Cap Choir; Anchor C; Chor; Ensm; NHS; Spch C; Y-Tns; Col Schol; Delta Beta Sigma; *NE La U; Acct.*

HANNA, Timothy Troy
W Holmes HS; Millersburg, OH (40-220) Band; Dbte Tm; Pres, 4H; Hmrm; Span C; Spch C; Tres, SC; Var C; Pres, Soph Cl; Bkbl; Ftbl; MVP, Tr; 4H A; Spch A; *Secondary Ed.*

HANNA, Willis Randall Jr
Hannah-Pamplico HS; Pamplico, SC (5%-110) Ann; Cpt, Band; Drama; NHS; Sci C; SC; Pres, Tres, Media C; Pep C; Fr A; *Furman U; Med.*

HANNAFORD, David Carlyle
Pottsville Area HS; Pottsville, PA (122-386) Drama; Fr C; Cr-Ctry; Tr; WW; *Lycoming Col; Bus.*

HANNAH, Angela Theo
E Peoria Comm HS; E Peoria, IL (1-391) Secy, Chem C; Chor; VP, Ger C; GS; Hmrm; Math C; NHS; A-Ed, Sch P; St Scholar; Val; Sterling Merit A; *Concordia Teachers Col; Elem Ed.*

HANNAH, Pamela Ann
Ed W Clark HS; Las Vegas, NV; A Cap Choir; Fr C; Madrigal; NHS; Hon Prog; *Ed.*

HANNAMAN, Jo Beth
Newton Comm HS; Newton, IL (50%-195) Parl, Band; Bus C; JV, Chldr; VP, 4H; Mjrte; Sftbl; 4H A; HCt; JA A; Yth Fel; Secy, Fresh Cl; *Oral Roberts U; Psych.*

HANNAN, Cynthia L
Laurel Highlands HS; Uniontown, PA (43-450) Band; FTA; Ski C; Span C; Jr Historians; *Biscayne Paramed Inst; Med Lab Tech.*

HANNAN, Leigh Ann
Jeffersontown HS; Jeffersontown, KY (33%-300) BC; Mgr, Bkbl; *Phys Therapy.*

HANNAY, Michelle Beth
Hightstown HS; Hightstown, NJ (13-254) A Cap Choir; Band; Chor; Drama; Ensm; Hmrm; Mjrte; NHS; SC; Thes; JV, Sftbl; HCt; Hon Prog; Most Out; Drum Mjrte; Regional, All St Band; Regional Ensm; Alt, GS; *Carnegie-Mellon U; Voice.*

HANNEMAN, Vicki Lynn
Arundel Sr HS; Gambrills, MD; Ann; Fr C; Hmrm; SC; Theatre C; Home Ec C; *Goucher Col; Psych.*

HANNEMANN, Anita Maurine
King City HS; King City, CA (4-157) Band; Chor; Drama; Mjrte; Span C; CSF; Summa Cum Laude; Yth Fel; Pianist, Church, Sch Choirs; Mus Yth Group; *Calif Lutheran Col; Child Mental Health.*

HANNU, Debra Ann
Robbinsdale Sr HS; Robbinsdale, MN (88-673) FBLA; Rptr, Lit Mag; Orch; Sodality; Spch C; Sftbl; COM; JA A; Type A; Usher C; Art A; HR; Jr Exec A; Achv A, Jr Achv; *Commercial Art.*

HANS, Dena Lynet
Calabasas HS; Calabasas, CA; Chor; JV, Sftbl; JV, Swim; Job's Daughters; *Pepperdine U; Social Sci.*

HANSARD, Pamela Kay
N Gwinnett HS; Suwanee, GA (2-150) Ann; Tres, BC; Ch, FHA; Math C; Secy, Jr Cl; Bio A; Crisco A; 4H A; *Home Ec.*

HANSCH, Deborah Ruth
St Joseph Sr HS; St Joseph, MI (96-363) Chor; Math C; Sch P; Sci C; Tr; Ntl Soc of Stu Organizations A; *Lake Mich Col; Special Ed.*

HANSCOM, Patricia Louise
Hinsdale Central HS; Hinsdale, IL (48-596) Band; Ger C; Var C; *DePauw Col; Lang.*

HANSE, Sharon Kay
Two Harbors HS; Two Harbors, MN (59-174) AFS; Ann; Fr C; Bkbl; Sonshine Singing Group; Secy, Christian Singing Group; Sunday Sch; V-P, Luther League; Christian Ed & Yth Ministry Comm; *Med.*

HANSEL, Donna Rene
N Iredell HS; Olin, NC; Drama; FHA; Hmrm; Monogram; Sci C; Cpt, Bkbl; Sftbl; Tr; HCt; Pres A; Sci A; Gov Page; *Appalachian St U; Radio and TV.*

HANSEN, Alice Marie
Estancia HS; Estancia, NM (3-68) Pres, FHA; SC; Bio A; COM; Type A; Young Hist Cert.

HANSEN, Beverly Jean
Spring Lake HS; Spring Lake, MI (25-180) Ann; NHS; Ski C; Tr; NMS; Sem-Fin, Royal Neighbors Schol, A's; St Schol, A; *Muskegon Comm Col; Retailing.*

HANSEN, Dennis Michael
Maryknoll HS; Honolulu, HI (36-110) NHS; Rptr, Sch P; Co-Cpt, Cr-Crcty; Swim; Co-Cpt, Tr; Gold Medal, CC Hawaii, 1st, Honolulu Marathon; *Oreg St U; Forestry.*

HANSEN, Fritz Robert
Charles A Lindbergh HS; Hopkins, MN (99-456) Pres, Demolay; Spch C; Spch A; *ND St U; Geol.*

HANSEN, Gail Jean
Spring Sr HS; Spring, TX (169-500) Mu Alpha Theta; Alg A; Math A; Homemaking A's; *Briar Cliff Col; Math.*

HANSEN, Gloria Jean
Wakefield Pub Sch; Wakefield, NE (21-46) Drama; S-T, 4H; Monogram; S-T, SC; Var C; Bkbl; Tr; Citz A; 4H A; Spch A; Dist Pres, SC; Pep C; Vlbl; Northeast Nebr Pork Qn; *Wayne St Col; Lib Sci.*

HANSEN, Janet Mary
Oak Park River Forest HS; Oak Park, IL (128-1042) A Cap Choir; Cum Laude Soc; Ensm; Hmrm; Madrigal; Math C; Orch; Sci C; *Liberal Arts.*

HANSEN, Jeff Owen
Dakota Adventist Acad; Bismark, ND (11-30) Chor; Pres, Soph Cl; *Union Col; Law.*

HANSEN, Jill
N Kitsap Sr HS; Poulsbo, WA (22-217) FFA; Co-Ch, GS; Hmrm; NHS; Orch; SC; Mgr, Bkbl; Coun of Teach A; Hon Prog; Cpt, Drill Tm; Jr Orthopedic Guild; Secy, GSC; Luther League; *Western Wash St Col; Environmental Stu.*

HANSEN, Joann Marie
Irene Public HS; Irene, SD (6-27) Cpt, Chldr; Chor; Dbte Tm; Drama; Ensm; FHA; Semi-Fin, GS; SC; Thes; Pres, Jr Cl; Mgr, Ftbl; Tr; Type A.

HANSEN, Jon Tyler
Ralston HS; Ralston, NE (55-300) NHS; Order/Arrow; Ski C; JV, Ftbl; Co-Cpt, Soccer; God & Country A; Hon Prog; Order/Arrow A; Pres A; Eagle Sct; *Sci.*

HANSEN, Karen Jean
Valley City HS; Valley City, ND (14-162) Band; Chor; Pres, 4H; Bkbl; Sftbl; Tr; Most Improved, Tr; Most Hustle, Bkbl A.

HANSEN, Linda Marie
Mercy HS; Red Bluff, CA; Chldr; Drama; Hmrm; K of C; Model UN; Spch C; SC; Swim; Bank Of Amer A; CSF; HCt; Hon Prog; K of C A; Lion A; Spch A; *Oral Roberts U; Art.*

HANSEN, Lora Ann
Hannibal Central Sch; Hannibal, NY; Hmrm; NHS; Var C; Bkbl; Soccer; HCt; Sci A; Buzzy Grant A; MVP, Vlbl.

HANSEN, Mary Kay
Cottage Grove HS; Cottage Grove, OR (20-200) NHS; SC; Bkbl; Hockey; Sftbl; VP, GRA; Vlbl; Most Inspirational Player; *George Fox Col; Social Services.*

HANSEN, Nancy Elizabeth
Mojave HS; Mojave, CA (3-119) Tres, Band; A-Ed, Sch P; Bkbl; COM; Journ A; Q&S A; Pres, Pep C; Cpt, Vlbl; *Pepperdine U; Med.*

HANSEN, Nancy Kay
Lindbergh Sr HS; Hopkins, MN (22-396) St Cloud St U; Bus.

HANSEN, Randy Eugene
Lowell Sr HS; Lowell, IN (45-299) Var C; Ftbl; Tr; Bus Adm.

HANSEN, Ronnie Earl
Frederic HS; Frederic, WI (4-78) Co-Cpt, Bkbl; MVP, Ftbl; Golf; Tnns; Star Student; MVP, Ftbl; *Eau Claire Col; Computer Sci.*

HANSEN, Sheryl Marie
Parkview HS; Springfield, MO; A Cap Choir; Chor; FBLA; NFL; Sch P; Spch C; Spch A; I Rating, St Mus Fest Piano Solo; *SW Mo St U; Mus Ed.*

HANSEN, Steven James
W Concord HS; W Concord, MN (4-43) Band; Chor; NHS; Spch C; Tr; Wrest; *U of Minn; Archt.*

HANSEN, Terri Lynn
John F Kennedy Sr HS; Bloomington, MN (10%-600) Band; Chor; NHS; Pres, MYF; Eng A; Mus As; Band A; Choir A; *Bethel Col.*

HANSEN, Thomas Kevin
Granite City S HS; Granite City, IL; JA A; Accolyte, Usher; *Math.*

HANSEN, Val Wayne
Hagerman HS; Hagerman, ID (1-32) Ann; Band; Rptr, FFA; Pres, NHS; Var C; Bkbl; JV, Ftbl; Tr; Chem A; Math A; MLS; Star Student; Val; *U of Idaho; Pre-Vet Med.*

HANSEN, Vicki Ann
Taft Union HS; Taft, CA (41-174) Pres, AFS; Fin, GS; Math C; SC; Soroptimist A; *Whitewater U; Secretarial.*

HANSEN, Vicki Lynn
Tyler Pub Sch; Tyler, MN (20-55) A Cap Choir; A-Ed, Ann; Band; Cpt, Chldr; Chor; Ensm; FHA; InterAct C; Jr Miss Pagent; Madrigal; Mod Mus Mas; Ntl Yth Conf; Spch C; Var C; Golf; Sftbl; Cpt, Swim; Tnns; Tr; COM; ARC A; Yth Fel; St Mus Ensm & Solo; Augie Band; *Willmar Col; Nurs.*

HANSLADEN, Robert Gerard
Chaminade HS; St Louis, MO (8-128) Cpt, Bsbl; Cpt, Ftbl; Hon Prog; Math A; *Ariz St U.*

HANSON, Amy Ellen
Forest Lake Sr HS; Forest Lake, MN (119-496) Tr; Stout U; Special Ed.

HANSON, Bruce Allen
Karlsruhe Amer HS; Karlsruhe, GERMANY; Ftbl; Soccer; Most Improved, All Conf, Ftbl; *U of Alaska; Wildlife Mgr.*

HANSON, Cheryl Lynn
Forest View HS; Arlington Heights, IL (1-750) Tres, HiY; NFL; NHS; Ntl Yth Conf; Ski C; Spch C; Var C; JV, Sftbl; COM; Hon Prog; Spch A; St Bowl Tm Champ; *Special Ed.*

HANSON, Christ Leo
Carpio Pub HS; Carpio, ND (3-24) VP, SC; Tres, Soph Cl; Co-Cpt, Ftbl; Citz A; *ND St U; Engr.*

HANSON, Christopher Alan
Forest View HS; Arlington Heights, IL (31-750) NHS; Var C; Bsbl; Cpt, Bkbl; Ftbl; Hon Prog; *U of Ill; Bus.*

HANSON, Claudia Jane
Mormon Trail HS; Humeston, IA; Secy, FHA; Tres, 4H; JV, Bkbl; Golf; Sftbl; *Elem Ed.*

HANSON, Craig Hilding
Rancho HS; North Las Vegas, NV (77-550) AFS; Ski C; Var C; VP, Sr Cl; Co-Cpt, Ftbl; Soccer; Amer Leg A; Sun Yth Forum; *US Air Force Acad; Astronautical Engr.*

HANSON, David Scott
Dassel-Cokato Jr Sr HS; Cokato, MN; Band; Chor; Madrigal; Order/Arrow; Bkbl; Ftbl; Golf; Order/Arrow A; Eagle Sct.

HANSON, David Wayne
Highline HS; Seattle, WA; Band; Rptr, Sch P; Sci A; *Math.*

HANSON, Denise Renee
Elk Point HS; Elk Point, SD (17-63) Band; JV, Chldr; Chor; Pres, 4H; JV, Bkbl; Tr; 4H A; *Augustana Col; Phys Ed.*

HANSON, Douglas Clinton
Hot Springs Co HS; Thermopolis, WY; Band; VFW A.

HANSON, Ellen L
Arlington Heights, IL (50%-570) Band; Key C; Sftbl; Pep C; HR; Office Aide; Mgr, Fencing; S-T, Job's Daughters; *U of Wisc; Animal Sci.*

HANSON, Erin Kay
Natrona Co HS; Casper, WY (150-650) Chldr; Chor; Drama; Ensm; Tr; Pres, Yth Group.

HANSON, Felicia Kay
Morningside HS; Inglewood, CA; SC; *Brayman's Col; Dentist Asst.*

HANSON, Hannah Jean
Charles Henderson HS; Troy, AL (15%-175) Pres, Anchor C; Band; VP, Bus C; Chldr; Parl, FBLA; FTA; InterClub Coun; Mjrte; ARC; Tres, Sci C; Span C; SC; Var C; Beauty; HCt; *Auburn U; Pol Sci.*

HANSON, Heidi Ruth
Bradley-Bourbonnais HS; Bradley, IL; FHA; Span C; *Olivet Nazarene Col; Early Childhood Ed.*

HANSON, Jane Melody
Erskine Pub HS; Erskine, MN (1-20) Band; Chor; Drama; Ensm; Pres, 4H; Madrigal; NHS; Ed, Sch P; Thes; Tr; COM; Citz A; 4H A; Math A; *Golden Valley Lutheran Col; Mus.*

HANSON, Janine Renee
Frank B Kellogg Sr HS; Roseville, MN (43-547) Band; Sftbl; Flute Ensm; Vlbl; St Flute Solo & Quartet Contest St; Piano Hon Concert; MMTA Piano & Theory Exam; *Mus.*

HANSON, John Mark
Reynolds HS; Portland, OR (15-540) AFS; VP, Ger C; Hmrm; VP, Order/Arrow; Co-Ed, Sch P; Ski C; SC; JV, Bsbl; JV, Ftbl; JV, Tr; Journ A; Order/Arrow A; Eagle Sct; *Pre-Law.*

HANSON, Julie Ann
Wahconah Regional HS; Dalton, MA (10-243) A Cap Choir; Band; Chor; Drama; Madrigal; Cpt, Mjrte; NHS; Pres, Yth Fellowship; *Russell Sage Col; Nurs.*

HANSON, Julie Lynn
Jefferson HS; Jefferson, WI; Band; Chldr; Chor; Ensm; Hmrm; Bkbl; Tr; COM; Hon Prog; *U of Wis-Whitewater; Instrumental Mus.*

HANSON, Karen Elaine
Viroqua HS; Viroqua, WI (1-147) Chor; FHA; Pres, 4H; Math C; NHS; Sch P; Sci C; Tres, Span C; Sftbl; Tr; COM; 4H A; Regent Schol; Val; CM Butt Schol; Pres, Church Yth League; Tres, Genealogy C; GAA; *Luther Col; Nurs.*

HANSON, Karen Sue
Roy Miller HS; Corpus Christi, TX; Band; Orch; Sch P; SC; Bkbl; Citz A; Sci A; *Phys Therapy.*

HANSON, Katherine Jane
Oshkosh W HS; Oshkosh, WI; A-Ed, Ann; Chor; Lit Mag; Golf; Hist A; Hon Prog; Journ A; Var Ltr Win for Golf; *U Wis; Elem Ed.*

HANSON, Kevin Alan
Antelope Valley HS; Lancaster, CA (100-700) *Azusa Pacific Col; Yth Ministry.*

HANSON, Kevin Lee
Benson Polytech HS; Portland, OR (10%-450) Band; JV, Tr; *Portland Comm Col; Machine Shop.*

HANSON, Kristeen Anne
Beaver Dam Sr HS; Beaver Dam, WI; Band; Chor; Ensm; 4H; Orch; Tnns; 4H A; Sci A; Marine Corps Yth Phys Fitness A; *U of Wisc; Mus.*

HANSON, Laurie Jean
Elma HS; Elma, WA (20-150) Bus C; Chor; Drama; FBLA; Pres, GS; NHS; Spch C; Cpt, Var C; Pres A; Vlbl; Girl o-t Mo; Qn, Town; *Bus.*

HANSON, Linda Kay
Fremont HS; Fremont, MI (25%-200) Band; 4H; Span C; Sftbl; Tr; *Western Mich U; Social Work.*

HANSON, Lisa Ann
Tyler Pub HS; Tyler, MN (30%-50) A Cap Choir; Ann; Band; Chor; Ensm; FHA; Var C; Bkbl; Golf; Mgr, Vlbl; Semi-Fin, Spch A; Med.

HANSON, Lori Sue
Arlington HS; Arlington Heights, IL; Rptr, Sch P; Jobs Daughters; Foreign Lang A; U of Ill; Home Ec.

HANSON, Mark Ralph
W Linn HS; W Linn, OR; City Conf; Bkbl; Citz A.

HANSON, Patrick David
Mormon Trail HS; Garden Grove, IA (2-50) Ftbl; Sftbl; Wrest.

HANSON, Richard Arin
Mormon Trail HS; Garden Grove, IA (8-50) Ann; Band; Chor; FFA; 4H; Sch P; Tres, Jr Cl; Bkbl; Ftbl; Tr; Beta Sigma Phi Schol; U of Iowa; Pre-Med.

HANSON, Sheila Ann
Rice Lake HS; Rice Lake, WI (10-300) A Cap Choir; Band; Dbte Tm; Fr C; Ger C; Key C; NFL; NHS; Sch P; SC; MVP, Bkbl; Sftbl; Mgr, Tr; COM; Job's Daughters; Co-Cpt, Vlbl; 1st, DAR Constitution Contest; U of Wis Eau Claire; Special Ed.

HANSON, Susan Marie
Pacific HS; San Leandro, CA (5-317) CYO; Chess C; InterAct C; Bkbl; CSF; Sailing C; No 1, Fund Raising; Span A; Falcon A; Pres Phys Fitness A.

HANSON, Terry LaVerne
Bardstown HS; Bardstown, KY (25%-155) Fr C; JV, Tnns; Pres, DECA; Computer Tech.

HANVEY, Phil R
Prospect HS; Mt Prospect, IL; A Cap Choir; Chor; NHS; Order/Arrow; Ftbl; NW Ill U; Bio-Med Engr.

HAPPEL, David Alan
Easton Area HS; Easton, PA; Cr-Ctry; Tr; Temple U; Archt.

HARABURDA, Karen Marie
Cecilian Acad; Philadelphia, PA; Chor; Fr C; Lat C; Hon Prog; NEDT.

HARADON, Joyce Lorraine
Princeton HS; Princeton, TX (14-58) Parl, FBLA; Span C; SC; Bkbl; Cl Fav; All-Dist, Hon Men, Bkbl.

HARALSON, Shirley Joan
Bogue Chitto HS; Bogue Chitto, MS (3-60) BC; Chldr; 4H; 4H A; Best Sch Spirit.

HARBAUGH, Barbara Ann
Taylor Center HS; Taylor, MI (14-470) NHS; Swim; COM; Co-Cpt, MVP, Gym; Bio.

HARBAUGH, Margie Esther
Riverton HS; Riverton, WY (5%-250) Lat C; Thes; Whitworth Col; Eng.

HARBAUGH, Paula Jaye
Penn-Trafford HS; Harrison City, PA (5-356) Pres, Chor; Secy, Drama; HiY; Lat C; NFL; NHS; Bus Mgr, Rainbow; SC; Thes; Swim; Cl Fav; Hon Prog; Yth Fel; WW; WW in Mus Stu; Yrbk Staff; Hospital Vol A; Citizens General Sch of Nurs; Nurs.

HARBER, Ann Elizabeth
Bishop Dwenger HS; Fort Wayne, IN (3-255) NHS; Chem A; Hon Prog; Math A; Co-Ed, Yrbk; Ger A; Tri Kappa A; Top 10% A; Parkview Sch of Nurs; Nurs.

HARBER, Dennis Paul
Douglass HS; Douglass, TX (1-12) A-Ed, Ann; Rptr, FFA; SC; Pres, Soph Cl; Bkbl; Tr; Hon Prog; Sci A; PA; Stephen F Austin Col; Sci.

HARBER, James Jackson
Claremont HS; Claremont, CA (37-450) Key C; Span C; Bio A; CSF; U of Calif; Environmental Sci.

HARBER, Mitzi Paulette
Douglass HS; Douglass, TX (1-8) Chldr; Pres, FHA; Hmrm; Co-Ed, Lit Mag; VP, SC; Tres, Sr Cl; Tres, Jr Cl; Pres, Soph Cl; Bkbl; Tr; COM; Cl Fav; Journ A; Poet A; Swtht; Panola Jr Col; Journ.

HARBIN, Holly
Calhoun HS; Calhoun, GA; Band; Chldr; Fr C; NHS; VP, Tri-HiY; U of Ga; Med.

HARBIN, Pamela Jean
Canyon HS; Canyon, TX (100-300) Band; FHA; Tres, FTA; Bkbl; Tex Tech U; Psych.

HARBIN, Steven Lee
Flathead HS; Kalispell, MT; Chor; Ensm; Order/Arrow.

HARBISON, Carey Lee
Eldorado HS; El Dorado, IL (10-125) Pres, 4H; NHS; JV, Bkbl; JV, Ftbl; JV, Tr; 4H A; Baylor U; Vet.

HARBISON, Carroll Joe
Eldorado HS; Eldorado, IL; Drama; Span C; Thes; Mgr, Bkbl; Mgr, Tr.

HARBMAN, Graham Campbell
Wm B Travis HS; Austin, TX (29-315) Fr C; Hmrm; NHS; Hon Prog; JA A; ROTC A; Trustee Schol A; Hon Graduate; U of Tex; Aerospace Engr.

HARBOR, Barbara Ann
Manatee HS; Bradenton, FL; FBLA; Delta Sigma Theta A; God & Country A; Hist A; NMF; Trevecca Nazarene Col; Computer Tech.

HARBOTTLE, Lisa Marie
Fort Hunt HS; Alexandria, VA (100-450) Band; Community Yth Symph; French NHS; Orch; SC; VP, Soph Cl; Lib Arts.

HARBOUR, Carolyn Dianne
Nederland HS; Nederland, TX (29-480) Anchor C; FTA; Lat C; NHS; Rptr, Sch P; Hist A; Lamar U; Acct.

HARBOUR, Ricky Klien
Monticello HS; Monticello, MS (2-145) Ann; BC; Order/Arrow; NEDT; Miss St U; Engr.

HARBRON, Nancy
Grand Blanc HS; Grand Blanc, MI; A Cap Choir; Chor; NHS; SC; Pres, Soph Cl; Art A; VP, Fresh Cl; Ferris St Col; Med Sci.

HARCAR, John Anthony
Cleveland Central HS; Cleveland, OH (25-150) Chess C; Span C; Bsbl; SCAT C.

HARCUS, Teri Jean
Pittsburg HS; Pittsburg, CA (48-281) Ann; Band; Mjrte; Sch Achieve Tm; F-Ed, Sch P; Ski C; COM; Citz A; Girl o-t Mo A; U of Ariz; Gen.

HARDACKER, Cecilia Teresa
Bryan Sr HS; Omaha, NE (56-367) Chess C; Key C; Var C; MVP, Bsbl; Golf; Sftbl; Tr; Co-Cpt, Bsbl; U of Nebr Col of Nurs; Nurs.

HARDACRE, Patricia Ann
Whitefish Bay HS; Whitefish Bay, WI (1-313) AFS; Chor; Pres, FTA; Ger C; Cpt, Mjrte; Sch Achieve Tm; Rptr, Lit Ral; Mgr, Bkbl; Amer Leg A; Q&S A; Val; Mortar Board; Piano; NHS; Most Outst Intelligent; Drill Tm; Wheaton Col; Natural Sci.

HARDAWAY, Melodie
Melrose HS; Memphis, TN (59-340) NHS; ARC; Memphis St U; Sci.

HARDAWAY, Melody
Melrose HS; Memphis, TN (1-340) NHS; ARC; Memphis St Col; Bio.

HARDCASTLE, Winilee Dawn
Breckinridge Co HS; Harned, KY (12%-200) Ann; VP, Chor; Tres, NHS; Rptr, Sch P; Campbellsville Col; Mus.

HARDEBECK, Susan Arlene
Crystal Lake Comm HS; Crystal Lake, IL (9-500) Band; Tres, NHS; Orch; Sftbl; NMS; St Scholar; Vlbl; McHenry Co Col; Vet Med.

HARDEE, Dudley Joseph
Marine Military Acad; Harlingen, TX; NHS; Ftbl; Tr; Hon Prog; U of Tex.

HARDEGREE, Alison Steel
Mena HS; Mena, AR (10%-120) Ann; NHS; A-Ed, Sch P; Rptr, SC; Tnns; Journ.

HARDEN, Amy Jo
Findlay Sr HS; Findlay, OH; Band; Chor; Ensm; Kiwanis A; Yth Fel; Bowling Green St U; Home Ec.

HARDEN, Janet Lynn
MacKenzie HS; Detroit, MI (32-352) NHS; Wayne Co Col; Bus.

HARDEN, Nathalyn Mercedes
Terrell Co HS; Dawson, GA (10%-112) BC; NHS; DARGCA; HCt; Andrew Col.

HARDEN, Sheena Angela
Northwestern Comm HS; Flint, MI; Chldr; Chor; City Conf; Hmrm; Rptr, Sch P; Tr; Cl Fav; ARC A; Yth Fel; U of Mich at Flint; Nurs.

HARDER, Juanita Ann
Hilbert HS; Hilbert, WI; Band; Ensm; NFL; Pom-Pon Squad; Vlbl.

HARDER, Mark Kevin
Lakeshore Sr HS; Stevensville, MI (5%-400) Band; Community Yth Symph; VP, SC; Bus.

HARDIE, Denise Suzanne
M B Smiley HS; Houston, TX (1-461) Mu Alpha Theta; NHS; Alg A; Bio A; COM; Citz A; Hist A; Math A; Most Out; Sci A; Type A.

HARDIE, Laurie Ann
Coupeville Jr Sr HS; Coupeville, WA (17-42) Chldr; Chor; 4H; NHS; HCt; Pres, Girls C; Puget Sound Col of The Bible; Teaching.

HARDIE, Leslie Helen
El Paso HS; El Paso, TX (5%-400) Chor; Ger C; Hmrm; Lit Mag; NHS; SC; Secy, Tri-HiY; Tres, Y-Tns; Beauty; COM; Citz A; Math A; Modern Dance; Art A; Interlochen Schol; Vanderbilt U; Pre-Med.

HARDIE, Tammie Sue
Coupeville HS; Coupeville, WA (6-78) Chldr; Chor; SC; Pres, Soph Cl; Bkbl; Tr; Amer Leg A; Puget Sound Col o-t Bible.

HARDIGREE, Scott Wayne
Aiken HS; Aiken, SC (5-710) Ann; BC; S-T, Chem C; S-T, Demolay; Hmrm; InterClub Coun; Key C; NHS; Pres, Sci C; Parl, SC; COM; Math A; Sci A; Pres, Rifle Tm; Mead Hall Hon A; Fr A; Presbyterian Col Jr Fel; MYF; Stu Coun A; Cert of Achv; NRA; Marksman, Sharpshooter A; Clemson U; Pre-Med.

HARDIMAN, Tara Lechia Rachael
Acad of Our Lady of Mercy; Milford, CT (2-88) CYO; Chor; Drama; Fr C; Key C; Sch P; Swim; NEDT; Law.

HARDIN, Barry Lynn
Malvern Sr HS; Malvern, AR (31-270) Band; Fr C; NHS; Golf.

HARDIN, Deborah Sharlene
Clyde A Erwin HS; Asheville, NC; Co-Cpt, Chldr; Chor; GS; Hmrm; Tr; HCt; Church Sftbl; FCA; Keywanette; Photography.

HARDIN, John Wesley
Lake HS; Lake, MS; BC; Math C; Order/Arrow; Var C; Ftbl; COM; God & Country A; Math A; Order/Arrow A; Q&S A; Yth Fel; Eagle Sct; Pres, Church Yth; Alt Del, St Church Conf; E Central Jr Col; Elec Engr.

HARDIN, Karan Ann
Weatherford HS; Weatherford, TX; FBLA; Cpt, Vlbl; DECA Stu o-t Mo; N Tex St U; Distributive Ed.

HARDIN, Lisa Karen
Washington Co HS; Springfield, KY (20-167) Fr-Ed, Ann; Band; BC; Ensm; FTA; Sftbl; Bio A; Chem A; Sci A; Sup, KMEA Solo Festival; All-Dist Band; Eastern Ky U; Social Work.

HARDIN, Melanie Elaine
R-S Central HS; Rutherfordton, NC (60-241) Fr C; FNA; FTA; S-T, Hmrm; ARC; W Piedmont Col; Nurs.

HARDIN, Neal Edward
W End Christian HS; Tuscaloosa, AL; Sci C; HiY; Mgr, Bkbl; Mgr, Ftbl; Mgr, Tnns; Mgr, Tr; ARC A; Sci A; Yth Fel; Athletic A; Trade Sch; Emergency Med Tech.

HARDIN, Paul David Norman
Hays HS; Hays, KS (95%-300) Band; 4H; NFL; Bsbl; JV, Bkbl; Cr-Ctry; Ftbl; Semi-Fin, Tr; Semi-Fin, Wrest; Cl Fav; 4H A; Yth Fel; Sci.

HARDIN, Ruth Ann
Morrison HS; Morrison, IL (9-156) Chldr; Dbte Tm; VP, FTA; GS; VP, 4H; NHS; Secy, Sr Cl; Pres, Jr Cl; Cpt, Bkbl; Co-Cpt, Tr; DARGCA; 4H A; Hist A; HCt; Hon Prog; St Scholar; VFW A; U of Iowa.

HARDIN, Sharon Marie
Meridian HS; Meridian, TX; BC; Chldr; VP, FHA; 4H; Bkbl; Tr; Cl Fav; 4H A; Type A.

HARDING, Charles Douglas Jr
Richard Montgomery HS; Rockville, MD (12-402) Chor; Hmrm; InterAct C; Co-Ch, NHS; Rptr, Sch P; SC; Var C; Bsbl; Co-Cpt, Ftbl; Co-Cpt, Wrest.

HARDING, David Scott
Miramonte HS; Orinda, CA (90-360) A Cap Choir; Drama; Fr C; Model UN; World Affairs C; CSF; BSct Eagle A; *U of Calif Santa Barbara.*

HARDING, Gale Sue
Green Ridge R-8 HS; Green Ridge, MO (4-36) Ed, Ann; Pres, Band; Cpt, Chldr; Chor; Ensm; FFA; FHA; SC; Cpt, Bkbl; Sftbl; COM; Cl Fav; Interlochen Ntl Mus; Pres A; ARC A; Regent Schol; Type A; Ann Qn; Ecology C; Most Popular; Glee C; GSct; Jubilee Day Qn Cand; Vlbl; Miss Mo Teenage Pageant; Pep C; Asst Church Pianist; *SW Mo St U;* Psych.

HARDING, Gilbert Jr
Guthrie HS; Guthrie, OK (45-200) A Cap Choir; Parl, Band; Bus C; Tres, Chem C; Chor; Cum Laude Soc; Drama; Ensm; FTA; JETS; VP, Key C; NFL; Order/Arrow; Phys C; ARC; Tres, Sci C; Spch C; SC; Bkbl; Cpt, Tnns; Chem A; Citz A; Cl Fav; Lion A; Math A; MLS; Regent Schol; Sci A; Yth Leg; Chaplain, FBLA; Mr FBLA; Ntl FBLA Del; Okla St U Alumni A; *Okla St U; Chem Engr.*

HARDING, Janice
North Side HS; Fort Worth, TX (19-222) Ed, Ann; Co-Cpt, Chldr; Chor; SC; Pres, Sr Cl; Cl Fav; Yth Fel; Ann Comp; *Tarrant Co Jr Col; Phys Ed.*

HARDING, Jonathan Francis
High Point HS; Beltsville, MD; Demolay; *Pratt Inst; Design.*

HARDING, Mary Louise
Decatur HS; Decatur, GA (15%-150) BC; Chor; Math C; Secy, Span C; Tnns; HCt; Type A; WSB Young Amer; *Bus.*

HARDING, Monica Lee
Patten HS; Oakland, CA; Pres, Chor; Orch; Cpt, Ftbl; Cpt, Soccer; COM; Citz A; Kiwanis A; Uniform A; *Patten Bible Col; Bible.*

HARDING, Paul Harvey
Nestucca Union HS; Cloverdale, OR (5-62) Chor; Drama; NHS; SC; Var C; VP, Soph Cl; JV, Bsbl; Wrest; NEDT; Var Ltr; Hugh O'Brien Leadership Win; *Willmette Col; Law.*

HARDING, Roberta Maria
Eldorado HS; Albuquerque, NM; Bus C; Drama; NHS; Span C; Spch C; Span NHS; Tres, SC; Tres, Thes; VP, Soph Cl; I Dare You; Spch A; City & Dist Win, Bicen Debate; *U of Miami; Interntl Bus.*

HARDING, Shelia Viola
Gumberry HS; Gumberry, NC (2-110) Chor; Fr C; GS; Sch P; SC; Soph Cl; B Crocker A; Citz A; Math A; Most Out; *NC St U; Bus.*

HARDING, Stanton Paul
Holyoke HS; Holyoke, CO (10-60) Chor; Sci C; JV, Ftbl; Golf; Sftbl; Swim; Tnns; JV, Wrest; *Life Sci.*

HARDING, Susan Elizabeth
Kirksville Sr HS; Kirksville, MO (30-197) Band; Chldr; Chor; FHA; Sftbl; Tnns; GAA; *Central Col.*

HARDING, Thelma Louise
Gumberry HS; Gumberry, NC; Secy, Jr Cl; *Winston Salem Col; Nurs.*

HARDISON, Angela Yvonne
Melbourne HS; Melbourne, FL; VP, FHA; NHS; SC; COM; Hon Prog; Math A; *Fla St U; Med.*

HARDISON, Charley Lynn
Brethren HS; Paramount, CA (20-90) A Cap Choir; VP, Ski C; Ftbl; MVP, Soccer; Tr; CSF; *Nampa Nazerene Col; Med.*

HARDISON, Sharon Ann
Williamston HS; Williamston, NC (3-230) Band; Chor; Fr C; Mjrte; Pres A; Presidential Phys Fitness; Ldrship Seminar; *E Carolina Col; Mus.*

HARDISTY, Sheila Lynn
Woodlake Union HS; Woodlake, CA (5-112) Pres, FHA; 4H; SC; Golf; Bank Of Amer A; CSF; COM; 4H A; St Scholar; Co Cow Bells Schol; *Fresno St Col; Home Ec.*

HARDLE, Peggy Susan
Anoka Sr HS; Anoka, MN (15%-1000) Band; Drama; Ensm; NHS; Sch P; Ski C; Golf; Vlbl; 1st Chair, Concert Band; *Bethel Col; Law.*

HARDMAN, Martha Jo
Albuquerque HS; Albuquerque, NM (25%-500) Fr C; GS; NHS; Sch P; SC; *U of NM; Fr.*

HARDMAN, Teresa Bell
Vista HS; Vista, CA (164-780) Band; Chor; Drama; NHS; Orch; COM; God & Country A; ARC A; Awana Ldr; Panther Christian Fel; Teacher, Good News C; Talents For Christ; Ntl Span Exam; *Los Angeles Baptist Col; Bible.*

HARDMAN, Van Clifford
Fort Payne HS; Fort Payne, AL (19-170) Hmrm; NHS; SC; Bsbl; Cpt, Bkbl; Cpt, Ftbl; HCt; Type A; Span A; Outst Sr; *U of Ala; Pre-Dentistry.*

HARDOMAN, William T
Charles E Hughes HS; NY, NY (134-425) *Hunter Col.*

HARDRICK, Andre Desmond
Lindblom Tech HS; Chicago, IL; JV, Bsbl; JV, Tr; *Bradley Col; Phys Ed.*

HARDS, Collin Del
Shorecrest HS; Seattle, WA; A Cap Choir; Chor; Hmrm; NHS; SC; Bkbl; Citz A; Coun of Teach A; Ntl Achv Schol; Star Student; Yth Fel; *Journ.*

HARDWICK, Mary Ruth
Cleveland HS; Cleveland, TN (25%-240) Anchor C; Drama; Fr C; Lat C; Pres, Sci C; Bkbl; Tnns; *Jefferson St U; Biol.*

HARDY, Anita Beryl
Banning HS; Banning, CA (44-171) A Cap Choir; Chor; Yth Fel; *Bus Adm.*

HARDY, Beverly Kay
Warsaw HS; Warsaw, IL (15-52) AFS; FHA; Secy, Hmrm; Sch P; Sftbl; 4H A; *Beautician.*

HARDY, Blakely Richard
Southern Guilford HS; Greensboro, NC (8-125) Chess C; Chor; NHS; Hist A; Yth Leg; Jr Marshal; *U of NC at Greensboro; Mus.*

HARDY, Cindy Ann
Warsaw HS; Warsaw, IL (10-55) AFS; Chldr; FBLA; FHA; VP, NHS; Ed, Sch P; SC; Var C; Sftbl; *NE Mo St U; Med Secy.*

HARDY, Dana Janette
Sunset HS; Beaverton, OR; JV, Golf.

HARDY, David Alfred
Kinston HS; Kinston, NC (35-330) Chess C; Dbte Tm; VP, Demolay; Ch, Drama; Secy, Order/Arrow; Pol Sci C; F-Ed, Sch P; SC; Swim; JV, Wrest; COM; Cl Fav; Journ A; Masonic A; MLS; Order/Arrow A; Hon Men, Schol Books; Short Story; 1st, NC Jr Wmn's C, Shrt Stry Con; *U of NC; Journ.*

HARDY, Debra Annette
Bowen HS; Chicago, IL; Band; COM; *Elem Ed.*

HARDY, Deena Anne
Marvell HS; Marvell, AR (4-120) Ann; BC; VP, FBLA; Ger C; SC; HCt; *Phillips Co Comm Col; Acct.*

HARDY, Jacqueline Lynelle
Minden HS; Minden, LA; Citz A; Jr Civitans; *Tex Sou Col; Pol Sci.*

HARDY, James Hartsfield
Reidsville Sr HS; Reidsville, NC (10-324) Order/Arrow; Ftbl; Co-Cpt, Wrest; *NC St U; Engr.*

HARDY, Jan Leigh
Monterey HS; Lubbock, TX (25%-600) A Cap Choir; Secy, Bus C; *Jacksonville Bapt Col; Mus.*

HARDY, Laura Virginia
Newton Co Comprehensive HS; Covington, GA; Band; BC; Chor; 4H; Span C; Tri-HiY; Y-Tns; Tnns; 4H A; Hon Prog; All St Chor; *Fashion Merchandising.*

HARDY, Letty Charmaine
Elston Sr HS; Michigan City, IN (100-350) Band; Mjrte; SC; Amer Leg A; COM; Choir; VP, Human Relations; Secy, Sunday Sch; Win, Trips to Spain & Guatemala; Steering Comm; *Ind U; Phys Therapy.*

HARDY, Lois Rebekah
Weymouth No HS; Weymouth, MA (50-501) Lit Mag; Ltr of Approval, Bible Memory Assn; *Barrington Col; Secondary Ed.*

HARDY, Marie
G W Carver HS; Birmingham, AL (16-237) Bus Mgr, Band; Ensm; Pres, Orch; HQn; HCt; *Lawson St Jr Col; Early Child Care.*

HARDY, Mary Jo
St Mary's HS; Lynn, MA (4-146) CYO; Hmrm; Bkbl; Sftbl; Alg A; Bio A; Hist A; Math A; Eng A.

HARDY, Michael Richard
Harrington HS; Harrington, WA (6-13) VP, Band; Chor; FFA; Sr Cl; Tnns; *Spokane Comm Col; Farm Agr.*

HARDY, Ralph Kennedy
Kinston HS; Kinston, NC (25-330) Chess C; Pres, Dbte Tm; VP, Demolay; Hmrm; Order/Arrow; Secy, Pol Sci C; Rptr, Sch P; Journ A; Masonic A; Order/Arrow A; Sci A; *U of NC; Law.*

HARDY, Rickey Eugene
Princeton HS; Cincinnati, OH (225-750) Span NHS; Tres, SC; Y-Tns; Tres, Sr Cl; Citz A; Hist A; Human Relations Cert; Span Hon Soc; Mgr, Bowl; *Engr.*

HARDY, Sandra Kay
Old Mill Sr HS; Glen Burne, MD (349-500) Co-Cpt, Chldr; Hmrm; Lit Mag; SC; Var C; Ch, Sr Cl; Ch, Jr Cl; Mgr, Tr; Cl Fav; HCt; Designer, Cl Ring; WW; *Col Misericordia; Social Work.*

HARDY, Stuart Keith
Tarboro Sr HS; Tarboro, NC (10%-250) Band; Chor; Drama; Ensm; Fr C; NHS; Pres, Order/Arrow; Sch P; Sci C; Order/Arrow A; Sci Hon Seminar; All-St Chorus; *UNC at Chapel Hill; Sci.*

HARDY, Suzanne Elizabeth
Moorefield HS; Moorefield, WV (12-88) Co-Cpt, Chldr; Chor; Fr C; NHS; Var C; Tr; Cl Fav; Type A; Yth Fel; *Marshall U; Dietetics.*

HARE, Barbara Sellers
Altoona HS; Altoona, PA (75-950) Fr C; Orch; Ski C; Tnns; Comm Symph; Most Improved, Tnns; Undefeated, Tnns Singles; *Pa St U; Pol Sci.*

HARELDSON, Gary Wayne
Lanesboro HS; Lanesboro, MN (8-32) Band; Chor; FFA; NHS; Bsbl; Ftbl; Tr; COM; *Rochester Votech Col; Elec.*

HARGER, Ronald Scott
Okemos HS; Okemos, MI; NHS; Golf; Tnns; Central Mich Amateur Radio T; FCC; *Architecture.*

HARGETT, Gloria Elaine
W Craven HS; Vanceboro, NC (7-160) Ann; Dbte Tm; FBLA; Hmrm; NHS; Co-Ed, Sch P; Sci C; Span C; SC; Secy, Sr Cl; Tnns; Citz A; Elk A; Most Out; Type A; Pep C; Eng, Span, A's; Bible C; Human Relations Committee; Hist, Jr Civitan; Journ C; *Appalachian Col; Phar.*

HARGETT, Icsolene
W Craven HS; Vanceboro, NC; Co-Ed, Ann; Dbte Tm; FBLA; Hmrm; NHS; Sci C; Span C; SC; VP, Sr Cl; Tnns; HQn; Most Out; Pep C; Vlbl; Bible C; Jr Civitans; Journ; *Appalachian St U; Psych.*

HARGIS, Elvin Kent
Spearman HS; Spearman, TX (20-84) Chor; Drama; SC; Thes; Cpt, Ftbl; Cl Fav; Yth Fel; *Amarillo Jr Col; Phys Ed.*

HARGIS, Karen Sue
Southwood HS; Shreveport, LA; Drama; FHA; Spch C; Y-Tns; Sftbl; Tnns; Pres A; Yth Fel; *LSU-S; Religion.*

HARGIS, Kirby Dean
Spearman HS; Spearman, TX; Band; VP, FFA; FTA; SC; Bkbl; Ftbl; Tr.

HARGRAVES, Cynthia Janelle
Kountze HS; Kountze, TX; Chldr; FHA; FTA; Jr Miss Pagent; NHS; Sci C; SC; Secy; B Crocker A; Cl Fav; H of F; HQn; Hon Prog; Yth Fel; Swtht, FFA; Drill Tm; *Lamar U.*

HARGROVE, Alicia Marie
Cumberland Valley HS; Mechanicsburg, PA (27-564) Chldr; Chor; French NHS; NHS; Var C; Hon Prog; Co- cpt, Gym; *Pa St U; Engr.*

HARGROVE, Belinda Gayle
Frederick HS; Frederick, OK (4-110) Secy, Band; Chor; Math C; Type A; St Hon Soc; *Okla St U; Math.*

HARGROVE, Cynthia Kay
Crockett HS; Crockett, TX (2-140) Band; FTA; Mjrte; Span C; SC; Kiwanis A; Band Private; HR; *Tex A&M U; Bus.*

HARGROVE, David Lee
Lowes HS; Lowes, KY (2-62) Ann; Secy, BC; VP, FFA; F-Ed, Sch P; Tres, Sr Cl; Co-Cpt, Bsbl; Mgr, Bkbl; Chamber of Comm A; Cl Fav; MLS; Opt A; Rotary A; Sal; Spch A; Star Student; Young Democrats; Ky Colonel; Young Democrats; Ky Colonel; Courier Journ Essay Contest Win; *Murray St U; Optometry.*

HARGROVE, Gwendolyn
Baker HS; Columbus, GA; BC; Secy, Chor; Pres, FHA; Semi-Fin, Lit Ral; NHS; ARC; B Crocker A; COM; ARC A; *Mercer U; Pediatrics.*

HARGROVE, Sibyl Yvette
G W Carver HS; Montgomery, AL (3-400) Chldr; Tres, Fr C; French NHS; Math C; Mu Alpha Theta; NHS; SC; Pres, Sr Cl; VP, Jr Cl; Secy, Soph Cl; HQn; HCt; Most Out; ROTC A; Very Important Tn; Outst Girl o-t Yr; Sr o-t Wk; ROTC School; *Ariz St U; Bus Mgr.*

HARGROVE, Steven Neill
Frederick HS; Frederick, OK (4-110) Band; Chor; Math C; *Okla City U; Mus.*

HARKEN, Dennis Eugene
Ackley-Geneva Comm HS; Ackley, IA (33%-83) Band; NEDT; Valor A, Band; *Archt.*

HARKER, Patrick Timothy
Gloucester Cath HS; Gloucester, NJ (1-192) CYO; Ger C; VP, NHS; JV, Bkbl; Cpt, Ftbl; Co-Cpt, Tr; Chem A; Val; MVP, Ftbl; Outst Schol Ath; Lang A; Brooks-Irvine A; *U of Penn; Civil Engr.*

HARKIN, Margaret Ann
Our Lady of Good Counsel HS; Newark, NJ (12-76) Cpt, Chldr; Chem C; Drama; Fr C; Hmrm; VP, NHS; Ed, Sch P; Ski C; VP, SC; VP, Jr Cl; Sftbl; B Crocker A; Hon Prog; Journ A; NEDT; *Montclair St Col; Math.*

HARKINS, Donnalynn
Darby-Colwyn Sr HS; Darby, PA (15-189) FBLA; NHS.

HARKINS, Eloise
Motley HS; Columbus, MS (12-70) BC; Hmrm; F-Ed, Sch P; Sci C; Tri-HiY; Secy, Jr Cl; Arch; COM; Cl Fav; Spch A; Eng A; *Alcorn St U; Acct.*

HARKINS, Randal Dean
Crockett HS; Crockett, TX (10%-110) Band; FFA; Hist A; *Tex A&M U.*

HARKNESS, Ricky
Fayette Co HS; Fayette, AL; A Cap Choir; Arch; Band; Chem C; Chor; Drama; VP, FFA; VP, 4H; Key C; Math A; Mu Alpha Theta; Phys C; Sci C; SC; Arch; Bsbl; JV, Bkbl; JV, Ftbl; JV, Tnns; Amer Leg A; Cl Fav; Math A; NEDT; Phy A; *Auburn U; Forestry.*

HARKRADER, Teresa Levorda
Pampa Sr HS; Pampa, TX (16-326) Chldr; FHA; Secy, Hmrm; NHS; Span C; Swim; Cl Fav; 1st Runner Up, Best Citz A; Span Qn; Foreign Study League, Tour Europe; *Texas Tech U.*

HARKRIDER, Michael Alan
Eastern Hills HS; Fort Worth, TX (30%-465) Hmrm; Bsbl; Nom, Cl Fav; Nom, Mr EHHS; Powder Puff Ftbl King; *U of Tex at Arlington; Agr.*

HARKSON, Esther Adreane
Lakeridge HS; Lake Oswego, OR; AFS; Hmrm; NHS; Span C; Pres, Jr Cl; Soccer; Tr; *Briar Cliff Col; Ed.*

HARKSON, Esther Ardeane
Millburn HS; Millburn, NJ (10%-350) Mgr, Bsbl; Mgr, Bkbl; *Lib Arts.*

HARLAN, David Anthony
University HS; San Diego, CA (3-311) Math C; NHS; Phys C; Sch P; Var C; Rptr, Sch P; MVP, Cr-Ctry; MVP, Tr; COM; Hon Prog; Most Out; *San Diego St U; Engr.*

HARLAN, Gloria Denise
Northwest HS; St Louis, MO (7-728) Swim; Hon Prog; Most Out; Type A; Amer Guild of Mus; Schol HR; Ntl Piano Playing Auditions; *Data Programmer.*

HARLAN, Laura Hope
Winnfield Sr HS; Winnfield, LA (39-159) Ann; Bus C; Drama; FBLA; FHA; FTA; Rainbow; Spch C; HCt; Yth Fel; Yth Foundation; Cpt, Drill Tm; *Baylor U; Nurs.*

HARLAN, Mitchele James
Ogemaw Heights HS; W Branch, MI (15-265) Cpt, 4H; Order/Arrow; JV, Golf; COM; Yth Fel; *Law.*

HARLAN, Rachel Elizabeth
Fremont Ross HS; Fremont, OH (48-527) AFS; Band; NHS; Orch; Clarinet Ensm, Sup; Best Dance A; *Ohio Northern U; Phar.*

HARLAN, Richard Alan
Sunbright HS; Sunbright, TN (10-66) Co-Ed, Ann; VP, BC; FFA; 4H; Var C; VP, Soph Cl; Bsbl; Bkbl; Ftbl; FFA, Ftbl, Bkbl, A's; *Tenn Tech U; Engr.*

HARLAND, Tina Marie
Texhoma HS; Texhoma, OK (5-20) Band; Chor; FHA; 4H; Jr Miss Pagent; NHS; Var C; Bkbl; Tr; Alg A; Cl Fav; DARGCA; Hist A; Masonic A; Math A; Sci A; Eng A; *Panhandle St U; Vet.*

HARLESS, Jolisa Kay
Merritt HS; Elk City, OK; VP, 4H; Sch P; Spch C; Bkbl; Tr; COM; Gov Honor Prog; Hist A; HQn; HCt; Hon Prog; Spch A; St Scholar; St Hon Soc; *Surgical Technologist.*

HARLESS, Lesa Annette
Moreno Valley HS; Sunnymead, CA (10-500) Fr C; French NHS; NHS; SC; Pres, Soph Cl; Tr; Hon Prog; *Pepperdine U; Foreign Lang.*

HARLESS, Randal Glenn
Scott HS; Madison, WV; Pres, 4H; InterAct C; Lat C; VP, NHS; SC; Bsbl; Co-Cpt, Ftbl; Mgr, Wrest; Alg A; 4H A; I Dare You; *W Va Inst of Tech; Engr.*

HARLEY, Cheryl Ann
Benjamin Franklin HS; New York, NY; Cpt, Chldr; Secy, Chor; Drama; Mjrte; Ntl Yth Conf; Sch Achieve Tm; Co-Ed, Sch P; Span NHS; St Stu Congress; Pres, SC; Pres, Jr Cl; Swim; Tr; COM; Yth Fel; HR; VP, Yth Choir; *Columbia U; Pre-Dentistry.*

HARLEY, Jack T Jr
Dillon HS; Dillon, SC (8-240) BC; Semi-Fin, BS; Var C; Mgr, Bkbl; *Col Charleston & Med; Surgery.*

HARLEY, Karola Patrice
W Holt HS; Atkinson, NE (6-73) Ann; Chor; Ensm; 4H; Tr; 4H A; Spch A; HR; *Mus.*

HARLIN, Tribune Verlisa
Westinghouse Area Voc HS; Chicago, IL (38-549) Chor; Drama; Amer Leg A; COM; Math A; *Pepperdine U; Nurs.*

HARLOW, Everett Tolman III
Elk Grove Sr HS; Elk Grove, CA; Arch; Band; Chess C; Drama; Fr C; Var C; Arch; Swim; Tnns; HR A; *Calif Baptist Col; Humanities.*

HARLOW, Mickey Lane
Treadwell HS; Memphis, TN (15-176) Math C; Mu Alpha Theta; NHS; VP, SC; Tres, Soph Cl; Bkbl; Cr-Ctry; Tnns; Tr; Cl Fav; H of F; Tn o-t Wk; All St Bkbl Tourn; Pres, Bible C; *Bus.*

HARLOW, Patricia Kiyono
Pana Sr HS; Pana, IL (71-175) Band; VP, FBLA; Pres, FHA; Sch P; *Secretarial Sci.*

HARLOW, Scott James
Watertown HS; Watertown, CT (10-300) Demolay; Hmrm; SC; Bsbl; Ftbl; S-T, Yth Fel; *Gordon Col; Religion.*

HARMAN, Jeffery Douglas
Bluefield HS; Bluefield, WV (28-364) Fr C; Key C; NHS; SC; Cpt, Ftbl; Hon Prog; Yth Foundation; Most Dedicated Ath; All Sectional Tm, Bsbl; *NC St U; Marine Bio.*

HARMAN, Joyce O
Muskogee HS; Muskogee, OK (25-550) AFS; Lat C; NFL; Spch C; VP, Thes; Wittiest; Most Versatile Performer; *Okla St U.*

HARMAN, Risa Renae
Huguenot HS; Richmond, VA (8-254) AFS; Co-Ed, Ann; VP, Chor; Pres, Drama; Ensm; InterClub Coun; NHS; Span C; Thes; Y-Tns; H of F; Best Actress; Most Talented; *Va Commonwealth U; Mus.*

HARMAN, Teresa Ann
Moorefield HS; Moorefield, WV (40-86) Ann; Chor; FHA; 4H; Sch P; *Fairmont St Col.*

HARMATA, Michael Andrew
Kelly HS; Chicago, IL; NHS; Ed, Sch P; Span NHS; Mgr, Bkbl; Lion A; Math A; NEDT; Q&S A; Val; *U of Ill; Chem.*

HARMON, Barbara
Franklin HS; Los Angeles, CA (5%-600) CYO; Chor; FTA; Hmrm; Key C; NHS; Cpt, Tr; CSF; PTA A; Pres A; Tres, Girls Coun; Nom, CYD Tn Qn; Cpt, Pres, Drill Tm; Auto C A; Church Yth Choir; Hazel Gross School; Nom, Outst Soph Girl; *Glendale Comm Col; Phys Ed.*

HARMON, Beverly Denise
D F Douglass HS; Montezuma, GA (5%-110) A-Ed, Ann; Drama; FBLA; FHA; Secy, Hmrm; Ed, Sch P; Sci C; Span C; SC; Tri-HiY; COM; Hist A; Yth Foundation; WW; *Ga SW Col; Pre-Dentistry.*

HARMON, Brian Allen
Anamosa HS; Anamosa, IA (116-135) Band; Chor; Drama; Ftbl; Tr; COM.

HARMON, Deborah Ann
Anniston HS; Anniston, AL; Ann; Chldr; Chor; *U of Ala; Rehabilitation.*

HARMON, Elizabeth Ann
W Point HS; West Point, MS; Anchor C; Band; Cpt, Chldr; GS; Hmrm; Sci C; SC; Tr; COM; Honorary Lt Col, Gov Staff; 'W' C; Spirit A; Miss Ntl Tn-Ager St Fin; Vlbl Tm; *Ms U For Women; Merchandising.*

HARMON, Frank Joseph
I C Norcom HS; Portsmouth, VA; Chor; Ensm; Hmrm; ARC; Span C; Var C; Bsbl; Bkbl; Sftbl; Swim; Most Out; ARC A; Yth Fel; Art C; Cpt, MVP, Tennis; Art As.

HARMON, Gary Dennis
B T Washington HS; Atlanta, GA; Band; Hmrm; Bkbl; Ftbl; Swim; Tnns; Tr; Wrest; COM; ROTC A; Library Aide; Sup Medal Band; *UCLA; Pilot.*

HARMON, James LaRue
Tallulah Acad; Tallulah, LA; Pres, Soph Cl; Bkbl; Ftbl; COM; Hist A; Math A; Sci A; Civics A; LISA St Civics A; Band A; *Engr.*

HARMON, Joyce Colleen
Beaman-Conrad-Liscomb HS; Conrad, IA (15-64) Chor; Drama; VP, 4H; Thes; Tres, Sr Cl; 4H A; HCt; Spch A; Vocal Mus A; *Hawkeye Inst of Tech; Horticultural Sci.*

HARMON, Mark Lane
Trinity Heights Christian Acad; Shreveport, LA (33%-50) Key C; Lit Ral; Math C; NHS; Sci C; Span C; SC; Bsbl; Bkbl; Ftbl; Tnns; FCA; Bsbl Scholastic A; *Med.*

HARMON, Melinda Kaye
Central HS; Savannah, TN (20-230) Ed, Ann; BC; FHA; Rainbow; Var C; Cpt, Bkbl; Sftbl; *Freed-Hardimen U; Phar.*

HARMON, Stephen
Diamond Hill Jarvis HS; Fort Worth, TX (75-150) Band; Chor; 4H; Rodeo C; Pres, Yth Group; *U of Tex; Agr Ed.*

HARMON, Velton James
Wadley HS; Wadley, GA (5-80) Co-Ed, Ann; VP, BC; Drama; VP, FFA; 4H; Math C; A-Ed, Sch P; Pres, Spch C; Rptr, Sr Cl; Mgr, Bkbl; Ftbl; Sftbl; COM; Cl Fav; Hist A; HKg; Journ A; JA A; Math A; MLS; Sci A; Spch A; Eng, Agr, Driver's Ed, A's; *Fort Valley St Col; Agr.*

HARMON, Vicki Sue
Dawson Bryant HS; Coal Grove, OH (3-114) Ed, Ann; Chor; GS; VP, NHS; DARGCA; Hist A; Hon Prog; Math A; MLS; Type A; Eng A; *Ashland Comm Col; Bus.*

HARMON, Wanda Ann
Garden City HS; Garden City, KS; A Cap Choir; Band; Chor; Ensm; Madrigal; NHS; Hon Prog; Ntl Achv School; Pres A; *Mid-Amer Nazarene Col; Mus.*

HARMS, Alison Ann
Heritage HS; Littleton, CO (34-382) Chor; 4H; Var C; JV, Bkbl; Cpt, Sftbl; Tnns; Citz A; 4H A; Hon Prog; Yth Fel; Vlbl; Butler Schol; *Doane Col; Elem Ed.*

HARMS, Gary Steven
Colton HS; Colton, CA; Band; Drama; Hmrm; Key C; NFL; Orch; F-Ed, Sch P; Spch C; Amer Leg A; Amer Leg Orator A; Aux Lat; COM; Citz A; Journ A; Kiwanis A; Lion A; Q&S A; Spch A; VFW A; VFW Orator Win; VofDEM; Eagle Sct; Key C; Lion's C Zone Fin; Journ Convention Del; *Pepperdine U; Pol Sci.*

HARMS, Robert L
MacArthur HS; Irving, TX (29-598) Drama; VP, Fr C; Hmrm; NHS; SC; *U of Tex; Radio-television.*

HARMS, Vickie Lynn
Benton Co R-1 HS; Cole Camp, MO (4-66) A Cap Choir; Chor; NHS; Co-Ed, Sch P; Var C; Secy, Jr Cl; Bkbl; Sftbl; Swtht.

HARMSEN, Laurie Kay
Eddyville HS; Eddyville, OR (1-13) Bus Mgr, Ann; Band; Chor; FFA; GS; Pres, 4H; VP, SC; MVP, Tr; 4H A; Vlbl; *Mt Hood Comm Col; Phys Therapy Assistant.*

HARNESS, Rene
Willard HS; Willard, MO (30-220) Chor; *SW Mo St U.*

HARNETT, Mary Catherine
St Joseph's Notre Dame HS; Alameda, CA (12-55) Ann; Cpt, Chldr; NHS; SC; CSF; Hon Prog; Fr II A; *Loyola-Marymount U; Communication.*

HARNEY, Janet Elaine
Lourdes Central HS; Nebraska City, NE (7-29) Co-Ch, Ann; Chldr; Chor; 4H; NHS; Pres, Span C; VP, Soph Cl; Tr; 4H A; HCt; Hon Prog; Opt Out Tn; WW; Anytown Alt; *U of Nebr at Lincoln; Journ.*

HARNEY, Mary Sue
Franklin Co HS; Frankfort, KY (163-500) Chor; Midway Col; Nurs.

HARNEY, Miriam Elizabeth
Goodlettsville HS; Goodlettsville, TN (20%-190) Chldr; Hmrm; Span C; VP, Spch C; SC; Secy, Soph Cl; JV, Bkbl; Tr; Spch A; Tn o-t Mo; *Samford U; Sci.*

HAROIAN, John
Belmont HS; Belmont, MA (25%-370) BS; Chor; Drama; SC; VP, Thes; Tres, Jr Cl; BS; *Harvard U; Bus.*

HARPER, Annette
Littlefield Jr Sr; Lumberton, NC (3-100) Ed, Ann; S-T, BC; Fr C; FHA; Math C; Bkbl; A-Ed, Ann; *E Carolina U; Spch Pathology.*

HARPER, Carol Sue
Clark Co R-1 HS; Kahoka, MO (5-96) Band; VP, Bus C; Chldr; Ensm; VP, FBLA; Pres, 4H; Mjrte; NHS; Sci C; Span C; Thes; JV, Bkbl; Alg A; 4H A.

HARPER, Cathy Lynn
Thayer R2 HS; Thayer, MO; A Cap Choir; Ann; Band; BC; Chor; Ensm; FHA; Cand, Miss Merry Christmas; Pres, Crusaders For Christ; *SW Mo St U; Secondary Ed.*

HARPER, Christopher Kendall
Elliott Co HS; Sandy Hook, KY (6-90) Pres, BC; Hist A; *Morehead St U; Law.*

HARPER, Cindy Dianne
Ole Main HS; N Little Rock, AR (30%-410) FBLA; Y-Tns; March of Dimes; DAHSS.

HARPER, Elaine Renee
Borah HS; Boise, ID (47-617) A Cap Choir; Band; NW Ariz Solo & Ensm A; *NW Nazarene Col; Elem Ed.*

HARPER, Hiram Gene
Columbia HS; Decatur, GA (12-300) BC; Mu Alpha Theta; NHS; Tnns; Wrest; COM; *Ga St Col; Bus Adm.*

HARPER, Irma Lou
Palmer HS; Palmer, TX (5-27) Ann; Chldr; Dbte Tm; Drama; Pres, FHA; ARC; Sch P; Rptr, Sr Cl; Bkbl; Sftbl; Tnns; Tr; Citz A; HQn; HCt; Swtht; Harvest Qn; *Stephen F Austin U; Fashion Merchandiser.*

HARPER, Jacquelyn Denise
Greenville HS; Greenville, MS; Chldr; Most Out; *U of Sou Miss; Phar.*

HARPER, Jeffrey Michael
Manalapan HS; Englishtown, NJ (29-350) Band; Community Yth Symph; Orch; Sci A; Festival Hon Band; *Engr.*

HARPER, Jennifer Gail
Metter HS; Metter, GA; Ed, Ann; Band; BC; Drama; FBLA; Pres, FHA; Pres, 4H; Hmrm; Inter-Club Coun; Pres, Key C; Cpt, Mjrte; Ed, Sch P; Tri-HiY; VP, Var C; Bkbl; Golf; Cpt, Tnns; Beauty; COM; DARGCA; 4H A; Hist A; HCt; Journ A; ARC A; Co-Cpt, Mjrte; MVP, Tnns; Attendance A; HR.

HARPER, John Robert
Holy Savior Menard Central HS; Alexandria, LA (9-121) A Cap Choir; BS; Chor; Dbte Tm; Drama; Ensm; Pres, Fr C; VP, FBLA; Hmrm; InterAct C; InterClub Coun; Lit Ral; Ed, Lit Mag; NHS; Spch C; SC; Amer Leg A; COM; Citz A; Cl Fav; Hon Prog; Most Out; Spch A; Exchange C A; 1st St Mus; Rally Solo; WW; *Louisiana Col; Mus.*

HARPER, Judy Dawn
Fairview HS; Boulder, CO (35-670) Ski C; Pres, Span C; Tr; Pres, Explorers; *Colo St U; Bus Adm.*

HARPER, Laurie
Statesville Sr HS; Statesville, NC; Band; Hmrm; Span C; Var C; Ftbl; Tr; COM; WW; Player o-t Yr; *Lenoir-Rhyne Col; Computer Sci.*

HARPER, Laurie Ann
Wayne HS; Wayne, OK; FFA; Pres, FHA; 4H; VP, SC; Tres, Sr Cl; B Crocker A; Cl Fav; Crisco A; *OSU; Farm Mgt.*

HARPER, Marilyn Eileen
Taylorville Sr HS; Taylorville, IL (26-267) Chor; Drama; Fr C; Mjrte; *U of Colo; Phys Therapy.*

HARPER, Melinda Lea
Northwestern HS; Sciota, IL (25%-55) AFS; Ann; Band; Chem C; Parl, FFA; FHA; Pres, 4H; Key C; Co-Ed, Sch P; Sci C; Chor; Sftbl; Citz A; 4H A; I Dare You; FFA A; 4-H Key C; WW; *Carl Sandburg Jr Col; Nurs.*

HARPER, Nina Lee
Columbia HS; Decatur, GA; Hon Prog; Alpha Beta; Impact; Kappa C; *Ga St U; Pol Sci.*

HARPER, Scott David
Broomfield HS; Broomfield, CO (33%-300) Var C; JV, Bkbl; Ftbl; Tnns; Wrest; Hon Prog; Pres, Yth Fel; Pres, Yth C; Pres, Yth Group; *Trinity Col; Doctrine.*

HARPER, Scott Michael
East HS; Cheyenne, WY; Chor; Sftbl; Yth Fel; Praise Found, Singing Group; *Seattle Pacific Col; Mus.*

HARPER, Tamelia Ann
Samuel Elbert Acad; Elberton, GA; Tres, Anchor C; Ed, Ann; BC; Co-Cpt, Chldr; Tres, Hmrm; Madrigal; Cpt, Bkbl; Sftbl; Tnns; Tr; Cl Fav; DARGCA; Swtht; MVP, Bkbl; Miss Commodore; *Lander Col; Elem Ed.*

HARPER, Teri Lucile
Wayne Co HS; Wayne, GA; Ann; JV, Chldr; Hmrm; Tres, SC; VP, Sr Cl; Citz A; HCt; *Brewton-Parker Col; Therapeutic Recreation.*

HARPER, Vanessa Denise
Channel Island HS; Oxnard, CA; *Calif St U; Social Work.*

HARPER, Will
Withrow HS; Cincinnati, OH;

HARPER, Willa Denise
Wilhrow HS; Cincinnati, OH;

HARPLING, Dawn Marie
Foreman HS; Chicago, IL (27-373) Band; Mod Mus Mas; Tres, NHS; Cpt, Bkbl; Cpt, Tr; *NE Ill U.*

HARPOLD, Dixie Lee
Ripley HS; Ripley, WV; VP, FHA; Pres, Lib C; GAA; *Marshall Col; Home Ec.*

HARPS, Michael John
Danbury HS; Danbury, CT; Hmrm; SC; Var C; Bsbl; Cpt, Bkbl; *Phys Ed.*

HARPS, Valariea Yuolanda
Centennial HS; Compton, CA; Chldr; MVP, Sftbl; Swim; Type A; Most Improved, Vlbl; Runner Up, Miss Dream Girl; *El Camino Col; Bus.*

HARPSTER, Linda Dee
Neshaminy Langhorne HS; Langhorne, PA (120-692) Band; Chor; WW in Mus; *Bucks Co Comm Col; Bus.*

HARPSTER, Lisa Ann
Warren Area HS; Warren, PA; Band; Mjrte; Orch; Span C; Tr; Civic Orchestra; Colorguard; *Jamestown Bus Col; Secy.*

HARPSTER, Timothy Lee
Upper Scioto Valley HS; McGuffey, OH (2-85) Band; BC; Pres, FFA; Pres, 4H; Sci C; Span C; SC; JV, Cr-Ctry; Ftbl; Tr; 4H A; Math A; Sci A; Drivers Ed A; *Ohio St U; Vet Sci.*

HARPSTER, Wendy Kay
Warren Area HS; Warren, PA; Band; Tres, Ger C; Mjrte; Orch; Civic Orchestra; Colorguard.

HARR, Pamela Ann
Sheyenne River Acad; Harvey, ND (4-25) Band; Chldr; NHS; SC; VP, Jr Cl; Tres, Soph Cl; Cpt, Bkbl; Cpt, Ftbl; Cpt, Sftbl; Social VP, Girls C; *Walla Walla Col; Teaching.*

HARRA, Susan Shirley
Clearwater HS; Clearwater, FL (37-850) Ger C; Ch, Lit Mag; NHS; Thes; Y-Tns; Amer Leg A; DARGCA; NML; Hon Stars, Thespians; Achv A; *St Petersburg Jr Col; Commercial Art.*

HARRAS, John Mark
Victoria HS; Victoria, TX (49-600) Sci C; Mgr, Bkbl; Mgr, Ftbl; Mgr, Tr; *Victoria Col; Bus.*

HARREL, Albert Tracy
Winnfield Sr HS; Winnfield, LA (6-122) Anchor C; A-Ed, Ann; Tres, BC; FBLA; FFA; FTA; Pres, 4H; Lit Ral; Spch C; VP, SC; VP, Sr Cl; Cr-Ctry; Ftbl; Tr; Cl Fav; 4H A; Most Courteous; FHA Beau; Anchor Admiral; Spch C Beau; *LSU; Industrial Tech.*

HARRELL, Ben Craig
Dalton HS; Dalton, GA (4-251) Pres, Band; Ensm; Pres, HiY; InterClub Coun; Madrigal; VP, NHS; Orch; Bausch & Lomb A; COM; Gov Honor Prog; Hon Prog; NEDT; Sci A; Yth Leg; Singing Ensm; Emmcee, Homecoming PC Jr Fel; Pres, VP, Church, Yth Coun; *Ga Tech; Chem Engr.*

HARRELL, Brenda Kaye
Marion HS; Marion, IN (32-675) BC; Bus Mgr, Drama; NHS; Sci C; Span C; Bus Mgr, Thes; Pres, Soph Cl; Bkbl; Mgr, Tr; Sci A; Span A; *Marion Col; Nurs.*

HARRELL, Charles LaBre
Crossland Sr HS; Camp Springs, MD; French NHS; NHS; *U of Md; Psych.*

HARRELL, Christopher John
E Richland HS; Olney, IL (14-258) VP, Chor; NHS; ARC; F-Ed, Sch P; VP, SC; Tres, Var C; Pres, Soph Cl; Bsbl; Ftbl; Golf; Amer Leg A; Stu Advisory Comm, St Board of Ed; *E Ill U; Engr.*

HARRELL, David Eaton
N Springs HS; Atlanta, GA; Golf.

HARRELL, Donna Renee
Junius H Rose HS; Greenville, NC; Yth Fel; Keywanettes; *E Carolina U; Elem Ed.*

HARRELL, Felecia Elizabeth
The Gilbert Sch; Brooklyn, NY (5-35) Chor; Drama; Tres, Sr Cl; Swim; COM; Star Student; *Va St U; Fine Arts.*

HARRELL, Jacquelyn Diane
Chicago Voc HS; Chicago, IL (124-956) Tres, Sr Cl; COM; Hon Prog; Secy Prac-Touch A; Drama A; Vlbl Champ A; Flag & Rifle Cpt; Civic A; Pom Pom A; Gym Ldr; Tres, Hostess C; Sr Exec Board; *SIU; Stenography.*

HARRELL, Joan Taylor
Bertie Sr HS; Windsor, NC (10-500) Band; Chess C; FBLA; Sci C; *E Carolina U; Nurs.*

HARRELL, Joyce Regina
Glenn Hills HS; Augusta, GA (96-226) F-Ed, Ann; Cpt, Chldr; Chor; FHA; FTA; Hmrm; Sch P; Ch, SC; VP, Jr Cl; HQn; Sci A; Home Ec A; *Stephens Col; Fashion Merchandising.*

HARRELL, Laura Ann
Goodlettsville HS; Goodlettsville, TN (10%-185) Chldr; FTA; Hmrm; NHS; SC; Tnns; COM; Citz A.

HARRELL, Leisha Kay
Rossville Comp HS; Rossville, GA (7-225) Tres, BC; FBLA; Pres, SC; Y-Tns; Math A; Sci A; Key C Swtht; *Dalton Jr Col; Vet.*

HARRELL, Leslie Elayne
Greenville Christian Acad; Greenville, NC (3-15) *Dentistry.*

HARRELL, Linda
Cainhoy HS; Huger, SC (3-45) Bus C; Chor; Drama; FHA; Hmrm; Math C; NHS; Span C; SC; Math A; WW; *Fla St U; Acct.*

HARRELL, Martha LaRosa
Silsbee HS; Silsbee, TX (55-235) VP, FHA; FTA; Sch P; Span C; SC; Masonic A; PA A; Worthy Adv, Rainbow Girls; Yth Lrdrship Seminar Schol A; Pres, Rep & Secy, Philatelist C; Secy, OEA; *Lamar U; Bus.*

HARRELL, Peggy Sue
Heritage Christian Sch; Indianapolis, IN (7-38) Ann; Cpt, Chldr; Chor; Ensm; Lit Mag; Tr; *Tenn Temple U; Special Ed.*

HARRELL, Robin Lynn
John A Holmes HS; Edenton, NC (3-130) Pres, Band; Chor; Secy, Mod Mus Mas; Rptr, Monogram; NHS; Rptr, Span C; SC; Pres, Sr Cl; VP, Soph Cl; Cpt, Bkbl; Sftbl; Gr Marshal; HQn; All St Band; Katherine Smith Reynolds Schol; *U of NC at Greensboro; Recreation.*

HARRELL, Sidney Dean
Greenville Christian Acad; Greenville, NC (1-3) Ann; Chor; Fr C; Bkbl; Sftbl; God & Country A; H of F; Pres A; *E Carolina U; Audiology.*

HARRELL, Stanley Leman
Bertie Sr HS; Windsor, NC (4-340) Band; BC; Hon Prog; WW; *Howard U; Hist.*

HARRELSON, Lonnie Ray
Goose Creek HS; Goose Creek, SC; Ftbl; Tr; *US Naval Acad.*

HARRELSON, Pamela
Loris HS; Loris, SC (1-142) Ed, Ann; Chor; Pres, FHA; 4H; NHS; Sci C; Secy, SC; 4H A; Val; WW; PC Merit A; FHA HERO Comm; Pres, St FHA; *NC St U; Sci.*

HARREN, Margaret Yvonne
Eufaula HS; Eufaula, OK (13-98) *Connors St Col; Acct.*

HARRER, Lori Lee
Mt Pleasant Sr HS; Mt Pleasant, PA (55-289) Band; Chor; Drama; Ger C; Math C; NHS; Sch P; Ski C; Pres, Span C; Span NHS; Var C; Bkbl; Cpt, Sftbl; Cpt, Tnns; Alg A; GT Fav; God & Country A; Math A; Most Out; Spch A; Star Student; Yth Fel; Cl Clown; *Computer Tech of Pitts; Computers.*

HARRIES, Renee Leone
McLouth HS; McLouth, KS (1-35) Ed, Ann; Pres, Band; Chldr; Chor; Ensm; 4H; Cpt, Mjrte; Model UN; Pres, NHS; SC; UN Council; Var C; Tres, Jr Cl; Tr; Alg A; Citz A; DARGCA; HCt; Hon Prog; MLS; St Scholar; Swtht; Val; Yth Fel; Vlbl; *Emporia St U; Early Childhood Ed.*

HARRINGTON, Carolyn Anne
Hardaway HS; Columbus, GA (27-407) AFS; Anchor C; Cpt, Chldr; Chor; Hmrm; InterClub Coun; Model UN; NHS; SC; Secy, Sr Cl; Sftbl; Tr; HCt; Hon Prog; All Bi-City Tr; OWC Schol; Outst Sprinter; Project D; Yth Coun; *Converse Col; Elem Ed.*

HARRINGTON, Debra Ann
Warren Hills Regional Sr HS; Washington, NJ; Band; Tr; COM; Yth Fel; Miss NJ St Tn; *Lee Col; Mus.*

HARRINGTON, Douglas William
Imlay City HS; Imlay City, MI (2-205) Pres, Chem C; VP, 4H; Math C; NHS; ARC; Pres, Sci C; Alg A; Bio A; COM; Chem A; 4H A; Sci A; Fin, AJQHA; Off, MTQHA; Registar of Merit; MT Show Mgr; *Mich St U; Med.*

HARRINGTON, Lisa Gaye
Herndon HS; Herndon, VA (120-521) NHS; Span C; *Mary Washington Col; Elem Ed.*

HARRINGTON, Mark Alan
Indian Hill HS; Cincinnati, OH (42-326) F-Ed, Ann; Hmrm; NHS; SC; Var C; MVP, Swim; Math A; Hon Men, All Amer Swim; *Miami U; Bus.*

HARRINGTON, Nancy Effie
Medford HS; Medford, MA (25%-800) Chor; Fr C; Madrigal; NHS; Hon Prog; Yth Fel; *Photography.*

HARRINGTON, Sandra Lee
Crete-Monee HS; Crete, IL (31-460) Ann; Chor; COM; Hon Prog; St Scholar; *Creative Writing.*

HARRINGTON, Steven Joe
Moulton-Udell HS; Moulton, IA; A Cap Choir; Band; Chor; Madrigal; Bsbl; Co-Cpt, Bkbl; Tr; HCt; All-Tourn Tm, Conf Bkbl; 2nd Tm, All-Conf Bkbl; 4th Tm, All Courierland Bkbl; St Chair Trumpet, Conf Band Fest.

HARRINGTON, Timothy David
N Augusta Sr HS; N Augusta, SC (50-450) Ann; Chor; Drama; Hon Prog; ROTC A; *US Naval Acad; Nuclear Physics.*

HARRINGTON, Tina Lynn
Howland Sr HS; Warren, OH (50%-437) Band; Ensm; Ger C; InterAct C; Orch; ARC; Sftbl; Pres A; 1st Pl A, Ger Skit Comp; 1st Pl, Ensm Comp; Band A; 1st Pl, Instrumental Quartet; *U of Tenn; Ed.*

HARRIS, Alan James
Brother Martin HS; New Orleans, LA (3-319) Cpt, Chldr; Key C; Cpt, Math C; NHS; Rptr, Sch P; SC; Tr; COM; Hon Prog; Math A; ROTC A; Computer Sci Merit A; Ntl On-Sets Champion; Eagle Sct; Brother Martin Golden Crusader A; *Tulane U; Engr.*

HARRIS, Alicia Renee
Booker T Washington HS; Tulsa, OK (10%-309) Fr C; French NHS; Hmrm; ARC; Amer Leg A; COM; Citz A; Hist A; Masonic A; Most Out; ARC A; Jr Cl Board; Camp Fire 7 Yr A; MS Vol Service A; *Criminal Psych.*

HARRIS, Anita Louise
Jesup W Scott HS; Toledo, OH (98-450) Chor; Tres, 4H; Hmrm; NHS; ARC; Sch P; Span C; SC; Tres, Y-Tns; 4H A; JA A; Soph Secy; *Toledo U; Law.*

HARRIS, Anthony
Alexander HS; Starkville, MS (5-25) *Social Studies.*

HARRIS, April Lynne
Lawrence HS; Lawrence, KS (191-668) A Cap Choir; Chor; Ensm; Orch; *Kans U; Social Work.*

HARRIS, Arthaniel Edgar Jr
Kinston HS; Kinston, NC; Band; Athletic As; Mus As; *Morehouse Col; Pre-Med.*

HARRIS, Barbara Anne
Rapid City Stevens HS; Rapid City, SD (92-459) ARC; Sci C; SC; S-T, Soph Cl; *Nurs.*

HARRIS, Bernice Delores
Phil Campbell HS; Phil Campbell, AL; S-T, Bus C; Dbte Tm; VP, FBLA; FHA; FTA; 4H; Hmrm; Pres, Soph Cl; Bkbl; Sftbl; Tr; 4H A; JA A; Type A; Yth Fel; *U of Ala; Bus.*

HARRIS, Bonita Louise
Dupont Park Seventh Day Adventist; Washington, DC; Chor; F-Ed, Sch P; Citz A; Type A; Mus A; PA; Candystriper Cert & Pin; *Journ.*

HARRIS, Cathy Lou
Del Valle HS; Walnut Creek, CA (15%-289) Chor; Fr C; Rptr, Hmrm; Tnns; Pres, Church Yth Coun; NJHS; *Tex U; Textiles.*

HARRIS, Celeste Roshell
Eau Claire HS; Columbia, SC; Secy, Chor; NHS; ARC; Sch P; Hon Prog; *Lander Col; Eng.*

HARRIS, Charlene Elizabeth
Jess Lanier HS; Bessemer, AL; Hmrm; ARC; COM; DARGCA; Pres A; Hon Roll; Bankteller; *Miles Col; Eng.*

HARRIS, Cherrie Dell
Loop Ind HS; Loop, TX (1-16) Band; BC; Dbte Tm; 4H; Mjrte; Bkbl; Tnns; Tr; Beauty; 4H A; NEDT; Pres A; WW; Schol A; 2nd in Dist, Reg Qualifer, Dbte; Runner-Up, Miss Tex Ntl Teen-Ager; Semi-Fin, Miss Teenage Amer Cand.

HARRIS, Cindy Rachelle
Boise HS; Boise, ID (20%-500) Ch, Band; *Northwest Nazarene Col; Phys Therapy.*

HARRIS, Cynthia Lynn
Forest Park HS; Beaumont, TX (18-500) Chor; Cum Laude Soc; Dbte Tm; FTA; Pres, Lat C; Lat NHS; Math C; NFL; NHS; Secy, Spch C; Tres, SC; Tr; Alg A; COM; Citz A; Hon Prog; Magna Cum Laude; Math A; Opt A; Spch A; WW; *Tex A&M U; Acct.*

HARRIS, Cyrus Louin
Tyner HS; Chattanooga, TN (100-350) Cpt, Band; BC; Chor; Ensm; Ch, Hmrm; SC; Most Talented; Church Pianist; All-St Band & Chor; *Lee Col; Mus.*

HARRIS, Dale William
Langley HS; McLean, VA (93-544) AFS; Chess C; Demolay; Ger C; Math C; NHS; Rptr, Sch P; Hon Prog; Yth Fel; Eng Tm; NML; District, Regional, Spell As; *U of Va; Bus.*

HARRIS, Darcy Lee
Wm R Boone HS; Orlando, FL (14-758) Secy, AFS; BC; Secy, Chor; NHS; Alg A; COM; Hon Prog; MLS; All Co, Chor; MV Chor Member; *Oral Roberts U; Nurs.*

HARRIS, David Lee
Salisbury Elklick HS; Salisbury, PA; BS; Chess C; Chor; SC; Bsbl; Bkbl; Golf; Soccer; Sftbl; Tnns; Type A; Phys Fitness A; Meritorious A, Soccer & Bkbl; *Penn St U; Dentistry.*

HARRIS, David Paul
Springfield HS; Springfield, PA (30%-459) A Cap Choir; Chor; Ensm; Order/Arrow; Ski C; Stu Director, Band; Pres, UMYF; *Lebanon Valley Col; Mus.*

HARRIS, Dean Hamilton
Hammond Baptist HS; Schererville, IN (1-90) VP, Band; Chor; Ensm; NHS; Span C; Cr-Ctry; Chem A; Magna Cum Laude; Sci A; Spch A; Val; WW; Talent Schol, Christ Ntl Contest; Eng A; *Baptist Bible Col; Pre-Pastoral Stu.*

HARRIS, Deborah Kay
Portage Central HS; Portage, MI; Chor; Word of Life Schol; *Grand Rapids Sch o-t Bible & Mus; Christian Ed.*

HARRIS, Deborah Lynn
Charleroi Area Sr Jr HS; Charleroi, PA; FNA; Ski C; Co-Cpt, Bkbl; Ballet, Pep C, A's; Dance Workshop Hon; *Slippery Rock Col; Med.*

HARRIS, Denise
Pittsburgh Learning Lab Cntr; Pittsburgh, PA (3-127) All Amer Yth; Chor; Pres, Dbte Tm; Secy, FTA; Pres, Hmrm; Ed, Lit Mag; VP, Math C; Ch, Sch Achieve Tm; Up Bound; Sftbl; Hist A; Hon Prog; I Dare You; Journ A; Most Out; Star Student; Ed.*

HARRIS, Denise Elayne
U S D 509 HS; S Haven, KS (3-22) Ann; Band; Chldr; Chor; Ensm; VP, FHA; VP, 4H; Madrigal; Sch P; Span C; SC; Y-Tns; Secy, Sr Cl; Rptr, Jr Cl; Rptr, Soph Cl; Co-Cpt, Bkbl; Tr; Cl Fav; 4H A; HQn; HCt; Type A; WW; *Oral Roberts U; Nurs.*

HARRIS, Donald Gene
Raytown HS; Raytown, MO (60-550) Pres, A Cap Choir; VP, Band; Ensm; NHS; Orch; Best Musician; Phi Mo Alpha Mus Comp A; William Jewell Schol A; All St Choir.

HARRIS, Edward
George Henry Corliss HS; Chicago, IL (24-485) Band; Hmrm; SC; Cr-Ctry; Tr; COM; Citz A; Hon Prog; MLS; Ntl Achv Schol; Star Student; *Mus.*

HARRIS, Ellen E
Ben C Bain HS; Mobile, AL; FBLA; Key C; ARC; Y-Tns; Hon Prog; Swtht; *U of Ala; Bus.*

HARRIS, F Gray Jr
Ayden-Grifton HS; Ayden, NC (16-179) Co-Ed, Ann; Pres, NHS; Rptr, Sch P; Pres, Sci C; Pres, Sr Cl; COM; *East Carolina U; Journ.*

HARRIS, Felicia Jewel
Ben Geyer Jr HS; Fort Wayne, IN (189-450) Orch; Bkbl; 1st Vocal & Piano, Nisbova; Art A; Orch A; *U of Notre Dame; Computor Math.*

HARRIS, George Walter III
Bartow Sr HS; Bartow, FL; Semi-Fin, BS; Rptr, Hmrm; VP, Key C; NHS; Rptr, SC; Var C; Bsbl; Cpt, Ftbl; Cpt, Swim; H of F; Hist A; Hon Prog; Yth Fel; Mr BHS; *Ga Tech; Bus.*

HARRIS, Gloria Anne
Westside HS; Augusta, GA (35-85) Co-Cpt, Chldr; Chor; *Phillips Col; Typist.*

HARRIS, Holly Kathryn
Stamps HS; Stamps, AR (1-76) Ann; Band; Fr C; GS; Mjrte; Mu Alpha Theta; NHS; Sci C; Bio A; Fr A; Co Cinderella Tn; All Region Band; *Ouchita Col; Pre-Med.*

HARRIS, Howard Dane
W A Berry HS; Birmingham, AL (20%-800) Order/Arrow; Span C; Cr-Ctry; COM; Eagle Sct; Nom, Most Talented; Span A; *Auburn U; Arts & Sci.*

HARRIS, Irish Rashall
F O Alexander HS; Starkville, MS; Chor; Up Bound; Y-Tns; Hon Prog; *Miss St U; Secy Procedures.*

HARRIS, James Mark
Forest Park HS; Beaumont, TX (25%-500) Lat C; SC; Sftbl; Tnns; Yth Fel.

HARRIS, James Patrick
Vernon HS; Vernon, TX (5%-169) Secy, Drama; Hmrm; NHS; Spch C; Parl, SC; Thes; Bkbl; Cpt, Ftbl; JV, Golf; Cl Fav; Hon Prog; Yth Fel; All District, Bkbl; All Sch Favorite; *Tex Christian U; Bus.*

HARRIS, Jan Marie
Ottumwa HS; Ottumwa, IA (155-550) A Cap Choir; Bus C; Chor; FBLA; VFW A; Yth Fel; Mus Hons; *Amer Inst of Bus; Acct.*

HARRIS, Janet Clarice
Seneca HS; Louisville, KY; Band; COM; Art A; *Western Col.*

HARRIS, Jann
Battle Mountain HS; Minturn-Vail, CO (3-55) Rptr, Ann; Chldr; Chor; Drama; NHS; Sci C; Ski C; Co-Cpt, Bkbl; Co-Cpt, Sftbl; JV, Tnns; Type A; Church Yth Group; *Textile Design.*

HARRIS, Jeffery Dean
Wonderview HS; Hattieville, AR (10%-44) FFA; Pres, Soph Cl; Cpt, Bkbl; Cl Fav; HKg; HCt.

HARRIS, Jeffrey Reed
Farmington Sr HS; Farmington, MO; Chess C; Chor; InterClub Coun; JETS; Sci C; Arch; Bkbl; Sftbl; Tnns; Tr; Sci A; HR; *Law Enforcement.*

HARRIS, Jim Bob
Clarke Central HS; Athens, GA; Var C; JV, Bkbl; MVP, Ftbl; Tr; 100% A; Tres, FCA; All NE Ga A, Ftbl.

HARRIS, John David
Denison HS; Denison, TX; Band; Chess C; Drama; Ensm; Lat C; Ski C; Hon Prog; Mus A; *U of Tex; Math.*

HARRIS, Joy Lindorius
Chester HS; Chester, PA; Band; Chor; Ger C; Hmrm; Mjrte; ARC; Span C; Bkbl; Swim; Masonic A; Colorguard Cpt A.

HARRIS, Judith Rhonda
Palmdale HS; Palmdale, CA (242-416) Chor; Most Achv; Vlbl; *Bus.*

HARRIS, Keitha Lynnette
Malverne HS; Malverne, NY (25-200) Cpt, Chldr; Var C; Fin, Tr; Hon Prog; Kiwanis A; Pres A; Cpt, Tr; *Norfolk St Col; Sociology.*

HARRIS, Kevin Dale
Checotah HS; Checotah, OK; FFA; Bkbl; Ftbl; Tr.

HARRIS, Kevin Mark
Bellefontaine Sr HS; Bellefontaine, OH (55-220) Pres, Band; Chor; Orch; Order/Arrow; *Ohio N U; Phar.*

HARRIS, Kimberly Rochelle
Kendrick HS; Columbus, GA (50-390) Cpt, Chldr; Chor; Drama; Fr C; FBLA; Jr Miss Pagent; Madrigal; NHS; VP, SC; Tr; Cl Fav; HCt; *Mercer U; Dental Tech.*

HARRIS, Kurt Arthur
Cambridge HS; Cambridge, NE (4-35) Ann; BS; Chor; Bkbl; Cr-Ctry; Wrest; NEDT; Yth Fel; *Vancouver Bible Col; Bible.*

HARRIS, La Tonya Dalphine
Wheeler Co HS; Alamo, GA (5-50) VP, BC; Chldr; Parl, FHA; NHS; Secy, Sci C; SC; VP, Sr Cl; VP, Jr Cl; HCt; Span A; Home Ec A; *Fort Valley St Col; Phar.*

HARRIS, Larry Jo
Pocatello HS; Pocatello, ID (150-480) Band; Dbte Tm; NFL; Hon Prog; Spch A; Type A; Band Ltr; Excel, Dist Mus Festival; *Forestry.*

HARRIS, Larry Lee
Checotah HS; Checotah, OK (10%-74) VP, FFA; Bkbl; Ftbl; St Hon Soc; WW; *Panhandle St U; Animal Sci.*

HARRIS, Lavone
Carroll HS; Monroe, LA; Ed, Ann; Rptr, Hmrm; SC; Tnns; HCt; Journ A; *Northeast U; Journ.*

HARRIS, Leslie Ann
Artesia HS; Artesia, NM (85-300) FHA; ARC; Var C; Bkbl; Sftbl; Tnns; ARC A; Worthy Advisor, Rainbow Girls; *Ariz St U; Dental.*

HARRIS, Linda O'Dean
Roosevelt HS; Gary, IN (61-580) Bus C; FTA; Pres, Lat C; NHS; Hon Prog; Math A; Booster C; Charm, Service & Culture; *Ind NW U; Respiratory Therapy.*

HARRIS, Lisa Annette
Rossville HS; Rossville, GA (15-211) BC; Co-Cpt, Chldr; Secy, Y-Tns; Sftbl; Gov Honor Prog; HQn; Hon Prog; Star Student; Yth Fel; *Ga Sou Col; Phys Ed.*

HARRIS, Lu Anne
Liberty HS; Bedford, VA (10-257) BC; Span C; Span NHS; Tri-HiY; Most Outst Stu, Practical Nurs; Highest Grade Avg; *Bedford Co Mem Hospital; Nurs.*

HARRIS, Marianne Laverne
Gov John R Rogers HS; Puyallup, WA (3-330) A Cap Choir; 4H; NHS; COM; Kiwanis A; VP, Church Yth Group; HR; SPU Schol; Entrance Hons; *Seattle Pacific U; Ed.*

HARRIS, Marie Antoinette
Acad of Our Lady; Chicago, IL (79-209) HR Cert; *Engr.*

HARRIS, Mark Allen
Greensville Co HS; Emporia, VA (9-155) Ann; BC; 4H; 4H A; *Va Commonwealth U; Bus.*

HARRIS, Marsha Lee
Cinnaminson HS; Cinnaminson, NJ (86-469) FTA; GS; Secy, NHS; Pres, SC; Cpt, Bkbl; Mgr, Cr-Ctry; WW; *Rutgers U; Engr.*

HARRIS, Mary Ann
Bullock Co HS; Union Springs, AL (5-148) Dbte Tm; 4H; Hmrm; VP, NHS; Tnns, Phys C; SC; Pres, Sr Cl; Bio A; COM; Chem A; 4H A; HCt; Hon Prog; I Dare You; Math A; Pres A; Sal; Sci A; Spch A; Ldrship A; *Ala St U; Biol.*

HARRIS, Melinda
Maryville R-II HS; Maryville, MO (1-186) S-T, Band; Chess C; Chor; Ensm; Tres, FHA; NHS; Sci C; Span C; Lib Sci; Win, Math Olympic Tm; Rotary Sponsored to Freedom Forum; Soph Pilgramage; Ambsdr to Bolivia; Experiment in Intrntl Living; *Lib Sci.*

HARRIS, Michael Allan
Harlingen HS; Harlingen, TX (4-635) Chess C; Dbte Tm; Hmrm; Key C; NHS; Bkbl; Tr; Alg A; Cl Fav; DARGCA; Hist A; Hon Prog; Math A; Pres, FCA; Exch Stu, Sweden, Yth Understnding; *USAF Acad; Computers.*

HARRIS, Michael Wayne
Cohn HS; Nashville, TN; Bkbl; Ftbl; Tr; *U of Tenn-Knoxville; Computer Programming.*

HARRIS, Mitchell A
Kolb Jr HS; Rialto, CA; Parl, Hmrm; Rptr, Ntl Teachers C; Rptr, SC; Cpt, Bkbl; Cpt, Ftbl; Mgr, Tr; Illustrator, Sch Paper; *UCLA; Bus Adm.*

HARRIS, Mitzi Darlene
Maplewood HS; Nashville, TN (30-426) Drama; NFL; Sch P; SC; Tnns; Cl Fav; MLS; Spch A; *U of Tenn; Social Sci.*

HARRIS, Nancy Clare
Shades Vly Resource Learning Ctr; Birmingham, AL (5-36) Drama; Hmrm; Lat C; Lit Mag; NHS; Sch P; Cl Fav; Hon Prog; MLS; Yth Fel; *Auburn U; Vet Med.*

HARRIS, Nathaniel Hawthorne
Wakefield HS; Arlington, VA; Drama; JV, Ftbl; COM; JA A; Human Relations Group; *Hampton Inst; Communication.*

HARRIS, Nelson Dale
Martinsville HS; Martinsville, VA (175-282) Span C; Rated Excellent St Fair; *Central Wesleyan Col.*

HARRIS, Opal Marie
Crockett HS; Crockett, TX; Pres, FHA; NHS; *Massey Bus Col; Bus.*

HARRIS, Pamela Rose
Little Rock Central HS; Little Rock, AR (27-576) BC; Parl, FBLA; GS; Hmrm; InterClub Coun; Jr Miss Pagent; NHS; Spch C; Co-Ch, SC; Thes; Pres, Jr Cl; Pres, Soph Cl; Cpt, Sftbl; Cl Fav; Hon Prog; MLS; Most Out; Opt A; Spch A; *Columbia Col; Acct.*

HARRIS, Patricia Ann
Seneca HS; Louisville, KY; Chor; Drama; HiY; Tr.

HARRIS, Patricia Delores
Bryant HS; New York City, NY;

HARRIS, Patricia May
Central HS; Davenport, IA (10%-700) Hon Prog; *Secy.*

HARRIS, Paula Rena
Chattanooga HS; Chattanooga, TN (7-203) BC; GS; Hmrm; Mu Alpha Theta; NHS; SC; Pres, Jr Cl; Alg A; Bio A; Citz A; Cl Fav; Hon Prog; Sci A; Type A; *U of Tenn; Sch Adm.*

HARRIS, Phillip Howard
Westport HS; Louisville, KY (110-400) VP, A Cap Choir; VP, Chor; Ensm; Pres, Hmrm; Madrigal; SC; VP, Jr Cl; Mgr, Bsbl; MVP, Ftbl; COM; Cl Fav; Hon Prog; Most Out; Star Student; *E Ky U; Acct.*

HARRIS, Phillip Todd
Claxton HS; Claxton, GA (25%-115) Band; Fin, Chess C; Tres, Industrial Arts C; *Swainsboro Tech Col; Elec.*

HARRIS, Phyllis Gail
Hatley HS; Amory, MS; BC; Chor; FHA; Co-Ed, Sch P; *Library Sci.*

HARRIS, Rebecca
Bible Baptist HS; Savannah, GA (6-34) *Armstrong St Col.*

HARRIS, Ricky
South Bay Baptist Schools; Gardena, CA; Pres, Sch Achieve Tm; Bkbl; Ftbl; Hon Prog; *UCLA; Math.*

HARRIS, Robert Glenn
Monticello HS; Monticello, MS; Ann; BC; Hmrm; VP, SC; JV, Ftbl; Cl Fav; *Alcorn St U; Agr.*

HARRIS, Robin Renelle
Steel Valley HS; Homestead, PA (41-390) Chor; Secy, Fr C; FBLA; Col Schol; *Penn St U; Bus Adm.*

HARRIS, Rodger Maurice
Eudora HS; Eudora, AR (1-98) A-Ed, Ann; Band; Chem C; Fr C; Math C; NHS; Order/Arrow; Sci C; Bsbl; Ftbl; COM; God & Country A; Hist A; Hon Prog; Ntl Achv Schol; Order/Arrow A; Val; Eagle Sct; *Delta Ouachita Vo-tech Col; Elec.*

HARRIS, Rodney Gene
Webster HS; Tulsa, OK; Hmrm; VP, SC; Pres, Soph Cl; Ftbl; Wrest; *Communications.*

HARRIS, Sandy Lee
Pinole Valley HS; Pinole, CA (219-425) *Simpson Bible Col; Missions.*

HARRIS, Saundra
John Adams HS; Cleveland, OH; Y-Tns; Citz A; Hon Prog; PA; *Cleveland St U; Eng.*

HARRIS, Scott Kirby
Niskayuna HS; Schenectady, NY (20%-550) Drama; Ger C; NHS; Order/Arrow; JV, Ski C; JV, Soccer; Amer Leg A; Citz A; Hon Prog; Order/Arrow A; Pres, Yth Fel; Eagle Sct, Bronze Palm; NHS A; *Law.*

HARRIS, Shanda Louise
Stuarts Draft HS; Waynesboro, VA; Drama; VP, FHA; Secy, FTA; Hmrm; Span C; SC; *Ed.*

HARRIS, Shanna Dawn
W Carter HS; Olive Hill, KY (15-189) Band; BC; Chor; FBLA; S-T, Soph Cl; Beauty; VFW A; Conservation A; Baton A; *Morehead St U.*

HARRIS, Shelia Cammile
Luther HS S; Chicago, IL (61-160) Spch C; Fin, Spch A; Clark Col; TV Broadcasting.

HARRIS, Shellye Cecila
Luther HS S; Chicago, IL (61-160) Chor; Sch P; Howard U; Ed.

HARRIS, Sherri Lorraine
Plainfield HS; Plainfield, NJ (36-443) VP, Bus C; Rptr, Hmrm; NHS; Mgr, Sftbl; DECA; Drew U; Math.

HARRIS, Sonia Nadine
Minden HS; Minden, LA; Chor; Pres, FHA; 4H; Hon Prog; Sci A; PA; Sou U; Computer Prog.

HARRIS, Sonya L
Carroll HS; Monroe, LA (10-200) Band; Ensm; FBLA; SC; Bkbl; Sftbl; Tr; Band A; PA; Drew U; Bus.

HARRIS, Stephene Denise
St Xavier Acad; Providence, RI; Chor; Drama; Model UN; Bkbl; Tnns; Tr; Citz A; Outst Yth Conservation; Social Work.

HARRIS, Steven Albert
Abraham Lincoln HS; Denver, CO (17-640) A Cap Choir; Key C; NHS; Orch; COM; Citz A; Elk A; Masonic A; Opt A; Regent Schol; ROTC A; U of Colo; Bus.

HARRIS, Steven Duane
Pell City Christian Sch; Pell City, AL (3-7) A Cap Choir; Bus Mgr, Ann; BC; Chem C; Math C; Sch P; SC; VP, Sr Cl; Alg A; COM; Cl Fav; Math A; MLS; Stu o-t Yr; Hobe Sound Bible Col.

HARRIS, Susan Renee
Tuscaloosa HS; Tuscaloosa, AL (295-561) Parl, FHA; St Yth Off; Warner Sou Col; Elem Ed.

HARRIS, Sylvia Gayle
Chapel Hill Sr HS; Chapel Hill, NC; Math A; Guidance Asst A; Durham Tech Inst; Secretarial Sci.

HARRIS, Sylvia Marie
Cinnaminson HS; Cinnaminson, NJ (10%-426) Chor; Fr C; Key C; SC; Mgr, Bkbl; Hockey; Tres, JA; Minorities in Engr Prog; Elec Engr.

HARRIS, Tonya Melinda
Coronado HS; Lubbock, TX; Rptr, FTA; NHS; Orch; Hon Prog; Outst Stu, Span Cl; Sociology.

HARRIS, Valerie Annette
Benton HS; Benton, AR (30-350) Sftbl; Swim; Squad Ldr, Drill Tm; Ed.

HARRIS, Vivian Ann
W Carter HS; Olive Hill, KY (10%-125) Chor; Dbte Tm; Drama; Ch, FBLA; Secy, 4H; COM; 4H A; Hon Prog; Most Out; Spch A; FBLA A; WW; Conservation A; Morehead St U; Communications.

HARRIS, Wendy Diane
Corning Comm HS; Corning, IA (6-68) Ann; Chor; NHS; ARC; Ch, SC; Thes; Var C; Ch, Y-Tns; Pres, Sr Cl; Bkbl; Cr-Ctry; Sftbl; Tr; Iowa St U; Recreation.

HARRIS, William James Jr
Suitland Sr HS; Suitland, MD; Dbte Tm; Lat C; ARC; Sci C; VP, Span C; Spch C; Tnns; ARC A; Air Force Acad; Aeronautics.

HARRIS, William Jennings
Loganville HS; Loganville, GA; Community Yth Symph; 4H; Parl, Key C; Order/Arrow; ARC; Sch P; SC; Var C; Cpt, Bsbl; Ftbl; Amer Leg Orator A; God & Country A; Order/Arrow; Yth Fel; Yth Foundation; Coaches A, Bsbl; Pres, Lib C; S Ga Col; Phys Ed.

HARRIS, William Monroe III
Homewood HS; Birmingham, AL (18-225) AFS; Ed, Ann; Mu Alpha Theta; NHS; NEDT; V- ch, Sr High Church Yth Group; Psych C; Most Dependable; Vanderbilt U; Hist.

HARRIS, William Scott
Lourdes Central HS; Nebraska City, NE (7-29) Ann; Band; Chor; Math C; Mu Alpha Theta; NHS; Span C; SC; Ftbl; Tr; HCt; Opt Out Tn; Anytown.

HARRISON,
Carole Ann Paulette
Berea HS; Greenville, SC; Span C; MVP, Bkbl; COM; All Tourn Player, Bkbl; All-Star Bkbl & Sftbl; Hon Camper; Pres, Lib C; Greenville Tech Col; Para-Legal Secy.

HARRISON, Carolyn Denise
Andrew Jackson HS; Jacksonville, FL; Chor; Ensm; Hmrm; NHS; SC; 3rd Pl, Talent Show; Schol Program; Fla Jr Col; Nurs.

HARRISON, Cathy Mae
Churchill HS; Eugene, OR (15-350) 4H; NHS; Tnns; St Scholar; Equestrian A; Pacific Lutheran U; Bus.

HARRISON, Cheryl Danette
Copeland HS; Copeland, KS (2-13) Chldr; Chor; Var C; Bkbl; Sftbl; HCt; Hon Prog; Drill Tm; Kayettes; Vlbl; Kans St Schol Test, 2 A's Clothing; Kans St Schol Test, Spelling; Sci.

HARRISON, Clay Kendall
Crockett HS; Crockett, TX; Band; Pres, FTA; Pres, Span C; SC; Tnns; Hon Prog; Tex A&M U; Engr.

HARRISON, D Wayn Michelle
Topeka W HS; Topeka, KS (42-428) Chldr; Mgr, Bkbl; Hon Prog; Kans St U; Home Ec.

HARRISON, Deanna Lynne
U S Grant HS; Oklahoma City, OK; Chor; Ensm; Rptr, FBLA; Hmrm; SC; Bus.

HARRISON, Debra Ann
Lake Wales Sr HS; Lake Wales, FL (40%-290) Chor; Drama; Hmrm; ARC; Span C; SC; Var C; Sftbl; Cpt, Swim; Pres A; Serviteens; Vlbl; Dream Girl; Tallahassee Comm Col; Med Secy.

HARRISON, Donald Kenneth
Washington HS; Fremont, CA; Order/Arrow; Oholone Jr Col; Criminal Law.

HARRISON, Ewell Gene
Port St Joe HS; Port St Joe, FL; Mobile Col.

HARRISON, Gay Lynn
Shamrock HS; Shamrock, TX; Band; Chor; FBLA; VP, FHA; Fin, Jr Miss Pagent; Mu Alpha Theta; NHS; Rainbow; Span C; Spch C; Beauty; COM; Mc Murry Col.

HARRISON, Gloria
Wakulla HS; Medart, FL; Pres, Band; Mod Mus Mas; NHS; Hon Band; John P Sousa A; Stu Ldrship A; Tallahassee Comm Col; Acct.

HARRISON, Gregory Scott
Lakeland Regional HS; Wanaque, NJ; Ed, Lit Mag; JV, Bsbl; JV, Bkbl; Tres, Yth Fel; Architecture.

HARRISON, Holly Renee
Gregory HS; Gregory, SD (15%-48) Ed, Ann; Band; Chldr; Chor; Tres, FHA; NHS; Span C; Pres, SC; Thes; MVP, Sftbl; MVP, Swim; MVP, Tr; HCt; Ntl Achv Schol; Brookings-SDSU; General Register.

HARRISON, James Anderson
Baton Rouge Magnet HS; Baton Rouge, LA; Chess C; Swim; Elec.

HARRISON, Janet Gayle
Central HS; Tulsa, OK (93-387) AFS; MVP, Sftbl; VP & Tres, Band; Bus Proffesnl Women, Girl o-t Mo; Tulsa Jr Col; Professional Secy.

HARRISON, Jean Marie
Crestview Sr HS; Crestview, FL (47-275) Band; BC; FHA; 4H; COM; Troy St U; Mus.

HARRISON, Jeanette
Blenheim HS; Blenheim, SC; Ann; Band; Chldr; Chor; Dbte Tm; 4H; Cpt, Mjrte; VP, Sch P; Sci C; Var C; Ntl Sci Found; Sci A; Type A; Mjrte A's & Cert; PA Certs; 1st Pl Runnerup A, Homecoming; Bendict Col; Secy Stu.

HARRISON, Jill Marie
Paramount Brethren HS; Paramount, CA; A Cap Choir; Drill Tm; Biola Col; Eng.

HARRISON, Jo Ann Louise
Clara Barton HS; Brooklyn, NY (318-500) Chor; Dbte Tm; Math C; ARC; COM; Sci A; Yth Fel; Bridgeport U; Dental Hygiene.

HARRISON, Joann Deloris
Booker T HS; Norfolk, VA; Bus C; Pres, Chor; Drama; FHA; 4H; 4H A; Ntl Conf Chr & Jews; VP, Chor; Tr A's; Bauder Col; Fashions.

HARRISON, Kellie Juanita
Chester HS; Chester, PA; Band; HiY; COM; Prinston U; Corporate Law.

HARRISON, Kimberly Jayne
Everett HS; Maryville, TN (72-400) BC; FHA; Span C; Y-Tns; Draughons Col; Bus.

HARRISON, Larry Jerome
Ballow Sr HS; Washington, DC (61-475) Parl, SC; Bsbl; Chem A; Math A; MLS; Howard U; Eng.

HARRISON, Leigh Palmer
Zion-Benton Township HS; Zion, IL (10%-500) Band; VP, Chor; Ensm; NHS; SC; Pres, Jr Cl; Bsbl; Golf; COM; Archt Engr.

HARRISON, Leo Ray
Deerfield Beach HS; Deerfield Beach, FL (10%-500) Ger C; Ftbl; Tr; Wrest; Industrial Arts A; Archt Drawing A; Mont St U; Archt.

HARRISON, Lillian
Blenheim HS; Blenheim, SC (13-50) Band; Pres, Fr C; Phys C; Rptr, Sch P; Sci C; Alg A; Chem A; Citz A; God & Country A; HQn; JA A; Math A; Phi Beta Kappa; Pres A; Sci A; Star Student; Yth Fel; Yth Leg; U of SC; Allied Health.

HARRISON, Marcia Dawn
Eastbrook HS; Marion, IN; Span C; Asbury Col; Elem Ed.

HARRISON, Marcia Jean
Elk Grove HS; Elk Grove Village, IL (17-632) Community Yth Symph; Tres, Ger C; Orch; Ed, Sch P; COM; Hist A; Hon Prog; Q&S A; Augustana Col; Sec Ed.

HARRISON, Marion Elizabeth
Henry Snyder HS; Jersey City, NJ; Color Guard.

HARRISON, Mary Beth
Man Sr HS; Man, WV (15-180) Band; GS; Hmrm; NHS; Span C; Prom Qn; W Va U; Phys Therapy.

HARRISON, Mollie Bea
Industry HS; Industry, IL (3-33) Ed, Ann; Drama; Pres, FHA; Rptr, Sch P; Sci C; Tres, Sr C; Tres, Jr Cl; VP, Soph Cl; Hon Prog; W Ill U; Home Ec.

HARRISON, Nancy Beth
Westminster HS; Westminster, CA; Band; Sftbl; Mus Schol; Goldenwest Jr Col; Med.

HARRISON, Pamela Kay
Fairfield Comm HS; Fairfield, IL (25-200) A Cap Choir; Chor; VP, Y-Tns; Bkbl; Sftbl; GAA; Wabash Jr Col; Cooking.

HARRISON, Pamela Kaye
Maryville HS; Maryville, TN; BC; Sch P; Secy, Spch C; Bkbl; Sftbl; Cl Fav; HQn.

HARRISON, Renita Marlene
Burnside HS; Burnside, KY (3-40) Ann; Sch P.

HARRISON, Roger Elvis
Williamsburg City Sch; Williamsburg, KY (10-60) Fr C; Hmrm; VP, Jr Cl; Bsbl; Ftbl; Cl Fav; Opt A; Tnns Trophies; Cumberland Col; Engr.

HARRISON, Russell Alan
Fountain Lake HS; Hot Springs, AR (5-42) BC; BS; Chor; Thes; Mgr, Tnns; Garland Co Comm Col; Law.

HARRISON, Sandy Lynn
Roanoke HS; Robersonville, NC (22-147) Ann; Band; Fr C; FBLA; FHA; Math C; SC; Ftbl; Hardbarger Bus Col; Med Secy.

HARRISON, Susan Alaine
Colo HS; Colo City, TX (13-90) NHS; Tr; Hon Prog; Cpt, Vlbl; W Tex U; Psych.

HARRISON, Terri Jo
Valley Union HS; Elfrida, AZ (7-28) Chor; Drama; FHA; NHS; Span NHS; Citz A; Sports-Ed, Ann & Sch Paper; Eastern Ariz U; Fashion Merchandising.

HARRISON, Vivian Elaine
Robert L Osborne Sr HS; Marietta, GA (15%-400) Ann; BC; Chor; Ensm; Hmrm; SC; Rotary A; WSB Great Young Amer; All St Chor; Belmont Col; Religion.

HARROLD, David Wayne
Central HS; Omaha, NE (25-485) Golf; Hon Prog; Anderson Col; Pol Sci.

HARROLD, Fred Eugene Jr
Plant City Sr HS; Plant City, FL (40%-900) Key C; SC; Var C; Co-Cpt, Wrest; Baptist Bible Inst; Ministry.

HARROP, Donald Ernest Jr
Phoenixville Area HS; Phoenixville, PA (30-263) Pres, Lat C; NHS; Pres, Var C; Cpt, Cr-Ctry; Cpt, Tr; Cpt, Wrest; Amer Leg A; Hon Prog; WW; Wrest, Cross Ctry; Replogle Soph Athlete A; Phila Bulletin Schol Athlete; HS All Amer; *Duke U; Pre-Med.*

HARROWA, Lonny James
Stanley Co HS; Ft Pierre, SD (10-40) A Cap Choir; Ann; BS; Chem C; Chor; Drama; 4H; Pres, SC; Var C; Pres, Soph Cl; Bsbl; Co-Cpt, Ftbl; Tr; Cpt, Wrest; Amer Leg A; 4H A; HCt; Pres A; *Dakota Westlyn Col.*

HARRUP, Tamara Jean
Sussex Central HS; Sussex, VA (10-186) Ann; BC; Chldr; Rptr, SC; Bkbl; Type A; Bus A; Lib A; *Smithdeal-Massey Col; Legal Asst.*

HARRY, Leboaz Barrow
Marshall Islands HS; Majuro, MARSHALL ISLANDS (18-103) VP, Jr Cl.

HARRY, Marsha Lee
Rapid City Central HS; Rapid City, SD (113-525) Band; Chor; Pres, FHA; Pres, ARC; 4H A; ARC A; *St John's Sch of Nurs; Nurs.*

HARRY, Sonja Valechia
Covington HS; Covington, LA; Band; Chor; FHA; Mjrte; Sci A; Home Ec A; *LSU; Med.*

HARSEY, Marcia
Berrien HS; Nashville, GA (29-173) BC; SC; Pres, Tri-HiY; WW.

HARSEY, Mary
Berrien HS; Nashville, GA; All Amer Yth; Bus C; FBLA; HiY; Tri-HiY; *Bus Ed.*

HARSH, Constance D
Manheim Township HS; Lancaster, PA (10-389) Band; Community Yth Symph; NHS; Orch; JV, Hockey.

HARSHAW, Karen Ilene
East HS; Columbus, OH (9-350) Band; Hmrm; Cpt, Mjrte; NHS; Rainbow; Span C; Span NHS; St Stu Congress; Tres, SC; Tnns; Tr; NMS; NEDT; Rotary A; *Benedict Col; Pol Sci.*

HARSHBARGER, Warren Peter
John F Kennedy Mem HS; Seattle, WA (150-300) Mgr, Bsbl; Mgr, Ftbl; Wrest; Crusader A; BSct.

HARSIN, Jeffrey Jay
Switzerland Co Jr Sr HS; Vevay, IN (4-137) Band; Tres, Drama; 4H; Pres, Span C; SC; 4H A; Sci A; Span C, Eng, HR, A's; WW; *Ind U; Pol Sci.*

HART, Barbara E
Lincoln E HS; Lincoln, NE; Band; Cpt, Bkbl; Sftbl; Tnns; Tr; MVP, Bkbl; Elks Outst Yth, Sprtscastr C, A's; *U of Nebr.*

HART, Brian Jack
Burges HS; El Paso, TX (3-650) Chess C; Hmrm; NHS; SC; Citz A; Ger Hon Soc; Ntl Piano Auditions; Ntl Federation of Stu Mus; Tex Mus Tchrs Assn Stu Affiliate; Medal, St Mus Theory Test; *Mus.*

HART, Chris David
Western HS; Anaheim, CA (100-600) NHS; Var C; Cr-Ctry; Ftbl; Tr; St Scholar; WW; Industrial Arts A; Most Improved Tr; Most Inspirational Tr; *Biola Col; Mech Engr.*

HART, Christopher William
Ottumwa HS; Ottumwa, IA (55-539) Band; Chor; Drama; Madrigal; Orch; Thes; *Vocal and Instrumental Mus.*

HART, David Alan
Permian HS; Odessa, TX (10%-800) Band; God & Country A; Hon Prog; Star Student; *U of Tex; Criminal Law.*

HART, David Morgan
Worth Co R-III; Grant City, MO (3-54) Band; Chor; Ensm; Pres, NHS; Orch; Var C; Pres, Sr Cl; Tres, Jr Cl; Bkbl; JV, Ftbl; Golf; Sftbl; Tr; Citz A; God & Country A; HCt; Regent Schol; Mic-O-Say; St Mus Con; Jr & Sr Pl; Eagle A; United Yth for Christ; Brain Bowl, Math Olympiad; I Rating, Dist Band & Chor Ensm; *NW Mo St U; Bus Adm.*

HART, Debbie Ann
Central HS; Memphis, TN (10-30) JA A.

HART, Diona Paulette
Overbrook HS; Philadelphia, PA (142-500) Hon Prog; *Community Col; Nurs.*

HART, Eric M
Northwest Classen HS; Oklahoma City, OK (23-460) Band; Community Yth Symph; VP, JETS; Mu Alpha Theta; NHS; Orch; Amer Leg A; COM; NMF; Order/Arrow A; *U of Tulsa; Mus.*

HART, Glenda Carol
Ashton HS; Ashton, IL (1-41) Ed, Ann; Chldr; Tres, Drama; NHS; Tres, SC; Var C; Tres, Jr Cl; Pres, Soph Cl; Amer Leg A; DARGCA; Hon Prog; Math A; MLS; Val; Stu o-t Month; *Ill St U; Secondary Ed.*

HART, Jacqueline Louise
Leominster HS; Leominster, MA (142-499) Chor; Christian Yth Fel; Choir; United Methodist Schol; Bowl A; Max-Ed Cert; *Boston Theological Col; Ministry.*

HART, James Eaton
Venice HS; Venice, FL (47-385) A Cap Choir; Chor; Ger C; Hmrm; Madrigal; NHS; Pres, SC; JV, Tnns; JV, Wrest; Hon Prog; Math A; Sci A; *Bob Jones U; Acct.*

HART, Jill Lynn
Lowes HS; Lowes, KY (10-64) All Amer Yth; FHA; 4H; MVP, Bkbl; All-Amer A; All-St Bkbl Sq; Presidential Sports A, Bkbl; *Paducah Comm Col; Secy.*

HART, John Edward
Venice HS; Venice, FL (12-385) A Cap Choir; Ed, Ann; Parl, BS; VP, Chor; Madrigal; NHS; Span C; Co-Cpt, Bkbl; Cpt, Ftbl; JV, Soccer; Cpt, Sftbl; Tnns; Hist A; Spch A; Eng A; WW; 1st Pl Schol, Barbershop Quartet; *Cedarville Col; Hist.*

HART, John Kyle
M B Smiley HS; Houston, TX (16-400) VP, FFA; Hmrm; Math C; Mu Alpha Theta; NHS; Sci C; Arch; JV, Bsbl; JV, Ftbl; Alg A; Bio A; COM; Chem A; Hist A; Math A; Sci A; *SW Tex St U; Agr Ed.*

HART, Jonathan Blake
Beaufort Acad; Beaufort, SC (6-38) Band; NHS; Secy, Order/Arrow; Hon Prog; Order/Arrow A; *Furman U; Econ.*

HART, Karen Denise
Withrow HS; Cincinnati, OH; Chor; Drama; Ensm; FHA; NHS; Math A; *Ohio St U; Nurs.*

HART, Karla Jean
Fairfield Sr HS; Fairfield, OH (47-621) Chor; Fr C; NHS; Sftbl; Vlbl; *Miami U; Hist.*

HART, Kenneth Craig
Claremore HS; Claremore, OK (4-217) Band; S-T, Chess C; Math C; Mu Alpha Theta; NHS; SC; Balfour A; Bio A; Chem A; Cl Fav; Elk A; Hist A; I Dare You; Math A; Phy A; Sal; All St Band; WW in Band Stu; OU Schol; Amer Airlines Schol; *U of Okla; Chem.*

HART, Laura Lynn
Parkway S Sr HS; Manchester, MO (4-358) Chor; NFL; Spch C; Spch A; *Eng.*

HART, Marvin Eugene
Marion Co HS; Lebanon, KY (13-298) CYO; NHS; Var C; Co-Cpt, Bkbl; Cr-Ctry; Tr; COM; Citz A; Hist A; Ch, Mayor's Advisory Committee; *U of Ky.*

HART, Page Vernon III
Dyersburg HS; Dyersburg, TN; Band; Fr C; NHS; Citz A; Achv A.

HART, Patrice Donnamarie
Philadelphia HS for Girls; Philadelphia, PA (34-375) Band; Chor; Bkbl; Co-Cpt, Hockey; MVP, Sftbl; COM; Star Student; LaCrosse; Mgr, Sftbl; MVP, Hockey; *Ursinus Col; Bio.*

HART, Raymond Edwin
New Brockton HS; New Brockton, AL (10-50) Ann; BC; Drama; Spch C; Bkbl; Ftbl; Sftbl; Cl Fav; Most Popular; *Enterprise Jr Col.*

HART, Robert Anderson
W Holmes HS; Millersburg, OH (3-168) Chor; Drama; FTA; Hmrm; NHS; VP, Sci C; SC; JV, Ftbl; JV, Golf; JV, Wrest; B Crocker A; Cl Fav; Sal; Sci A; *Taylor U; Pre-Med.*

HART, Robert Edward
Pathway HS; Savannah, GA (3-21) BC; Bsbl; Tr; Bio A; Citz A; HKg; Hon Prog; Bible A; Beta C; *Armstrong St U.*

HART, Steven Jerome
Central HS; Philadelphia, PA; Chor; NHS; Soccer; Amer Leg A; Hist A; Barnwell Credit.

HART, Susan Ann
St Mary's HS; S Amboy, NJ (3-185) Chor; F-Ed, Crown & Scepte; Pres, Fr C; French NHS; Secy, NHS; Hon Prog; Magna Cum Laude; Social Stu A; Fr A; *Rutgers Col; Fr.*

HART, Tanuya Rose
Cairo HS; Cairo, IL; Band; Chldr; Chor; Fr C; Secy, FHA; Mjrte; JV, Bkbl; *Occupational Therapist.*

HARTBERGER, Cynthia Darlene
Liberty HS; Bedford, VA; BC; Secy, Fr C; Mu Alpha Theta; Sci C; Up Bound; Rptr, Sr Cl; Alg A; COM; Math A; NHS; NEDT; Phy A; Sal; Sci A; Spch A; *Radford Col; Mus Ed.*

HARTDAGEN, Katherine Jean
St Josephs HS; Emmitsburg, MD (5-27) Pres, Bus C; Cpt, Chldr; Chor; Drama; Secy, NHS; Ed, Sch P; SC; Var C; Journ A; *Frederick Comm Col; Journ.*

HARTER, Andrea
Sutter Union HS; Sutter, CA (9-161) Span C; CSF; Pres, Jobs Daughters; *Fine Arts.*

HARTER, Carolyn Elaine
E J Wilson HS; Spencerport, NY (20%-370) Band; Chor; Model UN; SC; COM; Mus Cast; All Co & All St Chor; Vocal Soloist; Story A; *Teaching.*

HARTER, Joel Gregory
Cedar Crest HS; Lebanon, PA (95-405) Chor; Drama; Ger C; Lat C; Mod Mus Mas; Sci C; Thes; Var C; Ftbl; Swim; Tr; COM; Hon Prog; NEDT; Pres A; Yth Fel; Arion A, Mus; Most Outst Sr; Dist, Regional Mus Chor; *Penn St U; Pre-Med.*

HARTER, Julie Laura
N Augusta Sr HS; North Augusta, SC (20%-400) Chor; Secy, FTA; InterClub Coun; Fin, Lit Mag; Rainbow; Tri-HiY; Poet A; Hon All-St Chor; Acteen Schol; Hon Graduate; VP, SC Acteens; HR; Pres, Aiken Assn Acteens; Christian Leadership Schol; *Baptist Col; Elem Ed.*

HARTER, Suzette
Columbia HS; Columbia, IL; *Couiffure Beauty Sch; Beautician.*

HARTGROVE, Marcie Lee
Grimsley Sr HS; Greensboro, NC (2%-515) Ann; Chor; Ensm; Secy, Fr C; Pres, Hmrm; Bus Mgr, Lit Mag; NHS; Gov Honor Prog; Hon Prog; Tr, Jr Jaycettes; *U of NC; Med.*

HARTING, Carl Leo
Coldwater HS; Coldwater, OH; FFA; Pres, 4H; Ftbl; Tr; 4H A; JA A; Ftbl A.

HARTJE, Karen Sue
Cavalier HS; Cavalier, ND (6-64) A Cap Choir; Band; Chldr; VP, Chor; Ensm; Madrigal; Co-Ed, Sch P; SC; Ftbl; Sftbl; GAA; St Soloist; Curling-Skip; Bus Machines Gold Cert; 5th St, Curling; *Court Rptr.*

HARTLESS, Donna Denise
Ferguson HS; Newport News, VA (130-475) Parl, FBLA; FHA; Parl, FTA; Rptr, Hmrm; Lat C; ARC; Sftbl; Swim; Tnns; Citz A; Cl Fav; Most Out; Sci A; Yth Fel; Parl, Keyettes; Chaplin, SC; Delta Kappa Gama Schol; *Radford Col; Special Ed.*

HARTLEY, Cynthia Catherine
Cony HS; Augusta, ME (15%-455) Band; UMC St Yth Coun; Band Attendance Cert; *Thomas Col; Secretarial.*

HARTLEY, Jacque Elizabeth
Elbert Co Comp HS; Elberton, GA (24-260) Anchor C; BC; FHA; 4H; Hmrm; SC; Bkbl; Sftbl; Citz A; 4H A; WW; *Anderson Jr Col.*

HARTLEY, Kevin Neal
Putnam City HS; Oklahoma City, OK; AFS; *U of Okla.*

HARTLEY, Patrice Ann
East St Louis Lincoln Sr HS; E St Louis, IL (3-200) A Cap Choir; Cpt, Mjrte; Pres, NHS; Spch C; Secy, Sr Cl; Secy, Jr Cl; Secy, Soph Cl; Citz A; Cl Fav; MLS; Most Out; Spch A; *SIU Edwardsville; Bus Adm.*

HARTLEY, Richard Wayne
Logan HS; Logan, OH (95-310) Semi-Fin, BS; Chess C; Sci C; Span C; Up Bound; Bkbl; Sftbl; *Ohio U; Engr.*

HARTLEY, Ronald Beal
Elbert Co Comp HS; Elberton, GA (26-300) Band; BC; Ensm; VP, 4H; Hmrm; SC; 4H A; Math A.

HARTLEY, Thomas Mark
Marshall HS; Marshall, MO (8-189) BS; Orch; ARC; World Affairs C; Ftbl; Swim; Tr; Wrest; Hon Prog; Kiwanis A; Pres A; St Freedom Forum; *U of Mo; Med.*

HARTMAN, Betty Louise
Northside HS; Roanoke, VA (29-414) WW; *Ntl Bus Col; Med Secy.*

HARTMAN, Bonnie Sue
Steeleville HS; Steeleville, IL (50%-48) Chldr; Sftbl.

HARTMAN, Carol Jean
Thomson Comm HS; Thomason, IL; Chor; FHA; Pres, 4H; Bsbl; Bkbl; Sftbl; 4H A; Vlbl; *Sauk Valley Col; Marketing.*

HARTMAN, Charles Thomas
Karlsruhe Amer HS; Karlsruhe, GERMANY; Drama; Var C; Ftbl; Soccer; Wrest.

HARTMAN, Dale Ray
Kalamazoo Central HS; Kalamazoo, MI; Ski C; Cr-Ctry; Soccer; Tr; *Seattle Pacific U; Commercial Art.*

HARTMAN, David William
Bishop Union HS; Bishop, CA (20%-200) VP, 4H; Bkbl; CSF; 4H A; Val; Pres & VP, 4-H C; *Le Tourneau Col; Mech Engr.*

HARTMAN, Deborah Marie
Wonderview HS; Hattieville, AR (1-33) Bus Mgr, Ann; FHA; GS; Pres, 4H; Tres, Sr Cl; Sftbl; Alg A; Citz A; 4H A; Math A; MLS; Val; *Ark Tech U; Rehabilitation.*

HARTMAN, Kevin Gerald
Whitewater HS; Whitewater, WI (10-202) Band; Chor; VP, Drama; Ensm; Fr C; Madrigal; Order/Arrow; SC; Order/Arrow A; *U of Wisc; Bus.*

HARTMAN, Lisa Gennette
Southside HS; Elmira, NY (3-470) A Cap Choir; Band; Chor; Drama; Lat C; Madrigal; Model UN; Hon Prog.

HARTMAN, Mark Bently
Reidsville Sr HS; Reidsville, NC (5%-375) Key C; Math C; JV, Bkbl; JV, Ftbl; Tnns; NEDT; *Duke U; Med.*

HARTMAN, Mark Jonathan
King's Temple Christian Sch; Seattle, WA; Ann; Chor; Rptr, Sch P; Co-Cpt, Soccer; Citz A; Journ A; Yth Fel; *Air Force Acad; Career-Aviation.*

HARTMAN, Nadine Annette
Ramsey HS; Ramsey, NJ (20%-280) Band; Chor; Ensm; Fr C; Hmrm; Orch; Sch P; Var C; Cpt, Hockey; Chor Pianist; All League, Hon Men, Field Hockey; St Tm Cpt, Field Hockey; *Carson-Newman Col; Special Ed.*

HARTMAN, Nanette Amy
Ramsey HS; Ramsey, NJ (20%-300) Co-Ch, Band; Chor; Ensm; Var C; Hockey; Tr; All Lge, St Champ Tm, Field Hockey.

HARTMAN, Philip Thomas
Frayser HS; Memphis, TN (2-168) Band; BS; Community Yth Symph; Ensm; Secy, Key C; Lit Mag; S-T, Mod Mus Mas; Pres, NHS; Balfour A; I Dare You; Lion A; Most Out; Sal; Cpt, Rifle Tm; All St Band & Orch; Most Intelligent; WW; Pres, Church Yth Group; *Memphis St U; Engr.*

HARTMAN, Ruth Jenine
N Shore HS; W Palm Beach, FL (17-266) VP, Chor; Drama; Key C; Madrigal; Pres, NHS; Alg A; COM; Most Out; Sr Cl Coun; Most Talented, Choir; Yth o-t Mo; WW; Superior, Fla Vocal Assn; *FSU.*

HARTMANN, Cornelia
Liberty Sr HS; Liberty, MO (66-356) Band; NHS; Var C; Tr; Tr A; *Central Mo St U; Med.*

HARTMANN, Martha Emilie
Lutheran HS South; Affton, MO (1-153) Chor; NHS; B Crocker A; NMF; NMS; Opt A; Val; Pershing Schol; Shell Merit School; WW; *NE Mo St U; Math.*

HARTNETT, Edward Aloysius
St Peters Prep HS; Jersey City, NJ (1-250) Chor; Dbte Tm; Drama; Sch P; Ski C; Pres, SC; Pres, Sr Cl; Pres, Jr Cl; COM; Coun of Teach A; Math A; NEDT; Eng A; *Harvard U; Philosophy.*

HARTON, Lawrence Edward
Grafton HS; Grafton, WV (90-200) A Cap Choir; Band; Drama; Hmrm; Rptr, Key C; SC; Var C; JV, Bkbl; Ftbl; Tr; COM; Lion A; Nom, Hugh O'Brian A; *West Va U; Phys Ed.*

HARTON, Lawrence Edward Jr
Grafton HS; Grafton, WV (90-220) A Cap Choir; Band; Chor; Drama; Hmrm; Rptr, Key C; SC; Var C; Cpt, Bsbl; JV, Bkbl; MVP, Ftbl; Co-Cpt, Swim; Tr; COM; Lion A; Sanctuary Soc; Yth Fel; Yth Foundation A; Choir A; All Star, Bsbl; *W Va U; Phys Ed.*

HARTSHORN, Mary Frances
St Mary's Sch; Raleigh, NC (70-118) Ann; Band; Fr C; Sci C; Tres, Sr Cl; Tres, Jr Cl; Yth Fel; Outing C; Ambaj-Expeiment in Intrntl Living; *Hollins Col.*

HARTSO, Vanessa Wadean
Lenoir HS; Lenoir, NC; Band; Rptr, Sch P; Mgr, Bkbl; Mgr, Sftbl; VP, Explorers; Band Camp Schol; Black Hist C; Secy, Yth Today & Tomorrow; Mgr, Vlbl; *Wake Forest U; Psychiatry.*

HARTSOUGH, Robert Brian
North Liberty HS; North Liberty, IN (10-125) Span C; SC; Tr.

HARTSTACK, Denise Anne
Oak Park HS; Kansas City, MO (110-600) A Cap Choir; Ed, Ann; Band; Chor; Hmrm; Orch; Rainbow; ARC; Span C; SC; Arch; Bkbl; Golf; Hon Prog; Yth Fel; Stage, Pep, Bands; Mod Choir; *Nurs.*

HARTT, Quintin Hardtner
Holy Savior Menard HS; Alexandria, LA (58-167) Band; Ensm; Parl, FBLA; Orch; Order/Arrow; Bsbl; Ftbl; Swim; *LSU; Vet Med.*

HARTUNG, Jean Anne
Arlington HS; Arlington Heights, IL (48-564) Chor; NHS; COM; Magna Cum Laude; Summa Cum Laude; Hon Pins; *Purdue U; Food And Nutrition.*

HARTUNG, Lisa Marie
Benilde-St Margarets HS; St Louis Park, MN (61-192) A Cap Choir; CYO; Chldr; Drama; Madrigal; Span C; Var C; Tr; Swtht; Mgr, Gym; Gym A; Var A; Cl Proficiency; *St Cloud U; Elem Teaching.*

HARTUNIAN, Ruth Rosemary
Cudahy Sr HS; Cudahy, WI; Band; Chor; Ensm; Hmrm; Orch; Ed, Sch P; SC; Hon Prog; Pres A; Yth Fel; Rptr, F-Ed, Sch P; Yth Schol A; St Hon Band; Band Conductor A; Church Organist; Eng, Fr, A's; Band & Chor Accompanist; *Mus.*

HARTWELL, Lori Robin
Jamaica HS; Jamaica, NY (400-1102) Co-Cpt, Chldr; COM; Yth Fel; Creative Arts Soc; *NC Central U; Acct.*

HARTWIG, Sandra Ann
Luther HS S; Chicago, IL (3-175) A Cap Choir; Chor; Hon Prog; NEDT; Sal; Cpt, Vlbl; *Wesley-Passavant Nurs Col; Sci.*

HARTZ, Cynthia Jean
Hoopeston-E Lynn HS; Hoopeston, IL (12-156) Band; Span C; 4H A; Bkbl Statistician; Art A; GAA A; *Ind U; Optometry.*

HARTZ, Kristine Ann
Hilbert HS; Hilbert, WI (1-66) Band; Chor; NHS; Hon Prog; Val; Yth Fel; *LaCrosse Col; Computer Sci.*

HARTZ, Roberta Joann
Lincoln Park HS; Lincoln Park, MI (35-618) Chor; NHS; COM; Hon Prog; *Grand Canyon Col; Elem Ed.*

HARTZ, Warren Franklin III
Hamilton HS E; Trenton, NJ (109-715) Drama; Lat C; Tres, Sch P; NMS Ltr of Commendation; Director, Stu Tutoring Service A; Outdoor Ed Sci Cert; *Trenton St Col; Hist.*

HARTZELL, Jeffrey Alan
Wilson Area HS; Easton, PA (20-230) Ann; Chor; FTA; NHS; Hon Prog; *Olivet Nazarene Col; Mus.*

HARTZELL, Nancy Jean
Arlington Sr HS; Poughkeepsie, NY; Band; Ensm; 4H; Orch; 4H A; Yth Fel; Sr Coun; Sorority; A; Ratings, Solo Competition Candystriper; Schol Creative Writing A; *Dutchess Comm Col; Nurs.*

HARTZFELD, Jim E
Nevada HS; Nevada, MO (5-189) AFS; Band; BS; Chem C; Ensm; Lat C; NHS; Orch; Order/Arrow; SC; Var C; Bsbl; Bkbl; Ftbl; Tnns; Order/Arrow A; Sci Symp Del; Math Ral A; *Math.*

HARTZFELD, Kelly K
DuBois Area HS; DuBois, PA (5-370) NHS; Amer Leg A; *Penn St U; Forestry.*

HARTZFELD, Kimberly Ann
Nevada HS; Nevada, MO (9-259) AFS; Band; Co-Cpt, Chldr; Secy, FTA; Lat C; SC; Secy, Soph Cl; Tr; Alg A; Beauty; Math A; Type A; 'N' A; Gym; *SW Mo St U; Phys Ed.*

HARTZOG, Carlos Bridget
Choctaw Co HS; Butler, AL (68-110) Band; Chldr; Ch, Chor; Drama; Ensm; FHA; Rptr, 4H; Sci C; 4H A; Sci A; *Mericlian Jr Col; Nurs.*

HARVELL, David James
Elbert Co Comprehensive HS; Elberton, GA (78-293) Ann; Band; Fr C; 4H; Hmrm; SC; Thes; 4H A; *U of Ga; Art.*

HARVELL, Karen Denise
Cleveland HS; Cleveland, TN; Anchor C; Band; Chldr; Chor; Community Yth Symph; Ensm; Semi-Fin, Hmrm; Orch; Tri-HiY; Sftbl; Piano School; Church Orch; Prom Court; *Cleveland St Comm Col; Nurs.*

HARVESON, Robert Martin
Bridgeport HS; Bridgeport, TX (2-111) NHS; Span C; SC; Pres, Soph Cl; Bkbl; Ftbl; Tr; Citz A; Hist A; Span A; Hist A; Geography A; *Trinity U.*

HARVEY, Barbara Kay
Denton Pub Sch; Danton, MT (12-24) Ann; Secy, Chor; Drama; Pres, FHA; Sch P; Var C; Mgr, Bkbl; St FHA Convention; *Rocky Mountain Col; Elem Ed.*

HARVEY, Cynthia Ann
Englewood Sr HS; Jacksonville, FL (19-466) MVP, Band; Community Yth Symph; Hmrm; Key C; NHS; Orch; Rainbow; SC; Tri-HiY; Parl, Sr Cl; VP, Soph Cl; Tnns; COM; HCt; Most Out; Swtht; Yth Fel; Superlative, Most Sincere; 1st Runner-Up, Most Reliable; *U of Fla; Mus.*

HARVEY, Denise Jeanne
Briarcliff HS; Briarcliff Manor, NY (5-127) Ann; Chor; Community Yth Symph; Ensm; Lit Mag; NHS; Orch; Ed, Sch P; St Stu Congress; SC; Pres, Jr Cl; Co-Cpt, Bkbl; Cpt, Tnns; COM; Chamber of Comm A; Hon Prog; Q&S A; Regent School; All-Co & All-St Orch; Vlbl; WW; Jaycees Outst Tnage Yng Person A; *Hist.*

HARVEY, Howard Kirk
Athens HS; Athens, AL (50%-245) Pres, FBLA; Span C; Tres, Sr Cl; Most Courteous; Mr FBLA; *Calhoun Comm Col; Bus.*

HARVEY, Joseph Dwain
Fort Myers Sr HS; Fort Myers, FL; Lat C; JV, Ftbl; Tr; *Cincinnati Bible Col; Christian Ed.*

HARVEY, Julie Lynne
Lincoln Sr HS; Sioux Falls, SD (250-600) Band; Chor; Chamber Choir; *Social Work.*

HARVEY, Linda Louise
MacKenzie HS; Detroit, MI (35-352) NHS; SC; *Eastern Mich Col; Eng.*

HARVEY, Loni Jean
Winona Sr HS; Winona, MN (95-560) A Cap Choir; Chldr; Chor; Community Yth Symph; Ensm; Monogram; COM; Gym; 3 Ltr A; 1st Pl Medal, Sub-Section Gym; *Winona St U; Health.*

HARVEY, Marcia Lynn
Notre Dame HS; Clarksburg, WV (1-55) VP, Band; Chldr; Ensm; Lat C; Math C; Sci C; Pres, Med Careers; *St Mary's Col; Med Field.*

HARVEY, Maureen Ann
Mt St John Acad; Gladstone, NJ (3-25) CYO; Chldr; Drama; Fr C; Secy, Lit Mag; NFL; NHS; Ski C; Tres, Jr Cl; COM; NEDT; 1st Runner- up, Prom Qn; Top 5%, PSAT-NMSQT; St Fin, Miss Ntl Tnage Pageant; Candystriper A; *Princeton U; Law.*

HARVEY, Nancy
All Amer Christian Acad; Hollywood, FL (1-33) Band; Chess C; Chor; Drama; Ensm; NHS; Var C; Sftbl; Alg A; Hon Prog; 2nd Pl A, Vlbl; St Champ, Spelling; 4th Pl A, Girls Ensm; GSct; Best Academian; Cpt, PACE Bowl; Gray Hammond Sch; Ann Christmas Pag; *All Amer Bible Col; Ed.*

HARVEY, Nancy Jo
Corning E HS; Corning, NY (30-300) Band; Chor; Ski C; Swim; Sci A; Chor Accompanist.

HARVEY, Norma Grace
Highland HS; Ewing, MO (16-130) Ann; FBLA; GS; NHS; Sch P; Regent Schol; *NE Mo St U; Elem Ed.*

HARVEY, Paul Matthew
River Valley HS; Three Oaks, MI (150-200) Band; Orch; Var C; JV, Bsbl; JV, Ftbl; Wrest; *U of Mich; Law.*

HARVEY, Rebecca Lynn
Woodward Acad; College Park, GA (9-180) Bus Mgr, Ann; Cpt, Chldr; Hmrm; Key C; NHS; Tnns; HCt; Hon Prog; NEDT; Summa Cum Laude; FCA; Silver Eagle A; *Vanderbilt U; Econ.*

HARVEY, Sandra LeAnn
Plainview HS; Ardmore, OK (10-70) Ann; FHA; 4H; Band; Bkbl; Sftbl; Tr; COM; 4H A; Hon Prog.

HARVEY, Stephen Donald
Affton Sr HS; Affton, MO (18-343) Demolay; Fr C; SC; COM; Most Out; *U of Mo; Elec Engr.*

HARVEY, Terri Lynn
Sooner HS; Bartlesville, OK (79-280) AFS; FBLA; Span C; COM; Type A; Shorthand A; Professional Women's Schol; WW; Top Stu, Tri-Co Tech; *Wesleyan Col; Bus.*

HARVEY, Tony Keith
Vernon HS; Vernon, TX (25%-180) Drama; NFL; Thes; Ftbl; JV, Tr; Yth Fel; WW; All Around Stu & Ldrship; *VA Jr Col; Bus.*

HARVEY, Tracee Jolynn
Vernon HS; Vernon, TX; 4H; Cl Fav; Sec, HECE; *Tex Tech; Florist.*

HARVEY, Wanda Denise
Carver Sr HS; Montgomery, AL; Hmrm; Phi Beta Kappa; *U of Ala; Nurs.*

HARVEY, Wayne Russell
Capitol Christian Acad; Upper Marlboro, MD (10-22) Chess C; ARC; Sci C; SC; Bkbl; Ftbl; Wrest; Sci A; Bible Quiz Tm; *US Navy; Nuclear Physics.*

HARVEY, William Frederic
Philipsburg-Osceola Area HS; Philipsburg, PA (20%-246) Ann; Drama; Fr C; Pres, Hmrm; Mgr, Bkbl; MLS; NEDT; Yth Fel; Fr A; Drug & Alcohol Yth Forum; *Penn St U; Pre-Med.*

HARVEY, William Frederick
Sparks HS; Sparks, NV (1-386) NHS; SC; Bkbl; Tr.

HARVILL, Belinda Joyce
Pickwick Southside HS; Counce, TN (3-32) BC; Secy, FHA; 4H; Sci C; Var C; Bkbl; Star Student; Yth Fel.

HARWELL, David Carden
Battle Ground Acad; Franklin, TN (7-64) Key C; NHS; Order/Arrow; Var C; Swim; Tnns; Tr; DARGCA; Yth Fel; Order of St Vincent; *SMU; Engr.*

HARWELL, Donna Lynn
South HS; Bakersfield, CA (10%-385) Tres, Span C; Hon Prog; Hon C; Stu Aide A; *Calif St U; Acct.*

HARWELL, Joseph Wheeler
David Lipscomb HS; Nashville, TN (25-106) Chor; Fr C; Pres, NHS; Civitan Essay A; *David Lipscomb Col; Bus Adm.*

HARWELL, Randy
Lakewood HS; St Petersburg, FL; Secy, NHS; Span NHS; Bkbl; Hugh O'Brien A; *U of NC; Pre-Med.*

HARWOOD, Karen Eleise
John Marshall HS; Los Angeles, CA (15%-750) A-Ed, Ann; Span C; CSF; Drill Tm; *U of Redlands; Sociology.*

HASBROOK, John Frederic
Miramonte HS; Orinda, CA (40%-330) 4H; Bsbl; Cr-Ctry; Golf; Tr; *Pepperdine Col; Bus.*

HASEGAWA, Terry James
Hood River Valley HS; Hood River, OR (25-200) 4H; Model UN; Order/Arrow; Ski C; Var C; Soccer; Tr; 4H A; Order/Arrow A; Eagle Sct; Church Deacon; Tr A; *U of Calif at LA; Pre-Med.*

HASEMEYER, Pamela Sue
N Platte Sr HS; N Platte, NE; Band; Drama; Ensm; InterAct C; Job's Daughters; Alt, All St Band; *Mid Plains Comm Col; Med Tech.*

HASH, Jana Sue
Box Elder HS; Brigham City, UT (5%-450) FHA; NHS; Co-Cpt, Swim; Hon Prog; *Archt.*

HASHEIDER, Connie Beth
Phil Campbell HS; Phil Campbell, AL; Ann; Band; FHA; FTA; Hmrm; Cpt, Mjrte; Pres, SC; Tr; Beauty; Cl Fav; HCt; Ideal Miss; *U of N Ala; Phys Ed.*

HASHMAN, James Otis
The King's Temple Christian Sch; Seattle, WA; Ed, Ann; Band; Chor; Community Yth Symph; Drama; Ensm; Hmrm; Orch; Tres, SC; Bkbl; Soccer; COM; Hon Prog; NEDT; Pres A; Yth Fel; *Cornish Sch of Arts; Mus.*

HASKELL, Sandy Marie
Temple Christian HS; Detroit, MI (8-63) Chor; NHS; Ski C; Tr; Type A; Art C; *Bus.*

HASKILL, Michelle LeAnn
Cypress HS; Cypress, CA; NHS; Co-Cpt, Soccer; CSF; *Oral Roberts U; Med.*

HASKIN, Timothy Patrick
Wausau E HS; Wausaw, WI; Bkbl; Tr; *N Central Tech Inst; Residential Design.*

HASKINS, D William
Lancaster Sr HS; Lancaster, WI (7-133) AFS; Ann; Chor; Hmrm; Model UN; Order/Arrow; Sch P; Span C; SC; God & Country A; Order/Arrow A; NMS Commended; Eagle Sct; *St Ola[?] Col; Liberal Arts.*

HASKINS, Danita Tara
Charles B Glenn HS; Birmingham, AL; Fr C; Tres, FBLA; NHS; Sci C; COM; 4H A; Hon Prog; MLS; PTA A; *Law.*

HASKINS, Deborah Rene
Kickapoo HS; Springfield, MO; Chor; Ensm; Pres, FTA; Madrigal; Mjrte; Math C; Model UN; Span C; Kickapoo Faculty Schol; *SW Mo St U; Elem Ed.*

HASKINS, Freda Annette
Armstrong HS; Richmond, VA (104-280) FHA; Hmrm; Span C; SC; Most Serious; Most Sophisticated; *Va Union Col; Sociology.*

HASKINS, Kirk Lamar
Northwest HS; St Louis, MO (15-652) Band; Hmrm; NHS; SC; COM; *Howard U; Mus.*

HASKINS, Linda Louise
Broxton HS; Broxton, GA (5%-38) F-Ed, Ann; BC; Pres, FHA; Fin, GS; Hmrm; Cpt, Lit Ral; A-Ed, Sch P; SC; Secy, Var C; Bkbl; Amer Leg A; COM; Crisco A; HCt; Most Out; Yth Fel; VP, Tres, FHA; Yth Senate; Miss FHA; WW, Home Ec; Outst Ath o-t Yr; *Emery U; Hemotology.*

HASKINS, William Edward
Wakefield HS; Arlington, VA (56-420) Math C; NHS; JV, Bkbl; Math A; NROTC Schol; WW; *MIT; Engr.*

HASLERUD, David Robert
S St Paul Sr HS; S St Paul, MN (150-470) MVP, Golf; Tnns; *Col of St Thomas; Bus Adm.*

HASLEY, Christine Marie
Moline Sr HS; Moline, IL; *U of Manitoba; Social Work.*

HASS, Kristine Louise
Merrill Sr HS; Merrill, WI (85-321) A Cap Choir; Tri-HiY; Tr; Tres, Sr High Yth; GAA; Yth Cabinet; Co-Ed Yth Paper; *U of Wis-Stevens Point; Elem Ed.*

HASSE, Debra Ann
Freeport Sr HS; Freeport, IL (52-500) Band; Math C; SC; Cpt, Swim; Tnns; *Data Processing.*

HASSELBACH, Deborah Lynette
Ross HS; Fremont, OH (56-527) Pres, 4H; NHS; Woman's Auxilary A; *Capital U; Nurs.*

HASSELBECK, Diane Marie
Seton HS; Cincinnati, OH (20-305) Chor; Pres, Fr C; NHS; COM; Spch A; VofDEM; Church Mus Ministry; JA; Folk Mus Forum; Board of Pres; GAA; *Mt St Joseph Col; Nurs.*

HASSELL, Joe Bendal Jr
Pineville HS; Pineville, LA (2%-244) A-Ed, Ann; Dbte Tm; Hmrm; InterAct C; Key C; Fin, Lit Ral; NFL; NHS; Spch C; SC; Bkbl; COM; Hon Prog; Math A; Spch A; Pres, Sr Cl; 4th Pl Geom, St Lit Rally; *Acct.*

HASSIEN, Kimberly Kay
Van-Far R-1 HS; Vandalia, MO (4-90) Ann; Band; FHA; Pres, Hmrm; NHS; Sch P; Spch C; SC; Pres, Soph Cl; Bkbl; Secy, Hmrm; Schol Pin A; *PA.*

HASSKAMP, Mary Louise
Aitkin Pub HS; Aitkin, MN (50-150) A Cap Choir; Band; CYO; Chor; FHA; NHS; ARC; Vlbl; *Col of St Schlastica; Nurs.*

HASSLER, Cynthia Anne
Southside HS; Fort Smith, AR (96-430) A Cap Choir; CYO; FHA; 4H; Hmrm; InterAct C; Ch, InterClub Coun; Golf; Sftbl; Swim; Tnns; DECA; Cath Yth Singers; Art, Sewing, A's; *W Ark Col; Special Ed.*

HASSLER, Jean Mary
Staples HS; Staples, MN (13-150) Drama; Tres, FHA; NHS; Ski C; Spch C; SC; Sftbl; Tnns; Hon Prog; Spch A.

HASSLER, John Charles
Hall HS; Spring Valley, IL (8-145) NHS; Sci C; Var C; Cr-Ctry; MVP, Tr; Hon Prog; Summa Cum Laude; Most Improved, Cr; Ctry I Try A; *E Ill U; Physics.*

HASSMAN, Daniel Alfred
Lake Washington HS; Kirkland, WA (80-400) Band; Ensm; Orch; Order/Arrow; SC; JV, Bkbl; JV, Golf; Order/Arrow A; *NW Nazarene Col; Engr.*

HASSTEDT, Laura Lee
Bear Creek HS; Lakewood, CO (90-370) Cpt, Chor; Drama; Ensm; Madrigal; Curliest Hair; Mus; Most Outst; *U of Northern Colo; Mus.*

HASTINGS, Brenda Nell
Cypress Fairbanks HS; Houston, TX (206-612) VOE A; *Houston Comm Col; Acct.*

HASTINGS, Daniel Warren
Penn Hills Sr HS; Penn Hills, PA (10%-1331) Band; Orch; COM; Kiwanis A; Phys Fitness Tm & Trophy; *Engr.*

HASTINGS, Dawn Marie
Northfield Jr Sr HS; Northfield, VT (8-93) AFS; Fr C; FTA; Co-Ch, Hmrm; Sch P; Var C; Bkbl; Mgr, Sftbl; Swim; Tnns; Yth Fel; Field Hockey.

HASTINGS, Joel Miles
Hirschi HS; Wichita Falls, TX; A Cap Choir; Madrigal; MVP, Ftbl; MVP, Tr; Solo, UIL Gold Medal; *Pepperdine U; Phys Ed.*

HASTINGS, Karen Sue
Garinger HS; Charlotte, NC; Chldr; *Dancing.*

HASTINGS, Kathryn Elizabeth
Statesboro HS; Statesboro, GA (4-300) Band; BC; Ensm; NHS; Span C; Alg A; COM; Quiz Bowl; Hon Graduate; Outst Sr; Eng A; Lat A; *Ga Southern Col; Math.*

HASTINGS, Sonia Dene
Southeast of Saline Assaria HS; Assaria, KS (15-58) Band; Chldr; Chor; Ensm; FHA; 4H; NHS; Rptr; SC; Cl Fav; Hon Prog.

HASTINGS, Susan Diane
Hanston HS; Hanston, KS (1-12) Ed, Ann; Band; Cpt, Chldr; Chor; Pres, FFA; 4H; Cpt, Model UN; A-Ed, Sch P; VP, SC; Var C; S-T, Sr Cl; S-T, Jr Cl; S-T, Soph Cl; B Crocker A; COM; 4H A; NEDT; Spch A; Swtht; Val; WW; FFA Dist Rptr; *Kans Wesleyan Col.*

HASTINGS, Susan Rene
SE of Saline HS; Assaria, KS (13-54) Chor; Ensm;
FHA; Madrigal; NFL; NHS; 4H A; Hon Prog; Secy
& VP, 4-H C; Ntl Sch Choral A; *Bethany-
Lindsborg Col; Mus.*

HASTON, Tammy Jean
Bay Baptist HS; Gardena, CA (10%-6) Ed, Ann;
Cpt, Chldr; Ensm; Hmrm; Rptr, Sch P; Past Wor-
thy Adv, Rainbow Girls; Grand Cross of Color,
Rainbow Girls; *Tenn Temple U.*

HASTY, Robin Michelle
Gloucester HS; Gloucester, VA (15%-200) AFS;
Ann; Band; Chor; Ensm; Hmrm; SC; Sftbl; Friend-
liest; *Va Intermont Col; Photography.*

HATAJ, Jane Ellen
Edgerton Sr HS; Edgerton, WI (99-206) Chor;
Gym; COE; *Secretarial.*

HATALA, Gregory Joseph
Sacred Heart HS; Vineland, NJ (6-56) Ann; BS;
Chor; Co-Cpt, Dbte Tm; Hmrm; F-Ed, Sch P; Pres,
Sr Cl; Mgr, Bkbl; Co-Cpt, Golf; B Crocker A;
COM; MLS; Ntl Achv Schol; NMS; NEDT; *Rut-
gers U; Communications.*

HATAWAY, Anita
Hooper Acad; Hope Hull, AL (1-44) BC; Cpt,
Chldr; Chor; Drama; Fin, GS; 4H; Tres, Hmrm;
VP, Math C; NHS; Sch P; VP, Sci C; Pres, SC; Sftbl;
COM; Citz A; Cl Fav; 4H A; MLS; Sci A; Hugh
O'Brien Yth Found; Schol A; Step Ahead Prog;
Bio.

HATAWAY, Gary Thomas
Cache HS; Cache, OK (12-45) BC; FFA; SC; Tres,
Jr Cl; Bsbl; Bkbl; Ftbl; 4H A; St Farmer Degree;
Diversified Livestock Production; Livestock Show-
ing; Judging Livestock; *Cameron U; Agr.*

HATCH, Carolyn Anne
Northwest HS; Indianapolis, IN; *Bus.*

HATCH, Deborah Lee
Calvary Christian Acad; Midland, MI; Chor; *Oral
Roberts U; Mus.*

HATCH, Elaine Barbara
Dulaney HS; Timonium, MD (10%-750) Band;
ARC; *U of Del; Nurs.*

HATCH, Karen Ann
Gloucester HS; Gloucester, MA (50-500) Pres,
Band; Hmrm; SC; Pres, Jr Cl; VP, Soph Cl; Bkbl;
Tnns; Tr; Gr Marshal; Pres A; Field Hockey; Mus
A; *Pub Relations.*

HATCH, Linda Darlene
Atlantic HS; Delray Beach, FL (17-385) Chor;
NHS; Span NHS; Hon Prog; Star Student; Zeta C;
Soroptomist A Schol; *Palm Beach Jr Col; Lib Sci.*

HATCH, Marcia
Skyline HS; Salt Lake City, UT (25%-625) Campus
Coordinator US Sen Election; *Brigham Young U;
Social Work.*

HATCH, William Charles
Holliston HS; Holliston, MA (40-267) AFS; Chor;
Drama; Hmrm; NHS; ARC; SC; Co-Cpt, Cr-Ctry;
MVP, Swim; Tr; COM; Most Versatile; *Assump-
tion Col; Bio.*

HATCHELL, Debbie Lynn
First Colonial HS; Virginia Beach, VA (189-567)
Chor; 4H; Span C; Bkbl; Sftbl; *Mary Washington
Col; Sociology.*

HATCHELL, Jane Ellen
Kaukauna HS; Kaukauna, WI (14-366) A Cap
Choir; Ann; Band; Chldr; Chor; Ensm; NHS; Ed,
Sch P; Span C; SC; Hon Prog; Journ A; Q&S A;
Solo and Ensm; Pom Pom Squad; *La Crosse Col;
Phys Therapy.*

HATCHER, Cheryl Ann
Albemarle HS; Charlottesville, VA (130-580) *Radford Col; Bus.*

HATCHER, John Michael
Halifax Co Sr HS; S Boston, VA (20%-600) Pres,
Hmrm; Lat C; Sci C; SC; Bsbl; Ftbl; Hghst Grade
Point Avg, Indust Arts; *VPI; Forestry.*

HATCHER, Kathy Sue
Lake Taylor Sr HS; Norfolk, VA (30-720) Fr C;
FHA; GS; Hmrm; NHS; Girls Key C.

HATCHER, Kerry Annette
Douglass HS; Okla City, OK; Hmrm; NHS; SC;
Citz A; Cl Fav; Delta Sigma Theta A; HQn; Hon
Prog; NMF; NMS; Phi Beta Kappa; *Bishop Col;
Religion.*

HATCHER, Monty David
Dyersburg HS; Dyersburg, TN (21-130) VP, Ann;
Order/ Arrow; ARC; Span C; SC; Bsbl; Bkbl; Ftbl;
Golf; Cpt, Soccer; Tnns; Pres, Explorer Med Ca-
reer Group; *U of Tenn; Med.*

HATCHER, Rebecca Dawn
Jones Co HS; Gray, GA; BC; FHA; Secy, 4H;
Model UN; Secy, NHS; Sci C; Bio A; COM; 4H A;
Sci A; WW; *Ga Col; Bio.*

HATCHER, Theodoric Ronald
Ala Lutheran Acad; Selma, AL; Chor; Drama; Up
Bound; COM; Hon Prog; Humanitarian A; *Concor-
dia Lutheran Col; Theology.*

HATCHER, Theresa Victoria
Killeen HS; Killeen, TX (30-960) A Cap Choir;
Chor; Ensm; Delta Sigma Theta A; Mus Achv
Certs; Outst Service Church; *U of Tex; Bus Adm.*

HATERIUS, Ricky Dean
Stamford HS; Stamford, TX (1-55) Pres, FFA;
Pres, NHS; SC; Pres, Jr Cl; JV, Bkbl; Ftbl; Tnns; JV,
Tr; Alg A; Bio A; Math A; Val; Eng A; Slide Rule
A; Number Sense A; Lat A; *Tex Tech U; Pre-Med.*

HATESOHL, Gary Dean
Washington HS; Washington, KS; Tres, FFA; Pres,
4H; Bkbl; Ftbl; Tr; 4H A.

HATESOHL, Mark John
Linn HS; Linn, KS (3-46) Band; Chor; NHS; SC;
Bsbl; Mgr, Bkbl; Mgr, Tr; Chem A; Type A; Spell-
ing A; *Cloud Co Comm Col.*

HATESOHL, Paulette Leann
Linn HS; Linn, KS (2-47) Band; Chldr; Chor; Rptr,
FHA; NHS; A-Ed, Sch P; SC; Thes; Pres, Soph Cl;
Bkbl; Mgr, Tr; *Kans St U; Sci.*

HATESOHL, Steven Ernest
Linn HS; Linn, KS (4-40) A-Ed, Ann; Band; Chor;
NHS; Rptr, Sch P; VP, Thes; Pres, Var C; Cpt,
Bkbl; Cpt, Ftbl; MVP, Tr; Amer Leg A; Hon Prog;
St Scholar; Bookkeeping A; *Kans St U; Bus Adm.*

HATFIELD, Holly Louise
Archbold HS; Archbold, OH (13-143) Chor; 4H;
Span C; Co-Cpt, Tr; Nature C; Pep C; Co-Cpt, Tr;
Bowling Green St U; Elem Ed.

HATFIELD, Mark Edward
Warren Central HS; Indianapolis, IN (10-950)
Band; BS; Ger C; NHS; Orch; Sci C; Bio A; Scien-
tist A; Ger Hon Stu; Band, Solo, & Ensm
A; PA A; *Pre-Med.*

HATFIELD, Valerie Jean
Bellingham HS; Bellingham, WA (10%-300) CYO;
Vlbl; *Western Wash St Col; Math.*

HATHAWAY, Inge Mae
S Dade HS; Homestead, FL (9-600) Model UN;
Hon Prog; *Miami Dade Col; Secy.*

HATHAWAY, Marcy Lynne
Herndon HS; Herndon, VA; Chldr; NHS; ARC;
Pep C; Gym.

HATHAWAY, Scot Clay
Herndon HS; Herndon, VA (129-518) Hmrm; In-
terAct C; NHS; Var C; Cpt, Bkbl; Ftbl; Cl Fav; Jr
NHS; HS All Amer; All District, Bkbl; Sr Advisory
Coun; *VPI; Oceanography.*

HATHCOCK, Curtis Henry
Jefferson Co N HS; Nortonville, KS (7-39) Drama;
NHS; SC; Cpt, Bkbl; Golf; Tr; Duet A's; *Kans St U.*

HATHCOCK, Teresa Ann
Independence HS; Charlotte, NC (73-750) Fr C;
Rptr, FFA; NHS; Tr; *NC St U; Horticulture.*

HATLEN, Natalie Beth
Northgate HS; Walnut Creek, CA (25%-420) Chor;
Madrigal; Orch; ARC; Cpt, Swim; Cpt, Vlbl; Secy,
Sr League; Pres, Sr League; Yth Singing Group;
Pacific Lutheran U; Nurs.

HATLEY, Carl Brent
Lone Grove HS; Lone Grove, OK (1-40) FFA; VP,
4H; Pres, SC; Rptr, Sr Cl; VP, Soph Cl; Bsbl; Bkbl;
Ftbl; Alg A; Bio A; 4H A; Hist A; Masonic A;
MLS; Sci A; Val; St Hon Soc; 1st Run-Up, Co DAR
Good Ctznshp A; *SE Okla St U; Secondary Ed.*

HATLEY, Kelly June
Central HS; Memphis, TN; Ann; Fr C; Ed, Sch P;
Ntl Conf Chr & Jews; Most Dependable; Jr NHS;
Baylor U.

HATLEY, Phillip Ray
Lone Grove HS; Lone Grove, OK (20%-50) FFA;
Parl, 4H; SC; Secy, Soph Cl; Bsbl; Bkbl; 4H A; Sci
A; *SE Okla St U.*

HATMAKER, Betty Ann
West HS; Knoxville, TN; Band; Chor; Pres, Y-Tns;
Hon Prog; Outst Y-Tn; *Social Work.*

HATMAKER, John Edward
West HS; Knoxville, TN (8-291) AFS; Ann; Band;
Chor; Ger C; Rptr, Sch P; Alg A; Hon Prog; Math
A; Ntl Sci Found; Sci A; St Jr Sci & Humanities
Sym; *Engr.*

HATT, Lisa Jean
Flushing Sr HS; Flushing, MI (194-531) ARC;
COM; ARC A; Muppets; VP, Church Coun & Cab-
inet; Church Choir; *Hurley Sch of Nurs; Nurs.*

HATTAWAY, William Summey
Wallace O'Neal Day Sch; Sou Pines, NC (6-17)
AFS; Ann; Chess C; Cpt, Dbte Tm; Fr C; InterClub
Coun; JV, Ftbl; Swim; *U of NC; Phar.*

HATTEN, Cynthia Rene
Burges HS; El Paso, TX (6-715) Mu Alpha Theta;
COM; Math A; Opt A; HR; NJHS; *Ga Tech; Math.*

HATTEN, Jennie Lynn
Oak Grove HS; Hattiesburg, MS (10-35) BC; FHA;
4H; Rainbow; Span C; Bsbl; MVP, Bkbl; Sftbl; Tr;
FCA; Bkbl Trophies; Church Swtht; *William Carey
Col; Ath.*

HATTER, Dennis Wayne
Emerson HS; Emerson, AR; FFA; 4H; Up Bound;
Cr-Ctry; Tr.

HATTER, Gloria Laverne
Emerson HS; Emerson, AR (13-31) Chor; S-T,
FHA; GS; Secy, 4H; VP, SC; Bsbl; Cpt, Bkbl; Sftbl;
Tr; COM; Cl Fav; 4H A; HQn; MLS; Yth Fel; Most
Dependable; Miss EHS; Best Ath; *Sou Ark U; Bus.*

HATTER, Jacqueline Lew
Frankfort HS; Ridgeley, WV (10%-151) Anchor C;
Chor; Fr C; FHA; 4H; NHS; Var C; Bkbl; Tr; Vlbl;
Potomac St Col; Med.

HATTERY, James A
Creighton Prep Sch; Omaha, NE (25%-198) Dbte
Tm; Lat NHS; NHS; ARC; Sodality; JV, Ftbl; God
& Country A; Hon Prog; NEDT; Sal; Summa Cum
Laude; WW.

HATTLER, Kathleen Denise
Doane-Stuart Sch; Albany, NY (5-40) Ed, Ann;
Chor; Cum Laude Soc; Drama; Fr C; Lit Mag;
Model UN; Rptr, Sch P; SC; Pres, Sr Cl; Sftbl; Cpt,
Swim; COM; NEDT; *Georgetown U.*

HATTON, Keith Warren
Silsbee HS; Silsbee, TX; JETS; NHS; Pres, SC;
Ftbl; Cl Fav; Math A; Star Student; Rptr, Tres &
Pres, FFA; Highest Trig A; Mech Agr A; *Stephen F
Austin St U; Agr.*

HATTON, Lanny James
Lanesboro HS; Lanesboro, MN (6-33) BS; Chor;
Tres, FFA; Tres, 4H; NHS; SC; Pres, Soph Cl; Bsbl;
Bkbl; Ftbl; Sftbl; Tr; 4H A; Homecoming Dedica-
tee; FFA A's; Sports Ltrs; *Waseca Agr Col; Diver-
sified Farming.*

HATTON, Lisa Lea
Lanesboro HS; Lanesboro, MN (5-33) Ed, Ann;
S-T, Band; Chldr; Chor; Drama; Secy, FFA; Semi-
Fin, GS; VP, 4H; Mjrte; NHS; F-Ed, Sch P; Spch C;
Tres, SC; Pres, Jr Cl; Bkbl; 4H A; HCt; Masonic A;
Pres A; Spch A; Swtht; Singing A; Band A; Hon
Stu; *Rochester Comm Col; Nurs.*

HATTON, Robert Lynn
Silsbee HS; Silsbee, TX (129-230) Fr C; Key C; Ntl
Yth Conf; VP, SC; Bsbl; Bkbl; Ftbl; Tr; HCt; Yth
Fel; Best All Around; WW; *Stephen F Austin St U;
Phys Ed.*

HATTON, Robert Thomas
Gilmer Co HS; Glenville, WV (39-94) Chess C; VP,
FFA; Pres, 4H; Sci C; Bsbl; Bkbl; 4H A; FFA A;
WW; *W Va U; Agr.*

HATTON, Susan Elizabeth
Ben L Smith Sr HS; Greensboro, NC (5-503) Chor; Fr C; HR; Pres, Acteens; Qn Regent's A; Costume Mgr, Sunshine Puppeteers; Librarian, Church Yth Choir; Yth Ensm; S-T, Church Yth Coun; *U of NC at Greensboro; Hist.*

HATZ, Clyde George
Springfield Cath HS; Springfield, MO; Bsbl; Bkbl; JV, Cr-Ctry; *So Mo St U; Photography.*

HATZFELD, Robin Diane
Hall HS; Little Rock, AR; Band; Tres, Span C; Spch C; Most Out; *Baylor U; Mus Ed.*

HAUBEN, Rachel Ann
Lincoln HS; Stockton, CA; Drama; Lit Mag; Thes; *Allan Hancock-Performing Arts Col; Eng.*

HAUCK, Donna Rae
Los Altos HS; Hacienda Heights, CA (50-550) Hmrm; SC; Tres, Sr Cl; Secy, Jr Cl; Statistician, Ftbl; MYF Church Group; Section Ldr, ASB Conv; Campus Life; *Cal-St at Fullerton; Social Work.*

HAUCK, Gregory Lee
Exeter Township Sr HS; Reading, PA (90-250) Demolay; Drama; Rptr, Sch P; Cpt, Ftbl; Tr; *Penn St U; Pre-Law.*

HAUCK, Sandra Ann
Southside HS; Elmira, NY (5-550) Fr C; NHS; Span C.

HAUENSTEIN, Anita Louis
Lovett HS; Atlanta, GA (17-141) Chldr; Secy, Chor; Fr C; Tres, InterAct C; Secy, NHS; Co-Ed, Sch P; MVP, Bkbl; Sftbl; Tr; Hon Prog; NEDT; Sewanee C A for Excel; 3rd Pl, St Fr Contest; *Psych.*

HAUFLER, Bethanne Margret
Berks Christian Sch; Reading, PA; Band; Chldr; Chor; Ensm; Pres, SC; Hockey; Sftbl; JV, Swim; JA A; Band A; Spiritual Growth A; *Baptist Bible Col; Christian Ed.*

HAUGE, Lisa Renee
Stanley Co HS; Fort Pierre, SD (8-45) Band; Chldr; Chor; Community Yth Symph; Drama; Pres, FHA; Mjrte; Tr; Pres A; Yth Fel; FHA A; HR; PA; *Jamestown Col; Sociology.*

HAUGEN, Charlotte Dawn
Mayville-Portland HS; Mayville, ND; Secy, SC.

HAUGEN, Donn Robert
Havre HS; Havre, MT (70%-900) Bkbl; Ftbl; H-C; *N Mont Col; Bus.*

HAUGEN, James Marc
East HS; Green Bay, WI (3-410) Ger C; JV, Ftbl; Tr; Math A; MLS; Sci A; *UWGB; Bio.*

HAUGEN, Marie Elizabeth
Seguin HS; Seguin, TX (22-400) Drama; Pres, FHA; Secy, NHS; Tnns; COM; Hon Prog; Pres, Lutheran Yth League; Secy, FCA; Drill Tm; Explorer Sct; *Tex Lutheran Col.*

HAUGER, Richard Alan
E Knox HS; Howard, OH (3-80) Band; Secy, 4H; NHS; Sch P; SC; Ftbl; Sftbl; Elk A; Edmont-Wilson A; *Agr Tech Inst; Agr.*

HAUGHNEY, Shawn Scott
Hollywood Professional Sch; Hollywood, CA; USC; *Dramatic Arts.*

HAUK, Jeannine Karen
St Charles HS; St Charles, MO (40-541) A Cap Choir; Hon Prog; Yth for Christ C; Commencement Prayer Writer; *William Jewell Col; Math.*

HAUK, Steven Andrew
St Charles Sr HS; St Charles, MO; Cr-Ctry; Tr; Hon Prog; Cr-Ctry Hon A; *Math.*

HAUKEBO, Heidi Christine
Moorhead Sr HS; Moorhead, MN (93-605) Cpt, Chldr; Chor; City Conf; Community Yth Symph; Dbte Tm; Ensm; Fin, GS; Orch; Ski C; Pres, SC; Swim; Tnns; Cl Fav; HCt; Most Out; Yth Church Coun; Cpt, Vlbl; Syncronized Swim; Bank Jr Board of Directors; *Augsburg Col; Social Sci.*

HAULBROOK, Betsy Malinda
Greenwood HS; Greenwood, SC (8-508) Ann; BC; Pres, Hmrm; NHS; Sch P; Sci C; SC; 4H A; Journ A; Q&S A; *Piedmont Tech Col; Med Asst.*

HAUMSCHILT, Mark Edward
Parkway W HS; Ballwin, MO (50%-650) Drama; Hmrm; SC; Bsbl; Ftbl; Tnns; Ntl Conf Chr & Jews; Pres A; Pres, FCA; Pres, Campus Crusade for Christ; *U of Mo; Minister.*

HAUN, Karla Ann
Clearwater HS; Clearwater, FL; Chor; S-T, Dbte Tm; Ensm; Fr C; Key C; NFL; Ed, Radio Prog; Usherette; *U of S Fla; Mass Communications.*

HAUN, Mary Kaye
Western HS; Louisville, KY; A Cap Choir; BC; Chor; Ensm; Mod Mus Mas; COM; Superior, Solo; Sch Concert Soloist; WW; *Georgetown Col; Chem.*

HAUPT, Kirsten Lynne
Ferndale HS; Ferndale, MI (25%-490) Band; Chor; Ski C; Mgr, Tr; Choir Schol; *Nurs.*

HAUPT, Robert Jeffrey
Hazelwood Central Sr HS; Florissant, MO (80-1065) Dbte Tm; Math C; NHS; Spch C; JV, Cr-Ctry; JV, Tr; FCA; Pres, Yth Coun; Yth Valentine Court; Licensed S Baptist Minister; *Southwest Baptist Col; Religion.*

HAUSAUER, Ron Carl
Beulah Pub HS; Beulah, ND (18-44) Bkbl; Co-Cpt, Ftbl; Tr; *U of ND.*

HAUSENFLUKE, Marjorie Adell
Flatonia HS; Flatonia, TX (6-39) Band; Dbte Tm; Drama; Ensm; FHA; NHS; Co-Ed, Sch P; Secy, Var C; Bkbl; Tr; Hon Prog; Pres A; Type A; 4th, St Typing; All Dist, Vlbl; 2nd, Prose Reading; *U of Tx; Phys Ed.*

HAUSER, Janice Lucile
Pendleton Sr HS; Pendleton, OR (30-235) Chor; Drama; Math C; Mu Alpha Theta; NHS; F-Ed, Sch P; Sci C; Span C; Thes; Hon Prog; Journ A; Math A; Mu Alpha Theta A; WW; *Oreg Col of Ed; Elem Ed.*

HAUSER, LaDeana Marie
Aurora HS; Aurora, WV; Band; Chldr; Chor; VP, FHA; FNA; 4H; Mjrte; NHS; Sci C; Bkbl; Spch A; Swtht; VofDEM; Gun Safety; *Nurs.*

HAUSER, Regina
Blanchet HS; Seattle, WA (22-285) Ann; NHS; B Crocker A; U of Wash Alumni A; *U of Wash; Natural Sci.*

HAUSER, Ross George
Grundy Center Comm HS; Grundy Center, IA (5-83) Band; Pres, 4H; Bsbl; 4H A; VP, Tres, S-T, Rptr, 4-H C; *Broadcast Journ.*

HAUSSECKER, Anna Marie
Beech Grove HS; Beech Grove, IN (8-250) Band; NHS; St Scholar; Faith and Life A; *Ind U; Nurs.*

HAUSSECKER, John Carl
Beech Grove HS; Beech Grove, IN (29-224) Band; Drama; Thes; God & Country A; Eagle Sct; *Ind U; Comm.*

HAUSSLER, Steven Martens
John Muir HS; Pasadena, CA (16-527) Pres, Ger C; CSF; Hon Prog; NMS; Adelphians; Tres, Bridge C; *Cal-Poly San Luis Obispo; Archt.*

HAUT, Karen Leigh
Plymouth Salem HS; Plymouth, MI; Chldr; Fr C; Sch P; Hon Prog; ARC A; Chldr A; *Eng.*

HAUTALA, Jeff Arthur
Mark Morris HS; Longview, WA (1-318) Chess C; NHS; Swim; Hon Prog.

HAUTER, Lynne Annette
Metamora Twp HS; Metamora, IL (37-193) AFS; Band; Chor; Drama; Ger C; NHS; Sci C; Sunday Sch Teacher; Bible Sch Teacher; *Concordia Col; Elem Ed.*

HAUTHER, Robert L Jr
Pattonville Sr HS; St Louis County, MO; Chess C; HR; PA.

HAUX, Tony Louis
Leola HS; Leola, SD (12-43) Band; Fin, BS; Bkbl; Ftbl; Tr; Wrest; Alt, H King; Fin, Civic Oration; *SD St U; Engr.*

HAUXWELL, Elizabeth Sue
McCook Sr HS; McCook, NE (75%-170) Band; FBLA; Hist A; *Norfolk Christian Col; Mus.*

HAVARD, Christopher
Amite Co Attendance Center; Gloster, MS (1-23) BC; Hmrm; Bkbl; Ftbl; Tr; Alg A; COM; Citz A; MLS.

HAVARD, Reginald Michael
Amite Co Attendance Center; Gloster, MS (1-40) BC; FFA; Co-Cpt, Ftbl; *Southwest Miss Jr Col; Building Trades.*

HAVEN, Linda Charous
Glenbard W HS; Glen Ellyn, IL (72-534) Band; Ensm; Orch; *Carleton Col; Econ.*

HAVEN, Micki Lynn
Ponderosa HS; Shingle Springs, CA (3-402) A Cap Choir; Secy, Band; Chor; MVP, Bkbl; Swim; Amer Leg Orator A; CSF; Citz A; MLS; Odd Fellow Fin; Spch A; Stu o-t Yr; *Pepperdine U; Child Ed.*

HAVENS, Dana Shawn
Princeton HS; Cincinnati, OH (100-500) Band; Thes; Stage Directors A; Stage Tech A; *UC; Light Designing.*

HAVERKAMP, Janelle Marie
Lindsay HS; Lindsay, TX (1-31) Ed, Ann; CYO; Chldr; Pres, FHA; SC; Tres, Sr Cl; Pres, Jr Cl; Tres, Soph Cl; Co-Cpt, Bkbl; Tr; B Crocker A; DARGCA; Hist A; Most Out; Sci A; Val; Homemaking A; Eng As; Bus As; Gen Mill Ldr of Tomorrow A; St Fin, UIL; *Tex Tech; Pol Sci.*

HAVERKAMP, Karen Louise
S Choctaw Acad; Toxey, AL (5-26) BC; Chor; Mjrte; NHS; Bkbl; Beauty; MLS; *Nurs.*

HAVERKAMP, Robert George
Bern HS; Bern, KS (6-25) Ann; CYO; Chor; Ensm; Madrigal; Pres, NHS; Sch P; Var C; Ftbl; Tr.

HAVERKATE, Theodore Michael
Sweet Home HS; Sweet Home, OR (141-193) Band; Drama; 4H; Mgr, Cr-Ctry; Swim; *Chemeketa Comm Col; Criminal Justice.*

HAVERLAH, Steve Charles
Floresville HS; Floresville, TX (25%-125) Chor; VP, FFA; VP, 4H; JV, Ftbl; Tr; *Tex A&M U.*

HAVILAND, Randy L
Arvada Sr HS; Arvada, CO (39-540) BS; City Conf; FBLA; Lat C; NHS; Pres, SC; Var C; Bsbl; Bkbl; Ftbl; Coun of Teach A; DARGCA; Elk A; HCt; Hon Prog; Masonic A; MLS; *Trevecca Nazarene Col; Bus.*

HAVILAND, Vicki Sue
Arvada Sr HS; Arvada, CO; Chor; *Bethany Nazarene Col; Vocal Mus.*

HAVLAK, Steve Gerard
Paint Rock Rural HS; Paint Rock, TX (1-10) VP, BC; Pres, FFA; Pres, Hmrm; VP, SC; Bkbl; Cr-Ctry; Co-Cpt, Ftbl; Fin, Tr; Cl Fav; Star Greenhand FFA; FHA Beau.

HAWES, Pamela Mae
Luverne Jr And Sr HS; Luverne, MN (13-135) Band; Chor; *Canby Voc Sch; Dental Assisting.*

HAWES, Richard Alfred
Franklin Acad; Malone, NY (3-265) Chor; Drama; Fr C; Math A; WW; *Rensselaer Polytech Inst; Aerospace.*

HAWK, Brian Keith
Logan Sr HS; Logan, OH (45-310) Band; 4H; SC; Var C; Pres, Soph Cl; Bsbl; Bkbl; All SEOAL, All Dist, Bkbl; Hon Men, All St, Bkbl; *Ohio St U; Bus Adm.*

HAWK, Daphne Irene
John F Kennedy HS; Richmond, CA (99-352) Heald Bus Col; Secy.

HAWK, Gina T
Chipley HS; Chipley, FL (12-127) NHS; Span C; Sci A; High Hon's A; Span A; *Chipola Jr Col; Law.*

HAWK, Julia Elizabeth
Cleveland HS; Cleveland, TN (6-250) Band; BC; Drama; Fr C; Orch.

HAWK, Karen Ann
Weston McEwen HS; Athena, OR (1-41) Band; Tres, FFA; GS; Mjrte; VP, NHS; Span C; Secy, SC; S-T, Var C; VP, Jr Cl; Tnns; Tnns; HQn; HCt; Hon Prog; Spch A; Val; VofDEM; Vlbl; Outst Highland Lassie, Bagpipe Bnd; *Blue Mountain Comm Col.*

HAWK, Wynne Elizabeth
High Point HS; Beltsville, MD; NHS; Ski C; SC; Pres, Soph Cl; JV Vlbl; *U of Md; Med.*

HAWKE, Dawn Marie
Parkview HS; Orfordville, WI (1-150) Ann; Band; Fin, Dbte Tm; Drama; 4H; NHS; Hockey; Semi-Fin, Tr; 4H A; Hon Prog; Spch A; Val; *U of Wis-Whitewater; Acct.*

HAWKER, John Scott
Wichita HS W; Wichita, KS (12-588) Demolay; Model UN; NHS; Phys C; JV, Bsbl; JV, Ftbl; COM; Math A; St Scholar; Dean's A, Kans St U; *Tex Tech U; Elec Engr.*

HAWKINS, April Candace
Cooper Sr HS; New Hope, MN (20-684) NHS; Yth Fel; Ordained Elder; Sunday Sch Teacher; Membership Committee; *U of Minn; Child Development.*

HAWKINS, Barbara Ruth
Summit HS; Summit, NJ (25%-360) COM; Hon Prog; *Lib Arts.*

HAWKINS, Claudius Everette
Indian River HS; Chesapeake, VA; Band; Drama; 4H; Hmrm; Monogram; Bkbl; Ftbl; Tr; 4H A; Pres A; *Norfolk St Col; Bus Adm.*

HAWKINS, Clifton Renard
Cass Tech HS; Detroit, MI; *Wayne St U; Stenography.*

HAWKINS, Daniel John
University Sch; Hunting Valley, OH (25-90) Band; Orch; Order/Arrow; Pres, SC; World Affairs C; Pres, Sr Cl; Pres, Jr Cl; Soccer; Mgr, Wrest; COM; Citz A; Order/Arrow A; Eagle Sct; NML; *Princeton U; Econ.*

HAWKINS, Darryl Edward
Nw HS; St Louis, MO (5-595) NHS; SC; Bkbl; JV, Tr; COM; Citz A; Hon Soc, HR, Certs; *Kans U; Computer Prog.*

HAWKINS, Daryl Edward
Garland HS; Garland, TX (150-450) Lat C; Tr; Math A; Bookkeeping A; *Southwestern Col; Religion.*

HAWKINS, Derrek Cooper
Flint Central HS; Flint, MI (4-H; MVP, Bkbl; Ftbl; Tr; Most Out; MVP, Offensive Ftbl; All City Ftbl; V A; Hon Men, All Valley, Bkbl; *Bus Adm.*

HAWKINS, Donald Kenneth
Florida Air Acad; Melbourne, FL; Cpt, Band; Var C; COM; Special Achv A; *US Air Force Acad; Aviation.*

HAWKINS, Elizabeth Jane
Raleigh HS; Raleigh, MS; Sch P; Sci C; Spch C; Amer Leg A; Spch A; *Jones Co Jr Col; Nurs.*

HAWKINS, Graccine Alzette
Bakersfield HS; Bakersfield, CA (66%-450) Chor; Span C; Bsbl; Golf; Sftbl; Swim; Cl Fav; *Real Estate.*

HAWKINS, Harvey Eugene Jr
Westbury HS; Houston, TX (1-614) Pres, Key C; NHS; Co-Cpt, Ftbl; Amer Leg A; COM; Hon Prog; Most Out; NEDT; Senator, BS; *Tex A&M U; Engr.*

HAWKINS, Jay L
Buhl HS; Buhl, ID (30-140) BS; Drama; Key C; Ski C; Pres, SC; Pres, Soph Cl; JV, Bkbl; Cr-Ctry; Mgr, Ftbl; JV, Golf; Amer Leg A; *Boise St Col; Radio and Communication.*

HAWKINS, Judy Lynn
Villa Park HS; Villa Park, CA (10%-450) Co-Cpt, Hmrm; Y-Tns; COM; Cpt, Drill Tm; *Calif St U.*

HAWKINS, Kirk Douglas
Pinckneyville Comm HS; Pinckneyville, IL (5%-135) A-Ed, Ann; Drama; Span C; Spch C; Mgr, Bkbl; Ftbl; Co-Cpt, Swim; Tr; *Dentistry.*

HAWKINS, Mark Leslie
Paris HS; Paris, TX (15-315) Ger C; Key C; NHS; Tres, SC; Cpt, Ftbl; Tr; *Tex Tech U; Petroleum Engr.*

HAWKINS, Patricia Marie
R J Reynolds HS; Winston-Salem, NC; Chldr; Drama; Lat C; Tr; Most Improved Eng Stu; Most Congenial.*

HAWKINS, Phyllis Ann
Adlai E Stevenson HS; New York, NY (40-822) Chor; NHS; Sch Achieve Tm; Up Bound; Citz A; Regent Schol; *St U at Buffalo; Psych.*

HAWKINS, Rebecca Sue
Highland HS; Highland, IN (176-577).

HAWKINS, Robert Bradley
W Mecklenburg HS; Charlotte, NC; Ski C; Ftbl; Tnns; Opt A; ARC A; *Appalachian Col; Bus.*

HAWKINS, Ronald Lee
Norwayne HS; Creston, OH (30-150) Chor; Dbte Tm; Drama; Ensm; Rptr, Sch P; Spch C; God & Country A; Yth Fel; *Akron U; Span.*

HAWKINS, Sabrina Louise
San Jacinto HS; San Jacinto, CA; Cpt, Chldr; Fr C; Ski C; SC; Pres, Soph Cl; Service Above Self A; *U of Colo; Law.*

HAWKINS, Timothy Howard
Robert E Lee HS; Tyler, TX; Chem C; Hmrm; Pres, Span C; COM; Hon Prog; Rotary A; Yth Fel; Lee Gentlemen; Church Acolyte; Lead Bible Stu; *Tex U; Med.*

HAWKINS, Willie Mae
Woodrow Wilson HS; Camden, NJ; Chldr; Chor; Hmrm; Var C; Cpt, Bkbl; Cpt, Sftbl; *Rutgers Col; Engr.*

HAWKINSON, Cindy Sue
Radford HS; Honolulu, HI (15%-600) Mjrte; ARC; Swim; Yth for Christ; Campus Life; *Bus.*

HAWKINSON, Dorothy Ann
Christian Co HS; Hopkinsville, KY (49-350) Band; BC; Chldr; S-T, Hmrm; NHS; Orch; SC; *Lutheran Deaconess Col; Nurs.*

HAWKINSON, Kelley Colleen
McGregor HS; McGregor, MN (2-72) Chldr; Chor; Drama; Bus Mgr, Sch P; Sci C; Span C; *Southwest Minn St Col; Pre-Med.*

HAWKS, Cecil Duane
William Fleming HS; Roanoke, VA (15%-500) BC; Sci C; Bsbl; *Archt.*

HAWLEY, David Oren
N Clayton Sr HS; College Park, GA (15%-475) Band; Co-Cpt, Ftbl; Tr; *U of Ga; Hist.*

HAWLEY, James Russell
Salina Central HS; Salina, KS; Band; Hmrm; Bkbl; Golf; *Sports Broadcasting.*

HAWLEY, Judi Annette
Edmonds Sr High; Edmonds, WA (100-350) Chor; FBLA; HS Ldr; Candy Striper; *Shoreline SPC; Nursing.*

HAWLEY, Loralee
Sarasota HS; Sarasota, FL; Community Yth Symph; Orch; *Manatee Jr Col; Dentist Asst.*

HAWLEY, Steven Craig
N Clayton Sr HS; College Park, GA (20%-700) BC; Madrigal; Wrest.

HAWORTH, Leisha Vandever
Muskogee HS; Muskogee, OK; AFS; Chldr; VP, Fr C; GS; Jr Miss Pagent; NHS; Secy, Span C; SC; Thes; VP, Jr Cl; Tres, Soph Cl; Tnns; Hon Prog; Opt A; Spch A; Swtht; VofDEM; Qn, All Sch; Qn, ROTC; Swtht, St Demolay, St Knighthood; *Okla U; Radio & TV Broadcasting.*

HAWTHORNE, James Emanuel Jr
O D Wyatt HS; Fort Worth, TX (190-540) A Cap Choir; Chor; Dbte Tm; Drama; FHA; Tr; *U of Tex; Journ.*

HAWTHORNE, Jill Ann
Chappell HS; Chappell, NE (3-32) Co-Ed, Ann; Band; Chor; FHA; Fin, GS; 4H; NHS; Rptr, Sch P; SC; Var C; Secy, Jr Cl; Secy, Soph Cl; Bkbl; Tr; COM; 4H A; HCt; Hon Prog; Yth Fel; All Conf Vlbl & Bkbl; 4-H Citizenship Short Course; Hon Men, All St Bkbl; *Kearney St Col; Phys Therapy.*

HAWTHORNE, Keith Dwayne
Alma J Brown HS; Grambling, LA (3-70) Band; Chor; Parl, FTA; Hmrm; NHS; SC; VP, Jr Cl; Parl, Soph Cl; Bsbl; Ftbl; Alg A; Math A; Yth Fel; LSU Mixed Quartet; *Grambling St U; Elec.*

HAWTHORNE, Thomas Earl
O D Wyatt HS; Fort Worth, TX; Tr.

HAY, Gertrude Seabrook
Sea Island Acad; John's Island, SC (5-13) Bus Mgr, Ann; Cpt, Chldr; Chor; Drama; Fr C; ARC; Sch P; VP, SC; Pres, Sr Cl; Pres, Jr Cl; VP, Soph Cl; Bsbl; Bkbl; HCt; Miss Jr; Miss Sr; Most Sch Spirit; Most Popular; *Col of Charleston; Child Care.*

HAY, Jeffrey Scott
St John's HS; John's Island, SC (1-150) BC; Co-Ch, Chess C; Fr C; Pres, Math C; Mu Alpha Theta; Val; *Erskine Col; Hist.*

HAY, Karla Kay
Dublin HS; Dublin, GA (5%-199) A-Ed, Ann; Band; BC; FTA; Hon Prog; *Deaf Ed.*

HAY, Romona Lynn
Central HS; Bridgeport, CT; Hmrm; First & Second Hons; *Morehouse Col; Psych.*

HAYCOCK, Keith Allen
Andress HS; El Paso, TX (2-546) NHS; Math A; Scholastic Ltr; Nom, NMS Semi-Fin; *Math.*

HAYDEL, Nathan Joseph
Destrehan HS; Destrehan, LA (5%-200) BC; Hmrm; *U of New Orleans; Dentistry.*

HAYDEN, Angela Jeanine
Elmhurst HS; Fort Wayne, IN (33-341) Drama; Var C; MVP, Tr; COM; Citz A; JA A; Rotary A; Shorthand, Drama, A's; HR; Principle's List; *Ind St U; Clothing-Textiles.*

HAYDEN, Clara Lovell
MacDuffie Sch; Springfield, MA (15-47) A-Ed, Ann; Lit Mag; Rainbow; Pres, Sci C; S-T, Sr Cl; VP, Jr Cl; VP, Soph Cl; *Simmons Col; Art.*

HAYDEN, Denise Diane
Rantoul Township HS; Rantoul, IL (121-409) Secy & VP, Cultural Interest C; *U of Ill; Hist.*

HAYDEN, Joseph Thomas
Owensboro Cath HS; Owensboro, KY (1-225) CYO; Drama; Math C; NHS; Spch C; Thes; Amer Leg A; Amer Leg Orator A; COM; Chamber of Comm A; HCt; JA A; Math A; Opt A; Spch A; Ldrship A's; Newspaper Carrier o-t Mo; *Brescia Col; Math.*

HAYDEN, Mary Barbara
Albuquerque Acad; Albuquerque, NM; Mgr, Soccer; *Southern Methodist U.*

HAYDEN, Mary Monica
Owensboro Cath HS; Owensboro, KY; CYO; Drama; Spch C.

HAYDEN, Ollie
Madison Co HS; Gurley, AL (10-107) Pres, BC; BS; Chor; Pres, Var C; Bsbl; MVP, Bkbl; Tr; Amer Leg A; Hon Prog; Most Ath; Schol Bowl Tm; All-Amer Bkbl; Ath Schol; *Huntingdon Col; Acct.*

HAYDEN, Robin Lee
Lee Davis HS; Mechanicsville, VA (25%-600) AFS; Chldr; InterClub Coun; ARC; Span C; Secy, SC; Tri-HiY; Pres, Y-Tns; Tres, Soph Cl; Swim; Tr; Jacksonian A; *Madison Col; Sci.*

HAYDEN, Robin Nadine
Rantoul Township HS; Rantoul, IL (63-359) Mgr, Tr; *Ill Sou U; Acct.*

HAYDEN, Sean Kahlyl
Takoma Acad; Takoma Park, MD; Chor; Var C; Pres, Soph Cl; Bkbl; Ftbl; Tr; Citz A; Type A; *Oakwood Col; Child Psych.*

HAYDEN, Shelia Ann
Statesville Sr HS; Statesville, NC; Band; Mgr, Bkbl.

HAYES, Angela Maria
John F Kennedy HS; New Orleans, LA (40-435) A Cap Choir; Pres, Chor; Hmrm; ARC; Tres, Sr Cl; *Grambling U; Special Ed.*

HAYES, Brenda Gail
Jonesboro Hodge HS; Jonesboro, LA; 4H; JV, Bkbl; *NE Col; Child Care.*

HAYES, Cathy Ann
Ainsworth HS; Flint, MI (24-245) A Cap Choir; Secy, NHS; JA A; *Baker Jr Col of Bus; Court Reporting.*

HAYES, Christy Marie
Granite City HS S; Granite City, IL (179-693) Chor; *Bradley U; Child Care.*

HAYES, Clara Charlesetta
Bellaire HS; Bellaire, TX (5-700) Fr C; Hmrm; Span C; Span NHS; Cert of Merit; Hon Program; *Dillard U; Span.*

HAYES, Daniel Scott
Mt Gilead HS; Mt Gilead, OH (7-130) BS; Fr C; Pres, 4H; Pres, Key C; NHS; Span C; Ftbl; Sftbl; Hon Prog; WW; *General Motors Inst; Engr.*

HAYES, Danita Joyce
Fairfield HS; Fairfield, AL (9-167) Ann; BC; Chldr; Sch P; Parl, SC; Y-Tns; Beauty; HCt; WW; Outst Sr; *U of Ala; Med Records Adm.*

HAYES, Deborah Darlene
Nova HS; Ft Lauderdale, FL (15%-493) FBLA; Madrigal; NHS; Span NHS; Swim; *Fla St U; Bio.*

HAYES, Deborah Rochelle
Canton Acad; Canton, MS (25%-99) Ed, Ann; Band; BC; Chldr; Ensm; 4H; Cpt, Mjrte; ARC; Sci C; Y-Tns; Sftbl; Beauty; COM; 4H A; HCt; Hon Prog; Lion A; Spch A; Type A; Yth Fel; Century III A; Mus C Schol; Tau Beta Sigma A; Col Mus Schol; *Belhaven Col; Mus.*

HAYES, Don Kevin
Madison HS; Richmond, KY; F-Ed, Ann; Secy, Band; BC; Rptr, Fr C; Pres, 4H; F-Ed, Sch P; Rptr, Sci C; Bsbl; Ftbl; Alg A; COM; 4H A; I Dare You; Kiwanis A; Math A; Opt A; Opt Out Tn; Sci A; *U of Ky; Med.*

HAYES, Donald Joe Jr
Granite City HS S; Granite City, IL (172-656) Band; JV, Soccer; *Anesthesiologist.*

HAYES, Dorsene Annette
Midwest City HS; Midwest City, OK (285-520) A Cap Choir; Chor; FHA; Hmrm; *Oscar Rose Jr Col; Social Work.*

HAYES, Janet
N Natchez Adams HS; Natchez, MS (15%-220) Co-Ed, Ann; Band; BC; Lit Mag; Orch; S-T, Sr Cl; Beauty; Hon Prog; Masonic A; Swtht; Type A; *Alcorn St U; Elem Ed.*

HAYES, Janet Lee
Montgomery Co HS; Mt Sterling, KY (10%-290) FHA; GS; NHS; Jr, Chapter, St, FHA Degrees; Regional Hist; Outst Member, DECA; Swtht, Hon Stu, DECA; *U of Ky; Communications.*

HAYES, Jedaune
Chicago Voc HS; Chicago, IL (45-967) Commercial C; NHS; Var C; Bkbl; Cr-Ctry; Ftbl; Cpt, Tr; COM; Citz A; Hon Prog; Yth Fel; Yth Leg; *Memphis St U; Archit.*

HAYES, Jimmy Van
West Rome HS; Rome, GA; Band; Drama; Sch P.

HAYES, Judy Elizabeth
Gaffney Sr HS; Gaffney, SC (6-350) Tres, BC; Co-Ch, Chor; Ensm; FTA; Gov Honor Prog; Hon Prog; *Col of Charleston; Marine Bio.*

HAYES, Karen Jean
C L McLane HS; Fresno, CA; Stat Girl, Scorekeeper, Boy's Bkbl; *Fresno City Col; Social Welfare.*

HAYES, Kimberly Dawn
Hattiesburg HS; Hattiesburg, MS (35-392) Chldr; Chor; Ensm; S-T, Hmrm; Key C; Lit Mag; Ed, Sch P; Rptr, SC; Var C; Tres, Soph Cl; Hon Prog; Journ A; Swtht; Type A; FCA; Win, Jr Historical Soc; Activities A; Win, St Keyboard; All Superior, Piano; *Samford U; Mus Ed.*

HAYES, Lisa Danette
Lindsay HS; Lindsay, OK (30-120) Band; Span C; Bkbl; Cl Fav; Hon Prog; WW; Best Personality; *Okla U; Phys Ed.*

HAYES, Lisa Deanna
Bunker HS Dist R-3; Bunker, MO (3-55) Band; Tres, BC; Co-Cpt, Chldr; VP, FHA; Rptr, Soph Cl; HCt; JV, Vlbl; Home Ec A; World Lit A; *South West Mo St; Sociology.*

HAYES, Loy Archie
W Rome HS; Rome, GA (10-170) Band; Dbte Tm; NHS; Hon Prog; NEDT; NML; *Pepperdine U; Journ.*

HAYES, Marian Elizabeth
Berrien Co HS; Nashville, GA; Chldr; Hmrm; Rainbow; Tres, SC; Pres, Tri-HiY; Pres, Jr Cl; Cl Fav; DARGCA; HCt; WW; Ftbl Qn; Sr Superlative; *Valdosta St Col; Bus.*

HAYES, Marsha Lynn
Paris HS; Paris, TX (6-250) Chess C; Drama; Secy, Fr C; Lat C; Lit Mag; NHS; Thes; Tri-HiY; COM; Hon Prog; Summa Cum Laude; Cpt, Drill Tm; *U of Tex at Arlington; Physics.*

HAYES, Martha Dorene
Louisburg HS; Louisburg, NC (1-115) Ann; VP, BC; FBLA; Monogram; Bus Mgr, Sch P; VP, Span C; SC; VP, Jr Cl; Bkbl; Mgr, Sftbl; Q&S A; Type A; Fresh, Soph & Jr Marshal; *E Carolina U; Health.*

HAYES, Melanie Suzanne
Sweet Home HS; Sweet Home, OR (46-193) Band; Semi-Fin, GS; SC; Secy, Sr Cl; COM; Hon Prog; *George Fox Col; Mus.*

HAYES, Myra Lynn
Bessemer Acad; Bessemer, AL (1-76) BC; Ensm; Fr C; Tri-HiY; Beauty; COM; Type A; *Med.*

HAYES, Rhonda Kay
Woodward HS; Woodward, OK (12-181) Cpt, Chldr; Chor; 4H; Ch, Hmrm; Semi-Fin, Jr Miss Pa; Sch P; SC; Bkbl; Sftbl; COM; Citz A; 4H A; HQn; Hon Prog; Kiwanis A; St Scholar; Yth Fel; Pep C; Rptr, Sub Debs; *Okla U.*

HAYES, Robert Brian
C L McLane HS; Fresno, CA (20%-600) *Fresno City Col; Archt.*

HAYES, Robin Marie
W Columbus HS; Cerro Gordo, NC (17-180) Ann; BC; Fr C; FBLA; FHA; Shorthand A; Fin, Beauty Pageant; *U of NC; Commercial Art.*

HAYES, Rodney Eugene
St Augustine HS; New Orleans, LA (12-36) Ann; Chess C; Ed, Sch P; Hist A; Journ A; Tres, Med Careers; Yrbk; Pres, Hist C; *Xavier U; Bio.*

HAYES, Sally Ann
Cecilia Sr HS; Cecilia, LA; Secy, BC; Chor; Pres, Fr C; Pres, FBLA; 4H; Lit Ral; Most Out; Val; Val; *U of Sou LA; Med Tech.*

HAYES, Sonya Mellisa
Walter Wellborn HS; Anniston, AL (40-210) Chor; FBLA; Rptr, FHA; Hmrm; Math C; NHS; SC; HCt; Fin, Sch Beauty Contest; *South-Eastern Bible Col; Elem Ed.*

HAYES, Susan Margaret
Whitman-Hanson Regional HS; Whitman, MA (1-328) CYO; Chldr; Drama; GS; Key C; Math C; VP, NHS; Rptr, Sch P; Ski C; Cr-Ctry; Tnns; Bausch & Lomb A; Hist A; Hon Prog; Rensselaer A; Spch A; Val; VofDEM; *Williams Col; Hist.*

HAYES, Tawni Lee
Dexter HS Usd 471; Dexter, KS (2-25) Chor; Ensm; FHA; NHS; Sch P; S-T, Jr Cl; S-T, Soph Cl; JV, Bkbl; COM; Type A; Pep C; *Bus Adm.*

HAYES, Timothy Reed
Chelmsford HS; Chelmsford, MA (10%-650) Chess C; Math C; Order/Arrow; Ftbl; Tr; Alg A; COM; Hon Prog; Math A; Order/Arrow A; Sci A; Read Magazine; *US Air Force Acad; Sci.*

HAYES, Valerie E
Fernandina Beach Sr HS; Fernandina Beach, FL; Band; Chor.

HAYGOOD, Andrea Alise
Melrose Sr HS; Memphis, TN (20-360) Drama; NHS; Thes; Bkbl; Alg A; HCt; Sci A; Yth Fel; Secy, Choir; Cotton Makers Jubilee; *Pepperdine U; Journ.*

HAYGOOD, Diana L
Andrew J Terrell HS; Blanchard, OK; F-Ed, Ann; BC; Chldr; FHA; Hmrm; Math C; NHS; Sch P; Sci C; SC; Var C; Rptr, Jr Cl; Bkbl; Sftbl; COM; Citz A; Hist A; Hon Prog; Journ A; Magna Cum Laude; Yth Fel; Hist, FHA; *Okla St U; Elem Ed.*

HAYHURST, Brett Darren
Mannington HS; Mannington, WV (5-159) Bkbl; Tr; Hist A; Type A; HR; Ltrman, Bkbl & Tr; *W Va U; Law.*

HAYHURST, Nancy Arlene
Heritage Christian Acad; Ravenswood, WV (7-54) Band; Ensm; Sci C; Bkbl; Sftbl; Vlbl; *Nurs.*

HAYLES, Donna Louise
Chichester Sr HS; Boothwyn, PA (122-349) Cpt, Band; Chldr; Chor; Mgr, Bkbl; Mgr, Hockey; Chldr A; *Millersville Col; Child Psych.*

HAYLES, Judith Marie
Adlai E Stevenson HS; Bronx, NY (27-822) City Conf; Dbte Tm; Hmrm; Lit Mag; Model UN; NHS; Sch Achieve Tm; SC; COM; Citz A; Hon Prog; *Brown U; Arts & Sci.*

HAYMOND, Mark Whiteford
Marion HS; Marion, SC (20-210) Sch P; Pres, Var C; Bsbl; Cpt, Bkbl; Ftbl; HKg; Alt, BS; WW; *Presbyterian Col; Journ.*

HAYNES, Andrea
Encinal HS; Alameda, CA (12-360) JV, Chldr; Ntl Yth Conf; ARC; Tr; COM; Pres A; Type A; Shorthand A; *Heald's Bus Col; Secy.*

HAYNES, Argylene Kaye
Wheaton HS; Wheaton, MO (14-36) Band; Co-Cpt, Chldr; Chor; FHA; NHS; JV, Bkbl; Sftbl; HCt; Yth Fel; FFA Swtht; *Crowder Col; Phys Therapy.*

HAYNES, Bonnie
Towers HS; Decatur, GA; BC; Bus Mgr, Chor; Secy, Drama; Ensm; Hmrm; Span C; Thes; Cpt, Swim; Coaches A in Swimming; *Ga St U; Recreation.*

HAYNES, Catherine Merle
El Dorado Springs HS; El Dorado Springs, MO (5-132) Chldr; FHA; Fin, GS; NHS; Sch Achieve Tm; Secy, Soph Cl; Sftbl; Tr; Hon Prog; PTA A; Yth Fel; Yth Leg; *SW Mo St U; Sociology.*

HAYNES, Cheryl Densie
Miss Baptist HS; Jackson, MS (1-55) Bus Mgr, Ann; Co-Cpt, Chldr; Chor; 4H; NHS; Sch P; Pres, Jr Cl; S-T, Soph Cl; Bkbl; Tr; Alg A; Bio A; Cl Fav; DARGCA; Hist A; Math A; Sci A; Type A; Val; Home Ec A; Geom A; Bible A; Eng As; *Clarke Col; Home Ec.*

HAYNES, Cordelia A
Texas Sr HS; Texarkana, TX (39-435) All Amer Yth; Band; NHS; NHS A; *Tex Women's U; Nurs.*

HAYNES, Dallis Huguley
Scott Preparatory Sch; Opelika, AL (10-27) Anchor C; Co-Ed, Ann; BC; Cpt, Chldr; Chem C; SC; Var C; Secy, Jr Cl; Cpt, Bkbl; Cpt, Sftbl; COM; HCt; NEDT; Type A; Yth Fel; Chldr A; Sftbl A; Bkbl A; *Auburn U; Elem Ed.*

HAYNES, Dwain Stuart
Hendersonville HS; Hendersonville, NC (39-174) Chor; Span C; Bkbl; JV, Ftbl; JV, Tr; *U of NC; Math.*

HAYNES, Jay Harlan
N Caddo HS; Vivian, LA (8%-200) BS; Drama; Key C; NHS; ARC; Sci C; Spch C; Pres, SC; Cpt, Ftbl; Tr; Wrest; Cl Fav; Elk A; Hon Prog; MLS; Most Out; Opt A; Opt Out Tn; VFW Orator Win; VofDEM; MVP, Ftbl; Mayor For A Day; Pres, FCA; World Skeet Champ; Ch, CODAC; Win, Century III; *SW Col at Memphis; Pre-Med.*

HAYNES, Jeffery Sanford
Clay Co HS; Ashland, AL (4-72) BC; Chor; Ensm; S-T, Hmrm; Order/Arrow; Var C; Bsbl; Ftbl; *U of Houston; Engr.*

HAYNES, Keitha Ann
Claiborne Acad; Haynesville, LA (5-37) Ann; Band; Chldr; Chor; Lit Ral; Mjrte; NHS; Rptr, SC; B Crocker A; HCt; Jamboree Qn; Miss Claiborne Acad; WW; *La Tech U; Nurs.*

HAYNES, Kevin Christy
W Orange HS; Winter Garden, FL; Fin, Band; BC; Fin, Ensm; Pres, Hmrm; Lit Mag; Orch; Span C; Tri-HiY; Var C; Bsbl; Swim; COM; Hon Prog; Bsbl Trophies; AMVETS Drivers; Sunday Sch PA, As; Solo & Ensm; Master Bandsman; Co-Head, ACOLYTE; Excellence St Win & 6th-Ntl; *FSU; Mus.*

HAYNES, Nancy Loraine
Coleman HS; Coleman, TX (20-75) Bus C; Commercial C; JETS; Secy, Lat C; 'C' A, Bookkeeping; *McMurry Col; Bus Adm.*

HAYNES, Ralph Alan
Hale R-I HS; Hale, MO (6-28) Ann; Band; Chor; Dbte Tm; Drama; Ensm; Tres, 4H; Thes; Tres, Var C; Pres, Jr Cl; SC; MVP, Bkbl; Mgr, Sftbl; MVP, Tr; 4H A; Spch A; Type A; Aptitude Schol; PA; *SW Mo St U; Engr.*

HAYNES, Robert Dodd
Salisbury HS; Salisbury, NC (7-280) VP, AFS; A-Ed, Ann; Band; Pres, Hmrm; Key C; Pres, Lat C; Order/Arrow; COM; Citz A; Hon Prog; Journ A; Spch A; Eagle Sct A; SPEC Summer Ldrship Prog; Social Sci.

HAYNES, Stacy Jeanene
University Sch of Nashville; Nashville, TN (25-66) Band; Fr C; Fin, Jr Miss Pagent; Lat C; Orch; SC; Tr; Auburn U; Biochem.

HAYNES, Terence L
Leesville HS; Leesville, LA; ARC; Span C; Bsbl; MVP, Ftbl; Grambling St U; Computer Sci.

HAYNES, Timmy Joe
E Henderson HS; E Flat Rock, NC; Tres, AFS; Ann; Band; Chess C; Chor; Hmrm; Pres, Sci C; SC; Bsbl; Co-Cpt, Bkbl; Cpt, Sftbl; Fin, Swim; JV, Tnns; Mgr, Wrest; Citz A; 4H A; JA A; MLS; Most Out; Pres A; Sci A; Yth Fel; YMCA, Art, Easter Seal, A's; Bryan Col; Art.

HAYNES, Timothy John
Norton HS; Norton, OH (7-287) Pres, Band; Ensm; NHS; Orch; Order/Arrow; SC; VP, Soph Cl; Bsbl; Wrest; COM; Order/Arrow A; Ntl Assn of Rudimental Drummers; US Military; Elec.

HAYNES, Vanessa Elaine
Hemet HS; Hemet, CA; A Cap Choir; Kiwanis A.

HAYNES, William Gregory
Athens HS; Athens, AL (33%-350) Span C; Var C; Secy, Soph Cl; Bsbl; Bkbl; Ftbl; Cl Fav; Yth Fel; Phar.

HAYNIE, John Byron
Corsicana HS; Corsicana, TX; A Cap Choir; FFA; JV, Bkbl; JV, Ftbl; Chamber of Comm A; Cl Fav; Opt Out Tn; U of Colo; Communications.

HAYS, Charles Dudley
Crenshaw HS; Los Angeles, CA; Harvey Williams A; Chapman Col; Telecommunications.

HAYS, James Jeffrey
Salem Sr HS; Salem, OH (1-347) Fr C; Ger C; Tnns; FOE God, Flag & Ctry A; Cincinnati Bible Sem; Christian Ministries.

HAYS, Jon Riley
Herrin HS; Herrin, IL; Band; Fr C; Key C; Math C; Var C; Cpt, Golf; Alg A; Amer Leg A; COM; Math A; MVP, Golf; 1st, Sup Sci Fair; 1st, Solo Trombone Contest; Emory-Oxford Col; Med.

HAYS, Larry Mark
Eufaula HS; Eufaula, OK (10%-110) Rptr, Band; Rptr, FFA; God & Country A; Order/Arrow A; Spch A; Usher, Ntl FFA Convention; E Dist Hon Band; Win, St Spch; Okla St U; Agr Econ.

HAYS, Liana Renee
Highland HS; Highland, IN (300-600) Drama; FTA; 4H; Sftbl; PA; Los Angeles Baptist Col.

HAYS, Nelson Mark
Mannington HS; Mannington, WV (4-105) Monogram; NHS; VP, SC; Bsbl; Bkbl; Ftbl; Elk A; W Va U; Engr.

HAYS, Pamela
R J Reynolds Sr HS; Winston-Salem, NC (24-822) Tres, Fr C; Hmrm; NHS; Hon Prog; Co- ch, Yth Fel; Reynolds Dancing Boots; Girl's Coun; U of NC; Pol Sci.

HAYTER, Jamie Lynn
Benhaven HS; Olivia, NC (6-82) Ann; Band; BC; Chldr; FHA; Mjrte; Monogram; Orch; Sch P; Secy, Sci C; COM; Hon Prog; Band, Fr, Eng, A's; U of Tenn Hon Band; E Carolina U; Med.

HAYWARD, Daniel Arthur
Mira Costa HS; Manhattan Beach, CA (33%-625) Ftbl; Fin, Wrest; Most Out; PA; U of Sou Calif; Law.

HAYWARD, Ernest Jr
E E Smith Sr HS; Fayetteville, NC (17-297) Band; Pres, Key C; NHS; VP, SC; Pres, Jr Cl; COM; Gr Marshal; Most Out; Type A; VofDEM; Yth Fel; Fr A; Jr Service A; All-St Band; Ntl Brotherhood Essay, 2nd Pl; Marquette U; Pre-Med.

HAYWARD, Kimberly Jeanette
Pierce City HS; Pierce City, MO; Band; FHA; Secy, 4H; Tres, Jr Cl; Bkbl; HCt; Sal.

HAYWARD, Marty Albert
Frederick Douglass HS; Atlanta, GA (23-400) Band; Chor; JV, Tr; ROTC A; Med.

HAYWISER, Keith Michael
St Elizabeth HS; Pittsburgh, PA (30-112) All Amer Yth; CYO; Drama; Sci C; Ski C; Bkbl; Golf; Hockey; I Dare You; MLS; Star Student; Comm S Col; Computor Sci.

HAYWOOD, David Stuart
Fairfield HS; Fairfield, AL (15%-150) Ann; Band; BS; Hmrm; Orch; Order/Arrow; Sch P; S-T, Jr Cl; Order/Arrow A; Eagle Sct; Auburn U; Phar.

HAYWOOD, Keith Alan
Grand Rapids Baptist HS; Grand Rapids, MI (25%-32) A-Ed, Ann; Band; Ski C; VP, SC; Pres, Var C; Bsbl; Bkbl; Soccer; Journ.

HAYWOOD, Rita Lynn
Far Rockaway HS; Far Rockaway, NY (110-386) Chor; Co-Cpt, Bk'bl; Sftbl; COM; Citz A; Most Out; Spch A; Star Student; MVP A, Bkbl; 1980 Olympics; Chancellor's HR; Women's Sports Mag A; 1976 Olympic Fin; St Johns U; Psych.

HAYWOOD, Vanessa Irene
Southwest HS; Kansas City, MO; Fr C; Hmrm; Orch; ARC; JV, Swim; JV, Tnns; Art As; Secy, Soph Exec Board; Pep C; VP, Horse C; Pres, BYF.

HAYWOOD, Wanda
Olney HS; Philadelphia, PA; NHS; Hist A; Hon Prog; HR; Penn St U; Stenography.

HAYWOOD, Xeneida Elmira
Paraiso Jr Sr HS; Paraiso, CANAL ZONE; Band; FNA; ARC; Band A; PA; Drew U; Psych.

HAZARD, Donna Ann
Sparks HS; Sparks, NV (19-290) W Nev Comm Col; Bus.

HAZARD, Mark Douglas
Blair HS; Blair, NE (93-150) Tres, CYO; Var C; Bsbl; MVP, Bkbl; Tr; HCt; Hon Prog; Hastings Col; Forestry.

HAZARD, Nancy Lee
Oxford HS; Oxford, AL (10%-270) Ed, Ann; BC; Chor; Ensm; Superior Rating, Piano Contest; Excellent A, St & Dist Contest; Samford U; Sci.

HAZEL, David Henry
Marshall HS; Marshall, TX; Band; Sftbl; Jr Bowl League; Asst Coun, Royal Ambassadors; Church Yth Choir; E Tex Baptist Col.

HAZEL, Janet Lynn
Laurens Dist 55 HS; Laurens, SC; Ann; Fr C; FTA; NHS; Anderson Col; Secy Sci.

HAZELIP, Jeffrey Alan
Harding Acad; Memphis, TN; NHS; Var C; Cr-Ctry; Tr; All Co Cr-Ctry; Harding Col.

HAZELRIG, Susan Annette
Amer Christian Acad; Pomona, CA (1-21) Chor; Hmrm; S-T, SC; Tres, Soph Cl; Alg A; Bio A; COM; Citz A; Hist A; Hon Prog; Math A; Val; Vlbl; Bible A; Rep, TV Quiz Show; Hyles-Anderson Col; Christian Ed.

HAZELWOOD, Bonnie Gaye
Rufus King HS; Milwaukee, WI; Ann; FBLA; Bkbl; Pub Speaking A; Vlbl; Bryant And Stratton Col; Stenographic Secretarial.

HAZELWOOD, Pamela Hilda
Hopewell HS; Hopewell, VA (62-345) Ann; BC; Fr C; FHA; FTA; Jr Miss Pagent; Lit Mag; Tri-HiY; Richard Bland Col; Computer Prog.

HAZEN, Jeffrey Lewis
Boulder HS; Boulder, CO; BS; Chess C; Dbte Tm; 4H; Hmrm; Order/Arrow; Pres, SC; 4H A; Spch A; Eagle Sct; Semi-Fin, Opt A; Kenyon Col; Hist.

HAZEN, Jim Richard
Anderson HS; Anderson, IN (12%-620) Chor; Ensm; Madrigal; Var C; Co-Cpt, Bsbl; Anderson Col; Phys Ed.

HAZERJIAN, George Michael
Boston Latin HS; Boston, MA; Chess C; Hockey; Excellence, Aprobation; BSct; Fidelity; Boy's C; Amer Yth Fed; Modern Prize; Bowl; Aprobation with Distinction; Law.

HAZLETT, Christopher John
Lowell HS; Whittier, CA; Chor; Drama; Lit Mag; Sch P; Span C; Spch C; VP, SC; Ftbl; Drama A; Dentistry.

HAZLEWOOD, Joyce Irene
Tascosa HS; Amarillo, TX; FBLA; Hmrm; SC; Tr; 1st, De Area Comp; W Tex St U; Marketing.

HAZZARD, Donna Lynn
Texas City HS; Texas City, TX (65-443) A Cap Choir; Chor; Pres, Madrigal; Thes; WW; Region Choir; Outst Alto, Off, Mus; Lamar U; Deaf Ed.

HEABERLIN, Sherrill Denise
Rock Hill HS; Ironton, OH; Cpt, Band; BC; Drama; NHS; Rptr, Sci C; Home Ec A.

HEAD, Charles Malcolm
Abingdon HS; Abingdon, IL (10-100) Band; Dbte Tm; Pres, FFA; 4H; SC; Var C; Pres, Sr Cl; Co-Cpt, Ftbl; COM; 4H A; U of Ill; Agr.

HEAD, Debbie Jean
Dunedin Sr HS; Dunedin, FL; Band; Span C.

HEAD, Martha Sue
Dunedin HS; Dunedin, FL (1-817) Band; NHS.

HEAD, Pamela Kaye
Neville HS; Monroe, LA (14-150) Co-Cpt, Chldr; Secy, Fr C; VP, SC; VP, Soph Cl; Bkbl; Tnns; Hist A; HCt; Yth Leg; La Tech Col; Interior Design.

HEAD, Stephen Ray
Pontotoc HS; Pontotoc, MS (25%-90) Band; Chor; Drama; Ensm; Fr C; 4H; Orch; Rptr, Sch P; Christian Workers Training Band; 1st Pl Co Sci Fair; Jr HS All Co Band; Itawamba Jr Col; Vocal Mus.

HEAD, William Edward
Trion HS; Trion, GA; Band; BC; SC; Bsbl; Mgr, Bkbl; Academic 'T'; Ga Solo-Ensm Mus Medal; Ga Tech; Engr.

HEADEN, Deborah Lynne
Irvington HS; Fremont, CA; Ann; CSF; Hon Prog; Eng A; Baylor U; Lib Arts.

HEADINGS, Teddi Elaine
Penn View Bible Inst; Penns Creek, PA; Commercial C; Rptr, Sch P; VP, Soph Cl; Math A.

HEADLEY, Carol Kay
Calloway HS; Callaway, NE (8-24) Band; Chor; Parl, FHA; Pres, SC; S-T, Thes; S-T, Var C; Pres, Jr Cl; VP, Soph Cl; Co-Cpt, Bkbl; Tr; Co Cpt, Vlbl; Kearney St Col; Hist.

HEADRICK, John Lamar
Tabernacle Christian HS; Greenville, SC (2-12) A-Ed, Ann; Rptr, Sch P; VP, SC; Bkbl; Sal; Sprots Ldrship; 3rd Pl, Essay Contest; Acct.

HEADRICK, Tammy Lu
Rockdale HS; Rockdale, TX (15%-120) Band; Chem C; Mjrte; NHS; Phys C; Spch C; VP, UYF; Leo C; Regeneration Singers; Regeneration Small Group; SW Tex St Tech Col; Communications.

HEAGEY, Robert Cornell
El Dorado HS; Placerville, CA (20-421) Fin, Wrest; Alg A; Math A; Sci A; Cal Poly Col; Sci.

HEAGY, Terry Lee
John Piersol McCaskey HS; Lancaster, PA; ARC.

HEALY, Derrick Craig
Quartz Hill HS; Quartz Hill, CA; Chor; Math C; Bsbl; Ftbl; Tr; Math A; Drama; Ftbl A; Oral Roberts U; Ministering.

HEALY, Paulette Marie
McCracken HS; McCracken, KS; Band; CYO; Chldr; Chor; Drama; Ensm; Madrigal; Spch C; SC; Bsbl; Bkbl; Golf; COM; HCt; Spch A; Bat Girl, Bsbl; Kan St U; Home Ec.

HEARD, Deborah Kay
Lafayette HS; Lexington, KY (50-800) Crown & Scepter; Ensm; Sftbl; Tr; Explorers; Yth Choir; U of Ky; Dentistry.

HEARD, Jerry Dean
Lanier HS; Jackson, MS (10-522) 4H; NHS; Tnns; MLS; NMS.

HEARD, Nancy Ruth
Hanson Mem HS; Franklin, LA (4-67) Dbte Tm; Semi-Fin, Lit Ral; NHS; Bkbl; Tnns; Hist A; Type A; Yth Fel; Torch A; Eng A; Civics A; Fr A; LA St U; Sci.

HEARD, Patricia Anne
Central HS; Helena, AR; Ann; Chor; VP, FFA; Thes; Harlequins; Lit C; U of Central Ark; Spch.

HEARD, Samuel Thomas
Lakeland Sr HS; Lakeland, FL; Cpt, Band; Ensm; Orch; Trevecca Nazarene Col; Elec.

HEARD, Sandra Lynn
Lancaster HS; Lancaster, TX; FHA; Pres, FTA; NHS; SC; Cpt, Drill Tm; Mascot, Chldr; *Exec Secy Sch; Secy.*

HEARD, Stephen Alvandra
Sol C Johnson HS; Savannah, GA; Band; Chor; Mgr, Bkbl; Tr; *Elec.*

HEARD, Teddy Lewis
Lamar Sr HS; Houston, TX (25%-700) Chor; Hmrm; InterAct C; Sch P; VP, Soph Cl; Amer Leg A; Cl Fav; Spch A; Chaplain, Social Service C; Golden Carpet Day A, Baylor U; Chaplain, Sgt-Of-Arms; Ch, Choralette Singers; *Baylor U; Mus.*

HEARD, Willie
Luther Judson Price HS; Atlanta, GA (15-256) Chor; VP, SC; Bsbl; Cpt, Ftbl; Yth Fel.

HEARN, Edward Gregg
Rochester HS; Rochester, TX; FFA; Bsbl; Bkbl; Ftbl; Tr; *Mech.*

HEARN, Herschel Albert Jr
McGavock HS; Nashville, TN; *Nashville Auto-Diesel Col; Automobile Mech.*

HEARN, Laurie Layne
Monterey HS; Lubbock, TX; A Cap Choir; Band; Chldr; VP, Chor; Ensm; Hmrm; Orch; VP, SC; Pres, Tri-HiY; Bkbl; Sftbl; Tr; Citz A; Hon Prog; Secy, Yth in Govt; *Baylor U; Law.*

HEARN, Sandra Louise
Monticello HS; Monticello, MS; Ann; Band; BC; FHA; COM; *Co-Lin Jr Col; Secretarial Sci.*

HEARNE, Beverly Jean
Hannah-Pamplico HS; Pamplico, SC; Chor; Pres, Hmrm; NHS; JV, Bkbl; *TEC; Dental Asst.*

HEARNE, Bryant Levin
Hannah-Pamplico HS; Pamplico, SC (15-85) Chor; VP, Hmrm; NHS; Sci C; Var C; Bkbl; COM; Sci A; *Clemson U; Archt.*

HEARNE, Diana Leslie
Eureka HS; Eureka, IL (5-120) AFS; Band; NHS; Span NHS; Tres, SC; Tres, Jr Cl; Swim; Co Cpt, Vlbl; Outst Stu Coun; Stu Advisory Comm, St Sch Board; *Pre Med.*

HEARON, Kyle James
Duncanville HS; Duncanville, TX (15%-535) A-Ed, Ann; Chor; Key C; Rptr, Lit Mag; NHS; Span C; Hon Prog; WW; Q & S C; Miss Teenage Am Pageant Performer; *Pre-Dental.*

HEARON, Marsha Leah
Permian HS; Odessa, TX (350-700) FHA; Tri-HiY; *Lubbock Christian Col; Elem Ed.*

HEARRON, Mark Steven
McCullough HS; Spring, TX; A Cap Choir; Ann; Drama; Ftbl; *Sam Houston St U; PE.*

HEARTSILL, Michael Steven
Greenville HS; Greenville, AL (15%-216) BC; BS; Rptr, 4H; Rptr, Hmrm; Sci C; Semi-Fin, Bsbl; Amer Leg A; COM; 4H A; Hist A; ROTC A; Sci A; Yth Leg; ROTC Outst Leadership; Pres, Butler Co Yth Rally; Pres, Church Yth Coun; Commander, ROTC Drill Tm; *Samford U; Religion.*

HEASLEY, Carol Jean
Miller Public HS; Miller, SD (28-88) Chldr; Chor; FHA; Pres, 4H; Secy, Jr Cl; Sftbl; Citz A; 4H A; Type A; Secy, 4-H C; Home Ec A; Comm Service Ldrship A.

HEASTON, Norris Russell
Covington HS; Covington, TN (42-228) A Cap Choir; Ann; Bus C; Chor; Pres, Drama; Ensm; Fr C; FTA; Spch C; Mgr, Bsbl; Mgr, Bkbl; Cl Fav; Pres, Future Ldrs of Amer; *U of Tenn; Health & Physical Ed.*

HEATER, Robert Douglas
Regis HS; Stayton, OR (3-61) NHS; Ski C; Ftbl; Hon Prog; *Oreg St U; Agr.*

HEATH, Celeste Adele
Oak Ridge Acad; Oak Ridge, NC (3-30) Drama; Fr C; Monogram; VP, Jr Cl; Cpt, Sftbl; Cpt, Swim; Gr Marshal; HCt; *Appalachian St U; Early Childhood.*

HEATH, Diane Kay
Switzerland Co HS; Vevay, IN (1-109) Drama; GS; VP, 4H; NHS; Rptr, Sch P; Span C; 4H A; Hist A; Math A; Val; Band Lib; WW; *Ind St U; Chem.*

HEATH, Donald Neal
Switzerland Co Jr Sr HS; Vevay, IN (3-109) Band; BS; Drama; 4H; NHS; Order/Arrow; Sci C; Alg A; Chem A; 4H A; Math A; Sci A; VofDEM; Life Sct; *Rose-Hulman Inst of Tech; Elec Engr.*

HEATH, Doris Lynn
Switzerland Co HS; Vevay, IN (7-109) Drama; 4H; NHS; Sch P; 4H A; *Ind St U; Nurs.*

HEATH, Elizabeth Anne
Kinston HS; Kinston, NC (10%-340) Secy, Drama; Hmrm; Jr Miss Pagent; SC; Nom, NC Sch o-t Arts; New Bern Civic Ballet; Swtht, Babe Ruth World Series; *Wake Forest U; Math.*

HEATH, John Michael
S Allegheny HS; Liberty Boro, PA (15%-350) Cpt, Band; Mgr, Tr; Ntl Fed S Mus; Hon Band; WW; *Gannon Col; Pre-Med.*

HEATH, John Wesley
W Forsyth Sr HS; Winston-Salem, NC (69-504) Mgr, Bsbl; Bkbl; Sftbl; Eagle Sct; *Wake Forest U; Psych.*

HEATH, Kimberly Ann
Colonel Zadok Magruder HS; Rockville, MD; Secy, Band; Chldr; Drama; Hmrm; Mod Mus Mas; Sci C; SC; Var C; Sftbl; Tr; Most Out; NEDT; Rep, Sou Baptist Yth Conf; Pres, Church Yth Organization; Board of Christian Ed; *Fisk U; Med.*

HEATH, Len Claro
Central Baptist Sch; Hampton, VA (1-12) Ger C; VP, SC; Bsbl; Co-Cpt, Ftbl; JV, Sftbl; Citz A; H of F; Phys Ed A; DAR Hist A; 3 Academic Achv; *Archt.*

HEATH, Linda Sue
Rockland Dist HS; Rockland, ME (1-130) Ed, Ann; Chor; VP, Dbte Tm; Drama; InterClub Coun; Lat C; Pres, Math C; NFL; NHS; Hockey; Tr; Hon Prog; MLS; Val; Gym; Kippy Karnival Kween Kandidate; *Bates Col; Bio.*

HEATH, Linda Susan
Tuscola HS; Tuscola, IL (1-118) Lat C; NHS; Sch Achiev Tm; Sftbl; Gr Marshal; Val; Vlbl; *Sou Ill U; Pre-Med.*

HEATH, Michael David
Wade Hampton HS; Greenville, SC (150-400) Chem C; Chess C; Drama; V-Ch, Hmrm; Phys C; Sci C; Ftbl; Hon Prog; *Furman U; Pre-Med.*

HEATH, Shirley Jean
Coronado HS; Colorado Springs, CO (53-335) Chor; Community Yth Symph; Ensm; Fr C; Madrigal; Orch; COM; Hon Prog; Yth Fel; Yth Leg; All St Choir; Lead, 'Music Man'; St Solo Contest; *Westminster Choir Col; Chor Mus.*

HEATH, Terry Glen
Diamond Hill-Jarvis HS; Fort Worth, TX (2-150) Pres, Hmrm; Ski C; Span C; SC; Mgr, Bsbl; Ftbl; Tr; Cl Fav; HCt; All Zone Ftbl Defensive Tackle; *Tex U; Ath.*

HEATHERINGTON, Brian E
Haralson Co HS; Tallapoosa, GA (3-140) BC; COM; Math A; Star Student; *Ga Tech; Elec Engr.*

HEATHERLY, Marshall Rose
Campbell Co HS; LaFollette, TN; BC; Span C; *Lincoln Mem Col; Med.*

HEATHINGTON, Joni Denise
Farragut HS; Knoxville, TN (10%-450) Drama; NHS; *U of Tex.*

HEATLEY, Gregg Alan
Ripon Sr HS; Ripon, WI (2-175) Dbte Tm; Ger C; Math C; Var C; Bkbl; Ftbl; Tr; Bio A; COM; Math A; *U of Wisc; Med.*

HEATON, Brent Stanley
Industry HS; Industry, IL (11-36) Band; Chor; Pres, Drama; Rptr, Sch P; VP, Sci C; Thes; VP, Jr Cl; Pres, Soph Cl; JV, Bsbl; JV, Bkbl; Ftbl; JV, Tr; HCt; Kiwanis A; Spch A; *Pre-Engr.*

HEATON, Dave Nelson
Jefferson HS; Cedar Rapids, IA (33%-300) Bsbl; Bkbl; Ftbl; Golf; *Simpson Col; Acct.*

HEATON, Richard David
Saint Angela Acad; Aiken, SC (19-49) Ann; Demolay; Drama; Key C; Rptr, Sch P; SC; Pres, Soph Cl; Mgr, Bkbl; Hist A; HCt; Kiwanis A; Masonic A; MLS; Bicentennial Courier, Ger; Chevalier Degree, DeMolay; *Mars Hill Col; Pol Sci.*

HEAVNER, Chris Wise
Lincolnton Sr HS; Lincolnton, NC (20%-499) Band; BS; Span C; All St Band; *Mus.*

HEAVNER, Howard Kent
Valmeyer HS; Valmeyer, IL (10-49) CYO; Pres, FFA; Pres, 4H; Math C; Var C; VP, Sr Cl; Bsbl; Bkbl; Sftbl; 4H A; JA A; Order/Arrow A; Most Ath; *U of Ill; Agriculture.*

HEAVNER, John Mark
W Lincoln HS; Lincolnton, NC (18-145) Band; BC; Hist A; Stage Band; Bible C; Ntl HS A for Excellence; Century III Cert of Recognition; Band Merit A; *Davidson Col; Hist.*

HEAVNER, John Morrison
Mountain View HS; Mountain View, AR (33%-62) Ann; Band; Sch P; All Dist Band; WW; Applied Mus Schol; *U of Central Ark; Mus Ed.*

HEAVNER, Todd Wayne
South Point HS; Belmont, NC (2-250) A-Ed, Ann; Secy, BC; Fin, BS; Fr C; Hmrm; InterAct C; Inter-Club Coun; Key C; SC; Bkbl; Cr-Ctry; *Mus.*

HEBACH, Linda Marie
Forest Hill HS; W Palm Beach, FL; Tres, Rainbow; Tres, Church Yth; *Palm Beach Jr Col; Nurs.*

HEBDON, Wayne Philip
Dryden HS; Dryden, NY (40-200) Chess C; Fr C; MVP, Cr-Ctry; MVP, Tr; God & Country A; ARC A; Yth Fel; Mgr, Tr; *Religion.*

HEBERER, Amy Sue
Freeburg Comm Consolidates HS; Freeburg, IL (17-137) Ann; Band; Chldr; Chor; FTA; Pres, 4H; Cpt, Mjrte; Var C; S-T, Jr Cl; SC; Var C; Sftbl; 4H A; HCt; Hon Prog; I Dare You; JA A; Most Out; Pres A; Sci A; Yth Fel; Jr Grange Princess; Mus A; St Louis Dispatch Sci A; *Food and Nutrition.*

HEBERT, Carl Anthony
Fr Teurlings Cath HS; Lafayette, LA (12-78) S-T, Sci C; SC; Bkbl; Cr-Ctry; Mgr, Ftbl; Tr; Sci A; Serra C A; *U of SW La; Mech Engr.*

HEBERT, Darrell David
Burbank HS; Burbank, CA (75-400) A Cap Choir; Chess C; Chor; Tres, Demolay; Lat C; Madrigal; Order/Arrow; Bkbl; Masonic A; Pres A; Yth Fel; *Pepperdine U; Fine Arts.*

HEBERT, Debra Ann
Merryville HS; Merryville, VA (3-48) Ed, Ann; Band; Chldr; Dbte Tm; FBLA; 4H; Key C; Lit Ral; Mjrte; NHS; Pres, Sci C; Spch C; Tr; Beauty; Bio A; Cl Fav; 4H A; HCt; Hon Prog; Most Out; Sci A; Spch A; Ed, Yrbk; Col Schol; *McNeese St U; Horticulture.*

HEBERT, Kay Marie
St Joseph HS; Jeanerette, LA (2-30) Chldr; Semi-Fin, Lit Ral; Tres, NHS; Pres, Sch P; Pres, Soph Cl; COM; Math A; Sch Spirit A; Geom A; WW; *U of Southwestern La; Bus.*

HEBERT, Polly Sue
Berwick HS; Berwick, LA (45-141) CYO; FHA; 4H; Fin, Jr Miss Pagent; Sch P; SC; Swim; Tnns; Beauty; Swtht; Cpt, Dance Tm; Service A; Lib A.

HEBNER, Dennis Eugene
Calvary Christian Acad; Midland, MI; Chor; Drama; Sch P; Bkbl; Soccer; *Mid-Mich Comm Col; Advanced EMT.*

HEBRARD, Lynn A
Apollo HS; Simi Valley, CA (5-90) Ann; Drama; FTA; Secy, Hmrm; InterClub Coun; Math C; SC; Tres, Sr Cl; B Crocker A; Citz A; MLS; Most Out; Star Student; Yth Fel; *Moorpark Col; Elem Ed.*

HEBRINK, Wendy Jo
Midwest City HS; Midwest City, OK; NHS; Central St Art Festival; Bicentennial Art Contest; Art C.

HECHT, David Harvey
Horicon HS; Horicon, WI (15-117) Band; BS; City Conf; Pres, NHS; Var C; Bsbl; Cpt, Ftbl; Tr; Prom King; Wrest; HCt; Hon Prog; Rotary A; Prom King; *Madison Area Tech Col; Elec Tech.*

HECHT, Sheila Denise
Bern HS; Bern, KS (1-22) Tres, Band; Chldr; Chor; Ensm; Madrigal; Model UN; NHS; Sch P; Pres, Jr Cl; Bkbl; Tr; Alg A; Math A; Sci A; Type A; Yth Fel; Vlbl; Eng A; *Kans St U; Math.*

311

HECHT, Thomas Aquinas
Loyola HS; Baltimore, MD; Ger C; NHS; Swim; NHS A; *Ind U; Mus.*

HECK, John Stephen
Eisenhower HS; Washington, MI (33%-500) Ed, Ann; CYO; Model UN; Order/Arrow; ARC; Cr-Ctry; Ftbl; Tr; Order/Arrow A; Ldrship Corp; Eagle Set with Two Palms; Cpt, Sch Safety Patrol; *U of Mich; Archt.*

HECK, Scott Daniel
Wheaton HS; Wheaton, IL; Band; NHS; Var C; Bkbl; Co-Cpt, Soccer; Tr.

HECKARD, Delores Elaine
David Starr Jordan HS; Los Angeles, CA; Hmrm; SC; Tnns; Bank Of Amer A; Citz A; Cl Fav; Hon Prog; The Ladies C; *Bryan Col of Court Rptr; Court Rptr.*

HECKARD, Patsy Ann
David Starr Jordan HS; Los Angeles, CA; Chor; Rptr, Hmrm; Principal's HR; *Los Angeles Trade Tech Col; Bus.*

HECKEL, Barbara Elizabeth
Warwick HS; Newport News, VA (6-484) FHA; 4H; Secy, Lat C; NHS; Outst Lat Stu; *Riverside Nurs Sch; Nurs.*

HECKELER, Susan Jean
Burnt Hills-Ballston Lake HS; Burnt Hills, NY (4-389) Co-Ed, Ann; Hmrm; Tnns; Hon Prog; Regent Schol; Span Book A; Span Diploma of Merit; Gold Medals; *Russell Sage Col; Nurs.*

HECKER, Pamela Sue
Camdenton R III HS; Camdenton, MO (5-170) GS; VP, Math C; Secy, NHS; Tres, Sci C; SC; Pres, Sr Cl; Math A; MLS; Yth Fel; NML; Pres, Jr Historians; Tres, Explorers; 1st Pl, Explorer Dist Road Rall; *Sch o-t Ozarks; Religion.*

HECKERT, Trena Marie
Yough Sr HS; Herminie, PA (33%-293) Candystriper Vol A; *Westmoreland Co Comm Col; Clerical Asst.*

HECKMAN, Charles E
Garden Spot HS; New Holland, PA; Chor; Hmrm; NHS; Bkbl; Cr-Ctry; Tr; HCt; Yth Fel; Rotary Ldrship Camp.

HECKMAN, Patricia Lynn
Carmel HS; Carmel, IN (64-584) CYO; NHS; Mgr, Tnns; NEDT; VP, Art C; Span A; *Ball St U; Art.*

HECKMAN, Virginia Ellen
Loch Raven Sr HS; Towson, MD (41-471) FHA; NHS; Yth Rep, Christian Ed Committee; Sr High Fel; Sunday Sch Teacher; Piano Accompanist A; Ed.

HEDBERG, Janette Lee
Thomas Jefferson Sr HS; Bloomington, MN; Band; Chor; Community Yth Symph; Ski C; Job's Daughters; Pioneer Girls; Flag Corp.

HEDBERG, Joanne Rae
Thomas Jefferson HS; Bloomington, MN; Band; Bus C; Ski C; Swim; JA A; Job's Daughters; Pioneer Girls; Cadet Sct.

HEDDINS, Roland Jeffrey
Sulphur HS; Sulphur, LA (33%-500) DARGCA; Hon Prog; *McNeese St U; Elec.*

HEDELSON, Julie Lynn
Algona HS; Algona, IA (53-146) Band; Chor; FBLA; Golf; *U of Iowa; Bus.*

HEDENBERG, Renee
A C Reynolds HS; Asheville, NC (2-363) Ger C; Pres, Hmrm; Lat C; SC; Tr; COM; Hon Prog; NEDT; PTA A; Vlbl; *U of NC; Med.*

HEDGEPETH, Everette Lane
Mary Carroll HS; Corpus Christi, TX (10%-841) Mu Alpha Theta; NHS; Ftbl; A-B HR; *Baylor U.*

HEDGEPETH, Teresa Jo
Greenville Christian Acad; Greenville, NC; Chldr; Chor; Hmrm; Ed, Sch P; SC; HCt; Yth Fel; *Liberty Baptist Col; Ed.*

HEDGES, Kimberly Kay
Grant Co HS; Dry Ridge, KY (4-129) NHS; Y-Tns; COM; Math A; Acct A; Bus Ed A.

HEDLESTON, Wanda Lee
Broward Christian Sch; Plantation Acres, FL (1-5) Co-Cpt, Chldr; Sftbl; *Broward Comm Col; Acct.*

HEDMAN, Katherine Marie
River Valley HS; Three Oaks, MI (8-160) Band; Chor; Math C; NHS; Ski C; JV, Bkbl; COM; Math A; MLS; NMF; Yth for Understanding; Secy, Mich Christian Yth Fellowshp; *Moody Bible Inst; Christian Ed.*

HEDMAN, Kathleen Diane
Fremont HS; Sunnyvale, CA (1-572) Spch C; CSF; Spch A; Yth Leg; Christian Activities; *De Anza Jr Col; Commercial Art.*

HEDRICK, James David
Spruce Creek HS; Port Orange, FL (125-500) Band; Chem C; Chess C; Ensm; Orch; Tres, Order/Arrow; JV, Golf; JV, Sftbl; Tnns; Bio A; COM; Chem A; Citz A; Order/Arrow A; Poet A; Sci A; *Brooks Inst of Photography; Photography.*

HEDRICK, Linda Sue
Coldwater HS; Coldwater, OH (20-175) Ann; Tres, Band; Chor; Tres, FHA; Pres A; Tres, Young Active Christians; WW; *Wright St U.*

HEDRICK, Roger Barron Jr
Pampa HS; Pampa, TX (85-326) A Cap Choir; Key C; Order/Arrow; JV, Bsbl; *Tex Tech U; Civil Engr.*

HEDSTROM, Kris B
San Clemente HS; San Clemente, CA; Band; Golf.

HEDSTROM, Stephen Dale
Hettinger Pub Sch; Hettinger, ND (8-65) Band; Chor; Pres, FFA; Hmrm; NHS; Pres, SC; Pres, Soph Cl; Swim; Star Chapter Farmer, FFA; St Farmer Degree, FFA; *ND St U; Agr.*

HEEMSTRA, Maria Elaine
Kelloggsville HS; Grand Rapids, MI (10-205) InterAct C; Citz A; Saftey Duty, Tr, A's; Hon Stu.

HEER, Connie Sue
Mississinewa HS; Gas City, IN (43-212) Ann; NHS; Tri-HiY; Secy, Sr Cl; Type A; Shorthand A; District, St As, OEA; Jr Achv; Tres, OEA; *Marion Col; Bus.*

HEERES, Douglas Lee
Ellsworth Comm Sch; Ellsworth, MI (5-30) Tr; COM; Citz A; Math A; MLS; Ntl Radio Inst Hon Graduate; *DeVry Inst of Tech; Elec Engr.*

HEES, Philip Charles
Half Hollow Hills HS E; Dix Hills, NY (50-1100) Band; Chess C; Pres, 4H; Math C; NHS; Orch; Var C; Cr-Ctry; Tr; COM; 4H A; Hon Prog; Math A; NMF; Sci A; *Worcester Polytech Inst; Elec Engr.*

HEESZEL, Christine Marie
Steeleville Comm Unit HS; Steeleville, IL (14-48) Ann; Chldr; FBLA; VP, FHA; Fin, GS; Span C; VP, SC; Sftbl; Amer Leg A; HCt; Vlbl; Fin, Prom Qn; *Belleville Area Col; Beauty Sch.*

HEFFEL, Timothy Harold
Luray HS; Luray, KS (4-17) Band; Pres, Bus C; Chor; Secy, FBLA; Order/Arrow; VP, SC; VP, Sr Cl; Secy, Jr Cl; Pres, Soph Cl; Bsbl; Cpt, Bkbl; Cpt, Ftbl; Tnns; MVP, Tr; COM; H of F; HCt; MLS; Order/Arrow A; Pres, Lutheran League; All-St Ftbl Half-Back; WW; *Fort Hays St; Bus Adm.*

HEFFELFINGER, Marilyn Sue
Wellington HS; Wellington, IL (2-18) Ann; Chldr; Chor; Drama; FHA; NHS; Secy, SC; Rptr, Jr Cl; Cpt, Bkbl; Hon Prog; Sal; MVP, Vlbl; *Danville Jr Col; Horticulture.*

HEFFERMAN, Anne
T R Miller HS; Brewton, AL (20-120) Band; Bus C; Drama; FHA; Co-Cpt, Mjrte; SC; Swim; Math A; 'Neatest'; *U of Ala; Primary Ed.*

HEFFERNAN, Rory Fitzgerald
Libery HS; Bedford, VA (10-253) BC; Hmrm; F-Ed, Lit Mag; Sci C; Pres, Span NHS; SC; Sftbl; Bio A; Chem A; Sci A; Dist All Stars, Sftbl; Drama A; VJAS 2nd Pl Environmental Sci; Top 10 A; Span A; *Va Tech Col; Pol Sci.*

HEFFERNAN, Thomas Daniel
Blanchet HS; Seattle, WA (24-383) CYO; Soccer.

HEFFERNAN, Tom Paul
Brother Martin HS; New Orleans, LA; CYO; Lit Ral; NHS; ARC; Var C; Co-Cpt, Cr-Ctry; Cpt, Tr; Hon Prog; Most Out; MVP, Cr-Ctry & Tr; *LSU; Vet Med.*

HEFFINGER, Tamara Kaye
Sylmar HS; Sylmar, CA; Chldr; Chor; Drama; Rptr, Hmrm; SC; Thes; CSF; Cl Fav; Drama A; *Pepperdine U; Theater Arts.*

HEFFLEY, Kristin Lee
Reeds Spring HS; Reeds Spring, MO (10-77) AFS; Chor; Jr Miss Pagent; Sci C; Span C; COM; Citz A; Hon Prog; Type A; Shorthand A; *Special Ed.*

HEFFNER, Sheila March
Northern Chester Co Tech Sch; Phoenixville, PA (1-192) Chor; FBLA; Secy, NHS; ARC; Co-Ed, Sch P; Tres, SC; VP, Var C; Mgr, Bsbl; Bkbl; Co-Cpt, Hockey; Chamber of Comm A; Citz A; DARGCA; MLS; Miss NCCTS; Stu o-t Mo; *Cosmetology Teaching.*

HEFFNER, Shelia Robin
MacKenzie HS; Detroit, MI (34-350) Swim; Schol Prog; Hon Prog; *Sci.*

HEFLIN, Judith Lynn
Douglas Southall Freeman HS; Richmond, VA (141-550) A Cap Choir; Co-Ed, Ann; Chor; Hmrm; FBLA; Hmrm; Lat C; SC; Q&S A; *Va Commonwealth U; Bus.*

HEFLIN, Rhonda Elaine
Castleberry HS; Fort Worth, TX; Chor; FTA; U of Interscholstic League Comp; *Tarrant Co Jr Col; Nurs.*

HEFNER, Kelly Linn
Putnam City HS; Okla City, OK (2-850) Chor; GS; Hmrm; Lat C; Pres, NHS; SC; Amer Leg A; HQn; Sal; Off, St Lat C Board; Outst Lat; Med C; Outst, Pep C; Pres, Pep C; Acad Achv A; *Okla St U; Acct.*

HEFNER, Mark Alan
Bath HS; Lima, OH (4-150) A Cap Choir; Band; Chor; Community Yth Symph; Drama; Ensm; PTA A; Sch Talent Show; *Ohio N U; Mus.*

HEFTY, Blaine Lee
LuVerne Comm HS; LuVerne, IA; Bsbl; Bkbl; Tr; Hon Prog; Type A; Yth Fel; *Westmar Col.*

HEGARTY, Colleen Mary
St Augustine Acad; Lakewood, OH (15%-136) Bus C; NHS; Sch P; Bkbl; Sftbl; Hon Prog; NHS Schol; *Cleveland St Col; Allied Health Programs.*

HEGER, Karen Louise
Rosary HS; Aurora, IL (2-94) Bus C; Lit Mag; NHS; F-Ed, Sch P; Sci C; Span C; SC; VP, Sr Cl; Pres, Jr Cl; Tres, Soph Cl; Sftbl; COM; DARGCA; NMS; NEDT; Sal; St Scholar; Ed, Sch Paper; William Fletcher King Schol; *Cornell Col; Sci.*

HEGLIN, Catherine Lantz
Tecumseh Sr HS; Tecumseh, MI (10%-297) Dbte Tm; Drama; Fr C; 4H; NHS; Ntl Yth Conf; Ski C; VP, SC; Var C; Mgr, Bkbl; JV, Cr-Ctry; Soccer; Swim; Tr; COM; 4H A; Hon Prog; Spch A; VFW A; Yth Leg.

HEGSTAD, Lynn Ann
Brainerd Sr HS; Brainerd, MN; Hmrm; Jr Cl; Swim; Pres, Home Ec & Retarded Training; *Brnd Comm Col; Secondary Ed.*

HEGWOOD, Kathy Leigh
Stratford HS; Nashville, TN; Ann; Chldr; Chor; Hmrm; SC; Sportsmanship, Annual Staff, A's.

HEIBERGER, Therese Marie
Chilton HS; Chilton, WI (29-132) Band; Ensm; Hmrm; SC; Tres, Soph Cl; Tr; Vlbl; Prom Court; *U of Wis; Bus.*

HEID, Sue Edene
Rockford Guilford HS; Rockford, IL; 4H; Tr; 4H A; Tr A; *Lake Erie Col for Women; Horsemanship.*

HEIDE, Laura Ellen
Westbury Sr HS; Houston, TX (104-614) Anchor C; Chor; Ensm; NFL; Rptr, Sch P; SC; Journ A; NEDT; Spch A; Colonel, Drill Sq; *Baylor U; Psych.*

HEIDEL, Charles Frank
Winston Churchill HS; Potomac, MD (10%-576) NHS; Ftbl; Tr; Outst Schol Ath; *U of Va; Bus.*

HEIDEN, Lynda Marie
Brunswick HS; Brunswick, GA (41-416) FBLA; Hmrm; InterClub Coun; Lit Mag; Sch P; Span C; Tnns; Pres, Racquet C; *Brunswick Jr Col; Psych.*

HEIDENREICH, Bonna Brenda
Lyons Central HS; Lyons, NY (15-110) Band; Ger C; 100%, Algebra Regents; Piano, Saxophone, Stu; Bus.

HEIDGEN, Mary Elizabeth
Batavia HS; Batavia, IL (9-224) Drama; FTA; Math C; NFL; Spch C; Secy, Thes; Hon Prog; Math A; Spch A; *Eng.*

HEIDLOFF, Dale Richard
University HS; Normal, IL (19-105) BS; Semi-Fin, NHS; Bkbl; Cr-Ctry; Cpt, Tr; Rotary A; *Concordia Teachers Col; Math.*

HEIDORN, Elizabeth Jean
Mankato E HS; Mankato, MN (30-295) Band; Chldr; Co-Cpt, Sftbl; Tr; JA A; Pres A; *Pediatrics.*

HEIDORN, Jon Michael
Mankato E HS; Mankato, MN (45-300) Band; Golf; *U of Minn; Vet.*

HEIDT, Deborah Jane
Memorial HS; St Marys, OH (5-218) Band; Chor; Ensm; S-T, FTA; GS; Pres, 4H; InterClub Coun; Secy, NHS; Sch Achieve Tm; Sci C; VP, Thes; Y-Tns; Tnns; Tr; Amer Leg A; Cl Fav; God & Country A; 4H A; Journ A; Most Out; Rotary A; Yth Fel; WW; *U of Cincinnati; Med Tech.*

HEIDT, Diane Lynne
Booker T Washington HS; Tulsa, OK (3-288) Bus C; FBLA; Secy C; Mu Alpha Theta; NHS; *Richland Jr Col; Math.*

HEIGHT, William Hazel
Southwestern HS; Baltimore, MD; Bus Mgr, Chor; Drama; Up Bound; Var C; Cr-Ctry; Ftbl; Tr; COM; Citz A; Opt A; US Yth Games; *Pol Sci.*

HEIKAUS, Robert Carl Jr
W Haven HS; W Haven, CT (100-650) Demolay; Hmrm; Order/Arrow; Sci C; Ski C; SC; Var C; Cr-Ctry; Swim; Tr; Hon Prog; Order/Arrow A; ARC A; *Southampton Col; Marine Bio.*

HEIKES, Julie Ann
LaVeta HS; LaVeta, CO (2-23) NHS; SC; Bus A.

HEIKES, Raymond Lowery
T Roosevelt HS; Wyandotte, MI; Drama; Rptr, Sch P; Thes; *Theatrical Make-Up.*

HEIKKINEN, Donna Grace
Franklin HS; Livonia, MI (48-786) Band; Ensm; Orch; Citz A; Hon Prog; Yth Fel; Dist Solo & Ensm Comp; *U of Mich; Computer Programing.*

HEIL, Glenn Steven
Belleville Township HS W; Belleville, IL (60-800) Band; Orch; JV, Tr; Wrest; Yth Fel; *U of Ill; Math.*

HEIL, Julia Lynn
Belleville Township HS W; Belleville, IL (11-769) Secy, Band; Ger C; NHS; Orch; Citz A; Hon Prog; Yth Fel; John Philip Sousa A; Band A; Orch A; *Murray St U; Mus.*

HEILMAN, Peter Salem
Niskayuna HS; Schenectady, NY (20%-407) French NHS; NHS; Order/Arrow; Soccer; Amer Leg A; Co- cpt, Vlbl; Eagle Sct; *Clarkson Col of Tech; Elec Engr.*

HEIM, Cindy Lee
Ernest E Root HS; N Royalton, OH (30-300) Chor; Tres, Drama; Pres, Fr C; Secy, 4H; Madrigal; Thes; COM; 4H A; Hon Prog; Ath Bstrs A; *Baldin Wallace Col; Bus.*

HEIM, Michelle Renee
Duncan HS; Duncan, OK; JV, Chldr; Tres, Chor; FHA; Hmrm; Mgr, Bsbl; Sftbl; Citz A; Swtht, Key C; Outst Chldr; *Bio.*

HEIM, Reuben Charles
Ste Genevieve Pub HS; Ste Genevieve, MO (7-170) Band; BS; Pres, NHS; Phys C; Sch P; SC; Mgr, Bkbl; Co-Cpt, Ftbl; Tr; JV, Wrest; Amer Leg A; Hon Prog; Journ A; Rotary A; Type A; Vof-DEM; *U of Mo Rolla; Petroleum Engr.*

HEIMBERGER, Rebecca Ann
Saltsburg Jr Sr HS; Saltsburg, PA; Band; FHA; Sftbl; NEDT; 1st, Ntl Hunt & Fish Art Contest.

HEIMSOTH, Beverly Jean
Benton Co R-1 HS; Cole Camp, MO (2-51) Pres, A Cap Choir; Band; Chor; Ensm; Madrigal; VP, NHS; S-T, Thes; Var C; Bkbl; Sftbl; Regent Schol; Sal; Type A; *St Fair Comm Col; Elem Ed.*

HEIMSOTH, Cynthia Dianne
Benton Co R-1 HS; Cole Camp, MO (5-56) S-T, A Cap Choir; Band; Chor; Ensm; Madrigal; Secy, NHS; Secy, SC; Tres, Var C; Tres, Span C; Cpt, Bkbl; Sftbl; Type A; Rptr, NHS; All Conf, Vlbl & Bkbl; VP, Circuit Yth Organization; Pres, S-T, Church Yth; *SW Mo St U; Phys Ed.*

HEIN, Kathleen Virginia
Aurora Hoytlakes HS; Aurora, MN (164-208) FHA; Pres, 4H; *Duluth Bus U; Med Office Asst.*

HEIN, Lisa Louise
Lakeview HS; Battle Creek, MI (33%-425) Cpt, Chldr; Fr C; Hmrm; Secy, Ski C; SC; Tr; Vlbl; *Kellogg Comm Col.*

HEINDEL, Allen Wayne
Celina Sr HS; Celina, OH (44-300) Pres, 4H; 4H A; Yth Fel; Church Chor; Co-Cpt, Church Quiz Tm; Camper o-t Yr; Most Valuable Quizzer; *Fort Wayne Bible Col; Pastoral Ministries.*

HEINDEL, Timothy Raymond
Beaver Dam Sr HS; Beaver Dam, WI (3-331) Ski C; Ftbl; JV, Tnns; JV, Tr; JV, Wrest; COM; Hon Prog; Yth Fel; *U of Wis; Pre-Med.*

HEINE, Gail Collette
Lincoln Comm HS; Lincoln, IL; Fr C; *Lincoln Christian Col; Christian Ed.*

HEINE, Sally Kaye
Ventura Comm HS; Ventura, IA (3-32) Band; Chldr; Chor; Secy, FTA; VP, NHS; Spch C; Thes; Bkbl; Golf; Tr; HQn; Pres A; Spch A; FCA; Achv A; *U of N Iowa; Special Ed.*

HEINEMANN, Cyndee Sue
El Dorado Springs R-2 HS; El Dorado Springs, MO (78-103) A-Ed, Ann; Band; VP, Chor; Drama; FTA; A-Ed, Sch P; Mgr, Bkbl; Journ A; Yth Leg; Mgr, Vlbl; PA; Pep C Ltr; *SW Baptist Col; Elem Ed.*

HEINER, Scott D
Star Valley HS; Afton, WY (2-134) BS; Dbte Tm; FTA; Sch P; SC; Pres, Jr Cl; Tres, NHS; Bkbl; Ftbl; Sftbl; COM; 4H A; Hon Prog; *U of Wy; Math.*

HEINEY, Deborah Sue
Huntington N HS; Huntington, IN (1-589) Band; Tres, FTA; NHS; COM; Kiwanis A; Masonic A; Rotary A; Val; Yth Fel; Honored Qn, Job's Daughters; Cpt, Flag Corps; Tri-Kappa Schol; *Ball St U; Elem Ed.*

HEINIGER, Susan Marie
Bern HS; Bern, KS (4-25) All Amer Yth; Ann; Chor; Model UN; Secy, NHS; Type A; Yth Fel; *Kaw Valley Vo-tech; Data Processing.*

HEINLEIN, Brett William
Chaska Senior High; Chaska, MN (120-268) Band; Golf; Cpt, Hockey; Soccer; Pres, Luthern Yth Organization; *Dentistry.*

HEINLEIN, Daniel Lee
S Bend Jr Acad; S Bend, IN (2-12) Ann; Sch P; Bsbl; Cpt, Bkbl; Cpt, Ftbl; Cpt, Hockey; Soccer; Sftbl; Tnns; ARC A; *Andrews U; Engr.*

HEINOLD, Lynn Marie
Wisner-Pilger Jr-Sr HS; Wisner, NE (32-69) Chor; FBLA; FHA; Spch C; Bkbl; Mgr, Tr; Yth Fel; Pep C; *Fashion and Design.*

HEINRICH, Richard Franklin Jr
The Haft Tutoring Sch; New Albany, PA (3-5) Sch P; *Machinery.*

HEINRICHS, Jane Ellen
Southside HS; Fort Smith, AR (1-460) CYO; Lat C; NHS; Win, Mus Tchrs Ntl As St Comp; *U of Ark; Mus.*

HEINRICHS, Paula Ann
Highlands Sr HS; Natrona Heights, PA (95-493) HiY; Hmrm; Tri-HiY; Yth Fel; Family Squares; HR; Tn-Timer; Lrdship Citation; GSct; Jr Executive; *Westminster Col; Social Work.*

HEINTSCHEL, Joe A
Cardinal Stritch HS; Oregon, OH (52-180) CYO; Hmrm; Bkbl; MVP, Golf; HS Ath Yrbk; *Ohio U; Marketing.*

HEINTZ, Jeffrey George
Arlington HS; Arlington Heights, IL (175-575) Pres, 4H; Arch; BC; Band; Soccer; Tr; 4H A; *Forestry.*

HEINTZELMAN, Dianne Kay
Jamestown HS; Jamestown, NY (77-470) NHS; Swim; Tres, Synchronized Swim Tm; *Jamestown Comm Col; Acct.*

HEINTZELMAN, Jane Louise
Middleburg Joint HS; Middleburg, PA; Chldr; Chor; JV, Hockey; JV, Sftbl.

HEINTZMAN, Lynn Ann
Peoria HS; Peoria, IL; Ger C; ARC; SC; Var C; Bkbl; Sftbl; Most Out; ARC A; Sci A; Yth Fel; Vlbl.

HEIPLE, Bradley Keith
Academy HS; Erie, PA (50-210) Band; Ger C; Hon Prog; Hon Drum Major; *Bethel Col; Bib Lit.*

HEISEL, Gail Marie
Grace M Davis HS; Modesto, CA; Secy, Band; Community Yth Symph; Ensm; Orch; Span C; CSF; Pep Band; CSF C; *Modesto Jr Col; Behavioral Sci.*

HEISLER, Lori Theresa
S Park Sr HS; Library, PA (15-163) Tres, Band; Bus C; CYO; FBLA; FHA; Hmrm; SC; Pres, Jr Cl; Pres, Soph Cl; Hon Prog; Pres A.

HEISTER, Catherine Gayle
Fort Lupton HS; Fort Lupton, CO (8-130) Band; FBLA; Pres, 4H; Tres, Rainbow; COM; 4H A; Sci A; Type A; Yth Fel; Mus A; Welco Hon Band; *U of N Colo; Mus.*

HEITZ, Kerri Lynn
Jefferson HS; Jefferson, WI (19-208) Band; Chor; COM; Vlbl; Pom Pon Squad; Environmental Action C; Principal's A.

HEITZMAN, David Scott
Cascade Sr HS; Everett, WA; Ski C; JV, Ftbl; Church Yth Choir and Puppeteers; *Biola Col.*

HEIZER, Lisa Anne
Western Hills HS; Fort Worth, TX (3%-527) Lit Mag; NHS; Span C; Hon Prog; Math A; *SMU; Law.*

HELBERT, Ronnie Darryl
River Forest Sr HS; Hobart, IN (113-138) Drama; Hmrm; SC; Mgr, Bkbl; Mgr, Ftbl; SC Pin; Lib Asst Cert; Ftbl Mgr Ltr.

HELBIG, Arnold Paul
Thornton Township HS; Harvey, IL (35-750) Chor; Ensm; Madrigal; Swim; All St Choir; *Dentist.*

HELD, Lynne Anne
Glen Oak HS; Canton, OH; FHA; Ger C; Tr; *Med.*

HELD, Patty Jane
Hermann Sr HS; Hermann, MO (9-107) Band; Chldr; Drama; NHS; Pres, SC; HCt; Soph Pilgrimage; Best Support Actress A, HS Play; *U of Mo.*

HELDKE, Lisa Maree
Rice Lake Sr HS; Rice Lake, WI; Band; Ger C; Pres, 4H; Madrigal; NHS; Rptr, Sch P; God & Country A; 4H A; Journ A; St Hon Orch; *Instrumental Mus.*

HELDORFER, Charlotte Marie
Central Comm HS; Breese, IL (1-157) CYO; FHA; Mrk C; St Scholar; Val; WW; *St John's Hosp Sch of Nurs; Registered Nurs.*

HELDT, Lisa Wynell
Queen City HS; Queen City, TX (10%-73) Band; Ensm; NHS; Sci C; Span C; Band Medals; *Texarkana Jr Col; Wildlife Mgt.*

HELDT, Mark Jon
Rock Lake Pub HS; Rock Lake, ND (10%-19) Rptr, Ann; Chor; NHS; Bkbl; Mgr, Ftbl; Tr; *U of ND; Engr.*

HELGEN, Marcia Diane
Litchfield Sr HS; Litchfield, IL (34-147) Chldr; Chor; 4H; Span C; Pres, Jr Cl; Sftbl; 4H A; *Lincoln Land Comm Col; Acct.*

HELGESON, Elizabeth Rebecca
Preble HS; Green Bay, WI (5%-541) Band; NHS; Hon Prog; Phi Sigma Sigma.

HELGESON, Harold Gene
Mullan HS; Mullan, ID (10-29) Rptr, Ann; Band; Ski C; SC; VP, Sr Cl; MVP, Bsbl; Cpt, Bkbl; Ftbl; 200 Lb C; Weightlifting; Ftbl, Band, A's; *Elec.*

HELLARD, Dwayne Eric
Olympic HS; Charlotte, NC (95-675) NHS; Span C; Span NHS; Cpt, Bsbl; Hon Prog; Art As; *Winthrop Col; Art.*

HELLARD, Rhonda Sue
Olympic HS; Charlotte, NC (95-425) NHS; Hon Prog; Art As; Hon o-t Trojan; Rep, Stu Coun; *Winthrop Col; Art.*

313

HELLER, Don Allen
Stamford HS; Stamford, TX (10-50) VP, FFA; Pres, 4H; NHS; Ftbl; Tres, FFA; Agr A; Tex Tech U; Agr.

HELLER, Elizabeth Ellen
Thomas Jefferson Sr HS; Bloomington, MN (125-650) F-Ed, Ann; JV, Tr; Wash St U; Forestry.

HELLER, Janet Louise
Oceanside HS; Oceanside, NY; Pres, 4H; Ski C; 4H A; Tres, 4 H C; Hon Soc; U of Vt; Pol Sci.

HELLER, Mark John
Horicon HS; Horicon, WI (4-105) BS; Ger C; VP, NHS; Pres, Var C; Bkbl; Cpt, Cr-Crtry; Tnns; Prom Court.

HELLER, Suzanne
Germantown HS; Germantown, TN; Rptr, Ger C; GS; Lat C; Lit Mag; Model UN; Southwestern Col; Med.

HELLMAN, Joseph Michael
A D Johnston HS; Bessemer, MI (25%-95) ROTC A; Acct.

HELM, Kristi Joy
Montclair HS; Montclair, CA (1-500) A Cap Choir; Band; Chor; Amer Leg A; CSF; Hist A; WW; OPTA Schol; Mus Schol; Fr A; Mus.

HELMEN, Mollie Sommers
W Aurora HS; Aurora, IL (100-736) Band; Ensm; Mjrte; NHS; Ski C; Med.

HELMER, Kenneth Michael
Bayou Chicot HS; Ville Platte, LA (4-29) Co-Ed, Ann; Chem C; Pres, 4H; Math C; Spch C; Rptr, Sr Cl; VP, Jr Cl; Rptr, Soph Cl; Cpt, Bkbl; Cpt, Tr; Amer Leg A; 4H A; Math A; MLS; Most Out; Spch A; MVP, Tr; Mr Bayou Chicot; LSU at Alexandria; Agr Engr.

HELMER, Vicki Joann
Rockwall HS; Rockwall, TX (10-150) Band; Span C; Church Pianst; S-T, Yth Group; Ch, IWC; Church, Princess, Qn; Baylor U; Nurs.

HELMINK, Diane Lynn
Holland HS; Holland, MI; Secy, 4H; Var C; Co-Cpt, Swim; MVP, Swim; Central Mich U; Ed.

HELMS, Catherine Lynn
Rock Hill HS; Rock Hill, SC (75-614) Band; Winthrop Col; Mus.

HELMS, Lynda Love
S Gwinnett HS; Snellville, GA; Span C; Thes; Entertainment.

HELMS, Roberta Redfearn
Spartanburg Day Sch; Spartanburg, SC (3-28) SC; Var C; Co-Cpt, Bkbl; Hockey; Sftbl.

HELMS, Tracey Faye
Lyman HS; Longwood, FL; Chor; Tres, FBLA; Span C; Bkbl; Sftbl; Most Congenial; Hub; Parl Procedure Tm; Pres, Acteens; Alpha Omega; VP, Church Stu Coun; FTU; Legal Secy.

HELMS, Virginia Kathryn
Smithfield-Selma HS; Smithfield, NC (13-360) Fr C; Hmrm; NHS; Duke U; Biol.

HELPER, Katherine Chapin
South HS; Denver, CO (16-450) Secy, A Cap Choir; F-Ed, Ann; Band; Chor; City Conf; Community Yth Symph; Drama; Ensm; Fr C; Lat C; Madrigal; Secy, Model UN; Secy, NHS; Orch; Ed, Sch P; VP, Thes; COM; Curator A; Journ A; Oberlin Col; Lib Arts.

HELPLING, Donna Frances
Buchholz HS; Gainesville, FL (10%-490) Secy, 4H; NHS; Span C; 4H A; Sci A; Sewing A; U of Fla; Ed.

HELSEL, Mary Kathleen
Winfield Sr HS; Winfield, KS; Band; Chor; FHA; Tr; JA A; Math A; Ed, Church Paper; Candystriper; Valentine Qn; St John's U; Nurs.

HELSING, Julie Ann
Randolph Pub HS; Randolph, NE (7-63) A-Ed, Ann; Band; Chor; Drama; Parl, FHA; Pres, 4H; Madrigal; Pres, Span C; VP, Soph Cl; Tr; 4H A; Spch A; Type A; Yth Fel; Prom Server; Candidate, Swtht Ball; Wayne St Col; Acct.

HELTON, Annette
John Ehret HS; Marrero, LA (122-450) Hmrm; Rptr, Sch P; SC; VP, Sr Cl; VP, Jr Cl; Cl Fav; Hon Prog; Poet A; U of NO; Ed.

HELTON, Charlene Danita
Calvin Coolidge HS; Washington, DC (31-300) Co-Cpt, Chldr; FHA; 4H; Hmrm; NHS; SC; VP, Y-Tns; B Crocker A; Citz A; Crisco A; JA A; Most Out; Howard U; Pre-Med.

HELTON, Judy Kay
Midlothian HS; Midlothian, TX (36-84) Band; Bus C; VP, Chor; FHA; Span C; Most Out; Type A; Band A; UIL Typing A; Nelsons Beauty Col; Beautician.

HELTON, Melinda Sue
Laurel Co HS; London, KY (5-400) Ann; Secy, BC; Hmrm; VP, Lat C; Co-Cpt, Bkbl; Golf; Tnns; Bio A; Citz A; Lat A; Sociology A; Anatomy A; Health A; Physiology A; Eng As; Ntl Hon Schol; Psych A; Georgetown Col.

HELTON, Susan Lynn
Bishop Dwenger HS; Fort Wayne, IN (2-258) A Cap Choir; Chor; Sci C; Alg A; Aux Lat; Bio A; COM; Chamber of Comm A; Chem A; Citz A; Sal; Type A; Most Studious; St Vocal-Solo Gold Medalist; Tri-Kappa Schol A; Bio & Bookstore Service As; Ind U; Pre-Med.

HELVIE, Jacqueline Rachelle
Willows HS; Willows, CA (1-130) Band; Hmrm; Math C; Sci C; SC; Tres, Sr Cl; Tr; Bank Of Amer A; CSF; Citz A; Hon Prog; Val; Pres, Jr NHS; MVP, JV Vlbl; Savings & Loan A; Chico St U; Acct.

HELVIE, Michael Miles
Columbia City Joint HS; Columbia City, IN; FTA; Marion Col; Ministry.

HELWIG, Cheryl Lynn
Oak Park River Forest HS; Oak Park, IL (139-936) Chor; Cum Laude Soc; ARC; Ski C; Hon Prog; Yth Fel; Ill Wesleyan U; Nurs.

HELWIG, Gary Vernon
Hoisington HS; Hoisington, KS; Band; BS; Chor; Golf; Barton Co Comm Col; Computer Sci.

HELWIG, Wendy Jo
Elizabethtown HS; Elizabethtown, PA (8-262) Band; NHS; Yrbk; WW; Bus.

HELZER, Bryan John
N Platte Sr HS; N Platte, NE (65%-1000) Kearny Col; Computer Sci.

HEMAN, Kimberly Ann
Sahuaro HS; Tucson, AZ (171-631) Hmrm; NHS; Ski C; Hon Prog; Candy Striper; Vacation Bible Sch Teacher; Church Vlbl.

HEMAUER, Pamela Kay
Hilbert HS; Hilbert, WI; SC; Bkbl; Nurs.

HEMBREE, Connie Ruth
Burkeville HS; Burkeville, TX (1-36) Ann; Band; Dbte Tm; Drama; FHA; Math C; Pres, Soph Cl; NEDT; Fresh o-t Yr; Tex Tech U; Acct.

HEMBREE, Jeffrey Wayne
Grove HS; Grove, OK (2-90) BC; BS; Chor; Drama; Ensm; Rptr, 4H; NHS; Order/Arrow; SC; Thes; Swim; Tnns; Amer Leg A; B Crocker A; COM; Cl Fav; 4H A; Hon Prog; Order/Arrow A; Sal; Spch A; St Scholar; Yth Leg; Okla Bapt Acad; WW; Okla Baptist U; Religion.

HEMBREE, Regina Diane
Westville HS; Westville, OK (20-75) Band; VP, Chor; FHA; Mjrte; Rptr, Sch P; COM; HQn.

HEMENWAY, Joseph Jay
N Mercer R-III HS; Mercer, MO; VP, Jr Cl; Bkbl; Sftbl; Tr; NE Mo St U; Engr.

HEMENWAY, Martin Mayhew
Maryville R-II HS; Maryville, MO; Band; Chor; Ensm; Orch; Sftbl; JV, Tnns; U of Nebr; Bus.

HEMINGWAY, Sheryl Lynn
Saint Joseph HS; Saint Joseph, MI (165-363) Band; ARC; Var C; Bkbl; Cpt, Sftbl; Central Mich Col; Phys Ed.

HEMMELINE, Sharla
Richardson HS; Richardson, TX (119-942) Chor; Tri-HiY; Bkbl; HS All Amer; All District Spiker; MVP, Vlbl; Tex Tech U; Archt.

HEMMELSBACH, Janet Lynn
Grand Haven Sr HS; Grand Haven, MI (5-500) Chor; Ger C; VP, NHS; Yth Fel; Young Hist; Muskegon Comm Col; Bus Mgr.

HEMMERT, Mari Karol
Oakley HS; Oakley, KS (2-76) VP, CYO; FHA; Pres, 4H; NHS; Pres, SC; Cpt, Bkbl; Sftbl; B Crocker A; 4H A; St Scholar; Dodge City Comm Jr Col; Phys Ed.

HEMMES, Rebecca Jean
Harbor Springs HS; Harbor Springs, MI (5-75) A Cap Choir; Band; Chor; Co-Ch, Jr Cl; Cpt, Sftbl; Hon Prog; Band As; Cand, Christian Qn; Vocal Soloist; Baptist Bible of Penn; Mus & Bible.

HEMMINGS, Jamie Dawn
Northwest Sr HS; Cincinnati, OH; Co-Cpt, Chldr; Hmrm; Tres, InterClub Coun; K of C; SC; Sftbl; HCt; Hon Prog; Ath As; Marketing.

HEMMITT, Ollie Uvonnous Jr
Mullins HS; Mullins, SC; 4H; Math C; Span C; SC; Var C; Bsbl; Ftbl; Tr; 4H A; YPD Pres; Church Choir; SC St Col; Hist.

HEMP, William Ernest
N Plainfield HS; Plainfield, NJ (9-260) Band; Chor; Ger C; Pres, NHS; Orch; Bsbl; Ftbl; Swim; Pres, Episcopal Yth C; Tri-Hi-Y Yth Ldrship A; Engr.

HEMPEL, Karyl Jean
Stroman HS; Victoria, TX (33-375) Anchor C; FTA; Pres, 4H; Chamber of Comm A; 4H A; JA A; Victoria Col; Teaching.

HEMPEL, Nancy Dell
Nederland HS; Nederland, TX (45-482) Band; NHS; Lamar U; Math.

HEMPHILL, Mark Allen
Conroe HS; Conroe, TX (309-814) WW; Church Choir; Church Mission Trips; BSct; Sam Houston St U.

HENDERSHOT, Paula Jane
Shawnee HS; Shawnee, OK (8-365) Tres, FBLA; FTA; NHS; Tres, Span C; Hon Prog; East Central U; Bus.

HENDERSHOTT, Randall Ray
Stillman Valley HS; Stillman Valley, IL; Band; Var C; Co-Cpt, Cr-Crtry; Tr.

HENDERSON, Alan Clay
Madison Acad HS; Huntsville, AL (3-42) BC; Math C; Monogram; NHS; Var C; JV, Bsbl; JV, Bkbl; JV, Cr-Crtry; COM; Hon Prog; NEDT; Star Student; Bible A; David Lipscomb Col.

HENDERSON, Angelia Maria
Jackson HS; Jackson, GA (3-140) City Conf; Pres, FHA; NHS; Secy, Soph Cl; COM; Hon Prog; Most Intellectual; Essay A; Hon Guard; W Ga Col; Bus Adm.

HENDERSON, Armilla Kay
South HS; Youngstown, OH (6-348) Band; Chldr; NHS; Tres, Y-Tns; COM; MLS; PTA A; Sci A; Ohio St U; Elec Engr.

HENDERSON, Artis McKinley
South HS; Youngstown, OH; Band; COM; MLS; PTA A; Ohio St U; Aeronautical Engr.

HENDERSON, Barry Ralph
Pepperell HS; Rome, GA; Key C; NHS; SC; Bus Mgr, Jr Cl; MVP, Bsbl; JV, Bkbl; Ftbl; COM; Cl Fav; Sci A; Top 10%; U of Ga; Hist.

HENDERSON, Carl Anthony
Maggie L Walker HS; Richmond, VA; Hmrm; St Stu Congress; Tres, Soph Cl; Aeronautical Engr.

HENDERSON, Cheryl Ann
Dobyns-Bennett HS; Kingsport, TN (4-420) BC; CYO; Ger C; Tres, JETS; NHS; SC; JA A; NMF; Opt A; Opt Out Tn; Tres, Jr Civitan; Stu Ambassador, People to People; Outst Bus Woman, JA; VPI; Computer Sci.

HENDERSON, Cora
Harlem Park Sr HS; Baltimore, MD; SC; Drama Sch; Morgan St Col; Math.

HENDERSON, David Wayne
Guilford HS; Rockford, IL (80-650) Orch; SC; Soccer; Tnns; Wheaton Col; Psych.

HENDERSON, Debra Ann
Homer L Ferguson HS; Newport News, VA (161-482) Rptr, Sch P; SC; Hockey; Citz A; Best Defense Trophy, Hockey; Career Key; Poetry A; Hallmark A; Golden Thimble.

HENDERSON, Dolores
Danbury HS; Danbury, CT (203-864) VP, Hmrm; SC; Bkbl; Sftbl; Tr; Hon Prog; Howard U; Bus.

HENDERSON, Gail
Tallapoosa Acad; Dadeville, AL (5-22) BC; JV, Chldr; HCt; NEDT; *Alexander City Jr Col.*

HENDERSON, George Lawrence
Sparks HS; Sparks, NV (5-290) BS; NHS; VP, SC; Pres, Sr Cl; Ftbl; Cpt, Wrest; MVP, Wrest; WW; *Columbia U; Engr.*

HENDERSON, George Wesley
Garinger HS; Charlotte, NC (20%-749) Dbte Tm; Hmrm; Order/Arrow; ARC; SC; JV, Bsbl; JV, Bkbl; JV, Ftbl; Citz A; Cl Fav; DARGCA; God & Country A; JA A; MLS; Ntl Achv Schol; Star Student; Yth Fel; *U of NC; Theology.*

HENDERSON, Heather Alexandra
Lowes HS; Lowes, KY (10-55) Chldr; Secy, Chor; FHA; Secy, 4H; F-Ed, Sch P; PTA A; Cert of A.

HENDERSON, Holly Antoinette
Lowes HS; Lowes, KY (10-55) Chldr; Rptr, Chor; Ch, FHA; 4H; F-Ed, Sch P; Rptr, Jr Cl; Most Out; Cert of A; WW; 2nd Pl, Vocal Solo, Talent Show.

HENDERSON, Janet C
T F Riggs HS; Pierre, SD (53-253) F-Ed, Ann; Span C; Type A; NHS Cand; *USD; Phys Sci.*

HENDERSON, Janet Lynn
Martin Co HS; Stuart, FL (33-500) BC; Chldr; Lang C; Civinettes; Christian Fellowship C; Exchange C Stu o-t Mo; *U of Tenn; Bus Adm.*

HENDERSON, Jennifer Jane
Cushing HS; Cushing, OK (2-120) Rptr, FBLA; Pres, FHA; NHS; Co-Ed, Sch P; SC; Var C; Sal; Swtht; *Phillips U.*

HENDERSON, John Charles
NE HS; Elizabeth City, NC (30-425) Bus Mgr, Ann; Band; Pres, 4H; Tres, Key C; NHS; Span C; Order/Arrow A; Sci A; Eagle Sct, 3 Palms; *Atlantic Christian Col; Religion.*

HENDERSON, Joscelyn Denise
South Shore HS; Chicago, IL (135-500) *Ill St U; Bus Ed.*

HENDERSON, Judy Kay
Forest Park HS; Beaumont, TX; ARC; Sci C; Ski C; Tr; Bkbl; COM; Vlbl; Presidential Phys Fitness A; *Tex A&M; Bio.*

HENDERSON, Julie Frances
Wadley HS; Wadley, GA (10%-70) Co-Ed, Ann; Tres, BC; Ed, Sch P; Bkbl; COM; Chem A; Cl Fav; Gov Honor Prog; HCt; Math A; *Ga Sou Col; Bus.*

HENDERSON, Karen Ann
Joliet Township E Campus HS; Joliet, IL (50%-356) A Cap Choir; Madrigal; Spch A; VofDEM; WW; *Stephens Col; Theater Arts.*

HENDERSON, Kimberly Lynne
HS For Health Professions; Houston, TX (1-139) Chor; Hmrm; Pres, Math C; NHS; A-Ed, Sch P; COM; Hon Prog; Spch Choir; Yth Organization; Young Amer A; Nom, Amer Legion A; VP, NJHS; WW; *Spelman Col; Bio.*

HENDERSON, Lana Virginia
Leesburg HS; Leesburg, FL (100-300) Band; Mod Mus Mas; *Lake-Sumter Comm Col; Mus.*

HENDERSON, Lee J
Mtn View HS; Mtn View, OK (2-25) BS; Pres, FFA; NHS; Bsbl; Bkbl; Ftbl; Amer Leg A; Bio A; Chem A; FFA; Hon Prog; Phy A; Sci A; FFA Beef Production A; Kobs Mem A; *Okla St U; Engr.*

HENDERSON, Lilian Margaret
Burbank Sr HS; Burbank, CA; Beauty; Hon Prog; Demolay Swtht; Pep C; Hon Qn, Jobs Daughters; Gem & Mineral C; *Calif St U-Northridge; Law.*

HENDERSON, Lois Ann
Northeast Lauderdale HS; Meridian, MS; Anchor C; Secy, Fr C.

HENDERSON, Lori Ann
Stevens HS; Rapid City, SD (80-435) Secy, Bus C; *U of SD; Mus.*

HENDERSON, Lori Jeanne
Anamosa Comm HS; Anamosa, IA (15-140) Band; Pres, 4H; Sci C; Bkbl; 4H A; *Kirkwood Comm Col; Acct.*

HENDERSON, Margaret Delores
Weequahic HS; Newark, NJ; Computer Programming.

HENDERSON, Mark Anthony
George Washington HS; Los Angeles, CA; Bsbl; Bkbl; Ftbl; Sftbl; Swim; Tr; Citz A; Hon Prog; Tr, Art, Ath, A's; *Long Beach St Col.*

HENDERSON, Mary Elizabeth
Forest Park Sr HS; Forest Park, GA (1-614) Ann; BC; NHS; Span C; Sftbl; Alg A; COM; Coun of Teach A; Math A; Val; Pres, KAPPA C; Hon Stu; High HR; Semi-Fin, Gov's Hons Prog A; *U of Ga; Bus.*

HENDERSON, Matthew
Framingham S HS; Framingham, MA (182-440) A Cap Choir; AFS; Band; Ensm; Orch; Soccer; Wrest; *U of Mahe; Forestry.*

HENDERSON, Michael Eugene
Glasco HS; Glasco, KS; Band; Chor; Var C; Co-Cpt, Bkbl; Ftbl; Type A; Yth Fel; Purple Heart A, Bkbl; Tres, Church Yth Fel; HKing Candidate; Sr Cl Play; *Kans St Col; Rangeland Ecology.*

HENDERSON, Pamela Kaye
Hettinger HS; Hettinger, ND; Ch, Band; Chor; Ensm; Rainbow; SC; Var C; Bkbl; Sftbl; Tnns; Alg A; COM; Hon Prog; Math A; Mus A; *SD Sch of Mining Tech; Chem Engr.*

HENDERSON, Pamela Lee
Newburgh Free Acad; Newburgh, NY (89-850) Band; Chor; Orch; Tres, SC; Robert D Williams Mem A; Ntl Jr Hon Soc; Mus 'N'; Special Cert, Mus; Special Cert, Mus; *Albany Col of Phar; Phar.*

HENDERSON, Rachel Agnes
Ogemaw Heights HS; W Branch, MI; Chor; Swim; GSct; *Bus.*

HENDERSON, Randy Ray
Clay Co HS; Ashland, AL (10-60) A-Ed, Ann; VP, BC; VP, Chor; Dbte Tm; FTA; VP, SC; Var C; Cpt, Ftbl; MVP, Ftbl; *Auburn U; Engr.*

HENDERSON, Robert Craig
Headland HS; E Point, GA (5%-100) BC; BS; Hmrm; Model UN; Ed, Sch P; SC; Ftbl; Wrest; COM; Gov Honor Prog; Hon Prog; NEDT; Q&S A; Yth Fel; Eagle Sct; *Wake Forrest Col; Humanities.*

HENDERSON, Robin Jean
Georges Valley HS; Thomaston, ME (7-87) Chor; Drama; Ensm; Hmrm; Madrigal; NHS; ARC; SC; Bkbl; Hockey; Cpt, Sftbl; Hon Prog; *U of Del; Criminal Justice.*

HENDERSON, Roger Wayne
Albia Comm HS; Albia, IA (55-150) Ann; Band; Chor; Drama; Span C; SCIBA Hon Band; I Ratings, St Mus Contest; *Mus.*

HENDERSON, Sandra Jean
Thomas Jefferson HS; Los Angeles, CA; Chor; FNA; Alg A; Citz A; Pres, CSF; Hon Soc; Pep C; *Cal St U at Long Beach; Nurs.*

HENDERSON, Scotland Weaver
Langley HS; McLean, VA (20%-544) FBLA; Bkbl; Ftbl; Cpt, Rugby; Young Life Mus Schol; *VPI; Chem.*

HENDERSON, Sharon Ann
Cary Sr HS; Cary, NC (215-518) Bkbl; Soccer; Bkbl Statistician; Soccer Bat Girl.

HENDERSON, Sharon Jo
S Charleston HS; S Charleston, WV (35-294) Bus C; Rptr, FBLA; Rptr, Sch P; Span C; Hon Prog; JA A; Type A; *W Va St U; Bus.*

HENDERSON, Tammy Lynn
Ethel Attendance Center; Ethel, MS (25%-55) Rptr, Band; BC; Chldr; Ensm; S-T, FHA; GS; 4H; Mjrte; Ed, Sch P; Sci C; JV, Bkbl; Bio A; Type A; *Miss St U; Journ.*

HENDERSON, Tammy Renee
T R Miller HS; Brewton, AL (2-100) FBLA; FTA; NHS; Hon Prog; Sal; *Jefferson Davis Jr Col; Bus.*

HENDERSON, Teresa Anne
Glasco HS; Glasco, KS (4-28) Band; Chor; FHA; Var C; Y-Tns; MVP, Bkbl; Sftbl; Type A; Yth Fel; Vlbl; Alt, Met Tour; Tres, Church Yth Fel; Secy, Pep C.

HENDERSON, Terry Don
Plainview HS; Plainview, TX (15-350) A Cap Choir; Drama; Hmrm; NHS; Sch P; SC; JV, Ftbl; Amer Leg A; Amer Leg Orator A; COM; Journ A; NEDT; NML; Photography A; *E Tex St U; Photography.*

HENDERSON, Timothy Alan
Duncanville HS; Duncanville, TX (11-420) A Cap Choir; Band; Foreign Travel Prog; Bible Credit A's; Teacher's Asst; *Abilene Christian Col; Bible.*

HENDERSON, Timothy McKibben
Stafford HS; Falmouth, VA (25%-500) Fr C; Key C; Ftbl; Tr; WW; *Madison Col; Bus.*

HENDERSON, Tonya Kay
Goddard HS; Roswell, NM; Band; JV, Chldr; Pres, Chor; Ensm; Hmrm; NHS; Span NHS; SC; COM; Spch A; Yth Fel; *Ed.*

HENDERSON, Wanda Lavern
Paxon HS; Jacksonville, FL; *Fla Jr Col; Data Processing.*

HENDERSON, William Andrew
T R Miller HS; Brewton, AL; Chess C; Sci C; Var C; Ftbl; Sci A.

HENDON, Barry Clift
Memphis University Sch; Memphis, TN (16-94) Bus Mgr, Ann; Cum Laude Soc; Mu Alpha Theta; NHS; Ski C; Spch C; SC; Mgr, Bkbl; Mgr, Tr; COM; Hon Prog; NEDT; Sch Service A; NML; Leading Annual Ad Sales; *U of Tenn; Vet Med.*

HENDON, Susan
Shades Valley HS; Birmingham, AL (44-278) AFS; Ed, Ann; FTA; Hmrm; InterAct C; Secy, NHS; Span C; Hon Prog; Carol Brewton Sportsmanship A; G C Wallace Leadership Schol; *U of Ala in Birmingham; Ed.*

HENDON, Terry Hardy
Arapahoe HS; Littleton, CO; JV, Bsbl; Ftbl; Hon Prog.

HENDON, William David
Shades Valley HS; Birmingham, AL; Ftbl; *U of Ala; Engr.*

HENDRICK, Kevin Lee
E Alton-Wood River HS; Wood River, IL (25-253) Band; Chor; Ensm; Lat C; NHS; Orch; Rptr, Sch P; Var C; Bsbl; JV, Bkbl; Sftbl; Ed, Sch P; *St Louis Sch of Phar; Phar.*

HENDRICKS, Brenda Lu
Claremore HS; Claremore, OK (36-270) Chldr; Fr C; FHA; VP, Hmrm; Rptr, Sch P; Secy, Jr Cl; Lib A; Jr Attendant, Sch P; *Okla St U; Journ.*

HENDRICKS, Gustave Ralph
Highland HS; Bakersfield, CA; Ger C; JV, Bkbl; JV, Cr-Ctry; JV, Swim; *Bakersfield Col; Phys Ed.*

HENDRICKS, Jan Denise
A H Parker HS; Birmingham, AL; A Cap Choir; Tnns.

HENDRICKS, Judie Denise
Patrick Henry HS; San Diego, CA (28-1054) AFS; Co-Ed, Ann; Ensm; VP, Ger C; NHS; CSF; COM; Hon Prog; NMS; Ntl Sci Found; Sci A; Yth Fel; Ambassadors; Athenas; *Bethany Nazarene Col; Spch Communications.*

HENDRICKS, Kathy Renee
Foster HS; Seattle, WA (9-150) Band; NHS; Ski C; Span C; Alg A; Math A; Type A; Service, Mus, A's.

HENDRICKS, Linda Ann
Seekonk HS; Seekonk, MA (3-224) VP, CYO; Co-Cpt, Chldr; Fr C; FNA; Hmrm; Secy, NHS; *Boston Col; Bio.*

HENDRICKS, Myra Gwendaro
E St Louis Sr HS; E St Louis, IL (215-646) Chem C; *Sou Ill U; Radiology.*

HENDRICKS, Susie
Bonneville HS; Ogden, UT; A Cap Choir; FBLA; 4H; Sch Achieve Tm; SC; Secy, Sr Cl; Rptr, Jr Cl; Secy, Soph Cl; Tr; 4H A; Jr Prom Qn; *Weber Col; Cosmatology.*

HENDRICKS, Susie Fay
Plano Sr HS; Plano, TX; FHA; Yth Fel; *Richland Jr Col; Special Ed.*

HENDRICKSEN, Susan Carol
Edwin G Foreman HS; Chicago, IL (6-363) Drama; Key C; Semi-Fin, Tr; COM; Hon Prog; Special Ed.

HENDRICKSON, Bruce Peter
Neshaminy Maple Point HS; Langhorne, PA (2-415) Band; Demolay; NHS; Orch; Soccer; Wrest; Hon Prog; Masonic A; Mr Sandburg A; WW; US Naval Acad; Engr.

HENDRICKSON, Craig Randal
Levelland HS; Levelland, TX (25-230) Pres, Band; BS; Chess C; Ger C; NHS; Order/Arrow; Co-Ch, Sci C; SC; Tnns; US Air Force Acad; Bio Physics.

HENDRICKSON, Daniel Wayne
Albia Comm HS; Albia, IA (15-150) Band; Iowa St U.

HENDRICKSON, David Paul
Creston HS; Grand Rapids, MI; A Cap Choir; City Conf; Madrigal; Var C; Pres, Sr Cl; Tnns; WW Mus Stu; Outst Merit & Accomplishment; Grand Rapids Jr Col; Bus Adm.

HENDRICKSON, Gary Lee
Richfield HS; Richfield, MN (200-731) Yth Fel; Weather & Minerology.

HENDRICKSON, John Dean
Benton Co R-I HS; Cole Camp, MO (10-55) A Cap Choir; A-Ed, Ann; Parl, Band; Choir; Ensm; S-T, FFA; Pres, 4H; VP, HiY; NHS; Thes; Pres, Y-Tns; Ch, Jr Cl; Ch, Soph Cl; Tr; Wrest; 4H A; Spch A; Yth Fel; Yth Foundation; Star Greenhand; Sparkplug, FFA Dairy Found; U of Mo; Dairy Sci.

HENDRICKSON, Linda Joanne
Grinnell Sr HS; Grinnell, IA (20%-618) Secy, Band; Chldr; Chor; Fr C; VP, 4H; Hmrm; Bkbl; Mgr, Sftbl; Co-Cpt; Tr; 4H A; Christian Ed Board; All St Chor; Swing Choir; FFA Swtht; Stage Band; Yth Group; Spch.

HENDRICKSON, Susan Dalynn
Monterey HS; Lubbock, TX (25%-750) Chor; FHA; VP, Hmrm; NHS; Span C; VP, SC; Bkbl; Sftbl; Tr; Citz A; Most Out; WW; Church Swtht; Tex Tech U; Elem Ed.

HENDRIX, Barry Blaine
Alsea HS; Alsea, OR (10%-20) Ann; Chess C; Hmrm; Pres, NHS; SC; Var C; Pres, Sr Cl; Pres, Jr Cl; VP, Soph Cl; Cpt, Bkbl; Co-Cpt, Ftbl; Tr; Citz A; Math A; Most Out; Sal; Engr.

HENDRIX, Chet Evans
John L McClellan HS; Little Rock, AR; A Cap Choir; Chor; Art C; Art Survey; Human Relations C; U of Ark; Computer Sci.

HENDRIX, James Steven
Claxton HS; Claxton, GA (25%-116) Co-Ed, Ann; Sch P; VP, SC; Bkbl; Citz A.

HENDRIX, John Charles
Pleasant Grove HS; Pleasant Grove, AL (2-150) Ann; Parl, Chem C; Pres, NHS; Parl, Phys C; Tn Code A; Top 5%, Co; Birmingham Sou Col; Med.

HENDRIX, Karen
Trenton Central HS; Trenton, NJ; Drama; Citz A; Dancing A; HR; Clarion St Col; Lib Sci.

HENDRIX, Karen Sue
Tahlequah HS; Tahlequah, OK (59-245) Chor; FBLA; Secy, FHA; FTA; 4H; Math C; Math A; Northeastern Col; Bus.

HENDRIX, Kenneth Anthony
Booker T Washington HS; Atlanta, GA; Band; French NHS; Bkbl; Type A; Fr Cert; Bkbl As; Band Cert & Medal; Band Trophy; Drivers Ed Cert; Fla A&M U; Architecture.

HENDRIX, Lester Antonio
Svannah HS; Savannah, GA; Band; Hmrm; Ftbl; Savannah St Col; Acct.

HENDRIX, Mary Louise
Savannah HS; Savannah, GA; Chor; Eckerds Col.

HENDRIX, Michael Edward
Montgomery Co HS; Mt Sterling, KY (25%-300) Band; Hmrm; Math C; Tres, Tri-HiY; Bkbl; Ftbl; Tnns; U of Ky; Archt.

HENDRIX, Scott Alan
Alsea HS; Alsea, OR (2-20) Ann; Lit Mag; NHS; A-Ed, Sch P; Bkbl; Co-Cpt, Ftbl; Fin, Tr; HCt; Journ A.

HENEGAN, Judy Renee
Merced Union HS; Merced, CA (20%-950) FHA; Bkbl; Sftbl; Yth Church; Drill Tm; Berkeley U; Social Worker.

HENEGHAN, Robert Paul
Highland HS; Albuquerque, NM; Secy, K of C; Ftbl; Ftbl Ltr; Ariz St U; Bus Adm.

HENEREY, Donald Keith
James F Byrnes HS; Duncan, SC (44-240) Band; BC; Orch; Bkbl; Elec.

HENG, Christopher John
Lourdes Central HS; Nebraska City, NE (2-41) Chem C; Drama; Mu Alpha Theta; Span C; Spch C; VP, Jr Cl; Math A; Spch A; Nebr U; Sci.

HENG, Esther Maria
Center Sr HS; Kansas City, MO; A Cap Choir; Chess C; Chor; Ensm; Madrigal; Span C; Ftbl; Tr; Pres A; Yth Fel; 50% A, Gym; SW Baptist Col; Mus.

HENKE, Janet Clair
Anacortes HS; Anacortes, WA (25-200) S-T, Band; Chor; Ensm; HiY; Secy, NHS; SC; UN Council; S-T, Soph Cl; Bkbl; Cpt, Tnns; H of F; Hon Prog; Kiwanis A; Most Out; Pep C; WW, Mus; Torch Pin; Felicians; Hon Cord; Eng A; Swtht Royalty; Oral Roberts U; Aerobics.

HENKE, Kevin John
Valmeyer Comm HS; Valmeyer, IL; Ed, Ann; Tres, FFA; VP, Sr Cl; Pres, Industrial Arts C; Agr A; Yrbk A; Ill FFA Degree; Belleville Area Col; Agr.

HENKEL, Muffie Dolan
Mercer Island HS; Mercer Island, WA (35-553) Band; Fr C; NHS; Orch; Rainbow; Bkbl; Soccer; Tnns; Tr; COM; Hon Prog; Yth Fel; Yth Leg; Legislative Page; Stanford U; Med Research.

HENKELMANN, Kim Charlene
Luthern HS S; Afton, MO; Band; Hockey; Soccer; Tr; Eng.

HENLEY, Beverly Elaine
Alto HS; Alto, TX (6-50) Band; Chldr; Ensm; FHA; NHS; SC; Tnns; Hon Prog; Yth Fel; U of Tex at Austin; Psych.

HENLEY, Dawn Renae
Hoover HS; N Canton, OH (300-416) Chor; Booster C; Job's Daughters; Kent St U; Social Worker.

HENLEY, Grace Yvonne
Rufus King HS; Milwaukee, WI; Tres, Chor; Pres, Drama; Math C; NHS; Span C; MLS; Val; Yth Leg; Mortar Board A; Milwaukee Sch of Engr; Architectural Engr.

HENLEY, Kay Ellen
Booker T Washington HS; Norfolk, VA (40-500) Bus Mgr, Chor; Pres, FBLA; Hmrm; VP, Lat C; Rptr, Sch P; SC; VP, Jr Cl; VP, Soph Cl; Tnns; HCt; Hon Prog; Math Cert; Keyette C; Howard U; Bus Adm.

HENLEY, Kimberly King
Lebanon HS; Lebanon, VA (12-185) A-Ed, Ann; Drama; FTA; 4H; HiY; Hmrm; Fin, Jr Miss Pageant; Cpt, Mjrte; Math C; Model UN; NFL; Ntl Teachers Coun; Span C; Spch C; SC; UN Council; Var C; Tnns; Tr; VP, Yth Fel; Miss Lebanon HS; Fin, 4-H C A; Miss Mjrte; Fin, Beauty; Pres, Creat Writing C; Mod General Assembly Yth Govt; VPI; Law.

HENLEY, Larry James
Oak Ridge HS; Orlando, FL (10%-1200) AFS; Chor; Ensm; Gym; Co Hons Chor; Co All Around, Boys Gym; Oral Roberts U; Sci.

HENLEY, Lorraine Louise
Loyalton HS; Loyalton, CA (20-54) Chor; FBLA; FHA; Mgr, Sftbl; Nurs Aid Cert; Nurs.

HENLEY, Terry Lynn
Northwestern HS; Albion, PA (19-207) Band; VP, Chor; Fin, Dbte Tm; Drama; Madrigal; Spch C; Amer Leg Orator A; Pres, Bible Rap C; Eastern Nazarene Col; Christian Ed.

HENLEY, Timothy Brooks
Walter M Williams HS; Burlington, NC (55-337) Fr C; French NHS; NHS; Golf; Jr Civitan C; NC St U; Acct.

HENLEY, Walter Hodges
Harding Acad of Memphis; Memphis, TN (30-200) A Cap Choir; Hmrm; Ch, Key C; Lat C; A-Ed, Lit Mag; Math C; SC; Cr-Ctry; Tr; COM; NMS; NEDT; Swtht; Vanderbilt U; Pre-Med.

HENLEY, William Marine Jr
Holly Springs HS; Holly Springs, MS (30-96) BC; FFA; HiY; Tres, Ntl Yth Conf; S-T, Pol Sci C; SC; Up Bound; Var C; Parl, Jr Cl; Tres, Soph Cl; Bsbl; Bkbl; Ftbl; Amer Leg A; Cl Fav; MLS; Yth Fel; Tenn St U; Environmental Mgt.

HENNEMANN, Linda Sue
Notre Dame HS; St Louis, MO (85-125) VP, CYO; 4H.

HENNEN, Sandra Ann
Eden Valley-Watkins HS; Eden Valley, MN; Chor; Tres, FHA; Swim; Pep C; Co-Cpt, Pom Pon; Yrbk Staff; Mod Coll of Hair Design; Cosmetology.

HENNESSEE, Brenda Ellen
Geronimo HS; Geronimo, OK (10%-25) Drama; Pres, SC; Rptr, Jr Cl; Bkbl; HR; FFA Swtht; Cameron U.

HENNESSEY, Nancy Ann
Susquehanna Comm HS; Susquehanna, PA (1-110) Chldr; Drama; Ski C; COM; Penn St U; Journ.

HENNESSY, Christopher Gerard
Leo HS; Chicago, IL (4-115) NHS; Span C; Tr; Hon Prog; HR; Loyola U; Pre-Law.

HENNESSY, Darleen Elizabeth
Sharon HS; Sharon, MA; Chor; Drama; ARC; Sci C; Swim; Ldr, Church Yth; Sunday Sch Teacher; CAP; NE U; Nurs.

HENNESSY, Timothy James
Leo HS; Chicago, IL (2-152) Pres, Hmrm; Span C; SC; JV, Cr-Ctry; JV, Tr; Hon Prog; Iowa St U; Forestry.

HENNIG, David Paul
Finneytown HS; Cincinnati, OH (30-235) Chor; Demolay; Ensm; Madrigal; Monogram; NHS; Var C; Cr-Ctry; Tr; COM; Masonic A; Pres, Church Yth Group; Excel, Mech Drawing & Concert Choir; Wittenburg U; Bio.

HENNING, Cynthia Marie
Rufus King HS; Milwaukee, WI; Bus C; City Conf; Math C; Sci C; Span C; Secy, Jr Cl; Tnns; Hon Pin; Mount Mary Col; Fashion Designer.

HENNING, Donna Jean
Benton Co R-1 HS; Cole Camp, MO (7-56) A Cap Choir; F-Ed, Ann; JV, Chldr; Secy, Chor; FTA; GS; Secy, NHS; F-Ed, Sch P; VP, SC; Bkbl; Sftbl; HCt; Swtht; Type A; Co-Cpt, Vlbl; HR; Art Ed.

HENNINGER, Martha Alice
Upper Dauphin Area HS; Elizabethville, PA (10-127) Chor; Ensm; Pres, NHS; VFW Orator Win; Northeast Conf Foreign Lang A; Home Ec A; Most Studious; Most Courteous; Harrisburg Area Comm Col; Lib Arts.

HENNINGSGAARD, Beret Anne
Chisago Lakes Sr HS; Lindstrom, MN; Band; 4H; Rptr, Sch P; JV, Bkbl; Tr.

HENNINGTON, Sharon Yvonne
Bus And Mgmt Center; Dallas, TX; Secy, Bus C; U of Tex; Bus Adm.

HENNIS, Michael Allan
Cary Sr HS; Cary, NC (27-488) Fr C; Parl, FBLA; Jr Marshal; Drafting C; Bicentennial C.

HENNISON, Ronald Neil Jr
Hillsboro HS; Hillsboro, OH (35%-185) Band; Drama; Fr C; SC; VP, Soph Cl; Bkbl; Bkbl; Order/ Arrow A; Bronze Medal, Communication Elec; Sou St Col; Communication Elec.

HENNISON, Timothy Wayne
Hillsboro HS; Hillsboro, OH (25%-201) A Cap Choir; Band; Chor; Community Yth Symph; Drama; Ensm; Orch; Order/Arrow; Semi-Fin, Sch Achiev; Bsbl; JV, Bkbl; COM; Citz A; Order/ Arrow A; Sci A; Band, Ftbl, A's.

HENRICKSON, Kerry Nelle
Piedmont Hills HS; San Jose, CA (2%-500) Chor; 4H; NHS; Span C; VP, SC; VP, Sr Cl; Alg A; CSF; 4H A; Hon Prog; Math A; Yth Fel; Badminton; Vlbl; Math.

HENRIE, Saundra
Sky View HS; Smithfield, UT (4-570) Ch, Band; Community Yth Symph; Ensm; NHS; Orch; COM; Citz A; Hon Prog; WW; Outst Soloist A; All St; *Utah St U; Mech Engr.*

HENRIKSEN, Linda Ann
Westchester HS; Los Angeles, CA (25%-35) Hmrm; Orch; CSF; Athenians Hon Soc; *Sci.*

HENRIOTT, Mark Grover
Woodward Acad; College Park, GA (33%-178) Bsbl; *U of Ga; Pre-Vet.*

HENRIQUEZ, Aixa Regina
Dr Pila HS; Ponce, PR (12-703) Bus C; Sch Achieve Tm; Span C; COM; JA A; Poet A; *Cath U; Med.*

HENRIQUEZ, Anabel
The Macduffie Sch for Girls; Springfield, MA; Chldr; Chor; Cum Laude Soc; Span C; SC; JV, Hockey; Semi-Fin, Swim; Hon Prog; High Hon Prog; Cum Laude Assn; *St Mary Dominican Col; Bus Admin.*

HENRY, Anthony Leon
Suncoast HS; Riviera Beach, FL (50%-293) Band; *Morehouse Col; Pilot.*

HENRY, Barbara Elizabeth
Lawrence HS; Lawrence, KS; Band; Drama; Key C; Orch; Secy, Span C; *Kans U; Lib Arts.*

HENRY, Carol Leigh
Norwalk HS; Norwalk, CA (10-289) Cpt, Chldr; Secy, SC; CSF; COM; Citz A; HCt; Phi Beta Kappa; Vlbl; VP, Future Secy of Amer; Pres, Marantha C; YFU, Foreign Exchange Stu.

HENRY, Corletta Cornelia
Robert E Lee HS; Tyler, TX; Fr C; Bio A; Citz A; Hist A; Sci A; *Bradford Col; Sci.*

HENRY, Craig Manuel
Beaufort Acad; Beaufort, SC (12-38) Ann; NHS; Var C; Bsbl; Soccer; Hon Prog; *Clemson U; Plant Sci.*

HENRY, Donna Allyson
Tucker HS; Tucker, GA (40%-410) Tres, Anchor C; Chldr; Fr C; FHA; InterAct C; F-Ed, Sch P; *Ga Sou U; Bus Adm.*

HENRY, Edward Dwayne
Melville HS; Melville, LA; BC; Tres, FFA; Cpt, Bkbl; Ftbl; Alg A; COM; Hist A; 1st Pl, Lit Rally; *Huston-Tillotson Col; Pre-Law.*

HENRY, Errol
Flushing HS; Flushing, NY (115-913) SC; Hon Prog; *Wharton Col; Acct.*

HENRY, Gail Eugenia
Beaufort Acad; Beaufort, SC (3-43) Ann; Secy, SC; Var C; Bkbl; Sftbl; HCt; Hon Prog; Headmasters A.

HENRY, Gina Gaye
Maryville R-II HS; Maryville, MO (15%-131) Chldr; Fr C; Mjrte; NHS; Sch P; Spch C; SC; Bkbl; Tnns; Hon Prog; Opt A; Regent Schol; Experimenter in EIL to Austria; *NW Mo St U; Bus.*

HENRY, Herbert Harrison
Maynard Evans HS; Orlando, FL (166-730) FFA; Order/Arrow; Order/Arrow A; FFA Chpt School; *Bio.*

HENRY, Jamae Kathryn
McGavock HS; Nashville, TN; BC; Math C; Mu Alpha Theta; JV, Bkbl; Tnns; *Baylor U; Commercial Art.*

HENRY, Judy Lynn
Maple Shade HS; Maple Shade, NJ (4-241) Ed, Ann; Hmrm; Key C; NHS; Mgr, Bkbl; Mat Mate; JV LaCrosse; Classical & Modern Lang League; TNE; *Acct.*

HENRY, Karan Denise
Unicoi Co HS; Erwin, TN (10-200) Bus C; JV, Chldr; Secy, Drama; VP, FBLA; Tres, FHA; Pres, 4H; HiY; InterAct C; Co-Cpt, Mjrte; NHS; Bus Mgr, Ski C; Spch C; Tri-HiY; World Affairs C; JV, Arch; Swim; Beauty; HCt; Hon Prog; Most Out; Type A; Data Processing A; Drama A; FBLA A; Art A; Merit A; *Steed Col; Data Processing.*

HENRY, Kathi Elizabeth
Westland HS; Galloway, OH (98-540) Sftbl; JV Vlbl; Secy, Church Yth; Head Yrbk Artist; Bell Choir; *Ohio St U; Photography.*

HENRY, LaShaun Marie
Austin HS; Chicago, IL (35-440) Bus C; Drama; *De Paul; Bus Adm.*

HENRY, Levon B
Rehoboth Christian HS; Rehoboth, NM; Chor; Drama; Pres, Hmrm; ARC; Span C; VP, SC; Var C; Pres, Sr Cl; Bkbl; Tr; WW; *Calvin Col; Law.*

HENRY, Linda Jean
N Shore HS; W Palm Beach, FL (5-336) Anchor C; VP, Band; Chor; Ger C; Hmrm; InterClub Coun; Ch, Key C; Secy, NHS; ARC; Rptr, Sch P; Ch, SC; Ch, Jr Cl; Ch, Soph Cl; Mgr, Tr; COM; Hon Prog; Math A; ARC A; Spch A; Type A; Pres, GSct; Letterman; Ger A; Human Relations; Schol A; Outst Service, Band; 1st Cl, GSct.

HENRY, Lisa Anne
West HS; Davenport, IA (56-846) A Cap Choir; Chor; Ensm; Ger C; Madrigal; Orch; Hon Prog; Yth Fel; Tres, Mus C; St Solo & Ensm Contest; Tri-City Yth Symph; Bellringers; YWCA; *Spch Pathology.*

HENRY, Lori Ann
Lincoln HS; Lincoln, CA; Chor; Rptr, 4H; Citz A; Hon Prog; *Heald Bus Col; Secy.*

HENRY, Lydia
Durham HS; Durham, NC; Band; BC; Chldr; Chor; 4H; Hmrm; Bkbl; Sftbl; Tr; 4H A; Bkbl & Span A's; *NC Central U; Ed.*

HENRY, Mercie Dea
Manual Arts HS; Los Angeles, CA; *Cal Med Sch; Nurs.*

HENRY, Michael
Northeastern HS; Detroit, MI (1-201) NHS; COM; Citz A; Cl Fav; Hon Prog; MLS; Most Out; Phi Beta Kappa; Type A; Val; *Mich St U; Med.*

HENRY, Michael Paul
Lane Tech HS; Chicago, IL (180-2000) Band; Spch C; Var C; Cr-Ctry; Co-Cpt, Tr; COM; Swtht; Most Improved; Sprinter; *Sou Ill U; Bus.*

HENRY, Michelle Lee
William Howard Taft HS; Woodland Hills, CA; *Merit Col; Bus.*

HENRY, Patricia Ann
St Joseph HS; Toms River, NJ (20%-175) Co-Ed, Ann; Pres, CYO; Drama; Thes; Yth Rep, Parish Coun; *Georgian Court Col; Art.*

HENRY, Paul Gregory
Big Sandy HS; Big Sandy, TX (18-44) F-Ed, Ann; Drama; FFA; FTA; F-Ed, Sch P; Spch C; Var C; JV, Bkbl; Ftbl; JV, Tr; COM; Cl Fav; Spch A; Acting A; Hon Men, All Dist Ftbl; *Kilgore Col; Communications.*

HENRY, Paul Jamse
N Miami Beach Sr HS; N Miami Beach, FL; Band; Ntl Yth Conf; ARC; Swim; *Aviation.*

HENRY, Peter Joseph
Sutter Union HS; Sutter, CA (3-98) NHS; JV, Bkbl; CSF; *Calif St U; Social Work.*

HENRY, Raquel Hortensia
Paraiso Jr Sr HS; Paraiso, CANAL ZONE; Band; FNA; ARC; Hist A; Sci A; Band A; *UCLA; Computer Sci.*

HENRY, Regina Ann
T Wingate Andrews HS; High Point, NC (33%-400) Chldr; Chor; Ensm; NFL; Span C; Jr-Ettes; *Appalachian St U; Working With Handicapp.*

HENRY, Robert Scott
Stephens Co HS; Toccoa, GA (3%-434) BC; Dbte Tm; Hmrm; Secy, Key C; NHS; Bsbl; Co-Cpt, Ftbl; Chaplain, Hi-Y; *Emory at Oxford; Math.*

HENRY, Roger Dale
New Caney HS; Porter, TX (10%-215) FFA; Hmrm; NHS; SC; Co-Cpt, Ftbl; JV, Tr; Tmmate A; Lineman of Yr A; All-Dist Ftbl Tm; *Sul Ross St U; Phys Ed.*

HENRY, Samuel David
NE Acad; New York, NY; Drama; Bkbl; Sftbl; *Oakwood Col; Theology.*

HENRY, Shawna Raye
Big Spring HS; Big Springs, TX (26-450) A Cap Choir; Ann; City Conf; Ensm; NHS; Tres, Tri-HiY; Ftbl; Golf; Sftbl; Yth Leg; Pres, Acteens; FCA; *Tex Tech U; Social Work.*

HENRY, Stephen Brown
Maryville HS; Maryville, TN; AFS; Band; Chor; Hmrm; Order/Arrow; Swim; God & Country A; Order/Arrow A; MYF Yth Coun; Scuba Diving Cert; Eagle Sct.

HENRY, Tammy Elaine
Sunbright HS; Sunbright, TN (10-65) Band; Chldr; Chor; VP, FHA; Secy, 4H; Cpt, Mjrte; Sch P; Secy, Var C; Secy, Jr Cl; Mgr, Bkbl; Beauty; Cl Fav; *Interior Design.*

HENRY, Tori Lee
Hapeville HS; Hapeville, GA (1-100) F-Ed, Ann; BC; Chldr; Chor; VP, NHS; Span NHS; SC; Bkbl; Tr; COM; Math A; Sci A; Star Student; Type A; Val; Yth Fel; *U of Ga; Horticulture.*

HENSARLING, Rebecca Hazel
Castleberry HS; Fort Worth, TX (29-218) VP, FHA; Hmrm; NHS; *Calvary Bible Col; Bus.*

HENSDALE, Jane Raye
Terry Sanford Sr HS; Fayetteville, NC (40-340) Chor; Drama; Ensm; Fr C; F-Ed, Sch P; SC; Bkbl; Tnns; Tr; Journ A; Yth Fel; *Meredith Col; Journ.*

HENSE, Susan Louise
W Allis Central HS; W Allis, WI; Rptr, Ann; Band; Ensm; Hmrm; Mjrte; Orch; Rptr, Sch P; SC; Var C; Bsbl; Bkbl; Sftbl; Tnns; Tr; *Phys Ed.*

HENSEL, Laurie Beth
Watertown HS; Watertown, CT; Chor; JV, Bkbl; Cpt, Hockey; Tnns; Yth Fel; V Ltr & Jacket; *X-Ray Tech.*

HENSEL, Lynn Ellen
Watertown HS; Watertown, CT; A Cap Choir; Mgr, Bkbl; Cpt, Hockey; Swim; Yth Fel; V Ltr; Nurs.

HENSH, Denise Marie
Laurel Highlands HS; Uniontown, PA (180-430) Ski C; Arch; Bsbl; *Penn St HS; Social Work.*

HENSKE, Dawn Lynnette
Beaverton HS; Beaverton, OR; Band; Fr C; Hmrm; Rainbow; Sch P; SC; Bsbl; Drill Tm; *NW Nazarene Col; Phys Ed.*

HENSLER, Kimberley Kay
Carrollton HS; Saginaw, MI (3-150) A Cap Choir; Dbte Tm; Drama; NFL; NHS; *Concordia Col; Elem Ed.*

HENSLEY, April Marie
Los Altos HS; Los Altos, CA; *Davis Col; Nutrition.*

HENSLEY, Charles Clayton
Montrose Acad; Montrose, AR (9-40) NHS; Order/Arrow; Ftbl; Hist A; Order/Arrow A; *Agr Engr.*

HENSLEY, Cheryl Lynn
Montrose Acad; Montrose, AR; Band; Ensm; FHA; 4H; Mjrte; NHS; Citz A.

HENSLEY, Connie Lynn
Hillcrest HS; Springfield, MO; Tres, FFA; Dist Medal, Soils Judging; *SW Mo St U; Conservation.*

HENSLEY, Darla Gail
Franklin Co HS; Frankfort, KY (22-415) Band; BC; Community Yth Symph; Ensm; Tres, 4H; Hmrm; Ntl Yth Conf; Span C; Span NHS; Ldrship A; Reading Achv; *U of Ky; Psych.*

HENSLEY, Mark Kimball
George Washington Carver HS; Fieldale, VA (20%-150) Chor; Math C; SC; Span C; Mgr, Bsbl; JV, Ftbl; Math A; *Danville Comm Col; Drafting.*

HENSLEY, Marty Duane
Jefferson City Sr HS; Jefferson City, MO (33%-500) Band; Var C; Ftbl; Tr; *Baylor U.*

HENSLEY, Paula Jean
Tahlequah HS; Tahlequah, OK (175-280) Ed, Ann; Chor; VP, FBLA; FHA; Pres, FTA; InterClub Coun; 'S' C; *NE Okla St U; Home Ec.*

HENSLEY, Randy Michael
Bethel Baptist Sch; Memphis, TN (8-20) Hmrm; Pres, Sr Cl; Bsbl; Bkbl; Mgr, Ftbl; Mr Bethel; *Memphis St U; Psych.*

HENSLEY, Robin Melissa
Unicoi Co HS; Erwin, TN; FHA; FNA; Ger C; 4H; Citz A; DARGCA; 4H A; Hist A; Spch A; Ger A; *E Tenn St U; Med.*

HENSLEY, Shirley Faye
Galesburg Sr HS; Galesburg, IL (37-660) FTA; W Ill Col; Special Ed.

HENSLEY, Vicky Lynn
Olentangy HS; Delaware, OH (7-138) Pres, Band; S-T, Chor; Drama; 4H; Madrigal; NHS; Pres, Span C; Thes; JV, Bkbl; Tr; Powderpuff Ftbl; WW; Most Outst Sr, Marching Band; Ohio Valley Col; Math.

HENSLEY, William Heydon Jr
Texhoma HS; Texhoma, OK (1-25) Ann; Rptr, Band; Chor; Ensm; Pres, FFA; Pres, NHS; Co-Ch, Sch P; Pres, Sr Cl; Pres, Jr Cl; Alg A; Chem A; Hist A; Masonic A; Math A; Regent Schol; Type A; Val; Epsilon Sigma Alpha Outst Yth A; Okla St U; Archt.

HENSLIN, Sharon Lynn
St James HS; St James, MN (33%-140) Ch, FHA; VICA; Piano A, 6 Yrs; Outst, FHA; Alexandria Vo-tech Inst; Interior Design.

HENSON, Angela Jean
Clarke Central HS; Athens, GA (11-278) Cpt, Band; BC; JV, Chldr; Fin, Jr Miss Pageant; NHS; COM; Hon Prog; Athens Jr Miss; 1st Runner Up, Ga Jr Miss; Win, Poetry; Iliad Mag Lit Contest.

HENSON, Anthony Dewain
Tallulah HS; Tallulah, LA (13-75) Band; BS; Pres, 4H; Hmrm; F-Ed, Sch P; VP, SC; Mgr, Ftbl; Tnns; 4H A; I Dare You; NE La U; Police Sci.

HENSON, Arnell Saul
Oakland Tech HS; Oakland, CA (12-300) Chess C; Chor; City Conf; Dbte Tm; Drama; Ensm; Fr C; JETS; NHS; Spch C; St Stu Congress; V-Ch, SC; Cpt, Ftbl; Wrest; Citz A; Hon Prog; NMS; Spch A; Runner- up, Mr THS; Commissioner of Assemblies; San Francisco St Col; Television Communications.

HENSON, Arthur Leroy
Salem HS; Salem, NJ; Band; Drama; Ensm; Thes; Golf; Bucknell U; Math.

HENSON, Brenda Kay
Chattanooga Central HS; Harrison, TN (62-286) FBLA; FHA; Cleveland St Comm Col; Computer Tech.

HENSON, Catherine Anne
R J Reynolds HS; Winston-Salem, NC; Anchor C; Fr C; Hmrm; Pres, Soph Cl; Hockey; Swim; Tnns; Tr; Law.

HENSON, Connie Elaine
Trinity Christian Sch; Chattanooga, TN (10-13) Cpt, Chldr; VP, Hmrm; SC; HCt; HR A; Pensacola Christian Col; Bus.

HENSON, Connie Louise
Central HS; Newnan, GA (5%-325) Ann; S-T, BC; Sci C; SC; Bsbl; Ftbl; Sftbl; Swim; Tnns; Alg A; Bio A; COM.

HENSON, Jay Corbett
Eldorado HS; El Dorado, IL; FFA; 4H; Bsbl; Bkbl; Ftbl; 4H A; I Dare You; Vet Med.

HENSON, Kimberly Ann
McCluer Sr HS; Florissant, MO (97-677) Chor; Pres A; God & Comm A; GSct; Pres, MYF; Meramec Comm Col; Legal Asst.

HENSON, Luther Martin
Sandusky HS; Sandusky, OH; Co-Cpt, Ftbl; Fin, Wrest; MVP, Ftbl; Ohio St U; Food Mgr.

HENSON, Richard Gregory
Rutherfordton-Spindale Central HS; Rutherfordton, NC; ARC; Cpt, Ftbl.

HENSON, Sharon L
Robert E Lee HS; Thomaston, GA (9-112) Co-Ed, Ann; BC; Pres, Chor; FBLA; FHA; GS; NHS; Ntl Yth Conf; Tres, SC; Arch; Bsbl; Sftbl; Swim; Tnns; COM; Hon Prog; Alpha Y C; Nom, Cl Favorite; Delta Y C; John B Gardan Ldrship Schol; Lee High Singers; Gardan Jr Col.

HENSON, Tamara Susan
Powell Valley HS; Speedwell, TN; Tres, BC; FHA; 4H; Pres, Mu Alpha Theta; Rptr, Tri-HiY; Mgr, Bkbl; Tenn Tech Col; Med Tech.

HENSON, Teena
Gilmer HS; Gilmer, TX (17-129) F-Ed, Ann; Band; Ensm; Math C; NHS; Sci C; Span C; Hon Prog; Princess, Jamboree Pageant; Band Jacket & Medals; Span A's; Kilgore Col; Yth Work.

HENTGES, Diana Elaine
Eden Valley-Watkins HS; Eden Valley, MN (15-100) Band; S-T, Chor; Drama; Ensm; FHA; Fin, GS; VP, 4H; Orch; Rptr, Sch P; 4H A; Col of St Benedict; Elem Ed.

HENTRUP, Melinda Pearl
Twentynine Palms HS; 29 Palms, CA; CYO; Chor; HS Lit Contest; Vet Sci.

HENTZ, Barbara Ruth
Wasson HS; Colorado Springs, CO (11-564) Chor; Ensm; NHS; Orch; Alg A; COM; Hon Prog; Math A; VP, Walther League; Folk Group; Candystriper; Altar Guild; Concordia Col; Hist.

HENTZ, Mary Lillian
Cleveland HS; Cleveland, TN (50%-225) Band; JV, Chldr; Chor; Drama; FTA; A-Ed, Sch P; Tri-HiY; Rep, UN Seminar; Statistician, Bkbl, Tr; U of Miss; Pre-Med.

HENWOOD, Susan Marie
Ottawa Hills HS; Grand Rapids, MI; A Cap Choir; Chess C; Chor; Ensm; Sftbl; Lib Helper A; Mich St U; Med.

HEPBURN, Cecil Elkanah
Forest Hill HS; W Palm Beach, FL; Atlantic U; Coun.

HEPINSTALL, Kathy Ann
Montabella HS; Edmore, MI; VP, FHA; Ski C; Home Ec A.

HEPNER, Irene Ruth
Toulon HS; Toulon, IL (10-77) Ann; Chor; FHA; 4H; 4H A; Hon Prog; Art.

HEPNER, Lisa Ann
Bridgeton HS; Bridgeton, NJ; Span C; 4H A; Hon Prog; Explorers Law C; Ldrship A; Sportsmanship A; Cumberland Co Col; Legal Secy.

HEPPE, Martin
Irvington HS; Fremont, CA; Ger C; Sch Achieve Tm; Ski C; Swim; Kiwanis A; Foreign Exchange Stu, Germany; Pres, SG; Bus.

HEPPTING, LaNia G
South HS; Denver, CO; Rptr, Ann; Drama; Secy, ARC; Rptr, Sch P; SC; Hist A; Hon Prog; Journ A; Honored Qn; Job's Daughters; Brown Belt, Karate; Bowl Tm.

HERBERGER, James Anthony
Alisal HS; Salinas, CA (10%-400) A Cap Choir; Chor; Ensm; Hmrm; NHS; Order/Arrow; ARC; Span C; Var C; Ftbl; Cpt, Swim; COM; Cl Fav; Ntl Achv Schol; Order/Arrow A; St Scholar; MVP, Swim; Ntl Federation; HS Coaches; U of Colo; Archt Engr.

HERBERT, Craig Eugene
Sidney Sr HS; Sidney, MT (32-143) AFS; CYO; Key C; Span C; SC; Var C; Ftbl; All Conf, Ftbl; ND Sch of Sci; Elec Tech.

HERBERT, Donna Louise
Liberty HS; Bethlehem, PA; Ensm; Type A; Shorthand A's.

HERBERT, Glenn Robert
Liberty HS; Bethlehem, PA; Band; Hon Prog; Susquehanna U; Theology.

HERBERT, Kelly Mark
Permian HS; Odessa, TX (100-827) Ger C; SC; Soccer; Swim; Tex Tech U; Bus.

HERBERT, Richard Arden
Sam Houston HS; Lake Charles, LA (4-143) Dbte Tm; Demolay; Fr C; Fin, Lit Ral; Math C; Mu Alpha Theta; Spch C; Opt A; Sci A; Spch A; La Tech U; Elec Engr.

HERBIK, Michael Joseph
Cormichaels Area HS; Carmichaels, PA (2-81) Pres, NHS; Secy, Phys C; Tres, SC; Var C; Bkbl; Co-Cpt, Golf; Tr; Amer Leg A; NEDT; Sal; VFW A; W Va U; Phar.

HERBOLSHEIMER, Tammi Jo
Hartington HS; Hartington, NE (1-36) Ann; Chldr; Chor; Drama; Model UN; Spch C; Pres, SC; Bkbl; Tr; Alg A; Citz A; HQn; Hon Prog; Math A; Sci A; Spch A; Val; Semi-Fin, All GS; Math Contest; Latin A; Drama A; U of SD; Med Tech.

HERBST, John David
Spring Woods Sr HS; Houston, TX (10%-510) JETS; NHS; Bkbl; JV, Tr; Bio A; Hon Prog; JETS St Hon, Math.

HERCHEN, Harald
Grand Trunk HS; Evansburg, CANADA (1-71) Royal Roads Military Col; Elec Engr.

HERD, Judith Ann
Northeast Sr HS; N Little Rock, AR (1-439) Band; Fr C; GS; InterAct C; Pres, Mu Alpha Theta; NHS; Co-Ed, Sch P; Spch C; SC; Y-Tns; DARGCA; H of F; Hon Prog; Most Out; Spch A; Val; NMS Commended Stu; U of Ark; Chem.

HERDER, Susan Jean
Cooper Sr HS; New Hope, MN (84-684) Sch Mus; St Off Ed Assn Off Work Prog; Sunday Sch Teacher; SW St U; Secy Adm.

HERDINA, Thomas Richard
Red Hook Central HS; Red Hook, NY (40-250) Band; St U of NY; Engr.

HERDT, Gayann Christine
W Linn HS; West Linn, OR; FFA A; Oreg Col; Animal Sci.

HEREFORD, Kay Townsend
Hillwood HS; Nashville, TN (10%-200) Pres, Anchor C; GS; Cr-Ctry; Tr; COM; Ed.

HEREIM, Karl I
Highland HS; Salt Lake City, UT (4-430) A Cap Choir; Band; Chor; Dbte Tm; Key C; NFL; Orch; SC; Cr-Ctry; Sftbl; JV, Tr; Citz A; Kiwanis A; Lion A; Region A St Solo & Ensm Festival; Region Dbte & Leg Forum; St Leg Forum, Stu Congress; U of Utah; Mus.

HERGLOTZ, Helen Clair
Ursuline Acad; Wilmington, DE (1-43) A Cap Choir; Chor; Drama; French NHS; NHS; Sch P; Sci C; SC; Thes; Pres, Sr Cl; Tr; Amer Leg A; COM; Hon Prog; Poet A; Rensselaer A; Sacristan; Sci A; Val; 2nd Pl, Fr Contest; U of Dela; Chem.

HERIFORD, Pamela Sue
Shawnee Mission E HS; Shawnee Mission, KS (37-550) A Cap Choir; Chor; NHS; Schol Pin; William Jewell Col; Nurs.

HERING, Ann Marie
Yosemite Union HS; Oakhurst, CA (10-125) Ed, Ann; Drama; Tres, 4H; Hmrm; Model UN; NFL; Co-Ed, Sch P; Span C; Spch C; SC; Alg A; Bio A; COM; Citz A; 4H A; Hist A; Hon Prog; Journ A; Lion A; Math A; PTA A; Sci A; Spch A; Sci.

HERING, Anne Weaver
Tiffin Columbian HS; Tiffin, OH (52-370) Fin, AFS; Ann; Chor; Drama; Hmrm; Span C; Secy, SC; Thes; Var C; Bkbl; Tnns; Tr; HCt; Pres A; WW; Col of Wooster; Pol Sci.

HERING, Lisa Dawn
Shamrock HS; Decatur, GA (18-318) BC; NHS; F-Ed, Sch P; Cpt, Flag Corp; WW; DeKalb Comm Col; Acct.

HERMAN, Angie Dawn
Hibriten HS; Lenoir, NC (20%-250) Drama; Secy, FHA; FTA; Spch C; SC; Tres, Jr Cl; Swim; Tnns; Fashion Design.

HERMAN, Deborah Jill
Riverview HS; Sarasota, FL; Band; Chor; Drama; Ensm; Swim; Tnns; Tr; COM; Interlochen Ntl Mus; Yth Fel; Chor; Drama, Piano A's; Horsemanship; Gainesville Col; Drama.

HERMAN, Lynn Ann
Lutheran HS; La Verne, CA; CSF; Teaching.

HERMAN, Tami Jean
Riverview HS; Sarasota, FL (10-750) Chor; Ensm; Yth Fel; Yth Foundation A; Bible Quiz Tm; Candystriper of Mo; VICA; Nurs.

HERMAN, Thomas Anthony
Williamston HS; Williamston, NC (27-200) Band; Fr C; Monogram; Tr.

HERMANAS, Denis Julius
Gaga Park HS; Chicago, IL (1-625) NHS; Rptr, Sch P; SC; Hon Prog; Star Student; Ill Inst of Tech; Archt.

HERMANEK, Grace Barbara
Dwight D Eisenhower HS; Decatur, IL (78-362) Ann; Ger C; Orch.

318

HERMANN, Debbie Joanne
Wanamingo Pub HS; Wanamingo, MN (17-43) Ann; Band; Chor; VP, Drama; Ensm; Tres, Jr Cl; Secy, Soph Cl; Bkbl; HCt; Type A; Pres, Band Coun; Co-Cpt, Vlbl; Ensm St Comp; *Rochester Comm Col; Mass Media Tech.*

HERMANN, Doug Scott
Wichita HS E; Wichita, KS (25%-500) ARC; Bsbl; *Forestry.*

HERMANSON, David H
Eastbrook HS; Marion, IN (35-200) Mgr, Bkbl; Mgr, Ftbl; *Taylor U; Corporate Law.*

HERMENET, David John
Chrysler HS; New Castle, IN (68%-380) AFS; Chess C; Chor; FBLA; Key C; Order/Arrow; SC; Bsbl; Mgr, Swim; Tnns; COM; JA A; Order/Arrow A; Yth Fel; WW; Bsbl A; *Wabash U; Law.*

HERMES, Dwayne Joseph
Gainesville HS; Gainesville, TX (8-220) Secy, CYO; Drama; VP, NHS; A-Ed, Sch P; Spch C; Pres, SC; Bkbl; Tr; MLS; NEDT; Spch A; Schol A; *N Tex St U; Pol Sci.*

HERNANDEZ, Agueda Caridad
Colegio Santa Rita; Bayamon, PR (2-26) Secy, Span C; Arch; Tnns; Beauty; COM; Hon Prog; Eng A.

HERNANDEZ, Ana Laura
Miami Springs HS; Miami Springs, FL (37-816) *Miami Dade-South Col; Dental Hygiene.*

HERNANDEZ, Arturo Josaphat
Ben Franklin HS; Los Angeles, CA (40%-700) Band; Pres, CYO; Chor; Community Yth Symph; Drama; Ensm; Ger C; Hmrm; Rptr; Lit Mag; Orch; Spch C; Thes; COM; Opt A; Poet A; Spch A; Mus Fest Sup Rating; Pres, Ecology C; *CSU at LA; Mus.*

HERNANDEZ, Camille Ann
Hayden Cath HS; Topeka, KS (30-206) Band; Semi-Fin, GS; Rptr, Sch P; Span C; Sci A; Topeka Sci Sem; Hon Reward, Span Contest; *Ariz St U; Pre-Med.*

HERNANDEZ, Carlos Manuel
William Cullem Bryant HS; Long Island City, NY (273-983) Tres, Hmrm; Lit Mag; Co-Cpt, Bkbl; Co-Cpt, Sftbl; VP, Church Yth; *Bernard M Baruch Col; Bus Adm.*

HERNANDEZ, Diana
Greater New York Acad; New York, NY (12-72) NHS; Alg A; COM; Chem A; Type A; *Columbia Union Col; Phys Therapist.*

HERNANDEZ, Edward Eugene
Los Lunas HS; Los Lunas, NM (28-240) NHS; Bsbl; Bkbl; Ftbl; Tr.

HERNANDEZ, Edwin
Francisco Mendoza HS; Isabela, PR; A Cap Choir; Chor; COM; Hist A; Hon Prog; *U of PR; Natural Sci.*

HERNANDEZ, Gabriel Rico
Belton HS; Belton, TX (14-196) Band; CYO; Hmrm; A-Ed, Lit Mag; NHS; Sch P; SC; Amer Leg A; COM; Chamber of Comm A; Citz A; DARGCA; Hist A; Hon Prog; Journ A; Lion A; Q&S A; Rotary A; Art A; Social Stu A; PE A; Rotary C Swtht; *Southwest Tex St U; Commercial Art.*

HERNANDEZ, Jesus Gregorio
McAdoo HS; McAdoo, TX (4-9) Bkbl; Tr; *S Plains Jr Col; Auto Mech.*

HERNANDEZ, Joanna
Excelsior HS; Norwalk, CA (43-375) Hon Prog; Yth Fel; Church Choir; Church Span & Spch C'S; Mus A; *Pepperdine U; Interior Decoration.*

HERNANDEZ, Lawrence John
John F Kennedy HS; Tumon, GUAM (13-51) Band; JV, Bkbl; Ftbl; COM; *UOG.*

HERNANDEZ, Maria Consuelu
Temple Heights Christian HS; Tampa, FL (8-62) Ann; Drama; VP, NHS; Tres, Sr Cl; S-T, Jr Cl; Bkbl; HQn; HCt; *Southeastern Bible Col.*

HERNANDEZ, Marta Godinez
St Mary's Acad; Inglewood, CA; CYO; Chor; Fr C; Hmrm; ARC; Span C; Bkbl; Sftbl; Tnns; *LA Trade Tech Col; Secy Sci.*

HERNANDEZ, Mary Natalia
Stephen F Austin HS; Houston, TX; VP, CYO; Bkbl; Most Out; ROTC A; Sci A; Sgt at Arms A; *Law.*

HERNANDEZ, Mildred
Adlai E Stevenson HS; New York, NY; Band; Alg A; COM; Citz A; Hist A; Hon Prog; Math A; Sci A; Type A; *Franklin Pierce Col; Law.*

HERNANDEZ, Minerva
David W Carter HS; Dallas, TX; GS; Hmrm; Secy, Span C; SC; ROTC A; Pres, Church Yth Choir; Service A; NJHS; Scholastic Ribbon A; Pan Amer C; Conduct A; Academic Excellence Ribbon A; *Sou Methodist U; Law.*

HERNANDEZ, Nelda
Lydia Patterson Inst; El Paso, TX; S-T, Ann; Chess C; FHA; Bkbl; Tr; Beauty; Art A; *Tex Tech U; Vet Med.*

HERNANDEZ, Oscar Florencio
Quigley South HS; Chicago, IL (1-227) Chem C; Dbte Tm; Hmrm; Math C; Pres, NHS; SC; Var C; Swim; COM; H of F; Hon Prog; Lion A; Math A; Most Out; Ntl Sci Found; Sci A; Star Student; St Scholar; Art As; Eng As; Lat As; WW; Swim Gold Medal; *U of Ill at Urbana; Engr.*

HERNANDEZ, Pablo Gerard
Mendel Cath Col Prep; Chicago, IL (27-165) Span C; COM; Hon Prog; *Chicago St U; Law.*

HERNANDEZ, Ruben
Jose de Diego HS; Mayaguez, PR; Chem C; Dbte Tm; Phys C; Pres, Sci C; St Stu Congress; Var C; Bsbl; Sftbl; Bio A; COM; Summa Cum Laude; *UPR at Mayaguez; Elec Engr.*

**HERNANDEZ,
Saavedra Reinaldo A**
Francisco Mendoza HS; Isabela, PR; A Cap Choir; Band; BS; Chldr; Chor; City Conf; Hmrm; Math C; Order/Arrow; Pol Sci C; ARC; Rptr, Sch P; Span C; Cpt, Bsbl; Cpt, Bkbl; Sftbl; Cpt, Swim; Citz A; Cl Fav; Lion A; Math A; Order/Arrow A; Star Student; Summa Cum Laude; Ldrship A; Instructor A; *U of Puerto Rico; Econ.*

HERNANDEZ, Sandra Kay
Cache HS; Cache, OK (16-46) FHA; Secy, Sr Cl; Bkbl; Masonic A; *Cameron U; Secondary Ed.*

HERNDON, Elizabeth Ann
Bluestone Sr HS; Skipwith, VA (38-260) Fr C; FHA; Rptr, Sch P; Bkbl; Acteens; GAA; Rptr A; *Longwood Col; Lab Tech.*

**HERNDON,
 Jackquelyne Piccola**
Butler HS; Augusta, GA (20%-450) Chor; Ensm; VP, Up Bound; Y-Tns; Bkbl; Sftbl; Tr; Amer Leg A; COM; Cl Fav; Hon Prog; Poet A; *Paine Col; Phys Ed.*

HERNDON, Mary Jane
DeKalb Co HS; Smithville, TN (40-125) Ann; Pres, Band; Chor; Ensm; Pres, FHA; Orch; Sch P; Pres, Jr Cl; Sftbl; 4H A; Journ A; Most Out; Spch A; *Belmont Col; Nurs.*

HERNDON, Sherrie Ann
Warrior Acad; Eutaw, AL (6-26) F-Ed, Ann; Secy, BC; Chldr; Chor; Hmrm; Secy, Math C; SC; Secy, Var C; Secy, Sr Cl; Secy, Jr Cl; Secy, Soph Cl; Beauty; Bio A; HCt; Hon Prog; Sci A; Yth Fel; Chaplain, SC; VIP; *Troy St U; Nurs.*

HERNDON, Tim Allan
Weston-McEwen HS; Athena, OR (4-61) FFA; Hmrm; NHS; Span C; SC; Var C; Tr; Hon Prog; *Anthropology.*

HERNER, Rebecca Jean
Trotwood-Madison HS; Trotwood, OH (8-410) Chor; Drama; Pres, Ger C; NHS; Tr; COM; SMU, Stu Govt; Choir Soloist; Pres, Dist Fed of Ger Cs; Yth For Undrstnding Prog, Germany; *Journ.*

HERNGREN, Curt Howard
Ryan HS; Omaha, NE (35-250) Band; Chor; Dbte Tm; Pres, Demolay; Ensm; 4H; Hmrm; Bsbl; Bkbl; Ftbl; Golf; Mgr, Sftbl; 4H A; Pres A; Ice Skating.

HERNICK, John Thomas
T L Grace HS; Fridley, MN; Ed, Sch P; SC; Bkbl; Cr-Ctry; Tr; Journ A; Sci A; *U of Minn; Journ.*

HEROD, Steve Willis
Perry HS; Perry, OK (15-88) Chor; NHS; Tres, Soph Cl; Bsbl; Co-Cpt, Bkbl; Co-Cpt, Ftbl; Hist A; HCt; Rotary A; Yth Fel; All Dist Ftbl; SW Kans Col Ftbl Schol; *Southwestern Kans Col; Bus Adm.*

HEROLD, Beth Ann
S Allegheny HS; Liberty Boro, PA (133-324) Band; FNA; Y-Tns; Pres, Rainbow; Dist & Region Bands; Mid-E Mus Conf; *Mercy Hospital Sch of Nurs; Nurs.*

HEROLD, Deanna Rae
S Allegheny Sr HS; Liberty Boro, PA; Rainbow; Color Guard; *Pa St U.*

HERON, Hermine Josephine
Crenshaw HS; Los Angeles, CA; Chor; Tnns; Semi-Fin, Chem A; *W Los Angeles Col; Social Worker.*

HERPEL, Georgia Lee
Parkway W HS; Ballwin, MO (5%-650) NHS; Mgr, Swim; Hon Prog; *Med.*

HERPICH, Pamela Lynne
Troy HS; Troy, KS; Pres, Band; Chor; Ensm; 4H; NHS; SC; Secy, Jr Cl; Mgr, Bkbl; Tr; Alg A; B Crocker A; 4H A; HQn; Yth Fel.

HERR, Susan Kay
Conestoga Valley HS; Lancaster, PA (19-302) Ann; Band; Chldr; Chor; Community Yth Symph; Ensm; Mod Mus Mas; NHS; Orch; Sch P; Swim; Mgr, Tr; COM; Gov Honor Prog; Outst Underclass Musician; *Communications.*

HERRBOLDT, Curtis Lee
Yankton Sr HS; Yankton, SD (65-289) BS; Pres, Hmrm; SC; Var C; Bsbl; Cr-Ctry; Ftbl; Tr; COM; Hon Prog; JA A; VofDEM; Yth Fel; *SD St U; Criminal Justice.*

HERRELL, June Denise
Cloudcroft HS; Cloudcroft, NM (9-28) Parl, FFA; Pres, 4H; NHS; Var C; Pres, Jr Cl; Bkbl; Tr; 4H A; Yth Fel; Rodeo Princess; *Bio Sci.*

HERRERA, Chris Lynn
Sidney HS; Sidney, NE (45-109) Bsbl; Ftbl; Tr; Wrest; *Kearney St Col.*

HERRERA, Ernest Jr
Holy Cross HS; San Antonio, TX (52-77) CYO; Tres, SC; JV, Bsbl; Mgr, Bkbl; Co-Cpt, Ftbl; Tr; Church Coun; Pres, Yth C; *San Antonio Col; Mech Engr.*

HERRICK, James Louis
Pleasant Valley HS; Chico, CA (175-350) Ski C; Tnns; *Point Loma Col; Sci.*

HERRICK, John Joseph
Tampa Cath HS; Tampa, FL (25%-300) Bkbl; *Hillsborough Comm Col; Pre-Liberal Arts.*

HERRICK, Karen Lynn
Windham HS; Willimantic, CT (118-330) Band; Chor; Tr; Hist A; PTA A; CCD Teacher; Amer Stu Achv A; *U of Conn.*

HERRICK, Merilee Christine
Kewanee HS; Kewanee, IL (15%-210) S-T, AFS; A-Ed, Ann; Chldr; Chem C; Bus Mgr, Dbte Tm; Ger C; Semi-Fin, GS; Hmrm; Sci C; Spch C; SC; JV, Tnns; Amer Leg A; HCt; Spch A; *Special Ed.*

HERRIN, Donna Lynn
Denham Springs HS; Denham Springs, LA (40-213) Ann; Band; BC; FBLA; FHA; FNA; FTA; Parl, Lit Mag; Parl, NHS; Sci C; Ftbl; Coun of Teach A; 4H A; Hon Prog; Spirit Comm; VP, S-T, 4-H C; *Lady of Lake School of Nursing; Nursing.*

HERRIN, Elizabeth Ann
Jay Co HS; Portland, IN; Band; Hmrm; Mjrte; F-Ed, Sch P; Span C; SC; Y-Tns; Masonic A; Yth Fel; Past Hon Qn, Job's Daughters; *Ball St U; Journ.*

HERRIN, Kelly Jo
Centerville HS; Centerville, TX (5%-40) Band; Chldr; Chor; NHS; SC; *Sam Houston St Col; Bus.*

HERRIN, Rick Levi
N Salem HS; Salem, OR (15%-250) Pres, CYO; SC; Wrest; MIP, Wrest; Most Inspiring, Wrest; Head Choir Boy; *Hist.*

HERRIN, Sandra Ann
Simpson Co Acad; Mendenhall, MS; Hmrm; Math C; St Stu Congress; SC; Bkbl; Sftbl; JV, Tr; Cl Fav; Most Ath; Most Versatile; *U of Sou Miss; Phys Ed.*

HERRING, Albert Augustus
Thomas Jefferson HS; Richmond, VA (15-266)
Band; Chess C; Pres, Key C; Amer Leg A; Hon
Prog; *William & Mary Col; Hist.*

HERRING, Betty Karen
E Side Sr HS; East Saint Louis, IL; Chor; Sch P;
Bkbl; Soccer; Sftbl; Most Out; Sci A; Tn-
Challengers; Vlbl A; 3rd Pl, Art A; Phys Fitness A;
Church As; *Journ.*

HERRING, Bryan Lee
Phil Campbell HS; Phil Campbell, AL (12-72) Pres,
FFA; FTA; 4H; VP, NHS; Sch P; Var C; JV, Bkbl;
Ftbl; Tr; Best Sch Spirit; Scholastic A; Jaycee Schol
A; *Northwest Ala St Jr Col; Civil Engr.*

HERRING, Dave Alan
Ensley HS; Birmingham, AL; Ann; Lat C; Math C;
Ftbl; Golf; *Ala U.*

HERRING, Della J
William Brown HS; Sturgis, SD (10-200) Ed, Ann;
GS; S-T, NHS; Tres, Sr Cl; Amer Leg A; *U of SD.*

HERRING, Evan Lowell
Glenwood Sch Inc; Phenix City, AL (10%-78)
Band; BC; BS; Chor; Pres, Church Yth Fel; All St,
SE St Hon, Bands; *Birmingham Sou Col; Eng Ed.*

HERRING, Jill Renee
Lima Sr HS; Lima, OH (12-507) Chor; Drama;
Ensm; Hmrm; SC; COM; Yth Fel; NEDT; Piano
Sonatina A; Choir Accompanist; Church Mus
Comm Ch; Published Essay in Ntl Anthology; *An-
derson Col; Mus.*

HERRING, Johnna Lenelle
Edisto HS; Cordova, SC (1-120) Chldr; Chor; HiY;
Fin, Jr Miss Pagent; Lit Mag; VP, NHS; Sch P; Var
C; Bkbl; Beauty; Bio A; DARGCA; Gov Honor
Prog; HCt; Interlochen Ntl Mus; Journ A; Sci A;
Spch A; Fin, Hugh O'Brien Found; Miss Charm;
Clemson U; Journ.

HERRING, Kristin Joyce
S Dade HS; Homestead, FL (10%-1000) Ann;
Band; Co-Cpt, Mjrte; Model UN; NHS; Rainbow;
Swim; Order of Schol.

HERRING, Maureen Denise
Bolton HS; Alexandria, LA; Band; VP, Chor;
Hmrm; VP, Mod Mus Mas; Rainbow; SC; Y-Tns;
HCt; Hon Prog; Hon Choir; *Baylor U; Mus.*

HERRING, Paul Edward
Belmond HS; Belmond, IA; BS; Chor; NHS; Or-
der/Arrow; Var C; Secy, Soph Cl; Bsbl; Bkbl; Ftbl;
Golf; God & Country A; Order/Arrow A; Eagle
Sct; *Iowa St U; Architecture.*

HERRING, Retha Rochelle
Warren HS; Warren, AR (9-144) A Cap Choir;
MVP, Band; Chor; Ensm; Madrigal; Mjrte; Secy,
NHS; Secy, BC; WW; Most Outst Majorette; Hon
Stu; Jr Auxilary Schol; Beta C Schol; All Religion
Band; All-Religion All St Choir; *Ouachita Baptist
U; Spch Pathology.*

HERRING, Shirley Janelle
Starkville HS; Starkville, MS (5%-300) Band; Chor;
Ensm; FBLA; NHS; Tres, Span C; Type A; St Fin,
Sword Drill; Superior, Piano Festival; Band Solo
Contest A; Superior, Ntl Piano Playing Aud; *Med.*

HERRING, Waman June
John F Kennedy HS; Tumon, GUAM (33-511)
NHS; Alg A; COM; Citz A; Hist A; Sci A; Lang
Arts A; PA; HR; Home Ec A; *Oral Roberts U;
Med.*

HERRING, Wendy Yvonne
Oglethorpe Co HS; Lexington, GA (3-102) A-Ed,
Ann; Pres, BC; Dbte Tm; Rptr, Fr C; FBLA; GS;
4H; Lit Ral; Pres, Sci C; Tri-HiY; Alg A; Bio A;
Hon Prog; I Dare You; Math A; NEDT; Star Stu-
dent; Top 10% Sr Cl.

HERRING, William George
Metamora Township HS; Metamora, IL (36-193)
BS; NHS; SC; Var C; Cpt, Bsbl; Bkbl; Amer Leg A;
Ill Central Col; Acct.

HERRINGTON, Craig Eugene
Robertwood Johnson HS; Gainesville, GA
(175-350) Fr C; Key C; Opt A; *Gainesville Jr Col;
Graphic Arts.*

HERRINGTON, Denise
N Natchez Adams HS; Natchez, MS; BC; Hist A;
Hon Prog; Bookkeeping A; *Alcorn St U; Acct.*

HERRINGTON, Gerald Eric
Morgan Park HS; Duluth, MN; S-T, AFS; Tres,
Band; Chess C; Pres, Hmrm; Model UN; Spch C; Pres, SC; *U
of Minn; Ed.*

HERRINGTON, Rodney James
W Jones HS; Laurel, MS (10%-176) BC; Chess C;
Chor; VP, Ger C; Math C; Mu Alpha Theta; VP, Sci
C; Span C; Chem A; Citz A; Hist A; MLS; Pres,
Church Choir; Explorers; *Miss St Col; Petroleum
Engr.*

HERRIOT, Kim Sonolie
Central HS; Newark, NJ; *North Carolina Central
Col; Sociology.*

HERRMAN, Karen Jean
McHenry Comm HS; McHenry, IL (66-465) AFS;
Sch P.

HERRMANN, Brenda Jeanne
Gladewater HS; Gladewater, TX (10%-161) Lit
Mag; NHS; Art C; WW; 3rd, Dist Shorthand Con-
test.

HERRON, Kimberly Ann
Thomasville HS; Thomasville, AL (20%-105) BC;
Chldr; Ensm; FHA; 4H; Lat C; Cl Fav; 4H A; *Early
Child Development.*

HERRON, Linda Diane
Twin Lakes HS; Monticello, IN (50-230) Mjrte;
Span C; Tres, Hist C; *Secy.*

HERRON, Linda Pearl
Los Angeles HS; Los Angeles, CA; Drama; Tr; Ad-
vanced Career Trng Cert; Banking Cert; *Trade
Tech Col; Bus.*

HERRON, Marietta Verna
North HS; Nashville, TN (35-200) Bus C; VP,
Drama; Hmrm; Sch P; Spch C; SC; Y-Tns; Bsbl;
Tnns; COM; Hist A; Hon Prog; *Middle Tenn St U;
Bus Adm.*

HERRON, Patricia Ann
Spearville HS; Spearville, KS (10-25) Bus Mgr,
Ann; Band; Chldr; Fr C; Secy, FBLA; Rptr, Sch P; I
Dare You; *Dodge City Jr Col; Elem Ed.*

HERRON, Shawn Marie
Acad of Our Lady of Mercy; Louisville, KY (1-79)
Y-Tns; B Crocker A; *U of Louisville; Eng.*

HERSCHEID, Janelle Lee
Stanton Pub HS; Stanton, NE; Ann; VP, Band;
CYO; Chor; Drama; FHA; Tres, 4H; Sch P; SC; 4H
A; Pep C; Mus A.

HERSEMANN, Eliza Ann
E Peoria Comm HS; E Peoria, IL; Community Yth
Symph; Ensm; VP, Fr C; Math C; NHS; Pres, Orch;
COM; St Scholar; VP, Orch; Sterling Merit A;
WW; Top 10; *Augustana Col; Psych.*

HERSH, David Forrest
Paramus HS; Paramus, NJ (2-598) VP, NHS; Tnns;
Math A; MLS; Sal; *John Hopkins U; Chem.*

HERSH, Doreen Renee
Campus HS; Wichita, KS (16-248) A Cap Choir;
Co-Ed, Ann; Chor; Ensm; FHA; Madrigal; ARC;
Secy, Sci C; Sci A; Dist & All St Choir, KMEA;
Wichita St U; Mus.

HERSHBERGER, John Edward
Wheat Ridge HS; Wheat Ridge, CO (1-650) Band;
Drama; Ger C; NHS; Ski C; Hon Prog; Math A;
NMF; NMS; Phy A; Sci A; Yth Fel; Math, Sci
Seminar; *Cal Tech; Math.*

HERSHEY, Eric Wayne
Columbia HS; Columbia, PA (9-171) Band; Hmrm;
NHS; Order/Arrow; Span C; Secy, SC; Wrest; *Bio.*

HERSHEY, Renee Jeanette
Tulpehocken HS; Bernville, PA; Chor; Rptr,
FBLA; Hmrm; NHS; SC.

HERTEL, Martin Elliott
Taft HS; Chicago, IL (300-800) A Cap Choir; Chor;
Dbte Tm; Drama; FBLA; COM; PTA A; *Luther
Col; Religion.*

HERTELY, Joan E
G A R Mem HS; Wilkes-Barre, PA (1-190) Band;
FTA; NHS; ARC; Semi-Fin, Tr; Hon Prog; Sci A;
Ger A; *Pa St U; Med Tech.*

HERTENSTEIN, John W
Santa Monica HS; Santa Monica, CA (293-819)
Chldr; Drama; Ger C; Hmrm; Ski C; SC; *San Diego
St Col; Psych.*

HERTING, Kathryn Adele
N Plainfield HS; N Plainfield, NJ (80-230) Band;
Swim; 1st Cl, Sct A; All Sports Qn Court; S-T,
Church Yth; *Kutztown Col; Social Work.*

HERTLE, Daniel Dale
Armstrong Sr HS; Plymouth, MN (212-600) Or-
der/Arrow; ARC; Order/Arrow A; ARC A; *Pillsbury Bapt Bible Col; Bible.*

HERTWECK, Susan Paige
Hardaway HS; Columbus, GA (25%-410) Pres,
Anchor C; Secy, Ger C; Hmrm; Model UN; Mu
Alpha Theta; VP, SC; *Med.*

HERTZ, David Eldon
Herscher HS; Herscher, IL (1-221) Band; Lat C;
Orch; Amer Leg A; *U of Ill; Med.*

HERTZFELDT, Janet Kay
Highland Sr HS; Highland, IN (136-580) Chor;
Ensm; FHA; JV, Bkbl; Ftbl; Hon Prog; Ch, Yth
Banquet; Pres, Church Yth; Booster C; GAA; *Trng
Systems Inst; Bus.*

HERUTH, Doug Lee
Brooklyn Center HS; Brooklyn Center, MN
(30-200) Tres, NHS; Var C; Bsbl; Cpt, Bkbl; Ftbl;
HCt; All Conf Ftbl & Bkbl; FCA; *Hamline U.*

HERVEY, Rosetta Dyanne
Fern Creek HS; Louisville, KY; A Cap Choir; Chor;
FBLA; Pres, Hmrm; Jr Miss Pagent; Model UN;
Mod Mus Mas; ARC; Up Bound; Hon Prog; JA A;
Most Out; Spch A; St Scholar; Yth Fel; Cpt, Gym;
PA; Adden Voice A; Fashion Design A; Best
Dressed; Outst Personality; *Eckerd Col; Fashion
Designing.*

HERWECK, Kathy L
Kirkwood Sr HS; Kirkwood, MO (19-588) A Cap
Choir; Ensm; Hon Prog; HR; *SE Mo St U; Home
Ec.*

HERZOG, Jack Wade
Cleveland HS; Seattle, WA; Band; Ftbl; *George
Fox Col; You Adm.*

HESLER, Melissa Anne
Notre Dame-Bishop Gibbons HS; Schenectady,
NY; NHS; Hon Prog; NHS A; *St Bonaventure U;
Biol.*

HESS, Cynthia Lynne
Aldine Sr HS; Houston, TX (20%-500) A Cap
Choir; Chor; Ensm; FHA; FTA; Hmrm; Madrigal;
Mjrte; Swim; Yth Fel; *Tex A&M U; Fashions.*

HESS, David Lowell
Aldine Sr Ms; Houston, TX (25%-650) BS; Bsbl;
Cpt, Ftbl; Swim; *Air Force Acad; Sci.*

HESS, David Ray
Danville Comm HS; Danville, IN (8-138) BS; Ftbl;
Tr; Wrest; Chamber of Comm A; Math A; *Purdue
U; Elec Engr.*

HESS, Ilene June
Big Valley Jr-Sr HS; Bieber, CA; Ann; Band; Chor;
Secy, FFA; Ntl Yth Conf; Var C; Bkbl; Ftbl; JV, Tr;
Bank Of Amer A; Chamber of Comm A; Citz A;
4H A; Pres A; Mgr, Vlbl; Pres, VP & Secy, 4-H C;
Agr A; FFA A; *Chico St Col; Forestry.*

HESS, James Edward
Humboldt HS; Humboldt, TN (24-175) Bkbl; Chiz
A; Playmaker A; St Tourn Tm; *Tenn St U; Biol.*

HESS, Kathleen Ann
Owego Free Acad; Owego, NY (5-309) AFS;
Chldr; VP, Fr C; Mjrte; NHS; Tres, SC; Regent
Schol; NML; *SUNY at Albany; Acct.*

HESS, Kathleen Ann
Bloom Township HS; Chicago Heights, IL
(137-661) Band; Drama; NHS; SC; VP, Sr Cl; Bkbl;
Sftbl; Tr; *Ill St U; Social Welfare.*

HESS, Kenneth Ray
Manheim Central Sr HS; Manheim, PA (60-300)
BS; SC; JV, Tnns; Hist A; Hon Prog; Civil Service
Exam Merit A; *US Coast Guard Acad; Chem.*

HESS, Kimberly Frederica
Ironton HS; Ironton, OH (16-191) Fr C; GS; NHS;
Sch Achieve Tm; Pres, SC; Cpt, Bkbl; Sftbl; Sports
Ed, Ann; MVP, Bkbl; Pres, MVP, GAA; Cpt, Vlbl;
Marshall U; Ed.

HESS, Mary Patricia
East Ridge HS; Kankakee, IL (10%-320) Chor;
Drama; Madrigal; Swim; Lion A; *Math.*

HESS, Rebecca Sue
Greencastle-Antrim HS; Greencastle, PA; FBLA; Church Quiz Tm; Jr Choir; Fin, Typing A; Yth Group; *Secretarial.*

HESS, Sharon Edith
Lexington Sr HS; Lexington, NE (21-150) Band; Chldr; Chor; Rptr, FHA; Rptr, 4H; 4H A; Yth Fel; WW; HR; Cl Offices; *U of Nebr; Bus.*

HESSE, Ann Marie
Lyman Mem HS; Lebanon, CT (1-100) CYO; Pres, Fr C; GS; Secy, NHS; Amer Leg A; Chem A; JA A; Yth Foundation; Fr A; *Trinity Col; Pre-Med.*

HESSELBERG, Jeri Lee
La Farge HS; LaFarge, WI (2-24) Ann; Band; Chldr; Chor; Drama; Tres, FHA; Madrigal; Math C; NFL; NHS; Orch; Phys C; Secy, Jr Cl; Secy, Soph Cl; Tr; Arion A.

HESSELGRAVE, David Owen
Nyack HS; Nyack, NY; Band; InterAct C; Orch; Order/Arrow; Ski C; Hockey; Soccer; Lacrosse; *Aviation.*

HESSEY, Brian Keith
Wynford HS; Bucyrus, OH (38-105) FFA; Key C; Var C; Bsbl; Ftbl; COM; Sci A; *Ed.*

HESSLER, Carol Anne
Tatnall HS; Wilmington, DE (20%-68) A Cap Choir; Bus Mgr, AFS; Band; Chor; Dbte Tm; Drama; Lat C; Rptr, Sch P; Ski C; Secy, SC; Swim; Tnns; Tr; Beauty; HCt; Hon Prog; Outward Bound; All St Chor; *Amherst Col; Pol Sci.*

HESSONG, John Joseph
Northbrook Sr HS; Houston, TX (150-578) Band; Chess C; Hmrm; Sci C; SC; Pres, Y-Tns; VP, Tres, Church Yth Organization; Church Choir; Gold Medal of Achv, Royal Rangers; Rep, Frontiersman Camping Fratern; *U of Houston; Criminology.*

HESTER, Deborah Lynn
Mathiston HS; Mathiston, MS; Ann; Pres, BC; Pres, FHA; MLS; VofDEM; Most Intellectual; Mus Schol; HR.

HESTER, Dorothy Jean
Ft Pierce Central HS; Ft Pierce, FL; Bus C; Chor; FBLA; Hmrm; Ed, Sch P; St Stu Congress; Co-Ch, Soph Cl; Citz A; PA; Phys Fitness A; Sch Service Worker Teacher's Aide; Athletic Directors Aide; *U of Miami; Sociology.*

HESTER, Joe Bob Jr
Groveton HS; Groveton, TX (2-54) Rptr, BC; Pres, Span C; Mgr, Ftbl; Golf; *Drama.*

HESTER, Joseph David
Ramsay HS; Birmingham, AL (2-145) Band; Ensm; NHS; Rptr, Sch P; Cl Fav; Sal; Fresh Bk, Royal Ambas Serv, A's; *U of Ala; Hist.*

HESTER, Kalen Elizabeth
Boone HS; Boone, IA (24-210) 4H; Cpt, Cr-Ctry; Tr; Christmas Dance Qn; Schol Hon Soc; All St, Cr-Ctry; *Iowa St U; Ed.*

HESTER, Laura Ann
Pompano Bch HS; Pompano Bch, FL (55-530) Band; Hmrm; Key C; Lat C; NHS; Orch; Co Solo And Ensm A; *Jackson Mem Sch of Nurs; Nurs.*

HESTER, Lawrence Frederick
Bosse HS; Evansville, IN; *Olivet Col; Construction.*

HESTER, Lindsey Matthew
Groveton HS; Groveton, TX (3-54) Pres, Band; Tres, BC; A-Ed, Sch P; Span C; Tnns; *N Tex St U; Computer Tech.*

HESTER, Milton Mark
Norcross HS; Norcross, GA (3-240) BC; InterClub Coun; Tres, NHS; Bus Mgr, Sch P; Pres, SC; VP, Jr Cl; Bsbl; Bkbl; Ftbl; COM; Cl Fav; PC Jr Fellow; *Math.*

HESTER, Sandra Dawn
Crockett HS; Crockett, TX; Band; 4H; 4H A; World Geography A.

HESTER, Sue Ellen
John T Haggard HS; Wilmington, NC (25-650) Fr C; Hmrm; Soph Cl; COM; Citz A; Cl Office; *Campbell Col; Acct.*

HESTER, Terri Louvenia
West Union HS; Pinola, MS; Ann; Rptr, FBLA; SC; Sftbl; Beauty; Bio A; HCt; *Hinds Jr Col; Bus.*

HESTERBERG, Dean Louis Ralph
Valmeyer HS; Valmeyer, IL (3-38) Bus Mgr, Ann; Pres, Band; VP, Chor; 4H; Math C; NHS; Orch; JV, Bsbl; Cl Fav; 4H A; St Scholar; WW; *Sou Ill U; General Acad Stu.*

HESTERBERG, Sandra Sue
Rantoul Twp HS; Rantoul, IL (16-387) Chor; Secy, Fr C; *Wartburg Col; Elem Ed.*

HESTERMAN, Beth Ann
Glenbard S HS; Glen Ellyn, IL (63-305) Chor; Madrigal; Mgr, Pom Pon; *Concordia Teachers Col; Elem Ed.*

HESTERMAN, Nathan Donald
Valley Forge Sr HS; Parma Hts, OH (15%-750) Band; Ensm; Orch; Highest Hon; *Kent St U; Forestry.*

HETHERINGTON, Laurel Ann
Hinsdale Central HS; Hinsdale, IL (40%-600) Chor; Ski C; Thes; Variety Shows; Discovery; Operetta; Sch Play; Stu Rep, Church Mus Board; Pres, Church HS Choir; *Ohio Wesleyan U; Eng.*

HETICO, Hope Rachel
Glenbrook HS; Glenview, IL (55-597) Chor; Ensm; NHS; SC; Cl Fav; *Nurs.*

HETLAND, Penny Doreen
Crookston Central HS; Crookston, MN (5-200) Drama; NFL; Spch C; *Law Enforcement.*

HETRICK, Julie Lynne
Fremont Ross HS; Fremont, OH; A Cap Choir; Chor; Pres, 4H; Select Trio; Jr Choir Director; *Otterbien Col; Mus.*

HETSLER, Perry Guy
Keystone HS; LaGrange, OH (1-125) NHS; Bsbl; Ftbl; Hon Prog; *Mount Vernon Nazarene Col; Bus.*

HETZEL, Mark Scott
Purcell HS; Cincinnati, OH (48-191) Fr C; SC; Mgr, Tr; Hon Prog; Sacristan; Good Samaritan Safety Tm; Teacher of CCD A; *Animal Husbandry.*

HEUCHERT, Allen Carl
St Thomas HS; St Thomas, ND (4-16) Band; BS; Chor; Ensm; FFA; 4H; SC; VP, Jr Cl; Bsbl; Bkbl; Ftbl; 4H A; Bookkeeping A; Greyhound Hon Stu; MIP, Bkbl; Hon Men, All-Conf Ftbl; Ntl Baberuth A; *Agr.*

HEUCHERT, Shirley Jean
St Thomas HS; St Thomas, ND (1-18) Ed, Ann; Band; Chor; Drama; GS; Mgr, Bkbl; Type A; Interntl Mus Camp; Grey Gown; Ntl Sci Found; *U of ND; Computer Sci.*

HEUER, Lorinda Susan
Wyanet HS; Wyanet, IL (7-24) Ed, Ann; Mjrte; NHS; Span C; Spch C; SC; Pres, Thes; Tr; HQn; Spch A; VofDEM; Vlbl; Bicentennial Qn; *Ill Valley Comm Col; Psych.*

HEUER, Margo Rae
Harris-Lake Park Comm Sch; Lake Park, IA (5-36) Band; Chldr; SC; Parl, Sr Cl; JV, Bkbl; Sftbl; Tr; Hon Prog; Type A; *Mankato St U; Social Work.*

HEUER, Mary Lynn
Waupun HS; Waupun, WI (15-285) AFS; Band; Ensm; GS; Pres, 4H; NHS; Ski C; SC; Thes; Pres, Var C; Bkbl; 4H A; JA A; *U of Wis; Phys Therapy.*

HEUER, Steven Charles
Niagara Wheatfield Sr HS; Sanborn, NY (18-420) NHS; Tr; Hist A; NEDT; Sci A; Eng A; *SUNY at Buffalo; Chem Engr.*

HEUN, Terri Lynn
Holy Rosary Acad; Louisville, KY (13-86) JV, Chldr; Secy, Hmrm; NHS; Rptr, Sch P; *U of Louisville; Biological Sci.*

HEUPEL, Lavonne Joan
Medina Pub HS; Medina, ND (1-24) Ann; Band; Chldr; Chor; Ensm; FHA; GS; VP, 4H; Co-Ed, Sch P; Sftbl; B Crocker A; 4H A; Type A; Val; Yth Fel; WW; Angus Princess; *Jamestown Col; Optometry.*

HEUSCHKELL, Lisabeth Ann
Spring Woods HS; Houston, TX (190-530) AFS; Chor; FHA; NHS; Span C; Cr-Ctry; Tr; Yth Fel; *SW U.*

HEUSER, Christi Linn
Perry Meridian HS; Indianapolis, IN (178-538) Cpt, Chldr; Drama; FBLA; Hmrm; Span C; Pres, SC; HCt; ARC A; Type A; Yth Fel; GAA; Yth Congress; VP, Tres, SC; Bstr C; Secretarial Practice A; Service A.

HEVERLY, Jan-Sue
Kohala HS; Kapaau, HI (2-78) Band; Pres, 4H; NHS; VP, Span C; Cr-Ctry; Sftbl; Tr; HCt.

HEWELL, Gailyn
George Walton Acad; Monroe, GA (7-30) Ann; Chor; Pres, 4H; Jr Miss Pagent; Span C; Bkbl; COM; 4H A; JA A; *Ga Sou Col; Orthodontist.*

HEWELL, Janice Elizabeth
Northside HS; Atlanta, GA (41-350) BC; Fr C; FBLA; Hmrm; *Ga Sou Col; Law.*

HEWETT, Daniel Frank
Thomas B Doherty HS; Colorado Springs, CO (25-425) NHS; Secy, VICA; Computer C; VICA Statesman A; *U of Colo; Elec Engr.*

HEWGLEY, Sandra Marie
McMinn Co HS; Athens, TN; Tres, Anchor C; Chldr; NHS; Ski C; Tri-HiY; HCt; Type A; Yth Leg; Key C Calendar Girl; *U of Tenn.*

HEWITT, Cynthia Marie
Plymouth HS; Plymouth, NC (60-190) Band; Co-Cpt, Chldr; Drama; Sci C; Span C; Tnns; *St Mary's Col; Mus.*

HEWS, Mark Edward
Langley HS; McLean, VA; Ger C; Cr-Ctry; Tr; MYF; Rugby; *U of Maine; Agr.*

HEWTON, Joan Candace
Melbourne HS; Melbourne, FL; SC; Cr-Ctry; Swim; Pres A; Keyettes; Tres, JA; *Ga Sou Col; Ed.*

HEYD, Wendy Kay
Liberty Jr-Sr HS; Liberty, PA (5-54) Band; Chldr; Ensm; FHA; Ger C; Secy, Soph Cl; Schol A.

HEYER, Walter Thomas
Crawford Co R II HS; Cuba, MO (33%-77) Band; Chor; FFA; Pres, 4H; Bsbl; Citz A; 4H A; Yth Pastor; 4-H A's; Courier Schol; FFA A's; Yth Conservation A; *SW Baptist Col; Christianity.*

HEYLER, Donna Marie
Liberty Jr-Sr HS; Liberty, PA (5-54) Band; Chor; Ensm; Ger C; Band A.

HEYLIGER, Anthony Alonzo
Brooklyn Tech HS; Brooklyn, NY (700-1296) Hmrm; COM; NMS; *U of Del; Chem Engr.*

HEYMAN, Sarah T
Taylor Allderdice HS; Pittsburgh, PA; Arch; Chor; Drama; Model UN; Orch; Y-Tns; Cr-Ctry; Tr; COM; Hon Prog; Pres A; *Washington U at St Louis; Bio.*

HEYMANN, Nikki Elaine
Mission HS; San Fernando, CA; Co-Ed, Ann; Hmrm; Sch Achieve Tm; Sch P; Sci C; VP, SC; VP, Sr Cl; Citz A; Journ A; Star Student; *Art.*

HEYNE, Yvonne P
Lincoln Way HS; New Lenox, IL; Ski C; Span C; *Evangel Col.*

HIATT, Daniel Lester
Inglemoor HS; Bothell, WA (18-359) Band; NHS; Co-Cpt, Tnns; I Dare You; Masonic A; Drum Major; WW; *U of Wash; Natural Sci.*

HIATT, Malcolm Edward
Benson Polytech HS; Portland, OR (240-400) Pres, Church Yth Grp & Chapel Choir; *Forestry.*

HIBBARD, Amy Marie
Whitney Point Sr HS; Whitney Point, NY (8-160) Band; Chor; Drama; Fr C; 4H; Hmrm; VP, InterAct C; NHS; Ski C; Tr; COM; 4H A; Alt, Regents Schol; *Broome Comm Col; Med Lab Tech.*

HIBBITT, Michele Elizabeth
Denison Sr HS; Denison, TX (25%-380) FHA; Hmrm; NHS; ARC C; VP, Y-Tns; Tnns; ARC A; Yth Fel; *U of Tex; Med.*

HIBBITTS, Edna Katherine
Midland HS; Midland, TX (18-692) Ch, Span C; JV, Tnns; DARGCA; Hon Prog; 1st Cl Sct; Sr Planning Bd; Episcopal Young Churchmen; Acolytes.

HIBNER, John Anthony
Coldwater HS; Coldwater, OH (15-150) Secy,
CYO; Chem C; Chor; Drama; Span C; Tres, Jr Cl;
JV, Bkbl; Ftbl; *Ohio St U.*

HICKENBOTAM, Cena Ray
Crestview HS; Crestview, FL (10%-300) Band;
Hmrm; Rptr, Sch P; Secy, SC; COM; Cl Fav; HCt;
Archt.

HICKENBOTHAM, Lynn Kaye
Choctawhatchee HS; Ft Walton Beach, FL
(27-650) BC; Chor; NHS; Chaplain, Tri-Hi-Y; Mus
Hon; Guitarist Assn; Physics A.

HICKERSON, Sarah Ann
Finneytown HS; Cincinnati, OH (20-245) Tres,
Chor; Ensm; Secy, NHS; Secy, SC; Fin, Sr Cl;
COM; Math A; Lat As; Amer Hist A; Choir Med-
als; *U of Cincinnati; Nurs.*

HICKERSON, Scott Stuart
Mooresville HS; Mooresville, IN (6-310) Math C;
Sci C; JV, Bsbl; Cr-Ctry; Tr; Order/Arrow A; VP,
FCA; *Engr.*

HICKERSON, Steven Craig
Round Rock HS; Round Rock, TX (50%-300)
FFA; 4H; Order/Arrow; Pres, Sr Cl; Bkbl; Ftbl; Tr;
Order/Arrow A; *Baylor U; Bus.*

HICKERT, Dianne Louise
Lenora HS; Lenora, KS (1-22) Pres, CYO; Co-Cpt,
Chldr; Chor; Drama; Mjrte; NHS; Secy, Jr Cl; Pres,
Soph Cl; Math A; Spch A; *Benedictine Col.*

HICKEY, Beth Ann
Bedford Area HS; Bedford, PA (66%-245) 4H;
Hmrm; Rainbow; Pres, Soph Cl; Co-Cpt, Bkbl;
Mgr, Sftbl; 4H A; *Pittsburgh U; Eng Ed.*

HICKEY, Margaret Mary
Beaver Dam Sr HS; Beaver Dam, WI (7-330) AFS;
Bus Mgr, Ann; Band; Chldr; Tres, Chor; Ensm;
Secy, GS; 4H; Hmrm; Co-Ed, Sch P; Ski C; Span C;
Var C; JV, Swim; Tnns; St Forensics; *Marquette
Col; Med.*

HICKEY, Susan Margaret
Bedford HS; Bedford, PA (29-250) Rainbow; SC;
Bkbl; Sftbl; Hon Prog; *Penn St U; Archt Engr.*

HICKEY, William Thomas
Leo HS; Chicago, IL (14-140) Hmrm; NHS; F-Ed,
Sch P; SC; Bsbl; Bkbl; Cr-Ctry; Ftbl; Hon Prog; K of
C A; *Bus.*

HICKLIN, Arthur Vernon
Harrah HS; Harrah, OK (25-130) Chor; Ensm;
FFA; Tres, SC; Cpt, Bsbl; Co-Cpt, Bkbl; Co-Cpt,
Ftbl; Tr; COM; Spch A; MVP, Bsbl & Bkbl; Pres,
FCA; All St Bsbl; All City, Bsbl & Bkbl; *Okla Bap-
tist U; Religion.*

HICKMAN, David Paul
Kickapoo HS; Springfield, MO (30%-214) Band;
Community Yth Symph; Orch; Golf; Swim; SB
Pres; *Southwest Mo St U; Engr.*

HICKMAN, Jameye Lynn
Picayune Mem HS; Picayune, MS; Chldr; Pres,
Chor; Ensm; FHA; Hmrm; NHS; Sch P; Span C;
Spch C; SC; Fin, Sr Cl; Bsbl; Sftbl; COM; Cl Fav;
Best All Around; Most Talented; Pres, Church Yth;
U of Miss; Phys Therapy.

HICKMAN, Jo Ann
Cedar Bluff HS; Cedar Bluff, AL; BC; Secy, FHA;
Math C; F-Ed, Sch P; Cl Fav; HQn; Pep C; Pres,
Lib C; Vlbl; Highest Avg.

HICKMAN, L Winn
Denison HS; Denison, TX (25%-435) Ftbl; *Baylor
U; Bus.*

HICKMAN, Pamela Faye
Columbus Pub HS; Columbus, ND (4-20) Bus Mgr,
Ann; Band; Chor; Ensm; Bkbl; Tr; Hon Choir; Hon
Stu; St & Dist Mus Solo; *Concordia Col at Moor-
head; Mus.*

HICKMAN, Valeria Michelle
Eastside HS; Taylors, SC; A Cap Choir; CYO;
Chor; Tr; *Med.*

HICKMAN, Zarata Octavia
Woodbridge HS; Bridgeville, DE; Chor; FNA; 4H;
Span C; Spch C; Up Bound; Var C; Cpt, Bkbl;
Hockey; Cpt, Sftbl; Citz A; HCt; Sci A; Spch A;
Ath, Singing, A's; Personality, Ldrship, A's; *Psych.*

HICKMOTT, Gail Ann
Palo Duro HS; Amarillo, TX (7-285) Bus C; Pres,
FBLA; S-T, NHS; Math A; Type A; 1st St, FBLA
Data Processing; *Amarillo Col; Computer Sci.*

HICKOM, Scott Eric
Cartersville HS; Cartersville, GA (1-201) Hmrm;
SC; JV, Cr-Ctry; Pres, Yth Fel.

HICKORY, William Raymond
Glendale HS; Springfield, MO (130-412) Band;
Chess C; Ensm; Hmrm; Bsbl; Sftbl; Tnns; Wrest;
Ed, Sr High Church Yth Paper; VICA; Outst Drftg
Stu Schol; 1st Pl, Dist Archt Drftg; 2nd Pl, St Con-
test Archt Drftg; *Southwest Mo St U; Architecture.*

HICKS, Amy Catherine
Reeltown HS; Notasulga, AL (1-35) Ann; VP,
Band; BC; FHA; 4H; VP, SC; COM; Math A; Type
A; Gayfer Girl; Bicentennial Belle; Eng A; *Ala
Christian Col; Communications.*

HICKS, Billy Gerald
Claiborne Acad; Haynesville, LA; Ftbl; *NE La Col;
Art.*

HICKS, Carol Annette
Bauxite HS; Bauxite, AR (6-32) Bus Mgr, Ann;
S-T, Band; Secy, FBLA; FHA; Parl, FTA; Tres,
NHS; Sch P; Sci C; VP, Span C; Tres, SC; Pres, Sr
Cl; VP, Jr Cl; Fin, Bkbl; Sftbl; Cl Fav; Hon Prog;
NEDT; Spelling A; Ann Staff A; Stu Coun A;
Ouachita Baptist U; Art.

HICKS, Catherine Diane
Homewood HS; Birmingham, AL (11-250) *Jacksonville St U; Secy.*

HICKS, Christina Maria
Tyner HS; Chattanooga, TN (1-261) Pres, BC;
Chor; Drama; Fr C; GS; Model UN; Tres, NHS;
Ed, Sch P; SC; Cl Fav; Hist A; Hon Prog; Journ A;
Math A; MLS; Most Out; PTA A; Spch A; Star
Student; Val; Secy, Civinettes; CC Burgner, Princi-
pal's Sch, A's; *U of Tenn; Communications.*

HICKS, Connie Frances
Woodbridge HS; Bridgeville, DE (69-120) Co-Cpt,
Band; VP, Bus C; Chor; Drama; VP, FBLA; 4H;
ARC; Up Bound; 4H A; Hist A; ARC A; *Del Tech
& Comm Col; Secy.*

HICKS, Dawn Laraine
New Brighton Area HS; New Brighton, PA; Band;
Lat C; Orch; ARC; Thank You Trophy; 10 Yr GS
Pin; GS A; *Civil Engr.*

HICKS, Elizabeth Jean
Lakeland Christian Sch; Lakeland, FL; Chor; Pres,
Rainbow; Pres, Jr Cl; Masonic A; Grand Rep, St
Rainbow Girls; Most Improved, Outst Ability,
Mus.

HICKS, Henry William
Pickens HS; Pickens, WV (1-15) Drama; NHS;
Bkbl.

HICKS, Jacqueline
W Side HS; Newark, NJ; A Cap Choir; Drama;
Mjrte; Bkbl; Director, Chor; Most Lady Like; *Drew
U; Bus Adm.*

HICKS, James Monroe III
Edgewood Acad; Elmore, AL (10-24) BC; Hmrm;
SC; Var C; Pres, Soph Cl; JV, Bkbl; Ftbl; Cl Fav;
Auburn U; Marine Biol.

HICKS, Karen Sue
John Ehret HS; Marrero, LA (54-550) Pres, 4H;
ARC; VP, SC; Bio A; Chem A; 4H A; Journ A;
Math A; ARC A; Sci A; Scholastic A; *Touro Sch of
Nurs; Nurs.*

HICKS, Kevin Randoll
Queens Voc HS; Long Island City, NY; City Conf;
Drama; Orch; Bkbl; Ftbl; Sftbl; Tr; COM; Citz A;
Math A; *Syracuse U; Communications.*

HICKS, Kristi Dell
First Assembly Christian Sch; Memphis, TN
(4%-32) Lat C; Sftbl; Mgr, Tr; *Med.*

HICKS, Linda Sue
Boardman HS; Boardman, OH (266-602) A Cap
Choir; Ensm; Bkbl; Sftbl; Off Church Yth Group;
Most Improved, Bkbl; *Phys Ed.*

HICKS, Lowell Leonard
Strasburg HS; Strasburg, CO (4-28) NHS; SC; Bsbl;
JV, Bkbl.

HICKS, Michelle Lee
St Mary's Acad; Inglewood, CA; Drama; Ch, SC;
Cpt, Gym; Comm Serv A; Phys Ed A; SC A; HR;
Cal St at Long Beach; Police Sci.

HICKS, Peggy Ann
John L McClellan HS; Little Rock, AR; Band;
Chor; Drama; NFL; Beauty; Miss Congeniality; *U
of Ark.*

HICKS, Sharon Doloris
Kensington HS; Buffalo, NY; Chor; Drama; ARC;
Cpt, Tr; Phys Fitness A; Cert For Modeling; *Canis-
ius Col; Bus Adm.*

HICKS, Sherron Pertrice
Beaumont HS; St Louis, MO (60-742) Chor; Sci C;
Tnns; MLS; Sci A; Popularity; Jr Sword Drill; Ntl
Heart Assn; *Wash U; Med.*

HICKS, Tammy Denise
Hart Co HS; Hartwell, GA; Anchor C; Band; BC;
VP, Hmrm; Secy, Tri-HiY; Bkbl.

HICKS, Tammy Lynn
Carl Junction HS; Carl Junction, MO; Cum Laude
Soc; Math C; Bookkeeping, Frisbee, A's.

HICKS, Valerie Elizabeth
Ashbrook Sr HS; Gastonia, NC (295-510) Band;
UNC-Charlotte; Photography.

HICKSON, David James
Mt Gilead HS; Mt Gilead, OH (14-164) A Cap
Choir; Band; Chor; Pres, Demolay; Ensm; Fr C;
4H; VP, Key C; NHS; Sch Achieve Tm; Thes;
Chem A; Hon Men, Ohio St Achv Test; *Chem.*

HICKSON, Pamela Joy
Charles F Brush HS; Lyndhurst, OH (10%-650)
AFS; Co-Ed, Ann; Band; Drama; Hmrm; Orch;
Pres, Sci C; SC; Alg A; COM; Hon Prog; NEDT;
Sci A; Pres, UMYF; OMEA Cert; *Mount Union
Col; Sci.*

HICOK, Amy L
Peoria HS; Peoria, IL (48-450) NHS; ARC; Span C.

HIDA, Susan Elizabeth
Wauwatosa W HS; Wauwatosa, WI (25-444) AFS;
Ed, Ann; Band; Mu Alpha Theta; NHS; Orch;
Rptr, Sch P; Pres, Swim; COM; Wellesley Book A;
Spirit A; WW; Sup A, St Mus Contest; *Purdue U;
Civil Engr.*

HIDY, Paula Sue
Westside HS; Omaha, NE; A Cap Choir; Chor;
Ensm; Pres, 4H; Tr; Alg A; COM; 4H A; Math A;
Pres A; Mus As; Art As; *Elem Ed.*

HIDY, Terri Lynn
Miami Trace HS; Washington C H, OH (10-275)
Band; FFA; GS; Secy, 4H; Tres, NHS; Sci C; JV,
Tr; Spch A; FFA Ldrship A; Horse Production A;
Ohio St U; Vet Med.

HIE, Kie Kiong
Concordia HS; Oakland, CA; ARC; Swim; Tnns;
Iowa St U; Engr.

HIEATT, Janova Buckley
Franklin Co HS; Frankfort, KY (25%-430) Parl,
Band; Sci C; Span C; Span NHS; Sftbl; Secy, Ju-
niorettes; WW; *William Woods Col; Equestrian
Stu.*

HIEBERT, Robert Edwin Jr
Abilene HS; Abilene, KS (10%-165) Band; Chor;
Order/Arrow; Ftbl; 4H A; Directors A, Highest
Band Achv.

HIEHLE, Gregory Jackson
Findlay Sr HS; Findlay, OH (103-600) Band; Chor;
Parl, SC; COM; Most Outst Cadet, Civil Air Patrol;
Class 'A' Encampment; *US Air Force Acad; Aero-
Engr.*

HIEHLE, Mark Alan
Findlay HS; Findlay, OH; Band; Chor; Swim; Yth
Fel; *Sci.*

HIEMENZ, Louise Anne
Eden Valley-Watkins HS; Eden Valley, MN
(5-125) A Cap Choir; Ann; Band; Chor; Drama;
Ensm; Pres, FHA; 4H; Orch; Sci C; Spch C;
Pres, Jr Cl; VofDEM; Jr Rep, Band; Dist Pres,
FHA; St Mus Star, Solo & Dist Ensm; St Instru-
mental Stars; Drama A; *St Benedict Col; Hist.*

HIEMENZ, Mary Margaret
Eden Valley-Watkins Pub Sch; Eden Valley, MN (4-102) Ann; Pres, Band; Chor; Drama; Secy, FHA; Ger C; 4H; S-T, NHS; Orch; Rptr, Sch P; Ski C; Var C; COM; H of F; Hon Prog; Interlochen Ntl Mus; Journ A; ARC A; Spch A; House of Rep HS Page; Drama C, Choir & Band A's; *Col of Saint Benedict; Mus.*

HIER, Matthew R
Wethersfield HS; Kewanee, IL (25-108) Band; Drama; Bsbl; Bkbl; Ftbl; Tr; *Bradley Col; Engr.*

HIERS, Peter Leslie
P K Yonge Lab Sch; Gainesville, FL (1-74) Cpt, Band; Community Yth Symph; Hmrm; Span C; Span NHS; VP, SC; VP, Sr Cl; Pres, Soph Cl; JV, Bsbl; COM; Hon Prog; Outst Bandsman; Span C Ser A; 1st Chair Tuba, Fl All St Con Band; *U of Fla.*

HIERS, Rita Kay
Echols Co HS; Statenville, GA (4-42) BC; FHA; Hmrm; InterClub Coun; Ed, Sch P; SC; VP, Jr Cl; Bkbl; Hon Prog; Outst Fresh, Best Defense, Bkbl; *Valdosta Area Vo-tech Sch; Executive Secy.*

HIETBRINK, Steve Douglas
Norris Dist 160 HS; Firth, NE (30-83) Band; Chor; St Stu Congress; Bsbl; Co-Cpt, Bkbl; Cr-Ctry; Ftbl; COM; HKg; Yth Fel; Yth Leg.

HIGA, Megumu John
Kubasaki HS; Okinawa, JAPAN (8-355) Ann; Chess C; Lit Mag; NHS; Bsbl; Cpt, Bkbl; Cr-Ctry; Soccer; COM; Citz A; Gym A; Photo C; Schol Bowl Tm; Vlbl; Eng A; Philsophy C; Phys Sci A; Ger A; *Stanford U; Biochem.*

HIGA, Sheldon Yoshimi
Laupahoehoe HS; Laupahoehoe, HI (5-39) Sci C; Tnns; *Hilo Col.*

HIGDON, Denise Marie
Delavan Comm HS; Delavan, IL; Band; Chor; Ensm; Co-Ed, Sch P; Band A.

HIGER, Kristyn Jane
Pocatello HS; Pocatello, ID (69-500) Chor; NHS; Thes; Cl Fav; Soph Senator; Wilderness C; Off, Jobs Daughters; Best Dressed; Flagteam; Amer Harp Soc; *Performing Arts.*

HIGGENBOTTOM, Wanda Partrice
Independence HS; Independence, MS (15%-72) Ed, Ann; Band; BC; VP, FBLA; FHA; *Nurs.*

HIGGINBOTHAM, Julie Lynn
Webster Groves HS; Webster Groves, MO; Band; Chldr; SC; Soccer; Cpt, Vlbl.

HIGGINBOTHAM, Karen Lee
East HS; Columbus, OH (20-400) Fr C; Semi-Fin, NHS; JA A; Pres, JA; *Ohio St U; Engr.*

HIGGINBOTHAM, Kay Lynn
East HS; Columbus, OH;

HIGGINBOTHAM, Malinda Sue
Maryville R-II HS; Maryville, MO (1-135) Band; Ensm; SC; Type A; Best Marchr, Most Sprit, Ltr, Band.

HIGGINS, Angela Patricia
Libbey HS; Toledo, OH (3-301) Lat C; NHS; *Spellman Col; Med Tech.*

HIGGINS, Carey Shannon
Salem Sr HS; Salem, OH (110-325) AFS; Fr C; InterAct C; *Kent St U; Ed.*

HIGGINS, Cathy Jo
Tuscola Comm HS; Tuscola, IL (5-118) Ann; Band; FHA; Lat C; NHS; Rainbow; Hon Prog; Rotary A; *Parkland Col; Radiological Technology.*

HIGGINS, Don Jr
HS of Music and Art; New York, NY (65-525) Band; Fr C; HiY; Orch; Sci C; Cr-Ctry; Tr; Cl Fav; MLS; *Bio Sci.*

HIGGINS, Frank Leonard
Crestview Sr HS; Crestview, FL (23-247) Var C; Mgr, Ftbl; Hon Prog; ROTC A; VFW A; Presidential Nomin to West Point; *US Military Acad; Law.*

HIGGINS, George Andrew
Williston Northampton HS; Easthampton, MA (49-130) Arch; Band; VP, Chor; Lat C; Thes; JV, Ftbl; JV, Hockey; JV, Tnns; Yth Leg; Excel, Theatre Tech Aspects; *Bowman Tech Sch; Clock Making & Restoring.*

HIGGINS, Karen Eileen
Belvidere HS; Belvidere, IL (7-365) A Cap Choir; Chor; NHS; Amer Leg A; *Fla U; Mus Therapy.*

HIGGINS, Kenneth Milton Jr
Hillsdale HS; San Mateo, CA (318-458) Pres, A Cap Choir; Ch, BS; Pres, Chor; Ensm; VP, FBLA; Hmrm; NHS; Ntl Yth Conf; SC; Bkbl; Tnns; Co-Cpt, Wrest; Bank Of Amer A; Citz A; MLS; Most Out; Yth Fel; Yth Leg; *Baylor U; Retailing & Selling-Merch.*

HIGGINS, Linda Kay
Switzerland Co HS; Vevay, IN (6-137) FHA; Span C; Sci A; Eng A; HR; *Elem Ed.*

HIGGINS, Lori Beth
Athens HS; The Plains, OH; Band; 4H; Mjrte; Rainbow; Tr; 4H A; Bible Bowl; 1st Cl, GSct; *Ohio U; Ed.*

HIGGINS, Robin Lynn
N Gwinnett HS; Suwanee, GA (15%-120) Co-Ed, Ann; Chor; Dbte Tm; Co-Ch, FHA; 4H; ARC; Span C; Pres, SC; COM; Cl Fav; Gov Honor Prog; 4H A; VofDEM; 4-H Key A; WSB Young Amer; Miss Barker; *Gainsville Jr Col.*

HIGGINS, Roderick Dwayne
Thornton Township HS; Harvey, IL; *Bradley U.*

HIGGINS, Sandra Claudette
Libbey HS; Toledo, OH; Lat C; Arch.

HIGGINS, Sherry Ann
Adai Co R II HS; Brashear, MO (10%-17) A Cap Choir; Co-Ed, Ann; Chor; Ensm; VP, FHA; NHS; Thes; Var C; Tres, Jr Cl; Secy, Soph Cl; Bkbl; Sftbl; Tr; Cl Fav; HQn; HCt; WW; Yrbk Qn; Dist Contest.

HIGGINS, Teri Lynn
Madison Heights HS; Anderson, IN (20-375) Chor; Hmrm; Lat C; NHS; SC; Hon Prog; Lat A; *Ball St U; Bus.*

HIGGINS, Terri Lynn
Chase HS; Forest City, NC (8-160) Ed, Ann; BC; Bus C; Chem C; Fr C; FBLA; Secy, FHA; FNA; Bus Mgr, FTA; Secy, Hmrm; Monogram; Sci C; Bkbl; Cpt, Tnns; COM; Kiwanis A; Most Out; Fr A; Jr Marshal; *U of Va; Engr.*

HIGGINS, Thomas James
Ogemaw Heights HS; W Branch, MI (5%-260) A Cap Choir; Band; Chor; Community Yth Symph; Ensm; Hmrm; NHS; Orch; Ski C; Span C; Var C; Co-Cpt, Golf; Co-Cpt, Swim; Tr; Hon Prog; NMS; Order/Arrow A; Yth Fel; WW; General Mills Search for Ldrship; *Albion Col; Mus Ed.*

HIGGS, Dennis Edwin
Jupiter Christian Sch; Jupiter, FL (3-18) Ed, Ann; BS; Chor; Dbte Tm; Ensm; 4H; Hmrm; NHS; Rptr, Sch P; Pres, Jr Cl; Coun of Teach A; 4H A; Spch A; VP, Pep C; Pres, Prayer C; Lib A; *Palm Beach Atlantic Col; Ed.*

HIGGS, Joyce Lorene
Franklin D Roosevelt HS; Dallas, TX; Chldr; Chor; SC; COM; Hon Prog; NMF; ROTC A; Yth Fel; HOCT; *E Tex St U; Bus.*

HIGH, Arenda Jo
Christian Heritage Acad; Oklahoma City, OK; FHA; VP, Hmrm; Bkbl; Alg A; Cl Fav; Hist A; HCt; Math A; Pres A; Sci A; 1st, Essay; Bible A; Eng A.

HIGH, Deborah Jeannette
Azusa HS; Azusa, CA (97-313) Chor; Phys C; Cpt, Hockey; Tnns; Phy A; Cpt, Vlbl; Cpt, Badminton; *Covina Beauty Col; Cosmetologist.*

HIGH, Martha Joan
Whitmer HS; Toledo, OH (33-900) Band; S-T, Chor; Community Yth Symph; Pres, Ensm; InterClub Coun; Secy, NHS; Secy, Orch; VP, Thes; Hon Prog; Ntl Sch Orch A; Outst Choir Sr A; *Miami U-Ohio; Mus.*

HIGH, Marvona Gale
Green Forest HS; Green Forest, AR; Bus C; FBLA; FHA; Beauty; COM.

HIGHFILL, Michael Allen
Westen Hgts HS; Oklahoma City, OK; Parl, Band; FTA; Sch P; Citz A; Yth Fel; Yth Leg; Supt's HR; Principal's HR.

HIGHSMITH, William Samuel
W J Woodham HS; Pensacola, FL (4-530) Mu Alpha Theta; NHS; Span C; COM; Hon Prog; NMF; NEDT; Phy A; *Rice U; Elec Engr.*

HIGHT, Janet Kay
Statesboro HS; Statesboro, GA (2-355) Band; Bus C; FBLA; Pres, FHA; Pres, 4H; Secy, HiY; Hmrm; Lat C; Model UN; Span C; Spch C; SC; COM; Citz A; 4H A; JA A; Kiwanis A; Spch A; Yth Fel; WW; St Bus C A; *Ga Sou Col; Home Ec.*

HIGHT, Kathryn Jean
Terry Sanford HS; Fayetteville, NC; Chor; Drama; Secy, Hmrm; Lat C; Sch P; Tri-HiY; Pres, Methodist Yth Fel; Lat A; Distinguished Service A; Dramatic A; *U of NC at Greensboro; Special Ed.*

HIGHT, Regina Ann
Dongola Unit Sch; Dongola, IL (3-23) BC; FHA; Pres, FTA; 4H; NHS; Sci C; SC; Tres, Sr Cl; Secy, Jr Cl; Sftbl; 4H A; Hon Prog; Pres A; Sci A; Type A; Eng A; *Shawnee Jr Col; Nurs.*

HIGHTOWER, Andrea Jo
Shawnee Mission S HS; Overland Park, KS (33%-750) A Cap Choir; Chor; Ensm; Rainbow; Sci C; COM; Yth Fel; Chanterelles; Grand Cross of Color; Demolay Princess; Grand Page, Rainbow Girls; *Fashion Merchandising.*

HIGHTOWER, Cynthia Denise
John L McClellan HS; Little Rock, AR (33%-625) Chor; FBLA; Sci C; *Ouachita Baptist U.*

HIGHTOWER, Grethia
Edward Tilden HS; Chicago, IL (96-408) Chldr; Chor; Bkbl; Tr; COM; All City Chor; Mus A; *Sou Ill U.*

HIGHTOWER, Kathy Frances
Whitehouse HS; Whitehouse, TX (2-106) NHS; Bio A; *Computer Prog.*

HIGLEY, Deanna Faith
Oceanside HS; Oceanside, CA (68-407) Chor; Drama; Handbell Choir; Drill Tm; Gym.

HIGLEY, Helen Marie
St Mary's Regional HS; Lynn, MA (7-117) Ann; CYO; Rptr, Sch P; Co-Cpt, Swim; Tr; Alg A; Hon Prog; MVP, Swim; Secy, Jr Cath Daughters; Religion, Eng, A's; Photography C; Judicial Board; *Boston Col; Pre-Med.*

HILAND, Tami Maria
Northern Chester Co Voc-Tech Sch; Phoenixville, PA; Chor; Co-Ed, Sch P; SC.

HILBURN, Curtis R
Harrah HS; Harrah, OK; All Amer Yth; Tr; All-Amer, HS; Ath o-t Yr.

HILBURN, Holly Jean
Broadway Baptist HS; Houston, TX (2-17) Secy, Sci C; Tr; Sci A; Type A; Art C; Ftbl Swtht; Lieutenant, Drill Tm; Cpt, MVP, Vlbl; Hon Soc; *U of Houston; Acct.*

HILDEBRAND, Kathy Marie
Immanuel HS; Reedley, CA (1-83) A Cap Choir; Band; Chldr; Chor; S-T, 4H; Ski C; Tres, SC; Soph Cl; Bkbl; Cr-Ctry; MVP, Tr; CSF; 4H A.

HILDEBRAND, Linda Joann
Immanuel HS; Reedley, CA (1-91) Chor; Pres, 4H; Ski C; Mgr, Tr; CSF; 4H A; Spch A; Tres, Fresh Cl; *Med.*

HILDEBRANDT, Lisa Dawn
Harrodsburg HS; Harrodsburg, KY (9-84) Ed, Ann; Tres, BC; Sch Achieve Tm; Span C; Spch C; Mgr, Bsbl; Sci A; *Western Ky U.*

HILDEBRANDT, Mary Lise
Grimsley HS; Greensboro, NC (3%-500) Fr C; Orch; Soccer; Hon Prog; NMF; Yth Fel; *U of NC* Orch; Church Choir; *U of NC; Bio.*

HILDEBRANT, Brian Joseph
Doland HS; Doland, SD (1-34) Band; Semi-Fin, BS; CYO; Chor; Ensm; Madrigal; Amer Leg A; Most Out; Type A; All St Band & Chor; *Northern St U; Acct.*

HILDEBRANT, Lorna Caree
Moultrie HS; Moultrie, GA (10%-369) Anchor C; Co-Cpt, Band; Secy, BC; Chldr; Ch, Hmrm; Key C; Span C; SC; Secy, Tri-HiY; COM; Cl Fav; VP, Beta C; Local Schol A; WW; HR; *Ga Sou Col.*

HILDERBRAND, Merri Beth
Oroville HS; Oroville, WA (1-48) Ann; Band; Chor; NHS; A-Ed, Sch P; Ski C; SC; Secy, Jr Cl; Tr; Elk A; Q&S A; Val; Comm Princess, Ann May Festival; Pres, Art C; Pep C; 1st, Co Girls Single Badminton Trn; *Seattle Pacific U; Social Sci.*

HILDERBRAND, Myrna Darlene
Owyhee HS; Owyhee, NY (5-25) Parl, FBLA; Tres, FHA; Sch P; Bkbl; B Crocker A; Fleischman Schol; *Bacone Col; Bus.*

HILDRETH, Douglas Alan
Del Rio HS; Del Rio, TX (15-500) Ann; Semi-Fin, BS; Chor; Citz A; Span A; *U of Tex at Austin; Acct.*

HILDRETH, James Floyd
Big Walnut HS; Sunbury, OH (60-189) Band; VP, FFA; FHA; Pres, 4H; Pres, FFA; St & Star Chapter Degrees, FFA; *Ohio St U; Agr.*

HILDRETH, Jeffrey Charles
Charlotte Cath HS; Charlotte, NC (10-100) Tres, CYO; NHS; Hon Prog; *NC St U; Engr.*

HILDRETH, Susan Mary
J E B Stuart HS; Falls Church, VA (90-450) Secy, Chor; Drama; Madrigal; NHS; *VPI; Landscape Horticulture.*

HILDRETH, Terri Lynn
Tuscaloosa HS; Tuscaloosa, AL (29-561) Pres, FBLA; Pres, Hmrm; Mu Alpha Theta; NHS; Span C; *Auburn U.*

HILE, Gary Wayne
Pacifica HS; Garden Grove, CA (211-648) Wrest; Hon Prog.

HILEMAN, Kathy Joanne
Williamsburg Comm HS; Williamsburg, PA (25%-65) Ann; Chldr; Tres, FNA; GS; Ed, Sch P; Tres, Sr Cl; Var C; Bkbl; Ftbl; I Dare You; Journ A; Lion A.

HILEMAN, Lorri Beth
E L Bowsher HS; Toledo, OH; Hmrm; NHS; Ski C; Pres, Span C; Tnns; HCt; Hon Prog; Summa Cum Laude; Principal's A, Excel in School; *Wellesley Col; Pol Sci.*

HILES, Ronald Matthew
Hightstown HS; Hightstown, NJ (114-298) Drama; Tres, Lat C; SC; DARGCA; Hist A; VofDEM; Win, Ntl Landmark Search; *Mercer Co Com Col; Art.*

HILGART, James Edward
Batavia HS; Batavia, IL; Band; Drama; Lat C; Math C; NHS; Alg A; Hon Prog; Math A; St Scholar; St Lat Contest; *U of Ill; Engr.*

HILGENBERG, Becky Jean
Crestview Sr HS; Crestview, FL; Secy, Anchor C; Band; BC; Tres, SC; COM; Type A; Shorthand & Filing A; *Okaloosa-Walton Jr Col; Bus.*

HILGENDORF, Amy Parker
Minneapolis Lutheran HS; Minneapolis, MN; Ann; Band; Drama; Rptr, Sch P; JV, Bkbl; JV, Golf; JA A; *Social Work.*

HILGENDORF, Mary Elizabeth
Tuscola Comm HS; Tuscola, IL (3-118) Co-Ed, Ann; Dbte Tm; T/C, Ach Achieve Tm; Sch P; Spch C; Secy, Soph Cl; Hon Prog; Rotary A; Graduation Marshal; *U of Ill; Acct.*

HILGENDORF, Norman Alan
Lyons Township HS; La Grange, IL (70-1185) Band; Orch; Order/Arrow; JV, Soccer; Hon Prog; Kiwanis A; NEDT; Order/Arrow A; Eagle Sct; *Environmental Sci.*

HILGENDORF, Steve John
Cottage Grove HS; Cottage Grove, OR (55-300) Rptr, Sch P; Bsbl; JV, Bkbl; Ftbl; Phys Ed A; HR; *Broadcasting.*

HILGER, John Franklin
W Aurora Sr HS; Aurora, IL (170-300) Chess C; Yth Fel; Chess A; *Gulf Coast Bible Col; Bio.*

HILKER, Darla Lou
Littlestown HS; Littlestown, PA (29-150) Math C; NHS; Church Choir; Littonian; Yrbk Staff; Pres, Christian Endeavor; Pep C; Gym Ldrs C.

HILL, Alice Louise
Kiski Area Sr HS; Vandergrift, PA (10-525) Tri-HiY; Pep C; PA; Secy, PARC Yth Group; S-T, Church Yth Group; Acad Top 10; *Chem.*

HILL, Alisa Dawn
Sacramento HS; Sacramento, CA (100-482) CSF; Journ A; Sewing A; News Ed Trophy; *U of Calif; Acct.*

HILL, Audrey Elaine
Merced Union HS; Merced, CA; Black Stu Union; ROP Child Care; *Merced Community College; Business.*

HILL, Audrey Lynn
Sturgis HS; Sturgis, SD (2-240) Band; Chor; Fr C; Hmrm; Madrigal; Sci C; SC; Tnns; Alg A; COM; Math A; NMS; Hon Qn, Jobs Daughters; *SD St U; Interior Design.*

HILL, Brenda Kaye
Fairhope HS; Fairhope, AL (200-400) Band; Yth Fel; *Faulkner Junior College; Interior Decorator.*

HILL, Carol Ann
Waynoka HS; Waynoka, OK (3-35) Parl, FHA; GS; Pres, 4H; Sci C; Spch C; SC; Bkbl; Citz A; Gov Honor Prog; 4H A; Hist A; Hon Prog; MLS; Spch A; S-T, 4-H C; SC Rep; Art, 4-H Farmers Union, A's; *NW Okla St U.*

HILL, Carolyn Virginia
Walter Hines Page HS; Greensboro, NC (5%-700) Drama; French NHS; Hmrm; InterClub Coun; Pres, Key C; Ed, Lit Mag; Secy, NHS; ARC; Ski C; SC; Tnns; Hist A; Hon Prog; Poet A; Star Student; VP, Church Yth Fel; Yth o-t Mo; WW, City Yth; Poem Pub, NC Eng Teacher Mag; HR; *U of NC.*

HILL, Catherine Marion
Cleveland Heights HS; Cleveland Heights, OH (25-850) Chor; Swim; Hon Prog; Church Deacon; Biol.

HILL, Cathy Lynn
Gale-Ettrick-Trempealeau HS; Galesville, WI (1-123) A Cap Choir; Chor; Drama; Pres, 4H; NFL; NHS; SC; Math A; Ntl Sci Symposium; Val; Cpt, Color Guard; Fin, Curling; Tres, Lib C; Spoon A; Tres, Ecology C; JV Vlbl; *U of Wis; Engr.*

HILL, Celecia Lynn
Chipley HS; Chipley, FL (12-126) Ann; Band; Chor; Secy, FNA; FTA; NHS; F-Ed, Sch P; Var C; Rptr, Y-Tns; Tr; Beauty; Hon Prog; *Free Will Baptist Bible Col; Psych.*

HILL, Charles O'Neal
Meade Sr HS; Ft Meade, MD (15%-503) Sci C; JV, Wrest; Life Sct; Aviation Careers C; Church Yth Choir; *US Air Force Acad; Aeronautics.*

HILL, Cheryl Lynn
Wheaton-Warrenville HS; Wheaton, IL (24-356) AFS; Fr C; Cpt, Mjrte; NHS; Y-Tns; Swim; JV, Tnns; Amer Leg A; Chamber of Comm A; Hon Prog; Jr Chamber of Com A; Kiwanis A; Lion A; ARC A; *Purdue U; Sci.*

HILL, Claudia Gladys
Reeds Spring HS; Reeds Spring, MO (25%-90) BC; Tres, FHA.

HILL, Clifton Jr
Banks Co HS; Homer, GA (25%-62) 4H; HiY; Var C; Bkbl; Cl Fav; *Gainesville Jr Col.*

HILL, Connie Jean
Horseheads HS; Horseheads, NY (44-578) Chor; NHS; Sci C; Span C; JA A; JA Engr Day; *Alfred Agr and Tech Col; Acct.*

HILL, Constance La Treaste
Carroll HS; Monroe, LA (5%-160) Chldr; Drama; Fr C; Hmrm; Spch C; SC; HCt; Hon Prog; YES C; *Sou U; Speech & Hearing Pathology.*

HILL, Cynthia Louise
Pulaski Academy; Little Rock, AR (1-47) Ann; VP, BC; Ensm; FBLA; GS; NHS; SC; Pres, Y-Tns; Cl Fav; HCt; Val; Stu Activities Comm; Bkbl Swtht; Cpt, Drill Tm; Sr Sch A; Spirit A; VP, FCA; Best All Around, Sr Cl; Sou Method't U; Lang. Nt Alumni Sch; *Sou Methodist U; Lang.*

HILL, Cynthia Sue
Columbus HS; Columbus, IN; Hmrm; SC; Swim; COM; F-Ed, Sch P; Swim A; Singing A; *Evangelist.*

HILL, Darren Wayne
Fair Park HS; Shreveport, LA (41-345) BS; FFA; Cr-Ctry; Tr; Citz A; Delta Sigma Theta A; Hon Prog; *Bishop Col; Med.*

HILL, David
Motley HS; Columbus, MS (15-70) BC; Ftbl; *Miss St U; Elec Engr.*

HILL, David Houston Jr
Fairview Alpha HS; Coushatta, LA (1-31) 4H; Fin, Lit Ral; *Northwestern St U; Forestry.*

HILL, Debbie Sue
Forbush HS; East Bend, NC (30-290) Ann; Band; Chor; FTA; Hmrm; Mjrte; Monogram; Span C; Span NHS; Pres, SC; VP, Jr Cl; Pres, Soph Cl; Cpt, Sftbl; MVP, Tnns; Citz A; HCt; Most Out; Swtht; *High Point Col; Humanities.*

HILL, Deborah Lynn
Durant HS; Durant, OK; Chldr; Dbte Tm; Secy, Hmrm; Key C; Spch C; SC; Bkbl; Sftbl; Swim; MVP, Chldr.*

HILL, Debra L
Jackson HS; Jackson, MI (61-395) Bus C; Chor; Drama; S-T, Ski C; VP, MYF; Mgr, Girl's Gym; *Western Mich U; Bus Adm.*

HILL, Debra Loraine
Robt E Lee HS; Montgomery, AL (7-607) Chor; Ensm; Madrigal; Mu Alpha Theta; NHS; *U of Montevallo; Mus.*

HILL, Diane
Suffolk HS; Suffolk, VA; F-Ed, Ann; FHA; Semi-Fin, GS; NHS; SC; Pres, Sr Cl; Yth Fel; *Va Commonwealth U; Social Work.*

HILL, Donald Wayne
Washington HS; Sioux Falls, SD (5%-750) HiY; JV, Ftbl; Sftbl; JV, Tr.

HILL, Donna Lynn
York Comp HS; York, SC (5-272) Band; VP, FTA; V-Ch, Hmrm; InterClub Coun; NHS; Span C; Gr Marshal; HCt; Jr Cl Steering Comm; Co-Cpt, Color Guard; *Furman Schol; Clemson U; Bus Adm.*

HILL, Doris Fay
Stone HS; Wiggins, MS (80-210) 4H; Y-Tns; Sftbl; Tr; 4H A; *Eckerd Col; Nurs.*

HILL, Douglas Everitt
Campolindo HS; Moraga, CA (50%-350) Sci C; CSF; Yth Fel; MGM Prog; Hon Soc; *Sci.*

HILL, Edward Irving
Dell City HS; Dell City, TX (2-18) Dbte Tm; Drama; Secy, FFA; Pres, NHS; Ed, Sch P; Spch C; VP, SC; Var C; Bkbl; Ftbl; Tr; FFA A; All-Dist Ftbl; *UNM; Med.*

HILL, Elizabeth Ann
Columbus HS; Columbus, GA (10%-300) Chor; Ensm; Lit Ral; NHS; Accomp, Sch Chor & Church Yth Chor; *Columbus Col; Elem Ed.*

HILL, Elizabeth Ellen
Rutledge HS; Rutledge, TN (10%-170) Band; BC; Rptr, Chem C; FHA; HCt; Tr; 4H A; HCt; Outst Home Ec A; Best Frosh, Soph, Band; *U of Tenn; Vet Sci.*

HILL, Fred Earl
Ringgold HS; Ringgold, GA (11-229) VP, BC; VP, FFA; SC; MVP, Bsbl; MVP, Bkbl; Ftbl; Cl Fav; FCA A; *Phar.*

HILL, Georgette Casandra
Chicago Voc HS; Chicago, IL (150-670) Hon Prog; Type A; Film A; *U of Wisc; Mass Communications.*

HILL, Gerald Edwin Jr
Pinckneyville Comm HS; Pinckneyville, IL (18-133) Ann; NHS; Var C; Mgr, Bsbl; Ftbl; Hon Prog; WW; *Rend Lake Col; Drafting.*

HILL, Gordon Madison
Campbell HS; Smyrna, GA (100-200) SC; Pres, Jr Cl; B Crocker A; Cl Fav; Most Out; St Yth Conf; *Columbia Bible Col; Ministerial.*

HILL, Greg Paul
Lafayette HS; Lafayette, LA (20%-750) Band; FBLA; Order/Arrow; Bkbl; Life Sct; *USL; Acct.*

HILL, Hal Eugene
Dobyns-Bennett HS; Kingsport, TN (5-410) Band; VP, BC; VP, Lat C; NHS; Bkbl; Tnns; Hon Prog; MLS; *Pre-Med.*

HILL, Holly Anne
Alabama Sch of Fine Arts; Birmingham, AL (13-30) Band; Community Yth Symph; 4H; Orch; B'Ham Childrens Theatre; Church Drama Productions; ASFA Play; All-Co Band; 3rd Pl, Regional Sci Fair; *Drama.*

HILL, Jacqueline Ruth
Washington Sr HS; Sioux Falls, SD; Band; Bus C; FBLA; 4H; Span C; Tr; Mus As.

HILL, James Russell
United Township HS; E Moline, IL (1-750) Hon Prog; Acad Achv A; Top Quizzer; *Olivet Nazarene Col; Acct.*

HILL, James William Jr
Robert F Munroe HS; Quincy, FL (10-33) Ann; Demolay; Drama; Tnns; Most Talented; Boy o-t Month; *Stetson U.*

HILL, Jamie Irene
Lutheran HS; New Orleans, LA (7-50) SC; Secy, Jr Cl; Hon Prog; Vlbl; *Art.*

HILL, Janet Rose
Union Co HS; Morganfield, KY (20-230) Band; FBLA; FHA; NFL; NHS; Spch C; COM; Spch A; Type A; Fr A; Shorthand A; Home Ec A; Band A; *Western Ky U; Bus Adm.*

HILL, Jeanine Marie
Ellet Sr HS; Akron, OH (84-379) A Cap Choir; VP, Band; Chor; Semi-Fin, Ensm; Hmrm; Madrigal; NHS; Secy, SC; Citz A; HCt; Swtht; Schol A; PA; NHS A; Drum Ensm Excel A; *U of Akron; Bus Adm.*

HILL, Jeanne Gresham
Page HS; Greensboro, NC; Lat C; Lit Mag; Tnns; Inkling Staff; Soph Rep; Keywanetts; Interntl C.

HILL, Jeffrey Hudlow
Silver State Baptist HS; Denver, CO (50%-54) A Cap Choir; Band; Chor; Rptr, Sch P; Ftbl; Cl Fav; *W Bible Col; Bible.*

HILL, Jesse Mike
Phillips HS; Phillips, TX; Band; Hmrm; SC; JV, Bsbl; JV, Bkbl; JV, Ftbl; Golf; Amer Leg A.

HILL, Joan Elaine
Chopticon HS; Morganza, MD (3-307) Sch P; DARGCA; Sci A.

HILL, John Leroy
Ambridge Area HS; Ambridge, PA (154-476) AFS; Chor; VP, Drama; Ensm; FTA; Hmrm; Madrigal; Order/Arrow; ARC; Bus Mgr, Sch P; Span C; Spch C; SC; Thes; God & Country A; Journ A; Spch A; VofDEM; Yth Fel; Eagle Sct; Jr Sct Master; District Yth Coun; *US Navy.*

HILL, Julie V
Sky View HS; Smithfield, UT (5-611) Secy, Chess C; Chor; Dbte Tm; Lit Ral; Model UN; NFL; Sch Achieve Tm; Foreign Exchange Stu; *Brigham Young U; Sci.*

HILL, Karen Vetrica
Jones Co HS; Gray, GA; Sch P; Cl Fav; *Fla St U; Bus.*

HILL, Karl Geoffrey
Sutter Union HS; Sutter, CA (5-98) Chor; FFA; Pres, 4H; Sci C; Pres, SC; Var C; Golf; CSF; 4H A; WW; *UC at Davis; Dentistry.*

HILL, Karl Lonnie
Corliss HS; Chicago, IL; Commercial C; Monogram; SC; Bkbl; Ftbl; COM; Cl Fav; MLS; *Morehouse Col; Data Processing.*

HILL, Kathryn Ann
Lutheran HS W; Detroit, MI;

HILL, Kevin Craig
Dilce Combs Mem HS; Jeff, KY (12-111) BC; Hist A; *US Air Force Acad; Math.*

HILL, Kevin Eugene
Elmira Christian Acad; Elmira, NY (1-7) Band; Chess C; Rptr, Hmrm; NHS; SC; Var C; Tres, Sr Cl; VP, Jr Cl; VP, Soph Cl; Bsbl; Bkbl; Ftbl; Soccer; JV, Sftbl; JV, Tr; Wrest; COM; Hon Prog; *Cornell U; Elec Engr.*

HILL, Kevin Eugene
Columbus East HS; Columbus, OH; Band A; *Mass Inst Technology; Elec Technology.*

HILL, Kevin Leo
Shawnee Mission NW HS; Shawnee, KS; CYO; *Saint Mary's Col; Elec Engr.*

HILL, LaGloree Dawn
Pleasant Grove HS; Pleasant Grove, AL; Chem C; NHS; Phys C; MLS; *U of Ala; Nurs.*

HILL, Laura Jean
Old Forge HS; Old Forge, PA (12-121) Cpt, Chldr; FHA; Secy, NHS; Ensm; Ntl Fed of Eng Tchrs Writ; *Pa St U; Agr.*

HILL, Laura Marie
Taylor Allderdice HS; Pittsburgh, PA; Mjrte; Tres, Rainbow; Hon Prog; Masonic A; Yth Fel; Pres, Methodist Yth Organization; 3rd Pl, Patrl Primitive Camp, G Sct; *Edinbourogh St Col; Elem Ed.*

HILL, Lillian Erma Letitia
Kinston HS; Kinston, NC (190-330) Band; Ensm; Hmrm; Cpt, Mjrte; Orch; Span C; SC; Ftbl; *Livingstone Col; Elem Ed.*

HILL, Lillian Rose
Mount Olive HS; Ft Mitchell, AL (2-63) Co-Cpt, Chldr; Secy, Chor; 4H; Pres, Hmrm; Semi-Fin, Jr Miss Pa; NHSt; Ed, Sch P; SC; Pres, Jr Cl; S-T, Soph Cl; Bkbl; Sftbl; Beauty; B Crocker A; COM; 4H A; Hist A; Hon Prog; ROTC A; *Auburn U; Engr.*

HILL, Linda Shirlene
Turlock HS; Turlock, CA; Type A; Span A; *Modesto Jr Col; Bus.*

HILL, Lisa Louise
Odessa R-7 Pub HS; Odessa, MO (20%-133) Chor; FHA; FTA; NHS; Rainbow; ARC; Sch P; Worthy Advisor, Rainbow Girls; Regional & St VICA; *Research Sch of Nurs; Nurs.*

HILL, Lori Ann
Warwick Sr HS; Lititz, PA (2-275) Band; Chess C; Hmrm; Hon Prog; Math A; *Pre-Med.*

HILL, Lynn Marie
La Jolla HS; LaJolla, CA (192-534) AFS; Ski C; Mgr, Cr-Ctry; Cpt, Tr; COM; Soroptimist C; Secy, Vike Tr C; *U of Minn; Social Work.*

HILL, Marjorie Jonette
Fascosa HS; Amarillo, TX; Co-Cpt, Chldr; Pres, Orch; Bus Mgr, Sci C; Span C; Y-Tns; Tr; Hon Prog; I Dare You; Rebel Spirits; Span C Qn; Vlbl; Salutatorian, Fresh Cl; Orch Qn; Miss Sam Houston; *U of Tex.*

HILL, Mark Alan
Nevada HS; Nevada, MO; Band; VP, Sci C; Span C; Ftbl; Swim; Tr; Opt A; ROTC A; Sci A.

HILL, Mark Donald
Lutheran HS W; Detroit, MI (3-150) Pres, NHS; Tres, Sr Cl; Tnns; JA A; Math A; MLS; Phi Beta Kappa; Regent Schol; Sci A; Summa Cum Laude; Most Intelligent; *U of Mich; Engr.*

HILL, Martha Joyce
Queen City HS; Queen City, TX (2-41) Ann; Band; FHA; NHS; Rainbow; Sci C; Band Outst Service A; Band Medals; *Texarkana Comm Col; Bus.*

HILL, Melinda Lee
W Forest HS; Tionesta, PA (9-51) S-T, Band; Drama; FNA; 4H; Rainbow; Rptr, Sch P; Span C; Var C; Bkbl; Tr; 4H A; Yth Fel; Miss Teenage Amer; Pres, Phys Fitness; *Anderson Col; Nurs.*

HILL, Michael Dennis
Barringer HS; Newark, NJ (9-456) City Conf; Hmrm; Tres, NHS; Orch; Ed, Sch P; Pres, Ftbl; Tr; Citz A; Lat A; SC Service A; *Mo U at Columbia; Professional Broadcasting.*

HILL, Michael Wayne
Alma J Brown HS; Grambling, LA; Bus C; Pres, Community Yth; FBLAh; FTA; NHS; Hon Prog; Ntl Voc Guidance Assn; *Grambling St U; Bus Mgr.*

HILL, Michael Wayne
John Overton HS; Nashville, TN (75-375) Lat C; Var C; Tnns; *Acct.*

HILL, Miriam Leigh
W Mecklenburg HS; Charlotte, NC (10%-400) Fr C; NHS; ARC; DARGCA; Jr Marshal; *Nurs.*

HILL, Pamela Ann
Moore HS; Moore, OK (80-1000) Fr C; NHS; *U of Okla.*

HILL, Pamela Beth
Rising Star HS; Rising Star, TX (3-13) Ed, Ann; Secy, Band; Secy, Chldr; Pres, FHA; Ed, Sch P; Pres, Sr Cl; Secy, Jr Cl; Secy, Soph Cl; Cpt, Bkbl; Tr; Cl Fav; Hist A; MLS; Sal; Sci A; Most Attractive; One Act Play; All Dist Forward; *Abilene Christian U.*

HILL, Patricia Ann
Mount Olive HS; Seale, AL; Band; Chor; FFA; Secy, 4H; SC; Sftbl; 4H A; HQn; *Grambling St U; Mus.*

HILL, Patti Lynne
Borger HS; Borger, TX (66-250) BC; Chldr; Span C; Tr; Cl Fav; Vlbl; Cand, Bkbl Qn; *Westminster Col; Interior Design.*

HILL, Peggie Lynn
W Forest HS; Tionesta, PA (2-60) Band; Rainbow; Span C; Pres, Soph Cl; JV, Bkbl; Sftbl; 4H A; Yth Fel; Pres, Phys Fitness.

HILL, Ralph
J S Abrams HS; Bessemer, AL (5-94) Band; BS; Chor; 4H; Pres, Hmrm; SC; Var C; Bkbl; Cpt, Ftbl; Poet A; Pres A; *Tenn St Col; Elec Engr.*

HILL, Randall John
Hamilton HS; Hamilton, MI (30-145) Band; Ger C; Ftbl; Wrest; *Law.*

HILL, Raymond
J S Abrams HS; Bessemer, AL (15-94) Band; Chor; FBLA; Hmrm; SC; Var C; Bsbl; Bkbl; Cpt, Ftbl; Sftbl; HCt; Sportsmanship A; *Ala St U; X Ray Tech.*

HILL, Rickie Lavern
Motley HS; Columbus, MS; Ftbl; Pres A; *Miss St U; Computer Sci.*

HILL, Robbin Lynn
Westchester HS; Los Angeles, CA; Chldr; Tres, Drama; Pres, Hmrm; Tnns; COM; Most Out; Service A; *Pepperdine U; Bus.*

HILL, Robert Eugene Jr
Columbus HS; Columbus, GA (10%-450) Chor; Ensm; Hmrm; Lit Ral; NHS; 4H A; WW; Mus A; *Columbus Col; Mus.*

HILL, Robert Lynn
Highland HS; Anderson, IN (27-248) Lat C; Order/Arrow; Sci C; God & Country A; Hist A; Hon Prog; Ntl Sci Found; Order/Arrow A; Eagle Sct; *Christian Heritage Col; Geophysics.*

HILL, Robyn Lea
Vian HS; Vian, OK (1-90) Ann; Band; Cpt, Chldr; FHA; SC; Rptr, Jr Cl; Tr; HCt; Masonic A; Band A; St Hon Soc; Girl o-t Mo; *NE Okla St U; Bus.*

HILL, Ronald Dean
Lafayette HS; Lafayette, LA (25%-600) Band; Order/Arrow; Bkbl; Cr-Ctry; Tr; Order/Arrow A; Eagle Sct; *USL; Mech Engr.*

HILL, Sandra D'Ann
Bowman HS; Wadesboro, NC (10-377) A-Ed, Ann; NHS; Mgr, Sftbl; Advanced Bio C; FCA; James M Johnston Schol; Pres, Yth Coun; Span A; SPEC Summer Ldrship Prog; *U of NC; Spch Pathology.*

HILL, Sandra Regina
Surry Co HS; Dendron, VA (9%-90) Tres, Chor; Secy, FBLA; 4H; Piano Cert; *Norfolk St Col; Secy Sci.*

HILL, Sidney Lee
Levelland HS; Levelland, TX (14-192) Drama; FTA; Hmrm; NHS; Ed, Sch P; Pres, SC; Co-Cpt, Bsbl; Ftbl; Journ A; 4th St Journ Contest; *Tex Tech U; Journ.*

HILL, Simona Julietta
The Cecilian Acad; Philadelphia, PA; Fr C; Lat C; Sci C; *Chestnut Hill Col; Sci.*

HILL, Stanley
Smith HS; Atlanta, GA; Fin, Fr C; NHS; Secy, Sch P; Secy, St Stu Congress; Secy, SC; Var C; Fin, Ftbl; COM; Hist A; HKg; Math A; Val; *Iowa St U; Civil Engr.*

HILL, Stephen Anthony
Barringer HS; Newark, NJ (27-456) NHS; Ed, Sch P; Pres, Sr Cl; JV, Bkbl; Ftbl; Tr; Sports-Ed, Yrbk; Principals Adv Comm; Lat A; Schol Ath A; *U of Mo at Columbia; Journ.*

HILL, Susan Claudette
Claremore HS; Claremore, OK (60-400) AFS; Band; FBLA; Pres, FHA; Rainbow; Coun Asst; Band Qn Attendant; Fresh Cl Off; *T U; Social Work.*

HILL, Susan Elaine
Jefferson Davis HS; Montgomery, AL (74-742) Ensm; Mu Alpha Theta; Ed, Sch P; Tri-HiY; Yth Leg; Young Life; Acteens; Yth Coun; Ch, Mus Stu C; *Auburn U.*

HILL, Tami Jo
Valley City HS; Valley City, ND (45-152) Band; FBLA; FHA; Secy, 4H; Hmrm; Ski C; SC; Sftbl; 4H A; Valley City St Col; Social Work.

HILL, Tonya Denise
Bok AVT; Philadelphia, PA; Chldr; Drama; SC; Tnns; Cl Fav; Coun of Teach A; MLS; Type A; Eng A; Lib A; Saint Mary's Col; Nurs.

HILL, Toras Yul
Fair Park HS; Shreveport, LA (27-107) 4H; Orch; Mgr, Bsbl; Tr; 4H A; Sci A; Sen, SC; Bishop Col; Dentistry.

HILL, Tracy R
Harrah HS; Harrah, OK (1-116) VP, NHS; VP, Jr Cl; Bkbl; Sftbl; Alg A; Citz A; Hist A; Hon Prog; Math A; Secy, FCA; Eng A; Med.

HILL, Valerie Louise
Heidelberg American HS; Heidelberg, GERMANY; Hmrm; NHS; Rptr, Span C; Spch C; SC; Tri-HiY; Tnns; Homemaking Stu o-t Yr; Tnns Medals; Okla St U; Home Ec.

HILL, Van Eric
Arch-Bishop Carroll HS; Washington, DC (15-225) JV, Ftbl; Bio A; Hon Prog; Sci A; Morehouse Col; Med.

HILL, Vincent Troy
Fair Park HS; Shreveport, LA (38-455) Hon Prog; Bishop Col; Pediatrics.

HILL, Walter Davis Jr
Bolton HS; Alexandria, LA (10%-450) Fr C; Hmrm; Key C; Swim; Hon Prog; La Tech; Engr.

HILL, William Charles
The Blake Sch; Minneapolis, MN (45-94) Drama; Pres, Hmrm; Co-Cpt, Bsbl; Co-Cpt, Bkbl; Co-Cpt, Ftbl; HCt; Yth Fel; Pres, Yth Fellowship; U of Minn; Bus Adm.

HILL, William Murray III
Warren Area Sr HS; Warren, PA (2%-500) A Cap Choir; Band; Chor; VP, Drama; NHS; Orch; Ch, SC; VP, Thes; Var C; Co-Cpt, Swim; Tnns; God & Country A; Hon Prog; Yth Fel; Advanced Placement; Dickinson Col.

HILL, Yolande Renee
Villa Victoria Acad; Trenton, NJ (10-26) Chor; Math C; VP, NFL; Ski C; Ski C; Span C; Ch, Jr Cl; JV, Bkbl; JV, Hockey; COM; Hon Prog; Math A; Cert of Hon; Vol A; Cert of General Excellence; WW; Seton Hall U; Bio.

HILLARD, Jacqueline Sue
Landmark Christian HS; Cincinnati, OH (5-48) Band; JV, Chldr; Chor; SC; Tr; Qn, Swtht Banquet; Wheaton Col; Sociology.

HILLEGEIST, Douglas Ray
S P Waltrip Sr HS; Houston, TX (1-654) Band; Ger C; JETS; NHS; Order/Arrow; Sci C; God & Country A; Hon Prog; Bowl C; Eagle Sct; Rice U; Econ.

HILLEN, Kevin Francis
Brussels Comm HS; Brussels, IL (3-28) CYO; FFA; 4H; SC; 4H A; I Dare You; Math A; MLS; NEDT; St Scholar; PA; WW; Vanderbilt U; Engr.

HILLEN, Laura Ann
Brussels Comm HS; Brussels, IL (8-34) Band; S-T, CYO; FHA; Secy, 4H; 4H A; Math A; NEDT; PA A; Sou Ill U; Math.

HILLER, David Burgess
Webster Groves HS; Webster Groves, MO (96-550) Co-Ed, Ann; Fr C; Rptr, Lit Mag; Order/Arrow; SC; JV, Ftbl; Cpt, Soccer; Sftbl; Order/Arrow A; Pres A; Eagle Sct.

HILLER, Dean Harrison
Webster Groves HS; Webster Groves, MO (100-460) Band; Fr C; Order/Arrow; SC; Soccer; Sftbl; COM; Lion A; Order/Arrow A; Yale Book A; Yth Foundation; Yth Foundation A; Eagle Sct; Sr Service A; Lion's Band; U of Kans; Bus.

HILLER, Laurie Beth
La Canada HS; La Canada, CA; Drama; Mu Alpha Theta; Rptr, Sch P; Ski C; CSF; COM; Hon Prog; Win, Composer's Today; Psych.

HILLER, Rhoda Louise
Napoleon HS; Napoleon, ND (1-71) NHS; Rptr, Sch P; Sci C; Tr; B Crocker A; NMF; Sci A; Val; Golden Valley Lutheran Col; Bio.

HILLERBRAND, Eric Thomas
Montclair HS; Montclair, NJ (15-485) Band; Chess C; Community Yth Symph; Ger C; VP, Model UN; Orch; Ch, UN Council; World Affairs C; Bkbl; NMS; Serv A; Dbte A; Colgate U; Interntl Relations.

HILLERSON, Wendy Jean
Luverne Pub Sch; Luverne, ND; A Cap Choir; Pres, Band; Tres, Chldr; Co-Ch, Chor; Ger C; Phys C; Ed, Sch P; Pres, Jr Cl; Co-Ch, Bkbl; Amer Leg A; HCt; Hon Prog; MLS; GSct.

HILLERY, Joni Sue
Stoughton Sr HS; Stoughton, WI (80-237) AFS; Ski C; Span C; GAA A; Madison Area Tech Col; Interior Design.

HILLERY, Pandora Lee
Blacksburg HS; Blacksburg, VA (200-290) Fr C; Radford Col; Mus.

HILLHOUSE, Alicia Anne
Sou Baptist Educational Center; Memphis, TN (25-127) FBLA; NHS; Tri-HiY; Bkbl; Sftbl; U of Tenn; Bus.

HILLIARD, Cynthia Jean
Bishop Kelley HS; Tulsa, OK (21-175) Anchor C; Chor; Pres, FBLA; Hmrm; ARC; Co-Ed, Sch P; SC; COM; Journ A; JA A; Jr Chamber of Com A; ARC A; Outst Yth of Church; Tulsa Yth Coalition; Lib C; Outst VP, Personnel Fin; Okla U; Pre-Med.

HILLIARD, Greg Alan
St Mary's HS; Stockton, CA (3-270) Fr C; Rptr, Hmrm; NHS; SC; JV, Bkbl; MVP, Tnns; CSF; Hon Prog; Fin, Citizenship A; Fr A.

HILLIARD, Karen A
Lake Clifton Sr HS; Baltimore, MD (10%-500) Band; Hmrm; NHS; COM; Math A; U of Md; Sci.

HILLIARD, Leslie Mychelle
Silsbee HS; Silsbee, TX (7-265) JETS; Math C; NHS; A-Ed, Sch P; S-T, Span C; Spch C; SC; Swim; Mgr, Tr; Math A; Fin, Miss Tn Tex; Co-Cpt Drill Tm; Sr Beauty; Soc of Women Engr A; LSU; Chem.

HILLIARD, Mark Robert
St Mary's HS; Stockton, CA (20-204) Ann; BS; Hmrm; Key C; NHS; Pres, SC; Var C; Pres, Jr Cl; JV, Bsbl; JV, Bkbl; Cr-Ctry; Tnns; Amer Leg A; Citz A; Hon Prog; Math A; Opt A; Sci A; Ldrship A; Most Improved, Most Loyal, Tnns; SDAHSS; Stanford U; Bus.

HILLIGUS, Judy Jannell
Cabrillo Sr HS; Lompoc, CA; Pres, AFS; MVP, Band; Chem C; Chor; Community Yth Symph; MVP, Ensm; VP, FNA; Secy, InterAct C; Secy, InterClub Coun; Madrigal; Pres, Orch; ARC; Sci C; Spch C; Parl, SC; Cpt, Sftbl; Co-Cpt, Tnns; CSF; Interlochen Ntl Mus; MLS; ARC A; Spch A; Yth Fel; CMEA Mus; SCSBOA Mus; A's; Calif St U; Concert Pianist.

HILLIN, Doug Wade
Fort Stockton HS; Fort Stockton, TX; Pres, A Cap Choir; Ensm; Bsbl; Ftbl; Sftbl; Yth Fel; Eng A; Tex A&M U; Vet.

HILLIN, Mary Ann
Robert E Lee HS; Baytown, TX (25%-450) FTA; Lat C; Drill Tm; Lee Col; Ed.

HILLINCK, Allison Sharon
Reseda HS; Reseda, CA (1-750) A Cap Choir; Hmrm; Ski C; SC; VP, Jr Cl; Tnns; Pres, JA; HR; Engr.

HILLIS, Anne Louise
Maranatha HS; Arcadia, CA (50%-60) Chor; Sftbl; Pacific Coast Baptist Bible Col; Christian Ed.

HILLMAN, Caroline Louise
Aitkin HS; Aitkin, MN (9-150) Band; Chor; Dbte Tm; NHS; Spch C; SC; Beauty; COM; H of F; Spch A; Col of St Benedict; Eng.

HILLMAN, Deanne Kay
Boulder HS; Boulder, CO; Chor; VP, Fr C; Hockey; Alg A; Hon Prog; Math A; Sci A; U of Colo; Nurs.

HILLMAN, Gregory
Newton Co Comprehensive HS; Covington, GA (10%-450) Band; BC; Rptr, 4H; Hmrm; InterAct C; Pres, InterClub Coun; Key C; Pres, SC; Bkbl; 4H A; Hon Prog; All-St Band; Tuskegee Inst; Engr.

HILLMAN, Jeffrey Charles
Imlay City HS; Imlay City, MI (35-205) Ed, Ann; VP, FFA; NFL; Rptr, Sch P; Sci C; Spch C; SC; Y-Tns; Pres, Sr Cl; Cr-Ctry; Tnns; Tr; Alg A; HCt; Hon Prog; Journ A; Math A; Spch A; Forensics A; Mich St U; Pol Sci.

HILLMAN, Renata Holland
Leakesville HS; Leakesville, MS (3-68) Ann; BC; Pres, FHA; 4H; Sch P; Pres, Soph Cl; Alg A; Beauty; COM; Cl Fav; 4H A; Hon Prog; VofDEM.

HILLMAN, Robert Owen
Lebanon HS; Lebanon, VA; Dbte Tm; FFA; FTA; 4H; HiY; Model UN; NHS; SC; Bsbl; Bkbl; Ftbl; Yth Fel; Va Polytechnic Inst; Civil Engr.

HILLMAN, Robin Leigh
Blair HS; Hattiesburg, MS; Span C; Miss Col.

HILLMAN, Serafina Fredownia
E Atlanta HS; Atlanta, GA (16-142) Band; Chem C; Hmrm; Span C; Chem A; Outst, Band; Tuskegee Inst; Elem Ed.

HILLMER, Nancy Jean
Spencer HS; Spencer, IA (10%-175) Band; Chor; NHS; Span C; Var C; Bkbl; St Scholar; Concordia Col; Ed.

HILLMER, Paul Allan
Spencer HS; Spencer, IA (10%-225) A Cap Choir; Band; Chor; Drama; Ensm; Madrigal; Model UN; NHS; UN Council; Var C; Cr-Ctry; Tr; U of SD Mus Schol A; Mus.

HILLOCK, Suellen
Port Huron Northern HS; Port Huron, MI (25%-500) A Cap Choir; Chor; MVP, Ensm; 4H; Hmrm; Sftbl; 4H A; Hon Prog; Tres, Yth Fel; St Clair Co Comm Col; Secretarial Mgt.

HILLS, Brenda Marie
Elston Sr HS; Michigan City, IN; Hmrm; Mjrte; SC; Bkbl; Pres, Human Relations; Vlbl; Jr Concessions; Sterling Comm; RT; Ball St U; Phys Ed.

HILLSMAN, Karen
Danville HS; Danville, IL (22-612) Chldr; Hmrm; VP, Y-Tns; Sftbl; Mgr, Tr; Hon Prog; Rotary A.

HILMES, Chris Scott
Monte Vista HS; Monte Vista, CO (2-150) Band; VP, 4H; Secy, Model UN; SC; Ski C; Pres, SC; Fin, St Sci Fair; Med.

HILMOE, Mari Jo
Clark HS; Clark, SD; Ann; Band; Semi-Fin, GS; NHS; Sch P; Tres, Sr Cl; Q&S A; Lake Area Votech Col; Dental Asst.

HILPERT, Donald Walter
The Potter Public Sch; Potter, NE (6-14) Dbte Tm; Ensm; Pres, 4H; Sch Achieve Tm; SC; Bsbl; Cr-Ctry; Ftbl; Cpt, Wrest; COM; 4H A; HCt; Yth Fel; VP, 4-H C; Co- op Ldrship Sch; W Nebr Tech Col; Elec.

HILS, Mary Gabrielle
Villa Madonna Acad; Covington, KY (5-74) MVP, Chldr; NHS; COM; NEDT; Eng A; Thomas More School; Thomas More Col; Eng.

HILS, Maureen Louise
Aiken Sr HS; Cincinnati, OH (5%-830) Ann; Chor; Ensm; Span C; SC; Mgr, Bkbl; Mgr, Sftbl; Med.

HILTERBRAND, Gerald Dean
Temple Baptist Acad; Denver, CO (7-26) Ann; Band; VP, NHS; Spch C; Bsbl; Ftbl; COM; All Conf Ftbl; Bob Jones U; Pastoral Stu.

HILTON, Barbara Jean
Richwoods HS; Peoria, IL (295-450) Chor; Marion Col; Missionary Nurs.

HILTON, Diane
Twentynine Palms HS; Twentynine Palms, CA (9-150) Var C; Cpt, Bkbl; Tr; CSF; Citz A; Vlbl; Col o-t Desert; Math.

HILTON, Donald Elroy II
Simley HS; Inver Grove Hghts, MN; JA A.

HILTON, Karen Ann
Litchfield HS; Litchfield, IL; Fr C; NHS; U of Ark; Ed.

HILTON, Keith William
Litchfield HS; Litchfield, IL (16-150) Fr C; NHS; Bkbl; Yth Choir; Bible Stu; Okla Baptist U; Bus Mgt.

HILTON, Laurie Jeanne
S Broward HS; Hollywood, FL; Chor; Mjrte; Drill Tm; WW; *Ed.*

HILTS, Robert Jay
Dallas Sr HS; Dallas, OR (28-150) Band; Dbte Tm; NFL; NHS; Rptr, Sch P; Sci C; Span C; JV, Bsbl; Church Annual Conf; Dist Yth Coun On Ministries; *U of Oreg; Med.*

HILTZ, Murray L Jr
N Olmsted HS; North Olmsted, OH (120-650) AFS; Demolay; Hmrm; SC; Yth Fel; Bowl, Yth Del, SYNOD; *Cleveland St Col; Bus.*

HILVETY, Laura LaRue
Macon HS; Macon, IL (20-90) Band; Fr C; Yth Fel.

HILZENDEGER, Kevin Michael
Napoleon HS; Napoleon, ND (5-51) SC; Bsbl; Bkbl; Sftbl; *Jamestown Col.*

HIMES, Jerry Lee
Hammond Christian HS; Griffith, IN; Band; Chor; Drama; Hmrm; Orch; SC; Ftbl; Hist A; Hon Prog; Yth Fel.

HIMES, Kathy Lynn
Springbrook HS; Silver Spring, MD (3-620) Drama; NFL.

HIMES, Kenneth Warren
McCracken HS; Bluffton, SC (15%-72) Band; BC; 4H; Hmrm; Sftbl; JV, Tr; JV, Wrest; Citz A; Shop Stu o-t Yr; Home Ec Stu o-t Yr; *Air Force Acad; Air Traffic Control.*

HIMES, Lori Elizabeth
Assumption HS; Assumption, IL (20-50) VP, Band; Chldr; Drama; FHA; 4H; Sch P; SC; Thes; 4H A; HCt; Pres A; Drama A; *Eastern Col; Dentals Asst.*

HIMES, Rebecca Lynne
Fairfield Sr HS; Fairfield, OH (19-608) Band; Fr C; ARC; ARC A; *Eastern Ky U; Bio.*

HIMMELREICH, Peggy Lynette
Silsbee HS; Silsbee, TX (4-275) FHA; FTA; NHS; SC; Y-Tns; JA A; Poet A; ARC A; Secy, Creative Writing; NHS; Essay A; PA; Highest Eng III; *Bus.*

HIMMELWRIGHT, Cathy Ann
Burn And Hills Rallston Lk Sr HS; Burnt Hills, NY; Cpt, Chldr; Chor; Type A; Yth Fel; Pioneer Girls; Church Choir; *Secy.*

HINDERLITER, Richard Paul
Copeland HS; Copeland, KS (4-11) Ann; Band; BS; Chor; Ensm; Pres, Hmrm; VP, Rptr, Sch P; SC; VP, Soph Cl; Co-Cpt, Bkbl; Co-Cpt, Ftbl; Tr; 4H A; HCt; Spch A; Amer Royal Trip; 4-H St Key A; St 4-H Congress; 4-H Round- up; *Baker U; Phys Ed.*

HINDERMAN, Heidi Elen
N Royalton HS; N Royalton, OH; Chor; FTA; 4H; NHS; Church Choir; United Methodist Yth Fel; Church Handbells; Schol Excellence; *Tri-C.*

HINDMAN, Dana Ann
Dewey HS; Dewey, OK (22-94) Ann; S-T, FHA; 4H; Pres, Lit Ral; Ed, Sch P; Var C.

HINDMAN, Heather Mary
Memorial Sr HS; Houston, TX (1%-650) JETS; Math C; Mu Alpha Theta; NHS; Sci C; Span C; Span NHS; Bio A; COM; DARGCA; God & Country A; Hon Prog; Math A; Sci A; Eng A; Art A; *Scientific Art.*

HINDMAN, Karen Renee
Tyronza HS; Tyronza, AR; Ed, Ann; BC; Secy, Chor; NHS; Ed, Sch P; Pres, SC; Rptr, Sr Cl; Hon Prog; MLS; Sal; Yrbk Outst Work A; Clothing & Textiles A; Mus A; *Sou Baptist Col; Elem Ed.*

HINDMAN, Nell Elizabeth
Central HS; Memphis, TN (5%-250) A-Ed, Ann; Math C; Mu Alpha Theta; Span C; SC; Alg A; COM; Hon Prog; Journ A; Math A; Q&S A; Span, Drivers Ed, A's; Chief Marshal; Order o-t Redman; *Math.*

HINDMAN, Patricia Louise
Chester HS; Chester, IL; Ch, FHA; Tr.

HINDMAN, Sherry Lynn
Temple Christian HS; Detroit, MI (1-70) Rptr, Sch P; Secy, Sr Cl; Alg A; Citz A; Math A; Most Out; Sci A; *Pepperdine U; Med.*

HINDS, Clyde David
Oceana HS; Pacifica, CA; Bsbl; Ftbl; Golf; Soccer; Bank Of Amer A; Pres, Ceramics C; Best of Show A; Kemper Art A; Pacifica Tribune A; Tanforan Park Merchants Assn A; *Harding Col; Art.*

HINDS, Cynthia Ann
Sequoyah HS; Claremore, OK (10-70) Chor; Hmrm; SC; Spch A; Type A; VFW A; VofDEM; Yth Fel; Pres, Yth Fel; Mus A; *Claremore Jr Col; Mus.*

HINDS, Janice Diane
Bismarck HS; Bismarck, ND (25%-525) Chor; Pres A; ARC A; Secy, Church Yth; Church Choir; 1st Cl A; Jr Lifesaving.

HINDS, Kathryn Elizabeth
Bismarck HS; Bismarck, ND (5%-560) Lat C; Lat NHS; Orch; Swim; *Vet Sci.*

HINE, Douglas John
J M Coughlin HS; Wilkes-Barre, PA (42-410) Drama; Hmrm; Key C; NHS; Cpt, Order/Arrow; ARC; Pres, Ski C; Order/Arrow A; Vlbl; Skiing; *US Military Acad; Engr.*

HINER, LaDonna Kay
Lawrence HS; Lawrence, KS (163-528) Tnns; Tr; *Kans U; Ed.*

HINERMAN, Charles Paul
Washburn Sr HS; Minneapolis, MN (50-400) Band; Bsbl; Golf; *Asbury Col; Law.*

HINES, Benita Myra
John F Kennedy HS; Cleveland, OH (10%-600) A Cap Choir; HiY; Citz A; Yth Leg; Ohio YMCA Yth, Gov; *Ohio U; Law.*

HINES, Bonita Anne
Smithfield Selma Sr HS; Smithfield, NC (21-360) Chldr; Chor; S-T, Fr C; Hmrm; Mjrte; NHS; Ed, Sch P; NJHS; Graduation Marshal; Gym; WW; Pep C; Sub-Jr Women's C; SCA; Church Choir; Office Aid; Symphonic Band; Jr-Sr Prom Comm; *Meredith Col; Elem Ed.*

HINES, Brenda K
Warren Central HS; Indianapolis, IN (10%-600) Pres, Chor; NHS; Orch; Sch P; Spch C; Spch A; *Taylor U; Pre-Theology.*

HINES, Brooke Jennifer
Pierson HS; Sag Harbor, NY (1-63) Band; Chor; Drama; Ensm; Fr C; GS; NHS; Rptr, Sch P; SC; Tres, Jr Cl; Pres, Soph Cl; Hist A; Math A; Type A; Co Yth Recognition A; *Vet Med.*

HINES, Donna Kathleen
Porter HS; Maryville, TN (24-77) Bus C; Cpt, Chldr; Fr C; Pres, FHA; 4H; Sch P; Secy, Sr Cl; Rptr, Jr Cl; Crisco A; HCt; Yth Fel; Most Sch Spirit; Cand, Miss PHS; *Tenn Tech U; Wildlife Mgt.*

HINES, Jane Suzanne
Crockett HS; Crockett, TX (1-120) Band; Chor; Ensm; FTA; NHS; Span C; SC; Pres, Sr Cl; Tnns; Hon Prog; Most Out; Sci A; Val; Health A; WW Choir; *U of Tex; Ed.*

HINES, Jo Ellen
Midwest HS; Midwest, WY (5-20) Arch; Drama; Pres, NFL; NHS; SC; Golf; Bible A; *Casper Col; Bus.*

HINES, Judy Kay
Marshall-University HS; Minneapolis, MN (14-157) Secy, Sr Cl; Co-Cpt, Bkbl; Tr; HCt; Pres A; Vlbl; *U of Wis; Bus Adm.*

HINES, Keith Alan
Spring Woods HS; Houston, TX (75-510) Chor; Ensm; Madrigal; NHS; *Baylor U; Law.*

HINES, Keith David
Leo HS; Chicago, IL (6-140) Band; NHS; VP, Var C; Ftbl; Tr; *Milkin U; Bus Adm.*

HINES, Kevin Benjamin
Leo HS; Chicago, IL (3-140) Band; NHS; Secy, Var C; Ftbl; Tr; COM; Yth Fel; *Millikin U; Bus.*

HINES, Kevin David
Leo HS; Chicago, IL (3-140) Band; NHS; Ftbl; COM; Yth Fel; *Milikin Col; Bus.*

HINES, Lisa Gaye
Hobart HS; Hobart, OK (1-77) Chldr; VP, FHA; NHS; SC; Kiwanis A; Yth Fel; Mus As; *Altus Jr Col.*

HINES, Michael Lee
Northeastern HS; Detroit, MI; Band; Chess C; NHS; Ftbl; Amer Leg A; Citz A; *U of Mich; Math.*

HINES, Nancy Jo
Paris HS; Paris, TX; Tres, Chor; FTA; Key C; Madrigal; Span C; Tri-HiY; Drill Tm; *East Texas St U; Mus.*

HINES, Paula Kay
Emerson HS; Emerson, AR; Secy, FHA; GS; SC; S-T, Soph Cl; Bkbl; Tr; Alg A; COM; Hist A; Hon Prog; Best All Around; Homemaking A; Span Hon; *Sou Ark U; Math.*

HINES, Shanda Lee
Dilley HS; Dilley, TX; Band; Mjrte; Bkbl; Tnns; *U of Tex; Photography.*

HINES, Stessenie Denise
Hueytown HS; Hueytown, AL; *Ala A&M Col; Special Ed.*

HINES, Susan Carol
Vestavia Hills HS; Birmingham, AL (10%-300) Chor; Basic C; *Harding Col; Ed.*

HINES, Tammy Lynn
Thompson HS; Alabaster, AL (5-180) Band; Ch, Hmrm; Ch, NHS; Ch, Jr Cl; Tr; Gr Marshal; NHS A; Cl Off, 2 Yrs; *Auburn U; Math.*

HINES, Zerrie Levette
Forest Brook Sr HS; Houston, TX (5-400) Chor; Hmrm; Key C; Math C; Mu Alpha Theta; NHS; COM; Hon Prog; Magna Cum Laude; Math A; Drafting, Archt, A's; *Civil Engr.*

HINEY, Sharon Gertrude
W Orange HS; W Orange, NJ; Chor; Pres, Rainbow; *Computor Operator.*

HINISH, Apryle Lynn
Brooklyn HS; Brooklyn, OH; Ann; Band; Hmrm; Sch P; Span NHS; Tres, SC; Spa A; Piano A.

HINKELMAL, Lisa Jann
Sidney Lanier HS; Austin, TX (5-499) A Cap Choir; Ann; Chor; Hmrm; Sch P; VP, SC; Pres, Soph Cl; Bsbl; Bkbl; Cr-Ctry; Ftbl; Tr; Beauty; Cl Fav; HCt; Lion A; MLS; Most Out; Swtht; Yth Fel; WW; Homecoming Ct; Fin, Lion's C A; Semi-Fin, Beauty, Fin, MLS; Ftbl; Fin, Cl Fav; Fin, Most Outst; Semi-Fin; Fin Sch Swtht; *U of Tex; Public Relations.*

HINKLE, Bernadette Leanne
McMinnville HS; McMinnville, OR (150-250) Chor; Key C; Most Out; Yth Fel; *Airline Stewardess.*

HINKLE, Leslie Renee
Melbourne HS; Melbourne, FL (70-737) Cpt, Chldr; ARC; SC; Mgr, Bkbl; Alg A; DARGCA; Hon Prog; JA A; NEDT; Pres A; ARC A; Yth Fel; Vlbl; PA, Chldr, A's; Commission of Ed A of Excel; *Brevard Comm Col; Computer Prog.*

HINKLE, Linda Kay
Salisbury R-4 HS; Salisbury, MO (36-85) Chor; FHA; DARGCA; Sch Yrbk; *Moberly Jr Col; Practical Nurs.*

HINKLE, Pam Lynn
Cavalier Pub HS; Cavalier, ND (10-65) Band; Chldr; Chor; Ensm; Pres, 4H; Madrigal; Pres, Rainbow; Bkbl; MVP, Sftbl; Swim; Tr; Best Free Thrower; Most Dedicated, Bkbl; *Med.*

HINKLE, Pamela Lynn
Cavalier Pub Sch; Cavalier, ND (10-70) Band; Chldr; Chor; Ensm; Pres, 4H; Madrigal; Pres, Rainbow; Bkbl; MVP, Sftbl; Swim; Tnns; Tr; Best Free Throw Shooter; Bkbl & Tr Ltrs; Most Dedicated, Bkbl; *Med.*

HINKLE, Ron Eugene
Richland HS; Ft Worth, TX; Drama; VP, FHA; FTA; VP, SC; Pres, Jr Cl; Tr; *UTA.*

HINKLE, Thomas J
Anna-Jonesboro HS; Anna, IL (15-250) Band; Ensm; FBLA; Secy, Hmrm; Math C; Alg A; Math A; *Murry St U; Bus Mgr.*

HINKLEMAN, Cindy Jo
Eisenhower HS; Rialto, CA (10%-716) A Cap Choir; Chor; Key C; Madrigal; CSF; WW Among Amer HS Mus Stu; Chor Groups Accompianist A; *San Bernardino Valley Col; Computer Sci.*

HINKLEY, Genevieve June
Livermore Falls HS; Livermore Falls, ME (3-94) Pres, Band; Chor; Fr C; VP, FHA; GS; Hmrm; Math C; Secy, NHS; SC; Var C; Co-Cpt, Bkbl; Hockey; Sftbl; Bio A; HCt; U of Maine; Arts.

HINMAN, Carol Louise
Linn-Mar HS; Marion, IA (112-200) A Cap Choir; Chor; Madrigal; Thes; Hist, Thespians; Cornell Col; Mus.

HINMAN, Judy Ellen
Maranatha Christian Acad; New Hartford, NY (2-7) Chor; A-Ed, Sch P; VP, SC; Hockey; Soccer; Swim; VFW Orator Win; VofDEM; Spiritual Ldrship A; Best Athlete; 1st Pl, Pace Bowl, NY St; Baptist Bible Col; Christian Ed.

HINOJOSA, Alexandra Evangeline
M B Smiley HS; Houston, TX (3-400) VP, Math C; VP, Mu Alpha Theta; Pres, NHS; Bio A; COM; Hist A; Magna Cum Laude; Most Out; Sci A; VFW A; Eng, Data Process, Bookkeeping, A's; U of Houston; Acct.

HINOJOSA, Reynadlo
Mission HS; Mission, TX (100-365) Key C; SC; Rptr, Sr Cl; Co-Cpt, Ftbl; Cl Fav; H of F; Lion A; Rotary A; MVP, Ftbl; Trinity Col; Sci.

HINRICHS, Kevin Robert
Washburn HS; Minnapolis, MN (33%-300) Bkbl; COM; ARC A; Star Student; Sociology.

HINRICHS, Michelle Louise
Webb HS; Reedsburg, WI (20-200) CYO; Pres, Fr C; GS; NFL; VP, SC; Secy, Thes; HCt; Opt Out Tn; Type A; U of Wis-Madison; Ed.

HINRICHS, Miriam Jean
Springdale HS; Springdale, AR (93%-491) A Cap Choir; Chor; FTA; NHS; Sci C; Hendrix Col; Biol.

HINRICHS, William Peter
Fort Atkinson Sr HS; Fort Atkinson, WI (33%-260) Demolay; Ftbl; Wrest; U of Wis; Pre-Law.

HINSHAW, Catherine Ranning
Anacortes HS; Anacortes, WA; Ann; Band; Chor; Community Yth Symph; Tres, Dbte Tm; Ensm; FBLA; InterAct C; NHS; Orch; JV, Bkbl; COM; Hon Prog; VofDEM; Pep C; Teacher, Flute & Mus Theory; Thalians; Sr Prefect; Hon Choir; Felicians; Rotary Exchange Stu; GAC; Inner-Hi Exchange; U of Wash; Bus Mgr.

HINSON, Cynthia Lee
Schafer HS; Southgate, MI (30-310) Chor; Drama; Ensm; Rptr, Sch P; SC; Thes; Yth Fel; Wayne St U; Med.

HINSON, Michael Dean
Hapeville HS; Hapeville, GA (25%-115) Secy, Band; Hmrm; Orch; SC; VP, Soph Cl; ROTC A; Band, Ensm, Orch A's.

HINTON, Barry Frank
Coppras Cove HS; Coppras Cove, TX (166-310).

HINTON, Bernadette Maria
St Thomas Apostle HS; Chicago, IL (13-51) COM; GAA; Humanities A; Art A; PA; Vlbl; Yth Fitness Achv A; Vol Work A; Hon Prog; Tn A; Rptr, Co-Ed, F-Ed, CYO; Bradley Col; Journ.

HINTON, Bradly Thomas
Breckinridge Co HS; Harned, KY (12-200).

HINTON, Corine Renee
Bowen HS; Chicago, IL; Chor; SC; Law.

HINTON, Diane Marie
Holy Rosary Acad; Louisville, KY (6-86) Pres, Chor; NHS; SC; Ntl HS A for Execellence; WW; U of Louisville; Math.

HINTON, Dolores Faye
Breckinridge Co HS; Harned, KY (5%-207) FBLA; FHA; FTA; NHS; Sci C; 4H A; Western Ky U; Math.

HINTON, Edith Lorraine
Lakeland Sr HS; Lakeland, FL; JA A; Math A; Stu Advisory Comm; Fla AM Betham Cookman Col; Bus.

HINTON, Kevin Lee
Brookville HS; Brookville, OH; Band; Chess C; Ensm; Ed, Sch P; Var C; Pres, Sr Cl; VP, Jr Cl; VP, Soph Cl; Mgr, Bsbl; Mgr, Bkbl; Mgr, Ftbl; Wrest; COM; Chamber of Comm A; Star Student; Trainer, Bkbl, Ftbl, Wrest; OMEA; Bus Adm.

HINTON, Michelle LaRaye
McKinley Sr HS; Canton, OH; Chor; Ensm; Lit Mag; NHS; Circleville Bible Col; Mus.

HINTON, Nolan
Fenger HS; Chicago, IL; Band; Chor; FHA; 4H; Span C; Bkbl; Tr; Type A; Amateur Ath Union; Ill St U; Photography.

HINTON, Randy Dale
Zebulon HS; Zebulon, NC; Band; Ftbl; Wake Tech Inst; Elec.

HINTON, Robbie Lee
Gulfport HS; Gulfport, MS (97-238) Sftbl; Tr; Memphis St U; Sociology.

HINTON, Sharon Kay
Crosby HS; Crosby, TX; Ann; Band; FBLA; FTA; Secy, 4H; SC; COM; 4H A; St 4-H Win; Outst 4-H Girl; Grand Champ, Pigs; Tex A&M U.

HINTON, Vickie
Jordan HS; Columbus, GA (2-11) SC; Columbus Col; Chor.

HINTZ, Darla Jean
Hartington Pub Sch; Hartington, NE (5-40) Ann; Chldr; Chor; S-T, Hmrm; Model UN; Var C; S-T, Soph Cl; Tr; COM; Math A; Alt GS; Chldr A; Tr A; Phys Ed A; Mus A.

HINTZ, Pauline Elaine
Shawnee Mission S HS; Shawnee Mission, KS (150-850) Chor; NHS; NMF; NMS; VP, Church Yth Group; Vlbl; Hospital Jr Vol; Interntl C; U of Wis at Madison; Special Ed.

HINZ, Jane Adelaide
Shaker Hts HS; Shaker Hts, OH; Appreciation A, Art; Cleveland Inst of Art; Art.

HINZMAN, Connie Lynn
Norton HS; Norton, OH (100-349) Band; FHA; Beauty; COM; VP, VICA; Photography.

HIPP, Richard Pat
Claremore HS; Claremore, OK (20-318) Chess C; Dbte Tm; Fr C; Hmrm; Order/Arrow; SC; Ftbl; Golf; Tr; Yth Fel; North Eastern Okla A&M Col; Electro-Mech Tech.

HIPPLE, Carolyn Jean
Stratford Sr HS; Houston, TX (14-436) Dbte Tm; FTA; Fin, GS; Math C; Mu Alpha Theta; NFL; NHS; Spch C; VP, SC; Pres, Soph Cl; MVP, Swim; Hon Prog; Magna Cum Laude; MLS; Most Out; Yth Fel; Keyettes; Eng Hon Soc; Cpt, Drama; SC; PTA Schol; Eng A; Pres, Fresh Cl; LSU Alumni Hon A; Sr Girls C; UIL Poetry Contest; LSU; Child Psych.

HIPPOLYTE, Jacinta
Charlotte Amalie HS; St Thomas, VI; VP, Hmrm; VP, Span C; Alg A; Hist A; Avila Col; Pre-Med.

HIRAKAWA, Stacy Yae
Parlier HS; Parlier, CA; Bus Mgr, Ann; Band; Chldr; Chor; FHA; Semi-Fin, GS; Ski C; Tres, SC; Secy, Sr Cl; Pres, Jr Cl; Alg A; Bank Of Amer A; Bio A; CSF; COM; Chem A; Citz A; DARGCA; HQn; Math A; Q&S A; Sci A; Co- ed, Annual; Cpt, Cpt Trophy, Vlbl; Attendance A; Rep, Yth Conf; Reedley Jr Col; Liberal Arts.

HIRES, Angela Gail
Savannah HS; Savannah, GA; Chor; ROTC A; Cl Rep, Pres, Yth Coun; Yth Choir; Pianist, Yth Week; Armstrong Col; Mus.

HIRNING, David Mark
Hellgate HS; Missoula, MT (15-485) A Cap Choir; Co-Ed, Ann; Pres, Bus C; Chor; Drama; Ensm; Fr C; Hon Prog; JA A; U of Mont; Med.

HIRSCH, David William
Southwest HS; Kansas City, MO (5-471) AFS; Band; Cpt, Dbte Tm; Fr C; VP, Math C; NFL; NHS; SC; JV, Tnns; Opt A; All-Dist Band; BSct; Mic-O-Say Order of Arrow; Stage Band, Pres, Yth Group; Stage Crew; Bus.

HIRSCHI, Crystal Lynn
Rio Linda Sr HS; Rio Linda, CA (40-300) Chldr; Hmrm; A-Ed, Sch P; Spch C; Pres, SC; VP, Sr Cl; Pres, Jr Cl; Bkbl; Cl Fav; HCt; Spch A; VP, SC; American River Col; Dental Asst.

HIRST, Scott Oliver
Hempfield HS; Landsville, PA (93-500) Math C; Mu Alpha Theta; Pres, Order/Arrow; Cr-Ctry; JV, Ftbl; Tr; Air Force Acad; Math.

HIRTH, Janet Jean
Temple Heights Christian Sch; Tampa, FL; Band; Tres, NHS; Fin, Sci A; Fin, Bio A; U of Tenn-Knoxville; Pre-Law.

HIRYAK, Julie Marie
Oak Lawn Comm HS; Oak Lawn, IL (20-800) VP, A Cap Choir; Drama; Pres, Fr C; Madrigal; NFL; NHS; Thes; Ch, Sr Cl; Tnns; Most Out; Most Talented; Roosevelt U; Mus Ed.

HISAMOTO, Kaoru
Kubasaki HS; Okinawa, JAPAN (11-271) Pres, Fr C; Mu Alpha Theta; VP, NHS; PA; Radio C; Drafting A; Chinese Culture C; Vlbl C; UCLA; Engr.

HISE, Gretchyn Ernst
Marymount HS; Los Angeles, CA (1-60) Bus Mgr, Ann; Fr C; Ger C; Co-Ch, Hmrm; Co-Ch, Lit Mag; NHS; Sch Achieve Tm; Ski C; Span C; Spch C; Tres, SC; Tres, Jr Cl; CSF; COM; Hon Prog; Lion A; Most Out; NEDT; Spch A; HR; Span A; Attendance A; Harvard U; Med.

HISE, Kelly Diann
Perry HS; Perry, OK (25%-100) Band; Chor; FHA; Sch P; Bkbl; Citz A; Okla St U; Engr.

HISHMEH, Peggy Dawn
Wis Lutheran HS; Milwaukee, WI (30-282) Band; Drama; Ch, Hmrm; Co-Ed, Sch P; Var C; Secy, Y-Tns; Bkbl; Tnns; Cpt, Tr; Star Student; HR; Taylor U; Med.

HISSOM, David Virgle
E Liverpool HS; E Liverpool, OH (10%-300) Band; Key C; Tres, Order/Arrow; Order/Arrow A.

HITCH, David Martin
N Fulton HS; Atlanta, GA (3-187) BC; Hmrm; InterClub Coun; Pres, JETS; Ch, Model UN; Pres, NHS; Pres, Sci C; SC; Bausch & Lomb A; COM; Citz A; H of F; Hon Prog; Math A; NMF; ROTC A; Star Student; NCTE A; Ga Tech; Chem Engr.

HITCHCOCK, David Walter
Kiski Sch For Boys; Saltsburg, PA (3-87) Band; Hmrm; SC; Bsbl; Mgr, Bkbl; Ftbl; Pres, Yth Fel; Church Council; Pastor's Confirmation Schol A; Harvard Col; Law.

HITCHCOCK, Mary Ann
Hickory HS; Hickory, NC (58-359) Hmrm; Lit Mag; Rainbow; Span C; S-T, Jr Cl; Stu o-t Month; Hickory Rotary C; Church Coun; Homecoming Rep; UNC-GREENSBORO; Eng.

HITCHINGS, Douglas Alan
Westboro HS; Westborough, MA; Order/Arrow; Order/Arrow A; Ldr, Audio Visual C; BSct; Pres,; Acct.

HITE, David Gene
William Winlock Miller HS; Olympia, WA; Chor; Madrigal; Centralia Col.

HITE, Donald William Jr
Lee-Davis HS; Mechanicsville, VA (15-423) A Cap Choir; Band; BC; Chor; Ensm; Hmrm; Orch; SC; COM; Hon Schol; David-Lipscomb U; Special Ed.

HITE, Gary Alan
Temple Baptist Acad; Denver, CO (25%-35) Band; NHS; Cpt, Sch Achieve Tm; Ntl Champ Acad Tm; Baptist Bible Col; Ed.

HITE, Martha Ann
Paul M Dorman HS; Spartanburg, SC; VP, Drama; Secy, Hmrm; Bkbl; Sftbl; Hon Prog; Jr Civitan C; Drill Tm; Yth Coun; Acteens; Clemson U; Sci.

HITE, RaVonda LaChelle
Bosse HS; Evansville, IN; Ind U at Bloomington; Phys Ed.

HITT, Andrea Gayle
Alvin HS; Alvin, TX (34-512) Band; Mjrte; NHS; SC; Secy, Jr Cl; Secy, Soph Cl; JV, Bkbl; MVP, Sftbl; JV, Tnns; Outst Foreign Lang Stu; Tex A&M U.

HITT, Grace Elizabeth
Berea HS; Greenville, SC; Semi-Fin, Chldr; S-T, Chor; Hmrm; Semi-Fin, Mjrte; DARGCA; Hist A; Little Miss Greenville; Greenville Womans C Essay Win; Greenville Tech; Med.

HITT, William Otis
Avondale HS; Avondale Estates, GA (25-200) Ann; BC; Fr C; Key C; NHS; Sch P; SC; Cr-Ctry; Soccer; Botany.

HIVNOR, Michael Eugene
West HS; Columbus, OH (357-581) Demolay; Tres, Order/Arrow; Order/Arrow A; Yth Fel; Eagle Sct; Gold Medal Win, VICA Skill Olymp; *Heating-Air Conditioning.*

HIX, Rose Marie
Asher HS; Asher, OK (5%-21) FHA; Sch P; Pres, Jr Cl; Gen Bus A; Home Ec A; *ECU.*

HIX, Sandra Elaine
Pendleton HS; Pendleton, SC; BC; Fr C; WW; *Greenville Tech Col; Phys Therapy.*

HIXON, Charlsie Dianne
Fort Payne HS; Fort Payne, AL (50-127) Band; Chor; FBLA; FHA; FTA; SC; Pres, Tri-HiY; Yth Fel; Yth Leg; *Law.*

HIXON, Kelley Jane
Belton Sr HS; Belton, MO (195-350) Band; Crown & Scepter; *Christian Ed.*

HIXSON, Barbara Ann
Cottage Grove HS; Cottage Grove, OR (34-225) CYO; Hmrm; NHS; JV, Swim; Tr; Type A; *Oreg Inst of Tech; Dental Asst.*

HIZA, Cynthia Kaye
New Caney HS; Porter, TX (10%-220) Band; FHA; Tres, FTA; NHS; Math A; *Stephen F Austin St U.*

HJELLE, Patricia Eileen
Ingraham HS; Seattle, WA (5-25) Chor; Orch; Hon Prog; Scholastic Hon; Sch Service; Fin, Art Comp; *U of Wash.*

HJORT, Kevin James
Lincoln Comm HS; Lincoln, IL (150-350) Golf; *Tool & Die.*

HLOUSEK, Jerry Brent
Zillah HS; Zillah, WA (6-60) Band; BS; Cpt, Chor; Ensm; 4H; NHS; Spch C; JV, Tr; 4H A; Masonic A; Grange; NATS Mus A; Outst Musician; Grange Talent A; *Pacific Luthern Col; Mus.*

HNAT, Timothy Alan
Fort Madison Sr HS; Fort Madison, IA (135-276) Ann; Order/Arrow; Art C; Sct; *Construction.*

HNILICKA, Donna Marie
Valley Regional HS; Deep River, CT (7-140) Drama; Fr C; FNA; Hmrm; NHS; Ski C; SC; Var C; VP, Sr Cl; Bkbl; Hockey; Sftbl; Type A; *U of NH; Social Welfare.*

HOADLEY, Allison Lianne
Lyons Township HS; La Grange, IL (1-1210) A Cap Choir; Ensm; Madrigal; NHS; COM; Hon Prog; NEDT; Cert of Achv, Steinway Piano; HR; 1st Pl, Sch St Mus Contest; Hon Prog, Il St Mus Tchrs Assn; Outst Trophy, Geneva Swed Days Mus; *Ill St U; Mus Ed.*

HOAG, Alan Jon
Greene Central Sch; Greene, NY (14-140) Ann; Drama; Math C; NHS; Var C; Tres, Jr Cl; Co-Cpt, Bsbl; Bkbl; Co-Cpt, Ftbl; Ntl Achv Schol; *U of Ga; Bus.*

HOAG, Brian Chris
Wayland Acad; Beaver Dam, WI (1-78) BS; Cum Laude Soc; Order/Arrow; Span C; Var C; Cr-Ctry; Tr; Wrest; Alg A; God & Country A; Hist A; Hon Prog; Eagle Sct, Eng, Span, A's.

HOAG, David Russel
Don Bosco Tech HS; Boston, MA (11-215) *Elec.*

HOAGLAND, Cheryl Diane
Helix HS; La Mesa, CA (10%-700) Band; Orch; CSF; Citz A; Hon Prog; Band Ltr; *UCSD; Physiology.*

HOAGLAND, Garry Lee
Grimsley HS; Greensboro, NC (15%-500) Cr-Ctry; Tr; Yth Fel; Interntl Mgt Coun Sem; Tutor; *Wingate Col; Bus Adm.*

HOBART, Billie Anne
Fruita Monument HS; Fruita, CO (35-270) Band; Chor; Orch; ARC; Span C; JV, Bkbl; Tr; Yth Fel; VP, Church Dist Yth; Law Enforcement Explorers; Cadet; *Azusa Pacific Col; Mus.*

HOBART, Jean Ann
Weslaco HS; Weslaco, TX (5%-350) Band; NHS; ARC; Span C; Parl, SC; Y-Tns; JV, Tr; HCt; Hon Prog; ARC A; Semi-Fin, St Bkbl; Cpt, Vlbl; Pres, Hidalgo Cotillion; All Dist, Vlbl & Bsbl; *U of Tex; Med.*

HOBBIE, Denise Joy
Flagler Pub Sch; Flagler, CO (4-14) Ann; Chldr; Chor; FBLA; FHA; Semi-Fin, GS; 4H; SC; Secy, Jr Cl; Bkbl; Tr; Sci A; Type A; Yth Fel; Beta HR; Pres, Yth Fel; Mgr, Cpt, Vlbl; Semi-Fin, Typing A; Prom Princess; Fin, Sci A; *Northeastern Jr Col; Legal Secy.*

HOBBIE, Marcella Dea
Wichita East HS; Wichita, KS; Chor; Ensm; VP, Ger C; Matchmaker A.

HOBBS, Brenda Denise
Wichita N HS; Wichita, KS; Sftbl; Pom Pon Sq; Pom-Pon Cert; *Golf Coast Bible Col.*

HOBBS, Frances Elizabeth
Acme-Delco Jr-Sr HS; Delco, NC (2-98) Tres, BC; Cpt, Chldr; Fr C; Hmrm; Lit Mag; Math C; Monogram; Tres, NHS; Ed, Sch P; SC; Sftbl; Alg A; COM; Citz A; Gr Marshal; Sal; Yth Fel; Morehead Nom; *Peace Col; Phys Therapy.*

HOBBS, Frances Lane
Druid Park HS; Satsuma, AL (1-29) VP, Rainbow; Span C; Val; *Mobile Col; Bus Adm.*

HOBBS, Opal Marlena
Breckinridge Co HS; Harned, KY (10%-207) FBLA; VP, FHA; *Berea Col; Acct.*

HOBBS, Susie Denise
Clements HS; Athens, AL; S-T, Band; BC; Pres, FHA; FTA; 4H; Ed, Sch P; Rptr, Soph Cl; Cl Fav; Journ A; Harvest Festival Qn; Tn o-t Mo; Stu o-t Mo; FHA A's; *Calhoun Comm Col; General Ed.*

HOBBS, William Christopher
Newnan HS; Newnan, GA; A Cap Choir; Chor; Rptr, 4H; Key C; Citz A; *U of Ga; Sound Engr.*

HOBGOOD, Lynne Clark
Person Sr HS; Roxboro, NC (8-475) Chldr; Chor; Drama; Fr C; NHS; Tri-HiY; Med Explorers; *U of NC; Pharmacy.*

HOBGOOD, Mark Orion
Temple Christian HS; Redford, MI (2-57) BS; Pres, Chess C; Chor; Secy, Dbte Tm; Drama; Ger C; Ed, Sch P; Ski C; Span C; Spch C; Cr-Ctry; Soccer; Alg A; Bio A; COM; Journ A; Math A; *Henry Ford Comm Col; Elec Engr.*

HOBGOOD, Tina Renee
Cartersville HS; Cartersville, GA; Band; Mjrte; Sch P; *Ga U; Bus.*

HOBURN, Debbie Kay
S Moreland Sr HS; Alverton, PA (6-289) Tres, Ger C; Math C; Tri-HiY; World Affairs C; *Pediatric Nurs.*

HOCH, Andrew Steven
Regular Baptist HS; Martinez, CA (1-35) Hmrm; Span C; VP, SC; Golf; Tnns; Bank Of Amer A; CSF; Math A; Sci A; Val; Gospel Outreach Tm; NML; *U of Calif; Chem Engr.*

HOCH, David Lee
Central Dauphin HS; Harrisburg, PA (45-345) Chess C; Drama; Pres, SC; Ftbl; Soccer; Tr; *Elec.*

HOCH, Timothy Leroy
Central Dauphin HS; Harrisburg, PA; *Commercial Arts.*

HO CHEE, Ricky Neilson
Marist Brother's HS; Pago Pago, AMERICAN SAMOA (1-50) Bus C; Drama; Hmrm; Sch P; Spch C; Alg A; COM; Hon Prog; Journ A; Math A; Sci A; *Pepperdine U; Med.*

HOCHELLA, Tami Lynn
John I Leonard HS; Lake Worth, FL (100-800) Chor; Ensm; Fin, Jr Miss Pageant; Madrigal; Math A; Mus & Health Schol Pins; *Palm Beach Atlantic Col; Mus.*

HOCHSTEDLER, Jeryl Allen
Northridge HS; Middlebury, IN (50-125) 4H; Key C; Ntl Yth Conf; Cpt, Wrest; 4H A; HCt; Most Out; Pres A; MVP, Wrest; Most Points, Wrest; *Achcand Col; Elem Ed.*

HOCHSTEDLER, Kevin Ray
Northwood HS; Nappanee, IN (20-220) SC; Bkbl; Tr; HCt; Ltrman C; *Bus.*

HOCHSTETLER, Patricia Sue
Northridge HS; Middlebury, IN (33%-130) Band; Semi-Fin, GS; Rptr, Hmrm; Bkbl; MVP, Sftbl; Tr; Type A; *Tri-St U.*

HOCHULI, Cynthia Ann
Granite City HS-S; Granite City, IL (113-560) Band; Pres, Hmrm; JA A; Pres A; *Jewish Sch of Nurs; Nurs.*

HOCHULI, Stephan Urs
Northwestern Sr HS; Hyattsville, MD (1-673) Hon Prog; Math A; Rotary A; Val; Ntl Rifle Assn Jr Life Member; Fr A; Math A; Shop A; Gym A; *U of Med; Pre-Dentistry.*

HOCKADAY, James Edward
Lewiston Porter Sr HS; Lewiston, NY (50%-415) Chor; Key C; Ski C; Ftbl; Wrest; *U of Miami; Phys Ed.*

HOCKADAY, Janet Lynn
Spotsylvania Sr HS; Spotsylvania, VA (64-349) Ann; Bus Mgr, FBLA; FFA.

HOCKADAY, Rebecca Carol
Westwood Christian HS; Miami, FL (10%-21) Chldr; Sftbl; HCt; Home Ec A; HR; *NC St U; Secy.*

HOCKEN, Robbin Leigh
Neshaminy Maple Point HS; Langhorne, PA; *Agronomy.*

HOCKENBURY, R Todd
Seneca HS; Louisville, KY (3-322) BC; Pres, Ger C; Hmrm; Lat NHS; NHS; SC; Harvard Book A; MLS; Gym; *U S Military Acad; Engr.*

HOCKER, Eileen Cecile
Parkway Prog; Philadelphia, PA (23-205) Chor; Drama; VP, Hmrm; Rptr, Sch P; VP, SC; Bkbl; Sftbl; COM; *Clark Col; Mass Communications.*

HOCKERSMITH, Paul Duane
Waukegan Christian Sch; Zion, IL; Co-Ed, Sch P; SC; Bkbl; *Moody Bible Inst; Missionary Aviation.*

HOCRAFFER, Nancy Jean
Freeport Sr HS; Freeport, IL (150-600) Band; Ger C; Tri-Double-I; MVP, Badminton; Band Hon's; *Oral Roberts U; Ecology-Conservation.*

HOCUTT, Sameul Herbert III
Williamston HS; Williamston, NC (55-175) Band; Demolay; Fr C; Key C; Order/Arrow; Yth Fel; Pres, Wildlife C; Church Choir; Bus Driver; *NC St U; Elec.*

HODEL, David Beecher
Lakeridge HS; Lake Oswego, OR (90-250) Chor; Drama; Ski C; SC; Thes; Swim; Tr; Select Choir; Comm Chor; Sch Plays; Church Choir; Young Life; *Harvard U; Law.*

HODGE, Cynthia Ann
Aynor HS; Aynor, SC (15%-85) Ann; Fr C; GS; Var C; Mgr, Bsbl; Bkbl; Amer Leg A; *Clemson U; Early Childhood Ed.*

HODGE, David Keith
Russell HS; East Point, GA (15-147) Ann; BC; NHS; Ed, Sch P; JV, Tr; Hon Prog; Opt A; Opt Out Tn; Fire Marshal; PA; Faculty Cup; *Atlanta Christian Col; Ministry.*

HODGE, Gary Wade
Battiest HS; Battiest, OK (2-45) Chor; Drama; NHS; Sal.

HODGE, Gerald Kevin
Batavia HS; Batavia, IL; BS; Math C; SC; Bkbl; Cr-Ctry; Alg A; Hon Prog; Math A; St Scholar; St Span Contest; *Augustana Col; Pre-Law.*

HODGE, Jonathan Allen
Graham HS; Bluefield, VA; Chess C; Fr C; Sci C; Ftbl; Tr; NEDT; *VPI; Elec.*

HODGE, Randy Eugene
Lovington HS; Lovington, IL (9-43) Band; BS; Parl, FFA; VP, 4H; Sch P; SC; Pres, Jr Cl; Amer Leg A; 4H A; HCt; Kiwanis A; *E Ill U.*

HODGE, Rhonda Denise
Livingston HS; Livingston, CA; Drama; Parl, Hmrm; Mgr, Tnns; Spch A; *Morehouse Col; Eng.*

HODGE, Robin Ralene
E Clinton Local HS; Lees Creek, OH (40-128) Chor; Drama; 4H; Most Out; *Cincinnati Bible Col; Christian Secy.*

HODGE, Ronda Kay
Lovington HS; Lovington, IL (8-45) Chor; 4H; SC; 4H A; *Med.*

HODGEMAN, Sherri Lu
John Jay HS; Wiccopee, NY (20%-500) Ann; Band; Tnns; Hon Prog; Type A; 1st, 4th Pls, St Keyboard Comp; *The King's Col; Mus.*

HODGES, Anne Elizabeth
Andress HS; El Paso, TX; Jr Miss Pagent; Tri-HiY; Var C; Tnns; Spch A; Yth Fel; Church Cabinet; *Westmar Col; Hist.*

HODGES, Carla Rene
Carver HS; Columbus, GA (5%-300) Co-Ed, Ann; Hmrm; InterAct C; Secy, InterClub Coun; Key C; Rptr, Lit Mag; Model UN; NHS; Pol Sci C; Span C; Secy, SC; Tri-HiY; UN Council; Y-Tns; Pres, Jr Cl; COM; Cl Fav; Gov Honor Prog; Hon Prog; Most Out; Yth Fel; WW; Lit Meet; Nom, Ntl Senate Yth; Top Span Stu; Sci Fair; *Mercer U; Law.*

HODGES, Cecelia Anne
Washington HS; Washington, NC (10-290) Bus C; FHA; Hmrm; F-Ed, Sch P; Span C; Tr; Most Out; Sci A; Sch Marshal; NHS; DECA Stu o-t Yr; Legislative Page; *Campbell Col; Christian Yth Ed.*

HODGES, Charles Richard
Richardson HS; Richardson, TX (13-950) Band; Ensm; JETS; VP, Mu Alpha Theta; NHS; Order/ Arrow; Hon Prog; Math A; NMS; Eagle Sct.

HODGES, Cheryl Lynn
Eastside HS; Paterson, NJ; Chor; Ensm; COM; Pep Squad; Semi-Fin, Colorguard.

HODGES, Clemmon Howe Jr
Sweet Home Sr HS; Williamsville, NY (390-660) Band; BS; Co-Ch, InterClub Cou; Model UN; Co-Ch, SC; Pres, Jr Cl; JV, Bkbl; Interlochen Ntl Mus; *Morehouse Col; Pre-Law.*

HODGES, Debbie Elaine
Columbus HS; Columbus, GA; Chor; Church Choir; Helper, Mission Friends; Yth Helper, Bible Sch; *Columbus Voc Tech Inst; Secy.*

HODGES, Elizabeth Ann
John Carroll HS; Fort Pierce, FL (10-125) Secy, Drama; NHS; Span C; Thes; Var C; Bkbl; JV, Cr-Ctry; Tr; Alg A; Hon Prog; VP, Art C; Church Handbell Choir; Art A; Rho Alpha Mu; Secy, MYF; *Ringling Sch of Art; Art.*

HODGES, Elizabeth Mae
Miami Killian HS; Miami, FL (120-1200) Var C; Swim; Yth Fel; *Fashion Design.*

HODGES, Janice Lynn
Rio Americano HS; Sacramento, CA (12-378) A Cap Choir; AFS; Pres, Chor; Fr C; Ger C; Inter-Club Coun; Madrigal; Pres, Span C; Bsbl; COM; Citz A; Cl Fav; Ntl Achv Schol; Type A; Exchange Stu; Best Vocalist, Photography, A's; Vocal Competition, A; *Lang.*

HODGES, John Clarence Foight
Shenendehowa HS; Clifton Park, NY (14-650) A Cap Choir; AFS; Chem C; Chess C; Chor; Drama; Hmrm; Madrigal; NHS; ARC; Sci C; Span C; Spch C; Thes; Alg A; COM; Hon Prog; Math A; Ntl Achv Schol; NMF; NMS; NEDT; Regent Schol; *Mass Inst of Tech; Physics.*

HODGES, Kenneth Lee
Lake Taylor HS; Norfolk, VA; Chor; Hmrm; Span C; Citz A; Yth Fel; Yth Coun; DECA; Pres, Jr Civic League; Fin, Graphic Arts Fair; *Pepperdine U; Marine Bio.*

HODGES, Kevin Coles
Sweet Home Sr HS; Amherst, NY (32-625) Band; Co-Cpt, Ftbl; Tr; *Hampton Inst; Bus Adm.*

HODGES, Margaret Frances
Woodland Hills Baptist Acad; Jackson, MS (33%-55) Co-Ed, Ann; BC; Chor; Drama; SC; VP, Soph Cl; Hon Prog; *Ole Miss; Liberal Arts.*

HODGES, Mary Ann
Eastside HS; Paterson, NJ; Chor; Span C; *Passaic County Comm Col; Nurs.*

HODGES, Nancy Joan
Southfield-Lathrup HS; Lathrup Village, MI (64-605) Chor; Key C; Fin, HiL; Tr; Spch A; HR; *Lawrene Inst of Tech; Humanities.*

HODGES, Pamela Gale
Mooreville HS; Mooreville, MS; FHA; FNA; FTA; Ch, Y-Tns; Secy, Soph Cl; Mgr, Tr; Cl Fav; Most Spirited; *Nurs.*

HODGES, Robert Graham
Kinston HS; Kinston, NC (89-331) Co-Ed, Ann; VP, Order/Arrow; Phys C; Co-Ed, Sch P; Sci C; Ntl Sci Found; Order/Arrow A; Photo A; *NC St U; Textile Tech.*

HODGES, Robin Lee
Montclair HS; Montclair, CA (10-300) A Cap Choir; Fr C; Sch Achieve Tm; Arch; Bkbl; Hockey; CSF; Hon Prog; JA A; Pres A; Type A; Yth Fel; Hist, Drill Tm; *Humboldt Col; Forestry.*

HODGES, Shawn Halyane
Columbia HS; South Orange, NJ; Chldr; Pres, Chor; Drama; Span C; Tr; Dancing A; *Mus.*

HODGES, Tammy Elizabeth
Lumberton Sr HS; Lumberton, NC; Fr C; 4H; Acad A.

HODGES, Teresa Lynnette
Wellington HS; Wellington, TX; Band; Cpt, Chldr; Secy, Chor; Ensm; VP, FHA; Span C; Bkbl; Tr; Beauty; FHA Area Choir; FHA St Del; *Hardin-Simmons Col; Mus.*

HODGES, Theresa Louise
W Craven HS; Vanceboro, NC; BC; Chldr; Span C; Hist A; Jr Civitan; *U of NC; Sci.*

HODGES, Tina Marie
Franklin Co HS; Rocky Mount, VA (40%-249) Band; 4H; Span C; Pres, Tri-HiY; Var C; Sftbl; COM; 4H A; Vlbl; Band, Vlbl, Sftbl, A's; 1st Hon Role; *Roanoke Mem Sch of Nurs; Nurs.*

HODGES, Velma Jacqueline
Fort Johnson HS; Charleston, SC (35-235) Span C; Y-Tns; Type A; Pres, Bible C; Church Mus; *E Coast Bible Col; Mus.*

HODGES, Wayne
Anacostia Sr HS; Washington, DC (10-700) A Cap Choir; Chem C; Chess C; Chor; City Conf; Drama; Fr C; Hmrm; Lat C; Lat NHS; NHS; Pol Sci C; ARC; Ed, Sch P; Tres, St Stu Congres; Pres, Sr Cl; VP, Jr Cl; Pres, Soph Cl; Bsbl; Cpt, Cr-Ctry; Ftbl; Cpt, Sftbl; Tnns; Bio A; COM; Chem A; Citz A; HKg; Hon Prog; Journ A; Math A; MLS; PTA A; ARC A; ROTC A; Sci A; Val; DC Board Ed, Outst Work A; Mayor A; *Howard U; Pre-Med.*

HODGIN, Norris William
McMullen Co HS; Tilden, TX (4-18) Ann; FFA; Ch, 4H; NHS; Rptr, SC; Pres, Jr Cl; VP, Soph Cl; Bkbl; Tnns; COM; 4H A; Division I, UIL Piano; *Tex A&M U; Finance.*

HODGIN, Susan Elizabeth
Reidsville Sr HS; Reidsville, NC (11-324) Secy, AFS; Band; Drama; VP, Fr C; Gov Honor Prog; All-St Band.

HODGKINS, John Scott
Birmingham HS; Van Nuys, CA (10%-950) Band; Pres, Order/Arrow; CSF; God & Country A; Hon Prog; Secy, Order o-t Arrow; St Identified Gifted; *Calif St U; Bus.*

HODGKINS, Kevin Ronald
Summerville HS; Summerville, SC; NJROTC; *The Citadel U; Civil Engr.*

HODGKINS, Loraine Michele
Pacific HS; San Leandro, CA (83-356) Band; CYO; Chldr; Chor; Drama; Hmrm; SC; Sftbl; Math A; Pres A; SL Centennial Project; Stu Off Asst; St Mary Math Contest; PA; *Pepperdine U; Bus Adm.*

HODGKINS, Timothy John
Summerville Intermediate HS; Summerville, SC; Band; *The Citadel U; Elec Engr.*

HODGSON, Barbara Ellen
Norman HS; Norman, OK (93-662) Rptr, A Cap Choir; Secy, Chldr; Rptr, Chor; Drama; Ensm; Hmrm; Key C; NHS; Spch C; Spch A; Jr NHS; Mus, Drama, A's; *U of Okla; Drama.*

HODNETT, Billy Burke Jr
Fayetteville HS; Fayetteville, AR; FBLA; Bsbl; Ftbl; *Ark U at Fayetteville; Acct.*

HODNETT, Faye Elizabeth
Cooley HS; Detroit, MI (30-618) Bus C; NHS; Co-Cpt, Bsbl; Bkbl; Tr; Jr off Trng Soc; Fine Arts A; MVP, Bowl Tm; *E Mich U; Bus Adm.*

HODNETT, Tony Lynn
Warren Central HS; Vicksburg, MS;

HODO, Kevin Wayne
Penn Center HS; Washington, DC;

HODOWANES, Robert Daniel
Charles S Mott HS; Warren, MI (250-600) Band; VP, CYO; Co-Cpt, Hmrm; Sftbl; Tnns; *Control Data Inst; Computer Tech.*

HODSON, Cheryl Anne
Lebanon Union HS; Lebanon, OR (20%-450) Band; VP, FNA; NHS; Sci C; Mus o-t Yr; *Seattle Pacific U; Math.*

HODSON, Laurel Lynn
Upper Arlington HS; Columbus, OH (80-800) AFS; Band; Community Yth Symph; Fr C; Hmrm; Orch; Phys C; Ski C; Sftbl; JV, Tnns; Sci A; *Ohio St U; Phar.*

HODSON, Pamela Gaye
Wellston HS; Wellston, OK (1-51) A Cap Choir; Ed, Ann; Bus C; Chldr; Chem C; Pres, Chor; Drama; Ensm; Secy, FHA; Hmrm; Math C; NHS; Rptr, Sch P; Sci C; Pres, SC; Y-Tns; Rptr, Jr Cl; Pres, Soph Cl; Alg A; Amer Leg A; Bio A; COM; Cl Fav; Hist A; Hon Prog; Journ A; Math A; MLS; Sci A; Type A; Val; Candidate, Sch Swtht; Gen Mills Family Ldr of Tomorrow; St Hon Soc; Superintendents HR; *Okla Christian Col; Acct.*

HODSON, Susan Lee
Hillsboro HS; Hillsboro, OH (33%-181) Band; Chldr; Fr C; GS; Pres, 4H; Rptr, Sch P; Tres, SC; Amer Leg A; 4H A; Hon Prog; Statistician, Bkbl; Citz Shortcourse A; *Otterbein Col; Equine Sci.*

HOECHST, Christian John
Archmere Acad; Claymont, DE (5%-89) NHS; Tnns; Tr; Hon Prog; *Law.*

HOEFER, Lynne Annette
Glendale HS; Springfield, MO; AFS; Anchor C; Lat C; *U of Missouri in Columbia; Pre-Med.*

HOEGEMEYER, Debra Lynn
Lyons Pub HS; Lyons, NE (3-32) Band; FHA; Secy, 4H; Bkbl; Tr; 4H A; *U of Nebr; Math.*

HOEGH, Blair Duane
Treynor Comm Sch; Treynor, IA; All Amer Yth; Band; BS; 4H; NHS; Sci C; VP, SC; VP, Jr Cl; Tres, Soph Cl; Bsbl; Cpt, Bkbl; Co-Cpt, Ftbl; Golf; Swim; 4H A; Sci A; *Math.*

HOEMEYER, Andrea Jean
New Haven HS; New Haven, MO (1-50) Band; Chldr; Chor; Ensm; NHS; Pres, Jr Cl; Sftbl; Citz A; Type A; Vlbl; Acad Ltr; *U of Mo; Pol Sci.*

HOENIG, Joy Lynne
Adrian HS; Adrian, MI (20-400) Band; *Central Mich U.*

HOENIG, Julie Sue
Adrian HS; Adrian, MI (1-500) Band; Fin, GS; Mjrte; NHS; COM; Math A; NMS; Val; Yth Fel; *Central Mich U; Math.*

HOENSHELL, Jeffrey Lee
Ogemaw Heights HS; W Branch, MI; A Cap Choir; Band; Chor; Drama; Fr C; Madrigal; NFL; SC; Pres, Jr Cl; Spch A; *Mus.*

HOEPPNER, Mary Ellen
Glenbard W HS; Glen Ellyn, IL (13-507) Band; Chor; Mu Alpha Theta; GAA; Young Life; WW; *Denison Col.*

HOFELZER, Beth Anne
Midpark HS; Middleburg Hts, OH; Sftbl; Swim; Tnns; Hon Prog; *Hospital Adm.*

HOFER, Cheryl Lynne
St Louis Park Sr HS; St Louis Park, MN (14-724) Ensm; FHA; Lit Mag; NHS; Orch; COM; Hon Prog; Most Out; Star Student; 1st Pl, Dist Mus Comp; Valedictorian, Christian Inst; *King's Col; Elem Ed.*

HOFER, Craig Alan
Huron Sr HS; Huron, SD (3-330) Dbte Tm; Hmrm; NFL; Sci C; Amer Leg A; Sci A; Spch A; Win, Sch Writing Contest; *St Paul Bible Col; Missions.*

HOFER, Gena Ann
Hitchcock HS; Hitchcock, SD (1-12) Ed, Ann; Band; Chldr; Ensm; FHA; GS; Mjrte; Ed, Sch P; Amer Leg A; Citz A; Type A; WW; *U of SD; Law.*

HOFF, Connie Jo
Renville Pub HS; Renville, MN (12-45) Ann; Band; Chor; Drama; Ensm; FFA; FHA; FTA; Ger C; GS; *Willmar Comm Col; Elem Ed.*

330

HOFF, Denise Marie
St Joseph HS; Lowell, MA; Pres, CYO; NHS; Ski C; Tres, Jr Cl; Math A; *Northeastern U; Phys Therapy.*

HOFF, Gary Steven
Parkview HS; Orfordville, WI (2-148) A Cap Choir; Chor; Secy, Drama; Ensm; Madrigal; NFL; SC; Secy, Thes; Bsbl; Bkbl; Ftbl; Tr; Amer Leg Orator A; *U of Wis; Bio Sci.*

HOFF, Loraine
Secaucus HS; Secaucus, NJ (9-164) Ed, Ann; Chor; Semi-Fin, GS; NHS; Rptr, Sch P; Ski C; Tnns; MLS; *The Amer U; Pol Sci.*

HOFFERBER, Lori Jean
Lexington Sr HS; Lexington, NE (31-133) Chor; Pres, FTA; VP, 4H; NHS; Thes; 4H A; *Kearney St Col; Elem Ed.*

HOFFLUND, Mark
Clairemont HS; San Diego, CA (1-700) BS; Drama; Hmrm; Cpt, Cr-Ctry; Tnns; Cpt, Tr; Amer Leg A; Bank Of Amer A; CSF; COM; Citz A; DARGCA; Hon Prog; Sci A; Val; Best Supporting Actor; Most Inspirational Runner; Eng & Drama Hon's; Ntl Piano Playing Auditions; *Princeton U; Lib Arts.*

HOFFMAN, Carolyn Sue
Elkhorn Area HS; Elkhorn, WI (1-162) Band; Chldr; Pres, Chor; GS; NHS; DARGCA; Val; Church Yth Choir; Summer Band; Swing Chr Accomp; Mus Clinic Schol; Adult Choir Piano Accompanist; All Sch Musical Play Orch; *Wheaton Col; Bio.*

HOFFMAN, Cheryl Ann
Glenbrook S HS; Glenview, IL (278-600) Chor; Semi-Fin, Betty Crocker Homemaker; *Western Ill U; Recreation and Park Adm.*

HOFFMAN, Darrell Lee
Northwest HS; Omaha, NE (15-545) Chor; Tres, French NHS; Math C; NHS; Order/Arrow; Tres, Jr Cl; NEDT; Order/Arrow A; Yth Fel; Principal's HR; *Computer Sci.*

HOFFMAN, Dean Michael
Crestwood HS; Cresco, IA (8-209) A Cap Choir; Ensm; Madrigal; A-Ed, Sch P; Bkbl; MLS.

HOFFMAN, Doris Joan
Harrington HS; Harrington, WA (3-24) Band; Chor; Pres, FHA; VP, NHS; Var C; Secy, Sr Cl; Cpt, Bkbl; Tr; NEDT; Type A; Vlbl; Ath o-t Yr; St Homemaker Dg; *Spokane Comm; Bus Mgt.*

HOFFMAN, James Edwin
Crescent HS; Joyce, WA; Band; NHS; Bkbl; Ftbl; Tr; Most Out; Ltrmans C; *Idaho St U; Elec.*

HOFFMAN, Jeffrey Faulkner
Woodrow Wilson HS; Long Beach, CA; Ann; Semi-Fin, BS; Drama; Hmrm; InterClub Coun; Tres, Key C; Pres, SC; Pres, Sr Cl; Pres, Jr Cl; Secy, Soph Cl; Cl Fav; Hon Prog; DECA; Soph & Jr o-t Week; *Long Beach St U; Bus Adm.*

HOFFMAN, Jenny Lee
Leola Ind Sch; Leola, SD (2-42) Co-Ed, Ann; Band; Chor; Ensm; Pres, FBLA; FHA; Jr Miss Pagent; Amer Leg A; Cl Fav; Hon Prog; Journ A; Mus As.

HOFFMAN, Jerome Gerald
Leola Ind Sch; Leola, SD (20-43) Pres, 4H; 4H A; Type A; WW; *Presentation Col; Lab Tech.*

HOFFMAN, John Gerard
Glenbard W HS; Glen Ellyn, IL (120-500) Hmrm; NHS; A-Ed, Sch P; SC; VP, Sr Cl; VP, Jr Cl; Bkbl; COM; Q&S A; Legislative Schol; *Northern Ill U; Acct.*

HOFFMAN, Joyce Marie
St James HS; St James, MN (37-154) A Cap Choir; Band; Chor; 4H; 4H A; Hon Prog; Cpt, Color Guard; Gym; Band, Choir, Gym, Letters; Color Guard As; *Willmar Voc Inst; Adm Secy.*

HOFFMAN, Kathy Marie
Granada Hills HS; Granada Hills, CA (900-1500) Hmrm; CSF; Citz A; Hon Prog; *Nurs.*

HOFFMAN, Lori Ann
Northwest HS; Omaha, NE (33%-647) Band; French NHS; Swim.

HOFFMAN, Lydia Kay
Lompoc Sr HS; Lompoc, CA (130-525).

HOFFMAN, Mark Wayne
Garden Spot HS; New Holland, PA (53-259) Drama; Co-Ch, Ger C; NHS; Order/Arrow; Mgr, Bkbl; Mgr, Soccer; Sch Radio Station; Audio-Visual C; Eagle Sct; *Broadcasting.*

HOFFMAN, Michelle Dawn
Audubon HS; Audubon, NJ (89-225) Band; Chess C; Chor; FHA; Madrigal; Sftbl; Tnns; Tr; Yth Fel; Sftbl A; *Asbury Col; Social Work.*

HOFFMAN, Priscilla Joy
Luverne HS; Luverne, MN (8-160) Chor; FTA; Span C; Band A; Chor A; *Northwestern Col; Elem Ed.*

HOFFMAN, Stanley Scott
Woodlan HS; Woodburn, IN (4-145) Band; Ensm; 4H; Bsbl; JV, Ftbl; Citz A; Drafting A; *Sci.*

HOFFMAN, Stephen Henry
Audubon HS; Audubon, NJ (65-250) Band; Fr C; Lat C; MVP, Cr-Ctry; JV, Ftbl; Tr; JV, Wrest; Yth Fel; Cross-Country Tr; *Acct.*

HOFFMAN, Steven Lynn
Woodlan HS; Woodburn, IN (3-125) Band; BS; Chess C; Ensm; Ger C; 4H; JETS; NHS; JV, Bkbl; Golf; Chamber of Comm A; 4H A; Math A; *Purdue U; Chem.*

HOFFMAN, Tamara May
Ashley HS; Ashley, ND (18-42) Band; Chldr; Chor; Drama; Ensm; FHA; Madrigal; SC; Var C; Gym; *Concordia Col; Spch.*

HOFFMAN, Terri Lynn
Olney HS; Philadelphia, PA; FNA; ARC; Tres, Sr Cl; Sftbl; Tr; ARC A; *Villanova U; Nurs.*

HOFFMAN, Vaughn Allen
Hoopeston-E Lynn HS; Hoopeston, IL (21-130) BS; NHS; VP, Soph Cl; Bsbl; *Ill St U; Bus Adm.*

HOFFMAN, Diana Marie
George Washington Sr HS; Mangilao, GUAM (12-640) Drama; NHS; Hist A; Cl Offices.

HOFFMAN, Paul Stuart
Norfolk Catholic HS; Norfolk, VA (40%-150) Pres, Key C; Var C; Ch, Jr Cl; Ch, Soph Cl; JV, Bkbl; MVP, Co-Cpt, Fin, Wrest; Co-Cpt, MVP, Ftbl; *Col of William & Mary.*

HOFFMAN, Walter William
Lakeland Reg HS; Wanaque, NJ (33-330) NHS; Ftbl; Golf; Tr; Wrest; Hon Prog; *Beloit Col; Marine Sci.*

HOFFNER, Rebecca Ann
Lewiston Porter HS; Youngstown, NY (118-410) Co-Ed, Ann; Chor; FTA; Mgr, Bkbl; JV, VLBL; Stage Crew; DJ, Radio Station; *Fort Wayne Bible Col; Mus.*

HOFFPAUIR, Pamela Lynn
Del City HS; Del City, OK (10%-650) Chor; NHS; Rainbow; Tri-HiY; Secy, Sr Cl; HCt; Demolay Swtht; Off, Pep C; Del Aires Chor; *Central St; Med Tech.*

HOFMAN, Linda Diane
Buffalo Sr HS; Buffalo, MN; Yth Fel.

HOFMANN, Bryan Edwin
Oakdale HS; Oakdale, CA (10%-300) NHS; FFA; SC; VP, Soph Cl; Bkbl; Ftbl; JV, Tr; Amer Leg A; CSF; Good Sportsmanship A; *Pepperdine U; Engr.*

HOFMANN, Evelyn Ruth
Meade Sr HS; Fort Meade, MD; FBLA; Mjrte; Span C; Jr NHS; FBLA A; Art A; Mjrte A; *U of Md; Psych.*

HOFMANN, Holly Ann
Brown Deer HS; Brown Deer, WI (13-283) Ann; Fr C; NHS; Ski C; Var C; MVP, Bsbl; Bkbl; Tnns; Hon Prog; Masonic A; Powder Puff Ftbl; Miss Bethel; Honored Qn Bethel; Run-Up, Miss Intrntl Job's Daughtr; Miss Wis Job's Daughters; *U of Wis at Whitewater; Spch Communication.*

HOFMANN, Timothy Brian
Neshaminy Langhorne HS; Langhorne, PA (30-673) NHS; Var C; Cpt, Cr-Ctry; Tr; *Penn St U; Acct.*

HOFMEIER, Connie Lou
Southeast of Saline HS; Assaria, KS (10-84) Band; Chor; Ensm; FHA; NHS; Spch C; Pres, Sr Cl; Bus Mgr, Jr Cl; Bkbl; Sftbl; 4H A; Poet A; Spch A; Type A; *Brown Mackie Col; Secy.*

HOFSTETTER, Janis Sue
Hickory Co R-1 HS; Urbana, MO (6-50) Ed, Ann; Chldr; Chor; Dbte Tm; Ensm; VP, FHA; Secy, 4H; Mod Mus Mas; Secy, Sr Cl; 4H A; HQn; I Dare You; Journ A; Most Sch Spirit; Best Dressed; *Southwest Baptist Col; Lit.*

HOFSTRA, Cathy Anne
Thornton Fractional S HS; Lansing, IL (145-609) Chor; Span C; Sftbl; COM; Hon Prog; Spelling, Guitar, A's; *Moody Bible Inst; Counseling.*

HOFSTRA, Scott Allan
Holt HS; Holt, MI (25%-300) Swim; Yth Fel; *Aviation.*

HOFSTRAND, Joseph Kenneth
McKinley HS; Buffalo, NY; Bsbl; Hockey; Citz A; Yth Fel; 1st Cl BSct; Sr Patrol Ldr; *Air Conditioning.*

HOFT, Nancy Lee
Westover Sch; Middlebury, CT; A Cap Choir; Chldr; Chor; Fr C; JV, Soccer; Sftbl; Pres, Yth Fel; Art A's; *RI Sch of Design; Interior Design.*

HOFT, William Ernest
J S Morton W HS; Berwyn, IL (5%-500) Chor; NHS; Mgr, Swim; Hon Prog; NMS; *U of Ill at Urbana; Chem Engr.*

HOGAN, Bruce Nathaniel
Shaker Hts Sr HS; Shaker Hts, OH (150-500) A Cap Choir; Ensm; Order/Arrow; Ftbl; Mgr, Tr; Order/Arrow A; *Bus Adm.*

HOGAN, Charmaine Anne
Round Valley HS; Eagar, AZ (16-93) Band; Chor; Ski C; Mus A's; *Mus.*

HOGAN, James Bach
North State Acad; Hickory, NC (4-12) VP, Soph Cl; Bkbl; JV, Soccer; Acolyte; *Vanderbilt Col; Physics.*

HOGAN, Karen Leigh
Patrick Henry HS; Roanoke, VA (200-600) Ann; Drama; FHA; FTA; VP, Hmrm; Lat C; Sch P; Span C; *U of Va; Pre-Law.*

HOGAN, Kavin Reuben
St Augustine HS; New Orleans, LA (1-160) Band; CYO; Chor; Lit Mag; Mod Mus Mas; Orch; Alg A; Bio A; COM; Hon Prog; Math A; Most Out; Yth Fel; AFNA Stu; Altar Boy o-t Yr; *Pre-Med.*

HOGAN, Kimberly Elaine
Marion Co HS; Lebanon, KY (1-298) BC; FHA; NHS; Alg A; COM; Math A; Most Stu; *Campbellsville Col; Math.*

HOGAN, Larry Glenn
Phil Campbell HS; Phil Campbell, AL (3-75) Ann; Pres, Band; BS; Parl, FFA; Pres, NHS; VP, Sr Cl; Bkbl; All-St Tuba Player; John Philip Sousa A; Most Intelligent; *Mus.*

HOGAN, Michael Thomas
Don Bosco Tech HS; Boston, MA (1-177) CYO; JV, Bsbl; JV, Ftbl; JV, Hockey; COM; NEDT; *Boston Col; Acct.*

HOGAN, Peter Leo
Serra HS; San Matro, CA (4-180) NHS; Soccer; Bank Of Amer A; CSF; COM; Hon Prog; NMS; NEDT; *U of Santa Clara; Engr.*

HOGAN, Sharlo Beth
Bonita Vista HS; Chula Vista, CA (26-497) NHS; CSF; *Calvin Col; Law.*

HOGAN, Timothy Brian
Yough HS; Hermine, PA (50-150) Bsbl; Bkbl; Ftbl; Tres, Parish Coun; *Pa St U; Foresty.*

HOGBIN, Daryl Ray
Northwood-Kensett HS; Northwood, IA (15-68) Chor; Fr C; Cpt, Bsbl; Cr-Ctry; Tr; Pres A; Yth Leg; REC Govt School Trip; *Waldorf Col; Law Enforcement.*

HOGEN, Carol Ann
Northwood-Kensett Comm HS; Northwood, IA (10-64) Chor; VP, 4H; Secy, SC; Var C; Co-Cpt, Bkbl; Sftbl; Tr; Secy, Rptr, 4-H C; Girl's Recreational Assn; *N Iowa Area Comm Col; Phys Ed.*

HOGEN, Wendy Kay
Northwood-Kensett Comm HS; Northwood, IA (10-66) Chor; Pres, 4H; NHS; Sch P; Var C; VP, Sr Cl; MVP, Bkbl; Sftbl; MVP, Tr; COM; 4H A; Co-Cpt, Bkbl; VP, V-Ch, Rptr, Bus Mgr, 4-H C; DAR Cert; Girls Recreational Assn; N Iowa Area Comm Col; Acct.

HOGENSON, Steven Michael
William Kelley HS; Silver Bay, MN (8-152) VP, Band; Chor; NHS; Sci C; VP, Ski C; Var C; COM; Hon Prog; Sci A; Skiing; Concordia Col; Mus.

HOGG, Andrea DeeAnn
Cleburne HS; Cleburne, TX (10%-300) Band; Secy, Dbte Tm; Ensm; FHA; VP, FTA; 4H; Lat C; A-Ed, Lit Mag; Mjrte; NFL; NHS; Span C; Spch C; COM; Hon Prog; Eng A; U of Tex; Eng.

HOGG, Julie Ann
Ansley Pub Sch; Ansley, NE (33%-50) VP, Band; S-T, Chor; Ensm; Pres, SC; VP, Soph Cl; Pres, Pep C; Vlbl; FFA Swtht Candidate.

HOGGARD, Tammy Jo
Jonesboro Christian Sch; Jonesboro, AR; Pres, BC; Chldr; Chor; Ensm; Hmrm; Sch Achieve Tm; Sch P; Bkbl; Math A; Spiritual Ldrship A; Miss Jonesboro Christian; Choir A; Cert of Achv; Bob Jones U; Math.

HOGGARTH, Kim Korean
Courtenay Pub Sch; Courtenay, ND (2-8) A Cap Choir; Co-Ed, Ann; Band; Chldr; Chor; Drama; Ensm; Pres, 4H; NHS; Secy, Soph Cl; Bkbl; Sftbl; Tr; 4H A; Hon Prog; K of C A; U of ND; Med.

HOGGATT, Matthew Alan
William Winlock Miller Olympia HS; Olympia, WA; A Cap Choir; Chor; Community Yth Symph; Ensm; 4H; Madrigal; Orch; Most Out; Multnomah Sch o-t Bible; Bible.

HOGGE, Rebecca Ruth
Warwick HS; Newport News, VA (7-413) Ann; Chor; FHA; Hmrm; Key C; NHS; Span C; Sftbl; Citz A; Pres A; Yth Fel; Yth Foundation; Campus Life; Faculty A; Christopher Newport Col; Med Tech.

HOGNESS, Bruce Arthur
Niwot HS; Longmont, CO (163-311) A Cap Choir; Band; Bus C; Chor; FBLA; Key C; Bkbl; Ftbl; Tr; Comm Col of Denver; Archt Drafting.

HOHBEIN, Michael Allen
Lincoln NE HS; Lincoln, NE (65-500) JV, Bkbl; JV, Ftbl; Kiwanis A; Yth Fel; Campus Life; Bkbl Coach; Fin, Ftbl; Tnns; Bkbl & Bsbl; Phys Ed.

HOHENSTEIN, Eric Edward
University HS; Normal, IL (25%-121) 4H; Hmrm; Fin, Lit Ral; Spch C; SC; Bsbl; Bkbl; Cr-Ctry; Ftbl; 4H A; NEDT; Communications.

HOHENSTEIN, Julie Ann
Bishop Luers HS; Fort Wayne, IN (5-236) Chor; Pres, Ensm; COM; Hon Prog; Purdue U; Vet Med.

HOHENSTEIN, Pamela Jane
University HS; Normal, IL (25%-108) Secy, AFS; Chldr; Chor; Drama; Pres, Ger C; VP, 4H; Bkbl; 4H A; Pres, Walther League; Co Cpt, Flag Corps; Home Ec.

HOHLSTEIN, Brenda Kay
Waunakee HS; Waunakee, WI; Fr C; Cpt, Bkbl; Mgr, Cr-Ctry; Mgr, Tr; Yth Fel; Airline Stewardess.

HOHWIELER, Tamra Lynn
Chester Area HS; Chester, SD (1-35) Ann; Band; Chor; Ensm; FHA; Pres, 4H; F-Ed, Sch P; SC; Amer Leg A; 4H A; Journ A; S-T, 4-H C; Superior Vocal Solo; U of SD; Mus.

HOKANA, Carol Marie
Oakes HS; Oakes, ND (4-75) GS; S-T, 4H; SC; Pres, Jr Cl; Bkbl; Tr; 4H A; Pres, Secy, GAA; U of ND; Computer Prog.

HOKANA, Michael Edward
Robinson Secondary Sch; Fairfax, VA (125-525) Drama; Key C; JV, Ftbl; US Merchant Marine Acad; Nautical Sci.

HOKE, Billy Pershing
Borger HS; Borger, TX; A Cap Choir; Chor; Drama; Order/Arrow; Thes; Mgr, Bkbl.

HOKE, Janet Kay
NW Classen HS; Okla City, OK; Alg A; HR; Christian Ed.

HOKE, Marion Leah
Blytheville HS; Blytheville, AR (2-285) BC; JV, Chldr; Ger C; GS; Pres, NHS; Alg A; Amer Leg A; Bio A; COM; DARGCA; Pres A; Sal; Swtht; Ger, Econ, Civics, A's; Hendrix Col; Biol.

HOKE, Tina Marie
NW Classen HS; Okla City, OK (84-460) FHA; Tnns; Recording Secy, Pep C; Outst Home Ec A; SW Okla St U; Home Ec.

HOKINSON, Ehricke Roberts
Sacred Heart HS; Kingston, MA (7-85) Chor; Drama; Hmrm; NHS; Co-Ed, Sch P; Mgr, Cr-Ctry; COM; Hon Prog; Journ A; VFW A; Outst Sch Service; Outst Actor; Excellence in Acting A; Marquette U; Drama.

HOLBECK, Barbara Jil
Armour HS; Armour, SD (1-34) Ann; Band; Chor; Dbte Tm; Drama; Pres, FHA; Ger C; NFL; Pres, NHS; Spch C; SC; Pres, Soph Cl; Amer Leg A; Citz A; DARGCA; Elk A; Spch A; Val; Secy, FHA; Church Organist; Win, Local, Dist, Regional Declam; Superior, Piano Solos; Regional FHA Off; SD St U; Mus.

HOLBECK, Scott Alan
Armour HS; Armour, SD (2-40) Band; Chor; Drama; NHS; SC; Bsbl; All-Sch Plays; Stage Band; Swing Choir; SD St U; Agr.

HOLBEN, Lauren Leigh
Salisbury HS; Allentown, PA (21-238) Mgr, Bsbl; Tnns; Hon Prog; Yth Fel.

HOLBERT, Bret Hiram
Duncan U Fletcher Sr HS; Neptune Beach, FL; InterAct C; Ftbl; Church Sr High Yth Choir; Hon Men, All Conf Ftbl; Dentistry.

HOLBERT, Karen Sue
Moore HS; Moore, OK (7-676) Band; Ger C; NHS; Orch; Hon Prog; Jr Acad of Sci A; Tulsa U; Deaf Ed.

HOLBROOK, Beverly Anne
Jessamine Co Sr HS; Nicholasville, KY (30-240) Band; Secy, BC; Ensm; NHS; Span C; Alg A; Bkbl Qn Ct; Section Ed, Ann Staff; WW; U of Ky; Acct.

HOLBROOK, Billy Ray
Statesville Sr HS; Statesville, NC (15%-250) A Cap Choir; Fr C; Hmrm; Bkbl; Ftbl; Wrest; Art, Industrial, A's; W Carolina U; Art.

HOLBROOK, Clifton Neal
Tift Co HS; Tifton, GA; Biol.

HOLBROOK, Tommy Dean
Henryetta HS; Henryetta, OK (1-110) Ann; Key C; Pres, Mod Mus Mas; NHS; Span C; Bkbl; Mgr, Ftbl; Fin, Tnns; Alg A; Bio A; Citz A; Math A; Sci A; Okla U; Med.

HOLBROOKS, Jill Ann
Stamford HS; Stamford, TX (6-70) Ann; Band; Chor; FHA; NHS; Thes; Spch A; Lions C Swtht; WW; Mayor's Choice; Painting Merit A; Baylor U; Sociology.

HOLCOMB, Alma Jane
Greenville HS; Greenville, MS (17-526) FBLA; Span C; Hon Prog.

HOLCOMB, Angela Cherylene
Welch HS; Welch, WV; Up Bound; Vocational Sch; Typing.

HOLCOMB, Arnie Wallace
Bremerhaven American HS; Bremerhaven, GERMANY (8-31) Ann; NHS; Rptr, Sch P; Var C; Bsbl; Bkbl; Cpt, Ftbl; Cpt, Tr; HCt; Type A; MVP, Tr; Pepperdine U; Bus.

HOLCOMB, Barbara Jo
Springfield HS; Springfield, MI; JV, Chldr; Secy, FHA; NHS; SC; Tnns; Tr; Amer Leg A.

HOLCOMB, Cynthia Melissa
Calhoun HS; Calhoun, GA (10%-250) Chldr; NHS; Span C; Tri-HiY; Var C; 4H A; HCt; U of Ga; Dental Hygiene.

HOLCOMB, James Michael
Will Rogers HS; Tulsa, OK; Band; Community Yth Symph; Hmrm; Key C; NHS; Orch; SC; Bkbl; Kiwanis A; Scholastic A; Tulsa U; Sci.

HOLCOMB, Jay Anna
Alto HS; Alto, TX (7-41) Band; Drama; Lit Ral; Mjrte; Rptr, Sch P; Poet A; Yth Fel; UIL Solo & Ensm; Lib Staff; MYF; Stephen F Austin St U; Spch.

HOLCOMB, Julia Dianne
Forest Hill HS; Jackson, MS (99%-371) A Cap Choir; Co-Ch, BC; Hon Prog; Girl o-t Mo; Harding Col; Computer Sci.

HOLCOMB, Katrina Lynn
Alto HS; Alto, TX (2-30) Ann; VP, Band; Chor; VP, FHA; Mjrte; Rptr, Sch P; VP, SC; Bkbl; Tnns; HCt; Sal; Asst Drum Major; Eng A; Prose A; WW in Mus; Band Swtht; Most Scholarly; Bus A.

HOLCOMB, Laura Renee
Banks HS; Birmingham, AL (10%-250) Drama; Thes; Soccer; Sftbl; Nurs.

HOLCOMB, Randall William
Avondale HS; Avondale Estates, GA; Hmrm; Lat C; SC; Bsbl; Bkbl; Ftbl; Ga Col; Law.

HOLCOMB, Robert Perry
N Augusta HS; N Augusta, SC (5%-450) BC; NHS; JV, Bkbl; Tnns; Hon Prog; Jr Marshal; Augusta Col Achv A; Presbyterian Col Jr Fel; Law.

HOLCOMB, Rosa Lynn
Alto HS; Alto, TX (5%-45) Band; Chldr; MVP, Ensm; FHA; Jr Miss Pagent; Tres, SC; Secy, Jr Cl; Tnns; Beauty; Cl Fav; Hon Prog; Yth Fel; Tyler Jr Col; Interior Decorating.

HOLCOMB, Sandra Kay
Avondale HS; Avondale Estates, GA (22-250) BC; Secy, Chor; Ensm; Math C; NHS; Span C; Mgr, Bkbl; Soccer; Tr; Mgr, Wrest; Gov Honor Prog; Hon Prog; Star Student; Yth Fel; Fin, Vocal Solo; 1st Pl, Lit Meet; WW; Carson-Newman Col; Mus.

HOLCOMB, Stephen Roderic
Ripley HS; Ripley, TN (25-250) BC; Chor; VP, 4H; Hmrm; V-Ch, SC; Var C; Cpt, Bkbl; Cl Fav; Tenn St U; Acct.

HOLCOMB, Thomas James
Hueneme HS; Port Hueneme, CA; Order/Arrow; JV, Ftbl; JV, Wrest; Hon Prog.

HOLCOMB, Wayne Eugene
Royal Valley HS; Hoyt, KS (2-70) Ann; Co-Ed, Sch P; VP, SC; Bkbl; Cr-Ctry; Tr.

HOLDCRAFT, Linda Judith
Willingboro HS; Willingboro, NJ (100-432) Hmrm; NHS; Mgr, Sftbl; Mgr, Swim; Pres, Sou NJ Conf UMYF Conf; Conf Coun On Yth Ministries; Yth Del, Wrld Meth; Pres, Loc UMYF; Pres, Local UMYF; Lebanon Valley Col; Psych.

HOLDCROFT, Tamara Lynn
Switzerland Co HS; Vevay, IN (6-96) Band; Chldr; Drama; Pres, 4H; Sci C; Span C; Bkbl; MVP, Sftbl; Tr; 4H A; Purdue U; Vet Med.

HOLDEMAN, David Eugene
Shawnee Mission W HS; Overland Park, KS (25-688) Hon Prog; Fin, St Yth Bowl Tourn.

HOLDEN, Anthony Glenn
Osceola HS; Kissimmee, FL (250-499) Band; Drama; Ensm; InterClub Coun; Mjrte; Thes; COM; Hon Prog; JA A; Drum Major; WW; Pres, Bible C; Band & Vocal A's; Rollins Col; Mus.

HOLDEN, Carol Elizabeth
High Point Sr HS; Beltsville, MD (1-713) A Cap Choir; Co-Ed, Ann; Band; Chor; Community Yth Symph; Drama; Ensm; Fr C; Hmrm; NHS; Sch P; Bausch & Lomb A; COM; Hon Prog; NMF; NMS; Sci A; Service & Eng A's; Bryn Mawr Col; Psych.

HOLDEN, Darlene Scott
Storm King Sch; Cornwall on the Hudson, NY; Chldr; Chor; Drama; Lit Mag; ARC; Sch P; Var C; Soccer; Swim; COM; Citz A; God & Country A; Journ A; Poet A; ARC A; Karate; Highest GSct Rank; Drama, Sct, A's; Queens Col; Theater.

HOLDEN, Kristi Arlene
Elk Point HS; Elk Point, SD (7-56) Ann; Band; Chor; GS; 4H; Fin, Jr Miss Pagent; Madrigal; Sch P; Spch C; Var C; Bkbl; Sftbl; Swim; Tr; Amer Leg A; 4H A; Pres A; Pres, Luther League; Sportsmanship A; All St Hon Choir; Augustana Col; Elem Ed.

HOLDEN, Martha Prince
Petersburg HS; Petersburg, VA (30-600) Hmrm; Span C; Spch C; SC.

HOLDEN, Ryk Jeffrey
Tuscola HS; Tuscola, IL (13-145) Band; Pres, Lat C; NHS; Sch Achieve Tm; VP, Sci C; SC; Var C; Ftbl; Tr; COM; Cl Fav; Rotary A; St Scholar; *U of Ill; Engr.*

HOLDEN, Sharon Dorain
Oakdale HS; Oakdale, LA (10-205) NHS; Sci C; Hon Prog; Phys Ed A; *Computer Prog.*

HOLDER, Benny Ray
Elgin HS; Elgin, OK (32-73) Chess C; Chor; Ensm; 4H; VP, Hmrm; VP, Soph Cl; Cl Fav; Solo Medal; Chorus Medal; *Southwestern Col; Bio.*

HOLDER, Cheryl Joy
Concord Christian Sch; Concord, NH (2-5) Chldr; Chor; GS; VP, SC; Cpt, Bkbl; Swim; Alg A; Gr Marshal; Hon Prog; Sal; Yth Fel; Cert of Appreciation; Piano A; *NH Tech Inst; Secy Sci.*

HOLDER, David Lee
Newnan HS; Newnan, GA (22-307) Band; BC; Chor; Ensm; COM; Kiwanis A; Band A; Dist Hon Band; All St Band; *Jacksonville St U; Mus.*

HOLDER, Joni Marie
Colo HS; Colo City, TX (4-95) Secy, Band; Chor; Ensm; FBLA; Secy, NHS; Cl Fav; HQn; MLS; *Baylor U; Bio.*

HOLDER, Kasandra Lynne
Lake City HS; Lake City, TN (3-154) Ann; BC; Chor; Drama; 4H; Hmrm; VP, Span C; SC; Bkbl; Beauty; Bio A; Pres A; Span A; *U Tn; Religion.*

HOLDER, Linda June
Westside HS; Jonesboro, AR (6-102) Band; Chor; FBLA; Secy, FTA; NHS; SC; *Ark St U; Acct.*

HOLDER, Pamela Jo
Wilkes Central HS; N Wilkesboro, NC (118-290) Monogram; Span C; Sftbl; Most Improved; Vlbl.

HOLDER, Vicenzio
Rainbow City Jr Sr HS; Rainbow City, CANAL ZONE; Band; Chor; Secy, Drama; Rptr, Sch P; JV, Tnns; Hist A; Math A; Sci A; Chor A; SA A; *Canal Zone Col; Laboratory Tech.*

HOLDREN, Kenneth Roy
Central Baptist HS; Hampton, VA (1-13) Ann; 4H; Sch P; Ftbl; H of F; Type A.

HOLE, Timothy Scott
Wapakoneta Sr HS; Wapakoneta, OH (9-354) Chess C; Demolay; Pres, 4H; Rptr, Lat C; NHS; Sch Achieve Tm; Co-Ed, Sch P; 4H A; Q&S A; Hugh O'Brien A Yth Found; *Ohio St U; Sci.*

HOLIDAY, Margarette Louella
Winyah HS; Georgetown, SC; Co-Ed, Ann; Chldr; Hmrm; Fin, Jr Miss Pagent; SC; Var C; Bkbl; Cl Fav; HCt; *Anderson Jr Col; Bus.*

HOLIFIELD, Irene
East Tech HS; Cleveland, OH (60-625) Mjrte; Journ A; *Journ.*

HOLIFIELD, Jeffrey Kerry
East Central HS; Hurley, MS (4-115) BC; Sci C; Var C; Bsbl; MVP, Ftbl; Sci A; Star Student; JETS A; *Ga Inst of Tech; Chem Engr.*

HOLLAND, Alicia Doreen
Hillcrest HS; Dallas, TX (20-500) A Cap Choir; Band; NHS; Span NHS; *Baylor U; Sci.*

HOLLAND, Betty Lou
Big Sandy HS; Big Sandy, TN (3-28) Ed, Ann; VP, BC; Drama; FFA; FHA; MVP, Bkbl; Sftbl; MLS; Sci A; *Union U; Liberal Arts.*

HOLLAND, Beverly Janet
Memphis Tech HS; Memphis, TN; Chor; Hmrm; Mjrte; SC; Tr; Attendance A; *Nurs.*

HOLLAND, Carrie Ann
Broken Arrow HS; Broken Arrow, OK (86-467) Cpt, Band; FBLA.

HOLLAND, Cathy Renee
Bethany HS; Reidsville, NC; Anchor C; BC; Chldr; Fr C; Monogram; Sch P; *Mus.*

HOLLAND, Charles Martin
Hart Co HS; Hartwell, GA; Band; BC; HiY; Math C; Golf; Swim; Band Medals; *Ga Sou Col; Acct.*

HOLLAND, David Andrew
Wilburton HS; Wilburton, OK (9-60) BS; 4H; Math C; NHS; Order/Arrow; Sci C; Pres, Sr Cl; Ftbl; Amer Leg A; Bio A; Cl Fav; Sci A; *Eastern Okla St Col; Bio.*

HOLLAND, David Bruce
Austintown Fitch HS; Austintown, OH; Sftbl; VICA; *Emery Riddle Col; Aviation Maintenance.*

HOLLAND, Delfinia Antrice
Jessie H Jones HS; Houston, TX; Drama; *U of Houston; Nursing.*

HOLLAND, Diane Helen
Stafford HS; Stafford Springs, CT (9-149) Band; Chor; Drama; Madrigal; NHS; Thes; Most Out; *Nyack Col; Mus Ed.*

HOLLAND, Donna Carol
Franklin Co HS; Winchester, TN; Co-Ed, Ann; Drama; FHA; VP, FTA; 4H; Pres, Sci C; Bkbl; 4H A; Service A; *Middle Tenn St U; Elem Ed.*

HOLLAND, Gregory Martin
Stone Mountain HS; Stone Mountain, GA (27-289) Pres, Band; BC; VP, Chess C; Chor; Drama; Pres, Fr C; Lit Mag; SC; COM; DARGCA; Gov Honor Prog; Hon Prog; All St Band; All St Stage Band; DeKalb Hon Band; Arion A; *Ga St U; Mus Ed.*

HOLLAND, John Barry
Sophronia M Tompkins HS; Savannah, GA (3-184) Band; BC; Hmrm; NHS; Span C; SC; Bsbl; Alg A; Bio A; COM; Chem A; Cl Fav; Hist A; Hon Prog; Math A; Most Out; Sci A; Summa Cum Laude; Eng A; Ga Tech Sci Schol; WW; *Armstrong St Col; Chem.*

HOLLAND, Norman Gregory
Geneva HS; Geneva, AL (20-90) Band; Drama; Fr C; Sci C; Band A; *Enterprise St Jr Col; Drama.*

HOLLAND, Patricia Elaine
South HS; Columbus, OH (1-407) Chor; Ensm; Fr C; K of C; NHS; COM; Crisco A; Hon Prog; Val; *Ohio St U; Bus Adm.*

HOLLAND, Robert Keith
University of San Diego HS; San Diego, CA (1-374) Sci C; CSF; Hon Prog; Most Out; Rocket C; *Sci.*

HOLLAND, Robert William
Bremerhaven American HS; Bremerhaven, GERMANY (10-31) Co-Ed, Ann; CYO; Rptr, Sch P; VP, Var C; Tres, Sr Cl; Bsbl; Bkbl; Cpt, Cr-Ctry; Tr; COM; HCt; Order/Arrow A; *Police Work.*

HOLLAND, Sabina Drew
Archmere Acad; Claymont, DE (1-120) Cpt, Chldr; Fr C; French NHS; SC; Mgr, Tr; NEDT.

HOLLAND, Thomas Keating
Archmere Acad; Claymont, DE (1-100) Co-Ed, Ann; A-Ed, Lit Mag; NHS; A-Ed, Sch P; Spch C; Secy, Span NHS; Parl, SC; Secy, Jr Cl; Secy, Soph Cl; Mgr, Bkbl; Mgr, Ftbl; Mgr, Tr; Hon Prog; NEDT; Spch A; Eng A; Span A; *Pre-Law.*

HOLLAND, Travis Wayne
NW Classen HS; Oklahoma City, OK (114-460) A Cap Choir; Pres, Chor; Madrigal; JV, Ftbl; 1st Pl, NATS; *Okla Baptist U; Mus.*

HOLLAND, William Lewis
Sublette HS; Sublette, KS (20-48) Semi-Fin, BS; Pres, FFA; 4H; Var C; Ftbl; Tr.

HOLLANDER, Helaine Gail
Bruriah HS; Elizabeth, NJ (1-33) NHS; Hon Prog; *Stern Col For Women; Eng.*

HOLLEMAN, Stephen Bryan
Ridgedale Acad; W Monroe, LA; COM; NEDT; SRA Comp; PSAT-NMSQT Comp; WW; *Northeast La U; Computer Sci.*

HOLLENBECK, Teresa Ann
East HS; Salt Lake City, UT; A Cap Choir; FBLA; Madrigal; Rainbow; Ski C; SC; COM; Kiwanis A; *U of Utah; Pediatric Nurs.*

HOLLENBECK, Teresa Anne
East HS; Salt Lake City, UT (30-400) A Cap Choir; Ensm; FBLA; Hmrm; Madrigal; NHS; Rainbow; Ski C; SC; COM; Hon Prog; Kiwanis A; *U of Utah; Nurs.*

HOLLER, Mary Bruce
McLaurin HS; Sumter, SC; Chldr; Fr C; *Marine Bio.*

HOLLERS, Les Paul
Valentine HS; Valentine, NE (10%-78) Tres, FFA; Pres, 4H; Ftbl; Wrest; Alt, Jr Lawman; FFA A's; *U of Nebr; Vet Sci.*

HOLLEY, Barbara Therese
Robert E Lee HS; Montgomery, AL (123-649) Anchor C; Co-Ed, Ann; SC; Tri-HiY; Yth Leg; Pres, Yth Coun; Secy, Yth Fel; *Auburn U; Ed.*

HOLLEY, Belinda
Rockdale HS; Rockdale, TX (62-154) Band; Chldr; Chor; Golf; ARC A; Yth Fel; *Baylor U; Special Ed.*

HOLLEY, Carol Ellen
Sibley HS; Sibley, LA (3-54) Ed, Ann; FHA; GS; Pres, 4H; Lit Ral; NHS; Secy, SC; VP, Soph Cl; Cpt, Bkbl; Sftbl; Cl Fav; 4H A; Hon Prog; *La Tech U; Biomed Engr.*

HOLLEY, Jeri Shawn
Beech Hill HS; Pulaski, TN (10-25) VP, BC; Chor; Secy, FHA; Hmrm; F-Ed, Sch P; Secy, SC; Pres, Soph Cl; Bkbl; Sftbl; Beauty; Cl Fav; HQn; *Middle Tenn St U; Journ.*

HOLLEY, Jon Thomas
Washington HS; Los Angeles, CA (42-800) VP, Band; Drama; Pres, Ensm; Citz A; MLS; Most Out; *UCLA; Mus.*

HOLLEY, Joseph Eugene
Tupelo HS; Tupelo, MS (5%-375) Ch, Key C; NHS; Order/Arrow; Span C; Order/Arrow A; *U of Miss; Med.*

HOLLEY, Julie Elizabeth
Scott Preparatory Sch; Opelika, AL (10%-27) Anchor C; Ann; BC; Co-Cpt, Chldr; Secy, Hmrm; Var C; Secy, Jr Cl; Cpt, Bkbl; Phys Ed A; *Auburn U.*

HOLLEY, Kathy Diane
Burnsville HS; Burnsville, MS (2-70) BC; FHA; *Northeast Miss Jr Col; Art.*

HOLLEY, Susan Annette
Chester HS; Chester, IL (22-99) Ann; Band; VP, FTA; NHS; Sch P; Tr; COM; Hon Prog; St Scholar; *Sch o-t Ozarks; Amer Hist.*

HOLLEY, Virginia Linda
Maury HS; Norfolk, VA (25%-400) S-T, Band; Young Life; Comm Vol Service Cert; Candystriper; Band Swtht; Health Fair; *U of Va; Ed.*

HOLLIBAUGH, Lori Lee
Orofino HS; Orofino, ID; Chor; Drama; Ski C; Bkbl; Sftbl; Yth Fel; Qn of Orofino Fair Days Cand; Vlbl; Bible A; Cpt, Bkbl Intramurals; Badmitton.

HOLLICK, Steven Dale
North HS; Bakersfield, CA; Dbte Tm; Rptr, Sch P; Tnns; Hon Prog; Spch A; *Bakersfield Col; Bus.*

HOLLIDAY, Dawn Ranay
E Central HS; Brookville, IN (11-230) Ann; Band; BC; Chldr; Chor; FFA; Mjrte; NHS; F-Ed, Sch P; Secy, Span C; JV, Bkbl; Mus A; *Ky Christian Col; Missions.*

HOLLIDAY, Jeff Leigh
Whitehouse HS; Whitehouse, TX (5-140) Pres, FFA; NHS; *Tex A&M U; Agr.*

HOLLIDAY, Thomas John
Lakewood HS; Lakewood, OH (59-811) Ger C; NHS; Ski C; Mgr, Cr-Ctry; Mgr, Tnns; *Ohio St U; Mech Engr.*

HOLLIES, Donna Marie
West Side HS; Gary, IN (68-686) Band; Sci C; Span C; Bio A; COM; Citz A; Hon Prog; Sci A; *Okla St U; Vet Med.*

HOLLIFIELD, Kathy Jo
Tecumseh HS; New Carlisle, OH (110-368) Drama; 4H; COM; 4H A; *Cincinnati Bible Col; Bible.*

HOLLIMAN, Alice Faye
Leander HS; Leander, TX (1-170) Chldr; Pres, FHA; Secy, NHS; VP, Jr Cl; Secy, Soph Cl; JV, Bkbl; Alg A; COM; Type A; Cpt, Powder Puff Ftbl; A-HR; Varsity Vlbl; UIL Shorthand; OEA Rptr; *Secy.*

HOLLIN, Clara Joyce
Clay Co HS; Manchester, KY; FBLA; Phys Fitness A.

HOLLING, Cynthia Lou
Grand Junction HS; Grand Junction, CO (50-376) AFS; VP, Chor; Drama; NHS; DARGCA; H of F; Yth Fel; Outst Mus, Job's Daughters; Jr Mus C A; Rep, St Job's Daughters Pageant; *Colo St U; Mus Theory.*

HOLLINGER, Susan Anne
Crestwood HS; Mantua, OH; Band; BC; Hmrm; Ski C; SC; Sftbl; *Hiram Col; Biol.*

HOLLINGSWORTH, Cynthia
Rancho HS; N Las Vegas, NV (8-575) Chor; NHS; COM; Deans Schol; *Brigham Young U; Genealogical Research.*

HOLLINGSWORTH, Gregory Thomas
Marion Acad; Ocala, FL (2-18) Ed, Ann; Pres, Chess C; Pres, NHS; Ed, Sch P; Pres, Span C; Pres, SC; S-T, Var C; VP, Sr Cl; Pres, Jr Cl; Tres, Soph Cl; MVP, Bsbl; Co-Cpt, Bkbl; Co-Cpt, Ftbl; MVP, Golf; Tr; Alg A; Bio A; COM; Hist A; Hon Prog; I Dare You; Journ A; Math A; NMS; Opt A; Sal; Sci A; Spch A; Outst Ath; *Troy St U; Dentistry.*

HOLLINGSWORTH, Janet Kay
Lake Attendance Center; Lake, MS (3-40) Band; BC; FBLA; FHA; Sch P; Math A; ECJC Schol; *E Central Jr Col; Secretarial Training.*

HOLLINGSWORTH, Mildred Annette
Scott Central HS; Forest, MS; Co-Ed, Ann; S-T, Band; Secy, BC; Secy, Chor; Pres, Crown & Scepte; Drama; Ensm; FHA; Pres, 4H; Hmrm; VP, SC; VP, Sr Cl; VP, Jr Cl; Pres, Soph Cl; Beauty; COM; Citz A; Coun of Teach A; 4H A; HQn; Hon Prog; JA A; Most Out; Spch A; Type A; Yth Fel; Most Dependable; Miss SCHS; St Fair Dress Revue A; *U of Ala; Occupational Therapy.*

HOLLINGSWORTH, Rita Faye
Citronelle HS; Citronelle, AL; BC; Hmrm; Math C; NHS; Sci C; VP, Tri-HiY; Chaplin, NHS; CIOC; *Phys Therapist.*

HOLLINGSWORTH, Robert Dale
Panhandle HS; Panhandle, TX (41-60) Secy, FFA; FHA; 4H; Var C; Tr; 4H A; Most Courteous; *Amarillo Col; Diesel Mech.*

HOLLIS, Brian Lee
Sulphur HS; Sulphur, OK (4-84) Chem C; JETS; NHS; Sci C; Pres, SC; Math C; Bkbl; Cpt, Golf; Tr; Cl Fav; Gov Honor Prog; Ntl Sci Symposium; Pres A; Regent Schol; MVP, Golf; *Seminole Jr Col; Engr.*

HOLLIS, Gary Eugene
Maries R-I HS; Vienna, MO (10%-56) Parl, FFA; Cr-Ctry; *U of Mo at Columbia; Nuclear Engr.*

HOLLIS, Karen Esther
Pittsburgh Learning Lab Center; Pittsburgh, PA (4-127) All Amer Yth; Pres, Chor; Rptr, Dbte Tm; VP, FTA; Secy, Hmrm; Bus Mgr, Lit Mag; Math C; V-Ch, Sch Achieve Tm; Up Bound; Sftbl; Tnns; Cl Fav; Hon Prog; *All Comm Col; Special Ed.*

HOLLIS, Kristi Ellen
Lenora HS; Lenora, KS (6-25) NHS; Cpt, Bkbl; Tr; HCt; *Colby Comm Col; Art.*

HOLLISTER, Stephen Morse
Battle Ground Acad; Franklin, TN (1-98) Ann; Chor; Lat C; NFL; Spch C; Cr-Ctry; Tr; NEDT.

HOLLISTER, Susan Esther
Homer Central HS; Homer, NY (150-243) Chldr; Ch, Thes; Ch, Cl Homecoming Float; Alt, Bergamo Conf; Acolyte; Rep, Yth Conf; *W Los Angeles Comm Col; Respiratory Therapy.*

HOLLMANN, Lisa Ann
Armour HS; Armour, SD; Band; Chor; FHA; VP, 4H; Rptr, Sch P; Mgr, Bkbl; Mgr, Tr; 4H A.

HOLLOMAN, Cynthia Kay
Bladenboro HS; Bladenboro, NC (3-101) Ann; VP, BC; Fr C; FHA; Hmrm; SC; Tres, Jr Cl; B Crocker A; Hist A; Hon Prog; WW; *Pembroke St U; Elem Ed.*

HOLLOMAN, Gardnetta
Ahoskie HS; Ahoskie, NC; Chor; *Early Childhood Ed.*

HOLLOMAN, Leonardo Maurice
Palm Bay HS; Melbourne, FL (20-500) Chem C; Sci C; Bkbl; Swim; Chem A; Ntl Sci Found; Sci A; *Sci.*

HOLLOMAN, Scotty Alan
Clovis HS; Clovis, NM (1-546) BS; NHS; Tr; Val; Weightlifting; Danforth A; WW; Tn o-t Wk; *Bus.*

HOLLOMOND, Ruth Otelia
Greensville Co Sr HS; Emporia, VA; Pres, FBLA; FHA; Pres, 4H; HiY; Hmrm; Tri-HiY; Bkbl; *Smith Deal Meassey Col; Basic Secy.*

HOLLOT, Marissa Ludmila
Notre Dame HS; Clarksburg, WV (1-63) Dbte Tm; Drama; Lat C; Math C; NFL; NHS; Amer Leg Orator A; Spch A; Win, Knights of Pythias; Lat A; *W Va U; Med.*

HOLLOWAY, Brenda Jean
Terrell Co HS; Dawson, GA (10%-112) VP, BC; Pres, Sci C; Secy, Sr Cl; COM; Presbyterian Schol A; *Nurs.*

HOLLOWAY, Brian Douglass
Winston Churchill HS; Potomac, MD (33%-576) Lat C; Lat NHS; NHS; SC; Var C; Ftbl; Cpt, Tr; COM; H of F; Yth Fel; *Stanford U; Psych.*

HOLLOWAY, Bruce Alan
Bucyrus HS; Bucyrus, OH (2-200) BS; Var C; Tnns; *Math.*

HOLLOWAY, Bruce Vincent
Concord HS; Concord, NH (1-140) Band; Model UN; World Affairs C; *Tech.*

HOLLOWAY, Cheryl Ann
Plant City HS; Plant City, FL (18-560) F-Ed, Ann; Band; Chldr; GS; Secy, Model UN; NHS; Sr Superlative; Civinettes; Hon Stu; Tn For Christ; Tampa Times Hon Stu; Hosp Girls; Historian, Sr Cl; Soph Exec Coun; *U of Fla; Pol Sci.*

HOLLOWAY, Jack Walker
Jackson Central Merry HS; Jackson, TN (74-438) Ch, Hmrm; Mu Alpha Theta; NHS; SC; Cpt, Ftbl; Hon Prog; *Tenn Tech U; Engr.*

HOLLOWAY, Jamie L
Tivy HS; Kerrville, TX (17-281) Band; Drama; VP, InterAct C; NHS; COM; H of F; NMF; Opt Out Tn; Spch A; Pres, Art C; Art A's; Solo & Ensm Band A's; *Sam Houston St U; Art.*

HOLLOWAY, John Thomas
Garinger HS; Charlotte, NC (150-630) Tres, Key C; Rptr, Sch P; VP, Jr Cl; Ftbl; Tr; Co-Cpt, Wrest; Q&S A; Dey C Schol; SC Schol; *U of Ala; Bus.*

HOLLOWAY, Johnnie May
Lexington Sr HS; Lexington, NC (20%-256) Secy, FHA; Hmrm; SC; HCt; *NC A&T St U; Early Childhood Ed.*

HOLLOWAY, Kerry James
Homewood HS; Homewood, AL (1-240) BS; Chor; VP, Fr C; French NHS; InterClub Coun; VP, Key C; Math C; Mu Alpha Theta; NHS; SC; Alg A; Chamber of Comm A; Citz A; Hon Prog; Math A; MLS; NEDT; St HS Lions C Rep; Pres, Jr Park Board; *Auburn U; Pre-Med.*

HOLLOWAY, Mary Catharine
Gila Bend HS; Gila Bend, AZ (4-52) Pres, Band; Chldr; S-T, Chor; Pres, Drama; Cpt, Mjrte; NHS; Pres, Rainbow; Var C; Secy, Jr Cl; Bkbl; Tnns; Tr; HCt; Elks C Schol, Mus Camp; All Conf, Vlbl.

HOLLOWAY, Mary Kathryn
Bucyrus HS; Bucyrus, OH (60-200) Ed, Ann; Band; Mjrte; VP, Tri-HiY; *Ohio St U; Psych.*

HOLLOWAY, Max Leon Jr
Broken Arrow HS; Broken Arrow, OK (45-500) Band; NHS; Bsbl; Mgr, Bkbl; Ftbl; Swim; COM; Citz A; ARC A; Val; Stage Band; Achv A; VICA; Page, St House of Rep; 1st Pl, Dist Welding; *Okla St U; Engr.*

HOLLOWAY, Michele K
W P Davidson HS; Mobile, AL (2-500) BC; Co-Cpt, Chldr; Fr C; Fin, Jr Miss Pageant; NHS; SC; Tres, Sr Cl; Cl Fav; Hist A; HCt; Math A; NEDT; Sal; Sci A; Yth Fel; Co Jr Miss; Soph & Jr Cl Rep; Gayfers Tn- board; *Sci.*

HOLLOWAY, Remonia Vanessa
Baker HS; Columbus, GA (50-250) Ann; Band; Tres, FHA; Hmrm; SC; JA A; Cl Coun, HR, A's; *Morris Brown Col; Bus.*

HOLLOWAY, Ronda Faye
Dalton HS; Dalton, GA (10-300) Chor; NHS; JV, Bkbl; Hon Prog; Joyful Noise; Church Choir; Church Yth Coun.

HOLLOWAY, Sandra Elizabeth
Appalachian HS; Oneonta, AL (3-38) Ann; BC; VP, FHA; 4H; Secy, Hmrm; NHS; Sch P; Secy, Sr Cl; Cpt, Vlbl; Semi-Fin, HCt.

HOLLOWAY, Stephen Lloyd
Eastern HS; Middletown, KY; Fr C; Cr-Ctry; Tr; COM; Hon Prog; *Harding Col; Archt.*

HOLLY, Dawn Jenelle
Watsonville HS; Watsonville, CA; A Cap Choir; Chor; Drama; Madrigal; COM; Greatest Contributor, Mixed Chor; *Mus.*

HOLLY, Krislyn Faith
Watsonville HS; Watsonville, CA; Secy, Chor; Madrigal; CSF; Section Ldr, A Cappella Choir; *Biola Col; Psych.*

HOLLY, Renea Jeanenne
Glenwood HS; Glenwood, WA (2-12) 4H; Tr; 4H A; Hon Prog; Vlbl; *Walla Walla Comm Col; Med Secy.*

HOLLY, Tandi Lynn
Glenwood HS; Glenwood, WA (1-15) A-Ed, Ann; Chldr; Drama; Fr C; Pres, 4H; NHS; Phys C; Ed, Sch P; I Dare You.

HOLLYFIELD, Donna Lee
Crenshaw Christian Acad; Luverne, AL (3-24) Ann; BC; Chor; 4H; A-Ed, Sch P; Bkbl; Beauty; 4H A; Hon Prog; Hon Soc; *Art.*

HOLM, Jonathan Kent
Windom Area HS; Windom, MN; Chor; Ensm; Bkbl; JV, Ftbl; Tr.

HOLM, Lynette Rae
Windom Area HS; Windom, MN; Chor; Ensm; Fin, GS; VP, Candystripers; *NW Minn Col; Bible.*

HOLM, Pamela Jane
Columbus HS; Columbus, ND (5-20) Ann; Band; Chldr; Chor; Semi-Fin, GS; Sch P; Var C; Tres, Sr Cl; VP, Jr Cl; VP, Soph Cl; Cpt, Bkbl; Sftbl; Tr; Hon Stu; Hon Band; *Moorhead St U; Bus.*

HOLMAN, Debra Lynn
Winner HS; Winner, SD (20-105) Band; VP, Chor; Dbte Tm; Madrigal; VP, NFL; Ed, Sch P; SC; S-T, Thes; Journ A; Distinguished Musicianship; WW; WW, Mus Stu; *SD St U; Mus.*

HOLMAN, Dorothy Doloris
Hastings Sr HS; Hastings, MN (89-430) Ski C; Job's Daughter 'Qn'; VP, Pep C; *U of Minn of Duluth; Elem Ed.*

HOLMAN, Holly Faye
Jackson Prep Schl; Jackson, MS (90-117) A Cap Choir; Sch P; Fin, Tnns; Yth Fel; Tnns Trophies; *Comverse Col; Bio.*

HOLMAN, Kimberly Elise
Rockledge HS; Rockledge, FL (40-290) FBLA; Span C; COM; Eng A; *Spelman Col; Eng.*

HOLMAN, Marcia Jan
Charles H Darden HS; Wilson, NC; Band; Mjrte.

HOLMAN, Philippa Ann
Hightstown HS; Hightstown, NJ (36-283) Co-Ch, AFS; Chor; Fr C; Co-Cpt, Hockey; Swim; Tr; Hon Prog; Ath Yrbk; *Douglass Col; Engr.*

HOLMAN, Raoul Jr
Northwest HS; St Louis, MO (65-433) Tr; Ntl Achv Schol; *U of Ariz; Bus Adm.*

HOLMAN, Valarie Rene
Kathleen Sr HS; Lakeland, FL; Math C; *Secy.*

HOLMBERG, Karin Maurine
Batavia HS; Batavia, IL; AFS; Band; Orch; Band Solo's.

HOLMBERG, Kirsten Diane
Batavia Sr HS; Batavia, IL; Chldr; FTA; NHS; Orch; Sch P; SC; Co-Cpt, Tr; HCt; *N Park Col; Phys Ed.*

HOLMES, Allen Raymond
Thornton Fractional N HS; Calumet City, IL; *U of Miami; Phys Ed.*

HOLMES, Barbara Jean
Merced HS N Campus; Merced, CA; Yth Church; Yth Choir; *Merced Jr Col; Secy Sci.*

HOLMES, Brian Andrew
Holliston HS; Holliston, MA (40%-268) Wrest; Life Sct; *MIT; Engr.*

HOLMES, Bud Dewayne
Paris HS; Paris, TX; Ftbl; Tr; *Tex Tech U; Architecture.*

HOLMES, Christopher Conrad
Northeastern HS; Detroit, MI; Cr-Ctry; Tr; Tr, Cr Ctry, As; *Oakland Col; Engr.*

HOLMES, Cynthia Daphne
Midfield HS; Midfield, AL; Band; Chor; Ensm; Hmrm; NHS; Span C; SC; COM; Citz A.

HOLMES, Dale Hazen
Hartford HS; Hartford, VT (25%-160) Hmrm; Golf; Most Out; Comm Ctr A; Most Improved Stu o-t Yr; Skilled Comp A; Co-Op Work Stu Prog.

HOLMES, Darlene
Saginaw HS; Saginaw, MI; All Amer Yth; Chor; Secy, Hmrm; Phys C; Var C; Y-Tns; Bkbl; Tr; Attendance A.

HOLMES, David Ray
Elmira HS; Elmira, OR (10-147) Pres, Chess C; Math C; VP, NHS; Rptr, Sch P; Tr; H of F; Hon Prog; *OSU; Pre-Vet.*

HOLMES, Dawne Marie
Spruce Creek HS; Port Orange, FL; A Cap Choir; BC; Chor; Lit Mag; Span C.

HOLMES, Deborah Ann
Richardson HS; Richardson, TX (100-908) Band; Ensm; NHS; Orch; Tres, Tri-HiY; Hon Prog; Cpt, Drum Corp; Jazz Festival; NML; Advanced Placement Eng; All Region Band, Orch; Outst Drummer; *Baylor U; Bio Chem.*

HOLMES, Denise Lynn
Eaton Rapids HS; Eaton Rapids, MI (1-252) Ed, Ann; Secy, Band; Drama; NHS; Math A; Yth Foundation A; Church Chor; Band, School, Outst Eng Schol, A's; Geom, Yrbk Production, A's; *U of Ky; Eng.*

HOLMES, Denise Marie
Niles McKinley HS; Niles, OH (180-423) A Cap Choir; Drama; Ensm; FTA; ARC; Rptr, Sch P; Journ A; Sec, Mus Director; Future Shock C; Health Careers C; Chamber Chor, Ntl Comp U of Md; *Warren-Wilson Col; Eng.*

HOLMES, Edward
Clinton HS; Clinton, NC (2-230) Band; BC; Chess C; VP, Key C; Parl, Monogram; SC; Bsbl; Alg A; H of F; Math A; Nom, Gov Sch; *Wake Forest U; Law.*

HOLMES, Gay
Blytheville HS; Blytheville, AR (5-285) Ann; BC; Rptr, Chor; Drama; Ensm; FHA; GS; Lit Mag; Madrigal; NHS; VP, Span C; Span NHS; Amer Leg Orator A; Most Out; Choir Achv A; Ntl Guild of Piano Teachers; *U of Tenn at Martin; Mus Ed.*

HOLMES, Gayla Ann
Battiest HS; Battiest, OK (5-24) Co-Ed, Ann; Chor; Ensm; FHA; NHS; Parl, Sr Cl; Hist A.

HOLMES, Gregory Alan
Wheaton R-3 HS; Wheaton, MO (6-31) Ann; Pres, FFA; Secy, 4H; Pres, NHS; Pres, SC; Pres, Jr Cl; VP, Soph Cl; Mgr, Bsbl; Mgr, Bkbl; 4H A; MLS; Star Student; FFA, St Farmer Degree; FFA Beef & Crop Production A; FFA Star Greenhand & Star Chptr A; *SW Mo St U; Agr.*

HOLMES, Helen Elaine
Plano Sr HS; Plano, TX; Band; FHA; JV, Bkbl; JV, Tr; *E Texas St Col; Computer Sci.*

HOLMES, Jack Allen
Ottumwa HS; Ottumwa, IA (109-539) Hmrm; Var C; Ftbl; Tr; COM; Citz A.

HOLMES, James Edward III
S Pike HS; Magnolia, MS; Spch C; St Stu Congress; Hon Prog; *U of Sou Miss; Law.*

HOLMES, James Joseph
Prescott HS; Prescott, AZ (1-460) Chor; Dbte Tm; Drama; Hmrm; InterAct C; VP, Model UN; NFL; Rptr, Sch P; Spch C; Thes; Alg A; COM; DARGCA; Hon Prog; Lion A; Math A; Most Out; Poet A; Spch A; St Championships Spch; *U of Sou Calif; Law.*

HOLMES, James Martin
William Allen HS; Allentown, PA (300-800) Band; Pres, 4H; Co-Cpt, Hockey; 4H A; *Forestry.*

HOLMES, Joe Clinton
Corsicana HS; Corsicana, TX (28-310) Ftbl; Swim; *Tex A&M U; Finance.*

HOLMES, Joseph Daniel
Pearl HS; Pearl, MS (62-270) Co-Cpt, Tnns; Hon Prog; *Clarke Col.*

HOLMES, Julia Anna
Twentynine Palms HS; Twentynine Palms, CA (12-160) A Cap Choir; Co-Ed, Ann; Ch, CYO; Chor; Ensm; Fr C; Fin, GS; 4H; Madrigal; ARC; Pres, SC; Thes; Bsbl; JV, Bkbl; Ftbl; JV, Tr; Bank Of Amer A; CSF; Cl Fav; DARGCA; HCt; Hon Prog; Opt A; Star Student; Secy, SC; Fr A; Hon Guard; *Iowa St U; Vet Med.*

HOLMES, Julie Ann
Mason Sr HS; Mason, MI (10-270) Band; Chor; 4H; SC; COM; H of F; Hon Prog; Yth Fel; Jr NHS; Gen Excel A; *Acct.*

HOLMES, Kelly Kay
Jackson Hole HS; Jackson, WY (1-104) Co-Ed, Ann; Band; Ensm; Semi-Fin, GS; NHS; Ski C; Spch C; Pres, SC; Pres, Soph Cl; JV, Bkbl; Tr; Alg A; Hon Prog; Rotary A; Type A; Val; Yth Leg; *U of Idaho; Biochem.*

HOLMES, Lisa Ann
Freeport Sr HS; Freeport, IL (91-526) Band; Dbte Tm; FNA; *Highland Comm Col; Nurs.*

HOLMES, Mark William
Lawrence HS; Trenton, NJ (75-150) Hmrm; Ntl Yth Conf; Span C; Bsbl; Bkbl; Soccer; Citz A; Cl Fav; Yth Fel; *Sou U; Phenology.*

HOLMES, Paula Jo
Southside HS; Fort Smith, AR (169-430) Ensm; Lat C; Spch C; Pres, Y-Tns; Drill Tm; *Ouachita Baptist U; Elem Ed.*

HOLMES, Rebecca Hodges
Asheboro HS; Asheboro, NC; A-Ed, Ann; Chor; Pres, Hmrm; InterClub Coun; Rptr, Sch P; Span C; SC; Pres, Sr Cl; VP, Jr Cl; Bkbl; Mgr, Tr; HCt; Statistician, Tr; Typist, F-Ed, Sch P; *UNC-G; Social Work.*

HOLMES, Richard Cade
Pine Bluff HS; Pine Bluff, AR (30-700) Key C; Span C; Ftbl; Tnns; Tr; Square Dance C; Hon Roll; Lutheran Walther League; Ltr, Tnns; *U of Ark; Law.*

HOLMES, Stanley Robert
Ballou Sr HS; Washington, DC (3-30) A Cap Choir; Ntl Yth Conf; Citz A; Hist A; Hon Prog; MLS; Sci A; Yth Fel; Piano A; Sci Fair A; *Podiatry.*

HOLMES, Susan Lynn
Nettleton HS; Jonesboro, AR (7-120) A Cap Choir; Chor; Ensm; FBLA; FTA; Tres, Hmrm; Math C; Sci C; Secy, Span C; *Ark St U; Elem Ed.*

HOLMES, Terry Lee
Dows Comm Sch; Dows, IA (10-21) Band; BS; Tres, FFA; VP, 4H; Hmrm; SC; Co-Cpt, Ftbl; 4H A; HCt; Lion A; *Iowa Central Col; Farm Power & Equipment.*

HOLMES, Tina Maria
Frank W Ballou HS; Washington, DC; Chem C; Parl, Hmrm; Ntl Yth Conf; Bio A; COM; Chem A; Citz A; Hist A; Hon Prog; Most Out; PTA A; Sci A; Hon Soc; Mus A; Phys Ed A; *Wash Tech U; Lab Tech.*

HOLMQUIST, Joanne Beth
Kenowa Hills HS; Grand Rapids, MI (25%-275) Band; NHS; 4H A; Hon Prog; Solo & Ensm A.

HOLMQUIST, Tim John
Braham Westview HS; Braham, MN (10-98) Band; Ensm; Var C; Tres, Jr Cl; VP, Soph Cl; Co-Cpt, Bkbl; Ftbl; Cpt, Golf; Alt, BS; *St Olaf Col; Pre-Med.*

HOLOHAN, Debbie Joy
Madison C-3 HS; Madison, MO (2-27) Band; BC; Chldr; Chor; FHA; Rptr, Sch P; Var C; Pres, Jr Cl; Sftbl; Alg A; Amer Leg A; HCt; Candidate, Yrbk Qn; Soph Pilgrimage; Study C Eng Essay A.

HOLOHAN, Thomas Patrick
Greeley W HS; Greeley, CO (30-300) Chor; Swim; Tr; Math A; *Sound Engr.*

HOLONICS, Amy Elisabeth
Hightstown HS; Hightstown, NJ; Band; Chor; Hmrm; Sch P; Ski C; SC; Bkbl; JV, Hockey; Hon Prog; Ch, Yth Coun; *Ecology.*

HOLOVACH, Chris Alan
Sublette HS; Sublette, KS; Pres, Band; Ensm; Pres, 4H; InterClub Coun; SC; Var C; VP, Sr Cl; Co-Cpt, Bkbl; 4H A; HKg; HCt; Hon Prog; *Acct.*

HOLOVACH, Gina Shay
Sublette HS; Sublette, KS (33%-43) Band; Secy, 4H; *Colo Sch of Fine Arts; Dance.*

HOLSCHER, James Herman
Johnston Sr HS; Johnston, RI; Yth Fel.

HOLSCHER, Sheri Jo
Perkins Co HS; Grant, NE (1-30) Band; Chor; Ensm; FHA; S-T, 4H; JV, Bkbl; Sftbl; 4H A; Hist A; Math A; Yth Fel; JV Vlbl; Sumr Sch, St Peter's & Manhattan Co; *U of Nebr; Med Tech.*

HOLSCLAW, Donald Eugene
Elk Grove Sr HS; Elk Grove, CA (12-1200) JV, Ftbl; COM; Hon A; *USC; Bible Literature.*

HOLSCLAW, Pamela Sue
Days Creek HS; Days Creek, OR (5-26) Secy, FFA; NHS; Bkbl.

HOLSINGER, Pamela Jo
H H Dow HS; Midland, MI (100-424) Pres, Bus C; Drama; NHS; Co-Ed, Sch P; VP, Soph Cl; Golf; JA A; DECA; *Delta Col; Bus Adm.*

HOLSIPPLE, Andrea Donna
John Jay Sr HS; Hopewell Junction, NY (235-551) Ann; Band; Symphonic Band; Flag Girl; Band Ltr; Woodwind Choir; Sanctuary Choir; Librarian, Concert Band; Fin, HQN; March Bnd; Voc Ensm; Outst Bnd Mem; *Coble Skill Ag & Tech Col; Horticulture.*

HOLST, Jan Kay
Clinton HS; Clinton, LA; A Cap Choir; AFS; Chor; Drama; Ensm; Fr C; Madrigal; Tnns; Creative Writing A; *Harding Col; Elem Ed.*

HOLST, Tracy E
Simi Valley HS; Simi Valley, CA (170-675) AFS; Bkbl; Cpt, Soccer; Cpt, Sftbl; Swim; All Star, Soccer; Secy, Luther League; Art A; *Moorpark Col; Art.*

HOLSTON, Mary Patricia
Tuscaloosa HS; Tuscaloosa, AL (33-561) Lat C; Mu Alpha Theta; VP, NHS; Span C; Var C; Bkbl; Tr; *U of Ala; Microbio.*

HOLT, Alison
Bloomtrail HS; Chicago Heights, IL; Drama; Sci A; *Ill Mesonic Sch of Nurs; Nurs.*

HOLT, Beverly Jeanne
Williamston HS; Williamston, NC (7-200) Band; JV, Chldr; Chor; Drama; FBLA; Rptr, Monogram; NHS; Tres, Sci C; SC; Secy, Jr Cl; Mgr, Tr; Gr Marshal; Flag Tm; Women's C School; *Wake Forest U; Mus.*

HOLT, Brian Lee
Putnam City HS; Okla City, OK (343-850) Band; BS; Ger C; JETS; Sch Achieve Tm; Sci C; JV, Cr-Ctry; *Okla St U.*

HOLT, Bruce Allen
Burnt Hills-Ballston Lake Sr HS; Burnt Hills, NY; Band; Mgr, Ftbl; Tr; Mgr, Wrest; Regent Schol; *Taylor U; Chem.*

HOLT, Coleen Gracie
Glades Day Sch; Belle Glade, FL; BC; F-Ed, Sch P; *U of Fla; Bus.*

HOLT, David Glen
East HS; Duluth, MN; Chor; Pres, Hmrm; Ski C; Span C; Ftbl; Tnns; COM; Hon Prog; Church Choir.

HOLT, Doris Jean
Thornton Township HS; Harvey, IL (440-889) Prom Committee; Pom Pon Squad; Girl's C; *Prairie St Col; Nurs.*

HOLT, Gordie Bernard
Leesville HS; Leesville, LA; Band; Chor; Ensm; InterAct C; 1st Pl, Mus; Northwestern; Mus Schol; *Northwestern St U; Mus.*

HOLT, Holly Jean
Kenston HS; Chagrin Falls, OH; Fr C; HR Soc.

HOLT, Jacqueline Lee
Newton HS; Newton, IL; Band; Bus C; Chldr; Chor; Madrigal; Twirling Tm; *E Ill U; Interior Decorator.*

HOLT, John Ray
Meridian HS; Meridian, TX (4-36) BC; City Conf; Dbte Tm; Drama; FFA; Hmrm; InterClub Coun; NHS; Sch P; Pres, Ski C; Pres, St Stu Congres; VP, SC; Thes; Up Bound; Var C; VP, Jr Cl; Cpt, Bkbl; Cpt, Ftbl; Cpt, Hockey; Cpt, Tr; Cpt, Wrest; Cl Fav; Hon Prog; Sci A; Star Student; Drill Tm Beau; Outst Schol A; *Tex A&M U; Marine Biol.*

HOLT, John Thomas III
Loris HS; Loris, SC; Ann; Drama; Sch P; Sci C; Math A; *Archt.*

HOLT, John W III
Olanta HS; Olanta, SC (4-45) Ann; BC; Hmrm; Var C; Bsbl; MVP, Bkbl; Ftbl; Swim; Tnns; *U of SC; Pre-Med.*

HOLT, Judy Carol
Thornton HS; Harvey, IL; Band; SC; Swim; COM; Eng, A; *Art.*

HOLT, Katherine LeAnn
Jefferson City HS; Jefferson City, MO; Chor; Pep C; *Warrensburg Col; Psych.*

HOLT, Keith William
Central HS U S D 462; Burden, KS (1-47) Band; BS; VP, 4H; NHS; Sch P; SC; Var C; JV, Bkbl; Ftbl; Tr; Alg A; 4H A; Hist A; Math A; Type A; WW.

HOLT, Kelly Dean
Central o-t Burden HS U S D 462; Burden, KS (2-34) Band; BS; Chor; FFA; Pres, 4H; NHS; Sch P; Var C; Bkbl; Mgr, Ftbl; Tr; B Crocker A; 4H A; MLS; Sal; St Scholar; WW; St Lion's C Band; *McPherson Col; Elec.*

HOLT, Kenny Lee
North Side HS; Jackson, TN (20%-215) Co-Ed, Ann; Band; BC; Chess C; Drama; Bsbl; Bkbl; *Law.*

HOLT, Kim Ellen
N Love Christian Sch; Loves Park, IL (5-12) Ann; Spch A.

HOLT, Kirk Alan
Putman City HS; Oklahoma City, OK; Band; Fr C; NHS; Hon Prog; *Architecture.*

HOLT, Letitia Kathryn
Brunswick HS; Brunswick, GA (51-419) Tres, Chldr; Drama; InterClub Coun; Lit Mag; NHS; Span C; Pres, SC; Tnns; DARGCA; HCt; Cpt, JV Chldr; Pres, Raquet C; Outst Sr; *Ga Sou Col; Marine Biol.*

HOLT, Margaret Catherine
Greenville Sr HS; Greenville, TX (10%-430) Band; NHS; Academic Excellence A; *Psych.*

HOLT, Nancy Elizabeth
Williamston HS; Williamston, NC (14-250) Band; Ensm; Fr C; Key C; Monogram; Sci C; Tnns; Mgr, Tr; *U of NC; Phar.*

HOLT, Natalie Anne
Lead Hill HS; Lead Hill, AR (3-21) Ann; FBLA; VP, FHA; GS; Sch P; Secy, Sr Cl; Rptr, Jr Cl; Bkbl; Sftbl; HCt; MLS; Home Ec A; Most Courteous; Lib C; *U of Ark; Sociology.*

HOLT, Sherri Lynn
San Bernardino HS; San Bernardino, CA; Chor; Drama; Sales & Merchandise Cert; Worthy Princess; *San Bernardino Col; Bus Ed.*

HOLT, Steve Jerome
Coosa HS; Rome, GA; Band; Drama; 4H; Order/ Arrow; ARC; Opt A; Order/Arrow A; Sci A; *Berry Col; Eng.*

HOLT, Suzanne Lynn
Wheaton Central HS; Wheaton, IL (50-320) A-Ed, Ann; Band; Co-Cpt, Chldr; Community Yth Symph; Dbte Tm; Orch; Ski C; Spch C; Secy, SC; Beauty; Citz A; Opt A; Spch A; Star Student; Model o-t Yr; *Baylor U; Social Work.*

HOLTEN, Karen Kristine
Moorhead Sr HS; Moorhead, MN (90-610) Community Yth Symph; Ensm; Orch; Tr; *Concordia Col; Med.*

HOLTER, Brenda Lee
Grove City HS; Grove City, PA (21-225) AFS; Chldr; NHS; Secy, Sci C; Ski C; Secy, Span C; VP, Jr Cl; Win; Festival Ct; *Duff's Bus Inst; Ct Rptr.*

HOLTER, Kari DeAnn
Hatton Pub HS; Hatton, ND (4-20) Band; Chldr; Chor; Ensm; FHA; Tres, Hmrm; Math C; Co-Cpt, Bkbl; Sftbl; COM; Outst Rebounder, Bkbl.

HOLTER, Timothy Mark
Parkview HS; Orfordville, WI (34-161) A Cap Choir; Ann; Band; Chor; 4H; Tres, Sch P; Life Sct; Hon Stu; Teachers Fund Schol; Dorian Mus Camp Schol; *Carthage Col; Law.*

HOLTHUS, Velda Renae
Johnson-Brock Pub HS; Johnson, NE (1-24) Ann; Band; Chor; Ensm; Spch C; Alg A; COM; Hon Prog; Math A; *NW Mo St U; Mus.*

HOLTMAN, Linda Lee
Nw HS; Indianapolis, IN (30-530) Band; Community Yth Symph; Ensm; NHS; Orch; Ed, Sch P; COM; Hon Prog; Journ A; Q&S A; Sci A; *Purdue U; Vet Med.*

HOLTMEIER, Kristi Carol
Minn Luth HS; Minneapolis, MN (5-50) Ann; Band; Cpt, Chldr; Chor; Drama; 4H; Sch P; Tr; Great Books C; Ntl Poetry Press; *Concordia Col; Lit.*

HOLTON, Donna LaNell
Chickasaw Acad; Van Vleet, MS (2-10) Ed, Ann; Pres, BC; Co-Cpt, Chldr; A-Ed, Sch P; SC; Pres, Sr Cl; Rptr, Jr Cl; VP, Soph Cl; Cl Fav; DARGCA; Gov Honor Prog; 4H A; HQn; HCt; MLS; Eng A; Most Versatile; Bible C Church Yth Coun; *Northeast Jr Col; Elem Ed.*

HOLTON, Leslie Lucille
Parkway Prog Beta Unit HS; Philadelphia, PA; Chldr; Chor; Drama; Hmrm; Model UN; Orch; Co-Ed, Sch P; SC; Arch; JV, Bsbl; JV, Bkbl; JV, Hockey; JV, Soccer; JV, Sftbl; JV, Tnns; JV, Tr; Eng A; *Howard U; Dramatic Arts.*

HOLTON, Patricia Helen
Catholic Central HS; Troy, NY (10%-340) Cpt, Chldr; Chor; Ger C; Hmrm; NHS; Sch P; SC; Cr-Ctry; Tr; Elk A; K of C A; Sci A; *Union Col; Pre-Med.*

HOLTON, Priscilla Rose
P K Yonge Laboratory Sch; Gainesville, FL (20-94) Bus Mgr, Ann; Band; Chem C; Chor; Drama; VP, Ensm; InterClub Coun; Secy, Span C; SC; Bkbl; Cr-Ctry; Sftbl; *Microbio.*

HOLTON, Teresa Susan
Cath Central HS; Troy, NY (10%-350) NHS; Sch P; Cr-Ctry; Tr; Hist A; K of C A; *New Paltz Col; Art.*

HOLTON, Wayne Michael
Temple Heights Christian Sch; Tampa, FL (2-63) Chor; Pres, Sr Cl; COM; HCt; Hon Prog; Sal; Sci A; Photographer, Ann; Chp, NHS; Most Intellectual; *South-Eastern Bible Col; Ministerial.*

HOLTZ, DeEtta Jane
Walnut Comm HS; Walnut, IA (3-23) Chor; Ensm; FHA; FNA; NHS; Pres, Jr Cl; Hon Prog; Type A; Mus A; Stu Librarian; *SD St U; Med Tech.*

HOLTZ, Harold Fred
Clarke Central HS; Athens, GA (5-333) Band; BC; Fr C; Secy, Mu Alpha Theta; NHS; COM; Gov Honor Prog; Math A; Eagle Sct; *U of Ga; Computer Sci.*

HOLTZ, Julee Anita
Hinton Comm Sch; Hinton, IA; VP, Jr Cl; S-T, Soph Cl; *Western Iowa Tech; Secy.*

HOLTZ, Kathy Denice
M B Smiley HS; Houston, TX (11-400) NHS; Hist A; Eng, Homemaking, A's.

HOLTZ, Loren Eugene
AvoHa Comm HS; Avoca, IA (5-48) Band; Chor; Ensm; Ger C; Order/Arrow; Amer Leg A; God & Country A; Hon Prog; Order/Arrow A; Sci A; SWI Bandmasters Hon Band; WI Conf Hon Band; Band Jamboree Ct; *U of Iowa; Phar.*

HOLTZCLAW, Martha Jane
Gaffney Sr HS; Gaffney, SC (12-521) BC; Chor; NHS; SC; Tres, Sr Cl; Tres, Jr Cl; Citz A; Gr Marshal; Chorale, Off Coun Accompanist; Bible C; Outst Chor; Eng A; *Furman U; Religion.*

HOLTZCLAW, Susan Gayle
SE Whitfield HS; Dalton, GA (1-188) Secy, Anchor C; F-Ed, Ann; Chor; Drama; Rptr, FBLA; Secy, Lit Mag; NHS; Alg A; Bio A; Elk A; Gov Honor Prog; Hist A; Math A; MLS; Most Out; NEDT; Opt A; Sci A; Val; Type A; Chor Pianist; Fr, Span, Eng, A's; Dist Most Outst VOT Stu; *Berry Col.*

HOLUB, Eric Bohumil
Beloit HS Mem Campus; Beloit, WI (3%-550) Band; Chor; Pres, 4H; NHS; COM; 4H A; I Dare You; Opt Out Tn; Ntl 4-H Photo A; Del, 4-H St Congress; *U of Wisc; Pathology.*

HOLUB, Kraig Lee
Anamosa Comm HS; Anamosa, IA (4-139) BS; Fr C; NHS; Ftbl; St Scholar; *Math.*

HOLUBEC, Nanette
Bay City HS; Bay City, TX (25%-300) Band.

HOLUM, Douglas Maynard
Twin Valley Pub HS; Twin Valley, MN (3-36) Band; BS; FFA; NHS; Rptr, Sch P; Var C; Bsbl; Co-Cpt, Ftbl; Golf; H of F; MLS; Creativity As; Concordia Col Merit Schol; *Concordia Col; Bio.*

HOLZ, Kenneth Alan
Westwood Christian HS; Miami, FL; Co-Ed, Ann; Pres, Hmrm; Pres, Sr Cl; Bsbl; Bkbl; Cpt, Ftbl; Math A; Bible A; *U of Fla; Bus Adm.*

HOLZHACKER, Ronald Lindsey
Burnsville HS; Burnsville, MN (9-871) Band; 4H; Hmrm; Sch P; Soccer; Tnns; *U of Minn; Bus Adm.*

HOLZMAN, Karlene Ann
Waukegan Christian Sch; Zion, IL (4-6) Ann; Chor; Ger C; Ski C; Tr.

HOLZMANN, Ruth Naomi
Burnt Hills-Ballston Lake HS; Burnt Hills, NY (5-450) Band; Drama; Ensm; Citz A; Pat Cleary Nurs Schol; *Northeastern U; Nurs.*

HOLZWARTH, Jan Louise
Middle Park Jr Sr HS; Granby, CO (6-74) Band; City Conf; Secy, NHS; SC; COM; Vlbl; Hon Band; *W St Col; Phys Ed.*

HOMAN, Bruce Keith
Bridgeton HS; Bridgeton, NJ (10%-900) Secy, Church Yth Fel; Church Bsbl, Bkbl & Sftbl Tms; *Navy; Auto Mech.*

HOMAN, Janice Kay
Coldwater HS; Coldwater, OH (40-170) Band; Tres, CYO; Chor; Drama; Span C; CAC Church Committee; Candystriper; JV Vlbl; *Miami Valley Sch of Nurs; Nurs.*

HOMAN, Loraine Marie
Celina Sr HS; Celina, OH (1-275) Bus C; CYO; FBLA; FTA; Pres, Hmrm; VP, Lat C; NHS; VP, Sr Cl; VP, Jr Cl; Secy, Soph Cl; Type A; Val; GAA; WW; Ntl Schol Tm; Computer Games Tm; 1st Pl, St Acct; *Bus.*

HOMAN, Marilyn Ruth
Coldwater HS; Coldwater, OH (50%-170) CYO; Chor; Drama; 4H; K of C A; ARC A; Extra Ordinary Minister of Holy Com.

HOMARD, Deborah Lynn
Bridgeport HS; Bridgeport, OH; Band; NHS; Secy, SC; Y-Tns; John Philip Sousa A; Child Care A; Short Story A; Soph Eng A; *Ohio U Branch; Acct.*

HOMBURG, Kim Anette
Ralston HS; Ralston, NE; Chor; FBLA; Madrigal; SC; Golf; God & Country A; 1st Cl GSct.

HOMES, Alan Matthew
Yorktown Sr HS; Arlington, VA; Order/Arrow; Tr; Citz A; Order/Arrow A.

HOMESLEY, Karen Smith
E Gaston Sr HS; Mt Holly, NC; Fr C; FTA; Monogram; Bkbl; Sftbl; Citz A; All-Conf Sftbl A; *Appalachian St U; Criminal Justice.*

HOMEWOOD, Maureen Ann
The Cecilian Acad; Philadelphia, PA; CYO; Chldr; Chor; Lat C; Lit Mag; Rptr, Sch P; Hist A; Hon Prog; *Communications.*

HOMMEL, Sherrie Lynn
Selinsgrove Area HS; Selinsgrove, PA (50%-230) Chor; FBLA; 4H; Key C; 4H A; GSct; Church A's; *Bus.*

HOMOKI, Lorette Allison
First Baptist Christian Sch; N Las Vegas, NV (2-23) F-Ed, Ann; Chldr; Chor; Drama; Ger C; InterClub Coun; Sch Achieve Tm; F-Ed, Sch P; Spch C; Tres, SC; Bsbl; Soccer; Sftbl; Tr; COM; Cl Fav; Hon Prog; JA A; Most Out; Bible A; Art A; Hospital Vol; Off Work; *U of Las Vegas; Arts.*

HOMOLKA, Susan Grace
Morton W HS; Berwyn, IL (42-762) Chess C; Chor; Semi-Fin, Jr Miss Pa; Co-Ch, NHS; Orch; Ski C; Sftbl; Tnns; Amer Leg A; Girl's Service Trophy; Poise & Appearance A; Jr Miss Pageant; *Morton Col; Phys Therapy.*

HON, Donald Keith
Crossville HS; Crossville, IL (4-26) VP, BC; Math C; Co-Ed, Sch P; SC; Thes; VP, Jr Cl; VP, Soph Cl; Bsbl; JV, Bkbl; Tr; Gr Marshal; Hon Prog; Journ A; Type A; *Purdue U; Zoology.*

HON, Theresa Lynn
Pampa HS; Pampa, TX (38-300) Bus C; FHA; *S Plains Col; Bus.*

HONAKER, Helen Rose
Connellsville Area Sr HS; Connellsville, PA (5%-676) Span NHS; *Law Enforcement.*

HONAKER, Lisa Ann
Kickapoo HS; Springfield, MO; Band; Span C; Tnns; *Bus.*

HONEA, Mary Irene
Fertile-Beltrami HS; Fertile, MN (8-62) *Jamestown Col.*

HONEA, Priscilla Ruth
Tahlequah Sr HS; Tahlequah, OK (20-287) A Cap Choir; Band; Chor; Dbte Tm; NFL; NHS; Hist A; Outst Mus Stu; Mus A; *Northeastern Okla St U.*

HONEYCUTT, Debra Lyn
Assumption HS; Assumption, IL (5-50) Band; 4H; Cpt, Sftbl; Cpt, Tnns; Tr; 4H A; Pres A; Soc of Academic Achievement; *Eastern Ill U; Special Ed.*

HONEYCUTT, Gale Lynn
Ben Davis HS; Indianapolis, IN (40-856) Band; Chldr; Hmrm; Parl, Model UN; NHS; Ntl Yth Conf; Rptr, Sch P; VP, Span C; St Stu Congress; SC; Bkbl; MVP, Sftbl; COM; St Scholar; WW; Del, Yth-Power Conf; Del, Ntl Explorer Congress; Pres, Explorers; *U of Evansville; Child Psych.*

HONEYCUTT, Thomas Donald
Hall HS; Little Rock, AR (47-432) JETS; Lit Mag; Co-Cpt, Ftbl; I Dare You; Jaycees Salute to Ldrship A; *Hendrix Col; Eng.*

HONIG, Catherine Ann
Acad o t Holy Names; Tampa, FL (1-68) S-T, Fr C; Secy, NFL; Tres, NHS; Rptr, Sch P; Sci C; Span C; Span NHS; Secy, Jr Cl; Tres, Soph Cl; Hon Prog; MLS; Photography C; NFL Degree of Merit; Parameds; NFL Degree of Hon; Intramurals; Ntl Merit Ltr of Commendation.

HONORE, Giselle Denise
Dublin HS; Dublin, CA (2-330) VP, Fr C; Semi-Fin, GS; Model UN; NHS; SC; Pres, Sr Cl; VP, Jr Cl; Secy, Soph Cl; CSF; COM; Cl Fav; DARGCA; Elk A; Lion A; Sal; Spch A; St Fin, Hugh O'Brian Yth Ldrship; Most Service, Cl; *Mius Col; Med.*

HONSON, Lynnea Sue
Guilford HS; Rockford, IL (150-685) Fin, Sftbl; COE C; Summer Reach-Out Ministry; Vlbl Tm; Sunday Sch Teacher; *Bus.*

HONSTEIN, Gerahart Martinez
Crystal City HS; Crystal City, TX (4-107) Ann; Band; Chess C; Ensm; SC; Alg A; Math A; Phy A; Stage Band; *Tex A&I U; Engr.*

HOO, Edwina Jessie
Maryknoll HS; Honolulu, HI; Math C; NHS; Alg A; Hist A; Sci A; Social Stu A; Schol Pin.

HOOD, Anna Marie
Hapeville HS; Hapeville, GA (3-77) Band; BC; Cpt, Chldr; Hmrm; Cpt, Mjrte; Secy, NHS; Span NHS; SC; Y-Tns; Tr; COM; HCt; Bkbl, Bsbl, Statistician; FCA; Ltr C; *U of Ga; Lang.*

HOOD, Donna
Gibbons Alternative HS; New Brunswick, NJ (3-14) AFS; Band; Chor; Semi-Fin, Jr Miss Pa; Cpt, Mjrte; VP, SC; Ch, Y-Tns; Pres, Sr Cl; VP, Jr Cl; Secy, Soph Cl; Mgr, Bsbl; Mgr, Ftbl; Beauty; COM; Citz A; Most Out; Bar Assn A & Schol; *Rutgers Col; Pol Sci.*

HOOD, Elgene Edward
Denham Springs HS; Denham Springs, LA (1-222) Ann; Pres, Key C; Lit Ral; Pres, NHS; Var C; VP, Sr Cl; VP, Jr Cl; Parl, Soph Cl; Bsbl; Ftbl; Golf; Hon Prog; Val; *LSU; Pre-Dentistry.*

HOOD, Gary Allen
Middleburg HS; Middleburg, PA; Band; Ger C; Order/Arrow; Mgr, Bsbl; JV, Soccer; God & Country A; Order/Arrow A; ARC A; Yth Fel; *Phys Ed.*

HOOD, Glenda Marie
Thayer HS; Thayer, MO (30-50) Chor; Drama; FHA; Spch C; Bkbl; FHA o-t Mo; Choir; *Hillsdale Col.*

HOOD, Janice Lynn
Grace Christian Sch; Prattville, AL (3-11) Ann; Chldr; Chor; Ensm; Sftbl; Tr; HCt; *Auburn U; Math.*

HOOD, Jeffrey Allen
Elk Grove Sr HS; Elk Grove, CA (10%-400) Band; Drama; Sci C; Bsbl; Golf; Tnns; Alg A; Bio A; CSF; Hist A; Sci A; *Johns Hopkins U; Med.*

HOOD, Lynn Mari
Vincentian Inst; Albany, NY (2-166) Bus C; Chor; FBLA; Secy, 4H; Pres, NHS; ARC; Pres, Span C; Hist A; Sal; Vlbl; *Rochester Inst of Tech; Bio.*

HOOD, Matthew Eldon
Wayzata Sr HS; Wayzata, MN (32-500).

HOOD, Melvin Lee
Dunbar HS; Chicago, IL (137-600) *IIT; Elec Engr.*

HOOD, Pamela Jo
Bradley Central HS; Cleveland, TN (45-634) Ann; Fr C; JA A; Star Student; VP, Boosterettes; *Cleveland St Comm Col; Elem Ed.*

HOOD, Patricia Anne
Tivy HS; Kerrville, TX; Band; FHA; Pres, Ger C; InterAct C; Co-Ed, Sch P; HCt; St Ger A; *SW Tex St U; Journ.*

HOOD, Sandra Jo
Northside Christian HS; St Petersburg, FL (2-31) A Cap Choir; Cpt, Band; Chor; Ensm; Madrigal; Secy, NHS; Secy, SC; Secy, Jr Cl; Secy, Soph Cl; HQn; HCt; Hon Prog; Sal; Mus A; *St Petersburg Jr Col; Mus.*

HOOD, Sigrid Pernell
Lamar Sr HS; Houston, TX (226-529) FNA; NHS; Wittiest; *Howard U; Law.*

HOOD, Steven Allen
Baldwin HS; Wailuku, HI (80-300) Tres, Band; Chem C; Chess C; Ch, Ensm; VP, Key C; Secy, Order/Arrow; Spch C; Var C; God & Country A; Hon Prog; Pres, Cpt, MVP, Rifle & Pistol C; Select Band; Ltrman Trophy; *U of Hawaii; Engr.*

HOOD, Steven John
Marion HS; Marion, IN (40-840) God & Country A; Hon Prog; ARC A; Type A; BScts; CYF; Attendance A.

HOOD, Suzette Marie
Sulphur HS; Sulphur, LA (33%-450) A Cap Choir; Chor; Ensm; FHA; Outst Chor, 3 Yr Chor, A's; WW; *La Col; Special Ed.*

HOOD, Teresa Michele
Jonesboro Sr HS; Jonesboro, AR (18-401) Band; BC; Mjrte; Mu Alpha Theta; NHS; Math A; Type A; All-Region Band; *Ark St U; Bus Adm.*

HOOD, Tory L
Ruston HS; Ruston, LA (27-279) Chor; FBLA; Citz A; *La Tech Col; Home Ec.*

HOOD, Wendell Donald
Jones Co HS; Gray, GA (10%-250) BC; Sci C; Bio A; *ABAC; Wildlife Mgt.*

HOOEY, Wanda Maecheryl
Mary Brantley Smiley HS; Houston, TX (7-400) Fr C; Tres, Mu Alpha Theta; NHS; Bio A; COM; Chem A; Citz A; Hist A; Journ A; Math A; Most Out; Sci A; Type A; VFW A; Eng A; PA; St Reader's C; *U of Houston; Psych.*

HOOF, Mark Wayne
Jefferson HS; Jefferson, WI (80-184) A Cap Choir; Chor; Drama; Order/Arrow; VP, Sr Cl; VP, Jr Cl; Mgr, Bkbl; Order/Arrow A; *U of Wis; Mortuary Sci.*

HOOGENBOOM, Robert Scott
Muncie Central HS; Muncie, IN (7-300) BS; NHS; Span C; JV, Bsbl; Bkbl; Tnns; HCt; Kiwanis A; Opt A; Semi-Fin, Hugh O'Brien A; Busbey Sportsman A; FCA; *Purdue U; Sci.*

HOOK, Brian Roger
West HS; Columbus, OH (80-451) Golf; COM; Hon Prog.

HOOK, Lisa Lynn
Roy J Wasson HS; Colorado Springs, CO; Chor; SC; HQn; Bus A; Foreign Lang A.

HOOKER, Brian Keith
Glenvar HS; Salem, VA (66-241) InterClub Coun; Key C; Monogram; Bsbl; Cpt, Ftbl; Most Out; MVP, Ftbl; *Va Military Inst; Hist.*

HOOKER, Cheryl Dawn
Greater New York Acad; Woodside, NY (2-72) NHS; Tres, Sci C; VP, SC; Alg A; Bio A; Chem A; Citz A; Hist A; I Dare You; Phy A; Sal; Type A; *Atlantic Union Col; Dietetics.*

HOOKER, Karen Elaine
Rio Linda Sr HS; Rio Linda, CA (25%-295) Band; Chldr; Chor; Ensm; Orch; COM; 2nd Pl, Mus Medal; HR; Cert of Appreciation-Participation; *Calif St U; Mus.*

HOOKER, Mary Jane
Chiefland HS; Chiefland, FL (10-95) Co-Ed, Ann; Band; Parl, BC; Co-Cpt, Chldr; Rptr, FHA; 4H; Hmrm; Secy, SC; 4H A; Hon Guard; *Central Fla Comm Col; Med.*

HOOKSTRA, Kim Jeannette
Stanton HS; Stanton, NE (8-54) Chor; Drama; VP, FHA; Pres, 4H; NHS; Pres, SC; 4H A; *NE Nebr Tech Comm Col; Bus.*

HOOOK, Sheri Lynn
Vienna HS; Vienna, IL (1-99) S-T, BC; Cpt, Chldr; Math C; Secy, Thes; S-T, Sr Cl; Citz A; Cl Fav; DARGCA; HQn; Math A; MLS; Val; *Murray St U; Acct.*

HOOPER, Jan Denise
North Hall HS; Gainesville, GA; FBLA; FHA; 4H; Hmrm; ARC; Mgr, Bkbl; Acteen; Pres, Yth Choir; Childrens Church Workers; *Med.*

HOOPER, John Alan
Bristow HS; Bristow, OK (9-126) Chess C; Fr C; Co-Cpt, Bkbl; Soccer; Tr; Alg A; COM; Gov Honor Prog; Hist A; HKg; Math A; Sci A; Principal's HR; Presbyterian Yth Org; *U of Okla; Math.*

HOOPER, Julie Ann
St Augustine HS; Laredo, TX; Ed, Ann; Band; S-T, CYO; Chldr; NHS; SC; Rotary A; *St Thomas Col; Psych.*

HOOPER, Linda Gail
Marshall HS; Marshall, TX (55-424) Bus Mgr, Sch P; Wo-He-Lo; *E Tex Baptist Col.*

HOOPER, Margaret Lee
Banks Co HS; Homer, GA (7-70) Bus Mgr, Ann; BC; Ensm; 4H; DARGCA; Top Ten, Sr Cl; Officer's Service A; Publicity Ch, Co-Ed Y C; Ragger's Soc, St YMCA; Ed, Leopard Ltr; *N Ga Tech U; Bus.*

HOOPER, Patrick Lee
Hugh Manley HS; Chicago, IL (4-219) City Conf; Parl, NHS; Pres, Ski C; Span C; Bsbl; Bkbl; Cpt, Ftbl; Chem A; Hon Prog; Math A; ROTC A.

HOOPER, Sherry Faye
Hickman Mills Sr HS; Kansas City, MO (65-601) Orch; Tnns; COM; Gov Honor Prog.

HOOPER, Victoria Anne
Maple Shade HS; Maple Shade, NJ; GS; Hmrm; NHS; Alg A; Color Guard; Lacrosse; *Douglass Col; Pol Sci.*

HOOPER, William John
Glenbrook N HS; Northbrook, IL (200-700) Order/Arrow; Wrest; Eagle Sct; Pres, Explorer Post; Church Christian Ed Coun; Handbell Choir; *U of Wis-Stout; Industrial Ed.*

HOOPES, Barbara Jean
Clearwater HS; Clearwater, FL (10-850) Band; Ger C; Math C; NHS; Var C; Cr-Ctry; Tr.

HOOPES, Carol Elizabeth
Clearwater HS; Clearwater, FL (10%-900) Var C; Cr-Ctry; Tr; Keyettes.

HOOPES, Linda Louise
Clearwater HS; Clearwater, FL (15-850) Chor; Dbte Tm; NHS; St Stu Congress; SC; Pres, Soph Cl; God & Country A; NMF; Spch A; Ch, Keyettes; *Davidson Col; Pre-Law.*

HOOPINGARNER, Kirk Anson
Sturgis HS; Sturgis, MI (1-258) A Cap Choir; Band; Pres, Drama; Lat C; Madrigal; NHS; SC; Var C; Tr; Elk A; MLS; Hope Col Pres Schol; Rotary Ldrship Camp; *Hope Col; Pre-Law.*

HOOTEN, Terry Kent
Dallas Christian HS; Mesquite, TX; A Cap Choir; Chor; NHS; Co-Cpt, Ftbl; Hon Prog; *Harding Col; Acct.*

HOOVER, Belinda Sue
Wheelersburg HS; Wheelersburg, OH (33%-185) Band; Chor; Fr C; Bkbl; Tr; COM; Hist A; NEDT; Vlbl; Cert of Achv.

HOOVER, Bradley Ted
Dobyns-Bennett HS; Kingsport, TN (60-500) BS; Dbte Tm; Key C; ARC; Ski C; Span C; SC; Ftbl; Golf; *Adm.*

HOOVER, Brenda Lou
Wheelersburg HS; Wheelersburg, OH (33%-185) Band; Chor; Span C; Bkbl; Tr; Cert of Achv; *U of Cincinnati; Phys Therapy.*

HOOVER, Janice Lee
Northgate HS; Walnut Creek, CA (10-425) VP, Band; Model UN; Orch; Tr; CSF; Hon Prog; Pres A; Pres, CSF; Jobs Daughters; *U o-t Pacific; Phar.*

HOOVER, Janis Ann
Moline Sr HS; Moline, IL (319-831) Chor; Fr C; 4H; Rainbow; ARC; COM; 4H A; *York Col; Elem Ed.*

HOOVER, Jeffrey Jay
Franklin Jr Sr HS; Franklin, PA (60-274) Secy, Band; Community Yth Symph; Hmrm; SC; Var C; Bkbl; Tr; Cl Fav; *Ind U of Pa; Criminology.*

HOOVER, Julia Lee
Dobyns Bennett HS; Kingsport, TN; Cpt, Bkbl; Golf.

HOOVER, Kimberley Marie
Tupelo HS; Tupelo, MS (25%-435) Anchor C; Chor.

HOOVER, Phillip Allen
Alexander Central HS; Taylorsville, NC (150-450) Bsbl; Co-Cpt, Wrest; HCt; Yth Fel; Best All Around; *Elec Installation.*

HOOVER, Sharon Kay
Mechanicsburg Sr HS; Mechanicsburg, PA (218-343) Chor; Secy, Hmrm; Ntl Yth Conf; SC; Cr-Ctry; Mgr, Ftbl; HCt; Jr Women's Girl o-t Mo; Yrbk Staff A.

HOOVER, Tammy Kay
Henrico HS; Richmond, VA (5-240) Chor; Drama; Ensm; Fr C; FBLA; 4H; Hmrm; Tres, Mod Mus Mas; Mgr, Bkbl; JA A; *Randolph Macon Col; Special Ed.*

HOOVER, Vickie Lynn
Grapevine HS; Grapevine, TX; A Cap Choir; Span C; Thes; Future Med Workers; Co-Cpt, Drill Tm; *Tyler Jr Col; Gen.*

HOOVER, William Sanders
Avondale HS; Avondale Estates, GA (1-257) BC; Fr C; Math C; NHS; COM; Gov Honor Prog; Val; Acad Ltr; Stu o-t Mo; *Oxford Col; Psychiatry.*

HOPE, David Edwin
P K Yonge Laboratory Sch; Gainesville, FL (20-90) VP, SC; VP, Jr Cl; Cpt, Bsbl; Cpt, Bkbl; Cr-Ctry; Hist A; *U of Fla; Bus.*

HOPE, Debbie Faith
P K Yonge Laboratory Sch; Gainesville, FL (1-90) Band; JV, Chldr; Chor; Ensm; SC; Secy, Soph Cl; Swim; JV, Tr; Swtht; JV, Vlbl.

HOPE, Debbie L
Ridgeview HS; Atlanta, GA; Semi-Fin, Tr; Poet A; Type A; Poetry Published in Lit Mag; Tres, Church Yth Coun; *Interior Design.*

HOPE, Leslie Allison
Girls Prep Sch; Chattanooga, TN (62-95) Chor; Drama; Rptr, Sch P; Pres, Span C; *Art Ed.*

HOPE, Lori Lynne
Kearns HS; Kearns, UT (60-620) JV, Chldr; Fin, Jr Miss Pagent; HQn; Hon Prog; Secy, Drill Tm; Pep C; Service A; *Westminster Col; Psych.*

HOPE, Ossa Princess
Sch of Performing Arts; New York, NY; God & Country A; *Dance.*

HOPE, Ruth Odetta
Sterling Reg HS; Somerdale, NJ; Ann; Chor; Dbte Tm; Mgr, Tr.

HOPEWELL, Joyce Nadine
N Allegheny HS; Pittsburgh, PA; A Cap Choir; Chor; Ensm; Rptr, Hmrm; SC; Bsbl; *Atlanta U; Special Ed.*

HOPGOOD, Dorothy Lee
Rufus King HS; Milwaukee, WI (77-200).

HOPGOOD, Reopal Denise
Rufus King HS; Milwaukee, WI (10-21) JV, Chldr; Hmrm; Span C; *Northland Col; Nurs.*

HOPINKAH, Kathy Ann
Thomas Kelly HS; Chicago, IL (11-661) Chldr; Chor; City Conf; Hmrm; VP, SC; Swim; COM; HCt; Hon Prog; Most Out; Pres A; ARC A; Yth Foundation A; Ill Leadership; Kelly Hon Soc; *Loras Col; Bio.*

HOPKINS, Ann Louise
W Concord HS; West Concord, MN (23-46) Chor; FHA; Mgr, Bkbl.

HOPKINS, Ann Therese
Quincy Notre Dame HS; Quincy, IL (1-136) Hmrm; NHS; Pres, Span C; SC; Tnns; Kiwanis A; NEDT; St Scholar; Val; Ntl Merit Commended Stu; *Quincy Col; Span.*

HOPKINS, Craig Lee
Weatherford HS; Weatherford, TX (18-252) Bus C; Dbte Tm; FBLA; Parl, FTA; Math C; Tres, NFL; Parl, NHS; Order/Arrow; Sci C; Tnns; Order/ Arrow A; Spch A; VFW Orator Win; VofDEM; Yth Fel; WW; Eagle Sct; *Southwestern U; Pre-Law.*

HOPKINS, David Paul
Campbell HS; Fairburn, GA; *Clayton Jr Col; Sci.*

HOPKINS, Deborah Ann
Olney HS; Philadelphia, PA (84-855) A Cap Choir; A-Ed, Ann; Chor; Drama; S-T, Fr C; Lit Mag; Orch; Pol Sci C; Rptr, Sch P; Sci C; Span C; Swim; Tnns; Tr; COM; Citz A; Hon Prog; Human Relations A; Eng Hon Soc; *Heidelberg Col; Law.*

HOPKINS, Elizabeth Ann
Westminster HS; Westminster, MD (260-535) JA A; ARC A; Yth Fel; Pres, Church Yth Group; *Bethany Col; Missions.*

HOPKINS, Gail Elaine
Booker T Washington HS; Norfolk, VA; Tres, Band; Community Yth Symph; Drama; Pres, Hmrm; Math C; Orch; Co-Cpt, Bkbl; Sftbl; Tnns; Cl Fav; Hon Prog; Math A; Most Out; Sci A; *Eckerd Col; Mus.*

HOPKINS, James Frederick Jr
St Mary's Regional HS; Lynn, MA (35-117) All Amer Yth; CYO; K of C; Golf; Co-Cpt, Hockey; Citz A; Hon Prog; K of C A; Star Student; MVP, All Star, Hockey; Co-Cpt, Golf Tm; *Merrimack Col; Psych.*

HOPKINS, Lawrence Wayne
W W Samuell HS; Dallas, TX; Ann; Eng A; ROTC; *N Tex St U; Computer Elec.*

HOPKINS, LeeAnn
Hempfield Area Sr HS; Greensburg, PA (10%-885) A Cap Choir; Ann; Chor; Span C; Citz A; Hon Prog; Pres, Church Yth Group; Art A; Comm Ch, Greensburg Dist Yth Group; *Seton Hill Col; Span.*

HOPKINS, Lillian Ann
Van-Far Sr HS; Vandalia, MO (8-63) FHA; Tr; Crisco A; Most Out; P, VICA; Pep C; Vlbl Tm; *Mexico LPN Sch of Nurs; Nurs.*

HOPKINS, Loraine Marie
J W Hallahan HS; Philadelphia, PA (18-432) Pres, CYO; NHS; SC; Type A; *Chestnut Hill Col; Nurs.*

HOPKINS, Margaret Anne
Pine Bluff HS; Pine Bluff, AR (114-592) A Cap Choir; Ensm; Span C; *Ouachita Baptist U.*

HOPKINS, Marianne
Seaside HS; Seaside, CA; JV, Chldr; SC; VP, Jr Cl; Tres, Soph Cl; *San Jose Col; Bus Adm.*

HOPKINS, Nancy Michelle
Pendleton HS; Pendleton, SC (14-137) Cpt, Chldr; Fr C; 4H; Secy, Hmrm; A-Ed, Sch P; Tres, Jr Cl; Beauty; 4H A; Hon Prog; Q&S A; Pom-Pom Girl; Eng A; Allied Yth C; *Clemson U; Journ.*

HOPKINS, Sonya LaJean
John S Shaw HS; Mobile, AL (44-411) F-Ed, Ann; Ensm; NHS; Beauty; Citz A; Hon Prog; Q&S A; Chaplain, Jr Civitan C; *Mobile Col; Nurs.*

HOPKINS, Stephen Lon
Bluefield HS; Bluefield, WV (96-305) Ann; Chess C; Chor; Drama; Fr C; InterAct C; NFL; NHS; Spch C; Thes; Bausch & Lomb A; Cl Fav; Yth Fel; Fin, Interntl Sci Fair; Most Outst Project, St Sci Fair; Co Sci A; 1st Pl, Co & Regional Sci Fairs; *UNCG; Paleoantropology.*

HOPKINS, Sylvia R
Dixie Co HS; Cross City, FL (10%-120) Tnns; Jr Achv; *Baylor U; Textiles Interior Decorating.*

HOPKINS, Wanda Patrice
Sw HS; Detroit, MI (10-250) Chor; NHS; Amer Leg A; Magna Cum Laude; Type A; Shorthand A; Spelling A; US Bond; *U of Detroit; Acct.*

HOPPE, Weldon James
Farnam Pub HS; Farnam, NE (1-14) Ed, Ann; Band; BS; Pres, Sr Cl; Pres, Jr Cl; Pres, Soph Cl; Bkbl; Cpt, Ftbl; Tr; Alg A; Bio A; HKg; Regent Schol; Val; Yth Fel; *Northwest Mo St U; Bus.*

HOPPER, Elizabeth Ann
N Hollywood HS; N Hollywood, CA (100-600) Cpt, Chldr; Chor; Madrigal; Ski C; *Cal St U-Northridge; Psych.*

HOPPER, Jeffery Lee
Sheffield HS; Memphis, TN (35-138) Parl, Fr C; Var C; Bsbl; Cpt, Bkbl; Cr-Ctry; *US Air Force; Air Traffic Control.*

HOPPER, Ken Chris
Weatherford HS; Weatherford, TX (3-252) Ed, Ann; Band; Ensm; Math C; NHS; Sci C; SC; Hon Prog; Journ A; Opt A; Opt Out Tn; Rotary A; Sci A; Most Talented; 1st Pl Ntl, Yrbk Cover Design; *Baylor U; Orthodontistry.*

HOPPER, Marvin Keith
Goodlettsville HS; Goodlettsville, TN (20%-190) MVP, Bkbl; Ftbl; JV, Tr; Most Courteous; *U of Tenn; Engr.*

HOPPER, Michelle Marie
Saint Mary's Acad; Alexandria, VA; Math C; Model UN; Sftbl; Tnns; COM; Hon Prog; Math A; *Mary Washington Col; Pol Sci.*

HOPPER, Pamela Gale
St Petersburg HS; St Petersburg, FL (300-400) Bible C; *St Petersburg Voc Col; Med.*

HOPPER, Pamela Marilyn
Powell Valley HS; Speedwell, TN; BC; Secy, 4H; Mu Alpha Theta; Pres, Tri-HiY; Secy, Sr Cl; *St Mary's Nurs Sch; Nurs.*

HOPPER, Patricia Ann
St Mary's Acad; Alexandria, VA (10%-100) Sftbl; Hon Prog; Opt A; *Mary Washington Col; Lib Arts.*

HOPPER, Rachel Ann
Sheffield HS; Memphis, TN; Fr C; NHS; MVP, Bkbl; Sftbl; All Dist Bkbl; Jr NHS; *Oral Roberts U; Dentistry.*

HOPPER, Rachel Anne
Sheffield HS; Memphis, TN (25%-214) Fr C; Bkbl; Cpt, Sftbl; All-Dist; Jr High Hon Soc; *Oral Roberts U; Denistry.*

HOPPER, Richard Bruce
Mohawk Area Jr-Sr HS; Bessemer, PA (1-147) Pres, Lat C; Pres, NHS; SC; Pres, Soph Cl; Bsbl; Bkbl; Ftbl; Tr; Amer Leg A; Chem A; Val; *Allegheny Col; Physics.*

HOPPERDIETZEL, Joel Peter
Abbotsford Pub HS; Abbotsford, WI; Arch; Ch, CYO; Drama; Fin, NFL; Spch C; Arch; Tr; Spch A; Fin, St Forensics League.

HOPPERS, Marsha Dian
Humansville HS; Humansville, MO (1-29) Ed, Ann; Band; Cpt, Chldr; Chor; Pres, FHA; Ed, Sch P; VP, SC; S-T, Soph Cl; Cpt, Bkbl; Sftbl; I Dare You; MLS; Opt A; Val; Outst Home Ec Stu; Outst Bus Stu; Best Actress A; Miss Humansville; *Burge Sch of Nurs; Nurs.*

HOPPES, Terry Lee
Schuylkill Haven Area HS; Schuylkill Haven, PA; Secy, Bus C; Mgr, Sftbl; Mgr, Tr; *Bus.*

HOPPING, Andrew Jefferson
Westville HS; Westville, OK (30-60) Band; Chor; FFA; Bkbl; Ftbl; Tr; Wrest; VICA; 2nd Pl, Voc-Tech Regional A; *NW Okla St U; Industrial Arts.*

HOPPING, Clyde Franklin
Westville HS; Westville, OK (1-76) Band; Pres, Chem C; Chor; Drama; Ensm; NHS; Orch; Pres, Phys C; VP, Sci C; Spch C; SC; Var C; Bkbl; Cr-Ctry; Ftbl; Tr; COM; Cl Fav; Hon Prog; Math A; MLS; Sci A; St Scholar; Val; *NW Okla St U; Pre-Med.*

HOPPING, LaDonna Rose
Markema Bible Acad; Tahequal, OK (10-28) Band; Chor; Ch, FHA; Bkbl; Hockey; Tr; *NESU; Math.*

HOPSECKER, Michael Kenneth
New Bloomfield R III HS; New Bloomfield, MO (2-40) Ann; Fr C; VP, NHS; VP, SC; Tres, Var C; VP, Jr Cl; VP, Soph Cl; Bsbl; Bkbl; JV, Cr-Ctry.

HOPSON, Christine Elizabeth
W T Woodson HS; Fairfax, VA; Chor; FBLA; FTA; Mjrte; ARC; Citz A; Church Adm Board; *Madison Col; Med.*

HOPSON, Pamela
Carson HS; Carson City, NV (15-400) Bus C; FBLA; NHS; Span C; COM; Type A; Bus A; *Ricks U; Dentistry.*

HOPSON, Susan Kay
Pima HS; Pima, AZ (5-40) Model UN; NHS; SC; Hon Prog; Sci A; *ASU; Bus.*

HOPSON, Thomas Wade
Gladewater HS; Gladewater, TX; Hmrm; Bkbl; JV, Ftbl; Golf; *Tex A&M Col; Archt.*

HOPTON, Greg Wayne
Fairfield HS; Fairfield, OH (25-522) Band; Chem C; Ger C; Sftbl; Tr; *U of Cincinnati; Engr.*

HOPTON, Terri Lee
Fairfield Sr HS; Fairfield, OH (69-608) Band; Chor; Drama; Fr C; Orch; Thes; Off, Mod Mus Masters C; Historian, Monogram C; Timette, Swm; Bicen Coun Meet Piccilo Player; 'Spirit of 76' Fife & Drum Core; *Ohio St U; Mus.*

HOPWOOD, Angelic Denise
Thompson HS; Alabaster, AL (25%-190) Fr C; FHA; Semi-Fin, Jr Miss Pa; NHSt; Tr; Vlbl; *U of Montevallo; Eng.*

HORA, Bambi Arlene
Nathan Hale Sr HS; Tulsa, OK (10%-700) Secy, 4H; Math C; NHS; Span C; Span NHS; 4H A; 1st Cl, GSct; OSU Alumni Cert; *Okla St U; Home Ec.*

HORAN, Dennis Joseph
Cathedral HS; El Paso, TX (37-84) Drama; Fresh Orientation; Sch Musical; All-Around Serv A; *UTEP; Bus Mgt.*

HORD, Frederick Mark
Terre Haute S Vigo HS; Terre Haute, IN (33%-650) Fr C; MVP, Tnns; Audio-Visual Staff; Top 3 Soph Prog, Purdue U.

HORD, Grayla
Bennett HS; Buffalo, NY (79-319) Chor; Secy, SC; Co-Ch, Booster C; *St U of NY; Bus Adm.*

HORD, Teresa Darlene
Terre Haute S Vigo HS; Terre Haute, IN (1-625) A Cap Choir; Fr C; GS; NFL; VP, Spch C; VP, SC; Pres, Y-Tns; Citz A; JA A; MLS; Spch A; Optimist Oratorical St Win; DAC Citz; Alliances Francaises; *Law.*

HORGAN, Catherine Anne
St Mary's Regional HS; Lynn, MA (11-117) ARC; Alg A; Math A; Stu Gov Day; *N Shore Comm Col; Bus Adm.*

HORMAN, Janet Lynne
Plantation HS; Plantation, FL (84-540) AFS; ARC; SC; Tnns; Tres, Jr Sinawiks C; Soph Cl Service A; St Gov Service A; WW; *Furman U; Religion.*

HORN, Alexander Clayton
Cleburne HS; Cleburne, TX (20-335) Band; Dbte Tm; HiY; Hon Prog; *Tex A&M U; Vet Med.*

HORN, Ann Louise
Columbia HS; Columbia, PA (2-171) Chess C; Chor; Drama; NHS; VP, SC; Tnns; *Sci.*

HORN, Kathleen Cecelia
Springfield Sr HS; Springfield, PA (33%-450) Co-Ed, Ann; Chor; Pres, Ski C; Bkbl; Hockey; Q&S A; Lacrosse; *Elizabethtown Col.*

HORN, Lisa Mae
Centerville Sr HS; Centerville, IN (17-177) Band; Pres, 4H; NHS; Sci C; Span C; Y-Tns; COM; 4H A; Job's Daughters; *Ball St U; Med Tech.*

HORN, Margaret Jane
Danville HS; Danville, AR (10-36) Co-Ed, Ann; Pres, FHA; GS; Model UN; NHS; *U of Central Ark; Spch Pathology.*

HORN, Rebecca Jane
Osseo HS; Osseo, MN; Band; *Evangle Bible Col; Acct.*

HORN, Reve Roselene
Fridley Sr HS; Fridley, MN (95-475) NHS; ARC; Bkbl; Tnns; ARC A; *Evangel Bible Col; Nurs.*

HORN, Wanda Darnell
C F Vigor HS; Prichard, AL (12-400) Bus C; Chem C; Co-Ch, Jr Cl; *Twentieth Century Bus Col; Bus Adm.*

HORNAK, Andrea Louise
Strong Vincent HS; Erie, PA; Ed, Ann; Cpt, Chldr; Chor; Hmrm; NHS; ARC; Sch P; Span C; SC; Y-Tns; Swm; COM; Poet A; Win, Spelling Bee; Dynamite Stick, Friendliest, DCA; *Med.*

HORNBACK, Teresa Ann
Piedmont Hills HS; San Jose, CA (10%-800) Drama; Fr C; Hmrm; Hist A; *Biola Col; Sociology.*

HORNBACKER, Kent Michael
Limestone Comm HS; Bartonville, IL (35-387) Pres, NHS; Span NHS; Tres, SC; Var C; Bsbl; Ftbl; Hon Prog; Pres & Tres, Key C; Outst Key C Member; *Sou Ill U at Carbondale; Engr Tech.*

HORNBACKER, Kurt Alan
Limestone HS; Bartonville, IL (15-466) Parl, SC; Bsbl; Ftbl; *US Air Force Acad; Aviation.*

HORNBUCKLE, Charlette
S Oak Cliff HS; Dallas, TX (17-800) Band; Chor; Select Band; Home Ec A; MS Walk- a- thon; *Oral Roberts U; Mus.*

HORNE, Celia Lynn
Rocky Mount Sr HS; Rocky Mount, NC (75-588) SC; Tres, Jr Cl; Hon Prog; Yrbk; Sub-Deb C; *U of NC at Chapel Hill; Ed.*

HORNE, Donna Lynn
Tabernacle Christian Acad; Pougkeepsie, NY (8%-46) Tres, 4H.

HORNE, Edna Joyce
Deland Sr HS; Deland, FL; Chor; FBLA; FFA; VP, FHA; 4H; Mjrte; SC; Cr-Ctry; Sftbl; Tr; COM; 4H A; JA A; *Charleston Col; Child Care.*

HORNE, Juanita
Millbrook Sr HS; Raleigh, NC (40-509) A Cap Choir; Chor; Fr C; Secy, NHS; Bkbl; Sftbl; Swim; Tnns; COM; Citz A; Hist A; Hon Prog; MVP, Vlbl; Female Sportsmanship A; Most Ath Female; Eng A; Outst Cert, Hon Soc; Fr A; *NC St U; Life Sci.*

HORNE, Rita Faye
Wheeler Co HS; Alamo, GA (1-89) BC; FBLA; FHA; NHS; Sci C; *Medical Col of Ga; Therapy.*

HORNE, Sandra Gay
Bible Baptist HS; Savannah, GA (25%-54) Chldr; Pres, 4H; VP, Hmrm; Rptr, Sch P; VP, Soph Cl; HCt; Hon Prog; Yth Fel; WW; Ntl Fr Contest; *Armstrong St Col; Elem Ed.*

HORNER, Brenda Jean
Abbotsford Jr Sec HS; Abbotsford, CANADA; Band; Cpt, Bkbl.

HORNER, Brenda Lee
Napoleon HS; Napoleon, ND (27-71) *Bismarck Jr Col; Secy.*

HORNER, Glenda Kay
Napoleon HS; Napoleon, ND (15-71) Ann; Chor; Ch, FFA; Secy, FHA; Secy, SC; Bkbl; Tr; Tres, SC; *Valley City Col; Social Work.*

HORNER, Tamara Jane
Jenks HS; Jenks, OK (10%-280) Band; S-T, Drama; Ensm; Fr C; NHS; *Math.*

HORNER, Thomas William
Richardson HS; Richardson, TX (200-950) Key C; Span C; SC; Bsbl; *Baylor U; Bus Mgt.*

HORNICEK, Judy Marie
Lodgepole HS; Lodgepole, NE (5-16) Ann; Band; Chor; 4H; NHS; Sftbl; Tr; I Dare You; Kiwanis A; Vlbl; Meyer Mem Schol; Bank Schol; Col Schol; *W Nebr Tech Col; Professional Secy.*

HORNTVEDT, Peggy Jo
Columbus Pub HS; Columbus, ND; Ann; Band; Pres, Chor; Ensm; Ed, Sch P; SC; Secy, Sr Cl; Mgr, Bkbl; Alt, GS; Hon Choir; Hon Stu; St Mus Competition; *U of ND; Phys Therapy.*

HOROSCHAK, Suzanne
William H Hall HS; W Hartford, CT (120-550) Lit Mag; Secy, Span NHS; Co-Cpt, Cr-Ctry; Tr; Hon Prog; JA A; Q&S A; Acolyte; Pres, JA Company; Church Yth Coun; Eng Hon A.

HORSFALL, Michelle Yvette
El Cajon Valley HS; El Cajon, CA (1-417) JV, Hockey; Hon Prog; Val; *Grossmont Jr Col; Eng.*

HORSFORD, Edith Leona
Greater Ny Acad; Woodside Queens, NY (50%-73) Chldr; Secy, Chem C; Chor; Dbte Tm; ARC; Secy, Sci C; Spch C; Bkbl; Sftbl; Swim; Bio A; COM; Chem A; Citz A; Hon Prog; I Dare You; ARC A; Sci A; Yth Fel; Yth Foundation; Comm Service A; Pathfinder C; Vlbl; Good Conduct A; Secy, Treas, JMV; Nurses Aide A; Deaconess; HR; Sewing A; Vol Tutor; Delta Mus Chor; *Long Island U; Physicians Asst.*

HORSLEY, Belinda Mindell
St Andrew HS; Charleston, SC; Cpt, Chldr; Hmrm; SC; Bkbl; Mod Dance A; Bkbl HQn; *Oral Roberts U.*

HORSLEY, Robin Terressa
East HS; Columbus, OH; *Acct.*

HORSLEY, Vanessa Renee
Hoke Smith HS; Atlanta, GA (7-293) Band; *Nurs.*

HORSMAN, Kathy Ellen
W Middlesex HS; W Middlesex, PA (5-148) Band; Co-Cpt, Chldr; VP, Chor; S-T, FTA; 4H; Madrigal; NHS; Secy, Sr Cl; DARGCA; 4H A; HCt; MLS; NEDT; *Radiologic Tech.*

HORST, Michael Dean
Gurley Pub HS; Gurley, NE (6-12) Ann; Chor; Spch C; SC; Tres, Sr Cl; VP, Jr Cl; Tres, Soph Cl; Bsbl; Bkbl; Co-Cpt, Ftbl; Tr; HKg; Pres, Yth for Christ; Mech Drawing A; *Concordia Teachers Col; Director of Christian Ed.*

HORSTMANN, Tamra Lea
Central HS; Breese, IL (5-157) FHA; Amer Leg A; Bio A; Home Ec A; Eng A; Childcare A; Fin, Rural Elec Writing A.

HORTON, Ann Adeline
Karns HS; Knoxville, TN (60-235) Band; Chor; FHA; 4H; HiY; Hmrm; InterClub Coun; NHS; Ntl Teachers Coun; ARC; Sch P; SC; Y-Tns; Tnns; COM; 4H A; I Dare You; JA A; Most Out; Pres A; ARC A; Spch A; GS A; *U of Tenn; Home Ec.*

HORTON, Bobbye Nell
Walnut HS; Walnut, MS (5-50) BC; Chor; S-T, FHA; 4H; Beauty; COM.

HORTON, Connie Marie
Lyons Senior HS; Lyons, GA; FHA; 4H; Rptr, SC; Tri-HiY; Tres, Jr Cl; *Industrial Arts C.*

HORTON, Delwyn Carl
Thornton HS; Harvey, IL (150-700) Ann; Chess C; Cr-Ctry; Co-Cpt, Tr; Boy's C; Off Aid; Tr Record Holder; *Murray St Col; Phys Ed.*

HORTON, Donald Ray
Mart HS; Mart, TX (15-72) Chor; FFA; Math C; VP, Soph Cl; JV, Bkbl; Ftbl; Tr; *U of Tex; Phys Ed.*

HORTON, Donald Wayne
Walnut HS; Walnut, MS (1-55) Ed, Ann; Pres, BC; Dbte Tm; Tres, FFA; 4H; SC; Pres, Sr Cl; Pres, Jr Cl; Pres, Soph Cl; Gov Honor Prog; 4H A; H of F; HCt; Math A; MLS; Star Student; Type A; Star Chapter Farmer; Most Intelligent; SPATS; Miss St U; *Pre-Vet.*

HORTON, Elizabeth Leigh
Paducah Tilghman HS; Paducah, KY (10%-400) Chor; Drama; Ch, FHA; Marigal; Mu Alpha Theta; Sch P; SC; Var C; Swim; Tnns; Cl Fav; Head, Spirit Girl; Outst Christian Leadership; Miss RHS Court; *Journ.*

HORTON, Jeffrey Lynn
LaFarge HS; La Farge, WI (10-38) Drama; Fr C; Math C; NFL; Bsbl; JV, Bkbl; Most Improved, Bkbl.

HORTON, John Robert
Malta HS; Malta, IL; VP, FFA; Outst, FFA; Outst Comm Service; 2nd Pl, St Found A; *Bus Mgt.*

HORTON, Judy Diane
Rogersville HS; Rogersville, TN (46-155) FBLA; Pres, FHA; FTA; Sch P; Pres A; Candystriper.

HORTON, Julia Leigh
Wills HS; Smyrna, GA; Hmrm; InterAct C; SC; Parl, Pep C; PA; *Marietta Voca Sch; Medical Asst.*

HORTON, Julie Ann
John S Shaw HS; Mobile, AL; Band; Jr Civitan; Yth Choir; WW; Yth Handbells; Yth Coun; *Auburn U; Mus.*

HORTON, Kenneth Brian
Foothill HS; Tustin, CA; SC; JV, Ftbl; JV, Wrest; *U of Calif; Engr.*

HORTON, Leisa Lynn
Meadowbrook HS; Byesville, OH; Chor; Secy, FHA; Secy, 4H; Sci C; 4H A; Drill Tm; *Social Work.*

HORTON, Mary Louise
Karns HS; Knoxville, TN (20-210) Mgr, BC; Drama; GS; Pres, 4H; Hmrm; InterClub Coun; ARC; SC; Pres, Y-Tns; Sr Cl; Secy, Jr Cl; Sftbl; Amer Leg A; Citz A; 4H A; HCt; Opt A; PTA A; Home Ec A; Stu o-t Mo; *U of Tenn; Home Ec.*

HORTON, Micki Lynn
Henryville HS; Henryville, IN (10-75) NHS; Bkbl; Tr; HCt; Math A; Vlbl; Top Scorer, Tr.

HORTON, Nellie Jean
Baker Sr HS; Baker, LA (24-374) BC; Chor; FHA; FTA; Math C; Mu Alpha Theta; Tri-HiY; COM; Hon Prog; Math A; Yth Leg; Mu Sigma C; *Southeastern U; Pre-Dentistry.*

HORTON, Pamela Ann
William Penn HS; York, PA (300-515) Chor; NHS; Y-Tns; *Lincoln Col; Social Welfare.*

HORTON, Paula Deneice
Wm Penn Sr HS; York, PA (71-693) Hmrm; Y-Tns; Mgr, Tr; Amer Leg A; *Howard U; Psych.*

HORTON, Rebecca Louise
William Byrd HS; Vinton, VA (34-246) BC; FBLA; Math A; Spelling A; *Ntl Bus Col; Acct.*

HORTON, Rhonda Rene
N Beach HS; Moclips, WA; Chor; Tnns; Tr; *Zoology.*

HORTON, Shari Susan
Hudson HS; Lufkin, TX (1-66) Ann; VP, FHA; Pres, NHS; Rptr, Sch P; Spch C; Secy, SC; B Crocker A; Chamber of Comm A; Spch A; Star Student; Val; VFW Orator Win; Mgr, Vlbl; Ntl Merit Commended Stu; Eng A; NHS Schol A; *E Tex Baptist Col; Elem Ed.*

HORTON, Sherry Olien
Faith HS; Faith, SD (13-32) Band; Chldr; Chor; Drama; 4H; Span C; SC; Pres, Sr Cl; Secy, Soph Cl; Bkbl; Cpt, Tr; 4H A; HQn; HCt; Pres A; Spch A; Swtht; Type A; Yth Fel; Snow Qn Contest; Rodeo C; Declam; *Black Hills St Col; Criminal Justice.*

HORTON, Wade Alston
Columbia HS; Decatur, GA (20%-300) BC; Cr-Ctry; Soccer; Tr; Order/Arrow A; Sci A; *U of Ga; Ed.*

HORTON, Walter Floyd
Booker T Washington HS; Shreveport, LA (45-400) Top Tn of Amer; *Southern U; Engr.*

HORVATH, Bettyann
Philipsburg-Osceola Area Sr HS; Philipsburg, PA (41-204) Drama; FHA; Tres, FTA; HiY; Cpt, Mjrte; Secy, Rainbow; Ski C; Y-Tns; Beauty; Pres, Yth Fel; Fr A; Sr Ldr, GSct; Vlbl; *Williamsport Hospital Sch of Nurs; Nurs.*

HORVATH, Joyce Lynn
Elida HS; Elida, OH (47-190) Chor; Ensm; Span C; VP, Tres, JA; GAA; Church Sftbl & Bkbl; Dist Piano Guild; *Bluffton Col; Algebra.*

HORVATH, Linda Marie
McArthur HS; Hollywood, FL; NEDT.

HORVATH, Mark Bryon
Valley Forge HS; Parma Hts, OH (90-838) HiY; NHS; Order/Arrow; Var C; Tres, Sr Cl; Tres, Jr Cl; Cpt, Ftbl; Cpt, Wrest; Hon Prog; Most Out; Order/Arrow A; MVP, Ftbl & Wrest; Eagle Sct; All Amer, All Schol, Ftbl; All NE Ohio, Ftbl; *Kent St U; Bus Adm.*

HOSENTHIEN, Nancy J
Huntsville HS; Huntsville, AL (25-500) Band; Band Ltr; MVP, Bible Quiz Tm; *U of Ala; Physics.*

HOSEY, Robert H Jr
Decatur HS; Decatur, AL; Chem C; Hmrm; Key C; SC; Bsbl; Mgr, Bkbl; *U of Ala; Med.*

HOSIER, Barbara Ann
Cedarville HS; Cedarville, AR (5-30) Ann; Bus C; FBLA; FHA; Pres, 4H; NHS; Rptr, Sch P; SC; Swim; COM; 4H A; Swtht; Schol A; *Westark Jr Col.*

HOSIER, Edwin Eugene
Texhoma HS; Texhoma, OK (6-30) FFA; Var C; VP, Sr Cl; VP, Jr Cl; Bkbl; Co-Cpt, Ftbl; Tr; Alg A; Cl Fav; Masonic A; *Okla St U; Bus Adm.*

HOSIER, Elizabeth Ann
Pendleton Heights HS; Pendleton, IN (19-300) Band; BC; Mjrte; NHS; Span C; Var C; Bkbl; Tnns; Hon Prog; Type A; Cpt, MVP, Vlbl; Top 10%, Grand Ntl Twirling Tm; 6yr Ltr Win; White River Conf Tm; *Ball St U; Bus.*

HOSKIN, Kelly Ann
Mascoutah Comm HS; Mascoutah, IL (30-96) Chem C; Chess C; FFA; Ger C; Math C; Sci C; Swim; Tr; Karate; *Bradley U; Botany.*

HOSKINS, Carmen Alane
Deshler HS; Tuscumbia, AL; Parl, FHA; JA A; Gym; Miss Bronze Pagent; Debutante; *U of Ala; Phys Therapist.*

HOSKINS, Caryn Louise
Corbin HS; Corbin, KY (1-148) A-Ed, Ann; BC; S-T, Chor; Ensm; Hmrm; All Festival, All St, Choir; *Math.*

HOSKINS, David Springer
Corbin HS; Corbin, KY (15-120) BS; Fr C; Tnns; Tr; Co- cpt, All St, Table Tnns; Organizer, St Table Tnns Tourn; *Davidson Col; Pre-Law.*

HOSLER, Kimberly Ann
W Aurora HS; Aurora, IL (135-754) A Cap Choir; *Nurs.*

HOSLEY, Nancy
Cibola HS; Alameda, NM; FFA; Rptr, 4H; 4H A; Horse Shows; Rodeo.

HOSMAN, Ray Allyn
Southland HS; Arbyrd, MO (5-44) Band; Secy, FFA; VP, Soph Cl; Mgr, Bsbl; Bkbl; Cl Fav; Sci A; *SE Mo St U; Agr.*

HOSS, Kimberly June
Washington HS; Washington, IN; Bus C; Chor; Yth Fel; DECA A; *Secondary Ed.*

HOSTETLER, Karen Ann
Waverly-Shell Rock HS; Waverly, IA (104-198) Ger C; Secy, 4H; Golf; Poet A; Candidate, Co Fair Qn; *Hawkeye Tech Col; Commercial Art.*

HOSTETLER, Thomas LeRoy
Akron E HS; Akron, OH (62-328) Band; Ensm; NHS; Orch; Ed, Sch P; Tres, Sci C; Mgr, Soccer; Journ A; Q&S A; Sr o-t Wk; *U of Akron; Bus Adm.*

HOSTETTER, Beverly Day
Beaver Dam Sr HS; Beaver Dam, WI (5-321) Chldr; Chor; GS; Hmrm; Orch; Ski C; Var C; Tnns; JV, Tr; COM; JA A; *U of Wis; Sci.*

HOSTETTER, KarLee Louise
Warwick HS; Lititz, PA (58-262) Secy, FBLA; Hmrm; Span C; Mgr, Bkbl; Citz A; Type A; Yth Fel; GSct A Badges; *Bus.*

HOSTETTER, Sheila Maxine
Hickman Mills HS; Kansas City, MO (24-488) Chldr; Chor; Fr C; NHS; Ntl Teachers Coun; SC; COM; HCt; Hon Prog; Pep C; Piano A; Hon Schol; Pres, VP, Secy, MYF; Fr A; *William Woods Col; Interior Design.*

HOSTOFFER, Robert William
St Mary's Prep; Orchard Lake, MI (19-44) Co-Cpt, Chldr; Ensm; Order/Arrow; Ed, Sch P; Var C; Tr; Q&S A; Eagle Sct; 2nd Hon; Danis Vitar, BSct A; Ad Altaredei BSct A; Pope Pius X A.

HOSTUTLER, Carol Lynn
Scott Intermediate HS; Coatesville, PA; A Cap Choir; Chor; Community Yth Symph; Fr C; Orch; Rptr, Sch P; Ski C; Secy, Jr Cl; Citz A; Hon Prog; NEDT; DAR Essay A; Craig Ridgeway Schol A; *Lit.*

HOTCHKISS, Amy Louise
Statesboro HS; Statesboro, GA (136-300) Band; Ensm; HiY; Span C; Band A; *Ga Sou Col; Bus.*

HOTCHKISS, Grace Virginia
Brethern HS; Paramount, CA (3-110) Chem C; Ntl Yth Conf; Co-Cpt, Bkbl; JV, Sftbl; Alg A; CSF; COM; Citz A; Bookkeeping A; *Sci.*

HOTCHKISS, John Gordon
Grimsley Sr HS; Greensboro, NC (30-600) Order/ Arrow; Tr; Alg A; Industrial Arts A; *Ga Tech; Elec Engr.*

HOTCHKISS, Lois Jean
Brethren HS; Paramount, CA (27-88) Dbte Tm; CSF; Spch A; *Bob Jones U; Elem Ed.*

HOTTEL, Sara Ann
John Handley HS; Winchester, VA; Ann; Co-Cpt, Chldr; Chor; Swim; 3rd Pl, Bio A; 2nd Pl, Lat Certamen; *William & Mary Col.*

HOTTENSTEIN, Elizabeth Ann
W A Berry HS; Birmingham, AL (28-36) Chor; Pep, Charm, C'S; *U of Ala; Nurs.*

HOTTINGER, Scott Dane
Newark HS; Newark, OH; Var C; Mgr, Bkbl; Yth Fel; Pres, Yth Fel; HS Counselor; *Banking & Financial Mgr.*

HOTZE, Eric Robert
Hazelwood Central Sr HS; Florissant, MO (50-840) Band; Chess C; Demolay; Tres, NHS; Orch; Span C; Sftbl; Citz A; Curator A; All St Band; *Central Methodist Col; Bio.*

HOUCHEN, Rebecca Jane
Scarlet Oaks Joint Voc Sch; Cincinnati, OH (38-570) Band; Chldr; Chor; Drama; Ensm; Fr C; NHS; SC; Thes; Pres, Sr Cl; Hockey; Tr; COM; Citz A; Pres A; Pep C; NHS A; Russian Dancers; Ecology C; Mgr, Vlbl; Inter-Ntl Thespians Directors A; Ntl Hon, Ntl Fed of Mus C; *Ohio St U; Dentistry.*

HOUCHENS, Denise Elaine
William Monroe HS; Stanardsville, VA (10-90) BC; FBLA; FTA; Lit Mag; Type A; *Mary Washington Col; Secondary Ed.*

HOUCHIN, Denise Sue
Flagstaff HS; Flagstaff, AZ; Band; Ch, 4H; SC; 4H A; Yth Foundation A; Gym; Band; Judo; *N Ariz U; Sociology.*

HOUCK, Gary L
Pine Grove Area HS; Pine Grove, PA (90-160) Var C; Bsbl; Bkbl; Most Out.

HOUDEK, Lisa Lynn
Douglas MacArthur HS; San Antonio, TX (12-630) Band; CYO; Ensm; Rptr, Lat C; NHS; Ed, Sch P; Journ A; Q & S; St & Region Lat A; Gold Medals, Band Solo; *Special Ed.*

HOUG, James Donald
Jasper HS; Jasper, MN; CYO; FFA; Alt, BS.

HOUGER, Kevin Rodrick
Creston HS; Creston, WA (6-15) Order/Arrow; JV, Bkbl; *Spokane Comm Col; Carpentry.*

HOUGH, Deborah Ann
E Troy HS; W Troy, WI (19-119) Band; Rptr, FHA; NHS; Secy, Sr Cl; Secy, Jr Cl; Shorthand A's; *Milwaukee Area Tech Col; Med Secy.*

HOUGH, Julie Ann
Lansing Eastern HS; Lansing, MI; Band; Chor; Dbte Tm; Drama; Pres, Lat C; Lat NHS; Madrigal; Tres, NHS; Spch C; Tres, Soph Cl; NMS; Val; Abion Presidential Schol; Oakland U Founder's A Schol; *Albion Col; Bio.*

HOUGHTON, Julia Selina
Adolfo Camarillo HS; Camarillo, CA (1-650) Pres, Band; Hmrm; InterClub Coun; Pres, Sci C; Ski C; CSF; Hon Prog; Rensselaer A; *Sci.*

HOUK, Thomas Michael
Richwoods HS; Peoria, IL (35-520) Var C; Bsbl; Ftbl; All-Conf Bsbl Player; *Tex Christian U; Bus.*

HOULT, William S Jr
John H Francis Polytech HS; Sun Valley, CA; CSF; Christian C; NRA Rifle & Pistol C; Industrial A; *Calif St U; Math.*

HOULTON, Ramona Faye
Mio Au Sable HS; Mio, MI (1-80) F-Ed, Ann; Band; Chldr; Chor; 4H; NHS; Secy, Soph Cl; Bkbl; Sftbl; Tr; Alg A; Citz A; 4H A; Math A; Type A; Pres Phys Fitness A; *Ferris St Col; Bus.*

HOUNSHELL, Joyce
Belmont HS; Dayton, OH (19-467) SC; Var C; Secy, Soph Cl; JV, Bkbl; Swim; Hon Prog; Spch A; Yth Fel; Vlbl; Fencing; GSct; *U of Cincinnati; Bus Mgt.*

HOUNSHELL, William Wilder
E Peoria Comm HS; E Peoria, IL (9-515) Chem C; Chess C; Dbte Tm; Ger C; Hmrm; Sci C; Spch C; Cpt, Tnns; *U of Ill; Pre-Med.*

HOUPT, Ginger Mary
Summit HS; Summit, NJ (73-417) VP, AFS; Chor; Drama; Cpt, Mjrte; Orch; SC; Pres, MYF; All St Chor; *Oberlin Col; Ministry.*

HOUSE, Betsy Lynn
Irvin HS; El Paso, TX (10%-576) CYO; Chem C; Dbte Tm; Drama; FHA; Pres, Hmrm; Lit Mag; NHS; Sci C; Span C; Span NHS; MVP, Arch; Mgr, Bkbl; MVP, Ftbl; S-T, Sftbl; Swim; Tnns; Beauty; Hon Prog; Lion A; Teachers Apple A; Hikin Top 10%; 1st Runnerup, Hemisphere Pagent; Nurs Aid Course Cert; G A & Most Enthus, YWCA Camp; *U of Tex; Nurs.*

HOUSE, Betty Marie
Mt Whitney HS; Visalia, CA (74-462) S-T, Chor; Ensm; CSF; Chancel Choir; New Life Singers; Coun, Discipleship Prog; *Fresno Pacific Col; Ed.*

HOUSE, Bobbi Anne
Irvin HS; El Paso, TX (11-550) A Cap Choir; GS; NHS; Bkbl; Sftbl; Math A; Sci A; All Dist Vlbl; Math A; *U of Tex; Engr.*

HOUSE, Cindy Louise
Wood River HS; Hailey, ID (3-115) JV, Chldr; NHS; Ski C; Spch C; SC; Pres, Soph Cl; Bkbl; Tnns; HCt; Spch A; Vlbl; *Col of Idaho; Law.*

HOUSE, David Michael
Montgomery Bell Acad; Nashville, TN (41-87) Ann; Drama; Lat C; Lit Mag; NFL; Sch P; Spch C; Bkbl; Ftbl; Sftbl; COM; NEDT; Church Stu Coun; Church Yth Staff; *Vanderbilt U; Engr.*

HOUSE, Jeanne Ann
Banks Co HS; Homer, GA (12-67) Ann; BC; Ch, FHA; 4H; Tres, Tri-HiY; Bkbl; HCt; VofDEM; 1st R Up, Princess and Qn.

HOUSE, John Patrick
Cathedral HS; El Paso, TX (25-95) A Cap Choir; CYO; Chor; Drama; Hmrm; K of C; Bkbl; Sftbl; COM; Hon Prog; NEDT; Sci A; *Saint Mary's Col; Forestry.*

HOUSE, Kimberly F
Laurel Co HS; London, KY (10%-425) Chldr; Drama; Tres, FHA; GS; Hmrm; Spch C; Tnns; *Eastern Ky U; Bus.*

HOUSE, Lesa Anne
Glendale HS; Springfield, MO (45-475) AFS; Tres, Anchor C; FTA; Model UN; Sftbl; Tau Phi Gamma Sorority; *Drury Col; Home Ec.*

HOUSE, Mark David
Glendale HS; Springfield, MO (20%-500) A Cap Choir; AFS; Chor; JETS; SC; Ftbl; Sftbl; JV, Tr; Wrest; *U of Mo; Aerospace Engr.*

HOUSE, Patricia Lynn
Mathews HS; Vienna, OH (19-112) Band; Cpt, Chldr; FTA; GS; NHS; Span C; SC; Var C; Y-Tns; Pres, Soph Cl; Sftbl; Tr; HQn; Prom Court; VP, Future Secy; *Youngstown St U; Secy Studies.*

HOUSE, Terri Angela
Lowell HS; San Francisco, CA; *Calif St Col; Bus.*

HOUSEL, Dolly Ann
Lordstown HS; Warren, OH (25%-48) VP, Bus C; Ski C; VP, Jr Cl; Statistician, Tr; IOE Special A; Bkbl Prog Coordinator A; *Bus.*

HOUSER, Cindy Sue
Robinson Secondary HS; Fairfax, VA (1-501) Band; Ensm; Ger C; Fin, GS; Jr Miss Pagent; NHS; Orch; Sci C; Magna Cum Laude; Math A; NMS; Sci A; Val; Yth Fel; Jr Miss Scholastic Schol; AB Duke Mem Schol; Army Off Wives C Schol; *Duke U; Bio-Med.*

HOUSER, Denise
Germantown HS; Philadelphia, PA (12-551) FFA; Pres, Hmrm; NHS; SC; Amer Leg A; COM; Citz A; Hon Prog; MLS; Type A; Francis E Thole Essay Contest Win; AFNA Legal Prog; Magnet Hons Prog; *SC St Col; Eng.*

HOUSER, Lowell Phillip
Kenwood HS; Chicago, IL; A Cap Choir; Band; Pres, CYO; Chor; Tr; *U of Ill; Mus.*

HOUSER, Malinda Ann
W Point HS; W Point, MS (30-153) FBLA; Spirit C; WW; 1st, Northern Dist FBLA; *Miss St U; Secretarial Sci.*

HOUSER, Ruth Anne
Hardaway HS; Columbus, GA (1-415) Mu Alpha Theta; Secy, Jr Cl; Tnns; Outst Scholastic Achv; Principal's List A; *U of Ga; Computer Sci.*

HOUSER, Stephen Leslie
Temple Baptist Acad; Denver, CO; Band; NHS; Spch C; Ftbl; Sftbl; Ntl Pace Bowl Champ; *Baptist Bible Col W; Pastor.*

HOUSEWRIGHT, Tanya Yvonne
Crockett HS; Austin, TX (25%-850) Pres, Crown & Scepte; Hon Prog; Yth Fel; Gym; Bowl; *Baylor U; Art.*

HOUSH, Barbara Faie
Hay Springs Pub Sch; Hay Springs, NE (1-32) Ed, Ann; Chldr; Chor; Semi-Fin, GS; SC; Var C; Tr; Alg A; Amer Leg A; Bio A; HCt; Pres A; Regent Schol; Type A; Val; VFW A; VofDEM; Vlbl; Elk's Schol; Eng A; *Chadron St Col; Bio.*

HOUSIAUX, Mary Lynn
Huron Sr HS; Huron, SD (33%-320) Band; Chor; Pres, Hmrm; Ed, Sch P; SC; Var C; Mgr, Bkbl; JV, Tr; VP, Niki C; *Brookings-SDSU; Law.*

HOUSTON, Charla Beth
Early Co HS; Blakely, GA (1-220) BC; JV, Chldr; Pres, FHA; F-Ed, Sch P; Beauty; St FHA Off; FHA Natl Convention A; Beta Acad Bowl; Yth & Handbell Choir.

HOUSTON, Deana Marlene
Mexico Sr HS; Mexico, MO (45-310) Chldr; VP, Chor; COM; Citz A; Cl Fav; Fresh Attendent; Choral Dept; DAR Essay Win; *Stephens Col; Elem Ed.*

HOUSTON, Eric Von
Hollywood Professional Sch; Los Angeles, CA (30%-35) A Cap Choir; Dbte Tm; Secy, Lat C; VP, NHS; SC; Pres, Sr Cl; Swim; Tnns; Citz A; Hon Prog; Most Out; Sci A; *USC; Law.*

HOUSTON, Karl Jay
Athens Sr HS; Athen, TX; FFA; Ntl Yth Conf; Span C; Bsbl; Bkbl; JV, Ftbl; Yth Fel; Yth Foundation; RA A; Best Ath o-t Yr; *Tex Christian U.*

HOUSTON, Kimberly Anne
Early Co HS; Blakely, GA (30-165) Ann; Drama; Ensm; Fr C; FHA; Sch P; WW; *Troy St U.*

HOUSTON, Kurt Alan
Pocatello HS; Pocatello, ID (33-300) Band; Bkbl; Ftbl; Sftbl; Tr; Wrest; Yth Fel; Pres, Local, District Yth; *U of Idaho; Forestry.*

HOUSTON, R Scott
Imperial Christian Acad; Imperial, PA; Yth Fel; Social Work.

HOUSTON, Stephanie Rebecca
Pascagoula HS; Pascagoula, MS; Chor; Ensm; *Jackson Co Jr Col; Phys Therapy.*

HOUT, Bethanne
Mt Gilead Sr HS; Mt Gilead, OH (5-140) Ftbl; Sftbl; Swim; Tnns; GAA; Secy, Church Yth Fel; Adm Board; Yth Coun; *N Central Col; Retail Mgt.*

HOUTARI, Mark Thomas
Los Angeles Lutheran HS; Burbank, CA (5-85) Bausch & Lomb A; CSF.

HOUTCHENS, Steven Paul
Lancaster HS; Lancaster, TX (7-170) Secy, Band; Fr C; Pres, NHS; SC; Bus Mgr, Bkbl; Bus Mgr, Ftbl; Bio A; Chem A; Hon Prog; Math A; MLS; Ntl Sci Found; Phy A; Yth Fel; Interntl Sci & Engr Fair; Speaker, Tex Jr Sci Symp; Hons Group, Sci Talent Search; 1st Pl, Ntl Math Exam; *U of Tex at Austin; Aerospace Engr.*

HOUTKOOPER, Robin JoAnn
Vicksburg HS; Vicksburg, MI; Tnns; Hon Prog; Yth Fel; Word of Life A's; *Bronson Hospital Sch of Nurs; Nurs.*

HOUTS, Brenda Jean
Celina Sr HS; Celina, OH (1-275) Band; S-T, FTA; NHS; Bio A; Chem A; Hon Prog; Math A; Sci A; Val; GAA; GScts; S-T, Church Yth Fel; Church Choir; *Ohio N U; Phar.*

HOUTSMA, Kim Kay
Ogilvie HS; Ogilvie, MN (5-65) A Cap Choir; Chor; Jr Miss Pagent; Madrigal; Pres, SC; Var C; Bkbl; Sftbl; Tr; HCt; *Art.*

HOUTZER, Alan Rex
Pine View Sch; Sarasota, FL; Cr-Ctry; Tr; COM; Citz A; JA A; NEDT; Win, Spelling Bees; *MIT; Physics.*

HOUZE, Gwendolyn Elaine
Mattie T Blount HS; Prichard, AL (2-28) Drama; Pres, Hmrm; SC; Sftbl; HCt; Hon Prog; MLS; Best Dressed; *Faulkner Col; Acct.*

HOUZZ, Renee Almer
Willibroro Cath HS; Chicago, IL (5-81) Drama; Fr C; Hmrm; Secy, Math C; NHS; Secy, Pol Sci C; Tres, Sci C; SC; Thes; VP, Sr Cl; Amer Leg A; Bio A; Ntl Achv Schol; *NW U; Learning Disabilities.*

HOVEN, Elizabeth Diane
Jackson HS; Jackson, AL (3-132) A Cap Choir; Ann; VP, BC; Bus C; Chor; Drama; Ensm; FHA; VP, Math C; Pres, Rainbow; Bus Mgr, Sch P; Pres, SC; Secy, Sr Cl; Pres, Jr Cl; VP, Soph Cl; Co-Cpt, Sftbl; Cpt, Swim; Tnns; Alg A; Beauty; COM; Citz A; Cl Fav; Gr Marshal; 4H A; HQn; HCt; Jr Chamber of Com A; Math A; Most Out; Q&S A; Sci A; Swtht; VofDEM; Yth Fel; Miss Sou Belle; Worthy Advisor, Rainbow Girls; Miss JHS; *U of Ala; Nurs.*

HOVEN, Lucinda
Thornapple Kellogg HS; Middleville, MI; A-Ed, Ann; Band; Chor; NHS; Sch P; Secy, Ski C; HCt; Best Dressed.

HOVEN, Nancy Ann
Elmira HS; Elmira, OR (9-192) Rainbow; *Animal Sci.*

HOVEY, Carrie Fay
Williamston HS; Williamston, MI (15-160) AFS; Band; VP, 4H; Tnns; 4H A; Band Solos & Duet A's; *Math.*

HOVIS, Tamelia Lynn
N Fort Myers HS; N Fort Myers, FL (235-501) VP, Bus C; Lit Mag; Dist Display Contest; *Milligan Col; Med.*

HOVIS, Valerie Gaye
S San Antonio HS W Campus; San Antonio, TX (5-200) Band; NHS; Span C; Hon Prog; Art, Jr Spirit, C'S; *Hist.*

HOVLAND, Linda Ardis
Carpio Pub HS; Carpio, ND; Band; Chor; Ensm; Pres, 4H; Sch P; Var C; Tr; 4H A; Interlochen Ntl Mus; Spch A; JV Vlbl; Home Environment Achv Inst; *Art.*

HOWARD, Ann Carol
Melbourne HS; Melbourne, FL (25%-350) Band; Federation of Mus C As; Tres, Yth for Christ; *Pensacola Jr Col; Dental Hygiene.*

HOWARD, Anne Register
Fayetteville Acad; Fayetteville, NC (25%-60) A Cap Choir; FTA; Lat C; Span C; Sftbl; Yth Fel; *Eng.*

HOWARD, Arburdea Elaine
Central HS; Shelbyville, TN (20-264) Pres, FHA; VP, Hmrm; SC; Bkbl; Sftbl; SC A; *Middle Tenn St U; Acct.*

HOWARD, Belinda Cecilia
Plant City HS; Plant City, FL (5%-586) Chess C; Chor; FHA; NHS; Trustee Schol; *Hillsboro Comm Col; Mus.*

HOWARD, Beverlyn Lavern
Cainhoy HS; Huger, SC (4-84) Chldr; FHA; 4H; Sci C; Span C; Secy, SC; HQn; Sci A; *U of SC; Adm Asst.*

HOWARD, Billie Joe Jr
William Tennent Intermediate HS; Warminster, PA (350-1140) Chor; Drama; Sci C; Swim; Tr; Sci A; Outst Service A; Church Yth Mission Tours; *LSU; Archt.*

HOWARD, Bradley Moore
Daviess Co HS; Owensboro, KY; Key C; Ftbl.

HOWARD, Brenda Joyce
Crestview Sr HS; Crestview, FL (15-250) Anchor C; Ann; BC; Secy, Drama; Spch C; COM; Citz A; NMS; *Andrew Col; Social Work.*

HOWARD, Brenda Rene
Putnam City W HS; Oklahoma City, OK (40-715) Chor; Ensm; NHS; Pres, Span C; Span NHS; COM; Citz A; Hist A; Piano A; Mus A; *OKC Southwestern U; Bus.*

HOWARD, Brian Aden
Briarfield Acad; Lake Providence, LA (20-50) Ann; Hmrm; Ski C; SC; Pres, Sr Cl; *La Tech U; Agr Bus.*

HOWARD, Bruce Carl
Sunset HS; Beaverton, OR; Band; VP, Chess C; VP, Chor; Order/Arrow; ARC; JV, Bsbl; Mgr, Bkbl; JV, Ftbl; Swim; God & Country A; Dist Hon Band; *Oreg St U; Bus.*

HOWARD, Carolyn Sue
Clarkrange HS; Clarkrange, TN (3-51) Pres, BC; Chem C; Drama; FHA; 4H; Spch C; Pres, Jr Cl; 4H A; I Dare You; Pres A; Sub-Regional Pres, FHA; *Tenn Tech U.*

HOWARD, Cathy Darlene
Terrell Acad; Dawson, GA (15-35) FBLA; FTA; 4H; Bus Mgr, Sch P; Ch, Tri-HiY; Mgr, Bkbl; 4H A; Pep C; VP, Spirit C; VP, Church Yth; Gen Mills Family Ldr of Tomorrow; *Albany Voc Col; Secy.*

HOWARD, Cheryl Denise
E St Louis Sr HS; E Saint Louis, IL (80-845) Co-Cpt, Chldr; Lat C; NHS; *Eastern Ill; Journ.*

HOWARD, Curtis Lee
Carey HS; Carey, OH (16-106) BS; FTA; HiY; F-Ed, Sch P; Span C; Var C; MVP, Bkbl; Co-Cpt, Ftbl; MVP, Tr; MVP, Ftbl; *Ohio U; Journ.*

HOWARD, Daniel Ray
Rankin Twp HS; Rankin, IL (1-32) Band; Cpt, Chess C; Dbte Tm; NHS; S-T, Sci C; Bkbl; Phy A.

HOWARD, Deborah Mae
Laurel Valley Jr-Sr HS; New Florence, PA; Bus Mgr, Ann; Pres, FBLA; Rainbow; Rptr, Sch P; VP, Var C; Pres, Sr Cl; Cpt, Bkbl; Golf; Cpt, Vlbl.

HOWARD, Dianna Denise
Central HS; Shelbyville, TN; FHA; Secy, Hmrm; Tr; *Middle Tenn St U; Home Ec.*

HOWARD, Dianne Louise
Whitman-Hanson Regional HS; Whitman, MA (3-328) NHS; ARC; Cpt, Golf; Pres, Secy, Yth Fel; *Bridgewater St Col; Math.*

HOWARD, Donna Elisabeth
N University HS; Cedar Falls, IA; A Cap Choir; Chor; Drama; Madrigal; Thes; DARGCA; God & Country A; Journ A; JA A; Kiwanis A; Yth Fel; *Bartlesville Wesleyan Col; Mus.*

HOWARD, Doran
Buckhorn HS; Buckhorn, KY (5-63) BC; Bsbl; *Development of Lasers.*

HOWARD, Edward Dean
Weatherwax Sr HS; Aberdeen, WA (75-350) Chess C; 4H; NHS; ARC; Bkbl; Mgr, Ftbl; ARC A; Yth Fel.

HOWARD, Eileen Susan
Sterling HS; Somerdale, NJ (174-348) Bus Mgr, All Amer Yt; Ntl Yth Conf; COM; Yth Fel; *Fairleigh Diekerson U; Acct.*

HOWARD, Elaine Bernetta
Gloucester HS; Gloucester, VA (10%-150) Bus C; FBLA; 4H; Pres, Soph Cl; Bkbl; Cl Fav; 4H A; Hon Prog; Yth Fel; HR; PA; *Va St U; Bus Adm.*

HOWARD, Evelyn Lura
Elsworth J Wilson HS; Spencerport, NY (100-350) Band; Secy, Drama; 4H; Hmrm; SC; 4H A; Fr A; Band A.

HOWARD, Felise Kimberly
Charles Lincoln Harper HS; Atlanta, GA; CYO; Chor; Rptr, Hmrm; Sci C; SC; Sftbl; Tnns; Citz A; *Livingstone Col; Elec Engr.*

HOWARD, Fern Elise
James Madison HS; Vienna, VA (1-550) Hmrm; A-Ed, Lit Mag; NHS; ARC; Ed, Sch P; SC; Mgr, Bkbl; Pres, UMYF; Madisonettes; Optimist Orator A; Yth Coun; *Col of William and Mary; Eng.*

HOWARD, Fredrick Jay
Weatherwax Sr HS; Aberdeen, WA (175-350) 4H; ARC; ARC A; Yth Fel.

HOWARD, Gary Robert
Dyer Co HS; Newbern, TN (10%-117) Chor; Parl, FHA; Lat C; NHS; SC; Ftbl; Tnns; Hon Men, Conf Ftbl; *U of Tenn; Engr.*

HOWARD, Glenna Jo
Mariner HS; Everett, WA (76-398) Chor; VP, Western Wash Yth; *Seattle Pacific U; Psych.*

HOWARD, Jacquelyn Marie
Clarkstown S Sr HS; W Nyack, NY; Band; Hmrm; Tr; Sunday Sch Teacher's Organization; *Animal Tech.*

HOWARD, Jeffrey Michael
W Carteret HS; Morehead City, NC (72-300) A Cap Choir; Chor; Fr C; Madrigal; Var C; Ftbl; Wrest; Fin, Wrest; All St Chor; *Campbell Col; Bus.*

HOWARD, Kathy Marie
Holy Rosary Acad; Louisville, KY (2-86) Chor; Math C; NHS; ARC; Tr; NEDT; ARC A; Span A; WW; Ntl HS A; *Bellarmine Col; Acct.*

HOWARD, Kathy Pearlene
Swifton HS; Swifton, AR (3-28) Ann; FBLA; FFA; VP, FHA; B Crocker A; HR; *Pepperdine U; Bus.*

HOWARD, Kathy Sue
Sooner HS; Bartlesville, OK; Band; Bus C; Chor; Ensm; FBLA; Madrigal; NHS; Orch; COM; Elk A; VofDEM; Yth Fel; Demolay Outst Yth; Pres, Sr GSct; OSU Hon Schol; Pres, UMYF; UMW Recogn Cert; Ntl Merit Com Stu; Okla Northeast Dist Hon Choir; *Okla St U; Acct.*

HOWARD, Kiyo Vaughn
Merced HS; Merced, CA; Black Stu Union; *Reedley & Brook's Col; Fashion Merchandising.*

HOWARD, Laura Dawn
Niles E HS; Skokie, IL (155-499) A Cap Choir; Chor; Drama; Fr C; F-Ed, Sch P; Ski C; SC; Tr; NEDT; Q&S A; Co-Cpt, Vlbl; GAA Board; *Valparaiso U; Nurs.*

HOWARD, Lesha Anne
Niagara Wheatfield Sr HS; Sanborn, NY; Lion A; High Avg A; Phys Fitness A; *Cedarville Col; Eng.*

HOWARD, Leslie Annetta
W Philadelphia Cath Girls HS; Philadelphia, PA (3-388) CYO; Chor; Fr C; Hmrm; Lat C; Lat NHS; NHS; World Affairs C; COM; Chem A; Citz A; Hon Prog; Sci A; Lat A; HR; *La Salle Col; Bio.*

HOWARD, Leslie Marshall
Hastings Sr HS; Hastings, NE (122-304) Chor; Madrigal; Order/Arrow; God & Country A; Sci A; Yth Fel; Eagle Sct; Pres; Fel; Church Nom Comm; *U of Nebr; Art.*

HOWARD, Linda Jeannine
Taylor HS; North Bend, OH; Ann; Band; Chor; Pres, VP, Secy Yth Fel; Scottish Rite Choir; Sch Plays; *Oral Roberts U; Art.*

HOWARD, Lonnie Odell
Sunbright HS; Sunbright, TN (10-65) BC; FFA; 4H; Var C; Bsbl; Bkbl; Ftbl; 4H A; Bkbl A.

HOWARD, Marcia Louise
Jackson HS; Jackson, AL (10%-169) Band; Tres, BC; Chor; FHA; 4H; Mjrte; Sch P; Swim; Tnns; Cl Fav; 4H A; Spch A; Band Swtht; *Ga Tech; Journ.*

HOWARD, Mark Wayne
Texico HS; Texico, NM (2-38) FFA; Pres, NHS; Sch P; Pres, Sr Cl; Pres, Jr Cl; MVP, Ftbl; Amer Leg A; Hist A; HCt; Sal; *W Tex St U; Bus.*

HOWARD, Mary Louise
Owyhee HS; Owyhee, NV (3-25) JV, Chldr; FHA; GS; Bkbl; St Rptr, FBLA; Vlbl; *Links Sch of Bus; Secretarial.*

HOWARD, Mitchell Jay
Jay Howard HS; Columbus, GA;

HOWARD, Paul Stephen
Nitro HS; Nitro, WV (10-300) Band; Chor; Pres, Community Yth; NHSph; Span C; McDonald's All-Amer HS Band; Outst Bandsman; All-Co Band, Orch & Chor; All-St Band; *W Va U; Mus.*

HOWARD, Randle David
O D Wyatt HS; Fort Worth, TX (160-475) Ann; City Conf; FTA; Span C; SC; Pres, Sr Cl; Co-Cpt, Ftbl; JV, Tnns; COM; Citz A; JA A; MLS; Most Out; Opt A; Opt Out Tn; Spch A; MVP, Ftbl; Young Tex o-t Mo; Achiever o-t Yr; Art, Ldrship A's; *SW Tex St U; Marketing.*

HOWARD, Rebecca Anne
Fountain Lake HS; Hot Springs, AR (1-36) Ed, Ann; BC; GS; Sch P; Pres, SC; S-T, Thes; Pres, Sr Cl; Tnns; DARGCA; MLS; Opt Out Tn; Val; *UALR; Criminal Justice.*

HOWARD, Robert Stephen
Vanguard HS; Ocala, FL (7-350) Pres, Fr C; VP, FBLA; Pres, Ger C; Key C; Tres, Mu Alpha Theta; Tres, NHS; COM; Fr A's; *U of Fla; Med Tech.*

HOWARD, Rodney Gene
Mileur Co HS; Calhoun, KY (10-160) BC; Pres, Chess C; Sci C; Var C; Ftbl; Tr; Amer Leg A; ROTC A; Cpt, Rifle Tm; Superior Cadet, ROTC; High Rifle Firer; Colorguard A; *W Ky U; Chem.*

HOWARD, Rose Lynn
Melville HS; Melville, LA; BC; Tres, FBLA; Type A; *T H Harris Col; Bus.*

HOWARD, Sandra Marie
Connellsville HS; Connellsville, PA; Band; HiY; Pres, Hmrm; Swim; Tnns; *Seton Hill Col.*

HOWARD, Sherri Lynn
Wolfson Sr HS; Jacksonville, FL; Chor; Civinettes; Soph Girls; PREPS; *U of Fla; Bus.*

HOWARD, Sheryl Diane
Highland Park HS; Topeka, KS (39-400) Chor; NHS; Sch P; Pres, Y-Tns; Tr; Hist A; Type A; Mgr, Vlbl; Child Development A; Shorthand A; Home Ec Stu o-t Yr; Social Living A; Meal Mgt A; Modern Lit A; *Kansas Wesleyan Col; Bus.*

HOWARD, Susan Carlene
Terrell Acad; Dawson, GA; FBLA; Pres, 4H; F-Ed, Sch P; Tri-HiY; Mgr, Bkbl; Pres, Church Yth; Pres, Spirit C.

HOWARD, Tamra Dawn
Parchment HS; Kalamazoo, MI; Ski C; Span C; Y-Tns; Swim; Tnns.

HOWARD, Thomas Lee
Wayne Co HS; Jesup, GA (5%-402) BC; JV, Tnns; Scholastic Achv A; Arts & Crafts Sweepstakes A; *U of Ga; Bio.*

HOWARD, Tonda Lynne
Leedey HS; Leedey, OK (10-31) Ann; Secy, FHA; VP, 4H; Tres, Ski C; Rptr, Soph Cl; Bkbl; Tnns; COM; 4H A; Poet A; Spch A; *SWOSU; Med Tech.*

HOWARD, Wanda Susan
Thomas Jefferson HS; Pittsburgh, PA (47-372) Band; Chor; Span C; SC; Bkbl; Mgr, Sftbl; Hon Prog; Yth Fel; Jr Deacon; *Penn St U; Bio.*

HOWARD, William Francis
Southside HS; Elmira, NY; Lat C; NHS; Var C; Ftbl; Tr; Wrest; Hon Prog; MLS; Yth Fel.

HOWARTH, Jane Simms
Dublin HS; Dublin, CA (99-395) F-Ed, Ann; Cpt, Chldr; Fr C; GS; Hmrm; Model UN; Pol Sci C; Ch, SC; Pres, Var C; Cpt, Tnns; CSF; HQn; HCt; VFW A; VFW Orator Wn; C-Ed, Ann; MVP, Tnns; Asst-ailimar, St Girls Ldr; *San Jose U; Pol Sci.*

HOWDEN, Heather Gail
Washington Irving HS; NY, NY; Chor; Sch P; Type A; *Bernard M Baruch Col; Acct.*

HOWDEN, Sharon Faith
Washington Irving HS; New York, NY (99-817) Chor; Fin, Crown & Scepter; Hmrm; Ntl Yth Conf; Co-Ed, Sch P; S-T, SC; COM; Journ A; Rptr, Sch P; Singing Cert; *Hunter Col; Math.*

HOWDEN, Wendy Marie
Columbia HS; Richland, WA (1-427) NHS; Church Pianist; Masonic JA A; Pres, Yth Group; Candystriper; Amer Service C; *Bob Jones U; Phys Therapy.*

HOWE, Carole Lynn
Bay View HS; Milwaukee, WI; Arch; Band; Chldr; Pres, Chess C; Chor; Dbte Tm; Ensm; Hmrm; Math C; Orch; Pres, ARC; Span C; 3 JA A; Art A; Mus A; *Olivet Nazarene Col; Math.*

HOWE, Connie Catherine
Sacred Heart Acad; Salem, OR (10%-55) Chldr; Span C.

HOWE, Daniel Kevin
Coon Rapids Sr HS; Coon Rapids, MN (59-728) Band; NHS; Ski C; Var C; Mgr, Ftbl; Sftbl; Swim; JV, Tnns; COM; Cl Fav; Most Out; Yth Fel; Pres, Yth Group; *Bethel Col; Sci.*

HOWE, David Daniel
Mercer HS; Harrodsburg, KY (20%-120) Band; Sci C; VP, Span C; Tres, Span C; *Morehead Col; Biol.*

HOWE, Don J
Evergreen HS; Vancouver, WA; Chor; Drama; Ger C; SC; Tr; *Elec.*

HOWE, John Randall
Upper Darby Sr HS; Upper Darby, PA (26-1000) Ger C; Order/Arrow; Phys C; Ed, Sch P; Sci C; Order/Arrow A; Yth Fel; *Engr.*

HOWE, Lana Kay
Douglas S Freeman HS; Richmond, VA (393-650) Ann; FHA; Hmrm; *Nurs.*

HOWE, Timothy James
Whitman-Hanson Regional HS; Whitman, MA (35-328) Key C; NHS; Bsbl; Bkbl; Cr-Ctry; Ftbl; Jewish Brotherhood A; Friendliest; *Acct.*

HOWELL, Charles Thomas
Dodge Co HS; Eastman, GA; Chor; Ensm; Ftbl; Cl Fav; Church Yth Choir.

HOWELL, Cynthia Lee
Duncan HS; Duncan, OK; Ann; Chor; Hmrm; SC; Bkbl; Sftbl; Swim; Tr; Sci A; Swtht; Most Ath; Most Courteous; Best Dressed; *Southwestern OSU; Data Processing.*

HOWELL, Don Alan
Modesto HS; Modesto, CA; Tres, Bus C; Chor; Ensm; Madrigal; Var C; Swim; *Stanisbus St Col; Acct.*

HOWELL, Donna Lynne
Reidsville Sr HS; Reidsville, NC (5%-375) Band; Pres, 4H; 4H A; I Dare You; NEDT; *U of NC; Law.*

HOWELL, Donna Maria
Philadelphia HS For Girls; Philadelphia, PA; Chor; Y-Tns; COM; Cl Fav; Yth Fel; *Math.*

HOWELL, George B
Belgrade HS; Belgrade, MT (50-90) A Cap Choir; Chor; Demolay; Parl, FFA; 4H; Ski C; Ftbl; Tr; HCt; All-Conf & All-St Ftbl Tackle; *Harding Col.*

HOWELL, Janet Lynn
Ardmore HS; Ardmore, OK (160-400) Drama; FTA; Span C; Spch C; MVP, Golf; Tnns; Ltr, Golf & Tnns; Superior A'S, Ntl Fed of Mus C; *Phys Ed.*

HOWELL, Judy Carroll
Pine Bluff HS; Pine Bluff, AR (53-596) Chor; NHS; Span C; Consultant, FHA; Jr Social C; Church Yth Coun; Ch, St Yth Coun of March of Dimes; *U of Ark; Food Sci.*

HOWELL, Juleann
Post Falls HS; Post Falls, ID (3-154) Secy, Band; Chem C; Chor; Drama; Ensm; Fr C; Fin, GS; Mjrte; NHS; ARC; Spch C; VP, Sr Cl; JV, Bkbl; Tr; Hon Prog; Sal; Spch A; WW; Piano Medal; Lead Role in Play; *Whitworth Col; Nurs.*

HOWELL, Karen Christine
Lima Sr HS; Lima, OH (183-588) Mgr, Band; Drama; Hmrm; MVP, Tr; GSct; *U of Cinncinati; Interior Design.*

HOWELL, Keith Douglas
Alma J Brown HS; Grambling, LA (3-49) Band; FTA; NHS; Sci C; Cpt, Bsbl; Cpt, Bkbl; Hon Prog; All Dist Bkbl; Phys Ed & Band A's; *Grambling St U; Acct.*

HOWELL, Keith Gordon
Gospel Light Christian HS; Walkertown, NC (15-31) Chor; Rptr, Sch P; Var C; MVP, Bsbl; Cpt, Bkbl; Ftbl; Soccer; *Tenn Temple Col; Phys Ed.*

HOWELL, Lela Elizabeth
N Forrest Attd Center; Hattiesburg, MS; Ann; Band; FHA; Pres, Y-Tns; Secy, Soph Cl; Driver Ed; *U of Sou Miss; Secy Field.*

HOWELL, Lisa Jean
Duncan HS; Duncan, OK; Chor; Soccer; Sftbl; Swim; Tr; Sci A; Swtht; Semi-Fin, Sch Swtht; Most Ath.

HOWELL, Loretta Ferne
Lancaster HS; Lancaster, OH; Bus C; FBLA; FHA; Secy, 4H; Hmrm; Secy, Mjrte; Secy, Y-Tns; Arch; Swim; Cl Fav; 4H A; Type A; Spelling A; Eng A; *Ohio U; Bus Adm.*

HOWELL, Lori Ann
Pt Pleasant Boro HS; Pt Pleasant, NJ (15-350) Band; NHS; *Med.*

HOWELL, Lorra Lane
Cherryville Sr HS; Cherryville, NC (19-139) Band; Chor; Tres, 4H; Sftbl; 4H A; Jr Adv; Jr Bowl Assn; Ldr, Acteens; Secy, Jr Bowl Leagues; Board of Directors, Bowl; Hgh Sct Bowl Trophy; S-T Sundy Sch.

HOWELL, Marilyn Sue
Johnston City HS; Johnston City, IL (24-102) Band; Chor; FHA; SC; Thes; Sftbl; *John A Logan Col; Phys Ed.*

HOWELL, Mark Alan
Mission Viejo HS; Mission Viejo, CA (63-550) AFS; BS; Secy, Key C; Pres, Pol Sci C; Ski C; SC; Var C; Cpt, Ftbl; JV, Wrest; Amer Leg A; Hist A; Kiwanis A; MVP, Vlbl; Sheriffs A; Most Inspirational, Ftbl; *Stanford U; Pol Sci.*

HOWELL, Martha Lavern
Koshkonong HS; Koshkonong, MO (5-25) Ann; Chor; GS; Ch, Lit Mag; A-Ed, Sch P; Secy, Jr Cl; Tres, Soph Cl; Hon Prog; Type A; VFW A; Vof-DEM; Home Ec A; Span A; Pres, Fresh Cl.

HOWELL, Monette Jean
Estancia HS; Estancia, NM (7-55) Pres, Drama; VP, FFA; FHA; Pres, 4H; Hmrm; Mjrte; NHS; Pres, Rainbow; Span C; Rptr, SC; Bkbl; Tr; 4H A; Hon Prog; Spch A; Star Student; Rptr, Off Ed Assn; Vlbl; *NM St U; Bus.*

HOWELL, Robbie Nelle
Dublin HS; Dublin, GA (8-167) Ann; Band; BC; Dbte Tm; Ensm; Tnns; Hon Prog; NEDT; Type A; Director's A; *Emory U; Pre-Law.*

HOWELL, Robert Alan
H E McCracken HS; Bluffton, SC (5-110) BC; 4H; Sch P; Sci A; Art A; Eng A; Phys Ed A; *Clemson U; Engr.*

HOWELL, Ronald Wayne
DeSoto HS; De Soto, TX (60-250) Ed, Ann; Rptr, Band; FTA; VP, Sr Cl; Q&S A; *Tex Tech U; Mass Communications.*

HOWELL, Samuel Warren
New Bern Sr HS; New Bern, NC; Band; Order/Arrow; Order/Arrow A; Eagle Sct; *NC St U; Elec Engr.*

HOWELL, Sara Frances
Montgomery Co HS; Mt Sterling, KY; Pres, BC; Fr C; FHA; 4H; Y-Tns; Golf; Swim; Miss Soph; FHA Court; *U of NC; Acct.*

HOWELL, Vanessa Gaye
Gates Co HS; Gatesville, NC (29-130) Ann; FBLA; FHA; Ed, Sch P; Journ A; *Paul D Camp Comm Col.*

HOWELL, Vanessa Loraine
Nathan Hale HS; Tulsa, OK (66-677) Pres, Chor; FBLA; Pres, Hmrm; Math C; Mu Alpha Theta; Ch, SC; Type A; Mus A; Shorthand A; *Tulsa Jr Col; Legal Secy.*

HOWELL, Vikki Leigh
Silsbee HS; Silsbee, TX (30-250) Chess C; Dbte Tm; Drama; FHA; FTA; Jr Miss Pagent; Spch C; PA; *Lamar U; Lab Tech.*

HOWEN, Rebekah Sharlene
Alhambra HS; Martinez, CA (1-350) Band; Semi-Fin, GS; Ed, Sch P; Sftbl; JV, Tnns; Alg A; CSF; COM; Hist A; Journ A; Math A; Yth Fel; HR; Yth Del, Church Convention; WW; Eng A; VP, Secy, Church Group; *USC; Dentistry.*

HOWER, Randi Jo
McKinley Sr HS; Canton, OH (46-645) Hmrm; NHS; Ch, SC; COM; Best Soph Home Ec Stu; Poster Contest, 1st Prize; Alexis League; *U of Akron; Commercial Art.*

HOWERTON, Denise Marie
Ahrens HS; Louisville, KY; Fr C; Hmrm; VP, NHS; Ed, Sch P; Tres, SC; Up Bound; COM; Hist A; Journ A; Math A; MLS; Type A; Val; Fr A; *U of Louisville; Computer Sci.*

HOWERTON, Kent Edward
Richland HS; Fort Worth, TX; Cum Laude Soc; Tres, Ger C; NHS; Ftbl; Alg A; Hon Prog; Sal; Summa Cum Laude; *Baylor U; Acct.*

HOWERTON, Marsha Kay
Norman HS; Norman, OK (79-800) S-T, A Cap Choir; Band; Drama; Ensm; Hmrm; Lat C; NHS; Orch; St Stu Congress; Secy, SC; Thes; Swim; Lion A; MLS; Yth Fel; Girl o-t Mo; 1st Cl GSct; Superior Solo, St Band; Principal Hornist, Orch; *Okla U; Phys Theraphy.*

HOWES, Deborah Kaye
Van Horn HS; Independence, MO (20%-430) A Cap Choir; Semi-Fin, AFS; Chor; Community Yth Symph; Ensm; Lit Ral; MVP, Orch; Swim; COM; Most Out; Type A; Done Most A; Best Mus; KC Mus Teachers Assn A; St Mus As; *Mus.*

HOWIE, Genevieve Sharpe
York Comp HS; York, SC (1-261) Band; Fr C; FTA; JV, Bkbl.

HOWINGTON, Carol Diane
Hogansville HS; Hogansville, GA (5-65) Ann; Band; BC; Cpt, Chldr; Pres, FHA; FTA; Key C; Semi-Fin, Lit Ral; Sch P; VP, SC; 1st Runner-Up, Miss Hogansville; St Degree, Home Ec; *Ed.*

HOWLE, Cassandra Lynne
Lone Oak HS; Paducah, KY (66%-120) Band; FNA; Sci C; *Abilene Christian Col; Med.*

HOWSER, Stuart Michael
Jefferson City Sr HS; Jefferson City, MO; Rptr, Sch P; Ftbl; *Southwestern Mo St U; General Ed.*

HOWZE, Carolyn
Cass Tech HS; Detroit, MI; *Bradley U; Photo-Journ.*

HOXIE, Dale Allan
Stonington HS; Stonington, CT (18-267) Semi-Fin, BS; Math C; NHS; Hon Prog; Math A; Sci A; *Mech Engr.*

HOXIE, Sharon
Stonington HS; Pawcatuck, CT (6-282) Band; ARC A; Sci A; TNT Singers; HR; Rifle Guard; *Child Development.*

HOY, Denise Dorris
Burges HS; El Paso, TX; Secy, Span NHS; Hon Prog; Dean's List; HR; *U of Tex at El Paso; Journ.*

HOYE, Annette
Pascagoula HS; Pascagoula, MS; FHA; Bkbl; Sftbl; Phys Ed Trophy; Bkbl Trophy; Phys Fitness A; *Perk Col.*

HOYE, Wayne Edgar
Rosemark Acad; Millington, TN (20%-42) Ann; Chem C; Hmrm; Lat C; Rptr, Sch P; SC; Var C; Tres, Jr Cl; Bsbl; Bkbl; MVP, Ftbl; Cl Fav; Yth Fel; Co-Cpt, Ftbl; Nom Committee; Pres, Icthus C; Church Administrative Board; Coun on Ministries; *Tenn Tech U; Sociology.*

HOYER, Ann Lindsay
Chipley HS; Chipley, FL (10%-121) Band; Chor; Pres, 4H; NHS; Sci C; Span C; Tnns; 4H A; *Dance.*

HOYER, Georgia Kay
Weldon Valley HS; Weldona, CO (4-12) VP, FBLA; Tres, FHA; NHS; Ed, Sch P; S-T, SC; Tres, Sr Cl; COM; MLS; *Ft Lewis Col.*

HOYES, James Edward
Wyoming Seminary; Kingston, PA (15-73) Chess C; Demolay; Tres, Ger C; Math C; Ski C; Bsbl; Hon Prog; NEDT; Order/Arrow A; Tres, Christian Endeavor; Life Sct; Explorer; *Dentistry.*

HOYHTYA, Sharyl Rae
Kalama HS; Kalama, WA (50%-60) Band; Chor; Sftbl; Tr; HCt; Pres A; *Modeling.*

HOYLE, Wendy Ann
Shelby Sr HS; Shelby, NC; Chor; Ensm; Span C; *Appalachian Col; Mus.*

HOYLMAN, Rodney Lyle
Fairmont Sr HS; Fairmont, WV (41-310) Spch C; Var C; Cr-Ctry; Tr; *W Va U; Bus.*

HUCKABEE, Tom E
N Brook HS; Houston, TX (200-538) A Cap Choir; Band; Chor; Drama; FTA; Order/Arrow; ARC; Thes; Tnns; God & Country A; Order/Arrow A; ARC A; *U of Houston; Elem Ed.*

HUCKE, Diane Christine
S Park HS; Library, PA (6-180) CYO; Chldr; Chor; GS; NHS; Sch P; Ski C; Spch C; Var C; Y-Tns; NEDT; *Pitt Col; Med.*

HUCKS, Leslie Jean
South HS; Cleveland, OH; Tr; Hon Prog; *Pitt U; Law.*

HUDADOFF, Pamela A
Half Hollow Hills HS E; Dix Hills, NY (50-990) Band; Chor; Drama; NHS; Orch; Span C; Span NHS; Thes; Hon Prog; Ntl Sci Found; Yth Fel; *Meteorology.*

HUDAK, James T
Deerborne HS; Coral Gables, FL (3-78) Key C; NHS; Ch, SC; Bio A; Service, Golden Book, A's; *Miami Dade Comm Col; Bus.*

HUDAK, Nancy Lynn
Union Springs Acad; Union Springs, NY; Ann; Band; Chor; Hmmr; NHS; Sch P; SC; S-T, Soph Cl; Bkbl; Hockey; Soccer; Sftbl; Citz A; *Interior Design.*

HUDDLE, David Charles
Cary-Grove Comm HS; Cary, IL (50-315) Chor; FTA; NHS; Span C; JV, Ftbl; Tr; Hon Prog; CB C; BSct; Bowl League; 1st Yr Hon Pin; *Coe Col; Acct.*

HUDGEONS, Charles Randall
El Dorado HS; El Dorado, AR (115-398) Bsbl; Ftbl; Athlete o-t Yr; WW; Jr Civitans; Christian Athletes; *La Tech U; Petroleum Engr.*

HUDGEONS, Eva Dale
Diamond Hill-Jarvis HS; Fort Worth, TX (3-240) Band; Mjrte; Sci C; SC; Silver Eagle; *Bus.*

HUDGINS, Doyle Edward
Lamar Sr HS; Houston, TX; Drama; NHS; Thes; Bus Mgr, Swim; Amer Leg A; *Baylor U; Bus.*

HUDGINS, LaWanda Faye
Maggie L Walker HS; Richmond, VA (10%-222) Band; Jr Miss Pagent; Cpt, Mjrte; NHS; Secy, Sci C; Citz A; Hist A; Hon Prog; Most Out; Sci A; Type A; Yth Fel; Distinguished Stu; Mus A; *U of Va; Psych.*

HUDGINS, Rhonda Kay
N Hall HS; Gainesville, GA (10%-196) Band; BC; Chor; FTA; Math C; Sch P; COM; Hon Prog; *Gainesville Jr Col.*

HUDGINS, Ronnie Jay
N Hall HS; Gainesville, GA; *Gainesville Jr Col; Acct.*

HUDGINS, Terry Wayne
Buckingham Co HS; Dillwyn, VA; Band; Pres, FFA; 4H; JV, Ftbl; 4H A; FFA Greenhand; *VPI; Agr.*

HUDLER, Bobbie Ann
Starmount HS; Boonville, NC (16-204) Chldr; Secy, FFA; FHA; SC; Pres, Soph Cl; Sftbl; Tnns; HCt; FFA Swtht; *Forsyth Tech Col; Real Estate.*

HUDSON, Andrea Vonnett
Alfred Ely Beach HS; Savannah, GA (2-28) FHA; 4H A; Opt A; *Morehouse Col; Criminal Justice.*

HUDSON, Annette Kay
Central Valley HS; Spokane, WA (42-350) FTA; Drill Tm; Piano A; Girls Glee; Girls League; *Whitworth Col; Span & Eng Teacher.*

HUDSON, Becky Leigh
Moran HS; Moran, TX (2-8) A-Ed; Ann; Chldr; Tres, FHA; 4H; Rptr, Hmrm; Bkbl; Ftbl; Fin, Tnns; Tr; Cl Fav; HCt; *Tarleton St U; Sci.*

HUDSON, Brenda Lee
LeRoy HS; LeRoy, IL (2-100) Rptr, Ann; Band; Chor; Ensm; FHA; 4H; Madrigal; Tres, Soph Cl; Ftbl; Sftbl; Swim; Tr; Wrest; 4H A; Math A; Sci A; Spch A; Swim A; Band A; Soc of Academic Achv; Solo & Ensm A; *Hist.*

HUDSON, Carla Jo
Dustin HS; Dustin, OK (1-18) Ed, Ann; VP, FHA; GS; NHS; Ed, Sch P; S-T, Sr Cl; S-T, Jr Cl; S-T, Soph Cl; MVP, Bkbl; Sftbl; Citz A; Hist A; HQn; HCt; Hon Prog; Journ A; Sal; Sci A; Type A; Val; Co-Ed, Ann; Co-Ed, Rptr, Sch P; Spell, PA, Shorthand, A's; 1st Run-Up, Ms DHS; Bkbl Ltrs; Civics, Reading, Eng; Vlbl Ltrs; *Okla U; Occupational Therapy.*

HUDSON, Cathy Lee
Brandon Acad; Brandon, MS (4-50) BC; Sch Achieve Tm; *Wesley Col; Art.*

HUDSON, Cynthia Ann
Fairfield HS; Fairfield, AL (10%-168) BC; Chor; Ensm; NHS; SC; COM; Citz A; Hist A; HCt; Math A; MLS; NEDT; Sci A; Spch A; Oratorical A; VP, Bankboard.

HUDSON, Daniel Neil
Coleman HS; Coleman, TX (7-78) Ann; Hmrm; JETS; Lat C; NHS; SC; Pres, Jr Cl; Secy, Soph Cl; Cl Fav; DARGCA; Hist A; Pres, FCA; Regional Fin, Tr; *McMurry Col; Hist.*

HUDSON, Dianna Sue
Lead Hill HS; Lead Hill, AR (1-25) Co-Cpt, Chldr; FBLA; FHA; Ed, Sch P; SC; Secy, Jr Cl; Bkbl; Amer Leg A; Citz A; Hist A; Math A; Type A; All-Around Girl; Most Friendly; Most Dedicated Ath; Home Ec A; Best Defense, Bkbl; Eng A; All-Dist, Bkbl; *Fashion & Interior Design.*

HUDSON, Doris Ann
Midway HS; Dunn, NC (7-120) Chem C; Drama; Fr C; Sci C; Var C; Sftbl; Bio A; Chem A; Citz A; Ntl Sci Found; Sci A; *Fayeteville Tech Col; Dental Hygiene.*

HUDSON, Frederick A
Vashon HS; St Louis, MO; Hon Prog; VICA; *Eng.*

HUDSON, Jane Leigh
N Augusta Sr HS; N Augusta, SC; Ann; Band; NHS; St Off, FHA; *Winthrop Col; Home Ec.*

HUDSON, Jody Lynn
Two Harbors HS; Two Harbors, MN; Ann; Band; Fr C; FHA; Tr; Pres A; *Fashion.*

HUDSON, John Thomas
Salisbury HS; Salisbury, NC (40-229) BS; Pres, Demolay; Key C; Lat C; Span C; Secy, Jr Cl; Tr; Hon Prog; *UNC-Chapel Hill; Pol Sci.*

HUDSON, Joseph Robert
Bret Harte HS; Angels Camp, CA; AFS; Band; Drama; Sch P; Bkbl; Cr-Ctry; Ftbl; Tnns; Spch A; Drum Major; Mus Department Plaque; *U of Pacific; Mass Communication.*

HUDSON, Joseph Wade
E Henderson HS; Flat Rock, NC (38-230) Rptr, Key C; Ladies C Schol; *Tenneesse Temple Col; Religion.*

HUDSON, Kathleen Ruth
Northwest HS; St Louis, MO (12-652) NHS; Cpt, Hockey; Tr; *Mich St U.*

HUDSON, LaZelda Denise
Wadley HS; Wadley, GA; Ann; Secy, BC; Chor; Drama; FHA; Ed, Sch P; Bkbl; COM; Gov Honor Prog; HCt; Math A; *Emanuel Co Jr Col; Elem Ed.*

HUDSON, Leola
Cotton Plant HS; Cotton Plant, AR (6-23) BC; Pres, Drama; VP, FBLA; Pres, FHA; Pres, SC; Mgr, Bkbl; Alg A; Cl Fav; Math A; Choir A; *UAPB; Math.*

HUDSON, Lori Ann
Osseo Sr HS; Osseo, MN (38-400) Band; Ensm; FHA; NHS; Orch; ARC; Cpt, Swim; Most Out; Opt A; ARC A; All-Conf Swim A; *Ed.*

HUDSON, Lorraine
Provine HS; Jackson, MS; Secy, Chor; Rptr, City Conf; Drama; Jr Miss Pagent; Lit Mag; Mod Mus Mas; NHS; Orch; Sch P; Span C; Librarian, Band; Secy, DECCA; Stu Director A; Band A; VP, YWA; Miss Jr Metric; Missionary Soc; GSct; *Mus.*

HUDSON, Norma Jo
Monterey HS; Lubbock, TX; A Cap Choir; Chem C; Chor; NHS; Tri-HiY; Co-Cpt, Bkbl; Hon Prog; Co-Ch, Yth Fel; *Tex Tech U; Sci.*

HUDSON, Randall Keith
E B Erwin HS; Birmingham, AL (51-285) VP, Band; Chor; Ensm; Ger C; Orch; Thes; Super & Excel Ratings, Solo & Ensm; *U of Ala; Bus Adm.*

HUDSON, Rebecca Gail
Perry Co HS; Linden, TN (2-89) Secy, BC; 4H; Mgr, Bkbl; 4H A; Hon Prog; Sal; Sgt-at-Arms, Bus C; Most Studious; Presidential Schol; *Freed-Hardeman Col; Acct.*

HUDSON, Rhonda Sims
N Caddo HS; Vivian, LA; JV, Chldr; Drama; Semi-Fin, Jr Miss Pa; Spch C; Rptr, SC; Tr; Beauty; Citz A; Spch A; Dance Tm; *La Tech U; Spch Pathologist.*

HUDSON, Rosalind Veronica
Mayo HS; Darlington, SC (17-179) BC; Chor; Drama; SC; Bkbl; Sci A; Type A; Bus A; HR; Best All Around.

HUDSON, Susan Leslie
River Oaks Sch; Monroe, LA; Chldr; Span C; Spch C; HQn; Swtht; *NE La U.*

HUDSON, Thomas Freeman
York Comp HS; York, SC (7-240) Band; Drama; NHS; VP, Sci C; Span C; Bausch & Lomb A; NMS; Sci A; CAABA Bass Horn Solo A; *Rose-Hulman Inst of Tech; Chem Engr.*

HUDSON, Thomas William
Toms River HS S; Toms River, NJ (214-440) A Cap Choir; Chor; Model UN; Tr; Yth Fel; Tres, Yth Fellowship; Walk for Mankind Comm; Advanced Chor; *Springfield Col; Athletic Trainer.*

HUDSON, Timothy Mark
Hillsboro HS; Hillsboro, OH (20-181) A Cap Choir; Ann; Band; Drama; Ensm; Fr C; 4H; Math C; Pres, NHS; Order/Arrow; SC; Citz A; Cl Fav; Hon Prog; Lifeguard, Red Cross; Eng A; Most Talented; *U of Cincinnati; Elec Engr.*

HUDSON, Tommilea E
Churchill Area HS; Pittsburgh, PA (34-490) Secy, Band; Ensm; Hmrm; Orch; Co-Ch, SC; Co-Cpt, Bkbl; John Philip Sousa Band A; Librarian; WW; Yrbk; Musical; Hgh Hon Acad A; Bkbl Ltr; Tres, Church Group; Churchill Area Ed Assn School; *U of Pittsburgh; Engr.*

HUDSON, Velda Diane
Gosnell HS; Blytheville, AR (12-94) VP, BC; Chor; S-T, NHS; SC; JV, Hockey; JA A; WW; *Louise Salanger Acad of Fashion; Fashion Merchandising.*

HUDSON, Victoria Anne
Nova HS; Davie, FL (200-550) Ann; Band; Chor; Dbte Tm; InterClub Coun; Key C; Ed, Lit Mag; NFL; Rptr, Sch P; Sci C; St Stu Congress; SC; Journ A; Spch A; Amateur Fencers C of Amer; Pep C; Sch Photo; Safari C Intrntl; Amer Wildlife Ldrship Sch School; Civil Liberties Un; Co Yth Adv Comm; *U of Fla; Journ.*

HUDSPETH, Thomas Harold
Forbush HS; East Bend, NC (20-200) Demolay; Fr C; Monogram; NHS; Order/Arrow; Ftbl; Golf; *Math.*

HUECHTEMAN, Randal Bruce
Quincy Sr HS II; Quincy, IL (5%-620) Bsbl; Golf; Kiwanis A; Cert of Hon; Acad Achv Soc; *NW U; Math.*

HUEGEL, Anne Elizabeth
Homestead HS; Mequon, WI (1-390) Chor; Ensm; NHS; Sci C; Hon Prog; NMF; Val; Cpt, Color Guard; Mortar Board A; WW in Foreign Lang; Soc of Women Engr A; *U of Wisc at Madison; Chem.*

HUELER, Gregory Warren
Duluth E HS; Duluth, MN (40-548) VP, A Cap Choir; Chor; Ensm; Ger C; Hmrm; NHS; SC; Pres, Sr Cl; Pres, Jr Cl; Cr-Ctry; Hockey; Tr; COM; Rotary A; Cand, Snobeau; Hunt Schol A; *St Olaf Col; Math.*

HUENINK, Kathi Linn
Norris HS; Firth, NE (11-100) Band; Co-Cpt, Chldr; Chor; Drama; Ensm; FNA; VP, 4H; NHS; Secy, Jr Cl; S-T, Soph Cl; Sftbl; 4H A; Spch A; *U of Nebr; Home Ec.*

HUERGO, Humberto Rafael
Colegio Nuestra Sra de la Merced; Hato Rey, PR (5-92) VP, Arch; Chem C; VP, Chess C; Drama; Co-Ed, Lit Mag; Model UN; Order/Arrow; Phys C; Pres, Sci C; VP, Span C; Secy, Spch C; Arch; MVP, Swim; Bio A; COM; Chem A; Hist A; Hon Prog; MLS; Most Out; Order/Arrow A; Poet A; Spch A; Star Student; *Loyola U; Psych.*

HUETHER, Cynthia Cay
Lisbon HS; Lisbon, ND; A Cap Choir; Band; Chldr; Chor; Drama; FHA; GS; 4H; SC; Swim; Tnns; 4H A; Type A; *ND St U; Med Tech.*

HUETHER, Debby Kaye
Lisbon Pub HS; Lisbon, ND (7-70) Band; Chor; Drama; Ensm; FFA; VP, SC; Bkbl; Sftbl; Tr; Hon Prog; *Valley City St Col; Hist.*

HUETHER, John Jay
Washington Sr HS; Sioux Falls, SD (80%-622) Band; Chor; Community Yth Symph; Orch; Math A; Armstrong Installation Cert; 1st, Sml Grp & Solo, Tri-St Mus Fes; 1st, Solo & Sml Grp, St Mus Assn; *Northwestern Col; Math.*

HUETHER, Mary Lynn
Tripp HS; Tripp, SD (1-35) Chor; Pres, FHA; GS; 4H; S-T, NHS; Amer Leg A; DARGCA; Yth Fel; *Dakota Wesleyan U; Med Lab Technician.*

HUETHER, Roberta Lee
Lisbon Pub HS; Lisbon, ND (20-80) Bus Mgr, Ann; Band; Bus C; Chldr; Chor; Drama; Ensm; VP, FBLA; FHA; GS; 4H; Madrigal; Secy; SC; Var C; Bkbl.

HUEY, Kristine Diane
Franklin HS; Franklin, PA (36-243) Band; *New Castle Bus Col; Keypunch Operator.*

HUEY, Linda Lee
Christian Life Acad; McKeesport, PA (2-3) Chor; Sch P; *Central Bible Col; Span.*

HUFF, Alison Rozan
R J Reynolds HS; Winston-Salem, NC (10%-870) Tr; Vlbl; Art As; MIP, Vlbl; *NC St U; Sci.*

HUFF, Ann Louise
Notre Dame HS; Salinas, CA (6-120) 4H; Hmrm; Math C; Model UN; NHS; Ntl Yth Conf; Sci C; Ski C; Span C; Secy, SC; JV, Bkbl; CSF; Hon Prog; *Math.*

HUFF, Ann Marie
Bartram Sch; Jacksonville, FL; Chor; Drama; Fr C; Ed, Sch P; Tres, Sr Cl; Tres, Jr Cl; Bkbl; Soccer; Swim; Cpt, Tnns; *Fla Jr Col; Ed.*

HUFF, Carol Marie
Churchland HS; Portsmouth, VA; JV, Chldr; Chor; Ensm; Fr C; FBLA; Jr Miss Pagent; Swim; HCt; *Bus.*

HUFF, Cecil Scott
T R Miller HS; Brewton, AL; Rptr, Sch P; Sci C; VP, SC; JV, Bkbl; Ftbl; FCA.

HUFF, Cynthia Joy
Evans HS; Evans, GA; 4H; Tri-HiY; COM; 4H A; Hist A; JA A; Parl & Pres, FBLA; *Augusta Col; Pub Relations.*

HUFF, Dawn Elizabeth
Springfield S HS; Springfield, OH; *Clark Tech Inst; Nurs.*

HUFF, Deanna Jo
Springfield SE HS; Springfield, IL (30-402) Rptr, FBLA; NHS; Tres, OEA; Golden Laurel A; Mistress of Ceremonies, Co-Op Ed; *Lincolnland Comm Col; Acct.*

HUFF, Diane Carol
Douglas MacArthur HS; San Antonio, TX (25%-600) BC; FHA; Lat C; Secy, Sci C; Girls Chor; Health Occupations; Pep Sq Lassies; *Animal Sci.*

HUFF, John Michael
Potosi R-3 HS; Potosi, MO (33-207) A Cap Choir; Band; Parl, FBLA; FTA; Madrigal; Mjrte; NHS; Tres, Thes.

HUFF, Julie Marie
Potosi R-3 HS; Potosi, MO (13-210) A Cap Choir; FTA; NHS; Var C; Bkbl; Sftbl; Tnns; Tr; *SE Mo U; Phys Ed.*

HUFF, Katherine Ann
Notre Dame HS; Salinas, CA (7-98) A Cap Choir; Chor; Secy, 4H; Math C; Tnns; Amer Leg A; NHS; Pol Sci C; ARC; Ed, Sch P; Secy, Ski C; St Stu Congress; Var C; JV, Bkbl; Tnns; Amer Leg A; Bank Of Amer A; CSF; Math A; Sci A; Yth Leg; Ntl Merit Ltr of Commendation; Fin, Ntl Soc of Prof Engr; Semi-Fin, Hertz Found Schol; *U of Ca at Santa Barbara; Engr.*

HUFF, Linda Joyce
Fairfax HS; Fairfax, VA (179-480) Pres, FHA; Key C; Sch P; Hockey; Hon Prog; Opt A; GAA Ltr; Field Hockey Ltr; HR; *Richard Bland Col.*

HUFF, Margaret Elaine
Nederland HS; Nederland, TX (25-600) Tnns; CYO; Chor; Fr C; FHA; Tr; Hon Prog; Math A; Q&S A; Sci A; Co-Cpt, JV Vlbl; 'N' A; Presidential Patch Tex Readers C; *University of Texas; Law.*

HUFF, Marta K
Pleasure Ridge Park HS; Pleasure Ridge Park, KY (85-315) Ed, Ann; BC; NHS; Span C; Journ A; *Catherine Spalding Col; Nurs.*

HUFF, Michelle Kaye
Tiskilwa HS; Tiskilwa, IL;

HUFF, Samuel Lee
E Kemper HS; Scooba, MS (4-25) Drama; Math C; Hon A; Attendance A; *Tougaloo Col; Elec.*

HUFF, Sharon Kay
Curtis Baptist HS; Augusta, GA (6-18) VP, BC; Co-Cpt, Chldr; Ensm; Soccer; Tnns; Faculty A; All A HR; *Col of Charleston; Bus.*

HUFF, Theresa Marie
Notre Dame HS; Salinas, CA (4-93) Math C; VP, Model UN; Rptr, Sch P; Span C; SC; Var C; MVP, Bkbl; CSF; Math A; *Stanford U; Med.*

HUFFAKER, Donna Jean
Malden HS; Malden, IL (6-16) Cpt, Chldr; Chor; Drama; Fr C; Tres, FHA; Ed, Sch P; S-T, SC; DARGCA; HQn; HCt; Swtht; Type A; Vlbl; Shorthand A; *Ill Valley Comm Col; Secy Sci.*

HUFFAKER, Rob Faucette
McCallie Sch; Chattanooga, TN; Monogram; Ftbl; Sftbl; JV, Tnns; Wrest; Rep, Jr Cl; TEPS; Spirituals; Senant.

HUFFER, Kerry Lynn
Muskogee HS; Muskogee, OK; Band; Chor; Ensm; NHS; Orch; Amer Leg A; COM; Gov Honor Prog; Hon Prog; Most Out; All Dist, All St, Bands; Superior, Mus Solos; *W Tex St U; Mus.*

HUFFER, Kim Robert
Chelan HS; Chelan, WA; Band; Hmrm; Ed, Sch P; Ski C; SC; Var C; Pres, Sr Cl; Pres, Soph Cl; Bsbl; Bkbl; Co-Cpt, Ftbl; *Wash St U; Agr.*

HUFFMAN, Cathy Renee
Freedom HS; Morganton, NC; Ger C.

HUFFMAN, Debra Louise
Clark Co R-1 HS; Kahoka, MO (8-92) Pres, Bus C; Pres, NHS; Pres, Sr Cl; Pres, Jr Cl; Bkbl; Cpt, T; *Southeastern Comm Col; Bus.*

HUFFMAN, Janet Catherine
Mt Vernon Twp HS; Mt Vernon, IL (25%-400) Chor; 4H; 4H A; *Sou Ill U; Math.*

HUFFMAN, Jill Ann
Wichita Heights HS; Wichita, KS (10-400) Band; NHS; *Wichita St U; Acct.*

HUFFMAN, Jo Anna
Sullivan Central HS; Blountville, TN; Ann; Lat C; Yth Fel; Lat Hon Soc; Young Republicans C; People to People; *Bus.*

HUFFMAN, Keith Alan
Freedom HS; Morganton, NC; Chor; 4H; Bsbl; Bkbl; Cpt, Ftbl; Wrest; *Police Sci.*

HUFFMAN, Louis Lee
Weir HS; Weir, MS (5-51) BC; Chor; Tres, FFA; 4H; F-Ed, Sch P; VP, Sr Cl; Bio A; Hon Prog; Sci A; Star Student; *Holmes Jr Col; Engr.*

HUFFMAN, Robin Diane
Western Alamance HS; Elon College, NC (34-255) CYO; Fr C; VP, Hmrm; NHS; Bkbl; Tr; HCt; Hon Prog; Most Out; Pres, Bible C; 2nd Runner- up, Miss Western; *Oral Roberts U; Nurs.*

HUFFMAN, Sherri Lynne
Olathe HS; Olathe, KS (47-450) Chor; Ger C; NHS; Mgr, Swim; *Wichita St U; Engr.*

HUFFMAN, Susan Elizabeth
David Lipscomb HS; Nashville, TN; Chldr; VP, Chor; VP, Ensm; Fr C; Mjrte; Ftbl; Interlochen Ntl Mus; ARC A; *David Lipscomb Col; Nurs.*

HUFFMAN, Tammy Renee
St Albans HS; St Albans, WV (20%-500) AFS; Bus Mgr, Ann; Secy, Fr C; FBLA; Hmrm; SC; Sftbl; Semi Fin, Jr Achv A; *Marshall U; Bus.*

HUFFMAN, Terri Lea
Lyons Pub Sch; Lyons, NE (10%-36) Ann; Band; Chor; VP, FBLA; Secy, FHA; Pres, 4H; Sch P; Mgr, Bkbl; 4H A; Swtht; Type A; Spell A; Bus A; *U of Nebr; Home Ec.*

HUFFSTETLER, Donna Teal
S Point HS; Belmont, NC (10%-256) BC; Chor; Drama; Type A; Keyettes; Academic Excellence A; *Appalachian St U; Ed.*

HUFHAM, Mack Campbell
New Hanover HS; Wilmington, NC; Chor; Demolay; Key C; Bkbl; Yth Fel; Yth Leg; *UNC Wilmington; Engr.*

HUG, Kathryn Angela
Northside HS; Fort Smith, AR (20-535) CYO; Fr C; NHS; Tnns; Drill Tm; *Benedictine Col; Ed.*

HUGE, Duane Lowell
Twin Lakes Sr HS; Monticello, IN (11-245) Band; Chldr; FFA; NHS; Orch; Ftbl; Golf; 4H A; *Purdue U; Agr Ed.*

HUGEN, Kathrine Ann
Ottumwa HS; Ottumwa, IA (89-500) GS; Rptr, Hmrm; NHS; ARC; Var C; Mgr, Bkbl; MVP, Sftbl; COM; Citz A; H of F; Hon Prog; All St Tourn A, Sftbl; *Criminology.*

HUGGINS, Anthony Lance
E Bakersfield HS; Bakersfield, CA; Band; Orch; *Bakersfield Col; Mus.*

HUGGINS, Brian Joseph
Sw HS; Atlanta, GA (31-271) Band; VP, Hmrm; VP, Soph Cl.

HUGGINS, Brian Joseph
S Salem HS; Salem, OR (33%-300) Order/Arrow; Golf; Swim; Tr; *Oreg St Col; Bus.*

HUGGINS, Claud Henry III
Hickory HS; Hickory, NC (25-350) Math C; Order/Arrow; VP, Soph Cl; JV, Bkbl; JV, Ftbl; *NC St U; Engr.*

HUGGINS, Deborah Lynn
Owasso HS; Owasso, OK (3-230) FTA; Cpt, Hmrm; Rptr, Sch P; Sci C; Tres, Span C; Span NHS; Swim; Hon Prog; Sci A; Okla St U A; WW; Sch & Church Plays; *Tulsa U; Med.*

HUGGINS, Jerry Alan
Irving HS; Irving, TX (60-600) Semi-Fin, BS; Lat C; Math C; Mu Alpha Theta; NHS; Pres, SC; Tnns; Tr; *U of Houston; Phar.*

HUGGINS, Kimberly Louise
Hazelwood Central HS; Florissant, MO (130-879) Band; Chor; Drama; Orch; *Engr.*

HUGGINS, Lisa Jean
Charles Henderson HS; Troy, AL; BC; FTA; GS; Hmrm; Co-Ed, Sch P; Sci C; SC; Quill & Scroll; Prep Bowl Tm; Twilighters; *Broadcast Communications.*

HUGGINS, Tamee Sabrina
Reidsville Sr HS; Reidsville, NC (23-324) Fr C; Math C; *Childhood Ed.*

HUGGINS, Tammi Harriet
Churchland HS; Portsmouth, VA; AFS; Chldr; Hmrm; Lat C; Sch P; Tri-HiY; Tr; *Madison Col; Social Sci.*

HUGGINS, Terry Anthony
Crane Tech HS; Chicago, IL; Ftbl; Sftbl; Wrest.

HUGH, Stephen Albert
All Saints Cathedral Sch; St Thomas, VI (2-18) Ed, Ann; Chess C; Dbte Tm; Drama; SC; Hist A; Hon Prog; Eng Hon A; Lang A; Ntl Coun of Teachers of Eng Essay; *Brown U; Foreign Lang.*

HUGHBANKS, Kathy Jo
Richwood HS; Peoria, IL (28-550) Chor; Bkbl; Sftbl; Citz A; Hon Prog; Vlbl; *Bradley U; Eng.*

HUGHES, Alec Reid
Dublin HS; Dublin, CA (10-400) Dbte Tm; Rptr, Drama; Tres, Ger C; Hmrm; Lit Mag; Math C; Model UN; Sci C; SC; Rptr, Thes; UN Council; World Affairs C; CSF; COM; Hon Prog; Math A; Most Out; *Stanford U; Pol Sci.*

HUGHES, Amelia Susan
Sevier Co HS; Sevierville, TN (1-256) Rptr, AFS;
A-Ed, Ann; BC; Cpt, Chldr; Pres, Chor; Tres, Fr C;
InterAct C; Pres, InterClub Coun; Fin, Jr Miss Pa-
gent; Span C; Pres, SC; Var C; Amer Leg A; Hist A;
MLS; Spch A; Summa Cum Laude; Val; Gym; 1st
Runnerup, Miss SCHS; Schol, U of Tenn; Sevier-
ville Tn Board; Win, Co Hist Exam; *U of Tenn;
Secondary Ed.*

HUGHES, Bounita Lynn
Ind St U Laboratory Sch; Terre Haute, IN (1-61)
Ed, Ann; Chess C; Ch, Community Yth Sy; Dbte
Tm; Hmrm; Model UN; NFL; NHS; Orch; Sch P;
Spch C; SC; Pres, Sr Cl; COM; Citz A; DARGCA;
Elk A; Gov Honor Prog; Hon Prog; Journ A; Ki-
wanis A; MLS; NEDT; Opt A; Opt Out Tn; Q&S
A; Spch A; St Scholar; Val; AK Oliver A; DePauw
Talent Activity A; Fin, Gold Key Scholastic A; Ind
Fed of C Art A; *Ill Wesleyan U; Art.*

HUGHES, Carolyn
Rufus King HS; Milwaukee, WI; Ann; City Conf;
Drama; Hmrm; Y-Tns; Sftbl; Co-Cpt, Tnns; Cpt,
Tr; HCt; Most Out; *Milw Sch of Engr; Engr.*

HUGHES, Charles Matthew
Bluefield HS; Bluefield, WV (89-350) Chor; VP,
Drama; Fr C; Key C; VP, NFL; Pres, Spch C; VP,
Thes; Bkbl; Ftbl; Golf; Tr; Amer Leg A; Spch A;
VFW A; Yth Fel; Yth Foundation; Yth Leg; WW;
W Va Wesleyan Col; Pre-Law.

HUGHES, Cheryl Ann
Virgie HS; Virgie, KY (2-112) Ed, Ann; BC; Cpt,
Chldr; Chor; FTA; VP, SC; Tres, Jr Cl; Sftbl; HCt;
Hon Prog; Swtht; Val; Miss VHS; Most Spirited;
Eastern Ky U; Eng.

HUGHES, Christine Annette
Open Door Baptist HS; Kansas City, KS (3-18)
Ann; Chldr; Secy, Hmrm; *Baptist Bible Col; Bible.*

HUGHES, Doris Adele
N Donchester HS; Rhodesdale, MD; Band; Pres,
4H; COM; 4H A; Spch A; Gym; Church Choir;
Publicity Ch, NWMS; *Del Tec; Sci.*

HUGHES, Easter Mae
Ethel HS; Ethel, MS (2-54) BC; FHA; 4H; Sch
Achieve Tm; Pres, Tri-HiY; VP, Sr Cl; Chem A;
Hist A; HCt; Sal; Swtht; *Miss U For Women; Nurs.*

HUGHES, Harriett Yvette
Palm Bay HS; Melbourne, FL (189-375) Mgr, Sftbl;
Church Popularity A; *FAMU; Social Service.*

HUGHES, James Marlene
Geneva HS; Geneva, AL (70-90) A-Ed, Ann; Secy,
Drama; 4H; Bsbl; 4H A; Pres, MYF; *Auburn U;
Agriculture.*

HUGHES, James Russell
Roth Sr HS; Henrietta, NY (59-210) Band; Ensm;
Order/Arrow; Ski C; SC; Var C; Cpt, Hockey; Soc-
cer; Bio A; God & Country A; Order/Arrow A;
Stage Band A; Lacrosse; *Saint John Fischer Col;
Pre-Dentistry.*

HUGHES, Jeffrey Lynn
Greenville Sr HS; Greenville, PA; Band; Chor; Jr
Orpheus Mus C; *Mus.*

HUGHES, Jewell Christina
Francis Joseph Reitz HS; Evansville, IN (43-482)
Chor; Ensm; Hmrm; Lat C; Pres, NFL; NHS; ARC;
Spch C; SC; COM; Hon Prog; Magna Cum Laude;
Opt A; Sci A; Spch A; VofDEM; TNT A; Miss
Camper; *Marion Col; Nurs.*

HUGHES, Jimmie Luther
Central HS; St Joe, MO; Chor; ROTC A.

HUGHES, Joseph Gerard
Marquette HS; Ottawa, IL (10-100) Span NHS;
Bsbl; Bkbl; Ftbl; Sftbl; Religion A; Span A.

HUGHES, Karen Denise
Goodwater HS; Goodwater, AL (3-38) Ann; Arch;
Secy, BC; Chldr; Chor; Rptr, FBLA; FFA; Tres,
FHA; Secy, FNA; FTA; 4H; Math C; Phys C; 4H
A; HCt; Gym Medal & Trophy; *Alexander City St
Jr Col; Psych.*

HUGHES, Kelly
Jenks HS; Tulsa, OK (49-375) Span C; JV, Bkbl;
Co-Cpt, Soccer; *Bus.*

HUGHES, Laura Dee
Sam Rayburn HS; Pasadena, TX; Band; District,
Region Band.

HUGHES, Lisa Alyn
Louisville HS; Louisville, OH (34-384) Band; Chor;
Ger C; Swim; Tr; Tn Talk; *Med.*

HUGHES, Lori Lynn
North HS; Torrance, CA; Hmrm; *Pacific Christian
Col.*

HUGHES, Marlene Ann
Switzerland Co HS; Vevay, IN (8-96) Hanover Col;
Bus.

HUGHES, Matthew Russell
Sevier Co HS; Sevierville, TN (10%-304) AFS; BC;
Drama; Fr C; InterAct C; Span C; SC; Ftbl; Tr;
FCA; *U of Tenn; Bus.*

HUGHES, Melodie Marie
Faith HS; Faith, SD (12-34) JV, Chldr; Chor;
Drama; Rptr, FHA; Secy, 4H; Bsbl; Tr; COM; 4H
A; Hon Prog; S-T, Church Yth; Sch Solo A; *Drama.*

HUGHES, Michael Anthony
Coronado HS; Colorado Springs, CO (12-336) Cpt,
Chldr; Chor; Pres, Drama; InterClub Coun; Madri-
gal; Co-Ch, NHS; Pres, SC; Thes; Ch, Sr Cl;
Pres, Jr Cl; Math A; Most Out; Pres A; Rotary A;
Yth Fel; Yth Foundation A; WW; WW Among
Amer Chldr; OTA; Eng A; *Denver U; Pol Sci.*

HUGHES, Michael Joseph
Don Bosco Tech HS; Boston, MA (20-222) CYO;
K of C; *U of Lowell; Elec Engr.*

HUGHES, Michelle Lanette
Stratford HS; Nashville, TN (13-273) Band; BC;
Span C; Mgr, Bkbl; *Bartlesville Wesleyan Col;
Med.*

HUGHES, Milton Douglas
Denham Springs HS; Denham Springs, LA
(20-250) VP, FFA; Pres, Key C; Pres, NHS; Spch
C; Pres, Jr Cl; Bsbl; Ftbl; *LSU; Dentistry.*

HUGHES, Perrilyn Beatrice
Melbourne HS; Melbourne, FL; FHA; Rptr, Sch P;
SC.

HUGHES, Randy S
A J Terrell HS; Blanchard, OK; F-Ed, Ann; BC;
Chem C; Hmrm; Math C; NHS; Sch P, Span C; SC;
Var C; Pres, Jr Cl; Co-Cpt, Bsbl; Bkbl; Co-Cpt, Ftbl;
COM; Citz A; Cl Fav; Gov Honor Prog; Hon Prog;
Magna Cum Laude; St Scholar; Swtht; Yth Fel;
MVP, Bsbl; Secy of St A; *U of Okla.*

HUGHES, Raymond Alfred
Watson Chapel HS; Pine Bluff, AR (1-305) Cpt,
Band; Pres, BC; Key C; SC; Rotary A; Pres, Ark St
Beta C; *U of Ark; Elec Engr.*

HUGHES, Richard Gary
Fargo HS; Fargo, ND (33%-400) JV, Bkbl; Ftbl;
Yth Fel; *Computer Sci.*

HUGHES, Sandra Lynn
Columbia Acad; Columbia, MS; BC; Drama; NHS;
Sci C; COM; Hist A; Sal; Bookkeeping A; Short-
hand A; *U of Sou Miss; Acct.*

HUGHES, Sarah Anne
Lancaster Sr HS; Lancaster, WI (1-139) AFS;
Band; Chldr; Chor; Ensm; Secy, 4H; Hmrm; Math
C; NFL; NHS; Orch; Span C; SC; 4H A; Hon Prog.

HUGHES, Stanton Thomas
Center HS; Center, TX; A Cap Choir; Demolay;
FFA; Sch P; Span C; Ftbl; *East Texas Baptist Col;
Religion.*

HUGHES, Thomas Michael
Loyola HS; Towson, MD (1-134) NHS; Cr-Ctry;
COM; NEDT; *Archt.*

HUGHES, Toni Gayle
Central HS; Little Rock, AR (132-543) A Cap
Choir; Chor; Drama; Fr C; GS; Pres, Hmrm; Rain-
bow; Spch C; S-T, Thes; Y-Tns; Parl, Jr Cl; Amer
Leg A; Chem A; Hon Prog; Poet A; Sal; Most Tal-
ented Dramatically; Drama Contest A; Yth Coun
Rep; *U of Ark; Theatre Arts.*

HUGHES, Walter Michael Jr
Belton-Honea Path HS; Belton, SC (4-315) Band;
COM; *Newberry Col; Mus.*

HUGHES, Wendy Marie
St Andrews Episcopal Sch; Jackson, MS (1-46)
Chor; Drama; Mjrte; Mu Alpha Theta; NHS;
COM; Opt A; Star Student; Dance; Horseback
Riding.

HUGHES, Yvonne Lynnette
Beech Hill HS; Pulaski, TN; Pres, BC; Chor; FHA;
Hmrm; VP, SC; VP, Soph Cl; Beauty; Cl Fav; HCt.

HUGHEY, DeLynne
Westminster HS; Westminster, CO (32-605)
FBLA; NHS; JV, Tnns; Elk A; Jr Escort, Gradua-
tion; *St Paul Bible Col; Bus.*

HUGHEY, Marcia Ann
Fairfield HS; Fairfield, AL (25%-186) Ch, FHA;
COM; Hon Prog; Church A's; *Tuskegee Inst; Nurs.*

HUGHEY, Roger Keith
North Side HS; Jackson, TN; Bsbl; Bkbl; Tr; Spch
A; *Freed-Hardeman Col; Art.*

HUGHLEY, Regina Lynn
Warren W Reserve HS; Warren, OH (35-450) JV,
Bkbl; Bio A; Hon Prog; Yth Fel; *Ohio Northern U;
Art.*

HUGHLEY, Terry Jean
Garfield Sr HS; Hamilton, OH; Chor; NHS; SC;
Sftbl; COM; Cert, Hon Soc; *Law.*

HUGHLEY, Valerie Lee
Valley HS; New Kensington, PA (123-381) Pres,
SC; JV, Bkbl; Amer Leg A; Art Service C; Pres, Pep
C; *U of Pittsburgh; Special Ed.*

HUGLEY, Bridgette
John F Kennedy HS; Cleveland, OH; Mjrte; Citz
A; Merit Roll; HR; 1st Ladies; *Theatre.*

HUGO, Dennis Edward
Carlyle Comm HS; Carlyle, IL; Drama; SC.

HUGULEY, Laurie Elizabeth
Briarwood Christian HS; Birmingham, AL
(25%-48) Chldr; Chor; Dbte Tm; Drama; Ensm;
ARC; Spch C; Bkbl; Swim; COM; ARC A; Yth Fel;
Hospital Vol Cert of Achv; Girl's C of Amer Hon;
SE Bible Col; Med.

HUGUS, Jeffrey Edward
Steubenville HS; Steubenville, OH (45-300) A Cap
Choir; Key C; Lat C; Madrigal; Golf; Wrest; Most
Dedicated Wrest; Pres, Yth Fel; *Ky Christian Col.*

HUHTA, Bradley David
Heritage HS; Littleton, CO (30-400) BS; Bkbl; Cr-
Ctry; Tr; Hon Prog; Yth Fel; Pres, Yth Fel; WW;
Oral Roberts U; Psych.

HUISH, Amanda Rae
Austintown Fitch HS; Youngstown, OH (230-800)
Band; Community Yth Symph; Ensm; Ger C; Cpt,
Mjrte; Orch; ARC; *Nurse.*

HUISMAN, David Emery
Ellsworth Pub HS; Ellsworth, MN (1-33) NHS;
Var C; Amer Leg A; Opt A; *Northwestern U; Bus.*

HUISMAN, Sandra Joy
Pella Comm HS; Pella, IA (50%-102) Band; Chor;
SC; Thes; Mgr, Bkbl; Spch A; Yth Fel; Mus A; Pres,
Yth Fel; Service C; 4-Speeen Contest; Swing Chor;
Grls Glee C; All-Sch Musical and Play; *Central
Col; Social Work.*

HUIZENGA, Cary Lorin
Glasgow HS; Glasgow, KY; Band; Madrigal; Concert Choir; Attendance A.

HUIZINGA, Diana Jean
Amos Alonzo Stagg HS; Palos Hills, IL (39-565)
Band; Chem C; Dbte Tm; Ensm; Fr C; French
NHS; FNA; NHS; Sch P; Sci C; Var C; Bsbl; JV,
Bkbl; Cr-Ctry; Soccer; JV, Sftbl; Swim; Tr; COM;
Hon Prog; Interlochen Ntl Mus; Journ A; JA A;
Vlbl; Awana Ldr; Lib Aide; Fr A; Health Careers;
Homecoming Comm; Med Expl; Phys Ed A; Hgh
Hons A; Colorguard; Attendance A; *St Xavier Col;
Nurs.*

HULA, Patty Ann
Fountain Lake HS; Hot Springs, AR (4-40) Ann;
Rptr, BC; VP, FHA; Rptr, Thes; Secy, Sr Cl; Secy,
Soph Cl; MVP, Bkbl; HQn; *The Col of the Ozarks.*

HULETT, Donna Elizabeth
Swifton HS; Swifton, AR (1-28) Bus Mgr, Ann;
Band; Rptr, BC; Chldr; Secy, FBLA; VP, FHA; GS;
VP, 4H; Fin, Jr Miss Pagent; Rptr, SC; Pres, Jr Cl;
Rptr, Soph Cl; Sftbl; Alg A; Beauty; Cl Fav; 4H A;
Hist A; Hon Prog; Math A; Sci A; Val; Lib C; St
4-H Dance A; WW; St 4-H Off; Sou Assn of Dance
Masters; *William Woods Col; Math.*

HULETT, John Michael
Fayetteville HS; Fayetteville, AR; Key C; Mu Alpha Theta; NHS; Journ A; *U of Ark; Journ.*

HULETT, Michelle Rene
Frankton HS; Frankton, IN; Chor; 4H; Span C; Sftbl; 4H A.

HULL, Betsy Ann
Horseheads HS; Horseheads, NY (50%-650) Bkbl; Mgr, Sftbl; Tnns.

HULL, Eddie Eugene
Elston Sr HS; Michigan City, IN (98-415) Wrest; *Vinncenes U; Law Enforcement.*

HULL, Karen Yvonne
Herbert Hoover HS; Glendale, CA; A Cap Choir; Rainbow; *Oral Roberts U; Tele-Communications.*

HULL, Ray Brice
Cook HS; Adel, GA (25%-180) Secy, HiY; Art C; *Valdosta St Col; Pol Sci.*

HULL, Richard Wayne
Breckinridge Co HS; Harned, KY (1-207) Ann; Rptr, Math C; NHS; Rptr, Sch P; Span C; Tnns; WW; Span Cert; *U of Ky; Engr.*

HULL, Ricky James
Page HS; Greensboro, NC (10%-770) NHS; Cpt, Bkbl; Tnns; COM; Citz A; Opt A; Spch A; Yth Fel; G'Boro Yth Coun; Mgr, Sch Store; Best Personality; WW Among G'Boro Yth; *TV Journ.*

HULL, Sandra Sue
Central HS; Camp Point, IL (52-104) Band; Chor.

HULL, Steven Glen
Pinckneyville HS; Pinckneyville, IL (5%-160) Fr C; Monogram; Var C; Bsbl; JV, Bkbl; JV, Ftbl; Tr; Alg A; COM; Hist A; Hon Prog; Math A; Opt A; Spch A; *Med.*

HULL, Teresa Ellen
Zanesville HS; Zanesville, OH (20-356) Chldr; GS; Hmrm; NHS; Span C; SC; Secy, Sr Cl; Secy, Jr Cl; Beauty; HQn; HCt; Hon Prog; Journ A; Poet A; Buckeye; 3 5; *Ohio U; Bus Adm.*

HULL, Timothy Olen
Page Sr HS; Greensboro, NC (10%-550) NHS; MVP, Tnns; Hon Prog; Yth Fel; WW; NHS Stu o-t Mo; Gold Star Scholastic A; *Wake Forest U.*

HULS, Robbin Lee
Toluca HS; Toluca, IL (4-20) Secy, Band; FHA; NHS; Sci C; Span C; Bkbl; NEDT; Type A; HR; *Pre-Med.*

HULSE, Malcom Lynn
Adirondack Central Sch; Boonville, NY (87-160) ARC; Bsbl; Bkbl; Tr.

HULSEY, Norman Brian
Cleburne HS; Cleburne, TX (10%-220) Ann; Pres, Chor; Ensm; Madrigal; NHS; Hon Prog; *NTSU; Bus.*

HULSEY, Teresa Ann
Fountain Lake HS; Hot Springs, AR (2-55) BC; VP, FHA; NHS; S-T, Jr Cl; S-T, Soph Cl; Bkbl; Citz A; Cl Fav; HCt; Hon Prog; 9th Grade Valedictorian.

HULSEY, William Robert
Cedar Hill HS; Cedar Hill, TX (5-98) NHS; Bkbl; Ftbl; Tr; Tres, FCA; PA A.

HULSING, Jane Marie
Carroll Kuemper HS; Carroll, IA (40-285) CYO; Dbte Tm; S-T, 4H; Pres, Hmrm; Span C; Semi-Fin, Spch C; S-T, SC; Bkbl; Ftbl; Sftbl; 4H A.

HULTZ, Randy Lee
Madison C-3 HS; Madison, MO (1-27) Band; BC; Pres, 4H; Sch P; Secy, Soph Cl; Alg A; 4H A; Math A; HS Hon Prog, NE Mo St U; Academic Bowl Tm; DAHSS; Reynolds Corp Essay A; Federated Study C Eng Essay A; *NEMSU; Pre-Law.*

HULVEY, Lynne Elaine
Richwoods HS; Peoria, IL (73-463) Chor; Ensm; Cpt, Mjrte; NHS; Dance C; Yrbk; Sr PE Ldr; Vice Versa Escort; *Ariz St U; Lang.*

HUMAN, Basil Wayne
Harriman HS; Harriman, TN (5-148) Ed, Ann; VP, BC; VP, SC; Pres, Sr Cl; VP, Jr Cl; Golf; Citz A; DARGCA; MLS; Stu o-t Mo; *US Air Force Acad; Engr.*

HUMBERTSON, Angela Sue
Cleveland HS; Cleveland, TN; Band; Chor; Drama; Ensm; *Lee Col; Bus.*

HUMBERTSON, Anita Gay
Cleveland HS; Cleveland, TN (11-220) Anchor C; Band; BC; Chor; Ensm; FHA; Jr Miss Pagent; NHS; Orch; COM; Hist A; Top 5, Fresh; Jr Band Clinic; All St Band Clinic; Sr Hon Group; *Lee Col; Pre-Med.*

HUMBLE, David Christopher
East Ridge HS; Chattanooga, TN (112-288) Tres, Thes; Yth Fel; *U of Tenn at Chattanooga.*

HUMBLE, Sandy Lynn
Lawton HS; Lawton, OK; Ann; Secy, Key C; SC; Y-Tns; Type A; Highsteppers; Octagon; Drug Ed; *Okla U; Bus Ed.*

HUMBLE, Stevens Gregory
E Ridge HS; East Ridge, TN (113-288) Span C; Thes; Var C; Yth Fel; Member, Bible C; Member, Explores Sct; *U of Tenn; Pre-Med.*

HUMBYRD, Ronda June
Pasco Sr HS; Pasco, WA (113-400) Camp Qn Runner Up, Church of God; Secy, Young People's Endever; Yth Board; Win, Keyboard Solo & Vocal Ensm; *W Coast Bible Col; Mus.*

HUME, Liz Ann
River Valley HS; Three Oaks, MI; Span C; *Lake Mich Col; Social Worker.*

HUME, Robin Lee
Grove City Area HS; Grove City, PA (1-217) Band; Chor; Ed, Lit Mag; Math C; VP, NHS; Ski C; DARGCA; Opt Out Tn; Val; Bus & Professional Women's A; Pa St Schol Prog; Stu Law Day; Publication, Ntl Poetry Press; *Penn St U; Eng.*

HUMES, Teresa Lynn
Colchester HS; Colchester, IL (10-54) Bus Mgr, Ann; Band; JV, Chldr; Pres, Chor; Ensm; NHS; VP, Soph Cl; Bkbl; Sftbl; Tr; HQn; Swtht; Yth Fel; Stu Director, Musical; Vlbl; Pres, GAA; Pep C; Swing Choir; *Western Ill U; Phys Ed.*

HUMMEL, Brenda Jo
Vista HS; Vista, CA (150-720) Arch; Key C; Sftbl; Tnns; Tr; Citz A; Yth Fel; Phys Ed Asst A; Cl Teacher Aid A.

HUMMON, Glenn Arthur
Southfield Lathrup HS; Lathrup Village, MI; Swim; Yth Fel; *Mich St U.*

HUMPHREY, Darryl Wayne
South Side HS; Memphis, TN; Tres, Chess C; NHS; Bkbl; Swim; Co-Cpt, Tnns; Citz A; Cl Fav; Hon Prog; MLS; Committee Coun, Children's Theatre; *U of Tenn; Law.*

HUMPHREY, David Michael
Ainsworth HS; Flint, MI (33%-240) Band; Bkbl; 1st Pl MAEA Art Show; Merit, Band; Hon, Band; Fresh and Soph Band A; Var Ltr.

HUMPHREY, Douglas Joseph
Sandusky HS; Sandusky, MI (5%-150) Band; Ensm; VP, NHS; SC; JV, Bsbl; JV, Bkbl; Ftbl; COM; Opt A; VofDEM; Eagle Sct; *Engr.*

HUMPHREY, Gene Scott
Danville Comm HS; Danville, IN (10-150) Key C; Lat C; VP, NHS; Thes; Var C; Tres, Soph Cl; Bsbl; Ftbl; Bio A; COM; Hist A; Star Student; *Purdue U; Chem Engr.*

HUMPHREY, James Allen
Linton HS; Schenectady, NY (270-480) Chor; Hmrm; Sftbl; Tnns; Tr; *Ithaca Col; Health Services.*

HUMPHREY, Janis Lynn
S P Waltrip Sr HS; Houston, TX (63-654) Key C; NHS; SC; *Abilene Christian U; Ed.*

HUMPHREY, Jeffrey Alan
Prescott HS; Prescott, AZ (90-423) CYO; Order/ Arrow; ARC; Sch P; Var C; Co-Cpt, Cr-Ctry; JV, Ftbl; Tr; COM; God & Country A; Journ A; Order/ Arrow A; Life BSct; *Yavapai Col; Aquatics Bio.*

HUMPHREY, Johnnie Arty
Washington HS; Los Angeles, CA (60-601) Bsbl; Golf; Tnns; Bowl; Attendence A; *Associated Tech Col; Pre-Med.*

HUMPHREY, Linda Jean
Leesburg Sr HS; Leesburg, FL (10%-500) Ann; Chldr; Chor; Ensm; Tres, 4H; Hmrm; InterClub Coun; Lat NHS; Madrigal; Mod Mus Mas; NHS; SC; Tri-HiY; 4H A; VP, Fresh Cl; Horse Show Trophies; Reserve & Grand Champion Steer; Talent Show A's.

HUMPHREY, Mark Anthony
Valley HS; Santa Ana, CA; BS; Community Yth Symph; Tr; Citz A; HKg; Most Out; *Iowa St U; Med.*

HUMPHREY, Ronald David
Arkansas HS; Texarkana, AR (9-450) A-Ed, Ann; BS; Drama; Fr C; VP, Key C; Pres, NHS; Ed, Sch P; Tres, SC; DARGCA; Sci A; *SMU; Math.*

HUMPHREY, Sheri Deane
Leesburg Sr HS; Leesburg, FL; JV, Chldr; Chor; Ensm; Hmrm; Madrigal; Secy, Mod Mus Mas; SC; Secy, UN Council; Secy, Y-Tns; Beauty; 4H A; Pres A; Spch A; Secy, 4-H Co Coun; Powder Puff Ftbl; Talent Show A'S; Horseshow Trophies; Reserve & Grand Champion Steer; *Mus.*

HUMPHREY, Andrea Joyce
Duluth E HS; Duluth, MN; Fr C; Secy, Lit Mag; *Foreign Lang.*

HUMPHREYS, Carla
Irving HS; Irving, TX; Secy, Fr C; Mu Alpha Theta; NHS; Sci C; MVP, Swim; Most Out; Cpt, Fin, Swim; Swim Ltr; FC A; Top Tiger o-t Wk; Pres, Mat Mates; Pres, Christian Yth Fel.

HUMPHREYS, Stephen Cooper
Bethany Christian HS; Troy, MI (10-50) Chess C; Ensm; A-Ed, Sch P; Span C; SC; Bsbl; Bkbl; Cpt, Hockey; Soccer; VP, Choir; *Law.*

HUMPHRIES, Charles Aubrey
College Prepatory Sch; Charleston, SC (12-25) A-Ed, Ann; BC; Chldr; Drama; Lit Mag; Sch P; SC; JV, Bkbl; JV, Soccer; Tnns; Pres, VP & S-T, Hmrm; *Emmanuel Col; Math.*

HUMPHRIES, Elizabeth
Person Sr HS; Roxboro, NC (10%-500) Chldr; Chor; Drama; Chldr A; Tres, MYF; Mus Medal, Piano; *UNC-CHAPEL Hill; Dental Hygentist.*

HUMPHRIES, Francis Allen
College Preparatory; Charleston, SC (4-40) F-Ed, Ann; Chor; Drama; Ensm; Hmrm; Lit Mag; NHS; Rptr, Sch P; VP, Var C; Bkbl; Soccer; Citz A; Spch A; Furman Schol; Wofford Schol; Tn Talent Fin; *Emmanuel Col; Acct.*

HUMPHRIES, James King
Orangeburg-Wilkinson HS; Orangeburg, SC (18-414) Band; BS; Chess C; Dbte Tm; S-T, Drama; Key C; Model UN; NHS; S-T, Thes; Math A; Ger Hon Soc; *Davidson Col; Med.*

HUMPHRIES, Logan
Wilson Hall Acad; Sumter, SC (95%-75) JV, Chldr; Tres, FNA; VP, Span C; Sftbl; Tnns; Yth Fel; Fin, Tres, SB; *Med U of Charleston; Medicine.*

HUMPHRIES, Norma Jean
Vincent HS; Vincent, AL (7-100) Band; BC; FBLA; VP, Hmrm; Hon Prog; Yth Fel.

HUNDL, Anna Marie
Brazos HS; Wallis, TX (8-40) Pres, CYO; Drama; Rptr, FHA; Tres, 4H; Pres, NHS; Fin, Spch C; Rptr, Jr Cl; Tres, Soph Cl; Mgr, Bkbl; B Crocker A; Citz A; 4H A; I Dare You; Most Out; Pep C; Gold Star Girl; High P Girl; Mgr, Vlbl; Bread As; Encounter A; Drill Tm; Entomology A; Leadership A; *Victoria Col.*

HUNDLEY, Penny Elaine
Sou Alamance HS; Graham, NC; Drama; Tr; Pep C; Bible C; *Southeast Bible Col; Bus.*

HUNDLEY, Robert Spencer
Ft Worth Ctry Day Sch; Ft Worth, TX (19-56) AFS; Ann; Drama; Hmrm; Sch P; SC; Ftbl; Soccer; Tr; Wrest; Hon Prog; Photographer, Annual; Explorers; Soph Cl Rep; Young Life; Most Improved, Wrest; Poem Published, Eng Journ; *Washington & Lee Col; Psych.*

HUNDLEY, Wanda Yvonne
Southern HS; Graham, NC (110-350) Bus Mgr, Band; Tres, Bus C; Chor; Drama; Sci C; Span C; *Elon Col; Bus.*

HUNN, Sherry Ann
Shadyside HS; Shadyside, OH; Chldr; Chor; Jr Miss Pagent; Rainbow; ARC; Thes; Y-Tns; Bkbl; Tr; HCt; ARC A; Vlbl; Jr Miss Pageant, Personality A; Tr As; *Belmont Tech Col; Nurs.*

HUNNICUTT, Bradley Clark
Danville HS; Danville, AR (1-40) BS; VP, FFA; Model UN; NHS; MLS; Chor Accompanist; *Ouachita Baptist U; Math.*

HUNNICUTT, Lucille
Emerson HS; Emerson, AR (3-31) Chor; Pres, FHA; Span C; SC; VP, Jr Cl; Arch; Sftbl; Tnns; COM; Sci A; Most Stu; *Henderson St U; Social Services.*

HUNSAKER, Elizabeth Ann
Bellaire HS; Bellaire, TX (55-735) Bkbl; Cpt, Sftbl; COM; Sci A; Cpt, MVP, Vlbl; Jr NHS; Schol Merit A; *U of Houston; Med.*

HUNSAKER, Richard Lee
Valley HS; Las Vegas, NV; Demolay; Mgr, Ensm; *Elec.*

HUNSUCKER, Holli Vivian
DeSoto HS; De Soto, TX; Fr C; FHA; Hmrm; *Abilene Christian Col; Social Work.*

HUNSUCKER, Nancy Michele
Ashville HS; Ashville, AL (2-70) F-Ed, Ann; BC; Chldr; FHA; Hmrm; NHS; Var C; VP, Soph Cl; Beauty; DARGCA; HCt; Sal; *Gadsden St Jr Col.*

HUNT, Alicia Denise
East HS; Youngstown, OH; NHS; Sci C; Tr; COM; Sci A; Tr A; PA A; *Youngstown St Col; Psych.*

HUNT, Barbara Burton
Richardson HS; Richardson, TX (26-908) NHS; Pres, Tri-HiY; MVP, Tnns; VP, Girls Service League; Drill Tm; Most Outst Tnns; *U of Tex; Law.*

HUNT, Connie Kay
Oak Grove HS; Oak Grove, MO (15-110) AFS; Band; Chldr; Chor; Ensm; Tr; Type A; Sadi Hawkins Court; Mus A; *Central Mo St U.*

HUNT, Dana
Phelps HS; Phelps, KY (2-73) BC; NHS; MLS; Sal; *Sou Comm Col; Bus.*

HUNT, Daniel Garland
Bell Voc HS; Washington, DC;

HUNT, Darnel
Lumberton HS; Lumberton, NC; Math A; Sci Fair A.

HUNT, David Trent
Salisbury HS; Salisbury, NC (73-256) Band; Ch, Hmrm; Lat C; Span C; Tnns; Historian; Jr Civitan; Pres, MYF; Foreign Exchange Stu; *UNCC; Med.*

HUNT, Diane Teresa
Matoaca HS; Ettrick, VA (15-150) Ann; Drama; Fr C; VP, Key C; NHS; Tres, Sr Cl; Beauty; Citz A; Hon Prog; Swtht; Mgr, Gym; *Morgan St U; Psych.*

HUNT, Donald George
W Point HS; West Point, MS (10-30) Band; Ensm; Swim; Band Solo A; *Miss St U; Math.*

HUNT, Douglas Byron
Henry Hudson Regional HS; Highlands, NJ (10%-100) Fin, BS; JV, Bkbl; ARC A; *Sci.*

HUNT, Elizabeth Marie
Prestonsburg HS; Prestonsburg, KY (68-179) BC; FHA; Hmrm; Q&S A; *Prestonsburg Comm Col; Bus.*

HUNT, Eric Alan
New Life Christian Sch; Bridgeton, MO (1-8) F-Ed, Ann; *U of Mo; Biol.*

HUNT, Gregory Thomas
Thomas Jefferson HS; Clairton, PA; Ger C; Math C; Alg A; Hon Prog; Royal Amer Regiment; *Computer Programming.*

HUNT, Helene
Bonneville HS; Ogden, UT (8-429) A Cap Choir; Chor; Drama; InterClub Coun; Fin, Jr Miss Pagent; Key C; Madrigal; NHS; Tres, SC; Thes; Alg A; Beauty; Chem A; Elk A; Hon Prog; Kiwanis A; Magna Cum Laude; Most Out; PTA A; Spch A; Summa Cum Laude; Blue Key A; All-Around Sr; *Weber St U; Elem Ed.*

HUNT, Iris June
Canton HS; Canton, SD (50%-92) GS; 4H; *Dordt Col; Social Work.*

HUNT, Jane Marie
Newton Co Comprehensive HS; Covington, GA; Band; Pres, Chor; Ensm; Fr C; Secy, 4H; Key C; Tri-HiY; Citz A; 4H A; JA A; Kiwanis A; Most Out; Type A; All St Chor; *N Ga Col; Med Records.*

HUNT, John Arthur
Seekonk HS; Seekonk, MA (21-223) Tres, Span C; Span NHS; Tr; *Union Col; Civil Engr.*

HUNT, Laurie Jean
Narragansett HS; Narragansett, RI (20-80) A Cap Choir; Band; Chldr; Secy, Chor; Drama; Madrigal; Tnns; All St Choir; Most Outst Band; Solo & Ensm Medals, Chor & Band; *Dental Asst.*

HUNT, Leslie
West HS; Knoxville, TN (12-288) A Cap Choir; AFS; F-Ed, Ann; Band; Chor; Community Yth Symph; Crown & Scepter; Drama; Ensm; FNA; Hmrm; Madrigal; NHS; Orch; ARC; Rptr, Sch P; Y-Tns; Sftbl; COM; Citz A; Interlochen Ntl Mus; Journ A; Swtht; Yth Fel; God & Country A; Gov Honor Prog; ARC A; 1st Pl, St Drama A; St Choir Badge; *U of Tenn; Nurs.*

HUNT, Lillian Arletta
Independence HS; Charlotte, NC; Chldr; FHA.

HUNT, Lisa Wynne
Roy C Start HS; Toledo, OH (5-500) InterClub Coun; NHS; Ed, Sch P; Ch, Sr Cl; Amer Leg A; Hon Prog; Most Ambitious; Most Serious; Most Stu; *U of Toledo.*

HUNT, Lorana Denise
MacKenzie HS; Detroit, MI (32-352) FTA; NHS; SC; COM; Citz A; DARGCA; Hon Prog; *Ohio St U; Computer.*

HUNT, Marcy Loy
Stanton HS; Stanton, NE (2-46) Rptr, Band; Chor; Ensm; FHA; VP, 4H; SC; Bkbl; JV, Tr; COM; Pep C; VP, Yth Fel; Vlbl; *U of Nebr; Ed.*

HUNT, Marsha Jo
Chillicothe HS; Chillicothe, TX (5-25) Co-Ed, Ann; Chldr; VP, FHA; Secy, SC; Secy, Sr Cl; Tres, Jr Cl; Bkbl; Tr; Citz A; Cl Fav; HQn; WW; Personality Plus; FHA Ldrship A; *Vernon Regional Jr Col; Bus.*

HUNT, Michelle Susan
LaConner HS; LaConner, WA (3-50) Chldr; FHA; GS; 4H; VP, Math C; NHS; Secy, Phys C; A-Ed, Sch P; Pres, Span C; SC; Thes; Var C; Bkbl; Rptr, Ftbl; Mgr, Sftbl; CSF; Cl Fav; DARGCA; 4H A; Hon Prog; Jr Prom Qn; *Western Wash St Col; Law.*

HUNT, Patricia Diane
Batavia Sr HS; Batavia, IL; Lat C; NHS; Hon Prog; *Waubonsee Comm Col; Acct.*

HUNT, Paul William
Chanute Sr HS; Chanute, KS; Orch; Order/Arrow; Bkbl; Mgr, Tr; Star BSct; *Neosho Co Comm Col; Math.*

HUNT, Rebecca Lyn
Dayton Christian HS; Dayton, OH (20%-85) JV, Chldr; Sftbl; Mighty in Spirit Sftbl Trophy; Art Outst Achv A; Academics Outst Achv A; *Christian Col.*

HUNT, Rebecca Susan
Horicon HS; Horicon, WI (12-113) S-T, AFS; Ed, Ann; Chor; GS; NHS; A-Ed, Sch P; S-T, Span C; SC; Pres, Jr Cl; Tnns; B Crocker A; VofDEM; AFS Amer Abroad Stu; Trees for Tommorw Reps; St Forensics; *U of Wis-Madison; Pol Sci.*

HUNT, Ronald Eugene
Paris HS; Paris, TX (20-350) Band; VP, FTA; Pres, NHS; Order/Arrow; Tres, Span C; Hon Prog; Order/Arrow A; FCA; Bkbl C; *Baylor U; Hist.*

HUNT, Terri Lynn
Lexington HS; Lexington, AL; Band; Tr; Vlbl; Ltr Tr; Ltr Vlbl.

HUNT, Thomas Anthony
Levelland HS; Levelland, TX (10-230) Band; NHS; JV, Bkbl; JV, Ftbl; COM; Hon Prog; Math A; FCA; *Tex Tech U; Med.*

HUNT, Vicky Christine
Logan Elm HS; Circleville, OH (12-180) Pres, A Cap Choir; Band; Bus C; Pres, Chor; Community Yth Symph; 4H; Orch; Hon Prog; Yth Fel; Shorthand A; Chaplain, NHS; *Secretarial.*

HUNT, Virginia Carolyn
Ferguson HS; Newport News, VA; Drama; Span C; Outst Participation Cert Geography.

HUNT, Wendy Jill
Hardee HS; Wauchula, FL (30-268) Demolay; Drama; Span C; Bkbl; Cr-Ctry.

HUNTER, Amy Ruth
Willington Acad; Orangeburg, SC (5-30) Fr C; Rptr, Sch P; MLS; Sci A; *Clemson U; Nurs.*

HUNTER, Anthony Andre
Compton Sr HS; Compton, CA (100-800) Fr C; Bank of Amer A; CSF; HCt; *Long Beach St U; Industrial Arts.*

HUNTER, Audrey Belle
Friends Cent Sch; Philadelphia, PA (12-64) Chldr; Chor; Orch; Co-Ed, Sch P; Bkbl; Hockey; Tnns; Bio A; COM; Hon Prog; Magna Cum Laude; Spch A; F-Ed, Church Paper; Martin Luther King Schol A; Secy, Church Yth Choir; *Mus.*

HUNTER, Beth Ann
Paul Harding HS; Fort Wayne, IN (119-283) Band; Ensm; Orch; Outst Jr Band A; *Mus.*

HUNTER, Betty Smith
York Comp HS; York, SC (1-261) Band; Fr C; Tnns; *Clemson U; Elem Ed.*

HUNTER, Carol Ann
Pocatello HS; Pocatello, ID (60-500) Parl, NHS; Pres, Span C; SC; Tnns; MLS; Rensselaer A; Type A; Senator, Jr, Sr Classes; *U of Utah; Pre-Med.*

HUNTER, Catherine Jeanne
Elida HS; Elida, OH (70-190) Rptr, Ann; Band; Ch, FFA; Ch, 4H; Spch C; Church Chor; Annual Photographer; St FFA Band; *Ohio St U; Agr Communications.*

HUNTER, Cindy Renee
Union Co HS; Blairsville, GA (14-159) Chldr; 4H; SC; Var C; Mgr, Tr; 4H A; *Young Harris Col; Ed.*

HUNTER, Dena Renee
Saint Cecilia's Acad; Washington, DC (6-95) Drama; Secy, NHS; Alg A; Bio A; Hist A; Math A; Sci A; Religion A; A-B HR; *U of Md; Nurs.*

HUNTER, Denise Michele
John W Hallahan HS; Philadelphia, PA (8-431) CYO; Chldr; NHS; Sci C; Span C; Pres, Span NHS; Ftbl; Sftbl; Amer Leg A; Hon Prog; K of C A; Ntl Sci Symposium; Sci A; VofDEM; *U of Scranton; Psych.*

HUNTER, Edith Cornell
Chillicothe HS; Chillicothe, OH (4-425) Band; Orch; Rainbow; Span C; Tr; *Bennett Col; Child Stu.*

HUNTER, Elizabeth Greer
Horace Greeley HS; Chappaqua, NY; Tn Coun Adventures Unlimited.

HUNTER, Elliott Michaun
Rocky Mount HS; Rocky Mount, NC; Band; Bsbl; Bkbl; Ftbl; Tr; Opt A; Jazz Band; Bsbl A; *NC St U; Computer Sci.*

HUNTER, Evelyn Camelia
Luther HS S; Chicago, IL; A Cap Choir; Chor; Drama; Mjrte; Spch C; Swim; Tnns; Tr; Citz A; Cl Fav; JA A; MLS; Pom Pom Girl; Modeling A; Singing A; Tnns A; Sch Cert A, Sports; Tr & Field A; Piano A; *Psych.*

HUNTER, George Andrew
Rensselaer Jr-Sr HS; Rensselaer, NY (1-108) Pres, Chess C; Chor; Dbte Tm; Drama; FTA; Key C; NHS; ARC; F-Ed, Sch P; VP, SC; VP, Var C; Ftbl; Tnns; MVP, Wrest; Alg A; B Crocker A; Bio A; COM; Chem A; Hon Prog; Math A; NMF; Pres A; Regent School; Sci A; Type A; Val; Gym; *Siena Col; Psych.*

HUNTER, Gloria Latrice
Echols Co HS; Statenville, GA (2-40) Co-Ed, Ann; Pres, BC; Chldr; FBLA; FHA; InterClub Coun; Secy, SC; Tres, Sr Cl; Secy, Jr Cl; Hist A; Most Out; *Valdosta Vo-tech Sch; Radiology.*

HUNTER, Hollie Ann
Northwood HS; Silver Spring, MD; Chldr; Hon Prog; Hon Qn, Job's Daughters; Most Improved Trophy, Gym; *Pepperdine U; Recreation.*

HUNTER, Jan Caroline
Tates Creek HS; Lexington, KY (33%-550) Band; Span C; Ftbl; Swim; *Environmental Marine.*

HUNTER, Jane Ellen
Tates Creek Sr HS; Lexington, KY (33%-500) Band; Ensm; Orch; Ftbl; Swim; Ath o-t Wk; Swim A; *Fla St U; Marine Biol.*

HUNTER, Jonathan Chee
Chinle HS; Chinle, AZ (8-134) 4H; NHS; Bkbl; Ftbl; 4H A; *Northern Ariz U; Forestry.*

HUNTER, Kevin Craig
Towson Sr HS; Towson, MD (5%-700) Band; Hmrm; NHS; Tres, Span C; SC; Tr; Hon Prog; Yth Fel; AV A; Phys Ed A; *William & Mary Col; Bio-Chem.*

HUNTER, Leslie Jean
Rhinebeck Central HS; Rhinebeck, NY; Tres, AFS; Chldr; Oper, Rptr, 4H; Sch P; Citz A; Yth Fel; Gym; Jr Hist; Phys Ed A; Gym As; *Elem Ed.*

HUNTER, Marie Diane
Polytechnic HS; Fort Worth, TX; Chor; FHA; Tr.

HUNTER, Mark Alan
Connersville HS; Connersville, IN (4-397) BS; Pres, Ger C; Hmrm; Tres, NHS; Sci C; SC; Tres, Sr Cl; DARGCA; Lion A; Pres, Bible C; Pres, Church Yth; *Rose-Hulman Inst of Tech; Mech Engr.*

HUNTER, Mark Stanley
Karlsruhe Amer HS; Karlsruhe, GERMANY; VP, Band; Chor; Tnns; *Outdoor Ed.*

HUNTER, Melanie Anne
Ozark HS; Ozark, MO (38-134) Chldr; Tr; Hon Prog; *St Johns Sch of Nurs; Nurs.*

HUNTER, Michael John
St Mary's HS; Lynn, MA (10-146) CYO; Tres, Jr Cl; MVP, Bkbl; Cr-Ctry; Tr; Bio A; Math A; NMS; Lat A; *Teilhard De Chardin A.*

HUNTER, Patricia Louise
Sidney Lanier HS; Austin, TX (10%-500) FTA; Hmrm; Pres, Lat C; NHS; Spch C; SC; VP, Jr Cl; *Linguistics.*

HUNTER, Rachel Jo
South HS; Denver, CO (25-530) Chess C; Ed, Lit Mag; Sch P; Cl Fav; Pres, Church Yth Group; Choir Accompanist; Sunday Sch Teacher; Sacred Dance Group; *Colo Col; Eng Lit.*

HUNTER, Rebecca Lynne
St John's Lutheran HS; Ocala, FL (2-24) BC; Chor; Hon Prog; *Mus.*

HUNTER, Rickey Joe
Dongola HS; Dongola, IL (2-28) VP, Band; VP, BC; 4H; Sci C; SC; Cr-Ctry; Fin, Tr; Hist A; HCt; Hon Prog; Interlochen Ntl Mus; Math A; Ntl Sci Symposium; Sci A; Type A; Yth Fel; WW; *Sou Ill U; Physics.*

HUNTER, Robert Lawrance
Owyhee HS; Owyhee, NV (1-24) Tres, FFA; VP, Sci C; SC; Pres, Soph Cl; Cpt, Bkbl; Ftbl; Tr; *Med.*

HUNTER, Sandra Catherine
Ozark HS; Ozark, MO (3-134) FHA; Bkbl; Tr; Alg A; Hon Prog; Vlbl; *Sch o-t Ozarks; Teaching.*

HUNTER, Sandra Gay
Maplewod-Richmond Heights Sr HS; Maplewood, MO (143-216) Chor; Church Sftbl.

HUNTER, Susan Renee
Shawnee Mission W HS; Overland Park, KS; Band; COM; Ensm Group; Memorize Interp, Tyro Scripture; *Mid Amer Naz Col; Bus.*

HUNTER, Terri Jeanelle
Goodlettsville HS; Goodlettsville, TN (16-159) Secy, Chor; FTA; GS; Hmrm; Tres, Lat C; Lat NHS; NHS; Tres, SC; Tnns; Citz A; H of F; Swtht; Prom Qn; Teenboards; Sr Superlative; *U of Tenn; Clothing.*

HUNTER, William Michael Jr
Inkster HS; Inkster, MI; Parl, Bus C; NHS; SC; Tnns; Tr; Alg A; COM; Citz A; Hon Prog; Math A; Most Out; BOEC A; PA; Banking Prog As; *Ind U; Med.*

HUNTING, Daniel Wesley
Central HS; Phoenix, AZ (75-500) Band; Order/ Arrow; F-Ed, Sch P; Sci C; *MIT; Nuclear Engr.*

HUNTINGTON, Amy
Wethersfield HS; Wethersfield, CT (20%-600) Chor; Math C; Span C; Sftbl; Swim; Tnns; Photography C; *Math.*

HUNTLEY, James William
Sw HS; Saint Louis, MO (10-500) Co-Ed, Ann; Band; *U of Kans; Archt Engr.*

HUNTLEY, Kim Kay
Clearlake Comm HS; Clear Lake, IA (33%-135) Chor; Bkbl; HCt; Cpt, Vlbl; *Central Col; Psych.*

HUNTLEY, Lisa Frances
Hibriten HS; Lenoir, NC (50-150) Cpt, Chldr; Fr C; Semi-Fin, Miss NC Tnager Pageant; Fr C; *Lenoir Rhyne Col; Special Ed.*

HUNTLEY, Wendy Yvette
Greater New York Acad; Woodside, NY; Chor; NHS; Sch P; Bkbl; COM; Citz A; Hon Prog; Sports A; *Andrews U; Bus.*

HUNTON, Angela Dawn
Greater Atlanta Christian HS; Norcross, GA (40%-100) Chor; Fr C; HR; *Harding Col; Eng.*

HUNTON, Pamela Gail
Burnside HS; Burnside, KY (7-40) BC; VP, FBLA; Pres, FTA; Math C; Rptr, Sch P; COM; Hist A; Journ A; Q&S A; Sci A; FBLA A; *Somerset Comm Col; Lab Tech.*

HUNTSMAN, Anna Kay
Plant City HS; Plant City, FL (7%-599) F-Ed, Ann; Chor; Ensm; Ch, Model UN; Rptr, NHS; Tres, Span C; SC; Thes; Ch, UN Council; Beauty; Hon Prog; Church Yth Choir; FVA All St Chor; Cl Exec Comm; Fla St Hons Chor; Tns for Christ; Rptr, Jr Civinette; *Fla Tech U; Bus.*

HUNTSMAN, Patricia Lynne
Searcy HS; Searcy, AR; BC; Drama; Fr C; FTA; Tres, Thes; Jr Beethoven C; Eng A; Secy, St Chapter Ntl Fed of Mus C.

HUOTARI, Allen Joseph
Lutheran HS of Los Angeles; Burbank, CA (10%-85) Bsbl; Bkbl; CSF; Hon Prog; St Scholar; CSF Sealbearer; *Santa Monica City Col; Drafting.*

HUPP, Delores Eileen
Zane Trace HS; Chillicothe, OH (18-120) Band; Chem C; Chor; Fr C; 4H; NHS; Rptr, Sch P; Sci C; Var C; Y-Tns; Mgr, Tr.

HUPP, James David
Fairmont Sr HS; Fairmont, WV (20%-200) Hmrm; Yth Fel; Motor Cross Trophies; Ntl Win, Model Contest.

HUPP, Jodi Kay
N Canton Hoover HS; N Canton, OH (207-432) Ann; Chor; 4H; Rptr, InterAct C; Span C; Rptr, Sr Cl; Rptr, Jr Cl; JV, Tr; Hon Prog; Pres A; *U of Akron; Nurs.*

HUPP, John Stewart
Fairmont Sr HS; Fairmont, WV (39-233) A Cap Choir; Band; Bus C; Chor; Dbte Tm; COM; God & Country A; Hon Prog; Math A; Yth Fel; *Fairmont St Col; Econ.*

HUPP, Stephen Lee
Zane Trace HS; Chillicothe, OH (60-120) Band; Chor; 4H; NHS; Excel, Superior, St Hist Day; *Hist.*

HURD, Gerald Lyndon
Oakland Tech HS; Oakland, CA; Bus C; Cpt, Bsbl; Cpt, Ftbl; Spelling A; Bsbl A; JA; *Ohio St U; Real Estate.*

HURD, Janice Elaine
Chrysler HS; New Castle, IN (25%-300) Chor; Ensm; Semi-Fin, GS; 4H; NHS; Sci C; COM; Vlbl; *Purdue U; Consumer & Family Sci.*

HURD, Lori Sue
Weber HS; Pleasent View, UT; Ger C; Mgr, Bkbl; Tr; HR; *Utah St U; Sociology.*

HURD, Shirley Jean
Sumner HS; Sumner, WA; Chor; GS; NHS; Mgr, Sftbl; COM.

HURD, Susan Kay
Berean Christian Sch; Galesville, WI; Cpt, Chldr; Pres, Chor; Secy, SC; MVP, Tr; Vlbl; *Baptist Bible Col; Christian Ed.*

HURDER, Jay A
Freeport Sr HS; Freeport, IL (74-584) BS; Dbte Tm; Ftbl; JV, Tnns; JV, Wrest; HR; *Naval Acad; Astronautical Engr.*

HURDER, Kathryn Anne
Thomas Jefferson HS; Dallas, TX; Tri-HiY; Tr; *Teaching-Disabled.*

HURDZAN, Kathy M
Bridgeport HS; Bridgeport, OH (5-108) Ann; Band; Lat C; Co-Ch, NHS; SC; Y-Tns; Amer Leg A; H of F; Marian A; Cum Laude; *Ohio U; Bus Adm.*

HURLBURT, Catherine Jean
Richland HS; Fort Worth, TX (3%-600) Chor; FHA; NHS; Sch P; Span C; Hon Prog; Magna Cum Laude; Q&S A; Span A; Speed Reading A; *Baylor U; Ed.*

HURLBURT, Robert Scott
Mansfield Christian HS; Mansfield, OH (12-50) JV, Soccer; *Grace Col; Elem Ed.*

HURLBUT, Richard Dean
Ashland-Greenwood HS; Ashland, NE (1-74) Ann; Chor; NHS; VP, Sci C; Tres, Sr Cl; Tres, Jr Cl; Tres, Soph Cl; Mgr, Bkbl; Mgr, Ftbl; Bio A; COM; Chem A; Math A; Sci A; *Midland Col; Elec Engr.*

HURLEY, Anne Katherine
Northfield Jr-Sr HS; Northfield, VT (9-82) A-Ed, Ann; Band; Chor; Community Yth Symph; Drama; NHS; Orch; COM; Mus A; Drama A; *U of Vt; Med Tech.*

HURLEY, Cecilia Jane
West Point HS; W Point, GA (1-50) A Cap Choir; A-Ed, Ann; Band; VP, BC; Co-Cpt, Chldr; Chor; Dbte Tm; Drama; Ensm; FBLA; Ed, Sch P; Tnns; COM; Hon Prog; Musical A; Tnns Hons; *Social Work.*

HURLEY, James Joseph
Susquehanna Comm HS; Susquehanna, PA (2-110) Var C; Bkbl.

HURLEY, Kimberly Sue
Limestone Comm HS; Bartonville, IL (22-387) NHS; Span C; Span NHS; VP, SC; Var C; Co-Cpt, Bkbl; MVP, Tnns; Cpt, Tr; Amer Leg A; COM; Hon Prog; Rotary A; Yth Fel; Prom Qn; All-Conf Bkbl; Area Top 10 Women Ath; *Western Ill U; Phys Ed.*

HURLEY, Lance Duane
Bonita Vista HS; Chula Vista, CA (18-500) Band; Ger C; Var C; Bsbl; JV, Bkbl; Ftbl; *Manhattan Christian Col; Theology.*

HURLEY, Lisa Lynn
Lewistown Comm HS; Lewistown, IL; Band; Chor; FTA; Span C; Span NHS; SC; Thes; *Ill St U; Eng.*

HURLEY, Philip Wayne
Bel Air HS; El Paso, TX (20-651) Band; Chor; JETS; Pres, Lat C; Lit Mag; NHS; Thes; Opt A; *Tex A&M U; Chem.*

HURLEY, Susan Celeste
Bel Air HS; El Paso, TX (20-650) Chor; FHA; NHS; JV, Tnns; *Tex Tech U; Spch Therapy.*

HURLEY, William Randolph
Westfield Sr HS; Westfield, NJ (120-620) NHS; Sci C; Soccer; Alg A; *Lehigh U; Engr.*

HURN, Gwendolen
W Morgan HS; Trinity, AL (10%-59) F-Ed, Ann; VP, BC; Parl, FHA; Secy, Jr Cl; JA A; Vlbl; WW; Cert A; *John C Calhoun St Jr Col.*

HURSH, Kimberly Diane
Spring Grove Area Sr HS; Spring Grove, PA (23-303) Band; Chldr; Chor; NHS; Var C; Hockey; Gold Medal Mus A; Yth Comp Solo; *Bryn Mawr Col; Nurs.*

HURST, Anne Marjorie
Jackson Prep Sch; Jackson, MS; Secy, Chor; Ensm; NHS; Sch P; Secy, Girls Key C; Church Yth Coun; *Miss Col; Bus.*

HURST, Bertha Margarita
Westwood Christian HS; Miami, FL (10%-10) CYO; Sftbl; *Pepperdine U; Photo-Journ.*

HURST, Glenn Allen
St Helena HS; Greenburg, LA; Bus C; Chem C; Chor; Sci C; Up Bound; Bsbl; Bkbl; Ftbl; Sftbl; Swim; Tnns; Phy A; Agr, Ftbl & Bkbl A's; *Sou U; Agr.*

HURST, Gregory Joe
Fulton HS; Knoxville, TN (85-308) Anchor C; Chor; FFA; Key C; ARC; Var C; Y-Tns; Bkbl; Ftbl; Hockey; Tnns; Tr; COM; Citz A; Cl Fav; HCt; Hon Prog; PTA A; Swtht; Yth Fel; Cpt & MVP, Vlbl; *U of Tenn; Bus Adm.*

HURST, Jhan Bradley
Hilcrest HS; Springfield, MO (20%-300) Band; Drama; Bsbl; Cr-Ctry; Hon Prog; Spch A; Graduation Speaker; Ntl Church Bible Quiz Schol; Church Group Ldr; *Evangel Col; Religious Ed.*

HURST, Kevin Patrick
E Catholic HS; Manchester, CT (25-280) NHS; Bsbl; Ftbl; Kiwanis A.

HURST, Stewart Wesley
Sumter HS; Sumter, SC (5-800) A Cap Choir; Fr C; VP, Hmrm; Key C; NHS; Order/Arrow; SC; Pres, Jr Cl; JV, Bkbl; COM; God & Country A; Gov Honor Prog; Hist A; Hon Prog; Math A; Order/Arrow A; Eagle Sct; Furman Schol; Nom, Gov Sch; *Furman U; Bus.*

HURSTON, Byna Jo
Bremen HS; Bremen, GA; Band; FBLA; FTA; 4H; Fin, Hmrm; Fin, Jr Miss Pagent; Cpt, Mjrte; Tr; HCt; Cutest; 2nd, Jr Miss; *W Ga Col; Bus.*

HURSTON, Mitchell Gerold
Bremen HS; Bremen, GA; Bus C; Chor; FBLA; 4H; InterAct C; Thes; Var C; Bsbl; Bkbl; Cr-Ctry; Ftbl; Golf; Sftbl; Tr; Wrest; Cl Fav; Best All Round; MVP; *W Ga Col; Phys Ed.*

HURT, Vanessa Joy
Independence HS; Independence, MS (15%-72) Bus Mgr, Ann; BC; FHA; H of F; *Northwest Miss Jr Col; Lib Sci.*

HURWITZ, Clive Keatinge
Northgate HS; Walnut Creek, CA (1-500) Band; Chess C; Community Yth Symph; Cpt, Math C; Model UN; Orch; CSF; Hon Prog; Math A; NMS; *U of Calif; Math.*

HUSBAND, Decie Walter
Raleigh HS; Raleigh, MS (5%-74) Ann; Band; VP, BC; Math C; Order/Arrow; Sch P; Sci C; Span C; Spch C; Alg A; Amer Leg Orator A; COM; 4H A; H of F; Hon Prog; Journ A; Math A; Sci A; Spch A; Star Student; Type A; Fin, St Piano Festival; Literary Papers As; Super, Drum Major, Stu Conductor; *U of So Miss; Mus.*

HUSE, Belinda Beth
Chillicothe HS; Chillicothe, TX (3-15) Co-Ed, Ann; VP, FHA; 4H; Rptr; SC; Tr; 4H A; I Dare You; Court of Hon Jr; *Home Ec.*

HUSEBY, Jon Alan
Montevideo Sr HS; Montevideo, MN (33-149) AFS; Band; Pres, Hmrm; Pres, SC; Bsbl; Bkbl; HCt; Hon Prog; Lion A; Mus Cast; Pres, Stu Body; Luther League; Econ Advisory Comm; *Jackson AVTI; Land Construction.*

HUSEN, Tami Joyce
Montevideo Sr HS; Montevideo, MN (42-149) A Cap Choir; Band; Chor; Drama; Ensm; FHA; Pres, 4H; Swim; 4H A; Hon Prog; Mus Ensm A's; *Anoka Jr Col; Nurs.*

HUSHFIELD, Joan Ellen
Kimball HS; Dallas, TX (10%-500) Band; FHA; Span C; Hon Prog; Math A; Band; TAG Prog; *Tex A&M U; Vet Med.*

HUSKINS, Arnold Martin
W Lincoln Sr HS; Lincolnton, NC (11-146) BC; Sci C; Pep C; Bible C; Ntl HS A for Excellence; Most Sch Spirited; *NC St U; Vet Med.*

HUSSEINI, Joseph W
Marist Brothers' HS; Pago Pago, AMERICAN SAMOA (1-50) Ann; Dbte Tm; Hmrm; Sch P; Spch C; Secy, SC; Pres, Sr Cl; Bkbl; Alg A; COM; Hist A; Hon Prog; Math A; Phy A; Sci A; *Pepperdine U; Med.*

HUSSER, David Milton
Warwick HS; Lititz, PA (130-272) Band; Chor; Swim; Wrest; Yth Foundation.

HUSSEY, Paul Mark
Perry Meridian HS; Indianapolis, IN (66-600) Chem C; Phys C; Alg A; Hist A; Eng A; Industrial Arts A; *Purdue U; Engr.*

HUST, Diana Kay
San Benito HS; San Benito, TX; Var C; Bkbl; Soccer; MVP, Sftbl; Tr; MLS; *Sam Houston Col; Retarded Children.*

HUST, Glenda Ann
Foley HS; Foley, AL (10-300) Ann; Chor; Hmrm; NHS; Span C; Sftbl; Cl Fav; Opt A; Val; GSct 'Wider Opportunity'; Tres, Church Yth; *Huntingdon Col; Ed.*

HUSTED, Janice M
Johnstown HS; Johnstown, NY; Chor; COM; Citz A; Yth Fel; *Work With Retarded Children.*

HUSTED, Jeanette Louise
Johnstown Sr HS; Johnstown, NY; Chor; Swim; COM; Citz A; Yth Fel; Gym A; Most Points Trophy.

HUSTED, Robert Eric
Grace Davis HS; Modesto, CA; Dbte Tm; NFL; Spch C; Mgr, Ftbl; Tnns; Spch A; Steering Comm; *U SC.*

HUTCHENS, Christina Joy
D Russell Lee Vo-Ed HS; Hamilton, OH (150-620) Band; Ger C; Mod Mus Mas; Yth Fel; *Olivet Nazarene Col; Home Ec.*

HUTCHENS, Pamela Kay
Appalachian HS; Oneonta, AL (7-38) VP, BC; 4H; Sch P; VP, Sr Cl; MLS; WW; *Gadsden St Jr Col; Nurs.*

HUTCHERSON, Leigh Ann
Glasgow HS; Glasgow, KY (10%-144) Ann; Tres, BC; Fr C; Hmrm; Sch P; Sci C; Span C; Secy, SC; Var C; Pres, Soph Cl; Tr; Hon Prog; Span A; WW; *U of Ky.*

HUTCHERSON, Lesa Anne
Evangelical Christian Sch; Cordova, TN (1-57) Ed, Ann; S-T, Drama; Pres, NHS; Co-Ch, SC; Mgr, Bkbl; Tr; Alg A; Citz A; Hon Prog; Vlbl; *Memphis St U; Med.*

HUTCHESON, Cynthia Ann
Patton Springs HS; Afton, TX (2-11) Ann; Band; Cpt, Chldr; FHA; 4H; Sch P; MVP, Bkbl; Tnns; Tr; 4H A; Sal; Young Homemakers 'Little Sister'; FFA Swtht; *Temple Jr Col; Laboratory Technology.*

HUTCHESON, Myra Susan
Forsyth Co Day Sch; Lewisville, NC; Chor; Drama; Sci C; Span C; COM; Citz A; *Meredith Col; Religion.*

HUTCHESON, Penny Sue
Claxton HS; Claxton, GA (50%-116) Sci A.

HUTCHESON, Rhonda Alice
Jackson HS; Jackson, GA (2-253) Ann; Cpt, Chldr; FBLA; Semi-Fin, GS; Hmrm; Lit Ral; Math C; Tres, NHS; Tres, SC; Fin, Tnns; COM; HCt; Type A; Qn, Soph, Jr Cl; Ch, Co-Ed-Y; Chaplain, FCA; Tres Yth Choir; *Gordon Jr Col.*

HUTCHESON, William Randy
Claxton HS; Claxton, GA (25%-110) Chess C; COM.

HUTCHINS, Antonio Dwayne
Northeastern HS; Detroit, MI (9-202) Pres, NHS; *Central Mich U; Computor Programming.*

HUTCHINS, Donna Gail
Hunter Huss HS; Gastonia, NC (9-554) Band; BC; Community Yth Symph; Span C; Hon Prog; Co Yth Chor; Hon All St Band; Fel of Christian Stu; Marshal; Colorguard; Mus Camp Schol; All St Band; *Phys Therapy.*

HUTCHINS, Frances Nanettee
Miami Killian HS; Miami, FL; Ann; Chldr; Chor; Ensm; NHS; Sch P; HCt; Mus.

HUTCHINS, Lynda Michelle
Clyde A Erwin HS; Asheville, NC (105-260) Band; Fr C; Sci C; Tr; Yth Fel; *Montreat-Anderson Col; Sci.*

HUTCHINS, Paula Jo
Edgewood HS; Edgewood, TX (17-59) Band; Chldr; Parl, SC; Spirit C; Photographer, Ann; *Tyler Jr Col; Dental Hygiene.*

HUTCHINS, Ruth Ellen
Lee M Thurston HS; Redford, MI; Ger C; NHS; Orch; ARC; Bsbl; Swim; Hon Prog; Yth Fel; *Mich St U; Sci.*

HUTCHINS, Sherri Lynne
Andress HS; El Paso, TX; ARC; Pres, Tri-HiY; VP Personnal, JA; Most Outst Member, Tri Hi Y; *Ed.*

HUTCHINS, Susan Lynn
William J Brown HS; Sturgis, SD (33%-200) A Cap Choir; Band; Chor; Dbte Tm; Drama; Hmrm; Madrigal; NFL; Ski C; Parl, SC; Thes; Golf; COM; Dbte Ltr; *U of SD; Special Ed.*

HUTCHINSON, Al Vincent
Maggie L Walker HS; Richmond, VA (10%-250) Fin, BS; NHS; Ftbl.

HUTCHINSON, Anne
Greater Latrobe Sr HS; Latrobe, PA (84-518) Cpt, Chldr; Bus Mgr, Sch P; Ch, SC; VP, Var C; DARGCA; *U of Pittsburgh; Bus.*

HUTCHINSON, Brian O Shea
Cabrillo Sr HS; Lompoc, CA (32-450) Semi-Fin, BS; Pres, Key C; Orch; Rptr, Sch P; Sci C; Pres, SC; Var C; Pres, Jr Cl; Cr-Ctry; Tr; *Pepperdine U; Elec Engr.*

HUTCHINSON, David Lee
Coshocton HS; Coshocton, OH (14-250) BS; Chem C; HiY; Key C; Lat C; NHS; Span C; VP, SC; Pres, Soph Cl; Tnns; Hon Prog; Yth Fel; *Miami U; Acct.*

HUTCHINSON, Gregg Orrin
Hamden HS; Hamden, CT (140-735) Hmrm; JV, Cr-Ctry; Rifle Tm; Ldr, Perscriptive Phys Ed; Bio C; Phys Ed Outst Achv; Lt, Christian Service Brigade; *Gorden Col; Law.*

HUTCHINSON, Julie Lynn
Otsego HS; Otsego, MI; Band; Ensm; Ed, Sch P; Band A; PA; *Parsons Bus Sch; Secretarial.*

HUTCHINSON, Lorin Simpson
Hamden HS; Hamden, CT (170-865) VP, Bike C; Italian Outst Achv A; Church Mus Director; Vacation Bible Sch Teacher; *Psych.*

HUTCHINSON, Marcy Jean
Logan Elm HS; Circleville, OH (12-200) Ann; Band; Chldr; Rptr, 4H; NHS; ARC; Bsbl; Cpt, Swim; Tr; Beauty; COM; 4H A; Hon Prog; Yth Fel; Yearly Hlr; Stu o-t Mo; St Champion Swim Merit A; *Ohio U; Fashion Merchandising.*

HUTCHINSON, Randall Kevin
Lincoln HS; Ellwood City, PA; A Cap Choir; Chor; Drama; Hmrm; SC; Mgr, Tr; Music A; Yth Group; Jr Dramatics; Builders C; Church Choir; Art A; Academic Achv A; *Geneva Col; Mortuary Sci.*

HUTCHINSON, William Robert
Tower Hill HS; Tower Hill, IL (4-23) Chor; NHS; Span C; SC; Pres, Sr Cl; Pres, Jr Cl; VP, Soph Cl; Bsbl; Co-Cpt, Bkbl; Hist A; HCt; Crafts C; HR; *Lakeland Col; Data Processing.*

HUTCHISON, Anne Victoria
Churchill HS; Livonia, MI (3-800) Community Yth Symph; Orch; Phys C; ARC; JV, Cr-Ctry; Tr; Hon Prog; Dist & St Solo Ensm One Rating; Livonia Yth Symp Schol; Creative Writing A; *Capital U; Pre-Med.*

HUTCHISON, Clifford Ross Jr
Sam Houston HS; Arlington, TX (11-650) NHS; Pres, SC; JV, Bkbl; Golf; COM; DARGCA; Hon Prog; Sci A; *Baylor U; Pre-Dental.*

HUTCHISON, DeeAnn
Akeley HS; Akeley, MN; Ann; Chldr; Drama; FHA; 4H; Sch P; Sftbl; Tr; *Bemidji St Col; Teacher.*

HUTCHISON, Michael Shane
Dilley HS; Dilley, TX; Pres, FFA; Co-Cpt, Ftbl; Tr.

HUTCHISON, Ramona Ann
Horace Maynard HS; Maynardville, TN (12-121) Co-Ed, Ann; BC; Chor; FHA; 4H; Sci C; *St Mary's Sch of Nurs; Nurs.*

HUTSON, Debra Annette
Baker HS; Columbus, GA; Chldr; FTA; ARC; Span C; Swim; Church Choir; Skating, Swim, A's; *Emory U; Nurs.*

HUTSON, Gale E
London HS; London, OH (7-100) GS; VP, 4H; NHS; Co-Cpt, Bkbl; Sftbl; 4H A; Kiwanis A; Type A; *Phys Ed.*

HUTSON, Julianne
Beech Grove HS; Beech Grove, IN (43-239) Band; Drama; Thes; Var C; Cpt, Bkbl; *Taylor U; Eng.*

HUTSON, Kevin Eugene
Torrington HS; Torrington, CT (100-392) Order/Arrow; F-Ed, Sch P; God & Country A; NEDT; Past Master Councilor, Demolay; BSct; Little League Coach; Church Yth Fel; Eagle Sct A; Forum C; Intramural Hockey, Vlbl; *U of Conn; Eng.*

HUTSON, Kris Edward
Jacksonville HS; Jacksonville, TX (35-260) Band; Hmrm; Order/Arrow; Order/Arrow A; Jr Civitan; Eagle Sct; All Dist, All Region, Band; Solo & Ensm Medals; *Stephen F Austin St U; Mus.*

HUTT, Deborah Leann
West HS; Columbus, OH; Band; Chor; Ensm; Y-Tns; Sftbl; Tr; Most Musically Inclined; *Ohio St U; Vet Med.*

HUTT, Derreth E
Westboro HS; Westboro, MA (40-200) Chor; 4H; NHS; Bkbl; JV, Sftbl; Tr; Citz A; 4H A; Hon Prog; Pres A; Secy, Co-4-H Tn Coun; Jr Ldr Cert, 4-H; *Colo St U; Vet Med.*

HUTTO, Billye Renee
Andrew Jackson Sr HS; Jacksonville, FL; Ensm; Hmrm; Ntl Teachers Coun; Rainbow; Co-Ed, Sch P; SC; Secy, Sr Cl; Tnns; *Recreational Director.*

HUTTO, Walter Chisolm
Homewood HS; Homewood, AL (10%-240) Chor; Span C; Cr-Ctry; Tr; Wrest; COM; Citz A; Cl Fav; Lion A; ROTC A; Yth Fel; *Auburn U; Engr.*

HUTTON, Diane Alice
Greece Olympia HS; Rochester, NY (48-308) Chor; Ensm; Hmrm; Madrigal; Orch; Bkbl; Hon Prog; Hon Schol; *Geneva Col; Med Tech.*

HUTTON, Donald Lee
Anderson HS; Anderson, IN (15-565) Band; Chor; Madrigal; NHS; Mgr, Bsbl; Eagle Sct; *Ind U; Pol Sci.*

HUTTON, Douglas Scott
University HS; Spokane, WA; Pres, A Cap Choir; Pres, Chor; Span C; SC; Var C; Bsbl; Cpt, Ftbl; Sftbl; JV, Tnns; JV, Wrest; Tackle Trophy; *Law Enforcement.*

HUTTON, Laura Lee
Fredonia HS; Fredonia, KS; Co-Ed, Ann; VP, Band; Chor; Drama; Ensm; FHA; 4H; Sci C; Span C; SC; Golf; Tr; 4 Yr Merit Schol; *Friends U; Psych.*

HUTTON, Mark Lyal
Limestone Comm HS; Bartonville, IL (26-390) Band; Dbte Tm; Key C; Co-Ch, NHS; Spanish; Span NHS; VP, Var C; Ftbl; Tnns; MVP, Wrest; COM; Prom Kg; Sterling Merit; Most Improved Wrest; *Western Ill U; Bus Mgt.*

HUTTON, Michael William
Hall HS; Little Rock, AR (279-678) Band; Chess C; InterClub Coun; Pres, ARC; Arch; Ftbl; Swim; Tnns; Tr; *U of Ala.*

HUTTON, Shelli Danette
Ottumwa HS; Ottumwa, IA; Chldr; Chor; Hmrm; Orch; Tr; Gym.

HUTTON, Stacie DeAnne
Ottumwa HS; Ottumwa, IA; Chor; Hmrm; Bkbl; Tr.

HUTTON, Thomas John
St Albans HS; St Albans, WV (15%-600) Band; Ensm; Mu Alpha Theta; SC; Outst, Band; *Computer Sci.*

HUTZELL, Rebecca Lynn
Frankfort HS; Ridgeley, WV (10%-139) Band; FHA; NHS; Bkbl; Tres, Sonshiners; Tres, Pep C; Miss Pep Court; *W Va U; Elem Ed.*

HUTZELL, Rodney Dale
Frankfort HS; Ridgeley, WV (10%-139) Band; NHS; SC; Var C; Bkbl; Tr; All Tourn Bkbl Tm; *WVU; Computer Sci.*

HUTZLER, Charles Randall
S Rapides Acad; Lecompte, LA (1-23) Lit Ral; NHS; Bsbl; Bkbl.

HUTZLER, Debora Louise
Musselman HS; Bunker Hill, WV (20-92) Chor; FHA; FTA; *W Va U; Chem.*

HUUSKO, Pamela Lorraine
Aurora-Hoyt Lakes HS; Aurora, MN; Cr-Ctry; Tr; *Vet Asst.*

HUXHOLD, James Bartholomew
Park-Tudor HS; Indianapolis, IN (20-60) VP, Key C; Var C; Co-Cpt, Bkbl; MVP, Ftbl; Tr; Hilda Stewart Schol; Panther 500 C; Bkbl A; Alumni Grant; *Wittenberg Col; Bus.*

HUXHOLD, Wendy Lynn
Hinsdale HS; Clarendon Hills, IL (24-412) Chor; Drama; Fr C; Thes; *Oral Roberts U.*

HVASTA, Mark F
Washington-Lee HS; Arlington, VA (57-270) A-Ed, Ann; Secy, Chess C; Hmrm; Key C; Var C; Soccer; COM; HCt; Crew; *USC; Law.*

HWANG, Richard C
Holy Cross HS; Riverside, NJ (6-394) BS; Hmrm; NHS; SC; JV, Tr; Hon Prog; *St Joseph Col; Bio.*

HYATT, Benjamin Carroll III
Perryville HS; Perryville, AR (10-60) Ftbl.

HYATT, David Richard
Northeast HS; Oakland Park, FL (10%-570) Dbte Tm; NFL; NHS; Order/Arrow; Cpt, Swim; Hon Prog; Order/Arrow A; Sci A; Spch A; MVP, Swim; Eagle Sct A; WW; HR; *Furman U; Law.*

HYATT, James F
Newbury Park HS; Newbury Park, CA (9-636) BS; Hmrm; NHS; VP, Order/Arrow; Phys C; Var C; Co-Cpt, Wrest; Amer Leg A; CSF; COM; Citz A; Cl Fav; Elk A; God & Country A; Hon Prog; Opt A; Rotary A; MVP, Wrest; *Brigham Young U; Engr.*

HYATT, Mark James
Sodus Central Sch; Sodus, NY (2-130) Var C; Tr; Math A; Highest Avg, Boy; *Alfred U; Ceramic Engr.*

HYATT, Robert Stephen
Ne HS; Fort Lauderdale, FL (10%-550) NFL; Order/Arrow; Tnns; Hon Prog; Most Out; NEDT; Sci A; 'V' Ltrman; Eagle Sct; Jr NHS; Gifted Prog; *Med.*

HYDE, Bret Alan
Wallace HS; Wallace, ID (14-102) BS; Pres, Key C; Pres, Lat C; Lat NHS; Math C; NHS; Order/Arrow; SC; Var C; Bkbl; Cr-Ctry; Ftbl; Tr; *US Air Force Acad; Engr.*

HYDE, Cynthia Jane
Central Baptist HS; Hampton, VA (2-13) Chor; 4H; Co-Ed, Sch P; COM; Type A; Sunday Sch Teacher; Secy, Amer Party Yth; *Bob Jones U; Christian Worker.*

HYDE, Deborah Ann
Douglas HS; Douglas, AZ; Pres, AFS; Fin, GS; Pres, InterClub Coun; Co-Ed, Lit Mag; NHS; Rainbow; SC; Mgr, Tr; Amer Leg A; Q & S; Outst Jr; *U of Ariz; Med.*

HYDE, Jeffrey Dale
Frankston HS; Frankston, TX (10-40) VP, BC; FFA; NHS; VP, SC; VP, Jr Cl; Bsbl; Bkbl; Co-Cpt, Ftbl; Golf; Sftbl; Citz A; HCt; Semi-Fin, Ftbl; Best All Around; *Baylor U; PE.*

HYDE, Russell David
Tulsa Christian Sch; Tulsa, OK; Chess C; Chor; Dbte Tm; Semi-Fin, Tr; Spch A; 1st Pl, Pa Spch A; 1st Pl, Okla Spch A; Stu o-t Yr; *Baptist Bible Col; Elem Ed.*

HYDER, Anita Karen
Lincolnton Sr HS; Lincolnton, NC (29-260) Secy, Band; Secy, BC; Sch Achieve Tm; Span C; Secy, SC; Cl Fav; Sci A; Pres, Cystic Fibrosis C; Outst Mus; HR; *Pfeiffer Col; Christian Ed.*

HYDIE, William Resadell
S Philadelphia HS; Philadelphia, PA (40%-749) Temple Med Col; Med Tech.

HYLAND, Verien Fawn
Warren Central Sr HS; Vicksburg, MS (44-340) AFS; Chor; FTA; Pres, 4H; Lat C; Mu Alpha Theta; Math A; Drivers Ed A; Troubadour Group; *MSU; Landscape Architecture.*

HYLANDER, Sandy Lee
Sou Baptist Education Center; Memphis, TN (47-127) Bus C; FBLA; Rainbow; Var C; Bkbl; Sftbl; Tnns; Tr; Beauty; HCt; Hon Prog; Star Student; Type A; Civitan C; Sr Girls C; *Bus.*

HYLICK, Brenda Yvette
Ft Pierce Central HS; Ft Pierce, FL (8-597) Tres, Band; BC; Ensm; Math C; Secy, NHS; Tres, Orch; Hon Prog; Talent Search A; Symphonic Achv As; *Engr.*

HYLTON, Fiona Lorraine
Herndon HS; Herndon, WV (4-48) Band; Fr C; SC; Pres, Soph Cl; Bkbl; Sftbl; Phys Ed A; *Concord Col; Phys Ed.*

HYLTON, Jeffrey Scott
Handley HS; Winchester, VA (10-350) Chor; Hmrm; Tres, Key C; Monogram; Span C; SC; JV, Ftbl; Tr; Wrest.

HYMAN, Amos Stanley
Chester HS; Closter, PA; Chor; VP, Key C; Model UN; NHS; Up Bound; Soccer; Tr; Columbus Essay Contest; Chester's Crime Essay; *Lincoln U; Bus Adm.*

HYMAN, Jay Martin
Hillel HS; Lawrence, NY; Chess C; Chor; Dbte Tm; Math C; Parl, SC; Soccer; COM; Citz A; Hon Prog; NEDT; Sci A; Principal's List; Semi-Fin, Ntl Bible Contest; Ed- in-Chief, Yrbk; *Columbia U.*

HYMEL, Darlene Ann
Destrehan HS; Destrehan, LA (13-168) Bus C.

HYMEL, Marlene Marie
Destrehan HS; Destrehan, LA (12-168) BC; Bus C; HCt.

HYNES, Kathleen
Alameda HS; Lakewood, CO (50-600) Band; Tres, Chldr; COM; Citz A; Lang Arts A; PA A; Hon Soc; *Fort Collins Col; Social Work.*

HYNNING, Ron Andre
R A Long HS; Longview, WA (11-320) Span C; MVP, Bsbl; JV, Bkbl; Ftbl; Citz A; Cl Fav; JA A.

HYSLIP, Tammie Jo
Queen Anne HS; Seattle, WA; Chor; Key C; COM; God & Country A; *Comm Col; Social Sci.*

HYSON, Eric Allen
H D Woodson HS; Washington, DC; *Graphic Communications.*

I

IACONO, Brian D
Chester HS; Chester, PA; Bsbl.

IADAROLA, George Edward Jr
Notre Dame HS; W Haven, CT (1-229) Ed, Ann; Lit Mag; NHS; A-Ed, Sch P; VP, Span C; Pres, Span NHS; COM; St Scholar; Val; VofDEM; Math Hon Soc; Stage Mgr, Plays; Civitan Essay Cont As; Holy Cross A; Congress 10 Outst Srs; Notre Dame Schol o-t Yr; *Col o-t Holy Cross; Bio.*

IAMS, Lynn Ann
Barnesville HS; Barnesville, OH (1-115) Chor; Dbte Tm; Drama; Fr C; FTA; Rainbow; Co-Ed, Sch P; Tres, SC; Tres, Jr Cl; DARGCA; Elk A; Type A; Val; NML; *Washington & Jefferson Col; Biol.*

IASIELLO, Biagio Gino
St Edwards HS; Lakewood, OH (180-300) CYO; Bkbl; *Ohio St U; Archt.*

IBA, Wayne Franklin
Hershey Sr HS; Hershey, PA (80-266) Band; Chor; Ensm; Pres, Hmrm; Cpt, Model UN; Orch; Order/Arrow; SC; Bkbl; Cr-Ctry; Sftbl; Best Musician; *Hampshire Col.*

IBANEZ, Flora Palomo
George Washington Sr HS; Mangilao, GUAM; NHS; SC; Alg A; Citz A; Math A; Sal; Type A; *U of Guam; Acct.*

IBANEZ, Germaine Palomo
George Washington Sr HS; Agana, GUAM; Mjrte; Secy, NHS; SC; Secy, Jr Cl; Soc Stu; *Pasadena City Col; Astronomy.*

IBLINGS, Judy Lynn
Fair Park HS; Shreveport, LA (15-350) Chldr; Chem C; Chor; Ensm; FBLA; Hmrm; NHS; Phys C; Sci C; SC; Sftbl; Swim; Tnns; Tr; Hon Prog; Yth Fel; Secy, 'Z' C; Nom, GS; *La Tech U; Computer Sci.*

IBROM, Karen Ruth
Sam Houston HS; San Antonio, TX; A-Ed, Ann; A-Ed, Sch P; JV, Tnns; Crisco A; Journ A; Spch A; Lib C; Talent Mus A; Tr & Field A; CCD Cert A; *St Marys Dominican Col; Journ.*

ICE, Karen Sue
F J Reitz HS; Evansville, IN; Chor; Drama; Hmrm; Citz A; Magna Cum Laude; Schol HR; NJHS; NFSM Piano Guild As; Concert Choir; *ISU at Terre Haute; Acct.*

ICHNIOWSKI, Stephen Paul
Towson Cath HS; Towson, MD; Chor; Drama; NHS; Rptr, Sch P; Bsbl; Soccer; Bio A; COM; Hon Prog; NEDT; Fr A; Cpt, TV Quiz; *Columbia U; Hist.*

IDE, Constance Helene
Pittsburg HS; Pittsburg, KS (60-250) A Cap Choir; Band; Ensm; Bkbl; Sftbl; Bio A; COM; Pres A; St Mus Festival; *Pittsburg St U; Phys Ed.*

IDE, Miriam Marie
Pittsburg HS; Pittsburg, KS (50-200) A Cap Choir; Band; Ensm; VP, Ger C; SC; Mgr, Bkbl; Sftbl; Type A; Vlbl; *Pittsburg St U.*

IDE, William Lindsay
John S Shaw HS; Mobile, AL (10%-450) Key C; Up Bound; Hist A; Hon Prog; Math A; Sci A; *Radio & Television Elec.*

IDICA, Basilia Tumacder
Maui HS; Kahului, HI (20%-300) Band; Span NHS; Pres, Church Yth Choir; Comm Coun Board of Directors; *CSU; Phys Therapy.*

IDZIK, Donna Marie
Cecilian Acad; Philadelphia, PA; Fr C; Sci C; Bkbl; Sftbl; Vlbl; Lat Recognition A.

IGE, Kathy Akemi
Kubasaki HS; Okinawa, JAPAN (12-271) Drama; Secy, NHS; Ed, Stu Directory; Pres, S&Q; *U of Wash; Math.*

IGLESIA, Maria Concepcion
Bassick HS; Bridgeport, CT (50-500) Span A; *Sacred Heart U; Executive Bilingual Secy.*

IGO, Carl Gene
Eldorado HS; El Dorado, TX (4-56) Band; VP, FFA; 4H; Fin, Spch C; 4H A; NEDT; Spch A; FFA A; Semi-Fin, St Spch; *Tex A&M U; Agr.*

IGO, Johnny Robert
Corbin HS; Corbin, KY (32-70) Demolay; Ftbl; *Morehead U; Health.*

IGO, Katherine Elaine
Permian HS; Odessa, TX; Ch, A Cap Choir; Chor; Madrigal; Tri-HiY; Tr; Citz A; Sci A; UIL Mus A; Gym; Ntl Guild Piano; Ntl Fed of Mus C; *San Angelo St U; Elem Ed.*

IGOE, Donald Francis
Don Bosco Tech HS; Boston, MA (7-177) CYO; NHS; Semi-Fin, Bsbl; Semi-Fin, Bkbl.

IHRKE, Alan Kenton
Fosston HS; Fosston, MN (32-91) 4H; Var C; Ftbl; HCt; Pres, Christian Yth Fellowship; 1 of 2 in St, Radio Cl; *Northwestern U; Radio.*

IHRKE, Joyce Heidi
Fosston HS; Fosston, MN; 4H; JV, Bkbl; Secy, VP, Tres, Christian Yth Fel; *Math.*

IHRMAN, David Kryn
Holland HS; Holland, MI (10%-325) Band; Dbte Tm; NHS; Ed, Sch P; Cr-Ctry; Tr; Ntl Sci Found; Rotary A; VFW A; *Kalamazoo Col; Psych.*

IKARD, Stacy Lynn
Memorial HS; Houston, TX (18-650) A Cap Choir; Chor; Mjrte; Mu Alpha Theta; ARC; Span C; Span NHS; COM; God & Country A; Hon Prog; ARC A; Yth Fel; 1st Cl, GSct; *Baylor U; Med Tech.*

IKEY, Jack Dean
Bible Baptist Christian Sch; Wichita Falls, TX; Pres, SC; Bsbl; Bkbl; Cpt, Ftbl; Tr; *Arlington Baptist Col; Theology.*

IKNER, John Steven
Leroy HS; Leroy, AL; Ann; Band; BC; Pres, Jr Cl; Sftbl; Span A; Band A; *Patrick Henry Col; Computering.*

ILKO, Anna Louise
Struthers HS; Struthers, OH (37-325) CYO; Span C; Vol, Red Cross; Stenography A; *Computer Tech.*

ILKO, Jeanette Marie
Struthers HS; Struthers, OH (30-270) Bus C; CYO; NHS; Y-Tns; Mgr, Tr; Type A; Vol, Red Cross; Outst Bus Off Ed Stu; Shorthand A; *Youngstown St U; Court Reporting.*

ILTZSCH, Pamela Ky
Bennington Pub HS; Bennington, NE (13-38) Ann; Chor; Drama; 4H; Spch C; SC; Bkbl; Lion A; Vlbl Tm; Prom Qn Cand; VP, Pep C; Cpt, Pom Pon; *Fashion Merchandising.*

IMAE, Susan Hatsue
Maui HS; Kahului, HI (60-360) Pres, FNA; Hmrm; Sci C; Pres, Explorer's Med Post; Japanese C; *Health.*

IMAN, Anne M
Slater HS; Slater, MO (8-79) Ann; Band; Chldr; Chor, Secy, Drama; FTA; Secy, 4H; Hmrm; S-T, NHS; Pres, Rainbow; Span C; SC; Var C; Swim; Tr; 4H A; Hon Prog; Masonic A; Pres A; Yth Fel; Pep C; Sr Lifesaving; WW; FCA; Water Safety Aide; Gym; Courtwarming Court; *U of Mo; Eng.*

IMBLUM, Thomas Michael
Uniontown Area Sr HS; Uniontown, PA (3%-510) Key C; Span C; Alg A; DARGCA; Hist A; Math A; Sci A; Trainer, Ftbl.

IMEL, Nancie Lynn
Los Alamitos HS; Los Alamitos, CA; HCt; Board Rep Model, Bullocks Campus; Women's Auxiliary Schol; *Bethany Nazarene Col; Early Childhood Ed.*

IMER, Donald R
Highland Sr HS; Highland, IN (290-530).

IMER, Jack D
Highland HS; Highland, IN (290-565).

IMHOFF, Lori Ann
Inter-City Christian HS; Allen Park, MI; Band; SC; Tres, Jr Cl; Citz A; NEDT; Bkbl Statistician; Ribbons, St & Dist Solo & Ensm; *Phys Ed.*

IMMONEN, Cathy Louise
Luther L Wright HS; Ironwood, MI; Band; Mjrte; Orch; *Mich Tech U; Acct.*

IMMONEN, Mark Stephen
Luther L Wright HS; Ironwood, MI (11-192) Band; ARC; Ski C; Var C; Tr; HCt; Skiing Tm; Ntl Ski Patrol; Stage Band; *Mich Tech U; Engr.*

IMPERIAL, Frances Shirlene
Granby HS; Norfolk, VA (8-350) Pres, Band; Ensm; VP, NHS; Orch; H of F; Hon Prog; Most Out; Opt A; Drum Major; Mus Schol; Sch Swtht Contestant; Head Librarian, Band & Orch; *Old Dominion U; Mus Ed.*

IMRE, Rose Marie
Miami HS; Miami, FL; Band; Phys Ed A; *Eckerd Col; Nurs.*

IMRIE, David Darrell
Hopewell Valley Central HS; Hopewell, NJ; Band; Chor; Arch; JV, Bsbl; JV, Bkbl; Ftbl; Sftbl; Swim; Tnns; Tr; Wrest; Boy's Brigade; YMCA; *Ath.*

IMRIE, Joanne Elizabeth
Hopewell Valley C HS; Hopewell, NJ (78-311) Chor; Arch; Bkbl; Soccer; Sftbl; Swim; Tnns; ARC A; YMCA; Pres, Pioneer Girls; *Taylor U.*

INCLAN, Luisa Angelica
Colegio Puertorriqueno de Ninas; Caparra Heights, PR (3-61) VP, Band; Drama; Hmrm; Tres, Math C; Tres, NHS; F-Ed, Secy, P; VP, Spch C; SC; COM; Spch A; Ldrship A; *Bradley U; Ed.*

INDIHAR, Timothy Gerard
Gilbert HS; Gilbert, MN (11-62) Ann; Band; BS; CYO; Chor; Ensm; Math C; NHS; Orch; Sci C; SC; Thes; Bkbl; Cr-Ctry; Ftbl; Tnns; Amer Leg A; COM; HCt; Math A; *Mesabi Comm Col; Bus Adm.*

INGALLS, Brian Edward
Paris HS; Paris, IL (16-250) NHS; Cpt, Golf; *U of Ga; Bio.*

INGALLS, Teresa Dawn
Cleveland HS; Cleveland, OK; Chldr; FHA; Mjrte; NHS; Pep C; VICA; CT C; NHS, St Hon Soc, A's.

INGALSBE, Marilyn Ann
Kickapoo HS; Springfield, MO (80-279) Anchor C; Chor; Dbte Tm; Drama; Co-Ed, Lit Mag; NFL; Ed, Sch P; Span C; Spch C; Thes; COM; Journ A; WW; NFL Degree of Hon; *SW Mo St U; Life Sci.*

INGEBRITSEN, Sonja Carol
Lancaster Sr HS; Lancaster, WI (12-129) AFS; S-T, Band; Chldr; Chor; Ensm; 4H; Madrigal; Tres, NHS; Orch; DARGCA; Pres A; St Mus A; *UW-Platteville; Bus.*

INGELS, Lori Sue
Engleside Christian Sch; Alexandria, VA (2-4) Chldr; Chor; Dbte Tm; Hmrm; Co-Ed, Sch P; SC; Tres, Sr Cl; Hist A; Sal; Sci A; Type A.

INGERICK, Paul Kevin
Hugh M Cummings HS; Burlington, NC (75-250) MVP, Band; Most Supportive Sr in Band; *Tech Inst of Ala; Auto-Body Repair.*

INGERMAN, Shari Ruth
Hillel HS; Lawrence, NY (1-46) Ed, Ann; Chldr; Bkbl; B Crocker A; NEDT; Regent Schol; Vlbl; Principal's List; *Colgate U.*

INGIGNOLI, Annette
Secaucus HS; Secaucus, NJ (10-200) Band; Ensm; Hmrm; Orch; SC; Cr-Ctry; JV, Tr; *Marquette U; Phys Therapy.*

INGLE, Kelly Denise
Wm Chrisman HS; Independence, MO (30-488) A Cap Choir; Cpt, Band; Ensm; Hmrm; Cpt, Mjrte; Parl, SC; JV, Ftbl; Tr; *Wm Jewell Col; Bus.*

INGLE, Suzette
Asheville HS; Asheville, NC (10%-500) Band; Ski C; Span C; *UNEA; Special Ed.*

INGOLD, Jane Marie
Monroe Sr HS; Monroe, MI (40-255) Secy, Band; Secy, Fr C; Cr-Ctry; Tr; Pres A; High HR; *UW of La Crosse; Elem Ed.*

INGOLD, Mark Edmund
Glenbard W HS; Glen Ellyn, IL (278-486) A Cap Choir; CYO; Chor; Hmrm; SC; Var C; Bsbl; Ftbl; Wrest; *Iowa St U; Bus.*

INGOLD, Rhonda Lynn
Statesboro HS; Statesboro, GA (35-300) BC; Fr C; Ger C; Model UN; F-Ed, Sch P; Tres, Span C; *Young Harris Col; Biol.*

INGRAM, Debra Jean
Washington HS; Kansas City, KS (100-594) Bus C; Chor; FBLA; Hmrm; Madrigal; Span C; COM; Type A; Attendance A; *Kansas City Jr Col; Bus.*

INGRAM, Frankie Lane
Scotland HS; Scotland, AR (3-19) SC; Bkbl.

INGRAM, George
Simon Gratz HS; Philadelphia, PA (1-1000) CYO; FTA; Pres, Hmrm; JETS; Math C; NHS; Pol Sci C; SC; JV, Bsbl; JV, Bkbl; Wrest; Bio A; COM; Citz A; Hon Prog; JA A; Math A; MLS; Most Out; Ntl Achv Schol; *Temple University; Bus Adm.*

INGRAM, Geraldine Patricia
T Wingate Andrews HS; High Point, NC (114-298) *Bus Adm.*

INGRAM, Jeffrey Kirk
Edwards Co Sr HS; Albion, IL; Rptr, FTA; Sch P; JV, Bkbl.

INGRAM, John Richard
Robert E Lee HS; Jacksonville, FL (10%-500) BS; HiY; InterClub Coun; NHS; Pres, Jr Cl; Pres, Soph Cl; Bsbl; *Engr.*

INGRAM, Kathie Lynn
Katella HS; Anaheim, CA; Semi-Fin, Chldr; Ski C; Math A.

INGRAM, Leah LaVonne
Mabel Dean Bacon Voc HS; New York, NY; Chor; Drama; Cpt, Phys C; Sch Achieve Tm; Phy A; Yth Fel.

INGRAM, Marion Lorraione
Colbert Co HS; Leighton, AL (7-150) Ann; Chldr; FBLA; FHA; 4H; Math C; NHS; Secy, Jr Cl; Beauty; Cl Fav; 4H A; HCt; Pres A; *U of Tenn; Bus.*

INGRAM, Nelda Clorice
Thomas Jefferson HS; Louisville, KY (75-235) Bus C; Secy, Drama; Fr C; FHA; Ger C; *Western Ky U; Bus Adm.*

INGRAM, Renee Marie
Harrisburg HS; Harrisburg, IL (29-234) Band; Chldr; Chor; Ensm; FHA; 4H; Hmrm; Madrigal; Secy, SC; Cpt, Tr; 4H A; HCt; Cpt, Gym; *E III U; Special Ed.*

INGRAM, Tracy Leigh
Lewis Central Comm Sch; Council Bluffs, IA (14-207) Chor; FBLA; 4H; Hmrm; Madrigal; Mjrte; NHS; Span C; SC; JV, Bkbl; Tnns; Mgr; Tr; COM; Citz A; 4H A; Hist A; Hon Prog; Kiwanis A; Math A; Opt A; Pres A; Sci A; Yth Fel; Oration A; *Eng, Mus, Art As; Morningside Col; Religion.*

INGRAM, Vivian Eve
Bel Air HS; Bel Air, MD; Hmrm; Sftbl; Yth Fel; Most Improved Stu, Spch; All Star Sftbl; Best Camper, Christian Camp; *David Lipscomb Col; Phar.*

INGRAM, Wesley Mark
Carnegie HS; Carnegie, OK (1-77) Band; Chor; VP, 4H; NHS; Bsbl; Bkbl; Ftbl; Alg A; Amer Leg A; Bio A; Math A; Most Out; Eng II A; Geometry A; *Doctor.*

INGRAM, William Lawson
R L C Shades Valley HS; Birmingham, AL (15%-54) Key C; NHS; Amer Leg A; COM; Hon Prog; MLS; Sci A; Army Aviation A; US Army Sci A; Most Versatile; Med Explorers; *Pre-Med.*

INKLEBARGER, Doyle Randall
Horace Maynard HS; Maynardville, TN (1-127) Co-Ed, Ann; BC; BS; Chldr; 4H; Tres, Sci C; Pres, SC; Var C; Bsbl; JV, Bkbl; Val; Most Sch Spirit; WW; *U of Tenn; Engr.*

INMAN, Abe Benjamin
Monroe HS; Albany, GA; Band; Community Yth Symph; Drama; Ensm; NHS; COM; Citz A; Hon Prog.

INMAN, Deborah Ann
Snyder HS; Snyder, TX (3-200) Ann; FHA; NHS; Alg A; Citz A; Hist A; Top 10; Shorthand A; *Baylor U.*

INMAN, Faye Esther
Ithaca HS; Ithaca, NY; Tres, A Cap Choir; Fin, Jr Miss Pagent; Madrigal; Ideal Miss Talent; 1st Pl Vocal Solo; Miss Tompkins City Talent; Miss Ithaca Tn; Excel Mus; *Mus.*

INMAN, Jack Crozier Jr
Englewood HS; Jacksonville, FL (7-600) A Cap Choir; Band; Chor; City Conf; Drama; Ensm; Key C; NHS; COM; Citz A; VP, Yth Fel; Band Masters Assn A; *Med.*

INMAN, John Britt
Snyder HS; Snyder, TX; Band; Ftbl; Cl Fav; Stu Body Pres; *Hardensimins Col; Agr.*

INMAN, Robert Brian
Norfolk Cath HS; Norfolk, VA (80%-160) Ch, CYO; Chess C; Drama; Bsbl; Bkbl; HCt; Yth Rep, Parish Coun; Cpt, Bowl; *Old Dominion U; Eng.*

INMAN, Timothy Lee
Deshler HS; Tuscumbia, AL; Bkbl; MVP, Ftbl; Cl Fav; D-C; *Tenn Col; Coaching.*

INMAN, Vickie Jean
Warren HS; Monmouth, IL (20-60) Ann; Band; Chor; FHA; 4H; Pres, Span C; SC; Var C; Bkbl; Tr; *Nurs.*

INMON, Patrick Shawn
Mossyrock HS; Mossyrock, WA (5%-34) CYO; Chess C; Chor; Drama; Pres, Fr C; FBLA; FFA; NHS; Ed, Sch P; Pres, Sci C; SC; S-T, Soph Cl; JV, Bkbl; Tr; *U of Wash; Pre-Law.*

INSLEY, Kathyleen Adele
Rockville HS; Rockville, IN (15-83) Band; Mjrte; ARC; Sci C; Tr; God & Country A; *Ind St U; Criminology.*

INTEMANN, Robert Wayne
Poteau HS; Poteau, OK (5%-150) FFA; Secy, Key C; NHS; Sch P; Ftbl; Hon Prog; Stu o-t Week; Supt's HR; Principal's HR; St Hon Soc; *Okla U; Math.*

INZINA, Clinton Meredith
Carroll HS; Monroe, LA; Orch; Span C; COM; Mus Solo & Ensm; All St Orch; *USC; Law.*

IPACS, Kathleen Jeanette
Bulkeley HS; Hartford, CT (16-310) CYO; Chess C; Chor; Drama; GS; Hmrm; Lit Mag; NHS; Ed, Sch P; Span C; Span NHS; SC; Pres, Sr Cl; Tres, Jr Cl; Mgr, Golf; DARGCA; Hon Prog; 32 C; NML; Hon Pass; *Brown U; Eng.*

IPOCK, Bobby Russell
W Craven HS; Vanceboro, NC; NHS; *E Carolina U; Bus.*

IPOCK, Julia Rose
W Craven HS; Vanceboro, NC (10%-212) Pres, Band; BC; Hmrm; NHS; Span C; Bkbl; Tr; 4H A; Phys Ed, Bkbl Sportsmanship, A's; Co Hon Band; St Federation of Mus Stu Auditions; Ntl Piano Guild Auditions Cert.

IPOCK, Melanie Gay
W Craven HS; Vanceboro, NC; VP, BC; Chldr; Dbte Tm; Pres, Fr C; 4H; Pres, Hmrm; Monogram; NHS; Sci C; Co-Ch, SC; Tnns; DARGCA; 4H A; Hon Prog; *U of NC; Med.*

IRASEMA, Aguilar Espinoza
Abraham Lincoln HS; San Jose, CA; Bus C; Drama; Sftbl; *San Jose City Col; Secy Sci.*

IRBY, Kelvin Lemond
Sandusky HS; Sandusky, OH (130-430) All Amer Yth; Bsbl; Ftbl; Tr; Co-Cpt, Wrest; WW; All Amer, Wrest; *Ohio St U; Industrial Ed.*

IRBY, Lowell Kirk
Artesia HS; Artesia, NM; AFS; Band; Chor; Demolay; Order/Arrow; *Sci.*

IRBY, Roy Delaney
Hillcrest HS; Jamaica, NY; Chor; Cpt, Bkbl; COM; *York Col; Elec.*

IRELAND, Charlotte Ann
Starmount HS; Boonville, NC (28-151) A Cap Choir; Chor; Ensm; FFA; FTA; NHS; Span C; Citz A; Gov Honor Prog; NFMC As; Mus Camp Schol; *Brevard Col; Mus.*

IRELAND, Edward Scott
Jefferson Area HS; Jefferson, OH; Band; Spch C; Sftbl; *Elec.*

IRELAND, Jeff Elmer
Marion L Steele HS; Amherst, OH (98-500) Band; Chor; Drama; Ensm; Orch; COM; Pres A; A-Ed & Rptr; Sch Paper; Pres, Lib C; Marching Band; Pep Band; Stage Band; *U of Mont; Vet.*

IRETON, Daniel William
Bethel-Tate HS; Bethel, OH; Chess C; NHS; Parl, VICA; PA; *Cincinnati Tech Col; Art.*

IRICK, Tracy Carolyn
S Florence HS; Florence, SC (12-350) BC; Hmrm; Tres, SC; Tri-HiY; Hugh O'Brien A; *Med.*

IRISH, Sherree Linn
Midwest HS; Midwest, WY (6-21) Pres, Bus C; GS; VP, Hmrm; Secy, Ski C; Var C; Arch; Bkbl; Sftbl; Tnns; Tr; COM; Citz A; *Data Processing.*

IRIZARRY, Tannya Lynn
Consuelo Escalone Private Sch; Carolina, PR (5-28) Chldr; Chor; Drama; SC; COM; Hon Prog; *Mount Ida Jr Col; Pol Sci.*

IRIZARRY, Wanda
Lola Rodriguez de Tio; San German, PR (15-350) CYO; FHA; Pres, Hmrm; COM; Cl Fav; Hon Prog; Spch A; *Inter Amer U; Med Technology.*

IRMER, Douglas Daryl
NE HS; Lincoln, NE; Drama; Thes; Gym Ltr; Thespian Banquet Speaker; *U of Nebr; Dramatics.*

IRONS, Darla Kay
Linesville-Conneaut-Summit HS; Linesville, PA (2-90) Band; Ensm; Fr C; NHS; Var C; Bkbl; Sftbl; Band A; *Fla Inst of Tech; Marine Biol.*

IRONS, Janet Lynn
Manchester HS; Richmond, VA (15%-150) F-Ed, Ann; FNA; Hmrm; Mjrte; NHS; ARC; F-Ed, Sch P; Gym Tm; Chaplain, Span C; Chaplain, Tri-Hi-Y; *U of N Ala; Nurs.*

IRONS, Jennifer Kaye
Columbiana HS; Columbiana, OH (1-100) Secy, Band; JV, Chldr; Swim; Tnns; Tr; Hon Prog; Yth Fel; All St Fair Band; *Youngstown St Col; Mus.*

IRONS, Julie Faye
Columbiana HS; Columbiana, OH (25-100) Band; Span C; Swim; Tnns; Rotary A; Candystriper; Exchange Stu, Columbia S Amer; *Horticulture.*

IRSCH, Charles E
Robinson HS; Santurce, PR (1-38) Ann; Drama; A-Ed, Lit Mag; Math C; Mu Alpha Theta; NHS; VP, Phys C; Pol Sci C; Pres, SC; Bkbl; Co-Cpt, Cr-Ctry; Alg A; Math A; NMF; Sci A; *Communications.*

IRVAN, Philip Glenn
Duncanville HS; Duncanville, TX; *Arch.*

IRVIN, Debbie Lou
Friendswood HS; Friendswood, TX; Band; Chldr; FTA; Mjrte; NHS; Sci C; Bio A; Hon Prog; Sci A; Type A; UIL Regional Qualifier, Typing; St Qualifier, Band; *Baylor U; Nurs.*

IRVIN, Michele Lee
Philipsburg-Osceola HS; Philipsburg, PA (56-230) FHA; Mjrte; SC; Tres, Jr Cl; *Clarion Col; Elem Ed.*

IRVIN, Ronda Kay
LaMarque HS; LaMarque, TX (10-280) Ch, Bus C; VP, Chor; Hmrm; JETS; Ch, NHS; SC; Secy, Sr Cl; COM; Cl Fav; Elk A; Hon Prog; Marathon Schol; Safety A; Outst Choir Member; *Baylor U; Computer Sci.*

IRVIN, Stephan Ronald
North HS; Evansville, IN (226-363) Cpt, Ftbl; Kiwanis A; *U of Evansville; Bus.*

IRVINE, Daun Louise
Logan HS; Logan, OH (40-310) Band; 4H; Lat C; NHS; Rainbow; Co-Cpt, Bkbl; Ftbl; Sftbl; Tr; Yth Fel; Alt, GS; HS All Amer, Vlbl; Marching Band 90% C A; *Ohio U; Phys Ed.*

IRVINE, Mary Alice
Williamston HS; Williamston, MI (25%-150) PA; GAA; *Oakland U; Computer Sci.*

IRVING, Mary Jane
Beaver Dam Sr HS; Beaver Dam, WI (10-330) AFS; Cpt, Chldr; Chor; Ensm; Hmrm; Fin, Jr Miss Pagent; Madrigal; NFL; NHS; Ski C; Pres, Span C; SC; Var C; Tr; COM; Spch A; Solo-Ensm St A's; Soc of Women Engr Cert of Achv; Marine Corps A; Chldr A; *Carthage Col; Psych.*

IRWIN, Colette Joy
Argos Comm Sch; Argos, IN (5-67) Secy, Drama; FHA; Tres, FTA; GS; Secy, 4H; Secy, NHS; Amer Leg A; B Crocker A; Citz A; DARGCA; 4H A; Hist A; HCt; Spch A; Swtht; Yth Fel; Miss Sunshine; Pres, Sunshine Soc; *Valparaiso U; Bus Adm.*

IRWIN, David Ware
Westfield Sr HS; Westfield, NJ (151-669) Orch; Ski C; Wrest; Hon Prog; Math A; Yth Fel; LaCrosse; Gold Book A; Sunday Sch Teacher; *Lehigh Col; Bus Adm.*

IRWIN, Dean Lester
Newton Falls HS; Newton Falls, OH (23-200) Band; Chor; NHS; Rptr, Sch P; Sci C; Span C; SC; Tr; Yth Fel; Superior, Solo & Ensm; *U of Cincinnati; Engr.*

IRWIN, Kathryn Linda
Southside HS; Fort Smith, AR (50-500) CYO; Chor; Drama; Ensm; S-T, 4H; Hmrm; SC; JV, Bkbl; Golf; Swim; COM; Hon Prog; PTA A; Spch A; *Med.*

IRWIN, Lynda Kay
J J Pearce HS; Richardson, TX (350-500) *Stephen F Austin St U; Sociology.*

IRWIN, Sherie Darlene
Bentonia HS; Bentonia, MS; FBLA; FHA; JV, Bkbl; *Hinds Jr Col; Nurs.*

IRWIN, Terry Lynn
E Mecklenburg HS; Charlotte, NC; BC; Chor; Ski C; Sftbl; Tnns; COM; Citz A; Spch A; *Davidson Col; Journ.*

IRWIN, Tiffani Joy
E Mecklenburg HS; Charlotte, NC (53-587) SC; Vlbl; Hon Soc; Stu Cabinet; Interact C; *NC St U; Forestry.*

ISAAC, Emod
Carman HS; Flint, MI (30-450) Dbte Tm; Ftbl; Tnns; *Law.*

ISAAC, Oliver Fredrick
Monroe HS; Albany, GA (4-265) Ann; BS; Bus C; Dbte Tm; FBLA; Hmrm; Math C; Order/Arrow; Pres, Sci C; Tr; Amer Leg A; COM; Chamber of Comm A; Gov Honor Prog; Star Student; *U of Tenn; Engr.*

ISAAC, Sally Ann
Montgomery HS; Santa Rosa, CA (5%-500) Chldr; Chor; SC; St Scholar; Doyle School; *U C Davis; Human Development.*

ISAAC, Sara Ann
Montgomery HS; Santa Rosa, CA (5%-800) Chor; Ski C; SC; NEDT; Principal's A; *UC.*

ISAACS, LuAnn
Connersville Sr HS; Connersville, IN (160-380) Bus C; Chor; S-T, Bible C; *Liberty Baptist Col; Missionary Teacher.*

JACINTO, Martha Lardizabal
Science HS; Newark, NJ; Chor; Hist A; Vlbl; *UCLA; Med.*

JACINTO, Raquel Naomi
Claremont HS; Claremont, CA; AFS; Band; Secy, Madrigal; Rptr, Sch P; *Scripps Col; Journ.*

JACK, Donald Lafayette
Pattonville Sr HS; Maryland Heights, MO (120-820) Band; Ensm; Ger C; NHS; Orch; Sch P; JV, Ftbl; JV, Wrest; Citz A; Ntl Service Aide A's; *U of Mo; Bus Mgt.*

JACK, Joseph Benjamin
Eastside HS; Paterson, NJ (22-500) *Montclair St Col; Industrial Ed.*

JACK, Linda Sue
College HS; Bartlesville, OK (79-199) Chor; Sftbl; Citz A; Vlbl; 1st Cl GSct; *Nurs.*

JACK, Yvette Marie
Rosenwald HS; New Roads, LA (2-105) BC; Drama; FBLA; Amer Leg A; Hist A; Hon Prog; Math A; Sal; High Fighters Social C A; Eng A; FBLA A; Tobias-Kotzin Sch As Ntl Merit Sch; *Sou U; Civil Engr.*

JACKLE, John George
Bellevue HS; Nashville, TN (78-212) Drama; Pres, SC; Tnns; Elk A; Yth Fel; SAR A; *Lib Art.*

JACKMAN, Julie R
Davison Sr HS; Davison, MI (156-512) A Cap Choir; Joy Bus Helper; Health Career Vol; *Hurley Sch of Nurs; Nurs.*

JACKMAN, Julie Rene
Dawson HS; Davison, MI; A Cap Choir; Joy Bus Driver; Health Career Vol; *Huley Sch of Nurs; Nurs.*

JACKS, Daniel Richard
W Windsor Plainsboro HS; Princeton Junction, NJ (20-200) NHS; JV, Cr-Ctry; Hon Prog.

JACKS, Karl Heiko
Silsbee HS; Silsbee, TX (8-200) NHS; Span C; COM; 'S' A, Drafting & Ready Writing; *Lamar U; Elec Engr.*

JACKS, Luetta Sue
D C Everest Sr HS; Schofield, WI; ARC; COM.

JACKSON, Alfred Delano
University HS; Los Angeles, CA; Band; JV, Bsbl; *U of Chicago; Math.*

JACKSON, Amy Jo
Briarwood HS; East Point, GA (20%-150) A Cap Choir; AFS; Chor; Drama; Ensm; Span C; Mgr, Wrest; NEDT; VP, Candy Striper; Semi Fin, Ntl Span; SMENC Chor; Lt Gov, Jr Civitan; Flag Corp; *U of Wyo; Mus.*

JACKSON, Andrea Jill
Parkview Sr HS; Little Rock, AR (53-476) BC; Chor; FBLA; Sci C; Span C; Y-Tns; Hon Prog; Opt A; WW; *Ouachita Baptist U; Microbio.*

JACKSON, Andrew Jr
Northside HS; Atlanta, GA (96-393) Band; BC; Ensm; Math C; Hon Prog; ROTC A; Band A.

JACKSON, Andrew William
Englewood Sr HS; Jacksonville, FL (1-466) Tres, Key C; NHS; VP, Span C; Tnns; Amer Leg A; B Crocker A; COM; Elk A; H of F; Hon Prog; Val; *U of Fla; Elec Engr.*

JACKSON, Annette Crump
Dobbins Area Voc-Tech HS; Philadelphia, PA; Semi-Fin, Algebra A; Fin, Amer Leg A; Fin, Com; *U of Penna; Computer Sci.*

JACKSON, Antony Tyrone
Skyline Career Development Center; Dallas, TX (25%-1100) A Cap Choir; Band; Chor; Lat C; COM; Judo; US Jr Olympics Cert of Part; *Mus.*

JACKSON, Artus Maria
Olney HS; Philadelphia, PA (195-850) Drama; Jr Miss Pageant; Mjrte; Phys C; Sch Achieve Tm; Cpt, Tr; Citz A; MLS; Most Out; PTA A; Yth Leg; Dental A; Achv A; *Westchester Col; Data Processing.*

JACKSON, Barbara Ann
Lutheran North HS; St Louis, MO (10%-220) AFS; Band; Fr C; Hmrm; SC; COM; Pom-Pon A; Miss WMS 1977; United Spirit Assn Novelty A; United Spirit Assn Jazz A; *UMKC Mo; Med.*

JACKSON, Barbara Elaine
Colo HS; Colo City, TX (3-115) FHA.

JACKSON, Bart Wayne
Jonesco Acad; Gray, GA; BC.

JACKSON, Becky Ann
Tate HS; Gozlez, FL; Pres, Crown & Scepte; FHA; Jayettes; Servic Aide; Col Schol; Riding C; *PJC; Dental Hygienist.*

JACKSON, Belinda Gail
Clyde A Erwin HS; Asheville, NC (110-400) Cpt, Chldr; Fr C; GS; Tr; FCA; Most Improved Tr A.

JACKSON, Benard Brian
J E B Stuart HS; Falls Church, VA (200-450) Fr C; K of C; Span C; Spch C; Bkbl; Cpt, Cr-Ctry; Swim; Tr; DARGCA; Journ A; JA A; Kiwanis A; All-Dist Cr-Ctry; *Salem Col; Elem Ed.*

JACKSON, Bernice L
All Saints Cathedral Sch; St Thomas, VI (2-21) SC; Hon Prog.

JACKSON, Bethany Gail
Lafayette HS; Lafayette, LA; A Cap Choir; All Amer Yth; Chor; 4H; Rptr, Hmrm; Sftbl; Interlochen Ntl Mus; Pub Ch, Candy Striper; Nazarene Impact Tm; Church Pianist; Pianist, Jr-Sr Choir; Accomp, Jr Miss Pageant; *Hinds Jr Col; Bus Adm.*

JACKSON, Betty Ann
Belton HS; Belton, TX (50-200) Band; FHA.

JACKSON, Calvin Lorenzo
Monroe HS; Albany, GA (25-329) Co-Cpt, Ftbl; *Bethune Cookman Col; Social Studies.*

JACKSON, Carla Jean
Cherryville Sr HS; Cherryville, NC (3-146) Co-Ed, Ann; Drama; Fr C; FTA; Secy, InterAct C; Pres, NHS; SC; Ntl Sci Symposium; NEDT; Jr Marshal; Hon Stu; *U of NC; Math.*

JACKSON, Carmeleta Suzette
Pittsburg Sr HS; Pittsburg, CA (150-309) Bsbl; Bkbl; Cpt, Sftbl; MLS; Basic Opportunity Grant; *Los Angeles City Col; Special Ed.*

JACKSON, Carole Nadine
Carver HS; Columbus, GA (1-280) Hmrm; Key C; Co-Ed, Lit Mag; NHS; Ntl Teachers Coun; Span C; SC; Beauty; COM; Cl Fav; Gov Honor Prog; HCt; Hon Prog; Most Out; Top Academic Jr; Gov Hon Finals; Outst Span A; *U of Ga; Journ.*

JACKSON, Carolyn Denese
Los Angeles HS; Los Angeles, CA (35-750) Arch; S-T, CYO; Dbte Tm; Rptr, Sch P; Sci C; Span C; Spch C; SC; JV, Arch; JV, Swim; Beauty; CSF; COM; Citz A; Delta Sigma Theta A; Hon Prog; Sci A; Spch A; St Scholar; Principal's HR; Participation A; Roman Shield; Cert of Achv; *Mount St Mary's Col; Bus Adm.*

JACKSON, Catherine Aspasia
Jupiter Christian Sch; Jupiter, FL (2-18) Cpt, Chldr; Chor; Secy, Hmrm; Span C; Spch C; Cpt, Bkbl; Sftbl; HCt; Hon Prog; Sal; *Pensacola Christian Bus.*

JACKSON, Charles Maurice II
Trenton Central HS; Trenton, NJ (203-760) Band; Chor; Orch; *Rugters U; Graphic Arts.*

JACKSON, Charmaine
Terrell Co HS; Dawson, GA (4-200) BC; FBLA; SC; Tr; *Ga SW Col; Secy Sci.*

JACKSON, Cheryl Ann
Santa Fe HS; Alachua, FL (5%-175) BC; Dbte Tm; FFA; 4H; Co-Ed, Sch P; Sci C; Pres, Soph Cl; Cpt, Bkbl; Sftbl; Cpt, Swim; Tnns; Tr; Alg A; Beauty; Bio A; 4H A; Math A; Sci A; Spch A; VFW A; VFW Orator Win; VofDEM; Vlbl; Cand, Secy, St Beta; Interscholastic Spch A; FFA St Horticulture Judging Win; 4th, 4-H St Land Contest; *Oceanography.*

JACKSON, Cheryl Denise
Carroll HS; Monroe, LA; Band; Dbte Tm; Fr C; Secy, 4H; Hmrm; Math C; F-Ed, Sch P; SC; Bkbl; Sftbl; Tnns; Tr; COM; Citz A; 4H A; Hist A; HCt; Hon Prog; Journ A; Math A; Sci A; Yth Fel; Alpha Kappa Alpha Sorority; GSct; Pianist, Organist, Secy, Church; Band, Piano, Ath, PA, HR, A's; *LSU; Computer Sci.*

JACKSON, Cheryl Denise
John F Kennedy HS; Denver, CO; *Morehouse Col; Fashion Designing.*

JACKSON, Cheryl Lou
Van Horn HS; Independence, MO (11-415) F-Ed, Ann; Chor; Math C; NHS; Span C; Regent Schol; Cream o-t Crop; WW; Mo Sch-Col Rel Com Cert of Recogn; *Mo U.*

JACKSON, Cheryl Lynn
East HS; Columbus, OH (33-350) Socalite; *U of Cincinnati; Acct.*

JACKSON, Christopher Kent
Lafayette HS; Ballwin, MO; A Cap Choir; Madrigal; Ftbl; Tr; Wrest.

JACKSON, Clotele Diana
George Henry Corliss HS; Chicago, IL (5-485) Drama; NHS; PA; HR; Hon Soc; *U of Wis; Phys Therapy.*

JACKSON, Cynthia Lou
Lyon Co HS; Eddyville, KY (12-70) Ann; BC; Chor; FHA; SC; Pep C; Jr, Chapter, FHA Degrees; SDAHSS; Church Pianist; Murray Math Tourn.

JACKSON, Dale Edward
N Mesquite HS; Mesquite, TX; A Cap Choir; Band; Lat C; Orch; *Hardin-Simmons Col; Mus.*

JACKSON, Dana Leigh
Burkburnett HS; Wichata Falls, TX; ARC; ARC A; *Nurs.*

JACKSON, Darlene Ann
Reynolds HS; Greenville, PA (3-212) Co-Ed, Ann; VP, Chor; NHS; Bkbl.

JACKSON, Darryl Anthony
W Charlotte HS; Charlotte, NC (190-800) Bus C; FBLA; Monogram; Cpt, Bsbl; COM; JA A; Yth Kg, East Stonewall; Charlotte Merchants Assn Band A; Outst DECA Stu; *UNCC; Bus Mgt.*

JACKSON, Debbie Elaine
Pepperell HS; Lindale, GA (20%-157) F-Ed, Ann; Band; FHA; Hmrm; Mjrte; Sch P; Secy, SC; Pres, Sr Cl; Secy, Jr Cl; Cl Fav; HCt; Sr Superlative; Excel, Hist; *Floyd Jr Col; Med Asst.*

JACKSON, Debbie Sue
Clay Co HS; Manchester, KY (14-200) BC; Hmrm; Sch P; Art A; *Fine Arts.*

JACKSON, Deborah Carlotta
East Sr HS; Columbus, OH; GSct; *Acct.*

JACKSON, Deborah Kathryn
Williamston HS; Williamston, NC (57-221) BC; Secy, Chor; Drama; FBLA; Math C; Sci C; Mgr, Tr; Acteen Qn & Qn Regent; *Special Ed.*

JACKSON, Deborah Louise
Ragsdale HS; Jamestown, NC; BC; Fr C; FBLA; Pres, Exchangettes; *Bus.*

JACKSON, Deborah Lynn
Dunbar Voc HS; Chicago, IL (68-400) *Augustana Col; Acct.*

JACKSON, Denise Moani
Horizon Campus; Zion, IL (191-426) Pres, FSA; *Bethel Col; Lib Arts.*

JACKSON, Dennis Ray III
Old Mill HS; Glen Burnie, MD (85-600) Wrest; *U of Md; Criminology.*

JACKSON, Diane Lanette
Northern HS; Baltimore, MD; Chor; Drama; Tr; *Morgan U; Bus.*

JACKSON, Diann
Wendell Phillips HS; Chicago, IL (12-501) Bus C; Hmrm; ARC; SC; COM; Citz A; Hist A; Principal Schol; Future Counselor; GAA, Span, Attendance, A's; *U of Ill; Social Work.*

JACKSON, Diran Keith
George Henry Corliss HS; Chicago, IL (11-250) JETS; NHS; Sch P; COM; Hon Prog; Journ A; *U of Ill; Engr.*

JACKSON, Donna Jean
Belton HS; Belton, TX; Band; FHA; NHS.

JACKSON, Donna S
Dieterich HS; Dieterich, IL (5-55) Chor; FBLA; FHA; Sci C; Secy, Span C; 4H A; JA A; Type A; Span A; PA A; Scholastic A.

JACKSON, Doris Ann
Siloam Springs HS; Siloam Springs, AR (20%-150) Band; FHA; Bkbl.

JACKSON, Dorothy Jean
Bluefield HS; Bluefield, WV (100-311) F-Ed, Ann; Co-Cpt, Chldr; Chor; Hmrm; Secy, Lat C; Secy, SC; Pres, Jr Cl; Tnns; Cpt, Chldrs; Ctry C Swm Tm; Gym Tm; Cty Yth Comm; Jr Civitans; GAA; Beaver B'S; Phys Ed A; Gym A; Pep C; Mst Friendly; Tumbling Tm; VP, SC; *VPI; Phys Ed.*

JACKSON, Douglas Dean
Glen Burnie HS; Glen Burnie, MD; Band; Drama; Thes.

JACKSON, Dwayne Fitzgerald
Ebbert L Furr Jr-Sr HS; Houston, TX (1-211) Band; Fr C; Hmrm; Pres, NHS; Sch Achieve Tm; SC; Cl Fav; MLS; Ntl Achv Schol; Val; WW; Gulf Oil Engr Schol; UT Achv Schol; *U of Tex at Austin; Engr.*

JACKSON, Dwayne Michael
Inglewood HS; Inglewood, CA (76-464) BS; FBLA; NHS; Y-Tns; Cpt, Tnns; Amer Leg A; Amer Leg Orator A; CSF; COM; Citz A; Elk A; Hist A; Hon Prog; Opt A; Pres A; Rotary A; Spch A; MVP, Tnns; *U of Calif; Bio.*

JACKSON, Dwight David
Hall HS; Little Rock, AR; Up Bound; JV, Ftbl; *Ark St U; Sci.*

JACKSON, Elaine Gail
Furr HS; Houston, TX (16-200) Drama; FHA; Hmrm; Secy, NHS; Sci C; Span C; SC; Secy, Sr Cl; Tr; HCt; Opt A; WW; Hon Men, Outst Sr Girl; Semi-Fin, Optimist A; *Texas Women's U; Nurs.*

JACKSON, Everett Loenard
Seneca Voc HS; Buffalo, NY; Elec, Woodshop, Drawing, A's; *Elec.*

JACKSON, Gary
Zwolle HS; Zwolle, LA; *NW La U; Sci.*

JACKSON, Gay Letitia
Springbrook HS; Silver Spring, MD; Band; Chor; Dbte Tm; Mgr, Drama; Hmrm; Var C; Y-Tns; Bsbl; Bkbl; Swim; Tr; Spch A; Yth Fel; Yth Leg; *Col of St Benedict; Interior Design.*

JACKSON, Glenn Carl
Dan River HS; Ringgold, VA; Band; BC; Chess C; Dbte Tm; Drama; 4H; Gov Honor Prog; Gr Marshal; 4H A; All Co Band; *Engr Research.*

JACKSON, Gregory Allen
Middletown HS; Middletown, OH; Band; Hmrm; Sch P; Tnns; JA A; Opt A; Spch A; PA; Optimist Spch A; Supt, Sunday Sch; *U of Cincinnati; Arch.*

JACKSON, Gregory Terrall
Thornton HS; Harvey, IL (15-40) Chor; Ftbl; Tr; BTU Young Christian A; *Eastern Ill U; Bus Adm.*

JACKSON, Henry Robinson
Melbourne HS; Melbourne, FL; Band; Bkbl; Tr; Acad As; Band As; *U of Fla; Phys Ed.*

JACKSON, Jacqueline Louise
Levelland HS; Levelland, TX (9-200) Parl, Chor; Tres, FTA; NHS; Span C; SC; Thes; Tr; Swtht; *South Plains Col; Psych.*

JACKSON, James Ivory
Central HS; Philadelphia, PA; Drama; Lat C; Span C; JV, Cr-Ctry; JV, Tr; *Drexel Col; Computer Tech.*

JACKSON, James Kelvin
W Charlotte HS; Charlotte, NC; Pres, Chor; Drama; Pres, Ensm; Key C; Monogram; Var C; Sftbl; Swim; MVP, Wrest; COM; JA A; Most Outst; ROTC A; BSct; ROTC C; Vagabond C; Jr Usher Board; *Vet Med.*

JACKSON, James Stephen
Green Mountain HS; Lakewood, CO (79-484) A Cap Choir; Chor; Tres, Lat C; NHS; *Wheaton Col; Ministry.*

JACKSON, James Wesley Jr
Pendleton HS; Pendleton, SC (20-144) Fr C; FFA; Golf; *Clemson U; Engr.*

JACKSON, Jami Annette
Fairview HS; Ashland, KY (3-100) Co-Ed, Ann; GS; VP, NHS; Rptr, Sch P; JA A; *Ashland Comm Col; Acct.*

JACKSON, Jane Annette
Mar Vista HS; Imperial Beach, CA (100-350) FNA; Ntl Achv Schol; Pres, Sunday Sch; *Point Loma U; Nurs.*

JACKSON, Jane Ellen
DuQuoin HS; DuQuoin, IL (34-147) Band; FHA; VP, FTA; Secy, Spch C; Journ A; Newspaper Outst Sr A; *John A Logan Col; Bus.*

JACKSON, Janice Elizabeth
Independence HS; Independence, MS (15%-106) Ann; Tres, BC; FBLA; VP, FHA; Mjrte; Sch P; COM; PA; Water Safety Cert; *Northwest Jr Col; Home Ec.*

JACKSON, Jeanne Ann
Enka HS; Enka, NC (3-350) Band; Dbte Tm; NHS; *U of NC; Math.*

JACKSON, Jeffery
Luther Judson Price HS; Atlanta, GA (23-135) Tres, Chor; Pres, FBLA; Hmrm; Bus Mgr, Math C; Model UN; Pol Sci C; Co-Ed, Sch P; Span C; Pres, Jr Cl; Bsbl; Ftbl; Golf; Cpt, Tnns; *Morehouse Col; Bus.*

JACKSON, Jeffrey
Lead Hill HS; Lead Hill, AR (2-25) FBLA; Secy, FFA; Pres, 4H; Sch P; SC; Pres, Soph Cl; Mgr, Bkbl; COM; 4H A; Hon Prog; Agr A; Best Ldr; *U of Ark; Sci.*

JACKSON, Jeffrey Alan
J J Pearce HS; Richardson, TX (240-650) Church Functions; *Tex Tech U; Acct.*

JACKSON, JenRa
Jefferson Twp Sr HS; Dayton, OH (16-175) Secy, Band; FHA; NHS; Span C; Tres, CBYF; Pep C; *U of Cincinnati; Med.*

JACKSON, Jerri King
Marion Franklin HS; Columbus, OH (111-347) Ann; Band; Chor; Hmrm; Jr Miss Pagent; Orch; SC; Var C; Sftbl; COM; JA A; Yth Fel; Church Orch; Secy, Ushers; Asst Guidance Counselling; *W Va St Col; Archt.*

JACKSON, Jerry Simmons
Hall HS; Little Rock, AR; Up Bound; Bkbl; Sftbl; Tnns; *Ark St U; Art.*

JACKSON, JoMaria
Phillips HS; Birmingham, AL; FBLA; VP, Hmrm; *UAB; Surgical Nurs.*

JACKSON, Johnnie Edward
William Penn HS; New Castle, DE; Chor; Ch, St Stu Congress; VP, SC; Cpt, Bsbl; Ftbl; Soccer; Sftbl; Swim; Yth Leg; *Fla Inst of Tech; Psych.*

JACKSON, Juanita
Martin Luther King HS; Chicago, IL; Bus C; Citz A; Art, Attendance, A's; *Central YMCA Comm Col; Social Work.*

JACKSON, Julie Ann
Raytown S HS; Raytown, MO (10%-530) Ed, Sch P; COM; Journ A; Type A.

JACKSON, Julie Suzanne
Pendleton HS; Pendleton, SC (14-125) Chor; Crown & Scepter; Fr C; FHA; Ch, 4H; VP, Hmrm; Rptr, SC; Bkbl; 4H A; Spch A; Foreign Stu C; St 4-H Conf; Europe Trip; Wash Shortcourse; Acteens; Cooking Contest; Eng A; *Winthrop Col; Home Ec.*

JACKSON, Karen Ann
Reuben McCall Sr HS; Tallulah, LA; Chldr; Secy, Drama; FBLA; Tres, FHA; VP, 4H; Hmrm; Sch P; Pres, SC; Alg A; Beauty; Bio A; 4H A; Hist A; HQn; Type A; *Alcorn St U; Pre-Med.*

JACKSON, Karen Renee
Paul Laurence Dunbar Comm Sr HS; Baltimore, MD; Fr C; Tres, NHS; ARC; Var C; Bsbl; Hist A; Hon Prog; ARC A; Cpt, Semi- fin, MVP, Vlbl; Cpt, Fin, Badminton; Sign Lang; Physician's Asst A; Cty Summer Corps; Handicapped Swim; *Johns Hopkins U; Pre-Med.*

JACKSON, Karl Bernard
Randallstown HS; Randallstown, MD; Chor Outst Achv; All-Star Bkbl; Peabody Conserv of Mus Schol Nom; *W Point Acad; Mortuary Sci.*

JACKSON, Kathleen Elizabeth
Independent Methodist HS; Mobile, AL (1-55) F-Ed, Ann; Secy, BC; Drama; Sch P; Bkbl; Sftbl; HCt; Hon Prog; NEDT; Val; *U of S Ala; Radiology.*

JACKSON, Katrina Elaine
Hueneme HS; Oxnard, CA (8-800) JV, Bkbl; JV, Sftbl; *UCLA; Teacher.*

JACKSON, Kay Ellen
Webb HS; Reedsburg, WI (27-200) AFS; Band; Chldr; Pres, Drama; Fr C; Hmrm; NFL; Orch; SC; Pres, Thes; MVP, Bkbl; Tnns; Tr; HCt; Pres A; Yth Fel; Vlbl; Yth o-t Mo; Stu Director, Mus; All Conf Bkbl; *U of Wis; Ed.*

JACKSON, Kelvin Daniel
McNeil HS; McNeil, AR (9-34) Chem C; Hmrm; Math C; Sci C; Spch C; Alg A; Bio A; COM; Chem A; Cl Fav; Hist A; HCt; Math A; Sci A; Fire Marshal.

JACKSON, Kendra Ruth
Burnside HS; Burnside, KY (4-40) BC; Cpt, Chldr; FTA; Math A; Home Ec A; *Eastern U; Phys Therapy.*

JACKSON, Kimberli Elaine
Manual Arts HS; Los Angeles, CA; Tres, Chor; Drama; Rptr, Hmrm; Span C; Up Bound; Citz A; Ntl Sci Found; Sci A; Yth Fel; Yth Foundation A; Counselor's HR; Cert of Achv; Cert of A; Cert of Recog, Chrch Faithful Serv; *UCLA; Health Safety.*

JACKSON, Kimberly Dawn
Douglas Byrd Sr HS; Fayetteville, NC (19-410) BC; Chldr; Rainbow; Tri-HiY; Secy, Jr Cl; Fr A; Lang League C; *U of NC; Sociology.*

JACKSON, Laura Ann
Alfred Lawless Jr HS; New Orleans, LA; Y-Tns; *Sou U; Home Ec.*

JACKSON, Lawrence III
Scotland HS; Lauinburg, NC (25-400) Band; Ensm; Orch; Order/Arrow; Order/Arrow A; ARC A; Chor Pianist; Sup, Ntl Piano Guild; All-St Band; Church Minister of Mus; *N Carolina Central U; Mus.*

JACKSON, Linda C
F O Alexander HS; Starkville, MS (30-59) Y-Tns; VP, Soph Cl; *Miss St U; Bus.*

JACKSON, Lisa Ann
Philadelphia HS For Girls; Philadelphia, PA (40%-471) FHA; VP, Hmrm; SC; JV, Tnns; Alg A; Chem A; Cl Fav; Math A; Ntl Achv Schol; Ntl Sci Found; Sci A; *U of Pittsburgh; Phys Therapy.*

JACKSON, Lisa Ann
Jamestown HS; Jamestown, NY (20-500) Band; NHS; Sch P; Ski C; SC; Jr Cl; Ch, Soph Cl; Bkbl; Swim; 1st Cl GSct; Mus A; *SUNY Buffalo; Occupational Therapy.*

JACKSON, Lisa Dee
McClymonds HS; Oakland, CA; NHS; Span C; *UC at Berkeley; Audiology.*

JACKSON, Lisa Jean
United Township HS; E Moline, IL (126-624) Chor; ARC; Ldr, Pioneer Girls; GAA; Bible Instruction Cl; Secy, Health Occupations C; Camp Counselor; *Moline Pub Sch of Nurs; Nurs.*

JACKSON, Lorne Michael
John F Kennedy HS; Fremont, CA (10%-450) Ensm; Hmrm; Math C; Monogram; SC; Var C; Bsbl; Soccer; CSF; Math A; Yth Fel; *US Air Force Acad; Aerospace.*

JACKSON, Malcolm Gerard
Tascosa HS; Amarillo, TX (215-445) All Amer Yth; AFS; Band; BS; City Conf; Drama; Ensm; FTA; Key C; Lat C; NFL; Orch; Span C; Spch C; Pres, SC; JV, Tr; *Phillips U; Mus.*

JACKSON, Manya Lisa
Red Bay HS; Red Bay, AL; BC; FHA; Sch P; Bkbl; Sftbl; COM; Cl Fav; HQn; Math A; *Lee Col; Mus.*

JACKSON, Maree Elayne
Post Falls HS; Post Falls, ID; Chldr; Drama; Sch P; Spch C; SC; HCt; Hon Prog; Journ A; Spch A; *N Idaho Col; Forestry.*

JACKSON, Margaret Rose
Robbinsdale Sr HS; Robbinsdale, MN; Band; Community Yth Symph; NHS; A-Ed, Sch P; Bkbl; Cr-Ctry; Tr; *Augsburg Col; Media-TV.*

JACKSON, Marilyn Lynette
Havana HS; Havana, FL; Secy, NHS; Rptr, Sci C; *Fla A&M U; Mus.*

JACKSON, Marilyn Rhonda
Chester HS; Chester, PA; Band; Chor; Drama; *Northeastern Christian Jr Col; Mus.*

JACKSON, Michael
Northwest HS; St Louis, MO (7-652) NHS; Citz A; Most Out.

JACKSON, Michael Chikaiza
Screven Co HS; Sylvania, GA (18-200) Bus C; FBLA; 4H; A-Ed, Sch P; Var C; Mgr, Bkbl; Cpt, Cr-Ctry; Ftbl; Co-Cpt, Tr; WW; *Howard U; Bus Adm.*

JACKSON, Mike Ray
Timberline HS; Weippe, ID; Pres, 4H; NHS; Bkbl; 4H A; I Dare You.

JACKSON, Montree Lorraine
Sussex Central HS; Sussex, VA (7-260) BC; FHA; 4H; Sci C; Cpt, Bkbl; Sftbl; COM; HCt; Most Out; Type A; *Norfolk St Col; Nurs.*

JACKSON, Nancy Eiland
Coahoma Co HS; Clarksdale, MS (25%-91) Ed, Ann; Cpt, Chldr; Pres, FHA; GS; Secy, SC; B Crocker A; H of F; HCt; HR A; *U of Miss; Communications.*

JACKSON, Nancy Elizabeth
Phoebus HS; Hampton, VA (12-312) A Cap Choir; AFS; Chor; VP, Drama; Hmrm; Key C; Lat C; Lat NHS; Math C; Mu Alpha Theta; NHS; VP, Thes; Hon Prog; Best Soprano; Outst Service, Drama; *Madison Col; Drama Therapy.*

JACKSON, Nancy Virginia
Campbell HS; Fairburn, GA (20%-200) Ch, Bus C; Chor; Ch, FBLA; Hmrm; Lat C; SC; Hon Prog; Cpt, Drill Tm; Most Outst; GSct A; *Ga Col.*

JACKSON, Nell Denise
Newnan HS; Newnan, GA (10%-600) BC; S-T, Chldr; Drama; Span C; Span NHS; Tnns; COM; HCt; Jr Civinettes; 11 Yr PA, Sunday Sch.

JACKSON, Omega Michelle
McCall Sr HS; Tallulah, LA; Ann; Bus C; Chldr; Dbte Tm; Drama; Pres, FBLA; FHA; 4H; Hmrm; Sch P; SC; Alg A; B Crocker A; Cl Fav; 4H A; HCt; MLS; *Alcorn St U; Pre-Law.*

JACKSON, Pamela
Carroll HS; Monroe, LA; Secy, Chor; Fr C; Cpt, Mjrte; HCt; Hon Prog; Singing A; Mjrte A; *Robinson Bus Col; Key Punch.*

JACKSON, Patricia
East HS; Cleveland, OH; Band; Fr C; Co-Cpt, Bkbl; COM; PA; *Case Western Reserve Col; Engr.*

JACKSON, Patricia Ellen
Hickman Co HS; Clinton, KY (10-100) Secy, BC; Bus C; VP, FHA; Hmrm; NHS; Sci C; Ch, SC; Beauty; HCt; Most Out; Regional FHA Off; Top 5%, Ntl Merit Scores; *U of Ky; Journ.*

JACKSON, Pattie Lisette
O'Donnell HS; O'Donnell, TX (2-55) Secy, Band; Chor; VP, FHA; Hmrm; SC; Pres, Soph Cl; JV, Bkbl; Tnns; Pres, FHA; Ntl & St Projects Comm; St Exec Coun; NHS; Yrbk Staff; Home Ec Outst Achv A; Band A; Chrch Yth Adv Brd; Area Pres, FHA; *Tex Tech U; Home Ec.*

JACKSON, Paul Roger
Hanford HS; Richland, WA (15-290) A Cap Choir; Chor; Drama; Ensm; NHS; Mgr, Ftbl; COM; Citz A; Hon Prog; NEDT; *Bus.*

JACKSON, Paula Jean
Queen City HS; Queen City, TX (10%-73) Chldr; VP, FHA; Sci C; S-T, Soph Cl; JV, Bkbl; Tr; Cl Fav; HQn.

JACKSON, Paulette Christine
Windsor Forest HS; Savannah, GA; A Cap Choir; Chor; FHA; Fin, Mjrte; Swim; Tr; COM; Ntl Achv Schol; Yth Fel; Yth Foundation.

JACKSON, Penny Sue
Quincy Sr HS II; Quincy, IL (69%-772) A Cap Choir; Chor; Ensm; Hmrm; SC; Tr; S-T, GSct; *St Louis Christian Col; Mus.*

JACKSON, Phillip Howard
University City HS; University City, MO (2-28) FBLA; Bsbl; Bkbl; Cpt, Ftbl; COM; Handwriting A; *Wash U; Archt.*

JACKSON, Priscilla Ann
L E Rabouin HS; New Orleans, LA; *Charity Hospital Sch of Nurs; Nurs.*

JACKSON, Rebecca Lou
Parkway W Sr HS; Chesterfield, MO (132-619) Chor; Ensm; Hon Prog; Yth Fel; Ballet; Voice; Piano; Guitar; *Outdoor Christian Ed.*

JACKSON, Reginald DeMurris
Holly Springs HS; Holly Springs, MS; Ann; NHS; Order/Arrow; MVP, Bsbl; Bkbl; MVP, Ftbl; Tr; Order/Arrow A; Nat Brooks A; *Ohio St U; Enviromental Sci.*

JACKSON, Rex Sterling
Conway Sr HS; Conway, SC (2-364) Ed, Ann; Key C; NHS; Sci C; Span C; Tnns; *Furman U; Law.*

JACKSON, Rhonda Lee
McCullough HS; Spring, TX; A Cap Choir; Chor; FTA; Sci C; Span C; *Abilene Christian Col; Eng.*

JACKSON, Richard W Jr
St Augustine HS; New Orleans, LA (16-35) Dbte Tm; NFL; Spch C.

JACKSON, Rick Wayne
Lawerence D Bell HS; Hurst, TX (275-900) Band; Key C; Orch; Span C; Sftbl; COM; WW; *Baylor U; Govt.*

JACKSON, Ricky Alan
Marshall Co HS; Benton, KY (85-350) Band; BC; Chess C; Chor; Community Yth Symph; FBLA; Pres, Math C; Hon Prog; Most Improved Musician; *Murray St U; Chem.*

JACKSON, Robert Bradley
Naperville Central HS; Naperville, IL (20-430) Band; Chor; Ensm; Fr C; Madrigal; Math C; Ski C; Bsbl; Soccer; Alg A; COM; Citz A; Hon Prog; Math A; Phy A; Yth Fel; Am Assn of Fr Prof, Cert of Merit; *Chem Engr.*

JACKSON, Robert Roy
Parkland HS; El Paso, TX (1-226) BS; NHS; Cpt, Jr Cl; VP, Soph Cl; Co-Cpt, Bkbl; Cl Fav; Hist A; MLS; Opt A; Val; Appointment, USMA & USAFA; WW; NROTC Schol; *US Air Force Acad; Engr.*

JACKSON, Robert W
Ainsworth HS; Ainsworth, NE (3-80) VP, Band; Ensm; Fr C; Ch, Sci C; Thes; Var C; Cr-Ctry; Tr; Alg A; Bio A; COM; Spch A; Yth Fel; *Med.*

JACKSON, Robin Kim
Moravia Central Sch; Moravia, NY (10-105) Band; Chor; NHS; Tres, Sr Cl; *Powelson Bus Inst; Secy.*

JACKSON, Scarlet Leeann
Belton HS; Belton, MO; Band; Chor; Drama; Thes; Midwestern Mus & Art Camp Schol; *Mus.*

JACKSON, Senita Leveta
Carolina HS; Greenville, SC; Chor; Pres, FHA; *Bendict Col; Nurs.*

JACKSON, Shannon Cyphese
W Charlotte HS; Charlotte, NC (150-450) Chldr; Parl, Chor; Ch, Hmrm; Span C; SC; Bkbl; Sftbl; Swim; Tr; Cl Fav; JA A; Most Out; *Bus Adm.*

JACKSON, Sharon Denise
Walnut HS; Walnut, MS (10-55) Ed, Ann; VP, BC; FFA; H of F; Most Out; Most Dependable; *NE Miss Jr Col; Agr Econ.*

JACKSON, Shauneille Cassandra
Holly Springs HS; Holly Springs, MS (23-157) Ed, Ann; Band; Drama; FBLA; Pres, FHA; Hmrm; NHS; Ntl Yth Conf; Co-Ed, Sch P; SC; COM; HCt; Yth Fel; DECA; Qn, Miss Ldrship Trng Sch CYF; *Rust Col; Marketing.*

JACKSON, Sheila Kay
W Columbia HS; W Columbia, TX; AFS; Band; Ensm; Hmrm; Rainbow; Ch, SC; Bkbl; Sftbl; Hon Prog; Yth Fel; *Brazosport Jr Col; Bus.*

JACKSON, Sheila Maria
Brunswick HS; Brunswick, GA (5-416) Bus Mgr, Ann; Drama; Hmrm; InterClub Coun; Ch, Lit Mag; NHS; Secy, SC; COM; HQn; Outst Sr; Courtesy A; *Brunswick Jr Col; Pre-Law.*

JACKSON, Sheila Renee
Beaumont HS; St Louis, MO; Chor; Drama; Tnns; Choir A; *U of Calif; Dramatics.*

JACKSON, Shelly Gayle
Rudyard Pub Sch; Rudyard, MT (2-25) Chor; Drama; Ensm; NHS; F-Ed, Sch P; COM; Hon Prog; Type A; Pep C; Sun Sch Teacher, Pianist; Co Ch, Homecoming; Vlbl; EY.

JACKSON, Sonja Mae
Leavenworth HS; Leavenworth, KS (145-400) Mgr, Tr; Band Lib; Band A; *Kans City Col of Med & Dental Asst; Dental Asst.*

JACKSON, Suzanne
Arroyo Grande HS; Arroyo Grande, CA (8-640) Secy, A Cap Choir; Ensm; CSF; *Med Tech.*

JACKSON, Tamara Leigh
Camarillo HS; Camarillo, CA; AFS; Parl, Hmrm; Ski C; St Stu Congress; Stu Mayor, Inst of Local Govt; Interntl Cntr For Learning Achv A; *Pepperdine U; Mus Therapy.*

JACKSON, Tammy Lois
Thomasville HS; Thomasville, AL; Ann; BC; Pres, FHA; Span C; Lion A; Rep, Lion's C Camp; *U of Sou Miss; Home Ec.*

JACKSON, Tammy Renee
E Henderson HS; Flat Rock, NC; Chor; Citz A; NEDT; *Tenn Temple Col; Psych.*

JACKSON, Teresa Gail
Highland HS; Hardy, AR (4-92) Band; Chor; FHA; GS; SC; Outst Stu; *Ark St U; Acct.*

JACKSON, Terry Marie
Monticello HS; Monticello, MS; BC; Rptr, FHA; Sch P; COM; *Fashion Merchandising.*

JACKSON, Thysen Annette
Green B Trimble Tech HS; Fort Worth, TX; Bus C; FHA; Math C; Mgr, Tr; 2nd Pl, Data Processing Notebook; *Data Processing.*

JACKSON, Tiara Russia
Grace Dodge Tech HS; Bronx, NY; *Med.*

JACKSON, Timothy Charles
Jamestown HS; Jamestown, NY (25%-500) Band; Chor; Hmrm; Order/Arrow; Ski C; SC; Bkbl; JV, Ftbl; Sftbl; JV, Tr; Order/Arrow A; Meritorious A; *BSct A; Rochester Inst of Tech; Elec Tech.*

JACKSON, Timothy Michael
Brantley HS; Brantley, AL (1-46) Anchor C; Ann; BC; Chor; FFA; Cpt, Math C; NHS; Var C; Pres, Sr Cl; Pres, Jr Cl; Pres, Soph Cl; Bsbl; Bkbl; Ftbl; Alg A; Cl Fav; Hon Prog; Math A; MLS; Val; Composition A; Most Talented; Most Intellectual; *U of Ala; Elec Engr.*

JACKSON, Timothy Ray
Austin HS; Chicago, IL; Chor; JETS; Bsbl; Sftbl; COM; *Wright Col; Engr.*

JACKSON, Tina
Skyline HS; Dallas, TX; Ann; Band; FHA; Span C; Sftbl; Yth Fel; Yth Foundation A; VBS, Sunday Sch, A's; *Eastfield Col; Human Services.*

JACKSON, Tina Louise
Arts HS; Newark, NJ; Chor; Most Out; Tres, Church Yth Fel.

JACKSON, Tywannia Faye
Dougherty HS; Albany, GA (33-422) Citz A; Math A; Outst Stu; *Albany St Col; Elem Ed.*

JACKSON, Valerie Ann
Mem HS; San Antonio, TX (1-300) Ann; Co-Cpt, Chldr; FHA; Hmrm; Pres, NHS; Secy, SC; Tr; Most Out; Opt A; Val; Wards A; *U of Houston; Pub Relations.*

JACKSON, Vesta Renee
P L Dunbar Sr HS; Baltimore, MD (10-500) Bus C; Cpt, Chldr; Fr C; Secy, Hmrm; NHS; ARC; Span C; Var C; Bsbl; Sftbl; Swim; *Howard U; Nurs.*

JACKSON, Wanda Carnela
MacKenzie HS; Detroit, MI (18-352) FTA; NHS; SC; Sftbl; Citz A; Vlbl; Composition A; *Diesel Mech.*

JACKSON, Wanda Janine
Westside HS; Augusta, GA; Cpt, Chldr; FHA; Hmrm; Sch P; SC; Cl Fav; *Augusta Col; Bus Adm.*

JACKSON, William Michael
Pendleton HS; Pendleton, SC; Fr C; 4H; Sci C; Bsbl; Bkbl; Ftbl; Sftbl.

JACO, Michael Wayne
Broward Christian Sch; Fort Lauderdale, FL; A-Ed, Sch P; Bsbl; Bkbl; Cr-Ctry; Ftbl; Tr; Swtht; *Clearwater Christian Col; Phys Ed.*

JACOB, Jeannette
Booker T Washington Sr HS; New Orleans, LA; VP, Chor; Hmrm; NHS; SC; COM Spch; NEDT Test; *St Mary's Dominican Col; Pediatrician.*

JACOB, Steven Michael
Napoleon Pub Sch; Napoleon, ND; BS; FFA; SC; Bsbl; Ftbl; Wrest.

JACOBER, Beth Anne
Anglican School; Jerusalem, ISRAEL (1-6) Ed, Ann; Drama; Pres, SC; Pres, Sr Cl; Bio A; COM; Most Out; Eng A; Scripture A; *Taylor U; Eng Lit.*

JACOBER, Sally
Oppenheim-Ephratah Central Sch; St Johnsville, NY (1-39) Chor; FTA; NHS; Sch P; Alg A; Hist A; Math A; MLS; Val; *Easten Col; Social Sci.*

JACOBS, Beverly Lynn
Assumption Jr-Sr HS; Assumption, IL (2-35) Chor; VP, NHS; Tres, SC; VP, Sr Cl; Hon Prog; Sal; Swtht; Vlbl; GAA A; Vlbl Ltr; Scholastic Achievement A; *Dental Asst.*

JACOBS, Cindy A
St Joseph-Ogden HS; St Joseph, IL (71-100) Band; Sch P; *Parkland Col.*

JACOBS, David Gerald
Mendota Township HS; Mendota, IL; Hmrm; Order/Arrow; Span C; Order/Arrow A.

JACOBS, Dean Alan
Mendota Township HS; Mendota, IL (57-211) Bus C; Hmrm; Phys C; Co-Cpt, Bsbl; Bkbl; Cpt, Golf; Hon Prog; *Ill Valley Comm Col; Bus.*

JACOBS, Dwayne Edward
Boston Latin HS; Boston, MA; AFS; Drama; Tr; *Med.*

JACOBS, Elaine
W S Creecy HS; Rich Square, NC (4-42) Drama; VP, Fr C; VP, Hmrm; Cpt, Bkbl; Cpt, Sftbl; Tr; Eng A; HS All Amer; *E Carolina U; Math.*

JACOBS, Gretchen Anne
Edgewood HS; Ashtabula, OH (55-237) Drama; NHS; Thes; *Harding Col; Acct.*

JACOBS, Jeffrey Lyndon
Circleville HS; Circleville, OH; Band; 4H; All City Boy's Choir; Choir Boy o-t Yr; Luther League; BSct; *Law Enforcement.*

JACOBS, John Wesley
Lakeview Acad; Gainesville, GA (10-15) Key C; Bkbl; Golf; Soccer; Tnns.

JACOBS, Kevin Eugene
Shawnee HS; Shawnee, OK (26-400) Hmrm; Lat C; NHS; Sch P; SC; Var C; Pres, St Cl; Bsbl; Ftbl; Ideal Camper; Eng A; Friendliest A; Best All Around; *Bus Adm.*

JACOBS, Kimberly Kay
Booth HS; Des Moines, IA;

JACOBS, Kurt Hazlett
Highlands Sr HS; Natrona Heights, PA (5-493) Chor; Drama; Hmrm; NHS; SC; Hon Prog; Dist Chor; Human Relations Committee; Inter-Ntl C.

JACOBS, Lamont Bregg
Fairfield Sr HS; Fairfield, OH (72-625) Lat C; Swim; Math A.

JACOBS, Larry William
Edward H White HS; Jacksonville, FL (211-656) 4H; Lat C; NFL; Rptr, Sch P; *Fla Jr Col; Atomic Energy.*

JACOBS, Lisa Beth
Isle of Wight Acad; Isle of Wight County, VA (1-40) Chor; Pres, 4H; NHS; Ch, SC; Alg A; Bio A; COM; Chem A; 4H A; Math A; PTA A; Val; Most Stu; Gwaltney Schol; Church School; *U of Va; Pre-Med.*

JACOBS, Lois Emily
Valmeyer HS; Valmeyer, IL (2-46) Band; Chor; FHA; 4H; Math C; NHS; Sch P; SC; Pres, Soph Cl; 4H A.

JACOBS, Mark Lee
Albia Comm HS; Albia, IA (13-150) Band; Chor; Rptr, FFA; VP, 4H; Bkbl; Tr; Citz A; 4H A; *Iowa St U; Vet Sci.*

JACOBS, Michael John
Frankford HS; Philadelphia, PA; JV, Tnns; Hon Prog; Pres, Thanatopsis; Hyper Plus; Bus Mgr, Sr Advisory; Boy o-t Mo; Ch, Church Extension Committee; Tres, Fraternity; *Eastern Col; Bus Adm.*

JACOBS, Nadine Louise
Dublin HS; Dublin, CA (9-340) Bank of Amer A; CSF; Principal's HR; *Brigham Young U; Child Development.*

JACOBS, Pamela Lou
Eufaula HS; Eufaula, OK (1-100) Ann; Band; Chor; FHA; GS; NHS; Span C; S-T, SC; COM; DARGCA; MLS; Val; Band Qn; Hon Band; *Secondary Ed.*

JACOBS, Ted
Geronimo HS; Geronimo, OK (6-31) Drama; FFA; Cpt, Bkbl; COM; Drama, FFA, A's; *Okmulgee Tech Col; Diesel.*

JACOBS, Terry Lynn
Cumberland Valley Christian Sch; Chambersburg, PA (3-13) Band; Chor; Community Yth Symph; Drama; Ensm; Orch; Span C; Semi-Fin, Bsbl; JV, Bkbl; JV, Sftbl; Tr; Hon Prog; Chaplin, SC; Bkbl Trophy; Achv A; HR; Summer Misson for Chld Evangelism; Yth Fel; *Thomas Road Bible Inst; Pastoral Stu.*

JACOBSEN, Shelley Renee
Saline HS; Saline, MI; NHS; Secy, Sci C; Tr; Secy, Saline Steer C; Gym; President's Phys Fitness A; *U of Mich; Arct.*

JACOBSMUHLEN D'AMORE, Connie Jean
Othello HS; Othello, WA (10-150) Pres, A Cap Choir; Band; Chor; Dbte Tm; Drama; Ensm; FTA; 4H; Hmrm; Fin, Jr Miss Pagent; Lit Mag; NHS; Sch P; Span C; Spch C; SC; Thes; Jr Miss A; Most Inspirational; Sch Ltr; *Mental Deficency Ed.*

JACOBSON, Darla Mae
Belvidere HS; Belvidere, IL (1-434) JV, Bkbl.

JACOBSON, Elizabeth Marie
Texas City HS; Texas City, TX (6-410) VP, Band; Chor; Pres, Fr C; NHS; NEDT; Rotary A; Corresponding Secy, SC; Phys Ed A; Outst Female Band Member; *The U of Kans; Mus Therapy.*

JACOBSON, Eric Charles
Boulder HS; Boulder, CO (20-650) Band; Fin, Chess C; Ronald Raven A; *Mus.*

JACOBSON, Eric Lloyd
Redlands Sr HS; Redlands, CA; Pres, Bus C; Chess C; Dbte Tm; Pres, FBLA; NFL; NHS; Spch C; Mgr, Bsbl; Wrest; Amer Leg A; CSF; Opt A; Spch A; Retail Clerks Union Schol Win; *U of Calif at Riverside; Bus.*

JACOBSON, Gale Lee
Minnetonka HS; Minnetonka, MN (127-658) Fr C; Fr Travel Stu.

JACOBSON, Jeanne Marie
New Trier E HS; Winnetka, IL (27-950) Ensm; Tr; Girls C Board; Church Yth Group, Tri-Mu; Var Tr Ltr; *Ind U; Bus.*

JACOBSON, Michael Wayne
St Ignatius HS; St Ignatius, MT (5-32) Ann; Semi-Fin, BS; Chem A; Drama A; *Mont St U; Engr.*

JACOBSON, Sara Marie
Frank B Kellogg HS; St Paul, MN; Rptr, Ann; Chor; Pres, 4H; Orch; Thes; Soccer; COM; 4H A; *U of Minn; Liberal Arts.*

JACOBSON, Terry Julius
Viroqua Sr HS; Viroqua, WI (29-144) Chor; Drama; Ensm; Madrigal; Order/Arrow; Var C; Ftbl; Order/Arrow A; Pro Deo Patria; Barbershop Quartet; Drama A; *UW-Madison; Horticulture.*

JACOBSON, Wayne Allan
Washington HS; Cherokee, IA (90-144) Band; Chor; Chor; Madrigal; Order/Arrow; Thes; Ftbl; Swim; Tr; Wrest; God & Country A; Young Singers; Pres, Church HS; Sch Mus A; 1st, St Vocal; *Iowa Lakes Comm Col; Mus.*

JACOBSON, Wesley Ernest
Belvidere HS; Belvidere, IL (5-366) NHS; Elk A; WW; *Bradley U; Elec Engr.*

JACOCKS, Herbert
Humboldt HS; Humboldt, TN (49-150) Band; Tres, Fr C; ARC; Sch P; Tr; Salesman o-t Mo; Ntl News Carrier; *Memphis St U; Biol.*

JACQUES, Christina Louise
Lyman Mem HS; Lebanon, CT; Span C; SC; Nurs.

JACQUES, Theresa Marie
Livermore Falls HS; Livermore Falls, ME (2-94) Chor; Secy, Drama; Fr C; FNA; FTA; Math C; Mu Alpha Theta; NHS; SC; JV, Bkbl; JV, Hockey; Bio A; VofDEM; *Eng.*

JACQUOT, Kenneth Earl
Sycamore HS; Cincinnati, OH; Order/Arrow; Var C; World Affairs C; Bsbl; Mgr, Ftbl; JV, Tr; JV, Wrest; Eagle Sct; *Miami U; Biol.*

JADERHOLM, Ronald Russell
Glenbard W HS; Glen Ellyn, IL (351-488) Chor; Cr-Ctry; Fin, Tr; FCA; *Taylor U; Bus.*

JADICK, David
Old Forge HS; Old Forge, PA (15-121) NHS; Sci C; Chem A; Hon Prog; Ch, Yrbk Photo Department; *U of Scranton; Pre-Med.*

JAECKLE, Barbara Ann
Bishop Dwenger HS; Fort Wayne, IN; Band; Chor; Orch; COM; Hon Prog; JA A; Clothing A; Mus A; *Ind U.*

JAEGER, Holly Ann
Avondale HS; Avondale Estates, GA; VP, Chor; Ensm; Pres, Fr C; Swim; Gov Honor Prog; Hiking C; Drill Tm; Hon Soc; All St Chor; *Eckerd Col; Mus.*

JAEGER, Ron Peter
Reavis HS; Burbank, IL (125-746) Bsbl; Bkbl; Hon Prog; Comm Service, Cert, A's.

JAFFE, Stuart Henry
El Camino Real HS; Woodland Hills, CA (58-1095) Hmrm; Pres, K of C; NHS; CSF; COM; Hist A; Opt A; Ch, Ephepian Soc; *Berkeley U; Pre-Med.*

JAGELS, Rosalie Lorna
Benton Co R-1 Sch; Cole Camp, MO (4-56) A Cap Choir; Ann; Chor; VP, FHA; NHS; Regent Schol; Type A; *Central Mo St U; Secy.*

JAGER, Charles Gordon
Joliet W HS; Joliet, IL; Hmrm; Model UN; SC; UN Council; VP, Var C; Ftbl; Wrest; COM; Hist A; Hon Prog; DAHSS; *ISU; Phys Therapy.*

JAGGERS, Amy Miller
Cleveland HS; Cleveland, TN; Band; Fr C; Sci C; Tri-HiY; Cpt, Chldr; Bkbl; Swim; Tr; Hon Prog; Sci A; *U of Tenn; Home Ec.*

JAGGERS, Janet Maureen
Cleveland HS; Cleveland, TN; Anchor C; Band; BC; Chldr; Chor; VP, Fr C; Lat C; NHS; MVP, Bkbl; Tnns; Tr; HQn; Hon Prog; NEDT; Yth Fel; *U of Tenn.*

JAGLOWICZ, Joseph Michael
Marion Co HS; Lebanon, KY (15-324) CYO; Fr C; 4H; NHS; Bkbl; Ftbl; Swim; COM; Cl Fav; Hon Prog; *U of Ky; Acct.*

JAHN, David Alvin
Willamina HS; Willamina, OR (9-64) VP, Band; 4H; Cpt, Bsbl; Cpt, Bkbl; Cpt, Ftbl; Citz A; 4H A; Boy o-t Mo; Most Inspirational, Bkbl; *NW Nazarene Col.*

JAHN, Jeff David
Blair Comm HS; Blair, NE (71-172) CYO; Chor; VP, Drama; Sch P; VP, Thes; Golf; Choir Ltr; Best Tech; 3 Star Thespian; HR; *U of Nebr; Commercial Art.*

JAHN, Julie Ann
Plymouth Salem HS; Plymouth, MI; Band; Chldr; Chor; Madrigal; Orch; Ski C; COM; *W Mich Col; Psych.*

JAHN, Lennie Lee
Mulberry Grove HS; Mulberry Grove, IL (5-38) Ann; Pres, Band; VP, Chor; VP, Mod Mus Mas; Pres, NHS; Tres, Sci C; SAR Good Citz A; Hon Stu; Band A; Activities A; Chor A ; Dramatics A; Industrial Arts A; HR; US Marine Phys Achv A; *Greenville Col.*

JAHNKE, Judy Janene
Augusta HS; Augusta, MT (2-18) Band; Chor; 4H; Rainbow; SC; 4H A; HR; *E Mont Col; Phys Therapy.*

JAHNKE, LaVelle Ann
Hoisington HS; Hoisington, KS; Band; Dbte Tm; Ger C; Tres, NFL; Pres, Jr Cl; Bkbl; Golf; Rptr, GALS; Vlbl; Outst Novice Debator; *Med.*

JAHRLING, Kurt Vincent
Waltham HS; Waltham, MA;

JAKABOSKY, Kevin Charles
Robert E Lee HS; Midland, TX (171-632) Pres, Sunday Sch Department; *Mid-America Nazarene Col; Christian Ed.*

JAKEL, Debbie Jean
Spencer HS; Spencer, WI; Ann; CYO; Chldr; Chor; Drama; FHA; Sch P; Bkbl; Tr; Vlbl.

JAKOBE, Brenda Ann
Spring Hill HS; Spring Hill, KS (35-86) A Cap Choir; Chor; Ensm; Madrigal; Secy, Yth Fel; *Computer Data.*

JAKOBER, Duane Dean
Leota HS; Leola, SD (8-39) JV, Bkbl; Tr; Math A; Type A; *Jamestown Col; Math.*

JAKOBER, Gary Lynn
Leola HS; Leola, SD (6-42) All Amer Yth; Band; BS; Dbte Tm; Math C; Bsbl; Bkbl; Cr-Ctry; Ftbl; Soccer; Sftbl; Tr; Amer Leg A; Bank Of Amer A; COM; Citz A; Cl Fav; God & Country A; Hist A; Hon Prog; Math A; MLS; Most Out; Sci A; Spch A; Type A; Yth Fel; Yth Foundation; Reading A; PA; *Carpenter.*

JAKUBCZAK, Raymond Scott
Thornwood HS; S Holland, IL (138-1015) Order/ Arrow; Tres, UMYF; Eagle Sct; Gym; *Bio.*

JAM, Caroline Anne
Hall HS; Spring Valley, IL; Chldr; Chor; FHA; Sch P; Hist A; Stu Librarian A.

JAMBON, Jeanine Lafont
Pompano Beach Sr HS; Pompano Beach, FL (2-645) Pres, Ger C; InterAct C; InterClub Coun; Swim; Crisco A; Pres A; Vlbl; *U of Fla; Sci.*

JAMERSON, Brenda Diane
Springfield HS; Springfield, IL (40-480) A Cap Choir; JETS; Orch; Span C; Co-Cpt, Bkbl; Tr; COM; Hon Prog; Concert Master, Comm Yth Symph; Pres Coun Phys Fitness; Badminton; All City Badminton; Co-Cpt, Vlbl; Amer Cancer Soc Schol; *Phar.*

JAMERSON, Cynthia Renee
Charles Sumner HS; St Louis, MO (113-432) Band; Chor; FHA; Up Bound; HERO; *Forest Park Comm Col; Child Care.*

JAMES, Alan Paul
Alleghany Co HS; Covington, VA (2-194) VP, Fr C; Hmrm; SC; Pres, Jr Cl; JV, Bsbl; Tnns; Cl Fav; Hist A; Math A; Sci A; Yth Fel; Eng A; *Penn St U; Forestry.*

JAMES, Alex
W Side HS; Gary, IN (189-686) Band; *Ind U NW; Retail Mgt.*

JAMES, Amy Grace
Effingham HS; Effingham, IL (50-185) FHA; Pres, Rainbow; Span C; Amer Leg A; Spch A; Devotions Ldr, Church Yth Fel; Co-Ch, Jr Variety Show; Church Play & Mus; *E Ill U; Elem Ed.*

JAMES, Anita LaVeine
Harry P Harding HS; Charlotte, NC (30-235) Ch, FHA; GS; Sch P; Beauty; *NC Central U; Pol Sci.*

JAMES, Anita Viola
Kensington HS; Buffalo, NY; Tres, Chor; JV, Bkbl; Bus Adm A; *Bus.*

JAMES, Annett
Motley HS; Columbus, MS (10%-70) Ann; BC; FHA; Sci C; SC; Tri-HiY; Bkbl; Tr; Alg A; Bio A; Hist A; Hon Prog; Math A; Sci A; Val; Eng As; *U of Miss; Acct.*

JAMES, Becky Lynn
Sunbright HS; Sunbright, TN (10-65) Pres, FHA; Rptr, 4H; VP, Rainbow; A-Ed, Sch P; Bsbl; *Carson-Newman Col; Pol Sci.*

JAMES, Bruce Amon
Proviso E HS; Maywood, IL (26-967) Chor; Madrigal; Spch C; Thes; Tnns; *Bradley Col; International Stu.*

JAMES, David Michael
Wellsboro Sr HS; Wellsboro, PA (10-219) Fin, AFS; Chess C; Drama; Ger C; Model UN; NHS; Sci C; Ch, Ski C; Ftbl; Tr; NEDT; Sci A; *Eckerd Col; Bio.*

JAMES, Debra Lynn
Proviso E HS; Maywood, IL (277-950) Secy, Chor; Madrigal; Fin, Spch C; Thes; Spch A; *Hampton U; Nurs.*

JAMES, Diane Gina
Eastside HS; Paterson, NJ; Citz A; *Wilfred Acad; Beautician.*

JAMES, Dorian Orlando
Mendel Cath HS; Chicago, IL (1-164) Hmrm; NHS; SC; Tnns; COM; Hon Prog; Yth Fel; Christian Yth Cert; Excel A; WW; *Engr.*

JAMES, Doris Anette
E E Smith Sr HS; Fayetteville, NC (33%-200) A-Ed, Ann; Band; Dbte Tm; FHA; Hmrm; SC; JV, Bkbl; Type A; Senate Page, General Assembly; *E Carolina U; Spch Pathology.*

JAMES, Doris Felice
Seaside HS; Seaside, CA; Chldr; Commercial C; Hmrm; Mjrte; NHS; Ntl Yth Conf; SC; Tr; Pep C; Hon Soc; Cpt, NAACP Drill Tm; 2nd VP, NAACP Yth Coun; *UCLA; Psych.*

JAMES, Durell George
Mendel HS; Chicago, IL (18-147) Key C; NHS; Bkbl; Excel A; WW; 2nd Hon's; *Bus Adm.*

JAMES, Gail Lynne
S Charleston HS; South Charleston, WV (10%-291) Band; Chor; Community Yth Symph; Drama; NHS; Span C; Span NHS; *W Va U; Pre-Nurs.*

JAMES, Glendora
Williamston HS; Williamston, NC; Chldr; Chor; Drama; FHA; Tr; DECA C; Mus A; *Amer Bus & Fashion Inst; Fashion & Merchandising.*

JAMES, Hettie Denise
Harry P Handing HS; Charlotte, NC; Band; Secy, FHA; 4H; Rptr, Hmrm; NHS; ARC; Span C; SC; Sftbl.

JAMES, Jacqueline Cardellia
Western HS; Baltimore, MD; Chor; Drama; NHS; Alg A; COM; Type A.

JAMES, Janice Marie
East HS; Columbus, OH; *Ohio St U; Home Ec.*

JAMES, Jennifer Lynne
Cabrillo Sr HS; Lompoc, CA (9-409) Bank of Amer A; Legal Secy of Calif Schol; *Allan Hancock Jr Col; Bus.*

JAMES, Jonathan Joy
Castleberry HS; Ft Worth, TX; Bkbl; FCA; *Moody Bible Inst; Aviation.*

JAMES, Judy Loretta
Eastern HS; Baltimore, MD; Bus C; Chor; Jr Miss Pagent; COM; Pres A; Type A; Church A; Schol A; Cert of Hon; Departmental A; *Secretarial.*

JAMES, Kathleen Anne
Cabrillo Sr HS; Lompoc, CA (32-402) Home Ec Related Occupations C.

JAMES, Kathleen Suzan
Atlanta HS; Atlanta, TX; Band; Chldr; Chor; Secy, FHA; FNA; FTA; 4H; Rptr, Rainbow; Secy, SC; Sftbl; Tnns; 4H A; Rptr, SC; *Ouichita Baptist Col; Nurs.*

JAMES, Kerry Ann
Brazoswood HS; Clute, TX (50%-437) Drama; FTA; Orch; Thes; Sacristan; Violin Solo Medals; Col Schol; Pres, Vet C; 1st Cl GSct; *Brazosport Col; Drama.*

JAMES, Kevin Brian
Roosevelt HS; Gary, IN (60-560) Band; Span C; Golf; Citz A; Hon Prog; Spch A; *Howard U; Dentistry.*

JAMES, Kevin Corey
John Handley HS; Winchester, VA (50-250) Chor; Demolay; Hmrm; Key C; Monogram; SC; Wrest; *Va Polytechnical Inst; Bus Adm.*

JAMES, LaVerne
Abilene HS; Abilene, TX; Chldr; Sch Achieve Tm; MVP, Tr; Swtht; Yale Book A; Exchange C; Swtht of Church.

JAMES, Laura Marie
Bentley HS; Livonia, MI; Chor; Ski C; Swim; Hon Prog.

JAMES, Linda Diane
Elk Grove HS; Elk Grove Village, IL (140-630) Ski C; Span C; SC; VFW A; *Med.*

JAMES, Lisa Michelle
Caney Valley HS; Caney, KS (10%-70) JV, Chldr; Fr C; FHA; Tr; Cerebral Palsy Service A; *Coffeyville Comm Jr Col; Math.*

JAMES, Lori Kay
Hitchcock HS; Hitchcock, TX (8-135) Ann; Parl, FTA; Cpt, Mjrte; Secy, NHS; Secy, Soph Cl; Elk A; Lieutenant, Cpt, Drill Tm; WW; *Sam Houston Col; Bus Ed.*

JAMES, Magdalena Dolores
Colegio San Antonio Abad; Humacao, PR (1-96) Chldr; Pres, FHA; Secy, Hmrm; NHS; Sci C; Swim; Poetry A; Ntl Spelling Bee; *Saint Mary's Col; Bio.*

JAMES, Magna Moriama
Greater Ny Acad; Woodside, NY (9-73) NHS; Secy, Jr Cl; MVP, Tr; COM; Hon Prog; MLS; Most Out; Val; Win, Metropolitan Spelling Bee; *Atlantic Union Col; Nurs.*

JAMES, Magna Moriana
Greater New York Acad; Woodside, NY (15%-73) NHS; Semi-Fin, Tr; COM; Citz A; Hon Prog; Spelling As; *Atlantic Union Col; Nurs.*

JAMES, Maureen Teresa
Seton HS; Cincinnati, OH (46-299) Bus C; CYO; Chor; Drama; FBLA; Hmrm; Co-Ch, Lat C; NHS; ARC; SC; World Affairs C; Cpt, Soccer; Swim; Citz A; Hon Prog; Kiwanis A; MLS; Sci A; Swim A's; GSct A's; *Saint Mary's Col; Lib Arts.*

JAMES, Melinda Kaye
Grant Union HS; Sacramento, CA; Chor; Fr C; FBLA; Pres, Hmrm; Co-Ed, Lit Mag; NHS; Mgr, Sftbl; Tr; COM; Citz A; Math A; Most Out; Spch A; Type A; Psych A; HR; *Bauder Col; Bus Adm.*

JAMES, Michael Anthony
Bell Voc HS; Washington, DC; *Bowie St Col; Law.*

JAMES, Niccolo
Grant Union HS; Sacramento, CA; Band; Chor; Ensm; Pres, Hmrm; NHS; SC; Mgr, Bsbl; Alg A; COM; Math A; Most Out; Sci A; Schol; HR; Mus A; *U of Calif-Davis; Phys Therapy.*

JAMES, Patti Sue
John Overton HS; Nashville, TN; Chor; Fr C; Lat C; ARC; Span C; Theta Omega Sorority; *Freed Hardeman Col; Bible.*

JAMES, Penny Louise
T L Handy HS; Bay City, MI (49-369) Ann; Drama; NHS; SC; Secy, Soph Cl; Swim; Pres, Girl's League; *Ferris St Col; Med Record Tech.*

JAMES, Phillip Arnold
Wethersfield HS; Wethersfield, CT (40-400) Band; Hon Prog; *Chem.*

JAMES, Phyllis Rene
Dothan HS; Dothan, AL; Band; Chor; NHS; Hon Prog; *Acct.*

JAMES, Rebekah Markee
Monterey HS; Lubbock, TX (5%-723) Band; Chem C; FTA; 4H; NHS; Tri-HiY; JV, Bkbl; Tr; Vlbl; Phys Sci A; All Tourn Vlbl; 1st Medal, Bkbl; *McMurry Col; Coaching.*

JAMES, Rita Elaine
Bennett HS; Buffalo, NY; Chor; Jr Miss Pagent; Cl Fav; MLS; Most Out; Booster C; PA; Sherman Fisher A; *SE Acad; Airline-Travel.*

JAMES, Robert Earl
Aiken HS; Aiken, SC; Demolay; VP, InterClub Coun; Bkbl; Tnns; COM; Yth Fel; VP, Yth Fel; *U of SC-AIKEN; Bus.*

JAMES, Robert Leon
Mt Ida HS; Mt Ida, AR (14-29) FFA; Ntl Yth Conf; Bkbl; Ftbl; Tr; Yth Fel; Yth Leg.

JAMES, Sarah Josephine
Tillamook HS; Tillamook, OR; MVP, Chldr; GS; InterClub Coun; Pres, Jr Cl; Cr-Ctry; Tr; Tilla-High Qn; Girl o-t Month; *Tane Comm; Real Estate.*

JAMES, Sheri Lynn
W Carter HS; Olive Hill, KY (15-189) BC; Co-Cpt, Chldr; Chor; FBLA; 4H; Cl Fav; 4H A; HCt; Sci A; Achv Test A; *Morehead St U.*

JAMES, Tammy Sue
Cumberland HS; Toledo, IL (12-99) FHA; NHS; Pres, SC; VP, Sr Cl; Tr; Hon Prog; Home Ec A; *Dorothy Chrysler Beauty Sch; Beautician.*

JAMES, Thomas Wayne
Clay Center Comm HS; Clay Center, KS (15%-124) FFA; Tr; FCA; Kans Hon Soc; *Beloit Area Voc Tech Sch; Carpentry.*

JAMES, Vanessa LaFaye
Rufus King HS; Milwaukee, WI; FBLA; Pres, Hmrm; Fin, Bkbl; Bio A; Hon Prog; Sci A; Geography A; *U W at Madison; Law.*

JAMES, Welford Lamont
Forest Brook Sr HS; Houston, TX (3-40) *Stephen Col; Mus.*

JAMESON, Carol Yvonne
Providence Christian HS; Riverview, FL (8-26) Sftbl.

JAMESON, Harry Douglas Jr
Henry Clay HS; Lexington, KY (1-569) Chor; Community Yth Symph; Tres, NHS; Orch; Sch Achieve Tm; Cr-Ctry; Tr; I Dare You; NMF; Val; NCTE A; *Westminster Col; Biol.*

JAMESON, Maribeth Isabelle
Henry Clay HS; Lexington, KY; Community Yth Symph; Orch; MVP, Cr-Ctry; Tr; *Phys Ed.*

JAMESON, Stuart Curtis
Eupora HS; Eupora, MS (20-100) BC; JV, Bkbl; Ftbl; JV, Tr; Yth Fel; Life Sct; VP, Fresh Cl.

JAMESON, William Eugene
Davis Sr HS; Davis, OK (1-56) Band; VP, Fr C; FFA; 4H; Hmrm; Math C; Sci C; VP, Span C; Spch C; VP, SC; Bkbl; Alg A; Bio A; Most Talented 1976-77; FFA Pub Speaking A; *Okla St U; Pol Sci.*

JAMISON, Bryan Donald
Borup HS; Borup, MN (1-14) Cpt, A Cap Choir; Cpt, Band; BS; Cpt, Chess C; Cpt, Chor; Cpt, Dbte Tm; MVP, Drama; Cpt, Ensm; Pres, 4H; Cpt, Math C; Pres, NFL; NHS; Co-Ed, Sch P; Cpt, Spch C; St Stu Congress; S-T, Jr Cl; Bkbl; Cpt, Ftbl; Cpt, Tr; B Crocker A; 4H A; I Dare You; Spch A; Val; Yth Fel; MVP, Tr; St Ambassador, 4-H; Win, 4-H St Leadership; Minn Legislative Internship; NFL Highest Distinct; *U of Minn; Law.*

JAMISON, Cynthia Louise
Columbine HS; Littleton, CO (18-400) Chor; A-Ed, Lit Mag; SC; VP, Jr Cl; Tr; Citz A; Hon Prog; Kiwanis A; Pres A; Vlbl; 1st Cl GSct; Lifeguard; Outst Achv, Acad; Superior Art Achv; 'A' HR; *Colo St U; Environmental Engr.*

JAMISON, Julie Ann
Van Buren Comm HS; Keosauqua, IA; Var C; Bkbl; Tr; *Kirkwood Comm Col; Bus.*

JAMISON, Julie Lynn
Fairmont E HS; Kettering, OH (100-300) A Cap Choir; Chor; Ensm; Hon Prog; Yth Fel; *Fashion Merchandising.*

JAMISON, Lynda Carol
Butler Aizea Sr HS; Butler, PA (96-990) Band; Chor; Community Yth Symph; Semi-Fin, Jr Miss Pa; Orch; Rptr, Thes; COM; Dist Orch; Cpt, Acolyte Tm; Grand Usherette; Thespian Conf; Candystriper; Tour Poland, Rainbow; Past Worthy Adv, Rainbow Girls; *Duquesne U; Phar.*

JAMISON, Nancy Ann
Cabrillo Sr HS; Lompoc, CA (36-402) Bus C; Ski C; Mgr, Sftbl; *Calif Polytechnic Inst; Bus.*

JAMISON, Steven Micheal
Anacortes HS; Anacortes, WA; Key C; Model UN; F-Ed, Sch P; UN Council; *W Wash St Col; Journ.*

JANATKA, Nancy Ann
Lyons Twp HS; Lagrange, IL (86-1185) Orch; Ski C; HR; Guard C; Assn of Foreign Exchange Stu; *Knox Col; Nurs.*

JANES, Debbie Ann
Auburn HS; Auburn, WA; Band; Chor; Ensm; Hmrm; NHS; Orch; *Seattle Pacific Col; Interior Design.*

JangDHARI,
Kamini Shelly Wendy
McGavock HS; Nashville, TN (144-850) BC; Hmrm; InterClub Coun; Lat C; Math C; Mu Alpha Theta; Spch C; SC; Elk A; *Tenn St U; Med.*

JangDHARI,
Kathyann Shakuntala
McGavock HS; Nashville, TN; BC; Pres, Hmrm; Math C; Mu Alpha Theta; ARC; Ed, Sch P; SC; MVP, Sftbl; Honarary Page, St Leg; *Tenn St U; Med.*

JANICEK, Ivan Joseph
Brazos HS; Wallis, TX (29-72) FFA; Pres, 4H; Pres, Soph Cl; Bkbl; Ftbl; Cl Fav; *Wharton Co Jr Col; Mech.*

JANICKI, Robert Walter Jr
Bishop Ryan HS; Minot, ND (7-74) F-Ed, Ann; BS; Ger C; Hmrm; VP, Key C; Model UN; NHS; Ftbl; Tr; Chamber of Comm A; K of C A; MLS; Sci A; Ftbl & Tr Ltrs; Key C Intern; Hon Graduate; *St Thomas Col; Bio.*

JANKE, Judy Lynn
Spring N HS; Spring, TX (300-600) *N Harris Jr Col; Bus.*

JANKE, Matthew Lance
Monroe HS; Monroe, WI (100-200) VP, Bus C; Ch, Key C; VFW A; Yth Fel; Conservation C; Stu Exchange; VP, DECA; Church Coun; *U of Wis; Bus.*

JANKOWIAK, Kathy Lee
Manistee HS; Manistee, MI; S-T, Fr C; Journ A.

JANKOWSKI, James
Providence HS; New Lenox, IL (110-235) A Cap Choir; Chor; Span C; Amer Leg A; Sacristan; Sanctuary Soc; *Lewis U.*

JANMEY, Jeffrey Paul
Lutheran HS W; Rocky River, OH (25-100) Band; NHS; Cr-Ctry; Wrest; *Case W Reserve U; Engr.*

JANOSKO, Stephen Eric
Cave Spring HS; Roanoke, VA (25%-500) Band; Pres, Chess C; Hmrm; Fin, Lit Mag; Order/Arrow; COM; God & Country A; Order/Arrow A; Blue Belt, Judo C; Eagle Sct; Sr Patrol Ldr; Jr Asst Scoutmaster; *Art.*

JANOWSKY, Bruce Glenn
Sw Central HS; Jamestown, NY (10-190) NHS; Pres, Var C; Ftbl; Tr; Wrest; Opt Out Tn; Regent Schol; *Allegheny Col; Bus Adm.*

JANSEN, Darlene Sue
Maple Heights HS; Maple Heights, OH (225-550) Ensm; SC; Citz A; Close-Up; *Cedarville Col; Pre-Law.*

JANSEN, Donna Mae
Central Comm HS; Breese, IL (16-157) Band; CYO; VP, Drama; Fr C; FHA; Model UN; VP, Sr Cl; VP, Jr Cl; Amer Leg A; Bio A; All-Amer Band Hon.

JANSEN, Jacqueline Ann
Eden Valley-Watkins HS; Eden Valley, MN (15-100) CYO; Ger C; Colorguard; PA.

JANSEN, Jay Alden
Valley City HS; Valley City, ND (45-162) Band; Tres, FFA; FFA Ldrship A; *Botany.*

JANSEN, Josephine Elizabeth
Eden Valley-Watkins HS; Eden Valley, MN (5-100) Band; CYO; Ensm; FHA; NHS; Sftbl.

JANSEN, Sheila Ann
Mater Dei HS; Breese, IL (17-169) Ann; CYO; Chor; Drama; Cpt, Hmrm; Sch P; Sftbl; Hon Prog; Stats, Tr; MVP, Vlbl; WW; Drama A; *Ind U at Bloomington; Optometry.*

JANSKY, Denise Marie
Severson HS; Stanley, ND; Chor; 4H; Span C; Hon Prog; Magna Cum Laude; *UND; Farm & Ranch Mgt.*

JANTO, Carolyn Catherine
S Park HS; Library, PA (20-163) Hmrm; Ski C; Var C; Cpt, Bkbl; Cpt, Tnns; Hon Prog; *Shippensburg St Col; Hist.*

JANTSCH, Dawn Delisse
Arlington HS; Arlington Heights, IL; 4H A; Summa Cum Laude; *Bradly U; Eng.*

JANTZ, Gregory Lamar
Boise HS; Boise, ID (280-467) JA A; Outst Stu, Lions C; Sprts Med Trnr; Major Role, Pub Drama; VP, Exec Yth Co; Health Ed Achv Ce; Del, Nazarene Yth Interntl Conv; *Idaho St U; Pre-Med.*

JANUARY, Teresa Lynn
Raymore-Peculiar HS; Peculiar, MO (4-147) FHA; FTA; Ger C; Cpt, Mjrte; NHS; ARC; Secy, SC; Var C; Bkbl; Tr; *William Jewel Col; Law.*

JANZEN, Byron Kevin
Glendale Acad; Glendale, CA (80%-64) Band; Chor; ARC; Swim; Citz A; Type A; *Loma Linda U; Theology.*

JANZEN, James Keith
Augusto Sr HS; Augusta, KS (40-150) Band; Chor; Ensm; Madrigal; Cpt, Cr-Ctry; HCt; Dist Chor; *Tabor Col.*

JAQUIS, Juline Carin
New Hartford Comm HS; New Hartford, IA (5-32) Ann; Band; Chldr; Chor; VP, NHS; Sch P; VP, Sr Cl; Tr; Beauty; COM; HCt; *U of Northern Iowa; Bus.*

JARAMILLO, Angela
Goodard HS; Roswell, NM (71-310) CYO; Chldr; GS; Hmrm; Tres, NHS; Sch P; Ski C; Span C; Tres, St Stu Congres; Tres, SC; Tres, Jr Cl; Ftbl; Tr; Amer Leg A; COM; Citz A; AAUW, Girl o-t Month; *Columbia U; Journ.*

JARAMILLO, Dave Eugene
Bellarmine Jefferson HS; Burbank, CA; Bsbl; JV, Bkbl; Ftbl; Boxing; Altar Boy; *Truck Driving.*

JARAMILLO, Laura Maria
Colegio Universit Sagrado Corazon; Santurce, PR (3-37) A Cap Choir; CYO; Drama; FHA; Pres, Hmrm; COM; Math A; *CAAM; Industrial Engr.*

JARBOE, Charlotte Lynne
Breckinridge Co HS; Harned, KY (5%-250) 4H; Math C; Span C; Tres, Soph Cl; Bkbl; HR; Tres, Fresh Cl; Math C Comm; *Ambassador Col; Math.*

JARBOE, Rebecca Gayle
Breckinridge Co HS; Harned, KY (10%-200) Ann; Chor; FTA; NHS; Sch P; *U of Ky.*

JARCHOW, Timothy Scott
Roy C Start HS; Toledo, OH (17-441) NHS; *Aviation.*

JARECKIE, Ann Brittin
Mount Anthony Union HS; Bennington, VT; 4H; Ski C; Tr; 4H A; Most Out; *U of Vt; Art.*

JARECKIE, Ellen Carraway
Mount Anthony Union Sr HS; Bennington, VT; Ski C; Cr-Ctry; Tr; Patriol o-t Mo; *U of Vt; Studio Art.*

JARED, Garry Austin
Upperman HS; Baxter, TN; Co-Ed, Ann; BC; Dbte Tm; Drama; Secy, Fr C; VP, FFA; Pres, NFL; F-Ed, Sch P; Secy, Jr Cl; Pres, Soph Cl; Bsbl; Alg A; Amer Leg Orator A; Math A; Q&S A; VFW Orator Win; FFA Spch Win; *US Air Force Acad; Military Stu.*

JAREM, John Jeffry
Lakewood Sr HS; Saint Petersburg, FL (30-700) NHS; *U of Fla; Med.*

JARMON, Gawaja Danette
North HS; Nashville, TN; FHA; *Tenn St U.*

JAROSZ, Joan Ellen
D C Everest Sr HS; Schofield, WI (15-349) NHS; Orch; ARC; Sch P; SC; COM; Spch A; VofDEM; *Apostolic Bible Inst; Religious.*

JAROSZ, Melanie Frances
Nicholaus Senn HS; Chicago, IL (46-400) Band; Community Yth Symph; Fr C; Orch; Mgr, Swim; COM; Superior Rating, Flute Trio; All City, HS Band; Yth Del; Ntl Conv Lutheran Church; *DePaul U; Mus.*

JARRARD, Cynthia Ann
Broxton HS; Broxton, GA; F-Ed, Ann; Secy, BC; Cpt, Chldr; Pres, FHA; GS; VP, 4H; Sch P; SC; Pres, Jr Cl; Secy, Soph Cl; Tnns; Crisco A; 4H A; HQn; HCt; Most Out; Miss FHA; WW in Future Homemakers; *S Ga U; Legal Secy.*

JARRELL, Brenda Lynn
William Monroe HS; Standardsville, VA (5-78) Ann; Secy, BC; FBLA; FHA; A-Ed, Lit Mag; Sci C; Gifted Stu; WW; *Bridgewater Col; Sci.*

JARRELL, Cecelia Gail
Scott HS; Madison, WV; Band; JV, Chldr; Dbte Tm; Ensm; GS; Hmrm; NFL; Parl, NHS; Orch; SC; Thes; Tnns; MLS; Span A; *W Va U; Law.*

JARRELL, Patricia Ann
Estill HS; Estill, SC (2-56) Ann; BC; FHA; COM; Gov Honor Prog; *Columbia Col; Eng.*

JARVIS, Bobbye Lee
Germantown HS; Germantown, TN (153-425) A Cap Choir; Chor; FTA; ROTC A; Chor Cert; *U of Tenn; Mus.*

JARVIS, ByFord Thomas
Fairview HS; Boulder, CO (33%-600) Chor; SC; Bkbl; Ftbl; Tr; Opt A; Head Boy; *U of Colo; Bio.*

JARVIS, Cheryl Jeanette
Elida Sr HS; Elida, OH (193-250) Band; Chor; VP, FTA; NHS; *Evangel Col; Psych.*

JARVIS, Daniel Bailey
Fairview HS; Boulder, CO; Bkbl; Ftbl; Tr; *Colo U.*

JARVIS, Elizabeth Marie
Northwestern Sr HS; Hyattsville, MD; Rptr, Sch P; SC; Pres, Soph Cl; Alg A; COM; Sci A; Type A; Pom Pon Girl; Service to Sch A; *U of Md; Law.*

JARVIS, Kristie Lee
Asheville HS; Asheville, NC (2-375) Band; NHS; Span C; Sal; Drum Major; *E Tenn St U; Nurs.*

JARVIS, Nicolie Anne
Waukegan Christian Sch; Zion, IL (3-6) Ann; Chldr; Ensm; Jr Miss Pagent; Secy, Sr Cl; Rptr, Jr Cl; Memory & Bible As; Art As; *Trinity Col; Art.*

JARVIS, Patricia Elaine
Gilmer Co HS; Glenville, WV (13-122) Band; Ensm; Mjrte; *SE Okla St U; Med Tech.*

JARVIS, Paul Duncan
Fairview HS; Boulder, CO; Chor; JV, Tr; JV, Wrest; *Med.*

JARVIS, Reecia Ann
Pima HS; Pima, AZ (7-40) Band; Chldr; Drama; FHA; Hmrm; Mjrte; NHS; SC; Secy, Jr Cl; Sftbl; HQn; Type A; *Eastern Ariz Col.*

JARZABEK, Simone Lucie
Forest Ridge HS; Bellevue, WA (3-50) CYO; Fr C; Co-Ed, Lit Mag; NHS; Alg A; Amer Leg A; COM; Math A; NEDT; Phy A; Rensselaer A; *U of Wash; Engr.*

JASINSKI, Steven Arthur
St Anthony Village HS; Minneapolis, MN (88-195) Ann; Band; Community Yth Symph; Order/ Arrow; Sci C; Swim; God & Country A; JA A; Order/Arrow A; Eagle Sct; *St Thomas Col; Bus.*

JASKOWIAK, Robert Bryan
S St Paul Sr HS; S St Paul, MN (30-464) AFS; Drama; NHS; Span C; Mgr, Bkbl; Bio A; *St Olaf Col; Econ.*

JASPER, Bernard C
Estherville HS; Estherville, IA (2-173) BS; Chor; Drama; Hmrm; Madrigal; NHS; Pres, SC; Thes; Var C; Pres, Sr Cl; Bkbl; Cr-Ctry; Tr; Amer Leg A; Citz A; Elk A; Sal; St Scholar; Sports Schol; *U of SD; Bus.*

JASPER, Crecynthia Lavine
Channel Islands HS; Oxnard, CA (20-509) Beauty; COM; Hon Prog; *Oxnard Col; Bus.*

JASPER, Gail Kathryn
Estherville HS; Estherville, IA; Band; Chor; Drama.

JASPER, Mary Catherine
Hilbert HS; Hilbert, WI; A Cap Choir; AFS; Band; CYO; Chor; Ensm; Madrigal; Rptr, Sch P; Spch C; SC; Var C; COM; Hon Prog; Math A; Ntl Cath Mus Ed Asn; Spch A; Tri-M Piano, Marian, A's; Hon Camping Soc; *Mus.*

JASPER, Mozell
Bullock Co HS; Union Springs, AL (2-150) Rptr, FBLA; Hmrm; NHS; SC; COM; 4H A; Hist A; HQn; Hon Prog; Math A; Sci A; Val; Eng, PA, Service, Schol Achv, A's; *U of Ala; Acct.*

JASPER, Ruth Ann
Franklin Center HS; Franklin Grove, IL (3-49) Band; Tres, Fr C; 4H; NHS; Tres, SC; 4H A; JA A; Band A; PA at Sunday Sch; *Social Work.*

JASPER, Shelly Kay
Canyonville Bible Acad; Canyonville, OR (2-19) A Cap Choir; Band; Chldr; Chor; Drama; Spch Cl; Cr-Ctry; Tr; Alg A; HCt; Hon Prog; Most Out; Eng A; Band Trophy.

JASPERSE, Carol A
Dearborn HS; Dearborn, MI (5%-570) Ski C; Phi Beta Kappa; *Calvin Col; Biol.*

JAUREGUI, Philip DeWayne
Moreno Valley HS; Sunnymead, CA (20%-500) Drama; SC; Thes; Swim; Water Polo; Gym; Hon Hist Stu; *USC; Med.*

JAVORCKY, Cyndi Gail
Lakewood HS; Lakewood, OH; Band; Chor; Orch; Social Stu Departmental Hon; *Bus.*

JAVORCKY, Cynthia Gail
Lakewood HS; Lakewood, OH; Band; Chor; Orch; Bus.

JAWORSKI, Frank Joseph
Don Bosco Tech HS; Boston, MA (15-222) Rptr, Sch P; Tr; Pres, Radio C; *U of Dayton; Elec Engr.*

JAWORSKI, Thomas Martin
George J Penney HS; E Hartford, CT (75-376) Sch P; SC; Cpt, Bkbl; Bkbl Player o-t Wk; All League 1st Tm, Hon Men All St; *Central Conn St Col; Bus Adm.*

JAYNES, Cheryl Dianne
Independence HS; Charlotte, NC (40-579) Band; Ensm; NHS; Orch; Tres, Span C; Yth Fel; Yth Coun; *U of NC; Special Ed.*

JAYNES, Debbie Ann
West HS; Painted Post, NY; Alg A; Color Guard; Girls Routine; *Corning Comm Col; Secy.*

JAYNES, Patricia Anne
Berea HS; Greenville, SC (10-250) GS; Pres, Hmrm; NHS; VP, SC; Beauty; Pep C; *Vanderbilt U.*

JAYNES, Susan Kathy
Berea HS; Greenville, SC; Chor; GS; VP, Mod Mus Mas; NHS; DARGCA; HCt; *Furman U.*

JAYROE, William Charles
Winyoh HS; Georgetown, SC (58-140) Arch; 4H; Order/Arrow; Var C; JV, Arch; Ftbl; God & Country A; Order/Arrow A; Francis Marion A; *U of SC; Marine Bio.*

JEAN, Karen Rachelle
Tioga HS; Tioga, LA; BC; Chor; Q&S A; 3rd Pl, Foreign Lang Festival; *Math.*

JEANE, Joyce Marie
Leesville HS; Leesville, LA (32-290) Fr C; Lit Ral; Summer Workshop, La Tech U; Tn Involvement Coun; Parish Cattlemen Qn; *Northwestern of La; Social Work.*

JEAN FRANCOIS, Marie Junie
E Orange HS; E Orange, NJ (56-417) Fr C; FNA; *Cath U; Nurs.*

JEANLOUIS, Wendell
Jeanerette HS; Jeanerette, LA (3-160) CYO; Sch Achieve Tm; Bsbl; Cpt, Bkbl; Cpt, Ftbl; Sftbl; Tnns; Tr; Star Student; PA; *U of SW La; Hist.*

JEANSONNE, Jennifer Ann
Buckeye HS; Buckeye, LA; CYO; FBLA; FHA; Hmrm; Swim; *La Tech Col; Aviation Engr.*

JECKLIN, Jennifer Anne
Central HS; Davenport, IA (15-700) Ann; Fr C; Hon Prog; *Minneapolis Col of Art & Design; Photography.*

JEDLICKA, Tamra Sue
South Shelby HS; Shelbina, MO (2-110) Secy, CYO; Chor; Ensm; GS; Madrigal; Tres, NHS; Secy, Var C; Bkbl; Sftbl; Mgr, Tr; Bio A; COM; Hon Prog; K of C A; NEDT; Semi-Fin, REA Essay Contest; Dist Choir; *UMKC; Med.*

JEFFCOAT, Debra Charlene
Hannah-Pamplico HS; Pamplico, SC (15-100) Tres, FBLA; FHA; FTA; Tnns; Leadership A; *Florence Darlington Tech Col; Bus.*

JEFFCOAT, Ronald James
Eau Claire HS; Columbia, SC (79-375) Chess C; Sch P; Bkbl; Tr; Star Student; Type A; *U of SC; Bus Adm.*

JEFFERIES, Dawn LeAnn
Marion HS; Marion, IN; ARC; *Marion Col; Home Ec.*

JEFFERIES, Mary Ellen
Katella HS; Anaheim, CA; A Cap Choir; Chor; Home Ec A; Nurs Aide Cert; *Biola Col; Nurs.*

JEFFERIES, Roger Dean
T Wingate Andrews HS; High Point, NC; Band; Cpt, Bsbl; Co-Cpt, Bkbl; Hon Prog; Math A; Most Out; Phi Beta Kappa.

JEFFERS, Lana Rae
E St Louis Sr HS; E St Louis, IL (67-769) Fr C; 4H; Hmrm; Co-Ed, Lit Mag; Co-Ed, Sch P; SC; Amer Leg A; Cl Fav; 4H A; Hist A; Journ A; JA A; Pres A; Spch A; Type A; *Loyola U; Journ.*

JEFFERS, Lesa Jaleigh
Mt Carmel HS; Mt Carmel, IL (5-205) Chor; NHS; ARC; SC; Pres, Sr Cl; Tres, Jr Cl; WW; *Sou Ill U; Acct.*

JEFFERS, Scott Edward
Norwayne HS; Creston, OH (17-104) Ann; Band; BS; Chor; Ensm; 4H; Spch C; SC; Var C; Mgr, Bkbl; Tnns; *Bowling Green St U; Theater Arts.*

JEFFERSON, Charles Darryl
Baltimore City Col; Baltimore, MD (41-175) Chess C; Chor; Pres, Hmrm; Ftbl; Cpt, Tr; *Winston-Salem St Col; Photography.*

JEFFERSON, Frank William
St Ignatius College Prep; San Francisco, CA; A Cap Choir; MVP, Bkbl; Tr; *UCLA; Med.*

JEFFERSON, Freddie B
E Atlanta HS; Atlanta, GA (2-142) BC; Hmrm; ARC; Span C; SC; Pres, Sr Cl; COM; Harvard Book A; MLS; Most Out; ROTC A; Sal; Sci A; *Clark Col; Biol.*

JEFFERSON, Gwendolyn
Tunstall Sr HS; Dry Fork, VA; Ed, Ann; JV, Chldr; S-T, Chor; Parl, FHA; 4H; Hmrm; Madrigal; Monogram; SC; Mgr, Tr; Chor Ltr; Tr Ltr; *Va Commonwealth U; Mus.*

JEFFERSON, Janet Angelene
Tunstall HS; Dry Fork, VA; Ed, Ann; Chor; 4H; S-T, HiY; Madrigal; Monogram; Pres, SC; Secy, Y-Tns; Mgr, Tr; COM; Most Improved; Outst Y-Tn; Chor Ltr; Tr Ltr; *Danville Comm Col; Social Work.*

JEFFERSON, Janice Monique
Halter HS; St Louis, MO (1-110) Chldr; Jr Miss Pagent; Span C; SC; Jr Cl; Sftbl; HQn; Hon Prog; Math A; MLS; Type A; Span A; Homemaker A; *Engr.*

JEFFERSON, Kimberly
Martin Luther King HS; Philadelphia, PA; Chldr; Pres, Hmrm; Pres, SC; Pres, Jr Cl; *Drexel Col; Fashion Design.*

JEFFERSON, Pamela Joanne
Shawnee Mission NW HS; Shawnee Mission, KS (138-760) Band; Ensm; Vlbl; Past Worthy Adv, Job's Daughters; *Engr.*

JEFFERSON, Ronald Duane
Carver HS; Memphis, TN (12-24) VP, SC; JV, Bsbl; JV, Bkbl; Mgr, Ftbl; Hon Prog; Math A; MLS; *Memphis St U; Acct.*

JEFFERSON, Vanessa Rosa
Martin Luther King HS; Philadelphia, PA (17-690) FNA; Hmrm; NHS; Co-Ed, Sch P; Span C; Tnns; Tr; Alternative C; Lib Aide; Coun Aide.

JEFFERY, Connie Marie
Calico Rock HS; Calico Rock, AR (4-33) BC; Chor; FHA; Rptr, Soph Cl; Eng A; Win, Talent Contest; Runner-Up, Most Talented; *Stephens Col; Bus.*

JEFFERY, Dennis Dean
Centralia HS; Centralia, WA; Pres, Span C; Tres, Soph Cl; Bkbl; Tnns; HCt; Hon Prog; Yth Fel; Pres, Church Yth Fel; *Seattle Pacific U; Med.*

JEFFERY, Holly Lynn
St Albans HS; St Albans, WV; Span C; *W Va U; Lang.*

JEFFERY, John Allan
David Douglas HS; Portland, OR (10-650) Semi-Fin, BS; NHS; Order/Arrow; Ski C; Var C; JV, Soccer; COM; Cl Fav; Math A; Order/Arrow A; Yth Fel; Sr Patrol Ldr, Life Sct; 2nd V Man, Ski Racing Tm; *Portland St Col; Med.*

JEFFORDS, Cathy Lynn
Woodward Acad; College Park, GA (15%-200) A Cap Choir; Band; Chor; Ensm; Key C; Fin, Lit Mag; Var C; Bkbl; Sftbl; Drill Tm; *W Ga Col; Special Elem Ed.*

JEFFRES, Charlene Marie
Moorcroft HS; Moorcroft, WY (2-26) Ann; Band; FTA; Semi-Fin, GS; NHS; Co-Ed, Sch P; Tres, Sr Cl; Mgr, Bkbl; Tr; Alg A; Bio A; Chem A; Citz A; Cl Fav; Hist A; Math A; MLS; Sal; Bookkeeping A; WW; Eng A; *Sheridan Col; Counseling.*

JEFFREY, Diana Lynn
Classical HS; Providence, RI; Up Bound; Sftbl; *Bus Ed.*

JEFFREY, Sheila Kaye
Piqua Central HS; Piqua, OH (20-400) NHS; Span C; COM; Hon Prog; PTA A; Safety A; Spelling A; *Nurs.*

JEFFREY, Sherry Faye
Piqua Central HS; Piqua, OH (21-400) NHS; Span C; COM; Hon Prog; PTA A; First Aid & Safety A; Spelling A; *Nurs.*

JEFFREYS, Timothy Jay
Arvada HS; Aryada, CO; Dbte Tm; Spch C; *U of Colo; Physics.*

JEFFRIES, Ashley Mack
Seneca Valley HS; Germantown, MD; Co-Ed, Ann.

JEFFRIES, Christopher Coleman
St John's College HS; Washington, DC (117-235) Bkbl; Tr; Tots & Tns, Inc; Bowl League; Vol, Children's Hospital; *NC St U; Archt.*

JEFFRIES, Deborah Kaye
Castle Rock HS; Castle Rock, WA (14-143) A-Ed, Ann; Chldr; Secy, 4H; Hmrm; NHS; Pres, Rainbow; Secy, SC; Secy, Soph Cl; Mgr, Tr; COM; Citz A; 4H A; HQn; Hon Prog; Journ A; Spch A; Bell Telephone Savings Bond A; Creative Writing Trophy; Grnd Cross of Color, Rainbow Grls; Miss Service, Rainbow Girls; *Journ.*

JEFFRIES, Karen Elaine
Bedford-N Lawrence HS; Bedford, IN (22-486) Ann; BC; Chess C; Chor; Drama; Pres, Ensm; VP, Ger C; Hmrm; VP, Math C; Fin, Sch P; S-T, Sci C; VP, Span C; SC; Thes; Secy, Soph Cl; Bkbl; Cpt, Ftbl; Sftbl; Tr; Citz A; Journ A; Kiwanis A; Math A; MLS; Most Out; Sci A; Spch A; Star Student; Best Stu, Drama, Spch; Vocal Comp; Fin, 1st Pl, Mus A; *Pepperdine U; Mus.*

JEFFRIES, Robin Marie
Waukegan E HS; Waukegan, IL (89-551) A Cap Choir; Fr C; Madrigal; Ski C; Swim; Ch, Dolphins; Badminton; Ch, Prom; Diving; *Bio.*

JEFFRIES, Twyla Gail
Checotah HS; Checotah, OK; Tr; Home Ec A.

JEGHERS, Mark Steven
Tracy HS; Tracy, CA (375-400) Dbte Tm; Bank Of Amer A; CSF; *U o-t Pacific; Elec Engr.*

JEGLEY, Dawn Catherine
Stow Sr HS; Stow, OH (5%-550) Fr C; Math C; 1st Cl GSct; Schol Cert A; *MIT; Math.*

JELINEK, Timothy Downing
Polo R7 HS; Polo, MO (15-40) A Cap Choir; Ann; Chor; Ensm; Madrigal; A-Ed, Sch P; Pres, Span C; VP, SC; Tres, Sr Cl; Ftbl; Tr; God & Country A; Yth Fel; Hon Men, All Conf, Ftbl Offense; WW.

JELKS, Fredrick Lamar
Russell HS; Hurtsboro, AL; Chem C; Drama; FFA; 4H; Sci C; Bkbl; 4H A; HKg; Hon Prog; ROTC A; Spelling A; *Ala A & M Col; ROTC.*

JEMELA, Deborah Ann
Brazos HS; Wallis, TX (2-38) Ed, Ann; FHA; Secy, NHS; DARGCA; Sal; WW; Cl Secy; Most Studious; *Wharton Co Jr Col; Med Records.*

JEMISON, John Montgomery
Memphis University Sch; Memphis, TN (50%-100) Sch P; Ski C; Soccer; I Dare You; *Colorado Col; Hist.*

JEMISON, Karen Lashall
Hamilton HS; Memphis, TN (41-407) Pres, Drama; Lat C; NHS; Pres, Spch C; MVP, Tr; Spch A; Tn St Page; BCA; Choir Directress; Fin, Most Likely to Succeed; Young Amer A; Adv Stu Asst; Comm Theater; *Howard U; Drama.*

JENISON, Martha Diane
Myers Park Sr HS; Charlotte, NC (65-500) BC; Secy, Hmrm; Ski C; Secy, Y-Tns; COM; Girls Ambassador Civinettes; *Mich St U; Horticulture.*

JENISON, Stephen Hinsey
Paris HS; Paris, IL (6-236) Band; BS; Chem C; Hmrm; NHS; JV, Bkbl; Cpt, Ftbl; MVP, Swim; Tr; Wrest; Amer Leg A; Hon Prog; St Scholar; Yth Fel; United Methodist Good Sportsman A; *Rose Hulman Inst of Tech; Chem Engr.*

JENKINS, Barbara Ellen
Lafayette HS; Lafayette, LA (10%-650) Band; InterAct C; Cpt, Mjrte; NHS; Orch; HCt; Hon Prog; Ntl Champ, Trampoline.

JENKINS, Bernita Rose
McMain Magnet Sch; New Orleans, LA (23-82) All Amer Yth; Chem C; Chor; Ensm; Fr C; FHA; 4H; Hmrm; Jr Miss Pagent; Pres, Ntl Yth Conf; Sch Achieve Tm; SC; Cpt, Bsbl; Cpt, Bkbl; Cr-Ctry; Cpt, Sftbl; Tr; COM; Citz A; Cl Fav; HCt; JA A; Most Out; Yth Fel; AFNA Schol; WW; 1st Sr Maid; Gospel Soul Children; *Newcomb Col; Med.*

JENKINS, Billie Ann
Central HS; Little Rock, AR; FBLA; Rainbow; Y-Tns; Citz A; FBLA A; *UALR; Nurs.*

JENKINS, Brenda Elaine
Hutchinson HS; Hutchinson, KS; Chor; Fr C; Rptr, Sch P; Tr; JV, Vlbl; Church Choir; Psalm Quartet; VP, Yth Coun; *Hutchinson Jr Col; Home Ec.*

JENKINS, Charles Bennette
Hendersonville HS; Hendersonville, NC (26-172) Chor; Drama; Hmrm; Key C; NHS; Ed, Sch P; Span C; Thes; COM; Citz A; H of F; *U of NC; Creative Arts.*

JENKINS, Darrell Wayne
Gordon HS; Gordon, TX (10%-14) Ann; Tres, BC; VP, FFA; Pres, SC; Pres, Jr Cl; Pres, Soph Cl; Co-Cpt, Bkbl; Ftbl; Semi-Fin, Golf; Tr; Amer Leg A; Cl Fav; HCt; Hon Prog; Most Handsome; FHA Beau Cand; *Mech Engr.*

JENKINS, David Henry
Central Baptist HS; Hampton, VA (1-14) Ed, Ann; Chor; A-Ed, Sch P; MLS; Sci A; Val; Most Stu; Acad Achv A; Page, 94th Congress; *Col of William and Mary; Gov.*

JENKINS, David John Jr
Champion HS; Warren, OH (19-212) Band; Pres, Chor; Ensm; Fr C; NHS; Orch; ARC; Ftbl; Tr; God & Country A; Ntl Achv Schol; NEDT; ROTC A; Kent St U DSA; *US Air Force Acad; Aeronautical Engr.*

JENKINS, Dianne
Westside HS; Augusta, GA (10-35) Bkbl; Sftbl; Co-Cpt, Tr; COM; Cl Fav; Hon Prog; Math A; MVP, Tr; *Pepperdine U; Med.*

JENKINS, Gale Lynn
Newark Sr HS; Newark, OH (1-650) A Cap Choir; Chem C; Chor; Drama; Ensm; GS; Math C; Mu Alpha Theta; NHS; Thes; NMS; IAM Schol; PTA A; *Ohio Northern U; Phar.*

JENKINS, Genevieve Ann
Eminence Consolidated HS; Eminence, IN (2-51) Band; Semi-Fin, GS; Pres, NHS; HCt; MLS; Sal; St Scholar; *Purdue U; Home Ec.*

JENKINS, Grant William
St Louis Co Day Sch; St Louis, MO (4-78) Math C; Model UN; Order/Arrow; A-Ed, Sch P; JV, Bsbl; JV, Soccer; Chem A; God & Country A; Math A; Sci A; *Pre-Med.*

JENKINS, Greg Edward
Clark Co R-1 HS; Kahoka, MO (56-92) Bus C; Chor; VP, 4H; *Culver-Stockton Col; Art.*

JENKINS, Herbert Lee
Temple HS; Temple, TX; JV, Band; Ftbl; Tr.

JENKINS, Jacquelyn
E Anchorage HS; Anchorage, AK (83-515) Band; Chor; FBLA; Pres, Hmrm; Jr Miss Pagent; NHS; Cpt, Bkbl; COM; Hon Prog; JA A; Yth Fel; MVP; Best Drill Tm Mgr; Prettiest Smile; *Cosmetology.*

JENKINS, Janet Kay
Pacific Christian Acad; Graton, CA (2-6) JV, Chldr; S-T, FHA; Rptr, Sch P; Tres, SC; CSF; Hist A; Eng A; Bookkeeping A; Girls Ldrship Conf; Sunset Sch of Preaching; *Religion.*

JENKINS, Janice Lynn
Eupora HS; Eupora, MS (4-84) BC; FHA; Pres, SC; Best All Around; Miss EHS; *Miss Delta Jr Col; Phar.*

JENKINS, Jennifer Jenise
Serramonte HS; Daly City, CA; Chor; *CSM; Social Worker.*

JENKINS, Jill Elaine
Knob Noster Sr HS; Knob Noster, MO (8-115) Model UN; NHS; Co-Ed, Sch P; St Stu Congress; SC; Secy, Jr Cl; Mgr, Tr; Journ A; Regent Schol; Best Dressed; *Central Mo St U; Fashion Journ.*

JENKINS, Jill Elizabeth
La Jolla HS; LaJolla, CA (7%-500) JV, Chldr; Chor; Co-Ed, Lit Mag; Sci A; Royal Acad of Dancing; Elem A; 1st Hons; *Doreen Bird Col of Theatre Dance; Ballet.*

JENKINS, Judy Carol
Plano Sr HS; Plano, TX (10-850) Dbte Tm; Parl, FHA; NFL; NHS; Hon Prog; Spch A; Hon A, St Fair; St Off, FHA; *Tex Woman's U; Ed.*

JENKINS, Kelvin LeRoy
Jesuit HS; Shreveport, LA (4-97) F-Ed, Ann; Dbte Tm; Drama; Key C; Lit Ral; VP, Math C; Tres, NHS; Rptr, Sch P; COM; JA A; Ntl Achv Schol; NEDT; Schol; Mod Lang Medal; WW; *Northwestern U; Journ.*

JENKINS, Laraine Kim
Burke HS; Charleston, SC (20-210) Band; Tres, Drama; Spch C; *U of SC; Psych.*

JENKINS, Laura Helen
Jonesboro Sr HS; Jonesboro, GA (10%-250) BC; Drama; Fin, Jr Miss Pagent; Tri-HiY; Beauty; COM; Gov Honor Prog; Hon Prog; WW; Clayton Jr Col Schol; *Ga St U; Bus Adm.*

JENKINS, Linda Ann
Northeastern HS; Detroit, MI; Band; Secy, Chor; 4H; Secy, Sch Achieve Tm; Tr; Citz A; Cl Fav; 4H A; MLS; Most Out; *Math Teacher.*

JENKINS, Marcia Lea
Oxford HS; Oxford, KS (2-41) Bus Mgr, Ann; Band; Chor; Ensm; NHS; Rptr, Sch P; Tres, Span C; SC; Pres, Sr Cl; Hon Prog; Magna Cum Laude; Math A; Sal; *Baptist Bible Col; Missions.*

JENKINS, Martin Sam Jr
Arts HS; Newark, NJ (19-165) Chor; Hmrm; NHS; SC; Var C; JV, Bsbl; Soccer; JV, Tr; Cl Fav; Hon Prog; MLS; Future Physicians C; STEP; Talent Search Prog; Fencing Tm; Karate C; Phys Fit C; Merit Achv A; YMCA; Most Scholarly; Friendliest; *Howard U; Sci.*

JENKINS, Melanie Beth
H H Dow HS; Midland, MI (3%-300) Quiz Tm; Church Choir; Teacher; Nursery; *Marian Col; Teacher's Degree.*

JENKINS, Michael Raymond
Thomas Walter Josey HS; Augusta, GA (15-130) Band; Fr C; Math C; Phys C; Up Bound; Pres, Jr Cl; Bkbl; Ftbl; Tnns; Tr; Hist A; Hon Prog; Math A; *Morehouse Col; Vet Med.*

JENKINS, Moses Jr
Spartanburg HS; Spartanburg, SC (3-700) VP, Hmrm; Span C; Ftbl; Beauty; Sci A; *U of SC; Bus Mgr.*

JENKINS, Oneice
HS for Health Professions; Dallas, TX;

JENKINS, Patti Jean
Palestine HS; Palestine, TX (25%-250) InterAct C; NHS; Span C; Sftbl; Tnns; Drill Tm; *Stephen F Austin St U.*

JENKINS, Rae Ann
Ironton HS; Ironton, OH (24-191) Secy, Band; Chor; Drama; Hmrm; NHS; Span C; SC; Secy, Jr Cl; Secy, Soph Cl; JV, Sftbl; Magna Cum Laude; Yth Fel; Freshie A; WW; *Ohio U.*

JENKINS, Rita Viola
Savannah HS; Savannah, GA; Chor; Drama; Fr C; Tnns; Most Out; ROTC A; Scholastic Achv A; *Savannah St Col; Eng.*

JENKINS, Roxann
Northwestern HS; Flint, MI; Secy, Bus C; NHS; Hon Prog; Ntl Hon Cert; High Std Schol; *Mich St U; Psych.*

JENKINS, Russell Keith
Robert E Lee HS; Jacksonville, FL; VP, Chor; Ensm; Madrigal; Swim; VP, JA; Grad, Dale Carnegie Course; *Mus.*

JENKINS, Sally
Bayou Chicot HS; Bayou Chicot, LA (5-43) Pres, FHA; 4H; Lit Ral; HCt; Receptionist.

JENKINS, Sarah Elaine
Burke HS; Charleston, SC (13-201) Ed, Ann; VP, Drama; Secy, Hmrm; Mjrte; NHS; SC; Ed, Sr Cl; Pres, Jr Cl; VP, Soph Cl; MVP, Tr; COM; Hon Prog; JA A; WW; U of SC; Criminology.

JENKINS, Shari Jean
Zanesville HS; Zanesville, OH; Ski C; Span C; Tnns.

JENKINS, Sharon Kaye
Hazelwood E Sr HS; St Louis, MO (60-455) Co-Cpt, Chldr; NHS; SC; Sftbl; Mgr, Tr; Yth Fel; Young Life; Prom Court; Class Offices; Central Methodist Col; Elem Ed.

JENKINS, Shawn B
Star Valley HS; Afton, WY (6-100) BS; Chem C; Dbte Tm; FTA; Math C; NHS; VP, Order/Arrow; Phys C; ARC; Sci C; Var C; Sftbl; Wrest; Amer Leg A; Hon Prog; Order/Arrow A; Yth Leg; Fin, W Va Schol; U of Nev at Las Vegas; Vet Sci.

JENKINS, Shelia Ann
Waterproof HS; Waterproff, LA (4-62) Parl, Band; BS; Chor; FBLA; U of New Orleans; Acct.

JENKINS, Susan Christine
Pima HS; Pima, AZ (6-45) Chldr; FHA; Semi-Fin, GS; NHS; Ski C; Span C; SC; Pres, Jr Cl; Tnns; Eng A; Ariz St U; Sci.

JENKINS, Timothy Lavelle
St Andrews Parish HS; Charleston, SC; Bkbl; Tr; Morehouse Col; Criminal Law.

JENKINS, Vera Lisa
Chicago Vocational HS; Chicago, IL (98-935) Hmrm; SC; Secy, Jr Cl; COM; Hon Prog; Mus A; Howard U; Med.

JENKINS, Veronica Shay
Independence HS; Columbus, OH; Bkbl; Sftbl; Swim; Tr; Cl Fav; Philander Smith Col; Law.

JENKINS, Vicki Lyn
Kingsway Regional HS; Swedesboro, NJ (2-170) NHS.

JENKINS, Wanda Maureen
W Monroe HS; W Monroe, LA; Sch P; Spch A; Yth Fel; NE La U; Math.

JENKINS, William Earl
Leo HS; Chicago, IL (13-140) Hmrm; NHS; SC; Var C; Tr; HKg; HCt; Ed, Yrbk; Dance Comm; Middle Tenn St U; Psych.

JENKINS, Yolanda Yvette
Buena HS; Sierra Vista, AZ (12-500) Band; Minority Stu Union; Choshise Col; Health.

JENKS, John Robert
Chelan HS; Chelan, WA (3-50) VP, Bus C; Hmrm; NHS; Span C; Var C; Bkbl; Cpt, Tnns; Wash St U; Engr.

JENNER, Jane Elizabeth
Parkway Central Sr HS; Creve Coeur, MO (52-488) AFS; Ger C; Hockey; Tr; U of Mo at Columbia; Marketing.

JENNEY, Faith Elizabeth
Frank Scott Bonnell HS; Stratford, CT; Chor; Ensm; Lit Mag; Sch P; Span C; Span NHS; Bkbl; Pilgrim Fel; Yacht C; Best Racer, Sailing; Most Ath; Botany.

JENNINGS, Angela Junellie
Barringer HS; Newark, NJ; Band; Chor; Drama; Hmrm; Semi-Fin, Jr Miss Pa; SCnt; Citz A; Elk A; Colorguard; 2nd Runnerup, Miss Barringer; Drew U; Drama.

JENNINGS, Antonia
Guthrie HS; Guthrie, OK (32-186) A Cap Choir; Ann; Band; Chor; Ensm; FBLA; FFA; 4H; Sci A; Sch P; Span C; SC; Bkbl; COM; Citz A; Cl Fav; Journ A; Masonic A; PTA A; Spch A; Tri-St Hon Chor; Pres, Black Heritage C; Langston U; Bus Adm.

JENNINGS, Barbara Jo
Tri-Valley HS; Dresden, OH; Band; Drama; Tres, 4H; 4H A; Off, Drill Tm.

JENNINGS, Byron Lee
Patrick Henry HS; Roanoke, VA (1-575) BC; Pres, Fr C; SC; Bkbl; MVP, Tnns; Alg A; COM; Hist A; Math A; Sci A; Type A; Eng A; U of Richmond; Med.

JENNINGS, Cindy
Nordhoff HS; Ojai, CA (30-300) Swim; Ecology.

JENNINGS, David Anthony
Andrean High School; Merrillville, IN (107-220) Band; CYO; Drama; SC; Asst Drum Major; Band A; UCLA; Law.

JENNINGS, Donna Sue
Wilburton HS; Wilburton, OK (19-60) Band; Bus C; Chor; Ensm; Pres, FBLA; Pres, FHA; NHS; SC; VP, Sr Cl; Pres, Jr Cl; Cl Fav; Most Out; Eastern Okla St Col; Dental Hygienist.

JENNINGS, Elizabeth Bray
Marked Tree HS; Marked Tree, AR (2-110) Band; Chem C; Chor; Drama; Madrigal; NHS; Thes; HCt; Eng A; Ark St U; Blind Children Ed.

JENNINGS, James Alan
Battle Ground Acad; Franklin, TN (9-98) Lat C; Bsbl; Bkbl; Ftbl; NEDT; NCSU; Agr.

JENNINGS, James Edward
Oak Ridge HS; Orlando, FL; A Cap Choir; BS; Chor; Ensm; Pres, FBLA; Pres, FHA; NHS; Sci C; Stu Service A; Ntl Soc o-t Sons o-t Amer Rev; U S Air Force Acad; Air Force.

JENNINGS, Janice Larosa
Bartow Sr HS; Bartow, FL (24-300) F-Ed, Ann; Cpt, Chldr; Chor; Ensm; Parl, FHA; Parl, FTA; Fin, GS; 4H; VP, InterClub Coun; NHS; Sci C; Span C; St Stu Congress; Pres, SC; Secy, Jr Cl; Mgr, Cr-Ctry; Sftbl; Mgr, Tr; Amer Leg A; Beauty; COM; 4H A; Hon Prog; Pres A; Spch A; Howard U; Law.

JENNINGS, Jimmy Dale
Sylvan Hills HS; Sherwood, AR (316-383) Ch, A Cap Choir; Bus C; Chor; Demolay; Drama; FBLA; Hmrm; Key C; Sci C; Spch C; Var C; Bsbl; Mgr, Bkbl; Ftbl; Tnns; COM; Yth Leg; Medal & Mgr, A Cappella Choir; Jr Executive Trng; Ouachita Baptist U; Phys Ed.

JENNINGS, Julia Lynne
Sooner HS; Bartlesville, OK (1-289) A Cap Choir; AFS; A-Ed, Ann; Chor; COM; St Scholar; Ntl Piano Playing Auditions; Choral Accompanist; Acteens-Qn, Qn Wth Scepter & Regent; Okla St U; Marine Bio.

JENNINGS, Kathy Ellen
Sooner HS; Bartlesville, OK (8-289) Band; Co-Cpt, Chldr; Chor; Drama; JV, Tnns; Tr; Amer Leg A; Citz A; Hon Prog; Pres A.

JENNINGS, Kathy Jo
Greenwood HS; Greenwood, SC (350-570) Chor; Fr C; Spch C; Arch; JV, Bkbl; Hockey; Sftbl; Tr; Lander Col; Nurs.

JENNINGS, Kathy Melinda
Jamacia HS; Jamacia, NY (389-1133) Band; Cpt, Chldr; Chor; Ensm; Hmrm; SC; Tr; Most Out; Yth Fel; UCLA; Psych Social Worker.

JENNINGS, Katina Marie
East HS; Columbus, OH (1-330) Most Outst Jr, Band A; Ohio St U; Phys Therapy.

JENNINGS, Keith Allison
Central HS; Columbia, TN (45-433) BC; Fr C; Math C; Sci C; Mgr, Bkbl; Middle Tenn St U; Acct.

JENNINGS, Marci Chrisanne
Independence HS; Independence, MS (10%-118) BC; Chor; Mgr, Bkbl; Mgr, Tr; Northwest Jr Col; Nursing.

JENNINGS, Mary Elisabeth
Ethel HS; Ethel, MS (25%-50) Secy, Band; Rptr, BC; Ch, FHA; Sch P; Sci C; Cpt, Flag Corp; Most Improved, Band; Miss St U.

JENNINGS, Melanie Anne
Ballard Mem HS; Barlow, KY (10-108) Ed, Ann; Pres, Band; VP, BC; FFA; GS; SC; COM; Citz A; Hon Prog; Journ A; Lead, Jr & Sr Plays; Coffee Schol; Alumni Schol; Quad-St Band; Paducah Comm Col; Secondary Counseling.

JENNINGS, Nadine Otelia
Chester HS; Chester, PA (28-673) Band; U of Fla; Math.

JENNINGS, Peggy June
Coquille HS; Coquille, OR (25%-125) Band; Chldr; Ensm; Secy, Soph Cl; Sftbl; Oreg St U; Ed.

JENNINGS, Phyllis Karen
Lawton Sr HS; Lawton, OK; A Cap Choir; Chor; FHA; Bkbl; Sftbl; Tr; COM; 4H A; ROTC A; Cameron U; Law.

JENNINGS, Ramona
Columbus E HS; Columbus, OH (50-350) Chor; Ohio St U; Bus Adm.

JENNINGS, Randal Eugene
Oroville HS; Oroville, CA (32-220) NHS; Bsbl; Bkbl; Ftbl; Cpt, Tr; Citz A; Pres A; Humbolt St Col; Forestry.

JENNINGS, Suzanne Kathleen
Elk Grove HS; Elk Grove Village, IL; Chess C; Drama; Hmrm; Thes; Cl Fav; Drama & Costume A; Fr Achv A; Art A; Northern Ill U; Interior Design.

JENNINGS, Tina Renae
Fulton HS; Atlanta, GA; Drama; Eckerd Col; Bus Ed.

JENNINGS, Tony Neal
Kirkman Tech HS; Chattanooga, TN (1-550) Co-Cpt, Band; VP, Chor; Hmrm; Up Bound; Bkbl; Wrest; Best Dressed; Dist Choir; JC; Morehouse Col; Bus Ed.

JENSEN, Carolyn Bekins II
Sioux City N HS; Sioux City, IA (125-338) Band; Chldr; Fr C; Ski C; Tnns; Tn Board; Baton Feature; Sou Methodist U; Bus.

JENSEN, Eric James
Southwick HS; Southwick, MA (20-175) Tr; Engr.

JENSEN, Joan Louise
Cooperstown HS; Cooperstown, ND (3-32) Chor; FBLA; VP, 4H; NHS; 4H A; Mus A; Phys Fitness A; Bus.

JENSEN, Joyce Annette
Othello HS; Othello, WA (15%-230) Band; Chldr.

JENSEN, Julie Annette
Huntsville HS; Huntsville, AL (33%-450) Bkbl; Sftbl; Tr; ; Most Rebounds Bkbl; All Star Tm Sftbl; Best Offensive Player Vlbl; All-City Alt Bkbl; U of N Ala; PE Teacher.

JENSEN, Julie Jeanne
Hartford Union HS; Hartford, WI; AFS; Fr C; WW.

JENSEN, Katherine Sue
Mansfield HS; Mansfield, LA (7-95) Band; BC; Secy, Bus C; Secy, FBLA; GS; Fin, Lit Ral; Mjrte; Sch Achieve Tm; Tres, Span C; Pres, SC; Chem A; Cl Fav; Hon Prog; VFW Orator Win; VofDEM; Yth Fel; Yth Leg; All-Dist Hon Band; La All-Star Marching Band; All-Amer Band; Northeast La U; Eng Ed.

JENSEN, Kathy Lorinda
Detroit Lakes HS; Detroit Lakes, MN (50%-200) AFS; Ann; Band; Span C; Moorhead St U; Elem Ed.

JENSEN, Kenneth Wayne
Mendenhall Attendance Center; Mendenhall, MS; Math C; Bkbl; Golf; Sftbl; Miss St Col.

JENSEN, Lars Drew
Sky View HS; Smithfield, UT (40-617) Dbte Tm; Ger C; NHS; NMS; Utah St U; Physics.

JENSEN, Linda Kay
Kasson-Mantorville HS; Kasson, MN (3-101) Band; Secy, Chor; Ensm; GS; VP, 4H; NHS; Secy, SC; 4H A; MLS; Spch A; Secy, 4-H C; St HS Page; Hamline U; Span.

JENSEN, Lori Ann
Saint Agnes Acad; Memphis, TN (3%-80) A-Ed, Ann; NHS; Pres, Span NHS; VP, Jr Cl; Tres, Soph Cl; Hon Prog; Span A.

JENSEN, Lydia Lorraine
Montgomery Blair HS; Silver Spring, MD (20%-537) ARC; ARC A; Yth Fel; Church Chor; Judo C; Montgomery Col; Mental Health.

JENSEN, Marcia Lyn
Prairie HS; Cedar Rapids, IA; Chldr; Chor; FNA; VP, 4H; Secy, Jr Cl; U of Iowa; Spch and Hearing.

JENSEN, Mary Helen
Stanton Pub HS; Stanton, NE (7-45) Band; CYO; Chor; Drama; FHA; 4H; NHS; Var C; Bkbl; Tr; Alg A; 4H A; Math A; Pep C; Ltr A; Lib A; Mus A; Phys Fitness A.

JENSEN, Paul John
Notre Dame HS; W Haven, CT (15-280) French NHS; Math Hon Soc; *Math.*

JENSEN, Roxann Louise
Harris-Lake Park Comm Sch; Lake Park, IA (1-41) Band; Chor; Tres, 4H; VP, Soph Cl; JV, Bkbl; JV, Golf; COM; 4H A; Hon Prog; Type A; *Math.*

JENSEN, Scott Michael
Brainerd Sr HS; Brainerd, MN; Band; Bsbl.

JENSEN, Steven Fred
El Segundo HS; El Segundo, CA; Band; Fr C; Hmrm; Key C; Orch; JV, Ftbl; *BYU; Band.*

JENSEN, Teresa Lynn
Stafford HS; Falmouth, VA (100-600) InterClub Coun; Co-Cpt, Bkbl; Sftbl; Outst Band Stu; Outst Athlete; 1st Tm, All Commonwealth, Bkbl Tm; MVP, Summer Bkbl Camp; *Longwood Col; Recreation.*

JENSEN, Todd William
Chappell HS; Chappell, NE (6-21) Ann; Band; Chor; Ensm; FFA; Monogram; Co-Ed, Sch P; Pres, SC; Pres, Sr Cl; JV, Bkbl; Cr-Crty; Ftbl; Golf; Citz A; HCt; Hon Prog; Journ A; Sci A; Kent Brestel A; Outst Ath & Mus; Prom King; *Central Comm Tech Col; Auto Parts Distribution.*

JENSEN, Wenlee Dru
Sky View HS; Smithfield, UT (9-573) Dbte Tm; Fr C; Parl, GS; Parl, Hmrm; Model UN; NFL; NHS; A-Ed, Sch P; Swim; Amer Leg A; COM; Hon Prog; VP, Young Amer; Sterling Schol; Superior, USU Poetry Festival; *Utah St U; Hist.*

JENSON, Dawn Marie
Gilman Public HS; Gilman, WI (10-80) Band; Chldr; FHA; SC; Var C; Tr; MVP, Tr; *Nurs.*

JENTRY, Wanda Ranelle
McClymonds HS; Oakland, CA (1%-185) Hmrm; Span C; SC; Up Bound; Masonic A; *Loyola Marymount Col; Bio.*

JEPPSON, Lori
Sky View HS; Smithfield, UT (7-622) Ger C; Rptr, Hmrm; Orch; Bkbl; Sftbl; Tr; Sci A; *Brigham Young U; Civil Engr.*

JEPSON, Cynthia Ann
Luverne HS; Luverne, MN (20-163) Band; FTA; COM; Yth Fel; Cpt, Gym; *Hastings Col; Math.*

JERGER, Lori Lynne
Montpelier HS; Montpelier, OH (36-110) Band; Chldr; Chor; Rainbow; Sci C; Chldr A; Piano Contest A; Chor A; *Mus.*

JERIN, Jonette Ida
Helena HS; Helena, MT (1-285) Bus C; Chor; Ensm; Hmrm; NHS; Span C; SC; COM; Val; All NW Choir; Amer Yth Chor; *Pacific Lutheran U; Mus.*

JERIN, Susan Lynn
S Park HS; Library, PA (10-150) Band; Bus C; FBLA; FFA; FHA; Hmrm; NHS; Sch P; Secy, Sr Cl; Secy, Jr Cl; Secy, Soph Cl; *Bus.*

JERMAIN, Stacy Jo
Yukon HS; Yukon, OK; Drama; Pres, Fr C; FHA; GS; Hmrm; Span C; Amer Leg A; Spch A; *Okla St U; Linguistics.*

JERN, Michael Ivan
Metamora HS; Metamora, IL (50-190) Var C; Co-Cpt, Wrest; Church Usher; NHS Nom; *Ill Central Col; Drafting.*

JERNIGAN, Anne Bell
Shamrock HS; Atlanta, GA (17-306) PSAT-NSQT Consideration; *Psych.*

JERNIGAN, Clark Walter
Spring Woods HS; Houston, TX; Band; Chor; Drama; Key C; Math C; Mu Alpha Theta; Order/Arrow; Bkbl; Order/Arrow A; Yth Leg; Eng, Fr, A's; *Tex U; Acoustical Engr.*

JEROME, Carla Lynne
Green City R-1 HS; Green City, MO (6-39) Co-Ed, Ann; Band; Chor; VP, FBLA; FHA; GS; 4H; Sch P; SC; Tres, Jr Cl; Tres, Soph Cl; Bsbl; Mgr, Bkbl; Type A; *NE Mo St U; Clerical.*

JEROME, Ross Allen
John F Kennedy HS; Tumon, GUAM; NHS; *MIT; Biochemistry.*

JERRELL, Steven Wayne
Mount Vernon HS; Mount Vernon, MO (2-100) Chor; Math C; Pres, SC; Thes; Var C; Ftbl; DARGCA; MLS; Sal; I Rating, Dist Solo; *SW Baptist Col.*

JERRILS, William Albert
Tuscaloosa HS; Tuscaloosa, AL (50%-500) Inter-Act C; Lat C; Var C; Ftbl; *Anderson Col.*

JERVEY, Sarah Elaine
Whetstone HS; Columbus, OH (10%-547) Chor; Ger C; Secy, 4H; A-Ed, Lit Mag; NHS; Orch; Secy, Sci C; Hon Prog; Off, CampFire Girls; Lib Staff; Craft C; Knight Chancellor; *Home Ec.*

JESIONOWSKI, Sharon Lyn
McKeesport Sr HS; McKeesport, PA; Span C; SC; *Robert Morris Col; Bus.*

JESKE, Jeffrey Alan
Gilroy HS; Gilroy, CA (120-300) Chess C; Inter-Act C; Var C; Ftbl; Sftbl; Swim; Wrest; Sr Cl Coun; Yth Del, St & Ntl Convention; St Yth Board; *Gauilan Col; Bus.*

JESKE, Paula Jean
Westview HS; Kankakee, IL; JV, Chldr; Chor; Fr C; GS; Madrigal; NHS; Pres, Ski C; SC; Thes; Pres, Jr Cl; Tnns; *U of Iowa; Dental Hygiene.*

JESSE, Brian Jerome
West HS; Denver, CO; 4H A; ARC A; *ETI; Elec.*

JESSE, Janet Marie
West HS; Denver, CO (8-342) Secy, CYO; Secy, FBLA; Secy, NHS; Span C; COM; Citz A; 4H A; Denver Assn of Ed Schol; *Comm Col of Denver; Bus.*

JESSE, Julie Ann
West HS; Denver, CO (9-342) Band; Rptr, CYO; NHS; Orch; Tr; Hon Prog; *Colo St U; Foods and Nutrition.*

JESSEE, Kimberly Smith
Brandon Sr HS; Brandon, FL; Ensm; Beauty; COM; Dancerette; Gold Cup, Piano Solo; Keywanette; 1st Pl, St Piano Duet; Schol Letter; *U of NC; Psych.*

JESSEE, Lawrence Carroll
Cave Spring HS; Roanoke, VA (10-500) Lat C; NHS; Ftbl; *U of Va.*

JESSEN, Patrick Kelly
Battle Creek Pub HS; Battle Creek, NE (10%-47) Band; S-T, CYO; Chor; Community Yth Symph; Drama; Ger C; Pres, 4H; Math C; Order/Arrow; Spch C; SC; VP, Soph Cl; Mgr, Bkbl; Mgr, Ftbl; Tr; 4H A; Order/Arrow A; Star Student; VP, Cath Yth; Server A; *Creighton U; Med.*

JESSON, Jennifer Lou
Fort Smith Southside HS; Fort Smith, AR (35-400) Band; Ensm; Fr C; Mjrte; All Region, Band; *U of Ark.*

JESSUP, David Gordon
Southside HS; Elmira, NY (5-500) Band; NHS; Ed, Sch P; Regent Schol; NY St Film, Media Summer Sch & Sch.

JESSUP, Mary Rae
Lafayette HS; Ellisville, MO; A Cap Choir; Chor; FHA; *Mo Baptist Col; Hist.*

JESTER, Clarence Henry
Calhoun Co HS; Edison, GA (3-110) Band; BC; BS; Chor; FTA; Pres, 4H; NHS; Var C; Bsbl; Ftbl; Tnns; Tr; Amer Leg A; COM; 4H A; *Auburn U; Agr.*

JESTER, Douglas
Hoke Smith HS; Atlanta, GA (21-285) Band; SC; Pres, Jr Cl; Dbte Tm; Ftbl; Golf; ROTC A; *Civil Engr.*

JESTER, Robin Renee
E Randolph HS; Ramseur, NC (4-31) FHA; ARC; Sci C; MVP, Bkbl; MVP, Sftbl; Hon Prog; Cpt, Bkbl & Sftbl; *U of NC; Med.*

JESZECK, Thomas Michael
Ellenville HS; Ellenville, NY (11-115) Band; Chor; Drama; NHS; Orch; Ftbl; NEDT; Regent Schol; Co-Cpt, MVP, Tr; Mus A; Faculty Arts A; Montgomery Ward Young Amer; Co Mus Ed Schol; *Westminster Choir Col; Mus.*

JETER, Cheryl Lynne
Patterson Coop Sch; Dayton, OH (235-483) Pres, Bus C; Chor; Drama; Pres, Jr Cl; Pres, Soph Cl; Tr; HCt; Pres A; Type A; Secy, Del-Tn; OEA; *Howard U; Law.*

JETER, Jeffrey Frank
Webster Groves HS; Webster Groves, MO (115-450) Chem C; Chess C; Ger C; Order/Arrow; Phys C; Sci C; Bkbl; Ftbl; Tr; *U of Mo-Rolla; Chem Engr.*

JETER, Karen Rae
DuQuoin HS; DuQuoin, IL (6-140) Co-Ed, Ann; Band; Chor; FHA; S-T, 4H; Spch C; SC; Tr; 4H A; Math A; Opt A; Pep C; Schol A.

JETER, Melba Jean
Central of Lunenburg HS; Victoria, VA (10-192) Co-Cpt, Chldr; Chor; Hmrm; InterClub Coun; Secy, Span C; Tres, SC; VP, Tri-HiY; Bkbl; Mgr, Sftbl; 4H A; HCt; Yth Foundation; Best All Around Camper; Fin, St of Va Hugh O'Brien Yth Fond; *Radford U; Ed.*

JETER, Ralyn Lynch
Ponder HS; Ponder, TX (2-14) F-Ed, Ann; VP, FHA; Co-Cpt, Bkbl; Sftbl; Tr; Crisco A; HQn; Sal; Type A; PA; Best All Around; All-Dist Bkbl; *North Texas State Univ; Bus Mgt.*

JETT, Brian Erle
Thomas Carr Howe HS; Indianapolis, IN; Audio-Visual A; Pub Address A.

JETT, David Charles
Licking R 8 HS; Licking, MO (5-84) Chor; All Dist Hon Choir; Dist Spch Contest; Jr Play; Yth Ldrship Conference Win; *SW Baptist Col; Clergyman.*

JETT, James Michael
Phillips HS; Phillips, TX; Band; Chor; SC; Ftbl; Tnns; *Frank Phillips Jr Col; Phys Ed.*

JETT, Joseph Andrew
Phillips HS; Phillips, TX; Band; Ftbl; Golf.

JETT, Sheryl Laine
Thomas Carr Howe HS; Indianapolis, IN (47-660) Band; FTA; Hmrm; NHS; Orch; COM; *IUPUI; Bus Adm.*

JEUDE, Jeffrey Lynn
Kirkwood Sr HS; Kirkwood, MO (48-607) Rptr, Sch P; Mgr, Sftbl; Journ A; Gold N; Gold K; St Recognition; *St Pauls Col; Social Service.*

JEUNESSE, Mary Colleen
Holy Rosary Acad; Louisville, KY (15-86) Ann; Ed, Sch P; SC; COM; Journ A; *U of Louisville; Bus Mgt.*

JEWELL, Ann Louise
Shawnee Mission E HS; Shawnee Mission, KS (63-547) Chldr; NHS; Sci C; Ski C; JV, Tr; Alg A; Bio A; Citz A; Hon Prog; Math A; Sci A; JV, Vlbl; *Baylor U; Med.*

JEWELL, Anthony Thomas
Dominguez HS; Compton, CA (50-749) Tnns; *Long Beach St U; Hist.*

JEWELL, Karen Lee
Wilson HS; PA (40%-397) Ski C; SC; Hockey; Tnns; Alg A; HCt; JA A; Math A; Yth Fel; *The King's Col; Occupational Therapy.*

JEWELL, Scott Ralston
Warren Area HS; Warren, PA (20%-400) Band; Ger C; Golf; Tnns; Yth Fel; Dist Yth Coun; 'Silver B' A; Page, Annual Conf; Del, Yth Annual Conf; *Edinboro St Col; Psych.*

JEWELL, Walter H
Centerburg HS; Centerburg, OH (1-79) Band; Chem C; Chess C; 4H; NHS; Elk A; Hon Prog; Val; *Ohio St U.*

JEWETT, Deannine Lee
Nisrayuna HS; Schenectady, NY (30%-500) AFS; Drama; Ger C; Pres, 4H; Lit Mag; Bus Mgr, Sch P; Ski C; SC; Pres, Jr Cl; Mgr, Soccer; Swim; Citz A; 4H A; Kiwanis A; Rotary A; Comm Service C; Ballet Company; Rotary Exchange Stu; Ntl 4-H Dress Review Fin.

JEX, Nancy Irene
Santa Monica HS; Santa Monica, CA; Co-Cpt, Chldr; S-T, Chor; FNA; Hmrm; NHS; Sci C; Nurs.

JEZUIT, John Joseph
St Mary's Prep; Orchard Lake, MI (2-45) NHS; Hon Prog; Magna Cum Laude; First Hon; *U of Mich; Engr.*

JIAO, Conrad Rey
Karlsruhe Amer HS; Karlsruhe, WEST GERMANY; Co-Ed, Ann; Demolay; Hmrm; InterAct C; F-Ed, Sch P; St Stu Congress; Pres, SC; VP, Jr Cl; VP, Soph Cl; Tnns; Bio A; COM; Citz A; Hon Prog; Journ A; Kiwanis A; Math A; Most Out; Type A; *Engr.*

JICINSKY, Darla Jean
Spencer HS; Spencer, WI (20-60) Ann; Chor; Drama; VP, FHA; Ed, Sch P; Mgr, Bkbl; DARGCA; Journ A; Q&S A; Mgr, Vlbl; *Child Care.*

JICINSKY, Rhonda Catherine
Spencer HS; Spencer, WI (6-75) Band; JV, Chldr; Drama; FHA; Math C; Ed, Sch P; SC; Bkbl; Tr; Q&S A; Vlbl Tm; *Acct.*

JILES, Brian Paul
LeRoy HS; LeRoy, IL (10%-100) FFA; Pres, 4H; Wrest; 4H A; Schol A, FFA; St Outst Mem, 4-H C A; *Agr.*

JIM, Donald Thomas
White Oak HS; Jacksonville, NC (9-235) NHS; Bkbl; Ftbl; Sftbl; Marshal; Outst Sr; *Appalachian St U; Bus.*

JIMEIAN, Linda Julie
Satellite HS; Satellite Beach, FL (25%-694) Chor; Yth for Christ; FCA; *FSU; Social Work.*

JIMENEZ, Antonio
Academia Discipulos de Cristo; Bayamon, PR (10-122) *Universidad de Puerto Rico; Econ.*

JIMENEZ, Baltasar
Our Lady of Pilar HS; Rio Piedras, PR (20%-166) Pres, Chem C; Model UN; NFL; Ed, Sch P; SC; Jr Cl; Alg A; COM; Hist A; Math A; Fin, Judo; Religion A; Span A; PA A; UN Best Delegate; *Georgetown U; Sci.*

JIMENEZ, Billy
Roswell HS; Roswell, NM (50-340) Chor; Ensm; Fr C; NHS; *NM St U; Engr.*

JIMENEZ, Felix Alberto
Notre Dame HS; Caguas, PR (12-136) Chem C; Hmrm; NHS; Ed, Sch P; SC; COM; Q&S A; Academic Excellence A; *Yale U; Eng.*

JIMENEZ, Griselle
Colegio Universitario Corazon; Santurce, PR (3-25) Pres, Hmrm; NHS; Hon Prog; *Jamestown Col; Econ.*

JIMENEZ, Lourdes del Carmen
Colegio Espiritu Santo; Hato Rey, PR (1-96) Chldr; Pres, Hmrm; Secy, Math C; Spch C; SC; Cpt, Var C; Pres, Sr Cl; Pres, Jr Cl; Cpt, Bkbl; Swim; COM; Cl Fav; Hon Prog; Most Out; Cpt, Vlbl; *Oberlin Col; Sci.*

JIMENEZ, Marcos Daniel
Miami Christian HS; Miami, FL (3-60) A-Ed, Ann; VP, Band; Chor; Drama; Lit Mag; NHS; Orch; A-Ed, Sch P; Bkbl; Ftbl; Tr; COM; NEDT; Opt A; Spch A; Yth Fel; Chaplain, Soph Cl; HR Hall of Fame; Published Poems & Essays; 1st Pl Drama, Forensic Festival; Presidential Schol; *U of Miami; Law.*

JIMENEZ, Ruth Esther
Consuelo Escalona Private Sch; Rio Piedras, PR (1-38) Chor; Secy, Hmrm; ARC; Alg A; COM; Hon Prog; Magna Cum Laude; Math A; ARC A; Summa Cum Laude; Faculty A; Eng A; *U of PR; Natural Sci.*

JIMERSON, Jay Carey
Norman HS; Norman, OK; NHS; Span C; Span NHS; Var C; Bsbl; Cpt, Ftbl; Amer Leg A; MLS; All-St, All-Amer Ftbl; *Okla U.*

JIMMERSON, Cheryl
John Charles Fremont HS; Los Angeles, CA; FNA; Scorekeeper, Bkbl; *Saint's Mary Col; Nurs.*

JIMMERSON, Cynthia
Fremont HS; Los Angeles, CA; FBLA; Sftbl; Citz A; DARGCA; God & Country A; Most Out; Pres A; *CSU Long Beach; Sci.*

JINDRA, Nancy Christine
Cuyahoga Valley Christian Acad; Cuyahoga Falls, OH (3-65) COM; Citz A; Coun of Teach A; Hon Prog; Interlochen Ntl Mus; Sci A; Yth Fel; Yth Leg.

JIRA, Fran Elen
La Crosse HS; LaCrosse, KS; A Cap Choir; Bus Mgr, Ann; CYO; Chor; Dbte Tm; Pres, 4H; Secy, NFL; Tres, Span C; VP, Jr Cl; Sftbl; Tr; COM; Citz A; 4H A; Pres A; St Scholar; VofDEM; Vlbl; Pres, Co 4-H Coun; 4-H Key A; *Kans U; Pre-Med.*

JIRIK, Sarah Jane
Karlsruhe Amer HS; Karlsruhe, GERMANY; SC; *U of Minn; Sociology.*

JO, Richard Y
George Washington HS; Denver, CO; Ftbl; Soccer; *MIT; Engr.*

JOANES, Karen Renee
George Henry Corliss HS; Chicago, IL (25-481) Drama; Fr C; Hmrm; NHS; SC; Hon Prog; Attendance A; *U of Wis; Nurs.*

JOB, Christie Lee
Everett HS; Everett, WA; Band; 4H; Hmrm; Orch; Rainbow; 4H A; Pres, Yth Fel; Demolay Sr Princess; Drill Tm, Soroity, SOS; *Seattle Pacific U; Phys and Health Ed.*

JOB, Philip William
Goodlettsville HS; Goodlettsville, TN (20%-190) Lat C; JV, Bkbl; Cr-Ctry; Tr; COM; Sci A; Soc Stu, Lat, A's; *Med.*

JOBE, Brian Gregory
Jackson Central Merry HS; Jackson, TN (3-420) Math C; JV, Tr; Wrest; Alg A; Bio A; Hon Prog; Math A; Geom A; *Vanderbilt U; Math.*

JOBE, Suzanne
South Side HS; Counce, TN (5-26) FFA; Rptr, SC; Pres, Jr Cl; Pres, Soph Cl; Cl Fav; *NE Miss Jr Col; Vet.*

JOE, Sarlynn Rene
Coatesville Area Sr HS; Coatesville, PA (43-665) A Cap Choir; Band; Chor; Ensm; NHS; F-Ed, Sch P; SC; JV, Bkbl; JV, Tnns; Schol Achv A; Vol, Special Olympics; *Phar.*

JOENK, Brian Thomas
Ossining HS; Ossining, NY (50-400) Chor; Drama; Hmrm; Orch; ARC; Span C; Var C; Golf; Sftbl; Swim; DARGCA; Hist A; ARC A; Type A; Yth Fel; Yth Leg; Unicycle C of Amer; Lacrosse Varsity Ltr; *Midwest Col; Humanities.*

JOHANNESEN, Jeffrey Jay
Alta Comm HS; Alta, IA (1-75) NHS; SC; Bsbl; Cpt, Bkbl; Ftbl; Tr; Hon Prog; St Scholar; Val; Yth Fel; WW; Prep, Tr & Field Athletics; *Southwest St U; Bus.*

JOHANNSEN, Barbara Anne
North Toole County HS; Sunburst, MT (1-34) Ann; VP, Band; CYO; Drama; Math C; Sci C; Pres, SC; MVP, Bkbl; Sftbl; Tr; Amer Leg A; Bausch & Lomb A; Bio A; Cl Fav; Ntl Achv Schol; NEDT; Sci A; Val; Soroptomist Citz A; Heisey A; Grand A, St Sci Fair; *U of Mont; Bio.*

JOHANNSEN, Seth Christian
Spencer HS; Spencer, IA; Chor; Hon Prog; Spch A.

JOHANSEN, David Lewis
Glenbard W HS; Glenellyn, IL (100-507) Pres, Band; Hmrm; Orch; Ski C; SC; MVP, Bkbl; MVP, Golf; Mus Schol; *Tex Christian U; Bus.*

JOHANSEN, Ellen Marie
Lindenhurst HS; Lindenhurst, NY (3-790) NHS; MVP, Orch; Thes; Tnns; Hon Prog; Regent Schol; Julliard Schol; TAL Outst A; Fin, John Lyons Sr Schol; Symph A; Win, Mus Lovers C; Win, Friday Mus Lovers C; *Hofstra U; Engr.*

JOHANSEN, Julie Ann
CAL Comm HS; Latimer, IA (1-30) Band; Chldr; Chor; Drama; Ensm; Pres, 4H; Madrigal; Span C; Spch C; Mgr, Bkbl; JV, Golf; JV, Sftbl; 4H A; Merit A; *U of Iowa; Med.*

JOHANSEN, Laila Elaine
Tottenville HS; Staten Island, NY (722-1191) Chor; Tnns; Citz A; Bus.

JOHANSON, Robert Fred
Jamestown HS; Jamestown, NY (200-600) A Cap Choir; Ski C; *Thiel Col; Bus Adm.*

JOHLMAN, Linda Elizabeth
Glendale Acad; Glendale, CA; Chor; Ski C; VP, Soph Cl; Citz A; Schol Cert; *Loma Linda U; Med.*

JOHN, Rochelle Ann
Geibel HS; Connellsville, PA; Chor; NHS; Tnns; Tr; Chamber of Commerce Stu o-t Mo; 1st Pl A, Lat Classics Festival; Chldr & Tri-Co Stat Ltrs; Drama C Cert; *U of Pittsburgh; Nurs.*

JOHN, Soberta Jean
San Juan HS; Blanding, UT (6-98) Parl, FHA; GS; 4H; NHS; Sch P; Sftbl; Amer Leg A; 4H A; Hon Prog; Masonic A; Historian, FHA; Attendance A; Secy, Indian C; Social Sci A; Eng A; *Ariz St U; Bus Adm.*

JOHNS, Anita Louise
Midwest City HS; Midwest City, OK (25%-500) Chor; Ensm; Fr C; NHS; Sci C; Fr, Vocal Mus, A's; Bus & Professional Women, A; *Central Col; Ed.*

JOHNS, Barbara Lynne
Hanceville HS; Hanceville, AL (8-107) FHA; NHS; Ntl Achv Schol.

JOHNS, DeRhonda Lee
Northside HS; Fort Smith, AR (60-500) Chor; Hmrm; Secy, Sr Cl; Citz A; *U of Ark; Bus.*

JOHNS, Elaine Marie
Pontiac Central HS; Pontiac, MI (40-418) Chor; Dbte Tm; 4H; Hmrm; NFL; NHS; Ntl Yth Conf; ARC; Spch C; Y-Tns; COM; Citz A; Hon Prog; JA A; Most Out; Poet A; Spch A; Bus Woman of Pontiac; Executive, Jr Executive, A's; *Mich St U; Pol Sci.*

JOHNS, Elisa Marcia
Simon Gratz HS; Philadelphia, PA (10-1000) NHS; Punctuality & Attendance As; *Penn St U.*

JOHNS, Eloise Elizabeth
Delavan Comm HS; Delavan, IL; Band; Chor; Ensm; Secy, 4H; Spch C; 4H A; JV, Vlbl; Mus Contest A; Poster Contest A; *Mus.*

JOHNS, James Alan
S R Butler HS; Huntsville, AL (8%-750) Ann; Bsbl; Ftbl; Co-Cpt, Tr; JV, Wrest; Yth Fel; Golf Hobby; *Auburn U; Vet Med.*

JOHNS, Jennifer Louise
Linton Intermediate HS; Pittsburgh, PA (120-1200) A Cap Choir; Chor; Drama; Ensm; Fr C; Hmrm; Tr; COM; Math A; Bus Patrol; Ath A; *U of Pittsburgh; Med.*

JOHNS, Jo Ellen Kay
LuVerne Comm Sch; LuVerne, IA (2-19) Ann; Band; Chldr; Chor; SC; Tres, Jr Cl; VofDEM; Mus A; Pres, LYC; *U of Iowa; Spch.*

JOHNS, Karen Ann
Horicon HS; Horicon, WI; JV, Chldr; Chor; *Dental Asst.*

JOHNS, Kevin
Claymont HS; Uhrichsville, OH; Var C; Ftbl; *Ed.*

JOHNS, Kirsten J
Benton Harbor HS; Benton Harbor, MI; Band; Fr C; NHS; Tr; *Kalamazoo Col; Marine Bio.*

JOHNS, Lowrane
Fair Park HS; Shreveport, LA; Band; Chor; MVP, Tnns; Semi-Fin, Delta Sigma Theta A; Semi-Fin, Fleishman Found Schol; *Northwestern St U; Nurs.*

JOHNS, Michael David
McKinley Sr HS; Canton, OH (135-670) A Cap Choir; Demolay; Ensm; Span C; Span NHS; Thes; Arch; Hist A; Director, Church Choir; Demolay Service A; FJ Myers Schol A; *SE Bible Col; Ministry.*

JOHNS, Robert Paul
Ferndale HS; Ferndale, MI (10%-450) A Cap Choir; Rptr, Chldr; Chor; Rptr, Dbte Tm; Rptr, Drama; Ensm; Rptr, Fr C; Rptr, FBLA; Rptr, Ger C; Rptr, Key C; Madrigal; Rptr, NHS; Sch P; Rptr, Ski C; Rptr, Thes; JV, Bkbl; JV, Soccer; COM; Citz A; Coun of Teach A; Hon Prog; Journ A; PTA A; Yth Fel; *General Motors Inst; Bus Mgt.*

JOHNSEN, Gary Daniel
Alexander Ramsey HS; Roseville, MN (81-555) Dbte Tm; Drama; NFL; NHS; Sci C; Spch C; St Stu Congress; SC; Var C; MVP, Bsbl; MVP, Ftbl; MVP, Hockey; COM; Pres A; Sci A; Spch A; Yth Leg; Debate A's; *Wheaton Col; Philosophy.*

JOHNSEN, James David
El Monte HS; El Monte, CA (2-285) Hmrm; F-Ed, Sch P; Pres, Var C; Ftbl; MVP, Tr; Bank Of Amer A; CSF; H of F; St Scholar; Stu Govt Wk; Hon Serv C; *USC; Arch.*

JOHNSEN, Jonathan George
Tottenville HS; Staten Island, NY (171-1058) Band; Community Yth Symph; Ensm; Orch; Order/Arrow; Golf; COM; Hon Prog; Order/Arrow A; Regent Schol; Eagle Sct; All City HS Band; *Hartt Col of Mus; Mus.*

JOHNSEN, Vicki Lynn
West HS; Madison, WI (150-600) A Cap Choir; Chldr; Chor; Campus Life; Young Life; UMYF; Varsity Ltrs; *Therapy.*

JOHNSEN, Vida
Albany HS; Albany, NY; Tr; *Oakwood Col; Phys Ed.*

JOHNSON, Aaron Lee
Lewisville HS; Lewisville, TX (21-361) A Cap Choir; Ensm; Lit Mag; Madrigal; Math C; Mu Alpha Theta; NHS; Superior, St Solo-Ensm Contest; *N Tex St U; Mus Ed.*

JOHNSON, Adrena Elaine
Peabody HS; Pittsburgh, PA (33-480) Hmrm; NHS; Secy, Orch; Thes; Cpt, Swim; God & Country A; Pres A; Centers for Mus Talented; All City Orch; Swim Ltrs; *Mansfield St Col; Biol.*

JOHNSON, Alan Eugene
Richardson HS; Richardson, TX; Pres, A Cap Choir; Pres, Chor; Ensm; Madrigal; Most Out; *Bethany Nazarene Col; Religion.*

JOHNSON, Alisha Sussette
McDonogh 35 Sr HS; New Orleans, LA (17-38) Ann; Secy, Chor; Rptr, SC; COM; Citz A; Spelling, Eng, A's; Phys Ed, Reading, A's; *Mich St U; Philosophy.*

JOHNSON, Allison Marie
Hector HS; Hector, MN (6-64) Chor; Tres, FHA; Span C; JV, Bkbl; Vlbl; *Gustavus Adolphus Col; Nurs.*

JOHNSON, Alstrup Nordahl
Milo Adventist Acad; Days Creek, OR (7-75) Band; Tres, BS; Chor; Bkbl; *La Sierra Col; Med.*

JOHNSON, Andre William
Matoaca HS; Ettrick, VA; Key C; NHS; Ftbl; *U of Va; Dentistry.*

JOHNSON, Andy J
Sparta HS; Sparta, MO (1-32) Bkbl; Citz A; Sci A; Soph Cl Schol A; Cert of Attendance.

JOHNSON, Angela Darlene
Clio HS; Clio, SC (2-54) Ann; Band; Tres, Fr C; Secy, Hmrm; NHS; Secy, Sr Cl; Jr Cl; Pres, Soph Cl; Cpt, Bkbl; Cpt, Ftbl; Sftbl; Gov Honor Prog; HCt; NMF; Sal; Eng A; Fr A; Best All-Around; *Marshill Col.*

JOHNSON, Angela Doris
Dupont Sr HS; Hermitage, TN (27-200) Band; NHS; Rptr, Sch P; Soccer; Foreign Lang; Newspaper Photography, A; *Cumberland Col.*

JOHNSON, Angelia
Jonesboro Sr HS; Jonesboro, GA (5-25) All Amer Yth; Bus C; Chor; FBLA; FHA; 4H; Parl, Hmrm; ARC; Sftbl; COM; Cl Fav; 4H A; *Clayton Jr Col; Bus Ed.*

JOHNSON, Anita Louise
Crenshaw HS; Los Angeles, CA (50%-850) A Cap Choir; CYO; ARC; Beauty; COM; Citz A; Candystriper A; *El Camino Col; Mus.*

JOHNSON, Ann Darlene
Ysleta HS; El Paso, TX; Co-Ed, Ann; Mjrte; Swim; *Photography.*

JOHNSON, Anna Marie
Calvary Christian Acad; Midland, MI (4-18) Ed, Ann; Band; Chldr; Chor; Ensm; Sch P; COM; HCt; Most Out; Pep C; *Bob Jones U; Elem Ed.*

JOHNSON, Anne Elizabeth
Bound Brook HS; Bound Brook, NJ (16-218) Chor; Pres, Drama; GS; Lat C; F-Ed, Lit Mag; NHS; Secy, Thes; Good Theatre A; *NML; Eng.*

JOHNSON, Annette
John F Kennedy HS; Cleveland, OH (124-663) Rptr, Hmrm; Mjrte; SC; COM; Citz A; Hon Prog; Martha Holden Jennings Schol A; *Cincinnati U; Bus Ed.*

JOHNSON, Annette
Hilliard Jr-Sr HS; Hilliard, FL (3-76) Ann; Band; BC; Chess C; Chor; Ensm; Hmrm; Mjrte; Sch P; Span C; SC; COM; Cl Fav; Hon Prog; VofDEM; *Baptist Hospital; Radiology.*

JOHNSON, Annmarie
Jamestown HS; Jamestown, NY (100-500) A Cap Choir; Band; Pres, Hmrm; Madrigal; Orch; SC; Swim; *Fredonia Col; Mus.*

JOHNSON, Archie Herbert
Mullens HS; Mullens, WV (7-120) BC; Var C; Bkbl; Tr; Alg A; Hon Prog; *Concord Col; Math.*

JOHNSON, Ardell
Fairfield HS; Fairfield, AL (10%-160) BC; Inter-Club Coun; SC; Tri-HiY; COM; Hist A; HCt; Math A; Most Out; Sci A; Type A; Pres, Health Career C; VP, Candy- striper; Bankboard; *Tuskegee Inst; Nurs.*

JOHNSON, Arlene Marie
Morton HS; Morton, IL (28-351) Chor; Ensm; Spch A; Yth Fel; Secy, Church Choir; Campus Life; Choir Contest; 1st, Solo & Ensm Contest.

JOHNSON, Aubrey Lyn
Anoka Sr HS; Anoka, MN (5%-744) Yth Fel; Cr-Ctry Skiing; JA; *U of Minn; Pre-Dentistry.*

JOHNSON, Barbara Ann
Mabel-Canton HS; Mabel, MN (10-57) Band; Cpt, Chldr; FHA; Parl, 4H; Sch P; Pres, Jr Cl; Pres, Soph Cl; Bkbl; *Acct.*

JOHNSON, Barbara Ellen
Piscataquis Comm HS; Guilford, ME (10%-80) Band; Chor; Fr C.

JOHNSON, Barry Dean
Laurel Co HS; London, KY (25%-400) Lat C; Sci C; Golf; Alg A; Math A; *U of Ky; Civil Engr.*

JOHNSON, Becky June
Crittenden Co HS; Marion, KY (5%-125) S-T, A Cap Choir; Ann; Band; BC; Chldr; Chem C; S-T, Chor; Drama; FBLA; FHA; FTA; Hmrm; Mod Mus Mas; Sch P; Bkbl; Sftbl; Swim; COM; H of F; Hon Prog; NEDT; Type A; FBLA A; Mus A; All Amer Band; *Vanderbuilt U; Law.*

JOHNSON, Benjamin William
Simon Gratz HS; Philadelphia, PA; Chem C; *Lincoln Col; Med.*

JOHNSON, Bernadette Elaine
Rebecca Comer HS; Eufaula, AL (1-38) Ann; Chldr; 4H; Pres, Hmrm; Math C; NHS; Tres, Sch P; Spch C; S-T, SC; Bkbl; Beauty; COM; Hon Prog; Math A; Vlbl; *U of Ala; Med.*

JOHNSON, Berta Leone
Parkersburg HS; Parkersburg, WV (52-207) Chor; Ensm; Pres, 4H; Pres, Hmrm; SC; Bkbl; 4H A; Spch A; Yth Fel; GAA; Church Choirs; God & Comm A; Yth Rep, Coun On Ministries; Pres, GSct; Most Outst SC Member; Pep C; *W Va U; Art.*

JOHNSON, Beth Ann
Spearfish HS; Spearfish, SD (2-105) A Cap Choir; Band; Chor; Dbte Tm; Drama; Ensm; NHS; Rainbow; SC; Var C; S-T, Sr Cl; Mgr, Bkbl; Hon Prog; Kiwanis A; NMF; Sal; Co- ch, Pep C; Vlbl; Yth Tour, Wash DC; Stu o-t Mo; *SD St U; Pre-Med.*

JOHNSON, Beth Ellen
Leavenworth Sr HS; Leavenworth, KS; Band; CYO; Ntl Sojourners; *Kans St U; Computer Sci.*

JOHNSON, Beverly Ann
Bartow Sr HS; Bartow, FL (5-300) Anchor C; Band; FHA; Semi-Fin, US Hmrm; NHS; SC; Hon Prog; Phys Fitness A; Co Yth Fair Home Ec A; Sup Ratng, Solo & Ensm Band Cont; *FSU; Home Ec.*

JOHNSON, Beverly Jewell
Horace Maynard HS; Maynardville, TN (17-127) BC; Chldr; FHA; FNA; 4H; NHS; Bkbl; COM; HQn; Sports Qn; WW; *Med Secy.*

JOHNSON, Beverly Joan
Uintah HS; Vernal, UT; Chor; Pol Sci C; Pres A; Dance C; Secy, Uintah Safety Coun.

JOHNSON, Beverly Kaye
Latexo HS; Latexo, TX (5-16) Cpt, Chldr; Tres, FHA; Co-Ed, Sch P; Bkbl; Cl Fav; HQn; *Angelina Col; Bus.*

JOHNSON, Beverly Renee
Durham HS; Durham, NC; Chor; Secy, Hmrm; Tr; Reading Improvement A; *Bus.*

JOHNSON, Blake Martin
Bellevue Sr HS; Bellevue, NE (90-940) Ftbl; *US Naval Acad; Phys Sci.*

JOHNSON, Bonnie Rochelle
Theodore Roosevelt HS; Gary, IN (21-555) MVP, Chor; Drama; MVP, Madrigal; NHS; Cl Fav; Delta Sigma Theta A; Tri Kappa Mus Schol; Arts Coun Mus Schol; Delta Sigma Theta Schol; *Spelman Col; Mus.*

JOHNSON, Bradley Jay
Morton W HS; Berwyn, IL (35-800) Band; NHS; COM; PTA A; Pres, Church Yth; Span Merit A; *Hope Col; Biol.*

JOHNSON, Bradley Lynn
Harvard Pub Sch; Harvard, NE (6-45) Ann; Band; Semi-Fin, BS; Chor; Drama; Ger C; VP, 4H; Madrigal; VP, SC; Var C; VP, Jr Cl; Pres, Soph Cl; Bsbl; Bkbl; Ftbl; Tr; 4H A; Hon Prog; *Air Force Acad.*

JOHNSON, Brenda Carol
King William HS; King William, VA; BC; Chor; GS; 4H; F-Ed, Lit Mag; F-Ed, Sch P; COM; Q&S A; *Rappahannock Comm Col.*

JOHNSON, Brenda Dian
Corsicana HS; Corsicana, TX; FHA; Span C; *Tyler Jr Col; Dental Hygiene.*

JOHNSON, Brenda Fay
Fremont Sr HS; Fremont, NE (141-431) Math C; Mu Alpha Theta; Co-Ed, Sch P; Span C; Q&S A; Type A; Yth Fel; *Kansas Wesleyan Col; Nurs.*

JOHNSON, Brenda Ray
Moravia Comm HS; Moravia, IA (12%-52) Chor; Dbte Tm; Drama; FHA; S-T, 4H; Hmrm; Mjrte; Sch Achieve Tm; SC; Span C; Spch C; VP, SC; Var C; Bkbl; Mgr, Ftbl; Sftbl; Tr; Mgr, Wrest; Cl Fav; 4H A; JA A; Most Out; Sci A; Spch A; Yth Fel; Pres, Yth Fel; Bkbl A; Tr A; Clothing A; Band A; Twirling A; *Airline.*

JOHNSON, Brenda Ree
Gumberry HS; Gumberry, NC (7-97) Ann; BC; Chor; Drama; Fr C; SC; Co-Cpt, Bkbl; *A&T St U.*

JOHNSON, Brian C
Sidney Sr HS; Sidney, NE (40-119) Ftbl; Golf; Tr; Secy, Boys Ath C; *U of Nebr; Agr.*

JOHNSON, Brian David
Westmont Sr HS; Westmont, IL (10-150) VP, NHS; Pres, SC; PA; *U of Ill; Aeronautical Engr.*

JOHNSON, Brian Dean
Assumption HS; Assumption, IL (1-59) Drama; VP, Fr C; F-Ed, Sch P; SC; Thes; JV, Ftbl; Hon Prog; Journ A; Yth Fel; Soc For Academic Achievement; Sports Rptr, City Newspaper; *U of Minn.*

JOHNSON, Brian Keith
Goreville HS; Goreville, IL (1-45) Band; Chor; Drama; Ensm; FFA; Bus Arts A; Agr Arts A.

JOHNSON, Brian Randall
Thurston HS; Springfield, OR (100-300) Span C; Var C; Cr-Crty; Ftbl; Co-Cpt, Tnns; Vlbl; *U of Calif at San Diego; Law.*

JOHNSON, Brian T
St James HS; St James, MN (31-150) Pres, Chor; Drama; Madrigal; Golf; All St Choir; *Theater.*

JOHNSON, Brigitte F
Valley HS; Sanders, AZ (1-49) Ann; Span C; B Crocker A; JA A; Type A; Eng A; Acct A; *U of A; A Home Ec A; U of Ariz; Bus.*

JOHNSON, Brigitte Suezette
Continued Ed Project; St Louis, MO (10-46) Band; Hmrm; SC; *Forrest Park Col.*

JOHNSON, Bryan Keith
Starmount HS; Boonville, NC (9-150) Pres, Band; Ensm; FFA; Math C; Mu Alpha Theta; VP, NHS; Golf; Master Mus A; MVP, Band; All St Band; Michael Graham Mus A; *Mitchell Comm Col; Mus.*

JOHNSON, Camero Chano
Eastern HS; Washington, DC; *Maryland U at Eastern Shore; Art.*

JOHNSON, Carl
Grant Union HS; Sacramento, CA (10%-168) Band; Chess C; Chor; Drama; Orch; Var C; Pres, Soph Cl; JV, Bkbl; JV, Ftbl; Cpt, Soccer; Tr; Bank Of Amer A; Opt Out Tn; *Sac City Col; Law.*

JOHNSON, Carl Lynn
Marked Tree HS; Marked Tree, AR (4-75) Ann; BC; BS; Drama; Pres, NHS; SC; Thes; Cpt, Bsbl; Cpt, Bkbl; Ftbl; Cpt, Tr; Amer Leg A; 4H A; Hist A; Hon Prog; Type A; *U of Ark; Pre-Med.*

JOHNSON, Carol Ann
Maine Twp HS W; Des Plaines, IL (25%-800) Rptr, Ann; Band; Co-Ch, Ski C; Var C; Swim; Bio A; Hon Prog; Pool Guards; Audio-Visual C; *U of Ill; Acct.*

JOHNSON, Carol Lori
Norquay HS; Norquay, CANADA (1-17).

JOHNSON, Carol Lynette
Crenshaw HS; Los Angeles, CA; FBLA; Chem A; Pep C; Essay Contest A; *El Camino Col; Bus.*

JOHNSON, Carole Lynn
George Washington Carver HS; Montgomery, AL; Chor; Q&S A; *Psych.*

JOHNSON, Caroline Griffith
Bowling Green HS; Franklinton, LA (5-27) Co-Ed, Ann; Co-Cpt, Chldr; Chor; VP, Hmrm; Fin, Lit Ral; NHS; Pres, SC; VP, Jr Cl; Secy, Soph Cl; Bkbl; Cpt, Tnns; Amer Leg Orator A; Cl Fav; DARGCA; Hon Prog; I Dare You; *LSU; Hist.*

JOHNSON, Cassandra Yvette
Jess Lanier HS; Bessemer, AL; Chor; Tri-HiY; COM; Citz A; Hist A; Hon Prog; Spch A; Eng A; *Med.*

JOHNSON, Cathy Leann
Chester HS; Chester, PA (3-658) Co-Ed, Ann; Band; Chldr; Chor; Hmrm; Key C; St Stu Congress; Pres, SC; Up Bound; Swim; Tnns; Amer Leg A; Citz A; DARGCA; Elk A; *The Cath U of Amer; Communications.*

JOHNSON, Cathy Lynn
Berean Christian Sch; Olathe, KS (5-9) Chldr; Chor; Bkbl; Candystriper; *Elem Ed.*

JOHNSON, Celeste Otissa
Martin Luther King HS; Philadelphia, PA (64-692) Cpt, Chldr; World Affairs C; Most Out; *Moore Col of Art; Fashion Illustration.*

JOHNSON, Charlotte Elaine
Thompson HS; Siluria, AL (10-150) FBLA; FHA; *Bus.*

JOHNSON, Charlotte Lashay
Central HS; W Helena, AR; BC; JV, Chldr; Fr C; FHA; NHS; Sftbl; HCt; Kiwanis A; VFW A; Dionysians; Mgr, Gym; Secy, Sunday Sch Cl; *Phillips Co Comm Col; Dietetics.*

JOHNSON, Cheryl Anita
Lake Clifton Sr HS; Baltimore, MD (10%-315) NHS; Hist A; Math A; Bus A; Eng A; Art A; *Art.*

JOHNSON, Cheryl Lynn
Flambeau HS; Tony, WI (18-75) Ann; Band; JV, Chldr; Ensm; Mjrte; Rptr, Sch P; HCt; Chldr A's; *Rice Lake Voc Col; Med Secy.*

JOHNSON, Cheryl Lynn
Blaine Sr HS; Blaine, MN; Beta HR.

JOHNSON, Cheryl Lynn
John Ehret HS; Marrero, LA (49-470) Mu Alpha Theta; NHS; Up Bound; Hon Prog; Journ A; *U of Iowa; Journ.*

JOHNSON, Chester Lee
Virgie HS; Virgie, KY; FTA; Ger C; 4H; F-Ed, Sch P; VP, Spch C; Bsbl; Co-Cpt, Bkbl; Cpt, Ftbl; Tr; Cl Fav.

JOHNSON, Chiquita Monon
Avondale HS; Decatur, GA (10-308) Band; Chor; FHA; InterAct C; Lat C; Math C; Mgr, Bkbl; Tr; Beauty; God & Country A; Math A; Yth Fel; Christian Work A; Child Care A; *Spelman of Ga; Sociology.*

JOHNSON, Christa Marie
Galesburg Sr HS; Galesburg, IL (50-368) A Cap Choir; Band; Ensm; GS; NHS; Tres, Span C; Span NHS; Tnns; WW; Rep, Explorers Ntl Congress; *David Lipscomb Col; Math.*

JOHNSON, Christina Ann
S Mecklenburg HS; Pineville, NC (16%-581) A Cap Choir; Chor; FTA; Madrigal; Span C; SC; Swim; Tnns; Citz A; Hon Prog; GSct 1st Cl; *Appalachian St U; Elem Ed.*

JOHNSON, Christine
Kubasaki HS; Okinawa, JAPAN (16-271) NHS; Most Out; *U of S Fla; Elem Ed.*

JOHNSON, Claire Diane
Robert E Lee HS; Midland, TX (122-632) Ensm; NHS; Chaplain, A Cappella Choir; All St Choir; *Tex Tech U; Mus.*

JOHNSON, Clayton Mark
Luther HS S; Chicago, IL (40-160) A Cap Choir; Band; Chor; Spch C; *Concordia Teachers Col; Mus.*

JOHNSON, Connie Jeanine
Frontenac HS; Frontenac, KS (5-55) Cpt, Chldr; Drama; Span C; Spch A; Bkbl; Opt A; Spch A; VFW A; VofDEM; *Kans St Col.*

JOHNSON, Connie Lou
Harding HS; St Paul, MN (5%-850) Chor; Ensm; Ger C; Cpt, Mjrte; NHS; Sch P; Flagtwirler; Pres, Health Careers; *Gustavus Adolphus Col; Nurs.*

JOHNSON, Craig Owen
Yankton Sr HS; Yankton, SD (33-270) Band; Dbte Tm; Ensm; VP, Hmrm; NFL; JV, Cr-Ctry; JV, Golf; Alg A; Math A; Sup, Mus Contest; Church Organist; Accomp, Vocal Groups & Soloists; *U of SD; Pre-Med.*

JOHNSON, Curt Paul
Chatsworth HS; Chatsworth, CA (20%-600) Eagle Sct; Jr Schol; *Calif St U; Bus Adm.*

JOHNSON, Cynthia Anne
Unionville HS; Unionville, PA (66-216) Chor; Ensm; Harvest Qn Court; Concert Choir; Musical.

JOHNSON, Cynthia Denise
Springfeild SE HS; Springfield, IL (290-500) Drama; 4H A; *Bradley U; Nurs.*

JOHNSON, Cynthia Hope
Brown HS; Sturgis, SD; Math A; 2nd Pl Ribbon, Art; *Math.*

JOHNSON, Cynthia Jo
Loris HS; Loris, SC (46-153) Cpt, Chldr; Drama; Hmrm; Beauty; HQn; HCt; Hon Prog; Most Out; Swtht; Co-Cpt, JV Chldr; WW; Allied Yth; Pres & VP, SC; Pep C; WW; Harvest Qn.

JOHNSON, Cynthia Jo
Marion HS; Marion, IN; Band; Gym; *Psych.*

JOHNSON, Cynthia Joyce
Marion Co HS; Guin, AL (20-40) BC; Chldr; FHA; Co-Ed, Sch P; 4H A; *NW Ala St Tech Col; Cosmetology.*

JOHNSON, Cynthia Kaye
Union Cath Girls HS; Scotch Plains, NJ (68-150) Chor; Ensm; Hmrm; ARC; Tnns; Cpt, Tr; Citz A; ARC A; MVP, Tr; *Howard U; Bus Adm.*

JOHNSON, Cynthia Lee
Wheaton N HS; Wheaton, IL (10%-300) Lit Mag; Madrigal; NHS; Ntl Sci Found; *Wheaton Col; Physics.*

JOHNSON, Cynthia Lynn
Joliet Township HS W Campus; Joliet, IL (173-589) Chor; Hmrm; COM; Mod Dance; Scholastic Art A; *Animal Sci.*

JOHNSON, Cynthia Marie
John Bartram HS; Philadelphia, PA (50-900) Chor; Pres, Dbte Tm; Pres, Hmrm; ARC; Pres, SC; Pres, World Affairs; Swim; COM; Cl Fav; MLS; Most Out; ARC A; *U of NC; Pre-Law.*

JOHNSON, Cynthia Renee
London HS; London, OH (2-186) Band; Chor; Drama; Ensm; 4H; Hmrm; SC; 4H A; Tri-L; Pres, Yth Fel; Top Twenty; Soph Rep, Winter Prncss Court-Tri L; *EKU; Nurs.*

JOHNSON, Cynthia Sue
Atwater HS; Atwater, CA; S-T, A Cap Choir; Band; Qn, Church Yth; *California Baptist Col; Mus.*

JOHNSON, Dagne K
Washington HS; Cherokee, IA; Chldr; Chor; Community Yth Symph; 4H; Orch; Span C; Bkbl; Golf; Swim; Tr; *U of Iowa; Mus.*

JOHNSON, Dale Alan
Cary-Grove HS; Cary, IL; FBLA; Ed, Sch P; Hon Prog; Gold Key, Scholastic Art A; *Southwest Baptist Col; Bus Adm.*

JOHNSON, Dale Arthur
Cass Tech HS; Detroit, MI; *Automotive Mech.*

JOHNSON, Daniel James
Crystal Lake Comm HS; Crystal Lake, IL (16-590) Band; *Engr.*

JOHNSON, Daniel Leroy
Pine River HS; Pine River, MN (35-70) Ann; Chor; SC; VP, Sr Cl; VP, Jr Cl; Cpt, Bsbl; Co-Cpt, Ftbl; Co-Cpt, Wrest; HKg; Most Out; HS All Amer; All Conf Ftbl; *Bemidji St Col; Industrial Arts.*

JOHNSON, Daniel Scott
Clearlake HS; Lakeport, CA (1-90) Pres, Band; Chor; Ensm; Orch; A-Ed, Sch P; SC; Var C; Pres, Soph Cl; JV, Bsbl; Bkbl; Swim; CSF; Chem A; Elk A; Math A; ARC A; Hon Band.

JOHNSON, Daniel Scott
Brown Deer HS; Brown Deer, WI (20%-276) Ann; Band; JV, Cr-Ctry; Stage Band; Eagle Sct; Jr Asst Scoutmaster; Ntl Eagle Scout & Assn.

JOHNSON, Daniel Steven
Arlington HS; Arlington Heights, IL; AFS; Band; Chor; Dbte Tm; NFL; Span A; *Oral Roberts U; Telecommunications.*

JOHNSON, Darla Jeanine
Dr Martin L King HS; Chicago, IL (68-276) Bus Mgr, A Cap Choir; Bus Mgr, Chess C; Drama; Ensm; Hmrm; NHS; Sch P; SC; Bkbl; Cpt, Sftbl; Cpt, Swim; Tnns; Alg A; Beauty; COM; Hon Prog; Interlochen Ntl Mus; Yth Fel; Yth Foundation; Yth Foundation A; *Northern Ill U; Special Ed.*

JOHNSON, David Alfred
W Mecklemburg HS; Charlotte, NC (20%-350) F-Ed, Ann; InterAct C; InterClub Coun; Key C; Orch; Sci C; Golf; Soccer; VofDEM; Yth Fel; *Emory and Henry Col; Pre-Law.*

JOHNSON, David Allen
Hammond Tech HS; Hammond, IN (73-284) COM; Citz A; Spch A; VofDEM; Neatness, Behavior, A's; Shiest, Best Dressed, A's; *Purdue Calumet U; Child Psych.*

JOHNSON, David Arnold
Pepin HS; Pepin, WI (15-39) VP, FFA; JV, Bkbl; HCt; Dekalt Agr Achv; Mr Irresistible; Star Chapter Farmer; Crop Proficiency A; Leadership A; Pres, Church Yth Group.

JOHNSON, David Brooks
Bryant HS; Bryant, AR; Pres, Hmrm; Ftbl; Tr; Environmental A of Excel; Gov Adv Board, Environmental Ed; *Ark Tech Col; Wildlife Mgt.*

JOHNSON, David James
Portland HS; Portland, MI (48-150) Chess C; 4H; Ski C; Tr; 4H A; Yth Fel; *MSU; Bus.*

JOHNSON, David Michael
Beaver Dam Sr HS; Beaver Dam, WI (48-317) Tres, AFS; Ann; Chor; Ensm; Ski C; Span C; JV, Ftbl; JV, Tnns; JV, Wrest; Sci A; Stu Faculty Comm; Engr A; Tres, Art C; St Art Ed Assn A; Win, Sci Fair; Physics A; Summer Studio Art Workshop; *UW at Madison; Med.*

JOHNSON, David Wayne
Burkurnett HS; Burkurnett, TX (99-267) Band; Eng A; *Midwestern St U; Secondary Ed.*

JOHNSON, David Wayne
Sharpstown Sr HS; Houston, TX; Drama; Math C; *U of Houston.*

JOHNSON, Dawn Carole
Biggs HS; Biggs, CA (4-47) Ann; S-T, FHA; S-T, Hmrm; NHS; Ed, Sch Achieve Tm; Tres, Span C; Tres, SC; Bank Of Amer A; MLS; Type A; Bus A; Outst Stu A; *Tri-zity Western Col; Bus Adm.*

JOHNSON, Debbie Lynn
Anoka Sr HS; Anoka, MN; Band; SC; Tr; Opt A; Media A; *U of Minn; Ed.*

JOHNSON, Debbra Lynn
Central Jersey Christian Sch; Asbury Park, NJ (1-6) Chor; Pres, Fr C; Lit Mag; Alg A; Bio A; Hist A; HCt; Math A; Sci A; Fr A; Eng A; *Wheaton Col; Philosophy.*

JOHNSON, Deborah Ann
Neshaminy Maple Point HS; Langhorne, PA (3-415) Chor; Hmrm; NHS; SC; Thes; Hon Prog; Job's Daughters; *Ind U of Pa; Nurs.*

JOHNSON, Deborah Ann
Maryvale Sr HS; Cheektowaga, NY (20-650) Chor; City Conf; Drama; Fr C; NHS; Bkbl; COM; Cert of Hon; *Math.*

JOHNSON, Deborah Renee
Burke HS; Charleston, SC (10-210) Chldr; 4H; Pres, Hmrm; NHS; VP, SC; Pres, Sr Cl; Parl, Jr Cl; Bkbl; Foreign Lang A; Fin, HQn; *SC St U; Elem Ed.*

JOHNSON, Debra Jean
Banner Co HS; Harrisburg, NE (2-23) Bus Mgr, Ann; Band; Chor; VP, NHS; Co-Ed, Sch P; Span C; Cpt, Bkbl; COM; Journ A; Sal; Cpt, Vlbl; John Wiatt Mem Schol; Potery Pub, Ntl Potery Press; *U of Nebr; Bus Adm.*

JOHNSON, Debra Lynne
Alameda Sr HS; Lakewood, CO (33-620) Band; Chldr; Chor; Ensm; GS; Hmrm; NHS; ARC; Ski C; SC; Var C; Sftbl; Swim; Tnns; Citz A; Marching Band; Secy, Jr Exchange C; Pep Band; JV, Vlbl; Cand, Prom Qn; Ntl & St Ldrship Workshop; Friendliest Girl; *Azusa Pacific Col; Mus.*

JOHNSON, Deedy Allison
Canyon HS; Canyon, TX (25%-225) Band; Bus C; Chor; VP, Soph Cl; Cpt, Bkbl; Tr; Hon Men, Dist Bkbl Forward; All-Dist & All-St Bkbl Guard; Panhandle Plains Super Grls Bkbl Tm; Defensive Player o-t Yr; *Abilene Christian U; Lang.*

JOHNSON, Delbert Randolph
Mullens HS; Mullens, WV (5-125) Ann; Rptr, Sch P; Secy, Sci C; St Stu Congress; SC; Pres, Sr Cl; VP, Jr Cl; VP, Soph Cl; Tr; *W Va U; Pre-Med.*

JOHNSON, Della Suzanne
Clark Co R-1 HS; Kahoka, MO (37-92) Band; Ensm; COM; Yth Fel; All Conf Band; *Gem City Col; Bus.*

JOHNSON, Denise Ann
Beach Sr HS; Savannah, GA (11-32) *Bus.*

JOHNSON, Denise Annette
Oppenheim-Ephratah Central Sch; St Johnsville, NY (32-39) Chor; Mjrte; Cl Fav.

JOHNSON, Denise Louise
Simon Gratz HS; Philadelphia, PA (2-20) Co-Cpt, Mjrte; *Fisk U; Bus Adm.*

JOHNSON, Denise Louise
Searcy HS; Searcy, AR (10%-240) Drama; FTA; Thes; Tnns; COM; Val; Vlbl; *U of Central Ark; Med.*

JOHNSON, Dennis
East HS; Cleveland, OH; *Ohio U; Journ.*

JOHNSON, Diane Darcell
Simon Gratz HS; Philadelphia, PA (6-20) Cpt, Mjrte; *Fisk U; Art.*

JOHNSON, Dianne Carol
Jamestown HS; Jamestown, NY; Band; Chor; Madrigal; Co-Ed, Sch P; Hon Prog; NEDT; Clarinet NYSSMA; Evening News; Spell Bee A; Ntl Hon Soc; *Math.*

JOHNSON, Dixie Ann
Summit HS; Summit, SD (2-16) Ed, Ann; Chldr; Chor; Ensm; FNA; 4H; VP, SC; Pres, Jr Cl; Co-Cpt, Bkbl; Cr-Ctry; MVP, Tr; Beauty; 4H A; HCt; I Dare You; Sal; Type A; VofDEM; Stu o-t Yr A; *Eastern Wy Col; Animal Health Techology.*

JOHNSON, Donald Harvey
Sanger HS; Sanger, CA (9-521) AFS; Demolay; Ger C; 4H; Cr-Ctry; Tr; Wrest; CSF; NEDT; Luther League; *Reedley Col; Engr.*

JOHNSON, Donna Lee
Adlai E Stevenson HS; Bronx, NY (25-788) NHS; Tnns; *Simmon's Col; Phys Therapy.*

JOHNSON, Donna Lee
Forbush HS; E Bend, NC (8-300) A Cap Choir; Ann; Band; Chem C; Chor; Ensm; FNA; FTA; Hmrm; Mjrte; Monogram; NHS; Sr Span C; Span NHS; Secy, SC; Bkbl; Sftbl; Tnns; Beauty; Gov Honor Prog; Gr Marshal; HCt; Hon Prog; Secy, Fresh Cl; Bkbl HS All Amer; Gov Sch Nom; NC St Champ, Sftb; Marshal; *U of NC at Chapel Hill; Med.*

JOHNSON, Doreen Marie
Albert Lea Central HS; Albert Lea, MN (19-575) Band; Orch; Stage Band; Pep C; Big 9 Select Band; *Concordia Col; Phar.*

JOHNSON, Dorine Mary Beth
Chester HS; Chester, PA (20-643) Ann; Chor; Drama; NHS; Pol Sci C; Hon Prog; *Penn St U; Bus Adm.*

JOHNSON, Doris Glenda
George Washington HS; Los Angeles, CA; Chor; Span C; COM; Citz A; *UCLA; Bus.*

JOHNSON, Duncan Eric
Corliss HS; Chicago, IL (9-216) NHS; Sch P; COM; Citz A; Hon Prog; *Bradley U; Bus Mgt.*

JOHNSON, Dwayne Patrick
Central Baptist HS; Hampton, VA (8-14) Pres, Sr Cl; Cpt, Bkbl; Cpt, Ftbl; Co-Cpt, Sftbl; COM; Hist A; Most Ath A.

JOHNSON, Eddie Joe
Switzerland Co HS; Vevay, IN (10-108) BS; Drama; NHS; Cpt, Order/Arrow; Span C; Var C; Bus Mgr, Sr Cl; Co-Ch, Jr Cl; Bsbl; Mgr, Bkbl; Cr-Ctry; Tr; COM; Math A; Order/Arrow A; Eagle Sct; *Purdue U; Elec Engr.*

JOHNSON, Edie Jean
Cajon HS; San Bernardino, CA; Bus C; SC; Future Secy of Amer; Asst Secy, Baptist Stu Union; Phys Fitness A; *Skadron Col; Fashion Merchandising.*

JOHNSON, Elaine Marie
Patterson HS; Patterson, CA (12-99) Drama; Ski C; *Heald Bus Col; Legal Secy.*

JOHNSON, Elizabeth Carol
Mansfield HS; Mansfield, LA (15-100) Band; BC; VP, FBLA; Hmrm; Lit Rall; Mjrte; Secy, SC; Bkbl; Type A.

JOHNSON, Ella Mae
Martin Luther King Acad; Gary, IN; Chor; Drama; Sch P; SC; Bsbl; Bkbl; Soccer; Sftbl; Tnns; COM; Citz A; Hon Prog; MLS; Most Out; *Ind U NW; Computer Programming.*

JOHNSON, Ellen Marie
Isaac C Elston Sr HS; Michigan City, IN (25-355) Ann; NHS; 1st Cl, Pres, GSct; *U of Ariz; Math.*

JOHNSON, Emily Charlene
Grace Christian Sch; Blackstone, VA; Drama; Fr C; Tri-HiY; Valentine Qn.

JOHNSON, Ericka Michele
Hamtramck HS; Hamtramck, MI (9-107) Band; Chor; Drama; Pres, Fr C; Hmrm; Math C; NHS; Orch; F-Ed, Sch P; Sci C; SC; Y-Tns; COM; Citz A; Hon Prog; Journ A; JA A; Attendance A; Music A; NHS; *Mich St U.*

JOHNSON, Erin Helene
Morton Jr-Sr HS; Morton, WA (5-36) S-T, Band; CYO; Chldr; Drama; FHA; NHS; Rainbow; Ski C; Pres, Span C; Spch C; SC; Masonic A; NEDT; *Wash St U; Span.*

JOHNSON, Etheyl Quentella
Aiken Sr HS; Cincinnati, OH; Cpt, Sftbl; Cpt, Tr; Typing A; *St Mary's Dominican Col.*

JOHNSON, Eugenie Lee
San Diego HS; San Diego, CA (40%-246) Citz A; Badminton; *Pacific Col; Dental Asst.*

JOHNSON, Felicia Ann
Grove City HS; Grove City, OH; Chor; Ger C; Lit Mag; Sch P; Tr; COM; Hon Prog; Sci A; Pres, Yth Assn; *Ohio U; Lit.*

JOHNSON, Francis Melvin
J H Rose HS; Greenville, NC (19-429) BS; Pres, Chess C; Drama; Fr C; Math C; NHS; Pres, Order/Arrow; Sci C; COM; God & Country A; Secy, Ch, Order o-t Arrow; *Davidson Col; Pre-Med.*

JOHNSON, Fred Robert
Jefferson Davis HS; Montgomery, AL (46-742) Chor; Ensm; Mu Alpha Theta; NHS; Ntl Yth Conf; Span NHS; Bsbl; Bkbl; Sftbl; COM; Hon Prog; Phy A; Pres, VP, Yth Coun; Ensm Tour; All Star Bsbl; Yth Citz Seminar; *Auburn U; Engr.*

JOHNSON, Gary
East HS; Cleveland, OH; Band; Hmrm; Spch C; Mgr, Bkbl; Ftbl; Mgr, Sftbl; Citz A; Spch A; Martin Holdings Jennings, A; Off Service, A; *Cleveland St U; Bus.*

JOHNSON, Gary Dean
South HS; Springfield, OH (6-500) Band; Ger C; Math C; Pres, NHS; Alg A; Industrial Arts A; *Air Force-ROTC; Aviation.*

JOHNSON, Gary Lee
Madison Heights HS; Anderson, IN (199-397) Tres, Bus C; Order/Arrow; JV, Cr-Ctry; JV, Tr; JV, Wrest; Order/Arrow A; Young Democrats; FCA A; 1st Pl, Summer Tr Meet; *Ind U; Acct.*

JOHNSON, Gary Luke
Karlstad HS; Karlstad, MN (15-40) Tres, FFA; JV, Ftbl; Star Chpt Farmer; Crop Proficiency A; *Thief Riv Fall Area Voc Tech Inst; Agr.*

JOHNSON, George
St Augustine HS; New Orleans, LA (6-35) Band; Orch; *Xavier U; Architectural Engr.*

JOHNSON, Georgia Ann
Parkview HS; Orfordville, WI (55-138) JV, Chldr; Secy, 4H; SC; JV, Tr; 4H A; Gym; *Nova Col; Marine Bio.*

JOHNSON, Gigi Jill
Crestwood HS; Mountaintop, PA (10-232) Band; Cpt, Chldr; Chor; Drama; Hmrm; Jr Miss Pagent; Math C; Mu Alpha Theta; NHS; Rainbow; Ski C; SC; VP, Y-Tns; COM; NEDT; Yth Fel; *Franklin & Marshall Col; Pre-Med.*

JOHNSON, Ginger Lynn
McMinn Co HS; Athens, TN; Chem C; GS; Hmrm; InterClub Coun; Mu Alpha Theta; NHS; Span C; SC; Pres, Tri-HiY; MVP, Tnns; Citz A; Kiwanis A; Opt A; *Phys Ed.*

JOHNSON, Glendia Alfreda
Myrtle Beach HS; Myrtle Beach, SC (97-245) Rptr, Ann; Band; Chldr; Chor; Fr C; FHA; 4H; Pres, Hmrm; Rptr, Sch P; VP, SC; Var C; VP, SC; VP, Jr Cl; VP, Soph Cl; JV, Bkbl; JV, Tr; Beauty; 4H A; Showstopper; PA; *Winthrop Col; Fashion Merchandising.*

JOHNSON, Gloria LaTanya
Uniontown Sr HS; Uniontown, PA; Fr C; Secy, Hmrm; COBBE A; NJHS; *Psych.*

JOHNSON, Gregory Louis
Grace Christian Sch; Prattville, AL (8-50) Ann; Bsbl; Cpt, Bkbl; Cpt, Ftbl; Tr; Sportsmanship, Sch Ltr; Regular Attendance, Most Ath, A's; *U of Ala; Elec.*

JOHNSON, Gregory Wayne
Ponder HS; Ponder, TX; Rptr, FFA; SC; *N Tex St U; Animal Sci.*

JOHNSON, Guy Jeffrey
Colonel Zadok Magruder HS; Rockville, MD; Chess C; Drama; Thes; Thespians; *Navy.*

JOHNSON, Harriett Denise
Ft Pierce Central HS; Ft Pierce, FL; BC; *Eckerd Col; Acct.*

JOHNSON, Harry Andrew
F W Springstead HS; Spring Hill, FL (12-159) Pres, Chor; Tres, Key C; Order/Arrow; Bsbl; Ftbl; Citz A; God & Country A; Order/Arrow A; Eagle Sct; *Eckerd Col; Forestry.*

JOHNSON, Harry Duane
Boiling Springs HS; Spartanburg, SC (50-230) Ftbl; Tr; *Clemson U; Ath.*

JOHNSON, Helen Kristin
Sacred Heart Acad; Mt Pleasant, MI (4-50) Cpt, Chldr; Drama; Madrigal; NHS; ARC; Spch C; VP, SC; Cpt, Bkbl; Cpt, Sftbl; DARGCA; Hon Prog; Most Out; Rotary A; Spch A; Acad A; WW; *Central Mich U.*

JOHNSON, Hellene Vanessa
E Rome HS; Rome, GA (21-106) Drama; FBLA; Hmrm; Tri-HiY; Yth Comm Choir; Voc Off Trng A; Ch, Yth Coun; Shorthand; Bkbl & Tr Statistician; Church Yth Worker Cert; *Floyd Jr Col; Med Lab Tech.*

JOHNSON, Henry Etta
Block HS; Jonesville, LA (10%-89) Ann; Band; Pres, Chor; 4H; Tres, Hmrm; Sch P; 4H A; Hon Prog; JA A; Band A; Mu Sigma A; HR A; PA A; *NE La U; Lab Tech.*

JOHNSON, Herman Wayne
Savannah HS; Savannah, GA (12%-350) Band; Chor; Drama; Ensm; Hmrm; Bus Mgr, SC; Bsbl; Ftbl; COM; Cl Fav; Outst Mus; Eng, VIP Stu, A's; *Ga Sou Col; Mus.*

JOHNSON, Holly Ruth
Hinsdale Township HS Central; Hinsdale, IL (35-700) A Cap Choir; Cpt, Chldr; Chor; Pres, Ger C; NHS; Ski C; Tres, SC; Vlbl; *Concordia Col; Ed.*

JOHNSON, Ideliza
Orangewood Acad; Garden Grove, CA; Chor; Span C; Bkbl; Soccer; Sftbl; Tr; Citz A; Pres A; Type A; *Loma Linda U; Dentistry.*

JOHNSON, Ingrid Ellen
Batavia HS; Batavia, IL; NHS; St Scholar; *Waubonsee Comm Col; Bus.*

JOHNSON, Iris Marie
Cottonwood HS; Salt Lake City, UT; A Cap Choir; Drama; Ger C; NHS; Ski C; Thes; Demolay Swtht.

JOHNSON, J Paul
Valley City HS; Valley City, ND (35%-170) Ann; Drama; Hmrm; VP, Span C; SC; Bkbl; MVP, Tnns; Math A; *Concordia Col; Communications.*

JOHNSON, Jacqueline Antionett
Ahrens HS; Louisville, KY; Merit, Lib Service, Campers, A's; Cert of Attendance; *Fashion Designer.*

JOHNSON, James
Adlai E Stevenson HS; New York, NY; Band; NHS; Co-Cpt, Cr-Ctry; Co-Cpt, Tr; Hon Prog; Math A.

JOHNSON, James A
Kodiak HS; Kodiak, AK (6-103) Pres, Band; BS; Chor; Drama; Ensm; Pres, NHS; SC; Elk A; Hon Prog; NMF; All-St Jazz Band; John Philips Sousa A; *Rose-Hulman Inst of Tech; Elec Engr.*

JOHNSON, James Edward
Palmetto HS; Palmetto, GA (40-97) Bkbl.

JOHNSON, James Eric
NorthWood HS; Nappanee, IN; Band; Semi-Fin, BS; Chor; Drama; Mjrte; SC; Thes; Tr; Amer Leg A; Citz A; Drum Major; Director's Band A; *Taylor U; Secondary Ed.*

JOHNSON, James Lee
Trenton Central HS; Trenton, NJ (25%-700) Var C; Ftbl; Wrest; Citz A; Math A; *Trenton St U; Engr.*

JOHNSON, James Robert
Elmira Southside HS; Elmira, NY (20-500) Drama; Lat C; Regent Schol.

JOHNSON, James Rodney
Pflugerville HS; Pflugerville, TX; FFA; JV, Ftbl; JV, Tr.

JOHNSON, Jamie Robert
Dearborn HS; Dearborn, MI (25-570) AFS; Fin, NFL; NHS; Tres, SC; Thes; VP, Soph Cl; Bsbl; Bkbl; Cpt, Soccer; NMS; Phi Beta Kappa; St Fin, Forensic; Exchange Stu to Italy; *Ohio Wesleyan U; Sociology.*

JOHNSON, Janice Marie
York Comp HS; York, SC (1-272) Band; NHS; Sci C; Span C; Gov Honor Prog; Jr Marshal; Yth for Christ; All-Amer Band; All-Co Band; *USC; Computer Sci.*

JOHNSON, Jann Leslie
Union HS; Biggsville, IL; Chess C; Drama; NHS; SC; Bkbl; Tr; Spch A.

JOHNSON, Janna Patricia
Kecoughtan HS; Hampton, VA; Band; Fr C; 4H; Swim; COM; 4H A; JNHS; Reg Band; Most Talented; Tn A; Swim Ltr.

JOHNSON, Jean Marie
Kalama HS; Kalama, WA; Chldr; Secy, Chor; Dbte Tm; Bkbl; MVP, Sftbl; MVP, Tr; HQn; Type A; Bkbl Trophy; Home Ec A.

JOHNSON, Jeanne Marie
Moreau HS; Hayward, CA (12-348) Chldr; Ski C; Tr; *U of Cal at Berkeley; Bus Adm.*

JOHNSON, Jeannine Elizabeth
Lansing Christian HS; Lansing, MI (1-433) Cpt, Chldr; Chor; NHS; Rptr, Sch P; Sftbl; JV, Tnns; Tr; Hon Prog; Pres A; Hinman A; Right to Life; Yth Talent; Yth for Understanding; Morality in Media.

JOHNSON, Jeffery James
San Gabriel HS; San Gabriel, CA (160-529) Pres, Hmrm; Ski C; Thes; Bkbl; Ftbl; JV, Tr; Yth Fel; Ind Arts Achv; Sch Shows; Most Improved Player; League Champs; *Cal St Col; Interior Decoration.*

JOHNSON, Jeffrey Alan
Kuemper HS; Carroll, IA; Chor; Drama; Monogram; Mgr, Bkbl; Ntl Essay A; *Elec.*

JOHNSON, Jeffrey Durrah
Carver HS; Columbus, GA; *Jamestown Col; Wildlife.*

JOHNSON, Jeffrey Lee
Tartan HS; Oakdale, MN (60-430) NHS; Cpt, Tnns; Ski Tm; Young Life Work Crew; *Bethel Col; Engr.*

JOHNSON, Jeffrey Lyle
Luther L Wright HS; Ironwood, MI (25%-190) 4H; Bkbl; JV, Cr-Ctry; 4H A; Ntl Ath Hon Soc A; *Gogebic Comm Col; Architecture.*

JOHNSON, Jeffrey Michael
Plant City HS; Plant City, FL (50-800) Chor; FFA; Hmrm; SC; Var C; Bsbl; JV, Bkbl; Amer Leg A; COM; Citz A; Hon Prog; Highest Batting Avg A; *Stetson Col; Bus.*

JOHNSON, Jeffrey Paul
Valley City HS; Valley City, ND (35%-175) Ann; Drama; Span C; Var C; Bkbl; Tnns; Math A; *Concordia Col; Communications.*

JOHNSON, Jennifer Ann
Hector HS; Hector, MN (25-50) Ann; Band; Chor; FHA; F-Ed, Sch P; Spch C; Arch; Bkbl; Soccer; Sftbl; Swim; Tr; *Willmar Vo-tech Col; Photography.*

JOHNSON, Jennifer Gloria
Chester HS; Chester, PA; *Early Childhood Ed.*

JOHNSON, Jennifer Lynn
Armstrong Sr HS; Plymouth, MN; Hon Prog; Pres A; Gym; DECA; *Minn Sch of Bus; Sales Merchandising.*

JOHNSON, Jennifer Lynne
John Handley HS; Winchester, VA (57-264) Ann; Pres, Chor; Fr C; Pres, Hmrm; ARC; Soccer; Bio A; VP, Chor; Drill Tm; Fin, Fr Contest.

JOHNSON, Jerry James
Garfield Hts Sr HS; Garfield Hts, OH (207-480) Band; *Cleveland St Col; Acct.*

JOHNSON, Jerry Lee
Monticello HS; Monticello, MS; FFA; ARC; Var C; Bsbl; Cpt, Ftbl; Tr; Citz A; Cl Fav; H of F; HCt; Hon Prog; Most Out; Sci A; Most Handsome; Scholastic Achv A; *Alcorn St U; Bio.*

JOHNSON, Jerry Wayne
Colerain Sr HS; Cincinnati, OH; Band; Chor; Pres, Demolay; Ensm; Bsbl; Bkbl; Sftbl; JV, Tr; Wrest; COM; JA A; Pres A; Skating Trophy; Bsbl Trophy; Bowling Trophy; 1st Rating St Band Solo Comp.

JOHNSON, Jill Marie
Gaylord Pub HS; Gaylord, MN (1-79) Fin, Ensm; Pres, FHA; Jr Miss Pagent; Span C; COM; Hon Prog; Rotary A; Val; 1st Chair Band; Secy-Treas, Yth Fellowship; Med Careers C; *Gustavus Col; Ed.*

JOHNSON, Jimmy
McNeil HS; McNeil, AR (6-34) Hmrm; SC; Alg A; Bio A; COM; Citz A; Math A; Sci A; Star Student.

JOHNSON, Joan Adell
Brainerd HS; Brainerd, MN; Ann; Band; Dbte Tm; Hmrm; NFL; Sch P; Span C; Spch C; Bkbl; Tr; COM; Spch A; *Law.*

JOHNSON, Joan Dale
Kathleen HS; Lakeland, FL; St Assn of Women & Girls C; *Lakeland Bus Col; Fashion Design.*

JOHNSON, Joan Elizabeth
Plant City HS; Plant City, FL (228-835) Ch, Inter-Club Coun; Model UN; VP, SC; UN Council; Var C; Tnns; Pres A; Civinettes; Soph & Jr Executive Coun; Pres, Tns for Christ; *Stetson U.*

JOHNSON, Jody Rae
Rugby HS; Rugby, ND (5-110) Chor; Ensm; Madrigal; NHS; Pom Pon Girl; Pep C; *Concordia Col; Bus.*

JOHNSON, John Earl
Webster Groves HS; Webster Groves, MO (99-649) VP, Bus C; *Houston Col; Bus.*

JOHNSON, John Howard
S R Butler HS; Huntsville, AL; Bkbl; Pres, UMYF; Active, Church.

JOHNSON, John Nelson
Sharpstown Sr HS; Houston, TX (168-686) VP, Band; Chor; Ensm; Sch P; Journ A; Most Out; WW; Rptr, Yrbk; *U of Houston; Law Enforcement.*

JOHNSON, Johnella Olivia
Horace Mann Jr HS; Los Angeles, CA; *U of Sou Calif; Data Processing.*

JOHNSON, Jonna Kae
Crossville Comm HS; Crossville, IL; Ann; S-T, Band; Tres, BC; Hmrm; Cpt, Mjrte; SC; Sftbl; MVP, Tnns; Tr; Amer Leg A; Hon Prog; Drum Major.

JOHNSON, Joyce Anita
Crossland Sr HS; Campsprings, MD; *Computer Sci.*

JOHNSON, Joyce Sheree
Aquinas Dominican HS; Chicago, IL (83-175) Chor; Rptr, Sch P; Pres, Ski C; Swim; *Hist.*

JOHNSON, Juan Adrian
Avondale HS; Avondale Estates, GA; FBLA; Hmrm; SC; Ftbl; Sftbl; *Dekalb Comm Col; Bus Adm.*

JOHNSON, Judith Ann
Essex Comm HS; Essex, IA (3-35) Band; Pres, Chor; Ensm; Madrigal; NHS; Mgr, Bkbl; DARGCA; *North Park Col.*

JOHNSON, Judy Kay
Galesburg Sr HS; Galesburg, IL (78-648) Bus Mgr, Drama; Lat C; Thes; *Olivet Nazarene Col; Eng.*

JOHNSON, Judy Lynn
Tartan HS; Oakdale, MN (90-450) Band; Chor; Pres, Ski C; Tnns; HCt; Young Life; Ski Tm; *Bethel Col; Home Ec.*

JOHNSON, Julia Lorraine
Christian HS; El Cajon, CA (21-130) Drama; Ensm; Sundy Sch Tchr; Day Camp Counsellor; Jr Sr Banquet Comm; Dram A Church; Statistician, Bkbl; Drill Tm; Secy, Word of Life C; *Drama.*

JOHNSON, Julie Catherine
Everett HS; Everett, WA; Rainbow; Masonic A; Inspiration A; Friendship A; Girl o-t Mo; *Wash St U; Med.*

JOHNSON, Julie Dee
Fayetteville HS; Fayetteville, AR; A Cap Choir; Chor; Ensm; VP, Jr Cl; Secy, VICA; All St Choir; Outst Choir; *U of Ark; Mus.*

JOHNSON, Julie Lynn
Hoisington HS; Hoisington, KS (15-93) Chor; Dbte Tm; Drama; Ensm; NFL; Tres, NHS; 4H A; Hon Prog; Spch A; *US Air Force.*

JOHNSON, Kandace Kay
Lewis Central Comm HS; Council Bluffs, IA (9-165) NHS; Citz A; Eng A; Home Ec A; *Mid-Amer Nazarene Col; Nurs.*

JOHNSON, Kanitha GeJuana
Westinghouse HS; Chicago, IL (31-536) Chor; NHS; ROTC A; Hon Rib; Academic Achv; *Circle Campus Col; Bus Ed.*

JOHNSON, Karen Anita
E St Louis Sr HS; E Saint Louis, IL (200-617) Pres, Chor; F-Ed, Rainbow; JA A; Yth Fel; Pom Pom Sq Trophy; *SIU Edwardsville; Bus.*

JOHNSON, Karen Elaine
Belvidere HS; Belvidere, IL (80-366) A Cap Choir; St Scholar; WW; Choraliers; Swing Choir; *Bradley U; Elem Ed.*

JOHNSON, Karen Elise
Piscataquis Comm HS; Guilford, ME (1-65) Band; Drama; NHS; Phys C; Sch P; Secy, Sr Cl; Bkbl; Hockey; Alg A; Bausch & Lomb A; Chem A; Math A; Swtht; Val; Yth Fel; Fr A; Writing A; *USAF; Computer Sci.*

JOHNSON, Karen Elizabeth
New Bern Sr HS; New Bern, NC (10-436) Ann; Band; Chor; Drama; Ensm; Fr C; NHS; Rainbow; Sci C; NEDT; Sci A; Graduation Marshal; Prom Pagette; All-St & All-Co Band; *NCSU; Med Technology.*

JOHNSON, Karen Lisa
Olney HS; Philadelphia, PA (248-855) VP, Fr C; Sci C; Span C; Tr; Pres, Black Stu League; Stu Human Relations; *Community Col; Med Lab Tech.*

JOHNSON, Kari Lynn
Manistee HS; Manistee, MI; Band; Tri-HiY; Mus A.

JOHNSON, Katharine Johanne
J M Weatherway Sr HS; Aberdeen, WA (16-300) Dbte Tm; VP, Fr C; Tres, Math C; Mu Alpha Theta; NFL; Orch; Sci C; Hon Prog; NMS; Forensics Ltr; *Whitman Col; Bio.*

JOHNSON, Kathleen Ann
Hoover HS; Glendale, CA (4%-490) HiY; Tnns; CSF; COM; Hon Prog; Star Student; *Ed.*

JOHNSON, Kathleen Chiri
Alamosa HS; Alamosa, CO (22-181) CYO; Chldr; Pres, 4H; NHS; Pres, SC; 4H A; Prom Qn; Sch Drama A; St VP, 4-H; Ldrship A; *Loretto Heights Col; Nurs.*

JOHNSON, Kathleen Joyce
Albany HS; Albany, NY; Hmrm; Tr; *Oakwood Col; Nurs.*

JOHNSON, Kathleen Louise
Parkville Sr HS; Baltimore, MD (50-550) A Cap Choir; Chor; Drama; Fr C; Hmrm; Madrigal; Math C; NHS; ARC; SC; COM; Citz A; Hon Prog; Most Out; ARC A; Sci A; Co Cpt, Badminton; *Oral Roberts U; Nurs.*

JOHNSON, Kay Colleen
Lexington HS; Lexington, TN (10%-130) Co-Ed, Ann; BC; GS; Ed, Sch P; Sci C; Tres, Jr Cl; Cpt, Bkbl; MVP, Bkbl; *Union U; Phys Ed.*

JOHNSON, Kay Eugenia
Bowdon HS; Bowdon, GA (4-95) Band; BC; Chem C; Chess C; Drama; FHA; 4H; Tres, Hmrm; Math C; Span C; Rptr, Tri-HiY; Secy, Jr Cl; Bkbl; Cpt, Tnns; Alg A; Gov Honor Prog; Hon Prog; Math A; Sci A; Star Student; Hon Grad; Co Star Stu; Most Intelligent; Special Interests Research Prog; *Auburn U.*

JOHNSON, Keith
Grant Union HS; Sacramento, CA (10%-168) Pres, Chor; Var C; Bkbl; Tr; WW; *San Jose St U; Archt.*

JOHNSON, Keith Eugene
Orosi HS; Orosi, CA (1-126) Band; Fr C; HiY; SC; Bkbl; Ftbl; Co-Cpt, Tr; Amer Leg Orator A; Bausch & Lomb A; CSF; Val; B F Tunnel A; *Col of the Sequoias; Industrial Tech.*

JOHNSON, Kelly Ann
Lewistown Comm HS; Lewistown, IL; Ed, Ann; Chldr; Chor; NHS; SC; VP, Thes; Tres, Sr Cl; Tres, Jr Cl; DARGCA; St Scholar; Sr o-t Mo; Bus & Professional Women's Schol; Prom Princess & Prom Qn Attendant.

JOHNSON, Kelly Ann
Skyline HS; Salt Lake City, UT (127-675) F-Ed, Ann; Chor; FBLA; NHS; COM; Citz A; Hon Prog; *Brigham Young U.*

JOHNSON, Kenneth Alan
Brazosport HS; Freeport, TX (70-304) Band; Sftbl; *Brazosport Col.*

JOHNSON, Kenny J
Greenville HS; Greenville, TX (5%-366) Band; Chess C; Sch P; Span C; Tns Aid the Retarded; Acad Excel A; *U of Tex; Computer Sci.*

JOHNSON, Kerry Ray
Millbrook HS; Raleigh, NC (52-400) Band; Tres, Madrigal; NHS; Most Talented Male Sen; Outst Bandsman; Win, NCMTH; Win, Brady Corcerto Comp.

JOHNSON, Kim Elizabeth
Westborough Sr HS; Westborough, MA (105-240) A Cap Choir; AFS; Chor; Dbte Tm; Drama; Lit Mag; Madrigal; Rainbow; Span C; Tr; *N Adams St Col; Drama Arts.*

JOHNSON, Kimberlee Jill
Ephrata HS; Ephrata, WA; VP, AFS; 4H; NHS; JV, Bkbl; *Wash St U; Vet Med.*

JOHNSON, Kimberly Ann
Sunbright HS; Sunbright, TN (10-65) Band; Tres, BC; Chldr; FHA; VP, 4H; Var C; WW; *Tenn Tech U; Phar.*

JOHNSON, Kimberly Dawn
Smith Station HS; Smiths, AL (10%-188) BC; FHA; 4H; Mu Alpha Theta; Sci C; *Chattahoochee Valley Col; Optometric Tech.*

JOHNSON, Kimberly Elizabeth
N Beach HS; Moclips, WA (4-60) Band; Chldr; Chor; NHS; Rptr, Sch P; Span C; Hon Prog; Journ A; NMF; NMS; JV, Vlbl; Pres, Pep C; Miss Smile; VP, Christian C; WW, Mus Stu; Girls C; Girl o-t Mo A; *Seattle Pacific Col; Mus.*

JOHNSON, Korwin Oswald
Cooperstown HS; Cooperstown, ND (2-50) VP, Band; Chor; NHS; Orch; Var C; Co-Cpt, Ftbl; Chem A; Sal; Jazz Band; John Philip Sousa Band A; *ND St U; Engr.*

JOHNSON, Kris Marie
Belvidere HS; Belvidere, IL (17-366) Ger C; VP, 4H; WW; *Ill St U; Gen.*

JOHNSON, Kris Tina
Belaire HS; Baton Rouge, LA (47-400) A Cap Choir; Drama; Lat C; Mu Alpha Theta; Pres, Rainbow; ARC; S-T, Equations Tm; Grand Cross of Color; *LSU.*

JOHNSON, Kristi Lynn
Montevideo Sr HS; Montevideo, MN (5-170) AFS; Co-Ed, Ann; Band; Chldr; Ensm; FHA; Ger C; 4H; Mjrte; Rainbow; Beauty; 4H A; Most Out; Swtht; Jobs Daughters; Vlbl; Saxophone A's; Co-Ch, Prom Committee; Stage Band; VP, Yth Fel; Star, Fiddler On The Roof; *Ed.*

JOHNSON, Kristy Lee
Ralston HS; Ralston, NE (25%-350) AFS; Band; Chor; Ski C; Bat Girl, Bsbl; Fr A; *Wayne Col; Hist.*

JOHNSON, LaVetta Anne
Monroe Union HS; Monroe, OR (4-57) *Linn Benton Comm Col; Secretarial.*

JOHNSON, LaVita Denise
Eau Claire HS; Columbia, SC (30-375) Anchor C; VP, Chor; Drama; Hmrm; ARC; Bus Mgr, Sch P; VP, SC; HCt; Rptr, Sch P; *Atlanta U; Biol.*

JOHNSON, Larry Gene
South HS; Springfield, OH (5-500) Band; Math C; VP, NHS; Span C; Pres, Soph Cl; Top Soph Boy A; *Mount Vernon Nazarene Col; Pre-Law.*

JOHNSON, Laura Lee
Wachusett Regional HS; Holden, MA; Chldr; Chor; *Sch of Art; Art.*

JOHNSON, Laura Marie
Lanier HS; Austin, TX (10-500) Pres, FTA; Ger C; NHS; SC; COM; Most Out; UIL, Shorthand; *U of Tex; Bus.*

JOHNSON, Laura Sue
Spruce Creek HS; Port Orange, FL (8-450) Anchor C; Drama; A-Ed, Lit Mag; NHS; Pres, Span C; COM; Math A; Sci A; Summa Cum Laude; Rptr, Span C; Outst, Span; *Daytona Beach Comm Col; Liberal Arts.*

JOHNSON, Lauren Elizabeth
McMinn Co HS; Athens, TN; VP, Chem C; Fr C; Hmrm; Secy, Mu Alpha Theta; Secy, NHS; Span C; SC; Tri-HiY; MVP, Tnns; DARGCA; Opt A; Poetry A; May Ct; *UTK; Human Services.*

JOHNSON, Lavina Mae
North Toole County HS; Sunburst, MT (4-35) Band; Chor; Drama; Ensm; Pres, 4H; Math C; Sci C; S-T, Bkbl; Sftbl; COM; Citz A; HCt; NEDT; Sci A; Shorthand A; Heisey As; PTO Schol; Mem Schol; *Eastern Mont Col; Bus.*

JOHNSON, Leatha Ann
Hammond Tech HS; Hammond, IN; Chor; Drama; SC; Thes; COM; Citz A; Hist A; Sci A; Girl's C; Pom Pon Girl; *Purdue U; Secy.*

JOHNSON, Lee Ann
Palmer HS; Palmer, TX; Ed, Ann; VP, FHA; Sch P; Pres, Soph Cl; Bkbl; Tnns; COM; Journ A; Best Bicent Picture Story, UILPC; Yrbk Publication A; WW; Photo-Journ A; UILPC Photography Yrbk As; *Sam Houston St U at Huntsville; Photography.*

JOHNSON, Leon Curtis
Taylors Falls HS; Taylors Falls, MN (2-61) Band; 4H; Ski C; Mgr, Ftbl; Alg A; Bio A; 4H A; Math A; Star Student; Alpine Ski Raceing; *Mankato St U; Computor Sci.*

JOHNSON, Leonidas Alexander
Evanston Township HS; Evanston, IL (10%-1043) Band; Ensm; Ntl Yth Conf; COM; Cl Fav; Most Out; Tres, Church Chor; Cpt, MVP, Gym; Schol, St Rank, Excel, Gym Ldrship; *Ill Wesleyan U; Bio.*

JOHNSON, Lillian Gail
Hialeah-Miami Lakes Sr HS; Hialeah, FL (301-1000) Co-Cpt, Chldr; Sftbl; Tr; *Pepperdine U; Bus.*

JOHNSON, Linda
South Hills HS; Pittsburgh, PA (128-530) Chldr; Fr C; Pres, Hmrm; NHS; SC; Co-Cpt, Tnns; Outst Achv; *U of Pittsburgh; Law.*

JOHNSON, Linda Anne
Lynbrook HS; San Jose, CA (1-698) Dbte Tm; Pres, 4H; NFL; NHS; Span C; Spch C; 4H A; Hon Prog; Soph Cl Officer; *Med.*

JOHNSON, Linda Beth
Luther L Wright HS; Ironwood, MI (60-180) Band; Chor; Mjrte; Rptr; Sch P; Type A; Secy, Church Yth; Shorthand A; Jazz Band; Band A; Bible Quiz Tm; *Northland Col; Acct.*

JOHNSON, Linda Elaine
Miami Norland Sr HS; Miami, FL; Chor; Sch Service C; Secy, Chorus; Nom, Swtht of Key C; FCA; Statistician, Batgirl, Bsbl; Campers Life; *U of Fla; American Hist.*

JOHNSON, Linda Jane
John Foster Dulles HS; Stafford, TX (191-588) Tres, Drama; NFL; Spch C; Tres, Thes; Spch A; Best Thes; Drama Schol; *South West St; Elem Ed.*

JOHNSON, Linell Joy
Broward Christian HS; Fort Lauderdale, FL;

JOHNSON, Lisa Karen
Harding HS; Charlotte, NC (44-321) FHA; Orch; Span C; Sftbl; God & Comm A; *U of NC; Sociology.*

JOHNSON, Lisa Renee
Melville HS; Melville, LA; BC; Ch, 4H; Pres, Hmrm; Lit Ral; NHS; Ch, ARC; Spch C; Bkbl; Sftbl; Swim; Beauty; Hon Prog; ARC A; SDAHSS; St Fin, Ntl Tn Pageant; *La Col; Yth Director.*

JOHNSON, Lloyd Preston
Somerset HS; Somerset, KY (160-180) Chor; Bsbl; Bkbl; JV, Ftbl; Opt A; Spch A.

JOHNSON, Loreen Mae
Park Center Sr HS; Brooklyn Park, MN (82-523) F-Ed, Ann; Chor; Ensm; NHS; Ski C; SC; Co-Cpt, Swim; COM; Hon Prog; Church Camp Counselor; AAU Medals; Hon Qn, Jobs Daughters; VP, Church Yth Coun; Sr Personalities; St Swim Medals; *St Cloud St U; Aviation.*

JOHNSON, Loretta Joyce
Mart HS; Mart, TX (16-59) S-T, Band; Chor; Drama; Ensm; FHA; Math C; NHS; Ch, ARC; Sch P; Type A; WW; Dist & Regional Band A's; Most Talented; *McLennan Comm Jr Col; Computer Sci.*

JOHNSON, Lori Diane
Capital HS; Boise, ID; A Cap Choir; Secy, Chor; Ensm; Ski C; Ftbl; Beauty; Hon Prog; Yth Fel; Pianist, Swing Chor; Accomp o-t Ur; Ntl Piano Guild Soc Comp; Sch Mus Fest, I Rating; Cl Pres, Ch; Sup Rating; Command Performance Ao.

JOHNSON, Lori Lynn
Crystal Lake Comm HS; Crystal Lake, IL (10%-500) A Cap Choir; Band; Chor; Ger C; NHS; Pres, Ntl Yth Conf; Sftbl; Tr; Yth Fel; *Pepperdine U; Special Ed.*

JOHNSON, Lori Lynn
Santa Fe HS; Alachua, FL; JV, Chldr; Rptr, Sch P; Span C; SC; Citz A.

JOHNSON, Lowell Ross
Albert Lea Sr HS; Albert Lea, MN (117-537) Pres, Band; Chor; *Austin Comm Col; Pre-Dentistry.*

JOHNSON, Lynda Maureen
Valley HS; Hoople, ND; Rptr, Ann; Band; Co-Cpt, Chldr; Chor; Hmrm; Bkbl; Sftbl; Tr; MVP, Vlbl.

JOHNSON, Lyndon Ray
Leavenworth Sr HS; Leavenworth, KS; A Cap Choir; Band; Chor; ARC; Cpt, Bkbl; Tr; Wrest; COM; *Hutchinson Police Acad; Law Enforcement.*

JOHNSON, Lynette Sue
Chester HS; Chester, IL; Chor; Spch C; Amer Leg A; Spch A.

JOHNSON, Marcia Denise
Dassel-Cokato Jr-Sr HS; Cokato, MN (25%-137) Band; Chor; Drama; VP, Hmrm; Madrigal; SC; Bkbl; Sftbl; Vlbl; Ath Ltr A's.

JOHNSON, Marie Louise
Chester HS; Chester, PA; Y-Tns; Bkbl; Sftbl; Pres, Choir; Miss Popularity Qn; Bus.

JOHNSON,
Marilyn Jane Wilkerson
Hermitage HS; Hermitage, AR (2-75) S-T, BC; Chldr; FHA; 4H; Math C; Bkbl; Bio A; HCt; Lion A; Sci A; Swtht; Ideal Jr Girl; Most Popular; Freethrow & Assist Champ; All-Dist Bkbl Player; U of Ark at Monticello; Elem Ed.

JOHNSON, Marjorie Betty Ann
New Rochelle HS; New Rochelle, NY; As Cert, Recognition, Outst Achv; Yth Fitness Achv As; Col of New Rochelle; Nurs.

JOHNSON, Mark Alan
Northmont Sr HS; Clayton, OH (20%-593) Chor; Ski C; Hon Prog; Master Hon Carrier; St Fair Yth Ministry; Ch, Church Yth Coun; Asst Pee-Wee Soccer Coach.

JOHNSON, Mark Alan
Sisseton HS; Sisseton, SD (20-144) Band; Chor; Dbte Tm; S-T, 4H; Key C; Var C; Bsbl; Bkbl; Co-Cpt, Ftbl; Tr; Wrest; Hon Prog; Sch of Sci; Auto Mech.

JOHNSON, Mark Alan
Burns HS; Lawndale, NC (18-210) S-T, BC; Fr C; Secy, Key C; NHS; Cr-Ctry; Tr; Jr Marshal; UNCC; Bus.

JOHNSON, Mark Gregory
Cache HS; Cache, OK; SC; COM; Hon Prog; Win, Yth Auditions; Superior, Mus Festival; Hon Men, Composition Contest; Outst Stu, Art & Hist; U of Nev; Mus.

JOHNSON, Marla Kay
Germantown HS; Germantown, TN (17-404) Ed, Ann; BC; GS; S-T, NHS; Span C; VP, SC; H of F; Hist A; HCt; MLS; Mus; Church Choir; Memphis St U.

JOHNSON, Martha Evelyn
Marysville HS; Marysville, MI (13-156) Chor; Pres, Drama; NHS; Var C; Bkbl; COM; Hon Prog; Yth Fel; Times Herald Achv A; Mich Comp Schol A; St Clair Co Comm Col; General.

JOHNSON, Martin C V
Gull Lake HS; Richland, MI (30-240) Chem C; Fr C; Tres, JETS; NHS; Sci C; Tres, Var C; JV, Bkbl; Ftbl; Chem A; Citz A; HCt; Hon Prog; Kiwanis A; Yth Fel; Pres, FCA; Mich St U; Chem Engr.

JOHNSON, Mary Ann
Blue Valley HS; Randolph, KS (5-23) Ann; Band; Chor; Ensm; Pres, FHA; Tres, 4H; Orch; Sch P; SC; Secy, Jr Cl; Cpt, Bkbl; 4H A; Sci A; Type A; Secy, 4-H C; Vlbl; HR A.

JOHNSON, Mary Helen
Manual Arts HS; Los Angeles, CA (5%-560) Hmrm; Tres, SC; CSF; COM; Hon Prog; Kiwanis A; St Scholar; Principal's, Counselor's, HR'S; UCLA; Math.

JOHNSON, Mary Kathleen
Bradleyville HS; Bradleyville, MO (1-27) Drama; Fr C; FHA; Math C; Sch o-t Ozarks.

JOHNSON, Mary Kathryn
Bossier HS; Bossier City, LA; Yth Fel; Pres, Yth Fellowship; Northwestern Col; Nurs.

JOHNSON, Mary Lillian
Frederic HS; Frederic, WI; Bus C; Chldr; Chor; FBLA; Tres, FHA; Madrigal; Tres, Jr Cl; Bkbl; Tr; Singing Solo A; Swing Choir A; Stout St U; Fashion Merchandising.

JOHNSON, Mary Lynne
Arlington Sch; Fairburn, GA (3-35) Ann; BC; Lit Ral; Math C; Mu Alpha Theta; NHS; Sch P; JV, Bkbl; Sftbl; Alg A; Bio A; Hist A; Math A; NEDT; Sci A; Spch A; VP, Foreign Lang C; VP, Ga Federation of Jr Mus C; Top Schol; U of Ga; Vet Med.

JOHNSON, Mary Veline
Warrior Run HS; Turbotville, PA; Band; GSct; Fashion C; Cosmotology.

JOHNSON, Matthew
G W Carver Sr HS; New Orleans, LA; Dillard U.

JOHNSON, Mattie Lou
Hillsbourgh Jr HS; Tampa, FL; Secy.

JOHNSON, Melodee Lou
Black River Falls Sr HS; Black River Falls, WI (8-150) Bus Mgr, Band; Chor; FBLA; NHS; Co-Ed, Sch P; VP, Soph Cl; Amer Leg A; Hon Prog; Journ A; Lion A; ARC A; Type A; Shorthand A; Top Ten of Cl; Acct A; Off Practice A; SC Schol Win; Missionettes Hon; N Central Bible Col; Christian Ed.

JOHNSON, Michael Anthony
Leesville HS; Leesville, LA; A Cap Choir; Cpt, Band; VP, Chess C; Chor; InterAct C; Orch; Ftbl; Stage Band; Tn Involvement Coun; Chief of Police in Yth in Govt; WW; Pep Band.

JOHNSON, Michael Dwayne
Terra Linda HS; San Rafael, CA; Band; MVP, Ftbl; Tr; U of Sou Calif.

JOHNSON, Michael Euegene
Billings W HS; Billings, MT (33%-800) Band; SC; Bsbl; Bkbl; Cr-Ctry; Ftbl; JV, Tr; Mont St U; Mech Engr.

JOHNSON, Michael Eugene
Billings W HS; Billings, MT (33%-800) Bsbl; Bkbl; Cr-Ctry; Tr; Mont St U; Mech Engr.

JOHNSON, Michael Frank
Thompson HS; Alabaster, AL; A Cap Choir; Band; Chor; Ensm; Orch; Secy, Jr Cl; Co-Cpt, Tnns; Wrest; Bio A; MLS; Sci A; Attendance A; Band A; U of Montevallo; Dentistry.

JOHNSON, Michael Kenneth
Spring Lake HS; Spring Lake, MI (7-228) Ann; Drama; SC; JV, Ftbl; MLS.

JOHNSON, Michael Ray
Tyner HS; Chattanooga, TN (28-261) All Amer Yth; Ann; Band; BC; Semi-Fin, BS; Hmrm; JETS; Rptr, Key C; Lat C; NHS; Bsbl; Ftbl; Soccer; Star Student; Ga Tech; Elec Engr.

JOHNSON, Michael Richard
Denair HS; Denair, CA (10%-50) Ann; FFA; 4H; Sch P; SC; Var C; Pres, Sr Cl; Tres, Jr Cl; Ftbl; Tr; Wrest; Bank Of Amer A; Bausch & Lomb A; CSF; COM; H of F; Math A; MLS; Stanislaus St Col; Computer Sci.

JOHNSON, Michael Vernon
Hixson HS; Chattanooga, TN (28-381) Band; NHS; Bkbl; Sftbl; Order/Arrow A; ROTC A; Ga Tech; Elec Engr.

JOHNSON, Michele Alynn
N Hunterdon HS; Annandale, NJ (33%-260) Drama; 4H; Hmrm; Y-Tns; Hon Prog; The Kings Col; Social Work.

JOHNSON, Michelle Evette
Hempstead Sr HS; Hempstead, TX (5-53) BC; FTA; Span C; Tres, SC; Secy, Sr Cl; U of Houston; Acct.

JOHNSON, Mitzi Janeice
Hardin Co HS; Savannah, TN (7-221) Ed, Ann; BC; Fr C; FHA; DARGCA; H of F; Journ A; MLS; Art A; Hist, Hist C; VP, Sub Debs; Tumbling A; Stu for Christ; Miss CHS; Most Courteous; Freed-Hardeman Col.

JOHNSON, Monroe Willie
Woodmont HS; Piedmont, SC; BC; Tres, Hmrm.

JOHNSON, Myra Lynn
G W Carver Sr HS; New Orleans, LA; Dillard U; Bus.

JOHNSON, Myrna Ellen
Ruthven Cons HS; Ruthven, IA; Band; Chor; Drama; Ensm; 4H; Spch C; SC; Golf; Sftbl; 4H A; Spch A; 4-H Co Rptr A.

JOHNSON, Myron Dennis
Southland HS; Arbyrd, MO (7-38) S-T, Chess C; Chor; Drama; FTA; MLS; Central Bible Col; Evangelism.

JOHNSON, Nancy Anne
St Anthony HS; Minneapolis, MN; CYO; Chldr; Chor; Hmrm; ARC; Spch C; SC; JV, Sftbl; JV, Tr; COM; Citz A; Cl Fav; H of F; Most Out; Pres A; ARC A; Spch A; Star Student; Swtht; Yth Fel; Gym; Pep C; Ltr Win C; Fin, Sno Daze; Pre-sch Teacher; Pre-Sch Teacher; Gym Teacher.

JOHNSON, Nancy Catherine
Southern Reynolds Co R-2 HS; Ellington, MO (1-75) Band; BC; Chor; S-T, Soph Cl; Most Out; Eng A; Glee C A; Southwest Mo St U.

JOHNSON, Nancy Evalynn
Northern Chester Co Tech HS; Phoenixville, PA (1-193) Hmrm; Tres, NHS; SC; Var C; Co-Cpt, Bkbl; Tr; Stu o-t Mo; Distinguished Stu; Girl o-t Mo; Penn St U; Horticulture.

JOHNSON, Nancy Evelynn
Northern Chester Co Tech Sch; Phoenixville, PA (1-192) Tres, NHS; SC; Var C; Bkbl; Tr; Stu o-t Mo; Evening Bulletin; Most Athletic; Stu o-t Mo; Penn St U; Horticulture.

JOHNSON, Nicole Marie
Sidney Sr HS; Sidney, MT (8-143) A Cap Choir; VP, AFS; S-T, Band; VP, CYO; Ensm; Span C; Mont St U; Social Work.

JOHNSON, Ola Mae
Saginaw HS; Saginaw, MI; JV, Chldr; Chor; Secy, Hmrm; NHS; COM; Hon Prog; Type A; Spelling A; U of Mich; Dental Hygienist.

JOHNSON, Orelia Louise
Temple Heights Christian Sch; Tampa, FL (12-62) A Cap Choir; Chor; Drama; Ensm; NHS; Most Out; Vlbl; Lee Christian Col; Mus.

JOHNSON, Orlando Cecil
Chester HS; Chester, PA; Chor; Drama; NHS; JV, Bkbl; JV, Soccer; Tr; Acct.

JOHNSON, Ornetter
Sacramento HS; Sacramento, CA (271-482) Sacramento City Col; Nurs.

JOHNSON, Pamela
Virgie HS; Virgie, KY (33-112) Ann; Band; BC; JV, Chldr; Pres, FTA; 4H; Hmrm; NHS; Spch C; SC; 4H A; HCt; Hon Prog; Band A; Fin, HQn; Eastern Ky U; Psych.

JOHNSON, Pamela
Camden Co HS; St Mary's, GA (22-209) Secy, BC; S-T, Chess C; 4H; Pres, Span C; Bio A; Gov Honor Prog; Art A; Valdosta St Col; Phar.

JOHNSON, Pamela Jean
Forest Lake Sr HS; Forest Lake, MN (1-511) Band; Sftbl; Tnns.

JOHNSON, Pamela Louise
George Washington HS; Indianapolis, IN; Y-Tns; Vlbl; ITT Tech Col; Bus.

JOHNSON, Patricia Lynn
Charlottesville HS; Charlottesville, VA (16-329) Band; Ger C; NHS; Citz A; Math A; Sci A; Huff Schol; Hon Men, Classical Assn Lat Tourn; Del, Lutheran Va Synod Conv; Roanoke Col; Pre-Law.

JOHNSON, Patricia Marie
Cache HS; Cache, OK (4-46) Rptr, BC; Rptr, FHA; NHS; ARC; Tres, SC; VP, Jr Cl; Rptr, Soph Cl; JV, Bkbl; COM; Cl Fav; Hist A; Type A; Outst Stu, Home Ec, Lang Arts; N Ariz U; Conservation.

JOHNSON, Patricia Rose
Perry Meridian HS; Indianapolis, IN (3-568) Ed, Ann; Chem C; Secy, Chess C; Drama; GS; Pres, 4H; Math C; NHS; Phys C; Rainbow; Sci C; Span C; VP, SC; Pres, Soph Cl; Sftbl; Tnns; Alg A; Delta Sigma Theta A; 4H A; Hon Prog; Journ A; Math A; Most Out; Yth Fel; Hoosier Schol; Filmmakers A; Ind U; Bus.

JOHNSON, Patty Ann
Clovis HS; Clovis, NM; VP, FHA; Ntl Cand, FHA Hero Conv; Outst FHA; Valentine Swtht; Lubbock Christian Col; Home Ec.

JOHNSON, Paul Russell
Morton HS; Morton, IL; Chem C; Chess C; JETS; Sci C; Bkbl; Ftbl; Tnns; WW; Pres, Church HS Choir; Campus Life; VP, Church Yth Group; Bradley U; Civil Engr.

JOHNSON, Paula Arlene
Hemet HS; Hemet, CA; FBLA; Swim; CSF; Oral Roberts U; Bus.

JOHNSON, Paula Contessa
Central HS; Columbia, TN; Chem C; Sci C; Miss Duck River District.

JOHNSON, Paula Denise
Conway HS; Conway, SC (28-341) A Cap Choir; Anchor C; Chor; Fr C; FTA; NHS; SC; COM; 4H A; Sci A; All St Regional Chor; Mus, Spelling, PA, A's; Mus Ed.

JOHNSON, Paulette Elizabeth
Malcolm X Shabazz HS; Newark, NJ (71-272)
CYO; Chor; Hmrm; Sci C; SC; Mgr, Cr-Ctry; JV,
Sftbl; Hon Prog; Span A; Most Popular; *Psych.*

JOHNSON, Peggy Ann
Sioux Rapids Comm Sch; Sioux Rapids, IA (1-21)
Bus Mgr, Ann; Pres, Band; Cpt, Chldr; NHS; Tres,
Sr C; VP, Jr Cl; S-T, Soph Cl; Bkbl; Golf; Tr; B
Crocker A; COM; HQn; Star Student; St Scholar;
Type A; *Iowa St U; Family Environment.*

JOHNSON, Peggy Sue
Bridgeton HS; Bridgeton, NJ (22-718) Band; Mgr,
4H; Mjrte; NHS; 4H A; *Computer Sci.*

JOHNSON, Peggy Velma
Exira Comm HS; Exira, IA; Band; Tr; Vlbl; *Maryville Col; Elem Ed.*

JOHNSON, Penny Sue
Holt HS; Holt, MI (33-297) Band; Chess C; NHS;
Hon Prog; Ntl Achv Schol; Forensics C; Forensics
A; *Mich St U; Engr.*

JOHNSON, Perry Ken
Central HS; Jackson, MS (7-125) Chor; Tres, NHS;
Bio A; I Dare You; MLS; Modern Bus A; Chor A;
Most Intellectual; Metal Shop A; Geom A; *Jackson
St U; Bus.*

JOHNSON, Phillip Daniel
Northwest HS; St Louis, MO (20-433) *Parks College of St Louis U; Aero Mech.*

JOHNSON, Phyllis Ann
Gordon HS; Gordon, TX; BC; Chldr; Pres, FHA;
NHS; Co-Cpt, Bkbl; Tnns; Tr; Cl Fav; HCt; Lion A;
Miss GHS; FFA Swtht; Ranger Jr Col; Bus.

JOHNSON, Phyllis Theresa
Savannah HS; Savannah, GA; *Grady Mem Hospital; Nurs.*

JOHNSON, Polly Jan
Booker T Washington HS; Shreveport, LA; Hon
Prog; *Sou U; Clerical.*

JOHNSON, Priscilla Esther
The Open HS; Richmond, VA (4-27) Ann; Hmrm;
Rptr, Sch P; SC; Gov Honor Prog; Hon Prog; Thal-
heimers Art Show; *Drew U; Hist.*

JOHNSON, Rachel Ann
Bloomington HS; Bloomington, IL (118-408) A
Cap Choir; Ann; Band; Fr C; Orch; Phys C; Tr; VP,
Pep C; Tr Ltr; 1st Pl, IHSA Flute Trio Contest;
Trinity Col; Eng.

JOHNSON, Ranae Louise
Sky View HS; Smithfield, UT (3-622) Chor; Secy,
4H; Amer Leg A; Citz A.

JOHNSON, Randy Eugene
Concord Sr HS; Concord, NC; Band; Monogram;
Ftbl; Tr.

JOHNSON, Ranie Lin
Spring Valley HS; Spring Valley, WI; Cpt, Chldr;
Sftbl; Cl Fav; HCt.

JOHNSON, Raymond Virgust
Brazosport HS; Freeport, TX (69-206) Drama;
Thes; Sftbl; Best Actor; *Brazosport Col; Computer
Operating.*

JOHNSON, Rebecca Louise
Portales HS; Portales, NM; Secy, Band; Chor;
FHA; Mgr, Bkbl; Tr; Child Care C; VP, Hero C;
Band Aide A; WW; Church Swtht, Swtht Banquet.

JOHNSON, Rebecca Lynn
Winnfield Sr HS; Winnfield, LA (27-121) Ann;
Ensm; FBLA; FTA; GS; Fin, Jr Miss Pagent; Ch,
Spch C; Var C; Bkbl; Beauty; HCt; Mascot; Tres &
Rptr, Anchor C; *Louisiana Col; Mus.*

JOHNSON, Rebecca Sue
Bellingham HS; Bellingham, WA (10-320) A Cap
Choir; A-Ed, Ann; Chor; S-T, UMYF; Yth Rep,
Methodist Sch of Missions; *Wash St U; Commer-
cial Art.*

JOHNSON, Rebecca Yvonne
H D Woodson HS; Washington, DC (150-650)
Pres, Chor; NHS; ARC; Prep C; Hon A; Driver's
Ed; Letter of Commendation; *EKG Tech.*

JOHNSON, Regina Ann
Riverview Gardens Sr HS; St Louis, MO; *Florrisant Valley Col; Social Worker.*

JOHNSON, Regina Gay
Killeen HS; Killeen, TX (20%-966) Band; Chor;
FHA; COM; Masonic A; Pres A; Traffic Safety;
Lib A; Patrol A; *Tenn St U; Phys Therapy.*

JOHNSON, Regina Jo
Allendale HS; Allendale, IL (4-15) Tres, Band;
Chldr; 4H; Secy, SC; Pres, Soph Cl; Amer Leg A;
Hon Prog; Drama A; Pres, Pep C.

JOHNSON, Retha Renee
Morse HS; San Diego, CA (317-800) *Law.*

JOHNSON, Rhonda Ann
Peoria Central HS; Peoria, IL; Tr; JA A; Secy, Yth
Fel; *Ill Central Col; Bus Mgt.*

JOHNSON, Rhonda Jean
Sycamore HS; Sycamore, IL (3-277) Band; FHA;
4H; Hmrm; NHS; Amer Leg A; COM; 4H A; Hon
Prog; Type A; Phys Fitness A; Straight 'A' HR A;
U of Ill; Computer Sci.

JOHNSON, Richard Scott
New Life Christian HS; Bridgeton, MO; Ann;
Chor; SC; Ftbl; Tr; Wrest; HR; *Gateway Col of
Evangelism; Ministry.*

JOHNSON, Rickey Lamar
Rebecca Comer HS; Eufaula, AL (1-40) A-Ed,
Ann; Drama; VP, FFA; Hmrm; NHS; SC; Citz A;
U of Ala; Eng.

JOHNSON, Robert Burton
Jackson HS; Massillon, OH (105-320) Band; Fr C;
Tr; *Bob Jones U; Telecommunications.*

JOHNSON, Robert Charles
Carthage HS; Carthage, AR (5-24) Ann; Secy,
FFA; Bkbl; Beauty; Cl Fav; MLS; Fire Marshal; Mr
CHS; All Dist, Bkbl; *U of Ark-Pine Bluff; Hist.*

JOHNSON, Robert Charles
Maple Grove Jr-Sr HS; Bemus Point, NY (2-110)
Chor; Dbte Tm; NHS; *Math.*

JOHNSON, Robert David
S Hills HS; W Covina, CA (250-500) Fin, Chess C;
Order/Arrow; Cr-Ctry; Order/Arrow A; Yth Fel;
Church Choir & Ldrship; *Mount San Antonio Jr
Col; Bus.*

JOHNSON, Robert Erik
S Plainfield HS; S Plainfield, NJ (7-380) A Cap
Choir; Fin, BS; Chor; Drama; Ger C; NHS; Ski C;
Soccer; Amer Leg A; Citz A; Hon Prog; NJ Talent
Expo; *Hist.*

JOHNSON, Robert Jeffrey
Timothy Christian HS; Elmhurst, IL (13-100)
Chor; NHS; Omegans Yth Prog; Core Group; Call-
ing Prog; Church Choir; Asst Teacher, Sunday Sch;
Covenant Col; Bible.

JOHNSON, Robert L
Morris HS Annex; Bronx, NY (126-315) *Laguardia
Comm Col; Acct.*

JOHNSON, Robert L III
Tarrant HS; Tarrant, AL (15%-120) HiY; Hmrm;
InterClub Coun; Pres, NHS; SC; Var C; Cpt, Ftbl;
Citz A; Cl Fav; HCt; Sci A; Yth Fel; MVP, Ftbl;
FCA; Ath o-t Yr; WW; *U of Ala; Bus.*

JOHNSON, Robert Lee
John McDonogh HS; New Orleans, LA; All Amer
Yth; Arch; Hmrm; Ntl Yth Conf; Tri-HiY; Bsbl;
Co-Cpt, Ftbl; Tr; Yth Foundation; *Idaho U; Ed.*

JOHNSON, Robert Milo
Wautoma HS; Wautoma, WI (30-105) Chess C; Fr
C; Var C; JV, Bsbl; JV, Bkbl; JV, Ftbl; *Computer
Maintenance.*

JOHNSON, Robert Neal
Paris HS; Paris, TX (20-302) Band; VP, FTA; Ger
C; Key C; NHS; *N Tex St U; Bus Adm.*

JOHNSON, Robin Leroy
Logan Sr HS; Logan, OH; Key C; Span C; Var C;
Ftbl; God & Country A; Yth Fel; Eagle Sct; *Mt
Vernon Nazarene Col; Bus Adm.*

JOHNSON, Robin Sue
York Comp HS; York, SC (7-261) Ann; French
NHS.

JOHNSON, Rodger Dean
Rib Lake HS; Rib Lake, WI (29-60) AFS; Co-Ed,
Ann; Band; Chor; Fin, Ensm; SC; Var C; Cr-Ctry;
North Central Tech Sch; Auto Tech.

JOHNSON, Rosie N
McAdams HS; McAdams, MS (25%-60) Parl,
FHA; Tres, Jr Cl; Most Beautiful.

JOHNSON, Roy Jean
McCurtain HS; McCurtain, OK (2-11) NHS; Bsbl;
Bkbl; Hist A; Phys Fitness A.

JOHNSON, Rozalynn Loraine
Castlemont HS; Oakland, CA (25-650) Band;
Chor; Rptr, Hmrm; Model UN; Tres, NHS; Co-Ch,
SC; Bus Mgr, Jr Cl; Alg A; CSF; COM; Citz A; Hon
Prog; Math A; Star Student; Yth Fel; Yth Leg; Big
Sisters; *Spelman Col; Ed.*

JOHNSON, Ruby Lynnette
King William HS; King William, VA (1-80) Secy,
BC; FBLA; Tres, Sci C; Pres, Span C; Cpt, Bkbl;
Sftbl; Tr; HCt; Val; Most Ath Player, Bkbl; *Va
Commonwealth U; Med Technology.*

JOHNSON, Ruth Elaine
Suffolk HS; Suffolk, VA (1-150) NHS; Span C.

JOHNSON, Sammy Louis
Motley HS; Columbus, MS (2-81) Band; BC;
Chldr; VP, Drama; Hmrm; A-Ed, Sch P; VP, Sci C;
SC; Tr; Sci A; *U of Miss; Pre-Med.*

JOHNSON, Sandy Ray
Fyffe HS; Fyffe, AL (5-78) BC; FFA; Sch P; Sci C;
SC; Alg A; Outst Eng A.

JOHNSON, Scott A
W Bloomfield HS; West Bloomfield, MI (33%-400)
Drama; Semi-Fin, NHS; Span C; Var C; Cpt, Bkbl;
Ftbl; Tr; COM; Hon Prog; Yth Fel; Hon's Merit; *U
of Ga; Bus Adm.*

JOHNSON, Scott Daniel
Robbinsdale Sr HS; Robbinsdale, MN (500-750)
Hmrm; Soccer.

JOHNSON, Shannon Mark
Loyola-Sacred Heart HS; Missoula, MT; Ann;
Chor; Ensm; Var C; JV, Bkbl; Ftbl; Sftbl; Tr; *Heavy
Duty Equipment.*

JOHNSON, Shari Louise
Burke HS; Omaha, NE (89-668) AFS; Chor; Ger C;
Hmrm; COM; Citz A; Hon Prog; Nom, NHS; *U of
Nebr at Lincoln; Bio.*

JOHNSON, Sharon Ann
Chisago Lakes Area HS; Lindstrom, MN (16-178)
Chor; FHA; Spch C; *St Paul Vo-tech Col; Cosme-
tology.*

JOHNSON, Sharon C
Taylors Falls HS; Taylors Falls, MN (2-38) Band;
Chor; Ger C; Rptr, 4H; 4H A; HCt; *Concordia of
Moorhead Col.*

JOHNSON, Sharon Lynn
St Ignatius HS; St Ignatius, MT (8-40) Ann; Band;
CYO; Chldr; Chor; GS; 4H; Mjrte; Sch P; Mgr,
Bkbl; Sftbl; Tr; 4H A; Hon Prog; Outst Stage Band
Musician; Band Schol; *Eastern Mont Col; Sociol-
ogy.*

JOHNSON, Sheila Mae
Albemarle HS; Charlottesville, VA (275-550)
Chor; FHA; GS; 4H; Span C; Sftbl; 4H A; Pied-
mont Dist Schol; *Va Union U; Social Worker.*

JOHNSON, Shellia Rebecca
Crenshaw Christian Acad; Luverne, AL (3-30)
Ann; Band; Chor; 4H; NHS; Phys C; S-T, Jr Cl;
S-T, Soph Cl.

JOHNSON, Sherry
Edward Tilden HS; Chicago, IL (7-408) Co-Cpt,
Chldr; Chor; NHS; Tres, Jr Cl; Tr; All City Chor;
Attendance Secy, Sr Sem; *Sou Ill U; Eng.*

JOHNSON, Shirlene Michelle
Gardena HS; Gardena, CA; Fr C; FBLA; Hmrm;
Journ A; Type A; *Long Beach St Col; Bus.*

JOHNSON, Sondra Colette
W Lincoln Sr HS; Lincolnton, NC (40-180) Band;
Co-Cpt, Chldr; Drama; Hmrm; Tres, SC; Pres, Jr
Cl; HCt.

JOHNSON, Spencer Fry
Gilman HS; Baltimore, MD (11-98) Cum Laude
Soc; Lit Mag; Cr-Ctry; Cpt, Tr; Hon Prog; Ntl
Achv Schol; NMS; Brown Book A; WW; *Hopkins
Col; Pre-Med.*

JOHNSON, Stella Elizabeth
Lincoln HS; Dallas, TX; Chldr; Model UN; ARC;
Var C; Tr; ROTC A; Principal's A; Rifle Tm; *W Tex
St U; Nurs.*

JOHNSON, Stephen Paul
Markoma Bible Acad; Tahlequah, OK (25%-22) Chor; Ensm; VP, SC; Bsbl; Bkbl; Co-Cpt, Soccer; Hon Prog; Moody Bible Inst; Mus.

JOHNSON, Stephen Scott
Whetstone HS; Columbus, OH (25-582) BC; Chess C; Lat C; NHS; Ed, Sch P; Pres, Sci C; Hon Prog; Most Out; Sci A; Ntl Quill & Scroll Soc; Ntl Merit Commended Schol; 'In- the-Know' Tm; Ohio U; Journ.

JOHNSON, Steve Leon
Roseburg HS; Roseburg, OR (1-490) Demolay; Tres, NHS; Cpt, Tr; NEDT; Val; MVP, Tnns; WW; USNR Chief's Schol A; Acct.

JOHNSON, Steve Ray
Holston HS; Knoxville, TN; Band; Ensm; Orch; Order/Arrow; ARC; Spch C; ROTC A; John Philip Sousa A; U of Tn Schol; 10% Outst Stu A; Mus Schol; Sr Play; Hon of Good Friends; U of Tenn; Communications.

JOHNSON, Steven Neal
Auburndale Sr HS; Auburndale, FL; Tres, FFA; Outst Schol Achv A, Agr Sci; Polk Comm Col; Horticulture.

JOHNSON, Steven Paul
Newton Comm HS; Newton, IL (33%-139) 4H; Var C; Bsbl; Bkbl; JV, Golf; Tr; 4H A; HCt; E Ill U; Hist.

JOHNSON, Sue Nanette
Park View HS; Sterling, VA; Hmrm; Lat C; Ski C; Swim; Tr; HCt.

JOHNSON, Susan Ann
St Johns Ctry Day Sch; Orange Park, FL (18-27) Ed, Ann; Cpt, Chldr; Chor; Ensm; Fr C; Hmrm; SC; JV, Soccer; Tnns; Citz A; Cl Fav; HCt; Most Out; Yth Fel; Yth Leg; Fla Sou Col.

JOHNSON, Susan Elaine
Wachusett Regional HS; Holden, MA (196-500) Chldr; FHA; HiY; Hmrm; Mjrte; ARC; Mem Sch of Nurs; Nurs.

JOHNSON, Susan Elaine
Burlingame HS; Foster City, CA (33%-500) Chor.

JOHNSON, Susan Elizabeth
Bible Baptist HS; Savannah, GA (5-54) Ann; Chldr; Rptr, Sch P; Cpt, Bkbl; Sftbl; HQn; Armstrong St Col; Secondary Ed.

JOHNSON, Suzanne Charmaine
Forest Park HS; Beaumont, TX; VP, Chor; Parl, Drama; ARC; SC; Tr; Amer Leg A; Bio A; COM; Citz A; Pres A; Vlbl; Communications.

JOHNSON, Sydnie Dee
Holdrege HS; Holdrege, NE (20%-125) Band; Chor; SC; Thes; Type A; Conf Band; Swing Choir; 99% Ntl Guild, Piano; Superior Piano, St & Dist; U of Nebr; Mus.

JOHNSON, Sylvia Antionette
Aiken Sr HS; Cincinnati, OH; Rptr, Lit Mag; Span C; Co-Cpt, Tr; Beauty; COM; Citz A; Most Out; Tr A; Saint Mary's Col; Pol Sci.

JOHNSON, Tamara Lynne
Tyner HS; Chattanooga, TN; Band; BC; Chor; MTSU; Nurs.

JOHNSON, Tammie Maria
Charleston HS; Charleston, SC (9-62) Chor; Up Bound; Bkbl; Type A; Bookkeeping, Off Practice, Cert's; Hon Stu Recognition; WW; Johnson C Smith Col; Bus Adm.

JOHNSON, Tammy Michele
Grand Ridge HS; Grand Ridge, FL (10-65) BC; Cpt, Chldr; Chor; Secy, FFA; Tres, FTA; Secy, 4H; Cl Fav; 4H A; HCt; Hon Prog; Chipola Jr Col.

JOHNSON, Tanya Rae
Havre HS; Havre, MT (38-234) Ann; Band; Secy, 4H; Hmrm; NHS; SC; Tr; U of Mont; Fine Arts.

JOHNSON, Teal Marietta
Marvell HS; Marvell, AR (8-118) BC; Tres, FBLA; U of Ark; Bus Adm.

JOHNSON, Tenna Lynn
Corinth Christian Acad; Kinsman, OH (3-6) Chor; 4H; Ed, Sch P; Bkbl; Tr; Journ A; Secy-Treas, Library C; Faithful Attendance; Central Bible Col; Teaching.

JOHNSON, Teresa
Statesboro HS; Bulloch, GA; Type A; Phys Fitness A; Ga Sou Col; Elem Ed.

JOHNSON, Teresa Lynn
Wheelersburg HS; Wheelersburg, OH (70-130) Chor; FHA; Lib C; Historian, W HS; Sr Cl Play; Co Yth Adv Coun; Acct.

JOHNSON, Teresa Marie
Armstrong Twp HS; Armstrong, IL (10-50) FHA; Parkland Jr Col; Designing.

JOHNSON, Teri Lynn
Thompson HS; Siluria, AL (2-197) A-Ed, Ann; Band; VP, BC; Pres, FHA; Mjrte; Tres, Soph Cl; Hist A; MLS; Most Out; Eng A; WW; Auburn U; Spch Therapy.

JOHNSON, Terry L
Fairmont HS; Fairmont, MN (45-200) Bkbl; Ftbl; Tr; All Conf, Ftbl; Bus Adm.

JOHNSON, Thaylia Donna
North Comm HS; Minneapolis, MN; Chldr; Fr C; Ausburg Col; Social Sci.

JOHNSON, Tim Edward
Fairfield HS; Fairfield, OH; A Cap Choir; Ann; Band; Chor; Drama; Ensm; Mod Mus Mas; Orch; Sci C; Thes; Bsbl; Bkbl; Soccer; Sftbl; COM; Journ A; Q&S A; 3 Yr Chor A; U of Kansas Mus Festival, Schol A; Elec.

JOHNSON, Timothy Alan
Clear Lake HS; Lakeport, CA (1-90) Band; Chor; JV, Bkbl; JV, Swim; Tnns; CSF; Math A; Pres, Fresh Cl; Hon Band; San Francisco Conservatory of Mus; Mus.

JOHNSON, Timothy Dwayne
Northwestern Senior HS; Hyattsville, MD (4-750) Chor; Lit Mag; Orch; Harvard Book A; Hon Prog; Phi Beta Nu.

JOHNSON, Timothy Jack
Ogallala Sr HS; Ogallala, NE (7-126) NHS; Tres, St Stu Congress; SC; Ftbl; Cpt, Tr; Wrest; Tr Mem A; Tr, Ftbl, Wrest, Ltrs; U of Nebr; Engr.

JOHNSON, Timothy Karl
Shades Valley HS; Birmingham, AL (1-500) A Cap Choir; Math C; Mu Alpha Theta; NHS; Swim; COM; Hon Prog; Sci A; Drum Major; Hon Bands; Win, Mus Composition Contest; Eastman Sch of Mus; Mus.

JOHNSON, Tina M
McDonald Co HS; Anderson, MO; Chor; 4H; Pres, Sci C; Mgr, Bkbl; ROTC A; Jamestown Col; Home Ec.

JOHNSON, Tom Ralph
Ellensburg HS; Ellensburg, WA; Chor; Ensm; Hmrm; Ski C; Cr-Ctry; Tr; Hon Prog; Kiwanis A; Swing Choir; Win, City Talent Shows; Church Mus Group; U of Wash; Law.

JOHNSON, Tommy Ray
Judsonia HS; Judsonia, AR (2-35) Ed, Ann; BC; Chor; Drama; VP, FBLA; Tres, FFA; Cpt, Bkbl; Cr-Ctry; Sftbl; Tr; HCt; I Dare You; Sal; All-Co & All-Dist Bkbl; Agr A; St Pole Vault Champ, Tr; Top 5 Fin, St Star Agribusinessman; Hgh Pnt Dist Tr Mt; U of Ar Acad Sc; U of Ark; Agr.

JOHNSON, Tony Marvin
Granite City N HS; Granite City, IL; A Cap Choir; Chor; Hmrm; Madrigal; Mod Mus Mas; Ftbl; Sftbl; Tr; Bradly Col; Mus.

JOHNSON, Tore T
Olympia HS; Olympia, WA; Secy, FFA; InterClub Coun; FFA Advisors A; Horticulture Found A; Prairie Bible Inst; Horticulture.

JOHNSON, Tracey Ann
Detroit Lakes HS; Detroit Lakes, MN; Band; Ger C; Spch C; Tr; Band A; Nurs.

JOHNSON, Valda Yvonne
Plano Sr HS; Plano, TX (55-800) Drama; Lat C; Bkbl; Tr; Church Choir; Fr C; Span C; Special Singing Group; N Tex St U; Theatrical Arts.

JOHNSON,
Vanclive Alonzo St Joseph
Boys And Girls HS; Brooklyn, NY; AFS; Band; Pres, Hmrm; Orch; SC; JV, Var C; Bsbl; Bkbl; Ftbl; Sftbl; Tr; Alg A; Bio A; COM; Cl Fav; Hist A; Hon Prog; Math A; MLS; Sci A; Spch A; BSct; Ftbl A; Bsbl & Bkbl Trophies; Morehouse Col; Bio.

JOHNSON, Vanna
Palmer HS; Palmer, TX (2-28) FFA; Co-Ed, Sch P; S-T, Sr Cl; Pres, Jr Cl; Rptr, Soph Cl; Bio A; DARGCA; Hist A; Health Ed A; Phys Sci A; 1st Pl, Sci UIL; 3rd Pl, Journ UIL; Sou Methodist U; Communications.

JOHNSON, Velma Rebecca
Woodmont HS; Piedmont, SC; FHA; 4th Pl, Miss FHA; Rutledge Col; Fashion.

JOHNSON, Vendra
J E Brown HS; Atlanta, GA; Bus C; Chldr; Fr C; FBLA; FHA; Hmrm; Math C; Y-Tns; First Aid A; Med Self Help Training Course; Bus.

JOHNSON, Veronica Carol
Millard HS; Pikeville, KY; Band; Chem C; Chor; Fr C; Hmrm; Mjrte; Math C; NHS; Phys C; ARC; Sch Achieve Tm; Sci C; Spch C; SC; Pres, Sr Cl; Bausch & Lomb A; COM; Cl Fav; 4H A; Hist A; HCt; Hon Prog; JA A; Math A; Poet A; Sal; Sci A; Spch A; Star Student; Sr Achv A; Good Schol A; Band A; Mjrte A; Pikeville Col; Bus.

JOHNSON, Vicki
Livermore Falls HS; Livermore Falls, ME (2-124) JV, Mjrte; Bus Adm.

JOHNSON, Vickie Denise
Cook HS; Adel, GA (10%-162) Ann; Cpt, Band; Chor; S-T, Drama; Ensm; Pres, Ger C; Hmrm; Jr Miss Pagent; Orch; SC; Sftbl; WW, Foreign Lang; Acteen A; Besie Tift Col; Ed.

JOHNSON, Victor Lee
Harlem HS; Harlem, GA (10%-220) Var C; Mgr, Bsbl; JV, Bkbl; Mgr, Ftbl; Hon Prog; Sci A; Val; Phys Ed, Sch Spirit, A's; Outst Acad Achv, A; U of Ga; Phar.

JOHNSON, Victoria Lee
Grant HS; Sacramento, CA (30-260) Chldr; Chor; Ed, Lit Mag; Mjrte; Orch; VP, SC; Secy, Soph Cl; Vlbl; Jr Prom Princess.

JOHNSON, Virginia Hurt
Reidsville Sr HS; Reidsville, NC (6-344) VP, AFS; Co-Ed, Ann; Rptr, Band; Pres, Drama; Fr C; HiY; Hmrm; Jr Miss Pagent; NHS; Orch; Tres, SC; Pres, Jr Cl; Cl Fav; Gr Marshal; HCt; Hon Prog; Journ A; NEDT; Spch A; Morehead Schol Nom; Stuart Schol Nom; C D A Distinguished Acting A; Duke U; Fr.

JOHNSON, Virginia Louise
Carpio Pub HS; Carpio, ND (3-24) Band; Chor; Ensm; VP, 4H; Sch P; Var C; S-T, Soph Cl; MVP, Bkbl; Tr; 4H A; HCt; Interlochen Ntl Mus; Schol to Interntl Mus Camp; All Amer Outst Athletes; St U of ND.

JOHNSON, Vivian Parnell
Sou Normal HS; Brewton, AL (4-19) Band; FTA; Secy, Hmrm; Hist A; HCt; Type A; Bank Bicentennial Girl; Band, Eng, A's; Ala St U; Computer Sci.

JOHNSON, Wanda Kay
Altheimer HS; Altheimer, AR; Bus C; Drama; Fr C; FBLA; Ed, Sch P; VP, SC; Up Bound; Hist A; Journ A; Type A; Eng A; U of Ark; Journ.

JOHNSON, Wanda Renee
Terra Linda HS; Terra Linda, CA;

JOHNSON, Welborn Vernon
S Rowan Sr HS; China Grove, NC (11-300) Ann; BC; Hmrm; Pres, Lat C; Lat NHS; Tres, Math C; Sch P; Sci C; SC; Tres, Sr Cl; Aux Lat; Hist A; Hon Prog; Woodmen o-t World Amer Hist A; Hist Bowl; Forensics; NC St U; Nuclear Engr.

JOHNSON, Wendy
Hancock Central HS; Sparta, GA (13-123) A Cap Choir; Secy, All Amer Yth; Chor; Dbte Tm; S-T, Drama; FHA; 4H; Hmrm; Rptr, Math C; NHS; Tres, Phys C; Sch P; Spch C; Parl, SC; Up Bound; Cpt, Sftbl; Tnns; Alg A; COM; 4H A; Hist A; HCt; Journ A; Math A; Poet A; Sci A; Spch A; Type A; Clark Col; Mass Communication.

JOHNSON, Wesley Justin
Duluth Central HS; Duluth, MN (10%-491) Band; Chor; NFL; NHS; Spch C; Ftbl; COM; Spch A; VofDEM; Yth Fel; Mus A; Ftbl A; Math.

JOHNSON, William Alvin
Wheeler Co HS; Alamo, GA (7-50) BC; FFA; FHA; Ga Sou Col; Acct.

JOHNSON, William Arthur
Jefferson Davis HS; Montgomery, AL; Fr C; Order/Arrow; God & Country A; MCJROTC; Eagle Sct; *Engr.*

JOHNSON, William Kennard
Tara HS; Baton Rouge, LA (1-377) Pres, A Cap Choir; Tres, Band; BC; BS; Ensm; InterClub Coun; Fin, Lit Ral; Pres, Mu Alpha Theta; VP, NHS; Orch; SC; Masonic A; Math A; Most Out; Opt Out Tn; Val; Eagle Sct; All-St Choir; City Yth Coun 3rd Outst Sr; *LSU; Math.*

JOHNSON, William Truett
Northland Sr HS; Columbus, OH (15%-575) Band; Chor; Ensm; Hmrm; NHS; Span C; Span NHS; COM; Citz A; Hon Prog; Opt A; Sci A; Spch A; *Mt St Joseph Col; Theology.*

JOHNSON, Yolanda
Lanier HS; Jackson, MS (10-211) Secy, Drama; 4H; Pres, Hmrm; VP, NHS; Co-Ed, Sch P; Span C; Span NHS; SC; Secy, Thes; Pres, Jr Cl; Cl Fav; Hon Prog; Miss Lanier; 9th Grade Favorite; Miss Jr Cl; Miss Soph; Miss 8th Grade; *Hinds Jr Col; Sci.*

JOHNSON, Youlandean
Compton Sr HS; Compton, CA (50%-800) Sci C; CSF; *U of Calif; Psych.*

JOHNSON, Zavaan Blondell
Grove City HS; Grove City, OH; Band; Chor; Ensm; Orch; Opt Out Tn; Most Outst Bandsman; Win, Columbus Symph Yng Mus Comp; *Bowling Green St U; Mus Ed.*

JOHNSON, Ana Elizabeth
Paraiso Jr Sr HS; Paraiso, CANAL ZONE; Chor; Sch P; Span C; Swim; Type A; Acct A; Shorthand A; *Panama U; Archt.*

JOHNSTON, Anise Colley
Pike Liberal Arts HS; Troy, AL; Band; Chor; Drama; Fr C; Most Fun; Typical Tn; *U of Ala.*

JOHNSTON, Bernadette
Trinity HS; Euless, TX (17-624) CYO; Drama; VP, NFL; NHS; Spch C; Thes; Tr; Spch A; CYO Talent A; Fin, Spch Comp; Personal Poetry Published; Tr As; Outst Fresh Spch-Drama Stu; Outst Soph Stu; *U of Tex at Arlington; Criminal Justice.*

JOHNSTON, Billy Joe
Weir HS; Weir, MS (3-54) BC; Rptr, FFA; JV, Bkbl; Ftbl; Tr; COM; Hist A; *U of Miss; Mech Engr.*

JOHNSTON, David Ralph
Houston HS; Houston, MN (3-47) BS; Pres, FFA; Pres, 4H; NHS; SC; Pres, Soph Cl; Ftbl; Golf; Cpt, Wrest; HKg; Principals A; Principal's A; *U of Minn-Waseca; Agr Production.*

JOHNSTON, Dustin C
E Peoria Comm HS; E Peoria, IL (1-508) Tres, Chem C; Chess C; JV, Tnns; Citz A; Pres, Amateur Radio C; *MIT; Astronautics.*

JOHNSTON, Gayle Frances
Sooner HS; Bartlesville, OK (19-280) AFS; Band; FTA; Mjrte; NHS; Citz A; Gov Honor Prog; Bd Qn; Fr II Most Outs Stu; *Central St U; Speech Pathology.*

JOHNSTON, Glyndis Jael
Lutheran HS; Burbank, CA (8-84) Secy, A Cap Choir; Pres, AFS; A-Ed, Ann; VP, Bus C; VP, FBLA; Semi-Fin, GS; Madrigal; Pres, Math C; F-Ed, Sch P; Tres, Span C; Secy, SC; Bank Of Amer A; CSF; Journ A; Spch A; *Calif Lutheran Col; Psych.*

JOHNSTON, Gregory Charles
Tupelo HS; Tupelo, MS (33-355) BS; Chor; City Conf; Secy, Key C; Order/Arrow; VP, Sr Cl; Co-Cpt, Ftbl; Tnns; COM; HCt; Eagle Sct; *U of Miss; Engr.*

JOHNSTON, James Meade
Madison C-3 Sch; Madison, MO (7-29) Ann; BC; Var C; VP, Jr Cl; Pres, Soph Cl; Bsbl; Bkbl; Amer Leg A; Math A; *Northeast Mo St U; Acct.*

JOHNSTON, Janet Marie
Benton Harbor HS; Benton Harbor, MI (16-410) Band; Ensm; Span NHS; Hon Prog; *Mich St U; Nurs.*

JOHNSTON, Jon Lee
Moore HS; Moore, OK (500-800) FFA; Swim.

JOHNSTON, Jonathan David
Nathan Bedford Forrest Sr HS; Jacksonville, FL (20-540) NHS; COM; Math A; Joe Berg Soc; Ger A; Fr A; *Ga Inst of Technology; Computer Sci.*

JOHNSTON, Joy Lynn
Detroit Lakes Senior Sr HS; Detroit Lakes, MN (59-280) Secy, Chor; Sftbl; Tr; Alg A; 4H A; Math A; Vlbl; Candystripers; Campfire; *U of ND; Nurs.*

JOHNSTON, Karen Eason
Skyview Acad; Memphis, TN (63-95) A Cap Choir; Pres, Chor; Ensm; FTA; Fin, Jr Miss Pagent; Co-Cpt, Mjrte; Sci C; Secy, SC; Secy, Sr Cl; Pres, Jr Cl; Cl Fav; Chor A; *Memphis St U; Nurs.*

JOHNSTON, Kathy Lynn
Loudon Co HS; Loudon, TN (41-125) Ed, Ann; Co-Cpt, Band; Secy, Lat C; Math C; Sci C; Thes; Hon Prog; Poetry Win; Band A; Advanced Stu Prog; *Hiwasee Col; Secondary Eng Ed.*

JOHNSTON, Leslie Wayne
Nekoma Pub Sch; Nekoma, ND (3-6) Chor; Ed, Sch P; Pres, Sr Cl; Pres, Jr Cl; Tres, Soph Cl; Co-Cpt, Bkbl; Tr; Journ A; Most Out; Sal; *U of ND; Occupational Therapy.*

JOHNSTON, Linda Laurel
Oxford HS; Oxford, KS (1-44) Band; Chor; Ensm; Cpt, Mjrte; NHS; Secy, Sr Cl; Alg A; COM; Lion A; Regent Schol; St Scholar; Type A; Val; Bookkeeping A; Off Practice A; *U of Kans; Journ.*

JOHNSTON, Linda Sue
Poteau HS; Poteau, OK (50%-108) F-Ed, Ann; Rptr, Band; Ensm; Fr C; Jr Miss Pagent; Rainbow; SC; Treas, Art C; Outst Band Stu; Treas, GSA; St Solo; All St Band; Rotary Schol; All Dist Band; Mus Schol; Tri St Hon Band; *Carl Albert Jr Col; Mus.*

JOHNSTON, Margaret Elizabeth
Wilbur Wright HS; Dayton, OH; Tres, Chor; Fr C; Tres, JA; Off Aide; S-T, Yth Group; Choir Ltr; Sunday Sch Teacher; Pilot Rep; Coun Elder; Sch Plays; Hist C; Del, Conf Meet; Spch Cont; *Pepperdine U.*

JOHNSTON, Margaret Rosemary
El Camino Real HS; Woodland Hills, CA (35-1095) Bank of Amer A; CSF; COM; *CSU at Northridge; Bus.*

JOHNSTON, Mark Alan
Bryan Adams HS; Dallas, TX; *N Tex St U; Filmmaking.*

JOHNSTON, Michael Dale
Ole Main HS; N Little Rock, AR (125-425) Rptr, Ann; F-Ed, Sch P; Bkbl; *Ark St U; Journ.*

JOHNSTON, Nancy Lynn
Mount Whitney HS; Visalia, CA (11-500) Chor; Hmrm; Key C; Span C; Swim; CSF; Rally, Procrastinators, C'S; 1st Cl GSct; Wynanettes Cabinet; Church Choir; Tres, Church Yth; *U of Calif; Med.*

JOHNSTON, Patricia Jean
Maple Shade HS; Maple Shade, NJ (2-241) Band; CYO; Drama; NHS; SC; Mgr, Hockey; Mgr, Sftbl; *Glassboro St Col; Special Ed.*

JOHNSTON, Paul Michael
McConnellsburg HS; McConnellsburg, PA (1-86) Band; Fr C; NHS; Pres, SC; Pres, Jr Cl; Tres, Soph Cl; Bsbl; JV, Bkbl; Soccer; *Pa St U; Engr.*

JOHNSTON, Penny Annette
Clovis HS; Clovis, NM; Band; Church Valentine Swtht; Band Lib; *Lubbock Christian Col; Computers.*

JOHNSTON, Philip Scott
Central HS; Cheyenne, WY (1-369) Band; Hmrm; NHS; Sci C; Span C; SC; Lion A; Math A; NMF; NMS; Val; All St, Mus Clinic; All NW; Mus Clinic; *Pre-Med.*

JOHNSTON, Ramon Wilbur
Crosbyton HS; Crosbyton, TX (22-45) FFA; JV, Bkbl; Ftbl; *Lubbock Christian Col; Bus.*

JOHNSTON, Sally Ann
Sterling HS; Sterling, KS (8-50) Band; Chor; Drama; Ensm; Pres, FHA; NHS; Spch C; Parl, SC; Tnns; COM; Spch A; Joan Burkhead A; Mus As; *U of Kans; Spch Pathology.*

JOHNSTON, Sarah Elaine
Skyline HS; Dallas, TX (244-890) Chor; FFA; FHA; ARC; NJHS; *Eastfield Jr Col; Bus.*

JOHNSTON, Steven Arthur
Gresham HS; Gresham, OR; JV, Swim; *Mount Hood Col; Engr.*

JOHNSTON, Teena Well
Carterville HS; Carterville, IL (50-85) Bus C; Fr C; S-T, FBLA; FHA; Spch C; Secy, SC; MVP, Tr; HCt; Most Out; Swtht; Best Dressed; PA; *Bradley U.*

JOHNSTON, Thomas David
Griffith HS; Griffith, IN (10%-300) Chess C; Chor; Rptr, Sch P; COM; Journ A; Tn o-t Wk, Church Yth Wk; *Moody Bible Inst; Bible.*

JOHNSTON, Timothy Wayne
Litchfield Sr HS; Litchfield, IL (17-132) Band; BC; Fr C; Math C; NHS; Orch; Ed, Sch P; Tres, SC; Citz A; H of F; Hon Prog; Journ A; VFW A; Tres & Bus Mgr, Ann; Moose VFW Schol; *Ill Wesleyan U; Acct.*

JOHNSTON, Vicki Denise
Prairiland HS; Pattonville, TX (9-71) Chor; Drama; FHA; FTA; *Ed.*

JOHNSTON, Walter LeCharles
Tift Co HS; Tifton, GA (10%-350) Band; BC; 4H; Hmrm; Span C; COM; Hon Prog; Exchange C Boy o-t Mo; *Abraham Baldwin Col.*

JOHNSTON, William Richard Jr
Harlingen HS; Harlingen, TX (3-700) Dbte Tm; NHS; Co-Cpt, Ftbl; COM; Sci A; *U of Tex; Elec Engr.*

JOHNSTON, William Wilbur
Reynolds HS; Winston-Salem, NC (11-800) Fin, Dbte Tm; Hmrm; Math C; NFL; Order/Arrow; Span C; Spch C; Pres, SC; Pres, Sr Cl; Math A; Order/Arrow A; Spch A; St Debate Champs; Win, Simon Says; *Wake Forest U; Law.*

JOHNSTONE, Faith Sherie
Toms River HS S; Toms River, NJ (27-440) Band; Fr C; Pres, 4H; Model UN; NHS; Mgr, Tr; Yth Fel; Elder; Color Guard; Operation Friendship; Choir; *Sci.*

JOICE, Mary Lou
Bakersfield R-4 HS; Bakersfield, MO; Chldr; Chor; Pres, FHA; NHS; Sch P; VP, SC; Co-Cpt, Bkbl; Sftbl; Miss Merry Christmas Qn; Miss BHS; Best Dressed; Cutest Girl.

JOINER, Cindy Lee
Emerson HS; Emerson, AR; Ann; Bus C; Chor; FBLA; FHA; 4H; Arch; Bkbl; Golf; Sftbl; Tnns.

JOINER, Debra Cecile
W Columbus HS; Cerro Gordo, NC (13-180) VP, BC; Chldr; Tres, Fr C; FHA; Model UN; A-Ed, Sch P; SC; Beauty; HCt; Q&S A; Artist, Ann; Sr Superlative; Golden Star Nom; WW; Cl Marshal; *U of NC at Wilmington; Journ.*

JOINER, Dennis Ray
Leesville HS; Leesville, LA (30-262) BS; Chor; Lit Ral; Sci C; Var C; Cpt, Bkbl; Ftbl; Cpt, Tr; Cl Fav; Hon Prog; Most Out; Opt A; *Northeast St U; Computer Sci.*

JOINER, Dorrie
Dublin HS; Dublin, GA (75-250) F-Ed, Ann; S-T, Drama; Hmrm; SC; Thes; Pres, Jr Cl; Pres, Soph Cl; Gov Honor Prog; HCt; Lit Tm; One-Act Play; WW; *U of S Ala; Theatre.*

JOINER, Elera Sue
Christian Co HS; Hopkinsville, KY (10%-385) Ann; BC; Chor; Madrigal; NHS; All St Chor; WW; *Austin Peay St U; Mus.*

JOINER, Janice Lynn
Forest Park Sr HS; Forest Park, GA (25%-600) Chor; Ensm; Co-Cpt, Flag Corp; HR; *Clayton Jr Col; Early Childhood Ed.*

JOINER, Jocelyn Griselda
S R Butler HS; Huntsville, AL (15-566) Fr C; Hmrm; Mu Alpha Theta; NHS; Sci C; SC; Bkbl; Tnns; Alg A; Ntl Achv Schol; NEDT; Type A; Jr Civitans; Vlbl; WW; *U of Notre Dame; Bio.*

JOINER, Lynda Diane
Elgin HS; Elgin, IL (527-1011) *Central Bible Col; Bible.*

JOINER, Marcia Leigh
Thompson HS; Alabaster, AL (15-165) Band; BC;
Chem C; Chor; Fr C; VP, Hmrm; NHS; Sci C; SC;
Beauty; Cl Fav; Hon Prog; Eng A; *U of Montevallo;
Spch Pathology.*

JOINER, Sharon Joan
Cairo HS; Cairo, GA; Band; 4H; Tri-HiY; *Emergency Med Tech.*

JOKELA, Janet Arlene
Neil Armstrong Sr HS; Plymouth, MN (1-670) Co-
Ch, Band; Chor; Ensm; Hmrm; NHS; Orch; Cr-
Ctry; COM; Val; Co- cpt, Ski Tm; Rotary
Exchange Stu; *U of Minn; Lang.*

JOLIAT, Greg Scott
Karlsruhe Amer HS; Karlsruhe, GERMANY;
Chor; Order/Arrow; ARC; F-Ed, Sch P; SC; Var C;
MVP, Bsbl; Bkbl; Golf; Tr; Citz A; HCt; Pres A;
ARC A; Eagle Sct; *U of Maine; Wildlife Conservation.*

JOLLAY, Anne Elise
Lakeside HS; Atlanta, GA (28-350) BC; Cpt,
Chldr; FBLA; Hmrm; NHS; SC; Hon Prog; Young
Amer; Spirit A, Chldr; 1st Runner-Up, Miss LHS;
Outst Sr; *U of Ga; Bus Adm.*

JOLLEY, Dina Jolynn
West Side HS; Gary, IN (50-650) Secy, Fr C; Orch;
Citz A; *Communications.*

JOLLIE, Phyllis Louise
Aynor HS; Aynor, SC (12%-85) Ann; BC; Secy,
FHA; GS; Pres, 4H; Hmrm; Tres, Sci C; Span C;
SC; 4H A; I Dare You; VofDEM; St 4-H Food
Nutrition; *Food Nutrition.*

JOLLY, Jill Louise
Stillman Valley HS; Stillman Valley, IL; Band;
Drama; FHA; FTA; Secy, 4H; *Teaching.*

JOLLY, Laura Ann
Arlington HS; Arlington Heights, IL (12-543)
Band; Dbte Tm; Ger C; NHS; Swim; H of F; Hon
Prog; PTA A; Summa Cum Laude; Pres, Timette;
JV Vlbl; *Valparaiso U; Mech Engr.*

JOLLY, Michael John
Hoehne HS; Hoehne, CO (2-22) Band; VP, Chor;
Ensm; Pres, 4H; SC; Pres, Soph Cl; JV, Bkbl; Soc-
cer; Mgr, Swim; Tnns; Bio A; COM; 4H A; I Dare
You; Sci A; Band, Soc Stu, A's.

JOLLY, Roger Michael
Quincy Sr HS; Quincy, IL (120-735) Chor; Bkbl;
Cpt, Quiz Tm; C A's; Rptr, Church Paper.

JOLLY, Thomas Elwyn Jr
Monticello HS; Monticello, MS; Pres, BC; Bsbl;
Bkbl; Cl Fav; Star Student; *U of Miss; Bus.*

JONAS, Lori Jean Lois
Cary-Grove HS; Cary, IL (5-336) Cpt, Chldr; Fr C;
NHS; Secy, SC; Amer Leg A; Hon Prog; *Math.*

JONATHAN, Atmita
Marshall Islands HS; Majuro, MARSHALL IS-
LANDS (9-103) Sch P; Secy, Jr Cl; Star Student;
Bus Adm.

JONES, Albert Earl
Jackson S Abrams HS; Bessemer, AL (2%-106)
Pres, Band; BS; Ensm; F-Ed, Sch P; VP, Sr Cl;
Morehouse Col; Elec Engr.

JONES, Alesia
Edwin Denby HS; Detroit, MI; Chldr; Chor; Mus
A's; *Med.*

JONES, Alice Marie
HS for Performing and Visual Arts; Houston, TX;
Chor; Madrigal; NHS; SC; Amer Leg A; GSct
Board of Directors; *Reed Col; Mus.*

JONES, Alicia Sue
McLain HS; Tulsa, OK; Hon Prog; Sports A; Gym
A; *TU; Secretarial.*

JONES, Allyson Elisabeth
Cresset Christian Acad; Durham, NC (1-3) NHS;
Co-Ed, Sch P; SC; Hon Prog; Val; 2nd Baptist Col
Schol Essay Cont; *Bob Jones U; Nurs.*

JONES, Amy Louise
Winnebago Lutheran Acad; Fond du Lac, WI;
Band; Chldr; SC; Bkbl; Hon Prog.

JONES, Andre Earl
Covert Pub Sch; Covert, MI; Pres, Band; Chor;
FHA; NHS; Up Bound; Var C; Pres, Jr Cl; Bkbl;
Ftbl; H of F; Hon Prog; Interlochen Ntl Mus; Prin-
cipal's A; *Oakland U; Med.*

JONES, Angie Deloris
Yerba Buena HS; San Jose, CA (15-275) MVP,
Soccer; Sftbl; Tr; Hon Prog; St Scholar; *San Jose St
U; Criminal Law.*

JONES, Anita Louise
Sw McEvoy B HS; Macon, GA; DECA C; Tres,
GAA; *Phys Ed.*

JONES, Ann Sydnor
Hopewell HS; Hopewell, VA; Candystriping; Petersburg Gen Hosp Prof Sch Nurs; *Nurs.*

JONES, Anne Rebecca
Butler RV HS; Butler, MO (5-93) Chldr; Secy,
FHA; Secy, NHS; VP, Thes; B Crocker A; Pep C;
Mascot; WW; *Fla Col; Eng.*

JONES, Annette Maria
Tunstall HS; Dry Fork, VA;

JONES, Anthony George
Cascia Hall HS; Tulsa, OK (4-46) F-Ed, Lit Mag;
NHS; Rptr, Sch F; SC; Var C; Pres, Soph Cl; Bsbl;
Bkbl; Ftbl; Golf; Alg A; Bio A; NEDT; Val.

JONES, Arlee Jr
Altheimer HS; Altheimer, AR; VP, NHS; VP, Sr
Cl; Bkbl; Tr; Alg A; Bio A; Chem A; Hon Prog;
Math A; Sci A; *Henderson St U; Engr.*

JONES, Arlene
Jasper HS; Jasper, AR (3-21) Co-Ed, Ann; BC;
FBLA; FHA; Math A; Sci A; Type A; Eng A;
Shorthand A; Civics A; Hon Stu A; *Ark Tech U;
Elem Ed.*

JONES, Audrey Marie
Denton Sr HS; Denton, TX (157-564) Band;
Hmrm; NHS; SC; Ntl Teenage Pageant; *Pepper-
dine U; Bus Adm.*

JONES, Barbara Ann
Brooklyn Tech HS; Brooklyn, NY; Ann; Cpt,
Mjrte; *Eng.*

JONES, Barbara Elaine
Lexington Sr HS; Lexington, NC; FHA; *Fashion
Photography.*

JONES, Beatrice Isabella
Oleny HS; Philadelphia, PA; AFS; Chem C; Fr C;
Swim; Beauty; Math A; *Undertaker.*

JONES, Bertharee Louise
Soldan HS; St Louis, MO (6-23) SC; JA A; *UCLA;
Social Worker.*

JONES, Beverly Ann
Admiral King HS; Lorain, OH; HR; Nurs Home
Merit A; *Computer Programmer.*

JONES, Beverly Renata
Dublin HS; Dublin, GA (5-25) Co-Ed, Ann; BC;
Drama; Fin, Jr Miss Pagent; S-T, SC; Thes; Beauty;
HCt; *Eckerd Col; Elem Ed.*

JONES, Bonnie Jean
Hendersonville HS; Hendersonville, NC; Chor;
Tres, Hmrm; Key C; S-T, NHS; ARC; Rptr, Span
C; COM; Hon Prog; ARC A; Yth Fel; Secy, Art C;
Annual Artist; Co & Dist Art A's; *Bryan Col; Ed.*

JONES, Brenda Kay
North HS; Omaha, NE (25%-500) Band; Jobs
Daughters.

JONES, Brenda Lynn
Tuscola Comm HS; Tuscola, IL (16-118) Band; Tr;
Hon Prog; Rotary A; *Eastern Ill; Elem Ed.*

JONES, Brian Andre
E St Louis Sr HS; E St Louis, IL (1-800) Chess C;
Fr C; Math C; Sci C; Ftbl; Alg A; COM; Citz A;
Math A; Sci A; *Engr.*

JONES, Brian Keith
Cedartown HS; Cedartown, GA; Chess C; Most
Out; ROTC A; Excel Medals, Solo & Ensm Fest;
Military Order of World Wars.

JONES, Brian Walker
Claiborne Acad; Homer, LA (1-37) Band; Ensm;
Lit Ral; Orch; VP, SC; Pres, Jr Cl; Pres, Soph Cl;
Bkbl; Val; Tres, Sch Hon Soc; Most Intelligent;
Schol A; *La St U; Computer Sci.*

JONES, Bruce Edward
Ballou HS; Washington, DC (5-23) Band; Hmrm;
Bsbl; Bkbl; Ftbl; Sftbl; Swim; Tr; Citz A; Cl Fav;
Most Out; Spch A; *Howard U.*

JONES, Carentina
Williamson HS; Mobile, AL; JV, Chldr; Chor; Pres,
Hmrm; VP, InterClub Coun; Secy, Span C; Spch C;
SC; MVP, Bkbl; *Med.*

JONES, Carlos LaTrece
Ole Main HS; N Little Rock, AR (110-407) Band;
Drama; FBLA; Rptr, Sch P; Span C; Hon Prog;
Journ A; *Lane Col; Communications.*

JONES, Carol Anne
Highland HS; Highland, IN (47-530) FHA; F-Ed,
Sch P; *Ind U; Eng.*

JONES, Carol Jean
Tecumseh HS; New Carlisle, OH (50-500) AFS;
Band; Span C; *Mus.*

JONES, Carol Yvonne
Barrackville HS; Barrackville, WV (2-48) Pres,
Band; Chor; Ensm; NHS; Rptr, Sch P; Pres, Y-Tns;
Elk A; Hon Prog; Most Out; Phy A; Q&S A; Sal;
Outst Bandsmen; Bison Bellows A; WW; *Aiderson-
Broaddus Col; Nurs.*

JONES, Catherine Blain
Huguenot HS; Richmond, VA (2-254) F-Ed, Ann;
FBLA; NHS; Sftbl; COM; Sal; NMS Ltr of Commendation; FBLA St Comp Econ, 3rd Pl; *UPI; Forestry and Wildlife.*

JONES, Cathy Marie
Carroll HS; Monroe, LA; Band; Dbte Tm; Ensm;
Math C; SC; Band A; *Robinson Bus Col; Banking.*

JONES, Charles Alan
Texarkana Ark HS; Texarkana, AR (10-480) Fr C;
Pres, SC; Bsbl; Ftbl; COM; Citz A; Cl Fav; Hist A;
Hon Prog; *LSU; Forrestry.*

JONES, Charles Douglas
Beaufort Acad; Beaufort, SC (7-42) Band; Var C;
VP, Jr Cl; Tres, Soph Cl; Golf; Soccer; Hon Prog;
Citadel.

JONES, Charles Edward
West HS; Knoxville, TN (52-280) BS; Hmrm; Secy,
Key C; Lat C; NHS; Pres, SC; Var C; Pres, Jr Cl;
Arch; Bkbl; Co-Cpt, Ftbl; Tr; DARGCA; HKg;
Distinguished Yth A; *U of Tenn; Med.*

JONES, Charrae Delores
Presentation HS; San Francisco, CA (50-150) Co-
Cpt, Chldr; SC; Secy, Soph Cl; Amer Leg A; CSF;
COM; Cl Fav; MLS; *Fisk U; Psych.*

JONES, Cherie Lynn
McAdams HS; McAdams, MS; Ann; Beauty;
DARGCA; Star Student; *Holmes Jr Col; General
Col.*

JONES, Cherrie Anne
West HS; Billings, MT (100-735) A Cap Choir;
Chor; Ensm; Hmrm; NHS; Span C; SC; Swim; Tr;
Mont St U; Ed.

JONES, Cheryl Darlene
Warren Co Sr HS; McMinnville, TN (63-400) Pres,
Fr C; Pres, Span C; Pom-Pon; *Bauder Fashion Col;
Interior Decorating.*

JONES, Chonita Delphine
John F Kennedy HS; Suffolk, VA (4-230) Secy,
Chem C; NHS; Pol Sci C; Co-Cpt, Bkbl; Bio A;
Chem A; Citz A; HCt; Hon Prog; I Dare You; PTA
A; *Va Commonwealth U; Bio.*

JONES, Cindy Ranee
Wenatchee HS; Wenatchee, WA (125-397) Span
C; Yth Fel; *Okla Baptist U; Psych.*

JONES, Conchita Lynn
Woodrow Wilson Sr HS; Washington, DC; Hmrm;
Mjrte; Span C; *Lincoln U; Therapeutic Recreation.*

JONES, Connie Lee
Colo HS; Colo City, TX (11-90) Ed, Ann; FBLA;
VP, FHA; Pres, FTA; Math C; NHS; SC; Journ A;
Q&S A; Type A; Yth Fel; *W Tex Col; Secy Sci.*

JONES, Constance Viola
Camden Co HS; Camden, NC (24-95) Chor; Secy,
Drama; FHA; FTA; Hmrm; Jr Miss Pageant; COM;
HCt; JA A; Pres A; Jr Beta C; Debutante; *NC
Central U; Bus.*

JONES, Corliss Yolanda
West Side Sr HS; Gary, IN (33%-700) Lat C; Bkbl;
HS All-Amer; WW in Foreign Lang; *Purdue U;
Computer Tech.*

JONES, Craig Allen
Freeport Sr HS; Freeport, IL (42-545) ARC; JV,
Bkbl; Ftbl; Tnns; ARC A; Yth Fel; Bike C; Pres,
Yth Fel; Pres, FCA; Drafting A; *Carpentry-
Apprentice.*

JONES, Cydni Anne
San Angelo Central HS; San Angelo, TX (327-671)
FTA; *Abilene Christian U; Homemaking.*

JONES, Cynthia Vera
Apex Sr HS; Apex, NC; Chor; Hmrm; SC; Tres,
Soph Cl; Sftbl; *E Carolina U; Phys Ed.*

JONES, Dana Michelle
Burges HS; El Paso, TX (50-712).

JONES, Daniel
Rebecca Comer HS; Eufaula, AL (4-40) FFA; 4H;
SC; Pres, Jr Cl; Bsbl; *Tuskegee Inst; Bus.*

JONES, Daniel Ray
Yukon HS; Yukon, OK (40-300) Semi-Fin, Wrest;
Bethany Nazarene Col; Bus.

JONES, Darryl Wayne
Midwest City HS; Midwest City, OK (25%-550)
Band; Ensm; Key C; Order/Arrow; ARC; Order/
Arrow A; Eagle Sct, John Wesley, A's; *Oscar Rose
Jr Col; Med.*

JONES, David Caldwell
Council Rock HS; Newtown, PA (10-735) Hon
Prog; Stu Aides & Vol in Action; Yth Choir; Yth
Group; Ch, Retreat Committee; *Lehigh Col; Math.*

JONES, David Perry
Reidsville Sr HS; Reidsville, NC (9-344) BS; FFA;
Hmrm; Math C; NHS; Order/Arrow; Span C; Bsbl;
JV, Ftbl; Hon Prog; Order/Arrow A; Rotary A;
Eagle Sct Gold Palm; *Rockingham Comm Col.*

JONES, David Richard
Cumberland Valley HS; Mechanicsburg, PA
(25-650) NHS; Order/Arrow; Bkbl; Hon Prog;
NMS; Eagle A; *Muhlenberg Col; Pre-Med.*

JONES, David Ronald
Eastern Guilford HS; Gibsonville, NC (10-177) Fr
C; French NHS; Monogram; Order/Arrow; Sci C;
Var C; JV, Bkbl; Ftbl; COM; God & Country A;
Order/Arrow A; Eagle A; *Elec.*

JONES, Dawn Marie
Austin HS; Austin, MN (100-507) Band; Span C;
Mgr, Bkbl; Sftbl; Co- cpt, Vlbl; *Minn Bible Col;
Social Work.*

JONES, Debbie Lynn
E Hardin HS; Glendale, KY (35-186) Co-Cpt,
Chldr; Hmrm; Tres, Sr Cl; Pres, Jr Cl; Secy, Soph
Cl; Cl Fav; HCt; *Bus.*

JONES, Deborah Ann
Altoona Area HS; Altoona, PA; Chor; Hmrm; Up
Bound; Tr; Tr A; Filing A; Acct A; *Point Park Col;
Communications.*

JONES, Deborah Lynn
Crawford Co Jr-Sr HS; Marengo, IN (12-165)
Chor; Rptr, Sch P; *Covenant Found Col; Mus.*

JONES, Deborah Lynne
Lynn View HS; Kingsport, TN (2-120) Ch, Anchor
C; Ann; Band; Rptr, BC; Drama; Ch, FBLA; GS;
Fin, Jr Miss Pageant; Mjrte; NHS; Pres, SC; Thes;
DARGCA; HCt; MLS; Opt A; VofDEM; *U of
Tenn, Knoxville; Pre-Med.*

JONES, Deborah Suzanne
Brusly HS; Brusly, LA (1-76) Ann; Pres, BC; FHA;
GS; Pres, 4H; Fin, Lit Ral; Sch Achieve Tm; Sci C;
Mgr, Bkbl; Tr; Amer Leg A; B Crocker A; Chem A;
4H A; Hist A; Hon Prog; Sci A; Type A; Val; LSU
Fresh Hon A; Dow Chem Engr Schol; NASA A,
Outst Sci Achv; *LSU; Chem Engr.*

JONES, Debra Ann
Northwestern HS; Flint, MI (60-482) Chor; *Western Mich U; Bus Adm.*

JONES, Debra Lou
Paint Rock HS; Paint Rock, TX (8-12) F-Ed, Ann;
Tres, FHA; 4H; Bkbl; Semi-Fin, Tnns; Cl Fav; Re-
gional Champ, Tnns; Hon Men, Bkbl; *Angelo St U;
Phys Ed.*

JONES, Denise Lynne
Bluestone Sr HS; Skipwith, VA (25-200) FHA;
Blueridge Col; Vet Asst.

JONES, Denise Ruth
Mt Diablo HS; Concord, CA; Cpt, Chldr; Ch, Chor;
Pres, Var C; Bkbl; Sftbl; Tnns; Hon Prog; Most Out;
Pres A; St Scholar; Type A; Secy, V C; Most Im-
proved; Campus Life; Ath o-t Yr; Vlbl; WW; *Biola
Col; Christian Ed.*

JONES, Denise Sallie
John Bartrum HS; Philadelphia, PA (60%-749)
Pres, Var C; Bsbl; Cpt, Bkbl; Sftbl; Most Out; Yth
Fel; Art A; *W Chester St U; Commercial Art.*

JONES, Dennis G
McKinley HS; Buffalo, NY; Spch A; Yth Fel; Bowl
& Ftbl A's; *Morehouse Col; Law.*

JONES, Derek Sean
Osceola HS; Kissimmee, FL; A Cap Choir; Chor;
Drama; Ensm; HiY; Thes; Mgr, Bkbl; JV, Ftbl;
Swim; Yth Leg; Yth Group; Steer Comm.

JONES, Diana Leigh
E Hills HS; Fort Worth, TX; Drama; VP, Rainbow;
Thes; *U of Tex; Drama.*

JONES, Diana Lyn
Christiana HS; Newark, DE; AFS; Band; Pres, Bus
C; Hmrm; Span C; SC; Mgr, Bkbl; Cl Fav; Spch A;
Mgr, Vlbl; Job Interview Stu o-t Yr; *Goldey Bea-
com Col; Bus.*

JONES, Diane Gayle
Lafayette HS; Brooklyn, NY; Band; Chldr; Chor;
Dbte Tm; Hmrm; NHS; ARC; Bkbl; COM; Hist A;
Hon Prog; ARC A; Sci A; Type A; Yth Fel; Yth
Foundation A; Arkon Soc; *Phys Therapy.*

JONES, Diane Lavon
Theodore Roosevelt HS; San Antonio, TX
(175-700) AFS; Band; VP, Chess C; Chor; Ensm;
Hmrm; Sci C; Span C; Tres, SC; Sftbl; COM; Sci A;
Yth Fel; Vlbl; *Tex A&M U; Horticulture.*

JONES, Diedra Coleen
Flint Central HS; Flint, MI; SC; Hon Prog; Spch A;
Howard U; Math.

JONES, Donna Lee
Montgomery Co HS; Mt Sterling, KY (25%-290)
Rptr, Bus C; Chor; Pres, 4H; Hmrm; Lat C; Math
C; SC; Y-Tns; 4H A; Journ A; JA A; Explorers;
S-T, Church Yth Fel; Best Project Worker, DECA;
Most Supporting, DECA; *E Ky U; Hotel-Motel
Mgt.*

JONES, Donna Yavonne
Whitley Co HS; Williamsburg, KY (50-250) BC;
Chor; 4H; Opt A; Church Sftbl; WW; *Cumberland
Col; Nurs.*

JONES, Dori Lyn
Willows HS; Willows, CA (2-136) Secy, Band; 4H;
Tres, Sch Achieve Tm; Ski C; Tres, Y-Tns; VP, Jr
Cl; Swim; CSF; 4H A; JA A; MLS; Pres A; ARC A;
Sci A; *Math.*

JONES, Douglas Allen
Wausau E HS; Wausau, WI; Band; CYO; Tres, 4H;
Math C; Mu Alpha Theta; Tr; 4H A; Math A;
Pre-Med.

JONES, Dwayne Earl
Mart HS; Mart, TX (12-78) FFA; Cpt, Bsbl; Cpt,
Bkbl; Cpt, Tr; Cl Fav; *UCLA; Phys Ed.*

JONES, Eddie Glenn
Washington HS; Washington, NC (10%-280) Inter-
Act C; Span C; All Star Bsbl; Punt, Pass & Kick A;
NC St U; Pub Relations.

JONES, Edith Gay
Loraine HS; Loraine, TX; Band; Drama; Secy,
FHA; FTA; Mjrte; Bkbl; Tr; COM; Type A; Val; *N
Tex St U; Med.*

JONES, Elizabeth Anne
Danville HS; Danville, IL (61-600) A Cap Choir;
Chor; Drama; Ensm; Hmrm; Madrigal; Hon Prog;
Yth Fel; Top Vocal Stu; Talent Schol; *Butler U;
Mus Ed.*

JONES, Elizabeth Ivalee
Rye Cove HS; Clinchport, VA (9-77) BC; Pres,
FBLA; 4H; Sch P; COM.

JONES, Elizabeth Marie
Phineas Banning HS; Wilmington, CA; Chor;
Hmrm; ARC; ROTC; Gra Tnns; Bowl; Black Yth
Organization; Sr Vespers Committee; Pep C; *Ful-
lerton St Col; Pre-Med.*

JONES, Elona Denise
W Charlotte Sr HS; Charlotte, NC; Rptr, Ann;
Community Yth Symph; Drama; Rptr, Hmrm;
Orch; ARC; Span C; SC; Beauty; HCt; Most Out;
Type A; PA.

JONES, Emmett Charles
Daniel M Therrell HS; Atlanta, GA (6-351) Band;
BC; Dbte Tm; Model UN; VP, NHS; Pres, Order/
Arrow; Pres, Sci C; VP, Soph Cl; Mgr, Bkbl; COM;
JA A; NMS; ROTC A; Presbyterian Col Jr Fel; *US
Military Acad; Elec Engr.*

JONES, Gene Thomas
Norfolk Cath HS; Norfolk, VA (40%-150) Key C;
Monogram; Pol Sci C; SC; Var C; Cpt, Bkbl; Tr; Cl
Fav; HCt; *William & Mary Col; Pol Sci.*

JONES, Genecia Renee
Doss HS; Louisville, KY; SC; Tr; Human Relations
C; Tr A; *Bus Adm.*

JONES, Glenda Lorraine
Edneyville HS; Hendersonville, NC (20%-100)
Pres, Band; Chor; Pres, Hmrm; SC; Type A; Band
A; Eng A; *Brevard Col; Mus.*

JONES, Glenn Joseph
Springdale HS; Springdale, AR; Ntl Jr Hon Soc; *U
of Ark; Engr.*

JONES, Greg Allan
Wheeling Park HS; Wheeling, WV (282-842) Ftbl;
Tr.

JONES, Gregory Allan
Wheeling Park HS; Wheeling, WV (280-842) JV,
Ftbl; JV, Tnns; JV, Tr; Intramurals; Weight Lifting;
Sci.

JONES, Gregory Darin
Edgewood HS; Trenton, OH (60-245) Band; Ger
C; Span A; Bkbl; Ftbl; Golf; Tr; Wrest; Math A; Yth
Fel; Span A; Jr Deacon; Sunday Sch Teacher;
Georgetown Col.

JONES, Gregory E
Teaneck HS; Teaneck, NJ; Bkbl; BSct; Lib Coun;
Hist.

JONES, Gregory Lee
Mooresville HS; Mooresville, IN (36-300) Order/
Arrow; JV, Tr.

JONES, Gregory Norman
Moorestown HS; Moorestown, NJ (40%-300) Co-
Cpt, Ftbl; Tr; Ntl Achv Schol; NMF; Pres, Afro C;
HS All-Amer; All Star Tm Ftbl Co; *Hofstra U;
Psych.*

JONES, Gregory Scott
Stratford Central HS; Stratford, NY (4-18) Arch;
Band; Chor; Drama; Pres, Hmrm; VP, SC; VP, Var
C; Pres, Y-Tns; Pres, Sr Cl; Arch; Bsbl; Bkbl; Soc-
cer; Mgr, Sftbl; *Roberts Wesleyan Col; Phar.*

JONES, Gwendolyn Cheryl
Wakefield HS; Arlington, VA; Chor; *Howard U;
Nurs.*

JONES, Gwendolyn Elizabeth
Lincoln HS; Tacoma, WA (25%-500) Tr.

JONES, Hal O
Buford HS; Buford, GA (5%-76) BC; Chor; FBLA;
4H; Parl, HiY; Semi-Fin, Lit Ral; Gov Honor Prog;
4H A; Hist A; Type A; Mus A; Bookkeeping A;
Gregg Typing Pin; *N Ga Col; Mus Ed.*

JONES, Helen
Cottonwood HS; Cottonwood, AL (1-90) Ann;
Band; VP, BC; Rptr, FBLA; Secy, FHA; 4H; Sci C;
S-T, SC; S-T, Soph Cl; PTA A; Eng A; *Troy St U;
Phys Ed.*

JONES, Herbert Anderson II
W T White HS; Dallas, TX (20%-700) Key C; Ftbl;
Cl Fav; Young Life; FCA; Sr Executive Board; Hon
Men, All Dist Ftbl; *Bus Adm.*

JONES, Herbert Bernard
Bentonia HS; Bentonia, MS (1-55) FBLA; Bkbl;
Ftbl; *Holmes Jr Col; Elec.*

JONES, Jacqueline
Rebecca Comer HS; Eufaula, AL (5-64) FHA; 4H;
VP, Hmrm; NHS; Sftbl; 4H A; HQn; Hon Prog; Sci
A; Yth Fel; Stu Worker; Vlbl; *Talledega Col; Acct.*

JONES, James
Central HS; Providence, RI (60-370) Amer Leg
Orator A; CSF; Fin, Poetry Assn A; *Morgan St;
Physch.*

JONES, James Raymond
R B Worthy HS; Saltville, VA (10%-65) BC; Hmrm; Pres, Key C; Pres, Sci C; Span C; Bsbl; *VPI; Archt.*

JONES, James T
Borger HS; Borger, TX; Band; Hmrm; Order/ Arrow; Ski C; Span C; SC; Ftbl; God & Country A; Yth Fel; *TCU; Archt.*

JONES, Jamie Wallace
Monticello HS; Monticello, MS; BC; FFA; Hmrm; Pres, SC; Var C; Bkbl; *Miss St U; Engr.*

JONES, Jana Elizabeth
Oakhaven Bapt Acad; Memphis, TN (15-63) A-Ed, Ann; Secy, Span C; *U of Tenn at Martin; Ed.*

JONES, Janet Wesley
Lincoln HS; Stockton, CA (89-375) Cpt, Chldr; Chor; VP, SC; Ftbl; Kiwanis A; Prom Court; Del, Asilomar; *Westmont Col; International Pol.*

JONES, Janice Ann
Cousa HS; Rome, GA (5-350) Fr C; Tnns; COM; Hon Prog; *Shorter Col.*

JONES, Janice Lynne
Lutheran HS N; St Louis, MO (5-162) Fr C; VP, NHS; Sch P; SC; HR; Fin, Ntl Achv; *Bradley U; Acct.*

JONES, Jay Alan
Brookings HS; Brookings, SD (25-215) Monogram; NHS; Bsbl; Ftbl; Tr; Ftbl Spirit A; 1st, Ntl Assn of Teachers of Span; *SD St U; Broadcast Journ.*

JONES, Jay Harold
Cuyahoga Valley Christian Acad; Akron, OH (5-85) Chess C; Ski C; JV, Soccer; Citz A; Hist A; NEDT; Sci A; *Northeastern Ohio U; Pre-Med.*

JONES, Jeffrey Gray
Mars Area Sr HS; Mars, PA (14-200) NHS; Thes; Var C; Cr-Ctry; Tr; VP, Stage Crew; *Grove City Col; Communications.*

JONES, Jennifer Dale
Beavercreek HS; Xenia, OH; A Cap Choir; Chor; *Cincinnati Bible Col; Mus.*

JONES, Jennifer Denise
Mary Brantley Smiley HS; Houston, TX; Hmrm; SC; Tr; Yth Fel; Secy, Fresh Cl; Sign Lang C; *Special Ed.*

JONES, Jill Duncan
First Baptist HS; Charleston, SC (10-46) Chldr; VP, Chor; Drama; Ensm; Fr C; Hmrm; Sci C; SC; Y-Tns; Mgr, Soccer; Tr; Beauty; HCt; Miss Camelia Festival; *U of Va; Elem Ed.*

JONES, Jodi Ann
Linda Vista Acad; Oxnard, CA (2-15) A Cap Choir; Co-Ed, Ann; Band; Chor; Ensm; Hmrm; Bkbl; Ftbl; Soccer; Sftbl; Tr; Hon Prog; Swtht; Mus A; Pres, Social VP, SA; *Loma Linda U; Med.*

JONES, John Kevin
Texarkana Ark HS; Texarkana, AR (10-434) BS; Fr C; Key C; NHS; Sch P; Parl, SC; Pres, Soph Cl; Bsbl; Bkbl; Ftbl; COM; Citz A; Cl Fav; Hon Prog; Math A; NMS; Sci A; Interntl Sci Fair Fin; Alumni Acad A; *Stanford U; Law.*

JONES, John Wayne
Clovis HS; Clovis, CA; Ecology C; Campus Life; HR; *US Air Force Acad; Pilot.*

JONES, Joni Lea
Tift Co HS; Tifton, GA (20%-500) Band; Fin, GS; Pres, InterClub Coun; VP, SC; Tri-HiY; *Auburn U; Math.*

JONES, Joseph Bruce
Valley HS; Sanders, AZ; Drama; Pres, Sr Cl; Pres, Jr Cl; Bsbl; Bkbl; Ftbl; *NAU; Carpentry.*

JONES, Judith Leigh
The Cecilian Acad; Philadelphia, PA; Fr C; Lat C; Sacristan; *Psych.*

JONES, Judith Lynn
Edmond Mem HS; Edmond, OK; Band; Chor; *Oscar Rose Jr Col; Dental Health.*

JONES, Julia Faye
Hooper Acad; Hope Hull, AL (4-68) BC; S-T, Chor; Drama; 4H; Math C; Sci C; COM; Citz A; 4H A; Math A; Yth Fel; APSA St Champion Math Tm; *Auburn U at Montgomery; Bus.*

JONES, Karen Ann
Homewood HS; Homewood, AL; Chor; NHS; *Harding Col; Social Work.*

JONES, Karen Lee
Shaler Area HS; Glenshaw, PA (20%-823) Ann; Band; NHS; Rainbow; Ski C; Span C; Drill Tm; Westinghouse Sci Hons Inst; *Penn St U; Engr.*

JONES, Karen Leigh
Thomas Jefferson HS; Alexandria, VA (85-493) Tres, Band; Community Yth Symph; Dbte Tm; Drama; Hmrm; VP, Model UN; Orch; Phys C; Sci C; SC; Thes; Var C; Mgr, Bkbl; Mgr, Soccer; Mgr, Tr; Citz A; Sci A; *Madison Col; Special Ed.*

JONES, Karen Lynn
Pleasant Valley HS; Chico, CA (10%-300) A Cap Choir; Co-Ed, Ann; Madrigal; Soccer; Church Tn Coun; *Point Loma Nazarene Col; Mus.*

JONES, Karen Octavia
SW HS; Atlanta, GA (9-197) Co-Ed, Ann; Band; Tres, BC; VP, Hmrm; Math C; Mu Alpha Theta; NHS; SC; Bkbl; Cr-Ctry; Tr; HCt; Hon Prog; VP, Yth Fel; Debutante; Adv Placement; DECA A; *Ky St U; Chem Engr.*

JONES, Katherine Anne
Nordhoff HS; Ojai, CA (18-276) AFS; Chor; Secy, 4H; CSF; 4H A; Fr Academic Ltr A; Seal Bearer; Dean's List 4 Yr; *California Lutheran Col; Special Ed.*

JONES, Kathy Janine
Tivy HS; Kerrville, TX (25%-178) Band; Ensm; FHA; Hmrm; Key C; Mjrte; Rainbow; SC; Var C; VP, Jr Cl; MVP, Tr; *San Angelo St Col; Teaching.*

JONES, Kathy Paige
Lancaster HS; Lancaster, VA (30-98) FBLA.

JONES, Kathy Sue
Attica HS; Attica, IN (4-98) Ann; Pres, Fr C; VP, FTA; GS; VP, NHS; Span C; SC; Hon Prog; WW; Hoosier GS; *Ind U; Elem Ed.*

JONES, Kay Joann
Merced HS N Campus; Merced, CA; Alg A; Bank Of Amer A; Citz A; Math A; ARC A; Type A; Yth Fel; GAA; *Nurs.*

JONES, Keith Alan
Pershing HS; Detroit, MI; Var C; Ftbl; *Forestry.*

JONES, Keith Edward
Wausau E HS; Wausau, WI (50%-418) CYO; Pres, 4H; ARC T; 4H A; VP, 4-H C; *North Central Tech Inst; Police Sci.*

JONES, Kelli Denise
Powell HS; Powell, TN (15%-220) Band; BC; Secy, NHS; Tres, Rainbow; ARC; COM; Hon Prog; Masonic A; ARC A; Adv Foreign Lang, Eng, A's; *U of Tenn; Communications.*

JONES, Kelly Townes
Ware Shoals HS; Ware Shoals, SC (20%-100) F-Ed, Ann; Band; Secy, BC; Fr C; Cpt, Mjrte; Rptr, Sch P; Sci C; HCt; Christian C; Mjrte A; Academic A; Sr Play; Sr Standout; Hon Stu; *Lander Col; Nurs.*

JONES, Ken P
Box Elder HS; Brigham, UT (20-380) Ann; Chess C; Dbte Tm; Demolay; Hmrm; Model UN; NFL; NHS; Hon Prog; Masonic A; Math A; NMF; Spch A; *U of Utah; Pre-Law.*

JONES, Kenneth Dale
Sturgis HS; Sturgis, SD (31-193) BS; Chor; Drama; Ensm; Ger C; NHS; Sch P; VP, Sci C; SC; Thes; Stu o-t Mo; *Augustana Col.*

JONES, Kevin Richard
Kearney Sr HS; San Diego, CA (426-861) COM; Cl Fav; Type A; Off Practice A; *San Diego St U; Bus Adm.*

JONES, Kevin Scott
Dublin HS; Dublin, CA (30-160) Ger C; Lit Mag; Model UN; Ed, Sch P; Ski C; SC; Ftbl; Journ A; *UCLA; Pol Sci.*

JONES, Kimberly
Rockdale HS; Rockdale, TX; Band; FHA; I Rating, UIL Solo & Ensm.

JONES, Kimberly Sue
Wood River HS; Hailey, ID (1-62) Chldr; FHA; Pres, Ger C; GS; NHS; Rptr, Sch P; Ski C; SC; Pres, Var C; Pres, Sr Cl; Co-Cpt, Bkbl; Cr-Ctry; Tr; Bausch & Lomb A; Citz A; Hon Prog; Val; *Col of Idaho; Ath Trng.*

JONES, Kris Colette
Valley HS; W Des Moines, IA (1-550) A Cap Choir; Band; Chor; Ensm; Fr C; FHA; Madrigal; Mjrte; NHS; Sch P; SC; Bkbl; Sftbl; Tr; Yth Fel; Church Organist; Dist Piano Win; Symph Contest; *Applied Mus.*

JONES, Latanya Anita
C F Vigor HS; Mobile, AL; *Morehouse Col; Hist.*

JONES, Laura Anne
Harriton HS; Rosemont, PA (10-282) Co-Ch, Ger C; Lit Mag; Model UN; World Affairs C; Dbte Tm; NMF; *U of Ga; Psych.*

JONES, Laura Diane
Clear Creek HS; League City, TX; NHS; Alg A; Math A; Spelling A; *Fashion Design.*

JONES, Laura Jo
Lufkin HS; Lufkin, TX; A Cap Choir; Band; Chor; Drama; Ensm; Hmrm; Madrigal; ARC; SC; Sftbl; St Mus Contest; *Angelina Jr Col; Mus.*

JONES, Lawrence Alan
Irvin HS; El Paso, TX; A Cap Choir; CYO; Chor; Ensm; Orch; Order/Arrow; SC; Ad Altare Dei; Pope Pius XII; Panis Vitae; *St Marys Dominican Col; Ed.*

JONES, Lee Ann
De Soto Sr HS; De Soto, MO (25%-250) Pres, Band; FBLA; K of C A; Cpt, Pom Pons; MVP, Band; Jr Rotarian; *Nutrition.*

JONES, Lee Matthew
Brownfield HS; Brownfield, TX (10-174) A Cap Choir; BS; NHS; Order/Arrow; Span NHS; Pres, SC; Pres, Soph Cl; Bsbl; JV, Bkbl; Ftbl; JV, Tr; COM; Cl Fav; HCt; Most Out; Opt A; Order/Arrow A; Eagle Sct; Pres, FCA; All Region Choir; *Tex Tech U; Phys Therapy.*

JONES, Leonard Howard
Reidsville Sr HS; Reidsville, NC (36-344) Fr C; Hmrm; Tres, Key C; Math C; *Drew U; Econ.*

JONES, Leslie Teresa
John T Hoggard HS; Wilmington, NC (30-2000) Chor; Hmrm; Span C; *U of NC at Wilmington; Nurs.*

JONES, Lester Todd
Oakland, CA; Yth Fel; *Phys Sci.*

JONES, Lillian Vernelle
Tuskegee Inst HS; Tuskegee Institute, AL (10%-190) Secy, Chldr; Drama; FHA; Pres, Hmrm; NHS; Ed, Sch P; Secy, Span C; SC; Cl Fav; Hon Prog; Outst Chldr A; Gym Tm; Span Merit A; *Auburn U; Phys Ed.*

JONES, Linda Diane
Fayette Ware N HS; Somerville, TN (5-315) Tres, BC; FHA; Math C; SC; Up Bound; Bkbl; Alg A; Beauty; COM; Chem A; Math A; Most Out; Sci A; Most Conscientious; Stu o-t Wk; Eng Performance A; *U of Tenn; Math.*

JONES, Linda Gail
Forrest City HS; Forrest City, AR (11-327) Band; Parl, BC; Hmrm; Semi-Fin, Jr Miss Pa; Mjrte; Math C; Pres, Span NHS; Span A; Jr Miss Outst Sr; *Ark Comm Col; Math.*

JONES, Lisa Lynn
Alexandria Sr HS; Alexandria, LA (2-315) Chor; Ensm; Parl, Lat C; Fin, Lit Ral; NHS; Hon Prog; Sal; Pres Clrm For Young Amer; *Memphis St U; Engr.*

JONES, Lonnie Steven
East HS; Denver, CO; Wrest; City-Wide Orch.

JONES, Lori Ann
Lyndon Baines Johnson HS; Austin, TX (10%-400) NHS; Trustee A; Vlbl; *Stephen F Austin Col; Sci.*

JONES, Lottie Rose
Cary Sr HS; Cary, NC (134-590) BC; Sftbl; *U of NC; Law.*

JONES, Louise Marshelle
Pennsauken HS; Pennsauken, NJ; *Acct.*

JONES, Luanne Marie
Dows Comm Sch; Dows, IA (8-30) Bkbl; Co-Cpt, Cr-Ctry; Tr.

JONES, Ludell Marie
Jeannette Sr HS; Jeannette, PA; Chor; FHA; Cl Fav; Sanctuary Soc; Swtht; Church Chor; Planning Comm; *Cosmetology.*

JONES, Malcolm Wilkins
Perimeter S Christian Acad; Conley, GA (3-26)
Sch P; Bkbl; Ftbl; Sftbl.

JONES, Marcia Gale
Rio Linda Sr HS; Rio Linda, CA (33%-400) Chor;
Hon Prog; Art A.

JONES, Marcus Paul
Crowley HS; Crowley, TX (12-166) Band; Bus C;
Fin, Chess C; Order/Arrow; Order/Arrow A; *Air
Force Acad; Engr.*

JONES, Margaret Helen
J W Nixon HS; Laredo, TX (10-650) A-Ed, A Cap
Choir; GS; 4H; Hmrm; Lat C; Sci C; Ch, SC; Amer
Leg A; Hon Prog; Episcopal Yth Group; *Pamona
Col; Pre-Med.*

JONES, Margie Ellen
Wawasee HS; Syracuse, IN (38-242) FHA; Sftbl;
Hon Prog; Bus Mem A; 1st Pl, Essay Contest; *Air
Force Col; Bus Ed.*

JONES, Marianne
Hutchinson HS; Hutchinson, MN (35-220) AFS;
Secy, Band; Chor; NHS; Ed, Sch P; Pres, Thes;
Mus Contest A; *Hamline Col; Journ.*

JONES, Marie Annette
London HS; London, OH (4-96) Chor; Ensm;
FHA; GS; NHS; Jr Chamber of Com A; Pres, Tri-
L; Yrbk; Jr Kiwanianne; *Mt St Joseph o-t Ohio;
Mus Therapy.*

JONES, Marie Thomas
Leesville HS; Leesville, LA; *Secy.*

JONES, Marilyn Elaine
Highland HS; Highland, IN (12-585) Chor; Ensm;
FHA; French NHS; NHS; A-Ed, Sch P; *Valparaiso
U.*

JONES, Marilyn Ruth
N Augusta Sr HS; N Augusta, SC (2-389) BC;
Drama; Fr C; Mu Alpha Theta; NHS; Secy, Sci C;
COM; Hon Prog; JA A; NMS; Sal; *Purdue Engr
Stu A; Ga Tech; Aeronautical Engr.*

JONES, Marilyn Sue
Penny HS; Hamilton, MO (33%-77) Band; FHA;
Tres, 4H; Bkbl; Tr; 4H A; Type A; *Bus.*

JONES, Marinda Ann
L C Anderson HS; Austin, TX (25%-650) Band;
Ensm; Anderson Trojan Bells, Drill Tm; Choir Off,
Secy, Fresh Cl; Church Camp Far; Choir Accompa-
nist; Choir Accompanist; *Baylor U.*

JONES, Marion Leo
Marian HS; Houston, TX (30-70) Hmrm; SC; Bkbl;
Cpt, Ftbl; MVP, Tr; Amer Leg Orator A; Most
Rep; *Tex Tech U; Ed.*

JONES, Mark Allen
John Randolph Tucker HS; Richmond, VA
(102-446) HiY; Bkbl; Golf; Swim; DARGCA; *Va
Commonwealth U; Pre-Law.*

JONES, Mark Andrew
Big Spring HS; Big Spring, TX (3-400) A Cap
Choir; Secy, Key C; Order/Arrow; Alg A; Order/
Arrow A; *Tex A&M U; Nuclear Engr.*

JONES, Mark Farrell
Hendersonville HS; Hendersonville, NC; Pres, BC;
Chor; Fr C; Pres, Hmrm; ARC; VP, SC; H of F;
Hon Prog; Pres A; ARC A; Yth Fel; Art C; St Art
A; Women's C Art A; *Bryan Col; Art.*

JONES, Mark Kenneth
James Wood HS; Winchester, VA (58-523) Chess
C; FFA; 4H; A-Ed, Sch P; Mgr, Bkbl; Tr; 3rd Pl,
District Ntl Fr; 2nd Pl, Sci Fair; *Geology.*

JONES, Mark Thomas
Kearsley HS; Flint, MI (40-425) Chess C; NHS;
Mott Col; Agr.

JONES, Marsha Denise
North HS; Springfield, OH (125-390) *Engr.*

JONES, Marva Jannett
Pasadena HS; Pasadena, CA (286-640) GS; Hmrm;
SC; Sftbl; Swim; Tr; Beauty; COM; Citz A; I Dare
You; MLS; Type A; Pres, Yth Fel; Girls Z C; Vic-
tory Sq; Girls League; *Pasadena City Col; Bus
Adm.*

JONES, Marvin Loyd
Palmer HS; Palmer, TX (5-28) Rptr, FFA; Bkbl;
Cpt, Ftbl; Cpt, Golf; Tr; Cl Fav; HCt; Drama A;
FFA A; *Tarelton Col.*

JONES, Mary Beth
Lynchburg Clay HS; Lynchburg, OH (7-100) Ann;
Band; Chor; Ensm; NHS; Span C; SC; Bsbl; Bkbl;
Sftbl; Tr; Hon Prog; Magna Cum Laude; NHB;
Wilmington Col; Phys Ed.

JONES, Mary Jo
Louisville HS; Louisville, MS; Chem C; FHA; *Miss
Valley St Col; Army ROTC.*

JONES, Mary Lee
Block HS; Jonesville, LA; 4H; *Northeast Col;
Nurs.*

JONES, Mary Lena
Jeanerette Sr HS; Jeanerette, LA; Band; CYO;
Bkbl; Cpt, Sftbl; MVP, Tnns.

JONES, Mary Margaret
St Joseph Acad; Green Bay, WI (8-146) Pres,
CYO; Chor; Drama; Fr C; Rptr, Hmrm; Key C;
NHS; SC; Tres, Sr Cl; Ftbl; Tr; HCt; Pres A; *U of
Wis-Eau Claire; Phar.*

JONES, Maxine Suzanne
Baker Acad; Hawkinsville, GA (5-30) Ann; NHS;
Bkbl; Sftbl; Hon Prog; *U of Ga; Nurs.*

JONES, Melinda Delores
Suffolk HS; Suffolk, VA (10-118) Secy, Band;
Chor; Pres, FHA; Secy, NHS; Ch, SC; Mgr, Bkbl;
Chamber of Comm A; Regional Chor; *Hampton
Inst; Spch Pathology.*

JONES, Michael Albert
Central Baptist HS; Cincinnati, OH; Ed, Ann; Pres,
Chor; Pres, Hmrm; SC; Pres, Soph Cl; Alg A;
COM; Hist A; Sci A; Yth Fel; *Psych.*

JONES, Michael John
Bennington Pub HS; Bennington, NE (10-42) A
Cap Choir; Band; Chor; Ensm; SC; Var C; Bkbl;
Ftbl; Golf; Tr; Hon Prog; *Metro Tech Comm Col;
Restaurant Mgt.*

JONES, Michael Joseph
John F Kennedy HS; Barstow, CA; City Conf; Dbte
Tm; Hmrm; Ntl Yth Conf; SC; Var C; Cpt, Bkbl;
Cpt, Ftbl; Citz A; Cl Fav; Hon Prog; JA A; Kiwanis
A; Lion A; Most Out; Opt A; Yth Fel; Yth Founda-
tion; *Pepperdine U; Sociology.*

JONES, Michael Rex
Dixie Co HS; Cross City, FL (15-98) Band; Rptr,
BC; Drama; Span C; SC; Thes; Cl Fav; Rotary A;
Yth Fel; Early Admissions, Lake Cty Com Col; *Fla
St U; Ed.*

JONES, Michele
Fairhope HS; Fairhope, AL (15%-350) Secy, Band;
Drama; Ch, SC; Sftbl; Yth Fel; Church Chor; Rifle
Corp; *Auburn U; Engr.*

JONES, Michele Deanne
Willows HS; Willows, CA (1-148) Band; FTA; 4H;
Sch Achieve Tm; Ski C; Golf; Swim; Tnns; CSF;
4H A; JA A; Pres A; ARC A; Sci A; *U of Calif.*

JONES, Mickey Lynn
Liberty Jr-Sr HS; Liberty, PA (20%-64) Ger C;
Tres, Jr Cl; Bsbl; Bkbl; Soccer; Tnns; *Ind St U.*

JONES, Miriam Cecile
Oakland HS; Oakland, CA (10%-35) Chldr; Chor;
Secy, Hmrm; Cpt, Sftbl; Co-Cpt, Tr; Citz A; Princi-
pal's A; Outst Scholastic Achievement A; Ath A;
Tuskegee Inst; Med.

JONES, Monica Rose
Sequoia HS; Redwood City, CA; FBLA; Basic Ed
Opportunity Grant; *Notre Dame Col; Art.*

JONES, Monty Ray
Othello HS; Othello, WA (8-250) All Amer Yth;
Band; Key C; Ntl Yth Conf; Ftbl; Tr; Wrest; H of F;
Yth Fel; Top 10%; Pres Phys Fitness 100% A; *East-
ern Wa St Col; Health & PE.*

JONES, Morgan Evette
Killeen HS; Killeen, TX (87-850) *Central Tex Col;
Office Adm.*

JONES, Myra Lynn
Lincoln HS; Dallas, TX (10-200) A Cap Choir; Bus
C; Chor; NHS; Alg A; Hist A; Hon Prog; Math A;
Type A; Eng, Bus, Homemaking, Art, A's; *U of
Tex; Acct.*

JONES, Nancy Carol
Sou Wayne Sr HS; Dudley, NC (13-388) Pres,
FHA; NHS; FHA C A; Hon Graduate; *Wayne
Comm Col; Health Services.*

JONES, Nancy Lee
Harry Ells HS; Richmond, CA (4-309) A Cap
Choir; Ann; Drama; Ensm; Fr C; Rptr, Sch P; CSF;
Silver Tongue A; *Radcliffe Col; Pol Sci.*

JONES, Nancy Rose
Trent Acad; New Bern, NC (2-3) Co-Ed, Ann;
Chldr; Hmrm; SC; Co-Cpt, Bkbl; Sftbl; HCt; All
Conf Chldr.

JONES, Nancy Suzanne
Coatesville Area Sr HS; Coatesville, PA (8-619)
Chor; Fr C; NHS; Sch P; SC; Tres, Sr Cl;
DARGCA; Gym; Academic Schol, Clarion St Col;
Gym Schol; *Clarion St Col.*

JONES, Narci Lee
Wayne HS; Jesup, GA (20%-240) F-Ed, Ann;
Band; Drama; FBLA; Secy, 4H; Semi-Fin, Jr Miss
Pa; Lat C; Mjrte; F-Ed, Sch P; 4H A; HCt; VFW A;
Valdosta St Col; Art.

JONES, Natham Hanks
Hardaway HS; Columbus, GA (6-400) Chess C;
Math C; Mu Alpha Theta; Order/Arrow; COM;
Gov Honor Prog; JA A; ROTC A; Yth Fel; Eagle
Sct; BSA Pub Speaking A; JROTC; Sup Cadet;
Principal's List; *US Air Force Acad; Aerodynam-
ics.*

JONES, Norma Ann
E Aurora HS; E Aurora, NY (200-268) Chldr;
Chor; Hmrm; Ed, Sch P; Yth Fel; Best Dancer;
Lead, Sch Play.

JONES, Patricia Crane
Woodward Acad; College Park, GA (2-216) Inter-
Act C; NHS; Bkbl; Tr; COM; Hist A; Hon Prog; JA
A; Math A; NEDT; Sci A; Yth Fel; Eng A; 1 On 1
Champ; Highest Acad Avg; 2nd Pl, Most Congeni-
ality; *Ga Tech; Chem.*

JONES, Patricia Elaine
Marina HS; San Leandro, CA (270-300) Fr C;
Model UN; Ski C; Tnns; Tr; *U of Calif.*

JONES, Patti Ann
Nowlin Jr HS; Independence, MO; Sftbl; HR;
Church Yt Coun; *Religion.*

JONES, Patti Dale
Cherry Creek HS; Englewood, CO (152-680)
Harding Christian Col; Eng.

JONES, Patti Janice
Galena Park Sr HS; Galena Park, TX; A Cap Choir;
Chldr; Chor; Hmrm; Math C; Citz A.

JONES, Paul Edward
Lee's Summit HS; Lee's Summit, MO (33%-538)
Bkbl; JV, Ftbl; *Elec.*

JONES, Penny Janice
Cheraw HS; Cheraw, SC (5-159) A-Ed, Ann; Chem
C; Drama; GS; NHS; Thes; Var C; Bkbl; Sftbl; Alg
A; Gr Marshal; Hist A; Hon Prog; Ntl Achv Schol;
Sci A; *Ntl Jr Hon Soc; Clemson U; Sci.*

JONES, Peter Linn
Oroville HS; Oroville, CA (25-200) Yth Fel.

JONES, Rachelle Annette
John F Kennedy HS; Barstow, CA; Band; Hmrm;
Cpt, Sftbl; *Pepperdine U; Secy.*

JONES, Randall Benjamin
Little Cypress-Mauriceville HS; Orange, TX
(25%-210) Chor; Drama; Bsbl; Bkbl; *Acct.*

JONES, Randy Dwayne
Norman HS; Norman, OK (50%-662) A Cap Choir;
Chor; Hmrm; Order/Arrow; ASW; Ftbl; Tr; MVP, Wrest;
Cl Fav; Order/Arrow A; HS WW; *U of Okla.*

JONES, Rebecca Edna
N Iredell HS; Olin, NC (10%-320) Chor; Citz A;
Pres A; Sci A; *Mus.*

JONES, Rebecca Lynn
Morton HS; Morton, TX; Co-Ed, Ann; Chor; FTA;
Odesa Bus Sch; Bus.

JONES, Rhonda Kela
Chester HS; Chester, PA (16-673) Band.

JONES, Rhonda Lynn
Vanguard HS; Ocala, FL (3-350) VP, Anchor C;
Mu Alpha Theta; Secy, NHS; VP, SC; Most Out;
Pres A; Sci A; *Asbury Col; Bus Adm.*

JONES, Rhonda Patrice
Columbia HS; Decatur, GA; Band; Bkbl.

JONES, Richard Alan
New Bern Sr HS; New Bern, NC (25-502) Hmrm; Monogram; NHS; Tri-HiY; Bsbl; JV, Bkbl; HR; U of NC.

JONES, Richard Keith
Denison Sr HS; Denison, TX (25%-350) Hmrm; NHS; Order/Arrow; SC; Bkbl; JV, Ftbl; Tr; God & Country A; Hon Prog; Order/Arrow A; Pres A; Eagle A; Tex Tech U; Bus.

JONES, Richard Lee
Goodlettsville HS; Goodlettsville, TN (6-159) Band; Chem C; Chess C; Lat C; Phys C; Golf; MLS; NEDT; Phy A; Sci A; WW; Tenn Tech Col; Engr.

JONES, Richard Wayne
Lakewood HS; Lakewood, CO (191-570) Chor; Med Careers C; Lee Col; Psych.

JONES, Ricky Dale
Bell Voc HS; Washington, DC; Cpt, Ftbl; Woodward Found; WW; Va Union U; Mech Engr.

JONES, Ricky Redell
Wendell Phillips HS; Chicago, IL (9-350) Hmrm; Math C; NHS; Bkbl; Rensselaer A; Pres, Black Stu Union; Sr Senate; Northeastern U; Chem Engr.

JONES, Rita Faye
Stevenson HS; Stevenson, AL (11-83) Ed, Ann; Band; Cpt, Chldr; FHA; VP, Hmrm; Mjrte; Rptr, Sch P; VP, Soph Cl; 4H A; Pres & Secy, 4-H C.

JONES, Robert Charles
Lamar Sr HS; Houston, TX; Key C; NHS; Ftbl; Hon Men; All Dist Ftbl; U of H; Bus Law.

JONES, Robert Craig
Walter Hines Page HS; Greensboro, NC (40-550) Secy, Key C; NHS; JA A; Yth Fel; NC St U; Engr.

JONES, Robert Ralph
Stratford Central HS; Stratford, NY (5-18) Band; Chor; SC; Tres, Jr Cl; Bsbl; Bkbl; Soccer; Sftbl; Industrial Arts A; Roberts Wesleyan Col; Law.

JONES, Robin Elisa
Glendora HS; Glendora, CA; Pres, A Cap Choir; Pres, Chor; Orch; Amer Leg A; Bank Of Amer A; Hon Prog; Pres A; Spch A; Type A; Choir A; Most Outst Choir Girl As; Most Outst Orch; Azusa Pacific Col; Mus.

JONES, Robin Lenor
Westchester HS; Los Angeles, CA; W Los Angeles Col; Homemaking.

JONES, Roland Bradford III
Melbourne HS; Melbourne, FL; U of Fla; Hist.

JONES, Ronald Steven
Glynn Acad; Brunswick, GA; Morehouse Col; Social Stu.

JONES, Russell Robert
Mitchell Road HS; Memphis, TN; Fr C; COM; ROTC A; VP, Yth Choir; Jr Deacon; Phys Fitness, A; Church Attendance, A; Memphis St U; Hist.

JONES, Sandra Annette
Sigourney Comm HS; Sigourney, IA (12-95) Band; FHA; JV, Bkbl; Sftbl; Tr.

JONES, Sandra Faye
Tunstall HS; Dry Fork, VA; Oral Roberts U; Law.

JONES, Sandra Gail
Yukon HS; Yukon, OK (40-350) Chor; Drama; Ensm; FHA; NHS; Alg A; Hist A; Vocal A; Bethany Nazarene Col.

JONES, Sandra LaSalle
Union HS; Leslie, GA (1-64) Dbte Tm; Drama; FHA; SC; B Crocker A; COM; Hon Prog; Val; Spelling A; Mercer U; Elem Ed.

JONES, Sandra Lynn
Bethel Baptist HS; Memphis, TN (6-20) Ann; Cpt, Chldr; Chor; Cl Fav; HCt; Miss Total Christian Young Lady; Tri-St Baptist Col; Bible.

JONES, Saundra Denice
Aiken Sr HS; Cincinnati, OH (16-544) VP, Bus C; Rptr, Hmrm; NHS; Citz A; Hon Prog; PA; U of Cincinnati; Spec Ed.

JONES, Scott Lewis
Tuslaw HS; Massillon, OH (26-160) A Cap Choir; Chor; Ensm; NHS; JV, Bsbl; Tnns; Amer Leg A; Hon Prog; Comm Sounds of Praise Yth Choir; WW; Stark Tech Col; Computer Prog.

JONES, Sharon Lynn
G W Carver HS; Atlanta, GA; NHS; Atlanta Jr Col; Mod Dance.

JONES, Sharon Lynn
Fulton HS; Knoxville, TN (36-310) Ch, Anchor C; Fr C; Hmrm; NHS; Y-Tns; Tr; Art Achv Cert; WW; U of Tenn.

JONES, Sherea Diane
Ben L Smith HS; Greensboro, NC; Secy, FTA; Y-Tns; HCt; GTI.

JONES, Sherry Denise
Hancock Central HS; Sparta, GA; Co-Ed, Ann; 4H; Secy, Hmrm; Secy, NHS; Pres, SC; Up Bound; Secy, Sr Cl; Clark Col; Journ.

JONES, Shirley Ann
Canton Pub HS; Canton, MS; F-Ed, Ann; Drama; Tres, Math C; Tres, Mu Alpha Theta; NHS; Span C; Secy, Sr Cl; HCt; Math A; Sci A; Mary Holmes Col; Secy Sci.

JONES, Sonja Gail
Kingman HS; Kingman, KS; Chor; Sci C; Y-Tns; Hon Prog; Vocal Mus Contest As; Tabor Col; Secondary Ed.

JONES, Stanford Bernard
Hoke Smith HS; Atlanta, GA (4-293) Swim; Math.

JONES, Stephanie Leigh
W Birmingham Christian HS; Adamsville, AL; VP, NHS; SC; HCt; Sal; Hon Graduate; Psych A.

JONES, Stephen Frazier
Melbourne HS; Melbourne, FL (5%-500) Bus Mgr, Ann; Chor; Ensm; VP, 4H; Madrigal; Sch P; Citz A; 4H A; Spch A; Fla Tech U; Computer Sci.

JONES, Stephen Ray
Flint River Acad; Woodbury, GA (4-49) Ann; Chor; Drama; Fr C; Key C; NHS; Ntl Yth Conf; Order/Arrow; A-Ed, Sch P; SC; Mgr, Bkbl; Cpt, Ftbl; COM; Citz A; God & Country A; Hon Prog; NMF; Order/Arrow A; Yth Foundation; Eagle Sct; Big Brother A; U of Ga; Criminal Law.

JONES, Steven Anthony
Brewer HS; Brewer, ME (80-400) A Cap Choir; Band; Chor; Ski C; Span C; Var C; Mgr, Bsbl; Mgr, Bkbl; Mgr, Ftbl; Tres, Yth Fel.

JONES, Steven Mark
Drummond Pub Sch; Drummond, OK (3-21) Ann; Chor; Ensm; Pres, FFA; Order/Arrow; Pres, SC; Pres, Sr Cl; VP, Jr Cl; Pres, Soph Cl; Hon Schol, Central Col; Central Col of Kans; Med.

JONES, Steven Michael
S Pasadena HS; South Pasadena, CA (17-350) Ch, Bus C; Hmrm; Key C; Math C; NHS; Ch, Orch; Span C; Tres, SC; Cr-Ctry; Tr; COM; Hon Prog; Most Out; St Scholar; Pres, VP, Tres & Bus Mgr, Band; Highest Bandsman A; 2nd Pl Med, All-City Cr-Ctry Race; Rose Bowl Marathon Trophy; US Military Acad at West Point; Chem.

JONES, Sue Ellen
Horicon HS; Horicon, WI (18-111) Secy, NHS; Sch P; Ski C; Span C; S-T, Sr Cl; S-T, Jr Cl; Tnns; Tr; Amer Leg A; DARGCA; HCt; Spch A; VFW A; VofDEM; Forensics Tm; Musical; All Sch Play; U of Wis-LaCrosse; Computer Sci.

JONES, Susan Glennette
Clovis HS; Clovis, CA; Ecology C; Campus Life; HR; Fresno City Col; Nurs.

JONES, Susan K
Reeds Spring HS; Reeds Spring, MO (25%-90) BC; FHA; U of Mo at Columbia; Photo Journ.

JONES, Susan Lynn
Alton Sr HS; Alton, IL; Bus C; NHS; Semi-Fin, Dream Girl Court.

JONES, Susan Lynne
Sussex Central HS; Sussex, VA (4-200) Rptr, BC; Chldr; Chess C; Rptr, NHS; Sci C; Bkbl; Tr; Alg A; Math A; Art A; PA; Equitation.

JONES, Susan Pamela
Eastside HS; Paterson, NJ; Chor; HR Cert; Bus Adm.

JONES, Susan Renee
Windsor Acad; Macon, GA (2-42) BC; Pres, Jr Cl; COM; Gov Honor Prog; Bkbl Coach; Ldrship A; Ga Baptist Hospital Sch of Nurs; Nurs.

JONES, Suzanne Ruth
Highland HS; Albuquerque, NM (25%-900) Fr C; NHS; Hon Prog; Yth Fel; Young Life; U of NM.

JONES, Sylvia Ann
Rantoul Township HS; Rantoul, IL; Pres, Chor; Tnns; Tr; ARC A; Rensselaer A; Cpt & MVP, Vlbl; Ath A; Acct.

JONES, Synita
South Park HS; Buffalo, NY; Chldr; Sch P; Span C; SC; Bkbl; Sftbl; Tnns; COM; Citz A; Hon Prog; Math A; Gym A; Tutor's A; U of Ala; Radiologic Technology.

JONES, Tamara Jean
Madison HS; Richmond, KY; BC; Sch P; Eastern Ky U; Law.

JONES, Tammy
Paul Laurence Dunbar HS; Baltimore, MD; NHS; Hist A; U of Md; Biol.

JONES, Tammy Marie
Continued Ed Project; St Louis, MO (10-46) FBLA; COM; Citz A; Gym; U of Mo at St Louis; Bus.

JONES, Teresa Janette
N Iredell HS; Olin, NC (20%-326) Secy, FTA; MYF; Phys Fitness A; FCA; Chapel Hill Col; Dental Hygienist.

JONES, Teresa Lynn
Grace King HS; Metairie, LA; Drama; Secy, Span C; Close- up 77; Win, Lit & Social Stu; Explorers; Coun On Ministry; Sunday Sch Teacher; Pres, S-T, Yth Fel; SE La U; Ed.

JONES, Teresa Lynn
First Assembly Christian Sch; Memphis, TN (8-31) Chldr; Lat C; Math C; Ed, Sch P; Bkbl; Tnns; COM; Citz A; HCt; Hon Prog; Math A; Miss FACS; Evangel Col; Math.

JONES, Terri Rene
Allen Cons HS; Allen, NE; A Cap Choir; Ann; Band; Chldr; Chor; FHA; Sch P; Secy, Jr Cl; Bkbl; Swtht; Band Letter; Homecoming Usher; Mus Letter; Stewarts Hairstyling Sch.

JONES, Terry Lynn
Pasadena HS; Pasadena, CA (82-640) Pres, A Cap Choir; Secy, Chldr; Pres, Chor; Ch, Hmrm; SC; PCC; Med Asst.

JONES, TerryLee Estelle
Ossining HS; Ossining, NY (50%-359) All Amer Yth; CYO; Chldr; Chor; Bkbl; Co-Cpt, Hockey; Sftbl; Swim; All Conf, All Co, Field Hockey; All Amer, Field Hockey; Springfield Col; Phys Rehabilitation.

JONES, Thelma Marie
Fayette Ware HS; Somerville, TN (35-300) BC; Secy, Chess C; FHA; Math C; Up Bound; Bkbl; Alg A; COM; Citz A; HCt.

JONES, Thomas Gene
W Hills HS; Ft Worth, TX (133-616) Bsbl; Pres, Royal Ambassadors; 1st Pl, Ntl Rifle As Marksman; Solar Energy.

JONES, Thomas Randall
Ruthven Consolidated HS; Ruthven, IA; Band; Chor; Var C; Bsbl; Ftbl; Ellsworth Jr Col; Mortitian.

JONES, Timmy Ray
Monticello HS; Monticello, MS (3-145) Ann; Band; VP, BC; Ensm; Hmrm; Order/Arrow; Sch Achieve Tm; Bsbl; JV, Bkbl; Ftbl; COM; NEDT; Ole Miss; Engr.

JONES, Tina Lavon
Edgewood HS; Edgewood, TX (30-65) Band; FHA.

JONES, Tina Ruth
Scotland Sr HS; Laurinburg, NC (20%-500) A-Ed, Ann; Fr C; FFA; French NHS; Tres, Monogram; Pres, SC; Pres, Sr Cl; Tr; Vlbl; Bennett Col; Psych.

JONES, Tobin Jack
Kenai Central HS; Kenai, AK (1-170) BS; Tres, Chor; Community Yth Symph; Dbte Tm; VP, NHS; Orch; Pres, SC; Bsbl; Swim; B Crocker A; COM; Elk A; Lion A; MLS; Val; Cr-Ctry Skiing; Arion Found A; Barbrshp Qrt; All-St Chor & Orch; All-Northwest Orch; Century III Ldrs; St Alt; Rice U; Engr.

JONES, Vicki Sue
N Brunswick HS; Leland, NC; Chor; Tr; Secy, VICA; Nicholas Giovenetti Mem A; Indust Cooperative Train and Work; *Campbell Baptist Col; Med Sci.*

JONES, Vickie Lee
Central Sr HS; York, PA (7-282) NHS; Chem A; WW; *Pa St U; Chem.*

JONES, Vivian
Edward Tilden HS; Chicago, IL (60-408) Chor; Drama; Ensm; Math C; Sch P; Sci C; SC; Pres, Para-Medics; Vlbl; Bowl; *Ill St U; Special Ed.*

JONES, Vivian Orelene
Eastside HS; Paterson, NJ (10%-800) Chor; UN Council; Secy, Jr Cl; Bkbl; HR; *Montclair St Col; Lib Arts.*

JONES, Walter Bernard
Glynn Acad; Brunswick, GA; Ftbl; *Morehouse Col; Hist.*

JONES, Wayne Patterson
Coosa HS; Rome, GA (1-189) Cpt, Band; BC; Chor; Fr C; Key C; Tres, Math C; NHS; Alg A; Bio A; Gov Honor Prog; Hon Prog; NMS; Val; Sr Cl Officer; *Shorter Col; Pre-Med.*

JONES, William Daniel
Jellico HS; Jellico, TN (6-80) Ann; VP; BC; Parl, 4H; NHS; Secy, Var C; Pres, Jr Cl; Bsbl; Bkbl; Citz A; Cl Fav; 4H A; MLS; *Cumberland Col; Bus Adm.*

JONES, Yulanda Jean
Montgomery Co HS; Mt Sterling, KY (25%-300) Band; VP, SC; Y-Tns; MVP, Bkbl; MVP, Tr; Amer Leg A; HCt; *Acct.*

JOPHLIN, Anna Marie
Pana Sr HS; Pana, IL (29-133) FBLA; Secy, FHA; Secy, Hmrm; Ed, Sch P; Span C; *Tenn Temple Baptist Col; Elem Ed.*

JORDAN, Alphonso Capone
Benedictine HS; Cleveland, OH (24-125) CYO; Span C; SC; Pres, Y-Tns; Cpt, Bkbl; Ftbl; Sftbl; COM; Citz A; Hon Prog; JA A; MLS; Most Out; Ntl Achv Schol; Opt Out Tn; Pres A; Sacristan; Sanctuary Soc; Yth Leg; Human Relationship C; Pres, SCAT C; *Ohio St U; Sociology.*

JORDAN, Angela Dora
Burke HS; Charleston, SC (4-141) Bus C; Sch Achieve Tm; *SC St Col; Bus Adm.*

JORDAN, Angela Lee
Crestview Sr HS; Crestview, FL; BC; Chldr; Chor; Ensm; FTA; Beauty; COM; Hon Prog; Phys Ed A; Pianist, Chor; *U of Fla.*

JORDAN, Armetta Darlene
John F Kennedy HS; Cleveland, OH (20-650) Drama; COM; Citz A; Hon Prog; Type A; Service A; *Ohio U; Special Ed.*

JORDAN, Audrey Louise
Weatherwax Sr HS; Aberdeen, WA (69-320) AFS; Dbte Tm; Drama; Hmrm, 4H; NFL; NHS; Ski C; Pres, Span C; Thes; Tr; COM; 4H A; Hon Prog; Math A; Spch A; Rainfair Princess; *U of Wash; Computer Sci.*

JORDAN, Barbara Ann
Wadley HS; Wadley, GA (10%-70) Ed, Ann; Pres, BC; Chor; Ensm; Pres, FBLA; Mjrte; Alg A; COM; Hon Prog; Math A; Star Student; *Emanuel Co Jr Col.*

JORDAN, Beverly Ann
Ribault Sr HS; Jacksonville, FL; Y-Tns; Tr; *Fla Jr Col; Bus Ed.*

JORDAN, Bruce Alan
New Providence HS; New Providence, NJ (72-319) Band; Orch; Church Bkbl Sportsmanship A; Hon Band & Chem; *Fla St U; Biol.*

JORDAN, Cecilia Ann
Early Co HS; Blakely, GA; BC; Chldr.

JORDAN, Colaine Denise
Eastside HS; Paterson, NJ (12-519) Cr-Ctry; Cpt, Tr; HR Cert; *Computer Sci.*

JORDAN, David Lee
Asheboro HS; Asheboro, NC (25-349) Band; Chess C; Ensm; Tr; *Appalachian Col; Mus.*

JORDAN, Dianne
Emerson HS; Emerson, AR (10-32) FHA; 4H; Mgr, Bkbl; COM; Cl Fav; *Sou Ark U; Nurs.*

JORDAN, Janet Denise
Wheaton Christian HS; W Chicago, IL (4-40) A Cap Choir; BC; Cpt, Chldr; Tres, Chor; Ensm; HiY; Madrigal; NHS; SC; Tnns; Citz A; Pres A; Yth Fel; Hon Men, Lyon & Healy Mus A; Superior Ratings, St Mus A; *Biola Col; Psych.*

JORDAN, Janet Marie
Cumberland Valley HS; Mechanicsburg, PA (15-675) NHS; Sftbl; Swim; Hon Prog; *Lehigh U; Engr.*

JORDAN, Jeffrey Charles
Pennsville Mem HS; Pennsville, NJ; Band; Bkbl; Sftbl; Lib A; *Houghton Col; Hist.*

JORDAN, John Edward III
University Sch of Nashville; Nashville, TN (15-70) Fr C; NEDT; *Med.*

JORDAN, Joseph William
Charleston Sr HS; Charleston, WV (25%-350) A-Ed, Ann; Band; Lit Mag; Span C; UN Council; Tnns; Yth Fel; Dramatic A; Jeffersonian A; Band A; Attendance A; *W Va U; Social Work.*

JORDAN, Judith Kathleen
Wendell Phillips HS; Chicago, IL (3-501) Chldr; NHS; Tres, SC; VP, Jr Cl; Mgr, Swim; COM; Hon Prog; *U of Ill; Computer Engr.*

JORDAN, Karen Elizabeth
Wahconah Regional HS; Dalton, MA (25%-244) Band; Tres, Jr Cl; Tres, Soph Cl; *Vet Sci.*

JORDAN, Kathy Elaine
Waynesboro Central HS; Waynesboro, MS (25%-117) BC; Pres, Hmrm; Co-Ed, Sch P; SC; Var C; Y-Tns; Pres, Jr Cl; Bkbl; *Tuskegee Inst; Pol Sci.*

JORDAN, Keith Wayne
Inglewood HS; Inglewood, CA (16-323) Band; Math C; Orch; Sch P; CSF; Citz A; Hon Prog; Semi Fin, PSAT-NMSQT; *UCLA; Bus Adm.*

JORDAN, Lavelury Anne
Wadley HS; Wadley, GA (7-82) Chor; VP, FHA; 4H; Sch P; COM; Gov Honor Prog; HCt; *Emanuel Co Jr Col; Sociology.*

JORDAN, Lavonzella
Northside HS; Memphis, TN; FHA.

JORDAN, Luz Esperanza
Paraiso HS; Paraiso, CANAL ZONE; Commercial C; Dbte Tm; Co-Ed, Sch P; Tres, Span C; Tr; Journ A; Poet A; Spch A; Type A; *Briar Cliff Col; Bus Law.*

JORDAN, Lynne Revere
Chaminade-Julienne HS; Dayton, OH; CYO; Chor; Drama; HiY; SC; 4H A; *Northwestern U; Creative Writing.*

JORDAN, Mark Thomas
Momence HS; Momence, IL (12-139) CYO; Chess C; Drama; Math C; NHS; Span C; Spch C; SC; Thes; Var C; Bsbl; Co-Cpt, Bkbl; Tr; Citz A; Cl Fav; Math A; Pres A; St Scholar; *Math.*

JORDAN, Mark Wayne
Starkville HS; Starkville, MS (10%-300) Ann; Band; BS; VP, Chor; Key C; Pres, NHS; Sci C; Var C; Ftbl; Hon Prog; Most Out; *Miss St U.*

JORDAN, Mary Elizabeth
St Joseph's HS; W New York, NJ (7-232) Ann; CYO; Drama; Tres, Span NHS; COM; Hon Prog; NEDT.

JORDAN, Michele Renee
Jeannette Sr HS; Jeannette, PA (5-198) AFS; FBLA; Tres, Lat C; NHS; Pres, Rainbow; VP, Yth Fel; Grand Lecturer; Grand Cross of Color.

JORDAN, Nancy Louise
Northeast HS; Ft Lauderdale, FL (1-450) Tres, Drama; Fr C; InterClub Coun; Tres, Thes; VP, Y-Tns; Secy, Jr Cl; Hon Prog; Most Out; NEDT; Star Student; *Duke U; Pre-Med.*

JORDAN, Patti Ann
Grimsley Sr HS; Greensboro, NC (60%-525) Band; Chldr; Hmrm; Tres, SC; HCt; Homecoming & Prom Committees; *NC Central U; Psych.*

JORDAN, Paul Kim
Weston-McEwen HS; Athena, OR (4-39) Ann; Parl, Dbte Tm; FBLA; FFA; NHS; A-Ed, Sch P; Span C; Tres, SC; Thes; Var C; Bsbl; Bkbl; Mgr, Ftbl; Tnns; Hon Prog; Type A; Photography C; Academic A; *Oreg St Col; Bus.*

JORDAN, Peggy Ann
Harlingen HS; Harlingen, TX (105-650) NHS; SC; Var C; JV, Bkbl; Sftbl; Alg A; Bio A; Vlbl; *Tex A&I U; Coaching Bkbl.*

JORDAN, Richard Lee
Raytown HS; Raytown, MO (300-500) A Cap Choir; Chor; Ensm; Madrigal; Most Out; HR; Mus Minister; Assoc Pastor; Ldr Church Functions; Yth Week; Choir; *SW Baptist Col; Religious Stu.*

JORDAN, Sally McKenzie
W Florence HS; Florence, SC (13-250) BC; Bkbl; Gr Marshal; *Furman U; Elem Ed.*

JORDAN, Sheba Vanessa
Gumberry HS; Gumberry, NC (3-97) Secy, BC; Chor; Sch P; COM; HQn; Most Out; Page Duty, St House Rep; *NC Central U; Nurs.*

JORDAN, Sonja Jeneine
Moultrie Sr HS; Moultrie, GA (11-500) Pres, Hmrm; COM; Coed For United Progress; Fin, HCT; FHA; Fin, Hon Prog; Spirit C; Drama; *Albany St Col; Criminal Justice.*

JORDAN, Stanford Russell
Salisbury HS; Salisbury, NC (10-233) Band; Tres, Key C; NHS; Span C; Tres, SC; Var C; VP, Soph Cl; Ftbl; Golf; Hon Prog; Lion A; *U of NC; Acct.*

JORDAN, Susan Grace
Wheat Ridge HS; Wheat Ridge, CO (163-610) Band; Dbte Tm; Drama; NFL; Spch C; Tnns; Ntl Merit Commendation; *Colo St U; Engr.*

JORDAN, Thomas Stephen
Clinton HS; Clinton, MS; Var C; Bsbl; Bkbl; Ftbl; Tr; Most Out; All NLA Ftbl; HS All Amer, Ftbl; Most Handsome; *Miss St U; Phys Ed.*

JORDAN, Tomie Justine
Hollywood Professional Sch; Hollywood, CA (50%-20) Ann; Cpt, Chldr; Chor; Drama; S-T, K of C; Model UN; Fin, Bsbl; Fin, Cr-Ctry; Fin, Sftbl; Fin, Swim; MLS; Type A; Acreditation Comm; *Pepperdine U; Law.*

JORDAN, Valerie Celeste
Walnut Ridge HS; Columbus, OH; Pres, Chor; Span C; Tr; Ballet Dancer; Tres, Sunday Sch; Del, Ntl Baptist Convention.

JORDAN, Vernetha Louise
Galileo HS; San Francisco, CA; Bus C; Chor; FBLA; FTA; Pol Sci C; Bsbl; Bkbl; Sftbl; Pol Sci A; Black Stu A; *Cal-St of Hayward; Bus Adm.*

JORDAN, Vickie Wanetta
Percy L Julian HS; Chicago, IL; COM; *Tuskegee Inst; Eng.*

JORDAN, Walter Stephen Jr
Clinton HS; Clinton, MS (10%-270) BC; Lat C; Mgr, Bkbl; Mgr, Ftbl; WW; *Miss Col; Religion.*

JORDAN, Yvette Clarice
Galileo HS; San Francisco, CA; Chldr; Chor; Drama; Jr Miss Pagent; ARC; Bkbl; ROTC A; Spch A; Yth Fel; Dance A; Theatrical Training; *Bishop Col; Theatrical.*

JORDING, Dacia Elaine
St Thomas HS; St Thomas, ND (8-15) Chor; Ensm; Fr C; S-T, 4H; Co-Ed, Sch P; Mgr, Bkbl; Mgr, 4H A; Math A; *U of ND; Social Worker.*

JORDING, Timothy John
St Thomas Pub HS; St Thomas, ND (2-21) S-T, Chor; Mgr, Bkbl; Ftbl; Mgr, Tr; Cl Fav.

JORGENSEN, Eric Dale
Troy HS; Troy, KS (5-40) Band; Tres, 4H; Order/Arrow; Var C; JV, Bkbl; Cr-Ctry; Tr; Amer Leg A; 4H A; Math A; Sci A; Off, BSct; *Marine Sci.*

JORGENSEN, Gregory Mark
George Washington Carver HS; Montgomery, AL (20-375) Ann; Chess C; Demolay; Math C; Mu Alpha Theta; NHS; JV, Bkbl; JV, Ftbl; JV, Golf; JV, Tr; JV, Wrest; COM; Q&S A; *Computer Prog.*

JORGENSEN, John Russell
Lawton-Bronson HS; Lawton, IA (20-60) Ger C; JV, Bsbl; JV, Ftbl; JV, Tr; *Math.*

JORGENSEN, Suzanne Marie
Lawton-Bronson HS; Lawton, IA (5-60) Ann; Ger C; Sch P; Mgr, Bkbl; *Western Iowa Tech Comm Col; Acct.*

JORGENSEN, Valerie Lynn
Grand Trunk HS; Evansburg, CANADA (4-71) Soc Stu A; *Nurs.*

JORGENSON, Daniel Steven
Milford Township HS; Milford, IL (17-57) Band; Chor; NHS; F-Ed, Sch P; Bsbl; Bkbl; Co-Cpt, Ftbl; Golf; Fin, Wrest; HCt; I Dare You; MVP, Ftbl; Prom King; Prom Court; *Eureka Col; Bus.*

JORGENSON, Kenton Lee
Callaway Pub HS; Callaway, NE (25%-21) Band; Chor; Drama; NFL; SC; Thes; Bkbl; Ftbl; Tr; Spch A; Yth Fel; One Star Thespian; Best Actor; Best Tenor; *Archt.*

JORGENSON, Kimi Lee
Blaine Sr HS; Blaine, MN (464-734) Rptr, Sch P; ROTC A; *Waseca Col; Light Horse Mgt.*

JORGENSON, Melinda Sue
Amador Valley HS; Pleasanton, CA; Secy, CYO; JV, Chldr; Chor; Drama; Hmrm; Mjrte; F-Ed, Sch P; SC; Math A; Rally Commissioner; Ed, Newspaper; *Chico St; Physcology.*

JORGENSON, Shelly Lynne
Callaway Pub HS; Callaway, NE (4-24) Band; Chor; FHA; NHS; Sch P; VP, Thes; B Crocker A; Journ A; Spch A; Yth Fel; Pep C; Mgr, Vlbl; *U of Nebr; Human Development.*

JORISSEN, Dawn Marquerite
N Central of Bames HS; Rogers, ND (6-30) Band; Chor; Ensm; GS; Mgr, Bkbl; Sftbl; *ND St U; Child Care.*

JOSEPH, Cindy Ann
Ironton HS; Ironton, OH (36-186) Ann; Band; Chor; Drama; Ensm; FTA; Hmrm; NHS; Rainbow; Secy, Span C; Tr; COM; DARGCA; Hon Prog; *E Ky U; Ed.*

JOSEPH, Helen Mongique
John Ehret HS; Marrero, LA (50-500) CYO; Drama; NHS; Ed, Sch P; Hon Prog; *LSU.*

JOSEPH, Keith Anthony
Cardinal Spellman HS; Bronx, NY; Band; CYO; Chess C; Chor; Pres, Hmrm; Ntl Yth Conf; ARC; Bkbl; Cr-Ctry; Ftbl; Tr; Wrest; COM; Citz A; Cl Fav; I Dare You; JA A; MLS; NEDT; ARC A; Sci A; Spch A; Yth Foundation A; Yth Leg; Ldrship, Afro-Amer, A's; CCD & Cardinal Spellman, Cert's; *NC A&T Col; Engr.*

JOSEPH, Mary Beth
Chopticon HS; Morganza, MD; Band; Chldr; Rptr, FBLA; Secy, Jr Cl; VP, Soph Cl; COM; HCt; *U of Md; Math.*

JOSEPH, Michael Anthony
East HS; Columbus, OH (3-350) Span A; WW; *Case Western Reserve U; Biomedical Engr.*

JOSEPH, Paula Lynn
Hillel HS; Lawrence, NY (6-46) Math C; NHS; Span C; Span NHS; Bkbl; Tr; Hon Prog; NEDT; *Barnard Col; Liberal Arts.*

JOSEPH, Richard Scott
Walter H Page Sr HS; Greensboro, NC (10%-770) VP, Band; Pres, Hmrm; Lat C; NHS; Orch; Tres, SC; Bkbl; Cpt, Soccer; Citz A; Opt A; Spch A; Yth Fel; WW; Church Rep, Sr HS Assembly; Most Dependable; Outst Band Stu; Pres, MYF.

JOSEPHSON, Ivan LeRoy
Oroville HS; Oroville, CA (128-224) *Butte Comm Col; Law Enforcement.*

JOSEPHSON, Marjorie Jean
Lyons Township HS; LaGrange, IL (150-1150) Lit Mag; *Tex Christian U; Bus.*

JOSEY, Alicia Dianne
Coffee HS; Douglas, GA (10-285) Band; BC; Ensm; *Emory U; Med.*

JOSEY, Mike
Crestview Sr HS; Crestview, FL (15%-200) Chess C; Order/Arrow; MVP, Arch; ROTC A; *Paramedic.*

JOSEY, Ramona Denise
Coffee HS; Douglas, GA (3-280) Ann; VP, BC; Drama; Ensm; Pres, FHA; COM; Jr Homemaker A; Lora Drew A; Jr, Chapter & St Degrees, FHA; Secy, Beta C; *S Ga Col; Elem Ed.*

JOSHI, Mehul
Barringer HS; Newark, NJ (15%-500) Order/Arrow; Cpt, Tnns; Amer Leg A; Citz A; MLS; Order/Arrow A; VP, Future Physicians C; Eagle Sct; *Rutgers U; Zoology.*

JOSLIN, Shelia Maureen
Burnsville HS; Burnsville, MS (6-46) BC; Cpt, Chldr; FHA; Co-Ed, Sch P; Sftbl; H of F; *Northeast Jr Col.*

JOSLYN, Deborah Lynn
Luverne Jr-Sr HS; Luverne, MN (107-140) Band; Bus C; Chor; Dbte Tm; Drama; Ch, FHA; Ch, FTA; Pres, Hmrm; Monogram; ARC; Sch P; Spch C; VP, SC; Bkbl; Amer Leg A; God & Country A; Swtht; GAA; Secy, Dist Luther League; Secy, Asst Ldr, GSct; Church Lib Board; *Golden Valley Lutheran Col; Parish Worker.*

JOSLYN, Gail M
Mount Miguel HS; Spring Valley, CA (9-600) Bio A; CSF; COM; Citz A; Hon Prog; JA A; Masonic A; Cpt, Vlbl; Hon Aisle; Hon Stu; *Calif St U; Phys Therapy.*

JOSLYN, Gail Marguerite
Mount Miguel HS; Spring Valley, CA (10-500) Bio A; CSF; COM; Chem A; Hon Prog; JA A; Cpt, Vlbl; Hon Asle; San Diego Padre Hon Stu; *Long Beach Col; Phys Therapy.*

JOSUPAIT, John Peter
Luther HS S; Chicago, IL (1-170) Band; Ensm; NHS; Golf; Hon Prog; NEDT; Val; *Valparaiso U; Pre-Med.*

JOURDAN, Patricia Louise
Garinger HS; Charlotte, NC (23-639) Yth Fel; Commencement Marshal; *William and Mary Col; Dance.*

JOVEN, Zenaida Madarang
John F Kennedy HS; Tumon, GUAM; NHS; SC; Hist A; Math A; Lang Art A; Top Ten; *Nurs.*

JOYAUX, Chantelle Marie
St Mary of the Valley HS; Beaverton, OR; VP, CYO; Chor; Hmrm; Tres, SC; VP, Sr Cl; Hon Prog; Pres, Service C; *Pacific U; Elem Ed.*

JOYAUX, H Bernard
Jesuit HS; Portland, OR (30-125) CYO; Spch C; JV, Tr; NEDT; *Med.*

JOYCE, Angela Dawn
E Forsyth HS; Kernersville, NC (26-687) Anchor C; Ed, Ann; Bus C; FBLA; Lat C; Lat NHS; Q&S A; Jr Marshal; *U of NC at Greensboro; Acct.*

JOYCE, Brian Robert
Heidelberg American HS; Heidelberg, GERMANY (4-170) AFS; BS; Co-Ch, CYO; Drama; Pres, Fr C; French NHS; Key C; Model UN; Mu Alpha Theta; NHS; Ski C; VP, SC; Wrest; COM; Hon Prog; Most Out; ROTC A; Type A; ROTC Schol; WW; Acad A; *U of Va; Bio.*

JOYCE, Jeffrey Patrick
Temple Heights Christian Sch; Tampa, FL; NHS; NMS; Sci A; NPPA A; *U of Mich-Ann Arbor; Math.*

JOYCE, Kevin Campbell
Bellaire Sr HS; Bellaire, TX (10%-700) French NHS; Mu Alpha Theta; NHS; Bkbl; Amer Leg A; Masonic A; Yth Fel; Fr C A; Am As of Tchrs of Fr, Cert of Hon; *Rice U; Aerospace Engr.*

JOYCE, Lisa Gale
Newton Co Comprehensive HS; Covington, GA (22-300) BC; JV, Chldr; Chess C; Drama; Pres, 4H; Jr Miss Pagent; F-Ed, Sch P; Pres, Span C; Gov Honor Prog; 4H A; I Dare You; Civitan Essay A; 2nd Pl, Key A, 4-H; *W Ga Col; Geology.*

JOYCE, Lori Elizabeth
Riverview HS; Sarasota, FL (112-670) FBLA; *Fla St U; Fashion Merchandising.*

JOYCE, Nancy
St Angela Hall Acad; Brooklyn, NY; Math C; Pres, NHS; *NY Comm Col; Art.*

JOYCE, Richard Langford
Riverview HS; Sarasota, FL; Key C; NHS.

JOYCE, Teresa Marie
Andover Central Sch; Andover, NY (7-42) Chldr; Mjrte; NHS; Rptr, Sch P; Span C; Pres, SC; VP, Sr Cl; Pres, Soph Cl; MVP, Bkbl; Co-Cpt, Soccer; Co-Cpt, Sftbl; Tnns; DARGCA; H of F; Hist A; Regent Schol; Amer A; Outst Female Ath A; *St U Col; Phys Ed.*

JOYCE, Valerie Lynn
Clearence M Kimball HS; Royal Oak, MI (92-675) Chor; Drama; Hmrm; NHS; Hon Prog; *Central Mich U; Retail Mgt.*

JOYNER, Angela Marie
Camden Co HS; St Marys, GA (21-209) Chldr; FBLA; FHA; 4H; Sci C; Bio A; Type A; Highest Academic Achv in Art; Hon Graduate; Academic Excellence A.

JOYNER, Anice Earnestine
Hamilton HS; Memphis, TN (82-407) FBLA; Secy, Hmrm; Tr; Type A; Yrbk Bstr; 12 Yr C; *Shelby St Col; Off Adm.*

JOYNER, Crystal Belinda
Newtown HS; Elm Hurst, NY (5-14) Church Choir; *Nurses Aide.*

JOYNER, Debra Gail
Bel Air HS; El Paso, TX (2-650) Pres, Chor; Madrigal; NHS; SC; Beauty; NEDT; Opt A; Sal; Type A; Most Studious; Eng A; *Howard Payne U; Bus.*

JOYNER, Gregory
Bronx HS of Sci; Bronx, NY; Chess C; JETS; Sch P; Bkbl; Co-Cpt, Ftbl; Cl Fav; Service A; Teacher Aide A; *Columbia U; Engr.*

JOYNER, Lori Beth
Briarfield Acad; Lake Providence, LA; Ensm; Fr C; 4H; Tr; COM; Yth Fel; Pep Squad; One Way C; *La Tech U; Elem Ed.*

JOYNER, Lori Lynn
Calhoun HS; Calhoun, GA (3-340) Band; Fr C; SC; VP, Tri-HiY; Var C; Bkbl; Co-Cpt, Cr-Ctry; Sftbl; Co-Cpt, Tr; COM; Gov Honor Prog; Hon Prog; Pres A; Yth Leg; FCA; Pep C; Vlbl.

JOYNER, Vernon Douglas
Handley HS; Winchester, VA (60-275) Cpt, Band; Chess C; Chor; Ensm; Hmrm; ARC; Bio A; COM; Chem A; Hon Prog; Type A; Drum Major; VP, Jr Hist Soc; All Reg Bnd & Chor; Hosp Folly Bnd; Drum Major, St Bicentennial Band &; *Shenandoah Conservatory; Mus Ed.*

JUARBE, Wilma Imelda
Francisco Mendoza HS; Isabela, PR; Band; Secy, Chem C; Drama; Hmrm; Pres, Math C; Phys C; ARC; Tres, Sci C; VP, Span C; Secy, SC; Cpt, Bkbl; Alg A; Bio A; COM; Chem A; Citz A; Cl Fav; Coun of Teach A; Math A; Phy A; ARC A; Sci A; Summa Cum Laude; *U of Puerto Rico; Phar.*

JUAREZ, Jessica Monette
Incarnate Word HS; San Antonio, TX; CYO; Chldr; HQn; Jr Yth C; HR Moderator; CYO Outst Yth A; *Trinity U.*

JUARRERO, Isabel
Colegio Puertorriqueno de Ninas; Caparro Heights, PR (5-48) Fr C; Pres, NHS; Sch P; Tnns; Bio A; COM; Hon Prog; Sci A; *Sweet Briar Col; Bus.*

JUBELT, Jane Martha
Litchfield Sr HS; Litchfield, IL (4-142) BC; Pres, 4H; NHS; 4H A; Hon Prog; Sunday Sch Teacher; WW; *Lincoln Land Comm Col; Acct.*

JUDD, Jerilyn Edith
N Kingstown HS; N Kingstown, RI; Rainbow; Soccer.

JUDD, Kimberley Kaye
Wellington HS; Wellington, TX (5%-65) Ann; Band; Rptr, BC; VP, FHA; 4H; S-T, Soph Cl; JV, Bkbl; JV, Tnns; JV, Tr; Bio A; DARGCA; 4H A; Hist A; Sal; *Wayland Baptist Col; Secretarial.*

JUDD, Mary Elizabeth
Perry Meridian HS; Indianapolis, IN (20%-500) Tres, Lat C; Sci C; Span C; Schol Excellence; *Butler Col; Phar.*

JUDD, Nancy Marie
Belton HS; Belton, MO; Chor; Drama; Rptr, FHA; ARC; Var C; Mgr, Bkbl; Pep C.

JUDD, Tracy Lynne
Circleville HS; Circleville, OH (50%-205) Chor; Ensm; Rainbow; Rptr, Sch P; Spch C; Swim; Tr; *Capital Col; Vocal Mus.*

JUDD, Welton
Ben L Smith HS; Greensboro, NC (278-423) Band; Bkbl; *Johnson C Smith U.*

JUDGE, Karen Rochelle
Burke HS; Charleston, SC; Cpt, Chldr; *Voorhees Col; Elem Phys Ed.*

JUDGE, Roxeann
Lafayette HS; Lafayette, LA (10%-680) Drama; FBLA; Ch, Hmrm; NFL; Pres, Rainbow; Spch C; Thes; Bkbl; Ftbl; Spch A; Vlbl; *La Tech U.*

JUDICE, Darryl Edmond
Patterson HS; Patterson, LA (2-85) BC; Dbte Tm; SC; Ftbl; Wrest; 4H A; *U of SW La; Elec Engr.*

JUDKINS, Sheryl Kay
Putnam City HS; Oklahoma City, OK (371-850) Bus C; FBLA; FTA; Mjrte; Secy, Span C; Co-Cpt, Sftbl; Yth Fel; *Okla U; Bus.*

JUDKINS, Wanda Lee
Rumford HS; Rumford, ME (10%-230) Band; Chldr; Chor; 4H; Hmrm; Lat C; F-Ed, Sch P; JV, Sftbl; Amer Leg A; Bio A; 4H A; Hon Prog; Sci A; Bowl A; GSct Schol; *Nurs.*

JUDSON, Deborah Jeanne
Mission HS; San Fernando, CA; Co-Ed, Ann; Band; Bus C; Chldr; Chor; Hmrm; Pres, Math C; Sch Achieve Tm; Sch P; Sci C; Ski C; Secy, SC; Secy, Sr Cl; Ciz A; Star Student; *Pre-Med.*

JUDY, Denise Louise
Wellington HS; Wellington, IL (1-18) Co-Ed, Ann; Band; Chor; FHA; Pres, NHS; Co-Ed, Sch P; VP, SC; Pres, Sr Cl; Amer Leg A; DARGCA; HCt; Val; WW; *Milligan Col; Ed.*

JUDY, Jack Douglas
Cuyahoga Valley Christian Acad; Cuyahoga Falls, OH (5-56) F-Ed, Sch P; Sci C; Bkbl; Bio A; Sci A; Ohio Bio Scholastic Test; *Taylor U; Zoology.*

JUEL, Karen Elizabeth
Brookings HS; Brookings, SD (49-217) Community Yth Symph; NHS; Orch; Span C; Hon Prog; All St Orch; I Rating Mus Contest; *Augustana Col; Bus Adm.*

JUELFS, Jennifer Lynne
Potter Pub HS; Potter, NE (3-18) Ann; Band; Chldr; Chor; VP, NHS; Sch P; Var C; Tres, Jr Cl; Pres, Soph Cl; Bkbl; Sftbl; Vlbl; All-Conf Vlbl; All-Conf Bkbl.

JUELFS, Terri Jo
Potter HS; Potter, NE (7-14) Ann; Band; Chldr; Chor; GS; NHS; Sch P; Var C; Tres, Sr Cl; Pres, Jr Cl; Bkbl; Sftbl; MVP, Tr; B Crocker A; Vlbl; *Eastern Wy Col; Bus.*

JUETT, Courtney Kay
R L Turner HS; Carrollton, TX; Drama; NFL; Yth Fel; Drill Tm; Spch Tourn; Regional Champ, Figure Rollerskatng; *N Tex St U; Phys Ed.*

JUHAN, Louise Bryan
Jacksonville Episcopal HS; Jacksonville, FL (66-117) F-Ed, Ann; Lat C; JV, Swim; *Hist.*

JUHL, Lori Ann
Luverne Jr-Sr HS; Luverne, MN (18-163) Pres, Band; Chor; Pres, 4H; Mjrte; Co-Ed, Sch P; Co-Cpt, Bkbl; Co-Cpt, Tr; 4H A; Journ A; Secy, Tres, Ch, Co-Ch, 4 H C; Mgr Tr; *U of Minn; Light Horse Mgr.*

JUHNKE, Karna Kae
Wells Easton Pub Sch; Wells, MN (5-109) A Cap Choir; Bus Mgr, Ann; Band; Chor; Drama; Ensm; FHA; Hmrm; Spch C; SC; Bkbl; Tr; Spch A; VofDEM; Vlbl; *Phys Therapy.*

JULIAR, Jeffrey Scott
Burnsville Sr HS; Burnsville, MN (94-871) Pres, Band; Chor; Dbte Tm; Ch, Ensm; Bus Mgr, FBLA; 4H; Pres, Hmrm; Rptr, Sch P; Ski C; SC; Tnns; *Hamline U; Mus.*

JULIEN, Patricial Ann
Alma J Brown Lab HS; Grambling, LA (11-52) Fin, A Cap Choir; Chldr; Chem C; Pres, Chor; Cum Laude Soc; Ch, Drama; Rptr, FHA; Ch, FTA; 4H; Hmrm; Fin, Lit Ral; NHS; Sch P; Sci C; Span C; Rptr, SC, Sr Cl; Ch, Jr Cl; Ch, Soph Cl; B Crocker A; COM; Cl Fav; Hon Prog; Most Out; Poet A; Sci A; Summa Cum Laude; Swtht; Hi Ability Jr; Most Versatile; Most Popular; Peer Counselor; *Grambling St U; Criminal Justice.*

JULLIARD, Joy Ellen
Garfield HS; Hamilton, OH; Band; Secy, Bus C; NHS.

JULSON, Steven Michael
N Sr HS; Eau Claire, WI (33%-500) Bsbl.

JULY, Leslie Jordan
The Highland Sch; Jamaica, NY (20-57) Band; Chor; Drama; Ensm; Thes; World Affairs C; Most Respected; Most Creative; *Queens Col; Communications.*

JUNE, Karen Marie
Le Mars Comm Sr HS; Lemars, IA (112-224) A Cap Choir; Band; Chor; Community Yth Symph; Orch; Rainbow; Sup Rating Violin Solo; *Morningside Col; Mus.*

JUNEAU, Elizabeth Mary
Bordelonville HS; Bordelonville, LA; Pres, Band; S-T, BC; Pres, CYO; Chess C; FHA; Pres, 4H; Sch P; Sci C; SC; Pres, Jr Cl; MVP, Tnns; 4H A; Most Out; Sci A; *LSU at Alexandria; Nurs.*

JUNEAU, Matthew Kevin
Cottonport HS; Cottonport, LA (3-50) Band; BC; Lit Ral; Rptr, Sch P; Bkbl; MVP, Tnns; *LSU; Chem Engr.*

JUNG, Brenda Joy
Freeburg HS; Freeburg, IL (1-119) Ann; Band; Chldr; Chor; Mjrte; Model UN; NHS; Tres, SC; Thes; Var C; HCt; St Scholar; Val; Stu o-t Mo; *Belleville Area Col; Acct.*

JUNG, Wanda
Alhambra City HS; Alhambra, CA; Tri-HiY; CSF; COM; *U of Sou Calif; Med.*

JUNGCK, Mark Erwin
Ephrata HS; Eprata, WA (2-125) Band; Tr; *U of Wash; Engr.*

JUNGEMANN, Julie Marie
Clarkston HS; Clarkston, GA (10%-400) Anchor C; BC; Chldr; Chor; Sftbl; HCt; Gym; All St Chor; Miss CHS Pageant; *Ga St U; Bus Adm.*

JUNGEMANN, Marlo George Jr
Wolsey HS; Wolsey, SD (12-31) Ann; FFA; Hmrm; Sci C; SC; Bsbl; Cpt, Bkbl; MVP, Ftbl; Sftbl; MVP, Tr; HCt; Most Out; Type A; VP, HERD; *Northern St Col; Industrial Arts.*

JUNGEMANN, Russell William
Wolsey HS; Wolsey, SD (10-33) FFA; ARC; Sci C; Mgr, Bkbl; JV, Tr; B Crocker A; Hon Prog; Sci A; Type A; Yth Fel; Pres, Active Christian Serv; FFA Judging A; St Safety Coun Del; *SD St U; Dairy Sci.*

JUNGKLAUS, Matthew Walter
Monett HS; Monett, MO (18-130) Span C; Tr; Wrest; Hon Prog; Spch A; Geom A; Off, Walther League.

JUNGSLAGER, Donna Marie
Spring Lake HS; Spring Lake, MI (13-225) Chor; NHS; COM; 4H A; Yth Fel; *Mich St U; Pre-Med.*

JUNGWIRTH, Linda Luann
Durand HS; Durand, WI (30%-130) CYO; Drama; Ger C; NFL; Sodality.

JUNIOR, Ester James III
Maplewood HS; Nashville, TN (40-387) Band; BS; CYO; Chess C; Chor; Ensm; InterAct C; InterClub Coun; Pres, Lat C; Madrigal; NHS; Pres, SC; Var C; Bsbl; Bkbl; Cpt, Ftbl; Tr; Cl Fav; MLS; Most Out; MVP, Ftbl; Best Ath Schol; All-Amer Ftbl; Eagle Sct; Lat A; All-St Ath Ftbl.

JUNIOR, Keith Elliott
Maplewood HS; Nashville, TN; NHS; MVP, Bsbl; Bkbl; Ftbl; Tr; MLS; Eagle Sct; *Med.*

JUNKER, Margaret Ann
Our Lady of Angels HS; St Bernard, OH (3-136) CYO; Hmrm; NHS; SC; Sftbl; COM; Math A; Ohio House of Rep A; Hon A; U of Cin Admission with Distin; *U of Cincinnati; Law Enforcement Technology.*

JUNKINS, Laurelle
Chichester HS; Upper Chichester, PA; Band; Chldr; Chor; Mgr, Tr; God & Country A; Yth Fel; *Cazenovia Col; Merchandising.*

JUNSO, Sherry Ann
Bellflower HS; Bellflower, CA; Chor; Fin, Jr Miss Pagent; SC; Cr-Ctry; Beauty; HCt; Best Dressed; Miss Bellflower; 1st Runner-Up, Miss Calif Jr; *Charm Teacher.*

JUNTTI, Charles Edward
Castlewood Ind HS; Castlewood, SD (1-22) Ann; BS; Sch P; Mgr, Bkbl; Mgr, Tr; Amer Leg Orator A; Sci A; *SD St U; Elec Engr.*

JUPE, Eldon Ralph
West HS; West, TX (25%-130) Chess C; NHS; S-T, DECA; 1st Pl Tnage St Meet, Powerlifting; *Phys Ed.*

JUPITER, Mark Anthony
Alcee Fortier HS; New Orleans, LA; Band; Chor; *Sou La U; Engr.*

JUREK, Anne Catherine
University HS; San Diego, CA (26-374) Secy, Drama; Hmrm; NHS; Thes; VP, Soph Cl; JV, Swim; CSF; Hon Prog.

JUREY, Coleen Kay
Clifton HS; Clifton, KS (1-25) Band; Ensm; FHA; Pres, Sr Cl; Tres, Jr Cl; B Crocker A; Bio A; COM; Hon Prog; Sci A; St Scholar; Type A; Yth Fel; NML; St Hon Stu; Putnam Schol; Kayettes; *Kans St U; Acct.*

JURGENS, Rominy Jeannine
Lane Tech HS; Chicago, IL (125-1250) Band; Ski C; Soccer; Bio A; COM; Sci A; Printers C; Craftsman Printer A; Yth Group; *Eckerd Col; Biochem.*

JURGENSMEYER, Kenneth
Montrose HS; Montrose, MO (2-26) CYO; NHS; Bsbl; Cpt, Bkbl; Fin, Cr-Ctry; Chem A; Hist A; Math A; MLS; Regent Schol; Sal; *Central Mo St U; Industrial Technology.*

JURGENSMEYER, Ruth Ann
Montrose R-14 HS; Montrose, MO (2-26) CYO; Chldr; Chor; Ensm; Secy, NHS; Bio A; Hist A; K of C A; Sci A; VFW Orator Win; VofDEM; 1st Pl, REA Essay Contest; Geography A; 1st Pl, Sci Fair; Blue Ribbon Project Int Arts.

JUST, Denise Ann
Holy Rosary Acad; Louisville, KY (4-86) Ann; Math C; Pres, NHS; SC; Cpt, Bkbl; Cpt, Tr; Hon Prog; Glenn George Schol; Bellermine Col Academic Schol; *U of Louisville; Fine Art.*

JUSTICE, Gregory Martin
Carter Co HS; Ekalaka, MT (4-29) Ann; Band; BS; Drama; Math C; Model UN; SC; Var C; Pres, Sr Cl; Mgr, Bkbl; Ftbl; B Crocker A; *Engr.*

JUSTICE, Jennifer Lynn
Feds Creek HS; Feds Creek, KY (4-69) Fr C; HR Cert; Attendance A; *Pre-Sch Ed.*

JUSTICE, Jill Elizabeth
Waynesboro Central HS; Waynesboro, MS (25%-130) Ann; BC; Chldr; Drama; Pres, Hmrm; *U of Miss.*

JUSTICE, Pamela Ann
Thomas S Wootton HS; Rockville, MD (4-400) Chldr; Chor; Drama; Hmrm; Spch C; Thes; Bkbl; Tr; Type A; *Tex Christian U; Performing Arts.*

JUSTICE, Peggy Louise
Waukegan W HS; Waukegan, IL (5%-600) Fr C; NHS; JA A; NEDT; Type A; *U of Iowa; Anthropology.*

JUSTICE, ReVelle Bernice
Jones Co HS; Gray, GA (10%-200) Drama; Fr C; FHA; 4H; Pres, NHS; UN Council; Drama A; Spirit Medal; *Data Processing.*

JUSTICE, Sharon Dee
St Albans HS; St Albans, WV; AFS; Ann; Band; Fr C; Mu Alpha Theta; NHS; Span C.

JUSTIN, Kathryn Denise
George H Corliss HS; Chicago, IL (9-485) NHS; Secy, Span C; Hon Prog; Vlbl; Tres, Span C; HR; IIT; *Elec Engr.*

JUSTUS, Michael Donald
Northeast HS; Lincoln, NE (31-523) Hon Prog; *U of Nebr; Bus Adm.*

JUSTUS, Robyn Lynn
Katella HS; Anaheim, CA; Secy, Sr Cl; *Fullerton Jr Col; Child Development.*

K

KAAKE, Lori Lynette
Whitmer HS; Toledo, OH; Hmrm; VP, Span C; Span NHS; Tr; Alg A; COM; Hon Prog; Math A; Yth Fel; 1st Cl GSct; *US Air Force Acad; Engr.*

KAAKE, Robert Mark
Whitmer Sr HS; Toledo, OH (5-965) NHS; Order/
Arrow; Span C; Pres, Span NHS; COM; Hon Prog;
Math A; Sci A; Yth Fel; Eagle Sct; Span A; *Bowling
Green St U; Engr.*

KACERE, Michael Joseph
Gordon HS; Gordon, NE (3-87) Band; Drama; VP,
NHS; Var C; Bkbl; Ftbl; Tr; Most Out; *Math.*

KACHEL, Jean Ellen
Aquinas HS; LaCrosse, WI (6-186) Chor; Hmrm;
NHS; Span C; S-T, Jr Cl; COM; DARGCA; Hon
Prog; NEDT; *Viterbo Col; Dietetics.*

KADEL, Susan Gayle
Beloit Jr-Sr HS; Beloit, KS (3-70) Band; JV, Chldr;
Chor; Ensm; FTA; Orch; Y-Tns; Tr; Drill Tm; Pep
C; Shorthand, Mus, A's; *Kans U; Med.*

KADEL, Thomas Edward
Ne HS; Oakland Park, FL (20%-700) Cpt, Band;
Tres, Key C; Cr-Ctry; Tr; *Computer Sci.*

KADINGO, Anne Frances
Pampa HS; Pampa, TX (46-326) Drama; NHS;
Secy, Thes; Tnns; Parl, DECA; CYF; *Dance.*

KADLEC, Christine Lynn
Maine Township HS W; Des Plaines, IL (97%-890)
Band; Spch C; Bio A; Opt A.

KADLEC, Vickie Lynn
Maine Township HS W; Des Plaines, IL (99%-783)
NHS; Orch; Swim; Bio A; Chem A; Phy A; Art A.

KADUBEK, Laurie Ann
Goodman-Armstrong HS; Goodman, WI (1-29)
Stout Col; Dietetics.

KAEMPER, Amy Beth
Highland HS; Albuquerque, NM; Chldr; Chor;
Hmrm; Rainbow; Pres, Tri-HiY; VP, Soph Cl; 1st
Runner-Up, Demolay St Swtht; Secy, MYF; Rain-
bow Girl o-t Yr; *Pepperdine U; Rehabilitation
Therapy.*

KAEMPF, Patricia Ann
Oconomowoc Sr HS; Oconomowoc, WI; AFS; 4H;
ARC; JV, Bkbl; Tr; COM.

KAESMEYER,
Rebecca Charlotte
Martin Luther HS; Maspeth, NY; JV, Chldr;
Drama; Ger C; Monogram; Sch P; Hockey; Hon
Prog; Vlbl; *Wesleyan Col.*

KAESTNER, Susan Elizabeth
Adlai E Stevenson HS; Bronx, NY (19-788) Lit
Mag; Sch Achieve Tm; Sch P; Sci C; COM; Citz A;
Hon Prog; Sci A; Type A; Steno A; Romeo & Juliet
A; *Berkeley U; Bus.*

KAFKA, Dorcie Della
Havre HS; Havre, MT; Ann; Pres, Fr C; Secy, 4H;
Hmrm; InterAct C; Secy, NHS; Secy, SC; Secy,
Var C; Cr-Ctry; 4H A; Snowball Qn; Sports As;
Walk- athon As; *Mont St U; Agr.*

KAHANEK, Diana Marie
Spring Branch HS; Houston, TX (10%-570) NHS;
COM; NEDT; Pres A; Secy, Lutheran Yth; Future
Secy Assn; Vlbl All Dist & All Tourn; Church Bkbl
& Sftbl; *U of Houston; Bus.*

KAHL, Keith Edward
Valley Forge HS; Parma Heights, OH (173-838)
Cleveland St U; Acct.

KAHLE, Bradley Carl
West Sr HS; Aurora, IL; Band; Order/Arrow;
Hockey; COM; *Wheaton Col; Christian Ed.*

KAHLER, Cindy Louise
Normandy Sr HS; Parma, OH (120-230) Band; Fr
C; Lit Mag; Orch; Co-Ed, Sch P; Span C; Swim;
Kent St U; Interior Decorating.

KAHLER, Evan Quain
Amador Valley HS; Pleasanton, CA (50-462)
Band; Community Yth Symph; Drama; Ensm; VP,
Ger C; Math C; VP, Mu Alpha Theta; Orch; Or-
der/Arrow; SC; Thes; COM; Citz A; Hon Prog;
Order/Arrow A; Eagle Sct; Sct Lifeguard; Outst
Performance, Band; Mus Schol; *U of Calif at Davis;
Sci.*

KAHN, Richard A
Woodmere Acad; Woodmere, NY (1-51) Band;
Cum Laude Soc; Fr C; Cpt, Math C; Ed, Sch P; Ski
C; Tnns; Bio A; Chem A; Math A; Phy A; *Harvard
U; Math.*

KAIGHN, Louann
Haddon Township HS; Haddon Township, NJ
(5%-250) Chor; FHA; Lit Mag; Cpt, Mjrte; NHS;
Mgr, Sch P; Var C; MVP, Bkbl; Sftbl; Hon Prog;
Eng.

KAIL, Christopher Roland
Raleigh-Egypt HS; Memphis, TN (118-276)
Drama; Hmrm; SC; Mgr, Ftbl; Journ A; Sons o-t
Amer Revolution; Aircraft Recognition; Outst Ca-
det; ROTC Superior Performance; *Memphis St U;
Journ.*

KAILEY, Kevin William
Temple Baptist Acad; Denver, CO; A-Ed, Ann;
Band; Chor; Ensm; Pres, NHS; Orch; Semi Fin, Ntl
Piano Contest; Fin, Pace Bowl; Fin, Ntl Puppet
Contest; Life BSct; *Liberty Baptist Col; Mus.*

KAISER, Aissa Kim
Belleville Township HS E; Belleville, IL (20%-731)
Chldr; Chor; Co-Ed, Sch P; SC; Yth Fel; Job's
Daughters; *BAC; Social Sci.*

KAISER, Boyd Lynn
Chase Co HS; Imperial, NE (12-70) Tres, FFA;
NHS; Var C; VP, Jr Cl; Co-Cpt, Bkbl; Co-Cpt, Ftbl;
Tr; Regent Schol; *U of Nebr; Engr.*

KAISER, Dolores Emmi
Eastside HS; Paterson, NJ; *Col of Saint Benedict;
Nurs.*

KAISER, Judith Lillian
Rutherford HS; Rutherford, NJ; Bus Mgr, Ann;
Chor; Drama; Rptr, Sch P; Tr; Pep C; Flag Squad;
Rutgers U; Bio.

KAISER, Laura Marie
Melville HS; Melville, LA (10-38) BC; Secy, Sr Cl;
Bkbl; Sftbl; Alg A; COM; HCt; Math A; Sci A;
Type A; *LSU; Home Ec.*

KAISER, Nancy Ann
Westborough HS; Westborough, MA (30-250)
AFS; Chor; Drama; Tres, Sch P; SC; Bkbl; Fin,
Beauty; Entertainment Troupe; Secy, Yth Fel;
Lead, Dramatic Productions; Recreation Drama
Workshop; *Drama.*

KAISER, Randall Norman
Freeport Sr HS; Freport, IL (27-523) Chor; Com-
munity Yth Symph; Ensm; Ger C; Tres, 4H; JETS;
Orch; 4H A; Kiwanis A; Yth Fel; Church Organist;
All St Orch; *U of Ill; Vet Med.*

KAISER, Timothy Robert
Duluth Central HS; Duluth, MN; NCTE Nom;
Pres, Luther League; Yth Board; Co-Ed, FLY
Newspaper; *Writing.*

KAJDER, Carl J
St Hedwig HS; Detroit, MI (3-86) JV, CYO;
Hmrm; SC; JV, Bkbl; Hon Prog; Drafting A.

KAJDER, Sandra Marie
St Hedwig HS; Detroit, MI (1-70) Chor; Hmrm;
VP, NHS; Secy, Span C; Alg A; B Crocker A;
Chem A; Hist A; Hon Prog; *General Motors Inst;
Engr.*

KAKER, Kathy Ann
Azle HS; Azle, TX; Band; FTA; Jr Miss Pagent;
Cpt, Bkbl; Tr; Miss Flame; MVP, Bkbl; *Fashion
Merchandising.*

KAKER, Michael Wayne
Azle HS; Azle, TX; Rptr, Sch P; Cpt, Bkbl; Golf;
Tex A&M U; Engr.

KAKISH, William Randall
Hartshorne HS; Hartshorne, OK (1-70) Hmrm;
Secy, Order/Arrow; SC; Bkbl; COM; Alg A; Hist
A; Masonic A; Math A; St Scholar; Yth Fel; St Hon
Soc; Industrial Arts A; FCA; Eagle Sct; Superior,
Ntl Piano Auditions.

KALB, Sara Sue
Buckeye Central HS; New Washington, OH
(35-99) Ann; S-T, Band; Chor; 4H; Sch P; SC; Bkbl;
Tr; 4H A; Spch A; Vlbl; *U of Toledo; Health.*

KALCEVICH, Karen Ann
St Elizabeth HS; Pittsburgh, PA (2-101) Chor;
Drama; Lit Mag; Rptr, Sch P; US Stool Lectures;
Westinghouse Lectures; *Penn St U; Child Psych.*

KALIGIAN, Dikran Mesrob
Lexington HS; Lexington, MA (100-600) Orch.

KALIVODA, Cindy Elaine
Clifton HS; Clifton, KS (10-25) Co-Ed, Ann; Band;
Chldr; Chor; 4H; Secy, SC; HQn; Vlbl; *Kans St U;
Journ.*

KALIVODA, Jayne Beth
Clyde HS; Clyde, KS; Band; Chldr; Ensm; 4H; Sch
Achieve Tm; Tr; Chem A; 4H A; HCt; Hon Prog;
Pres A; Spch A; Type A; VFW A; Yth Fel; Stage
Band; S-T, Girl's Ath League; Tres, Kayette C;
Vlbl; *Kans St U.*

KALKE, Nancy L
Albert Lea HS; Albert Lea, MN (87-544) Bus C;
Drama; NHS; Sch Achieve Tm; Span C; Thes;
Golf; Hon Prog; JA A; Pres A; Type A; Sch Ltr; *Col
of Saint Benedict; Med.*

KALL, Scott Richard
Carrollton HS; Carrollton, MI (34-179) JV, Bkbl;
Engr.

KALLANDER, Robert Melvin
Moorhead Sr HS; Moorhead, MN (120-625) Chor;
Orch; Tnns; *Concordia Col.*

KALLAS, Kimberly Kaye
Wayne HS; Dayton, OH; Band; FTA; Ntl Jr Hon
Soc; Grosso Group; Outst Stu o-t Yr; Teacher's
Aid; Sup Rating, Flute; Pep Band; *Bus.*

KALLENBACH, Laurel Jane
Greeley Central HS; Greeley, CO (4-350) Band;
Drama; Orch; Bio A; Hon Prog; Opt A; Sci A; Yth
Fel; Eng A; Span A.

KALLESEN, Lisa Ann
Treynor Comm Sch; Treynor, IA (8-45) A-Ed,
Ann; Chldr; Fr C; Tres, FHA; SC; Golf; Swim; Sci
A; *U of Iowa; Med.*

KALSTEIN, Heidi Loreen
Lincoln Park HS; Lincoln Park, MI; Chor; Arch;
MLS; *Olivet Col; Bus.*

KALTENBACH,
Christopher Ignatius
Loyola HS; Towson, MD (18-134) Ger C; A-Ed,
Lit Ral; Ed, Lit Mag; NFL; NHS; Rptr, Sch P; Spch
C; Mgr, Bsbl; Mgr, Bkbl; COM; NEDT; Spch A;
Loyola Col; Hist.

KALTENBERG, Connie Rae
Crookston Central HS; Crookston, MN (19-189)
Chor; Ensm; Madrigal; Orch; VP, SC; Tnns; B
Crocker A; HQn; Ch, SC; Sunflower Qn Candi-
date; *E Grand Forks Col; Credit & Finance Mgt.*

KALWEI, Andrea Marie
Montrose HS; Montrose, MO (2-26) CYO; NHS;
Secy, Soph Cl; Alg A; Bio A; Eng A.

KAMBEITZ, Mark Francis
Napoleon HS; Napoleon, ND (43-71) Band; Chor;
Ensm; Madrigal; Sci C; Var C; Bsbl; Ftbl; Tr; Co-
Cpt, Wrest; Cl Fav; Ltr A; *Mary Col; Acct.*

KAME, Steve Earl
Bowman HS; Canyon Country, CA; *COC.*

KAMERLING, Julie Ellen
Brookfield E HS; Brookfield, WI (23-498) Band;
Chor; Drama; Mu Alpha Theta; NHS; Span C;
Secy, Span NHS; *U-W at Madison; Nutrition.*

KAMIEN, Eric Harold
Bklyn Tech HS; Brooklyn, NY; *Poly Tech; Engr.*

KAMILOS, Gerry Nick
Hiram W Johnson HS; Sacramento, CA (25%-499)
Chem C; VP, Dbte Tm; Fr C; Hmrm; Key C; NFL;
Phys C; VP, Sci C; Spch C; Secy, SC; Secy, Jr Cl;
VP, Soph Cl; Golf; Bio A; God & Country A; JA A;
Sci A; Spch A; *Sacramento St U; Biomed Engr.*

KAMINSKI, Neil Mitchell
Chillicothe HS; Chillicothe, OH (84-390) VP, Span
C; *Asbury Col; Theology.*

KAMITONO, Gale
Kohala HS; Kohala, HI (1-78) AFS; Band; Secy,
NHS; SC; *Cannon's Bus Col; Secreterial Sci.*

KAMLA, Craig Eugene
Haigler HS; Haigler, NE (33%-14) Band; Drama;
Pres, 4H; Order/Arrow; Pep Band; SC; Span C; St
Cl; Pres, Jr Cl; MVP, Bsbl; Bkbl; Cpt, Ftbl; Swim;
Fin, Tr; Alg A; COM; 4H A; Math A; MVP, Ftbl;
Contest Plays.

KASNIKOWSKI, Michelle
John S Fine Sr HS; Nanticoke, PA (3-355) Drama; Jr Miss Pagent; Key C; Sodality; Sci A; Spch A; *Med Sci.*

KASPAR, Kathy Kay
Norfolk Sr HS; Norfolk, NE (10%-330) Chor; Dbte Tm.

KASPAR, Steven Lee
Omaha S HS; Omaha, NE (12-648) Band; *Iowa St U; Engr.*

KASPARSON, Peter Karl
Wachusett Regional HS; Holden, MA; Yth Fel; Church Yth Comm; Usher; *Dartmouth Col; Eng.*

KASPER, Mary Ellen
Lyford HS; Lyford, TX; VP, FHA; NHS; Bkbl; Tr; Hist A.

KASPEROWICZ, David Eugene
Holy Cross HS; Delran, NJ; CYO; Bkbl; Hon Prog.

KASPERSON, Rebecca Ann
Lane Tech HS; Chicago, IL (135-1700) NHS; Hon Prog; Scholastic Art Fin; *Luther Col.*

KASSING, David Robert
Brebeuf Prep HS; Indianapolis, IN (1-150) Soccer; JV, Tnns; Fin, Wrest; JV, Bsbl; *Math.*

KASSING, Jeffrey Phillip
Peoria Heights HS; Peoria Heights, IL (8-77) Fr C; Ger C; Math C; NHS; Var C; Ftbl; Tnns; Cpt, Wrest; Alg A; HCt; *Ind U; Bus.*

KASSING, Judson Paul
Peoria Heights HS; Peoria Heights, IL (3-100) Ensm; Fr C; Ger C; Math C; NHS; Phys C; Ed, Sch P; Spch C; SC; Thes; Var C; Pres, Jr Cl; VP, Soph Cl; Bsbl; Bkbl; Ftbl; Soccer; HCt; Journ A; Q&S A; Spch A; Notre Dame C; *Bus.*

KASTEN, Jonathan Alan
Freeport Sr HS; Freeport, IL (325-550) Band; Ger C; COM; Citz A; Industrial Ed A; Civil Service A; *Highland Comm Col; Law Enforcement.*

KASTEN, Lori Kathryn
Hi-Plains Secondary HS; Seibert, CO (10%-19) Chor; Ensm; FHA; 4H; SC; Secy, Jr Cl; VP, Soph Cl; Tr; HCt; Hon Choir; *U of N Colo; Med Tech.*

KASTENS, Rhonda Lynn
Wellcome Mem HS; Garden City, MN (47-58) FFA; FHA; *Mankatoe Col; Nurs.*

KASWINKEL, Donna Carol
Hendersonville Sr HS; Hendersonville, TN; Band; BC; Chor; Tres, Fr C; FHA; Semi-Fin, GS; S-T, 4H; NHS; Alg A; 4H A; Sci A; Most Intelligent; Eng, Fire Prevention, Fr, A's; Home Ec, DECA, Bronze Merit, A's; *Commercial Pilot.*

KASZA, Suzanne Margaret
St Ladywig HS; Detroit, MI (3-86) Band; Chldr; Chor; Hmrm; Span C; SC; Hon Prog; Sci A; Swtht; High School Hon A; Win, Outs Cobo Hall; Spec Life Sci A, Sci & Engr Fair.

KATES, Gerald Jack
Gladewater HS; Gladewater, TX; Band; FTA; Rptr, Soph Cl; JV, Bkbl; JV, Ftbl; Golf; FCA; MVP, Church Sftbl; *Tex A&M U; Drafting.*

KATH, Diane Renae
Campbell-Tintah HS; Campbell, MN (10-40) Band; Chor; Semi-Fin, Spch C; VP, SC; Pres, Jr Cl; Pres, Soph Cl; Cpt, Bkbl; Tr; Hon Prog; Spch A; MVP, Bkbl; Vlbl; GRA A; Data Processing A.

KATH, Janet Lynne
Lindbergh HS; St Louis, MO (150-980) NHS; Christian Yth Fel; Job's Daughters; Bkbl; Tr; *Sociology.*

KATHEY, Shawn Kirk
Leesville HS; Leesville, LA (150-342) Band.

KATONA, Karen Sue
Riverside HS; Painesville, OH; Ed, Ann; JV, Chldr; Drama; 4H; Hmrm; Span C; SC; Thes; Sftbl; COM; Hon Prog; Sci A; Tn Board; *Bowling Green St U; Nurs.*

KATONA, Mark Allen
Riverside HS; Painesville Township, OH (93-286) Key C; Thes; NEDT; Yth Fel; *Ohio St U; Civil Engr.*

KATONA, William Elmer Jr
Harding HS; Fairport Harbor, OH (6-57) Bus C; NHS; Order/Arrow; Var C; Cr-Ctry; Ftbl; Tr; Bausch & Lomb A; *Ohio St U; Acct.*

KATS, Tammy Renee
Eldorado HS; Albuquerque, NM; Band; Chor; NHS; *Calvin Col; Nurs.*

KATTAN, Doris Lilian
Deerborne Sch; Coral Gables, FL; Tres, Sr Cl; *Eckerd Col.*

KATTAS, Sandra Kay
Admiral King HS; Lorain, OH (4-448) NHS; COM; Hon Prog; Math A; NEDT; Fr A; *U of Toledo; Nurs.*

KATUZNY, Carolyn Marie
Maria HS; Chicago, IL (13-371) Ed, Ann; CYO; Chldr; Pres, Chor; Ger C; Semi-Fin, Hmrm; NHS; Ed, Sch P; Secy, Sodality; SC; Semi-Fin, Soph Cl; Alg A; COM; Hist A; Hon Prog; Math A; Most Out; Sci A; Dancing Trophies; Essay A; Art A; Outst Yth Service Lib A; *Northwestern U; Med.*

KATYNSKI, John
Mott HS; Warren, MI; A Cap Choir; Bus Mgr, Bus C; CYO; Chor; Bkbl; Ftbl; Tr; *Macomb Co Comm Col; Public Relations.*

KATZ, Lois
Hillel HS; Lawrence, NY; Chldr; Drama; NHS; Ed, Sch P; Span C; Tr; NMS; NEDT; Regent Schol; Span A; Eng A; *Barnard Col.*

KATZ, Menashe
Talmudical Acad; Baltimore, MD (5%-20) NHS; *Brooklyn Col; Math.*

KAUDERER, Karen Lynne
Williamsville S HS; Williamsville, NY; Chor; Drama; Hmrm; InterAct C; SC; Sftbl; COM; Citz A; Hist A; Hon Prog; Math A; Most Out; Sci A; MIP, Sftbl; Fr A.

KAUFER, Deborah Anne
Forest Lake Sr HS; Forest Lake, MN (40-700) AFS; Band; Drama; Fr C; Lit Mag; Vlbl; *Interior Design.*

KAUFER, Stephen Anthony
Blanchet HS; Seattle, WA (1-308) Dbte Tm; Hon Prog; Spch A; Entrance Exam Schol; Hanford Nuclear Tour.

KAUFFMAN, John Michael
Octorara Area HS; Atglen, PA (60-201) A Cap Choir; Band; Co-Ch, Chor; Bus Mgr, Demolay; Drama; Hmrm; Bus Mgr, Key C; Madrigal; Math C; Bus Mgr, ARC; Span C; Gov Honor Prog; Sch Mus; Sch Play; Yth Choir; Pres, Yth Group; *Mus.*

KAUFFMAN, John Wallace
Perkins HS; Sandusky, OH (16-265) Band; Ensm; NHS; Chem A; Math A; Sci A; *Engr.*

KAUFFMAN, Kame Denise
Red Land HS; Lewisberry, PA; Band; Bus C; Chor; FBLA; FHA; Hmrm; SC; JV, Bkbl; JV, Hockey; JV, Sftbl; Tr; Math A; Type A; Acct A; Band Front A; Tr A; *HACC; Acct.*

KAUFFMAN, Pamela Sue
Bryan Adams Sr HS; Dallas, TX (216-734) Chem C; Ger C; 4H; ARC; Y-Tns; Swim; Dallas Aquadrons; York Synchronettes; *Eastfield Comm Col; Recreational Director.*

KAUFMAN, Brenda Kay
Wonderview HS; Hattieville, AR (10%-40) Co-Ed, Ann; Chldr; Tres, FHA; VP, 4H; Tres, Jr Cl; Rptr, Soph Cl; Sftbl; Beauty; Bio A; Cl Fav; 4H A; MLS; Sal; Eng A; Phys Fitness A.

KAUFMAN, Christine Ellen
Ashton Westview HS; Ashton, IL (6-55) Bus Mgr, Ann; Chldr; Chor; Pres, FHA; NHS; Pres, SC; Tnns; Tr; Hon Prog; *Lutheran Sch of Nurs; Registered Nurs.*

KAUFMAN, Douglas Carl
Warwick HS; Lititz, PA (50-250) Chem C; Dbte Tm; Order/Arrow; Span C; Spch C; JV, Bsbl; JV, Bkbl; JV, Cr-Ctry; Order/Arrow A; *Wake Forest Col; Bus.*

KAUFMAN, Scott Alan
Hitchcock HS; Hitchcock, TX (5-146) Demolay; Ger C; NHS; Bsbl; Cpt, Ftbl; Tr; Elk A; Hist A; Type A.

KAUFMAN, Sheila Ann
Wonderview HS; Hattieville, AR (10%-44) FHA; VP, 4H; S-T, Soph Cl; Bkbl; Cl Fav; 4H A; Math A; Eng A; Librarian; *Ark Tech U.*

KAUFMAN, Tony J
Winfield HS; Winfield, KS (30%-180) Band; BS; Pres, Key C; ARC; SC; JV, Bkbl; Cr-Ctry; Tnns; HCt; *Kans U; Lib Arts.*

KAUFMAN, Tracye Rose
Presentation Acad; Louisville, KY (50%-150) Chor; Sch P; Tr; *Drew U; Sci.*

KAUFMANN, Heidi Ann
Watertown Sr HS; Watertown, WI (1-388) Chor; Dbte Tm; Madrigal; Span C; Thes; Swim; *U of Wis; Mus.*

KAUFMANN, Joseph Steven
Shenandoah Valley Acad; New Market, VA;

KAUFMANN, Karen Leigh
Robert L Osborne Sr HS; Marietta, GA (25%-365) BC; Lit Mag; COM; Drill Tm; *Mercer Col; Sci.*

KAUFMANN, William Brian
Westminster Christian Acad; Huntsville, AL; Bus Mgr, Ann; VP, Chor; Ensm; Pres, Hmrm; F-Ed, Sch P; SC; Pres, Sr Cl; Cpt, Bkbl; Golf; Co-Cpt, Soccer; Tr; Sci A; *Covenant Col; Bus Adm.*

KAUK, Mitchell Kurt
Leedey HS; Leedey, OK (9-31) FFA; S-T, Soph Cl; Bsbl; Bkbl; Fish & Wildlife A; FFA; *SW Okla St U; Phar.*

KAUK, Monty Ross
Leedey Pub Sch; Leedey, OK; Tres, FFA; Var C; MVP, Bsbl; Cpt, Bkbl; Cl Fav; H of F; Most Out; All-St Bsbl; Nom, Jim Thorpe A; Nom, Okla All Star; *Phys Ed.*

KAUPHUSMAN, Kathy Ann
Cotter HS; Winona, MN (20-99) Cpt, Chldr; Chor; Sodality; Bkbl; Tnns; HQn; *St Mary's Col; Ed.*

KAURA, Suzanne Norma
Ashtabula Harbor HS; Ashtabula, OH (4-200) AFS; Ann; Band; Ger C; SC; Hist A; Hon Prog; Math A; Sci A; Ger A; Instr Mus A; Phys Fitness A; *Wittenberg U; Law.*

KAUSCH, Joseph Martin
Burnt-Hills Ballston-Lake Sr HS; Burnt-Hills, NY; JV, Bkbl; *St U of Oswego NY; Forestry.*

KAUTH, David Paul
Sprague HS; Salem, OR; *U of Portland; Engr.*

KAUTH, Jodene Lynn
Louisville HS; Louisville, OH; Band; Chor; Ensm; Tnns; Citz A; Kiwanis A; 2nd Bible Bowl Tm; Win, Thank God For Amer, Essay; High HR; Band, Choir As; *W Liberty St Col; Dentistry.*

KAUTSCH, Aimee Jo
Timken Sr HS; Canton, OH (55-475) A Cap Choir; Chor; Drama; Ensm; Hmrm; Secy, NFL; Secy, Spch C; SC; World Affairs C; Tr; Hon Prog; Rotary A; Spch A; *Navy; Drafting.*

KAUTZ, Rosamond Amelia
Apollo-Ridge HS; Spring Church, PA (51-204) Band; Chor; Ensm; FHA; Ger C; 4H; Madrigal; COM; 4H A; 1st Cl, GSct; *Westminster Col; Mus Ed.*

KAUTZMAN, Norine Margaret
Saint Mary's Central HS; Bismarck, ND (8-166) Chldr; Secy, Jr Cl; Tnns; Tr; Math A; Pom Pon Girl; 1st Cl GSct A; Sci.

KAVA, Mary Catherine
Fairview HS; Boulder, CO; CYO; Rptr, Hmrm; Orch; ARC; Tr; *St Mary's Col; Nurs.*

KAVANAGH, Gregory Robert
J W Robinson Secondary Sch; Fairfax, VA (84-501) Drama; Hmrm; InterClub Coun; NHS; Order/Arrow; Pres, Span C; Pres, Span NHS; Pres, Sr Cl; Mgr, Tnns; JV, Tr; COM; Hist A; Hon Prog; Order/Arrow A; Pres, Lutheran Yth; Tres, Span C; Best Dressed Sr; Eagle Sct; *Miami U of Ohio; Bus Adm.*

KAVANAGH, William Francis
St Mary's Regional HS; Lynn, MA (17-117) Drama; Hmrm; Pres, SC; Co-Cpt, Golf; Tr; Acct, Eng, A's; Stu Gov Day; *Boston Col; Acct.*

KAVET, Alexander Charles
Eldorado HS; Albuquerque, NM; Band; Community Yth Symph; NHS; Orch; Q&S A; WW; St Solo & Ensm, Mus Festival, A's; *Rockmont Col; Biblical Stu.*

KAWANO, Brian Nadao
H P Baldwin HS; Wailuku, HI (20-324) Parl, FTA; VP, Key C; NHS; St Stu Congress; SC; VP, Jr Cl; Pres, Soph Cl; Bsbl; COM; Citz A; Cl Fav; HCt; Pres A; Sci A; Bsbl A; Jr YBA Hon; Stu Govt Hon; *U of Hawaii; Bus.*

KAWWAS, Dena Lynn
Temple Christian HS; Detroit, MI (10%-57) Tres, Sr Cl; Tnns; COM; Chem A; Citz A; HQn; Hon Prog; MLS; Type A; Sewing A; *Mercy Col of Detroit; Med Records.*

KAY, Allison Ann
Robert E Lee; Tyler, TX (5-315) Span C; Piano As; Pres, Bicycling; S-T, Explorer; Pres Coun, ETEX; *Randolph Macon Col.*

KAY, David Brian
Glenwood Sch; Phenix City, AL (20%-77) Band; Chor; Math C; Tnns; Yth Fel; Most Talented; Outst, Band; Columbus Ldr, Page 1 Nom in Math; *Auburn U; Mech Engr.*

KAY, Laura Leigh
Dade Christian Sch; Hialeah, FL (1-79) Ann; NHS; Rptr, Sch P; Tres, Sr Cl; Tres, Jr Cl; Alg A; Amer Leg A; Bio A; COM; Chem A; Citz A; Hist A; Math A; Most Out; NMF; Phy A; Sal; Sci A; Val; Physiology A; WW at Dode Christian; Sr Superlotive; Miss Dode Christian; Phys Fitness A; *Duke U; Bio.*

KAY, May
Suffolk HS; Suffolk, VA (4-150) NHS; Span C; Math A; Sci A; *Med.*

KAY, Ron Dale
Cuyahoga Valley Christian Acad; Cuyahoga Falls, OH (1-56) Alg A; A-Ed, Sch P; Bkbl; Soccer; Bio A; Math A; NEDT; Sci A; *Theology.*

KAY, Sandra Lynn
N Clayton Sr HS; College Park, GA (5-417) Ch, BC; Bus C; Crown & Scepter; Drama; FBLA; Hmrm; NHS; Sci C; Ch, SC; Sftbl; COM; Hist A; Pres, Yth Coun; *Clayton Jr Col; Bus.*

KAY, Steve Jeffrey
Hart Co HS; Hartwell, GA (2-250) BC; Fr C; Pres, InterAct C; Sci C; Pres, Jr Cl; Ftbl; Alg A; Hon Prog; Math A; *U of Ga; Computer Programing.*

KAY, Thomas Scott
Hart Co HS; Hartwell, GA; Ann; BC; Fr C; VP, Hmrm; Math A; Language Arts A; Church Bkbl; Church Sftbl.

KAY, Timothy Ray
Tishomingo HS; Tishomingo, MS (50%-54) Bsbl; Bkbl; Tr; WW; *NE Miss Jr Col; Eng.*

KAYNOR, Laurel Aileen
Oak Park River Forest HS; Oak Park, IL (240-1057) A Cap Choir; Chldr; Chor; Drama; Madrigal; *U of Ill; Park Administration.*

KAYVONFAR, Indie
Crestview Sr HS; Crestview, FL (10%-247) Anchor C; Band; BC; Beauty; HCt; *U of Fla; Math.*

KAZA, Kimberly
Cuyahoga Falls HS; Cuyahoga Falls, OH (33%-830) Drama; Thes; Bsbl; Bkbl; MVP, Hockey; *Anderson Col; Eng.*

KAZANJIAN, Linda Dawn
Marpie Newtown Sr HS; Newtown Square, PA (250-650) Co-Ch, Hmrm; SC; COM; Ntl Achv Schol; Sewing A; *Philadelphia Col of Textile & Sci; Textile Design.*

KAZANJIAN, Nancy Christine
Marple Newtown Sr HS; Newtown Square, PA (45-600) Mgr, Chldr; Lat C; SC; Soph Cl; Bkbl; Tr; Young Life; Jr NHS; *U of Pa; Dentistry.*

KAZMIERCZAK, Margaret
St Angela Hall Acad; Brooklyn, NY (4-82) FNA; FTA; Math C; NHS; ARC; Sodality; Alg A; Chem A; Math A; Sci A; *NY U; Computer Sci.*

KAZMIERCZAK, Mary Frances
Ursuline Acad HS; Wilmington, DE (4-46) Chor; Drama; NHS; NEDT; Vlbl; HS Theatre; *Carnegie-Mellon Col; Chem Engr.*

KEA, Krista DeLaine
Rocky Mount Sr HS; Rocky Mount, NC (183-553) VP, Drama; S-T, Hmrm; 'B' HR; Drama Hon Soc.

KEAN, Caroline Hill
Roy J Wasson HS; Colorado Springs, CO (80-527) NHS; *Colo St U; Pre-Vet Med.*

KEANE, Janelle
Meadowdale Sr HS; Lynnwood, WA; A Cap Choir; Dbte Tm; Drama; NHS; 1st, St Drama Camp; Dist Best Actress; 1st, Dist Dbte; Drama A; *Whiteman Col; Dramatic-Arts.*

KEANE, Margaret Teresa
Mercy HS; Albany, NY (8-108) Fr C; A-Ed, Lit Mag; NEDT; *Sci.*

KEARNEY, Kevin David
Bishop Klonowski HS; Scranton, PA (1-106) CYO; Drama; Hmrm; Lat C; NHS; Ed, Sch P; Span C; Spch C; VP, SC; Bkbl; Cr-Ctry; COM; Hon Prog; Math A; NMS; NEDT; Spch A; St Scholar; Exchange Stu; Northeast Yth Coun; Interntl Stu Ldrship Inst; Amer Cultures A.

KEARNEY, Vanessa
Eastside HS; Paterson, NJ (26-519) Bus C; Ensm; FBLA; Hmrm; SC; Y-Tns; VP, Sr Cl; COM; Citz A; JA A; VP, Afro Amer C; Prom Committee; *Taylor Bus Inst; Lawyers Asst.*

KEARNS, Carolyn Ruth
Western Guilford HS; Greensboro, NC (1-250) BC; Sci C; Tres, Span C; COM; *NC St U; Bio.*

KEARSE, Eliza Barbara
Central HS; Bridgeport, CT; Co-Cpt, Chldr; Drama; Hmrm; Thes; Cert of Achv, Dance.

KEAS, Casandra Jean
Broken Arrow HS; Broken Arrow, OK; Band; Chor; FBLA; FHA; Hmrm; NHS; Bkbl; Sftbl; Okla St U Alumni Acad Achv A; St Hon Soc; *Okla U; Bus.*

KEATHLEY, Bruce Alan
Mt Vernon HS; Mt Vernon, AR; Ann; Pres, FFA; 4H; Rptr, Sch P; SC; Tres, Jr Cl; Bsbl; Cpt, Bkbl; Cl Fav; Sci A; Eng, Agr, A's; *U of Ark; Law.*

KEATHLEY, Kathy Lynn
Highlands HS; San Antonio, TX (29-663) Ann; FHA; Ger C; NHS; Tnns; MLS; Sigma Epsilon; Fin, Teamster Schol; Fin, Joske's Tn Board; Hon Men, UIL One Act Play; *Baylor U; Teaching.*

KEATING, Anthony Edward
St Peters Prep HS; Jersey City, NJ (5-250) Drama; Hmrm; A-Ed, Lit Mag; F-Ed, Sch P; SC; Cr-Ctry; JV, Tr; Hist A; Hon Prog; NEDT; Hon Fin; Marine Phys Fit A; Comm Action Prog; Partial Schol; *Liberal Arts.*

KEATING, Corland Gordon
Cashmere HS; Cashmere, WA (2-89) Chor; Dbte Tm; FFA; NHS; Pres, Soph Cl; Golf; JV, Wrest; Pres A; Yth Fel; Rotary Exchange Stu, New Zealand; *Oral Roberts U; Missionary.*

KEATING, Jeana Louise
Holy Rosary Acad; Louisville, KY (4-116) Ann; Chess C; Dbte Tm; Math C; A-Ed, Sch P; Span C; Mgr, Bkbl; Mgr, Hockey; Tr; COM; Hon Prog; JA A; *Bellarmine Col; Psychiatric Nurs.*

KEATING, Karla Laynne
Central Private HS; Baton Rouge, LA; Fr C; HR; 200 Hr A, Alpha Theta Psi, Pep, C'S.

KEATING, M Hope
Dixie Co HS; Cross City, FL; Ed, Ann; Band; VP, BC; GS; 4H; Cpt, Mjrte; Pres, Span C; Tres, Jr Cl; Tnns; Cl Fav; HCt; Hon Prog; MLS; Valedictorian; *Sweet Briar Col; Interntl Affairs.*

KEBLESS, Alan Wayne
Greenville HS; Greenville, MI; Secy, FFA; Ski C; 1st Chair, Sax, Band; 1st Pl Solo Ensm A; *Mich St U; Vet.*

KEE, Carolyn Columbus
Gumberry HS; Gumberry, NC; F-Ed, Ann; BC; Chor; Fr C; *A&T St U; Early-Childhood Ed.*

KEE, Rufus Tyrone
John F Kennedy HS; Suffolk, VA; BS; Chem C; Hmrm; Orch; SC; Up Bound; Bkbl; Adv Mus A; Band A; Stars & Bars.

KEECH, Brian Lee
Valentine HS; Valentine, NE (20-80) Chor; Ed, Sch P; SC; Pres, Var C; Pres, Sr Cl; Bkbl; Ftbl; Tr; HCt; *U of Nebr.*

KEEFE, Beverly Jean
Greater Latrobe HS; Latrobe, PA (222-554) AFS; Band; Chor; FNA; Ger C; ARC; Sch P; Ski C; SC; Tres, Jr Cl; Swim; *Nurs.*

KEEFE, Lorena Jane
Skyline HS; Salt Lake City, UT (33%-700) Drama; Fr C; NHS; Citz A; Drill Tm; Gym; Cert of Achv; Wings Service C; Dance C; Sub Debs & Squires; *U of Utah; Dance.*

KEEFE, Peggy Ann
Skyline HS; Salt Lake City, UT (10%-675) Drama; Secy, Fr C; NHS; Sci C; Citz A; Cl Fav; Honors at Entrance at U of Utah; Sub Debs And Squires; *U of Utah; Med.*

KEEFER, Donald Eugene
Cumberland Valley HS; Mechanicsburg, PA (13-564) Band; NHS; Orch; Spch C; COM; Math A; *Bradley U; Industrial Engr.*

KEEFER, Gregg Lee
Millersburg Area HS; Millersburg, PA (15-100) Band; Chor; Ensm; Hmrm; SC; Hon Prog; Drum Major; A-Ed, Yrbk; *Lebanon Valley Col.*

KEEFER, Jay Ramsey
James Ford Rhodes HS; Cleveland, OH (76-448) A Cap Choir; Tres, AFS; F-Ed, Ann; Band; Fin, BS; City Conf; Ensm; Hmrm; NHS; Orch; Sch P; Ski C; SC; Mgr, Bkbl; COM; HCt; Hon Prog; Co-Ch, Rally Committee; VP, Fresh Cl; Most Sch Spirit; *Grove City Col; Acct.*

KEEFER, Lori Jane
Warrior Run HS; Turbotville, PA; Chor; Rainbow; Tri-HiY; Tr; Yth Fel; *Williamsport Area Comm Col; Acct.*

KEEFER, Robin Ann
Cumberland Valley HS; Mechanicsburg, PA (22-585) Rptr, Hmrm; A-Ed, Lit Mag; NHS; SC; VP, Sr Cl; JV, Tr; COM; Cl Fav; Hon Prog; NEDT; Yth Festival Hon Tn; *Kutztown St Col; Special Ed.*

KEEFER, Tina Marie
Pine Grove Area HS; Pine Grove, PA (30-170) Dbte Tm; Drama; Tres, FHA; VP, Tri-HiY; JV, Bkbl; JV, Sftbl; DARGCA; God & Country A; 1st Cl Cadet; Sci Fair; *Computer.*

KEEFFEE, Margaret Lynn
Chipley HS; Chipley, FL; Chldr; Fr C; SC; Tr; Beauty; H of F; Sci A; Pres, Fresh Cl; *Gym.*

KEEL, LaDonna Lee
Tallapoosa Acad; Dadeville, AL; BC; Chldr; Var C; *Alexander City Jr Col.*

KEEL, Teresa Arlene
Hamill Road Christian Sch; Chattanooga, TN; Ann; Chor; Ensm; Miss Hamill Road; Schol; *Mus.*

KEELER, Rebecca Ann
Ponca City Sr HS; Ponca City, OK (128-525) AFS; Ann; Dbte Tm; Drama; FHA; Model UN; NHS; COM; Q&S A; OBU Acad; Bronze Schol Pin; *Okla Baptist U; Elem Ed.*

KEELS, Elgie
Coral Gables Sr HS; Coral Gables, FL; Up Bound; Ftbl; COM; Citz A; *Acct.*

KEEN, Darren Pressley
N Love Christian Sch; Rockford, IL; *Hyles-Anderson Col; Religion.*

KEEN, Donna Jo
Erwin HS; Erwin, NC (2-113) BC; Cpt, Chldr; Chor; InterClub Coun; Math C; Monogram; NHS; Phys C; A-Ed, Sch P; Sci C; Span C; Span NHS; HCt; Type A; Sch Spirit A; Scholastic A; *Campbell Col; Psych.*

KEEN, Martha Jean
Sparta R-III Sch Dist; Sparta, MO; Chor; Pres, FBLA; VP, FHA; Sftbl; Vlbl; Vocal A; Attendence.

KEEN, Melinda Gaye
North Side HS; Fort Worth, TX (1-206) Cpt, Chldr; Drama; Co-Ch, Fr C; FHA; Hmrm; Lit Mag; Ch, NHS; SC; Alg A; Cl Fav; Hon Prog; Spch A; VFW A; Drill Tm Dancer o-t Wk; Run-Up, Most Studious & Friedliest; *Pre-Law.*

KEEN, Randall Eugene
Person Sr HS; Roxboro, NC; Hmrm; Span C; SC; Bsbl; Cr-Ctry; Nom, Gov Sch; *U of N Carolina; Law.*

KEEN, Susan Gale
Dan River HS; Ringgold, VA (3-238) BC; FBLA; Rptr, Sch P; Span C; Bio A; Hon Prog; Jr Marshal; *Danville Comm Col; Journ.*

KEENAN, Jacy Lee
Moon Sr HS; Coraopolis, PA; Chor; Span C; Ftbl; *Nurs.*

KEENE, Ellen Elizabeth
Whitefish Bay HS; Milwaukee, WI (38-307) Chor; Ensm; NHS; Span NHS; *Edgewood Col; Art.*

KEENE, Phil L
Borah HS; Boise, ID (33%-650) Pres, Hmrm; Inter-Club Coun; Pres, Ski C; Var C; Bsbl; MVP, Ftbl; HCt; Q&S A; ARC A; All Sou Idaho, All St, Ftbl; Kicker o-t Yr; *The Col of Idaho; Pre-Med.*

KEENE, Richard Craig
Garden HS; Oakwood, VA; 4H; S-T, HiY; Hmrm; Model UN; NHS; Tres, SC; JV, Bkbl; Hist A; Math A; Geom A; Ch, Ways & Means Comm; Activity Comm; Prom Comm; *VPI; Optometry.*

KEENE, Susan Dale
Saint Albans HS; Saint Albans, WV (10%-500) Ann; Chor, Secy, Drama; Fr C; Bus Mgr, Sch P; Bkbl; Swim; COM; Pres A; Sunday Sch Teacher; All Co Chor; Church Altar Guild; Order of Arrow; 1st Cl GSct; *Bus.*

KEENER, Linda Sue
Red Lion Area Sr HS; Red Lion, PA (9-250) Band; NHS; Intramural Sports.

KEENER, Randy Robert
Mapleton HS; Ashland, OH (5-130) VP, Band; Chor; Ensm; FTA; Lat C; SC; Sci A; *North Central Tech Col; Acct.*

KEENER, Sharon Darlene
Waterproof HS; Waterproof, LA (33%-54) BC; Lit Ral; Most Out; Art A; *NE La U; Art.*

KEENEY, Lawrence C
Greenup Co HS; Greenup, KY (70-329) 4H; Semi-Fin, Prom King; Nom, Best All Around Boy; *Ashland Comm Col; Law.*

KEENEY, Lisa Jane
Tulpehocken Area HS; Bernville, PA (31-160) Chor; Drama; ARC; Mgr, Tnns; 4H A; NEDT; ARC A; Spch A; Yth Temperence Coun; 100 Hr Cert, Hospital Vol; *Phys Therapy.*

KEENEY, Sherri Lynn
Westminster Sr HS; Westminster, MD (5%-535) Ann; Hmrm; Lat C; Mgr, Bkbl; Tnns; Keyettes; Homecoming Comm; Rep, Co Stu Govt Assn; Ch, Jr Cl Fund-Raising Comm; Jr Prom Comm; *Phys Therapy.*

KEESAW, Barbara Luverne
San Lorenzo Valley HS; Ben Lomond, CA (10-225) Bkbl; Sftbl; Tr; CSF; Math A; *Nurs.*

KEESAW, Laurie Lee
San Lorenzo Valley HS; Felton, CA (10-225) Bkbl; Sftbl; Tr; CSF; Math A; Secy, Var Ltr Soc; Vlbl; *Law Enforcement.*

KEESE, Laurel Annette
A&M Consolidated HS; College Station, TX (10%-180) Chor; Fr C; Rptr, FTA; Semi-Fin, GS; Pres, NHS; Secy, SC; Secy, Soph Cl; Bkbl; Sftbl; Tnns; Tr; Hon Prog; Kiwanis A; WW; FCA; Tn Board; *Tex A&M U; Phys Ed.*

KEESECKER, Kathy Mae
Springfield Shawnee HS; Springfield, OH (43-168) Pres, A Cap Choir; Chor; Drama; Ensm; 4H; Sftbl; Citz A; 4H A; Yth Fel; *Wright St U; Rehabilitation.*

KEESEY, Kelly Lee
Dallastown Area HS; York, PA (28-450) AFS; Band; Orch.

KEESLING, Robert Lewis Jr
Jappatowne HS; Joppa, MD (10%-300) Band; Hmrm; SC; JV, Bsbl; Bkbl; Cpt, Ftbl; COM; Hon Prog; Yth Fel; PA.

KEFFER, Jeffery Dee
Haritage Christian Acad; Ravenswood, WV (7-58) Co-Ed, Ann; Chor; Pres, SC; Pres, Soph Cl; Cpt, Bkbl; Cpt, Ftbl; Tr; Pres A; *Liberty Baptist Col.*

KEHL, Monty Lynn
Lodgepole Pub HS; Lodgepole, NE (1-18) A Cap Choir; Band; Chor; Drama; Spch C; Tres, Soph Cl; Bsbl; Bkbl; Ftbl; Tr; Alg A; Bio A; Spch A; Hon Men, Geo, Bio, Social Contest; Superior, Instrumental Solo; *U of Nebr; Med.*

KEIBEL, Linda Jean
Whitney Point Central HS; Whitney Point, NY; GS; Mjrte; NHS; Ski C; Co-Cpt, Hockey; COM; Citz A; DARGCA; Alt, Regent's Schol; Elmira Key; *Albany Col; Bus Adm.*

KEIFFER, Wendy Ann
Meadowbrook HS; Byesville, OH (5%-170) Chldr; FHA; Tres, 4H; Ch, Hmrm; ARC; Sci C; SC; Sftbl; Crisco A; 4H A; ARC A; Tr Statistician; VP, Yth Fel; Confirmation Cl; Pep C; *Ohio U; Art.*

KEIGLER, Elizabeth Irene
Princeton HS; Princeton, NJ; AFS; Chor; Fr C; Soccer; Typing Mgr, Layout Staff, Sch News; Sr GSct; Laccross; *Social Sci.*

KEIL, Karl Roderick
Camden Central HS; Camden, NY (10%-225) Band; BS; NHS; Orch; Tres, SC; Var C; Bsbl; Bkbl; COM; Cl Fav; Math A; *Cornell U; Engr.*

KEIL, Nancy Jo
Sturgeon R-V HS; Sturgeon, MO (26-33) A Cap Choir; Pres, Band; Chldr; Chor; Ensm; VP, 4H; Pres, Orch; Secy, Jr Cl; Tr; 4H A; Type A; Mus A; Swtht, Qn Ct; *Westminister Col; Bus.*

KEILHOLTZ, Barbara Jean
Littlestown HS; Littlestown, PA (30-200) A Cap Choir; Band; Chor; Hon Prog; Type A; *Landscaping.*

KEILP, Judith Catherine
Acad of St Aloysius; Jersey City, NJ (1-103) Math C; Pres, NHS; F-Ed, Sch P; B Crocker A; COM; NEDT; Ntl Merit Commended; Academic Recognition; *St Peter's Col; Bus.*

KEIM, Bonnie Sue
Northridge HS; Middlebury, IN (10%-160) Band; Lightshine; Secy, Church Yth Group; Ch, Church Publicity Comm; *Ind U; Phys Therapy.*

KEIM, Patrick Thomas
Cass HS; Cassville, GA; F-Ed, Ann; BC; Fr C; JETS; VP, Math C; VP, Sci C; Alg A; Amer Leg Orator A; Bio A; Chem A; Cl Fav; Gov Honor Prog; HCt; Math A; St Scholar; Secy, Math C; *Ga Tech; Chem Engr.*

KEINATH, Tom Wayne
Ontario HS; Mansfield, OH (40-200) Chor; Drama; Ensm; NHS; Orch; Bsbl; Tnns; *Ohio St U; Hist.*

KEIRN, Richard Lee Jr
Clearfield Area HS; Clearfield, PA; Mgr, Bkbl; Ftbl; Yth Fel; V Ltr, Ftbl.

KEIRSTEAD, Rhonda Ann
Windsor HS; Windsor, CT; Chor; Cpt, Bible Quiz Tm; Win, Dist Bible Quiz; *AI Prince Tech Sch; Grafic Communications.*

KEISER, Nellie Marie
Casa Grande HS; Petaluma, CA;

KEISTER, Beth Ann
Winona Sr HS; Winona, MN (7-569) Ger C; Model UN; NHS; Tnns.

KEITH, Andrew Robert
Syosset HS; Syosset, NY (254-720) Drama; Tr; Citz A; Ham Radio C; Sailing C.

KEITH, Christy Lee
Weatherford HS; Weatherford, TX (16-252) Band; GS; NHS; Ed, Sch P; SC; Amer Leg A; COM; Citz A; Hon Prog; Opt Out Tn; Cpt, JV Vlbl; Cpt, Sch Spirit Group; Church Organist; Sunday Sch Teacher; *Weatherford Col; Elem Ed.*

KEITH, Donald Leroy
Geronimo HS; Geronimo, OK (10%-25) Drama; SC; Bsbl; Bkbl; HCt.

KEITH, Harlene Rose
Paradise HS; Paradise, CA (53-307) Chor; Spch C; *Butte Col; Legal Secy.*

KEITH, James Edward
Cheraw HS; Cheraw, SC; Fr C.

KEITH, Karen Jean
Amer Christian Acad; Pomona, CA (2-30) Chldr; Chor; Secy, SC; Secy, Soph Cl; Citz A; Hist A; HCt; Type A; Val; Secy, Yth Conf; Geography A; *Hyles-Anderson Col; Christian Ed Col.*

KEITH, Karen Lynne
William Byrd HS; Vinton, VA (17-246) Cpt, Band; VP, BC; Rptr, SC; Pres A; Tres, Band; Flag Squad; Ch, SC; *Va W Comm Col; Acct.*

KEITH, Kimberly Kay
Marion HS; Marion, IN (254-743) Chor; Pres, Sci C; Mgr, Tr; 1st Cl A, GSct; *Ball St U; Bus.*

KEITH, Lisa Nanette
Central Pinellas Christian HS; Largo, FL (3-8) Pres, Hmrm; Rptr, Sch P; SC; Pres, Sr Cl; VP, Jr Cl; VP, Soph Cl; HQn; Hon Prog; *Pensacola Christian Col; Nurs.*

KEITH, Perry Stan
Highland Park HS; Dallas, TX (110-415) AFS; Dbte Tm; VP, NFL; VP, Spch C; Var C; Co-Cpt, Bsbl; Bkbl; Sftbl; COM; Spch A; MVP, All Dist, Bsbl; Degree of Hon, Ntl Forensic League; *U of Okla; Bus Adm.*

KEITH, Samuel Ethan
Otsego HS; Otsego, MI (20-285) Chor; Ensm; Hmrm; Rptr, Sch P; SC; Jr Cl; Nom, BS; Sno-Coming Court; Lead, Plays; *Doctor Martin Luther Col; Ed.*

KEITH, Sandra Lynn
Dillon HS; Dillon, SC (6%-300) Anchor C; Ann; Secy, BC; Chor; VP, Hmrm; 1st Runnerup, Achv A; Semi-Fin, Beauty Pageant; *Columbia Col; Math.*

KEITH, Shari Ann
McCluer N HS; Florissant, MO (399-799) Swim; S-T, Outdoor C; V Ltrs; *Central Mo St U; Pub Relations.*

KEITH, Sheri Jo
Miramar HS; Miramar, FL; FBLA; *Lee Col; Bus.*

KEITH, Steven Paul
Norwood Sr HS; Norwood, OH; Tres, Chor; Demolay; Ensm; Hmrm; Mgr, Bsbl; Mgr, Bkbl; Mgr, Ftbl; *Northern Ky U; Mus Theater.*

KEITH, Susan Elizabeth
Colchester Jr Sr HS; Colchester, IL (1-54) Ann; Band; Chor; Ensm; Mjrte; Math C; NHS; Tres, SC; Bkbl; Hon Prog; Val; Tres & Pres, Drama C; Pom Pon; Vlbl; Tnage Miss Pageant; Art Contest; Yth Member, Coun On Ministries; S-T, Lib C; Art Womens C Schol; *Law Enforcement.*

KEITH, Terri Lee
Clinton Sr HS; Clinton, TN (15%-356) Band; Chor; Secy, 4H; Faculty Ed, Ann; Art C; Accompanist, Chor; Best Dressed; VP, Church Yth Coun; Church Swtht; 1st, Poetry Contest; *Carson Newman Col; Art.*

KEITH, Valerie Ann
Whiteface HS; Whiteface, TX; Band; FHA; JV, Bkbl; Tr; Amer Leg A; Scholastic Favorite; *S Plains Jr Col; Chem.*

KEITHAN, Cheryl Marie
Shenandoah Valley HS; Shenandoah, PA; Band; Chldr; Chor; Orch; JV, Bkbl; Co Band Pin; Chor Cert; Art Cert; JV Bkbl Ltrs; *Art.*

KEITHAN, Howard Robert
Shenandoah Valley HS; Shenandoah, PA (40-126) VP, Band; Orch; Cr-Ctry; Tr; JV, Wrest; COM; H of F; Type A; WW; Industrial Arts A; *Steven's Trade Sch; Masonry.*

KEITT, Regina Michelle
Savannah HS; Savannah, GA; Bsbl; Cr-Ctry; Soccer; Fin, Tr; Field Hockey; Tr As; *Tuskegee Inst; Phys Therapy.*

KEKAUOHA,
Jodie Ann Kanoeonalani
Laupahoehoe HS; Laupahoehoe, HI (7-39) Ed, Ann; Chor; Fin, Jr Miss Pageant; Spt Sr Cl; Cpt, Jr Cl; Cpt, Soph Cl; Tnns; Tr; HQn; HCt; Cpt, Vlbl; *Brigham Young U; Travel Industry.*

KELBAUGH, John William
Morrisville HS; Morrisville, PA (30-110) Band; Chor; Bsbl; Cl Fav; Best Actor A; *E Stroudsburg Col; Secondary Ed.*

KELCH, Vickie Lynn
W Ottawa HS; Holland, MI; Chor; Ensm; Explorers; *Grand Rapids Jr Col; Nurs.*

KELEMEN, Alex Daniel
Riverside HS; Painesville, OH (39-286) Hmrm; NHS; Sch Achieve Tm; F-Ed, Sch P; SC; World Affairs C; Amer Leg A; COM; Hist A; Journ A; Q&S A; VFW Orator Win; VofDEM; Yth Fel; Ohio U Hist Schol; 12th Pl St, Ohio Hist Comp; Ohio A of Distinction; Perfect Score, Am Hist Ap Test; *Ohio U; Communications.*

KELESHIAN, Dennis Joseph
Ridley HS; Folsom, PA (100-700) Drama; Ger C; Hmrm; SC; Thes; Mgr, Bsbl; Swim; Secy, ACYOA; Gym; *Math.*

KELLAM, Angela D
Hope HS; Hope, AR; BC; Chldr; GS; Span C; Tres, Soph Cl; Swim; Beauty; HQn; ARC A; SC, Jr Cl, Sr Cl, Rep; *U of Ark; X-Ray Tech.*

KELLAM, Kristi Karroll
Hope HS; Hope, AR (5%-220) BC; Cpt, Chldr; Tres, Span C; SC; Pres, Jr Cl; Citz A; Yth Fel; Church Choir; Soph Rep; Service A Committee; Nike C; *U of Ark; Law.*

KELLAMS, John Perry
Kountze HS; Kountze, TX (11-84) Band; Drama; Ensm; Fr C; VP, FTA; NHS; USMC Cert of Appreciation; Cpt, Rifle Tm; WW; *Lamar U; Pre-Med.*

KELLAR, Susan Marie
Hillsboro Sr HS; Hillsboro, OR (55-680) CYO; Chldr; 4H; NHS; Ski C; Bio A; COM; 4H A; Hon Prog; Swtht; Type A; May Pole Dancer; Dance-Drill Tm; *Ore St U; Home Ec.*

KELLER, Andrew Walter
Quigley South Prep Sem; Chicago, IL (145-260) Chess C; Ski C; SC; Tnns; Alg A; Sci A; *Aerospace Stu.*

KELLER, Brenda Eileen
Central Columbia HS; Bloomsburg, PA (17-200) Band; FTA; NHS; Penn Ambassador Band.

KELLER, Bruce Ralph
Lindbergh Sr HS; St Louis, MO (218-909) A Cap Choir; Chor; Demolay; Ch, Drama; Ensm; Madrigal; NHS; Ntl Yth Conf; Ch, Span C; Thes; Chamber of Comm A; Opt A; Best Thespian; *SE Mo St U; Psych.*

KELLER, Charles Robert
Notre Dame Bishop Gibbons HS; Schenectady, NY (45-150) JETS; ARC; Sch Achieve Tm; Bkbl; Golf; Sftbl; Math A; NEDT; PTA A; *Schenectady Comm Col; Fire Sci.*

KELLER, Dawne Denise
Lancaster Sr HS; Lancaster, WI (11-135) AFS; Ann; Band; Chor; Ensm; Pres, 4H; Ch, Hmrm; Jr Miss Pagent; Madrigal; Orch; Span C; SC; Mgr, Tr; 4H A; Hon Prog; ARC A; Spch A; VP, Secy & Tres, 4-H C; WW; *Nurs.*

KELLER, Deborah Ann
Nottaway Sr HS; Nottaway, VA (25%-285) Fr C; Hmrm; Sci C.

KELLER, Donald Rhea
DeSoto HS; De Soto, TX (100-234) *N Tex St Col; Bus.*

KELLER, Edmond Mack
Pampa HS; Pampa, TX (149-303) A Cap Choir; Key C; Span C; SC; VP, Jr Cl; Bsbl; Ftbl; JV, Tr; Opt A; Hi-Plain Area Disciples; Pres, FCA; *Tex Christian U; Religion.*

KELLER, Eric William
Moorefield HS; Moorefield, WV; Band; BS; Pres, FFA; 4H A; NHS; Var C; Bsbl; Bkbl; Ftbl; 4H A; Spch A; St Star Farmer; 4-H C Congress; FFA Dairy Found A; *Durham Tech Inst; Opticianry.*

KELLER, Florence May
Maple Shade HS; Maple Shade, NJ (10%-235) Semi-Fin, GS; NHS; Cpt, Sftbl; *Temple Col; Journ.*

KELLER, Gladys Elizabeth
Nottoway HS; Nottoway, VA (20-225) Ann; Dbte Tm; Fr C; Rptr, FTA; Hmrm; NHS; Sch P; Sci C; Pres, SC; Secy, SC; Jr Women's C School; Sch Pres A; WW; *VPI; Chem.*

KELLER, Jessie Marie
Lebanon HS; Lebanon, PA (32-398) A Cap Choir; Chor; COM; Ath Booster C; *Dickenson Col; Law.*

KELLER, Joseph Allen
Red Lion HS; Red Lion, PA (5-400) Band; BS; Chess C; Ensm; Tres, Mod Mus Mas; NHS; Order/ Arrow; Amer Leg A; COM; Hon Prog; Lion A; Math A; Pres, Biol C; Tn Action C; *Shelton Col; Theology.*

KELLER, Keith Richard
Brainerd Sr HS; Brainerd, MN (1-575) Ger C; Tr; *Embry-Riddle Aeronautical U; Aeronautical Engr.*

KELLER, Kolin Lane
Seguin HS; Seguin, TX (15%-450) Hmrm; Key C; Rptr, SC; JV, Bsbl; Ftbl; Hon Prog; *TSTI; Solar Engr.*

KELLER, Lesa Carole
Trezevant HS; Memphis, TN (8-157) Co-Cpt, Chldr; NHS; VP, Span C; SC; ROTC A; *Nurs.*

KELLER, Linda M
John F Kennedy HS; New York, NY; Band; Drama; GS; ARC; Cr-Ctry; Tr; Citz A; Cl Fav; Swtht; *U of Rochester; Psych.*

KELLER, Lucille Lynette
Fairfield HS; Langdon, KS (10%-42) Band; Chor; Dbte Tm; Ensm; Fin, Spch C; VP, Y-Tns; Spch A; St Scholar; Type A; Yth Fel; Outst Debators; Yth Assm Ldr; *Oral Roberts U; Drama.*

KELLER, Margaret Mary
Nekoma HS; Nekoma, ND (1-6) Band; 4H; A-Ed, Sch P; SC; Parl, Sr Cl; VP, Jr Cl; Cpt, Bkbl; B Crocker A; 4H A; Val; *ND St Sch of Sci; Gen Off.*

KELLER, Marie Elizabeth
Kaukauna HS; Kaukauna, WI (15%-400) Chor; Co-Ed, Sch P; Span C; Q&S A; Dance C.

KELLER, Marjo Rene
Cleveland HS; St Louis, MO; Chess C; Chor; Ensm; Ger C; SC; COM; *Kan U; Journ.*

KELLER, Mary Ann
Vicksburg HS; Vicksburg, MS; Band; FHA; Lat C; Pres, Math C; NHS; Secy, Sr Cl; Tnns; *Miss St U; Vet Sci.*

KELLER, Nancy Louise
Winona Sr HS; Winona, MN (14-558) Dbte Tm; VP, Ger C; Orch; COM; Yth Leg; Secy, Yth Task Force; Winona St U Symph Orch; Mate Sailing A.

KELLER, Nick W
Pleasant Ridge HS; Easton, KS (33%-65) Co-Cpt, Bkbl; Co-Cpt, Ftbl; Tr; Sci A; Cl Service A; *Phys Ed.*

KELLER, Randy Dale
Humansville HS; Humansville, MO; Ann; Tres, FFA; SC; S-T, Sr Cl; VP, Jr Cl; Bsbl; Citz A; Type A; Sr Personality; Most Friendly.

KELLER, Rodney Allen
Bishop Ryan HS; Minot, ND (6-105) Key C; NHS; Bkbl; Ftbl; Tr; Hon Prog; Monsignor Hogan A; *ND St Sch of Sci; Elec.*

KELLER, Ronald William Jr
Wakulla HS; Crawfordville, FL; Chess C; Ftbl; Wrest; Citz A; Sci A; *Oceanography.*

KELLER, Scott Michael
Oak Ridge Sr HS; Oakridge, OR (3-105) Ch, Hmrm; SC; Co-Ch, Soph Cl; *NW Nazarene Col; Math.*

KELLER, Werner Hans
Vincent Massey HS; Windsor, CANADA (10-118) Ger C; Math C; Soccer; *U of Windsor; Engr.*

KELLERHALS, Tricia Lynn
Milford Township HS; Milford, IL (15-45) Band; Chldr; Chor; Sftbl; HCt; *Ill St U; Social Work.*

KELLERMAN, Vanessa Jeanne
Elk Grove HS; Elk Grove, IL (1-630) S-T, AFS; Secy, Fr C; Semi-Fin, GS; NHS; Rptr, Sch P; Cpt, Swim; Magna Cum Laude; NMS; Summa Cum Laude; Val; Mgr, Swim; Hon Pin; *Knox Col; Math.*

KELLETT, Donna Rae
Biggs HS; Biggs, CA (15-67) Band; CYO; Bkbl; Sftbl; Most Inspirational; Bkbl; MVP, Vlbl; *Butte Col; Phys Ed.*

KELLEY, Amanda Bess
Pendleton HS; Pendleton, SC (25%-182) All Amer Yth; JV, Chldr; Chor; Fr C; 4H; S-T, Hmrm; A-Ed, Sch P; FHA; Mgr, Bkbl; 4H A; *Clemson U.*

KELLEY, Barbara Jane
Hueneme HS; Oxnard, CA (6-600) A Cap Choir; VP, AFS; Span C; Tres, Jr Cl; CSF; *Redlands Col.*

KELLEY, Bruce Phillip
Park Hill Sr HS; Kansas City, MO; Band; Var C; JV, Bsbl; Wrest; Yth Fel.

KELLEY, Cynthia Lou
Findlay HS; Findlay, OH (100-650) Band; Alg A; COM; H of F; Math A; *St Vincent's Sch of Nurs; Med.*

KELLEY, Daniel Anthony
Piedmont Hills HS; San Jose, CA (20%-750) Dist HR; *San Jose St U; Chem Engr.*

KELLEY, Dorsey Mae
Cotton Plant HS; Cotton Plant, AR (3-23) Ann; BC; Drama; Parl, Fr C; FBLA; FHA; Type A; *ASU; Bus.*

KELLEY, Emily Ilona
Tuscola Sr HS; Waynesville, NC (50%-400) Band; Chor; Ensm; *Help For Exceptional Children.*

KELLEY, Erin Rose
Monsignor Ryan Mem HS; Dorchester, MA; Ann; GS; Pres, NHS; Pres, Span C; VP, SC; Bkbl; Sftbl; Hon Prog; *Bridgewater St Col; Special Ed.*

KELLEY, Gregory Charles
Provine HS; Jackson, MS; Var C; Ftbl; *Jackson St U; Health.*

KELLEY, Gregory Dale
Northmont HS; Dayton, OH (10-300) Band; Chor; Drama; Ensm; Ger C; Orch; Ed, Sch P; Sci C; Spch C; Citz A; Regional Spelling Champ; Cpt, St Bible Quiz Champs; S-T, Yth Group; Yth Choir.

KELLEY, James Bryan
Wade Hampton HS; Greenville, SC (1-390) Pres, Hmrm; Pres, Soph Cl; Bkbl; Ftbl; Cpt, Golf; Gr Marshal; H of F; Hist A; Hon Prog; Val; *Clemson U; Bus.*

KELLEY, James Joseph
Blanchet HS; Seattle, WA (18-383) Bsbl; JV, Bkbl; JV, Ftbl; *U of Wash; Psych.*

KELLEY, Jeffrey Dale
Sarasota HS; Sarasota, FL; SC; JV, Bsbl; JV, Ftbl.

KELLEY, Jeffrey Lee
Wayne Co HS; Monticello, KY (1-180) Band; VP, BC; Pres, Ger C; SC; Var C; Co-Cpt, Bkbl; Ftbl; Chem A; Phy A; Val; Ch, Ky Yth Traffic Safety Comm; Yth Highway Safety Adv Comm; *Ky Wesleyan U; Ministery.*

KELLEY, Joel Don
Palestine HS; Palestine, TX; Chem C; Chor; Hmrm; SC; Bsbl; Ftbl.

KELLEY, John Byron
Eisenhower HS; Decatur, IL (10%-300) NHS; JV, Bsbl; Co-Cpt, Bkbl; Co-Cpt, Ftbl; Golf; Sftbl; Tr; Sci A; High HR.

KELLEY, Joseph Lee
Clay Co HS; Ashland, AL (4-56) Band; BC; Chor; FFA; FTA; 4H; Orch; Sci C; Var C; Bsbl; Ftbl; Citz A; 4H A; Sci A; Spch A; *Auburn U.*

KELLEY, Karen Michelle
Mortimer Jordan HS; Morris, AL; Bus C; FBLA; Pres, NHS; VP, SC; Sftbl; COM; Cl Fav; HCt; FBLA, Spell A; *Mgt.*

KELLEY, Kent Roland
Air Acad HS; Colorado Springs, CO (5%-300) Journ A; Interntl Honor Soc for HS Writers; *U of Colo; Journ.*

KELLEY, Lila Jeanette
Stephens Co HS; Toccoa, GA; JV, Chldr; FTA; Ch, InterAct C; HCt; Valentine Court; *Tri-County Tech Col; Marketing Distribution.*

KELLEY, Lisa Joy
Livermore Falls HS; Livermore Falls, ME (4-124) Sci C; JV, Bkbl; JV, Hockey; Tr; *U of Maine; Natural Resource Mgr.*

KELLEY, Melinda Lucille
Bible Baptist HS; Savannah, GA (1-34) Chor; *Armstrong St Col; Ed.*

KELLEY, Michael Stephen
Park Hill HS; Kansas City, MO (179-450) Band; Var C; Co-Cpt, Bsbl; JV, Wrest; Yth Fel; *NW Mo St Col; Eng.*

KELLEY, Rene Diane
Chester HS; Chester, PA; A-Ed, Ann; Band; Dbte Tm; Key C; Cpt, Tnns.

KELLEY, Roberta Virginia
Atchison Sr HS; Atchison, KS; Secy, A Cap Choir; Secy, Chor; Ensm; Sftbl; Mo W St Col; Secy.

KELLEY, Robin Lynette
Rossville Comp HS; Rossville, GA (16-212) Ann; BC; JV, Chldr; Fr C; Hmrm; SC; Ch, Y-Tns; COM; Gov Honor Prog; Hon Prog; Star Student; Pom-Pom Sq; Pep C; Mod Dance Tm; Dalton Jr Col.

KELLEY, Sam Anderson
Clovis HS; Clovis, NM; A Cap Choir; Chor; Ensm; Key C; Madrigal; Cpt, Bsbl; Bkbl; Ftbl; Sftbl; Tr; Wayland Baptist Col; Religion.

KELLEY, Sharon Susanne
Temple Heights Christian Sch; Tampa, FL (10-62) Chor; Ensm; Fr C; NHS; Ed, Sch P; Fin, Tnns; COM; Yth Fel; Quiz Tm A.

KELLEY, Sheila Diane
Sarasota HS; Sarasota, FL; FBLA.

KELLEY, Sherry Ann
Valdosta HS; Valdosta, GA (15%-600) Band; Hmrm; Semi-Fin, Jr Miss Pa; Hon Prog; Sci A; Juvenile Law Coun.

KELLING, Christopher Kent
E Troy HS; E Troy, WI (1-140) Arch; Band; Chess C; Ensm; NHS; Order/Arrow; Arch; Hockey; Soccer; Swim; Bio A; Chem A; Math A; Val; Eagle Sct; U of Wisc; Bio.

KELLISH, Christine Anne
Fayetteville-Manlius HS; Manlius, NY (219-420) Art A; WW; SUNY at Cortland; Ed.

KELLN, Kevin William
Marysville-Pilchuk HS; Marysville, WA; Ger C; NHS; Swim.

KELLNER, Terry Warren
Okeene HS; Okeene, OK; Secy, FFA; JV, Bkbl; Tr; Okla St U; Agr.

KELLOGG, Cindy Robin
Ada HS; Ada, OK (25-109) Arch; Chor; Drama; Ntl Yth Conf; Span C; Spch C; Thes; Arch; Bkbl; Sftbl; Swim; Tr; Interlochen Ntl Mus; Sci A; Swtht; E Central U; Nurs.

KELLOGG, Clark
Vandalia-Butler Sr HS; Vandalia, OH (4%-400) Band; Lat C; COM; Hon Prog; Fin, Ohio St Tn Talent; Hon Seminar of Metro-Dayton; Evangel Col; Mus.

KELLOGG, Julia Elizabeth
Belle Plaine HS; Belle Plaine, KS (5-65) Ann; Chor; Fr C; FHA; Madrigal; SC; Hon Prog; Type A; Fr Contest; Johnson Co Comm Col; Communications.

KELLOGG, Marcey Lynn
Edmeston Central Sch; Edmeston, NY (8-45) Pres, Band; Chor; Fr C; FHA; Pres, SC; Pres, Var C; Tres, Sr Cl; Tres, Jr Cl; VP, Soph Cl; Cpt, Bkbl; Hockey; Cpt, Soccer; Cpt, Sftbl; B Crocker A; Cpt, Vlbl; Clark Found Schol; Becker Jr Col; Travel and Tour Service.

KELLOGG, Shelly Jo
Antelope Valley HS; Lancaster, CA (1-500) Drama; Fin, GS; Thes; CSF; Hon Schol; Z C; Prom Comm; Fine Arts.

KELLOGG, Steven Arnold
Canton S HS; Canton, OH (10-285) Band; Ensm; Lat C; Math C; NHS; Sci C; COM; Hon Prog; U of Cincinnati; Engr.

KELLUM, Barbara Jane
Lancaster HS; Lancaster, VA (39-167) Band; Drama; Fr C; FBLA; 4H; Sci C; Sftbl; Old Dominion U; Dental Asst.

KELLUM, Malcolm Eric
Allen HS; Robeline, LA (1-37) Tres, Band; Bus C; Pres, 4H; Pres, Hmrm; Lit Ral; SC; Bsbl; Soccer; Sftbl; Swim; Tnns; Cl Fav; 4H A; HCt; Hon Prog; Sal; Camp A; 4-H Tree Id; Northwestern Col; Elec Engr.

KELLUM, Patricia Elizabeth
Lancaster HS; Lancaster, VA (16-145) Fr C; 4H; Sci C; Sci A; Yth Fel; Art A; Old Dominion U; Art.

KELLUM, Sylvia Elaine
Mary Brantley Smiley HS; Houston, TX (17-400) NHS; Sci C; Bio A; Chem A; 1st Pl, Sci Fair; 4th Pl, Ward Clerk; U of Houston; Pre-Med.

KELLUM, Tracy Ann
Bethel-Tate HS; Bethel, OH (6-130) Bus C; Cpt, Chldr; Dbte Tm; Hmrm; NHS; Sci C; SC; Tres, Sr Cl; Pres A; Type A; Cpt, Vlbl; 1st Pl, Comedy-Variety Show.

KELLY, Al Jerome
George Washington HS; Los Angeles, CA (33%-639) Hmrm; Sci C; Tr; Bio A; Yth Foundation A; Pepperdine U; Aerospace Tech.

KELLY, Anita Elaine
Columbia HS; W Columbia, TX; AFS; Band; Chess C; Rptr, FHA; FTA; Del, Close-Up Prog, Wash DC; Brazosport Jr Col; Bus.

KELLY, Beverly Jean
Sumner Hill HS; Clinton, MS; Ann; Band; Secy, BC; Secy, Chor; Secy, Jr Cl; 4H A; Most Out; Type A; Modeling A; Writing A; Test Achvs; Hinds Branch Col; Secy.

KELLY, Brett Alonzo
Lutheran HS; Los Angeles, CA (6-69) A Cap Choir; Chor; S-T, Key C; Madrigal; SC; Mgr, Ftbl; CSF; Figure Skate Comp; U So Calif.

KELLY, Bridget Sue
Johnson HS; Huntsville, AL; NHS; Span C; Hon Prog; Co-Cpt, Drill Tm; Christian Fel; FCA; New Vibrationstour Choir; Pres, Pres, HS Sorority.

KELLY, Bruce David
N Gwinnett HS; Suwanee, GA (10%-190) BC; Dbte Tm; Key C; Semi-Fin, Lit Ral; NHS; Var C; Bsbl; Bkbl; Ftbl; Gov Honor Prog; Ariz St U; Law.

KELLY, Calvin Cecil Leroy
Bell Gardens HS; Bell Gardens, CA; Chor; FFA; Var C; Ftbl; Tr; Cpt, Wrest; MVP, Wrest; Royal Ranger Ldr; Church Usher; Ltrman C.

KELLY, Carrie Dell
Bethel Baptist Sch; Memphis, TN (6-17) Bkbl; Sftbl; Draughons Col; Secy.

KELLY, Cheryl Rhea
McClymonds HS; Oakland, CA (10%-160) City Conf; FBLA; FHA; Hmrm; NHS; Rptr, Sch P; Span C; SC; Up Bound; Co-Ch, Sr Cl; Pres, Soph Cl; B Crocker A; Cl Fav; HCt; Hon Prog; MLS; Most Intelligent; Directress, Childrens Choir; Disciplinary Comm; USC; Communications.

KELLY, Clutheal Harriet
Burke HS; Charleston, SC (18-205) Chldr; Drama; Pres, FBLA; Hmrm; SC; Y-Tns; Type A; The Col of CHAS; Acct.

KELLY, Clyde Arthur
Rhinebeck Central Sch; Rhinebeck, NY; Band; Chor; Span C; Tr; Musicals; Math.

KELLY, Cynthia Lynne
Rancho HS; Las Vegas, NV; Chor; NHS; Ski C; COM; UNLV; Mus.

KELLY, Debbie Sue
Salem Sr HS; Salem, OH (31-35) Chor; Ensm; NHS; Sci C; Secretarial.

KELLY, Earlene
King Sr HS; Tampa, FL; Anchor C; Hmrm; SC; COM; Citz A; Hillsborough Comm Col; Secy.

KELLY, Edward Melton
Neville HS; Monroe, LA (4-180) Community Yth Symph; Ensm; InterClub Coun; Lat C; Lat NHS; NHS; Orch; Tnns; Hist A; NMS; Gov Program for Gifted Children; All St Orch; Emory U; Theology.

KELLY, Eileen Frances
Saint Joseph Acad; Cleveland, OH (10-185) A-Ed, Ann; Chor; Lit Mag; NHS; Rptr, Sch P; Span C; Thes; NEDT; Type A; Span Merit A; Shorthand Speed A; Mus Adjudication A; Cleveland St U; Pol Sci.

KELLY, Elizabeth Rae
Anoka Sr HS; Anoka, MN (75-800) Ramsey Jr Col; Bus Adm.

KELLY, Georgia Nell
Cape Fear HS; Fayetteville, NC (20-400) Hmrm; SC; Tr; MLS; Yth Fel; Stu o-t Yr, Sunday Sch; Stu o-t Month; VP & Rptr, Yth Dept; Morehouse Col; Hist.

KELLY, Heather Ann
Battle Mountain HS; Minturn-Vail, CO (3-55) Band; Fr C; Tr; Vlbl; Bio.

KELLY, Henry Boon
Pawhuska HS; Pawhuska, OK (1-124) Band; Key C; Mu Alpha Theta; NHS; Order/Arrow; SC; Alg A; Okla St U; Elec Engr.

KELLY, James Franklin
East Central HS; Hurley, MS (1-115) BC; Bus C; Var C; Co-Cpt, Bkbl; Miss St U; Bio Engr.

KELLY, Jeff William
Medina HS; Medina, NY; Ski C; Var C; Pres, Soph Cl; Ftbl; Tr; Wrest; COM; Citz A; Hon Prog; Skinner Mem A; General Motors Inst; Engr.

KELLY, Jim M
Highland HS; Pocatello, ID (128-325) FFA; Bsbl; Ftbl; Babe Ruth Ath o-t Yr; U of Idaho; Sociology.

KELLY, John Timothy
Holdrege HS; Holdrege, NE (34-140) Band; Ensm; Orch; SC; Tr; HCt; Hon Prog; Sacristan; FCA; Superior, Mus Clinic; Stage & Pep Bands; Co Govt Day; Calgary Stampede; 1st Choir, Dist Mus Clinic; U of Nebr; Archt.

KELLY, Karen Jane
J O Johnson HS; Huntsville, AL; Ed, Ann; Band; NHS; COM; Hon Prog; Outst Sr; Art League & Museum Assn; Flag Corps; 1st Pl Shrt Stry, Women's C Lit Con; Auburn U; Visual Arts.

KELLY, Karen Renee
Zephyrhills HS; Zephyrhills, FL (11-252) Tres, CYO; NHS; Bkbl; MVP, Sftbl; St Leo Col; Sci.

KELLY, Katharine Elizabeth
Sarasota HS; Sarasota, FL (180-617) Chor; Lit Mag; Rptr, Sch P; Y-Tns; Sftbl; Bible Quiz Tm; South Eastern Bible Col; Elem Ed.

KELLY, Kerry Lynn
Oil City Sr HS; Oil City, PA; Chor; Sch P; Span C; Y-Tns; Polk St Sch; Psych.

KELLY, Lillian
Altheimer HS; Altheimer, AR; Secy, Ann; Chor; Hmrm; Math C; NHS; Sci C; SC; Alg A; Bio A; COM; Math A; MLS; Sci A; Best Stu; Nurs.

KELLY, Mark Jay
Sidney Sr HS; Sidney, MT (98-120) Tres, CYO; K of C; VP, Key C; Var C; Ftbl; Tr.

KELLY, Martha Colleen
Guysborough Municipal HS; Guysborough, CANADA; Chem C; 4H.

KELLY, Mary Ann
Acad o-t Holy Names; Tampa, FL (26-68) Ann; Drama; VP, Hmrm; Tres, Sodality; Soccer; Sr Prom Ct; Nom, Soroptimist Yth Ldrship A; FSU; Med.

KELLY, Matthew S
Highland HS; Pocatello, ID (140-400) FFA; 4H; 4H A; Eng.

KELLY, Michael Sean
St Joseph HS; Hammonton, NJ (3-48) Chess C; FTA; Ch, Sci C; JV, Ftbl; Chem A; Hon Prog; Ntl Sci Found; Stage Crew; Dean's List; Lehigh U; Engr.

KELLY, Nancy Reed
Southwest HS; Fort Worth, TX (15-378) Band; Orch; SC; NASA Sym '77; All-City Band; Sci.

KELLY, Pamela Ann
Loyola HS; Mankato, MN (30-75) Chldr; Chor; Dbte Tm; Drama; Sch P; Co-Cpt, Bkbl; Sftbl; Spch A; Cpt, Vlbl; Ath A; Humor A; Ath o-t Sch Yr A; Winona St U; Nurs.

KELLY, Patrick Thomas
Chaminade Col Prep; St Louis, MO (10-118) A-Ed, Ann; Secy, CYO; Chess C; Lat C; NHS; Co-Ed, Sch P; Soccer; Alg A; Bio A; Chem A; Citz A; Hist A; Hon Prog; Math A; NEDT; Phy A; Sci A; Type A; Art.

KELLY, Paula June
Van Wert HS; Van Wert, OH (26-234) Cum Laude Soc; NHS; Cum Laude Hon Graduate; Bus Dept A; Adolf and Letticia Weck Schol; Defiance Col; Bus Ed.

KELLY, Renee Christine
Licking Heights HS; Summit Station, OH (20-100) Band; Ensm; FHA; FTA; NHS; Cpt, Drill Tm; WW; Nurs.

390

KELLY, Richard Paul
Anoka HS; Anoka, MN (70%-850) Chor; Order/Arrow; ARC; Swim; Order/Arrow A; ARC A; *Aeronautics.*

KELLY, Ruth Lynn
James Monroe HS; Fredericksburg, VA (11-206) Ann; Arch; Bus C; Chor; Fr C; FBLA; Hmrm; NHS; COM; Math A; Type A; *VPI; Math.*

KELLY, Sheila Lynn
Newton Co Comprehensive HS; Covington, GA (10-657) Band; VP, SC; *U of Ga.*

KELLY, Sherrie Yvette
Mission HS; San Fernando, CA; Ann; Bus C; Chldr; Hmrm; InterClub Coun; Math C; Pol Sci C; Sch Achieve Tm; Sch P; Sci C; Tres, SC; Tres, Sr Cl; Citz A; Star Student; Type A; *Sci.*

KELLY, Sonja Denise
Queens Vocational HS; Long Island, NY (73-299) Co-Cpt, Chldr; Cum Laude Soc; Var C; Chem A; Citz A; Magna Cum Laude; Sci A; *Nurs.*

KELLY, Sonya Yvette
Spartanburg HS; Spartanburg, SC; Beauty; Christmas Qn.

KELLY, Stacey Ann
North Babylon Sr HS; N Babylon, NY; NHS; Hon Prog; Regent Schol; *Suffolk Co Comm Col; Pre-Sch Ed.*

KELLY, Susan
Bristow HS; Bristow, OK (4-135) Cpt, Chldr; GS; Parl, Hmrm; Tres, Lat C; NFL; NHS; Co-Ch, ARC; Spch C; Secy, SC; VP, Sr Cl; Secy, Jr Cl; S-T, Soph Cl; Swim; Tnns; Amer Leg A; COM; Citz A; Gov Honor Prog; Hist A; HCt; Hon Prog; Math A; Sci A; Spch A; VFW A; Yth Fel; WW; Okla Hon Soc; *Sou Methodist U; Ed.*

KELLY, Vicki Joy
Robert E Lee HS; Midland, TX (10%-800) Chor; Rptr, Sch P; Span C; Hon Prog; Yth Fel; *Hardin-Simmons U; Eng.*

KELLY, William Steven
St Elizabeth HS; Pittsburgh, PA (70-102) CYO; Drama; Fr C; Hmrm; Ski C; SC; Tres, Sr Cl; VP, Jr Cl; COM; Star Student; *Engr.*

KELM, Rick Alan
Ripon Sr HS; Ripon, WI (20-179) Chess C; Math C; NHS; Ski C; JV, Bkbl; JV, Ftbl; JV, Tnns; COM; Hon Prog; *Stanford U; Archt.*

KELSCH, Rebecca Faye
Augusta Pub Ind HS; Augusta, KY (10-32) BC; Bkbl; Tr; Hist A; Presidential Phys Fitness A; *U of Ky; Math.*

KELSEY, Philip Joseph
Northeast HS; Ft Lauderdale, FL; Wrest; *Broward Comm Col.*

KELSH, Kathy Grayce
Duke Ellington Sch For Arts; Washington, DC (50%-200) Band; Community Yth Symph; Drama; Hmrm; Orch; Ed, Sch P; SC; Secy, Soph Cl; COM; Citz A; Hon Prog; NJHS; WW; Men, St Mus Teachers Comp; Friday Morning Mus C; Partial Sch Tanglewood Mus Center; *Eastman Col; Mus.*

KELSH, Kathy Grayce
Ellington Sch for Performing Arts; Washington, DC (33%-250) Band; Chor; Community Yth Symph; Hmrm; Orch; F-Ed, Sch P; Citz A; Hon Prog; NJHS; Tanglewood Schol A; Fedder String Comp; Sewanee Schol A; Summer Mus Camps; Supt Cert, Academic Excellence; *Eastman Col; Mus.*

KELSO, Alexandra Ruth
Spring Valley Sr HS; Spring Valley, NY; Rainbow; JV, Swim; Citz A; GSct; Sun Sch Teacher; *Mansfield St Col; Textile Designing.*

KELSO, Charles Andrew
Spring Lake Jr-Sr HS; Spring Lake, MI (10%-250) Band; Order/Arrow; Swim; MLS; *Aeronautics.*

KELSO, James Phil
Bryan Adams HS; Dallas, TX (12-783) Secy, Chess C; Math C; NHS; JV, Ftbl; Hon Prog; *SW Assembly of God Bible Col; Missions.*

KELSO, Michael
Abingdon HS; Abingdon, IL; Var C; Bsbl; Ftbl; Tr; Kappa Delta Chi Fraternity; Church Tn Choir; *Carl Sandburg Col.*

KELTNER, Kathleen Marie
Beloit Mem HS; Beloit, WI (129-582) Tnns; HQn; Yth Fel; *Med.*

KELTNER, Timothy Evans
F L Schlagle HS; Kansas City, KS (15%-450) A Cap Choir; Chldr; Demolay; Drama; Ensm; Ger C; Hmrm; Order/Arrow; Rptr, Sch P; SC; Swim; COM; Order/Arrow A; Mus St Medals; Best Supporting Actor; *Whichita St Col; Vocal Mus.*

KEMBLE, Jane Ellen
LaVille Jr Sr HS; Lakeville, IN (31-141) Band; 4H; NHS; Sci C; Span C; 4H A; *Purdue U; Agr.*

KEMERLING, Tammie Sue
Kewanee HS; Kewanee, IL; AFS; Chem C; Chor; Dbte Tm; Drama; FHA; Ger C; Hmrm; Sci C; Spch C; SC; Bkbl; Tr; *Pre-Law.*

KEMMER, Amy Marie
Clintonville Sr HS; Clintonville, WI; Chldr; NFL; NHS; Solo Ensm As; *Health.*

KEMMERLING, Larry Eugene
Hitchcock HS; Hitchcock, TX (8-132) Chess C; NHS; Bkbl; Ftbl; *Naval Acad; Drafting.*

KEMNER, Thomas Floyd
Burnt Hills Ballston Lk Central HS; Burnt Hills, NY (49-397) ARC; JV, Soccer; COM; Hon Prog; Regent's School Alt; Church Choir; Swim Instructor YMCA; Coach, YMCA Bkbl; YMCA Plaque; Plaque Presented Yrly in My Name; *Taylor U; Spch Communications.*

KEMP, Betty Ann
Washington And Lee HS; Montross, VA (44-205) Chldr; Secy, Drama; Secy, 4H; Lit Mag; Cpt, Mjrte; Bkbl; Sftbl; Amer Leg A; 4H A; Co-Ch, GAA; Gym; Art A; HR A.

KEMP, James Bryan
Warren Area HS; Warren, PA (40-430) Band; Pres, NHS; SC; Var C; Cr-Ctry; Co-Cpt, Wrest; *Grove City Col; Bus.*

KEMP, Jeffrey Allan
Winston Churchill HS; Potomac, MD (15%-600) NHS; Ski C; Bsbl; Ftbl; NMS; *Dartmouth Col; Econ.*

KEMP, Tracy Lee
Richard Montgomery HS; Rockville, MD (10-396) Band; Ensm; Hmrm; NHS; SC; Tr; NEDT; Opt A; Spch A; Co-Cpt, Drill Tm; *Carson Newman Col; Religion.*

KEMP, Vincent Billy
Shanti HS; Hartford, CT (5-72) Hmrm; Cl Fav; HKg; Hon Prog; I Dare You; JA A; MLS; Most Out; Yth Leg; *Moree Sch Of Bus; Fashion and Merchandising.*

KEMPE, Cindy Lou
Highland HS; Ewing, MO (3-130) JV, Chldr; Chor; NHS; Sci C; SC; Regent Schol; *U of Mo; Med.*

KEMPENICH, Jean Marie
Lake o-t Woods HS; Baudette, MN; Ann; Band; CYO; Chldr; NHS; Spch C; Spch A.

KEMPENICH, Mary Louise
Lake of The Woods HS; Baudette, MN (31-88) Ann; Ch, CYO; Drama; GS; NHS; Spch C; Tr; Sacristan; Spch A; Drama A; 1st Cl GSct A; *Rainy River Comm Col; Practical Nurs.*

KEMPER, Corinne Lee
Wallace HS; Wallace, ID (15-103) Band; Chldr; Tres, NHS; VP, Rainbow; Sup Rating, Piano Solo; *Mus.*

KEMPER, Crystal Marie
Checotah HS; Checotah, OK (10%-150) FHA; Chapel Choir; HR; Sunday Sch Teacher Aid.

KEMPER, Diane Lynn
Hobart Sr HS; Hobart, IN (67-399) Band; COM; Nishova Solo Flute A; *Commercial Arts Advertising.*

KEMPER, Dolores Ann
Hobart Sr HS; Hobart, IN (182-399) Band; Nisbova Solo As; *Secy.*

KEMPER, Judy Marie
El Dorado Spgs Jr-Sr HS; El Dorado Springs, MO (24-126) A Cap Choir; Chor; FHA; FTA; NHS; Shorthand A.

KEMPF, Dwight Clayton
Penn Manor HS; Millersville, PA (26-385) Order/Arrow; JA A; Order/Arrow A; Eagle Sct; Amateur Radio; Church Yth Fel; JA; *Penn St U; Elec Engr.*

KEMPF, Magdalene
Norwich Free Acad; Norwich, CT (95-738) Hon Prog; Ger A; Ger Prize Exam.

KEMPKES, Mary Ann
Lourdes Central HS; Nebraska City, NE (3-29) Chor; Drama; Lat NHS; Math C; NHS; Span C; Spch C; Pres, Jr Cl; Tr; Amer Leg A; B Crocker A; Elk A; Hist A; Journ A; K of C A; Spch A; VFW A; VFW Orator Win; VofDEM; Mayor, GS; Lead, Sch Plays; Pep C; Best Actress; Sup Actress; Secy & VP, Mu Alpha Theta; Vlbl; *Benedictine Col; Spch.*

KEMPLIN, David Edwin
Montgomery Co HS; Mt Sterling, KY; Band; BC; BS; HiY; Ftbl; Tnns; COM; PA; Band A; May Dance Court; *U of K; Phar.*

KENALL, Kevin Keith
Hillcrest HS; Springfield, MO (50-316) Co-Cpt, Ftbl; JV, Wrest; *Drury Col; Pre-Med.*

KENDALL, Carolyn
Altoona Area HS; Altoona, PA; Band; Chor; Community Yth Symph; Ch, Ger C; Pres, Hmrm; Mjrte; Orch; Ski C; SC; Interlochen Ntl Mus; Am Yth Symph & Chor European Tour; *Susquehanna U; Mus Therapy.*

KENDALL, Janet Lynn
Riverside HS; Greer, SC (15-214) BC; Chor; Ensm; Bkbl; Tnns; *Mus.*

KENDALL, Kerrie Lynn
Obion Co Central HS; Troy, TN (10-192) Band; BC; Chldr; FHA; GS; NHS; Var C; DARGCA; Hist A; *Bethel Col.*

KENDALL, Kimberly Dawn
Marion HS; Marion, IL; FBLA; Swim; Tnns; *Sch of Tech Careers; Secy.*

KENDALL, Leona Jene
Justin-Siena HS; Napo, CA; Ann; Hmrm; 1st Cl, GSct; Job's Daughters; *Teach Deaf And Blind.*

KENDALL, Linda Kay
Klein HS; Spring, TX (164-620) A Cap Choir; Chor; FHA; Ger C; COM; Most Out; Sci A; Art, Piano, Foreign Lang, A's; *Abilene Christian U; Mus Theory.*

KENDALL, Mark Christopher
Lawrence HS; Lawrence, KS (140-600) Co-Ed, Sch P; SC; JV, Bsbl; Bkbl; Citz A; *Kans U; Journ.*

KENDALL, Robert Andrew
Obion Co Central HS; Troy, TN (29-177) A Cap Choir; Pres, Band; BS; Chor; Ensm; Math C; Orch; Var C; Bkbl; Cr-Ctry; Golf; Tr; Amer Leg A; H of F; Yth Fel; *Bethel Col; Dentistry.*

KENDALL, Ronald Lynn
Elizabethton HS; Elizabethton, TN; VP, FBLA; Sftbl; *E Tenn St U; Bus Adm.*

KENDELL, Dorothy Lee
Halsey J HS; New York City, NY; Chldr; Reading A; *Queens Col; Math Ed.*

KENDELL, Nathaniel
Bushwick HS; NYC, NY; Band; Bsbl; DARGCA; *Med.*

KENDRICK, Audrey Lynn
Holy Family HS; Birmingham, AL (4-41) Miss Tornado; JCC & V Pageant; *Spellman Col; Fashion & Merchandise.*

KENDRICK, Cathy
N Shore HS; W Palm Beach, FL (31-266) VP, FBLA; NHS; Hist A; Acct A; Fr A; Civics A; *U of S Fla; Acct.*

KENDRICK, Dennis Jerome
Nettie Lee Roth HS; Dayton, OH (33%-260) Band; Orch; Math A; Mus A; AAHPER Test; Special Effort A; *US Air Force; Mus.*

KENDRICK, Gloria Rene
Plant City HS; Plant City, FL (10%-893) Type A; Tns for Christ; *Eckerd Col; Bus.*

KENDRICK, Jonathan Andrew
Orange Park Sr HS; Orange Park, FL (10%-620) Secy, Ger C; Lat C; Pres, NHS; Hon Prog; NMF; NMS; Alt, BS; Chaplin, SC; *U of Fla; Pre-Law.*

KENDRICK, Nancy Anne
Prescott HS; Prescott, AZ (17-450) Ed, Ann; Band; CYO; GS; NHS; VP, Jr Cl; Cpt, Bkbl; Tnns; Most Out; Coun, GS; MVP, Bkbl; Jr Women's C A; *U of Ariz; Phys Ed.*

KENDRICK, Paul Arthur
Forest Lake Sr HS; Forest Lake, MN; Ski C; Ftbl; Hockey; Sftbl; Tr; Pres A.

KENDRICK, Shirley Ann
Haynesville HS; Haynesville, LA; Bus C; Chldr; Chem C; FBLA; FHA; Tres, Hmrm; Spch C; Beauty; Song Ldr, Fr C; *Southern St U; Nurs.*

KENDRICK, Stephen Paul
Vines HS; Plano, TX (35-500) Band; Ensm; Bsbl; *Chem.*

KENDUS, Karen Elizabeth
Plymouth Whitemarsh Sr HS; Plymouth Meeting, PA (20%-600) Band; Fr C; Sci C; Ski C; Swim; *Del Valley Agr & Sci Col; Ornamental Horticulture.*

KENEIPP, Chris Ann
Mount Carmel HS; Mount Carmel, IL (34-170) Band; Cpt, Chldr; Chor; 4H; Kiwanis A; Art School; Valentine Qn; *Dance.*

KENEIPP, Shelly Sue
Mt Carmel HS; Mt Carmel, IL (70-180) Co-Ed, Ann; Chldr; 4H; Key C; 4H A; Journ A; Q&S A; Dancing Stu; Church Mus; Choreographer, Cl Plays; *Milliken U; Theater.*

KENELIA, Richele
Bridgeton HS; Bridgeton, NJ (24-718) Semi-Fin, GS; Pres, 4H; Secy, NHS; Pres, Var C; Co-Cpt, Hockey; Sftbl; Citz A; *Bio.*

KENFIELD, Jennifer Lee
Antioch HS; Antioch, CA (67-568) A Cap Choir; Ensm; Fr C; NHS; CSF; Hon Prog; *Simpson Col; Psych.*

KENIRY, Cyril Troy
Notre Dame HS; W Haven, CT (60-232) All Amer Yth; CYO; Hmrm; NHS; Tres, SC; Bsbl; Bkbl; Cpt, Ftbl; MVP, Ftbl; All-St Ftbl; Ath o-t Yr; *Boston Col; Bus Mgr.*

KENLEY, Diane Sue
Lakeland Sr HS; Lakeland, FL (67-780) Secy, Fr C; Hmrm; Key C; NHS; SC; COM; Hon Prog; Pres, Christian Yth Fel; Fr A; *Auburn U; Pre-Med.*

KENNARD, Nancy Norleen
Plymouth HS; Plymouth, OH (5-120) JV, Chldr; Parl, FHA; Span C; SC; Sftbl; Eng I; FHA Court; *U of Cincinnati; Nurs.*

KENNEBREW, Shelita Yvonne
Lufkin HS; Lufkin, TX; A Cap Choir; Chldr; Chor; Ensm; FHA; ARC; Up Bound; Tr; COM; Most Out; *U of Houston; Spch Therapist.*

KENNEDY, Ann Marie
Natrona HS; Casper, WY (9-634) Fr C; Secy, 4H; Orch; F-Ed, Sch P; 4H A; NMS; Cand, TASP; *Creative Writing.*

KENNEDY, Anne Lucille
Holy Cross HS; Marine City, MI (1-41) Chldr; NHS; Sch P; Ski C; Bsbl; COM; *Alma Col; Art.*

KENNEDY, Carolyn Sue
Queen City HS; Queen City, TX (25%-41) VP, FHA; Secy, NHS; VP, Sci C; Secy, SC; Rptr, Soph Cl; Cl Fav; *Texarkana Col; Bus Mgt.*

KENNEDY, Charles Darrell
Cresset Christian Acad; Durham, NC (2-3) A-Ed, Ann; Ensm; Span C; Pres, SC; Co-Cpt, Bsbl; Cpt, Ftbl; Sftbl; *Guilford Col; Law.*

KENNEDY, Cheri Lynn
Lyons Township HS; La Grange, IL; Swim; St Scholar; Pres, Yth Fel; Synchronized Swim Tm; Girls C Board; *Tex Christian U; Nurs.*

KENNEDY, Colleen Kay
Liberty HS; Liberty, IL; Ann; FHA; Sch P; Soc for Acad Achv A.

KENNEDY, Cynthia Jean
Katella HS; Anaheim, CA (8-560) CSF; Gold Seal Bearer; *Calif St U; Human Services.*

KENNEDY, Cynthia Lynette
El Reno HS; El Reno, OK (10%-205) Chor; Dbte Tm; Fr C; 4H; NHS; Rainbow; ARC; Sci C; Thes; Sftbl; Swim; COM; 4H A; PA; *Law Enforcement.*

KENNEDY, David Blaine
Windsor Forest HS; Savannah, GA; Drama; SC; JV, Bsbl; MVP, Cr-Ctry; Ftbl; MVP, Tr; Gov Honor Prog; NEDT; Sci A; Yearly HR.

KENNEDY, Deanna Kay
Sunbright HS; Sunbright, TN (8-63) Ann; BC; Chldr; Chor; FHA; Sch P; Secy, Sr Cl; Tres, Jr Cl; HQn; Most Popular; Most Dependable.

KENNEDY, Elizabeth Ann
Philipsburg-Osceola HS; Philipsburg, PA (29-235) Band; Chor; Drama; FTA; Rainbow; Charles Alsop Mus A; Fin, DAR Essay; Phys Fitness A; *Ind U of Penn; Mus.*

KENNEDY, Elizabeth Rychen
Riverside HS; Greer, SC (8-150) BC; Chess C; 4H; Bio A; COM; Chem A; Coun of Teach A; Hiking, Photography, C'S; 1st Cl, Off, GSct; Graduation Marshal; *Wildlife Mgr.*

KENNEDY, Ena Gwendolyn
Cass Tech HS; Detroit, MI; COM; Cl Fav; Yth Fel; *Morehouse Col; Bio.*

KENNEDY, Frances Louise
Vicksburg HS; Vicksburg, MS (11-244) Band; Fr C; FHA; GS; NHS; H of F; Hist A; WW; Superior Mus, Auxiliary Talent, A's; *Jackson St U; Bus Adm.*

KENNEDY, Gale ReNae
North HS; Youngstown, OH (7-111) Fr C; NHS; Sch P; Tres, SC; Secy, Y-Tns; Secy, Sr Cl; Secy, Jr Cl; Secy, Soph Cl; Mgr, Tr; Alg A; Bio A; Chem A; Hist A; Yth Fel; *Med.*

KENNEDY, George Stephen
New Castle Sr HS; New Castle, PA; Chor; Madrigal; Model UN; Pa Midwest District Chor; PMEA.

KENNEDY, Gerilyn Michelle
Franklin HS; Franklin, IL; FFA; Pres, NHS; Sci C; Hon Stu; *Biol.*

KENNEDY, Grace Ruth
Sooner HS; Bartlesville, OK (1-289) AFS; Chor; Fr C; Masonic A; *Okla U; Nurs.*

KENNEDY, Greg Wayne
Belleville W HS; Belleville, IL (98-842) Fr C; Mgr, Ftbl; Hist A; Opt A; *SW Baptist Col; Church Recreation.*

KENNEDY, Harry Benjamin Jr
Destrehan HS; Destrehan, LA (2-168) Band; BC; BS; Secy, Key Cl; Orch; SC; Math A; Band A's; *LSU; Acct.*

KENNEDY, James Michael
University HS; San Diego, CA (6-311) Drama; Hmrm; NHS; Sci C; SC; Mgr, Bsbl; Ftbl; Tnns; CSF; Hon Prog; Most Improved, Ftbl; *Whitman Col; Pre-Vet.*

KENNEDY, Jane Elizabeth
Sooner HS; Bartlesville, OK; Pres, Fr C; FBLA; S-T, NHS; Amer Leg A; VofDEM.

KENNEDY, Jeffrey Darnell
John Marshall HS; Okla City, OK; Pres, 4H; Var C; Ftbl; Tr; Amer Leg A; Citz A; 4H A; JA A; Co-Cpt, Gym; *Okla U; Commercial Arts.*

KENNEDY, Jeffrey Paul
Peabody HS; Pittsburgh, PA (14-600) NHS; Ski C; Var C; DARGCA; Hon Prog; Co-Cpt, Vlbl; VP, Pgh Dist United Meth Yth Fel; *Grove City Col; Sci.*

KENNEDY, Jimmy Dorsey
Briarwood Acad; Thomson, GA (10-26) Ann; Key C; S-T, SC; Bkbl; Cpt, Ftbl; Golf; Cl Fav; Pres, FCA; *Anderson Col; Bus.*

KENNEDY, Jo Ellen Marie
Marian Cath HS; Tamaqua, PA (11-173) Chor; S-T, French NHS; NHS; Ed, Sch P; Co-Cpt, Color Guard; *Penn St U; Civil Engineering.*

KENNEDY, John Groover
Savannah Ctry Day Sch; Savannah, GA (20%-60) AFS; Rptr, Lit Mag; Rptr, Sch P; Bkbl; Ftbl; Tnns; Hon Prog.

KENNEDY, Karen May
Butler Area Sr HS; Butler, PA (20%-1000) Chor; FBLA; Thes; JA A; ARC A; VP, Jr Achv; GSct A; Bus.

KENNEDY, Karis Ann
Campbellsville HS; Campbellsville, KY (20-100) FBLA; Tri-HiY; *Campbellsville Col; Eng.*

KENNEDY, Kevin Glen
Parkland HS; El Paso, TX (30-250) BS; Order/ Arrow; Ski C; SC; Var C; Pres, Jr Cl; Tnns; Opt A; Order/Arrow A; Eagle Sct; *U of Tex-Austin; Law.*

KENNEDY, Kimberly Ann
Industry HS; Industry, IL (6-33) Bus Mgr, Ann; Band; JV, Chldr; Chor; Drama; Tres, Fr C; Sci C; Tres, SC; VP, Sr Cl; HCt; *Monmouth Col; Bus.*

KENNEDY, Kimberly Michelle
E Davidson HS; Thomasville, NC (2-140) Rptr, BC; FBLA; FHA; Rptr, FTA; NHS; SC; Secy, Sr Cl; Sal; Co-Chief Marshal; Nom, Morehead A; Hon Stu; *U of NC; Sci.*

KENNEDY, Kriss Michael
Parkland HS; El Paso, TX (4-250) NHS; Order/ Arrow; Rptr, Sch P; Var C; JV, Bsbl; Mgr, Bkbl; Tnns; Chem A; Hist A; Eng A; Span A; *US Naval Acad; Engr.*

KENNEDY, Kyle Gregory
Parkview Sr HS; Little Rock, AR (20%-437) Key C; Math C; Mu Alpha Theta; ARC; Spch C; Ftbl; Co-Cpt, Soccer; Tr; *U of Tenn; Dental.*

KENNEDY, Laurie Elizabeth
Canton Acad; Canton, MS (9-95) A-Ed, Ann; BC; Cpt, Chldr; Chor; 4H; NHS; Spch C; Tres, SC; Y-Tns; Secy, Sr Cl; Tres, Jr Cl; Tres, Soph Cl; Balfour A; Beauty; COM; Cl Fav; 4H A; H of F; HQn; HCt; Lion A; Spch A; Yth Fel; Miss Pork Qn; Most Dependable; *U of Miss; Banking & Finance.*

KENNEDY, Linda Adele
Richland HS; Fort Worth, TX; Bkbl; Tr; *Stephen F Austin St Col; Phys Ed.*

KENNEDY, Lisa Marie
Lower Dauphin HS; Hummelstown, PA (25-318) Chor; 4H; NHS; SC; COM; Cl Fav; Sci A; VP, Christian Yth Group; *Interior Decorator.*

KENNEDY, Mark Owen
Bellingham HS; Bellingham, WA (15%-300) Order/Arrow; Order/Arrow A; Eagle Sct; *W Wash St Col; Forestry.*

KENNEDY, Mary Clare
Holy Cross HS; Marine City, MI; Chldr; NHS; Sch P; Ski C; Span C; VP, SC; Var C; Tres, Soph Cl; Sftbl; *Western Mich U; Bus Mgmt.*

KENNEDY, Mary Katherine
Ridgeview HS; Atlanta, GA (12-220) AFS; Ed, Ann; BC; Community Yth Symph; Drama; Fr C; French NHS; Orch; VP, Soph Cl; Gov Honor Prog; Hon Prog; Most Out; Drill Tm; All St Orch; *SW Col at Memphis; International Stu.*

KENNEDY, Michelle Yvette
Bloom Trial HS; E Chicago Hts, IL; A Cap Choir; Chor; Drama; Tnns; Tr; Star Student; *U of Calif; Mus.*

KENNEDY, Nina Gamble
McGavock HS; Nashville, TN; Band; BC; Chor; Fr C; Ger C; Lat C; NEDT; NJHS; Myra Jackson Blair Schol; Piano Soloist, Nashville Symph; 1st Pl, St Mus Teacher's Assn; Regional Win, Amer Mus Schol Assn; *Curtis Inst of Mus; Mus.*

KENNEDY, Rhonda Michelle
E E Smith Sr HS; Fayetteville, NC; Band; Secy, FHA; Span C; COM; HCt; Hon Prog; Ntl Achv Schol; WW; *NC St U; Secondary Ed.*

KENNEDY, Rodney Dean
Civic Mem HS; Bethalto, IL; Demolay; Co-Cpt, Bkbl; Cr-Ctry; Golf; Ind Art C; Varsity C; Pep C; Masonic A Merits; *Lewis & Clark Comm Col; Architectual Engr.*

KENNEDY, Scott Vincent
El Reno HS; El Reno, OK (66-195) Band; VP, Fr C; Math C; ARC; Sci C; Thes; Y-Tns; Ftbl; Swim; Tnns; Tr; Most Out; Spch A; VFW A; Pres & Secy, Key C; Cert of Excellence; *Okla St U; Med.*

KENNEDY, Shannon Rochelle
Stevens HS; Rapid City, SD (196-459) Band; JV, Chldr; Chor; SC; VP, Soph Cl; *U of SD; Forestry.*

KENNEDY, Shawna Jo
J E B Stuart Secondary Sch; Falls Church, VA (46-425) Ger C; NHS; Bkbl; COM; Bowl As; Bkbl Letters; Hist Hon Soc; Cand, Keyettes.

KENNEL, Cynthia Renae
Clark Co R-1 HS; Kahoka, MO (5-96) Pres, 4H; NHS; VP, Rainbow; Thes; *Columbia-MU; Business.*

KENNELL, Brian Patrick
Bishop McNamara; Kankakee, IL (30-150) CYO; K of C; SC; Y-Tns; Bkbl; Ftbl.

KENNER, David Harold
Maddock Pub Sch; Maddock, ND (10-28) Ann; VP, FFA; VP, SC; VP, Jr Cl; VP, Soph Cl; Cpt, Ftbl; Shop A; Vo-Ag A; *ND St U; Agr.*

KENNETT, Mary Alice
Warren Central HS; Indianapolis, IN; Sftbl; Yth Fel; Job's Daughters; Jr NHS; *Ind Central U; Vet Med.*

KENNETT, Stephen Allen
Warren Central HS; Indianapolis, IN; Key C; *Ind Central U; Religion.*

KENNEY, Connie Lynn
Barstow HS; Kansas City, MO; AFS; Band; Chor; Fr C; Hmrm; ARC; SC; Mgr, Swim; Yth Fel; Col Theatre; Church Choir; Duke Duncan A; *Special Ed.*

KENNEY, Joyce Anne
Wachusett Regional HS; Holden, MA; Co-Cpt, Chldr; *Fitchburg St Col; Nurs.*

KENNEY, Kristine Karen
Reseda HS; Reseda, CA (20%-800) Drama; Madrigal; MVP, Bkbl; Sftbl; Tr; Vlbl; *USC; Eng.*

KENNEY, Paul Randel
Amherst Pub HS; Amherst, NE; CYO; Pres, 4H; NHS; SC; VP, Var C; Pres, Jr Cl; Pres, Soph Cl; Ftbl; Tr; Wrest; COM; 4H A; St Wrest A; St Tr A; *U of Nebr; Ag Development.*

KENNEY, Paulette Andrea
Ritenour Sr HS; Overland, MO (90-668) Band; Hon Prog; *Stephens Col; Acct.*

KENNISON, Donna Lee
York Central Sch; Retsof, NY; Drama; VP, FTA; 4H; Hmrm; Tns, SC; 4H A; Pres, Color Guard; *Syracuse Col; Environmental.*

KENNISTON, Diane Louise
Sacred Heart HS; Kingston, MA (2-54) Chor; NHS; ARC; Bkbl; Hockey; Sftbl; Bausch & Lomb A; COM; Chem A; Hon Prog; Co-Ed, Yrbk; Highest Academic Avg; *Col o-t Holy Cross; Bio.*

KENNON, Kathleen Elizabeth
Cedar Shoals HS; Athens, GA; Band; S-T, Drama; Lat C; S-T, Thesp; Band; 3rd Pl, Regional Essay; *Young Harris Col; Special Ed.*

KENNY, Eric Richard
T C Roberson HS; Skyland, NC (10-250) BC; Chess C; Key C; Monogram; Pres, Span C; Var C; MVP, Bkbl; Cr-Ctry; Tnns; Gr Marshal; NMF; NMS; *UNC-Chapel Hill; Math.*

KENSING, Tracy Neal
New Braunfels HS; New Braunfels, TX (35-280) NHS; Co-Cpt, Ftbl; Co-Cpt, Tr; FCA; Theta Epsilon Nu; Blue Chippr; Iron Man A, All Zone, Offense, Ftbl; Defense, All Centr, Sup Centr, Ftbl; *Tex Tech U.*

KENT, Barbara J
Centralia HS; Centralia, WA (13-247) Chor; Dbte Tm; NHS; Var C; Mgr, Tr; Vlbl; Mgr, Gym; *NW Nazarene Col; Mus.*

KENT, Brenda Gail
S Garland HS; Garland, TX (25%-700) BC; Chldr; FHA; Sci C; Span C; *Eastfield Jr Col; Spec Ed.*

KENT, David Randall
Poway HS; Poway, CA (10-460) Band; Chor; Ensm; Hmrm.

KENT, Kelly Lee
Warwick HS; Lititz, PA (131-260) Band; Chor; Drama; Ensm; Mgr, Wrest; *Nurs.*

KENT, Larry Gene
Red Bay HS; Red Bay, AL (20-63) Hon Prog; *Phil Champbell Jr Col; Med.*

KENT, Letitia
East HS; Columbus, OH (32-350) All A's A; HR; WW; NJHS; *Columbus Tech Col; Nurs.*

KENT, Louis Ray
Wahama HS; Mason, WV (10-125) Chess C; Chor; Key C; NHS; COM; Citz A; DARGCA; Hon Prog; Rotary A; Yth Fel; Yth Foundation; *Glenville St Col; Ed.*

KENT, Richard Alan
N Canton Hoover HS; N Canton, OH (33%-435) A Cap Choir; Drama; Math C; NHS; Sci C; Thes; *U of Akron; Engr.*

KENT, Sandra Caye
Screven Co HS; Sylvania, GA (10%-250) Band; Chldr; Dbte Tm; Fr C; FBLA; Pres, 4H; Rptr, Hmrm; NHS; A-Ed, Sch P; SC; Tri-HiY; Var C; COM; 4H A; HCt; Opt A; Hon Grad; Farmers & Merchants Bank Acad Schol; *U of Ga; Journ.*

KENT, Vickie Michelle
Rossville Comp HS; Rossville, GA (10-212) BC; VP, FBLA; Math A; Sci A; Eng A; Semi-Fin, Gov Hon; *Tomlinson Col; Bus Adm.*

KENTON, Sally Elizabeth
Fremont HS; Sunnyvale, CA; Band; Chor; Sch P; Ski C; Tr; Sch Spirit C; HR.

KENWARD, Terry Katharine
Medina Sr HS; Medina, NY (3-200) A Cap Choir; Tres, 4H; Hmrm; SC; Citz A; 4H A; *U of Rochester; Med.*

KENYON, Janet Louise
Vista HS; Vista, CA; Band; Ensm; NHS; *Los Angelos Babt Col; Psych.*

KENYON, Lisa Gae
Lansdowne Sr HS; Baltimore, MD (10%-480) Bus C; Chor; FBLA; FTA; Hmrm; InterAct C; Inter-Club Coun; Rptr, SC; Sr Cl; Bio A; COM; Citz A; Puppet Ministry; Eng A; Choreography A; *Towson St U; Occupational Therapy.*

KENYON, Paul Saunders
Starpoint Central HS; Lockport, NY (17-253) Band; Drama; Fr C; Orch; Bkbl; Soccer; Tnns; Outst Male Musician A; *Eastman Sch of Mus; Piano.*

KENYON, Tammy Kay
Tahlequah Sr HS; Tahlequah, OK (5%-250) Band; FBLA; FTA; GS; Math C; NHS; Var C; Bkbl; Amer Leg A; Bio A; Kiwanis A; Type A; Band A.

KEPHART, Cheryl Marie
Hastings Sr HS; Hastings, MN (142-422) Band; DECA; Yth Resource Tm; *Bethel Col; Elem Ed.*

KEPLEY, James Donald
Lexington Sr HS; Lexington, NC (15-250) Ann; Pres, Fr C; Tres, Key C; Lit Mag; NHS; Pres, Soph Cl; JV, Bkbl; Tnns; *Wake Forest U; Law.*

KEPLINGER, Charles Everett
Potomac HS; Oxon Hill, MD; Band; Bsbl; Ftbl; *Ashland Col.*

KER, Kelly Lynne
Interlochen Arts Acad; Interlochen, MI; A Cap Choir; Band; Chor; Ensm; 4H; Madrigal; COM; 4H A; Hon Prog; Yth Fel; Yth Deacon; *U of Cincinnati Col Conserv of Mus; Piano.*

KERBO, Jimmy Neal
Mangum HS; Mangum, OK (10-70) Demolay; 4H; NHS; Bsbl; Bkbl; Ftbl; Gov Honor Prog; Hist A; HCt; Masonic A; Yth Fel; Stu of Today A; Dist Chmp Tm, Bsbl; Dist Chmp Tm, Reg Chmp Tm, Bkbl; Area Chmp Tm, St Semi-Fin, Bkbl; Conf Champ Tm, Bkbl.

KERBY, Cynthia D Lene
Sanger HS; Sanger, TX (1-70) Band; Drama; VP, FHA; NHS; Spch C; Tnns; Chamber of Comm A; Outst Band Stu; FHA St Degree; Drum Major; PA; *N Tex St U; Mus.*

KERKSIECK, Phillip John
Spencer HS; Spencer, WI (14-63) Ed, Ann; Band; Chor; Pres, Drama; Ensm; FFA; Pres, 4H; Mod Mus Mas; F-Ed, Sch P; Var C; Ftbl; Wrest; Elk A; 4H A; Masque & Gavel A; Q&S A; Drama A; Parl A; 4-H Citz Short Course; Ray Harrell Drama A; *Morehouse Col; Social Work.*

KERLEY, Daniel Francis
Western HS; Louisville, KY (62-363) Chor; Bkbl; JV, Cr-Ctry; Tr; *U of Ky; Forestry.*

KERN, Anthony Fitzgerald
Marian HS; Tamaqua, PA (8-138) Band; French NHS; Order/Arrow; SC; Hon Prog; NEDT; *Harvard U; Law.*

KERN, Debbie Lee
Brethren Christian HS; Osceola, IN (5%-26) Band; Chor; Ensm; Fr C; NHS; Ntl Yth Conf; ARC; Yth Fel; Nisbova Contest; *Grace Col.*

KERN, Diane Jean
Highland HS; Ewing, MO; FHA; Secy, 4H; NHS; Sch P; Sci C; Up Bound; Bio A; 4H A; Hon Prog; St Grange Princess; Grange, Foley, A's; *U of Mo; Commercial Art.*

KERN, Edward Lane Jr
Santa Monica HS; Santa Monica, CA (25%-980) Cpt, Cr-Ctry; *Carpentry.*

KERN, Kurt Christopher
Parkway Central Sr HS; Chesterfield, MO (15-550) Bkbl; Ftbl; HCt; Yth Committee; *Hillsdale Col.*

KERN, Paul Thomas
Ewing HS; Trenton, NJ (20-440) Band; Orch; Stage Band; Concertmaster, Concert Band.

KERNER, Deborah Ann
Watkins Mem HS; Pataskala, OH (20-215) Band; Drama; FTA; Span C; Pres, SC; Tr; Pres, BOE C; *Ohio U; Secy.*

KERNER, Pamela Lynn
Watkins Mem HS; Pataskala, OH (12-200) Co-Ed, Ann; Band; Drama; VP, FTA; 4H; Tres, Lit Mag; Ch, NHS; Rptr, Sch P; Span C; Sh, SC; Tres, Var C; Cr-Ctry; Swim; Co-Cpt, Tr; Magna Cum Laude; Tres, Pep C; Pres, Yth Fel; *Miami U; Ed.*

KERNICH, Thomas Paul
Bishop Klonowski HS; Scranton, PA (10-115) Pres, Chess C; Chor; Amer Leg A; Math A; *Penn St U; Engr.*

KERNS, Cathy Diane
Bardstown HS; Bardstown, KY (18-130) Ann; VP, Drama; NHS; SC; Tnns; Cl Fav; Regent Schol; Type A; Drama A; Sociology A; *Western Ky U; Broadcasting.*

KERNS, David Allan
Falls Church HS; Falls Church, VA (213-550) Chor; Soccer; *Bethany Col; Wildlife Mgr.*

KERNS, David Brian
Central Dauphin E HS; Harrisburg, PA; Band; Chor; Cr-Ctry; Swim; COM; Hon Prog; Order/Arrow A; Jr NHS; *Med.*

KERNS, David Clifford
Logan Elm HS; Circleville, OH; Band; Rptr, FFA; 4H; Ftbl.

KERNS, Debby Ann
Sherwood HS; Creighton, MO (15%-110) 4H; NHS; JV, Bkbl; Sftbl; JV Bkbl Trophies; *Central Mo St U; Clerical Practice.*

KERNS, Denise Marie
S Dade HS; Homestead, FL; FFA; NHS; ARC; Hon Prog; *Eckerd Col; Elem Ed.*

KERNS, Doris Elizabeth
Taylorville HS; Taylorville, IL (75%-266) Ann; Tres, Bus C; Chor; Drama; Lat C; Rptr, Sch P; Jr Chamber of Com A; GAA; God & Comm A; *Lincoln Land Comm Col; Computers.*

KERNS, Julia Rae
Springs Valley HS; French Lick, IN (11-97) Band; Chor; Fr C; GS; 4H; Fin, Jr Miss Pagent; Mjrte; NHS; F-Ed, Sch P; Citz A; DARGCA; Journ A; MLS; St Scholar; Outst Mus A; Rep, Boys Girls Nation; Twirling As; Pep C; Fr C; GAA; Rifle Squad; Job's Daughters; 4-H Fair Qn; Miss Cinderella.

KERNS, Karen Renee
Gladewater HS; Gladewater, TX (25%-180) Band; Secy, FHA; FTA; NHS; Yth Fel; Pres, Methodist Yth Fel; *Kilgore Jr Col; Ed.*

KERR, Bruce Edward
Smith Cotton HS; Sedalia, MO (230-339) All Amer Yth; Band; 4H; JV, Bkbl; Tr; JV, Wrest; COM; JA A; Most Out; NAIA Hurdle Champ; Outst Jazz As; Tr As; *Northeast Mo St U; Phys Ed.*

KERR, George Conrad
Sheyenne River Acad; Harvey, ND (33%-24) Ann; Sch P; Pres, Sr Cl; Cpt, Bkbl; Cpt, Ftbl; Sftbl; Tr; I Dare You; Pres Coun Phys Fitness A; Sergeant-At-Arms; Artist, Ann; *Union Col; Theology.*

KERR, Jeffrey Carroll
Wilkinsburg HS; Pittsburg, PA (52-287) A Cap Choir; Arch; InterClub Coun; Key C; ARC; Span C; Var C; Arch; Swim; Tr; Cpt, Wrest; PTA A; Yth Fel; Tr, Comm, A's; *U of Pittsburgh; Social Work.*

KEYS, Terry Louis
Breckinridge Co HS; Harned, KY (3%-207) Band; Ensm; FBLA; NHS; Span C; Span A; Dist Band; Sup Rating, Solo & Ensm.

KEYSER, Karen Lynn
Agnes Irwin HS; Rosemont, PA; Chor; Hmrm; Ski C; Cpt, Bkbl; Hockey; COM; Cpt, Lacrosse; *Math.*

KEYSER, Nancy Louise
Loy Norrix HS; Kalamazoo, MI (30-500) Band; Chldr; Ensm; Fr C; Orch; Sch P; Magna Cum Laude; Yth Fel; Ntl Solo & Ensm Festival; Ntl Band & Orch Festival; *Mich St U; Vet Med.*

KEZER, William Frank
Crater HS; Central Point, OR (35-600) Bus C; Cpt, Arch; West; Cert, Skills Contest A; *Oregon Col of Bus; Bus.*

KHAZOOM, Stephane
College De Ste Anne De La Pocatiere; La Pocatiere, CANADA (2-35) ARC A; *Med.*

KHOURY, Darlene Marie
Saint Vincent-Saint Mary HS; Akron, OH (37-260) A Cap Choir; Band; Mgr, CYO; Chor; Drama; Ensm; Madrigal; Math C; Mu Alpha Theta; NHS; COM; Hon Prog; Interlochen Ntl Mus; *Akron U; Hotel-Motel Mgr.*

KIANG, Michael
Liberty Central HS; Liberty, NY (10-130) NHS; Order/Arrow; JV, Ftbl; Sci A; Regents School Win; Math Academic Ltr; Physics Ltr; *Rensselaer Polytechnic Inst; Elec Engr.*

KIAR, Debbie Ruth
Jonesboro HS; Jonesboro, AR (10%-401) BC; VP, Chor; FBLA; Alpha Theta; NHS; COM; Math A; Type A; Jr Cl Play; Sch Typing A; Eng A; Art C; *Ark St U; Data Processing.*

KIBLER, Douglas Alan
Forest Park HS; Beaumont, TX; Math C; JA A; *Lon Morris Col; Archt Engr.*

KICHAK, Michelle Ann
Notre Dame HS; Clarksburg, WV (3-55) CYO; Chldr; Drama; FBLA; FTA; ARC; Tnns; Alg A; Hist A; Math A; *NEDT; W Va U; Med Field.*

KICK, Kimberly Lynn
Orrville HS; Orrville, OH (34-198) Band; Secy, FTA; Tres, Span C; JV, Bkbl; Poet A; *Malone Col; Elem Ed.*

KIDD, Carolyn LaFrance
Gumberry HS; Gumberry, NC (6-115) Chor; Fr C; FHA; Sch P; Secy, Soph Cl; *Hampton Inst; Child Development.*

KIDD, Dorian Christopher
E Tech HS; Cleveland, OH (12-460) VP, AFS; Fr C; Hmrm; Key C; Math C; NHS; Sch P; SC; Up Bound; COM; Chem A; Citz A; Hist A; Hon Prog; Journ A; Math A; Most Out; Q&S A; Sci A; 1st Pl, E Tech Sci Fair; Eng, Straight 'A', Fr, A's; *Morehouse Col; Pre-Med.*

KIDD, Gretchen Renee
East Tech HS; Cleveland, OH (3-460) Hmrm; Key C; NHS; A-Ed, Sch P; VP, Span C; SC; Up Bound; Bio A; Citz A; Hist A; Journ A; Kiwanis A; Most Out; Q&S A; Sci A; Attendance A; *Mus.*

KIDD, Kevin Earl
Diamond Hill-Jarvis HS; Ft Worth, TX (1-175) NHS; Bsbl; Ftbl; Bio A; Gold Eagle A; *Engr.*

KIDD, Kimberly Ann
Eau Gallie HS; Melbourne, FL; FBLA; VP, FHA; NHS; Rptr, Sch P; SC; Citz A; Q&S A; WW; *Fla St U; Acct.*

KIDD, Marcella Rene
Spur HS; Spur, TX; A Cap Choir; Ann; Pres, Band; VP, FHA; Co-Ed, Sch P; Sci C; SC; Cl Fav; HQn; *S Plains Jr Col.*

KIDD, Michael
Trenton Central HS; Trenton, NJ; Chor; Drama; Var C; Ftbl; Tr; Wrest; Citz A; Phys Ed A; HR; *Lincoln U; Med.*

KIDD, Sylvia Renee
Gumberry HS; Gumberry, NC (12-97) F-Ed, Ann; BC; Chldr; Chor; Drama; Fr C; SC; HCt; *Hampton Inst; Early Childhood Ed.*

KIDD, Tammy Deann
Whitney HS; Whitney, TX; BC; FHA; Secy, 4H; Secy, Span C; Bkbl; Co-Cpt, Drill Tm; Liber Socius C.

KIDDER, Jacque Sue
York HS; York, NE (49-152) Ger C; Sch P; VP, Var C; Cpt, Bkbl; Cpt, Sftbl; Tr; Job's Daughters; MVP, Super St All Cl, Bkbl; Cpt, MVP, Hon Men All St, Vlbl; Sertoma A; *U of Nebr; Ath Trng.*

KIDDER, Pauline
Berwick HS; Berwick, LA (20-157) CYO; Chldr; Lit Ral; *USL; Secy.*

KIDDER, Sherie Lynn
Central HS; Helena, AR; Band; Drama; Span C; *Hendrix Col.*

KIDWELL, Martin Clark
Ne HS; Oakland Park, FL (85%-600) Chor; JV, Bsbl; *Math.*

KIDWELL, Michael Lynn
E Central HS; Tulsa, OK (20-600) NHS; Bsbl; DARGCA; *Abilene Christian U; Forestry.*

KIEFER, Dawn Elise
Lakewood HS; Lakewood, CA; A Cap Choir; Chor; Lit Mag; Madrigal; NHS; CSF; Citz A; Yth Fel; Regional Guild Cover Girl, Church; *U of Calif; Ed.*

KIEFER, Georgia Lee
Chamblee HS; Atlanta, GA (40-342) Bus Mgr, Ann; BC; Drama; Secy, Fr C; Lat C; NHS; ARC; Hist A; Hon Prog; Eng A; Drill Tm; Lat A; Church Yth Group; Church Choir.

KIEFER, Lynda Lee
Luther S HS; Chicago, IL (90-160) Band; 4H; Ski C; Bkbl; Cpt, Sftbl; Tr; COM; 4H A; *Computer Math.*

KIEFER, Priscilla Jane
Chamblee HS; Chamblee, GA (11-280) Ann; BC; Ger C; Lat C; Mjrte; NHS; MVP, Tnns; COM; Hon Prog; *Agnes Scott Col; Eng.*

KIEFER, Thomas Aaron
Abbotsford Pub HS; Abbotsford, WI (15%-68) Band; CYO; Ensm; VP, FFA; VP, 4H; NHS; Tres, SC; Var C; Tr; Wrest; COM; 4H A; BS Nom; Dairy Cattle Proficiency; Stage Band; Jr Prom Kg; Tres, Marathon Co Jr Holstein Breed; Star Chap Farmer, FFA; *UN-River Falls.*

KIEFFE, Dana Lynn
Roma HS; Roma, TX (26-130) Chldr; FHA; S-T, 4H; Hmrm; Mjrte; ARC; 4H A; *Med.*

KIEFFER, Karla Marie
Newman HS; Wausau, WI; Ann; Hmrm; Cr-Ctry; Sftbl; HCt.

KIEFFER, William Norman
Hershey Sr HS; Hershey, PA (270-340) *HACC; Law.*

KIEL, Roger A
Castlemont HS; Oakland, CA (10%-620) Chess C; Math C; Span C; SC; Tr; Citz A; MLS; Sci A; Star Student; Type A; Rptr & A-Ed, Sch Paper; *Stanford Med Center; Med.*

KIELMAR, Kathleen Ann
Portsmouth HS; Portsmouth, OH (32-263) Tres, Hmrm; Lat C; NHS; Pres, Lib C; Vlbl; City Teacher's Assn Schol; Badminton; Ping-Pong; *Shawnee St Col; Acct.*

KIELSMEIER, Betty Jane
Leaf River HS; Leaf River, IL; Band; Chor; FHA; FTA; Fin, GS; Secy, Sr Cl; *Rock Valley Col; Lib Sci.*

KIELY, Thomas Joseph
Chaminade HS; Mineola, NY (25-297) Co-Ed, Ann; CYO; NFL; NHS; F-Ed, Sch P; Sodality; Pres, Spch C; SC; COM; Spch A; NY St Champ, Dramatic Interpret; *St John's U; Eng.*

KIENITZ, Rhonda LeAnn
LeMars Comm HS; LeMars, IA; Band; Chor; Community Yth Symph; Bkbl; Tr; Mgr, Wrest; 4H A; Interlochen Ntl Mus; Ntl Fraternity of Stu Musicians; Stage Band; *Westmar Col; Mus.*

KIER, Scott Alan
Perry HS; Massillon, OH (50%-470) Pres, A Cap Choir; Pres, Chor; Spch C.

KIERSTEAD, June L
Alvirne HS; Hudson, NH (100-200) Chor; FBLA; Win, Spelling Contest; Del, Interntl Church Yth Conf; Bible Quiz Trophies; *E Nazarene Col; Advertising.*

KIESOW, Sara Jane
Horicon HS; Horicon, WI; Band; Chldr; Chor; Sftbl; Tr; HCt; Solo-Ensm A; Color Guard; Statistician, Bkbl & Wrest; *Concordia Col; Teacher.*

KIESTLER, Deborah Lynne
Pickwick South Side HS; Counce, TN (1-32) Bus Mgr, Ann; BC; Co-Cpt, Chldr; VP, FHA; Sci C; Pres, SC; Rptr, Sr Cl; Rptr, Jr Cl; Val; *Memphis St U; Fashion Merchandising.*

KIESWETHER, Ronald Allen
La Center HS; La Center, WA (6-32) Band; NHS; JV, Bkbl.

KIEU, Quang Xuan
Lincoln HS; Seattle, WA;

KIEU, Thu Bich
Lincoln HS; Seattle, WA; Swim; *Warner Pacific Col; Law.*

KIGER, Jill Ann
Cleveland HS; St Louis, MO (12-940) Band; Cpt, Chldr; Hockey; Sftbl; Tr; Sci A; *William Jewell Col.*

KIHLE, Scott Anthony
Columbus Pub HS; Columbus, ND (4-21) Band; BS; Ensm; Pres, Jr Cl; MVP, Bkbl; Ftbl; Tr; Pres, Lutheran Yth Organization.

KIKER, Mark Allen
Lubbock Christian HS; Lubbock, TX (12-45) NHS; Cpt, Ftbl; Tr; MVP, Ftbl; *Tex Tech U; Acct.*

KIKER, Paula Wynn
Warrior Acad; Eutaw, AL; BC; Cpt, Chldr; Chor; Secy, Fr C; Math C; F-Ed, Sch P; Secy, SC; Var C; Tr; Beauty; Cl Fav; Sci A; Miss Warrior Contest; Bkbl & Bsbl Bookkeeper; *U of Ala; Med.*

KILBOURN, Lawrence Edward
Madison HS; Adrian, MI (5-60) BS; Bsbl; *Adrian Col; Acct.*

KILBURN, Toby Ann
Dilce Combs HS; Jeff, KY (14-110) Band; BC; Cpt, Chldr; FHA; Mjrte; Rainbow; Y-Tns; HCt; Hon Prog; *E Ky U; Acct.*

KILBY, Deborah Ann
John F Kennedy HS; Tumon, GUAM (1-511) Ch, NHS; Cpt, Swim; *Ariz St U; Engr.*

KILBY, Kevin Martin
Gridley HS; Gridley, CA (81-167) CYO; Span C; JV, Bkbl; JV, Ftbl; JV, Sftbl; Church Lector; *Med.*

KILBY, Mitchelle Darlene
Yates Center HS; Yates Center, KS (6-60) Band; FHA; Cpt, Mjrte; Bkbl; Sftbl; Swim; Tnns; *Iola Jr Col.*

KILBY, Penelope Marlaina
Takoma Acad; Takoma Park, MD; Band; Chor; Type A; *U of Md; Health Ed.*

KILCOLLINS, Bonnie Louise
Abraham Lincoln HS; Denver, CO (88-790) Chem C; FBLA; Pres, FNA; 4H; NHS; Secy, ARC; Sci C; Ski C; Swim; 4H A; ARC A; Type A; *Biola Col; Nurs.*

KILCREASE, Mar De Phle
Maplewood HS; Nashville, TN (10-390) S-T, FHA; Fin, GS; Secy, Lat C; NHS; SC; *U of Tenn; Pre-Med.*

KILDAHL, Heidi Christine
Houston HS; Houston, MN (14-47) Chor; Drama; Ensm; FHA; Sch P; Hon Stu; Piano A; Sextet A; *Luther Col; Eng.*

KILE, Russell Alan
Cheyenne Mountain HS; Colo Springs, CO (33%-200) Band; Ensm; Order/Arrow; Eagle Sct; *U of Colo; Hist.*

KILGORE, Ginger Colleen
N Clayton Sr HS; College Park, GA (43-400) Tres, BC; Ch, FHA; Tres, Sci C; Sftbl; Crisco A; HR; St Champ Flag Corp; *Ga Inst of Technology; Textile Sci.*

KILGORE, Linroy Manning
N Side HS; Ft Worth, TX; Golf; COM; Chem A; Sci A; Rodeo C; Pres, Royal Ambassador; Day Camper A; Hiker A; *Sci.*

KIMSEY, Jami Lynn
Campbell HS; Fairburn, GA; Secy, FBLA; Pres, Span NHS; SC; Y-Tns; HCt; Hon Prog; Drill Tm; Semi Fin, Beauty, Sch Swtht; *Ga Col; Secy Sci.*

KIMSEY, Tiago Norman
Claiborne Co HS; Tazewell, TN (5%-165) BC; Chess C; 4H; SC; Up Bound; Alg A; *Phys Sci.*

KINARD, Daryl Edward
Wm Penn HS; York, PA; Band; City Conf; Dbte Tm; Hmrm; InterClub Coun; Orch; SC; Coun of Teach A; Journ A; *Shippensburg St Col; Journ.*

KINCADE, Romielee Deborah
Hernando HS; Brooksville, FL (42-421) Chldr; NHS; Bkbl; Cpt, Ftbl; Sftbl; Tr; Vlbl; *Psych.*

KINCAID, Bruce Wade
Mission HS; Mission, TX (47-365) Var C; Co-Cpt, Ftbl; H of F; *Evangel Col; Foreign Lang.*

KINCAID, Donna Sue
Caney Valley HS; Caney, KS (13-66) Ann; Band; Chldr; Chor; FBLA; GS; NHS; Rainbow; SC; Sftbl; HCt; Dist Pres, FHA; *Coffeyville Jr Col; Bus Adm.*

KINCAID, Harold Blaine
Rockwood Area HS; Rockwood, PA (2-114) Pres, Fr C; VP, 4H; Hmrm; NHS; Ed, Sch P; Sci C; Pres, SC; Co-Cpt, Tr; COM; A; NEDT; Sch Rep, Penn St Schol Prog; *Penn St U; Sci.*

KINCAID, Kay
Falls Church HS; Falls Church, VA (50-509) Chor; Tres, FHA; French NHS; NHS; Secy, Keyettes; Certifcat de Merite; *David Lipscomb Col; Home Ec.*

KINCAID, Margaret Olivia
Stonewall Jackson HS; Mt Jackson, VA (25-115) F-Ed, Ann; Chor; Secy, 4H; Lat C; Monogram; NHS; Sch P; Ski C; SC; Mgr, Bkbl; Tr; DARGCA; 4H A; Parl, 4-H C; Secy, Yth Board, Va Lung Assn; 4-H Hon C; *Mary Baldwin Col; Hist.*

KINCAID, Mary Ella
W Division HS; Milwaukee, WI; Fr C; COM; *Law.*

KINCAID, Nona Leigh
The Altamont Sch; Birmingham, AL (20-41) Secy, Chor; Ensm; Fr C; Sci A; Citz A; Stu Intern For Graded Chors; Pres, Mus C; WW; *Samford U; Mus Therapy.*

KINCAID, William Burl
Bath Co HS; Owingsville, KY (20-100) BC; Sci C; Ftbl; Phys Ed A; *Morehead St U; Communications.*

KINCANNON, Elaine Kay
Melbourne HS; Melbourne, FL; Ann; VP, Drama; Fin, Hmrm; NHS; VP, Span C; SC; Tnns; COM; Hon Prog; Hospital Vol A; *U of Fla; Med.*

KINCER, Cindy Jane
George Wythe HS; Wytheville, VA (11-130) VP, HiY; Mu Alpha Theta; NHS; Sci C; Co-Cpt, Vlbl; Keyettes; *Old Dominion U; Marine Bio.*

KINCER, Michael Louis
Slaton HS; Slaton, TX (20-55) Parl, FFA; FHA; Ftbl; Golf; Sci A; *Tex Tech U; Geol.*

KINCIUS, Brian Craig
St Ignatius Col Prep Sch; Chicago, IL (4-224) Lat C; Cpt, Y-Tns; Wrest; Aux Lat; COM; Cl Fav; Hon Prog; CB Radio T; Schoenstadt Schol A; Pres, Altar Boy Soc; Talman Fed Schol A; *U of Notre Dame; Sci.*

KINDA, Tami Lynn
Williamsville S HS; Buffalo, NY; Chor; Drama; Orch; ARC; Span C; Soccer; Tr; COM; Citz A; NYSSMA Solo Festival A; *Mus Therapy.*

KINDBERG, Scott Alan
Jamestown HS; Jamestown, NY (33%-550) Band; Ensm; Hmrm; VP, SC; Bkbl; COM; Cl Fav; HKg; Yth Fel; *SUNY Fredonia; Journ.*

KINDER, Karol Ann
Richardson HS; Richardson, TX (53-980) Chor; Secy, Fr C; Tri-HiY; Y-Tns; Citz A; Hon Prog; *Baylor U; Bus.*

KINDER, Michelle Lynn
Brussels Comm HS; Brussels, IL (12-34) Band; CYO; Chor; FHA; VP, 4H; Tr; 4H A; I Dare You; *Lewis & Clark Col; Ed.*

KINDER, Risa Ann
Chase Co HS; Imperial, NE (24-78) Band; Ensm; JV, Bkbl; Sftbl; Swim; Tr.

KINDER, Susan Kay
North Sr HS; Springfield, OH (20-578) Band; Chldr; Drama; Ensm; Pres, Hmrm; Orch; Ski C; Span C; SC; Tr; Hon Prog; Star Student.

KINDRICK, Aquila Yvonne
Baker HS; Columbus, GA; Hmrm; SC; JA A; *Columbus Col; Health Ed.*

KINDSCHY, Lori Dawn
Havre HS; Haure, MT (45-292) Band; Chor; Hmrm; InterAct C; SC; Var C; Cr-Ctry; Golf; *N Mont Col; Acct.*

KINDY, Anna Olga
Alexander Galt Regional HS; Lennoxville, CANADA (8-439) Lat C; Tnns; JV, Tr; Swim; Hon Prog; Vlbl; Judo; Badminton.

KINDY, Nadine Alexandra
Alexander Galt Regional HS; Lennoxville, CANADA (4-539) VP, Ger C; Hmrm; Lat C; Ski C; S-T, SC; Soccer; Swim; Tnns; JV, Tr; Hon Prog; Lat A; Prom Comm; Judo; Vlbl; Stu Quiz Show; Modern Dance; Travel C; Badminton; Hostess; *Med.*

KINERK, Diane Elizabeth
Blanchet HS; Seattle, WA (33-285) Drama; Pres, Hmrm; NHS; Sch P; SC; Thes; VP, Soph Cl; Hon Prog; *U of Wash; Nurs.*

KING, Aaron Pike
Broadmoor Sr HS; Baton Rouge, LA (5%-530) BC; Ntl Teachers Coun; Alg A; COM; Chem A; Hon Prog; Math A; Most Out; NEDT; Sci A; Attendance A; Industrial Arts A; Phys Ed A; Eng A; *LSU; Computer Sci.*

KING, Amanda Evett
Frederick Douglass HS; Atlanta, GA; Y-Tns; Cl Fav; Journ A; Star Student; *Ga St U; News Rptr.*

KING, Annelle
Eureka HS; Eureka, IL (18-126) AFS; Band; Chldr; 4H; NHS; Span C; SC; Chor; HCt; St Band & Chor Contests; *Ill Wesleyan U; Bus Adm.*

KING, Annette Lorraine
James B Dudley Sr HS; Greensboro, NC; Band; Chem C; Ensm; Pres, Hmrm; Mjrte; Mod Mus Mas; Ntl Yth Conf; Sci C; Pres, SC; Var C; Pres, Jr Cl; Co-Cpt, Tr; Citz A; Gr Marshal; HCt; Hon Prog; Yth Leg; *U of NC; Med.*

KING, Anthony Raynard
Jesse H Jones Sr HS; Houston, TX; Band; Ensm; VofDEM; Yth Fel; Royal Ambassador; *Howard Payne U; Pol Sci.*

KING, Antoinette Marie
Windsor HS; Windsor, VA (2-130) Band; BC; Secy, Sci C; VP, Soph Cl; HCt; *Shenandoah Col; Mus.*

KING, Beth
Henderson Co Sr HS; Henderson, KY (1-600) A Cap Choir; Bus Mgr, Ann; Chor; Hmrm; Pres, NHS; VP, Sci C; Span C; SC; Swim; *Vanderbilt U.*

KING, Betty Jean
Bullock Co Sch; Union Springs, AL (7-148) Secy, Chor; Pres, 4H; Hmrm; NHS; Ed, Sch P; Tres, SC; Sftbl; Bio A; COM; Cl Fav; 4H A; HCt; Hon Prog; Math A; Pres A; Sci A; Spch A; Ldrship, PA, A's; *Tuskegee Inst; Phys Therapy.*

KING, Bobby Bryan Jr
Osborne HS; Marietta, GA; BC; JV, Bsbl; Bkbl; Ftbl; Mr Soph; Ftbl & Bkbl Ltrs; *Computer Prog.*

KING, Bonita
C F Vigor HS; Prichard, AL; Tr; ARC A; ROTC A; *Bishop St Jr Col; Child Care.*

KING, Bonnie Joy
Greece Arcadia HS; Rochester, NY (85-389) Band; Chor; Drama; Hmrm; 4H; 2nd Pl, Greece Performing Arts; All St Choir; 1st, NY Nazarene Talent Contest; *E Nazarene Col; Mus.*

KING, Bridget Kelley
McDonogh 35 HS; New Orleans, LA; SC; *Sou U; Med.*

KING, Cara Beth
Adairsville HS; Adairsville, GA; Fr C; FHA; Book, PA, A's; *Berry Col; Fr.*

KING, Catherine Louise
Arlington HS; Indianapolis, IN (19-344) A Cap Choir; Chor; Fr C; Ger C; Sci A; Pres, GSct; Pres, Church Yth Group; *Purdue U; Engr.*

KING, Celia Mariela
Neptune Sr HS; Neptune, NJ (40%-500) All Amer Yth; Arch; Semi-Fin, Chldr; Drama; Hmrm; Semi-Fin, Jr Miss Pa; Lat C; SC; Tr; Beauty; COM; JA A; Most Out; Sci A; Hon Lists; Academic Achv A; *Rutgers U; Psych.*

KING, Charles Alan
Montpelier HS; Montpelier, OH (40%-96) Band; Chor; VP, Demolay; Drama; Ensm; Fr C; FTA; 4H; Orch; Order/Arrow; ARC; Sch P; Spch C; 4H A; Order/Arrow A; *Ohio Northern U; Art.*

KING, Charles James
Marist Prep HS; Penndel, PA (4-21) Cpt, Bkbl; Cpt, Cr-Ctry; Fin, Ftbl; Fin, Tr; Bio A; Hist A; MVP, Bkbl; Semi-Fin Tr; Eng A; Theology A; *Drexel Col; Art.*

KING, Cheri Lynn
Fairhope HS; Fairhope, AL (48-327) AFS; Drama; NHS; Span C; JA A; Ldrship Grant; *U of Montevallo; Pre-Law.*

KING, Christina Anne
New Hope Solebury HS; New Hope, PA (2-65) AFS; Band; Chldr; Chor; Drama; Bkbl; Hockey; Citz A; LaCrosse; Cover's C; *Marine Sci.*

KING, Cindy Kay
Greenville HS; Greenville, TX (25%-320) FHA; FTA; NHS; Span C; Tnns; *Tyler Jr Col; Dental Hygiene.*

KING, Cynthia Lynne
New Edinburg HS; New Edinburg, AR (1-16) Ann; BC; VP, FHA; Pres, Sr Cl; Bkbl; Crisco A; Hon Prog; Type A; Val; Eng A; *U of Ark at Monticello.*

KING, David Alan
Harding Acad of Memphis; Memphis, TN (33%-200) Band; Math C; Sci C; NEDT; *Elec.*

KING, David Theodore
Clearfield HS; Clearfield, UT; Drama; Ed, Sch P; Journ A; *Weber St U; Photography.*

KING, Debra Ann
Adlai E Stevenson HS; Bronx, NY; Band; FTA; Orch; SC; Tres, Jr Cl; Bio A; COM; Hon Prog; Math A; *Pre-Med.*

KING, Debra Mae
Danbury HS; Danbury, CT (321-849) Hmrm; NHS; SC; JV, Bkbl; Phy A; Afro-Amer C; *NC A&T St U.*

KING, Donald Edwin
Miami Northwestern Sr HS; Miami, FL; Key C; Lat C; Sci C; Span C; Up Bound; Alg A; Bio A; COM; Citz A; Math A; Sci A; PA; Sr Service A; Citz A; *Oglethorpe U; Psych.*

KING, Edwin Carlton
Live Oak Acad; Moss Point, MS; BC; NHS; Sch Achieve Tm; Alg A; Bio A; COM; Elk A; HCt; Hon Prog; MLS; Val; *Jackson Co Jr Col.*

KING, Ellen Louise
Hinsdale Central HS; Hinsdale, IL (99-641) Band; Chldr; Chor; Var C; 1st Cl, GSct; *Denison U; Psych.*

KING, Emily Louise
LaVille Jr-Sr HS; Lakeville, IN (48-141) Band; Fr C; FHA; VP, 4H; 4-H Qn Candidate.

KING, Forrest Jay
Uniondale HS; Uniondale, NY; BC; Chess C; Bsbl; Bkbl; Co-Cpt, Ftbl; Swim; Alg A; COM; Citz A; Math A; Sal; Yth Fel; Athletic A; *Morehouse Col; Law.*

KING, Frances Lorene
Madison Co HS; Gurley, AL (10%-125) Pres, Band; Pres, BC; Math C; ARC; Sci C; VP, SC; Secy, Jr Cl; COM; *U of Ala in Huntsville; Chem.*

KING, George Warren
Memorial HS; Newark, CA (25-200) Bus C; Chess C; Chor; Drama; Ensm; Madrigal; Thes; *Calif St U; Acct.*

KING, Georgette Marie
Newark HS; Newark, OH (20%-2200) A Cap Choir; Chor; Tres, Drama; Ensm; Hmrm; NHS; Secy, Orch; Sci C; SC; Tres, Thes; *W Liberty St Col; Dental Hygiene.*

KING, Glen Neil
Sidney Lanier HS; Montgomery, AL (58-438) Chess C; Pres, Chor; Ensm; HiY; Key C; Span C; Var C; Bsbl; Bkbl; Sftbl; Sch Ltr; *Auburn U; Arts.*

KING, Hope Elane
Henry M Gunn Sr HS; Palo Alto, CA; Chor; ARC; JV, Soccer; Tr; JA A; Yth Ldr, Yth Conservation Corps; *Stanford U; Archt.*

KING, James Melvin
Athens HS; Athens, PA; Band; Mus A; Swim A; HiKing A.

KING, James Randolph
McCluer North Sr HS; Florissant, MO (35-790) Chor; Order/Arrow; ARC; Swim; Tnns; Citz A; Order/Arrow A; Type A; Life Sct; Sr Patrol Ldr; Mo E Conf Coun On Yth Ministries; *U of Mo; Eng.*

KING, Janet Marie
Canton S HS; Canton, OH; Drama; Lat C; Tri-HiY; JV, Tr; Gym; Ldr, Tn Talk; Fire Dept Qn; *Aultman Sch of Nurs; Registered Nurs.*

KING, JoAnn Marie
Bainbridge-Guilford Central HS; Bainbridge, NY (41-97) Band; Ski C; Yth Fel; *Alderson-Broaddus Col; Psych.*

KING, Joan Carol
Washington Sr HS; Cedar Rapids, IA (11-500) Chor; Community Yth Symph; Hmrm; NHS; Orch; JV, Tnns; Pres, Mozart Mus C; *Eng.*

KING, John David
Sarcoxie HS; Sarcoxie, MO (11-50) A Cap Choir; AFS; A-Ed, Ann; Chor; FTA; Math C; NHS; Rptr, Sch P; Alg A; COM; Citz A; Math A; Opt A; FFA A; Rural Electric Assn St A; Highest PSAT Test Score A; Chaplain, FFA; *Harding Col; Engr.*

KING, John Frank
Jones Co HS; Gray, GA (12-350) Band; NEDT; Sci A; *Ga Tech.*

KING, Joseph Lee
Oak Ridge Acad; Oak Ridge, NC (2-30) Chor; Ensm; Monogram; NHS; SC; VP, Soph Cl; Co-Cpt, Bkbl; Tnns; Gov Honor Prog; HCt; *U of NC at Chapel Hill; Pre-Med.*

KING, Julie Ann
Butler HS; Butler, MO (9-90) AFS; Band; Co-Cpt, Chldr; Chor; Ensm; Fr C; S-T, FBLA; Secy, 4H; Mjrte; Pres, NHS; F-Ed, Sch P; Tres, SC; Secy, Soph Cl; Alg A; 4H A; Hon Prog; Journ A; Type A; Rptr, 4-H C; *Avila Col; Nurs.*

KING, Karen Annette
Venice HS; Los Angeles, CA; CSF; Hon Prog; MYF; Yth Handbell Choir; Publicity Ch, Girls League; Girls Service C; Fencing C.

KING, Karen Annette
Bishop Hartley HS; Columbus, OH (27-135) Chldr; Drama; Span C; Ftbl; Tr; HCt; WW; Black Stu Union; Tr Statistician; Pep C; *Bowling Green St U; Journ.*

KING, Kathryn Grace
Hughson Union HS; Hughson, CA (25-140) Drama; FHA; Lit Mag; Ski C; VP, SC; Tres, Jr Cl; Ftbl; Sftbl; Vlbl; Co-Ch, Rally Commissioner; Homecoming Ch.

KING, Kelly Carl
Crenshaw Christian Acad; Luverne, AL (1-30) Band; Chldr; Chor; Math C; Phys C; Var C; Bkbl; Tnns; Alg A; Beauty; Sci A; Hon Soc; All Star Chldr; *U of Ala; Computer Prog.*

KING, Kelly Kaye
Faith HS; Faith, SD (50%-34) Chldr; Chor; Drama; FHA; Jr Miss Pageant; Sch P; Bkbl; Tr; *Steward's Col; Hair Styling.*

KING, Kenneth David
Rocky Mount Sr HS; Rocky Mount, NC (20-714) Band; Pres, Dbte Tm; Ensm; SC; Bsbl; Sftbl; COM; Citz A; Art Ed, Yrbk; VP, Yth Group; Jr Deacon; *Columbia U; Commercial Art.*

KING, Kimberly Ann
Maryville HS; Maryville, TN; AFS; Band; Lat C; Sch P; Golf; Swim; Tnns; 1st Cl, GSA; CISV; Candystriper; Maryville Gym Comp Tm; *U of Tenn; Med.*

KING, Kimberly Anne
Craigmont HS; Memphis, TN; A Cap Choir; Band; Chor; Community Yth Symph; Ensm; Orch; Bsbl; Cr-Ctry; Type A; Hon Star A; Church & Comm Hon As; Mus As; Qn, Sweetheart Banquet; May Day Qn.

KING, Kimberly V
Bellevue HS; Nashville, TN; Band; Lit Mag; Mgr, Bkbl; Rifle Sq; FSA; *Trevecca Nazarene Col; Bus.*

KING, Kristen Lorraine
Dryden Jr Sr HS; Dryden, NY; Band; Chor; Ski C; JV, Bkbl; Hockey; Pres, Yth Fel; Vlbl; *Social Work.*

KING, Kristi Jo
Sentinel HS; Sentinel, OK; BC; FHA; GS; Bkbl; Sftbl; COM; HQn; All Around Girl; *SW Okla St U; Math.*

KING, Larry Darnel
Chester HS; Chester, PA; Chess C; Ntl Yth Conf; Soccer; BScts; Young Adult Choir; Bowl League.

KING, Laurel Michaelle
South Shelby HS; Shelbina, MO (25%-100) A Cap Choir; Band; Pres, CYO; Chldr; Chor; Drama; Ensm; Hmrm; Madrigal; Sci C; SC; Bsbl; Bkbl; Sftbl; Mgr, Tr; HQn; Yth Leg; Sr GSct; Bkbl Qns Court; DAR Essay A; Vocal Solo, St I; *Central Mo St U; Special Ed.*

KING, Linda Elaine
Dublin HS; Dublin, OH (9-178) Ann; Secy, Band; Chor; Drama; Fr C; Pres, 4H; Hmrm; Pres, Lat C; NHS; Orch; SC; Var C; Secy, Sr Cl; Ch, Jr Cl; Secy, Soph Cl; JV, Bkbl; *Elem Ed.*

KING, Lolalisa DeCarlo
Baker HS; Baker, LA; A Cap Choir; BC; Madrigal; NHS; A-Ed, Sch P; SC; Semi-Fin, Arch; Journ A; Kiwanis A; Most Out; *Engr.*

KING, Lou Sherwood II
South Side Area HS; Hookstown, PA; Band; Ensm; Orch; Tr; *Mus.*

KING, Margretcher
Smithfield-Selma Sr HS; Smithfield, NC (16-355) Band; Monogram; NHS; Span C; SC; Cpt, Bkbl; *U of NC; Pre-Law.*

KING, Marlene Ann
Webster Groves HS; Webster Groves, MO (28-459) Secy, A Cap Choir; Band; Chor; Ensm; Madrigal; COM; DARGCA; Pres A; Yth Fel; Yth Leg; Miss CA; 3rd, Piano Solo; Stu Choral Director; Vocal Ensm; Nom, Sr Service A; 2nd, Vocal Solo; Tn Talent Win; *Secretarial.*

KING, Martha Ann
Theodore Roosevelt HS; San Antonio, TX (65-694) A Cap Choir; Tres, Band; Chor; Ensm; Secy, FTA; Hmrm; Key C; NHS; Span C; COM; *Angelo St U; Mus Ed.*

KING, Maxine
Ramsay HS; Birmingham, AL (4-139) NHS; Cl Fav; Type A; *U of Ala in B'Ham; Journ.*

KING, Michael Anthony
T C Roberson HS; Skyland, NC; Pres, Band; Chor; Ensm; Fr C; Sch P; Span C; Tnns; Jr Beta C; Outst Sr; Golden Ram Band A; *Guilford Col; Econ.*

KING, Michael Dwane
Canton S HS; N Industry, OH (20-275) Mgr, A Cap Choir; Chess C; Chor; Lat C; JV, Tnns; *Ohio St U; Astronomy.*

KING, Michael Franklin
Trenton HS; Trenton, MI (100-600) NHS; Ski C; Bsbl; JV, Bkbl; Yth Fel; Cl Spirit Kg; *Bradley U; Fine Arts.*

KING, Micheal Todd
Central HS; Harrison, TN (60-250) Demolay; HiY; Var C; Bkbl; Ftbl; Sftbl; Wrest; *U of Ala; Engr.*

KING, Mike J
Thomas Jefferson Sr HS; Cedar Rapids, IA (7%-573) Chor; Drama; Hmrm; NHS; VP, Order/Arrow; Tres, Thes; Amer Leg A; God & Country A; JA A; NMS; Order/Arrow A; Eagle Sct; CTAG A; *Iowa St U; Engr.*

KING, Monitetra Maude
McDonogh 35 Sr HS; New Orleans, LA; Band; B Crocker A; Jr NHS; HR; *Dillard U; Psych.*

KING, Myra Elizabeth
Cape Fear HS; Fayetteville, NC (28-359) BC; InterAct C; Span C; Mgr, Tr; COM; *U of NC; Phar.*

KING, Nanette Elaine
Batavia Sr HS; Batavia, IL (1-211) Hon Prog; *Bus.*

KING, Naoma Ruth
Cottage Grove HS; Cottage Grove, OR (17-215) Band; NHS; GPA A; Schol Merit A; *Lane Comm Col.*

KING, Norman Sherrill
Bellaire HS; Bellaire, TX (154-717) Pres, Chor; Ensm; Pres, Key C; Math C; Mu Alpha Theta; NHS; Mgr, Bkbl; Mgr, Ftbl; JV, Tr; Amer Leg A; WW; *Houston Baptist Col; Bus.*

KING, Odella
St Matthew HS; Melrose, LA (15-47) Band; Sftbl; Hon Prog; Most Out; General Mus A; Soloist A; WW Among Mus Stu A.

KING, Pamela Jean
Corinth Christian Acad; Kinsman, OH (2-10) Chldr; Chor; Bkbl; JV, Sftbl; *Bible Sch.*

KING, Paula Suzanne
Wade Hampton HS; Greenville, SC; Pres, Hmrm.

KING, Pebbles Leanne
Jackson HS; Jackson, GA; Drama; Ensm; Math C; NHS; Tres, Tri-HiY; JV, Bkbl; Citz A; *Tift Col; Elem Ed.*

KING, Peggy Lorraine
Longmont HS; Longmont, CO; AFS; Chor; Drama; NFL; NHS; Spch C; SC; VP, Jr Cl; Tr; Spch A; Cpt, FCA; Drill Tm; Gym; *Occupational Therapy.*

KING, Philip Andrew
Theodore Roosevelt HS; San Antonio, TX (10%-800) Band; Ensm; COM; Bowl Tm; *Archt.*

KING, Ramona
Northeast HS; Philadelphia, PA (361-1300) Chldr; Hmrm; SC; Bsbl; Cpt, Bkbl; Cr-Ctry; Sftbl; Tnns; Tr; HQn; *Early Childhood Ed.*

KING, Rebecca Anne
Washington Wilkes Comp HS; Washington, GA (14-177) Pres, FHA; Mjrte; NHS; Bkbl; Sftbl; Hon Prog; Para-Med A; Outst VICA Stu A; 3rd Pl, VICA St Skill Olympics; 1st CSRA Dist VICA Skill Olympics; *Berea Col; Nurs.*

KING, Regana Dionne
Westinghouse Area Voc HS; Chicago, IL (4-500) Band; Chor; ROTC Neatness A; Drill Participation A; CDT Sergeant; *Bus.*

KING, Robin Ann
Cushing HS; Cushing, OK; Band; Chor; *Jarvis Christian Col; Religion.*

KING, Ronald
Venice HS; Los Angeles, CA; Band; Hon Prog; NMS; MYF; Win, Search for Ldrship; Parl, Sci Fiction C; Secy, Computer C; *UMW A.*

KING, Sandra Gail
South Side HS; Memphis, TN (10%-370) Band; Chldr; Drama; Lat C; Math C; NHS; Bkbl; SC; Alg A; Hist A; Sci A; Mus, Schol, Achv, A's; *U of Tenn; Special Ed.*

KING, Sandra Jean
Cass HS; Cassville, GA (10%-197) BC; Fr C; FHA; Hmrm; Rptr, Sch P; SC; Thes; Cl Fav; PA; *Floyd Jr Col.*

KING, Sharon Jeanne
Bainbridge-Guilford Central Sch; Bainbridge, NY (19-97) Band; Ensm; NHS; Orch; Sch P; Ski C; Arch; Rotary Exchange Stu; Span Enthusiasm A; *Russell Sage Col; Medical Lab Tech.*

KING, Steve
Greeneville HS; Greeneville, TN (230-300) Band; Community Yth Symph; Ensm; Pres, 4H; Hmrm; Math C; Orch; Sch P; Pres, Soph Cl; Ftbl; Tnns; Cl Fav; Elk A; 4H A; Math A; Opt A; PTA A; Rotary A; Sci A; Spch A; Most Talented; Modern Woodmen A; *U of Tenn; Law.*

KING, Steven Roderick
Ross Shaw Sterling HS; Houston, TX; VP, Chor; Bkbl; COM; Most Out; Chor A; *Bishop Col; Mus.*

KING, Thomas John
Springfield HS; Springfield, OR (1-355) Chor; Var C; Cr-Ctry; Tr; Most Inspirational; Cr Ctry; *Engr.*

KING, Timothy Bruce
Woodlawn HS; Baton Rouge, LA (33%-300).

KING, Timothy J
Mona Shores HS; Muskegon, MI (5%-455) NHS; Sci C; Co-Cpt, Bkbl; Ntl Bio Hon Soc, Hon Stu; Acct A; Ath-Acdemic A; *Mich St U; Bus Adm.*

KING, Valerie
Lindblom HS; Chicago, IL (3-775) Math C; NHS; Alg A; Bio A; Hon Prog; Sci A; Hon Soc A; *Ill Inst of Tech; Engr.*

KINGAN, Jane Louise
Westlake HS; Westlake, OH (44-314) Chor; Lit Mag; Choir Medal & Pin; Special Service A; Vol o-t Yr, Camp Aowakiya; *Spring Arbor Col; Psych.*

KINGERY, Sylviabel Willa
New Monroe Comm HS; Monroe, IA (4-47) Band; Chor; Drama; Ensm; Secy, 4H; NHS; ARC; Spch C; Thes; JV, Bkbl; Cr-Ctry; JV, Sftbl; Tr; Bio A; COM; Citz A; 4H A; Hon Prog; ARC A; Sci A; Spch A; Type A; Mus As; Sports As; Drill Tm A; *Grandview Col; BSN Degree.*

KINGMA, Gregg Michael
Anacortes HS; Anacortes, WA (5-200) Pres, Hmrm; Ed, Sch P; SC; Arch; MVP, Bsbl; Cpt, Bkbl; Cr-Ctry; Cpt, Ftbl; Soccer; Sftbl; Cpt, Tr; Amer Leg A; Cl Fav; HCt; Journ A; Math A; MLS; Most Out; Spch A; Yth Fel; MVP, Bkbl & Ftbl.

KINGMA, John E
Anacortes HS; Anacortes, WA; Pres, A Cap Choir; VP, Chor; Tres, City Conf; Ensm; Hmrm; Pres, InterAct C; Pres, InterClub Coun; Madrigal; VP, NHS; Phys C; Ed, Sch P; Span C; Span NHS; Pres, St Stu Congres; VP, SC; Var C; Arch; Cpt, Bsbl; Cpt, Bkbl; Cpt, Ftbl; Alg A; Cl Fav; HCt; Hon Prog; Journ A; JA A; Jr Chamber of Com A; Math A; MLS; Most Out; Phy A; Rotary A; Spch A; Star Student; Yth Fel; Yth Leg; Pres, St SC; Stu Member, St Board of Ed; Del, Ntl Assn of SC; Top 10, Sr Cl; *Pacific Luthern U; Bus.*

KINGMA, Molly Greenwood
Fairfax HS; Fairfax, VA (48-448) Chor; NHS; Secy, SG; Pres, Church Choir; Contestant, Miss Fairfax Pageant; *The Col of William & Mary; Early Childhood Ed.*

KINGSBURY, Perry David
Redford Union HS; Redford, MI (15%-703) Band; BS; Chor; NHS; SC; Var C; Pres, Sr Cl; Pres, Soph Cl; Cpt, Bkbl; JV, Cr-Ctry; Ftbl; Tr; HCt; MLS; Drum Major; Eagle Sct; FCA Schol; *Judson Col; Mus.*

KINGSLAND, Terri Leigh
Pasco Sr HS; Pasco, WA (78-400) F-Ed, Ann; Chor; F-Ed, Sch P; Runner Up, Tn Talent Church of God; *W Coast Bible Col; Bus.*

KINGSLEY, Dorathea Beall
Campolindo HS; Moraga, CA (10%-398) GS; Hmrm; Model UN; NHS; St Stu Congress; SC; World Affairs C; Tres, Soph Cl; CSF; Hon Prog; Photo-Eb, Ann; Cpt, Spirit Group; NMS Top 5%; Sunday Sch Teacher; Ch, Jr Prom; Chrch Yth Grp; Grl Lge; Co-Ch, Constitution Revision Comm.

KINGSLEY, Susan Elizebeth
Campolindo HS; Moraga, CA (25%-350) Hmrm; NHS; Sci C; Hon Prog; Yth Fel; Tres, Girl's League; Vol, Church Sch; Stu Asst, Bio.

KINGSTON, Helen Frances
Tech Voc HS; Hammond, IN (57-234) Chor; Ensm; Jr Miss Pagent; Beauty; HCt; Mus Trophy & Certs; Jr Homecoming Princess; Cotillion Qn; *Ball St U.*

KINGSWOOD, Susan Ann
Ottawa HS; Ottawa, KS (10-259) Hon Prog; Yth Fel; Pep C; JV Vlbl; Ath A; Flag Twirler; *Art.*

KINION, Deborah Diane
Eddyville HS; Eddyville, OR (1-11) Chldr; Tres, FFA; Secy, Soph Cl; Bkbl; Wrest; HCt; Math A; Opt A; Sci A; Type A; Vlbl.

KINKADE, Debbie Darlene
Monroe Union HS; Monroe, OR (2-48) AFS; Cpt, Chldr; Chor; Drama; NHS; Tr; Ntl Achv Schol; Eng A; *Oreg St U.*

KINKEL, Alison Elizabeth
Red Lion Area Sr HS; Red Lion, PA (90-475) Band; Rainbow; Var C; Bkbl; Hockey; Mgr, Tr; *Police Sci.*

KINMAN, Katrina Marie
Franklin Co HS; Frankfort, KY (70-425) Band; Secy, Chor; Ensm; Tres, Ger C; Hmrm; Juniorettes; Drivers Ed A; *U of Ky.*

KINNA, Wanda Lynne
Damascus HS; Damascus, MD (5-234) Band; Semi-Fin, Chldr; Cpt, Mjrte; *Hagerstown Bus Col; Med Secretarial*

KINNAMON, Crystal Marie
Wyanet Comm HS; Wyanet, IL (2-25) Chor; SC; HCt; Home Ec A; WW; *Ill Valley Comm Col; Nurs.*

KINNETT, Robert Forest
Marion HS; Marion, SC (18-225) *Francis Marion Col; Psych.*

KINNETT, Territa Lucille
Shawnee HS; Shawnee, OK; FTA; Span C; Hon Prog; *Seminole Col; Nurs.*

KINNEY, Cindy Marie
Elkmont HS; Elkmont, AL (10-65) Band; BC; FHA; 4H; Mjrte; NHS; VP, Soph Cl; Beauty.

KINNEY, David Farrell
Ephrata Sr HS; Ephrata, WA; Tres, AFS; Tr; Wrest; UMY Ldrship Tm.

KINNEY, George Allen
Lowndes HS; Valdosta, GA (25%-476) CYO; Key C; Sci C; Bsbl; Ftbl; *Law.*

KINNEY, Kathy Karen
Brown HS; Sturgis, SD (115-230) Tres, Job's Daughters; Sunday Sch Teacher.

KINNEY, Lowell Richard
Ephrata Sr HS; Ephrata, WA; Ch, AFS; Band; Ski C; Cr-Ctry; Tr; Tres, United Methodist Yth Ldrshp.

KINNEY, Lynn Suzanne
Newman HS; Wausau, WI (10-122) A Cap Choir; Chor; VP, Ger C; MVP, Bkbl; Tr; *St Joseph Nurs Sch; Nurs.*

KINNEY, Patrick Joseph Jr
Hanceville HS; Hanceville, AL (10-104) Ann; BS; Math C; Pres, NHS; Var C; Bsbl; Bkbl; *Sou Benedictine Col; Acct.*

KINNEY, Rodney Eugene
Brown HS; Sturgis, SD (25%-195) Pres, Demolay; Bkbl; Ftbl; Master Councilor, DeMolay; *U S Navy; Elec.*

KINNISON, Pamela Ann
Weld Central HS; Keenesburg, CO (17-91) Drama; FHA; NHS; A-Ed, Sch P; COM; Art C; GAA; *York Col; Home Ec.*

KINSEL, Pamela Rae
Brookville HS; Brookville, OH; Ann; Band; Chldr; Chor; Pres, 4H; NHS; 4H A; *Sinclair Comm Col; Secretarial*

KINSELLA, Kevin George
Elk Grove HS; Elk Grove Village, IL (2-630) Band; NHS; Orch; Mgr, Bkbl; Tnns; COM; Acolyte; Rite, Cum Laude, A's; *U of Ill; Acct.*

KINSER, Nick Lynn
Red Oak Comm HS; Red Oak, IA (50-116) Band; Chor; Ensm; Madrigal; Piano As; Band As; Vocal As; Dramatic As; *Drake U; Mus.*

KINSEY, Carolyn Joy
Kamiakin HS; Kennewick, WA; Hon Prog; Jr Ldr Pioneer Girls.

KINSEY, Cathy Renee
Shawnee Mission NW HS; Shawnee, KS (10%-500) Orch; Thes.

KINSEY, Dean Micheal
Shawnee Mission NW HS; Shawnee, KS (259-650) AFS; Ed, Sch P; Thes; Journ A; Q&S A; Dram A; *U of Kan; Journ.*

KINSEY, James Shawn
Pascagoula HS; Pascagoula, MS (9-453) Chor; Ensm; Secy, Lat C; NHS; Tr; HCt; All Dist & St Choral; 2nd, Beta C Talent A; NHS Stu o-t Mo; *Oral Roberts U; Mus Ed.*

KINSEY, Robert Samuel
Hendersonville HS; Hendersonville, TN; Band; Orch; Bkbl; Hon Prog; Ntl Jr Hon Soc; 3rd, Bowl Tourn; Life Sct; *Math.*

KINSEY, Trudy Kay
Panora Linden Comm HS; Panora, IA; Band; Pres, FHA; SC; Var C; Bkbl; Sftbl; Tr; HQn; Design-A-Kitchen Home Ec A; Phys Fitness A; *Americana Acad of Beauty; Cosmetology.*

KINSINGER, Cherry Lynn
Fremont HS; Fremont, IA (3-21) Ed, Ann; Pres, Band; Cpt, Chldr; Pres, Chor; Pres, 4H; Madrigal; Cpt, Mjrte; VP, Sr Cl; Tres, Soph Cl; Sftbl; Tr; B Crocker A; DARGCA; 4H A; HCt; Rotary A; WW; YMCA Girl o-t Mo; Ch, Co 4-H Coun; V-Ch, SE Iowa 4-H Coun; *Iowa St U; Home Ec.*

KINSMAN, Lynne Rennee
Zion Benton Township HS; Zion, IL (200-450) Band; Chor; Swim; Talent Quest; Song Writing A; *Moody Bible Inst; Mus.*

KINSOLVING, Darlene Catherine
Minonk-Dana-Rutland HS; Minonk, IL (13-79) A Cap Choir; Cpt, Chldr; Chor; FHA; Span C; SC; Bkbl; Sftbl; Amer Leg A; Beauty; Chldr A; Chor A.

KINTNER, Cindy Ann
Warren HS; Warren, PA (10%-450) A Cap Choir; Chor; Drama; Ski C; Y-Tns; Tnns; Hon Prog; Yth Fel; VP, Ntl Jr Hon Soc; *Penn St U; Bio.*

KINTNER, Karen Aileen
Grinnell Sr HS; Grinnell, IA (8-200) Band; Chor; Ensm; Hmrm; Madrigal; SC; All-St Chor, 1975 and 1976.

KINTZ, Robert Allen
Southside Sr HS; Elmira, NY (20%-500) Pres, 4H; Hmrm; Ski C; Var C; JV, Ftbl; Tnns; COM.

KINUNEN, Lana Lee
Rock Lake Pub HS; Rock Lake, ND (3-24) Ed, Ann; Band; Chor; Drama; Ensm; FHA; NHS; Rptr, Sch P; SC; VP, Sr Cl; Ch, Jr Cl; Sal; Star Student; VofDEM; *Minot St Col; Mus.*

KINYAUO, Daisy Makyuwai
Boron HS; Boron, CA (2-76) Chor; Phi Beta Kappa.

KINZBACH, Kathy
University HS; Waco, TX; Band; NHS; Rptr, Sch P; Spch A; Page Ed, Sch P; Most Outst, Band; *Baylor U; Christian Psych.*

KINZEL, Bruce Michael
Freeburg Comm HS; Freeburg, IL (29-119) Pres, 4H; Ch, Model UN; VP, Ftbl; Pres, SC; Pres, Var C; Bsbl; Ftbl; 4H A; HCt; I Dare You; Journ A; All Conf Ftbl; *Ark St U; Journ.*

KINZEL, Carla Fay
Harlem HS; Harlem, MT (4-45) Ann; Secy, Band; Chor; 4H A.

KINZINGER, Douglas LaVerne
New Athens Comm HS; New Athens, IL (5-65) Band; Sci C; St Scholar; Yth Fel; Hon Graduate; WW; *Belleville Area Col; Engr.*

KIPER, John Christopher
New Albany HS; New Albany, IN (40-660) Band; Ger C; Hmrm; SC; JV, Bkbl; *Purdue U; Engr.*

KIPP, Kathy Jo
Bellmont HS; Decatur, IN (12-300) Band; Span A; Secy, Yth Fel; *Math.*

KIPP, Rosemary Ann
Chester HS; Chester, IL (10-98) Band; Bkbl; Sftbl; WW; Carrier o-t Week A; NCR A; Machine Bookkeeping A; Outst Carrier A.

KIPPEN, Debra Marie
Forest Area HS; Fife Lake, MI (25%-44) *Astronomy.*

KIPTA, Allison Lynn
Oak Park-River Forest HS; Oak Park, IL (422-958) Hmrm; Sci C; Ski C; Hockey; Bio A; Superior Rating, St Mus Comp; *Western Ill U; Mus Ed.*

KIRALY, Alan Philip
Forest Hills Central HS; Ada, MI (5%-241) Var C; Cr-Ctry; Tr; Alg A; Hon Prog; Math A; Opt A; Most Outst Soph, Phys Ed; *U of Mich; Structural Engr.*

KIRBY, Archie II
Red Mill HS; Odenton, MD; A Cap Choir; All Amer Yth; Band; Chess C; FBLA; 4H; Pres, Tri-HiY; Bsbl; Bkbl; Ftbl; Sftbl; Swim.

KIRBY, Carl George
Wichita Falls HS; Wichita Falls, TX (95-425) Chess C; Secy, Dbte Tm; FTA; Hmrm; Secy, NFL; Sch P; Spch C; Bkbl; Co-Cpt, Ftbl; Tr; Spch A; Tr A; *Child Psych.*

KIRBY, Deborah Faye
Warren Central HS; Bowling Green, KY (6-250) Band; BC; FHA; Hon Prog; Math A; Type A; Yth Fel; Pres, VP, Secy, Tres, UMYF; *Western Ky U.*

KIRBY, Jane Frances
Sacred Heart HS; Kingston, MA (1-85) JV, Chldr; Chor; Hmrm; Key C; Secy, NHS; SC; Mgr, Bkbl; Mgr, Hockey; COM; Hon Prog; Ger A.

KIRBY, Joline Marie
Tahlequah HS; Tahlequah, OK (100-300) Band; Parl, FHA; FTA; Sftbl; Amer Leg A; Citz A; Most Out; *Northeastern Okla St U; Hist.*

KIRBY, Karen Sue
Festus R-6 Sr HS; Festus, MO (1-250) Band; Chldr; Chor; Drama; Ensm; FHA; Gym.

KIRBY, Leslie Rhonda
John A Holmes HS; Edenton, NC (24-180) Anchor C; Secy, Band; Drama; FHA; Co-Cpt, Mjrte; Mod Mus Mas; Pol Sci C; Mgr, Bkbl; *E Carolina U; Primary Ed.*

KIRBY, Lynn Ellen
Silsbee HS; Silsbee, TX; F-Ed, Ann; Chldr; Fr C; Tr; COM; Yth Coun; Secy, Leo C.

KIRBY, Marshall Keith
Scottsboro HS; Scottsboro, AL; Band; NHS; God & Country A.

KIRBY, Patricia Lynn
Ft Pierce Central HS; Ft Pierce, FL; BC; NHS; Keyettes; *Indian River Comm Col.*

KIRBY, Stephanie Marie
Battle Creek Pub HS; Battle Creek, NE (8-53) Band; CYO; Chldr; Chor; Community Yth Symph; Drama; FHA; 4H; Math C; Sch P; Pres, SC; Sr Cl; Alg A; Amer Leg A; COM; Citz A; 4H A; Math A; Mascot; *Elem Ed.*

KIRBY, Tammy Sue
Buhler HS; Buhler, KS (15%-180) Pres, Span C; Church Yth Choir & Coun; Yth For Christ; Lay Witness Mission Tm; *Span.*

KIRCH, Maryann Louise
E Rockaway HS; E Rockaway, NY (4-176) Chor; Key C; NHS; Hockey; Amer Leg A; Hon Prog; Regent Schol; Knights of Pythias A; 1st Cl GSct; NML; Banking A; *St U of NY; Bus Mgt.*

KIRCHER, Tonya Kay
Winfield HS; Winfield, KS (58-185) A Cap Choir; Chor; Dbte Tm; Drama; Ensm; FBLA; 4H; Phys C; Pres, Rainbow; Sci C; Spch C; Bkbl; Co-Cpt, Sftbl; Tnns; Co-Cpt, Tr; COM; 4H A; Pres A; Spch A; Yth Fel; Cpt, Vlbl; Ntl Merit Magazine Read; Spirit A; Vet Asst; Piano As; *Kans St Col; Vet-Med.*

KIRCHNER, Charlene Jeanette
Fremont HS; Sunnyvale, CA (32-726) Chor; Ensm; Madrigal; Orch; Hockey; JA A; Most Out.

KIRCHOFFER, Kathleen Lynn
L D Bell HS; Hurst, TX (20-870) F-Ed, Ann; CYO; InterClub Coun; NHS; Span C; SC; Jr Cl; WW; Outst Stu in Span; *Biol.*

KIRCHOFFER, Wendy Renee
L D Bell HS; Hurst, TX (20-879) CYO; Ger C; InterClub Coun; Parl, NHS; ARC; Jr Cl; COM; Cl Fav; Hon Prog; Swtht; Ger Lang Festival A; Beauty Pageant; Fresh Chldr; *N Tex St; Biol.*

KIREJCZYK, Jane Marie
Cathedral HS; Springfield, MA (169-650) Drama; 4H; Hmrm; Tnns; COM; 4H A; Journ A; Type A; Liturgical Dancing; Church Lecturer; Minstrel Show; *Fashion Inst of Tech; Fashion Design.*

KIRK, Cheri Anne
Kermit HS; Kermit, WV (6-45) Band; Chor; 4H; Hmrm; Cpt, Mjrte; NHS; Span C; Pres, Jr Cl; Secy, Soph Cl; Bkbl.

KIRK, David Allen
Galion Sr HS; Galion, OH (102-275) Pres, HiY; Order/Arrow; ARC; St Stu Congress; Ch, Var C; Cr-Ctry; Tr; Order/Arrow A; *Ohio St U; Engr.*

KIRK, Dawn
Perry Co HS; Linden, TN (5-90) Ann; Pres, BC; Secy, Bus C; 4H; Sci C; Mgr, Bkbl; Citz A; DARGCA; Sci A; Best Dressed; 4-H All-St & Ldrship As; *Belmout Col; Social Work.*

KIRK, Donald Aaron
Frankfort HS; Ridgeley, WV (10%-151) FTA; NHS; Math A; VofDEM; *Potomac St Col; Horti-culture.*

KIRK, Gary Edward
Muskogee HS; Muskogee, OK (120-600) Band; Community Yth Symph; Ensm; Math C; Order/ Arrow; Phys C; Ski C; Opt A; Order/Arrow A; Eagle Sct; *NEOAM; Elec Engr.*

KIRK, Jeanette
Battle Creek Central HS; Battle Creek, MI (158-520) Bkbl; Hon Prog; *U of Mich; Law.*

KIRK, Joe Louis
Martin Luther King HS; Philadelphia, PA (4-692) Fin, Lat C; Math C; VP, NHS; Parl, Sr Cl; Mgr, Ftbl; Mgr, Wrest; Alg A; Citz A; Hon Prog; Law Seminar A; Lat A; *U of Penn; Pol Sci.*

KIRK, Lisa Frances
Dadeland Ctry Day Sch; Miami, FL (2-12) Ed, Ann; Cpt, Chldr; Mjrte; Sch P; VP, SC; COM; Chamber of Comm A; HQn; Hon Prog; Journ A; Most Out; Star Student; *U of Miami; Pre-Med.*

KIRK, Lisa Rose
Burlington Co Christian HS; Chesterfield, NJ; *W Minster Choir Col; Mus.*

KIRK, Lloydeane
Springtown HS; Springtown, TX; Dbte Tm; Drama; FHA; FTA; Fin, Jr Miss Pagent; Spch C; Co-Cpt, Bkbl; Tr; Beauty; Type A; Yth Fel; Vlbl; FCA; Pres, Modern Woodmen of Amer; *Elem Ed.*

KIRK, Pamela Lynette
Pike Central HS; Petersburg, IN (1-176) Ann; Band; Ensm; FHA; GS; NHS; COM; St Scholar; Type A; Val; Yth Fel; NML; WW; Yth Rep, Church Adm Board; U of Evansville Acad Alumni Schol; Pres Schol; *U of Evansville; Art.*

KIRK, Paula Kay
New Caney HS; Porter, TX (9-223) FHA; Hmrm; NHS; Rainbow; SC; Type A; Lt & Asst Chaplin, Drill Tm; *N Harris Co Col; Bus.*

KIRK, Rebecca Jo
Lakeland Sr HS; Lakeland, FL; Fr C.

KIRK, Zachary Cameron
Robert E Lee HS; Baytown, TX (175-415) Band; Drama; Ger C; Order/Arrow; Thes; Order/Arrow A; Octagon C; *Stephan F Austin Col; Mus.*

KIRKALDIE, Kathleen Marie
Central Dauphin HS; Harrisburg, PA (10-500) Co-Ed, Ann; Chor; Drama; Madrigal; Mod Mus Mas; A-Ed, Sch P; Thes; *York Col of Penn; Sociology.*

KIRKEBY, Beth Renee
Cranbrook Sch Kingswood; Bloomfield Hills, MI (25%-100) Secy, Band; Drama; Ensm; Orch; World Affairs C; Honored Qn, Job's Daughters; Cpt, Bowl; *Design.*

KIRKEEIDE, Star Marie
St Francis HS; St Francis, MN (50-210) 4H; Sci C; Ski C; Tnns; 4H A; Danceline; *U of Minn; Health.*

KIRKEGAARD, Bonnie Lynn
West HS; Sioux City, IA (5%-250) Band; Dbte Tm; Span C; Spch C; Span NHS; St Stu Congress; COM; Hon Prog; NMS; Spch A; St Band Solo A; *Pre-Law.*

KIRKING, Steven Craig
Viroqua HS; Viroqua, WI (7-141) Fin, Band; NHS; Tnns; HCt; Co-Cpt & MVP, Ftbl; JC A; *UW-Stevens Point; Fish & Wildlife Mgt.*

KIRKLAND, Charlotte Suzann
Marion Co HS; Lebanon, KY (14-298) Pres, FHA; Tres, 4H; Hmrm; Sci C; Spch C; SC; Mgr, Bkbl; B Crocker A; 4H A; Outst, FHA & 4-H; St Degree, FHA; *E Ky U; Nurs.*

KIRKLAND, Donna Kay
Nederland HS; Nederland, TX (86-463) AFS; InterClub Coun; Art A; Pres, Art C; Fin, Cl Fav; Interior Design A; *Lamar U; Art.*

KIRKLAND, Jerry Lynn
Levelland HS; Levelland, TX (7-200) A Cap Choir; Chor; NHS; Mgr, Cr-Ctry; MVP, Ftbl; Co-Cpt, Tr; VP, FCA; WW in Chor; All Reg; VP, Stu Christian As; All-Area; WW; WW in Math; All-St Choir; WW Among Mus Stu in Amer HS; *Tex A&M U; Pre-Med.*

KIRKLAND, Robin Beth
Coffee Co HS; Douglas, GA (5%-300) F-Ed, Ann; Band; BC; Secy, FHA; F-Ed, Sch P; COM; Gov Honor Prog; Mayor, GS; Gold Tn Vol; Jr Home-maker A; FHA St Degree; Color Guard Com-mander; *S Ga Col; Sci.*

KIRKLAND, Sharon Louise
LaVega HS; Bellmead, TX (4-128) Band; Co-Cpt, Mjrte; VP, NHS; PA A; Eng A; Hon Stu; *Baylor U; Elem Ed.*

KIRKLAND, Tracey Lee
William Penn Sr HS; York, PA; Ann; Chor; Dbte Tm; Drama; Hmrm; InterClub Coun; Sch P; SC; Thes; Y-Tns; Arch; Spch A; Type A; Yth Fel; Thea-tre Arts; *Mansfield St Col; Theatre Arts Major.*

KIRKLEY, Foster Dale
Porter's Chapel Acad; Vicksburg, MS; Ann; *Hinds Jr Col; Bus Adm.*

KIRKLEY, Sandra Elaine
Alfred Eli Beach Sr HS; Savannah, GA; Anchor C; Band; BC; NHS; Tnns; Tr; Span C; Band A; *Arm-strong St Col; Phys Therapy.*

KIRKPATRICK, Alfreda Denise
Alma J Brown HS; Grambling, LA; Band; Pres, FHA; Cpt, Mjrte; Sch P; SC; VP, Soph Cl; HQn; Cpt, Dancing Felines; Cpt, Modern Dance Group; *Grambling St U; Spch.*

KIRKPATRICK, JoAnn LaRee
Ainsworth HS; Ainsworth, NE (3-70) Fr C; Band; 4H; JV, Bkbl; Tr; 4H A; Yth Fel; JV, Vlbl; *Chadron Col; Ed.*

KIRKPATRICK, Julie LaRae
Ainsworth HS; Ainsworth, NE; Pres, 4H.

KIRKPATRICK, Scott Lyford
East HS; Madison, WI (10%-600) Band; Sch P; HR; *Art.*

KIRKPATRICK, Sharon Elise
Haltom HS; Ft Worth, TX; Fr C; FBLA; NHS; Amer Leg A; Hon Prog; *Harding Col; Elem Ed.*

KIRKPATRICK, Winona Annette
Greenland HS; Greenland, AR (3-38) Band; 4H; SC; Bio A; PTA A; Sci A; Driver's Ed, Piano, A's; *U of Ark; Biol.*

KIRKSEY, Carl Wayne
Druid Park Baptist HS; Satsuma, AL (2-29) BC; Sci C; Alg A; Cl Fav; Hist A; HKg; Math A; MLS; Opt A; Pres A; Eng A; *Math.*

KIRKSEY, James Edward
Canoga Park HS; Canoga Park, CA; Bkbl; Soccer; ROTC A; Yth Fel; *Air Force Acad; Sci.*

KIRKSEY, Nina Louise
Eisenhower HS; Lawton, OK (139-560) Fr C; FHA; NHS; SC; Tri-HiY; Sftbl; Yth Leg; Pom Pon Tm; HR; FCA; *Cameron Col; Bus Mgt.*

KIRKSEY, Wilma Jean
Winner HS; Winner, SD (20-105) Ed, Ann; Band; Chor; Dbte Tm; Ensm; GS; NFL; Sch P; Thes; Var C; Mgr, Bkbl; Tr; Beauty; Journ A; Spch A; Yth Fel; City Ed Assn A; *Black Hills St Col; Secondary Ed.*

KIRKWOOD, James Russell
Lakeview HS; Battle Creek, MI (1-600) Band; Ensm; Pres, NHS; Orch; Swim; Val; Eagle Sct; Dist Solo & Ensm As; Schol, Kellogg Co-Op; *Purdue U; Chem Engr.*

KIRKWOOD, Judy Lynn
Owyhee HS; Owyhee, NV (25%-25) Rptr, Ann; Pres, 4H; Tres, Hmrm; Rptr, Sch P; Bkbl; Tr; Fleischman Schol; 4H A; Sci A; Historian, FHA; Historian, FBLA; Outst FBLA Member; *U of New at Reno; Pre-Vet Sci.*

KIRKWOOD, Scott Alan
Lakeview HS; Battle Creek, MI (1-550) Band; Ensm; NHS; Orch; SC; Tnns; Citz A; Eagle Sct; Dist Solo & Ensm As; *Sci.*

KIRKWOOD, Shelly Rae
McDermitt Combined HS; McDermitt, NE (2-15) Band; GS.

KIRKWOOD, Thurman Eugene
Palm Springs HS; Palm Springs, CA; Calif Schol; Bank of Amer A; I Dare A Citz; *Pepperdine Col; Construction.*

KIRN, Jerome Paul
Brussels Comm HS; Brussels, IL (3-26) Pres, FFA; SC; Pres, Jr Cl; VP, Soph Cl; Bsbl; Bkbl; Citz A; HKg; *Lewis & Clark Comm Col; Acct.*

KIRSCH, Deborah Jo
Jasper HS; Jasper, MN (10-41) Band; CYO; Chor; Ensm; FHA; Orch; Secy, Soph Cl; Bkbl; Sftbl; Tr; Vlbl; *Dental Asst.*

KIRSCHNER, Stacy Lee
Woodmere Acad; Woodmere, NY (6-52) Drama; Rptr, Sch P; Sci C; Span C; Hon Prog; Regent Schol; Ntl Merit Commended Stu; *Pre-Med.*

KIRSH, Laurence Frederick
Clarkston HS; Clarkston, GA (8-380) BC; Chess C; Tres, Chor; Parl, Drama; Fr C; Math C; Model UN; Parl, NHS; COM; Hist A; Hon Prog; Math A; NMF; Presbyterian Col Jr Fel; Ga Tech Math Schol; Most Intelligent; *U of Va.*

KIRST, John Howard
Principia HS; St Louis, MO (16-100) Bus Mgr, Ann; Band; Drama; Ftbl; Soccer; COM; Citz A; NEDT; Co-Ch, Stage Crew; *NW Mo U; Law.*

KIRSTOWSKI, Beth Louise
Lutheran HS E; Harper Woods, MI (4-120) A Cap Choir; Ger C; Secy, NHS; Rptr, Sch P; JV, Bkbl; Tr; COM; NMS; Phi Beta Kappa; *Concordia Col; Deaconness Trng.*

KIRTLEY, David Lee
Sidney Lanier HS; Montgomery, AL (214-437) Fin, Auto & Petro, DELA; 1st Pl Auto & Petro Manuals, Banq; *Auburn U; Computer Prog.*

KIRTLEY, Robert Beckham
Enid HS; Enid, OK (145-538) Chor; Thes; Ftbl; *Okla St U; Art.*

KIRTON, Patricia Ann
Hillcrest HS; Jamaica, NY (66-667) Band; Church Yth Choir; Bowl Tm; Secy, Sunday Sch; Christian Seekr C; Basic Ed Opportunity Grant; Practical Nurs Prog; *Va Commonwealth U; Nurs.*

KIRWAN, Ann Lesa
Snake River HS; Blackfoot, ID (7-127) Pres, Dbte Tm; Drama; FHA; GS; Secy, 4H; NFL; NHS; Ed, Sch P; Secy, Span C; Amer Leg A; B Crocker A; Cl Fav; 4H A; Hon Prog; MLS; Sci A; Spch A; Pantherettes Drill Tm; Soroptomist A; LDS Sem Coun; *Utah St U; Amer Stu.*

KISCHER, Kim Noretta
Central HS; Waterloo, IA; Chor; Hmrm; Madrigal; SC; Y-Tns; Opt A; Spch A; Vlbl; *Psych.*

KISER, Randy Lee
Cherryville HS; Cherryville, NC (50-143) Band; Fr C; FFA; Rptr, 4H; Hmrm; Math C; Monogram; Sci C; Arch; Bsbl; Ftbl; Sftbl; Tr; 4H A; *Wildlife Mgr.*

KISER, Robert Scott
Brazil Sr HS; Brazil, IN (7-200) Pres, Key C; NHS; Sch P; Span C; Golf; Pep C; *Ind St U; Marketing.*

KISER, Sandra Jean
S Charleston HS; S Charleston, WV; Span C; Jr NHS; Intrntl Fel Exchng Stu, Columbia; *Archt.*

KISER, Susan Elaine
Brazil HS; Brazil, IN (18-200) FHA; Span C; *Ind St U; Bus.*

KISER, Tami Darlene
SW Randolph HS; Asheboro, NC (36-150) Chor; Ensm; Pres, FHA; VP, FTA; InterClub Coun; Rptr, Monogram; Mgr, Bsbl; COM; FHA' ER o-t Yr.

KISER, Theresa Gail
Monticello HS; Monticello, MS; Band; BC; Bus C; VP, Fr C; FHA; Semi-Fin, Jr Miss Pa; Mjrte; F-Ed, Sch P; Span C; Y-Tns; COM; *U of Sou Miss; Phar.*

KISER, Thomas Edward
William Penn Sr HS; York, PA (67-421) Demolay; Bkbl; Sftbl; Church Yth Choir; Pres, Luther League; Yrbk Photographer; *Pre-Med.*

KISER, Valerie Lynn
S Charleston HS; S Charleston, WV; Secy, FBLA; Span C; Beauty; JA A; Yth Fel; Future Secy's of Amer; *W Va Inst of Tech; Secy Sci.*

KISH, Grace Elizabeth
Tottenville HS; Staten Island, NY (72-1067) Ann; Band; NHS; Secy, Ski C; Var C; Bowl Tm; St George Assn Schol; *Bau Col; Acct.*

KISH, Sandra Kae
Bellbrook HS; Bellbrook, OH (30-201) Chor; Ensm; VP, 4H; Var C; Tr; Yth Fel; GAA.

KISHABA, Debora Renee
Heidelberg American HS; Heidelberg, GERMANY; Ann; Lit Mag; Secy, NHS; Ski C; SC; UN Council; Secy, Jr Cl; Hon Prog; Schol A; German A; Bus Law A.

KISHIHARA, Naomi
Fresno Adventist Acad; Fresno, CA (2-32) Ann; SC; Secy, Jr Cl; NEDT; *Pacific Union Col.*

KISS, Elizabeth Esther
Fort Hunt HS; Alexandria, VA (1-479) French NHS; Co-Ed, Lit Mag; Secy, Orch; Sch Achieve Tm; COM; Gov Honor Prog; Church Choir; Principal's A; Superior Learner's Prog; Stu Solo, Concerto Prog.

KISSEL, Brian Keith
W Genesee Sr HS; Camillus, NY (6-620) AFS; Hmrm; Rptr, Key C; Math C; NHS; Sch P; SC; Rptr, Sr Cl; Rptr, Jr Cl; Rptr, Soph Cl; Bsbl; Bausch & Lomb A; COM; Chem A; Hon Prog; JA A; Regent Schol; Yth Fel; Pres, Church Yth Fel; *US Naval Acad; Aeronautical Engr.*

KISSEL, Kathleen Yvette
Lyons Central Sch; Lyons, NY (10-100) AFS; VP, Band; Chldr; Chor; Fr C; FTA; Ger C; Secy, NHS; Ski C; SC; Var C; Soccer; Sftbl; Tr; Regent Schol; Yth Fel; Bishop's Pastor, Parish Committee; Dist Yth Tm; Coach, Elem Soccer Tm; Dist Conf Coun; Comm On Campus Conf; Director, Church Yth Choir; *Houghton Col; Mus Ed.*

KISSEL, Kevin Mark
Lyons Central Sch; Lyons, NY; Band; Lat C; Co-Cpt, Ftbl; Tr; Wrest; President's Phys Fitness A.

KISSEL, Linda Gayle
Central HS; Cheyenne, WY (10-503) 4H; Citz A; Pep C; HR; Powder-Puff Ftbl; St Fin, Miss United Teen Pageant; Scholastic Achv A; Phys Fitness A; *Bus.*

KISSEL, Ron Charles
Columbiana HS; Columbiana, OH (8-128) Fin, BS; Pres, Chess C; Chor; Pres, Hmrm; Span C; VP, SC; Var C; Pres, Soph Cl; Bsbl; Bkbl; Ftbl; Tr; Wrest; Cl Fav; Hon Prog; MLS; Most Out; Opt Out Tn; Yth Fel; Yth Foundation; All Area, All Co, All St, Ftbl; HR; *U of Pittsburgh; Phys Ed.*

KISSEL, Ronald Charles
Colonel Whit HS; Dayton, OH; Chor; Ftbl; MLS; ROTC A; Chor, Ftbl, A's; *Drew U; Mus.*

KISSINGER, Lori J
Niagara-Wheatfield Sr HS; Sanborn, NY (10%-425) Fr C; NHS; Tnns; Alg A; Bio A; Citz A; Hon Men, Cl Play; Secy, Sorority; Eng A; Secy, Yth Group; Champ, Tnns Doubles; Colorguard; Art.

KISSLING, Timothy Jon
Agoura HS; Agoura, CA (132-675) Band; CSF; Pres, Church Group; *Pepperdine U; Bus.*

KISTER, Karen Jeanne
Las Plumas HS; Oroville, CA (3-184) Co-Cpt, Chldr; GS; Bank Of Amer A; Girl o-t Mo; Top 10; *Point Loma HS; Religion.*

KISTLER, Deborah Joyce
Concord Comm HS; Elkhart, IN (102-241) Band; Orch; SC; Y-Tns; COM; Outst Service, Band; Band & Orch Ltrs; *Bus.*

KISTLER, Kenneth Michael
N Hills HS; Pittsburgh, PA (50-900) Tres, Hmrm; VP, JETS; Span C; COM; Cl Fav; Hon Prog; JA A; Ntl Achv Schol; Industrial Arts A.

KISTLER, Ricky Todd
Brownstown HS; Brownstown, IL (2-40) Fr C; FFA; Hmrm; VP, SC; Pres, Var C; VP, Sr Cl; Bsbl; Bkbl; Tr; HCt; MLS; Sal; St Scholar; *U of Ill; Chem Engr.*

KITA, Christina Mary
Lauralton Hall HS; Milford, CT (8-93) Chor; Drama; Sch P; Span C; Span NHS; *Clark U; Journ.*

KITCHELL, Anthony Lee
Wilmington HS; Wilmington, IL; Band; Fr C; Parl, 4H; Madrigal; Bsbl; 4H A; Spch A; Ntl Spch A; *U of Ill; Agr.*

KITCHEN, Carrie Lynne
Hart Co HS; Munfordville, KY; BC; Raiderette; S-T, Tns Who Care; *Western Col.*

KITCHEN, Donna Lee
Point Pleasant Boro HS; Point Pleasant, NJ (25-300) NHS; Mgr, Bkbl; Co-Cpt, Cr-Ctry; Co-Cpt, Tr; MVP, Tr; Sci Cert of A; *Phys Ed.*

KITCHEN, Julia Ann
Gideon HS; Gideon, MO (4-56) Band; CYO; Chor; Ensm; FHA; NHS; Citz A; Hist, FHA; Supt's List; Home Ec A; Band A; HR A; *U of Mo; Mus.*

KITCHEN, Karen Marie
Temple Christian HS; Detroit, MI (5-57) Chldr; Chor; Ensm; Cpt, Var C; Secy, Sr Cl; Cpt, Bkbl; Cpt, Sftbl; Citz A; Type A; MVP, Bkbl & Sftbl; Cpt, MVP, Vlbl; Shorthand A; *Liberty Baptist Col; Phys Ed.*

KITCHENS, Janice Voncile
Jones Co HS; Gray, GA; FHA; Hmrm; NHS; F-Ed, Sch P; SC; Bkbl; *Fashion.*

KITCHENS, Jill Elaine
MacArthur HS; Irving, TX; Span C; Drill Tm; *N Lake Jr Col.*

KITE, Brenda Mae
Pampa HS; Pampa, TX (74-326) Rainbow; Beauty; Radeo C; Playday's; Pony Show; *West Tx Col; Nurs.*

KITE, Dianna Lynn
Forest Hills Northern HS; Grand Rapids, MI (33%-250) Span C; *Kendall Sch of Art; Commercial Art.*

KITE, John Allan
Abraham Lincoln HS; Denver, CO (112-635) A Cap Choir; Chem C; Pres, Chor; Drama; Ensm; Ger C; Ski C; Tnns; Most Out; Superior A in Mus Writing; Superior A in Trio Arrangement; Superior A in Duet Arrangement; Super in Ntl & Postrie Comp, Chor; *Trinity Col; Mus.*

KITRON, Kathleen Deanne
St Joseph HS; St Joseph, MI (28-363) Band; Drama; Pres, Ger C; Hmrm; Tres, InterClub Coun; Mjrte; NHS; Bus Mgr, Sch P; Tres, SC; Beauty; Citz A; DARGCA; Hon Prog; Journ A; JA A; Q&S A; Sr Graduation Speech; Whirlpool Schol; IA Schol; *Mich St U; Marketing Adm.*

KITTELL, Rochelle D
Horicon HS; Horicon, WI (15%-110) FFA; NHS; GAA; Vlbl; Candidate, Trees for Tomorrow; *Commercial Art.*

KITTLE, Lisa Renee
J J Pearce HS; Richardson, TX (48-650) Chor; Drama; Lat C; Orch; *N Tex St U; Home Ec.*

KITZIGER, Kurt John
Jesuit HS; New Orleans, LA (2-165) Co-Ed, Ann; Fin, Lit Ral; Mu Alpha Theta; Pres, NHS; Sch P; Span C; VP, SC; Cpt, Ftbl; Bio A; COM; Chem A; Hon Prog; Sal; Summa Cum Laude; MVP, Ftbl; Eng A; Most Rep Cl Member; *Duke U; Chem.*

KITZMAN, Pamela Jean
Bayview Sr HS; Milwaukee, WI (70-672) Band; Chor; Ensm; GS; Orch; F-Ed, Sch P; God & Country A; PTA A; Q&S A; SG Historian; All City Band; Rep, City-Wide Sr HS Coun; Sr Hon Soc; All City Rifle Sq; Stu Promotion Mgr, Sch Musical; *Marquette U.*

KIVETT, Barbara Denise
Cottage Grove HS; Cottage Grove, OR (10-201) AFS; FBLA; Pres, FHA; VP, NHS; Var C; Tnns; Crisco A; Type A; *NW Nazarene Col; Family Relations.*

KIVI, Donna Rae
Aurora Hoyt Lakes HS; Aurora, MN; Band; Tr; Bemidj St Col; Social Service.*

KIVLIGHAN, John Abbitt
Greeneville HS; Greeneville, TN (122-200) Cpt, Band; Chor; VP, Order/Arrow; Bsbl; Cpt, Bkbl; Cpt, Ftbl; Sftbl; Tnns; Order/Arrow A; Yth Fel; Life Sct; HR; NRA Sharpshooter; CAA Archer; *Mus.*

KIZER, Donna Lee
Ardmore HS; Ardmore, OK (33%-300) Chor; Lat C; Pres, A; Sci A; Yth Fel; *Med Tech.*

KIZZIA, Linda
Chaparral HS; Las Vegas, NV (75-950) A Cap Choir; Band; S-T, Chor; Drama; Madrigal; VP, Soph Cl; Sftbl; COM; Cl Fav; Interlochen Ntl Mus; Yth Fel; DeVos Acting Schol; Co Drama Tour; Fin, Most Outst Choir Spirit; *U of Nev; Theatre And Mus.*

KLAHN, Douglas John
Wymore Sou HS; Wymore, NE (30-55) Var C; Bkbl; Golf; Swim; Tnns; *Milford Col.*

KLAHR, Karen Anne
Schuylkill Haven Area Sch Dist; Schuylkill Haven, PA (13-114) A-Ed, Ann; Pres, Band; Ger C; GS; Hmrm; VP, NHS; SC; Tri-HiY; Tres, Sr Cl; Tres, Jr Cl; Tres, Soph Cl; Arch; Amer Leg A; DARGCA; God & Country A; WW; Ger A; *Millersville St Col; Lib Sci.*

KLANN, Richard David
Freeburg Comm HS; Freeburg, IL (5-160) Model UN; Sci C; Pres, Soph Cl; Bsbl; JV, Bkbl; JV, Ftbl; Amer Leg A; DARGCA; *Bio.*

KLAPROTH, Deborah Lynn
Jackson HS; Jackson, MO (74-214) Ann; Band; Chldr; VP, Chor; Drama; Ensm; Madrigal; Pres, Span C; SC; Var C; Co-Cpt, Tr; Inspirational Ath, Mus, A's; Prom Court; Best Female Ath; CTA Schol; *Murray St U; Law Enforcement.*

KLAPROTH, Tammy Elaine
Jackson HS; Jackson, MO (5-274) Tres, Band; S-T, Chor; Drama; Ensm; VP, FHA; GS; Mjrte; NHS; Ed, Sch P; Tres, Span C; Pres, SC; Bkbl; Sftbl; Tr; Rptr, Sch P; All Dist Band; Excel, St Mus Contest; *SE Mo St U; Sci.*

KLASING, Donald Rollin
W A Berry HS; Birmingham, AL (38-400) Chor; Parl, Drama; Lat C; Sci C; Swim; NMF; Yale Bk A; *Vanderbilt U; Med Engr.*

KLASS, Jane Frances
Hinsdale Central HS; Hinsdale, IL (209-601) Band; Secy, CYO; Orch; Band A's; *Ill Benedictine Col; Bus.*

KLASS, Randy Paul
Montrose HS; Montrose, MO; CYO; VP, NHS; VP, SC; Bsbl; Bkbl; Cr-Crty; Alg A; Hist A; HCt; Sci A; Driver's Ed A.

KLASSEN, Mark Franklin I
Central Valley HS; Veradale, WA (150-350) Chor; Drama; Key C; Ski C; Parl, SC; Thes; Soccer; Citz A; Cl Fav; Yth Fel; Yth Leg; Spokane Yth Serv A; M S Tm Cpt; Coached Jr Soccer Tm; *Spokane Falls Comm Col; Pol Sci.*

KLASSEN, Marreta Yvonne
Ulysses HS; Ulysses, KS; Band; Tres, Chess C; Chor; Ensm; VP, FHA; Y-Tns; *Social Work.*

KLASSY, Paul Lamon
Lindbergh Sr HS; Hopkins, MN (100-415) Ski C; Cr-Crty; Eagle Sct; *U of Minn; Engr.*

KLAUKE, Martha Jean
St Louise de Marillac HS; Northfield, IL (10-222) CYO; Chor; Drama; Hmrm; NHS; Pol Sci C; SC; Ftbl; Sftbl; Tr; Hon Prog; St Scholar; VP, Bridge C; Eng C; Amer Cancer Soc Summer Schol; *U of Ill Champaign; Bio.*

KLAUM, Kevin Wayne
Gateway Sr HS; Monroeville, PA (35-740) Band; Amer Leg A; Pres, Yth Fel; *U of Pittsburgh; Engr.*

KLAUS, James Rupert
Oakland HS; Murfreesboro, TN (1-364) Pres, Band; BS; Dbte Tm; Drama; Ensm; Ger C; Key C; Lat C; A-Ed, Lit Mag; Pres, Mu Alpha Theta; NHS; Order/Arrow; Pol Sci C; Math A; NMS; NEDT; All St Chor; ROTC Schol; Mus Hon Soc; Eng Hon Soc; *Vanderbilt U; Pol Sci.*

KLAUS, Vicki Marie
Ashland HS; Ashland, WI (39-210) AFS; Chldr; Secy, 4H; Hmrm; SC; Var C; Ch, Sr Cl; Tres, Jr Cl; Sftbl; Swim; Tnns; Tr; Cl Fav; 4H A; HCt; Hon Prog; MLS; WW; *Mid-St Tech Sch; Respiratory Therapy.*

KLAUSEN, Robert Earl
Loup City HS; Loup City, NE (17-70) Ann; NHS; 4H A; Spch A; *Sch of Tech Agr; Agr Mech Technology.*

KLEBERG, Barbara Ann
Weymouth N HS; Weymouth, MA; *Mus.*

KLEE, Sharon Adele
Roy C Start HS; Toledo, OH; Chor; Dbte Tm; Ensm; Hmrm; NFL; SC; Thes; Outst Musician; *Bowling Green St U; Mus.*

KLEIBOEKER, June Alice
Pierce City HS; Pierce City, MO (3-48) Ed, Ann; Tres, FHA; GS; Math C; NHS; Sch P; Spch C; Secy, Jr Cl; Amer Leg A; Cl Fav; Journ A; Poet A; Psy A; Bicentennial Writing A; *SMSU; Home Ec.*

KLEIHAUER, Jolene Lori
Washington HS; Cherokee, IA (40-136) Chor; Drama; Spch C; Thes; Sftbl; COM; Spch A.

KLEIN, Gary Stephen
Oakville Sr HS; St Louis, MO (134-504) CYO; NHS; Order/Arrow; ARC; JV, Soccer; JV, Wrest; Hon Prog; Order/Arrow A; Page, House of Rep; *U of Mo; Engr.*

KLEIN, James Millard
Rutherford HS; Rutherford, NJ (25-250) Band; Chor; Pres, Hmrm; Tres, Key C; NHS; Order/Arrow; SC; Var C; Ftbl; Tnns; Wrest; Amer Leg A; COM; Hon Prog; NEDT; Eagle Sct; *Vanderbilt U; Engr.*

KLEIN, Jennifer
Wasatch HS; Heber, UT; A Cap Choir; Chor; NHS; Sch P; SC; *Brigham Young U; Bus Ed.*

KLEIN, Joy Dorothy
Crestwood HS; Dearborn Heights, MI (120-388) Band; Ensm; Ger C; VP, Key C; SC; Hon Prog; JA A; *U of Mich; Sociology.*

KLEIN, Lisa Ann
MacArthur HS; San Antonio, TX (14-632) AFS; CYO; Ger C; NHS; Span C; Soccer; Hon Guard; Span Merit Diploma; *Tex A&M U; Engr.*

KLEIN, Lisa Kay
Harlingen HS; Harlingen, TX (1-700) Ann; Chess C; Drama; Key C; NHS; Tres, Jr Cl; Swim; Alg A; Bio A; Hist A; Math A; ARC A; Spch A; Eng A; Swim As; Toastmasters Yth Leadership A; *Rice U; Med.*

KLEIN, Lisa Marie
Coronado HS; Colorado Springs, CO (175-425) Band; Chor; Orch; JV, Swim; JV, Tnns; *Physiology.*

KLEIN, Matthew Gene
Jamestown HS; Jamestown, NY (179-516) AFS; Drama; Fr C; Tres, Lat C; Yth Fel; 2nd Prize, Cultural Exhibit; *Art.*

KLEIN, Peter David
Sharon HS; Sharon, PA (10-296) Band; Ger C; HiY; NHS; Phys C; Cr-Crty; Tr; Hon Prog; Kiwanis A; NEDT; PTA A; Ntl Merit Sch Commended Stu; *Penn St U; Engr.*

KLEIN, Rebecca Anne
Hastings Sr HS; Hastings, MN (17-430) NHS; Cr-Crty; Golf; Tr; *Bethel Col; Phys Therapy.*

KLEIN, Rosemarie
The Buckley Sch; Sherman Oaks, CA (10-68) Ann; Dbte Tm; Drama; NHS; Sch P; Spch C; Alg A; Bio A; Hist A; Hon Prog; Math A; NEDT; Lat A; *Oregon St U; Engr.*

KLEIN, Theresa Ellen
Estancia HS; Estancia, NM (5-68) Bus C; CYO; Drama; NHS; SC; Up Bound; JV, Bkbl; Mgr, Tr; Chem A; 4H A; Math A; Spch A; Type A; Vlbl; *E NM U; Ed.*

KLEINSCHMIDT, Melody Joy
Merrill Sr HS; Merrill, WI; A Cap Choir; Chor; Drama; Pom Pon; *Olivet Col; Teaching.*

KLEKS, Jon A
Reseda HS; Reseda, CA; Sch Achieve Tm; CSF; COM; Hon Prog; *UCLA; Engr.*

KLEMAN, Kimberly Dawn
New Providence HS; New Providence, NJ (1-300) Ann; Rptr, Sch P; SC; Tres, Soph Cl; Hon Prog; Yth Fel; Tres, GSct; Mus School; Eng A; *Eng.*

KLEMASH, Kirk Steven
S Fayette Jr-Sr HS; McDonald, PA (40-115) Band; Drama; Fr C; Orch; Thes.

KLEMENT, Sally Evelyn
Coppers Cove HS; Coppers Cove, TX (21-345) FHA; Mjrte; NHS; Drill Tm; *Tarleton St U; Agri-Bus.*

KLEMM, Julie Ann
California HS; Whittier, CA (79-400) Jr Miss Pagent; ARC; Rptr, Sch P; Span C; SC; VP, Y-Tns; Bus Mgr, Jr Cl; S-T, Soph Cl; CSF; COM; Athenas; WW; HR; Candystriper; *Biola U; Nurs.*

KLEMM, Kathy Lee
California HS; Whittier, CA; Chldr; JV, Tr; Yth Fel; Tr Coaches A; Candystriper; HR.

KLEMME, Elizabeth Ruth
Hermann Gasconade R-1 HS; Hermann, MO (12-96) Band; Chor; Drama; Ensm; Mjrte; NHS; Sch P; Bsbl; Regent School; Yth Fel; Special Drama Worker; Outst Vocal Mus A; *Mo W U; Elem Ed.*

KLEMME, Esther Louise
Hermann Gasconade R-1 HS; Hermann, MO (10-96) Band; Chor; Drama; Ensm; Madrigal; Mjrte; Sch P; Yth Fel; Special Drama Worker; Outst Vocal Mus A; *Social Work.*

KLEMPEL, Lori Jo
Grand Haven Sr HS; Grand Haven, MI; Chldr; Muskegan Bus Col; Bus.

KLENKE, Dale Robert
Faith Christian Acad; St Louis, MO; Arch; Chess C; NHS; Arch; Soccer.

KLENKE, Kathy Marie
Faith Christian Acad; St Louis, MO; Chldr; Chor; Drama; Pres, 4H; NHS; SC; Sftbl; 4H A; Swtht; Yth Fel; Awana C; *Tenn Temple Col.*

KLENZ, Brenda Elaine
Delphos Jefferson Sr HS; Delphos, OH (1-120) Band; Y-Tns; Tr; Bio A; Hon Prog; Stu Highest Point Avg Medalion; *Bus.*

KLEPP, Mona Grace
Fox Lane HS; Bedford, NY (50-350) Ensm; Fr C; French NHS; Ski C; Bkbl; Hockey; Sftbl; Yth Fel; Choir; Fr Achv A; *Dartmouth U; Law.*

KLEPPER, Kimberlee Lynn
N Shore HS; W Palm Beach, FL (27-266) Secy, Fr C; NHS; ARC; Alg A; PA; Top 5%; *U of Mich; Physiology.*

KLEPPER, Melinda Kim
Sullivan Central HS; Blountville, TN (47-379) Sci C; Span C; Hon Diploma; Vlbl Tm; Pep C; *E Tenn St U; Dental Hygiene.*

KLEPZIG, Steven Richard
Grand Co HS; Moab, UT (45-104) Band; BS; Pres, Dbte Tm; Spch C; Bsbl; *Utah Tech at Provo; Arch.*

KLEVEN, Joel Rae
Mission HS; Mission, TX (10-355) Band; BS; Ensm; Pres, Fr C; Rptr, Key C; Math C; Mu Alpha Theta; Rptr, NHS; SC; H of F; Math A; Yth Fel; Fr A; *Iowa St U; Industrial Adm.*

KLEVEN, Laurel Jean
Cedar Shoals HS; Athens, GA; BC; Drama; Ger C; Sci C; COM; 1st Cl GSct; Ballet; *Sci.*

KLIMEK, Rose Marie
Joliet W HS; Joliet, IL (215-500) Chldr; Chor; Hmrm; Swim; Yth Fel; *Communications.*

KLIMOSKI, Karen Elizabeth
St Mary's Acad; Englewood, CO (4-50) Cpt, Chldr; Secy, Chor; Secy, Drama; French NHS; NHS; Soph Prom Attendant; Sch Contestant, St Writing Contest; *Colo St U; Secondary Ed.*

KLINDT, Kimarie Jane
Shelby-Tennant Comm HS; Shelby, IA (10-32) Band; Chor; Drama; Ensm; S-T, 4H; Spch C; JV, Bkbl; 4H A; Spch A; Candidate, Co Fair Qn; Sch Band A's; Sch Accompaist A.

KLINDT, Valerie Jean
Shelby-Tennant Comm HS; Shelby, IA (20%-30) Band; Chldr; Chor; Community Yth Symph; Ensm; FNA; Pres, 4H; NHS; Rptr, Sch P; 4H A; All St Orch; Co Fair Qn Cand; Sch Band A; Sch Accompanist A; *Mus.*

KLINE, David Bruce
Crestwood HS; Mountaintop, PA (70-207) Chor; SC; Bkbl; Cr-Crty; Tr; Dist Chorus; WW, Mus Stu; *Kutztown St Teachers Col; Lib Sci.*

KLINE, Dean Stephen
Wallace HS; Wallace, ID (50%-99) BS; Key C; Span C; Bsbl; Cpt, Bkbl; Cr-Crty; Ftbl; Tr; Mr Hustle A; Most Improved; *Air Force Acad.*

KLINE, Nancy Ruth
Nederland HS; Nederland, TX (203-463) Cpt, CYO; FHA; FTA; Sftbl; Art C; Cath Ed Cl Teacher A; Pep Sq; Miss Flame; Bowling Tm; Fin, Best Personality, Sr Cl; Publicity Ch, Diocesean Rep, CYO; *Mim's Sch of Beauty; Cosmetology Instructor.*

KLINE, Sandy Robin
Jewish Educational Center HS; Elizabeth, NJ (6-26) Chldr; VP, Hmrm; Ch, InterAct C; Mjrte; Math C; NHS; Sch P; Span C; Hon Prog; Yrbk; *Pre-Med.*

KLING, Bruce William
Tewksbury Mem HS; Tewksbury, MA (68-484) Ann; Demolay; COM; Yth Fel; Ecology, Computer, C'S; Pres, Yth Fel; HR; *Forestry.*

KLING, Daniel Harold
New Hope Solebury HS; New Hope, PA (5-65) AFS; Pres, Chess C; Drama; Cpt, Math C; NHS; Bkbl; Highest Score, NHS, ANHSE; *MIT; Math.*

KLING, Jeffrey Micheal
Shawsheen Valley Reg Voc Tech HS; Billerica, MA (141-361) Yth Fel; Pres, Yth Fel; *Machinist.*

KLING, Pamela Jean
Belmond Community HS; Belmond, IA (7-81) A-Ed, Ann; Band Schol; Chor; NHS; Span C; SC; Var C; Pres, Jr Cl; Sftbl; Tr; DARGCA; HQn; HCt; *U of Iowa; Pre-Med Technology.*

KLING, Susan Elizabeth
Tewksbury Mem HS; Tewksbury, MA (44-446) Ann; COM; Yth Fel; Ecology C; Rep, Church Coun; HR; *Fitchburg St Col; Nurs.*

KLINGBEIL, Julie Elizabeth
Mankato E HS; Mankato, MN (10%-350) Band; Chor; 4H; Ch, Hmrm; Orch; Ski C; Tnns; Interlochen Ntl Mus; Brett's Tm Board; Sch Play; Part Time Job; Gym; Modern Dance; *Mus.*

KLINGENSMITH, Charles Dana
Woodrow Wilson HS; Beckley, WV; Band; Chess C; Dbte Tm; Ensm; Lat C; Thes; *Hist.*

KLINGENSMITH, Janice Irene
Burrell Sr HS; Lower Burrell, PA (6-351) AFS; Pres, Chor; Pres, Ensm; Fin, Jr Miss Pagent; Key C; Mjrte; NHS; Sftbl; Tr; 2nd Runner Up, Jr Miss Pageant; District Chor; *Acct.*

KLINGERMAN, Gregory George
McCluer N HS; Florissant, MO (42-799) Chor; Fr C; Order/Arrow; Chem A; Ntl Sci Found; Puppet A; Dancing A; *Theatre.*

KLINGERMAN, Kevin Kenneth
McCluer N HS; Florissant, MO (154-764) Chor; Ger C; Order/Arrow; JV, Soccer; Order/Arrow A; *NE Mo St U; Law Enforcement.*

KLINGLER, Stephanie York
St Margaret's McTernan HS; Waterbury, CT (4-27) AFS; Rptr, Ann; Chor; S-T, Drama; Fr C; Hmrm; Lat C; Co-Ed, Lit Mag; Ed, Sch P; Soccer; Swim; Tnns; Hon Prog; Pres A; Fr A; WW; *Pre-Med.*

KLINGNER, Jennifer Lou
Central HS; Springfield, MO (69-278) Anchor C; Ed, Ann; Chldr; NFL; Sch P; Span C; Swim; Fin, Journ A; Fin, Q & S A.

KLINNER, John Burns
Scott Preparatory HS; Opelika, AL; BC; Hmrm; NHS; Cpt, Span C; SC; Bkbl; Cpt, Tnns; NEDT; Eng As; *Vanderbilt U; Med.*

KLOBUCAR, Lisa Lorraine
Convent o-t Sacred Heart HS; San Francisco, CA (22-50) A Cap Choir; Chor; Alliance Francaise A; *UCB; Journ.*

KLOCK, Thomas James
Kofa HS; Yuma, AZ (51-501) A Cap Choir; Band; Tres, Chess C; Chor; Ensm; InterClub Coun; Madrigal; NHS; Sci C; Math A; Optimist Schol; *Pacific Christian Col; Mus.*

KLOCKE, Deborah Lynne
Virden Comm HS; Virden, IL; Drama; Fr C; NHS; Co-Ed, Sch P; Sci C; Bio A; Hist A; Math A; NMS; NEDT; Rotary A; 1st Cl GSct; Christian Yth Group; Color Guard; GAA; Stu in Aid of Ed; Pres, Yth Fel; *Aurora Col; Fr.*

KLOCKE, Rhonda Jan
Highland HS; Ewing, MO (12-130) Pres, FHA; Tres, NHS; Rptr, Sch P; SC; Mgr, Ftbl; Mgr, Tr; Swtht; WW; Yrbk Qn; *Patricia Stephens Career Col; Fashion Merchandising.*

KLOCKE, Steven Paul
Hunter Huss HS; Gastonia, NC (57-554) Band; BC; Fr C; Order/Arrow; Eng A; S Central All St Band; *Acct.*

KLOCKENGA, Gail Ann
Lincoln Comm HS; Lincoln, IL (61-277) Bus C; Fr C; Rptr, Sch P; *Lincoln Land Comm Col; Acct.*

KLOEPPEL, Ronald Gene
Delphos Jefferson Sr HS; Delphos, OH (15-135) FFA; Bsbl; Pub Speaking; *Agr.*

KLOHN, Mark Jeffrey
Stephens Hempstead Sr HS; Dubuque, IA (143-627) Chor; Ger C; Order/Arrow; Sch P; Spch C; Y-Tns; God & Country A; Order/Arrow A; Sanctuary Soc; Spch A; Vlbl; Waterskiing; Eagle Sct; *U of Dubuque.*

KLOO, Kenneth John
Secaucus HS; Secaucus, NJ (10-164) BS; Tres, Key C; NHS; Cpt, Bsbl; Hon Prog; *St Peter's Col; Biol.*

KLOPFENSTEIN, Mary Sue
Grace Baptist HS; Decatur, AL (3-21) Ann; VP, Soph Cl; NEDT; *Ed.*

KLOPP, John Philip
Davenport Central HS; Davenport, IA (40-675) A Cap Choir; Band; Ensm; Madrigal; Orch; Order/Arrow; Thes; Hon Prog; Order/Arrow A; Hon Bands; *U of Iowa; Mus Ed.*

KLOR, Julie Dawn
Highland HS; Ault, CO (13-83) Band; Pres, FHA; VP, FTA; GS; NHS; SC; Var C; Parl, Soph Cl; Tr; *U of N Colo; Nurs.*

KLORFEIN, Tamara Joy
N Shore HS; W Palm Beach, FL (43-266) F-Ed, Ann; Co-Cpt, Chldr; Drama; Key C; SC; Var C; Tnns; Journ A; Civics A; Creative Writing A; Jr NHS; *Emory U; Eng.*

KLOS, Pamela Rae
Sparks HS; Sparks, NV (7-380) Fr C; COM; *Berkley Col; Acct.*

KLOSKY, Joyce Marie
Lutheran HS; Harper Woods, MI (3-154) A Cap Choir; Secy, Band; Hmrm; NHS; SC; Var C; Bkbl; Sftbl; Vlbl; *Concordia Seward Col; Phys Ed.*

KLOSS, Mary Ann
Riverside Jr-Sr HS; Taylor, PA (12-193) Drama; FBLA; NHS; Sch P; Sodality; NEDT; Type A; Shorthand, Drama C, A's; 200 Hour Candystriper, A; *Keystone Jr Col; Med Secy.*

KLOSSNER, Lisa Marie
Kasson-Mantorville HS; Kasson, MN (80-101) Chor; Drama; Ensm; 4H; Span C; Co-Cpt, Bkbl; Co-Cpt, Sftbl; Yth Fel; Mgr, Vlbl; All Conf Bkbl; Tm o-t Wk; *Rochester Comm Col; Phys Ed.*

KLOSTERMAN, Marcia Lynn
Highline HS; Seattle, WA (26-415) Tres, AFS; Cum Laude Soc; NHS; SC; Swim; Tnns; Most Inspirational, Swim; *W Wash Col; Health Sci.*

KLOSTERMAN, Matthew John
Chaminade Col Prep; St Louis, MO (18-118) NHS; Rptr, Sch P; Bsbl; Bkbl; Co-Cpt, Soccer; Alg A; Bio A; HCt; Hon Prog; Math A; Semi-Fin, ROTC; Plummers Essay Cert; *Washington U-Dartmouth; Pre-Med.*

KLOTZBUECHER, Karl Joseph
Little Wolf HS; Manawa, WI (6-80) Ann; Pres, Chor; Math C; NHS; Pres, Var C; SC; Var Cl; Pres, Soph Cl; Co-Cpt, Ftbl; Tr; Wrest; HKg; Math A; Pres A; MVP, Ftbl; *Mercy Medical Center Sch Nurs; Nurs.*

KLUSMEYER, Dennis John
South Shelby HS; Shelbina, MO (30-100) Arch; Chor; Ensm; Madrigal; NHS; Var C; Cpt, Bkbl; Ftbl; Golf; Wrest; St Choral Ratings; WW A; *Phys Ed.*

KLUTTS, Joe Douglas
Deweyville HS; Deweyville, TX (4-37) VP, Band; FFA; NHS; Citz A; Hon Prog; *Lamar U; Archt Engr.*

KLUZEK, Mark Thomas
Layton HS; Layton, UT (70-500) Hon Prog; *Concordia Col.*

KMETZ, Andrea C
St Elizabeth HS; Pittsburgh, PA (6-101) Bus Mgr, Ann; CYO; Chor; Drama; Phys C; Sch P; Ski C; VP, Span C; Tres, SC; COM; Hon Prog; Magna Cum Laude; NEDT; Tres, Span C; *U of Mich.*

KNAPP, Cynthia Louise
Birmingham Seaholm HS; Birmingham, MI; Chor; Ensm; Hmrm; SC; Yth Fel; *Western Mich U; Special Ed.*

KNAPP, Deborah Wanda
Auburn Christian Sch; Auburn, NY; Chor; A-Ed, Sch P; Bkbl; Sftbl.

KNAPP, Dorene Stacy
Yonkers HS; Yonkers, NY (21-400) Key C; Mjrte; Ski C; *Syracuse U; Communications.*

KNAPP, Kim Kay
Panhandle HS; Panhandle, TX (10-60) Band; Drama; FHA; FTA; NFL; NHS; Spch C; Pres, Thes; Golf; 1st, Co Bicentennial Essay Contest; 1st, Tex Women U Writer's Conf; *Tex Tech; Pre-Law.*

KNAPP, Michelle Irene
Benson HS; Omaha, NE (40-441) VP, AFS; Chor; Chamber of Comm A; Hon Prog; Regent Schol; Yth Fel; Board of Trustees Schol; Co Col Schol; Church Deacon; *Coe Col; Mus.*

KNAPP, Tami Lynn
Oak Hills HS; Cincinnati, OH (1-840) Pres, NHS; Mgr, Arch; DARGCA; Phy A; Val; Brown Book A; NML; Bicentennial Sch o-t Gifted; *Miami U; Bus Mgt.*

KNAPP, Trudie Jean
Highland HS; Ewing, MO (4-160) Band; Chor; Pres, 4H; NHS; Bio A; 4H A; Sci A; Spch A; Psych C; Mus A; *Med Sci.*

KNASEL, Susan Renee
Kalamazoo Central HS; Kalamazoo, MI; Chor; JV, Tr; JV Ltr; *Springarbor Col.*

KNAUF, Elizabeth Dianne
Taft HS; Lincoln City, OR (19-85) Ann; Chldr; Fr C; NHS; Spch C; Tr; COM; Kiwanis A; WW; *George Fox Col; Social Services.*

KNAUF, Libby Dianne
Taft HS; Lincoln City, OR (19-85) Ann; Chldr; Fr C; Tres, NHS; Spch C; SC; Tr; COM; H of F; Kiwanis A; WW; *George Fox Col; Eng.*

KNAUSS, Pamela Nora
William Allen HS; Allentown, PA (3-760) Band; VP, Ger C; Orch; World Affairs C; Y-Tns; Hosp Vol A; Band A; *Nurs.*

KNECHEL, Terri Kathryn
Palisades Jr-Sr HS; Kintnersville, PA (11-192) Chor; NHS; Orch; Mus Fed Gold Cup Win; Church Dist Keyboard Win; Co Pianist; Pres, NYI; World Conf, NYI, Switzerland; *Allentown Bus Sch; Acct.*

KNEE, Elizabeth Julie
Greeley W HS; Greeley, CO (50-279) Band; Chor; Ensm; Secy, Fr C; Secy, FHA; Achv Schol; *Nebr Wesleyan U; Art.*

KNEEDLER, Audrey Gail
NE Sr HS; Kansas City, MO (25%-300) Tres, Band; NHS; *Montessori Acad; Montessori Ed.*

KNEISEL, Teresa Beth
McCullough HS; Woodlands, TX (35-440) Chor; NHS; Sci C; Pres, SC; Pres, Soph Cl; Bkbl; Tr; Beauty; COM; Yth Fel; Gym; Guild Piano, A's; Imperial Miss Talent; *Baylor U; Nurs.*

KNEISLEY, Nancy Ellen
St Andrews Parish HS; Charleston, SC (75-550) COM; VP, Art C; Icthus C; Art A; *Col of Charleston; Art Ed.*

KNEKON, Linda Lee
Westchester Sr HS; Houston, TX (150-560) AFS; Bus C; Chor; FHA; Math C; Mu Alpha Theta; Span C; Hon Prog; Yth Fel; Keyettes; Homemaking A; *Banking & Finance.*

KNELL, Jeannie Kay
E Mecklenburg HS; Charlotte, NC; Hmrm; Sftbl; Good Sportsmanship A.

KNELLER, Judith Anne
Strong Vincent HS; Erie, PA (12-230) A Cap Choir; VP, Chor; Madrigal; NHS; Cpt, Swim; Dist Chor; GSct; Pres, Yth Fel; Chancel & Handbell Choir; *Villa Maria Col; Bio.*

KNERR, Kevin Scott
William Allen HS; Allentown, PA (47-778) NHS; *US Army.*

KNIBBS, Carol Lee
Chamberlain HS; Grassy Lake, CANADA (1-16) Tres, SC; Bkbl; Citz A; Hon Prog; Vlbl; *U of Calgary; Psych.*

KNIERIM, Lavigne Ann
Gulliver Acad; Coral Gables, FL (20%-17) Cpt, Chldr; Chor; Ensm; Fr C; Hmrm; Sch P; Pres, SC; HQn; *Fla St U; Nurs.*

KNIFONG, Linda Jean
Paradise HS; Paradise, CA (35-236) 4H; HiY; SC; Secy, Sr Cl; CSF; 4H A; Runnerup, Gold Nugget Qn; *Butte Col; Med Terminology.*

KNIGHT, Betty Howard
Temple Christian Sch; Redford, MI (5-70) Bkbl; Sftbl; Citz A; Math A; Sci A.

KNIGHT, Byron
Centerville HS; Centerville, TX (10-50) VP, FFA; NHS; Golf; Tnns; *Rice U; Med.*

KNIGHT, Cara Leigh
Vandalia-Butler HS; Vandalia, OH (50%-380) Bus C; FBLA; Ntl Yth Conf; COM; Type A; *Wright St U; Eng.*

KNIGHT, Diane Lynn
Thomas Stone HS; Waldorf, MD (8-361) Hmrm; Jr Miss Pagent; NHS; SC; Sftbl; Math A; *St Mary's Col of Md; Math.*

KNIGHT, Dianne Lorraine
Livermore Falls HS; Livermore Falls, ME (5-124).

KNIGHT, Donna Marie
Poteau HS; Poteau, OK (15%-108) Chor; Ensm; FBLA; Rotary A; OSU Hon Alumni Stu; *Carl Albert Jr Col; Elem Ed.*

KNIGHT, Elizabeth Anne
Central HS; Knoxville, TN; Chor; Hmrm; Span NHS; VP, Y-Tns; HCt; *U of Tenn; Pre-Law.*

KNIGHT, Eugene Turner
Donoho Sch; Anniston, AL (1-39) Mu Alpha Theta; NHS; S-T, Span C; SC; Pres, Jr Cl; Pres, Soph Cl; Alg A; God & Country A; NEDT; Eagle Sct; Physiology A; Span A; Lat A; *MIT; Engr.*

KNIGHT, Gaynel Kris
Lancaster HS; Lancaster, OH; FHA; HERO; *Ohio U; Ed.*

KNIGHT, Jacob William Jr
Hanceville HS; Hanceville, AL (38-104) FFA; FTA; VP, Hmrm; VP, Sr Cl; Bsbl; Bkbl; Cpt, Ftbl; *Wallace Tech Col; Elec.*

KNIGHT, Janice Kay
Minnehaha Acad; Minneapolis, MN (72-155) Chor; Drama; Fr C; Orch; VP, Span C; JV, Bkbl; Sftbl; Tr; Hon Prog; Vlbl; WW; Cl Clown; *Bethel Col; Elem Ed.*

KNIGHT, Jeffrey Neil
King's Acad; WPB, FL (4-60) Band; Chess C; Chor; Drama; Ensm; Hmrm; VP, NHS; VP, SC; Pres, Sr Cl; Pres, Soph Cl; Bkbl; Mgr, Ftbl; Hon Prog; Sci A; WW; Most Sch Spirit; Outst Mus & Drama A; Pres, Pep C; *Wake Forest U; Pre-Med.*

KNIGHT, John Anthony
Duncan HS; Duncan, OK (1-350) Chor; Secy, Key C; Madrigal; Tres, Soph Cl; Bio A; *Okla U; Law.*

KNIGHT, Judy Marie
Lockhart HS; Lockhart, TX; Ann; Band; Parl, Lib C; *U of Tex; Nurs.*

KNIGHT, Karen Elizabeth
Duncan HS; Duncan, OK (25-314) Rptr, Fr C; FHA; Hmrm; SC; Page, Carl Albert; Cl Offices; *Okla U; Pol Sci.*

KNIGHT, Karl Patrick
Thomasville HS; Thomasville, AL (10-70) FFA; 4H; WW; *Livingston U; Acct.*

KNIGHT, Kathryn Renee
Briarfield Acad; Lake Providence, LA (5-48) BC; Chldr; Ensm; 4H; Lit Ral; Sch P; Co-Ch, Span C; VP, St Stu Congress; Pres, SC; Up Bound; Tnns; Tr; 4H A; HCt; Hon Prog; Drill Tm; *La St Col; Fashion Merchandising.*

KNIGHT, Kathy Jo
Hatley HS; Hatley, MS; Secy, BC; Chldr; Chor; Ensm; Pres, FHA; Hmrm; SC; HCt; *Miss St U; Elem Ed.*

KNIGHT, Laura Catherine
Benhaven Sch; Olivia, NC; Tres, Band; BC; VP, Fr C; FHA; Secy, FTA; Pres, SC; Bio A; Gr Marshal; Hist A; Type A; *Elon Col; Bus Ed.*

KNIGHT, Mark Leslie
Hoopeston E Lynn HS; Hoopeston, IL; Band; Cr-Ctry; Tr.

KNIGHT, Melinda Beth
Ross S Sterling HS; Baytown, TX (25%-450) Ed, Ann; Chor; Ger C; Key C; *Psych.*

KNIGHT, Norma Jean
William Monroe HS; Stanardsville, VA (4-78) Ch, Ann; Tres, BC; Pres, FTA; Hmrm; Ed, Lit Mag; NFL; Tres, NHS; Parl, SC; VP, Sr Cl; Tr; Beauty; COM; Citz A; HCt; Hon Prog; Ntl Achv Schol; Type A; Miss Monroe; Miss Congenality; Nom, Col Schol; WW; *Mary Washington Col; Sci.*

KNIGHT, Patricia Ann
Beverly HS; Beverly, MA (54-580) 4H; Secy, Hmrm; Rainbow; 4H A; Hon Prog; Yth Fel; *Framingham St; Computer Sci.*

KNIGHT, Peggy Cornelia
Towering Oaks Baptist Sch; Memphis, TN (4-95) Chor; Ensm; FTA; Ntl Jr Hon Soc; Secy, Church Yth; Miss Colonial; Messenger Choir; *Christian Brothers Col; Vet.*

KNIGHT, Phillip Bruce
Chickasaw Acad; Satsuma, AL; Hmrm; Key C; Math C; Pres, SC; Var C; Sr Cl; Pres, Jr Cl; MVP, Bsbl; Bkbl; Cpt, Ftbl; Citz A; Cl Fav; HCt; MVP, Ftbl; VP, Pep C; Best All-Around; *Wesley Col; Ministerial.*

KNIGHT, Ronald D
Cowan HS; Muncie, IN (8-70) Band; BS; 4H; NHS; Bsbl; Bkbl; Golf; Tr; Alg A; 4H A; Hon Prog; Math A; Yth Fel; *Ball St U; Engr.*

KNIGHT, Russell R
Cleburne HS; Cleburne, TX; Chor; Demolay; Tri-HiY; Ftbl; Chor A; *Forestry.*

KNIGHT, Sandy Denise
Wayne Co HS; Jesup, GA; 4H; Ch, Hmrm; Lat C; SC; Gov Honor Prog; Hon Prog; Yth Fel; DECA; Pres, Sun Sch Cl; Tres, Cts; *ABAC; Bus Adm.*

KNIGHT, Stella Louise
Guthrie HS; Guthrie, OK; Cpt, Chldr; Chor; Drama; FBLA; Tr; Hist A; Hon Prog; JA A; Phy A; S Black Heritage C; PTA Schol; Secy Trng Cert; *Central St U; Pre-Law.*

KNIGHT, Tammy Annette
Lawton Sr HS; Lawton, OK (142-530) A Cap Choir; Chor; Drama; FHA; 4H; Semi-Fin, Hmrm; Spch C; Var C; Bkbl; Swim; Tr; COM; 4H A; Spch A; *Cameron Col; Bus Adm.*

KNIGHT, Teresa Louise
Aiken HS; Aiken, SC (15-640) BC; Hmrm; Jr Miss Pagent; NHS; Pol Sci C; Ch, SC; Secy, Sr Cl; Co-Ch, Jr Cl; Co-Ch, Soph Cl; Sftbl; Beauty; COM; HCt; Hon Prog; May Day Court; *U of SC; Nurs.*

KNIGHT, Tina Marie
Washington HS; Washington, IL (50%-425) Chor; Pres, FHA; VP, 4H; 4H A; *Ill Central Col; Secy.*

KNIGHT, Tony Kevin
Logan Sr HS; Logan, WV (60-350) Chor; Fr C; Pres, Key C; Golf; Tnns; Cl Fav; 4H A; Chor A; Tn A; Golf A; *Marshall U; Bus Adm.*

KNIGHT, William Ronald
W Carteret HS; Morehead City, NC (2-251) Band; BS; Chem; Fr C; Monogram; NHS; Phys C; SC; Pres, Sr Cl; JV, Bkbl; Cpt, Tnns; Chem A; Math A; NEDT; Phy A; Sal; VofDEM; MVP, Tnns; *Wake Forest U; Pre-Law.*

KNIGHTEN, Christopher Lydell
Terra Linda HS; San Rafael, CA; A Cap Choir; Band; Var C; Cpt, Bsbl; Ftbl; Hon Prog; Pres A; Mgr, JV Bsbl; Ath Achv A; Ath Block; Hon Mus A.

KNIGHTS, Edmund
Bell Voc HS; Washington, DC; Woodward Found; WW.

KNITT, Robert William
Flanagan HS; Flanagan, IL (10%-23) Band; Chor; Madrigal; SC; Bsbl; Bkbl; Ftbl; HCt; Type A.

KNITTEL, Bridgette Mary
Ayer Jr-Sr HS; Ayer, MA (37-397) Chor; Hmrm; SC; Bkbl; Sftbl; Tr; Pres A; Sci A; Yth Fel; Spelling A; *Hope Col; Engr.*

KNOBLOCH, Karen Lynne
Acad of Our Lady of Mercy; Milford, CT (4-86) CYO; Chldr; Fr C; Ski C; NEDT; Schol; *Conn Col; Dental Hygiene.*

KNOCH, Carole Jean
Bennington HS; Bennington, NE (12-65) Band; Chor; Ensm; VP, Var C; Co-Cpt, Bkbl; Tr; 4H A; Pres A; St Medallist; Tr; JV Vlbl; *Hastings Col; Phys Ed.*

KNODLE, Emily Ann
Leaf River HS; Leaf River, IL; Ann; Band; Chldr; Chor; Secy, FHA; Sch P; SC; Secy, Soph Cl; Bsbl; Bkbl; Ftbl; Soccer; Sftbl; Swim; Tr.

KNODLE, Wesley James
Leaf River HS; Leaf River, IL; Band; FFA; Pres, Hmrm; VP, Spch C; Var C; JV, Bkbl; Ftbl; MVP, Swim.

KNOELL, Jeffrey Scott
Kearny HS; San Diego, CA (90-800) Bkbl; *San Diego St U; Bus.*

KNOESPEL, Michael Lee
Mosinee Comm HS; Mosinee, WI (40-167) Band; Ensm; Var C; Bsbl; Ftbl; *Eng.*

KNOLHOFF, Gary Allan
Carlyle HS; Carlyle, IL (60-150) Secy, FFA.

KNOLHOFF, Sandy Kay
Carlyle HS; Carlyle, IL (57-138) Chor; Drama; Ch, FBLA; Sftbl; Tr; Type A; *Kaskaskia Col; Secy.*

KNOLL, Brian Donald
Patrick Henry HS; San Diego, CA (436-1173) S-T, Demolay; Campus Life C; *San Diego St U; Horticulture.*

KNOOP, Dean Edward
E Central HS; Tulsa, OK (250-674) Band; Order/ Arrow; Tr; Order/Arrow A; Nazarene Yth Dream Boat.

KNOP, Gretchen Elaine
Mt Olive HS; Mt Olive, IL (1-75) Band; Chor; Ensm; FHA; Ntl Fed Festival; Pres, Fresh Cl; Ntl Auditions; Ntl Fed Mus C; FHA 1st Yr Piano A; Co-Cpt, Bowl; Secy, Luth Yth Org; *Bus.*

KNOP, Kevin Dale
Stewardson-Strasburg HS; Stewardson, IL (2-40) Ann; VP, NHS; Pres, Soph Cl; MVP, Bsbl; MVP, Bkbl; Amer Leg A; Hon Prog; Sal; Co Cpt, Bkbl; *Bus Mgt.*

KNOPP, James Mark
Heritage Christian HS; Indianapolis, IN; Pres, Band; Chess C; VP, 4H; Lat C; Lit Mag; Var C; Bsbl; Mgr, Bkbl; Tnns; Mgr, Tr; Alg A; Sci A; *Butler U; Med.*

KNOTT, Princella Ann
Community HS; Houston, TX (10%-98) SC; Y-Tns; Hist A; Swtht; Miss CHS; Yth Fair; *Barbizon Fashion Col; Fashion Design.*

KNOTT, Robin Dale
McMinn Co HS; Athens, TN (50%-272) *Cleveland St Col; Math.*

KNOTT, William Edgar
East HS; Columbus, OH (25-350) Tres, Church Chor; WW; Straight A A; *Columbus Sch of Art & Design; Advertising.*

KNOWLES, Diane Marie
Campbell Central Sch; Campbell, NY (5-47) Band; Tres, Fr C; Ski C; Bkbl; Soccer; Sftbl; Spch A; Mjrte Colorguard; Ntl Tn-Age Pageant; *Corning Comm Col; Pol Sci.*

KNOWLES, Donald Lee
Maine Township HS W; Des Plaines, IL (92%-800)
Hmrm; Key C; Spch C; JV, Soccer; Bio A; Hist A;
Spch A; Optimist Oratorical Contest Win; Pres,
Church Yth Group; Yth Member, City Coun.

KNOWLES, Elaine Cecelia
Cleveland Heights HS; Cleveland Heights, OH
(10%-1000) Chor; Rptr, Sch P; COM; Hon Prog;
'A' Avg, Jr HS; *Sci.*

KNOWLES, Elizabeth Jane
Whitefish Bay HS; Milwaukee, WI (60-300) Phys
C; Span C; Swim; Tr; Hon Prog; Pres, Waterballet;
Waterballet, Tr, A's; *U of Minn; Nurs.*

KNOWLES, Janice Gaye
Fernandina Beach HS; Fernandina Beach, FL;
Band; Rainbow.

KNOWLES, Nancy Carol
Buchholz HS; Gainesville, FL; Fr C; Hmrm; NHS;
Secy, SC; COM; Keyettes; *Sociology.*

KNOWLTON, Karen Kay
Mankato W HS; Mankato, MN; Band; Golf; Can-
dystripper; *Concordia Col; Bus.*

KNOWLTON, Kenneth Lee
Beavercreek HS; Xenia, OH (100-650) Chem C;
Cr-Ctry; Ftbl; Soccer; Sftbl; Tnns; Tr; Wrest; Opt
A; Sci A; Gym; *Computer Engr.*

KNOWLTON, Richard Orin
Santa Monica HS; Santa Monica, CA (10-850) A
Cap Choir; Arch; Chess C; Chor; Ger C; Madrigal;
Pres, Model UN; NFL; Order/Arrow; Tres, Soph
Cl; Tres, Dbte Tm; JV, Swim; Bank Of Amer A; B
Crocker A; CSF; COM; Chem A; Spch A; St
Scholar; Yth Fel; JV, Water Polo; *Stanford U;
Chem.*

KNOX, Anne Winfield
Asheboro HS; Asheboro, NC; Chldr; Chem C;
Chor; FHA; FTA; Hmrm; Span C; SC; Swim;
COM; Hist A; HCt; Hon Prog; Ntl Achv Schol; Sci
A; HR; Ch, Lounge Comm; Ecology C; Best Dan-
cer; Poetry Published; *Meredith Col; Psych.*

KNOX, Donna Jean
Lake Clifton HS; Baltimore, MD (10%-500) NHS;
JA A; Math A; Eng A; Foreign Lang A; 100 Scho-
lastic Pts; *Nurs.*

KNOX, Garry Darnell
W Rome HS; Rome, GA (35-150) FBLA; Span C;
Ga St U; Acct.

KNOX, Jill Margaret
Newnan HS; Newnan, GA; Drama; Sftbl; *La-
Grange Col; Art.*

KNOX, Kim Marie
Weston-McEwen HS; Athena, OR (4-41) Band;
Chldr; Ensm; GS; Secy, NHS; Sch P; Span C; SC;
Pres, Var C; Bkbl; Tnns; Citz A; Hon Prog; Type A;
Grand off, Rainbow Girls; *Willamette U; Liberal
Arts.*

KNOX, Laura Katherine
Midwest City HS; Midwest City, OK; A Cap Choir;
Band; Chor; Hmrm; Math C; NHS; Sci C; SC; *Okla
St U; Sci.*

KNOX, Linda Lee
Asheboro HS; Asheboro, NC (60-310) BC; Pres,
Hmrm; Sci C; Span C; Yth Fel; Prom Princess; *NC
St U; Nurs.*

KNOX, LouAnn
Brownsville HS; Brownsville, PA (50-332) Band;
Drama; Pres, Rainbow; Tri-HiY; Var C; Bkbl; Sftbl;
Grand Cross of Color; *Calif St Col; Spch Pathol-
ogy.*

KNOX, Wendy Gunter
Seminole Sr HS; Seminole, FL (7-734) Tres, Band;
Ensm; InterClub Coun; Tres, Key C; Pres, Lat C;
NFL; Ch, NHS; Spch C; Secy, SC; Elk A; Kiwanis
A; Yth Fel; Section Ldr, Stage Band; Ch, Keyettes;
Hon Men, Co Math Comp; Lat A; 1st Pl, Wom-
ens's Foil; Superior Ratings, St Solo & Ensm; *U of
Ala; Acct.*

KNUCKLES, Sandy Pauline
Eminence R-1 HS; Eminence, MO (3-37) Band;
Alg A; Civics A; HR A; *Elem Ed.*

KNUDSEN, Luanne Jean
East HS; Des Moines, IA (15-477) A Cap Choir;
Chor; Ch, Hmrm; Model UN; Ed, Sch P; UN
Council; Y-Tns; Hon Prog; Ed, Saturday Page in
Local Paper; *Grand View Col.*

KNUDSEN, Ricarda Maria
West HS; Minneapolis, MN (36-312) Band; Ensm;
4H; NHS; 4H A; Spch A; Band A; *Augsburg Col;
Bio.*

KNUDSON, Gaye Alice
Montevideo Sr HS; Montevideo, MN (12-155)
AFS; Ed, Ann; Pres, Bus C; FFA; Ger C; Rainbow;
Journ A; Swtht; Type A; Pom-Pon; Jr Bus Women
C; Region A, OEA C; *Willmar Vo-tech Col; Phys
Therapy.*

KNUDSON, Pamela Jean
Albert Lea Central HS; Albert Lea, MN (57-575) A
Cap Choir; Chldr; Chor; Fr C; FHA; Tres, 4H; Var
C; Co-Cpt, Swim; 4H A; Lion A; WW; *U of Wis;
Bio Sci.*

KNUDTSEN, Stephen Fredrick
Palmer HS; Colorado Springs, CO (85-500) A Cap
Choir; VP, Chor; Drama; VP, Ger C; Madrigal; Var
C; Cr-Ctry; Hon Prog; Outst Achv, Mus Prog;
Lead, Sch Mus; 1st Pl German Language Festival;
Colo Col of Mines; Chem Engr.

KNUDTSON, Craig Alan
Minnehaha Acad; Minneapolis, MN; Chor; Ensm;
Fr C; Ski C; JV, Cr-Ctry; Soccer; Tr; *U of Minn; Ed.*

KNUDTSON, Kristine Marie
Minnehaha Acad; Minneapolis, MN; Ann; Chor;
Ensm; Fr C; Ger C; Tr; *St Catherine's Col; Nurs.*

KNUPP, Susan Joan
Southwest HS; St Louis, MO; A Cap Choir; Band;
Chor; Yth Fel; Mus; *Mo Baptist Col; Bus.*

KNUTILLA, Susan Diane
Williamston HS; Williamston, MI (14-167) Secy,
AFS; Band; Ski C; Sftbl; Yth Fel; Handicapped
Riding Prog; Interfaith Yth Singing Group; Teach-
ers Aid; 1st Cl GSct; *Mich Tech U; Forestry.*

KNUTSEN, Cornelius Kenneth
Sarasota HS; Sarasota, FL (10-645) Chem C; NHS;
Alg A; COM; Chem A; Hon Prog; Math A; Ntl Sci
Found; Sci A; *U of Fla; Med.*

KNUTSEN, Debora Lynn
Bacon Acad; Colchester, CT; Chor; Drama; Rptr,
FBLA; Hmrm; Mjrte; Y Swim Tm; Lions C Ex-
change; GSct; Stu Ex Dir; VP, Lib C; *Middlesex
Comm Col; Cable TV.*

KNUTSON, Denise Ardel
Oregon City HS; Oregon City, OR; Chldr; Service
A; Schol A; Hon A; *Oreg St U; Pre-Med.*

KNUTSON, Julie Kay
St Francis Sr HS; St Francis, MN; Band; Secy,
Drama; Semi-Fin, Ensm; Pres, 4H; Rptr, Sch P;
Thes; JV, Bkbl; Tr; 4H A; Drama Achv; Bkbl Nu-
meral.

KO, Yu Jin
Tappan Zee HS; Orangeburg, NY; NHS; ARC; F-
Ed, Sch P; SC; Cr-Ctry; Tr; COM; *Columbia U;
Med.*

KOBE, James Joseph
Gilbert HS; Gilbert, MN (5-67) CYO; Math C;
NHS; Sci C; SC; Bsbl; MVP, Ftbl; Hockey; Cpt, Tr;
Alg A; HCt; *Mesabi Comm Col; Biol.*

KOBS, Vicki Deanne
Preble HS; Green Bay, WI (275-606) Span C; JV,
Tr.

KOBUS, Jodi Lee
Shaler Area Sr HS; Glenshaw, PA (10%-1000)
Hmrm; NHS; Ntl Yth Conf; Ed, Sch P; Span NHS;
SC; Alg A; Hon Prog; NEDT; HR; *Communica-
tions.*

KOCH, Ann Elizabeth
Lima Sr HS; Lima, OH (10%-546) Band; Ensm;
Ger C; Orch; Hon Prog; JA A; Band, Orch As;
Wittenberg Col; Ed.

KOCH, Barbara Jean
Clearwater Sr HS; Clearwater, FL (300-900) Chor;
Drama; Key C; SC; Tres, Thes; Y-Tns; Sftbl; Cl
Fav; Yth Fel; Drama A; *Dentistry.*

KOCH, Judy Ann
Wisner-Pilger HS; Wisner, NE (1-70) Ann; Band;
Chldr; Chor; FBLA; FHA; Secy, 4H; NHS; Alg A;
4H A; Math A; Spch A; Type A; VofDEM; *U of
Nebr; Math.*

KOCH, Kassie Sybilla
Centennial HS; Gresham, OR (60-500) Band;
NHS; Ski C; SC; Var C; Mgr, Bkbl; Cpt, Tnns; Yth
Fel; *Mt Hood Comm Col; Juvenile Counselling.*

KOCH, Linda Jean
Earl L Vandermeulen HS; Port Jefferson, NY
(3-250) Hmrm; Mjrte; Yth Fel; VICA; 3rd, Nurs
Aide Contest; Sunday Sch Teacher; Pres & Founder, Sorority; *SUC at Brockport; Nurs.*

KOCH, Mark Franklin
Solanco Sr HS; Quarryville, PA (7-325) Chess C;
Reading Speed & Comprehension A; *Penn St U;
Engr.*

KOCH, Robin Lea
West HS; Madison, WI (144-596) Ed, Ann; Drama;
Ger C; NFL; Hon Prog; Q&S A; Forensics A; Year-
book A; *U of Wisc; Med.*

KOCH, Timothy Randall
Southmoreland Sr HS; Alverton, PA (1-300) Dbte
Tm; World Affairs C; Yth Fel; Yth Choir; Ch, Yth
Service Fund; Church Adm Board; Evangeli-
smcomm; Dist Yth Coun.

KOCHER, Roberta Kay
Easton Area HS; Easton, PA (66-662) SC; Bkbl;
COM; *Broadcasting.*

KOCUREK, Patricia Ann
Downers Grove Comm HS N; Downers Grove, IL
(199-752) A Cap Choir; Chor; Orch; SC; Tnns;
Hon Prog; 1st Pl, St Orch; 1st Pl, Orch Ensm Contest.

KODOSKY, Lawrence Gerard
Bishop McDevitt HS; Harrisburg, PA (3-300)
NHS; Co-Cpt, Cr-Ctry; Tnns; Hon Prog; Math A;
Sci A; Aviation & Flight Trng; Astronomy, Tr, C'S;
Fr Achv, Cath Womens Coun Sch, A's; *Penn St U;
Environmental Resource Mgr.*

KOEHLER, Beth Ellen
Nathan Hale HS; W Allis, WI (86-435) A Cap
Choir; Chor; Pres, Drama; Hmrm; NFL; Thes;
COM; HCt; St 'A' Cl Medal, Forensics; *U of Wis;
Oral Communications.*

KOEHLER, David Keith
Worthington Sr HS; Worthington, MN (87-300)
4H A; *Biol.*

KOEHLER, Duane Allen
Moulton-Udell HS; Moulton, IA (4-48) Band; VP,
FFA; Pres, 4H; Tres, Jr Cl; Cr-Ctry; Tr; Cpt, Wrest;
4H A; Type A; *Indian-Hills Comm Col; Elec Tech.*

KOEHLER, Kathy Ann
Belleville Township HS W; Belleville, IL (1-850)
Chor; Drama; Ger C; Tr; Hist A; Sci A; Hist C;
Secy, Yth Fel; Pep C.

KOEHLER, Margaret Mary
Hubbard HS; Chicago, IL (97-550) A Cap Choir;
FNA; Sftbl; Yth Fel; *Nurs.*

KOEHLER, Perry Lee
Liberty HS; Bethlehem, PA (10-780) Ger C; Math
C; Model UN; NHS; COM; Hon Prog; Math A; *US
Military Acad; Engr.*

KOEHLER, Susan Loverna
LaMoure HS; LaMoure, ND (10-40) Chldr; Hon
Prog; *Town & Ctry Beauty Col; Beautician.*

KOEHN, Charlene Anita
North Side HS; Jackson, TN (124-209) Chor; Span
C; Sftbl; *Tenn Temple Col; Mus.*

KOEHN, Kurt Wayne
Battle Ground Acad; Franklin, TN (15-64) Chess
C; Var C; Bsbl; Bkbl; Ftbl; COM; Hon Prog;
NEDT; All-Midst HM Ftbl; All-N Central Conf,
Ftbl; *Vanderbilt U; Biomed Engr.*

KOEHN, Leigh Ann
Deer Park HS; Deer Park, TX (25%-493) Band;
Ensm; NHS; ARC; COM; Type A; Drum Major;
Church Missionette Qn; All Dist & All Region
Band; Bible Quiz Tm; Hons Banquet; Chrch Chor;
Pres, Mission Group; *Oral Roberts U; Hist.*

KOEHN, Lisa Marie
The King's Temple Christian Sch; Seattle, WA;
Ann; Chor; COM; Hon Prog; Pres A; Yth Fel; *Seat-
tle Pacific U; Ed.*

KOEHN, Paul Richard
Minneapolis Lutheran HS; Minneapolis, MN (8-35) NHS; Pres, Sr Cl; Bsbl; Co-Cpt, Ftbl; HCt; VofDEM; Sno-Daze Kg; 3m Creativity A; All-Conf Ftbl; *Concordia Col; Pre-Theology.*

KOEHN, Terri Gay
Spring Woods HS; Houston, TX; JETS; Drill Tm; Geometry A; Art II A; *Baylor U; Med.*

KOELZER, Jane Ann
Centralia HS; Centralia, KS (2-30) Bkbl; All-League Bkbl.

KOENEMAN, Greogry Allan
Chester HS; Chester, IL; Var C; Tres, Soph Cl; Bkbl; Golf; WW; *Bus.*

KOENIG, Carol Ann
Brooten HS; Brooten, MN; Band; Chor; Rptr, Sch P; Sftbl; VP, Church Yth; Vlbl; MVP, Band Section; Outst Service A; *Naturalist.*

KOENIG, Elisabeth Ann
Pampa HS; Pampa, TX (69-350) Band; Lat C; All-Region Band; *W Tex St U; Bus.*

KOENIG, Jane Karla
Butterfield-Odin HS; Butterfield, MN (4-33) Co-Ed, Ann; Band; FHA; Ger C; GS; Sch P; Tres, Jr Cl; Tr; Mus A's; *Med.*

KOENIG, Reed Henry
Pine Grove Area HS; Pine Grove, PA; Band; Chor; Radio License; *Penn St U; Elec Tech.*

KOENIG, Richard Joseph
Cordova HS; Rancho Cordova, CA; Pres, Chess C; InterClub Coun; Math C; CSF; Math A; Elec A; *Cal Tech; Math.*

KOENIG, Ronald Wayne
Crystal Lake Comm HS; Crystal Lake, IL; Secy, Bsbl; Secy, Bkbl; *U of Wis; Agr.*

KOENIG, Theresa Ann
Holy Rosary Acad; Louisville, KY (5-86) Co-Ed, Ann; Chor; Math C; NHS; SC; Bio A; Hon Prog; Span A; Ntl HS A for Excellence; WW; *Bellarmine Col; Math.*

KOEPKE, Carol Jean
William M Kelley HS; Silver Bay, MN (1-145) AFS; Ann; Band; Dbte Tm; NFL; Pres, NHS; Sci C; Semi-Fin, Spch C; HCt; MLS; Ntl Sci Symposium; Sci A; Spch A; Star Student; Val; Debate A; Schol Win; *U of Minn at Duluth; Phys Therapy.*

KOEPPER, Glenda Ann
N Harford HS; Pylesville, MD (10%-310) Band; Ensm; 4H; Tr; Horticulture C; Band A; Presidential Phys Fitness A; Ltr A, HR; *Towson St U; Horticulture.*

KOEPSELL, Sharon Lorraine
Horicon HS; Horicon, WI (10-104) Co-Ed, Ann; Chldr; Chor; Hmrm; NFL; NHS; Sch P; SC; HCt; Hon Prog; Vlbl.

KOERNER, Cameron C
Wethersfield HS; Wethersfield, CT; Chor; Hmrm; Ski C; *Social Worker.*

KOERNER, Marlene Rose
Yankton Sr HS; Yankton, SD; Ann; Lit Mag; Tnns; Y-C; Tnns Major A; *SDSU; Interior Design.*

KOES, Alvin George
Hannibal Central Sch; Hannibal, NY (10-100) Bus Mgr, Band; Chor; Tres, Key C; Pres, NHS; Bus Mgr, Jr Cl; Bus Mgr, Soph Cl; NMS; Regent Schol; *NW U; Elec Engr.*

KOESJAN, Sandy Hideko
Palo Duro HS; Amarillo, TX; Ed, Ann; Chldr; Chor; FBLA; GS; VP, 4H; Hmrm; Madrigal; NHS; Orch; SC; MVP, Cr-Ctry; Tr; Amer Leg A; Cl Favr; 4H A; Hon Prog; Journ A; Most Out; PTA A; Q&S A; Ntl Guild.

KOESTER, Anita Louise
Mount Mercy Acad; Buffalo, NY; Chor; Madrigal; NFL; NHS; Pres, Spch C; NEDT; *Home Ec.*

KOESTER, Daniel Lee
Allen Cons HS; Allen, NE; Band; Chor; FFA; 4H; Sch P; Mgr, Ftbl.

KOESTER, Gregory Alan
Festus Sr HS; Festus, MO (68-214) Chess C; Dbte Tm; Pres, Demolay; Drama; Spch C; *Mo Baptist Col of St Louis; Bus Adm.*

KOETJE, Randal V
Oak Harbor HS; Oak Harbor, WA (6-343) Band; Span C; Span NHS; SC; Var C; Bkbl; Tr; Hon Prog; VP, CE Soc; *Engr.*

KOFFARNUS, Jayne Marie
Hilbert HS; Hilbert, WI (8-67) Ed, Sch P; HCt.

KOGER, John Keith
W Mecklenburg HS; Charlotte, NC (25%-350) Fr C; Sch & Ntl Art A's; *U of NC; Marine Bio.*

KOGER, William Brian
W Mecklenburg HS; Charlotte, NC;

KOHL, Charles McAllister
Jesuit HS; Sacramento, CA (30-130) Band; VP, 4H; Ski C; CSF; Jr Ldr Merit A; *U of Calif; Agr.*

KOHLER, Jacqueline Rae
Harry A Burke HS; Omaha, NE (137-793) Chor; Span C; SC; *U of Omaha; Phys Therapy.*

KOHLER, Joy Ann
N Plainfield HS; N Plainfield, NJ (47-265) Chor; NHS; Tres, SC; Tres, Jr Cl; JV, Bkbl; Hockey; Sftbl; Tres, Church Yth; God & Comm A; GSct; Laurel & Hardy Comedy A; Hand in Hand Mental Retarded Fest; *Phys Therapist.*

KOHLER, Kay Merie
Holy Trinity HS; Winsted, MN (13-46) Secy, Band; Chor; Secy, Var C; Bkbl; Cr-Ctry; Sftbl; Tr; HCt; Type A; *Bemidji St U; Bus.*

KOHLER, Robert Edward
MacArthur HS; San Antonio, TX; NHS; Bsbl.

KOHLMANN, Lori Jo
Northern HS; Flint, MI; VP, Yth Fel.

KOHLMANN, Marc Kenneth
Flint N HS; Flint, MI; Band; Ensm; Band Ltr.

KOHLS, Phyllis Louise
Ft Jennings HS; Ft Jennings, OH; Band; Chor; JV, Bkbl; Sftbl; Tr; Amer Leg A; NEDT; Sci A; Schol Tm; Math Tm; SC Pl Play; Musical; *Ohio St U; Phys Therapy.*

KOHN, Dorothy Edith
Milo Adventist Acad; Days Creek, OR (1-66) Ed, Ann; Band; Chor; Bkbl; Sftbl; Hon Prog; *Walla Walla Col; Elem Ed.*

KOHN, JoEllen Marie
S St Paul HS; St Paul, MN (81-450) AFS; Fr C; GS; SC; Hon Qn Job's Daughters, Ed, Yrbk; *St Paul Sch of Assn Arts; Commercial.*

KOHN, Mark Alan
St James HS; St James, MN; *St Paul Vo Tech; Watchmaking.*

KOHNE, Lynda Jane
Sparta HS; Sparta, IL (3%-200) Ed, Ann; Band; Bus C; Parl, FBLA; Pres, 4H; Lat NHS; NHS; Orch; Sci C; SC; Citz A; 4H A; Opt A; Q&S A; Lit A; *Sou Ill U; Med Tech.*

KOHRHERR, Robert Thomas
St Joseph's o-t Palisades HS; W New York, NJ (1-289) CYO; Chess C; Chor; Drama; Hmrm; Rptr, Sch P; Ski C; SC; Cl Favr; Hon Prog; Most Out; NEDT; Mother's Guild Schol; *Bio Sci.*

KOHRS, Kelly Jean
St Charles HS; St Charles, MO (33%-543) Chor; Pres, FBLA; *William Jewell Col; Mgt.*

KOKE, Carol Ann
Lincoln Comm HS; Lincoln, IL (118-282) Band; Bus C; Orch; Rptr, Sch P; *Ill St U; Bus.*

KOLANDER, Lisa Joy
Lutheran HS S; St Louis, MO (29-153) Tres, A Cap Choir; MVP, Band; Tres, Chor; Drama; Jr Miss Pagent; Ed, Lit Mag; Orch; Rptr, Sch P; Spch C; SC; VP, Sr Cl; Arch; Bkbl; Hockey; Sftbl; Cpt, Swim; Cpt, Tnns; God & Country A; HCt; JA A; MLS; Poet A; Spch A; Swtht; Composers A; Most All Around Talent A; *Communications.*

KOLANDER, Susan Kay
Webster HS; Webster, WI (2-60) Ann; Band; 4H; NFL; NHS; Span C; 4H A; Type A; Mus A; *Nurs.*

KOLARCHICK, Denise Marie
Northeastern HS; Detroit, MI; FBLA; NHS; Co-Ed, Sch P; Swim; Math A; Type A; PA; *Detroit Col of Bus; Bus.*

KOLB, Donna Leigh
White Plains HS; White Plains, NY (20-551) AFS; NHS; SC; NHS A; *Bio.*

KOLB, Michael Gregory
Acadiana HS; Lafayette, LA (1%-430) Tres, Key C; Lit Ral; VP, Mu Alpha Theta; NHS; Ftbl; Tr; Wrest; COM; Chem A; Hon Prog; Math A; NEDT; Sci A; Yth Fel; Alt, BS; Ltrman C; 1st Pl, Geom Lit Rally; 2nd Pl, Chem Lit Rally; *Engr.*

KOLB, Terri Sue
Acadiana HS; Lafayette, LA (10%-501) Mu Alpha Theta; NHS; Bkbl; Tr; Hon Prog; St Champs, Vlbl; Gym.

KOLBERG, Kathleen Mary
Wauwatosa W HS; Wauwatosa, WI; Band; Orch; COM; 4H A; Most Out; Summer Mus Clinic Schol.

KOLBUS, Elaine Diane
Bloomington HS; Bloomington, IL (28-418) Fr C; Mu Alpha Theta; Cpt, Bkbl; HCt; Hon Prog; Cpt, Vlbl; *Ill St U; Ed.*

KOLECKI, Mary Ann
Maple Shade HS; Maple Shade, NJ (13-241) Key C; NHS; *Rutgers U; Nurs.*

KOLESAR, Lydia Suzanne
Washburn HS; Minneapolis, MN (125-455) *Grace Bible Col.*

KOLLAR, Karl Eugene
Crystal Lake HS; Crystal Lake, IL (150-390) Phys C; Var C; Cpt, Bkbl; MVP, Golf; Yth Fel; Cpt, FCA; *Eastern Ill Col; Bus.*

KOLLASCH, Edward Earl
Alamosa HS; Alamosa, CO (34-200) Rptr, Anchor C; Band; Chess C; Ensm; VP, Key C; Wrest; SC; Var C; Cpt, Ftbl; Cpt, Swim; MVP, Tr; Most Valuable Athlete; Cpt, Tr; *Colo St U; Med Sci.*

KOLLER, DeWayne Jewell
Daviess Co HS; Owensboro, KY; Bsbl; Ftbl.

KOLLING, Rebecca Jean
Montgomery Co Joint Voc Sch; Clayton, OH (1-14) Band; Chor; Pres, 4H; Hon Prog; Yth Fel; A of Distinction of Cosmetology; *Dayton Sch of Pratical Nurs; Med.*

KOLLMEYER, Wilbur August Frederick III
Madison W HS; Madison, WI (180-725) Hmrm; Rptr, Sch P; SC; JV, Bsbl; JV, Bkbl; Pres, Yth Group; Co- cpt, Vlbl; Pre-Seminary Camp; *Broadcasting.*

KOLLMORGEN, Julie Lynn
Mountain Brook HS; Birmingham, AL (50%-347) Band; Chor; Solo and Ensm Medalist; PA; *U of Ala.*

KOMIVES, Shelley Kay
Avon HS; Avon, OH (32-142) Band; FHA; Yth Fel; Bowl; Schol; *Lorain Comm Col; Bus.*

KOMYATHY, Christine Ann
John Jay HS; Hopewell Junction, NY (10%-641) Band; Chor; Hmrm; COM; God & Country A; Hon Prog; Yth Fel; Church Choir; Ballet; Church Mus; MVP, Gym; Ice Skating Tm; *RI U; Marine Bio.*

KONDO, Muriel Etsuko
Waialua HS; Waialua, HI (20-183) Hmrm; Spch C; Hon Prog; *Leward Comm Col; Sociology.*

KONTOS, Annie Maria
West HS; Waterloo, IA (29-494) Pres, 4H; Crisco A; 4H A; Type A; *U of N Iowa; Med.*

KONVALINKA, Nancy Anne
St Louise de Marillac HS; Northfield, IL (3-197) Ensm; NHS; Amer Leg A; Opt A; Span A.

KONYA, Jeffry Alan
Maple Hts HS; Maple Hts, OH (325-460) Hmrm; Ski C; Co-Cpt, Ftbl; Tr; Wrest; *Bus Adm.*

KONYNENBELT, Cindy Jane
Noble Central HS; Nobleford, CANADA (2-16) ARC; Ed, Sch P; Secy, SC; Bkbl; *Col of Idaho; Ed.*

KONYNENBELT, Glenda June
Noble Central Sch; Nobleford, CANADA (3-28) Chor; Fr C; Tres, SC; Co-Cpt, Bkbl; Sftbl; Tnns; Tr; Acad A; *Col of Idaho; Ed.*

KOODA, Karen Ann
McGregor HS; McGregor, MN (3-66) Ann; Band; Chor; Drama; FHA; FTA; VP, 4H; NHS; Co-Ed, Sch P; Sci C; Var C; Bkbl; Tr; COM; 4H A; *U of Minn at Duluth; Acct.*

KOON, Melissa Louise
Coosa HS; Rome, GA (33%-125) Band; S-T, Yth Coun; Coun on Ministries; S-T & Tres, Sunday Sch Cl.

KOONS, Duane Melvin
Flushing HS; Flushing, MI (1-479) BS; Chess C; NHS; Pres, Sr Cl; Ftbl; Tr; Cpt, Wrest; B Crocker A; Cl Fav; DARGCA; Hon Prog; MLS; Val; Commencement Spch; Stu Rep, Ath Board of Control; *Mich St U; Med Research.*

KOONS, Jan Marie
Central Dauphin HS; Harrisburg, PA (20%-550) Chor; FNA; 4H; Var C; Cr-Ctry; Soccer; Sftbl; Cpt, Tr; Mgr, Wrest; 4H A; *Lancaster Gen Hosp Sch of Nurs; Nurs.*

KOONS, Lynn Dianne
Central Dauphin HS; Harrisburg, PA; 4H; Sftbl; 4H A; *Ed.*

KOONS, Patricia Rae
Fairmont Sr HS; Fairmont, MN (87-199) Chor; Tr; Jobs Daughters; GAA; GEMS; Ltrs, Vlbl, Bowl; *Mankato St U; Acct.*

KOONTZ, Debbie Lynn
Clearwater HS; Clearwater, FL; Band; Ger C; Semi-Fin, GS; Hist A; Friendship A; *Maryville Col; Special Ed.*

KOONTZ, Frankie Laverna
Lexington Sr HS; Lexington, NC (135-291) Chor; Drama; FHA; Hmrm; Yth Fel; Lib A; *Eckerd Col; Math.*

KOONTZ, Linda Helen
Westminster Sr HS; Westminster, MD (10-500) AFS; Band; Tres, CYO; Key C; NHS; Sftbl; MVP, Cath Yth Bkbl; Ath A's; CYO Outst Member; *Elem Ed.*

KOOY, Laura Lee
Timothy Christian HS; Elmhurst, IL (25-94) Band; Chldr; Drama; Ensm; Hmrm; Orch; Sch P; Ski C; SC; Secy, Soph Cl; Hon Prog; Fine Arts Instrumental A; Fine Arts Interpretive Reading A.

KOPA, Katherine
Dwight D Eisenhower HS; Rialto, CA (86-761) AFS; Bus Mgr, Drama; Rptr, Sch P; COM; Hon Prog; St Scholar; Hist, Thespians; Gen Mills Family Ldr of Tomorrow; *Calif Lutheran Col; Communications.*

KOPCIAL, Donald Jacob
Mansfield Christian HS; Mansfield, OH (23-46) Band; Chor; *Okla St U; Landscaping.*

KOPECKY, Maria Ann
Hilbert HS; Hilbert, WI (3-89) Cpt, Chldr; Chor; Cpt, Mjrte; SC; *Silverlake Col; Elem Ed.*

KOPKO, Joan Marie
John S Fine HS; Nanticoke, PA (9-355) Band; Chldr; Hmrm; Fin, Jr Miss Pagent; Key C; Rptr, Sch P; Var C; Tr; Amer Leg C; Citz A; Hon Prog; K of C A; *NEDT; Med.*

KOPLINKA, Carolyn Sue
Valhalla HS; Valhalla, NY (1-178) Band; Chor; Drama; Madrigal; Pres, NHS; Rptr, Sch P; Secy, SC; B Crocker A; Val; Alt, Regent's Schol; Family Ldr of Tomorrow; *Cornell U; Agr Econ.*

KOPPEL, Barbara Jeanine
Leland HS; San Jose, CA (130-600) SC; Sftbl; B Crocker A; COM; Citz A; Hon Prog; I Dare You; Opt A; Yth Fel; *UC at Santa Barbara; Ed.*

KOPPISCH, Christi Anne
Coronado HS; Colorado Springs, CO (2-337) Hmrm; InterClub Coun; Lat C; NHS; Tres, SC; Var C; Co-Cpt, Tr; HCt; PTA A; Pres A; Regent Schol; Sal; Star Student; MVP, Vlbl; *Colo St U; Food Sci.*

KORB, Gwen Teresa
Havre HS; Havre, MT (1-250) CYO; VP, InterAct C; NFL; SC; Bkbl; Tnns; Math A; Val; Soph Rep; Marion A; 1st Cl Sct; *N Mont Col; Math.*

KORB, Karen Elaine
Grand Blanc HS; Grand Blanc, MI (64-640) Band; 4H; SC; Tr; 10-10 C; Concern; MYF; *Ferris St Col; X-Ray.*

KORCHA, Rhonda Kay
Yucca Valley HS; Yucca Valley, CA; AFS; Cpt, Chldr; Hmrm; Secy, Jr Cl; CSF; Citz A; VP, Sr GSct; AFS Exchange Stu; Drill Tm; Yth Career Conf; Interntl Opportunity A, GSct; *Psych.*

KORDELLA, Robert Joseph
Uniontown Area Sr HS; Uniontown, PA (1-480) Band; Ensm; Orch; Span C; SC; Amer Leg A; Hist A; Hon Prog; Math A; PMEA Western Dist Band; Stu o-t Month; Schol A; *U of Pittsburgh; Phar.*

KOREN, Joyce Ann
Kelly HS; Chicago, IL (2-476) Secy, Math C; NHS; Hon Prog; NEDT; *Loyola U; Bio.*

KORESKO, Christine Gail
Moline Sr HS; Moline, IL; Pres, Chldr; Fr C; Co-Cpt, Hmrm; Sch P; H of F; Gym; *Elem Ed.*

KORLESKI, Karmon Luverne
Arlington HS; Arlington, TX (28-490) AFS; Pres, Ger C; Pres, JETS; Pres, Key C; NHS; Soccer; Hon Prog; WW; Ger; WW; *Bus.*

KORMAN, William Raymond
Penn Manor HS; Millersville, PA (143-389) Parl, FFA; Key C; Ftbl; Tr; Wrest; *Penn St U; Earth & Mineral Sci.*

KORN, Debby L
Hillel Acad; Pittsburgh, PA; Val.

KORNEGAY, Valerie Gale
Kinston HS; Kinston, NC; Chor; Drama; Jr Miss Pagent; HCt; Local Miss Black Tn Pageant; Miss Creative Expression; *Spellman Col; Social Worker.*

KORNKVEN, Eric William
Natrona Co HS; Casper, WY (230-600) Cr-Ctry; Wrest; *U of Wis.*

KORNMAYER, Kevin Casey
Fairhope HS; Fairhope, AL (88-311) AFS; Cpt, Band; Chess C; JV, Ftbl; HCt; Drum Major; Band St Contest Medal; *U of S Ala; Bus Adm.*

KORNREICH, Nancy Jane
Harrison HS; Harrison, NY (45-285) Mjrte; Secy, Sr Cl; VP, Jr Cl; Tr; *Eng.*

KORNRUMPF, Rodney Lin
Butler Area Sr HS; Butler, PA (3-2000) Bsbl; Bkbl; Sftbl; Yth Fel; *Slippery Rock St Col; Secondary Ed.*

KOROSHEC, John
Gilbert HS; Gilbert, MN (15-95) Band; CYO; Chor; SC; Var C; Ftbl; Hockey; Tnns; Tr; *Marine Biol.*

KORST, Timothy Jerome
Reseda HS; Reseda, CA; CYO; InterAct C; Bkbl; Tr; CSF; *U of Calif; Engr.*

KORTE, David Allen
Lincoln Way HS; New Lenox, IL; Cpt, Bowling; VP, Yth Group; Sanctuary Choir; Yth Choir; *N Central Bible Col; Ministry.*

KORTHUIS, Dawn Leanne
Alameda HS; Lakewood, CO; Chor; Ensm; Fr C; FHA; Hmrm; Cpt, Golf; Cpt, Sftbl; Hon Prog; Med Self Help; Fin, Sci A; Young Amer Singers; Sci Fair; HR.

KORZEKWA, Diane Veronica
Hobbs HS; Hobbs, NM; Band; CYO; Chor; Pres A; Type A; Sup, Piano Festival; Ntl Fed of Stu Musicians.

KOSBERG, Karen Marie
Mankato W HS; Mankato, MN (10%-350) Band; Ger C; ARC; Ed, Sch P; JV, Golf; Journ A; *Concordia Col; Mus.*

KOSCHMANN, Beth Marguerite
Highland HS; Salt Lake City, UT (45-480) NHS; Sftbl; Hon Prog; VP, Russian C; *St John's Lutheran Col; Lang.*

KOSCHNICK, Roxanne Marie
Robert L Osborne HS; Marietta, GA (125-400) Band; Chor; Jr Rep, Pep C; *Acct.*

KOSHUTA, Mary Monica
Oakton HS; Vienna, VA (105-500) Tres, CYO; FHA; ARC; Bkbl; Soccer; JV, Sftbl; Tr; Span Achv A; Most Improved, Bkbl, Sftbl; *VPI; Nurs.*

KOSHY, Soman Thomas
Wilson Area HS; Easton, PA (5-212) *Mech Engr.*

KOSINSKI, Sally Jean
Stoughton Pub HS; Stoughton, MA (263-431).

KOSKI, John Matthew
S Miami Sr HS; S Miami, FL (40-777) InterClub Coun; Key C; Ed, Lit Mag; Model UN; NHS; Ed, Sch P; Pres, Sr Cl; Co-Cpt, Golf; Journ A; Most Out; Rotary A; Swtht; Pres, Pep C; Sr Superlative; Calendar Couple; *U of Fla; Communications.*

KOSKOVICH, William Joseph
Eldorado HS; Albuquerque, NM (204-795) MVP, Bsbl; Bkbl; MVP, Ftbl; Rotary A.

KOSLEY, Penny Kay
East HS; Pueblo, CO (12-385) Secy, Fr C; Pres, FBLA; InterClub Coun; Key C; NHS; Hon Prog; VFW Orator Win; VofDEM; Pep C; Foreign Lang A; Eagle o-t Mo; *Colo St U; Data Processing.*

KOSPELICH, Brenda Marie
John Ehret HS; Marrero, LA (43-550) Hmrm; Lit Ral; Mu Alpha Theta; NHS; Sci C; SC; Sftbl; COM; Hist A; Hon Prog; PTA A; Co-Cpt, Flag Corp; Span A; Media Fair As; Lit Fair As; Academic A; *U of New Orleans; Biological Sci.*

KOSS, Timothy Dale
McHenry E Campus HS; McHenry, IL; *Med.*

KOSSOW, Colleen Rae
Mount Si HS; Snoqualmie, WA (12-136) Mu Alpha Theta; NHS; Hon Prog; *Northwest AOG; Missions.*

KOSTELNIK, Dena Marie
Mt Ida HS; Mt Ida, AR (7-55) A-Ed, Ann; BC; Chldr; FHA; SC; Pres, Soph Cl; Sftbl; COM; PA; Driver Trainer Cert; *U of Ark; Math.*

KOSTER, Nancee June
Freeland HS; Freeland, MI (6-152) Ed, Ann; Co-Cpt, Chldr; NHS; Sch P; Tnns; MLS; 'Sew-Biz' Win; *Delta Col; Interior Decor.*

KOSTOW, William Linden
Pocatello HS; Pocatello, ID (63-700) NHS; VP, Soph Cl; JV, Ftbl; JV, Wrest; Amer Leg A; Most Out; Sci A; Ath o-t Yr; Tres, Yth Fel.

KOSTYO, Kathryn Elaine
Poland Seminary HS; Poland, OH (25-385) Band; CYO; Drama; Ensm; Hmrm; Lat C; Orch; Y-Tns; Tr; Amer Leg A; Hist A; Hon Prog; JA A; Fin, JA Off o-t Yr; 1st Cl GSct.

KOTECKI, Karen Sue
St Bede Acad; Peru, IL (5-101) Chor; Amer Leg A; Hon Prog; K of C A; Parish Coun; Bible Sch Teacher; PGAA; Vlbl; May Qn; *Ill Valley Comm Jr Col; Special Ed.*

KOTEK, James Michael
Beaver Dam Sr HS; Beaver Dam, WI (2-330) Band; Ski C; Var C; Mgr, Bkbl; Ftbl; Tnns; *Law.*

KOTEN, Kathleen Louise
William Nottingham HS; Syracuse, NY; Band; Dbte Tm; Tres, Fr C; Tres, FBLA; 4H; Lat C; NFL; NHS; Co-Ed, Sch P; SC; Citz A; 4H A; Pres, Church Yth Fel; Lat Culture A; Zonta Achv A; Most Active; 4-H Home Ec Trip, NY City; *Georgetown U; Pol Sci.*

KOTESKI, Amy Lou
Oak Glen HS; New Cumberland, WV (16-245) Chor; Drama; GS; NHS; Sch P; Thes; Pres, Yth Fel; Pep C; Cl Ed, Yrbk; *W Va U; Mus.*

KOTH, Brenda Lee
Oregon City Sr HS; Oregon City, OR (46-400) Chldr; Ensm; Orch; Tnns; Citz A; Type A; Yth Fel; 2nd Pl, NW Orchestra Contest; Most Inspirational Tennis Player; *George Fox Col; Bus Adm.*

KOTHMANN, Rodney Duane
John H Reagan HS; Austin, TX (20-300) Tres, Ger C; Hmrm; NHS; Parl, SC; JV, Ftbl; Golf; DARGCA; Opt A; Trustee A; AAT Schol; *U Tex at Austin.*

KOTLOWSKI, Susan Marie
G A R HS; Wilkes-Barre, PA (4-198) Band; NHS; Orch; Var C; Bkbl; Hockey; Sftbl; *Kings Col; Sci.*

KOTSCHWAR, Lana Jo
Farnam Pub Sch; Farnam, NE (1-17) Chem C; Chor; S-T, 4H; Sch P; VP, Jr Cl; VP, Soph Cl; 4H A; Hon Prog; Math A; Spch A; Yth Fel; Cpt-Cornet Section, Band; Home Ec As; Nebr Farm Bureau Rep; Win, Nat Pilgrimage for Yth Tour; *Hastings Col; Elem Ed.*

KOTTIS, Kristy Ann
Randolph HS; Randolph, MA (350-562) Drama; Var C; MVP, Bkbl; Hockey; Cpt, Sftbl; Dave Cowens Bkbl Sch As; Miss Top Scorer; 3 on 3 Champ; 1 on 1 Champ; Foul Shooting Champ; *Eastern Nazarene Col.*

KOTTKE, Kerry Lee
Rogers HS; Toledo, OH (25%-525) Chem C; Ger C; Pres, HiY; JA A; Yth Fel; Fin, Secy o-t Yr; *Otterbein Col; Nurs.*

KOTTSCHADE, Kirk Christian
Pine River HS; Pine River, MN (13-60) Tres, 4H; 4H A; Sal; *Wadena Tech Col; Elec.*

KOUWENHOVEN, William Gerret
Fort Myers HS; Fort Myers, FL;

KOVACH, Daniel Joseph
Maple Heights HS; Maple Heights, OH; Band; Tres, Drama; Thes; COM; Citz A; *Cleveland St U; Computer Tech.*

KOVACH, Jean Marie
DeSales HS; Geneva, NY (5-54) All Amer Yth; CYO; Chldr; Drama; French NHS; Lit Mag; NHS; F-Ed, Sch P; Sodality; Soccer; Sftbl; Swim; Tnns; Tr; Amer Leg A; COM; Hon Prog; Regent Schol; *Humanitarian Service A; Boston U; Bio.*

KOVACIC, Janice Ruth
Oak Lawn Comm HS; Oak Lawn, IL (11-700) Fr C; Math C; Tres, NHS; Outst, Fr; *Augustana Col; Psych.*

KOVACS, Daniel Joseph
Thomas W Harvey HS; Painesville, OH (15-171) NHS; Sch P; Var C; MVP, Cr-Ctry; MVP, Tr; Hon Prog; Yth Fel; *Ohio U; Radio-television.*

KOVACS, James Edward
Bangor Area Sr HS; Bangor, PA (15-249) Model UN; NHS; Mgr, Bsbl; Tr; *Wilkes Col; Med.*

KOVACS, Theresa Ann
Ellet Sr HS; Akron, OH (48-385) Tres, Bus C; ARC; COM; JA A; ARC A.

KOVAL, Mark Peter
Liberty Central HS; Liberty, NY (19-140) Band; Chor; Ensm; 4H; NHS; Orch; Ski C; Most Out; Regent Schol; Co Eng A; Outst Musician; *SUNY at Binghampton; Mus.*

KOVAL, Mary Kathryn
Essex Junction Ed Center; Essex Junction, VT (10%-260) A Cap Choir; Band; CYO; Chor; Drama; Ski C; *Mass Col of Phar; Phar.*

KOVANIC, Diane Marie
Kelly HS; Chicago, IL (29-476) Cpt, Chldr; VP, FNA; VP, NHS; Span NHS; HCt; Hon Prog; St Scholar; Vlbl; GAA; *Bradley Col; Nurs.*

KOVSKY, Steven Dolph
Quartz Hill HS; Quartz Hill, CA (10-300) Drama; Fr C; Key C; Rptr; Sch P; Pres, SC; Thes; Pres, Soph Cl; Opt A; CASO Drama A; *Mich St U; Photojourn.*

KOWALCHUK, Lynn Kaye
Alexander Ramsey HS; Roseville, MN (50-564) Band; Cpt, Chldr; Chor; Bsbl; COM; HCt; Yth Fel; *St Paul Bible Col; Bible.*

KOWALEWSKI, Patty Louise
Immaculata HS; Leavenworth, KS (25-79) A Cap Choir; Chor; Ensm; Fr C; Mgr, Bkbl; Hon Prog.

KOWALIK, Barbara
Holy Child HS; Waukegan, IL (2-48) Chor; Dbte Tm; Lat C; NHS; Rptr, Sch P; Sci C; Span C; Spch C; SC; Pres, Jr Cl; Sftbl; Alg A; Bio A; COM; Chamber of Comm A; Citz A; Hist A; Hon Prog; Math A; Most Out; Sal; Sci A; Spch A; Hugh O'Brien Ldrship; WW; Jaycees A; Law Day; *Marquette U; Pre-Med.*

KOWALK, Wendy Lou
Ellsworth Comm HS; Ellsworth, MI (2-33) Chldr; NHS; Tres, Sch P; Tres, SC; Pres, Soph Cl; JV, Bkbl; Tr; Bio A; Bus Mgr, Sch P; Eng A; *Liberty Baptist Col; Nurs.*

KOWALSKI, Carl Marshall Jr
T L Hanna HS; Anderson, SC (10-310) Chem C; VP, FFA; Phys C; Sci C; Var C; Bsbl; JV, Ftbl; JV, Tr; H of F; MLS; ROTC A; Sportsmanship A; *Clemson U; Civil Engr.*

KOWALSKI, Kimberly Jane
T L Hanna HS; Anderson, SC (10-350) S-T, Hmrm; S-T, NHS; Tr; DARGCA; Interntl Relations C; Pep C; Stu Action For Ed; *Elem Ed.*

KOWELL, Patricia Ellen
Commack HS S; Commack, NY (20%-600) Ann; Arch; Co-Cpt, Chldr; Ski C; SC; HR; *Lib Arts.*

KOZAK, Craig Paul
Lyons Township HS; La Grange, IL (70%-1250) Arch; Community Yth Symph; Orch; NEDT; St Scholar; *Gustavus Adolphus Col; Bus.*

KOZAR, Georgia Ann
Meadowbrook HS; Byesville, OH (20%-200) Chldr; VP, Chor; Ensm; GS; VP, 4H; VP, Jr Cl; Sftbl; Bus.

KOZLOWSKI, John Eugene
N B Forrest HS; Jacksonville, FL; CYO; Drama; Hmrm; Thes; Ftbl; Hon Prog; HR; *NAVY; Nuclear Prop.*

KOZNED, Steven Alexander
Carlmont HS; Belmont, CA; WEC Missionary Training Col; Faith Acad; Mission Wrk, Far East Broadcast Co; *Elec Engr.*

KOZY, Terri Lee
Big Foot HS; Walworth, WI (2-176) Band; Chldr; Ensm; 4H; Math C; Mod Mus Mas; Span C; Sftbl; Amer Leg A; 4H A; Most Out; Sci A; Yth Fel; Band Director A; Chorus A; Outst Fresh Girl A.

KRABER, Jennifer Lynn
Albia Community HS; Albia, IA; Co-Cpt, Chldr; Fin, Chor; VP, Drama; FHA; 4H; VP, SC; Var C; JV, Bkbl; JV, Sftbl; Tr; COM; Citz A; 4H A; JA A; Yth Fel; All-St Chor; Albia Women's C; Top of Cl Art A; HR; I Rating, St Mus Contest; *Simpson Col; Liberal Arts.*

KRACKE, Gregory Arthur
Borger HS; Borger, TX (6-275) FTA; NHS; Parl, Span C; Span A; Academic A; *Tex A&M U; Engr.*

KRAFSIG, Cindy Marie
J W Robinson Secondary HS; Fairfax, VA (122-508) NHS; Span NHS; Sci A; Yth Group Off; Sunday Sch Teacher; Bible Sch Teacher; Drama Productions; *Shippensburg Col; Elem Ed.*

KRAFT, Connie Sue
Dixon HS; Dixon, IL (16-358) FNA; Semi-Fin, GS; St Scholar; WW; *Rockford Mem Hospital; Nurs.*

KRAFT, Jenny Sue
London HS; London, OH (2-186) Fr C; Secy, 4H; 4H A; 4-H Jr Ldrship A; Art C; Pres, Luther League; *Wittenberg Col; Bus Adm.*

KRAHN, Roger Alan
Wauwatosa W HS; Wauwatosa, WI; Chor; HR; *U of Wis; Engr.*

KRAJEWSKI, Elizabeth Ann
Gloucester Cath HS; Gloucester, NJ (9-158) Chor; Drama; Jr Miss Pagent; Mod Mus Mas; Hon Prog; Lincoln Bus Inst; *Legal Secy.*

KRAJEWSKI, Joan
Crestview Sr HS; Crestview, FL (10%-254) Anchor C; BC; GS; Mu Alpha Theta; SC; Tres, Jr Cl; COM; *U of Fla; Archt.*

KRAJEWSKI, Sandra Joan
St Joseph HS; Camden, NJ (10-76) Ger C; Ch, Hmrm; NHS; Sodality; *U of Penn; Chem.*

KRAKLOW, Linda Jean
Toulon HS; Toulon, IL (12-66) Band; Chor; FHA; Var C; Secy, Sr Cl; Tres, Soph Cl; Bkbl; Drum Major; Vlbl; SC Rep, AFS; *Moline Lutheran Hosp; Nurs.*

KRAMARCHYK, Andrew William
Cath Central HS; Troy, NY (20%-338) Pres, Hmrm; Sch P; Ski C; SC; Bsbl; Bkbl; Ftbl; Golf; Tnns; Math A.

KRAMER, Jana Dawn
Castleford HS; Castleford, ID (1-22) Bus Mgr, Ann; Pres, Band; Chldr; Dbte Tm; Pres, Ensm; Pres, FHA; GS; Hmrm; ARC; Sch P; Span C; Bkbl; Tr; Secy, VP, Tres, SC; OEA; Jr Ms A; Pres, Christian Yth Group; Tres, Jr Flower C; St Degree, FHA; MVP, Vlbl; *Col of Idaho; Elem Ed.*

KRAMER, Janice Sara
Dadeland Cnty Day Sch; Miami, FL (3-11) A-Ed, Ann; Chor; Sch P; Secy, SC; Citz A; Hist A; Journ A; Math A; Sci A; Type A; Sch Spirit; Sportsmanship; *U of Fla; Vet Med.*

KRAMER, Kirk Jeffrey
Miami HS; Miami, OK (10%-260) VP, CYO; NHS; SC; Ftbl; Tr.

KRAMER, Rebecca Ann
Holyoke HS; Holyoke, CO (10-60) FBLA; Pres, FHA; VP, FTA; GS; Pres, 4H; Rainbow; Sftbl; 4H A; Soc Stu A; *Northeastern Jr Col; Bus.*

KRAMER, Rene Marie
O'Neill HS; O'Neill, NE (2-90) Chldr; Drama; Tres, FHA; NHS; Alg A; Hon Prog; Math A; Sci A; Spch A; *U of NE; Sci.*

KRAMER, Richard William
Glenbard W HS; Glen Ellyn, IL (170-488) Chor; Hmrm; Ski C; Golf; Church Deacon.

KRAMER, Susan Marie
Villa Madonna Acad; Covington, KY (1-76) Chor; Secy, NHS; Tr; Aux Lat; B Crocker A; NMF; NEDT; Val; Eng A; Pres School Nom; *XU Schol; Xavier U; Psych.*

KRAMME, Clark Alan
Saydel HS; Des Moines, IA (10%-220) Band; BS; Chor; Drama; Key C; Thes; Bkbl; Ftbl; Tr; Most Out.

KRAMME, Mark Alan
Saydel HS; Des Moines, IA (12-205) Band; Chor; Drama; Key C; NHS; SC; Thes; Pres, Var C; Bkbl; Ftbl; Tr; *UNI; Pre-Med.*

KRAMP, Robyn Lee
Winston Churchill HS; Potomac, MD (25%-607) Chor; Fr C; SC; VP, Jr Cl; Mgr, Hockey; Tr.

KRAMPITZ, Cynthia Dawn
Lyons Township HS; LaGrange, IL (60-1250) Chor; Ensm; Math C; ARC; Swim; COM; Hon Prog; *U of Chicago; Med.*

KRANKER, Susan Michele
Northglenn HS; Northglenn, CO; *St Paul Bible Col; Secy.*

KRANTZ, David Paul
McCluer N HS; Florissant, MO (174-792) Band; Fin, BS; Demolay; Drama; Orch; Span C; Tnns; Masonic A; *U of Mo; Bus Adm.*

KRANTZ, Douglas Warren
Angola HS; Angola, IN (16-142) Band; Chor; Fr C; NHS; Orch; Order/Arrow; Thes; *Ind St U; Mus Ed.*

KRAPEK, Gary Joseph
Mason City Sr HS; Mason City, IA (25%-500) F-Ed, Ann; Chem C; Chor; Drama; NFL; F-Ed, Sch P; Sci C; Spch C; Thes; JV, Tr; Cl Fav; Hon Prog; Most Out; Q&S A; Spch A; Off, Outst Thespian; *US Army; Photrgraphy.*

KRASNIAK, Stephen
Auburn HS; Auburn, NY (12-600) Model UN; NHS; NMS; Regent Schol; *Mass Inst Tech; Chem.*

KRATZ, Michael Steven
Grover Cleveland HS; St Louis, MO (58-550) A-Ed, Ann; Fr C; Sch P.

KRAUS, Bill Dudley
Orangefield HS; Orangefield, TX (12-76) 4H; VP, Lit Mag; SC; Bsbl; Bkbl; Co-Cpt, Ftbl; Tr; Cl Fav; Gr Marshal; H of F; Most Out Ath Boy; Hall of Fame, Most Fun to Be With; *Polly Tech Inst; Architecture.*

KRAUSE, Carey Allen
Norman HS; Norman, OK; Band; Drama; Lat C; NHS; Orch; Band A; *U of Okla; Pre-Med.*

KRAUSE, Cindy Ruth
Riverton HS; Riverton, WY (39-198) Ger C; Yth Fel; Nom, NHS; Tres, Hist C; Foreign Lang C; *Central Wy Col; Psych.*

KRAUSE, Craig Allan
Merrill HS; Merrill, WI (220-375) A Cap Choir; Band; Chor; Ensm; Madrigal; JV, Cr-Ctry; Pres A; Yth Fel; *Northland Col; Mus.*

KRAUSE, Daniel Eugene
South HS; Fargo, ND (10-409) Schol Achv A; *U of ND; Law.*

KRAUSE, Frederick A
Lyman Mem HS; Lebanon, CT (20-90) Chor; Fr C; Bsbl; Cpt, Bkbl; Co-Cpt, Soccer; Co-Cpt, Bkbl; *Springfield Col; Phys Ed.*

KRAUSE, Kelly Clyde
Marshall Co HS; Benton, KY; A Cap Choir; Bus C; FBLA; 4H; Fin, Bkbl; Tr; 4H A; Rotary Bkbl; US Coast Guard Aux Boating Safety; *Murray St U; Sci.*

KRAUSE, Michael Joseph
Hinsdale Twp HS Central; Hinsdale, IL (68-601)
Band; Pres, CYO; Math C; Orch; St Scholar; U of
Ill; Pre-Med.

KRAUSE, Raymond Thomas
Pleasant Hill HS; Pleasant Hill, CA (50-255) Band;
Bsbl; Ftbl; JV, Swim.

KRAUSE, Steven John
Benet Acad; Lisle, IL (110-275) Band; Chess C;
Hon Prog; Lib Arts.

KRAUSE, Willow Ann
Alliance HS; Alliance, NE (15-152) Band; Pres,
4H; ARC; Y-Tns; 4H A; Spch A; NHS; Co-Ch,
Drill Tm; FFA Swtht Attendant; U of Nebr; Agr.

KRAUSEN, William Scott
Bardstown HS; Bardstown, KY; Chor; Ensm; Key
C; Madrigal; Bkbl; Mgr, Ftbl; Cpt, Sftbl; Tnns; Ar-
tistic Excellence A; Church Choir; Quad St Singing
A; Tn Who Care; Morehead St Singing A; Ftbl,
MG A; Choral Swing Choir Group; St Seminary;
Theology.

KRAUSS, Beth Renee
Attica Sr HS; Attica, NY; Band; Hmrm; SC; Tres,
Jr Cl; JV, Bkbl; Soccer; GAA; VP, Fresh Cl; Cornell
U; Vet Med.

KRAUTER, David William
Arvin HS; Arvin, CA (10-400) Chess C; Model
UN; Order/Arrow; Span C; Span NHS; SC; Var C;
Parl, Jr Cl; JV, Bkbl; JV, Tnns; CSF; Ntl Sci Found;
U of Colo; Mountain Research.

KRAUTSCHEID, Michael John
Hillsboro Sr HS; Hillsboro, OR (1-800) CYO; Ger
C; Pres, 4H; NHS; Ftbl; Wrest; 4H A; Pres A; Sci
A; VP, Tres, Rptr, 4 H C; Outst Ger Stu A; May-
pole Dancer, May Fete; Knighted For Acad Excel.

KRAWCZYKOWSKI,
Gloria Lynn
Thomas Kelly HS; Chicago, IL (9-635) Hmrm; In-
terClub Coun; NHS; Secy; SC; COM; Kiwanis A;
Math.

KREBS, Kathleen Marie
Maple Shade HS; Maple Shade, NJ (10%-235)
Secy, CYO; Chor; Drama; Key C; Mjrte; NHS;
Mgr, Bkbl; Rutgers U; Psych.

KREBS, Kathy Ruth
Valparaiso HS; Valparaiso, IN (30-490) Chor;
Drama; Ensm; Tres, 4H; NHS; Ski C; SC; Swim;
JV, Tnns; 4H A; Delta Theta Tu, Foreign Lang A;
Isaac Walton Nature A; Photography A; Valparaiso
U; Pre-Law.

KREBS, Theresa
Our Lady of Mercy Acad; Louisville, KY (2-77)
Chor; Drama; VP, Fr C; Tr; MLS; U of RI; Sci.

KRECEMAN, Victoria Lea
Battiest HS; Battiest, OK (3-45) Chor; FHA; Bkbl;
Elem Ed.

KREDELL, Kathleen
Cristobal Jr Sr HS; Coco Solo, CANAL ZONE
(4-150) FTA; Hmrm; Var C; Pres, Soph Cl; Bkbl;
Tnns; Med.

KREGER, Kirk James
Rockwood Area HS; Rockwood, PA (10-116)
Chess C; Sci C; Hon Prog; Drafting.

KREGNESS, Becky Ann
Brooklyn Center HS; Brooklyn Center, MN
(1-165) Co-Ed, Ann; Soc; Chor; Fr C; Pres, NHS;
Bkbl; Val; Q & S Soc; Parl, Danceline; Vlbl; First
Ntl Bank A; Bethel Col.

KREHBIEL, Lee Edward
Olathe HS; Olathe, KS (1-450) AFS; Band; BS;
Hmrm; NHS; Orch; Sch P; VP, SC; Rptr, Sr Cl;
Bkbl; Ftbl; Golf; Tnns; Hon Prog; Sal; St Scholar;
All St, All Dist, Band; All District, Orch; Midwest-
ern Jazz Festival; Wichita St Col; Engr.

KREIDER, Debra Ann
East HS; Cheyenne, WY; Band; Ger C; 4H; Swim;
Tnns; 4H A; Pres A; Ger A; Med.

KREIFELS, Jo Ann
Nebraska City Lourdes HS; Nebraska City, NE;
Ann; Cpt, Chldr; Chor; 4H; NHS; S-T, SC; Secy,
Var C; Sftbl; Tr; 4H A; HCt; Hon Prog; Cath
Daughter's Essay A; Grand Island Sch of Bus; Bus.

KREISEL, Rick Dean
Green Ridge R-8 HS; Green Ridge, MO (25%-37)
FFA; Pres, 4H; Spch C; Rptr, Soph Cl; JV, Bkbl;
JV, Tr; Spch A; Yth Fel.

KREITER, John David
Warwick HS; Lititz, PA (64-272) Hmrm; Pres,
Soph Cl; Tr; Elec Engr.

KREITZER, Susan Elaine
W Aurora Sr HS; Aurora, IL (99-631) Chor; NHS;
COM; Secy, DECA; N Ill U; Commercial Art.

KREIVENAS, Jane Elizabeth
Hubbard HS; Chicago, IL (31-657) Chor; Mu Al-
pha Theta; NHS; Rptr, Sch P; SC; COM; HCt; Hon
Prog; Q&S A; Type A; U of Ill; Bus Mgr.

KREKE, David Joseph
Central Community HS; Breese, IL; VP, Band;
Pres, CYO; Ger C; 4H; ARC; Golf; Hon Prog;
Math A; Mgr, CYO Bkbl; Mgr, CYO Sftbl; Fin,
VFW Essay Contest; Kaskaskia Col; Acct.

KREKE, Mary Therese
Stephen T Badin HS; Hamilton, OH (32-185)
CYO; Fr C; Co-Cpt, Mjrte; VP, SC; Bsbl; Co-Cpt,
Bkbl; Cpt, Tr; COM; Citz A; X-Ray Tech.

KRELL, Lisa Eileen
Joliet West Township HS; Joliet, IL (3-595) A Cap
Choir; Chor; French NHS; HiY; COM; Kiwanis A;
Spch A; Yth Fel.

KREMBS, Joseph Andrew
Northland HS; Columbus, OH (96-538) Serra C,
Knight, Page, Squire, A's; Navy; Mgr.

KREMER, Howard Louis
Parkview HS; Springfield, MO (5%-407) A Cap
Choir; BS; Chor; Lat C; Order/Arrow; JV, Tr; JV,
Wrest; God & Country A; JA; Eagle Sct A; SW Mo
St U; Sci.

KREMER, Julie Lynn
Crystal Lake Comm HS; Crystal Lake, IL
(139-585) AFS; Chor; Drama; Fr C; Ski C; Span C;
Thes; Tr; COM; Hon Prog; JV, Vlbl; Presidential
Fitness; Chicago Shell C; FCA; Luther League; Lu-
ther Col; Foreign Lang.

KRENEK, Michael James
E Bernard HS; East Bernard, TX (3-60) Band;
CYO; Chem C; Math C; Model UN; Phys C; Sch P;
Sci C; Tex A&I Col; Engr.

KRENTZ, Kristine Jo
Fruitport HS; Muskegon, MI (50-380) Pep C; Bus.

KREPPS, Steven Wayne
Central Dauphin HS; Harrisburg, PA (33%-477)
Band; God & Country A; Star Sct; Marine Biol.

KREPS, Marta Lise
Jameson Hall HS; San Rafael, CA (1-10) Drama;
Ed, Sch P; SC; CSF; Citz A; Val; VP, Stu Body;
Stanford U; Drama.

KRESGE, Jerry Glenn
Big Valley HS; Bieber, CA; Pres, FFA; Spch C; SC;
VP, Soph Cl; Pres A; Yale Book A; SB Pres; Big
Brother A; Agr.

KRESS, Beth Allison
Mother McAuley HS; Chicago, IL (70-475) Ed,
Ann; NHS; Sftbl; Hon Prog; St Mary's Col; Nurs.

KRESS, Kathleen Terese
Cabrini HS; Allen Park, MI (2-156) Chor; VP,
Drama; Ensm; GS; NHS; Rptr, Sch P; Sftbl; NMS;
Mus.

KRESSEL, Kim
Bruriah HS; Elizabeth, NJ (3-33) VP, Hmrm; NHS;
Ed, Sch P; Hon Prog; NEDT; Bernard Col.

KRESTAN, Ronald Mark
Kansas City Christian HS; Merriam, KS (5-22) A
Cap Choir; NHS; SC; Pres, Soph Cl; JV, Cr-Ctry;
Soccer; JV, Wrest; Citz A; Hon Prog; Bob Jones U;
Pre-Law.

KREUTZER, Paul Jerome
N Tonawanda Sr HS; N Tonawanda, NY (72-650)
Band; Chem C; Chor; Ensm; Hmrm; Sci C; Ski C;
Span C; Cpt, Soccer; Tnns; COM; St U of Buffalo;
Dentistry.

KREUTZER, Tammy Rae
La Veta HS; Sa Veta, CO (3-22) Band; Chldr; Secy,
FBLA; Mjrte; Pres, NHS; Rainbow; VP, SC; Cpt,
Bkbl; Mgr, Tr; Citz A; 4H A; MVP, Bkbl; All-Conf
Bkbl; Pres, VP & S-T, 4-H C; Top Stu; All-Conf
Vlbl; Home Ec A; Adams St Col; Bus.

KREVKO, Marianne
Old Forge HS; Old Forge, PA; Band; FNA; NHS;
Ski C; Span C; Chem A; Hon Prog.

KREY, Melody Lynne
John F Kennedy HS; Bloomington, MN;

KRHUT, Fred Alan
Fairhope HS; Fairhope, AL (179-300) Band; Chess
C; VP, Explorer Post; Marine Bio.

KRICK, Terry Lynn
Centerville Sr HS; Centerville, IN (9-160) Drama;
NHS; Y-Tns; Bible C; Bowl Tm; House of James
Beauty Col; Beautician.

KRIEG, Kenneth Joseph
Logan HS; Logan, OH (10-357) Fr C; Secy, Key C;
NHS; Pres, Soph Cl; Bsbl; JV, Bkbl; Alg A; Bio A.

KRIEG, Lisa Diane
Western Heights HS; Okla City, OK (45-260)
Hmrm; NHS; Sci C; SC; Chem A; JA A; Art C,
Schol Tm; Okla St U; Archt.

KRIEGEL, Joan Lisa
Las Cruces HS; Las Cruces, NM (15-566) Band;
Ensm; Pres, NHS; SC; Keyettes; Girl o-t Mon; Pi
Beta Phi; Vlbl; Amer Assn of U Women; NMSU
Schol; Angel Humanitarian A; IP Sousa Band A;
NM St U; Computer Sci.

KRIEGEL, Kathy Sue
Cy-Fair HS; Houston, TX; Chor; Sci C; Sftbl; Tex
A&M U; Floriculture.

KRIEGER, Angie Diane
Greeley W HS; Greeley, CO; Fr C; Ger C.

KRIEGER, Billy Joe
Big Piney HS; Big Piney, WY (13-40) Band; JV,
Ftbl; Stevens Henager Col; Acct.

KRIEGER, Carol Lois
Ft Lauderdale HS; Ft Lauderdale, FL; Chor; Pres,
FBLA; Lat C; Type A; Broward Comm Col; Nurs.

KRIEGER, Jesse James
Stanton HS; Stanton, ND (1-17) Bus Mgr, Ann;
Band; Chor; Drama; Pres, Hmrm; Golf; Whapeton
Col; Bus Mgr.

KRIER, Debra Lynne
McHenry HS W; McHenry, IL (1-550) AFS; Ann;
Dbte Tm; Tres, Fr C; Lit Mag; Secy, Model UN;
Sch P; Sci C; SC; Swim; Hon Prog; Kiwanis A; Sch
Spirit A; Marine Biol.

KRIGER, Mary Ruth
Houston HS; Houston, MS (10%-107) VP, Anchor
C; Co-Ed, Ann; Band; BC; Bio A; COM; Math.

KRIKKE, Robin Ann
Daviess Co HS; Owensboro, KY;

KRILL, Thomas Lawrence
Archbold Area HS; Archbold, OH (8%-143) Band;
Chor; Rptr, FFA; Pres, 4H; JV, Bsbl; Mgr, Bkbl; 4H
A; Yth Fel; Top 4-H Photography Project; Co
Rep, Photography St Fair; Co Rep, 4-H St Con-
gress; Ohio St U; Agr Engr.

KRIPPAEHNE, Naomi Jean
Gov John R Rogers HS; Puyallup, WA (5-413)
Ann; Band; Semi-Fin, GS; NHS; Orch; Rptr, Sch P;
Span C; SC; Var C; Secy, Jr Cl; Bkbl; Tr; Amer Leg
A; Amer Leg Orator A; Citz A; Hon Prog; Journ A;
Masonic A; Q&S A; Yth Fel; Yth Foundation; Pa-
cific Lutheran U; Phys Ed.

KRIPPENDORF, Wanda Joy
Dunedin HS; Dunedin, FL (32-830) Band; Ensm;
Hmrm; NHS; Tr; U of S Fla; Med Tech.

KRISKE, Charlotte M
Clarkstown HS; W Nyack, NY (44-550) Band;
Chem C; Chor; Bus Mgr, Drama; FTA; Ger C;
Madrigal; Mu Alpha Theta; NHS; Ski C; JV, Tnns;
Beauty; Future Doctors of Amer; Albany U; Lib
Arts.

KRISTENSEN, Linda Marie
Waukegan E HS; Waukegan, IL (81-453) Pres,
FNA; VP, Ger C; GS; NHS; ARC; Ski C; Swim;
Hon Prog; NEDT; ARC A; VFW A; Sunday Sch
Teacher; U of Wis-Madison; Marine Bio.

KRISTOF, Nicholas Donabet
Yamhill-Carlton Union HS; Yamhill, OR (1-89) Pres, BS; VP, Fr C; Pres, FFA; Tres, 4H; VP, NHS; Ed, Sch P; Spch C; St Stu Congress; Pres, SC; Var C; Pres, Soph Cl; Cr-Ctry; Tr; B Crocker A; Elk A; 4H A; Hon Prog; Journ A; NMF; NMS; Opt A; Spch A; St Scholar; Val; VFW Orator Win; Vof-DEM; St FFA Rptr; Ntl Merit Schol; Alt, Hon Soc Schol; Harvard U.

KRISTOFF, Olga Leticia
McKinley Sr HS; Canton, OH (2-597) A Cap Choir; Chor; Hmrm; NHS; Pres, Span C; Span NHS; Swim; Hardest Worker Swim A; Psych.

KRISTY, William Curtis
Northgate HS; Walnut Creek, CA (10-420) Model UN; Ed, Sch P; Span C; CSF; Journ A; U of Calif; Physics.

KRIZAN, David Paul
Gilman HS; Gilman, WI; FFA; Bsbl; FFA Winter Sports Area.

KRIZAN, Mark Thomas
Gilman HS; Gilman, WI (20-75) FFA; 4H; 4H A; Outdoor Recreation.

KROEGER, David William
Highland HS; Ewing, MO (1-150) Pres, CYO; NHS; Fin, Sch Achieve Tm; Sci C; VP, Soph Cl; Mgr, Bkbl; Citz A; Ntl Sci Symposium; Sci A; Jr Acad of Sci; Interntl Sci & Engr Fair; Army Sci & Engr A.

KROEGER, Kathy Ann
Beloit Cath HS; Beloit, WI; A Cap Choir; Chor; NHS.

KROENING, Terry Alan
Rogers HS; Michigan City, IN (35-585) Chor; Fr C; Sci C; COM; Citz A; Math A; Sci A; Star Student; Sci Fair, Chor, Schol, A's; Purdue U; Vet Med.

KROEPEL, Karen Sue
Carlyle HS; Carlyle, IL (23-138) Pres, Chor; Drama; Ensm; Madrigal; Hon Prog; WW; Mus Play; Run-Up, Ms Clinton Co-Op Beauty; Kaskaskia Jr Col; Special Ed.

KROHN, Susan Jean
Lakeview HS; Battle Creek, MI (10-410) Fr C; GS; NHS; Ftbl; Hon Prog; Yth Fel; Vol Recognition A; Ferris Col; Secy.

KROLDART, Patricia Ann
Orchard Park HS; Orchard Park, NY (10%-600) Chor; Demolay; Drama; Orch; Sci C; COM; Citz A; Triangle; Mus Bstrs A; Fr A; Deaf Ed.

KROLL, Douglas Donald
Kaukauna HS; Kaukauna, WI; Band; Lat C; Ed, Sch P; Ski C; Tnns; Journ A; Q&S A; Marquette U; Journ.

KROMMES, Laurie Meg
Emmaus HS; Emmaus, PA; Band; VP, Fr C; Hmrm; SC; Secy, Soph Cl; Mgr, Bkbl; Coun of Teach A; Citz A; Keyette; Ldrship A; HR; SG; Ministry.

KRONABLE, Gary Edwin
Brussels Comm HS; Brussels, IL; CYO; Dbte Tm; VP, FFA; 4H; Var C; Bkbl; Bio A; 4H A; HCt; Hon Prog; Lewis & Clark Col; Med.

KRONBERG, Hal Eric
Ralston HS; Ralston, NE; Band; Chor; Bsbl; MVP, Wrest; Wrest A, Inter-City Champ.

KRONBERGS, Leon Pete
Lake Braddock Secondary Sch; Burke, VA (227-695) JV, Ftbl; Tr; Indoor Tr; VP, Church Yth Group; Yth Rep, ALC Ntl Conv; Tex A&M U; Architecture.

KRONE, Carol Lynne
W York Area Sr HS; York, PA; Band; Mod Mus Mas; Tri-M.

KRONEBUSCH, Richard Lowry
Niceville HS; Niceville, FL (94-400) Key C; Ski C; JV, Bsbl; Co-Cpt, Ftbl; Colo St U; Criminology.

KRONEMER, Alexander
Charleroi HS; Charleroi, PA (30%-246) Hmrm; Ski C; Span C; Spch C; Pres, SC; Tr; JV, Wrest; Stu Forum VP, DPE; Georgetown Col; Econ.

KRONEMER, Dorothy
Charleroi Area HS; Charleroi, PA; Band; Rainbow; Secy, Sch P; Ski C; HCt; Co Band; Hospitality C; Orch Mus; Bus.

KRONEN, Bruce Frederick
Park Center HS; Brooklyn Park, MN (162-628) Band; Ftbl; Tr; St & Co Am Wilderness Ldrshp Sch; Wildlife Mgt.

KRONENWETTER, Tamara Ann
Newman HS; Wausau, WI; Co-Cpt, Chldr; Pres, 4H; NHS; Ski C; Secy, 4-H C; Art, Purchase, 4-H Qn, A's; U of Minn; Vet.

KRONER, Paul Gerard
Buckley HS; Sherman Oaks, CA; Drama; NHS; Sch P; SC; Mgr, Bsbl; Mgr, Bkbl; Mgr, Ftbl; JV, Soccer; Tr; Alg A; Citz A; Hon Prog; NEDT; Sci A; Eng A; Span A; Fr A; Stanford U.

KRONST, Kent William
Bradley-Bourbonnais HS; Bourbonnais, IL;

KROON, Robert Joseph
Hillsboro Sr HS; Hillsboro, OR (198-598) Pres, Band; CYO; Ensm; Hmrm; Pol Sci C; SC; Mgr, Bkbl; Citz A; Portland St U; Bus Adm.

KROPF, Nancy Patricia
Lutheran HS E; Harper Woods, MI (17-132) Band; Ensm; NHS; Orch; Var C; Mgr, Bkbl; Sftbl; Co-Cpt, Vlbl; MSBOA; Hope Col; Med Tech.

KROPKE, Darrylin Tamara
Granada Hills HS; Granada Hills, CA; Band; NHS; Beauty; CSF; Citz A; Hon Prog; Pres A; Secy, Schol Soc; UCLA; Social Stu.

KROS, Marcia Ruth
Clifton Sr HS; Clifton, NJ (2%-1000) Ger C; Key C; Math C; Star Student; VFW A; Math League; Eng A.

KROSTYNE, Marianne
St Benedict Acad; Pittsburgh, PA (2-60) S-T, Chor; Drama; NHS; Secy, Jr Cl; DARGCA; NEDT.

KROUSE, Andrew Mark
Roy C Start HS; Toledo, OH (30-250) Band; Dbte Tm; NFL; Orch; Hon Prog; Calvin Col; Mus.

KROUSE, John Samuel
Philipsburg-Osceola HS; Philipsburg, PA (87-235) Chess C; Fr C; Mgr, Ftbl; JV, Wrest; Math A; Westminster Col; Math.

KROUSE, John Samule
Philipsburg-Osceola HS; Philipsburg, PA (87-235) Chess C; Fr C; Mgr, Ftbl; JV, Wrest; Alg A; Math A; Math.

KROUT, Daniel E
Sycamore HS; Sycamore, IL (6-256) A Cap Choir; Chor; Madrigal; NHS; NEDT; Concordia Teachers Col; Ed.

KROUT, Karl William
Oak Lawn Comm HS; Oak Lawn, IL (5-800) ARC; Swim; Amer Leg A; Most Out; U of Ill; Aviation.

KRUCZAK, Sonia Lubomyra
Immaculate Conception Ukranian HS; Hamtramck, MI (5-43) Chor; Hmrm; NHS; Sch P; Var C; VP, Soph Cl; Bkbl; HCt; Kiwanis A; Ukranian Yth Organization; Ftbl, Bkbl Statistician; Cpt, Vlbl; Ukranian Mus Inst & Dancing; Wayne St U; Nurs.

KRUEA, Loree Lynne
Salisbury HS; Salisbury, NC (30-220) Co-Ed, Ann; Pres, Fr C; Hmrm; SC; Hon Prog; Q&S A; Secy, Jr Civitan; VP, Yth Fel; Appalachian St U; Ed.

KRUEGER, Cynthia Leigh
Clark Co R-1 HS; Kahoka, MO (1-95) Band; Chor; Ensm; FHA; 4H; NHS; Pol Sci C; Sci C; Hon Prog; Most Out; FHA Count; Culver Stockton Col; Sci.

KRUEGER, Jill Elizabeth
Waukegan E HS; Waukegan, IL (26-551) Chldr; Chor; Fr C; Fin, GS; NHS; Ski C; SC; Var C; Swim; HCt; Yth Foundation A; Gym; Hugh O'Brien Ldrship Runner-Up; Med Tech.

KRUEGER, Katherine Elise
New Braunfels HS; New Braunfels, TX (14-300) Band; Ensm; FFA; Ger C; Mjrte; Mu Alpha Theta; NHS; Tres, Rainbow; SC; Tnns; Amer Leg A; Pres A; Hugh O'Brien Ldrship Found A; Fashion Merchandising.

KRUEGER, Margie Jane
Edison HS; Huntington Beach, CA; Hmrm; Campus Life; Semi-Fin, Golden Key, Art; Publication, Sch Arts Magazine; Orange Coast Col; Art.

KRUEGER, Mark Anthony
Highland HS; Ewing, MO; Band; FFA; NHS; Sci C; Ftbl; Tr; U of Mo; Agr.

KRUEGER, Marlene Rose
Mississinewa HS; Gas City, IN (50-300) Chor; Drama; Ensm; Fr C; Talor U; Sociology.

KRUEGER, Mary Ann
Olympia HS; Stanford, IL (19-220) Band; Chem C; Chor; Ensm; Secy, FHA; Secy, 4H; Key C; Lit Ral; Math C; Orch; Sci C; COM; 4H A; Hist A; Hon Prog; I Dare You; Sci A; Spch A; Stu Bank Board; Clothing A; St Outst, 4-H.

KRUEGER, Mike Lee
Aldrich HS; Beloit, WI (20-35) Sftbl; Elec.

KRUEGER, Peter Heinz
Bridgman HS; Bridgman, MI (6-75) Fr C; Ger C; Lit Mag; NHS; Sci C; Var C; Ftbl; Soccer; Cpt, Sftbl; Tr; Cpt, Wrest; Amer Leg A; COM; Art A; Lake Superior St Col; Med Tech.

KRUEGER, Phillip Norman
Highland HS; Medina, OH (88-251) Chor; Ensm; Hmrm; SC; 4H A; Agr.

KRUEGER, Sue Marie
Hilbert HS; Hilbert, WI (25%-90) AFS; Band; 4H; SC; COM; 4H A; Hon Prog; Sci A; Spch A; Marquette U; Nurs.

KRUEGER, Thomas John
Fairmont Sr HS; Fairmont, MN (67-199) Chor; Ger C; Var C; Mgr, Bkbl; Mgr, Ftbl; Golf; Gustavus Adolphus Col; Acct.

KRUEL, Kay Ann
Horicon HS; Horicon, WI (35-100) Bkbl; Tr; Med Tech.

KRUELL, Christopher Paul
Minnetonka HS; Minnetonka, MN (90-660) Span NHS; Var C; Cr-Ctry; Tr; Chem.

KRUG, Daniel Jay
Rocky Grove HS; Franklin, PA; Fr C; Order/Arrow; Bsbl; Amer Leg A; Eagle Sct A; Penn St U; Forestry.

KRUGER, Anna Ruth
Columbus HS; Columbus, GA (5%-325) Band; Secy, Math C; Secy, Mu Alpha Theta; Orch; Hon Prog; Semi- fin, Gov Hon; St String A; All St Band & Orch; Mus.

KRUGER, Janice Elaine
Harrington HS; Harrington, WA (1-13) Tres, Band; Chor; Ensm; Fin, Jr Miss Pageant; VP, NHS; Orch; SC; Tres, Sr Cl; Pres, Soph Cl; Co-Cpt, Bkbl; COM; Citz A; Math A; NEDT; Type A; Val; Yth Fel; Pres, Pep C; Acct A; Pres, Ltr 'H' C; Pres, Ltr 'H' C;; Girls League; Vlbl; NW Col; Acct.

KRUGER, Sarah Lynn
LakeShore HS; St Clair Shores, MI; Chor; Sftbl; HR.

KRUIZENGA, Sandra Lee
Delavan-Darien HS; Delavan, WI (79-210) Bus C; FBLA; FFA; 4H A; FFA Greenhand & Chapter Farmer; U of Wis; Bus Adm.

KRULL, Linnae Karol
Holstein HS; Holstein, IA (1-47) A-Ed, Ann; Band; Chor; Ensm; Math C; NHS; Rptr, Sch P; St Stu Congress; SC; Pres, Jr Cl; COM; Hon Prog; Journ A; St Scholar; Secy, Luther League; Most Dependable; Hon Band; Hon Graduate; U of N Iowa; Bio.

KRUMMEL, LuAnn Marie
Avona Comm HS; Avoca, IA (23-42) Ann; Band; Chor; Drama; Y-Tns; Cl Fav; HCt; WW.

KRUMMERT, Katherine Ann
Holy Ghost HS; Pittsburgh, PA (1-48) Chldr; Drama; Sch P; Tres, SC; Y-Tns; VP, Jr Cl; Amer Leg A; MLS.

KRUMWIEDE, Kimberly Jane
Salina HS S; Salina, KS; Band; Tr; Kans St U; Acct.

KRUPICKA, Leonard Henry
Morton HS; Berwyn, IL; Cpt, Tnns.

KRUPKE, Kevin Jon
Monroe Sr HS; Monroe, WI (175-260) Band; Ensm; JV, Wrest; Prom Court.

KRUSCHKA, Gretchen Fawn
Mt Vernon HS; Alexandria, VA (25%-579) Cpt; Ann; Ger C; Ch, Hmrm; Soccer; Tr; Yth Fel; GSct; Challenges of Comm Outdoors; 1st Cl Citizenship; *Calif St U; Marine Biol.*

KRUSE, David Lee
Cathedral HS; El Paso, TX (7-35) Spch C; Hon Prog; Schol A; *U of Tex at Austin.*

KRUSE, Pamela Jane
Mankato W HS; Mankato, MN; Chor; A-Ed, Sch P; Sci C; COM; Solesteppers, Performance C.

KRUSE, William Cole
Cumberland Valley HS; Cumberland Valley, PA (70-697) Pres, Chess C; Co-Cpt, Dbte Tm; Hmrm; NFL; Sch P; Ski C; Spch C; Soccer; Hon Prog; Spch A; Type A; *Case Western Reserve U; Engr.*

KRUSKO, Alex
Saunders Trades And Tech HS; Yonkers, NY (1-158) Ann; Hmrm; NHS; Var C; Bsbl; Co-Cpt, Bkbl; Co-Cpt, Ftbl; Bausch & Lomb A; Regent Schol; Val; MVP, Bkbl; *Penn St U; Chem.*

KRUSZKA, Karen Lynn
Manistee HS; Manistee, MI (55-180) Band; NHS; WW; Candystriper A; *W Shore Comm Col; Nurs.*

KRUSZON, James Edward
Riverhead HS; Riverhead, NY (38-265) Drama; Ger C; Rptr, Sch P; COM; Bookkeeping Cert; Co-Ed, Yrbk Staff; *USAF; Bus.*

KRYSZEWSKI, Karen Denise
E Aurora HS; Aurora, IL (24-797) Band; *Wheaton Col; Bus Adm.*

KRZANOWSKI, Jeannine Anita
Mercy HS; Albany, NY (7-108) Drama; NHS; Sftbl; COM; *Maria Col; Nutrition.*

KUBACAK, Vickie Lynn
Wilson HS; Wilson, TX (6-25) CYO; Drama; VP, FHA; Tres, Jr Cl; WW; *S Plains Col; Sociology.*

KUBIC, Mark Michael
Chaney HS; Youngstown, OH (1-389) Dbte Tm; Ger C; Pres, Hmrm; NFL; NHS; F-Ed, Sch P; Spch C; SC; Bkbl; Golf; Alg A; Bio A; DARGCA; H of F; Hon Prog; MLS; Spch A; Val; Pres, Pol Speaker's Bureau; Vet Soc A; *Youngstown St U; Med.*

KUBIN, Linda Ann
Ennis HS; Ennis, TX; FHA; FTA; Semi-Fin, GS; Alg A; Amer Leg A; Bio A; NEDT; Asst Bus Mgr, Ann; VOE Stu o-t Yr A; Prog Ch, Off Ed Assn; 2nd Pl St Off Ed As Rec Mgt Cont.

KUBIN, Nancy Lee
St Louis HS; St Louis, MI (35-140) Band; 4H; Hmrm; Sch P; Span C; SC; VP, Soph Cl; Swim; 4H A; JA A; *Nazareth Col; Nurs.*

KUBOVICZ, Susan Kay
Bridgeport HS; Bridgeport, OH; Secy, Lat C; Secy, NHS; SC; VP, Y-Tns; Tnns; Art C.

KUCERA, Eva Rene
Havre HS; Havre, MT (78-269) CYO; Chldr; Chor; 4H; Hmrm; Secy; SC; Var C; VP, Sr Cl; S-T, Jr Cl; VP, Soph Cl; Bsbl; Bkbl; Tr; Cl Fav; 4H A; HCt; Swtht; Activity A; Friendliest; *Benedictine Col; Eng.*

KUCERA, Gary E
Prague HS; Prague, NE; Chor; Parl, FFA; Bsbl; Bkbl; Hon Prog; *Agr.*

KUCHAR, John Joseph
Old Forge HS; Old Forge, PA (1-121) Co-Ed, Ann; Pres, Band; NHS; Pres, Orch; Chem A; H of F; Val; Acad Achv A; Pres Schol; *U of Scranton; Pre-Med.*

KUCHTA, Janine Ann
Lutheran HS S; St Louis, MO; Band; Chor; Sftbl; Yth Fel; *Westminster Col; Social Work.*

KUECKER, Carol Jean
Chase Co HS; Imperial, NE (4-71) Band; Chldr; Chor; Secy, FHA; NHS; Co-Ed, Sch P; Spch C; Var C; Secy, Y-Tns; Bkbl; Tr; Regent Schol; Rptr, VP & S-T, Y-H C; St Tr HR; Yth League; Stage Band; VLBL; NMS Ltr of Commendation; *U of Lincoln; Med.*

KUECKER, Debra Jane
Francis Howell HS; Weldon Springs, MO; Band; Span C; Bkbl; COM; Citz A; Bell Choir Cert; *Journ.*

KUEFFNER, Gail Suzanne
Lakeview HS; Battle Creek, MI (25%-200) Community Yth Symph; Orch; ARC; Sci C; Span C; Var C; *Nurs.*

KUEHL, Barbara Ann
Los Alamos HS; Los Alamos, NM (10%-400) Band; Chor; Pres, 4H; NHS; Rainbow; COM; 4H A; NMF; Yth Fel; WW; Church Deacon; Jazz Ensm; *U of Tulsa; Special Ed.*

KUEHLER, Ingrid Edith
Bloomfield Sr HS; Bloomfield, NJ (58-651) Arch; Band; Chor; Hmrm; NHS; Arch; Stu Gov Assn; Gym.

KUEHN, Heidi Louise
Cristobal Jr-Sr HS; Coco Solo, CANAL ZONE (2-122) Co-Ed, Ann; Band; VP, FTA; Hmrm; Secy, NHS; Orch; Ed, Sch P; VP, Thes; COM; Citz A; Lion A; Math A; NMS; NEDT; Spch A; VofDEM; Mount Holyoke Col.

KUEHN, Leslie Ray
Gorley Pub HS; Gurley, NE (2-12) Ann; Semi-Fin, BS; Chor; 4H; Pres, Monogram; Sch P; Ski C; Spch C; SC; Pres, Var C; VP, Sr Cl; VP, Soph Cl; Co-Cpt, Bkbl; Co-Cpt, Ftbl; B Crocker A; COM; Elk A; 4H A; HCt; NEDT; Regent Schol; Sal; Acct A; *Chadron St Col; Agr.*

KUEHN, Michael David
Winthrop Comm HS; Winthrop, MN (5-61) Ann; Band; Chor; Drama; Ensm; FFA; Pres, 4H; Madrigal; NHS; Ed, Sch P; VP, SC; Ftbl; Golf; 4H A; Journ A; Spch A; Page, St Legislature; *U of Minn; Vet Med.*

KUEHNAST, Nancy Marie
Saint Croix Lutheran HS; West St Paul, MN (20-75) Bkbl; Sftbl; Swim; Tnns; Pres, Church Yth; *Concordia Col; Archt.*

KUEHNEL, Karen Elizabeth
Lindenhurst HS; Lindenhurst, NY (20-700) Chor; Lit Mag; Bus Mgr, Thes; COM; Hon Prog; Regent Schol; *Duke U; Psych.*

KUEHNEL, Kerry Lynne
Lindenhurst Sr HS; Lindenhurst, NY (10%-500) Chor; Key C; NHS; ARC; Sch P; Thes; Bkbl; Hon Prog; Sci A; Gym; Band; Phys Ed, A's; *Art.*

KUEHNER, Judith Ann
Technical HS; Scranton, PA; Bus C; Mjrte; Type A.

KUEHNERT, Jill Christina
Woodlan HS; Woodburn, IN (12-122) Chor; FFA; FHA; Arch; COM; Hon Stu; FFA Chapter Schol; HR; *Ivy Tech Col; Data Processing.*

KUENG, John Dennis
Anoka Sr HS; Anoka, MN (25%-851) Rptr, Sch P; Ski C; Mgr, Soccer; JV, Tnns; *Sci.*

KUENZI, Lynette Kay
Bern HS; Bern, KS (3-22) A Cap Choir; Band; Chor; Ensm; Pres, 4H; Madrigal; NHS; Sch P; Secy, SC; Bkbl; Alg A; Bio A; COM; 4H A; Math A; Type A; Yth Fel; *Washburn U; Bus.*

KUERBITZ, Ronald Jay
H H Dow HS; Midland, MI (10%-400) Band; Orch; JV, Tr; *Psych.*

KUES, Charles Edward Jr
W Carteret HS; Morehead City, NC; Band; Chor; Madrigal; Span C; Church Choir & Band; Band Serv, Percussion Ldr, A's; Chor, Pep Band, Stage Band, A's; *E Carolina U; Mus.*

KUESTER, Karen Kay
Belleville Township HS W; Belleville, IL (1-680) VP, Band; NHS; Orch; ARC; Citz A; Hon Prog; ARC A; St Scholar; Val; VFW A; Ntl Sch Orch A; *Belleville Area Col; Pre-Sch Ed.*

KUETTNER, Mark Eugene
Henderson HS; Atlanta, GA (50%-477) Chor; Swim; *W Ga Col; Communications.*

KUHL, Bonnie Lou
Central Comm HS; Breese, IL (11-157) Type A; Home Ec A; PE A.

KUHL, Elisabeth Jean
Bellevue HS; Bellevue, MI (42-100) Rptr, Sch P; Ski C; Span C; *Kellogg Comm Col; Special Ed.*

KUHLE, Kassie Lu
Assumption Jr-Sr HS; Assumption, IL (9-49) Pres, Band; Drama; FHA; 4H; Rptr, SC; Thes; Tr; Swtht.

KUHLENBERG, Catherine Ella
Our Lady of Angels HS; Cincinnati, OH (51-132) ARC; Span C; Citz A; God & Country A; Opt A; ARC A.

KUHLMAN, Crystal Kay
Warrensburg HS; Warrensburg, MO (57-196) Thes; Hon Prog; Schol Achv A; Thespian Stars; *Central Mo St U; Theatre.*

KUHLMANN, Kathy Jayne
Luther HS; Onalaska, WI (28-77) Band; Chor; Drama; Madrigal; Orch; Rptr, Sch P; Bkbl; Tr; Interlochen Ntl Mus; *Dr Martin Luther Col; Elem Ed.*

KUHN, Jeffery Michael
Montpelier HS; Montpelier, OH (3-110) BS; Bsbl; JV, Bkbl; Cr-Ctry; Yth Fel; Acad Achv A; *Air Force Acad; Engr.*

KUHN, Karen Ann
Columbia Jr-Sr HS; Columbia, PA (5-143) Band; Fr C; Hmrm; Cpt, Mjrte; NHS; VP, SC; Pres, Soph Cl; Presidential Clrm; Hist Fair; Twirling As; Essay A; Spelling Bee; *Villanova Col; Pol Sci.*

KUHN, Karen Louise
New Haven HS; New Haven, MO (16-58) Tres, FHA; NHS; SC; Secy, Yth Fel; Pep Squad; Vlbl; Harvest Ball Qn; *SE Mo St U; Elem Ed.*

KUHN, Marlene May
Chief Sealth HS; Seattle, WA (50-450) Chor; Ensm; Pres, Hmrm; Rptr, Sch P; Hon Prog; JA A; Pres, Church Yth Group; Candystriping A; Pres, Distributive Ed; Cert of Apprc Perform at Expo '74; *Simpson Col; Christian Ed.*

KUHN, Michael Brett
Gainesville HS; Gainesville, TX; CYO; Hmrm; Key C; SC; Bsbl; Bkbl; Girls Bkbl Fav; *Cooke Co Col; Elec.*

KUHN, Nancy Ann
Celina Sr HS; Celina, OH (26-285) Ed, Ann; Fr C; FTA; NHS; Thes; *Wright St Col; Public Relations.*

KUHN, Paula Kay
Gainesville HS; Gainesville, TX (5-247) CYO; Secy, Drama; FHA; FTA; Rptr, 4H; NHS; VP, Spch C; Spch A; DECA Pub Spkg A; *N Tex St U; Psych.*

KUHN, Terri Lee
Brooke HS; Wellsburg, WV (16-482) A Cap Choir; Chem C; Chor; Ensm; FNA; Secy, Hmrm; Lat C; Madrigal; NHS; Secy, Tri-HiY; Chem A; Hon Prog; Math A; 3rd Pl, Ntl Math Test; WW; Camper o-t Wk; *Ohio Valley Hospital Sch of Nurs; Registered Nurs.*

KUHNEN, Donald Lee
Prophetstown HS; Prophetstown, IL (10-67) Chess C; Chor; NHS; Sch P; Var C; Co-Cpt, Bkbl; JV, Cr-Ctry; MVP, Golf; Yth Fel; Cl Off; *Augustana Col; Bus.*

KUHRT, Morris Gene
Phillips HS; Phillips, TX (12-41) Pres, A Cap Choir; Band; Chem C; Pres, Chor; Drama; Ensm; Hmrm; Madrigal; Sci C; Spch C; SC; Pres, SC; Pres, Jr Cl; Pres, Soph Cl; Bsbl; Cpt, Bkbl; Cpt, Ftbl; Golf; Sftbl; Swim; Tnns; Cpt, Tr; Rotary A; Most Talented; Best All Around; Amer Yth Symph & Chor; All Regional Baritone, 1st Chair; *Frank Phillips Jr Col; Mus.*

KUIPERS, Susan Marie
Holland HS; Holland, MI; Ann; Band; Mjrte; Var C; Tnns; Tr; Hon Prog; Vol, Hospital; Horizon; Gym.

KUKLER, Jerry Joseph
Shawsheen Valley Tech HS; Billerica, MA (8-400) Chess C; Swim; Wrest; JA A; MVP, Chess C; Pres, Yth Fel; *Bradford Col; Math.*

KUKUK, Lynn Allen
Perry HS; Perry, OK; Band; Chor; VP, FFA; 4H; 4H A; Pres, Church Yth Jr Farm Bureau Cert; Farmers Union Jr Ldr; *Northern Okla Jr Col; Agr.*

KULIE, Karen Linda
Lakeview HS; Battle Creek, MI (14-416) NHS; Ski C; Span C; Amer Leg A; JA A; Sci A; NML; WW; *Mich St U; Bus.*

KULIK, Mark Allen
Bremerhaven American HS; Bremerhaven, GERMANY (4-24) Soccer; COM; Math A; Sports A; Math.

KULIK, Todd Allen
Bremerhaven American HS; Bremerhaven, GER-MANY (4-24) Fin, Tr; COM; *United States Military Acad; Math.*

KUMLER, Kimberly Ann
Bellflower HS; Bellflower, IL (10-20) Band; Ensm; Span C; Secy, Sftbl; Type A; Amer Legion Auxilary; Library C; Secy, Vlbl; Band, Lib, Schol, Shorthand, A's.

KUMOR, Maureen Kaye
Perkins Co HS; Grant, NE (3-30) Band; CYO; Chor; Ensm; 4H; Sch Achieve Tm; JV, Bkbl; 4H A; Head Drum Mjrte; Pep C; Vlbl; Home Ec, St 4h, Aksarben, A's; *U of Nebr; Sci Ed.*

KUMPF, Charlotte Diane
Cloverdale HS; Cloverdale, IN (10-120) 4H; Sci C; Span C; VP, SC; Bkbl; Tr; JV Vlbl; Phys Ed Attitude A; *Phys Ed Teacher.*

KUMPF, Kathy Ann
Cloverdale HS; Cloverdale, IN (5-75) VP, Band; Ensm; 4H; NHS; Span C; Span NHS; Thes; Tr; 4H A; Most Studious; GAA Plaque; GAA Sweater; Band Sweater; *Oral Roberts U; Math.*

KUNCE, Kevin Gregory
Herrin HS; Herrin, IL (9-251) Band; Key C; NHS; Rptr, Sch P; Bsbl; Ftbl; Amer Leg A; St Scholar; *Sou Ill U; Acct.*

KUNIYOSHI, Keri Lynne
Sacramento Union Acad; Carmichael, CA (1-54) Band; Madrigal; NHS; *Pacific Union Col; Nurs.*

KUNKEL, Ralph Kyle
Haltom HS; Ft Worth, TX (10%-550) Chess C; Ger C; NHS; A-Ed, Sch P; Sftbl; Chor A; *Journ.*

KUNKEN, Darrell James
Greenview HS; Greenview, IL (5-27) Ann; Band; Chem C; 4H; Sch P; SC; VP, Sr Cl; Bsbl; DARGCA; 4H A; MLS; NEDT; Century Ldr A; *Lincoln Land Comm Col; Agr Bus.*

KUNKLER, Kathleen Marie
Hickman Mills HS; Kansas City, MO (131-578) Chor; SC; Var C; Pres, Soph Cl; Co-Cpt, Bkbl; Tnns; Tr; COM; Hon Prog; Yth Fel; VP, Pep C; *William Woods Col; Child Psych.*

KUNNEMANN, Kevin Eugene
Chase Co HS; Imperial, NE (32-68) Pres, FFA; Pres, 4H; Var C; Bkbl; Ftbl; Tr; 4H A; HCt; *U of Wyom; Pre-Vet.*

KUNNEN, Joyce Marie
Douglas Macarthur HS; Saginaw, MI (13-323) NHS; Orch; Hon Prog; St Scholar; Top 20, Cl; WW; *Blodgett Sch of Nurs; Nurs.*

KUNSMAN, Gary Wayne
Liberty HS; Bethlehem, PA (100-770) Band; VP, Ger C; Secy, JETS; Parl, Model UN; NHS; VP, Orch; Bsbl; Bkbl; Sftbl; *VPI; Chem Engr.*

KUNTZ, Donald William
John R Buchtel HS; Akron, OH (4-420) A Cap Choir; Drama; Lit Mag; Thes; COM; Opt A; VFW Orator Win; VofDEM; Yrbk.

KUNTZ, Mark Henry
Beaver Dam Sr HS; Beaver Dam, WI (9-360) Band; Secy, Demolay; Ensm; Order/Arrow; Span C; Ftbl; JV, Tr; Wrest; God & Country A; Order/Arrow A; *U of Minn; Art.*

KUNZ, Paul Edward
Permian HS; Odessa, TX; Band; Demolay; Orch; Rptr, Sch P; Bsbl; Opt A; Sci A; Stage Band; Yth, Inc; Band Outst Spirit A; Region & St Band Medalist; *Tex Tech U; Bus Adm.*

KUNZ, Rainer A
Loara HS; Anaheim, CA (35%-600) Biola Col; Psych.

KUNZ, Steve Tod
Wanamingo Pub Sch; Wanamingo, MN (4-40) Ann; MVP, Band; MVP, Chor; Drama; NHS; SC; Var C; VP, Sr Cl; Pres, Soph Cl; Bsbl; Cpt, Bkbl; Ftbl; Citz A; ARC A; Sci A; Outst Musician; *Winona St Col; Nurs.*

KUPFER, Rita
Sky View HS; Smithfield, UT (67-573) Ed, Ann; FHA; Citz A; Nom, Sterling Schol; Homemaking A; *Utah St U; Home Ec.*

KUROHARA, Margaret Lei
S Pasadena HS; South Pasadena, CA (10-350) Ann; Fr C; ARC; CSF; Hon Prog; Scorekeeper, Wrest; Secy & Tres, GSct; WW; *Smith Col; Pre-Law.*

KUROIWA, Rene Harue
Waialua HS; Waialua, HI (26-183) Band; Hmrm; InterAct C; Spch C; Q&S A; *U of Hawaii.*

KUROSAKI, Glenn Michio
Reseda HS; Reseda, CA (22-640) City Conf; Hmrm; Pres, InterAct C; Pres, SC; Pres, Sr Cl; VP, Jr Cl; Tnns; CSF; Cl Fav; Elk A; Hon Prog; Opt A; 'A' Stu, Photography, A's; *Occidental Col; Psych.*

KUROWSKI, Christine Marie
Riverside Jr-Sr HS; Taylor, PA (5-195) Band; Chor; Tres, FTA; Hmrm; Co-Ch, NHS; Orch; Co-Ed, Sch P; Span C; COM; Hon Prog; JA A; NMS; NEDT; WW; *Marywood Col; Bus Adm.*

KURSCHNER, Danelle Jean
West HS; Green Bay, WI (200-412) Band; Sftbl; Church Sftbl; *Fox Valley Tech Inst; Child Care.*

KURTH, Barbara Joan
Lakeside HS; Atlanta, GA (80-400) Ger C; Lat C; Hon Prog; *Ga St U; Psych.*

KURTZ, Georgann
E Richland HS; Olney, IL (23-249) Ann; Band; Fr C; SC; Pow Wow Court; Intrntl Championship Bible Quiz Tm; *Greenville Col; Fr.*

KURTZ, John Andrew
Cumberland Valley HS; Mechanicsburg, PA (12-585) Pres, Demolay; Pres, Lat C; NHS; COM; Hon Prog; Rotary A; Demolay A; *Juniata Col; Pre-Dentistry.*

KURTZ, Kathi Jean
Mission San Jose HS; Fremont, CA (190-500) A Cap Choir; Chor; Drama; Ensm; Hmrm; Madrigal; Secy, Soph Cl; Lead Roles, HS Mus; Mus Director, Vacation Bible Sch; Actress-Tech, Ohlone Col Reper Thtr; *San Jose Bible Col; Psych.*

KURTZE, Sandra Lee
Pelham Mem HS; Pelham, NY; A Cap Choir; Chor; Drama; Ensm; Madrigal; Span NHS; *Math.*

KURTZWEG, Gail Renee
St James HS; St James, MN; Chor; MVP, Golf; Swim; Tr; Saintettes.

KURZ, Cathy Jeanne
Pekin Comm HS; Pekin, IL (22-807) Span NHS; Hist A; *Judson Baptist Col; Elem Ed.*

KUSCHEL, Kim Jo
Clintonville Sr HS; Clintonville, WI; Drama; Fr C; Tr; Pres A; Vlbl; *U of Wisc; Nurs.*

KUSCHEL, Mark Emanuel
Forest Hill HS; W Palm Beach, FL (25%-385) Band; Chor; Ensm; InterClub Coun; Pres, Sr Cl; Ftbl; Wrest; *Emory U; Dentistry.*

KUSCHMANN, Bernd
Klamath Union HS; Klamath Falls, OR; A Cap Choir; Community Yth Symph; Ger C; Bkbl; Cr-Ctry; Tr; Kiwanis A; Luther Leg; European Hndball Tm; Yth for Undrstndng Stu Exchange; Full Yr Stu Exchange Prog; Gold Plaque, Dutch-Ger Hiking.

KUSEK, Theresa Ann
Mercy HS; Albany, NY (5-115) Drama; InterAct C; Lat C; Hon Prog; *Bus Adm.*

KUSH, Paul
Neshaminy Maple Point HS; Langhorne, PA (3-415) NHS; Var C; MVP, Bkbl; Cr-Ctry; Tr.

KUSHTA, Susan Marie
Kelly HS; Chicago, IL (10-611) Band; Span NHS; Citz A; Type A; Lib Guild; Band A; Eng A; Kelly Hon Soc; *U of Ill; Vet Med.*

KUSZMAUL, Joel Scott
E Detroit HS; E Detroit, MI (1-950) Band; Chor; Dbte Tm; Co-Ed, Sch P; Sftbl; Spch A; Debate A; Pres, Yth Group; Sr Patrol Ldr, BSct.

KUTILEK, Janice Marie
Holdrege HS; Holdrege, NE; Chldr; Chor; VP, FBLA; Sch P; Sftbl; Tr; Type A; *Kearney Col; Bus.*

KUTSCHBACH, Carroll Lynn
New Caney HS; Porter, TX; Band; Bus C; VP, 4H; Math C; NHS; Sch P; Sci C; 4H A; *Tex A&M U; Bus.*

KUTZ, Ruth Lynn
Thomas Kelly HS; Chicago, IL (15-689) Band; Drama; Fr C; Hmrm; Key C; Math C; NHS; Sch P; Sci C; SC; Bkbl; Hon Prog; Journ A; Kiwanis A; Math A; NEDT; Spch A; Val; GAA; *Valparaiso U; Mus.*

KUUTTILA, Eric Kenneth
Bentley HS; Livonia, MI (25%-700) Band; Ski C; Hon Prog; *U of Mich; Engr.*

KUYKENDALL, Barbara Ann
Saks HS; Anniston, AL (8-205) Secy, FHA; FTA; NHS; Alg A; ARC A; Phys Ed A; *Samford U; Nurs.*

KUYKENDALL, Charles Fox
Putnam City; Oklahoma City, OK (70-900) BS; Dbte Tm; NFL; NHS; Thes; Hon Prog; *U of Okla; Law.*

KUYKENDALL, Judy Lynn
Lane Tech HS; Chicago, IL (550-1300) Band; *Faith Baptist Bible Col; Christian Ed.*

KUYKENDALL, Kevin Kent
Harlingen HS; Harlingen, TX; Mgr, Ftbl; Mgr, Tr.

KUZERA, Kelly Anne
Osborn HS; Detroit, MI; Chor; Cpt, Bkbl; Sftbl; Citz A; Pres A; Vlbl; *Med.*

KUZICHEV, Benjamin
John Marshall HS; Los Angeles, CA; Cr-Ctry; Mgr, Tr; VICA; *Los Angeles City Col; Fire Sci.*

KUZMIN, Kimberly Ann
Youngsville HS; Youngsville, PA (2-140) Chor; Secy, Fr C; Tr; Colorguard; Schols; *Specialized Teaching.*

KVAMME, Berta
Mabel-Canton HS; Mabel, MN (1-60) Band; Ensm; COM; Spch A; Top Hon; *St Olaf Col; Med.*

KVASNICKA, Nancy Joanne
Loyola HS; Mankato, MN (3-72) Ann; Chldr; Chor; Dbte Tm; GS; NFL; NHS; Sch P; VP, Sr Cl; Sftbl; HQn; MLS; *Col of St Thomas; Mus.*

KVETON, Cynthia Marie
St Elizabeth Acad; St Louis, MO (10-125) Chor; Lat C; NHS; Rptr, Sch P; Pres, SC; Cpt, Sftbl; COM; Chem A; Citz A; Hon Prog; WW; WW in Mus; *Washington U; Chem.*

KVIGNE, Anne Renee
N Crawford HS; Gays Mills, WI (5-72) VP, Band; Chldr; Chor; Ensm; FHA; GS; S-T, 4H; Madrigal; Pres, Math C; Secy, NHS; SC; COM; 4H A; HCt; Co Dairy Qn; Pres, Church Yth; WW; *U of Wis; Nurs.*

KWASINSKI, James Philip
W P Dainel HS; New Albany, MS; Bkbl; Tnns; St Champs, Bkbl.

KWASINSKI, Paul James
W P Daniel HS; New Albany, MS; Band; Spch C; Bkbl; Golf; Sci A; Eagle Sct.

KWAST, Kathy Leah
La Mirada HS; LaMirada, CA; Bio A; Phys Ed A; *Biola Col; Missions.*

KWIATKOWSKI, Josephine Ann
Riverside HS; Taylor, PA (2-180) Cpt, Band; CYO; Pres, Chor; Pres, NHS; Sch Achieve Tm; Sodality; SC; Tr; B Crocker A; COM; Hon Prog; NMS; NEDT; Spojnia Princess; Mayor's Prayer Breakfast; WW; *U of Scranton;; Bus Adm.*

KWOCHKO, Shirley Marie
J M Coughlin HS; Wilkes-Barre, PA (37-404) NHS; JV, Bkbl; Hockey; Mgr, Sftbl; Red & Blue C; Coughlin Pep C; VICA; *Luzerne Co Comm Col; Fashion Buying & Merchandising.*

KWOK, Daniel
Hollywood HS; Hollywood, CA; InterAct C; CSF; Camerights; *U of Sou Calif; Archt.*

KWON, Carolyn Sunye
Clarkstown Sr HS N; New City, NY;

KWONG, Lenelle Lon
Sacramento Ctry Day Sch; Sacramento, CA (1-14) A Cap Choir; Ann; Chor; Cum Laude Soc; Drama; Ch, Fr C; Hmrm; VP, Lat C; A-Ed, Lit Mag; Ch, Math C; Sch Achieve Tm; Rptr, Sch P; Ch, Sci C; Ski C; SC; Alg A; Aux Lat; Bank Of Amer A; CSF; COM; Citz A; Hon Prog; Magna Cum Laude; Math A; Most Out; Opt A; Sci A; Val; Yth Fel; Secy, Fr C; Cpt, Sailing Tm; Vlbl; Hospital Vol; Ski; Schol Win; HR; Tutor; Stu Activities A; NML; Cpt, Bowl Tm; *Brown U; Chem.*

KWONG, Robert Neal
John Marshall HS; Los Angeles, CA (75-750) Lat C; Lat NHS; Model UN; NFL; Pol Sci C; Spch C; World Affairs C; JV, Bkbl; Math A; Most Out; Opt A; Spch A; Young Author's Conf A; *Stanford U; Law.*

KYES, Vicki Lynn
Gull Lake HS; Richland, MI (43-248) Band; Drama; FTA; Span C; Spch C; JA A; NMS; 1st Cl, GSct; Pres, Bible C; Tres, Yth; Pianist, Tn Choir; *Bob Jones U; Elem Ed.*

KYLANDER, Janet Ellen
Tuscola Comm HS; Tuscola, IL (10-118) Ann; Band; Chor; Fr C; NHS; Rainbow; *U of Ill.*

KYLLO, Stanley John
Ingrahan HS; Seattle, WA; Rptr, Sch P; Swim; *Shoreline Comm Col; Archt.*

KYLLONEN, Kristie Kay
Cedar Cliff HS; Camp Hill, PA; Bus C; Chor; Bkbl; *CBC Bible Col; Bus.*

KYZER, Lisa Marie
Wilbur D Mills HS; Little Rock, AR (1-326) A Cap Choir; BC; Chor; Ensm; FHA; Madrigal; NHS; Span C; Arch; Tnns; Hon Prog; Sci A; *U of Ark; Sci.*

L

L'ROY, Juliana
McKinney HS; McKinney, TX (10-250) A Cap Choir; Fr C; Tnns; Hon Prog; *N Tex St U; Med.*

LAABES, Denise Teresa
Nuestra Senora de la Merced HS; Hato Rey, PR (4-92) Pres, Chem C; Chess C; Hmrm; Secy, Math C; VP, Model UN; Phys C; Pres, Pol Sci C; Secy, Sci C; Pres, Span C; Spch C; Alg A; Bio A; COM; Chem A; Hist A; Hon Prog; Math A; MLS; Most Out; Phy A; Sci A; Star Student; *Agr.*

LAABS, Cynthia Kay
Oshkosh N HS; Oshkosh, WI (27-377) A Cap Choir; VP, Drama; Pres, Key C; Madrigal; Kiwanis A; *U of Ill; Deaf Ed.*

LaBARRE, William Roof
All Saints Episcopal Sch; Vicksburg, MS (5-22) Ann; BC; BS; Soccer; Math A; MVP, Badminton; Vlbl; *U of Miss; Law.*

LABAT, Rose Marie
Marillac HS; Northfield, IL (26-221) Chor; A-Ed, Sch P; St Scholar; Eng C; Teacher Aide A; WW; *Purdue U; Acct.*

LaBAUVE, Lance Miguel
Antilles HS; Fort Buchanan, PR (7-124) F-Ed, Ann; Chess C; Chor; Hmrm; Secy, Key C; Tres, NHS; Co-Ed, Sch P; DAHSS.

LaBELLE, Dean Christian
Zion Benton Township HS; Zion, IL (1-450) Chor; Drama; Ger C; NHS; VP, Jr Cl; Bsbl; JV, Ftbl; Alg A; Amer Leg A; Citz A; Hon Prog; Math A; NEDT; Pres A; Boy A; Yr; Prom Court; *Math.*

LaBELLE, Marla Joy
Zion Benton HS; Zion, IL (10%-450) Co-Cpt, Chldr; Chor; Drama; Ger C; Ski C; SC; Tr; HCt; Pres A; S-T, Fresh Cl; Church Yth Group; Gym C; *Nurs.*

LaBERGE, Lise
College De Ste Anne De La Pocatiere; La Pocatiere, CANADA (2-28) CYO; Vlbl; *Universite Laval; Med.*

LaBINE, Robin Lee
Lutheran HS E; Harper Woods, MI (99-132) A Cap Choir; Hmrm; Sch P; SC; Var C; Co-Cpt, Vlbl; *Concordia Col; Ed.*

LABIOSA, Ana Judith
Colegio Puertorriqueno de Ninos; Rio Piedras, PR (5-48) Ann; Chor; NHS; Sch P; SC; Tres, Sr Cl; COM; Hon Prog; *Bus.*

LaBONTE, Monique Dolores
Acad o-t Holy Family; Baltic, CT (9-26) Chor; Drama; 4H; VP, SC; Bkbl; Sftbl; Tr; Mus A; *Drama A; Phys Therapy.*

LABOY, Frank Eric
Colegio San Antonio Abad; Humacao, PR (1-72) Chem C; Math C; ARC; Rptr, Sch P; JV, Tnns; Chem A; Historian, NHS; Essay Contest; *Yale Col; Med.*

LaBRANCHE, Meredith L
Dunbar Voc HS; Chicago, IL (192-670) Band; Chor; SC; Var C; Bsbl; Bkbl; Ftbl; Tnns; *Tuskege Inst.*

LaBREACHT, Nancy Louise
Chester HS; Chester, IL (30-97) Ann; Band; Chor; Dbte Tm; Drama; FHA; FTA; Hmrm; Spch C; SC; Spch A; Arion A; *Sou Ill U; Theatre.*

LaBUDA, Karen Jean
Kelly HS; Chicago, IL (11-500) Chor; Drama; NHS; Rptr, Sch P; Span NHS; Tnns; Journ A; Q&S A; Eng A.

LaCAZE, Donnis Karen
Hicks HS; Hicks, LA; Cpt, Chldr; Chor; Secy, FHA; 4H; Lit Ral; Sftbl; Beauty; Cl Fav; Hist A; HCt; MLS; Miss Hicks HS; Outst FHA; *Northwestern St U; Elem Ed.*

LACEY, Crystal Lynette
Lutheran HS W; Detroit, MI; Chor; VP, Highstepper; *Nurs.*

LACEY, Darrell
Canton Pub HS; Canton, MS (13-222) Math C; Mu Alpha Theta; NHS; Sci C; SC; Alg A; Hon Prog; NEDT; *U of Miss; Journ.*

LACEY, James Joseph
S Park Sr HS; Library, PA (1-163) BS; CYO; FNA; S-T, NHS; Co-Ch, ARC; Rptr, Sch P; COM; Chem A; Hon Prog; Journ A; MLS; ARC A; Val; *Penn St U; Bio-Chem.*

LACH, Norbert Allen
Thomas Kelly HS; Chicago, IL (6-485) Band; MVP, Chess C; Math C; NHS; Span NHS; COM; Math A; Pres, Chess C; Band A; Vlbl; Stu Exec Bd A; Civic Service A; Lib A; *U of Ill; Engr.*

LACK, Laurie Ann
Canby Union HS; Canby, OR (80-350) Ann; Band; Drama; VP, 4H; Orch; Thes; Citz A; Home Ec A; *Western Bus Col; Secy.*

LACK, Pamela Janiece
Canby Union HS; Canby, OR (70-250) Ann; Drama; Span C; Thes.

LACKER, Donna Gene
McCluer N Sr HS; Florissant, MO (101-776) A Cap Choir; Hmrm; Madrigal; SC; COM.

LACKEY, Dean Ellis
Newton-Conover HS; Newton, NC; BC; Bkbl; Ftbl; Tnns; Beta C A; *NC St U; Phys Ed.*

LACKEY, Jill Lorraine
Holly Sr HS; Holly, MI (29-274) A Cap Choir; Ensm; Interlochen Ntl Mus; *Oakland Comm Col; Bus.*

LACKEY, Lee Anne
Concord HS; Concord, NC (22-235) Band; Hmrm; Math C; Monogram; Mu Alpha Theta; NHS; Bkbl; Co-Cpt, Vlbl; *U of NC; Acct.*

LACKEY, Melanie Corrine
Munford HS; Munford, AL (20%-86) Band; VP, BC; Drama; GS; Math C; Val; Most Intellectual; *Auburn U; Chem Engr.*

LACKEY, Robert Cordell
Oroville HS; Oroville, CA (43-220) BS; Cpt, Dbte Tm; FFA; Spch C; Pres, SC; Amer Leg A; Spch A; WW; *Point Loma Col; Ministry.*

LACKORE, Jenny Lynn
Bishop Union HS; Bishop, CA; Chor; Drama; 4H; Hmrm; Span C; Y-Tns; Amer Leg A; COM; 4H A; Hon Prog; Pres A; *Lumbleau Real Estate Col; Real Estate.*

LaCOST, Renee Louise
Eastridge HS; Kankakee, IL (10-235) Band; Community Yth Symph; Pres, Fr C; NHS; Ntl Yth Conf; Orch; Rptr, Sch P; NMS; St Scholar; Match Points; Church Choir; Girl's Friendly Soc; Civil Air Patrol; *U of Ill; Biol.*

LACOUR, Anastasia Lair
St Matthew HS; Melrose, LA (11-47) VP, Chldr; Secy, 4H; Tres, Sr Cl; Secy, Jr Cl; Tres, Soph Cl; COM; 4H A; HCt; Hon Prog; Sci A; Swtht; VP, Secy & Tres, A Cappella Choir; Tres & S-T, Hmrm Rep; Choir A; Pres & Cpt, Soccer; Vlbl A; VP & Co-Cpt, Sftbl; *Northwestern St U; Bus Adm.*

LaCOUR, Donna Marie
Chippewa Falls Sr HS; Chippewa Falls, WI (50-300) NHS; Span C; Hon Prog; Athena; Pep C.

LaCOUR, Felecia Eloise
W Aurora HS; Aurora, IL; HCt; Black Stu Assn; *Chicago Inst; Mus.*

LaCOUR, Sherri Ann
St Matthew HS; Melrose, LA; CYO; FBLA; FHA; Hon Prog; Sal; Type A; *Northwestern U; Bus.*

LACY, Alicia Dianne
Kountze HS; Kountze, TX; FHA; Math C; Var C; Bkbl; Citz A; DARGCA; Ntl Conf Chr & Jews; Bkbl As; *U of Houston; Computer Operator.*

LACY, Debra Crystal
Phineas Banning HS; Wilmington, CA (15%-700) FTA; Pres, Hmrm; ARC; Span C; Co-Cpt, Bsbl; Co-Cpt, Sftbl; MLS; GSct Ldr; House of Rep; *Calif St U; Med.*

LACY, Elaine
Notre Dame HS; Portsmouth, OH (46-63) Chor; 4H; Bus Mgr, Sch P; Span C; Swim; Tr; Bio A; COM; 4H A; Journ A; Q&S A.

LACY, Linda Sue
Ysleta HS; El Paso, TX (10%-800) Cpt, Chldr; NHS; Hon Prog; *Tex Christian U; Religion.*

LACY, Robert E
Castlemont HS; Oakland, CA; Citz A; Gov Honor Prog; Sci A; *Laney Col; Social Sci.*

LACY, Zipporiah Jean
Abraham Lincoln HS; San Francisco, CA (42-350) Tnns; Math A; Secy, Black Stu Union; Stu Advisory Committee; VP, Yth Choir; *San Francisco St U; Bus Adm.*

LADA, Kathryn Ann
Wellsboro Area Sr HS; Wellsboro, PA (32-210) Band; CYO; Cpt, Chldr; Chor; Drama; Ger C; Hmrm; NHS; Ski C; SC; Secy, Var C; Cr-Ctry; Cpt, Tr; Amer Leg A; VofDEM; 1st Stu Rep, Coun Recreation Comm; *Pa St U; Social Welfare.*

LADBURY, Laurie Kathleen
Arvada W HS; Arvada, CO; Band.

LADBURY, Raymond Llewellyn
Arvada W HS; Arvada, CO; Band; NHS; NMS; Frontiers of Sci Inst Schol; Hon Inst, Engr; *Phys Sci.*

LADD, Bruce Alan
Ft Hunt HS; Alexandria, VA (63-446) Chor; NHS; JV, Soccer; Hon Prog; 1st Pl, Sci Fair A; *Wheaton Col.*

LADD, David Richard
N Shore HS; W Palm Beach, FL (1-266) NHS; Var C; Cr-Ctry; JV, Ftbl; Tr; Alg A; Bio A; COM; Hist A; Math A; Sci A; *Sci.*

LADD, Ellen Louise
Montabella HS; Edmore, MI; Chess C; Drama; GS; NHS; Ski C; Pres, Span C; Secy, SC; JV, Tr; NEDT; VofDEM; *U of Mich; Chem.*

LADD, Ernest Frank
Starmount HS; Boonville, NC (3-150) Ann; Band; Chess C; Chor; Drama; Ensm; FFA; 4H; Math C; Monogram; Mu Alpha Theta; NHS; Sch P; Pres, Sr Cl; Bkbl; Fin, Ftbl; Tnns; Summa Cum Laude; Jr Marshall; High Hon Graduate; SDAHSS; WW; Master Mus; *NC St U; Pre-Med.*

LADD, Terri Sue
SE HS; Oklahoma City, OK (4-250) A Cap Choir; A-Ed, Ann; Secy, Chor; Golf; Amer Leg A; COM; HCt; Tres, Pep C; All St Choir; Piano Achv; *Okla U; Journ.*

LADD, Timothy Edwin
Hall Sr HS; Little Rock, AR (24-434) Co-Ch, A Cap Choir; AFS; Band; BC; Pres, Bus C; City Conf; Fr C; Pres, FBLA; NHS; VP, Pol Sci C; COM; Citz A; Hist A; Hon Prog; JA A; Most Out; NEDT; Star Student; Type A; Sup, Piano, Ntl Fed of Music; Sup, Ntl Guild of Piano Teachers; 1st Pl, St FBLA Bus Communication; Bus Communications Achv; *Baylor U; Marketing.*

LADD, Virginia Carole
Emma Sansom HS; Gadsden, AL;

LADDIN, Michael Phillip
Pembroke Ctry Day Sch; Kansas City, MO (66%-60) AFS; Chess C; Ed, Sch P; Soccer; Journ A; Spch A; Ntl Schol Press Assn; 1st Grand A Sci Fair; NASA A Sci Fair; *Central Mo St U; Law Enforcement.*

LADDUSAW, Steve James
W Fargo HS; W Fargo, ND (53-187) Chor; St Stu Congress; Co-Cpt, Bsbl; COM; Yth Leg; *Moorhead St Col; Mus.*

LADESIC, Michelle Lynette
Turner HS; Kansas City, KS; Dbte Tm; Drama; Hmrm; ARC; Y-Tns; ARC A; Spch A; Type A; *Nurs.*

LADNER, Tonia Raythette
Chicago Voc HS; Chicago, IL (300-630) *Anderson Christian; Child Education.*

LADNER, Tracey Renee
Lindblom Tech; Chicago, IL (45-623) Chem C; NHS; SC; Tr; COM; Citz A; Hon Prog; Yth Fel; Emblem and Ltr, GAA; Ltr, Tr and Field; Lindblom Hon Soc; *U of Ill; Engr.*

LADYMAN, Susan LaVon
Rider HS; Wichita Falls, TX (25%-539) Crown & Scepter; FFA; Sftbl; FFA, Rodeo, A's; *Aviation.*

LAFARGE, Stephen Charles
Canby Union HS; Canby, OR (114-275) Chor; Drama; Thes; Industrial Arts A; *San Jose Col; Christian Ed.*

LaFAVER, Glenda Faye
Green City R-1 Sch; Green City, MO; Chldr; Rptr, FHA; Secy, 4H; 4H A; *NMSU.*

LaFEVER, Rebecca Joanne
Eastwood HS; El Paso, TX (10%-900) Band; Chor; VP, FHA; Pres, FTA; Sftbl; Tnns; Tr; Hon Prog; Sci A; Ntl Jr Hon Soc; Hist Fair A; Vlbl; Meritorous Service A; Tex Readers C; *Tex Tech U; Elem Ed.*

LAFFERTY, Roy Allen
William Tennent Sr HS; Warminster, PA; Band; Ftbl; Sftbl, Church.

LAGAREJOS, Lawrence John
Marist Brothers' HS; Pago Pago, AMERICAN SAMOA (1-50) Ann; Dbte Tm; Rptr, Sch P; Spch C; Ftbl; Bio A; COM; Hon Prog; Math A; Sci A; Martial Arts; *Drew U; Med.*

LAGAREJOS, Mark Gabriel
Marist Brothers' HS; Pago Pago, AMERICAN SAMOA (4-50) Alg A; COM; Hon Prog; Math A; Sci A; Martial Arts; *Drew U; Med.*

LAGENOEK, Brenda Jane
Merrillville HS; Merrillville, IN (10%-600) Band; Span C; Secy, SC; Sftbl; 4H A; Yth Fel; *Med.*

LAGENOEK, Joyce Ellen
Merrillville HS; Merrillville, IN (10%-600) Chor; Fr C; FTA; Hmrm; COM; Hon Prog; Opt A; Nisbova Mus; *Ill U; Spch Pathology.*

LAGESON, Wendy Lou
Maddock Pub Sch; Maddock, ND (9-28) Ann; Band; Chldr; Chor; Ed, Sch P; Pres, SC; Parl, FHA; HCt; I Dare You; Jr Chamber of Com A; WW; Jaycee's Schol; *Moorhead St U.*

LAGO, Brenton Jose
Portsmouth Cath HS; Portsmouth, VA; A Cap Choir; All Amer Yth; Chor; NHS; Span C; MVP, Swim; Alg A; Amer Leg A; Bio A; COM; Chem A; Citz A; Elk A; Gov Honor Prog; 4H A; Hist A; HKg; HQn; HCt; Hon Prog; Journ A; JA A; Lion A; Math A; Most Out; Ntl Cath Mus Ed Asn; Ntl Conf Chr & Jews; NMF; PTA A; Phy A; *U of Va; Psychiatry.*

LAGUANA, Liza E G
George Washington Sr HS; Mangilao, GUAM; Chldr; FNA; NHS; ARC; VP, SC; Citz A; Yth Leg; Cert of Appreciation; *San Jose U; Med.*

LA GUE, Jacqueline Lee
Analy Union HS; Sebastopol, CA; Band; Span C; CSF; Citz A; 4H A; MLS; Opt A; Spch A; Yth Fel; Fin, Mus A; Fin, Eng A; *Med.*

LaHAIE, Sheryl Marie
Cheboygan Area HS; Cheboygan, MI (28-227) 4H; NHS; 4H A.

LAHIKAINEN, Debbie Sue
Niles W Township HS; Skokie, IL (210-610) Swim; Hist A; Hon Prog; ARC A; Yth Fel; Sr Life Saving; *Art.*

LAHIKAINEN, Debra Sue
Niles Township Comm HS W; Skokie, IL (210-610) Hist A; Hon Prog; ARC A; Yth Fel; Bronze Key; *Art.*

LAHMAN, Mary Louise
E Knox HS; Howard, OH (21-80) Secy, Band; CYO; Pres, 4H; Tres, Jr Cl; 4H A; Off Helper; Tutoring; *Akron U; Elem Ed.*

LAHMON, Mary Louise
E Knox HS; Howard, OH (21-80) Secy, Band; CYO; Pres, 4H; Tres, Jr Cl; Bkbl; Ftbl; Sftbl; Off Help, Ath, Band, A's; *Akron U; Elem Ed.*

LAIBLE, Judy Lynn
Superior Sr HS; Superior, WI; A Cap Choir; Chor; Demolay; Drama; FBLA; Hmrm; F-Ed, Sch P; Secy, Ski C; SC; Tr; Citz A; Pres, Secy, Church Yth; Drama; Service A; Vocal A; Most Friendly; *Med.*

LAIDLAW, Paul Wayne
New London-Spicer HS; New London, MN (45-90) Pres, Church Yth Group; *N Central Bible Col; Ministerial.*

LAIL, Sam Dewitt Jr
Parkland HS; El Paso, TX (5-220) NHS; VP, Var C; Co-Ch, Sr Cl; Co-Cpt, Ftbl; Tr; Hist A; Hon Prog; WW; Ger Lang A; West Point Commission; Rice Summer Engr Prog; *W Point Acad; Engr.*

LAING, Roxanne Doreen
Bainbridge-Guilford Central Sch; Bainbridge, NY; Band; Chor; Orch; Yth Fel.

LAING, William Merion
Bainbridge-Guilford HS; Bainbridge, NY (15-70) Band; Fr C; InterAct C; NHS; Pres, Soph Cl; JV, Bsbl; Mgr, Bkbl; Ftbl; Golf; Yth Fel; Industrial Arts A; Courtesy A; *Law.*

LAIRD, Carl Lynn
Rockdale HS; Rockdale, TX; Band; Drama; Ensm; NHS; Sch P; Thes; 1st Pl, Chem Sci Fair; UYF; Navy Achv Cert; Band Coun; Regeneration Singers.

LAIRD, Debra Ann
Oakdale HS; Oakdale, LA; *Bolton Beauty Col; Beautician.*

LAIRD, Paul Frederick
Eastern HS; Middletown, KY (52-188) Ger C; Tres, Key C; F-Ed, Sch P; Ftbl; Soccer; Cl Fav; *Calif St Poly Inst; Archt.*

LAIRD, Sharon Kay
Lubbock Christian HS; Lubbock, TX (11-54) Band; Chor; NHS; Band Ltr; *Lubbock Christian Col; Elem Ed.*

LAIRD, Shrei L
Northmont HS; Clayton, OH (20%-485) A Cap Choir; Chor; Drama; Hmrm; SC; Hon Prog; Spch A; *Kettering Col of Med Arts; Med Off Asst.*

LAIRD, Tana Velisa
Kountze HS; Kountze, TX (5-92) Band; Chldr; Ensm; FHA; Tres, FTA; Mjrte; Sch P; Pres, SC; Cl Fav; HCt; Hon Prog; Drum Major; St Congress; *Lamar U; Data Processing.*

LAITAS, Rebecca Jane
Metamora Township HS; Metamora, IL (51-191) Chor; Fr C; NHS; Bkbl; Sftbl; Sadie Hawkins Qn; *Ill Central Col; Bus Adm.*

LAJEUNESSE, Pierre
College Ste-Anne De La Pocatiere; La Pocatiere, CANADA (2-30) Bsbl; Hockey; Tnns; Vlbl; *Sci.*

LAKE, James David
Pleasant Grove HS; Pleasant Grove, AL (3-150) Pres, Chem C; NHS; Pres, Phys C; MLS; NEDT; Outst Stu A, Am Inst of Indust Engr; *Auburn U; Elec Engr.*

LAKE, Jay Allen
Pender HS; Pender, NE (54-62) Band; Chor; Drama; Madrigal; Bsbl; Golf; Swim; Tnns; *Bus Adm.*

LAKE, Peter Stevenson
Russell HS; Russell, KY; BC; HiY; Hmrm; Span C; SC; Ftbl; Swim; Tr; Hon Prog; Sal; FCA.

LAKE, Sheryl Ann
Thornapple Kelloggs HS; Middleville, MI; FTA; NFL; Sci A; Spch A; *Col of William and Mary; Special Ed.*

LAKE, Thomas David
Bridgeton HS; Bridgeton, NJ; Pres, Hmrm; Bsbl; Cpt, Ftbl; Golf; Wrest; Sci A; Sci A Ribbon Excellent; FCA; *Med.*

LAKIN, Jack Randall
Fulton HS; Knoxville, TN; Chor; SC; Var C; Pres, Soph Cl; Ftbl; Tr; COM; ARC A; Swtht.

LAKY, Nancy Sue
Proviso W HS; Hillside, IL (300-900) Band; Orch; Swim; *Taylor U; Psych.*

LALEY, Steven Lawrence
Tuscola Comm HS; Tuscola, IL (27-118) Ann; CYO; Fr C; 4H; Monogram; Sch P; Sci C; Bsbl; Ftbl; Tr; HCt; I Dare You; *U of Ill; Liberal Arts.*

LALIMO, Hermi
Marshall Island HS; Majuro, MARSHALL ISLANDS (65-103) Tres, Jr Cl; Star Student; Yth Fel; *Arizona Col; Home Ec.*

LALLY, Joseph Michael
St Peters Prep Sch; Jersey City, NJ (4-260) Ann; Dbte Tm; Drama; NHS; Ed, Sch P; Ski C; SC; Cpt, Golf; Swim; Cpt, Tnns; Hon Prog; Journ A; NMS; NEDT.

LA LONDE, Beth Anne
Mt Rainier HS; Des Moines, WA (23-425) Band; Dbte Tm; FBLA; NFL; VP, NHS; Swim; Spch A; 1st Cl GSct; *Seattle Pacific U; Ed.*

LAM, Lily Bo Lien
McKinley HS; Honolulu, HI (70-850) Fr C; S-T, FBLA; NHS; Span C; COM; *U of Hawaii; Nurs.*

LAMAINE, Nicholas Andrew III
Princess Anne HS; Va Beach, VA; Order/Arrow; Outst Tnns Player.

LAMANCUSA, Lisa Rose
W Branch Local HS; Beloit, OH (23-240) Band; Tres, FHA; 4H; NHS; Wrest; MLS; St Off, FHA; Alt, GS; Wrest Statistician; WW; *Ohio St U; Home Ec.*

LAMB, Ann Rebecca
Mercy HS; Albany, NY (8-135) Chor; Rptr, Sch P; Sftbl; Journ A; K of C A; NEDT; Guitar Group; Editorial Board, Sch Paper; *Motion Picture.*

LAMB, Barbara Lynn
Wadley HS; Wadley, GA; Chldr; Mjrte; Cpt, Bkbl; COM; Cl Fav; WW.

LAMB, Barbara Rose
Franklin Co HS; Winchester, TN; S-T, CYO; Hmrm; Span C; Tnns; *Human Service.*

LAMB, Charla Rose
Shawnee HS; Shawnee, OK; FBLA; Pres, FHA; Outst Homemaker A; *Seminole Jr Col; Computer Programming.*

LAMB, Diane Lucille
Oakley HS; Oakley, KS (10-70) Chem C; Chor; Drama; FHA; Semi-Fin, GS; Fin, Jr Miss Pagent; Math C; NHS; Spch C; Pres, SC; Pres, Jr Cl; Swim; COM; Hist A; Spch A; Pres, Pep C; Talent & Art As; Cpt, Drill Tm; Phys Fitness A; Scholastic A; *Fort Hays St U; Fashion Merchandising.*

LAMB, Earnest Larone
Wilbur D Mills HS; Little Rock, AR (10-310) Ann; Band; Pres, BC; BS; Community Yth Symph; Inter-Club Coun; Pres, Span C; SC; MLS; Most Out; Span A; *Mus.*

LAMB, Horace Lee
Suffolk HS; Suffolk, VA (3-118) Semi-Fin, BS; Monogram; NHS; Bsbl; *Va Tech U; Acct.*

LAMB, James Manchester
J H Rose HS; Greenville, NC; Band; Order/Arrow; Stage Band; *NC St U; Engr.*

LAMB, Julie Denise
Balaton HS; Balaton, MN (1-30) Ed, Ann; Chor; FHA; Sch P; Spch C; Mgr, Bkbl; B Crocker A; Regent Schol; Type A; Alt, GS; 3 M Creativity A; PPG Indust Comm Commended Stu; *Augustana Col; Nurs.*

LAMB, Linda Ann
Atlanta HS; Atlanta, TX; Band; Ensm; Fr C; FBLA; FHA; Secy, FTA; Tres, 4H; Mjrte; Sci C; 4H A; CAR; *La Tech U; Home Ec.*

LAMB, Melissa Suzanne
Grove HS; Grove, OK (20-100) Band; Secy, BC; Drama; FBLA; Cpt, Mjrte; Rainbow; Spch C; Tr; HCt; Hon Prog; Type A; *Okla Baptist U; Nurs Anesthetist.*

LAMB, Michael Wayne
Truman HS; Independence, MO; Var C; JV, Ftbl; JV, Tr; Pres, Church Sr High Yth Group; Nom, Good Citz A.

LAMB, Rebecca Jeanne
Lafayette HS; Lafayette, LA (25%-560) Chldr; Chor; Drama; Fr C; 4H; Spch C; Arch; Sftbl; Tnns; Vlbl; S-T, VICA C; Cosmetology License; *U Southwestern La; Elem Ed.*

LAMB, Steven Matthew
Franklin HS; Franklin, OH; Bkbl; Ftbl; Tnns; *Cincinnati Tech Col; Auto Mech.*

LAMB, Wayne Vincent
Parkway Prog Beta HS; Philadelphia, PA; Co-Cpt, Bkbl; *Widener Col; Bus Adm.*

LAMBDEN, Bonnie Lynn
Seaford Sr HS; Seaford, DE (40-255) VP, Band; Bus C; FBLA; Ger C; Orch; ARC; F-Ed, Sch P; Semi-Fin, Bkbl; Cpt, Sftbl; ARC A; Ltr, MVP, Sftbl; Co Band; *Del Tech & Comm Col; Med Lab Tech.*

LAMBE, Beverly Carol
Marion Co HS; Lebanon, KY (1-324) Band; FHA; NHS; Sci C; Span C; Eng, Home Ec, Band, Hon Cert's; WW; *U of Ky; Med.*

LAMBE, Patricia Diane
Montabella HS; Edmore, MI (15-125) Ann; Band; Ensm; NHS; Span C; Drama Cl; *Central Mich U; Ed.*

LAMBERSON, David Scott
Port St Joe HS; Port St Joe, FL (6-120) A-Ed, Ann; Band; Mgr, Drama; Hmrm; Key C; Hon Prog.

LAMBERT, Alice Raynette
Science HS; Newark, NJ (10%-24) Band; Chor; 4H; Lat C; Orch; Sch P; SC; B Crocker A; Citz A; Hist A; Most Out; Sci A; Type A; Most Studious; Stu o-t Mon; *Douglass Col; Med.*

LAMBERT, Cavin Dale
Bennington HS; Bennington, KS (21-25) A Cap Choir; Band; Chor; Ensm; 4H; NHS; Orch; Var C; MVP, Bsbl; JV, Bkbl; Cr-Ctry; Cpt, Sftbl; Swim; Tnns; Cpt, Tr; 4H A; Yth Fel; FCA; *Chiropractics.*

LAMBERT, Cheryl Ann
Secaucus HS; Secaucus, NJ (13-187) Chldr; Chor; GS; Hmrm; Co-Ed, Sch P; Sci C; SC; S-T, Jr C; Hon Prog; Journ A; *Nurs.*

LAMBERT, Chuck Ervin
Monticello HS; Monticello, MS; BC; FFA; Bsbl; Ftbl; *U of Sou Miss; Acct.*

LAMBERT, Daniel Ray
C E Donart HS; Stillwater, OK (60-335) Drama; HiY; Hmrm; NFL; Spch C; Pres, SC; Thes; Tri-HiY; Cl Fav; DARGCA; Lion A; Most Out; Pres A; Spch A; Yth Leg; Presidential Clrm; Sr o-t Month; *Okla St U; Engr.*

LAMBERT, Janice Kay
New Monroe HS; Monroe, IA (15%-60) Ann; Band; Secy, Chor; FHA; Pres, Sci C; Secy, Jr Cl; Bkbl; Sftbl; Type A; Mus Pins Number 1; Shorthand Pin; Pom-Pon Girl; *Des Moines Area Comm Col; Developmental Disabilities.*

LAMBERT, Karla Kay
Lancaster Sr HS; Lancaster, WI (6-129) AFS; Band; Chor; Ensm; Pres, 4H; Model UN; NHS; Orch; Tres, Sr Cl; Bkbl; Tr; 4H A; Hon Prog; JA A; Vlbl; All-Conf Vlbl; *Phy Ed.*

LAMBERT, Lori Catherine
Stuarts Draft HS; Stuarts Draft, VA; FHA; NHS; Sch P; Sci C; Span C; Type A; *Nurs.*

LAMBERT, Mark Baxter
South Salem HS; Salem, OR (5%-400) Fr C; SC; MVP, Ftbl; Tr; MVP, Wrest; Soc Stu A; *USC; Marine Bio.*

LAMBERT, Patricia Leigh
Man HS; Man, WV (5-180) Chldr; Drama; GS; 4H; Hmrm; Key C; NHS; Span C; Pres, Span NHS; SC; COM; HCt; Type A; Drama, Principal's, Chldr, A's; *Marshall U; Early Childhood Ed.*

LAMBERT, Patty Faye
Aynor HS; Aynor, SC (15%-85) Secy, All Amer Yth; Co-Ed, Ann; Pres, BC; Fr C; VP, FHA; Secy, Sci C; Secy, SC; 4H A; Swtht; Mus A; *Coastal Carolina Col; Ed.*

LAMBERT, Raeanne
Ada HS; Ada, OK (1-217) Cpt, Band; VP, Chor; Ensm; Math C; Mu Alpha Theta; NHS; Cpt, Tnns; *Rice U; Med.*

LAMBERT, Robert Henry
Crestwood HS; Mountain Top, PA (130-288) Fr C; Yth Fel; Coun On Ministry; 22nd An Men's Phil Area Convocation; *Drew U; Law.*

LAMBERT, Vicky Jean
Seminole HS; Sanford, FL (10%-430) Anchor C; Ch, Chor; Ensm; InterClub Coun; Pres, Thes; MVP, Swim; Cl Fav; HCt; Opt A; Yth Leg; Chaplain, NHS; *Fla Sou Col; Drama.*

LAMBETH, Sonya Kaye
Flomaton HS; Flomaton, AL; Ann; Sch P; Bkbl.

LAMBIE, Lauren Kay
Fairview HS; Fairview Park, OH (38-278) A Cap Choir; AFS; Community Yth Symph; Secy, Drama; Ensm; Secy, Fr C; Hmrm; Model UN; Orch; Rptr, Sch P; Sci C; Thes; Pres, World Affairs; Sci A; 1st Cl GSct; U for Young Amer; Schol, Recognition, A's; *Pre-Law.*

LAMBERT, James Thomas
Smith Cotton HS; Sedalia, MO (225-340) Dbte Tm; Drama; Order/Arrow; Var C; Swim; JV, Wrest; Order/Arrow A.

LAMBRECHT, Andrew John
Whitnall HS; Greenfield, WI (1-260) Band; Chor; Math C; Golf; Math A; Band A; Choral A; *Med.*

LAMBRECHT, Beth Ann
Riverdale Sr HS; Port Byron, IL (9-140) GS; NHS; SC; VP, Jr Cl; Chamber of Comm A; HCt; St Scholar; 5% of Cl; Stu Board; *Lutheran Sch of Nurs; Nurs.*

LAMBRECHT, Frank Herbert
El Dorado R II HS; Eldorado Springs, MO; Sftbl; Radio Tech.

LAMBRIGHT, Kenneth Preston
La Puente HS; La Puente, CA (33-500) Band; Drama; Thes; *Mount Sanantonio Col; Hist.*

LAMBROS, Athanasia
Brooklyn Tech HS; Brooklyn, NY (147-1256) NHS; Ed, Sch P; Bkbl; Journ A; *Columbia U; Chem Engr.*

LAMBROS, Peter
Brooklyn Tech HS; Brooklyn, NY (300-1200) A Cap Choir; Band; Cpt, Bkbl; Soccer; Alg A; Chem A; Math A; Citation of Hon.

LAMELA, Cardona Demetrio J
Colegio San Antonio; Isabela, PR (1-46) Secy, Hmrm; Bkbl; Tr; Vlbl; Hon Prog; Magna Cum Laude; *U of Puerto Rico; Architecture.*

LAMENDOLA, Corey Jo
Batavia Sr HS; Batavia, IL (2-224) VP, Lat C; Hon Prog; St Lat Contest; *Home Ec.*

LAMKIN, Linda Landeros
Fremont HS; Sunnyvale, CA (1-618) A Cap Choir; Band; Chor; Community Yth Symph; Dbte Tm; Ensm; NFL; NHS; Orch; Spch C; JV, Bkbl; Swim; JV, Tr; CSF; Opt A; Co Hon Bands; NCTE Essay Contest Nom; Sup Rating, Chea Solo & Ensm Fest.

LAMLE, Juanita Dawn
Aline-Cleo HS; Aline, OK (3-24) Chldr; Chor; FHA; 4H; Sch P; SC; Bkbl; HCt; Hon Prog; Swtht; Gospelettes; *SW St Col; Nurs.*

LAMLE, Walter John
Aline-Cleo HS; Aline, OK (8-24) FFA; 4H; SC; Bsbl; Bkbl; 4H A; HCt; Yth Fel; FFA Livestock Showman; Chapter Farmer Degree; *SW St U; Agr.*

LAMON, Carolyn Gwen
Tallapoosa Acad; Dadeville, AL (5-34) Co-Ed, Ann; BC; Cpt, Chldr; Chor; Secy, FHA; 4H; Math C; Rptr, Jr Cl; 4H A; *U of Ala.*

LAMON, Douglas Edward
Fairfield HS; Fairfield, AL; Ann; Band; Chor; Key C; Sci C; *Auburn U; Phar.*

LAMON, Frederick Mancil III
Memphis Prep HS; Memphis, TN (30-100) HiY; Order/Arrow; Var C; Ftbl; God & Country A; Order/Arrow A; Pres, Yth Fel; Eagle Sct; Choir 0280002419c; *Miss St U; Animal Sci.*

LAMONS, John Wallace
Greenville HS; Greeneville, TN (38-193) A-Ed, Ann; Chor; Lat C; F-Ed, Sch P; Ftbl; Golf; Tnns; *Clemson U; Pre-Professional Health.*

LAMONT, Melissa Dee
Seaford Sr HS; Seaford, DE; Chor; 3rd Pl, Singing Advet-Zone Contest; *Secy.*

LAMONT, Michelle Dawn
Seaford Sr HS; Seaford, DE (9-235) Pres, AFS; Co-Ed, Ann; Chor; NHS; A-Ed, Sch P; SC; Mgr, Sftbl; Citz A; PTG A; Miss Blue Jay Court; Jr Sci Symp; 2nd Pl, St Sci Bowl; *Salisbury St Col; Bus Adm.*

LAMOTHE, David Joseph
St John HS; Plaquemine, LA (10-65) Bus C; Fr C; Hmrm; VP, Key C; VP, NHS; Pres, SC; Bsbl; Bkbl; Co-Cpt, Ftbl; Hon Prog; All-Dist Hons Sports; Service A; Outst Fresh Ath; Highest Avg, Phys Ed; Finance.

LAMOTTE, John Hunter
Sarasota HS; Sarasota, FL;

LAMP'l, Joseph Edward
S Miami Sr HS; Miami, FL; Drama; Hmrm; Rptr, Sch P; SC; Thes; Tnns; *Northwestern U; Photo Journ.*

LAMPA, Loreen Ann
Lancaster HS; Lancaster, WI (2-139) NHS; Span C; Tr; Hon Prog; *Madison Tech Col; Animal Technician.*

LAMPE, Fay Colleen
Ritenour Sr HS; Overland, MO (90-850) Hmrm; Span C; Hon Prog; Cert of Recognition; Glee C; *Harding Col.*

LAMPERT, Ervin Eugene III
Salisbury HS; Salisbury, NC (45-283) AFS; F-Ed, Ann; BS; Fr C; Hmrm; Lat C; NHS; Hon Prog; Q&S A; *Wake Forest Col; Law.*

LAMPHEAR, Gail Ellen
Whitesboro Sr HS; Marcy, NY; Rptr, SC; Secy, MYF; Church Choir; *Syracuse U; Fine Arts.*

LAMPKIN, James Charles
Vigor HS; Prichard, AL (13-37) *Morehouse Col; Archt.*

LAMPKIN, Terri Ellen
Voorhees HS; Glen Gardner, NJ (22-281) Ann; Band; Chor; Drama; Lat C; SC; DARGCA; Hist A; Bible C.

LAMPLEY, Shannon Gaye
Marion Co HS; Lebanon, KY (14-324) Ann; BC; Chldr; Drama; Mu Alpha Theta; NHS; Sch P; Secy, Span C; Spch C; Thes; Bkbl; Tr; COM; Pres A; Tr, Band, A's; *Murray St U; Nurs.*

LAMPLEY, Shirley
Bullock Co HS; Union Springs, AL (7-150) VP, Chor; FBLA; Secy, FHA; FNA; 4H; Hmrm; Secy, NHS; Pres, Sci C; COM; Cl Fav; 4H A; Hon Prog; JA A; Pres A; Sci A; Spch A; Ldrship, Achv, Recognition, A's; *Tuskegee Inst; Nurs.*

**LAMPRECHT,
Richard Joseph Jr**
Long Beach Polytechnic Sr HS; Long Beach, CA (97-831) A Cap Choir; Drama; Mgr, Bkbl; Mgr, Cr-Ctry; Mgr, Tr; Amer Leg A; ROTC A.

**LAMSON-SCRIBNER,
Bradford Hamilton**
St James Sch; St James, MD (7-26) Cum Laude Soc; Ski C; Span C; SC; Var C; Cpt, Bsbl; Bkbl; JV, Ftbl; Soccer; Math A; Sci A; Lib Prize; *Lehigh Col; Engr.*

LANARI, Marilyn Jo
Barberton HS; Barberton, OH (33%-500) FTA; Hon Prog; Yth Fel; JNHS; UL Light Ltr; *Akron U; Bio.*

LANCASTER, Jessica Katherine
Ft Stockton HS; Ft Stockton, TX (25-289) A Cap Choir; Band; Ensm; Fin, Jr Miss Pagent; Orch; Rptr, Span C; Tres, SC; Mgr, Bkbl; Beauty; COM; Cl Fav; Pres A; Swtht; Vlbl; All St Ensm; WW; Regional & Area Band; All St Solo; *W Tex St U; Mus.*

LANCASTER, Kathy Ann
N Gwinnett HS; Suwanee, GA (10%-190) BC; Secy, Soph Cl; Sci A; Eng Cert.

LANCASTER, Lisa Jo
S H Blair HS; Hattiesburg, MS; Chor; Hmrm; Span C; Most Out; Outst Sr Sct A; Jr Historical Soc; 1st Cl Sct; All Top Off, GSct; Presidential Environmental A; Secy, Sr Planning Board; *U of Sou Miss; Child Care.*

LANCASTER, Ronald Gene
Normal Comm HS; Normal, IL; AFS; Ger C; Hmrm; SC; *Ill St U; Bus Law.*

LANCASTER, Sarah Elizabeth
E Mecklenburg HS; Charlotte, NC (13-640) Ed, Ann; InterAct C; NHS; Mgr, Bsbl; NMF; NMS; Marshal; WW; *Appalachian St U; Early Childhood Ed.*

LANCASTER, Thomas Spigner
E Mecklenburg HS; Charlotte, NC; Ger C; Order/ Arrow; Tr; JV, Wrest; Order/Arrow A; Bronze Palm, BSA; Eagle Sct; Brotherhood, OA.

LANCASTER, Yvonne
Celina HS; Celina, TN (6-63) Ann; BC; FBLA; FTA; 4H; Math C; S-T, Sr Cl; COM; HCt; Hon Prog; Math A; *Tenn Technological U; Sec Ed.*

LANCE, Debby Lynn
East HS; Akron, OH (81-400) Chor; Community Yth Symph; Bkbl; Sftbl; Sci A; Lib A; *Akron U.*

LANCTOT, Anthony Charles
Thomas Jefferson HS; San Antonio, TX (175-575) Chess C; Parl, Lat C; Math C; Tnns; Alg A; COM; Magna Cum Laude; Math A; Spch A; Summa Cum Laude; Knights o-t Altar A; Lat A; BScts; Jr Classical League A; Cert of Service; NRA; *St Mary's U; Acct.*

LAND, Joscetta Nanette
Ben Davis HS; Indianapolis, IN (15%-800) Band; Bus C; Chor; Tr; Hon Qn, Jobs Daughters.

LAND, Kathy Lynn
Madison HS; Richmond, KY; BC; *U of Ky.*

LAND, Laura Elizabeth
Greenfield HS; Greenfield, IL (6-90) Amer Leg A; Regional Tres, Amer Baptist Yth; *Mus.*

LAND, Lillian Ann
Tallapoosa Acad; Dadeville, AL (1-27) Ann; S-T, Band; Secy, BC; Chldr; Chor; GS; Co-Cpt, Mjrte; Rptr, Sr Cl; VP, Jr Cl; Beauty; Citz A; DARGCA; Hist A; NEDT; Val; Graduation Monitor; *Auburn U; Law.*

LAND, Mary Carolyn
T R Miller HS; Brewton, AL (25-100) Band; Lit Mag; Span C; *Troy St Col; Photography.*

LAND, Otto Kenneth
Woodland Christian HS; Phenix City, AL (3-20) Ann; BC; Var C; Tres, Sr Cl; Bkbl; Cr-Ctry; Ftbl; Tr; Citz A; Cl Fav; Sci A; Star Student; Ftbl A; Most Outst Christian Athlete; *Jefferson St Jr Col; Horticulture.*

LAND, Roderick Vincent
Independence HS; Charlotte, NC; Ann; Chess C; Tr; *Math.*

LAND, Vicki Dianne
Port St Joe HS; Port St Joe, FL (9-125) F-Ed, Ann; Chldr; Ensm; NHS; Chrch Organist Chrch Ensm & Chor; Jr Cl Rep, Pres Clrm For Yng Amer; *Pediatrics.*

LAND, Vicki Lee
Centerville Sr HS; Centerville, IN; Band; Y-Tns; Bkbl; Sftbl.

LANDBERG, Gary Leroy
Willows HS; Willows, CA (9-136) Drama; Rptr, Sch P; Chamber of Comm A; Math A; *Soc Sci.*

LANDECK, Daniel Scott
Towson Sr HS; Towson, MD; Order/Arrow; ARC; SC; Mgr, Bkbl; Co-Cpt, Swim; JA A; Order/Arrow A; ARC A; Yth Fel; WW; St & Ntl DECA Conventions; Life Sct; *Bus Adm.*

LANDERDAHL, Julia Marie
Bozeman HS; Bozeman, MT (41-364) AFS; Ger C; NFL; Spch C; Soccer; Spch A; Degree of Excel; St Soccer Champ; Jr NHS; *US Air Force Acad; Physics.*

LANDEROS, Lupe Guadalupe
Colo HS; Colo City, TX (5-115) Band; S-T, FHA; SC; Amer Leg A; Star Student; Type A; Acad A; *W Tex Col; Teaching.*

LANDEROS, Martha
Harlingen HS; Harlingen, TX; Chor; Pres, 4H; 4H A; Type A; Prose Reading A; Tex Reading C; A of Hon; PA; *Saint Mary's Col; Mus.*

LANDERS, Janet Louise
Mason City HS; Mason City, IL (8-74) Band; Drama; FHA; Span C; Arch; Sftbl; Tr; JA A; Stu Secy; Forensics C; *Social Work.*

LANDERS, Kaye Lynne
Ysleta HS; El Paso, TX; Band; Chess C; Chor; Drama; Ensm; FFA; Hmrm; Sci C; SC; MVP, Bkbl; MVP, Sftbl; Tr; Most Out; Yth Fel; Secy, Church Yth Coun; FFA A's; Ntl FFA Band; *Tex A&M U; Agr.*

LANDERS, Tangelia Denise
Hendersonville HS; Hendersonville, TN (156-438) A Cap Choir; Ann; Chor; FHA; Co-Ch, Hmrm; Madrigal; SC; 4H A; Sunday Sch A; *Trevecca Nazarene Col; Special Ed.*

LANDES, Craig Neal
Mossyrock HS; Mossyrock, WA (1-40) Band; Rptr, FBLA; Secy, FFA; 4H; NHS; F-Ed, Sch P; VP, Sci C; Bus Mgr, SC; JV, Bkbl; Mgr, Ftbl; Tr; 4H A; NEDT; Pres A; Most Improved, Band; *Math.*

LANDES, John Christopher
Baldwin Sch; New York, NY (6-35) Pres, SC; Pres, Sr Cl; Cpt, Bkbl; COM; Citz A; Hist A; Math A; Pres A; Bicentennial Schol; Schol Athlete; Eng Merit; Art Studio Merit; *Hist.*

LANDESS, Aliza Cheryl
Lebanon HS; Lebanon, VA (2%-185) Chor; Dbte Tm; Fr C; Model UN; NHS; Tnns; 4H A; Hist A; Pres, Acteens; Fr A; *Med.*

LANDFAIR, Craig Darryle
Ventura Sr HS; Ventura, CA (199-670) Band; Chess C; Chor; Dbte Tm; Drama; NFL; Orch; Sch P; Spch C; SC; Var C; Wrest; COM; Lion A; Most Out; Opt A; Pres A; Spch A; Speaker o-t Yr; Talent A; *Pepperdine U.*

LANDGRAF, Paul Brian
Kenmore E HS; Tonawanda, NY (2%-800) Drama; Fr C; NHS; Hon Prog; JA A; NMS; Regent Schol; *Banking.*

LANDHOLT, Julie Kathryn
Westfield Acad i Central Sch; Westfield, NY; Band; CYO; Chor; Model UN; Sch P; SC; *Theater Arts.*

LANDINGHAM, Toy Ann
Ethel HS; Ethel, MS (6-55) 4H; Parl, Tri-HiY; Secy, Sr Cl; *Alcorn St U; Nurs.*

LANDIS, Donald Earl
Abilene HS; Abilene, TX; Lat C; NHS; JV, Ftbl; *Abilene Christian U; Bible.*

LANDIS, Mark Alan
Piqua Central HS; Piqua, OH (10%-400) Band; Secy, Key C; Span C; Soccer; *Archt.*

LANDIS, Nancy Anne
Phoebus HS; Hampton, VA (15-365) AFS; Band; Community Yth Symph; Fr C; Key C; NHS; Orch; Tnns; Most Out; Yth Foundation; *Mus.*

LANDIS, Rebecca Sue
Mogadore HS; Mogadore, OH (5-103) Pres, Band; Pres, Chor; Drama; Pres, 4H; Madrigal; Pres, NHS; Bkbl; Sftbl; Alg A; 4H A; Hon Prog; Secy, Chor; Secy, 4-H C; Outst, Band; All Amer Band Hon; *U of Akron; Nurs.*

LANDIS, Ronald William
Abilene HS; Abilene, TX; Lat C; JV, Ftbl; *Abilene Christian U; Bible.*

LANDOLF, Ellen Margaret
Harold L Richards HS; Oak Lawn, IL (35-645) Chess C; Lit Mag; NHS; Sci C; Q&S A; *Iowa St U; Eng.*

LANDOLF, Phyllis Gene
H L Richards HS; Oak Lawn, IL (43-794) Chess C; Fr C; NHS; Secy, Sci C; B Crocker A; St Scholar; WW; *Iowa St U; Biol.*

LANDON, Debbie Sue
Abingdon HS; Abingdon, IL (14-91) A Cap Choir; VP, Band; Tres, NHS; Span C; DARGCA; HQn; SAA A; WW; Ch, Jr Church Deaconists; Co-tres, Church Choir; *E III U; Acct.*

LANDON, Donna Jean
Grove HS; Grove, OK (5-100) Secy, Band; Parl, BC; Drama; FBLA; GS; Secy, 4H; Spch C; Secy, Sr Cl; VP, Jr Cl; VP, Soph Cl; Cpt, Bkbl; Tr; Amer Leg A; 4H A; Hist A; HQn; Spch A; All Conf Bkbl; *NE Okla A&M U; Spch.*

LANDPHAIR, David Russell
Mormon Trail HS; Garden Grove, IA (20-45) Ann; Band; Pres, Chor; FFA; Rptr, 4H; Ftbl; Wrest; 4H A; Most Mus; Valentine Dance Court; Hon Choir, Band; *Iowa St U; Agr Engr.*

LANDRAU, Marybel Areli
Colegio Universit Sagrado Corazon; Santurce, PR (1-37) Drama; Alg A; COM; Chem A; Hist A; Hon Prog; Most Out; Poet A; Summa Cum Laude; *U of Puerto Rico; Med.*

LANDRESS, Joyce Colleen
Miami Springs Sr HS; Miami Springs, FL (10-800) Anchor C; Lat C; Span NHS; COM; Hon Prog; ARC A; Type A; *U of Fla; Phys Therapy.*

LANDRUM, Andranette Anetra
Central HS; Tulsa, OK; All Amer Yth; Hmrm; Phys C; Bsbl; Bkbl; Sftbl; Tnns; *Art.*

LANDRUM, Bruce Dodd
Alfred B Maclay Jr Day Sch; Tallahassee, FL (1-21) BS; Hmrm; Key C; NHS; Secy, Order/ Arrow; Span NHS; SC; Mgr, Soccer; Alg A; Bio A; COM; Chem A; Hist A; Math A; Sci A; Span A; Span FLES Stu Director; *U of Fla Sci Prog School; Law.*

LANDRUM, Kelli Anne
Norland Sr HS; Miami, FL; Hmrm; Wrestlerrettes; *Ct Rptr.*

LANDRUM, Nellie Louise
Village Christian HS; Sun Valley, CA (20-38) Co-Ed, Ann; Chldr; Co-Ch, Rainbow; Rptr, Sch P; VP, SC; Citz A; Cl Fav; Stu o-t Month; *Child Development.*

LANDRUM, Ronald Hoy
Dixie Co HS; Cross City, FL (5%-100) Ann; Band; BC; Hmrm; Span C; VP, Jr Cl; Cl Fav; Hon Prog; MLS; Rotary A; WW; Soph Server; Graduation Usher; Early Admissions; *Air Force.*

LANDRUM, Tammy Linn
Donderd HS; Royal Oak, MI; *U of NC; Early Ed.*

LANDRUM, Terri Jayne
Loard HS; Anaheim, CA (16-300) A Cap Choir; Fr C; French NHS; Madrigal; NHS; Orch; Pol Sci C; CSF; Fr Department A; Mus o-t Yr; MGM C; WW; *Oral Roberts U; Mus.*

LANDRY, Jill Anne
John Ehret HS; Marrero, LA (36-450) VP, CYO; Dbte Tm; Drama; Hmrm; Semi-Fin, Jr Miss Pa; Lit Ral; NHS; Sci C; Spch C; St Stu Congress; VP, SC; Thes; Pres, Soph Cl; COM; Citz A; HCt; Hon Prog; JA A; Cath Yth Rally Comm; *U of New Orleans; Communications.*

LANDRY, Kelly Mack
Monterey HS; Lubbock, TX; Hmrm; Math C; SC; Co-Cpt, Bkbl; Sftbl; Citz A; Hon Prog; Gov's Phys Fitness A; *Tex Tech U; Archt.*

LANDRY, Lisa Marie
Holy Cross HS; Delran, NJ (8-360) Ed, Ann; Chor; Drama; GS; NHS; Hon Prog; PTA A; Yrbk A; Ntl Merit Ltr of Commendation; *Rutgers U; Engr.*

LANDRY, Lynette Marie
Our Lady of Fatima HS; Lafayette, LA (20-66) A Cap Choir; Chor; Ensm; Mjrte; VP, Math C; VP, Mu Alpha Theta; NFL; Spch C; Secy, SC; Swtht; S-T, La Yth Ldrship Seminar; Outst Group Del; WW; *U of Southwestern La; Spch Therapist.*

LANDRY, Patricia Anne
Saint Dominic Regional HS; Lewiston, ME; ARC; Sch P; Hon Prog; NEDT; Sci A.

LANDRY, Ralph Joseph
Bishop Byrne HS; Memphis, TN (3-191) Fr C; Math C; Mu Alpha Theta; NHS; Sci C; Var C; Bsbl; Bkbl; Cr-Ctry; Ftbl; Tr; NEDT; Phy A; Pres A; *Christian Brothers Col.*

LANDRY, Scott David
Palo Verde HS; Tucson, AZ (3-545) BS; Tres, Chess C; Community Yth Symph; Pres, Dbte Tm; Ensm; Math C; Model UN; NFL; NHS; VP, Orch; Fin, Spch C; Pres, SC; Tri-HiY; S-T, Jr Cl; COM; Hon Prog; Math A; Opt A; Spch A; Co-Ch, Yth Coun; Bicentennial Yth; Ch, Stu Adv Coun; Most Outst Jr; US Ser Yth; Key to The World; *Pol Sci.*

LANDS, Michael Kirk
N Mecklenburg HS; Huntersville, NC (5-430) Bus Mgr, Chess C; Bus Mgr, Chor; Ensm; Fr C; Ger C; Key C; NHS; Co-Ed, Sch P; Sci C; SC; Elk A; MLS; Fr A; George Foster Hankins Schol; Win, Mem Fund Schol; *Wake Forest U; Pol Sci.*

LANE, Allan Bryant
Whitney HS; Whitney, TX (1-45) Band; BC; BS; Ensm; Parl, FFA; NHS; Order/Arrow; VP, Span C; VP, SC; Rptr, Soph Cl; Hon Prog; Opt A; Order/ Arrow A; *Howard Payne Col; Religion.*

LANE, Ben Harold
Whitney HS; Whitney, TX; Band; BC; Chor; Ensm; FFA; Orch; Ftbl; Tnns.

LANE, Bridget Annette
Northwestern HS; Flint, MI; NHS; Hon Prog; March of Dimes A; *Northwood Col; Bus.*

LANE, Carolyn Geanean
Claxton HS; Claxton, GA (25%-116) Band; Sci C; SC; Secy, Jr Cl; Band A.

LANE, Claudia Jean
Elizabethton HS; Elizabethton, TN; Band; Tnns; Stage Band; FCA; Pep C; *E Tenn St U; Sci.*

LANE, Colethia Ann
Paul Laurence Dunbar Comm HS; Baltimore, MD; Drama; Fr C; Tres, NHS; ARC; Var C; COM; Hist A; MLS; ARC A; Sign Lang; Swim Prog; Physician's Asst; *U of Md; Pre-Med.*

LANE, Crystal Denise
James B Dudley HS; Greensboro, NC; Hon Prog; ROTC A; *U of NC; Acct.*

LANE, Curtis Lamont
James B Dudley HS; Greensboro, NC; Ftbl; Hon Prog; ROTC A.

LANE, Darrell William
Burlington HS; Burlington, IA (33%-450) A Cap Choir; Band; Ensm; Bkbl; Ntl Assn of Jazz A For Solo; *Mus.*

LANE, De Etta Patricia
Monterey Bay Acad; San Francisco, CA; Chor; Drama; Sch P; Ski C; Span C; Spch C; SC; Bkbl; Ftbl; Soccer; Tr; *Pacific Union Col; Journ.*

LANE, Drenda Mary
Sam Barlow HS; Gresham, OR (200-300) Band; CYO; 4H; NHS; COM; Citz A; Hon Prog; *Med.*

LANE, Freddie Lee Jr
Terrell Co HS; Dawson, GA (10%-147) FFA; Hon Prog.

LANE, Ginny Pauline
Scott Preparatory Sch; Opelika, AL (10%-25) Anchor C; BC; Chldr; SC; Var C; Bkbl; Golf; Sftbl; Swim; Tnns; Tr; Beauty; COM; HCt; PA; *Auburn U; Law.*

LANE, Gregory Ross
Crestwood HS; Atlanta, GA (10-152) Co-Cpt, Band; BC; Chess C; NHS; Orch; COM; *U of Ga; Mus.*

LANE, Jane Cherie
Pepperell HS; Lindale, GA (5%-180) Co-Cpt, Chldr; Pres, Fr C; FHA; Math C; NHS; Rainbow; Var C; Bkbl; Cr-Ctry; Tr; Alg A; Beauty; Cl Fav; Hon Prog; 1st Runner- up, Miss Pepperell; Scholastic Achv A; *Ga Tech; Engr.*

LANE, Jeffrey Paul
Pioneer HS; San Jose, CA (20-450) A Cap Choir; A-Ed, Ann; Chor; VP, Drama; Ensm; Ger C; SC; Thes; Tnns; CSF; Yth Fel; *UCLA; Television.*

LANE, Julie Wilson
Antioch HS; Antioch, CA (6-574) A Cap Choir; Bus C; Chor; Drama; FBLA; Mod Mus Mas; S-T, Mu Alpha Theta; S-T, NHS; Rptr, Sch P; CSF; COM; Journ A; Yth Fel; Outst, Mus; Pres Hon's; *U o-t Pacific; Mus.*

LANE, Larry Roy
Western Hills HS; Fort Worth, TX (7%-600) A-Ed, Ann; Arch; Ger C; Hmrm; NHS; Order/Arrow; SC; Cl Fav; Order/Arrow A; Drum Major; Sr Rep, SC; Eagle Sct; *Tex Tech U; Archt.*

LANE, Lisa Lynne
Sou Reynolds-R II HS; Ellington, MO; 4H; Rainbow; Bkbl; Cpt, Hockey; Sftbl; 4H A; PA A; *Phys Ed.*

LANE, Littie Christine
Bethany HS; Reidsville, NC; Chor; FHA; Hmrm; SC; Hon Prog.

LANE, Lorraine
Libbey HS; Toledo, OH; Fr C; *Med Tech.*

LANE, Marcia Anne
E Ridge HS; Chattanooga, TN (49-288) Ann; Band; BC; Chor; SC; Thes; Secy, Jr Cl.

LANE, Michael Bruce
Laurel Co HS; London, KY (25%-500) BC; Drama; Fr C; Lat C; SC; JV, Bkbl; Tr; Star Student; Yth Leg; *U of Ky; Dentistry.*

LANE, Michael Darryl
E E Smith Sr HS; Fayetteville, NC (25%-300) Key C; Span C; SC; JV, Ftbl; Tr; COM; HR; Most Improved, Span III; *Hampton Inst; Bus Adm.*

LANE, Michael Roger
Ouachita Parish HS; Monroe, LA; Band; Chor; Community Yth Symph; Ensm; SC; Bkbl; Alg A; Hist A; Math A; MLS; ROTC A; Yth Fel; Principal's List; Stage Band; HR; Church Ed Comm; 9th Coun; Comm Band; *Mus.*

LANE, Robert Arnold
E Hills HS; Fort Worth, TX (258-450) Chldr; Tnns; Twerp King; *Tex Wesleyan Col; Bus Adm.*

LANE, Roger Merrill
Central HS; Knoxville, TN; JV, Ftbl; FCA; S-T, Art C; *Carson Newman Col; Ministry.*

LANE, Roger William
Jennings Co HS; N Vernon, IN (180-430) Span C; Cr-Ctry; Tr; *U of Cincinnati; Broad Casting.*

LANE, Scott Alan
Covina HS; Covina, CA; S-T, Drama; VP, Model UN; VP, Thes; Cr-Ctry; Tr; Publicity Ch, Band; Most Promising Fresh; Most Improved, Cross-Ctry; Best Personality, Fresh Cl; *Drama.*

LANE, Sherry Anne
Chester HS; Chester, PA (116-680) *Acct.*

LANERGAN, Suzanne Catherine
Reseda HS; Reseda, CA (7-627) Hmrm; InterAct C; NHS; Bank Of Amer A; CSF; Citz A; Elk A; Hon Prog; Bicentennial Committee; Principal's Acad List; Cert of Accomplishment, Keypunch; *Calif St U; Pol Sci.*

LANEY, David Fredrickson
Norman HS; Norman, OK; BS; VP, Chess C; Ger C; Hmrm; InterClub Coun; JETS; Pres, Key C; Math C; Model UN; Pres, NHS; Pres, Order/ Arrow; Sch P; Sci C; SC; UN Council; Bsbl; Cr-Ctry; Ftbl; God & Country A; Eagle Sct; *Naval Acad; Oceanography.*

LANEY, Joseph Louis
Martin Luther King HS; Philadephia, PA (40-550) Cpt, Dbte Tm; Pres, Hmrm; Math C; Tres, NHS; Ed, Sch P; Mgr, Bsbl; Mgr, Ftbl; Tr; Wrest; *Penn St U; Sci.*

LANFORD, Thomas C Jr
Joseph Wheeler HS; Marietta, GA (25%-500) Dbte Tm; VP, Lat C; Order/Arrow; Gov Honor Prog; Soc Stu A; Freedom's Foundation; *William & Mary Col; Pol Sci.*

LANG, Arlyn Byron
Napoleon HS; Napoleon, ND; Chor; Sci C; Spch C; Golf; COM; Ntl Sci Found; NASA; Amer Meteorological Soc; *U of ND; Communications.*

LANG, Daryel Lee
San Marin HS; Novato, CA (65-310) Rainbow; Graduation Speaker; Henry L Hicks & Assoc Tuition Schol; *Col of Notre Dame; Early Childhood Ed.*

LANG, Dayton Robert
Westview Sr HS; Braham, MN; Band; Chor; Monogram; Spch C; Bkbl; Ftbl; Golf; Yale Book A; All Conf, Golf; *Bus.*

LANG, Eva Margaret
Montgomery HS; Montgomery, LA (1-63) Ann; Rptr, BC; Pres, FBLA; Pres, FHA; Semi-Fin, Lit Ral; Tres, SC; MLS; St Parl, FBLA; *NW St U; Bus.*

LANG, Evan David
West HS; Rockford, IL (157-455) Bus Mgr, Sch P; Tnns; Yth Fel; S-T, Yth Fel; Most Improved Ath; Ping Pong Tourn Champ; Semi- fin, City Tnns Tourn; *Bus.*

LANG, Kisso Alex
Marshall Islans HS; Majuro, MARSHALL ISLANDS (68-103) Bkbl; Sftbl; Hon Prog.

LANG, Lori Ann
Billings W HS; Billings, MT (40-800) A Cap Choir; Chor; Ensm; NHS; *Eastern Mont Col; Elem Ed.*

LANG, Robert Alan
Newman HS; Wausau, WI (11-134) Band; Chor; Ensm; NHS; Orch; Order/Arrow; Sch P; Sci C; SC; *U of Wisc at Marathon Campus; Engr.*

LANG, Robyn Lois Luanna
Trenton HS; Trenton, FL (2-40) Band; Secy, BC; Cpt, Chldr; Rptr, FBLA; FHA; 4H; Mjrte; SC; 4H A; Sal; Type A; Most Sch Spirit; *Lake City Comm Col; Law.*

LANG, Sandra Marie
Manasquan HS; Manasquan, NJ; Chldr; Fr C; Hmrm; NHS; Ski C; SC; Tnns; Tr; Kiwanis A; Keyettes; Board of Ed Academic A; Gym; *Law.*

LANG, Stephanie Sue
Ottawa HS; Ottawa, KS (10%-200) Band; Chldr; SC; Tr; MLS; Regent Schol; Type A; *Kans St U; Phys Therapy.*

LANG, Willie Junior
Tuscaloosa HS; Tuscaloosa, AL; Pres, Hmrm; VP, Key C; *U of Ala; Bus Adm.*

LANGAN, Michelle Kelly
Holy Cross HS; Marine City, MI (11-54) Chldr; Chor; NHS; Ski C; Hon Prog; *St Clair Comm Col; Legal Secy.*

LANGBAR, Adleina
Marshall Islands HS; Majuro, MARSHALL ISLANDS; Star Student.

LANGBEHN, Megan Terri
Hobart HS; Hobart, IN; A Cap Choir; AFS; Chor; 4H; Golf; Tr; 4H A; Chor A; Candystriper Cap; *Purdue U; Nurs.*

LANGDON, Beth K
Freeport Sr HS; Freeport, IL (21-558) A Cap Choir; Chor; 4H; Math C; MVP, Bkbl; Sftbl; Semi-Fin, Tnns; Sci A; *Math.*

LANGE, Carolyn Kay
Jamestown Sr HS; Jamestown, ND (84-300) Band; Chldr; Pres, 4H; Rainbow; VP, SC; Y-Tns; 4H A; Spch A; VP, Secy, Tres, Rptr, 4-H C; St 4-H Expo; Moorhead St Col; Mass Communications.

LANGE, Curtiss Calvin
Truman HS; Taylor, MI (1%-575) Chor; Ensm; Sch P; COM; Fred Waring Schol A's.

LaPLANTE, Kimberly Marie
St Francis de Sales Central HS; Morgantown, WV (2-69) Fr C; NHS; Sal; Cath Daughters of Amer Schol A; Rotary HS Exchange; *W Va U; Pre-Vet Med.*

LA PORTE, Vickie Lynn
Fairview HS; Sherwood, OH; Band; Chor; FHA.

LAPP, Aimee Christine
Rush Henrietta-Sperry HS; Rochester, NY (20%-550) Hmrm; SC; Tnns; Tr; Hon Prog; Yth Fel; Pres, Fresh Cl.

LAPP, Robert Hutchison
Nova HS; Davie, FL (46-496) Bsbl; Bkbl; JV, Ftbl; Yth Fel.

LAPPERT, Denise June
Crestview HS; Columbiana, OH (10-98) Ann; Chor; Ensm; 4H; 4H A; Type A; Shorthand A; *Bus.*

LAPRADE, James Thaddeus
Cathedral HS; Springfield, MA; JV, Ftbl; *Zion Bible Inst; Ministerial.*

LARAMORE, Julie Beth
SW HS; Flint, MI (5%-500) Chor; NHS; ARC; *Psych.*

LARBERG, Timothy Robert
Lyons Township HS; La Grange, IL (50%-1200) Band; Ensm; Orch; Order/Arrow; Swim; Order/ Arrow A; *Ferris St Col; Avionics.*

LARCADE, Lee Alan
Broken Bow HS; Broken Bow, OK (2-137) A Cap Choir; Band; Pres, Chor; Ensm; NHS; Sal; *Oral Roberts U; Med.*

LARDNER, Peter Cleaveland
Rock Island HS; Rock Island, IL; Ski C; Swim; Water Polo.

LARE, Lora Denise
Plymouth-Whitemarsh HS; Plymouth-Meeting, PA (20-649) Mjrte.

LARGE, Anthony Wayne
Pulaski Co HS; Somerset, KY (58-248) Chess C; FFA; FHA; Hmrm; Co-Cpt, Bkbl; Beauty; HCt.

LARGE, John Desmond
Kenwood HS; Chicago, IL (40-330) Band; Bus C; Drama; FBLA; Hmrm; SC; JV, Bsbl; Co-Cpt, Hockey; Co-Cpt, Sftbl; Semi-Fin, Swim; Fin, Tnns; Citz A; Yth Fel; *Drake U; Geol.*

LARGENT, Brian Lee
Frankfort HS; Ridgeley, WV (10%-149) Band; *Potomac St Col; Engr Tech.*

LARGY, Peter John
Alexander Galt Regional HS; Lennoxville, CANADA (22-539) Dbte Tm; Hmrm; InterClub Coun; Lat C; Ed, Sch P; Span C; Parl, SC; HR; Vlbl; *Arts.*

LARIMORE, Deborah Gale
Milford Township HS; Milford, IL (10-52) Band; Chldr; Chor; Ger C; Secy, 4H; A-Ed, Sch P; Prom Court; *Danville Jr Col; Executive Secy.*

LARINAN, Debi Darlene
Dos Pueblos HS; Goleta, CA; Chldr; Most Out; Type A; Yth Fel; Yth Leg; MVP, Gym; GAA; *Santa Barbara City Col; Bus.*

LARK, David Bruce
Covington HS; Covington, TN; NHS; *U of Tenn; Forestry.*

LARK, Mavis Elizabeth
Terrell Acad; Dawson, GA (10-42) Co-Ed, Ann; Chor; Fr C; VP, 4H; Pres, Hmrm; Ntl Yth Conf; Rptr, Sch P; VP, Tri-HiY; Pres, Jr Cl; VP, Soph Cl; Mgr, Bkbl; 4H A; Most Out; S-T, 4-H C; VP, Hmrm; Pres, Secy, Tri-Hi-Y; *U of Ga; Psych.*

LARKEY, Laurilyn Marie
Western HS; Anaheim, CA (15-525) A Cap Choir; Bank Of Amer A; CILT; Tres, Pioneer Girls; *Biola Col; Nurs.*

LARKIN, Janet Lynne
St Angela Hall Acad; Brooklyn, NY (8-90) Chor; Pres, Hmrm; NHS; SC; COM; Hon Prog; Math A; Ntl Achv Schol; WW; *The Wood Sch; Secy Stu.*

LARKIN, Nina Laverne
Jess Lanier HS; Bessemer, AL (50%-270) Pres, Bus C; FHA; ARC; Sftbl; Vlbl; PA; *U of Ala, Birmingham; Med.*

LaROCCA, Elizabeth
Cedar Shoals HS; Athens, GA (16-320) Band; BC; Chor; Community Yth Symph; Pres, Drama; Ensm; Ger C; Orch; ARC; Pres, Thes; Gov Honor Prog; Spch A; Yth Fel; Most Talented; All St, Orch, Chor; Hon Thespian; *Duke U; Psych.*

LaROCHELLE, Janine Marie
Mercy HS; Middletown, CT (60-200) Sch P; SC; Vol, Yth Assn of Retarded Children; Coach, Girl's Little League; Pianist, Stage Crew, Sch Play.

LaROCQUE, Bryan David
Sam Houston HS; Lake Charles, LA (50-140) BS; Hmrm; Pres, Sr Cl; Bsbl; Bkbl; Cpt, Ftbl; Cl Fav; HCt; Most Out; Pres, FCA; Mr Sam Houston; MVP, Ftbl; *Sowela Tech Inst; Welding.*

LARRABEE, Greg Daniel
Abraham Lincoln HS; Denver, CO (61-750) Monogram; NHS; Secy, Var C; Co-Cpt, Bsbl; Co-Cpt, Ftbl; Tr; Model Airplane C, Ntl; All City Bkbl; Prom Kg; *Colo St U; Engr.*

LARRIER, Craig
Brooklyn Tech HS; Brooklyn, NY; Chor; Tr; *Elec Engr.*

LARRIEU, Vanessa Ann
St Mary's Acad; New Orleans, LA; CYO; Chor; FHA; ARC; Math A; Mus A; *Xavieu U; Vocal Mus.*

LARRIMORE, Carolyn Susan
Springfield HS; Springfield, PA (25%-400) Ann; Chor; Pres, Fr C; Co-Cpt, Mjrte; Sch P; Bkbl; Mgr, Tnns; Yth Fel; Church Choir; Tnns, Chor & Mjrte A's; *West Chester U; Elem Ed.*

LARRIMORE, Mona Denise
Thomasville HS; Thomasville, AL (3-75) Band; VP, BC; JV, Chldr; FHA; SC; Tres, Sr Cl; Cl Fav; HCt; Sal; Pres, Foreign Lang C; *U of Montevallo; Spch Pathology-Audiology.*

LARRISON, Anna Darlene
Norwayne HS; Creston, OH; Band; Chldr; Chor; 4H; Mjrte; Tr; Math A; Yth Fel; Art A; *US Navy.*

LARRISON, Scott Lewis
Walter P Chrysler HS; New Castle, IN (185-400) Band; NFL; Ftbl; MVP, Swim; Tr; *U of Dayton; Communication Arts.*

LARSEN, Daniel Ray
Timberline HS; Weippe, ID (4-88) Ann; Band; Drama; 4H; NHS; SC; Thes; JV, Bkbl; Tr; 4H A; Hon Prog; *US Air Force Acad; Aeronautics.*

LARSEN, Donna Lynn
Denby HS; Detroit, MI (26-631) Chor; Secy, NHS; Orch; JV, Bkbl; Semi-Fin, Tnns; JV, Tr; Citz A; Poet A; Sci A; Art A; HR; Eng A; Sci Fair A; Brightest Blusher A; *Concordia Col; Nurs.*

LARSEN, Douglas Edward
Edina West HS; Edina, MN (137-552) Pres, Ger C; Order/Arrow; Order/Arrow A; Eagle Sct; AATG A; *St Olaf Col; Pol Sci.*

LARSEN, Jeffrey Allen
Denby HS; Detroit, MI (10-600) Band; Order/ Arrow; SC; JV, Bkbl; Tr; Alg A; Amer Leg A; NMS; *Engr.*

LARSEN, John Alexander
Edward H White HS; Jacksonville, FL; Chor; Chor A; Sch Ltr; *Jacksonville U; Mus.*

LARSEN, Laura Frances
Capital HS; Helena, MT; Chor; SC; *Blue Mountain Col; Bible.*

LARSEN, Mary Lee
West HS; Waterloo, IA (10-500) Band; Chor; Ensm; Ger C; Co-Ch, Hmrm; Pres, NHS; Ntl Yth Conf; Orch; Co-Ch, SC; Var C; Bkbl; Tnns; COM; Vlbl; *U of Iowa; Mus.*

LARSEN, Phil Grant
Byram Hills HS; Armonk, NY (98-183) Pres, Chor; JV, Bsbl; JV, Ftbl; *Muhlenberg Col; Bus.*

LARSEN, Wayne E
Sky View HS; Smithfield, UT; All Amer Yth; Var C; Soccer; Co-Cpt, Wrest; All Amer Ath; *Utah St U; Aviation.*

LARSON, Annette Joyce
Coon Rapids Sr HS; Coon Rapids, MN (261-676) Band; Chldr; Chor; City Conf; 4H; Hmrm; NHS; Ntl Yth Conf; SC; COM; ARC A; Pres, Church Sr High; JV Vlbl; MVP, Broomball; Cpt, Rookie o-t Yr, Cr-Ctry Skiing; *Interior Decorator.*

LARSON, Bradley Jon
Loomis HS; Loomis, NE (1-25) Ann; Pres, Band; BS; Key C; Order/Arrow; A-Ed, Sch P; Pres, SC; Var C; Pres, Sr Cl; Parl, Jr Cl; Parl, Soph Cl; Bsbl; Co-Cpt, Ftbl; Wrest; Alg A; B Crocker A; Bio A; Elk A; Hist A; HKg; Math A; Regent Schol; Val; Elks Teenager o-t Yr; Board of Trustees Schol; *U of Neb; Math.*

LARSON, Brian Robert
Norton HS; Norton, MA (37-152) Band; Hmrm; Key C; Pres, SC; Co-Cpt, Bkbl; Co-Cpt, Ftbl; Co-Cpt, Tr; DARGCA; WW; Sr Service Pin; Jewish Veteran's, Ftbl & Bkbl, A's; *Geneva Col; Computer Sci.*

LARSON, Cristy Jane
Fairfield HS; Fairfield, MT (11-46) Band; Chor; Ensm; Secy, 4H; Var C; Secy, Jr Cl; S-T, Soph Cl; Bkbl; Dist Spelling Bee; *Northwest Bible Col; Sociology.*

LARSON, Cynthia Lee
Watt Township HS; Wall, NJ (42-320) AFS; FHA; Hmrm; Key C; Secy, Ski C; SC; Mgr, Hockey; Tr; Candystriper; Church Del, Dist Yth Conf; *Keene St Col; Home Ec.*

LARSON, Dana Howard
Marina HS; Huntington Beach, CA (13-830) Chor; NHS; CSF; Hon Prog; *U of Calif Irvine; Bio Sci.*

LARSON, David Paul
Fountain Valley HS; Fountain Valley, CA (20%-1200) Cpt, Soccer.

LARSON, Deanna Marie
Pepin-Pub HS; Pepin, WI (1-37) Ann; Band; Chldr; Chor; FHA; NHS; Type A; Vlbl; PA; WW; Mus, Home Ec, Archor, A's.

LARSON, Denise Mae
Sunset HS; Beaverton, OR (18%-499) A Cap Choir; Chor; Drama; JV, Bkbl; Water Polo Tm; *Oreg St U; Fine Arts.*

LARSON, Doris Eileen
Sehome HS; Bellingham, WA; Band; Community Yth Symph; Cum Laude Soc; Hmrm.

LARSON, Douglas Scott
Westview HS; Braham, MN (13-81) NHS; Sch P; Var C; Cpt, Bsbl; Ftbl; Cl Fav; HCt; Hon Prog; Cl Spkr at Graduation; *U of Minn.*

LARSON, Elizabeth Louise
Ada HS; Ada, MN (10-64) Dbte Tm; FHA; 4H; Pres, NFL; Secy, SC; 4H A; HCt; Spch A; VFW A; *ND St U; Nurs.*

LARSON, Eric Dennis
Chisago Lakes Sr HS; Lindstrom, MN (60-180) Band; Bus C; Ensm; Sch P; Var C; Bsbl; Cpt, Bkbl; Ftbl; Tr; COM; Pres A; Career C; DECA; Phys Ed A; Mr Minn Tn; Best Dressed; *ND St U; Bus.*

LARSON, Fred Walter
Spring Valley HS; Spring Valley, WI (14-91) Band; FFA; Pres, 4H; HiY; Var C; JV, Ftbl; Tr; Wrest; Bio A; COM; 4H A; FFA Chapter Farmer; FFA Greenhand A; Ftbl; Area Citizen A; *U of Wyoming; Drafting.*

LARSON, Ingrid
Peru HS; Peru, IN (11-288) Chldr; GS; NHS; Var C; JV, Bkbl; Tnns; Beauty; COM; Vlbl; Gym; *Purdue U; Med Tech.*

LARSON, Janalee
Hueneme HS; Oxnard, CA (11-592) *Western Wash St U; Psych.*

LARSON, John Mark
Washington HS; Kansas City, KS; Band; Fr C; Secy, Order/Arrow; JV, Cr-Ctry; Semi-Fin, Tr; Order/Arrow A; Eagle Sct; *Kans U; Sci.*

LARSON, Kim L
Belvidere HS; Belvidere, IL (8-366) NHS; SC; S-T, Var C; Pres, Soph Cl; Bkbl; Ftbl; Bausch & Lomb A; Elk A; HCt; NMS; St Scholar; FCA; Pres, Fresh Cl; *U of Ill; Civil Engr.*

LARSON, Lona Susan
Lebanon Union HS; Lebanon, OR (35-203) AFS;
Chem C; Dbte Tm; Drama; FFA; Ger C; 4H;
Hmrm; JETS; NFL; VP, Thes; COM; Citz A; 4H
A; Hist A; Spch A; Ger A; St Forensics A; St Art A;
Trinity Bible Inst; Bible.

LARSON, Mary Elizabeth
Long Prairie Pub Sch; Long Prairie, MN (5-135)
Co-Ch, AFS; Bus Mgr, Ann; Band; Co-Cpt, Chldr;
Chor; Ensm; Madrigal; Co-Cpt, Mjrte; NHS;
Beauty; Bowl Trophy; Bethel Col; Elem Ed.

LARSON, Michael Leonard
Hononegah HS; Rockton, IL (49-195) Band.

LARSON, Patti Jane
Manistee HS; Manistee, MI (21-180) Band; NHS;
Ski C; Tres, Soph Cl; Bkbl; Sftbl; Tr; Skiing Tm;
Central Mich U; Math.

LARSON, Paula Jean
Brown Deer HS; Brown Deer, WI (25%-279) A
Cap Choir; Band; Dbte Tm; Fr C; S-T, 4H; Hmrm;
Madrigal; NFL; SC; Citz A; Spch A; St Hon Choir;
Pres, Church Luther League; Carthage Col; Mus.

LARSON, Randi Gay
Wakonda Pub HS; Wakonda, SD (6-18) Ann;
Band; Chor; Drama; FHA; Fin, GS; 4H;
NHS; Bkbl; Mgr, Tr; All St Chor; Hon Choir; Acct.

LARSON, Renee Ann
Sunset HS; Beaverton, OR (20%-499) Chor; Dbte
Tm; Drama; JV, Sftbl; Swim; Water Polo; U of
Oreg; Ed of Art.

LARSON, Rhonda Louise
Carl Schurz HS; Chicago, IL (17-2000) Drama;
Ensm; Thes; Bkbl; COM; Chamber of Comm A;
Citz A; Hon Prog; Pres A; Sci A; Child Psych.

LARSON, Rick Lee
O'Neill Pub Sch; O'Neill, NE (13-120) Band;
Chor; Math.

LARSON, Scott James
Central HS; Albert Lea, MN (103-708) Rptr, FFA;
Pres, 4H; Hmrm; 4H A; WW; Master Swine Pro-
ducer, FFA; Grnd Champ, Market Litter, Co Fair;
River Falls Col; Agr.

LARSON, Sharon Louise
Lindbergh Sr HS; Hopkins, MN (30-425) Chor;
Hmrm; SC; Hon Prog; MLS; Vlbl; Med.

LARSON, Thomas Allen
Winona Sr HS; Winona, MN (100-497) 4H; Var C;
Ftbl; Secy & Rptr, FFA; Winona St U; Med.

LARSON, Timothy Wayne
Dalhart HS; Dalhart, TX (10-86) A Cap Choir;
Band; Pres, Chor; Dbte Tm; Drama; Ensm; Pres,
FTA; Madrigal; NFL; NHS; Span C; Span NHS;
JV, Ftbl; Cpt, Swim; Tr; I Dare You; Spch A; Cal St
LA; Engr.

LARSSON, Todd Arthur
Springfield Southeast HS; Springfield, IL (27-503)
Church Yth; Church Maranatha Singers; Bible Stu
Prog; Summer Bsbl; Mich St U; Acct.

LaRUE, Arthur Paul
Pendleton HS; Pendleton, OR (8-269) A Cap
Choir; Dbte Tm; Drama; Ensm; Math C; Mu Alpha
Theta; Pres, NHS; Orch; Sci C; VP, Thes; Tr; Citz
A; Elk A; Hon Prog; NMF; Parl, Russian C; St Solo
Mus Contest; Reed Col; Sci.

LaRUE, Judy Ann
Houghton HS; Houghton, MI; Band; JV, Chldr;
4H; SC; Tr; 4H A.

LaRUE, Michael Randy
Enid HS; Enid, OK (100-500) Band; Hmrm; Math
C; Phys C; Bsbl; Ftbl; Sftbl; Tr; Wrest; Okla St U;
Archt.

LaRUE, Sally Ann
Sunbright HS; Sunbright, TN (11-63) FHA; Most
Courteous; Roane St Col.

LARY, Diane Denyse
Maquoketa Comm HS; Maquoketa, IA (1-150)
Band; Chor; NHS; Pres, Rainbow; Co-Cpt, Bkbl;
Tr; COM; Hon Prog; Opt A; Yth Fel; Iowa St U;
Phys Ed.

LASARSKY, Phil Stanely
Holland Hall HS; Tulsa, OK (10%-78) Lat C; Or-
der/Arrow; Pres, SC; Var C; Arch; Ftbl; JV, Soccer;
Swim; Wrest; COM; Citz A; MLS; Order/Arrow
A; PTA A; Yth Fel; Yth Leg; Eagle Sct; HR; Okla
St U; Vet Med.

LASCO, Mary Jane
Quincy Sr HS; Quincy, IL (138-700) A Cap Choir;
Rptr, Chor; Drama; Ensm; Madrigal; Span C; SC;
Thes; Tr; Soc For Academic Achv Schol Ltr; Di-
rector's A in Theatre; Major A in Choir; Mus.

LASCURAIN, Judy Ann
Monroe Union HS; Monroe, OR (5-43) NHS; Mgr,
Tr; Type A; Girls League; WW; Tri-Os; Lane
Comm Col.

LASERSOHN, Jeffrey Compton
Mercer Island HS; Mercer Island, WA; Swim; Central Wash St Col.

LASETER, Larry Joseph
Newton Co Comprehensive HS; Covington, GA
(10-500) HiY; Hmrm; Key C; Sch P; Span C; SC;
Ftbl; U of Ga; Engr.

LASETER, Timothy Marks
Newton Co Comprehensive HS; Covington, GA
(4-289) Bus C; FBLA; Hmrm; Key C; Ftbl; COM;
Chem A; NMF; PTA A; Star Student; Summa Cum
Laude; Ga Tech; Industrial Mgt.

LASH, Kathy Sue
Peabody HS; Pittsburgh, PA (195-600) Co-Ed,
Ann; Fr C; Rptr, Sch P; VP, Thes; VP, Yth Fel; City
Rep, W Pa Conf of Yth; Lead, Sr Cl Play; W Va
Wesleyan Col; Drama.

LASHER, Carrie Monroe
Hibriten HS; Lenoir, NC; Ski C; UNCC; Art.

LASHER, James Frederick
N Penn HS; Lansdale, PA (230-735) Band; Swim;
Hon Prog; Civil Air Patrol A; Swim Ltr; WW;
MVP; YMCA Swim Tm; Temple Col; Art.

LASHER, Kevin Scott
N Penn HS; Lansdale, PA; Band; Swim; Hon Prog;
MVP, YMCA Swim Tm; Swim Ltr; HR; Harvard
U.

LASHLEY, Dawn Elizabeth
Warrior Acad; Eutaw, AL (2-26) Ed, Ann; VP, BC;
Chor; GS; Pres, Math C; Pres, Span C; Tres, SC;
Pres, Sr Cl; Bio A; Citz A; DARGCA; Hon Prog;
Math A; MLS; Sal; Sci A; George C Wallace Schol;
Troy St U; Acct.

LASHLEY, Kevin L
West Co HS; Leadwood, MO (2-50) A Cap Choir;
Ed, Ann; Band; Chor; Ensm; Lit Mag; Madrigal;
VP, NHS; A-Ed, Sch P; Sci C; Tres, SC; Hist A;
Math A; Regent Schol; Sal; Acct A; Band A; Mus
A; Mus Schol; Southeast Mo St U; Acct.

LASHLEY, Sandra Suzanne
Gordon HS; Gordon, NE (29-78) CYO; Chor; VP,
FHA; Ger C; NHS; SC; Var C; Bkbl; Vlbl; Outst
Pep C; Chadron St U; Teaching.

LASKA, James Edwin
Tift Co HS; Tifton, GA; CYO; Chor; ARC; Swim;
Citz A; 4H A; Pres A; Yth Fel; Industrial Arts C;
2nd Pl, GAIAC Dreamhouse Contest; 1st Pl,
Crime Prevention Week; Industrial Arts.

LASKEY, Thomas James
Shawnee Mission W HS; Overland Park, KS; Bkbl;
Bowling; Sunday Sch Teacher; U of Ariz; Mus.

LASKOWSKI, Scott Matthew
Speedway Sr HS; Indianapolis, IN (95-170) Pres, A
Cap Choir; Band; Drama; Madrigal; Tnns; Tr; Pres,
Boys Glee; Hon Newsboy Carrier; Directors Choir
A; Johnson Bible Col; Ministry.

LASKOWSKI, Thomas Mark
Speedway Sr HS; Indianapolis, IN (40-204) A Cap
Choir; Band; Chor; Drama; Newsboy Hon Carrier.

LASKY, Mark Jeffrey
Valparaiso HS; Valparaiso, IN (3-400) BS; NHS;
Alg A; Math A; Bkbl Statistician; Geom A; Ind Sch
Math Journ A; Math.

LASLEY, Thomas O Neal
Smithfield-Selma Sr HS; Smithfield, NC (19-355)
Band; Fr C; Parl, Key C; NHS; Orch; Parl, Jr Cl;
Cr-Ctry; JV, Ftbl; Tnns; Tr; Wrest; Pres A; All St
Band; Duke U; Biol.

LaSORSA, Lillian O
Copiague HS; Copiague, NY (17-400) NHS; JV,
Bkbl; Mgr, Hockey; Mgr, Sftbl; SUNY at Farming-
dale; Dental Hygiene.

LASSAHN, Brian Michael
S Gwinnett HS; Snellville, GA; Band; Orch; Hon
Prog; Ga Tech; Engr.

LASSEN, William Brent
West HS; Wichita, KS; Ed, Sch P; Ftbl; Pres,
Church Yth Group; KC Sch of Optometry; Opto-
metry.

LASSETER, Raymonda Sue
J Sterling Morton HS; Cicero, IL; Secy, SC; Morehouse Col.

LASSETTER, Janet Elizabeth
Searcy HS; Searcy, AR (29-180) Ann; BC; Chldr;
Drama; Secy, FBLA; FTA; NHS; Sch P; SC; Thes;
Tnns; HQn; Swtht; U of Ark; Bus.

LASSITER, Lisa Renee
Allen Jay HS; High Point, NC; Pres, BC; Tres, Fr
C; Hmrm; Monogram; SC; Tres, Jr Cl; Sftbl; Tr; Jr
Cl Marshal; UNCG; Eng.

LASSMAN, Candace Linn
Nathan Hale Sr HS; Tulsa, OK; Band; Tulsa Jr Col;
Acct.

LASSWELL, Jane Ann
Lowpoint-Washburn HS; Washburn, IL (19-60)
AFS; Ann; Band; Chor; 4H; Sch P; Spch C; Tr; WW
Among Mus Stu in Amer HS; Western Ill U.

LASTER, Kathy Ann
Treadwell HS; Memphis, TN (13-200) NHS;
TOEC, Bible, C'S.

LASTER, Larry Edward
J W Sexton HS; Lansing, MI (140-480) Ann;
Drama; Phys C; Var C; Cr-Ctry; Tr; Citz A; Ki-
wanis A; Pole Vault; Lansing Comm Col; Lib Arts.

LASTER, Margaret Tate
Philadelphia HS For Girls; Philadelphia, PA
(253-400) Hockey; Sftbl; Pep Squad; Family A; W
Chester St Col; Elem Ed.

LATALL, Lisa Ann
W Springfield HS; Springfield, VA (350-800) Ann;
Drama; Chem A; Theatre Arts.

LATCHISON, Mark Cornelius
Soldan HS; St Louis, MO (120-460) Chor; Hmrm;
NHS; Columbia U; Bus Adm.

LATCHUM, Jane R
Hampton Roads Acad; Newport News, VA; Co-
Cpt, Chldr; JV, Hockey; Yth Fel; Pres, Pep C; Key-
ettes; Living Light Singers; Mary Baldwin Col;
Psych.

LATHAM, Charles Michael
Tuscumbia HS; Tuscumbia, MO (4-18) SC; Pres, Jr
Cl.

LATHAM, Don Loftis
T L Hanna HS; Anderson, SC; Secy, Ger C; Mu
Alpha Theta; VP, NHS; COM; NMS; NEDT;
Clemson U; Pre-Med.

LATHAM, Lesia Louise
Marion-Franklin HS; Columbus, OH (75-350)
Hmrm; Mjrte; ARC; Secy, Span C; Span NHS; SC;
Var C; Sftbl; Citz A; Yth Fel; Modern
Dance Group; Off Ed Assn; Tr & Wrest Statisti-
cian; Drill Tm; Big Friends Organization; Spelman
Col; Pre-Law.

LATHAM, Marc Anthony
Groveport Madison HS; Columbus, OH; Opt A;
Bus Adm.

LATHAM, Nancy Ellen
Benson HS; Omaha, NE; AFS; Chor; Pres, Hmrm;
Rptr, Sch P; SC; Thes; COM; Child Psych.

LATHAM, Terry Lee
Spearman HS; Spearman, TX (20%-86) Band; BS;
Chess C; Chor; Madrigal; VP, Sr Cl; Pres, Jr Cl;
Pres, Soph Cl; Co-Cpt, Ftbl; Tnns; Dan Berry A;
All St Ftbl; Amarillo Jr Col; Computer Tech.

LATHAN, Cassandra Denise
Alcee Fortier Sr HS; New Orleans, LA (13-274)
Chor; Ensm; Hmrm; NHS; Span C; SC; Y-Tns; Citz
A; Cl Fav; HCt; Hon Prog; Magna Cum Laude;
MLS; Mus Medals.

LATHAN, Susan Lynn
Alcee Fortier Sr HS; New Orleans, LA; Chldr; Hmrm; Hist A; HCt; *Dillard U; Elem Ed.*

LATHEM, Skippy Joe
Sebastopol HS; Sebastopol, MS (5%-40) Pres, BC; Pres, Drama; Pres, FFA; SC; Pres, Jr Cl; Bkbl; Mgr, Ftbl; Alg A; Cl Fav; Math A; Sci A; Agr A; *E Central Jr Col; Math.*

LATHION, Debora Inez
Soldan HS; St Louis, MO (60-481) Chor; *U of Mo; Acct.*

LATIMER, Julie Sue
Marysville-Pilchuck HS; Marysville, WA (12-392) Band; NHS; Rainbow; COM; Vlbl; *Bus.*

LATIMER, Kip Alan
Eastridge HS; Kankakee, IL (50%-500) Chor; Bkbl; Ftbl; Pres A; Part- time Job; *Olivet Nazarene Col; Bus.*

LATIMER, Roxena Dean
Elmira HS; Elmira, OR; Chor; 4H; Rainbow; Arch; Tr; Cl Fav.

LATIN, Linda Sue
Second Ward HS; Gloster, LA; Bus C; Math C; Sci C; SC; Bkbl; Sftbl; HQn; Hon Prog; *Sou U; Secy.*

LATIN, Michael Allen
El Camino Real HS; Woodland Hills, CA (150-1200) BS; Co-Ch, City Conf; Pres, Hmrm; InterAc C; InterClub Coun; Pres, SC; VP, Soph Cl; Amer Leg A; Chamber of Comm A; Citz A; Hon Prog; Most Out; Opt A; Opt Out Tn; Pres A; LA-CISD Ctu-Wide Stu Affairs Coun; DA Yth Coun; Adv Coun; Outst Member, SC.

LATIN, Michael Anthony
Second Ward HS; Gloster, LA (3-46) *Grambling Col.*

LATIN, Thelma Ruth
Second Ward HS; Gloster, LA (5-46) *Northwestern St U; Nurs.*

LATINA, Thomas Edward
Dundee Comm HS; Carpentersville, IL (34-340) Band; Chor; Ftbl; *Forestry.*

LATONI, Myrna Lisette
Robinson Sch; Santurce, PR (8-37) NHS; Span C; Hon Prog; *U of; Phys Therapy.*

LaTORRE, Pedro
Dillard HS; Fort Lauderdale, FL; Pres, Key C; Co-Ed, Sch P; Co-Cpt, Bsbl; Bkbl; Ftbl; *Ariz St U; Math.*

LATTA, Ricky Lynn
Kenai Central HS; Kenai, AR (3-185) Chor; NHS; Star Student.

LATTA, Sheryl Ann
Crowley HS; Crowley, TX (19-133) Chldr; Chor; NHS; Rainbow; SC; Bkbl; Tnns; Tr; MVP, Vlbl; *Tex Wesylan Col; Phys Ed.*

LATTANZIO, Anthony Mario
Nazareth Reg HS; Brooklyn, NY (12-250) Bus C; CYO; Chldr; Fr C; French NHS; Pres, Hmrm; NHS; Sch P; Var C; Mgr, Bkbl; Tr; Bowl; Distinguished Service A; Ath A; *NYU; Bus.*

LATTIMORE, Antoinette Denice
Yerba Buena HS; San Jose, CA (80-300) *Loma Linda U; Biochem.*

LATTIMORE, Gregory James
Harry S Truman HS; Bronx, NY (140-779) Var C; Tr; Bowl; Achv A; V A; Theater Arts A; *Elec.*

LATTIMORE, Jeffrey Wayne
Harry S Truman HS; Bronx, NY (320-1008) Var C; Tr.

LATTIMORE, Nena
Kensington HS; Buffalo, NY; SC; ARC A; Most Improved; SC A; *ECC; Home Ec.*

LATTUCA, Lisa Rose
Acad of Saint Aloysius; Jersey City, NJ (3-104) Hmrm; NHS; SC; NEDT; WW; Academic Recognition.

LAU, Grace
Adlai E Stevenson HS; New York, NY; NHS; Var C; Tnns; Hon Prog; *U of Calif Berkeley; Human Physiology.*

LAU, Nancy Jane
Hilbert HS; Hilbert, WI (4-66) Co-Ed, Ann; Co-Cpt, Chldr; NHS; Tr; Hon Prog; St Tr.

LAUBACH, Ann Pennington
William Nottingham HS; Syracuse, NY; Band; 4H; NHS; Tnns; Secy, Yth Fel; Semi-Fin, Amer Mus Schol Assn.

LAUBACH, Laura Brown
William Nottingham HS; Syracuse, NY (16-317) Dbte Tm; Lat C; Lit Mag; NFL; NHS; NMS; Regent Schol; Tres, Church Yth Fel; WW; *Colgate U.*

LAUBACHER, Mark Joseph
Carl Sandburg HS; Orland Park, IL (95-970) Drama; Mu Alpha Theta; Rptr, Sch P; SC; Thes; Var C; Swim; Hon Prog; Journ A; Q&S A; VP, Guard; *Princeton U; Elec Engr.*

LAUBE, Priscilla Elizabeth
Proviso E HS; Maywood, IL (157-964) Chor; Hmrm; SC; Tr; Prayer Group; Secy.

LAUBER, Caleb
Valley HS; Sanders, AZ (20-67) Ed, Ann; Band; Drama; Ed, Sch P; Span C; Spch C; SC; Pres, Soph Cl; Citz A; Type A; *Biola Col; Med.*

LAUCUS, Deborah Kaye
Hartshorne HS; Hartshorne, OK (1-60) Ed, Ann; Drama; FHA; NHS; Sch P; Spch C; Thes; Secy, Sr Cl; Rptr, Soph Cl; Alg A; Bio A; COM; Cl Fav; Gov Honor Prog; Hist A; Hon Prog; Journ A; Sci A; Type A; Val; WW; *E Okla U; Bus.*

LAUDENSLAGER, James Michael
Grandview Sr HS; Grandview, MO (100-430) Chess C; Madrigal; Bkbl; Tr; Alg A; Math A; Geog A; Principle's HR A; *U of Mo; Mech Engr.*

LAUDERMILK, Gregory James
McArthur HS; Hollywood, FL; FFA; Bsbl; Bkbl; Ftbl; Soccer; Yth Fel; Sunday Sch Teacher; Bus Ministry; VP, Yth Interntl; Puppet Ministry; Skate Board Assn; Choir; Tn Musical Productions; *Point Loma Col; Bio.*

LAUE, Brant Mitchell
Hanover HS; Hanover, KS (1-38) Drama; Rptr, FFA; Pres, 4H; NHS; Bkbl; Tr; Alg A; Bio A; 4H A; Hon Prog; JA A; Math A; Spch A; FFA, Eng, Livestock Judging, A's; *Oral Roberts U; Law.*

LAUE, Kim Kristine
J Burroughs HS; Burbank, CA; A Cap Choir; Chldr; Chor; Ensm; Hmrm; VP, Madrigal; Sch Achieve Tm; Spch C; SC; CSF; PTA A; Vocal Mus A; Sunshine Girls; *Biola Col; Communications.*

LAUER, Charles Robert
Clintonville Sr HS; Clintonville, WI; Mgr, Ftbl; Golf.

LAUER, Marie Antoinette
Bishop Carroll HS; Wichita, KS (34-211) Tres, CYO; Chess C; Co-Ch, City Conf; NHS; S-T, SC; Citz A; *Friends U; Bus.*

LAUER, Timothy John
Bishop Carroll HS; Wichita, KS (5-211) Co-Ed, BS; CYO; Chess C; Chor; Dbte Tm; Madrigal; NHS; JV, Golf; JV, Tnns; Amer Leg A; Hon Prog; St Scholar; Rptr & Secy, BS; *Wichita St U; Engr.*

LAUF, Douglas Frank
Jefferson City HS; Jefferson City, MO; Order/Arrow; ARC; God & Country A; Order/Arrow A; HR; Rifle C; Eagle Sct.

LAUFER, Robert Terrence
Hampton HS; Hampton, VA (221-581) A Cap Choir; Var C; Bkbl; Ftbl; Most Out; Regional, All St, Chor; V Ltr A.

LAUFER, Susan Helene
Royal HS; Simi Valley, CA (40-964) Dbte Tm; Hmrm; NFL; NHS; Spch C; St Stu Congress; CSF; COM; Citz A; Hon Prog; ROTC A; Spch A; Ntl Forensics League; Cl Off A; 4-H A; *UCLA; Pre-Law.*

LAUFFER, Teresa Ann
Warren Area HS; Warren, PA (20%-430) A Cap Choir; Chor; Dbte Tm; Drama; Madrigal; NHS; Span C; *Moody Bible Inst; Bible Theology.*

LAUGHLAND, Jean Marie
Vincent Massey Secondary Sch; Windsor, CANADA; Ftbl; Waterpolo; *U of Windsor; Fine Arts.*

LAUGHLIN, Carol Ann
Pojoaque HS; Pojoaque, NM; NHS; *Kans St U; Vet Med.*

LAUGHLIN, Kelly Lee
Sooner HS; Bartlesville, OK (6-280) AFS; Chor; NHS; Span C; COM; Citz A; St Scholar.

LAUGHLIN, Kristi June
Lancaster HS; Lancaster, OH; A Cap Choir; Band; Chldr; Chor; Drama; NFL; Thes; Semi-Fin, Spch A; *Dana Col; Special Ed.*

LAUGHLIN, Lynn Ann
Richardson HS; Richardson, TX (29-888) FHA; 4H; Co-Cpt, Mjrte; Tri-HiY; Y-Tns; Tr; DARGCA; MLS; Pres & VP, Ntls; Parl & Pres, SC; Lieutenant, Drill Tm; *Tex U; Bus.*

LAUGHLIN, Maren R
Superior Sr HS; Superior, WI (U%-700) A Cap Choir; Chor; Dbte Tm; Drama; Secy, Ger C; NHS; Orch; SC; Amer Leg A; NMS; *Mus.*

LAUGHLIN, Thomas Edward
McKeesport Area Sr HS; McKeesport, PA; Journ A; Sci A; Sci Fair; Mgr Ed, Sch P; *Food Service.*

LAUGHLIN, Vincent Gerard
Marist HS; Chicago, IL (118-457) Drama; Fr C; Ski C; Tutoring Fr.

LAUGHREY, Susan Lynn
Rogers HS; Michigan City, IN (65-500) A Cap Choir; Chor; NHS; SC; HCt.

LAUMEISTER, Joanne Mary
Holliston HS; Holliston, MA (42-256) Pres, AFS; Band; Chor; Drama; GS; NHS; Span C; Span NHS; Co-Cpt, Bkbl; Hon Prog; Stu-o-t Mo; Pres, Pilgrim Fel; Most Versatile; Usher; Stu Adv Comm; Christian Ed Comm; Drum Major; Minister Search Comm; *Worcester St Col; Span.*

LAUREANO, Magaly
H A Lehman HS; Bronx, NY; A Cap Choir; Chor; Sci A; Service A; Eng A; *Geneva Col; Child Psych.*

LAURENT, Yvonne Marie
Destrehan HS; Destrehan, LA (1-168) Tres, BC; Chldr; Semi-Fin, Lit Ral; Alg A; Hist A; Math A; Spch A; Type A; Econ, Shorthand, Eng, A's; *Nicholls Col; Ed.*

LAURICH, Jeffrey Andrew
Goodman HS; Goodman, WI (6-22) Bus Mgr, Ann; Band; CYO; Sch P; SC; Pres, Var C; Bkbl; Co-Cpt, Ftbl; HKg; HCt; ARC A; *U of Wis; Ecology.*

LAURIE, Brenda Jean
Sharon HS; Sharon, MA (20%-270) Co-Ch, TEVC; Cosmotology.

LAURIE, Sandra Eileen
Notre Dame HS; Clarksburg, WV (4-52) Drama; Fr C; FBLA; NHS; Bkbl; Runner Up, Century III; Forensics A; Girl o-t Mo; *Fairmont St Col; Med Tech.*

LAURIE, Susan Carol
Sharon HS; Sharon, MA (50-237) FNA; Hmrm; Mjrte; Tres, Young Churchmen; *Bentley Col; Acct.*

LAURILA, Mary Elaine
Rittman HS; Rittman, OH (9-131) Band; Chor; Drama; NHS; Sch Achieve Tm; Sci C; Tnns; COM; VP, Mat Maids; *Kent St U; Med Tech.*

LAURITZEN, Lisa Ellen
Whitewater HS; Whitewater, WI (5-176) Fr C; NHS; S-T, Ski C; Co-Cpt, Tr; Math A; Type A; Conf, St Champion, Tr; Horse Show Trophies; *Pre-Vet Med.*

LAURSEN, Paula Jean
J Sterling Morton W HS; Berwyn, IL; Ski C; Hon Prog; *Morton Col; Bus Ed.*

LAURSEN, Scott C
Manistee HS; Manistee, MI (25%-200) Bsbl; *Engr.*

LAUSE, Thomas Norbert
Fort Jennings HS; Fort Jennings, OH; SC; Bsbl; Bkbl; Cr-Ctry; DARGCA; Sci A; VFW A; Vof-DEM; Schol Tm; Soil Stewardship A; Sch Musical; *Ohio St U; Bus Adm.*

LAUTH, Linda Louise
S Park HS; Library, PA (5-163) FHA; Secy, FNA; NHS; *Duffs Bus Inst; Court Rptr.*

LAUVER, Annette Louise
Millersburg Area HS; Millersburg, PA; Band; Chor; Ensm; FTA; *Messiah Col; Sci.*

LAUVER, Lorrie Ann
Williamson Jr Sr HS; Tioga, PA (50%-103) Bus C; Type A; *Williamsport Col; Bus.*

421

LAUVSTAD, Kurt Kevin
Clarke Comm HS; Osceola, IA (14-110) Var C; Ftbl; Golf; Wrest; Pres, FCA; Iowa St U; Engr.

LAUX, Joseph John
Regis HS; Stayton, OR (3-56) NHS; Mgr, Bsbl; Mgr, Bkbl; Math A; Willamette U; Math.

LAVAGNINO, Andrew Frank
Casa Roble HS; Orangevale, CA (14-302) 4H; Bsbl; Bank of Amer A; Amer River Col; Engr.

LAVALLEE, William Robert
Bishop Guertin HS; Nashua, NH (61-148) Ski C; Ftbl; St Anselms Col; Bio.

LAVELLE, Marianne Patricia
Marian Cath HS; Tamaqua, PA (9-173) Pres, Band; French NHS; Ed, Sch P; Citz A; Spch A; Villanova Col; Eng.

LAVERGNE, Suzanne Louise
Our Lady of Fatima HS; Lafayette, LA; F-Ed, Ann; BC; Fr C; Co-Cpt, Mjrte; Bkbl; Tnns; Hon Prog; MLS; Vlbl; Ch, Hire-A-Kid; WW; Nicholls St U; Acct.

LAVERICK, Gregg Allen
Penns Manor Area HS; Clymer, PA (17-120) Bkbl; Ftbl; Tr; Ind U of Pa; Acct.

LAVERICK, Janice Kay
Penns Manor HS; Clymer, PA (3-160) A Cap Choir; Chor; FTA; Hmrm; NHS; SC; Tres, Jr Cl; Bkbl; Sftbl; Amer Leg A; Gov Intern; Sci.

LAVERTY, Kent J
Wood River HS; Hailey, ID (9-60) BS; NHS; Ed, Sch P; Span C; Pres, SC; Thes; JV, Bkbl; Tnns; Citz A; U of Oreg; Econ.

LAVERY, Barbara Lynne
Cherryville Sr HS; Cherryville, NC; Band; Chor; Pres, Crown & Scepte; Bkbl; Sftbl; Tnns; 4H A; Bowl Tm; Director, Church Children's Choir; Worker, Children's Church Soloist; Wildlife Mgr.

LAVIOLETTE, Kerry Drake
Maryvale Sr HS; Depew, NY (10-600) Fr C; Hon Prog.

LAVOIE, Linda Anne
Tignish Regional HS; Tignish, CANADA; Ann; Ntl Yth Conf; Pres, ARC; Amer Leg A; Chem A; 4H A; ARC A; Reach for The Top; U of Prince Edward Island; Lang.

LAW, Bobby
McIntosh Union HS; McIntosh, AL; FFA; Var C; Bsbl; Ftbl.

LAW, David Lawson
Gretna HS; Gretna, VA (7-274) Pres, Band; BC; Fr C; Tr; Alg A; All St Band; Outst Mus, Band Schol, A's; Madison Col; Mus.

LAW, Denise Leonne
Amer Christian Acad; Pomona, CA (3-21) Ann; Chor; Sch P; Bio A; HCt; Hon Prog; Sci A; Vlbl; Timothy A; Semi-Fin, TV Bible Quiz Show.

LAW, James Kenneth
Eisenhower HS; Hopkins, MN (49-423) Chor; Madrigal; Order/Arrow; Bkbl; Soccer; Tr; Life Sct; Sr Patrol Ldr; St Olaf Col; Gen.

LAW, Karen Eileen
Ray HS; Kearny, AZ (12-93) Drama; NHS; Elk A; Baylor U; Pre-Med.

LAW, Linda Hymes
Allen HS; Robeline, LA (1-32) Hon Prog; Cl Swtht; Northwestern St U; Bus.

LAW, Quinn Rolland
Ringgold HS; Donora, PA (25%-180) Arch; Hmrm; SC; Bkbl; Ftbl; Bus Adm.

LAWFER, Kay Leanne
Stockton HS; Stockton, IL (7-98) A Cap Choir; Chor; Drama; GS; NHS; Pres, SC; Bkbl; HCt; Hon Prog; St Scholar; Ill St U; Bus Adm.

LAWLER, Bradley Thomas
Western Hills HS; Fort Worth, TX; Hmrm; SC; Pres, Sr Cl; Cpt, Ftbl; Tr; Cl Fav; Southwestern Bible Col; Religion.

LAWLER, Christopher John
Maple Shade HS; Maple Shade, NJ (10%-235) Semi-Fin, BS; Drama; Hmrm; Lit Mag; NHS; SC; Alg A; Chem A; Glassboro St Col; Eng Ed.

LAWLER, Deborah Ann
Covington HS; Covington, TN (1-228) A Cap Choir; Pres, Band; Chor; Ensm; Fr C; Lat C; VP, NHS; Rptr, Sch P; SC; Tres, Sr Cl; Tnns; Ntl Achv Schol; Rotary A; Summa Cum Laude; Val; Yth Fel; Yth o-t Yr A; Band A; Vocal Talent A; Ch, Stu Adv Comm; Union U; Sci.

LAWLER, Diana Bernice
Hayfork HS; Hayfork, CA (33-45) A Cap Choir; Chor; Pres, Dbte Tm; Drama; Ensm; Secy, FFA; 4H; Madrigal; Tr; Basic Grants; Bethany Bible Col; Mus.

LAWLER, Elizabeth Ann
Holliston HS; Holliston, MA; AFS; Chor; Drama; Phys Therapy.

LAWLER, Martha Lynn
Covington HS; Covington, TN (5-295) Chor; Lat C; NHS; SC; Var C; VP, Soph Cl; MVP, Bkbl; Tr; Yth Fellowship Ldr; Union U; Sci.

LAWLER, Mary Elizabeth
Rock Lake Pub HS; Rock Lake, ND (4-24) Ann; Band; CYO; Chor; Drama; Ensm; VP, FHA; Hmrm; NHS; Rptr, Sch P; Pres, SC; Pres, Sr Cl; VP, Soph Cl; Tr; HCt; FHA C; U of ND; Med Tech.

LAWLER, Tonette A
Hayfork HS; Hayfork, CA; A Cap Choir; Chor; Bsbl.

LAWLES, Gay Lynn
Hydro Pub Sch; Hydro, OK; Chor; Ensm; FHA; Pres, 4H; Cl Fav; 4H A; Hon Prog; Most Out; SW St U; Bus Ed.

LAWLEY, Elizabeth Lynn
Goodwater HS; Goodwater, AL (1-38) Co-Ed, Ann; BC; Chor; Pres, FHA; FNA; Secy, FTA; 4H; Jr Miss Pagent; Secy, Sr Cl; Math C; Citz A; DARGCA; Lion A; MLS; Val; Yth Fel; Ala Forestry Qn Participant; Auburn U; Secondary Ed.

LAWMASTER, Katrina Marie
Will Rogers HS; Tulsa, OK; Sci A; Camp Fire Girls; Silk Line; S-T, CYF; Tulsa Jr Col; Legal Secy.

LAWRENCE, Amy Alice
Shenendehowa HS; Clifton Park, NY (100-670) Band; Ski C; Var C; Soccer; COM; Cl Fav; Co- cpt, Gym.

LAWRENCE, Beverly Anne
Statesville Sr HS; Statesville, NC (23-236) Cpt, Band; BC; FHA; Hmrm; Math C; SC; Mgr, Bkbl; Sftbl; Mgr, Tr; Citz A; HCt; Hon Prog; Math A; Most Out; Yth Leg; Girl o-t Mo; Best All Around; Math.

LAWRENCE, Brenda Jean
Hancock Central HS; Sparta, GA; Chldr; Chem C; Drama; Fr C; FHA; NHS; Sci C; Up Bound; Atlanta Area Tech Col; Med Asst.

LAWRENCE, Brenda Joyce
Hancock Central HS; Sparta, GA; Band; Chldr; FBLA; 4H; NHS; Sci C; Atlanta Area Tech Col; Bus.

LAWRENCE, Caesar Walter
Mount Olive HS; Seale, AL (1-53) Pres, 4H; NHS; Bsbl; Tr; 4H A; ROTC A; Most Intellectual; Math.

LAWRENCE, Cheryl Denise
Jones Valley HS; Birmingham, AL; Ann; Hmrm; Y-Tns; Secy, Soph Cl; COM; Cl Fav; HCt; ROTC A; Top 5%, Co Stu; Art Inst of Atlanta; Fashion Merchandising.

LAWRENCE, Christine Marie
Susquehanna Comm HS; Susquehanna, PA (17-116) Band; Bus C; Chor; 4H; Ski C; Med Secy.

LAWRENCE, Cynthia Leona
Russellville HS; Russellville, AL (25-160) Chldr; Secy, FFA; FHA; SC; Secy, Jr Cl; Hon Prog; Spirit A; Stu o-t Month; Stu o-t Yr; Most Dependable; Miss Etiquette; U of Ala; Health.

LAWRENCE, David Clifton
Forest Park Sr HS; Forest Park, GA (5%-700) Ann; Band; BC; COM; Most Out; All St Band; Ga Tech; Archt.

LAWRENCE, David K
Bridgeton HS; Bridgeton, NJ (145-663) Order/ Arrow; Bkbl; Amer Leg A; Citz A; God & Country A; Yth Fel; Eagle A; Americanism A Sct o-t Yr A.

LAWRENCE, Deborah Jean
Great Bridge HS; Chesapeake, VA; Chor; Drama; Ensm; Tri-HiY; Swim.

LAWRENCE, Delisa Ann
Fayette Co HS; Fayette, AL; F-Ed, Ann; S-T, Band; Chor; FBLA; FHA; FTA; Hmrm; InterClub Coun; Tres, SC; Swtht; Church Pianist; Prom Qn; Morehouse Col; Social Work.

LAWRENCE, Jean Louise
Hellgate HS; Missoula, MT; Chor; Mont Inst o-t Bible.

LAWRENCE, Jennifer Diane
Mahar Regional HS; Orange, MA (40-180) Greenfield Comm Col; Art.

LAWRENCE, Johanna
S Philadelphia HS; Philadelphia, PA (79-750) A Cap Choir; VP, Chor; Sch P; VP, SC; VP, Sr Cl; COM; Ch, Hostess, Usher; Ch, Dance Comm; Comm Col of Philadelphia; Radiologic Tech.

LAWRENCE, Julie Kay
Forest Hill HS; W Palm Beach, FL (100-450) A Cap Choir; Chor; Ensm; GS; NHS; Arch; Stu Activity A; Hon Home Ec A; Pianist & Secy, Yth Group; Toccoa Falls Bible Col; Mus.

LAWRENCE, Julie Margeurite
Shawnee Mission NW HS; Shawnee, KS; CYO; NHS; 150 Hr Hospital Vol; Grade Point Avg A; Kans St U.

LAWRENCE, Kathryn Mae
E Liverpool HS; E Liverpool, OH (1-320) GS; NHS; Val; Secy, Nike; Hi-Tri; Youngstown St U; Pre-Med.

LAWRENCE, Lisa Lynn
Grand Ridge HS; Grand Ridge, FL (10-52) BC; Chldr; FTA; Secy, Sci C; Amer Leg A; Chipola Jr Col; Nurs.

LAWRENCE, Lynda Lee
Herrin Township HS; Herrin, IL; SIU-EDWARDSVILLE; Computer Sci.

LAWRENCE, Lynn Marie
Gadsden HS; Anthony, NM (27-600) Band; Chor; Drama; 4H; Ed, Lit Mag; Madrigal; NFL; NHS; Orch; Rainbow; Rptr, Sch P; Spch C; Thes; Spch A; Yth Fel; McMurray Col; Mus.

LAWRENCE, Mark Alan
Reynolds HS; Greenville, PA (22-212) Chor; Secy, FFA; K of C; NHS; Spch A; FFA St Degree; DuPage Sch of Hort; Horticulture.

LAWRENCE, Mary Beth
Chaska Sr HS; Chaska, MN (50%-250) Band; Chldr; Chor; Drama; Hmrm; Tres, NHS; Ski C; Tres, SC; Cr-Ctry; Sftbl; MVP, Tr; Outward Bound; U of Minn Col of Lib Arts; Art.

LAWRENCE, Patricia Jean
Vanguard HS; Ocala, FL (10-350) Drama; Mu Alpha Theta; Pres, NHS; Shorthand A; 'S' C; Lee Col; Bus.

LAWRENCE, Randall P
Wheaton N HS; Wheaton, IL (100-400) Band; Chor; Community Yth Symph; Fr C; Orch; Rptr, Sch P; Mgr, Bkbl; COM; 1st Pl, IHSA Solo & Ensm Contest; Trinity Col; Mus.

LAWRENCE, Ronnie Everett
Eufaula HS; Eufaula, OK; VP, FFA; NHS; Var C; Cpt, Ftbl; HCt; Most Out; Co-Cpt, Ftbl; Talequah Col; Law.

LAWRENCE, Ruth Esstella
Hellgate HS; Missoula, MT (100-500) A Cap Choir; Ensm; Fr C; Orch.

LAWRENCE, Sharon Elizabeth
Myers Park HS; Charlotte, NC; A Cap Choir; AFS; Band; Chor; Drama; Ensm; Fr C; 4H; Hmrm; InterClub Coun; Lit Mag; Ski C; SC; Tr; U of NC at Chapel Hill; Law.

LAWRENCE, Sheila Dene
Jones Valley HS; Birmingham, AL; Ann; Chor; Pres, Hmrm; NHS; SC; COM; Hon Prog; Star Student; Fr, Eng, Hon A's; Herzing Col; Computer Operation.

LAWRENCE, Steve Grant
Taylor Center Baptist Acad; Taylor, MI (1-9) Chor; NHS; Sch P; Spch C; Var C; Ftbl; Soccer; Sftbl; Tr; Journ A; MLS; Q&S A; Val; Co-Cpt, MVP, Bkbl; Baptist Bible Col; Ed.

LAWRENCE, Susan Kay
LaFarge HS; LaFarge, WI (24-42) Ed, Ann; Chor; Drama; FHA; Sch P; *Greenville Col; Social Worker.*

LAWRENCE, Thomas Edward
Radnor Sr HS; Radnor, PA (80-400) Ch, Hmrm; Soccer; Hon Prog; Soccer A's; *Pre-Med.*

LAWRENCE, Timothy Stuart
Everett HS; Lansing, MI (10-350) NHS; Ski C; Bsbl; Bkbl; Ftbl; Amer Leg A; *Mich St U.*

LAWRENCE, Valerie Lynn
Nevada HS; Nevada, MO (19-230) Dbte Tm; Lat C; VP, Span C; Spch C; Sftbl; Taekwon-Do Green Belt; DAR Essay A; Semi-Fin, Spch A; NOW Essay A; Span Contest, Aural A; *Foreign Lang.*

LAWRENCE, Wendy Berrien
Fort Hunt HS; Alexandria, VA (1-502) Secy, NHS; Sci C; Rptr, Span NHS; Tnns; Co-Cpt, Tr; CSF; Hon Prog; NEDT; Sci A; Summa Cum Laude; Val; Outst Span Stu; NML; *US Naval Acad; Bio.*

LAWRENZ, Dawn Marie
Guilford HS; Rockford, IL (25-619) AFS; Band; NHS; NMF; NMS; WW; Hon Lit C; *Bethel Col; Math.*

LAWS, Donny Joel
Mt Heritage HS; Burnsville, NC (1-175) BC; Drama; Ed, Lit Mag; Monogram; NHS; Bsbl; Cpt, Bkbl; Tr; COM; Gov Honor Prog; Hist A; Math A; MLS; NEDT; Val; Eagle Sct; Drama A; *U of NC at Chapel Hill; Pol Sci.*

LAWS, Ruthie Louette
Monticello HS; Monticello, MS; Band; BC; Ch, Drama; FHA; Pres, 4H; Hmrm; Ed, Sch P; SC; COM; 4H A; Hist A; Journ A; MLS; Sci A; Pres, Sr GSct; Peer Group Coun Trng; Ch, Hospitality Comm; *Miss St U; Journ.*

LAWS, Sandra Yvonne
Laurel Co HS; London, KY (135-345) 4H; Lat C; 4H A; Hon Prog; Spch A; Del, Summa Cum Laude; *U of Ky; Adm.*

LAWSON, Bruce Edward
Woodrow Wilson HS; Portland, OR (125-384) A Cap Choir; Ann; Chor; VP, Drama; Ensm; Madrigal; Order/Arrow; VP, Thes; JV, Ftbl; Mgr, Tr; God & Country A; Order/Arrow A; Outst Newspaper Carrier; *U of Oreg; Ed.*

LAWSON, Catherine Ann
Sevier Co HS; Sevierville, TN (18-255) AFS; Ann; BC; Chldr; Fr C; InterAct C; I Dare You; Sr Superlative; WW; Parl, Tn Board; FCA; *U of Tenn; Interior Design.*

LAWSON, Charles Alexander
New Trier E HS; Winnetka, IL; Ann; NHS; *Sci.*

LAWSON, Christy Bowen
Claxton HS; Claxton, GA (25%-110) Chess C; FBLA; 4H; Sch P; Sci C; Y-Tns; 4H A; *Ga Sou U; Bus.*

LAWSON, Dawn Renae
New Bloomfield R III HS; New Bloomfield, MO (2-34) Ed, Ann; Tres, Band; Chor; Ensm; Pres, Fr C; Secy, NHS; Rptr, Sch P; Secy, SC; Secy, Var C; Secy, Sr Cl; Secy, Jr Cl; Secy, Soph Cl; Sftbl.

LAWSON, Dayla Jean
Highland HS; Anderson, IN (16-400) Span C; Citz A; Span A; *Anderson Col.*

LAWSON, Debbie Lynne
Lake City HS; Lake City, TN (18-132) F-Ed, Ann; Drama; Sch P; Span C; Hon Prog; Pep C; *U of Tenn; Marketing.*

LAWSON, Eric Hoffman
Jack Yates HS; Houston, TX (82-406) Pres, Order/Arrow; Pres, SC; God & Country A; MLS; *Howard U; Bus Adm.*

LAWSON, Joe Bryan
Wilburton HS; Wilburton, OK (25-69) FFA; 4H; Bkbl; Mgr, Ftbl; Mgr, Tr; *E Okla St Col; Engr.*

LAWSON, Joseph Wentworth
Goodlettsville HS; Goodlettsville, TN; Band; Lat C; *Christian Theology.*

LAWSON, Larry Jerome
Madison Acad HS; Huntsville, AL (4-51) VP, A Cap Choir; BC; VP, Chor; Ensm; Math C; Monogram; NHS; Sci C; Var C; JV, Bsbl; Ftbl; Bio A; COM; Cl Fav; HCt; Hon Prog; Math A; Sci A; Star Student; VP, Jr Civitan C; *Ala Christian Col; Elec Engr.*

LAWSON, Lori Denise
Ellen McCarter Stewart Private Sch; Houston, TX (10%-20) Band; Bus C; Commercial C; Dbte Tm; FFA; Ger C; Spch C; World Affairs C; Pres, Jr Cl; Mgr, Bkbl; Cpt, Soccer; Spch A; Sculpture, Art Shows; *Dramatics.*

LAWSON, Lori Lynette
William Monroe HS; Stanardsville, VA (5-78) F-Ed, Ann; Pres, BC; FBLA; Pres, FHA; A-Ed, Lit Mag; SC; Secy, Jr Cl; Cpt, Bkbl; Sftbl; DARGCA; Gov Honor Prog; Type A; Gen Mills Family Ldr; Dist Champ, Forensics; *Madison Col; Sci.*

LAWSON, Pamela Gayle
Pattonville HS; Maryland Heights, MO (20-1100) A Cap Choir; Band; Chor; Crown & Scepter; Drama; Ensm; Madrigal; Orch; Thes; Hon Prog; Outst All-Around Musician; Mus A; Schol Service Ltr and Chevron; *Mus.*

LAWSON, Paul Alvin
Wilburton HS; Wilburton, OK (15-80) 4H; Order/Arrow; Bkbl; Mgr, Ftbl; Fin, Tr; *Okla U; Phys Ed.*

LAWSON, Peggy Annette
York Acad; Shacklefords, VA (2-42) BC; Chor; Hmrm; Pres, Lat C; Pres, Span C; SC; Pres, Sr Cl; Tres, Jr Cl; Cpt, Tnns; COM; DARGCA; Hon Prog; Sal; *Col of William and Mary; Hist.*

LAWSON, Randall E
Winchester HS; Winchester, IL (3-80) A-Ed, Arch; BS; VP, Fr C; Pres, 4H; Pres, SC; Pres, Sr Cl; Pres, Jr Cl; Co-Cpt, Ftbl; Tr; Amer Leg A; COM; 4H A; I Dare You; St Scholar; *Pre-Law.*

LAWSON, Steve Douglas
Savannah HS; Savannah, GA (72-371) VP, Ga Yth; Church Jr Deacon; *Berkshire Christian Col; Ministry.*

LAWSON, Suzanne Rebecca
Delhi HS; Delhi, LA (4-95) Co-Ed, Ann; BC; Bus C; Chor; FBLA; FTA; Lit Ral; Ed, Sch P; S-T, SC; Mgr, Bsbl; Cl Fav; Clerical Practice A; Journ Ed A; *NE La U; Bus Adm.*

LAWTER, John Robert Jr
Columbus HS; Columbus, GA; Semi-Fin, BS; Key C; Tres, Var C; Ftbl; Co-Cpt, Soccer; JV, Tr; Co-Cpt, Wrest; Gov Honor Prog; Hon Prog; *Wofford Col; Math.*

LAWTHER, Alison Elizabeth
Virgil I Grissom HS; Huntsville, AL (25%-520) Co-Ed, Ann; Hmrm; Rptr, SC; Sgt- at-Arms, Sorority; Church Yth; League Pres; Del, Yth Convention; *U of Ala; Bus Adm.*

LAWTON, Denetris Elaine
Aquinas HS; Augusta, GA; Chor; Swim; Jack & Jill of Amer, Inc; Piano A; *Spelman Col; Ed.*

LAWTON, Donna Lynn
Orangeburg-Wilkinson HS; Orangeburg, SC; Cpt, Bkbl; Cpt, Sftbl; HCt.

LAWTON, Elaine Ann
St Joseph's o-t Palisades HS; W New York, NJ (2-289) CYO; Chor; Drama; Fr C; French NHS; Sch Achieve Tm; World Affairs C; Swim; Hon Prog; NEDT; Val; *Mich St U; Agr.*

LAWTON, Ronald William
Carver HS; Columbus, GA (5%-280) Chldr; Hmrm; Pres, Key C; VP, NHS; MVP, Golf; COM; Cl Fav; Hon Prog; Most Out; *Newberry Col; Theology.*

LAWTON, Shoune Colette
E Rome HS; Rome, GA (39-110) Bus C; Drama; FBLA; Hmrm; Span C; Tri-HiY; Allied Med C; UN Sem; Sch Swtht Court; Miss Asbury; Miss Metropolitan; *W Ga Col; Psych.*

LAWVER, Matthew Warren
Prague HS; Prague, NE (2-19) BS; Chor; Drama; Parl, FFA; Pres, 4H; Ntl Yth Conf; Pres, Pol Sci C; Spch C; Var C; VP, Jr Cl; Secy, Soph Cl; Tr; Amer Leg A; COM; Citz A; Gov Honor Prog; 4H A; Hon Prog; Jr Chamber of Com A; Pres A; Spch A; Yth Leg; FFA Star Farmer; FFA A; Runner- up, Farm Spokesman o-t Yr; *Harvard U; Law.*

LAWYER, Susan Marie
N Central Comm Sch; Manly, IA (14-66) Ann; Chor; Fr C; Pres, Rainbow; Rptr, Sch P; Golf; St Off, Grand Hope, Rainbow Girls; Grand Cross; *Iowa St U; Engr.*

LAY, Alma Faye
Horace Maynard HS; Maynardville, TN (9-127) Ann; BC; FHA; 4H; Sci C; Span C; Up Bound; DARGCA; *U of Tenn; Phar.*

LAY, Debra June
Wheaton HS; Wheaton, MO (1-36) Chor; Drama; 4H; Madrigal; Span C; 4H A; Hist A; Hon Prog; Math A; NEDT; Type A; HR; PA; Lang Arts A; Outst Camper.

LAY, George Mendel
Loris HS; Loris, SC (10%-189) Order/Arrow; COM; Gov Honor Prog; H of F; Principal's List; Hon Rating, St Mus Teacher's Assn; *Wake Forest U; Bus Adm.*

LAY, Lee Roy
Horace Maynard HS; Maynardville, TN (11-127) BC; Secy, FFA; Sci C; *Lincoln Mem U; Bus Adm.*

LAY, Linda Diane
L C Anderson HS; Austin, TX (30%-550) A Cap Choir; All Region Choir; UIL, Solo Ensm; *Tex A&M U; Bus.*

LAY, Linda Elaine
Baker HS; Columbus, GA; Chor; FTA; Eng C; *Columbus Col; Med.*

LAY, Olin Preston
Sulphur HS; Sulphur, OK (15-74) A Cap Choir; Chess C; Chor; Drama; Ensm; Phys C; Sci C; Var C; Bsbl; Bkbl; Mgr, Ftbl; Hon Prog; Yth Fel; *Cisco Jr Col; Engr.*

LAY, Randy Lee
Pineville HS; Pineville, LA (5%-230) Ed, Ann; City Conf; Hmrm; Key C; Lit Ral; VP, NHS; SC; Pres, Soph Cl; COM; Hon Prog; Journ A; Opt A; *McNeese St U; Med.*

LAYE, Melissa
Houston Acad; Dothan, AL (10%-33) Drama; Cpt, Mjrte; NHS; Span C; Bkbl; Swim; *Auburn U; Bus.*

LAYER, Jeffrey William
Crystal Lake Comm HS; Crystal Lake, IL (130-560) Var C; Bsbl; Ftbl; Tnns; Wrest; Most Out; Yth Fel; Ath o-t Yr; *Mich St U.*

LAYFIELD, Janice Lillian
Charles Henderson HS; Troy, AL (21-171) Band; Chor; Ensm; Sci C; Span C; *U of Ala; Nurs.*

LAYMAN, Cheri Lee
Wilson Mem HS; Fishersville, VA (3-250) Band; Fr C; Lat C; NFL; NHS; COM; *Bridgewater Col; Fr.*

LAYMAN, Nancy Lee
Southmoreland Sr HS; Alverton, PA (160-300) Chor; Fr C; HiY; Tri-HiY; *U of Pittsburgh; Phys Therapy.*

LAYMAN, Tracey Lynn
West Point HS; West Point, VA (9-60) Band; BC; Chldr; Chor; 4H; Span C; Mgr, Bsbl; Mgr, Soccer; HCt; Val; *U of Va; Bio Research.*

LAYNE, Elizabeth Hope
E C Glass HS; Lynchburg, VA (8-659) Band; Community Yth Symph; Fr C; NHS; Orch; Var C; Vlbl Tm; Section Ldr, Band; Ntl Fr Exam; S-T, UMYF; Church Choir; *Col of William & Mary.*

LAYNE, Karen Denise
El Segundo HS; El Segundo, CA; Band; Chldr; NHS; Span C; CSF; Citz A; Hon Prog; Span Achv A; *Brigham Young A;.*

LAYNE, Mark Garland
Charlottesville HS; Charlottesville, VA (114-369) Hmrm; Key C; Var C; Cpt, Bsbl; Cpt, Ftbl; Tr; Cpt, Wrest; Most Out; MVP, Bsbl; MVP, Ftbl; *Va Military Inst; Econ.*

LAYNE, Melissa Dawn
Homewood HS; Birmingham, AL (42-229) A Cap Choir; Ann; FHA; Lit Ral; Span C; Sftbl; *Samford U; Nurs.*

LAYTON, Audrey Beth
Neshaminy Langhorne HS; Langhorne, PA (150-659) AFS; Band; Chor; Ski C; Bkbl; Tr; *Bloomsburg Col; Sociology.*

LAYTON, Debbie Annette
Licking HS; Licking, MO (20-74) Ann; Chor; Rptr, Sch P; Sftbl; Tr; Citz A; WW, Mus; *SW Baptist Col; Mus.*

LAYTON, Jeffrey Floyd
Milford Sr HS; Milford, DE (37-271) Band; Community Yth Symph; Fr C; Orch; Order/Arrow; Order/Arrow A; Outst Musician; *Mus.*

LAZARO, Liza Marie
Notre Dame HS; Clarksburg, WV (10-50) CYO; Drama; FBLA; Parl, FTA; NFL; NHS; F-Ed, Sch P; VP, SC; Bkbl; Co-Cpt, Tnns; Journ A; Spch A; *Northwestern U; Journ.*

LEACH, Angela Rae
Longmont Sr HS; Longmont, CO (35-600) Chldr; NHS; VP, Ski C; Span C; Tres, SC; FCA; Art C; Yth Organization.

LEACH, Gregory Arthur
Homer Central HS; Homer, NY (10-252) A Cap Choir; Chor; Drama; VP, Fr C; Lat C; NHS; Rptr, Sch P; Thes; JV, Bkbl; JV, Soccer; Tnns; *W Va U; Med.*

LEACH, Judith Lynne
Baldwin-Whitehall HS; Pittsburgh, PA (88-900) Hmrm; NHS; Y-Tns; Urban Yth Action; VP of Personnel, JA; *Bus.*

LEACH, Kelly Ann
Russell HS; East Point, GA; Anchor C; Band; Chldr; Hmrm; Span C; SC; Swtht; Valentine Ct; *Ga Sou Col; Elem Ed.*

LEACH, Laura Ann
T F Riggs HS; Pierre, SD (69-237) Chor; Dbte Tm; Lat C; NFL; *U of SD; Soc Sci.*

LEACH, Marla Jane
Simms HS; Simms, MT (2-60) S-T, Band; Chor; 4H; NHS; S-T, Jr Cl; Math A; Singing Group; Pres, Church Yth.

LEACH, Michael Thomas
Western Hills HS; Fort Worth, TX (50%-496) CYO; *U of Tex; Acct.*

LEACH, Sarah Lou
E Hills HS; Fort Worth, TX; FHA; Hon Prog; Attendance A; *Tex Weslyan Col; Psych.*

LEACH, Susan Wadette
Mount Vernon HS; Mount Vernon, AR (1-17) Ann; VP, FHA; F-Ed, Sch P; SC; Secy, Sr Cl; Tres, Jr Cl; Tres, Soph Cl; Bkbl; Cl Fav; H of F; Hist A; HQn; HCt; Math A; MLS; Sci A; Home Ec A; *Home-Ec.*

LEACH, Suzanne C
Campbell Co Comprehensive HS; LaFollette, TN; BC; Chor; Drama; FHA; Math C; Alg A; Algebra A; *Math.*

LEACH, Tony Ray
Oak Ridge HS; Oak Ridge, TN; 4H; Hmrm; Sch P; VP, SC; Bkbl; Ftbl; Soccer; Sftbl; 4H A; Pres A; Cpt, Vlbl; Karate; Jr Usher, Choir, Church; Church Camp A's; *U of Tenn; Math.*

LEACHMAN, Teresa Marie
Alliance HS; Alliance, NE; Chor; Y-Tns; *Teaching.*

LEACHMAN, William Henry III
Saint James Sch; Saint James, MD (5-31) Ski C; Soccer; Swim; Sacristan; Tres, Vestry; Hist Soc; La Crosse; *U of Va; Bus Adm.*

LEACOCK, Karen Diane
Valencia HS; Placentia, CA; Band; Sftbl; COM; Math A; *Fullerton Jr Col; Social Worker.*

LEADILL, Tracy Leigh
Franklin HS; Franklin, IL (3-42) Chldr; FHA; NHS; Var C; HCt; Hon Prog; Type A.

LEAGUE, Beverly Regina
Travelers Rest HS; Travelers Rest, SC (18-198) S-T, Band; Chor; Community Yth Symph; Ensm; Orch; MVP, Band; Regional Orch; Superior, St Solo & Ensm; All St Band; Furman U Mus Schol; Span A; *Furman U; Mus Ed.*

LEAGUE, Vanesia Carole
Travelers Rest HS; Travelers Rest, SC; VP, Hmrm; JA A; *Columbia Col; Eng.*

LEAHY, Barbara Ann
St Joseph's Notre Dame HS; Alameda, CA (5-78) NHS; Alg A; Eng A.

LEAHY, Mary Elizabeth
Country Day Sch o-t Sacred Heart; Philadelphia, PA; A Cap Choir; F-Ed, Ann; Chor; Drama; Ski C; SC; Bkbl; MVP, Hockey; Tnns; COM; Hist A; Hon Prog; Math A; Sci A; Religion, Eng, Fr, A's; *Notre Dame U; Biol.*

LEAK, David Jeffrey
Peoria HS; Peoria, IL (60-500) JV, Tnns; JV, Wrest; Co-Cpt, Soccer; Yth Fel; YMCA Yth & Gov; Tres, Yth Fel.

LEAKE, Betsy J
York Central Sch; Retsof, NY; Chldr; VP, 4H; NHS; Soccer; 4H A; Hon Prog.

LEAKE, Susan Paige
Burleson HS; Burleson, TX; Band; Ensm; FHA.

LEAKE, Twyla Ann
Marion Co HS; Lebanon, KY (28-298) Band; CYO; VP, FBLA; FHA; Pres, SC; Pres, Soph Cl; HQn; HCt; Type A; Off Machines, Shorthand, A's; *Sullivan Bus Sch; Legal-Diplomatic Secy.*

LEAL, Anne Yolanda
Abilene HS; Abilene, TX (70-600) Band; Pres, CYO; Tri-HiY; Y-Tns; Sftbl; Most Out; Off Band A; Serv and Accomplishments CYO; *Hardin Simmons Col; Nurs.*

LEAL, Jessica
Stephen F Austin Sr HS; Houston, TX; CYO.

LEAMON, Michael David
Richmond Sr HS; Richmond, IN (25%-750) Chor; Hockey; Sftbl; Intra Mural Sports; YES Corps; *United Wesley Col; Pastorial Ministries.*

LEANDERSON, Gretchen Marie
Bellingham HS; Bellingham, WA (1-265) CYO; Ch, Chldr; GS; Tres, NHS; SC; Cpt, Tnns; Masonic A; MLS; Val; Soroptimist Schol; WW; *U of Wash; Nurs.*

LEAP, Denice
Switzerland Co HS; Vevay, IN (4-96) Secy, FHA; Span C; Alg A; COM; Math A; Attendance, Home Ec, Span, Eng, A's.

LEAR, Sheryl K
Crown Point HS; Crown Point, IN; Tres, A Cap Choir; VP, Drama; Madrigal; Secy, Spch C; VP, Thes; Federated Women's C Mus Schol; *Mus Ed.*

LEARNED, Tom M
Wyandotte HS; Kans City, KS; A Cap Choir; Chess C; Chor; City Conf; Drama; Ensm; Model UN; NFL; St Stu Congress; SC; Thes; World Affairs C; Citz A; Mus A; *Okla Christian Col; Drama.*

LEARY, Patricia
South Hunterdon Reg HS; Lambertville, NJ (4-111) CYO; Cpt, Chldr; Chor; Drama; Hmrm; NHS; Secy, SC; Bkbl; Cpt, Hockey; Sftbl; Elk A; Kiwanis A; St Scholar; *Boston U; Phys Ed.*

LEARY, Ruth Allison
Oak Ridge Acad; Oak Ridge, NC (1-30) BC; Monogram; NHS; Ed, Sch P; Bkbl; Sftbl; Tnns; Hon Prog; Nom, Morehead Schol; Nom, Gov Sch; Jr Marshal; *Sweet Briar Col; Special Ed.*

LEASURE, Evelyn E
East Bay Sr HS; Riverview, FL; Chor; Ensm; Fin, Jr Miss Pagent; NHS; Tres, SC; Beauty; Cl Fav; HCt; Stu Adv, Sr Planning, Committees; Pianist, Children's Choir; Tribal Coun; *Eckerd Col; Pub Relations.*

LEASURE, Jeannie
Estancia HS; Estancia, NM (10-67) Chem C; Drama; FBLA; NHS; Pres, Rainbow; Tres, Jr Cl; Bkbl; Tr; Vlbl; Filing A; *NM St U; Fashion Merchandising.*

LEASURE, Mimi Anne
Russell HS; Russell, KY; BC; Chldr; VP, Chor; Ensm; Fr C; Hmrm; Orch; SC; Swim; Tnns; Tr; HCt; Most Valuable Band Member.

LEASURE, Nona Jane
Estancia HS; Estancia, NM (6-46) Secy, Drama; GS; NHS; Rainbow; Var C; Bkbl; Tr; HCt; MLS; Vlbl; Off Ed Assn; *NM St U; Phys Ed.*

LEASURE, Teresa Lynn
Fairfield HS; Leesburg, OH; Drama; Sftbl; Yth Fel; Pres, Yth Group; *Bus.*

LEATH, Joanna Kay
Attica HS; Attica, IN (35-98) Band; Secy, FTA; Rainbow; Secy, Jr Cl; Tri Kappa Art A; *Ball St U; Nurs.*

LEATHERS, Wilbert
Durham HS; Durham, NC; Pres, Hmrm; Bsbl; Bkbl; Sci A; NJHS; *Engr.*

LEAVELLE, John Douglas
Andrews HS; Andrews, TX (39-176) Ger C; Hmrm; Orch; Bkbl; JV, Golf; *Rider Tech of Dallas; Deisel Tech.*

LEAVER, Karin Lynn
El Dorado Springs HS; El Dorado Springs, MO (8-104) Ed, Ann; GS; 4H; Secy, NHS; Sch P; Span C; SC; Secy, Var C; Sftbl; Tr; Beauty; Cl Fav; 4H A; HCt; Journ A; Vlbl; *U of Mo; Journ.*

LEAVITT, Harvey H III
Bowman HS; Wadesboro, NC (4-365) Band; Drama; Hmrm; Pres, Lat C; Pres, NHS; Order/Arrow; Tres, Sci C; SC; Co-Cpt, Bsbl; Cr-Ctry; Tnns; Citz A; Gov Honor Prog; H of F; Hist A; MLS; Order/Arrow A; Pres, Jr Civitan; Fin, Moorehead; Eagle Sct; WW; *Duke U; Pathology.*

LEAVITT, Mary Elizabeth
Marcus Comm HS; Marcus, IA (1-67) Ann; Band; Co-Cpt, Bkbl; Rotary A; Secy, Yth Fel; Church Choir.

LEAZENBY, Randy Lee
N Miami HS; Denver, IN (16-114) A Cap Choir; F-Ed, Ann; Band; Chor; Drama; Ensm; FTA; Madrigal; Tres, Mod Mus Mus; NHS; Sci C; Var C; Bkbl; Ftbl; Wrest; Band, Farrel Brower, A's; *Ind U; Mus.*

LEBA, Karen Marie
St Anthony Village HS; Minneapolis, MN (44-210) Band; 'A' HR; *Col of St Catherines.*

LEBAHN, Dawn Marie
Capital HS; Helena, MT; Chor; Fr C; Orch; Secy, Pres, Yth Group; *Helena Vo-tech Col; Nurs.*

LeBARON, Catharine Ann
Sutter Union HS; Sutter, CA (23-98) Cpt, Chldr; Chor; Drama; Ensm; 4H; Hmrm; Sch P; Ski C; SC; Secy, Var C; Rptr, Soph Cl; Bkbl; MVP, Hockey; Semi-Fin, Tr; HCt; MVP, Vlbl; MIP, Field Hockey; Co-Cpt, Drill Tm; *Chico St Col; Chem.*

LEBDER, Darla Lyn
Uniontown Area Sr HS; Uniontown, PA; Drama; Tres, Hmrm; *Soc Stu.*

LeBLANC, Mark Arnold
Fertile-Beltrami HS; Fertile, MN; Pres, AFS; CYO; Chor; Drama; Ensm; Madrigal; Ski C; Spch C; SC; Thes; Var C; Ftbl; Wrest; Coun of Teach A; Spch A; VFW A; VofDEM; Ftbl A; Ldrship A; *Communications.*

LeBLANC, Marvin Lucien
Nederland HS; Nederland, TX (31-482) VP, CYO; NHS; Order/Arrow; Bsbl; Ftbl; Tr; Alg A; Amer Leg A; COM; Math A; Order/Arrow A; Eagle Sct A; *U of Houston; Archt.*

LeBLANC, Michelle Marie
Ft Lupton HS; Ft Lupton, CO (7-125) Ann; Chor; Fr C; FTA; NHS; Rainbow; Sci C; VP, Yth Fel; Bkbl Statistician; Pres, Leo C; JV Gym; Pep C; GAA; *U of N Colo; Audiology.*

LeBLANC, Stephen Paul
Don Bosco Tech HS; Boston, MA (5-218) Lit Mag; NHS; Cpt, Cath Yth Bsbl & Bkbl; *Lowell U; Archt.*

LEBRON, Lourdes
Our Lady of Good Counsel HS; Newark, NJ (1-64) NHS; COM; Hon Prog; Reserve U; Ed.

LEBRON, Marie Delia
Colegio Espiritu Santo; Hato Rey, PR (8-96) Ann; Tres, Drama; Tres, Hmrm; NFL; Ed, Sch P; VP, Sci C; Sodality; Spch C; Tres, Sr Cl; Tres, Soph Cl; COM; Hon Prog; Spch A; Ann Talent Show, Poetry; *U of Puerto Rico; Sci.*

LeBRON, Ramona Lalita
All Saints Cathedral Schl; St Thomas, VI (1-28) Ann; Band; VP, Soph Cl; COM; Citz A; Hon Prog; Band A; Schol Attainment, GSct; *George Washington U; Med.*

LEBSACK, Laurie Lee
Holyoke HS; Holyoke, CO; Chor; FBLA; Secy, FFA; FHA; Pres, 4H; NHS; Var C; Tr; 4H A; Star Greenhand; High Point, Rodeo; *Colo U; Med.*

LEBSOCK, Jeff Todd
Fairview HS; Fairview, MT (6-53) Band; CYO; SC; Var C; Bsbl; Cpt, Bkbl; Cpt, Ftbl; Tr.

LECHLER, Earl David
Williamston HS; Williamston, MI; Key C; Ski C; Tr; Order/Arrow A; Automotive A; Denver Auto and Diesel Col; Automotive.

LECK, Susan Marie
Thomas Stone HS; Waldorf, MD (10-361) Ed, Ann; Chor; Drama; Hmrm; Secy, Mod Mus Mas; NHS; SC; COM; DARGCA; Elk A; MLS; VFW A; VofDEM; Guidance Aide; Hon Graduate; Marian Medal; Md Acord of Sci Stu Sem-In-Depth; U of Va.

LECLERC, Joanne Sylvie
Alexander Galt Regional HS; Lennoxville, CAN-ADA (5-539) Chldr; Fr A; Bus.

LECLERE, Randall Jay
Park Hill Sr HS; Kansas City, MO (30-420) Chor; Dbte Tm; NFL; Spch C; Golf; JV, Wrest; Citz A; God & Country A; Opt A; Spch A; VP, Ntl Forensic League; Mic- o- say; Art Merit A; Eagle Sct; Mic-O-Say; Fine Arts.

LeCOURT, Claudia Marie
St Joseph Regional HS; Lowell, MA; Hmrm; VP, NHS; SC; Bkbl; Tnns; COM; U of Lowell; Nurs.

LeCROY, Robert Thomas
Blair HS; Hattiesburg, MS (5%-350) Band; Key C; Order/Arrow; Span C; Miss Lions All St Band; Eagle Sct; Pres, Yth Choir; Miss Yth All St Symph Orch.

LeCROY, Scott Whitfield
Ensley HS; Birmingham, AL (1-356) A Cap Choir; Tres, Band; VP, Chor; Pres, Hmrm; Lat C; VP, NHS; Tres, Orch; Sci C; SC; COM; Hon Prog; Magna Cum Laude; Sci A; Star Student; Best Fresh, Faculty; U of A Scholastic Exc A; Excellence Prog Ind Stu; Eng A.

LEDBETTER, Anita Gwen
Douglas Co HS; Douglasville, GA; Chor; Drama; Yth Fel; Chorale; Lib Sci.

LEDBETTER, Anita Karen
Travelers Rest HS; Travelers Rest, SC (30-300) F-Ed, Ann; Pres, Hmrm; NHS; F-Ed, Sch P; SC; HR; Sftbl; Bkbl; Greenville Tech Col; Dental Hygienist.

LEDBETTER, Brenda Lee
Burnsville HS; Burnsville, MS; Band; Secy, BC; Chldr; FHA; Mjrte; VP, Sr Cl; Secy, Jr Cl; Cl Fav; HQn; HCt; Northeast Miss Jr Col; Pre-Vet.

LEDBETTER, Caroline Louise
Bennettsville HS; Bennettsville, SC (6-230) BC; FHA; NHS; Sci C; Var C; Bkbl; HQn; Hon Prog; Sci A; U of SC; Computer Sci.

LEDBETTER, Dave Bryce
L'Anse Creuse HS N; Mt Clemens, MI; Chor; Ger C; NHS; COM; Judson Col; Religion.

LEDBETTER, Frances Millicent
Benton Acad; Benton, MS (2-28) Secy, BC; JV, Chldr; Chor; 4H; Rptr, Hmrm; Key C; Co-Ed, Sch P; Rptr, Soph Cl; Cl Fav; Holmes Jr Col.

LEDBETTER, Letty
John A Brashear HS; Pittsburgh, PA; Community Yth Symph; Orch; Y-Tns; COM; Responsibility A; PA; UCLA; Bus Adm.

LEDBETTER, Lisa
John A Brashear HS; Pittsburgh, PA; Community Yth Symph; 4H; Orch; Y-Tns; PA; U of Pittsburgh; Phys Therapy.

LEDBETTER, Rachelle Leslie
Agnes Irwin Sch; Rosemont, PA (40%-44) Chldr; Mjrte; NHS; Ski C; SC; JV, Bkbl; JV, Sftbl; Hon Prog; Math A; Yth Fel; Bible Stu Group; Young Life; Jazz, Ballroom, Dancer; Current Events C; William Smith Col.

LEDBETTER, Rita Fay
Hermitage HS; Hermitage, AR (1-52) BC; Chor; FHA; French NHS; Secy, Math C; Mgr, Bkbl; U of Ark at Monticello; Elem Ed.

LEDBETTER, Stephen Lin
Haverford HS; Haverford, PA (18-95) Bsbl; Hockey; Hon Prog; JA A; Pres A; Yth Fel; High Hon A; Cert of Appreciation; Stanford U; Lib Arts.

LEDBETTER, Thomas Searcy
N Augusta Sr HS; N Augusta, SC; Ann; BS; Ensm; VP, NHS; Yth Fel; Sr High Choir; Clemson U.

LEDDY, Herbert Jon
John F Kennedy HS; Tumon, GUAM; Co-Ed, Ann; CYO; Hmrm; NHS; Sch P; St Stu Congress; SC; Amer Leg A; Most Out; ROTC A; Yth Leg; VP, Personnel, Sales, Jr Achv; UN Debate Tm; OICE for A Day; Squad Comm, ROTC; Stu Govt Day; Schol A; Pan Am Dir for A Day; Pol Sci.

LEDER, Brian Keith
Burley HS; Burley, ID (48-225) Band; Chor; Bus Mgr, Stage Band; Church Organist; Pres, Tres, Yth Group; Concordia Col; Christian Ed.

LEDFORD, Danny Ray
Tecumseh HS; Tecumseh, OK; Bsbl; Ftbl; Wrest; Okla Baptist U; Religion.

LEDFORD, Jeanne Marcella
Red Bank HS; Chattanooga, TN (50-350) NHS; Sch P; Span C; Yth Fel; U of Tenn; Pre-Law.

LEDFORD, Jeffrey Scott
Cleveland HS; Cleveland, TN (5-250) BS; Hmrm; VP, Key C; NHS; Alg A; Amer Leg Orator A; Bio A; Chem A; Hon Prog; Math A; Sci A; Top 5 C; Eng A; Vanderbilt Col; Physics.

LEDKINS, David Christopher
Lindale HS; Lindale, TX (22-68) VP, FFA; Hmrm; F-Ed, Sch P; Spch C; SC; Cpt, Bsbl; Cpt, Ftbl; Co-Cpt, Tr; Rotary A; Spch A; MVP, Bsbl; E Tex Baptist Col; Phys Ed.

LeDOUX, Patricia Jeralyn
Mercy HS; St Martinville, LA (1-18) CYO; Fr C; S-T, 4H; Hmrm; Fin, Jr Miss Pagent; Fin, Lit Ral; NHS; Sch Achieve Tm; Sci C; Pres, Sodality; Tres, Jr Cl; Swim; Alg A; Beauty; Bio A; COM; Citz A; 4H A; Hon Prog; PTA A; Pres A; Type A; Quebec Yth Ambassador; NCTE Achv A, Writing Nom; St 4-H Tres Cand; Ntl 4-H Comm; LSU; Nurs.

LeDOUX, Patricia Lynn
Orangefield HS; Orangefield, TX (3-74) CYO; Pres, FHA; VP, FTA; NHS; Sch P; SC; H of F; Math A; PTA A; Outst Homemaking Stu; Sabine Area Home Ec A; Lamar U at Beaumont; Acct.

LEE, Albert Lloyd
Sumter HS; Sumter, SC (115-753) Chess C; Fr C; Amer Leg A; ROTC A.

LEE, Allan Mark
Whitney Point HS; Whitney Point, NY (1-150) NHS; Rptr, Sch P; Var C; Cr-Ctry; Tr; COM; Math A; Regent Schol; Sci A; NML; The King's Col; Biol.

LEE, Alvin Yin
Belmont HS; Los Angeles, CA (80-835) All Amer Yth; Chess C; Chor; Cum Laude Soc; Hmrm; VP, InterAct C; InterClub Coun; Tres, NHS; Bkbl; Amer Leg A; CSF; COM; Citz A; Hist A; Hon Prog; Math A; Opt A; PTA A; Fr A; Industrial Arts A; Ephebians; U of Southern Calif; Archt.

LEE, Audrey Marie
St Andrew's HS; Charleston, SC (72-275) Lit Mag; Type A; Attendance A; U South Carolina; Communications.

LEE, Barbara Jean
E L Bowsher Sr HS; Toledo, OH; A Cap Choir; Chor; Ensm; Madrigal; ARC; Bkbl; Tr; COM; ARC A; Yth Fel; Piano A; U of Toledo; Mus Ed.

LEE, Barbara Lynn
William Monroe HS; Stanardsville, VA (33%-78) Rptr, BC; Pres, FHA; 4H; Sci C; Citz A; 4H A; Math A; Sci A; Va Comm Col; Acct.

LEE, Bill Edwin
Central HS; Camp Point, IL (10-115) Rptr, FFA; Ger C; Order/Arrow; Sch Achieve Tm; VP, SC; Var C; JV, Bkbl; Ftbl; Tr; COM.

LEE, Brenita Yvette
W Point HS; W Point, VA; Band; Chor; Parl, FHA; Mgr, Bkbl; Sftbl.

LEE, Bruce Robert
The Bronx HS of Sci; Bronx, NY (10%-900) VP, Chess C; Ed, Fr C; Parl, Hmrm; Co-Ed, Lit Mag; Math C; Parl, NHS; Pol Sci C; F-Ed, Sch P; Pres, Sci C; Ch, SC; Co-Cpt, Cr-Ctry; Tnns; Cpt, Tr; Bio A; COM; Hon Prog; Journ A; Math A; Regent Schol; Sci A; Yth Fel; Art School; Tutor Director; Cornell U; Biol Sci.

LEE, Cheryl Denise
Williamston HS; Williamston, NC (31-179) BC; Cpt, Chldr; FTA; Key C; Monogram; SC; NC A&T St U; Early Childhood Ed.

LEE, Chi Chi
Central HS; Little Rock, AR (279-650) BS; Chor; Hmrm; VP, Key C; Ftbl; Sftbl; Tr; Cl Fav; U of Little Rock; Bus.

LEE, Cynthia Gail
Smith HS; Atlanta, GA (6-200) Band; Chem C; Math C; NHS; Orch; Arch; Bkbl; Sftbl; Tr; Chem Engr.

LEE, Cynthia Robin
Whitman-Hanson Regional HS; Whitman, MA (1-418) Dbte Tm; Math C; NHS; Mgr, Cr-Ctry; Tr; Hist A; Hon Prog; Rensselaer A; Hist.

LEE, Dale Wayne
Lake Worth HS; Fort Worth, TX (3-104) VP, Band; Drama; Ensm; NHS; Pres, Spch C; Thes; Spch A; Bus Law, Outst Bandsman, A's; Eng, Best Supporting Actor, A's; U of Tex; Law.

LEE, Dana Ann
Encina HS; Sacramento, CA (1-400) Band; Chor; Secy, Community Yth; Ch,pEnsm; Ch, Fr C; Secy, Orch; Pol Sci C; Swim; Tnns; Bank OF Amer A; Hon Prog; Pres, CSF; Fin, Gemco School; Fin, Bank of Amer A; Win, Mus, Fin, COM; MGM C; Pres, Jr Sat C; Fin, Val; Win, Jr Bach Festival; Stanford U; Piano Performance.

LEE, Dana Whitney
Hesperia HS; Hesperia, MI (5-84) Ferris St Col; Bus Mgt.

LEE, Darryl Bernard
John Adams HS; Cleveland, OH; Fr C; Hmrm; Lit Mag; Phys C; Bsbl; Sftbl; COM; Citz A; Phy A; Type A; Eng A; Ohio St U; Eng.

LEE, David
James Marshall HS; W Sacramento, CA (10-250) BS; City Conf; Pres, Key C; Ed, Sch P; JV, Bsbl; Bkbl; Bank Of Amer A; CSF; Journ A; MLS; Q&S A; Sacramento Bee A; Sacramento City Col; Bus.

LEE, David Kenneth
University City HS; University City, MO (156-465) Co-Cpt, Bkbl; Cr-Ctry; Cpt, Tr; MVP, Tr; Semi-Fin, Schol Ath; Sou Ill U; Acct.

LEE, David Matthew
Dothan HS; Dothan, AL (5%-750) Chor; InterClub Coun; Pres, Key C; NHS; SC; Var C; Secy, Jr Cl; VP, Soph Cl; Bsbl; Mgr, Ftbl; Citz A; Cl Fav; DARGCA; Health Careers C; Secy, Teenage Vol; Bob Jones U; Mus.

LEE, Debbie Ann
Marion Co HS; Lebanon, KY (3-298) Band; Chor; Drama; Ensm; FTA; Pres, 4H; Jr Miss Pagent; NHS; Sci C; Span C; Spch C; Thes; Mgr, Bkbl; Tr; COM; Gr Marshal; Hist A; Spch A; Yth Fel; U of Ky; Law.

LEE, Deborah Jane
St Andrews Parish HS; Charleston, SC (40-375) S-T, Hmrm; SC; Mgr, Bkbl; WW; Pep C; Pres, Lib C; Icthus C; Sr Comm; Col of Charleston.

LEE, Deborah Jo
Greece Athena Sr HS; Rochester, NY; VP, Band; Chor; VP, Drama; Ensm; Hmrm; SC; Sftbl; Tr; COM; Hon Prog; Sci A; Yth Fel; 1st Pl, IESA Mus Contest; 1st Pl Voice, Church Dist Contest; Ntl Guild Piano Playing Auditions; Olivet Nazarene Col; Med.

LEE, Debra Renee
Winston Churchill HS; San Antonio, TX (319-800) Sftbl; UTSA; Acct.

LEE, Denise Renee
Compton Sr HS; Compton, CA (26-800) Chldr; Pres, Chor; NHS; Sci C; CSF; Citz A; Personality A; Zeta Phi Beta Debutante; Marymount Palos Verdes Col; Pre-Sch Ed.

LEE, Donald Craig
Ansley Pub HS; Ansley, NE (33%-49) Band; Chor; SC; Var C; Bkbl; Ftbl; Tr; Kearney St Col; Art.

LEE, Donna Marie
Cass Tech HS; Detroit, MI (100-800) 4H; U of Mich; Phys Therapy.

LEE, Doreen Ann
Belmont HS; Los Angeles, CA (5%-825) Chldr; Secy, Chor; GS; Secy, InterAct C; InterClub Coun; NHS; Var C; Y-Tns; Tnns; CSF; COM; Chem A; Citz A; Hist A; Hon Prog; Journ A; Ntl Achv Schol; PTA A; Poet A; Sci A; Yth Fel; Vlbl; Art A; *Acct.*

LEE, Dorie Andrea
Leroy HS; Leroy, AL (1-68) Ann; BC; Chldr; FHA; 4H; Jr Miss Pagent; Secy, Sr Cl; Secy, Jr Cl; Secy, Soph Cl; Beauty; HCt; Hon Prog; Val; Piano A; Sci A; Most Popular; Best Dressed; Eng A; Rep, Good Citz Seminar; *Meridian Jr Col; Ed.*

LEE, Douglyne Christine
West Point HS; West Point, VA; Band; FFA; FTA; Mjrte; Cpt, Bkbl; Cpt, Tr; COM; MVP, Bkbl; MVP, All District, Tr; *Va St Col; Health & Phys Ed.*

LEE, Eric Aaron
Stoughton Sr HS; Stoughton, WI (20-300) Math C; Model UN; Span C; JV, Bsbl; Ftbl; *U of Southern Cal; Journ.*

LEE, Esther Ruth
N Mesquite HS; Mesquite, TX; A Cap Choir; Band; NHS; Span C; Sftbl; Hon Prog; *SMU; Mus.*

LEE, Fonda Marsha
Pleasant Grove HS; Pleasant Grove, AL (5-145) Chldr; Chem C; NHS; Span C; *Xavier U; Med.*

LEE, Frank Nam
The Bronx HS of Sci; Bronx, NY (10%-961) Pres, Chess C; Parl, Hmmr; Ed, Lit Mag; Math C; Parl, NHS; Pol Sci C; F-Ed, Sch P; VP, Sci C; Ed, Span C; Co-Ch, SC; Bsbl; MVP, Bkbl; Co-Cpt, Cr-Ctry; Tnns; Cpt, Tr; Bio A; COM; Hist A; Hon Prog; JA A; Math A; Regent School; Sci A; Yth Fel; MVP Intramural Bkbl; *Cornell U; Pol Sci.*

LEE, Gina
Forest Park Sr HS; Forest Park, GA; Chldr; Inter-Club Coun; Span C; SC; HCt; *Med Asst.*

LEE, Glenn Lester
Madison HS; San Diego, CA (243-930) Hmmr; NHS; SC; Citz A; Pres A; St Scholar; Yth Fel; Yth Leg; Win, Calif Schol; *U of Calif; Bio.*

LEE, Gregory Earl
Lanier HS; Jackson, MS; Bkbl; Swim; Tnns; Star Student; *Jackson St U; Social Stu.*

LEE, Gregory Keith
Pleasure Ridge Park HS; Louisville, KY (9-315) F-Ed, Ann; BC; Drama; Fr C; Hmmr; Ch, NHS; SC; COM; WW; *U of Ky; Acct.*

LEE, Gwendolyn Renee
Texas City HS; Texas City, TX (25%-500) JV, A Cap Choir; Band; Chor; Drama; Ensm; Mjrte; Thes; Bkbl; Opt A; Spch A; Straight A A; *U of Texas.*

LEE, Hyun Suk
Largo Sr HS; Largo, MD; Cr-Ctry; Tr; *Med.*

LEE, Jan Elizabeth
Columbia HS; Decatur, GA; Span C; Kappa C; Drill Tm; Art C; *Eng.*

LEE, Janet Rebecca
Carlisle Intermediate HS; Carlisle, PA (10%-1000) Chor; NHS; Rptr, Sch P; COM; Citz A; 1st Cl Sct; Girl sr Mo; *Med.*

LEE, Janice Lynn
Las Lomas HS; Walnut Creek, CA (1-325) AFS; Ensm; Key C; NHS; Orch; Y-Tns; Semi-Fin, Tr; Hon Prog; Fin, Gym; *Math.*

LEE, Jennifer
Savannah Christian HS; Savannah, GA (33-137) Drama; NHS; Span C; Tri-HiY; Sftbl; Sci A; Drill Tm; Secy, Future Secys of Amer; Vlbl; *Armstrong St Col; Phys Therapy.*

LEE, Jimmy Robert
N Mesquite HS; Mesquite, TX; *Eastfield Jr Col; Acct.*

LEE, Joeli Kay
Mio AuSable HS; Mio, MI (7%-70) Chor; NHS; Pres, Jr Cl; Pres, Soph Cl; Co-Cpt, Bkbl; Type A; WW; Mus A; Bor Better Avg; PA; *Bus.*

LEE, John Mark
Corsicana HS; Corsicana, TX (2-200) A Cap Choir; Hmmr; Rptr, Sch P; SC; Tnns; Journ A; *Law.*

LEE, Jonathan Bruce
Stratford HS; Stratford, CT (70-400) Band; Fr C; Order/Arrow; Ski C; Var C; Hockey; Mgr, Soccer; Swim; Tr; Order/Arrow A; Type A; Photo C; Sr High Pilgrim Fel; Church Bkbl; Del, St Conference of Churches; *Natural Sci.*

LEE, Judith Anne
The Buckley Sch; Sherman Oaks, CA; Model UN; NHS; Alg A; Bio A; Hon Prog; NEDT; Yth in Govt; GSct; Lat A; Span A.

LEE, Julie Ann
Austin HS; Decatur, AL (10-350) Bus C; Mu Alpha Theta; NHS; NEDT; 3rd Pl, DECA District Advertising; *Auburn U; Pre Law.*

LEE, Julinda Letitia
Greenland HS; Greenland, AR (2-45) Ann; Band; VP, Hmmr; Sch P; Var C; Bkbl; Sftbl; Spelling, Civics, Band, A's.

LEE, Karen Louise
Alhambra HS; Alhambra, CA (147-758) Secy, Fr C; Art Ch, Girls League; Dance C; Graduation Night Committee; Hist, Social Ch; VP, Campus Service C; *Calif St U.*

LEE, Kathryn Malia
Yorkwood Jr-Sr HS; Monmouth, IL (3-44) Ann; Secy, Band; CYO; Chor; Drama; NHS; Rptr, Sch P; Span C; Spch C; SC; Tres, Sr Cl; Hon Prog; Journ A; Spch A; HR; Band A.

LEE, Kelly Ann
Beverly Hills HS; Beverly Hills, CA (150-700) Band; Chldr; Ger C; Swim; COM; Hon Prog; Most Out; Most Inspirational; *Dartmouth Col; Med.*

LEE, Kevin Edward
Coshocton HS; Coshocton, OH (14-233) Band; BS; Ensm; Pres, HiY; Key C; VP, NHS; Pres, Order/Arrow; Span C; SC; Pres, Sr Cl; NEDT; Order/Arrow A; Edmont Achv A; *Miami U; Acct.*

LEE, Kimberley Lynn
Inglewood HS; Inglewood, CA; Chldr; Sch P; Var C; MVP, Sftbl; PTA A; Lat A; *U of Calif; Law.*

LEE, Laura Jane
Waterproof HS; Waterproof, LA (25%-54) Tres, BC; Lit Ral; *NE La U; Bus.*

LEE, Laura Susan
DuVal Sr HS; Lanham, MD (10%-600) Chor; Tres, NHS; Tr; Fr A; *U of Md.*

LEE, Laurie Catherine
University HS; Baton Rouge, LA (1-60) A Cap Choir; Tres, BC; Community Yth Symph; Fr C; FHA; FTA; Fin, Lit Ral; Co-Ed, Lit Mag; NHS; Sftbl; Bio A; COM; Chem A; Citz A; Hon Prog; Ntl Sci Found; PTA A; Pres A; Sci A; Grand Prize Win, Sch Sci Fairs; Ntl Fed of Mus C; Social Stu A; *Baylor U; Math.*

LEE, Leta Anette
McGavock HS; Nashville, TN (1-830) BC; Fr C; NHS; ARC; Pres, SC; Pres, Sr Cl; Cpt, Bkbl; Tr; Alg A; Bio A; Hon Prog; Pres A; ARC A; Sci A; Val; Yth Fel; Sertoma Essay A; *U of Tenn; Med.*

LEE, Linda Dolores
Plant City HS; Plant City, FL (600-1200) VP, FBLA; Hmmr; Mjrte; SC; *Fla St U; Bus.*

LEE, Lisa Annette
Resource Learning Center; Birmingham, AL (32-60) Asst Teacher Kindergarten; Bible Sch Teacher; President Schol, Freed-Hardeman Col; *Freed-Hardeman Col; Elem Ed.*

LEE, Lucy Johnson
Giles Co HS; Pulaski, TN (20-148) Chldr; Chor; Lat C; Sch P; HCt; Hon Prog; Cpt, Rifle Corp; Pres, Pulaski Sub Deb C; Secy, Church Choir; Hon Schol; *Martin Col; Art.*

LEE, Lynn Marie
Robert E Lee HS; Jacksonville, FL (2-490) Anchor C; Lat C; Pres, NHS; HCt; Sal; Chaplain, Stu Coun; Chaplain, Tri-Hi-Y; Sci Hon; Most Outst A; *U of Fla; Pre-Med.*

LEE, Martha Carolyne
Westmont Hilltop HS; Johnstown, PA (8-205) Chor; Ensm; NHS; Ski C; COM; NEDT; *U of Va; Psych.*

LEE, Mathias James
Alamosa HS; Alamosa, CO (3-205) Band; CYO; Orch; SC; Thes; Pres, Soph Cl; Tr; Pres, Fresh Cl; SC A; *U of Col; Archt.*

LEE, Michael
Highlands HS; San Antonio, TX (5-601) Cum Laude Soc; JETS; Tres, Lat C; VP, Math C; VP, Mu Alpha Theta; Tres, NHS; Phys C; Sch Achieve Tm; Sci C; Co-Cpt, Tnns; Alg A; COM; Hon Prog; Math A; PTA A; Sci A; Summa Cum Laude; St Drafting A; St JETS Engr A; *Rice U; Architectural Engr.*

LEE, Michael Edward
Westside HS; Jonesboro, AR (35-102) FFA; *Hist.*

LEE, Norman Gilbert
Glen A Wilson HS; Hacienda Heights, CA (40-600) Band; BS; Chess C; Community Yth Symph; Ensm; Model UN; Orch; ARC; UN Council; Bsbl; Bkbl; Sftbl; Tnns; CSF; Band Medals; Mineral A's; *Calif St U; Forestry.*

LEE, Oliver Allen
DeLand HS; DeLand, FL; Co-Cpt, Bkbl; MVP, Bkbl; All St; All Conf; All-Amer; WW; All Area; *Communications.*

LEE, Pamela Ann
Merry HS; Cincinnati, OH; Swim; Vlbl; Choir; *U of Cincinnati.*

LEE, Pamela Jean
Westwood HS; Memphis, TN (17-212) A-Ed, Ann; Secy, Band; Chldr; Chor; Hmrm; Semi-Fin, Jr Miss Pa; S-T, Lat C; Rptr, Lit Mag; VP, Math C; Secy, NHS; Rptr, Sch P; Secy, SC; COM; Hon Prog; Band Hon; PA; *Tenn St U; Law.*

LEE, Pamela Noreen
Alexander Galt Regional HS; Lennoxville, CANADA (19-539).

LEE, Patricia Elaine
Banks HS; Birmingham, AL; Co-Ed, Ann; Band; Ensm; Jr Miss Pagent; Cpt, Mjrte; SC; Pres, Tri-HiY; VP, Sr Cl; Secy, Jr Cl; Beauty; Cl Fav; Journ A; Yth Leg; *U of N Ala; Fashion Merchandising.*

LEE, Peter Wing
Woodrow Wilson HS; Los Angeles, CA (70%-700) Chess C; Cpt, Dbte Tm; Fr C; Orch; Var C; MVP, Bkbl; Ftbl; Tnns; Yth Fel; *U of Calif; Computer Sci.*

LEE, Portia Alison
Kailua HS; Kailua, HI (25-570) Secy, Span C; SC; JA A; *U of Hawaii; Interior Design.*

LEE, Rebecca Dear
Mission Bay HS; San Diego, CA (87-433) Chor; Ensm; NHS; A-Ed, Sch P; COM; Hon Prog; Type A; Yth Fel; Yth Foundation; Yth Leg; Fin, Miss Tn San Diego; Secy, C-Ed, Church P; *Point Loma Col; Home Ec.*

LEE, Richard Carlton
Aurora-Hoyt Lakes HS; Aurora, MN (10%-245) AFS; Band; Chor; Order/Arrow; Span C; Ftbl; JV, Hockey; Tr; Hon Prog; Yth Fel; Pres, Church Yth; *Math.*

LEE, Richard Paul
John Overton HS; Nashville, TN (130-415) Span C; Bkbl; Sftbl; All Star, Church Sftbl; MVP, Church Bkbl; *Belmont Col; Religion.*

LEE, Richard Reed
Florence Township Mem HS; Florence, NJ (15-154) Math C; Ntl Yth Conf; Var C; Y-Tns; Bsbl; Bkbl; Ftbl; Pres, Yth Fel; PA; Sunday Sch; *Archt.*

LEE, Robert Daniel
John Muir HS; Pasadena, CA (50-750) Band; BS; Chess C; Pres, Ger C; Key C; Lat C; Tres, Mod Mus Mas; Orch; Rptr, Sch P; SC; Swim; Amer Leg A; Hon Prog; Water Polo; Commanding Off, Color Guard; *The Colo Col.*

LEE, Robin Clark
Hobbs HS; Hobbs, NM; Band; Chor; *NTSU; Mus.*

LEE, Rodney Reginald
Richard Arnold HS; Savannah, GA; Chor; Tr; *Astronomy.*

LEE, Rosalyn Wanda Gale
Beach Sr HS; Savannah, GA (38-42) FHA; 4H; Span C; Arch; Cr-Ctry; Tr; COM; Citz A; 4H A; Drill Tm; *Armstrong Col; Nurs.*

LEE, Rosemarie Antoinette
Duncan HS; Duncan, OK; Chor; SC; All Dist; Hon Choir; Superior, Excel, Solo; *Southwestern Col; Mus.*

LEE, Roy Daniel
Jackson HS; Jackson, LA (5%-92) S-T, BC; Pres, FFA; Parl, SC; DARGCA; *LSU; Engr.*

LEE, Ruth Ann
St Ignatius HS; St Ignatius, MT (1-32) Band; Chldr; Ensm; Hmrm; Co-Cpt, Mjrte; S-T, NHS; Rainbow; VP, SC; Secy, Soph Cl; Swim; COM; HCt; Type A; WW; *Mont St U; Vet.*

LEE, Sarah Lucienne
Central HS; Cheyenne, WY (24-370) Band; Hmrm; Lat C; NHS; Lion A; ROTC A; Alt, GS; Commander, Band Color Guard; HR; *U of Wy; Psych.*

LEE, Sonya Renita
W Charlotte HS; Charlotte, NC (164-601) A Cap Choir; All Amer Yth; Cpt, Chldr; Chor; Ensm; Pres, FHA; Hmrm; InterClub Coun; Order/Arrow; VP, ARC; Ed, Sch P; Spch C; Ch, SC; Beauty; Cl Fav; HCt; Journ A; Order/Arrow A; Q&S A; Yth Fel; 2nd Runner-Up, Carousel Qn; WW; Human Relation Trophy; Band A; Chldr A; *UNC-Charlotte; Criminal Justice.*

LEE, Susan Dianne
McCluer N HS; Florissant, MO (3-730) Band; NHS; *Mo Baptist Sch of Nurs; Nurs.*

LEE, Theodore Chan
Central HS; Philadelphia, PA (4-400) Chor; Ensm; Pres, Math C; Mu Alpha Theta; Orch; Sch Achieve Tm; COM; Citz A; Hon Prog; Math A; Sci A; Spch A; VFW A; VofDEM; Most Respected; Eng A; Fr A; *Yale U; Bio.*

LEE, Thomas H
La Jolla HS; La Jolla, CA; A Cap Choir; A-Ed, Ann; Band; Community Yth Symph; Ensm; Fr C; Hmrm; Secy, Key C; Madrigal; Orch; JV, Tr; Chem A; Citz A; Cl Fav; Math A; Sci A; Sou Calif, All St, Hon Orch; Symptonist, Key C Achv, A's; Key C Talent, Violin Solo, A's; Heart Assn, A's; *U of Calif; Med.*

LEE, Timothy Jacobus
Napa HS; Napa, CA (30-500) A Cap Choir; Demolay; VP, 4H; InterAct C; Key C; Lit Mag; Model UN; NHS; St Stu Congress; SC; VP, Sr Cl; Secy, Jr Cl; S-T, Soph Cl; MVP, Cr-Ctry; Soccer; MVP, Tr; Wrest; CSF; Chamber of Comm A; Citz A; 4H A; Masonic A; Most Out; Spch C; FCA School; *Berkely Col; Psych.*

LEE, Tina Lanett
Wade Hampton HS; Greenville, SC (107-386) Ensm; Mjrte; Span C; Bkbl; Sftbl; HCt; Pres, Acteens; All Star, Most Improv, Church Bkbl; *Winthrop Col; Fashion Merchandising.*

LEE, Todd Winfield
Thomas Jefferson HS; Richmond, VA; Band; Ensm; Pres, Hmrm; Key C; Orch; Tnns; *Mus.*

LEE, Tony Story
Vintage HS; Napa, CA (30-500) A Cap Choir; Chor; Drama; 4H; InterAct C; Secy, Key C; Model UN; NHS; Ntl Yth Conf; Spch C; Var C; Tres, Sr Cl; Cpt, Cr-Ctry; Cpt, Tr; Elk A; HKg; Opt A; Sports A's; *U of Calif; Psych.*

LEE, Tracy Jean
Wilson HS; Wilson, TX (2-14) CYO; Chldr; Drama; FFA; FHA; GS; 4H; Mjrte; Tres, Jr Cl; Rptr, Soph Cl; Bkbl; Tnns; Tr; Alg A; Bio A; Cl Fav; 4H A; HQn; Lion A; Math A; FFA Swtht; Area FFA Off; *S Plains Jr Col; Med.*

LEE, Travis J J Jr
Lyndon B Johnson HS; Austin, TX (75%-300) Bus C; SC; Partners; Pres, Church Yth Fel; Young Life; JA.

LEE, Velma Jean
Valley HS; Sanders, AZ (1-67) CYO; JV, Chldr; FFA; Hmrm; Model UN; SC; Cpt, Bkbl; Tr; COM; Citz A; HQn; Eng A; HS All-Amer; Outst Ath; Fin, Hqn; *Mesa Comm Col; Health.*

LEE, Vicki Lynne
Almont HS; Almont, MI (10%-100) Chor; Hmrm; Ski C; Span C; SC; Tr.

LEE, Vicki Victoria
San Bernardino HS; San Bernardino, CA (25-200) Bus C; Drama; NHS; Spch C; CSF; COM; Citz A; Hon Prog; JA A; Most Out; Opt A; Poet A; Spch A; Leo C; Inspirational Choir; JA; Checkmates; Schol Comm, Yth Coun; Supt, Jr Dept, Sunday Sch; Publicity Ch, Yth Coun; *UCLA; Psych.*

LEE, Virgil Wayne
Thomas Jefferson HS; Dallas, TX (10-422) NHS; Ftbl; JV, Tr; Chem A; I Dare You; Magna Cum Laude; Pres, Afro-Amer Culture C; *N Tex St U; Chem.*

LEE, Walter
Honokaa HS; Honokaa, HI (4-110) Span C; Tr.

LEE, Wanda Suzanne
Tabernacle Baptist HS; Virginia Beach, VA (2-13) Ann; Bus C; Cpt, Chldr; Chor; Span C; Tres, Sr Cl; Alg A; Bio A; Hon Prog; Chldr Cert; Chor Cert; Yrbk Cert; *Bob Jones U; Bus.*

LEE, Willie Otha
Lanier HS; Jackson, MS; NHS; Bkbl; Ftbl; Hon Prog; Industrial Arts A; *Miss Col; Eng.*

LEECE, Thomas Dean
Aurora-Hoyt Lakes HS; Aurora, MN; Band; Ftbl; Tr; *Concordia Col; Law.*

LEECH, Larissa Irene
Zion Benton Township HS; Zion, IL (110-396) VP, Chor; Ger C; NHS; Tres, Jr Cl; Cpt, Golf; NEDT; Col of Lake Co; Dental Asst.

LEEDS, Sherry Kay
Quincy Sr HS; Quincy, IL; Swtht; Yth Fel; Secy.

LEEDY, Ronald Lloyd
Lafayette HS; Lexington, KY; Band; Chess C; Bsbl; Mgr, Bkbl; JV, Ftbl; Golf; Swim; Kiwanis A; Most Out; IBM Bsbl All Stars; Kiwanis A, Bsbl All Stars; *U of Ky; Drama.*

LEEDY, Sharon Arlene
Naperville N HS; Naperville, IL (118-525) Ann; Arch; 4H; Acct.

LEEMAN, Elizabeth Irene
Marietta HS; Marietta, OK (10%-50) A Cap Choir; Chor; NHS; Fin, Spch C; Spch A.

LEES, Debra Ann
Penn Hills Sr HS; Pittsburgh, PA (10%-1225) Chor; FTA; Hmrm; Rptr, Sch P; Span C; SC; Var C; Swim; COM; Citz A; Ntl Cl GSct A; *Elem Ed.*

LEESE, Susan Elizabeth
George Washington HS; Philadelphia, PA (112-1200) Band; Orch; Church Choir; Pres, United Yth Fel; Candystriper; Nurs Aide; *Albright Col; Nurs.*

LE FEBER, Victoria Joy
Lakeview HS; Lakeview, MI (52-135) Band; Chor; Dbte Tm; Drama; FNA; FTA; Sci C; Ski C; God & Country A; John Wesely A; David Livingston A; Roy S Nicholson A; *Marion Col; Nurs.*

LEFEBVRE, Gigi Claire
St John HS; Plaquemine, LA (1-64) BC; CYO; Lit Ral; Secy, Math C; Secy, Mu Alpha Theta; NHS; Pres, Sci C; Mgr, Bkbl; Sftbl; Alg A; Bio A; COM; NEDT; Bell Sci A; Stu o-t Month; 1st, St Sci Fair; *LSU; Vet Med.*

LeFEURE, Brett Ronald
John F Kennedy HS; Cedar Rapids, IA; Thes; Yth Fel; Stage Mgr; Tech Director; *Theater.*

LeFEVER, Sherri Lynn
W Craven HS; Vanceboro, NC (3-160) Band; Fr C; Hmrm; Monogram; NHS; Sci C; Bkbl; JV, Tnns; Bio A; Citz A; Co- cpt, Vlbl; *Peace Col; Phys Ed.*

LEFEVRE, Perry Allen
Bedford HS; Temperance, MI (154-458) Drama; Thes; *Amer Hist.*

LEFFIN, Douglas Kent
Royal Oak HS; Covina, CA (20%-334) VP, Chor; Math C; Thes; Hon Prog; Yth Fel; Semi-Fin, So Cal Shakespearean Fes; 3rd Pl, Cal Poly Pomona Festival; Prog Coordinator, Church Yth Group.

LEFFLER, Margie Ann
Northern Heights HS; Allen, KS; FBLA; Type A.

LEFITI, Lillian Faletolu
El Camino HS; Oceanside, CA; Bus C; FBLA; Bsbl; Bkbl; Sftbl; Citz A; Math A; *San Diego St Col; Bus.*

LEFLER, James Clark Jr
Nathan Hale HS; Tulsa, OK (18-677) Math C; Mu Alpha Theta; NHS; St Stu Congress; Pres, SC; Pres, Soph Cl; JV, Ftbl; HCt; Hon Prog; Masonic A; St Scholar; Hon Men, Elk's C A; W of OK; Ranger-In-Review, Outst Stu A; *Okla St U; Fire & Safety Engr.*

LEFLER, Jennifer Harris
Loudon HS; Loudon, TN (1-150) VP, Bus C; Fr C; FHA; Lat C; NHS; Sci C; Secy, Sr Cl; Cpt, Bkbl; Cpt, Tnns; Citz A; DARGCA; HCt; Hon Prog; Val; Yth Fel; Secy, Prayer Group; *U of Ala; Phys Ed.*

LEGA, Mary Jeanine
Holy Rosary Acad; Louisville, KY (1-86) Math C; Secy, NHS; ARC; Hon Prog; Math A; ARC A; Val; Span A; Ntl HS A for Excellence; WW; *Bellarmine Col; Acct.*

LEGAKO, Jana Kay
Watonga HS; Watonga, OK (1-99) Ann; Chldr; VP, FBLA; GS; VP, NHS; Rainbow; Pres, SC; Bkbl; Tnns; Citz A; HCt; Yth Fel; WW; St VP, FBLA; *Okla St U; Radio and TV Broadcasting.*

LEGAN, Cheri Lynn
H M King HS; Kingsville, TX; A Cap Choir; Band; Drama; *Tex A&I Col; Secondary Ed.*

LEGAN, Ronald Allen
H M King HS; Kingsville, TX; A Cap Choir; Band; JV, Cr-Ctry; Tr; *A&I Kingsville Col; Mus.*

LEGARE, Helen Louise
Sea Island Acad; Johns Island, SC (4-13) F-Ed, Ann; Drama; Fr C; 4H; Sch P; Pres, SC; Var C; Ch, Sr Cl; VP, Jr Cl; Cpt, Bkbl; Ftbl; Cl Fav; 4H A; Intramural Bkbl Coach; WW; *Clemson U; Agr.*

LEGASPI, Lorenzo Santos
John F Kennedy HS; Tumon, GUAM; Band; Chess C; Hmrm; NHS; Co-Cpt, Bkbl; Soccer; Tr; Alg A; Math A; Sci A; HR; PE A; *U of Hawaii; Engr.*

LEGATE, Laurel Ann
Lakewood HS; St Petersburg, FL (70-547) Band; Chor; Span C; Swim; Tnns; Yth Fel; *Fla Tech U; Social Work.*

LEGER, Pascale
St Angela Hall Acad; Brooklyn, NY (3-82) CYO; Chor; Drama; Fr C; French NHS; Hmrm; Math C; NHS; ARC; Sci C; SC; Alg A; Bio A; Chem A; Math A; ARC A; *Downstate Med Col; Phys Therapy.*

LEGERE, Richard Alan
Valley Central HS; Montgomery, NY (33%-400) CYO; SC; Mgr, Bkbl; Swim; Lector; Fresh-Soph Play; Cath Yth Bkbl A; CCD Teaching A; *Orange Co Comm Col; Police Sci.*

LEGETTE, Josephine Ellen
Chester HS; Chester, PA; *Delaware Co Comm Col; Law Enforcement.*

LEGEZA, Sally Ann
S Park HS; Library, PA (8-163) Bus C; FBLA; FHA; NHS; Sch P; Ski C; Hon Prog; Q&S A.

LEGGETT, Eddrina Barbara
Thornridge; Dolton, IL (110-800) Chor; Drama; FNA; Lat C; Lat NHS; Spch C; Bkbl; COM; Cl Fav; Hon Prog; Most Out; Spch A; Highest Hon A; VICA; Best Dressed; *Trinity Christian Col; Med Lab Tech.*

LEGGETT, Mary Susan
Suffolk HS; Suffolk, VA (5-150) JV, Chldr; Pres, Lat C; NHS; Bus Mgr, Sch P; Secy, Tri-HiY; Tnns; Gov Honor Prog; Sci A; *Westhampton Col; Law.*

LEGGETT, Richard Lee
Rockdale HS; Rockdale, TX (50-150) Band; Orch; Ch, SC; Var C; Ftbl; Golf; Cl Fav; Yth Fel; Outst Bandsman A; St Band Festival; *Houston Baptist Col; Psych.*

LEGGITT, Lindy Dawn
Levelland HS; Levelland, TX; Chor; Ensm; VP, FHA; NHS; Span C; Y-Tns; AAUW Schol; Girl o-t Month; *S Plains Col; Nurs.*

LEHIGH, Louis Edwin
Secaucus HS; Secaucus, NJ (34-162) Band; Chor; Ski C; Secy, PTSA; *W Chester St Col; Hist.*

LEHMAN, Andrea Sue
Lake Braddock Secondary Sch; Burke, VA (375-625) Chor; Co-Ch, Hmrm; ARC; Pep C; 3 Mus A; All Regional Chor; *George Mason U; Early Childhood Ed.*

LEHMAN, Cathy Ann
Richfield Sr HS; Richfield, MN (125-705) Ed, Ann; Chor; Orch; Span C; Bkbl; Tnns.

LEHMAN, Deirdre Ann
Adams Central HS; Monroe, IN (2-120) Band; JV, Chldr; Chor; Cpt, Mjrte; VP, Span C; Tr; Hon Prog.

LEHMAN, Diane Marie
Cocoa Beach HS; Cocoa Beach, FL (1-250) BC; Pres, Chor; Tres, Mu Alpha Theta; Pres, NHS; Parl, SC; Chamber of Comm A; Chem A; MLS; Val; Rotary C Outst Girl A; Outst Scholastic Achievement A; Math.

LEHMAN, Douglas Allen
Adams Central HS; Monroe, IN (7-110) NHS; Span C; Pres, Jr Cl; Bsbl; Bkbl; Cr-Ctry; JV, Ftbl; Hon Prog; NEDT; Yth Fel; Tres, FCA.

LEHMAN, Laura Marie
Whitefish Bay HS; Whitefish Bay, WI (13-307) Fr C; VP, Church Yth Group, Awana Ldr; Grand Rapids Baptist Col; Bible.

LEHMAN, Nancy Helen
N Plainfield HS; N Plainfield, NJ (30-260) Secy, Band; Chor; Ensm; FHA; FTA; Rptr, 4H; Lit Mag; 4H A; Type A; Mus A; Camp Schol; Moravian Col.

LEHMAN, Sheri Lee
Sooner HS; Bartlesville, OK; Secy, FHA; Y-Tns.

LEHMANN, Diana Lynn
Ceylon Pub HS; Ceylon, MN (8-35) Band; Chor; FHA; NHS; SC; Bkbl; Pres A; UM at Minneapolis; Nurs.

LEHMANN, Gloria Ruth
Brooklyn HS; Brooklyn, OH; Band; Chess C; Chor; Drama; Ensm; Madrigal; Mu Alpha Theta; Orch; Rptr, Sch P; Secy, SC; Tres, Thes; Alg A; Bio A; Math A; Type A; Hon Men, Best Actress; Eng A.

LEHMANN, Lynn Catherine
Campolindo HS; Moraga, CA; Hmrm; NHS; SC; Var C; COM; Hist A; Hon Prog; ARC A; Gym; 1st Cl GSct; U of Calif; Social Sci.

LEHNERT, William Kolb
Del Rio HS; Del Rio, TX (10%-400) Band; VP, Chess C; Drama; Order/Arrow; F-Ed, Sch P; Pres, Spch C; Bsbl; Bkbl; Ftbl; Tnns; JV, Wrest; Bio A; Yth Fel; BSct; Explorer Sct; Church, Comm, Choirs; U of Tex; Oceanography.

LEHNING, Peggye Alyce
Pioneer Christian Acad; Whites Creek, TN (13-25) Ann; Cpt, Chldr; Chess C; FTA; Cpt, Bkbl; Sftbl; Swim; Bio A; HCt; Most Out; Puppet Ministry; Yth Coun; Choir; All Tourn, Bkbl; U of Tenn; Phys Ed.

LEHR, Carl Warren
Norman HS; Norman, OK (1-704) Hmrm; NHS; Pres, Span C; Span NHS; Ch, SC; VP, Sr Cl; JV, Bsbl; Hon Prog; Lion A; MLS; Yth Fel; WW; Cpt, MVP, Fin, Bsbl; Okla U; Social Sci.

LEHR, Nadine Frances
Ashley Pub Sch; Ashley, ND (1-42) A Cap Choir; Ann; Band; Chldr; Chor; Drama; FHA; 4H; NHS; ARC; Sch P; Swim; COM; Citz A; Hon Prog; Most Out; Val; Ed, Ann A; Ger.

LEHRER, Catherine Louise
Morristown-Hamblen W HS; Morristown, TN (1-335) Hmrm; InterAct C; Span C; Parl, SC; Tri-HiY; Tr; Pres, Church Yth Coun; Secy, Yth Choir; Sub-Debs; VP, Fresh Cl; U of Tenn; Home Ec.

LEHRER, Gary Mitchell
Woodmere Acad; Woodmere, NY (8-52) Co-Ch, Math C; Span C; Co-Ch, SC; NMS; Regent Schol.

LEHRER, Harry Frederick III
Morristown-Hamblen W HS; Morristown, TN (16-330) Tres, Key C; Tnns; Math A; Church Yth Coun; U of Tenn; Engr.

LEHRKE, Dean H
Jamestown HS; Jamestown, ND (25-350) Chor; Drama; Ger C; NHS; Bsbl; Tr; COM; VFW Orator Win; VofDEM; WW, Mus Stu; Letourneau Col; Mech Engr.

LEHRMANN, Steve Glenn
Cleburne HS; Cleburne, TX; Chor; InterAct C; Key C; Var C; Bsbl; Bkbl; Abilene Christian U; Acct.

LEHTO, Heidi Marie
Lordstown HS; Warren, OH (3-56) Band; Chor; Drama; GS; NHS; Ed, Sch P; Ch, Jr Cl; Pres, Soph Cl; Cpt, Bkbl; Cpt, Sftbl; Tr; Amer Leg A; Journ A; Akron Col; Med Tech.

LEHY, Amy J
Hempfield Area Sr HS; Greensburg, PA; Chor; NHS; Presidential A; Sunday Sch Teacher; Schol A; Dist & Regional Choir; VP, Yth Fel; Ch, Chmbr Sng & Reg; Instructor, Retarded Swim Prog; Ashland Col; Elem Ed.

LEIB, Deborah Suzanne
Flathead HS; Kalispell, MT (142-496) A Cap Choir; Band; Chor; Drama; Ensm; Semi-Fin, GS; NHS; Co-Ch, Span C; Golf; Sftbl; Swim; Jobs Daughters; W Point Military Acad; Mus.

LEIBBRANDT, Timothy Bruce
Chase Co HS; Imperial, NE (20%-71) Band; Chor; Pres, Soph Cl; Bsbl; Bkbl; Cpt, Ftbl; Fin, Tr; HCt; Hon Prog; Nebr U; Bus.

LEIBEL, Laurel Lou
Antilles HS; Ft Buchanan, PR (3-118) A-Ed, Ann; Chldr; Drama; Hmrm; Lit Mag; NHS; SC; Cr-Ctry; Sftbl; COM; Hon Prog; Secy, Keyettes; DAHSS; Ecology C; Stu Faculty; Lib Aide; U of Wash.

LEIBENSPERGER, Donna Jean
Marian HS; Tamaqua, PA (15-143) Chldr; Span NHS; Tr.

LEICHT, Kevin Timothy
Millard Sr HS; Omaha, NE (98-419) JV, Bkbl; Golf; Ntl Sci Found; Regent Schol; David Schol; Creighton U; Chem.

LEICHTENBERG, Laura Ann
Beaver Dam Sr HS; Beaver Dam, WI (158-331) Chldr; Chor; Orch; Ski C; Var C; Swim; Tr; Cl Fav; HQn; HCt; Pres A; WW; U of Wis at Stevens Point; Health Ed.

LEIGH, David Ralph
Caesar Rodney HS; Camden, DE (97-398) Drama; Sci C; WW.

LEIGH, Deborah Jean
Melbourne HS; Melbourne, FL (105-686) Band; Yth Fel; Yth for Christ; Brevard Comm Col; Lib Arts.

LEIGH, Debra Lynne
Gloucester HS; Gloucester, VA (10-260) AFS; A-Ed, Ann; BC; ARC; Phar.

LEIGH, Dona Denise
Callaway Pub Sch; Callaway, NE (15-30) Band; Chldr; VP, FHA; 4H; Cpt, Bkbl; Pres Phys Fitness A.

LEIGH, Richard D
Archmere Acad; Claymont, DE; NHS; Span NHS; SC; Cr-Ctry; Tr.

LEIGH, Thomas H
Stuyvesant HS; NY, NY; Tr; Amer Leg A; COM.

LEIGH, William Lester
Toluca HS; Toluca, IL (4-31) Bus Mgr, Ann; Band; BS; Chor; Ensm; FFA; Ch, 4H; NHS; Var C; Cpt, Bkbl; Cpt, Tr; 4H A; I Dare You; NEDT; St Scholar; Type A; Ed, Annual; St Farmer, FFA; Co-cpt, MVP, Bkbl; Co- ch, 4-H C; MVP, Tr; U of Ill; Agr.

LEIGHTON, Deborah Frances
Plant City HS; Plant City, FL (24-600) Ed, Ann; Model UN; NHS; Hon Prog; Hillsbourgh Comm Col; Nurs.

LEIGHTON, G Timothy
Mamaroneck HS; Mamaroneck, NY (2-554) Dbte Tm; FTA; NHS; Citz A; Hon Prog; Regent Schol; Rep. Fr C; Tutoring A; Asst Conductor, Orch; Adv to Pres, SC; NML of Commendation; Georgetown U; Govt.

LEIGHTY, Bonnie Sue
Southmoreland Sr HS; Alverton, PA (5-295) Band; Chor; Fr C; 4H; Pres, Hmrm; Pres, SC; World Affairs C; Pres, Soph Cl; Yth Fel; Special Ed.

LEIKER, James Norbert
Thomas More Prep Sch; Hays, KS (40-110) Pres, 4H; Citz A; 4H A; Hon Prog; K of C A; Opt A; Spch A; Fort Hays U; Sociology.

LeiKHIM, Paul Joseph
Notre Dame-Bishop Gibbons HS; Schenectady, NY (8-168) Math C; NHS; Pol Sci C; Rptr, Sch P; Cr-Ctry; Tr; Hon Prog; NEDT; St Bonaventure; Pol Sci.

LEIMER, Joni Lynn
Albert City-Truesdale HS; Albert City, IA (3-44) Band; Chor; Drama; Ger C; Spch C; SC; Tr; Hon Prog; NEDT; Pres A; Superior Ratings, St Mus Contest; Nurs.

LEIPPRANDT, Jeffrey Robert
Williamston HS; Williamston, MI (25-150) Band; Order/Arrow; Ski C; JV, Cr-Ctry; Sci.

LEIPZIGER, Lyle Seth
Woodmere Acad; Woodmere, NY (5-53) Chem C; Chess C; Math C; VP, Sci C; Chem A; Regent Schol; Sci A; 1000 Hr Hospital Vol A; Med.

LEISER, Karen Ann
St Louise de Marillac HS; Northfield, IL (3-222) Chor; NHS; Hon Prog; Vol Work; Choreleers; Church Play; Tutor; U of Ill; Acct.

LEISMAN, Suzanne Gayle
North HS; N St Paul, MN; A Cap Choir; Chor; Drama; Ensm; Tnns; Yth Fel; Jr Hospital Vol.

LEISS, Marty
Central Valley HS; Buxton, ND; Band; Sch P; Spch C; Mus A.

LEISSNER, Carole Elizabeth
New Braunfels Sr HS; New Braunfels, TX (41-299) Fr C; Ftbl; Drill Tm; Eng Hon C; U of Tex; Zoology.

LEISURE, Deiedre Jayne
Brookings HS; Brookings, SD (25%-200) A Cap Choir; Chor; 4H; Madrigal; Span C; All St Chor; Art Schol; Sup Musicianship; SDSU; Parish Ed.

LEITCH, Daniel Bruce
Moorhead Sr HS; Moorhead, MN (95-605) Secy, Key C; Ed, Sch P; Swim; COM; Journ A; Ntl Engr Wk Bridge Bldg A; WIEA A; U of ND; Aviation.

LEITER, Barbara Jo
Dauphin Co Voc-Tech HS; Harrisburg, PA (35-300) Chor; NHS; Sch P; SC; Jr NHS.

LEITH, Linda Joan
St Mary's Jr Col; Raleigh, NC (1-103) BC; Chldr; Chor; Ensm; Pres, Fr C; French NHS; NHS; Sch P; Tnns; COM; HCt; Sci A; Tres, Young Republicans; Volunteers; Pres, St Mary's Hon Soc; Academic Coun; Morehead Schol Cand; VP-PERSONNEL, JA; Nom, Govn Sch; NC; Bus Adm.

LEITHOLD, Joseph Scott
Mentor HS; Mentor, OH (92-820) JV, Cr-Ctry; JV, Tr; Hon Prog; ARC A; Chem Asst; St Paul's Choir Dir; Physics Asst; Concert B Stu Dir; Symph & Marching Bands; Gold Palm Eagle; 3 I-Ratings, OMED; Westminster Col; Med.

LEITKA, Letha Denise
Eldorado HS; Albuquerque, NM (66-744) NHS; JV, Sftbl; NM St U; Biol Sci.

LEITNER, Brenda Dellene
Chilton HS; Chilton, WI (10-155) CYO; Sftbl; GAA.

LEITZEL, Andrea Jane
Upper Dauphin Area HS; Elizabethville, PA; Band; Chor; Ensm; Hmrm; VP, NHS; Span C; SC; Tr; NEDT; Yth Fel; Band As; Civic C Girl o-t Month; Prom Court; Phys Therapy.

LEITZKE, Julie Ann
Horicon HS; Horicon, WI; Band; Chess C; Dbte Tm; Mjrte; Bsbl; Bkbl; Sftbl; Swim; Tr; COM; Hon Prog; Spch A; Yth Fel; Yth Leg; Lib C; Church Essay A; Water Ballet; Parl, Lutheran Yth; Stu o-t Mo; St Work Prog; U of Wis; Nurs.

LEIVICK, Neva Sue
N Mercer R-III HS; Mercer, MO (3-13) Ann; Band; JV, Chldr; Sch P; Sftbl; Trenton Jr Col; Secy.

LELAND, William Joseph
Robinson HS; San Juan, PR (2-54) Chess C; Hmrm; Lit Mag; Math C; Mu Alpha Theta; Tres, NHS; VP, Soph Cl; Bkbl; Cpt, Soccer; Tr; NEDT; Med.

LELE'a, Vaaalutasi Jr
Gardena HS; Gardena, CA; Key C; MVP, Ftbl; Wrest; Citz A; Kiwanis A; Principal's HR; Most Improved, Wrest; Player o-t Week, Ftbl.

LELEA, Vaaalutasi Jr
Gardena HS; Gardena, CA; Key C; MVP, Ftbl; MVP, Wrest; HR; Outst Player o-t Wk, Ftbl; Law.

LELITO, Francine Marie
Whitman-Hanson Regional HS; Whitman, MA (8-328) Tres, NHS; Cpt, Cr-Ctry; Tnns; Gym; Vet Med.

LEMA, Teresa Diane
Ferndale Union HS; Ferndale, CA (25-77) Band; FHA; 4H; COM; 4H A; Hon Prog; Type A; Col o-t Redwoods; Legal Secy.

LEMAIRE, Lonie Lucia
St Joseph HS; Jeanerette, LA (3-30) Ann; Lit Ral; NHS; Ed, Sch P; VP, Sr Cl; Bkbl; Tnns; COM; HCt; NEDT; *U of Southwestern La; Nurs.*

LEMANSKI, Raymond Joseph
St Peters Prep HS; Jersey City, NJ (30-260) A-Ed, Ann; NHS; Ski C; SC; Pres, Jr Cl; Tres, Soph Cl; Ftbl; COM; Elk A; NEDT; Cl Musician; *U of Denver Schol; U of Denver; Pol Sci.*

LeMASTER, Jeffrey Grant
Moline Sr HS; Moline, IL; A Cap Choir; Chor; Ensm; Lit Mag; Span C; Spch C; Tr; Citz A; Poet A; Pres A; Biblical A; Apostles C; *Augustana Col; Teaching.*

LEMBERG, Bryan Dean
Joseph A Craig HS; Janesville, WI (165-547) Band; Ger C; Mgr, Bsbl; 1st Pl, Vocal, Tn Talent Search; *North Central Bible Col; Pastoral Stu.*

LeMERE, Joy Beth
Kimball Union Acad; Meriden, NH (5-60) Arch; Chor; Ski C; Secy, SC; Y-Tns; Sftbl; Chem A; 4H A; Yth Fel; Cr-Ctry Skiing; Field Hockey; Girl's Lacrosse; *Pre-Med.*

LEMIEUX, Cherie Ann
W Hills HS; Cincinnati, OH (32-817) A-Ed, Ann; Tres, Chldr; Chor; Cum Laude Soc; Drama; Fr C; Hmrm; Lit Ral; Ntl Yth Conf; SC; Tres, World Affairs; Sftbl; Amer Leg A; COM; Hon Prog; Journ A; Q&S A; Yth Fel; Bus Mgr, Annual; *Miami U; Journ.*

LEMIEUX, Larry Myron
Taylor HS; N Bend, OH; Chor; Cpt, Bsbl; Mgr, Bkbl; Soccer; COM; Cl Fav; *U of Cincinnati.*

LEMIRE, Kathleen Mary
Acad o-t Holy Family; Baltic, CT (3-24) Chor; Hmrm; NHS; SC; Bkbl; K of C A; Pres A; VFW A; VofDEM; *Roger Williams Col; Creative Writing.*

LEMKE, Luke Patrick
Columbus Sr HS; Columbus, NE (25%-375) Pres, 4H; Secy, Soph Cl; JV, Bkbl; Co-Cpt, Ftbl; Semifin, Sch Swtht; *U of Nebr; Med.*

LEMLICH, Gabrielle Primavera
Woodmere Acad; Woodmere, NY (2-49) Band; Community Yth Symph; Cum Laude Soc; Pres, Fr C; Lat C; Math C; Ed, Sch P; Sci A; Alg A; Citz A; Math A; NMS; Regent Schol; Sci A; Ntl Fr Contest Win; Pres, Poetry C; Pres, Lib Aides; Future Physicians C; *Biochem.*

LEMMON, Angela Yvonne
Berkeley HS; Moncks Corner, SC (18-350) Chor; Dbte Tm; FHA; FTA; Hmrm; VP, Span C; SC; WW; *Johnson C Smith U; Bio.*

LEMMON, Elizabeth Ann
N Plainfield HS; N Plainfield, NJ (4-265) Co-Cpt, Chldr; Pres, Chor; GS; NHS; Rptr, Sch P; Tres, SC; Citz A; DARGCA; MLS; Russian C; Yrbk; Tres, Episcopal Young Christians; Best All Around; *Dickinson Col; Lang.*

LEMMON, Stephen Oscar
Central HS; Piqua, OH (114-395) Chor; Span C; *Ohio St U; Med.*

LEMOINE, Linda Ray
Bordelonville HS; Bordelonville, LA; Band; BC; Tres, CYO; Chess C; Chor; Fr C; FHA; 4H; Lit Ral; Phys C; Sch P; Sci C; VP, Sr Cl; Pres, Jr Cl; Secy, Soph Cl; Tr; Alg A; Bio A; Chem A; Cl Fav; 4H A; Hist A; ARC A; Sci A; Band A; Mus A; Sci Fair A; *Tulane Sch of Radiologic Tech; X-Ray Tech.*

LEMON, Benita Pearl
Roosevelt HS; Gary, IN (59-555) BC; NHS; *Ind U at Bloomington; Acct.*

LEMON, Brenda Anita
Gloucester HS; Gloucester, VA (25%-260) Chor; FBLA; Pres, FHA; 4H; ARC; Sch P; Span C; SC; Citz A; HCt; Pres A; Swtht; Yth Fel; Rptr, ICT; Cpt, Drill Tm; *Thomas Nelson Comm Col; Computer Operator.*

LEMON, Jacqueline Sue
Adrian HS; Adrian, MI; Orch; Swim.

LEMON, Jerry Wayne Jr
Seymour HS; Seymour, TX (5-50) Hmrm; NHS; Spch C; VP, SC; Bkbl; Tr; *Baylor U; Spch.*

LEMON, Lonny Brian
Aledo HS; Aledo, IL (2-135) Pres, Key C; Bsbl; Bkbl; Tr; *U of Ill; Social Sci.*

LEMONS, Keith George
Canadian HS; Canadian, TX (6-60) Band; 4H; NHS; Order/Arrow; Sch P; 4H A; Journ A; Math A; *Wayland Baptist Col; Mus Ministry.*

LEMONS, Loyce Ann
W W Samuell HS; Dallas, TX (8-360) Hmrm; NHS; Span C; Soccer; COM; Cl Fav; MLS; *N Tex St Col; Nurs.*

LEMONS, Mitchell Scott
Newton-Conover Sr HS; Newton, NC (20-275) Band; BC; Span C; SC; Drum Major; Pres, Church Yth; PA; Executive Board, SC; *U of NC.*

LEMONT, Mark Howard
Roy C Start HS; Toledo, OH (30-475) Band; Orch; Ch, Order/Arrow; God & Country A; Eagle Sct; *Northland Col; Forestry.*

LEMOS, Kelly Frances
Sharon Sr HS; Sharon, PA (10%-300) Chor; Ensm; Fr C; Hmrm; NHS; Sch P; SC; Swim; *Dance.*

LeMOSY, Lora Marie
Melbourne HS; Melbourne, FL; Band; Chor; Drama; Ger C; NHS; Rainbow; Secy, UMYF; *Fla Inst; Computer Sci.*

LEMP, Kevin Ray
Big Bay de Noc HS; Garden, MI (10%-60) 4H; Maranatha Baptist Bible Col; Pastoral Study.

LEMPA, Debra Ann
Kelly HS; Chicago, IL (2-661) Chor; City Conf; Math C; Tr; Hon Prog; Kiwanis A; Span A; Kelly Hon Soc.

LENGYEL-LEAHU, Pal Anthony
Marine Military Acad; Harlingen, TX (5-41) Band; Drama; NHS; Tnns; *Orange Coast Col; Med.*

LENK, John C
Clay Center Comm HS; Clay Center, KS (5-145) Band; Tr; *Oral Roberts U; Med.*

LENNING, Donna Lee
Wilmington HS; Wilmington, OH (43-304) Band; Chor; FTA; Pres, 4H; Rptr, Sch P; Tres, Span C; Phi Delta Sigma; 1st Cl GSct; *Wright St; Chem.*

LENNON, Kelly Robin
W Forsyth Sr HS; Clemmons, NC (7-504) Anchor C; Chor; Parl; Drama; FHA; Jr Miss Pagent; Lat C; Tres, NHS; Swim; Jr Marshall; JCL; Ixthous C; *Meredith Col; Math.*

LENOIR, Henry Joel
Sullivan Central HS; Blountville, TN (5%-350) Co-Ed, Ann; Lat C; Lat NHS; Order/Arrow; SC; JV, Ftbl; God & Country A; MLS; Opt A; Summa Cum Laude; Eagle Sct; *Emory U; Med.*

LeNOIR, William David
Hardaway HS; Columbus, GA (106-406) Fin, Model UN; ARC A; ROTC A; *Columbus Col; Marine Bio.*

LENSER, Ronda Leigh
Stratford Sr HS; Houston, TX (10-450) Band; JETS; Math C; Mu Alpha Theta; NHS; COM; Hon Prog; God & Comm A; 1st Cl GSct A; Top 5%, NMS; *Tex A&M U; Engr.*

LENSING, Cynthia Ann
Southside HS; Fort Smith, AR (164-430) Fr C; 4H; Bkbl; Sftbl; Tr; Most Out; Most Talented Female Artist; Pres, Art C; *U of Fayetteville; Art.*

LENSINK, Susan Elizabeth
Bozeman Sr HS; Bozeman, MT (1-300) Band; Ger C; NFL; NHS; Orch; Spch A; Val; *St Olaf's Col.*

LENT, Melissa Joyce
Robert H Goddard Sr HS; Roswell, NM (19-310) Tres, FHA; Ger C; NHS; WW; Outst HERO I Stu; 2nd Pl, Electric Company Bake-Off; *El Centro Jr Col; Police Sci.*

LENTZ, Edwin Mark
Clark Co R-1 HS; Kahoka, MO (2-93) Pres, Band; BS; Chor; Ensm; Pres, 4H; VP, NHS; Order/Arrow; S-T, Sci C; Var C; Cr-Ctry; Tr; God & Country A; 4H A; I Dare You; Order/Arrow A; Regent Schol; Sal; Mus A; 4 H Ntl Congress; Eagle Sct; *U of Mo; Agr.*

LENTZ, Thomas Allen
Glasgow HS; Newark, DE (10%-360) NHS; VP, Sr Cl; JV, Bsbl; Ftbl; Tr; Hon Prog; HR; *U of Del; Mech Engr.*

LENZ, Kathryn Elizabeth
East HS; Pueblo, CO (20-500) Band; Ensm; GS; Key C; NHS; Orch; Ski C; SC; Tr; Hon Prog; Recognition A, Candystriper; Civic Ballet Co; Oboe A; *St Olaf Col; Pre Med.*

LENZ, Kim Suzanne
Skyline HS; Salt Lake City, UT (230-650) Dbte Tm; NFL; Sch P; *U of Utah; Law.*

LENZER, Sherri Susan
N Pocono HS; Moscow, PA (80-200) Chor; 4H; Lat C; Mjrte; Ski C; SC; Rptr, Sr Cl; Rptr, Jr Cl; Rptr, Soph Cl; Mgr, Bkbl; Golf; Sftbl; Swim; Tnns; Tr; 4H A; Most Out; Feature Twirler; Horse Riding Cert; Phys Fitness A; Advance Sr Life Saving; Var Ltr, Tr; *Health Asst.*

LENZER, Tina
Western Hills HS; Cincinnati, OH (55-800) Cum Laude Soc; *Xavier U; Communication Arts.*

LEO, Matthew Francis
Don Bosco Tech HS; Boston, MA (4-177) Dbte Tm; SC; NEDT; Jr Asst Sct-Master; VP Manufacturing, JA; Secy, Radio C; Small Engine Repair C; *Elec.*

LEON, Mary Beth
Andover HS; Bloomfield Hills, MI (40-400) Hon Prog; Art A; High Hons; Secy, Church; *Hist.*

LEONARD, Barbara Ann
Wethersfield HS; Wethersfield, CT (10%-406) Dbte Tm; Drama; Sch P; Semi-Fin, Tnns; NEDT; Sci A; Pres, UCC Yth Organization; Church Choir; President's Phys Fitness A; *Biological Sci.*

LEONARD, Eloise
Charlotte Jr-Sr HS; Rochester, NY (67-160) Band; Soccer; Sftbl; Gregg Filing A; *Monroe Comm Col; Criminal Justice.*

LEONARD, James Arthur
Trotwood-Madison Sr HS; Trotwood, OH; Band; Orch; Order/Arrow; NEDT; Order/Arrow A; Jr NHS; *Miami St U; Chem.*

LEONARD, Jeffrey Lee
Trotwood-Madison Sr HS; Trotwood, OH; Band; Drama; Orch; Order/Arrow; NEDT; Order/Arrow A; Jr NHS; *Miami St U; Chem.*

LEONARD, Karen Elizabeth
Spencer HS; Spencer, IA; Band; Span C; *Sci.*

LEONARD, Kevin James
Reynolds HS; Greenville, PA (5-212) VP, Lat C; NHS; SC; Var C; Cpt, Bkbl; Tr; All Co, Bkbl; *Westminster Col; Pre-Med.*

LEONARD, Kimberly Kay
Louisburg HS; Louisburg, NC (25%-135) JV, Chldr; Secy, FHA; FTA; Monogram; Sch P; Span C; Bkbl; Sftbl; Citz A; HR; *NC St U; Agronomy.*

LEONARD, Levida Dawn
Joliet E HS; Joliet, IL (25%-450) Chor; Ger C; Ski C; SC; Swim; Gym; WW; SC A; *Lewis U; Pol Sci.*

LEONARD, Lori Sue
Holstein HS; Holstein, IA (90%-52) Band; Rptr, Bus C; Chldr; Chor; Community Yth Symph; Drama; FBLA; 4H; Madrigal; Mjrte; Sch P; JV; Bkbl; Swim; Tnns; COM; 4H A; Pep C; Sunday Sch Teacher; Vocal A; Yth Fitness Achv; *Iowa St U.*

LEONARD, LouAnn
Washington HS; Cherokee, IA (10%-140) Chor; Madrigal; S-T, SC; Bkbl; Cpt, Sftbl; *Amer Inst of Bus; Secy.*

LEONARD, Marilyn Kay
Fort Scott HS; Fort Scott, KS; Band; Chor; Swim; Tnns; *Math.*

LEONARD, Michael Emile
Hickory HS; Hickory, NC (80-375) Fr C; *U of NC; Phar.*

LEONARD, Richard Edward
Redondo Union HS; Redondo Beach, CA (2-400) VP, Band; French NHS; Key C; NHS; Orch; JV, Cr-Ctry; MVP; Tnns; Bank Of Amer A; CSF; Elk A; Hon Prog; Sal; St Scholar; Outst Musician; Ntl Merit Commendation; *The Ohio St U; Elec Engr.*

LEONARD, Stephen Victor
Potomac Sr HS; Oxon Hill, MD; JV, Soccer; *Aeronautics.*

429

LEONARD, Wayne Monroe
Fairfield HS; Fairfield, AL; Math C; Sci C; Span C; Cpt, Bkbl; Alg A; COM; MLS; Explorers; U of Ala; Med.

LEONARDS, Joan Maria
Notre Dame HS; Acadia Parish, LA (20-120) BC; Alg A; Cl Fav; Christian A; U of Southwestern La; Bio.

LEONARDS, Rachel Ann
Notre Dame HS; Crowley, LA (20-99) BC; 4H; Sodality.

LEON GUERRERO, Joseph Torres
George Washington Sr HS; Mangilao, GUAM; Hmrm; NHS; SC; Ftbl.

LEONHARDT, David Preston
Marist HS; Chicago, IL (60-460) Secy, Fr C; Ski C; Hon Prog; St Scholar; Acct.

LEONHARDT, Louis Anthony
J M Atherton HS; Louisville, KY (30-310) Demo-lay; Pres, SC; Var C; Pres, Sr Cl; Pres, Jr Cl; Sftbl; MVP, Swim; Cl Fav; HKg; JA A; Mr Atherton; Best Ldr; U of Louisville; Bus Adm.

LEONHART, Anne Elizabeth
Oak Park And River Forest HS; Oak Park, IL (248-1000) Band; Community Yth Symph; Ensm; Math C; Orch; Sci C; Swim; DePauw U; Mus.

LEONIAK, Cheryl Antonia
Old Forge HS; Old Forge, PA (21-121) VP, FHA; Hmrm; Cpt, Mjrte; NHS; Ski C; Secy, SC; Bkbl; Sftbl; Pres A; Pa St U; Dietetics.

LEOPOLD, Rita Max
Monroe Sr HS; Monroe, WI (80-245) Parl, FHA; Ger C; Hon Prog.

LEPAGE, Anne Marie
St Dominic Regional HS; Lewiston, ME (4-77) Secy, NHS; Ed, Sch P; B Crocker A; COM; NEDT; Sci A; Type A; Ntl Federation of Mus C A; Boston U; Psych.

LEPOUITZ, Leslie Lyn
St Augustine HS; Laredo, TX; Drama; Secy, SC; Bkbl; Tex A&M U; Law.

LEPP, Carol Ann
Hiram Johnson HS; Sacramento, CA (21-809) San Jose St Col; Lib Sci.

LERCH, David Eugene
Eaton Rapids Sr HS; Eaton Rapids, MI (20-243) Chor; Pres, Drama; NHS; Ed, Sch P; Span C; JV, Wrest; Journ A; VIP Stu A; Hon Schol; Creative Arts A; HR; Ferris St Col; Bus.

LERCH, Heidi G
Twin Lakes HS; West Palm Bch, FL (50-450) An-chor C; Drama; Bus Mgr, Ger C; Mod Mus Mas; Orch; Span C.

LERCH, Kathy Rae
Lordstown HS; Lordstown, OH (33%-50) Bus Mgr, Ann; BC; Chor; Secy, 4H; Secy, Hmrm; Bus Mgr, Sch P; Secy, Sr Cl; Sftbl; 4H A; Journ A; Q&S A; Type A; Bus.

LERCH, Laura Jane
Pocatello HS; Pocatello, ID (45-480) Chor; NHS; Excel Rating, Dist Choir; Home Ec.

LERCH, Reinhart Albert
Twin Lakes HS; W Palm Beach, FL (15-450) Com-munity Yth Symph; Dbte Tm; Tres, Ger C; Tres, Mod Mus Mas; NFL; NHS; Spch C; St Stu Con-gress; SC; Thes; Tres, Jr Cl; COM; Spch A; U of Fla; Communications.

LERCH, Tammy Lee
Valmeyer HS; Valmeyer, IL (2-45) Band; Chor; Ensm; Rptr, FHA; Pres, 4H; Hmrm; NHS; SC; 4H A; Math A; Mus As; SIU; General Stu.

LERCH, Terrie Lynn
Valmeyer HS; Valmeyer, IL (4-38) Bus Mgr, Band; Secy, Chor; FHA; Semi-Fin, GS; Pres, 4H; Key C; Tres, Math C; Secy, NHS; Orch; Sch P; Secy, SC; HCt; I Dare You; MLS; St Scholar; VofDEM; Mus Excellence A; Drama A; Vocal A; SC A; Eastern Ill U; Special Ed.

LERFALD, Susan Kay
Mayville-Portland HS; Mayville, ND; Band; Co-Cpt, Chldr; Tres, Chor; Ensm; FHA; GS; Secy, 4H; Fin, Jr Miss Pagent; Sch P; Secy, SC; Secy, Soph C; A; HCt; Most Out; VFW A; Babe Ruth A; St Tr Trophies; ND St U; Phys Ed.

LERICH, Glenn Allen
Floresville HS; Floresville, TX (5-119) BC; BS; Amer Leg A; Tex A&M U; Med.

LESHAY, Junear
Second Ward HS; Gloster, LA (3-46) Bus C; FBLA; FHA; Northwestern St U; Nurs.

LESHER, Cindy Barr
Taft HS; Lincoln City, OR (35-85) Chor; Ensm; Hmrm; SC; HCt; Yth Fel; WW Mus Stu; Vocal Mus; Most Talented A; Mus Achv A; Co Festival Soloist; 'Mus in May' Participant Soprano; George Fox Col; Mus.

LESHER, Kathy Darling
Valley HS; Las Vegas, NV; Drama; 4H; NHS; Ski C; Bsbl; Job's Daughters.

LESHER, Rochelle Janine
Norfolk Sr HS; Norfolk, NE (90-300) Chor; Evan-gel Col; Secy.

LESKERA, Elizabeth Ila
Collinsville HS; Collinsville, IL (10-650) Cpt, Chldr; Lat C; NHS; St Scholar; All St Chldr; U of Ill; Lib Arts.

LESLIE, Andrea Ruth
Auburn HS; Auburn, NE (7-95) Band; Chor; Ensm; Spch C; JV, Sftbl; Mgr, Tr; Kiwanis A; Math A; Spch A; HR; Acct.

LESLIE, Eddy R
Goddard HS; Roswell, NM (35-310) Band; Span C; JV, Bkbl; JV, Tr; Bio A; Sci A; NMSU; Sci.

LESLIE, John Loyd
McNeil HS; McNeil, AR (3-27) SC; 4H; Bkbl; Alg A; COM; Citz A; Cl Fav; Hist A; Math A.

LESLIE, Kim Suzanne
Carlmont HS; Belmont, CA; Cpt, Chldr; Beauty; Jr Prom Qn; Co-Ch, Sch Bible Stu; Campus After Dark; Church Executive Board; Sch Activities Board; Point Loma Col; Med.

LESLIE, Melanie Ann
Ft Pierce Central HS; Fort Pierce, FL (4-500) Ann; VP, BC; Secy, NHS; NEDT; Secy, Keyettes; Sr GSct; Pres, MYF; Med.

LESLIE, Robin Eileen
Eureka Sr HS; Eureka, CA; Ensm; Mjrte; Ski C; Cr-Ctry; Tr; Tr As; Vol Work A; Col o-t Redwoods; RN.

LESNY, Mark Eric
St Peters Prep HS; Jersey City, NJ (6-275) Drama; A-Ed, Lit Mag; COM; Hon Prog; NEDT; Dramat-ics Ltr; Eng Gold Medal; U of Va; Hist.

LESOING, Dean Curtis
Norris HS; Firth, NE (6-84) BS; Pres, FFA; 4H; NHS; Pres, SC; Wrest; Yth Fel; UNL Schol A; U of Neb; Animal Sci.

LESS, Wayne Scott
N Tonawanda Sr HS; N Tonawanda, NY; Band; Order/Arrow A.

LESSARD, Donald Anthony
E Ascension Acad; Gonzales, LA; LSU; Dentistry.

LESTER, Cindy Marie
Columbiana HS; Columbiana, OH (20%-105) 4H; Cl Fav; 4H A; Intensive Off Ed A.

LESTER, Donna Lorraine
Simon Gratz HS; Philadelphia, PA (7-350) Var C; Pres, Jr Cl; COM; Philadelphia HS China C; Future Careers; Girls Bowl Tm; Secy, Engr C; Mgr, Girl's Gym Tm; Pa St U; Math.

LESTER, Jane Irene
Elizabeth Seton HS; S Holland, IL (60-276) Chldr; Chor; Drama; Hon Prog; Sci A; U of Iowa; Bio.

LESTER, Kathy Lynne
Johnson HS; Gainesville, GA (10%-200) BC; Bus C; Chor; FBLA; Church Organist; Pres, Yth Group; Pianist, Primary Choir; Children's Choir Ldr.

LESTER, Kimberly Ann
Powell Valley HS; Speedwell, TN; FHA; Rptr, 4H; Bkbl; All Tourn Bkbl; Nurs.

LESTER, Mark Benton
N Miami HS; Denver, IN (10-127) Band; Semi-Fin, BS; Drama; Sch P; Sci C; Var C; JV, Bsbl; Ftbl; Wrest; Amer Leg A; Citz A; Most Out; Art.

LESTER, Niya Donderlyn
Philadelphia HS; Philadelphia, PA (161-375) FHA; Hmrm; Pa St U; Acct.

LESTON, James Gregory
Willowbrook HS; Villa Park, IL (333-844) Band; Chor; Model UN; SC; Preacher License; Cert Sun-day Sch Teacher; 1st Pl, Tn Talent Contest; Olivet Nazarene Col; Religion.

LETHERMAN, Debra Nadine
Baker HS; Baker, LA (33-374) Band; BC; LSU; Med.

LETOURNEAU, Linda Marie
Seekonk HS; Seekonk, MA (9-224) Hmrm; Lit Mag; Math C; NHS; Soccer; Hon Prog; Field Hockey; Fin, Most Musical; U of RI; Bio.

LETT, Aundrell
MacKenzie HS; Detroit, MI (18-352) NHS; Cpt, Cr-Ctry; Cpt, Tr; Mich St U; Bus Adm.

LETT, Danny Edwin
Tipton Comm HS; Tipton, IA; Bkbl; Cr-Ctry; Wild-life Mgt.

LETT, Debbie Rai
Tipton Comm HS; Tipton, IA (13-100) Ann; Chor; Bus Mgr, Fr C; Rptr, 4H; Bkbl; Golf; Sftbl; U of N Iowa; Elem Ed.

LETTEER, Elizabeth Ann
Bismarck HS; Bismarck, ND (143-450) Chor; ARC; Mgr, Var C; Mgr, Swim; ARC A; Yth Fel; 1st Cl GSct; Bismarck Jr Col; Nurs.

LEU, Connie Marie
Archbold Area HS; Archbold, OH (33%-140) Band; Chor; Pep C; Bowling Green St U; Special Ed.

LEUBA, Cynthia Louise
Santa Monica HS; Santa Monica, CA (30%-1000) Chor; Sunday Sch Teacher; Santa Monica Col; Theater Arts.

LEUNG, Conita
MacDuffie Sch; Springfield, MA; Math C; SC; JV, Bkbl; Archt.

LEUTHER, Thomas Edward
Ste Genevieve HS; Ste Genevieve, MO (40-170) Band; Order/Arrow; ARC; Bsbl; Bkbl; COM; 4H A; Order/Arrow A; ARC A; Scptr A; E Central Jr Col; Orthodontist.

LEUTHNER, Jean Marie
Holy Trinity HS; Winsted, MN (4-46) Band; Chor; 4H; COM; 4H A; Hon Prog; Type A; Hennipen Vo-tech Col; Secy.

LEUTZINGER, Richard R
Pattonville Sr HS; Hazelwood, MO; Citz A; Hon Prog; US Naval Sea Cadets; Unit Citation; Ntl Ci-tation; William Frazier A; US Navy; Elec Engr.

LEVELL, Patricia Ann
Killeen HS; Killeen, TX; Ger C; NHS; COM; Citz A; Sci A; Keywanettes; U of Tex at Austin; Nurs.

LEVERETT, Damon Keith
Cass Tech HS; Detroit, MI (20%-900) Band; Chess C; Bkbl; 'V' Ltr; Archt.

LEVERETT, Jeannine Marie
John F Kennedy HS; Tumon, GUAM; Hmrm; NHS; Rptr, Sch P; Hist A; Math A; ROTC A; Sci A; Top Ten; Outst Stu; Oral Roberts U; Social Work.

LEVESQUE, Daniel
Col De Ste Anne De La Pocatiere; La Pocatiere, CANADA (1-29) Phys C; Tnns; Sci.

LeVIER, Sandy Ann
Thomas Carr Howe HS; Indianapolis, IN; Chor; Pres, Fr C; Ger C; NHS; NMF; Earlham Col; Fr.

LEVIHN, Lynne Ann
Madison W Sr HS; Madison, WI (25%-700) Chor; Ski C; Soccer; JV, Swim; U of Wis; Dentistry.

LEVIN, Jeff Alan
Manhattan HS; Manhattan, KS (33%-450) AFS; BS; Model UN; Secy, Order/Arrow; Jr Cl; Soph Cl; JV, Ftbl; Wrest; Order/Arrow A; Yth Fel; WW; AFS Schol for Summer, Sweden; *Forestry.*

LEVIN, Susan Jean
Ulysses HS; Ulysses, KS; Ensm; FNA; FTA; Secy, 4H; Madrigal; NHS; Orch; Y-Tns; Accompanist, Chor; *Bethany Col; Biological Sci.*

LEVY, Ann Catherine
Cecilian Acad; Philadelphia, PA; Fr C; Sci C; Vlbl; *Med.*

LEVY, Helene Blanche
Jewish Education Center HS; Elizabeth, NJ (2-33) Tres, Hmrm; NHS; Co-Ed, Sch P; Hon Prog; NEDT; *Barnard U; Psych.*

LEVY, Karen Suzanne
Robert E Lee HS; Midland, TX; Chldr; Chor; Lat C; NHS; Type A; *Abilene Christian U; Phar.*

LEVY, Kathy Lynn
Booth-Temple HS; Des Moines, IA; Bsbl; Bkbl; Tr; Hon Prog.

LEVY, Stanley Uban III
Northside HS; Atlanta, GA; BC; Cpt, Bkbl; Ftbl; Tr; *Psych.*

LEWALLEN, Celeste Ann
Cando Pub HS; Cando, ND (11-47) A Cap Choir; Ann; Band; Chor; Drama; Fin, Ensm; FHA; Semi-Fin, GS; Pres, 4H; Hmrm; Madrigal; Sch P; Spch C; SC; S-T, Soph Cl; Mgr, Bkbl; Mgr, Ftbl; Swim; Tr; Citz A; 4H A; Spch A; Yth Fel; Mus A's; HR; Prom Qn Candidate; *McPherson Col; Elem Ed.*

LEWALLEN, Cynthia Jane
Claremore HS; Claremore, OK (9-217) Band; Chor; FHA; 4H; Madrigal; NHS; Bkbl; Sftbl; Bal-four A; St Hon Soc; Drum Major; Piano C; OSU Hon A; Anthology Co-Ed; PA A; Mus A; Girls in Action; Acteens; All St Choir; Page, Okla Sen; *U of Tulsa; Mus.*

LEWANDOWSKI, Kimberly Ann
Salina Central HS; Salina, KS (66-308) *Kans Tech Inst; Electronic Data Processing.*

LEWANTOWICZ, Ewa Ursula
Cathedral HS; Springfield, MA; CYO; Chess C; Drama; Math C; Sodality; Soccer; Sftbl; Tr.

LEWENCZUK, Jeffrey Scott
Hannibal Sr HS; Hannibal, MO (15-293) Band; NHS; Chem A; *U of Mo at Rolla; Chem Engr.*

LEWEY, Karen Ann
Tower Hill HS; Tower Hill, IL (1-30) Band; Chor; Rptr, FHA; Span C; Citz A; Type A.

LEWICKI, Margaret Susanna
A Crawford Mosley Sr HS; Panama City, FL (2-550) Mu Alpha Theta; Orch; Span C; Pres, GScts; Chaplain, NHS; Jr Marshal; Top Ten; *U of Fla; Phys Therapy.*

LEWIS, Anita Maureen
Dunbar Comm HS; Baltimore, MD; Pres, Hmrm; NHS; COM; Achv A; *Coppin Col; Bus.*

LEWIS, April Elizabeth
E Carteret HS; Beaufort, NC (25-178) Ann; Pres, Band; Fin, Chldr; GS; InterClub Coun; Lit Mag; Monogram; NHS; Orch; SC; Tres, Sr Cl; Tres, Jr Cl; Cpt, Bkbl; Tr; Most Out; Pres A; WW; Bkbl Schol; Nominee, Morehead Schol; *UNC-Wilmington; Phys Ed.*

LEWIS, Benjamin Eric
Myrtle Beach HS; Myrtle Beach, SC; Ann; Chor; Ensm; Cpt, Bkbl; Cpt, Ftbl; Tr; Best Defense, Bkbl; *Wake Forest U; Elec.*

LEWIS, Beverly Vonshea
Jonesboro Hodge HS; Jonesboro, LA (20%-127) Band; Drama; FBLA; FHA; VP, FNA; 4H; Up Bound; Bsbl; 4H A; JA A; *Nurs.*

LEWIS, Bonnie Kay
Danville HS; Danville, IL (25%-500) Yth Off, Church; Dist & St Win, Vocal Duet, Church; Church Choir.

LEWIS, Bradley Everett
Rio Amer HS; Sacramento, CA (50-400) Chess C; Fr C; Hon Prog; *Westmont Col; Sci.*

LEWIS, Brenda Julene
Dell City HS; Dell City, TX (4-24) Co-Ed, Ann; FFA; Tres, NHS; Var C; Cpt, Bkbl; Tnns; Tr; 4H A; HQn; Ftbl Swtht; FFA Swtht; Miss Dell HS; Most Ath; *Tex Tech U; Vet Med.*

LEWIS, Brian Dale
Gloucester HS; Gloucester, VA (33%-250) AFS; Band; Chor; Community Yth Symph; Pres, Drama; Ensm; InterAct C; InterClub Coun; VP, Madrigal; Orch; Thes; Gov Honor Prog; Regional Band & Choir; *James Madison U; Mus.*

LEWIS, Cathy Anne
Woodlake Union HS; Woodlake, CA (4-132) Co-Ed, Ann; Band; Fr C; Pres, FHA; Hmrm; Tres, SC; Var C; Bkbl; Bank Of Amer A; CSF; St Scholar; Vlbl; *Col o-t Sequoias; Lib Arts.*

LEWIS, Charles Leroy
Brethren HS; Paramount, CA; Chor; Dbte Tm; Span C; Mgr, Bsbl; Mgr, Bkbl; Mgr, Ftbl; Mgr, Tr.

LEWIS, Cindy Betty
Hernando HS; Brooksville, FL (20%-200) Key C; SC; Ch, Sr Cl; Co-Ch, Jr Cl; Art C; Art A; Pres, Yth Fel; *U of Fla; Art.*

LEWIS, Cynthia Annette
Minden HS; Minden, LA; Fr C; Hmrm; Fin, Lit Ral; SC; Up Bound; Shorthand A; *Grambling St U; Med Tech.*

LEWIS, Dana Kay
Glenwood Springs HS; Glenwood Springs, CO (1-160) Band; Cpt, Ensm; Mjrte; Math C; Var C; COM; Citz A; Hon Prog; Kiwanis A; Pres A; Cpt, Vlbl; *Colo Sch of Mines; Geological Engr.*

LEWIS, Darlene
Nettie Lee Roth HS; Dayton, OH; Hmrm; Mjrte; HR; *Wilberforce U; Bus.*

LEWIS, David Alan
Altus HS; Altus, OK (1-337) Hmrm; Model UN; VP, NHS; Sci C; SC; Var C; VP, Jr Cl; Bsbl; Ftbl; Tr; COM; Citz A; Hon Prog; Math A; Opt A; Pres A; Regent Schol; Val; Okla Hon Soc; Top 100 Stu, Okla; *W Okla St Col; Math.*

LEWIS, David Tyrone
N Natchez Adams HS; Natchez, MS; BC; Ch, Chem C; City Conf; Ch, Math C; NHS; Tres, Sci C; Pres, SC; Pres, Sr Cl; Pres, Jr Cl; Alg A; Bio A; COM; Chem A; Cl Fav; H of F; Hon Prog; Math A; MLS; Sci A; Mayor's Yth Coun; Hon Ram; St SC Rep; *Miss St U; Chem Engr.*

LEWIS, Debbie Sue
Mira Loma HS; Sacramento, CA (40-425) CSF; *U of Calif; Nutrition.*

LEWIS, Delenan Irene
Lakeland Sr HS; Lakeland, FL; *Trevcca Nazarene Col; Elem Ed.*

LEWIS, Doris Mae
Covina HS; Covina, CA (77-349) Dbte Tm; Drama; Model UN; Thes; Mgr, Swim; CSF; Lion A; VFW A; VofDEM; Yth Fel; Jr Statesman; *Biol.*

LEWIS, Douglas G
Barboursville HS; Barboursville, WV; Order/Arrow; Sch P; SC; Ftbl; Golf; Tnns; Tr; Cpt, Wrest; Order/Arrow A; Star, BScts; Champ of Champs Tri St Tr Meet; *Penn St U; Pre-Med.*

LEWIS, Eleanor Marie
Balboa HS; San Francisco, CA; Pres, Hmrm; Rptr, Sch P; SC; JV, Tnns; COM; Journ A; Block 'B' A; Cert of Appreciation; *USF; Bus.*

LEWIS, Elva Marie
Gardena HS; Gardena, CA; Cpt, Chldr; Chor; FNA; Pres, GS; Hmrm; Semi-Fin, Phi Delta Kappa; Fin, Baptist Training Union; Secy, Yth Fel; *Sci.*

LEWIS, Florence Lydia
Percy L Julian HS; Chicago, IL (41-184) Chor; Ensm; Rptr, Sch P; Span C; Spch C; Sftbl; Tnns; Beauty; COM; Citz A; Spch A; Yth Fel; Co-Op Work Training; *Chicago St U; Child Psych.*

LEWIS, Fred Clarke
Montgomery HS; Skillman, NJ (74-128) Band; Ger C; ARC; Ski C; Yth Fel; *Engr.*

LEWIS, Gary Claude
Lodi Union HS; Lodi, CA; Bsbl; JV, Ftbl; Wrest; *USC; Lib Arts.*

LEWIS, Gina Grace
Villa Angela Acad; Cleveland, OH (50-200) CYO; Chldr; Secy, Chor; Fr C; GS; NHS; SC; Tres, Sr Cl; Type A; Gym Ldrs A; Yth o-t Yr, Church; Best Singer A; *Toledo U; Bus.*

LEWIS, Gina Nannette
Wills HS; Smyrna, GA; A-Ed, Ann; Hmrm; NHS; SC; Bkbl; Sftbl; Cl Fav; Hon Prog.

LEWIS, Glenda Yvette
G W Carver Sr HS; New Orleans, LA; Chor; ARC; SC; Bsbl; Bkbl; Sftbl; Swim; Tr; Type A; Swim; *SUNO; Bus.*

LEWIS, Glenn Henry
SW Complex HS; Macon, GA (16-800) BC; Hmrm; Sch P; SC; COM; Hon Prog; *Macon Jr Col; Bus Adm.*

LEWIS, Greg Allen
Ritenour Sr HS; Overland, MO (90-800) NHS; Cr-Ctry; Swim; *U of Mo; Engr.*

LEWIS, Gwendolyn
Muncie Central HS; Muncie, IN; Co-Cpt, Chldr; FBLA; FHA; Mjrte; *Ball St U; Bus.*

LEWIS, Jacqueline Faye
G W Carver Sr HS; New Orleans, LA; Chor; Hmrm; NHS; ARC; Tri-HiY; Sftbl; Swim; Alg A; Bio A; COM; Citz A; Math A; ARC A; Sci A; *Dillard U; Nurs.*

LEWIS, James M
Delavan HS; Delavan, IL (3-66) Band; Drama; VP, FFA; 4H; Thes; Var C; Bkbl; Golf; 4H A; NEDT; Yth Fel; Star Chapter Greenhand; *U of Ill; Agr Engr.*

LEWIS, James Robert
Miami Palmetto Sr HS; Miami, FL; Tr.

LEWIS, James Scott
Woodland HS; Woodland, CA; Ann; Dbte Tm; Rptr, Sch P; Pres, SC; Bkbl; Ftbl; Tr; *Oreg St U; Forestry.*

LEWIS, Janet Gail
Decatur HS; Decatur, AL (33%-350) Chor; Hmrm; NHS; SC; COM; Math A; *Elem Ed.*

LEWIS, Jannett Renna
Fairfield HS; Fairfield, AL (25%-186) Band; Bkbl.

LEWIS, Jeanette
Martin L King Acad; Gary, IN; City Conf; SC; Hon Prog; *Ind U.*

LEWIS, Jennifer Elizabeth
Holton-Arms Sch; Bethesda, MD (20-60) Chor; Fr C; Lat C; A-Ed, Lit Mag; Pres, Madrigal; F-Ed, Sch P; Sci C; VP, World Affairs C; MVP, Hockey; Tnns; Hon Prog; Cpt, Hockey; JV Vlbl; 1st Pl, Lat Bowl; Hon Tour Guide; *Bucknell U; Biol.*

LEWIS, Jerry Lynn
Vicksburg HS; Vicksburg, MS (12-244) FHA; NHS; Span C; Alg A; COM; *Alcorn St U; Social Work.*

LEWIS, Jill Ann
Bridgeton HS; Bridgeton, NJ; Co-Ed, Ann; 4H; Hmrm; Pres, NHS; Hockey; Citz A; 4H A; HCt; Betty Crocker Search for Ldrship; *Douglass Col; Spch.*

LEWIS, John Douglas
Woodlawn HS; Birmingham, AL; Bsbl; Ftbl; Wrest; *U of Tenn; Archt.*

LEWIS, John Richard
Starkville HS; Starkville, MS (20-276) Ed, Ann; Band; BS; Chem C; 4H; NHS; VP, SC; Bio A; COM; 4H A; H of F; Hon Prog; *Miss St U; Pre-Vet Med.*

LEWIS, Jovanni Regina
Petersburg HS; Petersburg, VA (10%-585) Band; NHS; Sci C; Span C; COM; *Hampton Inst; Phar.*

LEWIS, Judith Marie
N Pocono HS; Moscow, PA (5-231) FTA; Span C; Co-Cpt, Bkbl; Sftbl; Vlbl; *E Stroudsburg St Col; Phys Ed.*

LEWIS, Katherine Lucille
Oregon HS; Oregon, IL (48-138) Sci C; *Rock Valley Col; Advertising.*

LEWIS, Keith Byron
West Side HS; Newark, NJ; VP, Fr C; NHS; Golf; JV, Soccer; Hon Prog; Fencing; *Harvard U; Psych.*

LEWIS, Kim Lorraine
Highland Sr HS; Highland, IN (150-582) Ski C; Tr; Hon Qn, Jobs Daughters; *Taylor Col; Phys Ed.*

LEWIS, Kimberly Terriera
Northview HS; Covina, CA; Chldr; Chor; Ensm; Hmrm; InterClub Coun; K of C; SC; Mgr, Bkbl; Mgr, Sftbl; Sewing, Chldr, Chor, A's; *Fashion.*

LEWIS, Laurie Gail
Fremd HS; Palatine, IL; SC; Hockey; Cpt, Vlbl; Badminton; 'Nicest Smile'; *Abilene Christian U; Child Psych.*

LEWIS, Leslie Diane
Cherry Creek HS; Englewood, CO (33%-700) A Cap Choir; AFS; Bus C; Chor; GS; Pres, SC; Pres, Sr Cl; JV, Tnns; Hon Prog; *Colo U; Bus Adm.*

LEWIS, Linda Marie
Vicksburg HS; Vicksburg, MS; Chor; Ensm; GS; Lat C; Secy, NHS; H of F; *Utica Jr Col; Acct.*

LEWIS, Lisa Ann
Warren Co Sr HS; McMinnville, TN; *David Lipscomb Col; Elem Ed.*

LEWIS, Lois Ruth
Northwest HS; St Louis, MO (15-700) FBLA; NHS; *Washington U; Acct.*

LEWIS, Loriann
Pleasantville Sr HS; Pleasantville, NJ; Chor; Schol & Achv A; *Med.*

LEWIS, Margaret Lynn
York Acad; Shacklefords, VA (3-44) Secy, BC; Lat C; Sftbl; COM; Athena Soc; Bookkeeping A; Academic Excellence A; Jr Beta C.

LEWIS, Maria Evonne
Inglewood HS; Inglewood, CA (317-469) Cl Fav; Hon Stu A; *Pepperdine U; Real Estate.*

LEWIS, Mark Andrew
Lake Placid HS; Lake Placid, FL (3-130) Ann; CYO; VP, Chess C; Tres, 4H; InterClub Coun; Pres, Key C; Tnns, NHS; Var C; Tnns; Tr; Amer Leg Orator A; DARGCA; Gr Marshal; 4H A; Spch A; Lieutenant, Band; Chaplain, BS; Lay Eucharistic Minister; *Spring Hill Col; Humanities.*

LEWIS, Melody L
E Atlanta HS; Atlanta, GA (9-142) Tres, Tnns; Hon Prog; ROTC A.

LEWIS, Michael LeRoy
Central Dauphin HS; Harrisburg, PA (54-554) Band; Ch, BS; Chor; Drama; Ger C; NHS; Bus Mgr, Thes; JV, Cr-Ctry; JV, Tr; COM; PTA A; ROTC A; Senator, Boys Nation; 1st Star, Thespian A; *Cornell U; Engr.*

LEWIS, Mike Claude
Daniel Boone HS; Jonesboro, TN (44-250) BC; Sci C; MVP, Ftbl; Tr; Phy A; *E Tenn St U; Engr.*

LEWIS, Mike D
Artesia HS; Artesia, NM (25%-330) Band; Bkbl; Golf; Hon Prog; Yth Fel; Woodshop A; Superior, Band Contest.

LEWIS, Monique La Shaun
Lincoln HS; Dallas, TX; Band; Tr; Principal's A; *El Centro Col; Chem.*

LEWIS, Monique La Shawn
Lincoln HS; Dallas, TX; Band; Tr; Pres A; *El Centro Col; Chem.*

LEWIS, Nancy Christine
First Baptist HS; Charleston, SC; F-Ed, Ann; Cpt, Chldr; S-T, Drama; Drama; Ensm; Pres, Rainbow; Rptr, Sch P; SC; HCt; NEDT; *Winthrop Col.*

LEWIS, Nathaniel Jerome
W End HS; Birmingham, AL (10-31) Band; Chor; Drama; FTA; Pres, Hmrm; Mod Mus Mas; Orch; Sch P; Spch C; SC; Thes; VP, Soph Cl; Hist A; Hon Prog; Math A; Ntl Conf Chr & Jews; Sci A; *Harvard U; Law.*

LEWIS, Ned Robert
Newman HS; Wausau, WI (104-136) Pres, K of C; Rptr, Sch P; Ski C; Mgr, Bkbl; Mgr, Ftbl; Swim; Mgr, Wrest; *U of Wis; Journ.*

LEWIS, Pamela Jane
Glendale HS; Springfield, MO (193-411) Band; Hon Prog; *Sou Mo St U; Instrumental Mus.*

LEWIS, Patricia Gayle
MacArthur HS; Irving, TX (20-400) Chor; Dbte Tm; Rptr, Drama; Hmrm; NFL; NHS; Sch P; Span C; Sch C; St Stu Congress; SC; Thes; NMF; Drill Tm; Spch Comp A; UIL Choir Contest; *Spch.*

LEWIS, Patricia Joyce
Corinth HS; Corinth, MS; FHA; DECA St Participant; Distributive Ed C of Amer; DECA Silver & Bronze A; Run-Up for Star Stu, DECA.

LEWIS, Patricia Lynn
Maysville HS; Maysville, KY (30-80) VP, FHA; Lat C; Sci C; WW; *Nurs.*

LEWIS, Paul Daniel
Walter Johnson HS; Bethesda, MD (30-450) Chess C; Fr C; Hmrm; Ed, Lit Mag; VP, SC; COM; Hon Prog; Cert of Achv; *Sci.*

LEWIS, Philip Edward
Eldorado HS; Eldorado, IL (10-130) Bsbl; Ftbl; *Bradley U; Chem.*

LEWIS, RaFaye Kathleen
N Natchez Adams HS; Natchez, MS (4-296) Band; Tres, Chor; Secy, City Conf; Fr C; DARGCA; *Ohio St U; Pre-Med.*

LEWIS, Rebecca Joy
Albemarle HS; Charlottesville, VA (5%-750) Fr C; Lit Mag; F-Ed, Sch P; Tr; Hon Prog; Jr Hon Soc; *Rice U; Biol.*

LEWIS, Rhonda Dee
E Ascension Acad; Gonzales, LA; FBLA; Lit Ral; Type A; *La Col; Ed.*

LEWIS, Rita Mae
Jasper HS; Jasper, MN (25%-50) CYO; Drama; FHA; Pres, 4H; Ayrshire Breeders Assn; Vlbl; 4-H, Top 10 Girls; Prom Waitress; Fin, 4-H A; *Commercial Bus.*

LEWIS, Robert James
Lisbon HS; Lisbon, ND (20-70) Band; Chor; JV, Bkbl; Ftbl; Golf; Math A; *U of Minn; Acct.*

LEWIS, Rodger Dale
Fairview HS; Fairview, TN (13-72) Pres, Jr Cl; Pres, Soph Cl; Cpt, Bsbl; Cpt, Ftbl; Cl Fav; MVP, Bsbl; *Tenn Tech U; Computer Sci.*

LEWIS, Sandy Dee
East Alton Wood River Comm HS; Wood River, IL (100-300) Sftbl; *N Ill U; Phys Ther.*

LEWIS, Sharolyn Denise
Mount Olive HS; Seale, AL (4-53) 4H; Co-Cpt, Mjrte; NHS; *Spch Therapy.*

LEWIS, Shawn Allen
Waynoka HS; Waynoka, OK (9-38) Ann; Pres, Band; Sch P; Sci C; Pres, SC; Pres, Jr Cl; Cpt, Bkbl; Cpt, Ftbl; Tr; HCt; Type A; Stu of Today; Eng Lit A; *NW Okla St U.*

LEWIS, Sherwood
Manley HS; Chicago, IL (12-500) Span C; VP, SC; Bsbl; Mgr, Bkbl; Tr; Fresh o-t Yr; *NW Col; Law.*

LEWIS, Sheryl Lynn
DeWitt HS; DeWitt, MI (20-143) Var C; Swim; Tr; Citz A; Yth Fel; Voice of Democracy, Atten, A's; *W Mich U; Special Ed.*

LEWIS, Sonjia Kaye
Monroe HS; Albany, GA (10-329) Band; Drama; SC; VP, Soph Cl; Tnns; Best All Around; *Morris Brown Col; Med.*

LEWIS, Stanley Malcolm
Joseph S Clark Sr HS; New Orleans, LA; Band; Ftbl; JA.

LEWIS, Steve A
Carroll HS; Monroe, LA (3%-205) VP, Band; Pres, Hmrm; Math C; Mod Mus Mas; Tres, Phys C; Alg A; MLS; Phy A; Band A; Jazz Festival A; *Grambling St U; Engr.*

LEWIS, Susan Faith
Gwynn Park Sr HS; Brandywine, MD (5%-283) Band; Chldr; Secy, 4H; Rptr, Lit Mag; Math C; NHS; Tr; COM; 4H A; Journ A; Q&S A; Spch A; Eng & Fr Proficiency As; *U of Md; Engr.*

LEWIS, Susan Kaye
Wetumka HS; Wetumka, OK (4-43) Band; GS; Mjrte; NHS; *U of Okla.*

LEWIS, Suzanne
El Camino Real HS; Woodland Hills, CA (1-1095) Fr C; CSF; Chem A; JA A; Pres, Ladies; Girls League; *Calif St U at Northridge; Ed.*

LEWIS, Tamara Ann
Mexico Sr HS; Mexico, MO; Chor; Fr C; VP, FBLA; SC; Pep C; *NMSU; Bus.*

LEWIS, Tamara Deane
Antelope Valley HS; Lancaster, CA (414-614) HiY; VP, Tri-HiY; Citz A; *Antelope Valley Jr Col; Bus.*

LEWIS, Teresa Gayle
W Carter Co HS; Olive Hill, KY (5%-127) FBLA; Pres, Lib C; Spelling A; *Morehead U; Nurs.*

LEWIS, Terri Dean
S Point HS; Belmont, NC (25%-240) Chldr; GS; Hmrm; InterAct C; Monogram; Bus Mgr, Sch P; SC; VP, Jr Cl; MVP, Bkbl; Sftbl; Amer Leg A; Citz A; DARGCA; *Appalachian St U; Elem Ed.*

LEWIS, Vance Clark
Fort Scott Sr HS; Fort Scott, KS; Dbte Tm; NFL; NHS; Span C; SC; Ftbl; Tnns; COM.

LEWIS, Vanessa Antoinette
W Side Sr HS; Gary, IN; Hmrm; Span C; SC; Y-Tns; VP, Jr Cl; Citz A; Cl Fav; Gov Honor Prog; Hon Prog; MLS; Most Out; *Ind U; Med.*

LEWIS, Vera Elizabeth
Kashmere Sr HS; Houston, TX (25%-670) Band; FHA; Hmrm; NHS; Ch, SC; Parl, Sr Cl; Parl, Jr Cl; Bsbl; Tr; Hon Prog; Sci A; St Readers C; Mus Talent Surver; Mus, Tex Safty, A's; *Prairie View Col; Elec Engr.*

LEWIS, Vincent Blair
Beecher HS; Flint, MI (20-40) Band; Var C; Y-Tns; Bkbl; Ftbl; Tr; JA A; *Central Mich U; Communication.*

LEWIS, Vivian Marie
Stone HS; Wiggins, MS; FHA; Y-Tns; *Miss Gulf Coast Jr Col; Health Care Mgt.*

LEWIS, Wayne Borden
N Shore HS; W Palm Beach, FL (19-266) Chor; Hmrm; InterClub Coun; Key C; NHS; Span C; SC; Var C; Pres, Sr Cl; VP, Jr Cl; Co-Cpt, Swim; Bio A; Hist A; NML; All Conf; *Emory Col; Pre-Med.*

LEWIS, William Michael
Enka HS; Enka, NC (30-360) Pres, Hmrm; VP, Lat C; Monogram; Bsbl; Ftbl; Tr; *VPI; Mineral Research.*

LEWIS, Yvonne Marlene
Will Rogers Sr HS; Tulsa, OK; VP, Bus C; Fr C; Tres, SC; Beauty; Citz A; Hist A; Hon Prog; JA A; Kiwanis A; Orch, Writing, A's; Stu Helper; Safety Patrol; *Med.*

LEWISON, Todd William
Anamosa HS; Anamosa, IA (3-153) Band; Chor; Ensm; Madrigal; Bsbl; JV, Bkbl; JV, Cr-Ctry; JV, Golf; NEDT; *Phys Therapy.*

LEWISTON, Susan Ellen
S Hamilton HS; Jewell, IA (12-96) A Cap Choir; Band; Chldr; Chor; Ensm; 4H; Madrigal; NHS; Mgr, Bkbl; Golf; Type A; Band Gold A; *Waldorf Col; Bus.*

LEY, Cynthia Joan
Warren Central HS; Indianapolis, IN; Chor; Ensm; Madrigal; *Span.*

LEY, Joel Quinten
North Kitsap HS; Poulsbo, WA (20-200) Pres, Band; Secy, NHS; Order/Arrow; Soccer; Band, Outst Sr; *Wash St U; Public Health.*

LEYDON, Thomas Paul
St Bede Acad; Peru, IL (40-126) Chor; Hmrm; Rptr, Sch P; SC; Tres, Sr Cl; Ftbl; JV, Tr; Stu Govt A; *St John's U; Natural Sci.*

LEYMEISTER, Clyde Luther Jr
Blue Mtn HS; Schuylkill Haven, PA (34-253) Mu Alpha Theta; JV, Tr.

LHAMON, Steven H
Marion HS; Marion, IN; Demolay; Order/Arrow; Ski C; Swim; *Ind U; Med.*

LIAKAKIS, Antonio Peter
Bible Baptist HS; Savannah, GA (25%-54) Pres, Sr Cl; Pres, Jr Cl; Pres, Soph Cl; Co-Cpt, Bkbl; Co-Cpt, Ftbl; Hon Prog; MLS; MVP, Bkbl & Ftbl; Most Academic; *Armstrong St Col; Phys Ed.*

LIANG, Grace Suie
John Jay Sr HS; Hopewell Junction, NY (5-550) S-T, Band; Ensm; Co-Ch, Lat C; Lat NHS; NHS; Ch, SC; Swim; Tr; Area & All St Band; *Biochem.*

LIBBE, John Allan
Maumee HS; Maumee, OH (6-361) NHS; Ski C; Tres, Var C; Tres, Sr Cl; Co-Cpt, Cr-Ctry; Mgr, Ftbl; Tnns; Alg A; Hon Prog; Bowl; Outst Jr; *U of Mich; Engr.*

LIBBY, Mark Wallace
Moberly Sr HS; Moberly, MO (23-212) BS; Math C; ARC; Mgr, Bkbl; Mgr, Cr-Ctry; Mgr, Ftbl; Mgr, Tr; Mgr, Wrest; *U of Mo; Bio.*

LIBERT, Michele Marie
Notre Dame HS; Clarksburg, WV (7-52) Band; Drama; Secy, FBLA; FTA; Cpt, Mjrte; NHS; HCt; *St Mary's Hospital; X-Ray Tech.*

LIBHART, Deborah Lee
Fort Lupton HS; Fort Lupton, CO (2-128) Ann; Chor; Fr C; VP, FTA; GS; NHS; Tres, Sci C; Y-Tns; COM; Jr Chamber of Com A; Masonic A; Most Out; Bkbl Statistician; Secy, Pep C; HR; Hon Choir; GAA; WW; *U of N Colo; Elem Ed.*

LICANTO, Nestor Peter Jr
John F Kennedy HS; Tumon, GUAM; Hmrm; Ed, Sch P; JV, Bkbl; Alg A; Sci A; *U o-t Philippines; Med.*

LICHA, Alicia Mercedes
Notre Dame HS; Caguas, PR (1-136) A Cap Choir; Chldr; Chem C; Chor; Dbte Tm; Drama; Fr C; Hmrm; Math C; Phys C; ARC; Sci C; Span C; SC; Alg A; Bio A; COM; Chem A; Hist A; Hon Prog; Math A; MLS; Most Out; Qtr A; Opt Out Tn; Phy A; Sci A; Spch A; Swtht; Span A; Excellency Cert; Conduct Cert; *Natural Sci.*

LICHAK, Nancy Ann
Riverside Jr-Sr HS; Taylor, PA (13-195) Bus Mgr, Ann; Chor; FNA; FTA; Cpt, Mjrte; NHS; Hon Prog; NEDT; Acad Schol; WW; *Col Misericordia; Nurs.*

LICHI, Jodi Marie
Broadmoor HS; Baton Rouge, LA; BC; Lat C; Lat NHS; St Missionette Qn; Campfire AE C; Bucerettes; Soc of Christian Ath; BBB'S; *U of NC; Bus Adm.*

LICHLYTER, Maria Ann
Shawe Mem HS; Madison, IN (1-24) NHS; A-Ed, Sch P; VP, SC; Bkbl; Hon Prog; Journ A; Val.

LICHOTA, Marc Helmut
Bedford HS; Bedford, OH (309-597) Chem C; Drama; Hmrm; Sci C; Ski C; Span C; Bkbl; MLS; *Ohio St U; Marketing.*

LICHT, Carol Eileen
Bell Gardens HS; Bell Gardens, CA (10-385) Secy, A Cap Choir; Ensm; Semi-Fin, GS; Hmrm; Jr Miss Pagent; SC; Bank Of Amer A; Cl Fav; HR; Top Ten; *U of Redlands; Communicative Disorders.*

LICHTE, Janeece Ilene
Lexington HS; Lexington, MO (2-110) NHS; Orch; Thes; Var C; Sftbl; Tr; *Central Mo St U.*

LICHTENBERG, Scott Evan
Woodmere Acad; Woodmere, NY (2-42) Band; Fr C; Co-Ed, Sch P; Sci C; Tres, Jr Cl; Mgr, Bkbl; Soccer; Tr; Bio A; Chem A; *Law.*

LICHTENBERGER, Erik Jacob
Kaiser HS; Honolulu, HI (11-350) Chor; Tres, Drama; Fr C; Hmrm; Pres, Key C; NHS, Ch, SC; Tres, Thes; JV, Cr-Ctry; JV, Wrest; COM; Sci A; *U of Mich; Med.*

LICHTENEGGER, Beverly Sue
Neshaminy Langhorne HS; Langhorne, PA (201-692) DECA; VICA; Basket Ballettes; *Bucks Co Comm Col; Early Childhood Ed.*

LICHTHARDT, Donna Lee
Arundel Sr HS; Gambrills, MD (98-750) Hmrm; ARC; Var C; Cpt, Bkbl; Cpt, Sftbl; Mgr, Tr; Cl Fav; ARC A; Cpt, Vlbl; Miss Arundel; *The Medix Sch; Nurs.*

LICHTY, Marla Irene
Bruning Pub Sch; Bruning, NE (5-17) A Cap Choir; Band; Chor; Madrigal; Spch C; Pres, Soph Cl; Bkbl; Tr; HCt; Hon Prog; Yth Fel; MVP, Vlbl; Milo Qn; VP, Pep C; All Star VB Player; *U of Nebr at Lincoln; Phys Ed.*

LIDA, Kim Anita
Rock Hill HS; Rock Hill, SC; *Gardner-Webb Col.*

LIDBECK, Glenn Jay
Kailua HS; Kailua, HI (10-570) Pres, NHS; Citz A; Most Out; Cpt, Vlbl; Eng A; *Ecology.*

LIDDELL, Donna Marie
Continued Education Project; St Louis, MO;

LIDDELL, Sarah Dorothea
Marquette HS; Michigan City, IN (15-57) Chor; Drama; Monogram; NHS; Ed, Sch P; Ski C; Span C; Secy, SC; VP, Soph Cl; Sftbl; Swim; MVP, Tnns; B Crocker A; HR of Hon Prog; Spch A; St Scholar; Mission; 1st Pl, NISBOVA; Sadie Hawkins Ct; Sch Musicals; Q&S; Outst Actress A; *Boston Col; Communications.*

LIDDY, Dawn Marie
Camden Central HS; Camden, NY; Chor; Mjrte; Chamber of Comm A; Citz A; Yth Fel; Ntl Baton Twirling Assn; WW; Jr & Sr Ntl Mjrte Champion; Bowl; 1st, Variety Showcase, NY St Fair; Performs For Nursing Homes, Charity.

LIDECKA, Jane Miriam
Aurora Sr HS; Aurora, IL (50-754) A Cap Choir; Chor; NHS; *General Ed.*

LIDECKA, Ruth Mary
W Aurora HS; Aurora, IL (20-625) Pres, A Cap Choir; NHS; St Scholar; Aurora Found Schol; *Augustana Col; Ed.*

LIDZ, David Gray
Princeton HS; Princeton, NJ (70%-250) A Cap Choir; Chor; Drama; Hmrm; InterAct C; SC; JV, Tnns; Tr; PHS Gold Key; *Cornell U; Mus.*

LIEBENSTEIN, Sharon Ann
Port Washington HS; Port Washington, WI (7-250) Band; Ensm; Orch; Arch; Yth Fel; Ltrs, St Ensm Contest; *Med.*

LIEBENSTEIN, Shirley Rae
Port Washington HS; Port Washington, WI (17-250) Band; Ensm; Orch; Arch; Yth Fel; Ltrs, St Ensm Contest; *Med.*

LIECHTY, Eric Newton
Zion Benton Twp HS; Zion, IL (18-450) A Cap Choir; Ntl Yth Conf; Span C; Bsbl; COM; Hon Prog; NEDT; Yth Fel; Sup HR; Nom, BS; 2nd Pl, Interntl Preacher Boy Con; *Wheaton Col; Bible Theology.*

LIEDER, Heidi Louise
Crookston Central HS; Crookston, MN (5-183) Band; Chor; Dbte Tm; Math C; NFL; Orch; Sch P; Spch C; Thes; COM; Spch A; Hon Thespian.

LIEFER, Doris Fay
Steeleville HS; Steeleville, IL (1-67) Co-Ed, Ann; Pres, FBLA; FHA; NHS; Cl Fav; DARGCA; Hist A; MLS; NEDT; St Scholar; Type A; Val; *Ill St U; Bus Adm.*

LIEKWEG, Paula Marie
Saint Mary's Acad; Alexandria, VA (4-67) Pres, Drama; VP, French NHS; GS; Key C; Mu Alpha Theta; S-T, NHS; ARC; SC; Secy, Jr Cl; Drama, NEDT, A's.

LIES, Sheila
Hillcrest HS; Ny, NY; Orch; Bkbl; *Stony Brook Col; Med.*

LIESSE, Sarah Margaret
St Bede Acad; Peru, IL (50-120) Chldr; Chor; Tr; *Ill Valley Comm Col.*

LIETZ, Charles Bradley
Denison Sr HS; Denison, TX (35-275) Band; Orch; Wrest; COM; Yth Fel; Pub Address Operator; PA; Excel, Orch; St Regional Solo & Ensm Medal; *Grayson Co Jr Col; Arch.*

LIFE, William Arthur
Maconaquah HS; Bunker Hill, IN (70-250) Order/ Arrow; Span C; Thes; Ftbl; JV, Swim; God & Country A; Sch Yrbk; Eagle Sct; Journalism C; *Ind U; Photography.*

LIGGET, Stephen Woodard
Spencer HS; Columbus, GA (48-208) Bsbl; Phys Ed A; Church MVP; Valley Rescue Mis Camp for Child.

LIGGETT, Thomas Shaw
Randolph Southern Sch; Shellman, GA (4-18) Ann; BC; Fr C; Bsbl; Bkbl; Tr; COM; NEDT; Pres, Church Yth Coun; *Ga Inst of Tech; Elec Engr.*

LIGGIN, Ben Wallis
Bay HS; Panama City, FL; FFA; VP, 4H; Bsbl; Ftbl; Tr; Wrest; *Fla Col; Drama.*

LIGGINS, Terri Eileen
Columbus East HS; Columbus, OH (10-350) WW; WW Among Amer Mus Stu; *Ohio U; Communications.*

LIGGINS, Toni E
East HS; Columbus, OH; *Med Assistant.*

LIGHT, Carol Annette
Chantilly HS; Chantilly, VA (1-360) Cpt, Chldr; FBLA; Jr Miss Pagent; NHS; Span C; Var C; Ch, Jr Cl; Fin, Tr; Beauty; Hon Prog; PTA A; Sci A; *U of Va at Charlottesville; Math.*

LIGHT, John
Penns Grove HS; Penns Grove, NJ (49-270) Bus Mgr, Chor; Drama; *Bradford Col; Drama.*

LIGHT, Robin Lynn
James River HS; Buchanan, VA (45-115) Dbte Tm; Sch P; WW; *Dabney S Lancaster Comm Col; Bus Adm.*

LIGHTCAP, Carole Virginia
Marple Newtown Sr HS; Newton Square, PA; Chor; Drama; FNA; Hmrm; Sch P; Chor A; Lib Aide; Hospital Vol; *Nurs.*

LIGHTFOOT, Bettie Jean
Fremont HS; Oakland, CA; *Merritt Col; Bus.*

LIGHTFOOT, Chandrea Denise
Broad Ripple HS; Indianapolis, IN; *Drew U; Psych.*

LIGHTFOOT, Larry Dean
Seabreeze Sr HS; Daytona Beach, FL; JV, Wrest; *Daytona Beach Comm Col; Pre-Law.*

LIGHTNER, Jeffrey Paul
Katella HS; Anaheim, CA; Tnns; Semi-Fin, Wrest; *Calif St U.*

LIGHTSEY, Linda Faye
Columbia Acad; Columbia, MS; Chldr; Chor; NHS; COM; *USM; Vet Sci.*

LIGHTSEY, Valerie Jo
Antelope Valley HS; Lancaster, CA; NHS; CSF; Hon Prog; Jr Cl Rep; Prom Committee.

LIGON, A Laurann
S Grand Prairie HS; Grand Prairie, TX; Chor; FTA; Bus Mgr, Drill Tm.

LIIMAKKA, Mia Emma
Luther L Wright HS; Ironwood, MI; Band; Tres, 4H; Swim; 4H A; 4-H Achv A; Swim A; Band A; HR; *Gogebic Comm Col; Archt.*

LIJEWSKI, Samantha Jean
St Bede Acad; Peru, IL (25-100) Sftbl; Tr; Hon Prog; GAA; *Bradley U.*

LILES, John Wall
Sanderson HS; Raleigh, NC (190-575) A Cap Choir; Band; Chor; Ensm; Madrigal; Orch; All-St Mus A; All-St Orch A; *Appalachian St U; Acct.*

LILES, Leesa Minette
Lake Highlands HS; Dallas, TX (55-690) Co-Ed, Lit Mag; NHS; Ed, Sch P; Secy, Jr Cl; Secy, Soph Cl; Hon Prog; Journ A; MLS; Q&S A; Val A of Excel; Girl o-t Mo; *Abilene Christian U; Communications.*

LILES, Lindsay Scott
Varina HS; Richmond, VA (35-150) FBLA; VP, 4H; Key C; Sodality; Co-Cpt, Bkbl; Tr; 4H A; Yth Fel; MVP, Bkbl; *Va Tech & St U; Agr.*

LILES, Robin Maree
Providence HS; Providence, KY (15-60) Band; FHA; Bkbl; Tr; Schol A; Home Ec A; *Nurs.*

LILES, Timothy Warren
Harding HS; Charlotte, NC; Band; Sci C; Hon Prog; ARC A; Yth Coun; Sportsmen Society; *UNC; Bus Adm.*

LILJEDAHL, Lisa Jo
Crescent HS; Joyce, WA (3-18) Ed, Ann; Band; Chldr; Secy, NHS; Secy, Jr Cl; Secy, Soph Cl; HCt; *Peninsula C C; Med.*

LILLARD, Laura Ann
Santa Fe HS; Alachua, FL (10%-173) BC; FBLA; FFA; Sftbl; 2nd Pl, Job Interview; *Santa Fe Comm Col; Bus.*

LILLARD, Natasha Lynn
Cohn HS; Nashville, TN; Tnns; Nashville St Tech Inst; Computer Programing.

LILLEGARD, Deborah Lynn
Luverne Jr-Sr HS; Luverne, MN (16-155) Band; Chor; Ensm; Co-Cpt, Sftbl; COM; 'A' HR; Bethany Jr Col; Mus.

LILLESKOV, Cynthia Lee
Cedar Falls HS; Cedar Falls, IA (25%-500) Band; Ger C; Orch; Golf; Yth for Understanding; U of Iowa; Med.

LILLEY, Stephen Harrison
Farmington Sr HS; Farmington, MO (65-269) Band; Rptr, Sch P; Sci C; Mineral Area Col; Journ.

LILLIBRIDGE, Robert Charles
Delavan Comm Unit HS; Delavan, IL (50%-60) Band; Drama; Pres, SC; Golf; Bradley U; Dentistry.

LILLIE, Cheryl Denise
M B Smiley HS; Houston, TX (10-400) FTA; Mu Alpha Theta; NHS; Bio A; COM; Chem A; Cl Fav; Swtht; 1st Ladies C; U of Houston; Bus.

LILLY, Cara Louise
W Mid-High Sch; Norman, OK; Ann; S-T, Chor; Ensm; Hmrm; NHS; Span C; SC; Amer Leg A; Citz A; Masonic A; Yth Fel; Sou Methodist U.

LILLY, Jan Elizabeth
Twin Lakes HS; Monticello, IN (13-265) Band; Chor; Ensm; Secy, 4H; Secy, Span C; JV, Bkbl; Tr; Yth Fel; JV, Vlbl.

LILLY, Kenneth Edward Jr
Northside HS; Fort Smith, AR (30-500) VP, A Cap Choir; BS; Chor; Drama; Ensm; Hmrm; Lat C; Mu Alpha Theta; VP, SC; Thes; Tnns; All St Choir; Baylor U; Biol.

LIM, Ray Dean
Woodrow Wilson HS; Los Angeles, CA (50%-500) Key C; Ftbl; Semi-Fin, Tr; Pasadena City Col; Bus.

LIMERICK, Thomas Stanley
Kemper Acad; DeKalb, MS (7-42) Ann; BC; Phy A; Sci A; Meridian Jr Col; Elec Tech.

LIN, Bob Tse Wen
Lane Tech HS; Chicago, IL (241-1400) Fr C; Hmrm; NHS; Orch; Ftbl; JV, Wrest; COM; Chem A; Hon Prog; Sup Rating, City Ensm Comp; St Champions, Orch; U of Ill-Urbana; Pre-Med.

LIN, Danny J H
Albany HS; Albany, CA; Chor; Ensm; Cr-Ctry; Tr; San Francisco St U; Broadcasting.

LINCICOME, Michelle Rae
Larkin HS; Elgin, IL (289-690) Band; Chor; Hmrm; Orch; JV, Tnns; Hist A; Stevens Point Col; Natural Resources.

LINCOLN, Daniel Arthur
Coral Gables HS; Coral Gables, FL; Band; Order/ Arrow; Rptr, Sch P; Bsbl; Bkbl; Yth Fel; Yth Leg; Eagle Sct; U of Miami; Marine Biol.

LINCOLN, Jane MacFarlane
Wilson HS; Washington, DC (15-501) Pres, Hmrm; NHS; COM; Hon Prog; Sal; Oberlin Col; Psych.

LINCOLN, Karla Ann
E Anchorage HS; Anchorage, AK (115-470) Band; Co-Ed, Sch P; St Stu Congress; Pres, Soph Cl; Bkbl; COM; MLS; Most Out; Co Cpt, Vlbl; Notre Dame U; Law.

LINCOLN, Laurie Lea
Portage Northern HS; Portage, MI; Chor; NHS; Sci C; Ski C; Var C; Cpt, Bkbl; MVP, Sftbl; COM; Citz A; Hon Prog; Sports A; All Star Bkbl Tm.

LINCOLN, Tami Robin
Cypress Lake HS; Ft Myers, FL; Cpt, Chldr; Drama; Hmrm; Lit Mag; Sci C; Beauty; Cl Fav; H of F; HCt; MLS; Most Out; WW; Prom Qn; Christmas Qn; Outst Sr; Muskingum Col; Creative Writing.

LIND, Arlen Christiaan
Bismarck HS; Bismarck, ND; Co-Ed, Ann; FFA; Var C; Ftbl; Tnns; Chapter Farmer; Commercial Photography.

LIND, Cynthia Ann
Jamestown HS; Jamestown, NY (2%-516) A Cap Choir; Band; Madrigal; NHS; ARC; Ski C; Amer Leg A; MLS; Most Out; Opt A; Regent Schol; Drum Major; Ski C; Colgate Col; Pre-Med.

LIND, Dawna
Clear Creek HS; League City, TX (1-456) A Cap Choir; Chor; Cum Laude Soc; Drama; Ensm; Parl, Hmrm; Madrigal; Mu Alpha Theta; NHS; Pol Sci C; Sch C; Parl, SC; Bkbl; Sftbl; Hon Prog; Magna Cum Laude; Opt A; Val; Pres, Church Yth Group; Choir A; Sch Musicals; Solo & Ensm Medals; Vlbl; Jesse Jones Schol; All St Hon Choir; Brigham Young U; Phys Tehrapy.

LIND, Karla Annette
Albert City-Truesdale HS; Albert City, IA; Band; Chldr; Chor; Ensm; Fr C; VP, 4H; Pres, Soph Cl; 4H A; Tres, FCYF; Pianist, Church Choir; 1st Pl, Ntl Church Mus; Piano, FCYF.

LIND, Kevin Robert
Santa Fe Preparatory Sch; Santa Fe, NM (10%-21) Co-Ed, Ann; BS; Chess C; Chor; Pres, Dbte Tm; Pres, Demolay; Pres, Model UN; Orch; Rptr, Sch P; Pres, Spch C; JV, Bkbl; JV, Soccer; Tr; COM; NMF; Spch A; Academic Achv; Rice U; Physics.

LIND, Sandra Jean
Winthrop Pub Sch; Winthrop, MN (19-69) Ann; Band; Chor; Drama; Semi-Fin, Ensm; FHA; Secy, 4H; NHS; Sch P; St Lucia Girl; Willmar Col; Acct.

LIND, Thomas William
Bismarck HS; Bismarck, ND; U of ND.

LINDBERG, Bruce Elroy
Albia Comm HS; Albia, IA (10-149) Band; Chor; FTA; 4H; NHS; Tr; JV, Wrest; HCt; Hon Prog; Pres, Art C; Art A; I Rating, Band; Indian Hills Comm Col; Med.

LINDBERG, Janelle Kay
Forest Lake Sr HS; Forest Lake, MN (75-511) Band; JV, Chldr; Chor; Ski C; Span C; SC; Golf; Sftbl; JV, Tnns; JV, Tr; Pres A; Med.

LINDBERG, Juanita Marie
Powers Lake HS; Powers Lake, ND; Chor; FFA; FHA; 4H; Bkbl; ND St U; Registered Nurs.

LINDBERG, Lynnette Sharon
Forest Lake HS; Forest Lake, MN (99-440) Ann; Band; Chldr; Lit Mag; S-T, Ski C; Span C; Sftbl; HCt; MMTA Syllabus & Theory Exams; St Cloud St U; Med Tech.

LINDBLOM, Anne Christine
Jamestown HS; Jamestown, NY (10-560) Parl, Band; NHS; Orch; Regent Schol; Pres, Mozart Mus C; Mus.

LINDELL, Jay Roger
Naperville Central HS; Naperville, IL (223-430) Ski C; Hon Prog; Yth Fel; Wheaton Col; Religion.

LINDEMAN, Diane Kay
Manistee HS; Manistee, MI (120-182) ARC; Tri-HiY; Amer Leg A; Registered Nurs.

LINDEMANN, Lori Ann
Golden Valley Pub HS; Golden Valley, ND (1-13) A-Ed, Ann; Pres, Band; Chor; Ed, Sch P; VP, Jr Cl; Bkbl; U of ND.

LINDEMANN, Mark Edwin
Western Hills HS; Cincinnati, OH (5-812) Band; Cum Laude Soc; HiY; Order/Arrow; Var C; Golf; Hist A; Hon Prog; Order/Arrow A; Eagle Sct; Rose-Hulman Inst; Computer Sci.

LINDEMANN, Roberta Gail
Bismarck HS; Bismarck, ND; Band; JV, Chldr; Chor; Tnns; Tr; Pres A.

LINDEMEYER, Richard John
Nordonia HS; Northfield, OH (102-518) Band; Ensm; Hmrm; Tnns; COM; Band A's; Mus.

LINDEMULDER, James Richard
Chicago Christian HS; Palos Heights, IL (30-158) Band; Ensm; Fr C; NHS; Orch; ARC; Ski C; Bkbl; Ftbl; Soccer; Sftbl; Puppet C; Short Story A; Fin, COM; Fin, Hons Prog; Fin, Red Cr A; U of Ill; Med Tech.

LINDENMUTH, Lorie Megan
Scott Comm HS; Scott City, KS (1-360) Band; Ensm; GS; NMS; Type A; Val; St of Kans Schol; Band A; Kans St U; Engr.

LINDER, David William
Starkville HS; Starkville, MS (20-250) Cpt, Band; Ensm; Pres, 4H; Pres, Lat C; NHS; Bsbl; Bkbl; Citz A; 4H A; I Dare You; JA A; Spch A; Sch P & Annual Photographer; Pres, Photo C; Mr Sr High, Church; Pres, Chrch Chor; Best Dress Boy A; Sr of Distinction; Miss St U; Acct.

LINDER, Paul David
Brentwood HS; Brentwood, NY (6%-1500) Cpt, Chess C; Drama; Ger C; NHS; Orch; Sci C; Bio A; COM; Hist A; Hon Prog; Regent Schol; Sci A; NY St Mus A; Rutgers Col; Chem.

LINDER, Sherry Kay
Sigourney Comm HS; Sigourney, IA (12-76) Pres, All Amer Yth; Band; Co-Cpt, Chldr; Chor; Ensm; Pres, Hmrm; Cpt, Mjrte; Var C; Co-Cpt, Tr; Gym; Mus As; Tr As; U of Northern Iowa; Interior & Fashion Design.

LINDER, Steve John
Aiken HS; Cincinnati, OH (10%-790) NHS; Var C; Tnns.

LINDGREN, Brenda Sue
Olivia HS; Olivia, MN (33%-65) Ann; Band; Chldr; Chor; Ensm; Madrigal; Rptr, Sch P; Span C; Pres, Jr Cl; Swim; Mgr, Tr; HCt; Star Student; Gym; Dist Solo; Dist Ensm; Dist Band; U of Minn; Nurs.

LINDGREN, Diane Louise
Meriden-Cleghorn HS; Cleghorn, IA; Ann; Band; Co-Cpt, Chldr; Chor; Semi-Fin, GS; Pres, 4H; NHS; Bkbl; Cr-Ctry; 4H A; Hon Prog; All Amer Chldr; St Mus A; Des Moines Area Comm Col; Med Asst.

LINDGREN, Rand Jonathan
Olivia Pub HS; Olivia, MN (20-87) Chor; Drama; Fin, Ensm; Fin, Madrigal; Rptr, Sch P; VP, SC; Var C; Ftbl; Swim; Tr; COM; Hon Prog; Sci A; St Mus Hon's; Concordia Col.

LINDGREN, Sara Lu
Dodgeville HS; Dodgeville, WI (1-135) AFS; Chor; Drama; Math C; Model UN; Span C; JV, Bkbl; Tr; Hist A; NEDT; UW-MADISON; Pol Sci.

LINDHOLM, David Eric
Miami Palmetto Sr HS; Miami, FL; Ftbl; Tr; Eagle Sct; Auburn U; Bus Adm.

LINDHOLM, Leslie Tyner
The Buckley Sch; Los Angeles, CA; NHS; Loyola Marymount Col; Math.

LINDHOLM, Matthew Scot
Blue Earth HS; Blue Earth, MN (10-104) Semi-Fin, BS; Chor; NHS; Pres, Jr Cl; JV, Bkbl; Co-Cpt, Ftbl; Golf; MVP, All Conf, Ftbl; Carleton Col; Econ.

LINDHOUT, Karen Jean
Manistee HS; Manistee, MI (5-200) Chor; Ensm; Secy, Madrigal; NHS; VP, Span C; Central Mich U; Sci.

LINDHURST, Marjorie Jean
N Tonawanda Sr HS; North Tonawanda, NY (2%-677) Chor; Fr C; Cpt, Sftbl; Hist A; Hon Prog; Sci A; Fr A; Pres, Church Yth Group; NJHS; Sunday Sch Teacher; Church Chor; Tres, GSct; Law.

LINDLEY, Cassandra Richelle
Skyline HS; Dallas, TX; Drama; FHA; Citz A; JA A; Math A; E Texas St Col; Counselor.

LINDLEY, Debra Kay
Herscher HS; Herscher, IL (61-176) Band; Ensm; 4H; Sftbl; 4H A; Olivet Nazarene Col; Nurs.

LINDLEY, Martin Robert
Herscher HS; Herscher, IL (5-190) Band; 4H; JV, Bsbl; JV, Ftbl; 4H A; Yth Fel; Bradley U; Elec Engr.

LINDNER, Gregg Richard
Hartford Union HS; Hartford, WI; Bsbl; Bkbl; Ftbl; Sftbl; Swim; HR; Math.

LINDQUIST, Jeanne M
Oconomowoc Sr HS; Oconomowoc, WI (100-525) FBLA; Church Bkbl League; GAA; Active Christian Tns; Pastors Christian Ath A; Waukesha Co Tech Inst; Acct.

LINDQUIST, Jennifer Diane
Fulda Pub HS; Fulda, MN (4-63) Band; Chor; VP, 4H; NHS; Spch C; Bkbl; Tr; COM; Citz A; 4H A; Hon Prog; JA A; Spch A; Yth Fel; Campus Life; Pres, Church Yth Fel; Vlbl; Mus & Band A's; Med.

LINDQUIST, Scott Lee
Luther L Wright HS; Ironwood, MI (1-210) Var C; Bkbl; Gogebic Comm Col; Secondary Ed.

LINDQUIST, William Edward
Fulda Pub HS; Fulda, MN (10-85) Band; Chor; Ensm; Pres, 4H; NHS; Fin, Soph C; Var C; Pres, Jr Cl; Bsbl; Bkbl; Cr-Ctry; Cpt, Sftbl; COM; Citz A; 4H A; HCt; Hon Prog; Pres A; Spch A; Yth Fel; Mus A's; Pol Sci.

LINDSAY, Amy Ann
Little Wolf HS; Manawa, WI (30-73) Band; JV, Chldr; Dbte Tm; Span C; Spch C; Type A.

LINDSAY, Anne R
Santa Monica HS; Santa Monica, CA (5%-961) Bkbl; U of Calif; Kinesiology.

LINDSAY, Barbara Ann
Hendersonville HS; Hendersonville, NC (15-145) Co-Cpt, Chldr; Hmrm; Span C; SC.

LINDSAY, Brenda Gail
Denbigh HS; Newport News, VA (252-450) Ann; City Conf; Pres, FBLA; 4H; Hmrm; InterClub Coun; Rptr, Key C; Span C; Ch, SC; Pres, Y-Tns; Ch, Sr Cl; Ch, Jr Cl; Rptr, Soph Cl; Tr; Sci A; DECA; Pres, Yth Fel; GSct; Pep C; Va Union U; Econ.

LINDSAY, Charles Brian
Ell-Saline HS; Brookville, KS (2-16) Chor; 4H; Secy, Jr Cl; Tres, Soph Cl; JV, Bkbl; Ftbl; Tr; Type A; Escort, Jr Cl Carnival; Escort, Jr Swtht.

LINDSAY, Colette Marie
Oconomowoc Sr HS; Oconomowoc, WI; Ski C; HR; 4 Hons Cl; Pep C; Vlbl; U of Wis; Engr.

LINDSAY, Gretchen Gail
Lyman HS; Longwood, FL (25%-650) AFS; Band; BC; Drama; Ger C; Orch; Secy, Tri-HiY; Amer Leg A; Yth Leg; VP, Chaplain, Tri-Hi-Y; Stu o-t Mo; WW; Foreign Exchange Stu; Foreign Lang.

LINDSAY, James John
Monroe-Woodbury Sr HS; Central Valley, NY (7-450) Lit Mag; NHS; Sch P; Bkbl; JV, Bkbl; Soccer; Hon Prog; NEDT; Sci A; Span Excel, Soc Stu Excel, A's; Journ.

LINDSAY, Kim R
Claremore HS; Claremore, OK (8-315) Bus C; Chor; Fr C; FBLA; FHA; VP, Hmrm; NHS; A-Ed, Sch P; SC; Y-Tns; JV, Bkbl; Tr; Balfour A; COM; Elk A; Type A; Archbearer; Cert of A; Fr 'C' A; Supt's HR; St Hon Soc; Bus.

LINDSAY, Patti Jo
Christian HS; El Cajon, CA (5-120) JV, Sftbl; JV, Swim; Banner Corps; Rifle Corp; Christian Heritage Col; Missions.

LINDSAY, Perry L
Spring HS N; Spring, TX (34-505) Mu Alpha Theta; NHS; F-Ed, Sch P; JV, Bsbl; Mgr, Ftbl; Hon Prog; Gulf Schol Semi-Fin; Natl Merit Commended Stu; Tex Tech U; Aeronautics.

LINDSAY, Robert Todd
Christian HS; El Cajon, CA (30-110) Chess C; JV, Ftbl; Chritian Heritage Col; Teaching.

LINDSEY, Ann
Vernon HS; Vernon, TX; FHA; FTA; Span C; Col o-t Ozrarks; Special Ed.

LINDSEY, Anthony
Wendell Phillips HS; Chicago, IL; A Cap Choir; Chor; Bradley U; Journ.

LINDSEY, Clayton Lynn
Crystal Lake Comm HS; Crystal Lake, IL (70-550) NHS; Cpt, Bsbl; Wrest; Hon Prog; Order/Arrow A; NHS A; Aurora Col; Psych.

LINDSEY, Earnest Douglas
R H Watkins HS; Laurel, MS;

LINDSEY, Jordan Paul
Moore HS; Moore, OK (48-676) Math C; NHS; Order/Arrow; Span C; Ch, SC; Tnns; COM; God & Country A; Hon Prog; Magna Cum Laude; Order/Arrow A; Eagle Sct; U of Okla.

LINDSEY, Karen Denise
Milwaukee Trade i Technical HS; Milwaukee, WI (25-500) A Cap Choir; Chor; Ensm; Hmrm; SC; Up Bound; COM; Hon Prog; MLS; Ntl Sci Found; Sci A; Yth Fel; Marquette U; Chem Engr.

LINDSEY, Kirby Lyle
Franklin Co HS; Frankfort, KY; Chor; Key C; Bkbl; Sftbl; Tnns; Tr.

LINDSEY, Laverne
F O Alexander HS; Starkville, MS (30-59) Chor; Y-Tns; Miss St U; Secy Sci.

LINDSEY, Melita
Westwood HS; Memphis, TN (28-248) NHS; Pres, Distributive Ed C of Amer; U of Tenn-Knoxville; Eng.

LINDSEY, Patricia Kathleen
Burges HS; El Paso, TX (15%-599) Drama; Hmrm; Span C; Thes; Rptr, Tri-HiY; Y-Tns; Masque & Gavel A; Jr NHS; U of Tex; Spch Pathology.

LINDSEY, Rhonda Lynn
Springs Valley HS; French Lick, IN (7-90) Ann; Band; JV, Chldr; Fr C; SC; Var C; Bkbl; Tr; COM; Hon Prog; VP, Photo C; Vlbl; Ind U; Clinical Psych.

LINDSEY, Ronald Jay
Devilbiss HS; Toledo, OH; Chor; Ed, Sch P; Up Bound; Journ A; MLS; Most Out; Yth Fel; Art As; Mus As; Bowling Green St U; Mgt.

LINDSEY, Suzanne Catherine
Central HS; Martinsburg, PA (140-215) Band; Drama; NFL; Secy C; Spch A; Outdoors C; Penn St U; Retailing.

LINDSTROM, Carol Elizabeth
Oroville HS; Oroville, CA (19-283) Chor; NHS; SC; Pres, Fresh Cl; Tres, CSF; Butte Jr Col; Eng.

LINDSTROM, Chris Ann
Zion-Benton HS; Zion, IL; Chor; Fin, GS; NHS; SC; Tr; Pres A; Yth Fel; Vlbl; Co-Ch, Prom; Prom Court; Bible.

LINDSTROM, Constance Colleen
Murdock HS; Murdock, MN (3-35) Ann; Cpt, Chldr; Chor; Bkbl; Tr; Special Ed.

LINDSTROM, Craig Edward
Forest Lake Sr HS; Forest Lake, MN (70-511) ARC; Ski C; Span C; Bsbl; Co-Cpt, Ftbl; COM; Cl Fav; Dance A; Cpt, Church Tm; Air Force Acad.

LINDSTROM, Joel Daniel
Fremont HS; Sunnyvale, CA (1-618) A Cap Choir; Chor; Drama; S-T, Math C; Thes; Tnns; CSF; NMS; NCTE Sch Rep; UCB; Physics.

LINDSTROM, Judith Kim
Raymore-Peculiar HS; Peculiar, MO (18-167) Band; Chldr; Chor; FTA; A-Ed, Lit Mag; NHS; JV, Bkbl; JV, Golf; Sftbl; VofDEM; Social Services.

LINDSTROM, Lori Ann
Maple Shade HS; Maple Shade, NJ; Bus Mgr, Ann; Secy, Band; JV, Chldr; Drama; Semi-Fin, GS; Hmrm; Key C; Rptr, Lit Mag; NHS; Orch; Ski C; St Stu Congress; Secy, SC; Var C; Hockey; Communications.

LINDSTROM, Marla Sue
Forest Park HS; Beaumont, TX (103-465) Rptr, FTA; Lat C; Lat MHS; Lit Mag; Rainbow; Hon Prog; Hon Men, Tex Short Story Contest; Cum Laude, Adv Lat; Jr Class Lge Poetry & Mottoes; LSU; Eng.

LINDUFF, Floyd Allen Jr
Midwest City Sr HS; Midwest City, OK (166-560) Band; Chess C; Lat C; Sci A; Bio A; U of Okla; Biochem.

LINE, Kathleen Louise
Mt Whitney HS; Visalia, CA (5%-450) A Cap Choir; Chor; Ensm; Fin, GS; Hmrm; InterClub Coun; Secy, Key C; Span C; SC; CSF; Citz A; Mgr, JV Vlbl; Girl o-t Mo; Lieutenant Apex, Keywannetts; Ed.

LINEBARGER, Daniel Jeffery
Weed HS; Weed, CA (7-57) Drama; Math C; NHS; Phys C; Pol Sci C; Var C; Cpt, Cr-Ctry; Cpt, Tr; CSF; Col o-t Siskiyous; Elec.

LINEBARGER, Lori Dene
Plano HS; Plano, TX (33%-850) Drama; ; Vac Bible Sch A; Lieut, Drill Tm; Historian, Drill Tm; Church, Yth Coun & Yth Choir; Best Personality & Smiles, Drill Tm; Baylor U; Elem Ed.

LINEBAUGH, David K
E Pennsboro Area HS; Enola, PA (17-225) NHS; Amer Leg A.

LINEBERGER, Martha Ann
N Augusta Sr HS; N Augusta, SC; Chor; Crown & Scepter; Ensm; Hmrm; Sftbl; Tnns; Sci A; Mars Hill Col; Pre-Sch Ed.

LINER, Nancy Jane
McMinn Co HS; Athens, TN; F-Ed, Ann; Chldr; Chem C; Tres, Sci C; Span C; Tri-HiY; Mgr, Bkbl; COM; Cl Fav; Journ A; E Tenn St U; Med.

LING, Susan Marie
Terra Linda HS; San Rafael, CA; Band; Chldr; Community Yth Symph; Fr C; CSF; U of Calif; Pre-Med.

LINGERFELT, Cynthia Ann
Tabernacle Christian Sch; Greenville, SC; Ann.

LINGERFELT, Donna Renee
Unicoi Co HS; Erwin, TN (33%-245) Chor; FNA; Secy, 4H; Model UN; ARC; Bkbl; Tr; Mus A; Tenn Baptist Hospital Sch of Nurs; Med.

LINGERFELT, Helen Ruth
Coconino HS; Flagstaff, AZ (33-331) F-Ed, Ann; Band; Ch, Chor; Community Yth Symph; Secy, Drama; Secy, Fr C; Madrigal; NHS; Co-Ed, Sch P; Spch C; SC; Rptr, Thes; Swim; Hon Prog; Spch A; Madrigal; Region St Bi-Centennial Bands; Poetry A; Hon Graduate; Westmont Col; Journ.

LINGERFELT, Julia Leigh
Coconino HS; Flagstaff, AZ (10%-375) Band; Chor; Dbte Tm; Swim; Spch A; Pom Pon; U of Washington; Mus.

LINGLE, David Russell
Big Sandy HS; Big Sandy, TX (10-42) NHS; SC; Pres, Soph Cl; Co-Cpt, Bkbl; Tr; Cl Fav; Stephen F Austin Col; Art.

LINGREN, Joan Emilia
Hood River Valley HS; Hood River, OR (73-184) Ann; 4th of July Princess; Girl League; Pres, Pep C; DECA; 'S' C; E Oreg St Col; Bus.

LINK, Daniel Robert
Douglas Co HS; Castle Rock, CO (60-450) Pres, Band; Chor; Drama; Hmrm; Ed, Sch P; Pres, SC; Pres, Jr Cl; Cpt, Ftbl; Fin, Tr; Wrest; Citz A; HCt; Most Out; Opt A; Opt Out Tn; Yth Fel; U of Colo; Law.

LINK, Dawn Leslie
Iroquois HS; Elma, NY; Mgr, Syncronize Swim; Aquatic C; Secy, Yth Fel; Boy's C; Ping Pong; Canisius Col; Acct.

LINK, Denise Lucille
Iroquois Central HS; Elma, NY (21-335) AFS; Chor; Model UN; NHS; A-Ed, Sch P; Swim; Tr; Ntl Sci Found; Regent Schol; Pres, Tres, Yth Fel; U of Rochester; Pre-Med.

LINK, John Stewart
Broad Run HS; Ashburn, VA (120-350) InterClub Coun; VP, Ski C; Var C; Co-Cpt, Bkbl; Cpt, Ftbl; Cpt, Soccer; Tnns; MVP, Ftbl; Madison Col; Pre-Dental.

LINK, Judith Ann
Fleetwood Area HS; Fleetwood, PA (25-149) Band; Orch; JV, Bkbl; JV, Hockey; JV, Sftbl; Tr; God & Country A; Hon Prog; NHS; Var Ltr, Girls Tr & Field; President's Phys Fitness A; VP, Jr Cl; Pres, Horizon C; Schlicher-Kratz Inst; Real Estate.

LINK, Nancy Lynn
Knoch HS; Saxonburg, PA (200-275) Band; Chor; Butler Comm Col; Bookkeeping.

LINK, Steven Craig
Beaver Dam HS; Beaver Dam, WI (10%-315) BS; Hmrm; NHS; Sci C; SC; Var C; Bkbl; Tnns; HCt; Yth Fel.

LINKLATER, Joseph Clyde
Wyle E Groves HS; Birmingham, MI; NHS; JV, Wrest; U of Mich; Med.

LINMAN, Mark James
Northgate HS; Walnut Creek, CA; Order/Arrow; Ski C; Soccer; Order/Arrow A; Eagle Sct; Church Yth Ldrship; Oreg St U; Natural Sci.

LINN, Jenny Lou
Lubbock Christian HS; Lubbock, TX (4-50) Bus Mgr, Chor; Ensm; GS; Madrigal; Rptr, NHS; Secy, SC; VP, Sr Cl; Secy, Jr Cl; Bkbl; DARGCA; HCt; PTA A; Runner Up, Miss LCHS; WW; Abilene Christian U; Homemaking.

LINN, Kenneth Carl
Lakeview HS; Stoneboro, PA (35-140) AFS; Band; Secy, Chor; Pres, Drama; Fr C; Pres, 4H; Lit C; Dist Chor; Westminster Col; Mus.

LINN, Malinda Anne
Frankfort HS; Ridgeley, WV (25%-151) Chor; NHS; Secy, Sr Cl; Secy, Jr Cl; Cl Fav; DARGCA; HQn; Service A; Potomac St Col; Secretarial Sci.

LINN, Timothy Peck
Hempfield HS; Landisville, PA (45%-465) A Cap Choir; Chor; Demolay; 4H; Lit Mag; ARC; Sci C; Bkbl; Ftbl; Sftbl; Freshmen's A, Group Sing Out; Father & Son o-t Yr A; Pa St U; Agr.

LINNA, Peni Jo
Cottage Grove HS; Cottage Grove, OR (19-240) S-T, NHS; Swim; Tr; COM; Type A; Outst Ath; PA; Oreg Inst of Tech; Radiology.

LINNE, Michelle Kay
Zion-Benton HS; Zion, IL (10-428) AFS; Chldr; Chor; Secy, Fr C; NHS; VP, Sr Cl; DARGCA; Elk A; St Scholar; Exchange C Stu o-t Mo; U of Ill Champaign; Law.

LINNEMAN, Stephen Louis
Permian HS; Odessa, TX (10%-700) A Cap Choir; Pres, Madrigal; NHS; Arch; Yth Fel; Top 10, Stu Body; Outst Choir Stu; Win, Bach Piano Competition; U of Tex; Pre-Med.

LINNEMEYER, Brian Keith
Central HS; Camp Point, IL (20-120) Band; Ger C; Orch; Var C; Ftbl; COM; NEDT; U of Ill; Agr Engr.

LINNEN, Kenneth Nathaniel
Burke HS; Charleston, SC; Ftbl; Tr; Sr Hon Soc; Math.

LINO, Palmira Maria
Richmond Hill HS; New York, NY (10-40) French NHS; Key C; Secy, Span C; Hon Prog; Type A; Queens Col; Lang.

LINSCHEID, Sylvia Kay
Jefferson HS; Cedar Rapids, IA; Orch; Bkbl; Sftbl; Mgr, Tr; Biola Col; Bible.

LINTNER, Gary Boden
New Brighton Area Sr HS; New Brighton, PA (7-223) Soph P; Var C; Swim; Co-Cpt, Tnns; Hon Prog; NEDT; Yth Fel; Rotary Boy o-t Month; Stu Photography Contest; 1st Pl, Pa Fed of Women's C; Carnegie-Mellon U; Civil Engr.

LINTON, Cynthia Louise
Corry Area Jr-Sr HS; Corry, PA; Chor; Chancel Chor; Old Time Radio C; Yth Group; Radio Amateurs of Corry; Cert of Code Proficiency; US Air Force; Elec.

LINTON, Felicia Dawn
Druid HS; Tuscaloosa, AL; S-T, HiY; NHS; SC; Secy, Sr Cl; Debutante Jabar Girl; U of Ala; Acct.

LINTON, Janet Rene
Godby HS; Tallahassee, FL; Chor; FHA; Span C; Amer Leg A; MLS; Pep C; Fla St U; Psych.

LINTON, Pamela Marshell
Miami Killiam Sr HS; Miami, FL (251-1102) Miami Dade Comm Col; Med.

LINTZ, Deidre Sue
Beavercreek HS; Xenia, OH (5%-700) AFS; Fr C; NHS; HR; Carson-Newman Col; Bio.

LINVILLE, Tracie Darlene
Riverdale HS; Fort Myers, FL (10%-450) Band; Chor; Drama; COM; Hon Prog; NEDT; Yth Fel; Lang Arts A; Prog VP, Yth Group; Candystriper; Sounds of Glory Gospel Group; Milligan Col; Eng.

LIO, Maria T
Bishop McDevitt HS; Harrisburg, PA (20%-300) Dbte Tm; Fr C; FBLA; Hmrm; VP, Lat C; VP, Ski C; Span C; SC; Soccer; COM; Cl Fav; Hon Prog; Most Out; Span A; Art Prog; Lang.

LIPP, Kelley Jay
South HS; Pueblo, CO; Journ A; Parl, VICA; 1st Pl St, VICA; U of Colo; Elec Engr.

LIPPENCOTT, Carolyn Teresa
St Joseph's o-t Palisades HS; W New York, NJ (5-225) CYO; Cpt, Chldr; Chor; Drama; GS; Pres, NHS; ARC; Span NHS; Sftbl; Bausch & Lomb A; JA A; NEDT; GSct; Duquesne U; Phar.

LIPPERT, Barbara Lynn
Highland HS; Bakersfield, CA (12-377) A Cap Choir; Pres, Bus C; Chor; Ensm; InterClub Coun; Madrigal; NHS; SC; Bank Of Amer A; CSF; Sr Cl Pub Committee; Fin, Achv A; Pres, Future Secy's of Amer; VP, Church Yth Group; YMCA; Gold Seal Bearer, CSF; Cincinnati Bible Col; Bus Ed.

LIPPERT, Tony Kim
Clay Co Comm HS; Clay Center, KS (7-124) NHS; Sci C; Bkbl; Ftbl; Sftbl; Tr; Hon Prog; Math A; Rotary A; Sci A; St Scholar; FCA; Kans St U; Agr Engr.

LIPPI, Theresa Marie
Bishop McDevitt HS; Harrisburg, PA (3-5) Cr-Ctry.

LIPPINCOTT, Tamara Joyce
Chelan HS; Chelan, WA (1-49) Ann; Band; Chor; Dbte Tm; Ensm; S-T, 4H; Hmrm; Secy, NHS; Rainbow; F-Ed, Sch P; Ski C; SC; Tnns; COM; 4H A; Magna Cum Laude; Val; Rodeo Qn; 1st Pl, DECA St; Eastern Wash St Col; Bus Adm.

LIPPOLD, Beth Ann
Kaneland Sr HS; Maple Park, IL (76-190) Chor; Drama; Span C; Swim; Hon Prog; Mus A; Lincoln Christian Col; Mus.

LIPPOLD, Bruce Alan
Avotta Comm HS; Avoca, IA (1-43) Pres, Band; Chor; Drama; Madrigal; NHS; Orch; Order/ Arrow; SC; Thes; Pres, Sr Cl; Bkbl; Ftbl; Bausch & Lomb A; COM; God & Country A; Masonic A; MLS; St Scholar; Val; Eagle A; All St Band; All St Ftbl; Iowa St U; Agr.

LIPPOLD, Kirk Staheli
Carson City HS; Carson City, NV (23-400) BS; Dbte Tm; VP, Key C; NFL; NHS; Spch C; Pres, SC; Golf; Tnns; Elk A; Most Out; Rotary A; Lt Gov, Key C; US Air Force Acad; Mech Engr.

LIPPS, Lynn Elwin
Pymatuning Valley HS; Andover, OH (7-140) Band; Chor; Dbte Tm; Drama; Ensm; Fr C; Lat C; NHS; SC; Thes; Var C; Bsbl; JV, Golf; Hon Prog; Pep Band; Co Band; Polar Bear C; Lat Banquet; Mus Solo Contest; Med.

LIPS, Jennifer Adrienne
Ossining HS; Ossining, NY (39-379) A Cap Choir; Band; VP, CYO; Chor; NHS; Secy, Orch; Thes; COM; Regent Schol; Type A; The King's Col; Ed.

LIPSCOMB, Gary Glenn II
Glendale HS; Springfield, MO (1-400) AFS; Chess C; Key C; Lat C; Pres, Math C; Order/Arrow; Curator A; Order/Arrow A; WW; U of Mo-Rolla; Chem Engr.

LIPSCOMB, Laura Anne
St Ignatius HS; St Ignatius, MT (1-36) Ann; Band; CYO; Chor; GS; NHS; Secy, SC; Hon Prog; NEDT; Type A; Bookkeeping A; Outst Band Stu; Outst Fresh in Band; U of Wash; Spch Pathology.

LIPSCOMB, Melvin Lavon
S H Archer HS; Atlanta, GA; Band; Chldr; Chor; Drama; Hmrm; Orch; SC; Tnns; Co-Cpt, Tr; MVP; PA; Best Chldr Stunt Man; Fin, Tr; Tr Certs & As; Co-Cpt, Gym; Church Choir A; Wash Close-Up Prog; Drama.

LIPSEY, Douglas Jay
Alvin HS; Alvin, TX; Band; Math C; Mgr, Bkbl; Tnns; Tex A&M U; Vet Med.

LIPSITZ, Amy Leigh
St Mary's HS; Raleigh, NC (24-100) BC; JV, Chldr; Fr C; FHA; Lit Mag; Var C; Bkbl; MVP, Tnns; Duke U; Med.

LIPSTRAW, John Arlyn
Fremont Ross HS; Fremont, OH (72-531) 4H; Key C; Tres, NHS; Tri-HiY; Var C; JV, Ftbl; Wrest; COM; 4H A; Wrest Coaches A; A of Distinction; MVP, 4-H Sftbl; Ohio St U; Pre-Med.

LIPTOW, Sandra Kay
Parkview HS; Orfordville, WI (25-164) AFS; Ann; NHS; Gifted Stu Found Schol; Airline Stewardess.

LISI, Deborah Ann
Springford Sr HS; Royersford, PA (10%-375) Band; Chor; NHS; Span C; VP, Soph Cl; Spch A; Spch Pathology.

LISS, Michael David
Robinson Sch; San Juan, PR (1-39) Drama; Ch, Hmrm; Lit Mag; Math C; Pres, Model UN; UN Council; Ch, Soph Cl; Soccer; JA A; Math A; NEDT; Secy & Pres, BSct; Pres, JA; Service A, NJHS; Mgr, Yrbk; NJHS; U of Pa; Bus.

LISSOLO, Janet Gail
Weldon Valley HS; Weldona, CO (4-12) A-Ed, Ann; Band; Chldr; Chor; FBLA; FHA; 4H; NHS; A-Ed, Sch P; Secy, SC; Bkbl; I Dare You; Masonic A; Sr Prom Comm; Best All Around.

LISSOLO, Patricia Annette
Weldon Valley Sch; Weldona, CO (1-19) Band; Chldr; Chor; FBLA; FHA; NHS; Tres, SC; Bkbl; Hist A; Math A; Sci A; Band A; Choir A; J Phillips Sousa A; Mus.

LIST, Cynthia Gaye
Struthers HS; Struthers, OH (4-275) Pres, Band; VP, Chor; Ensm; FTA; Tres, NHS; VP, Span C; NEDT; I Rating, Dist Solo & Ensm; Youngstown St Col; Elem Ed.

LIST, Marilyn Jane
Logan Elm HS; Circleville, OH (16-185) Band; Chor; Community Yth Symph; Secy, 4H; NHS; Sch Achieve Tm; Tr; 4H A; Yth Fel; Bowl; Circleville Forum; GAA; Luther League; Jr Ldrs; Pep Band; Young Life; Hons Band; Yth Orch; Miami U; Social Work.

LIST, Regan Eugene
Teays Valley HS; Ashvolle, OH (6-240) BS; Chem C; 4H; Pres, NHS; Sci C; VP, Jr Cl; MVP, Tnns; 4H A; Ohio St U; Sound Engr.

LISTELLA, Lisa Maria
N Salem HS; Salem, OR; AFS; VP, FBLA; FHA; FBLA Sr of Yr; Yth Rep, Diaconate; Candystriper; Chemeketa Comm Col; Nurs.

LISTELLA, Lorinda Kay
N Salem HS; Salem, OR; FBLA; Jr Vol; Chemeketa Col; Kinderarten Ed.

LISTER, Constance Ann
Barnwell HS; Barnwell, SC (12-150) CYO; Cpt, Chldr; Fr C; Bus Mgr, Sch P; VP, Soph Cl; Sftbl; Tnns; Tr; COM; Phar.

LISTER, Laura Ann
Harlingen HS; Harlingen, TX (120-700) Chor; NHS; Rptr, Sch P; Var C; Swim; COM; ARC A; Sci A; Keywanettes; 1st Cl, GSct; Baylor Col; Bus.

LISTER, Susan
Cochran HS; Cochran, GA; Chor; FHA; VP, 4H; VP, Hmrm; Lat C; Tri-HiY; Bkbl; COM; Cl Fav; 4H A; Sci A; Swtht Court; Most Cooperative; Grand Sweepstake A, Soc Sci Fair; Home Ec.

LITAKER, Anna Elizabeth
Nw Cabarrus HS; Concord, NC (25-210) Band; Drama; Fr C; FTA; Hmrm; Math C; Sci C; SC; Thes; Hon Prog; Yth Leg; Page; St Legislature; U of NC; Computer Sci.

LITAKER, Harry Lee Jr
NW Cabarrus HS; Concord, NC (33%-250) F-Ed, Ann; Band; Fr C; Orch; Order/Arrow; Sci C; Golf; COM; God & Country A; Q&S A; Eagle Sct with Triple Palms; Outst JV Bandsman; U of NC at Charlotte; TV and Radio Broadcasting.

LITCHFIELD, Lee Ann
Moberly Sr HS; Moberly, MO (33-250) Band; Orch; Rainbow; Rptr, Sch P; Span C; Sci A; Pep C; 3rd Pl, Essay Contest; Stu Del, Stu Govt Day; 1st Pl, Mo Mus Ed Assn A.

LITCHKOWSKI, Sandra Ann
John S Fine Sr HS; Nanticoke, PA (5-347) PTA A; Span A.

LITES, Regina Renee
Cathedral HS; San Francisco, CA; Cpt, Chldr; Pres, Hmrm; ARC; SC; Cl Fav; Most Out; Most Sportsmenship; Shorthand A; UCLA; Sociology.

LITHGOW, Susan Dawn
Richwoods HS; Peoria, IL (57-486) Mjrte; NHS; Royalett o-t Yr; Ill Central Col; Phy Therapy.

LITKA, Jay Allen
Inland Christian Sch; San Bernardino, CA (20%-30) Ann.

LITLAND, Paula Kae
DeSoto HS; De Soto, TX (28-250) Drama; FHA;
V-Ch, 4H; NHS; Span C; Thes; Citz A; 4H A; I
Dare You; Art, Homemaking, Bible, A's; Harding
Col; Homemaking.

LITLAND, Sharon Elaine
DeSoto HS; DeSoto, TX (10-263) Drama; Fr C;
Rptr, 4H; Lit Mag; Math C; Mu Alpha Theta; NFL;
NHS; Sch P; Spch C; Thes; Bkbl; 4H A; Journ A;
Q&S A; Spch A; Fr Poetry Reading, Bible, A's;
Abilene Christian U; Psych.

LITSEY, Stephen Edward
Daviess Co HS; Owensboro, KY (4-320) A Cap
Choir; Pres, Band; BC; Ensm; Math C; Sci C; Bio A;
Chem A; Cl Fav; U of Ky; Engr.

LITTER, Elizabeth Anne
Chillicothe HS; Chillicothe, OH (15%-320) Dbte
Tm; VP, NFL; NHS; Rainbow; Spch C; Spch A;
Karate Brown Belt; Miami U of Ohio; Law.

LITTLE, Angela Sue
Argenta-Oreana HS; Argenta, IL (17-110) Tres,
FHA; NHS; SC; Var C; Pres, Jr Cl; Sftbl; Tr; HCt;
Cpt, Vlbl; Weslyan Col; Nurs.

LITTLE, Anthony Arnold
Hamill Road Christian HS; Hixson, TN (1-9) Ed,
Ann; Band; BC; Ensm; Pres, Hmrm; VP, NHS;
ARC; Sch Achieve Tm; Ed, Sch P; SC; Pres, Soph
Cl; JV, Bkbl; Soccer; JV, Sftbl; Tr; Alg A; COM;
Math A; MLS; Pres A; Type A; Mr Hamill Road
Christian HS; Spiritual A; Most Dependable; Bible
Tm; Computers.

LITTLE, Barbara Ann
Cajon HS; San Bernardino, CA (20%-499) Chor;
Tr; Teacher, Bible Stu; Chaffey Jr Col; Physiology.

LITTLE, Charles Michael
Fairfield HS; Fairfield, AL (25%-180) Ann; Band;
Order/Arrow; ARC; Rptr, Sch P; COM; Order/
Arrow A; Eagle Sct; Auburn U; Vet Med.

LITTLE, Christine Helen
Maple Shade HS; Maple Shade, NJ (24-241) Tres,
CYO; Chldr; Drama; Hmrm; NHS; SC; Tres, Jr Cl;
VP, Soph Cl; Mgr, Sftbl; WW.

LITTLE, Darla Jeanne
Greenland HS; Greenland, AR (5-45) FHA; NHS;
Bkbl; Sftbl; Bio A; Hist A; Hon Prog; Sci A; Home
Ec; Eng, A's; U of Ark; Ed.

LITTLE, David Brian
Texas City HS; Texas City, TX; A Cap Choir;
Band; Dbte Tm; Madrigal; God & Country A;
NEDT; Opt A; Fr Luther Lge; Outst Choral
Mus; Tres, SE Conf Luther League; Jazz Ensm; All
Region Choir; UIL Solo & Ensm Contest; Mus.

LITTLE, Denice
Harlan HS; Chicago, IL (42-750) Chldr; Chor;
Drama; 4H; F-Ed, Sch P; Bsbl; COM; Cl Fav;
Teacher for a Day; Roosevelt Col; Journ.

LITTLE, Donna Jean
Bay HS; Panama City, FL; Ann; Band; Ensm; FTA;
4H; SC; Pres, Etude C; Explorer Post; Fla Col.

LITTLE, James Fredrick
Clay County HS; Ashland, KY (4-56) VP, BC; BS;
Chor; Dbte Tm; Pres, FTA; Sci C; Var C; Bsbl; Ftbl;
Chem A; DARGCA; Phy A; Ftbl Head Hunter A;
Southern Union Jr Col; Med Technology.

LITTLE, Jennifer Lynn
Cook HS; Adel, GA (3-190) BC; FBLA; Tri-HiY;
COM; Hon Prog; Shorthand, Eng, Top 10, A's; PC
Jr Fel; Valdosta St Col; Elem Ed.

LITTLE, Julia Elizabeth
Saint Albans HS; Saint Albans, WV (10-560) Band;
Ensm; Hmrm; VP, Lat C; NHS; Aux Lat; COM;
DARGCA; Hon Prog; Math A; MLS; Most Out;
Sci A; Sheriff's Yth Camp; Alt, All Co Band; Med.

LITTLE, Katherine Putnam
Ross Beatty HS; Cassopolis, MI (1-100) Band;
Chor; Drama; FTA; NHS; Ed, Sch P; Yth Fel; Most
Valuable Staffer, Sch P; Anderson Col; Eng.

LITTLE, LaDonna Claudine
Huttig HS; Huttig, AR (1-24) Ed, Ann; VP, BC;
Secy, Chem C; GS; Hmrm; Semi-Fin, Jr Miss Pa;
NHSt; Pres, SC; VP, Sr Cl; Tres, Jr Cl; Pres, Soph
Cl; Bkbl; Amer Leg A; COM; Citz A; Cl Fav'l;
DARGCA; HCt; I Dare You; MLS; Val; Yth Fel;
Sou Ark U; Nurs.

LITTLE, Larry Delon
Grace Baptist HS; Decatur, AL (30%-21) Chor;
Pres, Hmrm; SC; Var C; Pres, Soph Cl; Bkbl; Ftbl;
HCt; Friendliest; Auburn U.

LITTLE, Laura Ann
Dearborn HS; Dearborn, MI; Arch; Swim; Pres A;
ARC A; Stage Crew; Badminton; Alma Col; Bio.

LITTLE, Linda Diane
Central HS; W Helena, AR (54-356) Band; BC;
Hmrm; NHS; Rptr, Sch P; Phillips Co Comm Col;
Nurs.

LITTLE, Lisa Darlene
Jess Lanier HS; Bessemer, AL; Citz A; U of Ala;
Nurs.

LITTLE, Lisa Kay
Lawton HS; Lawton, OK (52-537) F-Ed, Ann;
Hmrm; NHS; Ski C; Bkbl; Sci A; Tn C; Protestant
Yth Organization; Pres, Yth Chapel; Army Rifle
As; Off, Jobs Daugh; Mst Improv, Bkbl; Ntl Rifle
As; Rifle Bdgs & Trophies; Okla U; Sci.

LITTLE, Lori Ann
Cooper City HS; Cooper City, FL; Band; FHA;
Sftbl; JA A; Teaching.

LITTLE, Mary Jane
Ind Acad; Cicero, IN (1-54) A Cap Choir; Chor;
Community Yth Symph; Madrigal; NHS; Orch;
Hon Prog; Val; Andrews U; Pre-Law.

LITTLE, Patricia Jean
Thornwell HS; Clinton, SC (2-20) BC; Fr C; Citz A;
Hist A; Hon Prog; Yth Fel; Presbyterian Col Jr Fel;
Jr Marshall; WW; Auburn U; Mus.

LITTLE, Richard N
Cypress Lake HS; Ft Myers, FL (110-450) MVP,
Bsbl; Bkbl; Leading Hitter, Bsbl A; Edison Comm
Col; Elec.

LITTLE, Tammy Kay
DeSoto HS; De Soto, TX; Co-Ch, FTA; VP, 4H;
Ch, Hmrm; Span C; 4H A; Hist A; Bible, Eng,
Reading, A's; Okla Christian Col; Hist.

LITTLE, Thomas Archer
Isle of Wight Acad; Isle of Wight, VA (5-42) Bus
Mgr, Ann; BS; NFL; Pres, NHS; SC; Bio A; Pres,
Service C; Jr Marshall; U of Richmond; Acct.

LITTLE, Trina Elise
E St Louis Sr HS; E St Louis, IL; Chldr; Sci A;
Millikin U; Med.

LITTLEFIELD, Bonnie Sue
Auburn HS; Auburn, NY; Math A; Home Ec A.

**LITTLEFIELD,
Henry Samuel III**
Franklin HS; Seattle, WA; A Cap Choir; JV, Ftbl;
Bellevue Comm Col; Med.

LITTLEFIELD, Tammy Kay
Inola Pub HS; Inola, OK (1-56) Bus C; Hmrm;
NHS; Sch P; Span C; Spch C; Span NHS; SC; Bkbl;
Sftbl; Tr; Alg A; Gov Honor Prog; Hist A; Math A;
Sci A; Type A; Val; 12 Yr C; Smithers Straight 'A'
A; Acct A; Hist A; NEA&M Miami Okla; Acct.

LITTLEJOHN, Darryl
Trotwood-Madison HS; Trotwood, OH; Chor;
Drama; Ensm; SC; Tres, Soph Cl; Bsbl; Bkbl; Ftbl;
Sftbl; Tr; COM; Ath A; Ohio St U; General.

LITTLEJOHN, James Randell
Patten Acad of Christian Ed; Oakland, CA (3-11)
Chem C; Sch P; Cpt, Sftbl; Citz A; Schol A; Pepper-
dine U; Math.

LITTLEJOHN, Orville Keith
Trotwood Madison HS; Trotwood, OH; SC; JV,
Bkbl; Cpt, Ftbl; Tr; HCt; Pres A; Wright St Col; Bus
Mgt.

LITTRELL, Dawn Marie
Burnside HS; Burnside, KY (5-40) F-Ed, Ann; VP,
BC; FTA; Secy, Sr Cl; Somerset Comm Col.

LIU, Joan Wai Yee
Concordia HS; Oakland, CA; Bank of Amer A; U
of Houston; Math.

LIU, Ka Man
George Washington HS; San Francisco, CA
(10-750) A Cap Choir; Chor; Community Yth
Symph; Ensm; Tres, JETS; Orch; Phys C; Tres, Sci
C; Bank Of Amer A; CSF; COM; Hon Prog; U of
Calif; Bio Sci.

LIVELY, Linda Gale
Woodrow Wilson HS; Beckley, WV; Band; Chldr;
Community Yth Symph; 4H; Rptr, Sch P; Tr; Yth
Fel; God & Comm A; 1st Cl, GSct; Secy, UMYF;
Church Choir; Journ.

LIVELY, Pamela Lynn
Walnut Hills HS; Cincinnati, OH (40%-412) A Cap
Choir; Span C; Span NHS; HR; Vacation Bible Sch
Teacher; Jr Cl Sunday Sch Teacher; Inspirational
Chor; Training U; Asst Superintendent, Sunday
Sch; Miami U at Oxford; Span.

LIVELY, Paula Ann
Lufkin HS; Lufkin, TX (10%-567) A Cap Choir;
Band; Drama; Ger C; COM; Citz A; All-Region,
Dist & Area Choirs; 1st Alt, All-St Choir; Baylor U;
Spch Therapy.

LIVENGOOD, Carole Susan
Starmount HS; Boonville, NC (3-151) Chor;
Drama; FHA; Secy, FTA; Jr Miss Pageant; Pres,
Math C; Pres, Mu Alpha Theta; NHS; Pres, Span
C; Alg A; Gov Honor Prog; Gr Marshal; Nom,
Morehead Schol; Soc Stu C; Nom, Peace Col
Schol; GAA; Parl, Health Careers C; Pep C; UNC;
Acct.

LIVENGOOD, Kelli Ranae
Norris HS; Firth, NE (5-108) Chldr; Semi-Fin, GS;
4H; NHS; SC; Var C; Tr; U of Nebr; Broadcasting.

LIVENGOOD, Sheryl Grace
Hamburg HS; Hamburg, IA (15-40) Ann; Band;
Chor; FHA; Co-Ed, Sch P; Bkbl; COM; HCt; NCE
Sch of Commerce; Secy.

LIVENGOOD, Victoria Ann
E Davidson HS; Thomasville, NC (8-135) BC;
Chldr; Chor; Dbte Tm; NHS; Sci C; Span C; SC;
Fin, Spch A; Jr Marshal; WW; Best All Around Stu;
Principal's A; Gov Sch Nom; Fin, Miss Merry
Christmas; U of NC; Bus Adm.

**LIVERGOOD,
Raymond Royce Jr**
Lakeview HS; San Angelo, TX; Chor; Ftbl.

LIVESAY, Keith Clark
Marion L Steele HS; Amherst, OH (25-325) Band;
Pres, Demolay; Lat C; Orch; Rptr, Sch P; Past Mas-
ter Coun Rep, DeMolay; Sr Acolyte; Law.

LIVINGSTON, Barbara Ann
Brookfield HS; Brookfield, OH (68-170).

LIVINGSTON, Brenda Fay
Georgiana HS; Georgiana, AL; FHA; Secy, NHS;
Alg A; Cl Fav; Math A; Span A; Eng A; Troy St U;
Nurs.

LIVINGSTON, Dawna Jean
Delavan-Darien HS; Delavan, WI (25-250) A Cap
Choir; Ann; Band; Chldr; Chem C; Chor; Commu-
nity Yth Symph; Ensm; Pres, FBLA; 4H; Madrigal;
NFL; Sch P; Secy, Sr Cl; Golf; 4H A; Spch A; Type
A; Yth Fel; Sunday Sch Teachers; Drum Major; St
VP, FBLA; Pres, BYF Assn; Outst Choir A; Colrgrd
Job's Daugh; St Solo & Ensm Con As; Sch Musical;
Bus.

LIVINGSTON, Denise Sue
Brookfield HS; Brookfield, OH (26-170) Span C.

LIVINGSTON, Gregory Dale
Osceola HS; Kissimmee, FL (28-276) Chem C;
Chor; Math C; Sci C; Span C; Spch C; JV, Bkbl;
Cr-Ctry; JV, Ftbl; Fla Tech U; Chem.

LIVINGSTON, Lee Ann
Warrior Acad; Eutaw, AL; BC; Chor; Math C; A-
Ed, Sch P; Rptr, SC; Var C; VP, Soph Cl; Cpt, Bkbl;
Soccer; Sftbl; Tr; Sci A; Yth Fel; Yth Leg; PA,
Sunday Sch; PA, Sch; All Tourn Bkbl; U of Ala;
Phys Ed.

**LIVINGSTON,
Percy Stanbrough**
McCall Sr HS; Tallulah, LA (20-131) Chor; Drama;
4H; Ch, Hmrm; Rptr, Sch P; Pres, Jr Cl; Cpt, Bsbl;
Mgr, Bkbl; Rptr, Ftbl; Swim; Tnns; Sou La U; Engr.

LIVINGSTON, Suzanne Marie
Monroe HS; Monroe, WA (6-140) Band; CYO;
Drama; FHA; Lat C; NHS; Sch Achieve Tm; Sch
P; SC; JV, Bkbl; Mgr, Ftbl; HCt; Hon Prog; JA A;
Kiwanis A; Lion A; Masonic A; MLS; Graduation
Faculty Speaker; Edmonds Col; Ed.

LIVINGTON, Randy Lee
York Co Voc-Tech HS; York, PA; Ger C; Cr-Ctry;
Golf; Tr; Concordia Col; Minister.

LIVIS, Lori Ann
John B Ehret HS; Marrero, LA (4-550) Pres, Chess C; Fr C; Lit Mag; Mu Alpha Theta; NHS; Rainbow; Swim; COM; Hist A; Hon Prog; Math A; PTA A; Sci A; *Computer Sci.*

LLANOS, Hernandez Evelyn
Centro Oportunidad Educativas HS; Guaynabo, PR; *U of Puerto Rico; Ed.*

LLERAS, Magda Idalia
Notre Dame HS; Caguas, PR (58-140) Chldr; Dbte Tm; Drama; Hmrm; NHS; ARC; Sci C; Beauty; COM; God & Country A; Hon Prog; Math A; Spch A.

LLORENS, Irma Eneida
Col Nuestra Sra de la Merced; Hato Rey, PR (1-92) Dbte Tm; Hmrm; NHS; Span C; Alg A; COM; Hist A; Hon Prog; Math A; Most Out; Poet A; Spch A; *U of Calif at La; Lit.*

LLORENS, Maria Dolores
Colegio Puertorriqueno de Ninas; Caparra Heights, PR (5-61) Drama; Tres, Math C; NHS; Sci C; Var C; COM; Math A; Pub Relationships; JV, Vlbl; Social Action C; Second Hon; Sports C; Activities C; *Sweet Briar Col; Computer Sci.*

LLORET, Rosado Clara Rosa
Centro Oportunidad Ed HS; Guaynabo, PR; *Universidad de Puerto Rico; Contabilidad.*

LLOYD, Dale Scott
Fort Lauderdale HS; Fort Lauderdale, FL (1-450) A Cap Choir; Madrigal; NHS; COM; Hist A; NMF; Val; *Duke U; Computer Sci.*

LLOYD, DeAnna
Wasatch HS; Heber, UT (10-140) Secy, FHA; Hmrm; Secy, Sr Cl; Ch, Jr Cl; Hon Prog; *Snow Col; Elem Ed.*

LLOYD, Elaine
David Brearley Regional HS; Kenilworth, NJ; Band; Pres, Chor; SC; Tr; Miss Black Fantasia Pageant.

LLOYD, Evelyn Denise
Metamora Township HS; Metamora, IL; AFS; Chor; Drama; Madrigal; Span C; 4H A; Art A; Chor Hons; *Art.*

LLOYD, Faith
George P Butler HS; Augusta, GA (19-425) Band; Tres, BC; Co-Cpt, Chldr; FHA; Hmrm; Sci C; Span C; SC; Mgr, Bsbl; Bio A; Hon Prog; Chldr A; *Augusta Col; Recreational Therapy.*

LLOYD, Janet Kay
Penncrest HS; Lima, PA (95-450) Band; S-T, Chor; Drama; Hmrm; Lit Mag; Madrigal; NHS; SC; ARC A; Swim Instructor, Red Cross; *W Chester St Col; Eng Ed.*

LLOYD, Jeannette Aleen
Mount Olive HS; Ft Mitchell, AL (1-63) Chor; 4H; Tres, Hmrm; NHS; Sch P; Tres, Jr Cl; B Crocker A; Bio A; 4H A; Hist A; Hon Prog; Sci A; Congeniality A; *Chattahoochee Valley Comm Col; Computer Sci.*

LLOYD, Joanna Marie
Driscoll HS; Addison, IL; Pres, Band; Lit Mag; Pres, NHS; Tr; St Scholar; Ntl Merit Commended Stu; *Bio.*

LLOYD, Julann Linnet
Westmont Hilltop HS; Johnstown, PA (1-195) Arch; Band; Chess C; Chor; Pres, JETS; NHS; Rainbow; COM; NMF; Bell Choir, Tn C; Explorers; Choir; *U of Pittsburgh at Johnstown; Engr.*

LLOYD, Kelly Lee
Lely HS; Naples, FL (30-300) NHS; Var C; MVP, Tnns; *Ed.*

LLOYD, Sandra Joyce
Russell HS; Hurtsboro, AL (5-75) *Bradley U; Counselor.*

LLOYD, Thomas Raymond
Miami Palmetto Sr HS; Miami, FL (10-1270) A Cap Choir; Bus Mgr, Chor; Hmrm; Lit Mag; Pres, Madrigal; Model UN; Mu Alpha Theta; Tres, NHS; Sci C; Span NHS; SC; COM; DARGCA; Hon Prog; Journ A; Math A; NMS; Q&S A; Sci A; Yth Fel; Ntl Amer Col of Mus; Hon Choir; Chptr Pres, Ntl Fed of Mus C; Drafting, Eng, NCTE, A's; Hon Soc's Dir, Double Quintet; *MIT; Archt.*

LLOYD, Vicki June
Judsonia HS; Judsonia, AR (1-35) A-Ed, Ann; BC; Chor; VP, Drama; Pres, FBLA; VP, FHA; NHS; VP, Spch C; VP, SC; Pres, Sr Cl; Bkbl; Sftbl; Chem A; Citz A; Hist A; HCt; I Dare You; MLS; Sci A; Val; Best All Around; Spelling, Eng, A's; Bus, Dist Off Procedure, A's; *Harding Col; Acct.*

LLOYD, Vicky May
Starkville HS; Starkville, MS (5%-300) Band; Chor; NHS; Y-Tns; Bkbl; Cpt, Swim.

LOADHOLTZ, Sherrye Jeanette
Fletcher Sr HS; Neptune Beach, FL (50-700) Type A; Bus Ed A; PA Cert; *Fla Jr Col; Dentistry.*

LOAR, Diana Marie
Palo Duro HS; Amarillo, TX (6-445) Drama; Hmrm; Sci C; SC; Thes; *Med.*

LOBB, Sue Lynn
Owen J Roberts HS; Pottstown, PA; Hmrm; Tr; Hockey; Indoor Tr; *Phys Therapy.*

LOBBY, Louise Victoria
Bound Brook HS; Bound Brook, NJ (52-237) Band; Bus C; Hmrm; Span C; SC; *Bus.*

LOBELL, Mark William
St Charles Borromeo HS; Destrehan, LA (10-79) BC; CYO; VP, Key C; Spch C; Pres, SC; Bsbl; Ftbl; Sftbl; Tnns; Tr; Cl Fav; Hon Prog; MLS; Most Out; Star Student; Most Courteous; Wittiest; Most Attractive; *Nicholls U; Bus.*

LOBSTEIN, Lisa Ann
Imlay City HS; Imlay City, MI (12-156) VP, Fr C; NFL; NHS; Bkbl; Stu Life Schol; *Oakland U; Bus Adm.*

LOBUE, Lisa Mae
Shawnee Mission NW HS; Shawnee Mission, KS (9-674) Rptr, Bus C; Ch, CYO; Co-Cpt, Chldr; Dbte Tm; NHS; ARC; Sci C; Ski C; Golf; Bio A; Hon Prog; Sci A; Win, Golf Championship; *Bus.*

LOCANTORE, Robert John
St Joseph HS; Camden, NJ (39-76) Fr C; Pres, Sr Cl; Pres, Jr Cl; Bsbl; Wrest; Cl Fav; *Camden Co Col; Phys Ed.*

LOCARRO, Mary Ann
Henry P Becton Regional HS; E Rutherford, NJ (5-201) Chldr; NHS; SC; Tr; Hon Prog; *Econ.*

LOCHA, Larry Noble
Karlsruhe Amer HS; Karlsruhe, GERMANY; Pres, Band; Chor; Demolay; NHS; Secy, Order/Arrow; Parl, SC; Var C; Pres, Jr Cl; Mgr, Bkbl; Ftbl; Tr; Hon Prog; Order/Arrow A; Win, Essay Contest; Life Sct; *Tex Christian U; Acct.*

LOCHOW, Constance Jean
Courtenay Pub Sch; Courtenay, ND; Ann; Band; Chldr; VP, Chor; Drama; GS; Pres, 4H; Sch P; SC; MVP, Bkbl; Sftbl; Tr; 4H A; *Moorhead St Col; Special Ed.*

LOCKARD, Barbara Diane
Lampeter-Strasburg HS; Lampeter, PA (30-205) Chor; FHA; Yth Fel; *Phys Therapy.*

LOCKARD, Carol Ann
Havre de Grace Sr HS; Harre de Grace, MD (12-220) Hmrm; Lit Mag; Pres, NHS; SC; Var C; Sftbl; Elk A; Pres, Yth Fel; *Salisbury St Col; Mass Communications.*

LOCKE, Anthony Darwin
Wheatland HS; Wheatland, WY (1-93) Band; Chor; Drama; Pres, SC; Thes; Var C; Pres, Jr Cl; Ftbl; Tr; Co-Cpt, Wrest; HCt; NHS; Thespian A; HR; Entertainers; All Conf Wrestler; Offensive Ftbl Player o-t Yr.

LOCKE, Bradley Merle
South HS; Denver, CO;

LOCKE, Buni Carol
Terrell Acad; Dawson, GA (12-46) Band; FTA; Pres, 4H; Span C; Tri-HiY; *Abraham Balwin Argi Col; Home Ec.*

LOCKE, Joseph Wofford Jr
Spartanburg HS; Spartanburg, SC (172-827) Cpt, Band; Chess C; Pres, Chor; Drama; Ensm; Inter-Club Coun; Orch; ARC; Bus Mgr, Sch P; Amer Leg A; Citz A; Opt Out Tn; ARC A; Yth Fel; All St Hon; *The Citadel Col; Bus Adm.*

LOCKE, Laura Diane
Thomasville HS; Thomasville, AL (1-110) VP, BC; Chldr; Drama; FHA; Span C; Var C; Chem A; Math A; Foreign Lang A; *U of Ala.*

LOCKE, Rachel Elizabeth
Elston Sr HS; Michigan City, IN (3-300) Ann; Band; Chor; Drama; Ensm; Hmrm; Orch; SC; VP, Soph Cl; JV, Golf; Swim; Hon Prog; Most Out; Opt A; Phy A; Rotary A; Sci A; Spch A; VP, Children's Intrntl Summer Vil.

LOCKE, Susan Marie
Reynolds HS; Greenville, PA (10-183) Ann; Band; Chor; FTA; Ger C; Math C; Span C; Tri-HiY; Drill Tm; Conservation A.

LOCKE, William Gregory
Druid Park Baptist HS; Satsuma, AL (2-16) Pres, Span C; VP, Jr Cl; Hist A; Hon Prog; Most Out; Sci A; Art A; Mus A; *Commercial Arts.*

LOCKERT, Charles Ray
Oak Ridge Acad; Oak Ridge, NC (4-30) AFS; VP, Arch; Band; Ch, Dbte Tm; Secy, FBLA; Ch, Hmrm; VP, Math C; Monogram; VP, NHS; Secy, Sci C; Pres, Span C; Spch C; Pres, SC; S-T, Var C; Pres, Sr Cl; S-T, Jr Cl; VP, Soph Cl; Cpt, Arch; Bsbl; Bkbl; JV, Ftbl; Soccer; Cpt, Swim; JV, Wrest; Alg A; Bio A; Citz A; DARGCA; Gr Marshal; Hist A; Hon Prog; MLS; Most Out; ROTC A; Sci A; Spch A; Star Student; Best Drill Cadet; Sup Cadet; *US Air Force Acad; Nuclear Engr.*

LOCKETT, Bertram Darius
Independence HS; Coldwater, MS (15%-72) BC; FBLA; FFA; Bkbl; Ftbl.

LOCKETT, Philip M
Victoria HS; Victoria, TX; FFA; *Texas A&I U; Agr.*

LOCKETT, Sonja Lanette
Havana HS; Havana, FL (3-124) Cpt, Chldr; NHS; Tres, Sci C; SC; Spch A; Chldr A; *Ind U; Nurs.*

LOCKETT, Valda Patrice
Independence HS; Independence, MS (10%-118) Chor; FHA; NHS; S-T, Sftbl; *Howard U; Sci.*

LOCKHART, Brent Allen
Southwest HS; Fort Worth, TX (150-594) A Cap Choir; AFS; Band; NHS; MVP, Swim; *Midwest Christian Col; Pre-Med.*

LOCKHART, Carolyn Suzanne
Ouachita Parish HS; Monroe, LA; Chor; *USC; Marine Bio.*

LOCKHART, Douglas Allan
Morenci Area HS; Morenci, MI (10-78) NHS; VP, SC; Var C; Pres, Sr Cl; Co-Cpt, Bkbl; Cl Fav; HCt; NMS; Pres A; *Spring Arbor Col; Phys Therapy.*

LOCKHART, Lisa Renee
East HS; Columbus, OH (26-350) *Bowling Green St U; Spch Pathology & Audiology.*

LOCKHART, Lorna June
Lawrence Acad; Groton, MA (15-73) A Cap Choir; Dbte Tm; Drama; Pres, Fr C; Hmrm; Rptr, Sch P; Bkbl; JV, Soccer; Tnns; Alg A; Bio A; Citz A; JA A; Most Out; Pres A; Highest Hon A; Martha Holding Jennings Schol; ABC Schol; *UCLA; Med.*

LOCKHART, Patricia Anne
McNeil Northside HS; McNeil, AR (3-27) Bus C; 4H; Hmrm; Math C; Pol Sci C; Sch P; Sci C; Bkbl; Sftbl; COM; Cl Fav; 4H A; Hist A; HCt; Sci A; Social Stu A; Lib A.

LOCKHART, Wendy Sue
Clifton HS; Clifton, NJ (86-900) Fr C; NHS; *Taylor U; Special Ed.*

LOCKLEAR, Clay
McColl HS; McColl, SC; Tres, FFA.

LOCKLEY, Glendia Jean
McDonogh 35 Sr HS; New Orleans, LA (100-316) Hon Prog; Type A; Shorthand Cert; Hon Cl; *SW La U; Off Adm.*

LOCKLIN, Linda Lee
Robert E Lee Sr HS; Jacksonville, FL; Swim; Alg A; Bio A; Hist A; *Med.*

LOCKWOOD, Amy Louise
Alexander Galt Regional HS; Lennoxville, CANADA (12-477) Band; ARC; Hon Prog; Home Ec A; *Bishop's U.*

LOCKWOOD, Kathryn Ann
Casady Sch; Okla City, OK (20%-92) Drama; Eng Riding C.

LOCKWOOD, Ruth Anne
Crossville Comm HS; Crossville, IL (3-26) Co-Ed, Ann; BC; FHA; Math C; Sch P; VP, SC; S-T, Thes; Secy, Sr Cl; VP, Jr Cl; Mgr, Sftbl; B Crocker A; HCt; St Scholar; Pres, Pep C; WW; Wabash Valley Col; Psych.

LOCKYER, Thomas George
Smithtown HS W; Smithtown, NY (45%-725) A Cap Choir; Pres, CYO; Chor; Drama; Lit Mag; Rptr, Sch P; Spch C; Thes; C W Post Col; Eng.

LODEN, Jeffrey Scott
Neshaminy Maple Point HS; Langhorne, PA (11-413) Chess C; NHS; COM; Hon Prog; Pa St U; Archt Engr.

LODER, Carla Suzanne
Dublin HS; Dublin, CA; JV, Chldr; JV, Tnns; HCt.

LODERBAUER, Joan Marie
Kaukauna HS; Kaukauna, WI (15%-379) NFL; Poet A; Spch A; Church Lector.

LODES, Denise Katherine
W E Boswell HS; Saginaw, TX (2-183) CYO; FBLA; VP, FTA; Secy, NHS; Mgr, Bkbl; Mgr, Tr; Citz A; Sal; Superior HR; Voc Off Ed A; U of Tex; Bus Mgt.

LODGE, Gregory Alan
Findlay HS; Findlay, OH; A Cap Choir; Chor; Drama; Orch; Soccer; Yth Fel; Bowling Green Col; Bio.

LODGE, Marvina Lynelle
Samuel W Wolfson Sr HS; Jacksonville, FL; A Cap Choir; Chor; Drama; Parl, FHA; Span C; Sr Play; Qn with Scepter, Acteens; Environmental Sci.

LODGE, Suzanne Dorothy
Haverford Sr HS; Havertown, PA; A Cap Choir; Chor; Ensm; Madrigal; Yth Fel; Nurs.

LOEB, Elizabeth Ann
Bakersfield HS; Bakersfield, CA; Community Yth Symph; Ensm; Secy, Ger C; Orch; Amer Leg A; CSF; Foreign Lang Festival; Mus Festival; Kern Philharmonic; Mus.

LOEB, Lola Jean
Manual Arts HS; Los Angeles, CA (30-700) Mus Ed.

LOEFFELBEIN, Peter James
Soap Lake Jr Sr HS; Soaplake, WA (8-42) Rptr, Sch P; VP, Soph Cl; Wrest; Lit.

LOEFFLER, Nathan James
Moorhead Sr HS; Moorhead, MN (77-560) Ann; Community Yth Symph; Orch; Order/Arrow; Order/Arrow A; Concordia Col.

LOEKS, Jennifer Ione
Campbell-Tintah HS; Campbell, MN; Ann; Band; Chor; Ensm; FHA; Sch P; Spch C; Secy, Soph Cl; Spch A; Ensm A; Bookkeeping Cert; HR; Accompaniment A; Choral A; Red Cross Cert.

LOESCH, Jonathan
Lutheran HS; Los Angeles, CA; A Cap Choir; Ger C; VP, Key C; NHS; Bkbl; JV, Ftbl; Tnns; Yth Fel; Yth Leg; Hugh O'Brian A; Pepperdine U; Ministerial.

LOESCH, Steven Mark
Parkwood HS; Joplin, MO (25-400) AFS; Band; Orch; Swim; Stage Band; Band A; Orch Ltr; Phototech.

LOESING, Arlene Amelia
Laura Speed Elliot HS; Boonville, MO (6-131) NHS; Span C; Regent Schol; U of Mo; Acct.

LOESING, Leann Elizabeth
Laura Speed Elliott HS; Boonville, MO (24-165) Chor; Secy, FHA; NHS; FHA A; Mo U; Med.

LOEWEN, Julia Ann
Garden Spot HS; New Holland, PA; AFS; Band; Secy, Chor; Community Yth Symph; Pres, Drama; Ensm; GS; 4H; Hmrm; Ch, NHS; Orch; Var C; Hockey; Tnns; Hon Prog; Yth Fel; Semi-Fin, Amer Leg A; Semi-Fin, Elk's C A; U of Pa; Dental Hygiene.

LOEWER, Renee Marie
University HS; San Diego, CA (4-311) NHS; Most Out; Summa Cum Laude; U of Calif; Biol.

LOEWER, Robbin Jean
Baker HS; Baker, LA (7-374) BC; Bus C; FBLA; GS; Rptr, 4H; InterClub Coun; Tres, NHS; Pres, Tri-HiY; Secy, Jr Cl; 4H A; Yth Leg; Steno A; Secy, Mu Sigma Hon Soc; Secretarial.

LOFLAND, Louanne Kay
N Montgomery HS; Crawfordsville, TN (1-225) A Cap Choir; Band; Chor; Drama; Madrigal; NFL; NHS; Pres, Rainbow; Span C; Spch C; Sunshine Soc; Writing, Band, Mus, A; Health & Eng Certs of Hon; Phys Ed, Home Ec, A's; Art, Sci, Hist, Math, A's; Ind U; Mus.

LOFLAND, Natalie Fay
N Montgomery HS; Crawfordsville, IN (24-214) Pres, 4H; NHS; VP, Rainbow; Sci C; Span C; 4H A; Hon Prog; Sci A; Ind U; Med.

LOFT, Lisa Dawn
C H Spurgeon Acad; Memphis, TN (5-18) Ann; Cpt, Chldr; Tres, Hmrm; Lat C; Rptr, Sch P; Span C; Sftbl; Cl Fav; HCt; Swtht; WW; Most Sch Spirited '76; Memphis St; Chem.

LOFTIN, Cassandra Eileen
Louis D Brandeis HS; New York, NY (10-1000) MVP, Var C; COM; Hon Prog; Type A; Personality, Attendance, A's; Bethany Col; Med.

LOFTIN, Jeffrey Kenneth
Southland HS; Arbyrd, MO (1-44) Band; Chor; Drama; Secy, Fr C; FTA; NHS; SC; Pres, Jr Cl; Alg A; Chem A; Sci A; Ark St U; Mus.

LOFTIN, Paul Richard
Reeds Spring HS; Reeds Spring, MO (25%-90) AFS; BC; Math C; S-T, Sci C; Var C; JV, Bkbl; Ftbl; JV, Tr; Citz A; Hist A; Math A; SMSU; Sci.

LOFTIN, Richard Henderson
Thomasville Acad; Thomasville, AL; BC; Rptr, 4H; F-Ed, Sch P; Cr-Ctry; JV, Ftbl; Tnns; Tr; 4H A; U of Ala; Law.

LOFTIS, Gregory Christopher
Ashbrook HS; Gastonia, NC (29-500) Pres, Band; NHS; Orch; SC; JV, Wrest; Ntl Achv Schol; Co-Cpt, Auditorium Crew; Gov Sch; All St Band; WW; Duke U; Physics.

LOFTIS, Teresa Carolyn
Bennington HS; Bennington, NE (15-40) Ann; Chor; Drama; 4H; Spch C; Tr; HCt; Spch A; Prom Qn; Spch Contest Medal Win.

LOFTON, John Henry
Santa Ana Valley Sr HS; Santa Ana, CA (1-30) Spch C; Usher Board Song Ldr; Boys C Tourn; Pres, Stu Adm BTU; CEP; YDP; BSU Kg & Qn Pag; Am Lit Hon Acad; NAACP; Green Belt, Martial Arts; Calif St U at Fullerton; Law.

LOFTON, Pamela Susan
Pineville HS; Pineville, LA (10%-244) Ann; FHA; Hmrm; Lit Ral; NHS; Sch P; Y-Tns; Bio A; Hon Prog; Sci A; Type A; La Col; Journ.

LOFTON, Thomas Allen
Denham Springs HS; Denham Springs, LA (57-220) Band; Art A; St Career & Guidance Post Contest.

LOFTUS, Timothy James
Loyola Acad; Wilmette, IL (150-369) Cum Laude Soc; Order/Arrow; Sch P; Ski C; Swim; Wrest; COM; Citz A; Hon Prog; Journ A; Rugby; Cum Laude; Ski Racing A; Photo Contests A; Marquette U; Bus Adm.

LOGAN, Catherine June
Lee Davis HS; Mechanicsville, VA (39-423) Band; BC; Chor; VP, NHS; Tri-HiY; Regional Chor; Pres, Yth Church Coun; U of Va; Nurs.

LOGAN, Danita Yvette
Joliet E Sch; Joliet, IL; Chldr; Pres, Chor; 4H; Pres, Hmrm; Sch P; Up Bound; MVP, Bsbl; MVP, Bkbl; Cpt, Sftbl; Co-Cpt, Tnns; Cl Fav; HCt; MLS; Yth Fel; Jackson St U; Fashion Designing.

LOGAN, Darryl Brian
Germantown HS; Philadelphia, PA (88-551) Cpt, Band; Ch, Ensm; Orch; Spch A; Val; Amer Acad of Broadcasting; Communications.

LOGAN, Debra Helen
Eastern HS; Macon, OH (10%-90) Chor; Fr C; Pres, FHA; GS; Secy, 4H; NHS; Sch P; Secy, Jr Cl; Outst Stu, Eng; General Bus A; Home Ec II A; Legal Secretarial.

LOGAN, Donna Marie
Neshaminy Langhorne HS; Langhorne, PA (41-700) Band; Mjrte; Tnns; Math A; Cedarville Col; Math.

LOGAN, Jeffrey Shawn
Abraham Lincoln HS; Denver, CO; Hmrm; Rptr, Sch P; DARGCA; PTA A; Yth Fel; Co-Ch, Church Christian Ed Board; U of Denver.

LOGAN, Lisa Ardette
Halifax Co Sr HS; South Boston, VA; Band; Chor; VP, FBLA; Rptr, NHS; Span C; HCt; 1st Lieutenant Rifle Corps; Jr Marshall, Graduation; Pianst, Church Choir; Mass Inst of Technology; Experimental Child Psych.

LOGAN, Marvin Ray
Benton Co R-1 HS; Cole Camp, MO; FFA; Var C; Bsbl; Bkbl; Cr-Ctry.

LOGAN, Melissa Nan
Peachtree HS; Atlanta, GA (25%-400) BC; Chor; Ger C; 4H; Cert of Pianistic Merit; Sup Rating, Ntl Piano Auditions; U of N Ala; Mus.

LOGAN, Robert Gary
Old Forge HS; Old Forge, PA (2-121) Ed, Ann; Chess C; Pres, NHS; Sci C; COM; Chem A; Sal; Scorekeeper, Bsbl & Bkbl; Pa St U Schol; Pa St U; Math.

LOGAN, Rolland Keith
Polo HS; Polo, MO (10-34) FFA; Var C; Pres, Bsbl; Pres, Bkbl; Pres, Ftbl; God & Country A; Yth Fel; Eagle Sct; Most Improved, Bkbl; Mo U.

LOGAN, Sandra Lucille
Ringgold HS; Ringgold, GA (1-229) BC; Secy, FBLA; FHA; SC; COM; Type A; Val; VP, Bible C; Presbyterian Col Jr Fel; Dalton Jr Col; Human Services.

LOGAN, Susan Caldwell
Trinity Heights Christian Acad; Shreveport, LA (2-65) Lit Ral; NHS; VP, Soph Cl; Bkbl; MVP, Tnns; Yth Fel; Zonta C; Schol A Bkbl; A-Ed, Yrbk Staff.

LOGAN, Wilbert Charles
Proviso E HS; Maywood, IL; VP, DO C; Triton Jr Col; Elec.

LOGAN, William Franklin
Kearny HS; San Diego, CA (120-113) Band; Tr; Wrest; Citz A; Most Out; Pres, Fresh Cl; Drum Major; Outst Jr Band Member; Air Force Acad.

LOGAN, Yvonne Mae
Columbiana HS; Columbiana, OH (18-110) A Cap Choir; Band; Chor; Ensm; Orch; Bkbl; Tr; Youngstown St U; X-Ray.

LOGGHE, Kevin Kyle
Worthington Sr HS; Worthington, MN (28-281) Dbte Tm; Drama; NHS; Ed, Sch P; Spch C; Amer Leg Orator A; HCt; Jr Chamber of Com A; Opt A; Spch A; Concordia Col; Teaching.

LOGGIN, Eugene
Kingsbury HS; Memphis, TN (10-250) Span C; Math.

LOGGIN, Eugenia
Kingsbury HS; Memphis, TN (9-250) Tres, NHS; TOEC; S-T, FSA; Bus.

LOGSDON, Mary Catherine
Durrett HS; Louisville, KY; U of Louisville; Bus.

LOGUE, Michael Cecil
Jessamine Co HS; Nicholasville, KY; Band; Ensm; 4H; Tr; Wrest; Central Ky Voc Sch.

LOGUE, Mike McLeod
Cedar Shoals HS; Athens, GA; VP, Chess C; Fr C; Order/Arrow; Soccer; COM; Order/Arrow A; Pres A.

LOHAUS, Agnes Marie
Holly Sr HS; Holly, MI; Ann; Band; Chor; Fr C; 4H; Tres, Sci C; Swim; Yth Fel; GSct; JA; Blue Ribbons, Excel in Report Qual; U of Mich; Archt.

LOHER, Donald Werner
Parsippany Hills HS; Parsippany, NJ; Band; Hockey; Alg A; Chem A; Math A; Sci A; Yth Fel; Ministry.

LOHMANN, Betsy Ann
Niwot HS; Niwot, CO; Band; Pres, 4H.

LOHMANN, James K
Mineral Wells HS; Mineral Wells, TX (100-208) Drama; Thes; Bkbl; Drama A; *Communications.*

LOHMEYER, Julie Ann
Linn HS; Linn, KS (12-42) Secy, Thes; Bkbl; *Emporia St U; Ed.*

LOHNES, Crystal Dawn
Valley HS; Hazelton, ID (1-70) A Cap Choir; Ann; Band; Chor; FHA; Ger C; GS; 4H; Madrigal; Mjrte; NHS; Ski C; Mgr, Wrest; *Moscow Col; Forestry.*

LOHR, Peter James
McLean HS; McLean, VA (94-420) Ger C; Cpt, Math C; Model UN; NHS; Spch C; Golf; Hon Prog; Math A; NMF; NMS; ROTC A; Pres, Ger Ntl Hon Soc; Tres, MYF; *U of Wash; Elec Engr.*

LOHRBERG, James Donald
Lincoln HS; Lincoln, NE (1-562) Key C; Var C; JV, Ftbl; Swim; COM; FCA; *U of Nebr; Sci.*

LOIZEAUX, Marc Alan
Cristobal HS; Coco Solo, CANAL ZONE (4-98) Band; Pres, FTA; Hmrm; VP, NHS; Span C; Var C; Swim; COM; Lion A; NMS; *Math.*

LOKKEN, Scott Leroy
Capital HS; Boise, ID (305-585) Order/Arrow; Var C; MVP, Cr-Ctry; Tr; Order/Arrow A; Eagle Sct; *Boise St U; Art.*

LOKKER, Wendy Sue
Holland HS; Holland, MI; Band; Bkbl; *Phys Ed.*

LOLLAR, Guynne
Goodrich HS; Goodrich, TX (1-15) Co-Ed, Ann; Tres, BC; Chldr; Pres, FHA; Co-Ed, Sch P; Miss GHS; Most Popular; Best Dressed; *Sam Houston St U; Elem Ed.*

LOLLING, Terry Lynn
Lincoln Comm HS; Lincoln, IL (25%-385) A Cap Choir; Ann; Chor; Drama; Fr C; Spch C; Thes; Soccer; *Mus.*

LOLLIS, Michelle L
Checotah HS; Checotah, OK (25-83) Band; Drama; Secy, FHA; SC; Crisco A; WW; *Connors Col; Lib Sci.*

LOLLIS, Thomas Anthony
Laurens District 55 HS; Laurens, SC (15-430) *Ed.*

LOMAS, Kimberly Gaye
Edwards Co HS; Albion, IL (5-110) Parl, Drama; FHA; S-T, FTA; SC; Secy, JV; Beauty; Cl Fav; St Scholar; *Wabash Valley Jr Col; Mgt.*

LOMAX, Eric Lee
Columbus East HS; Columbus, OH; *NCSU; Denistry.*

LOMAX, Faith Elizabeth
Trinity HS; Trinity, NC; Anchor C; Fr C; Keyette; *Davidson Co Comm Col; Phar.*

LOMAX, Laura Lea
Grimsley Sr HS; Greensboro, NC (5-600) VP, Chor; Ensm; Fr C; GS; Hmrm; Ed, Lit Mag; Pres, NHS; Tnns; NMF; Yth Fel; WW; Eng A; *UNC Chapel Hill; Pre-Med.*

LOMAX, Vanessa Tracey
Miami Springs Sr HS; Miami Springs, FL; *Miami Dade Jr Col; Nurs.*

LOMBARD, Deborah Eve
Warren Co R III HS; Warrenton, MO (16-115) Chor; Private HS Schol, S Africa; *Art.*

LOMBARDI, Paul D
LaSalle Sr HS; Niagara Falls, NY (31-496) BS; Pres, Hmrm; NHS; Parl, SC; Mgr, Ftbl; Mgr, Swim; Wrest; Yth Fel; Alt, ROTC A; Elmira Col Key A; *Cornell U; Hotel Adm.*

LOMBARDO, Virginia Myriam
Franklin HS; Seattle, WA; Mod Mus Mas; Span C; COM; Interlochen Ntl Mus; VP, Church Yth; Ntl Protestant Mus & Ed Assn; *Shoreline Comm Col; Mus.*

LOMBARDOZZI, Catherine Marie Theresa
Country Day Sch o-t Sacred Heart; Philadelphia, PA; Pres, Chor; NHS; A-Ed, Sch P; Co-Ch, SC; Bio A; Hist A; Math A; Sci A; NML; Gen Mills Fmly Ldr Tmrow, Spa, A's; *Villanova U; Secondary Ed.*

LOMELI, Sandye Marie
Round Valley HS; Springerville, AZ; Tres, CYO; Chor; FHA; InterAct C; Pom Pon A; *Mesa Comm Col; Bus.*

LOMEN, Paula Lynette
Lima Sr HS; Lima, OH; Rptr, 4H; Hmrm; Co-Cpt, Y-Tns; Tnns; Amer Leg A; Hon Prog; *Wittenberg Col; Nurs.*

LOMHEIM, Douglas Scott
Araphoe HS; Littleton, CO; Bkbl; Soccer; Tnns; Optimist's Yth Career; Close Up; *Metropolitan St Col; Aviation Maintenance Mgt.*

LOMONICO, Robert Anthony
Loyola HS; Baltimore, MD (1-180) CYO; Hmrm; Lat C; NFL; Spch C; Tnns; COM; MLS; NEDT; Opt A; Poet A; Spch A; Boy o-t Yr; Outst Christian; *Religious Stu.*

LONAS, John Robert
Hardaway HS; Columbus, GA (10-430) Hmrm; Model UN; NHS; Orch; SC; COM; Gov Honor Prog; All St Orch; *U of Ga; Pediatrics.*

LONDERGAN, Ellen Maureen
London HS; London, OH (5-187) Pres, CYO; Chor; Rptr, Sch P; 4H A; Sci A; Span Test A; *Law.*

LONDON, Darrell Wayne
Jackson HS; Jackson, LA (5%-92) BC; FBLA; FFA; Pres, FTA; 4H; Semi-Fin, Lit Ral; Math C; SC; Up Bound; Pres, Sr Cl; Pres, Jr Cl; COM; 4H A; Hon Prog; NMS; Spch A; *Howard U; Engr.*

LONDON, Robert Alan
Oscoda Area HS; Oscoda, MI; Golf; *U of Mich.*

LONESOME, Steve Donnell
Woodlawn Sr HS; Baltimore, MD; Sch P; Bsbl; Math A; Bsbl A; *Med.*

LONG, Amanda Canilla
Ponder High; Ponder, TX (3-14) S-T, Ann; Pres, FHA; S-T, Sr Cl; Cl Fav; HQn; MLS; Sal; Type A; *N Tex St U; Eng.*

LONG, Andrea Mignon
Cherry Hill HS; Inkster, MI (100-333) Sch P; Bkbl; *Wayne St U; Mortuary Sci.*

LONG, Anna Maribeth
Moore HS; Louisville, KY (1-391) AFS; Band; BC; Ensm; Fr C; Ger C; NHS; ARC; Y-Tns; Alg A; Hon Prog; Poet A; Band A; Sct A; Fr A; *U of La; Sci.*

LONG, Audrey Nicole
Smiths Station HS; Smiths, AL (5%-190) Ann; Band; BC; Drama; FHA; 4H; Mjrte; Tres, Mu Alpha Theta; Sci C; Secy, SC; Beauty; Hon Prog; Stand Up For Young Amer Wk; *Auburn U.*

LONG, Beverly Kay
Frederick HS; Frederick, OK (5-55) Bus C; Chor; VP, FHA; Math C; Mu Alpha Theta; NHS; SC; Mgr, Bkbl; B Crocker A; Cl Fav; Masonic A; MLS; Type A; Most Mus; *Cameron U; Bus.*

LONG, Brenda Joyce
Eisenhower HS; Rialto, CA (320-761) Band; Ger C; Sch P; Med Careers; *San Bernardino Valley Jr Col; Nurs.*

LONG, Carla Lee
N Carroll HS; Reisterstown, MD; Hmrm; Y-Tns; Cpt, Swim; Cl Fav; I Dare You; ARC A; Type A; Yth Fel; HR; Piano Cert; Sci Show; WW; Hospital Vol; Sr Cl Play; *Liberty Baptist Col; Elem Ed.*

LONG, Carol Ann
Union HS; Tulsa, OK; Chor; ARC; *Central Bible Col; Child Evangelism.*

LONG, Cecelia Elaine
S P Waltrip HS; Houston, TX (452-586) Band; Tr; Cl Fav; JA A; Tr A; *Tex Sou U; Social Work.*

LONG, Charlotte
Columbus East HS; Columbus, OH; Schol Ath; *U of Cincinnati; Bus Adm.*

LONG, Clay Arthur
Pine Grove Area HS; Pine Grove, PA (7-160) Ger C; NEDT; Pro Deo Patri A; *Environmental Sci.*

LONG, Cynthia Alice
Warren HS; Monmouth, IL (3-40) Chor; S-T, 4H; S-T, Math C; Span C; Secy, SC; Secy, Soph Cl; Mgr, Bkbl; Mgr, Hockey; Bausch & Lomb A; Citz A; DARGCA; 4H A; I Dare You; Spch A; Yth Fel; *Ill St U; Med Tech.*

LONG, Cynthia Ann
Westminster Sr HS; Westminster, MD (5%-475) Band; Cpt, Chldr; Chor; Dbte Tm; Jr Miss Pagent; Model UN; NHS; Pol Sci C; SC; Chor Choreographer; WW; WW, Chldrs; *Hagerstown Bus Col; Pol.*

LONG, David Benjamin
Greenville HS; Greenville, AL (2-216) Ann; BC; VP, 4H; Pres, NHS; Pres, Sci C; Tr; Citz A; 4H A; Ntl Sci Found; ROTC A; CAP A's; *Samford U; Engr Physics.*

LONG, Dawl Dwight
Paris HS; Paris, TX (130-291) FFA; VP, Sr Cl; Ftbl; *Tex Tech U; Bus.*

LONG, Debbie Ruth
River Valley HS; Three Oaks, MI (90-180) Chor; FHA; Hmrm; Bkbl; Sftbl; Tr; COM; Citz A; I Dare You; Pres A; Art, Reading, CEF Trng, A's; PA, Bible Reading, A's; *Moody Bible Inst; Nurs.*

LONG, Debra Diane
Vailsburg HS; Newark, NJ (40-240) Chor; VP, Drama; Hmrm; Secy, Span C; SC; Tres, Jr Cl; Bio A; Hon Prog; JA A; All City Chor; *Bentley Col; Acct.*

LONG, Field
Jena HS; Jena, LA; BS; Hmrm; Key C; Rptr, Sch P; SC; Pres, Jr Cl; Ftbl; Hon Prog; VofDEM; Handsome A; Hmcoming Escort, Sgt at Arms, Key C; *La St U; Bus Adm.*

LONG, Jody Renee
Springfield HS; Springfield, IL (14-600) Band; Chldr; Chor; Drama; Fr C; Pol Sci C; SC; JA A; Math A; Opt A; Pres A; Co-Cpt, Vlbl; Explorers, Vet-Sci; *U of Ill; Vet Sci.*

LONG, John Leon Jr
Robert L Paschal HS; Fort Worth, TX (26-587) Band; NHS; VP, Pol Sci C; Hon Prog; Magna Cum Laude; NMS; *Ga Tech; Engr.*

LONG, Judy Elizabeth
Patrician Acad; Butler, AL (33%-40) Ann; BC; Alg A; Cl Fav; Math A; *Math.*

LONG, Julie Lynn
Bolton HS; Alexandria, LA (25-260) FHA; NHS; Pres, Lib C; WW; *LSU; Social Work.*

LONG, Katherine Leola
Gumberry HS; Gumberry, NC (5-97) Bus Mgr, Ann; BC; Chor; SC; *NC Central U; Nurs.*

LONG, Kathy Ann
Pine Grove Area HS; Pine Grove, PA; Arch; FHA; FNA; Arch; God & Country A; *Thompson Inst; Med Asst.*

LONG, Kathy Ranel
Lookeba-Sickles HS; Lookeba, OK (2-26) Chldr; Sch Achieve Tm; SC; Rptr, Sr Cl; VP, Jr Cl; VP, Soph Cl; Cpt, Bkbl; Sftbl; Mgr, Tr; Amer Leg A; Bio A; Cl Fav; 4H A; HCt; Sal; Swtht; Type A; *SW St U; Bus.*

LONG, Kenneth Mark
Tippecanoe HS; Tipp City, OH (40-146) Band; Order/Arrow; Rptr, Sch P; SC; Wrest; Citz A; God & Country A; Yth Fel; BSct; Eagle Sct, Top 10 Schol, A's; Lamp of Learning; *SE Mo St U; Acct.*

LONG, Kim Elaine
J L Mann HS; Greenville, SC; Chor; Ensm; NHS; *Greenville Tech Col; Bus.*

LONG, Kimberly Ann
T L Handy HS; Bay City, MI; Chor; Choir As; *Olivet Nazarene Col; Bus.*

LONG, Leigh Ann
MacArthur HS; San Antonio, TX (33%-700) A Cap Choir; Band; Co-Cpt, JV Vlbl; Baptist All St Choir; *Wayland Baptist Col; Teacher of Disturbed Children.*

LONG, Lisa Lillian
Olathe Sr HS; Olathe, KS; Band; Chor; Drama; 4H; Orch; Sci A; NJHS; Span A; *Eng Lit.*

LONG, Mark Alvin
Douglas MacArthur HS; San Antonio, TX (33%-610) VP, A Cap Choir; Chor; Ensm; Madrigal; Bsbl; JV, Bkbl; Ftbl; Sftbl; JV; Tr; Pres, FCA; Nom, Best Looking; Nom, Most Talented; Nom, Best All Around Athlete; Nom, Best Dressed; *Wayland Baptist Col; Mus.*

LONG, Mary Claire
Blacksburg HS; Blacksburg, VA (40-300) Chor; VP;
Fr C; Lit Mag; Spch C; GAA; Pep C; 1st Cl Sct;
Semi-Fin, Miss BHS; *William and Mary Col; Law.*

LONG, Mary Frances
Permian HS; Odessa, TX (9-900) A Cap Choir;
Hmrm; NHS; Ski C; St Stu Congress; SC; Pres,
Tri-HiY; S-T, Jr Cl; Amer Leg A; Bio A; Hon Prog;
Eng A; Bkbl Swtht; *Tex A&M U; Pre-Med.*

LONG, Melanie Dawn
Stivers-Patterson HS; Dayton, OH; Chldr; ARC;
Tr; Hon Prog; Ntl Achv Schol; PTA A; Poet A;
Pres A; ARC A; Spch A; Type A; Yth Foundation
A; *Tuskegee Inst; Vet.*

LONG, Micheal Allen
Woodland Christian HS; Phenix City, AL; Band;
Ftbl; Tr; Arrow of Light; HR.

LONG, Nancy Ann
Alliance HS; Alliance, OH (23-500) A Cap Choir;
NHS; ARC; Ski C; Hon Prog; ARC A; Yth Fel;
WW; Gym; *Bob Jones U.*

LONG, Nancy Anne
Red Bluff Union HS; Red Bluff, CA (34-433) A
Cap Choir; Band; Ch, Chldr; Chor; Ensm; VP, 4H;
Key C; Madrigal; VP, Soph Cl; Swim; 4H A; Ki-
wanis A; Spirit Qn; Stu o-t Quarter; VP, Yth
Group; Most Spirited Chldr; *Mus.*

LONG, Nancy Margaret
Salina HS Central; Salina, KS (41-330) Band;
Chldr; Lit Mag; SC; Cr-Ctry; Cpt; Swim; Outstand-
ing Young Writers A; *Kans U.*

LONG, Pamela Rae
Frankfort HS; Ridgeley, WV (20-151) Chor; FHA;
4H; NHS; SC; Type A; Art A; *W Va U; Phys Therapy.*

LONG, Patricia Frances
George Washington Sr HS; Agana, GUAM; CYO;
Chldr; Hmrm; NHS; SC; Bsbl; Mgr, Bkbl; Mgr,
Soccer; Swim; HR; Yth Conservation Corp; Jr
NHS; *U of Hawaii; Psych Dev.*

LONG, Petrise Jayne
Parkway HS; Rockford, OH (35-92) Band; MVP,
Chldr; Tres, SC; Secy, Bkbl; Secy, Fresh Cl; Cam-
pus Life.

LONG, Rachel Yvonne
Bloomsburg HS; Bloomsburg, PA (17-155) NHS;
JV, Cr-Ctry; Tr; VofDEM; *Bloomsburg St Col;
Early Childhood Ed.*

LONG, Randy Keith
E Alton-Wood River HS; Wood River, IL (51-363)
Band; Bus C; Hmrm; Orch; SC; Tnns; Citz A;
DARGCA; *Bus Adm.*

LONG, Rebecca Jane
Dugway HS; Dugway, UT (1-50) Secy, Band; Chor;
Drama; Model UN; NHS; Tnns; Hugh O'Brien Yth
Ldrship A; *Mus.*

LONG, Regina
E St Louis Lincoln Sr HS; E St Louis, MO (64-291)
Dbte Tm; Bkbl; Swim; Tr; Sci A; Tr & Bkbl A's; *Sou
Ill U; Acct.*

LONG, Richard Allan
Breckenridge HS; Breckenridge, MI (5%-140)
Band; Ensm; NHS; VP, Order/Arrow; Ftbl; God &
Country A; Order/Arrow A; Yth Fel; Eagle Sct;
Outst News Carrier; WW; *Chem Engr.*

LONG, Robaire Marie
Poughkeepsie HS; Poughkeepsie, NY; A Cap
Choir; All Amer Yth; Cpt, Chldr; Chor; Y-Tns; JV,
Bsbl; JV, Bkbl; COM; Merit Cert; Athletic A; Bowl
A; *Dutchess Comm Col; Math.*

LONG, Robert Steven
East Central HS; Hurley, MS (5-115) BC; Bus C;
Sci C; SC; Bsbl; Bkbl; Cl Fav; *U of Miss.*

LONG, Sandra Bee
Elbert Co Comprehensive HS; Elberton, GA
(34-303) Anchor C; Band; BC; Mjrte; Parl, Mod
Mus Mas; Span C; H of F; NEDT; Jr NHS; Soil
Conservation Prog; *Middle Ga Col.*

LONG, Sara Ann
Roane Co HS; Kingston, TN (43-178) Secy, 4H;
Span C; 4H A; *U of Tenn; Mus Ed.*

LONG, Sheril Lynn
Wawasee HS; Syracuse, IN (33%-250) A Cap
Choir; Chor; Drama; Ensm; Secy, 4H; Lat C; NFL;
Spch C; 4H A; Spch A; *Hanover Col; Nursery Sch
Ed.*

LONG, Sidney Leville
Fort Pierce Central HS; Fort Pierce, FL (462-556)
Fisk U.

LONG, Susan Umstead
Grimsley Sr HS; Greensboro, NC (10%-515) Chor;
Ensm; Sch P; Secy, SC; Y-Tns; JA A; Pres A; Jr
NHS; Church Yth Coun; JA, Hon Salesperson;
Early Childhood Ed.

LONG, Suzanne Steward
Hartshorne HS; Hartshorne, OK; Secy, Band;
Chor; Pres, Drama; Ensm; FHA; GS; 4H; Mjrte;
NHS; Cpt, Spch C; Pres, Thes; COM; Gov Honor
Prog; Masonic A; Opt A; Rotary A; Spch A; St
Scholar; VFW Orator Win; VofDEM; Hon Prog;
Drum Major; Excel A; Band Qn; St Spch Contest;
St Yth Committee; *Okla St U; Bus Adm.*

LONG, Tammy Sue
James Ford Rhodes Sr HS; Cleveland, OH
(25-400) AFS; Fr C; French NHS; FTA; NHS;
Rptr, Sch P; Co-Cpt, Bkbl; Bio A; Citz A; Hon
Prog; Sci A; F-Ed, Sch P; Girls Ldr C; Vlbl; *Kent St
U; Journ.*

LONG, Toni Diane
Pleasant Grove HS; Birmingham, AL (12-150) Sci
C; Ch, Sr Cl; Tr; Hist A; *Nurs.*

LONG, Venessa
Pleasant Grove HS; Pleasant Grove, AL (6-145)
Chldr; Chem C; *Xavier U; Med.*

LONG, Verna Elizabeth
Lowndes HS; Valdosta, GA (8-540) BC; Thes; Tri-
HiY; *Psych.*

LONG, Wilbert Jr
Saginaw HS; Saginaw, MI (2-400) Band; HiY;
Math C; NHS; SC; Rptr, Bkbl; Rptr, Ftbl; Rptr, Tr;
COM; Chem A; Citz A; Gr Marshal; Most Out;
Don McGhee A; Prince Grand Lodge; Young,
Gifted & Black; *U of Mich; Med.*

LONGACRE, Jeffrey Lee
St Mary's HS; Stockton, CA (1-256) BS; Fr C; Key
C; NHS; Ski C; Pres, SC; Var C; Tnns; CSF; Hon
Prog; *UCLA; Med.*

LONGAN, Joy Lynn
Bowman HS; Canyon Country, CA (18-44) Col o-t
Canyons; *Journ.*

LONGARDNER, Nevin Lee
Goshen HS; Goshen, IN (31-260) Band; BS; Ensm;
Hmrm; NHS; Pres, SC; Ftbl; JV, Golf; God &
Country A; *W Mich U; Finance.*

LONGBERRY, Bret Douglas
Miami Trace HS; Washington Court House, OH
(84-239) Band; Chess C; Drama; FTA; Parl, 4H;
ARC; Rptr, Sch P; Pres, Sci C; 4H A; Spch A;
Church Vestry; WW; Head Acolyte; 'In The Know'
Tm; *Ohio St U; Earth Sci.*

LONGENECKER, James Marlin
Warwick HS; Lititz, PA (100-260) Band; Chor;
Drama; Hmrm; F-Ed, Sch P; Spch C; JV, Bsbl; JV,
Bkbl; Spch A; Phys Fitness A; *York Col; Radio-tV.*

LONGENECKER, James Robert
Annville-Cleona HS; Annville, PA (50-175) Chor;
Tr; Gold Key A; Jaycee Art A; Plaza Art Show A;
Kutztown St Col; Art.

LONGENECKER, Karen Louise
Lampeter-Strasburg HS; Lampeter, PA (80-210)
AFS; FHA; 1st Cl GSct; Fin, JA A; International
C; *Miami-Dade Comm Col; Dietetics.*

LONGEST, Cyrana Letitia
Holly Springs HS; Holly Springs, MS (13-166) Bus
Mgr, Ann; Chor; FBLA; FHA; Mjrte; NHS; Ntl
Yth Conf; Ed, Sch P; SC; Amer Leg Orator A;
COM; Cl Fav; H of F; Drum Major; 2nd Pl, DECA
Girl Stu o-t Yr; Col Schol; WW; *Vanderbuilt U; Bus
Adm.*

LONGEST, Debra Lynn
Richard Montgomery HS; Rockville, MD
(15%-396) Band; Chldr; Pres, Chor; Hmrm; Pres,
Madrigal; NHS; SC; HCt; Hon Prog; Band Monogram; Chldr Bars; *Montgomery Col; Bus Mgt.*

LONGEST, Kim Diane
King William HS; King William, VA (25%-90) VP,
BC; Fr C; FHA; 4H; A-Ed, Lit Mag; A-Ed, Sch P;
Journ A; Q&S A; *Math.*

LONGEST, Tom Bruce
Florence HS; Florence, MS (1-189) Pres, BC; VP,
Drama; Rptr, Fr C; Secy, Sci C; Ch, SC; Mgr, Bkbl;
Mgr, Tr; COM; I Dare You; MLS; Star Student;
Val; Most Intellectual; *U of Miss; Computer Sci.*

LONGLEY, Fran Jane
Lompoc Sr HS; Lompoc, CA; A Cap Choir; Chor;
Pres, Dbte Tm; NFL; Pres, Spch C; Gym Tm; Eng
Achv; Phys Fitness Achv; Var Ltr, Gym; *North-
ridge Col; Communicative Disorders.*

LONGMAN, David Clay
Richwoods HS; Peoria, IL (50-435) *Bradley U;
Mech Engr.*

LONGO, Nicholas J
Morton HS; Berwyn, IL (99-762) Lat C; Pres, Sci
C; Mgr, Bkbl; JV, Sftbl; Pres A; President's Envi-
ronmental Merit; *U of Cincinnati; Bio.*

LONGORIA, Rafael Roberto
St Augustine HS; Laredo, TX; NHS; Spch A; Art
A; Craft A; *Tecnologico de Monterrey; Architec-
ture.*

LONIE, Gregory Lind
Campolindo HS; Moraga, CA (125-250) Rowing C;
Col of Idaho; Lib Arts.

LONN, Christopher Robert
Glenbrook N HS; Northbrook, IL; VP, Jaycees;
Gym; *Harper Jr Col.*

LONSBERRY, Gay L
Pojoaque HS; Santa Fe, NM (10-111) Band; NHS;
Rptr, Sch P; Bio A; Math A; Type A; Eng A; Spell-
ing A.

LONSINGER, Brenda Jill
Ashland HS; Ashland, OH (20%-387) Chor; Tri-
HiY; 1st HR; Cpt, Gym; Secy, Jr Ldr C;
Youngstown St U; Phys Ed.

LONTZ, David Michael
Central Dauphin HS; Harrisburg, PA (40%-800)
Hmrm; Order/Arrow; Var C; Cr-Ctry; Swim; Co-
Cpt, Tr; Order/Arrow A; MVP, Tr; Eagle Sct; *Ind
U of Penn; Criminology.*

LOOK, Leonard Edwin
El Cerrito HS; El Cerrito, CA (15-500) Band; CSF;
Hon Prog; Yth Fel; *U of Calif; Computer Programming.*

LOOMER, Laura Jean
Huguenot HS; Richmond, VA (1-254) AFS; Ed,
Ann; GS; NHS; Pol Sci C; Y-Tns; Co-Cpt, Hockey;
Hon Prog; MLS; Val; Echols Schol, U of Va; U of
Va, du Pont Regional Schol; Richmond Chptr o-t
Mortar Brd Alum; *U of Va; Pre-Law.*

LOOMIS, Kimberly Sue
Reynolds HS; Greenville, PA (4-183) AFS; Chldr;
Chor; Ensm; FTA; Ger C; Lat C; Math C; Tri-HiY;
Secy, Jr Cl; Secy, Soph Cl; Conservation C; *Iowa
Central Col; Vet Sci.*

LOOMIS, Pauline Bertha
Champaign Central HS; Champaign, IL (60-351)
NHS; Tr; Ger Hon Soc; *U of Ill; Med.*

LOOMIS, Ruth Angeline
Champaign Central HS; Champaign, IL (60-470)
Ger C; Tr; Math A; Pres A; Ger Hon Soc; *Med.*

LOOMIS, Virginia Knight
Alleghany Co HS; Covington, VA (9-240) Chldr;
HiY; NHS; VP, Span C; Tri-HiY; Var C; Gym;
DAHSS; WW; *Radford Col; Nurs.*

LOONEY, Alan Paul
Leavenworth HS; Leavenworth, KS (8-374)
Chess C; VP, Demolay; Drama; Fr C; French NHS;
Hmrm; Math C; NHS; Order/Arrow; Thes; Tres,
Sr Cl; Citz A; Hist A; Hon Prog; Math A; NMF;
NMS; NEDT; St Scholar; Sommerfield Schol; *U of
Kans; Engr.*

LOONEY, Celia Ellen
Paris HS; Paris, AR (7-125) Rptr, Fr C; FBLA; S-T,
4H; Tnns; Hist A; Sci A; Eng A; PA; *Harding Col;
Hist.*

LOONEY, Michael L
Andrew Terrell HS; Blanchard, OK; F-Ed, Ann;
Dbte Tm; Drama; Math C; Sch P; Sci C; Span C;
Var C; Mgr, Bkbl; Co-Cpt, Ftbl; *Okla St U; Bus.*

LOONEY, Teresa Carolyn
Cleveland HS; Cleveland, TN (9-220) Band; Chor; Drama; Fr C; NHS; Bus Mgr, Sch P; Spch C; Pres, Thes; Hon Prog; NMF; NMS; Spch A; Yth Fel; Eng A; All St Band; All St Chor; *Middle Tenn St U; Drama.*

LOOPER, Debra Ruth
Travelers Rest HS; Travelers Rest, SC; Chor; FHA; 4H; Type A.

LOOPER, Pamela Kay
Clarkrange HS; Clarkrange, TN (11-51) Ann; Rptr, BC; Co-Cpt, Chldr; Drama; FHA; 4H; F-Ed, Sch P; Secy, Sci C; Spch C; Var C; Pres, Sr Cl; Bkbl; Bio A; Sci A; Swtht; Miss CHS; Most Popular; Air Force Zoology A; *Tenn Tech U; Bus.*

LOOTENS, Janet Lee
Shrine HS; Royal Oak, MI (11-158) Ed, Ann; Chor; NHS; Journ A; Phi Beta Kappa; Hospital Vol; *Hope Col; Eng.*

LOPES, Sharon Elizabeth
Riverdale Joint Union HS; Riverdale, CA (10-125) Pres, Band; Drama; Hmrm; SC; Secy, Soph Cl; *Calif St U at Fresno; Early Childhood Ed.*

LOPEZ, Adolph Jr
Arlington Heights HS; Fort Worth, TX;

LOPEZ, Alfredo Freddy
Herbert H Lehman HS; New York, NY; SC; Bank of Amer A; ROTC A; VofDEM; *John Jay Col; Sci.*

LOPEZ, Amanda Patricia
Joliet Township W HS; Joliet, IL (250-500) AFS; Drama; Ensm; Secy, Orch; ARC; Thes; Tr; COM; Citz A; Sci A; Amer Hospital Assn; *Evangel Col; Med Tech.*

LOPEZ, Anna
Luis Munoz Rivera HS; Lajas, PR (9-175) VP, CYO; VP, Drama; Pres, 4H; Hmrm; Monogram; NHS; ARC; Sch P; Bsbl; COM; 4H A; Hon Prog; I Dare You; *Recinto U de Mayaguez; Chem Ingeneering.*

LOPEZ, Anthony Robert
Reseda HS; Reseda, CA; Chess C; SC; *Loyola Col; Eng.*

LOPEZ, Benjamin
Luis Munoz Rivera HS; Lajas, PR (30-170) FFA; Bsbl; Bkbl; *Inter Amer U; Ciencias Policiacas.*

LOPEZ, Bruce David
Oneida Baptist Inst; Oneida, KY (4-42) Chem C; Chess C; Chor; Span C; Soccer; Swim; Yth Fel; Best All-Around; HR; Top 5, Sr Cl; *Eastern Ky U; Sci.*

LOPEZ, Ciriaco J R
Ralls HS; Ralls, TX; Band; CYO; Lat C; Sci C; Bus Mgr, Var C; MVP, Bsbl; Bkbl; Cpt, Ftbl; Tr; WW; *Auto Mech.*

LOPEZ, Clarissa Amelia
La Sierra HS; Carmichael, CA (25%-600) Rptr, Sch P; Span C; Sftbl; Swim; COM; Citz A; *Pima Col; Law Enforcement.*

LOPEZ, Edie Lynn
Jones HS; Lynnville, TN; BC; Chldr; FTA; 4H; Sch P; SC; Bkbl; Math Contest; *Columbia St Comm Col.*

LOPEZ, Ileana
Acad Ntra Sra Providencia; Rio Piedras, PR (12-58) A Cap Choir; Cpt, Band; CYO; Chor; Dbte Tm; Drama; Tres, Hmrm; Lit Mag; Sci C; Span C; Spch C; Tres, SC; Tres, Soph Cl; Sftbl; Tnns; COM; Hon Prog; Sci A.

LOPEZ, Iris Violeta
Dr Pedro Perea Fajardo Voc HS; Mayaguez, PR; Hon Stu; *Med Technology.*

LOPEZ, Joanne Marie
Miami Springs Sr HS; Miami Springs, FL (31-816) Anchor C; Secy, Fr C; Ger C; Hmrm; InterClub Coun; NHS; VP, Sci C; Ftbl; Sftbl; Tnns; Hon Prog; Sci A; *U of Fla; Vet Med.*

LOPEZ, Joseph Alexander
Harlandale HS; San Antonio, TX (14-470) AFS; Secy, Band; BS; Chess C; Math C; NHS; Sci C; Amer Leg A; Hist A; Hon Prog; Opt A; Pres A; Ensm & Solo Contest Medals; *U of Tex at Austin; Med.*

LOPEZ, Karen Elizabeth
Santa Fe HS; High Springs, FL; A Cap Choir; BC; NHS; Span C; Span NHS; Fleischman Schol; Ntl Achv Schol; Regent Schol; *Gardner-Webb Col.*

LOPEZ, Nora Ivette
Manuela Toro HS; Caguas, PR; Math Hon; *U of Puerto Rico; Ed.*

LOPEZ, Pedro Francisco
Christopher Columbus HS; Miami, FL; Fr C; Sci C; Hon Prog; NEDT; Top Ten Gold Medal; *MIT; Sci.*

LOPEZ, Polly Eloise
Santa Fe HS; Santa Fe Springs, CA; SC; Pres, Jr Cl; S-T, Soph Cl; JA A; VP, ASB; *Rio Hondo Jr Col; Bus Ed.*

LOPEZ, Raymond
Harry S Truman HS; Bronx, NY; *S Eastern Bible Col; Ed.*

LOPEZ, Roseli
San Jorge Acad; Santurce, PR (5-75) Chor; Fr C; Secy, InterAct C; Pres, NHS; Secy, Jr Cl; Secy, Soph Cl; Bio A; Hon Prog; Eng A; *Col o-t Sacred Heart; Bus Adm.*

LOPEZ, Susan Bernadette
Pojoague HS; Santa Fe, NM (10%-111) Ann; FHA; 4H; NHS; Secy, Span C; SC; Bio A; COM; Type A; *NM St U.*

LOPEZ, Victor Manuel
Hobbs HS; Hobbs, NM (256-458) Ch, CYO; Chor; Pres, FTA; Pres, Hmrm; *NM Jr Col; Registered Nurs.*

LOPEZ-PEREIRA, Marisa Patricia
Calif Preparatory Sch; Encino, CA; Pres, SC; *Northridge Col; Sci.*

LORAH, Jeffrey Layne
Geronimo HS; Geronimo, OK (5-31) BS; Drama; Rptr, FFA; 4H; Pres, SC; Bsbl; Bkbl; Alg A; Amer Leg A; COM; 4H A; HKg; Math A; MLS; Drama, FFA, WW, A's; *Cameron U; Law.*

LORBEER, Charles Floyd
N B Forrest HS; Jacksonville, FL (25-600) Pres, Band; Secy, Key C; Order/Arrow; Order/Arrow A; Best Musician HS Band A; 2 St Bands.

LORBEER, John Bryan
Nathan Bedford Forrest HS; Jacksonville, FL (50-600) Order/Arrow; Order/Arrow A; Sci A; Elec.

LORCH, Scott Alan
El Camino Real HS; Woodland Hills, CA (110-1100) Drama; Hmrm; VP, SC; Thes; Mgr, Swim; CSF; Chem A; Hon Prog; NMS; *UCLA; Bio.*

LORD, Debra Darlene
R B Stall HS; Charleston, SC (25%-300) Pres, FHA; *Okla Baptist U; Nurs.*

LORD, James Marshall
Huntsville HS; Huntsville, AL (22-500) Chem C; Dbte Tm; Lat C; Math C; Mu Alpha Theta; NHS; Phys C; Ftbl; Co-Cpt, Soccer; Tr; *Vanderbilt U; Psych.*

LORD, Kenneth Allan
Springfield HS; Springfield, PA (10%-444) Band; Community Yth Symph; Ger C; NHS; Orch; Order/Arrow; Hon Prog; NMF; Dist Band & Orch; *Houghton Col; Biochem.*

LORE, Deborah Ann
Garner Sr HS; Garner, NC (45-300) Hmrm; *U of NC; Med.*

LOREK, Steven John
Medina Sr HS; Medina, OH (28-370) Span C; Bsbl; Ftbl; COM; *Akron U; Acct.*

LORELLI, Alison Anne
Lindenhurst HS; Lindenhurst, NY (25-720) Band; Ger C; Orch; *Med.*

LORENZ, L Bruce
College View Acad; Lincoln, NE; A Cap Choir; Ed, Ann; Pres, Band; Ensm; NHS; Ski C; SC; Pres, Jr Cl; Cpt, Bkbl; Cpt, Ftbl; Hockey.

LORENZ, Linda Marie
Romeo Sr HS; Romeo, MI; Ch, CYO; Chor; 4H; Ftbl; Sftbl; Swim; Tr; COM; Citz A; 4H A; HR; PA; GScts; *Oakland U; Archt.*

LORENZ, Steve Frederick
St Mary's HS; Stockton, CA (30-203) Chess C; Drama; Key C; Lit Mag; NHS; Sci C; Ski C; SC; Golf; CSF; Hist A; *U o-t Pacific; Biol.*

LORENZ, Steve Robert
Cary-Grove HS; Cary, IL (16-336) Var C; Bsbl; Ftbl; *Bio.*

LORENZEN, Cynthia Anne
Chrisman HS; Chrisman, IL (10-58) Cpt, Chldr; Chor; Drama; Ensm; Pres, 4H; Sch P; Secy, Jr Cl; Tr; Vlbl; Chor A; Outst 4-Her; *Concordia Col; Art.*

LORENZEN, Wendy Louise
Jasper HS; Jasper, MN (18-44) Band; Chor; Ensm; FHA; Luth Yth League; Solo A For Singing; *St John's Col; Elem Ed.*

LOREY, Jan Michelle
Summerville HS; Summerville, SC; FHA; FTA; MVP, Sftbl; *Bus.*

LORIA, Lorna Lynn
Ne Sr HS; Kansas City, MO (3-318) AFS; Chor; Dbte Tm; Drama; Ensm; Semi-Fin, NFL; NHS; ARC; Pres, Span C; Spch C; Hon Prog; Math A; Phi Beta Kappa; Summa Cum Laude; The Hundred HS Girl's C; Courier Schol; Combined Admission Schol; St Mus Solo Contest; *SW Baptist Col; Lib Arts.*

LORICK, Mary Louise
Humboldt HS; Humboldt, TN; FHA; 4H; 4H A; VICA.

LORIGAN, Deborah Fay
Clark Co R-1 HS; Kahonka, MO (7-96) Band; Chor; Ensm; Cpt, Mjrte; NHS; Var C; COM; Hon Prog; JA A; NJHS; Phys Ed Sr Merit; *Stephens Col; Bus.*

LOSCHIAVO, John Edward
Don Bosco Tech HS; Boston, MA (3-177) SC; NEDT; *Air Force Acad.*

LOSEE, Lori Nola
Heritage Christian Sch; Indianapolis, IN (4-61) Lit Mag; NHS; Citz A; Hon Soc; Cl Off; Ltr of Commendation PSAT; *Chem Engr.*

LOSEE, Michael Dwight
Hamburg Sr HS; Hamburg, NY (60-550) NHS; Wrest; Hon Prog; Regent Schol; Yth Fel; Prog Director, Sch TV; Producer, JA TV Company; *Clarkson Col; Elec Engr.*

LOTAKIS, Elizabeth Ann
St Andrew Acad; New York, NY (3-27) VP, A Cap Choir; Ann; VP, Chor; Pres, SC; Pres, Sr Cl; Alg A; I Dare You; *St John's U; Broadcasting.*

LOTT, Cynthia
Campolindo HS; Moraga, CA (5-400) A Cap Choir; Band; Orch; CSF; 1st Cl GSct; *Col of Idaho; Ger.*

LOTT, Morris Wilburn
Sumrall HS; Sumrall, MS (2-140) Ann; Pres, BC; VP, Sci C; Bkbl; Tr; Alg A; Cl Fav; Best Sch Spirit; Best Defensive Player; Mr Hustle.

LOTT, Nancy Ellen
Campolindo HS; Moraga, CA (10%-400) Chor; CSF; *Ed.*

LOTTRIDGE, Teresa Lynn
Benton Harbor HS; Benton Harbor, MI (35%-392) Ann; Band; Fr C; Orch; Tnns; Church Chor; Vlbl; Pres, Yth Fel; *Lake Mich Col; Psych.*

LOUDAMY, Anthony William
Robert E Lee HS; Tyler, TX; Hmrm; Math C; NHS; Span C; SC; Co-Cpt, Sftbl; Hon Prog; Yth in Gov A; Schol A; *Tex A&M U; Landscape Horticulture.*

LOUDERMILK, Carol Anne
Woodrow Wilson HS; Beckley, WV; Tres, Band; Cpt, Chldr; GS; VP, 4H; Hmrm; Rptr, Sch P; SC; Bkbl; Tr; 4H A; I Dare You; Math A; Tr-Letter, Ribbons; 4-H As; *W Va U; Interior Decorator.*

LOUDERMILK, Gregg Sawyer
Columbus HS; Columbus, GA; Secy, InterAct C; Ftbl; Cl Fav; Hon Prog; Most Out; Nom, Gov Hon; *U of Ga; Dentistry.*

LOUDERMILK, Kathern Lynn
Crestline HS; Crestline, OH; Pres, Sr Cl; Bio A; Citz A; Sci A; Star Student; Type A; Yth Fel; *Nurs.*

LOUERS, Craig
McKinley HS; Washington, DC (150-754) Bkbl; Ftbl; Citz A; Cl Fav; Most Out; WW; Art As; *Hampton Col; Architecture.*

LOUERS, Kevin
McKinley HS; Washington, DC (76-754) Ftbl; Citz A; Attendance As; Art A; Outst PE Stu; *Howard Col; Architecture.*

LOUGEE, Richard Scott
N Pocono HS; Moscow, PA (23-225) Ski C; JV, Golf; *Ind U of Pa; Computer Sci.*

LOUGHEED, Kathryn Isobel
Bradley Central HS; Cleveland, TN (155-441) Tres, CYO; Fr C; FBLA; InterAct C; Fin, Spch; *Cleveland St Col; Psych.*

LOUGHLIN, Christopher Andrew
Rockland Dist HS; Rockland, ME (5-180) A Cap Choir; Band; Chor; Ensm; Hmrm; Fin, Math C; NHS; Orch; Ski C; Golf; Alg A; Hist A; Hon Prog; Math A; Sci A; Yth Fel; *Bowdoin Col; Math.*

LOUGHMAN, Kimberly Jo
Edmond Mid-High Sch; Edmond, OK (102-650) Parl, NHS; VP, Thes; Hon Prog; Secy, PTSA; *Math.*

LOUIE, Lawrence Woo
Lowell HS; San Francisco, CA (85%-775) JETS; NHS; *Cal Poly St U at San Luis Obispo; Mech Engr.*

LOUKAKOS, Penny
Brooklyn Tech HS; Brooklyn, NY (250-1356) NHS; Bkbl; Secy, Jr GOYA; Longfellows; Sunday Sch Teacher; *Columbia U; Architecture.*

LOUKO, Jane Ellen
Elk Grove HS; Elk Grove Village, IL (40-580) Ed, Ann; Chem C; Jr Miss Pageant; NHS; Secy, Sr Cl; Hon Prog; Journ A; Q&S A; St Scholar; Pom-Pon Sq; *Ill Wesleyan U; Bus Adm.*

LOUQUE, Terrie Ann
Lutcher HS; Lutcher, LA (2-310) BC; Bus C; FBLA; Secy, 4H; Bkbl; Sftbl; COM; Citz A; 4H A; Phi Beta Kappa; Pres A; Type A; FBLA A; Chem Industry A; *Nicholls Col; Bus Adm.*

LOURENCE, Karen Jean
Mercy HS; Red Bluff, CA (1-25) Chor; Drama; Semi-Fin, GS; Pres, 4H; Model UN; Rptr, Sch P; SC; Tres, Jr Cl; Parl, Soph Cl; Bkbl; Sftbl; Tr; CSF; 4H A; Hon Prog; NEDT; Shakespeare C; Grnd A Win, Yng Men's Inst Essy Con; *U of Calif at Davis; Med Technology.*

LOUTH, Dorrie Jean
Lutheran HS W; Rocky River, OH (10-87) Bus C; Chldr; Chor; FBLA; Hmrm; NHS; Orch; Rptr, Sch P; Ski C; SC; Secy, Sr Cl; Tres, Jr Cl; Bsbl; Bkbl; Sftbl; Beauty; COM; Cl Fav; HCt; Hon Prog; MLS; ROTC A; Yth Fel; Air Force Acad Nominee; Organist; S-T, GAA; Pianist; String Quartet; Yth Group; *Toledo U; Pre-Med.*

LOVATO, Henry Michael
Battle Mountain HS; Minturn, CO (5-74) NHS; Ed, Sch P; Cpt, Bkbl; Cpt, Ftbl; JV, Tr; Journ A.

LOVE, Beverly Ann
Apollo HS; Owensboro, KY (33%-320) BC; Fr C; FHA; Pol Sci C; Mgr, Bkbl; Sftbl; Pol Sci C; FCA; WW; Ldrship A; Young Historians; Drill Tm; Pres Phys Fitness A; Pep C; Gifted & Talented; *Brescia Col; Acct.*

LOVE, Beverly Ann
Northwest HS; St Louis, MO (8-433) Math C; NHS; Sch P; SC; COM; Citz A; Type A; Yth Recreation A; *U of Iowa; Phys Therapy.*

LOVE, Charmaine Renee
Denby HS; Detroit, MI (230-634) Y-Tns; Tr; HR; Green Belt Karate; *Wayne St U; Nurs.*

LOVE, Dale Melvin
W Mecklenburg HS; Charlotte, NC (50%-504).

LOVE, David Nash Wilkins III
Rose HS; Greenville, NC; Ftbl; *E Carolina U.*

LOVE, Deborah Ann
Monroe HS; Sepulveda, CA; Bkbl; Sftbl; *LA City Col; Phys Ed.*

LOVE, Diane Elizabeth
Dunkirk Sr HS; Dunkirk, NY (10-285) VP, AFS; Band; Chor; Drama; Fr C; Hmrm; NHS; Ed, Sch P; Sci C; Ski C; SC; Mgr, Swim; COM; Hon Prog; Math A; Fr, SC, A's; *Math.*

LOVE, Don Eldon
Westbury Sr HS; Houston, TX (5%-767) A Cap Choir; Chor; Ensm; Key C; Sftbl; Jr Newscaster; Asst Coach, Ftbl; *Baylor U; Oral Communications.*

LOVE, Geraldine
Motley HS; Columbus, MS (10-81) BC; FBLA; FHA; Sci C; Tri-HiY; Pres, Jr Cl; Bkbl; *Miss St U; Bus Adm.*

LOVE, Gerard Anthony
Springfield Cath HS; Springfield, MO (37-53) AFS; Drama; Fr C; Rptr, Sch P; Bio A; Opt A; Sci A; *Viterbo Col; Psych.*

LOVE, Gerry Andrew
Willard HS; Willard, MO (12-196) AFS; BS; Chem C; Chess C; Dbte Tm; Drama; NFL; Phys C; Pres, Sci C; Bkbl; Fin, Optimist A; Fin, Sci, Spch As; *U of Mo; Med.*

LOVE, Linda Sue
Sulphur Springs HS; Sulphur Springs, TX (10%-220) Bus C; FHA; FTA; Lat C; NHS; *Baptist Bible Col; Christian Ed.*

LOVE, Marcia Jane
Sheffield HS; Sheffield, AL; Band; Bus C; FBLA; Tres, InterAct C; Bus Mgr, SC; *U of N Ala; Social Work.*

LOVE, Maurice Jerome
F W Ballou HS; Washington, DC (73-387) Pres, Order/Arrow; Var C; Mgr, Ftbl; Wrest; Citz A; God & Country A; Order/Arrow A; Eagle Sct, Silver Palm; Gold Cross Acolyte A; NRA Expert Rifleman; *NC A&T U; Med Technology.*

LOVE, Nash W III
Rose HS; Greenville, NC; Ftbl; *E Carolina U.*

LOVE, Otis Larue
Canton Pub HS; Canton, MS; Ch, Hmrm; VP, Math C; Mu Alpha Theta; NHS; Sci C; Span C; Bsbl; Math A; Phi Beta Kappa; Sci A; *Tougaloo Col; Phar.*

LOVE, Rodney Glen
N Shore HS; W Palm Beach, FL (18-266) Secy, Key C; NHS; Sci C; Span C; Alg A; Hist A; Math A; Eng A; Jr NHS; *U of NC; Engr.*

LOVE, Sandra Janette
Zwolle HS; Zwolle, LA; Band; FHA; 4H; Sftbl; *Tex Sou Col; Bus Adm.*

LOVE, Sarah Elizabeth
Northwestern HS; Rock Hill, SC (73-388) A Cap Choir; BC; Chor; Dbte Tm; Parl, Ensm; Math C; Monogram; Span C; JV, Bkbl; Tnns; *Clemson U; Nurs.*

LOVE, Shellie May
Billings Sr HS; Billings, MT; Fr C; *Psych.*

LOVE, Stephen P
Notre Dame HS; W Haven, CT (7-225) Drama; Ed, Lit Mag; NHS; Ed, Sch P; Span NHS; Cr-Ctry; JV, Tnns; St Scholar; Intramural Bkbl; VP, Current Affairs C; Span A; Jaycee Ten Outst Sr; *Fordham Col; Philosophy.*

LOVE, Stephen Radford
Avon Old Farms Sch; Avon, CT (16-83) Order/Arrow; Ski C; Ftbl; Hockey; Tr; Wrest; Hist A; Order/Arrow A; Yth Leg; LaCrosse; Ath A.

LOVE, Theodis Emmett Jr
Max S Hayes Voc HS; Cleveland, OH (3-15) Dr of Motors Citation.

LOVE, Troy Douglas
Palo Verde HS; Blythe, CA; SC; Bkbl; Ftbl; Tr; Most Out; Yth Fel; Letterman's C; Yellow Jacket A.

LOVE, Valorie Joyce
Thornton Twp HS; Harvey, IL; Beauty; B Crocker A; Citz A; I Dare You; Journ A; JA A; MLS; Most Out; *Prairie St Col; Interior Design.*

LOVE, Willa Jean
Lincoln HS; San Diego, CA; Sch P; Bsbl; Bkbl; Tnns; Citz A; *St U; Nurs.*

LOVEDAY, Troy Esther
Seymour HS; Seymour, TN (30%-97) Chor; FHA; GS; VP, 4H; Jr Miss Pagent; Madrigal; Sftbl; 4H A; Journ A; Pres, Acteens; 1st Aid Cert; WW; *U of Tenn; Lib Arts.*

LOVELACE, Cindy Dee
Bells HS; Bells, TN (12-50) FHA; S-T, Art C; Historian, FHA; *Freed-Hardeman Col; Radiology.*

LOVELACE, Dina Ann
Oak Ridge HS; Orlando, FL (10%-800) NHS; Acad Excel; Outst Achv, DECA; *Med.*

LOVELACE, Diresa Mae
Dan River HS; Ringgold, VA; Drama; Sch P; Cl Fav; Most Out; *Modeling.*

LOVELACE, Michael Sidney
Tabernacle Baptist Sch; Va Beach, VA; Band; Chor; Drama; Ensm; FTA; Orch; Bsbl; Bkbl; *Bob Jones U; Ed.*

LOVELACE, Monica Rose
Vernon HS; Vernon, TX; A Cap Choir; Band; Chor; 4H; Hmrm; Sch P; Spch C; Bkbl; Sftbl; Tnns; Tr; 4H A; Spch A; Dist-Vlbl, Tnns, Horse Show; Bkbl, Tr, Piano, Rodeo, A's; *Tex A&M U; Ath.*

LOVELESS, Mark Todd
SW HS; Flint, MI (5%-600) JV, Ftbl; *U of Mich.*

LOVELESS, Randy Scott
Welch Christian HS; Columbus, OH (3-20) Ann; Chor; Hmrm; NHS; SC; Bsbl; Co-Cpt, Bkbl; Page, Ga Senate; Page, Jimmy Carter.

LOVELL, Miller Co R III Hs
Miller Co R III HS; Tuscumbia, MO (9-27) Band; Military Service.

LOVELL, Randall Anderson
Weatherford HS; Weatherford, OK (2-93) Chor; VP, FFA; NHS; Var C; Bsbl; Bkbl; Golf; COM; I Dare You; Regent Schol; Rotary A; Sal; St Scholar; Yth Fel; St Farmer A; Academic Agr; Sen Page; Pres, Dist Methodist Yth; *Okla St U; Pre-Vet.*

LOVELL, Ruth Ann
Caldwell Co HS; Princeton, KY (70-160) Band; Ensm; Lat C; Sftbl; MLS; Yth Fel; *U of Louisville; Pre-Med.*

LOVELY, Glenn
Technical HS; Oakland, CA (10%-300) Band; Chess C; Chor; 4H; JETS; NHS; Span C; Var C; Bsbl; Cpt, Bkbl; Cpt, Ftbl; MVP, Sftbl; Citz A; Hon Prog; MLS; Most Out; Marcus Foster A; Gilmore A; Pop Warnes Schol A; *UCLA; Civil Engr.*

LOVELY, Kathy Annette
Newnan HS; Newnan, GA (88-305) Band; Bus C; Chor; Drama; VP, FBLA; Lit Mag; WW; *Ga Sou Col; Spch.*

LOVETT, Alesia Marie
Orange Glen HS; Escondido, CA; Elk A; Pep C; Explorers C; *USC; Journ.*

LOVETT, Fiesta Ann
Rockledge HS; Rockledge, FL; Chor; FBLA; Span C; Mgr, Tr; COM; Citz A; HCt; *Fla St U; Elem Ed.*

LOVETT, Gregory Wayne
St Elmo Community HS; St Elmo, IL (7-46) Band; Tres, 4H; NHS; SC; Pres, Soph Cl; JV, Bkbl; JV, Ftbl; JV, Tr; 4H A; Private Pilot License; *Lake Land Col; Aeronautical.*

LOVETT, Jerry Wayne
George P Butler HS; Augusta, GA (13-425) BC; Fr C; Hon Prog; U of Ga Cert of Merit; Geom A; Semi-Fin, Gov Hon; 1st Pl, Sci Fair; Drafting A; *Augusta Col; Physics.*

LOVETT, Rusty Bob
Pearland HS; Pearland, TX (50-350) Chess C; Chor; NHS; JV, Bkbl; Ftbl; Soccer; Sftbl; Tr; HCt; Journ A; FCC; Pres, Yth Coun; Secy, Yth Choir; *SW Tex St U; Law.*

LOVETT, Sharon Sue
Columbia Central HS; Columbia, TN (15-457) Rptr, FHA; Secy, 4H; Lat C; Math C; Citz A; 4H A; Spch A; Math Tournament Tm; Candystriper; Ch, Co Dairymonth; *Middle Tenn St U; Med Research.*

LOVGREN, Mark Wayne
Clay Center HS; Clay Center, NE (9-33) Band; Chor; Drama; NHS; Spch C; Ftbl; Spch A; *U of Nebr; Arts And Sci.*

LOVICK, Kelvin
Allen HS; Allen, LA (2-32) FBLA; Pres, Hmrm; Hon Prog; *Sou U; Computer Technology.*

LOVINGOOD, Rebecca Lynn
Kempsville HS; Virginia Beach, VA (10%-700) Band; Ger C; Sci A; *Col of William & Mary; Oceanography.*

LOVINGS, Leigh Ann
Eastern Guilford HS; Gibsonville, NC (12-164) NHS; *U of NC.*

LOVINGTON, Wayne Michael
Frank Scott Bunnell HS; Stratford, CT; Band; Ensm; Orch; Ski C; Ftbl; Hon Prog; Muscular Dystrophy A of Merit; *Mus.*

LOVINS, Linda Sue
Kermit HS; Kermit, WV (8-35) Ann; Bus C; FBLA; Sch P; VP, SC; *Berea Col; Bus.*

LOW, James Richard
Castro Valley HS; Castro Valley, CA (5-250) Band; Fin, BS; Chor; Pres, 4H; Rptr, Hmrm; Math C; Mu Alpha Theta; NHS; Orch; SC; Bank Of Amer A; CSF; COM; Chamber of Comm A; Citz A; 4H A; Yth Fel; Yth Leg; *U of Calif Berkeley; Elec Engr.*

LOW, Leslie Jean
Brownfield HS; Brownfield, TX (30-150) Band; GS; Tres, Rainbow; Golf; *Tex Tech U; Phys Ed.*

LOW, Rebecca Joyce
Amer Heritage Christian Sch; Hayward, CA; Bkbl; CSF; DAR Essay A; *Pensicola Christian Col; Bible.*

LOW, Sharon Denise
Alto HS; Alto, TX (3-50) Band; Dbte Tm; Ensm; FHA; SC; Hist A; Hon Prog; Math A; Sci A; Yth Fel; C-Ed, Newsltr; ESAA Comm; S-T, MYF; *Sam Houston St U; Biological Sci.*

LOWBER, Adrianne Clare
Monroe HS; Monroe, WA; Band; CYO; HiY; Hmrm; InterClub Coun; ARC; Sch Achieve Tm; Span C; St Stu Congress; Var C; Soph Cl; Bkbl; Soccer; Sftbl; Tnns; Cl Fav; JA A; Type A; Vlbl; *U of Wash; Law.*

LOWDER, Ellen Marie
Peebles HS; Peebles, OH (1-100) Chor; FTA; Hon Prog; Bio Schol Tm; Alg I Schol Tm; *Acct.*

LOWDER, John Charles
Peebles HS; Peebles, OH (1-105) Drama; VP, FFA; FTA; Hmrm; Co-Ed, Sch P; Sci C; VP, Sr Cl; Mgr, Bkbl; Q&S A; Spch A; Val; VofDEM; Bus Mgr, Sch Paper; St FFA Degree; 2nd Pl, St Farm Mgt Test; Conservation Essay A; St FFA Off Nom; *The Ohio St U; Civil Engr.*

LOWDER, Richard David II
Lexington Sr HS; Lexington, NC (2-250) F-Ed, Ann; Chor; Rptr, Fr C; Key C; Lit Mag; Tres, NHS; Cpt, Sch Achieve Tm; Tnns; COM; Hon Prog; NMS; NEDT; Opt A; Poet A; Rotary A; Sal; Spch A; Yth Fel; *Duke U; Pre-Med.*

LOWE, Debora Jean
Logan HS; Logan, OH; Yth Fel.

LOWE, Dee Ann
Maine N HS; Des Plaines, IL; SC; Var C; JV, Bkbl; Sftbl; Swim; Vlbl; Badminton; *Eastern Ill Col; Phys Ed.*

LOWE, Jabby Duane
McMullen Co HS; Tilden, TX (2-6) Ed, Ann; Pres, FFA; 4H; VP, NHS; Rptr, SC; Thes; VP, Sr Cl; VP, Jr Cl; Rptr, Soph Cl; Tnns; COM; 4H A; FFA Dist A; WW; *Schreiner Col; Bus Adm.*

LOWE, Jeffery Trent
N Gaston Sr HS; Dallas, NC (62-235) Secy, FFA; 4H; WW; *Gaston Col; Computer Sci.*

LOWE, Jennifer Sue
Oak Hills HS; Cincinnati, OH (179-822) Secy, Chldr; Chor; Ensm; Tr; Citz A; Yth Fel; *Ohio St U; Dietetics.*

LOWE, Joyce Eileen
Eastern Guilford HS; Gibsonville, NC (12-164) Ann; Chor; Pres, FTA; Secy, NHS; Yth Fel; *U of NC; Elem Ed.*

LOWE, Laura Marie
Fort Scott Sr HS; Fort Scott, KS (15-160) Co-Cpt, Chldr; Drama; GS; Hmrm; Rainbow; SC; Tr; Pres A; Yth Fel; Yth Leg; *Washburn Col; Acct.*

LOWE, Laurie Lyn
Litchfield HS; Litchfield, IL (21-155) BC; Chor; Drama; FTA; NHS; Span C; *Liberty Baptist Col; Missions.*

LOWE, Linda Janell
du Pont Manual HS; Louisville, KY; Chor; Ensm; Hmrm; NHS; Tr; Hebrew C; Ky All-St Chor; *Sullivan Jr Col of Bus; Legal-Diplomatic Secy.*

LOWE, Lisa Lynn
W A Berry HS; Birmingham, AL (125-350) Band; FHA; Span C; *U of Montevallo; Fashion Merchandising.*

LOWE, Martha Kaye
Hardaway HS; Columbus, GA (1-407) Secy, Anchor C; Ed, Ann; Pres, Fr C; Hmrm; Mu Alpha Theta; NHS; SC; COM; Journ A; Math A; Most Out; Q&S A; Val; Yth Fel; Page One A; *Vanderbilt U; Engr.*

LOWE, Pamela Sue
Campolindo HS; Moraga, CA; Hmrm; NHS; ARC; Spch C; SC; Bank Of Amer A; Citz A; Jr Rep, Girls League; V Crew; 1st Cl GSct; Church Deacon; Rowing C; *Calif Polytech Inst; Dietetics & Nutrition.*

LOWE, Perry Ernest III
Eastern Guilford HS; Gibsonville, NC (10-164) Ann; Monogram; NHS; Order/Arrow; Sci C; Span C; Span NHS; Bsbl; Bkbl; Ftbl; Golf; Order/Arrow A; Eagle Sct, Bronze Palm; *U of NC; Bus Adm.*

LOWE, Phyllis Ann
Independence HS; Columbus, OH; *Med.*

LOWE, Ricky LaVerne
Bluestem HS; Leon, KS (6-48) SC; Pres, Sr Cl; Bkbl; Tr; COM; Chem A; Phy A; *Wichita St U; Engr.*

LOWE, Robert Lee
John Bartram HS; Philadelphia, PA (72-200) Drama; Ensm; Phys C; Span C; Citz A; ARC A; Adv Coun Board; Stu Assn; Ath Assn; BSct; DA HS; Neal Ensm.

LOWE, Susan Marie
Zion-Benton Township HS; Zion, IL (32-429) Secy, Chor; Bus Mgr, Hmrm; Secy, NHS; Bus Mgr, Sch P; Span C; Secy, SC; Var C; COM; HQn; HCt; Most Out; NEDT; Most Congenial; Span Cert; HR Cert; *Eastern Ill U; Social Sci.*

LOWE, Vance Edward
Riverdale HS; Riverdale, ND; Chess C; Drama; Math C; Span C; Spch C; Bsbl; Golf; Soccer; Tr; ROTC A; Spch A.

LOWELL, Ernest Gibson
Chelmsford HS; Chelmsford, MA; Band; Ensm; NFL; Spch C; *Bus Adm.*

LOWELL, Karen Dean
Pascagoula HS; Pascagoula, MS (25%-455) Chor; Drama; Ensm; NHS; Orch; Rainbow; F-Ed, Sch P; Span C; Sftbl; Swim; Tnns; Bio A; Hon Prog; *William Carey Col; Mus Therapy.*

LOWER, John Charles
Brooke HS; Follansbee, WV (36-483) Dbte Tm; NHS; SC; Bkbl; Wrest; Star Student; WW; *Jefferson Co Tech Sch; Food Mgt.*

LOWER, Kelvin B
Valentine HS; Valentine, NE (20%-80) Chess C; Drama; Var C; Cr-Ctry; Mgr, Ftbl; Tr; Mgr, Wrest; Yth Fel; Ath Trnr Course; *Elec.*

LOWER, Rodney Charles
Copperas Cove HS; Copperas Cove, TX (65-371) Arch; JV, Ftbl; Sftbl; Tr; Gov Honor Prog; *Tex St Tech Inst; Hist.*

LOWERY, Anita Jo
Wayne HS; Fort Wayne, IN; MVP, Bsbl; Bowl Tm; Art, Bowl; A's; All Star Bowl; *Art.*

LOWERY, Billy DeWayne
Cartersville HS; Cartersville, GA (50-125) Hmrm; Bus Mgr, Sch P; SC; HCt.

LOWERY, Bryce Blakney Jr
Concord Sr HS; Concord, NC (9-220) Tres, Demolay; Drama; Fr C; Hmrm; Pres, InterAct C; Math C; Monogram; Mu Alpha Theta; NHS; Order/Arrow; Sci C; Thes; Golf; Cpt, Soccer; Wrest; Gr Marshal; *NC St U; Vet Sci.*

LOWERY, Charles Wayne
Chattooga HS; Summerville, GA (20%-150) JV, Ftbl; Tres, VICA; US Naval Sea Cadet Corps; 1st Cl Petty Off; Outst Sea Cadet of Yr; *Ga Tech U; Industrial Mgt.*

LOWERY, Doyle L
Glenoak E Campus HS; Canton, OH; Band; Pres, NFL; Spch C; Ftbl; COM; Interlochen Ntl Mus; Most Out; Sci A; Spch A; Georgetown U Schol; Preacher Boy Contest; Boy Camper o-t Wk; 1st Pl, Most Improved Spkr; *Cincinnati Bible Sem; Minister.*

LOWERY, John Douglas
Robert E Lee HS; Midland, TX (42-649) NHS; Bsbl; Bkbl; Ftbl; Tr; Explorers C; WW; Rebel Brigade; Acad Letterman; All District, All So Plains, Ftbl; *Tex Tech U; Engr.*

LOWERY, Karen Lee
Vancleave HS; Vancleave, MS (10-80) Ann; BC; Co-Cpt, Chldr; Chor; VP, SC; Tres, Jr Cl; Alg A; Bio A; Chem A; Citz A; Hist A; HCt; Type A; Chor A; Eng A; *U of W Fla.*

LOWERY, Kim Louise
Eastern HS; Baltimore, MD; *Nurs.*

LOWERY, Laura Lynne
Adrian Sr HS; Adrian, MI (20%-394) Bus Mgr, A Cap Choir; Chor; Ensm; Ski C; Mgr, Bkbl; Swim; HCt; *Siena Heights Col; Legal Secy.*

LOWERY, Linda Sue
Gallia Acad; Gallipolis, OH; Fr C; Secy, FHA; FTA; Sci C; Sftbl; Most Out.

LOWERY, Pamela Jeanine
Rainier HS; Rainier, WA (10-43) Pres, Band; Dbte Tm; VP, 4H; NHS; Rptr, Sch P; Secy, SC; Var C; Bsbl; Cpt, Bkbl; MVP, Tr; COM; HQn; Hon Prog; Journ A; NEDT; *U of Wash; Mus.*

LOWERY, Rebecca Ann
Sanford Acad; Sanford, MS (33%-11) Ann; BC; Chor; 4H; Rainbow; Sch P; SC; Rptr, Soph Cl; Mgr, Bkbl; Bio A; Cl Fav; HCt; Sci A; *Belhaven Col; Med.*

LOWERY, Thomas Duane
Palm Beach Gardens HS; Palm Beach Gardens, FL (86-451) Band; Ensm; Civitans; Mass Coun; St Tn Talent Win, Keyboard Solo; Ntl Tn Talent Win, Instrum Ensm; *Palm Beach Jr Col; Mus Ed.*

LOWREY, Paul Michael
Forsyth Ctry Day Sch; Lewisville, NC (5-43) A-Ed, Ann; Chor; Secy, Key C; Madrigal; NHS; Soccer; Yth Fel; Art Hon; *Haverford Col; Philosophy.*

LOWREY, Sharon Lavonne
Van-Cove HS; Cove, AR (1-26) Ed, Ann; FHA; Cpt, Bkbl; Citz A; HQn; MLS; Star Student; Val.

LOWRIE, Dane Joseph
Scotch Plains-Fanwood HS; Scotch Plains, NJ (30-650) A Cap Choir; Chor; Sch P; Tr; All St Chor; Jr Olympic Decathlon Champion; Runnerup, Opt Contest.

LOWRY, Denise Lynn
Avondale HS; Avondale Estates, GA; Band; S-T, Chor; Ensm; Lat C; Ga All St, Chor; *Sci.*

LOWRY, Freda Beth
McKinney HS; McKinney, TX (3-250) FTA; Hmrm; Span C; Pres, SC; S-T, Band; Stage Band A; S-T, NHS; Miss Sr; All Around Girl; *Baylor U.*

LOWRY, James Keith
Hueytown HS; Hueytown, AL (1-383) A-Ed, Ann; Chess C; Chor; Ensm; Fr C; HiY; Bus Mgr, Hmrm; Co-Ed, Lit Mag; Math C; ARC; F-Ed, Sch P; Sci C; SC; COM; Cl Fav; Most Out; NEDT; Val; Outst Soph; Resource Learning Center; *Birmingham Sou Col; Pre-Med.*

LOWRY, Lisa Bea
Leeton R-10 HS; Leeton, MO (10%-24) Ann; Band; Chor; Pres, Mjrte; Sch P; FBLA; COM; Band A; Bkbl & Sftbl Ltr; Mus Ltr; *Elem Ed.*

LOWRY, Michelle Reinna
Salisbury-Elk Lick HS; Salisbury, PA; Chldr; Chor; Hmrm; SC; Bkbl; Sftbl; PA.

LOWRY, Nancy Ann
Sooner HS; Bartlesville, OK (14-280) Chor; NHS; Rptr, Sch P.

LOWS, Julia Catherine
Rockville HS; Rockville, IN (19-87) Band; Chldr; VP, Chor; Drama; Cpt, FHA; 4H; Mjrte; Pres, Rainbow; Sch P; Sftbl; Tnns; Tr; Amer Leg Orator A; God & Country A; 4H A; Masonic A; Spch A; Grand Cr of Colors, Rainbow Girls; Solo & Ensm A; *Creative Writing & Comp A; Ind St U; Journ.*

LOX, Jeffrey Earl
Union HS; Biggsville, IL; Ann; FFA; Bsbl; Bkbl; Sftbl.

LOY, David Lee
Freeburg Comm HS; Freeburg, IL (6-120) Ann; Band; Model UN; NHS; Tres, Sci C; Var C; Cpt, Bsbl; Bkbl; Amer Leg A; HCt; NMS; St Scholar; Yth Fel; WW; Outst Del, Mod UN; Prom Kg; *Westminster Col; Pre-Med.*

LOY, Patrick Kevin
Valley Forge HS; Parma Hts, OH; A Cap Choir; Chor; Drama; Fr C; Hmrm; Madrigal; Sch Achieve Tm; Thes; COM; Gov Honor Prog; Hon Prog; *OMEA A; Psych.*

LOYD, Eric Dylan
Inglewood HS; Inglewood, CA; Var C; JV, Bkbl; Ftbl; Tr; *CSF; UCLA; Elec Engr.*

LOYD, Mary Annetta
Lincoln HS; Dallas, TX (10-190) Secy, Hmrm; Tres, Key C; Math C; Model UN; VP, NHS; Sci C; Span C; Up Bound; Cl Fav; HCt; Math A; MLS; Most Out; Cpt, Pep C; Church, Special Attendance, A's; Sch Cert's; *Tex A&M U; Computer Sci.*

LOYD, Sheryl D
Glenbrook HS; Glenview, IL (80-600) A Cap Choir; Chor; Drama; NFL; NHS; Spch A; Spch A; Commendations As; IMEA Dist Mus Festivals; IHSA St Mus Contest As; *Northwestern U; Mus Ed.*

LOYER, Dale Allen
Tri-Rivers HS; Marion, OH (11-22) Ftbl; Yth Fel; VICA; *Law Enforcement.*

LOYOLA, Natalie Ann
Laupahoehoe HS; Laupahoehoe, HI (3-24) NHS; Secy, Soph Cl; *Hawaii Comm Col; Clerical.*

LOZADA, Nicolas
Luis Munoz Marin HS; Cabo Rojo, PR (6-200) Pres, 4H; Pres, Hmrm; ARC; Pres, SC; Semi-Fin, Bsbl; Semi-Fin, Bkbl; Semi-Fin, Sftbl; Semi-Fin, Tr; Alg A; Bio A; COM; Cl Fav; 4H A; H of P; Hist A; Hon Prog; Math A; MLS; Most Out; Pres A; Spch A; Star Student; Summa Cum Laude; *CAAM UPR; Med.*

LOZADA, Wanda Marisol
Eastside HS; Paterson, NJ;

LOZANO, Margaret Ann
Stonewall Jackson HS; Charleston, WV; Chor; Span C; *Marshall U; Eng.*

LOZANO, Rose Anne
Thomas Jefferson HS; San Antonio, TX (75-398) Chor; Hmrm; ARC; Citz A; Ntl Jr Hon Soc; Cert of Service; Social C; Runner-Up, All Around Fav; *SAC; Bio Sci.*

LOZANO, Sarah Lynn
McClellan HS; Little Rock, AR (13-430) Ann; Band; FBLA; FHA; Lit Mag; NHS; Sch P; Hon Prog; Type A.

LOZINSKI, Brenda Lee
Norquay HS; Norquay, CANADA (2-22) Ann; Drama; Sch P; Alg A; Amer Leg A; Hist A; Sci A; Curling; *U of Saskatchewan; Phar.*

LUBKIN, Tracy Lynn
Beaufort Acad; Beaufort, SC (1-43) SC; JV, Bkbl; Sftbl; Hon Prog; Val; Headmasters A; *Math.*

LUBNIEWSKI, Lisa Marie
Moreau HS; Hayward, CA (1-345) CYO; Pres, Fr C; InterClub Coun; ARC; COM; Hon Prog; Sci A; Star Student; VFW A; HR; *Mills Col; Med.*

LUBNIEWSKI, Paula
Moreau HS; Hayward, CA (1-383) Fr C; ARC; COM; Hon Prog; Sci A; Spch A; VFW A; HR; *Mills Col; Law.*

LUCAS, Barbara Jean
Switzerland Co Jr Sr HS; Vevay, IN (5-108) Band; Chor; Tres, Mod Mus Mas; NHS.

LUCAS, Cheryl Ann
Crockett HS; Austin, TX (25%-650) Span NHS; Cr-Ctry; Sftbl; Tr; Yth Fel; Trustees A; *Sociology.*

LUCAS, Gayla Regina
W S Creecy HS; Rich Square, NC (2-42) FFA; FHA; NFL; NHS; Alg A; Sal; Fr A; WW; *NC Central U; Psych.*

LUCAS, Jerrell Keith
Brookhaven Acad; Brookhaven, MS (4-32) F-Ed, Ann; Tres, BC; Pres, Fr C; Fin, French NHS; Cl; Bsbl; Ftbl; Tr; Bio A; Cl Fav; HCt; Hon Prog; Most Dignified Sr; Cutest; *U of Miss; Phar.*

LUCAS, John David
Jackson HS; Jackson, AL (10%-250) Ann; Hmrm; Sch P; COM; Boy o-t Yr; *Art.*

LUCAS, Judith Lynne
N Kingstown HS; N Kingstown, RI (39-283) Chor; Hmrm; ARC; Swim; Citz A; Cand, HQn; *U of RI; Natural Resources.*

LUCAS, Kenneth Earl Jr
S Choctaw Acad; Toxey, AL; BC; NHS; MLS; *Agr.*

LUCAS, Lewis Ray
Jackson HS; Jackson, AL (10%-140) Band; Chor; FFA; NHS; COM; Most Talented; *Mus.*

LUCAS, Mae Ellen
Bosse HS; Evansville, IN (70-370) 4H; Sch P; *Ind U; Telecommunications.*

LUCAS, Mary Elizabeth
St Louise de Marillac HS; Northfield, IL (18-222) NHS; Ed, Sch P; VP, Sodality; Span C; *U of Ill; Nurs.*

LUCAS, Nicholas Daniel Boyd
Cameron Co HS; Emporium, PA (55-109) Band; Chor.

LUCAS, Rebecca Lynn
Levelland HS; Levelland, TX (2-180) Secy, A Cap Choir; Ensm; Ger C; Madrigal; NHS; Bio A; Math A; Sal; Vlbl; All St, All Region, Choir; WW; Superior, UIL Solo & Ensm; *Lubbock Christian Col; Mus.*

LUCAS, Samuel Lamar Jr
Broomfield HS; Broomfield, CO (25%-315) SC; JV, Bkbl; Ftbl; Tr; Citz A; FCA; *Colo St U; Engr.*

LUCAS, Sandra Lee
Mary D Bradford HS; Kenosha, WI (24-521) Chldr; Drama; GS; NHS; Pres, SC; Mgr, Swim; COM; Citz A; NHS; Hon Prog; *U of Wisc; Spec Ed.*

LUCAS, Stephanie Lynne
Robert E HS; Montgomery, AL; BC; Chldr; Chor; Rptr, 4H; Pol Sci C; Bkbl; Sci A; Pianist, Childrens Church; Assn Pianist, Church; Secy, Acteens; *Special Ed.*

LUCAS, Sylvia Michelle
Banning HS; Banning, CA (61-218) Fr C; Bkbl; Sftbl; Sci A; MVP, Sftbl; GSct; Usherette, Graduation; AAYA; Usher Board, Choir, Church; Block B; Jr Deaconess, Church; *U of Calif; Police Sci.*

LUCAS, Timothy Herman
First Assembly Christian Sch; Memphis, TN (10-32) Hmrm; Ftbl; Citz A; Christ Ambassadors; Jr Cl Chaplin; *Memphis St U; Broadcasting.*

LUCCA, Lynanne Marie
Kenmore E Sr HS; Kenmore, NY (15%-850) Band; Ch, City Conf; Sftbl; Yth Fel; NY St Mus Competition A; Best All Around; *Baptist Bible Col; Bible.*

LUCE, Barbara Ann
Chickahominy Acad; Richmond, VA (3-18) Chldr; Tres, Sr Cl; Tres, Jr Cl; Sftbl; Bio A; *Econ.*

LUCE, Gregg
S Vermillion HS; Clinton, IN (12-178) BS; SC; Var C; Bsbl; Bkbl; VFW A.

LUCERO, Delores Milligan
Thoreau HS; Thoreau, NM (2-89) Ann; CYO; Chldr; Hmrm; NHS; Pres, SC; Tr; Bio A; Math A; *W NM Col; Bus.*

LUCERO, Ralph Joseph
Alamosa HS; Alamosa, CO (32-182) CYO; Pres, Home Ec Related Occupations; Outst Stu for HERO; *Denver Inst of Tech; Elec.*

LUCHTENBURG, Brian Paul
Edgerton Pub HS; Edgerton, MN (20-34) Band; Chor; VP, 4H; Var C; Ftbl; Tr; 4H A; Tr A; Ftbl A.

LUCIANO, Carmen Migdalia
Dra Maria Cadilla HS; Arecibo, PR (51-636) FBLA; 4H; Hmrm; ARC; Co-Cpt, Sftbl; Cpt, Swim; COM; *UPR; Bus Adm.*

LUCIANO, Sandra
Francisco Mendoza HS; Isabela, PR; VP, 4H; COM; Sci A; *Foreign Lang.*

LUCIE, Lesa Jean
Hilton Central HS; Hilton, NY (16-350) Band; Hmrm; Math C; NHS; Orch; Ski C; Span C; SC; Tnns; Tres, A Cappella Choir; Church Chor; S-T, Church Yth; Church Ensm; Bible Quiz A; Soph & Jr Cl Rep; *E Nazarene Col; Bus.*

LUCK, Diane Marie
Holy Cross HS; Marine City, MI; Chor; NHS; Ski C; Hon Prog; *Mich St U; Biochem.*

LUCKENBILL, Debra Ann
Muhlenberg Sr HS; Laureldale, PA (38-310) Hmrm; Pol Sci C; Sci C; COM; Hon Prog; Tres, Art C; Pep C; Lib Aide.

LUCKETT, Barbara Carol
Lexington Sr HS; Lexington, NE (9-132) Chor; Tres, FHA; 4H; Regent Schol; *Cosmetology.*

LUCKETT, Carmen Aurelia
Crenshaw HS; Los Angeles, CA; Type A; Tres, Faithful Serv, Teachers, A's; *Calif St U; Bus.*

LUCKETT, Cynthia Marie
Canton Pub HS; Canton, MS (1-222) Pres, Math C; Pres, Mu Alpha Theta; NHS; VP, Sci C; VP, SC; VP, Sr Cl; Bkbl; Tr; Alg A; Bio A; Chem A; Cl Fav; HCt; Hon Prog; Math A; Sci A; Swtht; Val; *Tougaloo Col; Biol.*

LUCKETT, Vivian
Northeastern HS; Detroit, MI (16-206) All Amer Yth; VP, Mjrte; NHS; SC; Citz A; I Dare You; *Wayne St U; Nurs.*

LUCKO, Marianne Geraldine
John W Hallahan HS; Philadelphia, PA (14-431) Dbte Tm; Hmrm; Mod Mus Mas; NHS; Aux Lat; COM; Hon Prog; Ntl Sci Symposium; Vlbl; *Penn St U; Math.*

LUDEWIG, Gerald Wayne
Polo Comm HS; Polo, IL (95-110) Band; Bkbl; Aviation.

LUDEWIG, Laurie Marie
Roosevelt HS; Minneapolis, MN (10-500) Band; Chor; Madrigal; Mgr, Accompanist, Select Singers; *Augsburg Col; Ed.*

LUDLAM, Danna Lunita
Warrensburg HS; Warrensburg, MO (15-224) A Cap Choir; Chor; FHA; GS; Secy, NHS; SC; Hon Prog; Opt Out Tn; Intramural Sports; Mo Yth Leg Coun; Optimist Tnager o-t Yr; *Central Mo St U; Home Ec.*

LUDLOW, Karen Marie
Mississinewa HS; Gas City, IN (33%-200) Chor; Drama; Fin, Jr Miss Pagent; ARC; Swim; Miss Congeniality; *Ball St Col.*

LUDWICK, Alison Joy
In-Erlochen Arts Acad; Interlochen, MI (7-165) Band; JV, Chldr; Community Yth Symph; Dbte Tm; Rptr, Soph Cl; JV, Bkbl; St Scholar; Sr Acad Hon Stu; *Carelton Col.*

LUDWIG, Barbara Lynne
Copiague HS; Copiague, NY (6-399) Hmrm; NHS; Secy, SC; Fin, Regent's Schol; *SUNY at Stoneybrook; Bio.*

LUDWIG, Bruce Logan Jr
Worthington HS; Worthington, OH (30-600) Ensm; Hon Prog; *Sci.*

LUDWIG, Christy Lynn
Parkwood HS; Joplin, MO; A Cap Choir; VP, Chor; Drama; Ensm; Orch; SC; Swim; Tnns; Co-Cpt, Yth for Christ Group; *Mus.*

LUDWIG, Kamilla Jean
Hoehne HS; Hoehne, CO; Ann; Chem C; Rptr, Chor; Drama; Fr C; NHS; Phys C; Sch P; Spch C; Hist A; Math A; Type A; Mgr, Vlbl; Choir Accompanist; *Bethel Col; Pol Sci.*

LUEBBERING, Deborah Jean
Benton Co R-1 HS; Cole Camp, MO; A Cap Choir; CYO; Chor; Drama; Ensm; Pres, FHA; 4H; NHS; Sch P; Spch C; SC; Thes; Spch A; Growth Encounter, FHA; *St Fair Comm Col; Drama.*

LUEBBERT, Bonnie Beth
Granite City HS S; Granite City, IL; Chor; St Louis Civic Ballet; Sunday Sch, Piano Player; Church Organist; *Liberal Arts.*

LUECHTEFELD, Ray Anthony
Maries R-1 HS; Vienna, MO (10%-56) Band; Span C; Cr-Ctry; Alg A; Plumb Ind Coun, Speak Up for Amer; *U of Mo; Ceramic Engr.*

LUECK, Catharine Hellen
Bay HS; Panama City, FL; A Cap Choir; Secy, BC; Chor; Ensm; HCt; Kiwanis A; Yth Fel; Miss Valentine Pageant; TAP Ch; Jr Exchangettes; *Gulf Coast Col; Med.*

LUECK, David Ronald
Ord Pub HS; Ord, NE (18-93) FFA; 4H; Bsbl; Ftbl; St Farmer A; *Bob Jones U; Pre-Med.*

LUECKE, Nancy Ann
Souderton Area Sr HS; Souderton, PA (50%-375) JV, Chldr; Hmrm; SC; Tr; *Pinebrook Jr Col; Bible.*

LUEDECKE, Carrie Lynn
Eastwood HS; El Paso, TX; Band; FTA; Band A's.

LUEDKE, Gail Lynn
Troy HS; Troy, KS; Ann; Band; Cpt, Chldr; Chor; Ensm; Pres, 4H; NHS; SC; S-T, Sr Cl; Secy, Soph Cl; JV, Bkbl; Tr; 4H A; HQn; GS Alt; *St Joseph Beauty U; Cosmetology.*

LUEDTKE, Milan Frederick
Mankato W HS; Mankato, MN; Chor; Bkbl; *Mankato St U; Computer Prog.*

LUEKEMEYER, Deborah Ann
Corona Sr HS; Corona, CA (375-575) Chor; Rptr, FFA; Thes; Jobs Daughters; 1st Pl Painting, Co Fair; *Calif Poly-Tech Inst; Agr.*

LUEKER, John Frederick
Mt Olive HS; Mt Olive, IL (20-55) Chor; Pres, Hmrm; Phys C; Var C; Ftbl; Cpt, Wrest; COM; Cl Fav; HCt; Pres A; Yth Leg; MVP, Wrest; *Lincoln Land Col; Drafting.*

LUEKING, Nita Marie
Carlyle HS; Carlyle, IL (2-140) Drama; NHS; Sci C; Sal; St Scholar; Ger A; Fin, Co Math; 1st Pl, Variety Show; *Kaskaskia Jr Col; General Stu.*

LUENINGHOENER, Peter Donald
Stanton Comm Sch; Stanton, NE (4-55) Ann; VP, CYO; FFA; Ger C; Pres, 4H; Var C; VP, Sr Cl; VP, Jr Cl; Bkbl; Bausch & Lomb A; COM; Chem A; 4H A; Ntl Sci Found; Sci A; *Knox Col; Bio.*

LUENSER, Susan Kay
Patrician Acad; Butler, AL (8-38) A-Ed, Ann; BC; Co-Cpt, Chldr; Chor; Ensm; Secy, Hmrm; *U of Ala; Nurs.*

LUETH, Wendy Annette
Everett HS; Everett, WA; A Cap Choir; Chor; Drama; Ensm; *Mus.*

LUETJEN, Shirley Jean
Benton Co R-1 HS; Cole Camp, MO; A Cap Choir; Band; Chor; Secy, Drama; Ensm; Secy, FHA; Secy, NHS; Secy, Spch C; SC; Secy, Thes; Var C; Pres, Jr Cl; Bkbl; Vlbl; Growth Encounter, FHA; *St Fair Comm Col; Acct.*

LUETZOW, Annette Marie
Dearborn HS; Dearborn, MI (1%-558) Cpt, AFS; Co-Ed, Ann; Drama; NHS; Cpt, Swim; B Crocker A; COM; DARGCA; Hon Prog; NMF; MVP, Swim; UOP Schol; *Mich St U; Pre-Med.*

LUETZOW, Kyle Renee
Mankato E HS; Mankato, MN (1-278) Ann; Band; Chor; Pres, Hmrm; Orch; Thes; Choir Coun Rep; JV Vlbl; *Concordia Col; Mus.*

LUFF, Robert John Jr
Colorado Springs Christian Sch; Colorado Springs, CO (1-24) Chldr; Chor; Pres, Soph Cl; Co-Cpt, Bkbl; Sftbl; COM; Hon Prog; Pres, SB; *JBU; Bus Adm.*

LUFT, Margaret Ellen
Valley Central HS; Montgomery, NY (128-350) F-Ed, Ann; Co-Cpt, Chldr; Chor; Drama; Hmrm; Lit Mag; ARC; Secy, SC; Secy, Var C; Cr-Ctry; Soccer; Tr; Beauty; Citz A; Hon Prog; ARC A; Pres, Cpt, Tn C; Cardinal Spellman Yth A; Miss Walden Bicentennial; Service C A; Most Congenial; *St U of NY; Foreign Lang.*

LUFT, Mark Stephen
Valley Central HS; Montgomery, NY (40-300) Tres, CYO; Chor; Fr C; French NHS; Hmrm; Order/Arrow; Var C; Cr-Ctry; JV, Soccer; Tr; Order/Arrow A; Pres A; Tres, Parish Tn C; Church Lector; Folk Group Mus; Parish Coun; *W Point Military Acad; Engr.*

LUGINSLAND, Nennette Dee
Northern Heights HS; Allen, KS (3-31) Pres, 4H; Model UN; Secy, NHS; 4H A; Type A; *Kans St U; Vet Med.*

LUGO, Aida Maria
Acad Ntra Sra Providencia; Rio Piedras, PR (5-58) A Cap Choir; Bus C; CYO; Chem C; Chor; Cum Laude Soc; Dbte Tm; Drama; Hmrm; Phys C; Span C; Spch C; SC; Sftbl; COM; Hon Prog.

LUGO, Ange Luis
Barringer HS; Newark, NJ (2-450) Chess C; NHS; Ed, Sch P; VP, Sr Cl; Tr; Citz A; Journ A; Math A; Rensselaer A; Sal; Human Rights Schol; *Rutgers Col; Bio.*

LUGO, Edwin
Jose de Diego HS; Mayaguez, PR; Math C; Sci C; SC; Bio A; COM; Cl Fav; Magna Cum Laude; Math A; Sci A; C Becarios.

LUGO, Iris Isabel
Colegio San Antonio Abad; Humacao, PR (8-90) Sci C; COM; *Colegio Univ De Humacao; Med.*

LUGO, Jesus
Jose de Diego HS; Mayaguez, PR; Math C; Sci C; COM; Cl Fav; Magna Cum Laude; Math A; C de Becarios.

LUGO, Maria De L
Adolfo Grana Rivera HS; Penuelas, PR (3-342) VP, Band; Chldr; Chor; Drama; GP; Pres, Hmrm; Span C; Bio A; COM; Chem A; Lion A; Phy A; Pres A; Mus A; *U of Puerto Rico; Med.*

LUGO, Marissa
Lola Rodriguez de Tio; San German, PR (8-350) CYO; FHA; ARC; Sci C; Span C; COM; Hon Prog; Lion A; Phy A; Sci A; Summa Cum Laude; *U of Puerto Rico at Mayaguez; Med.*

LUHMAN, Scott Jeffrey
Hutchinson HS; Hutchinson, MN (50%-210) Band; Hmrm; SC; Var C; Pres, Sr Cl; Co-Cpt, Bsbl; Ftbl; Co-Cpt, Hockey; HCt; All Conf Bsbl; St Tn Prog; *U of Minn; Bus.*

LUKACH, Fred
Castle Park HS; Chula Vista, CA (27-426) City Conf; Drama; Hmrm; InterAct C; InterClub Coun; NFL; Spch C; Pres, SC; Thes; VP, Jr Cl; CSF; COM; Spch A; Drama A; *San Diego St U; Bus Adm.*

LUKACHKO, Helen Denise
Riverside HS; Taylor, PA (11-193) FTA; Hmrm; Cpt, Mjrte; NHS; Ski C; Sodality; Tr; COM; Hon Prog; NEDT; Mayor's Prayer Breakfast; *Bloomsburg St Col; Special Ed.*

LUKE, Brenda Susan
Compton HS; Compton, CA (24-800) City Conf; NHS; Ntl Yth Conf; CSF; Opt A; Opt Out Tn; Spch A; *Calif Polytech Inst; Med.*

LUKE, Brick Fortune
Coffee HS; Douglas, GA (5-211) Golf; Pres, Industrial Arts; Hmcoming Escort; Hon Graduate; *South Ga Col; Pharmacy.*

LUKE, James O
Pinckneyville Comm HS; Pinckneyville, IL (13-130) CYO; Math C; Span C; Bsbl; Ftbl; Tnns; Chamber of Comm A; HCt; Hon Prog; Math A; *Ill St U; Gen.*

LUKE, Patricia Ann
B T Washington HS; Atlanta, GA (8-425) Pres, Hmrm; Lat C; Lat NHS; NHS; Sch P; SC; Bio A; COM; Hon Prog; *Law.*

LUKE, Robert Alan
Hillcrest HS; Springfield, MO (10%-330) Key C; Math C; Sch Achieve Tm; JV, Bkbl; MVP, Golf; Swim; *Sci.*

LUKE, Robert Anthony
Holbrook HS; Holbrook, AZ (2-241) Band; S-T, Chess C; Drama; InterAct C; S-T, Math C; Span C; Spch C; Alg A; Hon Prog; Math A; Ntl Sci Symposium; Chess A; *MIT; Engr.*

LUKE, Stan
Crestview Sr HS; Crestview, FL (10%-250) Anchor C; Pres, Band; Parl, BC; *U of Fla; Bus.*

LUKE, Stanley Keith
Crestview Sr HS; Crestview, FL (10%-242) Anchor C; Pres, Band; Parl, BC; Chor; Key C; SC; *U of Fla; Bus.*

LUKE, Vicki Dawn
Berrie N Co HS; Nashville, GA (10-202) Band; Secy, Chor; Semi-Fin, Lit Ral; Tres, Tri-HiY; JV, Bkbl; 4H A; JA A; Pianist, Chor; Piano A's; Pianist, Drama C; Church Pianist; All St Chor; 'Miss Rebel' Pianist; *Valdosta St Col; Mus Ed.*

LUKER, Roger Wayne
Thompson HS; Alabaster, AL; A Cap Choir; Chor; Ensm; FFA; Var C; Ftbl; Hon Prog; Sci A; *U of Montevallo.*

LUKES, Gloria Kaye
Merrill Sr HS; Merrill, WI (18-379) Rptr, Ann; Band; Chor; Pres, 4H; Madrigal; Citz A; 4H A; Spch A; Job's Daughters; Mus Camp School; *Marquette U; Mass Communications.*

LUKEY, Phyllis Louise
Norquay HS; Norquay, CANADA (1-22) Ed, Ann; Pres, Drama; Rptr, Sch P; Bkbl; Amer Leg A; Spch A; Curling; Stu o-t Yr; Drama A; Eng A; *Acct.*

LUM, Judi Rae
Henry J Kaiser HS; Honolulu, HI (7-402) AFS; Ann; Lit Mag; NHS; Sch P; Secy, SC; Cpt, Cr-Ctry; COM; Hon Prog; Pres, Keywanettes; B'Nai B'Rith Yth o-t Yr A; Span Heritage Assn A; Outst Ldrship & Service A; *Pre-Med.*

LUMPFORD, Shirley Jean
E Side Sr HS; E St Louis, IL; Chor; Bsbl; Sftbl; Swim; Tn Challenge; *Nurs.*

LUMPKIN, Debbie Sue
Eastern Hills HS; Fort Worth, TX (133-450) A Cap Choir; FHA; Hist A; Hon Prog; *U Tex at Arlington; Pol Sci.*

LUMPKIN, Karen Lynn
Ensley HS; Birmingham, AL (5%-350) Co-Ed, Ann; Pres, Hmrm; Lat C; Tres, Math C; NHS; Secy, SC; Y-Tns; Amer Leg A; Citz A; Magna Cum Laude; Most Out; Soroptimist A; Bank Board; Exchange C Stu o-t Month; BTNB Outst Stu; U of Ala Dimes; Mayor's Yth Adv Comm; *U of Ala; Interior Design.*

LUMPKIN, William Ivan III
Ensley HS; Birmingham, AL (1%-346) Ann; Lat C; Mgr, Bsbl; Mgr, Bkbl; Mgr, Ftbl; Amer Leg A; COM; Citz A; Hon Prog; Magna Cum Laude; Head Sports Mgr; *U of Ala; Journ.*

LUMSDEN, James Wayne
Parker HS; Janesville, WI (126-460) NHS; JV, Ftbl; Tr.

LUNA, Guadalupe
Memorial HS; San Antonio, TX (23-300) Ann; FBLA; FTA; Secy, NHS; Span C; *Bus Adm.*

LUNCFORD, Barbara Diane
Admiral King HS; Lorain, OH (190-438) Band; Drama; Ensm; Hon Prog; *St Joesph Sch of Practical Nurs; Nurs.*

LUND, Barbara
Silver HS; Silver City, NM (7-213) Drama; Secy, NHS; SC; Thes; B Crocker A; *NM St U; Engr.*

LUND, Jeanine Kay
Neil Armstrong HS; Plymouth, MN (130-700) Chor; Dbte Tm; NFL; NFL Degree of Hon & Merit; *St Cloud St U; Special Ed.*

LUND, Jeri Sue
Wanamingo Pub HS; Wanamingo, MN (12-41) Ann; Band; Chldr; Chor; Drama; Ensm; FHA; Mjrte; NHS; Span C; SC; Var C; Co-Cpt, Tr; HCt; All-Conf Tr; Tr Ribbons; St Chor Ensm Comp Medal; *Lowthian Col; Fashion Merchandising.*

LUND, Julie Kay
Robert E Lee HS; Montgomery, AL (200-600) Pol Sci C; Thes; Alg A; Hist A.

LUND, Marcia Louise
Parker HS; Janesville, WI (41-491) NHS; SC; Bkbl; Tnns; HCt; St Olaf Col; Sociology.

LUND, Mike E
Sparks HS; Sparks, NV (2-380) Span A; U of Nev; Arts.

LUND, Richard A
Lincoln HS; Stockton, CA (18-468) S-T; Demolay; Ger C; Order/Arrow; JV, Ftbl; Golf; CSF; Hon Prog; U of Colo.

LUND, Sheba Lori
Hobe Sound Bible Acad; Hobe Sound, FL (8-32) Chor; Orch.

LUND, Teri Ann
Wanamingo Pub HS; Wanamingo, MN; Band; Chor; Drama; FHA; SC; Bkbl; Sftbl; Type A; Vlbl.

LUND, Thomas Andrew
Lincoln HS; Lincoln, RI (50-280) Chess C; NHS; Var C; Bkbl; Cpt, Ftbl; Tr; HCt; Hon Prog; U of RI; Bus Adm.

LUND, Yvonne Irene
Crestwood Sr HS; Cresco, IA (2-208) A Cap Choir; Band; 4H; Var C; Bkbl; Cpt, Cr-Ctry; Tr; 4H A; Church Choir; Sunday Sch Teacher; Secy, Walter League Zone; All-St Cr-Ctry; Med.

LUNDBERG, Ross Eugene
Houston HS; Houston, MN (15-47) Band; Sch P; Bkbl; Ftbl; Hon Prog; St Olaf Col; Mus.

LUNDBERG, Susan Michelle
Mehlville St HS; St Louis, MO (5%-560) Chor; Ensm; Ger C; NHS; ARC; Yth Fel; Yth Leg; Ger Achv A; Central Bible Col; Applied Mus.

LUNDE, Karyn Sue
Wissahickon Sr HS; Ambler, PA (20-360) Band; Chor; Drama; Swim; Phila Col of Bible; Mus.

LUNDEEN, Karen Louise
New London-Spicer HS; New London, MN (3-96) A Cap Choir; Pres, AFS; Band; Chor; Drama; Pres, FHA; 4H; Madrigal; Math C; NHS; Span C; SC; Tres, Soph Cl; 4H A; Hon Prog; Lion A; Waukesha Co Tech Inst; Acct.

LUNDEEN, Paul Harold
Hastings Sr HS; Hastings, NE (30-302) A Cap Choir; AFS; Fin, BS; Chor; Dbte Tm; Madrigal; NFL; Order/Arrow; Swim; Hon Prog; Eagle Sct; U of Nebr; Journ.

LUNDGREN, Larry Allen
Henry Sibley HS; Mendota Heights, MN (11-575) Pres, A Cap Choir; Band; Pres, Chor; Ensm; 4H; Madrigal; NHS; Sci C; Var C; Golf; COM; 4H A; Hon Prog; 1st, Quartet Contest; Northwestern Bible Col; Acct.

LUNDQUIST, Anne Elizabeth
Loy Norrix HS; Kalamazoo, MI; Chor; Var C; Co-Cpt, Cr-Ctry; Tr; Yth Fel; Ger A; U of Mich; Eng.

LUNDQUIST, Myra Jean
Clifton HS; Clifton, KS (25%-25) A-Ed, Ann; Pres, Jr Cl; Bkbl; Journ A; Type A; Vlbl; Cloud Co Comm Jr Col; Acct.

LUNDSGAARD, Timothy Jay
Aurelia Comm HS; Aurelia, IA (7-61) Chem C; FFA; Math C; Phys C; Var C; Bsbl; Bkbl; Cpt, Ftbl; Tr; Chem A; Pres A; Type A; Luther Col; Bookkeeping.

LUNDSTROM, Linda Sue
Hoover HS; N Canton, OH (23-463) A Cap Choir; Chor; Community Yth Symph; Ensm; Fr C; 4H; NHS; Orch; Sch Achieve Tm; Citz A; 4H A; Canton Symph Orch; Saddle C Assn A's; Mus Ed.

LUNDSTROM, Richard Allan
Albia Community HS; Albia, IA (7-148) Band; Chamber of Comm A; Iowa St U.

LUNDY, Brenda Lillian
Virginia HS; Bristol, VA; Ann; SC; FHA; Sci C; Span C; Pres, Y-Tns; Va Highlands Col; Nurs.

LUNDY, James Russell
Lyons Township HS; La Grange, IL (173-1207) Fin, Spch C; COM; Hon Prog; Spch A; St Scholar; Gustavus Adolphus Col.

LUNNING, Laura Kaye
Cottage Grove HS; Cottage Grove, OR (19-250) A Cap Choir; Chldr; Chor; InterClub Coun; Spch C; SC; Sftbl; Tr; Most Talented.

LUNSFORD, Anna Lee
Taft HS; Hamilton, OH (21-500) Fr C; Miami U at Oxford; Law.

LUNSFORD, Beatrice Rose
Pacelli HS; Columbus, GA (9-93) Hmrm; Model UN; Span C; Span NHS; Var C; VP, Soph Cl; Tr; JA A; Phys Ed A.

LUNSFORD, Cindy Lynne
N Iredell HS; Olin, NC (7-190) Band; BC; Drama; Monogram; F-Ed, Sch P; Sci C; Bkbl; Gr Marshal; Yth Fel; Top 10%; Mitchell Comm Col; Phys Therapy.

LUNSFORD, Clyde Courtney
E Coweta HS; Senoia, GA (3-100) Band; BC; Dbte Tm; Secy, Key C; Ftbl; COM; Kiwanis A; All Amer HR; Math, Lit, Tms; Sr Play; Ga Tech; Engr.

LUNSFORD, Eddie Gene
N Iredell HS; Olin, NC (15-256) BC; FFA; Hmrm; Sci C; Jr Marshal; Appalachian St U; Bus Adm.

LUNSFORD, Kevin Dee
Choctaw HS; Choctaw, OK; BC; Pres, Chor; Ensm; Pres, 4H; Secy, Key C; NHS; Bsbl; Bkbl; Cpt, Tnns; Tr; 4H A; Yth Fel; All St Chor; Southwestern St U; Mus.

LUNSFORD, Larry Allan
Macon HS; Macon, MO (2-115) BS; Co-Ch, Key C; Ed, Sch P; S-T; Var C; Tres, Soph Cl; Bsbl; Co-Cpt, Bkbl; Tr; Alg A; COM; Curator A; Hist A; HCt; Journ A; Math A; Regent Schol; Sal; Yth Fel; MVP, Bkbl; Pershing Schol; NE Mo St U; Acct.

LUNSFORD, Loretta Laureen
Pacelli HS; Columbus, GA (15-83) Ann; CYO; Hmrm; NHS; SC; Pres, Jr Cl; VP, Soph Cl; JA A; Religion A; WW; Speak Up For Young Amer; Columbus Col; Pol Sci.

LUNSFORD, Pamela Jean
Calvary Christian Acad; Midland, MI; Cpt, Chldr; Liberty Baptist Col; Nurs.

LUNZER, Cynthia Louise
Bolsa Grande HS; Garden Grove, CA (35-378) F-Ed, Key C; NHS; Orange Coast Col; Dental Hygiene.

LUPBERGER, Tina Marie
John F Hodge HS; St James, MO (2-121) Rptr, FHA; S-T, Sci C; COM; Hist A; Pom Pon Squad; 2nd St James, Sci Fair; 1st U of Mo, Sci Fair; U of Mo.

LUPER, Debra LaDenna
Carnegie HS; Carnegie, OK (10-56) Chor; Rptr, FHA; NHS; SC; Bkbl; Tr; HQn; Outst Tr Girl; Outst HS Girl; Home Ec Service A; Okla St U.

LUPER, Denise Lea
Carnegie HS; Carnegie, OK (1-70) Chor; FHA; GS; NHS; VP, Span C; SC; Secy, Jr Cl; Alg A; Bio A; Type A; NHS; St Hon Soc; Span A; Eng A; Okla St U.

LUPO, Mark Ramsey
Smith Station HS; Smith Station, AL; BC; VP, Key C; Pres, Math C; Pres, Mu Alpha Theta; VP, Sci C; Math A; Auburn U; Med.

LUQUETTE, Stephen Paul
Crosby HS; Crosby, TX; Ann; BS; Chess C; Cpt, Ftbl; Tr; San Jacinto Col; Drafting.

LURIE, Frances Ann
Homewood HS; Homewood, AL (100-245) Band; Orch; Span C; Psych C; Miss Sorority; WW; Co-cpt, Flag Corp; Jr Civitan; Religion Committee; U of Ala; Phys Therapy.

LURRY, Mary Frances
Jena HS; Jena, LA (33-165) Band; Drama; Ensm; Arch; Bkbl; Ftbl; Sftbl; Tr.

LUSHINA, Salina Ann
Hillsboro Sr HS; Hillsboro, OR (232-651) Band; CYO; Chor; Cpt, Mjrte; ARC; Tnns; Tr; Bio A; Chem A; ARC A; Sci A; Portland St U; Obstetric Nurs.

LUSK, Claire Eileen
Gainesville HS; Gainesville, TX (5-190) Band; Fr C; FTA; NHS; Math A; NMS; NEDT; VofDEM; Spelling A; Tex Tech U; Food Tech.

LUSK, Gregory Brian
Herndon HS; Herndon, WV (1-48) Fr C; SC; Bkbl; Alg A; Hist A; W Va U; Med.

LUSK, Gwendolyn
Altheimer HS; Altheimer, AR; Ann; Chor; Fr C; Pres, FBLA; Rptr, Hmrm; Secy, NHS; Secy, SC; Bio A; Citz A; Most Out; Sci A; Most Courteous; Biol.

LUSK, Lee Ann
Richland HS; Fort Worth, TX (15%-500) Secy, Chor; FTA; NHS; Chor A; PA A; TCJC; Math.

LUSK, Linda Darlene
Herndon HS; Herndon, WV (3-58) FBLA; FHA; S-T, Hmrm; S-T, NHS; SC; HCt; Eng A; Bus.

LUSK, Pamela Diane
Herndon HS; Herndon, WV (3-37) Cpt, Chldr; Chor; Pres, FHA; GS; VP, NHS; MLS; Most Out; Eng A; Home Ec A; Marshall U; Dentistry.

LUSK, Sharon Lynn
Herndon HS; Herndon, WV (9-48) Chldr; Fr C; Bkbl; Sftbl; HCt; All-Tourn Bkbl; All-St Bkbl; All-SMA Girls Cage Bkbl; Chldr A; Concord Col; Phys Ed.

LUSK, Terri Lee
Mullens HS; Mullens, WV (6-144) BC; FBLA; HiY; Rainbow; SC.

LUSSKY, Karen Jean
Armstrong Sr HS; Plymouth, MN (1-731) Band; Chor; NHS; Orch; Bethel Col; Psych.

LUSTER, Antoinette Delass
Jean Ribault HS; Jacksonville, FL (20%-700) A Cap Choir; Chor; Hmrm; Pres, Span C; Parl, SC; DARGCA; MLS; Yth Fel; Key C Swtht; Les Jolies; U Fla; Med.

LUSTER, Deborah LaFaye
Jean Ribault Sr HS; Jacksonville, FL (13-545) Chor; Pres, Fr C; Hmrm; NHS; Ntl Yth Conf; U of Fla; Phar.

LUSTER, Sheila Elaine
Ribault Sr HS; Jacksonville, FL (4-500) Band; Ensm; Pres, Hmrm; Key C; NHS; Ntl Yth Conf; SC; COM; 4H A; Hon Prog; Yth Fel; Duke U; Sci.

LUTES, Edmund Kevin
Weymouth S HS; Weymouth, MA (63-516) A Cap Choir; Band; Chor; Demolay; Ensm; Madrigal; Math C; COM; Hon Prog; Cpt, Church Bkbl; Philadelphia Col of Bible; Pastoral Stu.

LUTH, Karla Diane
Walnut Comm HS; Walnut, IA (6-26) Band; Chor; Ensm; FHA; Ger C; 4H; Madrigal; Sch P; JV, Bkbl; Tr; Missionary.

LUTHER, Kelly Diane
Aptos HS; Aptos, CA (70-300) Ed, Ann; Bus C; Chor; 4H; InterClub Coun; Secy, Lit Mag; Ed, Sch P; Var C; Mgr, Bkbl; MVP, Tr; COM; Citz A; Math A; Most Out; Rotary A; Type A; Vlbl; Poster A; Pepperdine U; Bus.

LUTHER, Tammy Elsie
Acad of Our Lady of Mercy; Milford, CT (9-93) Chor; Drama; Fr C; Key C; Lit Mag; Pres, NHS; NEDT; Psych.

LUTHER, Wendy Lynn
Crescent HS; Joyce, WA (3-26) Chldr; Tres, NHS; Co-Ed, Sch P; Pres, Jr Cl; JV, Bkbl; Tr; HCt; Secretarial.

LUTTRELL, Gregory Leon
Park Center HS; Brooklyn Park, MN (30-600) A Cap Choir; Chess C; Chor; Orch; Order/Arrow; Tr; Engr.

LUTTRELL, Johnny Price
Franklin Co HS; Frankfort, KY; Chor; Parl, FFA; 4H; Hmrm; Secy, Key C; Cpt, Sftbl; Wrest; 4H A; U of Ky; Agr.

LUTTRELL, Leta Mae
Elizabethton HS; Elizabethton, TN; Chor; Ensm; FHA; ARC A; DECA; E Tenn St U; Nurs.

LUTTRELL, Richard Brian
San Carlos HS; San Carlos, CA (10%-501) Band; ARC; SC; Cpt, Cr-Ctry; Cpt, Tr; MVP, Cr Ctry; MVP, Tr.

LUTZ, Barbara Ann
John S Fine Sr HS; Nanticoke, PA (2-347) Chor; Ed, Sch P; Sodality; SC; Var C; Bkbl; Hockey; MVP, Sftbl; Tr; NEDT; Phys Therapy.

LUTZ, Bryan Kent
Madisonville N Hopkins HS; Madisonville, KY; Chess C; *Madisonville Voc Sch; Machinist.*

LUTZ, Gary David
Ironton HS; Ironton, OH (50-200) Hmrm; Bsbl; Bkbl.

LUTZ, Kathy Louise
Columbus HS; Columbus, GA (20%-250) Cpt, Chldr; NHS; Var C; Secy, Soph Cl; Most Out; Jr Civitan; *Columbus Col; Phys Therapy.*

LUTZ, Kelley Lea
Brookville HS; Lynchburg, VA (30-350) Pres, AFS; Ann; Secy, Band; Ch, NHS; Orch; Sch P; Tnns; COM; Journ A; *James Madison U; Radiology.*

LUTZ, Kimberlee Joanne
Holyoke HS; Holyoke, CO (1-60) Ann; Band; Chor; Secy, FHA; Ch, Mjrte; Rainbow; SC; Var C; Bkbl; Sftbl; Mgr, Tr; Alg A; Hon Prog; Math A; Yth Fel; Vlbl; Home Ec A; Director, Pep Band; Tres, Pep C; Secy, Yth Fel; Pom Pon Girl; Flag Corp; *Bus.*

LUTZ, Ronald Craig
Cumberland Valley HS; Mechanicsburg, PA (7-585) NHS; Sci C; Bio A; Hon Prog; *Pa St U; Chem Engr.*

LUTZ, Terry Lee
Lake HS; Hartville, OH; Band; Drama; Bkbl; *Johnson Bible Col; Mus.*

LYAUTEY, Henry Jules
Vidalia HS; Vidalia, GA (28-150) Band; Ger C; Tr; NROTC Schol Fin; *Ga Tech U; Mech Engr.*

LYBARGER, Karen Leigh
Odessa HS; Odessa, MO (24-129) Bus C; Chldr; FBLA; NHS; Rainbow; Type A; DECA A; FBLA Contest Win.

LYBECKER, Kristan Jaye
Weston McEwen HS; Athena, OR (1-41) Ann; Band; Chor; NHS; Sch P; Span C; SC; Var C; Tnns; Hon Prog; Sal; Type A; Nth Choral A; *Blue Mountain Comm Col; Photography.*

LYBRAND, Robert David
Whitehall HS; White Hall, AR (68-149) BS; Ch, Order/Arrow; SC; Co-Cpt, Ftbl; Order/Arrow A; Secy, FCA; Leadership A; Eagle Sct; *Ark Tech U; Parks and Recreation Mgt.*

LyBRAND, William
White Hall HS; Pine Bluff, AR; BC; Parl, Order/Arrow; Sci C; Order/Arrow A; Sci A; Eagle Sct; Koskalakas; *US Air Force Acad; Aviation.*

LYCES, Vicky Veronica
Thomas Stone HS; Waldorf, MD (73-390) Chor; FTA; NHS; Mgr, Bkbl; Cr-Ctry; MVP; Tr; COM; Yth Fel; Cpt, Tr; FTA B Avg; *Morgan St U; Art.*

LYDA, Janet Dawn
Franklin Co HS; Carnesville, GA (15%-250) Band; Rptr, Fr C; FHA; 4H; Hmrm; Sftbl; 4H A; *Home Ec.*

LYDA, Patricia Ann
Asheville HS; Asheville, NC (90-400) Band; Chldr; Drama; Hmrm; Secy, Span C; SC; Thes; *E Carolina U; Chem.*

LYDDY, Dennis Michael
St Joseph Regional HS; Lowell, MA; Chess C; Chor; Dbte Tm; Hmrm; Tres, NHS; Order/Arrow; Span C; SC; Bsbl; Bkbl; COM; Order/Arrow A; VofDEM; *Northeastern U; Chem Engr.*

LYDE, Ronald Kendrick
S Gate HS; Los Angeles, CA; Band; Drama; Ntl Yth Conf; Var C; Bsbl; Bkbl; Ftbl; Swim; COM; Cl Fav; Band A; Bkbl A; Scholastic Achv A; *Fullerton U; Religion.*

LYDON, Lori Jean
McKeesport Area Sr HS; McKeesport, PA; Bus C; Chor; Drama; Hmrm; Orch; Rainbow; Sch P; SC; Amer Leg A; COM; Yth Fel; Academic Games; ATP Schols A.

LYDON, Timothy Gerard
Pacific HS; San Leandro, CA (29-312) Cpt, Chess C; Chor; Math C; Sch P; SC; Soccer; Tnns; Hon Prog; Math A; *U of Calif; Aerospace Engr.*

LYERLY, Cynthia Lynn
Hickory HS; Hickory, NC; AFS; Fr C; French NHS; Mgr, Sftbl; COM; Yth Fel; Catechism A; Del, Reenactment, 2nd Contin Cong; *Med.*

LYGA, Andrew Mark
Terryville HS; Terryville, CT (30-158) Cr-Ctry; Cpt, Tnns; Tr; Wrest; *Manchester Comm Col; Respiratory Therapy.*

LYKES, Sonia Yvette
Inglewood HS; Inglewood, CA; Band; Cpt, Bkbl; Cpt, Sftbl; Cl Fav; Elk A; Cpt, Vlbl; Band A; MVP, Vlbl & Sftbl; *U of Sou Calif; Stenography.*

LYKINS, Patsy Irene
Marion HS; Marion, IN (28-706) NHS; Span C; Tres, Booster Bloc.

LYLE, Earl Kenneth
John F Kennedy HS; Richmond, CA (65-307) AFS; NFL; Rptr, Sch P; Parl, St Stu Congres; Cr-Ctry; Tr; CSF; *San Jose St Col; Pol Sci.*

LYLE, Julie Anne
Santa Monica HS; Santa Monica, CA; Chldr; Pres, Hmrm; Model UN; NHS; SC; Cpt, Ftbl; CSF; Citz A; United Methodist Women's Schol; Jesse Rodriguez A, Outst Sr; Comm of Girl's Actv, SC; *Calif St U; Psych.*

LYLE, Kermit Allen
Ahoskie HS; Ahoskie, NC (34-240) Hmrm; Order/Arrow; F-Ed, Sch P; Bsbl; Ftbl; Sftbl; Swim; COM; Citz A; Life Sct; *Atlantic Christian Col; Bus.*

LYLE, Margaret Ann
Mantachie HS; Mantachie, MS (33%-51) VP, CYO; Drama; FHA; ARC; Rptr, Sch P; Lib A; Sociology A; *Itawamba Jr Col; Nurs.*

LYLE, Marilee Anne
John F Kennedy HS; El Cerrito, CA; A Cap Choir; AFS; Chor; Drama; Ensm; Madrigal; NFL; NHS; CSF; COM; Chem A; Math A; Sci A; Spch A; Geom A.

LYLE, Mark DeWayne
MacArthur HS; San Antonio, TX (2-653) A Cap Choir; Drama; Pres, Hmrm; Math C; Sci C; Secy, Span C; Mgr, Bkbl; Ftbl; Alg A; COM; Citz A; Math A; Sci A; Spch A; Type A; Bowling Trophies; *San Antonio Jr Col; Data Processing.*

LYLE, Teresa Ann
Tecumseh HS; New Carlisle, OH (42-420) AFS; NHS; Var C; Tr; Concert & Marching Band; FCA; Campus Life; School Athlete A; *Sci.*

LYLES, Alana Ruth
Vanguard HS; Ocala, FL (16-350) FBLA; Mu Alpha Theta; NHS; Pres, Rainbow; 2nd Pl, FBLA Bus Communications; *Central Fla Comm Col; Bus.*

LYLES, Lawrence Alan
John F Kennedy HS; Richmond, VA (59-309) Community Yth Symph; Drama; VP, Orch; Span C; SC; *Madison Col; Mus.*

LYMAN, Donna Ann
Livermore Falls HS; Livermore Falls, ME (5-104) Chor; GS; Hmrm; SC; DARGCA; *Pepperdine U; Journ.*

LYMAN, Kent Marvin
San Juan HS; Blanding, UT (1-89) Pres, Band; BS; Chor; Pres, NHS; Math A; Val; Best All-Around Boy; John Philip Sousa Band A; *U of Utah; Mus.*

LYMAN, Sharon Kay
Oakland HS; Oakland, IA (24-49) Ann; Chor; Rainbow; Rptr, Sch P; Golf; Worthy Advisor, Rainbow Girls; *Nettleton Comm; Acct.*

LYMANSTALL, Ted Douglas
Tinora HS; Defiance, OH; Chor; Demolay; FFA; Pres, 4H; Var C; Bkbl; Cr-Ctry; 4H A; HCt.

LYMAS, Carla Rene
Sacramento HS; Sacramento, CA (176-376) Pres, A Cap Choir; Chldr; Secy, Chor; Secy, Ntl Yth Conf; Cpt, Bsbl; Cpt, Sftbl; COM; Chamber of Comm A; Citz A; Interlochen Ntl Mus; JA A; Jr Chamber of Com A; Most Out; Ntl Sch Chor A & Patches; Mus Bars; *Mus.*

LYNCH, Amanda Pauline
Greensville Co Sr HS; Emporia, VA (18-215) BC; Math C; Sci C; *Emory & Henry U; Archt Drafting.*

LYNCH, Barry Jack
Coosa HS; Rome, GA; JV, Bkbl; Ftbl; Tr.

LYNCH, Bobby Carroll
Monterey Sr HS; Lubbock, TX; Band; Chor; Mgr, Bkbl; Hon Prog; Church SC; Church Soph Rep; Church Choir; For Love of Children.

LYNCH, Bryan Edwin
Memorial Sr HS; Houston, TX; Hmrm; Order/Arrow; JV, Tr; Citz A; Order/Arrow A; Eagle Sct A; *Tex A&M U; Engr.*

LYNCH, Byron Claude
Episcopal Sr HS; Baton Rouge, LA (20-75) BC; Key C; Lat C; Bkbl; Cr-Ctry; Swim; Tr; *Engr.*

LYNCH, David Harry
Hart HS; Hart, MI (1-145) Band; Bus Mgr, Drama; NFL; NHS; Ski C; Pres, SC; Thes; Mgr, Bsbl; Mgr, Bkbl; Golf; NMS; Pres, UCC Sr HS Group; BSct; Pep Band; Del, Annual Meeting UCC; Academic Workshop; Citz Seminar; *Law.*

LYNCH, Gregory Alvin
Lindbergh Sr HS; Crestwood, MO (25%-1015) A Cap Choir; Lat C; Orch; Swim; *U of Mo; Mech Engr.*

LYNCH, Helen Ann
Southmoreland Sr HS; Alverton, PA; *Pitt Col; Nurs.*

LYNCH, Ian Robert
Altoona Area HS; Altoona, PA; Band; Chor; Ch, Order/Arrow; NEDT; *Clergy.*

LYNCH, Jack Dowell
T C Williams Sr HS; Alexandria, VA (390-885) Bus Mgr, Lit Mag; Secy, Order/Arrow; Mgr, Bsbl; Order/Arrow A; Pres, Yth Coun; Life Sct; WW; *Engr.*

LYNCH, Jean Ann
Notre Dame HS; Clarksburg, WV (7-52) Ann; Band; Chor; Drama; Key C; NHS; Bkbl; *W Va U; Dietetics.*

LYNCH, Julie Anne
Joel E Ferris HS; Spokane, WA (100-430) S-T, Chor; Dbte Tm; Drama; *U of Wash; Law.*

LYNCH, Lisa Linfield
Episcopal HS; Baton Rouge, LA (8-70) BC; Lat C; Sch P; Thes; Swim; Tnns; ROTC A; Sci A; Vlbl; Geo A; Civics A; Drama A; *Sweet Briar Col; Eng.*

LYNCH, Machelle Jean
Valley HS; Sanders, AZ (10-50) Ann; JV, Chldr; FHA; *NAU.*

LYNCH, Marvin Woodrow
W Florence HS; Florence, SC (10%-250) BC; Pres, InterClub Coun; VP, Key C; VP, SC; Co-Cpt, Bkbl; Tr; Hon Prog; *Pre-Dental.*

LYNCH, Mary Louise
Moreau HS; Hayward, CA (17-383) Chor; Hmrm; Bsbl; Bkbl; Cr-Ctry; General Excellence A; *Vet.*

LYNCH, Melissa Jane
Parkwood HS; Joplin, MO (1-412) AFS; Chor; ARC; Swim; Win, 9 Yrs, Ntl Piano Guild; *Kans U; Sci.*

LYNCH, Michael John
Troy HS; Troy, TX (18-49) Ann; Pres, Band; BC; BS; Ensm; Tres, FFA; Co-Ed, Sch P; Span C; Spch C; Pres, SC; JV, Bkbl; Co-Cpt, Ftbl; Tnns; Tr; Amer Leg A; COM; PTA A; Sci A; Dist Band; Dist Champ, Tnns; Mr THS; WW; All Dist, Ftbl; *Tarleton St U; Landscape Archt.*

LYNCH, Ramona Marie
Darby Township HS; Glenoden, PA; Band; Chor; Fr C; Hmrm; Sch P; SC; Yth Fel; Driver Ed A; Dist Play; *Lancaster General Hospital; Nurs.*

LYNCH, Rosalynn
Berkner HS; Richardson, TX (14-595) FTA; COM; Hon Prog; PTA A; Outst Bible Quizzer o-t Yr; *Bethany Nazarene Col; Psych.*

LYNCH, Steve Allen
Bulloch Acad; Statesboro, GA (1-10) Ann; BC; 4H; VP, SC; Var C; Bkbl; Ftbl; Tr; 4H A; *Sci.*

LYNCH, Thomas Francis
Edison HS; Minneapolis, MN (1-550) Band; CYO; Chess C; Cpt, Dbte Tm; Fr C; K of C; NFL; VP, NHS; Cpt, Spch C; St Stu Congress; Bkbl; Cr-Ctry; Golf; Amer Leg Orator A; Hon Prog; Cpt A; Spch A; VFW Orator Win; VofDEM; St Stu Congress A; All City Band A; Outst Spch A; *US Military Acad; Law.*

LYNCH, Timothy Marvin
Bayless Sch; St Louis, MO (33%-165) Hmrm; SC; Mgr, Bkbl; Mgr, Tr; *U of Mo; Chem Engr.*

LYNCH, Zoe Lynne
Nova HS; Ft Lauderdale, FL (41-466) Chor; French NHS; NHS; Yth Fel; Teacher Aide; Bible Quiz Tm; Sunday Sch Teacher; NYI; Health Aide Prog; Missionary Soc; *Trevecca Nazarene Col/ Ed.*

LYND, Elizabeth Atkins
Shawnee Mission E HS; Prairie Village, KS (34-569) A Cap Choir; Chor; Community Yth Symph; Ensm; NHS; Orch; Span C; SC; Tres, Jr Cl; COM; Chem A; Ntl Achv Schol; Sci A; Diving Tm; Vlbl; Mus A's; *Sci.*

LYNG, Nancy Joanne
Central Valley HS; Buxton, ND (4-33) Ann; Band; Chor; Ensm; FHA; Pres, 4H; Mod Mus Mas; Sch P; 4H A; Journ A; Spch A; *Mayville St Col; Elem Ed.*

LYNN, Gloria
South Fork Comm HS; Kincaid, IL (49-50) Band; Church Pianist; Band Accompanist; 'A' C; Stu Acad Achv.

LYNN, Kimberly Kay
Manchester HS; Manchester, OH (33-99) Chor; 4H; Span C; Bkbl; Sftbl; Most Ath; *Phys.*

LYNN, Laurie Jean
Wallace HS; Wallace, IA (22-101) Band; Chor; Drama; FHA; Rainbow; Ski C; MVP; Tr; Beauty; Citz A; Lion A; Yth Fel; Jazz Band; WW; Vlbl; Superior, Mus Festival; Worthy Advisor, Rainbow Girls; *U of Idaho; Mus.*

LYNN, Robert Lee
Virden HS; Virden, IL (33-110) All Amer Yth; Band; Chor; FFA; Sci C; Sci A; *Paducak Comm Col; Sci.*

LYNNE, Shari Phyllis
Hightstown HS; Hightstown, NJ (25%-250) Band; FHA; French NHS; FTA; Pres, 4H; Hmrm; Cpt, Mjrte; NHS; Span C; SC; Citz A; 4H A; Lion A; *Fairleigh Dickinson U; Bus.*

LYON, Barbara Ann
Clear Creek HS; Kewah, TX (25-460) Drama; GS; Hmrm; Lit Mag; NHS; Ski C; S-T, SC; Thes; Sftbl; Beauty; Cl Fav; HCt; Yth Leg; Co-Cpt, Vlbl; All-Dist Vlbl Tm; HR; WW.

LYON, Connie Elaine
Portsmouth HS; Portsmouth, OH (68-263) Ann; Chor; Pres, Drama; Ensm; Lat C; Co-Ed, Sch P; Span C; SC; Journ A; Q&S A; Superior, St & Ensm Mus Camp; Talents for Christ; Stu Director, Sch Mus; Amer Hist Schol Tm; *Holzer Sch of Nurs; Nurs.*

LYON, Diann Kay
United Township HS; E Moline, IL (76-700) Band; Pres, 4H; Span C; COM; 4H A; Hon Prog; Most Out; Spch A; 4-H Key C; *Meteorology.*

LYON, Karl Victor
W Columbus HS; Cerro Gordo, NC (20-350) FFA; Hmrm; Span C; Bsbl; Golf; Order/Arrow A; RA Achv Pins; *Mars Hill Col; Law Enforcement.*

LYON, Kenneth William
Rio Linda Sr HS; Rio Linda, CA (10%-292) Chor; AR; *Elec Engr.*

LYON, Leland Earl
Doyle HS; Knoxville, TN (25%-350) S-T, HiY; Pol Sci C; Ed, Sch P; COM; WW; *Carson-Newman Col; Ministerial.*

LYON, Sande Jean
Hamburg Sr HS; Hamburg, NY (10%-500) AFS; Fr C; Pres, Hmrm; Lat C; Orch; SC; Secy, Soph Cl; Hockey; Sftbl; Hon Prog; Sci A; Cpt, Vlbl; Industrial Arts A; W NY Sci Congress; All Star, Sftbl; *Math.*

LYON, Sara Catherine
Sheffield HS; Memphis, TN (10-160) Pres, FHA; Hmrm; NHS; Sch P; Secy, SC; Tr; *MSU; Home Ec.*

LYON, Sara Jean
Gale-Ettrick-Trempealeau HS; Galesville, WI (16-140) Secy, Band; Chor; Drama; Ensm; Pres, 4H; Madrigal; NHS; Sci C; Secy, Sr Cl; Secy, Jr Cl; Secy, Soph Cl; Tr; 4H A; Lion A; *Hamline U; Environmental Stu.*

LYON, Suzanne Lee
University HS; Irvine, CA; Band; Co-Cpt, Chldr; 4H; Hmrm; Swim; Co- cpt, V Songleader; Prom Committee; Gym; Prom Court Fin; *UCLA; Nurs.*

LYONS, Adrian Dewizz
Dunbar Sr HS; Washington, DC (10%-502) Hon Prog; *Howard U; Archt Drafting.*

LYONS, Arnella Louise
Covington HS; Covington, TN (17-195) A Cap Choir; Drama; *Nurs.*

LYONS, Beatrice Laverne
Westside HS; Augusta, GA; Band; Chor; Bkbl; Sftbl; Tr; Top Underclassman; *Augusta Col; Oceanography.*

LYONS, Calvin LaMarr
Emerson HS; Gary, IN (1-222) BS; Chess C; Fr C; Pres, NHS; Up Bound; Mgr, Bkbl; Ftbl; Tr; Alg A; Bio A; Chem A; Hon Prog; Math A; Sci A; Type A; Val; Eng A; *Purdue U; Bus Mgr.*

LYONS, Cassandra Jean
Northwest HS; St Louis, MO (18-433) *Mizzou Col; Lib Sci.*

LYONS, Kathleen Kay
Paradise HS; Paradise, CA (40-238) Hmrm; SC; Beauty; CSF; HQn; ARC A; Type A; Yth Fel; Yth Choir; Piano As; Yth Staff; *Col of Idaho; Humanities.*

LYONS, Kathryn Sue
Moreau HS; Hayward, CA (25-383) Chldr; Fr C; VP, 4H; Ski C; Cr-Ctry; Tr; Alg A; COM; 4H A; Hon Prog; Math A; *UC at Berkely.*

LYONS, Lillie Vanessa
Weldon HS; Weldon, NC (5-125) AFS; Ann; FBLA; FHA; Hmrm; Math C; Sci C; SC; Bkbl; Sci A; Most Ambitious; Home Ec A; Varsity Ltr, Bkbl; DAHSS; *Howard U; Psych.*

LYONS, Lisa Marie
Washington Jr Sr HS; Washington, PA (12-230) Band; Secy, Fr C; Mjrte; Orch; S-T, Rainbow; Secy, SC; Y-Tns; Secy, Band Coun; Campus Life; Stu UN; Co Band Hon; S-T, Project '81'; Pres, MYF; *Med.*

LYONS, Mary Margaret
West HS; West, TX (25%-130) CYO; Chldr; Chem C; Chess C; Drama; FHA; FTA; Math C; NHS; Sch P; Fin, HQn; *Baylor U; Math.*

LYONS, Nancy Maureen
Mercy HS; Albany, NY (13-108) CYO; Fr C; Hmrm; Sci C; NEDT; Regent Schol; Type A; *Plattsburgh St Col; Child-Family Service.*

LYONS, Natolyn Joyce
Maggie L Walker HS; Richmond, VA (10%-222) Chldr; Tres, Commercial C; Pres, Hmrm; Key C; Tres, Sr Cl; Tnns; Hist A.

LYONS, Pamela June
Gainesville HS; Gainesville, TX (25-250) Bus C; Chem C; Chor; *Tex Women's U; Lib Sci.*

LYONS, Pamela Sue
Franklin Comm HS; Franklin, IN; Chor; FHA; Tri-HiY; *Saint Mary's Col; Bus.*

LYONS, Sandra Ann
Glenn Hill HS; Augusta, GA (30%-340) BC; Chor; Mjrte; ARC; *Albany St Col; Nurs.*

LYONS, Shawn Jeffrey
Robinson Secondary Sch; Fairfax, VA (18-469) NHS; VP, Sr Cl; Co-Cpt, Ftbl; Citz A; Gov Honor Prog; MLS; NMS; Booster C Ftbl A; *Bio.*

LYONS, Stacy Lynne
Hammond Hills Baptist HS; Memphis, TN; Ann; Chldr; Chess C; Drama; Ensm; Fr C; Spch A; Yth Fel; *Liberty Baptist Col; Yth Work.*

LYONS, Thomas Robert III
John T Hoggard HS; Wilmington, NC; Chor; Ensm; Hmrm; Key C; Order/Arrow; Ftbl; JV, Tr; Order/Arrow A; Yth Fel; *NC St U; Bio.*

LYONS, Tonya Lea
Gainesville Comm HS; Gainesville, TX (10%-250) Chor; NHS; Schol A; *U of Tex; Mus.*

LYSDAHL, Holly Joyce
Anoka Sr HS; Anoka, MN (10%-926) Orch; Ski C; *Sci.*

LYSTER, Christopher Guy
Goddard HS; Roswell, NM (16-300) BS; Chess C; Drama; InterClub Coun; NHS; Sci C; Spch C; Wrest; Amer Leg Orator A; Kiwanis A; Sci A; VFW Orator Win; VofDEM; DECA Stu of Yr; *Marketing.*

LYTEL, Bernice Arlene
Bellflower Township HS; Bellflower, IL (6-20) Ann; VP, Band; Pres, FHA; SC; Var C; Sftbl; Tr; Ntl Achv Schol; Pres A; Outst, Lib; Friendliest; *Oakland City Col; Elem Ed.*

LYTEL, Brenda Kay
Bellflower HS Dist 311; Bellflower, IL (7-15) Ann; Band; Chor; FHA; Ed, Sch P; Pres, Span C; S-T, SC; Sftbl; Tr; Citz A; Schol A; Alt, GS; *Social Work.*

LYTLE, Robert Edward
J E B Stuart HS; Falls Church, VA (100-500) Chor; NHS; Ftbl; Cpt, Tr; Most Ath; *VPI; Civil Engr.*

LYTLE, Robert Edwart
J E B Stuart HS; Falls Church, VA (100-500) Chor; NHS; Ftbl; Cpt, Tr; Most Ath; *VPI; Civil Engr.*

LYTLE, Roberta Louise
Francis Lewis HS; St Albans, NY (90-500) Band; Orch; COM; Hon Prog; Yth Fel; Sunday Sch A's; *St John U; Nurs.*

LYTTON, Katherine Ann
Princeton HS; Princeton, WV (28-280) NHS; Span C; GAA; WW; Pep C; Co Cpt, Pom Pon; Ch, Sr UMYF; *Concord Col; Acct.*

LYTTON, Sally Jane
Bridgeport HS; Bridgeport, OH; Band; Sci C; Span C; SC; Y-Tns; Span A.

M

MAAKESTAD, Kelly Jean
Fairmont Sr HS; Fairmont, MN (76-199) Secy, Band; Chldr; Chor; Ger C; Hmrm; Mjrte; SC; Secy, Jr Cl; Secy, Soph Cl; HCt; *St Cloud U; Ed.*

MABON, Lois Jane
Laurel Valley Jr Sr HS; New Florence, PA (6-126) AFS; Band; Bus C; Chess C; Chor; FBLA; Ed, Sch P; Tnns; Hon Prog; Type A; DAR A; 2nd Pl, St Typing.

MABREY, Dana Carol
Southland HS; Arbyrd, MO (2-38) F-Ed, Ann; Chldr; FHA; FTA; VP, NHS; Co-Ed, Sch P; Cl Fav; HCt; Sal; *Cape Girardeu Col; Dietetics.*

MABRY, Jonathan Blum
Henry Clay HS; Lexington, KY; Band; Drama; Span C; Span NHS; Soccer; Swim; *Anthropology.*

MACADANGDANG, Agnes Premia
Henry Perrine Baldwin HS; Wailuku, HI (16-317) Band; NHS; Spch C; VP, SC; Jr Prom Court; Aloha C; SCHWA Soc.

MACARIO, Belkis Valerio
Academia Santa Monica; Santurce, PR; Ann; CYO; VP, SC; Bio A; COM; *Colegio Regional de Carolina; Phys Therapy.*

MacARTHUR, Beth Ann
Point Pleasant Boro HS; Point Pleasant, NJ (25%-309) COM; Yth Fel; Sanamic C; *Drew U; Secy.*

MacARTHUR, Thomas Raymond
Point Pleasant Borough HS; Point Pleasant, NJ (20%-291) Band; Chess C; Cpt, Soccer; COM; God & Country A; Yth Fel; Glenn Palen Mem A; Weblos Achv A; BSct; *Construction-Engr.*

Mac BAIN, Allison Elizabeth
Adlai E Stevenson HS; New York, NY; *Pre-Law.*

MacBAIN, Robbin Elizabeth
Adlai E Stevenson HS; New York, NY (46-814) Band; Orch; *Queens Col; Mus.*

Mac BAIN, Robbin Elizabeth
Adlai E Stevenson HS; New York, NY (46-788) Pres, All Amer Yth; Band; Ensm; Orch; *Queen's Col; Mus.*

MACBETH, Scott Edward
Tecumseh Sr HS; Tecumseh, MI (24-276) Bkbl; Golf; *Hope Col; Bus Adm.*

MACCHIAROLI, Lea Velia
MacDuffie Sch; Springfield, MA (3-13) Drama; Fr C; Key C; Ski C; Tnns; Hon Prog; Ecology, Photography, Crafts, C'S; Ski Tm; Am As of Tchrs of Fr Ntl Contest; *Med.*

MacCOLL, Katherine June
Springbrook HS; Silver Spring, MD (10%-619) Ch, NHS; Sci C; Cpt, Hockey; Bkbl Trainer; VP, Stu Trainer Assn; Varsity Ltr; Church Yth Drama; NCTE Writing As; Church Choir; *U of Md; Horticulture.*

MacCORMACK, Steven Eliot
Lansing Baptist HS; Lansing, MI (1-3) Ed, Ann; Band; Chor; Ensm; 4H; Hmrm; Orch; Pres, SC; Pres, Sr Cl; VP, Jr Cl; Co-Cpt, Bkbl; Soccer; Fin, Wrest; DARGCA; Marines Phys Fitness A; *Hyles-Anderson Col; Pastoral.*

MacCORMACK, Valerie Ann
Lansing Baptist Sch; Lansing, MI (1-9) A-Ed, Ann; Co-Cpt, Chldr; S-T, SC; S-T, Soph Cl; Math A; Eng A; *Hyles Anderson Col; Missions.*

MacCOY, Bruce Robert
Carlmont HS; Belmont, CA (125-400) Chess C; Fr C; Math C; Order/Arrow; ARC; God & Country A; United Methodist Dist Yth Coun; Eagle Sct; *Col of San Mateo; Wildlife Management.*

MacDONALD, Cheryl Jeanne
E Brunswick HS; E Brunswick, NJ (30%-700) Swim; Pres, Protestant Yth Organization; *Middlesex Co Col; Early Childhood Ed.*

MacDONALD, Denise Gail
George Washington HS; Philadelphia, PA (12-1000) Secy, Band; Chor; Community Yth Symph; Ensm; Math C; Mu Alpha Theta; NHS; Secy, Orch; SC; COM; Math A; NMF; WW; *VPI; Forestry.*

MacDONALD, Elizabeth Annice
Franklin Co HS; Frankfort, KY; Drama; Fr C; ARC; Spch C; 4H A.

MacDONALD, Gary Bruce
Burncoat Sr HS; Worcester, MA; SC; Pres, Church Yth Fel; *Westfield St Col; Journ.*

MACDONALD, Kimberly Sue
Nordonia Hills HS; Macedonia, OH (3-439) Band; Drama; Ensm; NHS; Alg A; Citz A; Hist A; Hon Prog; Math A; Sci A; Yth Fel; Drill Tm; Intra-Amer Stu Found; Geom A; *Med Tech.*

MacDONALD, Marilyn Sarah
Alexander Galt Regional HS; Lennoxville, CANADA (2-477) Band; Hon Prog; Type A; ISCF; MSD A; Excel A.

MacDONALD, Pamela Denise
Eastside HS; Paterson, NJ; Band; MVP, Bsbl; MVP, Sftbl; Phy A; Mod Dance A; *Air Passenger Services.*

MacDOUGALL, Carla Jean
Brockton HS; Brockton, MA (415-1500) Yth Fel; Sun Sch Teacher; Deacon; *Waynesburg Col; Secondary Ed.*

MACEK, Richard Joseph
St Andrew HS; Detroit, MI (2-82) Pres, NHS; Cpt, SC; Var C; Co-Cpt, Bkbl; Cr-Crty; Ftbl; COM; Citz A; Hist A; HCt; Hon Prog; Math A; MLS; Most Out; Sal; Sanctuary Soc; PA; 4-Yr Hon Stu; Police Dept Yth A; Acct A; *U of Detroit; Elec Engr.*

MACEMON, Cynthia Ann
Hutchinson HS; Hutchinson, MN; AFS; Ski C; Span C; SC; Golf; Swim; *Luther Col; Nurs.*

MACEMON, David John
Woodford Co HS; Versailles, KY (10-250) Ann; Band; BC; Chor; Drama; Fr C; 4H; NHS; Order/Arrow; Sch P; Hist A; *U of Ky; Elec Engr.*

MacEWEN, Rebecca Jean
Towson Sr HS; Towson, MD (20%-578) Band; Fr C; GScts; Hospital Vol; Band Ltr & Pin; *UMBC; Pre-Med.*

MacGILVRA, Sara Davies
Washington HS; Fremont, CA (40-462) Band; Tr; CSF; HR; *Humboldt Col; Forestry.*

MACH, Lyle David
Prague HS; Prague, NE (33%-19) Band; Chor; Tres, FFA; Var C; JV, Bkbl; Ftbl; Tr.

MACH, Roger Allan
Prague HS; Prague, NE (33%-19) Band; VP, FFA; NHS; Var C; Bkbl; Ftbl; Tr; Hon Prog; I Dare You; *U of Nebr; Bus Adm.*

MACH, Steven Donald
St Joseph HS; St Joseph, MI (30-375) A Cap Choir; Chor; Drama; Math C; NHS; Sci C; Span C; Thes; NMS; Rotary A; St Scholar; Hon Graduate; Art A; Art Show A's; *W Mich U; Commercial Art.*

MACHA, Carolyn Ann
E Bernard HS; East Bernard, TX (1-60) Band; CYO; Commercial C; Drama; Ensm; FHA; FTA; JETS; Math C; Model UN; NHS; Sch P; Sci C; Tnns; Alg A; B Crocker A; NMS; Val; Sci Sym; *Tex A&M U; Acct.*

MACHADO, Mayra
Francisco Mendoza HS; Isabela, PR; FHA; Cpt, Bkbl; Sftbl; Cpt, Vlbl; Highest Hon; *Col of Agr & Mech Arts; Ed.*

MACHADO, Ricardo
Francisco Mendoza HS; Isabela, PR; Drama; Parl, FFA; Tr; Hon Prog; Spch A; Oratory A; *Col of Agr & Mech Art; Med.*

MACHADO, Rolando
Francisco Mendoza HS; Isabela, PR; 4H; Chem A; Hist A; *U of PR; Politics.*

MACHADO, Soraya Gina
Rainbow City HS; Rainbow City, CANAL ZONE; Band; Secy, CYO; Chldr; Chor; Dbte Tm; Drama; COM; Spch A; Chor; Declamatory A; *Pepperdine U; Sci.*

MACHAN, Jason Paul
Liggett Sch; Grosse Pointe Woods, MI (3-77) Cum Laude Soc; Pres, Sci C; Soccer; Tr; NMF; Rensselaer A; *Rensselaer Polytechnic Inst; Phys.*

MACHART, Jill Marie
Erskine Pub Sch; Erskine, MN (4-20) Ed, Ann; Band; JV, Chldr; Chor; Drama; Hmrm; NHS; Sch P; Spch C; S-T, Jr Cl; VP, Soph Cl; Bkbl; Tr; 4H A; Hon Prog; Best Actress, Sch & Sub-Dist; *U of ND; Social Work.*

MACHEN, Michael James
Winnfield Sr HS; Winnfield, LA; Anchor C; BC; Spch C; SC; *La Tech Col; Civil Engr.*

MACHORRO, Ernestina
Castle Park HS; Chula Vista, CA; Chldr; GS; Hmrm; InterClub Coun; St Stu Congress; SC; Amer Leg A; CSF; COM; Citz A; DARGCA; Most Out; Span A; *UC at San Diego; Social Sci.*

MACIAS, Inez Marie
Benjamin Franklin HS; Los Angeles, CA (12%-600) Band; CYO; Community Yth Symph; Ensm; Key C; Orch; Secy, Sr Cl; Bank Of Amer A; Marian Medal; *UCLA; Special Ed.*

MacINNES, Barbara Kay
Denfeld HS; Duluth, MN; Hon Prog; Yth Fel; *Med Inst of Minn; Vet Med.*

MacINTYRE, Craig Robert
Conard HS; West Hartford, CT (148-461) Chor; Demolay; DeMolay Ldrship A; *Vermont Col; Math.*

MacIVER, Mark David
Southfield-Lathrup HS; Lathrup Village, MI (262-605) Ski C; Cr-Crty; Hockey; JV, Tnns; Tr; Citz A; Yth Fel; Outst Industrial Arts Stu; *Ferris St Col; Dental Tech.*

MacIVER, Paul Donald
Southfield-Lathrup HS; Lathrup Village, MI (61-605) Co-Cpt, Hockey; JV, Tnns; Hon Prog; NMF; Secy, Yth Fel; *Ohio Wesleyan U; Pre-Dentistry.*

MACK, Antoinette
Murray Wright HS; Detroit, MI; FBLA; Hmrm; Sch P; SC; Up Bound; Var C; Citz A; JA A; Ntl Achv Schol; Val; Hockey Tm A; Gourmet Cooking A; *U of Mich; Pre-Med.*

MACK, Barbara Ann
Marion HS; Marion, IN (146-674) Chor; NHS; Sch P; Vocis; GAA; Secy, Yth Group; *Marion Col; Eng.*

MACK, Byron
Francis Lewis HS; Flushing, NY; A Cap Choir; All Amer Yth; Band; Chor; Drama; Ntl Yth Conf; Orch; Swim; Tr; COM; Citz A; Most Out; Spch A; Yth Fel; Yth Foundation; St John's Schol Prog; *Fla St U; Mus.*

MACK, Carey P
Grossmont HS; LaMesa, CA (25%-750) Bsbl; JV, Bkbl; *San Diego St U; Bus.*

MACK, Cheryl Lynn
Southside HS; Greenville, SC; Secy, CYO; Chor; Pres, Hmrm; VP, SC; Bkbl; Tr; Amer Leg A; Cert of Appreciation; CCD Teacher-Aide; Tr & Intramurals Certs; *Mus.*

MACK, Chris Alan
Plano Sr HS; Plano, TX (5%-1080) Band; NHS; Order/Arrow; *U of Mich; Chem.*

MACK, Eric Lawrence
Halter HS; St Louis, MO (4-110) Chor; Hmrm; NHS; Ntl Yth Conf; SC; Var C; Cpt, Bkbl; Hon Prog; *Alcorn U; Natural Sci.*

MACK, Jack Lee
Kenmore W HS; Kenmore, NY; *Paramedics.*

MACK, Jackie Kay
Leola Ind HS; Leola, SD (1-43) Ann; Band; Chor; Ensm; FBLA; FHA; Madrigal; Sch P; Hon Prog; Most Out; Type A; Fresh Schol.

MACK, James Gavin
Glendale HS; Springfield, MO (12-418) A Cap Choir; Math C; Orch; Order/Arrow; COM; Curator A; Eagle Sct; *Drury Col; Pre-Med.*

MACK, Jeffery Edwin
Stephen F Austin Sr HS; Houston, TX (25%-500) FFA; *U of Houston; Law.*

MACK, Joyce Eunice
Burke HS; Charleston, SC (1-177) Pres, NHS; MLS; Val; *Math.*

MACK, Julie Marie
Vines HS; Plano, TX (25%-700) Span C; *Rochester Inst of Tech; Photography.*

MACK, Kyle Donald
St Mary's Central HS; Bismarck, ND (15-177) Pres, Band; BS; CYO; Chor; Ensm; Var C; Bsbl; Bkbl; JV, Ftbl; Cpt, Hockey; JV; Tr; Amer Leg A; Elk A; All St, Tri-St, Bands; Alt, Boy's Nation; Ntl As of Jazz Educator Outst Mus A; *Dickinson St Col; Mus.*

MACK, Marcia Kay
Leola HS; Leola, SD (50%-47) Ed, Ann; Band; Tres, Bus C; CYO; FBLA; 4H; Sch P; Co-Cpt, Bkbl; MVP, Tr; Journ A; *Northern St; Acct.*

MACK, Michael Fredrick
Forest Brook Sr HS; Houston, TX; Band; Hmrm; Key C; Bsbl; Cpt, Bkbl; Ftbl; *Kansas Wesleyan Col; Religion.*

MACK, Pearline
Chicora HS; Charleston, SC (28-82) Y-Tns; Cpt, Bkbl; Cpt, Sftbl; Tr; HQn; *Baptist Col; Phys Ed.*

MACK, Rhonda Sue
Kalamazoo Seventh-Day Ad Jr Acad; Kalamazoo, MI; Fin, Hockey; Sftbl; Tr; *Mich St U; Vet Med.*

MACK, Sherri Kay
Marion HS; Marion, IN; Band; Chor; Drama; Unlimited Progress; *Taylor U.*

MACK, Thomas John
Secaucus HS; Secaucus, NJ (1-200) Sci C; Tr; Hon Prog; Bowl Tm; Jr NHS; *Princeton U; Biol Sci.*

MacKENZIE, Janet Sue
Grand Haven Sr HS; Grand Haven, MI (33%-477) Commercial C; Swim; Tr; ARC A; Pres, Calalina C; Candystriper; *Alma Col; Sci.*

MACKEY, Amy Luann
Robert E Lee HS; Tyler, TX (88-620) Band; Chem C; Fr C; Lit Mag; NHS; Hon Prog; NEDT; Opt C Yth Appreciation A; *Tyler Jr Col; Fashion Merchandising.*

MACKEY, Cheryl Ann
Albany HS; Albany, NY (180-1500) A Cap Choir; Chor; Hmrm; Var C; Sftbl; Tr; *Med.*

MACKEY, Cynthia Kay
Tivy HS; Kerrville, TX (50%-193) FHA; ARC; Mgr, Bkbl; Drill Tm; FCA; GSct; *SW Tex Col.*

MACKEY, Janet Beth
Waukegan HS; Waukegan, IL (162-453) Chldr; Ski C; Thes; Y-Tns; Ath A; Gym; *Ill St U; Special Ed.*

MACKEY, Jennifer Rose
Seymour HS; Seymour, MO (66%-63) Band; Chess C; Demolay; FHA; Bkbl; Sftbl; COM; Swtht; Mus A; FHA A; *SMSU; Mus.*

MACKEY, Martha Ann
Tivy HS; Kerrville, TX (9-284) FHA; NHS; SC; Secy, Var C; Bkbl; Tr; COM; DARGCA; GSct; Cpt, All Dist, Vlbl; Drill Tm; Secy, FCA; Tr Regionals; *U of Tex; Pre-Law.*

MACKEY, Melinda Ann
Jackson HS; Jackson, GA (20%-140) JV, Chldr; Parl, FBLA; GS; Pres, HiY; Hmrm; SC; Secy, Sr Cl; JA A; Kiwanis A; Swtht; Type A; *Gordon Jr Col; Core Courses.*

MACKEY, Nancy Lynne
Central U S D 462 HS; Burden, KS (3-48) Ann; VP, Band; Chldr; VP, 4H; S-T, NHS; Pres, Jr Cl; 4H A; Hist A; *Cowley Co Comm Jr Col; Bus.*

MACKEY, Stephen Wiley
Marvell HS; Marvell, AR (3-151) BC; Cl Fav; Sci A; Eng, Civics, Band A's.

MACKIE, Scot Dennis
Palestine HS; Palestine, TX (25%-234) A Cap Choir; Band; Chor; Co-Ch, Drama; Ensm; Fr C; Parl, Ger C; Hmrm; Madrigal; Orch; Thes; Best Actor; All Star Cast; All Region Choir; *Baylor U; Mus.*

MACKINTOSH, James Todd
Regis HS; Denver, CO (25-150) Ann; VP, CYO; Hmrm; Ed, Lit Mag; NHS; Ski C; SC; JV, Soccer; JV, Tr; *Trinity U; Eng.*

MACKLEY, James Fowler
Grand Junction HS; Grand Junction, CO (75-378) Ger C; NHS; Co-Ed, Game Prog Staff; Acad Schol; *Mesa Col; Acct.*

MACKLIN, Andre
Carver Sr HS; New Orleans, LA; SC; Bsbl; Ftbl; *UNO; Police Sci.*

MACKLIN, Cynthia Ann
St Mary's Acad; New Orleans, LA; Chor; ARC; SC; MVP, Bsbl; MVP, Sftbl; PA; *Sou U; Chem.*

MACKLIN, Joyce Marie
Cape Henlopen HS; Lewes, DE (41-250) AFS; Band; FNA; 4H; JV, Hockey; PA; Co Band; *Salisbury St Col; X-Ray Tech.*

MACKOWIAK, Anita Florence
Roseville HS; Roseville, MI (144-485) Rainbow; Ski C; Type A; *Concordia Col; Social Worker.*

MACKSEY, Susan Cabanne
Ojai Valley Sch; Ojai, CA; Drama; Soccer; Span A; Eng A; Poetry A; *Drama.*

MacLAUCHLAN, Susan Elaine
Piscataquis Comm HS; Guilford, ME (10%-81) Band; VP, Chor; Drama; NHS; *Boston Conservatory; Mus.*

MacLAUGHLIN, Susan Annette
Walnut Hills HS; Cincinnati, OH (20%-500) Band; Ger C; NHS; COM; Yth Coun; Yth Fel; MYF Jr HS Coun.

MacLEAN, Bradley Weir
Bentley HS; Livonia, MI (125-500) Chor; Drama; Hmrm; Ski C; Tr; Yth Fel; Pres, St Amer Baptist Yth Fel; Industrial Arts A; *U of Mich; Biomed Engr.*

MACLEAN, Catherine Marie
Noble Central Sch; Nobleford, CANADA (5-16) *Jamestown Col; Sci.*

MACLEAN, Isabelle Marguerite
Noble Central Sch; Nobleford, CANADA (2-28) Chor; Fr C; Co-Cpt, Bkbl; Tr; MVP, Bkbl; Acad A; All Star; *Col of Idaho; Ed.*

MacLEAN, Vicky Marie
Muscle Shoals HS; Muscle Shoals, AL; Anchor C; Chldr; Hmrm; InterClub Coun; Math C; Mu Alpha Theta; Span C; SC; Pres, Soph Cl; Tr; Presidential Phys Fitness A; *Samford U; Guidance Counselor.*

MacLEOD, Karen Elizabeth
Evanston Township HS; Evanston, IL (10%-950) Chor; Ensm; InterClub Coun; Madrigal; Bronze & Silver, Ntl Hebrew Coun; Cl Hebrew As; AP Eng; Special Recognition, Eng & Bio; Israeli Culture C; *AP Hist; Sociology.*

MacLEOD, Kenneth Robert
Aquinas HS; Augusta, GA (10%-130) Co-Ed, Ann; Dbte Tm; Drama; NHS; Sodality; Bkbl; NMF; Star Student; WW; *Ga Inst of Tech.*

MacLEOD, Kimberly Ileen
Weymouth N HS; Weymouth, MA (94-465) Ski C; Sftbl; Swim; Tnns; Tr; *U of Maine; Home Ec.*

MACLIN, Carolina
Proviso E HS; Maywood, IL (33-968) Orch; COM; Hon Prog; Yth Leg; Yth & Gov; Bronze Schol Medal; *Ill St U; Computer Sci.*

MacMAHON, Carolyn Leslie
San Lorenzo Valley HS; Felton, CA; Chldr; Key C; NHS; SC; Sftbl; Swim; Tnns; Hon Prog; *Cabrillo Col; Sci.*

MacMANNIS, Stephen Hall
Arlington Sr HS; Lagraneville, NY (20%-700) *Cornell U; Bio.*

MacMILLAN, Anne Meredith
Forest Hill HS; W Palm Beach, FL (8-501) A Cap Choir; Chor; Ensm; Madrigal; Secy, Soph Cl; Tnns; COM; Hon Prog; Exchange C; Sch Music; Civic Opera; Secy, Fresh Cl; Sch Production; President's Phys Fitness A; Outst Fresh Choral Stu; *Duke U; Med.*

MacMONEGLE, Jill Maureen
MacDuffie HS; Springfield, MA (3-45) A Cap Choir; Chor; Ensm; Ntl Sci Symposium; *Med.*

MacMURTRY, Peter William
Penney HS; E Hartford, CT; JV, Wrest; *Elec.*

MacNUTT, Alicia Ann
Clearwater HS; Clearwater, FL (60%-800) Chor; Drama; SC; Y-Tns; Bkbl; Swim; Tr; Beauty; MLS; Yth Fel; *Phys Therapy.*

MACON, Katherine Lynn
Southeast HS; Bradenton, FL (20-250) Chor; Ensm; Fr C; Pres, Lit Mag; Madrigal; Secy, Mod Mus Mas; *Manatee Jr Col; Mus.*

MACON, Marie Faith
Independence Jr Sr HS; Columbus, OH; Band; Fr C; Hmrm; Tnns; HR; Attendance A; Drill Tm; *Morehouse Col; Psych.*

MACON, Sharon Lynne
Robert E Lee HS; Baytown, TX (47-411) Band; French NHS; Math C; NHS; C Swtht; *Lee Col.*

MacPHAIL, Keith Thomas
Rhinebeck Central HS; Rhinebeck, NY (9-112) NHS; Tr; DAR A for Excellence; AAA Safe Drive A; *Marist Col; Bus Mgt.*

MACPHERSON, Pam M
Westfield HS; Westfield, NJ (143-669) Fr C; Pres, Y-Tns; Piano Stu; Church Choir; 1st Cl GSct; *Gettysburg Col; Bus.*

MacPHERSON, Pam M
Westfield Sr HS; Westfield, NJ (140-669) Fr C; Ski C; Pres, Y-Tns; Type A; Yth Fel; Church Choir; *Gettysburg Col; Bus Adm.*

MACRI, Jean Elizabeth
G A R HS; Wilkes-Barre, PA (8-179) Band; NHS; *Misericordia Col; Nurs.*

MACSHERRY, Clinton Kilty
Loyola HS; Towson, MD (7-134) NHS; NEDT; JV Lacrosse; WW; *Bowdoin Col; Eng.*

MacTAMMANY, Cheryl Elaine
Deerfield Beach HS; Deerfield Beach, FL; Band; Presidential Phys Fitness A; Band Medal; Marching Medal; Meritorious A; *Lee Col; Bible.*

MacWILLIAMS, Sandra Louise
Wilton-Lyndeboro Cooperative HS; Wilton, NH (10%-55) Ed, Ann; Drama; GS; NHS; Ed, Sch P; Journ A; WW; Amer Leg Auxilary; *U of NH; Social Work.*

MADARAS, Sally Ann
Lawrence HS; Lawrence, MI (14-54) Band; WW; *SW Mich Col; Chem Tech.*

MADDEN, Julie Lynn
Whitmer HS; Toledo, OH (195-900) Ann; Inter-Club Coun; Span C; Journ A; Q&S A; *Baptist Bible Col; Bus.*

MADDEN, Kenneth Wayne Jr
Waverly Central HS; Waverly, TN (25-204) Band; BC; 4H; Mu Alpha Theta; Span C; Bsbl; Bkbl; Ftbl; *Theology.*

MADDEN, Lora Lee
Parkwood HS; Joplin, MO; AFS; *Mo Sou Col; Math.*

MADDOX, Donna Rene
James F Byrnes HS; Duncan, SC (40%-227) Fr C; Co-Ch, InterAct C; Secy, Sci C; Span C; HCt; *Spartanburg Methodist Col; Early Childhood Ed.*

MADDOX, Elizabeth Dianne
Riverdale Joint Union HS; Riverdale, CA (10%-130) Chldr; FFA; 4H; Hmrm; SC; VP, Jr Cl; Pres, Soph Cl; Bkbl; Tnns; HCt; Cpt, Gym; FFA Star Greenhand; *Calif Polytech U; Dairy Sci.*

MADDOX, Gregory Houston
Central HS; Phenix City, AL (1-400) BC; Model UN; NHS; Ch, UN Council; Var C; MVP, Ftbl; Outst Young Amer; Darnell A.

MADDOX, Julia Anne
Riverdale Joint Union HS; Riverdale, CA (5-85) Cpt, Chldr; Tres, FFA; Fin, GS; Hmrm; Secy, SC; VP, Sr Cl; VP, Jr Cl; Rptr, Soph Cl; Tnns; Bank Of Amer A; CSF; MLS; MVP, Cpt, Gym; *Calif Polytech St U; Agr Bus Mgt.*

MADDOX, Kathryn Blair
W P Davidson HS; Mobile, AL; Fr C; Soccer; Hon Prog; NEDT; Yth Fel; Yth Leg; Civinettes; Candystriper; Secy, Yth SC; *U of Ala; Med.*

MADDOX, Kathryn Ruth
E Laurens HS; Dublin, GA (10%-90) Bus Mgr, BC; FBLA; FFA; Lit Ral; Bus Mgr, NHS; Bio A; Hist A; Math A; Sci A; Spch A; WW; Wittiest; Sr Superlative; PA; *Ga Sou Col; Psych.*

MADDOX, Mary Angeline
Fayette Co HS; Fayette, AL; FBLA; Scorekeeper, Tr; Ltr A; *Secy.*

MADDOX, Mavis LuAnn
Pleasant Grove HS; Pleasant Grove, AL (6-150) Cpt, Chldr; Chem C; Hmrm; VP, NHS; SC; MVP, Bkbl; Type A; Soccer; Dance C; Most Sch Spirit; WW; *U of Montevallo.*

MADDOX, Pamela Gail
Susan Miller Dorsey HS; Los Angeles, CA; Band; City Conf; Drama; Pres, Hmrm; Rptr, Sch P; Y-Tns; Cpt, Bsbl; Cpt, Bkbl; Co-Cpt, Sftbl; Swim; Tnns; Tr; Citz A; Cl Fav; Hon Prog; Journ A; Kiwanis A; Lion A; Opt Out Tn; Yth Fel; NAACP; Nitwit C, Outst Choir, A's; Word of Mouth Film Soc; *W Point Military Acad; Law Enforcement.*

MADDOX, Teresa Ann
Geraldine HS; Geraldine, AL; Band; Chor; FTA; MVP, Bkbl; MVP, Sftbl; MVP, Swim; MVP, Tnns; *Med.*

MADDOX, William Andrew
Calhoun HS; Calhoun, GA (10%-300) Band; Chess C; Chor; Dbte Tm; Fr C; Pres, HiY; Hmrm; Key C; NHS; St Stu Congress; SC; Thes; Tnns; Gov Honor Prog; Boy's Quartet, Lit Region & St; Boy's Solo, Region; *Baylor U; Law.*

MADDUX, Melinda Marie
Springfield HS; Springfield, OR (20-350) A-Ed, Ann; Band; Chor; Ensm; A-Ed, Sch P; Rptr, SC; COM; Journ A; Mus A; WW; *Pacific U; Mus.*

MADDUX, Robert Alfred
W Memphis Sr HS; W Memphis, AR; Band; BC; Lat C; Citz A; Sci A; Regional Sci Symp; *Memphis St U; Television Production.*

MADER, Lori Alisa
Los Altos HS; Hacienda Heights, CA (10%-600) Band; Hmrm; CSF; Hon Prog; Outst, Concert Band; *Ed.*

MADER, Tynie Lyn
Carter Co HS; Ekalaka, MT (4-28) Ann; Band; Chldr; Chor; GS; 4H; NHS; Sch P; Bkbl; Amer Leg A; 4H A; *Mont St U; Acct.*

MADERA, Angel Francisco
Central HS; Santurce, PR (10-300) Ann; CYO; Chess C; Hmrm; Bkbl; Bio A; Chem A; *U of Puerto Rico; Chem.*

MADERA, Jaime
Yauco HS; Yauco, PR; Bsbl; Bkbl; *Jamestown Col; Acct.*

MADERE, Kim Ann
Destrehan HS; Destrehan, LA (4-150) BC; Key C; SC; COM; Gov Honor Prog; Mgr, Vlbl; *LSU; Public Relations.*

MADILL, Julie Bliss
Briarcliff HS; Atlanta, GA (20-263) Span C; Span NHS; Drill Tm; *U of Ga; Art.*

MADISON, Brenda Lynn
Matthew Fontaine Maury HS; Norfolk, VA (19-388) FBLA; NHS; Span C; NMS; *Old Dominion U; Astronomy.*

MADISON, Geoffrey Craig
Palmdale HS; Palmdale, CA (20-400) BS; Inter-Club Coun; Ed, Sch P; Tres, SC; Bank Of Amer A; CSF; Hon Prog; Journ A; Lion A; Opt A; Spch A; VFW A; VFW Orator Win; VofDEM; *U of Mo; Journ.*

MADISON, Joe Louis
Manley HS; Chicago, IL (10-219) Tres, Bus C; Chess C; FBLA; NHS; Bkbl; Tr; Citz A; Math A; Bkbl Ltr; Chess A; Checker A; Tr A; *Eastern Ill U; Bus Adm.*

MADISON, Nanette Virginia
Cottonwood HS; Salt Lake City, UT (9-150) Fr C; Ger C; NHS; Co-Cpt, Swim; Tr; COM; Hon Prog; NEDT; Sr Princess, Job's Daughters; Secy, United Ministries Yth Coun; *Lewis & Clark Col; Ed.*

MADISON, Richard Kent Jr
Warren Co Sr HS; McMinnville, TN (4-423) Band; BS; Tres, Fr C; InterAct C; COM; Hon Prog; NHS, Pres, Interact C; Band, Concert, Sight Reading; Band Clinic; *U of Tenn; Elec Engr.*

MADISON, Teresa Gail
Matthew Fontaine Maury HS; Norfolk, VA (26-388) Secy, FBLA; Span NHS; *Old Dominion U.*

MADL, George Victor
John S Fine Sr HS; Nanticoke, PA (5-297) Var C; Bsbl; Bkbl; *Pa St U; Math.*

MADORE, Linda Joan Ann
R H A M HS; Hebron, CT; *Manchester Comm Col; Executive Secy.*

MADRAY, Terri Lynn
Wayne Co HS; Jesup, GA (20%-420) Ann; Bus C; *Brunswick Jr Col; Acct.*

MADRID, Edwina Helen
Saipointe Cath HS; Tucson, AZ (53-193) CYO; *U of Ariz; Nurs.*

MADRID, Joann Elizabeth
Clovis HS; Clovis, NM; Pres, 4H; HiY; VP, Span C; 4H A; Lieutenant, Drill Tm; VP, Church Group; Outst Girl A.

MADRIGAL, John Robert
Marie Sklodowska Curie HS; Chicago, IL (2-200) Band; Lat C; Lat NHS; NHS; Sci C; Span C; Span NHS; Ftbl; Hon Prog; Band, Span Hon Soc, A's; *US Air Force Acad; Aerospace.*

MADSEN, Paul Matthew
John F Kennedy Sr HS; Bloomington, MN; Band; Order/Arrow; Order/Arrow A; *U of Minn; Elec.*

MADSEN, Timothy Arthur
John F Kennedy HS; Bloomington, MN (21-668) Chess C; Phy A; 1st Pl, St HS Chess Tourn; *U of Minn; Elec Engr.*

MADURO NIEVES, Grisel Margarita
Juan Jose Alvarez HS; Hato Rey, PR (3-101) A Cap Choir; Drama; FHA; FTA; Hmrm; ARC; Sch P; Span NHS; Swim; Tnns; Alg A; COM; Cl Fav; Hist A; Hon Prog; Math A; Spch A; High Hon; *U of PR; Literature Lit.*

MAE, Robert Martin Takashi
Waialua Intermediate HS; Waialua Oahu, HI (79-209) Mgr, Tr; *Lee Ward Comm Col.*

MAEDCHE, Kathleen Diane
Hebron Pub Sch; Hebron, ND (17-33) Ann; Fin, Band; Cpt, Chldr; Chor; Drama; Ensm; FHA; GS; 4H; NHS; Pres, Rainbow; Rptr, Sch P; Var C; Tr; Amer Leg; K of C A; *ND St U; Interior Design.*

MAES, Daniel Benjiman
Rib Lake HS; Rib Lake, WI (29-70) Band; Ensm; Order/Arrow; VP, SC; Var C; Bsbl; Bkbl; Ftbl; HCt; Order/Arrow A; *W Point Military Acad; Hist.*

MAESAKA, Clifford Toshihiko Jr
Burnsville Sr HS; Burnsville, MN (35-765) A Cap Choir; Chor; Ch, Hmrm; Madrigal; Ski C; JV, Soccer; Tnns; COM; NHS; All St Choir; *Carlton Col; Dentistry.*

MAGALSKI, Michael James
Abbeville HS; Abbeville, SC (5-167) BC; Chess C; Model UN; NHS; Span C; Cert of A.

MAGANN, Kelli Teresa
Dugway HS; Dugway, UT (4-50) Band; Bus C; CYO; Cpt, Chldr; Chor; Dbte Tm; Drama; Model UN; NHS; F-Ed, Sch P; VP, SC; VP, Soph Cl; Bkbl; Tnns; Tr; Cl Fav; HCt; Type A; Vlbl; VP, Girls Ltrman's C; Outst Soph Nom; St Drama Tm; Drill Tm; *U of Utah; Psych.*

MAGANN, Tony T
Dugway HS; Dugway, UT; Drama; Ger C; Model UN; NHS; Pres, SC; Var C; Pres, Jr Cl; Pres, Soph Cl; Co-Cpt, Bkbl; Co-Cpt, Ftbl; Golf; Tnns; Cl Fav; Elk A; Spch A; All-St Bkbl; Rep, Freedom Acad Bus.

MAGARO, Carol Ann
Cumberland Valley HS; Mechanicsburg, PA (45-585) Drama; Pres, Fr C; NHS; Spch C; Thes; *U of Pittsburgh; Social Work.*

MAGEE, Angie Lynn
Eureka HS; Eureka, IL (3-130) Band; Cpt, Chldr; Chor; Ensm; Swim; Tr; Amer Leg A; HCt; Outst Mus; *Dentistry.*

MAGEE, Carey Lynn
Mt Vernon Twp HS; Mt Vernon, IL (18-409) Band; Cpt, Chldr; GS; 4H; NHS; ARC; Rptr, Sch P; SC; Tr; HCt; Prom Qn; *W Ky U; Phys Ed.*

MAGEE, Craig Stephen
Gulfport E HS; Gulfport, MS; *Alcorn St U; Elec.*

MAGEE, Cynthia Louise
Eureka HS; Eureka, IL (1-140) AFS; Band; Chldr; Chor; Ensm; NHS; Span NHS; SC; Secy, Jr Cl; Pres, Soph Cl; Tr; HCt; Highest Soph Schol A; *Denistry.*

MAGEE, David Bryan
Bowling Green HS; Franklinton, LA (8-30) Chor; VP, Hmrm; Tres, NHS; Sch P; VP, SC; Bsbl; Bkbl; Ftbl; Cl Fav; *Pepperdine U; Law.*

MAGEE, Diane Carol
Whitman-Hanson Regional HS; Whitman, MA (14-328) Hmrm; Key C; Math C; NHS; Rainbow; Ski C; Tres, Sr Cl; Hon Prog; *Babson Col; Bus.*

MAGEE, James Shipman
Brookhaven Acad; Brookhaven, MS; VP, BC; Pres, Fr C; Hmrm; VP, SC; Pres, Jr Cl; Pres, Soph Cl; Bsbl; JV, Bkbl; Ftbl; Tr; Alg A; Bio A; COM; Math A; NEDT; Sci A; *Miss St U; Med.*

MAGEE, Janice Lee
Columbia HS; Columbia, MS (15-230) Chldr; 4H; Hmrm; Sftbl; Tr; Cl Fav; Type A; Yth Fel; Pep, CYASC, Bible, DECA, C'S; *Nurs.*

MAGEE, Teresa Ann
McCleur Acad; Jackson, MS (10-65) Chor; Win, St MMTA; 16 Group; Revelation Choir, Piano; *Miss Col; Mus.*

MAGER, Dianna Jo
Rosedale HS; Rosedale, IN (5-58) Band; JV, Chldr; Chor; VP, 4H; NHS; Secy, Sr Cl; Secy, Soph Cl; DARGCA; HCt; St Dress Review Fin; *Ind St U; Eng.*

MAGERS, Barbara Ann
Virgie HS; Virgie, KY; FTA; A-Ed, Sch P; Secy, Spch C.

MAGERS, Dick Lawrence
Lexington HS; Lexington, OH (30%-280) Band.

MAGGARD, Joyce Renee
Bradleyville Sch; Bradleyville, MO (2-30) Bus Mgr, Ann; Chor; Secy, FHA; Secy, SC; Secy, Sr Cl; Secy, Jr Cl; Sftbl; Citz A; HQn; Journ A; Type A; Cpt, MVP, Vlbl; Annual Qn; Home Ec A.

MAGGIONCALDA, Michael David
Holy Cross HS; Delran, NJ (25%-400) JV, Bkbl; Ftbl; Tr; HCt; *Med.*

MAGGITT, Valerie Renee
Luther HS N; Chicago, IL; Soul C; *NW Bus Col; Acct.*

MAGGITT, Zelda Lynnette
Luther N HS; Chicago, IL (155-260) Soul C; *NW Col; Bus.*

MAGNANT, Aimee Francoise
St Mary's Acad; Alexandria, VA; Swim; Alg A; Hist A; NEDT; Geom A; DAR Hist A; *Med.*

MAGNESS, Kristi Lynn
Farwell HS; Farwell, TX (15-45) Ann; Chor; FHA; NHS; Sch P; JV, Bkbl; Mgr, Ftbl; Tnns; Tr; Cl Fav; *McMurry Col; Med.*

MAGNUS, Carl Joseph
Adlai E Stevenson HS; New York City, NY (50-822) Chem C; City Conf; Dbte Tm; Pres, Hmrm; InterClub Coun; NHS; SC; Var C; Ftbl; Hon Prog; Sci A; Var Ltr; *Rochester U; Dentistry.*

MAGNUS, Carol Lynn
Tisdale Unit Composite Sch; Tisdale, CANADA (5-97) Sch P; 4H A; Spch A; Geography, Typing, C'S; Intramurals; *U of Saskatchewan; Nurs.*

MAGNUSON, Daniel Lee
Staples HS; Staples, MN (7-156) Band; Ensm; NHS; Spch C; Mgr, Bkbl; JV, Golf; NMS; *U of Minn; Pol Sci.*

MAGNUSON, Laurie Lynn
Harding Sr HS; St Paul, MN (32-770) Chldr; Chor; Drama; Hmrm; Fin, Jr Miss Pagent; NHS; Co-Ed, Sch P; SC; Pres, Soph Cl; Mgr, Bsbl; Beauty; HCt; Journ A; Rotary A; Spch A; Gym; Comm Service A; *Col of St Catherines; Nurs.*

MAGNUSSEN, Pamela Lynn
Lincoln Comm HS; Lincoln, IL (1-340) BC; Chldr; Chor; Ensm; Spch C; SC; Sci A; Spch A; HS High Hon; *Lincoln Christian Col; Christian Ed.*

MAGONI, Cheryl Lee
Columbus HS; Columbus, GA (15%-379) Chldr; NHS; SC; Var C; Tres, Sr Cl; Hon Prog; Spch A; Swtht; Yth Fel; Jr Civitan; Pep C; Sr Life Saving; *Occupation Therapy.*

MAGOR, Janelle Lynn
Grand Co HS; Moab, UT; Band; Chor; Ski C; Golf; Swim; Tnns; Type A; Band A; *Bus.*

MAGRUDER, Barbara Ann
Adair Co R II HS; Brashear, MO (10%-17) VP, FHA; Tres, SC; Thes; Up Bound; Mgr, Bkbl; Tr; Hist A; PTA A.

MAGRUDER, Karen Rose
E Hartford HS; E Hartford, CT (50-360) Chor; Drama; Ensm; GS; Hmrm; Madrigal; NHS; DARGCA; *Columbia U; Nurs.*

MAGUIRE, Thomas Edward Jr
Chaminade Col Prep; St Louis, MO (20-120) Band; Chess C; Chor; Drama; Fr C; Lit Mag; NHS; Orch; Rptr, Sch P; Spch C; Bkbl; Soccer; Swim; Alg A; Citz A; Hist A; Hon Prog; Math A; NEDT; Opt A; Sci A; Spch A; *Washington U; Bus Adm.*

MAGULAC, Laura Jean
San Carlos HS; San Carlos, CA (10%-500) Band; Co-Cpt, Chldr; ARC; SC; JV, Bkbl; MVP, Swim; Mgr, Tr; CSF.

MAGWOOD, Anita Joyce
Moultrie Sr HS; Moultrie, GA; Vesper Choir; CVP C; *Fort Valley St Col; Social Work.*

MAHAFFEY, Cynthia Kay
Fairfield HS; Fairfield, AL; Band; BC; FHA; Orch; Co-Ed, Sch P; Y-Tns; Beauty; COM; HCt; Ala Alumni A.

MAHAFFEY, Richard Alan
Fairfield HS; Fairfield, AL (25%-186) Band; Key C; Bus Mgr, Sch P; SC; COM; *Math.*

MAHAFFEY, William Michael
MacArthur HS; Irving, TX (30%-2000) Band; Order/Arrow; Soccer; Sftbl; Order/Arrow A; Eagle Sct.

MAHAN, Dennis Morris
Copiague HS; Copiague, NY (1-399) Pres, Ger C; Pres, NHS; Tr; Bausch & Lomb A; Most Out; Regent Schol; Val; Ger Ntl Hon Soc; Paragon Oil Stu Incentive; *SUNY at Stonybrook; Dentistry.*

MAHAN, Priscilla Ann
Salem HS; Salem, NJ (25%-270) Ann; Band; John Philip Sousa Band A; *Salem Comm Col; Secretarial.*

MAHAR, John Donnell
Calvary Christian Sch; Glens Falls, NY; Var C; Bkbl; Ftbl; Tr; Wrest; Cl Fav.

MAHAR, Lisa Anne
Calvary Christian Sch; Glens Falls, NY (3-6) Cpt, Chldr; Chor; Drama; Ensm; Sch P; Ski C; Span C; Secy, SC; Var C; Sftbl; Cl Fav; Vlbl; *Special Ed.*

MAHER, Daniel Wesley
Inglewood HS; Inglewood, CA; Semi-Fin, AFS; Chor; Demolay; Parl, HiY; F-Ed, Sch P; Span C; SC; Parl, Tri-HiY; S-T, Jr Cl; Co-Cpt, Swim; Cl Fav; HCt; JA A; Masonic A; PTA A; ARC A; Parl, Yth & Govt; *San Jose St Col; Psych.*

MAHER, Philip William
Brimfield HS; Brimfield, IL (10-59) CYO; FFA; Pres, 4H; NHS; SC; Bsbl; JV, Bkbl; Co-Cpt, Ftbl; Golf; Swim; Tnns; Tr; 4H; Sci A; *Ill Central Col; Mech.*

MAHLER, Anne Marie
Granada HS; Livermore, CA (88-582) A Cap Choir; Hmrm; Rally C; *Stephens Col; Liberal Arts.*

MAHLER, Jonathan Lee
Owego Free Acad; Owego, NY (49-309) Fr C; NHS; Var C; JV, Cr-Ctry; Tr; Hon Prog; Yth Fel; Pres, Yth Fel; *Wheaton Col; Lang.*

MAHLER, Laurel Kay
Owego Free Acad; Owego, NY (10-398) Band; Chor; Ensm; *Wheaton Col; Sci.*

MAHLERWEIN, Tara Lee
Mt Healthy HS; Cincinnati, OH (31-567) Band; BC; Drama; Ensm; VP, Ger C; Semi-Fin, GS; NHS; Tnns; *Duke U; Ger.*

MAHNKE, Tamera June
Shawnee HS; Shawnee, OK; Band; Chor; Fr C; FHA; FHA A; Outst Home Ec A; BCYC Sportsmanship A; HR; *Okla Christian Col; Elem Ed.*

MAHNKEN, Glenn Allen
St Charles HS; St Charles, MO (20%-550) Bsbl; Bkbl; Ftbl; Citz A; *Mo U; Dentistry.*

MAHON, Furman Lewis Jr
Laurens Dist 55 HS; Laurens, SC (12%-280) BS; Fr C; FTA; 4H; Secy, Key C; Rptr, Sch P; Bkbl; Ftbl; Tr; *Clemson U; Adm Mgt.*

MAHON, Philip August
Pendleton HS; Pendleton, SC (3-133) BC; Fr C; Secy, Hmrm; Var C; Ftbl; Golf; NMS; FCA; Commencement Marshal; *Air Force Acad; Hist.*

MAHONEY, Deborah Ann
Palo Duro HS; Amarillo, TX (2-285) Drama; VP, Fr C; FHA; FTA; Hmrm; NHS; Spch C; Thes; COM; Hon Prog; Most Out; Spch A; 'Learn & Live' Regional Champs; Outst Fr Stu; *Amarillo Col.*

MAHONEY, Mary Helene
Freeport Sr HS; Freeport, IL (66-584) Chldr; JV, Dbte Tm; HCt; Pres A; *Biochem.*

MAHONEY, Paula Ann
Franklin Co HS; Frankfort, KY (50-460) FFA; Ger C; Lit Mag; Arch; Sftbl; Math A.

MAHONEY, Tamara Nadine
Eastern HS; Washington, DC; *Printing.*

MAHOOD, Margaret Ann
Elkhorn Valley HS; Tilden, NE (10-32) Band; Chor; Ensm; Pres, 4H; Arch; Bkbl; Tr; 4H A; Admiral-St Navy; *Maridoth Manor Col; Horse Trnr.*

MAHURIN, Ronald Paul
Christopher Dock Mennonite HS; Lansdale, PA (20-82) Bus Mgr, Ann; F-Ed, Sch P; Bkbl; Soccer; Pres, Yth Fel; *Pinebrook Jr Col; Biol.*

MAIDEN, Glen Byron
Las Vegas HS; Las Vegas, NV; Cpt, Ftbl; Cpt, Soccer; All Conf Ftbl & Soccer; *Forestry.*

MAIDEN, Michael Wayne
Marshalltown Sr HS; Marshalltown, IA (14-497) Band; Chor; Drama; Ensm; Ger C; Order/Arrow; Spch C; Hon Prog; Spch A; Pres, Lutheran Yth Organization; *St Paul's Col; Bus.*

MAIDES, Dabney Ragland
Terry Sanford Sr HS; Fayetteville, NC (20%-400) Fr C; Order/Arrow; Sci C; JV, Bkbl; Cr-Ctry; God & Country A; Yth Fel; Chamber of Comm A.

MAIDLOW, Margaret Louise
Maderia HS; Cincinnati, OH (23-208) AFS; Chldr; Chor; Span NHS; Tn Counselor; Sunday Sch Teacher; *Bluffton Col; Ed.*

MAIER, Carol Jean
Ashley HS; Ashley, ND (5-42) Band; Chldr; Chor; Sch P; Var C; VP, Jr Cl; Bkbl; Tr; Presidential Phys Fitness A.

MAILHES, Linda Carol
Broadmoor HS; Baton Rouge, LA; A Cap Choir; Band; Span C; *LSU; Psych.*

MAIO, Peter Vincent
Neshaminy Maple Point HS; Langhorne, PA (1-413) Band; Ensm; NHS; COM; Hon Prog.

MAIO, Steve Michael
St Pius X HS; Albuquerque, NM (25-200) Band; BS; Drama; Tnns; Hon Prog; *Ariz St Col; Philosophy.*

MAIONE, Angela
St Joseph HS; Hammonton, NJ (1-50) JV, Chldr; Chor; Drama; Fr C; Semi-Fin, Jr Miss Pa; Pres, NHS; Sch P; Ski C; Tres, SC; Parl, Soph Cl; Mgr, Bkbl; Mgr, Cr-Ctry; Mgr, Ftbl; Beauty; Hon Prog; Ntl Sci Found; NEDT; VP, Ecology C; WW; Art C; Principal's List; Yrbk; Dance C; *Law.*

MAIORANO, Ann Bernadette
W Philadelphia Cath Girls HS; Philadelphia, PA (11-354) Chem C; GS; Hmrm; NHS; F-Ed, Sci C; Spch C; Alg A; Bio A; Hon Prog; Math A; Sci A; Spch A; Type A; Italian C; CS C; News Rptr; *Math.*

MAITLAND, Jill Cathrine
Chippewa Falls Sr HS; Chippewa Falls, WI (4-366) Band; Cpt, Chldr; Dbte Tm; GS; Model UN; NFL; NHS; Rptr, Sch P; Ski C; Spch C; Pres, SC; Sftbl; Tnns; Tr; DARGCA; Ntl Sci Found; Ntl Sci Symposium; Sci A; Spch A; Yth Fel; Co- cpt, Gym; Athena A; *US Air Force Acad; Pre-Med.*

MAITLAND, Richard Perkinson
Matoaca HS; Ettrick, VA (3-151) Tres, Fr C; French NHS; Secy, Key C; Pres, NHS; Church Organist; *U of Richmond; Orthodontist.*

MAIZE, Gerri Lynn
Spearman HS; Spearman, TX (10-75) Band; Pres, Drama; Secy, FHA; NFL; Pres, Spch C; Bkbl; Tnns; COM; Yth Fel; Drama A; Spirit A; *Journ.*

MAJCHER, Cheree Lynne
L'Anse Creuse HS; Mt Clemens, MI; Band; Chldr; Chor; Drama; Rptr, Sch P; Span C; Secy, Soph Cl; Sftbl; Tnns; *Mich St U; Law.*

MAJESKI, Kathleen Ruth
Iroquois Central HS; Elma, NY (21-350) Chor; Tres, Hmrm; Pres, Model UN; NHS; SC; Bkbl; Hockey; MVP, Sftbl; COM; Citz A; HCt; Hon Prog; Kiwanis A; S-T, Model UN; Co- cpt, Vlbl; NHS A; *Special Ed.*

MAJOR, Audrey C
Norman Thomas HS; NY, NY; Dbte Tm; NHS; F-Ed, Sch P; SC; MVP, Bkbl; COM; Citz A; Hon Prog; Journ A; Math A; Most Out; Phy A; Type A; Acct, Data Processing A's; Schol, Service, A's; *NY U; Lib Arts.*

MAJOR, Bruce Michael
Southeast of Saline HS; Assaria, KS (1-58) Band; Chor; Tres, 4H; Madrigal; Pres, Soph Cl; Ftbl; Wrest.

MAJOR, Glenna Elaine
Somerset HS; Somerset, KY (5%-175) Ann; Band; NHS; Sch P; Sci C; Schol Prize; Pep C; Tns Who Care; PA; Lit C; Secy, UMYF; Schol Medal; Candystriper; Prom Server; Statistician, Bsbl; *U of Ky; Computer Sci.*

MAJOR, Lee Ann
Coosa HS; Rome, GA (5%-265) Band; Tres, BC; JV, Chldr; Chor; Hmrm; NHS; Tres, SC; Gov Honor Prog; Hon Prog; Type A; Pres, Tres, Yth Fel; Ntl Fed of Mus C; St Mus Teachers Assn, Fin; *Mus.*

MAJOR, Marlene Marcella
Howard Lake-Waverly HS; Howard Lake, MN (7-97) Band; Chldr; Tr.

MAJOROS, Daniel George
Mehlville Sr HS; St Louis, MO (126-550) A Cap Choir; Chor; Drama; Spch C; Thes; Amer Leg A; Hon Prog; Spch A; Schol Art A; *U of Calgary; Theatre.*

MAJORS, Stacy DeeAnn
Eufaula HS; Eufaula, OK (10%-114) Band; Bus Mgr, Drama; NHS; A-Ed, Sch P; Span C; Bus Mgr, Spch C; Bus Mgr, Thes; *Bus Adm.*

MAJORS, Steven Charles
Eufaula HS; Eufaula, OK (10%-113) Band; Chor; Ensm; NHS; Citz A; *Okla St Tech Col; Elec.*

MAK, To Ming
Martin Luther King HS; Philadelphia, PA (1-692) Cpt, Chess C; NHS; Sci C; Mgr, Soccer; Mgr, Tnns; Alg A; COM; Hon Prog; Math A; Most Out; Phy A; Sci A; Geom A; Elem Funct A; *U of Penn; Mech Engr.*

MAKARA, James Joseph
W Middlesex HS; W Middlesex, PA (11-146) Chess C; Co-Cpt, Hmrm; NHS; JV, Bkbl; Ftbl; Tr; Type A; *Penn St U; Mech Engr.*

MAKAREWICZ, Marion Joseph
St Thomas Seminary; Hannibal, MO (1-20) A Cap Choir; Rptr, Ann; CYO; Chor; Drama; 4H; Pres, Hmrm; Monogram; Rptr, Sch P; Sodality; Var C; JV, Bkbl; Soccer; Sftbl; 4H A; Spch A.

MAKELA, James W
John F Kennedy HS; Bloomington, MN (314-688) Ski C; Tr; HCt; Tri-Cpt, Ftbl; HS All-Amer A, Ftbl; All-Conf A, Offensive Tackle; Lineman of Yr A; *U of SD.*

MAKELY, Phillip McBurney
Forest Hills HS; Marshville, NC (19-200) Ann; Band; Community Yth Symph; Drama; Fr C; VP, NHS; Sch P; Gov Honor Prog; 4H A; Hon Prog; All St Hon Band; *Kent St U; Mus.*

MAKI, Bonnie Lou
Stanley HS; Stanley, ND (18-55) Chor; Ensm; FHA; GS; Jr Miss Pagent; Arch; Tr; COM; *ND St Sch of Sci; Bus Mgt.*

MAKI, Curtis Matthew
Birmingham HS; Van Nuys, CA; Hmrm; St Stu Congress; Pep C; Play Production; Semi-Fin, Drama Festival; Fin, Shakespear Festival; *UCLA; Hist.*

MAKILA, Bonnie Lynn
Ben Franklin HS; Livonia, MI (10-700) A Cap Choir; Summa Cum Laude; WW; *Oral Roberts U.*

MAKUCH, Linda Ann
Massey Secondary Sch; Windsor, CANADA; *U of Windsor; Communication Stu.*

MALARCHICK, Jo Ann
Robert H Goddard HS; Roswell, NM; Band; Drama; Mjrte; NHS; Rainbow; Span C; Twirler; *Eastern NM U at Roswell; Vet Med.*

MALARCHICK, Tim
Orofino HS; Orofino, ID (11-100) CYO; Pres, Chor; Drama; Ensm; Madrigal; NHS; A-Ed, Sch P; Spch C; St Stu Congress; Pres, SC; Var C; Pres, Sr Cl; VP, Jr Cl; Bsbl; Co-Cpt, Ftbl; Tr; Cl Fav; HCt; Most Out; Spch A; Yth Leg; All Cont, All St, Ftbl; St Champ, Declamation; WW; Up With People; *Law.*

MALATOS, Scott
Leominster HS; Leominster, MA; Hmrm; Swim; Tnns; Hon Prog; Yth Rep; Tres, Fine Arts C; VP, CYF; *Tufts Col; Biol.*

MALAVE, Benjamin
Deerfield Acad; Deerfield, MA (97-141) Span C; Var C; Wrest.

MALAVE, Rafael Jr
Deerfield Acad; Deerfield, MA (120-183) ARC; VP, Span C; Var C; JV, Ftbl; Soccer; Wrest; *Georgetown U; Pre-Med.*

MALCOLM, Patricia Sue
Fairfield Comm HS; Fairfield, IL (53-155) Chor; 4H; Ed, Sch P; Span C; 4H A; *E Ill U; Eng.*

MALCOM, Carl Ray
Athens HS; Athens, TX; Chor.

MALCOM, Janice Elaine
Stapleton HS; Stapleton, NE (1-20) Ed, Ann; Chor; Secy, FHA; NHS; Secy, Sr Cl; Secy, Jr Cl; Secy, Soph Cl; HCt; NEDT; Vlbl; Highest Grade Avg, Jr Yr.

MALCOM, Kathy Jean
Allen Cons Sch; Allen, NE (5-23) Band; Chldr; Chor; Ensm; FHA; Semi-Fin, GS; 4H; NHS; Secy, SC; Pres, Var C; Bkbl; Sftbl; Tr; Hon Prog; Tres, S-T, Yth Group; Vlbl; Homecoming Usher; Prom Waitress; *Midland Lutheran Col; Phys Ed.*

MALCOM, Lori Ann
Allen Cons HS; Allen, NE; Band; JV, Chldr; SC; Tr; *U of Nebr; Hist Ed.*

MALCOM, Shandee Marsha
Oxon Hill Sr HS; Oxon Hill, MD (60-210) 4H; SC; 4H A; GSct; *Prince George's Comm Col; Med.*

MALDJIAN, Pierre Dikran
Barringer HS; Newark, NJ (1-500) Orch; Rensselaer A; Pres, Future Physician C; Ntl Merit Top 5%; All-City Orch; St Win, Earthwatch; Outst Jr; *Drew U; Pre-Med.*

MALDONADO, Jaime Luis
Juan Jose Owsuna HS; Hato Rey, PR (5-150) Pres, Dbte Tm; Drama; Pres, Hmrm; A-Ed, Lit Mag; Ed, Monogram; Mu Alpha Theta; ARC; Sch P; Span C; VP, SC; Swim; Tnns; COM; God & Country A; Hon Prog; Lion A; Ntl Conf Chr & Jews; Opt A; Sanctuary Soc; Spch A; *U of Cayey; Psych.*

MALDONADO, Mara
Colegio San Antonio HS; Rio Piedras, PR (8-103) VP, Hmrm; Math C; NHS; NEDT; Sci A; *U of Puerto Rico; Chem.*

MALDONADO, Maria Santa
Dra Maria Cadilla HS; Arecibo, PR (74-429) FBLA; *Universidad de Puerto Rico; Social Worker.*

MALDONADO, Roberto
Our Lady of Pilar HS; San Juan, PR; Hmrm; Pres, NHS; Span C; Bsbl; Bkbl; Alg A; Bio A; COM; Hist A; Math A; Sci A; Span A; Newspaper Rptr; *Bradley U; Social Sci.*

MALDONADO, Zulma
Lola Rodriguez de Tio; San German, PR (22-350) CYO; FHA; Secy, 4H; Hmrm; Fin, Lit Ral; Bio A; COM; Cl Fav; 4H A; *Inter Amer U; Med Technology.*

MALECKI, Martin Henry III
Hinsdale Township HS Central; Hinsdale, IL (68-659) Band; VP, Lat C; Math C; Monogram; Co-Cpt, Swim; Hon Prog; NMF; NMS; St Scholar; Gym Tm; Dean's List; WW; Tns Now Together; Lector; Knight o-t Altar; *Stanford U; Engr.*

MALEK, Jody Lynn
Canarsie HS; Brooklyn, NY (8-945) Band; FTA; Cpt, Math C; NHS; A-Ed, Sch P; Alg A; Amer Leg A; COM; Citz A; Hist A; Hon Prog; Math A; Regent Schol; Sci A; Type A; Mus A; Span A; *Brooklyn Col; Math.*

MALEK, Rose Marie
Tampa Cath HS; Tampa, FL (20-300) Ann; CYO; JV Vlbl; *Math.*

MALEY, Carla E
Pottsville Area HS; Pottsville, PA (153-376) A Cap Choir; Arch; Band; Rainbow; Y-Tns; Arch; JA A; Order/Arrow A; Type A.

MALEY, Dirk
Ogallala HS; Ogallala, NE (15%-150) Band; 4H; NHS; F-Ed, Sch P; Var C; Bsbl; Bkbl; Cr-Ctry; Wrest; Elk A; 4H A; Pres A; Cr Ctry A; Scholastic A, Silver & Bronze; NHS A; Band A; *U of Nebr; Journ.*

MALICHI, Randall Spencer
Bennettsville HS; Bennettsville, SC (56-220) VP, Band; VP, Chem C; FFA; FHA; Hmrm; VP, Phys C; SC; Bkbl; Ftbl; Fin, Lion's C; John Philip Sousa A; *N Carolina A&T Col; Bus Adm.*

MALICK, Randall Joseph
St Vincent-St Mary HS; Akron, OH (10-230) Pres, CYO; Drama; Math C; Mu Alpha Theta; NHS; Sch P; Pres, SC; COM; Hon Prog; Best Supporting Actor; *Akron U; Communications.*

MALIN, Terri Ann
Clio Area HS; Clio, MI (10%-352) A Cap Choir; Band; Chor; Drama; Ensm; Cpt, Hmrm; Cpt, Mjrte; Ski C; Span C; Secy, SC; Pres, Sr Cl; Tres, Soph Cl; Tr; Cl Fav; HCt; Hon Prog; Star Student; Yth Fel; Tres, Church Dist Yth; *Mott Comm Col; Eng.*

MALINIAK, Maurice Marcus
Sam Rayburn HS; Pasadena, TX; Chem C; Lat C; JV, Bsbl; JV, Bkbl; *San Jacinto Jr Col; Sci.*

MALINOWSKI, Andrea V
Gar Mem HS; Wilkes-Barre, PA (3-186) NHS; Pres, SC; Bkbl; Sftbl; Mgr, Tr; Vlbl; Statistician, Ftbl; *U of Pa; Phys Therapy.*

MALINSKI, Sandra Lynne
Villa Park HS; Villa Park, CA (70-631) AFS; Secy, Chor; Sftbl; Tnns; CSF; COM; Citz A; Hon Prog; Pres A; Cert of Completion; Ath A's; *Calif St U; Ed.*

MALISKA, Deborah Jane
St John HS; Ennis, TX (7-34) Ann; Chor; FTA; Fin, GS; NHS; Sch P; Tr; Nike C; WW; *Navarro Jr Col; Bus.*

MALL, Susan Margaret
Eureka HS; Eureka, IL (13-125) A Cap Choir; AFS; Cpt, Band; Pres, Chor; Ensm; Co-Ch, Span C; Span NHS; Amer Leg A; Spch A; *Eureka Col; Religious Ed.*

MALLARD, Brenda Faye
Callaway HS; Jackson, MS (25%-511) Ann; Mu Alpha Theta; NHS; COM; Math A; Yth Fel; *Pre-Med.*

MALLERY, David Benton
Auburndale HS; Cordova, TN (11-55) A Cap Choir; Arch; Band; Bus C; Chess C; Chor; Drama; Ensm; Ntl Yth Conf; ARC; VP, Span C; Var C; Arch; Bsbl; Bkbl; Cr-Ctry; Golf; Tr; All City A, Violin; Jr Postman A; *U of Tenn; Mech Engr.*

MALLETT, Sharon Kay
Douglas Co HS; Douglasville, GA (10-287) Pres, Lat C; NHS; Ed, Sch P; SC; Pres, Sr Cl; Pres, Soph Cl; HCt; Sr Favorites; Contributed Most A, Newspaper; *Ga Col; Bus.*

MALLETTE, Brenda Lee
Franklin Acad; Malone, NY (1-265) Fr C; Math C; Regent Schol; Val; Secy, Hist C; Secy, Rifle C; Epsilon Hon Soc; *Clarkson Col; Acct.*

MALLICOAT, Frank Wells
Miramonte HS; Orinda, CA (20%-370) Span NHS; Var C; Bsbl; Soccer; Wrest; Bank Of Amer A; CSF; Cl Fav; Most Improved, Wrest; Eagle Sct A's; *U of Calif; Liberal Arts.*

MALLICOATE, Laura Elizabeth
Talawanda HS; Oxford, OH; A Cap Choir; Drama; FHA; Key C; Thes; *Bauder Fashion Col; Fashion Merchandising.*

MALLINCKRODT, David Paul
Stoutland HS; Stoutland, MO; Tres, BC; Ed, Sch P; VP, Sr Cl; Bsbl; Bkbl; Tr; Bio A; MLS; Sci A; *SW Mo St U; Sci.*

MALLIS, Lawrence Marc
Hightstown HS; Hightstown, NJ (17-310) Var C; Y-Tns; Tr; Hon Prog; Math A; Sci A; *Rutgers Col; Pre-Med.*

MALLORY, Jennifer Lyn
Jefferson City HS; Jefferson City, MO; AFS; Chor; NHS; Span C; Span NHS; SC; S-T, Jr Cl; *Mo U; Ed.*

MALLORY, Margaret Kathleen
The Donoho Sch; Anniston, AL (25%-52) Chldr; Ensm; Span C; Tri-HiY; Hon Coun; Vlbl; *Auburn U; Sci.*

MALLORY, Melvin
Wm Monroe HS; Stanardsville, VA (25%-90) BC; Chor; FFA; Sch P; Bkbl; Ftbl; Tr; Beta C A.

MALLORY, Victor Bernard
D M Therrell HS; Atlanta, GA (30-300) A Cap Choir; Band; Bus C; Chor; Drama; FBLA; Hmrm; Citz A; Hon Prog; JA A; Pres A; ROTC A; Type A; Band A; Attendance A; Drivers A; *Ga St U; Bus Mgt.*

MALLOS, Johm Thomas
Benson Polytechnic HS; Portland, OR (8-375) Band; Chem C; Ensm; Key C; Math C; NHS; Ntl Yth Conf; Orch; SC; Var C; JV, Bkbl; Ftbl; Tr; Cpt, Wrest; Alg A; HKg; Kiwanis A; Pres A; Yth Foundation; Yth Leg; MVP, Wrest; All City Ftbl; City Champ, Wrest; *US Merchant Marine Acad; Dual Merchant License.*

MALLOW, Jo Lynn
Hobbs HS; Hobbs, NM (103-440) A Cap Choir; Ann; Chor; Rainbow; Most Dependable, Sr Cl; Choir Librarian; *Mus.*

MALLOY, Craig Brown
Santa Ana HS; Santa Ana, CA (15-636) Band; Chor; Pres, Ger C; NHS; Orch; SC; Pres, Soph Cl; Cpt, Swim; Amer Leg A; Hon Prog; Yth Fel; MVP, Water Polo; Outst, Band; Swim Medals; *UCLA; Med.*

MALLOY, Jacqueline Irene
Clark Co R-1 HS; Kahoka, MO (5-95) Sci C; JV, Bkbl; Pep C; NJHS.

MALLOY, Todd Webster
Santa Ana HS; Santa Ana, CA (8-388) Fin, BS; Chor; Ger C; NHS; Sch Achieve Tm; St Stu Congress; SC; Cpt, Swim; Amer Leg A; Bank Of Amer A; Hist A; Hon Prog; Music A; ROTC A; Yth Fel; Rifle Drill Tm; Water Polo; WW; T Medal, ROTC; Exchange C A; *Naval Acad.*

MALLOY, William Michael
Independence HS; Independence, OH; Secy, Band; Chor; Drama; Ensm; Mod Mus Mas; Thes; Pres, Photography C; *Eng.*

MALNOR, Kevin Paul
Green Bay HS; Green Bay, WI (50-350) All Amer Yth; Ann; Band; Bus C; Dbte Tm; FBLA; Hmrm; Math C; Sch P; Var C; Bkbl; Ftbl; Golf; Alg A; COM; Citz A; HCt; JA A; Math A; Opt A; DECA A; *U of Wisc; Bus.*

MALONE, Cedric Eugene
Halter HS; Wellston, MO (7-125) Cr-Ctry; Journ A; Spch A; *Journ.*

MALONE, Cheri Marie
Lincoln Sr HS; E St Louis, IL (1-400) Fr C; Math C; NHS; *Northern Ill U; Nurs.*

MALONE, Jackie Glen
Pampa HS; Pampa, TX (1-308) Chor; Pres, NHS; Chem A; Hon Prog; Math A; Val; Most Scholarly; Tex Chem Coun A; WW; Eng A; *Tex Tech U; Engr.*

MALONE, Joe Hal
Greeneville HS; Greeneville, TN; Chess C; Chor; Pres, Demolay; Key C; Ski C; Bkbl; Ftbl; Tnns; Tr; *Clemson U; Bus Adm.*

MALONE, John Michael
Amador Valley HS; Pleasanton, CA (103-450) Band; Parl, CYO; Chor; Ensm; Orch; Bsbl; Ftbl; Hockey; Star Student; Yth Fel; *Archt.*

MALONE, Lynn Marie
Hannibal Central Sch; Hannibal, NY (5-100) VP, AFS; Ed, Ann; Chor; FTA; Secy, Key C; Math C; NHS; Tres, Jr Cl; Regent Schol; *Canton Col; Bus Adm.*

MALONE, Matthew Todd
Paris HS; Paris, TX (10%-250) Key C; JV, Ftbl; Cl Fav; Hon Prog; *E Tex St U; Elec.*

MALONE, Michael Wayne
Argos Comm Sch; Argos, IN (15-80) FTA; Bkbl.

MALONE, Norma Ev
Coronado HS; Lubbock, TX; Rainbow.

MALONE, Pertricia Lee
W Charlotte Sr HS; Charlotte, NC; Band; Chldr; Dbte Tm; Hmrm; InterClub Coun; Span C; SC; COM; Ltr-Girl; Pres, Civinettes; *U of NC Central; Bus Adm.*

MALONE, Robert Archie
McKinley Tech HS; Washington, DC (95-754) *Sch of Visual Arts; Photography.*

MALONE, Salvatore Elliott
Mendel Cath HS; Chicago, IL (16-147) NHS; Var C; Bsbl; Mgr, Bkbl; COM; Hon Prog; Excel A; *NW U; Acct.*

MALONE, Susan Claire
St Mary's Regional HS; Lynn, MA (1-129) Drama; Fr C; Bkbl; Cr-Ctry; Tnns; Tr; Alg A; COM; Citz A; Hist A; Hon Prog; Math A; MLS; NEDT; Sci A; Val; VFW A; VofDEM; Fr, Eng, A's; Mass Inst of Tech; Engr.

MALONEY, Laura Jo
Nolan HS; Ft Worth, TX (30-200) Chor; Drama; Semi-Fin, Hmrm; Madrigal; ARC; Spch C; Semi-Fin, SC; Thes; COM; Hon Prog; Math A; Sci A; Spch A; Tex A&M U; Vet Med.

MALONEY, Lori Ann
Eldorado HS; Eldorado, IL (50%-114) Ger C; Mgr, Bkbl; Mgr, Sftbl; Mgr, Tr; Mgr, Vlbl; Lockyear Col; Bus.

MALOUF, Michael Alan
La Canada HS; La Canada, CA (10%-450) Band; Chor; Community Yth Symph; Demolay; Madrigal; Orch; Swim; CSF; Cpt, Water Polo; Humanitarian A; Pasadena City Col.

MALOY, Joseph Dwight
T R Miller HS; Brewton, AL (10-95) Ann; Chess C; Lit Mag; SC; VP, Sr Cl; VP, Jr Cl; Bsbl; MVP, Ftbl; Cl Fav; Lion A; Most Christian Ath; Best Personality; J I Edwards Schol; Most Friendly; Jefferson Davis Jr Col; Pre-Vet Med.

MALOY, Sally Ann
Mercy HS; Albany, NY (5-108) CYO; Fr C; Ed, Lit Mag; NEDT; Regent Schol; St Bonaventure U; Journ.

MALPICA, Ruth Elizabeth
Roberto Clemente HS; Chicago, IL (25%-500) Anchor C; Chor; Fr C; French NHS; Hmrm; Spch C; Bsbl; Bkbl; Soccer; Sftbl; Amer Leg A; Amer Leg Orator A; COM; ROTC A; Spch A; ROTC Sponsor; Pres, Flag Detail Committee; Pres, Fancy Drill Committee; Fr.

MALTBIE, Michael Kenneth
Lincoln HS; Stockton, CA (42-468) JV, Bkbl; Cr-Ctry; Excellence As, Span; Top Span Stu; San Jose St Col; Acct.

MALTHANER, Kevin
Norman HS; Norman, OK (15%-545) JV, Bkbl.

MALVEAU, Rozena LaFonda
Crockett HS; Crockett, TX (10%-110) Bus C; Bus A; Sam Houston St U; Bus.

MAMALO, Christina Ruth
Hershey Sr HS; Hershey, PA (95-300) Yth Fel; Jobs Daughters; Bloomsburg St Col; Med.

MANAHAN, Nancy Alane
Ralston HS; Omaha, NE; AFS; Chldr; Span A; William and Jewell Col; Nurs.

MANAHAN, Timothy Edward
Hall Township HS; Spring Valley, IL; Golf; Elec.

MANAK, Ralph Martin
Eldorado HS; Albuquerque, NM (32-744) Band; NHS; Span NHS; Cr-Ctry; Tr; U of New Mexico; Bio.

MANALO, Marissa Rizarre
Castle Park HS; Chula Vista, CA (9-400) Ed, Ann; Cpt, Chldr; Chor; Hmrm; Ed, Lit Mag; ARC; SC; Pres, Jr Cl; CSF; Citz A; Journ A; UC at San Diego; Med.

MANAMTAM, Alden Yanuaria
McKinley HS; Honolulu, HI (216-766) A Cap Choir; Chor; Drama; Thes; VP, Yth Fel; U of Hawaii; Communications.

MANCHESTER, Robert George
Oppenheim-Ephratah Central Sch; St Johnsville, NY (7-39) BS; NHS; Pres, Sr Cl; Bkbl; Soccer; Chem A; DARGCA.

MANCINA, Lisa Ann
Notre Dame HS; Clarksburg, WV (6-52) CYO; Cpt, Chldr; Drama; FBLA; GS; Hmrm; Math C; Tres, NHS; ARC; Sci C; SC; Y-Tns; HCt; W Va U; Spch Path.

MANDL, Cynthia Sue
Stanton HS; Stanton, NE; Band; S-T, CYO; Drama; FHA; Pres, Y-Tns; Mgr, Tr; COM; Mus Camp Schol; Northern U of Colo; Ed of Handicapped.

MANDL, Janet Leota
Stanton HS; Stanton, NE (4-56) Ann; CYO; Chor; Drama; FHA; Ger C; GS; A-Ed, Sch P; Rptr, Y-Tns; Mgr, Cr-Ctry; Mgr, Wrest; Hon Prog; U of Nebr; Nurs.

MANDORCA, Brent Girard
Alton Sr HS; Alton, IL; Bsbl; Bkbl; Sftbl; Sch Ltr; Letterman's C Trophy; Bsbl Pin; Lewis & Clark Col; Math.

MANDRELL, Vivian Lorraine
Big Sandy HS; Big Sandy, TN (10-30) Chldr; FHA; 4H; Bkbl; Sftbl; HCt; Union Col; Med Asst.

MANDY, Lynda Anne
Homewood HS; Homewood, AL (80-229) Chor; Ensm; FHA; All St Jazz Choir; Auburn U; Child and Family Development.

MANEA, Mirela Christine
The Cecilian Acad; Philadelphia, PA (1-29) A-Ed, Ann; CYO; Fr C; Hmrm; Lat C; NHS; Pres, Sci C; Tres, SC; JV, Bkbl; COM; Chem A; Hon Prog; Magna Cum Laude; NEDT; Fr A; Dance C; Lib Aide; Vlbl; Chestnut Hill Col; Chem.

MANECKE, Linda Irene
Fostoria HS; Fostoria, OH (6-225) Band; FHA; NHS; Tr; Pres A; Secy, Jr Ldrs; Diving; Gym; Secy, Yth Fel; Tres, JA; Cpt, Vlbl.

MANER, Cynthia Ann
W Morgan HS; Trinity, AL (1-63) F-Ed, Ann; Band; BC; Tres, SC; Bio A; Hist A; Type A; WW; HR; Calhoun Comm Col; Secretarial Sci.

MANER, Sarah Elizabeth
Kings Mountain Sr HS; Kings Mountain, NC (3-250) Ann; Band; BC; Chem C; Drama; Ensm; Fr C; FTA; Hmrm; Lat C; NHS; Phys C; Sci C; SC; JV, Bkbl; Tnns; MLS; Most Stu; Jr Marshall; Nom, Gov Sch; All St Band; Appalachian St U; Special Ed.

MANERS, Barry Alan
Sam Rayburn HS; Pasadena, TX (25%-600) Hmrm; JETS; Key C; Straight 'A' Stu A; Tex A&M U; Enviromental Design.

MANERS, Robert Leonard
Towering Oaks Baptist HS; Memphis, TN (10%-90) Hmrm; Key C; NHS; Span C; SC; Pres, Soph Cl; Bkbl; Ftbl.

MANESS, Amanda Jane
New Bern Sr HS; New Bern, NC (175-500) Secy, Anchor C; Chor; Pres, FHA; Hmrm; Sci C; SC; Tnns; Tri-Chi; FHA A; E Carolina U; Special Ed.

MANESS, Dale Anthony
Glenvar HS; Salem, VA (8-300) Lat C; NHS; COM; Cum Magna Laude; Best Producer of Sch Play; Freed-Hardeman Col.

MANESS, Jane
John Ehret HS; Marrero, LA (5-550) Band; Chess C; 4H; Hmrm; Fin, Lit Ral; Mu Alpha Theta; Secy, NHS; ARC; Rptr, Sch P; Secy, Span C; SC; VP, Jr Cl; Bio A; Hon Prog; Journ A; Sci A; Scholastic A; Span A; LSU; Spch Therapy.

MANESS, Karen Lea
All Amer Christian Acad; Hollywood, FL (1-36) Chess C; Chor; Drama; Ensm; FHA; Var C; Cpt, Sftbl; Hon Prog; Most Out; Val; Cpt, Vlbl; HR; Rep, PACE Bowl; 4th, Grls Ensm; 1st Solo A; Outst Christian Testimony A; 3rd Pl, Dressmaking & Fashion A; All Amer Bible Col; Ed.

MANESS, Tambra Kaye
Temple Baptist Acad; Denver, CO (5-29) Ann; Chldr; Ensm; Fin, Jr Miss Pagent; Tres, NHS; Ski C; Spch C; Sftbl; HCt; Vlbl.

MANESS, Val Anne
John Ehret HS; Marrero, LA (42-480) Hmrm; Lit Ral; VP, Math C; Mu Alpha Theta; ARC; Pres, Span C; Parl, SC; Hon Prog; ARC A; Sci A; WW; U of Southwestern La; Acct.

MANFULL, Julie Marie
Hot Springs Co HS; Thermopolis, WY (10-79) Band; NFL; Tres, Job's Daughters; Span A; Hon Stu As; U of Wy; Sci.

MANGAN, Cindy Jean
N Quincy HS; N Quincy, MA (35-463) Ann; NHS; Secy, Span C; Span NHS; JV, Sftbl; COM; Hon Prog; Secy, Church Fellowship; Wheaton Col; Law.

MANGER, Laura Beth
Shelton HS; Shelton, CT (73-432) Fr C; NHS; Span C; Span NHS; COM; Fr A & Cert; Span Cert; Eckerd Col; Lang.

MANGER, Lexanne Rhea
Shelton HS; Shelton, CT (200-420) Drama; Ch, Hmrm; MVP, Bkbl; MVP, Sftbl; Citz A; Coun of Teach A; Spirit A; Law Enforcement.

MANGER, Victoria Annette
W Jefferson HS; West Jefferson, OH (10%-120) Tres, A Cap Choir; Band; Ensm; NHS; Sftbl; Swim; Tnns; COM; VofDEM; Med.

MANGIGIAN, Debra
Upper Darby Sr HS; Upper Darby, PA (259-1063) A Cap Choir; Chess C; Community Yth Symph; Drama; Ensm; Hmrm; Madrigal; VP, Orch; Sch P; Thes; Mgr, Bkbl; Hockey; Chor Lib; Church Member-o-t Yr; W Chester St Col; Mus Ed.

MANGIGIAN, Matthew
Upper Darby HS; Upper Darby, PA (253-365) Archt.

MANGLE, Elisa Ann
Cumberland Valley HS; Mechanicsburg, PA (2-585) Cpt, Chldr; Hmrm; NHS; SC; Tnns; COM; NEDT; Pa St Schol; Pa St U; Chem.

MANGOLD, Carol Anne
Norwalk Sr HS; Norwalk, OH (25-204) Band; 4H; Orch; Span C; Tres, Church Yth Group.

MANGOLD, Rose Marie
Norwalk HS; Norwalk, OH (25-204) Band; 4H; Orch; Span C; Pres, Church Yth Group.

MANGUM, Billy Todd
Florence HS; Florence, MS (10-239) BC; Chess C; Bsbl; PA; Ole Miss; Engr.

MANGUM, James Stuart
N Gaston Sr HS; Dallas, NC (5%-377) Band; Chess C; Span C; SC; Most Out; U of NC; Math.

MANGUM, Linda Ruth
Jim Hill HS; Jackson, MS; Chldr; FHA; Jr Miss Pagent; Sci C; Bkbl; Sftbl; Tnns; Tr.

MANHOLLAN, Ray Robert
Woodrow Wilson HS; Youngstown, OH (48-350) Drama; Pres, Church Yth Group; Pres, DECA; Youngstown St U; Bus.

MANIBUSAN, Esther Suba
John F Kennedy HS; Tumon, GUAM (4-511) Ger C; NHS; Bio A; COM; Hon Prog; Lit A; Top Ten; Int'l Bus Col; Bus.

MANIGOLD, Lori Kathryn
Pflugerville HS; Pflugerville, TX (10%-108) Drama; FHA; VP, 4H; Span C; Spch C; Baylor U; Med Research.

MANION, Marka Ann
Longmont Sr HS; Longmont, CO; Chor; Drama; VP, FHA; Pres, 4H; NHS; Citz A; 4H A; Yth Fel; Child Care.

MANIS, James Douglas
Chattanooga Central HS; Harrison, TN (40-268) Co-Ed, Ann; BS; Tres, HiY; Hmrm; SC; Pres, Var C; Ftbl; Amer Leg A; Cl Fav; HKg; Journ A; ROTC A; Star Student; Mr Central; UTC; Bio.

MANKE, Donald Gary
Jefferson HS; Jefferson, WI (30-206) Chor; Drama; JV, Bkbl; JV, Ftbl; Swim; Hon Prog; U of Wis; Wildlife Forestry.

MANKOWSKI, Marsha Ann
Joliet Central HS; Joliet, IL (2-581) Chor; Yth Fel; Yth Leg; No 1, Soph Cl; Ed.

MANLEY, Beverly Lynne
Greenville HS; Greenville, MS (71-569) Lee Col; Spec Ed.

MANLEY, Cathy Jean
Memorial HS; Elkhart, IN; Cpt, Band; Chor; Community Yth Symph; Dbte Tm; Fr C; 4H; Madrigal; Cpt, Mjrte; NFL; NHS; Orch; Rainbow; Spch C; Swim; Tr; Most Out; Spch A; Star Student; MVP, Band; Eastman Col; Mus Performance.

MANLEY, Danny Ray
S Choctaw Acad; Toxey, AL (1-32) BC; NHS; SC; Bio A; Math A; MLS; Val.

MANLEY, Deborah Elise
Marantha Christian Acad; New Hartford, NY; A-Ed, Ann; Chor; 4H; Sch Achieve Tm; A-Ed, Sch P; SC; Soccer; Cpt, Vlbl; *Baptist Bible Col; Religious Ed.*

MANLEY, Diane Rae
S Plantation HS; Plantation, FL; Chor; SC; Cr-Ctry; Tr; Cr-Ctry Ltr; Tr Ltrs; *U of Fla; Med Technology.*

MANLEY, Jan Renee
Montpelier HS; Montpelier, OH; *Child Therapy.*

MANLEY, Karen Lynne
Red Bay HS; Red Bay, AL; FHA; FNA; 4H; Sch P; Sftbl; Swim; Tnns; 4H A; HCt; Spch A; *Lee Col.*

MANLEY, Tina Darlene
Hazlewood HS; Town Creek, AL (5-65) Band; BC; Pres, Bus C; Pres, FBLA; FHA; 4H; Sftbl; Beauty; 4H A; HCt; Type A; Bowl; 1st Pl, FBLA Talent; Shorthand A; Clarinet Medal.

MANN,
Catherine Claiborne Warwick
Cedar Bluff HS; Cedar Bluff, AL; BC; Rptr, FHA; Math C; A-Ed, Sch P; Rptr, SC; Tres, Soph Cl; Alg A; Sci A; Pep C; Mgr, Vlbl; Space C; VP, Lib C; Tigerette; *U of Montevallo; Social Work.*

MANN, Charles John
Winside HS; Winside, NE (3-37) Chem C; Chor; Drama; NHS; Order/Arrow; Sci C; S-T, SC; Var C; Bkbl; Ftbl; Tr; Hon Prog; Order/Arrow A; Sci A; Yth Fel; *U of Nebr; Engr.*

MANN, Cynthia Jean
Springfield Southeast HS; Springfield, IL (38-402) Secy, Band; NHS; Tres, SC; Bkbl; JV, Cr-Ctry; Tr; Vlbl; Marine Bank Stu of Week; Nth Ath Soc Schol A; *Sou Ill U at Carbondale; Outdoor Recreation.*

MANN, Cynthia Louise
Wauseu W Sr HS; Wausau, WI (10%-430) A Cap Choir; Band; Orch; Swim; Sch HR; *U of Wis; Communicative Disorders.*

MANN, Elizabeth Jayne
W Memphis Christian Sch; W Memphis, AR (5-23) Fr C; Tr; *Harding Col; Acct.*

MANN, Iris Valencia
Kecoughtan HS; Hampton, VA (48-585) Ann; Chor; City Conf; Tres, Drama; Fr C; French NHS; Hmrm; SC; Thes; COM; Hon Prog; Best Dressed; *Fashion Merchandising.*

MANN, Jeanne Sue
Panhandle HS; Panhandle, TX (10-50) Pres, FHA; FTA; NFL; NHS; Thes; Tnns; Spch A; Drum Major; Devotional C; Homemaking A; Ntl Piano Auditions; *Tex Tech U; Elem Ed.*

MANN, Jeffrey Lee
Springfield Southeast HS; Springfield, IL (63-525) SC; Cr-Ctry; Tr.

MANN, Jeffrey Scott
Del City Sr HS; Del City, OK (134-564) Hmrm; Pres, JETS; Ftbl; *Eastern Okla St Col; Drafting Technology.*

MANN, Kathleen Elizabeth
Robert E Lee HS; Midland, TX (98-649) Ann; JV, Chldr; Semi-Fin, Dbte Tm; Tres, NFL; NHS; Fin, Spch C; SC; JV, Hockey; Tnns; Spch A; Yth Fel; Rebelette; *Tex A&M U; Liberal Arts.*

MANN, Kenneth Dewayne
Hermitage HS; Hermitage, AR (1-60) Ed, Ann; BC; Chem C; Tres, FFA; VP, 4H; Math C; Sch P; Var C; JV, Bkbl; Ftbl; Tr; COM; 4H A; Hist A; HCt; Hon Prog; Math A; NMS; Val; All-Dist Ftbl; Trigonometry A; *U of Ark at Monticello; Archt Engr.*

MANN, LeAnn Joy
Campbell Tintah; Campbell, MN (1-38) Ann; MVP, Band; Chldr; Chor; Drama; Ensm; FHA; Ed, Sch P; Secy, SC; COM; Hon Prog; Journ A; Val; John Philip Sousa Band A; Chldr A; *U of Minn.*

MANN, Linda Nadine
Victory Christian Acad; Jacksonville, FL (10%-100) Rptr, Hmrm; NHS; Span C; SC; Sftbl; Hon Prog; *Stetson U; Bus.*

MANN, Phyllis Lorraine
Menchville HS; Newport News, VA (253-563) A Cap Choir; Pres A; Yth Fel; *Fashion Designer.*

MANN, Regina
Menchville HS; Newport News, VA (240-600) A Cap Choir; FTA; GS; NHS; Hockey; Yth Fel; Drill Tm; Black Humanities C; *Va St U; Med.*

MANN, Renee
Barringer HS; Newark, NJ; 2nd VP, Jr Quire.

MANN, Romme Rena
Southwest R-1 Sch; Ludlow, MO (1-24) F-Ed, Ann; Chor; NHS; Sch P; Alg A; Math A; Type A; Fr A; Shorthand A; Geography A; Ann Staff A; *Mo Western St Col; Law.*

MANN, Rose Marie
Pinckneyville Comm HS; Pinckneyville, IL (5%-135) CYO; Fr C; FHA; Sci C; SC; Pres, Soph Cl; Hon Prog; Flag Corps Christmas Court; SIU Math Day; *U of Ill; Math.*

MANN, Sharon Rhena
Hermitage HS; Hermitage, AR (1-60) BC; Chldr; Chor; FHA; Math C; COM; HCt; Sci A; *UAM; Bus.*

MANN, Stephen Carl
Falls Church HS; Falls Church, VA; Band; MVP, Chess C; Journ A; Sci A.

MANN, William Douglas Jr
Jackson Prep Sch; Jackson, MS (25%-180) Chor; Hmrm; Key C; Lat C; Madrigal; NHS; Ftbl; COM; Citz A; NMS; *Pre-Med.*

MANNEL, Eric James
Valparaiso HS; Valparaiso, IN (25-450) Chess C; SC; Bkbl; Soccer; Hon Prog; Ntl Jr Hon Soc; Foreign Exchange C; *Valparaiso U; Math.*

MANNING, Alice Kaye
Sharkey-Issaquena Acad; Rolling Fork, MS (10-29) BC; Chldr; 4H; JV, Hmrm; Sch P; Pres, Y-Tns; Bkbl; COM; Citz A; 4H A; HCt; *Delta St U; Nurs.*

MANNING, Anna Kay
John A Holmes HS; Edenton, NC (20-130) A Cap Choir; Ann; Chor; FHA; Type A; Bio C; Special Ed Teacher Aide; S-T, Health Careers C; *E Carolina U; Special Ed.*

MANNING, Belinda Ann
George Washington HS; Los Angeles, CA (40%-500) Chor; Mjrte; MVP, Sftbl; Fin, Tnns; Fin, Tr; Citz A; Yth Foundation; NAACP; Jr Counselor; *U of Sou Calif; Med.*

MANNING, Beth Ann
Hall HS; Spring Valley, IL (50-145) Ann; Band; Drama; FNA; Sci C; Var C; 4H A; Pres A; Sci A; Bowl; Presidential Clrm; *St Francis Sch of Nurs; Nurs.*

MANNING, David Wayne
El Camino HS; Oceanside, CA; A Cap Choir; Band; Bsbl; Bkbl; Ftbl.

MANNING, Debbie Renee
Sonora Union HS; Sonora, CA (17-296) AFS; Drama; FNA; 4H; InterAct C; NHS; Ch, Rainbow; Pres, Sci C; Secy, Ski C; Span C; Amer Leg A; CSF; 4H A; Sci A; Spch A; S-T, Sci C; Pres, Ski C; Co-ch, Tres, Rainbow Girls; 2nd VP, Rainbow Girls; *Fresno St U; Nurs.*

MANNING, Frances Patricia
Eldorado HS; Albuquerque, NM (16-744) Drama; Pres, Fr C; NHS; St Stu Congress; *U of NM; Computer Sci.*

MANNING, Geri Lynn
Hall HS; Spring Valley, IL (50%-130) Pres, CYO; Chldr; Secy, Drama; 4H; COM; Hist A; ARC A; Sci A; Art A's; *Ill Valley Comm Col; Designing.*

MANNING, J Frederick
Marian HS; Tamaqua, PA (42-153) CYO; Hmrm; SC; Bkbl; Tr; Hon Prog; Math A; Religion A; *U of Penn; Bus.*

MANNING, Kimberly Dobbs
Bowling Green HS; Bowling Green, KY (68-390) Pres, A Cap Choir; JV, Chldr; Drama; Ensm; Hmrm; InterClub Coun; Math C; SC; Tri-HiY; SC Executive Board; Ky Fed Woman's C; 4th Runner-Up, Jr Miss; Spirit of Jr Miss; *Georgetown Col; Mus Therapy.*

MANNING, Laura Jo
Weslaco HS; Weslaco, TX (12-350) Chem C; Sci C; Y-Tns; Co-Cpt, Bkbl; Tr; *Tex A&M U; Pre-Med.*

MANNING, Lynne Alison
Gates-Chili Sr HS; Rochester, NY (48-560) Band; Ensm; NHS; Swim; Church Sftbl; *St U of NY; Acct.*

MANNING, Michael Scott
Carl Sandburg HS; Orland Park, IL (300-880) *Lewis U; Bus.*

MANNING, Teresa Ann
El Camino HS; Oceanside, CA (40-325) A Cap Choir; Bus.

MANNING, Virginia Rene
Rock Hill HS; Rock Hill, SC (10%-350) Band; VP, BC; Drama; 4H; Hmrm; Span C; SC; Var C; Bkbl; MVP, Sftbl; Tnns; 4H A; HCt; Interlochen Ntl Mus; Yth Fel; Best Actor; *Lander Col; Phys Ed.*

MANNING, William Charlie Jr
Washington HS; Washington, NC (10-307) Span C; Ftbl; Church Yth Coun; FCA; *U of NC.*

MANNING, William Leroy
Lansdowne Sr HS; Lansdowne, MD; Band; BS; Chess C; Chor; ARC; Sch Achieve Tm; Sci C; Span C; Bkbl; JV, Soccer; COM; ARC A; Cert of Achv; *Mental Health.*

MANNING, William Oliver
Lee Acad; Clarksdale, MS (12%-96) Band; Mu Alpha Theta; Sci C; Tr; *US Air Force Acad; Aeronautical Engr.*

MANNION, Grainne Louise
Country Day Sch o-t Sacred Heart; Philadelphia, PA; Ann; Drama; NHS; F-Ed, Sch P; Ch, SC; JV, Hockey; Hon Prog; Effort, Good Sportsmanship, A's; HS School; *Lafayette Col; Civil Engr.*

MANNO, Loretta Jean
Lake Shore Central HS; Angola, NY (101-296) Bkbl; Tr; *Alfred Agr And Tech Col; Med Off Asst.*

MANNS, Ruby Jean
Ripley HS; Ripley, TN; Band; Chldr; Chor; Drama; Fr C; FHA; VP, 4H; Hmrm; Spch; Var C; Bkbl; 4H A; Spch A; Piano A; *Tenn Tech U; Child Psych.*

MANOS, Kevin Ross
Sylvan Hills HS; Atlanta, GA; BC; BS; Model UN; Pres, NHS; Orch; Sch P; Span C; SC; Cr-Ctry; Co-Cpt, Tnns; Tr; COM; ROTC A; *US Military Acad; Engr.*

MANRY, Susan Frances
Early Co HS; Blakely, GA (33%-180) Tres, BC; Ensm; 4H; Tri-HiY; Co-Cpt, Bkbl; Sftbl; 4H A; Co-Ed & Ed, Ann; Ch & Tres, FHA; *Mus.*

MANSFIELD, Cheryl Kay
Alma J Brown Lab HS; Grambling, LA (6-49) Pres, Band; Chem C; Drama; Secy, FTA; Tres, NHS; S-T, Sci C; Span C; VP, SC; Pres, Jr Cl; Pres, Soph Cl; Cpt, Bkbl; Cl Fav; HCt; Hon Prog; WW, Mus; *Grambling St U; Criminal Justice.*

MANSFIELD, Jon Keith
Bath Co HS; Owingsville, KY (30-129) Band; VP, FFA; 4H; Sci C; Rptr, Soph Cl; Bkbl; Ftbl; 4H A; Sci A; Spch A; *Morehead St U; Psych.*

MANSFIELD, Joyce Maureen
Ferndale Union HS; Ferndale, CA (2-64) Chldr; Bkbl; JV, Tr; CSF; Rptr & Parl, FFA; JV, Vlbl; *Animal Researcher.*

MANSHOLT, Nancy Ann
Litchfield HS; Litchfield, IL (15-150) Chor; Ensm; NHS; Span C; Bkbl; Rptr, Ftbl; GAA; Secy, Service C; *U of Ill; Bus.*

MANSON, Carole Elaine
Gilbert Sch; Brooklyn, NY (1-35) Cpt, Chem C; Cpt, Hmrm; A-Ed, Lit Mag; Rptr, Sch P; Pres, Span C; VP, Jr Cl; Citz A; Hon Prog; HR; *Hofstra U; Vet Med.*

MANSTROM, Cynthia Ann
Valley City HS; Valley City, ND (31-162) Chor; 4H; Hmrm; Sftbl; 4H A; Hon Prog; Yth Fel; Evangelism Outreach Comm; *Columbus U; Fine Arts.*

MANSUR, George Shahade
Elkhart HS; Elkhart, TX (20-30) VP, Band; Chor; Drama; FTA; Spch C; Thes; Outst Academic Achv, Drama; *S F Austin St Col; Drama.*

MANTA, Virginia Carolyn
Bellevue HS; Bellevue, MI (30-97) Chor; Ski C; Sftbl; HQn; Vlbl; *Kellogg Comm Col; Bus Courses.*

MANTAS, Claudia Margrit
Martin Luther HS; Maspeth, NY (21-70) Drama;
Bkbl; NEDT; Hunter Col.

MANTAY, Ron A
Vincent Massey Secondary Sch; Windsor, CAN-
ADA (10-100) Ger C; Math C; Soccer; Swim; Tr;
Wrest; Private Pilot's License; U of Windsor; Math.

MANTEGARI, Evon Mirene
Notre Dame HS; Salinas, CA; Hmrm; NHS; VP, Jr
Cl; CSF; Span A; U of C Davis; Biol Sci.

MANTEI, Mark Edmund
Cheboygan Area HS; Cheboygan, MI (30-190)
Rptr, Sch P; SC; Hockey; Yth Fel; U of Mich; Bus.

MANTELL, Marjorie Dolores
Notre Dame HS; Portsmouth, OH (30-64) Chor;
Span C; Bkbl; Tr; Pep C; Vlbl; Best Stu, Art; PA;
Shawnee St Col; Commercial Art.

MANTELL, Robert Edwin Jr
Sprayberry HS; Marietta, GA (3-550) Ch, Hmrm;
SC; Ga Tech; Elec.

MANTHE, Don Phillip
Payson HS; Payson, AZ (17-82) Drama; NHS;
Span C; Spch C; Var C; Bsbl; JV, Bkbl; N Ariz U;
Marine Biol.

MANTZ, Daniel John
Maranatha Christian Acad; New Hartford, NY
(1-7) Ed, Ann; Band; Pres, Chor; Ensm; Ed, Sch P;
Ch, SC; Cpt, Soccer; Tr; Best Ath; Highest Acad
Average; Tr A; Cedarville Col; Ed.

MANUEL, Gail
Jones Co HS; Gray, GA; Fr C; NHS; WW; Valdosta St Col; Nurs.

MANUEL, Joseph Devon
MacKenzie HS; Detroit, MI (28-352) NHS; Cr-
Ctry; Fla A&M U.

MANUS, Sally Ann
Delavan HS; Delavan, IL (6-64) Ed, Ann; Band;
Chor; Drama; Madrigal; Thes; St Civil Defense, A;
St Vocal Music, A; Ill Wesleyan U; Social Sci Ed.

MANVILLE, Marianne
North Park HS; Walden, CO (5-30) Ann; Band;
Chor; Drama; Ensm; Pres, 4H; Sch P; Ski C; SC;
Co-Cpt, Bkbl; COM; 4H A; NEDT; Spch A; VFW
A; VofDEM; Sen, 4-H St Coun; Pom-Pons; Colo U;
Law.

MANYAK, Diane Marie
Uniontown Area Sr HS; Uniontown, PA; Ann;
FBLA; NHS; Penn St U at Fayette; Bus Mgt.

MANYPENNY, Lynda Marie
Sebring McKinley HS; Sebring, OH (25-83) Band;
Chor; Pres, Drama; Lat C; NHS; SC; COM; Yth
Fel; Band A's; Nurs.

MANZANEDO, Julie Ann
Los Banos HS; Los Banos, CA (5-230) Secy, AFS;
Bus C; CYO; Secy, 4H; Math C; Sci C; SC; CSF;
Crisco A; 4H A; Math A; Most Out; Sci A; Tres,
AFS; Davis Col; Phys Therapy.

MANZANO, Roberto
Academia Ntra Sra Providencia; Rio Piedras, PR
(10-58) Bus Mgr, Ann; Band; Bus C; CYO; Chem
C; Chor; Dbte Tm; Drama; Lit Ral; Phys C; Span C;
Spch C; Tr; COM; Hon Prog; Phy A; Sci A; U of
Puerto Rico; Law.

MAPES, Mary Cheryl
Daviess Co HS; Owensboro, KY; Secy, Pol Sci C;
Bio A; COM; Brescia Col; Psych.

MAPLE, Anna Kathleen
Eastside HS; Gainesville, FL; A-Ed, Sch P; Citz A;
Pres, Yth Group; Sunday Sch Teacher; Fla Sou Col;
Journ.

MAPLE, Howard D
Kennedy HS; Cedar Rapids, IA (28-700) Band;
Community Yth Symph; Drama; NHS; Orch; Thes;
Sch Dist Schol; Cornell Schols; Cornell Col; Mus.

MAPLES, LaDonna Kay
Anna-Jonesboro Comm HS; Anna, IL (40-150) S-
T, Band; Fr C; FTA; Orch; Co-Ed, Sch P; Cl Fav;
HCt; Drill Tm; Pep C; Band Coun; SE Mo St U.

MAPLES, Patricia Kay
Oak Grove HS; Hattiesburg, MS; FHA; Spch C;
Var C; Bsbl; Sftbl; Beauty; Best Defensive, Bkbl; U
of Sou Miss; Home Ec.

MAPP, Debbie S
Brookhaven Acad; Brookhaven, MS (3-32) Ann;
BC; S-T, Hmrm; Mgr, Bkbl; Sftbl; Beauty; Cl Fav;
HQn; Most Dependable; U of Miss; Marketing.

MAPP, Pamela Denise
Oakland HS; Oakland, CA (5%-600) Bus C; VP,
Chor; Pres, Drama; Secy, Fr C; Hmrm; Pres, ARC;
Sch Achieve Tm; SC; World Affairs C; Tnns;
Beauty; COM; Citz A; HQn; Hon Prog; NEDT;
ARC A; Yth Foundation A; Leading Actress A; U
of San Francisco; Psych.

MAPP, Paula Louise
Port Richmond HS; Staten Island, NY; Tres,
Hmrm; Bkbl; Tr; US Navy.

MAPPS, Leah Grace
S Bay Bible Baptist Sch; Gardena, CA (10%-6)
Band; Ensm; A-Ed, Sch P; Cpt, Bkbl; Co-Cpt, Sftbl;
Tr; Psych.

MAPU, Vaasoaia
El Camino HS; Oceanside, CA; Var C; Ftbl; Phys
Ed.

MARABLE, Teresa Elizabeth
Matoaca HS; Ettrick, VA (5-149) Ann; Secy,
Chldr; FHA; NHS; SC; VP, Jr Cl; Secy, Soph Cl;
Secy, Keyettes; WW; Jr Marshal; Richard Bland
Col.

MARAGONI, Nathan Eustace
Sanger HS; Sanger, CA (34-417) A Cap Choir;
Chess C; Demolay; 4H; NHS; Orch; Sci C; Wrest;
CSF; COM; Citz A; WW; Reedly Jr Col; Bus.

MARBLE, Barbara Ann
Ralph C Mahar Regional HS; Orange, MA (6-165)
Band; Chor; SC; Sch Comm Adv, SC; Mus A; Field
Radio.

MARBLEY, Theodore Charles
Spring Brook HS; Silver Spring, MD; Hmrm; SC;
Tr.

MARBURY, Connie Darlene
Howard HS; Chattanooga, TN (79-150) Band;
Chor; Eckerd Col; Psych.

MARBURY, Juanita
Howard HS; Chattanooga, TN (6-300) Fr C;
Hmrm; Mjrte; S-T, Mu Alpha Theta; NHS; Sci C;
SC; Sftbl; Math A; Knoxville Col; Sci.

MARBURY, Milton Peter
Howard HS; Chattanooga, TN; Band; Key C;
Morehouse Col; Sociology.

MARCHAND, Mary Elizabeth
Saint Agnes HS; Rochester, NY (10%-120) CYO;
NHS; Ski C; SC; Pres, Sr Cl; Secy, Jr Cl; Secy, Soph
Cl; Niagara U; Nurs.

MARCHESE, Cathy Lynn
Sam Houston Sr HS; Houston, TX; VP, Hmrm;
NHS; SC; U of Houston; Bus Adm.

MARCHESE, Debra Lee
N Shore HS; W Palm Beach, FL (8-266) A Cap
Choir; Chor; InterClub Coun; Pres, Key C; Madri-
gal; NHS; Rptr, Sch P; Span C; SC; Alg A; Key C
Swtht; Geo A; Mt Holyoke Col.

MARCHESE, Dorothy N
Abington HS; Abington, PA (314-867) Ensm;
FBLA; FTA; Houghton Col; Elem Ed.

MARCHMAN, Clinton Daniel
Greene Co HS; Greensboro, GA (2-148) Band;
Rptr, BC; Ftbl; Cpt, Tnns; Tr; COM; Cl Fav; Gov
Honor Prog; HCt; Georgia Southern Col; Acct.

MARCIANO, Natalie Marie
Acad of Our Lady of Mercy; Milford, CT (5-88) A
Cap Choir; Secy, Chor; Drama; Key C; Madrigal;
NHS; VP, Span C; Hon Prog; NEDT; Hugh O'B-
rien Ldrship Seminar Nom; Med.

MARCIN, Jacqueline Ann
Marian HS; Tamaqua, PA (1-150) CYO; Hmrm; Jr
Miss Pagent; NHS; Sch P; SC; Co-Cpt, Bkbl; Cr-
Ctry; Tr; Amer Leg A; Hon Prog.

MARCIN, John Joseph
Marian HS; Tamaqua, PA (1-140) CYO; NHS; Or-
der/Arrow; JV, Bkbl; Cr-Ctry; Tr; Amer Leg A;
COM; Hon Prog; Order/Arrow A.

MARCIN, Judith Ann
Marian Cath HS; Tamaqua, PA (11-150) CYO;
Hmrm; Jr Miss Pagent; NHS; Sch P; SC; Co-Cpt,
Bkbl; Cr-Ctry; Tr; Amer Leg A; Hon Prog.

MARCINKOWSKI, John James
John S Fine Sr HS; Nanticoke, PA (4-347) Chor;
Drama; Key C; Rptr, Sch P; Pres, Soph Cl; COM;
Lion A; MLS; NEDT; PTA A; Span A; Pol Sci.

MARCOLINI, Carla Rene
Highland HS; Albuquerque, NM; CYO; NHS;
ARC; U of NM; Med.

MARCOOT, Marla Jean
Greenville HS; Greenville, IL (15-168) Ann; Band;
Chldr; Pres, 4H; Hmrm; Key C; NHS; Span C; SC;
Pres, Sr Cl; Mgr, Tr; Citz A; 4H A; HCt; Hon Prog;
I Dare You; St Jersey Qn; Pres, Yth Fel; Pres,
Jersey C; Pom Pom Sq; S-T, 4-H C; Greenville Col;
Ed.

MARCOTTE, James Leonard
South HS; Pueblo, CO; BS; CYO; Order/Arrow;
SC; Amer Leg A; COM; God & Country A; Order/
Arrow A; ARC A; City Wide SC; Eagle Sct.

MARCUSON, Karen A
York HS; York, NE (120-185) Cpt, Chldr; Chor;
4H; Secy, Hmrm; Bsbl; Sftbl; Cl Fav; 4H A; Pres A;
Art A's; U of Nebr; Commercial Art.

MAREK, Sarah Ellen
Exeter HS; Exeter, NE; Ann; Band; Chor; Drama;
GS; Pres, 4H; Monogram; Pres, Mu Alpha Theta;
NHS; Pres, Y-Tns; Secy, Jr Cl; B Crocker A;
DARGCA; Spch A; Vlbl; Williams Col.

MARENCHIN, Donna Suzanne
Hickory Sr HS; Sharon, PA (75-250) Secy, Chor;
Ensm; Rainbow; Mercy Hurst Col; Acct.

MARENGO, John Christopher
Gulfport HS; Gulfport, MS (33%-250) A Cap
Choir; Pres, Chor; Pres, Drama; Parl, NHS; Span C;
SC; Ftbl; COM; Most Talented; St Choir; Clarke Jr
Col; Church Mus.

MARES, Terena Sue
Las Plumas HS; Oroville, CA (40-283) Cpt, Chldr;
Drama; GS; Span C; SC; Pres, Jr Cl; HQn; Butte Jr
Col.

MARESCO, Ralph Anthony
Sacred Heart HS; Vineland, NJ; Chess C; Golf;
COM; NEDT; Villanova U; Math.

MARET, Lynn Marie
Hart Co HS; Hartwell, GA (10%-250) Band; BC;
Secy, Fr C; Hmrm; S-T, Math C; Sci C; SC; Tnns.

MARG, Lauren Louise
Forest Lake Sr HS; Forest Lake, MN (42-447) Ed,
Lit Mag; NHS; Ski C; Hon Prog; U of Minn-
Duluth; Home Ec.

MARGOLIS, Janice Michelle
Hillel Academy; Pittsburgh, PA (6-18) Chor;
Drama; Pres, Fr C; NHS; VP, Ntl Yth Conf; Co-Ed,
Sch P; SC; COM; Cert of Hon; Sr Service A; Horn
Col; Communications.

MARGOSIAK, John Stephen
Cathedral HS; Springfield, MA (200-650) U of
Mass; Engr.

MARIANO, Tamara Marie
The Gilbert Sch; Winsted, CT (15%-200) Lat C;
Span C; COM; Hon Prog; NEDT; Schol A; Fla St
U; Law.

MARIN, Elsa
St Augustine HS; Laredo, TX (1-66) Drama;
Hmrm; Secy, NHS; Bkbl; Tr; Swtht; Val; Bayani-
han A; WW; U of Houston; Tech Theatre.

MARIN, Genie
Tabernacle Christian Acad; San Diego, CA (2-6)
Cpt, Chldr; Sch P; Pres, SC; Sftbl; Journ A; San
Diego St Col; Law.

MARINI, Joseph Gerard
Archmere Acad; Claymont, DE (10-100) Chem C;
Drama; NHS; Span NHS; SC; Pres, Jr Cl; Cr-Ctry;
Tr; NEDT; Dartmouth Col; Math.

MARINO, Angela
Dover Sr HS; Dover, OH (19-273) NHS; Span C;
JV, Bkbl; Bio A; Math A; Vlbl; Eng A; Broadcast-
ing.

MARINO, Dawn Angela
Destrehan HS; New Sarpy, LA (1-200) Secy, BC;
JA A; Eng A; Highest Rank, Jr; Co-Cpt, Drill
Squad; Newcombe Col; Eng.

MARINO, Mary Theresa
John W Hallahan HS; Philadelphia, PA (25-431)
CYO; Chor; VP, Dbte Tm; Fr C; Hmrm; Pres,
Math C; Ch, Model UN; NFL; NHS; Sch P; Sci C;
VP, Spch C; Ch, St Stu Congress; World Affairs C;
Hon Prog; Spch A; Ntl Cath; Forensics League, Ntl
Comps; *Drexel U; Retail Mgt.*

MARION, Charlotte
Russell HS; Hurtsboro, AL (8-75) Chldr; Chor;
FBLA; Pres, FHA; 4H; Secy, Hmrm; Up Bound;
Secy, Jr Cl; Sftbl; 4H A; JA A; ROTC A; *Ala A&M
U; Bus Adm.*

MARION, Sharon Elaine
Burke HS; Charleston, SC (2-201) Chldr; Chor;
Drama; 4H; NHS; ARC; SC; Pres, Y-Tns; Secy,
Soph Cl; Alg A; COM; Gov Honor Prog; Math A;
Pres A; ARC A; Sal; WW; *Tuskegee U; Math.*

MARK, Darrell Wai On
Skyline HS; Oakland, CA (10%-700) InterClub
Coun; Key C; ARC; Fin, Tr; CSF; COM; Citz A;
Outst Schol A; Principal's A; Stu Participation A;
Pres, Church Yth, Comm Yth Leader; *San Jose St
U; Criminology.*

MARK, James Wing
S Pasadena HS; S Pasadena, CA; JV, Tnns; *Med.*

MARK, Patricia Ruth
El Reno HS; El Reno, OK; Band; Tres, Hmrm;
Mjrte; ARC; Span C; Spch C; Thes; Sftbl; Swim;
Tnns; COM; Band Cert; *Phys Ed.*

MARK, Wally E
Canton S HS; Canton, OH (10-300) Chor; Hmrm;
NHS; VP, Sr Cl; JV, Bsbl; COM; NEDT; PTA A;
Yth Fel; *Tenn Temple Col; Acct.*

MARKEL, Jessie Clare
W York Area HS; York, PA; Band; Co-Cpt, Chldr;
HCt; Yth Fel; Vlbl; Vol Action.

MARKEL, Mary Anne
Holy Cross HS; Marine City, MI; Chor; NHS; Ski
C; Var C; Sftbl; *U of Mich; Med.*

MARKER, Pamela Gayle
Dexter HS; Dexter, KS (2-26) Ann; Secy, Band;
Tres, FHA; NHS; Sch P; VP, SC; Pres, Jr Cl; S-T,
Soph Cl; Cpt, Bkbl; Cl Fav; HQn; Yth Fel; Vlbl;
Pride Committee; Friendliest; Most Ath; *Bus.*

MARKER, Tamara
Potter Pub HS; Potter, NE (3-14) Ann; Band; Chor;
Ensm; S-T, NHS; Pres, SC; VP, Jr Cl; Bkbl; Sftbl;
Mgr, Tr; Alt, GS; Miss Potter HS; Ltrman's C;
Outst Pep C Member; Secy, Pep C; Mgr, Vlbl; *W
Nebr Gen Hospital Sch of Nurs; Nurs.*

MARKER, Tamy
Potter Pub HS; Potter, NE (3-14) Ann; Band; Chor;
Ensm; GS; S-T, NHS; Pres, SC; VP, Jr Cl; Bkbl;
Sftbl; Mgr, Tr; Mgr, Vlbl; Miss Potter, MVP, Pep C;
W Tech Comm Col Schol; Memorial Hosp Schol;
W Nebr Gen Hospital Sch of Nurs; Nurs.

MARKERT, Tamara Ileen
Independence HS; Charlotte, NC (52-670) A Cap
Choir; Ensm; Tres, Fr C; InterClub Coun; Tres,
Key C; NHS; Pres, Fine Arts Hon Soc; Nom, Gov
Sch; WW; Opera Apprentice Prog; *U of NC; Mus.*

MARKEY, John II
Lord Botetourt HS; Daleville, VA (5-230) Chor;
Dbte Tm; FTA; Hmrm; Pres, Mod Mus Mas; NFL;
NHS; Order/Arrow; SC; COM; God & Country A;
Gov Honor Prog; 4H A; Hon Prog; Lion A; Order/
Arrow A; Spch A; Merit Badges, Eagle Sct; Mus C
Contest Win; Debate Trophies; 1st Pl, Extempora-
neous Spkr; *William and Mary Col; Law.*

MARKHAM, Carolyn Sue
Lake Highlands HS; Dallas, TX (25%-745) Fr C;
HiY; Y-Tns; Bkbl; MVP, Sftbl; Tr; *Oral Roberts U;
Elem Ed.*

MARKHAM, Jesse Lee
McDonogh 35 Sr HS; New Orleans, LA; Band;
Most Musical A; Best Dressed A; *Xavier U; Mus.*

MARKHAM, Sheri Krishena
Francis T Nicholas HS; New Orleans, LA; Band;
4H; Sftbl; *Dillard U; Nurs.*

MARKIS, Susan Marie
Whitmer Sr HS; Toledo, OH (2-895) Dbte Tm;
French NHS; NFL; Ch, NHS; Sch Achieve Tm;
Spch C; Up Bound; Amer Leg A; Hon Prog; NMF;
Opt A; Sal; Spch A; Governor's Art Exhibit; Natl
Scholastic Art A; *U of Dayton; Fine Art.*

MARKLE, Karla Louise
Elmwood HS; Bloomdale, OH (25-150) Ann; Chor;
NHS; Sch P; Yth Fel; Barbara Hillard A; *Nurs.*

MARKMAN, Sandi Kaye
Worthington Sr HS; Worthington, MN (24-268)
Chor; Ensm; Madrigal; Ski C; Tr; Stu of Excel, Bus;
Cert of Hon, 3 5 GPA; *Jackson Vo-tech; Bus.*

MARKMAN, Sonja Jo
Worthington Sr HS; Worthington, MN (13-280)
Pres, Ger C; Bkbl; Sftbl; Cert of Hon; Excel Stu,
Phys Ed & Acct; *Concordia Col; Ger.*

MARKS, Barbara Lee
Beavercreek HS; Xenia, OH; Thes; Tr; JV Gym;
Most Witty; *Ohio U.*

MARKS, Melissa Gaye
Nederland HS; Nederland, TX; Church Choir;
Secy, Church Yth; Sunday Sch Teacher; *Lamar U;
Secy.*

MARKS, Ty Stewart
Constantine HS; Constantine, MI; Band; Sch P;
Var C; Bsbl; Bkbl; MVP, Golf; Yth Fel; HR; *Ath.*

MARKSBERRY, Gary Dean
Sherwood HS; Creighton, MO (2-82) Ger C; Pres,
NHS; SC; Pres, Soph Cl; Bsbl; Bkbl; Curator A;
Math A; MLS; Sal; St Scholar; Soph Pilgrimage; *U
of Mo; Vet Sci.*

MARKUS, James Louis
Chief Sealth HS; Seattle, WA (30-500) Band; Chess
C; Bus Mgr, Hmrm; Pres, NHS; Tres, Soph Cl;
Golf; Soccer; Hon Prog; Rotary A; WW; *W Wash
Col; Bus Adm.*

MARKWELL, April
Manchester HS; Manchester, OH (25-117) Band;
Chor; 4H; Span C; 4H A; Yth Fel; *Ohio U; Teacher.*

MARLAN, Ruth Elizabeth
Highland HS; Albuquerque, NM (50-732) Chor;
NHS; ARC A; WW; Vol Hospital Worker; *Baylor
U; Pre-Med.*

MARLAR, Cheryl Kaye
Burnsville HS; Burnsville, MS (2-46) BC; Co-Cpt,
Chldr; FHA; Secy, Sr Cl; Tres, Jr Cl; Sftbl; Crisco
A; H of F; Best Sch Spirit; WW; *Northeast Jr Col.*

MARLATTE, Travis Earl
Downers Grove Hs-N; Downers Grove, IL
(79-555) NHS; Pres, Audio Visual; *Purdue U; Elec
Engr.*

MARLER, David Harvey Jr
Lumberton Sr HS; Lumberton, NC (39-269) Band;
Drama; Fr C; Key C; Monogram; A-Ed, Sch P; Sci
C; Bsbl; Swim; WW; *Campbell Col; Bus Adm.*

MARLER, Paula Jean
West Co HS; Leadwood, MO (5-48) Ed, Ann; S-T,
Band; GS; Secy, NHS; VP, Sr Cl; Alg A; Math A;
Pep C; Edison Yth Sci Day; Comm Teachers Assn
Schol; Hon Band; Dist Mus Festival; Carnival Qn;
Mineral Area Col.

MARLER, Penny Carole
Lumberton Sr HS; Lumberton, NC; Ann; Band;
Tres, Span C; SC; Swim.

MARLER, Steven Von
Hobart HS; Hobart, OK (15-52) Ann; FTA; Key C;
Sci C; Var C; VP, Jr Cl; Ftbl; Cpt, Wrest; St Champ,
N-S Tm.

MARLER, Vickie Lynn
Lumberton Sr HS; Lumberton, NC; Band; Drama;
Secy, Fr C; Hmrm; SC; Tri-HiY; Swim.

MARLIN, Peggy
Shaler Area HS; Glenshaw, PA; Chor; Pres, Rainbow; Hon Prog; *Grove City Col; Mus.*

MARLIN, Ronald David
Cuyahoga Falls HS; Cuyahoga Falls, OH (16-819)
Ger C; NHS; Hon Prog; PTA A; Rotary A; Ntl
Merit Ltr of Commendation; *U of Akron; Geol.*

MARLOW, Douglas Jay
Boone Grove HS; Boone Grove, IN (6-81) Pres,
Chess C; Drama; NHS; Phys C; A-Ed, Sch P; Sci
C; Span C; Bio A; COM; Hist A; Hon Prog; Sci
A; VP, Art C; 1st Pl, Sci Fair, Local, Regional; AV
A; *Purdue U; Bio.*

MARLOW, Wanda Lee
W Tech HS; Cleveland, OH (179-737) Chor; Ensm;
FTA; ARC; Rptr, Sch P; COM; Citz A; Service;
Western Ky U; Med Secy.

MARME, Annette Marie
Driscoll HS; Addison, IL (2-144) Cpt, Chldr; Chor;
Drama; NHS; Pres, SC; Pres, Jr Cl; HCt; St
Scholar; *St Mary's Col; Pre-Dentistry.*

MARMON, Gwen
Scott Comm HS; Scott City, KS (39-126) Band;
Chor; SC; Bkbl; Golf; Tnns; Tr; 4H A; Pres A; Secy,
Parl & Rptr, 4-H C; 4-H St Win, People-To-People;
4-H Congress; High Jumping A; 4-H St Food Judg-
ing Tm; *TV Commontator.*

MARNEY, Ellan Kaye
Commerce HS; Commerce, OK (2-70) Ann; JV,
Chldr; Chor; Secy, FHA; Secy, 4H; NHS; Bkbl; Tr;
Citz A; 4H A; Hist A; HCt; Sal; Spch A; *Northeast-
ern Okla St U; Home Ec.*

MAROLT, Anthony
Gilbert HS; Gilbert, MN (1-64) Ann; Band; CYO;
Chor; Dbte Tm; Orch; Co-Ed, Sch P; Sci C; SC;
Thes; VP, Sr Cl; Pres, Soph Cl; Co-Cpt, Ftbl; Tr;
Citz A; HCt; Math A; Val; Eagle Sct; VP, Explorers
Pres Assn; *U S Naval Acad; Oceanography.*

MAROLT, Louise
Gilbert HS; Gilbert, MN; Band; CYO; Chldr; Chor;
Dbte Tm; Orch; SC; Thes; Pres, Jr Cl; Pres, Soph
Cl; Cpt, Tnns; Citz A; HCt; *St Scholastica Col.*

MAROLT, Marie
Gilbert HS; Detroit, MI (-58).

MARONA, Cindy Maria
E Henderson HS; Hendersonville, NC (50%-290)
AFS; BC; Chor; FHA; 4H; Hmrm; ARC; Rptr, Sch
P; SC; COM; 4H A; Hist A; Most Out; ARC A; Sci
A; Yth Fel; JV Vlbl; Art A; Equestrian A; PA.

MARONEY, John Groves
Ouachita HS; Monroe, LA; Chor; Ensm; JV, Bkbl;
Cl Fav; *La Tech U; Drafting.*

MAROSE, David Paul
Minneapolis Lutheran HS; Minneapolis, MN; A
Cap Choir; Chess C; Chor; Math C; Model UN;
NHS; Phys C; Bsbl; Bkbl; Ftbl; Tr; HCt; *Concordia
Teacher's Col; Math.*

MAROTZ, Connie Sue
James Madison Mem HS; Madison, WI (325-520)
Bus C; Chor; Ski A; Mgr, Bkbl; Ftbl; Cooperative
Ed; *MATC; Merchandising.*

MAROTZ, Michael Maynard
Stanton HS; Stanton, NE (10-55) Ann; Chor;
Drama; Pres, FFA; Pres, 4H; Sch P; SC; Var C;
Bkbl; Ftbl; Tr; Citz A; 4H A; HCt; *U of Nebr;
Range Mgmt.*

MARPLE, Cheryl Ann
John Jay HS; San Antonio, TX (191-639) Band; Sci
C; *U of Tex at San Antonio; Nurs.*

MARPLE, Rhonda Blanche
Crockett HS; Crockett, TX (4-120) FTA; 4H;
NHS; Mgr, Bkbl; Hon Prog; Eng A; Art A; *U of
Denver; Mus.*

MARQUARD, Jeanne Louise
N Olmsted HS; N Olmsted, OH (57-700) Pres,
Chor; Bus Mgr, Drama; Secy, NHS; SC; Thes; Solo
& Ensm Contest; *Mt St Joseph on- the-Ohio Col;
Mus Therapy.*

MARQUARD, Karen Elizabeth
N Olmsted HS; N Olmsted, OH (25%-750) VP,
Chor; Bus Mgr, Drama; Bkbl; COM; Hon Prog;
Singing Angels; Pre-Sch CCD Prog; HS Asst, Ar-
cheaological Dig Pro Er; *Col of Mount St Joseph;
Sci.*

MARQUARDT, Donna Rae
Westfield HS; Westfield, WI (10-97) Ann; NHS;
Act C; Lib C; *Madison Area Tech Col; Printing.*

MARQUART, Dale William
Effingham HS; Effingham, IL (13-202) Band; Pres,
4H; Pres, Lat C; Order/Arrow; Mgr, Bkbl; Cpt,
Cr-Ctry; Tr; 4H A; Hon Prog; I Dare You; Order/
Arrow A; St Scholar; Yth Fel; MVP, Cross Ctry; *U
of Ill; Engr.*

MARQUEZ, Juanita
Diamond Hill-Jarvis HS; Fort Worth, TX (3-240)
Band; Pres, Hmrm; SC; Silver Eagle; *Bus.*

MARQUIE, Thomas James
St Bonaventure HS; Sturtevant, WI (1-50) NHS;
SC; Co-Cpt, Bsbl; Cpt, Bkbl; Hon Prog; K of C A;
NMF; Val; All Conf Bkbl & Bsbl; *U of Wis at
Madison; Bus Mgt.*

MARQUIS, Esther
College De St Anne De La Pocatiere; La Pocatiere, CANADA (2-30) Pres, Hmrm; VP, Var C; Co-Cpt, Bkbl; Cpt, Sftbl; Swim; Fin, Tr.

MARQUIS, Markey Jon
Del Rio HS; Del Rio, TX; God & Country A; Order/Arrow A; Eagle Sct; U of Tex; Eng.

MARQUISS, Trudy Lynn
Zion Benton HS; Zion, IL (140-470) Chldr; Chor; InterAct C; Ski C; Sftbl; Tr; Most Out; Yth Fel; Bethel Col; Early Childhood Ed.

MARQUITH, Karen Lee
Moore Haven Jr-Sr HS; Moore Haven, FL (10%-60) BC; Chldr; Chor; Rainbow; Sch P; Troy St U; Computer Sci.

MARQUITH, Ronald Kent
Moore Haven HS; Moore Haven, FL (12-79) Band; Bsbl; JV, Bkbl.

MARR, Nick Lloyd
Sam Rayburn HS; Pasadena, TX (276-578) InterAct C; Key C; Ftbl; Sftbl; Sam Houston St Col; Marine Biol.

MARR, Patricia Lee
Collingswood HS; Collingswood, NJ (40%-400) Fr C; GS; Rptr, Sch P; SC; Bkbl; Hockey; Tnns; Journ A; PTA A; Spch A; LaCrosse; Ed, Church Yth Group Newspaper; Messiah Col; Eng.

MARR, Paul Douglas
Gull Lake HS; Richland, MI; Band; Ensm; Orch; Order/Arrow; Hon Prog; Order/Arrow A; Eagle Sct A; Ntl Eagle Sct Assn; Sci.

MARR, Sarah Alice
Suffolk HS; Suffolk, VA (2-118) Drama; Monogram; NHS; Pres, SC; Thes; Co-Cpt, Bkbl; Cpt, Tnns; U of NC; Psych.

MARRA, Therese Anne
Country Day Sch o-t Sacred Heart; Overbrook, PA; Ann; Fr C; Sch P; Hon Prog; Math A; Sci A; 5th Pl City, Ntl Fr A; PA; Great Bks, Fr, Eng, Fine Arts, A's; Villanova Col; Lit.

MARRERO, Maria Victoria
Immaculata HS; Chicago, IL (16-157) NHS; Span C; Pres, Span NHS; Hon Prog; Century III Ldrs; Span Ntl Exam; Loyola U; Acct.

MARRERO, Yamil Edgardo
Wesleyan Acad; Guaynabo, PR (3-29) Chor; Drama; Model UN; NHS; Co-Ed, Sch P; VP, SC; VP, Sr Cl; Pres, Soph Cl; Mgr, Bkbl; NEDT; Stu o-t Yr; Exchange Stu; Pol Sci.

MARRIOTT, Paul Wayne
Los Angeles Baptist HS; Sepulveda, CA (12-114) Rptr, Hmrm; SC; MVP, Bsbl; Cpt, Bkbl; CSF; COM; Hon Prog; PTA A; MVP, Bkbl; Stu Assembly; Commissioner of Ath & A's; Dress Committee; Spiritual Life Coun.

MARRS, Caryn Sue
Valparaiso HS; Valparaiso, IN; Chor; Sftbl; Tnns; Citz A; Hon Prog; Pres A; Awana A; Typing HR; Grand Rapids Baptist Col; Secretarial.

MARS, Karen Lynn
Palmdale HS; Palmdale, CA (10%-550) A Cap Choir; Mgr, Band; Chor; Ensm; Fr C; Citz A; Hon Prog; PTA A; Antelope Valley Col; Bus.

MARS, Mark Edward
Azle HS; Azle, TX (10-245) NHS; Bio A; Sci A; Spch A; Calif Inst of Tech; Physics.

MARSELLA, Karen Elizabeth
Warwick Vetrans Mem HS; Warwick, RI (15%-406) French NHS; Hon Prog; Fr Hon Soc; WW; URI; Sci.

MARSELLOS, Tami LaVerne
Foothill HS; Bakersfield, CA; Chldr; Ger C; GS; SC; Sftbl; CSF; Bakersfield Col; Math.

MARSH, Arthur Andrew
General McClane HS; Edinboro, PA (30-230) FFA; JV, Bkbl; Tr; Rotary Exchange Stu; Edinboro St Col; Social Stu.

MARSH, Beverly Ann
Middle Park Jr Sr HS; Granby, CO (11-76) Arch; Chor; Span C; Type A; Brigham Young U; Bus.

MARSH, Brian Dean
Belen HS; Belen, NM (55-268) Pres, Demolay; Hist A; Sci A; Spch A; Pres, Church Yth; Meritorious Service, NRA Rifle, A; Past Master Coun, Blue Hon Key, A's; Member o-t Yr, De Molay, A's; E NM U; Religion.

MARSH, Clay S
Salina HS Central; Salina, KS (2-326) Band; Pres, Dbte Tm; HiY; Co-Ed, Lit Mag; NFL; Orch; Fin, St Stu Congress; SC; Mgr, Bkbl; Coun of Teach A; Hon Prog; NMF; NMS; Spch A; Yth Leg; Tn Republicans; Most Improved Debater; Nom Comm; Church Officers, Pastors; U of Kans; Bus Adm.

MARSH, Darrel Arnes
Overbrook HS; Philadelphia, PA (77-750) Parl, Band; Community Yth Symph; Ensm; Hmrm; NHS; Orch; Pres, Jr Cl; Cr-Ctry; COM; Cl Fav; Hon Prog; Kiwanis A; New England Conservatory of Mus; Mus.

MARSH, Dwane Dee
Charlotte HS; Charlotte, TX; Ann; Band; FFA; NHS; Sch P; Bkbl; Ftbl; Tr; Citz A; Yth Fel.

MARSH, Henry E
Prosser Voc HS; Chicago, IL; Ftbl; Tnns; Cpt, Wrest; Hon Prog; Yth Fel; Pres, Church Tns; Melodyland Sch of Theology; Bible.

MARSH, Jeffrey Charles
Middle Park Jr Sr HS; Granby, CO (20-78) Arch; Chor; Mgr, Bkbl; Colo St U; Wildlife Mgr.

MARSH, John Allen
Frankford HS; Philadelphia, PA; Chess C; SC; Ftbl; Tr; JV, Wrest; Law.

MARSH, John Howard
Hastings Sr HS; Hastings, NE; Dbte Tm; NFL; Var C; Cr-Ctry; Tr; Hastings Col.

MARSH, Judy Lynn
Douglas HS; Ellsworth A F B, SD; Hmrm; Secy, SC; Co-Cpt, Tr; HCt; Ltr Women C; MVP, Tr; Cpt, Gym; Most Dedicated Tm Mate, Runner; Concordia U; Phys Ed.

MARSH, Kathryn Lynn
Charlotte HS; Charlotte, TX; Band; Chldr; Ensm; VP, FHA; 4H; Bkbl; Tr; Cl Fav; Swtht; Yth Fel.

MARSH, Marguerite Lee
Gloucester HS; Gloucester, VA (25%-200) AFS; Chor; Hmrm; SC; Va Commonwealth U; Bus.

MARSH, Mary Paulette
Beebe HS; Beebe, AR (3-94) BC; Chor; Ensm; FBLA; FHA; Math C; Model UN; SC; Alg A; COM; Hist A; Opt A; Opt Out Tn; Home Ec A; Hon Stu A; U of Central Ark; Home Ec.

MARSH, Michael Eric
James Monroe HS; Fredericksburg, VA (14-159) AFS; Pres, Band; Dbte Tm; Fr C; Key C; Lit Mag; NHS; Sch P; Sci C; Ski C; Soccer; H of F; Hon Prog; Ntl Hon, Ntl Fed of Jr Mus Guild; Tour Choir; Pres, Jazz Ensm; WW; Ga Tech; Engr.

MARSH, Russell Hiram
Batavia HS; Batavia, IL; Band; Math C; NHS; SC; Bkbl; Ftbl; Tr; Alg A; Hon Prog; Math A; St Scholar; Augustana Col; Math.

MARSH, Shari Lynn
Carroll HS; Ozark, AL; FHA; Enterprise St Jr Col.

MARSH, Stephanie Jane
Darlington Acad; Darlington, SC (6-16) F-Ed; Ann; Chor; Ensm; Fr C; Sch P; Sci C; HQn; HCt; Francis Marion Col; Early Childhood.

MARSH, Ted A
Bremerhaven American HS; Bremerhaven, GERMANY (3-31) JV, Bkbl; Co-Cpt, Soccer; Alg A; COM; Citz A; Math A; Type A; Eng A; Sou Ill U; Archt.

MARSHALL, Barbara Louise
LaFarge HS; LaFarge, WI (3-42) F-Ed, Ann; Chor; Secy, Fr C; FHA; Secy, 4H; Ed, Sch P; Bpch C; VP, Jr Cl; Secy, Soph Cl; B Crocker A; DARGCA; 4H A; Journ A; Spch A; VFW A; VofDEM; U of Wis; Journ.

MARSHALL, Charles Jay
Winchester HS; Winchester, IL (2-80) Pres, Band; Chor; Ensm; 4H; Orch; St Scholar; NAJE Citations; WW; St Mus Educators; All St Band; Northwestern U; Med.

MARSHALL, Clara Ruth
Auburn HS; Auburn, AL (100-200) Arch; Chor; Ensm; FBLA; Secy, Pol Sci C; St Stu Congress; Yth Leg; Pres, Yth Fel.

MARSHALL, David Brian
Littleton HS; Littleton, CO (103-513) Chor; Drama; Ski C; Thes; Y-Tns; JV, Bsbl; Ftbl; COM; Ntl Achv Schol; Opt A; Pres A; Colo Sch of Mines; Sci.

MARSHALL, Diana Lynn
Winnfield Sr HS; Winnfield, LA (1-103) Tres, Anchor C; Secy, Band; BC; Chor; Ensm; FBLA; FTA; Lit Ral; Mjrte; Orch; Ch, Spch C; Hist A; JA A; MLS; Drum Mjrte; Outst Soph, Band; All Star Marching, All Dist, Bands; NE St U; Mus Ed.

MARSHALL, Elaine Esther
Spotswood HS; Spotswood, NJ (10%-114) AFS; InterClub Coun; Cpt, Mjrte; Hon Prog; All Around Stu; Elem Ed.

MARSHALL, Elizabeth Jane
Clarence M Kimball HS; Royal Oak, MI (27-678) A Cap Choir; Chor; Madrigal; NHS; Thes; Mich St U; Criminal Justice.

MARSHALL, Ellen Lillie
Gladstone HS; Gladstone, OR (15-130) Bus C; FBLA; NHS; Spch C; Type A; Shorthand A; Puget Sound Col o-t Bible; Mus.

MARSHALL, Gwen Ellen
Gurley HS; Gurley, NE (1-14) A-Ed, Ann; Mgr, Bkbl; NEDT; Type A; Highest Avg A; Pep C; Mgr, Vlbl; Concordia Col; Religion.

MARSHALL, James David
Osceola Sr HS; Kissimmee, FL; Band; JV, Tnns; COM; Sci A.

MARSHALL, James Edward
Ala Lutheran Acad; Selma, AL (2-12) Band; Bkbl; Hon Prog; Ala Lutheran Jr Col; Theology.

MARSHALL, James Llowell
Lowndes HS; Valdosta, GA; FHA; Bsbl; Ftbl; Tr; Ltrman; Davidson Col; Math.

MARSHALL, Jeffrey Allen
Turtle Creek Area HS; Turtle Creek, PA (25%-150) Hmrm; Span C; VP, Sr Cl; Mgr, Bkbl; Ftbl; Tnns; Amer Leg A; COM; Yth Fel; Cl V-P; Asbury Col; Philosophy and Religion.

MARSHALL, John Fredric
La Farge HS; LaFarge, WI (1-25) Secy, FFA; 4H; Sch P; Tres, SC; Ftbl; Tr; Wrest; COM; 4H A; Spch A; FFA Solerman A; FFA Cl Schol A.

MARSHALL, John Rambo
Morrisville HS; Morrisville, PA (25-120).

MARSHALL, Karen Denise
Southwest HS; Fort Worth, TX (78-780) Band; FHA; Mgr, Bkbl; COM; Secy, Jack & Jill of Amer; Jr Debutante; U of Tex; Communication.

MARSHALL, Karen L
Greater Latrobe HS; Latrobe, PA (30-560) Ann; French NHS; Secy, Sr Cl; Q&S A; Pres, Biol C; Vlbl; U of Pittsburgh; Nurs.

MARSHALL, Kiela Marie
Battle Creek Central HS; Battle Creek, MI; A Cap Choir; Band; Chor; Ensm; GS; Hmrm; Madrigal; SC; Bkbl; Hon Prog; Vlbl; Most Talented; Hon Library Pass; Top Female Vocalist; Olivet Col; Phar.

MARSHALL, Kimberly Anne
NC Sch o-t Arts; Winston-Salem, NC (3-60) Span Mgr, Ann; Dbte Tm; Fr C; Orch; Sch Achieve Tm; Bio A; Gov Honor Prog; Gr Marshal; Hon Prog; JA A; NMF; 1st Pl, Talent Competition; Morehead Schol; 2nd Pl, Ntl Secy o-t Yr; 1st Pl, St Mus Tchrs As Auditions; U of NC; Mus.

MARSHALL, LaSylvia Delores
Corliss HS; Chicago, IL (102-730) Chor; Drama; COM; Citz A; Coun of Teach A; MLS; Nurs.

MARSHALL, Linda Joyce
Blairsville Sr HS; Blairsville, PA (61-143) Cpt, Band; Chor; Hmrm; Mod Mus Mas; Orch; SC; Tr; HR; Bus Careers Inst; Legal Secy.

MARSHALL, Lynette Louise
Sparland Comm HS; Sparland, IL (1-34) Co-Ed, Ann; Secy, Band; VP, Chor; FFA; VP, FHA; Pres, 4H; Spch C; Secy, SC; 4H A; I Dare You; Lion A; NEDT; Spch A; Type A; Yth Foundation; 4-H Key C; Director's Band A; FFA Schol Pin; *N Ill U; Med.*

MARSHALL, Marilyn Rae
DuBois Sr HS; DuBois, PA (22-325) Co-Cpt, Chldr; 4H; Hmrm; NHS; SC; Var C; HCt; Nicest Smile; *Nurs.*

MARSHALL, Marilyn Sue
Granville HS; Granville, OH (7-130) Drama; Fr C; NHS; Span C; Bsbl; Tr; Hon Prog; Vlbl; HR; Ntl Fr Test; GAA; *Earlham Col; Foreign Lang.*

MARSHALL, Martha Marie
Osceola HS; Kissimmee, FL (11-276) Type A; VP, Drill Tm; Span A; *Atlanta Christian Col; Secy Sci.*

MARSHALL, Melinda Lorraine
Mexico Sr HS; Mexico, MO (10%-310) Chor; Drama; Hmrm; NFL; SC; JV, Tnns; Citz A; Opt A; Pres, Fresh Cl; FCA; Outst Yth A; *U of Mo; Journ.*

MARSHALL, Michelle Lenaye
Inglewood HS; Inglewood, CA; Chldr; Chor; Madrigal; SC; Pres, Sr Cl; Pres, Jr Cl; CSF; Cl Fav; HCt; Pres A; Chair; WW; *Long Beach St Col; Sci.*

MARSHALL, Mike Wayne
Columbia HS; Columbia, IL (6-127) Band; BS; Tres, 4H; Pres, NHS; Var C; Bkbl; Tr; 4H A; Pres A; Type A; *U of Mo at Rolla; Elec Engr.*

MARSHALL, Pamela Lynn
Argenta-Oreana HS; Argenta, IL (1-100) AFS; Band; Chldr; Chor; Fr C; VP, FHA; Secy, 4H; NHS; Pres, SC; Amer Leg A; B Crocker A; Cl Fav; 4H A; MLS; St Scholar; *Millikin U; Vocal Mus Ed.*

MARSHALL, Patrick Michael
Gurley Pub Sch; Gurley, NE (2-12) Chor; JV, Bkbl; NEDT; Sci A.

MARSHALL, Rebecca Holly
Milford Sr HS; Milford, DE; Ger C; Hmrm; NHS; SC; Var C; MVP, Tnns; 2nd, Lawn Tnns Assn; *Med.*

MARSHALL, Rhonda Alease
Charles A Brown HS; Charleston, SC (4-145) F-Ed, Ann; Tnns; Band; Pres, BC; Chor; Community Yth Symph; 4H; Pres, Hmrm; Mu Alpha Theta; NHS; Orch; Ed, Sch P; COM; Cl Fav; Hon Prog; Most Out; Pres A; Val; Yth Fel; *Communication.*

MARSHALL, Richard Henry
Franklin Acad; Malone, NY (200-265) Drama; Rptr, Hmrm; BSct; Altar Boy; Lector for Church.

MARSHALL, Richard Ledell
Saint Rita HS; Chicago, IL (121-400) CYO; Bsbl; Sftbl; Hon Prog; *Devry Inst of Tech; Elec Engr.*

MARSHALL, Sandra Lynn
John D Bassett HS; Bassett, VA (15-300) F-Ed, Ann; Chor; Ensm; Secy, 4H; Jr Miss Pagent; NHS; COM; Citz A; Cl Fav; 4H A; Yth Fel; A-Ed, Annual; Mus A's; *Patrick Henry Col; Social Services.*

MARSHALL, Shari Elizabeth
Lincoln HS; Ellwood City, PA (40%-252) Band; Drama; Ger C; 4H; Math C; Rainbow; Y-Tns; COM; 4H A; Hon Prog; *Penn St U; Computer Sci.*

MARSHALL, SueAnn
McConnellsburg HS; McConnellsburg, PA; Bus C; FHA; COM; 4H A; VP & Secy, 4-H C; *Harrisburg Thompson Inst; Data Processing.*

MARSHALL, Tammy Virginia
William Monroe HS; Stanardsville, VA; Chor; Sci C; Art A; *Blue Ridge Comm Col; Vet Asst.*

MARSHALL, Teresa Rene
Owsley Co HS; Booneville, KY (5-50) BC; Cpt, Chldr; Chor; Pres, FHA; Pres, 4H; Rptr, Sch P; Up Bound; COM; 4H A; Swtht; Yth Fel; WW; Co Fair As; Win, Calif Trip; Soil Conserv, Regional Runner-Up; *U of Ky; Dentistry.*

MARSHALL, Terri Lynn
Plant City HS; Plant City, FL; A-Ed, Ann; Band; NHS.

MARSHALL, Tessie Lynn
Madison HS; Richmond, KY; BC; Pres, Chor; Drama; Ensm; Spch C; COM; Opt A; Chor A; *Eastern Ky U; Nurs.*

MARSHALL, Thomas Ernest
MacArthur HS; Irving, TX (2-555) Ann; Band; NHS; Order/Arrow; Hon Prog; Eagle Sct; Highest GPA, Jr Cl; *Tex A&M U; Language.*

MARSHALL, Timothy Paul
Jefferson Sr HS; Cedar Rapids, IA; Acct.

MARSOLEK, James Ralph
Courtenay Pub Sch; Courtenay, ND (5-7) Bkbl; Sftbl; Tr; Bkbl Ltr.

MARSTALLER, Mark Douglas
Livermore Falls HS; Livermore Falls, ME (7-94) BS; VP, Chess C; Chor; Drama; Math C; NHS; Sci C; VP, Span C; Mgr, Bkbl; Alg A; DARGCA; Math A; S-T, Chess C; *U of Maine; Chem Engr.*

MARSTELLER, Helen Elizabeth
Kennard-Dale HS; Fawn Grove, PA (43-170) Chor; FBLA; Pres, 4H; 4H A; Hon Prog; *Ntl Legal Secy Sch; Legal Secy.*

MARTELLO, Matthew
Loyola HS; Towson, MD (7-134) Chor; NHS; Span C; Span NHS; Bsbl; Co-Cpt, Bkbl; Cpt, Ftbl; Hon Prog; MVP, Ftbl; Coaches' A; 3rd, St Fr; Lacrosse; Schol-Ath; Span Medal; *U of Sou Calif; Med.*

MARTENS, Emily Luise
Marcus Whitman HS; Rushville, NY (1-130) Band; Ensm; NHS; JV, Tnns; Citz A; 4H A; Pres, VP & Tres; *Cedarville Col; Acct.*

MARTENS, Joni Sue
Vestavia Hills HS; Birmingham, AL (33%-290) Band; FHA; Basic C; Band Solo & Ensm Medals.

MARTENS, Judi Kay
Vestavia Hills HS; Vestavia Hills, AL (30-300) Citz A; Basic C.

MARTENS, Leona Marie
Rosati-Kain HS; St Louis, MO (1-112) Band; CYO; Chldr; Chor; Ensm; NHS; Orch; Alg A; COM; Hon Prog; Math A; Opt A; NMSQT-PSAT Top 5%; Municipal Opera All HS Band; *Actuarial Sci.*

MARTENS, Linda Kay
Leavenworth Sr HS; Leavenworth, KS; Ann; Band; Chess C; Chor; 4H; Cpt, Mjrte; Orch; Scq; Schol-Ath; SC; Bkbl; Cr-Ctry; Tnns; Tr; Citz A; 4H A; Journ A; Q&S A; Yth Fel; 1st Runner Sunflower Miss Pageant; *Patricia Stevens Col; Modeling.*

MARTH, Janet Leigh
Civic Mem HS; Bethalto, IL (115-250) S-T, Band; Drama; FTA; Ger C; 4H; Mjrte; 4H A; VofDEM; *Concordia Teachers Col; Elem Ed.*

MARTHALER, Monica May
Brooten HS; Brooten, MN (3-36) A Cap Choir; F-Ed, Ann; Band; Bus C; Pres, CYO; Chldr; Chem C; Chor; Drama; Ensm; NHS; Rptr, Sch P; Thes; Secy, Jr Cl; Tres, Soph Cl; Cpt, Bkbl; COM; Citz A; Lion A; Most Out; Star Student; MVP, Bkbl; Missing Spoon, Thespian; A's; Chldr Trophy; Most Rebounds, Most Assists, Bkbl; *Minn Sch of Bus; Court Rptr.*

MARTIN, Abby LaTranquil
Stephens Co HS; Toccoa, GA (8-295) Pres, Anchor C; BC; Dbte Tm; GS; Mjrte; Pres, NHS; Tri-HiY; VP, Soph Cl; JV, Bkbl; Amer Leg A; COM; Hist A; Yth Choir; CAR; Prom Ch, Jr Cl; *Social Stu.*

MARTIN, Alice Frances
Truman HS; Independence, MO (82-663) Ann; CYO; Hmrm; Sch P; Span C; Span NHS; Citz A; Cl Fav; Q&S A; Pep C; *SW Mo Col; Bus.*

MARTIN, Amy Louise
William Fleming HS; Roanoke, VA (8-500) BC; Chldr; Chor; Tres, FBLA; VP, FTA; COM; *Comm Hospital Sch of Nurs; Nurs.*

MARTIN, Anna Gayle
Huntsville HS; Huntsville, AL (10%-480) Anchor C; NHS; ARC; VP, Yth Fel; St Del, Ntl Yth Ministry Congress; Tres, Dist VP, CYF; Regional Tres & Pres, CYF; *U of N Ala; Nurs.*

MARTIN, Annette Gaye
Clifton Forge HS; Clifton Forge, VA (6%-65) BC; FBLA; Tri-HiY; Hon Prog; Hugh O'Brien Jaycees A; *Dabney S Lancaster Comm Col; Secretarial Sci.*

MARTIN, Barry William
Augusta Christian Acad; Augusta, GA (2-40) Soccer; Sftbl; Swim; Tnns; COM; Citz A; Hon Prog; Schol A; *Augusta Col.*

MARTIN, Becky R
Harrah HS; Harrah, OK (22-122) A-Ed, Ann; Fr C; SC; Cpt, Bkbl; Sftbl; Tr; COM; Citz A; HQn; HCt; Hon Prog; WW; HS All Amer, Bkbl; Fin, FCA Female Ath o-t Yr; City All Star, Bkbl; *Okla St U; Phys Ed.*

MARTIN, Beverly Lynn
Washington HS; Los Angeles, CA (10%-500) Chor; Span C; SC; Citz A; Hon Prog; Choir A; Usher; *Trade Tech Col; Bus.*

MARTIN, Bonnie Lou
Proviso W HS; Hillside, IL (72-890) Tres, Chor; GS; Pres, Madrigal; NHS; Co-Cpt, Drill Tm; Mus Schol; WW; Bronze Cert; Audition, Universal Acad of Mus.

MARTIN, Brenda Anna
Grover Cleveland HS; Brooklyn, NY; Bus.

MARTIN, Brian Harris
Starmount HS; Boonville, NC (16-204) Span C; Cr-Ctry; Tnns; *U of NC; US Hist.*

MARTIN, Bruce Allen Scott
Ballard HS; Seattle, WA (89-439) Band; Soccer; Hon Prog; *Shoreline Comm Col.*

MARTIN, Candaca
Northeast HS; Oklahoma City, OK (5-185) Chor; Drama; Secy, Fr C; VP, Ger C; Math C; Mu Alpha Theta; NHS; Sci C; COM; Hist A; Type A; Panhellenic Assn A; Woodman A; Cum Praestantic; Glen Morgan Schol; *Okla City U; Pre-Med.*

MARTIN, Cathy Elaine
Civic Mem HS; Bethalto, IL; FHA; FNA; *Lewis & Clark Col.*

MARTIN, Charlie Hurst III
Franklin HS; Rocky Mount, VA (80-450) Pres, Hmrm; Span C; SC; Pres, Var C; Bsbl; Ftbl; Most Out; Pres & VP, Yth Fel; Sr Mirror; Cpt, Defense Ftbl; All-Metro Bsbl; FCA; *Madison Col; Communications.*

MARTIN, Cheryl Ann
Hobbs HS; Hobbs, NM (36-485) JV, Band; NHS; Tres, Rainbow; *NM Jr Col; Acct.*

MARTIN, Christi Ann
Aurora Central HS; Aurora, CO (33-475) S-T, A Cap Choir; S-T, Chor; Drama; Secy, Ensm; FBLA; NHS; Thes; *U of Northern Colo; Mus Ed.*

MARTIN, Christopher Scott
Albemarle HS; Charlottesville, VA (161-624) SC; Spch A; Yth Wk Pastor; Pres, Secy, Church Yth Coun; *VPI; Marketing.*

MARTIN, Colleen Ann
Amity Regional HS; Woodbridge, CT (37-638) 4H; 4H A; Hon Prog; Math A; ROTC A; Outst Poetry; *Ariz St U; Psych.*

MARTIN, Creston Michael
Del Norte HS; Albuquerque, NM; *Baylor U; Med.*

MARTIN, Cynthia Dawn
St Andrews Parish HS; Charleston, SC; JV, Chldr; FHA; VP, Hmrm; Y-Tns; *Col of Charleston; PE Ed.*

MARTIN, Cynthia Dianne
Antioch HS; Nashville, TN (190-392) Chess C; Chor; FHA; Bkbl; Sftbl; St Off Ed C; Most Cooperative Stu; *Acct.*

MARTIN, Daniel Joseph
Don Bosco Tech HS; Boston, MA (3-211) CYO; Secy, NHS; SC; Swim; Tr; Pres A; *US Naval Acad; Oceanography.*

MARTIN, Daniel Keith
Lyons Township HS; LaGrange, IL (65%-5000) Chor; Ftbl; Wrest; St Scholar; *Augustana Col.*

MARTIN, Darrell Lloyd
Macon Drive Christian HS; Atlanta, GA (2-10) Ann; Chor; Ensm; SC; Bsbl; Bkbl; Ftbl; Soccer; Ftbl Ltr; *Mus.*

MARTIN, Darren Michael
Arvada W HS; Arvada, CO; VP, Demolay; VP, 4H; 4H A; Church Sch Cadet; Ldrship Conf & Course; Scribe, De Molay; *Chem Engr.*

MARTIN, David Anthony
Cardinal Spellman HS; Bronx, NY; CYO; Chess C; Hmrm; Bkbl; COM; *Syracuse U; Acct.*

MARTIN, David Bruce
Buchholz HS; Gainesville, FL (75-400) AFS; Fr C; Hmrm; NHS; Order/Arrow; Sci C; SC; Ftbl; Swim; Tnns; Eagle Sct; *U of Fla; Sci.*

MARTIN, Deborah Lynn
Madison Comprehensive HS; Mansfield, OH; Band; Fr C; FHA; Tnns; Yth Fel; Parl, St Off Ed Assn; *Bus.*

MARTIN, Denise Elaine
Temple Heights Christian HS; Tampa, FL; Chor; Ensm; NHS; Bkbl; Tnns; Hon Prog; *Lee Col; Mus.*

MARTIN, Denise Marie
Amherst HS; Snyder, NY (5-249) Chldr; Hmrm; ARC; Bkbl; Tnns; JA A; *Fashion Inst; Fashion Design.*

MARTIN, Donald James
Northern Lebanon HS; Fredericksburg, PA; Cr-Ctry; Tr; JV, Wrest; Bicycling & Backpacking A.

MARTIN, Donna Lynn
Iowa HS; Iowa, LA (1-100) F-Ed, Ann; GS; Fin, Lit Ral; NHS; Ed, Sch P; Sci C; Bio A; COM; Chem A; *McNeese St U; Computers.*

MARTIN, Donna Mae
Springtown HS; Springtown, TX; FHA; FTA; Fin, Jr Miss Pagent; Mgr, Bkbl; Mgr, Tr.

MARTIN, Dwight Eric
Western Grove HS; Western Grove, AR; 4H; Bkbl; 4H A; *U of Ark; Agr.*

MARTIN, Earl Jamel
Withrow HS; Cincinnati, OH; Bsbl; JV, Bkbl; JV, Ftbl; *U of Cincinnati; Med.*

MARTIN, Eileen Elizabeth
Blair HS; Blair, NE (6-150) Ann; CYO; Chor; Secy, FHA; Sci C; VP, Span C; JV, Bkbl; Sftbl; Tr; DARGCA; Pres A; Type A; Phys Fitness A; Alt, All-St Choir; HR; WW; Ltr, Pep C & Varsity Choir; *West Point; Military.*

MARTIN, Elizabeth Millie
Rufus King HS; Milwaukee, WI; *Bryant And Stratton Col; Keypunch.*

MARTIN, Elizabeth Suzanne
Park View Sr HS; S Hill, VA (6-209) Ann; Secy, BC; Chldr; Chor; Fr C; FTA; Hmrm; Alg A; Math A; Choir; All Region Choir; Handbell Choir; Acteens; Girls Action; *Old Dominion U.*

MARTIN, Enith Pearl
Walton HS; Bronx, NY; Chess C; Drama; Fr C; S-T, ARC; Sch P; Arch; Bkbl; Soccer; Bio A; COM; Hist A; MLS; Most Out; Sci C; HR Fel; Social Stu A; Attendance A; *Columbia U; Med.*

MARTIN, Eric Ostrom
Community HS; Houston, TX (10%-98) Hmrm; NHS; VP, SC; Tnns; COM; Citz A; DARGCA; Most Out; ROTC A; *Sam Houston St U; Law Enforcement.*

MARTIN, Floyd Allen Jr
Ash Fork HS; Ash Fork, AZ; Band; 4H; SC; Pres, Soph C; 4H A; Hon Prog; Sal; Band A; Jr Phys Fitness A; *PE Ed.*

MARTIN, Francis Marion
Tallulah Acad; Tallulah, LA (5-30) Ann; Cpt, Chldr; Chor; FHA; 4H; Hmrm; Lit Ral; Secy, NHS; Spch C; SC; Beauty; Cl Fav; HC; Spch A; Type A; Miss Tallulah Acad, WW; *Northeast La U; Elem Ed.*

MARTIN, Freddie Ann
Marvell HS; Marvell, AR (9-120) Chor; FHA; Spch C; SC; Hon Graduate; Health & Safety, Chor, A's; *Home Ec.*

MARTIN, Gail Elizabeth
Francis Lewis HS; Flushing, NY (50%-794) Chor; Span C; Up Bound; Hockey; *Ind St U; Communications.*

MARTIN, Georgine
Meridian HS; Meridian, TX; Band; BC; Drama; FHA; Mjrte; Sch P; Bkbl; Fin, Tr; Swtht; Band, Ftbl, Swtht's; *Tex A&M U; Special Ed.*

MARTIN, Glenn David
Greenville HS; Greenville, TX (10-325) BS; Pres, Ger C; VP, Math C; VP, Order/Arrow; Ftbl; JV, Tr; Bausch & Lomb A; Cl Fav; Math A; Opt A; Order/Arrow A; Sci A; Eagle Sct; *Austin Col; Engr.*

MARTIN, James Craig
S R Butler HS; Huntsville, AL; Cpt, Band; Ensm; Orch; COM; NEDT; *U of Ala; Engr.*

MARTIN, Jane Elaine
Eufaula HS; Eufaula, OK (1-100) Chor; FHA; 4H; NHS; Span C; COM; Hist A; Val; Best Dressed; HR; St Hon Soc; *NE Okla St U; Pre-Law.*

MARTIN, Jean Camille
Valley City HS; Valley City, ND (25%-160) FHA; Tr; Gym; *Valley City St Col; Bus.*

MARTIN, Jeffrey Alan
Austintown-Fitch HS; Youngstown, OH (124-750) Youngstown St U; Psych.

MARTIN, Jeffrey Donald
East Central HS; Tulsa, OK; Chem C; Tnns; Wrest; Hist A; Pres A; Christian Ath Outreach; *Oral Roberts U; Law.*

MARTIN, Jeffrey Layne
Medford Sr HS; Medford, OR (20-700) Pres, A Cap Choir; Ensm; Madrigal; NHS; SC; Thes; Var C; Ftbl; Tr; NMS; All NW Choir; WW; All St Choir; *Sou Oreg St Col; Ed.*

MARTIN, Jerry Paul
Gila Bend HS; Gila Bend, AZ (2-50) Var C; Bsbl; Bkbl; Ftbl; Amer Leg A; *Mech.*

MARTIN, Jill
Buckley HS; Sherman Oaks, CA (5-63) Chldr; Hist A; *USC; Eng.*

MARTIN, Jill Kathleen
Oregon City Sr HS; Oregon City, OR (30-500) Hmrm; Sch P; Swim; Win, Ntl Jr Olympics Medal; *U of Oreg; Bus.*

MARTIN, Jill Marie
Notre Dame HS; Salinas, CA (12-100) Chldr; Fr C; GS; NHS; Bkbl; NEDT; *Santa Clara Col; Social Sci.*

MARTIN, John Lind
Mountain Brook HS; Mountain Brook, AL (38-375) Chor; Ensm; NHS; JV, Bkbl; Ftbl; Tr; Eagle Sct; *Samford U; Religion.*

MARTIN, John P
Oil Trough HS; Oil Trough, AR (1-16) Ann; Tres, FTA; Pres, 4H; Pres, SC; Bio A; 4H A; Val; Lib, Sch Service, A's; *Ark St U; Computer Sci.*

MARTIN, Jorge
St Peters Prep HS; Jersey City, NJ (1-260) Band; Ed, Lit Mag; Pres, Span C; Amer Leg A; COM; Hon Prog; NEDT; Val; Eng A; Lat A; Span A; *Yale Col; Mus.*

MARTIN, Karen Kay
Fairfield Comm HS; Fairfield, IL (10-200) Band; Chor; Ensm; Pres, Fr C; FTA; WW; *Lincoln Christian Col; Semitic Lang.*

MARTIN, Kari Ann
Bear Creek Sr HS; Lakewood, CO; Band; Russian C; 1st Pl, Short Story Comp; Fin, Sr Div Comp; *Lang.*

MARTIN, Katherine G
St Charles HS; St Charles, IL; 4H; Sftbl; COM; 4H A; *U of Ill; Bus.*

MARTIN, Kathy Elaine
Duncan HS; Duncan, OK (17-314) FBLA; FHA; NHS; JV, Bkbl; Sftbl; Tr; COM; Hist A; Opt A; Sci A; St Phar Assn; *Okla St U Acad Achv A; WW; Okla Christian Col; Bus.*

MARTIN, Kathy Marie
Central HS; Columbus, OH (40-400) Co-Cpt, Chldr; Pres, IOE; Ath A Cert; Cert of Schol Achv; Cert of Appr, Outst Serv Acct; *Phys Therapy.*

MARTIN, Keith Daniel
Kenmore E Sr HS; Tonawanda, NY (15%-700) Band; NHS; Orch; Order/Arrow; Var C; Ftbl; JV, Swim; Tr; Hon Prog; Regent Schol; Stage Band; Eagle Sct Sr Patrol Ldr; Jr Asst Sct-Master; *St U of NY; Bio.*

MARTIN, Keith William
Claremore HS; Claremore, OK; VP, Jr Cl; Bsbl; Ftbl; Tr; FCA; Pres, Yth Coun; *Okla Baptist U; Religion.*

MARTIN, Ken Edward
N Gwinnett HS; Suwanee, GA (10%-190) BC; Chess C; MVP, Dbte Tm; Key C; Fin, Lit Ral; NHS; Var C; JV, Bkbl; Tnns; COM; Gov Honor Prog; *Baylor U; Debate.*

MARTIN, Kenneth Edwin Jr
Olmsted Falls HS; Olmsted Falls, OH (1-227) Band; Ensm; NHS; Orch; Sch Achieve Tm; Bsbl; Bio A; COM; Chem A; Hon Prog; Math A; *Life Sci.*

MARTIN, Kristin Coy
Plano Sr HS; Plano, TX (10%-1150) Drama; Fr C; NHS; Thes; *Biol.*

MARTIN, Laura Virginia
Starmount HS; Boonville, NC (35-204) Chldr; FHA; Span C; Co-Cpt, Sftbl; MVP, Sftbl; *Forsyth Tech Col; Dental Hygiene.*

MARTIN, Laurie Jean
Rock Lake Pub HS; Rock Lake, ND (2-23) Tres, CYO; Chor; FHA; 4H; Bkbl; Sftbl; Tr; 4H A; Sci A; *ND St U; Sci.*

MARTIN, LeAnn
Central Dauphin HS; Harrisburg, PA (10%-520) Band; Chor; Ger C; Madrigal; NHS; ARC; *Penn St U; Pre Med.*

MARTIN, Lee Ann
Wade Hampton Acad; Orangeburg, SC (29-72) Band; JV, Chldr; Chor; Rptr, Sch P; Span C; Co-Cpt, Bkbl; Sftbl; Cheerer; *Clemson U; Bus Adm.*

MARTIN, Lisa Gay
Texas City HS; Texas City, TX; Band; Mjrte; Alg A; Outst Band; Ntl Jr Hon Soc; Drum Major; *U of Tex; Math.*

MARTIN, Lisa Laraine
Parkview Sr HS; Orfordville, WI (7-150) A-Ed, Ann; Band; FHA; 4H; Math C; NFL; NHS; Arch; Tr; *Madison Area Tech Col; Med Lab Tech.*

MARTIN, Lori Ann
Beemer Pub HS; Beemer, NE (1-21) Co-Ed, Ann; VP, Band; Chldr; Chor; GS; Pres, 4H; Secy, NHS; Secy, Jr Cl; Pres, Soph Cl; JV, Bkbl; 4H A; H of F; HQn; HCt; Hon Prog; Vlbl; WW; *Kearney St Col; Nurs.*

MARTIN, Lori Lynn
Ellet HS; Akron, OH (25%-380) A Cap Choir; Chor; Ger C; Madrigal; Fin, NHS; Sftbl; COM; Gym C; Vol Service Recognition; Schol A; *Akron U; Mus.*

MARTIN, Lydia
Seward Park HS; New York, NY; Band; Yth Fel; *Acct.*

MARTIN, Marguerite Virginia
Immaculata HS; Chicago, IL (5-157) Secy, Fr C; French NHS; 4H; Hmrm; NHS; F-Ed, Sch P; SC; 4H A; Hon Prog; St Scholar; Ntl Merit Commended Stu; *Purdue U; Acct.*

MARTIN, Marianne
Notre Dame HS; Clarksburg, WV (13-52) Bus; Bus C; CYO; Chor; Drama; FBLA; FTA; Bkbl; *W Va U.*

MARTIN, Marie Antoinette
Niagara Falls HS; Niagara Falls, NY; A Cap Choir; Chor; Fr C; Rptr, Hmrm; Co-Cpt, Bkbl; Sftbl; *Psych.*

MARTIN, Marie Lanette
Shawnee Mid-HS; Shawnee, OK (5-325) FHA; VP, Hmrm; SC; Tri-HiY; Sftbl; Hon Prog; Type A; Soph Spirit Ldr; Spirit A; VP, Pep C; *OBU; Mus.*

MARTIN, Marlon Brent
Fayetteville Sr HS; Fayetteville, AR; A Cap Choir; Pres, Band; Chor; Madrigal; Most Out; All St Choir; All St Band; Drum Major; *U of Ark; Mus Ed.*

MARTIN, Martha Kimberly
Tecumseh HS; Tecumseh, OK (15-101) A Cap Choir; Band; Pres, Chor; Ensm; 4H; Span C; Var C; Bkbl; Sftbl; Tr; Hon Prog; Tres, Pep C; Tr A; Academic Achv A; Outst Mus A; Camp Fire A; *Cottey Col; Home Ec.*

MARTIN, Mary Elizabeth
Walnut HS; Walnut, MS (10-50) F-Ed, Ann; BC; Chldr; Chor; Pres, FHA; Spch C; JV, Bkbl; Beauty; B Crocker A; H of F; Most Talented; *Miss St U; Banking.*

MARTIN, Matt J
Ponder HS; Ponder, TX (3-16) Rptr, FFA; Pres, Jr Cl; Bkbl; Tr; Chem A; Hist A; MLS; Sci A; *Tex Women's U; Nurs.*

461

MARTIN, Michael Hamilton
S Salem HS; Salem, OR; MVP, Band; Ensm; NFL; Spch C; Interlochen Ntl Mus; MLS; Spch A; Jazz Mus; CRISP, Band Involvement Prog; *North Western Col; Mus.*

MARTIN, Michael John
St Mary's Prep; Orchard Lake, MI (1-32) Ski C; Secy, SC; Pres, Jr Cl; Tr; Summa Cum Laude; Highest Hon; *Med.*

MARTIN, Michael Louis
Renton HS; Renton, WA (39-303) Chess C; Dbte Tm; Drama; Ger C; VP, Hmrm; Thes; Var C; Mgr, Bsbl; JV, Bkbl; Ftbl; Tr; Hon Prog; Star Student; Baccalaureate Speaker; *Oral Roberts U; Theology.*

MARTIN, Milla Kay
Carney HS; Carney, OK (2-12) Ed, Sch P; Pres, Sr Cl; Tres, Jr Cl; Secy, Soph Cl; Bkbl; Tr; Citz A; Masonic A; Most Out; 1st, St UICA Skill Contest; *Printing.*

MARTIN, Mimi
Penncrest HS; Media, PA (33%-500) A Cap Choir; Band; Chor; Ensm; Pres, 4H; Hmrm; Madrigal; Orch; SC; Hockey; Mgr, Soccer; Mgr, Swim; 4H A; Hon Prog; Mus A; Pres, Church Yth Group; *W Chester St Col; Mus.*

MARTIN, Molly Dearman
Hattiesburg HS Rowan Center; Hattiesburg, MS (5%-500) Cpt, Chldr; Y-Tns; B Crocker A; Hon Prog; Most Sch Spirit; Special Hon; *Miss St U; Home Ec.*

MARTIN, Monique Marie
Our Lady of Fatima HS; Lafayette, LA; BC; Bus C; Chess C; Drama; Fr C; Lit Ral; Pres, Math C; Pres, Mu Alpha Theta; NHS; SC; Thes; Swtht; Ntl Bus Hon Soc; *U of Southwestern La; Acct.*

MARTIN, Natalia
Maria Reina Acad; Rio Piedras, PR; CYO; Chor; Fr C; Model UN; NFL; NHS; Sch P; COM; NEDT; 3rd Pl, Ntl Fr Exam; *Georgetown U; Econ.*

MARTIN, Natalie Ann
Circleville HS; Circleville, OH (25%-217) JV, Band; JV, Chldr; GS; Secy, 4H; Lat C; NHS; Bkbl; Co-Cpt, Tr; Most Out; Cpt, Vlbl; Luther League; *OSU; Phys Ed.*

MARTIN, Patricia
Maria Reina Acad; Rio Piedras, PR (1-80) Fr C; French NHS; NHS; Sch P; Pres, SC; Bio A; NEDT; Spch A; *Bio.*

MARTIN, Patricia Gale
Miller Co R III HS; Tuscumbia, MO (3-28) Band; Cpt, Chldr; Chor; Pres, 4H; Tres, NHS.

MARTIN, Patrick
St Bede Acad; Peru, IL (60-127) CYO; Hmrm; Rptr, Sch P; Sodality; Ch, SC; MVP, Ftbl; MVP, Tr; Amer Leg A; COM; Journ A; Summa Cum Laude; Ed, Sch P; Phys Fitness, Ftbl, Tr, Sci, A's; *Worsham Col of Mortuary Sci; Mortician.*

MARTIN, Phillip Wade
Cass City HS; Cass City, MI (11-157) Band; Ensm; NHS; Orch; ARC; Bkbl; Ftbl; Sftbl; Swim; Tnns; NHS A; WW; *Ferris St Col; Phar.*

MARTIN, Phyllis Lynn
Levelland HS; Levelland, TX (50%-260) Band; JV, Bkbl; Tr; JNHS; Swtht, Lion's C; FCA; *S Plains Col.*

MARTIN, Raymond Charles
John Muir HS; Pasadena, CA (23-600) Fr C; Pres, HiY; Swim; CSF; Hon Prog; NMS; Water Polo; PUC-ESAA Fr Merit; *Westmont Col; Phys Ed.*

MARTIN, Rhonda Lee
Edison Sr HS; Lake Station, IN (1-160) Pres, Chor; Drama; Ensm; VP, Fr C; Hmrm; Madrigal; VP, NHS; Secy, SC; MLS; Val; Yth Fel; HR; PA; 12 Yr Church Pin; *Purdue U; Nurs.*

MARTIN, Robert Anthony
Marion Co HS; Lebanon, KY (40-324) Secy, Band; Fr C; NHS; *Georgetown Col; Mus.*

MARTIN, Robert Hiram
Woodward Acad; College Park, GA (50%-200) Band; Chor; Community Yth Symph; Bsbl; JV, Bkbl; Ftbl; Pres A; Bsbl A.

MARTIN, Robert LeAndrew
Finney HS; Detroit, MI; MVP, Arch; HiY; MVP, Arch; MVP, Hockey; Swim; COM; Citz A; Masonic A; Yth Foundation; Bowl A's & Trophies; *John Wesley Col; Phys Ed.*

MARTIN, Robin Elizabeth
West End Acad; Franklin, LA (4-15) Dbte Tm; Hmrm; Fin, Lit Ral; Secy, SC; Bkbl; Tr; HCt; Hon Prog; Yth Fel; Church Choir; Fin, Typing A; *U of Southwestern La; Home Ec.*

MARTIN, Sally Ann
John Ehret HS; Marrero, LA (33-450) Pres, 4H; Hmrm; Lit Ral; Pres, Mu Alpha Theta; NHS; ARC; Sci C; SC; Secy, Jr Cl; COM; 4H A; Hon Prog; I Dare You; Math A; Sci A; Bowling; WW; Bicen Comm Cert of Appreciation; *Nicholls St U; Computer Sci.*

MARTIN, Samuel Thornton
R Nelson Snider HS; Ft Wayne, IN (99-501) Band; Chor; Orch; St Scholar; Choir Ltr; Orch & Band Cert; St Vocal 1st Division; *Moody Bible Inst; Theology.*

MARTIN, Sandra Rhenelle
Benhaven HS; Olivia, NC; Ann; Band; BC; FHA; Cpt, Mjrte; Sch P; SC; Miss BHS; Eng, Mjrte, A's; *Central Carolina Tech Inst.*

MARTIN, Sara Lee
Robinson Sch; Santurce, PR (4-37) NHS; Span C; Math A; NEDT; Val; Art A; High Hon A; Adv Placement Prog; *Occupational Therapy.*

MARTIN, Sara Sue
W Mid-High Sch; Norman, OK (100-300) VP, Chor; Drama; Ensm; Hmrm; SC; Citz A; Asst Director, Children's Choir; Bell Chor; Church Sftbl; Cpt, Bowl; Puppet Ministry; Mus Medals; Page, St House of Rep; *Okla U; Drama.*

MARTIN, Scott Anthony
N Las Vegas Christian Sch; N Las Vegas, NV (1-9) Ed, Ann; Band; Pres, Chess C; Chor; NHS; Phys C Ed, Sch P; Sci C; SC; COM; Citz A; Hon Prog; Math A; Most Out; Sci A; Yth Leg; Amateur & Commercial Radio Oper; *Med.*

MARTIN, Scott Patrick
Bret Harte HS; Angels Camp, CA (85-120) Spch C; SC; Var C; Pres, Jr Cl; Cpt, Bkbl; Cpt, Ftbl; Cpt, Tr; Most Ath; All League Ftbl & Bkbl; *Hartnell Jr Col; Archt.*

MARTIN, Sheila Jo
Panhandle HS; Panhandle, TX (25%-45) Band; Drama; Secy, FHA; Pres, FTA; Secy, 4H; NFL; Spch C; Secy, Thes; 4H A; JA A; *Angelo St U; Interior Design.*

MARTIN, Sheila Ruth
Brandon Acad; Brandon, MS; Ann; BC; Rptr, 4H; NHS; A-Ed, Sch P; Secy, SC; Beauty; Citz A; 4H A; Yth Fel; VP, Yth Coun; *Miss St U; Mus.*

MARTIN, Sheila Yvonne
Spruce Creek HS; Daytona Beach, FL; Chor.

MARTIN, Siri Lou
Winona Sr HS; Winona, MN; Band; Chldr; Drama; GS; Span C; SC; Var C; Y-Tns; Pres, Sr Cl; Swim; *Ed.*

MARTIN, Stanley John
Genoa HS; Genoa, OH (1-10) BS; Chor; Rptr, 4H; Bsbl; Cpt, Bkbl; Tr; 4H A; Pres, 4-H C; *NE Jr Col; Agr.*

MARTIN, Susan Camille
Wayne Co HS; Jesup, GA; Band; JV, Chldr; FBLA; Hmrm; S-T, SC; COM; HCt; Semi-Fin, Swtht Contest.

MARTIN, Suzanne Helene
N Beach Jr Sr HS; Moclips, WA (20%-73) Rptr, Ann; Chor; FHA; Semi-Fin, GS; NHS; F-Ed, Sch P; Tnns; Tr; Journ A; Math A; Type A; Most Improved, Tr; *Grays Harbor Jr Col; Secretarial Sci.*

MARTIN, Teena Jane
Ralph L Fike HS; Wilson, NC (100-500) Dbte Tm; Drama; Key C; Math C; ARC; Span C; COM; ARC A; Florence Kidder Participant; Qn Regent in Service, Service Aid; Wilson's Write to Win Essay Contest; Acteens; *U of NC; Med.*

MARTIN, Terence Buell
Scotia-Glenville HS; Scotia, NY (20-450) AFS; Chor; Drama; Order/Arrow; Eagle Sct; *Math.*

MARTIN, Teresa Eileen
Miami Edison Sr HS; Miami, FL; Dbte Tm; Secy, Drama; SC; Secy, Thes; Superior, Dist Thes Conf; *Bethune Cookman Col; Eng.*

MARTIN, Terry Bernard
Humboldt HS; Humboldt, TN; Chor; Spch C; Cpt, Bkbl; Tr; MVP, Bkbl; Tr A; *Lambuth Col; Bus Adm.*

MARTIN, Terry Clayton
Tabernacle Baptist Sch; Va Beach, VA (13-27) NHS; Bsbl; Ftbl; Wrest; Pres, Yth Fel; Pro-tns; Homiletics, Phys Ed, Preach, A's; *Bob Jones U; Homiletics.*

MARTIN, Terry Dan
Bret Harle Union HS; Angels Camp, CA (20-125) A-Ed, Sch P; SC; Bkbl; Hon Prog; Yth Fel; Young Life C; *Law.*

MARTIN, Thomas Gregory
Winnfield Sr HS; Winnfield, LA; FTA; Spch C; Bkbl; Ftbl; Tr; *La Tech U; Elec Engr.*

MARTIN, Timothy
William Penn Sr HS; York, PA (104-400) Band; Chor; Drama; Thes; Swim; Gov Honor Prog; MLS; Most Out; *Mus.*

MARTIN, Timothy Andrew
R Nelson Snider HS; Ft Wayne, IN (80-600) Band; Orch; Mgr, Tr; Hon Prog; Math A; Art A; Orch A.

MARTIN, Timothy Joseph
St Bede Acad; Peru, IL (87-126) Chor; Ftbl; *Ill St U; Forrestry.*

MARTIN, Timothy Richard
Lyons Township HS; La Grange, IL (50-1200) Ftbl; Hon Prog; NEDT; *Sci.*

MARTIN, Tobi Roxane
Woodlawn HS; Shreveport, LA (1-400) A Cap Choir; Ann; Chor; VP, Fr C; Hmrm; InterClub Coun; Lit Ral; Math C; Mu Alpha Theta; NHS; Rptr, Sch P; Thes; Pres, Y-Tns; Tnns; Alg A; Math A; Close Up Govt A Schol; *LSU; Lang.*

MARTIN, Tonia Lynn
Nettie Lee Roth HS; Dayton, OH; Chldr; Drama; Hmrm; Gym; *Sinclar Comm Col; Modeling & Drama.*

MARTIN, Valerie Annette
Adlai E Stevenson HS; Bronx, NY; NHS; Tnns; Hon Prog.

MARTIN, Vicki Camille
Parkview Sr HS; Little Rock, AR; Ann; BC; Chor; Community Yth Symph; Ensm; FBLA; Hmrm; Fin, Jr Miss Pagent; Madrigal; Sci C; St Stu Congress; SC; Y-Tns; Cl Fav; H of F; Spch A; Swtht; Ark Jr Miss; *Ouachita Baptist U; Communications.*

MARTIN, Vienna Lyn
Canal Winchester HS; Canal Winchester, OH (16-110) Band; S-T, Drama; FTA; GS; Hmrm; NHS; Span C; Spch C; Thes; JV, Bkbl; Amer Leg A; COM; Hon Prog; Spch A; Type A; Yth Fel; *U of Va; Pol Sci.*

MARTIN, Wanda Joyce
Carver HS; Birmingham, AL (21-237) FBLA; Secy, SC; Tri-HiY; HQn; HCt; Hon Prog; ROTC A; *Ala A&M U.*

MARTIN, Wayne Alan
San Jacinto HS; San Jacinto, CA (2-75) Fr C; VP, InterAct C; Span C; SC; Var C; VP, Soph Cl; Cpt, Bsbl; Ftbl; Tr; Bank Of Amer A; CSF; Hon Prog; Rotary A; Jr Cl Rep; *Calif Polytech Inst; Elec.*

MARTIN, Wayne Thomas
Wilcox Co HS; Rochelle, GA (10-97) Ann; Drama; FFA; 4H; Var C; Mgr, Bkbl; Ftbl; Tnns; Tr; Cl Fav; Hon Prog; *Ga SW Col.*

MARTIN, William Doss Jr
Fern Creek HS; Louisville, KY (11-264) BC; Fr C; NHS; Cr-Ctry; Sr Superlative; WW; Opt C; PA A; *U of Ky.*

MARTIN, William Kenneth
Southwood HS; Shreveport, LA (52-510) FFA; InterAct C; *LSU; Gen Stu.*

MARTIN, William Riley
Mannington HS; Mannington, WV (7-115) NHS; Bsbl; Ftbl.

MARTIN, William Robert III
Princeton HS; Princeton, NJ (33%-250) A Cap Choir; Ann; Secy, Chor; Drama; VP, InterAct C; Madrigal; Rptr, Sch P; Span C; SC; Soccer; COM; Yth Fel; Gold Key A; 2nd, Co Essay Contest; Presbyterian Elder; *Davidson Col; Religion.*

MARTIN, Yolanda Kay
Booker T Washington HS; Houston, TX; F-Ed, Ann; Chor; Dbte Tm; Tres, Drama; Tres, NFL; Tres, NHS; Tres, Spch C; St Stu Congress; Pres, SC; Alg A; Bio A; COM; Citz A; Cl Fav; God & Country A; Hon Prog; JA A; Math A; MLS; Most Out; Spch A; *U of Tex; Pre-Law.*

MARTIN, Yvonne Ellen
Pleasant Valley Sr HS; Chico, CA (115-250) Chor; Drama; FHA; Hmrm; Spch C; SC; Bsbl; Hockey; Soccer; VP, Sftbl; Most Inspiring Soccer; *Pt Loma Col; Phys Ed.*

MARTINDALE, Della Anita
Walnut HS; Walnut, MS (10-65) Band; Pres, Chor; FFA; FHA; Agr A; *NE Jr Col; Dental.*

MARTINELLI, Michael Joseph
Sacred Heart HS; Vineland, NJ; Chor; NHS; SC; Pres, Jr Cl; VP, Soph Cl; Bsbl; JV, Bkbl; JV, Cr-Ctry; Amer Leg A.

MARTINELLI, Rosemaria
E Aurora HS; Aurora, IL (18-563) VP, A Cap Choir; Band; Drama; Ensm; Ger C; NHS; Thes; Superior, St Solo Contest; *Wheaton Col; Mus.*

MARTINELLI, Teresa Maria
San Gabriel Mission HS; San Gabriel, CA (10%-80) Pres, Chem C; Rptr, Fr C; Rptr, Hmrm; Madrigal; Pres, Math C; Mu Alpha Theta; VP, NHS; Phys C; Sch Achieve Tm; Pres, Sci C; VP, St Stu Congress; SC; Var C; Rptr, Soph Cl; Bkbl; Bank Of Amer A; COM; Hon Prog; Math A; Vlbl; Academic Achv; WW; NHS Cert to Stu Aboard; GAA Achv; *Calif St U at Los Angeles; Engr.*

MARTINETTI, Thomas Albert
St Joseph's o-t Palisades HS; W New York, NJ (3-225) NHS; Span NHS; Cpt, Bkbl; Hon Prog; MLS; NEDT; Rensselaer A; *Pre-Med.*

MARTINEZ, Amarylis
Jose de Diego HS; Mayaguez, PR; Sci C; COM; Hist A; Hon Prog; Summa Cum Laude; C de Becarios.

MARTINEZ, Ana de Fatima
Academia Ntra Sra Providencia; Rio Piedras, PR (1-58) Ann; CYO; Chor; Dbte Tm; Drama; Hmrm; Fin, Jr Miss Pageant; Lit Ral; Span C; Spch C; SC; Beauty; COM; Hon Prog; Spch A; Conduct A; *Saint Mary's Dominican Col.*

MARTINEZ, Carlos
Gomper HS; Bronx, NY (9-30) Chor; JETS; NHS; COM; Hon Prog; *City Col; Elec Engr.*

MARTINEZ, Christopher Conrad
Luther Burbank Sr HS; Sacramento, CA; Band; Ensm; Math A; Eng A; *U of Calif-Berkley; Bio.*

MARTINEZ, Darlene
Simon Gratz HS; Philadelphia, PA; Secy, Chldr; FTA.

MARTINEZ, Debbie Renee
Alamosa HS; Alamosh, CO; Band; CYO; Sftbl; *Adams St Col; Bus.*

MARTINEZ, Doramir
Luis Munoz Rivera HS; Lajas, PR (5-175) BC; Chldr; Chor; Cum Laude Soc; Drama; FHA; 4H; ARC; Thes; Beauty; H of F; Opt A; Poet A; Swtht; Type A; Yth Foundation; *Cath U of Ponce; Psych.*

MARTINEZ, Fred Steven
Alamosa HS; Alamosa, CO (100-200) Band; *ASC.*

MARTINEZ, Gerald Dean
Alamosa HS; Alamosa, CO; SC; Var C; Cr-Ctry; Pres A; Guitar Band; Bsbl A's; *Calif St U; Med.*

MARTINEZ, Hilda Denise
Dr Pila HS; Ponce, PR; CYO; Hmrm; NHS; COM; Cl Fav; Hon Prog; Lion A; St Scholar; Lib C; *Cath U of PR; Sci.*

MARTINEZ, Hugo
Academia del Sagrado Corazon; Santurce, PR (12-65) Ann; NHS; ARC; Sch P; Alg A; COM; Hist A; *Embry Riddle Col; Aeronautical Engineer.*

MARTINEZ, Iraida
Jose de Diego HS; Mayaguez, PR; Bus C; Chor; 4H; Sci C; COM; Magna Cum Laude; C de Becarios.

MARTINEZ, Joseph
Miguel Melendez Munoz; Bayamon, PR (2-250) Hmrm; Order/Arrow; ARC; Ed, Sch P; Alg A; COM; Hist A; Math A; Order/Arrow A; Eagle Sct A; *U of Puerto Rico; Dentistry.*

MARTINEZ, Juanita Louise
Albuquerque HS; Albuquerque, NM (33%-500) CYO; Chldr; Tres, Rainbow; Ski C; Bsbl; Bkbl; Yth Vol; *U of NM; Ed.*

MARTINEZ, Lidia
S San Antonio HS; San Antonio, TX (34-415) Chor; Math C; Hon Prog; *E Tex Baptist Col; Mus.*

MARTINEZ, Lino Louis
Richmond HS; Richmond, CA (27-287) A Cap Choir; Co-Ed, Ann; Chor; Ensm; Lat C; Madrigal; VP, Sr Cl; COM; Hon Prog; Hon Graduate; Alma La Raza Schol; *W Baptist Bible Col; Biblical Lang.*

MARTINEZ, Luis Alberto
Our Lady of Pilar HS; Rio Piedras, PR (20%-166) Chem C; Model UN; NHS; *Pepperdine U; Interntl Law.*

MARTINEZ, Luis Antonio
Dr Pila HS; Ponce, PR; VP, CYO; VP, Dbte Tm; Rptr, Sch P; Sftbl; Bio A; COM; Cl Fav; Spch A; *Cath U; Law.*

MARTINEZ, Maria Ivonne
Luis Munoz Marin HS; Cabo Rojo, PR (1-200) Pres, Chldr; Pres, Dbte Tm; Drama; Pres, Hmrm; NHS; ARC; Cpt, Swim; Fin, Tnns; Alg A; Amer Leg A; Bio A; COM; Chem A; Hist A; Hon Prog; Magna Cum Laude; Math A; Pres A; Sci A; Spch A; Exchange C A; *CAAM-UPR; Med.*

MARTINEZ, Mary Jane
Jefferson Davis Sr HS; Houston, TX (5-312) Pres, Bus C; CYO; FHA; Ch, Hmrm; NHS; Amer Leg A; COM; Citz A; Outst HERO Stu; *Sam Houston St U; Sociology.*

MARTINEZ, Monica Maria
Alpine HS; Alpine, TX; CYO; Span C; JV, Bkbl; 'A' HR.

MARTINEZ, Pablo Alberto
St Augustine HS; Laredo, TX (15%-70) BS; NHS; Tres, Soph Cl; Alg A; Hist A; Hon Prog; Math A; Sci A; NCTE Achv A; WW Nom; Contestant, My Ctry, Right Or Wrong; *UT at San Antonio; Med.*

MARTINEZ, Ramon Luis
Jose de Diego HS; Mayaguez, PR; Band; ARC; Bsbl; Bkbl; Sftbl; Bio A; COM; Magna Cum Laude; Sci A.

MARTINEZ, Rivera Elmer
Francisco Mendoza HS; Isabela, PR; A Cap Choir; AFS; BS; CYO; Chldr; Chem C; Chess C; Chor; City Conf; Drama; Hmrm; Order/Arrow; Pol Sci C; ARC; Sch P; Sci C; Span C; Cpt, Bsbl; Cpt, Bkbl; MVP, Sftbl; Cpt, Swim; Bio A; COM; Citz A; Cl Fav; Lion A; Order/Arrow A; Sci A; Star Student; Summa Cum Laude; Instructor A; Ldrship A; *U of Puerto Rico; Laws.*

MARTINEZ, Steven Dale
Windber Area HS; Windber, PA (20%-146) Band; Ensm; F-Ed, Lit Mag; NHS; Orch; Order/Arrow; Citz A; Order/Arrow A; Yth Fel; Yth Leg; Sch Quizz Television; Drum Major; Com Ch, Worship Redbrd Tsk Force Co; Gov Sch for Arts, Summer 1977; *U of Penn; Liberal Arts.*

MARTINEZ, Sylvia
Benjamin Franklin HS; Los Angeles, CA; CYO; FTA; Hmrm; Pres, Rainbow.

MARTINEZ, Sylvia Iris
San Antonio HS; Rio Piedras, PR (3-103) Chor; Drama; NHS; Spch C; Christian Ethics A.

MARTINEZ, Tomas
Academia Santa Monica; Santurce, PR; Ann; VP, Drama; Model UN; NHS; Co-Ed, Sch P; Spch C; VP, SC; Tnns; COM; Spch A; Hon A; *St Mary's U; Med.*

MARTINEZ, Tony
Chillicothe HS; Chillicothe, TX (5%-15) FFA; VP, SC; Pres, Soph Cl; Bsbl; Cpt, Ftbl; Fin, Tr; Citz A; *Tex A&M U; Agr.*

MARTINEZ, Virginia Cecilia
Alpine HS; Alpine, TX; Band; Rptr, CYO; S-T, FHA; Hmrm; SC; COM; Chem A; Hist A; Eng A; Homemaking A; *Sul Ross St University; Bus Adm.*

MARTINEZ, Yvonne Carol
Windber Area HS; Windber, PA (20%-154) Band; Drama; Ensm; Orch; Yth Fel; Lib C; St Yth Fel; FPT Yth Adv Board; *Edinboro Col; Art.*

MARTINI, Cindy Sue
Bridgeport HS; Bridgeport, OH; Ann; Pres, Bus C; Cpt, Chldr; GS; VP, Lat C; Secy, NHS; Rainbow; Sch Achieve Tm; SC; VP, Y-Tns; Hist A; Rotary A; Val; Rptr, Y-Tn; WW; Lat A; Eng A; Nts A; *Wheeling Col; Bus Ed.*

MARTINO, Larry Joseph
Hartford HS; White River Jct, VT (10-175) Band; JV, Bsbl; Mgr, Bkbl; Oratory A; *Bus Field.*

MARTINO, Val Keith
Harding Acad of Memphis; Memphis, TN; Band; Dbte Tm; Sch P; Sci C; Spch C; World Affairs C; COM; NEDT; Church Bsbl; Drama Production; Big Brother Prog; *U of Tenn Psych C; ACT School.*

MARTINSON, Ronny James
Fairmont HS; Fairmont, MN (44-215) Ger C; Bkbl; Ftbl.

MARTOCCIA, Catherine L
Cardinal Newman HS; W Palm Beach, FL (10-300) Tres, CYO; Bio A; COM; Hon Prog; Math A; Civitan C; Yth Fitness Achv A; HR; *Sci.*

MARTSOLF, Teresa Dale
Oakridge HS; Oakridge, OR (45-90) Band; Chor; *Airline Stewardess.*

MARTUCCI, Paul David
St Peters Prep HS; Jersey City, NJ (102-275) Bsbl; Cpt, Swim; *Rutgers U in Newark; Acct.*

MARTY, David Edward
LuVerne Comm Sch; LuVerne, IA (3-18) Ann; Semi-Fin, BS; Pres, 4H; Secy, Jr Cl; VP, Soph Cl; Bsbl; Bkbl; Tr; 4H A; Type A; VofDEM; Yth Fel; All Conf, Bkbl & Bsbl; *Iowa St U; Agr.*

MARTY, Diane Marie
LuVerne Comm Sch; LuVerne, IA (4-14) Ann; Pres, Band; Chldr; VP, Chor; 4H; Rainbow; Secy, SC; B Crocker A; 4H A; HCt; Type A; Yth Fel; REC Yth Tour; *Iowa Central Comm Col.*

MARTZ, Deborah Elizabeth
Bishop Klonowski HS; Scranton, PA; Chor; NHS; Sodality; Bkbl; Amer Leg A; Col Essay Contest; *U of Scranton; Med.*

MARTZ, Teresa Marie
Goodlettsville HS; Goodlettsville, TN (10%-185) CYO; FTA; Lat C; NFL; Ed, Sch P; Bio A; Citz A; NEDT; VFW A; *Eng.*

MARUMOTO, Wendy Hideko
George C Marshall HS; Falls Church, VA (36-471) SC; Ntl Fin, Accordian Assn.

MARUNA, Linda Marie
Coldwater HS; Coldwater, OH; Band; CYO; Chldr; Chor; Drama; Ger C; Secy, Jr Cl; Co-Cpt, Bkbl; Swim; Tr; Chldr A.

MARVIN, Lois Marie
Colonel Crawford HS; N Robinson, OH (20-150) Band; Chor; Ensm; Fr C; FTA; Co-Ed, Sch P; Yth Fel; *Bowling Green St U; Vocal Mus Ed.*

MARVIN, Raymond Francis
Whitmer HS; Toledo, OH (33%-925).

MARX, Winfield
Malcolm X Shabazz HS; Newark, NJ (2-354) NHS; Pres, SC; Up Bound; Cpt, Ftbl; Cpt, Tr; COM; Hist A; MLS; Sal; Sci A; Schol Ath A; Stu Achv A; *Rutger's Col; Pre-Med.*

MARYOTT, Cheryl Susan
Minnechaug HS; Wilbraham, MA; Drama; *Bus.*

MARZE, Dianne
Merryville HS; Merryville, LA (7-46) VP, Fr C; Pres, FBLA; Key C; Fin, Lit Ral; Secy, Sci C; Spch C; Cpt, Bkbl; Sftbl; DARGCA; HCt; WW; McNeese St Trustees Schol; Most Ath A; Delta Kappa Gamma Schol; *McNeese St U; Phys Ed.*

MASAR, Margaret Louise
Orofino HS; Orofino, ID (3-135) CYO; HR; *U of Idaho.*

MASARO, Mary Angela
Burnsville HS; Burnsville, MS; Band; BC; Fin, Ensm; VP, FHA; 4H; SC; Pres, Soph Cl; Mgr, Bkbl; Sftbl; Tr; Beauty; Cl Fav; H of F; HCt; *Northeast Ms Jr Col; Secretarial Sci.*

MASCHMEYER, William Alan
Perry Meridian HS; Indianapolis, IN (51-572) Band; Chess C; Dbte Tm; Order/Arrow; Spch C; Var C; JV, Bsbl; Wrest; Order/Arrow A; Eagle Sct.

MASCO, Anthony Paul
Luther HS S; Chicago, IL (22-175) Order/Arrow; Spch C; JV, Bsbl; JV, Wrest; Hon Prog; Order/Arrow A; ARC A; Spch A; Val; Mayor's Clean- up Chicago A.

MASEDA, Maureen Emelia
Notre Dame HS; Clarksburg, WV (7-63) Band; Dbte Tm; Drama; Ensm; Lat C; Lit Mag; Math C; NHS; S-T, ARC; Sci C; Spch C; Spch A; *Med Sci.*

MASEK, Sue Elizabeth
Lemont Township HS; Lemont, IL (23-195) Ann; NHS; Thes; Tr; Amer Leg A; COM; Library Aide; Statistician, Wrest & Bkbl; Accompanist for Piano; *Wheaton Col; Bus.*

MASENHEIMER, David Charles
York Suburban Sr HS; York, PA (22-298) Pres, Chor; Tres, Drama; Ensm; NHS; SC; Amer Leg A; COM; God & Country A; NMF; NMS; Jr & Sr Cl Senator; Dist, Region, St, Chor; WW; *Dickinson Col.*

MASERANG, Daniel Philip
Belleville Twp HS W; Belleville, IL (33-842) Tres, Band; BS; Chess C; Community Yth Symph; Drama; Orch; Bus Mgr, Sch P; Soccer; Alg A; Math A; VFW A; Drum Major; *MIT; Physics.*

MASH, Connie Diane
Putnam City W HS; Oklahoma City, OK; Drama; Hmrm; NFL; Pres; Spch C; Thes; COM; Spch A; Ntl Tn Talent with Singing Group; First Regionals in DI Drama; Miss Life Lineer of Okla Center; *Central St U; Drama.*

MASHBURN, Connie Louanne
Sou Baptist Educational Center; Memphis, TN (19-127) Ann; Chldr; Chor; Ensm; Span C.

MASHBURN, Jan E
Carrollton HS; Carrollton, GA (100-200) Band; FHA; Semi-Fin, Jr Miss Pa; SCnt; Tri-HiY; *Emory Col; Law.*

MASINGILL, Joan Elizabeth
Girl's Prep Sch; Chattanooga, TN (40-95) Co-Cpt, Chldr; Chor; Drama; Fr C; ARC; Rptr, Sch P; Soccer; Sftbl; Citz A; Art & Mus Cert's; *Auburn U; Fashion Merchandising.*

MASK, M Timothy
Frayser Baptist HS; Memphis, TN (30-66) Chor; Hmrm; Bsbl; Bkbl; Ftbl; Wrest; Cl Fav; Mr Frayser Baptist; Most Dependable; Most Talented; *Memphis St U; Engr.*

MASLOFF, Emily Short
Albemarle HS; Charlottesville, VA (15%-650) Ann; NHS; Secy, Span C; Span NHS; Mgr, Hockey; Dist Fin, Ntl Span Exam.

MASMINSTER, Mary Carol
Western Hills HS; Cincinnati, OH (12%-900) Hmrm; ARC; Span C; Cr-Ctry; Mgr, Swim; Mgr, Tnns; Bio A; MVP, Tr; *Col of Mount St Joseph; Nurs.*

MASNY, Mark Stephen
Freeport Sr HS; Freeport, IL (40%-575) Band; Order/Arrow; Ftbl; JV, Tr; JV, Wrest; Order/Arrow A; Sci A; Yth Fel; Bike C; Beekeepers Assn; BScts; *Forestry.*

MASON, Barbara Faye
Berkeley HS; Berkeley, CA; *U of New Orleans; X-Ray Technician.*

MASON, Bernita Selena
Ahoskie HS; Ahoskie, NC (20-300) Chor; FHA; Hmrm; InterClub Coun; SC; *U of NC; Phys Therapy.*

MASON, Brian William
East Side HS; Newark, NJ (1-426) BS; Chor; Hmrm; NHS; Tnns; Citz A; Hon Prog; Lion A; PTA A; Rotary A; Val; Yth Fel; Penn Savings & Loan Assn A; Outst Member o-t Cl of 1977; *Brown U; Pol Sci.*

MASON, Cheryl Ann
Bishop Dunne HS; Dallas, TX; Chor; Tnns; *N Tex St U; Psych.*

MASON, Claude Alan
Rossville Comp HS; Rossville, GA (1-225) Pres, Band; BC; Chor; Fr C; Pres, FTA; Hmrm; Lit Mag; NHS; Sci C; SC; Var C; Tnns; Alg A; Bio A; COM; Gov Honor Prog; Hist A; Hon Prog; Math A; NEDT; Sci A; Alt, All-St Band; Nom, McDonalds All-Amer Band; Presbyterian Col Schol; Highest Fresh Eng A; *Oberlin Col; Mus Ed.*

MASON, Danette Renee
Westchester HS; Los Angeles, CA (3-20) Chldr; Tnns; *U of Sou Calif; Sci.*

MASON, Daniel Burton
Moulton-Udell HS; Moulton, IA; A Cap Choir; Pres, Band; Chor; Drama; FFA; Madrigal; Math C; Orch; B Crocker A; Yth Fel; WW; *McPherson Col; Agr.*

MASON, Deanna Marie
Findlay HS; Findlay, OH (76-587) Band; Chor; Pres, FNA; *St Vincents Sch of Nurs; Sci.*

MASON, Diane Marie
Logan HS; Logan, OH; Band; Secy, 4H; 4H A; Hon Prog; Yth Fel; Director, Jayteens; Jayteen o-t Yr; *Dietitian.*

MASON, Dinah Carol
Montgomery Co HS; Mt Sterling, KY; Band; Y-Tns; Sftbl; Tr; *Lexington Tech Inst; Data Processing.*

MASON, Georgie Latham
Vanguard HS; Ocala, FL (11-350) ARC; Mu Alpha Theta; NHS; COM; VofDEM; *Fla Sou Col; Phys Sci.*

MASON, Hugh William
Henry Sibley Sr HS; Mendota Heights, MN (198-548) A Cap Choir; Chor; Key C; Spch C; Thes; Swim; Spch A; *ND St U; Engr.*

MASON, Jacqueline Lorraine
W S Creecy HS; Rich Square, NC (10-42) Pres, BC; Chldr; Chor; Drama; Pres, Fr C; VP, SC; Pres, Sr Cl; Co-Cpt, Bkbl; Pres A; *NC Central U; Pol Sci.*

MASON, James Ewell
Douglas MacArthur HS; San Antonio, TX; Ger C; Bsbl; Golf; *Tex A&M U; Agr.*

MASON, John Albert
Clear Creek HS; League City, TX (2-453) Drama; JETS; Tres, NHS; Order/Arrow; Ski C; Thes; Swim; Hon Prog; Order/Arrow A; Rotary A; Sal; Yth Fel; Water Polo; Most Dependable; Eagle Sct; *US Air Force Acad.*

MASON, John William
E C Glass HS; Lynchburg, VA (10%-450) VP, Band; BS; Ensm; Hmrm; Lat C; Sch P; Sci C; SC; Tnns; Tr; Drum Major Band; Sup Rating, Solo Band Fest; *UVA.*

MASON, Jonathan Whitcomb
Parkersburg HS; Parkersburg, WV (25%-840) Bkbl; Bus Adm.

MASON, Julie Ann
Polytechnic HS; Riverside, CA (50-493) AFS; ROTC A; Hon Men; 'Talking Hands' Pin, Deaf Interp; *Central Col; Fr.*

MASON, Kelvin
Williamston HS; Williamston, NC; FFA; Monogram; Bkbl; Ftbl; Swim; Tr; Cl Fav; Most Out; Sports A.

MASON, Linda Elaine
Zion Benton Twp HS; Zion, IL (110-394) Fr C; French NHS; Ger C; Sci C; Bkbl; Sftbl; Tnns; COM; Pres A; Co Cpt, Vlbl; A of Excel, Eng; *Greenville Col; Phys Ed.*

MASON, Lori Ann
Susan Wagner HS; Staten Island, NY (33-700) Fin, Chldr; Pres, Hmrm; Rptr, Sch P; Cr-Ctry; Tnns; Tr; Pres, Yth Fel; *Sou Methodist U; Acct.*

MASON, Marilyn Jene
Naperville N HS; Naperville, IL (20-450) A Cap Choir; AFS; Fr C; NHS; Curator School; *Central Methodist Col.*

MASON, Mary Kay
Douglas Co HS; Castle Rock, CO (39-315) Fr C; NHS; Calculus A; Fr A; Soc of Women Engr Math & Sci A; St Energy Research Inst Schol; *Colo St U; Mech Engr.*

MASON, Matthew Kirk
St Mary's Prep; Orchard Lake, MI (4-44) AFS; NHS; Rptr, Sch P; Ski C; COM; Hon Prog; Journ A; WW.

MASON, Melanie
Cartersville HS; Cartersville, GA (30-150) Secy, Chor; Ensm; Fr C; Hmrm; F-Ed, Sch P; Pres, Tri-HiY; *Eng.*

MASON, Melanie Elizabeth
Robert E Lee HS; Houston, TX (Chor; Drama; FHA; Secy, FTA; Hmrm; F-Ed, Sch P; Pres, Span C; SC; Pres, Young Amers for Freedom; Pres, Christian Stu Union; Yth Adv Board; Prog Coun; Spirit C; Tex Hist C; Stu Adv Coun; *U of Tex; Communications.*

MASON, Melvin
Williamston HS; Williamston, NC (60-219) Drama; Tres, Fr C; FBLA; Hmrm; Monogram; VP, SC; MVP, Tnns; Alg A; Citz A; *E Carolina U; Art.*

MASON, Mitzi Jo
Herndon HS; Herndon, VA; Band; Soccer; *U of Va; Nurs.*

MASON, Patty Marie
Franklin HS; Franklin, IL; Chldr; FHA; NHS; Span C; Tr; HCt; *Radiology.*

MASON, Reginald Prentiss
Matoaca HS; Chesterfield County, VA (10-175) Chor; Key C; Ftbl; *Va St Col; Bio.*

MASON, Sandra Denise
Mary Brantley Smiley HS; Houston, TX (24-400) Cpt, Chldr; FTA; Math C; Mu Alpha Theta; NHS; Tnns; COM; *U of Houston; Med Tech.*

MASON, Sandra Denise
Penn View Bible Inst; Penns Creek, PA; Ann; Band; Chor; Type A; Acct A.

MASON, Tina Marie
East Central HS; Hurley, MS;

MASON, Victoria Jean
Montgomery Co HS; Mt Sterling, KY; Band; Y-Tns; Bkbl; Sftbl; PA.

MASON, Wayne Brian
Susan E Wagner HS; Staten Island, NY (152-762) City Conf; Pres, Hmrm; InterClub Coun; Ntl Yth Conf; Pres, Ski C; Var C; Ftbl; Cpt, Tnns; COM; Coun of Teach A; God & Country A; Pres A; Yth Fel; MVP, Tnns; Stu Athlete A; *U of Tenn Chattanooga; Pre-Law.*

MASON, Wayne Gary
Miami Jackson Sr HS; Miami, FL; ARC A; Reading A.

MASONHALL, Connie Lou
Okeene HS; Okeene, OK (2-38) Band; Fin, Jr Miss Pagent; Mjrte; Rptr, Sch P; Bkbl; Cl Fav; 4H A; HQn; St Hon Soc; St Jr Miss Pageant; 1st Run-Up, Whea-Esta Pageant; Miss Congeniality, Whea-Esta Pag; *OSU; Bus.*

MASOTTO, Michael Steven
Parkway W Sr HS; Chesterfield, MO; *Archt.*

MASSARO, Fred Joseph
Montclair HS; Montclair, NJ (33%-450) Band; Ensm; SC; Bkbl; Wrest; *Montclair St Col; Bus Adm.*

MASSARO, Gina Maria
Plymouth Salem HS; Canton, MI (4-400) Dbte Tm; Drama; NFL; NHS; Ski C; *U of Mich; Bio.*

MASSARO, Laurie Ann
Greater Latrobe HS; Latrobe, PA (7-518) AFS; Chldr; Tres, Chor; Hmrm; Secy, NHS; Ed, Sch P; Sci C; Ski C; Span C; Thes; Var C; World Affairs C; Tres, Sr Cl; Sftbl; Cpt, Tnns; Chem A; Hon Prog; Journ A; Q&S A; ARC A; Rotary A; Rptr, Sch P; Director, Jr Cl Play; Sch Mus; *U of Pittsburgh; Phar.*

MASSE, Ronald Roland
Montachusett Regional HS; Fitchburg, MA; Tres, Christ Ambassadors; Jr Commander, Royal Rangers; Christian Service A; Ranger o-t Yr; *Zion Bible Inst; Ministerial Major.*

MASSENBURG, Dwane Edgar
Sussex Central HS; Sussex, VA (6-186) BC; Hmrm; Pol Sci C; Sci C; Span C; Co-Cpt, Ftbl; Co-Cpt, Tr; COM; Semi-Fin, Tr; Marine Corps YPF; *Ga Inst of Tech; Civil Engr.*

MASSENBURG, Michael Arnold
George Washington HS; Los Angeles, CA (87-575) Tres, A Cap Choir; Pres, Tri-HiY; JV, Bkbl; Citz A; Hon Prog; Yth Fel; Bicentennial Observance A; Amer Lit A; Faithful Service A; Art A; *Long Beach St U; Art.*

MASSEY, Anne Patricia
Notre Dame-Bishop Gibbons HS; Schenectady, NY; Rptr, Sch P; Bkbl; Tnns; NEDT; Sci A; Vlbl.

MASSEY, Becky Jane
Maysville HS; Maysville, OK (9-40) Band; FBLA; Tres, NHS; Sch P; Co-Cpt, Bkbl; Alg A; Cl Fav; HQn; Swtht; Type A; Eng, Stu o-t Mo, A's.

MASSEY, Con Smith
Greater Atlanta Christian Sch; Norcross, GA; Fr C; VP, Sci C; Pres, Soph Cl; Bkbl; Alg A; Citz A; HCt; *Law.*

MASSEY, Essie B
McAdams HS; McAdams, MS (2-52) Ed, Ann; FFA; FHA; Rptr, Hmrm; Beauty; Citz A; Cl Fav; Hist A; HQn; HCt; Hon Prog; MLS; Sal; Bookkeeping A; Most Intellectual; Miss McAdams; *Holmes Jr Col; Acct.*

MASSEY, Gina Lea
Dexter HS; Dexter, KS (1-23) Band; Cpt, Chldr; Pres, FHA; GS; NHS; Ed, Sch P; Secy, SC; Pres, Soph Cl; *Emporia St Col; Social Stu.*

MASSEY, Joe Carol
Ross S Sterling HS; Houston, TX (10%-485) Dbte Tm; Span C; Tr; *U of Houston; Phys Ed.*

MASSEY, Karen Elaine
The Immaculata HS; Chicago, IL (4-157) Co-Ed, Ann; CYO; Hmrm; Lit Mag; VP, NHS; A-Ed, Sch P; Span NHS; SC; Hon Prog; Journ A; NMS; St Scholar; Marian Medal A; *Northwestern U; Econ.*

MASSEY, Pamela Marie
Rule HS; Knoxville, TN (14-128) Chor; Key C; NHS; Y-Tns; HCt; Hon Prog; Swtht; Outst, Foods; Mus As; Faithful Support A; Sore Foot As; *Health.*

MASSEY, Sheryl Lynn
Northbrook Sr HS; Houston, TX (80-650) GS; JETS; Mu Alpha Theta; NHS; Span C; Hon Prog; Off, Drill Tm; *Corrective Therapy.*

MASSEY, Wyatt
H D Woodson Sr HS; Washington, DC (7-596) Secy, Sci C; Fel A; Tool A; *Howard U; Archt Dwg.*

MASSIE, Layland Ray
Baker HS; Columbus, GA; Hmrm; Var C; Sftbl; DARGCA; ROTC A; DAR Military Achv A; *Columbus Col; Criminal Justice.*

MASSIE, Mark Alan
MacKenzie HS; Detroit, MI (8-352) Hmrm; VP, NHS; SC; Var C; VP, Sr Cl; Ftbl; Hon Prog; St Scholar; The Det New Mich Indust Ed A; Mich St Fair Yth Indust Arts A; WW; *U of Mich; Architecture.*

MASSINGILL, Laura Denise
Theodore HS; Theodore, AL; Band; 4H; 4H A; Yth Fel; Band A; *20th Century Col; Secretarial Work.*

MASSINGILL, Stacy Lynn
Lufkin HS; Lufkin, TX (10%-520) Chor; Dbte Tm; Drama; Secy, Fr C; NFL; Tr; Hon Prog; Drill Tm; *Baylor U; Med Tech.*

MASSO, Jose F
Colegio San Antonio Abad; Humacao, PR (5-110) NHS; Tnns; High Hon; *Chem.*

MAST, Charles David
Smithfield-Selma HS; Smithfield, NC (9-300) Fr C; NHS; Y-Tns; God & Country A; Pep C; Soph Marshall; Sct Merit Badges; *Wake Forest U.*

MAST, Gregory Clark
Colerain Sr HS; Cincinnati, OH; Band; Drama; VP, JETS; Sci C; Sftbl; Mgr, Wrest; COM; Sci A; Bible Bowl; Ohio Mus Ed Assn Contest A; Ch, Yth Group Renovation; Mus A; *Bio Sci.*

MAST, Steven James
Quincy Notre Dame HS; Quincy, IL (21-141) Tres, Key C; NHS; Mgr, Bkbl; Mgr, Ftbl; Mgr, Soccer; WW; SAA; *Engr.*

MAST, Susan Marie
Quincy Notre Dame HS; Quincy, IL (3-141) Secy, Bus C; Chor; Hmrm; Secy, NHS; Tres, Span C; SC; JV, Tnns; COM; Hon Prog; Type A; SAA A; WW.

MASTEN, Eric William
Seaford Sr HS; Seaford, DE (58-238) JV, Soccer; Tr; Parl & Rptr, DECA; Tr HR; Tr Ltrs; Intramural Tnns Championships; *Salisbury St Col; Bio.*

MASTEN, Lynn Ann
Wallkill Sr HS; Wallkill, NY (1-235) VP, Band; Chldr; Chor; Ensm; GS; Hmrm; NHS; Pres, Jr Cl; Bkbl; Hockey; Tr; Amer Leg A; Citz A; Hon Prog; Yth Fel; Span A; Bkbl Trophy; GS Rep; Jr Prom Qn; All St Band; SC A; *Cornell U; Vet Sci.*

MASTERS, Charla Marion
Monte Vista HS; Danville, CA (1-357) Fin, AFS; Band; Ger C; Orch; Pres, Rainbow; Spch C; Bank Of Amer A; CSF; COM; DARGCA; MLS; Val; Cal Teachers Assn Schol; UCLA Alumni Schol; Tanglewood Inst of Mus, Yng Pianists; *UCLA; Mus.*

MASTERS, James Lee III
Tahlequah HS; Tahlequah, OK; Band; SC; Dist, Tri-St Hon, Bands; Directors A, Band; Superior, Solo Contests; *Mus.*

MASTERS, Laurie Ann
LaConner HS; LaConner, WA (1-52) Chor; Math C; NHS; ARC; Ski C; Span C; Tr; *Col of Sou Idaho; Med Technician.*

MASTERS, Lisa Ann
Stratford HS; Nashville, TN; Cr-Ctry; Tr; Bowl A; PA.

MASTERS, Megan Beth
McNary HS; Salem, OR (24-420) GS; Jr Miss Pageant; NHS; V-Ch, SC; Pres, Jr Cl; VP, Soph Cl; Rotary A; *Oreg St U; Social Sci.*

MASTERS, Michael Guy
Liberty HS; Bethlehem, PA (15-694) A Cap Choir; Pres, Band; Chor; Key C; S-T, NHS; Thes; Hon Prog; Lion A; Band A; Glee C A; 2 Var Scholar A; *Duke U; Eng.*

MASTERSON, Daniel Joseph
Mt Morris HS; Mt Morris, IL (4-75) Band; Chor; Ensm; Madrigal; VP, Order/Arrow; Hon Prog; NEDT; Mus Contest; *McPherson Col; Math.*

MASTERSON, Debra Lynn
Madison Central HS; Richmond, KY (20-500) Tres, BC; Chor; Drama; Ensm; Hmrm; Lat C; SC; Var C; Golf; Hon Prog; All St Chor; *E Ky U; Math.*

MASTERSON, Melanie Viola
Bloomington HS; Bloomington, CA (20%-350) Chldr; Ger C; Rptr, Sch P; Var C; JV, Bkbl; Swim; CSF; Girl o-t Mo; *Sou Oreg Col; Psych.*

MASTIN, Linda Anderson
Franklin Delonor Roosevelt HS; Hyde Park, NY; Cpt, Chldr; Chor; Drama; Hmrm; Var C; Sftbl; Tr; Cl Fav; Most Hon & Respected; *Home Ec.*

MASTRACEHIO, Joseph Antonio
Leesville HS; Leesville, LA (25-300) BS; CYO; FBLA; Hmrm; Var C; Bsbl; Ftbl; Tnns; Ftbl A; Superior, Bookkeeping Rally; *NW St U; Acct.*

MASTRINI, Michelle Lynn
Centennial HS; Pueblo, CO; Band; Chor; Ensm; Hmrm; ARC; Rptr, Sch P; Swim; Concert, Pep, Marching, Bands; Hist C; Miss Bethel; God & Comm A; Hon Qn; Jobs Daught; 1st Cl GSct; Fin, Ms Colo Jobs Daughter Pageant; *Trinity U.*

MASTROGIACOMO, Paul Michael
Don Bosco Tech HS; Boston, MA (13-222) CYO; NHS; SC; Tr; NEDT; Marine Phys Fitness A; *NE Col; Computer Sci.*

MASUGA, Laura Kay
Green HS; Greensburg, OH (20-300) Chor; Ensm; Hmrm; VP, NHS; SC; Y-Tns; Pres, Jr Cl; Pres, Soph Cl; HQn; HCt; Yth Fel; *Akron U; Cyto Tech.*

MATACOTTA, Ernest Albert
Marine Military Acad; Harlingen, TX; NHS; Ftbl; Elk A; Tnager o-t Month; *US Naval Acad; Sci.*

MATAUTO, Spohn
Emmaus HS; Koror, PALAU, WESTERN CAROLINE ISLANDS (1-17) A Cap Choir; Chem C; Hon Prog.

MATEIKA, Debra Lynn
Stoughton Sr HS; Stoughton, WI (80-224) Band; Chor; VP, FHA; FTA; Span C; Mgr, Bkbl; JV, Tnns; Yth Fel; Tnns Ltr A; Bkbl Mgr Ltr A; GAA Ltr A; 2nd Pl Dist Solo-Ensm Mus Festival; *Lakeshore Tech Inst; Optometric Asst.*

MATER, Dee Ann
Ripon HS; Ripon, WI (7-174) Fin, AFS; Chldr; Hmrm; NHS; A-Ed, Sch P; SC; Bkbl; Sftbl; CSF; COM; Hon Prog; Journ A; Cpt, Vlbl; *Communication.*

MATERO, Philip M
Vista HS; Vista, CA (33-800) Chess C; Chor; Dbte Tm; NHS; Bsbl; Bkbl; Ftbl; Sftbl; Swim; Tr; Wrest; COM; Most Out; Pres A; Yth Fel; Cl Offices; Awanas C; Ntl Span Exam; *Moody Bible Inst; Missionary Work.*

MATHER, Lynn Marie
Lisbon HS; Lisbon, ND (3-80) Chor; Drama; Ensm; FHA; Ger C; JV, Bkbl; Bronze Pin; *ND St U; Math.*

MATHER, Paula Jane
Gurley Public Sch; Gurley, NE (6-12) Ann; Chor; Pres, SC; Secy, Tr; VP, Soph Cl; Bkbl; Tr; Lion A; Alt, GS; Pep C; Vlbl; Home Ec A; Swing Choir; Commercial A; Triple Trio; Bicentennial Qn; Christ Yth Fel; Lucille Larson Sch; *Kearney St Col; Elem Ed.*

MATHERNE, Brian Patrick
Hahnville HS; Boutte, LA (118-350) A Cap Choir; Band; CYO; Ensm; Pres, Church Choir; *Nicholls St U.*

MATHERNE, Gaynell Ann
Hahnville HS; Boutte, LA (72-430) Band; BC; VP, CYO; Chor; FHA; Secy, 4H; Lit Ral; Secy, Sci C; Bkbl; Sftbl; Hon Prog; NEDT; Vlbl; English A; Parish Oust CYO Girl; Numerous A Sch Parsh & Reg Sci Fair; *Nicholls St U; Phys Ed.*

MATHERS, Marianne
John F Kennedy HS; Denver, CO (183-435) Ger C; Mgr, Bkbl; JA A; Opt A; ROTC A; 1st Pl, Art A; Rifle Tm A; WW; *Metro St of Colo; Elem Ed.*

MATHES, Karen Denise
John Muir HS; Pasadena, CA; FBLA; SC; Up Bound; Pres A; *Pacific Oaks Col; Early Childhood Ed.*

MATHES, Scott Hamilton
Riverview HS; Sarasota, FL (100-750) InterAct C; Order/Arrow; Golf; Order/Arrow A; Yth Fel; Eagle Sct; *Citadel Col; Bus.*

MATHES, Susan Jane
Brookhaven Acad; Brookhaven, MS; BC; Chldr; Fr C; FHA; Ed, Sch P; Mgr, Bkbl; Mgr, Tr; Beauty; Citz A; HCt; *U of Ark; Journ.*

MATHEWS, Craig Floyd
Thomas A Edison HS; Alexandria, VA (112-350) Hmrm; Var C; Ftbl; Tr; All District, All Region, Ftbl; *Clemson U; Engr.*

MATHEWS, Eddie James
Brimfield HS; Brimfield, IL (14-61) Fin, BS; Fin, City Conf; Sch P; Bsbl; Bkbl; Cr-Ctry; Tr; Hon Men, All St Bkbl; All Star, Conf Bkbl; *Notre Dame U.*

MATHEWS, Elsie Marie
Stonington HS; Pawcatuck, CT (11-283) Band; FNA; Hmrm; Math C; Sftbl; *Health Sci.*

MATHEWS, Ernestine LaVerne
Amherst Co HS; Amherst, VA; Chor; Span C; Pres, DECA; Ch, Jr Sisterhood C; Pep C; Ch, Jr Usher Board; Pres, Jr C; *Lynchburg General Hospital; Nurs.*

MATHEWS, James Hunter
Red Springs HS; Red Springs, NC (8-130) FFA; FTA; Order/Arrow; B Crocker A; Order/Arrow A; Eagle Sct; *Berea Col; Chem.*

MATHEWS, Karen Lynn
Briarwood HS; E Point, GA; AFS; Chor; Drama; Fr C; Parl, Hmrm; NHS; SC; Hon Prog; NEDT; *U of Ga; Eng.*

MATHEWS, Kenny Paul
Ponchatoula HS; Ponchatoula, LA; Band; InterAct C; Bsbl; Ftbl; Sci.*

MATHEWS, Loyd Duwane
Paris HS; Paris, TX; Pres, Band; Ger C; NHS; *Paris Jr Col; Law Enforcement.*

MATHEWS, Sara Lee
Grinnell Comm Sr HS; Grinnell, IA (5-200) Band; GS; NHS; SC; MVP, Swim; Tnns; Amer Leg A.

MATHEWS, Sheri Lynn
John Yeates HS; Suffolk, VA (25%-155) Co-Ed, Ann; Band; BC; FBLA; Tri-HiY; Citz A; Pom Pom Sq; WW; *Legal Secy.*

MATHEWS, Terri Lynn
Havre de Grace Sr HS; Havre de Grace, MD (5-260) Band; Chor; Drama; *Towson St Col; Mus Ed.*

MATHEWS, Yvonne Carmel
Fairfield Comm HS; Fairfield, IL (35-188) F-Ed, Ann; Band; Ensm; FTA; InterAct C; NHS; Tres, Sci C; Span C; Secy, Sr Cl; Pres, Jr Cl; JV, Bkbl; Mgr, Cr-Ctry; Tr; Semi-Fin, William R Heart A; Co Pres, US Yth Sen Prog; HS Columnist.

MATHEWSON, John Turner
Bertie Sr HS; Windsor, NC (14-340) Chess C; Ch, FBLA; Monogram; A-Ed, Sch P; Sci C; Pres, SC; Bkbl; Rotary A; WW in NC FBLA; NC School; *Duke U; Chem.*

MATHIAS, Jody Ann
Stuarts Draft HS; Stuarts Draft, VA (11-152) Ann; Chor; Rptr, FHA; FNA; Lat C; NFL; NHS; Sci C; Sodality; Tnns; *U Va; Nurs.*

MATHIAS, Karen Marie
W Concord HS; W Concord, MN (1-57) Band; Chldr; Chor; Drama; Ensm; Pres, FTA; Mjrte; NHS; Spch C; Spch A; Best Actress A; WW, Mus A; *Concordia Col; Bio.*

MATHIEU, Brian Elliott
Rockford Guilford HS; Rockford, IL (160-850) Kiwanis A; Schol Art A's; *RI Sch of Design; Photography.*

MATHIEU, Jay Dee
Horseheads HS; Horseheads, NY (33%-550) Chor; Hmrm; ARC; SC; Tnns; COM; PTA A; Pres A; Lib A; US Army Phys Ed Prog; Outst, Chor; US Lawn Tnns Assn; *Elmira Col; Criminal Justice.*

MATHIOT, Mary Lou
Columbia HS; Columbia, PA (10-109) Chldr; Var C; DARGCA; *Penn St U at York; Bio Chem.*

MATHIS, Deborah
Booker T Washington HS; Atlanta, GA (5-350) Rptr, Band; Fr C; French NHS; HiY; Pres, Hmrm; Secy, NHS; ARC; F-Ed, Sch P; Secy, SC; Y-Tns; Tres, Sr Cl; Tres, Jr Cl; Rptr, Soph Cl; COM; Hon Prog; NMS; NEDT; Most Congenial; PC Jr Fel A; WW; Gov Hons Nom; *Georgia St U; Acct.*

MATHIS, Frederick Lewis
Ahrens HS; Louisville, KY; NHS; MLS; *U of Louisville.*

MATHIS, John Paul
Charles Henderson HS; Troy, AL (2-200) Band; Parl, BC; Dbte Tm; InterAct C; VP, NFL; Spch A; Outst Male; *U of Ala; Pre-Med.*

MATHIS, Joy Pamela
Starmount HS; Boonville, NC (10%-211) Co-Cpt, Chldr; Chor; Sftbl; Tnns; HCt.

MATHIS, Marcia Anna
Wakulla HS; Crawfordville, FL (40-120) Ed, Ann; VP, FBLA; FHA; Hmrm; Co-Ed, Lit Mag; SC; HCt; Cpt, Vlbl; Messenger, House of Rep; 1st Pl, FBLA Talent Comp; *Tallahassee Comm Col.*

MATHIS, Mark Eugene
N Clayton Sr HS; College Park, GA (180-417) Hmrm; ARC; SC; JV, Ftbl; JV, Sftbl; HCt; Hon Cadet AFJROTC; HR.

MATHIS, Marvin LaVet
Scott HS; Toledo, OH; FBLA; FHA; Hmrm; Model UN; Var C; Arch; Bsbl; Bkbl; Ftbl; Sftbl; Swim; Tnns; Wrest.

MATHIS, Melody Gaye
Hardaway HS; Columbus, GA (10%-450) Band; BC; Tri-HiY; Type A; Home Ec A; *Columbus Col; Span.*

MATHIS, Philip Freeman
Vanguard HS; Waco, TX (5-25) Chor; Drama; Ensm; Hmrm; Lit Mag; NHS; Sch P; SC; Bkbl; Tnns; Cl Fav; Hon Prog; Champ, Tnns Tourn; Bkbl Ltrs; *Oral Roberts U; Bus Adm.*

MATHIS, Rebecca Jean
Robert E Lee HS; Tyler, TX (10-685) Secy, Band; Chem C; Rptr, Lit Mag; Hon Prog; *Abilene Christian U; Hist.*

MATHIS, Shelley Ann
Lompoc Sr HS; Lompoc, CA (10%-507) Chor; Principle's List.

MATHIS, Steven Mark
N Gwinnett HS; Suwanee, GA (15%-120) Pres, Key C; *Ga St U; Bus Mgt.*

MATHISEN, Andrew Stephen
New Rochelle HS; New Rochelle, NY; Alg A; Bio A.

MATHISON, Kathy Jeanne
Southwood HS; Shreveport, LA (41-494) Fr C; NHS; *LSUS; Vet Asst.*

MATHISON, Paul James
Maryville HS; Maryville, TN (10%-183) Hmrm; Key C; Mu Alpha Theta; NHS; Order/Arrow; Pres, SC; Cr-Ctry; Tr; Order/Arrow A; Eagle Sct; *Engr.*

MATHRE, Keith A
Thomas McKean HS; Wilmington, DE (8-283) Band; BS; NHS; A-Ed, Sch P; Swim; Hon Prog; Math A; *Sci.*

MATICH, Kenneth Andrew
Oakton HS; Vienna, VA (102-546) CYO; Chess C; Drama; Ensm; NFL; NHS; Thes; Ftbl; JV, Wrest; Star Sct; *Wake Forest U; Pol Sci.*

MATLACK, Tim Alan
Clearwater HS; Clearwater, KS (14-88) A-Ed, Ann; Band; Chor; Dbte Tm; Drama; Ensm; 4H; Madrigal; Wrest; Lion A; St Drama A; St Mus A; *K-State Kans St; Law.*

MATLICK, Cari Jo
Brown HS; Sturgis, SD (30-230) Fr C; FTA; Semi-Fin, GS; 4H; NHS; Ski C; Pres, Job's Daughters; *SD St U; Child Development.*

MATLON, Susan Marie
Grace HS; Minneapolis, MN (10%-250) CYO; Chor; Drama; Ed, Lit Mag; Secy, Sci C; S-T, SC; Thes; S-T, Soph Cl; MVP, Bkbl; Cl Fav; Most Out.

MATOS, Franklin
Jose de Diego HS; Mayaguez, PR; Band; Order/Arrow; COM; Magna Cum Laude; Order/Arrow A.

MATOS, Maria Francisca
Adlai E Stevenson HS; Bronx, NY (26-788) Span C; Secy, Aspira.

MATSCHULLAT, Jan Marie
O'Neill Pub HS; O'Neill, NE (8-82) Ann; Chldr; Pres, Chor; Secy, Drama; Ensm; NHS; Secy, Sr Cl; Secy, Jr Cl; Hon Prog; Type A; Yth Fel; *U of Lincoln; Legal Secy.*

MATSON, David Lertis
N Torrance HS; Torrance, CA (10%-700) Hmrm; A-Ed, Sch P; Var C; Bsbl; Bkbl; Pres A; Most Ath; HS All-Amer Bkbl; Outst Broadcaster.

MATSON, Donna Ray
N Torrance HS; Torrance, CA; Chor; Drama; Thes; *El Camino Col.*

MATSON, Heidi Nadine
Evergreen HS; Vancouver, WA; Band; FHA; 4H; NHS; SC; Yth Fel; *Clark Col; Nurs.*

MATSON, Todd Allen
Princeton HS; Princeton, WV (22-279) Hmrm; VP, Key C; NHS; Co-Cpt, Cr-Ctry; Tr; Cl Fav; HCt; Hon Prog; Kiwanis A; *W Va U.*

MATSUNAMI, Rhonda Beth
Northwest HS; Omaha, NE (34-652) Band; Chldr; SC; Hon Prog; Yth Fel; Gym; *Bus.*

MATSUOKA, Betsy Tamame
John F Kennedy HS; Tumon, GUAM; NHS; Sftbl; Alg A; Spch A.

MATT, Dorothy Ann
Morton E HS; Cicero, IL; *Lee Col; Bible-Mission Field.*

MATTEI, Dina Ann
Springfield HS; Springfield, PA (130-444) Chor; ARC; Cpt, COM; Yth Fel; Yth Leg; Work Stu; Ed, Church Yth Paper; Church Yth Coun; Church Choirs & Ensms; *Banking.*

MATTESON, Marilou Eileen
Spur HS; Spur, TX (6-33) Band; FHA; Tres, NHS; Secy, Sci C; *S Plains Col; Acct.*

MATTESON, Martha Lynn
Lincoln-Way Comm HS; New Lenox, IL (20-629) Band; Chess C; Cpt, Dbte Tm; Drama; Ensm; Ger C; Pres, 4H; Math C; Mu Alpha Theta; Orch; Spch C; Thes; Alg A; Hon Prog; NMS; *Pre-Med.*

MATTESON, Max Zechmeister
Worth Co R-III HS; Grant City, MO (3-55) Band; BS; Tres, FTA; NHS; Var C; Pres, Jr Cl; VP, Soph Cl; Bkbl; Ftbl; Tr; Citz A; HCt; Rotary A; IA A; Scts; *U of Mo; Engr.*

MATTEUCCI, Julie Ann
Albuquerque HS; Albuquerque, NM (17-500) CYO; Chor; NHS; SC; Sftbl; DARGCA; CCD Teacher; *U of NM; Dental Hygiene.*

MATTEUCCI, Linda Marie
Albuquerque HS; Albuquerque, NM (20-600) CYO; Chor; NHS; Bkbl; Sftbl; Hon Prog; *U of NM; Law.*

MATTHEES, Naomi Ann
Minneapolis Lutheran HS; Minneapolis, MN (4-37) Chor; Drama; VP, NHS; Rptr, Sch P; Hon Prog; Ntl Merit Ltr of Commendation; Ger A; Schol A; *Concordia Col; Elem Ed.*

MATTHEWS, Brenda Louise
East Sr HS; Nashville, TN; Rptr, Sch P; Up Bound; Crisco A; Hon Prog; PA; Home Ec Cert; Sci Cert; Forensic Medal; *U of Knoxville.*

MATTHEWS, Charles Hugh
Winston Co HS; Double Springs, AL (2-70) BC; BS; Chor; Drama; FTA; Sch P; Sci C; Amer Leg A; COM; Citz A; Most Out; Phy A; Sci A; Eng A; Dist Sci Paper Reading A; Phys Ed A; *Lee Col; Engr.*

MATTHEWS, Daniel Greene Jr
Shenandoah Valley Acad; New Market, VA; BC; Parl, Ski C; JV, Bkbl; JV, Ftbl; *Andrews U; Theology.*

MATTHEWS, Edward Donald
Scranton Central HS; Scranton, PA; Bsbl; Bkbl; Jack Pasco Mem A; Leading Scorer, Bkbl League.

MATTHEWS, Ellen Kay
E E Root HS; N Royalton, OH (30-313) Band; NHS; Orch; Span C; Var C; Bkbl; Sergeant at Arms, Girls Ath Ldrs; *Slippery Rock St Col; Bus Adm.*

MATTHEWS, Gloria Louise
The New William Penn HS; Philadelphia, PA; S-T, Chor; Drama; Secy, Sch P; Span C; Cpt, Bkbl; Alg A; Math A; MVP, Bkbl; Qn of Church; Attendance A; Computer A; Bkbl A; *Secy.*

MATTHEWS, James Coert
Sidney HS; Sidney, OH; Chess C; Soccer; Swim; JV, Tr; Nom, Gov's A for Bravery; *Forestry.*

MATTHEWS, Jeffrey Bruce
Doland HS; Doland, SD (13-34) Band; Chor; Dbte Tm; Madrigal; NFL; Orch; Ed, Sch P; Spch C; St Stu Congress; JV, Bkbl; Spch A; Yth Fel; *Vermillion Col; Law.*

MATTHEWS, John Connor
Knob Noster HS; Knob Noster, MO; A Cap Choir; Band; Chor; Demolay; Ensm; Madrigal; Var C; Bsbl; JV, Bkbl; Ftbl; Eagle Sct; Warrior of Mic-O-Say; *Central Methodist Col; Med.*

MATTHEWS, John MacDowell
Dearborn HS; Dearborn, MI (10%-560) Hmrm; NHS; Order/Arrow; Sch P; Var C; Tnns; COM; Hon Prog; Yth Fel; *Gen Motors Inst; Bus.*

MATTHEWS, John Mark
Starkville HS; Starkville, MS (10%-250) Chem C; NHS; Sci C; SC; Parl, Var C; VP, Sr Cl; Bsbl; Co-Cpt, Ftbl; Hon Prog; Star Student; Sr of Distinction; Ldrship A; *Miss St U; Med.*

MATTHEWS, Kandee LaVerne
Crenshaw HS; Los Angeles, CA (50%-750) Tnns; Tr; HCt; Drill Tm; *Northridge Col; Sci.*

MATTHEWS, Karla Renee
Crenshaw HS; Los Angeles, CA; Gym; Pres, Jr Ushers.

MATTHEWS, Kathleen
W Platte Rii HS; Platte City, MO; Chor; Ensm; FHA; Model UN; NHS; A-Ed, Sch P; Span C; Mgr, Bkbl; Sftbl; *U of Mo-Columbia; Hist.*

MATTHEWS, Keith Allen
Bloom Carroll HS; Carroll, OH (24-145) Ann; FFA; NHS; Sch Achieve Tm; *Ohio St U; Law.*

MATTHEWS, Luanne Spencer
Dothan Sr HS; Dothan, AL (20%-780) Lit Mag; Hon Prog; ROTC A; Ensm; Pres; SC; Co-Cpt, Bkbl; Alpha Phi Chi Sor; *U of S Ala; Bio.*

MATTHEWS, Marcia Denise
Union HS; Tulsa, OK (2-221) Dbte Tm; Drama; Fr C; NHS; Co-Ed, Sch P; Spch C; Pres, SC; Var C; Bkbl; Sftbl; Journ A; Merit A; Highest Schol Achv in Ath; Secy, Parent Teacher Stu Assn; *Journ.*

MATTHEWS, Mary Lou
Lone Grove HS; Lone Grove, OK (10-56) Ann; Cpt, Chldr; Chor; FHA; Sch P; SC; Bkbl; St Hon Soc; Principal HR; *Hist.*

MATTHEWS, Neal Cameron
Waukegan Christian Sch; Zion, IL (1-6) Ann; Ensm; Pres, SC; Co-Cpt, Bkbl; COM; Chamber of Comm A; Most Out; Val; Highest Avg, Soph; Yth Assn Meritorious A; *Le Tourneau Col; Aviation Tech.*

MATTHEWS, Reba Darlene
Booker T Washington HS; Atlanta, GA (10-345) Co-Cpt, Chldr; Fr C; NHS; Secy, Scha SC; COM; Hon Prog; Math A; *U of Pa; Bus Adm.*

MATTHEWS, Reed Eugene
Grove City Area HS; Grove City, PA (83-234) Chor; Community Yth Symph; Ensm; Lat C; Orch; String Quartet; PMEA Dist Orch; Pres, Grove City Mus C; Piano Accompanist, Chor; HS Mus Prod; PA Westrn St Orch; *Grove City Col; Mus.*

MATTHEWS, Richard Leon
Eastside HS; Paterson, NJ (28-1500) Cpt, Bsbl; Bkbl; Ftbl; Sftbl; Tnns; MVP, Bkbl; *Miami Dade Comm Col; Phys Ed.*

MATTHEWS, Robert Dean
Walker HS; Jasper, AL (1-350) Band; BC; Pres, Chess C; Ensm; VP, Hmrm; Pres, Key C; Math C; NHS; Ch, Order/Arrow; Rptr, Sch P; SC; Var C; VP, Soph Cl; MVP, Cr-Ctry; Tr; Math A; NEDT; Eagle Sct; Hon Stage, Hon Concert, Bands; *Med.*

MATTHEWS, Ruth Lynette
Grace Baptist HS; Decatur, AL (1-10) A-Ed, Ann; Band; Chor; Math C; Tres, NHS; Sch P; Span C; Cl Fav; Hist A; Val; Cpt, Vlbl; Bible A; As Dist Yng Am Build Qual Wth Mean; *Bob Jones U; Mus Ed.*

MATTHEWS, Scott Andrew
Niles McKinley HS; Niles, OH (12-421) AFS; Chor; Drama; Ensm; Key C; Order/Arrow; Thes; *Bio.*

MATTHEWS, Sonja Kay
W Wyman King Acad; Batesburg, SC (50%-24) Cpt, Chldr; Drama; JV, Bkbl.

MATTHEWS, Starla Gay
San Benito Joint Union HS; Hollister, CA (20%-320) Band; JV, Bkbl; COM; Hist A; Math A; *Bus.*

MATTHEWS, Stephen Alan
Niles Mckinley HS; Niles, OH; Ftbl; COM; *Butcher.*

MATTHEWS, Stephen Mark
Burges HS; El Paso, TX; *Pacific Coast Baptist Bible Col; Pastor.*

MATTHEWS, Steven Paul
Dearborn HS; Dearborn, MI (10-550) F-Ed, Ann; NHS; Order/Arrow; F-Ed, Sch P; SC; Var C; Tnns; God & Country A; Hon Prog; Journ A; Q&S A; MIPA A; *Henry Ford Comm Col; Hotel Motel Mgt.*

MATTHEWS, Tanya Denise
Malcolm X Shabazz HS; Newark, NJ (1-272) Co-Cpt, Band; Chor; Drama; FHA; Secy, FNA; Hmrm; Lit Mag; Secy, NHS; Orch; Rptr, Sch P; Sci C; SC; Mgr, Bkbl; Sftbl; COM; Citz A; Hist A; Hon Prog; Math A; MLS; Most Out; PTA A; Sci A; Val; Phys Ed A; Eng A; Span A; *Armed Forces.*

MATTHEWS, Timothy Lynn
Grace Baptist HS; Decatur, AL (5-25) Band; MVP, Ensm; Math C; Sci C; Bkbl; Soccer; Cl Fav; HCt; Most Out; *Bob Jones U; Bus Adm.*

MATTHEWS, Vern Blanche
Ossining HS; Ossining, NY; Band; Tr; Hon Prog; Dancing A; Sing A; Reading A; *Sociology.*

MATTHEWS, Villian Ilean
Crestview Sr HS; Crestview, FL (10%-300) *Okla St U.*

MATTHEWS, William Evan
Walker HS; Jasper, AL (10%-350) Band; BC; Pres, Chor; Ensm; InterAct C; NHS; VP, Order/Arrow; Var C; Cr-Ctry; Tr; Eagle Sct A; Hon Stage Band; *U of Ga; Forest Mgr.*

MATTICK, Kelly Therese
Mercy HS; Albany, NY (6-135) NEDT; VFW A; Partial Schol; Marian Medal A; *Phys Therapy.*

MATTINGLY, Chara Belle
Daviess Co HS; Owensboro, KY (34-316) Cpt, Chldr; Key C; HCt; Young Hist; Most Spirited; *U of Ky; Oceanography.*

MATTINGLY, Denise Ann
Holy Rosary Acad; Louisville, KY (1-116) Math C; ARC; Span C; Pres, Spch C; SC; COM; 4H A; K of C A; Opt A; Spch A; *Bellarmine Col; Psych.*

MATTINGLY, Garland Jay
Washington Co HS; Springfield, KY (50-200) Band; Drama; Ensm; Hmrm; Var C; Bsbl; Bkbl; Sftbl; Tnns; Cl Fav; Type A.

MATTINGLY, Janet Lee
Daviess Co HS; Owensboro, KY (30-320) F-Ed, Ann; Hmrm; Key C; SC; Var C; Tres, Sr Cl; Cpt, Bkbl; Tnns; Tr; Cl Fav; HQn; MVP, Bkbl; Rptr, Young Hist; Most Rebounds; *U of Ky; Med Tech.*

MATTINGLY, Joseph Earl
Green Ridge R-8 HS; Green Ridge, MO (8-36) CYO; Pres, FFA; Pres, 4H; Pres, Sr Cl; Bsbl; Bkbl; Cr-Ctry; Amer Leg A; 4H A; MLS; FFA A's; MFA Schol; *U of Mo; Agr.*

MATTINGLY, Martha
Memorial Sr HS; Houston, TX (65-640) GS; Pres, Mjrte; NHS; COM; God & Country A; Magna Cum Laude; NMF; Rotary A; WW; Cpt, Mjrte; *Tex A&M U; Pre-Med.*

MATTISON, Angela Renee
Asheville HS; Asheville, NC; Chor; Crown & Scepter; Hmrm; ARC; Span C; SC; Swim; Tnns; Phi Beta Kappa; Yth Fel; Yth Coun; Debutant Ball; Distributive Ed C; *Nurs.*

MATTISON, Barry James
Burlington City HS; Burlington City, NJ; Band; Pres, Chess C; Chor; Drama; Orch; JV, Bkbl; Bkbl; Co-Cpt, Ftbl; JV, Tr; COM; *USC; Elec Engr.*

MATTMILLER, Kendra Lynn
Carlyle HS; Carlyle, IL (9-138) FBLA; NHS; Pres, SC; HCt.

MATTOS, Angela Kay
San Marcos HS; Santa Barbara, CA; Tres, Rainbow; CSF; Masonic A; *Eng.*

MATTOX, Frederick Eugene
Burkesville HS; Burkeville, TX (9-47) Chor; Dbte Tm; Pres, Drama; Rptr, FFA; FHA; Rptr, Hmrm; Secy, Cpt, Bsbl; Cpt, Bkbl; Cpt, Ftbl; Cpt, Tnns; COM; Sch Hon Soc; *Engr.*

MATTOX, Kimberly Ann
Indian Hill HS; Cincinnati, OH (28-300) City Conf; Hmrm; NHS; Tres, SC; COM; Citz A; Hon Prog; Most Out; Pres, S-T & MVP, Band; Pres, Yth Fel; *Miami U; Elem Ed.*

MATTOX, Melody Dawn
Highland HS; Marengo, OH (10%-140) Band; Ensm; 4H; Orch; Span C; Tr; 4H A; Section Ldr, Chor; Art C; Tr A; All-Co Choir; Band Choir; Pep Band; Solo Contest; Stage Band; Marching Band; *Mus.*

MATTSON, Joseph Charles
N Shore HS; W Palm Beach, FL (25-266) Tres, Key C; NHS; Order/Arrow; Bus Mgr, Sch P; Var C; Tres, Sr Cl; Tres, Jr Cl; Cr-Ctry; Tr; God & Country A; Order/Arrow A; Eagle Sct A; Yth o-t Mo; *Bio.*

MATTSON, Kay Alina
Antioch HS; Antioch, CA (10%-540) VP, A Cap Choir; Drama; Secy, Mod Mus Mas; Span C; *Willamette U; Mus Therapy.*

MATTSON, Mark Donald
Cannon Falls HS; Cannon Falls, MN (9-147) Band; VP, BS; Dbte Tm; Ensm; Pres, 4H; Cpt, Model UN; NHS; Ski C; Spch C; SC; Tnns; Amer Leg A; COM; 4H A; K of C A; Rotary A; Spch A; VFW A; All Star Band; WW; Century III Ldr A; NHS A; *St Olaf Col; Social Sci.*

MATTSON, Todd Merlyn
Marshall Sr HS; Marshall, MN (40-264) Chor; Drama; Fr C; Spch C; Mgr, Bsbl; Chem A; Citz A; Most Out; Sci A; Spch A; Eagle Sct A; Hon Piano A; Tutor A; Talent A; *Southwest St U; Religion.*

MATTUCCI, Mark Michael
Marist Prep HS; Penndel, PA (1-13) CYO; Choi, Order/Arrow; SC; Bkbl; Hockey; Alg A; Math A; Order/Arrow A; *U of Penn; Hist.*

MATUZAK, Mark Steven
Colonie Central HS; Albany, NY (110-650) Key C; NHS; Bsbl; Soccer; *Hudson Valley Comm Col; Math Sci.*

MATZDORFF, Kyra Lynn
Esko HS; Esko, MN (20%-98) Chor; Rptr, 4H; Spch C; Cr-Ctry; Tr; Pep C; *Duluth Vo-tech Col; Nurs.*

MATZEK, Becky Sue
Maryville HS; Maryville, TN; Hmrm; Math C; Swim; Tnns; Yth Fel; Jr Beta C.

MATZEK, Michelle Marie
Maryville HS; Maryville, TN; Lat C; NHS; Swim; Hon Prog; NEDT; Yth Fel; Beta Epsilon; Jr Beta C.

MAUCH, Brian Anthony
Valley Central HS; Montgomery, NY (56-320) A Cap Choir; Tres, CYO; Chor; Span NHS; Var C; Ftbl; JV, Tr; Co Chor A; Social Stu Hon Soc; *West Point; Engr.*

MAUCHE, Christopher Wayne
Southside HS; Elmira, NY (2-435) Parl, Model UN; Pres, NHS; Rptr, Sch P; Hon Prog; Math A; NMS; Regent Schol; Sal.*

MAUCHLEY, Dan Steven
Anchor Christian Acad; Salt Lake City, UT; A Cap Choir; Ann; Chor; Drama; Ensm; Pres, SC; Pres, Soph Cl; Bkbl; Ftbl; Sftbl; Tr; Cl Fav; MLS; Most Out; Pres A; Best Christian Attitude; Best Ath; Highest Pace Avg; Best Dressed.

MAUCHLEY, Daniel Steven
Anchor Christian Acad; Salt Lake City, UT; A Cap Choir; Ann; Chor; Drama; Ensm; SC; Soph Cl; Ftbl; Sftbl; Tr; Cl Fav; MLS; Pres A; Best Christian Attitude; Best All Around Boy; Pres, Cl Rep.

MAUDLIN, Laurel Leigh
Portage HS; Portage, IN (35-769) Band; Chem C; Chor; Ensm; Lit Mag; A-Ed, Sch P; Spch C; Sftbl; COM; Citz A; Hon Prog; Journ A; Spch A; Vof-DEM; All Star Quizzer; *Journ.*

MAUER, Elizabeth
Hebrew Acad of Nassau Co; Uniondale, NY; Chldr; Chor; Drama; NHS; Bus Mgr, Sch P; Fr A; Hebrew Cert of Hon; Sewing A; *Cornell U.*

MAUER, Leslie Anne
Hartshorne HS; Hartshorne, OK (1-70) Chor; NHS; DARGCA; Hist A; Spch A; Service Above Self; *U of Okla; Biol.*

MAUGE, Carmen Estrellita
Rainbow City Jr Sr HS; Rainbow City, CANAL ZONE; Swim; *Santa Maria La Antigua; Finance And Banking.*

MAUGHN, Christina Marie
Danville HS; Danville, AR (437-625) Chldr; VP, FHA; Hmrm; Pres, NHS; SC; Tres, Soph Cl; Citz A; HCt; Swtht; *Ark Tech U; Commercial Ed.*

MAULDIN, Charlotte Marie
Spring Woods Sr HS; Houston, TX (10%-510) FHA; Mu Alpha Theta; NHS; COM; Hon Prog; Art A; *Tex A&M U; Acct.*

MAULDIN, Jeff Paul
New Brockton HS; New Brockton, AL (20%-70) 4H; Bkbl; Ftbl; Cl Fav.

MAULDIN, Libby Alesia
Pascagoula HS; Pascagoula, MS (33%-450) Ann; Chor; Lat C; Span C; 1000 Hr Candystriper; Page, St House of Rep; *Nurs.*

MAULDIN, Russell Brian
Berea HS; Greenville, SC (38-250) Band; Var C; Tnns; Amer Leg A; *Furman U; Mus Theory.*

MAULDIN, Russell Bryan
LaGrange Sr HS; LaGrange, GA (20%-350) 4H; Math C; Var C; Mgr, Bsbl; Mgr, Bkbl; Mgr, Ftbl; 4H A; Bkbl Ltrman; *Jacksonville St U.*

MAUND, Mark Timothy
Westside HS; Augusta, GA (10%-300) Pres, Band; Key C; WW, Mus Stu; Auburn U; Law.

MAUNEY, Karen Mavia
Everett HS; Maryville, TN; Community Yth Symph; Drama; Fr C; Excel, Solo & Ensm Contest; Grnd Champ, Cert of Excel, Sci Fair.

MAUNEY, Nancy Jewell
Buffalo Grove HS; Buffalo Grove, IL (30-550) Swim; COM; Hon Prog; Pres A; Yth Foundation; Pom-Pons; Schol Art A; Hon Yth JC; U of Colo; Archt.

MAUNEY, William Kelly
St Stephens HS; Hickory, NC (2-20) BC; Chess C; Fr C; Span C; Mgr, Bkbl; Sftbl; Yth Fel; E Tenn U; Bio.

MAUPIN, Barbara Gayle
William Monroe HS; Stanardsville, VA; Ann; BC; Cpt, Chldr; Lit Mag; Pres, SC; Rptr, Jr Cl; Tr; Duke U; Bus Adm.

MAURER, Astrid Michelle
Marina HS; Huntington Beach, CA; AFS; JV, Tnns; CSF; Nom, Golden Shields A; Golden W Col; Bus.

MAURER, Barbara Jean
Holdrege Sr HS; Holdrege, NE; Band; Chldr; Golf; Sftbl; Tr; Candy Striper; Coach Little League; Nurs.

MAURER, Charles Alfred
Vanguard HS; Ocala, FL (21-350) Mu Alpha Theta; NHS.

MAURER, Cynthia Ann
Lindbergh Sr HS; St Louis, MO (173-909) NHS; HCt; Journ A; Q&S A; Yth Fel; Ed-in-Chief, Yrbk; Ger C; Co-Pilot's; Close-Up; U of Mo; Ed.

MAURER, Joanna Bea
Shawnee Mission N HS; Shawnee Mission, KS; Tr; Stu Teacher, Dance Studio; Gym, Tr, Ltrs; Yth Group Planning Committee; St John's Jr Col; Secy.

MAURER, Joy Yvonne
Exeter Sr HS; Reading, PA (45-210) Chor; Ed, Sch P; JA A; Color Guard; Social Work.

MAURER, Kimberly Ilene
Mansfield Christian HS; Mansfield, OH (7-46) Drama; Pres, 4H; JV, Bkbl; 4H A; Spch A; Vof-DEM; F-Ed, Yrbk; 4-H Saddle C Qn; Vlbl; 4-H MV Member; Teacher's Aide; Cpt, Quiz Tm; Grace Col; Lang Arts.

MAURER, Lorie Lynn
Highlands Sr HS; Natrona Heights, PA (10%-510) Drama; Fr C; NHS; Yth Fel; Explorers; Tn-Timer; Jr Cl Executive Committee; Gym; Duke U; Psych.

MAURER, Robin Denise
Exeter Sr HS; Reading, PA (25%-300) Chor; Hmrm; ARC A; HR; Golden Eagle A; Chor A; Psych.

MAURER, Vernette Eve
Grand Prairie HS; Grand Prairie, TX (30-384) A Cap Choir; Chor; Baylor U; Nurs.

MAURICE, David Ronald
Mabel-Canton HS; Mabel, MN; Ger C; S-T, Lat C; SC; JV, Wrest; Phys Sci.

MAURO, Teresa Nicole
Doane-Stuart Sch; Albany, NY (10%-39) Cum Laude Soc; Lit Mag; Sch P; Ski C; SC; Var C; Pres, Sr Cl; Bkbl; Soccer; Bio A; NMS; Regent School; Eng, Span, Gen Foods Ldr, A's; Harvard Col.

MAUSER, Alice Catherine
W Albany HS; Albany, OR (6-300) Band; Ensm; Pres, FBLA; NHS; Type A; Shorthand A's; Dist Hon Band; Girl o-t Mo; Seattle Pacific U; Bus.

MAUSER, James Irwin
Denby HS; Detroit, MI; Pres, Chor; Ensm; Ski C; Swim; Amer Leg A; Citz A; Hon Prog; Math A; St Scholar; U of Mich; Lit.

MAUST, Nina Lynn
Uniontown Area Sr HS; Uniontown, PA (31-435) Arch; Chor; FNA; Ger C; Secy, NHS; SC; Span C; Alg A; Hist A; Hon Prog; JA A; Rotary A; St Rep, Ntl Bicenten Handbell Choir; Alderson-Broaddus Col; Nurs Practitioner.

MAUTONE, Lucia Ida
Acad of St Aloysius; Jersey City, NJ (3-127) Band; Chor; Drama; Ensm; Hmrm; Lit Mag; JV, Math C; NHS; Sch P; SC; Pres, Soph Cl; Tnns; COM; Cl Fav; Hist A; Hon Prog; K of C A; MLS; Most Out; PTA A; Sal; Sci A; High Series 1st Pl Tm, Bowl; WW; Best Play Design; Co-Ed, Yrbk; Hudson Co Vocalist; Semi-Fin, Talent Expo; Pratt Inst; Advertising.

MAVER, Kathryn Joan
Prospect HS; Mt Prospect, IL (120-596) Lit Mag; Secy, Pol Sci C; Art Show Recognition; Carthage Col; International Bus.

MAW, Charles Ray
O'Neill Pub HS; O'Neill, NE (8-85) Ann; Order/ Arrow; Var C; JV, Cr-Ctry; Order/Arrow A; Yth Fel.

MAXEY, David Alan
Raytown South HS; Raytown, MO; Drama; NHS; Thes; Spch A; Art A; WW; Most Promising, Drama; Art.

MAXEY, Laura Mayfield
Westminster Christian HS; Miami, FL (8-103) Chor; Ensm; Pres, NHS; DARGCA; NEDT; Opt A; Piano Soloist; Pres, Fl Fed of Mus; Silver Knight Nom; Irene Muir Schol; Miami Beach Symph; 1st Pl, HS Auditions, Fla St Mus; Ariz St U; Mus.

MAXEY, Lauri Ellen
Tuscola Comm HS; Tuscola, IL (11-118) Chor; Ensm; Fr C; Sch P; Spch C; Co-Cpt, Pom Pon Sq; Parkland Jr Col; Acct.

MAXEY, Margaret Page
Harlingen HS; Harlingen, TX (293-700) A Cap Choir; Chor; Ensm; Madrigal; Baylor U; Mus.

MAXEY, Melanie G
Capital Sr HS; Boise, ID (150-640) Band; Chor; Ensm; Orch; Sftbl; COM; Co-Cpt, Rifle Corps; Northwest Nazarene Col.

MAXEY, Pamela Jean
Grace St Lukes HS; Memphis, TN; Hmrm; Lat C; Math C; SC; VP, Sr Cl; Sal; Sci A; Pres, Yth Coun; Memphis St U; Pre-Med.

MAXFIELD, Janetta Ruth
Jonesboro HS; Jonesboro, AR; BC; FBLA; Type A; NJHS; Ark St U; Criminology.

MAXWELL, Bryan Scot
Pinole Valley HS; Pinole, CA (73-547) Ger C; Wrest; U of Calif at Berkeley; Bus Adm.

MAXWELL, Catherine Jane
N Mecklenburg HS; Huntersville, NC (29-437) Chess C; Fr C; FTA; Ger C; Lit Mag; Model UN; Monogram; NHS; NMS; U of NC; Eng.

MAXWELL, Elizabeth Ann
High Point HS; Beltsville, MD (15%-750) FTA; Hmrm; NHS; Frostburg St Col; Elem Ed.

MAXWELL, James Dale Jr
Casady Sch; Oklahoma City, OK; A Cap Choir; Ski C; Bsbl; Bkbl; Sftbl; COM; Yth Fel; Intrntl Mem, Ntl Piano Play Aud; Okla St U; Med.

MAXWELL, James Stephen
L C Anderson HS; Austin, TX (200-600) Order/ Arrow; Ftbl; Tr; Order/Arrow A; U of Tex; Archt.

MAXWELL, Katherine Elaine
W J Woodham HS; Pensacola, FL (15-350) FBLA; NHS; Pensacola Jr Col; Special Ed.

MAXWELL, Laura Lynn
High Point HS; Beltsville, MD (15%-700) Chor; NHS; SC; Ntl Sci Found; Sci A; Stu Page, Co Page Prog; U of Md; Bio.

MAXWELL, Lisa Dianne
Pleasant Grove HS; Pleasant Grove, AL (13-150) Bus Mgr, Ann; Secy, Sr Cl; Outst Sr; Jefferson St Jr Col; Med Secy.

MAXWELL, Lori Lynn
Cheboygan Area HS; Cheboygan, MI; Band; Band A; Lake Superior St Col; Secy Sci.

MAXWELL, Mary Louise
Cairo HS; Cairo, GA (20-250) Ann; FBLA; Hmrm; Sch P; SC; Cpt, Bkbl; COM; Morehouse Col; Secy Sci.

MAXWELL, Mary Lynne
Jacksboro HS; Jacksboro, TX (2-61) Ed, Ann; Secy, BC; Chor; Secy, FBLA; FTA; Fin, Jr Miss Pagent; Secy, NHS; SC; Beauty; COM; Citz A; HCt; Hon Prog; Journ A; Most Out; Sal; Type A; Most Dependable; Most Courteous; Best Groomed; Most Versatile.

MAXWELL, Michael Craig
N Garland Sr HS; Garland, TX; A Cap Choir; BC; Chor; Pres, Drama; Ger C; NFL; NHS; Pres, Thes; Amer Leg A; Hon Prog; Acting A; Abilene Christian U; Bio.

MAXWELL, Nancy Alyson
Portsmouth Cath HS; Portsmouth, VA (1-33) Band; Chor; Fr C; Parl, Lat C; Lat NHS; Math C; ARC; Sftbl; COM; Sci A; Principal's List; 2nd Pl, Lat Declamation Contest; Early Bach A, Ntl Piano Tchrs Assoc.

MAXWELL, Ramona Faye
W J Woodham HS; Pensacola, FL (11-530) Fr C; NHS; Sci C; COM; Hist A; WW; Ntl Merit Commended Stu; U of S Ala; Nurs.

MAXWELL, Sandra
Northern Chester Co Voc-Tech Sch; Phoenixville, PA (10%-192) Mgr, Wrest; HCt; Qn, Sr Cl; Quietest Girl, Sr Cl.

MAXWELL, Susan Janelle
Bedford-N Lawrence HS; Bedford, IN; Band; Drama; Span C; Heart Fund A; U of Evansville; Industrial Arts Ed.

MAXWELL, Susan Leake
Wade Hampton HS; Greenville, SC (2-371) Pres, Hmrm; Pres, NHS; Secy, Sr Cl; DARGCA; H of F; Hon Prog; Math A; NMF; Sal; St Pres, FTA; Tres, Pep C; Secy, Pep C; Furman School; Clemson U; Eng.

MAXWELL, Suzan Malinda
Acad of Our Lady; Chicago, IL (212-150) Co-Ch, Chldr; Chor.

MAXWELL, William Leroy
Turner HS; Portage, WI (46-209) AFS; Band; Drama; Ger C; VP, 4H; Orch; Bsbl; Bkbl; Ftbl; Soccer; Sftbl; 4H A; AFS Exchange Stu, Brazil; Pres, Christ Ambassadors; Milwaukee Sch of Engr; Elec Tech.

MAY, Carol Lynn
Switzerland Co HS; Vevay, IN (16-108) VP, Band; Pres, Chor; Drama; Cpt, Mjrte; Pres, Mod Mus Mas; NHS; Rainbow; Bkbl; Tr; COM; Hon Prog; All St Choir; Dist Tr, Bkbl, A's; Ball St U; Mus Ed.

MAY, Charles Anderson
Central HS; Phenix City, AL (3-336) Chor; Dbte Tm; Drama; Ensm; Rptr, Sch P; Spch C; Hon Prog; Journ A; Sci A; Spch A; Drama A; Art A; Outst Young Amer; U of Ala; Communications.

MAY, Charlynn
Alto HS; Alto, TX (7-41) Band; Chldr; Drama; Mjrte; Rptr, Sch P; Tnns; Yth Fel; Prose Interpretation; UIL Dist Meet; Kilgoe Jr Col; Rehabilitation.

MAY, Cheryl Yvonne
Osborn HS; Detroit, MI; Chor; Ensm; FTA; Yth Fel; Mercy Col; Nurs.

MAY, Debbie
W Point HS; W Point, MS (30-153) Anchor C; Band; Miss St U; Elem Ed.

MAY, Denise
Kirksville St HS; Kirksville, MO; Chldr; Chor; Drama; NE Mo St U; Mus.

MAY, Dennis Oliver
N Little Rock Ole Main HS; N Little Rock, AR (12-407) BS; Mu Alpha Theta; NHS; VP, Span C; SC; COM; Citz A; DARGCA; Delta Sigma Theta A; H of F; I Dare You; Ntl Achv Schol; NMF; NMS; Q&S A; Rotary A; WW; U of Ark; Pub Adm.

MAY, Gillian Annie
Alexander Galt Regional HS; Lennoxville, CAN-ADA (11-477) A Cap Choir; Hmrm; InterClub Coun; Ski C; Bsbl; Hon Prog; Tres, Yth C; Broomball; MSD A.

MAY, Jack L
Troy HS; Troy, OH (120-366) Chess C; FFA; Var C; Bsbl; Bkbl; Mgr, Ftbl; Semi-Fin, Tnns; Mich Christian Col; Engr.

MAY, Janice Elaine
Cass Tech HS; Detroit, MI; Gospel Choir; Wagne
Co Comm Col; Data Processing.

MAY, John Allen
Central Cath HS; Pittsburgh, PA (127-274) Dbte
Tm; Pres, Y-Tns; Bsbl; Tr; Grove City Col; Reli-
gion.

MAY, Karen Elizabeth
Lyons Township HS; LaGrange, IL (125-1500)
Chor; Ensm; Yth Fel; Gym; Purdue U; Math.

MAY, Margaret Ann
Lincoln Comm HS; Lincoln, IL (107-282) Band;
Dbte Tm; Ensm; Pres, 4H; Hmrm; Lat C; NHS; SC;
Ill St U; General.

MAY, Maura Elizabeth
Acad of Our Lady of Mercy; Milford, CT (1-93) A
Cap Choir; CYO; VP, Chor; Drama; Madrigal;
NHS; Ski C; Span C; Span NHS; SC; Tres, Jr Cl;
COM; Hon Prog; Math A; NMS; NEDT; Sci A;
Yale U.

MAY, Perry Charles
Puckett Attendance Center; Puckett, MS (4-23)
Ann; Bkbl; Sftbl; COM; HCt; Most Courteous;
Clarke Col; Bus.

MAY, Peter John
Buckley Sch; Sherman Oaks, CA (4-63) NHS; Var
C; Ftbl; Soccer; JV, Tr; Alg A; Hist A; Hon Prog;
Math A; NEDT; Sci A; Stanford U; Bus Law.

MAY, Sandra Elaine
W Lincoln HS; Lincolnton, NC; Band; Gifted &
Talented Eng; Wake Forest U; Bus.

MAY, Sharyl Lee
Malden Comm HS; Malden, IL (6-19) Bus Mgr,
Ann; Chor; Drama; Fr C; Sch P; Secy, SC; Pres, Jr
Cl; Rptr, Soph Cl; Alg A; Hon Prog; Math A; Type
A; W Ill Col; Acct.

MAY, Sherry Jean
Carter HS; Knoxville, TN (50-300) Ann; Chor;
FHA; 4H; Bkbl; Sftbl; Tnns; 4H A; Sci A; Yth Fel;
Yth Rep; Coun On Ministries; Adm Board; U of
Tenn; Bio-Chem.

MAY, Tamalah Jean
Paint Rock HS; Paint Rock, TX (2-10) Ann; BC;
FHA; 4H; Mjrte; SC; Bkbl; Semi-Fin, Tnns; Type
A; Regional Champ, Tnns; Cl Tres; 1st, Twirling
Street Routine; Angelo St U.

MAY, Tammy Renee
Monticello HS; Monticello, MS; BC; Pres, Bus C;
GS; Beauty; HQn; MLS; Co-Lin Jr Col.

MAYBECK, Sheryl Anne
Shelton HS; Shelton, CT; Chor; Drama; 4H;
Hmrm; Pres, Rainbow; Secy, SC; Arch; Swim; Tr;
4H A; Southern Conn St Col; Med Secy.

MAYBEN, Monica Ruth
Chadron HS; Chadron, NE; Band; Bus C; FTA;
GS; NHS; Orch; Sch P; Span C; SC; Var C; Bkbl;
Sftbl; VP, Jr Pep C; Sunday Sch Teacher; Pres, Sr
Pep C; Co-Cpt, Drill Tm; S-T; Church Group; U of
Tex; Med.

MAYBERRY, Connie Sue
Glenwood Sr HS; Glenwood, IA (7-135) Ed, Ann;
Band; Chor; Hmrm; Mjrte; NHS; SC; JV, Sftbl; Tr;
Activities, Shorthand, A's; Iowa St U; Bus Adm.

MAYBERRY, Dewey Scott
Maroa-Forsyth HS; Maroa, IL; Secy, FFA; Free
Will Baptist Col; Bible.

MAYBERRY, Lori Anne
Deshler HS; Tuscumbia, AL; BC; U of N Ala; Med.

MAYBERRY,
Mary Patricia Anne
Cleveland HS; Cleveland, TN (93-240) Secy, CYO;
Fr C; Sch P; Mgr, Bkbl; Tnns; JA A; U of Tenn at
Knoxville; Home Ec.

MAYBERRY, Thomas Patrick
O D Wyatt HS; Fort Worth, TX (195-456) Hmrm;
Sci C; Mgr, Bkbl; U of Tex at Arlington; Bus Mgt.

MAYBERRY, Vanessa Lynn
Scott Preparatory Sch; Opelika, AL (10-27) VP,
Anchor C; VP, BC; Hmrm; Span C; SC; Pres, Jr Cl;
Pres, Soph Cl; MVP, Bkbl; Chem A; Cl Fav; HCt;
NEDT; Auburn; U.

MAYEAUX, Sheila Ann
E Ascension Acad; Gonzales, LA; F-Ed, Ann; 4H;
Rptr, Hmrm; Lit Ral; SC; JV, Bkbl; JV, Sftbl; 4H A;
Hon Prog; Sci A; CBM Bus Col; Computer Prog.

MAYER, Kelley Jo
Eldorado HS; Albuquerque, NM (84-750) Band;
NHS; Orch; Ind U; Nurs.

MAYER, Laura Jeanne
Druid Hills HS; Atlanta, GA (4-200) Band; BC;
Ensm; Ger C; 4H; Orch; Sch Achieve Tm; Sch P;
Sci C; Tres, Soph Cl; Bkbl; JV, Soccer; MVP, Tr;
Alg A; Hon Prog; Geometry A; HR.

MAYER, Michael Lloyd
Steeleville HS; Steeleville, IL (15-43) Span C; Bsbl;
Bkbl.

MAYERS, Charles Collins
Conway HS; Conway, SC (150-325) Bkbl; Cpt,
Ftbl; Tr; Yth Fel; Most Handsome; Jr Civitan;
FCA; U of SC; Pre-Law.

MAYERS, Daniel Ericson
Newtown HS; New York, NY; Band; Pres, Chor;
Orch; Cpt, Bsbl; Bkbl; Cr-Ctry; Tr; COM; Phy A;
Cert of Recognition; Yth Choir; Mus A; More-
house Col; Mus.

MAYERS, Patricia Estella
Paraiso Jr-Sr HS; Paraiso, CANAL ZONE (1-75)
Pres, Band; Dbte Tm; VP, Hmrm; ARC; Sch P;
Span C; VP, SC; Bsbl; Sftbl; COM; H of F; Hist A;
Interlochen Ntl Mus; Math A; MLS; ARC A; Sci
A; Briar Cliff Col; Engr.

MAYES, Linda Lee
Hanes HS; Winston-Salem, NC (10-29) A Cap
Choir; Chor; Rptr, InterClub Coun; Rptr, ARC;
Mgr, Arch; Mgr, Bsbl; Mgr, Sftbl; MLS; Star Stu-
dent; Yth Fel; Sewing C; PA; Ohio St; Teacher.

MAYES, Patricia Annette
Edmond Mem HS; Edmond, OK; Sftbl; Pep C;
Vlbl; VP, JA; Okla Christian Col; Acct.

MAYES, Terri Jean
Spring Woods Sr HS; Houston, TX (75%-600)
AFS; Chor; Ensm; Citz A; Drill Tm; Baylor U; Bus.

MAYES, Theron Tyrone
Arsenal Tech HS; Indianapolis, IN; Hmrm; SC; Jr
Cl; Mgr, Bkbl; COM; VP, VICA; Purdue U; Aeros-
pace Engr.

MAYEUX, Dawn Monique
Lafayette HS; Lafayette, LA (5%-630) Fin, Dbte
Tm; Hmrm; Secy, Mu Alpha Theta; NFL; NHS;
Tr; Hon Prog; Opt A; Spch A; Yth Fel; Church
Bkbl; Fin, St Spch; Mgr, Cpt, City Ftbl & Sftbl; VP,
Methodist Yth Fel; Ntl Fin, Catholic Forensics; U
of Sou La; Pre-Vet.

MAYFIELD,
Charles Anderson Jr
Inglewood HS; Inglewood, CA; Ann; Chor; VP,
Madrigal; Sch P; Pres, SC; Bsbl; Cpt, Ftbl; Wrest;
CSF; Hon Prog; Math A; PTA A; VP, SC; Stu o-t
Mo; Cl Service Plaque; Sou U; Math.

MAYFIELD, Clyniece
Waynesboro Central HS; Waynesboro, MS
(25%-99) Bus Mgr, Ann; Pres, BC; Drama; Pres,
FHA; Ch, Hmrm; Secy, Lit Mag; Co-Ed, Sch P;
Tres, SC; Secy, Y-Tns; Sr Cl; Amer Leg A; Hon
Prog; MLS; Most Out; Swtht; Val; Cert of Attend-
ance; Med.

MAYFIELD, Debora Jane
Saline HS; Saline, MI; Band; Drama; FHA; NHS;
Ski C; Span C; Sftbl; Hon Prog; NMS; Bus Schol;
Eastern Mich U; Bus Mgt.

MAYFIELD, Diane
Waynesboro-Central HS; Waynesboro, MS
(25%-99) BC; Drama; FHA; Hmrm; Sch P; SC;
Secy, Y-Tns; Pres, Sr Cl; Pres, Jr Cl; Secy, Soph Cl;
S-T, Lit C; Jones Co Jr Col; Hist.

MAYFIELD, Ruth Nellein
Phillis Wheatley Sr HS; Houston, TX; Rptr, Bus C;
Hmrm; Mjrte; NHS; SC; COM; Hist A; Hon Prog;
Type A; Bus Mgt.

MAYFIELD, Stephanie Michelle
Regina HS; Norwood, OH (30-118) Fr C; Hmrm;
Spch C; SC; Citz A; Cl Fav; H of F.

MAYFIELD, Steve Curtis
Douglas MacArthur HS; San Antonio, TX
(200-620) Lat C; Lat NHS; Var C; JV, Bkbl; Ftbl;
Citz A; Blinn Jr Col.

MAYFIELD, Wyzetta Lynn
Phillis Wheatley HS; Houston, TX; Cl Fav; Most
Out; Yth Foundation A; Band A; U of Houston;
Acct.

MAYHEW, Annette Jeanne
Wellston HS; Wellston, OH; Band; Chor; Rptr, Sch
P; Tri-HiY; Gym, Band, Choir, A's.

MAYLE, Cathy Ann
Franklin HS; Livonia, MI; Band; Hon Prog; Madonna Col; Nurs.

MAYNARD, Jeffery Bryant
Cleburne HS; Cleburne, TX (101-313) FTA; Lat C;
Phys C; Ski C; Ftbl; Tnns; Tr; Tex A&M U; Vet Sci.

MAYNARD, Lisa Theodora
Bayshore Christian Sch; Tampa, FL (1-24) Hmrm;
VP, SC; Pres, Soph Cl; Dance Schol; Principal HR;
U of NC; Theatrical Arts.

MAYNARD, Martha Christiana
Concord HS; Concord, NH (66-376) 4H; VP, Lat
C; Model UN; World Affairs C; Hockey; Law.

MAYNARD, Nancy Kathryn
Barboursville HS; Barboursville, WV (173-330) Bus
C; FBLA; FHA; FTA; 4H; Lat C; Marshall U; Elem
Ed.

MAYNARD, Randy Glen
Whiteland Comm HS; New Whiteland, IN; Bus
Ministry; Yth, Adult Choir; Sun Sch.

MAYNARD, Sheila Rae
Edgerton Sr HS; Edgerton, WI; Chor; Chldr; Secy,
Soph Cl; Swim; Tr; Pres A; ARC A; Gym; Swim
As; Madison Col; Acct.

MAYNEZ, Roland Stephen
Manual HS; Denver, CO (10%-700) Chor; Drama;
FBLA; Hmrm; Key C; NHS; Spch C; SC; Thes; Tr;
Alg A; COM; Cl Fav; Hon Prog; Math A; Opt Out
Tn; Spch A; US Sen Page Nom; Choral Group; HR;
Principal's List; Candystriper; Graduation Escort;
Pres, SB; Fashion Design.

MAYNIE, Tamra Gladys
Flint Southwestern HS; Flint, MI; Chldr; NHS;
Citz A; Hon Prog; U of Mich; Med Tech.

MAYO, Anna Mareta
Balmont HS; Dayton, OH; Drama; Hmrm; 4H A;
Spch A; Self Defense C; Art C; Capitol U; Journ.

MAYO, Cindy Jane
Ruston HS; Ruston, LA (38-270) Band; Chor;
Ensm; FHA; Lit Ral; NHS; Hist A; Solo & Ensm
Festival, Eng, A's; Lib A; La Tech U; Computer
Sci.

MAYO, Gerald Robert
Mt Vernon Township HS; Mt Vernon, IL (52-385)
Band; Drama; Co-Ed, Lit Mag; NHS; Orch; Thes;
Rend Lake Jr Col; Journ.

MAYO, Kenneth Wilson Jr
Goodlettsville HS; Goodlettsville, TN (20%-190)
Fr C; Bsbl; MVP, Wrest; Hon Prog; Fr A; Engr.

MAYOTTE, David Paul
St Joseph's Regional HS; Lowell, MA; NHS; Bkbl;
Hist A; Hon Prog; NEDT; Photo; Cert of Achv;
Sustained School Effort; US Naval Acad; Naval Sci.

MAYS, June Marie
Block HS; Jonesville, LA; Band; Bkbl; Sou U; Ed.

MAYS, LaJuan
George Washington Carver HS; Fieldale, VA;
FBLA; Pres, FHA; Sftbl; Ldrship A; Most Depend-
able.

MAYS, Patricia Gail
Medina HS; Medina, TN; Jackson St Col; Secy
Field.

MAYS, Randal Lee
Simsboro HS; Simsboro, LA (1-29) Ed, Ann; Lit
Ral; VP, SC; Pres, Sr Cl; Mgr, Bkbl; Amer Leg A;
Bio A; Citz A; Math A; Val; VofDEM; Sch Service
A; La Tech U; Elec Engr.

MAYS, Rebecca
Norfolk Collegiate HS; Norfolk, VA (10-70) Fr C;
French NHS; NHS; Co-Ed, Sch P; Citz A; NEDT;
Yth Fel; Lib A; Ntl de Concours Francais A; Va
Gov Sch for the Gifted; WW Nom; WW Nom;
William and Mary Col; Eng.

MAYS, Suzanne Elaine
Horseheads Sr HS; Horseheads, NY (114-573) Chor; Fr C; Ski C; Sftbl; DARGCA; Shorthand A's; *Alfred Agr & Tech Col; Secy Sci.*

MAZ, Elizabeth
Hollywood HS; Los Angeles, CA; Citz A; *Valley Col; Stenographer.*

MAZA, Jorge Luis
Amer Military Acad; Guaynabo, PR (3-68) JV, Cr-Ctry; Cpt, Wrest; Alg A; Bio A.

MAZE, Champ Arthur
Bath Co HS; Owingsville, KY (20-150) BC; Bus C; FBLA; Sci C; Bkbl; Cr-Ctry; Soccer; Sftbl; Cpt, Tnns; Tr; Hist A; Pres A; *Bus.*

MAZIQUE, Lovey Clarissa
Charlotte Amalie HS; St Thomas, VI; Hmrm; Rptr, Sch P; SC; Alg A; Bio A; Hist A; Span A; Eng A's; *Columbia Union Col; Nurs.*

MAZO, Rodolfo
Academia Santa Monica; Santurce, PR (5-55) NHS; SC; Tr; COM; JA A; *Annapolis Acad; Engr.*

MAZUREK, Edward Dana
Sweet Home Sr HS; N Tonawanda, NY (59-600) Band; NHS; Order/Arrow; Sci C; COM; Hon Prog; Regent Schol; Sci A; *SUNY at Binghampton; Pre-Med.*

MAZUROWSKI, Joseph Charles
York Central Sch; Retsof, NY; VP, Band; Ensm; Pres, 4H; NHS; Orch; Co-Cpt, Cr-Ctry; Co-Cpt, Tr; JV, Wrest; Bausch & Lomb A; 4H A; Hon Prog; *U of Rochester; Engr.*

MAZZEI, Tami Ann
Weed HS; Weed, CA; Chldr; NHS; Sch P; Ski C; VP, Jr Cl; CSF; HQn; Pres, YMCA; Cougar Rally; GAA; *Col o-t Siskiyous; Spch Pathology.*

MAZZEO, Maria Denise
Old Forge HS; Old Forge, PA; A Cap Choir; FNA; NHS; Pol Sci C; Sch P; Ski C; Span C; Mgr, Sftbl; Chem A; Hon Prog; Sacristan; Sanctuary Soc; Yth Leg; *U of Scranton; Pre-Law.*

McADAM, Charles Weston
Park Hill Sr HS; Kansas City, MO; Band; JV, Bsbl; Ftbl; Tr; Wrest; Drum Major; Soph Pilgramage; *Mo W U; Bus.*

McADAMS, Mark William
Iroquois HS; Louisville, KY (40-400) BC; Chor; Ensm; Fr C; JV, Bsbl; JV, Bkbl; Golf; WW; *U of Louisville; Med.*

McADAMS, Susan Marie
Reynolds HS; Greenville, PA (7-207) Chor; 4H; Piano, Organ C; St Jr Grange Instrumental.

McADOO, Jernice Lucille
Redford HS; Detroit, MI (91-650) NHS; Bsbl; Hon Prog; Spch A; *U of Mich; Pediatrics.*

McADOO, Lisa Labrie
Medina HS; Medina, TN (10%-25) BC; Chldr; Bus Mgr, FHA; Hmrm; Var C; Secy, Soph Cl; Most Courteous; *Special Ed.*

McAFEE, Deedra Kay
Mabank HS; Mabank, TX (20-130) Band; Chldr; SC; JV, Bkbl; Mgr, Tr; COM; Cl Fav; FCA; *Bus.*

McAHREN, Becky Ann
Adams Central HS; Monroe, IN (1-107) Ann; Ger C; NHS; Tr; Ger A; *International Bus Col; Acct.*

McALAHNEY, Cheryl Lynn
Campbell HS; Campbell, CA (12-350) A Cap Choir; Pres, SC; Bsbl; Bkbl; Ftbl; Tr; CSF; Hon Prog; Math A; ROTC A; Pantomine C.

McALDUFF, Susan Marie
Tignish Regional HS; Tignish, CANADA; Pres, 4H; Rptr, Hmrm; ARC; Spch C; SC; Swim; Tr; COM; Citz A; 4H A; JA A; Spch A; Sew A; *U of New Brunswick; Med.*

McALEXANDER, Rhonda Carol
John D Bassett HS; Bassett, VA (15%-138) Band; 4H; NHS; Sci C; Math A; Sci A; PA; Participation A.

McALILEY, Lydia
Olney HS; Philadelphia, PA; All Amer Yth; Band; Dbte Tm; Mjrte; Sch P; SC; Cpt, Bkbl; Cr-Ctry; JV, Sftbl; Cpt, Tr; All Public; *Phys Ed.*

McALISTER, Edwinna Beth
Jonesboro HS; Jonesboro, AR (88-349) BC; Chldr; Chor; Fr C; Hmrm; Pres, InterAct C; SC; COM; Yth Fel; Jr Cl Play; FMC; Church Choir Ldr; *Ouachita Baptist U; Home Ec.*

McALISTER, Leah Kay
York Comp HS; York, SC (20-240) Pres, Drama; FBLA; Span C; Mgr, Tnns; *Drama.*

McALISTER, Mary Alice
McNeil HS; McNeil, AR (7-34) A-Ed, Ann; BC; Chem C; FHA; 4H; Math C; Sch P; Span C; Pres, Soph Cl; Mgr, Bkbl; Cl Fav.

McALLASTER, Douglas Lawrence
Warren Area HS; Warren, PA (3%-450) A Cap Choir; Pres, Chor; NHS; Order/Arrow; Var C; Cr-Ctry; Wrest; Math A; ROTC A; Dist, Regional, All St, Chor; Eagle Sct; *US Military Acad; Engr.*

McALLISTER, Bradley Scott
Bakersfield HS; Bakersfield, CA; Bsbl; Bkbl; Ftbl; Sftbl.

McALLISTER, Debra Ann
Piqua Central HS; Piqua, OH (11-371) Bus C; Chor; 4H; NHS; Co-Ed, Sch P; Span C; *Wright St U; Eng.*

McALLISTER, Lisa Kay
Castleberry HS; Fort Worth, TX; Band; Math C; NHS; Hon Prog; *Baylor U; Sci.*

McALLISTER, Mary Anne
Smithfield HS; Smithfield, VA (68-157) Pres, Fr C; FBLA; Secy, FHA; Hmrm; Math C; Rptr, Sch P; COM; Chaplain, SC; Semi-Fin, Sch Swtht; *Longwood Col; Mus Ed.*

McALLISTER, Scott James
Kirkwood HS; Kirkwood, MO (39-592) Ger C; Order/Arrow; JV, Tr; COM; Eagle Sct; *U of Mo Columbia; Forestry.*

McALLISTER, Vanessa Bonita
Northwest HS; St Louis, MO (37-433) *Jewish Hospital Sch of Nurs.*

McALPHIN, Robert Timothy
Richard James Reynolds HS; Winston-Salem, NC (200-1700) Fr C; ARC; Ftbl; Swim; *UNC-Wilmington; Marine Bio.*

McALPINE, Barney Clark
Eldorado HS; Eldorado, TX (11-41) Tres, FBLA; FFA; 4H; NHS; VP, Var C; Ftbl; Tr; COM; Yth Fel; *Baylor U.*

McALPINE, Katreana Sanaria
Immaculata HS; Detroit, MI (25%-93) Chor; Fr C; NHS; *Albion Col; Pre-Med.*

McALPINE, Susan Kay
Schleicher Co HS; Eldorado, TX (2-30) Band; Dbte Tm; FHA; NHS; Spch C; VP, SC; Mgr, Bkbl; Highest Grade A; *Baylor U; Med.*

McANDREW, Melinda Kay
Clark Co R-I HS; Kahoka, MO (12-92) Bus C; CYO; FBLA; NHS; Pres, Pol Sci C; FHA; Bkbl; Tr; *U of Mo at Columbia; Bus.*

McANESPEY, Karen Ann
Holy Cross HS; Delran, NJ; CYO; JV, Bkbl; Sftbl; Math A; McCusker Mem Grant; *Bus.*

McANN, Karen Lorraine
Bossier Acad; Haughton, LA (2-13) F-Ed, Ann; Chldr; Lit Ral; Co-Ed, Sch P; Secy, SC; VP, Sr Cl; Alg A; Sal; Type A; Shorthand A; *LSU at Shreveport; Med Technology.*

McARTHUR, Jamelle Tonyalisa
Lindblom Tech HS; Chicago, IL (33-600) Secy, Ger C; Tres, Mjrte; NHS; Tr; Hon Prog; Mjrte; *Bradley U; Math.*

McARTHUR, Mark Allen
N Forrest HS; Hattiesburg, MS; Sci C; Var C; Bsbl; Mgr, Ftbl; Sftbl; DARGCA; Pres, Church Yth Coun; Pres, Church RA Chapter; Pres, Church BTU Cl; Outreach Ch, Sunday Sch Cl; *U of Sou Miss; Wildlife Biol.*

McARTHUR, Tambra Rene
College View Acad; Lincoln, NE (1-25) Band; Chor; NHS; Ski C; SC; Bkbl; Hon Prog; Type A; Jr Vol A; *Union Col; Teaching.*

McARTHUR, Teresa Ruth
College View Acad; Lincoln, NE; Band; NHS; Ski C; Hon Prog; Type A; *Union Col.*

McARTHUR, Thomas Kevin
Brazos HS; Wallis-Orchard, TX; FFA; Sch P; Var C; Bsbl; Bkbl; Ftbl; Semi-Fin, Golf; Soccer; Sftbl; Swim; Tr; Phy A; Sci A.

McATEE, Frank Junior II
Horseheads Sr HS; Horseheads, NY (317-570) Band; Chess C; Demolay; Ger C; 4H; Orch; *Marine Drum & Bugle Corp; Mus.*

McATEE, Jo Alyce
Trigg Co HS; Cadiz, KY (10%-200) BC; Bus C; CYO; FBLA; FHA; Secy, 4H; NFL; Rptr, Jr Cl; Cl Fav; 4H A; Type A; Yth Fel; *Murray St U; Acct.*

McATEE, John Douglass
Hobbs HS; Hobbs, NM (66%-580) BS; Ftbl; Amer Leg A; Cl Fav; *Bus.*

McATEE, Mary Jane
Trigg Co HS; Cadiz, KY; Band; FBLA; FHA; Pres, 4H; Sftbl; 4H A; *Hopkinsville Comm Col; Secretarial Sci.*

McATEER, Patricia Joan
Blanchet HS; Seattle, WA (3-285) Chor; Hmrm; NHS; A-Ed, Sch P; Tres, SC; Soccer; Tnns; *W Wash St Col; Lit.*

McAULEY, Ann Elizabeth
N Mecklenburg HS; Huntersville, NC (16-430) Band; Fr C; NHS; ARC; Type A; Sportsmanship, Catechism, A's.

McAULEY, Diane Lyndell
N Mecklenburg HS; Huntersville, NC; Band; GS; Hmrm; *Bus.*

McAULIFFE, Ann Marie
Lourdes HS; Chicago, IL (46-309) Band; VP, Drama; Hmrm; NHS; Span C; SC; Pres, Sr Cl; Pres, Soph Cl; Bkbl; Ftbl; UN; Hon Prog; I Dare You; NEDT; Sal; St Scholar; Drama A; Religion A; Friendliest Girl; NHS Outst Member; *Marquette U; Phys Therapy.*

McAVOY, Mary Ruth
Washington Wilkes Comp HS; Washington, GA (9-185) NHS; Sch P; Tres, Sci C; Secy, Span C; Tri-HiY; Gov Honor Prog; HR; Mus A; Sr Tal Win, Dist YMCA Beauty Pag; 2nd Pl, St Lit Meet-Piano; 2nd Pl, Piano-Dist Lit Meet; *Mus.*

McAWARD, Mary Jeanne
Huntington HS; Huntington, NY; Arch; Band; CYO; Secy, Hmrm; Ed, Sch P; Sci C; Ski C; Arch; Bkbl; Sftbl; COM; Math A; Ntl Sci Found; Ntl Sci Symposium; Sci A; Yth Fel; F-Ed, Sch P; *Bennington Col; Journ.*

McBEATH, Deborah G
Sebastopol HS; Sebastopol, MS (5%-45) Ann; Band; BC; Ensm; Hmrm; SC; Bkbl; Tr; Alg A; Cl Fav; Math A; Sci A; Band, Bkbl, A's.

McBEATH, Paula Denise
Moss Point HS; Moss Point, MS; *Pepperdine U; Teacher.*

McBETH, Laura Frances
Arkadelphia HS; Arkadelphia, AR (8-200) Ann; Band; Rptr, Dbte Tm; Rptr, FHA; GS; Hmrm; Mjrte; Tres, NHS; St Stu Congress; SC; Tres, Soph Cl; Ntl; Kiwanis A; Regional Band; Solo & Ensm; *Ouachita Baptist U; Ed.*

McBRAYER, David Kevin
NW Guilford HS; Greensboro, NC; Bsbl; Bkbl; Ftbl; Soccer; Sftbl; Tnns; Tr; Wrest.

McBREEN, Ann Marie
Gretna HS; Gretna, NE; NHS; Span C; Var C; Bkbl; *Anderson Col.*

McBRIDE, Beverly Ann
Cedar Rapids HS; Cedar Rapids, NE (5-35) Ann; Band; Chor; Ensm; Fin, GS; 4H; S-T, NHS; SC; Pres, Jr Cl; HQn; All Conf Vlbl; Pres Clrm; *Secy.*

McBRIDE, Debbie Kay
Stevens HS; Rapid City, SD (45-426) Summa Cum Laude; Pep C; Cpt, Dancing Group; Tres, Yth Fel; Top Dancer o-t Mo; *U of SD; Acct.*

McBRIDE, Elva Yvonne
Winona HS; Winona, MO (3-30) BC; Chldr; Chor; Pres, FBLA; Pres, FHA; Citz A; I Dare You; Math A; Pres A; Fin, Bicentennial Qn; *Amanda Jane Beauty Acad; Cosmetology.*

McBRIDE, James Ronald
Southport HS; Indianapolis, IN (50-501) CYO;
Chem C; Ger C; Hmrm; Math C; Phys C; Sci C; SC;
Var C; Bsbl; Ftbl; JV, Swim; Tr; Alg A; Math A;
Ger A; *Pre-Med.*

McBRIDE, Janine
Thatcher HS; Thatcher, AZ (1-66) Band; Drama;
Madrigal; NHS; Tnns; Type A; Outst HS Jr A; Mus
Camp A; Hugh O'Brien Rep; *Eastern Ariz Col;
Elem Ed.*

McBRIDE, Jeanetta Diana
Samuel F B Morse HS; San Diego, CA (142-465)
Tr; *U of Calif; Vet Med.*

McBRIDE, Jill Colleen
Church Point HS; Church Point, LA (13-122) A-
Ed, Ann; BC; CYO; VP, FHA; Pres, 4H; Key C;
A-Ed, Lat HS; NHS; Secy, Sr Cl; Secy, Jr Cl;
Secy, Soph Cl; 4H A; MLS; Most Out; St Secy,
4-H; St Bankers Assn; Agr-Bus Sem For Yths; Pres
Pep Sqd; Amer Leg A; VP, Jr Ldrship; Search;
Neatest, Most Spirited, Cl; *U of SW La; Elem Ed.*

McBRIDE, Kathleen Alison
Waukegan W HS; Waukegan, IL (27-469) Chor;
NHS; SC; Hon Prog; Type A; Phys Ed A; Pres,
Church MYF; VP and S-T, Sycronized Swim C;
Alverno Col; Mus Therapy.

McBRIDE, Keith Alan
John McEachern HS; Powder Springs, GA (3-250)
BC; Chess C; Fr C; Pres, Math C; Pres, Mu Alpha
Theta; Mgr, Ftbl; Amer Leg A; COM; Gov Honor
Prog; Math A; NMS; Sci A; *Ga Inst of Tech; Archt.*

McBRIDE, Kenneth Blair
Shiloh Seventh-Day-Adventist Acad; Chicago, IL
(6-27) Band; Mgr, Chor; Drama; Hmrm; Orch;
F-Ed, Soph P; Bus Mgr, Sr Cl; Parl, Jr Cl; Pres, Soph
Cl; Cpt, Bkbl; MVP, Sftbl; COM; Citz A; Most Out;
Swtht; Most Talented; *Andrews U; Pre-Dental.*

McBRIDE, Patricia Jean
Sky View HS; Smithfield, UT (5-611) FHA; Ski C;
Math A; Ntl Achv Schol; *Ricks Col; Bus.*

McBRIDE, Sharon Jean
Butler Area Intermediate HS; Butler, PA; Band;
Orch; Law Explorers C; *Law.*

McBRIDE, Steve J
Valley HS; Sanders, AZ (1-60) Dbte Tm; VP, FFA;
Model UN; Var C; VP, Soph Cl; Bsbl; JV, Bkbl;
Ftbl; Tr; Sci A; Type A; Val; General Bus A; De-
bate A; *Brigham Young U; Law.*

McBRIDE, Wendell Lee
Robert E Lee HS; Midland, TX; Mgr, Bkbl; JV,
Swim; Mus A; *Tex Tech U; Elec Engr.*

McBRIEN, Mary Melissa
Liggett Sch; Grosse Pointe Woods, MI (1-74) VP,
A Cap Choir; VP, Chor; Cum Laude Soc; Ensm; Fr
C; Ed, Lit Mag; Math C; Sci C; Swim; COM; Hon
Prog; Star Student; Mich Yth Arts Coun, Cert of
Merit; Hon Men, Detroit Scholastic As; Ntl Fr
Contest Level 1 As; Highest Schol; *Med.*

McBROOM, Dee Ann
Brawley Union HS; Brawley, CA (1-450) Ann; Cpt,
Chldr; SC; Amer Leg A; CSF; Job's Daughters;
Semi-Fin, Gettysburg Address.

McBRYDE, Pamella Jayne
Fayetteville HS; Fayetteville, AR (25-450) A Cap
Choir; Band; FHA; Sci A; Fr Hon; 1st Division
Medal, Clarinet Comp; Sup, Piano Playing Guild;
U of Ark; Mus.

McBURNETT, Lesia Diane
Glencoe HS; Glencoe, AL (10%-106) Anchor C;
Band; FHA; 4H; B Crocker A; Flag Twirler; *Ala
Tech Col; Legal Secy.*

McCABE, April Dawn
Pinckneyville Comm HS; Pinckneyville, IL
(73-133) FHA; Pres, 4H; NHS; Sci C; Soph Cl;
Arch; 4H A; JA A; Most Out; VP, Secy, Tres, Rptr,
4-H C; Jr Ldr A; *Rend Lake Jr Col; Med Secy.*

McCABE, Cindy Helen Marie
Orleans HS; Orleans, NE (7-29) A-Ed, Ann; Band;
Chor; Pres, 4H; Monogram; SC; Cpt, Bkbl; Sftbl;
Tr; 4H A; HCt; Type A; Yth Fel; JV Vlbl; Safety
Coun Merit; 1st, Dist Solo Mus Contest; *Kans
Wesleyan U; Lang Arts.*

McCABE, Marla Jean
Union HS; Biggsville, IL; Co-Ed, Ann; VP, Drama;
SC; Bkbl; Tr; Spch A; Vlbl; Faculty List; Pom-Pom
Girl; *Monmouth U; Phys Ed.*

McCABE, Mary L
Carl Sandburg HS; Orland Park, IL (109-764) Tres,
CYO; Drama; Ger C; NHS; Spch C; SC; Thes; Spch
A; WW; *N Ill U; Bus.*

McCABE, Michael Henderson
Naperville Central HS; Naperville, IL (75-430)
Model UN; F-Ed, Sch P; Ski C; Pres, SC; Mgr,
Bsbl; Bkbl; DARGCA; Hon Prog; Journ A; Q&S A;
VFW A; Yth Fel; Young Life; *Ill U; Journ.*

McCABE, Patrick William Ed
Orleans Pub HS; Orleans, NE (5-30) Pres, Dbte
Tm; 4H; Tres, SC; VP, Soph Cl; Tr; JV, Wrest; 4H
A; Spch A; Yth Fel; Sr Choir; *Kans Wesleyan U.*

McCAFFERTY, Therese Lynette
McCurtain HS; McCurtain, OK (1-18) Cpt, Chldr;
Pres, 4H; Secy, Hmrm; NHS; Bkbl; Sftbl; Tr; 4H A;
Hist A; HCt; Type A; Phys Fitness A; PA; HR;
Northeastern Okla St U.

McCAGG, Betty Jean
Poughkeepsie HS; Poughkeepsie, NY; Chor; *Evangel Col; Mus.*

McCAHAN, Lori Lynn
Sherman E Burroughs HS; Ridgecrest, CA
(38-378) Band; Ch, InterClub Coun; Key C; Orch;
SC; Sftbl; Hon Prog; Miss Amer Pageant Prog;
Calif Polytech U; Bio Sci.

McCAIN, Kathleen Grace
Arcata HS; Arcata, CA (20%-350) A Cap Choir;
Band; Drama; Hmrm; InterAct C; Madrigal; Spch
C; SC; COM; Girl o-t Mo; *Baylor U; Mus.*

McCAIN, Sandra Lee
Durant HS; Durant, OK; A Cap Choir; Cpt, Chldr;
S-T, Chor; Ensm; Hmrm; Madrigal; SC; COM; Cl
Fav; Key C Swtht; Pres, Girls Chapter FCA; MVP,
Chldr; Secy, Bryan Baptist Assn Yth Coun; *South-
eastern Okla St U; Phys Ed.*

McCAIN, Shelia LaKequia
Lake Clifton HS; Baltimore, MD (10%-300)
Drama; Model UN; ARC; Cpt, Swim; Hist A; Hon
Prog; JA A; Star Student.

McCALEB, Phil Allen
Quincy Sr HS II; Quincy, IL (3-700) Tr; SAA; *John
Wood Comm Col; Bus.*

McCALEB, Phyllis Kay
Hueytown HS; Hueytown, AL; Secy, Chor; Ensm;
ARC; SC; Secy, Jr Cl; Secy, Soph Cl; Beauty; Cl
Fav; Spch A; VFW Orator Win; Choir Swtht; *U of
Ala; Phys Therapy.*

McCALL, Ann Elizabeth
N Reynolds Sr HS; Winston-Salem, NC; Fr C;
Bkbl; Sftbl; Citz A; Yth Fel; Lat A.

McCALL, Barbara Ann
Scotland HS; Laurinburg, NC; Dbte Tm; FFA;
FHA; Math C.

McCALL, Jack Humphreys Jr
Battle Ground Acad; Franklin, TN (11-98) F-Ed,
Ann; Band; Chor; 4H; Lat C; NFL; Spch C; Mgr,
Cr-Ctry; Mgr, Tr; God & Country A; 4H A;
NEDT; Spch A; *Vanderbilt U; Hist.*

McCALL, James Lamar
Norman HS; Norman, OK (167-662) Band; BS;
Order / Arrow; Span C; Span NHS; Var C; Ftbl;
Wrest; Amer Leg A; Order / Arrow A; Yth Fel;
Outst Tm Contribution A, Wrest; Eagle Sct; Sct
World Jamboree; *Okla St U; Forestry.*

McCALL, Karen Eunice
Independence Sr HS; Charlotte, NC (35-700) A
Cap Choir; Ann; Band; Chor; Community Yth
Symph; Drama; Ensm; Hmrm; Co-Ch, InterClub
Cou; Lit Mag; Madrigal; NHS; Orch; Pres, Span C;
Tres, SC; Hist A; Type A; Church Swtht; Church
Yth Coun; GAA; Fine Arts Hon Soc; Civinettes;
Flute Ensm.

McCALL, Laurie
Silsbee HS; Silsbee, TX (1-240) Pres, A Cap Choir;
Chor; Fr C; French NHS; FTA; JETS; Madrigal;
Pres, NHS; SC; Alg A; Bio A; Chem A; Math A;
MLS; Summa Cum Laude; Type A; Val; WW; Fr A;
Choir A; WW Among Amer HS Mus Stu; *Baylor
U; Med.*

McCALL, Margaret Anne
Sarasota HS; Sarasota, FL (250-600) Hmrm; Ch,
SC; Ftbl; HCt; WW; Pres, Booster C; Ch, Home-
coming; Statistician, Bkbl; Counteract; Cl Offices;
Abilene Christian Col; Journ.

McCALLA, Stacy Lee
Weatherford HS; Weatherford, OK (12-100) Cpt,
Chldr; Chor; FBLA; FTA; Model UN; NHS; SC;
Hist A; HCt; *SW Okla St U; Computer Prog.*

**McCALLUM,
James Meredith Jr**
Palatka S HS; Palatka, FL (9-285) Chor; Key C;
NHS; Bkbl; Tnns; Hist A; Sci A; Sch Schol A; *St
Johns River Comm Col.*

McCALLUM, Jane Meador
Palatka S HS; Palatka, FL (1-230) Ann; BC; NHS;
Sch P; SC; VP, Jr Cl; Hist A; Journ A; Math A;
NMS; Star Student; Val; Eng, Span, A's; Cl Schol &
Sch Schol A; *St Johns River Comm Col; Paralegal.*

McCALLUM, Laurie LuAnne
Broxton HS; Broxton, GA (5%-50) Co-Cpt, Chldr;
Ch, FHA; Rptr, 4H; Pres, Soph Cl; Mgr, Tnns; 4H
A.

McCAMEY, Krista LaJune
Henry Ford HS; Detroit, MI; Chor; Sftbl; Pioneer
Girls; Pom Pom Girls; Bus.

McCAMMON, David Thomas
Porter HS; Maryville, TN (30-75) Tres, FFA; Key
C; Order / Arrow; Span C; Eagle Sct; St Farmer,
FFA; *Tech Sch; Refrigeration.*

McCANDLESS, James Clayton
Daviess Co HS; Owensboro, KY (26-316) Order /
Arrow; H of F; Hon Prog; NMS; Jr Crime Coun;
Eagle Sct; *U o-t South; Psychiatric Med.*

McCANDLESS, Mary Jo
Butler Area Intermediate HS; Butler, PA
(2%-1100) Chor; Ensm; Yth Fel; Fin, W Pa Dist
Chor Comp; Rep, Church Budget & Finance
Comm.

McCANDLESS, Susan Jane
Ross S Sterling HS; Baytown, TX (175-600) Chor;
Drama; InterClub Coun; Spch C; SC; Thes; Swim;
Type A; DeMolay Swtht; GSct; Drill Tm; VP, Jr
Optimist; *U of Tex; Bus Field.*

McCANE, Debra Sue
Northwest HS; Cincinnati, OH (61-378) Band;
Hmrm; SC; Bkbl; Sftbl; Citz A; Adv Board, Jr Cl;
Ohio St; Phys Therapy.

McCANN, Joseph James
Tech HS; Scranton, PA (357-400) Ftbl; *Pinebrook
Jr Col; Ministry.*

McCANN, Kevin Luke
Reynolds HS; Greenville, PA (7-212) VP, HiY;
Math C; Pres, NHS; Rptr, Sch P; Bsbl; Tr; Pres
Clroom for Young Amer; *Dickinson Col; Law.*

McCANN, Margaret Jeanne
Scotch Plains-Fanwood HS; Scotch Plains, NJ
(75-594) A Cap Choir; Chor; Dbte Tm; Orch; Rainbow; Sch P; PTA A; Yth Fel; WW; Region Choir;
Vocal Mus Schol; *Rutgers Col; Nurs.*

McCANN, Michael Lee
Bryan HS; Bryan, OH; A Cap Choir; Band; Chor;
Ensm; FFA; 4H; Ftbl; Church Bkbl & Sftbl.

McCANN, Sonja Dylisa
John McDonogh Sr HS; New Orleans, LA; *Nurs.*

McCANN, Stacey Lee
S Garland HS; Garland, TX (50%-700) Chldr;
FHA; Sci C; *Eastfield Jr Col.*

McCARLEY, Janet Elaine
Del Norte HS; Albuquerque, NM (241-650) Jr Cl;
U of NM; Art.

McCARLEY, Marjorie Lucille
Danbury HS; Danbury, CT (414-718) Chor;
Hmrm; Sch Art A; Sch Gym A; *Bus.*

McCARROLL, Tammie Yvonne
Lenoir City HS; Lenoir City, TN; Thes C; VP,
Chor; 4H; InterAct C; Fin, Jr Miss Pagent; Lit
Mag; NHS; Distributive Ed As; *Tenn Tech; Mus
Ed.*

McCARTER, Dolan Craig
Northbrook Sr HS; Houston, TX (159-529) Chor;
NHS; Bus.

McCARTER, Virginia Marie
Gatlinburg Pittman HS; Gatlinburg, TN (33%-75) Band; FHA; Hmrm; Jr Miss Pagent; SC; *E Tenn St U; Law Enforcement.*

McCARTHA, Sarah Jerene
Lakeland HS; Lakeland, FL; Hmrm; Math C; COM; Kiwanis A; Opt A; Secy, Sunday Sch; PA, Part, Ann Walk- a- thon, A's; *Polk Voc-Tech Sch; Secy Practices.*

McCARTHY, David Anthony
St Mary's HS; Lynn, MA (1-146) Chor; Hmrm; NHS; Rptr, Sch P; Bsbl; Bkbl; Bio A; Hon Prog; Math A; Sci A; Essay Contest, Span, Religion, A's.

McCARTHY, David Daniel
Clintonville Sr HS; Clintonville, WI (1-175) Band; Ensm; Ger C; Math C; NHS; Var C; Bkbl; MVP, Tnns; Math A; Rotary A; Val; Yth Fel; Win; Guidance Lab For Superior Stu; Local, Top 10% St, MAA Math Cont; *U of Wis; Health Field.*

McCARTHY, Eric M
Northwest HS; St Louis, MO (8-728) Cpt, Bkbl; Cl Fav; Spch A; Church A Cappella Choir & Band; Schol, Med Self-Help, A's; *Law.*

McCARTHY, James Thomas
MacArthur HS; San Antonio, TX (70-600) CYO; Lat C; NHS; Bkbl; *Tex A&M U; Archt.*

McCARTHY, Jerry Francis
Sprague HS; Salem, OR (123-475) CYO; Bkbl; Golf; HCt; *Willamette U; Biol.*

McCARTHY, Joan Coreen
Fowler HS; Fowler, CO (15-60) Ann; Cpt, Chldr; Chor; Drama; Ensm; GS; Jr Miss Pagent; Madrigal; Fin, Model UN; NFL; S-T, Rainbow; Sch P; Ski C; Spch C; Thes; Secy, Jr Cl; Sftbl; Swim; Tr; Journ A; NEDT; Odd Fellow Fin; Q&S A; Type A; Hist, FBLA; S-T, Ltrmen's C; Pom Pon; Pep C Adv Board; St Tr Placer; *Colo St U; Bus.*

McCARTHY, Judith Maureen
Fowler HS; Fowler, CO (10-58) Ann; Cpt, Chldr; Chor; Drama; VP, FBLA; FHA; GS; Madrigal; NFL; Rainbow; Spch C; Secy, SC; Thes; VP, Sr Cl; Tr; Amer Leg A; Spch A; Yth Fel; Worthy Advisor, Rainbow Girls; *Colo St U; Bus.*

McCARTHY, Megan
J H Linton Intermediate Sch; Penn Hills, PA (5%-1300) Chldr; Fr C; Tr; COM; NEDT; ARC A; Cert of Achv; Phys Fitness Tm; Cert of Ath Accomp, Marine Corp; *Phys Therapy.*

McCARTHY, Michele Dianne
Blanchet HS; Seattle, WA (28-383) Cpt, Cr-Ctry; Swim; Cpt, Tr; MLS; Most Inspirational, Sports; HR; Ray Segal A; *Seattle U; Phys Ed.*

McCARTHY, Virginia Ann
Robert E Lee HS; Midland, TX; Chor; Dbte Tm; NFL; NHS; Rainbow; Spch C; SC; JV, Swim; Pres A; Spch A; *Baylor U; Nurs.*

McCARTNEY, Charmaine
Pawhuska HS; Pawhuska, OK (17-89) Ed, Ann; S-T, Band; Drama; GS; NHS; Span C; Secy, SC; Amer Leg A; Citz A; Cl Fav; DARGCA; Rotary A; Band Qn; John Philip Sousa A; *Northern Okla Col; Acct.*

McCARTNEY, Tammiela Annette
Springdale HS; Springdale, AR; Church Yth Group; Missionette; CA; Children's Phase 5 Worker; *U of Ark; Secy.*

McCARTNEY, Tammy Annette
Springdale HS; Springdale, AR; *U of Ark; Acct.*

McCARTY, Bruce
Quitman HS; Quitman, MS (10%-203) BC; Chor; FTA; HiY; Pres, Hmrm; Span C; SC; Pres, Soph C; Alg A; Type A; Reading Cert; All St Chor A; *Miss St U; Med.*

McCARTY, Kenneth
Sandusky HS; Sandusky, OH; Bkbl; COM; Fr Cert of Merit; HR, Schol Achv; *Computer Sci.*

McCARTY, Kimberly Marie
Tuscola HS; Tuscola, IL (6-118) VP, Band; Ensm; VP, Fr C; NHS; Bkbl; Secy, Jr Cl; Sftbl; Cl Fav; HQn; HCt; Hon Prog; Rotary A; Spch A; St Scholar; Tuscola Beauty Pageant; Pom Pon Sq; Marshal; *U of Ill.*

McCARTY, Shari Lynn
Southeast HS; Springfield, IL (23-557) Chor; Hmrm; ARC; SC; Hon Prog; Ger A; Superior Hon; Bus.

McCARVER, Neta Beth
Pine Bluff HS; Pine Bluff, AR (78-592) A Cap Choir; FHA; NHS; All Region Choir; *Ouachita Baptist U; Special Ed.*

McCARVER, Rhonda Sue
Springdale HS; Springdale, AR (47-427) Chor; Fr C; FHA; S-T, FTA; Sci A; 1st Pl, Local & Regional Sci Fair; VP, S-T, Church Yth Group; Jr Swtht, Vica HOE; FTA Schol; *U of Ark.*

McCASKEY, Sandra Jean
Polo HS; Polo, MO (10-37) VP, Band; Chor; Ensm; S-T, Span C; Pres, Soph Cl; Cpt, Bkbl; Tr; *Central Mo St U; Special Ed.*

McCASKILL, Jane Chandler
Robert F Munroe HS; Quincy, FL (2-33) Ed, Ann; Secy, BC; Cpt, Chldr; Hmrm; SC; Bkbl; COM; HCt; NEDT; Sal; Spch A; Yth Fel; *Presbyterian Col; Biol.*

McCASKILL, Kenneth Patrick
St Andrews HS; Charleston, SC; Mgr, Band; Chess C; Dbte Tm; Bkbl; Sftbl; Tr.

McCASKY, Melanie Joy
Limestone HS; Peoria, IL; Band; Chor; Orch; Bkbl; COM; Hon Prog; *ICC; Span Ed.*

McCASLIN, Soni Kay
Guthrie HS; Guthrie, OK; Masonic A; Pres, Church Yth Fel; *Central St U; Bus Law.*

McCASLIN, Trenton Hayes
Copeland Rural HS; Copeland, KS (50%-9) 4H; Hmrm; SC; Bkbl; Ftbl; Tr; 4H A; Swtht.

McCATHERN, Gregory
W Side HS; Newark, NJ (50%-250) Chor; Span C; Spch C; SC; Var C; JV, Bsbl; JV, Bkbl; Cr-Ctry; Tr; Interlochen Ntl Mus; JA A; Math A; *Delaware St Col; Archt.*

McCATHERN, Kenneth Ricciardi
Sci HS; Newark, NJ (50-160) Chor; Hmrm; JETS; Math C; Orch; Up Bound; Bkbl; Ftbl; Alg A; Sci A; Type A; *USC; Bio.*

McCATHRAN, Charles Eric
N Caddo HS; Vivian, LA (1-200) BS; Pres, Key C; NHS; Pres, SC; Ftbl; Tnns; Cl Fav; *Med.*

McCAULEY, Brian Holden
Trumbull HS; Trumbull, CT; Chor; Co-Cpt, Dbte Tm; Ensm; Fin, Ntl Yth Conf; Y-Tns; Soccer; Tr; Hon Prog; ARC A; Spch A; Yth Fel; Yth Foundation; Singing A; VP, FCYF; Mgr, Stage Crew; *Gordon Theological Sem; Theol.*

McCAULEY, Dana Lee
French HS; Beaumont, TX;

McCAULEY, Dwight William
Belen HS; Belen, NM (33%-350) A Cap Choir; Chess C; Chor; Demolay; Drama; Ensm; Bsbl; Bkbl; Ftbl; Math A; Poet A; Yth Fel; All-St Chor; Preceptor A For Demolay; Bd of Dir, Albuquerque Bowl; *U of New Mexico; Mus.*

McCAULEY, Gayle Regina
Normandy Sr HS; St Louis, MO (69-742) Band; Secy, Chor; Drama; Hmrm; VP, SC; COM; Citz A; Cl Fav; *Psych.*

McCAY, Sandra Lee
Medford Sr HS; Medford, OR (20%-600) Band; Chor; Community Yth Symph; Drama; Hmrm; Orch; SC; Thes; Bsbl; Band A; *Med.*

McCHAREN, Suzanne
Aiken HS; Aiken, SC (11-640) BC; Tres, Ger C; Hmrm; InterClub Coun; Fin, Jr Miss Pagent; Mu Alpha Theta; NHS; SC; HCt; Pres, Keyette C; Co-ordinator, Casual Hut Tn Board; *Clemson U; Ceramic Engr.*

McCHRISTIAN, Elizabeth Hester
Mena HS; Mena, AR (7-147) FHA; 4H; Sci C; Pres, Span C; 4H A; HCt; Hon Prog; Band Lib; All Region Band; Flag Tm; Fel of Christian Stu; VP, United Meth Yth; *Sci.*

McCLAIN, Adrienne Renee
Amer Heritage Christian Sch; Hayward, CA (2-12) A Cap Choir; Ann; Cpt, Chldr; Chor; Dbte Tm; Ensm; Hmrm; Semi-Fin, Jr Miss Pa; Orch; Sch P; SC; Bkbl; Sftbl; Tnns; Tr; Bank Of Amer A; CSF; Journ A; Sal; Spch A; *Stanford U; Journ.*

McCLAIN, Barbara Ann
Jesup W Scott HS; Toledo, OH (20-354) Secy, Chor; Bkbl; Sftbl; Hon Prog; Stu o-t Mo; Pres, Sr Girls; Coun Comm; WW; *U of Toledo; Legal Secy.*

McCLAIN, Bonita Yulanda
W Edgecombe HS; Rocky Mount, NC (2-130) BC; Chldr; Chor; Tres, Fr C; FHA; Monogram; Sci C; SC; Secy, Soph Cl; Citz A; Gov Honor Prog; Hist A; Ntl Sci Found; *Mich St U; Med.*

McCLAIN, E Michelle
Marshall HS; Marshall, TX (23-424) Chldr; FTA; Secy, NHS; Span C; Tres, SC; Beauty; HCt; Swtht; Yth Fel; Tres, Girl's FCA; WW; S-T, Horizon C; Drill Tm; Jr Civitan; *Baylor U.*

McCLAIN, Janet Marie
Wilcox HS; Rochelle, GA (8-116) BC; 4H; Math C; Sci C; Span C; COM; Hon Prog; *U of Ga; Lab Tech.*

McCLAIN, Janice Laree
Wilcox HS; Rochelle, GA (6-116) BC; 4H; Math C; Sci C; Span C; COM; Hon Prog; *U of Ga; Lab Tech.*

McCLAIN, Lesa
Rancho HS; N Las Vegas, NV; Cpt, Sftbl; Tnns; Type A; MVP, Sftbl; Cpt, Vlbl; *UNR; Interior Design.*

McCLAIN, Marcia Lynn
Vicksburg HS; Vicksburg, MS (10%-300) F-Ed, Ann; Band; Lat C; *U of Miss; Nurs.*

McCLAIN, Murenda Vanessa
Central HS; Columbia, TN; FHA; SC; *U of Detroit; Law.*

McCLAIN, Samuel Lorenza
Vancleave HS; Vancleave, MS; Var C; Ftbl; Tr.

McCLAIN, Sharen LaVon
W Edgecombe HS; Rocky Mount, NC (5-130) BC; Chldr; Chor; Fr C; FBLA; FHA; Jr Miss Pagent; Monogram; ARC; Sci C; Rptr, SC; Citz A; Gov Honor Prog; Ntl Sci Found; *Ohio St U; Med.*

McCLANAHAN, Mark Walter
Benjamin Franklin HS; Philadelphia, PA (9-375) Dbte Tm; Hmrm; Secy, SC; Up Bound; *Moorehouse Col; Econ.*

McCLARD, Peter Tracy
Thomas Jefferson HS; Denver, CO;

McCLARD, Timothy Marion
Farmington Sr HS; Farmington, MO (178-258) A Cap Choir; Band; BS; Chor; Ensm; Madrigal; Bkbl; JV, Cr-Ctry; *SEMU; Mus.*

McCLAREN, Charlene Kay
Bellevue Sr HS; Bellevue, NE (140-851) Chor; Tres, ARC; ARC A; *Tex Christian U; Child Care.*

McCLARY, Michael Duane
Pinedale HS; Pinedale, WY (2-50) Band; Chor; Ensm; NHS; JV, Bkbl; Ftbl; Bio A; Hon Prog; 1 Rating, District Comp, Trombone; *Mus.*

McCLARY, Susan Beth
Fairfield HS; Langdon, KS (10-54) Band; Chor; Ensm; VP, FHA; Rptr, Hmrm; Mjrte; NHS; SC; Thes; Var C; Tr; COM; WW; Solo, Trio, Mus Fest; VP, Pep C; Co Cpt, Vlbl; VP, S-T, Young Peoples Group; *Chadron St U; Law Enforcement.*

McCLASKEY, Pena Lea
Arkansas City HS; Arkansas City, KS (10%-250) Chor; Ensm; Rptr, FFA; Rptr, FHA; Semi-Fin, GS; Hmrm; Madrigal; Span C; Y-Tns; All St, Dist, Choirs; Schol, Mus & Art Camp; *Okla Christian Col; Mus.*

McCLAY, Linda Marie
W J Woodham HS; Pensacola, FL (10-530) Chess C; Mu Alpha Theta; NHS; Orch; F-Ed, Sch P; SC; Bausch & Lomb A; COM; Elk A; JA A; NMF; NEDT; *NC St U; Pulp & Paper Tech.*

McCLEAN, David Robert
Minneapolis Lutheran HS; Minneapolis, MN (7-49) Band; BS; Chor; Ger C; NHS; Bsbl; Bkbl; Ftbl; New Wine, Swing Choir; Delta Epsilon Phi; *Concordia Col; Theology.*

McCOMB, Tracy Cheryl
Bethel HS; Hampton, VA (49-566) Fr C; Rptr, Sch
P; Co-Ch, Jr Cl; Campus Life; Church Yth Fel Yth
Coun; *Duke U; Psych.*

McCOMBS, Nancy Joan
Connersville Sr HS; Connersville, IN (33%-407)
Band; Ger C; Hmrm; *Purdue U; Communication.*

McCOMBS, Robin Louise
Coronado HS; El Paso, TX (83-750) Semi-Fin,
Chldr; Drama; Hmrm; Secy, InterClub Coun; Span
C; SC; VP, Tri-HiY; Golf; Spch A; Swtht; Yth Fel;
Yth Leg; Pres, Honorary Dance C; Outst Christian
Yth; Bkbl Duchess; *SW Tex St U; Dance Therapy.*

McCONAHA, Sharon
Bellmont HS; Decatur, IN (14-270) Fr C; Secy,
NHS; SC; Pres, Yth Fel; Sunshine Soc; Pep C; Co-
Ch, Young Republicans; Pres, Church Dist Yth
Coun; *Hanover Col; Pub Relations.*

McCONDICHIE, LaDonna Joi
Booker T Washington HS; Tulsa, OK (78-290)
Semi-Fin, Chldr; Chess C; Chor; Drama; Fin,
Hmrm; Phys C; ARC; Rptr, Sch P; Span C; Ch, Sr
Cl; Secy, Jr Cl; Hon Prog; MLS; Swtht; Yth Fel;
Secy, Yth Fel; Gym C; Win, Dance Contest; *Tenn
St U; Phys Therapy.*

McCONEGHY, Sharon Lynn
William Tennent Sr HS; Warminster, PA; S-T,
CYO; FNA; NHS; Ed, Sch P; SC; Hon Prog; Hosp
Vol; *Nurs.*

**McCONNAUGHAY,
Thomas Allen**
Batavia Sr HS; Batavia, IL (4-224) Band; Hmrm;
Pres, Lat C; Math C; Tres, SC; Hon Prog; Math A;
Dist Mus Contest; St Lat Contest; Soph Yth
Ldrship Seminar; *U of Ill; Finance.*

McCONNELL, Betty Jane
Nova HS; Davie, FL (240-436) Chor; FBLA;
Church Adult Choir; Church Yth Group & Chor;
Sunday Sch Teacher; Vacation Church Sch
Teacher; *Bus Ed.*

McCONNELL, Elsie Lenae
Springhill HS; Springhill, LA (10%-190) GS; Math
C; NHS; Sch P; Q&S A; *La Tech U; Ed.*

McCONNELL, Kathy
Blanchard HS; Blanchard, OK; F-Ed, Ann; BC;
Dbte Tm; Pres, FHA; 4H; Hmrm; JETS; Math C;
NHS; Sch P; Sci C; SC; Rptr, Soph Cl; Mgr, Bkbl;
Sftbl; B Crocker A; COM; Gov Honor Prog; 4H A;
HCt; Hon Prog; Journ A; Yth Fel; Hist, Rptr, FHA;
Secy, Tres, Pep C; *Okla St U.*

McCONNELL, Robert Harold
Grinnell Sr HS; Grinnell, IA (23-300) A Cap Choir;
Band; Chor; Ensm; SC; Tnns; Hon Prog; Band A;
FCA; *General Art.*

McCONNELL, Scott P
Attica Central HS; Attica, NY (10%-200) Tres,
AFS; Band; Ski C; Soccer; Swim; Tnns; *Rensselaer
Poly Tech Inst; Archt.*

McCONNELL, Susan Jane
Auburn Sr HS; Auburn, NE (7-105) Band; Chor;
Math C; Sci C; Span C; MVP, Swim; MVP, Tnns;
Mus.

McCONNELL, Susan Lay
Dobyns-Bennett HS; Kingsport, TN; Ed, Ann; BC;
Chor; Sch P; Citz A; Opt A; Tn o-t Wk; Hon Men,
Ntl Writing Contest; *Mus.*

McCONVILLE, Janice Susan
N Fort Myers HS; N Fort Myers, FL (25%-500)
Ch, FBLA; Ch, Hmrm; Hon Prog; Opt A; Opt Out
Tn; Yth Fel; Pres, A, Candystripers; *Edison Comm
Col; Bus.*

McCOOK, William Rufus Jr
Tupelo HS; Tupelo, MS (25%-381) Order/Arrow;
JV, Ftbl; Tnns; JV, Tr; God & Country A; Order/
Arrow A; VP, Yth Fel; Jr Civitan C; Eagle Sct;
Coun, Sct Camp; Page, St House of Reps; Tnns C;
Miss St U; Petroleum Engr.

McCOOL, Jamie Leigh
R H Watkins HS; Laurel, MS; Cpt, Band; Chor;
Rainbow; Miss Rainbow; Drum Major; Horse Tro-
phies; *U Sou Miss; Eng.*

McCOOL, Timothy Lee
Mortimer Jordan HS; Morris, AL (4-94) Band;
Chor; Ensm; NHS; Sci C; NEDT; Eng Develop-
ment A; Span Excel A; *Mus.*

McCORD, Gregory Lyle
Dunlap Comm HS; Dunlap, IA (30-58) A Cap
Choir; Ed, Ann; Band; Chor; Ensm; Fr C; Madrigal;
ARC; Sch P; Spch C; SC; Bkbl; Ftbl; Swim; Tr;
Journ A; Most Out; Spch A; *Nebraska Wesleyan.*

McCORD, James Michael
Giles Co HS; Pulaski, TN (8-160) Fin, BS; Order/
Arrow; Pres, Soph Cl; Bkbl; Co-Cpt, Ftbl; Tnns;
Order/Arrow A; ARC A; Fr A; Eagle Sct; Ftbl All
Amer; BS Rep; *U of Tenn; Med.*

McCORD, Mary Helen
Norman HS; Norman, OK (94-676) VP, Chor;
Community Yth Symph; Ensm; Hmrm; NHS;
Orch; SC; Swim; All St Orch; Swim C; All St Chor;
Church Bell Choir; Foreign Stu League; *Okla Bap-
tist U; Mus.*

McCORD, Rebecca Adair
Winter Park HS; Winter Park, FL; Chor; *Seminole
Comm Col; Legal Secy.*

McCORD, Sallyanna
Clear Lake HS; Clear Lake City, TX (213-600)
Ann; FTA; Key C; Span C; Tnns; *Baylor U; Pub
Relations.*

McCORD, Steven Paul
Spencer HS; Spencer, IA (45-182) Chor; Drama;
Spch C; Thes; Ftbl; JV, Wrest; *Morningside Col;
Drama.*

McCORKLE, David Frederick
King's Garden HS; Seattle, WA; NHS; Mgr, Ftbl;
Type A; Schol Achv A.

McCORKLE, Debra Jean
Pathway Day Sch; Savannah, GA (1-22) Ed, Ann;
Rptr, Sch P; Hon Prog; Journ A; Sci A; Bible A;
Armstrong St Col; Hist.

McCORKLE, Gina Lynn
Godley HS; Godley, TX; FHA; Mjrte; Tres, Soph
Cl; Bkbl; Tnns; Tr; *Tex Womens U; Phys Therapy.*

McCORKLE, James Wayne
Union HS; Union, MS (10%-50) VP, Band; BC; VP,
Chess C; Pres, FFA; Hmrm; SC; 1st Pl, Skeet
Shoot; *Miss St U; Agr.*

McCORKLE, Martin Dale
Mesa Verde HS; Citrus Heights, CA (30-250) A
Cap Choir; Band; Chor; Drama; Ensm; Madrigal;
Orch; *San Frans Col; Mus.*

McCORMACK, Richard Joseph
St Aloysious HS; Jersey City, NJ (69-110) Drama;
Sch P; Mgr, Bsbl; Mgr, Bkbl; Journ A; Cl Writer,
Pres, Bowl; Most Valuable Staffer, Sch Paper; Ch-
Finance, Prom; *Hudson Co Comm Col; Journ.*

McCORMACK, Steven Russell
San Jacinto HS; San Jacinto, CA; Cpt, Bkbl.

McCORMICK, Alison Anne
Washington HS; Cedar Rapids, IA (20%-400)
Band; Chor; Community Yth Symph; JETS; Orch;
JV, Swim; *Ia St Col; Sci.*

McCORMICK, Denise
Bovina HS; Bovina, TX (10-25) Cpt, Chldr; FHA;
Hmrm; Var C; Bkbl; Cr-Ctry; Tr; Beauty; Math A;
S Plains Col; Coach.

McCORMICK, James Dean
Hueytown HS; Hueytown, AL; COM; *U of Ala;
Engr.*

McCORMICK, Jeffrey Martin
E Alton Wood River HS; Wood River, IL; Ger C;
Thes; *Sou Ill U; Archt.*

McCORMICK, Jill Lynn
E Alton-Wood River HS; Wood River, IL
(1-253) Chor; Tres, Ger C; GS; Hmrm; NHS; SC;
Secy, Thes; Hon Prog; *SIU-Edwardsville; Med
Tech.*

McCORMICK, Karen Marie
George Washington Carver Sr HS; New Orleans,
LA; SC; Tri-HiY; Swim; COM; Citz A; Math A;
Star Student; *St Mary's Dominican Col; Math.*

McCORMICK, Kimberly Jo
McCracken HS; McCracken, KS (2-14) Band; Pres,
CYO; Cpt, Chldr; Chor; Drama; Ensm; F-Ed, Sch
P; Spch C; Pres, SC; Cpt, Bkbl; Golf; Cpt, Tr; COM;
HCt; Most Out; Spch A; *Washburn Col; Eng.*

McCORMICK, Lauren Jane
Desales HS; Geneva, NY (1-53) A-Ed, Ann; VP,
NHS; F-Ed, Sch P; Tres, Ski C; Tri-HiY; VP, Sr Cl;
COM; MLS; NEDT; Val; *Mass Col of Phar; Phar.*

McCORMICK, Margaret Ellen
Hightstown HS; Hightstown, NJ (23-253) AFS;
Chor; Fr C; 4H; NHS; Cpt, Hockey; Sftbl; Cpt, Tr;
4H A; Hon Prog; Ath Yrbk; Tr Half-Mile; *Bowdoin
Col; Hist.*

McCORMICK, Mary Kathryn
Streator HS; Streator, IL (118-350) MVP, Band;
Pres, 4H; Fin, Sftbl; 4H A; Secy, Band; Band A;
Vlbl Ltr; VP, Lat, 4-H C; Art C; Vlbl; *Ill Valley
Comm Col; Nurs.*

McCORMICK, Maureen Ann
Aquiras HS; La Crosse, WI (6-186) Chldr; Chem C;
Drama; Hmrm; NHS; Sftbl; Tnns; Tr; Chamber of
Comm A; Hon Prog; Candystriper Service A; *La-
Crosse St U; Bus.*

McCORMICK, Patricia Michelle
East Noble HS; Kendallville, IN (4-259) Ann;
Band; Chldr; Ger C; 4H; NHS; Spch C; Var C; Cpt,
Bkbl; Amer Leg A; Math A; Sci A; Dist & St Solo &
Ensm Contest; *Ind U; Math.*

McCORMICK, Peggy Ann
Central of Lunenburg HS; Victoria, VA; Band; Cpt,
Chldr; Chor; Fr C; FBLA; Pres, 4H; Mjrte; Tri-
HiY; Sftbl; Band Ltr; Chldr Ltr; *Eckerd Col; Psych.*

McCORMICK, Peggy Eileen
W Liberty-Salem HS; W Liberty, OH; Mgr, Tr;
Springfield Comm Col; Nurs.

McCORMICK, Sandra Dee
Fairfield Sr HS; Fairfield, OH (122-641) *Elem Ed.*

McCORMICK, Scott III
Hastings Sr HS; Hastings, NE (1-285) Chor; Bsbl;
Cr-Ctry; Tr; COM; Elk A; Hon Prog; Tiger o-t Wk;
Semi Fin, Pres Schol; NML; *Coe Col; Bio.*

McCORMICK, Steven Andrew
Logan HS; Logan, WV (2-387) A Cap Choir; Chor;
Pres, Key C; VP, Lat C; Span C; Alg A; I Dare You;
Journ A; NMS; Q&S A; Sal; Newspaper Ed; *Duke
U; Bio-Med Engr.*

McCORMICK, Susan Diane
Marquette HS; Ottawa, IL (30%-100) Band; Rptr,
4H; Lat C; Bsbl; Sftbl; 4H A; Val; *Ill Valley Comm
Col; Secy.*

McCORMICK, Tanya Dawn
Staunton River HS; Moneta, VA (49-160) Chldr;
Chor; Drama; Fr C; Rptr, FBLA; Monogram;
Roanoke Col; Journ.

McCORMICK, Terri Raye
Sapulpa HS; Sapulpa, OK (33%-350) Band; Bsbl;
Tr; Hist A; *General Bus.*

McCORMICK, Warren Austin
Danville Pub Sch; Danville, AR (2-50) Band; FFA;
Hmrm; Model UN; NHS; SC; Bkbl; Bkbl; Ftbl;
Tnns; Tr; Citz A; MLS; Most Out; *U of Ark-
Fayetteville; Pre-Med.*

McCORQUODALE, Betty Ann
Palo Duro HS; Amarillo, TX (5-445) Band; Chor;
Drama; FBLA; Lat C; Mjrte; SC; Pres, Fresh Cl; *W
Tex U; Bus.*

**McCORQUODALE,
Sharen Louise**
Middlesex Regional HS; Townsend, MA (63-300)
Chor; Co-Ch, Dbte Tm; 4H; Pres, Lat C; Tr; COM;
4H A; Yth Fel; Subordinate Grange; Sr Choir; Lady
Asst Steward; Co of Ministries; Home & Comm
Comm; Church Adm Board; Yth Com, Grange;
Sacred Dance Group; *Northeastern U; Phys Ther-
apy.*

McCORRY, Maureen Ann
Quincy Notre Dame HS; Quincy, IL; Chor; Ensm;
VP, Fr C; NHS; Rptr, Sch P; SC; Pres, Jr Cl; Swim;
Hon Prog; Journ A; Q&S A; Stu o-t Month; *Bene-
dictine Col; Bio.*

McCOVERY, Estella Renee
John Meiwr Jr Sch; Los Angeles, CA; Beauty; Citz
A; Cl Fav; Spch A; *Pepperdine U; Reporter.*

McCOY, Angela Denise
W Craven HS; Vanceboro, NC; BC; Fr C; FBLA;
FHA; NHS; Alg A; Bible C; Jr Civitan; *U of NC;
Pre-Med.*

McCOY, Angela Gail
Clyde A Erwin HS; Asheville, NC (20-210) Ann;
Band; BC; Cpt, Chldr; FTA; Hmrm; Lit Mag;
Mjrte; Monogram; Bus Mgr, Sch P; Secy, Span C;
JA A; Co-Cpt, Chldr; Best Personality; Secy,
Church Yth Coun; Miss August; Hillcrest Court; W
Carolina U; Bus.

McCOY, Anne Danielle
N Fla Christian Sch; Tallahassee, FL (20%-60)
Chor; NHS; Secy, SC; Most Dependable; Tallahas-
see Comm Col; Ed.

McCOY, Beverly Ann
Eastside HS; Paterson, NJ; Bus.

McCOY, Cheryl Lynne
Lutheran W HS; Detroit, MI; A Cap Choir; Chor;
ARC; Jr Cl; Sftbl; Swim; ARC A; Olivet Col; Med.

McCOY, Cindy Bee
Bluefield HS; Bluefield, WV (256-520) Band;
Ensm; Fr C; Bluefield St Col; Nurs.

McCOY, Dale Jerome
South HS; Bakersfield, CA (56-82) Band; Bkbl.

McCOY, Dave Ellis
Cotton Plant HS; Cotton Plant, AR (4-46) BC;
Drama; Fr C; Rptr, FFA; 4H; SC; Bsbl; Bkbl; Ftbl;
Tr; Hon Prog.

McCOY, Debbie Kay
Chillicothe HS; Chillicothe, OH; Chor; Ensm; Tr;
Sci A; Yth Foundation; Swing Choir; Church Nurs-
ery Teacher.

McCOY, Donna Marie
Chapel Acad; Pine Bluff, AR (2-18) Ann; Pres, GS;
Hmrm; Semi-Fin, Jr Miss Pa; Pres, SC; VP, Sr Cl;
Secy, Jr Cl; Bkbl; Citz A; Cl Fav; HQn; HCt; MLS;
Sal; Bus A; Ouachita Baptist U; Mus.

McCOY, Elizabeth Ann
L D Bell HS; Hurst, TX (217-750) FHA; Sftbl; JA
A; Opt A; DECA Stu o-t Yr; Northwood Col;
Fashion Merchandising.

McCOY, Judith Corrine
Wm A Wirt HS; Gary, IN; Y-Tns; Tr; Tr Ltr; Med.

McCOY, Judy Marie
Lutcher Stark HS; Orange, TX; Drama; Sci C; Spch
C; Thes; Kiwanis A; Poet A; Spch A; McNeese St
U; Criminal Law.

McCOY, Kathy Ruth
Mercy HS; St Martinville, LA (1-18) Fin, Lit Ral;
Secy, NHS; Secy, SC; Pres, Jr Cl; Cpt, Bkbl; Hist A;
PTA A; Alpha Kappa Alpha Jr A; EAP Part; All-
Dist Bkbl; 1st St Lit Rally; 2nd, Dist Lit Rally; U of
New Orleans; Geol.

McCOY, Lisa Carole
W Craven HS; Vanceboro, NC; BC; Cpt, Chldr;
Hmrm; Ed, Sch P; Parl, Span C; Secy, SC; Hist A;
VP, Jr Civitan; Miss Jr Civitan Contestant; Pre-
Med.

McCOY, Mamie Izetta
John Brone HS; Flushing, NY (592-977) COM;
Citz A; Type A; Attendance Cert; Home Ec A;
Asst Yth Advisor.

McCOY, Margaret Elody
W Charlotte Open HS; Charlotte, NC; Drama; Fr
C; Hmrm; SC; Tnns; Fine Arts Internship; NY In-
ternship; Ball Boy at 100,000 WCT Cl; U of NC;
Nurs.

McCOY, Mark Bryan
Eastwood HS; El Paso, TX (64-720) A Cap Choir;
Chor; Tnns; Lat C; Madrigal; NHS; Sr Cl; Hon
Prog; Ntl Conf Chr & Jews; Tex All Region Choir;
Tex Baptist All St Yth Choir; Baylor U; Mus Ed.

McCOY, Michael Lee
Southeast HS; Oklahoma City, OK; NHS; JV,
Wrest; Principals Acad A; Distributive Ed A; Okla
St U; Fire Protection Tech.

McCOY, Michael Vernon
Midwest City HS; Midwest City, OK (275-550)
Pres, Hmrm; Lat C; SC; JV, Ftbl; Tr; JV, Wrest; Yth
Fel.

McCOY, Patricia Ann
Thomas Jefferson Sr HS; Council Bluffs, IA
(17-400) Chem C; Chor; Fr C; St Scholar; I'Ll
Never Smoke C; Olivet Nazerene Col; Chem Engr.

McCOY, Patricia Kathleen
Gallia Acad HS; Gallipolis, OH (11-243) Band;
Chor; 4H; NHS; Sch Achieve Tm; F-Ed, Sch P; Sci
C; VP, Span C; Tri-HiY; 4H A; St BYF Publicity
Ch; Win, Essay Contest; Girl o-t Mo; Col Schol;
Georgetown Col; Eng.

McCOY, Paula Christine
Gallia Acad HS; Gallipolis, OH (12-250) Band;
Chor; Ensm; FNA; NHS; Rptr, Sch P; Tri-HiY;
WW; Girl o-t Mo; Win, Local Merchant Marine
Essay; Georgetown Col; Religious Ed.

McCOY, Rhonda Ann
Gloucester HS; Gloucester, VA (15%-207) Chor;
Drama; Madrigal; Cpt, Mjrte; Thes; WW; Radford
Col; Dance.

McCOY, Richard Donald
Central Cambria HS; Ebensburg, PA (20-232).

McCOY, Sharon Kay
Pike HS; Indianapolis, IN (28-305) Band; VP,
FBLA; Semi-Fin, GS; Mjrte; NHS; JA A; WW; 1st
Pl St, FBLA Off Procedures; Ball St U; Bus.

McCOY, Sheryl Anne
John H Reagan HS; Austin, TX (208-530) Band;
Ensm; Ger C; Orch; Var C; Tnns; Tr; Citz A; U of
Tex; Book-Keeping.

McCOY, Timothy Wade
Gloucester HS; Gloucester, VA (30%-325) Band;
Chor; Drama; Thes; Mgr, Bsbl; Bkbl; Ftbl; Tr; Math
A; Sci A; Bsbl A; Outst Stu A; Auto Mech.

McCOY, Wendell Ira
Charles A Brown HS; Charleston, SC (27-115) Sch
P; SC; Cpt, Bsbl; Cpt, Ftbl; MVP, Bsbl; Highest
Academic A, Ftbl; All-Star Tm, Bsbl; Saint Augus-
tine's Col; Bus Mgt.

McCRACKEN, Donna Ruth
David Crockett HS; Jonesboro, TN; Rptr, Bus C;
Chldr; Pres, Chor; Pres, Commercial C; Pres,
Ensm; FHA; Rptr, 4H; Ch, Hmrm; Fin, Jr Miss
Pagent; Ntl Yth Conf; Sch P; Beauty; 4H A; HCt; E
Tenn St U.

McCRACKEN, Larry Joe Jr
Terre Haute N Vigo HS; Terre Haute, IN; VP,
CYO; Chor; HiY; Ftbl; Wrest; Amer Wilderness
Ldrship Sch.

McCRACKEN, Lynn Ann
Pendleton HS; Pendleton, SC (7-140) Tres, BC;
Co-Cpt, Chldr; VP, Fr C; VP, Hmrm; F-Ed, Sch P;
Clemson U.

McCRACKEN, Marc Russell
Wheaton R 3 HS; Wheaton, MO (16-31) VP, FFA;
Hmrm; VP, SC; Cpt, Bsbl; Cpt, Bkbl; Cr-Ctry; Tr;
Cl Fav; HKg; HCt; FFA Proficiency A; Most Im-
proved, Bkbl; All Conf, Bsbl; Best Sportsmanship;
SW Mo St U; Phys Ed.

McCRADY, Brenda Lee
Hastings Sr HS; Hastings, NE (1-296) Band; Chor;
Ensm; Semi-Fin, GS; Swim; COM; Val; Hastings
Col; Bus Adm.

McCRADY, Dan Eugene
Gilroy HS; Gilroy, CA (25%-375) Bkbl.

McCRAE, Emma Loraine
MacKenzie HS; Detroit, MI (27-352) FTA; Math
C; NHS; Ntl Yth Conf; Orch; Rptr, Sch P; VP, Sci
C; Sch Comm Comm; Mich Barber Col; Cosmetol-
ogy.

McCRANEY, David Patrick
Bartow Sr HS; Bartow, FL; Pres, Chess C; Inter-
Club Coun; Pres, Key C; VP, Lat C; NHS; Golf;
Hon Prog; Most Out; NMF; NMS; 2nd, St Ora-
tory, Key C; WW; Cpt, High-Q Tm; U Fo Fla;
Pre-Med.

McCRANIE, Rodney Dean
Tift Co HS; Tifton, GA (40-400) Band; S-T, Chess
C; Lit Mag; Span C; Carson-Newman Col; Mus.

McCRARY, Barry Douglas
Dora HS; Dora, AL (7%-180) Ann; Band; Hmrm;
Math C; Orch; Sci C; SC; Var C; Ftbl; Auburn U;
Archt.

McCRARY, June Lynne
Washington HS; Fremont, CA (34-334) Bus Mgr,
SC; Tres, Sr Cl; CSF; Yth Fel; Young Life; St Schol;
Sunday Sch Ldr; Ohlone Jr Col; Secy Sci.

McCRARY, Martha Dianne
Bible Baptist HS; Savannah, GA (2-34) Armstrong
St Col; Bus Adm.

McCRARY, Nettie Lee
Jones Co HS; Gray, GA (10%-190) F-Ed, Ann;
Cpt, Chldr; Chor; FBLA; FHA; 4H; Hmrm; Model
UN; Ch, NHS; F-Ed, Sch P; Span C; SC; VP, Soph
Cl; Beauty; Cl Fav; HQn; HCt; Type A; WW; Bowl
Trophies; Most Popular; Spelman Col; Child De-
velopment.

McCRARY, Christine
Williamsburg HS; Andrews, SC (12-105) FHA; 4H;
Bkbl; Nurs.

McCRAY, Levoular Denise
Bridgeton HS; Bridgeton, NJ (50%-700) Hmrm;
Bkbl; Drew U; Med.

McCRAY, Paula Sue
Hartshorne HS; Hartshorne, OK; Chor; NHS; Hist
A; Sci A; Okla City U; Mus.

McCRAY, Randy
Williamsburg HS; Andrews, SC; 4H; Art.

McCRAY, Wendy Rose
S Plainfield HS; S Plainfield, NJ; Tres, Chor; FNA;
Sci C; Tr; Candystriper; A&T St U; Nurs.

McCRAY, William Benjamin
Northwest HS; Indianapolis, IN (90-300) Chor;
Ensm; Ftbl; Tr; Wrest; COM; Citz A; Most Out;
Yth Fel; UCLA; Bus.

McCREA, Duane Mark
Charlotte Valley Central HS; Davenport, NY
(4-41) BS; Hmrm; NHS; Pres, SC; Var C; Pres, Sr
Cl; Pres, Jr Cl; VP, Soph Cl; Bsbl; Cpt, Bkbl; Soccer;
Tr; MVP, Bkbl; NY St U; Bus Adm.

McCREA, Valerie Eve
South HS; Denver, CO; Bkbl; Bkbl A; Phys Fitness
A; Art.

McCREARY, Brenda Sue
Pauls Valley HS; Paul Valley, OK (5-110) Band;
VP, FHA; Span C; Citz A; Type A; Band Qn; Girl
o-t Mo; St Hon Soc; Church Secy; Okla Christian
Col; Elem Ed.

McCREARY, Dena Kay
Milburn HS; Milburn, OK; Chldr; Chor; 4H; NHS;
VP, SC; B Crocker A; Hist A; MLS; Sci A; SE Ok
St U.

McCREARY, Kevin Eugene
Del Norte HS; Albuquerque, NM; A Cap Choir;
Band; BS; Chor; Demolay; SC; U of Tex at El Paso;
Mus.

McCREARY, Pamela Gail
Zion-Benton Township HS; Zion, IL (65-389) Ann;
Band; Chor; Drama; Secy, Ger C; F-Ed, Lit Mag;
NHS; VP, Thes; NEDT; Art.

McCREARY, Scott Alan
Mohawk Area HS; Bessemer, PA (15-143) Lat C;
NHS; SC; WW; Hon Schol, Col; VP, Yth C; Mt
Jackson UP; Geneva Col; Bus Adm.

McCREARY, Sheri Lynn
Tarpon Springs Sr HS; Tarpon Springs, FL (8-249)
Band; Cpt, Chldr; Chor; Ensm; FHA; Hmrm; Lat
C; Lat NHS; NHS; ARC; SC; Secy, Sr Cl; Secy, Jr
Cl; MVP, Tr; Magna Cum Laude; Pres A; ARC A;
Summa Cum Laude.

McCREARY, Sue Marie
Zion-Benton Township HS; Zion, IL; Band;
Drama; Secy, Ger C; NHS; Secy, Thes; Hon Prog;
Best Jr Actress; Theatre.

McCRERY, Elizabeth Ann
Southwood HS; Shreveport, LA; Band; VP, Chor;
SC; ROTC A; Yth Fel; Yth Foundation; Yth Leg;
Win, Talent Show; La Tech U; Journ.

McCRORY, Deborah Elaine
Jena HS; Jena, LA (20-160) Band; Chor; Ensm;
FHA; 4H; NHS; 4H A; Hon Prog; Acteens A's; NE
La U; Spch Therapist.

McCRORY, Glenda Ann
Jeffersontown HS; Louisville, KY (90-420) Drama;
Fr C; Hmrm; SC; Thes; Var C; Ch, Jr Cl; Mjrte; Tr;
Cl Fav; Hon Prog; Best Thes A; Elizabeth Breckin-
gridge A; Wesian Special Ed A; Western Ky Col;
Special Ed.

McCRORY, Rosalind
Compton Sr HS; Compton, CA (10-800) Ed, Sch P; Sci C; SC; Bank of Amer A; CSF; COM; Cl Fav; Hon Prog; Journ A; Jr Chamber of Com A; Most Out; Spch A; Highest Avg, Department; U of Sou Calif; Engr.

McCROSKEY, Charles Richard
Herbert Hoover HS; Clendenin, WV (16-278) NHS; Bkbl; Ftbl; Pres A; Clendenin Womens C Schol; W Va Inst of Technology; Computer Sci.

McCROSKEY, Chris Alan
El Dorado HS; El Dorado, AR; Band; Chor; Ensm; Madrigal; Span C; Lynchburg Baptist Col; Mus.

McCROSKEY, Kellie Colleen
St Francis DeSalles Central HS; Morgantown, WV (2-83) Ann; JV, Chldr; Chor; VP, Fr C; Fin, GS; Math C; NHS; Sci C; Secy, Jr Cl; Co-Cpt, Tnns; Jr Orch Dance C; Astronomy.

McCROSKEY, Mary Elizabeth
Porter HS; Maryville, TN; BC; Bus C; Co-Cpt, Chldr; FFA; FHA; 4H; Math C; Span C; Secy, Y-Tns; HQn; Type A; WW; Runner-Up, FFA Swtht; FFA Dist Off; Maryville Col; Bus.

McCRUMMEN, Steva Ann
New Brockton HS; New Brockton, AL (10%-75) FBLA; FHA; 4H; 4H A; Enterprise St Jr Col; Bus.

McCUISTIAN, Bridgett Ann
Claremore HS; Claremore, OK (70-350) AFS; Chor; Ensm; FBLA; FHA; COM; Yth Fel; Chor A; Secy of Creativity, Yth Coun; OBU; Bus.

McCUISTION, Danny Ray
Olustee HS; Olustee, OK (5-18) Ann; 4H; Sch P; VP, Jr Cl; Bsbl; Bkbl; Cl Fav; HCt; Mr OHS; Best Physique; W Okla St Col.

McCUISTION, Linda Sue Wilburn
Olustee HS; Olustee, OK (3-18) Co-Ed, Ann; Chldr; Secy, Chor; Parl, FHA; Pres, 4H; Co-Ed, Beauty; B Crocker A; Bio A; Cl Fav; Gov Honor Prog; 4H A; Hist A; HCt; Hon Prog; Most Out; Sci A; Type A; Most Popular; Bus Ed; Best Looking; Best Dressed; Best All Around; W Okla St Col; Elem Ed.

McCUISTON, Danny Fayne
Geronimo HS; Geronimo, OK (4-29) FFA; VP, Math C; Bsbl; Bkbl; Amer Leg A; COM; Star Greenhand; Best Looking; Cameron U; Bus.

McCULLAH, Gail
Williamsburg HS; Williamsburg, KY (1-54) Band; BC; Pres, Fr C; Rptr, FHA; Mjrte; Sch P; Alg A; COM; Hist A; HCt; Math A; MLS; Opt A; PTA A; Val; Top Five Stu; Smartest; U of Ky; Med Technology.

McCULLIN, M Cregg
Ouachita Parish HS; Monroe, LA; Band; Math A; Puppetteer; Church Choir; NE La U; Sci.

McCULLOCH, Susan Edith
Ripon Sr HS; Ripon, WI (20-180) AFS; Chldr; Chor; Drama; Hmrm; ARC; SC; Pres, Jr Cl; Tr; Spch A; U of Wisc; Med.

McCULLOUGH, Alton Devonne
Darby Township HS; Glenolden, PA (30-165) Chor; Drama; Fr C; Var C; Bsbl; Cpt, Bkbl; Ftbl; Swim; Tr; Most Out.

McCULLOUGH, Belinda Anne
Washington Co HS; Sandersville, GA; Pres, Drama; FFA; 4H; Secy, InterAct C; Semi-Fin, Jr Miss Pa; Rptr, Sch P; Sci C; SC; JV, Tnns; HCt; Hon Prog; Type A; FFA Swtht & A.

McCULLOUGH, Clayton Lee
Gervais Union HS; Gervais, OR (25-75) Band; Chor; Ensm; FFA; 4H; Bsbl; Ftbl; Yth Fel; Agr.

McCULLOUGH, Gary Ernest
Bible Baptist HS; Savannah, GA (1-39) Chess C; COM; Fr A; Covenant Col; Math.

McCULLOUGH, Joanne Gale
Tabernacle Christian Acad; Hopewell Jct, NY; Bkbl; Tnns; Sprtsmnshp, Memorization, Hon, A's; Baptist Bible Col; Christian Ed.

McCULLOUGH, Jodonna Marie
Gervais Union HS; Gervais City, OR (13-75) Band; Chor; Ensm; FHA; 4H; Tr; Yth Fel; Chemeketa Col; Nurs.

McCULLOUGH, Joe Grady
Henryetta HS; Henryetta, OK (7-110) Ann; Band; Ensm; Secy, Key C; NHS; Spch C; Pres, Jr Cl; Spch A; Dist & Conf Yth Fel; St Hon Soc; Okla St U; Communications.

McCULLOUGH, John Joseph
Bethel Christian Acad; Hopwell Jct, NY (2-3) Chor; Pres, Hmrm; Hist A; Baptist Bible Col; Bible.

McCULLOUGH, Joseph Ray
Hobart Sr HS; Hobart, IN (114-404) Ger C; Order/ Arrow; Sci C; SC; Var C; Bsbl; Mgr, Bkbl; Sftbl; COM; Order/Arrow A; Sci A; Eagle Sct A; Purdue U; Forestry.

McCULLOUGH, Laura Elaine
Thomas Jefferson Elder Jr HS; Sandersville, GA; Secy, Band; 4H; InterAct C; F-Ed, Sch P; Sci C; Bkbl; 4H A; Hon Prog; Band Excel A; Phys Ed A; Solo & Ensm Medals; Most Improved, Bkbl.

McCULLOUGH, Susan
Crockett HS; Crockett, TX (10%-140) Band; Secy, Drama; Mjrte; Span C; Hist A; Math A; Most Out; Type A; Eng A; Rice U; Psych.

McCULLOUGH, Tammy Jo
Zion-Benton Horizon Campus HS; Zion, IL (76-400) Ann; Band; Chor; Ensm; Ger C; Sch P; Tr; Awana A's; Trinity Col; Bus.

McCULLOUGH, Telara Leigh
Weston-McEwen HS; Athena, OR (3-61) Ed, Ann; Band; Drama; 4H; NHS; Rainbow; Rptr, Sch P; Thes; Pres, Soph Cl; JV, Bkbl; JV, Tnns; Hon Prog; Spch A; VofDEM.

McCULLOUGH, Valerie Anita
Harlem Park Jr HS; Baltimore, MD; 4H; SC; COM; Citz A; 4H A; Ntl Achv Schol; Attendance A; Conduct A; Math A; Cert of Recogn Vacation Chrch Sch.

McCULLOUGH, William DeValle
Darby Township HS; Glenolden, PA (26-155) Chor; Hmrm; SC; Tres, Soph Cl; Bkbl; Ntl Achv Schol; Co-Cpt, Ftbl; Most Out; Ntl Achv Schol; Pres A; Wake Forest U; Phys Therapist.

McCULLY, Denise Ann
Yorktown HS; Yorktown, IN (53-187) Drama; Pres, Span C; Thes; Grand Cross of Colors, Piano, A's; Span Workshop, Interntl Fel; Ball St U Exchange Stu; Ind U; Span Lang Arts.

McCULLY, Vicki Lynn
Lowpoint-Washburn HS; Washburn, IL (7-59) AFS; Band; Chor; NHS; Sch P; Northern Ill U; Bus.

McCUMBER, Scott Alan
Parker HS; Janesville, WI (5-454) NHS; Elk A; U of Wis-Whitewater; Acct.

McCUNE, Catherine Beth
Maine Township HS W; Des Plaines, IL (50%-500) Chor; FNA; Hmrm; Ntl Yth Conf; Sci C; Span C; SC; Tr; Suomi Col; Nurs.

McCUNE, Donald Bruce
Elk Grove Sr HS; Elk Grove, CA (30-1200) Ger C; Sci C; Tnns; Most Out; Outst Eng Stu; Arts & Crafts A; Sacramento St Col; Hist.

McCURDY, Scott Terry
Grand Rapids Baptist Acad; Grand Rapids, MI; French NHS; NHS; Bsbl; JV, Bkbl; Wrest; Med.

McCURRY, Craig Arlen
Dobyns-Bennett HS; Kingsport, TN (125-453) Hmrm; SC; Pres, Sr Cl; JV, Bsbl; Mgr, Bkbl; HKg; SC Exchange Prog; Emory & Henry Col; Med.

McCURRY, Paul Lee
Bob Jones Acad; Greenville, SC (60-120) Chess C; Ger C; S-T, InterAct C; JV, Soccer; JV, Sftbl; NMS; Clemson U; Computer Sci.

McCURRY, Rickey Neal
Humboldt HS; Humboldt, TN (22-189) BC; BS; FFA; 4H; NHS; Ntl Yth Conf; Span C; JV, Bkbl; JV, Ftbl; Hon Prog; MLS; Lane Col; Pol Sci.

McCUTCHAN, Richard Shannon
Atlanta HS; Atlanta, TX (5-183) JETS; NHS; VP, Sci C; Col Computer Prog Course; MIT; Physics.

McCUTCHEN, Carole Anne
Scottsboro HS; Scottsboro, AL (33%-200) Anchor C; Band; Drama; FHA; Fin, Jr Miss Pageant; Mjrte; Math C; NHS; Span C; Beauty; Scholastic Achv A; Birmingham Sou Col; Dance.

McCUTCHEN, Mark Anthony
E Prairie HS; E Prairie, MO (9-112) VP, FBLA; NHS; Pres, Span C; SC; VP, Jr Cl; COM; Math A; Type A; SE Mo St U; Bus Adm.

McCUTCHEON, Myra Lynn
Science HS; Newark, NJ; A Cap Choir; Band; Chor; VP, FNA; VP, Hmrm; SC; Up Bound; Bkbl; Tr; COM; HR A; Gym A's; SC A; Rutgers U; Sci.

McCUTCHEON, Philip Earl
Dunedin Sr HS; Dunedin, FL; Montreat-Anderson Col; Ministry.

McDADE, Kenneth Alan
Provine HS; Jackson, MS (54-267) Lat C; Lit Mag; Sch P; Best in Overall Prod A, Cl Capers; Miss St U; Elec Engr.

McDADE, Micky Tori
Custer HS; Milwaukee, WI; Co-Cpt, Sftbl; U of Wis at Milwaukee; Photography.

McDADE, Tina Louise
Sandy Valley HS; Magnolia, OH; Band; Pres, 4H; B Crocker A; 4H A.

McDANIEL, Angela Robin
Cabrillo Sr HS; Lompoc, CA (35-435) Yth Leg; Principals List; HR; Tutor.

McDANIEL, Anthony Dale
Boise City HS; Boise City, OK (2-50) FFA; Parl, NHS; SC; Var C; Mgr, Bkbl; Ftbl; Hist A; Hon Prog; Star Student; Okla St Hon Schol; Phar.

McDANIEL, Barbara Catherine
Merryville HS; Merryville, LA (8-47) F-Ed, Ann; Pres, Fr C; FBLA; FFA; 4H; Key C; Lit Ral; F-Ed, Sch P; Secy, Sci C; Spch C; SC; Mgr, Bsbl; Sftbl; Amer Leg A; Citz A; Cl Fav; HQn; HCt; VofDEM; Secy, Fr C; Hist, FHA; Fair Princess; Runnerup, Miss Yambilee; McNeese St U; Elem Ed.

McDANIEL, Bradley Steven
Perry HS; Perry, OK (21-120) Chem C; Math C; Bsbl; Bkbl; Ftbl; Tr; Cl Fav; Yth Fel.

McDANIEL, Cheryl Lynn
Waynesboro HS; Waynesboro, VA (73-251) BC; Chor; Lit Mag; COM; Phys, Ldrship Ch, DECA; Intramural Special A; Pep C; Secy, Christ Ed; Blue Ridge Comm Col; Mental Health Tech.

McDANIEL, Dale Leon
Labette Co HS; Altamont, KS (10-160) A Cap Choir; Band; Chor; Drama; 4H; HiY; Tres, Mod Mus Mas; NHS; Sch P; Var C; Bsbl; JV, Bkbl; Co-Cpt, Tnns; Alg A; Hon Prog; St Scholar; Dist, St, Hon Choir; Win, St Federation of Mus Auditions; Coffeyville Comm Jr Col; Mus Ed.

McDANIEL, Danny Nelson
Jefferson City HS; Jefferson City, MO (317-483) Co-Cpt, Bsbl; Co-Cpt, Bkbl; MVP, Ftbl; Outst Ath; Wichita St U; Bus Adm.

McDANIEL, Duane Earl
Columbus HS; Columbus, MT (1-32) Band; BS; Chor; Drama; Ensm; Pres, NHS; Ed, Sch P; S-T, SC; Var C; Bsbl; Co-Cpt, Bkbl; Ftbl; B Crocker A; DARGCA; MLS; Val; Augustana Col; Phys Therapy.

McDANIEL, Earl Whitson
Stratford HS; Stratford, TX; Band; Ftbl; Stage Band; FCA; Tex St Tech Inst; Auto Mech.

McDANIEL, Eugene Loir
Santa Fe HS; Alachua, FL; BC; Star Student; U of Fla; Mech Engr.

McDANIEL, Grace Ann
Grove City HS; Grove City, OH; Band; Community Yth Symph; Orch; COM; Sci A; Ohio St U.

McDANIEL, James Patrick
Alvin HS; Alvin, TX (25%-586) Golf; Tnns; Tr.

McDANIEL, Janice Diane
Silver Creek HS; Sellersburg, IN (20-144) Co-Ed, Ann; Secy, Fr C; NHS; Rptr, Sch P; Sci C; Var C; Bkbl; Ind U; Journ.

McDANIEL, Judy Ann
York Comp HS; York, SC (3-272) FTA; Ch, Hmrm; NHS; Span C; Gr Marshal; Hon Prog; Jr Cl Steering Comm; Clemson U; Span.

McDANIEL, Lori Ann
Macon HS; Macon, IL; Band; Cpt, Chldr; Chor; Ensm; Fin, Jr Miss Pagent; SC; Sftbl; Tr; JA A; Spch A; Yth Fel; Yth Leg; VP, Fresh Cl; Jr Miss Qn; Mus A's.

McDANIEL, Marsha Lynn
Enterprise HS; Enterprise, AL (1-390) Drama; Tres, FBLA; NHS; Rainbow; Enterprise St Jr Col; Bus.

McDANIEL, Nancy Ann
John Ehert HS; Marrero, LA; 4H; Hmrm; Mjrte; Sci C; SC; Bkbl; U of New Orleans; Bus.

McDANIEL, Ondra Ophedia
Forest Hill HS; W Palm Beach, FL; Chor; FHA; 4H; Tres, Soph Cl; Sftbl; Tr; Gov Honor Prog; 4H A; Pres A; Yth Fel; VP, Ponsetta's C; Fla A&M U; Mus.

McDANIEL, Patricia Lynne
William Monroe HS; Stanardsville, VA (3-129) FBLA; FHA; Rptr, FTA; 4H; Rptr, SC; Tr; Type A.

McDANIEL, Reginael Dimarco
DeVilbiss HS; Toledo, OH; Fr C; Bsbl; JV, Bkbl; Hon Prog; Church Choir; Asst Sunday Sch Pianist; UCLA; Bus.

McDANIEL, Rhonda
St Vincent-St Mary HS; Akron, OH; CYO; Bkbl; Swim; COM; Citz A; MYF; Karate C; Mich St U; Chem.

McDANIEL, Shannon Kaye
Canadian HS; Canadian, TX (19-55) Co-Ed, Ann; Chor; Drama; Ensm; FHA; Secy, FTA; NHS; Mgr, Bkbl; Golf; Tnns; Mgr, Tr; WW Ann 1st Pl SMU; CAR St Off; Advanced Photo Journ Workshop; Tex Woman's U; Photography & Interior Design.

McDANIEL, Sylvania
Central HS; St Louis, MO (50-450) Chor; Drama; Ntl Yth Conf; Rptr, Sch P; COM; Citz A; Star Student; Yth Fel; Good Conduct; PA; Columbia U; Elec Tech.

McDANIEL, Thomas Lee
St James HS; Montgomery, AL (9-42) BC; Chor; Ensm; InterClub Coun; Key C; VP, Lat C; NHS; Ed, Sch P; Bsbl; Bkbl; Hon Prog; NEDT; Auburn U; Elec Engr.

McDANIEL, Timothy Roger
Lake Clifton Sr HS; Baltimore, MD (10%-1079) Pres, Band; Chor; Drama; Ensm; Pres, Mod Mus Mas; NHS; Pres, Jr Cl; Alg A; CSF; COM; Citz A; Gov Honor Prog; Hist A; Hon Prog; Interlochen Ntl Mus; Math A; Most Out; Ntl Achv Schol; NMF; Sci A; Guitar A; Mus A; Peabody Inst of Mus; Guitar.

McDANIEL, Vivian Kathleen
Battiest HS; Battiest, OK (3-24) F-Ed, Ann; Chor; FHA; NHS; Southeastern Okla St U; Sociology.

McDANIEL, William Jeffrey
Dalton HS; Dalton, GA (13-300) Band; Chor; Ensm; NHS; Swim; Pre-Med.

McDANIEL, Xavier Maurice
Temple HS; Temple, TX; Span C; Bkbl; U of NC; Pre-Law.

McDAVID, Martha Erin
Terre Haute S Vigo HS; Terre Haute, IN (36-640) CYO; VP, Per C; Ch, Hmrm; Rptr, Sch P; Spch C; SC; Y-Tns; Ch, Jr Cl; Cpt, Bkbl; Tr; Aux Lat; COM; Yth Fel; GAA; Deans A; Jr Lifesaving; Forum; Jr Advisory; V Ltrs; Biochem.

McDAVID, Patrick Andrew
Terre Haute S Vigo Sch; Terre Haute, IN (32-590) CYO; City Conf; VP, Ger C; Math C; NHS; Order/Arrow; Sch P, SC; Var C; Pres, Sr Cl; Co-Ch, Soph Cl; JV, Bkbl; Ftbl; Tr; Life Sct; Ftbl A; Tulane U; Law.

McDERMOTT, John Dennis
Don Bosco Tech HS; Boston, MA (1-222) Ch, Ann; CYO; NHS; Co-Ed, Sch P; COM; Hon Prog; JA A; Notre Dame U; Archt.

McDERMOTT, Karen Mary
Acad of Saint Aloysius; Jersey City, NJ (1-127) Chor; Drama; Fr C; Lat C; Math C; NHS; Span C; Hist A; Hon Prog; Math A; NEDT; Stu Service Corps; Horseback Riding C; Dance C.

McDERMOTT, Maureen Elizabeth
Summit HS; Summit, NJ; Band; Chldr; Chor; Lit Mag; Tnns; COM; Hon Prog; Most Out; Yth Fel; Art A's; Art.

McDERMOTT, Sherri Lynn
Wayne Mem HS; Wayne, MI; Chor; Virginia Farrells Col; Cosmetology.

McDEVITT, Lynn Marie
John W Hallahan HS; Philadelphia, PA (22-432) Fr C; Hmrm; Math C; NHS; Orch; Hon Prog; Chestnut Hill Col; Mus.

McDEVITT, Ona Sue
Virginia HS; Bristol, VA (75-250) Ed, Ann; S-T, Chor; FBLA; HiY; InterClub Coun; Span C; HCt; Type A; Ed A; Service A, Ann; Outst Choir Member; Va Highlands Col; Elem Ed.

McDILL, David James
Callaway HS; Jackson, MS (35-538) Band; Chor; Ensm; Lat C; Math C; Mu Alpha Theta; Order/Arrow; Sch P; Bsbl; Hon Prog; JA A; Math A; Ntl Sci Found; Ntl Math Test; Geom A; Miss Col; Mus.

McDONALD, Brad Jay
Cowan HS; Muncie, IN (1-70) Chem C; Var C; Co-Cpt, Golf; Alg A; Bio A; Math A; Sci A; Yth Fel; Skill Bowl Tm; Ball St U.

McDONALD, Brian Allen
Silsbee HS; Silsbee, TX (1-300) JETS; NHS; Span C; Ftbl; Tr; Alg A; Bio A; Chem A; Hon Prog; Yth Fel; PA; High Span, A; Church Choir; Lang Teachers Assn Hon Soc; High Geom, High Eng, A's; Lamar U; Chem Engr.

McDONALD, Carhlotte Jean
Klein HS; Spring, TX (425-600) Band; Bus C; Secy, Chor; Fin, Ensm; FBLA; FHA; Bsbl; Cpt, Sftbl; Cl Fav; Most Out; PTA A; Dist & St A'S, Cosmetology; Most Popular; Tex Sou U; Bus.

McDONALD, Cynthia Ann
Medina Sr HS; Medina, NY; A Cap Choir; Fr C; Hmrm; SC; COM; Hon Prog; Med.

McDONALD, Darrell Henry
Dudley Sr HS; Greensboro, NC; Band; Drama; Ensm; Cl Fav; HKg; Tenn St U; Pol Sci.

McDONALD, David Kyle
Mansfield HS; Mansfield, LA (1-100) Band; Tres, BC; Fin, BS; 4H; Order/Arrow; SC; Bkbl; Mgr, Ftbl; Golf; Amer Leg A; Citz A; Val; VofDEM; Pres & Tres, FBLA; St Band Schol; St Rptr, FBLA; Yth Achv A; Most Intellectual; Ntl Merit Commended Stu; La Tech U; Acct.

McDONALD, Eileen Ann
William Allen HS; Allentown, PA (10%-750) Band; Chor; FNA; Mod Mus Mas; NHS; World Affairs C; Swim; COM; God & Country A; Hon Prog; Most Out; Spelling A; Hospital Vol; Secy of Yth; Mus Ministry A; Roberts Wesleyan Col; Mus.

McDONALD, Elaine Michelle
Fairview Alpha HS; Coushatta, LA (5-18) F-Ed, Ann; Ch, Chldr; Parl, FHA; Rptr, Hmrm; Lit Mag; Bkbl; Sftbl; Cl Fav; HQn; Most Spirited; Pres, Spirit Comm; Northwestern St U; Photography.

McDONALD, Ellen Louise
Forest Park Sr HS; Forest Park, GA; Secy, Chor; FBLA; Semi-Fin, NHS; Span C; COM; Math A; All St Chor.

McDONALD, Frank Russell
Silsbee HS; Silsbee, TX (10-300) JETS; Rptr, Span C; Tnns; Chem A; Hon Prog; Yth Fel; High Eng, High Span, A's; Hon Stu; PA; Lamar U; Elec Engr.

McDONALD, Holly Sue
Madison Central HS; Richmond, KY; Band; Sci C; Golf; Sftbl; Church Choir; Band Clinic; FCA; Beta C; Girls Ath C; Wind Ensm; Drama C; GS; Golf Tm; Sci C; 4-H C; E Ky U.

McDONALD, John Allan
N Crawford HS; Gays Mills, WI (33%-75) A Cap Choir; Ann; Band; Chor; Drama; Ensm; Hmrm; Madrigal; Orch; Sch P; Ski C; Tr; Cpt, Wrest; Spch A; 1st, St Solo & Vocal Contests; Wrest Pins; SWWTI; Auto Body & Mech.

McDONALD, Karen Sue
Sacred Heart Acad; Mt Pleasant, MI; Drama; Lat C; Span C; SC; JV, Bkbl; Sftbl.

McDONALD, Kathryn Diane
Putnam City W HS; Okla City, OK (29-800) NHS; Span C; Okla U; Computer Sci.

McDONALD, Kathy Anne
Mansfield HS; Mansfield, LA (1-90) Band; Pres, BC; Fin, GS; 4H; VP & Parl, FBLA; Pres, Jr Civitan; La Tech U; Nurs.

McDONALD, Keith Erwin
Reynolds HS; Greenville, PA (16-212) Pres, Band; Chor; Ensm; FTA; Pres, HiY; Lat C; Math C; Sci C; SC; District, Reg Chor; Penn St U.

McDONALD, Kenneth John
Fairview Alpha HS; Coushatta, LA; Lit Ral; Bkbl; Ftbl; Tr; H of F; HCt; Northwestern U; Pre-Law.

McDONALD, Lavita Gaye
Malabar Sr HS; Mansfield, OH; A Cap Choir; Cpt, Chldr; Chor; Dbte Tm; 4H; Secy, HiY; Ch, Hmrm; Lit Mag; Secy, Rainbow; Spch C; SC; Citz A; Math A; Secy, JA; Eng A; Mansfield Bus Col; Bus Adm.

McDONALD, Loretta
Sandusky HS; Sandusky, OH; Band; Mgr, Bkbl; Tr; COM; Math A; Teacher's Aide; Ohio St U; Bus Adm.

McDONALD, Paul Douglas
Ballard HS; Louisville, KY; Chor; Drama; Hmrm; ARC; Pres, Sr Cl; Co-Cpt, Bkbl; Soccer; Sftbl; Pres, Sunday Sch Cl; Med.

McDONALD, Preston Edward
Tabernacle Christian HS; Greenville, SC (6-12) Lat C; Bible.

McDONALD, Rebecca Anne
Englewood Sr HS; Jacksonville, FL; Tri-HiY; Amer Leg A; Sci A; Math.

McDONALD, Renee Darlene
Edward Kennedy Ellington Sch of Art; Washington, DC; Drama; Hmrm; SC; Semi-Fin, Jr Cl; Alg A; COM; Hon Prog; Most Out; Theater Arts.

McDONALD, Rhonda Gay
Diamond Hill-Jarvis HS; Fort Worth, TX; Chor; Rptr, FBLA; Pres, NHS; VP, Sr Cl; Tr; HQn; Secy, OEA; Tarrant Jr Col; Secretarial.

McDONALD, Robin Clara
King's Acad; W Palm Beach, FL (8-61) Ed, Ann; Chor; Drama; Ensm; NHS; Mgr, Bsbl; Bkbl; Sftbl; Swim; Amer Leg A; COM; VofDEM; Co-Cpt, Vlbl; Southeastern Bible Col; Secondary Eng.

McDONALD, Sally Jean
New Haven HS; New Haven, MO (4-58) Band; Chor; Ensm; Pres, FHA; NHS; SC; Secy, Soph Cl; VP, Yth Fel; Vlbl; Pep Squad; Mo Yth Del; Occupational Therapy.

McDONALD, Sandra Lynn
Sandusky HS; Sandusky, OH; Pres, 4H; Bsbl; 4H A; ARC A; Davis Jr Bus Col; Computing Clerk.

McDONALD, Sharon
Sandusky HS; Sandusky, OH; Pres, Bus C; Hmrm; SC; Tres, Jr Cl; Sftbl; Tr; COM; Cl Fav; Math A; MLS; Most Out; ARC A; Type A; Yth Fel; Ohio St U; Bus Adm.

McDONALD, Shirley Marie
Marion Abramson Sr HS; New Orleans, LA; Chor; Tnns; Dillard U; Typiest.

McDONALD, Susan Maria
New Haven HS; New Haven, MO (3-41) Band; Chldr; Ensm; NHS; Mgr, Sftbl; Hon Prog; Span A; E Central Jr Col; Acct.

McDONALD, Tammy Jo
Chambersburg HS; Chambersburg, PA (84-725) Chldr; Chess C; Chor; 4H; Lat C; Co-Cpt, Bkbl; Aux Lat; 4H A; Pres A; Yth Fel.

McDONALD, Teresa Renee
Canyon HS; Canyon, TX (77-255) Bkbl; All St, All Dist, St Champs, Bkbl; SWAAU Outst Guard; Abilene Christian U; Health.

McDONALD, Terri Jean
Livermore Falls HS; Livermore Falls, ME (3-124) Drama.

McDONALD, Thomas Groomes
E Hills HS; Fort Worth, TX (20%-500) Pres, SC; MVP, Tnns.

McDONALD, Thomas Raymon
Malcolm X Shabazz HS; Newark, NJ; A Cap Choir; Bus C; Chor; Fin, Hmrm; Model UN; Ntl Yth Conf; Rptr, Sch P; SC; Up Bound; COM; Cl Fav; Most Out; Sanctuary Soc; Spch A; Type A; Yth Fel; Best Dressed; Outst Camp Counselor; Hospital Vol; Essex Co Col; Sociology.

McDONALD, Thomas Stanley
Fridley Grace HS; Fridley, MN (60-310) Chor; Drama; Bsbl; Wrest; Drama A; Best Character Actor; *St Johns U; Bus.*

McDONALD, Vickie Sue
McClellan HS; Little Rock, AR (38-456) BC; Ensm; FBLA; FHA; NHS; Baccalaureate Usher; Hon Banquet.

McDONEL, Robin Marie
Tustin HS; Tustin, CA; Drama; Co-Cpt, Hockey; Co-Cpt, Soccer; Swim; *Drama.*

McDONNELL, Katherine Lynne
Wheaton N HS; Wheaton, IL (4-400) Band; Dbte Tm; Ensm; NFL; NHS; Rptr; Sch P; Tres, SC; Bkbl; Sftbl; Tr; Chem A; Hon Prog; Math A; *Wheaton Col; Sci.*

McDONNELL, Julie Ann
Fowler HS; Fowler, CO (1-70) Band; Chldr; Chor; VP, Drama; Ensm; FBLA; GS; Madrigal; NHS; Spch C; Thes; Secy, Soph Cl; JV, Bkbl; COM; Hon Prog; Yth Fel; Tr Statistician; Hon Band; *Colo U; Sci.*

McDONNELL, Maureen Patricia
Glenbard W HS; Glen Ellyn, IL; AFS; Mgr, Bsbl; Mgr, Bkbl; Amer Leg A; *St Mary's Col; Nurs.*

McDONNELL, Nancy Kay
Levelland HS; Levelland, TX (12-220) Ed, Ann; Pres, Band; Chess C; A-Ed, Sch P; Pres, Span C; SC; Journ A; Swtht; *Tex Tech U; Med.*

McDONNELL, Suzanne
Woodlake Union HS; Woodlake, CA (45-145) F-Ed, Band; Ch, Chldr; Chor; Sch P; Secy, SC; Var C; Pres, Soph Cl; Swim; Tr; Vlbl; *Pepperdine U; Bus.*

McDONOUGH, Kevin Colby
Charles H Roth HS; Rochester, NY; Band; Orch; Bsbl; Ftbl; Soccer; Sftbl; Tr; Wrest; Hon Prog; Most Out; DECA; Outst De Stu; RHAA League Champs; PA; Numeral Sports; Division Champs; *Math.*

McDONOUGH, Regina Rose
Carmel HS; Carmel, NY (40-320) CYO; Cpt, Chldr; Pres, Hmrm; Lat C; NHS; Secy, SC; Var C; Y-Tns; COM; Hon Prog; WW; DAHSS; Towners Ath & Social C Schol; *Buffalo U; Lang.*

McDOUGAL, Cheryl Ann
Waupun HS; Waupun, WI (104-300) Ann; *Northland Col.*

McDOUGALD, Linda Kay
White Hall HS; Pine Bluff, AR; SC; Bkbl; Sftbl; Tr; Qn, Little League; Babe Ruth; Bkbl, Tr As; *Monticello Col; Phys Ed.*

McDOUGALL, Catherine Ann
Cumberland Valley Sr HS; Mechanicsburg, PA (38-564) Fr C; NHS; ARC; Var C; Swim; COM; Water- polo; WW; *Beaver Col; Art.*

McDOUGALL, Cathryn Edna
La Mirada HS; La Mirada, CA (1-440) Ann; Tr; Type A; Vlbl; *Biola Col.*

McDOUGALL, Colin Stewart
La Mirada HS; La Mirada, CA (5-410) Co-Ed, Sch P; JV, Bkbl; Cr-Ctry; Tr; JV, Wrest; CSF; Kiwanis A; EBELL Schol; *Biola Col; Phys Ed.*

McDOUGALL, Patricia Anne
Celina Sr HS; Celina, OH (20-255) Ed, Ann; S-T, Band; CYO; Fr C; FTA; Lat C; Pres, NHS; Bkbl; Cpt, Tr; COM; Pres, GAA; Vlbl; *Ohio St U; Phys Therapy.*

McDOUGALL, Sheri
Holy Rosary Acad; Louisville, KY (3-90) Math C; NHS; ARC; A-Ed, Sch P; COM; Hon Prog; Math A; Poet A; Pres, Bowl; Span Cert; WW; Ntl HS A for Excellence; *U of Louisville; Special Ed.*

McDOUGLE, Tammy Sue
Uniontown Area Sr HS; Uniontown, PA (16-450) Band; Fr C; Tres, Hmrm; NHS; Amer Leg A; Hon Prog; NMS Ltr of Commendation; *Calif St Col; Elem Ed.*

McDOWELL, Alphonso
Jackson Central HS; Jackson, MS (10-175) Band; HiY; Ntl Yth Conf; Bsbl; COM; Citz A; Hist A; Math A; Eng A; Social Stu A; Mus A; *Jackson St U; Engr.*

McDOWELL, Andrea Louise
Richfield HS; Waco, TX; Band; Chldr; Secy, FTA; SC; Y-Tns; Beauty; COM; Citz A; Cl Fav; HCt; PTA A; Alpha Kappa Alpha As; *Baylor U; Bus Adm.*

McDOWELL, Beverly Kay
Paris HS; Paris, TX (10-400) Rptr, Fr C; French NHS; Key C; Math C; NHS; Tri-HiY; *Baylor U; Law.*

McDOWELL, Carol Bunn
The Wheatley Sch; Westbury, NY (8-166) Band; Cpt, Chldr; Chor; Hmrm; NHS; Orch; Secy, SC; Mgr, Tr; Hon Prog; JA A; Math A; Math Tutor; Title IX Comm; Make-Up Artist, Sch Productions; Ch, Alumni Col Day; Secy, Church Yth Fel; *Lafayette Col.*

McDOWELL, Deborah Lynn
Collingswood Sr HS; Collingswood, NJ; A Cap Choir; Band; Mjrte; Orch; SC; Layout Ed, Sch P; *Messiah Col; Journ.*

McDOWELL, Donna Anne
Fairmont Sr HS; Fairmont, WV; A Cap Choir; Secy, Chor; Drama; Ensm; Madrigal; Rainbow; Span C; Spch C; COM; WV All-St Chor; *WV Wesleyan Col; Mus Therapy.*

McDOWELL, Donna Kaye
Farmington Sr HS; Farmington, MO (61-279) A Cap Choir; Band; Chldr; Chor; Ensm; 4H; HiY; Hmrm; Madrigal; Swtht; Yth Fel; HR; St Mus A; All District Choir; Church St Mus; *SW Baptist Col; Mus.*

McDOWELL, Hank Leigh
Treadwell HS; Memphis, TN (100-179) Bkbl; Cr-Ctry; Tr; Mr Treadwell; All Tourn Dist-Region-St; 10 Best Dressed; *Belmont Col; Elem Ed.*

McDOWELL, Jamie Tyron
Chester HS; Chester, PA; Hmrm; *Drafting.*

McDOWELL, Leotis
Springfield Southeast HS; Springfield, IL (115-501) Coach Bkbl; *Sou Ill Col; Med.*

McDOWELL, Mark David
Cuyahoga Valley Christian Acad; Cuyahoga Falls, OH (1-56) Alg A; Bio A; Chem A; Hist A; NEDT; Life Bible Inst Schol; Chem A, Ohio Scholastic Test; *Le Torneau Col; Mech Engr.*

McDOWELL, Martha Ellen
Airport HS; W Columbia, SC (5%-310) A Cap Choir; Secy, Chor; Pres, Fr C; Pres, Hmrm; Inter-Club Coun; Ed, Lit Mag; NHS; Sch P; COM; Hon Prog; Pres, VIA Service C; Adm Board; Jr Marshal; Coun On Ministries; GSct; Pres, Yth Choir; HARP Prog; Secy, Yth Coun; *Winthrop Col; Eng.*

McDOWELL, Mary Louise
Central HS; Jackson, MS; Chor; Pres, Hmrm; SC; Sftbl; COM; Hist A; JA A; Math A; Phys Ed A; Social Stu A; *Jackson St Col; Bus Adm.*

McDOWELL, Ronald Ray
Buena Vista HS; Imperial, TX (3-16) Tres, FFA; Tres, NHS; Bkbl; Cpt, Ftbl; Golf; Tr; COM; Spch A; All-W Tex Defensive Lineman; Top Rank Boy, Cl; All-Dist Defensive Lineman; WW.

McDOWELL, Steve Lawrence
N Babylon Sr HS; N Babylon, NY; A Cap Choir; Chess C; Chor; Dbte Tm; Drama; 4H; ARC; Rptr, Sch P; Span C; Pres, SC; Arch; Bsbl; Bkbl; Mgr, Ftbl; Soccer; Sftbl; Co-Cpt, Tr; Wrest; COM; Cl Fav; 4H A; I Dare You; Pres A; ARC A; Swtht; Tr A; BSct A; Sportsmanship A; *Bradford Col; Acting.*

McDOWELL, Terrilee D
Maple Shade HS; Maple Shade, NJ (7-241) Pres, Band; B Crocker A; 4H A; *Tulsa U; Deaf Ed.*

McDOWELL, William Lewis
Airport HS; W Columbia, SC (10%-600) Band; Order/Arrow; Order/Arrow A; *Photography.*

McDOWELL, Yolanda Renee
George H Corliss HS; Chicago, IL (2-700) Ann; Dbte Tm; NHS; COM; Citz A; Hon Prog; Principal's Schol; PA; HR; *Northwestern U; Sci.*

McDUFF, Bruce Edward
Campbell HS; Smyrna, GA; Band; Math C; VP, NHS; Order/Arrow; Bsbl; Cr-Ctry; Cpt, Soccer; God & Country A; US Air Force Acad.

McDUFFEE, Katharine Louise
North Sr HS; N St Paul, MN (25%-450) Yth Fel; Church Choir; 1 to 1 Swim w-Handicapped; 1st Cl GSct; *U of Minn; Vet Med.*

McDUFFIE, Wallace Howell Jr
Gadsden HS; Gadsden, AL; Key C; Var C; VP, Sr Cl; Bsbl; Ftbl; Citz A; H of F; WW; *Eng.*

McDUFFIE, Yvonne Dale
Eastside HS; Paterson, NJ (16-519) NHS; Hon Prog; Most Out; *Taylor Bus Inst; Legal.*

McEACHERN, Edward Barry
Fayette Co HS; Fayette, AL (35-153) Band; VICA; *Livingston U; Bus Law.*

McEACHERN, James Sterling III
Bremen HS; Bremen, GA (15%-80) FBLA; VP, Inter-Act C; Ftbl; Tr; Wrest; Art C; FCA; PA.

McEACHERN, Robert Allen
Fayette Co HS; Fayette, AL; Bus Mgr, Ann; Band; Chor; Drama; FFA; 4H; Math C; Sci C; 4H A; Math A; NEDT; Sci A; Prom, Coronation, Committees; *Brewer St Jr Col; Bus Adm.*

McELFRESH, Robin Lynn
Coshocton HS; Coshocton, OH; Band; 4H; Span C; Var C; Co-Cpt, Bkbl; Sftbl; Tnns; Tr; 4H A; Yth Fel; Most Improved A, Tnns; *Phys Ed.*

McELHANEY, James Vinson
Broxton HS; Broxton, GA; Tres, Ann; Tres, FFA; Tres, 4H; Tres, Bkbl; Most Dependable; *Mech.*

McELHANEY, Karen Lee
Rutledge HS; Rutledge, TN (1-190) BC; Chem C; Math C; Span C; S-T, Jr Cl; Bkbl; Tnns; School Athletic A; *Psych.*

McELHATTAN, Jeffery Dean
Temple Baptist Acad; Denver, CO; Ed, Ann; Band; Chor; Drama; Ensm; Fr C; VP, Ger C; NHS; Ftbl; Linquistics.

McELMURRAY, Alice Nell
Aiken HS; Aiken, SC (5%-700) Semi-Fin, Jr Miss Pa; Mjrte; Mu Alpha Theta; NHS; Sci C; Span NHS; COM; Opt A; Type A; S-T, Lib C; Jr Miss Scholastic Achievement A; *Med Technology.*

McELMURRAY, Sherri
Franklin Co HS; Frankfort, KY; Ann; Band; Span C; Academic Achievement A.

McELMURRAY, Terri
Franklin Co HS; Frankfort, KY; Co-Ed, Ann; Band; Span C; Academic Achievement A.

McELREATH, Ricky Lynn
Hobart HS; Hobart, OK (2-52) NHS; Span C; Lib C; *Western Okla St U; Acct.*

McELROY, Melinda Sue
Columbia HS; Decatur, GA; Fr C; FBLA.

McELROY, Stan Phillip
Amer HS; Fremont, CA; Hmrm; Tr; Wrest; MLS; Royal Ranger Advancements; Recogn, Co Fair Indust Ed Exhibit; *Bethany Bible Col; Mus.*

McELVAINE, Bryan David
Hightstown HS; Hightstown, NJ (1-309) BS; Pres, Jr Cl; Soccer; Tr; Amer Leg A; Hon Prog; *Pol Sci.*

McELWAINE, Joann
Independence HS; Charlotte, NC (356-641) Pres, UICA; *Central Piedmont Col; Early Childhood Aide.*

McELWEE, Deborah Ann
Mercy HS; Albany, NY (6-115) Lat C; Hon Prog; NEDT.

McELWEE, Donna Marie
Reading Sr HS; Reading, PA (25%-700) Bus C; FBLA; Hon Prog; *Bus.*

McENDREE, Belinda Lee
Bridgeport HS; Bridgeport, OH (3-108) French NHS; Lat C; NHS; Sci C; Y-Tns; Secy, Sr Cl; Secy, Jr Cl; Alg A; H of F; Hist A; MLS; Prom Qn; Art C; Zoology.

McENTIRE, Christopher Thomas
Wilkes Central HS; Wilkesboro, NC (25-290) Monogram; NHS; VP, SC; VP, Jr Cl; Golf; *U of NC; Law.*

McENTIRE, Deborah Anne
Grace Baptist HS; Decatur, AL (2-26) Ann; Chor; Math C; NHS; Rainbow; Ed, Sch P; Sci C; COM; Hon Prog; NEDT; Excel A, Eng; *Sociology.*

McENTIRE, Edward Le Monte
Wilkes Central HS; N Wilkesboro, NC (27-340)
Chor; VP, Jr Cl; JV, Bkbl; Golf; *UNC at Chapel Hill; Acct.*

McEVENY, Kathleen Karil
Westside HS; Omaha, NE (25%-786) FBLA; Rainbow; Tr; 1st Cl GSct; *U of Nebr Med Center; Nurs.*

McEWAN, Robert Paul
Oak Ridge HS; Orlando, FL; A Cap Choir; Band; *Auburn U.*

McEWEN, Jennifer Jo
Antelope Valley HS; Lancaster, CA (60-625) Semi-Fin, GS; Hmrm; VP, SC; Pres, Tri-HiY; Fin, Homecomng Ct; Eng A; Fin, Com; Activities A; Fin, PTA A; PTSA Rep A; Fin, Ca Schol Fed; Stu Rel Comm; *Azusa Pacific; Communications.*

McEWEN, Melissa
Shelby Co HS; Columbiana, AL; Band; BC; Ensm; Pres, FHA; Pres, 4H; Hmrm; InterClub Coun; Sch P; SC; S-T, Soph Cl; Beauty; 4H A; Hon Prog; MLS; Most Out; Type A; *U of Montevallo; Mus.*

McEWING, Alexander Douglas
Trinity Christian Sch; Williston, VT (2-16) Chor; Pres, SC; Bkbl; JV, Soccer; JV, Tr; Hist A; Sch Spirit, A; Indoor-Outdoor Field Events, A; *Bob Jones U; Med Aviator.*

McFADDEN, Colleen Marie
University HS; San Diego, CA (10-315) Badminton.

McFADDEN, Dawn Marie
Lawrence HS; Lawrence, MI; Cpt, Chldr; 4H; Pres, Jr Cl; Pres, Soph Cl; COM; Pres A; Outst Achv.

McFADDEN, Lorna Jean
Uniontown Area Sr HS; Uniontown, PA; *Western Penn Hospital Sch of Nurs; Nurs.*

McFADDEN, Russell Eugene
Bishop Carroll HS; Wichita, KS (17-211) St Scholar; *Wichita St U; Aeronautical Engr.*

McFADDEN, Susan Rebecca
North HS; Eastlake, OH; Span C; Citz A.

McFADDEN, Wendy Kay
Homestead HS; Mequon, WI (130-450) Band; Ski C; Sftbl; Hon Prog; Pres A; Prom Committee; Lutheran Yth; Modeling; Cert 1st Aid; *U of Minn; Occupational Therapy.*

McFADDIN, Colleen Marie
Estherville HS; Estherville, IA (30-180) MVP, Band; Chldr; MVP, Chor; VP, FHA; MVP, Bkbl; MVP, Golf; Pres A; *Bus.*

McFADYEN, Beth Ann
Sarasota; Sanasota, FL (217-619) Drama; Jr Miss Pagent; WW; Sanctuary Choir; Yth C Staff; Witness Comm; Jr HS Advisory Comm; Lay Witness Comm; Search Comm; Evang Tribe, Montreat Anderson Col; *U of Fla; Child Development.*

McFALL, Marshan
Huge Manley HS; Chicago, IL; Chor; 4H; Model UN; Beauty; 4H A; HQn; Journ A; JA A; Phy A; Sci A; Star Student; Swtht; Type A; Yth Fel.

McFALL, Phyllis Anne
Duncanville HS; Duncanville, TX (114-435) A Cap Choir; Chor; FTA; Rptr, Ger C; JETS; Secy, Lit Mag; Madrigal; NHS; Span C; SC; COM; Hon Prog; *U of Tex; Bio.*

McFALLS, James Clifford Jr
Columbia HS; Columbia, PA (48-109) Ann; Band; Chor; Orch; Co-Ed, Sch P; Pres, Span C; VP, SC; Ftbl; Tr; HCt; Dist Band; Co Band; Co Orch; *Navy Sch of Mus; Mus.*

McFARLAN, Alice Louise
Sweet Home HS; Sweet Home, OR (30-190) AFS; Ann; Fin, GS; Hmrm; NHS; Pres, Rainbow; Bus Mgr, Sch P; Pres, Sr Cl; Swim; JV, Tr; Elk A; Lion A; Elks Ldrship Schol; Sec, Linn Co As For Retard Citizens; Grand Rep, Order of Rainbow Girls; *Seattle Pacific Col; Journ.*

McFARLAND, Barbara Jean
Copperas Cove HS; Copperas Cove, TX (20-300) Band; FHA; Lat C; Sftbl; Cl Fav; HCt; Drill Tm; *Central Texas Col; Secretarial.*

McFARLAND, Bobby Jack Jr
Copperas Cove HS; Copperas Cove, TX (21-320) Demolay; Lat C; NHS; Sci C; *Tarleton St U; Engr.*

McFARLAND, Laura Gayle
North Co HS; Desloge, MO (10-184) Band; NHS; *Mineral Area Col.*

McFARLAND, Lori Marie
Valley HS; Hazelton, ID (7-52) Ed, Ann; Band; SC; Pres, Sr Cl; Mgr, Tr; Jr Cl Rep, SC; *Col of Sou Idaho; Psych.*

McFARLAND, Mary Beth
Hoopeston-E Lynn HS; Hoopeston, IL (5-150) Chor; Math C; NHS; Pres, Span C; Thes; *Ill Wesleyan U; Drama.*

McFARLAND, Mary Jane
Wheelersburg HS; Wheelersburg, OH (10-130) Band; Chor; Ensm; Secy, Fr C; Cpt, Mjrte; NHS; Rainbow; Sch P; Sci C; SC; VP, Soph Cl; Tr; HCt; Hon Prog; *Capital U; Nurs.*

McFARLAND, Matthew Curtis
Washburn Rural HS; Topeka, KS (10%-200) Hmrm; NHS; A-Ed, Sch P; SC; Pres, Sr Cl; Bkbl; Ftbl; Sftbl; Tnns; COM; HCt; Hon Prog; Journ A; King of Courts; Dist Coun; Variety Show; WW; *Washburn U; Journ.*

McFARLAND, Pamela Joy
Norton Comm HS; Norton, KS (4-82) Band; Chor; Ensm; Ch, FHA; SC; Rptr, Thes; Hon Prog; St Homemaker Degree; Kans St Chor; *U of Northern Colo; Bilingual-Bicultural Ed.*

McFARLAND, Pamela Sue
Burleson HS; Burleson, TX (150-300) Chldr; FHA; Tnns; Cl Fav; HCt; *Mus.*

McFARLAND, Silas Robert II
Tyrone Area HS; Tyrone, PA; Chor; Ski C; Ftbl; *Ind U of Pa; Natural Sci.*

McFARLAND, Suzanne Lynn
Valley HS; Hazelton, ID (5-50) Ann; Band; FHA; Mgr, Tr; Type A; *U of Idaho; Mus.*

McFATRICH, Bobbie Dean Jr
Fort Osage HS; Independence, MO; Jr Fireman; Osage Fire Dept; *U of Mo; Fire Sci.*

McFETERS, Abby Rose
South Side HS; Ft Wayne, IN (2-490) Chor; Ensm; Sci A; Rifle C; Sign Lang C; Mus Ltr; Bus Worker; St Win, Ensm; Ambassadors in Mission; Bible Qz Tm; 3rd Pl, Math Contest; *Oral Roberts U.*

McFETERS, Marianne
S Side HS; Ft Wayne, IN (89-438) Chor; Ensm; NHS; Service C; Secy, Christ Ambassadors; Rifle C; Church St Tn Talent Win; Hobby C; Mus Ltr; Sr Mus A; Church Mission; Win, in St Audition; *Purdue U; Nurs.*

McGAHEE, Byron Kelly
Essex Cath HS; Newark, NJ (94-202) Hmrm; Pol Sci C; Delta Sigma Theta A; Hist A; *Morehouse Col; Pol Sci.*

McGANNON, Mark Thomas
Marist HS; Chicago, IL (14-495) CYO; Cr-Ctry; Ftbl; NMS; St Scholar; Vol, Sch for Ment Handi-Capped; *U of Ill; Bus Adm.*

McGARITY, Rocky Lavelle
W Point HS; W Point, MS (50%-250) VP, NHS; Sci C; VP, SC; Var C; Bsbl; Ftbl; Eng A; Lit A; *Miss U; Law.*

McGARRY, Kevin John
De La Salle HS; Chicago, IL (30-285) Hmrm; Pres, NHS; Span NHS; Tres, SC; JV, Bsbl; Co-Cpt, Ftbl; JV, Tr; Cpt, Wrest; *Bradley U; Law.*

McGARY, Daniel Edwin
Madisonville N Hopkins HS; Madisonville, KY (50%-363) Secy, Key C; Var C; Pres, Soph Cl; Cpt, Swim; Homecoming Escort; MVP, Swim; Jr Deacon; *E Ky U; Bus.*

McGAUGHEY, Gail Lynn
Ulysses HS; Ulysses, KS; Chor; Ed, Ensm; NHS; Y-Tns; Tres, Tigerette.

McGAUGHY, Jane Louise
Chalker HS; Southington, OH (8-70) BC; Chor; NHS; Yth Fel; Candystriper; *Ohio St U; Phys Therapy.*

McGEE, Bonnie Sue
Oak Lawn Comm HS; Oak Lawn, IL (3-734) Fr C; Math C; NHS; Cr-Ctry; Tr; *U of Ill; Math.*

McGEE, Brenda Kaye
Fayette Comm HS; Fayette, IA (31-37) Chor; Mgr, Bkbl; CIA A; *Secretarial.*

McGEE, Carol Luann
Hannibal Sr HS; Hannibal, MO (26-293) Secy, FFA; NHS; Span C; WW; Alt, GS; *U of Mo; Floriculture.*

McGEE, Cynthia
Baker HS; Columbus, GA (68-295) Bkbl; Hon Prog; ROTC A; Eng C; VICA; Feb Calendar C; *US Air Force Acad; Secy.*

McGEE, Cynthia Kay
Bogue Chitto HS; Bogue Chitto, MS (1-60) BC; FHA; 4H; Rptr, Sch P; Cl Fav; *Copiah-Lincoln Jr Col; Sci.*

McGEE, Cynthia Lee
Central Bucks E HS; Buckingham, PA (40-450) Pres, A Cap Choir; Chldr; Pres, Chor; Tres, Drama; Ensm; Hmrm; InterAct C; Madrigal; Secy, SC; WW; *Temple U; Mus Therapy.*

McGEE, Debra Dennis
W A Berry HS; Birmingham, AL (2-413) VP, AFS; Anchor C; F-Ed, Ann; Chor; FHA; FTA; InterClub Coun; NHS; Beauty; DARGCA; Hon Prog; *U of Montevallo; Elem Ed.*

McGEE, Eleanor
Jane Addams Voc Sch; Cleveland, OH (187-225) FHA; Tr; *Cuyahoga Comm Col; Nurs.*

McGEE, Ellis Clanton
Gumberry HS; Gumberry, NC; BC; Chor; Fr C; 4H; Pres, Jr Cl; 4H A; *Halifax Comm Col; Mech Tech.*

McGEE, Hattie Marie
McCurtain HS; McCurtain, OK (2-18) Bus C; Co-Cpt, Chldr; Pres, Hmrm; NHS; Pres, Soph Cl; Hist A; *Secy.*

McGEE, James Lloyd
R J Reynolds HS; Winston-Salem, NC (20%-750) Order/Arrow; Ski C; God & Country A; Order/Arrow A; *Davidson Col; Religion.*

McGEE, James Wayne
Battle Ground Acad; Franklin, TN (8-64) Ann; Key C; Lat C; NHS; Order/Arrow; Co-Cpt, Swim; God & Country A; NEDT; Order/Arrow A; Yth Fel; Eagle A; *Tulane U; Bio.*

McGEE, Jennifer Lynne
Ballard Memorial HS; Wickliffe, KY; Band; FTA; Hist A; *Nurs.*

McGEE, Johnnie Earl
Lanier HS; Jackson, MS (75%-301) Chor; Pres, Ensm; Fr C; A-Ed, Newsletter; *Tougaloo Col; Mus.*

McGEE, Kelvin Brian
South HS; Bakersfield, CA; Band; BSUP C; Young Life; Yth Against Cancer; *USC; Eng.*

McGEE, Mark Allen
San Juan HS; Citrus Heights, CA (16-450) Arch; Bsbl; Bkbl; Swim; Tnns; Tr; *Carpenter.*

McGEE, Norine Edna
Pine Island HS; Pine Island, MN (13-73) CYO; Ger C; NHS; COM; Citz A; Hon Prog; Lion A; Stu o-t Month; Outst Yth; Hon Stu; *Rochester Comm Col; Bus.*

McGEE, Pamela Charisse
W Wyman King Acad; Batesburg, SC; Chor; Jr Miss Pagent; Model UN; Swim; Tnns; Beauty; Professional Model; Miss Sr; Runnerup, Miss Fresh; *Peidmont Tech Col; Bus Mgr.*

McGEE, Pandora Lois
Roosevelt HS; Gary, IN (5-510) Bus C; Chor; FHA; FTA; Sci C; Bkbl; Attendance A; Service A; *Purdue-Calumet U; Bus.*

McGEE, Peter Evred
De La Salle HS; Chicago, IL (64-364) Band; CYO; Chess C; NHS; Bsbl; Bkbl; Hon Prog; *Drama.*

McGEE, Shirley Ann
Motley HS; Columbus, MS (10%-70) Ann; Tres, BC; Secy, FHA; 4H; Secy, Sci C; Ch, Tri-HiY; Bio A; Sci A; Eng A; *Miss U For Women; Home Ec.*

McGEEHAN, Maryanne Theresa
John W Hallahan HS; Philadelphia, PA (7-432) Pres, CYO; Hmrm; NFL; Tres, NHS; Ch, Orch; Spch C; Ftbl; Sftbl; Spch A; Mus A; *U of Del; Lang.*

McGEHEE, Ann Scott
Trinity Episcopal Day Sch; Natchez, MS (33%-34) NHS; Parl, Jr Cl; Bkbl; Co-Cpt, Swim; Mgr, Tr; NEDT; Yth Fel; Span Academics A; Sch Spirit A; Acad Betterment Test; Character Spch, Hon Soc; Eng.

McGEHEE, Jannet Clair
Walter Wellborn HS; Anniston, AL; A Cap Choir; Band; Chor; FHA; Hmrm; Sci C; SC; All St Chor; Pres, MYF; Head Color Guard; U of Ala; Anthropology.

McGEHEE, Michael Ralph
Hitchcock HS; Hitchcock, TX (1-146) NHS; Engr.

McGEHEE, Michele Andrew
Mt Vernon HS; Mt Vernon, MO; FFA; Cpt, Bsbl; Cpt, Bkbl; MVP, Ftbl; Tr; Amer Leg A; COM; DARGCA; HCt.

McGETTIGAN, Pamela Ruth
Wilton-Lyndeboro Cooperative HS; Wilton, NH (5-52) Drama; FNA; NHS; Mgr, Bkbl; WW; 2nd, Ntl St Bookkeeping Contest; HR; Acct.

McGHEE, Billy Kevin
Lindblom Tech HS; Chicago, IL (36-620) Chess C; NHS; COM; Hon Prog; JA A; WW; JA; High Schol; U of Chicago; Archt.

McGHEE, Debbie Lynn
Washington-Lee HS; Arlington, VA (60-560) Drama; Ensm; Church Choir; Ger Hon Soc.

McGHEE, Deborah Jean
Buena Park HS; Buena Park, CA; Chess C; NHS; Sci C; Cr-Ctry; Tr; CSF; John Hopkins U; Sci.

McGHEE, Karen Dawn
Franklin Co HS; Rocky Mount, VA; FBLA; Bus.

McGHEE, Patrice Rechel
Melrose HS; SE Memphis, TN; Schol 2nd; Karate C; Shelby St; Secretarial.

McGHEE, VeLisa Michelle
Anacostia HS; Washington, DC; Maryland U; Econ.

McGHEE, Wendy Gale
Carroll HS; Monroe, LA (5%-205) Secy, Band; Pres, Drama; Secy, FBLA; Tres, Hmrm; Phys C; SC; Up Bound; HCt; Grambling St U; Journ.

McGHEE, William Richard
Crenshaw Christian Acad; Luverne, AL (5-24) Co-Ed, Ann; Pres, NHS; Sch P; Var C; Pres, Jr Cl; Bsbl; Bkbl; Ftbl; Davidson Col; Engr.

McGILL, Velda Darlene
Seventy First HS; Fayetteville, NC (40%-600) Parl, FBLA; 4H; Rptr, Hmrm; Delta Sigma Theta A; 4H A; U of NC; Bus Adm.

McGILLEY, Meg Mary
Loretto HS; Kansas City, MO (1-42) Fr C; French NHS; Cpt, Var C; Bausch & Lomb A; Bio A; Chem A; Hist A; Math A; Sci A; Type A; U of San Diego.

McGILLVREY, Lori Jean
Wolsey HS; Wolsey, SD (2-31) Co-Ed, Ann; Band; Chor; Drama; Ensm; FHA; ARC; Bkbl; Hon Prog; Sal; Spch A; John Philip Sousa Band A; 1st Run-Up, Miss Congen, Snow Qn; Presentation Col; RN.

McGILVARY, Gloria Ann
King And Queen Central HS; King & Queen Co, VA; Chldr; Chor; FBLA; FHA; 4H; Va Union Col; Phys Therapist.

McGILVRA, Kelly Dawn
Batavia HS; Batavia, IL (7-224) Band; Lat C; Math C; Orch; Hon Prog; Math A; JV, Vlbl; St Lat Contest; Dist Mus; U of Ill; Math.

McGILVRAY, Victoria Anne
George J Penney HS; E Hartford, CT; Fr C; Cr-Ctry; Tr; Hon Prog; Yth Fel; Gym; Med.

McGIMSEY, Mary Caroline
Lenoir HS; Lenoir, NC; Ann; Band; Bus C; Rptr, Hmrm; Co-Cpt, Mjrte; Monogram; ARC; Span C; SC; Swim; Spring Formal Court; U of NC; Interior Design.

McGINLEY, Mary Louise
Gordon HS; Gordon, NE (10%-80) Ed, Ann; Band; Chor; Orch; SC; Mgr, Tr; Mt Marty Col; Oral Communication.

McGINNIS, Bryan Haldean Jr
Hemet HS; Hemet, CA (70-600) Ann; Span C; Los Angeles Baptist Col; Mus.

McGINNIS, Elizabeth Mary
Monsignor Robert Nolan HS; Fort Worth, TX (32-162) Pres, Hmrm; Pres, Lat C; Lat NHS; NFL; Spch C; Hon Prog; Spch A; MV, Vlbl; Academic Achv A; U of Dallas; Pre-Med.

McGINNIS, Jenne Lynde
Mahar Regional HS; Orange, MA (1-188) Band; NHS; Orch; Hon Prog; Yth Fel; Womens C A; Cornell U; Horticulture.

McGINNIS, Mark Robert
Woodrow Wilson HS; Beckley, WV (1-500) Pres, A Cap Choir; BS; NHS; Sci C; Bkbl; Co-Cpt, Cr-Ctry; Tr; NMS; Regent Schol; Val; Amer Yth, Concert; W Va U; Bio.

McGINNISS, Deborah Jean
Milford HS; Milford, DE; NHS; Sci C; Var C; Hockey; Tnns; HCt; Hon Prog; Alt, GS; U of Del; Art.

McGLAUGHLIN, Rhonda Faye
Cambridge-S Dorchester HS; Cambridge, MD (19-298) Band; Chor; Commercial C; FNA; NHS; Swim; Tr; Miss Congeniality; Salisbury St Col; Nurs.

McGLONE, Leah Orene
W Carter Co HS; Olive Hill, KY (5%-127) Sci A; Rptr, Lib C.

McGLONE, Lois Jean
W Carter Co HS; Olive Hill, KY (5%-135) Bus C; FBLA; Bkbl; Lion A; Pep C; Newspaper C; Lib C; Morehead St U; Elem Ed.

McGLONE, Margaret Mary
Hyde Park HS; Hyde Park, MA (15-232) CYO; FNA; Hmrm; NHS; Ch, ARC; SC; Ftbl; Tr; Hon Prog; Sci A; 3-Yr Hon; Northeastern U; Nurs.

McGLOTHLIN, Angela Dawn
Fauquier HS; Warrenton, VA (33%-600) Chess C; Lit Mag; Tr; NJHS; Most Artistic; Home Ec A; Win, Sci Fiction Story.

McGLOTTEN, Sharon
Lake Clifton Sr HS; Baltimore, MD (10%-500) Chor; Hmrm; NHS; Ch, ARC; Sci C; Hist A; PA; Extra Curriculum A; Johns Hopkins U; Phys Therapy.

McGONAGILL, Robin Ann
S Plantation HS; Plantation, FL (19-600) Cpt, Chldr; Hmrm; NHS; Tres, SC; DARGCA; HCt; Acct A; Ldrship A; Most Outst Chldr; U of S Fla; Acct.

McGOVERN, James Peter
St Peters Prep Sch; Jersey City, NJ (12-250) Drama; 4H; Jr Cl; JV, Soccer; Hist A; NEDT; Hist.

McGOVERN, Kathryn Alyce
Seekonk HS; Seekonk, MA (17-224) Drama; NHS; Ski C; Cr-Ctry; Swim; Tnns; Tr; Boston Col; Bus Adm.

McGOWAN, Monica Mary
St Joseph's Notre Dame HS; Alameda, CA (1-72) Fr C; Hmrm; Pres, NHS; Ski C; COM; Hist A; Hon Prog; Most Out; PA; Eng A; Religion A; U of Santa Clara; Law.

McGOWEN, Elizabeth Ann
Norman HS; Norman, OK (67-662) Ch, Hmrm; NHS; Pres, Health Occupations Stu of Am; U of Okla; Nurs.

McGRADY, Mark Ennis
Fountain Central HS; Veedersburg, IN (3-120) Ed, Ann; 4H; NHS; Ed, Sch P; Bsbl; Tnns; Hist A; I Dare You; Journ A; NMF; NMS; Sal; Wabash Col; Pol Sci.

McGRAIN, Diane Michelle
Neshaminy Maple Point HS; Langhorne, PA; JV, Chess C; NHS; Temple Col; Psych.

McGRATH, John Daniel Jr
Marist HS; Chicago, IL (35-380) Band; VP, CYO; Drama; Hon Prog; St Scholar; Notre Dame U; Pre-Law.

McGRATH, Kathleen Elaine
Lake Oswego HS; Lake Oswego, OR (55-290) A Cap Choir; Chor; Dbte Tm; NFL; NHS; ARC; Secy, Spch C; Hon Prog; Spch A; Tres, Inter-Ntl Relations C; Church Social Concerns Committee; 1st St, Debate; 4th, St Poetry Interpretation; Reed Col; Biol.

McGRAW, Amanda
Estill HS; Estill, SC (50%-50) Ann; Chor; Drama; Cl Fav; 4H A; HQn; NMS; Med Col of Ga; Nurs.

McGRAW, Dana Lee
Tupelo HS; Tupelo, MS (10-359) Anchor C; Ann; Band; Fr C; NHS; Thes; NE Miss Jr Col; Spch.

McGRAW, Donna Frances
Bentonia HS; Bentonia, MS (2-50) Dbte Tm; Drama; A-Ed, Sch P; Cpt, Bkbl; Cl Fav; Miss BHS; Delta St U; Phys Ed.

McGRAW, Gregory Alan
Pattonville HS; Hazelwood, MO; Chor; NHS; Hon Prog; U of Mo at St Louis; Acct.

McGRAW, Janice Elaine
Shenandoah Valley Acad; New Market, VA; Ed, Ann; Secy, Band; NHS; Ski C; VP, Soph Cl; Bkbl; Soccer; Fin, Sftbl; COM; Citz A; DARGCA; Pres A; Columbia Union Col; Nurs.

McGRAW, Jennifer Loren
Central HS; Carrollton, GA; Band; Tri-HiY; Mgr, Bkbl; Pres A.

McGRAW, Kyle Alan
Robert E Lee HS; Midland, TX; Ger C; SC; Bsbl; Tr; Tex Tech U; Arch.

McGRAW, Melinda Letitia
Cony HS; Augusta, ME (65-350) Ann; Fr C; Secy, Sci C; B Crocker A; WW; U of Maine; Secondary Ed.

McGRAW, Susan Carol
Alexandria Sr HS; Alexandria, LA (50-352) S-T, Chor; Fr C; FHA; French NHS; GS; Key C; Var C; Y-Tns; Beauty; HCt; Hon Prog; Swtht; Royalty Court; WW; La Tech Col; Interior Design.

McGREEVY, John William
Bishop Carroll HS; Wichita, KS (44-211) VP, CYO; NHS; Var C; Bsbl; Ftbl; Hon Prog; Benedictine Col; Law.

McGREGOR, Amy Jo
T L Handy HS; Bay City, MI (22-397) Band; Chldr; Chor; Dbte Tm; Fin, Ensm; Mjrte; NHS; Orch; ARC; SC; MVP, Sftbl; Swim; Tr; COM; Hon Prog; ARC A; Citz A; Band A; Co-Ed, Yth Paper; Choir; Solo Ensm A; NYI; PA A; Art A; YMCA Swim Tm A; Tn Talent; CST A; Olivet Nazerene Col; Sci.

McGREGOR, James Morrison
Thomas Lincoln Handy HS; Bay City, MI (231-325) Ann; FFA; Bkbl; Sftbl; Walkathon; Delta Col; Clerical.

McGREGOR, Susan Jean
Mount Pleasant HS; Wilmington, DE (30-380) AFS; VP, NHS; SC; Tres, Sr Cl; Tres, Soph Cl; Sftbl; DARGCA; NEDT; Yth Fel; Cpt, Vlbl; Opera C; Ch, Comm Action, Comm of SC; Yth Rep, Coun on Ministries; Mount Holyoke Col; Span.

McGREGORY, Sheila Renee
Benhaven HS; Olivia, NC; VP, Band; BC; Chldr; VP, FHA; Rptr, FTA; Pres, Hmrm; SC; VP, Soph Cl; Alg A; COM; Math A; MLS; Most Out; Band, Phys Sci, Eng, A's; NC St U; Eng.

McGREW, Julie Ann
John Ehret HS; Marrero, LA; CYO; Lit Ral; VP, Mjrte; NHS; Co-Cpt, Sftbl; Bio A; COM; Hon Prog; PTA A; Lib C; Academic A; Asst Life Guard; Tres, Swtht, Spirit C; Q&S Swtht; Maid for Poseidon; UNO; Elem Ed.

McGREW, Vincent Roy
Fairfield HS; Fairfield, AL (25%-184) SC; Bsbl; Bkbl; All Metro Tm.

McGRIFF, Kathleen Ethel
Buchholz HS; Gainesville, FL (10%-350) VP, 4H; Hmrm; NHS; Span C; SC; JV, Sftbl; COM; 4H A; Hon Prog; Keyettes; Vet.

McGRIFF, Michelle
N Nashville HS; Nashville, TN; Ann; Band; Chor; Cpt, Dbte Tm; Hmrm; ARC; Sch Achieve Tm; Sch P; SC; Golf; Sftbl; Tr; COM; Hon Prog; NEDT; ARC A; Spelman Col; Med.

McGROGAN, Frank Patrick III
Yough Sr HS; Herminie, PA (10%-292) Band; NHS; Tr; NEDT; Outdoor's C; St Vincent Col Schol; Saint Vincent Col; Pre-Math.

McGRUDER, Darlene Letitia
Northwestern Sr HS; Adelphi, MD (10%-600) BC; Var C; MVP, Tr; Citz A; ROTC A; Type A; Psych.

480

McGUFFEY, Jonathon Trent
Newnan HS; Newnan, GA; 4H; Ftbl; *Auburn U; Trainer.*

McGUINTY, Robert Wayne
Wilcox Co HS; Rochelle, GA (5-110) Band; BC; FFA; Tres, 4H; Hmrm; 4H A; Hon Prog; JA A; Eng, Mus A's; *Agr.*

McGUIRE, Brian Keith
Blackwell HS; Blackwell, OK; Ann; Band; BS; Chor; Drama; Sch P; Mgr, Ftbl; Wrest; Pres, Church Yth Coun; Pres, Sch Christian Organization; 3rd Pl, Wrest; 1st Pl Dist, 1st Pl St, Mus; *Okla St U; Mus.*

McGUIRE, Carl Lee
Claymont Sr HS; Uhrichsville, OH (190-320) Bsbl; Bkbl; Ftbl; Sftbl; Swim; Tnns; Tr; Wrest.

McGUIRE, Colleen Anne
Greater Latrobe HS; Latrobe, PA (60-554) AFS; SC; Secy, Jr Cl; Bio A; *Robert Morris Col; Secy.*

McGUIRE, David Wayne
Gibbs Sr HS; St Petersburg, FL (20-390) Key C; NHS; Ftbl; Bio A; *Trevecca Nazarene Col; Bus.*

McGUIRE, Esther Jo
Woodlawn HS; Shreveport, LA (4-421) Secy, Dbte Tm; Secy, Drama; Secy, Math C; NFL; NHS; Rptr, Sch P; Secy, Sci C; Secy, Spch C; St Stu Congress; COM; Spch A; Rep, Astra C; Comm Affairs; GSct; Q&S; *La Tech U; Pre-Law.*

McGUIRE, LaGertha Anne
Springfield S HS; Springfield, OH; Band; Chor; Ensm; NFL; Spch C; St Stu Congress; Spch A; Star & Chevron A; *Bowling Green St U; Bus Adm.*

McGUIRE, Lewis Randall
John M Morehead HS; Eden, NC (50-430) Pres, Band; Chor; Pres, Hmrm; Orch; A-Ed, Sch P; SC; Cpt, Soccer; Chem A; Opt A; Sci A; Type A; HR; *U of NC; Psych.*

McGUIRE, Patricia Gail
Obion Co Central HS; Troy, TN (10-183) BC; NHS; Ntl Achv Schol; WW; *U of Tenn; Nurs.*

McGUIRE, Patricia Louise
Western Hills HS; Cincinnati, OH (84-840) Hmrm; Secy, Lat C; NHS; Rainbow; ARC; Ed, Sch P; Ch, SC; Hon Prog; Q&S A; WW; *Christ Hospital Sch of Nurs; Nurs.*

McGUIRE, Shari Lynn
East HS; Columbus, OH (17-350) *Ohio St U; Child Development.*

McGWIRE, Linda Carol
Hopewell Valley Central HS; Pennington, NJ; AFS; Pres, Hmrm; Rptr, Sch P; SC; Var C; Tnns; *Wilkes Col; Nurs.*

McHAM, Donna Carole
Whiteface HS; Whiteface, TX; Band; FHA; Mjrte; Spch C; JV, Bkbl; Sftbl; Tnns; UIL Solo As; *Tex Tech U; Mus.*

McHAM, Jacque De Ann
Whiteface HS; Whiteface, TX; Ann; Band; FHA; Mjrte; Band A; *S Plains Jr Col.*

McHAN, Kathleen Elizabeth
Milo Adventist Acad; Days Creek, OR (3-66) A Cap Choir; Co-Ed, Ann; Band; Chor; Pres, GS; Ed, Sch P; Ski C; Cpt, Bkbl; Fin, Cr-Ctry; Sftbl; Semi-Fin, Tr; *Walla Walla Col; Elem Ed.*

McHENRY, Brenda Joyce
Center HS; Monaca, PA (13-280) Span C; Secy & Tres, Alliance Yth Fel; Voices o-t Loud Singing Group; Campus Life C; *Geneva Col; Psych.*

McHENRY, Terry Kaye
Zanesville HS; Zanesville, OH (12-400) Chldr; 4H; Hmrm; Sch P; SC; Swim; 4H A; HCt; Most Out; Showing Horses As; *Sciota Tech Col; Dental Hygiene.*

McHUGH, Margaret Marie
St Joseph's Notre Dame HS; Alameda, CA (1-78) Chor; NHS; Eng A; *Fashion Design.*

McILHENNY, Beverly Jean
Bensalem Sr HS; Cornwells Heights, PA; Chor; Hmrm; SC; Most Humorous; Sr Cl Play; *Bucks Co Comm Col; Human Services.*

McILROY, Melissa
Arkadelphia HS; Arkadelphia, AR (10%-230) Cpt, Chldr; VP, FHA; NHS; Pres, Sci C; SC; Gym A; *U of Miss.*

McILROY, Rebecca Stewart
Independence HS; Charlotte, NC (32-597) Ed, Ann; Chor; VFW A; Golden Eagle A; Rptr, Spirit of '77; Ann A; Choir; Women's Chorale; Marshal; Keyettes; *UNCC; Special Ed.*

McILVAIN, Sandra Kay
East HS; Cheyenne, WY (50-430) AFS; Chor; FTA; 4H; NHS; Ntl Teachers Coun; World Affairs C; Soccer; Tr; Hist A; Hon Prog; Yth Fel; Yth Leg; Select Musical Group; *Tabor Col; Elem Phys Ed.*

McILWAIN, Lori Elizabeth
Waynesboro Central HS; Waynesboro, MS (20%-100) FHA; Sch P; Y-Tns; *Jones Co Jr Col; Bus & Commerce.*

McILWAIN, Miranda Jane
W A Berry HS; Birmingham, AL; S-T, Lat C; Lat NHS; Amer Leg A; COM; *Engr.*

McINDOO, Dean Ellsworth
Broomfield HS; Broomfield, CO; Ann; Chor; Opt A; *CAP.*

McINNIS, Carol Lynne
Tara HS; Baton Rouge, LA; Pres, Hmrm; NHS; Swim; *LSU; Phys Therapy.*

McINTEE, Dennis Patrick
Carmel HS; Carmel, IN (350-587) Var C; MVP, Cr-Ctry; Tr.

McINTIRE, Christie Lynn
Elk Grove HS; Elk Grove Village, IL (90-599) Secy, Chor; Drama; Ensm; Mod Mus Mas; Thes; Elk A; *Eng.*

McINTIRE, Jeffrie Shawn
Winona R-III HS; Winona, MO (1-32) Ed, Ann; Band; BC; BS; FBLA; NHS; F-Ed, Sch P; SC; Sftbl; Tnns; Alg A; B Crocker A; COM; Hon Prog; Math A; Type A; Val; *Southwest Mo St U; Acct.*

McINTIRE, Karen Kay
Laurelwood Acad; Gaston, OR; Bsbl; Bkbl; Soccer; *Portland Comm Col; Vet.*

McINTIRE, Karen Key
Laurelwood Acad; Gaston, OR; Cpt, Bkbl; *Portland Comm Col; Vet.*

McINTOSH, Daniel Freeman
Seminole HS; Sanford, FL (5-481) BS; Fr C; French NHS; InterAct C; InterClub Coun; Mu Alpha Theta; Pres, NHS; Cpt, Soccer; Swim; Citz A; HCt; Sr Cl Coun; VP, FCA; Schol Ath A; *Duke U; Law.*

McINTOSH, Darlene Sue
Warren Central HS; Indianapolis, IN; Chor; Ensm; Church Ensm; Yth Ldr; *Dental Assistant.*

McINTOSH, Elva Sue
Buckhorn HS; Buckhorn, KY (4-63) BC.

McINTOSH, Eunice Michelle
Thornton Township HS; Harvey, IL (204-899) Drama; Spch C; SC; Spch A; *Ill St U; Law.*

McINTOSH, Gregory Allen
Kickapoo Sr HS; Springfield, MO (45-280) Chor; Ensm; VP, Hmrm; Madrigal; Math C; SC; JV, Sftbl; JV, Tr; Alg A; Math A; *SW Mo St U; Elec.*

McINTOSH, Guy Bryon
Deerfield HS; Deerfield Beach, FL; Chor; Co-Ed, Sch P; Span C; JA A; *Eckerd Col; Ministry.*

McINTOSH, Holly Dene
Box Elder HS; Brigham City, UT (4-360) Chor; FHA; GS; Madrigal; NHS; Swim; Tnns; Elk A; Gracious Womanhood A; Chopin Piano A; Top 3%; *Brigham Young U; Elem Ed.*

McINTOSH, James Andrew
Hemet HS; Hemet, CA (88-475) FFA; Var C; Cr-Ctry; Ftbl; Tr; CSF; *Los Angeles Baptist Col; Bus.*

McINTOSH, Johnny Wilburn
Richland HS; Ft Worth, TX; Ensm; Hmrm; SC; Tres, Soph Cl; JV, Bkbl; Co-Cpt, Ftbl; Chamber of Comm A; Most Out.

McINTOSH, Joyce Marie
Altheimer HS; Altheimer, AR; Ann; FBLA; Rptr, Hmrm; Sch P; VP, SC; COM; Citz A; HCt; MLS; Most Out; Type A; *U of Ark at Pine Bluff; Bus Ed.*

McINTOSH, Lisa J
Naperville N HS; Naperville, IL (10%-500) Band; Drama; Ger C; *Math.*

McINTOSH, Marilyn Darlene
Lincoln HS; Dallas, TX (10%-263) Band; Bus C; Drama; FHA; Tres, Math C; Tres, NHS; ARC; Sci C; Type A; Bus, Band, Piano, Exec Asst, A's; *Bishop Col; Nurs.*

McINTOSH, Mark Allen
William Fremd HS; Palatine, IL (4-756) Pres, AFS; Fr C; Co-Ed, Sch P; Spch C; SC; Tr; Amer Leg A; Spch A; Stu Rep, District Board of Ed; District Area Coun; Jr Cl Rep, Principal's Advisory Brd; *Yale U; Pol Sci.*

McINTOSH, Mary Ann
Edison HS; Huntington Beach, CA (285-995) Fr C; Pres A; *Calif Baptist Col; Bus Adm.*

McINTOSH, Paul David
Westford Acad; Westford, MA (30-250) Ftbl; Tr; *Biol.*

McINTOSH, Philip Elbert
Somerset HS; Somerset, KY (10-180) Ann; Bkbl; Cr-Ctry; Ftbl; Golf; 3 S Schol A; Ntl Athletic Schol Soc; *U of Ky.*

McINTOSH, Robert Charles
Bishop McDevitt HS; Harrisburg, PA (4-271) Band; Ensm; NMF; Sal; *U of Pittsburgh; Chem Engr.*

McINTOSH, Zoe Camille
Thornton Township HS; Harvey, IL (252-863) Chor; Drama; NFL; Tr; Spch A; *Chicago St U; Chem.*

McINTYRE, Barbara Ann
Scotland HS; Laurinburg, NC; Tr; Vlbl; *A&T U; Phys Ed.*

McINTYRE, Bruce Herndon
Cypress Lake HS; Ft Myers, FL (30-500) Pres, NHS; Order/Arrow; Ftbl; *U of Fla; Bus Mgt.*

McINTYRE, Christy Gay
Daviess Co HS; Owensboro, KY (1-320) Pres, BC; 4H; Sch Achieve Tm; Sch P; Co-Cpt, Bkbl; Chem A; 4H A; Hon Prog; Coaches A; *U of Ky; Animal Sci.*

McINTYRE, David L
Steinmetz HS; Chicago, IL; Band; JV, Ftbl; JV, Tr; *Loyola U; Law.*

McINTYRE, Denise Elaine
Warwick HS; Lititz, PA (1-263) VP, Chor; GS; Secy, SC; Var C; Tres, Jr Cl; Tres, Soph Cl; Bkbl; Hockey; Tnns; Amer Leg A.

McINTYRE, Lisa M
San Houston HS; Arlington, TX (11-600) Sch P; Sci C; Spch C; SC; JV, Tnns; Sci A; Spch A; Photo A; *Photography.*

McINTYRE, Margaret Susan
Valley Central HS; Montgomery, NY (106-347) Secy, CYO; Co-Cpt, Chldr; VP, 4H; Hmrm; ARC; Ski C; Secy, SC; Var C; 4H A; HCt; Cand, Prom Qn; *SUNY at Oswego; Bio.*

McINTYRE, Naomi Linda
Lonis D Brandis HS; New York, NC; Cpt, Chldr; Chess C; Fr C; Fin, Jr Miss Pagent; Pres, Soph Cl; MVP, Bkbl; *Eckerd Col; Fr.*

McINTYRE, Sandra Alethea
Saint Dominic Acad; Jersey City, NJ (25-122) Chor; FNA; GS; Ed, Lit Mag; NFL; Span C; COM; Hon Prog; NEDT; Karate C Founder; Jr Altar Guild; Probationary Member, NHS; *Rutgers U; Social Sci.*

McIVER, Molly Elizabeth
Sidney HS; Sidney, OH; Band; Orch; Tr; Cpt, YMCA Gym Tm; *Ohio St U; Phys Therapy.*

McIVER, Willie Mae
Rancho HS; Las Vegas, NV (29-578) NHS; Hon Prog; Arthritus Found Distin Serv A; *UNLV; Banking & Finance.*

McKAMEY, Mike Robert
Cloverdale HS; Cloverdale, IN (20-100) Chor; Fr C; Sch P; S-T, SC; Thes; Tr; Wrest; FCA; VP, Church Yth.

McKAN, Margie Laverne
Monroe HS; Albany, GA (20-265) Bus C; Secy, Drama; FBLA; Hmrm; NHS; COM; Hon Prog; *Knoxville Col; Sociology.*

McKARNS, Polly Anne
Montpelier HS; Montpelier, OH (10%-110) Secy, Band; Secy, Chor; Ensm; Fr C; NHS; Rainbow; Acad Achv C; Grand Cross of Color, Rainbow; *Med.*

McKAY, Darla Jean
Switzerland Co Jr-Sr HS; Vevay, IN (4-108) Pres, NHS; Rptr, Sch P; Span C; Bio A; Math A; Sci A; Spelling, Eng, Home Ec, A's.

McKAY, Dorine Louise
Pass Christian HS; Pass Christian, MS (25%-110) BC; Pres, Hmrm; SC; Bkbl; Hon Prog; Sci A; Phys Ed A; Ntl HS A for Excellence; WW; Ntl Beta C; *Tex Sou U; Acct.*

McKAY, Lisa Charlene
Miami Palmetto Sr HS; Miami, FL (527-1075) Span NHS; Yth Fel; Yth Leg; Yth Cluster; Campus Life; United Church of Christ; *Catawba Col; Elem Ed.*

McKAY, Marla Suzanne
Alexandria Sr HS; Alexandria, LA (12-26) Band; Hmrm; Pres, SC; Pres, Y-Tns; COM; Hon Prog; Pres A; *LSU; Bus Adm.*

McKAY, Micah Kevin
Lenape Regional HS; Medford, NJ (20%-800) Hmrm; ARC; Var C; Soph Cl; Co-Cpt, Bsbl; Bkbl; Ftbl; Sftbl; COM; ARC A; ROTC A; VFW A; Sq Com, Civil Air Patrol; Amelia Earhart A; Billy Mitchell A; Most Outst Cadet; Big Stick Carrier; *U of Tex; Archt.*

McKAY, Robert Alan
Upper Arlington HS; Columbus, OH (65-699) AFS; Bus Mgr, Ann; NHS; Ed, Sch P; Span C; VP, Span NHS; Hon Prog; Journ A; Q&S A; Sertoma Yth Service A; *U of Ala; Bus.*

McKAY, Scott A
Everett HS; Everett, WA (15-360) Secy, Var C; Co-Cpt, Ftbl; Co-Cpt, Soccer; Wrest; *Sci.*

McKAY, Stephen Michael
Perryton HS; Perryton, TX (17-140) Band; BS; Pres, CYO; Dbte Tm; FFA; NFL; A-Ed, Sch P; Semi-Fin, Ftbl; COM; Hist A; HCt; Spch A; Citation Cert, St House of Rep; *Odessa Jr Col; Law.*

McKEE, Anthony Duane
Marion HS; Marion, IN; Ger C; JV, Cr-Ctry; Hon Prog; Yth Fel; Art A.

McKEE, Carolyn May
S Garland HS; Garland, TX;

McKEE, Cristy Lynne
Ainsworth HS; Flint, MI (36-250) Hmrm; Hon Prog; Co-Op Stu; Sch Store Secy; *Michigan Christian Col; Bus.*

McKEE, Darla Fay
Boulevard Baptist Sch; Burleson, TX (1-3) Ed, Ann; Cpt, Chldr; Chor; Ensm; Span C; Secy, SC; Cpt, Bkbl; Co-Cpt, Sftbl; Tr; MLS; Most Valuable Ath; Miss BBS; *Tarrant Co Jr Col; Bible.*

McKEE, Douglas James
Novinger R-1 HS; Novinger, MO (2-26) Pres, NHS; Pres, SC; Var C; Tr; Curator A; Hon Prog; I Dare You; Regent Schol; Yth Leg; Soph Pilgrimage; PTA Legislative Committee; Yrbk King; *U of Mo.*

McKEE, Jackie Sue
Buena HS; Sierra Vista, AZ (300-511) Ger C; Alt, Hmrm Rep.

McKEE, James Gil
Pearland HS; Pearland, TX; A Cap Choir; Pres, Band; BC; Pres, Chor; Ensm; Madrigal; VP, SC; Bsbl; Bkbl; JV, Ftbl; Sftbl; Tr; COM; Most Out; Most Friendly; Ntl Fed of Mus C; Piano Ass; Choir; MIP, Ftbl; *Med.*

McKEE, James Robert
Santa Rosa HS; Santa Rosa, CA (10%-379) Co-Ed, Ann; Chor; Math C; Co-Ed, Sch P; Var C; Tr; Citz A; Hon Prog; Journ A; Yth Fel; *Bus.*

McKEE, Jerry Ray
Burns Sr HS; Lawndale, NC (3-250) BC; Parl, BS; FBLA; Pres, Key C; Monogram; NHS; Rptr, Sch P; Cpt, Ftbl; Tr; Hon Prog; Journ A; NMS; Q&S A; *Guilford Col; Biol.*

McKEE, Jonathan Thomas
Roswell HS; Roswell, NM; Chor; Ensm; Ftbl; Wrest; COM; *ROTC.*

McKEE, Kelly Stuart
Wayne Co Day Sch; Goldsboro, NC (7-33) A-Ed, Ann; Chldr; Chor; NHS; Sch P; Secy, SC; Bkbl; Sftbl; Tnns; COM; HCt; Yth Fel; Most Improved, Tnns; *Sweet Briar Col; Math.*

McKEE, Patrick Kevin
Christian Brothers Col HS; St Louis, MO (5-130) Ed, Ann; NHS; Ed, Sch P; Bkbl; Ftbl; Tr; COM; Journ A; JA A; NEDT; Q&S A; *U of Mo at Columbia; Journ.*

McKEE, Paula Ann
Billy Mitchell HS; Colorado Springs, CO; Span C; Swim; JV, Tnns; Citz A; 4H A; I Dare You; Pres, VP, Secy & Ch, 4-H C; *CSU.*

McKEE, Peg Kadel
Fernandina Beach HS; Fernandina Beach, FL (10%-250) Band; Secy, Ensm; Madrigal; Tres, NHS; Rainbow; Tres, Sci C; Thes; *Stetson U; Mus.*

McKEE, Sherri Lynn
Pottstown Sr HS; Pottstown, PA (16-285) Band; Secy, NHS; Sch P; SC; Lacrosse; *Secretarial.*

McKEEVER, Kenneth Duane
Medina Senior HS; Medina, NY (3-190) A Cap Choir; Band; BS; Hmrm; NHS; Orch; Tres, Order/ Arrow; Cpt, Cr-Ctry; Co-Cpt, Swim; Chem A; Hist A; Jr Chamber of Com A; NEDT; Regent Schol; ROTC A; Alfred U Pres Schol; NMS Ltr of Commendation; *Alfred U; Ceramic Engr.*

McKELVEY, Stephen Cameron
Lakeside HS; Atlanta, GA; BC; Chor; Pres, Ger C; InterClub Coun; A-Ed, Lit Mag; NHS; Order/ Arrow; SC; Pres, Soph Cl; Swim; Tr; COM; Gov Honor Prog; Hist A; Hon Prog; Eagle Sct; *W Point Military Acad.*

McKELVIE, Sandra Joan
Wethersfield HS; Wethersfield, CT; Hmrm; Lat C; ARC; Hon Prog; Church Search Committee; Art A; Church Board; Asst Teacher, Church Sch Cl; TV Debate; *Pre-Med.*

McKENNEY, David Richard
Kimball HS; Royal Oak, MI; Dbte Tm; Life Sct; Sr Patrol Ldr; Highest Off, Sct Troop; *Law.*

McKENNEY, William Girard
Holly HS; Holly, MI (50-150) A Cap Choir; Fr C; NHS; Ed, Sch P; VP, SC; Var C; Bkbl; Ftbl; Tr; MLS; Vince Lombardi Ftbl A; Stu Advisor, Board of Ed; *Marquette University; Journalism.*

McKENZIE, Anna Marguerite
Mossyrock HS; Mossyrock, WA; Secy, FBLA; Pres, FHA; VP, NHS; Sci C; Bkbl; Tr; NEDT; *Math.*

McKENZIE, Carla Renee
Richland HS; Ft Worth, TX (50%-610) Chor; FHA; FTA; Rainbow; Rptr, Sch P; COM; Spirit C; Ntl Piano Guild; Secy, GSct; *U of Tex; Journ.*

McKENZIE, David Austin
Highland HS; Ewing, MO (7-160) NHS; Soph Pilgrimage.

McKENZIE, James Elbert Jr
Sparta Acad; Evergreen, AL (1-24) Ann; BC; Secy, Key C; NHS; Rptr, Sch P; JV, Bkbl; Ftbl; COM; Chem A; Hist A; Hon Prog; Sci A; Eng A; ACT A; Most Academic V Ftbl; Sci Fair As; *Auburn U; Chem Engr.*

McKENZIE, Mark Howard
Lawrence HS; Lawrence, KS (230-553) Secy, Bus C; Drama; Fr C; Hmrm; SC; Thes; Tres, Jr Cl; Swim; Gym; *Kans U; Bus.*

McKENZIE, Martin Leslie
Plymouth HS; Plymouth, OH (25-120) VP, Band; BS; Tres, Demolay; Drama; Fr C; VP, SC; Var C; Bsbl; Mgr, Bkbl; Ftbl; Tnns; Wrest; Amer Leg A; COM; Masonic A; Sci A; Demolay Ohio Gov Day; *Math.*

McKENZIE, Michael M
Russell HS; Russell, KY; HiY; Bkbl; FCA; *Transylvania U; Computer Sci.*

McKENZIE, Michael Shawn
Madras Sr HS; Madras, OR; Fr C; FBLA; VP, Ger C; 4H; Hmrm; Pres, NHS; Co-Ed, Sch P; SC; Thes; Var C; Pres, Soph Cl; Tnns; Alg A; Math A; Q&S A; Oreg Scholastic Press; Ger A; *Willamette Col; Journ.*

McKENZIE, Ralph Blake
Russell Ind Sch; Russell, KY (15-300) A Cap Choir; Band; Chor; 4H; Bsbl; Bkbl; Ftbl; 4H A; Spch A; Win, Talent Contest; *Wake Forest U; Criminal Law.*

McKENZIE, William Blake
Fort Stockton HS; Fort Stockton, TX (5-198) BS; VP, FFA; VP, NHS; Mgr, Bkbl; Mgr, Ftbl; Mgr, Tr; Amer Leg A; COM; Citz A; Hist A; Math A; MYF; Bookkeeping A; Hon Stu; Agr A; Farm Bureau Citz Seminar; Univ Interscholastic League, Poetry; *Tex Tech U; Agr.*

McKEOWN,
Mary Margaret Anne
John S Fine HS; Nanticoke, PA (5-347) Secy, CYO; Sch P; SC; Eng, Span, A's; Jr NHS; *Bloomsburg St Col; Nurs.*

McKERLEY, Cheryl Lynn
Merrimack Valley HS; Penacook, NH (10-147) Pres, Drama; Secy, NHS; Pres, World Affairs; Secy, Jr Cl; VofDEM; Pub Relations, Sr Cl; *U of NH; Occupational Therapy.*

McKETCHER, Willie Lewis
Saginaw HS; Saginaw, MI; Ftbl; Tr; Phy A; Ath A; *Adrian Col; Archt.*

McKIBBIN, Jay G
Dulaney Sr HS; Timonium, MD; Ensm; Lacross; *Mus.*

McKIBBIN, Mark Anthony
Horseheads HS; Horseheads, NY (350-600) Chor; Hmrm; Soccer; Tr; 4H A; Tr Medals & Trophy; *Criminal Justice.*

McKIE, Erin Lee
Reeds Spring HS; Reeds Spring, MO (1-75) BC; Rptr, FHA; 4H; Jr Miss Pagent; Math C; Ed, Sch P; Hon Prog; Val; *Sch o-t Ozarks; Ed.*

McKIE, Faye Elizabeth
Brown HS; Sturgis, SD (5-220) Dbte Tm; Ger C; GS; NFL; Pres, NHS; Ski C; SC; Tr; Pres A; Spch A.

McKIE, Marci Jill
Reeds Spring HS; Reeds Spring, MO; BC; FHA; Sch o-t Ozarks; Home Ec.

McKIE, Ross William
Brown HS; Sturgis, SD (69-224) BS; Chor; V-Ch, Demolay; SC; Var C; Wrest; Pres, Black Hills Jr Angus Assn; *SD St U; Pol Sci.*

McKILLIP, Barbara Jo
Lincoln E HS; Lincoln, NE (48-305) Band; Chor; Community Yth Symph; Math C; Orch; COM; Math A; Secy, St Yth Fel; *U of Nebr; Pre-Med.*

McKIM, Lori Ann
Grinnell-Newburg Sr HS; Grinnell, IA (35-200) Band; Chor; Ensm; ARC; Secy, Span C; Var C; Golf; Sftbl; Yth Fel; Ath A; *Elem Ed.*

McKIMSON, Linda Kay
Westview HS; Kankakee, IL (23-250) Band; Secy, Fr C; NHS; SC; VP, Thes; Yth Fel; Band Qn; Pres, Yth Fellowship; *Evangelical Sch of Nurs; Nurs.*

McKINLAY, Andrew Cameron
Oak Harbor HS; Oak Harbor, WA (20-350) BS; Bus C; Pres, Chem C; S-T, Chess C; Chor; Dbte Tm; Fr C; InterClub Coun; Key C; Madrigal; VP, NHS; VP, Order/Arrow; Pres, Sci C; Ski C; Var C; Bus Mgr, Sr Cl; Cr-Ctry; Tr; JV, Wrest; Citz A; God & Country A; NMS; Order/Arrow A; Pres A; *Yale U; Pre-Med.*

McKINLAY, Leigh Ann
Momence HS; Momence, IL (43-126) Chor; Drama; 4H; Math C; Span C; Spch C; SC; Sftbl; Chor A; *Bradley Col; Nurs.*

McKINLEY, Helen Marie
S Page Comm Sch; College Springs, IA (25%-39) Chor; Drama; FHA; Pres, 4H; NHS; Pres, Y-Tns; Co-Cpt, Bkbl; Mgr, Cr-Ctry; Mgr, Ftbl; Cpt, Tr; 4H A.

McKINLEY, Larry Dale
Hobbs HS; Hobbs, NM (35-497) A Cap Choir; Order/Arrow; Bkbl; HKg; HCt; Masonic A; MLS; Most Out; Yth Fel; CI Offices; *NM Jr Col.*

McKINLEY, Lindsay Keese
Redlands HS; Redlands, CA (23-778) Chess C; InterClub Coun; Order/Arrow; Ftbl; Soccer; Alg A; CSF; Math A; Order/Arrow A; Eagle Sct; *Ga Tech; Chem.*

McKINLEY, Robert Charles
Shawnee HS; Lima, OH; A Cap Choir; Band; BS; Chor; Orch; Span C; Bsbl; Ftbl; Golf; Tr; Wrest; JA A; Spch A; Yth Fel.

McKINLEY, Wilbert Sterling
Paul Lawrence Dunbar HS; Baltimore, MD; Parl, City Conf; Drama; Pres, Hmrm; NHS; Order/Arrow; A-Ed, Sch P; Parl, St Stu Congres; Pres, SC; Co-Cpt, Ftbl; Cpt, Tr; Cl Fav; Hist A; Hon Prog; Most Out; Star Student; Peer Coun; Church Worker; Drafting A; *George Washington U; Religion.*

McKINNEY, Brenda Kay
Reidsville Sr HS; Reidsville, NC (6-344) Math C; Co-Ch, Span C; SC; Bkbl; Sftbl; Tnns; Gr Marshal; Hon Stu; *U of NC at Raleigh; Computer Sci.*

McKINNEY, Carol Ann
Miami HS; Miami, OK (3-220) Band; Bus C; Pres, CYO; Drama; Ensm; FBLA; Jr Miss Pagent; Cpt, VP, Span C; Spch C; Tres, SC; VP, Thes; Golf; COM; Cl Fav; HQn; Lion A; Most Out; ARC A; Spch A; St Scholar; NML; St Senate Page; HR; Sch Executive Board; *Okla U; Bus Adm.*

McKINNEY, Elizabeth Ann
Del Rio HS; Del Rio, TX (93-436) VP, Lat C; Ed, Lit Mag; Gym A; *Baylor U; Med.*

McKINNEY, Frank Thompson
Fairfield Sr HS; Fairfield, OH (242-619) Band; Ensm; Orch; Bsbl; Bkbl; Ftbl; Soccer; Sftbl; Wrest; Citz A; ARC A; Star Sct; Scribe; Church Yth Choir; *Bradley U; Industrial Arts.*

McKINNEY, Ghitiana Marie
Carroll HS; Monroe, LA (10%-205) CYO; FBLA; Pres, Hmrm; Math C; Phys C; SC; HCt; Hon Prog; Star Student; YES A; *NE U; Pre-Med.*

McKINNEY, Ginger Deanne
Tulare Union HS; Tulare, CA (1-448) Cpt, Chldr; Chess C; Hmrm; Math C; Amer Leg A; COM; Outst Part Plaque; Ath o-t Week; Reading Cert; MVP o-t Yr; HR; Tchrs Aid; Grls Leg; Soph Cl Princs; Gym Tm; Vol & Actv Dir, Hosp; *Col o-t Sequioes; General.*

McKINNEY, Harold Wayne
Wellington HS; Wellington, TX (20-63) FFA; Key C; Bkbl; Cpt, Ftbl; Tr; Charter Farmer, FFA; *TSTI-Amarillo; Welding.*

McKINNEY, Jeffrey Dale
Bothell Sr HS; Bothell, WA (73-500) Band; Ensm; Orch; Bio A; All-St Band; *NW Nazarene Col; Mus Ed.*

McKINNEY, Joel Robert
Niantic-Harristown HS; Niantic, IL (12-60) Drama; SC; Var C; MVP, Cr-Ctry; MVP, Tr; *Eastern Ill; Communications.*

McKINNEY, John Kevin
Southwest HS; Fort Worth, TX (44-678) Order/Arrow; Hon Prog; Math A.

McKINNEY, Joni Alaine
Macon HS; Macon, IL (5-55) BC; Chor; Drama; Ensm; FHA; NHS; Ed, Sch P; Span C; *E Ill U; Acct.*

McKINNEY, Kathleen Diane
Miami HS; Miami, OK (7-320) Band; CYO; Chldr; Drama; Spch C; Thes; Golf; Sftbl; Swim; Tnns; *U of Colo; Child Psych.*

McKINNEY, Mark Allan
Edison HS; Huntington Beach, CA; Band; Chor; SC; Bsbl; Bkbl; *Calif Baptist Col; Mus.*

McKINNEY, Mary Jane
Sooner HS; Bartlesville, OK (13-291) AFS; Lat C; NHS; Orch; Dist Mus Win; Lat Service A; *Baylor U; Eng.*

McKINNEY, Mary Katherine
Tuscarawas Valley HS; Zoarville, OH (17-145) Band; VP, Bus C; 4H; Sftbl; MVP, Tr; COM; Hon Prog; Most Out; Ntl Achv Schol; NMS; Yth Fel.

McKINNEY, Patricia Ann
York Comp HS; York, SC (6-240) Band; Fr C; Hmrm; Cpt, Mjrte; Secy, NHS; Sci C; SC; JV, Bkbl; Tnns; Gr Marshal; Hon Prog; St Scholar; *Winthrop Col; Cytotechnology.*

McKINNEY, Paul Kevin
Justin F Kimball HS; Dallas, TX (10%-40) Chor; Demolay; NHS; ARC; Tnns; VP, Art C; Sct.

McKINNEY, Robin Kaylor
W A Berry HS; Birmingham, AL (15%-380) Lat C; Lat NHS; Bkbl; Jr NHS.

McKINNEY, Sherri Lynn
Yukon HS; Yukon, OK (33%-267) Chor; Drama; Ensm; FHA; Pres, Pep C; Church Yth Group; WW; Sup Rating, Piano; *Okla Baptist U; Elem Ed.*

McKINNEY, Stephen Foster
Wicomico Sr HS; Salisbury, MD (3-250) Hmrm; Pres, NHS; Var C; Tnns; *Wash & Lee U; Pre-Med.*

McKINNEY, Susan Lyn
Cary-Grove Comm HS; Cary, IL (11-326) AFS; Ger C; 4H; Hmrm; Math C; NHS; SC; Co-Ch, Jr Cl; Co-Ch, Soph Cl; Soccer; Tr; Citz A; Hon Prog; Vlbl; *Wheaton Col; Bio-Physics.*

McKINNEY, Timothy Lee
Robert E Lee HS; Midland, TX (157-712) FFA; Order/Arrow; Hon Prog; Order/Arrow A; Eagle Sct; WW; *Abilene Christian Col; Wildlife Mgt.*

McKINNEY, Vicki Deneise
Whitney HS; Whitney, TX (7%-43) Secy, FHA; 4H; Jr Miss Pagent; Pres, Rainbow; JV, Bkbl; Sftbl; Tnns; JV, Tr; VP, Rainbow Girls; Jr Cl Play; Off, Drill Tm; Graduation Usher; PA; Bus A; UIL Typ-ing; *Hill Jr Col; Secy Stu.*

McKINNEY, Wendell O Neal
Westminster Christian Acad; Huntsville, AL (4-6) Rptr, Ann; Chess C; Chor; Drama; ARC; Rptr, Sch P; Co-Cpt, Sci C; Tres, SC; Bkbl; Soccer; Tnns; Tr; COM; ARC A; Sci A; Hugh O'Brian Yth Found Ldrship Sem; Alt, Ala Mus Ths Assn; *Covenent Col.*

McKINNIS, Diana Kay
Daviess Co HS; Owensboro, KY (13-316) BC; Chor; Pres, FNA; Hmrm; Math C; Pol Sci C; Sci C; SC; COM; Hon Prog; Type A; 500 Hour A, Can-dystriper; *Murray St U; Nurs.*

McKINNIS, Linda Joy
Episcopal HS; Baton Rouge, LA (1-61) Pres, BC; Fr C; InterClub Coun; Ftn, Lit Ral; NHS; Bkbl; Bio A; Hist A; Math A; Opt A; Opt Out Tn; Pres A; Val; Fr A; Superior, Fr Prose; *LSU; Hist.*

McKINNON, Al
Coffee HS; Douglas, GA (33%-208) JV, Band; BC; Key C; F-Ed, Sch P; Var C; Bsbl; Bkbl; MVP, Ftbl; Wrest; Bsbl Ltr; All Region, Ltr, Ftbl; Best All Around Lineman, Ftbl; *S Ga Col; Engr.*

McKINNON, Ann Marie
Hamady HS; Flint, MI (4-156) Band; Ensm; NHS; Tr; Explorers; Semi Fin, Ntl Exploration A; S-T, Church Yth Group; *Pre Med.*

McKINNON, Debra Sue
Bossier Acad; Haughton, LA (1-11) Ann; Chldr; Lit Ral; SC; Bkbl; Alg A; Hon Prog; Math A; Type A; PA; Soc Stu A; *La Tech U; Acct.*

McKINNON, Karen Michelle
Amador Valley HS; Pleasanton, CA; CYO; Chor; VP, Hmrm; Ski C; SC; Mgr, Bsbl; Soccer; Yth Fel; Yth Leg; *Chico St U; Eng.*

McKINNON, Pandra Lynn
Greenon HS; Springfield, OH; Band; Cpt, Chldr; Chor; FTA; VP, 4H; A-Ed, Lit Mag; A-Ed, Sch P; SC; Hockey; Sftbl; Tr; 4H A.

McKINSTRY, Dennis Joseph
Weber HS; Chicago, IL;

McKINZIE, Sandra Louise
Chester HS; Chester, PA; Sci A; *Cheyney St Col; Biol.*

McKIRDY, Donna Marie
Shelton HS; Shelton, CT (347-439) Sftbl; COM; Yth Fel; Foul Shoot A; *Housatonic Comm Col; Child Care.*

McKISSACK, Kim
Lutheran HS W; Detroit, MI; *Mich St U.*

McKISSION, Neal Currin
Kenston Forest HS; Blackstone, VA (18-40) Bkbl; Ftbl; Swim; Tnns.

McKITTRICK, Kimberly
Spring Branch Sr HS; Houston, TX (5%-550) Fr C; Fin, GS; Mu Alpha Theta; NHS; Pres, Orch; Joyful Echo; *Del U.*

McKITTRICK, Melanie
Spring Branch HS; Houston, TX (5%-550) Fr C; JV, Tnns; NEDT; Yth Fel; Joyful Echo.

McKLEMURRY, Ricky Lee
Byram Attendance Center; Jackson, MS; Ftbl; *Hinds Jr Col; Mech Engr.*

McKNEELY, Phillip Engler
Brazoswood HS; Clute, TX (10-450) Pres, Chem C; Pres, JETS; Math C; VP, NHS; Cpt, Golf; Bio A; Chem A; Hon Prog; Math A; Ntl Sci Found; Phy A; Sci A; Type A; *Tex A&M U; Chem Engr.*

McKNIGHT, Barbara Ann
Carver Voc Tech HS; Baltimore, MD; NHS; SC; COM; Delta Sigma Theta A; Most Out; Spch A; *U of Morgan; Bus Law.*

McKNIGHT, Donald Taylor
Southwest HS; Wichita, KS; JV, Bkbl; Ftbl; *U Okla; Bus.*

McKNIGHT, Janice Marie
The Cecilian Acad; Philadelphia, PA; Chor; Fr C; JV, Bkbl; Hon Prog; Magna Cum Laude; Sacristan; Ath, Vocal, A's; *U of Pa; Pre-Med.*

McKNIGHT, Karen Diane
N Del Rio HS; Sacramento, CA (20%-500) Band; Bowl; AJBC As; Badminton; Bluebirds; Camp Fire.

McKNIGHT, Susan Nan
South Side HS; Bee Branch, AR (2-26) BC; FHA; Jr Miss Pagent; Ed, Sch P; S-T, Sr Cl; Cpt, Bkbl; HQn; I Dare You; Sal; All-Co Bkbl; *U of Central Ark; Home Ec.*

McKNIGHT, Tina Rae
Flora HS; Flora, IL (56-124) Chor; FBLA; *Olney Central Col; Nurs.*

McKNIGHT, Windsor Jr
E St Louis HS; E St Louis, IL (67-600) Band; Bus C; Chess C; Hmrm; Orch; Ftbl; Tr; Alg A; COM; Hon Prog; Math A; Sci A; *Med.*

McKOY, Brian Renwick
Ben L Smith Sr HS; Greensboro, NC; Pres, Inter-Act C; InterClub Coun; Ftbl; COM; *A&T St U; Bus.*

McLAIN, Becky Blanche
Vian HS; Vian, OK (10-105) Band; Ensm; FHA; NHS; COM; Yth Fel.

McLAIN, Jerry LeRoy
Hatton Pub Sch; Hatton, ND (1-19) Band; Chor; Ensm; VP, SC; Bsbl; Bkbl; Ftbl; Tr; COM; Math A; Med.

McLAIN, Paul King
Monticello HS; Monticello, MS; Bus Mgr, Ann; BC; Order/Arrow; COM; *Miss St U.*

McLAIN, Tammy
Van Buren Comm HS; Keosauqua, IA (13-80) Pres, 4H; NHS; Bkbl; COM; 4H A; Secy, Off Ed; *Amer Inst of Bus; Secretarial.*

McLAMB, Dennis Lynwood
Midway HS; Dunn, NC; FFA; *Farmer.*

McLANE, Linda Kay
W A Berry HS; Birmingham, AL (25-450) A Cap Choir; AFS; Chor; Drama; Ensm; FHA; Lat C; Math C; Thes; Cr-Ctry; Tr; Pres A; Yth Fel; Vlbl; Classical Jr League; Secy, VP, Jr Civitan; *Montevallo Col; Marine Biol.*

McLAREN, Christina Althea
Fullerton Union HS; Fullerton, CA (35-360) Pres, Chor; Drama; Ensm; FFA; Ch, Hmrm; Madrigal; SC; HCt; Yth Fel; Yth Leg; Most Talented; Pow-Wow Princess; *Calif St U; Mus.*

McLAREN, Kirk Lewis
Auburn Sr HS; Auburn, WA (37-480) Chess C; Orch; JV, Ftbl; *W Valley Comm Col.*

McLAREN, Phillip Duane
Fairview Alpha HS; Coushatta, LA (5-20) 4H; Hmrm; Lit Ral; Bus Mgr, SC; Cpt, Var C; Cpt, Bkbl; Sftbl; Tr; H of F; HCt; *Northwestern St U; Phys Ed.*

McLAUD, Eric Scott
Bainbridge-Guilford HS; Bainbridge, NY (60-98) Band; Chor; Ensm; InterAct C; Ntl Yth Conf; Orch; Span C; Co-Cpt, Bkbl; Cr-Ctry; Ftbl; Co-Cpt, Tnns; Cl Fav; Pres, Yth Fel; *St U at Cobleskill; Acct.*

McLAUGHLIN, Alita Monique
E Atlanta HS; Atlanta, GA (1-175) BC; Hmrm; Ed, Sch P; Var C; Pres, Jr Cl; Alg A; Bio A; Hon Prog; Journ A; Math A; Type A; Yth Fel; *Spelmar Col; Computer Sci.*

McLAUGHLIN, Brian Thomas
San Angelo Central HS; San Angelo, TX; Order/
Arrow; JV, Ftbl; Order/Arrow A; Eagle Sct; U of
Tex; Law.

McLAUGHLIN, Carol
Charles Evans Hughes HS; New York City, NY
(135-427) Ed, Ann; Chor; FHA; FTA; Pres,
Hmrm; SC; Tr; Yth Foundation; Secy, College
Group; Baurch Col; Communications.

McLAUGHLIN, Cynthia Ann
Hopewell HS; Aliquippa, PA (35-525) NHS; Span
C; COM; Cpt, Church Bible Quiz Tm; Cpt, Co Dist
Bible Quiz Tm; Church Choir; Coastal Carolina
Col; Eng.

McLAUGHLIN, Linda
HS of Mus and Art; New York, NY (375-517)
Band; Chor; FHA; FTA; Orch; ARC; Yth Fel; Lat
Amer Stu A; Mus A; Attorney General's Triple 'C'
A; Tr Tm A; Morgan St U; Psych.

McLAUGHLIN, Lola Leigh
Silsbee HS; Silsbee, TX (50%-300) Drama; JETS;
Ntl Yth Conf; ARC; Span C; Spch C; HCt; ARC A;
Spch A; S-T & Secy, Sr Cl; 'B' HR; Drill Tm; Sat-
suma Cand; Leo C Director; United Methodist
Church; Lamar U; Nurs.

McLAUGHLIN, Michael L
Niagara Falls HS; Niagara Falls, NY (30-530)
Chess C; Hmrm; Ed, Sch P; Pres, Soph Cl; Co-Cpt,
Bsbl; Co-Cpt, Ftbl; Lion A; Swtht; U of Buffalo;
Law.

McLAUGHLIN, Nanci
Largo Sr HS; Upper Marlboro, MD; Chor; Secy,
Ensm; Sch P; Thes; Yth Fel; Yth Leg; German A;
Eng.

McLAUGHLIN, Robin Elizabeth
Hinsdale Township HS Central; Hinsdale, IL
(11-601) AFS; Band; NHS; Orch; Tres, Sr Cl; Tres,
Soph Cl; St Scholar; WW; Miami U; Acct.

McLAUGHLIN, Shamus Patrick
University HS; San Diego, CA (1-315) Hmrm;
NHS; Swim; CSF; Water Polo; All W League Tm;
U of Calif; Med.

McLAUGHLIN, Shawn Patrick
Belmond Comm HS; Belmond, IA (1-94) Co-Ed,
Ann; Pres, CYO; Dbte Tm; Hmrm; NHS; Span C;
S-T, SC; Thes; Bkbl; Golf; Hon Prog; Emergency
Med Tech; Georgetown U; Pre-Law.

McLAUGHLIN, Toni Ann
Boston Tech HS; Boston, MA; American U; Liberal Arts.

McLAUGHLIN, William Arnold
Hopewell HS; Aliquippa, PA (10-500) JV, Bsbl;
Ftbl; COM; NMS; U of Pittsburgh; Law.

McLAWHORN, Nancy Sue
W Craven HS; Vanceboro, NC (1-160) Co-Ed,
Ann; Parl, FBLA; Lit Mag; VP; NHS; Sch P; Sci C;
Span C; SC; VP, Soph Cl; Most Out; Eng A; 2nd, St
FBLA Parliamen Procedure Tm; Atlantic Christian
Col; Ed o-t Hearing Impaired.

McLAWYER, Carol Laraine
John F Kennedy HS; Granada Hills, CA (201-814)
Drama; Church Choir; 1st Pl Bowling Trophy; Ho-
tel & Restaurant Mgt.

McLAWYER, Sharron Lenise
John F Kennedy HS; Granada Hills, CA; Span C;
JV, Bsbl; JV, Tnns; Calif St of LA; Sociology.

McLEAN, Barrington O'Neal
Albany HS; Albany, NY (280-500) Chor; Dbte Tm;
COM; God & Country A; JA A; MLS; Spch A;
VofDEM; Health C; Nazareth Col; Span.

McLEAN, Billy W A Jr
England HS; England, AR (5-50) Band; BC; Chess
C; Orch; Chess A; Solo & Ensm A; Band A; Hen-
drix Col; Med.

McLEAN, Carl Jones
Independence Sr HS; Charlotte, NC; Livingstone
U; Bus Adm.

McLEAN, Carol Lee
W Carteret HS; Morehead City, NC (33-300)
NHS; WOW Hist A; Orch A; Meredith Col; Mus
Ed.

McLEAN, Caroline Jane
Hardaway HS; Columbus, GA (40-450) Band;
Chor; Mjrte; Yth Fel; Yth Coun; Ch, Open House;
Band Ltr; UNC; Mus.

McLEAN, Elizabeth Stuart
Fairhope HS; Fairhope, AL; A Cap Choir; Band;
Chor; NHS; Mgr, Bkbl; Sftbl; Tnns; Tr; Vlbl; South-
western at Memphis; Bio.

McLEAN, John Jay
Virgil I Grissom HS; Huntsville, AL (20-800)
Band; Mu Alpha Theta; NHS; Order/Arrow; Tr;
Wrest; Yth Fel; Eagle Sct; Drum Major; Superior
Solo A; All City Tr Tourn.

McLEAN, Mary Ellen
Rosary HS; Aurora, IL (2-85) Ann; Chor; JV, Bkbl;
NEDT; Sch Musical; Special Ed, Sch Prog; Pep C;
NEDT Cert of Educational Develop.

McLEAN, Sheila
Frank H Morrell HS; Irvington, NJ; Secy, Hmrm;
Bkbl; Archt.

McLEAN, Sylvia Ann
Independence Sr HS; Charlotte, NC; FHA; Jr Miss
Pagent; Cpt, Sftbl; Beauty; Dancing A; Modeling
A; Winsalm St U; Computer Programmer.

McLEER, Elizabeth Mary
Mercy HS; Albany, NY (3-135) NEDT; Nurs.

McLELLAND, Jeffrey Randal
Beeson Acad; Hattiesburg, MS (6-33) BC; InterAct
C; Sci C; SC; Var C; Bsbl; Bkbl; Cpt, Ftbl; Tnns; Tr;
Phy A; William Carey Col; Mus.

McLELLAND, Robin Madison
Patrick Henry HS; Roanoke, VA; Chldr; F-Ed, Sch
P; SC; Radford Col; Journ.

McLELLAND, Virginia Faye
Walter M Williams HS; Burlington, NC (45-350)
Chldr; VP, Hmrm; Monogram; NHS; Span C; Span
NHS; Span A; UNC-Greensboro.

McLEMORE, William Brown
Gilbert HS; Gilbert, LA (3-35) Ann; Chor; FFA;
4H; Ftbl; NE La St U; Agr.

McLENDON, Cathy Rae
Robert E Lee Acad; Bishopville, SC; Chldr; Chor;
Drama; Lat C; Florence-Darlington Tech Col; So-
cial Service.

McLENDON, Michael Andre
John F Kennedy HS; Richmond, VA (22-309) Ann;
Band; Fr C; Orch; Sch P; SC; JV, Bkbl; Ftbl; Wrest;
COM.

McLENDON, Michelle Andrea
John F Kennedy HS; Richmond, VA (10-309) Ed,
Ann; Tres, Chldr; Pres, Hmrm; Tres, Lat C; SC;
Mgr, Tr; COM; Madison Col; Math.

McLENDON, Shelby Jean
Smith's Station HS; Smith's, AL; Chor; FTA; Math
C; Mu Alpha Theta; Sci C; 4H A; Hist A; Math A;
MLS; Sci A.

McLEOD, Christene Elizabeth
Tisdale Unit Composite Sch; Tisdale, CANADA
(3-99) Secy, ARC; Lib C; Wascana Inst of Applied
Arts & Sci; Dental Asst.

McLEOD, Christy Jean
Coppell HS; Coppell, TX (4-23) VP, BC; Chldr;
Drama; Sch P; VP, SC; Bkbl; Sftbl; Tnns; Tr; Cl
Fav; HQn; Swtht; VFW A; Miss CHS; Most Spir-
ited; WW; E Tex St U; Gen Ed.

McLEOD, Keith Alan
Ramona HS; Riverside, CA; Baylor U; Law.

McLEOD, Robert Parker
Clarke Central HS; Athens, GA (9-295) BC; De-
molay; VP, HiY; Hmrm; InterAct C; InterClub
Coun; SC; VP, Tri-HiY; Pres, Var C; Mgr, Bsbl; JV,
Bkbl; Cpt, Ftbl; Tr; COM; Most Out; FCAP; Mr
CCHS; HR; US Military Acad; Engr.

McLERNON, Aidan Hugh
St Nicholas of Tolentine HS; New York, NY
(7-107) Cpt, Swim; Regent Schol; US Merchant
Marine Acad; Engr.

McLERRAN, Douglas M
Champaign Central HS; Champaign, IL (164-408)
Band; Ger C; Var C; Wrest; Jazz Band; Intramural
Sports; Ill St U; Bus Adm.

McLIN, Darlene Elizabeth
Belaire HS; Baton Rouge, LA; Ensm; FHA; Pres,
Hmrm; SC; Tr; SE Col; Bus.

McLIN, Frank
Hamilton HS; Memphis, TN;

McLURKIN, Kimberly Elana
Newton Co Comprehensive HS; Covington, GA
(30%-504) Band; S-T, 4H; Key C; Span C; Tri-HiY;
Bkbl; Tr; COM; Gov Honor Prog; 4H A; Fisk U;
Hist.

McMAHAN, David Blaine
Princeton HS; Princeton, TX (2-51) A-Ed, Ann;
Chor; Pres, FFA; Pres, NHS; Sch P; Sci C; Tres,
SC; Bkbl; COM; Chem A; Hon Prog; Most Out;
Sal; Spch A; FFA Merit; NHS Ldrship A; FFA
Outst Sr; Tex Tech U; Agr.

McMAHAN, Kent Pierce
Porter HS; Maryville, TN (40-73) Key C; VP, Or-
der/Arrow; Span C; Mgr, Bkbl; S-T, Order o-t Arrow; Eagle Sct; U of Tenn; Forestry.

McMAHAN, Myra Elaine
Sevier Co HS; Sevierville, TN (22-268) AFS; Ann;
BC; Chor; Fr C; Span C; Magna Cum Laude; E
Tenn St U; Nurs.

McMAHAN, William Wayne
Stevenson HS; Stevenson, AL; Ann; FFA; Bkbl;
HKg; Most Improved, Bkbl.

McMAHON, Karen Therese
Scecina Mem HS; Indianapolis, IN; CYO; Cpt,
Chldr; NHS; SC; Sftbl; Alg A; COM; HCt; Hon
Prog; Kiwanis A; ARC A; Off, Sch C; Ind U; Law.

McMAHON, Norine Elizabeth
St Mary's Acad; Alexandria, VA (5-98) Band; Tres,
CYO; Ensm; French NHS; Mu Alpha Theta; Bkbl;
NEDT; All Star Sftbl & Vlbl; Hist.

McMAHON, Sharon Elaine
Sacred Heart Acad; Salem, OR (2-35) Chor; Pres,
NHS; Ed, Sch P; SC; Pres, Jr Cl; Sal; Co Yth Coun;
Commercial Bank Jr Board; Pep C; Loyola & Mar-
ymount Col; Bus Adm.

McMAINS, Barbara Rose
Wm B Travis HS; Austin, TX; Thes; Accompanist,
Beauty Pageant; Organizer, Bible C; Kans Wes-
leyan U; Spch Therapy.

McMANEMON, James Edgar
Martin Co HS; Stuart, FL (46-500) Fin, BS; Tres,
CYO; Chldr; Fin, Dbte Tm; Drama; Hmrm; Pres,
InterAct C; Pres, Key C; VP, NHS; Span C; SC; Sr
Cl; JV, Ftbl; Soccer; JV, Tnns; COM; Hon Prog;
Rotary A; Spch A; Lang C; Christian Fellowship;
Foreign Exchange, RSVP, Rotary; U of Fla; Acct.

McMANUS, Bridget Kathleen
Blanchet HS; Seattle, WA (6-285) Chor; Amer Leg
A; Hon Prog; Closeup Fel; U of San Francisco;
Lang.

McMANUS, Julia Malpass
Red Springs HS; Red Springs, NC; Ed, Ann; FHA;
FTA; MVP, Golf; Tnns; U of NC; Law.

McMANUS, Paul Gerard
St Mary's HS; Lynn, MA (1-146) Band; Chor;
Drama; Hmrm; NHS; Orch; Rptr, Sch P; VP, SC;
Pres, Jr Cl; Ch, Soph Cl; Alg A; Bio A; COM; Hist
A; Hon Prog; Journ A; Math A; Sci A; Religion A;
Most Spirited; Harvard U.

McMASTER, Dana Leigh
George Washington HS; Alexandria, VA; NHS; U
of NC; Art.

McMASTERS, Shawn Elaine
Monroe Co HS; Monroeville, AL (35-157) Band;
BC; Chor; Ensm; Hmrm; Rainbow; A-Ed, Sch P;
Spch C; SC; COM; Yth Fel; Rptr, Sch P; Computer
Tech.

McMICHAEL, Allen Raines
Johnson Co HS; Wrightsville, GA (5%-90) Band;
Rptr, BC; Pres, HiY; Rptr, Var C; Pres, Jr Cl; Bsbl;
Ftbl; Golf; COM; U of Ga; Law.

McMICHAEL, Charles M III
D M Therrell HS; Atlanta, GA (61-298) Pres,
Chor; Hmrm; Pres, Sr Cl; Colorguard Ribbon,
ROTC; Fashion Designing.

McMICKEN, Marlene Kay
Robert E Lee HS; Baytown, TX (40-550) Band;
Chor; JV, Bkbl; Christian Stu Union; Lee Col;
Math.

McMILLAN, Alkatrina Yvette
Kathleen Sr HS; Lakeland, FL; Span C; Citz A; Foreign Lang, Vac Bible Sch, A's; *Moorehouse Col; Span.*

McMILLAN, David Scott
Red Springs Sr HS; Red Springs, NC (10-118) FTA; Ftbl; All Conf Ftbl; All Co Ftbl; Best Defensive Lineman; *E Carolina U.*

McMILLAN, James Everett
Mt Vernon Sr HS; Mt Vernon, OH (33%-430) Y-Tns; Mgr, Bkbl; Mgr, Ftbl; Tr; COM; Hist A; Most Out; PTA A; Yth Fel; *Tech Sch; Construction.*

McMILLAN, Kimberly Sarah
Weston McEwen HS; Athena, OR (4-41) Ed, Ann; Chor; Semi-Fin, GS; Hmrm; Pres, NHS; ARC; Sch P; Span C; SC; Tres, Var C; Tnns; B Crocker A; Chem A; Citz A; Hon Prog; Journ A; Math A; Sal; Type A; Cpt, Vlbl; Ntl Choral A; *George Fox Col; Engr.*

McMILLAN, Lynda Kay
Robert H Goddard HS; Roswell, NM (13-310) Rptr, FHA; GS; InterClub Coun; NHS; A-Ed, Sch P; Sci C; Span C; Pres, Span NHS; VP, SC; Secy, Jr Cl; Swim; JV, Tnns; Citz A; HQn; 1st Pl, Elec Co Cake Bake-Off; WW; Service League A; Page, NM St Leg; *Ariz St U; Home Ec.*

McMILLAN, Matthew Emmett
Apex HS; Apex, NC (5%-250) Ann; Fr C; Var C; Bsbl; Ftbl; Wrest; Yth Foundation; *Stetson U; Pre-Law.*

McMILLAN, Melanie Sue
Wilkes Central HS; Wilkesboro, NC (63-254) Co-Cpt, Band; VP, Chor; Hmrm; InterAct C; NHS; SC; HQn; HCt; *Appalachian St U; Elem Ed.*

McMILLAN, Michael Ivan
Johnstown HS; Johnstown, NY (70-250) Chor; Hockey; Tr; Wrest; *Le Tourneau Col; Elem Ed.*

McMILLAN, Molly Jeane
Industry HS; Industry, IL (4-33) Band; Chldr; Chor; Drama; Ensm; Fr C; 4H; Mjrte; Sci C; Bkbl; Golf; Sftbl; Tr; B Crocker A; St Scholar; Vlbl; Schol Achv, Chldr, A's; *W Ill U; Acct.*

McMILLAN, Nancy Gail
Holliston HS; Holliston, MA; AFS; Drama; Fr C; Span C; Choir; Substitute Sunday Sch Teacher; *Sci.*

McMILLAN, Sylvia Michelle
Frederick Douglass HS; Atlanta, GA (31-343) Chor; Bus Mgr, Hmrm; Cpt, Mjrte; NHS; Most Out; WW; *Howard U; Pol Sci.*

McMILLEN, Charles Joseph
Sulphur HS; Sulphur, LA; Band; Community Yth Symph; *McNeese St U; Mus.*

McMILLEN, Latricia Ann
Sulphur HS; Sulphur, LA; Mjrte; Ed, Sch P; Tres, Spch C; Future Christian Ath; Secy, Dist Gov, Art C; Art A; *La Tech U; Art.*

McMILLEN, Thomas Owen
Grand Junction HS; Grand Junction, CO; Demolay; Drama; Sci C; Thes; *Colo St U; Bus.*

McMILLER, Cheryl
Northeastern HS; Detroit, MI; Co-Cpt, Chldr; Pres, Hmrm; Pres, SC; Soph Cl; Amer Leg A; Citz A; Hon Prog; *Bus Adm.*

McMILLIAN, James Edward Jr
Gadsden HS; E Gadsden, AL (52-378) Key C; Var C; Ftbl; Tnns; Tr; HCt; *DeVry Inst of Tech; Elec Engr.*

McMILLIAN, Lander Jean
Inkster HS; Inkster, MI (27-249) Var C; Tnns; *Central Mich U; Acct.*

McMILLON, Annette
Woodlawn HS; Shreveport, LA (41-420) SC; Hon Prog; Scholastic Achv A; *Southern U; Bus Adm.*

McMINAMEN, Mark Steven
Holdrege Sr HS; Holdrege, NE (75%-120) Bkbl; Ftbl; Golf; *Kearney St; Engr.*

McMINN, Elizabeth Colleen
Weir Attendance Centre; Weir, MS (5-54) Band; Rptr, BC; 4H; Bkbl; Tr; 4H A; Most Out.

McMINN, Kimberly Jean
Hendersonville HS; Hendersonville, TN; Anchor C; Chldr; Chem C; Sci C; Ch, Prom Committee; Art Show A's; *Med.*

McMINN, Woody Temple
L B Johnson HS; Austin, TX (23-326) Pres, Chor; Ensm; SC; Bsbl; Bkbl; Ftbl; Golf; Sftbl; Trustee A; Top 10%; *Baylor U; Acct.*

McMONIGLE, Debra Lynn
Arundel Sr HS; Gambrills, MD (20%-400) JV, Chldr; Hmrm; Fin, JETS; Fin, Jr Miss Pagent; Fin, ARC; Sci C; SC; Sftbl; Swim; Tnns; Beauty; COM; Chamber of Comm A; Cl Fav; HCt; JA A; Ntl Achv Schol; ARC A; Sci A; Yth Fel; Gym; Soloist, Yth Choir; Miss Md Ntl Tn; Inst of Environment Sci, Art, A's.

McMULLEN, Diane Lynne
Knob Noster Sr HS; Knob Noster, MO (4-115) VP, FNA; NHS; ARC; Ski C; SC; Bio A; COM; PTA A; Sci A; *Tex Woman's U; Nurs.*

McMULLEN, Anne Blaine
Walnut Hills HS; Cincinnati, OH (20%-700) Drama; Lit Mag; Bkbl; Sftbl; ARC A; VAST Tutor; Hospital Vol; Phys Fitness A; *Phys Therapy.*

McMULLEN, Brock Alan
Rockville HS; Rockville, IN (28-85) Chem C; Pres, FFA; Pres, 4H; Lat C; NHS; Sci C; Pres, SC; Bsbl; Bkbl; Cr-Ctry; Ftbl; 4H A; St Scholar; Outst Sr FFA; *Purdue U; Agr Ec.*

McMULLEN, Donna Suzanne
William Monroe HS; Stanardsville, VA; Ann; BC; FBLA; Secy, FTA; Lit Mag; Co-Cpt, Tr; COM; Hist A; S-T, Art C; Most Promising Artist; Hon Cert, Bookkeeping; *Longwood Col; Art Ed.*

McMULLEN, Ellen Nanette
Sharpstown Sr HS; Houston, TX (304-686) Drama; FHA; DAR St Conf A; DAR Jr Amer Citz; *Houston Baptist U; Elem Ed.*

McMULLEN, Guy Herbert
Twin Valley Jr Sr HS; Elverson, PA (50-158) Hmrm; SC; Pres, Sr Cl; *Kutztown St Col; Communication.*

McMULLEN, Lorrie Ann
David Starr Jordan HS; Los Angeles, CA; A Cap Choir; Fr C; Hmrm; Alg A; Citz A; Hon Prog; Math A; Most Out; Type A; Prin HR; Achv A; *Pepperdine U; Math.*

McMULLEN, Shawn Emil
Western Hills HS; Cincinnati, OH; Arch; Drama; Fr C; Hmrm; Thes; COM; Kiwanis A; Most Out; Most Talented; Best Musician; Best Artist; Conservatory of Mus Schol; *Berkley Col of Mus; Mus.*

McMULLEN, Veda Marie
Gloucester HS; Gloucester, VA (10%-210) AFS; Ed, Ann; BC; Pres, Chor; Secy, Drama; Fin, GS; InterAct C; Madrigal; NFL; NHS; ARC; Secy, SC; Thes; Citz A; 4H A; 1st Cl GSct; WW; *Va Commonwealth U; Mass Communications.*

McMULLIN, Broderick Keith
A H Parker HS; Birmingham, AL (4-30) A Cap Choir; Band; Chor; FTA; Bus Mgr, Sci C; Tres, SC; VP, Soph Cl; COM; Sci A; Ushers C; Bank Board; *Clark Col; Secondary Ed.*

McMULLIN, William Arrel
Cumberland HS; Maben, MS (1-27) Ann; Band; BC; Fr C; Ed, Sch P; Pres, Sr Cl; Pres, Jr Cl; Ftbl; Tr; Wrest; Alg A; COM; Chem A; Cl Fav; Hist A; Math A; MLS; NMS; Star Student; Type A; Val; Schol Ath; Sportsmanship A; *Anderson Col; Chem.*

McMURDIE, Paul Joseph
Sky View HS; Smithfield, UT; Dbte Tm; Drama; Key C; NHS; Ed, Sch P; Var C; Mgr, Bkbl; Mgr, Ftbl; Mgr, Tnns; Spch A; *Utah St U; Communications.*

McMURRAY, Denise Lynn
Long Prairie Pub HS; Long Prairie, MN (14-127) Band; Chor; Ensm; NHS; *Oak Hills Bible Inst; Bible.*

McMURRAY, Janet Ruth
Pascagoula HS; Pascagoula, MS (1-452) Pres, BC; Chor; Ensm; Hmrm; Lat C; Madrigal; Amer Leg A; Hist A; Math A; NEDT; Val; Tres, Jr Civitan; Lat A; NHS Stu o-t Mo; Bus & Profesnl Women's Stu o-t Mo; *Miss Col.*

McMURRAY, Larry Dean
Passaic HS; Passaic, NJ (30-600) Bus C; FBLA; SC; Cpt, Bsbl; Cpt, Bkbl; Cpt, Ftbl; Cpt, Tr; *Fairleigh Dickson U; Acct.*

McMURRAY, Mary Susan
Pascagoula HS; Pascagoula, MS (10%-790) Chldr; S-T, Chor; Ensm; VP, Hmrm; Pres, Lat C; NHS; Sch P; Sftbl; Bkbl.

McMURRY, Malinda Bea
Duncan Sr HS; Duncan, OK; Ann; 4H; Hon Prog; Okla Hon Soc; Jr NHS; *Okla St U; Vet Med.*

McMURRY, Robin Lynne
Canyon HS; Canyon Ctry, CA; Math C; Phys C; Rptr, Bkbl; Professional Women's C; JV, Badminton; Calif St Schol; *Westmont Col; Math.*

McMURTRY, Donna Kay
Goodlettsville HS; Goodlettsville, TN (15-159) Cpt, Chldr; Secy, FTA; Hmrm; SC; Sftbl; Tnns; Tn o-t Mo; Outst Tn; *David Lipscomb Col; Psych.*

McNAB, Steven Leo
Brewster Pub Sch; Brewster, MN (3-28) BS; Pres, FFA; NHS; SC; Var C; Bkbl; Ftbl; Sftbl; Tr; HCt; Star Greenhand A; Beef A, FFA; Creed Contest Win, FFA; *Agr.*

McNABB, Carol Louise
Bonneville HS; Ogden, UT; GS; Swim; Hon Prog; Span As; Swim As; *Interior Desgin.*

McNABB, Linda Sue
Sooner HS; Bartlesville, OK (5-290) Bus C; Chor; Drama; FBLA; NHS; Span NHS; Bkbl; Tr; Secy of St A; *Okla St U; Phys Ed.*

McNABB, Pauline Marie
Marycliff HS; Spokane, WA (1-40) Fin, Chldr; Fin, GS; Model UN; Ski C; COM; Math A; NMS; NEDT; WOHELO Medallion, Camp Fire Girls; 1st, St Traffic Safety Essay; *Wash St U; Nurs.*

McNAIR, Christopher Allen
Andress HS; El Paso, TX; Cr-Ctry; ROTC A; Math.

McNAIR, James Timothy
Andress HS; El Paso, TX; Ann; Lat C; Lit Mag; Ftbl; Tr; Jr NHS; *Med.*

McNAIR, Michael Kevin
J J Pearce HS; Richardson, TX (138-751) Band; Dbte Tm; Ger C; Model UN; Order/Arrow; Spch C; Soccer; COM; God & Country A; JA A; Order/Arrow A; Spch A; *MIT; Physics.*

McNAIR, Wanda Lenae
Central HS; Newark, NJ; *Typing Secy.*

McNAIR, William Robert
Quitman HS; Quitman, AR (2-40) Ann; BC; Drama; FFA; Mgr, Bkbl; Alg A; Bio A; Hist A; Alg As; Geom A; *Hendrix Col; Math.*

McNALL, Leland Ray
Lakeland HS; La Grange, IN (20-150) City Conf; Hmrm; SC; Var C; Bsbl; JV, Bkbl; JV, Cr-Ctry; Hon Prog; *IUPU; Bus.*

McNAMARA, Harold John III
Lamar HS; Rosenburg, TX (100-450) Band; CYO; FHA; 4H; JETS; COM; Sci A; First Chair, Band As; *Tex A&M U; Petroleom Engr.*

McNAMARA, Laurie Gwen
Southwest HS; St Louis, MO; Ann; Sci C; Var C; Cpt, Bkbl; Sftbl; Swim; Hon Prog; Pres A; Yth Fel.

McNARE, Carol Lynne
Falls Church HS; Falls Church, VA (50-500) NHS; Span C; DARGCA; *George Mason Col; Bus Adm.*

McNAUGHTON, John Robert
Word of God Acad; Erie, PA (3-5) Band; Chess C; Chor; Model UN; Var C; Ftbl; Hon Prog; NEDT; *Gannon Col; Elec Engr.*

McNAUGHTON, Yvonne Elaine Marcia
Evanston Township HS; Evanston, IL (50%-1075) Y-Tns; Hon Prog; JA A; 1st Runner-Up, Ms Sophisticated; Pom-Pon Kitten; Pep C; *Psych.*

McNEAL, Doris Ellen
Tipton HS; Tipton, OK (10%-48) Chor; S-T, FHA; 4H; NHS; Span C; Mgr, Bkbl; Sftbl; *Okla Christian Col; Home Ec.*

McNEAL, John Larry
Asheville HS; Asheville, NC; Drama; NHS; Thes; Bkbl; *Tex Christian U; Ministry.*

McNEELY, Marjorie
Bok Voc Tech HS; Philadelphia, PA; *NY Inst of Tech; Textile.*

McNEELY, Tamara Lynne
Bryan Adams HS; Dallas, TX (25%-900) Ann; Chor; Drama; Fr C; Hmrm; Lat C; Sch P; SC; Tri-HiY; Hon Prog; *Baylor U; Religion.*

McNEELY, Vicki Cheryl
Mooresville Sr HS; Mooresville, NC; Chldr; FHA; *Child Development.*

McNEER, Rodetta Lu
Hinton HS; Hinton, WV (10%-160) F-Ed, Ann; Drama; FBLA; FHA; Secy, 4H; Math C; NHS; Tres, SC; Type A; VP, Bible C; *Liberty Baptist Col; Bus.*

McNEIL, Dianne
Central HS; High Point, NC; Bus C; Hmrm; SC; Swim; Tnns; HCt; *GTI; Child Care.*

McNEIL, Linda
Lake Wales Sr HS; Lake Wales, FL (36-260) FHA; HiY; Math C; Sci C; Tr; Bio A; Elk A; Page, Fla Capitol; *U of Fla; Phar.*

McNEIL, Pamela Ann
Homestead HS; Mequon, WI (259-425) AFS; Chor; Drama; Fr C; Dist Solo; Ensm; Cl A Pl.

McNEIL, Richard John
Palisades HS; Pacific Pausades, CA (96-788) Pres, A Cap Choir; AFS; Band; BS; Chor; Community Yth Symph; Dbte Tm; Drama; Fr C; Pres, Hmrm; Pres, Madrigal; NHS; Orch; Co-Ed, Sch P; Ski C; VP, SC; Var C; Pres, Sr Cl; Tres, Soph Cl; Cr-Ctry; Ftbl; Tnns; JV, Tr; CSF; COM; Cl Fav; Hist A; Hon Prog; Journ A; Ntl Achv Schol; Regent Schol; WW; Alumni Schol; Administrative Ltr, Academic Achv; Century III Ldr Runner-Up; Pres, Ephebiams; *Yale U; Pre-Law.*

McNEIL, Robbin Renee
Ocean Springs HS; Ocean Springs, MS (15-265) F-Ed, Ann; VP, BC; Fr C; VP, FHA; Hmrm; SC; Swtht; Yth Fel; WW; Sr o-t Month; High Hon Graduate; *U of Sou Miss; Med.*

McNEIL, Sarah Anne
Abilene HS; Abilene, TX (132-540) VP, FHA; S-T, Hmrm; Secy, Ftbl; Outst Jr Girl in Bold Gold; Spirit C; *Abilene Christian U; Pre-Nurs.*

McNEIL, Sarahan
Oak Ridge Acad; Oak Ridge, NC (1-30) Chldr; Chor; Ensm; NHS; SC; S-T, Soph Cl; Bkbl; Sftbl; HCt; Top Schol A; *Wake Forest U; Zoology.*

McNEIL, Stanley
Mullins HS; Mullins, SC; JV, Ftbl; *SC St U; Phys Ed.*

McNEIL, Tony Antonio
Loris HS; Loris, SC; Band; Hmrm; Sci C; Bkbl; Most Out; *USC; Bio.*

McNEILL, Cynthia Jenese
Benhaven HS; Olivia, NC (6-84) Band; BC; Rptr, Hmrm; Monogram; SC; Tres, Jr Cl; Bkbl; Sftbl; COM; Band A; MVP, Bkbl; *Biol.*

McNEILL, Daphne Elaine
Benhaven HS; Olivia, NC (1-84) Secy, BC; Cpt, Chldr; Monogram; Tres, SC; Bio A; Hist A; Math A; Drama, Home Ec, Phys Ed, A's; *A&T Col; Elem Ed.*

McNEILL, Harold Gregory
Lexington Sr HS; Lexington, NC (15-356) Dbte Tm; Drama; Fr C; Hmrm; NFL; F-Ed, Sch P; SC; Mgr, Bkbl; Ftbl; Golf; Hist A; NEDT; Phi Beta Kappa; Rotary A; Spch A; *U of NC; Journ.*

McNEILL, Jeffery Dwain
Whitehouse HS; Whitehouse, TX (4-140) Band; NHS; Bsbl; JV, Bkbl; JV, Ftbl; *Tyler Jr Col; Phys Ed.*

McNEILL, Kathy Joanne
Benhaven HS; Olivia, NC; Co-Ed, Ann; Pres, Band; Tres, BC; Chor; Secy, Fr C; FHA; FTA; Secy, 4H; Rptr, Sch P; Secy, SC; Tres, Jr Cl; Mgr, Bkbl; Sftbl; Bio A; Chem A; 4H A; Hist A; Math A; Sci A; Director's A, Band; Eng, Fr, A's; *E Carolina U; Journ.*

McNEILL, Nancy Lea
Santa Fe HS; Alachua, FL (10%-270) Co-Ed, Ann; BC; JV, Chldr; Hmrm; Math C; Sch P; Span C; SC; VP, Soph Cl; Citz A; Pa; Outst Leadership; Ntl Fed of Mus C; Outst Schol; St Mus Teachers Assn; Patriotism & Sportsmanship; *U of Fla; Med.*

McNEILL, Richard Vance
Benhaven HS; Olivia, NC (1-82) Ann; BC; FFA; Monogram; VP, SC; Pres, Jr Cl; Pres, Soph Cl; Bsbl; Alg A; Hist A; Hon Prog; Math A; Sci A; Eng, Agr, A's; *Fayettville Tech Inst; Civil Engr.*

McNEILL, Warren Scott
Happy HS; Happy, TX; Ann; VP, Band; BS; Pres, FTA; NHS; Sch P; JV, Bkbl; Drum Major; *Lubbock Christian Col.*

McNENNEY, Aurora U
Academia Maria Reina; Rio Piedras, PR; CYO; Drama; Fr C; Span C; COM; Hon Prog; PA; Second Hons; Cpt, Vlbl.

McNEW, Charles William
West HS; Knoxville, TN (95-255) Band; Chldr; Hmrm; Ch, Key C; Cpt, Var C; Co-Cpt, Ftbl; Co-Cpt, Tr; COM; HCt; Swtht; Yth Fel.

McNIEL, Martha Celeste
Ft Dodge Sr HS; Fort Dodge, IA (18-500) A Cap Choir; Ann; VP, Band; Co-Cpt, Mjrte; Model UN; Pres, NHS; Span C; St Scholar; All St Band; All St Orch; St Woodwind Young Artist Win; *Baylor U; Mus.*

McNIEL, Paul Douglas
Beavercreek HS; Xenia, OH (80-800) Band; Cpt, Chess C; Chor; Orch; Ski C; Sftbl; JV, Tnns; Superior, Solo & Ensm Contest; *Wright St U; Acct.*

McNIEL, Philip Curtis
Beavercreek HS; Xenia, OH (80-800) Band; Pres, Chess C; Chor; Ensm; Orch; Ski C; Sftbl; JV, Tnns; Superior, Solo & Ensm Contest; *Wright St U; Acct.*

McNULTY, Dennis Joseph
Cooper HS; Abilene, TX (75-600) COM; Hon Prog; *NEDT; Liberty Baptist Col; Mus.*

McNULTY, James Donald
Garden HS; Oakwood, VA (2-90) A-Ed, Ann; Pres, Chess C; NHS; F-Ed, Sch P; Sci A; Eng A; *Astronomy.*

McNULTY, Timothy Patrick
Glenbard W HS; Glen Ellyn, IL (28-507) Lat C; Ch, Model UN; NHS; Rptr, Sch P; VP, SC; Hon Prog; Q&S A; Century III Leadership A; Memco Schol; Randolph Hearst, Sen Yth Prog Win; *Indiana U; Pol Sci.*

McNUTT, Pamela Jean
New Caney HS; Porter, TX (25%-350) Band; Tres, FTA; NHS; Ed, Sch P; Tres, Soph Cl; Alg A; Hon Prog; Eng A; *Sam Houston St U; Journ.*

McNUTT, Susan Elizabeth
Maryville HS; Maryville, TN (15%-207) AFS; Band; Chor; FHA; Secy, Lat C; NEDT; *Med Tech.*

McNUTT, Teri Lea
Sterling HS; Sterling, KS (3-50) NHS; Pres, Sr Cl; Hon Prog; St Scholar; *Kans U; Phys Therapy.*

McPADDEN, John Thomas
Manatee HS; Bradenton, FL (80-572) Hmrm; InterAct C; Lat C; Tres, SC; JV, Ftbl; Tr; Pres, Jr Exchange C; *Wheaton Col; Pre-Med.*

McPEAK, Jessica Rae
Amarillo HS; Amarillo, TX; A Cap Choir; Madrigal; FCA; Church Yth Coun; Social Ch, Church Yth Choir; *W Tex St U; Mus Therapy.*

McPEEK, Lisa Gay
Gilmer HS; Gilmer, TX (12-130) Ann; Band; Chem C; Crown & Scepter; Drama; Ensm; FHA; FTA; NHS; Sci C; S-T, Span C; Spch C; Thes; DARGCA; Spch A; *E Tex St U; Computer Sci.*

McPETERS, Brian Clayton
Hillsborough HS; Tampa, FL (110-1200) Chor; Ensm; Mod Mus Mas; Sftbl; God & Country A.

McPHAIL, Eric Ray
Rolling Fork HS; Rolling Fork, MS (5-70) Ann; Band; NHS; Sch P; SC; Bsbl; Ftbl; Tr; Hist A; ROTC A; VFW A; *Air Force Acad; Air Traffic.*

McPHAIL, Preston Charles
Tahlequah Sr HS; Tahlequah, OK (10-285) Chor; Dbte Tm; Demolay; Math C; NHS; Mgr, Bkbl; Alg A; Geom A; Eng A; *Math.*

McPHERSON, Bennie Jr
Walnut Hills HS; Cincinnati, OH (70%-435) JV, Band; Bsbl; JV, Bkbl; Ftbl; Tr; *West Point Prep Sch; Engr.*

McPHERSON, Carol LeAnn
Timberline HS; Weippe, ID (1-88) Ann; Band; Chldr; Secy, Drama; Secy, FHA; Rptr, 4H; NHS; Sch P; SC; JV, Bkbl; Tr; 4H A; Hon Prog; *Boise St U; Sociology.*

McPHERSON, Cynthia Reina
Benhaven HS; Olivia, NC; BC; FHA; Alg A; Hist A; Sci A; Lib C; Eng A; *Sandhills Comm Col; Ed.*

McPHERSON, David Scott
Orange Glen HS; Escondido, CA (40%-500) Band; Chem C; Ger C; *San Diego St Col.*

McPHERSON, Janet Gale
Atherton Sr HS; Burton, MI (100-156) Mgr, Bsbl; JV, Tnns; Yth Fel; Yth Foundation.

McPHERSON, Jerry Thomas
Gilmer Co HS; Glenville, WV (19-94) BS; Drama; Fr C; Hmrm; SC; Var C; Bsbl; Co-Cpt, Bkbl; Ftbl; Golf; Tr; HCt; *Glenville St Col; Bus Adm.*

McPHERSON, John Lemon
Cass HS; Cassville, GA (25-180) Chor; Fr C; Math C; Sci C; Mgr, Cr-Ctry; Mgr, Ftbl; COM; *Oglethorpe U; Chem.*

McPHERSON, Kathy Elaine
Bremen HS; Bremen, GA; Mgr, Chldr; FBLA; 4H; Span C; S-T, VICA; *W Ga Col; Sociology.*

McPHERSON, Kim LaRue
Snyder HS; Snyder, TX; Band; Rptr, FHA; 4H; Mjrte; Rainbow; JV, Bkbl; Citz A; 4H A; Twirler; *W Tex Col; Secy.*

McPHERSON, Linda Sue
Atherton Sr HS; Burton, MI; Bus C; ARC; Tr; ARC A; Yth Fel; Yth Foundation; Speedball; *Bus.*

McPHERSON, Lisa Ann
West HS; Columbus, OH (238-573) Band; Dbte Tm; Orch; Ski C; Y-Tns; Bkbl; Tnns; Wrest; Yth Fel; Past Hon Qn, Jobs Daughters; *Ohio St U; Dentistry.*

McPHERSON, Lynda Dian
Mayfield HS; Las Cruces, NM (10%-630) Band; Tr; Keyettes; 1st Cl, GSct; Math.

McPHERSON, Mary Denise
Overbrook HS; Philadelphia, PA (5-1150) Pres, Chor; Hmrm; Model UN; Secy, ARC; World Affairs C; Y-Tns; Hon Prog; Engr Post Drexel U; AFNA; *Indiana U; Pharmacology.*

McPHERSON, Pamela Sue
Oregon HS; Oregon, IL (1-140) AFS; Chor; Secy, Fr C; NHS; Amer Leg A; COM; Citz A; Hon Prog; *Ill St U; Bio.*

McPHERSON, Patricia Ann
Oregon HS; Oregon, IL (3-140) AFS; Fr C; NHS; COM; Citz A; Hon Prog; *Ill St U; Bio.*

McPHERSON, Paula Kay
Oregon HS; Oregon, IL; AFS; Band; Ensm; Sftbl; Mgr, Wrest; COM; Interlochen Ntl Mus; *Rock Valley Col; Secy.*

McQUADE, Thomas Patrick
Notre Dame-Bishop Gibbons HS; Schenectady, NY (6-161) Chess C; NHS; COM; NEDT; Regent Schol; Rensselaer A; *Rensselaer Polytechnic Inst; Elec Engr.*

McQUAIG, Winston Adolph Jr
Columbus HS; Columbus, GA (12-350) F-Ed, Ann; Tres, NHS; Span C; Var C; Golf; COM; Hon Prog; Q&S A; WW; *Columbus Col.*

McQUAIN, Susan Marie
Falls Church HS; Falls Church, VA (140-503) Co-Ed, Ann; French NHS; NHS; Tri-HiY; *George Mason U; Bus Adm.*

McQUAY, Phyllis Denise
Paul Lawrence Dunbar HS; Baltimore, MD; Hmrm; NHS; Var C; Co-Cpt, Bkbl; Hist A; Hon Prog; Math A; Prom Qn A; Most Contributing Jr; Radio Broadcast, Tech Theatre, A's; *U of Md; Computer Sci.*

McQUEARY, Jon Patrick
Colerain Sr HS; Cincinnati, OH (250-600) Chess C; Math C; Sci C; Span C; Var C; Mgr, Bkbl; Mgr, Ftbl; Sftbl; Mgr, Tr; Mgr, Wrest; Hist A; JA A; ARC A; Sci A; BSct.

McQUEEN, Barbara Rosezenia
Scotland HS; Laurinburg, NC; All Amer Yth; Cpt, Chldr; Drama; VP, Monogram; Ntl Yth Conf; VP, SC; UN Council; Sftbl; Most Out; Opt A; Methodist Schol; *High Point Col; Early Childhood Ed.*

McQUEEN, Brenda Joyce
Blenheim HS; Blenheim, SC (2-41) Band; Chldr; Dbte Tm; Fr C; FHA; 4H; Sch P; SC; DARGCA; Hon Prog; MLS; Most Out; Rotary A; *U of SC; Broadcasting.*

McQUEEN, Gregory Keith
Franklin HS; Franklin, IL (5-41) FFA; Var C; VP, Jr Cl; Bsbl; Bkbl; Cr-Ctry; HCt; Swtht Swirl Court; Pres, Greenhand; *Bradley Col.*

McQUEEN, Loretta
Carver Sr HS; Montgomery, AL (5-400) Band; Pres, FBLA; Hmrm; NHS; VP, Soph Cl; COM; Hist A; *Ala A&M U; Med Tech.*

McQUEEN, Melinda
Rebecca Comer HS; Eufaula, AL (2-64) Secy, FHA; Secy, Hmrm; NHS; Hon Prog; Eng A; Art C; FHA A; *Trenholm St Tech Sch; Keypunch and Code Operating.*

McQUINN, Mark Alan
Highline HS; Burien, WA (115-415) Band; Drama; Sci C; Thes; NHS; *Wash St U; Life Sci.*

McQUOID, Grace Florence
Caprock HS; Amarillo, TX (10-350) A Cap Choir; Span C; JV, Hockey; *U of Tex; Eng.*

McQUOID, Malcolm David
Caprock HS; Amarillo, TX; Dbte Tm; Drama; Fr C; Lat C; Span C; Ftbl; Swim; Tnns; 2nd Prize Fr; Review Schol; *Southwestern U; Fr.*

McRAE, Jacqueline Louise
Pasco Comprehensive HS; Dade City, FL (50-250) FHA; Span C; SC; Tr; Secy & Sargeant of Arms, DCT; DCT Dist Acct First Pl A; *Fla Mem Col; Acct.*

McRAE, Jeanice
Hernando HS; Brooksville, FL; Band; Chldr; FHA; 4H; Secy, Jr Cl; Tr; Beauty; 4H A; *Kans St U; Law.*

McRAE, Jeannette
Hernando HS; Brooksville, FL; Band; JV, Chldr; Chor; FHA; 4H; Hmrm; Tr; 4H A; Cosmetology A; Band Riflecorp; *Army; R Nurs.*

McRAE, Lonina Kay
Miami Norland Sr HS; Miami, FL; Band; Pres, Math C; NHS; SC; Sftbl; Swim; Alg A; Bio A; Hon Prog; Math A; Service to Youth; Sci A; Type A; Best All Around; Phys Ed A; Gifted Program; Service to Church; HR; Sci, Math, Typing Trophies; *Pediatrician.*

McRAE, Mary Ann
Melbourne HS; Melbourne, FL; SC; Keyettes; Dance C; *Fla St U; Child Care.*

McRAE, Regina Leigh
Kemper Acad; DeKalb, MS; Co-Ed, Ann; BC; Chor; COM; Hist A; Eng, Mus, A's; HR; *Miss U For Women; Ed.*

McRAE, Rhonda Louise
Kemper Acad; DeKalb, MS (1-37) A-Ed, Ann; S-T, BC; Chldr; Chor; Var C; Beauty; Eng, Lit, HR, A's; *U of Tenn; Eng.*

McRAE, Susan Dawn
Huntsville HS; Huntsville, AL (40-489) Anchor C; Fr C; NHS; Phys C; Sch P; Tnns; NEDT; WW; *U of Ala.*

McRAE, Wendy Lee
Sanford Central HS; Sanford, NC (150-350) Hmrm; Jr Miss Pageant; SC; Sftbl; Commercial Sewing A; Safety Bus Driver A; *Fayetteville St Col; Phys Ed.*

McRANEY, Kathryn Ruth
Sanford Acad; Sanford, MS; Ed, Ann; BC; Chldr; S-T, Hmrm; Sch P; SC; S-T; S-T, Jr Cl; S-T, Soph Cl; Bkbl; Cl Fav; H of F; HQn; Journ A; Math A; Star Student; Eng A; *William Carey Col; Acct.*

McRAY, David Murray
Duncanville HS; Duncanville, TX (17-438) Chor; Ensm; FTA; NHS; *Abilene Christian; Elem Ed.*

McRAY, Julie Marjorie
Washington Co HS; Springfield, KY (6-150) Band; BC; FHA; Sch Achieve Tm; Spch C; Y-Tns; Cpt, Bsbl; Cpt, Swim; Phi Beta Kappa; *Eastern U.*

McREDDIE, Warren B
Sleepy Hollow HS; Tarrytown, NY (85-260) Pres, CYO; Key C; ARC; MVP, Bsbl; Co-Cpt, Bsbl; All Co Bsbl.

McREDDIE, Warren Boyesen
Sleepy Hollow HS; Tarrytown, NY (85-260) Key C; ARC; Co-Cpt, Bsbl; Yth Fel; MVP, Bsbl.

McREYNOLDS, Harold Scott
Holy Family HS; Birmingham, AL (5-41) Drama; Pres, Jr Cl; Bkbl; *UA; Bus.*

McSHAFFREY, David Gerard
Carrollton St Edward's HS; Carrollton, OH (1-9) Chess C; Hmrm; Order/Arrow; Sch P; Sci C; Ski C; Bkbl; Alg A; Bio A; Chem A; God & Country A; HCt; Math A; NMS; Order/Arrow A; Sci A; 6th Pl, St Biol Test; *U of Miami; Biol.*

McSHAY, Patricia Coleen
Collingswood HS; Collingswood, NJ (10%-250) A Cap Choir; NHS; Ed, Sch P; JV, Hockey; Amer Leg A; COM; Citz A; Hon Prog; Journ A; NEDT; PTA A; VFW A; Yth Fel; Girls Citz Inst; *Messiah Col; Eng.*

McSHERRY, Herbert Thomas
St Joseph o-t Palisades HS; W New York, NJ (3-289) Span NHS; Mgr, Bkbl; COM; Hon Prog; NEDT.

MC*SHERRY, Mary Catherine
St Josephs o-t Palisades; W New York, NJ (2-232) Span NHS; Bio A; COM; NMS; NEDT; *Eng.*

McSPEDDEN, Thomas Ray
DeSoto HS; Desoto, TX (100-250) Span C; SC; Bsbl; Bkbl; JV, Ftbl; JV, Tr; Citz A; *U of Tex; Bus Adm.*

McSWAIN, Rickey Lamar
R H Watkins HS; Laurel, MS; *Jackson St U; Ath.*

McSWAIN, Teresa Anne
Cherryville Sr HS; Cherryville, NC (22-150) Band; Chldr; Chem C; Fr C; Hmrm; InterAct C; Mjrte; Monogram; Sci C; SC; Sftbl; Tnns; *Appalachian St Col; Bio.*

McSWAIN, Theresa Lorraine
Kensington HS; Philadelphia, PA; *Comm Col; Bus.*

**McTAGGART,
Patricia Josephine**
West HS; Iowa City, IA (33%-353) A Cap Choir; Co-Cpt, Chldr; Chor; Co-Ch, Drama; GS; Ch, Hmrm; Lit Mag; Co-Ed, Sch P; Span C; SC; Thes; Pres, Jr Cl; Pres, Soph Cl; Amer Leg A; Journ A; Q&S A; Spch A; *St Mary's Col; Pre-Law.*

McTHENIA, Karen Lee
Marion Sr HS; Marion, VA; Bus C; Chor; Drama; FBLA; Secy, FHA; 4H; HiY; Pres, Hmrm; Jr Miss Pageant; ARC; Sci C; SC; Pres, Tri-HiY; Y-Tns; Tnns; 4H A; PTA A; Sci A; Yth Fel; Piano Concert; FHA Chapter Degree; Valentine Qn; *Tenn Temple Col; Bible.*

McTIER, Calvin
James H Bowen HS; Chicago, IL (50-518) Pres, Chem C; Drama; Pres, Phys C; Pres, Sci C; COM; Hon Prog; Sci C; Yth Fel; Galaxy Chptr Pres, Future Sci of Am; Women's C, Chrch Daugh o-t Year; Pac Christian Col Merit Schol A.

McVEY, Jimmy Dean Jr
Mullens HS; Mullens, WV (16-110) Bus Mgr, Ann; Band; Tres, BC; Chess C; City Conf; Drama; Parl, FBLA; VP, HiY; Tres, NHS; ARC; Ed, Sch P; Pres, Sci C; Span C; St Stu Congress; Var C; Mgr, Bkbl; Mgr, Ftbl; Mgr, Wrest; Journ A; Q&S A; Sci A; Yth Fel; Yth Leg; BSct; UHSP Convention; 3rd Pl, Parl; *W Va U; Bus.*

McWATTERS, Sarah Frances
Eastwood HS; El Paso, TX (129-706) Span NHS; Hon Prog; Most Out; Most Outst Bkkg II; Most Outst Girl, Yth Dept; 1st Pl, Yng Designers Drafting Con; *Liberty Bible Col; Bus.*

McWATTERS, Tom Albert III
Delta HS; Delta, OH (7-120) Tres, NHS; Co-Ed, Sch P; Bsbl; Bkbl; Rotary A; Sci A; Highest Batting Average; *Taylor U; Physics.*

McWHERTER, Wendy Chloe
Irving HS; Irving, TX (375-558) A Cap Choir; Drama; Fr C; Tri-HiY; V-Ch, Y-Tns; Tnns; Best Member, Theta Sigma Rho; Young Life; Jr Hist C; *Abilene Christian U; Hist.*

McWHITE, Pamela Denise
T L Hanna HS; Anderson, SC; Band; Ger C; Mjrte; NHS; NEDT; Band Block Letter; *Furman U; Lib Sci.*

McWHORTER, Cathy Ann
Wellston HS; Wellston, OK (1-50) A Cap Choir; Ed, Ann; Band; Chor; Drama; Ensm; Rptr, FHA; Hmrm; NHS; Rptr, Sch P; SC; Pres, Sr Cl; Rptr, Jr Cl; Secy, Soph Cl; Alg A; Amer Leg A; Bio A; COM; Cl Fav; Hist A; Journ A; Sci A; Spch A; Swtht; Val; Vlbl; Superintendent's HR; Mus & Band A's; Best Personality; *Central St U; Special Ed.*

McWHORTER, Kathleen Faith
Wills HS; Smyrna, GA (5%-350) Co-Ed, Ann; Hmrm; SC; Pres, Soph Cl; Tr; Beauty; COM; 4H A; Sci A; Spch A; FCA; Pep C; *U of Ga; Drama.*

**McWHORTER,
Kathryn Elizabeth**
Fayette Co HS; Fayette, AL (8-151) Ed, Ann; Band; Cpt, Chldr; Pres, FHA; GS; Jr Miss Pagent; Math C; VP, Mu Alpha Theta; NHS; Co-Ed, Sch P; Sci C; Ch, Span C; SC; Mgr, Bkbl; B Crocker A; NEDT; Opt A; Spch A; Miss VICA Dist Outst Stu; Win, Dist VICA Speaking; Win, Century III Ldrs; Span A; *Freed-Hardeman Col; Early Childhood Development.*

**McWHORTER,
Russell Franklyn**
Tates Creek HS; Lexington, KY; Band; BC; Chor; Mu Alpha Theta; NHS; Soph A; *U of Ky; Bio.*

McWILLIAMS, Bernice
Adlai E Stevenson HS; Bronx, NY; Lib Service A; Black Unity C; Tutoring; *Law.*

McWILLIAMS, Thomas Edward
Wellston HS; Wellston, OH; Ann; Band; Chor; Ensm; Fr C; Rptr, 4H; Sch P; 4H A; Pres, Yth Fel.

McWILLIAMS, Todd Clayton
Gainesville HS; Gainesville, TX; Ann; Band; Sch P; Golf; *Math.*

McWRIGHT, Kathy Dewonda
Winnfield Sr HS; Winnfield, LA (23-122) BC; FBLA; 4H; Lit Ral; Sch P; SC; Cpt, Bkbl; COM; Excel, Superior, Acad Achv; *NW St U; Ed.*

MEACHEM, Matthew John
Notre Dame-Bishop Gibbons HS; Schenectady, NY (9-161) Chor; Drama; NHS; Mgr, Bkbl; Tnns; NEDT; Regent Schol; Sci A; Stage Crew; WW; *Siena Col; Bus Math.*

MEAD, Kathy LaNell
Woodward HS; Woodward, OK (30%-186) Ann; Pres, Chor; Drama; FTA; Hmrm; Jr Miss Pagent; Ski C; SC; Var C; Bkbl; Cr-Ctry; Golf; Sftbl; Tnns; Tr; Beauty; Cl Fav; HQn; HCt; Interlochen Ntl Mus; Pres A; Swtht; Yth Fel; Soph, Jr & Sr Rep, Peppers; Jr Cl Play; Powder Puff Ftbl; ReDink Coun; *SW Okla St U; Elem Ed.*

MEADE, Patricia Anne
Philadelphia HS For Girls; Philadelphia, PA; Chldr; St Stu Congress; Cpt, Soph Cl; Bkbl; Hockey; *Penn St U; Bone Surgeon.*

MEADE, Ronald Vincent
Parkhill Sr HS; Parkville, MO (100-520) Band; Ftbl; Tr; Wrest; Yth Fel; Pres, Sunday Sch; Church Choir.

MEADE, Steven Jerome
Westminster HS; Westminster, CA (223-817) VP, Band; S-T, Lat C; Var C; Cpt, Swim; Cpt, Waterpolo; Lion Band Sr Service A; *Bus.*

MEADER, Marilyn Ruth
Brethren HS; Paramount, CA (40-88) A Cap Choir; Drama; Secy, SC; JV, Bkbl; Sftbl; Cl Fav; Most Out; WW; *Long Beach City Col; Child Ed.*

MEADOR, Gary Don
Pampa HS; Pampa, TX (50-450) A-Ed, Ann; A-Ed, Sch P; JV, Ftbl; JV, Tr; COM; Journ A; Tex Historical Comm; *Tex Tech U; Photography.*

MEADORS, Nathaniel
Haynesville HS; Haynesville, LA (10%-60) Band; FBLA; Lit Ral; Math C; ARC; Sch P; SC; Bkbl; Ftbl; Swim; Tnns; Tr; H of F; Math A; ARC A; Bkbl Coach A; All-Dist Tr; St Tr Tm; *Sou U; Mgt.*

MEADOWS, Don Tracy
Atkins HS; Atkins, AR (8-76) Band; BC; Chor; S-T, Demolay; Rptr, Sch P; Sci C; Rptr, Jr Cl; H of F; Masonic A; WW; All Region Band; *Ark Tech U; Mus.*

MEADOWS, Kathryn Jane
Lorain HS; Lorain, OH; A Cap Choir; AFS; Tres, NHS; *U of Toledo; Pol Sci.*

MEADOWS, Lisa Darlene
Lufkin HS; Lufkin, TX (72-600) A Cap Choir; Chor; Drama; VP, FHA; JETS; Mu Alpha Theta; Citz A; UIL Medalist; *Stephen F Austin Col; Mus Ed.*

MEADOWS, M James
Falls Church HS; Fairfax County, VA (10%-600) Semi-Fin, Wrest; *U of Va; Med Field.*

MEADOWS, Mary Catherine
Loraine HS; Loraine, TX (1-21) Pres, Band; Cpt, Chldr; Ensm; Pres, FHA; 4H; NHS; Parl, SC; Rptr, Sr Cl; Secy, Jr Cl; Tres, Soph Cl; Bkbl; Tnns; Beauty; Citz A; Cl Fav; 4H A; HQn; MLS; Val; Band Swtht; Miss Sch Spirit; Friendliest; Most Courteous; *Hardin-Simmons U; Art.*

MEADOWS, Regina Carole
Broomfield HS; Broomfield, CO (78-288) Cpt, Band; Pres, Chor; Drama; Ensm; Pres, FHA; Thes; Most Out; Opt A; Mus, Achv, A's; Outst Achv, Outst Soph, Drama; *Wayland Baptist Col; Missions.*

MEADOWS, Sandra Ann
Estancia HS; Estancia, NM (5-68) Chor; Rptr, FFA; Rptr, NHS; Rptr, Jr Cl; Cl Fav; Journ A; Art Cert; Eng, FFA, Parl, A's; *NM St U; Journ.*

MEADOWS, Yvonne
Baker HS; Columbus, GA (2-340) Fr C; Tri-HiY; Cl Fav; Most Out; Swtht; Most Intellectual; *Columbus Col; Math.*

MEADS, Edward Wimmer II
Army Navy Acad; Carlsbad, CA (14-50) Demolay; Rptr, Sch P; Ftbl; Cpt, Tr; COM; Citz A; Hon Prog; Masonic A; Most Out; PTA A; ROTC A; Hon Drill Tm; *US Naval Acad; Sci.*

MEANS, Karen Lynnette
Irving HS; Irving, TX (25%-650) Band; JV, Tnns; *Stephen F Austin Col; Special Ed.*

MEANS, Kathleen Ann
Bear Creek HS; Lakewood, CO (7-350) Ntl Yth Conf; Span C; Yth Fel; Bible Quiz A; Church Yth Choir A; *Wheaton Col; Child Ed.*

MEANS, Marc Elliott
Arts HS; Newark, NJ (6-175) A Cap Choir; Chess C; Chor; Hmrm; NHS; SC; Var C; Cr-Ctry; Tr; Math A; Academic Achv A; Vocal A; *U of Pa; Bus.*

MEANS, Robin Ann
Moore HS; Moore, OK (22-676) A-Ed, Ann; Drama; FBLA; Rptr, Lat C; NHS; Thes; HCt; Pep C; Fin, Miss MHS; *U of Okla.*

MEANS, Stephanie Ann
Wilburton HS; Wilburton, OK (15%-60) Secy, Band; Bus C; Chor; Ensm; 4H; Secy, SC; Cl Fav; 4H A; HQn; HCt; Yth Fel; St Hon Soc; Dist Hon Band; WW Amer Band Members; Dist Mus Solo A; All Dist Chor; *Eastern Okla St U; Mus Ed.*

MEANS, Terri Lynn
Irving HS; Irving, TX (50-560) Chor; FTA; Hmrm; VP, Lat C; NHS; Rainbow; Sodality; Span C; Tres, Sr Cl; Citz A; Church Evangelism Commission; Church Coun On Ministries; Secy, Yth Ministry Coun; *Southwestern U; Hist.*

MEAR, Marcia Lynn
Claxton HS; Claxton, GA (25%-116) 4H; Hmrm; SC; HCt; Yth For Christ; *Ga Sou Col; Stewardess.*

MEARES, Eva Marie
W Columbus HS; Cerro Gordo, NC; BC; Fr C; FHA; Secy, Hmrm; Math C; SC; VP, Jr Cl; Art As; *U of NC.*

MEARES, Lisa Rene
N Gaston Sr HS; Dallas, NC (24-210) BC; Hmrm; Monogram; Span C; SC; Pres, Sr Cl; Pres, Soph Cl; Bkbl; Cpt, Tr; HCt; Pres A; Yth Fel; MVP, Tr; Sr Ldrship A; Civinettes; Friendliest; Sr Superlative; *Appalachian St U; Sociology.*

MEARS, Gary Wayne
Putnam City W HS; Okla City, OK (507-707) Hmrm; Span C; SC; Sftbl; Yth Fel; Page, St Senate; Church Usher; Church PA System Controller.

MEASE, Gary Warren
Hightstown HS; Hightstown, NJ (39-252) Bus Mgr, Ann; NHS; Bus Mgr, Sch P; Golf; Cl Fav; *Trenton St Col; Computer Sci.*

MEBERG, Ruth Diane
Briarcliff HS; Briarcliff Manor, NY; Band; Chor; Bkbl; Sftbl; Hon Prog; *St Olaf Col; Law.*

MECHLING, Todd Alan
William J Brown HS; Sturgis, SD (11-238) 4H; Pres, Hmrm; Sch P; SC; Bkbl; Ftbl; Golf; *Pepperdine U; Eng.*

MECHTEL, Joyce Marie
Chaska Sr HS; Chaska, MN (29-292) CYO; Chldr; Chor; Ger C; Tres, 4H; NHS; Var C; Arch; Bkbl; Cr-Ctry; Sftbl; Tr; COM; 4H A; Hon Prog; JA A; Math A; Type A; Ath A.

MECOY, Charles Donald
Moore HS; Moore, OK; Ger C; Sch P; NMS; *Okla U; Journ.*

MEDDERS, Eugenia DeLoyce
Battiest HS; Battiest, OK (1-45) Chor; Ensm; FHA; NHS; Bkbl; Val; Piano A.

MEDDLEY, Alan Ray
M B Smiley HS; Houston, TX (13-400) Band; Ensm; Ch, Fr C; Math C; Mu Alpha Theta; NHS; Sci C; Bio A; COM; Citz A; Cl Fav; Magna Cum Laude; Good Sportsmanship League; WW; Mgr, Drill Tm; *Tex A&M U; Fisheries Sci.*

MEDER, Frederick Louis Jr
Commack HS S; Commack, NY; A Cap Choir; Chor; Community Yth Symph; Drama; Hmrm; Co-Ch, Ski C; Mgr, Cr-Ctry; Mgr, Tr; Tres, Cr-Ctry; All Suffolk Chor; Tres, Tr; All St Choir; Eagle Sct; Chor Soc; Fin, NY St Summer Sch o-t Arts; *St U Col; Mus Ed.*

MEDILL, Deborah Ann
James B Conant HS; Hoffman Estates, IL (58-646) CYO; Hmrm; Rptr, Sch P; Span C; Ch, SC; Amer Leg A; *U of Ill; Eng.*

MEDINA, Alfredo Bernardo
Dra Maria Cadilla HS; Avecibo, PR (46-636) MVP, Chess C; Monogram; Order/Arrow; Bkbl; Amer Leg A; COM; Lion A; Order/Arrow A; Pres A; Eagle Sct A; *Colegio Agvigultuva Avtes Mecanica; ROTC.*

MEDINA, Arnaldo Luis
Juan Jose Osuna HS; Hato Rey, PR (7-150) Drama; Pres, Hmrm; Tres, ARC; Rptr, Sch P; Tres, Span C; Parl, Spch C; SC; Fin, Bsbl; Semi-Fin, Bkbl; JV, Ftbl; Semi-Fin, Sftbl; Mgr, Tr; COM; Citz A; Hon Prog; Lion A; MLS; Pres, Lib C; Lib A; Civic A; Stu o-t Yr; Ldrship A; *U of Puerto Rico; Law.*

MEDINA, Deborah Ivelisse
Juan Jose Osuna HS; Hato Rey, PR (1-150) Ann; Chor; Drama; Hmrm; S-T, SC; Cpt, Bkbl; JV, Sftbl; COM; Hon Prog; Sal; Sci A; *U of Puerto Rico; Computer Sci.*

MEDINA, Elsa
Dra Maria Cadilla HS; Arecibo, PR (24-482) Alg A; COM.

MEDINA, Eric Abraham
Juan Jose Osuna HS; Rio Piedras, PR (2-150) A Cap Choir; Ann; Band; Chor; Bus Mgr, Commercial; Drama; Hmrm; Fin, Lit Ral; A-Ed, Lit Mag; ARC; Rptr, Sch P; Sci C; Spch C; Arch; Cpt, Bsbl; JV, Bkbl; MVP, Ftbl; Semi-Fin, Golf; MVP, Soccer; MVP, Sftbl; Semi-Fin, Swim; Fin, Tnns; Fin, Tr; Alg A; Bio A; COM; Chem A; Cl Fav; Hist A; Math A; Most Out; Sci A; Spch A; AHPER Phys Fitness A; *MIT; Computer Sci.*

MEDINA, Jose A
Francisco Mendoza HS; Isabela, PR; Band; CYO; Chor; Drama; Hmrm; Rptr, Sch P; COM; Hon Prog; Math A; Sci A; Painting A; *Inst de Cultura de PR; Painting.*

MEDINA, Lorena Tinoco
Battle Mountain HS; Minturn, CO; Secy, FBLA; FHA; Var C; Mgr, Bkbl; Sci A.

MEDINA, Noelia
Antonio S Pedreira HS; Moca, PR (3-45) VP, CYO; Chor; FHA; COM; Hon Prog; *UPR at Mayaguez; Nurs.*

MEDLAND, Jeffrey Dale
Carl Sandburg HS; Orland Park, IL (135-832) CYO; Dbte Tm; Ger C; Order/Arrow; Swim; Eagle Sct; *Baylor U; Pre-Med.*

MEDLAND, Norman Thomas
Wm Tennent Intermediate HS; Warminster, PA (20%-1000) NHS; God & Country A; ROTC A; A Lay Discipleship Cert; *The King's Col; Psych.*

MEDLAR, Susan Laura
Shelton HS; Shelton, CT (10-430) Drama; Span C; Bkbl; Sftbl; Tnns; Tr; COM; Pres A; Span A; *Central Comm St Col; Bio.*

MEDLEY, Barbara Ann
Pocatello Sr HS; Pocatello, ID (1-459) Band; NHS; Amer Leg A; COM; Math A; Spch A; Type A; *Idaho St U.*

MEDLEY, R Sutton
Eminence HS; Eminence, MO (5-40) Band; BC; SC; MVP, Bsbl; Cpt, Bkbl; Tnns; Citz A; MLS; Conf All Star, Schol, Bkbl; Ath o-t Yr; *SW Baptist Col; Bus.*

MEDLEY, Thomas Joseph Jr
James Monroe HS; Fredericksburg, VA (19-195) BS; Chess C; 4H; Hmrm; Lit Mag; Ch, Order/Arrow; Ski C; Bus Mgr, Span C; Amer Leg Orator A; 4H A; Hon Prog; Eagle Sct; Sr Patrol Ldr; *VPI; Oceanography.*

MEDLIN, Keith Floyd
Garinger HS; Charlotte, NC (5%-750) JV, Bsbl; JV, Soccer; HR; *U of NC; Engr.*

MEDLIN, Thomas Eastwood Jr
Smithfield Selma Sr HS; Smithfield, NC (5-400) BS; Chor; Fr C; Key C; Monogram; NHS; SC; Ftbl; Co-Cpt, Tnns; I Dare You; Kiwanis A; Math A; *UNC Chapel Hill; Bus.*

MEDLOCK, Jacqueline Darlene
Miramar HS; Miramar, FL (94-595) Chor; Lat C; NHS; Sftbl; Bible Quiz A; Del, NYI Conv; Puppet Ministry; Bus Ministry; Tres, NYI; *Eckerd Col.*

MEDLOCK, James Edward
Mart HS; Mart, TX (15-62) Ftbl; Tr; Cl Fav; Most Out; All Dist Ftbl; Regional Qualifier, Tr; Most Popular; All Star Ftbl; *Phys Ed.*

MEDLOCK, Linda Faye
Mart HS; Mart, TX (15-60) JV, Bkbl; JV, Tnns; JV, Tr; *Pepperdine U; Phys Sci.*

MEE, Terry Allen
McGavock HS; Nashville, TN (50-800) Band; Fin, BS; Ensm; Lat C; Tr; Church Yth Coun; Most Christ-Like; St Champ, Marching Band; Superior, Mus Festivals; *Ouachita Baptist U; Psych.*

MEECE, Melissa Beth
Forest Park HS; Cincinnati, OH (28-368) Ann; Bus C; Drama; Ger C; Hon Prog; Type A; *Raymond Walters Col; Bus Adm.*

MEEK, Bregitta Deloice
Harrison HS; Colorado Springs, CO (100-500) VP, Hmrm; Bkbl; Sci.

MEEK, Gary Anthony
Harrison HS; Colorado Springs, CO (200-400) Bkbl; ROTC A; *Colo St U; Biol.*

MEEK, Laurie Sue
El Camino Real HS; Woodland Hills, CA (88-1095) A Cap Choir; Chor; Drama; Hmrm; Madrigal; Thes; Bank Of Amer A; CSF; Hon Prog; NMS; *San Diego St Col; Theatre Arts.*

MEEK, Mary Louise
Tuscarawas Valley HS; Zoarville, OH; Chldr; Drama; VP, 4H; Sftbl.

MEEKER, Barbara Jean
Venice Sr HS; Venice, FL; FBLA; InterAct C.

MEEKER, Candace Ann
Cumberland Co HS; Crossville, TN (40%-375) Co-Cpt, Chldr; Dbte Tm; Fin, Hmrm; SC; Beauty; Cl Fav; *Oral Roberts U; Geography.*

MEEKER, Diana Lynn
Eastern Local HS; Macon, OH (5-84) Fr C; FTA; NHS; S-T, Sr Cl; Secy, Jr Cl; Secy, Soph Cl; Math A; Home Ec A; *U of Cincinnati; Nurs.*

MEEKER, William Albert
Cumberland Co HS; Crossville, TN (55-480) Chor; SC; Co-Cpt, Ftbl; Hon Men, All St Ftbl; U of Tenn; Police Sci.

MEEKS, Danny Neal
Walnut HS; Walnut, MS (1-63) BC; VP, FFA; Hist A; Most Out; NE Miss Jr Col.

MEEKS, Patricia Jo
Ben Davis HS; Indianapolis, IN; A Cap Choir; Pres, AFS; Rptr, Bus C; Chor; Commercial C; Drama; Ensm; SC; Thes; Most Out; Job's Daughters; 1st, St Vocal Mus Contest; Ball St U; Elem Ed.

MEEKS, Philip Douglas
Webster Groves HS; Webster Groves, MO; Band; Demolay; Ensm; Order/Arrow; Bsbl; Sftbl; Pres, UMYF; Eagle Sct; Phar.

MEEKS, Richard Eugene
Benson Polytechnic HS; Portland, OR (16-375) VP, Band; NHS; Hon Prog; Tres, Band; Portland St U; Bus Adm.

MEEKS, Robin Rena
Villa Victoria Acad; Trenton, NJ; VP, A Cap Choir; Model UN; Span C; Bkbl; Bkbl A; Rider Col; Psych.

MEESE, Mark Russell
Sooner HS; Bartlesville, OK (12-280) Chor; FBLA; Key C; NHS; Bsbl; Bkbl; Summa Cum Laude.

MEESE, Michael James
Valhalla HS; El Cajon, CA (16-430) BS; Chess C; Ger C; Hmrm; Key C; Pres, Math C; Mu Alpha Theta; NFL; Order/Arrow; Parl, Pol Sci C; Ski C; Spch C; Fin, St Stu Congress; SC; Bank Of Amer A; CSF; Math A; Opt A; ROTC A; Spch A; Yth Leg; Water Polo; Eagle Sct; Jr Statesman; Pres, Church Yth; US Military Acad; Gov.

MEESKE, Alisa Jyl
Chase Co HS; Imperial, NE (15-70) Co-Ed, Ann; Band; Chor; Tres, FHA; NHS; Secy, SC; Q&S A; Type A; U of Wy; Agr.

MEEVES, Victoria Ann
Bennington HS; Bennington, NE (3-65) Band; Chor; Secy, Soph Cl.

MEFFORD, Craig Stuart
Mason HS; Mason, MI; Band; Chor; Ch, 4H; Sci C; Bkbl; JV, Ftbl; Co-Cpt, Sftbl; 4H A; Yth Fel; Creative Writing; Church Choir; Band As; Hope Col; Radio-tV.

MEFFORD, Merrie Lee
Melbourne HS; Melbourne, FL; Drama; Secy, Mu Alpha Theta; NHS; Span C; Hon Prog; Art-Ed, Lit Magazine; WW; Appalachian St U; Span.

MEFFORD, Patricia Sue
Franklin Co HS; Frankfort, KY (38-428) Co-Ed, Ann; BC; Span C; Span NHS; Outst Sr HS Women's Recog, U of Ky; U of Ky; Med.

MEFFORD, William Carl
Riggs HS; Pierre, SD; U of Ariz; Drafting.

MEGEE, Eric Thane
Ceres HS; Ceres, CA (80-350) AFS; Band; Bsbl; Bkbl; Ftbl; Aerospace.

MEGGINSON, Kathryn Lynn
Tupelo HS; Tupelo, MS; BC; Chor; Tri-HiY; Sftbl; Yth Fel; Northeast Col; Secy.

MEGILL, Dale Marie
Wall HS; Wall Twp, NJ; Band; Chor; Ensm; Hmrm; VP, Span C; SC; Bkbl; Sftbl; Tr; Hist A; Sal.

MEGUIAR, Rebecca Denise
Wheeler Co HS; Alamo, GA (2-50) BC; Chor; FBLA; Hmrm; Secy, NHS; SC; VP, Tri-HiY; Cl Fav; Type A; Middle Ga Col; Legal Secy.

MEHAFFEY, Amy Louise
Potomac Sr HS; Oxon Hill, MD; VP, Chor; Madrigal; All St Chor; Prince George Hon Chor; Sweet Briar Col; Home Ec.

MEHALL, Kimberly Ann
Laurel Highlands HS; Uniontown, PA; Uniontown Beauty Acad; Cosmetology.

MEHRTENS, Denise Ann
Valmeyer HS; Valmeyer, IL (5-40) Co-Ed, Ann; Chor; VP, FHA; Pres, 4H; Secy, Math C; VP, NHS; Sch P; B Crocker A; Citz A; 4H A; I Dare You; Math A; St Scholar; WW; Key C; District Chor, Solo Ensm Contests; 4-H Offices; Ill St U; Bus Adm.

MEHUS, Heidi Lyn
Ingraham HS; Seattle, WA (37-458) A Cap Choir; Band; Chor; City Conf; Drama; Ger C; Co-Ch, Hmrm; Ntl Yth Conf; Span C; SC; Var C; Bus Mgr, Sr Cl; Bus Mgr, Jr Cl; S-T, Soph Cl; MVP, Bkbl; Sftbl; Semi-Fin, Swim; Mgr, Tnns; Semi-Fin, Tr; COM; Hon Prog; ARC A; Torch Soc; Cpt, Bkbl; Cpt, MVP, Vlbl; Shoreline Comm Col; Ger.

MEIER, Cindy Lou
Juda Pub HS; Juda, WI (4-27) Ed, Ann; Chor; Drama; Ensm; Pres, FHA; Model UN; NFL; Co-Cpt, Tr; Hon Prog; VofDEM; Yth Fel; Vlbl; Social Sci.

MEIER, David Kent
L D Bell HS; Hurst, TX; Chor; NHS; Ftbl; Wrest; Baylor U; Bus Law.

MEIER, Debra Sue
Monroe Sr HS; Monroe, WI (1-255) VP, FHA; Pres, Ger C; VP, 4H; Fin, NFL; 4H A; Opt A; Spch A; Yth Fel; Conservation Speaking and Poster; UW Madison; Radio and TV Broadcasting.

MEIER, Elizabeth Ann
Ogallala HS; Ogallala, NE (17-150) Band; Chor; NHS; Girl's Quartet; Nurs.

MEIER, Kristi Lynn
Giles Co HS; Pulaski, TN (33%-178) Chldr; Chor; Fr C; Hmrm; Lat C; SC; Sftbl; Tnns; Cl Fav; HCt; I Dare You; Swtht.

MEIER, Mary Kristine
Las Cruces HS; Las Cruces, NM; Ann; Band; FHA; Key C; Tres, SC; New Mexico St U; Deaf Ed.

MEIER, Sally Ann
Edgewater Sr HS; Orlando, FL (78-687) Co-Cpt, Ann; Chor; Drama; Hmrm; Ntl Yth Conf; Span C; Span NHS; SC; VP, Tri-HiY; VP, Jr Cl; Mgr, Bsbl; Tnns; Mgr, Tr; Yth Fel; Span A; Appreciation A; Sou Col of Optometry; Assoc of Sci.

MEIER, Susan Carol
Bartow Sr HS; Bartow, FL (7-300) Ch, Anchor C; Drama; Ch, FHA; NHS; Rptr, SC; Tnns; Hist A; Hon Prog; High-Q Tm; Auburn U; Phar.

MEIGS, Jody Neal
Silsbee HS; Silsbee, TX (46-230) Pres, Key C; Math C; Span C; SC; Hon Prog; Photographer, Ann; WW; Lamar U; Med.

MEIGS, Keith Lance
Daviston HS; Daviston, AL; Co-Ed, Ann; VP, BC; 4H; Phys C; Var C; Pres, Jr Cl; VP, Soph Cl; Bsbl; Bkbl; 4H A; Halloween King; Engr.

MEILI, Marsha Ann
Lincoln HS; Lincoln, KS (1-66) Band; Ger C; Bkbl; NEDT; St Scholar; Val; Kans St U; Engr.

MEINHARDT, Lyndel Wayne
Clark Co R-I HS; Kahoka, MO (7-92) FFA; NHS; Sch P; VP, Sr Cl; Bkbl; Cpt, Ftbl; Tr.

MEISE, Kerry Dwayne
Permian HS; Odessa, TX (22-668) Band; Chor; Demolay; Ensm; Math C; NHS; Orch; Sftbl; COM; Hon Prog; Most Out; Stage Band; Search Comm; All Region Band; Outst Ger Stu; Top Ten; Outst Drafting Stu; Scholastic; AAAA Hon Band; Tex Tech U; Petroleum Engr.

MEISEL, Michael John
Valley Central HS; Montgomery, NY (10-350) BC; CYO; Hmrm; Math C; Ed, Sch P; Span NHS; Mgr, Bkbl; Amer Leg A; Amer Leg Orator A; NEDT; Spch A; US Coast Guard Acad; Law.

MEISINGER, Gregory Allen
Pekin Comm HS; Pekin, IL (2-702) Band; Ensm; JETS; NHS; Orch; Bkbl; COM; NEDT; Sal; WW; U of Ill; Elec Engr.

MEISNER, Cari Lynn
LaVille Jr Sr HS; Lakeville, IN (23-179) Band; FHA; Fin, GS; NHS; Sftbl; Hon Prog; Flag Corp; Fashion Merchandising.

MEISNER, Timothy Donald
Vincent Massey Secondary Sch; Windsor, CAN-ADA; Math C; Hon Prog; Ontario Schol; U of Windsor; Math.

MEJIA, Gloria M
Colegio Puertorriqueno de Ninas; Caparra Heights, PR (2-48) CYO; Dbte Tm; Fr C; Hmrm; Pres, Math C; NFL; Tres, NHS; Co-Ed, Sch P; Spch C; SC; Bio A; COM; Chem A; HQn; Hon Prog; Sci A; Spch A; Val; Poetry & Short Stories in Span A; Prima Ballerina; Yrbk Staff; Mod; Qn Caparra Cntry C; Bradford Col; Clinical Psych.

MELANCON, Dale Paul
Cecilia Sr HS; Cecilia, LA (10-150) Fr C; VP, 4H; Fin, Lit Ral; Sci C; Bsbl; Sftbl; 4H A; Math A; NEDT; Sci A; Social Stu A; Fr A; U of Southwestern La; Architecture.

MELAND, Kevin Ray
Bowman HS; Wadesboro, NC; Band; Order/Arrow; Sftbl; Tnns; God & Country A; Order/Arrow A; All St Band A; Most Improved, Bsbl.

MELANDER, Mark Steven
Daviess Co HS; Owensboro, KY (53-316) 4H; Mgr, Ftbl.

MELANDER, Ruth Astrid
Scotch Plains-Fanwood HS; Scotch Plains, NJ (25-500) Mod UN Legislature; Psych.

MELDER, Lisa Gay
Glenmora HS; Glenmora, LA (9-42) JV, Chldr; FBLA; FHA; Rptr, Hmrm; Jr Miss Pagent; Lit Ral; SC; Bkbl; Cl Fav; Opt A; Yth Fel; Health and Phys Ed A; Chldr A.

MELENDEZ, Aracelis
Fernando Suria Chaves HS; Barceloneta, PR; VP, FBLA; 4H; Pres, Hmrm; COM; 4H A; Spch A; Type A; Pres, Lib Assistant; Miss FBLA; Eng As; Dancing As; Universidad de Puerto Rico; Bus Adm.

MELENDEZ, Arturo
Francisco Mendoza HS; Isabela, PR; Tres, Band; CYO; Pres, Chldr; Chor; Rptr, City Conf; Rptr, Dbte Tm; Order/Arrow; ARC; MVP, Bsbl; Bkbl; MVP, Sftbl; COM; Citz A; Delta Sigma Theta A; Order/Arrow A; Star Student; UPR-CAAM at Mayaguez; Bio.

MELENDEZ, Daniel J
Central HS; Santurce, PR (4-300) Hmrm; ARC; F-Ed, Sch P; COM; Chem A; Math A; Sci A; Exchange C; Radio Operator; A Earheart A; Cert of Proficiency; Civil Air Patrol; PR Sci Fair; Fla St U; Meteorology.

MELENDEZ, David
Central HS; San Juan, PR (3-300) Hmrm; ARC; Sci C; Sr Cl; Alg A; Chem A; Col Agr Art & Mech; Bio.

MELGAR, Veronica Jean
Snyder Sr HS; Snyder, TX (63-200) Fin, AFS; Band; Chor; Drama; Hon Prog; Rotary A; WW; AFS Abroad Stu, Finland; Western Tex Col; Ed.

MELICHAR, June Lee
Hempfield Area Sr HS; Greensburg, PA (25%-800) VP, Band; Chor; Ensm; NHS; Most Out; WW; Hons Band; Percussive Arts Soc; Band, Percussion Section; Stage Band; Symph Orch; Ind U of Pa; Mus Ed.

MELIKIAN, Christine Andrea
Marple Newtown Sr HS; Newtown Square, PA (80-640) Chor; Mgr, Mjrte; Mgr, Sftbl; Sec, Armenian Chrch Yth Organ of Am; Pa St U; Psych.

MELLA, Nancy Isabelle
Deerborne HS; Miami, FL; BC; Cpt, Chldr; NHS; Cl Fav; HCt; Golden Book, Home Ec, A's; Drew U; Psych.

MELLAS, James Manuel
Hiram W Johnson HS; Sacramento, CA (4-680) Band; BS; VP, Chem C; Dbte Tm; Ger C; Hmrm; Math C; NFL; VP, NHS; VP, Phys C; VP, Sci C; Spch C; Ftbl; Tr; Wrest; Amer Leg A; Bank Of Amer A; CSF; COM; Chem A; Math A; Opt A; Sci A; Order of AHEPA Schol; Soroptimist A; Outst Orator; Gemco; Calif St U of Sacramento; Chem.

MELLEMA, Dan Ray
Colorado Springs Christian Sch; Colorado Springs, CO (11-26) Chldr; Chor; SC; Pres, Soph Cl; Bkbl; Sftbl; Colo St U; Construction Engr.

MELLIES, Dawn Elizabeth
MacArthur HS; San Antonio, TX (72-610) Band; Chor; NHS; Span C; VP, Span NHS; COM; 3rd Pl, Ntl Span Poetry Contest; Diploma, Dist Bnd; Reg Band A; NHS Med of Excel, Am As Tchrs Span; 1st, UTSA Span Recitation Contest; *U of Tex-San Antonio; Nurs.*

MELLING, Terrie Kay
Graham HS; St Paris, OH (1-18) Chor; FHA; FNA; NHS; Var C; Bsbl; Bkbl; Cr-Ctry; Sftbl; Tr; COM; Pres A; PA; St Comp VICA; *Wright St U; Mortuary Sci.*

MELLO, Barbara Liane
St Mary's HS; Lynn, MA (10-146) Drama; Fr C; NHS; Bkbl; Sftbl; Alg A; Math A; SIGN A; Lat A; Phys Ed A; Eng A; *Pre-Med.*

MELLON, Caprice Anne
York Comp HS; York, SC (19-240) Semi-Fin, GS; Span C; Bkbl.

MELLON, Teresa Jean
York Comp HS; York, SC (8-272) NHS; Bkbl; Marshal; Block Y.

MELLOTT, Susan Leigh
McConnellsburg HS; McConnellsburg, PA (10-80) Band; Chor; Tres, FFA; FNA; VP, 4H; Hmrm; NHS; Co-Ed, Sch P; Span C; SC; JV, Bkbl; JV, Hockey; *Pa St U; Nurs.*

MELLS, Bradley Neil
The Buckley Sch; Sherman Oaks, CA (5-52) NHS; Var C; Tr; Alg A; Bio A; Chem A; Hon Prog; NEDT; Sci A; Fr, Lat, A's; Trigonometry & Analytic Geom A; Eng A; Geom A; *Pomona Col; Chem.*

MELNICK, Anne Marie
Boardman HS; Youngstown, OH (3-602) A Cap Choir; Drama; Ensm; Fr C; GS; NFL; NHS; Spch C; Spch A; VofDEM; Mus A; Appeals Panel; *Eng.*

MELNYK, Elizabeth Anne
Norquay HS; Norquay, CANADA; Chor; 4H; A-Ed, Sch P; Tr; 4H A; Math A; Canadian Legion Essay Zone A; *U of Saskachewan; Vet Med.*

MELONE, JoAnn
Madonna HS; Chicago, IL (100-350) Co-Cpt, Chldr; VP, Hmrm; Span C; SC; Bkbl; Hockey; Sftbl; COM; HCt; Pres A; Sci A; Sch Olympics A; Chldr A; GSct A; Attendance A; *Moser Col; Secy.*

MELOVIDOV, Platonida May
John F Kennedy HS; Tumon, GUAM; NHS; Alg A; ROTC A; Sci A.

MELSTAD, Gretchen Marie
Bismark HS; Bismarck, ND; Span C; Swim; Tr; *Vet Asst.*

MELTABARGER, Brenda Lou
Ardmore HS; Ardmore, OK; Band; Chldr; Lat C; Golf; *Okla St U; Secretarial Work.*

MELTON, Bradley Gene
Effingham HS; Effingham, IL (31-201) Band; Bkbl; Cr-Ctry; WW.

MELTON, Cathy Sue
Paw Christian Acad; Paw Creek, NC; Co-Ed, Ann; Var C; Bkbl; Sftbl; 'A' HR.

MELTON, Cynthia Gayle
Peach Co Comp HS; Fort Valley, GA (5-200) Ann; Secy, BC; Chldr; Lit Ral; Lit Mag; NEDT; Alpha Kappa Alpha Cert; Spelling A; *Macon Jr Col; Math.*

MELTON, David Myron
Wm Chrisman HS; Independence, MO; Ann; Fr C; Hmrm; Pres, Key C; ARC; Mgr, Swim; Citz A; Yth Fel; VP, Key C; *U of Mo; Hist.*

MELTON, John Walker
Henderson Co Sr HS; Henderson, KY (8-549) Band; BC; Fr C; Lat C; NHS; Fr A; HS Completion, 3 Yrs; Classical Piano Stu; *The Johns Hopkins U; Natural Sci.*

MELTON, Julie Kathryn
Putnam City HS; Oklahoma City, OK (320-850) Bus C; Chor; Ensm; Fin, Jr Miss Pagent; Span C; Sftbl; Type A; Chor Accompanist; Okla U Schol; Outst Mus; *Okla U; Mus.*

MELTON, Karen Faye
Paw Creek Christian Acad; Paw Creek, NC (4-22) Pres, Drama; Tres, Hmrm; Monogram; Co-Ed, Sch P; Var C; Bkbl; Sftbl; Girl's C; 'A' Hon A; *Lee Col; Phys Ed.*

MELTON, Kathy Belinda
Clyde A Erwin HS; Asheville, NC (20-250) BC; Fr C; Square Dance Tm; FCA; Acteens.

MELTON, Larry Kent
Putnam City HS; Oklahoma City, OK; JV, Ftbl; Sftbl; Swim; JV, Tnns; JV, Tr; JV, Wrest; HCt.

MELTON, Perry Allen
Claremore HS; Claremore, OK (30-295) Band; Chor; Ger C; Mu Alpha Theta; NHS; A-Ed, Sch P; Sci C; SC; DARGCA; Most Dependable; *Yale U; Psych.*

MELTON, Sandra Lynn
Gaffney Day Sch; Gaffney, SC; Co-Ed, Ann; Chldr; Secy, SC; Arch; MVP, Hockey; Sftbl; Cpt, Hockey.

MELTON, Vincent Dale
West End HS; Birmingham, AL; Band; Mod Mus Mas; *Regional Tech Inst; Bio-Chem.*

MELVIN, Amy Celeste
Walnut Hills HS; Cincinnati, OH; Chor; COM; Drill Tm; Church Yth Coun; Church Yth Fel; Drama.

MELVIN, David L
Hinsdale Central HS; Hinsdale, IL; Chor; Ensm; V-Ch, InterClub Coun; Lat C; Madrigal; NHS; Phys C; F-Ed, Sch P; Pres, SC; Bkbl; Swim; COM; Hon Prog; *Wheaton Col; Liberal Arts.*

MELVIN, Helen Elaine
Spencer HS; Columbus, GA; Dbte Tm; NHS; SC; JA A; *Ga Baptist Col; Nurs.*

MELVIN, June Louise
Acad of St Aloysius; Jersey City, NJ (8-104) A Cap Choir; Chldr; Chor; Drama; NHS; Rptr, Sch P; Alg A; Amer Leg A; Hist A; Hon Prog; Math A; Val; Baptist Yth Fel; GSct; *Pre-Med.*

MELVIN, Keith Randolph
Lake Taylor Sr HS; Norfolk, VA (75-511) Chor; Jr Hon Soc; DECA; *Old Dominion U; Engr.*

MELVIN, Michael Christain
Warwick HS; Newport News, VA (80-490) Semi-Fin, BS; Hmrm; Sci C; VP, Span C; SC; Var C; Soccer; JV, Tr; JV, Wrest; COM; Chem A; Sci A; Soph Cl Executive Board; Elec C; Aeronautics C; *NC St U; Engr.*

MELVIN, Susan Marie
La Farge HS; LaFarge, WI (5-43) F-Ed, Ann; 4H; Mgr, Sftbl; Vlbl; *Western Wis Tech Inst; Med Sec.*

MENA, Roland
Oliver Wendell Holmes HS; San Antonio, TX; CYO; Cpt, Bsbl; Bkbl; Mgr, Ftbl; Soccer; Sftbl; Tnns; Bio A; COM; Sci A; Cert of A; Cert o-t Knights o-t Altar; Cert of Service; *Sam Houston St U; Pre-Vet Med.*

MENARD, Elizabeth Rose
St Dominic Regional HS; Lewiston, ME; Ch, CYO; Chor; Drama; FTA; Rptr, Sch P; Bkbl; Hockey; Sftbl; Type A; *U of Maine; Broadcast Journ.*

MENARD, Jean Paul M
Notre Dame HS; Sherman Oaks, CA (34-165) CYO; Drama; French NHS; Monogram; NHS; Thes; Cpt, Bkbl; CSF; Hon Prog; Magna Cum Laude; *Calif St U; Bus.*

MENARD, Margaret Mary
Seton HS; Cincinnati, OH (38-299) Chldr; Chor; FBLA; Tres, Lat C; NHS; World Affairs C; Cpt, Soccer; Sftbl; Swim; Tr; Amer Leg A; COM; Sci A; *St Mary's Col; Ed.*

MENARY, Carole Ann
Williamsburg Comm HS; Williamsburg, IA (1-107) Band; Chor; Ger C; NHS; Bkbl; Cr-Ctry; Tr; *Sci.*

MENCER, Elisa Ann
Zion Benton Township HS; Zion, IL (120-450) A Cap Choir; Secy, AFS; Chor; Ensm; Ger C; NHS; A-Ed, Sch P; Sci C; SC; Cpt, Sftbl; Co-Cpt, Tnns; Beauty; St Scholar; Cpt, Vlbl; Christian Ldrship A; Special Talent A; Vocal Mus A; Incentive A; *Union U; Vocal Mus.*

MENCHINGER, Cindy Lin
Benton Harbor HS; Benton Harbor, MI; Band; *Lake Mich Col; Bus.*

MENCY, Kelvin DesMond
Henry Grady HS; Atlanta, GA (50-200) Pres, Hmrm; SC; Bsbl; Cpt, Bkbl; Ftbl; ROTC A; *Morehouse Col; Engr.*

MENDEL, Lisa Lynette
Freeport Sr HS; Freeport, IL (50-450) Band; Chor; 4H; Span C; Y-Tns; Yth Fel; *Sci.*

MENDENHALL, Corletta Lorene
Herbert Hoover HS; San Diego, CA; Chor; Drama; 4H; Y-Tns; Bkbl; Tnns; Tr; Citz A; 4H A; Pres A; Yth Fel; Modeling A; *Calif St U; Drama.*

MENDES, Steve Manuel
Los Banos HS; Los Banos, CA; CYO; Dbte Tm; FFA; 4H; Var C; Bsbl; Cpt, Bkbl; Co-Cpt, Ftbl; Rotary A; Pres, SB; *Merced Jr Col; Broadcasting.*

MENDEZ, Ann Nelida
Centro Oportunidad Educativas B HS; Guaynabo, PR; Drama; Swim; *U Central; Social Worker.*

MENDEZ, Maritza Estrellita
John W Hallahan HS; Philadelphia, PA (15-432) CYO; NHS; Orch; COM; Hon Prog; *Temple U; Pre-Dentistry.*

MENDEZ, Norma Evelyn
Francisco Mendoza HS; Isabela, PR; A Cap Choir; Chor; Bsbl; Tnns; Alg A; Bio A; COM; Chem A; Cl Fav; Hist A; Hon Prog; Math A; Phy A; Sci A; *U of PR; Med.*

MENDEZ, Susie Marie
Sam Houston HS; San Antonio, TX; Span C; JV, Tnns; COM; Citz A; Hist A; Hon Prog; Pres, Library C; *Saint Marys U; Phys Therapist.*

MENDHAM, Natalie Anne
Wilton-Lyndeboro HS; Wilton, NH (2-60) FNA; Tres, NHS; B Crocker A; MLS; Sal; VofDEM; Yth Leg; *U of RI; Phar.*

MENDOZA, Brenda Marie
Academia Maria Reina; Rio Piedras, PR; Pres, Model UN; NFL; Rptr, Sch P; Spch C; *Drew U; International Stu.*

MENDOZA, Debbie Ann
Notre Dame HS; Clarksburg, WV (6-63) Fr C; FBLA; Ger C; Lat C; Lit Mag; ARC; Span C; Tnns; Photo C; Tres, Future Med Careers; Pres Phys Fitness A; *W Va U; Med.*

MENDOZA, Dora Marie
Belton HS; Belton, TX; Tnns; VP & S-T, CYO.

MENDOZA, Evelyn Dimalanta
Queen Anne HS; Seattle, WA (12-388) Tnns; Vlbl; Schenebele A; *U of Wash; Acct.*

MENDOZA, Magdalena
Manuela Toro HS; Caguas, PR; *U of Puerto Rico; Technician.*

MENEFEE, Dwight Wesley
Artesia HS; Artesia, NM (4-273) Pres, Demolay; VP, FFA; Pres, 4H; NHS; Sch P; Parl, SC; COM; 4H A; Math A; Star Farmer, FFA; *Tex Tech U; Agr.*

MENEFEE, Lynette Alice
Alamogordo Sr HS; Alamogordo, NM (22-652) Band; Dbte Tm; Drama; Ensm; NFL; NHS; Pres, Rainbow; Spch C; COM; Kiwanis A; Most Out; Spch A; VFW A; VFW Orator Win; VofDEM; Yth Fel; Ntl Piano Playing Auditions; Bicentennial Spch Contest; Mus Composer's Pin; Creative Writing A; *NMSU; Psych.*

MENENDEZ, Claire Elizabeth
Valley Central HS; Montgomery, NY (10%-400) CYO; Co-Cpt, Chldr; Chor; Pres, 4H; Sch Achieve Tm; Var C; 4H A; Hon Prog; Secy, Rptr, Ch, 4-H C; Cardinal Spellman Yth, Com Serv, As.

MENESES, Sandra Lynn
Thomas A Edison HS; San Antonio, TX;

MENG, Cathy Elise
Berea HS; Greenville, SC; Secy, Community Yth; Fr Ch; Orch; COM; Most Christlike A; Member Fr C; Outst Piano A, SCMTA Auditions; Concert Mistress, All-St Orch; Member, Brevard Mus Center; *Mus.*

MENG, Julie Ann
Jefferson Sr HS; Jefferson, WI (10-200) Band; Chor; Secy, Var C; Bkbl; Tr; Yth Fel; *Milton Col; Sci.*

MENGER, Jenny Lena
N Augusta HS; N Augusta, SC; ROTC A; Sons o-t Amer Revolution A; Band A; ROTC Exemplary Conduct A; Yth Coun; Ldrship A; *Rising Jr Col.*

MENGES, Lorie Jenniene
Douglas HS; Douglas, AZ; Chor; Ensm; Thes; St Solo & Ensm Mus Festival; U Acad For Mus.

MENGHETTI, Anita Lyn
Modesto HS; Modesto, CA (34-400) Band; Chldr; Hmrm; NFL; Sch P; Rptr, Soph Cl; Gym; *U of Calif; Social Sci.*

MENICHELLO, Gina Marie
Old Forge HS; Old Forge, PA (10-121) Chldr; Chor; Drama; FHA; Hmrm; NHS; Ski C; SC; Chem A; WW; *Pa St U; Nurs.*

MENICHIELLO, Arthur Anthony
Old Forge HS; Old Forge, PA (16-121) Chess C; VP, NHS; Sci C; Ski C; SC; Cpt, Golf; Hist A; Sci A; *Pa St U; Physics.*

MENINNO, David Michael
Avon Jr Sr HS; Avon, MA (36-89) Chor; Drama; Sch P; SC; Yth Fel; *Johnson and Wales Col; Culinary Arts.*

MENKE, Jan Elaine
Perry Meridian HS; Indianapolis, IN; Chor; Yth Fel; *Horticulture.*

MENNENGA, Julie Ann
Waverly Shell Rock HS; Waverly, IA (80-250) A Cap Choir; Band; Chldr; Chor; Ensm; 4H; Hmrm; Madrigal; Tres, Rainbow; Secy, SC; Yth Fel; JA Ntl Conv; Shorthand As; Singing Contest As; *Mankato St Col; Child Developement.*

MENNENGA, Marla Denise
Rantoul Twp HS; Rantoul, IL (25%-364) Band; Ensm; Pres, 4H; Key C; ARC; Span C; Tr; Amer Leg A; COM; Citz A; Cl Fav; 4H A; I Dare You; Kiwanis A; Pres A; ARC A; Spch A; Swtht; Type A; *Parkland Jr Col; Med Off Asst.*

MENNING, James Ronald
United Local HS; Hanoverton, OH (11-130) BS; Chor; Pres, 4H; NHS; Span C; Pres, Sr Cl; Pres, Jr Cl; Pres, Soph Cl; Bkbl; Ftbl; Tr; Amer Leg A; 4H A; HCt; All-Ohio Ftbl; *Pol Sci.*

MENSING, Ramona Lynne
Carlyle HS; Carlyle, IL (66-138) A Cap Choir; Pres, Chor; Ensm; 4H; Madrigal; Ch, SC; Var C; Arch; Bkbl; Sftbl; 4H A; Miss Congeniality; WW; Bowl As; *Kaskaskia Jr Col; Cosmetology.*

MENTER, David Robert
Imlay City HS; Imlay City, MI (8-200) Band; Fr C; Cr-Ctry; Tr.

MENTER, Deborah Anne
Imlay City HS; Imlay City, MI (3-150) Band; Secy, FBLA; Semi-Fin, NFL; VP, NHS; VP, SC C; SC; Spch A; *Northwestern U; Psych.*

MENTON, Eddie Lee
Palmer Ind Sch; Palmer, TX (6-28) FFA; NHS; Span C; Bsbl; JV, Bkbl; Cpt, Ftbl; Tr; *Navarro Jr Col; Math.*

MENTZER, Connie Faye
Biglerville HS; Biglerville, PA (39-130) Chldr; Chor; Secy, Sr Cl; HCt; Yth Fel; May Day Attendant; *Central Penn Bus Sch; Fashion Merchandising.*

MENTZER, Judy Kae
Biglerville HS; Biglerville, PA (40-148) A Cap Choir; Band; Cpt, Chldr; Chor; Ensm; FHA; 4H; NHS; Span C; Var C; Bkbl; Hockey; Sftbl; WW; Co Band; Ath, Fair, A's; *Art.*

MENTZER, Patricia Anne
Greater Latrobe HS; Latrobe, PA (6-518) Co-Ed, Ann; Band; French NHS; Tres, NHS; Ski C; Journ A; GSct; Q&S; *Lehigh Col; Engr.*

MENZEL, Scott Lynn
Lincoln Comm HS; Lincoln, IL (1-348) Band; JV, Wrest; Math A; Yth Fel; Soc of Amer Magicians; Drafting, Principal's, A's; Spelling, A; *Engr.*

MENZEL, Victoria Lee
Denfeld HS; Duluth, MN (15%-450) Band; Bus C; Fr C; FBLA; Hon Prog; Yth Fel; *Central Col; Bus.*

MENZIE, William Lee
Norman HS; Norman, OK (20%-704) BS; Chem C; Demolay; 4H; Lat C; Lit Mag; Math C; Order/ Arrow; ARC; Sci C; JV, Tr; 4H A; Hon Prog; Kiwanis A; Order/ Arrow A; ARC A; Yth Fel; God & Country A; 1st Pl, Ntl Kodak A; Co Bird C; 1st Pl, Ntl Wildlife Fed A; Top 20 Fin, Essay Contest; MYF; Church Yth Choir; Eagle Sct; *U of Okla; Engr Physics.*

MENZING, Laura Ruth
James Ford Rhodes HS; Cleveland, OH (120-460) A Cap Choir; AFS; Bus C; Chor; FHA; FTA; Ger C; Hmrm; SC; Y-Tns; Mgr, Cr-Ctry; Mgr, Tr; Citz A; Most Out; Type A; Stu Lib A; *Evangel Bible Col; Bus Adm.*

MERA, Ann Elizabeth
John S Fine HS; Nanticoke, PA (2-297) Mgr, Swim; NEDT; Vlbl; NML; *Pa St U.*

MERANTA, Kim Mark
Berwick Sr HS; Berwick, LA (28-114) CYO; Rptr, Drama; Spch C; SC; Pres, Sr Cl; Ftbl; Citz A; HCt; K of C A; Pres, FCA; Schol A.

MERBLER, Michelle A
R H A M HS; Hebron, CT (10-253) A Cap Choir; Band; Chor; Drama; Fr C; Madrigal; Alg A; Amer Leg A; Bio A; Hon Prog; Math A; Sci A; Mus A; Home Ec A; Eng A.

MERCADO, Julia
Francisco Mendoza HS; Isabela, PR; CYO; Chor; Drama; FHA; Bsbl; Alg A; COM; *U of PR; Med Tech.*

MERCADO, Paul
Luis Munoz Marin HS; Cabo Rojo, PR (9-200) Chem C; Chor; Dbte Tm; Drama; Hmrm; InterAct C; Lit Ral; Sci C; Span C; Spch C; SC; Bkbl; Chem A; Cl Fav; JA A; Magna Cum Laude; Masonic A; Poet A; Sci A; Spch A; VFW Orator Win; *Recinto Universitario Rio Piedras; Law.*

MERCER, Christina Kay
Limestone Comm HS; Bartonville, IL (43-435) Chor; Drama; NHS; Sftbl; Hon Prog; Young Life.

MERCER, Connie Ann
Zebulon HS; Zebulon, NC (35-80) *Art.*

MERCER, Constance Marie
Dublin HS; Dublin, GA; Co-Cpt, Band; VP, Tri-HiY; Swim; 1st Pl, Piano, St Lit Meet; 1st Runner-Up, Miss Dublin; Outst Jr; John Philip Sousa A; Mst Outst Bndsmn; Distin Mus Cert; *Shorter Col; Piano.*

MERCER, Debora Ann
Virgie HS; Virgie, KY (20-110) Secy, BC; FTA; 4H; A-Ed, Sch P; Secy, Spch C.

MERCER, Helen Elizabeth
Samuel W Wolfson HS; Jacksonville, FL (12-670) Ann; Secy, Chor; VP, Drama; Ensm; Hmrm; Lat C; Madrigal; NHS; Bio A; COM; Hist A; Hon Prog; Most Academic; Drama A; Ensm Dist & St Sup, Chor; FVA St Clinic; Dist Sup, Solo; *Eng.*

MERCER, Lynn
Hemet HS; Hemet, CA (135-425) Cpt, Gym; *Physiology.*

MERCER, Melinda Elizabeth
East Sr HS; W Chester, PA (25-500) Ed, Ann; Band; Dbte Tm; Drama; Ensm; Fr C; Hmrm; NHS; Orch; ARC; Rptr, Sch P; SC; Sftbl; COM; Hon Prog; Yth Fel; Juvenile Justice Committee; *Juniata Col; Pre-Med.*

MERCER, Patti Gail
N Mesquite HS; Mesquite, TX (51-400) A Cap Choir; Ensm; FHA; Madrigal; NHS; Span C; Y-Tns; Tnns; *Eastfield Col; Secy.*

MERCHANT, Ernestine Manise
Middletown HS; Middletown, OH; A Cap Choir; Chor; FHA; Hmrm; Y-Tns; Bkbl; Sftbl; Swim; *Allan Hancock Jr Col; Child Psych.*

MERCHANT, Susan Gale
Marshall HS; Marshall, MO (11-209) Bus C; Chor; FBLA; Pres, Rainbow; Span C; Regent Schol; Vlbl; *Central Mo St U; Spch Therapist.*

MERCIER, Ginger Lynn
Ashwaubenon HS; Green Bay, WI; Band; SC.

MERCIER, Gustavo Alberto
Colegio San Antonio; Rio Piedras, PR (1-103) VP, Chor; NFL; NHS; Spch C; SC; Alg A; Bio A; Hist A; Hon Prog; Sci A; Spch A; Judo As; Fr A; Span A; *Natural Sci.*

MERCIER, Juan Carlos
Colegio San Antonio HS; Rio Piedras, PR (1-103) Chor; NHS; SC; Tnns; Alg A; Hist A; Hon Prog; NEDT; Sci A; Judo As; Span A; Fr A; Lib Sci A; Eng A.

MERCIER, Marc
College De Ste Anne De La Pocatiere; La Pocatiere, CANADA (2-34) CYO; Co-Ch, 4H Ldrship; Var C; Ftbl; Hockey; Sftbl; 4H A; Most Out; ARC A; *Universite Laval; Med.*

MERCK, James Edward
Travelers Rest HS; Travelers Rest, SC; *N Greenville Col; Percussion Mus.*

MERCURY, Carolyn Elaine
Palm Beach Gardens HS; Palm Beach Gardens, FL (340-460) *Bethune Cookman Col; Child Psych.*

MEREDITH, Carol Ann
O D Wyatt HS; Fort Worth, TX (43-435) A-Ed, Ann; Ensm; NHS; Hon Prog; Magna Cum Laude; WW; People; Photographer, FTA; Bible C; *Tarrant Co Jr Col.*

MEREDITH, Jane Leigh
Ft Johnson HS; Charleston, SC (19-212) Tres, Chor; Fr C; Madrigal; Y-Tns; Hon Prog; WW; All St Chor; *Winthrop Col; Mus.*

MEREDITH, Kathryn Lizbeth
Lincoln HS; Stockton, CA (25-530) Drama; GS; Orch; Ski C; Tres, SC; VP, Jr Cl; JV, Bkbl; CSF; Tres, Jr Cl; Drill Tm; Foreign; Acad Ed, Yrbk; N Exchng Correspon; Pres, VP, GAA; Historian, Ree C; Ldrship Conf; Church Yth Group; *UC Berkley.*

MEREDITH, Marie Elaine
Charlottesville HS; Charlottesville, VA (25%-501) Band; FBLA; Math A; Span A; Keyette C; *Med.*

MEREDITH, Robin Ann
Middleburg HS; Middleburg, PA (1-135) Band; Chor; Drama; Semi-Fin, JV Miss Pa; Mod Mus Mas; Rptr, Sch P; Bkbl; Hockey; Sftbl; Swim; Tnns; Hist A; Yth Fel; WW.

MEREDIZ, Maria de la Paz
Academia Ntra Sra Providencia; Rio Piedras, PR (3-64) CYO; Commercial C; Drama; Rptr, Sch P; Sci C; Bkbl; Bio A; COM; Summa Cum Laude; Conduct A; Sci.

MERICAL, Terry Lynne
Vandalia Butler HS; Vandalia, OH; Fr C; Sftbl; Swim; Vlbl; *Evangel Col; Bus.*

MERIEDETH, Jeanna Kay
Ballard Mem HS; Barlow, KY (3-108) Secy, BC; Chldr; Tres, FBLA; FHA; Tres, SC; Thes; VP, Sr Cl; Pres, Jr Cl; VP, Soph Cl; Sftbl; Beauty; Citz A; HCt; Math A; Spch A; Type A; Secy, Parl, FBLA; Miss BMHS; Alt, GS; Best All Around; Hon Graduate; *Murray St U; Nurs.*

MERINGA, Susan Beth
E Kentwood HS; Kentwood, MI; A Cap Choir; Chor; NHS; Sftbl; Citz A; Most Out; PA; 1 Rating, Dist & St Mus; Pep A; *Mus.*

MERIWETHER, Cindy D
Claremont HS; Claremont, CA (1-550) F-Ed, Ann; Tres, Band; Secy, Ensm; JV, Tnns; CSF; COM; Hist A; Hon Prog; Humanities A; *Med Sci.*

MERIWETHER, Lee Ann
McGavock HS; Nashville, TN; Ger C; *MTSU; Childrens Ed.*

MERIWETHER, Steven Herschel
McGavock Sr HS; Nashville, TN (150-860) Tres, BC; Hmrm; NHS; ARC; SC; Cl Fav; Yth Fel; *Middle Tenn St U; Plant and Soil Science.*

MERKATORIS, Mary Ann
St Joseph's Acad; Green Bay, WI (49-150) Chor; Drama; Hmrm; SC; Pres A; Neatest; Most Efficient; Creativity A; *Stout Col; Social Work.*

MERKEL, David George
Huron Sr HS; Huron, SD (25%-330) A Cap Choir; Chor; Ensm; Madrigal; NHS; ARC; Type A; SD Honors Choir; 40; Superior Mus A *St Olaf; Mus.*

MERKET, Dondi
Colo HS; Colo City, TX (5-95) Band; City Conf; NHS; Parl, SC; Tr; *Tex Tech U; Pre-Med.*

MERKL, Daniel Lee
Ensley HS; Birmingham, AL (20%-300) Band; Ensm; Math C; Orch; Sci C; Sftbl; Math A; *U of Ala at Tuscaloosa; Engr.*

MERKT, Joanne Louise
William H Taft HS; Chicago, IL (190-780) Band; Ensm; Hmrm; JETS; Orch; Span C; SC; COM; Hon Prog; Sci A; VICA; Choir; S-T, Church Yth Group; Jr Prin, Job's Daughters; Church Acolyte; Altar Guild; *Bradley U; Tech.*

MERLINO, David Peter
Saint Joseph HS; Camden, NJ (1-96) BS; Chess C; Fr C; NHS; Order/Arrow; Ftbl; Amer Leg A; Citz A; Hon Prog; Pres A; VFW A; Eagle Sct; Ad Altare Dei Cross; Film Lib A; *US Naval Acad; Aeronautics.*

MERREOT, David Allen
Columbiana HS; Columbiana, OH (54-101) Order/Arrow; Cr-Cxtry; Eagle Sct.

MERRICK, Priscilla Pinckney
St Vincents Acad; Savannah, GA (20-103) Ann; CYO; Fr C; Tnns; Off, Church Yth; Swim C; Yoga C; Del, SC Yth Conservation Workshp; *U of Ga; Art.*

MERRIETT, Regina Gale
M B Smiley HS; Houston, TX (25-400) Parl, FTA; Math C; NHS; JV, Tnns; Bio A; Type A; Pep Squad; Homemaking A; *U of Houston; Engr.*

MERRIFIELD, Donna Lee
Iowa HS; Iowa, LA (10-91) Crisco A; Type A; Christmas Qn; *McNeese Col; Nurs.*

MERRIFIELD, Joe Kieth
Okeene HS; Okeene, OK (10%-38) Ann; Band; BS; Sci C; Var C; VP, Sr Cl; VP, Jr Cl; Bkbl; Ftbl; Tr; COM; HCt; Hon Prog; Sci A; All St, Tr; *Okla St U; Acct.*

MERRILL, Ann Adelia
The Kinkaid Sch; Houston, TX (2-100) AFS; Chor; Lit Mag; Span C; JV, Soccer; Yth Fel; *Stanford U; Foreign Lang.*

MERRILL, Christopher Paul
Grossmont Union HS; La Mesa, CA; A Cap Choir; Rptr, Sch P; Ftbl; Soccer; MVP, Tr; *Wesmont Col; Psych.*

MERRILL, John Mark
Memphis University Sch; Memphis, TN (24-95) Bus Mgr, La Cap Choir; Ann; Bus Mgr, Chor; Lat C; Lit Mag; NHS; Sch P; COM; NMF; NMS; NEDT; *Vanderbilt U; Pre-Law.*

MERRILL, Mark Berg
Skyline HS; Salt Lake City, UT; A Cap Choir; Chor; Key C; Ski C; God & Country A; Duty to God; Eagle Sct; Outst Sct As; *U of Utah; Aviation.*

MERRILL, Martha Eizabeth
Rockland Dist HS; Rockland, ME (10-126) A Cap Choir; Band; Chor; Community Yth Symph; Dbte Tm; Drama; GS; Lat C; Madrigal; NFL; NHS; Orch; Spch C; Thes; All St Orch; WW, Mus Stu; *U of Maine-Farmington; Emotional Disturbance.*

MERRILL, Sandra Jo
Campbell Central Sch; Campbell, NY (9-62) Tres, Band; Chldr; Secy, Chor; Fr C; NHS; Sch P; Ski C; Var C; Soccer; Sftbl; COM; Cl Fav; Hon Prog; Shorthand Cert; *Comm Col; Acct.*

MERRILL, Tom Glen
Memorial HS; Houston, TX (150-635) Band; Chor; Ensm; NHS; Yth Fel; *Trinity Col; Chem.*

MERRILLS, James Lee
Wisconsin Acad; Columbus, WI; Chor; Bkbl; Cpt, Ftbl; Cpt, Sftbl; *Andrews U; Tech.*

MERRIMAN, Frank Walter III
Paul Harding HS; Fort Wayne, IN; Ch, Order/Arrow; ARC; Span C; Swim; JV, Wrest; Eagle Sct A; *Ind U.*

MERRINER, Micky Ray
E Jordan HS; E Jordan, MI (47-88) Band; Drama; Sch P; Span C; Span NHS; Var C; Bsbl; Bkbl; Ftbl; Golf; Sftbl; Tr; Hon Prog; *Social Services.*

MERRITT, Julie DeAnn
Genoa-Kingston HS; Genoa, IL (13-100) Band; Fr C; NHS; Sci C; Var C; JV, Sftbl; Cpt, Tr; Pres A; Yth Fel; *Iowa St U; Applied Art.*

MERRITT, Kurt Pascal
Negreet HS; Negreet, LA (10-52) Bus C; CYO; Dbte Tm; FBLA; FFA; 4H; Pres, Hmrm; Ed, Sch P; Parl, SC; Pres, Soph Cl; Bsbl; Bkbl; Tr; COM.

MERRITT, Miki
Northwest HS; St Louis, MO (1-433) NHS; Tres, Sr Cl; Bsbl; Ftbl; *Wash U; Acct.*

MERRITT, Ricky Alvin
Horace Maynard HS; Maynardville, TN (2-127) Co-Ed, Ann; BC; 4H; Sci C; SC; Pres A; Sal; Most Stu; WW; *U of Tenn; Engr.*

MERRITT, Sarah McAden
N Olmsted HS; N Olmsted, OH (200-600) Hmrm; Ski C; Tres, SC; UN Council; VP, Sr Cl; VP, Jr Cl; VP, Soph Cl; Tnns; *Ferrum Col; Child Care.*

MERRITT, Stacey Elizabeth
Arcadia HS; Arcadia, CA; Band; NHS; Orch; Swim; CSF; *U of Calif; Vet Med.*

MERRIWETHER, Steven Scott
Southwood HS; Shreveport, LA;

MERROW, Jeffrey Allan
White Mt Regional HS; Whitefield, NH (14-120) Band; Thes; *Brigham Young U; Computer Sci.*

MERRY, Joella
Eldorado HS; Albuquerque, NM; Band; Chor; Band Ltr; Drum Major; *Southwestern Col; Ed.*

MERRYMAN, Elizabeth Anne
Rustburg HS; Rustburg, VA; Span C; Tri-HiY; Tnns; 4H A; Best Office Asst.

MERSHON, Cynthia Marie
Eastern HS; Louisville, KY (33%-300) Band; BC; Bkbl; Sftbl; Tr; COM; Opt A.

MERTZ, Mary Carol
Conestoga Valley HS; Lancaster, PA (11-324) Hmrm; NHS; Pres, Tres, Yth Fel; Amer Bus Women's Assn; *Shippensburg St Col; Social Welfare.*

MERVOSH, Steven Paul
E Peoria Comm HS; E Peoria, IL (3-515) Chem C; Ger C; JV, Bsbl; Hon Prog; *Math.*

MERZ, John Paul
Canfield HS; Canfield, OH; AFS; Drama; Fr C; Rptr, Hmrm; SC; Hon Prog; *Law.*

MERZ, Julie Ann
Montgomery HS; Santa Rosa, CA (20%-650) Secy, Chor; 4H; Mgr, Bkbl; CSF; *Eng.*

MESA, Osvaldo A
Academia Santa Monica; Santurce, PR (3-53) NHS; Pres, Var C; MVP, Bsbl; Bkbl; Tr; Hon Prog; *UPR at Recinto de Mayaguez; Engr.*

MESARCHIK, David Michael
Meadowbrook HS; Byesville, OH (1-165) Math C; Pres, NHS; Sch Achieve Tm; Sci C; Span C; Bio A; COM; Cl Fav; Hon Prog; MLS; Most Out; Sci A; St Scholar; Val; PA; Ohio Scholastic Achv; Marine Phys Fitness A; *Ohio St U; Optometry.*

MESEROLE, Barbara Anne
Lindenhurst Sr HS; Lindenhurst, NY (7-897) VP, InterAct C; NHS; ARC; Cpt, Bkbl; Regent Schol; Rotary A; Wittenberg Alumni Schol; *Wittenberg U; Pol Sci.*

MESKIMEN, James Paul
Hubbard HS; Chicago, IL (173-475) *Green Tech Col; Refrigeration.*

MESKUS, Eric Andrew
Rhinebeck Central Sch; Rhinebeck, NY; *Elec.*

MESLER, Linda Kaye
Andress HS; El Paso, TX; VP, JA.

MESMER, Donna Lynn
Weldon Valley HS; Weldona, CO (2-12) Chor; FBLA; Parl, FHA; NHS; Sch P; SC; Secy, Sr Cl; Alg A; Bio A; HCt; Masonic A; Math A; Sci A; Yth Fel.

MESS, Elizabeth Ann
Metro HS; St Louis, MO (7-52) Bus Mgr, Sch P; Bkbl; Sftbl; Rptr, Sch P; *SW Baptist Col; Sociology.*

MESSA, Cheryl Ann
Cecilian Acad; Philadelphia, PA; CYO; Fr C; VP, Hmrm; Lat C; Lit Mag; Sci C; SC; JV, Bkbl; Sftbl; Alg A; Citz A; HS Schol; *Sci.*

MESSENGER, Laura Lynn
A P Baldwin HS; Wailuku, HI (86-313) Chldr; FTA; Aloha Service C; Booster C; *U of Hawaii; Ed.*

MESSER, Les Marsh
Ellen McCarter Stewart Sch; Houston, TX (10%-20) Spch C; World Affairs C; Soph Cl; Bkbl; Cpt, Ftbl; Tnns; Semi-Fin, Wrest; JA A; Spch A; MVP, Ftbl; *Tex A&M U; Psych.*

MESSER, Malinda Darlene
Tuscola Sr HS; Waynesville, NC (5%-406) Band; Chor; InterAct C; Alg A; COM; Yth Fel; Gold Key Art A.

MESSER, Tony Eugene
Wayne Co HS; Jesup, GA; Band; Orch; Ftbl; Wrest.

MESSERKLINGER, Joe Gottlieb
Batavia HS; Batavia, IL (3-211) Band; Lat C; Mus A; Lat A; *U of Ill; Engr.*

MESSERSCHMIDT, Julie Lynn
Sheffield-Chapin Comm Sch; Sheffield, IA (15%-58) Band; Chldr; Chor; FBLA; VP, 4H; Span C; Var C; Tres, Soph Cl; Tr; 4H A; *U of Northern Iowa; Librarian.*

MESSERSMITH, Gerald Alan
Alliance HS; Alliance, NE; AFS; Band; Chor; Demolay; 4H; Hmrm; JV, Wrest; Amer Leg A; Bio A; Citz A; DARGCA; 4H A; Hist A; Spch A; *Mus.*

MESSERSMITH, Pam Sue
Farnam Pub Sch; Farnam, NE (2-18) Band; Cpt, Chldr; Chem C; Chor; Rptr, Sch P; Tres, Jr Cl; Pres, Soph Cl; Bkbl; Sftbl; Tr; Hist A; Hon Prog; Yth Fel; VP, Fresh Cl; Home Ec A; Vlbl; WW; *Kearney St Col; Bus.*

MESSICK, Rodney Joseph
Fairview Alpha HS; Coushatta, LA (4-19) Drama; Pres, 4H; Hmrm; Fin, Lit Ral; SC; Var C; MVP, Bkbl; 4H A; Sportmanship A; St Eng Rally; *Northwestern Col; Phar.*

MESSINGER, Carmen
Ellenville HS; Ellenville, NY (99%-100) Chor; Pres, Dbte Tm; Drama; Lit Mag; Soccer; Tr; Vof-DEM; *Ariz St U; Bus.*

MESSMER, Jeffrey Robert
Wheatland-Chili HS; Scottsville, NY; JV, Bkbl; JV, Soccer; JV, Swim; *Monroe Comm Col; Social Work.*

MESSMER, Mary Ellen Kathleen
Eastmoor Sr HS; Columbus, OH; Ensm; Co-Ed, Sch P; *Ohio St U; Real Estate.*

MESSMER, Stephen Wayne
Artesia HS; Artesia, NM (8-300) BS; Pres, Hmrm; NHS; Order/Arrow; Ski C; VP, SC; Pres, Soph Cl; JV, Bkbl; Cpt, Tnns; Bio A; COM; Citz A; Cl Fav; Gov Honor Prog; Hist A; HCt; Hon Prog; JA A; Order/Arrow A; Pres A; Q&S A; Sci A; Spch A; Yth Fel; Yth Foundation A; Pres, SC; Eagle Sct Ntl Yth Rep; Tn o-t Yr; Soil Conservation Soc of Amer; *NM St U; Bus.*

MESSMORE, Toni Lee
Melvin Sibley HS; Melvin, IL (9-31) GS; Hist A; Prom Court.

MESSNER, Karen Lyn
Lancaster HS; Lancaster, OH (33%-650) Chem C; Chor; FHA; FNA; Sftbl; Yth Fel; *Mt Carmel Hospital; Surgical Nurs.*

METCALF, Christopher Ray
University HS; San Diego, CA (26-374) Bsbl; Most Out.

METCALF, Clifton Blake Jr
Tuscola Sr HS; Waynesville, NC (5%-406) Band; Key C; MLS; Sci A; VofDEM; Asst Coach, Yth Bkbl; Nom, Gov Sch; Church Yth Coun; VP, Yth Choir; Handbell Choir; *U of NC; Journ.*

METCALF, Sheri Renee
Denair HS; Denair, CA (5-69) AFS; Chldr; Math C; Span C; Var C; Bkbl; Tr; Bank Of Amer A; Bausch & Lomb A; CSF; COM; H of F; Math A; MLS; Bowling; Co- cpt, Vlbl; YMCA Jr Girls Ldrship; Top 10% of Cl, Span, Eng, A's; *Stanislaus St Col; Computer Sci.*

METCALF, Victoria Lynn
Madison HS; Marshall, NC (11-75) Bus C; Chor; FBLA; FHA; *Bus.*

METCALF, William Douglas
Granite City HS S; Granite City, IL (16-656) NHS; NEDT; Yth Fel; St Stu Hist o-t Mo; *U of Mo; Elec Engr.*

METEYER, Paul William
Anchor Bay HS; New Baltimore, MI (8-250) NHS; Ski C; Cpt, Tnns; Alg A; *Bradley U; Engr.*

METOYER, Anita Marie
St Matthew HS; Melrose, LA (2-47) VP, CYO; Chor; FBLA; Secy, FHA; 4H; Co-Ed, Sch P; Bkbl; B Crocker A; 4H A; Hist A; Hon Prog; Journ A; Sal; *Northwestern St U; Journ.*

METOYER, David Keith
St Matthew HS; Melrose, LA; Band; CYO; FBLA; Bkbl; Sftbl; Alg A; Hon Prog; *Northwestern U; Hist.*

METTICA, Brenda Lee
Williamsville S HS; Williamsville, NY (168-338) Band; InterAct C; Orch; Bkbl; Sftbl; Tr; HCt; *Roberts Wesleyan Col; Nurs.*

METZ, Sarah Louise
McConnellsburg HS; McConnellsburg, PA (10-90) Chor; FHA; Co-Ed, Yrbk; *Armed Forces.*

METZ, Terri Lynn
S Park HS; Library, PA (23-153) Hmrm; Ski C; VP, Jr Cl; HCt; NEDT; WW; *Pittsburgh Beauty Acad; Cosmetology.*

METZ, Timothy Brian
Lindsay HS; Lindsay, CA (20%-120) Band; VP, Drama; FTA; 4H; Lit Ral; Swim; Tr; 4H A; Rotary Intl Leadership Conf; Stu Involvement Comm; Stu Rep, Sch Human Relations Tm; Arts & Crafts C; *Porterville Comm Col; Drama.*

METZGER, Don Ray
Moore HS; Moore, OK (1%-700) NHS; Cpt, Golf; MVP, Golf; *Okla U; Bus.*

METZGER, Don William
Coronado HS; Colorado Springs, CO (2-400) Band; NHS; Orch; Mgr, Bkbl; *Biola Col; Chem.*

METZGER, Donald William
Francisco Vasquez De Coronado; Colorado Springs, CO (2-400) Band; NHS; Orch; Mgr, Bkbl; *BIOLA Col; Chem.*

METZGER, John Tucker
Christopher Columbus HS; Miami, FL; CYO; Pres, Hmrm; NHS; Ftbl; Tr; Hon Prog; Top Ten; *Sci.*

METZGER, Laura Jean
Delphos Jefferson Sr HS; Delphos, OH (10-82) Pres, A Cap Choir; S-T, Band; Pres, Chor; Ensm; Fr C; NHS; Sch Achieve Tm; Y-Tns; Tres, Jr Cl; Co-Cpt, Bkbl; Sftbl; MVP, Tr; Amer Leg A; Pres A; Co-Cpt, Vlbl; Director's A, Band; *Adrian Col; Biological Sci.*

METZGER, Lori Ann
Peoria HS; Peoria, IL (9-230) Chor; Ensm; Ger C; NHS; Sterling Merit; Top 10; *Ill Central Col; Elem Ed.*

METZGER, Melinda Jean
E Aurora HS; Aurora, IL (24-498) Secy, A Cap Choir; Chor; Hmrm; NHS; St Scholar; USMC Fitness A; *Judson Col; Elem Ed.*

METZGER, Michael Gene
Alton Sr HS; Alton, IL (125-860) Chor; Order/ Arrow; Span C; Thes; Mgr, Bsbl.

METZGER, Randy Duane
Homestead HS; Ft Wayne, IN (13-242) Chess C; Drama; NHS; Orch; Mgr, Bkbl; Chamber of Comm A; Hist A; Eagle Sct A; *Ball St U; Med Tech.*

METZGER, Reggie Leroy
Northwood HS; Nappanee, IN; Band; Drama; Span C; Thes; Spch A; Art As; *Ashland Col; Art.*

METZGER, Richard Gerard
Fort Jennings HS; Fort Jennings, OH; BS; Pres, Jr Cl; Co-Cpt, Bkbl; Cr-Ctry; Golf; Amer Leg A; HKg; MLS; NEDT; Sci A; Schol Tm; Math Tm; *Bowling Green St U; Computer Sci.*

METZGER, Susan Elizabeth
Alfred Ely Beach HS; Savannah, GA (4-325) Anchor C; BC; 4H; NHS; Sci C; Alg A; Bio A; COM; 4H A; Math A; NEDT; Sci A; Yth Fel; Semi-Fin, Govn Hon; *U of Ga; Pre-Med.*

METZLER, Charlotte Ann
John Ehret HS; Marrero, LA (23-450) Bus C; FBLA; Hmrm; Lit Ral; NHS; Co-Ed, Sch P; Span C; SC; Pres, Soph Cl; Amer Leg A; Amer Leg Orator A; COM; Citz A; Hist A; Hon Prog; Journ A; K of C A; VFW A; VFW Orator Win; *U of New Orleans; Sci.*

METZLER, David Jerome
Taft HS; Hamilton, OH (100-525) Band; NHS; Wrest.

METZLER, Julie Lynne
Sooner HS; Bartlesville, OK (8-277) AFS; Chor; Secy, Mod Mus Mas; NHS; Span C; COM; Citz A; Kiwanis A.

METZLER, Kim Eric
Sylvania Northview HS; Sylvania, OH; Chess C; Dbte Tm; NFL; ARC; Hon Prog; Eagle Sct; *Duke U; Law.*

METZLER, Linda Jean
Appalachian HS; Oneonta, AL (2-38) Rptr, BC; 4H; Ed, Sch P; VP, Jr Cl; 4H A; Most Out; Sal; WW; *Rosedale Bible Inst; Bible.*

METZLER, Maribeth Sue
Taft Sr HS; Hamilton, OH (1-500) Chor; City Conf; Drama; Secy, Ger C; Fin, GS; NHS; Pres, Rainbow; JV, Bkbl; Tnns; COM; Ger A; *Xavier U; Radiology Tech.*

METZNER, Christine Marie
Douglas Macarthur HS; San Antonio, TX (100-516) JV, Band; Ch, Ger C; Arch; Tres, DECA; *U of Tex; Acct.*

MEUER, David John
Chilton HS; Chilton, WI (57-120) CYO; Drama; VP, FFA; Pres, 4H; JV, Wrest; 4H A; K of C A; Extem Speaking Fin; FFA As; FFA Degrees; *UW at Madison; Agr.*

MEUMANN, Deborah Jean
Redlands Sr HS; Redlands, CA; Model UN; Tres, Jobs Daughters; *Brooks Col-Long Beach; Art.*

MEURER, Elizabeth Jane
Concordia HS; Oakland, CA; Sch P; JV, Sftbl; JV, Swim; *Bio.*

MEVERDEN, Susan Marie
Newman HS; Wausau, WI (12-136) Band; GS; Sch P; Mgr, Bkbl; Co- cpt, Vlbl; WW.

MEWIS, Doralee Alice
Milano HS; Milano, TX (6-17) Ann; Cpt, Chldr; Hmrm; Lat NHS; Secy, NHS; Secy, SC; VP, Soph Cl; Cpt, Bsbl; Tr; Beauty; Cl Fav; Most Out; Swtht; Yth Fel; *Sam Houston St U; Elem Ed.*

MEYENBURG, Royce Wayne
Granite HS N; Granite City, IL (145-425) Tres, Chor; Madrigal; Mod Mus Mas; Var C; Bkbl; Cr-Ctry; Tnns; Tr.

MEYER, Barbara Ruth
Sharpsville HS; Sharpsville, PA (18-156) Chor; Ensm; NHS; S-T, Orch; VofDEM; WW; Dist Chor; Dist Orch; *Thiel Col; Bio.*

MEYER, Bruce Allan
Spring Branch Sr HS; Houston, TX (7-531) Co-Cpt, Golf; Hon Prog; Magna Cum Laude; NEDT; Pres A; Regent Schol; St Nuclear Sci Sym; *Tex Christian Col; Bus Adm.*

MEYER, Bryanna Gail
Monett HS; Monett, MO (5-125) AFS; Band; FHA; GS; NHS; SC; Tr; *Mont U; Engr.*

MEYER, Christine Ruth
Rib Lake HS; Rib Lake, WI; AFS; Band; Chor; Rptr, 4H; 4H A; S-T, Lutheran Yth.

MEYER, Cindy Lou
Ceylon Pub Sch; Ceylon, MN (3-29) VP, Band; Chldr; VP, Chor; Secy, NHS; Rptr, Sch P; SC; VP, Sr Cl; Secy, Jr Cl; Cr-Ctry; Tr; B Crocker A; HCt; Spch A; Dist, Select Band; Dist, Ensm Win; Alt, GS; Alt, Dist Spch; *Mankato St U; General Secy.*

MEYER, Cynthia Marie
Crookston Central HS; Crookston, MN (6-189) Band; *Moorhead St U.*

MEYER, David Michael
Shenandoah Valley Acad; Newmarket, VA; Pres, BC; Chor; Sci C; SC; Arch; Ftbl; Sftbl; Math A; Tumbling; Gym; *Andrews U; Industrial Arts Ed.*

MEYER, David Thomas
Gates-Chili Sr HS; Rochester, NY (94-563) Pres, Chor; Drama; Church Choir; Lay Speakers A; Director, Jr Choir; VP, Church Yth; Tres, Yorker C; *Roberts Wesleyan Col; Mus Ed.*

MEYER, Diane Ruth
Lutheran HS S; Affton, MO (36-158) Cpt, A Cap Choir; Chor; Ensm; Hmrm; Var C; Bkbl; Tr; Var Ltr, Vlbl; *U of Mo-Columbia; Home Ec.*

MEYER, Jack Allen
Ripon Sr HS; Ripon, WI (25-170) Tres, Chess C; FFA; VP, Span C; Var C; Ftbl; Bio A; COM; 4H A; Hon Prog; Spch A; *Moraine Park Tech Col; Food Manufacturing Tech.*

MEYER, James Daniel
LaFayette Central HS; LaFayette, NY; Band; Tr; *Cayaga Comm Col; Vet.*

MEYER, Jane Marie
Ripon HS; Ripon, WI (31-170) FBLA; Tres, FHA; Pres, 4H; 4H A; 4-H Co A; *Moraine Park Tech Inst; Secy Sci.*

MEYER, Janet Kay
Alta Comm HS; Alta, IA (2-73) Band; Drama; Ensm; VP, FHA; S-T, 4H; NHS; Orch; Secy, SC; Pres, Jr Cl; Bkbl; Tr; 4H A; Spch A; *Nurs.*

MEYER, Jeffrey Scott
Orchard Park HS; Orchard Park, NY (5-500) NHS; Sch P; SC; Secy, Var C; World Affairs C; MVP, Bkbl; JV, Ftbl; Tr; Hon Prog; Most Out; *Wheaton Col; Law.*

MEYER, Kathleen Ann
Fremont Ross HS; Fremont, OH (10%-494) Drama; NHS; Var C; Bkbl; Mgr, Tr; Alg A; COM; 4H A; Hon Prog; Librarian, A Cap Choir; Historian, FTA; Church Choir; Pianist, Church Choir; Vlbl; Tres, Church Luther League; *Ed.*

MEYER, Kim J
Armour HS; Armour, SD (2-29) Ann; Band; Chor; Ensm; S-T, FHA; Semi-Fin, GS; 4H; Mjrte; NFL; NHS; SC; Secy, Jr Cl; VP, Soph Cl; Bkbl; Cpt, Tr; 4H A; Outst 4-H Girl; *SD St U; Phar.*

MEYER, Laura Lynn
Moscow Sr HS; Moscow, ID (83-204) A Cap Choir; AFS; Chor; VP, Drama; Hmrm; Tnns; 4H A; Songldr, 4-H C; *U of Idaho; Coun.*

MEYER, Laura Therese
Los Alamitos HS; Los Alamitos, CA (1-680) Hmrm; Sch P; Ski C; Spch C; SC; CSF; Journ A; Most Out; Yth Fel; Orange Jr Vol Hospital; *UC-DAVIS; Landscape.*

MEYER, Lori Marlene
Lakeview HS; Battle Creek, MI (10%-400) BC; Co-Cpt, Chldr; Hmrm; NHS; SC; Bkbl; Sftbl; Tr; Hon Prog; Pres A; Sportsmanship A; Personality A.

MEYER, Marcella Jean
Washington HS; Kansas City, KS; Band; Dbte Tm; Type A; Scholastic Achv A; Yth Choir; Span A; Job's Daughters; Ambass; Yth Coun; *Nurs.*

MEYER, Mark Thomas
Glenbard S HS; Glen Ellyn, IL (21-324) Ger C; Ed, Lit Mag; NHS; Var C; MVP, Bsbl; MVP, Bkbl; Hon Prog; St Scholar; Marine Corp 'Devil Dog' A; *Trinity U; Bus Adm.*

MEYER, Marvin William
Bonner Springs HS; Bonner Springs, KS (10%-200) Band; Dbte Tm; Lat C; Order/ Arrow; JV, Bkbl; JV, Ftbl; Golf; Hon Prog; Order/ Arrow A; *Kans St U; Med.*

MEYER, Randal Dean
Benton Co R-1 HS; Cole Camp, MO; Pres, FFA; VP, Jr Cl; Greenhand; Chapter Farmer; Star Chapter Farmer; Beef Production; *St Fair Comm Col; Agr.*

MEYER, Sheryl Diane
Cissna Park HS; Cissna Park, IL (8-41) Band; Chor; VP, FHA; Pres, Ger C; VP, 4H; NHS; VP, Sr Cl; Secy, Jr Cl; Bkbl; Sftbl; Tr; NEDT; Pres A; St Scholar; Type A; *U of Ill; Phys Ed.*

MEYER, Stephanie Louise
Rib Lake HS; Rib Lake, WI (2-63) AFS; Band; Chor; Ensm; Pres, 4H; SC; B Crocker A; 4H A; NMF; Sal; Ftbl Statistician; Jazz Band; Horeographer, Swing Choir; Accompanist-Choreographer, Swing C; Schol Win, Aid As for Lutherans; *Boston U; Theater.*

MEYER, Stuart Douglas
San Ramon Valley HS; Danville, CA (44-373) BS; Pres, 4H; Pol Sci C; Pres, SC; Bank Of Amer A; CSF; 4H A; Spch A; Yth Fel; Cpt, Fin, Skiing; JV Water Polo; St Bankers Assn, Soroptomists A's; *George Washington U; Gov.*

MEYER, Susan Marie
Illinois Valley HS; Cave Junction, OR (2%-130) Band; CYO; Chor; Ensm; GS; NHS; ARC; Pres, Jr Cl; Bkbl; Sftbl; Swim; Tnns; Tr; Amer Leg A; Hon Prog; Lion A; MVP, Vlbl; Sports A; Band A; Choir A; *Therapist.*

MEYER, Terri Lyn
Stevens HS; Rapid City, SD (78-411) Chor; Dbte Tm; NFL; St Stu Congress; SC; Var C; Co-Cpt, Bkbl; Sftbl; Tr; Ntl Stu Congress; *Chadron St Col; Secondary Ed.*

MEYER, Terri Lynn
Dieterich HS; Dieterich, IL (12-54) Band; Chor; Rptr, FBLA; FHA; Sci C; VP, SC; Scholastic A; Phys Ed A; *Secy.*

MEYER, Theresa Elizabeth
Elgin HS; Elgin, IL (31-1050) Drama; Ger C; NFL; Spch C; Hon Prog; Rotary A; Drama A; *U of Ill at Urbana; Special Ed.*

MEYER, Trudy Ann
Bern HS; Bern, KS (5-25) A Cap Choir; Ann; Band; Ensm; Madrigal; Pres, SC; COM; Math A; Type A; Mus A; *Stormant Vail Sch Nurs; Surgical Technician.*

MEYER, Valerie Jeanne
John Marshall HS; San Antonio, TX (99-657) Band; Orch; 1st Cl, GSct; Region, Solo-Ensm As; St Solo; *N Ariz U; Forestry.*

MEYER, Valerie Kay
Verdi HS; Verdi, MN (3-9) A Cap Choir; Pres, Ann; Band; Chor; Ensm; 4H; Sch P; Spch C; SC; 4H A; Swtht; Mus As; Spch As; *Mankato St U; Mus.*

MEYER, Virginia Louise
Avon HS; Indianapolis, IN; A Cap Choir; Band; Chor; Drama; Pres, 4H; Madrigal; Tri-HiY; 1st Pl Solo, St Contest; *Mus Therapy.*

MEYERHOLTZ, Lois Ann
Charleston HS; Charleston, IL (47-292) Secy, AFS; Parl, FTA; NHS; Sch P; SC; VP, Jr Cl; *Eastern Ill U; Elem-Special Ed.*

MEYERS, Barbara Lynn
Ridgefield HS; Ridgefield, CT; Cpt, Chldr; Community Yth Symph; Orch; Tr; Yth Fel; Gym; *Child Psych.*

MEYERS, Cecilia Marion
Barnwell HS; Barnwell, SC (3-130) Ann; S-T, CYO; Drama; Fr C; NHS; Presbyterian Col Jr Fel; Pres HR; Jr Marshal; Hon Graduate; *U of SC; Psych.*

MEYERS, Claydon Regis
Tex City HS; Texas City, TX (31-440) Ed, Ann; Band; Secy, Key C; Amer Leg A; Journ A; Pres A; Sandy Nininger A; *Stephen F Austin St U; Communication.*

MEYERS, David Mattew
Pennsauken HS; Pennsauken, NJ (10%-600) Band; JV, Ftbl; Tr.

MEYERS, David Matthew
Pennsauken HS; Pennsauken, NJ; Band; JV, Ftbl; Tr; *Dartmouth Col.*

MEYERS, Dennis Richard
Roman Cath HS; Philadelphia, PA (45-245) Pres, CYO; Co-Ch, Hmrm; Ntl Yth Conf; Mgr, Ftbl; Co-Cpt, Hockey; Ntl Conf Chr & Jews; Pres, CYO; CYO Leadership A; *St Joseph's Col; Bus.*

MEYERS, Donald James
Ridgefield HS; Ridgefield, CT (100-500) Ann; Bus C; FBLA; Chamber of Comm A; Hon Prog; Folk Choir; VP, Church Yth; *Bryant Col; Bus Adm.*

MEYERS, Janeen Renee
South Side HS; Ft Wayne, IN (60-460) JV, Chldr; NHS; F-Ed, Sch P; Spch C; Co-Ch, Sr Cl; Tnns; Spch A; Tr Timers; Philo; Vlbl & Spch Ltrs; Service C; Hi-Y Best Citizen A; Tutors; Tourguides; *Bethel Col; Drama.*

MEYERS, JoAnne
JoAnne; Milford, CT (2-93) A Cap Choir; Pres, Chor; Drama; Madrigal; NHS; Sch P; Span C; Span NHS; VP, Jr Cl; NEDT; Type A; VFW A; *Bus Adm.*

MEYERS, Linda Elaine
Arapahoe HS; Arapahoe, NE (15-29) Band; Chor; FHA; Tnns.

MEYERS, Lisa Ann
Freeport Sr HS; Freeport, IL;

MEYERS, Marlon K
Hannibal Sr HS; Hannibal, MO; Bus C; Secy, Spch C; ROTC A; Yth Fel; Honor Cadet; *Broadcasting.*

MEYERS, Mary Beth
Ponchatoula HS; Ponchatoula, LA (18-181) Secy, BC; Bus C; FBLA; Hmrm; Jr Miss Pagent; NHS; Art C; Tres, Yth Choir; Activity Ldr, Acteens; Runner-Up, Best Dressed Fresh Yr; La Strawberry Princess; *Southeastern La U; Acct.*

MEYERS, Robbin Eileen
Iowa HS; Iowa, LA (4-94) FHA; NHS; SC; Beauty; Hist A; Math A; Key C Swtht; Best Dressed; DAR A; Eng A; *McNeese St U; Social Work.*

MEYERS, Roy Lee
Pennsauken HS; Pennsauken, NJ (39-580) Band; Model UN; Pres, NHS; Order/Arrow; Bkbl; Tr; Odd Fellow Fin; *Bowdoin Col.*

MEYERS, Susan Marie
Alton Sr HS; Alton, IL (1-820) Cpt, Chldr; Ger C; Ed, Sch P; Spch C; Cpt, Bkbl; Star Student; Vlbl; *Art.*

MEYLE, Terry Ann
William Tennent HS; Warminster, PA (4-27) Chor; Hmrm; SC.

MEYNE, Linda Kay
Pender HS; Pender, NE (1-42) Band; Chldr; Chor; Drama; FHA; 4H; NHS; SC; Var C; Bkbl; MVP, Tr; 4H A; HCt; Regent Schol; Spch A; Type A; Val; *VofDEM; Cpt, Vlbl; Shorthand A; U of Nebr; Acct.*

MEZERA, Joan Helena
Waupun Sr HS; Waupun, WI (50-320) CYO; Dbte Tm; FBLA; Church Coun; *Sci.*

MICHAEL, Beth Ann
Gibsonburg HS; Gibsonburg, OH (27-122) Ann; Band; Chldr; Fr C; 4H; SC; Var C; MVP, Bkbl; Cpt, Sftbl; Cpt, Tr; COM; Yth Fel; MVP, Tr; All League Vlbl; *Ohio St U.*

MICHAEL, Daniel Wayne
Raytown S HS; Raytown, MO (45-580) COM; Regent Schol; *SW Mo St U; Bio.*

MICHAEL, Elizabeth Carol
S Mecklenburg HS; Pineville, NC (9%-630) NHS; Ski C; Art C; Governor's Sch, 1976; *UNC-Chapel Hill; Art.*

MICHAEL, Flora Denise
William Penn Sr HS; York, PA (33%-300) Band; Bus C; Hmrm; SC; Y-Tns; Hockey; Amer Leg A; Beauty; HCt; Hon Prog; Yth Fel; *Western Maryland Jr Col; Legal Secy.*

MICHAEL, Gary Eugene
G A R Mem HS; Wilkes-Barre, PA (4-179) Chor; NHS; *Wilkes Col; Med.*

MICHAEL, Heather Milada
Washington HS; Washington, PA; Band; Pres, Hmrm; Model UN; SC; Thes; Y-Tns.

MICHAEL, Joann
Kingsway Regional HS; Swedesboro, NJ (17-166) Ann; Chem C; FNA; Key C; NHS; Phys C; SC; JV, Bkbl; Tr; Ntl Sci Symposium; Yth Fel; Stat, Bsbl; *Cedar Crest Col; Nurs.*

MICHAEL, Kimberly Rene
Bremen HS; Bremen, IN (35-120) Bkbl; Sftbl; Tr; Vlbl; *Phys Ed.*

MICHAEL, Mallorie L
Schenley HS; Pittsburgh, PA (10-200) Fr C; Hmrm; NHS; Orch; Tnns; COM; Citz A; DARGCA; Hon Prog; JA A; Math A; *U of Pa; Engr.*

MICHAEL, Raymond John III
Manheim Central HS; Manheim, PA (61-264) Bsbl; COM; VICA; *Elec Engr.*

MICHAEL, Toni Lynn
Deshler HS; Tuscumbia, AL (25%-150) FHA.

MICHAEL, Vicki Lynn
Haxtun HS; Haxtun, CO (11-27) Band; Chldr; Chor; FBLA; Pres, FHA; Secy, Jr Cl; Swtht; Type A; Vlbl; Fin, FFA Swtht; *Stenography.*

MICHAEL, Wesley William
Arvin HS; Arvin, CA (15%-243) Band; Chor; Drama; Ensm; Golf; *US Air Force; Elec.*

MICHAELIAN, Richard Charles
Menchville HS; Newport News, VA (15%-650) Rptr, Ann; Chess C; Var C; Golf; COM; Citz A; Newspaper Carrier A; *Math.*

MICHAELS, Brian James
St Charles Sr HS; St Charles, MO (30-615) A Cap Choir; Key C; NHS; Cpt, Ftbl; Tr; NCAA Schol; *Sou Ill U; Med Tech.*

MICHAELSON, Elizabeth Jane
Courtenay Pub Sch; Courtenay, ND; Chldr; Chor; 4H; Sch P; Bkbl; Sftbl; Tr; Sci A; Type A.

MICHAL, Eunice Lorraine
Flagler Pub Sch; Flagler, CO (5-14) A-Ed, Ann; Band; Bus C; Chldr; Chor; FBLA; VP, FFA; FTA; 4H; Pres, Hmrm; Mjrte; Sch P; Spch C; SC; VP, Jr Cl; Tres, Soph Cl; Bkbl; Tr; 4H A; Spch A; Swtht; Type A; *Barbizon Col; Fashion.*

MICHALIK, Michael Jay
Big Bay de Noc HS; Cooks, MI (10%-60) VP, Soph Cl; JV, Bkbl; JV, Tr; Phy A; Bkbl Ltr; Tr Hon A; *Maranatha Baptist Bible Col; Sacred Mus.*

MICHALSKI, Mary Josephine
Phoenixville Area HS; Phoenixville, PA (20%-500) Ski C; Tnns; Riding C; Art.

MICHALSKI, Paul Peter
Amsterdame HS; Amsterdam, NY (2%-400) Hmrm; NHS; Order/Arrow; Rptr, Sch P; SC; Var C; Mgr, Wrest; Hon Prog; JA A; 1st, St Newspaper Carrier o-t Yr; Mem Conservation A; 1st, Rotary Essay Contest; Woodworking A; Art A; *Law.*

MICHALSKY, Linda Sue
Connellsville Sr HS; Connellsville, PA (40%-600) A Cap Choir; Chor; Hmrm; Rptr, Sch P; Span NHS; Tri-HiY; Sftbl; *Duff's Bus Inst; Med Transcriptionist.*

MICHAUD, Jacques
Col De Ste Anne De La Pocatiere; La Pocatiere, CANADA (2-30) CYO; Swim; Spch A; *Hist.*

MICHAUD, Nelson
College De Ste Anne De La Pocatiere; La Pocatiere, CANADA (1-29) CYO; Drama; Pres, Sch P; Bsbl; Bkbl; ARC A; Spch A; Ntl Photo A; Lat A; *CEGEP de La Pocatiere; Health Sci.*

MICHAUD, Renee
College De Ste Anne De La Pocatiere; La Pocatiere, CANADA; CYO; Pres, Hmrm; SC; Var C; Bkbl; Athletic A.

MICHEL, Brenda Sue
Whitehouse HS; Whitehouse, TX (7-99) Band; BC; NHS; Bkbl; Fin, Tr; *Tyler Jr Col; Drafting.*

MICHEL, Charles Eugene
Halifax Co Sr HS; S Boston, VA (10%-700) Band; Chor; Bsbl; Band A's; *Engr.*

MICHEL, Dianne Lee
Roxborough Sr HS; Philadelphia, PA; Chldr; Mgr, Wrest; Amer Leg A; Bowl; Sr GSct; Associate Ldr, Jr GSct; BYF; *Art.*

MICHEL, Mark Bachdon
Chester HS; Chester, PA; Hmrm; Math C; Pol Sci
C; Ftbl; Tnns; *Widener Col; Pol Sci.*

MICHEL, Paul Donald
Lake Oswego HS; Lake Oswego, OR (56-267) Sci
C; Sftbl; Ch, Lutheran Yth; Church Chor; *U of
Oreg; Acct.*

MICHEL, Susan Jean
York Sr HS; York, NE (13-156) Chldr; Chor; VP,
Fr C; Rptr, NHS; Pres Schol, Nebr Weselyan U;
Nebr Wesleyan U.

MICHELON, Susan Dorothie
Weed HS; Weed, CA (1-162) Band; Pres, CYO;
4H; NHS; Co-Ed, Sch P; Ski C; SC; Cpt, Bkbl; Ftbl;
Sftbl; Tr; CSF; COM; WW; *Chico St Col; Bus Adm.*

MICHELS, Stephen Link
Greenville HS; Greenville, IL; Fr C; Cr-Ctry; Tnns;
Tr; Yth Fel; Yth Foundation; Pres, Southern Ill
Conf Yth Coun; *U of Ill; Drafting.*

MICHELSEN, Karen Joyce
Blacksburg HS; Blacksburg, VA (52-300) Pres,
Drama; Monogram; NHS; SC; Co-Cpt, Cr-Ctry;
Cpt, Tr; *Bucknell U; Lib Arts.*

MICHELSON, Andi L
Manchester HS; Akron, OH (16-250) A Cap Choir;
AFS; Band; VP, Drama; Fr C; NFL; Tr; COM;
Spch A; *Wittenberg Col; Psych.*

MICHIE, Anne Marie
Royal HS; Simi, CA (141-454) CYO; Cpt, Chldr;
Spch C; Swim; Tr; Vlbl; *Communications.*

MICHL, Alan Richard
Exeter Pub Sch; Exeter, NE (14-140) A-Ed, Ann;
Band; BS; Drama; FFA; Pres, 4H; Math C; NHS;
Spch C; Var C; Bkbl; Ftbl; Tr; Citz A; Math A; Spch
A; WW; *U of Nebr at Lincoln; Agr.*

MICHL, Robert Wayne
Exeter Pub HS; Exeter, NE (8-32) A-Ed, Ann;
Band; Chor; Drama; Ensm; Pres, FFA; 4H; Hmrm;
Math C; NHS; Spch C; Var C; Bsbl; Bkbl; Ftbl;
MVP, Golf; Citz A; Hist A; Yth Fel; FFA Star
Greenhand; *Hastings Col; Phys Ed.*

MICHNIEWICZ, Gary Gerard
Quigley Prep Sem S; Chicago, IL (34-240) Pres,
CYO; Ski C; Co-Cpt, Bsbl; Cr-Ctry; Tr; JV, Wrest;
Hon Prog; Ch, Retreat Committee; HR; Dean's
List; *Niles Col; Pre-Med.*

MICHNIEWICZ, Martin Edwin
Quigley Prep Sem S; Chicago, IL (26-257) Pres,
CYO; Chor; NHS; SC; Sftbl; Tr; Wrest; Hon Prog;
Loyola Col; Med.

MICK, Susan Loraine
Hendersonville Sr HS; Hendersonville, TN; Bus C;
Span C; Ntl Piano Playing Auditions; *Olivet Naza-
rene Col; Secretarial Sci.*

MICKELSON, Steven Robert
Coshocton HS; Coshocton, OH (12-244) Secy, Key
C; NHS; SC; Pres, Jr Cl; VP, Soph Cl; Ftbl; *Miami
U; Law.*

MICKEY, Frank Doebler IV
Parkdale Sr HS; Riverdale, MD; Chor; Orch; Orch
Letters; Yth Chor; *Computer Related.*

MICKEY, Victoria Kathleen
Parkdale Sr HS; Riverdale, MD; Chor; Tr; Tr A;
Candy Striper; Yth Choir; Sch Letter, High Grade
Point; *Nurs.*

MICKLE, Collier Edwards
Notre Dame HS; Shreveport, LA (2-22) Ann;
CYO; Hmrm; NHS; ARC; Sodality; Mgr, Bkbl; Alg
A; COM; Citz A; HCt; I Dare You; Journ A; Math
A; Sal; *LSU; Acct.*

MICKLES, Patricia Elizabeth
SW Miami Sr HS; Miami, FL; Chor; FBLA; FHA;
Hmrm; SC.

MICKOW, Laurie Adeline
Kingfisher HS; Kingfisher, OK (23-96) A Cap
Choir; Band; Chor; Dbte Tm; Drama; Ensm; Pres,
4H; Model UN; A-Ed, Sch P; Spch C; SC; 4H A;
Spch A; Yth Fel; Pres, Yth Fellowship; Okla Hon
Soc; Pres, Art C; 1st Pl, Ensm A; Yth Phys Fitness
A; Outst Bandsman.

MIDDLEBROOK, Cynthia Joy
Craigmont Sr HS; Memphis, TN; Chor; Drama;
Rptr, Sch P; *Oral Roberts U; Pol Sci.*

**MIDDLEBROOK,
Marian Elizabeth**
Immaculata HS; Detroit, MI; *Lake Superior Col;
Ed.*

**MIDDLEBROOKS,
Gregory Lynn**
Bowdon HS; Bowdon, GA (15-144) Pres, Hmrm;
Key C; Span C; Ftbl; Golf; Eng A; *W Ga Col; Law.*

**MIDDLEBROOKS,
Michael Lloyd**
Plant City HS; Plant City, FL (100-700) VP, Band;
BS; Model UN; *U of S Fla; Engr.*

MIDDLEBROOKS, Tamara Kay
Dothan HS; Dothan, AL (26-520) Drama; NHS;
Span C; Thes; *Religion.*

**MIDDLEKAUFF,
William Bradford**
Walnut Hills HS; Cincinnati, OH; Rptr, Sch P; SC;
Tnns; Hon Prog; Ntl Sci Symposium; Yth Fel;
Psych.

MIDDLESTEAD, Lynn
El Toro HS; El Toro, CA; Hon Prog; Folk Mus
Group; Limeaide Prog; Church Yth Ldrship; *Ed.*

MIDDLETON, Cynthia Ann
Rio Grande HS; Albuquerque, NM (18-750) FFA;
Secy, NHS; Swim; Hon Prog; *Tarleton Col; Bio.*

MIDDLETON, David Dean
Dalton HS; Dalton, GA (42-241) Key C; NHS; JV,
Bkbl; Ftbl; Tr; COM; Cl Fav; Hon Prog; Spch A;
Yth Fel; FCA Christian Ath o-t Yr; St Part, Baptist
Speakers Tourn; Sportsmanship A; Best All-
Around; *Furman U; Christian Work.*

MIDDLETON, David Owen
Kalamazoo Loy Norrix HS; Kalamazoo, MI
(55-418) Ann; VP, SC; VP, Chor; Sr Cl Cab; VP
Camera C; WW; Photographer Yrbk; Pres, Co In-
tersch Coun; Presidental Clrm for Yng Amers;
Northwestern U; Econ.

MIDDLETON, Debra Ann
George Washington Carver Sr HS; Montgomery,
AL (13-400) Chor; Ensm; Hmrm; Madrigal; NHS;
Tri-HiY; Sci A; Home Ec, Gavel, Best Mannered,
A's; All St Chor; *Troy St U; Special Ed.*

MIDDLETON, Debra Joy
New Smyrna Beach HS; New Smyrna Beach, FL
(11-341) Pres, FNA; InterClub Coun; Lit Ral;
NHS; COM; Hon Prog; Magna Cum Laude; Math
A; Yth Fel; *Flagler Col; Special Ed.*

MIDDLETON, Denise Bertha
Deer Park HS; Deer Park, NY; Band; Span C; Bkbl;
Tnns; Dance A.

MIDDLETON, Dianne Pauline
Columbia HS; Columbia, IL (15-127) Band;
Drama; Fr C; FTA; Math C; NHS; Arch; Tr; Opt
A; *Drama.*

MIDDLETON, Gwenevere Avis
Hardy Jr HS; Jackson, MS; Chor; Hmrm; Secy,
NHS; Mgr, Sch P; Sci C; St Stu Congress; SC; Citz
A; Pres, Yth Group; Ntl Explorers Post; *Miss Col;
Psychiatry.*

MIDDLETON, Lisa Lynne
Anna Jonesboro HS; Anna, IL (33%-180) FHA;
Sftbl; Home Ec A; *SE Mo U; Mus.*

MIDDLETON, Rannie Lee Jr
Raleigh HS; Raleigh, MS (50%-76) BC; BS; FFA;
4H; Math C; Sch P; Sci C; Span C; *Jones Jr Col;
Med.*

MIDDLETON, Rita Jo
Van-Far R-1 HS; Vandalia, MO; Band; F-Ed, Sch P;
Secy, Sr Cl; Tres, Jr Cl; Q&S A; PA.

MIDGETT, Kemberly Mark
John Overton HS; Nashville, TN (15-422) BC;
Chess C; NHS; Span C; COM; Hon Prog; Math A;
Tenn Tech U; Engr.

MIDKIFF, Susan Elaine
Mission HS; Mission, TX (4-356) Band; GS; Secy,
NHS; SC; Pres, Sr Cl; Pres, Jr Cl; Cr-Ctry; Tnns;
Cpt, Tr; Cl Fav; NEDT; Co-Cpt, Vlbl; *West Point
Military Acad; Pre-Med.*

MIDLAND, Mark David
Maryville R-2 HS; Maryville, MO (4-190) Band;
Chor; Dbte Tm; Fr C; NFL; NHS; Sci C; Tr; Engr.

MIDLICK, Annette Marie
Neshaminy Maple Point HS; Langhorne, PA
(9-417) Chldr; NHS; Var C; Ch, Jr Cl; Ch, Soph Cl;
Med Tech.

MIDURE, Karen Ann
St Joseph HS; Hammonton, NJ (4-63) Cpt, Bkbl;
Sftbl; *Nurs.*

MIDYETTE, Allen Dale
Mattamuskeet HS; Swan Quarter, NC (2-100) BC;
Fr C; Pres, 4H; Sci C; SC; Pres, Soph Cl; Bsbl; Mgr,
Bkbl; Ftbl; Alg A; 4H A; Type A; PA; *Math.*

MIDYETTE, James Emery Jr
Mattamuskeet HS; Swan Quarter, NC (6-70) Co-
Ed, Ann; BC; Fr C; Pres, 4H; Monogram; Sci C;
SC; Parl, Jr Cl; Rptr, Soph Cl; Bsbl; Ftbl; 4H A;
Type A; PA; *NC St U; Agr.*

MIEDEMA, Lana Sue
Warren Central HS; Indianapolis, IN (71-935)
Chor; Drama; 4H; Crisco A; *Ball St U; Ed.*

MIELKE, Christine
Seguin HS; Seguin, TX; Ger C; Hmrm; SC; Hon
Prog; Tres, Candystriper; Yth Choir; Happy Soles
Squaredance C; Duchess, Luth Charity Corona-
tion; Secy; Yth Ministry Com; Luther Lge; *Med.*

MIELKE, Suzann Kay
Albert Lea HS; Albert Lea, MN (111-575) Band;
Chor; Drama; Orch; Thes; Thespians Actor o-t Yr;
St Olaf Col; Drama.

MIERS, Barbara Sue
E Hills HS; Fort Worth, TX (85-565) Chor; A-Ed,
Lit Mag; Citz A; Hist A; Spch A; Ntl Piano Guild
Auditions; Camp Bible Stu; Mus Teachers Forum;
Baylor U; Mus.

MIERTSCHIN, Mark Alan
Spring Branch Sr HS; Houston, TX (3-531) Chess
C; JETS; Secy, Math C; Secy, Mu Alpha Theta;
Pres, NHS; Alg A; Magna Cum Laude; Math A;
MLS; Most Out; NMF; Phy A; *U of Tex; Engr.*

MIERZEJEWSKI, Stephen John
Xavier HS; Middletown, CT (7-176) NHS; JV,
Bkbl; JV, Tr; Ntl Merit Commended Stu; *U of
Conn; Elec Engr.*

MIESSE, Mark Bennett
Christian Brothers HS; Memphis, TN (35-250)
CYO; Tres, Fr C; Soccer; Swim; Hon Prog; Sci A;
Yth Fel; *U of Tenn; Med.*

MIFFLIN, Annette Elizabeth
Zion Benton Township HS; Zion, IL (60-475)
Chor; Ensm; Sftbl; VP, Yth Exec; Yth Choir; *Trin-
ity Col; Elem Ed.*

MIGENES, Victor
Academia Discipulos de Cristo; Bayamon, PR
(10-122) A Cap Choir; Chem C; Chess C; Chor;
Pres, Drama; FTA; Secy, Hmrm; Math C; NHS;
Order/ Arrow; Phys C; F-Ed, Sch P; Sci C; Span C;
Spch C; SC; Secy, Sr Cl; Secy, Jr Cl; Secy, Soph Cl;
Co-Cpt, Ftbl; Co-Cpt, Soccer; Tnns; Alg A; Bio A;
Chem A; Citz A; Hist A; Hon Prog; Journ A; Math
A; Order/ Arrow A; Phy A; Sci A; Spch A; Summa
Cum Laude; Eagle Sct; *US Air Force Acad; Aeros-
pace Sci.*

MIGHTY, Colin Anthony
Evander Childs HS; New York City, NY (28-917)
Attendance A; *Bradford Col.*

MIGLER, Donna Lynn
St Barbara HS; Chicago, IL (2-80) Chor; *Math.*

MIGLIOZZI, Ralph Joseph
L B Jordan HS; Long Beach, CA (35-631) Tres, SC;
Bsbl; Co-Cpt, Ftbl; Tr; Co-Cpt, Wrest; Citz A; Elk
A; Hon Prog; Opt A; Spch A; All League Ftbl; Fin,
MVP, Wrest; *Stanford U; Biol Ed.*

MIGUES, Patrice Theresa
St Joseph HS; Jeanerette, LA (3-28) CYO; NHS;
COM; X-Ray Tech.

MIHALCAK, Daniel Joseph
W Middlesex Area HS; W Middlesex, PA (2-170)
Span NHS; VP, Jr Cl; Co-Cpt, Ftbl; Tr; Type A;
Ftbl Tri-Ctry All Star Hon Men; *Art Inst of Pitts-
burgh; Photography.*

MIHALICK, Jolene Dawn
Central Fulton HS; McConnellsburg, PA; Band;
Chor; FHA; 4H; InterAct C; Arch; Bkbl; Hockey;
Soccer; Sftbl; Tr.

MIHELICH, Carolyn Denise
New Caney HS; Porter, TX (25%-280) Band; Secy,
FHA; 4H; Mjrte; NHS; Tex A&M St U.

MIHOK, Marsha
Laurel Highlands HS; Uniontown, PA (6-407)
Chor; Span C; Swim; Amer Leg A; Yth Fel; Bio.

MIHURA, Joni Lynn
Tecumseh HS; Tecumseh, OK (5-135) Band; Chor;
Community Yth Symph; Ensm; FHA; Bkbl; Sftbl;
Tr; Hon Prog; NEDT; Phy A; St Scholar; Yth Fel;
St Hon Soc; Best Contributing Bkbl Player; OSU
Academic A; Chem.

MIKALOFF, Karen Louise
River Forest HS; Hobart, IN (6-130) Band; Pres,
NHS; SC; B Crocker A; MLS; St Scholar; Type A;
Fr A; Valparaiso U; Home Ec.

MIKALOFF, Robert Scott
River Forest HS; Hobart Twp, IN; Band; Ind U;
Optometry.

MIKEL, Allen Bret
Lafayette HS; Ellisville, MO (33%-451) Bsbl; Ftbl;
Hon Prog; FCA.

MIKEL, Julie Louise
Lafayette HS; Ellisville, MO (33%-600).

MIKEL, Mark Steven
North Wood HS; Nappanee, IN (5-200) Chor;
Ensm; Monogram; NHS; Thes; Ftbl; Tr; FCA.

MIKKOLA, Carolyn Nadine
Houghton HS; Houghton, MI (3-125) Band; Span
C; Tres, Soph Cl; JV, Bkbl; Swim; HCt; NEDT.

**MIKOLAJCZYK,
Michelle Marie**
St Andrew HS; Detroit, MI (1-83) Ed, Ann; Bus C;
Drama; Math C; NHS; COM; Journ A; MLS; Re-
gent Schol; Val; Secy, Adm Comm; PA; Mich
Comp Schol; U of M-Ann Arbor; Pre-Bus.

MIKULA, Gregory John
Leo HS; Chicago, IL (1-152) Ftbl; JV, Tr; Hon
Prog; Purdue U; Math.

MILAM, Lisa Michelle
Lloyd V Berkner HS; Richardson, TX (25%-600) A
Cap Choir; Ensm; Rptr, Sch P; Arch; Journ A; Q&S
A; Church Choir; UIL Solo & Ensm A; Church SC;
All-Dist Hon Choir A; Chrch Hndbel Chr; Gold
Med-Archery; Al-Dist Solo & Ensm As; Al-Co
Olymp; Journ.

MILAM, Stacey Ann
Decatur HS; Decatur, AL; VP, Fr C; Hmrm; NHS;
SC; Alg A; Hon Prog; Auburn U; Fashion Mer-
chandising.

MILAN, Russell Earl
Marine Military Acad; Harlingen, TX (4-43) NHS;
Ftbl; VFW A; Superintendent's List; Sch Schol A;
Tex A&M U; Computer Sci.

MILBOURNE, Phillip Kenneth
Woodson Sr HS; Washington, DC; Band; JETS; Tr;
Industrial Arts A; Wash Tech Inst; Architecture.

MILBY, Janet Rhea
Pike Co HS; Zebulon, GA (1-154) F-Ed, Ann; BC;
JV, Chldr; Chor; FHA; Parl, 4H; Hmrm; Secy,
Math C; Span C; SC; Bio A; 4H A; HCt; Hon Prog;
JA A; Math A; Ga Key A; Square Dance Ribbon;
Leadership Medal; Berry Col; Conservation.

MILDRUM, Cora Sue
Carroll HS; Ozark, AL (47-290) Ann; Band; Yth
Fel; Festival of Arts A; George C Wallace St Jr Col;
Art.

MILES, Amy Ruth
Holland HS; Holland, MI; Band; High Grades Hon
Pin; Pep Band; Expedition C; Dutch Dance C;
Schol; Dutch Dance C; Schol A; Central Mich U;
Teaching.

MILES, Awanda
J F Kennedy HS; NY, NY;

MILES, Candy Ann
Kelly HS; Chicago, IL (24-485) Mjrte; NHS; ARC;
Sci C; Bio A; Hon Prog; ARC A; Sci A; Type A;
Service A.

MILES, Charles Amos
McMullen Co HS; Tilden, TX (1-6) Pres, FFA;
Pres, 4H; Pres, NHS; Pres, SC; Tnns; COM; 4H A;
Tex A&M U; Vet Sci.

MILES, Dana Beth
Norman HS; Norman, OK; A Cap Choir; Rptr,
Ann; Hmrm; Ed, Lit Mag; Orch; Span C; Journ A;
Candy Striper; HS Symphonic Orch; Campfire
Hon; Chapel Choir; News-Ed, Sch Paper; Worth
Adv, Rain; Personal Column, City Newspaper;
Okla U; Journ.

MILES, Debra Kay
Apollo HS; Owensboro, KY (33%-390) Band; BC;
FHA; Hmrm; SC; JA A.

MILES, Diane
Compton HS; Compton, CA (12-800) NHS; CSF;
Hist A; Chapman Col; Communications.

MILES, Earnest Edward II
Alma J Brown Lab HS; Grambling, LA (15-50)
Chor; Pres, Drama; FBLA; Pres, FTA; InterClub
Coun; VP, NHS; Pres, Sci C; SC; Parl, Sr Cl; Co-
Cpt, Ftbl; Bio A; COM; Hon Prog; Math A; Most
Out; NEDT; Sci A; Eng A; All Star Ftbl; La Tech
U; Elec Engr.

MILES, Gail Anne
Holland HS; Holland, MI (7-300) Band; NHS;
Bkbl; Tr; Bio A; Church Yth; Dutch Dance; Mich
St U; Med.

MILES, Jimmy Jerome
St Angela Acad; Aiken, SC (5-40) Pres, Hmrm; VP,
Key C; NHS; Sci C; SC; Var C; Bkbl; Ftbl; Golf; Bio
A; Cl Fav; Hist A; Math A; MLS; Sci A; Ger A;
Phys Ed A; U of SC; Denistry.

MILES, Karen Addie Elizabeth
Heidelberg American HS; Heidelberg, GER-
MANY (19-170) Tres, Ger C; NHS; Spch A; Sou
Methodist U; Bus.

MILES, Karen Annette
Marshall HS; Marshall, MO (4-189) Chor; Pres,
4H; Hmrm; SC; VP, Soph Cl; Sftbl; Swim; Bio A;
4H A; Math A; Mo Freedom Forum; Vlbl; Stephens Col; Natural Sci.

MILES, Larry Travis
Tanner HS; Tanner, AL (5-70) Mu Alpha Theta;
JV, Bsbl; JV, Bkbl; U of Ala; Pre-Law.

MILES, Lois Rose
Eastern Guilford HS; Gibsonville, NC (10-175)
Band; Hmrm; Sci C; SC.

MILES, Marvin Nathaniel
Southfield HS; Southfield, MI (45-600) Bkbl; Tr;
Citz A; H of F; Yth Fel; Most Determination; Most
Free Throws; Wayne St U; Mgt.

MILES, Melinda Sue
St Johns HS; Darlington, SC (11-175) Tres, Drama;
NHS; Yth Fel; Jr Marshal.

MILES, Pamela Ruth
Loyalton HS; Loyalton, CA (1-38) Ann; Band;
Chor; Drama; FBLA; GS; Tres, 4H; Spch C; Secy,
SC; Cpt, Bkbl; Sftbl; Semi-Fin, Band of Amer A;
Fin, 4-H C A; Fin, Lion's C A; Fin, Spch A; Yuba
Col; Sociology.

MILES, Peggy Lee
John F Kennedy HS; New Orleans, LA (39-368)
BC; VP, Drama; Fr C; Hmrm; Math C; S-T, Mu
Alpha Theta; NHS; Spch C; Tri-HiY; COM; Hon
Prog; Math A; Ntl Cath Mus Ed Asn; Pres A; Yth
Fel; Centenary Col of La; Broadcast Journ.

MILES, Rebecca Sue
Springfield HS; Springfield, IL (92-509) Chor; 4H;
SC; 4H A; Pep C A; Scholastic A; Greenville Col;
Bus.

MILES, Sandra Jean
Okeene HS; Okeene, OK; Band; Chor; FHA; Jr
Miss Pagent; Hmrm; Rptr, Sch P; Var C; Bkbl;
HQn; HCt; Okla St Col; Bus.

MILES, Scott Greg
Cypress HS; Cypress, CA; Hmrm; NHS; Ski C;
CSF; Mentally Gifted Minors; Systems Engr.

MILES, Sherilyn Regina
Gardena HS; Gardena, CA (178-1000) FHA;
FNA; 4H; Fin, Jr Miss Pagent; Mjrte; Span C; Y-
Tns; Sftbl; 4H A; Hist A; I Dare You; Kiwanis A;
Swtht; Occupational Therapy.

MILES, Stephanie Ann
Leeton HS; Leeton, MO; Chldr; Chor; Ensm; FHA;
Pres, 4H; Sch P; Rptr, Soph Cl; 4H A; Mus A; PA;
CMSU; Med Secy.

MILES, Theresa Lynn
Calhoun HS; Calhoun, GA (9-230) Band; BC;
Chor; Fin, Jr Miss Pagent; Mu Alpha Theta; Rptr,
Sch P; Thes; COM; Gov Honor Prog; Kiwanis A;
Outst Sr; Shorter Col; Voice.

MILES, Tracy Ann
Cleveland HS; Cleveland, TN; All Amer Yth; BC;
VP, CYO; Sch P; SC; Pres, Tri-HiY; Cpt, Bkbl;
COM; Converse Col; Lib Arts.

MILEWSKI, Diana Monica
Amos Alonzo Stagg HS; Palos Hills, IL (168-512)
Ann; Ger C; SC; Var C; Tres, Jr Cl; HCt; Pres,
Health Occupations; Pom-Pons; Scorekeeper, Bsbl;
VICA; Moraine Valley Col; Gen.

MILEWSKI, Linda Alice
Naperville Central HS; Naperville, IL; Band; Math
C; Hon Prog; Bus.

MILEY, Everett Gerrard
Gibbs HS; St Petersburg, FL;

MILEY, Everette Gerrad
Gibbs HS; St Petersburg, FL;

MILEY, Jenyne Louise
Prescott HS; Prescott, AZ (50%-400) 4H; Yauapai
Col; Bus.

MILEY, Lisa Ann
Dothan HS; Dothan, AL (10-240) Band; Chor; Jr
NHS; Yth Choir; UAB; Phys Therapist.

MILEY, Michelle Marie
Prescott HS; Prescott, AZ (50%-418) Chldr; Chor;
Ensm; FHA; Secy, 4H; Rainbow; ARC; COM; 4H
A; ARC A; Type A; Ariz St U; Nurs.

MILHOLLIN, Danita Faye
Broxton HS; Broxton, GA (2-37) Secy, BC; Tres,
FHA; Rptr, Sch P; Pres, SC; Var C; Bkbl; COM;
WW Among Tomorrow's Homemakers; Abraham
Baldwin Agr Col; Secondary Ed.

MILHOUS, John William
Turlock HS; Turlock, CA (10%-410) Pres, Band;
Bank of Amer A; CSF; COM; Math A; Calif Poly-
tech Col; Archt.

MILHOUS, Kathryn Banks
Athens Acad; Athens, GA (1-20) Bus Mgr, Ann;
Pres, Ger C; VP, 4H; Co-Ed, Lit Mag; Secy, NHS;
Rptr, Sch P; VP, Sci C; SC; Bkbl; Bio A; Gov Honor
Prog; 4H A; Hon Prog; I Dare You; Most Out;
NEDT; St Key A; WW; Biol.

MILHOUS, Lisa Ann
Turlock HS; Turlock, CA (10%-535) Band; Orch;
CSF; COM; Type A; Calif St U; Psych.

MILLAR, Barbara Patrice
Central HS; Rapid City, SD; Sioux Falls Col; Ed.

MILLARD, Brian Lee
Bridgeport HS; Bridgeport, OH (8-128) HiY; Pres,
NHS; Span C; Cpt, Bkbl; VofDEM; Law.

MILLARD, Elaine
Emerson HS; Gary, IN (15-222) Chor; Fr C; NHS;
Up Bound; St Scholar; Purdue U; Linguistics.

MILLARD, Mary Elizabeth
Fenton HS; Bensenville, IL; 1st Pl, Shorthand Con-
test; Secy, Office Ed C; Outst Office Ed Stu o-t Yr;
Ntl Piano Auditions; Secy.

MILLARD, Thomas Alan
Red Bank HS; Chattanooga, TN (2%-400) Band;
Chem C; Chess C; Demolay; Ensm; Lat C; Model
UN; NHS; Order/Arrow; JV, Bkbl; Sftbl; Tr; JV,
Wrest; Alg A; Amer Leg A; Aux Lat; Hon Prog;
NMS; Order/Arrow A; Star Student; U of Tenn;
Computer Sci.

MILLER, Alan S
Notre Dame-Bishop Gibbons HS; Schenectady,
NY (21-280) Cpt, Chess C; NEDT; Regent Schol;
Union Col; Physics.

MILLER, Alvin Earl
Banning HS; Banning, CA (143-218) Cpt, Band;
VP, Chor; Co-Ch, Dbte Tm; Fr C; VP, Ushers; Yth
Conf; Ch, Jr Deacons; Calif St U; Ed.

MILLER, Andrea Michelle
Lamden HS; Camden, NJ (5-406) Secy, Band;
Hmrm; VP, NHS; Secy, Orch; SC; Hist A; WW;
Brandeis U; Pol Sci.

MILLER, Andrew John
Vandalia Christian Sch; Greensboro, NC (3-14) Ann; Monogram; Rptr, Sch P; VP, Span C; Bkbl; Soccer; HCt; High Point Col.

MILLER, Anne Liese
Fremont Christian HS; Fremont, CA (5-83) Chor; Var C; Bus Mgr, Soph Cl; Bkbl; Sftbl; Tr; Hon Prog; Yth Leg; Hon Men; Principal's HR.

MILLER, Annis Powel
Morristown-Hamblen HS W; Morristown, TN (49-294) Anchor C; Band; Tres, Chor; Lat C; Carson-Newman Col.

MILLER, Arlezer Le Verne
Buena HS; Sierra Vista, AZ; Hmrm; Bus Mgr Minority Stu Union; Art A; Poetry A; Pima Jr Col; Psych.

MILLER, Babette Teresa
Sky View HS; Smithfield, UT (7-622) FHA; 4H; Sci A; Schol A.

MILLER, Barbara Jean
Holland HS; Holland, MI (12-300) Band; Ger C; Lat C; NHS; Orch; Var C; Cpt, Swim; Hon Prog; MVP, Swim; Schol, Holland Coun for Arts; Furman U; Pre-Med.

MILLER, Barbara Lynn
Granite City HS; Granity City, IL (75-700) Drama; Spch C; Bellville Area Col; Med.

MILLER, Belinda
East HS; Cleveland, OH (36-292) Chor; SC; COM; Pres A; A of Hon; Martha Holdens Jennings A; Dyke Col; Secretarial Sci.

MILLER, Belinda Jean
Booker T Washington HS; Norfolk, VA (2-500) Drama; VP, Fr C; FBLA; NHS; Sch Achieve Tm; Thes; Citz A; Opt A; Newspaper Scholastic Tm; Fr.

MILLER, Beth Ann
Clear Lake HS; Clear Lake, IA (1-150) AFS; Ed, Ann; Band; Pres, 4H; Lat C; Tres, NHS; Golf; Citz A; Crisco A; 4H A; Spch A; Vlbl; Iowa St U; Vet Med.

MILLER, Betty Jane
Gateway Regional HS; Woodbury Heights, NJ (1-257) Hmrm; Model UN; Tres, SC; Mgr, Bkbl; JV, Hockey; JV, Tnns; Bio A; Hon Prog; Lion A; Rensselaer A; Sci A; Med Tech.

MILLER, Beverly Ann
Martin Co HS; Stuart, FL (74-500) Cpt, Chldr; FBLA; InterAct C; Tr; US Air Force.

MILLER, Brenda Bernice
Campbell HS; Smyrna, GA (10%-350) Band; BC; FHA; Hon Prog; Math.

MILLER, Brian Allen
Watson Chapel HS; Pine Bluff, AR (30-228) BC; Bsbl; Bkbl; Ftbl; Golf; HCt.

MILLER, Brian Ralph
N Miami HS; Denver, IN (18-114) Chor; Drama; Ger C; Pres, 4H; NHS; Sci C; Secy, Var C; VP, Sr Cl; Bkbl; Cr-Ctry; Tr; 4H A; Yth Fel; Purdue U; Agr.

MILLER, Bruce Earl
Dublin HS; Dublin, GA (2-220) BC; BS; Dbte Tm; HiY; Math C; Sci C; Ftbl; Fin, COM; Fin, NEDT Cert; Fin, Cl Fav; Fin, Sci A; Semi-Fin, Elk's C A; Fin, Math A; Fin, PC Jr Fel; Ga Southwestern Col; Bio.

MILLER, Bruce Jeffrey
Harbor HS; Ashtabula, OH; AFS; Band; Tres, Ger C; Hmrm; SC; Hon Prog.

MILLER, Bryan Douglas
Madison HS; Richmond, KY; Ann; Drama; Sch P; Spch C; Up Bound; Var C; Pres, Jr Cl; VP, Soph Cl; Bsbl; Ftbl; Boxing; Co-Cpt, FCA.

MILLER, Cammy Caroline
Midwest HS; Midwest, WY (3-21) Ann; Band; S-T, Bus C; Chess C; Drama; FHA; 4H; NHS; Sch P; Ski C; Secy, Sr Cl; Citz A; 4H A; Type A; Eastern Wyo Col; Bus.

MILLER, Carol Ann
Montpelier HS; Montpelier, OH (23-117) Band; Chor; Var C; MVP, Bkbl; Cr-Ctry; MVP, Tr; HCt; Toledo Col; Teaching.

MILLER, Cassandra Lynn
Pleasantville HS; Pleasantville, NJ; Tnns; Amer Leg A; Hist A; Eng, Lang Arts, A's.

MILLER, Cecilia Alissia
The Flint Acad; Flint, MI (3-6) A Cap Choir; Band; Chldr; Chor; Ensm; Pres, FHA; Ger C; 4H; Rptr, Hmrm; Semi-Fin, Jr Miss Pa; Lat C; NHS; Orch; ARC; SC; Pres, Sr Cl; Bkbl; Tr; Beauty; Citz A; 4H A; Hon Prog; JA A; ARC A; VofDEM; GSct; Pol Sci.

MILLER, Chanda Alberta
Abraham Lincoln HS; Denver, CO; DARGCA; ROTC A; Drill Tm Commander.

MILLER, Cheryl Denise
John Tyler HS; Tyler, TX; Chor; S-T, FHA; Ch, Hmrm; Math C; Sci C; Spch C; Tnns; COM; Chem A; Citz A; Cl Fav; Star Student; Swtht; Modeling A; E Tex St U; Radio & TV.

MILLER, Cheryl Katherine
Turner Ashby HS; Dayton, VA (3-270) Rptr, Band; Fr C; Rptr, 4H; Pres, Hmrm; Orch; Rptr, Sch P; SC; Var C; Secy, Soph Cl; JV, Bkbl; Sftbl; Stage Band; Law.

MILLER, Christine Penelope
Thomas A Edison HS; Lake Station, IN (20%-185) Ntl Yth Conf; Ivy Tech Col; Child Care.

MILLER, Christopher T
Church Farm Sch; Paoli, PA (2-17) Drama; Ger C; Rptr, Sch P; Mgr, Bkbl; Mgr, Soccer.

MILLER, Christy Lynne
Suffern HS; Suffern, NY (5%-500) Ed, Ann; Band; Chor; Key C; NHS; Soccer; Sftbl; Church Yth; Vlbl; Liberal Arts.

MILLER, Clarence Everett
Inkster HS; Inkster, MI (21-200) Band; Span C; Var C; Bsbl; HCt; Morehouse Col; Computer Sci.

MILLER, Clayton William
Oak Harbor HS; Oak Harbor, WA (39-343) Band; Secy, Chess C; City Conf; Ensm; Key C; Sci C; Span C; Cr-Ctry; Tr; ROTC A; VP, Amateur Radio C; Co- opt, Rifle Tm; US Naval Acad; Astronautics.

MILLER, Connie Lyle
Crestview Sr HS; Crestview, FL (12-275) Anchor C; Band; FTA; Cpt, Mjrte; NHS; Sch P; Tr; COM; Citz A; Type A; Hon Stu; Okaloosa Walton Jr Col; Nurs.

MILLER, Connie Lyn
Whitehouse HS; Whitehouse, TX (10-99) Pres, Band; VP, BC; Mjrte; Secy, NHS; S-T, Sci C; Bkbl; Cl Fav; HQn; All Campus Fav; Drum Major; Top 10; Tyler Jr Col; Sociology.

MILLER, Craig Alan
Huntington E HS; Huntington, WV; Band; Director's A, Band; Sectional Ldr, Stage Band; Marshall U; Broadcasting.

MILLER, Craig Martin
John F Kennedy Sr HS; Cedar Rapids, IA (85-540) Drama; Ski C; Thes.

MILLER, Craig Steven
Yough HS; Herminie, PA (40%-320) Semi-Fin, NHS; Ski C; Bsbl; Bkbl; Co-Cpt, Ftbl; Hon Prog; 'Y' C; Hon Men, Conf Ftbl; Clarion St Col; Bus.

MILLER, Creola Lee
George Washington HS; Los Angeles, CA; Ed, Sch P; Rptr, SC; Rptr, Tr; Hon Prog; Journ A; JA A; Calif Polytech Col; Journ.

MILLER, Curtis Lee
Liberty HS; Bethlehem, PA (40%-743) Band; Mgr, Bsbl; Bkbl; Sftbl; HR; Penn St U; Archt.

MILLER, Cynthia Anne
Holly HS; Holly, MI (9-235) NHS; Var C; Tr; Ferris St Col; Phar.

MILLER, Cynthia L
Bowman HS; Canyon Country, CA; Cpt, Bsbl; Sunday Sch A; Col o-t Canyons; Legal Secy.

MILLER, Cynthia Lynn
Abraham Lincoln HS; Denver, CO (25%-1000) HEO C; Arapahoe Comm Col; Health.

MILLER, Cynthia Sue
Dos Pueblos HS; Goleta, CA; A Cap Choir; AFS; CSF.

MILLER, Daniel
Church Point HS; Church Point, LA (45-122) Ch, FFA; Ch, Hmrm; SC; Ftbl; Bank Of Amer A; Citz A; Horticulture A.

MILLER, Danny Kaye
East Noble HS; Kendallville, IN (34-251) Var C; Wrest; COM; Eagle Sct A.

MILLER, David Charles
Emmerich Manual HS; Indianapolis, IN (1-480) Tres, Fr C; Pres, Key C; NHS; Mgr, Bkbl; Tnns; Tr; Amer Leg A; DARGCA; Type A; Yth Fel; City SC; Fra; 500 Festival o-t Arts; VP, Ind St Yth o-t Church of God; Top Ten Jr; Ball St U; Architecture.

MILLER, David Dean
Will Rogers HS; Tulsa, OK; Key C; Sch P; SC; Co-Cpt, Bsbl; Co-Cpt, Bkbl; Ftbl; Cl Fav; Yth Fel; Soph Board; FCA.

MILLER, Deadra Edwinna
Plainfield HS; Plainfield, NJ; Pom Pon Squad; Brotherhood A.

MILLER, Debbie Elizabeth
Benjamin N Cardozo HS; New York, NY; Bsbl; Swim; Manhattan Comm Col; Acct.

MILLER, Deborah Eugenia
Cass HS; Cassville, GA (10%-189) Semi-Fin, Lit Ral; Tri-HiY; S-T, Sr Cl; Cpt, Bkbl; Type A; Sr Superlative; Shorthand A.

MILLER, Deborah Lynn
Carterville Comm HS; Carterville, IL (30-113) FHA; JV, Vlbl; Pa; John A Logan Col; Bio Sci.

MILLER, Deborah Ruth
Miller Place Jr-Sr HS; Miller Place, NY (23-185) Chor; Drama; Lit Mag; Math C; NHS; Secy, Thes; Alg A; COM; Hist A; Hon Prog; Triangle Girls; Pol Sci.

MILLER, Debra Diane
Colerain Sr HS; Cincinnati, OH (127-630) Chldr; Tres, Chor; Drama; Ensm; Fr C; Hmrm; Madrigal; SC; Thes; Var C; VP, Sr Cl; Cl Fav; HCt; Daisey Chain; Best Personality; Evangel Col; Psych.

MILLER, Debra Jean
Pamlico Co HS; Bayboro, NC; Ann; Band; BC; Chldr; Drama; 4H; Bsbl; Bkbl; Sftbl; Eng A; E Carolina U; Nurs.

MILLER, Debra Sue
Quincy Sr HS; Quincy, IL; Fr C; Hmrm; NHS; U of Sou Calif; Law.

MILLER, Denice Lynn
Sparks HS; Sparks, NV (2-290) Dbte Tm; Pres, Drama; Co-Ed, Lit Mag; Pres, NFL; NHS; Rptr, Sch P; Spch C; SC; Lion A; NMF; Spch A; Willamette U; Pol Sci.

MILLER, Denise Ann
Rockdale HS; Rockdale, TX (21-130) Secy, Band; Pres, Commercial C; Ensm; NHS; Orch; SC; JV, Bkbl; Tr; Cl Fav; Outst, Band; Tyler Jr Col; Dental Hygiene.

MILLER, Denise Marcell
Forest Park Sr HS; Lake City, GA; Chor; 4H; HR; Office Work.

MILLER, Denise Marie
Davison HS; Davison, MI (90-350) Chor; Ger C; Tr; ARC A; Olivet Col; Teaching.

MILLER, Diana
Weir HS; Weir, MS (4-54) F-Ed, Ann; BC; Chor; FHA; S-T, 4H; Mgr, Var C; Ch, Jr Cl; Ch, Soph Cl; Mgr, Bkbl; Mgr, Tr; Cl Fav; 4H A; Math A; Swtht; Eng A; Most Courteous; Holmes Jr Col; Acct.

MILLER, Don Franklin
Falls Church HS; Falls Church, VA (100-503) Cr-Ctry; JV, Tr; George Mason U; Bus Adm.

MILLER, Donald Elton
Civic Mem HS; Bethalto, IL (10%-300) Band; Tr; Spelling, Mus, A's; Sou Ill U; Elec.

MILLER, Donald James
Van Buren Comm HS; Keosauqua, IA; Ann; BS; 4H; Span C; Var C; Ftbl; Golf; JV, Wrest; 4H A; Fred Perkins Mem A; NE Mo St U; Acct.

MILLER, Donna Jean
Quincy Sr HS; Quincy, IL; SC; Christ Ambassadors; Tn Choir; Sanctuary Choir; Bible Quiz Tm; Gem City Bus Col; Legal Secy.

MILLER, Donna Lynn
Butler Intermediate HS; Butler, PA (20%-1500) Chor; Ensm; Mus.

MILLER, Douglas John
Salisbury-Elk Lick HS; Salisbury, PA (2-55) BS; Chess C; NHS; Ed, Sch P; VP, SC; Pres, Soph Cl; Bsbl; Bkbl; Soccer; Amer Leg A; Hon Prog; PTA A; Type A; Pepperdine U; Lib Arts.

MILLER, Douglas Keith
Bryan Adams HS; Dallas, TX (25%-900) Secy, Key C; SC; Bsbl; Ftbl; Tr; COM; Yth Fel; Jr NHS; Pres, Sr High Yth Group; FCA; Young Life; Baylor U; Law.

MILLER, Douglas Morgan
Hinsdale Central HS; Hinsdale, IL (25%-630) Tnns; U of Ill.

MILLER, Douglas Scott
Rio Grande HS; Albuquerque, NM (3-749) Band; BS; Chess C; NFL; NHS; Spch C; SC; Bsbl; JV, Ftbl; Sci A; Spch A; NM St U; Engr.

MILLER, Elizabeth Anne
Penn View Bible Inst; Penns Creek, PA; Williamsport Area Comm; Med Secy.

MILLER, Ellen Jean
Bangor Sr HS; Bangor, PA; MVP, Chess C; MVP, Chor; MVP, Drama; MVP, Bkbl; Drama Tm Trophy; Allentown Sch of Nurs; Nurs.

MILLER, Eric Dean
Coronado HS; Lubbock, TX (75-725) Chor; Hmrm; NHS; SC; COM; Citz A; Hon Prog; Math A; Sci A.

MILLER, Eugene David
Connellsville Sr HS; Connellsville, PA (74-600) Cr-Ctry; Tr; COM; Yth Fel; Bowl C; Ohio Inst of Tech; Elec Engr.

MILLER, Eugene Thomas
Guymon HS; Guymon, OK; FFA; Pres, 4H; Key C; Ski C; JV, Ftbl; Chem A; 4H A; Spch A; Lubbock Christian Col; Agr.

MILLER, Faith Victoria
Wardensville HS; Wardensville, WV; Sheperd Col.

MILLER, Gabriel
James F Byrnes HS; Duncan, SC (47-261) Ann; BC; FFA; Pres, Hmrm; SC; MVP, Wrest; U of SC; Socialogy.

MILLER, Gail Lynne
Pekin Comm HS; Pekin, IL (60-706) A Cap Choir; Chor; Fr C; French NHS; Madrigal; NHS; Hon Prog; Iowa St U; Fr.

MILLER, Gail Maxine
Campbell HS; Smyrna, GA (15%-300) Band; BC; FTA; Hmrm; NHS; Hon Prog; Hon Band; HR; Schol Ltr; Kennesaw Jr Col; Special Ed.

MILLER, Glenn Todd
Buena HS; Sierra Vista, AZ; Ftbl; Tr; Air Force; Missle Tech.

MILLER, Greg Scott
Norfolk Sr HS; Norfolk, NE (20%-275) NNTCC; Broadcasting.

MILLER, Gregg William
Clear Creek HS; League City, TX; Drama; Pres, Soph Cl; Law.

MILLER, Gregory Alan
Elston Sr HS; Michigan City, IN (69-375) Hmrm; NHS; Span C; Cr-Ctry; Golf; Ind U; Pre-Dentistry.

MILLER, Gregory Lawrence
Daviess Co HS; Owensboro, KY; Chess C; Secy, Fr C; Sci C.

MILLER, Gwendolyn Sue
Paul Harding HS; Fort Wayne, IN (50%-280) ARC; Var C; Caving C; Anthropology; Earth Sci.

MILLER, Harold Lee III
Bluefield HS; Bluefield, WV; Chor; Span C; Sci A; Jr NHS; Social Stu A; 3rd Pl, Sci Fair A; Soph o-t Yr Nom; Archt.

MILLER, Heidi L
Chelan HS; Chelan, WA; Chor; Dbte Tm; Pres, FFA; NHS; Ski C; 4H A; HCt; Hon Prog; Spch A; Swtht; Ldrship A; WW; Western Wash St Col; Marine Bio.

MILLER, Jack Scott
Montabella HS; Edmore, MI (10-120) Band; NHS; Ski C; Span C; Co-Cpt, Bkbl; Golf; Tr; Yth Fel; St Fin, Golf; Chem.

MILLER, James Daniel
Leakesville HS; Leakesville, MS (6-66) Parl, BC; FFA; Order/Arrow; Ed, Sch P; VP, Sr Cl; Bkbl; Ftbl; Tr; Yth Fel; U of S Ala; Marine Biol.

MILLER, James Edward
Pascagoula HS; Pascagoula, MS; Chor; Drama; Ensm; Madrigal; Sch P; Ftbl; Swim; Tr; Church Bkbl & Sftbl; Mus A; Licensed Preacher; U of Sou Miss; Archt.

MILLER, James Issac
Patterson Sch; Lenoir, NC (5-12) Band; Ftbl; Mgr, Soccer; Most Improved, Band; 1st Cl BSct; Haywood Tech Inst; Wood Sci.

MILLER, James Richard
Highlands HS; Natrona Heights, PA (5-450) Chor; Drama; Ensm; Hmrm; NHS; Sci C; SC; Swim; Co-Cpt, Wrest; COM; Citz A; NMF; Opt Out Tn; Graduation Spkr; Carnegie-Mellon U; Chem.

MILLER, Jane Elisabeth
Greece Arcadia HS; Rochester, NY (8-360) Band; CYO; Drama; Math C; NHS; Rptr, Sch P; Ed.

MILLER, Janet Lynn
Marvell Acad; Marvell, AR (11-33) Co-Cpt, Chldr; GS; Fin, Jr Miss Pageant; NHS; Sch P; Pres, SC; Pres, Soph Cl; MVP, Bkbl; Tr; Cl Fav; HQn; HCt; Type A; Central Ark Jr Miss; WW; Lib C; U of Central Ark; Phys Therapy.

MILLER, Janice Dawn
Glen A Wilson HS; Hacienda Heights, CA; A Cap Choir; Ensm; Key C; Secy, SC; CSF; Hon Prog; St Scholar; Principal's HR; 'A' Stu; Pacific Christian Col; Early Childhood Ed.

MILLER, Jeff Roger
Sevier Co HS; Sevierville, TN (33%-300) AFS; Band; Drama; Ski C; Span C; Tenn Tech Col; Engr.

MILLER, Jeffrey Craig
Valley City HS; Valley City, NC; Ann; Band; Order/Arrow; God & Country A; U of ND.

MILLER, Jenella Maria
Plainfield HS; Plainfield, NJ (102-453) Band; Cpt, Chldr; FBLA; 4H; Hmrm; Citz A; 4H A; Yth Foundation A; Best Pom Pon o-t Yr; Schol Achv, PA, A's; Livingston Col; Journ.

MILLER, Jennifer Haile
Mahopac HS; Mahopac, NY (10-350) Chldr; Tnns; JV, Tr; Hon Prog; Dartmouth Col; Lang.

MILLER, Jennifer Junean
R B Stall HS; Charleston Hgts, SC; Bus Mgr, Ann; Hmrm; Span C; SC; Mgr, Bkbl; U of SC; Law.

MILLER, Jerry Michael
Benson HS; Portland, OR (50%-360) NHS; JV, Bkbl; Mgr, Ftbl; Rose Festival Driver; Caravan Amer Driver; Machine Shop Foreman; E Wash St Col; Ed.

MILLER, Jimmy Ray
Dexter HS; Dexter, KS (4-22) Band; Chor; JV, Ftbl; Type A; Auto Mech.

MILLER, Joanne Eleanor
Loch Raven Sr HS; Baltimore, MD (10%-500) Band; COM; Hon Prog; ARC A; Sci A; Fin, Miss Tn Baltimore; Sunday Sch Teacher; Jr NHS; Loyola Col; Med Tech.

MILLER, Joe Lester
Waynesboro Central HS; Waynesboro, MS (25%-130) Var C; Pres, Bkbl; Amer Leg A; God & Country A; Most Out.

MILLER, Joel David
Lewis Central HS; Council Bluffs, IA (10%-270) Band; Chor; Ensm; Madrigal; Var C; JV, Bkbl; Ftbl; JV, Golf; Tr; Mid-Amer Nazarene Col; Law.

MILLER, John Joseph
West HS; West, TX (25%-130) VP, Band; Ensm; Math C; NHS; Var C; Parl, Jr Cl; Ftbl; JV, Tr; Mech Engr.

MILLER, John Melville
Indian Springs HS; Helena, AL (2-50) Dbte Tm; Fr C; Lat C; NFL; Bkbl; Soccer; Alg A; 2nd St Lat Trans; Ancient Hist A; Srd St, Concourse.

MILLER, John Thomas
Burkevile HS; Burkeville, TX (2-46) FFA; Math C; NHS; COM; Math A; Lamar U.

MILLER, Johnnie May
Montgomery Blair HS; Silver Spring, MD (20%-537) ARC; COM; ARC A; Yth Fel; Judo C; Salisbury Col; Art Design.

MILLER, Jolene Phyllis
Beemer Pub HS; Beemer, NE (8-22) Ed, Ann; Band; Chor; Secy, Sr Cl.

MILLER, Joseph Jude
Notre Dame-Bishop Gibbons HS; Schenectady, NY (40-160) Ed, Sch P; VP, SC; Ftbl; Tr; NMS; Regent Schol; Fin, Regent's Schol; McGill U; Bio Chem.

MILLER, Julia Ann
Ada HS; Ada, MN (18-58) A-Ed, Ann; Band; Chldr; Chor; Drama; Ensm; Spch C; Thes; Mgr, Bkbl; Vlbl; GSct.

MILLER, Julie Gayle
Dodge Center HS; Dodge Center, MN (16-59) FHA; Mankato St U.

MILLER, June Ellen
St Angela Hall Acad; Brooklyn, NY; Tres, NHS; Catherine Gibbs-Wood Col; Secy.

MILLER, Karen Ann
Mars Area Sr HS; Mars, PA (58-227) Band; Bus C; FNA; NHS; WW; Villa Marie Col; Nurs.

MILLER, Karen Diane
Fremont Christian HS; Fremont, CA (5-36) Span C; Bus Mgr, SC; Ch, Soph Cl; Sftbl; CSF; Type A; VP, CSF; Med Asst.

MILLER, Karen Marie
Montpelier HS; Montpelier, OH (17-97) Chor; GS; Pres, SC; Secy, Var C; Tr; HCt; U of Toledo; Nurs.

MILLER, Karen Renee
Mechanicsburg Area Sr HS; Mechanicsburg, PA (68-355) Ann; Rainbow; Home Ec Clothing A; Messiah Col; Home Ec Ed.

MILLER, Karen Sue
Beaver Local HS; E Liverpool, OH; Secy, 4H; Var C; Bkbl; COM; Camper o-t Wk.

MILLER, Karen Yvonne
T C Roberson HS; Skyland, NC (75-200) Band; BC; Mjrte; Degree Nurs.

MILLER, Katherine Blackall
Oak Grove Coburn Sch; Vassalboro, ME (3-35) Ann; Chor; Drama; Ensm; Lat C; NHS; Co-Ed, Sch P; Ski C; Hockey; Chem A; Eng A; Radcliffe Col; Law.

MILLER, Kathleen Ann
Our Lady of Mercy Acad; Louisville, KY (3-78) Drama; Fr C; A-Ed, Sch P; Alg A; Bio A; Chem A; Hist A; Regent Schol; Spch A; U of Western Ky; Dental Hygiene.

MILLER, Kathy D'Ann
Weatherford HS; Weatherford, TX (72-250) Chldr; FBLA; FTA; Rptr, Sch P; Tres, SC; Secy, Jr Cl; HCt; Opt A; Opt Out Tn; Weatherford Col; Bus.

MILLER, Kenneth Lee
Sooner HS; Bartlesville, OK; Span C; Ftbl; Tr; Wrest; Cl Fav; Yth Fel; Yth Foundation; Yth Choir Church; Okla St U; Sci.

MILLER, Kenneth Ray
Buckhorn HS; Buckhorn, KY (4-41) BC; SC; Alice Loyd Col; Heavy Equipment.

MILLER, Kent Alan
Glen A Wilson HS; Hacienda Heights, CA (3%-425) A Cap Choir; Soccer; Tr; CSF; Hon Prog; Principal's HR; Essay A; U of Sou Calif; Dentistry.

MILLER, Kevin O'Neal
Arvada HS; Arvada, CO (425-790) Swim; Yth Fel; Yth Pres, Church of God; Yth Choir, Church of God; Metro St Col; Mgt.

MILLER, Kevin Troy
McGavock HS; Nashville, TN (20%-1000) BC; Hmrm; InterClub Coun; Lat C; Lat NHS; Pres, ARC; Sch P; Spch C; Secy, St Stu Congres; Pres, SC; Pres, Sr Cl; Pres, Jr Cl; Pres, Soph Cl; Cpt, Bkbl; Ftbl; Sftbl; Tr; Citz A; Most Out; ARC A; Yth Leg; Eng A; Bus.

MILLER, Kim Marie
Lakeview HS; Stoneboro, PA (15-175) Chor; 4H; VP, Tri-HiY; 3rd Pl Shadow Box; 1st Pl Poster Division; DECA Dist Career Development.

MILLER, Kim Patrick
Monticello HS; Monticello, MS; FFA; Sch P; COM; Cert of Scholastic Achv.

MILLER, Kimberly Ann
King's Acad; W Palm Beach, FL (15-43) Choir; Lat C; NHS; Hon Prog; Penmanship A; Top 4% of Cl A; *Oral Roberts U.*

MILLER, Kimberly Joy
Glynn Acad; Brunswick, GA (32-390) Chor; Drama; FBLA; Span C; SC; Tnns; HCt; Yth Fel; Church Organist; Outst Sr; Yth Coun; Win, Talent Show; Most Talented; WW; *Mus.*

MILLER, Kimberly Louise
Granite City HS S; Granite City, IL (69-650) Chldr; Fr C; FHA; Secy, Pol Sci C; *Ill St U; Bio.*

MILLER, Kristi Kae
Waverly-Shell Rock Sr HS; Waverly, IA (37-204) Chldr; Chor; Ger C; Bkbl; Sftbl; Tr; Type A.

MILLER, Lane Vance
Hettinger HS; Hettinger, ND (25%-69) FFA; Bsbl; Bkbl; Ftbl; Fin, Tr; Most Improved Trackster; *Ntl Col of Bus; Bus Adm.*

MILLER, Lauri Lynn
Stephan Watts Kearny HS; San Diego, CA (200-749) NHS; *Point Loma Col.*

MILLER, Laurie
Star Valley HS; Afton, WY (10%-145) Band; FTA; VP, 4H; Ski C; Tr; 4H A; Sup Mus Medal; *BYU; Computer Sci.*

MILLER, Laurie Ann
Greater Latrobe Sr HS; Latrobe, PA (21-518) Band; Chor; Ger C; Sci C; *Westminster Col; Biol.*

MILLER, Laurie Beth
Fremont HS; Sunnyvale, CA (1-618) Band; Dbte Tm; Drama; VP, Fr C; Hmrm; Math C; NFL; Tnns, Ski C; Spch C; SC; Thes; Swim; Tnns; Alg A; CSF; COM; Citz A; Hon Prog; Math A; Most Out; *UC at Santa Barbara; Math.*

MILLER, Laurie Beth
Beaman-Conrad-Liscomb Comm HS; Conrad, IA (10%-59) Band; Chor; Drama; Madrigal; Sch P; Spch C; Secy, SC; Thes.

MILLER, Leigh Ann
Norman HS; Norman, OK; Band; Hmrm; VP, SC; VP, Soph Cl; JV, Bkbl; Sftbl; Tr; Yth Fel; *U of Okla.*

MILLER, Leon S
Randolph Pub HS; Randolph, NE (29-68) Ann; Band; Chess C; Drama; Order/Arrow; SC; Thes; JV, Wrest; H of F; Order/Arrow A; Art C; WW; *Central Technical Comm Col; Elec Tech.*

MILLER, Leroy Herman
Abraham Lincoln HS; Bloomington; MN (18-512) Ger C; VP, NHS; Soccer; Pres A; Church Chor; *N Central Bible Col; Elec.*

MILLER, Leslie Ann
Lincoln HS; Ellwood City, PA; Drama; FHA; Span C; Y-Tns; NEDT; Yth Fel; Yth Prayer Group; Bowl C; Acad Achv A.

MILLER, Leslie Sue
Bedford HS; Bedford, PA; JV, Chldr; SC; Tr; Past Worthy Adv, Rainbow Girls; Teach Gym; Pep C; Church Yth Group.

MILLER, Letha Denene
Sulphur Springs HS; Sulphur Springs, TX (25%-300) Dbte Tm; Pres, FHA; FTA; Hmrm; NHS; Sci C; Spch C; SC; JV, Tnns; Pres A; Q&S A; Spch A; MVP, FHA; Photography C; Outst Future Jr Homemaker; *Tex Tech U; Nurs.*

MILLER, Linda Kay
Worth Co R III HS; Grant City, MO (50%-62) Band; Chldr; FHA; FTA; Golf; Mgr, Tr; *Child Development.*

MILLER, Linda Rae
Mars Area HS; Mars, PA; Band; NHS; Thes; *Grove City Col; Ed.*

MILLER, Lisa
Star Valley HS; Afton, WY; Secy, 4H; Ski C; 4H A; Drill Tm.

MILLER, Lisa Jane
Bedford HS; Bedford, PA (12-240) Ann; Band; Chor; NHS; Ed, Sch P; Bkbl; Q&S A; Past Worthy Adv, Rainbow Girls; Winter Sport's Qn Cand; Vlbl; Grnd Cr Clr; Yth Chor; Chrch Yth Gp; Sch Med; Europe Tour; Fn Mss Cen Pn; *Ind U of Pa; Journ.*

MILLER, Lizbeth Anne
Duval HS; Lanham, MD; Chor.

MILLER, Loren Jane
Manheim Central Sr HS; Manheim, PA (26-263) Chor; Pres, FNA; Hmrm; Ed, Sch P; Var C; Bkbl; Hockey; Med Careers C; Yrbook A; *Shippensburg St Col; Bus Adm.*

MILLER, Lori Ann
Landmark Christian Sch; Cincinnati, OH (5-60) Chor; Spch A.

MILLER, Lori Ann
Belvidere HS; Belvidere, IL (202-374) FHA; JA A; Yth Fel; GAA; 10 Yr GSct; Sunday Sch Teacher's Aid; *Rock Valley Col; Bus.*

MILLER, Lori Jean
Hickory Sr HS; Hermitage, PA (85-275) Tri-HiY; JA A; *Johnson & Wales Col; Culinary Arts.*

MILLER, Malone E
Binghamton N HS; Binghamton, NY (8-230) CYO; Tres, Chem C; Fr C; Hmrm; NHS; Sci C; Tres, SC; Var C; Tres, Soph Cl; Bkbl; Sftbl; Swim; Tnns; Co-Cpt, Tr; Citz A; PTA A; MVP, Tr; *St Lawrence U; Health Profession.*

MILLER, Marcia Kay
Centerburg HS; Centerburg, OH; JV, Chldr; Chor; Dbte Tm; NHS; F-Ed, Sch P; Pres, Sci C; Pres, Span C; Spch C; Secy, SC; Var C; Bkbl; Tr; HCt; ARC A; Star Student; Powder Puff Ftbl.

MILLER, Margaret Alice
Leesville HS; Leesville, LA (20-289) CYO; Chor; Ensm; Alg A; Hist A; *Northwestern St U; Ed.*

MILLER, Marianne
Maud HS; Maud, OK (3-45) BC; Bus C; FBLA; FHA; 4H; Secy, SC; Bkbl; Sftbl; Tr; Hist A; Civics A; *E Central St Col; Nurs.*

MILLER, Marilyn Kay
New Athens Comm HS; New Athens, IL (7-65) Secy, FHA; FTA; Rptr, 4H; Secy, NHS; ARC; Var C; 4H A; NMF; ARC A; Rotary A; Yth Fel; Cpt, Vlbl; FHA Qn; *Belleville Area Col; Phys Therapy.*

MILLER, Marilyn Sue
Heritage Christian Sch; Indianapolis, IN (1-61) Fr C; 4H; Lit Mag; Tres, Jr Cl; Mgr, Bkbl; Sftbl; Citz A; 4H A; Hon Prog; *Law.*

MILLER, Mark A
Adolfo Camarillo HS; Camarillo, CA (27-600) Chess C; Ger C; Key C; Tnns; CSF; Hon Prog; HR; *US Airforce Acad; Aerospace Engr.*

MILLER, Mark Andrew
Burnsville Sr HS; Burnsville, MN (25%-450) A Cap Choir; Chor; Fr C; Order/Arrow; SC; JV, Ftbl; *Norman Dale Comm Col; Pre-Law.*

MILLER, Mark Stephen
Charles H Roth HS; Henrietta, NY (5-200) Pres, Chor; Drama; NHS; Order/Arrow; Thes; Var C; Tres, Jr Cl; Soccer; Hon Prog; MLS; VFW A; Outst Thes; *Alfred U; Ceramic Engr.*

MILLER, Mark Wendell
Lewis Central HS; Council Bluffs, IA (90-178) Band; Chor; Madrigal; Var C; Ftbl; Cl Fav; Toby A; *Mid-Amer Nazarene Col; Mus Ed.*

MILLER, Mark William
Nicolet HS; Glendale, WI (20-530) NHS; Tnns; Alg A; Hon Prog; Math A; Wis Section Math Assn of Amer A; 1st Pl, Si-System Tnns Tourn; *U of Wis at Madison; Law.*

MILLER, Marvin
Weir HS; Weir, MS (16-52) Bkbl; Ftbl; Tr; Bio A; Math A; *Trade Sch; Welding.*

MILLER, Mary Bernice
Provine HS; Jackson, MS; Band; Bus C; Chor; VP, FBLA; Sci C; Span C; SC; Bsbl; Beauty; Cl Fav; Best Dressed; *Tougaloo Col; Eng.*

MILLER, Mary Ellen
Eisenhower Sr HS; Washington, MI (301-589) VP, CYO; Chor; Hmrm; Sch P; SC; Mgr, Tr; SC A; *S Macomb Comm Col; Executive Secy.*

MILLER, Mary Teresa
Asheville HS; Asheville, NC; Chor; NHS; Span C; JV, Sftbl; COM; Art A; *UNC-Asheville; Psych.*

MILLER, Maureen Ann
Sabino HS; Tucson, AZ (4-396) Chor; NHS; Outst Schol; *U of Ariz; Sci.*

MILLER, Meredith Lynn
Parkview HS; Little Rock, AR; BC; Dbte Tm; FBLA; GS; Rptr, InterClub Coun; Co-Ed, Sch P; Sci C; Span C; St Stu Congress; Pres, SC; Y-Tns; Pres, Soph Cl; Spch A; Secy, SC; Handbell Choir; Sch Board; Most Courteous; Ballet Stu; *Baylor U; Communications.*

MILLER, Merrill Thomas
Marked Tree HS; Marked Tree, AR (2-75) BS; FFA; NHS; Order/Arrow; Ed, Sch P; Thes; Pres, Jr Cl; Bsbl; Ftbl; Alg A; Bio A; Chem A; Order/Arrow A; Sci A; Geom A; *ASU; Biol.*

MILLER, Michael M
Glenbard W HS; Glen Ellyn, IL (20%-550) Bsbl.

MILLER, Michael Marvin
Lincoln Northeast HS; Lincoln, NE (21-501) BS; Chor; Var C; JV, Golf; Tnns; Amer Leg A; Elk A; Opt A; *U of Nebr; Math.*

MILLER, Miles Weston
The Williams Sch; New London, CT (4-27) Hmrm; Order/Arrow; Pol Sci C; Sci C; SC; Soccer; *Sci.*

MILLER, Milo Steven
Brazil Sr HS; Brazil, IN; HiY; Var C; Cpt, Ftbl; Wrest; All Conf, Defensive End, Ftbl; *Bus.*

MILLER, Nancy Joye
Winside HS; Winside, NE (2-31) Band; Dbte Tm; HiY; NFL; NHS; Bus Mgr, Sch P; Span C; Swim; *Catawba Col; Pre-Med.*

MILLER, Nick Arthur
Boone Jr-Sr HS; Boone, IA (10%-225) Chor; NHS; Co-Cpt, Hockey; Goeppinger A; *Iowa St U; Eng Ed.*

MILLER, Nora Lee
Central HS; Davenport, IA; VP, Chor; Ensm; Bkbl; Sftbl; Vlbl; Stu Trainer, Tr; Sunday Sch Teacher; *Therapist.*

MILLER, Pamela Ann
Exeter Pub HS; Exeter, NE (6-40) Ann; Band; Chor; Drama; 4H; Secy, Math C; Pres, NHS; Sch P; Pres, SC; Y-Tns; Alg A; Spch A; *U of Nebr; Child Development.*

MILLER, Pamela Jean
John F Hodge HS; St James, MO (3-109) Chldr; SC; Alg A; Citz A; Hist A; HCt; MLS; Phy A; Regent Schol; Vlbl; Eng, Basic Bus, A's; Arthropology Sociology; *SW Mo St U; Acct.*

MILLER, Pamela Jo
Lakeland Christian Sch; Lakeland, FL; Cpt, Chldr; Drama; Secy, Hmrm; Spch C; SC; MVP, Sftbl; HCt; Pres A; Type A; MVP Piano; Fin, Tns in Tune; *Baptist Bible Col; Ed.*

MILLER, Pamela Kim
Lakeview HS; Battle Creek, MI; Chldr; Tr; *Med.*

MILLER, Pamela Lynn
Oakdale Joint Union HS; Oakdale, CA (20-250) Chor; Drama; Lion A; Spch A; Service C; Camper o-t Yr; Lions C Spch A; *Modesto Jr Col; Bus.*

MILLER, Pamela Sue
Topeka W HS; Topeka, KS (1%-570) Span A; *U of Denver; Acct.*

MILLER, Patricia Naomi
St Pius V HS; Bronx, NY (47-101) Chess C; Secy, Chor; COM; *LaGuardia Col; Secy.*

MILLER, Paula Marie
New Albany HS; New Albany, IN; Lat C; JV, Sftbl.

MILLER, Paula Michelle
Plano Sr HS; Plano, TX; Chor; FHA; FTA; COM; ARC A; Fr A; *Lubbock Christian Col; Elem Ed.*

MILLER, Peter Karl
William Penn Sr HS; York, PA (5-425) Band; Chor; Ensm; Mu Alpha Theta; NHS; Orch; Thes; Co-Cpt, Cr-Ctry; Tr; Sr A; Finkbinder A; Ed, Sch Book; *Indiana U of Pa; Mus.*

MILLER, Phillip Ray Jr
Palo Duro HS; Amarillo, TX (25-445) Chor; FTA; Hmrm; SC; JV, Bkbl; JV, Ftbl; JV, Tr; Runner- up, Smiler; FTA Fav; *Tex Tech U; Med.*

MILLER, Phyllis Joan
Church Point HS; Church Point, LA (12-145) BC; CYO; FFA; FHA; Alg A; Sci A; Secy, Jr Cath Daughters; Pep Squad; Parish & Area Horticulture A's; *U of SW La; Horticulture.*

MILLER, Ralph Carl
Schulte HS; Terre Haute, IN (7-83) BS; CYO; Ger C; Key C; Phys C; F-Ed, Sch P; JV, Bsbl; JV, Bkbl; Cr-Ctry; Tr; Alg A; COM; Hon Prog; Rotary A; St Scholar; Ind St U; Aerospace Technology.

MILLER, Ramona Pauline
Dallas Christian HS; Mesquite, TX (13-53) Cpt, Chldr; Rptr, FHA; NHS; F-Ed, Sch P; Parl, Span C; Secy, Sr Cl; Math A; Sci A; Type A; Richland Jr Col; Bus Adm.

MILLER, Raymond Edward Jr
New Albany HS; New Albany, IN (86-610) VP, Demolay; Ger C; NHS; Mgr, Ftbl; Ind U Southeast; Social Stu.

MILLER, Rebecca Darlene
Graham HS; St Paris, OH (23-185) Band; Bus C; Chor; Orch; Type A; A of Dist St Bd of Ed in Voc Bus Ed; Mount Vernon Nazarene Col; Bus.

MILLER, Rebecca Lynn
San Lorenzo Valley HS; Felton, CA (10-280) NHS; Keywanettes.

MILLER, Regina
Monroe HS; Albany, GA (5-329) Hmrm; NHS; SC; Tres, Y-Tns; Tres, Jr Cl; Citz A; Hon Prog; Honorary Page, House of Reps & Sen; Clark Col; Eng.

MILLER, Rene Avanell
Pender Pub HS; Pender, NE (5-62) Parl, Band; Chor; Drama; Ensm; Secy, FHA; Tres, Jr Cl; Vlbl; WW; U of Nebr; Art.

MILLER, Renee
Northwest HS; St Louis, MO (14-433) Hmrm; Math C; NHS; Ed, Sch P; Sci C; Spch A; U of Mo; Civil Engr.

MILLER, Renee Lyn
Marion HS; Marion, IN (280-750) Ger C; Eng.

MILLER, Rhonda Lea
Sam Rayburn HS; Pasadena, TX (35-600) Band; Fr C; VP, FHA; Tres, FTA; Hmrm; Mjrte; Mu Alpha Theta; Orch; Rainbow; SC; Tres, Soph Cl; Yth Fel; Academic Excellence; St Twirling; Region Band; St Orch; Tex A&M U; Computer Sci.

MILLER, Richard William
Valhalla HS; El Cajon, CA (10%-500) Math C; NHS; Bkbl; JV, Soccer; Hon Prog; Pres A; Dist Archt Design A; Cal-Poly Pamona; Archt Design.

MILLER, Rick Bernard
Ruthven Consolidated Sch; Ruthven, IA; Band; Chor; Bsbl; Cpt, Bkbl; Ftbl; Golf; Yth Fel.

MILLER, Robert Scott
Spruce Creek HS; Port Orange, FL (50-480) Anchor C; Band; BC; Drama; Ensm; SC; VP, Jr Cl; Co-Cpt, Swim; Cl Fav; HCt; Swtht; St Photography A; WW, Band; U of Fla; Pre-Med.

MILLER, Robert William
R Nelson Snider HS; Fort Wayne, IN (3-510) Sci C; Alg A; Bio A; COM; Chamber of Comm A; Chem A; Math A; Ntl Achv Schol; Purdue U; Engr.

MILLER, Robin Anne
Hickory HS; Hickory, NC (16-380) French NHS; NHS; Confirmation A; Stu o-t Mo; Jr Marshal; Appalachian St U.

MILLER, Robin Elaine
Zwolle HS; Zwolle, LA; Band; FHA; 4H; Bkbl; Tnns; Southern U; Bus Adm.

MILLER, Robin Jolene
West HS; Denver, CO (14-386) Drama; Secy, NHS; Thes; JV, Tr; Hesston Mennonite Col; Engr.

MILLER, Robin Kay
Grace Baptist HS; South Bend, IN (2-23) Ann; Chor; Drama; 4H; Church Mus Group; Tenn Temple Col.

MILLER, Robin Louise
Mechanicsburg HS; Mechanicsburg, PA; Sftbl; Tres & VP, DECA; Central Penn Bus Sch; Travel.

MILLER, Roderick Kent
Turner Ashby HS; Dayton, VA (1-270) VP, FFA; Pres, 4H; VP, NHS; Tres, SC; JV, Bkbl; Gov Honor Prog; 4H A; Pres A; Spch A.

MILLER, Ruth Ann
W Lincoln Sr HS; Lincolnton, NC (4-146) VP, BC; Sch P; Sci C; Bkbl; Sftbl; Q&S A; Lib A; All-Conf Sftbl; Ntl HS A for Excellence; WW; Schol Ath A.

MILLER, Ruth Jane
Ahrens HS; Louisville, KY; Drama; FBLA; Hmrm; NHS; SC; U of Louisville; Bus.

MILLER, Samentha Germaine
Petersburg HS; Petersburg, VA; Drama; FBLA; 4H; Hmrm; Semi-Fin, Jr Miss Pa; Lat C; NHS; Sci C; Co-Cpt, Tr; COM; Cl Fav; Hon Prog; JA A; Va St Col; Pol Sci.

MILLER, Scott Alan
St Francis HS; St Francis, MN; Chor; Ensm; Madrigal; Ski C; COM; Ansko Ramsey Jr Col; Elec Engr.

MILLER, Sharon Elaine
Madison HS; Madison, TN (1-300) Bus C; Tres, NHS; Sch P; Bio A; Chem A; Val; Jamie Shields Secretarial Schol; Trevecca Nazarene Col; Bus.

MILLER, Sharon Marie
Covenant Christian Sch; Logansport, IN (1-4) Orch; Rptr, Sch P; Covenant Foundation Col; Nurs.

MILLER, Sheri Lyn
Northwest HS; Jackson, MI (62-308) A Cap Choir; Chor; COM; 4H A; Hon Prog; NMS; Secy & Pres, 4-H C; Bus A; Jackson Bus U; Acct.

MILLER, Sherry Donalda
Bethany HS; Reidsville, NC (12-52) Band; Chem C; Secy, Fr C; FHA; Hmrm; Monogram; Secy, Jr Cl; Pres, Soph Cl; ARC; Co-Cpt, Sftbl; Tr; HCt; ARC A; Co- cpt, Vlbl; Watts Hospital Sch of Nurs; Nurs.

MILLER, Sidney Dale
Zion Benton Township HS; Zion, IL (1-550) Span C; Tr; JV, Wrest; Highest Avg, Span; Superintendent's HR; Moody Bible Inst; Math.

MILLER, Sonja Ann
Whitehouse HS; Whitehouse, TX (1-140) Tyler Jr Col.

MILLER, Stacey Ann
Alfred E Beach HS; Savannah, GA; Ch, Anchor C; Band; ARC; Span C; Pres, Jewish Yth Organization; U of Ga; Math.

MILLER, Stephen Anthony
Columbus Briggs HS; Columbus, OH (15-350) Chor; Ensm; Pres, Fr C; NHS; Tnns; Wrest; Ohio Tn Tempos; VP, Sunday Sch Cl; Frontiersman Camping Fraternity; OCTM Tm; Royal Rangers Gold Medal; VP, CA; Engr, Day Pro; Ntl Rif As; Ohio U; Engr.

MILLER, Stephen Frederick
James Island HS; Charleston, SC; Chor; Fr C; VP, Tres & Drum Major, Band; Hon All-St Chor; WW; Anderson Jr Col; Mus.

MILLER, Susan Kay
Muskogee HS; Muskogee, OK (230-700) Bus C; Chor; VP, Hmrm; Sci C; Span C; HQn; Hon Prog; Yth Fel; Literary Soc; Okla St U; Ed.

MILLER, Tammi Renee
Lakeview HS; Battle Creek, MI; A Cap Choir; Chor; Orch; SC; Mgr, Tr; COM; Yth for Understanding; Health Careers C; Stu Listener; Beta HR; U of Mich; Med.

MILLER, Tammy Lynn
Choctaw Co HS; Butler, AL (18-150) Ann; Rptr, Band; Chor; Drama; Ensm; FHA; Pres, 4H; Sci C; Bio A; COM; 4H A; WW, Mus Stu; Livingston U; Mus Ed.

MILLER, Teresa Ann
Booker T Washington HS; Norfolk, VA (3-600) Band; Drama; Secy, Ger C; NHS; Orch; Rptr, Sch P; Secy, SC; Swim; Tr; Hon Prog; Opt A; Duke U; Pre-Med.

MILLER, Teresa Lynne
Eastern Guilford HS; Gibsonville, NC (10-175) BC; FBLA; NHS; Bkbl; King's Col; Bus.

MILLER, Thomas Harold
William Penn Sr HS; York, PA (54-693) Hmrm; Ntl Jr Hon Soc; Ntl Jr Historical Soc; Yrbk Staff; Eagle A; Sci.

MILLER, Timothy Carl
Sparks HS; Sparks, NV (15-380) NHS; JV, Wrest; Hon Prog; Math A; Jr NHS; Stanford U; Chem.

MILLER, Timothy Mark
Park View HS; Sterling, VA (20%-295) Chess C; Ger C; Cr-Ctry; Tnns; Cpt, Tr; Most Talented; George Mason Col; Acct.

MILLER, Toby Joe
Valentine HS; Valentine, NE (10-64) Semi-Fin, BS; Var C; VP, Soph Cl; JV, Bkbl; Cr-Ctry; JV, Ftbl; Golf; JV, Tr; JV, Wrest; Yth Fel; Northwood Inst; Automotive Marketing.

MILLER, Tonia Larnett
John C Fremont HS; Los Angeles, CA (45-550) Band; Cpt, Chldr; Cpt, Mjrte; CSF; COM; Sal; Sr Cl Qn; Cosmetology Trophy and A; HR; Career Expo '77 A; Pepperdine U.

MILLER, Vanessa Donella
Charleston HS; Charleston, SC; Ann; BC; Bus C; FTA; Hmrm; SC; Y-Tns; Tres, Soph Cl; Tnns; COM; Cl Fav; JA A; Spch A; SC St U; Journ.

MILLER, Vanessa Donnell
Charleston HS; Charleston, SC (25-105) BC; Commercial C; Hmrm; Lit Mag; SC; Tres, Soph Cl; Cl Fav; Hon Prog; Journ A; JA A; Spch A; S Carolina St Col; Journ.

MILLER, Vanessa Lonette
Alfred Ely Beach HS; Savannah, GA; A Cap Choir; Chldr; FBLA; 4H; ARC; VP, Jr Cl; Sci A; Cpt, Girls Drill Tm; Memorial Med Center; Radiology.

MILLER, Vesta Leona
Williamsburg HS; Andrews, SC (1-59) Ann; Chess C; Tres, Drama; Secy, 4H; A-Ed, Sch P; COM; Gr Marshal; Journ A; WW; Assistant Jr Cl Rep; Rural Elec Yth Tour Participant; Francis Marion Col; Chem.

MILLER, Vicki Jane
Cowan HS; Muncie, IN (1-70) FHA; Hmrm; NHS; SC; Tr; Bio A; Math A; Yth Fel; Bkbl Timer; Cpt, Bkbl; Ball St U; Math.

MILLER, Vicki Lynn
Zion-Benton Twp HS; Zion, IL (7-396) Chor; Tres, NHS; Secy, Span C; COM; Hon Prog; Most Out; St Scholar; Superior HR; Stu o-t Mo; Moody Bible Inst; Elem Ed.

MILLER, Vicklyn Patricia
Prospect Heights HS; Brooklyn, NY (10-35) COM; K of Pythias; Art A; CCNY; Lib Arts.

MILLER, Victor Craig
Daviess Co HS; Owensboro, KY; Chess C; Fr C; Lat C.

MILLER, Victoria Marie
Ithaca HS; Richland Center, WI (4-43) A-Ed, Ann; Band; Chldr; Parl, FHA; Secy, 4H; MVP, Tr; 4H A; Most Out; U of Wis; Phys Ed.

MILLER, Virginia Alice
Saucon Valley HS; Hellertown, PA (50-201) Sci.

MILLER, Walter Braxton
Russell County HS; Russell Springs, KY (12-151) Chess C; Drama; Ftbl; Cl Fav; Reg Win, VICA St Skill Olympics; Reg Plymouth Trouble Shooting Comp; U of Ky; Pre-Law.

MILLER, William Bruce
Waltrip Sr HS; Houston, TX (99-660) A Cap Choir; Chor; Drama; Ensm; Madrigal; NHS; All Region, All St, Choir; Outst Thespian; Best Actor & Stu Director; Abilene Christian U; Missions.

MILLER, William Michael
Morgan City HS; Morgan City, LA (50-250) Chor; Ensm; Thes; Ftbl; La Tech U; Bio.

MILLER, William Richard
Wyom Valley W HS; Kingston, PA (85-477) Cpt, Band; Secy, Demolay; Lit Mag; Rptr, Sch P; SC; Thes; NEDT; Yth Leg; DeMolay Rep; WW; Attendance A; Ldrship Course; Wilkes Col; Bus Adm.

MILLETT, Karen Elaine
Green Bay E HS; Green Bay, WI (25%-479) Band; Pres, CYO; Chor; Dbte Tm; Ensm; Sch P; Span C; SC; Sftbl; Swim; Tr; UW Madison; Psych.

MILLETT, Mary Megan
E Green Bay HS; Green Bay, WI (12-474) Secy, CYO; Community Yth Symph; Dbte Tm; Fr C; QS; Secy, NHS; Orch; Swim; Citz A; DARGCA; HCt; Hon Prog; Rensselaer A; Ripon Col; Hist.

MILLETT, Sally Ann
Moline Sr HS; Moline, IL; Rainbow; Worthy Advisor, Rainbow Girls; Black Hawk Col; Secy.

MILLEY, Barbara Ann
William H Hall HS; W Hartford, CT (220-463) SC; V-Ch, Fund Raising C; Social C; JV, Vlbl; GEOG Grant; *Nyack Col; Elem Ed.*

MILLHOUSE, Lori Lee
Cheboygan Area HS; Cheboygan, MI (24-220) Band; Fr C; *Ferris St Col; Court & Conference Reporting.*

MILLICK, John Thomas
All American Christian Acad; Hollywood, FL (33%-33) Chess C; Chor; Ensm; Sch P; Var C; Bsbl; Cpt, Cr-Ctry; Ftbl; Sftbl; Cpt, Tr; Wrest; Hon Prog; 2nd Pl, ACE St Convention; *Ed.*

MILLIGAN, Bryan Gilbert
Smiths Station HS; Smiths, AL (8-148) BC; BS; Parl, FFA; 4H; VP, Key C; Mu Alpha Theta; NHS; Sci C; Bsbl; Ftbl; Golf; *Auburn U; Marketing.*

MILLIGAN, Charlotte Elaine
Loganville HS; Atlanta, GA; Ann; Chor; FHA; Rptr, 4H; Sch P; Tri-HiY; Bkbl; Tr; 4H A; *Brewton-Parker Col; Med.*

MILLIGAN, Cheryl Marie
Burke HS; Charleston, SC (15-151) VP, Hmrm; F-Ed, Sch P; Y-Tns; Beauty; Bio A; COM; JA A; Jr Coun; Art A; *Clemson U; Architecture.*

MILLIGAN, Clifford Neil
Oakdale HS; Oakdale, LA (5-129) Ed, Ann; Band; Drama; Ensm; Key C; NHS; Spch C; Chem A; H of F; Hon Prog; Journ A; Jr Chamber of Com A; Spch A; VofDEM; *LSU; Bio-Chem.*

MILLIGAN, Judith Lynn
Lindbergh HS; St Louis, MO (33%-964) Band; Outst Cadet o-t Yr; Counselor, Sch Camp; *Southeast Mo St U; Special Ed.*

MILLIGAN, Thomas Edwin
Lead Hill HS; Lead Hill, AR (2-21) Ed, Ann; BS; FFA; Tres, Key C; Bus Mgr, Sch P; SC; VP, Jr Cl; Bsbl; Mgr, Bkbl; Alg A; Hist A; Bookkeeping A; Eng A; *N Ark Comm Col; Bus.*

MILLIGAN, Thomas Patrick
Sidney HS; Sidney, OH (24-270) BS; Hmrm; Inter-Club Coun; VP, Key C; NHS; SC; Pres, Jr Cl; Bkbl; Cr-Ctry; Tnns; Kiwanis A; *Georgetown U; Foreign Service.*

MILLIGAN, Tina Renee
Berry HS; Berry, AL;

MILLIKEN, Scott Marlyn
Holdrege HS; Holdrege, NE (67-140) Band; Chor; Dbte Tm; Drama; SC; Thes; Var C; JV, Bkbl; Cpt, Cr-Ctry; Tr; JA A; Spch A; Yth Fel; Dbte A; *U of Nebr; Ed.*

MILLIKIN, Rhonda Jean
Marion Sr HS; Marion, AR; BC; Fr C; Hmrm; Math C; NHS; SC; COM; Hist A; HCt.

MILLINGTON, Seth Douglas
W Mid-High Sch; Norman, OK; A Cap Choir; Chor; Order/Arrow; Bsbl; Bkbl; Ftbl; *Northwestern U; Elec.*

MILLION, Charles Alan
Danville HS; Danville, KY; Band; Hmrm; Key C; Tres, Lat C; Tres, Math C; Mu Alpha Theta; NFL; Spch C; SC; Tnns; John Phillip Sousa A.

MILLIRON, Barbara Louise
Southmoreland Sr HS; Alverton, PA (20%-350) JV, Chldr; Fr C; Co-Ed, Sch P; Ski C; Tri-HiY; World Affairs C; *Bio.*

MILLIRON, Dennis Richard
Frankfort HS; Ridgeley, WV (10%-151) Band; Fr C; FTA; NHS; Pres, Sr Cl; Tres, Jr Cl; VP, Soph Cl; Cr-Ctry; *Potomac St Col; Bio.*

MILLIRON, Thomas Ernest Jr
Southmoreland Sr HS; Scottdale, PA (40%-300) Fr C; Hmrm; Order/Arrow; Ski C; Var C; World Affairs C; Ftbl; Wrest; Order/Arrow A; Yth Fel; *Hist.*

MILLNER, Darrell Thomas
Barringer HS; Newark, NJ (65-456) Chess C; City Conf; VP, SC; Ed & Rptr, Sch Paper; SC Service A; Martin Luther King Schol; *Seton Hall U; Communications.*

MILLON, Edward Lloyd
Proviso E HS; Maywood, IL (25-712) NHS; Hon Prog; NMF; NMS; St Scholar; WW; Silver Medalist; Eileen S Andrew Schol A; *Ill Inst of Tech; Civil Engr.*

MILLS, Candence Lynne
Sheffield HS; Memphis, TN (4-160) Hmrm; Lat C; Secy, Mu Alpha Theta; NHS; ARC; Sch P; SC; Tres, Jr Cl; Govn, SW Region; Mu Alpha Theta; Mu Alpha Theta; WW; *Memphis St U; Home Ec.*

MILLS, Cheri Lynn
Westport HS; Louisville, KY (77-348) Tr; Type A; *Secretarial Stu.*

MILLS, David William
Quartz Hill HS; Lancaster, CA (25-600) A Cap Choir; Madrigal; Tres, Soph Cl; JV, Tnns; Amer Leg A; CSF; COM; Ed, ASB Newspaper; *Pacific Christian Col; Religion.*

MILLS, Donna Louise
Colo HS; Colo City, TX (12-95) A Cap Choir; Band; VP, Chor; FHA; NHS; Rainbow; Pres, Span C; SC; Most Dependable; *Angelo St U; Elem Ed.*

MILLS, Douglas Jay
Bay HS; Panama City, FL; Key C; Mu Alpha Theta; NHS; Ftbl; FCA; *Pre-Med.*

MILLS, Emily
Bogalusa HS; Bogalusa, LA; BC; Key C; Fin, Lit Ral; SC; Yth Fel; Golden B Hon Soc; Dance Tm; Eng A; SC Adv Board; Pres Campfire Girls; Ntl Soc of Gifted & Talented Stu; Torch C; Secy, Horizon Cabinet; *Pediatrics.*

MILLS, Gregory Curt
Hartley Comm HS; Hartley, IA (15-55) Band; Chor; SC; Var C; Bsbl; Bkbl; Mgr, Ftbl; Tr; Oracle Attendant; *Iowa Lake Col; Bus.*

MILLS, Jinie Beth
Ogemaw Heights HS; W Branch, MI (20-200) Ann; Band; Dbte Tm; FHA; Pres, 4H; NHS; Ski C; Co-Ch, SC; Var C; Bkbl; Sftbl; Tr; 4H A; Hon Prog; Mgr, Vlbl; *Ferris Col; Law.*

MILLS, John Clifford
Edison HS; Milan, OH (30-213) BS; NHS; Var C; Tres, Sr Cl; Tres, Jr Cl; Bkbl; Ftbl; Tr; Amer Leg A; VP, Sr Luther League; *Pre-Optometry.*

MILLS, John D
Minnetonka Sr HS; Minnetonka, MN (5-650) Band; Order/Arrow; Cpt, Cr-Ctry; Tr; JV, Wrest; Order/Arrow A; Sci A; Yth Fel; Jazz Ensm; Eagle Sct; Eagle Sct; *U of Minn; Sci.*

MILLS, Joyce Marie
Ballston Spa HS; Ballston Spa, NY (4-252) FNA; Pres, 4H; A-Ed, Lit Mag; Secy, NHS; A-Ed, Sch P; COM; Most Out; Regent Schol; Vlbl; *Albany Med Center; Nurs.*

MILLS, Karen Eileen
Bellevue HS; Nashville, TN; Chldr; VP, FTA; SC; Sftbl; Tr; Beauty; HCt; Miss Bellevue; WW; Best All Around; *Trevecca Nazarene Col; Pub Relations.*

MILLS, Karen Louise
Miami Northwestern Sr HS; Miami, FL (2-400) Ann; Drama; Pres, InterClub Coun; Pres, NHS; Ed, Sch P; Sci C; Thes; VP, Sr Cl; Bio A; COM; Citz A; Hon Prog; Most Out; Sci A; Sci Fair A; Most Understanding; CRTI Schol; *U of Wis Minority Pre-Engr Prog.*

MILLS, Kathy Renea
Ulysses HS; Ulysses, KS; Secy, FBLA; FHA; SC; Y-Tns; Sftbl; Swim; Tres, Art C; Gym; Art As; *Art.*

MILLS, Kenneth Eugene
Lynwood HS; Lynwood, CA;

MILLS, Kevin Andrew
Daviess Co HS; Owensboro, KY; Sci C; Cr-Ctry; Tnns; Sci A.

MILLS, Laura Ellen
Hickman Co HS; Clinton, KY (1-105) VP, BC; FHA; Jr Miss Pagent; Ntl Yth Conf; Sci C; Most Out; Spch A; Superior, Piano Festival; *Murray St U; Math.*

MILLS, Lauri Beth
Lone Tree Comm Sch; Lone Tree, IA (11-43) Band; Cpt, Chldr; Chor; Drama; Mjrte; NHS; JV, Bkbl; Tr; Spch A; Mus A; Highest Grade Point Avg, GAA.

MILLS, Lemuel Vassar
Xaverian Brothers HS; Westwood, MA; CYO; Sch Achieve Tm; Var C; Bsbl; Bkbl; Soccer; Sftbl; Tnns; COM; Hist A; Math A; Val; *Harvard U; Econ.*

MILLS, Marlene Denise
Adlai E Stevenson HS; Bronx, NY (20-822) Band; City Conf; Dbte Tm; Lit Mag; Model UN; NHS; Sch Achieve Tm; COM; Citz A; Hon Prog; *Pace U; Math.*

MILLS, Mary Jo
Redmond HS; Redmond, OR (30-229) A Cap Choir; Ann; Ensm; Pres, 4H; InterAct C; Orch; Sch P; HQn; Magna Cum Laude; Summa Cum Laude; Secy, Keyettes; WW in Mus; All St Choir; Amer Yth in Concert; All NW Choir.

MILLS, Melinda Ann
Sam Houston Sr HS; Houston, TX (1-660) Bus C; InterAct C; NHS; Interact Schol Fin; PTA Schol; Candidate, Valedictorian; *U of Houston; Bus Adm.*

MILLS, Melinda Carol
Clara HS; Clara, MS (6-60) Ann; BC; Mgr, Bkbl.

MILLS, Nancy Diane
Concord HS; Concord, NC (11-231) AFS; Band; Fr C; FTA; Cpt, Mjrte; Math C; Mu Alpha Theta; NHS; Sch P; NC All St Band; Jr Marshal; *Wake Forest U; Math.*

MILLS, Rickey Tyrone
Cocoa HS; Cocoa, FL; Chor; Ntl Yth Conf; Ftbl; Wrest.

MILLS, Susan Danielle
Tecumseh Sr HS; Tecumseh, MI (6-263) A Cap Choir; Band; JV, Chldr; Chor; Drama; NHS; Advance Placement, Eng; Fin, Ctry Western Singing Comp; *Theatre Arts.*

MILLS, Teresa Lynn
D H Conley HS; Greenville, NC (46-271) FBLA; Lit Mag; Co-Cpt, Bkbl; Sftbl; *Secy Work.*

MILLS, Venetta Louise
Highlands HS; N Highlands, CA (18-260) Chor; Community Yth Symph; Secy, Fr C; NHS; Orch; Bkbl; Type A; Silver Echo A; Sports A; Mus A; Church Participation A; *CSUS; Bus Adm.*

MILLS, Vicki Renee
Prosser Sr HS; Prosser, WA (3-123) Ann; S-T, Chor; FHA; Pres, NHS; SC; Amer Leg A; Cl Fav; MLS; *Northwest Nazarene Col; Dental Hygiene.*

MILLS, Wanda Jernell
D H Conley HS; Greenville, NC (18-222) BC; Chldr; Fr C; Lit Mag; Math C; NHS; Tr; *Mt Olive Col; Chem.*

MILLSAP, Jeanne J
Del City HS; Del City, OK (10%-600) Band; Ensm; GS; NHS; Secy, Span C; Span A; *Natural Sci.*

MILLSAP, Patricia Kay
John A Holmes HS; Edenton, NC (7-200) Bus Mgr, Ann; Secy, Chess C; FHA; Monogram; Sftbl; Flag Corp; *Wake Forest U; Law.*

MILNE, Linetta Shawne
LaConner HS; LaConner, WA (1-50) FHA; NHS; ARC.

MILNER, April Joy
Kelly Walsh HS; Casper, WY; Secy, Chor; Semi-Fin, Tr; ARC A; Phys Fitness A; Drivers Ed A; *Central Bible Col; Mus.*

MILNER, Diane Lynn
Grapevine HS; Grapevine, TX; Ann; Chor; Co-Ed, Sch P; Span C; Journ A; Mgr, Vlbl; *SMU; Acct.*

MILNER, Linda Gwen
Ft Myers HS; Fort Myers, FL;

MILNER, Melissa Gail
Winnfield Sr HS; Winnfield, LA (8-119) Secy, Anchor C; Rptr, BC; FBLA; Ch, FTA; GS; Lit Ral; Rainbow; Spch C; Type A; *La Tech U; Gen Stu.*

MILNIKEL, Sheryl Lynn
St Joseph HS; St Joseph, MI (76-350) Pres, Chor; Hmrm; Thes; *Lake Mich Col; Bus Asst.*

MILSTEAD, Gary Wayne
Thomas A Edison HS; Alexandria, VA (64-363) Band; Chess C; Ensm; Mod Mus Mas; Orch; Order/Arrow; Order/Arrow A; *George Mason U; Religion.*

MILSTEAD, James Martin
Pascagoula HS; Pascagoula, MS (10%-760) Pres, Hmrm; Pres, Key C; NHS; SC; JV, Bkbl; JV, Golf; Cl Fav; Lion A; *U of Miss; Law.*

MILSTEAD, Virginia Elise
Pascagoula HS; Pascagoula, MS (31-452) F-Ed, Ann; BC; Chldr; Tres, GS; Pres, Hmrm; Lat C; St Stu Congress; SC; Pres, Sr Cl; Pres, Jr Cl; Amer Leg A; Beauty; B Crocker A; Citz A; Cl Fav; DARGCA; H of F; HQn; HCt; Magna Cum Laude; Most Out; Pres A; Yth Leg; Outst Girl Ldrship A; Miss PHS; Secy, Jr Civitan; U of Sou Miss; Interior Design.

MILTON, Carla Kay
Blue Springs HS; Blue Springs, MO (40-459) A Cap Choir; Band; Chor; Fr C; Hmrm; SC; Marching Band; Camp Fire Dist Rep; Clarinet Trio; Church Sr HS Group; PTSA; Secy, VP, Pep C.

MILTON, Deborah Joyce
Emerson HS; Emerson, AR (6-31) Ed, Ann; JV, Chldr; Tres, FBLA; GS; Ed, Sch P; SC; Rptr, Sr Cl; Pres, Soph Cl; Bkbl; HCt; Type A; WW; Most Dependable; Sou Ark U; Bus.

MILTON, Gregory Boyd
Crowley HS; Crowley, LA; Band; Secy, Key C; Semi-Fin, Lit Ral; Mu Alpha Theta; NHS; Bkbl; Sup, Band Solo & Band Trio; Bronze Academic Medal; USL Prog for Gifted Stu.

MILTON, Jonathan
Linsly Military Inst; Wheeling, WV (6-62) Key C; NHS; SC; Var C; Tres, Sr Cl; Tres, Jr Cl; VP, Soph Cl; Bkbl; Ftbl; Tr; Hon Prog; Miami U of Ohio; Acct.

MILTON, Robert Craig
Wolfson Sr HS; Jacksonville, FL (190-500) Sci C; JV, Ftbl; Sci A; Bible C; Ecology C; Trevecca Nazarene Col; Religion.

MILTON, Sharon Denise
Andrew Jackson HS; New York, NY (8-401) Ensm; Math C; NHS; Orch; Arch; Alg A; Bio A; COM; Citz A; Hist A; Hon Prog; Magna Cum Laude; Math A; Sci A; Summa Cum Laude; Personality Cert; Orch Pin; Columbia U; Med.

MILUM, Raymond Lee Jr
Malabar HS; Mansfield, OH (10%-261) Band; Key C; Order/Arrow; JV, Wrest; God & Country A; Hon Prog; Yth Fel; Eagle Sct; Law.

MIMMS, Karen Denise
Southeast HS; Springfield, IL (26-501) Band; Fr C; Lincoln Land Comm; Law.

MIMS, Emma Maxcine
Jackson HS; Jackson, LA; Ann; VP, BC; Chldr; VP, FBLA; FHA; 4H; Cpt, Hmrm; Lit Ral; Math C; Sch P; Sci C; SC; Cpt, Jr Cl; Cpt, Soph Cl; Cl Fav; 4H A; Hon Prog; Sou U; Computer Sci.

MIMS, Janie Marie
Castlemont HS; Oakland, CA (20%-749) Cpt, Sftbl; Yth Fel; Secy, Med C; Hon A; Service Cert; A of Merit; Cert of Completion; U of Notre Dame; Registered Nurs.

MIMS, Reginald Dwayne
Captain Shreve HS; Shreveport, LA (219-551) Band; Citz A; School Achv A; Superior, Solo Festival; Sou U; Archt.

MIMS, Vincent Craig
Abraham Lincoln HS; Houston, TX (10%-98) Band; Chess C; Chor; COM; Ecology C; U of Houston; Bio.

MINAKER, Mark Judson
Lindbergh HS; Renton, WA (10-300) Band; Hmrm; Rptr, Sch P; SC; Northwest Col; Ministry.

MINARD, Kathy Lisa
John F Kennedy HS; Richmond, CA (90-350) Ski C; Mgr, Soccer; Swim; COM; Psych.

MINARDI, Linda Ann
Cecilian Acad; Philadelphia, PA; Pres, Fr C; Lit Mag; Sci C; Tnns; HS Schol; U of Pa; Med.

MINCE, Melanie Ann
Lawrence HS; Lawrence, MI (12-90) Band; Chldr; Chor; Ensm; Ch, Mjrte; NHS; COM; Hon Prog; Outst Attendence A; Hope Col; Mus Ed.

MINCER, David Edward
Hamburg Comm Sch; Hamburg, IA (10-36) Band; FFA; 4H; Mgr, Bkbl; Cr-Ctry; Mgr, Ftbl; Tr; Wrest.

MINCER, Karen Lynn
Columbus Comm HS; Columbus Junction, IA (16-68) Pres, Jr Cl; Kirkwood Col; Environment.

MINCEY, Betty Anne
First Baptist HS; Charleston, SC (3-45) JV, Chldr; S-T, Chess C; Fr C; FTA; NHS; S-T, Sci C; Fin, Tnns; Hon Prog; Math A; NEDT; Journ.

MINCEY, Jimmie Russell
Hunter Huss HS; Gastonia, NC; Band; BC; Fr C; Hmrm; Hon Prog; Math.

MINCHOW, Byron Raymond
Olympus HS; Salt Lake City, UT (175-700) Band; Chem C; Chess C; Swim; Chem A; ROTC A; U of Utah; Meteorology.

MINDRUP, David Thomas
Lenora HS; Lenora, KS (2-22) CYO; NHS; Rptr, Sch P; Bkbl; Mech Drawing, Woodworking, A's; Schol Pin; Jr Cl Play; Kans St Col; Mech Engr.

MINDRUP, Margaret Mary
Lenora HS; Lenora, KS (4-26) VP, CYO; Chldr; Chor; Drama; NHS; Pres, SC; Bkbl; B Crocker A; HCt; Marymount Col; Eng.

MINE, William Edward
Lancaster HS; Lancaster, VA; Ann; Chess C; Sch P; Acolyte; Church Usher; Church Nom Committee; Ferrum Col.

MINEER, Edith Denise
Mt Notre Dame HS; Reading, OH (5-111) Model UN; Bus Mgr, Sch P; Span C; UN Council; World Affairs C; COM; Citz A; Lib Arts.

MINER, Brenda Gay
East HS; Madison, WI (20%-520) Chldr; Chor; 4H; Hmrm; Var C; Ftbl; Sftbl; Swim; Tr; ARC A; Type A; Yth Fel; Sunday Sch Teacher; Presidential Phys Fitness A; MATC; Elec.

MINER, Daniel McCrae
Chambersburg Area Sr HS; Chambersburg, PA; Ftbl; Co-Cpt, Wrest; Amer Leg A; Wilkes Col; Elec Engr.

MINER, Steven Richard
Highland HS; Pocatello, ID (70-450) Span C; Bsbl; Bkbl; Idaho St U; Social Stu.

MINER, Teresa Denise
E Union HS; Manteca, CA (45-240) Secy, Band; Chldr; Chor; Pres, 4H; Bkbl; Sftbl; Tr; COM; 4H A; Secy, Tres, Rptr, 4-H C; Chldr Mascot; Delta Col; Bus Adm.

MINERD, Scott Allen
Connellsville Area HS; Connellsville, PA (450-600) Band; Chess C; God & Country A; Order/Arrow A; Penn St U; Bus Adm.

MINERVA, Anne Therese
Good Counsel HS; Chicago, IL (130-252) Tres, Bus C; CYO; Chor; Drama; Hmrm; Sch P; Tres, Sr Cl; Secy, Jr Cl; Hon Prog; Sci A; Creative Writing A; Candystriper A; Felician Col; Acct.

MINGEE, Charles Wayne
Champaign Central HS; Champaign, IL (66%-425) Parl, FFA; Mgr, Bsbl; Yth Fel; Rptr, FFA; Col o-t Redwoods; Forestry Tech.

MINGER, Christy Joanna
Lindblom Tech HS; Chicago, IL (262-433) Drama; COM; VP, Lib C; NML; Campus Life; Stu Aide; New Expression Newspaper; Modern Dance; U of Ill at Chicago; Psych.

MINGO, Lionel
McClymonds HS; Oakland, CA (153-210) ROTC A; Healds Col; Acct.

MINGUS, Pamela Ann
Mission Viejo HS; Mission Viejo, CA (20%-500) Ski C; Rank Ldr, Drill Tm; Powder Puff Ftbl; Loma Linda U; Dental Hygiene.

MINICK, Cynthia Leigh
Southwestern Central HS; Jamestown, NY (20-189) VP, Band; Ger C; GS; Fin, Jr Miss Pagent; NHS; Ski C; Var C; Sftbl; Gov Empire, GS; Jr Miss Schol; Pol Sci.

MINKS, Michelle Marie
O'Fallon Township HS; O'Fallon, IL (20-352) Chor; Drama; Ensm; Mod Mus Mas; Spch C; Sci A; Future Med Careers; Pres, Acteens; Jr NHS; Phys Therapy.

MINKS, Richard Dean
Brazos HS; Wallis, TX (3-39) BS; Drama; FFA; NHS; Pres, SC; Pres, Sr Cl; Pres, Jr Cl; Pres, Soph Cl; Bkbl; Ftbl; Tnns; Cl Fav; DARGCA; Hon Prog; Lion A; MLS; Star Student; Mr BHS; Most Dependable; Most Handsome; Wharton Co Jr Col; Special Ed.

MINKS, William Dale
Brazos HS; Wallis, TX; Rptr, FFA; SC; VP, Sr Cl; Rptr, Jr Cl; Bkbl; Ftbl; Tr; Cl Fav; Wharton Co Jr Col; Phys Ed.

MINNER, Judy Belle
W Middlesex Area HS; W Middlesex, PA (2-168) Chor; SC; JV, Bkbl.

MINNICK, Denise Lori
Joliet E HS; Joliet, IL (37-400) A Cap Choir; Chldr; Chor; Secy, Drama; Fr C; Madrigal; NHS; Rptr, Sch P; Ski C; SC; Secy, Sr Cl; Secy, Jr Cl; Secy, Soph Cl; Swim; Tr; HCt; Semi-Fin, Spirit A; Semi-Fin, Band Sponsor; Nurs.

MINNICK, Robert E Jr
Hightstown HS; Hightstown, NJ (126-300).

MINNICK, Sharon Lynn
Hightstown HS; Hightstown, NJ; COM; Hon Prog; Math A; Ldrship Bible Stu A; Bus.

MINNICK, Sherryl Kay
Lindbergh HS; St Louis, MO; A Cap Choir; Ensm; Madrigal; NHS; COM; Yth Fel; Variety Show; Co-Pilots; Meramec Col; Mus.

MINNIEAR, John Steven
Yreka HS; Yreka, CA (26-200) Var C; Sftbl; Tr; Wrest; CSF; Top 100; Point Loma Col; Psych.

MINNIX, Dale Edward
Fairmont E HS; Kettering, OH (50-560) Pres, Chor; Ensm; NHS; Orch; Drum Major; All St Choir; Falcon A; Musical Lead; Ohio Yth Chorale; Bowling Green St U; Bus Mgt.

MINOR, Denise Jacqueline
Paul Lawrence Dunbar HS; Washington, DC (11-225) NHS; Wash Tech Inst; Architecture.

MINOR, James Edward
Durrett HS; Louisville, KY; Chor; Mod Mus Mas; All St Choir; Peer-Ldr; Stu Advisory Committee; Mus.

MINOR, John Halley
Centennial Sr HS; Compton, CA; Cpt, Dbte Tm; NHS; Ed, Sch P; Span C; Bus Mgr, Spch C; SC; Bsbl; Ftbl; CSF; COM; Citz A; NMS; U of Calif; Eng.

MINOR, Julie M
Franklin Sr HS; Franklin, LA; Lit Ral; NHS; Rainbow; Span C; Thes; JV, Bkbl; Swim; La St U; Vet Sci.

MINOR, Mary Sue
Germantown HS; Germantown, TN; VP, BC; GS; 4H; Hmrm; Model UN; NHS; Co-Ed, Sch P; Span C; SC; VP, Jr Cl; Rptr, Soph Cl; Sftbl; Mgr, Tr; COM; 4H A; Journ A; Yth Leg; WW; Delta Alpha Delta Sorority; Journ.

MINTER, Kimberly Sue
Woodrow Wilson HS; Beckley, WV (33%-550) BC; Secy, City Conf; FHA; ARC; Rptr, Sch P; Span C; Attendance A; U of Miss; Dentistry.

MINTER, Stephen Craig
Hempstead HS; Hempstead, NY (27-285) Cr-Ctry; Swim; Tr; Regent Schol; Yth Fel; Syracuse U; Engr.

MINTON, Donna Lynn
Athens HS; Athens, AL (10%-254) A-Ed, Ann; InterAct C; Math C; Tres, NHS; Sci C; SC; Beauty; Hon Prog; Auburn U.

MINTON, Pamela Anne
Lordstown HS; Warren, OH (10-56) Band; JV, Chldr; Community Yth Symph; Hmrm; Ski C; Span C; SC; Hon Prog.

MINTON, Willa Dean
Clay Co HS; Manchester, KY (10-200) Band; Secy, BC; Orch; Rptr, Sch P; Drum Mjrte; WW; U of Ky; Fashion Design.

MINTURN, Jennifer Lee
Nathan Hale HS; West Allis, WI (78-432) A Cap Choir; Chor; Madrigal; Gym; Luther League; Prom Court; St Comp, A Cappella Chor & Madrigal; Pom Pon Girls; Swing Choir; U-Wis at Madison; Bus.

MITCHELL, Karen Renee
Checotah HS; Checotah, OK (20%-85) A Cap Choir; Chldr; Chor; V-Ch, FHA; 4H; NHS; Secy, SC; Secy, Sr Cl; VP, Jr Cl; VP, Soph Cl; Bkbl; Tr; COM; 4H A; Hon Prog; St Hon Soc; FFA Swtht; Connors Col; Elem Ed.

MITCHELL, Karl Thomas
Churchill Co HS; Fallon, NV (10%-191) Band; Secy, Chor; Ensm; NHS; Var C; Ftbl; Eagle Sct; NW Nazarene Col.

MITCHELL, Kathleen Ann
St Louis HS; Saint Louis, MI (11-130) 4H; Inter-Club Coun; Fin, Jr Miss Pagent; NHS; Rptr, Sch P; Cpt, Pom Pon Girl; St Louis Jr Miss; Central Mich Col; Art.

MITCHELL, Kent Edward
Paul Harding HS; Ft Wayne, IN (3-300) VP, Chess C; Sci C; Span C; Co-Cpt, Wrest; Chamber of Comm A; I Dare You; Robert Sauer Humanitarian; Purdue U; Chem Engr.

MITCHELL, Kimberly Ann
Chillicothe HS; Chillicothe, OH (140-400) VP, Band; Chldr; Dbte Tm; NFL; Orch; Sci C; SC; Tr; Spch A; Forensics, Mus, A's; Fla Tech U; Nurs.

MITCHELL, Kimberly Gayle
N Wilkes HS; Hays, NC; Ann; BC; Ensm; Fr C; FHA; Yth Fel; Mus A; Appalachian Col; Ed.

MITCHELL, Laura Ann
Levelland HS; Levelland, TX (10%-210) Band; Parl, FHA; NHS; Rainbow; Span C; COM; Amer Col of Mus; Baylor U; Home Ec.

MITCHELL, Laura Jo
Maysville HS; Maysville, KY (5-76) Ann; Band; Chor; Ensm; Fr C; Parl, FHA; Sch P; Sci C; Golf; Outst Ach A, Gym; Maysville Comm Col; Math.

MITCHELL, Linda Mary
Uniontown HS; Uniontown, PA (3%-510) Drama; Fr C; Tres, Hmrm; NHS; Sci C; Alg A; COM; Chamber of Comm A; Sci A; Eng A; Fr A; Stu o-t Month; Penn St U; Med.

MITCHELL, Loretta Anita
John F Kennedy HS; Richmond, VA (25%-309) City Conf; GS; Hmrm; ARC; SC; JA A; ROTC A; Pep C; Hampton Inst; Social Worker.

MITCHELL, Louise Annette
Navasota HS; Navasota, TX; Pep Sq; Blinn Col; Registered Nurs.

MITCHELL, Marilee
Albia Comm HS; Albia, IA (9-145) Band; Ger C; NHS; Var C; Bkbl; JV, Sftbl; Mgr, Tr; Christmas Qn; Band Qn; Simpson Col; Bus.

MITCHELL, Mark Everett
New Caney HS; Porter, TX; Hmrm; NHS; Bsbl; Bkbl; Alg A; Hist A; Hon Prog; Math A; U of Houston.

MITCHELL, Marth Jayne
Carmi Comm Unit 5 HS; Carmi, IL (50-125) Co-Ed, Ann; Band; Chor; Ensm; Secy, FHA; Cpt, Mjrte; ARC; Rptr, Sch P; Tri-HiY; Hon Prog; In-terlochen Ntl Mus; Q&S A; ARC A; Yth Fel; 1st Cl GSct; Church Choir; Life & First Aider, GSct Day Camp; Comm Choir; Drum & Brass Corp; Yth Del, Evang Comm & Mission Coun; Southeastern Ill Jr Col; Journ.

MITCHELL, Mary Angela
Morristown-Hamblen HS E; Morristown, TN (6-239) Pres, Anchor C; Co-Ed, Ann; Band; BC; Pres, FHA; ARC; Secy, Thes; Anchor Service A.

MITCHELL, Melanie Darling
Teaneck HS; Teaneck, NJ; A Cap Choir; JV, Chldr; Drama; Hmrm; SC; Hon Prog; Best Vocalist; Most Versitile; Hon Men, Outst Stu; The Arts.

MITCHELL, Melinda Kay
Cardinal Newman HS; Columbia, SC (3-68) Bus Mgr, Ann; JV, Chldr; Fr C; Hmrm; NHS; SC; Soc-cer; B Crocker A; Bio A; Hon Prog; NMF; NEDT; Psych A; Principal's List; U of SC.

MITCHELL, Melonia Renea
Marvell HS; Marvell, AR (16-120) Chor; FBLA; Spch C; Parl, SC; Thes; Hon Prog; Nurs.

MITCHELL, Mona Fay
New Caney HS; Porter, TX (12-219) Tres, Band; Hmrm; NHS; SC; 4H A; HCt; Historian, 4-H C; Band Swtht; Tex A&M U; Sci.

MITCHELL, Pamela Eileen
St John HS; Ennis, TX (5-43) Ann; VP, NHS; SC; Bkbl; Sftbl; Tr; NEDT; Health A; Bazaar Qn; Secy, Nike C; St Champ Girls Bkbl Tm; Navarro Jr Col; Med.

MITCHELL, Patty Lynn
Chatham Central HS; Bear Creek, NC (15-130) Band; Drama; FHA; Secy, SC; Bio A; Marshall; A&T Col.

MITCHELL, Paul Alan
Fargo N HS; Fargo, ND (19-380) A Cap Choir; AFS; Drama; NHS; Swim; Amer Leg A; Citz A; I Dare You; NMF; Ch, Ntl Meth Coun On Yth Min-istry; Amer U; Law.

MITCHELL, Penny
Newtown HS; New York City, NY; Type A; Sci A; Star Stu; Most Outst; Sci Teacher.

MITCHELL, Richard James
Cainhoy HS; Huger, SC (1-62) Chor; FFA; 4H; NHS; Span C.

MITCHELL, Robert Vincent
Saint Elizabeth HS; Pittsburgh, PA; Vlbl Tm; Du-quesne U; Law.

MITCHELL, Robin Rennee
Sch Within A Sch; Newark, NJ (10%-80) Chldr; Chor; Ensm; NHS; Tr; Alg A; Bio A; PTA A; Sci A; Med.

MITCHELL, Ronda Cherie
Jane Adams HS; Cleveland, OH;

MITCHELL, Rose Renate
Cass HS; Cassville, GA; Bus Mgr, BC; Co-Cpt, Chldr; Jr Miss Pagent; Math C; Secy, Span C; Secy, SC; Golf; Tres, Tr; Dalton Jr Col; Nurs.

MITCHELL, Royce Dale
Texas City HS; Texas City, TX (27-420) FFA; Cpt, Ftbl; Tr; Cl Fav; Star Student; Acad A, Co-Cpt, Ftbl; Outst Christian Ath; Area FCA A; Steven F Austin U; Bio.

MITCHELL, Russell Dale
Big Spring HS; Big Spring, TX; Band; Pres, Demo-lay; Howard Col; Elec Technology.

MITCHELL, Shareene Lynn
Ralston HS; Ralston, NE (13-296) Chor; Semi-Fin, GS; Key C; Model UN; NHS; Thes; Hon Prog; Nom, NCTE Achv Writing A; Pre-Med.

MITCHELL, Sherril Agatha
St Pius V HS; Bronx, NY (8-101) Chldr; Fr C; Semi-Fin, Jr Miss Pa; NHSt; ARC; Sch P; VP, SC; VP, Sr Cl; Bkbl; Sftbl; COM; Cl Fav; HCt; Hon Prog; Journ A; Star Student; Regents Schol Alt; Psych A; NYU; Journ.

MITCHELL, Sondar Jeanne
Centennial HS; Pueblo, CO (6-350) Pres, A Cap Choir; Chor; Hmrm; Pres, Madrigal; Tres, NHS; Span C; Rotary A; Chopin Piano A; Prom Court; U of N Colo; Nurs.

MITCHELL, Sondra Jeanne
Centennial HS; Pueblo, CO (6-350) Pres, A Cap Choir; Chor; Hmrm; Pres, Madrigal; Tres, NHS; Rotary A; Chopin Piano A; Prom Court; U of N Colo; Nurs.

MITCHELL, Susan Elaine
Manhattan HS; Manhattan, KS (32-440) Cpt, Chldr; Chor; Fr C; Model UN; Tres, Soph Cl; Ki-wanis A; Kans Hon Stu, KU Alumni Assn; U of Mo at Columbia; Bus.

MITCHELL, Sybil Suzette
Cainhoy HS; Huger, SC (1-45) Chor; Drama; FHA; 4H; Hmrm; Math C; NHS; Phys C; Ed, Sch P; Sci C; Span C; SC; Pres, Sr Cl; Gov Honor Prog; JA A; WW; PC Jr Fellow; U of Md; Law.

MITCHELL, Teena Marie
Patrick Henry HS; Glade Spring, VA; Band; Chor; Ensm; Co-Ch, Hmrm; Ch, Sch P; Tres, Tri-HiY; Var C; Bkbl; Tr; Yth Fel; All Region Chor; Del Conf Yth; Hon Men, Writing Contest; Journ.

MITCHELL, Terry Lee
Northside HS; Memphis, TN (70-480) Co-Ed, Ann; Dbte Tm; FBLA; Ch, Hmrm; Phys C; SC; Swim; COM; Citz A; Hon Prog; U of Tenn-Knoxville; Engr.

MITCHELL, Vanesia Rae
Cokeville HS; Cokeville, WY (4-12) Ed, Ann; Chldr; Chor; FHA; GS; Journ A; Type A; U of Wyo; Psych.

MITCHELL, Veronica
Proviso E HS; Maywood, IL; Chldr; Hmrm; Madri-gal; Thes; Cpt, Bsbl; Cpt, Soccer; Cpt, Sftbl; Most Out; Sci A; Cpt, Vlbl; Triton Col; Interpreter For Deaf And Dumb.

MITCHELL, William Howard
Bristow HS; Bristow, OK (1-141) Chor; Fr C; SC; Bkbl; Ftbl; Swim; Amer Leg A; COM; Cl Fav; Hist A; Sci A; Most Inspirational; Principal's HR; Best Attitude; Eng A; Okla Hon Soc; Okla St U; Vet.

MITCHEM, Deborah Ann
Man HS; Man, WV (14-180) Band; GS; Span C; All Co Band; W Va U; Med Tech.

MITCHEM, Deborah Ann
Palatka S HS; Palatka, FL (7-285) BC; Lat C; Span C; Tri-HiY; COM; Pres A; JV Vlbl; Commissioner of Ed A of Hon; Civics, Phys Ed, Eng, Certs of A; St Johns Jr Col; Lib Arts.

MITCHENER, Devonne Camille
Smithfield-Selma HS; Smithfield, NC (14-355) Chor; FHA; Rptr, Hmrm; NHS; Bus Mgr, Sch P; Rptr, SC; U of NC; Ed.

MITOMA, Terri Tsuyako
Sacramento Union Acad; Carmichael, CA (3-45) Bus Mgr, Ann; Band; VP, Madrigal; NHS; Rptr, Sch P; Ski C; S-T, SC; Cpt, Bkbl; Golf; Cpt, Soccer; Cpt, Sftbl; Semi-Fin, Tnns; Tr; Bank Of Amer A; Pres A; Type A; Schol A; Band A; Piano A; Pacific Union Col; Med.

MITTAG, Angela Marie
Fairfax HS; Los Angeles, CA (105-827) Pres, A Cap Choir; Chldr; Pres, Chor; Pres, City Conf; Drama; Pres, Fr C; Fin, GS; Pres, Hmrm; InterClub Coun; Pres, Madrigal; VP, Mu Alpha Theta; NHS; Semi-Fin, Ntl Yth Co; Spch C; St Stu Congress; Pres, SC; Var C; VP, Sr Cl; Bkbl; Co-Cpt, Sftbl; COM; Citz A; Cl Fav; HQn; HCt; MLS; Most Out; Phi Beta Kappa; Pres A; Yth Fel; Yth Leg; Vlbl; Ldrship A; Secy, SC; Sen Yth Semi-Fin; Phys Ed A; Calif Lutheran Col; Sociology.

MITTEL, Cynthia Gail
Eldorado HS; Eldorado, TX (5-44) Band; FHA; 4H; NHS; 4H A; Bus.

MITTLER, Michelle Louise
Crystal Lake HS; Crystal Lake, IL (99-537) A Cap Choir; Band; Chem C; Chor; FNA; NHS; F-Ed, Sch P; Span C; COM; Hon Prog; St Scholar; Yth Fel; March of Dimes Nurs Schol; United Church of Christ A; WW; Elmhurst Col; Nurs.

MITTON, Brett Lewis
Carmel HS; Carmel, NY (170-350) Band; Chor; Orch; Mus Production Workshop; Choir; SUNY; Bus Adm.

MITTS, Diane Elizabeth
Homewood Flossmoor HS; Flossmoor, IL (36-936) Chor; Fr C; NHS; ARC; Q&S A; ARC A; Sunday Sch Teacher; Swim Timers C; HR; Activities Coor-dinator, Yrbk; Augustana Col; Eng.

MITTS, Helen Marie
Bonner Springs HS; Bonner Springs, KS (15-175) VP, Band; VP, Lat C; NFL; SC; VP, Thes; K St U; Special Ed.

MITTS, Steven Jon
Marcus Comm HS; Marcus, IA (6-67) NHS; Tres, Soph Cl; JV, Bsbl; JV, Bkbl; Ftbl; Tr; Rotary A; Spch A; VofDEM; Iowa St U; Compter Sci.

MITTS, Valerie Ann
Stratford HS; Stratford, TX (10-93) Band; JV, Chldr; SC; Bkbl; Tnns; Tex Tech U; Eng.

MITZEL, George Dean
Fruitport HS; Muskegon, MI (180-250) Tres, Lit Mag; Sch P; Mgr, Bkbl.

MIX, Amy Eileen
Northmont HS; Clayton, OH (50-546) SC; Hon Prog; Yth Fel; Math.

MIX, Greggory Robert
Duluth E HS; Duluth, MN (33-548) A Cap Choir; Chor; Ensm; Hmrm; NHS; Co-Ed, Sch P; SC; VP, Jr Cl; Rotary A; U of Minn; Pre-Med.

MIXON, Charlotte Elaine
Jackson S Abrams HS; Bessemer, AL; Band; Chldr; Tres, Hmrm; Cpt, Mjrte; Beauty; Mjrte A; Stu Teacher; *Grady Col; Nurs.*

MIXON, Lisa Lynne
Sou Choctaw HS; Silas, AL (3-90) Band; BC; FHA; Secy, Soph Cl; Alg A; 4H A; Math A; Sci A; Type A; Eng A's.

MIXON, Michael Anthony
Ross S Sterling HS; Houston, TX (25%-485) Chess C; *Tex A&M U; Engr.*

MIXON, Mitzi Regina
New Augusta HS; New Augusta, MS; Band; BC; FBLA; FHA; FTA; 4H; NHS; Sci C; Span C; *Jones Co Jr Col; Foreign Lang.*

MIZDAIL, Brenda Lee
John S Fine Sr HS; Namtioke, PA (7-347) Chldr; Chor; Drama; Hmrm; Rptr, Rptr, Sch P; Sodality; SC; Pres, Soph Cl; JV, Hockey; Hon Prog; NEDT; *Phar.*

MIZE, Karen Elaine
Brazos HS; Wallis, TX (50%-69) Band; Ensm; Pres, FHA; SC; Type A; FHA Encounter; FHA Girl o-t Yr; FHA Girl o-t Month; Band Ensm Div I; *Wharton Co Jr Col.*

MIZE, Michele Daun
Dulles HS; Stafford, TX (25%-900) Chor; FNA; Ger C; NFL; Spch A; *Houston Baptist Col; Nurs.*

MIZE, Michele Dawn
John Foster Dulles HS; Stafford, TX (33%-1000) Chor; FNA; Ger C; NFL; Spch C; Spch A; Sunday Sch Teacher; *Houston Baptist Col; Nurs.*

MIZELL, Bruce Lane
Fletcher Sr HS; Jacksonville Beach, FL (33%-54) Ann; Span C; Hon Prog; Acolyte Guild; Sheriff's Explorers; *Criminology.*

MIZELLE, Scott Payne
Oak Ridge Acad; Oak Ridge, NC (2-30) Band; Chor; Fr C; Lat C; NHS; ARC; Var C; VP, Soph Cl; Bsbl; JV, Bkbl; Ftbl; Soccer; Tr; Hon Prog; ROTC A; Good Conduct; HR Expert Marksman A; Good Sportsman A; *Air Force Acad; Engr.*

MIZER, Rebecca Lynne
Walla Walla HS; Walla Walla, WA (295-488) Semi-Fin, Jr Miss Pa; Rptr, Lit Mag; ARC; *NW Bible Col; Ed.*

MLODZIENSKI, Linda Christine
Riverside HS; Taylor, PA (7-195) Chor; FTA; Bus Mgr, Hmrm; Co-Cpt, Mjrte; Secy, NHS; Orch; SC; Bus Mgr, Sr Cl; Coun of Teach A; Hon, Prog; NEDT; PTA A; WW; Driving Cert; *U of Scranton; Bus Adm.*

MLODZIK, Donna Jean
Cabrini HS; Allen Park, MI (15-153) Drama; GS; Key C; NFL; NHS; F-Ed, Sch P; Thes; Var C; Tr; COM; Journ A; Kiwanis A; Pres A; Q&S A; Spch A; Service A; Yrbk A; Hon A; Theology A; *U of Mich; Med Technology.*

MO, Justina Margaret
All Saints Cathedral Sch; St Thomas, VI (5-18) Math C; Secy, Jr Cl; *Fla Sou Col; Acct.*

MOAK, Roger Alan
Jackson Preparatory HS; Jackson, MS (103-174) Key C; Order/Arrow; Bsbl; Order/Arrow A; Eagle Sct; *U of Miss; Bus.*

MOALLI, Karen Beth
St Mary's HS; Lynn, MA (15-146) Chldr; Hmrm; SC; Bkbl; Tr; Alg A; Math A; Religion, Fr, Eng, A's; *Boston Col.*

MOBERLY, Kenneth Allen
Lafayette Sr HS; Lexington, KY (50-800) Wrest; NJROTC Lt; *U of Ky; Math.*

MOBLEY, Berthenia Rosetta
Groves HS; Garden City, GA (13-215) Chldr; Fr C; NHS; SC; Beauty; COM; Fr A.

MOBLEY, Charlene Joanne
Groves HS; Garden City, GA; Fr C; FHA; Span C; *Armstrong Col.*

MOBLEY, Darlene Janice
Groves HS; Garden City, GA; Fr C; FHA; Span C; *Armstrong Col.*

MOBLEY, Marcie Lynn
Uintah HS; Vernal, UT (16-323) Ann; Hmrm; Ed, Sch P; Sftbl; Swim; COM; Pres, Church Yth; Sunday Sch Teacher; *Cosmetology.*

MOBLEY, Michele
Martin Luther King HS; Philadelphia, PA; Pres, Hmrm; COM; Drill Tm; Fr A.

MOBLEY, Yvette Lynn
Simon Gratz HS; Philadelphia, PA (10-1000) Cpt, Chldr; Secy, FBLA; JETS; *Penn St U.*

MOCK, Carol Jean
Parma Sr HS; Parma, OH (49-1009) Band; Fr C; NHS; Ski C; Sftbl; NEDT; *Cuyahoga Comm Col; Psych.*

MOCK, Daniel Edsel
Bible Baptist HS; Savannah, GA (25%-54) Ann; Band; Chor; 4H; Rptr, Hmrm; Rptr, Sch P; Rptr, Sr Cl; Tnns; Cl Fav; Hon Prog; JA A; *Armstrong St Col; Mus.*

MOCK, Donna Marie
S Salem HS; Salem, OR (50-350) AFS; JV, Chldr; Secy, Span C; Soccer; Tnns; *Oregon St U; Forestry Mgt.*

MOCK, Linda Gayle
Strongsville HS; Strongsville, OH; Orch; Span C; 1st Cl GSct; Solo & Ensm; St Orch Contest; *Rockhurst Col; Bus.*

MOCK, McCord Lee
Austin HS; Decatur, AL (5%-460) Band; Mu Alpha Theta; Sci C; NEDT; All St, Band; All St Jazz Band; Mensa; *Memphis St U; Mus.*

MOCK, Roy Edward
St Ignatius Col Prep Sch; Chicago, IL (63-199) A Cap Choir; Tnns; Hon Prog; Ntl Achv Schol; NMS; NEDT; Yth Fel; Yth Leg.

MOCK, Steven Elliott
Mahar Regional HS; Orange, MA (15-150) Band; Chor; Hmrm; Key C; St Stu Congress; SC; JV, Bsbl; JV, Bkbl; Soccer; Wrest; Citz A; HKg; Sci A; *U of NH.*

MOCK, Susan Dawn
Hopewell HS; Aliquippa, PA (50-425) Ensm; Pres, Fr C; Hmrm; SC; Bkbl; *Geneva Col; Med.*

MOCK, Vanessa B
W J Woodham HS; Pensacola, FL (16-530) Secy, BC; Ger C; InterClub Coun; VP, Mu Alpha Theta; NHS; ARC; Chem A; NEDT; Type A; Ger A; *Pensacola Jr Col; Psych.*

MOCKENSTURM, Thomas Raymond
Cardinal Stritch HS; Oregon, OH; Rptr, Sch P; Thes; Tnns; Hon Prog; Art A; *Toledo U; Journ.*

MODE, Clarissa Jo
Vega HS; Vega, TX; 4H; JV, Bkbl; Tnns; Tr; *Pepperdine U.*

MODE, Marvin Wilbur
Vega HS; Vega, TX; BS; Pres, FFA; 4H; NHS; SC; JV, Bkbl; Ftbl; Citz A; 4H A; I Dare You; *Tex A&M U; Agr Bus.*

MODEROW, Debra Ellen
Hubbard HS; Chicago, IL (63-600) Band; Hon Prog; Russian C; *Art Inst of Chicago; Art.*

MODESITT, Brenda June
Arlington Heights HS; Fort Worth, TX (1-440) Community Yth Symph; Semi-Fin, GS; NHS; Orch; Ch, SC; DARGCA; Hon Prog; Summa Cum Laude; All Region Orch; All St Symph Orch; All City HS Orch; *Baylor U; Mus Ed.*

MODISETTE, John Pat
Silsbee HS; Silsbee, TX (35-300) Fr C; Pres, JETS; Key C; Orch; Spch C; SC; Tnns; Mgr, Tr; COM; Drum Major, Band; Human Relation Comm A; *Stephen F Austin St U; Computer Sci.*

MODLICH, Linus William
W Jefferson HS; W Jefferson, OH; Bsbl; Cpt, Bkbl.

MOE, Nancy Gail
Grafton HS; Grafton, ND (7-118) VP, Band; Chor; Drama; Madrigal; NHS; Sci C; COM; 4H A; Hon Prog; Star Student; Type A; *Association Free Lutheran Bible Sc; H.*

MOE, Randall Arthur
Lincoln HS; Thief River Falls, MN (39-255) Chor; Drama; Ensm; Orch; VP, Church Yth Group; Church Organist; *U of ND; Eng.*

MOEGERLE, Nannette Denise
Centerville HS; Centerville, IN (20-136) Band; Rptr, 4H; NHS; 4H A; Model Legislature; *Ball St U; Eng.*

MOEHRING, Kari Lynn
Galva HS; Galva, IL (15-88) Ann; Band; Chor; Drama; JV, Bkbl; Cpt, Sftbl; JV, Tr; 4H A; Hon Prog; Type A; VP, Art C; Ftbl Qn Ct; Ath Ltr; Pres, VP, Secy, 4-H C; GAA; Cpt, Vlbl; *Bradley U; Archt.*

MOEHRKE, Kathleen Lois
Sheboygan S HS; Sheboygan, WI (80-500) Band; Dbte Tm; NFL; Spch A; Solo, Ensm, A's; *Concordia Teachers Col; Elem Ed.*

MOELLENKAMP, Cheryl Ann
Lisbon HS; Lisbon, ND (25%-69) Band; Bus C; Chldr; Secy, FBLA; FHA; SC; Bkbl; Sftbl; Tr; *ND St U; Interior Design.*

MOELLENKAMP, Joel Eugene
Lisbon HS; Lisbon, ND; Dbte Tm; VP, FFA; Var C; Bsbl; Wrest; FFA St Farmer; *Carpentry.*

MOELLER, Jeffrey Wayne
Wilton Comm HS; Wilton, IA (50-85) Chor; FFA; SC; Bkbl; Ftbl; Tr; Pres, Yth Fel; *Auto Repair.*

MOEN, Barbara Kay
Arkadelphia HS; Arkadelphia, AR (6-160) A Cap Choir; Chor; Fr C; NHS; Sch P; *Ouachita Baptist U; Vet Med.*

MOEN, Gregory Scott
Forest Park Sr HS; Forest Park, GA; Band; S-T, Key C; DECA; *Ga Tech; Mech Engr.*

MOEN, Jeffrey Charles
Burnsville Sr HS; Burnsville, MN; A Cap Choir; Band; VP, Chor; Ensm; Ger C; Madrigal; Orch; Bkbl; Golf; Pop Group; Mus Ltr; *Wheaton Col; Mus.*

MOENNIG, Glen Richard
Pierce City R-6 HS; Pierce City, MO (7-47) BS; Pres, FFA; Math C; NHS; SC; Ftbl; Tr; MLS.

MOENNIG, Shirley Diane
Pierce City R-6 HS; Pierce City, MO (18-72) Band; Chldr; Secy, FFA; FHA; Math C; Tres, Soph Cl; Bkbl; Tr; 4H A; Val; Miss Merry Christmas Qn; PA, Pep C; Bkbl A; Tres, Church Walter League; Vlbl; Farm-Home Improvement, FFA; FFA Meat Judging Tm; *SW Mo St U; Phys Ed.*

MOERTLE, George Eric
Sycamore HS; Cincinnati, OH; Band; *Mech Engr.*

MOESEL, Douglas Dean
Northwest Classen HS; Oklahoma City, OK (6-470) Drama; Pres, 4H; Key C; Math C; Mu Alpha Theta; NHS; Thes; JV, Bsbl; Ftbl; Cpt, Wrest; COM; Citz A; 4H A; H of F; Hist A; Hon Prog; I Dare You; Regent Schol; Spch A; St 4-H Pub Spch, Gardening A's; Alt, All St, Wrest; Ntl 4-H Conf; *Okla St U; Horticulture.*

MOEWS, Angela Marie
Central Heights Sch; Richmond, KS (11-54) Chor; FHA; 4H; NHS; Type A; Eng, Secy, Ger, A's; Pep C; *St Mary Col; Secy.*

MOFFATT, Glenn Edwin Jr
North Toole County HS; Sunburst, MT; Band; CYO; Chem C; 4H; Hmrm; Math C; SC; Bkbl; Ftbl; Swim; Tr; Amer Leg A; Chem A; I Dare You; Most Out; PA; WW; Sportsmanship A; Altar Boy & Lector, Church; NASA Chem A; Sup, St Sci Fair; *U of Mont; Forestry.*

MOFFATT, Holly Ruth
Parsippany Christian Sch; Parsippany, NJ; Ann; Band; Chor; *Ed.*

MOFFETT, Debbie Ann
Danbury HS; Danbury, CT (177-864) Hmrm; SC; COM; Hon Prog; *NC Agr Col; Data Processing.*

MOFFETT, Kenneth Jerome
Hugh Manley HS; Chicago, IL (1-219) City Conf; Model UN; NHS; Sci C; Up Bound; Co-Cpt, Bsbl; Bkbl; Ftbl; Tr; Alg A; COM; Hon Prog; Math A; Most Out; Sci A; Val; *Northeastern U; Elec Engr.*

MOGENSEN, Karin Ruth
Bellevue Christian Sch; Bellevue, WA; Chldr; 4H; SC; Soccer; Drill Tm; *Pepperdine U; Psych.*

MOGENSEN, Krista Jean
Alexander Hamilton Sr HS; Milwaukee, WI (33%-800) CYO; Drama; Hmrm; Ski C; S-T, Span C; Secy, SC; Jr Cl; Bsbl; JV, Swim; COM; Hon Prog; K of C A; Sports A; CCD Teacher; Art A; Service A; Eng A; *UW Milwaukee; Occupational Therapy.*

MOGENSEN, Marlene Joan
Cedar Rapids Pub Sch; Cedar Rapids, NE (4-35) Ann; Band; Chr; Drama; Ensm; Spch C; Var C; S-T, Sr Cl; Tres, Jr Cl; Bkbl; MVP, Tr; Hon Prog; Spch A; Type A; MVP, Vlbl; *Wayne St Col; Bus.*

MOGISH, David John Jr
Jacksonville HS; Jacksonville, AR (83-528) Ann; *U of Ark at Little Rock; Engr.*

MOHAMMED, Greg S
Dugway HS; Dugway, UT (4-50) CYO; Drama; NHS; Sch P; SC; VP, Var C; VP, Jr Cl; Pres, Soph Cl; Bkbl; Ftbl; Tnns; *U of Utah; Med.*

MOHAN, Barbara A
Tottenville HS; Staten Island, NY (81-1200) Band; Key C; NHS; ARC; COM; Citz A; Hon Prog; Interlochen Ntl Mus; ARC A; Yth Fel; Fireman Schol; *Nurs.*

MOHL, Lynn Bluette
Hatboro-Horsham HS; Horsham, PA (132-415) Chor; JV, Hockey; JV, Sftbl; JV, Swim; Citz A; *Bob Jones U; Eng.*

MOHLER, Diane Sue
Heights HS; Cleveland Height, OH (30%-900) JA; Swim Timers; Diversified Ed; *Dyke Col; Bus.*

MOHLER, Mary Anne
E Mecklenburg HS; Charlotte, NC; BC; NHS; Vagabond C.

MOHLER, Nancy Jo
Claiborne Acad; Haynesville, LA (3-34) Co-Ed, Ann; Fr C; Semi-Fin, Lit Ral; Rptr; NHS, Secy, Soph Cl; Secy, Tres, Church Yth Fel; Tres, Cpt Asst, Drill Tm; 1st Pl Fr, 2nd Pl Spelling, Rally; Outst Attitude, Drill Tm; *NE La U; Occupational Therapy.*

MOHNEY, James Edward Jr
Fredonia HS; Fredonia, NY (63-216) Chor; Community Yth Symph; Ensm; Orch; Co Mus Teacher's Schol; Yth Orch; Church Choir; Audio-Visual Service C; Church Yth Group; *Mus.*

MOHNEY, Kirk Franklin
York Central Sch; Retsof, NY (3-96) Hmrm; NHS; VP, SC; VP, Soph Cl; Ftbl; Regent Schol; *U of Rochester; Physics.*

MOHR, Gerald David
Beaumont Charlton Pollard HS; Beaumont, TX (29-305) Band; Dbte Tm; Key C; NHS; Orch; Order/Arrow; SC; JV, Bkbl; COM; UIL Solo and Ensem; Eagle Sct BSA; All Region Band; *Lamar U; Criminal Justice.*

MOHR, Shawn Anne
Bennington HS; Bennington, NE (7-42) Band; Chor; 4H; Math C; NHS; Bkbl; Sftbl; Tr; Alg A; 4H A; Hon Prog; Math A; *Midland Lutheran Col; Agr.*

MOHR, Stephen Joseph
Carroll HS; Dayton, OH (11-265) Band; Math C; NHS; Hon Prog; Math A; NMS; HR; *U of Dayton; Elec Engr.*

MOJARRO, Shirley Ann
Whittier Christian HS; Whittier, CA; Cpt, Chldr; Chor; Ensm; Hmrm; Rptr, Sch P; Sci C; Cpt, Bkbl; Cpt, Sftbl; Cpt, Tr; COM; Citz A; Cl Fav; Hon Prog; Swtht; *LIFE Bible Col; Christian Ed.*

MOJTA, Theresa Ann
St Joseph's HS; Camden, NJ (28-111) CYO; Cpt, Chldr; Drama; Fr C; NHS; Span C; Tres, SC; Var C; Tres, Soph Cl; Hon Prog; Individual Chldr A.

MOKREN, Linda Elizabeth
Oak Hills HS; Cincinnati, OH (97-855) Rptr, Sch P; GSct; Baton Corp; Yth Group; GAA; *Miami U; Interior Design.*

MOLARTE, Cynthia Blones
George Washington Sr HS; Mangilao, GUAM (16-740) Band; Cpt, Chldr; NHS; Rptr, SC; SC; Hon Prog; Swtht; Achv A; *Ind St U; Mus.*

MOLDE, Kathy Louise
Montevideo Sr HS; Montevideo, MN (42-170) AFS; Ann; Band; Span C; Bkbl; COM; Hon Prog; Cpt, Vlbl; Conf Vlbl A; *U of Minn; Phys Ed.*

MOLDEN, Jeffrey Bernard
Walnut Hill HS; Cincinnati, OH (50%-400) Band; Golf; Swim; *Universal Training Inc; Deisel Mech.*

MOLDENHAUER, Susan LaVonne
LaCrescent Jr-Sr HS; LaCrescent, MN (33%-140) S-T, A Cap Choir; Chor; FHA; Ger C; Madrigal; Pres A; Choir Ltr & A; *Viterbo Col; Nurs.*

MOLDENHAVER, Susan LaVonne
La Crescent HS; LaCrescent, MN (33%-140) A Cap Choir; Chor; FHA; Ger C; Madrigal; Choir A & Ltr; Phys Fitness A; *Viterbo Col; Nurs.*

MOLENAAR, James Harry
Danube HS; Danube, MN (4-37) Band; BS; Chor; Secy, FFA; Tres, 4H; NHS; Ftbl; 4H A; Hon Prog; Alt, BS; Chpt Swine Feeding A; FFA Dist Star Farmer; Spkr A; Chpt Mech A; Chpt Livestock A; Chpt Record A; Dist Extemporaneous; *Willmar Jr Col; Agr.*

MOLES, Terri Lynn
Lowndes HS; Valdosta, GA; Anchor C; BC; Chor; Span C; Tri-HiY.

MOLETT, Glen
Temple HS; Temple, TX (45-100) Ch, Hmrm; Ch, Ntl Yth Conf; SC; Ftbl; Tr; Most Out; *Psych.*

MOLINA, Eva B
Douglas HS; Douglas, AZ; Ch, Dbte Tm; NHS; Co-Ed, Sch P; Arch; Bkbl; Sftbl; Tnns; Amer Leg A; Cl Fav; DARGCA; Elk A; Hist A; Q&S A; GAA; Piano Medals; *Bethany Col; Med.*

MOLINER, Carmen Elizabeth
Alexander Galt Regional HS; Lennoxville, CANADA (3-539) Hmrm; Hockey; Cpt, Soccer; Swim; Tnns; Tr; MVP, Soccer; MVP, Vlbl; Astronomy C; Badminton; *Lester B Pearson Col; Sci.*

MOLL, Linda Elin
Wilton HS; Wilton, CT (20-400) Chor; Fr C; Madrigal; Math C; *Wheaton Col; Sci.*

MOLL, Theresa Michele
Lakeview HS; Battle Creek, MI (50%-390) A Cap Choir; Chor; Hon Prog; Yth Fel; Beta Stu; Cert of Recogn, St Board of Ed; *W Mich U; Special Ed.*

MOLLER, Dean Richard
Dassel-Cokato HS; Dassel, MN; FFA; Swim; Church Sr High League; *Bemidji St Col; Commercial Art.*

MOLLER, James Edward
Thomas Jefferson HS; Denver, CO (4-625) Band; Madrigal; Bkbl; Soccer; JV, Wrest; *Metro St Col; Sci.*

MOLNAR, Charles Andrew
Southwood HS; Miami, FL; Fin, Soccer; Fin, Sftbl; Fin, Tr; Amer Leg A; COM; Math A; MLS; Most Out; Phys Ed Hon A; Ath A; Career Awareness A.

MOLNAR, Marcia Anne
Acad of Our Lady of Mercy; Milford, CT (3-86) Key C; Lat C; Sch P; Sodality; NEDT; Schol; *Georgetown U; Lang.*

MOLNAR, Margery Sue
Canton S HS; Canton, OH (25-297) Ann; Band; Cpt, Chldr; Chor; FNA; Hmrm; Spch C; Thes; Tri-HiY; Secy, Jr Cl; Tnns; Tr; COM; Sci A; Yth Fel; *Med.*

MOLTER, Donald Raymond
Whitmer Sr HS; Toledo, OH (33%-991) CYO; Order/Arrow; JV, Bsbl; Cpt, Bkbl; Cpt, Ftbl; Tr; Hon Prog; Math A; Order/Arrow A; Pres A; Eagle Sct A; Bsbl All-Star Tm; Par Vuli Dei A; Bridge Builder A; *Bus.*

MOLTZAN, Bruce David
W Fargo HS; W Fargo, ND; NFL; Spch C; Pres, SC; Ftbl; Cpt, Wrest; HKg; Spch A; Pres, Local, Dist Act; *Moorhead St U; Spch.*

MOLZAHN, Marilyn
Clearwater HS; Clearwater, FL (15%-1000) Church Choir; *Auburn U; Phar.*

MOLZAHN, Robert James
Columbine HS; Littleton, CO (120-375) A Cap Choir; Chor; Ensm; Co-Ed, Lit Ral; Semi-Fin, Ntl Yth Co; Mgr, Bkbl; Yth Fel; *Letonrneau Col; Drafting.*

MOMANY, Timothy Dale
St Joseph HS; Saint Joseph, MI (8-355) Secy, Lat C; NHS; Parl, SC; Var C; Swim; Ntl Sci Found; Hospital Vol; *Pre-Med.*

MOMON, Belinda Natarcha
Bass HS; Atlanta, GA; Band; Fr C; FHA; Pres, Hmrm; NHS; SC; HCt; Hon Prog; PA; Fr A; *Clark Col.*

MON, Stephanie Kim
Governor Livingston Regional HS; Berkeley Heights, NJ (20-320) Band; JV, Chldr; Drama; 4H; Tr; COM; Sci A; PA; *Computers.*

MONAHAN, Peggy Baker
Jefferson Comm HS; Jefferson, IA (42-122) Bus C; Tres, FHA; FTA; Spch C; Var C; Golf; Tr; Spch A; Pep C; Shorthand A; HR; *U of N Iowa; Elem Special Ed.*

MONCRIEF, Dale Edward
Cuyahoga Valley Christian Acad; Cuyahoga Falls, OH (1-56) Drama; Co-Ed, Sch P; SC; Pres, Jr Cl; Soccer; Tr; Bio A; Journ A; Math A; NEDT; Sci A; Young Citizens A; Ger A; Art A; *Bio.*

MONDAY, Denise Darlene
Central Cabarrus HS; Concord, NC (60-280) BC; VP, FHA; COM; HCt; Hon Prog; Pep C; Travel C; Schol Excel A; Cosmetology Voc A; *Cosmetology.*

MONDIMORE, Donna Marie
John W Hallahan HS; Philadelphia, PA (24-432) Chldr; Dbte Tm; Fr C; Hmrm; NHS; Spch C; Swim; Dbte As; Forensic Distinction; Jr Acad of Sci; Attendance & Punctuality A; *St Joseph's Col; Chem.*

MONETTE, Cathy Lynn
Cloutierville HS; Cloutierville, LA; CYO; Chldr; Tres, FBLA; VP, Sr Cl; VP, Jr Cl; *NW St U; Bus Adm.*

MONEY, Janet L
Powell Valley HS; Speedwell, TN; SC; 4H; Math C; Mu Alpha Theta; Span C; Tri-HiY; *Lincoln Mem Col; Secy.*

MONEY, Jerry Howard
Geronimo HS; Geronimo, OK (10-31) FFA; Bkbl; Ftbl; COM.

MONG, Deanna Lee
Roy HS; Roy, UT; F-Ed, Ann; Band; Chor; Sftbl; Yth Fel; Mus A's; Jobs Daughters; Bell Choir; *Bus.*

MONG, Rebecca Jane
Logan HS; Logan, OH; Band; Co-Cpt, Chldr; 4H; ARC; SC; Tri-HiY; Var C; Sftbl; Tr; COM; Cpt, Gym; Ohio Bicentennial Comm; *Coaching.*

MONGE, Crispin
Yauco HS; Yauco, PR; Bsbl; Sftbl; *Bradley U; Med Surgery.*

MONGE, Gianna Ivette
Colegio San Antonio; Rio Piedras, PR (2-105) Chor; NHS; Span A; *Natural Sci.*

MONGELLI, Rita
St Joseph's o-t Palisades HS; W New York, NJ (4-225) Chor; Drama; Hmrm; NHS; Span C; Span NHS; Hon Prog; *Fairleig Dickinson U; Med Tech.*

MONHOLLON, Kathryn Allie
Forest Park HS; Forest Park, GA (54-425) Ger C; Semi-Fin, GS; *Secy.*

MONINGER, Richard Allen
Chartiers-Houston HS; Houston, PA (20%-125) Ann; Band; Co-Ed, Sch P; Ch, Art C; Semi Fin, Penn Gov Sch o-t Arts; *Washington & Jefferson Col; Med.*

MONK, Charlotte Anne
R L Turner HS; Carrollton, TX (190-843) A Cap Choir; Band; Chor; FHA; Hmrm.

MONK, Drema O'Neal
Herndon HS; Herndon, WV (1-37) Chor; FBLA; Pres, FHA; NHS; Alg A; Hist A; Fr A; Eng A; Pep C; Sportsmanship A.

MONK, Julie Ann
Washington HS; Fremont, CA (51-378) Band; Chor; Orch; Tr; Hon Star, Missionette's; *Secy Sci.*

MONK, Marion Denise
Duncanville HS; Duncanville, TX (32-600) FBLA; Bkbl; *Abilene Christian U.*

MONK, Mildred Deanne
Duncanville HS; Duncanville, TX (75-600) FBLA; Type A; Office Ed Assn.

MONLLOR, Lilliam Tvette
Central HS; San Juan, PR; Chldr; Chor; Drama; FHA; Bkbl; COM; God & Country A; Hist A; Hon Prog; *U of Puerto Rico; Natural Sci.*

MONMOUTH, Dennis Earl
Booker T Washington HS; Houston, TX (5%-220) Chor; Dbte Tm; Pres, Drama; Ensm; JETS; NFL; NHS; Pres, Spch C; SC; Thes; VP, Sr Cl; COM; JA A; Most Out; Poet A; Spch A; *Stanford U; Biol.*

MONN, Kristina
Salisbury-Elk Lick HS; Salisbury, PA (7-36) Co-Ed, Ann; Band; Chor; Secy, SC; Bkbl; Sftbl; Amer Leg A; COM; Citz A; Cl Fav; Type A; Yth Foundation; Soroptomist Ltr of Merit; Salisbury Maple Princess; Miss Congeniality; *Erie Bus Center; Airline Travel.*

MONROE, Debra Kim
Moore HS; Moore, OK (10%-800) Band; Chldr; FBLA; Hmrm; NHS; SC; Mgr, Bkbl; HCt; PTA A; Fin, Gym St; Young Talent; Art C; Secy, Gym; Ltrman's C; Fin, St Homisphere Pageant; Stu o-t Month C; *OSU; Computer Sci.*

MONROE, Donna Michelle
Bible Baptist HS; Savannah, GA (25%-54) Ann; Secy, Chor; Hon Prog; Miss Bible Baptist HS; Outst Christian Ldrship; *Baptist U of Amer; Missions.*

MONROE, Lydia Ann
Westover HS; Albany, GA; Chor; Ensm; Pres, 4H; Lit Ral; Spch C; Tri-HiY; Bkbl; COM; Citz A; 4H A; Fin, Citz A; Fin, Com; Fin, 4-H A; *U of Ga; Home Ec.*

MONROE, Lynette Lea
Limestone Comm HS; Bartonville, IL (135-435) Fr C; Pep C; Voice of Democracy A; Usherettes; *Bradley U; Art.*

MONROE, Mary Ann
Lowndes HS; Valdosta, GA (40-450) Chor; FBLA; *Valdosta St Col; Bus.*

MONROE, Monte Auburn
New Caney HS; Porter, TX (25%-300) Drama; NHS; Bsbl; Bkbl; Ftbl; Tnns; Int Thespian; *U of Houston; Bus.*

MONROE, Ricky David
John F Kennedy HS; Richmond, VA (5-309) Band; Fr C; NHS; Phys C; Cpt, Wrest; *VPI; Civil Engr.*

MONSEES, Brenda Joy
Kirkwood HS; Kirkwood, MO (33%-550) A Cap Choir; Chor; Ensm; Sftbl; *Warrensburg Col; Elem Ed.*

MONSEGUE, Anne Carmen
Fort Hamilton HS; Brooklyn, NY; Chor; Jr Miss Pagent; Cpt, Ftbl; Cl Fav; Hist A; Piano A; Jr A, Qn Contest; *W Va U; Law.*

MONSHOWER, Cathy Ann
S Garland HS; Garland, TX; DECA; *Eastfield-UJD; Bus.*

MONSON, Julie Lynne
Cut Bank HS; Cut Bank, MT (1-101) Band; Chor; Ensm; Fr C; Secy, NHS; SC; Amer Leg A; COM; Citz A; Hon Prog; NMF; NMS; Val; St Hon Schol; Ntl Choral A; Choir Director's A; *Eastern Mont Col; Eng.*

MONTAGUE, Robert Joseph
Parlier Union HS; Parlier, CA (4-85) A-Ed, Sch P; SC; Var C; Bsbl; Mgr, Bkbl; Mgr, Ftbl; Journ A; Lion A; Math A; SC A; *Fresno City Col; Bus.*

MONTAGUE, Sandra Althea
Northwest HS; St Louis, MO (10-728).

MONTAGUE-BLACK, Nicole Suzanne
Albuquerque HS; Albuquerque, NM; Chor; Fr C; Church Choir; Secy, Yth Coun; Candystriper; *Lit.*

MONTALTO, Mary Jane
The Immaculata HS; Chicago, IL (19-157) Chor; Drama; Fr C; French NHS; Lit Mag; Secy, NHS; Ed, Sch P; SC; Pres, Thes; Hon Prog; *U of Ill at Champaign; Pre-Journ.*

MONTALVO, Dorianne
Consuelo Escalona Private Sch; Carolina, PR (5-56) Chldr; Chor; Dbte Tm; Math C; Phys C; ARC; Span C; Sftbl; Swim; Alg A; COM; Cl Fav; Hon Prog; Most Out; Sci A; Swtht; Secy, JA; Loyalty A; *U of PR; Executive Secy.*

MONTALVO, Giselle Venus
Adlai E Stevenson HS; Bronx, NY (32-724) Berkley U; Secretarial.*

MONTALVO, James
Jose de Diego HS; Mayaguez, PR; ARC; COM; Magna Cum Laude.

MONTALVO, Noemi
Consuelo Escalona Private Sch; Carolina, PR (5-28) Dbte Tm; Drama; Hmrm; ARC; Bkbl; COM; Chem A; Hon Prog; Loyalty A; *U of PR; Natural Sci.*

MONTALVO, Wilma
Adlai E Stevenson HS; New York, NY; NHS; Pres, Jr Cl; Hon Prog; Attendance A; *Syracuse U; Acct.*

MONTANEY, Jane Rene
Tahoma HS; Kent, WA (70-176) Hmrm; SC; Positive Attitude C; Girl o-t Yr; Secy, Girls C; Pep C; VP, Service C.

MONTANEZ, Lizzie M
Academia Sagrado Corazon; Santurce, PR (1-92) Drama; NHS; ARC; Sci C; Alg A; Bio A; COM; Hist A; Hon Prog; Math A; Phy A; Sci A; Type A; Geography A; Span A; Eng A; *Albright Col; Psych Bio.*

MONTANO, Aileen
Maria Cadilla de Martinez HS; Arecibo, PR (1-636) COM; Tutoria; *U of Puerto Rico; Phar.*

MONTANO, Racel
N Babylon HS; N Babylon, NY; JV, BC; Var C; Bsbl; JV, Bkbl; Hockey; Soccer; Sftbl; Tr; *Pepperdine U; Religion.*

MONTAS, Florence Diane
William H Hall HS; W Hartford, CT (100-550) Fr C; Span C; Co-Cpt, Cr-Ctry; Tr; Ntl Fr A; *Middlebury Col; Romance Lang.*

MONTE, Susan Louise
Spruce Creek HS; Port Orange, FL; Anchor C; Band; BC; Fr C; Hmrm; NHS; Orch; Rptr, Sch P; SC; Tres, Jr Cl; Cpt, Swim; COM; Citz A; Hon Prog; Yth Fel; GS Nom; March of Dimes A; MVP, Swim; DAR Essay A; Fr Congres A; *Daytona Beach Comm Col; Eng.*

MONTEFERRANTE, Mark Letterio
Loyola HS; Towson, MD; Chess C; *Johns Hopkins U; Med.*

MONTES, Lucas
Dr Pedro Perea Fajardo Voc HS; Mayaguez, PR; COM; High Hon; *Eckerd Col; Marine Bio.*

MONTGOMERY, Angela Lynn
Macon Jr-Sr HS; Macon, MO (16-126) Band; VP, Drama; Mjrte; Band Ldrship A; Anti-Rust C; Prom Steering Committee; Drama Cl Play; *NE Mo St U; Bus Ed.*

MONTGOMERY, Brenda Sue
Bogue Chitto HS; Bogue Chitto, MS (1-60) BC; FHA; S-T, Soph Cl; Mgr, Bkbl; *Miss Col; Mus.*

MONTGOMERY, Clark Alan
Flomaton HS; Flomaton, AL; Band; Chor; FFA; Citz A; *Jefferson Davis St Col; Drafting.*

MONTGOMERY, Craig W
Oak Park and River Forest HS; Oak Park, IL (164-1050) Hmrm; JV, Cr-Ctry; Tr; Hon Prog; VP, Church Yth Group; *St Olaf's Col; Pre-Med.*

MONTGOMERY, Donna Louise
John Glenn HS; New Concord, OH; Bus C; S-T, 4H; NHS; Hon Prog; MLS; Secy, OOEA; Victory's Ldr Band; Bible Quiz Tm; Pianist, Yth Group; *Bus Adm.*

MONTGOMERY, Gaye Cherise
Melbourne Central Cath HS; Melbourne, FL (2-85) Chldr; Chor; Drama; Pres, Fr C; SC; Alg A; COM; Hon Prog; Math A; Most Out; Congres Francaise En Floride; *Fisk U; Pre-Law.*

MONTGOMERY, Gwynne Marie
Denton HS; Denton, TX (10%-700) A Cap Choir; Band; Chldr; 4H; NHS; MVP, Bkbl; Citz A; HCt; Most Out; Yth Fel; VP, SC; Pres, VP, Yth Fel; *Mus.*

MONTGOMERY, Katherine Danette
York Comp HS; York, SC (1-261) Ann; Band; Fr C; FTA; *Wintrop Col; Ed.*

MONTGOMERY, Keith William
Nathan Hale HS; Tulsa, OK (15-678) A Cap Choir; Mgr, Band; Chor; Math C; Mu Alpha Theta; NHS; Orch; Bkbl; Tnns; Alg A; Hon Prog; Math A; Regent Schol; WW; *Okla St U; Engr.*

MONTGOMERY, Patricia Ann
Glenwood HS; Chatham, IL (76-185) A Cap Choir; AFS; Secy, Chor; Ensm; FHA; FNA; Ger C; Semi-Fin, Hmrm; Fin, SC; *Bus.*

MONTGOMERY, Paul John
Glenbard W HS; Glen Ellyn, IL (90-510) Band; Chor; Rptr, Hmrm; InterClub Coun; Key C; Monogram; Rptr, Sch P; Parl, SC; Var C; Pres, Sr Cl; Pres, Jr Cl; Pres, Soph Cl; COM; Co- cpt, Gym; *US Air Force Acad; Chem.*

MONTGOMERY, Susan Mary
Oak Park-River Forest HS; Oak Park, IL (48-1025) Hmrm; SC; Hon Prog; *Smith Col; Art.*

MONTGOMERY, Suzanne
Midfield HS; Midfield, AL (14-164) Band; BC; Tres, FBLA; FHA; Hmrm; Sch P; S-T, SC; Tres, Jr Cl; *Bessemer Tech Col; Computer Prog.*

MONTGOMERY, Theresa Lynn
Russell County HS; Russell Springs, KY (21-151) Ed, Ann; Ed, Sch P; Cl Fav; Journ A; PA; *Western Ky U; Journ.*

MONTGOMERY, Walter Dee
Mission San Jose HS; Fremont, CA (20%-750) Chor; Dbte Tm; Drama; FFA; Pres, 4H; NFL; Spch C; JV, Swim; CSF; COM; Cl Fav; 4H A; MLS; Spch A; Eng A; Timothy A; Meritorious A; *Western Baptist Bible Col; Yth Ministry.*

MONTGOMERY, Wendy Allison
Delavan-Darian HS; Delavan, WI (37-249) A Cap Choir; AFS; Band; Ensm; Hmrm; Orch; SC; Jobs Daughters; Pres, Church Yth Fel; Sch Mus Schol; *Sioux Falls Col; Mus.*

MONTIE, Mark Wilott
Cuyahoga Valley Christian Acad; Cuyahoga Falls, OH (3-30) MVP, Chess C; Hist A; NEDT; 10th, Am Hist, St Tests Schol Abil; *Christian Heritage Col; Paleontology.*

MONTOYA, Anthony Henry
Abe Lincoln HS; Denver, CO (69-715) Chess C; NHS; VP, Span C; JV, Tnns; Citz A; Hon Prog; Rotary Schol; *Colo Sch of Mines; Engr.*

MONTOYA, Diane T
Pojoaque HS; Santa Fe, NM (24-87) 4H; Math C; NHS; Var C; Fin, Bkbl; Sftbl; Tr; Co-Cpt, Bkbl; Co-Cpt, Vlbl; *NM St U; Bus.*

MONTOYA, Janet Jessie
Albuquerque HS; Albuquerque, NM; CYO; Span C; *NM St U; Special Ed.*

MONTS, Britton David
L O Bell HS; Hurst, TX (135-760) Drama; Order/Arrow; SC; Ftbl; COM; *Abilene Christian Col; Law.*

MONTZ, Deborah Jean
Willows HS; Willows, CA (5-130) Band; Chor; Ensm; Hmrm; Mjrte; Ski C; SC; Secy, Sr Cl; Orch; Bkbl; Ftbl; JV, Sftbl; CSF; Hon Prog; Band Drum Major; *U of Calif; Math.*

MONZIONE, Linda Joyce
Julia R Masterman Lab and Dem Sch; Philadelphia, PA; Drama; Hmrm; Span C; Tnns; COM; Communications.

MONZO, Maria Christine
Acad of St Aloysius; Jersey City, NJ (7-104) Math C; NHS; Amer Leg A; COM; Math A; NEDT; WW; *St Peter's Col; Acct.*

MONZON, Migdalia
Colegio San Antonio HS; Rio Piedras, PR (17-100) Math C; NHS; COM; Hon Prog; Yale Book A; *Colo St U; Med.*

MOODY, Christina Marie
Canby Union HS; Canby, OR (125-275) Drama; Thes; *George Fox Col; Sci.*

MOODY, Darlene
Bloom Trail HS; Chicago Heights, IL (59-1405) Band; Cpt, Bkbl; Sftbl; *Fla A&M U; Math.*

MOODY, David Keith
Columbus HS; Columbus, GA; Star Student; Lib C; PA.

MOODY, Gray
W Charlotte HS; Charlotte, NC (5%-700) Band; Chor; Drama; Ensm; Fr C; Mod Mus Mas; NHS; Orch; Fin, Charlotte Piano Tchr's Forum; *Mus.*

MOODY, Jeffrey Lynn
Fairmont Sr HS; Fairmont, WV (45-225) A Cap Choir; Band; InterAct C; Mu Alpha Theta; Ftbl; God & Country A; Ed Tours; *Fairmont St Col; Phar.*

MOODY, Jerald Ernest
Philo HS; Philo, OH (24-183) Band; Chor; Ensm; Fr C; NHS; Mgr, Tr; Math A; *Ohio N U; Mech Engr.*

MOODY, Justine Joy
Ansley Pub HS; Ansley, NE (9-26) Ann; Chor; Var C; Bkbl; Sftbl; Tr; HCt; Hon Prog; Yth Fel; St Champ, Vlbl Tm; Superior, District Mus; Job's Daughter's; Secy, Pep C; *Med Asst.*

MOODY, Marcia Juette
Northern HS; Flint, MI (1%-600) Ch, Community Yth Sy; SCh; Citz A; Hon Prog; Bluelake Fine Arts Camp; Interntl Yth Symph; Sound of 76; Yth Arts Festival; Gifted Stu Prog; All-Mi Hon Orch; Church Serv A; *U of Mich at Ann Arbor; Mus.*

MOODY, Marcy Jean
Norwood HS; Norwood, OH; BC; Fr C; InterClub Coun; SC; Var C; Swim; Flag Corp; *Nurs.*

MOODY, Mark McKelway
Saint Augustine HS; New Orleans, LA (22-193) JETS; Co-Cpt, Math C; Orch; Secy, Order/Arrow; Sch P; Bsbl; COM; Citz A; Hon Prog; JA A; Most Out; Yth Fel; MVP, Tr Meet; *Tulane U; Engr.*

MOODY, Melva Lea
Dilley HS; Dilley, TX (25%-64) Band; Chldr; Chor; Dbte Tm; 4H; Sch P; Span C; Var C; Cpt, Bkbl; Tnns; Tr; Cl Fav; 4H A; Fine Arts C; VP, MYF; Waitress, Jr-Sr Banquet; *Tex A&M U; Communications.*

MOOLCHAN, Elva Julie
Cristobal Jr Sr HS; Coco Solo, CANAL ZONE (1-150) VP, FNA; FTA; VP, Rainbow; Rptr, Sch P; Span C; Thes; Var C; Mgr, Bkbl; COM; Masonic A; *John Hopkins U; Med.*

MOON, Douglas Edward
Oscoda Area HS; Oscoda, MI (5%-250) NHS; Ski C; Pres, Soph Cl; Bsbl; MVP, Ftbl; Fin, Hugh O'Brien Leadership Found.

MOON, Gregory
Hart Co Comprehensive HS; Hartwell, GA (35-242) FBLA; FFA; 4H; Sch P; COM; 4H A; Journ A; Math A; Sci A; VICA.

MOON, James Barry
Osborne HS; Marietta, GA (10%-365) BC; Chor; Ensm; COM; Hon Prog; Choral A; *Math.*

MOON, Laura Ann
Roxana HS; Roxana, IL (82-230) Bus C; Chldr; Chor; Drama; FHA; FNA; F-Ed, Sch P; Pres, SC; Var C; HCt; Kiwanis A; High HR; Rptr, SC; WW; *Nurs.*

MOON, Nena Beth
Vestavia Hills HS; Vestavia Hills, AL (1-301) A-Ed, Ann; Ensm; Mjrte; Tri-HiY; *Bus Adm.*

MOON, Rick Dale
Wethersfield HS; Kewanee, IL (40-110) AFS; Pres, Band; Dbte Tm; Drama; Math C; Orch; Phys C; Spch C; Arch; Cpt, Bsbl; Bkbl; Cr-Ctry; Ftbl; Golf; Soccer; Sftbl; Swim; Tnns; Tr; COM; Spch A; *U of Ill; Archt.*

MOON, Sara Frances
Swifton Pub Sch; Swifton, AR; Ann; Band; Secy, BC; Chldr; FBLA; Pres, 4H; SC; Bkbl; Cl Fav; 4H A; HCt; MLS; 4-H Citizenship Short Course.

MOON, Terence Bernard
Terrell Co HS; Dawson, GA (7-200) FFA; Ftbl; Hon Prog; *Agr.*

MOON, Timothy LaMarre
Bethany Jr-Sr HS; Bethany, IL; Band; Chor; Ger C; Sch P.

MOONEY, Alicia Gay
Hobbs Sr HS; Hobbs, NM; Band; Pres, Chor; VP, Lat C; Parl, SC; JV, Bkbl; JV, Tr; Ntbl; Math A; Most Out; Pres A; Sci A; S-T, Lat C; All St Choir; Outst Choral Stu; Band A; *W Tex St U; Mus.*

MOONEY, Sherrie Renae
Madisonville N Hopkins HS; Madisonville, KY (50-300) Ann; BC; Cpt, Chldr; Rainbow; Tres, SC; Secy, Thes; Tri-HiY; Tr; Key C Swtht; All Dist Chldr; *W Ky U.*

MOONEY, Vauneida Ruth
Parkview HS; Little Rock, AR (20-800) BC; Chldr; Fr C; Hmrm; Mu Alpha Theta; SC; Y-Tns; *U of Ark; Med.*

MOONEYHAM, Deborah Elaine
Oglesby HS; Oglesby, TX (1-10) Co-Ed, Ann; Secy, BC; Cpt, Chldr; Pres, Drama; Hmrm; NHS; A-Ed, Sch P; VP, Spch C; SC; Var C; S-T, Jr Cl; VP, Soph Cl; Bkbl; Cpt, Sftbl; B Crocker A; COM; Cl Fav; HQn; MLS; Phy A; Spch A; Swtht; Val; *McLennan Comm Col; Radiology.*

MOOR, Pamela Jeanne
Ottawa HS; Ottawa, KS (7-203) Band; Chor; Drama; Ensm; Fr C; NHS; Bus Mgr, Sch P; Spch C; COM; Chamber of Comm A; Hon Prog; Journ A; NEDT; Pres A; Spch A; St Scholar; Yth Fel; Mus, Eng Hon, A's; St Choir; NML; *Kans U; Journ.*

MOORE, Adrianne Meredity
Ysleta HS; El Paso, TX (25%-500) Indian Marimba Band; Drum Major; *N Tex St Teachers Col; Pre-Med.*

MOORE, Alexander Herman
Lincoln HS; Dallas, TX; Chor; Cpt, Ftbl; Tr; Ath A; *E Tex St U; Phys Ed.*

MOORE, Angela Gail
Whitney HS; Whitney, TX (50%-35) Chor; FHA; Cpt, Mjrte; Sch Achieve Tm; Span C; Mgr, Bkbl; Cr-Ctry; Sftbl; Tr; Alg A; Math A; Poet A; Yth Fel; *Art.*

MOORE, Ann Elizabeth
R Nelson Snider HS; Ft Wayne, IN (120-529) Drama; 4H; Sch P; Art A; Drama A; *Lutheran Hospital Sch of Nurs; Nurs.*

MOORE, Anthony Randall
Fulton HS; Knoxville, TN (18-350) Ann; Chor; Secy, Key C; Lat C; NHS; JV, Bkbl; Ftbl; Tr; COM; Hon Prog; Math A; Sci A.

MOORE, Arnetta Jane
Plymouth HS; Plymouth, NC; Pres, A Cap Choir; Dbte Tm; FBLA; Math C; Sci C; Var C; Bsbl; Bkbl; Ftbl; Sftbl; Tr; *A&T St U; Bus Adm.*

MOORE, Arthur Burney
Dilley HS; Dilley, TX (10-75) Band; Pres, FFA; 4H; Bkbl; Ftbl; Swim; Tr; *A&M Col.*

MOORE, Belinda E
Greencastle HS; Greencastle, IN (34-150) Chldr; Chor; Fr C; FTA; Secy, 4H; Tres, Hmrm; ARC; S-T, SC; Thes; Swim; *Ind U; Elem Ed.*

MOORE, Benjamin Franklin
Southwest HS; Atlanta, GA; BC; Chess C; Pres, Hmrm; NHS; Span C; Tr; Citz A; Hon Prog; Sci A; Eng A; *Law.*

MOORE, Brenda Lee
Spencer HS; Columbus, GA; Outst Stu in Home Ec; HR; Poetry Contest; *Columbus Col; Bus Adm.*

MOORE, Bret A
Crestview Sr HS; Crestview, FL; BC; Pres, Math C; Mu Alpha Theta; VP, Order/Arrow; SC; Cr-Ctry; Tr; COM; Order/Arrow A; Eagle Sct; *U of Fla; Pre-Law.*

MOORE, Bridgett LaVerne
Shaw HS; E Cleveland, OH; Sftbl; Sftb Player A; *Virginia Mart Col; Fashion Designing.*

MOORE, Carl Lee
Ne HS; North East, MD; Band; NHS; Orch; Interlochen Ntl Mus; Yth Fel; Usher; Yth Coun; *Pipe Fitting.*

MOORE, Cathy Ann
S Haven HS; S Haven, KS (2-22) Ed, Ann; Band; Chldr; Chor; Ensm; Pres, FHA; Tres, 4H; Madrigal; Mjrte; Sch P; Y-Tns; Tres, Sr Cl; Pres, Jr Cl; Pres, Soph Cl; Bkbl; B Crocker A; Hon Prog; Sal; Co-Cpt, Vlbl; FFA Swtht; Band A; WW; Amer Yth in Concert Tour; Dist FFA Secy; *Okla Christian Col; Bus.*

MOORE, Charlene Ann
Campbell Central HS; Campbell, NY (6-52) Band; Chldr; Chor; Ski C; Var C; Bkbl; Soccer; Sftbl; Tnns; Alg A; Pres A; Type A; St Ping Pong A; Phys Fitness A; *King's Col; Legal.*

MOORE, Charles Albert Jr
Midwest City HS; Midwest City, OK (68-562) Band; Chess C; Ger C; Math C; NHS; Bio A; Citz A; Sci A; Eagle Sct; Band A; *Okla St U; Engr.*

MOORE, Christine
Forest Park HS; Cincinnati, OH (130-480) Chor; Drama; ARC; Cr-Ctry; Tr; COM; Vlbl; Mus A; *Bio Sci.*

MOORE, Claude Barnes Jr
Virgil I Grissom HS; Huntsville, AL (90-600) Key C; Mu Alpha Theta; Ftbl; Wrest; Ideal Sr; Ldrship A; WW; *U of Ala.*

MOORE, Cynthia Denise
Phyllis Wheatley HS; Houston, TX; A Cap Choir; Band; Chor; Fr C; FHA; Hmrm; Secy, Jr Cl; Sftbl; Tnns; Tr; COM; Citz A; Hon Prog; JA A; ROTC A; Yth Fel; Booster C; *Prairie View A&M U; Fashion Designer.*

MOORE, Dana Lin
Ritenour Sr HS; Overland, MO (51-850) Cpt, Chldr; Hmrm; NHS; SC; Tr; HCt; Regent Schol; Rotary A; *NE Mo St U; Acct.*

MOORE, Daniel Paul
Hood River Valley HS; Hood River, OR; Order/Arrow; Rptr, Sch P; Wrest; Order/Arrow A; *Sci.*

MOORE, Danny William
M D Collins HS; College Park, GA; Var C; Bsbl; Ftbl; Pres, Leo C; Pres, Explorers; *Atlanta Christian Col; Minister of Yth.*

MOORE, Daren Lee
Evander Childs HS; New York, NY; All Amer Yth; Bkbl; Math A; *Bradley U; Computer Programmer.*

MOORE, David Alan
Hope HS; Hope, AR (10%-250) Band; Hmrm; Key C; Span C; SC; Pres, Soph Cl; Bsbl; Golf; Leo C; *Ouachita Baptist U; Bus.*

MOORE, David Quentin
Putnam City HS; Oklahoma City, OK; Band; BC; Bkbl; JV, Ftbl; Sftbl; Alg A; COM; Citz A; Hist A; DAP Poster A; *Emanuel Col; Christian Ed.*

MOORE, Dawna June
Arnett HS; Arnett, OK (1-14) Secy, Band; Chldr; Chem C; Chor; Ensm; Pres, 4H; Math C; NHS; Var C; Bkbl; Swim; Tnns; Beauty; 4H A; St Scholar; Type A; Val; FFA Swtht; Sup, Home Ec Contest; NHS A; Supt's HR; Bus A; Rodeo Qn; *Okla St U; Med Tech.*

MOORE, Debbie Sue
Tupelo HS; Tupelo, MS (50%-675) Ann; Bus C; Drama; FHA; HiY; InterAct C; Lit Mag; Model UN; Sch P; Spch C; Thes; Tri-HiY; Y-Tns; Swim; Sci A; VFW A; Yth Fel; Dancing Sch; *Miss St U; Interior Design.*

MOORE, Debbie Sue
Smithfield-Selma HS; Smithfield, NC (22-355) Fin, FTA; Hmrm; NHS; Span C; SC; Co-Cpt, Vlbl; *U of NC; Phys Therapy.*

MOORE, Debra Elaine
Booker T Washington HS; Tulsa, OK; Bus C; FBLA; Y-Tns; Fresh Schol; *Northeastern A&M U; Nurs.*

MOORE, Debra Louise
Ellenville Central HS; Ellenville, NY; Band; Chor; Orch; Tnns; Ulster Co Lady Trapshooting Champ; Church Choir A; *Ulster Co Comm Col; Bus.*

MOORE, Donald Keith
Vestavia Hills HS; Birmingham, AL (25%-250) Cr-Ctry; Ftbl; Tr; Leo C; Church Puppet Ministry; Sr Board of Stewards, Church; *Aviation.*

MOORE, Douglas Don
Copeland Rural HS; Copeland, KS (2-10) Pres, 4H; Sch Achieve Tm; VP, Jr Cl; VP, Soph Cl; Co-Cpt, Bkbl; Co-Cpt, Ftbl; Tr; Amer Leg A; Gr Marshal; 4H A; Hon Prog; St Scholar.

MOORE, Douglas Owen
Hanceville HS; Hanceville, AL; Ann; Chem C; FTA; Math C; NHS.

MOORE, Eileen Cecile
Pekin Comm HS; Pekin, IL (6-705) Chor; Ensm; NHS; Span C; Hon Prog; VP, Tres, Yth Fel; WW; SDAHSS; *Ill St U; Phys Handicapped.*

MOORE, Erma Jean
Marvell HS; Marvell, AR (2-120) Tres, BC; FBLA; Pres, FHA; Pres, Ger C; Spch C; SC; COM; Cl Fav; Hist A; HCt; Sal; Spch A; Swtht; Type A; Miss MHS; Pep C; PA; WW; *U of Ark; Elem Ed.*

MOORE, Felicia
Dublin HS; Dublin, GA; FHA; HCt; *Tuskegee Inst; Sociology.*

MOORE, Glenn Edward
Arvada HS; Arvada, CO (148-695) A-Ed, Ann; Band; Key C; NHS; Span C; Var C; Bkbl; Sftbl; Tr; JV, Wrest; Yth Fel; Hallmark Art A; Pres, Yth Fel; *Architecture.*

MOORE, Gregory Claire
Bridgeton Sr HS; Bridgeton, NJ (15-500) NHS; Span C; Math A; Sci A; *U of Ky; Computer Sci.*

MOORE, Hubert Phillip Jr
Sw Ga Acad; Damascus, GA (2-36) Bus Mgr, Ann; BC; BS; Secy, Chor; Ensm; Fr C; VP, HiY; Hmrm; InterClub Coun; Lit Ral; Var C; Pres, Jr Cl; Pres, Soph Cl; Bsbl; Co-Cpt, Bkbl; Ftbl; Alg A; COM; Cl Fav; Hist A; Hon Prog; 2nd St, Boy's Solo; Yth Minister of Mus.

MOORE, Janet Elaine
Kirkwood HS; Kirkwood, MO (3-600) Chor; Drama; Hon Prog; Yth Fel; Pres, Regional CYF; Pep C; *Sociology.*

MOORE, Janet Sue
Wilbur D Mills HS; Little Rock, AR (9-320) BC; FBLA; Fin, Lit Mag; Hist A; *U of Ark; Pre-Med.*

MOORE, Joanne
Terrell Co HS; Dawson, GA (8-200) BC; Cpt, Sftbl; Tr; Hon Prog; Math A; Sci A; Eng A.

MOORE, John Morgan
Washington Sr HS; Washington, OH (4-185) AFS; Fr C; SC; Var C; Cpt, Golf; Amer Leg A; All League Golf; *Law.*

MOORE, Johnny Reese
Huntington HS; Shreveport, LA; Band; Chem C; Secy, FFA; Key C; Phys C; Ftbl; COM; *Engr.*

MOORE, Joyce Annette
Mt Carmel HS; Mt Carmel, IL (32-189) Band; Chldr; Bsbl; *Lockyear Col; Secy.*

MOORE, Judy Elaine
Winyah HS; Georgetown, SC (20%-170) Fr C; Pres, Yth Group; Band As; *Marine Bio.*

MOORE, Judy Lynn
Ellenville Central HS; Ellenville, NY; Chor; Church Choir A; *Ulster Co Comm Col; Home Ec.*

MOORE, Judy Teresa
Lincoln Consolidated HS; Ypsilanti, MI; Band; Bkbl; Best All Around; Math A; Vlbl; *Olivet U; Sci.*

MOORE, Julia Ann
Isle of Wight Acad; Isle of Wight, VA (4-42) Ed, Ann; Secy, Chor; Semi-Fin, GS; Monogram; NHS; Ed, Sch P; SC; Tres, Soph Cl; COM; Hon Prog; Journ A; Type A; Yth Fel; Sch Emblem A; PA; *Old Dominion U; Special Ed.*

MOORE, Julie Ann
Westside HS; Omaha, NE (260-796) Jr Miss Pagent; Rainbow; Demolay Swtht; WW; Drill Sq; Coun on Ministries; Z C; Exchange Prog to Mexico; UMYF; *U of NE-Lincoln; Med.*

MOORE, Karen Lee
Willows HS; Willows, CA (12-130) Ann; Chldr; Secy, FFA; Semi-Fin, GS; 4H; Hmrm; VP, SC; VP, Soph Cl; Co-Cpt, Bkbl; Ftbl; Hockey; Sftbl; Bank Of Amer A; CSF; 4H A; Hist A; Pres, FFA; *Calif Polytech U; Animal Sci.*

MOORE, Kathie Lorraine
Brookfield Central HS; Brookfield, WI (280-517) AFS; Chor; Ger C; Bkbl; Sftbl; Vlbl; *U of Wis-Oshkosh; Criminal Justice.*

MOORE, Kathleen Elizabeth
Broadview Acad; La Fox, IL (10%-77) Ann; Band; Chor; Hmrm; Sci C; Ski C; Tres, SC; Tres, Jr Cl; Cpt, Bkbl; Tr; Hon Prog; Choir; Courtesy Qn; *Andrews U; Nurs.*

MOORE, Kathy Brooks
Wade Hampton HS; Greenville, SC (200-380) Bus Mgr, Ann; FTA; Secy, Hmrm; Heart Fund A; *Col of Charleston; Social Sci.*

MOORE, Kathy Lynn
NW Classen HS; Oklahoma City, OK; Chldr; VP, Chor; Bkbl; Cl Fav; Type A; Girl o-t Yr; Clothing A; Eng A.

MOORE, Katrina Sue
Dan River HS; Ringgold, VA (1-236).

MOORE, Katrina Yvette
Wm Penn Sr HS; York, PA (46-465) AFS; Hmrm; NHS; Var C; Cpt, Hockey; Mgr, Swim; Mgr, Tr; Amer Leg A; Phys Ed Outst A; *Drexel U; Bus Adm.*

MOORE, Kevin Dale
Breckinridge Co HS; Harned, KY (2%-250) Chess C; Math C; Tnns; Lib C; Joseph Holt Hist C; Bio C; Lat A; *U of Chicago; Med Research.*

MOORE, Kevin Lenn
Romulus Sr HS; Romulus, MI (5-400) Tres, Band; BS; Chor; Tres, NHS; Mgr, Bsbl; Tnns; WW; WW Mus Stu; *Tenn Temple Sch; Mus.*

MOORE, Kimberly Ann
Great Bridge HS; Chesapeake, VA; Ann; Band; Chldr; Dbte Tm; Drama; NFL; NHS; VP, SC; Alg A; COM; Citz A; Math A; Spch A; NJHS; All-City Band As; Forensics A; *Bennett Col; Child Psych.*

MOORE, Larry Roger
Fairhope HS; Fairhope, AL (25%-250) *Troy St U; Biol.*

MOORE, Laurie Lynn
Skyline HS; Dallas, TX (25%-1104) Rainbow; SC; JV, Bkbl; Co-Cpt, Sftbl; Bio A; Hon Prog; Sci A.

MOORE, Lavernia
Terrell Co HS; Dawson, GA (10%-112) BC; FBLA; FHA; 4H; NHS; Up Bound; Tr; HCt; *Albany St Col; Criminal Justice.*

MOORE, Lawrence Elton Jr
Craigmont HS; Memphis, TN (43-240) Band; Chess C; 4H; Math C; Sci C; Bsbl; Bkbl; Citz A; *St Tech Col; Elec Engr.*

MOORE, Lee Nathan
John C Fremont HS; Los Angeles, CA; Hon Prog; HR; *Calif St U; Mus.*

MOORE, Leslie Leanne
Colo HS; Colo City, TX (6-126) Ann; Chldr; Rptr, FHA; NHS; Sci C; Amer Leg A; Cl Fav; Q&S A; Type A; Most Dependable; Most Courteous; Most Stu.

MOORE, Lisa Diane
Boardman HS; Boardman, OH; 4H; Sci C; Art C; Math.

MOORE, Lisa Dianne
Logan HS; Logan, OH (40-330) Band; 4H; Pres, SC; Sftbl; 4H A; *Mt Vernon Nazarene Col; Elem Ed.*

MOORE, Lisa Jelynne
Milan C 2 HS; Milan, MO (3-45) Band; Chldr; Chor; Ensm; GS; NHS; SC; Secy, Jr Cl; COM; Type A; Yth Fel; *Sch o-t Ozarks; Elem Ed.*

MOORE, Lori Denise
Logan HS; Logan, OH (10-367) Band; 4H; NHS; Sch Achieve Tm; SC; Sftbl; 4H A; Fin, Miss United Tn Pageant.

MOORE, Lori Kaye
Milan C-2 Sch; Milan, MO (10-60) Ann; Band; Cpt, Chldr; Chor; Ensm; NHS; SC; COM; HQn; Type A; Stenographic, Band, A's; *The Sch o-t Ozarks; Psych.*

MOORE, Lori L
Muskogee HS; Muskogee, OK; Ed, Ann; Drama; NFL; Thes; Tnns; Citz A; Journ A; Opt A; Spch A; Yth Fel; *Okla St U; Law.*

MOORE, Lori Lynn
Montpelier HS; Montpelier, OH (27-93) Ann; VP, Band; Chor; Pres, 4H; NHS; Sch P; Tres, Sr Cl; Bsbl Batgirl; Arion A, Mus; Sr Court; *Bowling Green St U; Mus Ed.*

MOORE, Lynette Ann
Powell Valley HS; Speedwell, TN; Thes; BC; FHA; *E Tenn St Col; Real Estate.*

MOORE, Lynne Etta
Zanesville HS; Zanesville, OH (2-300) Band; Drama; Secy, Lat C; NHS; Orch; Sch Achieve Tm; Rptr, Sch P; Span C; Thes; Tr; Hon Prog; Journ A; Q&S A; William Shinnick Educational A; *Ohio Wesleyan U; Bacteriology.*

MOORE, Marie Jean
Green Oaks HS; Shreveport, LA; Pres, Band; Dbte Tm; Drama; FBLA; FHA; Lit Ral; NHS; Rptr, Sch P; Type A; *Math.*

MOORE, Marjorie Ann
Jennings Co HS; North Vernon, IN (59-300) Band; VP, Bus C; Parl, FHA; Pres, 4H; Rainbow; Var C; Tr; 4H A; PA.

MOORE, Mark Edward
Petersburg HS; Petersburg, VA (10-550) Chess C; Dbte Tm; Fr C; Pres, Jr Cl; Ftbl; Alg A; Elk A; God & Country A; Math A; Acad Ftbl A; *U of Va; Law.*

MOORE, Mark Granger
Wortham HS; Wortham, TX (5-31) BC; Rptr, FFA; VP, Jr Cl; Co-Cpt, Bsbl; Ftbl; COM.

MOORE, Martha Phyllis
Southwest Ga Acad; Damascus, GA (9-26) Ed, Ann; Drama; Fr C; Hmrm; F-Ed, Sch P; Secy, Sr Cl; Rptr, Jr Cl; Cl Fav; Accompanist, Chor; Chapl, Tri-Hi-Y; Outst Acting A; *Ga Sou Col.*

MOORE, Mary Fran
Bethel Christain Sch; Ruston, LA (5-12) A-Ed, Ann; Chor; Pres, Hmrm; Lit Ral; Pres, Jr Cl; VP, Soph Cl; Bsbl; Bkbl; Beauty; HCt; Church Pianist; *La Tech U; Bus.*

MOORE, Mason Armistead
Norfolk Acad; Norfolk, VA (40-80) Drama; ARC; Pres, SC; Var C; Cr-Ctry; JV, Ftbl; Soccer; Tr; COM; Hon Prog; NMS; LaCrosse; Hon Ct; *U of Va; Engr.*

MOORE, Mellisa Sue
La Canada HS; La Canada, CA (60-375) Drama; Fr C; FTA; CSF; Hon Prog; Cpt, Drill Tm; Tres, Keywannetes; *U of Redlands; Ed.*

MOORE, Merry Lee
Castle Park HS; Chula Vista, CA (4-425) Chldr; Drama; Fr C; 4H; St Stu Congress; SC; Thes; Ch, Sr Cl; MVP, Bkbl; CSF; COM; H of F; Spch A; Yth Fel; Cpt, Bkbl; Pep C; Torch Bearer, Camp Fire Girls; Cpt & MVP, Vlbl; VP, Anthropology C; *Calif Poly St U; Phys Ed.*

MOORE, Michael Vincent
Peru HS; Peru, IN (50%-180) Ed, Lit Mag; NFL; Spch C; Poet A; Spch A; Art As; Hist, Eng C; Ice Skate C; Ed A; Art C; Yth for Christ; *Grace Col; Art.*

MOORE, Michael Wilson
Clements HS; Athens, AL (3-55) BC; 4H; Sch Achieve Tm; Bus Mgr, Sch P; Tres, Sr Cl; VP, Soph Cl; Bsbl; 4H A; Spch A; WW; *Math.*

MOORE, Molly M
St Mary o-t Valley HS; Beaverton, OR (10%-88) CYO; Fr C; French NHS; Orch; Sch P; Beauty; Hon Prog; Folk Group; *Santa Clara Col; Sci.*

MOORE, Monica Dana
Mercy HS; University City, MO (11-32) Band; Chldr; Chor; Drama; Hmrm; SC; JV, Bsbl; Sftbl; MVP, Tnns; Citz A; Cl Fav; HCt; JA A; Most Out; *Journ.*

MOORE, Myrna Ruth
Princeton HS; Princeton, MO (10%-52) Band; FHA; S-T, Hmrm; Mjrte; NHS; Rainbow; Bkbl; Fin, Tr; St Champ & Rec Hold, 80 Yd Low Hurd.

MOORE, Neadie Louise
Matoaca HS; Ettrick, VA; Ann; Tres, Band; Drama; Jr Miss Pagent; Lat C; NHS; Rptr, Sch P; SC; Var C; VP, Sr Cl; Tr; JA A; Gym; WW; *U of Sou Calif; Pre-Med.*

MOORE, Needa Renetta
Kalamazoo Central HS; Kalamazoo, MI (101-517) Drama; 4H; Up Bound; Tr; COM; Citz A; Hon Prog; Most Ntl Achv Schol; Pres, Yth Fel; *W Mich U; Bus Adm.*

MOORE, Nina Patrice
Lindblone Tech HS; Chicago, IL (210-689) All Amer Yth; Commercial C; FTA; Pres, Hmrm; Ntl Teachers Coun; SC; Bkbl; Sftbl; Swim; Tnns; Tr; Alg A; Beauty; Bio A; Citz A; Cl Fav; Coun of Teach A; Hist A; Hon Prog; I Dare You; Math A; Sci A; Star Student; Swtht; Type A; Yth Fel; *Ill St U; Special Ed.*

MOORE, Norman Eric
Grandview Heights HS; Columbus, OH; Band; Chor; Drama; Ensm; Ski C; Thes; Yth Fel; CCAD Sch School; *Art.*

MOORE, Pamela Anne
Summerville HS; Summerville, SC (101-548)
Drama; Pres, Fr C; FTA; A-Ed, Lit Mag; SC;
NEDT; *Col of Charleston; Eng.*

MOORE, Pamela Renee
Skyline HS; Dallas, TX; Lat C; NHS; Hist A; WW;
Jr Classical League; Life Ldrship A; *U of Houston;*
Psych.

MOORE, Patricia Ann
Gosnell HS; Blytheville, AR (15%-103) BC; Fr C;
SC; Good Schol, Phys Fitness, A's.

MOORE, Patricia Ruth
Adlai E Stevenson HS; Bronx, NY (50-788) Hon
Prog; Type A; *John Jay Col of Criminal Justice;*
Criminal Justice Adm.

MOORE, Peggy Christine
Balmorhea HS; Balmorhea, TX (4-18) Band; Dbte
Tm; FFA; Pres, FHA; NHS; F-Ed, Sch P; Mgr,
Bkbl; Tnns; DARGCA; Hist A; Photographer,
Ann; Young Homemaking A; Assn Drum Major;
Odessa Col; Nurs.

MOORE, Ramona Carolyn
Winona HS; Winona, MO (25%-40) Band; BC;
Chor; VP, FBLA; FHA; 4H; Orch; Sftbl; Tr; 4H A;
Most Out; Pres A; Type A; Best Sport.

MOORE, Rebecca Louise
Hood River Valley HS; Hood River, OR (4-156)
NHS; Tres, SC; Church Chor; Vlbl; Mushbl; Jr
Deaconess; Service C; Grand Bethel Rep to Alaska;
Hon Qn, Job's Daughters; *Mt Hood Comm Col;*
Adm Secy.

MOORE, Richard Russell
Kirkwood HS; Kirkwood, MO; JV, Ftbl; JV, Tr.

MOORE, Robert David
Flint Northwestern HS; Flint, MI (40-500) Band;
Bus C; Dbte Tm; Ensm; Hmrm; NHS; Orch; Pres,
ARC; Span C; Bsbl; Bkbl; Soccer; COM; Citz A;
Hon Prog; Most Out; Pres A; ARC A; Band A;
Sports A; *Mott Comm Col; Elec.*

MOORE, Robert Lee
James Madison HS; Dallas, TX (30-188) Bkbl;
Ftbl; Most Out; Star Student; *Saint Mary's Col;*
Math.

MOORE, Robert Lewis
Starkville Acad; Starkville, MS (2-43) BC; BS;
Pres, Key C; NHS; Spch C; SC; Var C; Ftbl; Tnns;
Hist A; NEDT; Sal; Star Student; Exchange C Stu
o-t Mo; Win, Civitan Essay; *Miss St U; Pol Sci.*

MOORE, Robin Gay
Edward Best HS; Louisburg, NC; FHA; Sftbl; Billy
Graham Crusade Diploma; *Nash Tech; Auto*
Mech.

MOORE, Robin Marion
Olanta HS; Olanta, SC (15-43) BC; Chor; FFA; 4H;
Bsbl; Ftbl; Golf; Swim; Tnns; *Frances Marion Col.*

MOORE, Roger Bernard
Halifax Co Sr HS; S Boston, VA (75-550) Arch;
Chess C; Drama; HiY; Order/Arrow; Span C;
Tnns; JV, Tr; Order/Arrow A; Eagle Sct; *Commu-*
nications.

MOORE, Ronald Howell
Grissom HS; Huntsville, AL (20-634) BS; Hmrm;
InterClub Coun; Pres, Key C; Mu Alpha Theta;
NHS; Order/Arrow; SC; VP, Sr Cl; Tr; Cl Fav;
Auburn U; Chem Engr.

MOORE, Rose Marie
Melville HS; Melville, LA; Tres, BC; Pres, FBLA;
Ch, SC; Bio A; Hist A; HQn; *Grambling St U; Phys*
Ther Asst.

MOORE, Russell Joseph
Newnan HS; Newnan, GA (9-400) Rptr, BC; Chor;
Drama; Fr C; Ger C; Ch, Key C; Lit Mag; Order/
Arrow; MVP, Soccer; Sftbl; COM; Hon Prog; Math
A; Star Student; Yth Fel; Hon A; U of Dallas Schol;
Ga Tech; Mech Engr.

MOORE, Sally Ann
Raytown HS; Raytown, MO (59-593) NHS; Span
C; Bkbl; Sftbl; *Longview Comm Col; Sci.*

MOORE, Sally Teresa
Pisgah HS; Canton, NC (6-337) Pres, Band; Ensm;
Hmrm; Lat C; SC; COM; Citz A; Hon Prog; Most
Out; Sci A; Win, Scripture Exploring Drill; PA;
Excel Trumpet Solo; Band A.

MOORE, Sam G
Eisenhower HS; Decatur, IL; Chor; Tnns; Wrest;
Harding Col; Med.

MOORE, Samuel DeWayne
Menchville HS; Newport News, VA (200-563) Bus
C; Chor; FBLA; FTA; Hmrm; ROTC A; PA An-
nouncer A; *Va Commonwealth U; Acct.*

MOORE, Sandra Marie
Harlingen HS; Harlingen, TX (32-700) Ann; JV,
Chldr; Chor; Drama; FHA; 4H; ARC; Rptr, Sch P;
Sci C; Arch; Golf; Sftbl; MVP, Tr; 4H A; JA A; Phy
A; Pres A; ARC A; Sci A; GAA; Leo C; Co-Cpt
Vlbl; PA; Athletic A; Meritorious A, Tr; Cert of
Hons; PA; *Secy.*

MOORE, Sara Chmampion
Wade Hampton HS; Greenville, SC; A Cap Choir;
Pres, Hmrm; Jr Miss Pagent; Sftbl; Backpacking C;
Gym; *Law.*

MOORE, Sharon Gayle
Central Acad; Macon, MS (5%-63) Anchor C;
Ann; BC; SC; S-T, Soph Cl; COM; Hist A; Math A;
Sci A; Eng, Home Ec, HS, A's; Friendliest; *U of*
Miss; Phar.

MOORE, Shearon Dawn
Goodlettsville HS; Goodlettsville, TN (10%-185)
Chor; Fr C; FTA; Hmrm; ARC; A-Ed, Sch P; SC;
Bkbl; Tr; Hist A; Q&S A; Stu European Prog.

MOORE, Sheila Patricia
Spingarn HS; Washington, DC; *Bus.*

MOORE, Shelby Jean
Oliver Springs HS; Oliver Springs, TN; Fr C; FHA;
4H; *Nurs.*

MOORE, Sherrill Elizabeth
East HS; Columbus, OH (16-350) WW; *U of Cin-*
cinnati; Child Psych.

MOORE, Sherye Leigh
J F Kennedy HS; Winston-Salem, NC (10-170)
Band; Chldr; SC; Sftbl; HR; *Wake Forest U; Psych.*

MOORE, Shirley Irene
Philadelphia HS For Girls; Philadelphia, PA
(130-375) Band; Chldr; Ensm; Mjrte; Orch; Bkbl;
God & Country A; Fin, Beauty; PSFS Art A; Balch
Museum Art A; *Gordon Col; Phys Ed.*

MOORE, Stephanie Irene
Kinston HS; Kinston, NC; Band; Chor; Ensm;
Hmrm; Mjrte; Parl, SC; Bkbl; Sr GSct; MOD
Dance Groups; Candystriper; *Mus.*

MOORE, Stephen Whitney
Zanesville HS; Zanesville, OH; Band; Lat C; Orch;
Pres, Sci C; Hon Prog; Dance Band; *Sci.*

MOORE, Steve Raymond
Newnan HS; Newnan, GA (15-400) BC; Drama;
Rptr, Fr C; Hmrm; Key C; SC; Outst Actor; *U of*
Ga; Journ.

MOORE, Steven David
Walter Hines Page HS; Greensboro, NC; God &
Country A; Ldr, Church Yth Fel; *Psych.*

MOORE, Susan Diane
Evart Pub HS; Evart, MI (8-85) FHA; Tres, 4H;
NHS; F-Ed, Sch P; Bkbl; Sftbl; *Bob Jones U; Ed.*

MOORE, Susan Lynette
Steelville R-3 HS; Steelville, MO (18-63) Chor;
Drama; VP, SC; Harvest Festival Court; *Harding*
Col; Eng.

MOORE, Susan Marie
St Joseph's o-t Palisades HS; W New York, NJ
(9-232) NHS; Span NHS; VP, Jr Cl; Mgr, Bkbl;
Hon Prog; NEDT; *Seton Hall U.*

MOORE, Tammy Ann
Montpelier HS; Montpelier, OH (30-120) Band;
Chor; Fr C; Secy, Soph Cl; Acad Achv; *Foreign*
Lang.

MOORE, Teresa Ann
Starkville Acad; Starkville, MS (10-44) BC; FTA;
NHS; Y-Tns; COM; Gov Honor Prog; NEDT; PA;
Nom, 'Serious Senior'; Patriotic Amer Yth; Eng A;
Nom, Most Intellectual; *U of Miss; Elem Ed.*

MOORE, Teresa Jean
Parkview HS; Orfordville, WI (6-138) A Cap
Choir; AFS; Ann; Band; Drama; 4H; Madrigal;
NFL; Thes; 4H A; Spch A; Swing Choir; JV, Vlbl;
Stage Band; Mus Festival A; Finance Comm; Band
Camp Schol A; Secy, Luther League; *Whitewater*
Col; Mus.

MOORE, Terri Larraine
Blackhawk HS; Beaver Falls, PA; AFS; Pres, FNA;
Tr; Candystriper; *Jameson Mem Hospital; Nurs.*

MOORE, Terry Ann
Estancia HS; Estancia, NM (6-67) Bus C; Chor;
Drama; NHS; Rainbow; Bkbl; Swim; Tr; Type A;
Driver Ed A; Rainbow Girl o-t Yr; *Hist.*

MOORE, Thomas Joseph
Jesuit HS; Portland, OR (5-122) CYO; Chess C;
Hmrm; NHS; Order/Arrow; ARC; Elk A; Hon
Prog; St Scholar; *Santa Clara Col; Engr.*

MOORE, Tonya Natushi
Plymouth HS; Plymouth, NC (33-207) Span C;
MLS; Eng C; Social Stu; Cpt, Girls Ftbl; Bluebird
Schol; *NC Central U; Bus Adm.*

MOORE, Verlinda Gale
Hendersonville HS; Hendersonville, NC (60-165)
Fr C; S-T, 4H; Key C; 4H A; Nom, Gov Hon Prog;
Math.

MOORE, Wanda Faye
Jones HS; Lynnville, TN (3-22) Ann; VP, BC;
Chldr; Drama; FHA; GS; VP, 4H; Sch P; Spch C;
Tres, SC; Var C; Bkbl; Cl Fav; HCt; Type A; Vof-
DEM; Yth Fel; *Columbia St Col; Nurs.*

MOORE, Wesley Tate
NW Classen HS; Oklahoma City, OK; Cpt, Ftbl;
Tr; Citz A; FCA; *Langston U; Phys Ed.*

MOORE, Yolanda Denise
Milburn HS; Milburn, OK (3%-18) VP, 4H; Sci C;
SC; Cl Fav; 4H A; Sal; *Murray St Col.*

MOOREHEAD, Jeff Allen
Juanita HS; Kirkland, WA (25%-340) Band; JV,
Ftbl; Tnns; Church Evangelism; Yth Choir; Disci-
pleship C; *Pacific Christian Col; Ministry.*

MOORER, Erna Elaine
Woodbridge HS; Bridgeville, DE; Band; Mgr,
Chldr; Ensm; FBLA; Secy, 4H; SC; Mgr, Bsbl; 4H
A; JA A; Math A; OEA A; *Syracuse U; Bus Adm.*

MOORER, Karen Lynn
Rancocas Valley Regional HS; Mount Holly, NJ
(28-401) A Cap Choir; All Amer Yth; Chldr; Pres,
Hmrm; Semi-Fin, Jr Miss Pa; NHS; Var C; JV,
Sftbl; Amer Leg A; Hon Prog; Pres A; Yth Fel; HS
Mascot; Cpt, Gym; HS All Amer; *Acct.*

MOORER, Monica Renee
Buchtel HS; Akron, OH (165-394) Chor; NHS;
Beauty; COM; Hon Prog; *Med.*

MOORES, Cynthia Lucille
Ashtabula HS; Ashtabula, OH; A Cap Choir; Chor;
FTA; 4H; Madrigal; Rainbow; Sch P; Span C; Spch
C; Citz A; 4H A; VofDEM; Yth Fel; FTA A; *Oral*
Roberts U; Elem Ed.

MOORHEAD, Beth Ann
Hart Co HS; Hartwell, GA (10%-220) Ch, Anchor
C; VP, FHA; Cpt, Mjrte; Sci C; SC; Secy, Sr Cl;
HCt; FHA St Degree; Hon Grad A; *Augusta Col;*
Phy-Therapy.

MOORHOUS, Linda Sue
Mt Vernon Twp HS; Mt Vernon, IL; Band; Chor;
Ensm; Orch; Tri-HiY; *St Mary's Sch of Radiology;*
X-Ray Tech.

MOORHOUSE, Becky Lou
Science Hill HS; Johnson City, TN (20%-350)
Chor; Community Yth Symph; Ensm; Mod Mus
Mas; Orch; Span C; Cr-Ctry; Tr; Alg A; COM; All
St Orch; *Milligan Col; Math.*

MOORHOUSE, Bonnie Marie
Sci Hill HS; Johnson City, TN (20%-440) Chor;
Span C; Bkbl; Sftbl; *Milligan Col; Sci.*

MOORMAN, Claude Tee
Concord HS; Concord, NC (10%-250) Tres, Key C;
Math C; Monogram; Order/Arrow; Sci C; SC; VP,
Soph Cl; Ftbl; Tnns; MVP, Wrest; Pres, Bible C;
VP, Church Yth Fel; *Duke U; Med.*

MOORMAN, Diana Lynn
Manhattan HS; Manhattan, KS; Band; Chor; 4H;
SC; Bsbl; Sftbl; JV, Tr; 4H A; Yth Fel; Pres, Kay-
ettes; Vlbl.

MOORMAN, Mary Ellen
Carmel HS; Carmel, IN (53-585) Ann; Drama;
Hmrm; NHS; Span C; VP, Sr Cl; COM; JA A; Opt
A; Spch A; Secy, GSct; Span, Drama, A's; Marion
Medal; *NW U; Spch.*

MOORMAN, Michael Carroll
Christopher Columbus HS; Miami, FL (4-200) *Tulane U; Med.*

MOOSE, Kimberly Kay
Charleston HS; Charleston, WV; Ch, Bus C; Ch, FBLA; Hmrm; Lat C; NHS; Secy, SC; Mgr, Tr; MLS; Pres A; Yth Fel; VP, Bowl; Pres, St Yth; Pres, Church Yth; Board Member, FSA; *Morris Harvey Col; Bus Adm.*

MOOTY, Debra Rae
Grundy Center Comm HS; Grundy Center, IA; Ann; Band; FBLA; Sch P; Ski C; Bkbl; Golf; Sftbl; Tnns; *U of N Iowa; Sociology.*

MOOTY, Mark Edwin
Claiborne Acad; Haynesville, LA (4-37) A Cap Choir; Pres, Band; Chem C; Pres, Chor; Ensm; Tres, Hmrm; Lit Ral; Math C; Mod Mus Mas; Parl, NHS; Orch; Spch C; Tres, SC; Tr; Chem A; Cl Fav; Type A; WW; La Mus Ed, Band, A's; Wittiest; *La Tech U; Biomed Engr.*

MOQUIN, Teresa Ann
Mercy HS; Albany, NY (4-115) InterAct C; Lat C; Chem A; Hon Prog; NEDT; *Sci.*

MORACE, Judy Elaine
Waterproof HS; Waterproof, LA (25%-54) BC; Tres, Chldr; Tres, SC; Bio A; HCt; Win, Art Contest; *NE La U; Art.*

MORAIN, Tammy Sue
W Mind HS; Norman, OK; Chldr; Chor; Parl, NHS; Sftbl; Amer Leg A; COM; Coun of Teach A; Masonic A; Choral W Mus A; Ntl Fed Piano Festival; *Okla U; Fashion Merchandising.*

MORALE, Nick John
Bryan Adams HS; Dallas, TX; Lat C; ARC; SC; Swim; Yth Fel; *Harding Col; Bible.*

MORALES, Diana Grace
Hobbs HS; Hobbs, NM; A Cap Choir; Band; Tres, CYO; Chor; Amer Leg A; COM; Math A; *Psych.*

MORALES, Janet Lynn
Antilles HS; Fort Buchanan, PR (3-124) Cpt, Chldr; Chor; NHS; Hon Prog; NMS; *Carnegie-Mellon U; Math.*

MORALES, Janice Kelita
Dr Pedro Perea Fajardo Voc HS; Mayaguez, PR; Hon Medal; *Secy.*

MORALES, Jorge Rafael
Academia Discipulos de Cristo; Bayamon, PR (20-122) COM; Most Out; Good Conduct A; PA; Eng, Span & Social Stu Merit Cert; Top, Physics Cl; *U of Puerto Rico at Mayaguez; Physics.*

MORALES, Luis
St Augustine HS; Laredo, TX (9-67) Drama; VP, NHS; Spch C; MVP, Bsbl; Bkbl; WW Nom; *Laredo Jr Col; Drama.*

MORALES, Luz Amelia
Juan Jose Osuna HS; Hato Rey, PR (3-150) Chldr; Drama; FHA; ARC; Bsbl; Bkbl; Tr; Alg A; Hist A; Phy A; *Universidad de Puerto Rico; Ed.*

MORALES, Mayra Isabel
Manuela Toro HS; Caguas, PR; CYO; *U of Puerto Rico; Pub Relations.*

MORALES, Mitzi Ivelisse
Colegio Universit Sagrado Corazon; San Juan, PR (2-25) VP, Hmrm; NHS; COM; Hist A; Magna Cum Laude; Phy A; Bicentennial Contest Creative A; *Sociology A.*

MORALES, Rafael Ramos
Dr Pedro Perea Fajardo HS; Mayaguez, PR; COM; Exc Hon; *Drew U; Mech Ingeniery.*

MORAN, Carol Anne
Warren Central HS; Indianapolis, IN (20%-850) Tres, CYO; Sftbl; *Acct.*

MORAN, Ginger Lee
Daviston HS; Daviston, AL; Ann; Pres, BC; Cpt, Chldr; Pres, 4H; Secy, Sr Cl; Amer Leg A; Amer Leg Orator A; Citz A; Cl Fav; DARGCA; 4H A; HCt; Hon Prog; JA A; MLS; Val; VFW A; VFW Orator Win; VofDEM; Church Yth Coun; *Auburn U; Phar.*

MORAN, Katherine Suzanne
Herndon HS; Herndon, VA; Cpt, Bkbl; Cpt, Hockey; Cpt, Sftbl; Yth Fel; GAA; *Phys Ed.*

MORAN, Kathleen
McCluer N HS; Florissant, MO (100-824) Rainbow; Tnns; Type A; Vlbl; *U of Mo; Bus Adm.*

MORAN, Phyllis Eileen
Winston Churchill HS; Livonia, MI (10%-900) Orch; Sch P; Bkbl; S-T, Luther League; *Sch Craft Comm Col; Med Rec Tech.*

MORAN, Regina Sue
Douglass HS; Douglass, KS (3-48) Ann; Chldr; Parl, FHA; GS; NHS; Pres, Jr Cl; Parl, Soph Cl; Alg A; Citz A; HCt; Math A; Sci A; Geom A; *Math.*

MORAN, Susan Louise
Warren Central HS; Indianapolis, IN (159-857) Pres, CYO; Fr C; Sftbl; COM; Citz A; Journ A; Most Out; VP, CYO; Church Paper; Tns Against Cancer; *Marian Col; Journ.*

MORAVEC, Alan Mark
Northeast HS; Lincoln, NE (309-538) A Cap Choir; Chor; Bkbl; Ftbl; Sftbl; Swim; Yth Fel; Acolyte; Swim Tm; Church Yth Rep.

MORAVEC, Alise Anne
Lincoln Ne HS; Lincoln, NE (34-501) Chor; VP, 4H; NHS; Y-Tns; Swim; 4H A; Spch A; VofDEM; Yth Fel; Pres, Lutheran Yth Fel; Yr o-t Arts A; Concordia Col A of Excellence; Nebr St Mus Clinic; *Concordia Col; Mus.*

MORBY, Raeleen Sage
Stillwater Central Sch; Stillwater, NY (6-83) Co-Ed, Ann; Band; Chor; Fr C; NHS; SC; COM; Hon Prog; Yth Fel; Constellation; Mus A; *Oral Roberts U; Social Work.*

MORCONE, Mary Beth
Acad of Our Lady of Mercy; Milford, CT (4-93) NHS; F-Ed, Sch P; Span C; Span NHS; SC; *Boston Col; Marketing.*

MORDAS, Terri Lynn
Nordonia HS; Macedonia, OH (100-420) Band; Chor; Drama; Ensm; Hmrm; Orch; ARC; Bkbl; Tr; Bkbl A Tr Statistician; Cpt, JV Vlbl; *Ohio St U; Nurs.*

MORDECAI, David K A
Montclair HS; Bloomfield, NJ; Yth Fel; CPR Rescuer; Cpt, Police Explorer; Singing Group; *Johns Hopkins U; Med.*

MORDT, Julie Ann
Hickman HS; Columbia, MO (123-566) A Cap Choir; Chor; Rptr, Sch P; *Mo U; Dental Hygiene.*

MORE, Ramona Dawn
Bedford-N Lawrence HS; Bedford, IN (2-400) Band; BC; S-T, Chess C; Chor; Fr C; NHS; Spch C; Alg A; Amer Leg A; COM; Citz A; DARGCA; Math A; NMS; Sal; Sci A; Spch A; St Mus Assn Solo & Ensm A's; Most Valuable Rank Ldr, Band; *Ind U; Instrumental Ed.*

MOREAU, David Anthony
De La Salle HS; New Orleans, LA (36-250) Model UN; NHS; Co-Cpt, Bsbl; Bkbl; Torch A; *Southeastern La U; Phys Ed.*

MOREAU, Lynda Perrianne
Winnfield Sr HS; Winnfield, LA; Band; Ch, BC; Ch, CYO; Chor; Dbte Tm; Fr C; Secy, 4H; Fin, Lit Ral; Orch; Pres, Rainbow; Ed, Sch P; Secy, Spch C; 4H A; Hon Prog; Flag Girl; WW; Fin, Miss Tn Amer; City Acad Excel A; *Tulane U; Theater.*

MOREDOCK, Jayne Ann
Daviess Co HS; Owensboro, KY (16-316) Secy, Band; BC; Community Yth Symph; Ensm; Secy, Fr C; COM; Hon Prog; Sci A; *U of Ky; Law.*

MOREE, Alice Jeanne
Dunedin Sr HS; Dunedin, FL; Ann; Chor; Span C; Schol, Art Center.

MOREHEAD, Darren Bryant
Sutter Union HS; Sutter, CA (13-111) BS; Sci C; Ski C; Ftbl; Tnns; Alg A; Kiwanis A; *Constructional Engr.*

MOREHEAD, James Barry
Comm Preparatory Sch; Erie, PA; Arch; Chess C; Span C; Pres, SC; Sftbl; Tr; COM; Cl Fav; Hon Prog; Vlbl; *US Air Force; Pilot.*

MOREHOUSE, Dawn Marie
Greenwich Central HS; Greenwich, NY (25-105) Band; Tres, FBLA; 4H; Hmrm; Ch, ARC; SC; Var C; Pres, Sr Cl; Tres, Jr Cl; Tres, Soph Cl; Bsbl; Co-Cpt, Bkbl; Cpt, Hockey; Sftbl; Tr; Cl Fav; Constellation; Qn Jr Prom; *Hudson Valley Comm Col; Phys Ed.*

MOREHOUSE, Suzzanna Kimberly
Algonac HS; Algonac, MI; NHS; *Secy Career.*

MORELAND, Donald William
Marvell HS; Marvell, AR (11-120) BS; FBLA; Ger C; Bsbl; Mgr, Bkbl; Ftbl; Tr; Cl Fav.

MORELLA, Alan Thomas
Springfield Local HS; Petersburg, OH (13-130) Band; CYO; HiY; Span C; H of F; *Akron Col; Engr.*

MORELLI, Eugene Arcangelo
Williamsburg Comm HS; Williamsburg, PA (10%-65) Band; Co-Ed, Sch P; SC; Var C; Bkbl; Co-Cpt, Ftbl; Amer Leg A; Blue Pirate Achv A; Most Improved Sr, Bkbl; Newspaper Schol A, Ftbl; *Bucknell U; Mech Engr.*

MORELLI, Kathleen Marie
Catholic Central HS; Troy, NY (33%-339) CYO; Chldr; Chor; FNA; Ski C; Span C; Span NHS; Hon Prog; Sci A; Cl Comedian; *Samaritan Hospital Sch of Nurs; Nurs.*

MORELOCK, Lynne Allyn
Clarke Central HS; Athens, GA (5-280) Pres, BC; Chor; Hmrm; InterClub Coun; Mu Alpha Theta; Secy, NHS; Sch Achieve Tm; Sci C; Ch, SC; COM; Hon Prog; MLS; Gov Hon Prog Alt; *Emory U; Vet Med.*

MOREN, Louis Stanley
Gilbert Sr HS; Gilbert, MN (3-65) Ann; Band; Pres, CYO; Chor; Dbte Tm; Rptr, Sch P; Sci C; SC; Thes; Mgr, Bkbl; Cpt, Cr-Ctry; COM; HCt; Hon Prog; Spch A; VofDEM; Win, Govt in Action; Win, St & Region Mus; *Mesabi Comm Col; Bio.*

MORENCY, Danae Alline
Quilcene HS; Quilcene, WA; Chldr; Rainbow; A-Ed, Sch P; SC; Rptr, Jr Cl; Tres, Soph Cl; Mgr, Bkbl; *Lower Col; Sociology.*

MORENCY, Pauline Rita
St Dominic Regional HS; Lewiston, ME (2-98) Chor; Drama; Secy, Fr C; GS; Sch P; Hockey; Sftbl; Type A.

MORENO, Juan Alberto Jr
Wilcox HS; Santa Clara, CA; Span C; Soccer; Swim; Asian C; Drafting A; *U of Calif; Arch.*

MORENO, Nestor
Francisco Mendoza HS; Isabela, PR; Cr-Ctry; Tr; Marathon A; *Drew U.*

MORENO, Norma Irene
Roma HS; Roma, TX (9-144) Pan Amer U; Ed.

MORETTI, Eugene William
Old Forge HS; Old Forge, PA (8-121) Band; CYO; Chess C; Ensm; NHS; Orch; Sodality; COM; Span A; Hon Prog; PTA A; VFW A; VofDEM; WW; Bicentennial Song Writing A; *U of Scranton; Pre-Med.*

MOREY, Pamela Yvonne
Mansfield Sr HS; Mansfield, OH (26-375) Band; Mjrte; SC; Var C; Bkbl; Sftbl; Vlbl.

MOREY, Steven Gale
Wood River HS; Hailey, ID (12-115) Math C; NHS; Rptr, Sch P; Sci C; Ski C; Spch C; Var C; Cpt, Bkbl; Cpt, Ftbl; Tr; Citz A; Odd Fellow Fin; Pres A; Spch A; Most Inspirational; Ftbl; *Col of Idaho; Math.*

MORFORD, Jana Carol
Bethel-Tate HS; Bethel, OH (1-160) Chor; NHS; Span C; SC; Amer Leg A; Pep C; *Foreign Services.*

MORFORD, Jeffrey Scott
Madison Heights HS; Anderson, IN (10%-450) Ann; Fr C; Hmrm; SC; JV, Bsbl; JV, Bkbl; H of F; Opt A; Yth Fel; FCA; *Olivet Col.*

MORGAN, Allen Coleman
Hermitage HS; Hermitage, AR (1-55) Ann; VP, BC; Pres, FFA; Pres, 4H; VP, Math C; Ed, Sch P; Tres, Var C; Cpt, Ftbl; Bio A; COM; Chem A; 4H A; Hist A; MLS; Spch A; Val; FFA A; *U of Ark at Monticello; Forestry Adm.*

MORGAN, Angela J
Thomasville Acad; Thomasville, AL (8-20) Ann; BC; Chldr; Sch P; Tr; Beauty; Cl Fav; HCt; *Troy St U; Bus.*

MORGAN, Anita Lynn
Tygarts Valley HS; Mill Creek, WV (3-89) Band; 4H; 4H A; Co Math Field Day Cert; *Phys Therapy.*

MORGAN, Brenda Gail
Parker HS; Greenville, SC; Sftbl.

MORGAN, Carla Kay
Reagan Sr HS; Houston, TX; InterAct C; NHS; Sci C; Swim; Tnns; COM; Sci A; Schol A; *U of Houston; Journ.*

MORGAN, Carol Lee
S Salem HS; Salem, OR; A Cap Choir; Chor; Drama; Ensm; 4H; Thes; Var C; Tr; 4H A; Drill Tm; *Oregon Col of Ed; Art.*

MORGAN, Carolyn Sue
Middletown HS; Middletown, OH; Bus C; Span NHS; Bkbl; *Spelman Col; Pre-Law.*

MORGAN, Catherine Elaine
A&M Cons HS; College Station, TX; A Cap Choir; Band; FTA; 4H; 4H A; All Dist Band.

MORGAN, Deborah Ann
Halter HS; Wellston, MO; InterClub Coun; SC; Secy, Soph Cl; Bsbl; Sftbl; Swtht; Yth Fel.

MORGAN, Donna Jean
Miami Coral Park Sr HS; Miami, FL (167-667) HR Achv; *Miami Dade Comm Col; Art.*

MORGAN, Donna Lee
Eastside HS; Paterson, NJ;

MORGAN, Dorothy Ann
Eastside HS; Paterson, NJ (2-520) Hon Prog; Montclair *St Col; Acct.*

MORGAN, Erskine Ellis II
Northeast HS; Elizabeth City, NC; VP, Chor; Key C; Bsbl; Co-Cpt, Bkbl; Ftbl; Tr; Citz A; *Norfolk St Col; Bus Ed.*

MORGAN, Jamie T
Thomasville Acad; Thomasville, AL (9-17) Bsbl; Bkbl; MVP, Ftbl; Sftbl; Cl Fav; Mr Thomasville Acad; *Patrick Henry Jr Col.*

MORGAN, Jeffrey Smith
Parkersburg HS; Parkersburg, WV; Order/Arrow; Ftbl; God & Country A; Order/Arrow A; Yth Fel; Eagle A; Rep, Know Your St Gov Day; *W Va U; Law.*

MORGAN, Joe Leta
Thrasher HS; Booneville, MS (33%-38) F-Ed, Sch P; Sci C; VP, SC; VP, Jr Cl; Sci A; Type A; *NE Miss Jr Col.*

MORGAN, John Howard
Eastwood HS; El Paso, TX (20%-1000) Jr NHS; VP, Church Yth; Church League Sports; *Baptist Bible Col; Theology.*

MORGAN, Jonathan B
Westside HS; Omaha, NE (14-800) Fin, BS; FBLA; Hmrm; NHS; Ski C; SC; Bkbl; Tr; Hon Prog; Rotary A; Pres, Order of St John; *Nebr U; Phys Sci.*

MORGAN, Judith Ann
Jackson HS; Jackson, LA (4-82) Ann; BC; Chldr; Dbte Tm; VP, FBLA; Secy, FFA; Secy, FHA; Secy, 4H; Hmrm; Lit Ral; Math C; VP, SC; VP, Jr Cl; Cl Fav; HQn; WW; *U of Southwestern La; Nurs.*

MORGAN, Kathy Lynn
Neshaminy Langhorne HS; Langhorne, PA (250-689) Chor; VP, Drama; Hmrm; SC; VP, Jr Cl; Distinguished Service A; *Barbizon Sch; Fashion Merchandising.*

MORGAN, Kimberly Lynn
Polo HS; Polo, MO (10-40) A Cap Choir; Secy, Band; Chor; Ensm; Fr C; Tres, FHA; 4H; Sci C; Bkbl; Sftbl; Tr; Type A; WW; US Collegiate Wind Band; Cand, Swtht Qn; Letter C; Girls Glee C; Math.

MORGAN, Larry Dale
North Side HS; Fort Worth, TX (10-214) Demolay; Sci C; Co-Cpt, Ftbl; Tr; 3rd Pl, Regional Discus; *Baylor U; Law.*

MORGAN, Leslie Renee
Cass Tech HS; Detroit, MI; Band; FTA; Sftbl; ROTC A; *Mich St U.*

MORGAN, Linda Lee
Hinsdale Township HS Central; Hinsdale, IL (7-601) Tres, Band; NHS; Orch; Mgr, Soccer; *Northwestern U; Pre-Law.*

MORGAN, Lisa Jo
Fairhope HS; Fairhope, AL (56-350) Co-Cpt, Chldr; FNA; NHS; SC; Var C; COM; Hon Prog; Girl's Service C; Sr Ath A; All St Chldr A; Hospital Vol A; Outst Chldr Performance A; *Providence Sch of Nurs; Nurs.*

MORGAN, Mary Margaret
Saint Agnes Acad; Memphis, TN (11-58) F-Ed, Ann; Chor; Fr C; VP, NHS; NEDT; *U of Tenn-Martin; Med.*

MORGAN, Melody Ann
Natchitoches Acad; Natchitoches, LA (5-20) Chldr; Chor; Ensm; Fr C; Math C; F-Ed, Sch P; SC; Pres, Jr Cl; VP, Soph Cl; Sftbl; Alg A; Cl Fav; HCt; MLS; WW; *La Tech U; Acct.*

MORGAN, Michael Lowell
Marion Ind HS; Marion, IA (66-161) Order/Arrow; Pres, SC; Var C; Bsbl; Cpt, Ftbl; Tr; Yth Fel; All Conf Ftbl; Eagle Sct; *Iowa Wesleyan Col; Religion.*

MORGAN, Michael Paul
Henderson Co Sr HS; Henderson, KY (6-618) Ann; Band; BC; Ensm; Fr C; Hmrm; NHS; Spch C; Parl, SC; VP, Thes; JA A; Spch A; VofDEM; *U of Ky; Communications.*

MORGAN, Micheal O'Neal
Eupora HS; Eupora, MS (30-84) Pres, Band; Ensm; FFA; Hmrm; SC; Ftbl; Type A; *Holmes Jr Col; Engr Technician.*

MORGAN, Michele
Olney HS; Philadelphia, PA; Chor; Orch; Usher; Gospel Choir; HR; *Berean Inst; Stenography.*

MORGAN, Miranda
Carver Area HS; Chicago, IL (19-200) Co-Cpt, Chldr; Chor; Drama; Ski C; Swim; Tr; COM; Citz A; Cl Fav; MLS; Swtht; *Michael Reese Nurs Sch; Nurs.*

MORGAN, Nancy Carol
Beverly Hills HS; Beverly Hills, CA (3-520) Ger C; Bio A; *Lewis & Clark Col; Bio.*

MORGAN, Nancy Carroll
Sunbright HS; Sunbright, TN (12-63) Ann; Chldr; FHA; Sch P; Var C; Pres, Soph Cl; Bkbl; Most Sch Spirit; *Tenn Tech U; Secondary Eng.*

MORGAN, Neill Sagen
Greenville Sr HS; Greenville, TX (28-358) Ann; BS; Rptr, Fr C; Math C; SC; Swim; Amer Leg A; Hon Prog; Journ A; Q&S A; Yth Fel; *Austin Col; Pre-Med.*

MORGAN, Nora Elizabeth
Tompkins HS; Savannah, GA (76-194) FBLA; SC; Home Ec Hon.

MORGAN, Paul David
Columbine HS; Littleton, CO; Band; Ger C; Hmrm; NFL; NHS; F-Ed, Sch P; JV, Cr-Ctry; JV, Tr; JV, Wrest; Hon Prog; MLS; NEDT; Spch A; *Pastoral Stu.*

MORGAN, Paul Eugene
Robert E Lee HS; Baytown, TX (50%-400) Co-Ch, Key C; V-Ch, SC; Ftbl; Ltr, All Dist, Ftbl; All Greater Houston, Ftbl; *Tex A&I Col; Bus.*

MORGAN, Paula Ann
Paint Valley HS; Bainbridge, OH (13-90) F-Ed, Ann; JV, Chldr; Lat C; Span C; Secy, Jr Cl; S-T, Soph Cl; VP, Pep C; Yth Ministries Board.

MORGAN, Raquel Janet
Joel Elias Spingarn HS; Washington, DC (10%-789) Sch P; Citz A; Tres, Church Yth; Secy, Church Usher Board; Jr NHS; *Occupational Therapy.*

MORGAN, Richard John
Clifton HS; Clifton, KS (19-25) Chor; Pres, FFA; Pres, 4H; Type A; Church Choir; FFA Judging Tm; *Colby Jr Col; Agr.*

MORGAN, Robert Devan
Lake Clifton Sr HS; Baltimore, MD (10%-500) NHS; ARC; Hist A; *Wash U; Bio.*

MORGAN, Robert Lowell
Kanland HS; Maple Part, IL (50-183) Span C; Ftbl; Tnns; *Northland Col; Psych.*

MORGAN, Robert Theodore
Babylon Jr Sr HS; Babylon, NY (25%-203) A Cap Choir; Chor; Bsbl; Mgr, Bkbl; Ftbl; Episcopal Yth Organization; Equestrian As; BSct; Acolyte.

MORGAN, Ronald Jay
A&7 Cons HS; College Station, TX (5%-150) A Cap Choir; BS; NHS; Pres, SC; Bsbl; Co-Cpt, Bkbl; Ftbl; Tnns; Amer Leg A; Opt Out Tn; Rotary A; VFW A; MVP, Bkbl; Mister A&M Cons HS; WW; *Abilene Christian U; Bible.*

MORGAN, Roy Charles
Eastside HS; Paterson, NJ; Sch P; JV, Ftbl; COM; *Rutgers U; Law.*

MORGAN, Shirley Melissa
Shaker HS; Latham, NY; Type A; *Oakwood Col; Bus Ed.*

MORGAN, Stephen Derek
Shelby HS; Shelby, NC (6-340) BC; Pres, Chor; Ensm; FTA; VP, NHS; Span C; NML; *U of NC; Astronomy.*

MORGAN, Tammy
Wheeler Co HS; Alamo, GA (4-79) Hist A; *Med.*

MORGAN, Theresa Delane
N Iredell HS; Statesville, NC (3-23) Band; FHA; Citz A; *Wingate Col; Sociology.*

MORGAN, Theresa Lynne
Linden McKinley HS; Columbus, OH (6-400) VP, Bus C; VP, Chor; Dbte Tm; Secy, NHS; SC; Citz A; Hon Prog; Journ A; Ntl Achv Schol; Yth Fel; Stu o-t Yr; *Ohio St U; Bus Adm.*

MORGAN, Thomas Wayne
Thomasville HS; Thomasville, AL (2-75) VP, BC; Chor; Community Yth Symph; Drama; VP, Hmrm; S-T, Var C; Bsbl; Bkbl; Co-Cpt, Ftbl; Tr; Bio A; Citz A; Hist A; Sal; Vlbl; *U of Ala; Engr.*

MORGAN, Valerie Denise
Leilehua HS; Wahiawa, HI (132-455) AFS; Commercial C; Drama; Ger C; *Leeward Comm Col; Lib Arts.*

MORGAN, William Dale
Wayne HS; Fort Wayne, IN; Cr-Ctry; Ftbl.

MORIKAWA, Steven Masami
Kailua HS; Kailua, HI (1-556) Span C; Tres, Soph Cl; Tnns.

MORIMIZU, Ann Keiko
Reseda HS; Reseda, CA; Community Yth Symph; Ensm; Hmrm; Orch; ARC; SC; Secy, Jr Cl; Hon Prog; ARC A; VFW A; VofDEM; Church Worker; Girl's League; Nom, GS; Nom, Writing A; *Calif St Col; Home Ec.*

MORIMIZU, Robert Keiji
Reseda HS; Reseda, CA (5%-800) Band; Tnns; CSF; Hon Prog; Math A; 'A' Stu, Photography, A's; St Mus Conserv Mst Outst Flute Play; *UCLA; Engr.*

MORIN, Douglas Martin
Marion HS; Marion, IN (33%-650) Band; Chor; Dbte Tm; Demolay; Drama; Span C; Spch C; Thes; *Ind U; Math.*

MORIN, Michelle Jeanne
Marianhill Centoal Cath HS; Southbridge, MA (3-31) CYO; Drama; VP, Fr C; French NHS; Pres, NHS; ARC; Ski C; Tres, Sr Cl; Tres, Jr Cl; Tres, Soph Cl; Cpt, Bkbl; Cr-Ctry; Cpt, Sftbl; Citz A; Hon Prog; K of C A; NEDT; Rotary A; VFW A; MVP, Bkbl; *Marquette U; Phys Therapy.*

MORING, Chrisea Denise
Jordan Voc HS; Columbus, GA (5%-530) CYO; Journ.

MORING, Ellen Ruth
William Cullen Bryant HS; New York, NY (5-989) Lit Mag; NHS; Swim; COM; Regent School; Gym; Bowl; Dance; *Bernard Baruch Col; Bus.*

MORIOKA, Katherine Hiromi
Woodlake Union HS; Woodlake, CA (1-120) Chldr; Secy, Fr C; FHA; Sch Achieve Tm; Sci C; Ski C; SC; Var C; Bkbl; Swim; Tnns; Bank Of Amer A; CSF; HQn; Math A; Pres, GAA; Cpt, Vlbl; *Calif St U; Math.*

MORITZ, David Lee II
Portsmouth W HS; W Portsmouth, OH; Band; Chor; FTA; Span C; Sci A; Type A; Co-Cpt, Bowl Tm; Eng Schol Tm; Missionary Tm; Church Organist.

MORIWAKE, Dawn Michie
Waimea HS; Waimea, HI (6-199) Fin, Jr Miss Pagent; S-T, NHS; Spch C; Co-Ch, Sr Cl; Ch, Soph Cl; Golf; B Crocker A; Yth Fel; Tres & Pres, FTA; Leg Lobbyist; Swtht, Key C; Church Choir; Ch & VP, SC; Bus A; Na Menehune Hanohano A; *U of Hawaii; Acct.*

MORLAN, Ruth Elizabeth
Highland HS; Albuquerque, NM (57-725) Chor; Ensm; NHS; ARC A; WW; 300 Hrs Vol Work, Hospital; *Baylor U; Pre-Med.*

MORLAND, Lisa Kay
Coronado HS; Colorado Springs, CO; Fr C; Advisory Panel, Acteens.

MORLEDGE, David Walker
Westchester HS; Houston, TX (147-520) A Cap Choir; Chor; Hmrm; F-Ed, Scn P; Bsbl; Bkbl; Ftbl; Sftbl; Tnns; Spch A; Runner-Up, Cl Fav; *U of Tex; Law.*

MORLEY, Curtis William
McNary Sr HS; Salem, OR (119-390) AFS; Band; Ger C; 4H; Orch; Sch P; Sci C; 4H A; *Chemeketa Comm Col.*

MORLEY, Jennifer
N Shore HS; W Palm Beach, FL (2-336) Chor; Ensm; Key C; NHS; Alg A; Math A; WW; All St Mus A; FVA St Contest A; Eng A; *Bus Adm.*

MORNINGSTAR, Lori Sue
Mt Vernon HS; Mt Vernon, OH (30-320) Band; Chor; Fr C; VP, 4H; Orch; 4H A; Hon Prog; Math A; Band A; Solo, Ensm A; Orch A; *Milligan Col; Teaching Handicaps.*

MORRELL, Laura Ann
William H Hall HS; W Hartford, CT (8-500) GS; NHS; Orch; Ski C; Secy, Span C; Tr; Tri-St Ski Tm; Jr Altar Guild; 1st St Scholastic Writing Contest; Co-Cpt, Field Hockey; Hon Men, St Scholastic Art Contest; *Sci.*

MORREN, Lesa Kay
Colo HS; Colo City, TX (1-115) Chor; Math C; NHS; Secy, Soph Cl; JV, Bkbl; Interlochen Ntl Mus; Star Student; Type A.

MORRILL, Judith Alice
Livermore Falls HS; Livermore Falls, ME (2-104) Fr C; GS; Math C; Ski C; SC; Var C; Pres, Soph Cl; Cr-Ctry; Hockey; Sftbl; Alg A; Math A; *U of Maine; Sci.*

MORRILL, Judy Lynn
Brown HS; Sturgis, SD (14-237) Band; Chldr; Chor; Dbte Tm; Hmrm; NFL; Ski C; Secy, SC; Secy, Soph Cl; Cr-Ctry; Alg A; COM; Math A; Spch A; Job's Daughter's; God Squad; MVP, Gym; VP, Pep C; *U of SD; Bus.*

MORRIS, Adrian Gregory Jr
E Side Sr HS; E St Louis, IL (10-28) Tnns; *Sou Ill U; Psych.*

MORRIS, Anthony Durand
Waukegan W Campus HS; Waukegan, IL (240-518) Drama; Spch C; Thes; Cr-Ctry; Tnns; Spch A; Piano A; Phys Fitness A; Boy o-t Yr; *Roosevelt Col; Mus.*

MORRIS, Billy Joe
Leilehua HS; Wahiawa, HI (230-500) ARC; Bsbl; Sftbl; Hon Prog; *Photography.*

MORRIS, Brenda Dee
Southwest HS McEvoy B; Macon, GA (25-900) Band; Ensm; Hmrm; COM; Yth Fel; Hon Band A; Mus Festival A; *Art Inst of Atlanta; Photography.*

MORRIS, Bryan Mac
Hobart HS; Hobart, OK (13-68) Chor; 4H; Pres, Key C; NHS; SC; Var C; Ftbl; Tnns; Tr; Citz A; S-T & Pres, Key C; Comm Theater; *Okla St U; Phys Ed.*

MORRIS, Carla Anne
Gemantowne Acad; Fort Washington, PA (60-106) Chor; Hockey; Tr; *Drew U; Special Ed.*

MORRIS, Cynthia Ann
Charlottesville HS; Charlottesville, VA; Bus C; FBLA; Sci C; Span C; Co-Cpt, Bkbl; Sftbl; Ntl Bible Bowl Comp; Church Tn Choir.

MORRIS, Cynthia Irene
W Craven HS; Vanceboro, NC (8-160) VP, FBLA; NHS; S-T, Jr Cl; *Craven Comm Col; Acct.*

MORRIS, Darla Kay
Liberty Eylau HS; Texarkana, TX (8-170) NHS; Pres, Home Ec Related Occupations; *Early Childhood Ed.*

MORRIS, Deana Marie
Bayshore Methodist Christian Sch; Tampa, FL (2-6) Chor; A-Ed, Sch P; Hon Prog; Sal; Church Pianist & Choir Director; Pres, Church Yth Fel; Ntl Fed Mus C; Am Guild Eng Handbell Ringers; Ntl Piano Playing Auditions; *Mus.*

MORRIS, Debra Lee
London HS; London, OH (3-165) Hmrm; NHS; Span C; SC; Kiwanis A; Yth Fel; Tri-L; OSU Dist Span A; *Cedarville Col.*

MORRIS, Donna Faye
William Monroe HS; Stanardsville, VA (10-90) BC; Drama; FHA; FTA; Lit Mag; Tr; Type A; *Madison Col; Eng.*

MORRIS, Douglas Barry
R A Taft HS; Cincinnati, OH (31-192) Ann; Band; Chess C; Hmrm; JETS; Bus Mgr, Var C; Bus Mgr, Sr Cl; Pres, Jr Cl; Pres, Soph Cl; Cr-Ctry; Cpt, Tr; Citz A; Cl Fav; MLS; Phy A; WW; *Wilberforce U; Elec Engr.*

MORRIS, Elizabeth Bernell
Fayetteville HS; Fayetteville, AR (147-352) Band; Chor; FHA; 4H; Hon Prog; Ch, VICA; Dental Asst; PA; *Stephens Col; Acct.*

MORRIS, Elizabeth Kay
South Dade Sr HS; Homestead, FL (50%-836) *Young Harris Col; Bio.*

MORRIS, Eric Wayne
Mascoutah Comm HS; Mascoutah, IL; JV, Ftbl.

MORRIS, Gene
Wyoming HS; Wyoming, OH (100-180) Hmrm; Var C; Bsbl; Mgr, Bkbl; *Amer U; Journ.*

MORRIS, Jacqueline Marie
E L Furr HS; Houston, TX; Chor; Secy, FHA; NHS; Y-Tns; Arch; Sftbl; ICU; YWIA; *U of Houston; Med.*

MORRIS, Janet Lynn
Phillips HS; Phillips, TX (7-41) Band; SC; Bkbl; *W Tex St; Nurs.*

MORRIS, Jay Kevin
N Hills HS; Pittsburgh, PA (47-782) Key C; NHS; Order/Arrow; Ski C; JV, Bsbl; Ftbl; Tr; V Ltr; *U of Okla; Chem Engr.*

MORRIS, Jeanie Louise
George Walton Acad; Monroe, GA; Ann; Secy, BC; Chldr; Secy, Chor; Fin, Jr Miss Pagent; Lit Ral; Span C; S-T, SC; Beauty; Gov Honor Prog; HCt; Most Out; *Emory U; Med.*

MORRIS, Jeannie Marie
DuQuoin HS; Du Quoin, IL (25%-105) FHA; *E Ill U; Home Ec.*

MORRIS, Jeffery Glenn
Pelham HS; Pelham, AL; Band; Sci C; Eng A; *U of Ala.*

MORRIS, Jeffrey Neal
William Monroe HS; Stanardsville, VA (3-90) BC; JV, Ftbl; *Madison Col; Astronomy.*

MORRIS, Jeffrey Scot
Elkhart Mem HS; Elkhart, IN (20-500) A Cap Choir; Chor; Bsbl; Bkbl; Ftbl; Sftbl; Tr; Hon Prog; Stu o-t Month; *Med.*

MORRIS, Jerri Lynne
Hazlewood HS; Town Creek, AL (5-45) Band; Drama; FHA; Sch P; Sci C; Spch C; 4H A; Ala Band Masters A; *Med.*

MORRIS, Joan Ellen
Hopewell Valley Central HS; Pennington, NJ (87-300) Band; Chor; Community Yth Symph; Ger C; Pres, Hmrm; NHS; F-Ed, Sch P; Secy, SC; Bkbl; St Scholar; Mgr, Church Bkbl; Ch, Church Yth Fel; *Columbia Bible Col; Bible.*

MORRIS, John Kenyon
North Chicago Comm HS; N Chicago, IL (216-395) All Amer Yth; Chess C; Bsbl; Bkbl; Ftbl; Tnns; Wrest; COM; *Tuskegee Inst; Bus Adm.*

MORRIS, Karen Darlene
Hopewell HS; Hopewell, VA (3-425) Co-Ed, Ann; BC; Monogram; VP, NHS; Pres, Sr Cl; Co-Cpt, Hockey; Tr; HCt; *Madison Col; Bus.*

MORRIS, Katherine Jane
Hampton Roads Acad; Newport News, VA (24-48) Ann; Fr C; Hockey; Citz A; Sci A; HR; GScts Presidential Clrm; Dist Parl, Keyettes; Pres, Hospital Jr Vols; Pres, Church Yth Coun; *U of Richmond; Bus.*

MORRIS, Kathryn Louise
Madison Acad HS; Huntsville, AL (4-43) Ann; BC; Dbte Tm; GS; NHS; Sch P; Tres, Sr Cl; COM; Citz A; Hon Prog; NEDT; Star Student; Eng A; Home Ec A; Bible A; *UAH; Acct.*

MORRIS, Kathy Ann
Fullington Acad; Pinehurst, GA (8-40) FBLA; HCt; *Middle Ga Col; Secy.*

MORRIS, Kelly Lynn
Riverdale HS; Fort Myers, FL; Band; SC; Hon Prog; S-T, Christian C; Hon Prog; Band As; Cleverest A; *Eckerd Col; Dental Hygeinst.*

MORRIS, Kelly Renee
Madeira HS; Madeira, OH (64-214) Band; Chor; Ger C; Hmrm; Sch P; Swim; Tnns; Secy A; Clarinet Mus A; Chor A; Sup & Outst Piano As; *U of Cincinnati; Elem Ed.*

MORRIS, Kena Lanette
Union Co HS; Morganfield, KY; Fr C; FHA; Cl Fav; Most Out; *Henderson Comm Col; Psych.*

MORRIS, Kent Douglas
Grace Baptist Sch; South Bend, IN (3-14) Pres, Band; Chor; Drama; 4H; Cpt, Bkbl; Ftbl; Co-Cpt, Soccer; Co-Cpt, Tr; HKg; *Bob Jones U; Archt.*

MORRIS, Kevin James
Jennings HS; St Louis, MO (43-279) Hon Prog; *Westminster Col; Aerospace Sci.*

MORRIS, Kevin Jeffery
Drumright HS; Drumright, OK; A Cap Choir; FFA; 4H; Amer Leg A; 4H A; Kiwanis A; FFA St Greenhand A; 4-H Demonstration Beef A; *Heavy Equipment.*

MORRIS, Kim Louise
E Jordan HS; E Jordan, MI (30-120) Band; Chldr; Span C; Tr.

MORRIS, Lavado Rebecca
Columbia Acad; Columbia, MS (35-53) FHA; Worthy Advisor, Rainbow Girls; Miss Rainbow.

MORRIS, Lee Ellen
Columbia Acad; Columbia, MS (23-46) Band; Rainbow; Sci C; Sftbl; Wittiest.

MORRIS, Leslie Lynn
Nathan Bedford Forrest HS; Jacksonville, FL (70-590) Band; Hmrm; Span C; SC.

MORRIS, Lisa Gaye
Franklin Comm HS; Franklin, IN (7-300) A Cap Choir; Bus C; Chor; Ensm; Fr C; FBLA; FHA; Pres, 4H; Madrigal; NHS; Secy, SC; Tri-HiY; Y-Tns; 4H A; Hon Prog; *Harding Col; Dietetics.*

MORRIS, Lisa Renee
Scribner HS; Scribner, NE (5-37) Ann; Band; Chor; FHA; GS; Tri-HiY; Bkbl; Tr; *U of Nebr.*

MORRIS, Lizbeth Jaye
Wilbur L Cross HS; New Haven, CT (44-287) CYO; Bkbl; Bio A; Tres, Church Yth; Gym; Col Early Entrance Prog; *E Nazarene Col.*

MORRIS, Lloyd Ray
Cloutierville HS; Cloutierville, LA; VP, FBLA; Co-Cpt, Bkbl; *Sou U; Photography.*

MORRIS, Lynda Ann
Prospect HS; Mount Prospect, IL (365-598) Chor; Community Yth Symph; Soloist, Roche Ch, Church Choir; Program Ch, Sr Tuxis; *Eng.*

MORRIS, Lynne Hope
John F Kennedy HS; Granada Hills, CA; JA A; Gym; JA.

MORRIS, Malinda Lea
S Dade Sr HS; Homestead, FL (169-470) Church Lib Staff; Interntl C; Religious C; *Miami Dade Jr Col; Eng Lit.*

MORRIS, Marilyn Monroe
Williamsburg HS; Andrews, SC (4-30) Ann; Co-Cpt, Chldr; Drama; Sch P; *SC St U; Eng.*

MORRIS, Marla Kay
Grand Ridge HS; Grand Ridge, FL (1-49) Ann; Rptr, BC; Chldr; Semi-Fin, Jr Miss Pa; Cl Fav; Val; Jr Miss Scholastic A; *U of Fla; Acct.*

MORRIS, Martin Brent
Bellflower HS; Bellflower, CA (220-382) A Cap Choir; Co-Ed, Ann; Chor; Ensm; Co-Ed, Sch P; Tr; *Baptist Bible Col; Missions.*

MORRIS, Mary Ann
Carroll HS; Monroe, LA (10%-205) Fr C; Secy, FBLA; Math C; SC; Hon Prog; Star Student; Yth Fel; Eng A; YES A; *Grambling U; Eng Ed.*

MORRIS, Michael Anthony
Columbia Acad; Columbia, MS (3-60) Pres, Band; NHS; Orch; Sftbl; COM; Hist A; Hon Prog; Sci A; All St Band; Superior Rating, Solo Comp; MV Member, Band; *U of Sou Miss; Mus.*

MORRIS, Michael Lane
Cleveland HS; Cleveland, TN (25%-220) F-Ed, Ann; Cpt, Band; BC; BS; Chor; Drama; Ensm; Hmrm; Key C; Orch; ARC; Bsbl; Hon Prog; Phy A; ARC A; Star Student; Yth Fel; Composers Clinic, Hon Band; All-St E Band; Ntl Tenn Talent, Chor Ensm; *Lee Col; Aeronautics.*

MORRIS, Natalie LaFay
Dorsey HS; Los Angeles, CA; *Cal St; Law.*

MORRIS, Pamela Jean
Stephens Co HS; Toccoa, GA (28-250) Anchor C; Ann; VP, BC; Co-Cpt, Chldr; Secy, Tri-HiY; VP, Jr Cl; VofDEM; Valentine Qn; 1st Alt, GS; 1st Run-Up, Miss NE Dist Ga Pag; *Young Harris Jr Col.*

MORRIS, Patricia Ann
Van-Far R-I HS; Vandalia, MO (4-64) Pres, Band; Drama; Pres, FTA; Pres, 4H; VP, NHS; Rptr, Sch P; DARGCA; 4H A; I Dare You; *Central Mo St U; Elem Ed.*

MORRIS, Patricia Ann
Altoona Area HS; Altoona, PA; Chor; Hmrm; *Penn St U; Home Ec.*

MORRIS, Paula Jeanne
Miller Co R III Tuscumbia HS; Tuscumbia, MO (2-18) Co-Cpt, Chldr; Chor; 4H; Bkbl; Tr; Soph Pilgrimage; *Home Ec.*

MORRIS, Phyllis Gay
Round Rock HS; Round Rock, TX; Bus C; ARC; Sci C; Tr; *Dentistry.*

MORRIS, Rebecca Lou
Cedarville HS; Cedarville, OH (4-51) Co-Ed, Ann; Band; Chldr; Drama; FTA; Pres, 4H; NHS; Tres, Jr Cl; Tres, Soph Cl; Candystriper; *Wright St U; Phys Therapy.*

MORRIS, Richard Allan
Central Union HS; El Centro, CA (30-500) F-Ed, Ann; Ger C; InterAct C; Key C; Secy, Math C; V-Ch, Var C; JV, Bkbl; MVP, Ftbl; Swim; Tr; Alg A; CSF; Math A; Pres A; Spch A; *Grossmont Jr Col; Math.*

MORRIS, Rickey
Robert A Taft HS; Cincinnati, OH; JV, Cr-Ctry; Cpt, Wrest; COM; Hon Prog; Drafting A; Merchantile Card.

MORRIS, Robert Freeman
Sarasota HS; Sarasota, FL (300-617) Chor; Key C; *Law.*

MORRIS, Robert Kevin
Cheraw HS; Cheraw, SC; Fr C; Key C.

MORRIS, Roberta Michelle
River Valley HS; Marion, OH (75-171) Ann; Chor; FHA; Ftbl; Stu Aide; Bkbl & Vlbl Statistician; Church Bible Quiz Tm; Off Worker; St Degree, FHA; Prom Ch; Superior Sci Fair A; *Working with the Deaf.*

MORRIS, Rodney Wayne
Anniston HS; Anniston, AL; CYO; Drama; Hmrm; Rptr, Sch P; Ftbl; Tr; Wrest; Cl Fav; Journ A; Stu Safety A; Ftbl Ltr; Tr Ltr; Wrest Ltr; *Journ.*

MORRIS, Ronald
Robert A Taft HS; Cincinnati, OH (1-192) Chess C; Sch Achieve Tm; Sch P; Sci C; Up Bound; Var C; MVP, Tnns; COM; Chamber of Comm A; Harvard Book A; I Dare You; Journ A; Kiwanis A; Math A; MLS; Val; Drafting A; *U of Dayton; Civil Engr.*

MORRIS, Ronald David II
Robert E Lee HS; Baytown, TX (5%-400) Band; Dbte Tm; VP, Math C; NHS; Tex Nuclear Sci Symp; *U of Tex; Math.*

MORRIS, Roslyn Diane
The Cecilian Acad; Philadelphia, PA (8-29) Cpt, Chldr; Fr C; Sci C; World Affairs C; Alg A; WW; *Brandeis U; Pre-Law.*

MORRIS, Sara Josephine
Winyah HS; Georgetown, SC (50%-200) Band; Sch P; Citz A; *Dental Hygiene.*

MORRIS, Sharon Lodean
McClymonds HS; Oakland, CA; FHA; NHS; Citz A; *Tex Sou U; Phar.*

MORRIS, Teresa Jane
Manchester HS; Manchester, GA;

MORRIS, Teresa Marie
Bishop Carroll HS; Wichita, KS (24-211) Bkbl; Tnns; *Kans Newman Col; Cytotechnology.*

MORRIS, Terri Lynn
Jim Hill HS; Jackson, MS; Lat C; Lat NHS; Math C; Mu Alpha Theta; NHS; Sch P; COM; Journ A; Lat A; *Hinds Jr Col; Phys Therapy.*

MORRIS, Terri Lynn
John F Kennedy Sr HS; New Orleans, LA (48-348) Co-Cpt, Chldr; Hmrm; NHS; Pres, Tri-HiY; Hon Prog; Yth Leg; Eng A; Service A; *La Tech U; Nurs.*

MORRIS, Thomas Arthur
Columbia Acad; Columbia, MS (10-37) SC; Var C; Pres, Sr Cl; Bkbl; Ftbl; Citz A; Most Improved A, Bkbl; *Pearl River Jr Col; Bus Adm.*

MORRIS, Tim Scott
Cambridge HS; Cambridge, OH (25-282) BS; HiY; VP, Key C; NHS; WW; *Ohio St Col; Adm Sci.*

MORRIS, Timothy Scott
Abilene HS; Abilene, KS (10%-119) SC; Bkbl; Cr-Ctry; Ftbl; Tr; Hon Prog; Opt A; Board of Regents St Schol; *Kans St U; Milling.*

MORRIS, Tyler Glen
Temple Baptist Acad; Marion, IN; Chor; Pres, 4H; Span C; Bkbl; Soccer; Tr; Hist A; NRA Rifle Tm; Highest Academic Improvement; Oration A; *Bob Jones U.*

MORRIS, Valarie Jean
Waurika HS; Waurika, OK (6-26) Pres, FHA; NHS; VP, SC; Pres, Sr Cl; Pres, Jr Cl; Pres, Soph Cl; Tnns; Masonic A; MLS; Friendliest A; *Okla Christian Col; Social Work.*

MORRIS, Vicki Carol
Medicine Bow HS; Medicine Bow, WY (1-19) Ann; Band; Pres, 4H; Jr Miss Pagent; NHS; Sch P; Cpt, Bkbl; Chem A; Citz A; I Dare You; Val; Mod Woodmen of Amer Schol; *Northeast Miss Jr Col; Liberal Arts.*

MORRIS, Vicki Lynn
Mannington HS; Mannington, WV (1-105) Band; Drama; GS; Mjrte; NHS; Secy, SC; Y-Tns; Bkbl; Hist A; Spch A; Prom Court; Know Your St Govt Day; St-Area All Festival Band; *Fairmont St Col; Nurs.*

MORRIS, Vickie Ann
Parkersburg South HS; Parkersburg, WV; Type A; DECA C; *Parkersburg Comm Col; Acct.*

MORRIS, Wayne Allan
Sycamore HS; Sycamore, IL (20-256) NHS; Bkbl; Cpt, Cr-Ctry; Tr; *Archt.*

MORRIS, Wayne Matthew
Hughson HS; Hughson, CA; FFA; Key C; Monogram; Ski C; Var C; MVP, Ftbl; Fin, Tr; Co-Cpt, Wrest; Cl Fav; Fin, Wrest; Ftbl All-League; Defensive Player o-t Yr; *MJC; PE.*

MORRIS, William Carl Jr
Headland HS; East Point, GA (10-145) BC; NHS; Ed, Sch P; Span NHS; COM; Hon Prog; NEDT; *U of Ga; Forestry.*

MORRISEY, Randolph
Clinton HS; Clinton, NC; BC; Math C; *UCLA.*

MORRISON, Ann Marie
Delta HS; Delta, UT (15-100) Chldr; Chor; Ski C; SC; *U of Utah; Ed.*

MORRISON, Beverly Jane
Patrick Henry Acad; Estill, SC (4-25) *Eng.*

MORRISON, David James
Hastings Sr HS; Hastings, MN (50-475) *Physics.*

MORRISON, David Robert
Aquinas HS; La Crosse, WI (3-185) Rptr, Ann; BS; Dbte Tm; Drama; NFL; NHS; Rptr, Sch P; Span C; Spch C; Pres, SC; Amer Leg Orator A; COM; Citz A; Journ A; MLS; NMF; NMS; NEDT; Opt A; Spch A; VFW Orator Win; VofDEM; Span A; Photography C; Debate A; *U of Wis; Bus.*

MORRISON, Deborah Demetri
C E Byrd HS; Shreveport, LA; Band; Chldr; Chor; Ntl Advisory Committee; Jr Prom Court; *Engr.*

MORRISON, Dennis Ray
Humansville HS; Humansville, MO (2-37) VP, Band; Chor; Pres, FFA; Rptr, Soph Cl; COM; Cl Fav; Hon Prog; Spch A; Type A; Pres, S-T & Rptr, 4-H C; St Capital Soph Pilgrimage; Acct A; Area FFA Off; Co 4-H Coun Off; Win, Bicen Essay; *SW Mo St U; Acct.*

MORRISON, Garry Robert
Morgan Park HS; Duluth, MN (52-116) AFS; Hmrm; K of C; Ftbl; Golf; Hockey; Tr; HCt; K of C A; Rotary A; *U of Wis; Bus.*

MORRISON, Jackie Lee
Venice HS; Venice, FL (33%-450) Chor; Hmrm; SC.

MORRISON, Jody Lynne
Kenmore-E Sr HS; Tonawanda, NY (30%-700) ARC; Swim; ARC A; Yth Fel; Booster C; Cpt, Kipettes; GAA; Yth Choir; *Phys Therapy.*

MORRISON, John Daniel
Charles Henderson HS; Troy, AL (1-187) BC; Chor; Dbte Tm; NHS; Ed, Sch P; Span C; SC; COM; Journ A; Math A; NMF; NMS; Val; Span A; GC Wallace Schol; Prep Bowl A; *Troy St U; Bio.*

MORRISON, John Mark
Gadsden HS; Gadsden, AL; Fr C; VP, HiY; Key C; Math C; Span C; VP, Tri-HiY; Bsbl; Bkbl; Ftbl; Tr; Sci A; Yth Fel; Alg A; Church Chr; All St YMCA Bkbl Tm; All Star, Little League, Bsbl; City Putt Putt Golf Championship; Pony League & Colt League, Bsbl; *U O Ala; Phys Ed.*

MORRISON, Joy Albertine
Lincoln HS; Wisconsin Rapids, WI (25-560) A Cap Choir; Bus C; Secy, Chor; Drama; Ensm; FBLA; Madrigal; Mod Mus Mas; NHS; Orch; COM; HCt; Hon Prog; Math A; NMS; Sanctuary Soc; Type A; Yth Fel; Yth Foundation; Fin, Secy o-t Yr; Swing Choir; HR; St Win, Bible Quiz Tm; Mus A; FSA; Pres, Missionettes; Pep C; Christ's Ambassadors; *N Central Bible Col; Sacred Mus.*

MORRISON, Joy Elaine
Montgomery Co HS; Mt Sterling, KY; Band; FBLA; Cpt, Mjrte; NHS; *Nu Teck Acad; Beautician.*

MORRISON, Juanita Gayle
Montgomery Co HS; Mt Sterling, KY; Chor; FBLA; Math C; Mu Alpha Theta; NHS; ROTC A; NJROTC Swtht; *U of Ky; Social Work.*

MORRISON, Laura Diane
Shelton HS; Shelton, CT (272-432) Band; Ski C; Span C; Tnns; Span A; *Sou Ct Col; Social Work.*

MORRISON, Lisa Ann
Grimsley Sr HS; Greensboro, NC (10%-550) Band; Pres, Fr C; VP, NHS; Hon Prog; St Sci Symposium Schol; Natl Merit Commended Stu; *U of NC; Phar.*

MORRISON, Louis Paul
Vanguard HS; Ocala, FL (22-350) Anchor C; Mu Alpha Theta; NHS; Bsbl; Bkbl; Ftbl; Tr; Most Out; Outst Knight; Span A; *Eckerd Col; Hist.*

MORRISON, Marti Minet
Andress HS; El Paso, TX; A Cap Choir; Band; Yth Fel; *U of Texas at El Paso; Nurs.*

MORRISON, Richard Thomas
Jeannette Sr HS; Jeannette, PA (80-181) HiY; Bsbl; Ftbl; Sftbl; Tr; Amer Leg A; COM; Citz A; *Westmd Co Comm Col; Police Sci.*

MORRISON, Sarah Darlene
Hickman Mills Sr HS; Kansas City, MO (121-577) Pep C; Pom Pon; *Acct.*

MORRISON, Scot Alan
Sterling Heights HS; Sterling Heights, MI (73-900) NHS; Sci C; Span C; Bio A; Citz A; Jr Deacon; *U of Mich-Ann Arbor; Med.*

MORRISON, Vonda Kay
Kings Temple Christian Sch; Seattle, WA; Chor; COM; Hon Prog; Pres A; Yth Fel; Harvard U; Theology.

MORRISON, Zachary Charles
Dominguez Sr HS; Compton, CA; Band; Chor; Community Yth Symph; Ensm; NHS; Orch; Spch C; CSF; Citz A; Interlochen Ntl Mus; Most Out; Spch A; Calif St U; Mus.

MORRISSET, Mark Madison
Granite Hills HS; El Cajon, CA (1-439) Tres, Band; V-Ch, Ger C; Tres, Orch; Order/Arrow; Secy, Spch C; Tr; Wrest; Amer Leg Orator A; Bank Of Amer A; CSF; Elk A; Harvard Book A; Hon Prog; Lion A; Math A; MLS; Most Out; Sci A; Spch A; Val; Soroptomist Yth Ldrship A; CSF Seymour A Fin; Eagle Sct; Outst Band; The Calif Inst of Tech; Physics.

MORRISSEY, Patricia Joan
Lourdes HS; Chicago, IL (8-288) Chor; Drama; Ensm; Ger C; Madrigal; NHS; COM; Hon Prog; NEDT; Sci A; Spch A; St Scholar; Outst Vocal; WW; Rosary Col; Mus.

MORROW, Claudia Leigh
Girls' Prep Sch; Chattanooga, TN (8-90) A-Ed, Ann; Chldr; Chor; Drama; Lat C; Madrigal; NHS; Span C; Span NHS; SC; Citz A; Hist A; NEDT; AATSP Ntl Span Comp; Span A; Bus.

MORROW, Gordon Ray
Alan B Shepard HS; Palos Heights, IL (22-350) Chess C; Span C; Wrest; IIT; Elec Engr.

MORROW, Levern
East HS; Buffalo, NY (1-18) Chess C; Sch P; Span C; Bkbl; Ftbl; Tr; Eng A; Morehouse Col; Journ.

MORROW, Lori Lee
Armour HS; Armour, SD; Secy, Band; Chldr; Chor; FHA; SC; Var C; Bkbl; Tr; PA; Mitchell Area Voc Sch; Nurs.

MORROW, Mary Harding
Millbrook Sr HS; Raleigh, NC (70-463) Chor; Ensm; NHS; Span C; Ftbl; Salem Col; Hist.

MORROW, Rhonda Lynn
Lindale HS; Lindale, TX (12-70) Band; BC; Ensm; Pres, FHA; Semi-Fin, Jr Miss Pa; Mjrte; SC; HQn; Coronation Qn Nom; Miss Lindale HS; Tyler Jr Col; Fashion Merchandising.

MORROW, Virginia Lee
Dodgeville HS; Dodgeville, WI (5-140) AFS; Chem C; Chor; Dbte Tm; Lit Mag; Math C; Co-Ch, Model UN; Fin, NFL; NHS; Ski C; Span C; Var C; Bkbl; Tr; COM; Hon Prog; GScts; God & Comm A; Prom Ct; Bus Mgt.

MORROW, Warren Roy
Interlake HS; Bellevue, WA (10%-300) SC; Ftbl; Soccer; Wrest; Bus.

MORSE, Barbara June
Granada HS; Livermore, CA; Band; Chor; Drama; Span C; Cpt, Bkbl; MVP, Soccer; Sftbl; Most Improved A, Bkbl; Camp Fire Girls A; Pres, Tres, Episcopal Yth Organ; Fresno St U; Psych.

MORSE, Chynsia Princetta
Greater NY Acad; Woodside, NY (20-73) Bkbl; Sftbl; Citz A; Atlantic Union Col; Nutrition.

MORSE, Cynthia Marie
Aiken HS; Cincinnati, OH (3-800) Band; NHS; SC; Swim; COM; Citz A; DARGCA; Hon Prog; MLS; Most Out; Schol Achv; Cincinnati Bible Col; Bible.

MORSE, Delores Kay
East Greene Comm HS; Grand Junction, IA (2-28) Ed, Ann; JV, Chldr; Pres, Chor; Drama; Pres, 4H; Pres, NHS; Rptr, Sch P; Mgr, Bkbl; B Crocker A; Citz A; 4H A; Journ A; PTA A; Q&S A; Sal; Yth Fel; PA; Choir Coun; Vocal A; Bar Assn A; Iowa St U; Elem Ed.

MORSE, Jane Elizabeth
Warwick HS; Newport News, VA (1-484) Co-Ed, Ann; Key C; Math C; NHS; Span C; Hockey; Gov Honor Prog; Alt, GS; U of Va; Math.

MORSE, Kaye Lynne
Hanna Elk Mountain HS; Hanna, WY (9-29) Ann; Band; Drama; Pres, 4H; NHS; Thes; 4H A; Dist off, FHA.

MORSE, Mark Russell
Aiken Sr HS; Cincinnati, OH (1-600) Ann; Band; BS; Chess C; Pres, Fr C; French NHS; Pres, Hmrm; Co-Ch, Model UN; NHS; SC; UN Council; Var C; JV, Tnns; COM; Citz A; Harvard Book A; Hon Prog; MLS; Most Out; Spch A; Fin, Swim; Cincinnati Bible Col; Christian Ministries.

MORSE, Michelle Ann
Virgil I Grissom HS; Huntsville, AL; Drama; Rptr, FBLA; Co-Ch, Hmrm; Ed, Sch P; Thes; Sftbl; Span A; Type A; Yth Fel; Yth Leg; Troy St U; Journ.

MORSE, Sharon Aleshia
Savannah HS; Savannah, GA; Chor; FHA; Span C; Math A; ARC A.

MORTA, Carolyn Diana
John F Kennedy HS; Tumon, GUAM; Effort A; Determination A; Psych.

MORTELLARO, John Charles
N Salinas HS; Salinas, CA (50-450) A Cap Choir; Bible.

MORTENSEN, Barbara
Union HS; Roosevelt, UT (4-165) Dbte Tm; Secy, Drama; FBLA; FHA; 4H; Secy, Spch C; 4H A; Spch A; WW; Brigham Young U; Bus.

MORTENSEN, Mary Lee
Fairmont HS; Fairmont, MN; Chor; Swim; Yth Fel; Yth Singing Group; Work Part Time; Exec Adm Board, Church.

MORTENSON, James Herbert
Vista HS; Vista, CA (13-670) Band; NHS; CSF; Citz A; Hon Prog; Ntl Achv Schol; NMS; California St U; Mus.

MORTENSON, Jay Arthur
Bismarck HS; Bismarck, ND; Chor; Demolay; S-Sgt, Civil Air Patrol; U of ND; Aviation.

MORTHORST, Pamela Jean
James E Sperry HS; Henrietta, NY (18-476) A Cap Choir; Secy, 4H; NHS; SC; Citz A; Hon Prog; Regent School; 4h School; Monroe Comm Col; Acct.

MORTIMER, Jean Elizabeth
Avon HS; Avon, CT (40-200) AFS; Chor; Fr C; Lit Mag; Ski C; JV Vlbl; Allegheny Col; Hist.

MORTON, Beverly Jan
Kress HS; Kress, TX; Ed, Ann; FHA; VP, FTA; GS; Pres, Sr Cl; Mgr, Bkbl; Tr; Outst FHA A; Lions C Swtht; St FHA Choir; St Baptist Yth Choir; Wayland Baptist Col; Homemaking.

MORTON, Bruce Howard
Fairview HS; Sherwood, OH (51-154) All Amer Yth; Band; Chor; Ensm; Fr C; FTA; Madrigal; Poet A; Yth Fel; Heidelberg Col; Mus Performance.

MORTON, Candace Marlayne
Lowell HS; San Francisco, CA; Beauty; Swtht; Fin, Gym; VP, Yth at Church; Gospel Director And Soloist; Fashion Inst of Design & Merch; Fashion Merchandising.

MORTON, Cathy Mary
Devilbiss HS; Toledo, OH; Hmrm; Mjrte; Sch Achieve Tm; Arch; Bkbl; Sftbl; Tnns; Tr; Beauty; Citz A; MLS; Swtht; All Around Sportsmanship A; UCLA; Bus Ed.

MORTON, Cynthia Ann
C F Brewer HS; White Settlement, TX; Band; Ensm; Fr C; Jr Miss Pagent; Key C; SC; Bkbl; Tr; Pres A; N Tex St U; Recreation.

MORTON, James Richard
South Shelby HS; Shelbina, MO (4-100) Chor; Var C; Bkbl; Ftbl; Tr; US Air Force Acad.

MORTON, Jill Anne
S Plantation HS; Plantation, FL (10%-550) VP, Chor; NHS; Pres, Yth Fel; Secy, Yth Coun; Cpt, Drill Tm; Fla Sou U; Sci.

MORTON, Martha Lynn
Plainview HS; Plainview, TX (33-334) A Cap Choir; Co-Ed, Ann; Band; Chldr; FBLA; FHA; FTA; Hmrm; SC; HQn; Interlochen Ntl Mus; Kiwanis Swtht; Tex Tech U; Home Ec.

MORTON, Paul Anthony
Wakulla HS; Medart, FL; Drama; Parl, Thes; Band; Ftbl; Tr; FSU; Geology.

MORTON, Robin Marie
Switzerland Co HS; Vevay, IN (6-108) Band; Cpt, Chldr; Dbte Tm; FHA; 4H; Cpt, Mjrte; NHS; Span C; SC; Cpt, Tr; HCt; Poet A; Eng, WW, A's; Ind St U; Bus Mgr.

MORTON, Shawn Camille
Huffman HS; Birmingham, AL; Bus C; FBLA; FTA; Lat C; U of Ala in Birmingham; Ger.

MORTON, Sheri Yvette
Los Angeles HS; Los Angeles, CA; FHA; Hmrm; NHS; SC; CSF; COM; Citz A; Hon Prog; Most Out; Opt A; Cpt, DAPS; Explorers; DAP o-t Yr Trophy; USC; Fashion Design.

MORTON, Tom Leslie
Bremen Sr HS; Bremen, IN (1-120) Bus Mgr, Band; Fin, BS; Drama; Ensm; Tres, HFV; Hmrm; Tres, NHS; Sci C; Span C; Rptr, SC; Tres, Jr Cl; Cpt, Bkbl; Tr; Alg A; COM; Purdue U; Met-Architectural Design.

MORTRUD, Debra Ann
Lincoln Sr HS; Thief River Falls, MN (14-255) Ann; Band; Chor; Rptr, Sch P; Span C; JV, Tnns; Assoc Free Lutheran Bible Sch; Bible.

MOSAL, Jonathan Scott
Valley City HS; Valley City, ND (30-185) Ann; Dbte Tm; NFL; Order/Arrow; Sci C; Ski C; Spch C; St Stu Congress; Citz A; Order/Arrow A; Spch A; U of Minn.

MOSBARGER, Deana Lee
Salem Comm HS; Salem, IL (126-202) Band; City Conf; Pres, 4H; Span C; 4H A; Opt A; Opt Out Tn; PTA A; Yth Fel; Bus Ministry; Christ in Yth Conf; Puppet Ministry; Yth For Christ; St Fair; Photo; Top Sales Person, Band; St Louis Christian Col; Christian Ed.

MOSBY, Joseph Lamont
Benedictine HS; Cleveland, OH (11-135) CYO; Drama; Var C; Bsbl; Cr-Ctry; Sftbl; Swim; Tr; Wrest; Hist A; Mich St U; Chem.

MOSBY, Martha Helen
Canton Acad HS; Canton, MS (5-95) Ann; BC; S-T, CYO; Co-Cpt, Chldr; Chor; 4H; Hmrm; NHS; Sch P; Sci C; VP, Span C; Spch C; St Stu Congress; VP, SC; Y-Tns; Swim; Cpt, Tnns; Balfour A; Beauty; COM; Cl Fav; 4H A; Fr A; F; HCt; MLS; Most Out; Rotary A; Yth Leg; WW; Miss St U; Lib Arts.

MOSCA, Stephanie Ellen
Gloucester HS; Gloucester, VA (50-260) Tres, AFS; F-Ed, Ann; Chor; Secy, 4H; InterClub Coun; Madrigal; Sch P; Most Improved Vocal Mus; Col of William & Mary; Journ.

MOSCHETTIERI, Grace Darlene
Bible Baptist HS; Savannah, GA (4-34) Armstrong St Col; Bus Adm.

MOSELEY, Andre Perez
Terry Sanford Sr HS; Fayetteville, NC; Ann; Chor; Drama; Ensm; HiY; Sch P; Thes; NC Sch of Arts; Mus.

MOSELEY, Douglas Harry
Buckingham Co HS; Buckingham, VA (11-130) FFA; VP, 4H; Math C; VP, Sci C; Span C; COM; 4H A; Math A; Sci A; Eng, Span, A's; Jr Deacon; Col of William & Mary; Span.

MOSELEY, Ellen Arthur
I C Norcom HS; Portsmouth, VA (1-280) Monogram; NHS; Sci C; Bkbl; Sftbl; HR A; Scholastic Tm A; Span A; PA A; U of Va; Bio.

MOSELEY, Linda Marie
Wayne Co HS; Jesup, GA (20-390) FHA; 4H; Bsbl; Sftbl; COM; FHA St Degree A; Shorthand A; Ga Southwestern Col; Elem Ed.

MOSELEY, Melissa Diane
Montrose Acad; Montrose, AR (5-32) Ann; Band; Ensm; Fr C; Mjrte; NHS; NE La U; Phar.

MOSELEY, Patrice Cathrene
Woodrow Wilson HS; Dallas, TX (25%-300) NHS; Sci C; Span C; Bkbl; Drill Tm; Choir; Med.

MOSELEY, Patricia Anne
Wayne Co HS; Jesup, GA (10%-325) Fr C; VP, FHA; 4H; NHS; SC; Sr Cl; Sftbl; COM; Citz A; Rotary A; Home Ec, FHA St Degree; Ga Sou Col; Home Ec.

MOSELEY, Patsey Rivers
Gumberry HS; Gumberry, NC (2-97) Ann; BC; Chldr; Chor; Fr C; FHA; Pres, 4H; COM; 4H A; HQn; I Dare You; Sal; *U of NC at Chapel Hill; Pub Health Ed.*

MOSELY, Jami Louise
Tuscaloosa HS; Tuscaloosa, AL (48-561) Anchor C; Chldr; FHA; Pres, Hmrm; NHS; Span C; SC; Cpt, Sftbl; Beauty; Elk A; HCt; Sci A; Tnboard Model; Hosp Explorer Post; *U of Ala; Phys Therapy.*

MOSEMAN, Laura Kay
Oakland-Craig HS; Oakland, NE (1-48) Ann; Band; Chor; S-T, Drama; Madrigal; Sftbl; Regent Schol; Val; VofDEM; *U of Nebr; Bus Adm.*

MOSEMAN, Neil Patrick
Oakland-Craig HS; Oakland, NE (7-55) Fr C; VP, Soph Cl; Bsbl; JV, Bkbl; *U of Houston; Criminology.*

MOSER, Cynthia Lynn
Garner Sr HS; Garner, NC (33%-500) Chldr; Fr C; Tnns; COM; Hon Prog; *Paralegal.*

MOSER, Karen Louise
Guttenberg Comm HS; Guttenberg, IA; Rptr, Ann; JV, Chldr; Chor; FHA; Madrigal; Sch P; JV, Bkbl; Tr; Spch A; I Rating, Small Groups Contest; *Kirkwood Comm Col; Legal Secy.*

MOSER, Lynn Robert
Guttenberg Comm HS; Guttenberg, IA; *Loras Col; Pre-Vet.*

MOSER, Mary Catherine
Battle Mountain HS; Minturn, CO (6-55) Ann; Chor; FHA; Pres, 4H; Model UN; NHS; SC; Var C; Mgr, Tr; Art C; High Scholastic Achv A; Ski Tm; Most Improved Vlbl Player; Vlbl; Earth Sci A; *U of Colo; Psych.*

MOSER, Paul F
Clairemont HS; San Diego, CA (150-750) Ger C; Orch; Hist A; Sci A; Church Chor; Church Yth Coun; Bio C; *Cal Poly-San Luis Opisbo; Architecture.*

MOSER, Ronald Dean
Van Wert HS; Van Wert, OH (12-165) Band; Chess C; Chor; Fr C; NHS; Var C; Ftbl; Tr; *The Cincinnati Bible Seminary; Soc Sci.*

MOSER, Wade Leslie
Calico Rock HS; Calico Rock, AR (13-42) A Cap Choir; FBLA; FFA; Hmrm; Bsbl; Cpt, Bkbl; Spch A; Bkbl Defense A.

MOSER, Yvonne LaNelle
Marshalltown Sr HS; Marshalltown, IA (2%-489) A Cap Choir; BC; Bus C; Chldr; Chor; Ensm; Span C; Tr; COM; Chamber of Comm A; Citz A; HCt; Lion A; NMS; Opt A; *Harding Col; Bus Mgt.*

MOSES, Debra Lynn
Winner Sr HS; Winner, SD (3-105) Fin, GS; Golf; COM; Magna Cum Laude; Pres A; Yth Fel; Pres, DECA; Pep C; Safety Coun Adv; VP, MYF.

MOSES, Dennis Leon
Carolina HS; Greenville, SC; Ftbl; Wrest; Most Out; MVP, Ftbl; *Machinery.*

MOSES, Donna Renna
Simon Gratz HS; Philadelphia, PA; FTA; NHS; Hist A; Math A; MLS; Punctuality & Attendance As.

MOSES, Karen Sue
N Mesquite HS; Mesquite, TX (256-452) A Cap Choir; Band; Rainbow; Span C; *Sam Houston St U; Elem Ed.*

MOSES, Loraine Denise
W S Creecy HS; Rich Square, NC (6-42) Tres, BC; Cpt, Chldr; Drama; Fr C; Hon Prog; Beta A; WW; *NC Central U; Elem Ed.*

MOSES, Mark Alan
Leesville HS; Leesville, LA (12-265) Pres, BC; BS; FBLA; Pres, 4H; InterClub Coun; K of C; VP, Sr Cl; Cl Fav; *La Tech U; Bus Adm.*

MOSHENEK, Mary Elizabeth
Dan River HS; Ringgold, VA (8-238) Secy, BC; Co-Cpt, Chldr; FHA; Hmrm; Monogram; SC; Tres, Tri-HiY; Acad Chldr A; WW; *VPI; Acct.*

MOSHER, Mark Keith
Rogers HS; Michigan City, IN; 4H; Orch; VICA C; VP, Church Yth Fel; St Gold Medal, Solo Violin; Silver Medal, Trio Ens Strings; *Mus.*

MOSIER, Christine Elizabeth
Argyll Episcopal Acad; N Hollywood, CA (1-25) Band; Chor; Drama; VP, Jr Cl; Bkbl; Sftbl; Tnns; MVP, Tr; CSF; COM; Citz A; Hon Prog; Val; Yth Fel; Vlbl; *Claremont Col; Mus.*

MOSIER, Linda Kay
Bonner Springs Sr HS; Bonner Springs, KS (10-188) Band; Fin, GS; Span C; Var C; Cr-Ctry; Sftbl; Tr; COM; Hon Prog; NEDT; Kayettes; S-T, Herpitological Soc; Secy, Rainbow Girls; Vlbl; *Pittsburg St U.*

MOSIER, Lora Beth
Chardon HS; Chardon, OH (33-100) A Cap Choir; Band; Chldr; Chor; Dbte Tm; Ensm; Fr C; Rptr, 4H; Mod Mus Mas; ARC; 4H A; FCA; Chor A; *Phys Therapist.*

MOSIER, Mike Charles
Bonner Springs HS; Bonner Springs, KS (10%-150) Band; Order/Arrow; JV, Cr-Ctry; Swim; Tr; JV, Wrest; COM; Order/Arrow A; *Bio.*

MOSIER, William Louis
Flint N HS; Flint, MI; Band; Co-Ch, Sci C; *Mich Tech U; Bio Sci.*

MOSIOR, Mark William
R E Lee HS; Springfield, VA (100-500) Band; Ensm; Orch; Bkbl; Tnns; ETTA Preliminary Cert; Church Orch; *Washington Bible Sch; Mus.*

MOSKOVICS, Helen Shirley
Bruriah HS; Elizabeth, NJ (5-33) NHS; Pres, Soph Cl; Hon Prog; Cert of Service.

MOSKOVITZ, Ronald Bruce
Parkway Prog-Beta Unit HS; Philadelphia, PA; Rptr, Sch P; *Comm Col of Philadelphia; Restaurant Mgt.*

MOSLEY, Cynthia Lynn
River Forest HS; Hobart, IN; NHS; Hist A; Math A; Sci A; Val.

MOSLEY, Everett
John F Kennedy HS; New Orleans, LA; Band; Bkbl; Tr; Yth Fel; Church Coun; Yth Choir; Mr Beecher Mem Unted Chrch of Chrst; *Sou U; Elec.*

MOSLEY, Janet
Lyons Sr HS; Lyons, GA (10%-30) Tri-HiY; COM; HR A; Cert of A; Bible Sch Teacher's Cert; *Ga Sou Col; Eng.*

MOSLEY, Jimmie R III
Ayer HS; Milpitas, CA (24-454) Chess C; Order/Arrow; CSF; Eagle Sct; *U of Calif; Sci.*

MOSLEY, Jocelyn Gail
Roxborough HS; Philadelphia, PA; Orch; Yth Fel; *Child Psych.*

MOSLEY, Judith Lynn
Albia Comm HS; Albia, IA (33%-150) Band; Chldr; Chor; Ensm; SC; Var C; JV, Bkbl; JV, Sftbl; Tr; Yth Fel; Christmas Court; *Stevens Col; Mus.*

MOSLEY, Karen Denise
Wade Hampton HS; Greenville, SC (124-438) Pres, CYO; Chldr; Dbte Tm; Ed, Sch P; SC; I Dare You; Brotherhood A; *Ga Southern Col; Pol Sci.*

MOSLEY, Mark Allen
Albia Comm HS; Albia, IA (80-160) Band; Chor; FFA; Var C; JV, Bsbl; Ftbl; Tr; Yth Fel; *Indian Hills Comm Col; Building Trades.*

MOSLEY, Melody Grace
McGavock HS; Nashville, TN (1-840) BC; Chor; Dbte Tm; Drama; Ensm; Fr C; Ger C; GS; Madrigal; NFL; NHS; Rptr, Sch P; Spch C; Amer Leg Orator A; Hon Prog; NEDT; Spch A; All St Chor; Dist Win & Rep, Ntl Forensic League; *William Jewel Col; Mus.*

MOSLEY, Patricia Ann
S Choctaw Acad; Toxey, AL (3-32) BC; Cpt, Chldr; Chor; NHS; MVP, Bkbl; Sftbl; Most Out; Spch A; *Eng.*

MOSLEY, Sharron Ann
Allen HS; Robeline, LA (3-32) FHA; VP, Hmrm; NHS; Hon Prog; Cl Swtht; *NSU; Nurs.*

MOSLEY, Sheila Ann
William A Bass HS; Atlanta, GA (13-160) Band; Chldr; Dbte Tm; Fr C; FHA; FNA; Hmrm; Sftbl; Co-Cpt, Flag Girls; 1st Alt, Ms ROTC; Co-Ch, ROTC Sponsors; *Clark Col; Court Stenographer.*

MOSLEY, Yolanda Renee
Manual Arts HS; Los Angeles, CA; Hon Prog; JEP; Vol Service A; Schol A; Cert of Recognition; *Bus.*

MOSS, Arlenia
Chester HS; Chester, PA (10%-760) NHS; Tres, Sr Cl; *Lincoln U; Law.*

MOSS, Carol Ann Mary
Kings Park HS; Kings Park, NY (84-980) AFS; Chor; Drama; NHS; Sch P; Span C; Ch, Thes; CCD Teacher; Folk Choir; Adv & Pres, Order of St Francis; *U of Scranton; Psych.*

MOSS, Debra Renee
Wayne HS; Fort Wayne, IN (8-352) Bio A; Hist A; Hon Prog; Type A; Foreign Lang A; *Olivet Nazarene Col.*

MOSS, Joy Lynnette
Grenada HS; Grenada, MS (4-160) Secy, Anchor C; FFA; 4H; Pres, NHS; A-Ed, Sch P; DARGCA; Type A; Piano A; Humanities A; Shorthand A; Eng A; *Delta St U; Mus Ed.*

MOSS, Kevin Ray
Quincy Sr HS; Quincy, IL; Chor; Demolay; Tres, 4H; SC; Thes; 4H A; Safety Town A; *U of Ill; Mus.*

MOSS, Marzetta Cassandra
Central HS; Providence, RI; *Tuskegee Inst; Obstetrician.*

MOSS, Nola Jean
Short Ridge HS; Indianapolis, IN (16-568) Lat C; NHS; *Indiana U; Med.*

MOSS, Teressa Ann
Logan Elm HS; Circleville, OH; Yth Qn; VP, Yth Group.

MOSS, Walter Lee
Rutherford Spindale HS; Rutherfordton, NC (65-250) VP, FFA; InterAct C; ARC; VP, Span C; JV, Bsbl; Golf; 4H A; Forestry A; *NC St U; Forestry.*

MOSSER, Debbie Renae
Maddock Pub Sch; Maddock, ND (3-23) Band; Chor; Pres, 4H; Var C; Secy, Soph Cl; Bkbl; Sftbl; 4H A; Asst Secy, FHA; NRA Rifle C Medal; FHA A; *Bismark Junior College; Criminology.*

MOSSMAN, James Joseph
Vincent Massey Secondary Sch; Windsor, CANADA; Chem C; Math C; *U of Toronto; Math.*

MOST, Cynthia Jean
Prescott Sr HS; Prescott, WI (5-81) Ed, Ann; Chor; GS; NHS; Secy, SC; Secy, Jr Cl; DARGCA; Type A; *Dr Martin Luther Col; Elem Ed.*

MOSTAJO, Emilynn Lee
George Washington Sr HS; Mangilao, GUAM; NHS; Tres, Sch P; COM; Citz A; Journ A; Sci A; Type A; Val; PA; Penmanship A.

MOTE, Kevin L
Valhalla HS; El Cajon, CA (40%-500) Lit Mag; Pres, Skyline Wesleyan; Yth for Christ; Coun, Billy Graham Crusade; Art, Lit Mag & Various Sch Pub; *San Diego St U; Grafic Arts.*

MOTEN, Jerry
Cedar Bluff HS; Cedar Bluff, AL; BC; FFA; Math C; Secy, Soph Cl; Bsbl; Bkbl; Ftbl; Tr; Sci A; Pep C.

MOTEN, Michael Anthony
Burke HS; Charleston, SC (7-210) Math C; Tres, NHS; Co-Cpt, Ftbl; Tr; WW; Sr Hon Stu; *Sou U; Elec Engr.*

MOTEN, Terri Lynn
Beaumont HS; St Louis, MO (8-800) Tnns; Delta Sigma Theta A; *U of Mo; Psych.*

MOTES, Amy Lou
Robert E Lee HS; Tyler, TX; A Cap Choir; BC; Ensm; *Baylor U; Voice.*

MOTHERSHED, Kimberly Diane
Jeffersontown HS; Jeffersontown, KY (19-409) BC; Community Yth Symph; Hmrm; Lit Mag; NHS; Orch; Span C; SC; Sci A; Art As; *Phar.*

MOTLEY, Charlene
Buchtel HS; Akron, OH (180-390) Co-Ch, Bus C; Chor; Fr C; 4H; Tr; COM; 4H A; Swtht; Type A; Yth Fel; Gregg A; *Ohio St; Clerical Typist.*

MOTLEY, Douglas Lee
Dan River HS; Ringgold, VA (20-238) Pres, BC; Tres, FFA; Gr Marshal; Secy, FFA; *Danville Comm Col; Elec.*

MOTLEY, Gertrude Louise
Fairview HS; Dayton, OH; Chor; Vlbl A; *Bowling Green St U; Criminology.*

MOTLEY, Malinda Williams
Gumberry HS; Gumberry, NC; Chor; Fr C; FHA; Sch P; *NC Central U; Mus.*

MOTO, Brian Tetsuo
Maui HS; Kahului, HI (1-299) Bus Mgr, Ann; VP, Bus C; Dbte Tm; FBLA; Secy, 4H; Hmrm; Pres, NHS; Eng A; Outst, Soph & Jr; NML; *U of Hawaii; Bus Adm.*

MOTON, Janet Adrienne
J M Morehead Sr HS; Eden, NC (33-308) Bus Mgr, Ann; Chor; Drama; FTA; Math C; NHS; Sci C; WW; NML; *NC St U; Chem Engr.*

MOTON, Joyce Ann
Coahoma Agr Sch; Clarksdale, MS; FHA; *Jackson Col; Elem Ed.*

MOTON, Richard Claude
S Philadelphia HS; Philadelphia, PA (18-30) 4H; Ftbl; *UCLA; Math.*

MOTT, David Hollie
Putnam County Sr HS; Cookeville, TN (7-377) Gov Honor Prog; St Fin, Hearst Sen Yth Prog; *Tenn Tech U; Law.*

MOTTA, Anne Patricia
John Adams HS; Ozone Park, NY; Hon Prog; *Acct.*

MOTTER, Lisa Ann
Piqua Central HS; Piqua, OH (1-420) Band; Chor; Span C; Top 100; Acomodadores; *Law.*

MOTZ, Natalie Ann
Alamosa HS; Alamosa, CO (5-186) Ann; MVP, Band; Ensm; GS; Model UN; Secy, NHS; Sch P; VP, Spch C; SC; Thes; Tres, Sr Cl; Bkbl; Cr-Ctry; Swim; Tr; Amer Leg A; Bio A; HQn; I Dare You; Journ A; Pres A; Regent Schol; Spch A; Drama A; *Adams St Col; Pre-Med.*

MOTZER, Brenda Kay
W Forest HS; Tionesta, PA (10%-70) Band; Pres, 4H; SC; Golf; Sftbl; 4H A; Pres A; Vlbl; *Erie Bus Col; Bus.*

MOUGHLER, Debbie Kay
Clara Co R-1 HS; Kahoka, MO (13-92) FBLA; NHS; *NMSU; Bus.*

MOULLIET, Maria Theresa
John Ehret HS; Marrero, LA; S-T, CYO; S-T, 4H; Bio A; 4H A.

MOULTON, Carl Rick
Lexington HS; Lexington, OK (16-75) Var C; Mgr, Bkbl; Ftbl; Tr; Yth Fel; *Okla U; Oceanography.*

MOULTON, Kim Albert
Sky View HS; Smithfield, UT (158-573) BS; Drama; Key C; Pres, SC; Var C; Bkbl; Ftbl; Tr; Citz A; God & Country A; Rotary A; Spch A; Sterling Schol Nom; *Ricks Col; Law Enforcement.*

MOULTRIE, Patricia Ann
E Ridge HS; East Ridge, TN (7-288) Band; BC; Chor; Ensm; GS; NHS; Rainbow; Thes; COM; 4H A; Hon Prog; Math A; Star Student; Eng A; ETEA Chor Rep; 3yr Chldr; Member, Bible C; Chor A; Member, Jaycetts; 10y Attendance A; *U of Tenn at Chattanooga; Med.*

MOUND, Frederic Charles
Warren Travis White HS; Dallas, TX (196-727) Drama; Hmrm; VP, Ntl Yth Conf; Span C; SC; Secy, Ntl Yth Conf; *Baylor U; Bus.*

MOUNTAIN, Teresa Gail
Ahoskie HS; Ahoskie, NC (58-243) Band; Parl, Jr Cl; GSct; Flag Corp; *U of NC; Pre-Med.*

MOUNTJOY, Leanna Carol
Oreg City Sr HS; Oreg City, OR (59-400) AFS; Hmrm; SC; Var C; Tr; Most Inspirational; Vlbl; *Linfield Col; Phys Ed.*

MOURING, Stephen Earl
Central Baptist HS; Hampton, VA (1-21) Chor; Cpt, Dbte Tm; Ger C; VP, Hmrm; Var C; Cpt, Bsbl; JV, Bkbl; Co-Cpt, Ftbl; Cpt, Sftbl; *Liberty Baptist Col; Law Enforcement.*

MOURLAS, Mark Allen
J Sterling Morton E HS; Cicero, IL;

MOUSER, Kenneth Wayne
Bossier Acad; Haughton, LA (2-11) Pres, Hmrm; Pres, Jr Cl; VP, Soph Cl; Bkbl; Alg A; Bio A; Cl Fav; MLS; *La Tech U at Ruston; T V Elec.*

MOUTON, Jennifer Marie
Headland HS; East Point, GA (25-150) Drama; FBLA; 4H; Hmrm; Cpt, Model UN; Sch P; Span NHS; SC; Tr; B Crocker A; Most Out; Opt Out Tn; Q&S A; *Catawba Col; Pub Adm.*

MOUTRAY, Janet Denise
Mt Carmel HS; Mt Carmel, IL; Chor; FHA; Key C; Sftbl; VP, NYI.

MOUZON, Elizabeth De Vineau
St Mary's Acad; Alexandria, VA; Drama; ARC; Bio A; NEDT; Fr A; Highest Fresh NEDT Score; *Med.*

MOWDY, Reba Gail
Neshoba Central HS; Philadelphia, MS; Typist, Sch Paper; WW; Tres, Bible C; *Meridian Jr Col; Acct.*

MOWER, David Eugene
South HS; Pueblo, CO; Mgr, Bsbl; *Area Voc Center; Elec Communications.*

MOWERY, Chandra Lynne
Cumberland Valley HS; Mechanicsburg, PA (9-585) Secy, Band; Parl, Hmrm; Math C; Pres, NHS; Pres, Orch; Ski C; Span C; Parl, SC; Tres, Var C; Tr; Rotary A; Yth Fel; GSct o-t Mo; Summer Schol, Dickenson Col; *Pa St U; Earth Sci.*

MOWERY, Kenneth Harold
Salisbury HS; Salisbury, NC (25%-250) AFS; Ann; Band; Lat C; Order/Arrow; Tnns; Hist A; Hon Prog; Order/Arrow A; Type A; Secy, Church Yth; Jr Civitan; SPEC Prog; Ealge Sct; *Corpate Law.*

MOWERY, Lillian Ann
St Pius X HS; Pottstown, PA (59-154) Type A; Spirit C; Shorthand Cert.

MOWREY, Edward Leland
Kiski Area HS; Leechburg, PA (40%-517) Chess C; Chor; Drama; Ger C; Writing A; *Art.*

MOWREY, Jacquelene Marie
Oppenheim-Ephratah Central Sch; St Johnsville, NY (4-39) NHS; Sch P; Tres, Sr Cl; B Crocker A; Regent Schol.

MOWRY, Stephen Lewis
Nevada Sr HS; Nevada, MO (19-165) A Cap Choir; Chess C; VP, Chor; Ensm; Pres, Lat C; Madrigal; NHS; Thes; Type A; BS Alt; Pres, Bio C; Ex-Officio City Coun; Mus A's; *U of Mo-Kansas City; Law.*

MOY, Lily Mei
Foreman HS; Chicago, IL (7-373) Ann; Chor; Drama; FTA; Ger C; Hmrm; Lit Mag; Pres, Mu Alpha Theta; Secy, NHS; COM; Hon Prog; Sci A; St Scholar; VFW A; VofDEM; Sch Service Ltr; HR Pins; *U of Ill; Biol.*

MOYE, Eugene
Motley HS; Columbus, MS (2-70) Ed, Ann; Pres, BC; S-T, HiY; Ed, Sch P; Pres, Sr Cl; Pres, Jr Cl; Bsbl; B Crocker A; Bio A; Cl Fav; Hist A; Hon Prog; MLS; Sal; Sci A; Star Student; *Miss St U; Sci.*

MOYE, Larry
Motley HS; Columbus, MS (3-95) JV, Bkbl; Cl Fav; *Miss St U; Hist.*

MOYER, Brian Walter
Gulf Comprehensive HS; New Port Richey, FL (1-300) Ann; JV, Ftbl; Amer Leg A; Citz A; Hon Prog; Eng A; Church Yth Choir; Yrbk A; HR; Tres, Church Yth Coun; *Law Enforcement.*

MOYER, Carrie Jo
W Middlesex Area HS; W Middlesex, PA (2-147) Co-Cpt, Chldr; Secy, Chor; FTA; Tres, 4H; VP, NHS; SC; Tres, Sr Cl; HQn; NEDT; PTA A; *X-Ray Tech.*

MOYER, Kimberly Ann
S Plantation HS; Plantation, FL (11-600) Co-Ed, Ann; NHS; SC; Tres, Jr Cl; I Dare You; Journ A; Kiwanis A; Q&S A; Drill Tm; VP, Exchange C; *Broward Comm Col.*

MOYER, Mark Daniel
Paris HS; Paris, IL; Hon Prog; Co-Ed, Yrbk; Art Schol; *Mech Engr.*

MOYER, Robert James
N Penn HS; Lansdale, PA (20%-960) Drama; Stage Crew; *Pa St U; Engr.*

MOYER, Robert William
Blue Mountain HS; Schuylkill Haven, PA (120-240) Chor; Var C; Cr-Ctry; Tr; *Game Commission Trng Sch; Wildlife Mgr.*

MOYER, Sharon Lynn
Wilson Mem HS; Fishersville, VA (38-200) JV, Chldr; Drama; Parl, FBLA; Secy, FFA; FHA; FTA; 4H; Hmrm; Sci C; Secy, Jr Cl; Pres A; Keyettes; FBLA Math A; Spelling A.

MOYERS, Kathy Ann
Powell Valley HS; Speedwell, TN; Ann; BC; Bus C; FFA; 4H; Sch P; Tri-HiY; Sftbl; Tr; Cl Fav; 4H A; Sr Merit, 1st Aid, A's; Sr Bar.

MOYLAN, Eleanor Kellogg
Avondale HS; Avondale Estates, GA (15-230) Anchor C; BC; Chor; Fr C; Math C; NHS; COM; NMS; Vlbl; *St Andrews Presbyterian Col; Bio.*

MOYLE, Lori Lea
Central HS; LaCrosse, WI (88-535) A Cap Choir; Band; *Sioux Falls Col; Social Work.*

MOZELESKI,
Mary Ann Theresa
Riverside HS; Taylor, PA (7-187) Chor; FNA; NHS; Span C; Amer Leg A; Hist A; Eng A; *E Stroudsburg Col; Nurs.*

MOZELL, Arttie Lee
S Miami Sr HS; S Miami, FL (34-777) Secy, NHS; Sci C; SC; Amer Leg A; Citz A; Hon Prog; Sci A; *Miami Dade Comm Col; Med Tech.*

MOZES, Michael Joseph
Morris Knolls HS; Denvill, NJ; Band; Order/Arrow; Ski C; Wrest; Order/Arrow A; Pres A; *Voc Sch; Heating-Air Cond-Ventilation.*

MOZINGO, Jennifer Earle
Princeton HS; Princeton, NC (21-73) Band; Chor; FFA; Pres, FTA; Monogram; Co-Ed, Sch P; HCt; Stu o-t Mo; *E Carolina U.*

MRASEK, Jayne Christine
Perkins Co HS; Grant, NE (15-30) Band; Chor; Ensm; FHA; VP, Rainbow; Soph Cl; *Doane Col.*

MRAZ, Donna Alison
Delavan-Darien HS; Delavan, WI (3-230) A Cap Choir; VP, Band; Chor; Dbte Tm; Drama; Ensm; Hmrm; NHS; Rptr, Sch P; SC; Var C; Tres, Sr Cl; Bkbl; Tr; Q&S A; John Philip Sousa Band A; Outst Actress; Outst Band Front; *U of Wis-Madison; Acct.*

MROZ, Donald Dean
Carl Sandburg HS; Orland Park, IL (180-932) Secy, CYO; Secy, NHS; Sci C; Span C; SC; Cpt, Cr-Ctry; Gov Honor Prog; NHS Off; St Off, Mike's Yth Group; *Loyola Col; Psych.*

MROZ, Richard Joseph
St Mary's Prep; Orchard Lake, MI (3-44) NHS; Rptr, Sch P; Hon Prog; Journ A; Magna Cum Laude; *Wayne St U; Phar.*

MSUYA, Philemon
Luthern W HS; Detroit, MI; Bsbl; Bkbl; Ftbl; Sftbl; Tnns; Tr.

MUCKLE, Holly Lee
Charleroi Area HS; Charleroi, PA (66%-255) Band; Chor; Drama; Hmrm; Mjrte; Rainbow; Ski C; Sftbl; Swim; Cl Fav.

MUCKLE, Lori Kay
Charleroi Area Jr Sr HS; Charleroi, PA; Chor; Hmrm; Ski C; Sftbl; Swim; *Therapy.*

MUDD, Michael Thomas
Oakville Sr HS; Saint Louis Co, MO; CYO; Order/Arrow; Order/Arrow A; Ad Altare Dei; Christian Service A; Parvuli Dei; *U of Mo; Mech Engr.*

517

MUDD, Robert Lynn
Union HS; Union, OR (32-95) Chess C; Chor; Dbte Tm; Spch C; Y-Tns; Swim; Citz A; *Agr.*

MUDRA, Cheryl Ann
Morton W HS; Berwyn, IL; Teachers Aid; Nursery Vol; Girls Sftbl; Church Choir; Vacation Bible Sch Vol; Church Yth Group; *Pediatrics.*

MUDRINICH, Carolyn Sue
Hickory Sr HS; Sharon, PA (20-330) A-Ed, Ann; Chor; Fr C; Ger C; HiY; Pres, Hmrm; Math C; Secy, NHS; Sch P; Span C; Span NHS; Tri-HiY; Tr; Chamber of Comm A; Citz A; Health Careers C; Candystriper A; Vlbl; Century III Ldrship A; CPR Certified Adm; 1st Cl GSct; *Penn St U; Pre-Med.*

MUEHLBRAD, Timothy Wayne
Pflugerville HS; Pflugerville, TX (10%-110) FFA; NHS; Ftbl; Tnns; JV, Tr; Alg A; *Tex Lutheran Col.*

MUEHLICH, Jeanette Ellen
Nelson HS; Nelson, NE; JV, Chldr; Chor; FHA; Y-Tns; *Computer Tech.*

MUELLER, Catherine Marie
Anamosa HS; Anamosa, IA (3-160) Band; Chor; Ensm; Mjrte; JV, Golf; NEDT; *Med.*

MUELLER, Charles William
Winona Sr HS; Winona, MN (65-575) Band; Hmrm; Model UN; NHS; Var C; Co-Cpt, Bkbl; Ftbl; Cpt, Golf; COM; *Luther Col; Bus Adm.*

MUELLER, Chris Eugene
St James-John T Hodge HS; St James, MO (45-106) Band; Ensm; Var C; Bsbl; MVP, Bkbl; Golf; Swim; Tnns; Tr; HCt; *Sou Mo St U; Bus Mgt.*

MUELLER, David Scott
Steeleville HS; Steeleville, IL (9-68) VP, NHS; Pres, SC; VP, Soph Cl; JV, Bkbl; Cpt, Golf; Amer Leg A; NEDT; St Scholar; Tres, SC; MVP, Golf; *U of Mo; Civil Engr.*

MUELLER, Debra Lynn
Kingman HS; Kingman, KS (5-100) Band; Ensm; Pres, 4H; Y-Tns; Bkbl; Tnns; Tr; 4H A; *Kans St U; Vet Med.*

MUELLER, Elena Cecile
Theodore Roosevelt HS; St Louis, MO (22-575) Band; Ger C; NHS; God & Country A; Secy, Church Yth Group; Bell Choir; GSct; Bus Mgr, Ongoing Ambass for Christ; Hosp Vol; *Bus.*

MUELLER, Erik Thomas
Hightstown HS; Hightstown, NJ (9-247) AFS; Pres, Fr C; Math C; *MIT; Elec Engr.*

MUELLER, James Michael
Notre Dame-Bishop Gibbons HS; Schenectady, NY (19-160) CYO; Var C; Bsbl; Co-Cpt, Bkbl; Co-Cpt, Golf; Lorica Hon Soc; *St Bonaventure Col; Acct.*

MUELLER, Jeanne Lynn
Cedarburg HS; Cedarburg, WI (24-335) F-Ed, Ann; Band; Ensm; 4H; F-Ed, Lit Mag; NHS; 4H A; Yth Fel; *U of Wis; Art.*

MUELLER, John Herrmann
Los Alamitos HS; Los Alamitos, CA (42-690) Band; Ch, Ensm; NHS; Orch; Ftbl; CSF; COM; Hon Prog; JA A; Star Student; Yth Leg; Outst Academic A; Acolyte Tm; MGM Program; Handbell Choir; Church Yth Coun.

MUELLER, Kyle Marie
Niagara Wheatfield Sr HS; Sanborn, NY (37-453) Chor; NHS; COM; Hon Prog; WW; Pres, Luther League; Pep C; *Niagara Co Comm Col; Bus.*

MUELLER, LaVonne Emma
Los Banos HS; Los Banos, CA (20-235) HCt; Hon Prog; Math A; VP, Art C; Pres, Church Yth Group; *PLU; Math.*

MUELLER, Mary Elizabeth
Lutheran HS S; St Louis, MO (3-170) Band; Chor; Drama; Ensm; Fr C; 4H; Pres, Tri-HiY; COM; 4H A; Hon Prog; Math A; Secy, Tri-Hi-Y; Ntl Mus Guild; Candystriper; Pep C; *Sci.*

MUELLER, Melinda Christine
Richmond Sr HS; Richmond, IN; Chor; Community Yth Symph; Ensm; VP, FBLA; FTA; Hmrm; Madrigal; Y-Tns; Pres, Church Yth Fel; Nom, Outst Luther League Member; *Ball St U; Elem Ed.*

MUELLER, Nadean R
College HS; Bartlesville, OK; *U of Tulsa; Mus.*

MUELLER, Nancy Joy
Skyline HS; Salt Lake City, UT; A Cap Choir; Community Yth Symph; Ensm; S-T, Ger C; NHS; Orch; Ski C; Span C; St Stu Congress; Co-Cpt, Tnns; Citz A; Hon Prog; Utah Yth Symph; Outst Orch Player A; *U of Utah; Dentistry.*

MUELLER, Nancy Marie
E Rockaway HS; E Rockaway, NY (11-178) Band; Chor; Fr C; French NHS; Secy, Key C; Kiwanis A; PTA A; March of Dimes A; Adelpi Schol; Alt, Regent Schol; *Adelphi U; Nurs.*

MUELLER, Pamela Ann
Bay View HS; Milwaukee, WI (28-600) Span C; SC; Regional Rep, YOU; *U of Wis-Milwaukee; Journ.*

MUELLER, Patricia Anne
Overbrook Regional HS; Pine Hill, NJ; Band; Chor; Ensm; Fr C; VP, 4H; NHS; Ntl Yth Conf; Var C; Mgr, Wrest; 4H A; Hon Prog; *Glassboro St Col; Child Developement.*

MUELLER, Paul Louis
Olympus Sr HS; Salt Lake City, UT (129-700) Band; FFA; Bsbl; Bkbl; Hon Prog; *U of Utah; Elec Engr.*

MUELLER, Robert Jay
Belleville Twp HS W; Belleville, IL (300-900) SC; Bsbl; Bkbl; Ftbl; *U of Ill; Agr.*

MUELLER, Roylee Herbert
New Athens Comm HS Unit 60; New Athens, IL (17-65) Band; Chem C; S-T, Chess C; VP, FFA; Sci C; Tres, SC; Pres, Jr Cl; VP, Soph Cl; Bkbl; Cr-Ctry; Tr; Spch A; Ill St FFA Farmer; 4th Pl St FFA Small Grains; *Belleville Area Col; Bus.*

MUELLER, Timothy Karl
Winona Sr HS; Winona, MN (14-560) Band; NHS; Orch; Order/Arrow; Sci C; JV, Cr-Ctry; Tr; JV, Wrest; Order/Arrow A; Eagle Sct; Amateur Radio A; *Elec.*

MUELLER, Tina Marie
New Braunfels HS; New Braunfels, TX (20-285) Band; Ensm; FTA; Ger C; GS; Math C; Mu Alpha Theta; NHS; Sci C; Tnns; NEDT; Yth Fel; FCA; *U of Tex; Psych.*

MUESBECK, Tammy Lynn
Ashwaubenon HS; Green Bay, WI (20%-314) Ger C; NHS; Ntl Yth Conf; Sch P; Var C; Secy, Jr Cl; Bkbl; Tr; Yth Fel; Yth Foundation; Yth Leg; Candystriper; Prom Ct; Tr A; Vlbl; Med First Aid; Sunday Sch Teacher; VP, Luther League; *Nurs.*

MUFFLEY, Cathy Leigh
Treadwell HS; Memphis, TN (1-172) Band; Chem C; Tres, Lat C; Secy, NHS; Phys C; Co-Ed, Sch P; Ntl Sci Found; Val; *Memphis St U; Nurs.*

MUFFLY, Kevin Ray
Warrior Run HS; Turbotville, PA (90-187) Var C; Bsbl; Ftbl; Wrest; *Lincoln Tech Inst; Drafting.*

MUGGERUD, Todd B
Hettinger Pub Sch; Hettinger, ND; Var C; Cpt, Bkbl; Cpt, Ftbl; Tr; MVP, Ftbl; *Bismarck Jr Col; Bus.*

MUGLER, Marcella Dawn
Winfield HS; Winfield, KS; A Cap Choir; NHS; Hon Prog; *Southwestern Col; Home Ec.*

MUGLIA, Marlene Ann
South Plainfield HS; S Plainfield, NJ; Chor; Fr C; SC; Tri-HiY; Pres, Jr Cl; Pres, Soph Cl; Mgr, Bsbl; JV, Hockey; Mgr, Wrest; Hon Prog; MLS; Pres A; Done Most A; *Law.*

MUHLENBRUCH, Christa Lee
Dows Comm Sch; Daws, IA (5-21) Ann; Band; Chor; Secy, FFA; Rptr, FHA; Pres, 4H; NHS; SC; 4H A; FFA A; Co Pork Qn; *Iowa Central Comm Col; Nurs.*

MUHM, Patricia Joy
Bradley Bourbonnais Comm HS; Bradley, IL (10%-372) Band; FNA; Band A; *Olivet Nazarene Col; Secy Sci.*

MUI, Ming Ying
Tilden HS; Chicago, IL (1-408) A-Ed, Ann; NHS; Pres, Sci C; Sci A; St Scholar; Val; *Loyola U.*

MUIR, Jennifer Gail
Thomas Jefferson HS; San Antonio, TX (12-575) Secy, Ger C; JETS; Lit Mag; NHS; Sch Achieve Tm; Hon Prog; Yth Fel; Eng Hon Soc; *St Mary's U; Pre-Law.*

MUIR, Karen Lee
Richwoods HS; Peoria, IL (24-450) A Cap Choir; Chor; Ensm; Ftbl; St Scholar; *Augustana Col; Biol.*

MUIR, Marcia Lee
Billings W HS; Billings, MT (16-725) Semi-Fin, GS; Hmrm; Lat C; Mjrte; NFL; NHS; Secy, SC; Mgr, Tnns; Amer Leg A; Hon Prog; NMF; Spch A; *U of Mont; Home Ec.*

MUIRHEAD, Benjamin Michael
Frederick HS; Frederick, OK (12%-55) Band; BS; Chor; VP, Math C; VP, Mu Alpha Theta; NHS; F-Ed, Sch P; Sci C; VP, SC; Var C; Pres, Jr Cl; Pres, Soph Cl; Co-Cpt, Bsbl; Bkbl; Ftbl; Golf; Cl Fav; Lion A; Masonic A; MLS; Drum Major; All St Chor; Mr FHS; OSU Alumni, Hon Stu; All District, Ftbl; *Cameron U; Vocal Mus.*

MUIRHEAD, Karen Winona
Warren Central HS; Vicksburg, MS (230-384) Rainbow; *La Tech U; CPA.*

MUKAI, Vicki Emi
Fremont HS; Sunnyvale, CA (14-572) CSF; Type A; Featherette Drill Tm; Cascaids Service C; *U of Santa Clara; Bus.*

MULBERRY, Larry Wayne
Northeast Sr HS; Kansas City, MO (62-307) Bsbl; MVP, Bkbl; Cr-Ctry; Sftbl; *Central Bible Col; Bible.*

MULCH, Cindy Louise
Warsaw HS; Warsaw, IL (25%-60) AFS; Band; Chor; FBLA; VP, FHA; SC; Type A; SAA A; Chor A; FHA A.

MULCHI, Vicki Lynne
Norlina HS; Norlina, NC (9-115) Chor; VP, FBLA; Tres, Hmrm; Citz A; HCt; Sci A; Band A.

MULDER, Tamara Sue
Rogers HS; Wyoming, MI (17-256) NHS; Mgr, Swim; COM; Hon Prog; Ntl Achv Schol; MVP, Swim.

MULDROW, Steven Carl
Cincinnati Co Day HS; Cincinnati, OH; MVP, Bkbl; Ftbl; Tr; COM; WW; *Duke U; Engr.*

MULERO, Orlando
Acad Nuestra Sra Providencia; Rio Piedras, PR (1-64) CYO; Cum Laude Soc; ARC; Sch Achieve Tm; Semi-Fin, Bsbl; Semi-Fin, Bkbl; COM; Hon Prog; Summa Cum Laude; Conduct A; *Med.*

MULFORD, Cynthia Alice
Columbia Acad; Columbia, MS (12-50) Eng Academic Achv Cert; ABC Alg Test; *U of Sou Miss; Bio.*

MULFORD, Jonathan Anderson
Glen Oaks Sr HS; Baton Rouge, LA; Band; Rptr, Band C; *Mus.*

MULFORD, Samuel Campbell
Shelton HS; Shelton, CT; A Cap Choir; Band; Chor; Span C; God & Country A; Yth Fel; Green Belt Karate; Vol, Library; Explorers; 1st Fife, Ancient Fife & Drum Corp; *Acct.*

MULFORD, Sherri Denise
Central HS; Thomasville, GA; JV, Chldr; FHA; Hmrm; Pres, Tri-HiY; Sci A; *Lee Col.*

MULFORD, Tammi Lynn
Bogalusa HS W; Bogalusa, LA; 4H; Y-Tns; 4H A; Candystriper; Art Asst; S-T, Church Young Ladies Auxilary; St Win, Church Poetry Contest; *Lee Col; Off Adm.*

MULGREW, Catherine Bridget
St Joseph Acad; Cleveland, OH (125-250) A Cap Choir; All Amer Yth; S-T, CYO; Fr C; MVP, Bkbl; Sftbl; Cpt, Tnns; COM; Journ A; Foreign Lang A; Poetry A; *Cleveland St Col; Sociology.*

MULHERON, John Francis
Thomas S Wootton HS; Rockville, MD; A Cap Choir; Chor; Span NHS; JV, Ftbl; Tr; Hon Prog; Kappa Alpha; *Md U.*

MULHOLLEM, Timothy Alan
Clearfield HS; Clearfield, PA (65-375) Wrest; Citz A; Pres A; Ntl Sci Found; DAR Art A; Champ, Jr Olympic Wrest; 5 Time Area Champ, Wrest; *Palmer Col; Chiropractic.*

MULITAUAOPELE, Tamotu Jr
Marist Brothers HS; Pago Pago, AMERICAN SAMOA (2-50) Band; Sch P; COM; Hon Prog; Math A; Sci A.

MULKEY, Gail Renee
Burlington Comm HS; Burlington, IA (15%-500) A
Cap Choir; Chor; Madrigal; NHS; GSct.

MULKEY, Mark Stephen
Wade Hampton Acad; Orangeburg, SC (50-75) BS;
Fr C; Key C; NHS; Order/Arrow; Var C; Secy, Sr
Cl; Tres, Jr Cl; JV, Bsbl; Bkbl; Ftbl; Tr; COM;
NEDT; Sci A; Fin, Cert of Merit; Fin, NEDT Cert;
Fin, Sci A; *Clemson U; Microbio.*

MULLEN, Brian John
Liberty Central HS; Liberty, NY (20-120) CYO;
SC; JV, Bsbl; Ftbl; Golf; *Pre-Law.*

MULLEN, Elisa Sue
Ottawa HS; Ottawa, KS (41-203) Chor; Drama;
Ensm; NHS; VP, SC; COM; Regent Schol; St
Scholar; St Choir; Arion A Nom; *Ottawa U; Mus.*

MULLEN, Gabrielle Denise
Acad of Our Lady; Chicago, IL (64-209) A Cap
Choir; Chor; FNA; Madrigal; Swim; Fin, Tr; COM;
Citz A; Math A; Sci A; Art, Achv, Attendance, A's;
Dillard Col; Nurs.

MULLEN, Julia Brooke
Norfolk Cath HS; Norfolk, VA (5-157) CYO;
Drama; Swim; *Health Field.*

MULLEN, Karen Lynn
Central HS; Little Rock, AR (1-666) A Cap Choir;
VP, BC; FBLA; Mjrte; Math C; Mu Alpha Theta;
NHS; Sch P; Spch C; Y-Tns; COM; Citz A;
DARGCA; Hon Prog; NEDT; Spch A; Type A;
Val; Miss Ark FBLA; *SW Col at Memphis.*

MULLEN, Lillian Hope
Ayden-Grifton HS; Ayden, NC (7-180) Ann; 4H;
Tres, NHS; Co-Ed, Sch P; Sci C; Alg A; Math A;
Appalachian St Col; Math.

MULLENIX, John Stephen
Simi HS; Simi Valley, CA; Order/Arrow; Cpt, Tr;
CLC; Teaching.

MULLENS, Donna Venice
Rossville Comprehensive HS; Rossville, GA
(4-254) BC; FBLA; Hmrm; A-Ed, Lit Mag; SC;
Y-Tns; COM; Gov Honor Prog; Math A; NEDT;
Type A; *U of Ga; Journ.*

MULLER, Carilyn Jean
Miramonte HS; Orinda, CA (2-360) AFS; F-Ed,
Ann; Band; Chor; Hmrm; Ski C; CSF; *U of Calif;
Comm Nutrition.*

MULLER, Jana Kaye
Portageville HS; Portageville, MO (2-97) Band;
FBLA; FHA; VP, FNA; FTA; NHS.

MULLER, Katherine Theresa
Carmel HS; Carmel, NY (8-250) Secy, Band; Chor;
Drama; Ensm; Madrigal; Tres, NHS; Orch; Hon
Prog; Regent Schol; NYSSMA Competion; Mus
Dept Schol; WW Among Amer HS Mus Stu;
SUNY at Fredonia; Mus Ed.

MULLER, Lynne Marie
Liberty Jr-Sr HS; Liberty, PA (5-64) Chldr; Chor;
Secy, Ger C; Co-Cpt, Bkbl; Tr; *Air Force Acad;
Aircrafts.*

MULLER, Patricia Jo
La Farge HS; La Farge, WI (5-42) F-Ed, Ann;
Band; Cpt, Chldr; Chem C; Chor; Ensm; Fr C;
Secy, FHA; Madrigal; Mjrte; Phys C; Sci C; Spch
C; Hon Prog; Spch A; Hon Stu; Prom Ct; 1st Run-
Up KVA Princess Contest; *UW-Eau Claire; Nurs.*

MULLET, Mark Scot
Superior HS; Superior, NE (6-82) JV, Bkbl; Ftbl; *U
of Nebr; Bus Adm.*

MULLETT, Susan Dian
Arapahoe HS; Littleton, CO (10-400) *Lubbock
Christian Col; Psych.*

MULLICAN, John Christopher
I S U Sch; Terre Haute, IN (8-64) MVP, Band; BS;
CYO; Community Yth Symph; Fin, Model UN;
Tres, NHS; Pres, SC; Var C; Pres, Jr Cl; JV, Bkbl;
MVP, Cr-Ctry; MVP, Tr; Hon Prog; Rotary A; Ind
St Mus Assn; WW, Mus Stu; 1st Rating, ISMA
Contest; *Ind St U; Mus Ed.*

MULLICAN, Melinda Kay
St High Lab Sch; Terre Haute, IN (14-65) Bus C;
CYO; Chor; Drama; Span C; Y-Tns; Hon Prog;
Vlbl; *Eng.*

MULLIN, Brian Ellis
Wheatland Chili Central HS; Scottsville, NY
(30-137) Band; Bsbl; JV, Bkbl; Soccer; Hon Prog;
Elim Bible Inst; Ministerial.

MULLIN, Kimberly Irene
Virgil I Grissom HS; Huntsville, AL (33%-500)
Ann; Hmrm; SC; Mgr, Vlbl; *Auburn U; Sci.*

MULLIN, Patti Allyce
Hoquiam HS; Hoquiam, WA (52-190) Chor; Ensm;
Span C; SC; WW; *Grays Harbor Comm Col; Bus
Adm.*

MULLINAX, Susan Lynn
Faith Christian HS; Hendersonville, NC; VP, A
Cap Choir; Chldr; Chor; FTA; VP, 4H; Sch P; SC;
Bkbl; HQn; Pep C; Secy, Civitan C; *Tenn Temple
Col; Phys Ed.*

MULLINGS, Joseph Wayne
Coronado HS; El Paso, TX; Hmrm; Ftbl; JV, Tr; Sci
A; *U of Tex; Engr.*

MULLINO, Reida Vesta
Rochester HS; Rochester, TX (5-13) A-Ed, Ann;
Band; FFA; VP, FHA; 4H; Mjrte; Cpt, Bsbl; Tnns;
Tr; 4H A; Swtht; Type A; Church Organist; *Tex
Tech U; Agr.*

MULLINS, Becky Jeanine
El Capitan HS; Lakeside, CA (16-377) Chldr;
Chor; Drama; Tres, NHS; Gym Tm; *Pepperdine U;
Home Ec.*

MULLINS, Brenda Sue
Crawford Co R II HS; Cuba, MO (15-110) Chldr;
Chor; NHS; Var C; Sftbl; Tr; PA.

MULLINS, Cheryl Diane
Franklin HS; Somerset, NJ (199-420) Pres, FNA;
Bkbl; JV, Sftbl; Tr; GSct; Ntl Achv Commended
Stu.

MULLINS, Curtis Lee
Independence HS; Independence, MS (10%-118)
Pres, Demolay; Rptr, FFA; Ed, Sch P; Mgr, Ftbl; *U
of Miss; Chiropractor.*

MULLINS, Eric Lewis
Marion HS; Marion, IN; *Bus.*

MULLINS, Janice Ann
Lakeview HS; Battle Creek, MI (10-400) A Cap
Choir; NHS; *U of Mich; Med.*

MULLINS, Kevin John
George Washington Carver Sr HS; Montgomery,
AL; Ensm; NHS; Span C; Sftbl; NEDT; *Auburn U;
Sci U.*

MULLINS, Lisa Anne
Springville HS; Springville, AL; FHA; Hon Prog;
Eng A; Off A; YOU; *Data Processing.*

MULLINS, Lynda Elise
Westwood HS; Atlanta, GA; FBLA; NHS; Co-Ed,
Sch P; Span C; Cert of A, Acad Excel; *Bus Adm.*

MULLINS, Natalie Ann
Whiteville HS; Whiteville, NC (4-187) Chor; Rptr,
FTA; Math C; Model UN; Tres, NHS; Secy, Sr Cl;
Tres, Jr Cl; Sftbl; Tnns; Hist A; Most Intelligent;
Most Improved; Best All-Around Sr; *NC St U;
Math.*

MULLINS, Patricia Ann
Binghamton HS; Binghamton, NY (5-230) Band;
NHS; Most Out.

MULLINS, Richard Dewey III
McClymonds Sr HS; Oakland, CA; NHS; *Archt-
Elec Engr.*

MULLINS, Robert Wayne
Bethel Baptist Sch; Memphis, TN (1-22) Chess C;
Phys C; Sci C; Tres, Sr Cl; VP, Soph Cl; Bkbl;
Co-Cpt, Ftbl; Swim; Alg A; COM; Cl Fav; Hon
Prog; JA A; Math A; MLS; Most Out; Sci A; All
Conf, Ftbl; Wittiest; Most Intelligent; Friendliest;
Congeniality A; *Navy; Physics.*

MULLINS, Sandra Elaine
Prairiland HS; Pattonville, TX (5-73) BC; Chem C;
VP, FHA; Hist A.

MULLINS, Stephanie Ann
Calhoun HS; Calhoun, GA (10%-231) Band; Fr C;
Hmrm; Jr Miss Pagent; NHS; Tri-HiY; Var C;
Swim; Tnns; *U of Ga; Acct.*

MULLINS, Susan Leslie
Mount de Sales HS; Macon, GA (8-120) Chor; Lit
Mag; Math C; ARC; Span C; VP, Yth Fel; *U of Ga;
Elem Ed.*

MULLINS, Terri Lynn
Bixby HS; Bixby, OK (10%-200) A-Ed, Ann;
Chldr; Sch P; Span C; Parl, SC; *Okla St U; Psych.*

MULLINS, Valerie Marie
Virgie HS; Virgie, KY; BC; JV, Chldr; Chor; FTA;
Ger C; Spch C; *Pikeville Col; Eng.*

MULLINS, Mincey Regina
Victory Christian Acad; Jacksonville, FL
(10%-100) Arch; Chldr; Chor; Drama; Ensm; Fr C;
Pres, 4H; Math C; NHS; Sch P; Spch C; Arch; Bkbl;
Swim; COM; Lang Arts A; Telephone Operator's
A; *Med.*

MULLIS, Thad McCoy
Lenoir HS; Lenoir, NC (10%-100) Band; Mgr, Bsbl;
Tr; Wrest; Schol A to Mus Camp; Scts; Sup Rating,
Solo Contest; HR; All St Band; *Math.*

MULLNER, Timothy Paul
Mandan Sr HS; Mandan, ND (70-325) A Cap
Choir; Band; BS; CYO; Chor; Drama; Ensm; Mad-
rigal; NHS; Rptr, Sch P; Span C; St Stu Congress;
SC; JV, Tr; COM; US Jaycee War Mem Fund
Schol; Young Life Fellowship; *Col of St Thomas;
Instrumental & Vocal Mus.*

MULLOY, Patrick Stapp
Ysleta HS; El Paso, TX (99%-673) Band; Commu-
nity Yth Symph; NHS; SC; Hon Prog; WW; *Tex
A&M U; Engr.*

MULROY, James Francis
St Joseph's o-t Palisades HS; W New York, NJ
(1-232) Hmrm; Sci C; Span NHS; Jr Activities
Comm; Hist C; *Fordham U; Computer Sci.*

MULVIHILL, Kathleen Ann
Immaculate Heart of Mary HS; Westchester, IL
(40-220) Chldr; Chor; Hmrm; NHS; ARC; Ftbl;
Sftbl; Tnns; NEDT; VP, Fresh Cl; HS Schol; *St
Mary's Col; Med Tech.*

MUMAW, Bob John
Columbiana HS; Columbiana, OH; HiY; Bus Mgr,
Jr Cl; Bkbl; Swim; Art A; *Milligan Col; Bus Acct.*

MUMFORD, Angela Marie
Nette Lee Roth HS; Dayton, OH; Beauty; Cosmetology A; *Central St Col; Beauty Culture.*

MUMFORD, Bart L
Sky View HS; Smithfield, UT; NHS; Order/Arrow;
Citz A; Order/Arrow A; Sci A; Type A; Duty to
God, Eagle Sct, Engr, A's; *Utah St U; Elec Engr.*

MUMFORD, Gloria Ann
Patterson Co-Op HS; Dayton, OH; Type A; Choir;
Wright St Col; Bus.

MUMM, Julie Anne
Holy Name HS; Omaha, NE (33%-63) Co-Ed,
Ann; Cpt, Chldr; Chor; Semi-Fin, GS; Ed, Lit Mag;
Model UN; VP, NHS; SC; Secy, Sr Cl; Tres, Soph
Cl; HCt; HS Schol; Rambler Rumor, Local Paper;
Hastings Col; Eng.

MUMM, Rita Ellen
Oregon City HS; Oregon City, OR; Chor; Bkbl;
Cr-Ctry; Tnns; *Mt Hood Comm Col; Elem Ed.*

MUMMA, Joel Marc
Hempfield HS; Landisville, PA (2-550) Band;
Chess C; Orch; Soph Cl; Mgr, Swim; Exchange C
Yth o-t Mo; *Millersville St Col; Hist.*

MUMMERT, Cheryl Ann
Aurelia Comm HS; Aurelia, IA (6-46) F-Ed, Ann;
Band; Pres, Chor; Ensm; VP, FHA; Pres, 4H; NHS;
Co-Ed, Sch P; Secy, Jr Cl; MVP, Bkbl; Golf; Tr;
Amer Leg A; COM; Citz A; DARGCA; 4H A; Hist
A; HQn; Spch A; Swtht; Type A; Young Men's C
Schol; *Waldorf Col; Acct.*

MUMY, Tamira A
Mount Pleasant HS; Mount Pleasant, MI
(67-300) Dbte Tm; 4H; Span C; 4H A; Demolay
Swtht; Gym; Outst Novis Debator; Acad A; *Ga
Tech; Archt.*

MUNA, Roke Diaz
George Washington Sr HS; Mangilao, GUAM
(19-600) CYO; Hmrm; NHS; Bkbl; Sftbl; Rotary A;
Yth Leg; *U of Calif; Archt.*

MUNCHBACH, Thomas Paul
Capitol City Baptist Sch; Lansing, MI (1-8) Bkbl; MVP, Soccer; Tr; Wrest; Math A; MLS; Sci A; Social Stu A; Eng A; *Baptist Bible Col; Sci.*

MUNCRIEF, Sherri Carol
Colo HS; Colo City, TX (7-95) F-Ed, Ann; Band; Chldr; FHA; VP, NHS; Span C; Tr; B Crocker A; HCt; WW; VP, Q&S; *Tex Tech U; Bus.*

MUND, Cheryl Lee
John F Kennedy HS; Cedar Rapids, IA (62-495) Ed, Ann; Ger C; Co-Ed, Lit Mag; JV, Tnns; *U of Iowa; Bus Adm.*

MUNDLE, Elaine M
Eastside HS; Paterson, NJ; Hon Cert; *Rutgers Col; Pediatrics.*

MUNDO, Sergio
Antilles HS; Fort Buchanan, PR (6-124) NHS; *U of Puerto Rico; Humanities.*

MUNDY, Frances Ruth
Lumberton Sr HS; Lumberton, NC; Ann; Fr C; Sci A; *Archt.*

MUNDY, Lisa Anne
Cherryville Sr HS; Cherryville, NC (34-130) Band; S-T, Chor; Pres, FTA; InterAct C; Tnns; *Appalachian Col; Early Childhood Ed.*

MUNDY, Sarah Kathryn
Person Sr HS; Roxboro, NC (40-410) Pres, Chor; Drama; Secy, Fr C; Pres, 4H; Hmrm; Jr Miss Pageant; NHS; Secy, Tri-HiY; Gr Marshal; Yth Fel; Woman's C A; *Meredith Col; Psych.*

MUNFORD, Edmund Forrest
Mars Area Sr HS; Mars, PA (20%-236) Band; VP, Chor; Drama; Hmrm; NHS; Order/Arrow; SC; COM; Citz A; Rotary A; Hugh O'Brien Yth Ldrship A; Hons Chor; Dist Chor; Amer Yth Chor; *Communications.*

MUNFORD, Mildred Caintic
Matoaca HS; Ettrick, VA (1-153) Fr C; VP, French NHS; Key C; Lat C; NHS; Pres, SC; Century III Ldrship A; WW; *Pepperdine U; Pol Sci.*

MUNGER, Julie Ann
Hannibal Sr HS; Hannibal, MO (71-337) Band; Drama; FTA; Mjrte; SC; Bkbl; Tr; Pres A; Sci A.

MUNGY, Annika Karen
New Trier W HS; Northfield, IL; Ensm; NHS; COM; Hon Prog; Pres A; Sociedad Honoraria Hispanica; Vlbl; Badminton; *Northwestern U.*

MUNIZ, Avid Jose
Nuestra Senora de la Merced HS; San Juan, PR (2-92) Chem C; Order/Arrow; Phys C; Span C; Eagle A; BSct of Amer; Art Contest A; *Cornell U; Med.*

MUNIZ, William
Kolbe Cathedral HS; Bridgeport, CT; Bkbl; Cr-Ctry; Tr; *New Haven Col; Law Enforcement.*

MUNIZ RIVERA, Jorge Luis
Nuestra Senora de la Merced HS; San Juan, PR (1-92) Chem C; Order/Arrow; Phys C; Span C; Order/Arrow A; Eagle A, BSct of Amer; Art Contest A; *Cornell U; Med.*

MUNN, Cassie Jill
Emmaus HS; Emmaus, PA (68-512) Chor; FTA; Hmrm; Ski C; Tnns; Hon Prog; Yth Fel; Leadership A; Vol A; *E Stradsburg St Col; Nurs.*

MUNN, Nannette
Cartersville HS; Cartersville, GA (35-150) Band; Chor; Ensm; Fr C; FTA; Math C; Mu Alpha Theta; Sch P; Cr-Ctry; *LaGrange Col; Nurs.*

MUNN, Nathan Allen
Quilcene HS; Quilcene, WA (1-31) Band; Ed, Sch P; Pres, SC; VP, Jr Cl; Bkbl; Ftbl.

MUNNELL, Carrie Lou
Reynolds HS; Greenville, PA (6-183) 4H; Lit Mag; Thes; Tri-HiY; 4H A; Yth Fel; VP, DECA, Co Chapter; 1st Pl, Job Interview, DECA; *Ind St Col; Distributive Ed.*

MUNNELL, Pamela Kay
LaFayette Central HS; La Fayette, NY (15%-145) JV, Chldr; FFA; Ski C; Mgr, Wrest; *St U of NY; Computer Sci.*

MUNOZ, Sahira
Adlai E Stevenson HS; New York, NY; COM; Hon Prog.

MUNOZ, Yvonne Marie
Notre Dame HS; Caguas, PR (12-140) COM; Hon Prog; Lib C; Excellence A; *Med.*

MUNROE, Gloria
William Howard Taft HS; Bronx, NY; Sch Achieve Tm; *Marriage Coun.*

MUNSELL, Carla Joy
Cottage Grove HS; Cottage Grove, OR (9-200) Bus C; Chldr; FBLA; NHS; SC; Bkbl; Tnns; *NW Col of Bus; Med Receptionist.*

MUNSON, Colleen Renee
Dryden Central Sch; Dryden, NY; Band; Chldr; Chor; Drama; *Social Work.*

MUNSON, Heidi Jo
Sycamore HS; Sycamore, IL; Chor; Fr C; Madrigal; JV, Sftbl; Bowl; Rotary Mus Schol; *Art.*

MUNSON, Laura Faye
The Buffalo Sem; Buffalo, NY; A Cap Choir; AFS; Chor; Fr C; Model UN; NHS; SC; VP, Soph Cl Mgr, Hockey; NEDT.

MUNSON, Terry Lynn
Dryden Jr-Sr HS; Dryden, NY; Hmrm; SC; JV, Bkbl; Sftbl; Swim; Secy; Yth Fel; Pres, GSct; Vlbl; *Conservation.*

MUNSTERMAN, Lisa Ann
Montrose Pub Sch; Montrose, MO; Band; CYO; Chor; Dbte Tm; Ensm; NHS; VP, Span C; Spch C; Bio A; Hist A; Math A; Most Out; Spch A; Type A; VFW A; VofDEM; Miss Mo Tn Age Pageant; Mus A; Driver's Ed A; VFW Essay A; Eng A; Span A; *Mus.*

MUNYAN, Jean Ellen
Woodstown HS; Woodstown, NJ (10-180) NHS; Span NHS; *Glassboro St Col; Art.*

MURA, Lisa Ann
Leavenworth HS; Leavenworth, KS; A-Ed, Ann; CYO; Hmrm; Rptr, Sch P; Span C; Tr; St Span Hon; *St Mary Col; Elem Ed.*

MURAI, Wendy Maile
Kohala HS; Kapaau, HI (3-78) Secy, AFS; Band; Tres, Hmrm; NHS; F-Ed, Sch P; Span C; Ch, SC; Var C; Tres, Jr Cl; Bsbl; Tnns; *Kapiolani Community College; Accounting.*

MURBY, Erik Ernest
Seekonk HS; Seekonk, MA (21-224) NHS; Swim; Fin, ROTC; Appointed to US Military Acad; Appointed to Merchant Marine Acad.

MURCH, Jerry L Jr
Smoky Hill HS; Denver, CO (33-515) A Cap Choir; Madrigal; NHS; Var C; Bsbl; Ftbl; Hon Prog; Opt Out Tn; *Colo U; Journ.*

MURCHISON, Phyllis Diane
Benhaven HS; Olivia, NC; FHA; FTA; SC; VP, Jr Cl; *Fayetteville St U; Sociology.*

MURCHISON, Tanya Marie
Wetumpka HS; Wetumpka, AL; A-Ed, Ann; BC; Chldr; Drama; FTA; SC; *Troy St U; Elem Ed.*

MURDOCH, Michael Edward
Valley Forge HS; Parma Heights, OH (290-878) A Cap Choir; Chor; Madrigal; ARC; Bkbl; Sftbl; MVP, Tnns; Yth Fel; Ger A; *Cleveland St Col; Journ.*

MURDOCK, Alexis Nan
Whitewater HS; Whitewater, MT (2-9) Chor; 4H; Pres, NHS; Co-Ed, Sch P; Pres, Jr Cl; Cpt, Bkbl; Sftbl; Cpt, Tr; 4H A; Most Out; Sal; *Mont St U; Phys Ed.*

MURDOCK, Angela Gayle
Colonial Hills Christian Sch; E Point, GA (10-30) F-Ed, Ann; BC; Cpt, Chldr; Chor; Dbte Tm; VP, Hmrm; Sftbl; HQn; Most Out; Swtht; *Tenn Temple Col; Nurs.*

MURDOCK, Beth Lynn
Rossville HS; Rossville, GA (18-212) Secy, BC; Cpt, Chldr; Hmrm; SC; Gov Honor Prog; Hon Prog; Yth Fel; Social Ch, Y-Tn; Seekers Yth Choir; Pep C; Pres GAL; *Dalton Jr Col; Interior Decorating.*

MURDOCK, Donna Gwinn
Model HS; Rome, GA (4-198) 4H; Math C; Sci C; Bkbl; Sftbl; Alg A; Math A; Asst Church Pianist; *Shorter Col; Psych.*

MURDOCK, Jean Marie
Colonial Heights HS; Colonial Heights, VA (17-310) Ann; Band; BC; Fr C; NHS; WW; *Old Dominion U; Med Tech.*

MURDOCK, Jeffrey Lynn
Whitewater HS; Whitewater, MT (1-7) Ann; Pres, 4H; NHS; Sch P; Pres, SC; Cpt, Bsbl; Cpt, Bkbl; Cpt, Sftbl; Cpt, Swim; Cpt, Tr; Citz A; Cl Fav; 4H A; MLS; Most Out; Val; Yth Fel; MVP, Tr; SC A; *Mont St U; Vet Sci.*

MURDOCK, Laurie Corvett
Arbishop Keough HS; Baltimore, MD; Cpt, Chldr; Chor; Semi-Fin, Jr Miss Pa; Sch Achieve Tm; Sci C; Var C; Arch; Bkbl; Soccer; Sftbl; Tnns; COM; Hon Prog; Most Out; Sci A.

MURDOCK, Mark Hamilton
Rossville HS; Rossville, GA (8-212) BC; Hmrm; NHS; Pres, SC; Bkbl; Ftbl; Golf; COM; Citz A; Math A; Jr Exchange, Pep C; FCA; Presyter; *Dalton Junior; Dentistry.*

MURFF, Joy Lee
Crescent City Jr Sr HS; Crescent City, FL (10-120) Band; BC; FBLA; Pres, Span C; SC; COM; Sci A; Span, Mus, Band, A's; *St Johns River Jr Col; Secy Sci.*

MURIEL, Rose Kathleen
O D Wyatt HS; Fort Worth, TX; Band; Bkbl; Sftbl; Tr; *Tarrant Co Jr Col; Elem Ed.*

MURILLO, Carlos Arturo
Glendale Acad; Glendale, CA (3-100) Pres, Hmrm; K of C; Bsbl; Bkbl; Ftbl; Soccer; Tr; Industrial A; *Med.*

MURKERSON, Loretta Joyce
Waipahu HS; Waipahu, HI (26-558) Chor; Rptr, Sch P; *Leeward Comm Col; Journ.*

MURLICK, Cynthia Lorraine
Carrollton HS; Saginaw, MI (70-150) Ann; Cpt, Chldr; SC; Sftbl; Tr.

MURO, David Lee
Hiram Johnson HS; Sacramento, CA (80-809) Sftbl; *Sacramento St U.*

MURO, Stephen Paul
Hiram Johnson HS; Sacramento, CA; Band; Orch; Yth Leg; Soph Cl Senator; Marching Drum & Bugle Corps; *Sacramento St U.*

MURPHREE, Donna Irene
Mt Carmel HS; Mt Carmel, IL; FHA.

MURPHY, Alice Dela Cruz
Compton HS; Compton, CA (2-800) Cpt, Chldr; Sci C; Span C; Mgr, Tnns; Bank Of Amer A; CSF; Cl Fav; Hon Prog; Most Out; Sal; *U of Calif; Vet Med.*

MURPHY, Andrea Susan
E Gaston Sr HS; Mount Holly, NC (30-271) BC; Pres, Fr C; Hmrm; Secy, Sci C; SC; NEDT; Comm Chor; Warrior o-t Wk; Sch For The Gifted; *Lenior-Rhyne Col; Biol.*

MURPHY, Angela Patrice
Cardinal Mooney HS; Sarasota, FL (10-73) Ann; Drama; Lit Mag; Sch P; Spch C; SC; COM; Fr A; *Maryville Col; Broadcasting.*

MURPHY, Brady C
Red Lion Sr HS; Red Lion, PA (25-400) BS; Chem C; Chess C; NHS; Var C; Cpt, Bkbl; Ftbl; God & Country A; Pres A; *Penn St U; Chem.*

MURPHY, Carole Suzanne
N Fulton HS; Atlanta, GA (38-158) Chor; Drama; ARC; Sch P; VP, Secy, Yth Coun; Piano; Board of Yth Ministries; Adm Board; Sound of Mus C; Sup Ratng, Ntl Fed Jr Festival; *Wesleyan Col; Mus.*

MURPHY, Carolyn
John Fitzgerald Kennedy HS; Cleveland, OH; VP, Bus C; Chldr; Chor; Dbte Tm; ARC; Highstepper; *Eckerd Col; Bus.*

MURPHY, Celestine Elona
Claxton HS; Claxton, GA (25%-110) Rptr, FHA; Hmrm; VP, Sci C; Secy, SC; Rptr, Sr Cl; Pres, Jr Cl; Bio A; Citz A; Sci A; *Grady Mem Col; Nurs.*

MURPHY, Charles William
Stuyvesant HS; New York, NY (50-780) Fr C; Hmrm; Cpt, Math C; ARC; Ch, SC; Bkbl; Swim; Tnns; Alg A; COM; Citz A; Gov Honor Prog; Hist A; Math A; Sci A; Type A; Val; Co-Ldr, JHS Group; Pres, Church Ushers; Ch, Graduation Comm; Church Pub Worship Comm; Princeton U; Math.

MURPHY, Cheryl Suzanne
Richwoods HS; Peoria, IL (32-480) A Cap Choir; JV, Chldr; Chor; Drama; Ensm; GS; Madrigal; Mjrte; NHS; Ed, Sch P; Thes; COM; Hon Prog; Journ A; Q&S A; Sterling Merit; Wheaton Col; Pre-Med.

MURPHY, Clyde Caldwell III
Trinity Christian Acad; Jacksonville, FL (50%-54) Chor; Demolay; Drama; Opt A; Pres, Rod & Gun C; Chor Service A; Winthrop Col; Bus Adm.

MURPHY, Donna Sue
Laurel Valley Jr-Sr HS; New Florence, PA (10-135) Chor; FBLA; NFL; SC; Cpt, Silks Squad; Mercy Hospital Sch of Nurs; Nurs.

MURPHY, Elizabeth
Continued Ed Project; St Louis, MO; Sch P; Citz A; Forest Park Col; Exray Tech.

MURPHY, Elspeth Anne
Spring Branch HS; Houston, TX (150-600) Chor; Hockey; Co-Cpt, Tr; Yth Fel; Sou Methodist U; Broadcasting.

MURPHY, Erin Ann
Fernandina Beach HS; Fernandina Beach, FL (10%-319) Chor; Cpt, Hmrm; NHS; Sch P; COM; H of F; Hist A; Hon Prog; Most Out; Opt A; Spch A.

MURPHY, Gail Ellyn
Glendale Acad; Glendale, CA (6-68) A Cap Choir; AFS; Band; Chor; NHS; ARC; Secy, Sr Cl; Fin, Tnns; Hon Prog; Pres A; Loma Londa U; Bio.

MURPHY, Glenn Allan
Ash Fork Unified Sch; Ash Fork, AZ (1-11) Ed, Ann; BS; Pres, SC; VP, Jr Cl; Pres, Soph Cl; Bsbl; Bkbl; Cpt, Ftbl; Tr; Elk A; Hon Prog; Most Out; Type A; Val; NAU Cert of Achv; Elec.

MURPHY, Jacqueline Suzanne
Gamewell-Collettsville HS; Lenoir, NC (3-104) BC; Cpt, Chldr; Chor; Fr C; FHA; FTA; COM; Jr Marshal; Stu o-t Yr; WW.

MURPHY, James Frederick
Catholic Central HS; N Troy, NY; CYO; Hudson Valley Comm Col; Environmental Stu.

MURPHY, Jeanmarie
El Camino Real HS; Woodland Hills, CA; Tres, Bus C; Ch, City Conf; VP, Dbte Tm; FBLA; Hmrm; InterClub Coun; Model UN; S-T, Pol Sci C; Rptr, Sch P; Span C; VP, Spch C; S-T, World Affairs C; CSF; COM; Citz A; Hon Prog; Most Out; Spch A; Type A; Producer, ECR TV News Show; Creative Writing A; Columbia U; Journ.

MURPHY, Jennifer Lynn
Preble Shawnee HS; Camden, OH (15-160) Band; Rptr, Bus C; Chldr; Fr C; FHA; FTA; Fin, Jr Miss Pagent; Rainbow; Grand Mus, Rainbow Girls.

MURPHY, Joanne Eileen
Star o-t Sea Acad; San Francisco, CA (1-50) Sci C; Bank of Amer A; COM; Math A; Most Out; Val; Life Member CSF; Drill Tm; Hon Stu; U of San Francisco; Bus.

MURPHY, Judy Lynn
Westinghouse HS; Pittsburgh, PA; FHA; Mjrte; Tr; Duff Bus Col; Fashion Merchandising.

MURPHY, Julie Ann
Saint Ursula Acad; Cincinnati, OH (35-76) CYO; Hmrm; SC; Tnns; Photographer, Sch P; WW; U of Cincinnati; Industrial Design.

MURPHY, Karan Denisse
Fayette Co HS; Fayette, AL (20%-145) S-T, Band; Chor; FHA; 4H; Hmrm; VP, Math C; Mu Alpha Theta; NHS; SC; Tres, Span C; SC; HCt; Royal Court; Brewer St Col; Social Work.

MURPHY, Karen Dianne
L V Berkner HS; Richardson, TX (6%-600) A Cap Choir; Chor; Ensm; Rptr, Sch P; SC; Sftbl; Exploring C; Gym; TMEA Region III Choir; All UIL District, Solo, Ensm As; District Hon Choir As; Baylor U; Mus.

MURPHY, Kathleen Ann
Somerville HS; Somerville, MA; A-Ed, Ann; JV, Hockey; Swim; Italian C; Travel C; Bunker Hill Comm Col; Human Services.

MURPHY, Kevin Lawrence
Lyon Co HS; Eddyville, KY (25-70) Ann; Pres, BC; FFA; SC; Cpt, Bkbl; Co- cpt, MVP, Bkbl; Most Ath; Greenhand Degree; Paducah Comm Col; Engr.

MURPHY, Lesa Marie
Greenbrier HS; Green Brier, TN (6-124) BC; Parl, FHA; Farm Bureau A; UT Martin; Social Work.

MURPHY, Linda Joyce
McNeil HS; McNeil, AR (2-33) BC; Sci C; Spch C; Alg A; Cl Fav; Hist A; Sci A; Eng A; Sou Ark U; X-Ray Technician.

MURPHY, Lisa Gaye
Robert L Osborne Sr HS; Marietta, GA (10%-486) Band; Secy, BC; VP, Hmrm; Mjrte; Ga Tech; Archt Engr.

MURPHY, Lisa Sue
Truman HS; Independence, MO; A Cap Choir; Ann; CYO; Chor; Hmrm; SC; Bkbl; Sftbl; Tr; Hon Prog; Pres A; Yth Leg; Sailing C; Pep C; Citizenship List; Foreign Stu League; Pres, Bowl League; Campfire Girls; Med.

MURPHY, Marilyn Sue
Colchester HS; Colchester, IL (5-52) Ch, Chor; Pres, Drama; Chor A; NHS; Sci C; COM; St Scholar; Best Actress; Monmouth Col; Bio.

MURPHY, Marjorie Lynn
Lenoir HS; Lenoir, NC (2-116) Bus C; FBLA; Rptr, Lit Mag; NHS; Span C; VP, Church Yth Fel; Yth Ever Serving.

MURPHY, Mary Ellen R
Seekonk HS; Seekonk, MA (6-224) CYO; Chor; Fr C; Lit Mag; NHS; Tnns; Yrbk Staff; GAA; Pre-Med.

MURPHY, Maureen Anne
Susquehanna Comm HS; Susquehanna, PA; Bus C; Drama; NHS; Ski C; Ch, Sr Cl; Cpt, Bkbl; Sftbl; Tr; HCt; Lock Haven St U; Phys Ed.

MURPHY, Maureen Theresa
Qn o-t Rosary Acad; Amityville, NY (3-86) Hmrm; NHS; Rptr, Sch P; Pres, SC; Pres, Sr Cl; Pres, Jr Cl; Bkbl; Sftbl; Swim; Ntl Conf Chr & Jews; A-Ed, Yrbk; Del, Citizenship A; WW; Co-Cpt, Vlbl; Alt, Regents Schol; Ntl Fr Cont; Rotary C Essay Contest; Del, Knights of Columbus A; Adelphi U; Pre-Med.

MURPHY, Megan Patricia
Secaucus Middle Secondary Sch; Secaucus, NJ (16-164) Chor; Drama; Ensm; GS; Sch P; Pres, SC; JV, Bkbl; JV, Sftbl; Jr Women of Achv; Region Chor; Drama.

MURPHY, Melinda Cherry
Quitman HS; Quitman, MS (15%-210) BC; FBLA; VP, FHA; FTA; Rptr, 4H; Co-Cpt, Hmrm; Rptr, SC; Parl, Tri-HiY; Pres, Soph Cl; COM; Hon Prog; Journ A; Type A; Encounter A; March of Dimes; Meridian Jr Col; Journ.

MURPHY, Michelle A
Mother McAuley HS; Chicago, IL (200-485) CYO; Math C; Ski C; Span C; Med Sci.

MURPHY, Patricia Ann
Tower Hill HS; Tower Hill, IL (2-32) Band; Chor; FHA; Tres, Hmrm; Span C; Home Ec A.

MURPHY, Patricia Anne
John W Hallahan HS; Philadelphia, PA (3-432) Chldr; Chem C; Fr C; Hmrm; Math C; Pres, NHS; Rptr, Sch P; Sci C; SC; Alg A; Bio A; Ntl Sci Symposium; Fr As; Lat As; Distinguished Stu; Lat Classical Soc A; Villanova U; Nurs.

MURPHY, Patricia Gail
Walnut HS; Walnut, MS (10-55) Ann; BC; Chldr; Chor; FFA; FHA; Beauty; Spch A; WW; Agr A; Blue Mountain Col; Ed.

MURPHY, Patrick Brendan
Chaminade Col Prep; St Louis, MO (2-125) A-Ed, Ann; Chess C; Dbte Tm; Drama; NFL; NHS; Rptr, Sch P; Spch C; JV, Tr; Alg A; Bio A; Chem A; Hist A; Hon Prog; Math A; NEDT; Sci A; Spch A; Lat A; Scholastic Excellence A; HS Schol; Harvard U; Sci.

MURPHY, Paul Douglas
Anoka HS; Anoka, MN (142-750) Fin, AFS; Ger C; NHS; Rptr, Sch P; Sci C; Ski C; Cr-Ctry; Augsburg Col; Lang.

MURPHY, Paula Jacqueline
Magnolia Acad; Jackson, MS; Chldr; FHA; 4H; Sch P; Span C; Sftbl; Swim; Tr; 4H A; Hinds Jr Col; X-Ray Tech.

MURPHY, Richard Michael Jr
DuPont HS; Hermitage, TN (10-323) Pres, Band; Demolay; NHS; Pres, Swim; NEDT; SAR Good Citz A; Outst Sr; Vanderbilt U; Engr.

MURPHY, Robert Earl
Highland Sr HS; Highland, IN (300-625) Bkbl; Ftbl; Sftbl; Wood Working.

MURPHY, Sarah Anne
Lakewood HS; St Petersburg, FL (5-500) Band; Community Yth Symph; Ensm; Tres, French NHS; Lit Mag; Math C; NHS; JV, Swim; Tr; Hon Prog; Math A; Amer Yth Fel; Anatomy-Physiology A; PYF; Page, St Sen; Creative Writing A; Fr A; Sup, St Clarinet Solo & Trio As; Liberal Arts.

MURPHY, Susan Ruth
Duncan MacMillan HS; Sheet Harbour, CAN-ADA (5-24) St Martha's Sch of Nurs.

MURPHY, Thomas Kelly
Montgomery Co HS; Mt Sterling, KY; Ftbl; Ftbl Ltr; Lexington Teach Col; Archt.

MURPHY, Vicki Marie
Livingston HS; Livingston, TX; Band; JV, Bkbl; Sftbl; Tr; Stephen F Austin St U; PE.

MURPHY, William Robert
Somerville HS; Somerville, MA (30-450) Fr C; Sci C; Fin, Sci A; Northeastern U; Criminal Law.

MURRAINE, Fitzgerald Terrance
Charlotte Amalie HS; St Thomas, VIRGIN IS-LANDS (15-450) Bus C; Drama; Rptr, Hmrm; Rptr, Lit Mag; Rptr, Sch P; Sci C; Tnns, SC; Up Bound; Var C; Bsbl; Bkbl; Ftbl; Bio A; COM; Cl Fav; Hist A; Hon Prog; Sci A; Sch Govt; Drama A; Computer Sci.

MURRAY, Annie Laurie
Melborne HS; Melbourne, FL; Fr C; Pres, Mu Alpha Theta; Secy, NHS; SC; Alg A; Chem A; DARGCA; Math A; NHS; Ntl Sci Found; Sci A; Keyettes; Pres, St Luther League; Sci Fair; Chancel Choir.

MURRAY, Audrie Karel
Bonita Vista HS; Chula Vista, CA (33%-250) Co-Cpt, Chldr; Hmrm; InterAct C; Y-Tns; Tr; Citz A; Pep C; Campus Life; Gym; Nursery Sch Aide; McMurry Col; Nursery Sch Teacher.

MURRAY, Beneta Ann
Goodwater HS; Goodwater, AL (2-38) Co-Ed, Ann; Tres, BC; Tres, Bus C; Ch, Chldr; Chor; Tres, FBLA; FHA; FNA; VP, FTA; Math C; Secy, Jr Cl; Sal; Yth Fel; Troy St U; Nurs.

MURRAY, Beth Ann
Kiski Area HS; Vandergrift, PA (20%-573) Band; Var C; Bkbl; Hon Prog; Pres A; Yth Fel; Top 10%; Yth in Prtnrshp With Missions Trip; X-Ray Tech.

MURRAY, Carole Mary
Whitman-Hanson Regional HS; Whitman, MA (20-328) CYO; Chldr; NHS; Ski C; Pres, Sr Cl; Tres, Jr Cl; Tres, Soph Cl; DARGCA; Gr Marshal; HQn; Hon Prog; St Joseph's Col; Food Marketing.

MURRAY, Cindy Marlene
Newbury Park HS; Newbury Park, CA (38-691) JV, Bkbl; Golf; Soccer; JV, Sftbl; Swim; Most Improved, Vlbl; PA; Recreation Ed.

MURRAY, Colette Doreen
George Washington HS; Denver, CO; Band; Chor; 4H; ARC; Rptr, Sch P; SC; BSA; Tempe Ariz Col; Archt.

MURRAY, Connie Ann
Salisbury Elk-Lick Jr-Sr HS; Salisbury, PA (12-44) Commercial C; Span C; Amer Leg A; Citz A; Hon Prog; Type A; Yth Fel; Church Consistory; Americanism Makes A Difference A; WW; Pittsburgh Beauty Acad; Cosmetology.

MURRAY, Crystal Renee
Gainesville HS; Gainesville, TX (16-225) Band; Chor; Ensm; FTA; NHS; Secy, Span C; Hon Prog; NEDT; Miss FTA; U of Tex; Hist.

521

MURRAY, David Herschel
Mississinewa HS; Gas City, IN (1-250) Ann; Band; BS; VP, Drama; VP, Fr C; Key C; NHS; VP, Thes; Alg A; Bio A; Hist A; Math A; Hugh O'Brien Yth Schol; Eng A; Fr A; Band Cert; *Taylor U.*

MURRAY, Deborah Ann
Cache HS; Cache, OK (10%-62) BC; Chldr; Parl, FHA; Pres, 4H; NHS; Tres, Soph Cl; Masonic A; Sci A; 1st Runner- up, St Spelling Bee.

MURRAY, Delores
Frank W Ballou Sr HS; Washington, DC; Co-Cpt, Dbte Tm; Tr; Vlbl; 'It's Academic'.

MURRAY, Dennis Joe
McLoud HS; McLoud, OK (10%-90) Ftbl; Tr; COM; Defense A, Ftbl; *Athletics.*

MURRAY, Diane
Leesville HS; Leesville, LA (24-262) Hmrm; Lit Ral; Tres, Lit Mag; Sch P; Sci C; Span C; SC; JA A; Fresh Hon Schol; Acad Col Schol; *NW St U; Pol Sci.*

MURRAY, Diane Lynna
John A Brashear HS; Pittsburgh, PA (8-220) Cpt, Chldr; Hmrm; NHS; SC; COM; Hon Prog; DECA C; Co-Cpt, Vlbl; Yth Motivation Task Force Schol; Sportsmanship A, Vlbl.

MURRAY, Evangela
Johnson HS; Savannah, GA; Chldr; Hmrm; SC; Beauty; Cl Fav; Swtht; *Savannah St Col; Early Child Ed.*

MURRAY, George Jr
Sacramento HS; Sacramento, CA; Cr-Ctry; Sftbl; Tr; Art; *City Col; Mus.*

MURRAY, Gwendolyn
Scarlet Oaks Joint Voc Sch; Cincinnati, OH (115-333) Band; Fin, Demolay; FHA; Swim; Mgr, Drill Tm; PA; HR; Demolay Swtht; Co-Ed Rep; Cincinnati Red's Straight 'A' Stu; Job's Daughters; *Raymond Walters Gen & Tech Col; Lib.*

MURRAY, Gwinnette Adonicas
Burke HS; Charleston, SC; Band; Drama; Jr Miss Pagent; Mjrte; Sptch C; SC; Pres, Jr Cl; Beauty; COM; Coun of Teach A; Hon Prog; MLS; Sptch A; VofDEM.

MURRAY, James J III
Weequahic HS; Newark, NJ (183-426) Band; BS; Dbte Tm; Drama; Hmrm; Rptr, Ntl Yth Conf; Rptr, Sch P; SC; Ch, Soph Cl; Mgr, Bkbl; Mgr, Ftbl; Amer Leg A; Amer Leg Orator A; HKg; Masonic A; Most Out; V-Ch, City Conf Boy's C; NJ; Band A; Boy o-t Yr; Top City Mayor; *Kean Col; Communications.*

MURRAY, Janet Lynn
Northwest HS; Omaha, NE (25-471) Fin, GS; Hmrm; Math C; NHS; Orch; Phys C; Span C; VP, Span NHS; Var C; Golf; Ntl Sci Found; Sci A; Pep C; US Army Excellence A; Job's Daughters; Nebr St Sci Win; Ntl Westinghouse Sci Fin; Amer Sptch & Hearing Assn A; *U of Omaha; Sci.*

MURRAY, Jean
Faith Christian HS; Collingswood, NJ; Chor; Hmrm; Pres, SC; Cpt, Bkbl; Cpt, Hockey; Cpt, Sftbl; Sal; MVP, Bkbl, Hockey & Sftbl; *King's Col; Phys Ed.*

MURRAY, Karen Jean
Kecoughtan HS; Hampton, VA (19-453) Secy, Band; Hmrm; Key C; VP, Math C; NHS; Orch; SC; VP, Jr Cl; HCt; S-T Band; Secy, Church Yth Fel; Regional, All City, Bands; Highest Hon Graduate; *U of Va; Social Services.*

MURRAY, Kimberly Michelle
Cathedral HS; Chicago, IL (10-30) CYO; Chldr; City Conf; Cpt, Sftbl; Cpt, Tr; Sci A; *Loyola U; Law.*

MURRAY, Laura Susan
W Allegheny HS; Imperial, PA;

MURRAY, Leslie Ruth
Peru Sr HS; Peru, IN (6-355) SC; Var C; JV, Bkbl; Tnns; COM; Hon Prog; JV, Vlbl; GAA; Sectional Tnns Champs; *Teaching.*

MURRAY, Lisa Kay
Charlotte HS; Punta Gorda, FL (50%-650) Drama; Secy, InterAct C; ARC.

MURRAY, Lorraine
Morrisville HS; Morrisville, PA (53-183) A Cap Choir; Band; Chor; Drama; Hmrm; Mgr, Sftbl; Tres, Yth Fel; Co Mus Festival; Band, Achv, A's; Sci.

MURRAY, Lynda Hope
Philadelphia HS for Girls; Philadelphia, PA (37-400) Cpt, Math C; Math A; *Howard Harvard Col; Acct.*

MURRAY, Lynn Margaret
Abington HS; Abington, PA (280-867) Fr C; Hmrm; COM; *Mansfield St Col; Special Ed.*

MURRAY, Marjorie Ann
Lauralton Hall HS; Milford, CT (7-93) Chor; Lit Mag; Span C; Span NHS; NEDT; *U of Hartford; Pre-Med.*

MURRAY, Marjorie Lynne
Thomas Jefferson HS; Pittsburgh, PA (6-372) Chor; NHS; Span C; Westinghouse Sci Hon Inst; *Col of Wooster; Hist.*

MURRAY, Matt Neal
Central HS; Waterloo, IA (30-350) Rptr, Ann; Chor; Madrigal; NHS; Rptr, Sch P; Pres, Jr Cl; Bkbl; Tr; *U of N Iowa; Bio.*

MURRAY, Maureen Colette
St Joseph's Acad; Cleveland, OH; CYO; Chor; Rptr, Sch P; Pres, CYO; SJA News A; *Cleveland Comm Col; Practical Nurs.*

MURRAY, Mona Rebecca
Indian River HS; Frankford, DE (83-193) Chor; Drama; Pres, Jobs Daughters; Art As; Librarian A; *Salisbury St Col; Ed.*

MURRAY, Nancy Ann
Chagrin Falls HS; Chagrin Falls, OH (58-205) Ann; Lat C; A-Ed, Lit Mag; NHS; Rptr, Sch P; VP, Jr Cl; Tres, Soph Cl; Bkbl; Sftbl; Secy, Fresh Cl; Church Nusery; Ch & Mgr, Ftbl Concessions; VP, Ldr's C; Regional Art Show; Coach, Girls Bkbl Tm; *Hiram Col; Bio.*

MURRAY, Nancy Susan
Homewood HS; Homewood, AL (81-249) Chor; Drama; Ensm; Parl, SC; Thes; Thespian Conv; Thespian Troupe A; *U of Ala in Birmingham; Early Childhood Development.*

MURRAY, Patrick Michael
Greater Latrobe Sr HS; Latrobe, PA (4-518) Ch, CYO; Dbte Tm; NFL; Pres, NHS; A-Ed, Sch P; Sci C; Span C; Span NHS; Var C; Cr-Ctry; Tr; COM; Chem A; Harvard Book A; Hon Prog; Q&S A; Sci A; Sptch A; *Washington and Jefferson Col; Pre-Med.*

MURRAY, Paul Bailey
N Mesquite HS; Mesquite, TX; Band; Ensm; Orch; Hockey; Sftbl; COM; Citz A; Sci A; Outst Band A; *Baylor U; Mus.*

MURRAY, Peter Marshall
Parkersburg HS; Parkersburg, WV (15-779) A Cap Choir; Band; Ensm; Pres, Hmrm; SC; JV, Bsbl; Golf; Elk A; ROTC A; Sci A; Yth Fel; All St, Choir; VPI; Chem.*

MURRAY, Theresa Marie
Tuscola Comm HS; Tuscola, IL (9-118) Co-Ed, Ann; CYO; Chor; Ensm; GS; 4H; NHS; Pres, Soph Cl; Tr; Cl Fav; DARGCA; 4H A; Hon Prog; MLS; Pres A; St Scholar; Pres, Med Explorers; Cpt, Vlbl; Badminton; *St Francis Sch of Nurs; Med.*

MURRAY, Timothy Garrett
Kubasaki HS; Okinawa, JAPAN (1-271) Chess C; Chor; Dbte Tm; Fr C; Hmrm; NHS; Order/Arrow; ARC; Pres, Sci C; Cpt, Golf; Tnns; Alg A; COM; Hon Prog; Math A; NMS; Order/Arrow A; ARC A; Yth Fel; Pres, Med Explorers; Eagle Sct; *Johns Hopkins U; Med.*

MURRAY, Timothy Paul
Saint Elizabeth HS; Pleasant Hills, PA; Co-Ch, Band; Drama; UN Council; Bio A; NEDT; *U of Pittsburgh; Hist.*

MURRAY, Timothy Wayne
Sw Willingham B HS; Macon, GA; Band; Fr C; Sch P; Church Choir A; *Archt.*

MURRAY, Todd Alan
Nickerson HS; Nickerson, KS; Arch; Band; 4H; Arch; Bkbl; Golf; Sftbl; Tnns; Wrest; Citz A; Cooking A; *Sterling Col; Wildlife.*

MURRAY, Warren Lee
Dewey HS; Dewey, OK (5%-95) NHS; Phys C; Pres, Soph Cl; MVP, Bsbl; Bkbl; Cpt, Ftbl; HKg; HCt; Hon Prog; St Scholar; WW; All Around Schol; Bsbl All Amer; *Col of The Ozarks; Dentistry.*

MURRAY, Wayne Darrell
Jim Hill Sr HS; Jackson, MS (10%-207) Band; Drama; Hmrm; Math C; Mu Alpha Theta; Sch P; Tnns; COM; Journ A; NEDT; Opt A; Band A, Holly Mus; Amer Ed Week; Essay Winner; *Med.*

MURRAY, William Kent
Wayne HS; Jesup, GA; Hmrm; Y-Tns; Bsbl; First Lt, Band, Adult Chor; Yth Dir; VP, Industrial Arts C; Stage Band; Church Handbell Choir; Jazz Ensm; Yth Chor; Yth Pastor; Chrch Yth Co; *Brewton-Parker Col.*

MURRELL, Beverly Dorress
Palm Springs HS; Palm Springs, CA (155-568) Bus Mgr, A Cap Choir; 4H; InterClub Coun; Madrigal; COM; 4H A; Lion A; Yth Fel; *Psych.*

MURRELL, Janette Renia
Burke HS; Charleston, SC (12-177) S-T, Band; Drama; VP, Y-Tns; Math A; MLS; Most Out; VP, Band; WW; WW in Band; *Baptist Col; Sci.*

MURRELL, Phillip Stanley
Hogansville HS; Hogansville, GA; Sci C; SC; Bkbl; Ftbl; Cl Fav; Hon Prog; Math A; Most Out; Sci A; PA; Milliken Schol; All-Area Ftbl Tm; Co-Lib Asst o-t Yr; *LaGrange Col; Bus Adm.*

MURRELL, Susan Jane
Waverly HS; Waverly, OH (11-184) Band; FTA; Cpt, Mjrte; Span C; NHS; Pres Phys Fitness A; 1st Pl, Drum Mjrte A; *Math.*

MURRELL, Vicki Lou
Putnam City HS; Oklahoma City, OK (183-850) Hmrm; Lat C; NHS; Sptch C; SC; Sftbl; Tr; Pres, Church Group; Historian, DECA; Chperson, DECA; Chapter o-t Yr Bk, 1st-St.

MURREY, Marshall Cary
Giles Co HS; Pulaski, TN (12-200) A Cap Choir; BC; Ntl Yth Conf; Order/Arrow; SC; Pres, Soph Cl; Cpt, Ftbl; Golf; Eagle A; Stu o-t Yr; *Sci.*

MURROW, Jean Ann
Little Wolf HS; Manawa, WI (10%-80) Span C; Citz A.

MURTHA, Jennifer Eileen
Mount Pleasant Area Sr HS; Mount Pleasant, PA (1-300) AFS; Band; Drama; Secy, Fr C; FTA; Var C; Swim; Amer Leg A; Theatrical Appreciation Group; GAA, Winter and Summer Mus.

MUSCARELLA, David Micheal
York Central HS; Retsof, NY; Pres, Key C; Ski C; JV, Ftbl; JV, Tnns; *RPI; Energy Research.*

MUSCARI, Michael Allen
Mullens HS; Mullens, WV (1-120) BC; BS; NHS; Var C; Bsbl; Co-Cpt, Ftbl; Golf; Val; *W Va U; Pre-Med.*

MUSE, Jennie Lyn
Kossuth HS; Kossuth, MS (11-95) Ann; Band; BC; Bus C; FHA; Mjrte; SC; JV, Bkbl; Sftbl; COM; Most Improved, Band; Best Overall, Advertising; Christian Ldr; 2nd, Sci Fair.

MUSE, Lynda Gayle
Southwood HS; Shreveport, LA; Chor; 4H; *La Tech U; Psych.*

MUSE, Tondra Lynne
Southwood HS; Shreveport, LA;

MUSGRAVE, Kathryn Sue
Ashland Sr HS; Ashland, OR (100-250) Tres, FBLA; Bus Mgr, Sch P; *Sou U; Bus.*

MUSGRAVE, Lisa Gae
Norwayne HS; Creston, OH (10%-120) Band; JV, Chldr; Tres, Chor; Tr; Lion A; Schol Achv A; Span A; *Foreign Lang.*

MUSGROVE, Celeste Ann
Cy-Fair HS; Cypress, TX (25%-650) JETS; NHS.

MUSGROVE, Gordan Scott
Spring Woods Sr HS; Houston, TX (90-520) Chor; Math C; Mu Alpha Theta; Tres, SC; JV, Ftbl; *SW U; Computer Sci.*

MUSGROW, Deirdre Marietta
Minden HS; Minden, LA (2-200) Band; Cpt, Chldr; Secy, Fr C; FBLA; GS; Semi-Fin, Lit Ral; Tres, NHS; Pres, Span C; SC; Most Out; Semi-Fin, Sch Swtht; *LSU; Sci.*

MUSHALA, Mary Elizabeth
Susquehanna Comm HS; Susquehanna, PA (12-119) Arch; Band; Bus C; Chldr; Chor; Drama; Mjrte; Sch P; Ski C; Type A; WW Among HS Mus Stu; *Robert Packer Hosp Sch of Nurs; Nurs.*

MUSICK, Jim Wayne
Western Hills HS; Fort Worth, TX; Band; Drama; Hmrm; VP, Sci C; SC; JV, Tnns; Hon Prog; Best Actor; *Baylor U; Psych.*

MUSIL, Kari Irene
Stevens HS; Rapid City, SD (51-459) Band; NHS; *Augustana Col; Ministry.*

MUSIL, Mary Lyn
Sheboygan Falls HS; Sheboygan Falls, WI (44-158) Ann; Chldr; Chor; Var C; Bkbl; Sftbl; Tr; Tr A's; Vlbl A; Yth Tutor; *Oskosh Col; Math.*

MUSILLO, Diane Marie
Saint Elizabeth HS; Pittsburgh, PA (5-101) F-Ed, Ann; Drama; Ski C; Tres, Sr Cl; Tres, Jr Cl; Tres, Soph Cl; Bio A; Chamber of Comm A; Hon Prog; NEDT; Pres A; Type A; Vlbl; Geom A; Shorthand As; Primary Tutor; *Pittsburgh Beauty Acad; Cosmetology.*

MUSKOPF, Merribeth Ann
Belleville Township HS W; Belleville, IL (1-850) AFS; Band; Chor; Drama; Tres, Ger C; Hmrm; Orch; SC; Tr; Amer Leg A; Hist A; Sci A; Pep C; Pres, Tres, Yth Fellowship; Hist C.

MUSLAND, Roy Allan
Edgeley Pub Sch; Edgeley, ND; 4H; JV, Bkbl; Tr; 4H A.

MUSSARI, Theresa Marie
Westminster HS; Westminster, MD (10-570) A Cap Choir; Ed, Ann; CYO; Chor; Fr C; GS; Hmrm; Key C; NHS; SC; Hon Prog; Q&S A; Keyetts; *York Col; Nurs.*

MUSSER, Lisa Ann
Marion HS; Marion, AR (5-104) Chldr; Math C; Tres, NHS; *U of Ark; Elem Ed.*

MUSSETTER, Kevin Jon
Abraham Lincoln Sr HS; Bloomington, MN (43-586) Co-Cpt, Band; Ensm; JV, Bsbl; *N Central Bible Col; Theology.*

MUSSEY, Arthur William
William J Palmer HS; Colorado Springs, CO; Chess C; Citz A; JA A; *Offset Printing.*

MUSSEY, Steven Walter
Lee HS; Springfield, VA (1-300) Chor; Pres, City Conf; Drama; VP, Ger C; Pres, Hmrm; VP, Math C; NHS; Sci C; JV, Tr; H of F; NMS; Phy A; Sal; Sci A; Ntl Capital Optical Soc A; Patent Office Soc A; Soc of Automotive Engr; GW U Sch of Engr; *U of Va; Pre-Med.*

MUSSO, Cynthia Marie
South HS; Pueblo, CO (65-500) CYO; Chldr; Ski C; Var C; Tr; Yth Fel; Yth Foundation; Cpt, Gym; Gym Ltr; Co-Ch, Yth Fel; Silver Cord Sr; Young Life Ldr; *Saint Mary's Col; Elem Ed.*

MUSTAIN, Cynthia Jean
Greenhills HS; Cincinnati, OH (2-250) Bus Mgr, Ann; Drama; Fr C; Tres, NHS; Bus Mgr, Sch P; JV, Tr; Q&S A; Natl Merit Schol Stu; Greenhills HS Schol A; *U of Cincinnati; Engr.*

MUSTER, Sue Marie
Eisenhower HS; Washington, MI (76-588) Ch, CYO; Chldr; Ger C; Sch P; Swim; *Oakland U; Med Technology.*

MUSTOE, Margaret Hope
Alleghany Co HS; Covington, VA (1-197) Fr C; Hmrm; NHS; Ski C; Secy, Tri-HiY; Gov Honor Prog; Sci A; *Pre-Med.*

MUSTONEN, Julie Margaret
Brainerd Sr HS; Brainerd, MN (4-432) A Cap Choir; Chor; Co-Ed, Lit Mag; S-T, Span C; *Concordia Col; Sociology.*

MUSUMECHE, Tammy Elizabeth
Bellaire HS; Bellaire, TX (5-750) Rptr, A Cap Choir; Ensm; FHA; Hmrm; NHS; Rainbow; SC; COM; Hon Prog; Home Ec Rally A; Mus A; *Houston Baptist U; Elem Ed.*

MUTCH, Mary Lou
Lakeview HS; Battle Creek, MI (79-416) Yth for Christ; Hon Schol A; *Spring Arbor Col; Psych.*

MUTCH, Robin Kaye
Wallace Sr HS; Wallace, ID (20-100) Chldr; Drama; Lat C; Lat NHS; Math C; Sftbl; Type A; GS Alt; *U of Mont; Forestry.*

MUTH, Donald Ray
Chester Area HS; Chester, SD (5-40) BS; Rptr, FFA; Pres, 4H; Pres, NHS; Bkbl; Cr-Ctry; Mgr, Ftbl; *SD St U; Agr.*

MUUS, Paul M
Bishop Ryan HS; Minot, ND (8-118) CYO; Pres, Ger C; Hmrm; Tres, Key C; NHS; ARC; Sci C; Ski C; Var C; MVP, Bkbl; Tr; Bio A; Hist A; Hon Prog; Math A; Ntl Sci Found; Sci A; Inter-Ntl Solar Energy Soc; Am Meteorological Soc, Jets, A's; Dept of Comm, Air Force, Army, A's; Navy Sci, Erda, A's; *Archt.*

MUYSKENS, Mark Alan
Piscataway HS; Piscataway, NJ (10-600) Band; Drama; JV, Soccer; Tr; Val; *Central Col of Iowa; Chem.*

MUZIO, Sheryl Lynn
Turlock HS; Turlock, CA (3-400) F-Ed, Sch P; Bio A; CSF; Hist A; Eng As; *USC; Journ.*

MYART, Robin Lois
Chicago Voc HS; Chicago, IL (20-956) VP, NHS; Secy, Sr Cl; COM; Hon Prog; JA A; MLS; Ntl Achv Schol; Type A; *Sou Ill U; Acct.*

MYATT, Jennifer Jill
Fuquay-Varina Sr HS; Fuquay-Varina, NC (65-171) Chor; Ensm; Lat C; COM; *Mus.*

MYCHALCZAK, Borys Roman
Immaculate Conception Ukrainian HS; Hamtramck, MI (3-30) Chor; Ensm; Pres, NHS; SC; Bkbl; Mgr, Ftbl; Soccer; COM; HCt; Ntl Sci Symposium; Rotary A; Yth Fel; Col Merit Schol; Lector C; *Wayne St U; Pre-Med.*

MYCHALOWYCH, Andrew Wasyl
Immaculate Conception HS; Hamtramck, MI (3-50) Band; Bus C; CYO; VP, Chess C; Chor; Dbte Tm; Ensm; VP, Ger C; Pres, Hmrm; Pres, NHS; Orch; Ed, Sch P; VP, Ski C; Pres, Jr Cl; VP, Soph Cl; Bkbl; Ftbl; Soccer; Semi-Fin, Swim; Tnns; Bio A; COM; Chem A; HCt; Hon Prog; MLS; Sci A; St Scholar; Yth Foundation; *Wayne St U; Med.*

MYERS, Amanda Lorie
Independence HS; Independence, MS (15%-72) BC; FBLA; FHA; COM; *Miss Col; Nurs.*

MYERS, Amy Priscilla
Essex Junction Educational Center; Essex Junction, VT; Chor; Drama; Tr; MYO; *U of Vermont; Phys Therapy.*

MYERS, Anne Polk
Hattiesburg HS; Hattiesburg, MS; JV, Chldr; Ensm; GS; Pres, Hmrm; Fin, Jr Miss Pagent; Pres, Span C; Secy, SC; Tnns; Schol A, Jr Miss Pageant; Win, Mental Illness Essay; Miss Congeniality, Jr Miss Pageant; Run-Up, Spch Contest, Drug Abuse; *U of Miss; Span.*

MYERS, Barbara Ruth
Harding Acad; Memphis, TN (139-200) Band; Hist, FHA; Pres, Spirit C; VP, Explorers; *Methodist Sch of Nurs; Nurs.*

MYERS, Carl Rodney
Cainhoy HS; Huger, SC (6-45) Band; FFA; Pres, Hmrm; Math C; Sci C; Var C; Co-Cpt, Bkbl; Ftbl; Bio A; 4H A; Hist A; Math A; Sci A; *Morris Col; Bus Mgr.*

MYERS, Carolyn Jean
NW Sr HS; Hyattsville, MD; All Amer Yth; Band; Chor; Mjrte; Y-Tns; Fin, Arch; Swim; ARC A; Type A; Pom Pons; GSct; *Social Work.*

MYERS, Charlene
Polytech HS; Long Beach, CA; Chor; MVP, Sftbl; *UCLA; Secy.*

MYERS, Charles Jeffrey
Attica HS; Attica, IN (4-97) Span C; VP, SC; Var C; MVP, Bsbl; MVP, Bkbl; MVP, Cr-Ctry; Swim.

MYERS, Cheryl Lynn
Norwin HS; N Huntingdon, PA (130-860) A Cap Choir; Chor; Hmrm; Swim; Beauty; VP, Yth Fel.

MYERS, Cindy Lee
Hempfield HS; Landisville, PA (152-485) Band; Chor; Var C; Swim; *E Stroudsburg St Col; Spch Pathology & Audiology.*

MYERS, Cynthia Marie
Warwick HS; Lititz, PA (105-247) Band; Chor; Ensm; F-Ed, Sch P; Mgr, Hockey; *Millersville St Col; Psych.*

MYERS, Debra Sue
Anselmo-Merna HS; Merna, NE; Band; Chor; Ensm; FBLA; S-T, 4H; Bkbl; Sftbl; Tr; COM; 4H A; *Phys Ed.*

MYERS, Dianna Lynn
Sandy Valley HS; Magnolia, OH (5-153) A Cap Choir; 4H; NHS; Outst Bus Stu; Ohio DEA Regional Contest 2nd Pl; OEA St, 2nd Pl.

MYERS, Donna Joyce
Woodlake Union HS; Woodlake, CA (11-155) Band; Chldr; Fr C; JV, Bkbl; JV, Tnns; *Col o-t Sequoias; Mus.*

MYERS, Eric Duane
Red Lion Area Sr HS; Red Lion, PA (37-360) NHS; Ftbl; Co-Cpt, Wrest; MVP, Wrest; *U of Md; Bus.*

MYERS, James Herbert
Schenley HS; Pittsburgh, PA (10-253) Drama; Var C; Tr; Math A; MLS; Pres A; Yth Fel; *U of Pittsburgh; Engr.*

MYERS, James Walter
Pennsville Mem HS; Pennsville, NJ (80-275) BS; Demolay; Pres, InterAct C; NHS; MVP, Bsbl; Ftbl; Wrest; Citz A; Rotary A; Best All Around; *The Citadel; Bio.*

MYERS, Jane Elaine
Mount Gilead HS; Mount Gilead, OH (20-130) Ann; Band; Drama; Fr C; GS; 4H; Sch Achieve Tm; Sch P; Thes; Yth Fel; Amer Private Enterprise System Fin; *Ohio St U.*

MYERS, Janet Lynn
Abraham Lincoln HS; Council Bluffs, IA (25%-400) Band; Job's Daughters; Candystripers; *Med.*

MYERS, Jeffrey D
Northern Chester Co Tech Sch; Phoenixville, PA; Chess C; SC; Ftbl; Hockey; *U of Cincinnati; Engr.*

MYERS, John Earl
Madison W HS; Madison, WI (45-600) Band; Ensm; Soccer; Kiwanis A; *U of Wisc Madison; Engr.*

MYERS, Julie Ellen
Hunterdon Central HS; Flemington, NJ; Key C; Ski C; Hockey; *Nurs.*

MYERS, Katherine S
Bethel HS; Hampton, VA (27-566) NHS; COM; Sci A; Service Aide; WW; *Old Dominion U; Pediatrician.*

MYERS, Kathryn Elizabeth
Comstock HS; Comstock, TX (3-7) Ann; Chldr; VP, 4H; Fin, Lit Ral; S-T, Rainbow; Ed, Sch P; St Stu Congress; S-T, Sr Cl; Jr Cl; Soph Cl; Cpt, Bkbl; Tnns; B Crocker A; Cl Fav; 4H A; Journ A; Poet A; Win, St 4-H; 4-H Gold Star Girl; UIL A, District, Regional; *Tarleton St U; Food Tech.*

MYERS, Kenneth Roy
Greencastle HS; Greencastle, IN; Ensm; Key C; Orch; Span C; Var C; Tnns; Tr; Wrest; WW, Mus; Ntl Sch Orch A; All St Orch; Stu o-t Wk; *Depauw U; Mus.*

MYERS, Kevin Leslie
Parkway Epsilon HS; Philadelphia, PA (30-200) Hmrm; Tres, Jr Cl; Swim; Tnns; *Drexel U; Computer Sci.*

MYERS, Kimberly Ann
DeSoto HS; De Soto, TX; FHA; Span C; Pres, Jr Cl; Bkbl; Sftbl; Tr; Yth Fel; *Abilene Christian U; Phys Ed.*

MYERS, Laura Lynn
Cypress Lake HS; Fort Myers, FL (2-492) A Cap
Choir; Band; Chor; Community Yth Symph; Ensm;
NHS; Sci C; Hon Prog; Magna Cum Laude; Pres A;
Sal; *New Col of USF; Math.*

MYERS, Linda Sue
Lakeview HS; Stoneboro, PA (33-140) Band; NHS;
Var C; Cpt, Bkbl; Cpt, Tr; MVP, Bkbl Sr Yr; *Slippery Rock St Col; Phys Ed.*

MYERS, Lisa Maxine
Erie HS; Erie, IL (25%-89) Bsbl; Bkbl; Sftbl; Tr;
Lion A; Pres A; Yth Fel.

MYERS, Margaret Ann
Cumberland Valley HS; Mechanicsburg, PA
(16-608) NHS; Span C; JV, Bkbl; Mgr, Hockey;
Sftbl; COM; Hon Prog; *Harrisburg Area Comm
Col; Law Enforcement.*

MYERS, Marilyn Joan
Dekalb HS; Waterloo, IN (20-360) Band; BC;
Chor; Ensm; Fr C; FTA; 4H; Hmrm; Mjrte; Orch;
SC; Swim; JV, Tnns; 4H A; Interlochen Ntl Mus;
JA A; Pres A; *Mus.*

MYERS, Mark Leland
Madison W HS; Madison, WI (13-595) JV, Soccer;
U of Wis at Madison; Mech Engr.

MYERS, Mary Beth
Will Rogers HS; Tulsa, OK (5%-846) Band; Dbte
Tm; Drama; Pres, Hmrm; ARC; Sch P; SC; VP,
Soph Cl; Journ A; Masque & Gavel A; ARC A; Yth
Fel; HR; Page in St Capitol; Billy Graham A; *Okla
St U; Fashion Merchandises.*

MYERS, Mary Cassandra
Schenley HS; Pittsburgh, PA; Pres, Hmrm; Orch;
Span C; SC; Co-Cpt, Bkbl; Sftbl; COM; Citz A;
Math A; Bkbl, Orch, Acad, Safety, A's; *Math.*

MYERS, Mary Elizabeth
Kenmore HS; Akron, OH (10%-240) Chor; Orch;
Bkbl; Tr; Chaplain, Job's Daughters; *Akron U;
Med.*

MYERS, Mary Elizabeth
St Elmo HS; St Elmo, IL (12-50) Tres, FHA; NHS;
Tr; Vlbl; WW.

MYERS, Maurice Wayne
Holy Family HS; Birmingham, AL (3-41) CYO;
Bus Mgr, City Conf; Pres, Fr C; Pres, Hmrm; VP,
NHS; ARC; VP, Sci C; VP, SC; Var C; Bkbl; Alg A;
Bio A; COM; Chem A; Hist A; Hon Prog; Math A;
MLS; Most Out; *Computer Programmer.*

MYERS, Patricia Louise
Central Acad; Macon, MS (5%-63) Anchor C;
Band; BC; Chor; Alg A; Amer Leg A; COM; Hist
A; Math A; Sci A; Drum Mjrte; S-T, Jr Mus C; Lat,
Eng, A's; *Miss St U; Math Ed.*

MYERS, Peggy Ann
Fort Scott Sr HS; Fort Scott, KS (8-169) Band; Cpt,
Chldr; Dbte Tm; Pres, Drama; 4H; Hmrm; Math C;
NFL; Pres, Rainbow; Span C; Spch C; SC; Beauty;
DARGCA; 4H A; *Kans St Col of Pittsburg; Phys
Therapy.*

MYERS, Sharon Kay
Arlington HS; Arlington Heights, IL (125-500) 4H;
Sch P; Cr-Ctry; Tr; Journ A; Ltr & Pin, Cr-Ctry;
Journ.

MYERS, Susan Dee
Arvada W Sr HS; Arvada, CO (10%-700) 4H;
NHS; *Platte Valley Bible Col; Bible.*

MYERS, Susan Ellen
SW Christian Acad; Ruth, MS (1-9) BC; Chldr;
Tres, SC; Pres, Soph Cl; Bkbl; Sftbl; Cl Fav; Hist A;
Math A; Sci A; Eng A; *Copiah-Lincoln Jr Col;
Nurs.*

MYERS, Susan Lee
Highland Park HS; Dallas, TX (300-500) AFS;
Chor; Ensm; InterClub Coun; Thes; Pres, Tri-HiY;
Tex Tech U; Bus.

MYERS, Terry Lynn
Sw HS; Kansas City, MO (48-450) Pres, Band; BS;
NHS; Orch; ARC; Sci C; St Stu Congress; UN
Council; Var C; MVP, Bsbl; JV, Ftbl; Tr; Hon Prog;
Opt A; Spch A; Cpt, Bowl; *Rockhurst Col; Med.*

MYERS, Toni Jean
Morgan HS; McConnelsville, OH (45-254) Band;
NHS; Stu C Hon; Candystriper; Statistician, Bkbl;
Demolay Swtht; Pre Med C; Firemen's Festival
Qn; Pep C; Ath Dir Aid; Past Hon Qn; *Muskingum
Area Tech Col; Radiology.*

MYERS, Valerie Lynn
Lutheran HS W; Detroit, MI; Chldr; Secy, Drama;
Hmrm; Secy, InterClub Coun; NHS; SC; Y-Tns;
Attendance C; Tres, Mod Dance C; Pep C; *Mich St
U; Psych.*

MYERS, Vicki Renee
Neshoba Central HS; Philadelphia, MS; BC; Chldr;
Drama; Tres, FHA; Pres, Hmrm; SC; Pres, Soph Cl;
Beauty; Cl Fav; *Meridian Jr Col; Nurs.*

MYERS, Wanda Jean
Palestine HS; Palestine, TX (25%-350) Pres,
Hmrm; Cl Fav; *Ed.*

MYFELT, Lynn Georgia
Elmira Christian Acad; Corning, NY (1-11) Band;
Chldr; Chor; Hmrm; NHS; SC; Tres, Soph Cl; Citz
A.

MYHAN, Jimmie Ann
Muscle Shoals HS; Muscle Shoals, AL; Rptr,
FBLA; FHA; NHS; *U of N Ala; Bus.*

MYKYTIUK, Marion Sue
Durango Sr HS; Durango, CO (27-283) Chor; Most
Talented; WW; Gregg Shorthand A; *Rockmont
Col; Mus.*

MYLER, Douglas Joseph
Sky View HS; Smithfield, UT (2-573) A Cap Choir;
BS; Community Yth Symph; Dbte Tm; NFL; NHS;
Orch; Citz A; DARGCA; Accompanist, A Cappella Choir; Gen Schol Sterling Schol; *U of Utah;
Phar.*

MYLES, Carey Deland
Rufus King HS; Milwaukee, WI; City Conf; Mgr,
Ftbl; Wrest; Sports As; *U W M; Math.*

MYLES, Carolyn Denise
Minden HS; Minden, LA (100-251) Fr C; 4H;
Hmrm; Cpt, Bkbl; Sftbl; Tr; Yth Fel; *Southern
Branch Col; Bus.*

MYLES, Ruby Lee
Hugh Manley HS; Chicago, IL (7-219) Secy, Band;
Drama; Model UN; Pres, NHS; Sch P; Span C; SC;
Alg A; COM; Cl Fav; Hon Prog; Math A; MLS;
Type A; Band A; Art A; Service A; Most Outst
Gym Stu; *Northern Ill U; Mus.*

MYLES, Willie Lee
Amite Co Attendance Center; Gloster, MS (3-40)
Band; Pres, BC; Tres, Chor; Tres, Drama; Pres,
FFA; VP, Hmrm; Tres, Lit Mag; Orch; VP, SC; VP,
Sr Cl; Tres, Soph Cl; COM; Citz A; Hon Prog; I
Dare You; Jr Bus Mgr A; *Jackson St U; Med Technology.*

MYNATT, Mark David
Daingerfield-Lone Star Isd; Daingerfield, TX; Span
C; *Hist.*

MYNATT, Matt D
Daingerfield HS; Daingerfield, TX (4-225) Demolay; Math C; NHS; Sci C; Math A; De Stu o-t Yr;
Kilgore Col.

MYRICK, Paul Davis III
John Graham HS; Warrenton, NC (50-158) VICA
C; *Vance Comm Col; Drafting.*

MYRON, David Pius
St Elizabeth HS; Pittsburgh, PA (10%-112) Co-Cpt,
Chess C; Rptr, Hmrm; Pres, K of C; Lat C; Model
UN; Rptr, Sch P; SC; Mgr, Var C; Pres, Jr Cl; Mgr,
Bkbl; Hockey; Alg A; COM; Citz A; Cl Fav; K of C
A; Math A; Co- cpt, Vlbl; Geom A; *St Francis Col;
Acct.*

MYRON, Jerome Anthony
St Elizabeth HS; Pittsburgh, PA; Fr C; K of C; Sch
P; JV, Bkbl; Vlbl; Pius X Book A's.

MYTINGER, Margaret Lee
Sarasota HS; Sarasota, FL; Chor; Secy, Rainbow; *Manatee Jr Col; Lab Tech.*

N

NABB, Kristan Anne
Moline Sr HS; Moline, IL; Chor; Drama; Ensm;
Hmrm; F-Ed, Sch P; Span C; H of F; Opt A; Win,
Fire Prevention Essay; Runner-Up, Amer Legion;
Nom, Crystal Court; *Span.*

**NABORS,
Michael Charles Ramon**
Kalamazoo Central HS; Kalamazoo, MI (383-517)
All Amer Yth; Dbte Tm; Lat C; NFL; Span C; Spch
C; Yth o-t Yr; MLK Creative Win; Ch of Black Hist
& Brotherhood Wk; *East Mich Col; Journ.*

NABORS, Shirley Ann
Albany HS; Albany, NY; Span C; *Computer Sci.*

NABORS, William Henry
Decatur HS; Decatur, AL (10%-300) Chem C;
Hmrm; Key C; Math C; Mu Alpha Theta; NHS; Sci
C; Span C; Var C; Bsbl; Bkbl; Alg A; *Auburn U;
Vet.*

NABOZNY, Mary Elizabeth
St Hedwig HS; Detroit, MI (4-70) Band; Chor;
Tres, NHS; SC; Sftbl; Hon Prog; *Wayne St U; Med
Technology.*

NACHTIGAL, Ron Allan
Wheaton HS; Wheaton, MN (12-81) 4H; Var C;
Bkbl; Ftbl; Tr; 4H A.

NACKO, Debra H
Riverside Jr-Sr HS; Taylor, PA (9-196) Co-Ed,
Ann; Chor; FTA; NHS; Span C; Sftbl; Hon Prog;
Sftbl Ltr; *Col Misericordia; Psych.*

NADEAU, Tracy Leigh
Sooner HS; Bartlesville, OK (50-289) Fr C; FBLA;
NHS.

NADEKOW, Robert Paul
Miramar HS; Miramar, FL; Bsbl; Bkbl; Yth Fel;
Life Rank Sct; *US Air Force Acad; Math.*

NADGE, Valerie Ann
Moravia Central Sch; Moravia, NY (3-105) Band;
Chor; Drama; NHS; Regent Schol; John Philip
Sousa Band A; Span A; Alfred T Atwood Spelling
A; *Eisenhower Col; Human Relations.*

NADLER, Antoinette Rose
Chilton HS; Chilton, WI (13-129) Ann; Pres, Chor;
Ensm; Madrigal; Sch P; COM; Hist A; Type A;
Dist & St Festival Mus A's; Church Organist; Concert Pianist; *Silver Lake Col; Mus.*

NAFF, Kim Eileen
Lawrence HS; Lawrence, KS (425-750) Band; Tr;
Hon Prog; Ntl Achv Schol; Phi Beta Kappa; *Kans
U; Bus Law.*

NAFFZIGER, Deborah Ellen
Waukegan Christian Sch; Zion, IL; Ann; Chldr;
Chor; Hmrm; VP, SC; COM; S-T, SC; Bible Memory A; *Bethel Col; Elem Ed.*

NAGAHIRO, Rae Reiko
Henry Perrine Baldwin HS; Wailuku, HI (3-292)
Secy, NHS; Ed, Sch P; Pres, Sci C; Bausch & Lomb
A; *U of Hawaii; Chem.*

NAGANO, Linda Tami
Inglewood HS; Inglewood, CA; Band; Chor; SC;
Cpt, Sftbl; Tnns; CSF; Citz A; Gold Key; Pres Phys
Fitness A; Athletic C A.

NAGENGAST, Mary A
Immaculata HS; Chicago, IL (2-149) Chldr; Chess
C; Drama; Secy, Ger C; Hmrm; Lit Mag; NHS; Sch
P; Ski C; SC; Pres, Sr Cl; COM; Hon Prog; Sci A; St
Scholar; Vlbl; WW; *DePaul U; Chem.*

NAGLE, Laura E
Franklin Regional Sr HS; Murrysville, PA
(10%-400) AFS; Band; Chor; Ensm; Hmrm; SC;
Soccer; Hon Prog; Yth Fel; Rep, Yth Coun; Fin,
Telluride Schol; Phys Fitness A; *Harvard U; PreLaw.*

NAGLER, Cathy Jo
Angola HS; Angola, IN (10-170) FTA; GS; Lat C;
NHS; Jr Classical Lat; *Ind U; Pre-Med.*

NAGLER, Robin Lynn
Angola HS; Angola, IN (33%-190) Band; FTA; *Ball
St U; Ed.*

NAGLEY, Nancy Lee
John Handley HS; Winchester, VA (20-283) Ann; Bus C; Chor; Secy, Hmrm; NHS; Pres, ARC; SC; Rptr, Tri-HiY; Arch; Fin, Swim; Tnns; Tr; Hon Prog; Type A; Yth Fel; Phys Ed A; *Radford Col; Elem Ed.*

NAGORE, Kathy Mary
Salpointe Cath HS; Tucson, AZ (140-236) CYO; Chor; Y-Tns; Bsbl; Tr; Choir; *Ariz St U; Social Working.*

NAGY, Janet Paige
Westminster Christian Sch; Miami, FL (20-115) NHS; Mgr, Tr.

NAIL, Cynthia Karen
Eupora HS; Eupora, MS (10-84) BC; Chor; FHA; FTA; Rptr, Sch P; SC; Rptr, Jr Cl; Type A; *Miss St U; Acct.*

NAIL, Leah Jewel
Mortimer Jordan HS; Morris, AL (5-97) F-Ed, Ann; Chor; Pres, Hmrm; NHS; SC; Sr Cl; Beauty; Most Courteous; Sr Cl Officer; *U of S Ala; Foreign Lang.*

NAIL, Pamela Ann
Mortimer Jordan HS; Morris, AL (10%-150) Band; NHS; Chaplain, Band, Homeroom.

NAIL, Sandy Kae
E Greene HS; Grand Junction, IA (19-50) Band; Chldr; FHA; Rptr, 4H; Sci C; SC; Bkbl; JV, Sftbl; Mgr, Tr; *Social Work.*

NAIL, Vickie Delilah
Mortimer Jordan HS; Morris, AL (25%-150) Band; Ensm; FHA; Tr; *Sanford U; Foreign Lang.*

NAILOR, Duane A
Grover Cleveland HS; Buffalo, NY (5-30) A Cap Choir; Band; S-T, Bus C; Chor; Drama; Wrest; Cl Fav; MLS; Spch A; Swtht; Industrial Arts A; Tailoring A; Communications A; Richmond Speaking A; *Media Col; Communications.*

NAISER, Nancy Lynn
Springwoods HS; Houston, TX (275-600) Bus Mgr, Chor; Drama; Sch P; Cr-Ctry; Sftbl; Tr; Pres A; Pres, Church Yth Coun; VP, Church Choir; Dist Coun; Church Board.

NAJAR, Leona
Franklin HS; Los Angeles, CA; CYO; Chldr; Chor; Pres, Hmrm; Ed, Sch P; Sftbl; Tnns; COM; Citz A; Hon Prog; MLS; Sci A; Police Department A; *Pepperdine U; Legal Secy.*

NAKAMA, Renee Kinuko
Kubasaki HS; Okinawa, JAPAN (17-271) Ann; Drama; S-T, Lit Mag; NHS; MVP, Bkbl; Sftbl; COM; Powderpuff Ftbl; Co Ed, Stu Directory; *U of Hawaii; Recreation.*

NAKATANI, Shigeki James
Sacred Heart HS; San Francisco, CA; CSF; Sci A; *U of San Francisco; Bus.*

NAKAYAMA, Susan Miye
Bridgeton HS; Bridgeton, NJ (4-718) Tres, Fr C; NHS; Ed, Sch P; JV, Tnns; Citz A.

NALEPA, Kathleen Mary
Our Lady of Mercy Acad; Syosset, NY (50-150) SC; Pres, Sr Cl; Cpt, Bkbl; Coach, Cath Yth; Cpt, Vlbl; *NY U; Phys Therapy.*

NALEY, Ingrid Susan
Meadowdale Sr HS; Lynnwood, WA (2-355) A Cap Choir; Ensm; VP, NHS; Citz A; Sal; *Seattle Pacific U; Math.*

NALL, Brent Carlton
John F Kennedy Sr HS; Sacramento, CA (27-629) Ger C; Lat C; Bank of Amer A; CSF; *U of Calif; Hist.*

NALL, Susan Ann
Ft Stockton HS; Ft Stockton, TX (10-180) Band; Chor; GS; Hmrm; Mjrte; Secy, Sr Cl; Rptr, Soph Cl; Tnns; Tr; Beauty; COM; Most Out; Pres, Yth Fel; Tex Jr Miss Nom; All Dist Band; Miss Ft Stockton HS; Hon Stu; *Angelo St U; Phys Ed.*

NALLS, Gary Wayne
Brazos HS; Wallis, TX (5-37) FFA; Golf; Chor A; Reading A; *Wharton Jr Col; Mus.*

NALLY, Judy Sue
Defiance Sr HS; Defiance, OH (38-334) ARC A; Bible Quiz A; Lib Worker; DECA C; Bus Mgt.

NAMANNY, Lee Arthur
Antioch Sr HS; Antioch, CA (57-630) Ger C; Math C; Mu Alpha Theta; Sch P; Alg A; Math A; Attendance A; *San Jose St U; Engr.*

NANCE, Bradley Warren
Webster Co HS; Dixon, KY (17-157) Ann; Drama; Hmrm; Sci C; SC; Bio A; 4H A.

NANCE, Brian Kenneth
Levelland HS; Levelland, TX (10-260) Pres, Soph Cl; Cpt, Bkbl; Ftbl; Tr; HCt; Chaplain, SC; FCA; *Tex A&M U; Hist.*

NANCE, Cindy Lee
E Peoria Comm HS; E Peoria, IL (25%-400) Chor; Ensm; GS; Pres, Hmrm; Jr Miss Pagent; Madrigal; St Stu Congress; VP, SC; VP, Sr Cl; Bkbl; COM; HCt; Sci A; Yth Fel; Yth Leg; GAA; *Social Work.*

NANCE, Janice Laine
Wade Hampton HS; Greenville, SC (22-390) Chor; GS; Pres, Hmrm; NHS; Ed, Sch P; SC; Bkbl; Sftbl; COM; Hon Prog; NMS; Yth Fel; Yth Leg; *Clemson U; Math.*

NANCE, Jeff T
Rio Americano HS; Sacramento, CA; *Amer River Col.*

NANCE, Leroy Jr
Wakefield HS; Arlington, VA; Tr; Photography; PA; *U of Maryland; Photography.*

NANCE, Mary Elizabeth
Marshall HS; Marshall, TX; A Cap Choir; VP, Band; Chor; Ensm; FTA; Pres, Hmrm; Fin, Jr Miss Pagent; Lat C; Lit Mag; Madrigal; Mod Mus Mas; SC; Hon Prog; Lion's C Dist Qn; All St Yth Choir; Octagon C; Reading Writing, UIL; Swing Choir; Ntl Guild Auditions; *E Tex Baptist Col; Ed.*

NANCOLLAS, Daryl
Sky View HS; Smithfield, UT (2-611) Band; Order/ Arrow; Bsbl; Ftbl; Mgr, Swim; Tr; Wrest; Alg A; Citz A; God & Country A; Order/Arrow A; Eagle Sct; HR; *Utah St U; Med.*

NANGLE, Kirsten Erika
Immaculate Conception Acad; San Francisco, CA; Co-Ch, Ann; Chldr; Chor; Drama; Black Soc; *City Col of San Francisco; Drama.*

NANNEY, Jackie Lynn
College Park HS; College Park, GA (25%-141) Band; Drama; Lat C; Math C; Orch; Secy, SC; Sftbl; Tres, Candystripers; Bus Ministry; Acteens; *Primary Ed.*

NANTZ, Barbara Ann
Paul Harding HS; Fort Wayne, IN (7-281) Bus C; NHS; Span C; B Crocker A; Chamber of Comm A; Type A; Tri Kappa A; Instrument Ensm A; *Secretarial.*

NANTZ, Katherine Marie
Freedom HS; Morganton, NC (45-470) Anchor C; Ger C; Ch, Hmrm; InterAct C; NHS; ARC A; *Pfeiffer Col; Phys Therapy.*

NAPIER, Mark Alan
Buckhorn HS; Buckhorn, KY (2-63) Pres, 4H; 4H A; Ger A; Conservation Essay A; *U of Ky; Med.*

NAPOLI, Elyse Bernadette
Paramus HS; Paramus, NJ (9-600) NHS; Sci C; SC; Ch, Sr Cl; Cpt, Tnns; Hon Prog; Mgr, Boys Tr; Fr A; MVP, Tr; Girls Citz Inst; NCTE A; *Princeton U; Pre-Law.*

NAPPE, Tim M
Northwood-Kensett HS; Northwood, IA (7-68) *Waldorf Col; Comm Service.*

NAPPE, Timothy Mark
Northwood-Kensett HS; Northwood, IA (7-68) NHS; Mgr, Cr-Ctry; Mgr, Tr; COM; Swensrud Schol; *Waldorf Col; Comm Service.*

NAPPER, Gabriele Maria
Karlsruhe Amer HS; Karlsruhe, GERMANY; Vlbl; Ger A.

NAPUDA, James Michael
Pennsville Mem HS; Pennsville, NJ (68-240) Band; Ensm; Mgr, Ftbl; Bio A; Sci A.

NAPUTI, Joseph Tedpahogo
George Washington Sr HS; Mangilao, GUAM (4-740) NHS; SC; Co-Cpt, Ftbl; Soccer; Hon Prog; Math A; Type A; *US Naval Acad; Systems Analysis.*

NARAGON, Eric Wayne
N Liberty HS; N Liberty, IN (26-122) Monogram; Span C; SC; Var C; Bsbl; Ftbl; Co-Cpt, Wrest; HCt; Phys Ed A.

NARANJO, David
Castle Park HS; Chula Vista, CA; VP, Drama; InterAct C; Spch C; Parl, SC; Thes; COM; *Designing.*

NARCISSE, Calvinetta Christine
Buena HS; Sierra Vista, AZ (91-504) Fr C; NHS; Ski C; SC; Tri-HiY; Pres, Soph Cl; MLS; *Boston U; Med Tech.*

NARED, Daymon George
The Bronx HS of Sci; Bronx, NY; Drama; K of C A; Blk Organization for Stu Strength; *Child Psych.*

NARGI, Ronald Joseph
St Thomas Aquinas HS; Ft Lauderdale, FL (20-300) Ann; Pres, CYO; Dbte Tm; Fr C; Hmrm; Lat C; Ntl Yth Conf; Rptr, Sch P; Bsbl; JV, Bkbl; JV, Ftbl; Alg A; Bio A; COM; Chem A; Citz A; Hist A; Hon Prog; Sci A; Yth Fel; Yth Foundation; Yth Leg; *Bradley U; Engr.*

NARIOS, Elsicher
Williamston HS; Williamston, MI; AFS; HCt; Bus.

NARR, Roberta Susan
Pekin Comm HS; Pekin, IL (8-800) Chor; Community Yth Symph; Ensm; NHS; Orch; Rptr, Sch P; Tr; Q&S A; Mus.

NARVAEZ, Jo Ann
Mem HS; San Antonio, TX (21-300) Ann; Secy, FTA; NHS; Secy, Sci C; *U of Tex at Austin; Nurs.*

NASH, Brenda Dawn
Wachusett Regional HS; Holden, MA; Band; 4H; JV, Hockey; Tr; Jr Central Dist Band; Art.

NASH, Carol
Lamar Sr HS; Houston, TX; Dbte Tm; Hmrm; NFL; Orch; Math A; Spch A; *Howard U; Law.*

NASH, Dawn Marie
HS of Mus & Arts; Manhattan, NY; Sci C.

NASH, Donnie Louise
Beaumont HS; St Louis, MO (130-440) Hmrm; SC; Hon Prog; Journ A; *Harris Stowe Col; Special Ed.*

NASH, Janine Lois
Mt Healthy HS; Cincinnati, OH; Chor; Fr C; Tr A; *CTC; Tailor.*

NASH, Kim Vertina
Jonesboro Hodge HS; Jonesboro, LA; Bsbl; Bkbl; Ftbl; Tr; *NW La U; Religion.*

NASH, Kimberlee T
Wachusett Regional HS; Holden, MA (133-500) Band; Ensm; FHA; VP, 4H; Rainbow; ARC; Bkbl; 4H A; JA A; Field Hockey; *Children's Ed.*

NASH, Kimberly Hazen
Resource Lrng Ctr Shades Vly Annx; Birmingham, AL (5-36) Hmrm; NHS; Citz A; *U of Ala; Retail.*

NASH, Terri Ann
Valdosta HS; Valdosta, GA (10%-300) Ed, Ann; BC; Co-Ch, Model UN; Gov Honor Prog; Hon Prog; WW; Jr Cl Ed, Yrbk; *Phys Therapy.*

NASH, Timothy Alan
Summertown HS; Summertown, TN (3-72) Ann; VP, BC; Chess C; Ger C; Hmrm; NHS; A-Ed, Sch P; Pres, Sci C; SC; Bsbl; Bkbl; Hist A; Chess Champion; Most Studious; Civitan Essay Contest Win; *Vanderbilt U; Chem.*

NASIF, Donald Bowman
Vicksburg HS; Vicksburg, MS (19-244) AFS; BS; Key C; Bsbl; JV, Bkbl; JV, Tnns; Most Versatile; *La St U; Archt.*

NASLUND, Michelle Sue
Schaller Comm HS; Schaller, IA; Band; Cpt, Chldr; Chor; 4H; Var C; Sftbl; Swim; Tr; HCt; JA A; Yth Fel; Sunday Sch Teacher Asst; *Secretarial.*

NASRABADI, Alireza
St Agnes HS; New York, NY (7-34) Cpt, Soccer; Steven Inst; Elec Engr.

NASSRAWAY, Sandra Marie
Downey HS; Downey, CA (310-575) CYO; FTA; Sch Achieve Tm; Ski C; Span C; Tr; Cpt, Vlbl; Instructional Aid with Deaf; *Golden W Col; Teaching the Deaf.*

NATER, Sylvette Marie
Colegio Puertorriqueno de Ninas; Rio Piedras, PR (3-48) Chor; NHS; Pres, SC; COM; Hon Prog; Kiwanis A; *Acct.*

NATH, Terri Lynn
Luverne Jr-Sr HS; Luverne, MN; Chor; Ensm; Span C; Secy, SC; Bkbl; Tr; COM; Pres A; Yth Fel; *Westmar Col.*

NATHAN, Cecelia
Terrell Co HS; Dawson, GA (10%-112) Ann; BC; Co-Ed, Sch P; Tres, Sci C; COM; Ntl Sci Found; *Ga SW Col; Acct.*

NATHAN, Mathan Nelson
Marshall Islands HS; Majuro, MARSHALL ISLANDS; Cpt, Bsbl; Hon Prog; Star Student; Yth Fel.

NATION, Jacqueline Marie
Buchholz HS; Gainesville, FL (10%-500) Mu Alpha Theta; Span C.

NATION, Mark Alan
Kings Mtn Sr HS; Kings Mtn, NC; BC.

NATION, Sharon Marie
N Caddo HS; Vivian, LA (3-20) FHA; 4H; Pol Sci C; Sci C; Beauty; *Mr Lynn's Modeling Sch; Modeling.*

NATIONS, Christine Therese
Pass Christian HS; Pass Christian, MS (25%-110) Lit Ral; *Jeff Davis Col; Social Work.*

NATIONS, Laura Elizabeth
Webster Groves HS; Webster Groves, MO; SC; Swim.

NATOLI, Maria Grace
Tottenville HS; Staten Island, NY; *Kings Col; Med.*

NATVIG, Kim Kristina
Preble HS; Green Bay, WI (50%-606).

NATZKE, Susan Ann
Merrill Sr HS; Merrill, WI (1-374) Band; Ger C; JV, Bkbl; K of C A; Math A; Alleulia Bellringer; Vlbl.

NAUGHTON, Timothy Joseph
St Patrick HS; Chicago, IL (47-357) Chor; Pres, Hmrm; Tres, NHS; SC; Bsbl; Mgr, Bkbl; Mgr, Ftbl.

NAUGLE, Edward Dean
Windber Area HS; Windber, PA (16-139) Hmrm; NHS; Ftbl; Tr; Yth Fel; *Penn St U; Computer Sci.*

NAUGLER, Ellen Marie
Brewer HS; Brewer, ME (126-284) Bus C; FHA; Tres, Rainbow; F-Ed, Sch P; Hon Prog; Yth Fel; Vol Service A.

NAUMAN, Stephen Russell
Mt Vernon Sr HS; Mt Vernon, OH (40-402) Pres, 4H; Hmrm; Lat C; Orch; 4H A; Hist A; *Milligan Col; Bio.*

NAUMANN, Laura Ann
Montville Township HS; Montville, NJ (98-289) Rifle Sgt, Color Guard; Service C; WW; *Susquehanna U; Acct.*

NAUMANN, Susan R
Scranton Central HS; Scranton, PA (100-358) Band; NHS; Orch; Ski C; Type A; *Lackawanna Jr Col; Executive Secy.*

NAVALTA, Leonida F
Laupahoehoe HS; Laupahoehoe, HI (5-41) Secy, FHA; Hmrm; Sch P; Bkbl; Cr-Ctry; MVP, Tr; H of F; Pres A; Vlbl; *Hawaii Sch of Bus; Travel Mgr.*

NAVARRE, Christopher Paul
Robert E Lee HS; Baytown, TX (144-411) Key C; Ftbl; VP, FCA; *Stephen F Austin St U; Forestry.*

NAVARRO, George Henry II
Leesville HS; Leesville, LA (70-350) Rptr, CYO; VP, Chess C; Fr C; Lit Ral; SC; Rptr, Jr Cl; *LSU; Astronomy.*

NAVARRO, Marissa Baronia
John F Kennedy HS; Tumon, GUAM (13-511) Hmrm; NHS; Sch P; Arch; Tnns; COM; Citz A; Math A; Type A; *Pepperdine U; Med.*

NAVARRO, Taft Daniel
Cresset Christian Acad; Durham, NC; Ch, Ann; Chor; Drama; Ensm; Ntl Yth Conf; ARC; Ed, Sch P; Pres, SC; Pres, Sr Cl; Pres, Jr Cl; Pres, Soph Cl; Cr-Ctry; Tr; Wrest; Cl Fav; Journ A; MLS; Most Out; Spch A; Yth Fel; Christian Service A; *Bob Jones U; Ministry.*

NAVAS, Jorge Pedro
Our Lady of Pilar HS; Rio Piedras, PR (2-148) Chem C; Hmrm; VP, NHS; COM; Hon Prog; Sci Fair A; *U of Notre Dame; Pre-Med.*

NAVRATIL, Kurt David
E Mecklenburg HS; Charlotte, NC (36-589) Key C; Model UN; Rptr, Sch P; Pres, SC; Bkbl; Cr-Ctry; *Wake Forest U; Bus.*

NAWYN, Bruce Alan
Clifton HS; Clifton, NJ (350-863) Psych C; Automotive C; Yth Group Off; *LeTourneau Col; Aviation Technology.*

NAY, Freddie Homer
George Washington Sr HS; Manigalao, GUAM (3-740) NHS; Co-Cpt, Ftbl; Tnns; I Dare You; Industrial Arts A; *FSU; Engr.*

NAYLOR, Charles Laurence
Park Hill HS; Kansas City, MO (300-550) Band; Chor; Pres, Hmrm; SC; Var C; VP, Jr Cl; VP, Soph Cl; Bkbl; Ftbl; Golf; Soccer; Swim; Tnns; Tr; Pres A; Spch A; Type A; World, Ntl Jamboree, BSA; Jr Deacon; Heart of Amer Coun; Jr Assembly; Mic-O-Say; *U of Mo; Dentistry.*

NAYLOR, Gregory Philip
Lynchburg-Clay HS; Lynchburg, OH (20-100) VP, Band; Chor; Drama; Ensm; Span C; Pres, Soph Cl; *Sou St Col; Liberal Arts.*

NAYLOR, Mark Richard
Warren Western Reserve HS; Warren, OH (73-448) InterAct C; Span C; HR; *Youngstown St U; Law Enforcement Admin.*

NAYLOR, Suzanne Marie
S Hills HS; Covina, CA (20-420) F-Ed, Ann; Drama; Hmrm; SC; High HR; Daisy Chain; *Behavior Sci.*

NAYLOR, Thomas Glenn
Bret Harte HS; Altaville, CA (25-145) Co-Ed, Ann; Sch Achieve Tm; VP, Sr Cl; VP, Jr Cl; Bkbl; Cr-Ctry; Tnns; COM; 4H A; HCt; Lion A; MLS; *Delta Jr Col; Automotive.*

NEADOW, Viola Mae
Big Bay de Noc HS; Cooks, MI; Chldr; Chor; Fr C; 4H; Sch P; 4H A; JA A; WW; *Bay de Noc Comm Col; Bus Mgr.*

NEAL, Ellen Marie
Bel Air HS; El Paso, TX; Chor; Pres, FHA; Citz A; Know The Bible; Bicentennial, Choir; 'B' Avg, A's; *U of El Paso; Counselor.*

NEAL, Jana Lee
S Houston HS; S Houston, TX; A Cap Choir; Hon Prog; *Baylor U; Bus.*

NEAL, Julie Anne
Edgewood HS; Trenton, OH (20-294) Band; NHS; *Ohio St U; Horticulture.*

NEAL, Karen Denise
Independence HS; Independence, MS (15%-106) BC; FBLA; FHA.

NEAL, Katherine Elizabeth
Fayetteville HS; Fayetteville, AR; Tr; *U of Ark.*

NEAL, Leah Susan
Oak Hill HS; Oak Hill, OH (7-110) Band; BC; Chor; Secy, Fr C; FNA; 4H; NHS; Sch P; Secy, Tri-HiY; 4H A; *Ohio U; Phys Therapy.*

NEAL, Linda Susan
Colerain Sr HS; Cincinnati, OH (25-630) Pres, Ger C; NHS; Rainbow; SC; Var C; COM; HCt; Hon Prog; Yth Fel; Ger Hon Soc; Pres Coun; *U of Cincinnati; Spch Pathology.*

NEAL, Mildred Flowers
Columbus HS; Columbus, GA; NHS; Var C; Tres, Sr Cl; Secy, Jr Cl; Sftbl; *Converse Col.*

NEAL, Nancy Kirsten
S Houston HS; S Houston, TX (10-506) F-Ed, Ann; Band; Ensm; FTA; Hmrm; Mu Alpha Theta; NHS; Tres, Tri-HiY; Journ A; Chaplain, SC; Chaplain, Tri-Hi-Y; NHS Schol Nom; UIL Medal Win; *Baylor U; Mus Ed.*

NEAL, Percy Jr
Peoria HS; Peoria, IL (300-450) Cpt, Bkbl; Ntl Achv Schol; MVP, Bkbl; *Grandview Col; Social Psych.*

NEAL, Robin LaSandra
Lincoln HS; Dallas, TX; Secy, A Cap Choir; Band; Bus C; Key C; Math C; NHS; Sci C; S-T, SC; Beauty; HCt; Hon Prog; Swtht; Sch Cert's; SC A; Band, Choir, Medals; *Tex Women's U; Nurs.*

NEAL, Sherry
Corsicana HS; Corsicana, TX (59-273) A Cap Choir; Chor; Span C; *Baylor U.*

NEAL, William Robert Jr
Sidney Lanier HS; Montgomery, AL; Drama; Ensm; COM; ROTC A.

NEARMYER, Lana Rae
New Monroe Comm HS; Monroe, IA (10-44) Band; Chor; Dbte Tm; Ensm; Secy, FFA; Secy, 4H; Co-Cpt, Mjrte; Sci C; Var C; Cpt, Bkbl; Sftbl; Mgr, Tr; Yth Fel; *Iowa St U; Voc-Agr.*

NEARY, Christine Elizabeth
St Mary's HS; Lynn, MA (16-117) Co-Ed, Ann; CYO; Drama; Span C; Alg A; Chem A; Math A; Sci A; *Stonehill Col; Med Tech.*

NEASOM, Sandra Lee
Schenley HS; Pittsburgh, PA (25-283) Tres, Chldr; Drama; Math C; Co-Ed, Sch P; '25 Mst Influen Blck Yths Pittsb; *Drexel U; Bus Mgt.*

NEBELSICK, Janet Gail
Harris-Lake Park Comm HS; Lake Park, IA (4-39) Band; Chor; Mjrte; Bkbl; COM; Hon Prog; *U of N Iowa; Med Tech.*

NEBGEN, Linda Gale
Tyrone Area HS; Tyrone, PA (10%-216) Band; Chor; Fr C; Secy, 4H; 4H A; Kiwanis A; Most Out; Ch, Rptr, Fin, Semi-Fin, 4-H C; Farm Credit Coop; *Pa St U; Nurs.*

NEBGEN, Patricia Joy
Bern HS; Bern, KS (1-25) Ann; GS; Tres, NHS; Sch P; Phy A; Type A; *U of Kans; Math.*

NECAISE, Polly Jane
Pass Christian HS; Pass Christian, MS (25%-110) BC; VP, Hmrm; Co-Cpt, Bkbl; Sftbl; Tnns; Amer Leg A; COM; Cl Fav; Hon Prog; Sci A.

NECKLES, Kevin Carlson
Martin Luther HS; Maspeth, NY (40-102) Fr C; Soccer; *U of Albuquerque; Med Technology.*

NEDIC, Mira
Foreman HS; Chicago, IL (20-373) SC; COM; *Loyola U; Biol.*

NEDRELO, Laurie Jo
Seneca HS; Seneca, WI (4-44) Band; Chldr; Drama; Ensm; FHA; Mjrte; NFL; NHS; Spch C; Var C; Secy, Soph Cl; Tr; Spch A; Vlbl; Underclassman A; Ntl Hon Soc; Prom & Swtht Court.

NEE, Patricia Jean
Dobyns-Bennett HS; Kingsport, TN (45-500) Band; BC; CYO; Community Yth Symph; Mjrte; NHS; Orch; Span C; Span NHS; Soccer; COM; Hon Prog; JA A; Kiwanis A; Most Out; 1st Chair, All St & All E Tn, Bands; *U of Tenn; Pre-Law.*

NEEB, Kathleen Mary
Westfield HS; Westfield, WI (2-118) Band; Chldr; Chor; Ensm; Mjrte; Secy, NHS; VP, Span C; Span NHS; Var C; Sftbl; Wrest; Tres, Span C; WW, Foreign Lang; *UW-Eau Claire; Social Work.*

NEEBE, Deborah Lynn
Westminster HS; Westminister, CA (10-800) NHS; CSF; Hon Prog; Mentally Gifted Minors; *Pepperdine U; Acct.*

NEECK, Catherine Elizabeth
Rosary Acad; Sparkill, NY (5-69) Pres, NHS; Bkbl; Soccer; Sftbl; *Health.*

NEEDHAM, Becky Lee
Lafayette Sr HS; Lafayette, LA; Lit Mag; Rainbow; Bkbl; Ftbl; Sftbl; 4H A; JA A; Yth Fel; *U of SW La; Bus Ed.*

NEEDHAM, Kathy Gay
Charles Francis Adams HS; Clarkston, WA; A Cap Choir; *NW Nazarene Col; Bus.*

NEEL, Danny Jay
Dixie Co HS; Cross City, FL (3-90) VP, BC; Pres, Sr Cl; Ftbl; Rotary A; All Conf Ftbl; *Air Force.*

NEEL, Jefferson L
N Ridgeville HS; North Ridgeville, OH (1-311) Monogram; Pres, NHS; SC; Var C; Tres, Jr Cl; Bkbl; Co-Cpt, Ftbl; Tr; COM; Hon Prog; MLS; Most Out; NMF; Val; MVP, Ftbl; Col Schol; TV Acad Challenge; WW; Prom King; *Yale U; Engr.*

NEEL, Kimberly Lynne
Breckinridge Co HS; Hardinsburg, KY (15%-273) JV, Chldr; FTA; HCt.

NEEL, Mark Alan
Grand Ridge Sch; Grand Ridge, FL (8-49) Ann; BC; Bkbl; Cl Fav; *Chipola Jr Col; Communications.*

NEEL, Stanley Charles
Sumter Acad; York, AL (1-40) Ann; Pres, BC; Order/Arrow; Sci C; SC; Var C; Pres, Sr Cl; Pres, Jr Cl; Pres, Soph Cl; Ftbl; Balfour A; Math A; NMF; NMS; Q&S A; Val; *Birmingham Sou Col; Math.*

NEEL, Stephen Charles
Warren Area HS; Warren, PA (40%-450) All Amer Yth; Chor; Drama; Ntl Yth Conf; Sci C; Spch C; Tri-HiY; Golf; Sftbl; Swim; Tnns; Chem A; Hon Prog; Opt A; Spch A; Yth Fel; *Alliance Col; Chem.*

NEELEY, Sue Anne
Riverview HS; Sarasota, FL; Chor; Ensm; Tri-HiY; U of Tenn; Dental Hygiene.

NEELY, Alison Claire
R L Turner HS; Carrollton, TX (33%-800) Chldr; Fr C; Tnns; *E Tex St Col; Engr.*

NEELY, Gregory Warren
F L Schlagle HS; Kans City, KS (17-435) A Cap Choir; BS; Chor; Dbte Tm; Ensm; Madrigal; Model UN; NFL; Pres, NHS; Order/Arrow; Tr; COM; Citz A; Math A; Spch A; St Scholar; McDowell & Fine Arts C Schol; *William Jewell Col; Med.*

NEELY, James Anthony
York Comprehensive HS; York, SC (25-274) Fr C; Hmrm; NHS; Order/Arrow; Sci C; Pres, SC; Var C; JV, Bkbl; Ftbl; Hon Prog; Order/Arrow A; Yth Fel; *Col of Charleston; Pre-Med.*

NEELY, Johnny Dee
Simpson Co Acad; Mendenhall, MS (1-36) Hmrm; Math C; SC; Pres, Sr Cl; Bkbl; Co-Cpt, Ftbl; Alg A; Amer Leg A; B Crocker A; Bio A; COM; Chem A; Cl Fav; H of F; Hist A; HCt; Hon Prog; Math A; Phy A; Sci A; Star Student; Val; MVP, Ftbl; All-Star Ftbl; Spirit of Amer A; *U of Miss; Pre-Med.*

NEELY, Terri Elizabeth
Simpson Acad; Mendenhall, MS (4-21) A Cap Choir; Chldr; Ensm; S-T, Hmrm; Math C; Rptr, NHS; VP, SC; Bsbl; Bkbl; COM; Cl Fav; HCt; Hon Prog; Cutest; Drill Tm; *Ole Miss; Math.*

NEENO, Timothy Masanobu
Lane Tech HS; Chicago, IL (279-1152) *Westminster Col; Law.*

NEES, Michael Frederick
Sarasota HS; Sarasota, FL; Ftbl; JV, Golf; Gold Card A; Sarasota Journ; *U of Fla.*

NEESE, Elaine Carol
Brazil Sr HS; Brazil, IN (11-200) Rptr, Chor; VP, Drama; Secy, FHA; Hmrm; Mjrte; Model UN; NHS; VP, Thes; DARGCA; Yth Fel; Page for St Rep; WW; Drama A; *Ball St U; Fashion Merchandising.*

NEESE, Katherine Elaine
W S Neal HS; E Brewton, AL (3-114) Ed, Ann; JV, Chldr; Pres, Drama; FHA; FTA; NHS; Sci C; B Crocker A; Cl Fav; MLS; Eng A; *Jefferson Davis Jr Col; Bus.*

NEFF, Ellen Elizabeth
Catasauqua HS; Catasauqua, PA (48-150) Band; Yth Fel; Pres, Yth Group; Church Choir; Church Sftbl Tm; David Livingston A; *United Wesleyan Col; Sociology.*

NEFF, Kathy Sue
Rochester Comm HS; Rochester, IN (20%-177) Band; Chor; Ch, Drama; Fr C; 4H; NHS; Spch C; Thes; Sftbl; Swim; Tr; Spch A; Art A; Intl Thespian; Vet Sci A; *U of Evansville; Drama.*

NEFF, Kim Loraine
Borger HS; Borger, TX (5-206) Co-Ed, Ann; Dbte Tm; Rptr, Drama; FHA; FTA; NHS; Ski C; Span C; Rptr, Thes; Citz A; Elk A; Hon Prog; Journ A; Yth Fel; Church Lib; Board of Deacons; Christian Ed Comm; *Southwestern Ok St U; Phar.*

NEFF, Louise
Manila HS; Manila, UT (2-19) Chldr; Chem C; Ger C; GS; Pres, 4H; Math C; Phys C; Ed, Sch P; Sci C; Span C; S-T, SC; Var C; Bkbl; Tr; Alg A; Bio A; Chem A; Cl Fav; 4H A; Hist A; Hon Prog; Math A; Phy A; Sci A; HCt; Secy, 4-H C; Jr Prom, Rodeo Qn; Cl Off; *Ricks Col; Animal Health.*

NEGAS, Charles John
George Walton HS; Marietta, GA; Ann; Band; Key C; Bkbl; Tnns; Annual Photographer; Hon Camper; Outdoor Adventures C; Church Yth Group; BSct; *Harding Col; Law.*

NEGREY, Robert Alexander
Central HS; Thomasville, GA (40-325) JV, Bkbl; Golf; Sftbl; Citz A; Church Choir; *Bus.*

NEHRENZ, Kathryn Ruth
Lutheran HS W; Rocky River, OH (5-103) JV, Chldr; Chor; Ger C; Tres, Soph Cl; Tr; Hon Prog; JA A; Yth Fel; *Interior Decorating.*

NEIBLING, Anita Louise
Highland HS; Highland, KS; Ann; Band; Chor; Ensm; Mjrte; Secy, Soph Cl; B Crocker A; Cl Fav; MLS; Yth Fel; Pres, Board Member, Kayettes; Cpt, Pep C; John Philip Sousa Band A; *Highland Jr Col; Dietetics.*

NEIBLING, Robert Floyd
Highland HS; Highland, KS (1-24) Band; BS; FFA; VP, Jr Cl; Ftbl; Cl Fav; Kiwanis A; Val; *Kans St U; Mech Engr.*

NEIDLINGER, Susan Marie
Pine Grove Area HS; Pine Grove, PA (40-156) Band; Chldr; Chor; Hmrm; Sch P; Var C; Bkbl; Phys Achv A; Bkbl A; PA; *Reading Hospital Nurs Sch; Nurs.*

NEIGHBORS, Linda Elaine
Homewood HS; Homewood, AL (10%-270) Dbte Tm; Drama; Fr C; French NHS; NHS; Thes; Swim; Tnns; Hon Prog; NEDT; Spch A; Sr Lifesaving Cert; Church Yth Choir; *Auburn U; Vet Medical.*

NEIL, Gerald Dennis
Mitchell HS; Memphis, TN; Bsbl; Art A; *Eckerd Col; Engr.*

NEILL, David Wayne
Stockton R-1 Sch; Stockton, MO (5-77) Chor; FBLA; FFA; Secy, NHS; Rptr, Sch P; SC; Var C; Bsbl; Bkbl; Ftbl; Golf; Tr; Cl Fav; HCt; Best Dressed Sr; All Conf, All Dist, Ftbl; Hon Men All St, Ftbl; *SW Mo St U; Bus.*

NEILL, Jeffery Steven
Colonial Hills Christina HS; E Point, GA (2-35) Band; Pres, BC; Chor; Ensm; NHS; Sch P; Ftbl; Mus As; All-St Band; Nom, McDonalds All-Amer Band; *Applied Mus.*

NEILL, Terri Faye
Temple HS; Des Moines, IA; *Amer Inst of Bus; Mgr Trng.*

NEISLER, Melissa Marlene
Gaston Day HS; Gastonia, NC (14-40) Ann; Chldr; Chor; Fr C; ARC; Citz A; Sanctuary Soc; Yth Fel; Yth Leg; Gastonin Girls C; *Interior Decorating.*

NEITHAMMER,
John George III
Everett HS; Maryville, TN (20-230) BC; VP, Drama; 4H; ARC; Rptr, Sch P; Bsbl; Bkbl; Ftbl; Sftbl; DARGCA; Sci A; Star Student; Pres, Fresh Cl; *U of Tenn; Med.*

NEITZEL, Carla Jean
Albert Lea Sr HS; Albert Lea, MN (101-580) Chor; Ensm; Swim; COM; Type A; Yth Fel; 1st Pl, Information Communications; *Austin Col; Med Secy.*

NEJEDLY, Mary Patricia
St Mary's HS; Stockton, CA (14-204) Chor; Drama; Hmrm; NHS; Ski C; SC; Thes; VP, Jr Cl; Citz A; HCt; Hon Prog; MVP, Vlbl; *UCLA; Nurs.*

NEJEDLY, Susan Carol
St Mary's HS; Stockton, CA (1-256) Ann; Chldr; Drama; Fin, GS; Hmrm; NHS; Ski C; SC; Thes; CSF; Hon Prog; Vlbl.

NEKUZA, Andrea Ramona
Ennis HS; Ennis, TX (5%-237) F-Ed, Ann; Fr C; FTA; GS; Rptr, JETS; NHS; COM; Hist A; 3rd, Dist Miss FTA; *Stephen F Austin St U; Eng.*

NELDON, Lori Ann
Litchfield HS; Litchfield, IL; Chor; Drama; Rptr, Fr C; Dist Semi-Fin, VFW Loyalty Day.

NELL, Joan Marie
Capital HS; Helena, MT (10%-350) *Mont St U; General.*

NELL, Nancy Jane
Capital HS; Helena, MT (80-340) 4H; COM; 4H A; VFW A; St Parl, DECA; Secy, Rodeo C; Secy, Saddle C; *Powell Col; Horse Mgt.*

NELLE, Laurel D Anne
Lewisville HS; Lewisville, TX (25-450) Band; Ensm; NHS; SC; Yth Fel; Sup Rating, UIL Solo & Ensm; St Solo & Ensm; WW; *Social Work.*

NELMS, Donna Kay
Middleton HS; Middletown, OH (30-26) Pres, FHA; Bkbl; *Ohio St U; Phys Ed.*

NELMS, Doris Faith
Sheffield HS; Memphis, TN (9-160) Ann; Band; Cpt, Chldr; Chor; Secy, FHA; 4H; Hmrm; Pres, Mod Mus Mas; Mu Alpha Theta; Secy, NHS; Spch C; Thes; Tr; 4H A; Opt A; Spch A; Dist Oratory; Best in Oratory; WW; *Murray St U; Radio-tV Communications.*

NELMS, Willard Bruce Jr
Bellaire Sr HS; Bellaire, TX; *Houston Comm Col; Auto Mech.*

NELOMS, Sharon Yvette
Compton Sr HS; Compton, CA (25%-900) Rptr, Hmrm; SC; CSF; Hon Prog; Kiwanis A; *U of Sou Calif; Bus.*

NELSEN, Glen Richard
Riverview Gardens Sr HS; St Louis, MO; Order/Arrow; Sftbl; Tr; Order/Arrow A; PA.

NELSEN, Lori Irene
Lyons Pub Sch; Lyons, NE (4-33) Ann; Band; Chor; Secy, FBLA; Rptr, FHA; Pres, 4H; NHS; Var C; Bkbl; Tr; 4H A; Vlbl; FHA A; FBLA A; FHA Swtht Candidate; *U of Nebr; Home Ec.*

NELSEN, Mark LeRoy
Lyons Pub Sch; Lyons, NE (17-31) Band; Chor; Rptr, FFA; Pres, 4H; Var C; Mgr, Bkbl; Mgr, Ftbl; 4H A; St Farmer; DeKalb Agr Accomplishment; *NE Tech Comm Col; Agr.*

NELSEN, Adella Fay
Red Bluff Union HS; Red Bluff, CA (16-378) Chor; Fr C; VP, 4H; F-Ed, Lit Mag; NHS; Tr; COM; Lion A; Spch A; Social Ch, Yth Group; Teach, Sun Sch; Seal Bearer, CSF; *Southwestern Bible Col; Cristian Ed.*

NELSON, Alan Rex
Arkadelphia HS; Arkadelphia, AR (5-200) VP, Key C; Order/Arrow; Ftbl; Kiwanis A; Eagle Sct; *Communications.*

NELSON, Angela Marie
Loomis Pub HS; Loomis, NE (12-42) Chldr; Secy, Chor; Tres, 4H; Key C; Mjrte; NHS; Spch C; Tres, Y-Tns; Sftbl; Tr; Bio A; COM; 4H A; Hon Prog; Spch A; Vlbl Tm; *Mus Ed.*

NELSON, Ardis Re
Bonneville HS; Ogden, UT; A Cap Choir; Chor; InterClub Coun; ARC; Ski C; Thes; Mgr, Wrest; *Mus Ed.*

NELSON, Barbara Ann
Bell Voc HS; Washington, DC; Hmrm; NHS; Sch P; SC; Woodward Found A; Harry O Street A; *Federal City Col; Bus Ed.*

NELSON, Barbara Jean
Clear Lake HS; Clear Lake, WI (4-72) Band; Chem C; Chor; Fin, Ensm; FHA; Mjrte; Math C; NHS; Type A; St Solo, Ensm, A's; Mus Champion, Gen Baptist Conf; *Bethel Col; Math.*

NELSON, Becky Ann
Immanuel Baptist Christian Sch; Menomonie, WI; Ann; Band; Chldr; Chor; Rptr, Sch P; Pres, SC; Pres, Sr Cl; Citz A; Hon Prog; Val; HWANA; Vlbl; Christian Service; *Hyles Anderson Col; Christian Ed.*

NELSON, Brian Allen
Alvin HS; Alvin, TX (42-360) Dbte Tm; Swim; *Alvin Comm Col; Elec Engr.*

NELSON, Bruce Lee Jr
Ingleside HS; Ingleside, TX (50%-80) Parl, NHS; Bsbl; Cpt, Ftbl; Cl Fav; MVP, Ftbl; *Tex A&M U; Game Warden.*

NELSON, Carl Borja
George Washington Sr HS; Mongmong, GUAM (17-740) NHS; SC; JV, Cr-Ctry; Most Out; *U of Guam.*

NELSON, Carol Ruth
San Dimas HS; San Dimas, CA (103-254) Badminton; *Bethel Col; Law.*

NELSON, Cathy Sue
John Marshall HS; San Antonio, TX; Pres, FHA; FTA; Span C; Swim; Tr; Pep Squad Dance Tm; S-T Church Yth; PSAF; Pres Phys Fitness As.

NELSON, Charles Daniel
Cartersville HS; Cartersville, GA (18-148) Band; BC; Chor; Dbte Tm; Ensm; HiY; Hmrm; Lit Ral; Math C; Mu Alpha Theta; Sci C; SC; Thes; Gov Honor Prog; Hon Prog; Kiwanis A; Opt A; All St Chor; St Cl A, Boy's Solo; *Jacksonville St U; Vocal Mus.*

NELSON, Cheryl Ann
Maranatha HS; Arcadia, CA (3-63) Band; Chldr; NHS; Alg A; CSF; Most Valuable Song Girl; Pres, Pep C; *Biola Col; Nurs.*

NELSON, Cheryl Sue
Litchfield HS; Litchfield, MN (33%-175) Chor; Ensm; Span C; Mus Contest A; Ensm A; *NW Col; Airline Ticket Agent.*

NELSON, Christie Jan
Fort Pierce Central HS; Fort Pierce, FL (2-600) Tres, Key C; NHS; Secy, Span NHS; Secy, Jr Cl; Hist, Beta C; *Ed.*

NELSON, Christine Annette
Modesto HS; Modesto, CA (10-250) Ed, FFA; Tres, Ger C; Tnns; CSF; Star Student; Outst Secy; Outst Debator; *U of Calif; Vet.*

NELSON, Christine Louise
Twin Falls HS; Twin Falls, ID; Band; Ger C; VP, 4H; Fin, Jr Miss Pageant; Mjrte; 4H A.

NELSON, Cindy Marie
Wanamingo Pub Sch; Wanamingo, MN (9-40) Band; Chldr; Chor; Drama; Mjrte; Tr.

NELSON, Claudia Baxter
Shaker Hts HS; Shaker Hts, OH (10%-520) A Cap Choir; Chor; Dbte Tm; Model UN; Co-Cpt, Spch C; St Stu Congress; Hon Prog; NMF; Spch A; VP, Stu Congress A; Piano A's; Sch School Key; *Bryn Mawr Col; Anthropology.*

NELSON, Craig Lind
Gordon HS; Gordon, NE (11-86) Ann; Band; Chor, Secy, Drama; Ensm; 4H; Math C; NHS; Sch P; SC; Secy, Thes; Pres, Sr Cl; VP, Jr Cl; Bsbl; Mgr, Ftbl; JV, Sftbl; Mgr, Tr; Mgr, Wrest; Citz A; Cl Fav; Outst Service A; *Chadron St Col; Pre-Law.*

NELSON, Cynthia L
N Natchez Adams HS; Natchez, MS; Ann; BC; Parl, Chor; Ensm; COM; H of F; Hon Prog; Ability Count A; *Dillard U; Nurs.*

NELSON, Daniel Duane
Eastridge HS; Kankakee, IL (175-300) *Kishwakee Jr Col; Bus Adm.*

NELSON, David Albert
Harold L Richards HS; Oak Lawn, IL (82-629) Band; Order/Arrow; JV, Swim; *Sci.*

NELSON, David Scott
Sequoyah HS; Doraville, GA (5-365) Chess C; Dbte Tm; Ger C; Hmrm; MVP, Bsbl; JV, Bkbl; Cr-Ctry; Tnns; Gov Honor Prog; Hon Prog; MLS; Straight A's A; *Ga Inst of Technology; Architecture.*

NELSON, Dean Howard
Souris Pub Sch; Souris, ND (5-11) Chor; Mgr, Bkbl; Sftbl; 4H A; Co Fair A, Cattle & Showmanship; Jr Ldrs C; Asst Head Usher, Church; VP, Tres, Rptr, 4-H C; *Fargo Agr Col; Agr Sci.*

NELSON, Deborah Ranee
Spring Lake HS; Spring Lake, MI; Band; Chor; FNA; 4H; Mjrte; 4H A; ARC A; *Muskegon Comm Col; Nurs.*

NELSON, Dee Ann
Chantilly Secondary Sch; Chantilly, VA (25-300) Band; Ger C; Orch; Most Out; NMS; *Longwood Col; Hist.*

NELSON, Diana Marie
Lutheran HS Los Angeles; Los Angeles, CA (1-85) AFS; Band; MVP, Community Yth S; FBLA; Semi-Fin, GS; Math C; Span C; Bank Of Amer A; CSF; MLS; *UCLA Alumni Schol; UCLA; Dentistry.*

NELSON, Duane Alan
W View HS; Braham, MN; Band; Drama; Bsbl; Bkbl; Ftbl; Hon Stu.

NELSON, Edward John
Brown HS; Sturgis, SD (12-195) FFA; NHS; Var C; Bsbl; Cpt, Bkbl; Ftbl; COM; Hist A; Rep, St Hist Conf; *SD St U; Chem.*

NELSON, Eric Arnold
Seaholm HS; Birmingham, MI (7-30) Lat C; NHS; Golf; COM; Citz A; Journ A; Ntl Achv Schol; *Mich St U; Engr.*

NELSON, Gina Gwena
Ripley HS; Ripley, TN; Fr C; *Lane Col; Elem Ed.*

NELSON, Gretchen Shelea
Booker T Washington Sr HS; Tulsa, OK (50%-315) HQn; *OSU; Bus Mgt.*

NELSON, James Lowell
Moline Sr HS; Moline, IL (110-832) Band; Ensm; A-Ed, Lit Mag; NHS; Orch; Ed, Sch P; Sci C; Span C; Span NHS; Hon Prog; Journ A; Pres A; Q&S A; Rotary A; Pres, Church Yth Fel; Interviewer; Church Coun; Rosalynn Carter; Best Staffer, Newspaper; Dept Hon, Social Stu; *Gustavus Adolphus Col; Sociology.*

NELSON, James Otis
Lansdowne-Aldan HS; Lansdowne, PA (5-225) Band; Hmrm; NHS; SC; Ftbl; Hockey; Tnns; JV, Wrest; Hist A; Yth Fel; Ecology C; Distinguished HR; Pres, MYF; *Econ.*

NELSON, James Wesley
Iowa City City HS; Iowa City, IA (10%-330) Pres, Dbte Tm; NFL; NHS; Degree of Excellence A; *Law.*

NELSON, Jeannine
Deland Sr HS; Deland, FL; *Home Ec.*

NELSON, Jennifer Lisa
Laurel Co HS; London, KY (33%-450) Fr C; FBLA; *David Lipscomb Col; Eng.*

NELSON, Jeri Mae
Lakota HS; Lakota, ND (5-48) Secy, Band; Chldr; Ensm; VP, NHS; VP, SC; Var C; Bkbl; Sftbl; MVP, Tr; *US Air Force Acad.*

NELSON, Joan Elizabeth
Gridley Union HS; Gridley, CA (34-116) Ann; Pres, CYO; Chldr; Chor; Drama; Secy, FNA; Ski C; Span C; VP, Y-Tns; Ftbl; *Sacramento St Col; Nurs.*

NELSON, John Carl
Mt Vernon HS; Mt Vernon, MO; FFA; Ftbl; Tr; *Farming.*

NELSON, John Joseph
Battle Creek Pub Sch; Battle Creek, NE (13-55) CYO; Var C; Bsbl; Bkbl; Ftbl; Tr; *Kearney Col; Eng.*

NELSON, Jolene Jaye
Cedar Falls HS; Cedar Falls, IA (30-465) A Cap Choir; Band; Chor; Community Yth Symph; Madrigal; NHS; Orch; Rptr, Sch P; Span C; St Scholar; All St Band; *U of N Iowa; Mus Ed.*

NELSON, Jon LaVern
Norte Del Rio HS; Sacramento, CA (90-250) Mod Mus Mas; Bkbl; Soccer; Swim; Tr; *Calif Baptist Col; Theology.*

NELSON, Judith Margaret
Lansdowne-Aldan HS; Lansdowne, PA (40-220) Chor; VP, Drama; Arch; Bkbl; Sftbl; Swim; Tnns; Poet A; Yth Fel; *Temple U; Drama.*

NELSON, Julie Katherine
Mankato HS; Mankato, MN (30-302) Chor; Hmrm; Ski C; Y-Tns; Golf; Mgr, Swim; Distinguished Stu Hon, Drafting; *U of Minn; Archt.*

NELSON, Kathleen Denise
Englewood Christian Sch; Independence, MO (4-16) A-Ed, Ann; Chess C; Chor; Secy, Drama; Rptr, Sch P; Tres, SC; Bkbl; *Mo U; Journ.*

NELSON, Kathy Renee
Sunset HS; Dallas, TX (10%-350) A Cap Choir; Tres, Chor; VP, Drama; Ensm; NHS; Span C; Secy, Spch C; Thes; Cl Fav; Hon Prog; All Star Cast A; DAHSS; Cand, Clark Found Schol; *U of Tex at Arlington; Dental.*

NELSON, Kenneth Philip
Evergreen Park Comm HS; Evergreen Park, IL (117-432) AFS; Cr-Ctry; Tr; Swim Guard; *DePaul U; Acct.*

NELSON, Kenny Ray
Owensboro HS; Owensboro, KY; Chor; Dbte Tm; Drama; Hmrm; SC; Bkbl; Ftbl; Sftbl; Tr; HCt.

NELSON, Kimberly P
Tartan Sr HS; St Paul, MN (6-400) Pres, Band; Community Yth Symph; Jr Miss Pagent; NHS; Tnns; Jr Miss Pageant Scholastic A; St Mus Contest Sup Rating; Congeniality A; *U of Texas-Arlington; Medicine.*

NELSON, Kirsten Renee
Bridgemont HS; San Francisco, CA (3-15) Chor; Hmrm; Ch, SC; JA A; Type A; AKA A; *Bishop Col; Bus.*

NELSON, Kristen Elizabeth
Holliston HS; Holliston, MA (117-257) Secy, AFS; Band; Chor; Drama; Secy, Fr C; Orch; Secy, Span C; Sftbl; Tr; Hon Prog; Most Out; Type A; Yth Fel; Cl Mus; Dist Chor; Town Drama C; *Becker Jr Col; Animal Tech.*

NELSON, Kristen Elizabeth
Clarkston HS; Clarkston, GA (12-378) BC; Drama; Fr C; COM; Hon Prog; Math A; Jr Civitan; Mus Productions; *Wheaton Col; Art.*

NELSON, Laura Marie
Belle Fourche HS; Belle Fourche, SD (8-106) Fr C; Math C; NHS; Math A; Church Choir; Coach, Girls Sftbl; Beef Cook- off; *Phys Therapist.*

NELSON, Laurel Diane
Balaton Pub HS; Balaton, MN (15-40) Band; JV, Chldr; Chor; FHA; Spch C; Mgr, Bkbl; COM; Vlbl; Ltr A; Numeral A.

NELSON, Linda Kay
Lewis & Clark HS; Spokane, WA; Chldr; Fin, GS; Hmrm; Key C; NHS; Tres, Sr Cl; Secy, Jr Cl; Golf; JA A; Masonic A; Swtht; Girls Service C; Rep, Photography Studio; *U of Wash; Ed.*

NELSON, Linda Sue
Fountain Valley HS; Fountain Valley, CA (141-1125) Band; Hmrm; Pres, Key C; ARC; SC; JV, Tnns; COM; Citz A; Hon Prog; MOD; Cornet A; *Child Development.*

NELSON, Linda Sue
Highlands HS; San Antonio, TX (13-594) Band; Ger C; NHS; Hon Prog; *Southwest Tex St U; Elem Ed.*

NELSON, Lisa Dale
Castleberry HS; Fort Worth, TX (80-209) FHA; JV, Bkbl; JV, Cr-Ctry.

NELSON, Lisa Kaye
Sumner HS; St Louis, MO (27-419) Ch, Hmrm; NHS; Co-Ed, Sch P; VP, SC; Citz A; Art A & Hon's; *Stephens Col; Art.*

NELSON, Lois M
Dix Pub HS; Dix, NE (1-13) Co-Ed, Ann; Chor; Drama; 4H; Mjrte; Spch C; Var C; Tres, Jr Cl; Bkbl; Tr; 4H A; Pres A; Spch A; Star Student; VofDEM; Vlbl; Yth Ldrship A; *U of Nebr.*

NELSON, Lorae Lynn
Emmons HS; Emmons, MN (1-28) Co-Ed, Ann; Band; NHS; Ed, Sch P; Spch C; Secy, Sr Cl; Tr; Spch A; Type A; NMS Commendation; WW; Gen Mills Family Ldr of Tomorrow; *St Paul Bible Col; Christian Ed.*

NELSON, Lori Ann
Annville Cleona HS; Annville, PA (50%-140) Chor; FHA; HiY; Hmrm; Secy, SC; MVP, Sftbl; Kg & Qn of Hearts Ct; Outst Stu, Vo-tech; *Med.*

NELSON, Lori Ann
Balaton Pub HS; Balaton, MN (15-30) Band; FHA; SC; Bkbl; Golf; 4H A; Pom Pon; Pres & Tres, 4-H C; *Child Care.*

NELSON, Lori Marie
Ralston HS; Ralston, NE; AFS; Chor; Ensm; Madrigal; JV, Tnns; Church Yth Choir; Church Pianist.

NELSON, Lorie Diane
Issaquah HS; Issaquah, WA (228-570) Yth Fel; *San Jose Bible Col; Ed.*

NELSON, Lorraine Gail
Sun Valley HS; Aston, PA (40%-500) FNA; *W Chester St Col; Nurs.*

NELSON, Lynne Alison
Eastwood HS; El Paso, TX; A Cap Choir; Chor; Hmrm; SC; Ch, Church Sr Social Committee; Jr NHS; Eng A; *Phys Therapy.*

NELSON, Marcia Gay
Parsons Sr HS; Parsons, KS (12-201) HR; *SW Col; Elem Ed.*

NELSON, Mark Michael
Dassel-Cokato HS; Cokato, MN (3-130) A Cap Choir; Band; Chor; Madrigal; Orch; JV, Bkbl; Golf.

NELSON, Mark Shane
Oak Valley Christian Sch; Oakdale, CA; Band; NHS; ARC; Sch P; Var C; Bkbl; Ftbl; MVP, Swim; Tnns; Wrest; ARC A; Spch A; Yth Fel; *Col of Idaho; Law.*

NELSON, Michael Gene
Clifton HS; Clifton, KS (5-25) BS; Chor; Ensm; FFA; 4H; VP, Jr Cl; Co-Cpt, Bkbl; Ftbl; Tr; COM; 4H A; Yth Fel; WW; Yth for Mus; *Bethany Col; Phys Ed.*

NELSON, Michael Scott
Harry A Burke HS; Omaha, NE (74-668) NHS; Sftbl; Amer Leg A; ROTC A; Type A; Omaha World-Herald Merit A; Retired Off Assn Plaque; Dept o-t Army Superior Cadet A; *Wheaton Col; Chem.*

NELSON, Nancy Ann
Willow Comm Sch; Quimby, IA (2-32) Band; Pres, 4H; NHS; Var C; Bkbl; Cr-Ctry; Tr; COM; 4H A; *Nurs.*

NELSON, Nancy Elaine
Sweet Home HS; Sweet Home, OR; Band; Chor; Ensm; Semi-Fin, GS; Hmrm; Fin, Key C; Mod Mus Mas; NHS; Pres, Rainbow; SC; VP, Var C; Cpt, Bkbl; Tr; GAA; Cpt, Vlbl; *Oreg St U.*

NELSON, Pamela Cecile
Fremont HS; Sunnyvale, CA; Band; Ensm; NHS; CSF; *Humboldt Col; Sci.*

NELSON, Pamela Gail
Paul Lawrence Dunbar HS; Fort Worth, TX; Ann; Band; Chor; Hmrm; Mjrte; Mod Mus Mas; NHS; SC; Homemaking A; Karate A; Eng A; PA; *U of Houston; Med.*

NELSON, Patricia Ann
Nettie Lee Roth HS; Dayton, OH (4-270) Chem C; Fr C; FHA; Hmrm; SC; Citz A; Prom Qn; PA; *Wright St U; Med.*

NELSON, Paul Ross
Petoskey HS; Petoskey, MI (10%-350) A Cap Choir; Band; Chor; Community Yth Symph; Drama; Ensm; Fr C; Madrigal; Sci C; Spch C; Bio A; Citz A; Spch A; Hons Band; *Albion Col; Theater.*

NELSON, Paul Snider
Eastern Hills HS; Fort Worth, TX (50-485) Ntl Merit Commendation; *U of Tex at Arlington; Bus Adm.*

NELSON, Rebecca Faith
Jenkins HS; Chewelah, WA (4-60) Honors A; Bkbl; DAR A; Var C; Tr.

NELSON, Robert Jay
Elgin HS; Elgin, IL (3-845) Ger C; Ski C; Var C; Tnns; Wrest; COM; Hon Prog; Rotary A; St Scholar; Yth Fel.

NELSON, Robin Ellen
Roosevelt HS; Minneapolis, MN (3-545) Chor; Ger C; NHS; H of F; Outst, Ger; Outst, Creative Writing; 'Smartest'; *Augsburg Col; Math.*

NELSON, Ronald Eugene
Rockledge HS; Rockledge, FL (15%-319) All Amer Yth; Hmrm; Rptr, Sch P; VP, SC; Ftbl; Cpt, Tr; COM; Citz A; Most Out; MVP, St Champ, All Conf, Tr; *Fla St U; Phys Therapy.*

NELSON, Ronald Oscar
Jamestown HS; Jamestown, NY (168-486) Tres, A Cap Choir; Tres, AFS; Madrigal; SC; *Jamestown Comm Col; Journ.*

NELSON, Ronda Lisa
Highland Park HS; Dallas, TX (108-328) Chor; Hmrm; SC; Tri-HiY; Art A; *Tex Tech Col; Art.*

NELSON, Susan Mae
Kerkhaven HS; Kerkhoven, MN (14-60) Ann; FHA; 4H; ARC; Spch C; Bkbl; Tr; 4H A; ARC A; Spch A; Hon Men, Bkbl; *Mankato St U; Phys Therapist.*

NELSON, Susan Marie
Martin Luther HS; Greendale, WI (12-119) Band; Chldr; Fin, GS; NHS; JV, Bkbl; JV, Sftbl; Tr; Secy, YCC; Vlbl; Prom Court; *Math.*

NELSON, Susan Marie
Williams Bay HS; Williams Bay, WI (9-45) Band; Chor; Ensm; Span C; Bkbl; HQn; *Moody Bible Inst; Missions.*

NELSON, Tammy Lee
Ashland Sr HS; Ashland, WI (25%-200) Band; Co-Cpt, Chldr; Chem C; Hmrm; Fin, Jr Miss Pagent; Model UN; NFL; NHS; Ed, Sch P; Ski C; SC; UN Council; Var C; World Affairs C; Tr; Beauty; Poet A; Spch A; Composition A; Chldr A; *Eau Claire U; Med.*

NELSON, Teresa Ann
McLoud HS; McLoud, OK (10,-120) Band; FHA; FTA; Tres, SC; Bkbl; Sftbl; Tr; HCt; FCA; Christian Ath o-t Yr; *Okla St U; Bus.*

NELSON, Teresa Joy
Cushing HS; Cushing, TX (1-34) Ann; FHA; 4H; Pres, NHS; SC; Secy, Sr Cl; Pres, Jr Cl; Pres, Soph Cl; Bkbl; Citz A; Cl Fav; HCt; Type A; Val; All-St Forward, Bkbl; Miss CHS; *Stephen F Austin St U; Bus.*

NELSON, Terri Lynn
Minnetonka Sr HS; Minnetonka, MN (141-638) Orch.

NELSON, Thomas Allen
Jamestown HS; Jamestown, NY (48-524) Fin, Dbte Tm; NFL; NHS; Order/Arrow; Amer Leg Orator A; God & Country A; Order/Arrow A; Spch A.

NELSON, Tracy Ann
Edgerton Sr HS; Edgerton, WI (1-185) Chldr; Chor; Fr C; GS; SC; Tres, Soph Cl; Social Rep, Sr Cl; Vlbl; Gym; NML; *Carroll Col; Bus.*

NELSON, Troy
N Mesquite HS; Mesquite, TX; Parl, FHA; Mgr, Ftbl; PA; *Mech Drawing.*

NELSON, William James
Barringer HS; Newark, NJ (240-615) Band; Bkbl; *Jersey City St Col; Communications.*

NENOW, Mark Charles
Blair HS; Blair, NE (13-150) Order/Arrow; Ftbl; Tr; Order/Arrow A; *Pre-Med.*

NEPTUNE, Enid Rose
Plymouth HS; Plymouth, NC (3-240) A-Ed, Ann; Math C; Secy, SC; Hon Prog; 1st Pl, Read- a- thon; WCU Gifted Prog; Nom, Governor's Sch; *UNC Chapel Hill; Hist.*

NEPTUNE, Lionel William
Plymouth HS; Plymouth, NC (3-192) A-Ed, Ann; Hmrm; Math C; NHS; Sch P; Span C; Pres, SC; Bkbl; JV, Ftbl; Gr Marshal; HCt; NHS Del; Gov's Sch; *Engr.*

NERHOOD, LaDawn Marie
Middleburg HS; Middleburg, PA (5-200) Chor; Ensm; Cpt, Bkbl; 4H A; Sports Ltr; *Wiallsompont Comm Col; Bus.*

NERVIG, Denis Jeffrey
Simi Valley HS; Simi Valley, CA (475-681) Arch; Var C; Arch; Ftbl; Tr; JV, Wrest; Most Out; Pres A; *Biol.*

NESBIT, Byron David
Southwest HS; Miami, FL; Ch, Hmrm; NHS; SC; Bsbl; Bkbl; COM; God & Country A; Hon Prog; Sci A; Swtht; Presidential Phys Fitness A; Bkbl A; Jr NHS A; Stu Service A; Schol A; Principal's A; Attendance A; Excellence A; SC & Yrbk Staff; *Dentistry.*

NESBIT, Robin Lyn
Greenville HS; Greenville, IL; Band; Hmrm; VP, Fresh Cl; *Art.*

NESBITT, Connie Marie
Ticonderoga HS; Ticonderoga, NY (68-116) Squadron Ldr; Pres, Church Yth; Bus Secy; Sundy Sch Tchr & Superintendent.

NESBITT, Elizabeth Regina
Mother Cabrini HS; New York, NY (1-102) Band; GS; NHS; Sci C; COM; NEDT; Regent Schol; Usher; HS Schol; Vol Serv C; Theatre C; Empire GS; VP, Interntl C; Extra Duty A; Sch Win, Century Three Comp; *Manhattan Col; Chem.*

NESBITT, Rosalee
N Charleston HS; N Charleston, SC; Chor; FHA; 4H; Hmrm; InterClub Coun; ARC; Y-Tns; Secy, Sr Cl; COM; ARC A; Yth Fel; Most Versatile; VP, Afro-Amer C; *Columbia Commercial Col; Bus.*

NESMITH, Brenda Lynette
Falkville HS; Falkville, AL (25%-67) PA A; *Lee Col; Mus.*

NeSMITH, Marti Ella
Fairfield HS; Fairfield, AL (1-160) Ann; Band; Pres, BC; Chor; Ensm; GS; InterClub Coun; Sch P; SC; Y-Tns; HQn; *Auburn U; Special Ed.*

NESMITH, Queen Christine
Williamsburg HS; Andrews, SC; Ed, Sch P; Co-Cpt, Bkbl; *Denmark Tech Col; Bus Adm.*

NeSMITH, Stephen Louis
York Comp HS; York, SC (9-240) Ch, Hmrm; NHS; Sci C; Span C; Var C; Wrest; *Clemson U; Elec Engr.*

NESMITH, Sylvia Loretta
English HS; Boston, MA; *Nurs.*

NESS, Rolf Olin
Worley HS; Worley, ID (2-11) Ann; Band; JETS; Order/Arrow; ARC; Var C; VP, Sr Cl; Bkbl; Tr; COM; Order/Arrow A; Sal; Eagle Sct A; *N Idaho Col; Engr.*

NESTER, Brenda Lee
Pottstown Sr HS; Pottstown, PA (8-275) Band; NHS; Past Grand Lecturer, Rainbow Girls.

NESTER, Donna Jean
Man HS; Man, WV (4-180) Band; Bus C; Cpt, Mjrte; Tnns; Beauty; Interlochen Ntl Mus; Type A; Yth Fel; Bookkeeping, Shorthand, A's; Band, Majorette, A's; *Marshall U; Secondary Ed.*

NESTOR, Laura Ann
Acad o-t Holy Names; Tampa, FL (6-68) Hmrm; VP, InterClub Coun; NHS; ARC; Sci C; Sodality; Span C; S-T, Span NHS; VP, SC; Tr; Yth Fel; Most Sincere Sr; Prom Qn; Ntl Merit Commended Stu; *U of Va; Pre-Med.*

NESTOROWICZ, Daria Roksulana
Immaculate Conception HS; Hamtramck, MI (10-45) A Cap Choir; CYO; Chldr; Chor; Ensm; NHS; Orch; Sch P; Bkbl; Mgr, Cr-Ctry; Mgr, Tnns; Hon Prog; MLS; Most Out; Mus, Bowl, A's; *Wayne St U; Dentistry.*

NETBURN, Peter Craig
Karlsruhe Amer HS; Karlsruhe, GERMANY; F-Ed, Ann; Drama; InterClub Coun; Ntl Teachers Coun; St Stu Congress; SC; Mgr, Ftbl; Tnns; Hon Prog; Pres A; Yth Leg; Drama A; *Med.*

NETH, Joann Marie
Lauralton Hall HS; Milford, CT (3-93) CYO; Chor; Drama; Lat C; Lit Mag; NHS; Ski C; Pres, Span C; Span NHS; VP, Sr Cl; Cpt, Tnns; NEDT; HS All-Amer; *Pre-Med.*

NETHERLAND, Don
Brookhaven Acad; Brookhaven, MS; Band; BC; Chess C; Fr C; JV, Bkbl; Ftbl; Tr; Bio A; COM; Math A; NEDT; Sci A; *U of Miss; Med.*

NETHERS, Gail Charolette
West HS; Columbus, OH (30-581) Band; Chess C; Chor; Ensm; Mod Mus Mas; NHS; Span C; Sftbl; VCY; Vocal Hon Trophies; Quad; St Touring Choir; Missionette Hon Star; Tres, Yth Fel; *SW Tex Col.*

NETHERY, Kathryn Ann
Washington HS; Fremont, CA; Chldr; Hmrm; Secy, InterClub Coun; Co-Ed, Lit Mag; Secy, SC; Pres, Soph Cl; JV, Soccer; Swim; Fin, Cl Favorite; Fin, Homecoming Ct; Semi-Fin, Yth Fel; MVP, Gym; Al Ord Jobs Daugh Ment Gift Minors; *Law.*

NETT, Denise Carol
Kingman Rural HS; Kingman, KS (50-100) S-T, Fr C; FFA; VP, 4H; Rainbow; Y-Tns; Horse Show A; Tex St Tech Inst; Saddlemaking.

NETTERVILLE, Sherry Lynn
Grace King HS; Metairie, LA; Chor; Drama; Pres, Hmrm; Mjrte; COM; Journ A; Yth Fel; Journ Ldrship A; SE La U; Journ.

NETTLES, Debra Diann
Wilson HS; Wilson, TX (5-14) Band; Chldr; Drama; FFA; FHA; Secy, 4H; Secy, Hmrm; Secy, Jr Cl; Bkbl; Tr; Cl Fav; 4H A; S Plains Jr Col; Nurs.

NETTLES, Gena Renee
Brookhaven Acad; Brookhaven, MS; BC; Fr C; Rainbow; Miss U for Women; Bus Adm.

NETTLES, Gwendolyn Geneen
T R Miller HS; Brewton, AL (35-99) Bus C; Pres, Chor; FBLA; VP, FHA; VP, FTA; Lit Mag; ARC; SC; Bkbl; Sftbl; Tr; Beauty; Cl Fav; Phys Fitness A; Troy St U; Bus Adm.

NETTLES, John David
Crenshaw HS; Los Angeles, CA; Co-Cpt, Ftbl; Tr; PA.

NETTLES, Rose Marie
C F Vigor HS; Prichard, AL; Chor; Carver St Trade Sch; Off Ed.

NETTLES, Viola
Halter HS; Wellston, MO (5-58) Rptr, Sch P; Rptr, Jr Cl; Parl, Soph Cl; Hon Prog; Journ A; Asst-Secy, Sr Cl; Forest Park Comm Col; Pediatrics.

NETTLESHIP, Micaela Denise
Copperas Cove HS; Copperas Cove, TX; FBLA; SW Tex St U.

NEU, Gail Dawn
Lindbergh HS; St Louis, MO (300-900) Semi-Fin, Swim; Hon Prog; Camp Counselor; U of Mo; Dietetics.

NEU, Kim Marie
Lindbergh HS; St Louis, MO (33%-980) Ger C; Cpt, Swim; Hon Prog; Fin, MVP, Swim; Camp Counselor; U of Mo; Marine Bio.

NEU, Tamala Sue
Eastern Local HS; Sardinia, OH (1-83) Band; Chor; Pres, Fr C; FTA; NHS; Ed, Sch P; DARGCA; I Dare You; MLS; Val; Sou St Col; Social Work.

NEU, Teri Linn
Lindbergh HS; St Louis, MO (33%-950) Fin, Swim; Hon Prog; Yth Fel; Camp Counselor; U of Mo.

NEUBAUER, Julie Jan
Normal Comm HS; Normal, IL (188-535) VP, AFS; Secy, Ger C; Pres, 4H; ARC; 4H A; Yth Foundation; Secy-Tres, AFS; Tres, Ger C; 4-H St Outst; 4-H Project Hon; E Ill U.

NEUBAUER, Kathleen Anne
St Joseph Sr HS; St Joseph, MI (95-347) A Cap Choir; F-Ed, Ann; Chor; Drama; Fr C; Hmrm; A-Ed, Sch P; SC; Bkbl; Tr; COM; Yth Fel.

NEUBER, Jo Ann
Chilton Pub HS; Chilton, WI; CYO; Rptr, FHA; 4H; Span C; Tres; B Crocker A; 4H A; Moraine Park Tech Inst; Child Care.

NEUERBURG, Marge JoAnn
Brethren Christian HS; Osceola, IN (5%-26) Chldr; ARC A; Cederville Col; Math.

NEUGEBAUER, Jeanette Rose
Parkston HS; Parkston, SD; Chor; Ensm; FHA; Math C; Sci C; SC; Secy, Jr Cl; Golf; St FHA Degree; Food Service Training; Runner-Up, Sch Swtht; Vo-tech Col at Watertown; Med Asst.

NEUMAN, Connie Jo
Catlin HS; Catlin, IL (1-65) Secy, FFA; 4H; NHS; ARC; SC; Sftbl; Tr; 4H A; Spch A; VFW A; Vof-DEM; Yth Fel; Girls Ath Assn; FFA Schol; S-T, Stu Libarians of E Cen Ill; Danville Jr Col; Agr.

NEUMAN, Kimberlee Ann
Campbell Tintah HS; Campbell, MN (14-42) Band; Chldr; Chor; Drama; FBLA; FHA; VP, 4H; Sch P; S-T, Sr Cl; Mgr, Bkbl; Tr; COM; 4H A; HCt; Hon Prog; Bookkeeping Cert; ND St Sch of Sci; Secretarial.

NEUMANN, Janine Minnie
Pinconning Area HS; Pinconning, MI (25-250) Ann; Band; Chldr; Drama; FNA; FTA; ARC; Vof-DEM; Solo, Ensm Medals.

NEUMANN, Paula Eileen
Glenbard W HS; Glen Ellyn, IL (68-507) A Cap Choir; Arch; Secy, Band; Ensm; Semi-Fin, GS; Hmrm; Rptr, Lit Mag; Rptr, Sch P; SC; Thes; Arch; COM; DARGCA; Hon Prog; Journ A; Yth Fel; Trs, GAA; Steer Co; Chrch Lucia Qn; Choir Soloist; Staff Search Comm; Fairest o-t Fair Beauty Qn; Wayfolk, Sing Grp; Sundy Sch Tchr; Baylor U; Pre-Med.

NEUMANN, Rachel Ellen
Maddock Pub HS; Maddock, ND (4-23) Band; Chldr; Chor; Ensm; FHA; SC; NMS; ND St U; Elem Ed.

NEUMEISTER, Karen Louise
Glastonbury HS; Glastonbury, CT (19-497) Orch; Med.

NEUMILLER, Carol Jean
Medina Pub HS; Medina, ND (3-24) Band; FHA; Sch P; Tres, Sr Cl; Hon Prog; Sal; Shorthand A; Valley City St Col; Special Ed.

NEUMILLER, Sandra Jean
Maddock Pub HS; Maddock, ND (3-23) Band; Chor; Ensm; FHA; GS; 4H; Var C; VP, Jr Cl; Secy, Soph Cl; Bkbl; Golf; 4H A; NMS; Sci A; ND St U; Med.

NEVELLS, Susan Gwenith
Stratford HS; Stratford, CT (11-319) Band; Drama; Secy, FBLA; NHS; Span NHS; Bkbl; COM; St Scholar; Pilgrimage Fel; Bell Choir; Yth Choir; Church Coun; Rep, United Church of Christ Conf; SC Outst Serv A, FBLA; Sou Conn St Col; Special Ed.

NEVES, Diane Marlene
Oak Grove Attendence Center; Hattiesburg, MS (5%-130) BC; Pres, Fr C; Hmrm; ARC; Sch P; Secy, SC; Pres, Jr Cl; Type A.

NEVES, Tammy Jane
Victory Christian Acad; Jacksonville, FL (10%-100) Span C; Span A.

NEVIL, Rebecca Ruth
Peebles HS; Peebles, OH (1-100) Band; Chldr; Drama; FFA; 4H; NHS; ARC; Tres, Jr Cl; Sftbl; Tr; 4H A; Poet A; Type A; FFA Qn; Old Timer's Day Qn; Sch Schol Tm; WW; Ohio St U; Nurs.

NEVILL, Connie Denice
Nassau Christian Acad; Yulee, FL; Ensm; 4H; Bkbl; Tr; HCt; Math A; Vlbl Tm; Baptist Bible Col; Mus.

NEVILL, Lexie Lee
Worthington Sr HS; Worthington, MN (5-280) NHS; ARC; Regent Schol; Augustana Col; Nurs.

NEVILLE, Diane Shirley
W Technical HS; Cleveland, OH (37-659) Band; Chor; Drama; Rptr, Ger C; Hmrm; NHS; Orch; Hon Prog; NMS; Yth Fel; Job's Daughters; Comm Theater; Torch; Cleveland St U; Communications.

NEVILLE, Gregory Alan
J F Kennedy HS; La Palma, CA (1-650) Golf; CSF; NMS; Rice U; Math.

NEVIN, Lorrie Ann
Riverview HS; Sarasota, FL (298-664) Chldr; Tres, Fr C; FHA; Hmrm; Rainbow; HCt; Keyettes; Eckerd Col; Travel.

NEVINS, Laurie Ann
South Shelby HS; Shelbina, MO (24-102) Band; Chor; NHS; SC; Bkbl; Tr; HCt; NEDT; Yth Fel; Ltrwomens C; Soph Pilgrimage; All-Conf Tr; All-Conf A All-Dist Bkbl; Northeast Mo St U.

NEW, Brynda Elaine
Miami Killian Sr HS; Miami, FL (94-1002) Jacksonville St U.

NEW, Deletha Lynn
Richland HS; Richland Hills, TX (200-600) Ann; Band; Chor; Ensm; FHA; FTA; Secy, Hmrm; Lit Ral; Secy, SC; Secy, Soph Cl; Tnns; Drill Tm; Abilene Christian U; Fashion.

NEW, Edwin Eugene
Miami Killian Sr HS; Miami, FL;

NEWBERRY, Deborah Ann
Niwot HS; Longmont, CO (1-325) Parl, Bus C; Chldr; Chor; Drama; FBLA; GS; Pres, 4H; NHS; Orch; Sch P; SC; Thes; Tr; COM; Elk A; 4H A; JA A; MLS; Most Out; Pres A; Regent Schol; Type A; Powder Puff Ftbl; Srs Academic A; AFPAW A; WW; Welker Schol; Teenager o-t Mo; Zonta Girl o-t Mo; U of Colo; Bio.

NEWBERRY, Julianne
Momence HS; Momence, IL (29-135) Chor; Drama; Hmrm; Spch C; SC; Thes; Mgr, Sftbl; Marycrest Bus Col; Secy Stu.

NEWBERRY, Kathy Eleen
Green Forest HS; Green Forest, AR (10-60) BC; FHA; Sci C; Math A; Parl, Lib C; Civics A; Twin Lakes Voc Tech Sch; Bus.

NEWBERRY, Michel Dean
O D Wyatt HS; Fort Worth, TX (1-435) A-Ed, Ann; Ensm; NHS; Pres, SC; Cpt, Tr; Cl Fav; Hist A; Hon Prog; PTA A; Summa Cum Laude; Pres & VP, FTA; People; WW; Bible C; CTA Schol; U of Tex at Arlington; Chem.

NEWBERRY, Nanci Gail
Heritage Hall-Upper Sch; Oklahoma City, OK; Fr C; JETS; Math C; Mu Alpha Theta; Sch Achieve Tm; Sci C; COM; Oklahoma City U; Ed.

NEWBILL, Leah Jeanine
McKenzie HS; McKenzie, TN (7-79) F-Ed, Ann; Band; Rptr, BC; Sci C; SC; Hon Prog; U of Tenn; Zoology.

NEWBRAUGH, Kala Tiffany
Musselman HS; Bunker Hill, WV (7-92) Secy, Chor; FHA; Pres, FTA; 4H; ARC; Tres, Jr Cl; Shepherd Col; Bus Adm.

NEWBY, Lisa Diane
Bend Sr HS; Bend, OR (318-480) A Cap Choir; Chor; Ensm; Type A; Filing A; Poster A; Amer Cancer Soc.

NEWBY, Myra Lynn
Manual HS; Denver, CO; Chor; NHS; F-Ed, Sch P; COM; Journ A; Rptr, Sch P; Pres, Church Yth Group; Rep, St Church Yth Committee; Elem Ed.

NEWBY, Regina LaVon
Little Rock Central HS; Little Rock, AR (20-543) Drama; Model UN; NHS; F-Ed, Sch P; Spch C; VP, Thes; Y-Tns; Journ A; Q&S A; Spch A; St HS Press Assn A; U of Mo; Broadcast Journ.

NEWCOMB, Holly Ann
S Burlington HS; S Burlington, VT; Yth Fel; Church Chor; Whitewater U; Elem Ed.

NEWCOMB, Jerry Scott
Daviess Co HS; Owensboro, KY; Bsbl; W Ky U; Geol.

NEWCOMB, Katherine R
Interlochen Arts Acad; Interlochen, MI (6-160) Band; Orch; NMF; Rensselaer A; Stanford U; Premed.

NEWCOMB, Michael Alan
Blanchet HS; Seattle, WA (33-297) Pres, Hmrm; NHS; SC; Ftbl; Cpt, Soccer; Hon Prog; Air Force Acad; Life Sci.

NEWCOMB, Terry Elizabeth
South Burlington HS; South Burlington, VT; Chldr; Chor; Y-Tns.

NEWCOMBE, Michelle Suzanne
Von Steuben HS; Chicago, IL (44-205) Chor; ARC; Mgr, Bkbl; Swim; Cpt, Tr; Secy, GSct; All City HS Choir; Mgr, Tr; Co-Cpt, Vlbl; W Ill U; Recreational Therapy.

NEWCOMER, Lisa Mae
Oregon Comm HS; Oregon, IL (1-116) Tres, NHS; Rptr, Sch P; Pres, Sr Cl; Tres, Jr Cl; Secy, Soph Cl; Mgr, Tr; Regent Schol; St Scholar; VofDEM; Yth Fel; Pom Pon Squad; 1st Cl, GSct; Luther Col; Med.

NEWE, Karen Marie
Reseda HS; Reseda, CA; Hmrm; Secy, Jr Cl; CSF; Gym; Girl's League; Calif St U; Foreign Lang.

NEWELL, Angela Janine
Egyptian HS; Tamms, IL (5-86) Band; BC; Chldr; FHA; Mjrte; 1st, Band Ensm; Teaching.

NEWELL, Georgia Ann
Phoebus HS; Hampton, VA (23-280) A Cap Choir; Chor; NHS; Tnns; U of Va; Pre-Law.

NEWELL, Hilary Minton
Westfield Acad; Westfield, NY (6-95) Band; Chor; Ensm; Pres, Key C; Sftbl; Citz A; Hon Prog; GScts Chor; Stage Band; Westwinds; HS Bowl; Photographer, Yrbk; Prog Aide, GScts.

NEWELL, Janice Marlene
Burnside HS; Burnside, KY (2-70) BC; Pres, Soph Cl; Mgr, Bkbl; Alg A; Most Out; Home Ec A; *U of Ky; Social Work.*

NEWELL, Leroy B
Verona HS; Verona, NJ (120-280) A Cap Choir; Chor; Hmrm; Arch; JV, Bsbl; Bkbl; Soccer; Sftbl; Pres A; Yth Fel; Pres, Yth Group; *NE Bible Col; Christian Ed.*

NEWELL, Margaret Ann
Flushing HS; Flushing, NY (279-913) A Cap Choir; Chor; Ensm; Hmrm; Madrigal; Bkbl; Co-Cpt, Sftbl; COM; Cl Fav; PTA A; Sanctuary Soc; Yth Fel; Yth Foundation; *SC U; Mus.*

NEWELL, Robert Earl
S Jones HS; Ellisville, MS (7-36) Hmrm; Bsbl; Ftbl; Hist A; *Jones Co Jr Col; Brick Layer.*

NEWELL, Ronald Harold
Kemper Co Acad; DeKalb, MS (1-42) A-Ed, Ann; Bus Mgr, BC; Chor; F-Ed, Sch P; Alg A; COM; Cl Fav; Hist A; Math A; Star Student; 2nd Pl, St Physics; Sr o-t Mo; 1st Pl, Sch & Dist Physics A; Most Intellectual; Eng A; *Miss St U; Math.*

NEWELL, Susan Leigh
N Shore HS; W Palm Beach, FL (14-336) Ger C; Key C; NFL; Spch C; Secy, Jr Cl; COM; Hon Prog; Math A; *Pol Sci.*

NEWELL, Vicki Denise
New Hanover HS; Wilmington, NC; Hmrm; Key C; SC; Nom, Halyburton A; *Teaching Deaf.*

NEWENDORP, Mark Alan
Norman HS; Norman, OK (10%-700) Band; Fr C; Hmrm; NHS; Rptr, SC; Mgr, Bsbl; Mgr, Bkbl; Mgr, Ftbl; Bio A; COM; Yth Fel; *Med.*

NEWENS, Kenneth Wilson
Fowler HS; Fowler, CO (1-60) Band; BS; Chor; Dbte Tm; Secy, FFA; Madrigal; NFL; NHS; Spch C; Pres, Jr Cl; Masonic A; NEDT; Spch A; *Colo St U; Vet Med.*

NEWHALL, Sharon Lee
Bonita Vista HS; Chula Vista, CA (95-460) Chor; Sftbl; Voc Cl Cert; *SW Col; Airline Services.*

NEWHOUSE, Melody Kay
Cache HS; Cache, OK (1-46) FHA; NHS; Span C; Citz A; Cl Fav; Hist A; Masonic A; MLS; Opt A; Opt Out Tn; Val.

NEWMAN, Anna Christine
Phillips HS; Phillips, TX (20%-40) Band; Chor; FHA; Cpt, Tr; *Amarillo Col; Criminology.*

NEWMAN, Charlotte Bernice
Eldorado HS; Albuquerque, NM (72-744) Tres, CYO; NHS; *NM St U; Psych.*

NEWMAN, Debi Ann
Kalama HS; Kalama, WA; Chldr; Sftbl; Pep C; *Secretarial.*

NEWMAN, Douglas Richard
Detroit Lakes HS; Detroit Lakes, MN; Band; Chor; Ensm; Hmrm; Madrigal; Ftbl; Wrest; MLS; Most Out; All St Choir; Win, Dist, St, Solo, Ensm; *Mus.*

NEWMAN, Gary Lee
South Plainfield HS; S Plainfield, NJ (6-312) NHS; Sci C; Cpt, Tnns; Opt A; Alt, BS; NHS Schol; MVP, Tnns; St Schol; Middlesex Co Coaches Schol, Ath A; Jaycee Mem A; *Rutgers Col; Phar.*

NEWMAN, Jane Lee
Pisgah HS; Canton, NC (150-300) Fr C; Monogram; Cr-Ctry; Tr; FCA; *Lees McRae Col; Ed.*

NEWMAN, Kathy Ann
Thomas Carr Howe HS; Indianapolis, IN (44-691) Band; Chor; NHS; Tnns; *Ind U; Phys Therapy.*

NEWMAN, Linda Diane
Guthrie HS; Guthrie, OK (15-186) Parl, Band; Ensm; FBLA; Secy, FTA; GS; Pres, NHS; ARC; SC; Secy, Jr C; Secy, Soph Cl; Tnns; Beauty; COM; DARGCA; Gov Honor Prog; Hist A; HQn; Lion A; Masonic A; Most Out; NHS; Fr C; Demolay Swtht; AAUW Art A; VP, FTA; WW in Baton Twirling; Feature Twirler, Mjrte; Past Worthy Adv, Rainbow Girls; *Okla St U; Art Ed.*

NEWMAN, Lori Louise
Fairview HS; Dayton, OH (17-285) All Amer Yth; Bus C; Drama; Hmrm; Lit Mag; Secy, NFL; NHS; Ntl Yth Conf; Ed, Sch P; SC; Pres, Thes; Bkbl; Cpt, Sftbl; Swim; Cpt, Tnns; COM; Cl Fav; Hon Prog; Journ A; Ntl Achv Schol; Odd Fellow Fin; PTA A; Poet A; Pres A; Spch A; Type A; Yth Fel; Cpt, Vlbl; Fitness As; Chor As; Children Home A; *Ohio St U; Bus.*

NEWMAN, Mark Franklin
Daviess Co HS; Owensboro, KY (8-320) Ed, Ann; Fr C; 4H; Key C; Pres, Sci C; JV, Bsbl; Chem A; JA A; Ntl Sci Symposium; Phy A; Sci A; Miles Sci, Sci Fair, A's; Fin, St Jr Sci Sym; *W Ky U; Chem.*

NEWMAN, Marlene Kay
Albia Comm HS; Albia, IA; Chor; FHA; 4H; *Mentally Retarded Ed.*

NEWMAN, Martha Mae
Morristown HS; Morristown, MN (4-35) Ann; Secy, Band; Cpt, Chldr; Pres, Chor; Dbte Tm; Drama; Ensm; GS; Hmrm; S-T, NHS; Ed, Sch P; SC; Var C; Cpt, Bkbl; Tr; COM; Select Band; Select Chor; Star at St Mus Contest; *Bemidji St U.*

NEWMAN, Mica Kaye
Holyoke HS; Holyoke, CO (3-57) Ed, Ann; Pres, Band; Chor; Ensm; Secy, FHA; Secy, NHS; Orch; Pres, Rainbow; F-Ed, Sch P; Sci C; Span C; SC; Pres, Soph Cl; Cpt, Tr; Mgr, Wrest; Amer Leg A; Citz A; Math A; Q&S A; Sci A; Swtht; Cpt, Vlbl; Co-Op Yth; Pres, MYF; Attd, Prom Qn; Swing Choir; *SD St U; Nurs.*

NEWMAN, Michael Duane
Kalama HS; Kalama, WA (23-60) Band; Chem C; Chor; Dbte Tm; Drama; Fr C; Sch P; SC; Ch, Thes; Mgr, Bkbl; Cl Fav; Hon Prog; Most Out; Yth Foundation; Outst Choral Yth; *Mt Hood Comm Col; Pol Sci.*

NEWMAN, Michelle Patrice
HS of Charleston; Charleston, SC; BC; Community Yth Symph; FTA; NHS; Y-Tns; COM; Hon Prog; *Bethune-Cookman Col; Computer Tech.*

NEWMAN, Nikki Marie
Mabel-Canton HS; Mabel, MN (1-50) Co-Ed, Ann; Band; Co-Cpt, Chldr; Chor; Ensm; Ch, FHA; Mjrte; NHS; Co-Ed, Sch P; Secy, Sr Cl; Secy, Jr Cl; Tres, Soph Cl; Bkbl; Tr; COM; HCt; Hon Prog; Pres A; Swtht; Yth Fel; Dorian Band; Phi Beta Mu Band; Hon Band; WW; St Olaf Col; Pol Sci.

NEWMAN, Rebecca McCartt
Harpeth Hall HS; Nashville, TN (25%-84) AFS; Chor; Lat C; Sears Tn Board; Church Pianist; *Vanderbilt U; General Stu.*

NEWMAN, Rudolph Mitch
Wilson Hall Acad; Sumter, SC; Pres, BC; Order/Arrow; Tres, SC; Bkbl; Alg A; God & Country A; Eagle Sct; May Court; *Math.*

NEWMAN, Scott Lee
Normal Comm HS; Normal, IL (10-485) JV, Bsbl; Swim; Sci A; *Marine Biol.*

NEWMAN, Sharon Michelle
S R Butler HS; Huntsville, AL; Ann; Band; FBLA; *U of N Ala; Secy Sci.*

NEWMAN, Shelly Kay
Blanchet HS; Seattle, WA (2-383) Drama; Hmrm; SC; *Law.*

NEWMAN, Tracy
Williamston HS; Williamston, MI (10-160) Band; Chldr; SC; Var C; *Early Elem Ed.*

NEWMAN, William Maynard
Swain Co HS; Bryson City, NC; Band; Fr C; JV, Bkbl; Tr; Sci A.

NEWMARK, Marlene
New Rochelle HS; New Rochelle, NY; Ski C; Swim; Tnns; Hon Prog; *Pepperdine U; Law.*

NEWMILLER, Lisa Ann
Thornton Township; Harvey, IL (80-926) NHS; Tres, SC; Tri-HiY; *Ill St U; Med Technology.*

NEWNAM, Cindy Lynn
Bethany HS; Reidsville, NC; Ed, Ann; Pres, Fr C; FHA; Hmrm; Pres, Monogram; F-Ed, Sch P; SC; Co-Cpt, Bkbl; Co-Cpt, Sftbl; DARGCA; *U of NC.*

NEWNHAM, Margie B
Antelope Valley HS; Lancaster, CA (30-636) A Cap Choir; Fr C; JV, Tnns; Tr; CSF; Hon Prog; *Antelope Valley Col; Nurs.*

NEWSHUTZ, Patricia Joan
Gallia Acad HS; Gallipolis, OH (46-250) NHS; Span C; Tri-HiY; HCt; *Ohio St U; Bus Adm.*

NEWSOM, Angela
Virgie HS; Virgie, KY (2-120) Rptr, Band; BC; Secy, Chem C; Chess C; Ensm; FTA; Secy, Ger C; 4H; Hmrm; Key C; Math C; Rptr, NHS; Orch; Sci C; Spch C; Rptr, SC; Sftbl; COM; 4H A; Hon Prog; MLS; Swtht; Type A; All Co Hons Band; Spelling A; Sup Solo A; *U of Ky; Mus.*

NEWSOM, Debra Elaine
Bethany HS; Reidsville, NC (3-52) Pres, Anchor C; Chldr; FHA; Tres, Monogram; Rptr, Sch P; Secy, SC; VP, Jr Cl; HCt; Miss Pineburr; Biggest Flirt; *Rockingham Comm Col; Cosmetology.*

NEWSOM, Karen Lynn
Martinsville HS; Martinsville, VA (80-600) Band; Chor; Drama; *Central Wesleyan Col; Law.*

NEWSOM, Lynn Chloia
Carlsbad HS; Carlsbad, CA (40-450) AFS; Band; FHA; CSF; Hon Prog; *U of Nev; Foreign Lang.*

NEWSOM, Ricky James
Enterprise HS; Enterprise, AL; Tr; Wrest.

NEWSOM, Sherri Lynn
Bethany HS; Reidsville, NC; VP, Anchor C; Ann; BC; FHA; HCt; 'B' HR.

NEWSOM, Teresa Carol
Virgie HS; Virgie, KY (12-110) Ann; Rptr, BC; FTA; Ger C; 4H; Co-Ed, Sch P; Spch C; DARGCA; HCt; Sci A; *Pikeville Col.*

NEWSOM, Teresa Celeste
Red Bank HS; Red Bank, TN (3-300) Span C; Silk Corp; *Edmondson Col; Acct.*

NEWSOME, Abbie Gail
Marvell HS; Marvell, AR (4-118) Band; Tres, BC; FBLA; FHA; NHS; Secy, SC; *U of Ark; Phar.*

NEWSOME, Curtis Wayne
Ahoskie HS; Ahoskie, NC (18-243) Band; 4H; InterClub Coun; Order/Arrow; SC; VP, Var C; VP, Jr Cl; Pres, Soph Cl; Bsbl; Bkbl; Ftbl; Tnns; 4H A; Band A; *U of NC; Dentistry.*

NEWSOME, Jacqueline McDarry
Ahoskie HS; Ahoskie, NC (69-246) Band; FHA; Nurs.

NEWSOME, Jeffery Kent
Virgie HS; Virgie, KY (10-112) F-Ed, Ann; BC; FTA; NHS; Sci C; Bsbl; Bkbl; HCt; Hon Prog; *U of Ky; Engr.*

NEWSOME, Jeffrey Morrell
Virgie HS; Virgie, KY; A-Ed, Sch P; Bsbl; Bkbl; Tr; Hon Prog; All Tourn; *Pikeville Col; Mining Tech.*

NEWSOME, Monique Elizabeth
Alamogordo HS; Alamogordo, NM (481-500) Drama; Secy, Thes; *NM St U; Drama.*

NEWSOME, Richetta Vanessa
Ahoskie HS; Ahoskie, NC (81-243) Cpt, Chldr; Chor; FHA; Pres, SC; Var C; Co-Cpt, Bkbl; *Norfolk St U; Phys Ed.*

NEWSOME, Robert Lee
Virgie HS; Virgie, KY; BC; VP, FTA; Var C; Pres, Jr Cl; Bsbl; Cpt, Bkbl; MVP, Bkbl; *U of Ky.*

NEWSOME, Sue Allison
Hixson HS; Chattanooga, TN; Tres, Chor; Ensm; Span C; Tri-HiY; Y-Tns; Yth Fel; Secy, TAL C; Jr NHS; Most Improved; *Fla St U.*

NEWSON, Lorenzo
Brandon HS; Brandon, FL (731-854) *Morehouse Col; Dentistry.*

NEWTON, Barbara
Carroll HS; Monroe, LA (12-205) VP, Chor; Ensm; Hon Prog; *NE U; Special Ed.*

NEWTON, Carlton Wayne
Wakefield Sr HS; Arlington, VA (155-323) A Cap Choir; Band; Chor; Ensm; Hmrm; Orch; SC; Pres, Soph Cl; Bsbl; JV, Bkbl; Ftbl; Tr; Most Out; Star Student; Outst Sportsmanship; Outst Musical Achv As; Band.

NEWTON, Christopher Jay
Monroe-Woodbury HS; Central Valley, NY; Chess C; Hmrm; Lit Mag; NHS; Rptr, Sch P; Ski C; NMS; NEDT; Social Studies.

NEWTON, David Brainerd
Harold G Hoffman HS; South Amboy, NJ (8-70) NHS; ARC; Ski C; Var C; JV, Bsbl; Bkbl; Cpt, Cr-Ctry; Sci A; Yth Fel; Phys Ed Highest Avg; NJFTA A, Foreign Lang Stu; *The King's Col; Bus Adm.*

NEWTON, David Paul
Saugerties HS; Saugerties, NY; Sch P; *New Paltz Col; Art.*

NEWTON, Debbie Kay
Maryville R-II HS; Maryville, MO (62-128) Band; NHS; Rptr, Sch P; Sci C; SC; Experiment in Interntl Living; Soroptimist Interntl A; Bus & Professional Women's Schol; *NW Mo St U; Pre-Law.*

NEWTON, Deborah Ann
Asheboro HS; Asheboro, NC (37-310) Band; Chldr; Hmrm; InterClub Coun; VP, Monogram; Tres, NHS; Sci C; Span C; SC; Secy, Sr Cl; Tnns; Civinettes; Med Explorers; *U of NC; Dental Hygiene.*

NEWTON, Denise Ann
Obion Co HS; Troy, TN (3-192) Tres, BC; Tres, Bus C; Chor; Fr C; Tnns, FBLA; GS; Hmrm; NHS; SC; Pres, Jr Cl; Beauty; Cl Fav; HCt; Miss Soph; Miss Jr; Hon Marshall; VP, St FBLA; *Finance.*

NEWTON, Jeffrey Duke
Leesburg HS; Leesburg, FL (20-360) NHS; *Acct.*

NEWTON, Kathy Sue
Commerce HS; Commerce, OK (13-55) Chor; VP, FHA; 4H; NHS; Ftbl; Sftbl; Hon Prog; St Scholar; Agr Achv Day; FHA Worker o-t Yr; *NEO A&M U; Psych.*

NEWTON, Melinda Alleene
N Little Rock Northeast HS; N Little Rock, AR (87-486) Pres, Chor; FBLA; FHA; Mu Alpha Theta; Secy, NHS; Sci C; Tr; *U of Ark; Med.*

NEWTON, Neal Ross
Patrick Henry HS; Glade Spring, VA (20-168) Cpt, Dbte Tm; Drama; FFA; Rptr, Hmrm; SC; COM; Most Out; VP, Art C; Horticulture, Art, A's; *VPI; Art.*

NEWTON, Pamela Sue
Glenwood HS; Chatham, IL; AFS; FHA; Mgr, Tr; Colorguard; GAA; *W Ill U.*

NEWTON, Robin Lorranie
Eastside HS; Paterson, NJ; NHS; COM; *Acct.*

NEWTON, Steven Daniel
Boardman HS; Boardman, OH (10-602) BS; Dbte Tm; Secy, Math C; NFL; NHS; A-Ed, Sch P; Sci C; VP, Span C; Amer Leg A; Journ A; Q&S A; Outst Jr Span Stu, N Ohio; *Princeton U; Econ.*

NEWTON, Walter Lou
Leetonia HS; Leetonia, OH (20-100) BS; 4H; Span C; Bkbl; Tr; *Pepperdine U; Secondary Ed.*

NEWTON, William Albert
Mira Mesa Jr-Sr HS; San Diego, CA; A Cap Choir; Demolay; Bkbl; Athlete o-t Wk; *Officers Candidate Sch; Mus.*

NEYLAND, Joseph Blake
Sullivan Central HS; Blountville, TN; Ann; NHS; Secy, SC; JV, Bkbl; Ftbl.

NEYLAND, Ruthie Senette
John C Fremont HS; Los Angeles, CA; Cpt, Mjrte; Type A; *Trade Tech Col; Bus.*

NEYMAN, Judith Marie
Cedar Bluff HS; Cedar Bluff, AL; BC; Chldr; FHA; Semi-Fin, Jr Miss Pa; Math C; Secy, SC; Var C; Beauty; HCt; Tigerette; Phys Ed A; Secy, Tn Involvement; Tres, Lib C; Diligence A.

NEZWISKY, Nina
Northeastern HS; Detroit, MI; Ntl Yth Conf; Secy, Sch P; Journ A; *US Air Force Acad; Pol Sci.*

NG, Kevin Kin
Abraham Lincoln HS; San Francisco, CA (35-334) Chess C; *U of Calif at Berkeley; Elec Engr.*

NGIRACHEDENG, John
Emmaus HS; Koror, PALAU, WESTERN CAROLINE ISLANDS (2-17) Chem C; Bsbl; Bkbl; Hon Prog.

NGIRMECHAET, Melwis
Emmaus HS; Koror, PALAU, WESTERN CAROLINE ISLANDS (2-13) Math C; Sftbl; Hon Prog.

NGUYEN, Chau Huu
Kubasaki HS; Okinawa, JAPAN (8-421) PA; *Med.*

NGUYEN, Hanh Huu
Kubasaki HS; Okinawa, JAPAN (8-421) Sci A; Elec A; PA; *Med.*

NIBBE, Dennis Johanes Adolf
Tillamook HS; Tillamook, OR (10-180) Dbte Tm; NFL; Spch C; *U of Oreg; Pre-Law.*

NIBECK, Christopher Robert
Hinsdale Central HS; Hinsdale, IL; JETS; Pres, Math C; Phys C; Hon Prog; *Elec Engr.*

NIBLETT, Shari Leigh
Milburn HS; Milburn, OK (4%-22) 4H; NHS; Bkbl; Sftbl; Cl Fav; 4H A; HCt; Sal; *Wayland Baptist U; Phys Ed.*

NICCUM, Jan Carter
Effingham HS; Effingham, IL (10-200) Ann; Band; Fr C; VP, 4H; SC; Mgr, Bkbl; Mgr, Cr-Ctry; Mgr, Tr; Amer Leg A; COM; Hon Prog; Sci A; Soc of Academic Achv; *Ind U; Optometry.*

NICELY, Kathy Diane
Sylvan Hills HS; N Little Rock, AR; Co-Ed, Ann; Tres, BC; Drama; FHA; FTA; NHS; Thes; Y-Tns; Hon Prog; Spch A; Drill Tm; *U of Ark; Special Ed.*

NICHELSON, Amy Jo
Columbiana HS; Columbiana, OH; Secy, A Cap Choir; Ann; Chor; Fr C; Sch P; Tri-HiY; Secy, Church Yth; *Bowling Green St U; Bus.*

NICHOL, Roy William
Castle Heights Military Acad; Lebanon, TN (6-51) Pres, Monogram; Pres, NHS; F-Ed, Sch P; Pres, SC; Pres, Soph Cl; Bsbl; Ftbl; Citz A; Q&S A; Mr Castle Heights; Jr Hon Star; *Baylor U; Dentistry.*

NICHOLAS, Donald Gene Jr
John Marshall HS; San Antonio, TX (4-677) InterClub Coun; JETS; Mu Alpha Theta; NHS; Span NHS; Bio A; Cl Fav; Hon Prog; NMF; *Baylor U; Pre-Med.*

NICHOLAS, Edward Francis
Cardinal Mooney HS; Sarasota, FL (5-75) Key C; Lit Mag; NHS; Span C; SC; Ftbl; Cpt, Tnns; Most Out; Showfolks Schol; *Manatee Jr Col; Psych.*

NICHOLAS, Pamela Jean
Knappa HS; Astoria, OR (5-54) Dbte Tm; Pres, Drama; FFA; Rptr, Spch C; Y-Tns; Spch A; VofDEM; Leadership A; *Col of Idaho; Med.*

NICHOLAS, Terrie Ann
Marion Sr HS; Marion, AR (20%-200) FBLA; FHA; *Draughons Bus Col; Acct.*

NICHOLAS, Tina Renee
Schoolcraft HS; Schoolcraft, MI (15-64) Band; Chor; Drama; Rptr, Hmrm; NHS; VP, SC; Rptr, Jr Cl; Secy, Soph Cl; Bkbl; Tr; Hon Prog; Yth Fel; PA; Purdue Mus Camp; *Oral Roberts U; Art Ed.*

NICHOLS, Marc Carter
George Washington HS; Denver, CO (33%-712) Band; Chess C; Ensm; Lat C; Lat NHS; Order/Arrow; Ski C; Arch; Bsbl; Bkbl; Ftbl; Golf; Sftbl; Swim; Tnns; Order/Arrow A; Church Yth Choir; Life Sct; Sr Patrol Ldr; Tres, Church Yth Group; *U of Colo; Med.*

NICHOLS, Arthur David
Beavercreek HS; Xenia, OH (338-601) A Cap Choir; Band; Chor; Ftbl; Sftbl; *Police Acad; Military Police.*

NICHOLS, Becky Jane
McClellan HS; Little Rock, AR (4-450) Band; BC; FBLA; FHA; NHS; Church Chor, Ensm & Orch; COE A; Bible Quiz Tm; Hon Banquet; VP, Yth Group; S-T, Girl's Yth Group.

NICHOLS, Billie Dawn
Concord HS; Concord, NC (128-220) Safe Driving A; Bus Driver A; *Pfeiffer Col.*

NICHOLS, Bobbi Mae Reda
N Beach HS; Moclips, WA (10%-59) Ann; Chldr; NHS; Rptr, Sch P; SC; Bkbl; Tnns; Tr; H of F; Pres A; Type A; Secy, Gym; Vlbl; PA; *Central Wash St Col; Ed.*

NICHOLS, Christian Lars
Nicholas Senn HS; Chicago, IL (171-707) JV, Bsbl; Co-Cpt, Cr-Ctry; JV, Golf; Co-Cpt, Swim; *Hesston Col; Aviation.*

NICHOLS, Christopher John
Ashland Sr HS; Ashland, OR (5-230) Band; 4H; Hmrm; InterClub Coun; Math C; NHS; Ntl Yth Conf; Var C; Wrest; 4H A; Rensselaer A; Del, Nation 4-H Congress; *Cornell U; Agr Engr.*

NICHOLS, Craig W
D D Eisenhower HS; Saginaw, MI (33%-350) SC; Bsbl; JV, Bkbl; JV, Ftbl; JV, Golf.

NICHOLS, David Peter
Bella Vista HS; Fair Oaks, CA (5%-500) Orch; Tnns; CSF.

NICHOLS, Donna Kay
Central Baptist HS; Hampton, VA (3-13) Cpt, Chldr; Chor; 4H; Secy, Sch P; Sftbl; H of F; Type A; Piano A; *Bob Jones U; Mus.*

NICHOLS, Elizabeth Deverlin
Faith Christian Acad; Palmyra, MI; *Secretarial.*

NICHOLS, James William
Ashland Sr HS; Ashland, OR (22-250) Band; VP, 4H; NHS; Wrest; 4H A; Yth Fel; *Oreg St U; Sci.*

NICHOLS, Janet Marie
Claxton HS; Claxton, GA (25%-115) Chldr; Sch P; Var C.

NICHOLS, Jeff T
N Gwinnett HS; Suwanee, GA (10%-150) Dbte Tm; Key C; JV, Ftbl; Wrest; *Ga Tech; Elec Engr.*

NICHOLS, Judith Keturah
Louisville HS; Louisville, MS; Band; Chem C; Chor; VP, FHA; Math C; Sftbl; Cl Fav; Hon Cert; *U of Miss; Med Technology.*

NICHOLS, Juliann Marie
Clark Co R-I HS; Kahoka, MO (2-95) Chor; 4H; NHS; Pol Sci C; Sch Achieve Tm; Citz A; Hist A; K of C A.

NICHOLS, Karla Kay
Raytown HS; Raytown, MO (14-600) NHS; Span C; Church Bkbl & Sftbl; *SW Baptist Col; Psych.*

NICHOLS, Kelli Diane
Wichita S HS; Wichita, KS (6-550) Drama; Semi-Fin, GS; NHS; F-Ed, Sch P; Span C; Thes; COM; Hon Prog; Drill Tm; Pom-Pon Squad; *Archt.*

NICHOLS, Laura Loraine
Temple HS; Temple, TX (144-443) Band; Swim; Yth Fel; Regional Exec, Christian Yth Fel; *Tex Christian U; Mus Theory.*

NICHOLS, Linda Gwen
Pleasure Ridge Park HS; Louisville, KY (33-315) Lat C; Up Bound; COM; Scholastic Service A; *U of Louisville; Phar.*

NICHOLS, Linda Sue
Pike HS; Indianapolis, IN (2-300) Fr C; FBLA; GS; Mu Alpha Theta; NHS; Secy, Sr Cl; Tnns; Hon Prog; Math A; Sal; Vlbl; 1st Pl Bus Law, FBLA St Contest; All Col Schol; *Valparaiso U; Pre-Law.*

NICHOLS, Lucy Karen
Burkeville HS; Burkeville, TX (5-47) Ed, Ann; Band; Cpt, Chldr; Hmrm; NHS; Sch P; SC; Cl Fav; HCt; Type A; Most Popular; Cl Play; Miss Tex Ntl Teenager Pageant; *Lamar U; Bus.*

NICHOLS, Marietta
Enid HS; Enid, OK (35-485) F-Ed, Ann; Chor; Dbte Tm; Drama; GS; Hmrm; Secy, Math C; NFL; NHS; Spch C; SC; Thes; Sftbl; Lion A; Math A; Q&S A; Yth Fel; *Okla St U; Acct.*

NICHOLS, Mark Daniel
Mountain View HS; Mountain View, AR (5-68) Pres, Band; BC; BS; Community Yth Symph; Drama; Key C; *Evangel Col; Sci.*

NICHOLS, Mary Ellen
Forest Brook Sr HS; Houston, TX; Pres, FHA; SC; *U of Houston; Fashion Designer.*

NICHOLS, Mary Julia
Ridgeview HS; Atlanta, GA (40%-200) Anchor C; Ann; Drama; Hmrm; Model UN; VP, Sr Cl; Var C; Cl; VP, Soph Cl; Cpt, Tr; Tr Ltr; *U of Ga; Ed.*

NICHOLS, Nancy Jean
Rock Hill HS; Rock Hill, SC; Band; Candy-Striper; Colorguard; Pres, MYF; *Nurs.*

NICHOLS, Norma Lou
Chenango Valley Jr-Sr HS; Binghamton, NY; NHS; Span C; NML; Regents Nurs Schol; *Roberts Wesleyan Col; Nurs.*

NICHOLS, Richard David
Hobart HS; Hobart, IN (10%-437) Ann; Chor; Drama; Ensm; NHS; COM; God & Country A; Outst Choir Member; Eagle Sct; *Computer Engr.*

NICHOLS, Rita Jean
Shawnee HS; Louisville, KY (5-250) VP, Fr C; NHS; VP, Span C; Up Bound; Cr-Cty; Co-Cpt, Tr; COM; Cl Fav; Hist A; Span A; *Foreign Lang.*

NICHOLS, Robert Henard Jr
W Memphis Christian Sch; W Memphis, AR (5-31) VP, Hmrm; Semi-Fin, Bkbl; Mgr, Ftbl; Fin, Golf; Fin, Tnns; Fin, Tr; Cl Fav; Reading; Bible; *Harding Col; Public Relations.*

NICHOLS, Ruth Ann
Classen HS; Okla City, OK (3-176) FBLA; NHS; Span C; SC; Tnns; Hist A; Okla St U Alumni Cert, Top Jr; Medal, Conf Tnns; *Central St U; Acct.*

NICHOLS, Sabrina Joy
W Side HS; Gary, IN (18-700) Band; Bus C; FBLA; NHS; Span C; COM; Hon Prog; Type A; *W Mich U; Acct.*

NICHOLS, Sandra Gail
Frankston HS; Frankston, TX (10%-39) Band; FHA; Mjrte; Cpt, Bkbl; Tnns; Citz A; Type A; *Tyler Jr Col.*

NICHOLS, Shari Lee
Pine View HS; Sarasota, FL; Drama; SC; Bio A; NEDT; *Lang Arts.*

NICHOLS, Sharyn Elaine
Springfield Local HS; Petersburg, OH (8-135) Fr C; FTA; NHS; COM; H of F; Poet A; Top Ten; Amer Bus Women's Assn Schol; *Youngstown Col of Bus; Acct.*

NICHOLS, Susan Irene
Dixie Co HS; Cross City, FL (20-160) Ann; Secy, Band; Chor; Rptr, FHA; Tres, Sci C; FHA, Band, Acteens, A's; Acteens Schol; *Judson Col; Elem Ed.*

NICHOLS, Tammy Marie
Swain Co HS; Bryson City, NC (18-131) Cpt, Chldr; VP, Chess C; Fr C; NHS; Sci C; Rptr, Soph Cl; Mgr, Bkbl; Hist A; *Wake Forest Col; Pre-Med.*

NICHOLS, Teresa Ann
Port St Joe Jr-Sr HS; Port St Joe, FL (5%-135) Chor; VP, Ntl Jr Hon Soc; Keyettes.

NICHOLS, Thelma Ruth
Wayne Comm HS; Corydon, IA; Chor; Rptr, Y-Tns; Type A; Yth Fel.

NICHOLS, Theresa Lynne
Karlsruhe Amer HS; Karlsruhe, GERMANY; JV, Chldr; SC; Secy, Soph Cl; COM; HQn.

NICHOLS, Wendy Elizabeth
Cheyenne Central HS; Cheyenne, WY (11-402) Band; Chor; Rptr, FBLA; Hmrm; InterClub Coun; Lat C; NHS; Rptr, Sch P; Mgr, Bkbl; Mgr, Ftbl; Mgr, Tr; Mgr, Wrest; Hon Prog; Type A; Acct A; Pres, Tn Action Prog; Bus Ed A; Sunday Sch Teacher; Academic Achv A; Candystriper; *U of Wy; Bus Ed.*

NICHOLS, William Arthur
Dixie Co HS; Cross City, FL (5%-80) Ann; Cpt, Band; BC; Sci C; Cl Fav; Rotary A; Most Stu; GP Schol; *Fla Tech U; Engr.*

NICHOLS, William Burton
San Benito Joint Union HS; Hollister, CA (40-210) Chor; Drama; 4H; Rptr, Sch P; Tnns; Sci C; VP, SC; Thes; VP, Soph Cl; JV, Cr-Ctry; JV, Golf; Citz A; 4H A; Sci A; WW; *Gavilan Col; Elec.*

NICHOLSON, Bonnie Gayle
Glenbrook S HS; Glenview, IL (236-600) Ed, Ann; Ski C; Var C; JV, Bkbl; Golf; Sftbl; Q&S; Sewing A; Commendation Interior Design; Commendation Phys Ed; *Photography.*

NICHOLSON, David Lee
Springs Valley HS; French Lick, IN (16-89) All Amer Yth; Chem C; Fr C; 4H; HiY; Hmrm; Key C; NHS; SC; Var C; Bsbl; Cpt, Bkbl; Ftbl; COM; 4H A; Hon Prog; Lion A; MLS; Star Student; St Scholar; Swth; WW; *Purdue U; Engr.*

NICHOLSON, Dean Gregory
Pattonville HS; Hazelwood, MO (170-1050) BS; Dbte Tm; NFL; VP, Var C; Cr-Ctry; Co-Cpt, Tr; *Social Stu.*

NICHOLSON, Deidria Claresse
Eisenhower HS; Rialto, CA (98-761) Hmrm; CSF; Hon Prog; Ntl Sci Found; *UCLA; Eng.*

NICHOLSON, Edward Brown
Sussex Central HS; Sussex, VA (2-173) BC; BS; Pres, FFA; InterClub Coun; Co-Ed, Sch P; Sci C; SC; Mgr, Bsbl; Mgr, Ftbl; JV, Wrest; Math A; Sal; St Farmer Degree; *Va Tech U; Civil Engr.*

NICHOLSON, Elaine Joy
Pattonville Sr HS; Maryland Heights, MO (40-743) A Cap Choir; Chor; Drama; Ensm; NFL; NHS; Thes; Citz A; Hon Prog; PA; Mus Ltr; Church Campus A; Best Female Cameo; Top 10 Sr Musicians; *William Jewell Col; Lib Art.*

NICHOLSON, James Matthew
Dilley HS; Dilley, TX; BS; FFA; Ftbl; Amateur Radio Operator; *Elec.*

NICHOLSON, Jane Marie
Kalamazoo Loy Norrix HS; Kalamazoo, MI (3-400) A Cap Choir; Chor; Fr C; NHS; Var C; Y-Tns; Co-Cpt, Swim; Hon Prog; Yth Fel; Mgr, Swim; JV Vlbl; *Albion Col; Pre-Med.*

NICHOLSON, Jennifer Lynn
New Brockton HS; New Brockton, AL (10%-75) Ann; BC; FBLA; Sftbl; *Enterprise Jr Col; Computer Sci.*

NICHOLSON, Joey Lee
Lakeview Acad; Gainesville, GA (3-28) BC; Chor; Bkbl; Soccer; Lat A; *Law.*

NICHOLSON, June Marie
Hastings HS; Hastings, MI (6-289) Chor; Ensm; NHS; Pres, Y-Tns; NEDT; Rotary A; WW; *Olivet Nazarene Col; Nurs.*

NICHOLSON, LaVetta Maria
McKinley Tech Sr HS; Washington, DC;

NICHOLSON, Phillip Brent
Watsonville Union HS; Watsonville, CA; Chor; Drama; CSF; Soloist, The Freedom Singers; *Westminster Choir Col; Mus.*

NICHOLSON, Robert Michael
Stratford Acad; Macon, GA; Key C; SC; Cpt, Bsbl; Bkbl; Tr; Bio A; S-T, Sr Cl; VP, Pep C; AKO Fraternity; Inter-Fraternity; All-St Bsbl; *Columbus Col; Bio.*

NICHOLSON, Roger Lee
Jessamine Co HS; Nicholasville, KY (10-290) Pres, BC; SC; Bkbl; Sftbl; COM; Eng A; *Georgetown Col; Pre-Law.*

NICHOLSON, Ronaldo Terrez
Lincoln Sr HS; E St Louis, IL (4-412) Chess C; Math C; *U of Sou Calif; Engr.*

NICHOLSON, Steven Michael
Sandy Valley HS; Magnolia, OH (96-160) MVP, Bsbl; Bkbl; Co-Cpt, Ftbl; 2nd Tm All-Ohio Def Tm, Ftbl; Sonny Thomas A; Varsity Ltrs; *Otterbein Col; Ed.*

NICKEL, Victor Eugene
Manchester HS; Manchester, GA (12-102) Chess C; 4H; Sci C; Bsbl; Bkbl; Ftbl; Math A; Most Outst Math A; *Troup Tech U; Elec.*

NICKELL, Sherry Ann
Linn Co R-I HS; Browning, MO; Chor; 4H; Bkbl; Sftbl; DARGCA; *NE Mo St U; Child Development.*

NICKELSON, Gail Louise
Waynoka HS; Waynoka, OK; Ann; Band; Tres, FHA; VP, 4H; VP, Sci C; 4H A; Masonic A; Okla Hon Soc.

NICKERSON, George Mark
Hermon Christian Sch; Hermon, ME; Fin, Chess C; Chor; Ensm; Math C; Phys C; Sci C; Ski C; Span C; VP, SC; Var C; Bsbl; Bkbl; JV, Cr-Ctry; Golf; Sftbl; Swim; Tr; Wrest; *Eastern Maine Voc-Tech Inst; Photography.*

NICKERSON, Kay Frances
Palisades HS; Pacific Palisades, CA; A Cap Choir; Band; Chldr; Chor; Drama; Madrigal; HCt; MLS; Yth Fel; Outst Singing A; Excel, Dancing; Spring Mus; *El Camino Jr Col; Mus.*

NICKERSON, Kevin John
Bellevue Comm HS; Bellevue, MI (15-110) Span C; *Olivet Col; Pre-Law.*

NICKERSON, Kimberlee T
Beverly Hills HS; Beverly Hills, CA; Chldr; Drama; Tr; COM; Citz A; Yth Fel; Yth Leg; Semi Fin, Fall Drama Festival; Bicentennial A; Principal's Hon List; Human Relation Comm; *The Juilliard Sch; Drama.*

NICKERSON, Paul Laurence
M B Smiley HS; Houston, TX (31-400) Math C; Cr-Ctry; Ftbl; Tr; Archt Drafting A; *Civil Engr.*

NICKERSON, Robert Murray
Linesville Conneaut Summit HS; Linesville, PA (5-90) Band; Chess C; Bsbl; Bkbl; Cr-Ctry.

NICKERSON, Suzanne Joy
Grace Baptist HS; South Bend, IN (2-14) Band; Chor; 4H; *SW Mich U; Nurs.*

NICKESON, Linda Lanae
Barneston HS; Barneston, NE (3-22) Band; Chldr; Chor; Cpt, Bkbl; Sftbl; Mus A; Mus Accompanist; Cpt, Vlbl; Pres, Luther League; *University; Nutrition.*

NICKMEYER, Gwyn Allyn
Redlands Sr HS; Redlands, CA (30-750) Band; NHS; Phys C; Ski C; SC; Tr; Jobs Daughters; JV Vlbl; Daisy Chain; WW; *U of Calif; Bio.*

NICKOLAISEN, Niel Raymond
Box Elder HS; Brigham City, UT (13-418) Hmrm; NHS; Order/Arrow; Pres, Var C; Cpt, Bkbl; Co-Cpt, Ftbl; Cpt, Tr; Steven Josephsen A; All-St Ftbl; All-Area Ftbl; All-Region Ftbl; *Brigham Young U; Chem.*

NICKOLAISEN, Scott
Box Elder HS; Brigham City, UT (5%-450) Hmrm; VP, NHS; Order/Arrow; Co-Cpt, Ftbl; Tr; Hon Prog; *Brigham Young U; Chem Engr.*

NICKSE, Jay Scott
Shelton HS; Shelton, CT (20%-450) Ski C; Golf; Bus.

NICOLA, Joseph Paul
St Elizabeth HS; Pleasant Hills, PA (10-101) Band; Cpt, Hockey; Nom, Dorothy Lombardi A; Geom A; Lab Assistance A; *Comm Col of Allegheny Co-South; Architecture.*

NICOLA, Karen Ruth
Warsaw HS; Warsaw, IN (40-425) A Cap Choir; Band; Chor; Drama; VP, Fr C; FHA; Hmrm; NFL; Spch C; Tres, SC; Amer Leg A; Amer Leg Orator A; Bio A; Citz A; Gov Honor Prog; Hist A; Hon Prog; JA A; Spch A; Yth Fel; *Oral Roberts U; Drama.*

NICOLAIDES, Steven Thomas
Chester HS; Chester, PA; Demolay; Hmrm; JV, Wrest; Hon Prog; *Swarthmore Col; Engr.*

NICOLL, Jessica
Dover HS; Dover, NH (12-396) Ann; Fr C; Lit Mag; Secy, NHS; Hon Prog; MLS; Nom, NCTE A; Sch Rptr, City News; Schol Achv Ltr; *U of NH; Liberal Arts.*

NICOLL, Theresa Ann
Cath Central HS; Troy, NY (40%-350) Drama; Hmrm; Key C; SC; *Marketing.*

NICOLLS, Angelo David II
Huntington E HS; Huntington, WV (33%-365) Key C; Sch P; Pres, SC; Pres, Jr Cl; Bsbl; Ftbl; *Marshall U; Psych.*

NICOLSON, Laurie Anne
W A Berry HS; Birmingham, AL (10-353) VP, Band; Hmrm; Mu Alpha Theta; NHS; Span C; NMF; All St Band; WW; *U of Ala.*

NICOSON, Laura Lin
Brazil Sr HS; Brazil, IN (6-196) Chor; Secy, Drama; FHA; Rptr, Sch P; Sci C; Span C; Thes; Eng.

NIDO, Fernando Juan
Academia del Sagrado Corazon; Santurce, PR (17-65) NHS; ARC; Sch P; SC; VP, Jr Cl; Bsbl; Bkbl; MVP, Tr; COM; Span A; *U S Air Force Acad; Sci.*

NIEDERHAUSER, Donald Brent
Quincy Sr HS II; Quincy, IL (116-772) A Cap Choir; Chor; VP, Demolay; Hmrm; Madrigal; Span C; SC; Mgr, Soccer; Bus.

NIEDERHISER, Leonard
Salem HS; Salem, OH (77-327) VP, InterAct C; Math C; Mu Alpha Theta; Tr; Heidelberg Col; Ed.

NIEDRICH, Mary Jane
Doss HS; Louisville, KY (4-325) BC; NHS; MLS; WW.

NIEDZIALEK, Elizabeth Ann
LaSalle Sr HS; Niagara Falls, NY (200-600) Rptr, Sch P; Ch, Church Yth; Cedarville Col; Elem Ed.

NIEDZIELKO, Marian Kathryn
Chetek HS; Chetek, WI (7-94) Co-Ed, Ann; Band; CYO; Chldr; Chor; VP, FHA; S-T, FNA; Semi-Fin, GS; NFL; NHS; Sch P; Sci C; Ski C; JV, Bkbl; Tr; Bio A; Pres A; Spch A; JV, Vlbl; St Off, FHA; St Tourn Forensic A; Church Coun; U of Wis-Eau Claire; Med Tech.

NIEHAUS, Brenda Lee
Litchfield HS; Litchfield, IL (23-150) Cpt, Chldr; Chor; Pres, 4H; NHS; Span C; VP, SC; Var C; Tres, Soph Cl; Sftbl; Tr; COM; 4H A; Pres A; VofDEM; VP, Secy, 4 H C; Secy, SC; Phys Ed.

NIEHAUS, Mark L
Wooster Sr HS; Wooster, OH (12-382) Band; Drama; Fr C; Math C; NFL; NHS; Spch C; Thes; Magna Cum Laude; Spch A; NML; Psych.

NIELSEN, Beth Naomi
Kinder HS; Kinder, LA (12-101) Band; BC; Chor; Community Yth Symph; Drama; Ensm; FHA; 4H; Jr Miss Pagent; Lit Mag; Sch P; COM; 4H A; Band A; McNeese St U; Vocal Sch Mus.

NIELSEN, Diane Lynn
Port Washington HS; Port Washington, WI; AFS; Ger C; Silver Lake Col; Vet Assist.

NIELSEN, Joan Louise
Dunlap Comm Sch; Dunlap, IA (19-64) Ch, FHA; Var C; Bkbl; Sftbl; Vlbl; Computer Prog.

NIELSEN, Julie Marie
Cambridge Sr HS; Cambridge, MN; FNA; VP, 4H.

NIELSEN, Kevin Robert
Spencer HS; Spencer, IA (15%-185) BS; Drama; NHS; Span C; SC; Pres, Var C; Pres, Jr Cl; Pres, Soph Cl; Co-Cpt, Bkbl; Co-Cpt, Ftbl; Tr; Amer Leg A; HCt; Hon Prog; Most Out; Yth Fel; MVP, Bkbl; U of Iowa; Med.

NIELSEN, Kurt Charles
James I O'Neill HS; Highland Falls, NY (40-187) Ann; NHS; Var C; Bsbl; JV, Bkbl; Soccer; Regent Schol; Bio C; Merrimack Col.

NIELSEN, Leslie Renee
Columbus Sr HS; Columbus, NE; Ger C; Pres, 4H; NHS; ARC; Sch P; SC; Tnns; 4H A; Jr Ed, Ann; Thespians; Vlbl; St Fair 4-H Model; German.

NIELSEN, Lori Ann
Harold L Richards HS; Oak Lawn, IL (144-600) Band; Drama; Mod Mus Mas; NFL; Spch C; Thes; Spch A; Best Marching Band; Wartburg Col; Teaching.

NIELSEN, Robert Jorgen
Cabrillo Sr HS; Lompoc, CA (40-430) Band; Fin, BS; Chem C; Dbte Tm; Pres, InterClub Coun; Key C; Span C; VP, SC; Var C; Swim; Amer Leg A; H of F; Spch A; Water Polo All Amer; Dean's List; Pepperdine U; Bus.

NIELSEN, Robert William
Fairmont HS; Fairmont, MN (160-230) Tres, FFA; 4H; Arch; Bsbl; Sftbl; Wrest; 4H A; Star Student; U of Mn; Agr.

NIELSEN, Sheila Rena
Cedar Falls HS; Cedar Falls, IA (5%-519) COM; Bus.

NIELSON, Janine Marie
Erskine HS; Erskine, MN (3-25) Band; Chor; Ensm; Semi-Fin, NHS; Rptr, Sch P; Bkbl; Band A; Chor A; Bsbl A.

NIELSON, Julie Lynn
LuVerne Comm HS; LuVerne, IA (4-18) Band; Chor; 4H; SC; Pres, Jr Cl; Cpt, Bkbl; Tr; Type A; VofDEM; MVP, Bkbl; Eckerd Col; Phys Ed.

NIELSON, Lisa Mary
Sprague HS; Salem, OR (10-431) A Cap Choir; CYO; Chor; Madrigal; JA A.

NIELSON, Nancy Diane
James Island HS; Charleston, SC; Chor; InterClub Coun; Secy, SC; Pres, Y-Tns; WW; Col Charleston; Psych.

NIELSON, Nancy Nydia
Wheaton HS; Wheaton, MN (5-78) Ann; Band; Chor; Ensm; FHA; GS; SC; Mus A; Nurs.

NIEMAN, Debra Ann
Auburndale HS; Auburndale, WI (25-110) Chor; NFL; Cpt, Bkbl; JA A; ARC A; Clara Barton A; Pres, Health C; St Joseph's Sch of Nurs; Nurs.

NIEMAN, Jonathan Henry
Rosemead HS; Rosemead, CA (1-380) A Cap Choir; Fr C; Hmrm; Bank Of Amer A; President's HR; Church Organist; CSU-LOS Angeles; Mus.

NIEMAN, Ruth Joy
Grandview Park Baptist HS; Des Moines, IA; Ed, Ann; Chldr; Chor; ARC; Rptr, Sch P; Sftbl; God & Country A; MLS; John Brown U; Pre-Law.

NIEMANN, Nancy Ellen
Litchfield Sr HS; Litchfield, IL (12-132) Chor; Ensm; 4H; NHS; 4H A; St Scholar; VofDEM; Eastern Ill U; Acct.

NIEMANN, Nancy Lucille
Valley HS; Hoople, ND (4-26) Ann; Band; Chor; 4H; Pres, Soph Cl; JV, Sftbl; 4H A; JV Vlbl.

NIEMEIER, James Allan
Mayville-Portland HS; Mayville, ND (4-70) Band; Var C; Ftbl; Tr; Wrest; Hon Prog; Yth Fel; ND St U; Mech Engr.

NIEMEIER, Rodney Orland
Mayville Portland HS; Mayville, ND (3-68) VP, Band; BS; Tres, Sr Cl; VP, Soph Cl; Wrest; Hon Prog; Yth Fel; Schol to MSC; Mayville St Col; Engr.

NIEMEYER, Linda Sue
William Chrisman HS; Independence, MO (33%-484) Dbte Tm; Secy, 4H; NFL; Sch P; Thes; 4H A; Q&S A; Head Photographer, Sch P; Photographer, Yrbk.

NIEMEYER, Martha Lee
Norris HS; Firth, NE (6-84) Chor; Bus Mgr, Drama; Fr C; GS; Secy, 4H; NFL; NHS; Spch C; Sftbl; B Crocker A; 4H A; Spch A; U of NE; Journ.

NIEMEYER, Phillip Clarke
Rolling Meadows HS; Rolling Meadows, IL (230-640) Chor; Ger C; Ntl Fraternity of Stu Musicians.

NIEMITALO, Felecia Ranae
Stanley Comm HS; Stanley, ND (20%-55) Band; Chor; FHA; Bacone Col; Lit.

NIENOW, John Robert
Santa Ana HS; Santa Ana, CA (1-525) Bus Mgr, AFS; Band; Fin, BS; Pres, Ger C; NHS; Order / Arrow; Rptr, Sch P; Golf; CSF; COM; Hist A; Hon Prog; Stanford U; Med.

NIESCHLAG, Russell Alan
Metamora Township HS; Metamora, IL (71-193) Band; Community Yth Symph; Ensm; Swim; Wrest; All St, All Star, Bands; Bradley U; Elec Engr.

NIESS, Robert Andrew
N Penn HS; Lansdale, PA (125-900) Ski C; Ftbl; Gettysburg Col.

NIETHOLD, Arlyn Bernice
Sharon HS; Sharon, MA (35-250) Sftbl; Swim; Pres, Yth Fel; Gym; Tumbletts; Bus.

NIETUPSKI, Paula Jean
Ne Clinton Central HS; Champlain, NY (6-150) Band; Sci C; Span C; Hockey; Vlbl.

NIETZ, Cindy Ann
Gilman HS; Gilman, WI (61-74) VP, AFS; Ann; Band; Chor; Sch P; Mgr, Tr; Pres, Yth Group; VP, Fellowship Interntl; U of Wisc; Communicative Disorters.

NIEUWSMA, Janice Kay
Pollock HS; Pollock, SD; Chor; Pres, FHA; 4H; A-Ed, Sch P; Sci C; 4H A; Sci A; U of ND; Sci.

NIEVES, Daniel
Morris HS; New York, NY; Chor; Bsbl; Alg A; Hon Prog; Math A; Attendance, Gym, A's; Fine Arts.

NIEVES, Manuel Jesus
Olney HS; Philadelphia, PA;

NIEVES, Maria
Miguel Melendez Munoz; Bayamon, PR (6-250) Escuela Miguel M Munoz.

NIEVES, Mariemma Rosa
Acad Nuestra Sra de la Providncia; Rio Piedras, PR (4-64) Band; CYO; Chor; Pres, Drama; InterAct C; Rptr, Sch P; Sci C; Spch C; Cpt, Bsbl; Cpt, Tr; Bio A; COM; Poet A; Sci A; Summa Cum Laude; Vlbl; Conduct A; Civics A; PR Women Federation A; St Mus A; Sci.

NIEVES, Narda Teresa
Dr P Perea Fajardo Voc HS; Mayaguez, PR; COM; Sci A; Exc Hon Stu; Bradford Col; Med Technology.

NIEWALD, Joyce Alice
Lutheran HS N; St Louis, MO (8-160) Chor; JV, Bkbl; Sftbl; GAA; St, Campfire Girls; Secy, Fresh Cl; PTL Schol, HS; Journ.

NIEWALD, Laurie Kay
Glendale HS; Springfield, MO (25%-410) AFS; Ger C; Bus & Professional Women's C Schol; SW Mo St U; Ed.

NIEWOHNER, Laura Lee
Lyons Pub HS; Lyons, NE (8-33) Ann; FBLA; FHA; Pres, Ger C; Sch P; SC; VofDEM; U of Nebr; Nurs.

NIEZNANSKI, Valerie Kay
Aurora E HS; Aurora, IL (102-797) Band; Drama; Ger C; Orch; Thes; Waubonsee Col.

NIGHTINGALE, Annette
Lee Co HS; Beattyville, KY (50%-125) Band; Drama; Cpt, Mjrte; Rptr, Sch P; HQn; Morehead St U; Vet Technology.

NIGRO, Mario Luigi
Ursuline HS; Youngstown, OH (120-380) Anesthesiology.

NIKIRK, David Bruce
Richland HS; Fort Worth, TX (10%-700) Cum Laude Soc; Spch C; Ftbl; Opt A; Rotary A; St & Ntl Champ, Judo; Industrial & Martial Arts A's; Pepperdine U; Med.

NIKOLAY, Paul Alexander
Abbotsford HS; Abbotsford, WI (6-65) AFS; Secy, Band; BS; CYO; Chem C; Chess C; Dbte Tm; Drama; Ensm; Pres, Fr C; NFL; NHS; Ntl Yth Conf; ARC; Pres, Spch C; Pres, SC; Var C; Pres, Sr Cl; Pres, Soph Cl; Bkbl; Bkbl; Cpt, Ftbl; Semi-Fin, Tr; Alg A; Amer Leg A; COM; Elk A; HKg; HCt; MLS; Most Out; Spch A; Yth Leg; Laird Yth Ldrship; NASC Conf; Math League A; UW-Madison; Pre-Law.

NILEMO, David Bertil
Cherry Creek Sr HS; Englewood, CO (100-700) Band; Chor; Span C; Cr-Ctry; Soccer; Swim; Tr; VP, Church Yth Fel; Band Cert; Bus Adm.

NILES, Kelly Jean
Hopkinsville HS; Hopkinsville, KY (20%-350) Band; Yth Fel; Yth Leg; Murray St Col; Elem Ed.

NILES, Melida Cecilia
Clara Barton HS; Brooklyn, NY (200-400) COM; Wendell Felman A; Bus Ed A; Attendance A; Atlantic Union Col; Dietitics.

NILES, Stacey Rae
Edmond Memorial HS; Edmond, OK; Band; Chldr; Chor; FHA; FTA; 4H; HiY; SC; Tri-HiY; Var C; Bkbl; Tr; HQn; Hon Prog; Pres A; Assembly Com; Okla Christian Col; Interior Design.

NILSEN, Eva Annette
Montgomery HS; Skillman, NJ; A Cap Choir; Band; Chor; Soccer; Sftbl; Yth Fel; Dental Asst; Band Letter A; Church Young Peoples Soc; Soccer Letter A; Sun Sch Teacher; Nurs.

NILSON, David Alan
S R Butler HS; Huntsville, AL; Band; Ensm; COM; Yth Fel; Solo & Ensm A; Sch Ltr; Oral Roberts U; Med.

NIMMO, Janis Ann
Snyder HS; Snyder, TX (45-195) Band; Drama; Type A; Hardin-Simmons Col; Ed.

NIMMO, Julie Kay
Cheshire HS; Cheshire, CT (25%-375) Pres, Rainbow; Span C; Cpt, Bkbl; Masonic A; Pres A; Flour Hockey; GAD; U of New Haven; Criminology.

NIMMO, Kimberly Lynn
DuPont Sr HS; Hermitage, TN; FHA.

NIMMO, Lois Ann
Staunton River HS; Moneta, VA (20%-169) Chldr; Drama; 4H; Monogram; SC; Roanoke Col; Elem Teaching.

NIMMO, William Thomas
Seaside HS; Seaside, OR (2-96) Ann; Band; BS; Chor; HiY; NHS; Pol Sci C; Ed, Sch P; Sci C; Ski C; Pres, Span C; Spch C; SC; Pres, Sr Cl; Cr-Ctry; Ftbl; Golf; Tnns; Amer Leg A; Elk A; Gov Honor Prog; Hon Prog; Journ A; Sal; Spch A; Tres, Span C; Vocal Jazz Ensm; A-Ed, Sch Paper; Arion Mus A; VP, Stu Body; Ltrman's C; Sch Fin, St Yth Prog; U of Oreg; Pre-Law.

NIMMONS, Billy Truett
Tupelo HS; Tupelo, MS (15%-400) Chor; Tnns.

NIMMONS, Rhonda Lee
Tupelo HS; Tupelo, MS (10%-350) A Cap Choir; Anchor C; Chor; Ensm; Fr C; FHA; Madrigal; NHS; Thes; Magna Cum Laude; Chor A; Outst Girl Choral Stu; Delta St Hon Chor; Soprano Soloist; Samford U; Mus.

NIMMONS, Willie James
Estill HS; Estill, SC; Chor; Ensm; Var C; Bkbl; Ftbl; Tr; Tr A; Ftbl A; U of SC; Bus.

NINNEMANN, Mark David
Chisago Lakes Sr HS; Lindstrom, MN; Drama; Spch C; Golf; Hockey; Spch A; Best Actor, Sub Dist & Dist; U of Minn at Duluth; Theatre.

NINNEMANN, Steven David
S St Paul HS; S St Paul, MN (25-428) Bsbl; Cr-Ctry; Ftbl; Hockey; Sftbl; ARC A; Math.

NINO, Leonor Carlotta
Notre Dame HS; Salinas, CA (23-89) Model UN; NHS; Rptr, Sch P; Span C; SC; Hon Prog; Yth Leg; Secy, Action C; Pep C; Gavilan Jr Col; Nurs.

NIPP, Bruce Dean
Caprock HS; Amarillo, TX (10-350) HiY; Lat C; NHS; Ch, SC; VP, Soph Cl; Bsbl; Bkbl; Cl Fav; Most Out; All-Dist Bsbl; Soph of Yr, Bkbl; Archt.

NIPPER, Carla Dawn
Earlsboro HS; Earlsboro, OK (3-26) Cpt, Chldr; FBLA; Tres, FHA; 4H; Hmrm; NHS; SC; VP, Var C; VP, Jr Cl; Tres, Soph Cl; Bsbl; Bkbl; Hon Prog; Val; Vlbl; Best Personality; WW; Oklahoma Christian Col; Bus.

NIPPER, Martina Michelle
Julia Richman HS; New York, NY (160-300) Chldr; Chor; Manhattan Comm Col; Psych.

NIPPERT, Leesa Susan
Mangum HS; Mangum, OK (6-68) Chor; Drama; Ensm; FHA; 4H; NHS; SC; Var C; Bkbl; Swim; Tnns; Gov Honor Prog; 4H A; Hist A; Masonic A; St Hon Soc; Okla U; Sociology.

NIRENSTEIN, Debra Lisa
Canarsie HS; Brooklyn, NY (7-945) FTA; Mjrte; Math C; NHS; Sch P; Alg A; Amer Leg A; Math A; Regent Schol; Rensselaer A; Sal; NMSQT Commendation; Ed, Math Magazine; Governor's Cert; Sci Magazine; Cornell U; Math.

NISBET, Ginger Eileen
Conroe HS; Conroe, TX (91-814) FTA; Ger C; 4H; Rptr, NHS; Church Chor; off, Drill Tm; Houston Baptist Col; Social Work.

NISHIYAMA, Curtis Hideo
Pasadena HS; Pasadena, CA; Cpt, Soccer; Water-Polo; Pepperdine U; Dentistry.

NISPERLY, Barbara Ann
Bridgeport HS; Bridgeport, OH (20-108) Band; Secy, Chor; Ensm; FTA; 4H; NHS; Span C; SC; Y-Tns; Chor A; Span A.

NISSEN, Barbara Lynn
Spencer HS; Spencer, IA (8-200) Band; 4H; Span C; N Iowa Area Comm Col; Acct.

NISSEN, Kimberly Kay
Ralston HS; Ralston, NE (45-300) A Cap Choir; Bus C; Chor; Madrigal; NHS; Sftbl; Hon Prog; Interlochen Ntl Mus; Mus Service A.

NISSEN, Terry Lynn
O'Neill Pub HS; O'Neill, NE; Band; Chor; Ensm; NHS; Bkbl; Swim; Hon Prog; FCA; Vlbl; Sioux Falls Col.

NISSWANDT, Beret Serena
Two Harbors HS; Two Harbors, MN (15-210) Chor; Ensm; Fr C; NHS; Tr; COM; Curling; U of Minn; Med.

NISWONGER, Michael Glenn
Fairmont E HS; Kettering, OH (30-600) Ger C; COM; Hon Prog; PA; Cincinnati Col; Engr.

NITSCHKE, Paul Jeffery
Wis Lutheran HS; Milwaukee, WI (15-275) NHS; Rptr, Sch P; JV, Cr-Ctry; Tr; COM; NMF; NMS; UW-EAU Claire; Acct.

NITZ, Amber Elaine
NW HS; Canal Fulton, OH; Chor; FBLA; FHA; Hmrm; Sch P; SC; Y-Tns; MLS; Type A; Fla Col Camper o-t Yr; Fla Col; Sociology.

NITZ, Randolph Carl
Reavis HS; Burbank, IL (76-790) Ger C; NHS; Sci C; SC; COM; NEDT; ROTC A; Bradley U; Elec Engr.

NITZ, Rita G
Reavis HS; Burbank, IL (192-790) Chldr; Ger C; Sci C; COM; Bus.

NITZSCHKE, Rhonda Faye
Remsen-Union Comm HS; Remsen, IA; Ed, Ann; Band; FHA; FNA; NHS; Ed, Sch P; S-T, Jr Cl; Secy, Soph Cl; Bkbl; NHS A; HR; 2nd, Oktoberfeast Court; Patricia Stevens Fashion & Bus Col; Executive Secy.

NIVER, Sara Elizabeth
Oak Ridge Acad; Oak Ridge, NC (6-30) Ed, Ann; Chor; Drama; Fr C; Ger C; 4H; Monogram; ARC; Ski C; Var C; Arch; Bkbl; Sftbl; Swim; Tnns; Citz A; ARC A; ROTC A; Appalachian U; Special Ed.

NIX, Christie Lynn
James W Robinson HS; Fairfax, VA (180-500) Co-Ed, Ann; Chor; Hmrm; InterAct C; Mgr, Soccer; COM; Hon Prog; Regional Chor; Lenoir Rhyne Col; Med.

NIX, Janet Carol
Carbon Hill HS; Carbon Hill, AL (10-85) BC; HiY; NHS; Sci C; Most Stu; Knox Col.

NIX, Kenneth Wayne Jr
Brazos HS; Wallis, TX (10-75) Band; Dbte Tm; Demolay; Span C; SC; Cpt, Ftbl; Semi-Fin, Tr; COM; Gov Honor Prog; Pres A; Most Friendly; Most Talkative; Baylor U; Med.

NIX, Robert Lincoln
First Assembly Christian Sch; Memphis, TN (10-30) Chor; Lib C; Lib As; Central Bible Col; Bible.

NIXDORF, Renate Gabriele
St Joseph Sr HS; St Joseph, MI (25%-372) F-Ed, Ann; Band; Hmrm; Co-Ed, Sch P; SC; Bkbl; Sftbl; Candystriper; Christian Witness A; Med.

NIXON, Alan Mangrum
Scott Preparatory Sch; Opelika, AL (10%-28) BC; Demolay; Ger C; Span C; MLS; Auburn U; Engr.

NIXON, Beverlye
Scott Preparatory Sch; Opelika, AL (4-29) Pres, Anchor C; Ed, Ann; BC; Chor; Pres, Ger C; 4H; Pres, Hmrm; Tres, SC; Pres, Soph Cl; Chem A; DARGCA; Math A; MLS; NMS; NEDT; WW; Auburn U; Bus.

NIXON, Charon Reshea
Lincoln HS; Dallas, TX; Band; Tnns; B Crocker A; Cl Fav; Math A; Yth o-t Yr; Pres, Yth Ushers.

NIXON, Deborah Jean
North HS; Omaha, NE (60-413) Band; Chor; Community Yth Symph; Ensm; NHS; Orch; Cl Fav; Hon Prog; JA A; Most Out; Type A; JA; All St Chor; Sch Musicals; Explorers; VP, Church UMY; VP, Camera C; Orch A; All City, All St Orch; U of Nebr at Omaha; Fine Arts.

NIXON, Dedra Kaye
Calhoun Co HS; Edison, GA (10%-95) Band; Rptr, Hmrm; Orch; Sci C; Var C; Tnns; Albany Jr Col; Dental Hygiene.

NIXON, Donna Ruth
Omaha HS; Omaha, NE (2-403) Chor; Dbte Tm; Semi-Fin, GS; Parl, Lat C; NHS; Sch Achieve Tm; Var C; Sftbl; COM; Citz A; Hon Prog; ROTC A; Yth Fel; U of Nebr at Lincoln; Sci.

NIXON, Lewis Carroll II
Charter Oak HS; Covina, CA (11-300) A Cap Choir; Band; Chor; Ensm; Hmrm; Pres, Lat C; Lat NHS; Orch; Spch C; SC; Var C; Mgr, Cr-Ctry; Swim; Mgr, Tnns; Mgr, Wrest; Bio A; CSF; COM; Chem A; Hon Prog; JA A; Phy A; Sci A; Yth Fel; Lat Proficiency A; Chapman Col; Mus.

NIXON, Lewis Cawthon
Spruce Creek HS; Port Orange, FL (56-450) Band; Drama; Fr C; VP, Lat C; Bkbl; Cr-Ctry; Most Out; Yth Fel; Pres, TV Production C; Wittiest; Mr Spruce Creek; Sch Radio Rptr; Appalachian St U; Communications.

NIXON, Lori Ruth
Star Spencer HS; Spencer, OK (30-381) FBLA; Key C; U of Okla; Nurs.

NIXON, Michael Alan
Argenta-Oreana HS; Argenta, IL (5-106) Band; FFA; NHS; Order/Arrow; Sci C; SC; Var C; Cr-Ctry; Wrest; U of Ill; Aeronautical Engr.

NIXON, Pamela Jeanette
Piedmont HS; Monroe, NC; FBLA; 4H; Sftbl; U of NC; Bus.

NOAK, Lisa Diann
Rockdale HS; Rockdale, TX (15-146) Band; Chldr; Tex St Tech Inst; Commercial Art.

NOAK, Lizette Dawn
Rockdale HS; Rockdale, TX (30%-150) NHS; SW U; Elem Ed.

NOAKES, Teresa Ann
Carver HS; Montgomery, AL (28-375) Band; NHS; Span C; VP, Jr Cl; Cpt, Bkbl; Cr-Ctry; Cpt, Sftbl; Tnns; Hist A; Cpt, MVP, Vlbl; Phys Fitness A; Radford Col; Phys Ed.

NOBBE, Susan Eileen
Edmond Mem HS; Edmond, OK; Band; Ensm; NHS; Span C; Sftbl; Alg A; Hist A; Hon Prog; Type A; S-T, Yth Group; St Hon Soc; Masopust Polka Band; Okla St U; Acct.

NOBLE, Anthony Allen
Las Vegas HS; Las Vegas, NV (20%-387) Fin, Chess C; Pres, SC; Bio C; Pres, Yth Leg; U of Nev, Las Vegas; Anthropology.

NOBLE, David Andrew
Holdrege Sr HS; Holdrege, NE (1-150) Band; Chor; St Stu Congress; Pres, Jr Cl; Ftbl; Bio A; Chem A; Hon Prog; MLS; NMS; Phy A; Regent Schol; ROTC A; Sci A; Pres, FCA; MIT; Elec Engr.

NOBLE, Deborah Marie
Washington Sr HS; Cedar Rapids, IA; Chor; Drama; NHS; Artist, Sch P; Art C; Work Experience Prog; Iowa Weslyan; Commercial Art.

NOBLE, James Crispin II
New Bern Sr HS; New Bern, NC; Chor; Drama; FBLA; Ger C; Hmrm; Pres, SC; Wrest; Harvard Col; Bus Adm.

NOBLE, Kevin Ray
Comm Preparatory Acad; Erie, PA; Chess C; Chor; Drama; Rptr, Hmrm; Sci C; Span C; VP, SC; Co-Cpt, Bkbl; COM; Hon Prog; JA A; Sci A; Oceanography.

NOBLE, Nancy Jeanne
Seton HS; Cincinnati, OH (10%-315) ARC; Span C; Mgr, Sftbl; JV, Tr; COM; Hon Prog; Kiwanis A; Bradley U; Home Ec.

NOBLE, Peter Lawrence
Pavilion Central Sch; Pavillion, NY (24-80) Chor; FFA; 4H; Ftbl; Wrest.

NOBLE, Suzanne Louise
Pennsburg HS; Fairless Hills, PA (167-1048) Chldr; Lat C; NHS; ARC; Ski C; Cl Fav; I Dare You; Odd Fellow Fin; Opt A; Swtht; Sr GSct; Sr Lifesaver; Red Cross Canoeing; Penn St U; Liberal Arts.

NOBLE, Tammy Jane
Farmington Sr HS; Farmington, MO (32-280) A Cap Choir; Chor; Drama; Ensm; Ed, Sch P; SC; Thes; Pres, Jr Cl; COM; Journ A; Q&S A.

NOBLEMAN, Blythe Dren
El Camino Real HS; Woodland Hills, CA; City Conf; Ski C; SC; Pres, Soph Cl; Tr; VP, Fresh Cl; Co-Ed, Yrbk; Rep, Interscholastic Ath Comm; COBA Conf; Activity Period Coordinator; *Social Sci.*

NOBLES, David O'Dell
Tex Sr HS; Texarkana, TX (10%-479) Fr C; Rptr, Sch P; Swim; Journ A; *Ouachita Baptist Col; Journ.*

NOBLES, Deborah Jane
Texas Sr HS; Texarkana, TX (54-465) A Cap Choir; Ensm; VP, FTA; Pres, Hmrm; Madrigal; NHS; SC; Pres, Thes; All St Choir; Outst, Mus; Most Talented; *Baylor U; Vocal Mus.*

NOBLES, Donna Irene
Denair HS; Denair, CA (1-69) Co-Ed, Ann; Math C; Sch P; Span C; Tres, Jr Cl; Bkbl; JV, Sftbl; CSF; COM; Hist A; Math A; Val; Cpt, Bowl; GAA Vlbl; YMCA Jr Girl's Ldrship, A; Span, Eng, Home Ec, A's.

NOBLES, Gladys
Waynesboro Central HS; Waynesboro, MS (25%-99) *Jackson St U.*

NOBLES, Quenton Orlanda
Lincoln HS; Dallas, TX; Ch, Band; Mod Mus Mas; Ed, Sch P; Sci C; Cpt, Soccer; Cpt, Tnns; Cl Fav; Journ A; JA A; Kiwanis A; MLS; Ntl Achv Schol; Q&S A; Sci A; *U of Tex; Law.*

NOBLES, Sandra Dianne
Bladenboro HS; Bladenboro, NC (1-117) Ann; Band; BC; Chldr; FHA; Pres, FTA; Hmrm; Mjrte; SC; 4H A; Hist A; Sci A; Fin, Miss NC Tn Pageant; Home Ec A; WW; Chldr A; Ecology A; *Wake Forest Col; Med.*

NOBLES, Shelly Deanne
Bremerhaven American HS; Bremerhaven, GERMANY (2-24) Chldr; Sch P; Riding C; Ballet; Pageant of Masters Art Festival; *Saddleback Jr Col; Pre-Med.*

NOBLITT, Mary Melinda
Union HS; Biggsville, IL (10%-80) Band; Tres, Chor; Drama; Ensm; 4H; Madrigal; NHS; 4H A; Spch A; Yth Fel; Chor As; *Ill Wesleyan U; Psych.*

NOBOA, Doris S
Annandale HS; Annandale, VA (25-375) Band; BC; Bus C; Drama; S-T, Fr C; FBLA; Span C; Mgr, Bsbl; Yth Fel; *N Va Comm Col; Bus Adm.*

NOCITA, Stephen Michael
Lourdes Central HS; Nebraska City, NE (1-33) Mu Alpha Theta; Spch C; SC; Bkbl; Tr; Woodmen o-t World.

NOE, Terri Ann
Riverview HS; Sarasota, FL (20-700) Chor; Ensm; Span C; Swim; Keyettes; Jr Board; *Nutrition.*

NOEL, Allan Douglas
East HS; Salt Lake City, UT (1%-420) Chess C; Drama; NHS; Tri-HiY; JV, Wrest; COM; NMS; Dance Company.

NOELL, Theresa Lee
Oglethorpe Co HS; Lexington, GA (2-110) Band; BC; Fr C; GS; Rptr, 4H; Lit Ral; Sci C; Tri-HiY; Amer Leg A; COM; 4H A; Most Out; Achv A; Eng A; Fr A; *U of Ga; Computer Sci.*

NOENS, Nancy Kelly
Chicago, IL (27-157) Ger C; Hmrm; Rptr, Sch P; SC; Beauty; Hon Prog; WW; *Loyola U; Criminal Justice.*

NOGA, Glenn Allen
Moreau HS; Hayward, CA (11-346) VP, Ger C; Cr-Ctry; Tr; Ntl Sci Found; Ntl Sci Symposium; *Princeton U; Engr.*

NOGALES, Louis Charles
Albuquerque HS; Albuquerque, NM (7-35) Band; CYO; Rptr, Hmrm; JV, Bsbl; JV, Ftbl; *U of NM; Med.*

NOGUERAS, Jaime
Tampa Cath HS; Tampa, FL; Cpt, Ftbl; Cpt, Soccer; Cpt, Tr; Mod Mus; Best Performer; Coach's A; Best Ath; Best Best Bowler; *U of S Fla; Engr.*

NOID, Marion Jeanette
Ben Lomond HS; Ogden, UT (33%-450) AFS; Community Yth Symph; Dbte Tm; Model UN; NHS; Orch; Span C; Spch C; Amer Leg A; COM; Rotary A; Spch A; Pres, Yth Fel; *Weber St Col; Anthropology.*

NOLAN, Barbara Carol
Fall River Jr-Sr HS; McArthur, CA (1-54) AFS; A-Ed, Ann; Chess C; Drama; Secy, FHA; Semi-Fin, GS; Pres, Rainbow; Ed, Sch P; Spch C; Bkbl; Sftbl; Alg A; Amer Leg Orator A; Bank Of Amer A; CSF; Chem A; Cl Fav; Hist A; Journ A; Lion A; Math A; MLS; Most Out; Sci A; Spch A; Val; Schol; Eng, Trig Medals; Union Oil Schol; *U of Calif; Engr.*

NOLAN, Claudia Ann
Central HS; Little Rock, AR (177-666) A Cap Choir; Y-Tns; *Okla U.*

NOLAN, Joseph Douglas Jr
Clay Co HS; Ashland, AL (10-55) A-Ed, Ann; Pres, BC; FTA; Sci C; Var C; Bkbl; Ftbl; *Southern Union Jr Col; Mus.*

NOLAN, Wendell Lee
Hamtramck HS; Hamtramck, MI (42-107) Chess C; Hmrm; Sci C; Var C; Bkbl; Ftbl; Citz A; Cl Fav; Hon Prog; JA A; Ftbl, All City & All Metro; *Wayne St U; Social Work.*

NOLAND, Bobbie Jo
Baker HS; Baker, LA (11-374) BC; Chem C; Drama; Fr C; FTA; Lit Ral; ARC; Span C; Spch C; SC; Alg A; ARC A; 1st Pl, Fr Ral; *LSU; Med.*

NOLAND, Dawn Alena
Moses Lake HS; Moses Lake, WA; A-Ed, Ann; Chor; Drama; 4H; Rainbow; A-Ed, Sch P; SC; Acct.

NOLAND, Gary Neil
Baker HS; Baker, LA; Key C; Mu Sigma; *LSU; Commercial Art.*

NOLAND, Pamela Lynne
West End Christian HS; Tuscaloosa, AL (11-43) Chor; Drama; Ensm; Hmrm; InterAct C; Mod Mus Mas; SC; Pres, Sr Cl; Tres, Jr Cl; Cl Fav; MLS; Outst Sr; WW; Pres, Lib C; *U of N Ala; Arts & Sci.*

NOLAND, Phyllis Kay
Northeast HS; N Little Rock, AR; Band; FBLA; Bus Adm.

NOLAND, Tonya Kay
Ben Davis HS; Indianapolis, IN (2-960) Tres, A Cap Choir; Cpt, Band; Chor; Secy, Drama; Ensm; GS; Madrigal; NHS; Secy, Thes; Alg A; COM; 4H A; Masque & Gavel A; St Scholar; *Ind U; Bus.*

NOLEN, Becky Ann
Hartshorne HS; Hartshorne, OK (7-81) FHA; 4H; SC; Alg A; COM; DARGCA; Sci A; *E Okla St Col.*

NOLEN, Julia Lynn
La Porte HS; La Porte, TX (96-343) Bus C; NHS; Outst, Bus; Outst, VOE; St Win, Acct; *Baylor U; Bus.*

NOLEN, Karrie Lynn
Hartshorne HS; Hartshorne, OK; Rptr, FHA; 4H; NHS; Pres, SC; Bkbl; Sftbl; HQn; *E Okla St Col.*

NOLEN, Michael
Redlands HS; Redlands, CA (1-900) Model UN; Rptr, Sch P; UN Council; CSF; Journ A; NMS; Journ.

NOLES, Bonnie Dee
Sunset HS; Beaverton, OR; Drama; Fr C; Rptr, Sch P; Tnns; *Col of Fashion; Fashion Design.*

NOLES, David Lee
Whiteface HS; Whiteface, TX; Band; FFA; Bkbl; Ftbl; Tr; Cl Fav; Spch A; Most Ambitious; Cl Rptr; *Tex Tech U; Elec Engr.*

NOLES, Jana Kay
Whiteface HS; Whiteface, TX; Rptr, Ann; Rptr, Band; Ensm; FBLA; FHA; Mjrte; Sch P; Sci C; Bkbl; Tnns; Tr; HCt; Math A; Sci A; *Tex Tech U; Mus.*

NOLES, Mike Dean
Sunset HS; Beaverton, OR; Chess C; Span C; World Affairs C; JV, Ftbl; Co-Cpt, Tr; *NNC; Cartoonist.*

NOLF, Jan Elizabeth
Highlands Intermediate HS; Natrona Hgts, PA; Chor; FNA; InterAct C; Ntl Jr Hon Soc; *Temple Col; Med.*

NOLL, Mary Lea
Wonderview HS; Hattieville, AR (2-33) Ed, Ann; FHA; Secy, Sr Cl; Sftbl; 4H A; Sal; Type A; Librarian; *Ark Tech U.*

NOLTA, Jan Aileen
Willows HS; Willows, CA (2-136) Tres, Band; Ensm; Hmrm; Sch Achieve Tm; SC; Secy, Y-Tns; Pep C; *Lang.*

NOLTING, Cindy Lu
Preston Comm HS; Preston, IA (10-40) Band; Chor; FTA; 4H; Rainbow; Sch P; Thes; 4H A.

NOMURA, Randy Ichiro
Sacramento Union Acad; Carmichael, CA (15-47) F-Ed, Ann; Pres, Band; Madrigal; VP, Ski C; Pres, SC; Var C; Tres, Jr Cl; Cpt, Bsbl; Cpt, Bkbl; Ftbl; Soccer; Sftbl; Fin, Tr; CSF; Hon Prog; Pres A; Pastor, Sr Cl; Outst Gymist A; AAPHER 95%; *Pacific Union Col; Dentistry.*

NOONAN, David Alan
St Bede Acad; Peru, IL (50-122) CYO; Chldr; Hmrm; SC; Var C; Bkbl; Ftbl; Tnns; Amer Leg A; Fresh Hmrm Ldr.

NOONE, Kevin James
Blanchet HS; Seattle, WA (67-286) Chor; Dbte Tm; Drama; Bsbl; COM; Chamber of Comm A; Order/Arrow A; *U of Wash; Oceanography.*

NOONING, Nora Judith
Shawnee HS; Louisville, KY; Band; CYO; Drama; Rainbow; Span C; Tres, Soph Cl; JV, Tnns; *Eastern Ky U; Eng.*

NOONKESTER, Lila Dawn
Blair Center Hattiesburg HS; Hattiesburg, MS (5%-400) Band; Chor; Ensm; Ger C; GS; Hmrm; Jr Miss Pagent; Rptr, Mu Alpha Theta; Ed, Sch P; SC; Pres, Jr Cl; Semi-Fin, Tnns; Amer Leg A; Hon Prog; Most Out; Eng A; Achv A; St Win, Ntl Fed Mus C; *Mus.*

NOONKESTER, Teresa Lynn
Union HS; Tulsa, OK (28-181) Chldr; Chor; Hmrm; Key C; NHS; SC; Var C; Pres, Jr Cl; VP, Soph Cl; Mgr, Bsbl; Bkbl; Cr-Ctry; Sftbl; COM; Cl Fav; HCt; Hon Prog; Most Out; Yth Fel; *Dentistry.*

NOPONEN, Christine Kathryn
Wachusett Regional HS; Holden, MA (168-500) Rainbow.

NOPONEN, David August
Wachusett Regional HS; Holden, MA (40%-500) Demolay; Ski C; Bsbl; Bkbl; Ftbl; COM.

NORBERG, Shary Faith
Grand Blanc HS; Grand Blanc, MI; Band; 4H; Nurs.

NORCROSS, Kenneth Robert
Flushing Sr HS; Flushing, MI (185-600) A Cap Choir; Chor; Ensm; Madrigal; Orch; Bsbl; Ftbl; Hockey; Citz A; *SE Bible Col; Theology.*

NORD, Ross Stewart
Wheaton HS; Wheaton, MN (3-83) Band; Chor; Span C; Mgr, Bkbl; Mgr, Ftbl; COM; Math A; *U of Minn Morris; Physics.*

NORDAHL, Dennis James
Ogilvie HS; Ogilvie, MN (17-56) Pres, Chor; Madrigal; Var C; Pres, Sr Cl; Ftbl; Tr; Cpt, Wrest; Tres, Church Yth Fel; Sr Ath A; Church Choir; Ntl Chor A; Choir A; *Moorhead St U; Law.*

NORDAHL, Mary Kay
Aurora-Hoyt Lakes HS; Aurora, MN; AFS; Band; VP, Soph Cl; Co-Cpt, Swim; Tnns.

NORDEEN, Faye Marie
W Fargo HS; W Fargo, ND (10%-211) A Cap Choir; Chor; Ger C; NHS; Orch; Tnns; Tnns A; Church Organist; S-T, Church Yth Group; *ND St U; Acct.*

NORDEEN, Philip Michael
Ottawa HS; Ottawa, KS (10%-200) Band; BS; NHS; Order/Arrow; Tnns; God & Country A; Order/Arrow A; Eagle Sct; *Emporia St U; Journ.*

NORDEEN, Roger Alan
Ottawa HS; Ottawa, KS (10%-250) Band; Hmrm; Order/Arrow; JV, Tnns; God & Country A; NEDT; Order/Arrow A; Eagle Sct; *Washburn Col; Law.*

NORDGAARD, Susan Elise
Tottenville HS; Staten Island, NY (329-1058) A Cap Choir; Chor; Pres, Hmrm; Swim; God & Country A; HR; Merit Roll; 1st Cl GSct; Pres, GSct Troop; Katherine Von Bora A; *Katharine Gibbs Sch; Secretarial.*

NORDMAN, Wesley William
E Union HS; Manteca, CA (10-300) CSF; Hon Prog; *Bethany Col; Ministry.*

NORDQUIST, Rene Connie
West Bend West; West Bend, WI; Cpt, Sftbl; Outst Clubber o-t Yr, AWANA C; Church Yth Group; *Citadel Bible Col; Bible.*

NOREEN, Laurel Andrea
Glenbrook S HS; Glenview, IL (98-612) NHS; Bio A; Hist A; Yth Fel; Yth Leg; Pres, Church Choir; Tutoring C; *National Col of Ed; Pre-Sch Ed.*

NOREN, Kara Jean
Minnetonka Sr HS; Minnetonka, MN (14-700) Community Yth Symph; Orch; Cr-Ctry; Mgr, Swim; Tr; 4H A; All Conf Cr-Ctry; 4-H Talent Show; *Hamline-Gustavus Col; Med.*

NORFLEET, Debbie Sue
Jefferson City HS; Jefferson City, MO (144-524) Tres, Band; Chor; Drama; Rptr; Sch P; Spch A; Type A; *Central Mo St U; Elem Ed.*

NORFLEET, Jesse O'Dell
Southside HS; Memphis, TN (3%-317) Math C; Pres, NHS; MLS; Most Out; Fin, Ntl Achv Schol; *Pre-Law.*

NORFOLK, Lori Lynn
Jefferson City Sr HS; Jefferson City, MO (400-900) Parl, Bus C; Parl, FBLA; Secy, Span C; Bkbl; Sftbl; 2nd, Area Key Punch; Area Secy, Bus C; Church Yth Coun; FBLA Dist Contest Recognition; *Hannibal La Grange Col; Bus.*

NORINKAVICH, Kathryn Marie
Monsignor Ryan Mem HS; Dorchester, MA (3-88) NHS; Span C; Bkbl; Sftbl; Swim; Hon Prog; Yth Leg; 2nd Pl, Accordion Contest; *NE U; Nurs.*

NORLING, Diane Marie
Washington Sr HS; Sioux Falls, SD; FBLA; VICA; *SE Area Voc Tech Sch; Advertising Design.*

NORMAN, Brenda Leah
McKinley HS; Buffalo, NY; A Cap Choir; CYO; Chldr; Chor; Hmrm; Bkbl; COM; Poet A; Sports, Attendance, Art, A's; *Adv Art.*

NORMAN, Brian Kent
Marion HS; Marion, IL (133-314) Ftbl, Fin, Wrest; Camera C; Project Partner; Sunday Jr Church Vol; *Sou Ill U; Aero Space Engr.*

NORMAN, Catherine Jean
Menchville HS; Newport News, VA (22-563) Band; Chldr; Ensm; Secy, Hmrm; Cpt, Mjrte; NHS; COM; Citz A; Cl Fav; Lion A; NMF; Superior A'S, Piano Competition; Piano Schol; *Greensboro Col; Mus.*

NORMAN, Catherine Lucille
Hastings Sr HS; Hastings, NE; Ed, Ann; Band; Ch, Chor; Dbte Tm; Madrigal; NFL; Y-Tns; Tr; Journ A; Type A; Chor, Madrigal A; Stu Mgr, Vlbl; Lead, Mus; Drill Tm; *U of Nebr; Mus Ed.*

NORMAN, Cheri Ann
Perkins Co HS; Grant, NE (2-30) Band; Secy, CYO; Chor; Ensm; Ch, FHA; Co-Cpt, Mjrte; Secy, Soph Cl; JV, Bkbl; Sftbl; Swim; HCt; Type A; Swing Choir; JV Vlbl.

NORMAN, Dale Vanessa
Gates HS; Gatesville, NC (15-132) BC; Fr C; Hmrm; Monogram; SC; VP, Sr Cl; Pres, Jr Cl; Bkbl; Cpt, Sftbl; HQn; *Elizabeth City St Col; Bus Adm.*

NORMAN, Elizabeth Ann
University Christian Sch; Jacksonville, FL (10%-30) Chldr; Chor; Ensm; Lat C; NHS; Yth Fel Qn; Secy, Church Yth Group; Private Tutor; VBS Worker; Mus A's; *Toccoa Falls Christian Col; Christian Elem Ed.*

NORMAN, Gregory Paul
John F Kennedy HS; Barstow, CA; MVP, All Amer Yth; Chor; City Conf; Dbte Tm; Co-Ch, Hmrm; Spch C; Bkbl; JV, Cr-Ctry; Ftbl; Sftbl; Swim; Fin, Tr; Wrest; Most Out; Sanctuary Soc; Fin, Citz A; Art A; Sunday Sch Attendance A; MVP A; Witnessing Cert; *U of Calif-Berkeley; Social Work.*

NORMAN, Kathleen
Douglas Co HS; Castle Rock, CO (67-411) JV, Chldr; 4H; Orch; SC; VP, Soph Cl; Cpt, Bkbl; Sftbl; Citz A; Opt A; Opt Out Tn; Star Student; Orch A; *Med.*

NORMAN, Kim
Williamston HS; Williamston, NC; Band; Chor; Drama; Secy, FBLA; FTA; Hmrm; Mjrte; Monogram; Sch P; Mgr, Tnns; Cl Fav; HQn; Yth Fel; *E Carolina U; Primary Ed.*

NORMAN, Laurie Jane
Wilkes Central HS; Wilkesboro, NC (5-235) Key C; SC; Pres, Jr Cl; Pres, Soph Cl; Tnns; Hist A; Hon Prog; Journ A; NEDT; Sci A; All-Conf Tnns Doubles; *U of NC at Chapel Hill; Special Ed.*

NORMAN, Mark Dewayne
Odessa HS; Odessa, TX; Pres, NHS; Cpt, Bkbl; Chem A; Section Ldr, A Cappella Choir; Atl, BS; All-Region Choir; *Angelo St U; Civil Engr.*

NORMAN, Patricia Ann
Terra Nova HS; Pacifica, CA; Mgr, Bsbl; Badminton.

NORMAN, Robert Edward Jr
Bellevue HS; Nashville, TN; NYI; Impact Tm; *Trevecca Col; Theology.*

NORMAN, Steven Aaron
John F Kennedy HS; Barstow, CA; *Sociology.*

NORMAN, Tara Damita
Glenn HS; Birmingham, AL; Band; Secy, Bus C; Tnns; HR; *Bus Adm.*

NORMAN, Tony Brooks
B T Washington HS; Shreveport, LA (10-205) Dbte Tm; Drama; Fr C; Span C; SC; Tri-HiY; COM; Hon Prog; ROTC A; Yth Leg; Band, Drama, Art, A's; *NE La U; Pre-Law.*

NORMAN, William Nielsen
Augusta Christian Acad; Augusta, GA (3-40) Sftbl; Swim; Tnns; COM; Hon Prog; *Augusta Col; Math.*

NORMANN, Cynthia Diane
Governor Mifflin HS; Shillington, PA (180-380) Band; Chor; Ensm; Rptr, Lit Mag; Orch; Accompanist, Chor; *Geneva Col; Eng.*

NORMENT, Sandra Lynn
Bolivar Central HS; Bolivar, TN; *Memphis St.*

NORNES, Gretchen Louise
Harding HS; St Paul, MN; Type A; Marching Unit.

NORR, Bradley Donald
Proctor HS; Proctor, MN (10%-250) Ch, Bsbl; Bkbl; Ftbl; Golf; MLS; *Art.*

NORRIS, Alfred Alfonso III
Central Union HS; El Centro, CA (50-1000) Bkbl; Ftbl; Swim; Tr; *Long Beach St Col; Bus.*

NORRIS, Alfred Lloyd Jr
Saint Augustine's HS; New Orleans, LA (20-165) Cpt, Band; Orch; Hon Prog; Yth Fel; JA; *Morehouse Col; Civil Engr.*

NORRIS, Ann Elizabeth
San Ramon Valley HS; Danville, CA (33-336) Chor; Pres, InterClub Coun; VP, Key C; Pres, NHS; Orch; Pres, Span C; SC; Tnns; Swim Cl; CSF; Hon Prog; Art C; Jr Vol Service A; Eng Tutor; Graduation Archbearer; Candystriper; Commercial Art A; Comm Newspaper Sch Columnist; *Diablo Valley Jr Col; Med.*

NORRIS, Cynthia Anne
St Mary's Academy-Chopticon HS; Leonardtown, MD; Tres, Band; COM; *Stephens Col; Psych.*

NORRIS, Gail Elaine
Clarkrange HS; Clarkrange, TN (10-50) FHA; Sch P; Spch C; Bkbl; DARGCA; *Tenn Tech U; Pre Law.*

NORRIS, Jamie Louise
York Comp HS; York, SC (3-240) Tres, Band; Secy, Drama; Fr C; FTA; GS; Ch, Hmrm; Tres, NHS; Ed, Sch P; Tnns; Furman Schol; Jr Marshal; Newberry Summer Schol; *Clemson U; Psych.*

NORRIS, Leah Charlene
Goodlettsville HS; Goodlettsville, TN (37-159) Cpt, Chldr; Fr C; Tres, FTA; 4H; Hmrm; InterClub Coun; SC; Secy, Jr Cl; Tnns; Cl Fav; H of F; HQn; HCt; Tn o-t Mo; Most Sch Spirit; *W Ky U; Fashion Merchandising.*

NORRIS, Linda Helene
Foley HS; Foley, AL; Hon Prog; *U of S Ala; Med.*

NORRIS, Lisa Jo
Clovis HS; Clovis, NM; Chor; 4H; VP, Hmrm; NHS; Rptr, SC; VP, Soph Cl; Citz A; Cl Fav; 4H A; Banquet Qn; Principal's A; Cand, Miss Teenage; *Lubbock Christian Col; Ed.*

NORRIS, Marsha Kay
Cumberland Co HS; Crossville, TN (18-338) Ann; BC; FTA; Sch P; *Middle Tenn St U; Elem Ed.*

NORRIS, Marshall Alexander
Wayne Co HS; Jesup, GA (35-485) JV, Bkbl; JV, Ftbl; Sftbl; Tr; COM.

NORRIS, McCormick Thompson
Northside HS; Atlanta, GA; Hmrm; Bkbl; ROTC A; Drivers Ed; Home Ec; *Livingstone Col; Bio.*

NORRIS, Sara Elaine
Great Mill HS; Great Mills, MD; Band; Chor; Ensm; A-Ed, Sch P; Var C; Sftbl; Swim; Yth Fel; Band Hon; Chor Hon; *Shenandoah Col; Mus.*

NORRIS, Tammy Jodette
Oak Ridge HS; Oak Ridge, TN (82-519) Drama; Fr C; Hmrm; NHS; ARC; SC; Sears Tn Fashion Board; *Middle Tenn St U; Foreign Lang.*

NORRIS, Valerie Lynne
Red Bank HS; Chattanooga, TN (20%-362) Band; FHA; Hmrm; Parl, SC; B Crocker A; Hon Prog; *Middle Tenn St U; Nurs.*

NORSBY, Rochelle Jo
Rugby HS; Rugby, ND (1-112) Band; Chldr; Chor; Ensm; S-T, Ger C; NHS; S-T, Soph Cl; Tr.

NORSWORTHY, Jeanetta
Waynesboro Central HS; Waynesboro, MS (25%-130) Math C; SC.

NORSWORTHY, Tanzie Lei
Jackson HS; Jackson, GA; Chldr; Y-Tns; Sftbl; Batgirl, Bsbl; C Swtht; Sr Superlative; *Dental Assistant.*

NORTAVAGE, Donna Marie
Shenandoah Valley HS; Shenandoah, PA (23-125) Chldr; Y-Tns; Yth Fel; Jr Olympics; CROP; *Pa St U; Lib Arts.*

NORTH, Brian Kelly
Bryan HS; Bryan, OH (85-130) Bsbl; JV, Bkbl; *Bowling Green St U; Bus.*

NORTH, Dennis Edward
East Noble HS; Kendallville, IN (30-290) Cpt, Band; VP, Drama; Ensm; NHS; Thes; Golf; H of F; Drum Major; Artist, Ann & Sch P; Purdue U Mus Hall of Fame; Outst Honorary Thespian; *IU; Comm Art.*

NORTH, Kathleen Ann
Reynolds HS; Greenville, PA (17-212) Cpt, Chldr; Chor; Ensm; Secy, Math C; Span C; Tres, SC; Hon Prog; *Thiel Col; Lib Arts.*

NORTH, Lisa Ann
Jonathan Alder HS; Plain City, OH (30-128) Band; JV, Chldr; Chor; Drama; Ensm; Fr C; FTA; 4H; Hmrm; Ed, Sch P; SC; Y-Tns; Tr; COM; 4H A; Yth Fel; *Communications.*

NORTH, Steven Bruce
Charleston HS; Charleston, IL (20-292) Band; NHS; Rptr, Sch P; Var C; Secy, Sr Cl; Bsbl; Co-Cpt, Bkbl; Cr-Ctry; Golf; Tr; Bio A; COM; Chem A; Hon Prog; Best Dressed; Most Ath; Most Stu; WW; *Sou Ill U; Dentistry.*

NORTH, Terry Allen
Shawnee Mission Nw HS; Shawnee, KS (33%-650) A Cap Choir; Band; Ensm; Tnns; Bio A; Sci A; *Agr.*

NORTHCUTT, Albert Curr
William Mitchell HS; Colo Springs, CO (15-733) Chor; Dbte Tm; Drama; Fr C; InterClub Coun; Madrigal; NFL; Order/Arrow; Ski C; Thes; Hon Prog; Opt A; Order/Arrow A; Spch A; *Julliard Sch; Mus.*

NORTHCUTT, Anita Jo
Shawnee HS; Shawnee, OK; Ann; CYO; Chor; Parl, FHA; Hmrm; Tri-HiY; Tr; *St Gregory's Col; Fashion Merchandising.*

NORTHCUTT, Diane Elizabeth
Greeneville HS; Greeneville, TN (10%-225) Tres, FHA; Hmrm; NHS; S-T, Span C; Bio A; Math A; NEDT; Home Ec A; Span A; US Yth Ambassador to Europe; Jr Marshal.

NORTHCUTT,
Douglas Wingfield
Jesse O Sanderson HS; Raleigh, NC; Lat C; Order/
Arrow; MVP, Bsbl; Bkbl; JV, Ftbl; Tr; Order/
Arrow A; Hon Sct.

NORTHCUTT, Jeanie Marie
DuPont Sr HS; Hermitage, TN (10%-300) Secy,
Ensm; Hmrm; Lat C; Lat NHS; VP, NHS; SC; Mgr,
Bkbl; Citz A; Cl Fav; HCt; Hon Prog; Best All
Around; *Oral Roberts U; Bus Adm.*

NORTHEY, Robert Michael
Blacksburg HS; Blacksburg, SC (50%-130) Pres,
Dbte Tm; Drama; FFA; 4H; VP, Hmrm; Rptr, Sch
P; Spch C; SC; Sftbl; *U of SC; Engr.*

NORTHINGTON,
Timothy Gerand
Hopkinsville HS; Hopkinsville, KY (25%-300)
Ann; Tres, BC; Ch, Hmrm; Key C; NHS; SC; *Ky
Wesleyan U; Bus Adm.*

NORTHRIP, Scott
Hobart HS; Hobart, OK (3-77) Band; Secy, Key C;
SC; JV, Bsbl; JV, Bkbl; JV, Ftbl; *Architecture.*

NORTHRIP, Valerie Kay
Parkview HS; Springfield, MO; Orch; Tr; *SW Baptist Col; Recreation.*

NORTHROP, Jennifer Jane
Brookstone Sch; Columbus, GA (5%-45) Cpt,
Chldr; Chor; Cum Laude Soc; Sftbl; Swim; Tnns;
Tr; COM; Cl Fav; HCt; Hon Prog.

NORTHRUP, Lori Jeanne
Montpelier HS; Montpelier, OH (3-117) Band; BC;
Chor; Ensm; Pres, 4H; Rainbow; Sch Achieve Tm;
Var C; VP, Soph Cl; Tr; COM; Citz A; 4H A; 4-H
St A; Eng A.

NORTHRUP, Susan Jean
Temple Heights Christian HS; Tampa, FL (14-62)
NHS; Span C; Bkbl; MVP, Sftbl; Vlbl; Most Outst
Ath; *Hillsborough Comm Col; Phys Ed.*

NORTHUP, Audrey Lynn
Sanford Central HS; Sanford, NC; AFS; Band;
Rainbow; SC; *Vet Sci.*

NORTON, Bryan John
Salina HS Central; Salina, KS (10%-400) Co-Cpt,
Bkbl; Cpt, Golf; HCt; MVP, Golf; *Bus.*

NORTON, Cynthia Diana
W Morgan HS; Trinity, AL; Bus Mgr, Ann; Band;
Secy, BC; Math C; Span C; JA A; WW; Most Par-
ticipating Jr; Span A; HR; *UAB; Pol Sci.*

NORTON, Eileen Lee
N Phoenix HS; Phoenix, AZ (37-386) COM;
ROTC A; Parnassus; Hon Cotillion; Secy, Church
Yth; Secy, Church Yth; *Police Sci.*

NORTON, Glen Allan
Minnetonka Sr HS; Minnetonka, MN (211-663)
Band; JV, Dbte Tm; Pol Sci C; Sci C; Spch A;
Gustavus Adolphus Col.

NORTON, Kimberly Ann
Cedar Grove Acad; Philadelphia, PA; Chldr; Chor;
MVP, Bkbl; Choir Cert; Spelling Bee; Sportsman-
ship Ltr, Chldr; *Mus.*

NORTON, Laurie Lynne
Cedar Springs HS; Cedar Springs, MI (12-143)
Band; Community Yth Symph; Ensm; NHS; Span
C; Hon Prog; J P Sousa A; Director's A; Marine's
A; Cl Musician; *Central Mich U; Mus.*

NORTON, Nancy Marie
Pima HS; Pima, AZ (3-38) Chor; VP, FHA; 4H;
Var C; Co-Cpt, Sftbl; Cl Fav; 4H A; Sci A; Type A;
Vlbl; Lib A; Sewing A; *Eastern Ariz Col; Secretar-
ial.*

NORTON, Nancy Ruth
Nantucket HS; Nantucket, MA (1-60) French
NHS; NHS; B Crocker A; Hist A; Val; VFW A;
VofDEM; WW; Fr Merit; *Southeastern Mass U;
Hist.*

NORTON, Pamela Ann
Jasper HS; Jasper, AR (2-25) BC; VP, FBLA; Pres,
FHA; GS; Pres, Sr Cl; Pres, Jr Cl; Pres, Soph Cl;
Bkbl; Alg A; Citz A; MLS; Most Out; 1st Runner-
up, Homecoming Qn; *Ark Tech U; Ed.*

NORTON, Rae Ann
Norfolk Cath HS; Norfolk, VA (30-160) Drama;
Secy, FFA; SC; Mgr, Swim; Tr; Span Craft A; *VPI;
Animal Sci.*

NORTON, Richard Byrd
Christopher Columbus HS; Miami, FL (3-200)
CYO; Chess C; Span NHS; Alg A; Math A; Dean's
List; Top Ten; *Math.*

NORTON, Roberta Jean
Western Hills HS; Fort Worth, TX (79-642) Band;
Math C; Orch; Citz A; Math A; Safety Patrol A;
Hardin-Simmons Col; Math.

NORTON, Shari Lynn
Hutchinson HS; Hutchinson, KS (160-475) A Cap
Choir; Bus C; Chldr; Chor; Ensm; Sftbl; Yth Fel;
Yth Church Choir & Coun; *Bolivar Col of Mo;
Child Psych.*

NORTON, Virginia Ann
Odessa-Montour Central Sch; Odessa, NY (6-121)
Ed, Ann; VP, 4H; Hmrm; NHS; Span C; SC; Var C;
Pres, Sr Cl; Secy, Soph Cl; Cpt, Sftbl; Cpt, Vlbl; Fin,
4-H C A; Fin, Regent's Schol; *Syracuse U; Bio.*

NORVILLE, Joseph Stanley
Bells HS; Bells, TN (7-50) F-Ed, Ann; Tres, BC;
BS; Lat C; Rptr, Sch P; Pres, Thes; S-T, Jr Cl; Bsbl;
God & Country A; Journ A; Lion A; Spch A; 1st
Lambuth Col Spch Tourn; Best Actor, Bells High;
Memphis Press Sem Tnage o-t Week; *U T Martin
Col; Pre-Phar.*

NORWOOD, Christy Paula
Clay Co HS; Ashland, AL (1-56) Tres, BC; Chor;
Dbte Tm; Ensm; FHA; FTA; Hon Prog; NEDT;
Val; *Auburn U; Pre-Med.*

NORWOOD, Gloria Lovell
Southeastern HS; Detroit, MI (20%-248) Chor;
Drama; Rptr, Hmrm; Jr Miss Pagent; Secy, SC;
COM; Citz A; Math A; Sci A; WW A; BICP A; *U
of Mich; Med.*

NORWOOD, Jeffrey Scott
Cleveland HS; Cleveland, TN (30-275) Cpt, Band;
Drama; Hmrm; Key C; Order/Arrow; Soccer; Tr;
Wrest; Order/Arrow A; Eagle Sct o-t Yr; *Emory U;
Med.*

NORWOOD, Robert Earl
Aquinas HS; Southgate, MI; Chor; Drama; Rptr,
Sch P; Spch C; VP, SC; Bkbl; Hockey; Citz A; Sci
A; *Bradley U; Criminal Law.*

NORWOOD, Teresa
Crawford Mosley HS; Panama City, FL (12-350)
Chor; Mu Alpha Theta; NHS; *U of Fla; Psych.*

NOSAKA, Jonathan Riyoso
Kalani HS; Honolulu, HI (450-749) Key C; Orch; *U
of Hawaii.*

NOSALIK, Chester Steven
Saint Bede Acad; Peru, IL (57-126) Order/Arrow;
Bsbl; Bkbl; Ftbl; Tr; *U of Ill; Engr.*

NOSS, Janet A
Hatton HS; Hatton, ND (2-20) Band; Chldr; Chor;
Rptr, FHA; Tres, Hmrm; Tr; COM; 4H A; Hon
Prog; *ND St U; Psych.*

NOTT, Robert Duane
Harlingen HS; Harlingen, TX (24-700) Pres, A Cap
Choir; Chor; Ensm; Madrigal; SC; Arch; Golf; Mgr,
Sftbl; Hist A; Lion A; Math A; Pres A; All Region,
All St Choir; Lit A; Rep, LEO C, Hawaii
Convention; Major Offices, LEO C; *U of Tex; Bus
Adm.*

NOTTAGE, Eugene O Hara
Miami Jackson Sr HS; Miami, FL; Band; SC; Tr;
COM; Citz A; J Tns.

NOTTESTAD, Nancy Jo
Maddock HS; Maddock, ND (8-28) Band; Ensm;
GS; Cpt, Bkbl; Sftbl; Tr; Alg A; HQn; WW; Home
Ec A; Phys Ed A; *U of ND; Phys Ed.*

NOTTINGHAM, Derrick Andrea
Norview HS; Norfolk, VA; Band; Fr C; SC; Ftbl;
Law.

NOTTINGHAM,
Tawana Levette
Norview HS; Norfolk, VA; Band; Community Yth
Symph; Key C; Lat C; Orch; SC; HCt; Interlochen
Ntl Mus; Miss Jr; *Phys Therapy.*

NOURSE, Nancy Maude
Wachusett Regional HS; Holden, MO (57-527) A
Cap Choir; Chor; Pres, 4H; Madrigal; NHS; 4H A;
Emergency Med Tech; Police & Fire Dispatcher; *St
Anselm's Col; Nurs.*

NOVACK, Patricia Marie
Cecilian Acad; Philadelphia, PA; Secy, CYO; Fr C;
VP, Hmrm; Lat C; Lit Mag; SC; Sftbl; Hon Prog; K
of C A; *Chestnut Hill Col; Nurs.*

NOVAK, David H Jr
Old Forge HS; Old Forge, PA (13-121) Mgr, Band;
Hmrm; NHS; SC; WW; Ch, Yrbk Art Committee;
U of Scranton; Dentistry.

NOVAK, Robert James
Gilbert HS; Gilbert, MN (6-62) NHS; S-T, Soph
Cl; Bsbl; Bkbl; Ftbl; HCt; *Mesabi Comm Col; Com-
puter Sci.*

NOVASKY, Robert William
Moses Lake HS; Moses Lake, WA (15%-375) VP,
A Cap Choir; Band; VP, Chor; VP, Drama; Ensm;
NHS; Orch; COM; Yth Fel; Sgt at Arms, Thespi-
ans; Mus Schol; Cert of Comp, Mt Raimier Semi-
nar; *Whitworts Col; Music.*

NOVICKI, William Henry
Xavier HS; Middletown, CT (23-176) CYO;
Hmrm; NHS; SC; Ftbl; Tr; Cpt, CYO Bkbl; Sr A,
Ftbl; *Williams Col.*

NOVOA, Jose R
Adolfo Grana Rivera HS; Penuelas, PR (4-342)
Drama; Tres, 4H; SC; Bsbl; Bkbl; Sftbl; COM; 4H
A; Hon Prog; Lion A; *U of PR; Med.*

NOVOSHIELSKI, Cheryl Leona
Holy Cross HS; Riverside, NJ (111-400) Band;
Drama; NHS; Bkbl; Cr-Ctry; Sftbl; Tr; Pres A;
DAHSS; Religion A; *Trenton St U; Bus Ed.*

NOVOTNY, Charles Joseph
Downers Grove S HS; Downers Grove, IL
(346-763) A Cap Choir; Chor; Ger C; Var C; Bsbl;
JV, Bkbl; Soccer.

NOVOTNY, William Joseph
Broadmoor HS; Baton Rouge, LA (22-490) Band;
BC; CYO; Ensm; Key C; NHS; Span C; Bkbl; Sftbl;
COM; Hon Prog; Pres, Church Yth Group; Stu
Service Assn; *LSU; Banking.*

NOWAK, Maria J
St Joseph's HS; Camden, NJ (12-76) Fr C; NHS;
Cpt, Bkbl; Cpt, Sftbl; Hon Prog; WW; *Rutgers U;
Nutrition.*

NOWDEN, Cynthia J
Halter HS; St Louis, MO (2-110) *Nurs.*

NOWER, Daniel Lee
W Platte R-II HS; Weston, MO (9-85) A Cap
Choir; Chor; Ensm; NHS; Sci C; Var C; Bsbl; Bkbl;
Ftbl; Cl Fav; Sci A; *Mo U; Agr.*

NOWICKI, Joseph Paul
St Peters Prep HS; Jersey City, NJ (60-259) Ftbl;
NEDT; *Econ.*

NOWICKI, Susan
Lawrence HS N; Lawrenceville, NJ (4-304) AFS;
Lat C; Madrigal; NHS; Orch; JV, Hockey; NMF;
Yth Fel; Brown U Alumni A; Polish Arts C A;
Stokes Mus A; Gindhart Piano Fin; *Philadelphia
Col of Performing Art; Mus.*

NOWINSKY, James Joseph
Boulder HS; Boulder, CO (85-680) A Cap Choir;
Chess C; Chor; Drama; Ger C; 4H; Lat C; Span C;
Spch C; Mgr, Bkbl; Mgr, Tr; VP-SALES, JA; Var-
sity Ltrs; *AF Acad; Engr.*

NOWLEN, David Tyrrell
Benton Harbor HS; Benton Harbor, MI; Band;
MYF; *Albion Col; Sci.*

NOWLIN, Mary Virginia
Weir Cons Sch; Weir, MS (2-53) BC; Chor; Most
Out; Home Ec, Eng, A's; *Miss St U; Nurs.*

NUCKOLS, Dona Rene
Mullens HS; Mullens, WV (11-144) Ann; Bus Mgr,
BC; FBLA; VP, Rainbow; MVP, Bkbl; Sftbl; Cpt,
Tnns; HCt; Pres A; Yth Fel; All Co, All St, Bkbl;
Athlete o-t Wk; Cpt, Bkbl; Semi Fin, Regional
Tnns; Clerical Test, FBLA Convention; *Ed.*

NUCKOLS, Larry Ray
University HS; Greeley, CO (29-80) Band; Chem
C; Cpt, Dbte Tm; Ger C; Math C; Monogram;
NFL; Phys C; ARC; Sci C; Pres, Spch C; Var C;
Soccer; COM; ARC A; Spch A; Hon Band; *Denver
Inst of Tech; Engr.*

**NUERMBERGER,
D Arcy Renee**
Lookout Mountain Christian Sch; Lookout Mountain, GA (3-7) Cpt, Chldr; Chor; Sftbl; Tr; Secy, Yth Conf; *Covenant Col; Psych.*

NUGTEREN, Randal James
Pella Christian HS; Pella, IA (2-78) BS; Pres, 4H; NHS; Co-Ed, Sch P; JV, Bsbl; Bkbl; JV, Cr-Ctry; Tr; Bausch & Lomb A; 4H A; *Dordt Col; Engr.*

NUHFER, Cynthia Marie
Reynolds HS; Greenville, PA (1-207) Chldr; Span C; SC; Gym; *Penn St Col; Archt.*

NULL, Mary Kathleen
Bethel Christian Sch; Ruston, LA (10%-15) Cpt, Chldr; Pres, Hmrm; Semi-Fin, Lit Ral; Sch P; SC; Pres, Sr Cl; Bkbl; Sftbl; Tr; Yth Fel; Beauty; COM; Citz A; 4H A; HCt; Hon Prog; Poet A; VFW A; VofDEM; Yth Fel; Most Courteous; Schol A; PA; All Dist, Sftbl & Tr; *La Tech U; Bus.*

NULL, Suzanne Patricia
Western Grove HS; Western Grove, AR (3-15) Bus Mgr, Ann; Chor; Sch P; Tres, Sr Cl; HCt; Sal; *N Ark Comm Col; Bus Adm.*

NULTON, Jill Susan
Grossmont HS; La Mesa, CA; MVP, Bkbl; MVP, Vlbl; 1st Tm, All League Vlbl; *Commercial Arts.*

NULTON, Timothy Donald
G A R Mem HS; Wilkes-Barre, PA (5-190) Band; Key C; NHS; Orch; Wrest; WW; *Luzerne Co Comm Col; Bus Adm.*

NUNAN, Laurie Jean
Evergreen HS; Vancouver, WA (10-600) Band; Chor; NHS; *Clark Comm Col; Med.*

NUNES, Pamela Joy
Los Banos HS; Los Banos, CA (27-185) Band; CYO; Tres, FBLA; Cpt, Mjrte; SC; HCt; Hon Prog; Type A; FBLA Central Section; Mjrte A; *Heald's 4c's Col; Bus.*

NUNES, Sherry Renee
Ferndale Union HS; Ferndale, CA (8-60) Band; CYO; Cpt, Chldr; MVP, Drama; 4H; Ch, Model UN; Span C; SC; Var C; Rptr, Sr Cl; Secy, Jr Cl; S-T, Soph Cl; Cpt, Bkbl; Sftbl; Tr; CSF; Citz A; Cl Fav; 4H A; HQn; Hon Prog; Kiwanis A; Lion A; Most Out; Pres A; Swtht; Sr Girl Ath; All-Co Bkbl Player; *Col o-t Redwoods; Liberal Arts.*

NUNEZ, Lorraine
Central HS; Pueblo, CO; *Sou Colo Col; Cosmetology.*

NUNEZ, Luz Elena
St Sebastian HS; Chicago, IL (1-3) Lat C; Lat NHS; First Hon; Eng A; PA; *Loyola U; Nurs.*

NUNEZ, Maria Elena
Colegio Santa Rita; Bayamon, PR (1-33) A Cap Choir; Ch, Chor; Hmrm; NHS; Sch P; Tnns; Bio A; Chem A; Citz A; JA A; Excellence A; Principals A; *U of Houston; Mus.*

NUNLEY, Arthur Gale
Sheffield HS; Memphis, TN; ARC; Bsbl; Bkbl; Yth Fel; *U of Miss; Sci.*

NUNLEY, Diann Shawn
Callaway Pub HS; Callaway, NE (12-24) Secy, Ann; Band; Chor; Drama; Ensm; FHA; GS; 4H; HiY; F-Ed, Sch P; Spch C; Thes; Coun of Teach A; I Dare You; Journ A; Most Out; Opt Out Tn; Poet A; Q&S A; Spch A; VFW A; VofDEM; Outst Soprano, Chor; Best Female Actress; Song Ldr, FHA; *Calvary Bible Col; Elem Ed.*

NUNLEY, Lisa Gail
Friendswood HS; Friendswood, TX (25%-250) Drama; NHS; Golf; *Tex A&M U; Bus.*

NUNLEY, Mark Allen
East HS; Columbus, OH (159-350) CYO; Cr-Ctry; Lib C; HR; Merit Roll.

NUNLEY, Rebecca Sue
Villa Christian Sch; Broadview, IL; A-Ed, Ann; Pres, Ger C; Secy, Hmrm; COM; Spch A; Scripture A; Personal Appearance; Christian Character; *Baptist Bible Col; Elem Ed.*

NUNN, Andrea Michelle
Humboldt HS; Humboldt, TN (30-175) Rptr, BC; FHA; GS; Span C; Bkbl; *U of Tenn at Martin; Home Ec.*

NUNN, Elaine Kaylyn
Sonora Union HS; Sonora, CA (3-396) Band; Pres, 4H; Span C; SC; CSF; 4H A; Pres A; *Stanislaus St Col; Child Development.*

NUNN, Glenda Lee
Marvell HS; Marvell, AR (13-120) Ed, Ann; BC; Tres, FBLA; VP, FHA; Rptr, Ger C; Spch C; Tres, Sr Cl; Tres, Jr Cl; Cl Fav; HQn; HCt; Ch, Stu Adv Committee; WW; *U of Central Ark; Phys Ed.*

NUNN, Karen Diane
Highland HS; Ewing, MO (8-130) Band; Ensm; Fr C; Mjrte; Secy, NHS; Secy, Sci C; Var C; Bkbl; Tr; Bio A; COM; Ntl Sci Found; Ntl Sci Symposium; Regent Schol; Sci A; Conf Band; WW; Soph Pilgrimage; Ntl Sci Found Trng Prog; *NE Mo St U; Pre-Med.*

NUNN, Mark Alexander
Aragon HS; San Mateo, CA; A Cap Choir; Ensm; Ski C; Pres, Yth Choir; Puppets; *Calif Baptist Col; Mus.*

NUNN, Mary Susan
John Carroll HS; Fort Pierce, FL (1-134) Tres, CYO; NHS; Span C; Var C; Cr-Ctry; Sftbl; Tr; Alg A; Citz A; Hist A; Hon Prog; NEDT; Pres A; VofDEM; Sch Liturgy C; Sing-Out; Lit A; Dean's List A; *Ed.*

NUPEN, Terri Lin
Brookings HS; Brookings, SD; Chor; Dbte Tm; NFL; Span C; Citz A; Kiwanis A; Lion A; Opt A; Spch A; Type A; Miss Job's Daughters; Grand Rep to Ill; *SD St U.*

NURRE, Susan Margaret
Sherman HS; Sherman, TX (1-400) Pres, FTA; Semi-Fin, GS; Pres, NHS; ARC; Span C; Parl, SC; Cl Fav; DARGCA; NEDT; Yth Fel; WW; Girl o-t Mo; *N Tex St U; Bus.*

NURSE, Bertram Lawerence
E Orange HS; E Orange, NJ; Soccer; Tr; *Bradley U; Mech Engr.*

NUSBICKEL, Edna Ruth
Salisbury HS; Allentown, PA (20-180) Band; NHS; NMS; *Moriavian Col; Math.*

NUSS, Patricia Lea
Ashville HS; Ashville, AL (88-110) Rptr, BC; Co-Cpt, Chldr; FHA; Sftbl; Yth Leg.

NUSSBAUM, Elizabeth Ann
Corsicana HS; Corsicana, TX (3-280) A Cap Choir; NHS; SC; Yth Leg; Pres, UMYF; Yth & Govt; *Tex A&M U; Recreation & Park Adm.*

NUSSBAUM, Jay
Greenville Sr HS; Greenville, TX (10%-335) BS; Rptr, NHS; Order/Arrow; Rptr, Sr Cl; Cl Fav; Head Photographer, Ann; Yth o-t Month; *U of Tex; Dentistry.*

NUTCHENS, Susan Lynn
T Wingate Andrews HS; High Point, NC (58-327) Pres, BC; Pres, Chor; Sci C; Chor A; *Guilford Tech Inst; Nurs.*

NUTT, Catherine Diane
Boswell HS; Saginaw, TX (10-241) Pres, Band; Chem C; Dbte Tm; Drama; Ensm; Fr C; GS; Math C; NHS; Sci C; Spch C; Pres, SC; Thes; Hist A; Spch A; Drum Major; *Law.*

NUTT, Randy Lee
Robbinsdale Sr HS; Robbinsdale, MN; Chor; Tr; *Concordia Col; Art.*

NUTTALL, Leal Frances
Vicksburg HS; Vicksburg, MS (3-244) AFS; Ed, Ann; Ensm; Pres, Fr C; FHA; Lat C; Math C; Pres, NHS; Crisco A; H of F; MLS; DAR Amer Hist A; *U of Sou Miss; Hotel & Restaurant Mgt.*

NUTTER, Leona Marie
Notre Dame HS; Clarksburg, WV (2-52) F-Ed, Ann; CYO; Dbte Tm; FBLA; FTA; Lat C; Lat NHS; Ed, Lit Mag; Secy, NHS; Ed, Sch P; VP, Spch C; SC; Aux Lat; Hist A; NEDT; Sal; Sci A; Spch A; 1st, Century III Essay; *VPI; Civil Engr.*

NYBECK, Lisa Anne
Cedar Crest HS; Lebanon, PA (99-418) Stage Crew; *Messiah Col; Mus Ed.*

NYBERG, Deborah Ann
Harold L Richards HS; Oak Lawn, IL (80-700) NFL; NHS; Co-Ed, Sch P; Spch C; Thes; Hon Prog; *U of Ill; Nurs.*

NYCZEPIR, David Jon
Arlington HS; Poughkeepsie, NY (2-70) Chess C; ARC; Ski C; SC; Var C; JV, Bkbl; JV, Soccer; Tnns; COM; Hist A; Math A; NEDT; Eng A; *Virginia Commonwealth U; Dentistry.*

NYE, Alison Catherine
Aloha HS; Aloha, OR (32-500) Chor; Co-E, Church Newspaper; Secy, S-T, Church HS Yth; Most Creativity A; Calif Del, Mock Democratic Conv; *Psych.*

NYE, Jeanne Lynn
W Middlesex HS; W Middlesex, PA (1-161) A-Ed, Ann; Band; Mjrte; Rptr, Sch P; Span C; Span NHS; Arch; Swim; Beauty; NEDT; Q&S A; *Acct.*

NYGREN, Tamera Martha
Henley HS; Klamath Falls, OR (2-176) Band; FFA; Tres, 4H; NHS; Spch C; MVP, Tr; 4H A; *Health Field.*

NYMAN, Karin Susan Ruth
Oakmont Regional HS; S Ashburnham, MA; JV, Chldr; Drama; Rainbow; Mgr, Bkbl; Mgr, Hockey; *Northeastern U; Acct.*

NYMAN, Susan Lynn
A D Johnston HS; Bessemer, MI (2-42) Band; *Med.*

NYQUIST, Eric James
Henry Sibley HS; W St Paul, MN (37-595) Ger C; NHS; JV, Soccer; Cpt, Swim; Tr; MVP, Swim; Special Hon Stu; *Hamline U; Bus.*

NYUL, Terri Ann
Garden Spot HS; New Holland, PA (9-247) Pres, AFS; Band; Chor; Drama; Ensm; NHS; Secy, SC; JV, Tnns; *Delhi Col; Vet Sci.*

O

O'BANNER, Debra Yvonne
Estill HS; Estill, SC; Ann; Chldr; Drama; Pres, Hmrm; Sch P; Span C; SC; Pres, Soph Cl; Cpt, Sftbl; Tnns; *USC; Psych.*

O'BANNION, Charles Edward II
Dell City HS; Dell City, TX (4-33) FFA; Cpt, Var C; Pres, Soph Cl; Bkbl; Cpt, Ftbl; Tr; Coaches A; All-Dist Ftbl; *Air Force Acad; Aeronautical Engr.*

O'BANNON, Randall Keith
Cleveland HS; Cleveland, TN (10-220) A-Ed, Ann; Co-Cpt, Band; BC; Chor; Pres, Drama; Ensm; Key C; Sch P; SC; Thes; COM; Hon Prog; NMF; NMS; Sr Executive Comm; Most Talented; Sr Hon Graduate; All St Band; *Lee Col; Mus.*

O'BLANC, Glinda Sue
Sulphur HS; Sulphur, LA (278-500) Cert, Chamber of Commerce; *Bethany Col; Art.*

O'BLANC, Gwendolyn Kay
Sulphur HS; Suphur, LA; *Bethany Col; Hist.*

O'BRIEN, Bill Lawrence
Sunnyvale HS; Sunnyvale, CA (49-529) Order/Arrow; JV, Swim; Order/Arrow A; Waterpolo; Eagle Sct; *Calif Inst of Technology; Aerospace Engr.*

O'BRIEN, Billy Alan
O D Wyatt HS; Fort Worth, TX; JV, Ftbl; Tnns; Alg A; Bio A; Hon Prog; FCA; *U of Tex; Bus.*

O'BRIEN, Brian
Alleghany Co HS; Covington, VA (50%-232) Drama; Fr C; NFL; ARC; Mgr, Ftbl; *Video Tape.*

O'BRIEN, Eleanor Anne
Hightstown HS; Hightstown, NJ (10-253) Band; Fr C; Ger C; NHS; *UCLA; Communications.*

O'BRIEN, Frances Helen
Delone Cath HS; McSherrystown, PA (35-178) CYO; Rptr, Sch P; MVP, Bkbl; NHS; Hist A; Pres A; Cpt, Bkbl; Bowl; Vlbl; GSct.

O'BRIEN, Jeffrey Allen
E Troy HS; E Troy, WI; Ski C; Bsbl; Yth Fel; *Aeronautics.*

O'BRIEN, Jeremiah M
Crystal River HS; Crystal River, FL (25-260) Band; BC; VP, CYO; Chor; 4H; JV, Ftbl; COM; Math A; *Ga Tech; Mech Engr.*

O'BRIEN, Michael Patrick
St Joseph HS; Ogden, UT; NHS; Spch C; SC; Pres, Soph Cl; Hist A; NEDT; Religion A; Eng A; *Fordham U; Law.*

O'BRIEN, Patricia Ann
R U C E HS; Reddick, IL (1-30) Arch; Band; Chldr; Chor; Bus Mgr, FHA; Math C; S-T, NHS; SC; Pres, Sr Cl; VP, Jr Cl; Secy, Soph Cl; Arch; Bkbl; Sftbl; Tr; Amer Leg A; HCt; Hon Prog; Math A; MLS; Val; Activities A; Research A; *Ill St U; Applied Computer Sci.*

O'BROCKTO, Christopher Lee
Hernando HS; Brooksville, FL; A Cap Choir; Pres, Chor; Ensm; Madrigal; Thes; Ftbl; Golf; VP, Chor.

O'BROCTO, Steven Mark
Hernando HS; Brooksville, FL (72-350) Fin, Band; Fin, Ensm; Key C; Tr; Hon Prog; Most Out; Yth Fel; Outst Fresh, Bnd A; Most Outst Mus; Sup Rating, Solo & Ensm Contest; Excellent Rating, St Solo & Ensm; Fla All Star Marching Band; *Bucks Co Comm Col; Mus Ed.*

O'BRYAN, Michael David
Hannibal Central Sch; Hannibal, NY; Band; Ensm; Hmrm; NHS; F-Ed, Sch P; Bus Mgr, Jr Cl.

O'CAIN, Burney W
Wilson Hall HS; Sumter, SC (20-55) Eagle Sct; Troop Instr A; Church Adm; Octagon C; *Clemson U; Bus Adm.*

O'CALLAGHAN, William John
Lovett Sch; Atlanta, GA (66-139) Dbte Tm; Drama; Rptr, Sch P; Pres, SC; Thes; JV, Bkbl; Tnns; Citz A; HCt; NEDT; Alumni A; Stu o-t Day A; *Ga Tech; Industrial Engr.*

O'CONNELL, Christopher John
Saint Thomas More Sch; Colchester, CT; Chldr; Mgr, Hockey; Soccer; Tnns; *New Hampshire Col; Bus Adm.*

O'CONNELL, Colleen Lorraine
Western Hills HS; Fort Worth, TX (119-622) FFA; FHA; Lit Mag; Sftbl; Hist A; Child Development Cert; *Stephen F Austin St Col; Bus Adm.*

O'CONNELL, Margaret Rose
Elizabeth Seton HS; S Holland, IL (76-215) Hmrm; Span C; Var C; Hon Prog; Math A; Sci A; Dance & Prom Comm; Hon Stu; Vlbl; *U of Ill; Occupational Therapy.*

O'CONNER, Cheryle Jean
Washington HS; Washington, NC; FHA; Hmrm; Sch P; Tr; *E Carolina U; Social Work.*

O'CONNOR, Brian Kevin
Gloucester Cath HS; Gloucester, NJ (3-171) Ger C; NHS; F-Ed, Sch P; Mgr, Bkbl; Ftbl; Tr; Sci A; *U of Notre Dame; Pre-Med.*

O'CONNOR, Constance Louise
Ogallala HS; Ogallala, NE (20-115) VP, Band; Chor; Dbte Tm; Drama; Ensm; 4H; Mjrte; NHS; Spch C; Thes; Var C; Mgr, Bkbl; Sftbl; Swim; Tnns; Spch A; Pep C; Secy, Spirit C; SW Conf Band Clinic; VP, Singing Sisters; Band A; *U of Nebr at Lincoln; Law.*

O'CONNOR, Darby Jane
Carmel HS; Carmel, NY (100-500) A Cap Choir; Band; Chor; Drama; Orch; MYF; Singing Group; *Fredonia Col; Musical Theater.*

O'CONNOR, David Joseph
Loyola HS; Towson, MD; Lit Mag; NHS; NEDT; Campus Ministry; Lounge Committee; Frisbee Tm; *Georgetown Col; Math.*

O'CONNOR, David Kevin
St Ignatius HS; Cleveland, OH (115-300) CYO; Ski C; Spch A; *Lib Arts.*

O'CONNOR, Diane Rose
Elizabeth Seton HS; Pittsburgh, PA (43-66) Chor; Fr C; Co-Cpt, Sftbl; Religion; John J Kane Hospital; *Computer Tech; Computer Programing.*

O'CONNOR, Gerard Joseph
Clintonville Sr HS; Clintonville, WI; CYO; Chor; FFA; Pres, Hmrm; Pres, SC; Var C; Ftbl; Tr; Wrest; HCt; Most Out; Pres A; 2nd Tm, All Conf, Ftbl; Rookie o-t Yr, Ftbl; Tr Records; Punt Return Record.

O'CONNOR, Paul Barry
Don Bosco Tech HS; Boston, MA (17-222) CYO; Fin, City Conf; K of C; Math C; NHS; Hon Prog; Star Student; NHS A; *Suffolk U; Lib Arts.*

O'CONNOR, Peggy Lee
Brown HS; Sturgis, SD (4-195) Chldr; Dbte Tm; Secy, FHA; Ger C; NHS; Ski C; Tr; COM; Pres A; Spch A; AAUW Schol; Fire Chief's Assn of SD Schol; *Black Hills St Col; Social Sci.*

O'DANIEL, Beverly Ann
Marion Co HS; Lebanon, KY (37-298) CYO; FTA; Pres, 4H; Jr Miss Pagent; Tres, NHS; St Stu Congress; SC; Thes; Tr; Pres, Tns Who Care; *U of Ky; Fashion Merchandising.*

O'DAY, Alan Leroy
Newman Smith HS; Carrollton, TX (160-314) A Cap Choir; VP, Chor; Drama; Ensm; Fr C; Madrigal; Thes; Citz A; Sci A; Yth Fel; Yth Foundation; Yth Leg; Outst Effort A; UIL Solo; Superior Performance Medals & Cert; *N Tex St U; Mus.*

O'DEA, Alan Francis
Boston Latin HS; Boston, MA; *Auto Mech.*

O'DEA, Anthony Alan
Boston Latin Sch; Boston, MA; A Cap Choir; K of C; Bsbl; Ftbl; Hockey; Swim.

O'DELL, Bob Edward
Brownstown HS; Brownstown, IL (4-37) Ann; FFA; Pres, St Stu Congres; Var C; JV, Bsbl; Bkbl; Hon Prog; Yth Fel; Yth Leg; Lib C; Home Improvement A; *Gulf-Coast Bible Col; Minister.*

O'DELL, Judith Elaine
Valley Forge HS; Parma Heights, OH; Chor; Span C; Pres, Chi Rho Fel; HR; VICA; Eudoreans; S-T, Christian Yth Fel; *Baldwin Wallace Col; Nurs.*

O'DELL, Lowell John
Gahr HS; Cerritos, CA; Hmrm; Ftbl; *Calif St Col; Bus Adm.*

O'DELL, William Lee
Flora HS; Flora, IL (28-137) A-Ed, Sch P; Span C; Amer Leg A; *Journ.*

O'DONAHUE, Patrick J
Monroe Sr HS; Monroe, WI (30-260) AFS; Band; Community Yth Symph; Drama; Fr C; F-Ed, Lit Mag; SC; *U of Wisc; Psych.*

O'DONNELL, Kate Marie
The Fannie A Smith Prep Sch; Bridgeport, CT;

O'DONNELL, Kathleen Ann
Havre HS; Havre, MT (45-233) Ann; Dbte Tm; FHA; Hmrm; Pres, NFL; NHS; St Stu Congress; VP, SC; Spch A; Alt, GS; Blue Pride A's; HR; *Carroll Col; Dental Hygiene.*

O'DONNELL, Mary Catherine
Fowler HS; Syracuse, NY; Cpt, Chldr; Chor; NHS; SC; Regent Schol; *Morrisville Col; Data Processing.*

O'DONNELL, Susan
Driscoll HS; Addison, IL (6-144) Drama; VP, NHS; St Scholar; *Loyola U of Chicago; Med.*

O'DONNELL, William Joseph
Havre HS; Havre, MT; Dbte Tm; Hmrm; VP, NFL; SC; Opt A; Spch A; VofDEM.

O'FARRELL, Cathleen Monica
St Marys HS; Stockton, CA (1-270) Chem C; 4H; NHS; Phys C; SC; VP, Soph Cl; JV, Bkbl; JV, Tr; CSF; Eng, Span, A's.

O'FARRELL, Deirdre Ann
St Mary's HS; Stockton, CA (8-204) Rptr, Ann; Chem C; Chor; Drama; Fin, GS; 4H; Hmrm; Model UN; NHS; Phys C; SC; Thes; Secy, Jr Cl; Secy, Soph Cl; Bank Of Amer A; CSF; COM; Hist A; HCt; Hon Prog; NEDT; Director of Elections, SC; Candystriper; Soroptomist, YMI, Eng, Chor, A's; *U of Calif; Spch Therapy.*

O'FLYNN, Denise Marie
Acad of Mount Saint Ursula; Bronx, NY; CYO; Parish Altar Grl; Untd Hosp Fund A; Parish Altar Girl; Teens Encounter Christ; Parish Serv Com; CCD Tchng Cert; *Col of Mt St Vincent; Social Sci.*

O'GALLAGHER, Paul
Alexander Galt Regional HS; Lennoxville, CANADA (15-539) Tres, Y-Tns; Bkbl; Cpt, Hockey; Cpt, Soccer; Hon Prog; Type A; *Champlain Col; Pure & Applied Sci.*

O'GORMAN, Corey Walther
Palm Cove Beach Sch; Pompano Beach, FL (1-25) NHS; Hist A; Math A; Star Student; *USC; Architecture.*

O'GORMAN, Elizabeth Ann
Mt St Ursula HS; New York, NY (85-184) CYO; Chor; Drama; Ch, InterClub Coun; Cardinal Spellman Yth A; Co-Ordinator Altar Girls; Ch, Spiritual Ed Comm; *Leeman Col.*

O'HAGAN, Deirdre Rachel
Nyack Sr HS; Nyack, NY (79-311) VP, AFS; Fr C; NHS; *Purchase Col; Eng.*

O'HANLON, Ellen Marie
Mercy HS; Albany, NY (8-115) Drama; Fr C; Hmrm; SC; Hon Prog; NEDT.

O'HARA, Linda
S Bay Baptist Sch; Gardena, CA (1%-440) Chor; FHA; Hmrm; Lat C; ARC; Co-Ed, Sch P; Citz A; Hon Prog; Deaf C; Girl o-t Mo; Homemaking C; Athenians; Girls League; *Biola Col; Nurs.*

O'HARA, Lynette Rae
Antelope Union HS; Wellton, AZ (3-75) Sci C; Kiwanis A; Schol 'A'; *Lamson Bus Col; Secy.*

O'HARA, Marie Ann
George Washington HS; Denver, CO (62-650) Ed, Ann; Cpt, Dbte Tm; Drama; Ger C; NHS; ARC; Co-Ed, Sch P; Hon Prog; *SW Bible Col; Communications.*

O'HARA, Patricia Lea
F D Roosevelt HS; Hyde Park, NY; Drama; 4H; Sch P; *Psych.*

O'HEARN, Edward Charles
Saint Elizabeth HS; Pittsburgh, PA (35-107) Pres, Chess C; Drama; Model UN; Ski C; Span C; Bsbl; JA A; Sci A; Spch A; Dale Carnegie Course A; *Duquesne U; Acct.*

O'KEEFE, Nancy Anne
Secaucus HS; Secaucus, NJ (27-164) Co-Ed, Ann; Pres, CYO; Fin, GS; VP, Sci C; SC; Pres, Sr Cl; Pres, Jr Cl; Tres, Soph Cl; JV, Tnns; Cl Fav; *Montclair St Col; Pol Sci.*

O'KEEFE, Patricia Dianne
Moscow HS; Moscow, ID (53-190) Rptr, Ann; CYO; Chem C; GS; S-T, 4H; Hmrm; Ntl Yth Conf; Rptr, Sch P; Sci C; Pres, SC; Var C; Pres, Jr Cl; Tr; 4H A; Hon Prog; Yth Leg; VP, SC; *U of Idaho; Pol Sci.*

O'KRESIK, Sandra Elaine
W Middlesex HS; W Middlesex, PA; Cpt, Chldr; Chor; Ensm; Sci C; Span C; SC; Sftbl.

O'LEARY, Doreen Elizabeth
Guysborough Municipal HS; Guysborough Co, CANADA; Secy, Chem C.

O'LEARY, Jack Michael
T L Handy HS; Bay City, MI (20-460) NHS; JV, Bkbl; JV, Cr-Ctry; Tr.

O'LEARY, Kathleen Ann
Ursuline HS; Youngstown, OH; Ski C; Mus As; *Med Field.*

O'LEARY, Susan Patricia
Permian HS; Odessa, TX (65-670) VP, FHA; NHS; Sci C; Magna Cum Laude; Yth Fel; FHA St Del; *Baylor U; Med.*

O'LOUGHLIN, Thomas F
Fordnam Prep Sch; New York, NY (4-25) Bsbl; Bkbl; Dramatics A; Second Hons; *Fordham U; Writing.*

O'LOUGHLIN, Thomas Francis
Fordham Prep HS; New York, NY (4-20) Hmrm; Bsbl; Bkbl; Dramatics A; Second Hon; *Fordham Col; Writing.*

O'MALLEY, Maureen Kelly
Pittsburgh Learning Lab Center; Pittsburgh, PA (5-127) All Amer Yth; Chor; Dbte Tm; Pres, FTA; VP, Hmrm; Rptr, Lit Mag; Math C; V-Ch, Sch Achieve Tm; Sftbl; Tnns; Beauty; B Crocker A; Hon Prog; JA A; Opt A; *Pitt Comm Col; Special Ed.*

O'MALLEY, Patrick Geary
Loyola HS; Towson, MD (10-134) Drama; Fr C; Hmrm; Math C; NHS; Pol Sci C; ARC; Sch Achieve Tm; Ski C; Var C; JV, Bkbl; JV, Ftbl; JV, Golf; Tnns; Cl Fav; Hon Prog; Ntl Achv Schol; Star Student; *U of Md; Eng.*

540

O'MARA, Andrew Paul
Springdale HS; Springdale, AR (75-469) Pres, CYO; Hmrm; VP, SC; Bsbl; Ftbl; COM; *U of Ark; Archt.*

O'MEARA, Maureen Erin
Blanchet HS; Seattle, WA (2-383) Bkbl; Sftbl; Vlbl.

O'MEILIA, Marianne
N Shore HS; W Palm Beach, FL (47-266) CYO; Tres, Span C; Var C; Sftbl; COM; Hist A; Math A; Pres A; Pres, Canoe C; Art A; Jr NHS.

O'NEAL, Beverly Ann
N Natchez Adams HS; Natchez, MS; Band; BC; Chor; Alg A; Chem A; Math A.

O'NEAL, Brian Keith
Walnut Hills HS; Cincinnati, OH (40%-459) Ensm; COM; *U of Cincinnati; Sci.*

O'NEAL, James Clem
Technical HS; Oakland, CA;

O'NEAL, Javhan
Cherry Hill E HS; Cherry Hill, NJ (53%-865) Stage Mgr, Spring Play Tourn; Dancer, Pace Setters; *Rutgers U; Special Ed.*

O'NEAL, Karen Sue
Mullens HS; Mullens, WV (13-144) A-Ed, Ann; FBLA; SC; Secy, Jr Cl; Sftbl; HCt; *Concord Col.*

O'NEAL, Kelly Jean
Pampa HS; Pampa, TX; Chor; Lat C; JV, Bkbl; VP, Keywanettes; *Tex Tech U; Psychiatry.*

O'NEAL, Patricia Anne
N Gwinnett HS; Suwanee, CA (15%-120) Ann; BC; Chor; Dbte Tm; VP, FHA; 4H; Fin, Lit Ral; SC; COM; WSB Young Amer A; *Atlanta Col of Interior Design; Interior Design.*

O'NEAL, Stacy Lea
Lamar Sr HS; Houston, TX (20%-560) Bus C; Chor; Drama; Hmrm; NHS; SC; Acteens; Baptist Yth Group; Drill Sq; Social Service C; *Sam Houston Col; Bus.*

O'NEAL, Towanna Faith
Terry Sanford HS; Fayetteville, NC (60-270) Chor; FHA; Sch P; *Methodist Col; Sociology.*

O'NEIL, Adele Eugenie
St John HS; Plaquemine, LA (5-64) Pres, Fr C; 4H; Lit Ral; Secy, Math C; Mu Alpha Theta; Co-Ed, Sch P; Spch C; Hist A; *LSU; Acct.*

O'NEIL, Brian Jeffrey
Industry HS; Industry, IL (2-30) Ed, Ann; Chor; Rptr, Sch P; Sci C; SC; Var C; Drama; Fr C; Bkbl; Tr; Kiwanis A; Math A; NEDT; Spch A; Type A; *Ill Col; Pol Sci.*

O'NEIL, Nuel Harding
Northwest HS; St Louis, MO (8-652) Tnns; Hon Prog; *Wash U; Dentistry.*

O'NEIL, Shawn Frances
Northrop HS; Fort Wayne, IN; Chor; Citz A; Swing Choir; Nisbova A's; Mus Ltr & Jacket; *Cosmetology.*

O'NEILL, Christine Ann
Regis HS; Stayton, OR (4-56) Chem C; Drama; Math C; S-T, NHS; Sci C; Ski C; S-T, Sr Cl; Sftbl; Tr; Hon Prog; Ntl Sym Symposium; Century III Ldr; Creighton U Acad Hon Schol; *Creighton U; Pre-Med.*

O'NEILL, Jeanne Bridget
Catholic Central HS; Troy, NY (5-328) Sftbl; *Communications.*

O'NEILL, Moira Kathleen
Marianapolis Prep Sch; Thompson, CT (8-22) 4H; Rptr, Sch P; Ski C; Co-Cpt, Bkbl; Cpt, Soccer; *Hist.*

O'NEILL, Pamela Dawn
Blue Valley HS; Randolph, KS (1-23) A-Ed, Ann; Band; Bus C; Cpt, Chldr; Chor; VP, FHA; Ed, Sch P; SC; Tres, Soph Cl; Bkbl; Sftbl; Tr; Bio A; HQn; Type A; Yth Fel; 3rd Pl Dist, Miss FHA; *Kans St U; Phys Ed.*

O'NEILL, Sean Gerard
Cardinal Hayes HS; Bronx, NY (50-370) Sci C; Bkbl; Ftbl; Sftbl; Swim; Hon Prog; Span Honorable Men; *Manhattan Col; Acct.*

O'NEILL, Violet Rose
Haines City Sr HS; Haines City, FL (53-230) Bus C; Bus Mgr, FBLA; FHA; Pres, Rainbow; SC; S-T, Y-Tns; Tres, Soph Cl; Swim; Tnns; Masonic A; *Acct.*

O'PRY, Rebecca Earline
Latexo HS; Latexo, TX (4-18) VP, FHA; VP, Jr Cl; JV, Bkbl; COM; HCt; Annual Qn; Vlbl; *Sam Houston St U; Bus.*

O'QUENDO, Carmen Socorro
Rockledge HS; Rockledge, FL; *Brevard Comm Col; Child Developement.*

O'QUINN, Kelly Lee
Arkadelphia Sr HS; Arkadelphia, AR (10-210) A Cap Choir; Chldr; Fr C; FTA; Hmrm; Sch Achieve Tm; SC; Bkbl; Golf; Fin, Swim; Tr; COM; Citz A; Gov Honor Prog; Yth Fel; Page A; *Memphis St U; Med.*

O'QUINN, Michael Darren
Arkadelphia HS; Arkadelphia, AR (100-170) Chess C; Fr C; Order/Arrow; Cpt, Bkbl; Cpt, Ftbl; Order/Arrow A; All Star, All Dist, Ftbl; *Memphis St U; Engr.*

O'REAR, Jenny Lynn
Chattanooga Central HS; Chattanooga, TN (48-280) Bus C; Ensm; VP, FBLA; Hmrm; Sch Rep, Spelling Contest; Adult Choir; Handbell Choir; Pres, Acteens; *Chattanooga St Comm Col; Bus.*

O'REILLY, Patricia Eileen
Blanchet HS; Seattle, WA (1-305) Swim; Hon Prog; Math A; Skiing A; *Psych.*

O'RILEY, Evangeline Ruth
Colorado Springs Christian Sch; Colorado Springs, CO (3-25) Ann; Band; Chldr; Chor; Ensm; Rptr, 4H; Hmrm; Tres, SC; VP, Soph Cl; Sftbl; COM; 4H A; Cpt, Vlbl; *Mus.*

O'RORKE, Daniel Klein
Toms River HS N; Toms River, NJ (85-700) Band; Order/Arrow; Yth Fel; Stu Walk Dir, Walk For Mankind; *Drexel U; Engr.*

O'ROSKY, Marissa Ann
Brazos HS; Wallis, TX; Drama; FHA; Sch P; JV, Bkbl; Fin, Golf; Spch A; *Sam Houston St U; Psych.*

O'ROSKY, Michael Joseph
Brazos HS; Wallis, TX (5-71) Band; CYO; Dbte Tm; FFA; SC; Mgr, Bkbl; Ftbl; Cpt, Golf; Sci A; Spch A; *Tex A&M U; Solar Engr.*

O'ROURKE, Ruthanne
Nardin Acad; Buffalo, NY (9-66) Band; Chldr; Lit Mag; Rptr, Sch P; SC; Swim; Tr; COM; Hon Prog; Regent Schol; Gym Tm; It's Academic; Yrbk; *U of Calif at Berkeley; Eng.*

O'SELL, Kelly Ann
Fairmont HS; Fairmont, MN (25%-214) Band; Sch P; Ski C; *Phys Therapy.*

O'SHEA, John
Oceanside Sr HS; Oceanside, NY; Hmrm; COM; Regent Schol; Yth Fel; Pres, Christian Yth Organization; *Syracuse U; Forestry.*

O'TOOLE, Daniel Gerard
All Hallows Inst; Bronx, NY (63-200) CYO; Sodality; Span C; Bkbl; COM; Glee C; Coach, Elem Sch Bkbl; *Jamestown Col; Hist.*

OAK, Dyanne Linae
Arlington HS; Arlington Hts, IL (11-575) A Cap Choir; Band; Mod Mus Mas; NHS; Orch; Ski C; Tr; Gym; Sr HR.

OAKES, Angela Kay
S Charleston HS; S Charleston, WV; Span C; Span NHS; Lion A; Co Sheriff's Yth Camp.

OAKES, Loren
Hightstown HS; Hightstown, NJ (7-300) Band; Hmrm; Span C; SC; JV, Soccer; Sftbl; Mgr, Tr; COM; Outst, B'Nai Brith Yth Organization; *Ed.*

OAKES, Mark Luther
Niles McKinley HS; Niles, OH (1-423) A Cap Choir; AFS; BS; Chem C; Dbte Tm; Pres, Key C; NFL; VP, NHS; Sch Achieve Tm; Sci C; Spch C; Var C; Ftbl; Bausch & Lomb A; COM; Chem A; Hon Prog; Kiwanis A; Magna Cum Laude; Most Out; Val; *Mount Union Col; Chem.*

OAKES, Susan Gale
Coleman HS; Coleman, TX (8-63) Band; Chldr; Chor; Ensm; VP, FHA; NHS; Citz A; Lion A; Type A; Yth Fel; Secy VP, FTA; St Degree in FHA; UIL Medals; *McMurry Col; Mus.*

OAKLEY, James Jeffry
T L Hanna HS; Anderson, SC (10%-250) Sci C; *U of SC; Pre Law.*

OAKLEY, Janice Eileen
Tuscola HS; Tuscola, IL (7-118) CYO; Chldr; S-T, Chor; Fr C; Madrigal; NHS; Spch C; Cl Fav; HCt; *Eastern Ill U; Acct.*

OAKLEY, Teresa Ann
Brazil HS; Brazil, IN (5-200) Chor; Drama; FHA; Lat C; NHS; Rptr, Sch P; Sci C; Span C; Thes; Alg A; Bio A; WW; *Journ.*

OAKLEY, William Ennis Jr
Falls Road Baptist Church Sch; Rocky Mount, NC (1-24) F-Ed, Ann; Chor; NHS; F-Ed, Sch P; Bsbl; Soccer; *UNC; Med.*

OAKMAN, Laura Jean
Liberty HS; Liberty, IL (18-54) Ann; Chor; Secy, Drama; Ensm; FHA; Rptr, 4H; Secy, Sci C; Var C; Sftbl; Tr; 4H A; Semi-Fin, Winter Carnival.

OATIS, Cheryl Lynn
Carroll HS; Monroe, LA (15%-205) Chor; Drama; FBLA; Secy, Hmrm; Phys C; SC; Secy, Soph Cl; Beauty; HCt; YES A; *NE U; Nurs.*

OBARA, Jon S
McKinley HS; Honolulu, HI (124-819) Band; Community Yth Symph; Math C; NHS; Pres, SC; Rptr, Jr Cl; Rptr, Soph Cl; Band A; *U of Hawaii; Sci.*

OBERDORFER, Robert Michael
New Buffalo HS; New Buffalo, MI (6-95) F-Ed, Ann; Drama; VP, NHS; Span NHS; Thes; Tr; COM; Drama C & Annual Photographer; Jr Miss Escort; Schol A, Tr; *Mich St U; Landscape Archt.*

OBERFOELL, Becky Ann
Bowman HS; Bowman, ND (3-74) Chor; VP, FBLA; Pres, 4H; NHS; Cr-Ctry; MVP, Tr; Citz A; 4H A; Pres A; Alt, GS; *ND St Sch of Sci; Elec.*

OBERG, June Norma
Tonasket HS; Tonasket, WA (12-80) Band; Chor; Drama; 4H; Lat C; Tres, SC; Secy, Jr Cl; Pres, Soph Cl; *Eastern Washington Col; Registered Nurs.*

OBERG, Tammi Diane
Downers Grove S HS; Downers Grove, IL; Band; Drama; Ski C; Yth Fel; *Dental Asst.*

OBERHAUSER, Sara Gretchen
Clintonville Sr HS; Clintonville, WI; Band; Drama; Ensm; Fr C; NHS; Var C; Bkbl; Tr; Pres A; Vlbl; Ath Ltrs; *Med.*

OBERHELLMANN, Jill Anne
Bellevue HS; Nashville, TN (25-211) FHA; Span C; Cpt, Bkbl; Sftbl; Tr; Pres A; MVP, Bkbl; Sr Superlative.

OBERLANDER, Carol Sue
Sarasota HS; Sarasota, FL; Chor; Ensm; Tnns; Counteract; Horseback Riding; Crafts; *Dental Asst.*

OBERMEIER, Helmut Francois
Alexander Galt Regional HS; Lennoxville, CANADA (2-539) Hmrm; Soccer; Tr; Vlbl; *Lester B Pearson Col o-t Pacific; Sci.*

OBHOF, Sally Katherine
Geneva HS; Geneva, OH; Chor; Ensm; Secy, FTA; 4H; Lat C; 4H A; Hon Prog; Solo & Ensm Contest; *Math.*

OBISPO, Theresa Field
George Washington HS; Mangilao, GUAM; *U of Guam; Acct.*

OBLINGER, Tabitha Jane
Wichita N HS; Wichita, KS; Chess C; Dbte Tm; Drama; S-T, NFL; Thes; *Emporia St Col; Drama.*

OCASIO, Esther
Miguel Melendez Munoz; Bayamon, PR (5-220) Secy, Ann; CYO; VP, Chem C; Chor; Tres, FHA; Tres, Math C; Orch; Phys C; S-T, ARC; F-Ed, Sch P; Sci C; Span C; SC; Alg A; Beauty; Bio A; COM; Chem A; Citz A; Math A; Phy A; Poet A; ARC A; Sci A; Spch A; Summa Cum Laude; Assitence A; Conduct A; *U of Puerto Rico; X-Ray Tech.*

OCASIO, Francisco
Francisco Mendoza HS; Isabela, PR; Band; Hmrm; JV, Bkbl; Tr; COM; Hon Prog; *U of Puerto Rico; Mus.*

OCASIO, Olga
Academia Sagrado Corazon; Santurce, PR (12-65) Chor; Secy, Drama; 4H; Madrigal; NHS; ARC; Sci C; Span C; VP, SC; Alg A; COM; Hon Prog; Pres, SC; Damasco Yth Movement; Drama Secy A; *Bradley U; Math.*

OCHOA, James Philip
Paris HS; Paris, TX (50-273) Band; Chess C; FTA; NHS; Span C; Louis Armstrong Jazz A; All Region Band; Outst Soloist, Tri-St; *E Tex St U; Mus Ed.*

OCHOA, June Adele
Thomas A Edison HS; San Antonio, TX (11-543) CYO; Chor; COM; Citz A; Hon Prog; Most Out; Tres, Pep Squad; Jr NHS; Spelling Bee Champ; Qn, Monterrey C; *U of Tex; Med.*

OCHOA, Nora Lee
Highlands HS; San Antonio, TX (1-600) Parl, InterClub Coun; Mu Alpha Theta; NHS; Span C; Parl, SC; Pres, Sr Cl; Secy, Jr Cl; DARGCA; Val; Ready Writing As; Ntl Sci Found Summer Sci Prog; *U of Tex at Austin; Law.*

OCHSNER, Maria Suzanne
Mountlake Christian HS; Mountlake Terrace, WA (1-28) Chldr; Orch; Pres, Soph Cl; Bkbl; Soccer; Tr; Best Defense, Bkbl; *Seattle Pacific Col; Bus.*

OCKERBLOOM, Linda Emily
Penncrest HS; Lima, PA (47-460) Chor; NHS; JV, Hockey; COM; Mus A; LaCrosse A; *Gettysburg Col; Psych.*

ODAFFER, Opal Marie
Parsons Sr HS; Parsons, KS (25%-150) Chldr; Tres, NHS; SC; Tnns; Tr; HQn; Yth Fel; Pres, Yth Fel; Nurs Schol; 'P' A; *Labette Jr Col; Nurs.*

ODEE, Cheryl Ann
Coon Rapids Sr HS; Coon Rapids, MN (7-676) Chldr; NHS; Secy, SC; Var C; COM; Citz A; Gym; Outst Achv Schol Cert; *U of Minn.*

ODEGAARD, Twyla Jane
Stevens HS; Rapid City, SD (48-483) Chor; Star Student; *Clerical.*

ODELL, Pamela Denise
Leavenworth Sr HS; Leavenworth, KS; Chor; Rainbow; Hon Prog; Sci A; PA; Mus A; *Math.*

ODEM, Carla Jean
Bastrop HS; Bastrop, LA (10%-320) VP, 4H; Lat C; 4H A; Co Fair A's; *NE La U; Art.*

ODEN, Deborah Denise
John A O'Connell; San Francisco, CA (1-236) Pres, Chldr; Chess C; VP, Drama; Math C; Secy, NHS; Rptr, Sch P; Tres, SC; Pres, Jr Cl; Bsbl; Bkbl; Sftbl; Tnns; Beauty; COM; Citz A; Hon Prog; JA A; Opt A; *Cal Poly Inst; Archt.*

ODEN, Elra Clint
Morton HS; Morton, TX; Chess C; MVP, Chor; Order/Arrow; Swim; MVP, Tnns; Cl Fav; Order/Arrow A; Cpt, Tnns; Tr; St Hon Chor; Choir UIL Comp; Dist Tnns A; Tranquility Chor; Guitarist & Write Songs; *S Plains Col; Bus Adm.*

ODEN, Gerald Karl
Madison Acad HS; Huntsville, AL (2-43) Pres, BC; Dbte Tm; Math C; Monogram; Order/Arrow; Var C; Ftbl; COM; Hon Prog; NEDT; Star Student; *UAH; Elec Engr.*

ODENTHAL, Patricia Ann
Regis HS; Stayton, OR (7-56) Ann; Chor; Drama; Pres, NHS; Ski C; Mus, Religion, Spch, A Fin; *Oreg Col of Ed; Ed.*

ODEY, Susanne Marie
Kewanee HS; Kewanee, IL; Band; Chem C; 4H; Pres, Hmrm; Sftbl; Tr; *Phys Therapy.*

ODLE, David Martin
Moreno Valley HS; Sunnymead, CA (90-400) Band; S-T, InterAct C; Ski C; Mgr, Wrest; *Optometry.*

ODLE, Gregory Alan
Moreno Valley HS; Sunnymead, CA (53-380) BS; Ger C; Pres, InterAct C; NHS; Sci C; Ski C; Wrest; CSF; Rotary A; ROTC A; Deputy Gov, Dist Inter-Act C; Outst Cadet, CAP; Lang Arts Hon; *U of Calif at Riverside; Bio-Med.*

ODOM, Amy Lynne
Vancleave HS; Vancleave, MS (30-75) Band; BC; Chor; Ensm; Rainbow; Entertainers; Home Ec A; *U of Sou Miss; Hist.*

ODOM, Belva Shea
Hubbard HS; Hubbard, TX (4-35) Ann; Chldr; Pres, FHA; FTA; NHS; Pres, Sr Cl; S-T, Soph Cl; Bkbl; Tnns; Citz A; PTA A; Bkbl Swtht; *Sam Houston St U; Dental Hygiene.*

ODOM, Bertha Mae
Waterproof HS; Waterproof, LA; BC.

ODOM, Cindy Kay
Leroy HS; Leroy, AL; Ann; Band; BC; Chor; FHA; 4H; Semi-Fin, Jr Miss Pa; Sch P, Rptr, Sr Cl; Pres, Soph Cl; COM; 4H A; Val; Creat & Perf Arts Win, Jr Miss Pag; *U of Montevallo; Elem Ed.*

ODOM, Dawn Margaret
Maple Shade HS; Maple Shade, NJ (20-241) GS; Hmrm; Key C; Color Guard; Cooperative Ed; Lacrosse; 1st Pl, Knights of Colum Essay Con; *Rutgers U; Eng.*

ODOM, Rebecca Lynn
Reidsville Sr HS; Reidsville, NC (32-344) AFS; Ann; Chor; Drama; Fr C; NHS; NEDT; *U of NC at Greensboro; Nurs.*

ODOM, Rodney Gene
Sequoia HS; Redwood City, CA; MVP, Bkbl; Tr; Most Outst; *Pepperdine U; Med.*

ODOM, Vicki Diane
S Rapides Acad; Lecompte, LA (5-13) Secy, 4H; Semi-Fin, Lit Ral; Sch P; *La Col; Mus.*

ODUM, Cynthia Michelle
Pathway HS; Savannah, GA; BC; Chldr; Drama; Secy, SC; *Armstrong St Col; Dental Hygiene.*

ODUM, Melinda Susan
Carlmont HS; Belmont, CA; A Cap Choir; CSF; Pres, Bicycle C; Job's Daughters Musician; Church Deacon; Co-Ch, Church Sr Hi Yth Group; *Nurs.*

OEHLERTZ, Joyce Elaine
Avo-Ha Comm HS; Avoca, IA (5-49) Band; Chor; FNA; 4H; Madrigal; NHS; S-T, Thes; Tres, Y-Tns; JV, Sftbl; 4H A; *Phys Therapy.*

OEHMLER, Dorothy Drew
Huntington HS; Huntington, NY (11%-667) AFS; Band; A-Ed, Lit Mag; Tr; Regent Schol; Gym; Ntl Merit Ltr of Commendation; *Harvard U.*

OELAND, Glenn David
Wade Hampton HS; Greenville, SC (23-400) Chess C; V-Ch, NHS; Span NHS; COM; Gr Marshal; Hon Prog; *Clemson U; Religion.*

OELSCHLAGER, Lynn Susan
Elston Sr HS; Michigan City, IN (60-365) Ann; NHS; Sch P; St Scholar; Yth Fel; Secy, VICA; Stu Store; CHO; *DePauw U; Nurs.*

OENBRINK, Elaine Verna
Cardinal Newman HS; W Palm Beach, FL (101-265) CYO; Chor; Ensm; Bkbl; Sftbl; Bio A; Citz A; Sci A; Miss Bicentennial Lake Park; Mus A; *Palm Beach Jr Col.*

OESTERREICH, Paul Edwin
Lakeview HS; Battle Creek, MI (125-450) Band; Ensm; Orch; Tr; Amer Leg A; Hon Prog; 1st Div Rating, St Jazz Band Fest; *Mich Tech U; Engr.*

OESTMAN, Jim Lee
Auburn HS; Auburn, NE (10-100) Dbte Tm; Math C; Pol Sci C; SC; Var C; Bsbl; Bkbl; Golf.

OESTREICH, Danita Jeannette
Llano HS; Llano, TX (3-72) Chldr; Chor; VP, FHA; FTA; Secy, Jr Cl; VP, Soph Cl; Cr-Ctry; Tr; Cl Fav; HCt; *Angelo St Col; Phys Ed.*

OESTREICH, LaJean Renee
Norfolk Sr HS; Norfolk, NE (70-330) Secy, 4H; Ch, Span C; Var C; Mgr, Bkbl; 4H A; Co-Cpt, Vlbl; *U of Nebr Lincoln; Pre-Vet Sci.*

OETH, Gregory Ray
Mt Vernon Sr HS; Mt Vernon, IN; Band; Order/Arrow; Mgr, Tr; God & Country A; Order/Arrow A; Yth Fel; Eagle Sct A; *Vincennes U; Law Enforcement.*

OETKEN, Kathleen Pearl
Burlington Comm HS; Burlington, IA; Band; Chldr; 4H; Secy, Church Yth; Future Secy's of Amer; Office Ed; *Patricia Stevens Secy & Fash Col.*

OFFDENKAMP, Gail Lynn
East HS; Pueblo, CO (1-412) Fr C; Tres, FBLA; GS; NHS; Hist A; Regent Schol; Rotary A; Val; Keyettes; Zonta Girl; Golden Scroll A; *U of Colo; Med.*

OFFER, Brad William
King's Garden HS; Seattle, WA (10-60) Band; Chor; Ensm; Hmrm; NHS; Var C; Pres, Soph Cl; Bsbl; Bkbl; Cr-Ctry; Ftbl; MVP, Swim; NMS; Type A; *U of Wash; Engr.*

OFFERMANN, Laurie Ann
Lafayette HS; Lafayette, LA (104-527) Band; Drama; Ch, Hmrm; Key C; SC; Tres, Sr Cl; Beauty; Cl Fav; HCt; NEDT; Spch A; Swtht; *LSU; Bus Adm.*

OFSTHUN, Norma Jean
Maryvale Sr HS; Cheektowaga, NY (1-562) AFS; Chor; NHS; Span C; JV, Arch; Bkbl; Tr; Amer Leg Orator A; Bausch & Lomb A; COM; Citz A; DARGCA; Hon Prog; Math A; Regent Schol; Rensselaer A; Val; Vlbl; Most Improved Player, Bkbl; GAA Ath o-t Yr; Most Brilliant; *Calif Inst of Tech; Chem.*

OFSTHUN, Stanley Clifford
Maryvale HS; Cheektowaga, NY (1-600) Band; Order/Arrow; Tr; Order/Arrow A; Vlbl.

OGAN, Matthew Rene
Tehachapi HS; Tehachapi, CA (15%-171) JV, Bsbl; Co-Cpt, Ftbl; Best All Round Player, Jr Var Ftbl; Hon Math; Hon Eng.

OGDEN, David Richard
Hamilton Taft Sr HS; Hamilton, OH (40%-489) A Cap Choir; Chor; Ger C; Ftbl; Tr; JV, Wrest.

OGDEN, Jane Ann
Midwest HS; Midwest, WY (20%-21) A Cap Choir; Ann; Band; Bus C; Chess C; Chor; Drama; Pres, FHA; Math C; S-T, NFL; NHS; Rptr, Sch P; Thes; Var C; Ch, Sr Cl; Ch, Jr Cl; Ch, Soph Cl; Co-Cpt, Bkbl; Tr; Alg A; Cl Fav; I Dare You; Journ A; Math A; Spch A; Type A; Pres, Ntl Forensics League; MVP, Vlbl; *Central Wyom Col; Social Sci.*

OGDEN, Shirley Peebles
Kountze HS; Kountze, TX (1-84) Band; Pres, FTA; VP, NHS; SC; Tnns; Cl Fav; H of F; Hon Prog; Lion A; Val; *Lamar U; Math.*

OGDEN, Steve Ray
Wilmington Sr HS; Wilmington, OH (50-350) JV, Wrest; *Bio.*

OGDEN, Susan Jean
Midlakes HS; Phelps, NY (26-190) Chor; VP, Church Yth Group; Social Comm; Secy, Church Missionary Group.

OGDEN, Timothy Wayne
Jessamine Co HS; Nicholasville, KY (100-225) A Cap Choir; MVP, Band; Chor; Ensm; 4H; Madrigal; ARC; Sch Achieve Tm; Var C; MVP, Bsbl; Co-Cpt, Ftbl; Golf; Swim; Tnns; Wrest; Cl Fav; Band; Sports; Most Dependable; *Georgetown U; Sci.*

OGERLY, Chris Randall
Littlefield HS; Littlefield, TX; Band; Bus C; Fin, Ensm; All-Region Band; Solo-Ensm Contest Fin; *Archt.*

OGG, Cheri Lynn
Christian Co HS; Hopkinsville, KY (29-300) Band; BC; Chor; Fin, Jr Miss Pagent; SC; S-T, UMYF; WW; Worship Comm; *Miss U for Women; Lib Sci.*

OGILVIE, Jay Scott
Coshocton HS; Coshocton, OH (28-205) Pres, Chem C; Chess C; Drama; S-T, HiY; Key C; NHS; ARC; Span C; JV, Bkbl; COM; Hon Prog; Ntl Sci Symposium; ARC A; A of Distinction; *Purdue U; Forestry.*

OGILVIE, Melanie Way
McGavock HS; Nashville, TN (88-836) BC; Bus C; FBLA; FHA; Ger C; Ch, Hmrm; Mjrte; NHS; ARC; SC; Sftbl; Tnns; Ntl Achv Schol; *Fisk U; Bus Mgt.*

OGILVIE, Tim Wayne
Poteau HS; Poteau, OK (10-150) Ann; Band; Sch P; Sci C; Journ A; *Okla St U; Photo Journ.*

OGLES, Edith Ann
Gardendale HS; Gardendale, AL (57-167) Hmrm; Tnns; Drum Major; Band A; Band Ldrship A; Art A; 1st Pl, Painting Art Show; All-Amer Hall of Fame A; *U of Ala; Art.*

OGLESBY, Beth Ann
Madisonville N Hopkins HS; Madisonville, KY; Band; Sftbl.

OGLESBY, Clifford William
Byrd HS; Shreveport, LA (51-450) BS; Pres, Inter-Act C; S-T, Lat C; A-Ed, Sch P; Var C; Bsbl; Ftbl; Yth Fel; Secy, FCA; V-P, Christian Yth Fellowship; *La Tech; Engr.*

OGLESBY, Elaine Sue
Danville Comm HS; Danville, IN (36-146) Co-Ed, Ann; Band; Ger C; VP, 4H; Tres, NHS; Sch P; Tri-HiY; Tnns; Citz A; 4H A; Q&S A; Yth Fel; Secy, 4-H C; Chaplain, Tri-Hi-Y; Booster C; *Purdue U; Phar.*

OGLESBY, Elizabeth Ann
Byrd HS; Shreveport, LA; Key C; Pres, Lat C; Rptr, Sch P; VP, Soph Cl; Tnns; Swtht; Bkbl Court Maid.

OGLETREE, Rodney Bernard
Skyline HS; Dallas, TX (600-800) Bkbl; JV, Ftbl; Art; Bowl; *Navy.*

OGREN, Jill Benita
Hinsdale Central HS; Hinsdale, IL (48-691) Chor; Ensm; NHS; Var C; Ensm Mus A; Dean's List; Operettas.

OH, Kwangho
George Washington HS; Denver, CO (100-700) VP, FHA; Ski C; Pres, Karate Kata C; HEO Contest A; *GW KATA A; U of Colo; Engr.*

OH, Ruth Kim
Whitewater HS; Whitewater, WI (10-176) Fin, AFS; Ed, Ann; Pres, Band; Cpt, Chldr; S-T, Chor; Community Yth Symph; Semi-Fin, GS; Lat C; Madrigal; Mjrte; Math C; NFL; NHS; SC; Var C; Q&S A; St Hon Choir; All Reginal Band; Pres, Q & S; *Psych.*

OHL, Lynne Cheryl
Central Columbia HS; Bloomsburg, PA (18-167) Bus C; JV, Chldr; Secy, Chor; City Conf; Fr C; FBLA; FTA; Hmrm; NHS; Pres, SC; NMS; Dist & Regional Chor; *Johnson Bible Col; Ed.*

OHLAU, Sue Ann
Chester HS; Chester, IL (2-100) Ed, Ann; Band; Pres, NHS; VP, SC; Swim; Hon Prog; Sal; St Scholar; Cpt, Vlbl; WW; Sou Ill Outst Stu; *SE Mo St U; Nurs.*

OHLSON, Robert Edward
Calistoga HS; Calistoga, CA (8-51) Ann; Sch P; CSF; PTA A; Video Tape, Ftbl & Bkbl; Stats, Ftbl; *UC at Davis; Statistics.*

OHLSSON, Cynthia Jo
Southside Sr HS; Fort Smith, AR (79-430) Span C; *Westark Jr Col; Nurs.*

OHM, Michael Lynn
Detroit Lakes HS; Detroit Lakes, MN; Band; Tr; Amer Legion Safety Patrol Cert; *Drafting.*

OHNIKIAN, Barbara Katherine
Pascack Hills HS; Montvale, NJ (49-328) Mjrte; NHS; *The Berkeley Sch; Med Secy.*

OHRN, Catherine Louise
Minneapolis Central HS; Minneapolis, MN; Band; Community Yth Symph; NHS; Tr; COM; Hon Prog; Yth Fel; Church Choir; PTSA; Actress-Tech Staff, HS Plays; Reg Solo Semi-Fin, Bnd & MMTA Cont; *U of Minn; Art.*

OIE, Sandra Jane
Eisenhower HS; New Berlin, WI (189-275) Band; Span C; *Baptist Bible Col; Teaching.*

OJA, Debra Joy
Stanley HS; Stanley, ND; Ann; Band; Chor; Secy, FBLA; Secy, FHA; 4H; 4H A; Parish Yth Group; *Grand Forks Col; Social Work.*

OJA, Mary Elizabeth
Detroit Lakes Comm HS; Detroit Lakes, MN (24-250) Band; Chor; Span C; Tr; Cpt, Gym; Wohelo Medallion; Synchronized Swim; MMTA Mus A, Piano; 1st Pl, Dist Gym; *Wartburg Col; Span & Mus.*

OJAKANGAS, Gregory Wayne
East HS; Duluth, MN (70-550) VP, Band; Chor; Ensm; NHS; Orch; Span C; Thes; COM; Hon Prog; Silver Cross Acolyte; Life Sct; Band Ltr; Norma Screwoff Choir Schol; *U of Minn; Physics.*

OKADA, David Shigeji
George Washington HS; Mangilao, GUAM; NHS; Tres, SC; Mgr, Bkbl; Mgr, Tr; Most Out; *U of Hawaii; Archt Engr.*

OKER, Carolina Jean
Crystal Lake Comm HS; Crystal Lake, IL (148-505) A Cap Choir; Hon Prog; Yth Fel; Gym; Secy, Personal Serv Occupation C; Outst Atten On Job-In Cl A; *Childcare.*

OKRINA, Bradley Scott
Washington HS; Sioux Falls, SD (76%-720) Chess C; Chor; Dbte Tm; Ensm; Madrigal; NFL; Bsbl; Ftbl; Tr; Wrest; JA A; All St Hon Choir.

OKRUHLIK, Geralyn Marie
Flatonia HS; Flatonia, TX (1-38) Rptr, Band; FHA; Rptr, Sch P; Secy, Soph Cl; WW; *Blinn Col; Ed.*

OKUNIEWSKI, Laura
Interlochen Arts Acad; Interlochen, MI (4-165) Band; Chldr; Chor; Community Yth Symph; Ensm; Mod Mus Mas; Orch; COM; Cl Fav; Interlochen Ntl Mus; Spch A; Louis Sudler A; Pres, N Mich Chapter Amer Harp Soc; High Hon Stu; Concerto Win, Interlochen Arts Acad; *Cleveland Inst of Mus; Harp.*

OLANO, Peggy Susie
St John HS; Plaquemine, LA (5-50) Drama; Fr C; Hmrm; Lit Ral; Mjrte; NHS; Spch C; Thes; Spch A; Yrbk C; 2nd Pl, Dist Lit Ral; Secy, Lib C; Academic Ltr; Pep Sq; Best Over All Spch Stu; Keywanettes; *LSU-Baton Rouge; Spch.*

OLARTE, Enrique Tomas
Deerborne HS; Coral Gables, FL (9-72) BC; Tnns; Soccer Tm; Home Ec, Yth Fair, A's; *Miami Dade Comm Col; Econ.*

OLDENBURG, Karen Sue
Alexander Hamilton HS; Milwaukee, WI (175-820) A-Ed, Ann; Band; CYO; Chor; Ensm; Hmrm; Orch; Rptr, Sch P; Mgr, Cr-Ctry; JV, Tr; COM; 1st A, Wis St Mus Assn; Mus Hon's; *Alverno Col; Mus.*

OLDER, Jacqueline Dean
Park Hill HS; Kansas City, MO (165-450) A Cap Choir; Chldr; FHA; Secy, Soph Cl; *U of Mo; Public Adm.*

OLDFIELD, David Keith
Bellflower HS; Bellflower, CA (64-400) A Cap Choir; Chor; Hmrm; Var C; Co-Cpt, Ftbl; Principal's HR; VP, Athletes in Christ; Ind Art As.

OLDHAM, Carolyn Ann
Jefferson HS; Tampa, FL; Mjrte; COM; Spch A; Span Spch A; *U of S Fla; Fashion Merchandising.*

OLDHAM, Sheila Ellen
Bowling Green Sr HS; Bowling Green, KY; Hmrm; Cl Fav; ARC A; *Morehead St U; Radiology.*

OLDHAM, Zachary Carnell
Montgomery Co HS; Mt Sterling, KY; HiY; Span C; Ftbl.

OLDHAM-WOLF, Debbie Lee
Lake Clifton HS; Baltimore, MD (10%-315) Ch, NHS; Sci C; Mgr, Bkbl; Bio A; Eng A; *Bio.*

OLDING, Mary Colleen
Warren Central HS; Indianapolis, IN (25%-1000) VP, CYO; Fr C; Bus Mgr, Sch P; Co-Cpt, Sftbl; *Ball St U; Journ.*

OLDING, Teresa Kathryn
Warren Central HS; Indianapolis, IN (220-813) CYO; FHA; FTA; 4H; Secy, SC; Tri-HiY; Bkbl; Mgr, Sftbl; Rptr, CYO Paper; *Ball St U; Elem Ed.*

OLDS, Kevin Lee
Grand Blanc HS; Grand Blanc, MI (200-666) Swim; *Jacksonville U; Hist.*

OLDS, Kurt Andrew
Grand Blanc HS; Grand Blanc, MI (300-630).

OLEAR, Andrea Sue
Uniontown Sr HS; Uniontown, PA (25-435) NHS; Ed, Sch P; *Westmoreland Hospital Assn; Lab Techology.*

OLECH, Marcia Mary
St Hedwig HS; Detroit, MI (5-71) NHS; Opt A; VofDEM; Acct A; *Detroit Col of Bus; Secretarial.*

OLESEN, Nanci Linnea
Crystal Lake Comm HS; Crystal Lake, IL (95-570) A Cap Choir; APS; Band; Chor; Drama; Fr C; Madrigal; NHS; Orch; Ski C; SC; Pres, Thes; *Gustavus Adolphus Col; Mus.*

OLESON, Sean Mark
Shawnee Mission NW HS; Shawnee, KS (69-725) Yth Fel; *Oral Roberts U; Yth Ministry.*

OLFASON, Ole John
Ripon Union HS; Ripon, CA (20-63) A Cap Choir; A-Ed, Ann; Dbte Tm; VP, Drama; Ski C; JV, Cr-Ctry; Tnns; NMS; VofDEM; Swedish Heritage A; *N Park Col; Urban Studies.*

OLIMSKI, Mary Jo
Whitehall HS; Whitehall, MI; Band; Chor; Drama; Thes; JV, Cr-Ctry; Pres, Yth Theatre; Camera C; Musical Theatre Schol; *Sthnic Stu.*

OLIPHANT, Sharmon Arvetta
Philadelphia HS For Girls; Philadelphia, PA (200-475) Chor; Drama; Hmrm; Orch; Bkbl; Sftbl; Tnns; Tr; *Howard U; Social Work.*

OLIVA, Claude Michel
Marine Military Acad; Harlingen, TX (5%-50) NHS; Ftbl; Tnns; VofDEM; *Tulane U; Med.*

OLIVARES, Lazaro
Watsonville HS; Watsonville, GA; Bus.

OLIVE, Bonnie Sue
East Central HS; Tulsa, OK; Chor; Masonic A; Sci A; *Mus.*

OLIVE, Sandra Rene
West End Christian Sch; Tuscaloosa, AL (1-40) Ed, Ann; Pres, BC; Chor; Ensm; Sci C; Bkbl; Sftbl; Cpt, Tr; Cl Fav; Most Out; Val; Miss WEC; *U of Ala; Arts and Sci.*

OLIVE, Vivian Elaine
Corning Comm HS; Corning, IA (10-90) A Cap Choir; Bus Mgr, Ann; Co-Cpt, Chldr; Chor; Ensm; Tres, 4H; Madrigal; NHS; Thes; Y-Tns; Tr; 4H A; Hon Prog; Cpt, Chldr; VP, Secy, Rptr, 4-H C; Schol HR A's; *Kirkwood Col; Floriculture.*

OLIVENCIA, Julie Marie
Colegio San Antonio HS; Rio Piedras, PR (11-100) NHS; ARC; COM; Hist A; Hon Prog; *Eckerd Col; Sci.*

OLIVER, Barbara Elaine
Alfred E Beach HS; Savannah, GA; FHA; *Morehouse Col; Bus.*

OLIVER, Brenda Lee
Loraine HS; Loraine, TX; Ed, Ann; Chldr; FHA; FTA; NHS; SC; VP, Sr Cl; Cpt, Bkbl; Tnns; Tr; Cl Fav; Miss Sch Spirit; Ftbl Swthtf Candidate, HQn.

OLIVER, Cathy Jane
Columbiana HS; Columbiana, OH; Band; Drama; Fr C; Bsbl; Swim; Tr; Yth Fel; Pep C; Pep Band; Yth Choir; Accompanist, Piano & Trumpet; *Ky Christian Col; Ed.*

OLIVER, Charles Lewis
Parkview HS; Springfield, MO (50%-390) Hmrm; SC; Var C; Ftbl; Tr; JA A; FCA; VICA; *William Jewel Col; Bus Adm.*

OLIVER, Christine Louise
Carson HS; Carson City, NV (15-390) FBLA; NHS; Rainbow; Sci A; *U of Nev at Reno; Kindergarten Ed.*

OLIVER, Dianne Dalene
Greeley W HS; Greeley, CO; FHA; Pres, Span C; Spch A; *Nurs.*

OLIVER, Elise E
Roseburg Sr HS; Roseburg, OR (117-480) Band; Dbte Tm; Ensm; Ch, Model UN; NFL; NHS; Spch C; UN Council; Opt A; VofDEM; S-t & 2nd Pl, Debate; 2nd Pl, Optimist; 3rd, Expository Speaking; UN A; *Sou Oreg St Col; Spch.*

OLIVER, Elise Elma
Roseburg HS; Roseburg, OR (117-485) Band; Dbte Tm; Model UN; NHS; Spch C; Opt A; Spch A; VofDEM; Dbte A; *Sou Oreg St Col; Pub Relations.*

OLIVER, Joyce Ann
R L Paschal HS; Fort Worth, TX; *N Tex St Col; Nurs.*

OLIVER, Kandy Lee
Bristol HS; Bristolville, OH (5%-60) BC; Chor; Drama; Co-Ed, Sch P; B Crocker A; Math A; Vof-DEM; Hon Stu; *God's Bible Sch; Ed.*

OLIVER, Karen Elaine
Phil Campbell HS; Phil Campbell, AL (1-72) Ann; Band; FHA; Pres, FTA; Pres, 4H; Hmrm; NHS; VP, SC; 4H A; Val; Outst Bandsman; Most Talented; *NW Ala St Jr Col; Chem.*

OLIVER, Karen Elizabeth
Fountain Lake HS; Hot Springs, AR (6-42) BC; FHA; VP, 4H; Treas, Library C; Vlbl Tm; WW; *Nurs.*

OLIVER, Kate Lorraine
Boulder HS; Boulder, CO (250-517) Chor; Span C; Lit A; *Rockmont Col; Special Ed.*

OLIVER, Keith Alexander
Coshocton HS; Coshocton, OH (40-209) Arch; Chem C; Chess C; Drama; Pres, 4H; HiY; NHS; Ch, Order/Arrow; ARC; Span C; SC; Arch; Cr-Ctry; Co-Cpt, Swim; Tr; Elk A; 4H A; Math A; ARC A; Ntl Math Assn A; *U of Cincinnati; Engr.*

OLIVER, Kristy Jean
Davenport HS; Davenport, WA; S-T, Band; JV, Chldr; Drama; Fin, Jr Miss Pageant; Rptr, Sci C; Ski C; Span C; Mgr, Bsbl; Sal; Vlbl; Miss DHS; WW; People to People, Europe; *Ariz St U; Biol.*

OLIVER, Lythea Denise
Burke HS; Charleston, SC (38-207) Co-Ed, Ann; Secy, Drama; VP, Hmrm; VP, Sr Cl; Beauty; *Johnson C Smith U; Phys Therapy.*

OLIVER, Maria Teresa
Colegio Espiritu Santo; Hato Rey, PR; Co-Ed, Ann; Drama; Pres, Hmrm; F-Ed, Lit Mag; Math C; NFL; VP, NHS; Pres, Span C; SC; Var C; Pres, Sr Cl; Alg A; COM; Math A; *U of Puerto Rico; Phar.*

OLIVER, Mike Clyde
Kearns HS; Kearns, UT (15%-800) NHS; Orch; Order/Arrow; COM; Citz A; God & Country A; Hon Prog; Eagle Sct.

OLIVER, Mike Gill
Cedar Shoals HS; Athens, GA; F-Ed, Sch P; SC; JV, Ftbl.

OLIVER, Natalie Dawn
Carlisle Sr HS; Carlisle, PA (57-526) Pres, A Cap Choir; Band; Chor; Fin, Crown & Scepter; Bus Mgr, Drama; Pres, Ensm; Pres, 4H; Tr; COM; Kiwanis A; Dist, Regional, Chor; Gov Sch for Arts; The New Virginians; Amer Yth in Concert; *Applied Vocal Performance.*

OLIVER, Pamela Kaye
St Johns HS; Ocala, FL (6-24) Anchor C; Amer Leg A; COM; God & Country A; Sci A; Home Ec A; GSct Arrow; GSct Star; *U of Fla; Sci.*

OLIVER, Raylynn
Longmont HS; Longmont, CO; NHS; Orch; Rainbow; Span C; Tr; Pres, Tres, GSct; Span A; FCA; Tres, MYF; *DU; Lib Sci.*

OLIVER, Ronald Cary
St Charles HS; St Charles, IL (129-425) Bkbl; Yth Fel; *Judson Col; Religion.*

OLIVER, Teresa Renee
Dora HS; Dora, AL (10-130) Tres, Band; Secy, BC; VP, Chor; Drama; Ensm; Hmrm; Jr Miss Pageant; Madrigal; NHS; Phys C; Sch Achieve Tm; Tres, Sci C; SC; Pres, Jr Cl; Pres, Soph Cl; Beauty; Drum Major; Hon Chor; Outst Female Vocalist; Most Musical All St Chor; Hon Band; Madrigal Singers; *Samford U; Dentistry.*

OLIVER, Terry Phillip
Coshocton HS; Coshocton, OH (9-250) Band; Chem C; Chess C; HiY; Lat C; Tres, Order/Arrow; Swim; Excellent, Dist Sci Fair.

OLIVER, Tona Gedese
Bob Jones HS; Madison, AL (2-120) Band; FHA; MLS; Sal; Pres, Fresh Cl; *Law.*

OLIVER, Vera Lovern
Paul Lawarnce Dunbar HS; Dayton, OH (50-360) AFS; Bus C; Chor; Commercial C; Secy, Hmrm; Jr Miss Pageant; Model UN; Sch P; Bkbl; Soccer; Tnns; Beauty; Cl Fav; MLS; Fashion Arts Hon; Painting Hon; *Pepperdine U; Fashion Artist.*

OLIVERAS, Gilberto
Academia Santa Monica; Santurce, PR (12-28) NHS; Tnns; Tr; *U of Puerto Rico; Med.*

OLIVERIA, Susan Ann
Sacred Heart HS; Kingston, MA (8-85) Chldr; Drama; Key C; NHS; VP, Jr Cl; Sftbl; COM; Win, Miss VFW Tnager; *Interntl Fine Arts Col; Fashion Mercandising.*

OLIVERO, Laurie Louise
LaSalle Peru Township HS; Peru, IL (10-490) AFS; Band; Lat C; NHS; SC; Tnns; Hon Prog; Rotary A; Ushers C; Tnns Tm; Cavalettes; Pep C; HS Schol; Modern Dance C; Gym C; *U of Ill; Acct.*

OLIVIER, Barbara Ellen
Our Lady of Fatima HS; Lafayette, LA; A Cap Choir; Ann; BC; Chor; Fr C; Hmrm; Math C; Ed, Sch P; SC; Bkbl; Ftbl; Mgr, Sftbl; COM; Cl Fav; Hon Prog; JA A; Secy, JA; Secy, Pep Sq; *Med.*

OLK, Paul Michael
Clintonville Sr HS; Clintonville, WI (7-180) AFS; Band; Secy, Drama; Ger C; Math C; NHS; Cr-Ctry; Golf; COM; Spch A; Yth Ldrship Conf; Forensics Tm; *U of Wis; Psych.*

OLLIE, Linda Faye
Charles B Glenn HS; Birmingham, AL; Band; Hmrm; Co-Cpt, Mjrte; NHS; St Stu Congress; VP, SC; Parl, Y-Tns; Amer Leg A; COM; Cl Fav; Hon Prog; MLS; Most Out; Spch A; Band Ltr; *Samford U.*

OLLIS, Karen Lee
St Albans HS; St Albans, WV (50-500) Ann; Chor; Drama; GS; VP, 4H; Pres, Hmrm; Lat C; NHS; Span C; SC; Tri-HiY; 4H A; Vlbl; *W Va U; Phar.*

OLLISON, Julia Vernae
Southwest HS; Fort Worth, TX; FHA; Jr Miss Pageant; COM; *U of Houston; Radio-tV.*

OLMO, Luz Divina
Dra Maria Cadilla de Martinez HS; Arecibo, PR (45-636) Pres, Hmrm; COM; H of F; Most Out; Hon Med, Eng, Spn, Mth, Sci, Soc St; *Universidad de Rio Piedras; Executive Secy.*

OLMOS, Alma
South Pasadena HS; South Pasadena, CA (10%-400) Span C; Span NHS; Cpt, Bkbl; Soccer; Sftbl; CSF; COM; Citz A; *Occidental Col.*

OLMSTEAD, Barbara Ellen
Coventry HS; Coventry, CT (5-145) Band; 4H; NHS; SC; 4H A; Hon Prog; Math A; Star Student; *U of Conn; Sci.*

OLMSTEAD, Karen Lee
Christian Acad; Waverly, NY; *Bradford Col; Mus.*

OLMSTEAD, Kelly Murphy
MacArthur HS; Irving, TX (1-400) Demolay; Hmrm; SC; Var C; Tnns; Opt A; Opt Out Tn; Jr NHS; Pres, Church Yth; FCA; Beau; *Tex A&M U; Marine Biol.*

OLNEY, Janet Jean
Harrison HS; Colo Springs, CO (1-400) Pres, Band; Ensm; Semi-Fin, GS; Hmrm; Lat C; Semi-Fin, Madrigal; NHS; Bus Mgr, Sci C; SC; Secy, Stage Band; Pre-Med C; Fin, WW; *Johns Hopkins U; Biol.*

OLSCHEWSKI, Angelika
Greece Athena Sr HS; Rochester, NY (100-650) Band; Bus C; Chor; Hmrm; SC; *Computer Prog.*

OLSEN, Andrew Dalen
Luverne Pub Jr Sr HS; Luverne, MN (10-140) A Cap Choir; Ann; Band; Madrigal; NHS; SC; Ftbl; Tnns; COM; *Concordia Col; Sci.*

OLSEN, Betty Jean
Niles N HS; Skokie, IL (244-592) Chldr; Chor; Ski C; JV, Bkbl; Sftbl; Tr; Citz A; Pres A; JV, Vlbl; Tr A; Vlbl A; High Achv A; Vol Service A; Bkbl A; *Nurs.*

OLSEN, Cindra J
Mt Eden HS; Hayward, CA (50%-400) Square Dance Caller; Ntl Yth Conf; Stu, PTA Board; Candystriper; Yth Conf; *Chabot Col; Child Care.*

OLSEN, Cynthia Gail
London HS; London, OH (13-98) Chess C; Secy, Fr C; GS; Pres, 4H; Ed, Lit Mag; NHS; Pres A; Sci C; Co-Cpt, Tnns; COM; Gov Honor Prog; 4H A; Kiwanis A; Sci A; Pork Qn; Conservation A; Sci Fair; *Ohio St U; Research Bio.*

OLSEN, Darren Timothy
Livingston HS; Livingston, NJ; Orch; Cr-Ctry; Pres, Church Yth Organization.

OLSEN, Deborah Ann
Toms River HS N; Toms River, NJ (10%-700) A Cap Choir; Pres, Chor; Drama; Madrigal; COM; Pres A; Yth Fel; *Mus.*

OLSEN, Debra Jean
Staples HS; Staples, MN (3-150) Drama; NHS; Spch C; SC; Sal; *St Cloud Voc Sch; Acct.*

OLSEN, Debra Kay
Plantation HS; Plantation, FL (100-300) Anchor C; Co-Ed, BC; Ftbl; *Broward Comm Col; Acct.*

OLSEN, Donna Jean
Durango Sr HS; Durango, CO (35-290) Ann; Chor; Drama; Fr C; GS; 4H; Model UN; NHS; Ed, Sch P; SC; Thes; Var C; Tnns; Amer Leg A; 4H A; Masonic A; WW; *Westmont Col; Bus.*

OLSEN, Eugene Martin
Xavier HS; NY, NY (2-16) *W Point Acad; Math.*

OLSEN, Kristin
Monett HS; Monett, MO (18-125) Co-Cpt, Chldr; Secy, FHA; 4H; SC; 4H A; *Psych.*

OLSEN, Lori Gaye
White Bear Mariner HS; White Bear Lake, MN (14-456) Ann; Band; NHS; Co-Cpt, Vlbl; *U of Minn; Hist.*

OLSEN, Lynn Rae
Mariner HS; White Bear Lake, MN (8-456) Ann; *Lakewood Jr Col; Hist.*

OLSEN, Martin E
London HS; London, OH (2-100) BS; Pres, 4H; Hmrm; Secy, NHS; Span C; Pres, SC; Ftbl; Co-Cpt, Tr; Amer Leg A; 4H A; Hist A; NMS; Best Ftbl Defensive Back; 3-Yr Tr A; 4-H Tribe 2000 A; *Muskingum Col; Pre-Law.*

OLSEN, Sonya Kim
White Bear Mariner Sr HS; White Bear Lake, MN (5-440) Band; Chor; MLS; JV Vlbl; Superior, St Mus Contest; Win, Mn Mus Tchrs Assn Piano Cont.

OLSEN, Thomas John
Whitman-Hanson Regional HS; Whitman, MA (32-324) BS; CYO; Tres, Key C; NHS; Pres, Jr Cl; Bkbl; Ftbl; Tr; Gr Marshal; Hon Hist Soc; All Star, Ftbl; *West Point Military Acad; Engr.*

OLSON, Allen James
Paynesville HS; Paynesville, MN (75-147) Ann; Rptr, FFA; Sch P; *N Central Bible Col; Photography.*

OLSON, Ann Marie
Clintonville Sr HS; Clintonville, WI (25%-150) Band; Parl, FHA; 4H; 4H A; 1st Pl, 4-H Play.

OLSON, Averyl Beth
Westview Sr HS; Braham, MN (4-85) Band; Chor; Secy, FHA; NHS; VofDEM; FHA Secy Pin; FHA Ltr; NHS Pin; *Bethel Col; Elem Ed.*

OLSON, Carla Mae
S Hamilton Comm HS; Jewell, IA (60-91) Chor; Pres, 4H; Madrigal; Bkbl; Sftbl; Tr; 4H A; *Iowa St U; Applied Arts.*

OLSON, Cynthia Ann
Lafollette HS; Madison, WI (150-600) Chor; Homecoming Chr; *Hospital Nursery.*

OLSON, Cynthia Kay
Maddock Pub Sch; Maddock, ND (7-28) Band; Chldr; Alg A; 4H A; Type A; *Minot St Col; Acct.*

OLSON, Cynthia Lynne
Loveland Hurst HS; Loveland, OH (32-260) Ann; Band; Fr C; InterAct C; World Affairs C; NEDT; Drill Tm; *Ohio St U; Social Work.*

OLSON, Debra Gay
Sealy HS; Sealy, TX (57-93) JV, Chldr; Drama; Semi-Fin, Jr Miss Pa; Fin, Cr-Ctry; Cpt, Tr; Drama A; *Special Ed.*

OLSON, DiAnne Ellen
Hettinger HS; Hettinger, ND; Band; Chldr; Chor; Pres, 4H; Rainbow; Sch P; SC; Tr; WW; WW, Mus Stu; Hon Band; Str Ratng, Clarin Solo, St Mus Fest.

OLSON, Diane Renae
Kerkhoven HS; Kerkhoven, MN (51-61) Chor; Drama; FFA; FHA; 4H; Sch P; Spch C; Bkbl; Tr; 4H A; Star Student; *Wilmar Col.*

OLSON, Elizabeth Ann
Tartan Sr HS; St Paul, MN (22-427) Band; NHS; Bkbl; Tnns; *St Catherines Col; Nurs.*

544

OLSON, Gary Stig
Arlington HS; Arlington, MA; Sci C; Cpt, Tr; Lib C; Photography C; BSct; Boy's C; Top Ten; Pro Deo et Patria; Arlington Plan Com Slogan Search; *Mass Inst of Technology; Engr.*

OLSON, Gayle Lynne
Hettinger Pub Sch; Hettinger, ND; Chor; 4H; Rainbow; Bkbl; Sftbl; Swim; Tnns; Tr; COM; 4H A; Carnival Qn; Pep C A.

OLSON, Gwen Delene
Aberdeen Central HS; Aberdeen, SD (15%-500) A Cap Choir; NHS; Golf; 3rd Pl, Talent Show; *Bartlesville Wesleyan Col; Sci.*

OLSON, James Lloyd
Homewood-Flossmoor HS; Flossmoor, IL (68-914) A Cap Choir; Chor; 1st St, Ping Pong; Sportsmanship A; Pres, Area Yth Groups; Off, Boys Chor; *Wheaton Col; Natural Sci.*

OLSON, Jane Marilyn
Windom Area HS; Windom, MN; Band; Chor; FNA; Orch; GSct; *Nurs.*

OLSON, Janelle Jodi
Valley City HS; Valley City, ND (50%-175) Band; Chldr; FBLA; Ski C; Sftbl; Swim; Tnns; Tr; *Valley City St Col; Elem Ed.*

OLSON, Janet Elaine
Blue Valley USD 384 HS; Randolph, KS (10%-18) Band; Chor; Ensm; FHA; Pres, 4H; 4H A; Co, St, Youthpower; *Kans St U; Home Ec.*

OLSON, Jason Scott
Aurora W HS; Aurora, IL; Band; Chor; Community Yth Symph; Drama; Ensm; Tres, Math C; Orch; Span C; Thes; Wrest; Math A; Ntl Achv Schol; Mus Schol; *Mus.*

OLSON, Jenifer Lynn
Hastings Sr HS; Hastings, MN (159-422) AFS; Chor; Fin, Ensm; Ski C; Swim; Fin Solo Contest; HR; Hastings House Registration Project; *Golden Valley Lutheran Col; Missionary Work.*

OLSON, Jonathan Allen
Port Washington HS; Port Washington, WI (5-269) Band; Chor; Dbte Tm; Pres, Demolay; Ensm; NHS; Orch; Tr; DARGCA; Hon Prog; NMF; WW; *Coe Col.*

OLSON, Judy Marie
Minidoka Co HS; Rupert, ID (20-300) Chor; Dbte Tm; GS; Secy, NFL; NHS; ARC; Ski C; Secy, Jr Cl; COM; Spch A; 2nd, Dist Debate; *Idaho St U; Phar.*

OLSON, Karen Maja
Alhambra HS; Martinez, CA (15-300) Band; Secy, Chor; 4H; Amer Leg A; 4H A; Most Out; CSF; Gym Tm; *Fr.*

OLSON, Kathy Joleen
Milo Adventist Acad; Days Creek, OR (4-75) Chor; *Pacific Union Col; Bus.*

OLSON, Kim Luanne
Underwood Pub HS; Underwood, ND (7-29) Secy, Band; Chldr; Chor; Drama; Sch P; Tr; John Philips Sousa Band A; Star Rating, St Mus Contest; *Minot St Col; Mus.*

OLSON, Lori Marie
Oak Lawn Comm HS; Oak Lawn, IL (59-734) *N Park Col; Bus.*

OLSON, Margaret Christine
Apollo HS; Simi Valley, CA; Ann; Chldr; Drama; Hmrm; Sci C; Ski C; Bsbl; Bkbl; Ftbl; Soccer; Sftbl; Swim; Tnns; Tr; Most Out; Q&S A; Star Student; *Moorpark Col; Asst Vet.*

OLSON, Marlin Arthur
Twin Valley HS; Twin Valley, MN; A Cap Choir; Band; Chor.

OLSON, Mary Kay
Maine S HS; Park Ridge, IL (70%-690) SC; Thes; *U of Ill; Nutrition.*

OLSON, Nancy Alice
Park Center HS; Brooklyn Park, MN; Orch; JV, Bsbl; JV, Sftbl; Swim; *Phys Ed.*

OLSON, Nancy Ann
Wasco Co Union HS; Maupin, OR (10-21) Band; Chor; Ensm; FTA; SC; Pres, Sr Cl; Tr; Yth Fel; Math Assn of Amer A; *George Fox Col; Mus.*

OLSON, Pamela Jo
Saline HS; Saline, MI (35-265) Band; Chor; NHS; COM; Yth Fel; *Bus Ed.*

OLSON, Patricia Kay
Jefferson Davis HS; Montgomery, AL; CYO; Chor; Ensm; Tri-HiY; Swim.

OLSON, Rebecca Jo
Hibbing HS; Hibbing, MN (25%-425) City Conf; Fr C; Hon Prog; Math A; Type A; *U of Wis-Eau Claire; Bio.*

OLSON, Renae Lynn
Century HS; Bismarck, ND (25-192) Band; Chor; NHS; Var C; Golf; Cpt, Dance Tm; *Bismarck Jr Col; Interior Design.*

OLSON, Reuel Matthew
Kings Temple Christian Sch; Seattle, WA; Band; BS; Chor; Hmrm; SC; Bkbl; Soccer; COM; Hon Prog; Yth Fel; *U of Wash; Engr.*

OLSON, Robert Eugene
Morgan Park HS; Duluth, MN (8-116) Pres, Hmrm; NHS; Bsbl; Cr-Ctry; Golf; Hockey; Rotary A; Hunt Schol; *Gustavus Adolphus Col; Pre-Med.*

OLSON, Ronald Lee
Shabbona HS; Shabbona, IL (1-42) Ann; Sci C; Amer Leg A; Spch A; Annual Photographer; *Sci.*

OLSON, Rosa Catherine
Blue Valley HS; Randolph, KS (1-27) Band; Chor; Ensm; FHA; 4H; SC; Secy, Soph Cl; Mgr, Bkbl; Mgr, Tr; 4H A; Type A; St Piano Contest; *Emporia St Col; Mus.*

OLSON, Roxe Ann
The King's Temple Christian Sch; Seattle, WA; Ed, Ann; Band; Chor; GS; Ed, Sch P; Amer Leg Orator A; COM; Hon Prog; Journ A; Pres A; Spch A; Yth Fel; *Harvard U; Theology.*

OLSON, Sandra Marie
Wachusett Regional HS; Holden, MA (61-504) Cpt, Chldr; Hockey; Dance Theater; Jr-Sr Prom Committee; Hi-League; Homecoming Float Committee; *Clark U; Econ.*

OLSON, Sharon Louise
King's Garden HS; Seattle, WA (4-59) Chor; NHS; Commencement Spkr; *Shoreline Comm Col; Ed.*

OLSON, Steven E
Aurora W HS; Aurora, IL (55-650) Chor; Drama; Thes; Bsbl; Bkbl; Ftbl; St Scholar; Yth Fel; *Bradley U; Civil Engr.*

OLSON, Susan Lynn
Paynesville HS; Paynesville, MN (17-120) Band; Co-Cpt, Chldr.

OLSON, Susan Mary
Albert Lea Sr HS; Albert Lea, MN (99-557) A Cap Choir; Chor; Mjrte; Orch; Golf; Church Schol; *Bethany Lutheran Col; Nurs.*

OLSON, Thomas Richard
Burlington Sr HS; Burlington, WI (78-317) Ann; Chor; Fin, Dbte Tm; VP, Drama; Ensm; Fin, NFL; NHS; Ski C; Var C; JV, Golf; JV, Wrest; *U of Wis; Int Liberal Stu.*

OLSON, Timothy Mark
N Crawford Sr HS; Gays Mills, WI (25%-71) VP, FFA; 4H; St Farmer Degree, FFA; *Farm.*

OLSON, Viola Jayne
Redwood HS; Visalia, CA (10%-350) NHS; SC.

OLSON, Wanda Kay
Rugby HS; Rugby, ND (50%-104) Band; Chldr; Chor; Ensm; FHA; 4H; Sci C; Bkbl; Sftbl; Swim; Tr; 4H A; Sci A; *Bismark-Joseph's Sch of Hair; Beautician.*

OLSZEWSKI, Julia Mary
Valmeyer HS; Valmeyer, IL (1-40) Band; Chor; Secy, FHA; Pres, 4H; Math C; NHS; Sch P; 4H A; Math A; *Sou Ill U at Edwards.*

OMURA, Kevin Hiroshi
Maryknoll HS; Honolulu, HI (31-110) CYO; NHS; St Stu Congress; SC; Pres, Sr Cl; Pres, Jr Cl; Pres, Soph Cl; Mgr, Bkbl; Tnns; Hon Prog; Ldrship A; Ath o-t Yr; *U of Hawaii.*

ONARECKER, Cheyn Damon
New Caney HS; Porter, TX (4-216) Chess C; Chor; Dbte Tm; Drama; NFL; NHS; Span C; Spch C; Thes; Bkbl; Ftbl; Tnns; JV, Tr; Hon Prog; Math A; Ntl Sci Symposium; NEDT; Sci A; VFW Orator Win; VofDEM; Mr New Caney; *Oral Roberts U; Chem.*

ONCKEN, Brenda Kay
Stoughton Sr HS; Stoughton, WI (50-288) Band; Cpt, Chldr; Chor; FFA; Secy, 4H; Math C; Model UN; Spch C; SC; JV, Bkbl; Tr; 4H A; Spch A; Parl Procedure; Champion Dairy A; Pep C; Chldr A; Vlbl; Prom Ct.

ONDREJKA, Therese Marie
Boulder HS; Boulder, CO (350-600) FFA; Ger C; Alg A; Citz A; Spch A; *Agr.*

ONEY, Vanessa Lyn
Hammond Christian Acad; Griffith, IN; Co-Ed, Ann; Drama; Ensm; Orch; Pres, SC; Pres, Sr Cl; VP, Soph Cl; HQn; Eng, Drama, A's.

ONGMAN, Kirk John
Homewood-Flossmoor HS; Flossmoor, IL (59-929) A Cap Choir; Chor; Drama; Ensm; Key C; VP, NHS; SC; Thes; Var C; Bsbl; Bkbl; Golf; Amer Leg A; Ntl Achv Schol; St Mus A; *Berkley U; Chem Engr.*

ONION, Steve Edward
Industry HS; Industry, IL (6-30) Drama; Fr C; VP, Soph Cl; Bkbl; Ftbl; Golf; Tr; *Carl Sandburg Col; Agr.*

ONKEN, Jerry Scott
Bellevue HS; Bellevue, NE (41-847) Bsbl; Bkbl; Ftbl; Cert of Achv & Ltrman, Bsbl & Bkbl; Cert of Achv & Ltrman, Ftbl; *Forestry.*

ONORATO, Maria Antoinette
St Benedict Acad; Pittsburgh, PA (4-65) CYO; NHS; Sci C; Ski C; Amer Leg A; Bausch & Lomb A; Chem A; Hon Prog; NEDT; Type A; *Allegheny Col; Biochem.*

ONTTO, Carol Lou
Rock HS; Rock, MI (33%-28) Drama; GS; Tres, 4H; Ed, Sch P; Tres, Sr Cl; Tres, Jr Cl; 4H A; NEDT; Type A; *Northern Mich U; Nurs.*

ONUFER, Mary Fran
Glenbrook S HS; Glenview, IL (18-600) Secy, CYO; Key C; NHS; Ski C; SC; JV, Bkbl; JV, Swim; Alg A; Bio A; Hon Prog; Opt A; Sci A; St Scholar; *U of Ill; Bio.*

ONUFRAK, Patricia Ann
McLean HS; McLean, VA (34-408) Band; Lit Mag; NHS; Orch; Rptr, Sch P; COM; NEDT; St Fin, Bowl; All Regional Band; Jr Hons Prog; *Duquesne U; Russian Area Stu.*

OOMMEN, Cherian Santhosh
Southwick HS; Southwick, MA (14-176) Math C; Tr; Tres, Yth Fel; Church Choir; *Saint Mary's Col; Pre-Med.*

OOSTERHOUSE, Randy Scott
Thornapple Kellogg HS; Middleville, MI; Band; Swim; Tnns; *Ferris Col; Bus.*

OPACHKO, Sharon Ann
James Madison HS; Vienna, VA (89-489) Band; Bus C; CYO; FBLA; NHS; Var C; Mgr, Bkbl; Mgr, Sftbl; Tr; Regional Band; PA; *WSS; Secretarial Procedures.*

OPDAHL, Gwendolyn Renae
Timberline HS; Weippe, ID (8-47) Ann; Band; Chem C; VP, 4H; NHS; Pol Sci C; Ski C; Spch C; Bkbl; 4H A; Hon Prog; *Waldorf Jr Col; Med Technology.*

OPEL, Kevin Earl
Marysville-Pilchuck HS; Marysville, WA (80-330) Ger C; Hmrm; Key C; SC; Var C; Bsbl; Bkbl; Ftbl; Swim; JA A; Masonic A; *U of Wash; Phys Therapy.*

OPFER, Mark Cameron
Arlington HS; Arlington, NE (6-98) Chess C; Ger C; Monogram; NHS; Order/Arrow; Var C; Bsbl; Bkbl; Cr-Ctry; Tr; Hon Prog; Math A; Order/Arrow A; Tr Ltr; Declam; *Physics.*

OPLAND, Monica Marie
Washington HS; Sioux Falls, SD (10%-600) Chor; Dbte Tm; Fr C; 4H; 4H A; *Augustana Col; Med.*

OPPEL, Gary Louis
Shelton HS; Shelton, CT (30-200) Band; Fr C; Soccer; *Sou Conn U; Bus.*

OPPERMAN, Betsy Jo
Parma Sr HS; Parma, OH (212-855) Chldr; Chor; Ensm; SC; Sftbl; HQn; Most Improved, Chldr; Bible Sch Aid; HR; Church Nursery Attendant; Tn Board; Sch Morning Show Announcer; *Cuyahoga Comm Col; Elem Ed.*

OPRYSHEK, Keith Alan
Robert E Lee HS; Baytown, TX (5%-500) Rptr, Band; Lat NHS; NHS; SC; Mgr, Bkbl; Secy, St Lat C; S-T, Octagon C; Sch News Rptr, Baytown Sun; *U of Houston; Bus Adm.*

OQUIN, Rodney Paul
Stratford HS; Stratford, TX (10-68) Chor; FFA; Golf; Ntl Sci Symposium; HR; PA; *Drafting.*

ORANGE, Samuel Glenn Jr
Springhill HS; Springhill, LA (10-147) BS; Var C; MVP, Bkbl; Hon Prog; High Ability Prog; Pre-Engr Inst; *Sou U; Civil Engr.*

ORBIN, Deanna Jane
Macon HS; Macon, MO; Band; Mjrte; Most Out; *Hannibal LaGrange; Youth Work.*

ORCZYK, Natalie Mary
Greece Olympia HS; Greece, NY (15-360) A Cap Choir; Chor; Drama; ARC; Secy, Sodality; Pres, Y-Tns; MVP, Cr-Ctry; Swim; Hon Prog; *Cornell U; Fashion Design.*

ORD, John Ellwood
Warren Area HS; Warren, PA (20%-420) Hmrm; Tres, NHS; Rptr, Sch P; Var C; Bsbl; Bkbl; Rptr, Ftbl; Most Improved; *Grove City Col; Bus.*

ORD, Kenneth Paul
Richardson HS; Richardson, TX (677-954) Pres, HiY; Cpt, Bkbl; MVP, All Tourn, Bkbl; *Bus.*

OREBAUGH, Jeanette Lynn
Camdenton HS; Camdenton, MO; A Cap Choir; Band; Chor; 4H; PTL C; Cpt, Yth for Christ; Band A; *Mus.*

OREDSON, Susan Elgene
Blaine Sr HS; Blaine, MN (41-734) Band; Drama; Hmrm; NHS; Swim; Mus Instrumental A; *Suburban Vo-tech Col; Dental Asst.*

ORENCH, Jose A
Antilles HS; Fort Buchanan, PR (15-118) Fin, Wrest; Hon Prog; *Col of Agr & Mech Arts-Mayaguez; Elec Engr.*

OREWILER, Janel Claire
United Township HS; E Moline, IL (21-600) Drama; NHS; Span C; VP, Span NHS; Var C; Tnns; Chamber of Comm A; Hon Prog; Span Hon Medal; *Wheaton Col.*

OREWILER, Jonathan Paul
United Township HS; E Moline, IL (11-600) NHS; Span C; Span NHS; Cr-Ctry; Tr; Hon Prog; Jr Rotarian.

ORIANS, Maureen Mary
Shawnee HS; Shawnee, OK (33%-319) Secy, FTA; *St Gregory's Col; Family Life.*

ORIENTALE, Michael Eugene
Briarcliff HS; Briarcliff Manor, NY (10-127) Drama; NHS; Rptr, Sch P; Tres, SC; Tres, Jr Cl; Cpt, Ftbl; Tr; COM; Hon Prog; ROTC A; Star Student; WW; *U of Colo at Boulder; Mech Engr.*

ORINGDERFF, Nelda Fern
Diamond Hill-Jarvis HS; Ft Worth, TX (7-134) S-T, FHA; VP, FTA; Secy, NHS; Rainbow; Altrusa A; Jr Woman's C Schol; Ntl HS A for Excellence; Gold Eagle A; *TCJC; Elem Ed.*

ORIOLD, Donna Lee
Central Bucks HS W; Doylestown, PA (50-513) Drama; Madrigal; Cpt, Mjrte; Span NHS; Thes; Sftbl; *Westminster Choir Col; Mus Ed.*

ORLANDO, Michael Eugene
St Thomas Aquinas HS; Louisville, OH (75-225) Chem C; Chess C; Commercial C; ARC; Sch P; Sci C; Span C; COM; Most Out; ARC A; Most Outst Ldr A of Merit; *Sci.*

ORLANDO, Toni Marie
Madonna HS; Weirton, WV (13-117) Cpt, Chldr; Chor; Drama; Secy, InterAct C; NHS; Rptr, Sch P; Secy, SC; Tnns; HCt; Hon Prog; Pep C; WW; WW Among HS Chldr; *Duquesne U; Nurs.*

ORLYK, Linda June
Fenton HS; Bensenville, IL (30-446) Chor; NHS; Rptr, Sch P; SC; Hon Prog; St Scholar; F-Ed, Sch P; WW; Ntl Col of Ed School; *Ntl Col of Ed; Ed.*

ORMAN, Andrea Kay
Del Valle HS; Austin, TX (1-209) VP, A Cap Choir; VP, Chor; Ensm; VP, FHA; Hmrm; Lit Mag; Madrigal; NHS; ARC; Sci C; Span NHS; Parl, SC; VP, Soph Cl; Swim; Amer Leg A; Bio A; COM; Citz A; Hist A; Hon Prog; JA A; Lion A; Math A; Most Out; Sci A; Star Student; Type A; Val; Ntl Span Hon Soc; Choir Accompanist; Rptr, Pep C; Lion C Swtht; Pep C; SG; Secy & VP, Church Yth Choir; Yth for Christ; Runner-Up; Bio A; *Baylor University; Nursing.*

ORMOND, Susan Kathryn
Alamosa HS; Alamosa, CO (1-200) VP, NHS; Pres, Thes; Bkbl; Alg A; Bio A; Chem A; Masonic A; Math A; Sci A; Val; Vlbl; Drama A; *Colo St U; Sociology.*

ORMSBEE, Anna Loraine
Diamond Hill-Jarvis HS; Fort Worth, TX; *Air Force Acad.*

ORMSBY, William Patrick
Bronx HS of Sci; Bronx, NY (300-900) Ski C Instructor; *Bradford Col; Dentistry.*

ORNDOFF, Cynthia Jane
Paris HS; Paris, IL; Band; Chem C; Chor; Drama; 4H; Secy, GSct; *Stephens Col; Ed.*

ORNDORFF, Cheryl Leigh
Central HS; Woodstock, VA (25-195) FBLA; FHA; Lat C; Co-Cpt, Mjrte; NHS; Sch P; *Madison Col; Teaching.*

ORR, Bart Wayne
Obion Co HS; Troy, TN (3-178) BC; BS; Secy, FFA; Hmrm; NHS; Ed, Sch P; JV, Bkbl; Most Reliable; St Farmer; *U of Tenn; Computer Programming.*

ORR, David John
Treynor Comm HS; Treynor, IA (2-48) Band; Chor; Drama; Fr C; NHS; VP, Soph Cl; St Scholar; *Iowa St U.*

ORR, Debbie Lynne
Parsons Sr HS; Parsons, KS (24-125) Chor; Hon Prog; Gen Ed Schol; *Labette Comm Jr Col; Bus.*

ORR, Deborah Louise
Sprague HS; Salem, OR; Chor; Ensm; 4H; Ntl Yth Conf; JV, Bkbl; Fin, Cr-Ctry; Cpt, Sftbl; Fin, Tr; Beauty; 4H A; MLS; Cross Ctry, Tr As; *Multnomah Col; Bible.*

ORR, Elizabeth
Arkadelphia HS; Arkadelphia, AR (35-163) Band; Chor; Ensm; Fr C; FHA; Tres, GS; Hmrm; Mjrte; Orch; Sci C; Band A; *Ouachita Baptist U; Art.*

ORR, Jeffrey Stuart
Batavia HS; Batavia, IL (12-224) Band; Math C; Order/Arrow; Ski C; JA A; Math A; Order/Arrow A; *Law.*

ORR, Julian Marie
St Ignatius HS; St Ignatius, MT (2-30) Chldr; GS; Mjrte; Pres, NHS; A-Ed, Sch P; VP, Sr Cl; Tres, Jr Cl; Tres, Soph Cl; Cpt, Bkbl; Type A; WW; Shorthand A; HR; *Missoula Vo-tech Center; Accountant Asst.*

ORR, Kate Joanna
Marion HS; Marion, IN (10-750) GS; NHS; Bkbl; Tr; Pres A; *Taylor U; Phys Ed.*

ORR, Kathleen Ann
James W Robinson Secondary HS; Fairfax, VA (370-501) JV, Soccer; Swim; VP, Lutheran Yth; Most Improved, Swim; *Ferrum Col; Social Work.*

ORR, Kathryn Elizabeth
Grissom HS; Huntsville, AL (33%-576) Cpt, Swim; All City Swim; V Ltr, Swim; *Ga St U; Phys Ed.*

ORR, Laurie Beth
Chickasha HS; Chickasha, OK (10%-200) JV, Chldr; Sci C; Span C; SC; Thes; Tnns; HQn; *Bethany Nazarene Col; Law.*

ORR, Linda Susan
New Brighton HS; New Brighton, PA (1-209) Ann; Secy, Drama; Hmrm; Rptr, Sch P; SC; Tri-HiY; Secy, Jr Cl; Hon Prog; NEDT; Val; Vlbl; Principal's Cert of Soph Ed Achv; May Ct; *Westminster Col; Bus Adm.*

ORR, Lynette Kay
Lutheran HS E; Harper Woods, MI; Band; Sftbl; *Secretarial.*

ORR, Rebecca King
Highlands Sr HS; Natrona Hgts, PA (160-493) Chor; Var C; Bkbl; Sftbl; Tnns; COM; Hon Prog; *Med Tech.*

ORR, Sylvia Elaine
E Rome HS; Rome, GA; Drama; FBLA; B Crocker A; High HR; *Floyd Jr Col; Nurs.*

ORRELL, Laura Louise
Grants HS; Grants, NM; Band; Pres, 4H; Hmrm; Mjrte; NHS; Ntl Yth Conf; ARC; Span NHS; SC; Bkbl; JV, Ftbl; Swim; Rptr, Wrest; Cl Fav; Interlochen Ntl Mus; MLS; Sci A; Yth Leg; Semi-Fin, Cl Favorite; Fin, Interlochen Ntl Mus Comp A; Semi-Fin, MLS; Fin, Sci A; *Tex Womens U; Special Ed.*

ORRENDER, Kimberly Dawn
Bellbrook HS; Bellbrook, OH; Mjrte; 1st Pl, St Baton Comp; *Computer Service.*

ORRICK, Marlene La Nea
River Valley HS; Three Oaks, MI; Chor; FHA; *Moody Bible Inst; Christian Ed.*

ORRICK, Marsha Kay
Washington HS; Kansas City, KS (5%-600) Band; Chor; Drama; Ensm; Fr C; French NHS; 4H; NHS; Orch; Thes; COM; 4H A; Hon Prog; Math A; Girls Pep Band; Gold Medal, St Drum Solo; Gold Medal, St Drum Ensm; *Performing Arts.*

ORRIS, Helen Jeanne
Clark HS; Clark, SD (7-65) AFS; Ann; Dbte Tm; FHA; NHS; Ed, Sch P; B Crocker A; Journ A; Q&S A; Spch A; Stu o-t Mo A; *SD St U; Journ.*

ORSBURN, Derrin Keith
Gainesville HS; Gainesville, TX; Chor; Ensm; Hmrm; Secy, Key C; NHS; Spch C; SC; Pres, Jr Cl; Pres, Soph Cl; Bsbl; Ftbl; Citz A; Kiwanis A; *Baylor U; Law.*

ORTEGA, Victor O
Wilson HS; Wilson, TX (10%-25) Band; FFA; VP, Span C; Pres, Soph Cl; Co-Cpt, Bkbl; Ftbl; Tr; *Tex Tech U; Bus.*

ORTH, Lorinda Irene
Central HS; Aberdeen, SD (10%-498) Band; Dbte Tm; Ensm; Orch.

ORTIZ, Iris R
Luis Munoz Rivera HS; Lajas, PR (20-170) Commercial C; FBLA; SC; *Colegio Regional de Aguadillo; Secy.*

ORTIZ, Luis Angel Garza
Thomas A Edison HS; San Antonio, TX; Band; CYO; Chess C; Fr C; Ger C; COM; Hon Prog; ROTC A; Scholastic Achv; City Chapion; Semi-Fin, St Bowl; *St Mary's U; Pol Sci.*

ORTIZ, Luis Manuel
Colegio San Antonio Abad; Humacao, PR (7-90) Sci C; *Wake Forest U; Microbiology.*

ORTIZ, Marisabel
Francisco Mendoza HS; Isabela, PR; A Cap Choir; Band; GS; Pres, Hmrm; ARC; Swim; COM; *Col Regional Aquadilla; Ed.*

ORTIZ, Marta R
Antonio S Pedreira HS; Moca, PR (4-38) CYO; FHA; Secy, Hmrm; COM; *Mayaguez U; Sci.*

ORTIZ, Orlando
Adlai E Stevenson HS; New York City, NY (1-822) Chem C; Chor; City Conf; Dbte Tm; Drama; Hmrm; InterClub Coun; Math C; Pres, NHS; Sch Achieve Tm; SC; Pres, Sr Cl; Bio A; COM; Chem A; Citz A; Gov Honor Prog; Hon Prog; Math A; Most Out; Ntl Sci Symposium; Phy A; Regent Schol; Sci A; Val; Homework Helpers A; *Columbia U; Pre-Med.*

ORTIZ, Thomas
Barringer HS; Newark, NJ (5-550) Band; Orch; Tres, Span C; Hist A; Hon Prog; Math A; Tres, Future Physicians of Amer; Span A; Musical A; Poa Bass; *Dukes U; Biomed Engr.*

ORTIZ, Wanda Enid
Academia Santa Monica; Santurce, PR; *U of Puerto Rico; Med.*

ORTIZ, Zwinda Sahyly
Academia del Sagrado Corazon; Santurce, PR (17-65) NHS; ARC; *Natural Sci.*

ORTIZ-ROBLEDO, Christine
Antilles HS; Fort Buchanan, PR (10-118) Ann; Hmrm; Lit Mag; NHS; Ed, Sch P; SC; Tres, Soph Cl; Mgr, Sftbl; COM; Hon Prog; NJHS; Tres, Keyettes; Ecology C; *Counselor.*

ORTMAN, Raymond Charles Jr
Benjamin Cardoza HS; Bayside, NY (5-1000) Band; Hon Prog; Math A; Yth Fel; Tres, Yth Fel; Win, Math Fair Bronze Medal; *Drew U; Math.*

ORTON, Janice Lynn
Ensley HS; Birmingham, AL (5%-300) Bus Mgr, Ann; Math C; Y-Tns; Amer Leg A; Citz A; Harold B Johnson A; Top 5%, Co Jr's; *U of Ala.*

ORTON, Paul David
Moberly Sr HS; Moberly, MO (17-200) Chor; VP, Math C; Mu Alpha Theta; NHS; Co-Cpt, Ftbl; Tr; DARGCA; MLS; Cl Offices; *Mo U; Engr.*

ORTON, Susan Marie
Williamston HS; Williamston, NC (17-219) BC; Chldr; Drama; Monogram; Mgr, Tnns; Alt, Foreign Ambassador.

ORVIN, Edna Pamela
St Stephen HS; St Stephen, SC; Chldr; Chor; *Col of Charleston; Ed.*

ORWIG, Matthew Daney
Coronado HS; Lubbock, TX (15%-580) Dbte Tm; Drama; Lat C; Pres, NFL; NHS; Sci C; Tres, Thes; Citz A; God & Country A; Spch A; *Tex Tech U; Pre Law.*

ORZA, Lisa Jane
Briarcliff Manor HS; Briarcliff Manor, NY; F-Ed, Ann; Chldr; A-Ed, Lit Mag; NHS; Hockey; Tr; COM; Q&S A; WW; Alt, Regent's Schol; *SUNY at Albany; Sci.*

OSAKI, Carl Hiroshi
Maryknoll HS; Honolulu, HI (1-115) CYO; VP, Hmrm; Math C; NHS; Tres, Jr Cl; Tres, Soph Cl; Bsbl; Hist A; K of C A; NEDT; Spch A; Cpt, Bowl; CAP A; Eng A; Japanese A; Schol A; *Drake U; Law.*

OSANKA, Jeffery Franklin
Naperville N HS; Naperville, IL (10-400) Hmrm; Math C; Sch P; Spch C; JV, Swim; Tr; VofDEM; Yth Leg; Forensics Tm; *Law.*

OSBECK, Mark Kenneth
Forest Hills N HS; Grand Rapids, MI (25-160) Band; Cpt, Dbte Tm; Orch; JV, Bkbl; COM; Spch A; St Scholar; *Calvin Col; Pre-Law.*

OSBORN, Brian Lynn
Winnebago Pub Sch; Winnebago, MN; Tres, FFA; Ftbl; MVP, Wrest; *Jackson Voc Sch; Auto Body Mech.*

OSBORN, Dorothy Bockel
Buckley HS; Sherman Oaks, CA (10-65) Chess C; Community Yth Symph; NHS; Orch; Alg A; Bio A; COM; Citz A; Hist A; Math A; NEDT; Sci A; Yth Fel; Calif All-St HS Hon Orch, Viola; *Stanford U; Math.*

OSBORN, Jimmy Lee
Haltom HS; Ft Worth, TX; JV, Tnns; Amer Leg A; Citz A; Jr Chamber of Com A; *Math.*

OSBORN, Katherine Marie
Burnsville HS; Burnsville, MS; Tres, BC; Rptr, FBLA; FHA; 4H; *Northeast Miss Jr Col; Secy.*

OSBORN, Kent Alan
Ainsworth HS; Ainsworth, NE (20%-73) Band; Chor; Monogram; SC; Thes; Bkbl; Ftbl; Tr; Lion A; NHS; PeeWee Bkbl Coach A; Tr A; Outst Baritone, Chor; Swing Choir; City Tn Coun; Scholastic HR; *Sci.*

OSBORN, Paul Thomas
East HS; Rockford, IL; BS; City Conf; Orch; SC; Cr-Ctry; JV, Swim; Tr; COM; Pres A; 1st Area Fresh Scorer, St Tr Meet; Marine Fitness A; *Social Work.*

OSBORNE, Anita Estelle
Marshall HS; Marshall, TX (3-500) Chor; FTA; 4H; Alg A; 4H A; Hon Prog; Poetry, Span, Schol, A's; *U of Tex; Math.*

OSBORNE, DeAnna
Ashtabula HS; Ashtabula, OH; AFS; FTA; Hmrm; Sch P; SC; *Harding Col; Home Ec.*

OSBORNE, Dennis Eugene
Attica HS; Attica, IN (10-98) NHS; Eagle Sct; *Ind Central U; Bus Adm.*

OSBORNE, Katherine Elizabeth
Huguenot Acad; Powhaton, VA (5-88) Ann; Drama; Secy, FHA; 4H; Hmrm; VP, NHS; Secy, SC; Mgr, Bkbl; Sftbl; COM; DARGCA; 4H A; Magna Cum Laude; *U of Va; Nurs.*

OSBORNE, Ladd Bruce
Greens Farms Acad; Greens Farms, CT (12-36) Pres, Var C; MVP, Bsbl; Co-Cpt, Bkbl; Co-Cpt, Soccer; Tr; Yth Fel; Co-Cpt, Bsbl; Good Citz A; Eng A; *Drew U; Religion.*

OSBORNE, Linda Gay
Karlsruhe Amer HS; Karlsruhe, GERMANY; Chor; Drama; FTA; ARC; Sch P; Bkbl; Tr; Hon Prog; *U of Tenn; Chem.*

OSBORNE, Lori Jane
Goodlettsville HS; Goodlettsville, TN; Cpt, Chldr; FTA; GS; Hmrm; NFL; NHS; Span C; SC; Tnns; Citz A; HCt; Butch Douglas A; Tn o-t Mo; Civitan A; *U of Tenn.*

OSBORNE, Louise Ann
Parma Sr HS; Parma, OH (390-855) Chor; Mjrte; SC; Sftbl; VP, AYF; Kindergarden Sunday Sch Teacher; Girls Gym Ldr; Pres, Hockey C; *Child Care.*

OSBORNE, Rachel Beverly
W Orange HS; Ft Myers, FL; Band; Chor; Hmrm; A-Ed, Sch P; Bkbl; Mgr, Cr-Ctry; Mgr, Tr; Church Schol; *Trevecca Nazarene Col; Sci.*

OSBORNE, Theodore
Ahoskie HS; Ahoskie, NC (10-29).

OSBORNE, Tracy Louise
Freeport II HS; Freeport, IL (2%-550) Math C; Swim; Hon Prog; Redeem Yth Fel; GSct; *Ill St Col; Chem.*

OSBORN SWANGO, Michelle Elise
Switzerland Co HS; Vevay, IN (7-120) Band; 4H.

OSBURN, Blake Lee
Del Norte HS; Albuquerque, NM; Chor; JV, Bsbl; JV, Ftbl; Tnns; *Iowa Western Col; Bus Adm.*

OSBURN, Gaye Lynn
Churchill HS; San Antonio, TX (33%-625) FTA; Y-Tns; Sftbl; *Baylor U.*

OSBURN, Pamala Kay
Del City HS; Del City, OK (10%-564) Chor; Fr C; Hmrm; NHS; SC; Amer Leg A; Citz A; Masonic A; Yth Fel; Secy, VP, Yth for Christ; Chaplain, Tri-Hi-Y; Secy, Yth Coun; Secy, Prayer & Ministry; Yth Coun; *NE A&M Col; Bus.*

OSDRAS, Mark Anthony
Milford HS; Milford, MI (365-390) Chor; Hmrm; Ch, SC; Ed, Yth Newspaper; Parish Coun; Yth Coun Rep; Vol Director, Children's Choir; Accompanist, Folk Group; *Sacred Heart Sem; Religious Mus.*

OSEAS, David Lee
El Camino Real HS; Woodland Hills, CA (53-1095) Band; Chem C; Chess C; Tres, Ger C; CSF; COM; Citz A; Elk A; Hist A; Boy's League; Gold Seal Bearer; Cpt, Tm Sports; VP, Kingsmen; *George E Hale A.*

OSENBAUGH, Judy Elaine
Bellevue HS; Bellevue, MI; Cpt, Chldr; Drama; Ger C; Ski C; *KCC; Teaching.*

OSGOOD, David Dale
Cy-Fair HS; Cypress, TX (375-750) NHS; *Concordia Lutheran Col; Pastor.*

OSGOOD, Karen Ellen
Mercy HS; Red Bluff, CA (2-27) Chor; Secy, 4H; Model UN; VP, Soph Cl; Bkbl; Ftbl; Sftbl; Tr; CSF; 4H A; Sal; *UC at Davis; Engr.*

OSGOOD, Robert Thornton Jr
Sweet Home Sr HS; Amherst, NY (90-610) Model UN; Rptr, Sch P; Var C; Soccer; Tnns; Pres A; *St U of NY at Buffalo; Architecture.*

OSHER, Robert Micheal
Buckley HS; Sherman Oaks, CA; Co-Ed, Ann; Pres, NHS; Ski C; Tres, Var C; Cpt, Bsbl; Cpt, Ftbl; Cpt, Hockey; Soccer; Cpt, Tr; Hon Prog; MVP, Bsbl; Fin, Bio A; Fin, MLS; MVP, Ftbl; Span A; Sports A; MVP, Tr; Semi-Fin, Alg A; *Stanford U; Bus.*

OSHIMA, Randy Y
Piedmont Hills HS; San Jose, CA (2%-750) Chor; Ger C; NHS; VP, Var C; Cpt, Ftbl; CSF; God & Country A; *Bethel Col; Christian Ed.*

OSINSKI, Therese M
Lourdes HS; Chicago, IL (18-288) Chor; Tres, Drama; NHS; Thes; COM; Hon Prog; NEDT; Type A; Drama A; Candystriper Pin.

OSLAND, Lori Faye
Erskine Pub HS; Erskine, MN (6-20) Chldr; Chor; NHS; Sch P; Secy, SC; MVP, Bkbl; Tr; HQn; Vlbl; *Northland Comm Col; Acct.*

OSLAND, Mark Allen
May-Port HS; Mayville, ND (10-63) SC; Var C; JV, Bkbl; Ftbl; Tr; *Wichita St U; Bus.*

OSMANSKI, Sue Marie
St Mary's Acad; Englewood, CO (1-50) Chor; Fr C; NHS; Ski C; Swim; Bio A; Spirit C; Swim A; *Colo St U; Sci.*

OSNER, Leonard Mark
Cunningham HS; Cunningham, KS (5-20) Ann; CYO; Chor; VP, HiY; Secy, Sr Cl; Bkbl; HCt; *Farming.*

OSNESS, Kimberley Jo
Kofa HS; Yuma, AZ; FBLA; Semi-Fin, GS; *Pacific Christian Col; Christian Ed.*

OSSEGE, Sharon Patricia
Seton HS; Cincinnati, OH (20%-330) CYO; Hmrm; NHS; S-T, Span C; SC; Sftbl; Hon Prog; Psych C; *Xavier U; Med Tech.*

OSSWALD, Kimberly Raye
Brookville HS; Brookville, OH; Band; Tres, NHS; Alg A; *Sinclair Col; Nurs.*

OSSWALD, Scott Allen
Brookville HS; Brookville, OH (30-175) Pres, Band; SC; Var C; Wrest; *Miami U of Oxford; Ed.*

OST, Catherine Rose
Albert Lea Central HS; Albert Lea, MN (22-597) Band; ARC; Var C; Bkbl; Tr; Citz A; Pres A; ARC A; ISE Trip to Ger; Outst, Mus; Vlbl; Outst Sportsmanship; PA; NASA Viking Stu Profect A; Stu Tutor; 5 Yr Choir Attendance; *Augustana Col; Deaf Ed.*

OSTER, Robert Faircloth
Rocky River HS; Rocky River, OH; Band; Bus C; Rptr, Sch P; *Bus Adm.*

OSTERHOF, Debra Jean
Sulphur HS; Sulphur, LA (19-430) Band; Rptr, BC; FTA; Pres, 4H; Lit Ral; Math C; Mu Alpha Theta; Span C; SC; COM; Citz A; DARGCA; 4H A; I Dare You; Pres A; Swtht; Yth Fel; WW; DeMolay Swtht; GS Alt; Sadie Hawkins Ct; Miss Conclave, St of La; VP, Keyettes; Rifle Corps Swtht; *La Tech U; Ed.*

OSTERLOH, Timothy E
Verona R7 HS; Verona, MO (6-15) BS; Chor; Pres, Sr Cl; Pres, Jr Cl; VP, Soph Cl; Cpt, Bkbl; Fin, Tr; Amer Leg A; HKg; MVP, Bkbl; Semi-Fin, Tr; Leading Hitter, Bsbl; Woodworking A.

OSTHEIMER, Edward McIlvain
St Ignatius HS; St Ignatius, MT (1-60) Tres, 4H; Var C; VP, Soph Cl; MVP, Bsbl; Ftbl; Tr; NEDT; Pres A; Type A; Drafting A; *MIT; Engr.*

OSTRAND, Pamela Jean
Rosalie Pub Sch; Rosalie, NE; Chldr; Chor; Spch C; Secy, Jr Cl; VP, Soph Cl; Sftbl; Tr; Hist A; HCt; Cpt, Vlbl; *U of Nebr; Fashion Merchandising.*

OSTRANDER, Dixie Ann
Cedar Rapids Pub HS; Cedar Rapids, NE (33%-62) Chldr; Chor; Bkbl; *Midland Lutheran Col; Mus.*

OSTROFF, Virginia Annelle
Skyline HS; Dallas, TX (25%-950) Choir; Fr C; Beauty; Key C Swtht; Ntl Mus Guild; Travis A; N Tex St U; Home Ec.

OSUNA, Albert
McAdoo HS; McAdoo, TX (5-9) Cpt, Bkbl.

OSUNA, Frederick James
University HS; San Diego, CA (18-315) BS; CYO; Hmrm; NHS; Sch Achieve Tm; Tres, SC; Var C; MVP, Swim; CSF; COM; Hon Prog; Pep C; Water Polo; Med.

OSWALD, John David
Pendleton Sr HS; Pendleton, OR (1-233) VP, Ger C; Mu Alpha Theta; NHS; Sci C; Kiwanis A; St Scholar; Oreg St U; Sci.

OSWALD, Susan Dawn
N Canton Hoover HS; North Canton, OH (15-465) A Cap Choir; Chor; Drama; Ensm; Fr C; F-Ed, Sch P; Tr; Pres A; Young Citizens A; Art.

OSWALT, Denise Elaine
Palisade HS; Palisade, CO (20-69) Ann; Band; Drama; Tres, FBLA; Span C; Mgr, Bkbl; COM; Kiwanis A; Ottawa U; Art.

OSWALT, Margaret Elizabeth
Briarcrest Baptist HS; Memphis, TN; Mu Alpha Theta; Sftbl; Pep C; Chem Tourn; Hon A; Sci.

OSWALT, Rachel Yvonne
Sou Baptist Ed Center; Memphis, TN (59-127) Band; Ensm; FHA; Orch; Sci C; Beauty; PTA A; Church Sftbl; Band Schol; 2nd Pl, DAR Essay Contest; 3 8 Early Avg A; Memphis St U; Elem Ed.

OTEN, Jeraldine Denise
East HS; Denver, CO; Bkbl; Hockey; Soccer; Sftbl; Tnns; COM; Citz A; Kans Wesleyan Col; Computer Programmer.

OTERO, David Anthony
Los Lunas HS; Los Lunas, NM (1-245) JV, Bkbl; JV, Cr-Ctry; Alg A; Bio A; Hist A; Math A; Sci A; MIT; Chem.

OTERO, Edgard E
Juan Jose Osuna HS; Hato Rey, PR (5-101) All Amer Yth; Commercial C; Drama; Pres, Lit Mag; ARC; Sci C; Span C; St Stu Congress; Alg A; COM; Cl Fav; God & Country A; Hist A; Hon Prog; JA A; Lion A; Math A; Pres A; Star Student; St Scholar; Summa Cum Laude; High Hon; Universidad de PR; Contabilidad.

OTERO, Rosita
Adolfo Grana Rivera HS; Penuelas, PR (5-263) Dbte Tm; FHA; Tres, Hmrm; Pres, ARC; Bkbl; Soccer; COM; Hon Prog; Cath U; Math.

OTERO, Ruth E
Juan Jose Osuna HS; Hato Rey, PR (13-101) All Amer Yth; FHA; Lit Mag; ARC; Secy, Sci C; Pres, Span C; St Stu Congress; Alg A; Beauty; COM; Cl Fav; H of F; Hist A; Hon Prog; JA A; Math A; Pres A; Sci A; Star Student; St Scholar; Summa Cum Laude; Hon A; Universidad de PR; Farmacia.

OTERO MARTINEZ, Jose A
Academia Disipolos Cristo; Bayamon, PR (20-122) Chess C; Drama; S-T; Hmrm; Pres, Sch Achieve Tm; Cpt, Var C; MVP, Bsbl; Cpt, Bkbl; Ftbl; Golf; Mgr, Sftbl; Swim; Tnns; Fin, Tr; Alg A; Bio A; COM; Chem A; Hist A; Hon Prog; Phy A; Sci A; Val; Universidad de Puerto Rico; Biochem.

OTHON, Jessie Jo
Pima HS; Pima, AZ (2-39) Chor; FHA; Hmrm; NHS; Ed, Sch P; SC; Sftbl; Bio A; Cl Fav; Sci A; Type A; BPW Girl o-t Yr; Choir A; Commercial A; 4-Yr Hon Stu.

OTIS, Gregory Harold
Homestead HS; Fort Wayne, IN (35-234) A Cap Choir; Chess C; Chor; Drama; Ensm; Ger C; Madrigal; Spch C; Alg A; Hon Prog; Mus As; Chess A; Indiana U; Mus.

OTIS, Micheal Fredrick
Delton Kellogg HS; Delton, MI; Arch; Chess C; Fr C; 4H; Sch P; Arch; Bsbl; Tnns; 4H A; 1st Pl, Woodworking; New Tribes Bible Inst; Bible.

OTKINS, Richard Allen
John Marshall Harlan HS; Chicago, IL (200-570) Ky St U; Bus Admn.

OTT, Carma Jean
Parkersburg HS; Parkersburg, WV (8-739) A Cap Choir; GS; COM; Coun of Teach A; VP, GAA; Book, Pep, C'S; VPI; Engr.

OTT, George Montague
Spruce Creek HS; Port Orange, FL (290-390) A Cap Choir; Key C; Order/Arrow; Var C; Cpt, Ftbl; Golf; JV, Soccer; Swim; Tr; Order/Arrow A; Pres A; Eagle Sct; U of Ky; Elec.

OTT, Jay Lester
Superior Sr HS; Superior, WI (70-750) Bus C; Chor; Drama; Order/Arrow; Ski C; God & Country A; Yth Fel; U of Wisc; Bus.

OTT, Jeanette Louise
Superior Sr HS; Superior, WI; Band; Drama.

OTT, Jerri Jann
Prague HS; Prague, OK (7-73) FHA; NHS; S-T, Sr Cl; HQn; Drill Tm; BPW.

OTT, Lisa Jayne
Nordonia HS; Macedonia, OH; Secy, Band; Drama; Ensm; NHS; Ski C; Thes; Hon Prog; Drill Tm; Miami U; Special Ed.

OTT, Mark Rippey
Mancos HS; Mancos, CO (2-45) 4H; NHS; Order/Arrow; Var C; Bkbl; Cpt, Ftbl; Tr; 4H A; Order/Arrow A; Sci A; Fort Lewis Col; Engr.

OTTAVIANI, William Louis
Uniontown Area Joint Jr HS; Uniontown, PA; Chess C; Span C; Alg A; Hon Prog; Sci A; Schol A; Penn St U; Sci.

OTTAWAY, Brent Michael
Corry Area Sr HS; Corry, PA; Hmrm; SC; Bkbl; Golf.

OTTE, Bonnie Marie
Gordon HS; Gordon, NE (30-72) CYO; NHS; Outst Co-Op Voc Ed Stu; Chadron St Col; Elem Ed.

OTTE, Bruce Eugene
Denver Christian HS; Denver, CO (10-67) A Cap Choir; Ger C; NHS; Var C; Ftbl; JV, Wrest; 1st Pl, Piano Comp; U of Colo; Engr.

OTTE, Candi Louise
Gordon HS; Gordon, NE (6-84) Band; CYO; FHA; 4H; NHS; Tr; Citz A; 4H A; 3rd Pl, Ntl Lenox China Contest; Drill Tm; 2nd, Schol A; Pep C; 2nd, Co Spelling; U of Nebr-Lincoln.

OTTE, Debra Jean
Gordon HS; Gordon, NE (7-72) S-T, CYO; Chor; FHA; Pres, 4H; NHS; S-T, SC; Tr; B Crocker A; Citz A; 4H A; WW; Top 10%; PA; Pres, Usher C; Co- op Yth Ldrship Conf; Pep C; Chadron St Col; Med Tech.

OTTE, Frederick Eugene
Gordon HS; Gordon, NE (4-85) Band; Semi-Fin, BS; CYO; Chor; Drama; Ensm; Ger C; VP, 4H; NHS; Orch; Sch Achieve Tm; F-Ed, Sch P; Pres, SC; Thes; VP, Soph Cl; COM; 4H A; Hon Prog; NMS; All Star Band; Humorous Mus A; Foreign Lang A; Engr.

OTTE, Pamela Rose
Clark Co R-1 HS; Kahoka, MO (1-96) CYO; Tres, FHA; NHS; Thes; Secy, Jr Cl; Bkbl; Golf; Math A; Academic Ltr; WW.

OTTENDORF, Wendy Elaine
Scotia-Glenville HS; Scotia, NY (7-342) Chldr; Chor; Span C; Y-Tns; Swim; Bio A; Hon Prog; Gym; Social Stu, Eng, Acad Avg, A's; Math.

OTTESON, Ann
Sky View HS; Smithfield, UT (3-622) Citz A; Utah St U; Computer Sci.

OTTESON, David F
Sky View HS; Smithfield, UT (16-611) Var C; Ftbl; Tr; Utah St U; Sci.

OTTO, Brenda Lee
Quincy Sr HS; Quincy, IL; FBLA; Rainbow; Span C; Citz A; NEDT; Church Yth Group; Cl 1 Rating, District Piano; Bus.

OTTO, Cheryl Jean
Illiana Christian HS; Lansing, IL (70-204) A Cap Choir; Ensm; Northland Baptist Bible Col; Mus.

OTTO, Cindy L
Bad Axe HS; Bad Axe, MI; Drama; VP, NHS; Sci C; SC; Co-Cpt, Bkbl; Co-Cpt, Sftbl; COM; NMS; Regent Schol; Sal; U of Mich; Eng.

OTTO, Elisabeth Ann
Portland Christian HS; Portland, OR (18-44) A Cap Choir; Drama; F-Ed, Sch P; Var C; Y-Tns; Cr-Ctry; Tr; V Cr-Ctry Ltr; NW Nazarene Col; Mus Ed.

OTTO, Janet Louise
Madison E HS; Madison, WI; MATC; Data Processing.

OTTO, Julie Ann
Middle Park HS; Granby, CO (1-72) Band; Chess C; Dbte Tm; NFL; Spch C; Kiwanis A; Spch A; JV Vlbl; St Solo A; Graduation Escort; Phi Kappa Delta.

OTTO, Mike Wayne
West HS; West, TX (12-130) Chess C; FFA; FTA; Hmrm; NHS; SC; Pres, Sr Cl; Bsbl; Ftbl; Cl Fav; MCC; Bus.

OTTO, Pamela Lynn
Homestead HS; Mequon, WI (25%-430) AFS; Fr C; Hon Prog; Prom Committee; Pep C; Secy, Tres, Lutheran Yth; Valparaiso U; Nurs.

OTTO, Sandra Lynn
Holt Sr HS; Holt, MI (20-280) Chor; NHS; Tnns; Alma Col; Ed.

OTTO, Steven Laird
James Lick HS; San Jose, CA (20%-300) Cum Laude Soc; Pres, FFA; 4H; InterClub Coun; CSF; 4H A; Calif St Schol; Methodist Dist Yth Coun; Yth Empowerment Service Intern; Cal Poly San Luis Obispo; Agr.

OTTO, Vince J
Kuemper HS; Carroll, IA (90-287) CYO; Fr C; Hmrm; S-T, Key C; Monogram; ARC; Pres, SC; Bsbl; Ftbl; MVP, Swim; Tnns; Tr; Wrest; Iowa St U.

OTTS, Dennis Mark
Homewood HS; Homewood, AL (97-229) Key C; Math C; Order/Arrow; Rptr, Sch P; Soccer; Order/Arrow A; ROTC A; Eagle Sct; U of Montevallo.

OTTUSCH, Monica Paula
Bridgman HS; Bridgman, MI (20-79) A-Ed, Ann; Band; Chor; Sch P; Bus Mgr, Sci C; Sftbl; Amer Leg A; COM.

OTTUSCH, Susan Helen
Bridgman HS; Bridgman, MI (15-70) Ann; NHS; Sci C; SC; Var C; Sal; Parsons Bus Sch; Med Secy.

OUE, Ross Akiyoshi
Kailua HS; Kailua, HI (12-683) Bsbl; U of Hawaii; Bus.

OUELLETTE, Cindy Lucille
Clyde HS; Clyde, KS (25%-35) Ann; Chldr; Chor; F-Ed, Sch P; SC; Tr; COM; Crisco A; HQn; Type A; Co-Cpt, Vlbl; Cloud Co Comm Col; Secy.

OUREN, Marianne Kay
Monte Vista HS; Monte Vista, CO (10%-111) Secy, 4H; Ed, Sch P; Ski C; Co-Cpt, Bkbl; Sftbl; 4H A; Masonic A.

OURSLAND, James Paul
Flathead HS; Kalispell, MT (10%-500) Band; Var C; Cr-Ctry; Tr.

OURSLAND, Mark David
Flathead HS; Kalispell, MT (20-600) JV, Bkbl; Tr; Sci A; Pres, Tn for Christ.

OUSLEY, Terry Edward
Dekalb HS; Waterloo, IN (236-340) Chor; Olivet Nazarene Col; Religion.

OUTLAND, Angela Yvonne
Liberty Christian Sch; Durham, NC (2-6) Ed, Ann; Co-Cpt, Chldr; Chor; Hmrm; Pres, SC; Bkbl; Co-Cpt, Vlbl; Christian Character A; Freewill Baptist Bible Col; Elem Ed.

OUTLAW, Kerry Lyn
Truman HS; Independence, MO; Chor; F-Ed, Sch P; Citz A; Hon Prog; Stephens Col; Journ.

OUTLAW, Pamela Louise
Broward Christian HS; Plantation, FL; Ann; Cpt, Chldr; Chor; Beauty; COM; Citz A; HCt; Hon Prog; Drill Tm; Palm Beach Atlantic Col; Christian Ed.

OUTLAW, Tammie Anita
Johnson Co HS; Wrightsville, GA; Ann; FHA; Ed, Sch P; Tri-HiY; Creative Writing A; Emmanuel Co Jr Col; Ed.

OUZOUNIAN, Sheri Joyce
University HS; Los Angeles, CA (21-900) Cum Laude Soc; NHS; SC; CSF; Hon Prog; Byron Holland Schol; Gold Seal Bearer; *UCLA.*

OVERALL, Mary Lisa
L C Anderson HS; Austin, TX (270-525) A Cap Choir; Chor; FHA; FTA; Madrigal; U Interscholastic League; Vocal Solo & Ensm Contest As; Most Outst Girl Camper; Lead, Musical; Young Life; *Abilene Christian U; Primary Ed.*

OVERALL, Michael Dean
Northeast HS; Okla City, OK; NHS; Bkbl; Ftbl; Citz A.

OVERBY, Ann Mears
Henry Sibley HS; W St Paul, MN; A Cap Choir; Band; Cpt, Chldr; Hmrm; Ski C; Tr; PTA A; Pres A; Yth Fel; Yth Foundation; Best Dressed; Dayton's Tn Board; *UMD; Art.*

OVERBY, Gay Michele
Lubbock Christian HS; Lubbock, TX; Band; Dbte Tm; GS; NFL; NHS; A-Ed, Sch P; WW; *Lubbock Christian Col; Pre-Med.*

OVERBYE, Mark David
Henry Sibley HS; W Saint Paul, MN (100-586) Fr C; Hmrm; Pres, Ski C; Hon Prog; I Dare You; Pres A; Yth Fel; MVP, Ski C; Pres, Scuba Diving; *U of Minn.*

OVERCASH, Lisa Dawn
Allen Jay HS; High Point, NC; Ann; BC; Fr C; Monogram; Sci C; SC; Bkbl; Tr; Marshal; *Sci.*

OVERDORF, James Rowland
Eden Sr HS; Eden, NY (10%-220) NHS; Ski C; Var C; Swim; Co Cpt, Vlbl; *Ariz St U; Eng.*

OVERFIELD, Diana Jean
Warren Western Reserve HS; Warren, OH (114-500) Band; Ensm; Ger C; Orch; Sftbl; Journ A; Sci A; *Nurs.*

OVERFIELD, Joy Clare
Northbrook Sr HS; Houston, TX; JV, Chldr; Chor; Ch, Hmrm; Sftbl; Swim; Tr; Outst Choir Mem; All Star Sftbl Player; *SW Tex Col.*

OVERFIELD, Richard Lee
Warren Western Reserve HS; Warren, OH (74-493) A Cap Choir; Band; Chor; Ensm; Ger C; InterClub Coun; Orch; Bkbl; Sftbl; COM; *Tenn Temple Col; Acct.*

OVERLIE, Denise Joyce
Lutheran HS Mayer; Mayer, MN (6-71) Band; Chor; Drama; FHA; Mus A's; *U of Minn; Food Industry.*

OVERLY, Tonya Sue
Wilmington HS; Wilmington, OH (70-305) Band; Cpt, Chldr; Ensm; Fr C; 4H; Cpt, Mjrte; Sch P; Pres, SC; Ftbl; Sftbl; COM; Math A; Yth Fel; Qn, Yth Group; *Columbus Bus Col; Secy.*

OVERMANN, Deborah Ann
Thomas Jefferson Sr HS; Cedar Rapids, IA (31-609) Chor; Drama; JV, Bkbl; JV, Cr-Ctry; Golf; *Iowa St U; Engr.*

OVERMEYER, Patricia Jane
Columbia HS; Columbia, PA (9-171) Mgr, Bkbl; JV, Hockey; *Math.*

OVERSTREET, Jill Marie
Everett HS; Everett, WA (33%-280) Ann; Dbte Tm; GS; Hmrm; Rptr, Sch P; Secy, SC; Semi-Fin, JA A; Exchange Stu to Japan; Exchange C Girl o-t Mo; Pres, UMY; *Wash St U; Hist.*

OVERTON, Albert Daniel III
Lindbergh Sr HS; St Louis, MO (200-1000) A Cap Choir; Chem C; Ensm; Madrigal; Orch; Rptr, Sch P; Mgr, Tr; God & Country A; *U of Mo; Engr.*

OVERTON, Jeff Alan
Crystal Lake Comm HS; Crystal Lake, IL (1-613) Band; Ensm; 4H; NHS; 4H A; Hon Prog; Marching Band; 1st Pl, Park Dist Free Throw Con; *Engr.*

OVERTON, Kimberly Jo
Jefferson Davis HS; Montgomery, AL (53-752) Math C; Mu Alpha Theta; NHS; Span C; Span NHS; *Auburn U; Fashion Merchandising.*

OVERTON, Priscilla Ann
Sanford Central HS; Sanford, NC (73-350) FHA; Elk A; Most Out; Bus Driver; Pres, VICA C; Fin, NC Federation, Woman's C; Hon Men, Bette Elliott, Sew Cont; *NC Central U; Early Childhood Ed.*

OVERTON, Sherri Neese
St Helena HS; Greensburg, LA (7-53) Chor; FHA; Ch, 4H; Hmrm; Mod Mus Mas; Sci C; Bio A; COM; 4H A; HCt; Hon Prog; OALL; Lib C; Bookkeeping A; Best Dressed A; *Sou U; Acct.*

OVERTON, Teresa Lynn
John A Holmes HS; Edenton, NC (20-135) Chldr; Chor; Ensm; Pres, FHA; Mod Mus Mas; Monogram; Sports-Ed, Ann; Chldr A; Candystriper A; Phys Fitness A; *E Carolina U; Nurs.*

OVERTON, Teresa Mae
N Daviess Jr And Sr HS; Elnora, IN (6-100) Type A; Shorthand, Filing, A's; *Lincoln Christian Col; Christian Ed.*

OVERY, Mary Vivian
Amer Heritage Christian Sch; Hayward, CA; Sftbl; CSF; Citz A; DAR A; *Vet.*

OWCZARCZAK, Cynthia Ann
Villa Maria Acad; Buffalo, NY; Mgr, Band; Fin, Jr Miss Pagent; Lat C; NHS; SC; COM; 2nd & 3rd Prize, Polish Arts C; Citations, Mercy Hospital; WW; *U of Buffalo; Pre-Med.*

OWEN, Archibald Alexander
Penncrest HS; Media, PA (20-463) Chor; Mu Alpha Theta; NHS; Co-Cpt, Ftbl; Tr; Hon Prog; *Engr.*

OWEN, Carter Brown
Penncrest HS; Media, PA (40-450) Swim; Math A; Yth Fel; *Chem Engr.*

OWEN, Catherine Viola
Edwin G Foreman HS; Chicago, IL (13-373) Key C; S-T, Mu Alpha Theta; Hon Prog; St Scholar; *Loyola U; Biol.*

OWEN, Christopher Lee
Andrew Lewis HS; Salem, VA (40-300) BC; Golf; Hockey; *U of Va; Engr.*

OWEN, Cylia Cyd
Pleasanton HS; Pleasanton, TX (5-150) Co-Ed, Ann; Band; Fr C; FHA; FTA; VP, NHS; Orch; SC; Var C; Pres, Sr Cl; Pres, Jr Cl; MVP, Golf; Citz A; Eng A; Co Band A; Ntl Mus Guild; *Baylor U; Bio.*

OWEN, Cynthia Leigh
Bluestone Sr HS; Skipwith, VA; BC; Fr C; Pres, FHA; Monogram; SC; Bkbl; Sftbl; COM; Yth Fel; Acteens.

OWEN, Dayna Mary
Plainview HS; Plainview, TX (75-350) A Cap Choir; F-Ed, Ann; Band; Bus C; Hmrm; SC; Tr; Outst Band; *Baylor U; Spch Therapy.*

OWEN, Frances Kathryn
W Mecklenburg HS; Charlotte, NC (20%-352) InterAct C; Ski C; *U of NC at Char.*

OWEN, Glenn Paul
Abilene HS; Abilene, TX; Chor; Hmrm; NHS; Mgr, Bkbl; Mgr, Ftbl; Mgr, Tr; Amer Leg A; COM; Hon Prog; Opt A; *Abilene Christian U; Med.*

OWEN, Gloria Louise
Harrisburg Union HS; Harrisburg, OR (9-47) Chor; Drama; Ensm; Pres, Fr C; Rptr, FHA; 4H; NHS; Pres, Span C; Secy, Sr Cl; Tr; Vocal Jazz Choir; St Mus Teacher's Assn; Fin, Annual Spelling Contest; Tr A; *Walla Walla Col; Nurs.*

OWEN, Jill Dianne
Fargo N HS; Fargo, ND (4-397) Band; NHS; Orch; COM; Citz A; 4H A; Yth Fel; Church Choir; *U of ND; Med.*

OWEN, Kathy Louise
Emerson HS; Emerson, AR (2-28) VP, Bus C; Chor; Pres, FHA; Mgr, Bkbl; Tnns; COM; Hon Prog; Rptr, FHA; Eng A; *Sou Ark U; Mus.*

OWEN, Lee Ann
Westminster HS; Westminster, SC; Band; Fr C; Sch P; MVP, Bkbl; *Clemson U; Phar.*

OWEN, Lou Ann
Dubach HS; Dubach, LA (5%-46) Ann; Band; Rptr, FBLA; Rptr, 4H; Lit Ral; Sci C; Pres, Soph Cl; Mgr, Bkbl; Cl Fav; Poet A; *LSU; Pol Sci.*

OWEN, Mark Douglas
U S Grant HS; Portland, OR (5-386) Chess C; Tres, NHS; Bausch & Lomb A; H of F; Hon Prog; Math A; Opt A; St Scholar; Yth Fel; MVP, Gym; City Champion, Gym; Outst Sr Draftsman; Stu in Govt; *U of Wash; Engr.*

OWEN, Martha Jean
Central Davidson Sr HS; Lexington, NC (15-218) Ann; FHA; Monogram; NHS; Mgr, Bkbl; Sftbl; Yth Fel; *Cabarrus Mem Hospital; Nurs.*

OWEN, Mary Frances
Holy Rosary Acad; Louisville, KY (4-96) Ann; NHS; Pol Sci C; A-Ed, Sch P; JV, Bkbl; Sftbl; Tr; COM; Hon Prog; Ntl Sci Found; NEDT; WW; *Sci.*

OWEN, Mary Margaret
Dubach HS; Dubach, LA (1-35) Band; Pres, Fr C; VP, FBLA; FHA; VP, 4H; Lit Ral; Model UN; Ed, Sch P; S-T, Sci C; Pres, Sr Cl; Pres, Jr Cl; Pres, Soph Cl; Cpt, Bpbl; COM; Cl Fav; 4H A; MLS; Poet A; Pres A; Val; All Dist Bkbl; Most Courteous; Gold 'D' Service A; *LSU; Pre-Med.*

OWEN, Michael David
Marion HS; Marion, IN (175-706) NHS; *Marion Col.*

OWEN, Nancy Ann
Choctaw Co HS; Butler, AL (2-168) Band; Chor; Ensm; FHA; 4H; NHS; Sci C; Beauty; 4H A; Hon Prog; Phy A; Sci A; *Auburn U; Acct.*

OWEN, Patricia Jean
Telstar Regional HS; Bethel, ME; Band; NHS; Bkbl; Sftbl.

OWEN, Randel Glenn
Abilene HS; Abilene, TX (40-525) Chess C; Ger C; Key C; Lat C; NHS; SC; Soccer; Sftbl; Tnns; Hon Prog; *Abilene Christian U; Acct.*

OWEN, Steven Keith
George Washington Carver HS; Montgomery, AL (6-400) Chess C; Chor; Drama; Ensm; Hmrm; Pres, Math C; Ch, Mu Alpha Theta; VP, NHS; Order/Arrow; Sch Achieve Tm; Rptr, Sch P; Sci C; Sftbl; Math A; Order/Arrow A; ARC A; ROTC A; Eagle Sct; Church Yth Pastor; ROTC Saber Day Spch; *Auburn U; Engr.*

OWEN, Susan Michelle
Reeds Spring HS; Reeds Spring, MO (25%-90) AFS; Chldr; Drama; Sci C; Span C; Var C; Pres, Jr Cl; Bkbl; Sftbl; Tr; Citz A; HCt; Math A; *SMSU; Ed.*

OWEN, Terri Lea
Winnebago HS; Winnebago, MN; A Cap Choir; All Amer Yth; Chor; Commercial C; Ger C; ARC; VP, Jr Cl; Bkbl; Sftbl; Swim; Tnns; Type A; Yth Fel; *Austin Jr Col; Nurs.*

OWEN, Thomas Clifford
Savannah Ctry Day Sch; Savannah, GA (10%-70) Tres, Bus C; Chor; Order/Arrow; Ski C; SC; Bkbl; Cr-Ctry; Cpt, Tr; Eagle Sct; *Ga Tech; Industrial Mgt.*

OWEN, Virginia Cheryl
Breckinridge Co HS; Harned, KY (7-200) Band; FTA; 4H; Math C; NHS; Rainbow; Sci C; Tres, Sr Cl; Mgr, Ftbl; 4H A; St Grand Tres, Rainbow Girls; *U of Louisville; Pre-Med.*

OWEN, William Conally
Eastern Guilford HS; Gibsonville, NC (1-164) Ann; Fr C; French NHS; Pres, Monogram; NHS; Order/Arrow; Sci C; SC; Co-Cpt, Ftbl; Math A; Marshal; Nom, Morehead Schol; *U of NC; Math.*

OWENS, Antwinette Lynn
West Side Sr HS; Gary, IN (16-686) A Cap Choir; Chor; Ensm; Fr C; Lat C; Madrigal; Secy, NHS; VP, Sr Cl; Citz A; Hon Prog; Yth Fel; Best Personality; *Mich St U; Nurs.*

OWENS, Betty Carol
Pearl HS; Nashville, TN; Chldr; Sftbl; JA A; *Middle Tenn St U; Teacher.*

OWENS, Celeste Louise
West Side HS; Gary, IN; Chor; Span C; Y-Tns; VP, Soph Cl; Mus Achv A; JNHS; Schol As.

OWENS, Charles William
Fairhope HS; Fairhope, AL (33-365) Band; Key C; NHS; Superior, Drum Major; *S Ala Col; Sci.*

OWENS, Cheryl Annette
Carlisle Sr HS; Carlisle, PA (40%-500) A Cap Choir; Pres, FTA; Mgr, Bkbl; JV, Hockey; Tr; Computor Prog.

OWENS, David Thomas
Mineral Wells HS; Mineral Wells, TX (31-210) Chem C; Drama; NHS; VP, Order/Arrow; Phys C; Pres, Span C; Pres, Span NHS; Mgr, Bkbl; Ftbl; Tr; Order/Arrow A; Eagle Sct; Angeleo St U; Bio.

OWENS, Donna Marie
Liberty Christian Sch; Durham, NC (1-4) A Cap Choir; Ann; Chldr; Chor; Ensm; Ed, Sch P; Vlbl; Freewill Baptist Bible Col; Christian Ed.

OWENS, Gerald Francis
Frankfort HS; Ridgeley, WV (25%-151) NHS; Var C; Ftbl.

OWENS, Gerald Travis
Texas City HS; Texas City, TX (42-472) Band; Hist A; Baylor U; Hist.

OWENS, Gina Renee
Central HS; Thomasville, GA; Chldr; Drama; Tri-HiY; Bsbl; Bkbl; Sftbl; Pres A; Pres, Fresh Cl; Bsbl & Sftbl Scorekeeper; Phys Ed.

OWENS, Glenn William
E J Wilson HS; Spencerport, NY (10%-300) A Cap Choir; Band; Parl, BS; Chor; Drama; Fr C; Madrigal; Math C; Model UN; NHS; Order/Arrow; Swim; Order/Arrow A; Eagle Sct; Hope Col; Computer Sci.

OWENS, Greg
Central HS; Minneapolis, MN (48-400) Band; Hmrm; SC; Semi-Fin, Soph Cl; Bsbl; Cpt, Bkbl; Ftbl; Citz A; Cl Fav; H of F; HCt; MLS; Most Out; Yth Fel; Drum Major; Most Promising, Bkbl; MVP, Bkbl; Snowdays Ct; Mgr, Bkbl; Ath Camp Schol; Pres, Drum & Bugle Corps; Engr.

OWENS, Greg A
ElDorado HS; El Dorado, AR (20%-457) Bus Mgr, Hmrm; COM; Sr Steering Committee; Sou Ark U.

OWENS, Gregory Alan
El Dorado HS; El Dorado, AR (20%-357) Bkbl; VICCA C; Sr Steering C; Southern Ark U; Elec.

OWENS, Gwendolyn Aletha
Redford HS; Detroit, MI; Cpt, Bkbl; Tr; ROTC A.

OWENS, Hugh Thomas
Eau Gallie HS; Melbourne, FL (1-650) Band; BS; VP, Math C; VP, Mu Alpha Theta; NHS; Orch; Golf; Alg A; COM; Hon Prog; Math A; NMS; U of Fla; Math.

OWENS, Janet Lynn
Winyah HS; Georgetown, SC; Ann; Chldr; Chor; Ensm; Rptr, 4H; Span C; VP, Sr Cl; Cl Fav; HCt; Col of Charleston; Psych.

OWENS, Janette Catheleen
Hudson Sr HS; Hudson, WI (30-250) AFS; Drama; Ed, Sch P; Span C; Bus Achv A.

OWENS, John Charles
Wyoming Valley HS; Kingston, PA (10%-550) Chor; NHS; Math A; Sci A; Penn St U; Elec Engr.

OWENS, Joseph Paul
Butler Area Sch; Butler, PA (3%-1000) Demolay; Ger C; Hmrm; NHS; SC; Ftbl; Tr; DARGCA; Law.

OWENS, Judi Jo
Cheyenne Mountain HS; Colorado Springs, CO (100-683) Tr; Sci A; Sci School; Powder Puff Ftbl; 1980 Olympics; Figure Skating; Colorado Col; Sci.

OWENS, Karen June
David H Hickman HS; Columbia, MO (54-566) Chor; Secy, FHA; Type A; Kewpie C, Pep Sq; Burge Sch of Nurs; Nurs.

OWENS, Kathy Lynn
Midfield HS; Midfield, AL; FHA; 4H; Hmrm; Jr Miss Pagent; Yth Fel; 4H A; Miss Reflection; Sou Jr Col of Bus; Bus Adm.

OWENS, Lisa Lynn
Clear Creek HS; League City, TX (25%-635) Hmrm; NHS; Professional Service.

OWENS, Marilyn Denise
Marvell HS; Marvell, AR (8-120) Chldr; FBLA; FHA; Spch C; Thes; WW; U of Ark; Bus Adm.

OWENS, Mark Anthony
Central HS; Philadelphia, PA; Barnewell A; 1st Cl BSct; Med.

OWENS, Melanie Denise
Bowling Green Sr HS; Bowling Green, KY (95-360) Band; Bkbl; Sftbl; Sci A; Variety Stor Manual, Eng, A's; DECA Swtht Court; U of Ky; Phys Therapist.

OWENS, Michelle
Adlai E Stevenson HS; Bronx, NY; NHS; Hon Prog; Amer Assn of Teachers of Span; Upsala Col; Math.

OWENS, Michelle Ranae
Don Bosco HS; Gilbertville, IA (11-69) Cpt, Chldr; Chor; Ensm; Hmrm; NHS; Sch P; Secy, SC; Swim; Hon Prog; U of N Iowa; Med.

OWENS, Omega Lynn
Fairfield HS; Fairfield, AL (25%-184) Bkbl; Tr; Swim A; Nurs.

OWENS, Rebecca Prinetta
Sheffield HS; Sheffield, AL; Chldr; Span C; Sftbl; U of Ala; Med.

OWENS, Regina Karol
Inglewood HS; Inglewood, CA; Cpt, Chldr; Chor; Hmrm; Madrigal; SC; Pres, Soph Cl; Tr; CSF; COM; Citz A; Hon Prog; MLS; Most Out; Drill Tm; Merit Roll; UCLA; Math.

OWENS, Renee
Kettering Sr HS; Detroit, MI;

OWENS, Robin Kimberly
Ware Shoals HS; Ware Shoals, SC (15-111) Band; BC; Sci C; Span C; Sftbl; Hon Prog; Band A; U of SC; Pol Sci.

OWENS, Ronda Marie
Abilene HS; Abilene, TX; Bus C; Drama; FHA; Sci C; COM; Cisco Jr Col; Bus Adm.

OWENS, Samuel Venoy
Bluefield HS; Bluefield, WV (15-350) Band; Chor; Ensm; Hmrm; Lat C; NHS; JV, Bkbl; Golf; Aux Lat; COM; Hon Prog; Math A; Sci A; Choir, Band, Creative Writing, A's; VPI; Engr.

OWENS, Shari Lee
Dana Hills HS; Dana Hills, CA; COM; Yth Fel; Co Ed, Church Paper; Del, Yth Convo Camp Coun; Yth Leadership Training; Del, Yth Rally; Calif Lutheran Col; Interior Design.

OWENS, Sterling David
Howe Military Sch; Howe, IN; Var C; Bkbl; Ftbl.

OWENS, Susan Elizabeth
Tartan HS; Oakdale, MN (3-430) Chldr; Chor; NHS; Ski C; Tnns; Hon Prog; Math A; Sci A; Summa Cum Laude; Moorhead St Col; Math.

OWENS, Tamara Leigh
Central HS; Thomasville, GA (8-250) Semi-Fin, Jr Miss Pa; NHSt; A-Ed, Sch P; Pres, Tri-HiY; Var C; Mgr, Bsbl; Bkbl; COM; Cl Fav; Gov Honor Prog; Hon Prog; Abraham Baldwin Agr Col; Architecture.

OWENS, Toni Mirianda
F O Alexander HS; Starkville, MS (10-59) Y-Tns; Pres, Soph Cl; Tr; Hon Prog; Soph Cl Qn; Miss St U; Social Work.

OWENS, Twyman Rene
Miami Northwestern Sr HS; Miami, FL (4-387) Key C; NHS; Sci C; Bkbl; Cr-Ctry; Swim; Citz A; Hist A; Hon Prog; Kiwanis A; Math A; Ntl Sci Symposium; Sci A; Best All Around; Principals HR; Morehouse Col; Med Research.

OWENS, Valerie Layne
Georgetown HS; Georgetown, TX (8-157) Ed, Ann; 4H; NHS; Span C; SC; Tr; NMF; Opt A; Span A; UIL Shorthand A; WW; Tex A&M U; Vet Med.

OWENS, Vara Helene
Seventy-First HS; Fayetteville, NC (486-786) Bus C; FHA; Span C; Y-Tns; Pep C; Fayetteville St Col; Ed.

OWENS, Yvonne Denise
Northern Chester Co Tech; Phoenixville, PA (10%-132) Hon Prog.

OWENSON, Annette Myrtle
S Hamilton HS; Jewell, IA (8-92) Ann; Chor; Madrigal; Math C; Model UN; Iowa Methodist Sch of Nurs; Nurs.

OWINGS, Lynette Cecelia
Herndon HS; Herndon, VA; Span C; Span NHS.

OWNBY, Melissa Gay
Sevier Co HS; Sevierville, TN; AFS; Ann; Band; BC; Ensm; Fr C; Orch; Tn Board; Win, Talent Show; Win, Piano Audition; U of Tenn; Mus.

OWNBY, William Vaden
Wichita SE HS; Wichita, KS (70-675) A Cap Choir; Chor; Ensm; Sch Achieve Tm; Var C; Co-Cpt, Ftbl; HKg; Hon Prog; All City, All St, Ftbl; Butler Co Jr Col; Public Relations.

OXE, Karla Lynn
Helux HS; La Mesa, CA (1-500) Hmrm; Y-Tns; CSF; PTA A; Val; Bartlesville Wesleyan Col; Ed.

OXENDINE, Darlene
R B Stall HS; Charleston, SC (1-230) Ensm; FHA; FTA; Hmrm; NHS; Span C; SC; JV, Bkbl; MVP, Sftbl; Gov Honor Prog; Gr Marshal; Hon Prog; Secy, Pep C; Vlbl Tm; WW; Med U of SC; Psych.

OXENDINE, Gail Adrienne
Cass Technical; Detroit, MI; Fr C; Hmrm; SC; Dance Workshop; Bus Adm.

OXFORD, Hazel Gay
W Monroe HS; W Monroe, LA; Chor; FHA; 4H; Pres, Hmrm; SC; Thes; Y-Tns; Bkbl; Golf; Sftbl; Tnns; Most Out; Yth Fel; Yth Foundation; Drill Tm; Outst Phys Ed Stu; Swim A; Jr Cl Rep; All St Swim; Secy, Church Yth Group; Cpt, AAU Swim Tm.

OXFORD, Judy Ann
Fairview HS; Fairview, TN (2-75) Band; Rptr, BC; Chor; Hmrm; Orch; Ed, Sch P; MLS; Sal; Ntl Defense A; Mary T Anderson Eng A; Band A; Belmont Col; Mus.

OXFORD, Laura Sue
Rossville Comp HS; Rossville, GA (5-212) BC; Pres, FBLA; SC; COM; NEDT; Type A; Eng A; 1st Pl, Typing Olympics; 2nd Pl, Shorthand Olympics; Berry Col School Bowl Tms; Bus Adm.

OXLEY, Anthony Franklin
Stephens Co HS; Toccoa, GA (20%-258) Cpt, Ftbl; Tr; Wrest; Ftbl & Tr Ltrs; FCA; WW; Scholastic Schol; Piedmont Col; Industrial Mgt.

OYAMA, Oliver Neal
Melbourne HS; Melbourne, FL (10%-668) Chor; Ensm; VP, Ger C; InterClub Coun; ARC; COM; Math A; U of Fla; Med.

OZAWA, Janine Emiko
Sacramento Union Acad; Sacramento, CA (4-48) Chor; VP, Madrigal; NHS; Rptr, Sch P; Ski C; Pres, Sr Cl; VP, Jr Cl; Pres, Soph Cl; Bsbl; Soccer; Sftbl; Tnns; Tr; Bank Of Amer A; Citz A; Hon Prog; Type A; Princess, Courtesy Qn Court; Pacific Union Col; Secondary Ed.

OZBUN, Candy Marita
Roswell HS; Roswell, NM (15-500) Band; Chor; NHS; Med Tech.

OZBUN, Cathy Marina
Roswell HS; Roswell, NM (85-325) Band; Chor; Ensm; Bach A; WW; 'Up with People'; NM St U; Mus.

OZIAS, Arlene Hope
Monta Vista HS; Cupertino, CA (135-552) Chor; CSF; DeAnza Col; Nursery Sch Ed.

OZIER, Ella Mae
Sullivan HS; Sullivan, IL (1-118) Dbte Tm; Pres, FHA; FTA; Pres, 4H; NHS; Sci C; Bkbl; St Scholar; Val; Pom Pom; WW; Church Yth; VP, S-T, FHA, 4-HC; U of Ill; Commerce.

OZIMA, Roger Yoshio
Albert G Lane Tech HS; Chicago, IL (30-1376) Chess C; NHS; Hon Prog; NMS; Service Ltr; Ill Inst of Tech; Engr.

OZMENT, Cynthia Frances
Hermitage HS; Hermitage, AR (1-55) BC; Chor; Dbte Tm; Drama; Ensm; Secy, FHA; 4H; Math C; Span C; Alg A; Math A; Val; Choral A; Bicentennial Essay A; U of Ark at Monticello; Math Ed.

OZMORE, Jeanne Lee
Nottoway Sr HS; Nottoway, VA (25-240) Ann; Chor; Hmrm; NHS; Sci C; Span C; SC; Pres A; Sci A; Yth Fel; Hist, FHA.

P

PAAOAO, Mary Kehaulani
Kailua HS; Kailua, HI; FBLA; Hmrm; InterClub Coun; NHS; SC; Tr; COM; *Moody Bible Inst; Christian Ed.*

PAAP, Kevin Donald
Wellcome Mem HS; Garden City, MN (12-48) Pres, FFA; SC; Var C; Ch, Jr Cl; Secy, Soph Cl; Mgr, Bkbl; Mgr, Ftbl; Funk's Seed Interntl A; *U of Minn; Agr Production.*

PACAK, Pamela Marie
Monessen HS; Monessen, PA (42-230) Band; Chor; Ensm; FNA; Mjrte; NFL; NHS; Bus Mgr, Sch P; Ski C; Secy, Sr Cl; Secy, Jr Cl; Secy, Soph Cl; Citz A; Hon Prog; Westmoreland Co Chor; Ed, Yrbk; Co Band; 1st Alt, Amer Leg A; Dist Band; Cand, Sch Highest A; St Band; *Washington Sch of Nurs; Nurs.*

PACCIORINI, Susan Marie
Notre Dame HS; Salinas, CA (25-94) NHS; Span C; SC; Pres, Jr Cl; Bkbl; *Gavilan Col.*

PACE, Audrey McCormick
Wade Hampton Acad; Orangeburg, SC (10-80) Chor; GS; Fin, Jr Miss Pagent; Span C; Spch A; Yth Fel; Jr Amer Legion Auxilary; Cotillion C; HR; *Col of Charleston; Acct.*

PACE, Corinne Lee
Old Forge HS; Old Forge, PA (10-134) A Cap Choir; Drama; NHS; Ski C; Span C; Chem A; Hon Prog; *Wilkes Col; Med Tech.*

PACE, Donna Marie
Landrum HS; Landrum, SC (25%-56) Ann; BC; S-T, FBLA; FHA; Sch P; Gr Marshal; Type A; Shorthand, Phys Ed, Acct, A's; WW; *Spartanburg Tech Col; Secy Sci.*

PACE, Eddie Nathaniel
Smiths Station HS; Smiths, AL (1-148) F-Ed, Ann; BC; BS; Secy, Key C; Mu Alpha Theta; Rptr, Sch P; Pres, Sci C; Pres, SC; Alg A; Cl Fav; Val; *U of Ala; Chem.*

PACE, Esca Howard
Jackson HS; Jackson, GA (10-180) BC; Chor; Ensm; Hmrm; Key C; NHS; SC; Bsbl; JV, Bkbl; Ftbl; Tnns; COM; Hon Prog; Yth Fel; Drafting A; Most Improved, Tnns; *Ga Tech; Textiles.*

PACE, James Russell
Monticello HS; Monticello, MS; BC; Secy, FFA; 4H; Hmrm; Order/Arrow; A-Ed, Sch P; SC; COM; Hist A; Sci A; *Miss St U; Med.*

PACE, Leighea Mae
Bentonia HS; Bentonia, MS (2-52) Chor; Cpt, Dbte Tm; FHA; Y-Tns; Bkbl; Sftbl; COM; Hon Prog; Cert of Attendance; Cert of Achievement; *Hinds Jr Col; Lab Technician.*

PACE, Marinell
Gainesville HS; Gainesville, TX (4-200) Band; Pres, Fr C; NHS; Orch; Sch P; NEDT; Most Outst Fr Stu; *U of Tex; Pol Sci.*

PACE, Nancy Gail
Wm Mason HS; Mason, OH (35-180) Band; Drama; Tres, Fr C; FHA; FTA; Fin, Jr Miss Pagent; NHS; Rainbow; Sch P; COM; Sci A; Writing A; *Ohio St U; Radiology.*

PACE, Oscar Harold Jr
Benhaven HS; Olivia, NC; BC; FFA; Hmrm; Tres, Monogram; SC; Pres, Soph Cl; Bsbl; Mgr, Bkbl; Ftbl; Hist A; Band, Eng, Ath, A's; *U of NC; Law.*

PACE, Teresa Irene
Wm Mason HS; Mason, OH; Band; Fr C; Sci C; Tr; Amer Leg A; COM; Citz A; Ntl Achv Schol; *Ohio St U; Med.*

PACE, Valerie Ann
Chester HS; Chester, PA; 4H; Tnns.

PACE, Wayne Edward
North HS; Columbus, OH (200-450) Cr-Ctry; Ftbl; Cpt, Tr; *Bowling Green St U; Audio Visual Tech.*

PACELEY, Peter Johnson
J O Johnson HS; Huntsville, AL; Ger C; Sch P; Hon Prog; *Vanderbilt U; Chem Engr.*

PACHECO, Helida Blanca
Eastside HS; Paterson, NJ (8-519) Hmrm; NHS; VP, SC; Bus A; Hon Achv Sch Schol Cert; *Seton Hall U; Pre-Law.*

PACHECO, John Gilbert
Salpointe Cath HS; Tucson, AZ (66-170) All Amer Yth; CYO; Order/Arrow; Sci C; Span C; Var C; Y-Tns; JV, Bsbl; JV, Ftbl; Cpt, Swim; Cpt, Wrest; COM; Elk A; Order/Arrow A; Sci A; Sct of Yr; Silver Palm Eagle Sct As; Hiking As; Ad Altare Dei; *Vet Sci.*

PACHECO, Miranda
Hebrew Acad of Nassau Co; Uniondale, NY (4-26) Drama; NHS; Val; Fr A; NY Sch Mus Assn Festival; Ed, Yrbk; *Brandeis Col; Eng.*

PACHECO, Norma
Notre Dame HS; Caguas, PR (9-128) NHS; Tres, Jr Cl; Alg A; COM; Cl Fav; Math A; JA; Art A; Ath A; *Executive Secy.*

PACHECO, Robert James
St Raphael Acad; Pawtucket, RI (13-130) NHS; Secy, Span NHS; Ftbl; Hon Prog; *U of Notre Dame; Math.*

PACIOREK, James Joseph
St Mary's Prep; Orchard Lake, MI (3-32) NHS; Bsbl; Cpt, Bkbl; Co-Cpt, Ftbl; Tr; Hon Prog; Magna Cum Laude; MLS; MVP, Bkbl; MVP, Ftbl; Ath Schol A; Cl VP; *Business.*

PACK, Belinda June
W Morgan HS; Trinity, AL (4-60) F-Ed, Ann; BC; FHA; Bio A; Mgr, Vlbl; Eng A; WW; *Tenn Temple Col; Art.*

PACK, Kimberly Dru
Sharpstown Sr HS; Houston, TX (192-700) Key C; NHS; Secy, Span C; Type A; *Abilene Christian U; Elem Ed.*

PACK, Sherry Lynn
Vian HS; Vian, OK (10-83) A-Ed, Ann; Band; Chldr; FHA; Cpt, Mjrte; Rptr, SC; Yth Fel; Band Princess; St Hon Soc; Jr Play; *NE Okla St U.*

PACKARD, Julianne Elaine
W Albany HS; Albany, OR (75-300) A Cap Choir; Band; Ensm; FBLA; *Liberty Baptist Col; Mus.*

PACKARD, Marc David
Telstar Regional HS; Bethel, ME (10%-87) Drama; Math C; Mgr, Cr-Ctry; Alg A; Math A; Sci A; *Oral Roberts U; Acct.*

PACKER, Charles Henry Jr
Austintown Fitch HS; Austintown, OH (229-675) Arch; Band; Dbte Tm; Order/Arrow; ARC; Spch C; Arch; Bsbl; Sftbl; Swim; Order/Arrow A; Eagle Sct A; *Youngstown St U; Bus.*

PACKER, Lance Kem
Sky View HS; Smithfield, UT (11-622) Bsbl; Bkbl; Ftbl; Schol A's.

PACKER, Lynda
Christian Sch; Mesquite, TX (5-42) Ann; Chldr; Drama; FHA; NHS; SC; *Abilene Christian U; Interior Design.*

PACKER, Timothy Joseph
Austintown Fitch HS; Youngstown, OH; Band; Order/Arrow; Sftbl; Swim; Order/Arrow A; *Youngstown St U; Bio.*

PACKER, William
Andrew Jackson HS; Los Angeles, CA;

PACKER, William Joseph
Whitman-Hanson Regional HS; Whitman, MA (10-324) Math C; NHS; *SE Mass U; Biol.*

PACOCHA, Marion Thomas
Thomas Kelly HS; Chicago, IL (5-676) NHS; VP, Span NHS; Bsbl; Journ A; NEDT; Q&S A; *IIT; Elec Engr.*

PACOT, Cynthia Parreno
Auburn HS; Auburn, NE; Band; Math C; Sci C; Span C; *U of Nebr; Bus Adm.*

PADDEN, Eileen Marie
St Louis de Marillac HS; Northfield, IL (12-222) A-Ed, Lit Mag; NHS; A-Ed, Sch P; SC; COM; Hon Prog; Ntl Scholastic Art A; *Marquette U; Journ.*

PADELETTI, Teresa Patricia
Bishop Klonowski HS; Scranton, PA; Chldr; Chor; NHS; Hon Prog; Math A; *Social Work.*

PADEN, Sandy Kay
Shannon HS; Shannon, MS; JETS; Rptr, Sch P; *Itawamba Jr Col; Bus.*

PADGETT, Alvin Broadus
Aiken HS; Aiken, SC; Ann; Band; Chor; Community Yth Symph; Ensm; VP, 4H; Co-Ch, Hmrm; Orch; SC; Var C; Bsbl; Mgr, Bkbl; Ftbl; Sftbl; Swim; Tnns; Citz A; 4H A; Phy A; Sci A; Yth Fel; Young Life; All St Band & Orch; *Mus.*

PADGETT, Bradley Kent
Washington HS; Washington, KS (7-45) SC; Arch; Bsbl; Bkbl; Cr-Ctry; JV, Ftbl; Swim; Tr; ARC A; Type A; HR; Life Guard; *U of Kans; Bus.*

PADGETT,
Catherine Sara Marie
Thomas Edison HS; Elmira Heights, NY (75-150) Chor; FHA; World Affairs C; Bkbl; *Elmira Bus Inst; Bus.*

PADGETT, Charles Francis
Loogootee Comm HS; Loogootee, IN (21-113) Pres, 4H; VP, Sci C; Span C; 4H A; 4-H Ldrship Trophy; *Purdue U; Engr.*

PADGETT, Melva Jahnette
Watauga HS; Boone, NC; Chor; Ensm; VP, Fr C; FTA; Hmrm; Jr Miss Pagent; NHS; SC; Hon Prog; *U of NC at Greensboro; Psych.*

PADGETT, Robert James
New Albany HS; New Albany, IN; Band; Demolay; Mgr, Bsbl; Ftbl; Tr; Wrest; *Engr.*

PADGETT, Roger Brent
Marysville-Pilchuck HS; Marysville, WA (20-380) Ger C; Hmrm; NHS; Phys C; Var C; Cpt, Bsbl; Bkbl; Ftbl; Hon Prog; JA A; Jr Chamber of Com A; *W Wash Col; Computer Sci.*

PADGETT, Russell Edwin
Saluda HS; Saluda, SC (10%-150) BC; Bsbl; Ftbl; Var Ltrman, Ftbl & Bsbl; Bus Driver's C; Furman, Wofford, Scholar; *Furman U; Bus Adm.*

PADGITT, Karen Denise
Arlington HS; Arlington Heights, IL (79-575) Chor; Dbte Tm; Ger C; Mod Mus Mas; Secy, NFL; Rptr, Sch P; St Stu Congress; Hon Prog; Yth Leg; Nom, NOTE A; Hospital Service A; Foreign Lang A; *U of Ill; Communications.*

PADILLA, Ivelisse
Luis Munoz Marin HS; Cabo Rojo, PR (1-150) Chldr; 4H; VP, Hmrm; COM; Hon Prog; Masonic A; *Recinto Universitario Mayaguez; Biologia.*

PADILLA, Manuel
Jose de Diego HS; Mayaguez, PR; Math C; Sci C; Bsbl; Bkbl; COM; Cl Fav; Magna Cum Laude; Sci A.

PADILLO, Gabriel Paul
Broadview Acad; La Fox, IL (20-77) Co-Ch, A Cap Choir; Co-Ch, Chor; Ch, Ensm; Hmrm; Co-Ch, Madrigal; Ski C; SC; Journ A; Most Musical; Frederic Chopin Piano A; *Columbia Union Col; Mus Ed.*

PADIN, Iris Nereida
Dr Pedro P Fajardo Voc HS; Mayaguez, PR; Math A; Hon Medal; Span A; *Arts.*

PADRNOS, Thomas Stuart
Boulder HS; Boulder, CO (60-600) CYO; Monogram; Span C; Var C; Bkbl; Cr-Ctry; Tr; Span, Eng, A's.

PADWICK, Jane
Kohala HS; Kapaau, HI (2-68) Secy, AFS; SC; Tres, Soph Cl; HCt; Dr Michael Padwick A; *Stanford U; Math.*

PAFFENBARGER, John Andrew
Monroe-Woodbury Sr HS; Central Valley, NY (1-417) Hmrm; Tres, Lit Mag; Math C; Pres, NHS; Soccer; COM; Hon Prog; Math A; MLS; NMS; NEDT; Phy A; Regent Schol; Val; Yth Fel; Span As; *Sci.*

PAFFHAUSEN, James Vernon
La Jolla HS; La Jolla, CA (17-480) Hmrm; Tres, Key C; Ed, Lit Mag; Mgr, Bsbl; CSF; Opt Out Tn; Acolyte A; Author, Acolyte Handbook; Episcopal Young Churchman; NMS Commended Stu; *U of Chicago; Hist.*

PAFFORD, Becky Sue
Chilhowie HS; Chilhowie, VA; Band; VP, BC; Chor; InterClub Coun; Monogram; A-Ed, Sch P; Tri-HiY; Mgr, Bkbl; Tr; 4H A; VofDEM; GSct A; *Lynchburg Baptist Col; Yth.*

PAFFORD, Kevin Ray
Haywood HS; Brownsville, TN; Tnns; *Air Force ROTC; Pilot.*

PAFFORD, Sherry Elaine
Chilhowie HS; Chilhowie, VA; Chor; FBLA; 4H; Jr Miss Pagent; Monogram; Tr; 4H A; *Tenn Temple Sch; Child Evangelism.*

PAGAN, Awilda
Juan Jose Osuna HS; Hato Rey, PR (2-101) Chldr; Chor; Dbte Tm; Drama; Parl, FHA; 4H; Hmrm; InterAct C; ARC; Sch P; Swim; Alg A; COM; Cl Fav; Hon Prog; Opt A; Star Student; *U of Cayey; Occupational Therapy.*

PAGAN, Bryan Gaylon
N Augusta Sr HS; N Augusta, SC (33-515) Band; Drama; NHS; Hon Prog.

PAGAN, Debbie
Luis Munoz Marin HS; Cabo Rojo, PR (2-150) Band; Chldr; Chor; FHA; Semi-Fin, Tr; Beauty; COM; Cl Fav; Hon Prog; Masonic A; Pres A; Swtht; *Recinto Universitario de Mayaguez; Bio.*

PAGAN, Omell
Jose de Diego HS; Mayaguez, PR; Dbte Tm; VP, Hmrm; ARC; VP, Sci C; SC; Alg A; Bio A; COM; Hist A; Hon Prog; Magna Cum Laude; Math A; JEME.

PAGAN, Pagan Maritza
Central de Oportunidades Edu HS; Guaynabo, PR; VP, SC; *U of Puerto Rico; Med.*

PAGAN, Waleska C
San Jorge Acad; Santurce, PR; *Cornell U; Optometry.*

PAGE, Bruce Allen
Plant City HS; Plant City, FL; F-Ed, Ann; InterClub Coun; Model UN; Photography; *Hillsborough Comm Col; Photography.*

PAGE, Cleveland Smith
Robert E Lee Sr HS; Jacksonville, FL; Band; Hmrm; Order/Arrow; SC; Sftbl; Most Out; Order/ Arrow A; Yth Fel; Secy, Yth Fel; Eagle Sct.

PAGE, David Kirk
Longmont Sr HS; Longmont, CO; Ch, Ann; Band; Co-Ed, Sch P; VP, SC; Cpt, Bkbl; Ftbl; Tr; All-Tourney Bkbl Tm; CCYM Rep; *TV & Radio Broadcasting.*

PAGE, David Ryan
Robert E Lee HS; Jacksonville, FL; Band; Community Yth Symph; Order/Arrow; Order/ Arrow A; Yth Fel; Eagle Sct; Mass Transit Seminar.

PAGE, Golphin
Lucy C Laney HS; Augusta, GA (71-265) Hmrm; Sch P; Bsbl; Ftbl; Co-Cpt, Sftbl; Cpt, Tnns; Tr; Chem A; Poet A; Art Achv A; *Clark Col.*

PAGE, Janet Elaine
Neshoba Central HS; Philadelphia, MS; BC; VP, Hmrm; Mgr, Bkbl; MVP, Sftbl; All Star Bkbl Trophy; *E Central Jr Col; Lib Arts.*

PAGE, Jennifer
Franklin HS; Seattle, WA; Hon Prog; Journ A.

PAGE, Karen Michelle
Neville HS; Monroe, LA (93-158) Chldr; Chor; Pres, Hmrm; F-Ed, Sch P; SC; Beauty; Cl Fav; Twin City Civic Ballet; Commission, Worship, Church; *NE La St Col; Art.*

PAGE, Kenny Earl
McKee HS; Staten Island, NY (50-300) Bkbl; Jaques A; Newspaper All Star; Prep All Star.

PAGE, Lori Dawn
Lancaster Elsie Robertson HS; Lancaster, TX (10-280) Band; Lat C; Band, Art, A's; All Region Band; Fr Horn C; *Tex A&M U; Vet Med.*

PAGE, Mary Jane
Queen City HS; Queen City, TX (9-44) FHA; NHS; Pres, Sr Cl; Bkbl; Tr; Most Dependable; *Texarkana Col; Art.*

PAGE, Mary Jo
Lexington Sr HS; Lexington, NE (40-150) Pres, FHA; 4H; B Crocker A; VP, FHA; *U of Nebr; Bus Ed.*

PAGE, Monty C
Buffalo HS; Buffalo, OK (2-34) Ann; Band; Sch P; MLS; Regent Schol; St Scholar; Type A; *Okla St U; Bus.*

PAGE, Myra Lyniece
Mullins HS; Mullins, SC (10%-499) Sci C; Sch Bus Driver A; *U of SC; Elem Art.*

PAGE, Paul Kevin
Leesville HS; Leesville, LA; CYO; Chess C; FBLA; Lit Ral; Sci C; Ftbl; Golf; Type A; *NE La U; Law.*

PAGE, Ronald James
Longmont HS; Longmont, CO; Band; Pres, Chor; Ensm; FTA; NHS; Ski C; Tr; Citz A; Kiwanis A; Lion A; Yth Fel; Solo Contest As; Outst Musician; *SMU; Mus.*

PAGE, Ronald Steven
St Matthew HS; Melrose, LA (4-42) *La St U; Journ.*

PAGE, Sabre Beeann
Burges HS; El Paso, TX; Chem A; Attendance A; Secy, Sunday Sch Cl; Span A; Art Cert.

PAGE, Shelia Marie
Midwest HS; Midwest, WY (6-21) CYO; Chor; Drama; Sch P; Spch C; Alg A; Hist A; Math A; Type A; Choir A.

PAGE, Tamera Lou
Prospect HS; Saratoga, CA; A Cap Choir; Band; Chor; Ensm; Orch; SC; Cpt, Bsbl; Cpt, Bkbl; Cpt, Soccer; Cl Fav; Yth Fel; Dance, Baton, Swim, Mus, A's.

PAGE, Terrie Rae
Coventry HS; Coventry, RI (11-414) NHS; Sftbl; Ntl Sci Found; Span A; St Hon Soc; WW; *RI Jr Col; Chem Tech.*

PAGE, Tom William
Montpelier HS; Montpelier, OH (4-120) Sch Achieve Tm; SC; Bkbl; Acad Achv A; *Ohio St U.*

PAGE, Valerie Rene
Ingewood HS; Inglewood, CA (71-325) Chldr; Chor; Var C; Sftbl; CSF; Citz A; Swtht; *Bryan Comm Col; Stenographer.*

PAGE'S, Luisa
Adlai E Stevenson HS; Bronx, NY; CYO; NHS; Sci C; Sftbl; Hon Prog; Sci A; *Acct.*

PAHL, Diane Marie
Beaver Dam Sr HS; Beaver Dam, WI (16-317) Band; Chldr; Chor; Ski C; SC; JV, Tnns; COM; JA A; Pres A; Spch A.

PAHL, Pamela Marie
Maria HS; Chicago, IL (14-350) CYO; Ch, Hmrm; S-T, Lat C; NHS; Pres, Sodality; SC; WW; *Loyola Col; Nurs.*

PAHLKE, Daniel Lavern
Todd Co HS; Mission, SD (15-60) Pres, 4H; NHS; Bkbl; Ftbl; 4H A; *SD St U; Econ.*

PAHMIYER, Gayle Lynn
Samuel Clemens HS; Schertz, TX (25-328) A Cap Choir; Pres, Chor; Ensm; VP, 4H; Madrigal; NHS; Bio A; 4H A; Outst Choir; PTA Schol; *Tex Christian U; Ed.*

PAIGE, Brenda Louise
Paul G Blazer HS; Ashland, KY (85-415) Chor; GS; Hmrm; Math C; VP, Span C; Pres, Y-Tns; Type A; Yth Fel; Co-Cpt, Vlbl; WW; *E Ky U; Bus Adm.*

PAIGE, Glenda Yvonne
East Tech HS; Cleveland, OH (25%-393) Bus C; Hmrm; Jr Miss Pagent; NHS; SC; COM; Citz A; JA A; Math A; Most Out; Type A; Attendance A; Bus.

PAIGE, Jeffery Scott
W Hills HS; Fort Worth, TX (5%-635) Band; NHS; Order/Arrow; Alg A; COM; Citz A; DARGCA; Math A; Opt A; Order/Arrow A; Eagle Sct; *Tex Tech U; Sci.*

PAIGE, Jeffrey Sumner
Shelton HS; Shelton, CT (50%-500) Chess C; JV, Golf; Gym C; *Southern Conn St Col; Phys Ed.*

PAIGE, Nancy Ann
Granada HS; Livermore, CA (125-406) Span C; Soccer; Sftbl; Bishop's Acolyte; Soccer A; Swim A; EYC Off; *Chabot Col; Sci.*

PAIGE, Sandra Louise
Ne Sr HS; Philadelphia, PA (612-1000) Chor; Hmrm; Citz A; Yth Fel; Yth Foundation; Gym; Special Ed.

PaIgE THOMAS, Darlene A
Rebecca Comer HS; Eufaula, AL (3-40) Pres, Hmrm; NHS; Pres, Sr Cl; Hist A; Hon Prog; Math A; Phy A; Eng A; Art C; *Chauncey Sparks St Tech Sch; Nurs.*

PAIN, David Daniel
Spring Woods HS; Houston, TX (10%-510) Chem C; Ftbl; Chem C; *U of Texas; Chem Engr.*

PAINE, Julia Ann
Northbridge HS; Northbridge, MA (8-150) VP, Band; Secy, Fr C; NHS; Sch P; JV, Bkbl; JV, Hockey; Tnns; *Boston Col; Bio.*

PAINE, Peter Earl
Hampton Roads Acad; Newport News, VA (19-50) Chess C; Key C; Lat C; Golf; Soccer; Ntl Fr Contest; *William & Mary U; Pre-Law.*

PAINTER, Barrett T
Cleveland HS; Cleveland, TN (50%-230) Band; S-T, InterAct C; Bsbl; Wrest; Yth Fel; *U of Tenn; Law.*

PAINTER, Charles Gregory
Buffalo HS; Buffalo, OK (25-51) Tres, FFA; Spch C; Var C; Bsbl; Bkbl; Ftbl; Tr; COM; Citz A; Hon Prog; Star Student; Yth Fel; *Panhandle Col; Agr.*

PAINTER, Patricia Ann
Woodlake Union HS; Woodlake, CA (3-166) Band; Ensm; JV, Golf; JV, Tnns; CSF; JV Vlbl.

PAK, Wonkyu
Fremont HS; Sunnyvale, CA (1-600) Chess C; Math C; Cr-Ctry; Alg A; COM; Hon Prog; Math A; Most Out; Ntl Sci Found; Rensselaer A; *Stanford U; Math.*

PAKULA, Bradley Alan
El Camino Real HS; Woodland Hills, CA (10-1000) Semi-Fin, BS; Fr C; French NHS; Ch, Hmrm; Ed, Lit Mag; Model UN; Pol Sci C; Ski C; SC; Ch, Soph Cl; CSF; COM; Hon Prog; Type A; *Stanford U; Med.*

PALACINO, John Michael
Trumbull HS; Trumbull, CT (40-750) A Cap Choir; Pres, Band; Chor; Ensm; Madrigal; NHS; Ntl Yth Conf; Hon Prog; Best Drum Major A; Tres & Pres, Church Yth Group; Ldrship A; Sem-Fin, Unted Technologies Schol; *Taylor U; Math.*

PALACIOS, Blanca N
Adlai E Stevenson HS; Bronx, NY; *Queens Col.*

PALACIOS, Rufus Junior
Abilene HS; Abilene, TX; VP, CYO; NHS; Citz A; Hon Prog; Industrial Arts; *TSIT; Archt.*

PALACIOS, Veronica
Abilene HS; Abilene, TX; FHA; Sftbl; COM; Mus A; Courage A, Daughters of Mary; Apprec Religious Ed Train Asst.

PALASEK, Carol Anne
Monsignor Ryan Mem HS; Dorchester, MA; Ann; Chor; Secy, NHS; Sch P; Span C; Hon Prog; Journ A; Avon Writing A; Diocesan Art A; *Simmons Col; Foods and Nutrition.*

PALERMO, Alex John
Orange HS; Orange, CA; Band; Chor; Drama; Ensm; Best Actor A; *Fullerton U; Mus.*

PALERMO, Darren Anthony
St John HS; Plaquemine, LA (2-30) Hmrm; Key C; Fin, Lit Ral; Tres, Mu Alpha Theta; NHS; Secy, Soph Cl; Mgr, Bsbl; Ftbl; NEDT; Sci A; Highest Religion Avg; Highest Eng Avg; *LSU; Conservation.*

PALES, Marisol
La Merced HS; Hato Rey, PR (2-92) Dbte Tm; Hmrm; NHS; Span C; Alg A; COM; Hist A; Hon Prog; Math A; Most Out; Poet A; Spch A; *MIT; Architecture.*

PALFRAMAN, Claudia Christine Hedwig
Sharon HS; Sharon, MA (100-200) Co-Ch, CYO; Community Yth Symph; Sci C; Ballet Stu; *Sci.*

PALKOVICH, Paula Jean
Bellaire HS; Bellaire, OH (7-225) A Cap Choir; Secy, Band; Chldr; Pres, Chor; Ensm; Fr C; 4H; VP, NHS; Rainbow; Ski C; Thes; Y-Tns; Golf; Swim; Tnns.

PALKOVITZ, Barry Joel
Hillel Acad of Pittsburgh; Pittsburgh, PA (3-11) Band; Fr C; Tres, Hmrm; Lit Mag; Math C; Order/Arrow; ARC; SC; Var C; Y-Tns; Bsbl; Bkbl; Cpt, Ftbl; Co-Cpt, Soccer; Sftbl; COM; Citz A; God & Country A; Hon Prog; Order/Arrow A; Q&S A; ARC A; Yth Leg; *U of Pittsburgh; Life Sci.*

PALLESEN, Cynthia
Manila HS; Manila, UT; Band; Chldr; GS; Pres, 4H; Math C; Sch P; VP, SC; VP, Soph Cl; Co-Cpt, Bkbl; Tr; COM; 4H A; HQn; HCt; Hist, SC; Rodeo Qn; MVP, Vlbl; Jr Prom Attendant; Swtht Ball Attendant; *Snow Col; Ath.*

PALLETTE, Kathy Lynn
Odessa R7 HS; Odessa, MO (58-130) Ann; FHA; FTA; Sch P; COM; Journ A; Type A; Scholastic Art A; *ADYA WW.*

PALLOTTA, Dino Joseph
Swiss Vale Area HS; Pittsburgh, PA (60-195) Band; Fr C; Rptr, Sch P; *Pitt U; Sci.*

PALM, Darryl Glenn
Huntsville HS; Huntsville, AL (50-450) *U of Ala-Huntsville.*

PALM, Rena Marie
Ashtabula Harbor HS; Ashtabula, OH (38-183) AFS; Chldr; Chor; Hmrm; Ski C; SC; Sftbl; Hon Prog; Math A; Sci A; GAA; Pep C; Vlbl, Bkbl, Intramural, Sftbl, A's; *Ohio St U; Phys Ed.*

PALMER, Alison
Richfield HS; Waco, TX (30-400) Span C; Swtht; Drill Tm; Cotillion; Ntl Span Exam; Dancer; *Tex Tech U; Span.*

PALMER, Barry Neal
Engleside Christian Sch; Alexandria, VA (4-22) Ed, Sch P; VP, Jr Cl; *Pensacola Christian Col; Art.*

PALMER, Brent Randal
Lake Worth HS; Fort Worth, TX; VP, FFA; VP, SC; Co-Cpt, Ftbl; Tr; HCt; Pres, FFA; *Tex A&M U; Law.*

PALMER, Brian Keith
Greece Arcadia HS; Rochester, NY (92-379) Band; Chor; Drama; Mgr, Bsbl; Swim; Tnns; Brigadier o-t Yr; *Houghton Col; Phys Ed.*

PALMER, Carl Arthur
St Charles Borromeo HS; Destrehan, LA; BC; Tres, Key C; VP, SC; Ftbl; Cl Fav; *LSU; Journ.*

PALMER, Catherine Lea
Blytheville Sr HS; Blytheville, AR (25-284) Band; BC; FBLA; GS; NHS; Span C; Pres, Secy, Am Legion Jr Auxilary; *Ark St U; Bus.*

PALMER, Catherine Mary
Whitman-Hanson Regional HS; Whitman, MA (22-328) FTA; Ski C; Hon Prog; *Northeastern U; Nurs.*

PALMER, Clydell
Amite Co Attendance Center; Gloster, MS (4-40) Band; Parl, BC; VP, Chor; Pres, Drama; Ensm; FFA; Pres, Hmrm; VP, Lit Mag; Orch; Pres, SC; Secy, Sr Cl; COM; Citz A; Most Out; Type A; *Jackson St U; Mus.*

PALMER, David Charles
Plant City Sr HS; Plant City, FL (15-670) FFA; 4H; Model UN; NHS; VP, Order/Arrow; Hon Prog; Order/Arrow A; Eagle Sct; *Fla St U; Bio.*

PALMER, David Terry
New Caney HS; New Caney, TX (25%-320) Chor; JV, Bkbl; *Sci.*

PALMER, David William
Terra Linda HS; San Rafael, CA (15-500) Band; Secy, InterAct C; Pres, Sci C; Regent School; ROTC A; Schol, Cal Alumni; Schol, Fed Personnel Coun of NCA; *U of Calif, Berkeley; Elec Engr.*

PALMER, David William
Morristown-Hamblen HS W; Morristown, TN (21-276) Bus Mgr, Band; SC; Rptr, Hmrm; Key C; SC; Ftbl; Cpt, Sftbl; Tr; Wrest; Alg A; Chem A; Hon Prog; Math A; Geom A; *US Air Force Acad; Aeronautical Engr.*

PALMER, Denise Janice
Norman Thomas HS; New York, NY (279-805) *Cheyney St Col; Acct.*

PALMER, Edward James Jr
Haverling Central HS; Bath, NY; Chor; VP, FFA; NHS; FFA Empire Degree; FFA Mgt A; *Marrisiville Col; Agr.*

PALMER, Elizabeth Anne
Charleston HS; Charleston, IL (10-282) A Cap Choir; AFS; Chor; Fr C; SC; Fr A; *Ill Wesleyan Col; Mus.*

PALMER, Gregory Lawrence
Sumner HS; St Louis, MO (3%-780) Hmrm; Math C; Span C; Bio A; Citz A; Hist A; Hon Prog; Math A; *Med.*

PALMER, James Anthony
Henry Hudson Regional Sch; Highlands, NJ (15%-127) Band; Chor; Ensm; Hmrm; Orch; Order/Arrow; ARC; SC; Bkbl; Ftbl; Hon Prog; Order/Arrow A; VofDEM; Yth Fel; Life Sct; BSct; *Drew U; Social Sci.*

PALMER, Joel Craig
Marshall Sr HS; Marshal, TX (20-550) A Cap Choir; Band; Ensm; Lat C; Tres, Mod Mus Mas; NHS; SC; Hon Prog; Swing Choir; All Dist Choir; Pres, Astronomy C; Co-Cpt, Church Bkbl; *E Tex Baptist Col; Phys Sci.*

PALMER, Karen Elizabeth
Sunset HS; Dallas, TX (65-350) Co-Ed, Ann; Chor; Fr C; Hmrm; Rainbow; SC; Tnns; Hon Prog; Q&S A; Nom, Swtht; Co-Cpt, Drill Tm; *U of Tex; Nutrition.*

PALMER, Katharine Anne
Kalama HS; Kalama, WA (12-60) Band; Chldr; Drama; Fr C; Ski C; SC; Sftbl; Swtht; *Clark Col; Dental Hygiene.*

PALMER, Lance Eugene
Centralia Sr HS; Centralia, WA (5%-350) Band; Ensm; FBLA; NHS; Sch P; VP, Soph Cl; JV, Ftbl; *U of Wash; Mus.*

PALMER, Martha Paulette
Glencoe HS; Glencoe, AL (10-115) BC; FHA; Gov Honor Prog; Sci A; Home Ec A; *Gadsden St Jr Col; Med Asst.*

PALMER, Mary Ellen
Morristown-Hamblen W HS; Morristown, TN (5-380) BC; Chor; Fr C; Hmrm; Math C; SC; Tri-HiY; *Carson-Newman Col; Med.*

PALMER, Michael Jason
Blytheville Sr HS; Blytheville, AR (9-435) BC; Ger C; Bsbl; Math A; ROTC A; *Air Force Acad; Astronautical Engr.*

PALMER, Phillip Carl
Walnut HS; Walnut, MS (15-55) Ann; Band; BC; Drama; FFA; Mod Mus Mas; Spch C; JV, Bkbl; Swim; Tnns; Most Talented; *Miss St U; Mus.*

PALMER, Robert John
Oxon Hill Sr HS; Oxon Hill, MD (20%-480) Bsbl; COM; Hon Prog; Sci A; Sch Service A; Academic Achv A; Yth Fitness A; *Engr.*

PALMER, Rosemary
W Side Sr HS; Gary, IN (140-700) VP, Chor; Hmrm; SC; WW; *Odessa Beauty Sch; Beautician.*

PALMER, Sharon H
Hollidaysburg Sr HS; Hollidaysburg, PA; Chor; Tres, FNA; Ger C.

PALMER, Sue Eileen
E Central HS; Tulsa, OK (135-630) Chem C; VP, FHA; Ger C; Hmrm; NHS; SC; *Okla St U; Spch Pathology.*

PALMER, Vincent Isaac
Wyoming HS; Wyoming, OH (137-215) Band; Cpt, Bsbl; Bkbl; Ftbl; *Raymond Walters Col; Lib Arts.*

PALMISANO, Debra Lynn
Lansdowne Sr HS; Baltimore, MD; HR; Mgr, Vlbl; *Towson St Col; Choreography.*

PALMORE, Kathryn Anne
Fairhope HS; Fairhope, AL (20%-340) Band; Orch; *Nurs.*

PALMORE, Pamela Ernesta
Druid HS; Tuscaloosa, AL; Band; NHS; Rptr, Sch P; Span C; Tri-HiY; Beauty; COM; Citz A; HQn; Cpt, Dance Group; Miss Varsity; *UA; Communications.*

PALOMARES, Roberto
Saddleback HS; Santa Ana, CA; MVP, Cr-Ctry; MVP, Tnns; MVP, Tr; Math A; Pres A; Rensselaer A; *Santa Ana Col; Dentist.*

PALOMBO, Mark Jeffrey
Beaufort Acad; Beaufort, SC; Co-Ed, Ann; Band; Drama; NHS; Hon Prog; *Wofford Col; Bus Adm.*

PALOS, Elisa
Harlingen HS; Harlingen, TX (217-640) Pres, CYO; Ch, FHA; Fin, Hmrm; Pres, Span C; SC; Cl Fav; PTA A; Good Neighbor Commission; Stu o-t Month; *Del Mar Col; Human Services.*

PALOS, Ester
Harlingen HS; Harlingen, TX (73-647) Secy, CYO; Hmrm; VP, Sr Cl; VP, Jr Cl; VP, Soph Cl; Cl Fav; DARGCA; Swtht; Chaplain, SC; PASF Good Neighbor A; *Pan Amer U; Sociology.*

PALS, Brian Joseph
Belmond Community HS; Belmond, IA (1-81) Band; Drama; Pres, 4H; NHS; Bus Mgr, Sch P; Thes; 4H A; St Scholar; Val; Yth Fel; *Iowa St U; Elec Engr.*

PALUSAK, Vikki
Reynolds HS; Greenville, PA (2-183).

PAMPLIN, Holly Kay
New Albany HS; New Albany, IN; Community Yth Symph; Ger C; Orch; Spch C; Most Out; Vlbl; Outst Schol As; Outst Orch A; St Contest As; *Math.*

PAMPLONA, Marla Ann
Los Banos HS; Los Banos, CA (90-198) AFS; Band; CYO; 4H; Mjrte; ARC; 4H A; HQn; *Solano Comm Col; Animal Tech.*

PANA, Evelyn Kathleen
Euclid Sr HS; Euclid, OH (86-835) Ann; Cpt, Chldr; Hmrm; F-Ed, Lit Mag; NHS; Ntl Yth Conf; COM; Hon Prog; Q&S A; Yth Fel; Cl Cabinet, Soph, Jr, Sr; Spirits C; Vlbl; Co-Ch, Sr Talent Show; Powder Puff Ftbl; Job's Daughters; Ad C; Sunday Sch Teacher; *Ohio U; Interior Design.*

PANES, Meninet Patriarca
George Washington Sr HS; Mangilao, GUAM; NHS; COM; Citz A; Most Out; Sci A; PA; Span A; Home Ec A; *Pepperdine U; Med.*

PANG, Darlene Mew Wah
McKinley HS; Honolulu, HI (40-837) Co-Cpt, Chldr; HiY; NHS; Tr; Sch Rep, Shorthand Contest; *U of Hawaii.*

PANG, Hyo Song
Lane Tech HS; Chicago, IL (240-1420) VP, Lat C; ARC; JV, Tr; Citz A; Post A; *U of Chicago; Pre-Med.*

PANG, Whee Song
Lane-Tech HS; Chicago, IL (300-1300) HiY; Sch Achieve Tm; Hockey; Soccer; COM; City Champ, Speed Skating; Sch Ltrman, Print, Phys Achv, A's; *U of Ill; Pre-Law.*

PANIAGUA, Blanca Ivette
Juan Jose Osuna HS; San Juan, PR (10-101) Chess C; Drama; Fr C; VP, Hmrm; ARC; Span C; SC; Hon Prog; Math A; MLS; ARC A; Hon A; *U of Puerto Rico; Lit.*

PANIZZI, Anne Marie
Hall HS; Spring Valley, IL (25-150) HCt; *Ill St U; Ed.*

PANKOW, Matthew David
Merrill Sr HS; Merrill, WI (2-324) BS; Dbte Tm; Ger C; Hmrm; Mgr, Bkbl; Ftbl; Tr; Amer Leg A; NMF; Opt A; *Notre Dame U; Engr.*

PANKOWITZ, Paula Ann
Acad of Our Lady of Mercy; Milford, CT (1-86) Drama; NEDT.

PANKRATZ, Michele Patricia
Abbotsford Jr Secondary HS; Abbotsford, CANADA; Band; Hmrm; Ski C; SC; Cr-Ctry; Tr; Hon Prog; *Eng.*

PANN, Marcia Ann
Old Forge HS; Old Forge, PA (7-121) FHA; Mjrte; NHS; Chem A; Hon Prog; *Geisinger Med Center; Nurs.*

PANNELL, Ina Simone
Adlai E Stevenson HS; Bronx, NY (5-788) Chor; Math C; NHS; Hon Prog; Eng A; Span A; *Psych.*

PANNETON, Linda Marie
Ste Joseph's Regional HS; Lowell, MA; NHS; *U of Lowell; Art.*

PANNONE, Greg Micheal
Cambridge Acad; Greenwood, SC (4-16) Semi-Fin, BS; Chess C; S-T, Hmrm; SC; Hon Prog; *Mont St U; Archt.*

PANSCH, Jane Marie
Graceville Pub HS; Graceville, MN (1-58) Band; Chldr; Drama; FHA; Key C; NHS; Sftbl; Citz A; 4H A.

PANTER, Janet Marie
Red Bank HS; Chattanooga, TN; Lat C; Secy, NHS; Mgr, Bkbl; Sftbl; Lat A; Bkbl Ltrs; Most Improved Bkbl Trophy; League Champ Trophy; *Chattanooga St Tech Comm Col; X-Ray Tech.*

PANTOZZI, Donna Grace
Acad of Saint Aloysius; Jersey City, NJ (17-127) S-T, Fr C; FTA; S-T, Lat C; NHS; S-T, Span C; Ch, SC; Ch, Jr Cl; VP, Soph Cl; Hon Prog; Type A; Ch, Stu Service Corps; SG; *Montclair St Col; Foreign Lang.*

PANWITZ, Angela Elaine
Alliance HS; Alliance, NE (24-149) Band; Chldr; 4H; Y-Tns; Swim; Tr; *Kearney St Col.*

PANYAN, Mary Catherine
Gilbert HS; Gilbert, MN (2%-83) Band; CYO; Chldr; Chor; Bkbl; Tnns; Best Citizen; Star Schol; *St Scholastica Col; Med.*

PANZENHAGEN, Janis Dee
N Shore HS; W Palm Beach, FL (1-353) Community Yth Symph; Key C; NHS; Orch; COM; Ragtime Ensm; Jr NHS; Fr, Eng As; Superior, District Ensm; *Mus.*

PAPENFUSS, David William
Wilton HS; Wilton, CT (72-425) Pres, Var C; Cpt, Bkbl; Cpt, Ftbl; Cpt, Lacrosse; All St Ftbl & Lacrosse; Hon All Amer; *U of Pa; Bus Adm.*

PAPKE, Marilyn Cecile
Douglas Co HS; Castle Rock, CO (43-300) Band; Chor; NFL; Tres, NHS; Spch C; Sftbl; Spch A; God & Comm A; NHS A; *Colo St U; Spch Therapy.*

PAPKE, Robert Edwin
Falls Church HS; Falls Church, VA (150-590) Band; Pres, Key C; NHS; VP, Key C; *U of SC; Bus.*

PAPP, Andrew Christopher
Arcadia HS; Arcadia, CA (94-806) VP, Band; Cpt, Ensm; Orch; SC; Ftbl; CSF; Hon Prog; VP, Sr Men C; Pep Band; *U of Calif; Agr Bus Mgt.*

PAPPALARDO, Elizabeth Ann
Kelly HS; Chicago, IL (2-611) *Bio.*

PAPPAS, Denise Marie
Arcadia HS; Arcadia, CA; Hmrm; Vlbl; Assembly Commission; *Pasadena City Col; Dental Hygienist.*

PAPPAS, Katherine
Eau Gallie HS; Melbourne, FL; InterAct C; NHS; Citz A; Star Student; *Stetson U; Bus Adm.*

PAPULAS, Julie Ann
Roosevelt HS; Minneapolis, MN (52-569) Chor; Drama; NHS; Ski C; Tri-HiY; Sftbl; Sr Exec Board; Vlbl; Bush Foundation Schol; Slalom; Yth for Understanding.

PAPUSCH, Richard George
Western Hills HS; Ft Worth, TX (1-500) Band; NHS; Orch; Distinguished Mus Cert; John Philip Sousa Band A; *Tex Christian U; Mus.*

PAQUIN, Robin Jane
L L Wright HS; Ironwood, MI; Chor; VP, FTA; Ski C; Var C; MVP, Bkbl; MVP, Golf; MVP, Tr; Phys Fitness A; *Gogebic Comm Col; Social Work.*

PARADIS, Darral Wayne
N Little Rock Ole Main HS; N Little Rock, AR (20%-500) VP, Band; Drama; Lit Mag; NHS; Orch; Co-Ed, Sch P; COM; Citz A; Hon Prog; Journ A; Pres A; Q&S A; Spch A; *Communications.*

PARADISE, Pierre Lamonte
George Rogers Clark HS; E St Louis, IL (30-260) Chess C; Drama; Sch P; Sci C; Cpt, Cr-Ctry; Cpt, Tr; *FSU; Civics.*

PARANTO, Mary Elizabeth
Kingsway Regional HS; Swedesboro, NJ (10-140) Key C; Cpt, Mjrte; NHS; *Med Technology.*

PARDIN, Cheryl Annette
Smyrna HS; Smyrna, TN (26-250) BC; Bus C; Drama; Rptr, Hmrm.

PARDOE, Noel Douglas
Jefferson City HS; Jefferson City, MO;

PARDUE, Andrew Scott
Starmount HS; Boonville, NC (18-204) FFA; Ger C; MVP, Bsbl; Bkbl; Ftbl; *U of NC; Law.*

PARDUE, Christine Ann
S Dade Sr HS; Homestead, FL (47-820) Bus C; F-Ed, Lit Mag; NHS; F-Ed, Sch P; Journ A; PA; Paper Contests; Golden & Silver HR; *Miami Dade Comm Col; Journ.*

PARDUE, John Howard
Wooddale HS; Memphis, TN; Band; Ensm; Hmrm; SC; All West Band; HR; *Archeology.*

PARDUE, Lauren Rose
Obion Co HS; Troy, TN (7-177) Ed, Ann; BC; Chor; FBLA; FHA; GS; NHS; Span C; Bkbl; Amer Leg A; DAC A; *U of Tenn; Office Adm.*

PAREDES, Mary Gail
Nordhoff HS; Ojai, CA (5-315) AFS; Swim; Tnns; CSF; VP, CSF; World Lit A; *Occidental Col; Law.*

PARELIUS, Marianne
Bret Harte Union HS; Angels Camp, CA (3-137) AFS; Ski C; Span C; Secy, Sr Cl; CSF; Educators A; *U of Santa Clara; Pre-Med.*

PARENTE, Victoria Anne
Country Day Sch o-t Sacred Heart; Philadelphia, PA; Ann; Chor; VP, Drama; NHS; Ed, Sch P; Hist A; Hon Prog; HS Schol; Eng Lit, Good Sportsmanship, A's; *Villanova U; Eng.*

PARES, Odemaris
Academia Santa Monica; Santurce, PR; NHS; Rptr, Sch P; Tres, SC; COM; Hon Prog; *U of Puerto Rico; Bus Adm.*

PARET, Robert York
Del Rio HS; Del Rio, TX (30-410) 4H; NHS; Order/Arrow; SC; Golf; 4H A; Order/Arrow A; Span A; *Tex A&M U; Range Sci.*

PARHAM, Christopher Brian
Eastmoor Sr HS; Columbus, OH (110-397) Band; Orch; Ftbl; Tr; All-City Concert Band; Ftbl and Tr Ltr; *Ohio St U; Bus Adm.*

PARHAM, Kenneth Rene
E Atlanta HS; Atlanta, GA (1-142) BC; Math C; NHS; Span C; SC; Alg A; COM; Math A; MLS; NEDT; ROTC A; Sci A; Star Student; Val; PC Fellow; Sewanee C A; Span A; *Howard U; Chem Engr.*

PARHAM, Larry Allen
Gordon Ind Sch District; Gordon, TX (7-17) FFA; Var C; Bkbl; Cr-Ctry; Ftbl; Tr.

PARHAM, Vicki Lee
Hatley HS; Amory, MS (2-38) Rptr, BC; Chldr; Chor; S-T, FHA; VP, Jr Cl; Rptr, Soph Cl; Bkbl; Amer Leg A; Beauty; Bio A; Cl Fav; HCt; HR; *Itawamba Jr Col.*

PARIS, Rhonda Laine
Saks HS; Anniston, AL (50%-165) Band; Ger C; Pres, Tri-HiY; Sftbl; Yth Fel; Yth Leg; Drill Tm; *Jacksonville St U; Mgt.*

PARISE, Russell Edward
Dobyns-Bennett HS; Kingsport, TN (25-429) BC; BS; Ger C; Hmrm; InterAct C; NHS; SC; Bsbl; Bio A; JA A; *Tenn Tech U; Chem Engr.*

PARISER, Susan E
Uniontown Area Sr HS; Uniontown, PA (16-435) Arch; Pres, FTA; NHS; Sci C; Chamber of Comm A; Hist A; NMS; Brown U Eng A; *Ed.*

PARISH, Brenda Joyce
Riverside HS; Avon, MS; Ann; Band; Drama; Pres, Hmrm; Ch, Mjrte; Sch P; SC; Pres, Sr Cl; Rptr, Jr Cl; Mgr, Bkbl; HCt; Miss Riverside HS; *Miss Col; Law.*

PARISH, Candace Elizabeth
E Syracuse-Minoa HS; E Syracuse, NY (50%-580) A Cap Choir; Band; Chor; *Oral Roberts U; Mus Ed.*

PARISH, Cherie Kristen
Derby Sr HS; Derby, KS; Chldr; Chor; Drama; Ensm; 4H; Hmrm; NFL; Orch; Span C; SC; Tres, Soph Cl; Tr; Jr Cl Rep; FCA; Jr NHS; Gym Tm; *Kans St U; Dental Tech.*

PARISH, David Carl
N Garland HS; Garland, TX; A Cap Choir; Band; Ensm; Ger C; Ftbl; Golf; Tr; *Law Enforcement.*

PARISIO, Deborah Jeanne
Willows HS; Willows, CA (9-136) Chess C; Drama; CSF; Pres A; *Engr.*

PARISOT, Michael John
Chaminade HS; St Louis, MO (22-128) NHS; SC; Bsbl; Ftbl; Alg A; Math A; *Ariz U; Communications.*

PARK, David Bryan
Watonga HS; Watonga, OK; Key C; NHS; Bsbl; Bkbl; Ftbl; *Okla U; Ath.*

PARK, David James
Riggs HS; Pierre, SD (12-250) V-Ch, Hmrm; Monogram; NHS; SC; Var C; Y-Tns; Pres, Jr Cl; Bsbl; Bkbl; Ftbl; JV, Tr; *MIT; Engr.*

PARK, Karen Kyong-Ai
John F Kennedy HS; Tumon, GUAM; Hmrm; NHS; Sal; Sci A; Type A; Geo A; *U of Minn; Nurs.*

PARK, Kay Frances
Mexico HS; Mexico, MO (20%-300) Band; Chldr; Drama; Pres, Fr C; NFL; 2nd & 3rd Trophies, Spch Tourn; *William Jewell Col; Bus.*

PARK, Kyung Hwan
McKinley HS; Honolulu, HI (25-819) Math C; NHS; Secy, Sci C; *Civil Engr.*

PARK, Steve H
John F Kennedy HS; Bronx, NY (5-35) Fr C; Math C; NHS; Sch P; Sci C; Soccer; *MIT; Engr.*

PARK, Toni Lynn
Emmanuel Baptist Christian HS; Toledo, OH (3-22) Cpt, Chldr; Chor; Ensm; Ed, Sch P; Semi-Fin, Tnns; Beauty; COM; ARC A; Sci A; Yrbk; Vocal A; Ath A; *Baptist Bible Col; Mus.*

PARKE, Pamela Jo
Woodlake Union HS; Woodlake, CA; Band; 4H; Mjrte; Tnns; CSF; Best Dressed; Most Improved, Vlbl; *Vet.*

PARKE, Tamera Jean
Wood River HS; Hailey, ID (3-60) Secy, Band; Chor; Drama; Secy, 4H; Cpt, Mjrte; NHS; Orch; Ski C; Span C; Thes; Cpt, Sftbl; Tr; Beauty; COM; 4H A; Hon Prog; Math A; Most Out; ARC A; Sal; Spch A; Type A; Win, Drill Down Camp; Ntl Thespian Soc, A; Ntl Mus Federation, A's; *Ricks Col; Elem Ed.*

PARKER, Alan Charles
Norman HS; Norman, OK (50-680) Band; Fr C; NHS; SC; Amer Leg A; COM; Masonic A; Rotary A; *Okla U; Chem.*

PARKER, Alliane
VanCleave HS; Vancleave, MS (20-90) Chor; FHA; Rptr, Sch P; Span C; Citz A; Hist A; Eng A; *Sou Mo U; Hist.*

PARKER, Andrea Kay
Mission HS; St Ignatius, MT (33%-37) Band; Chldr; Chor; Ensm; 4H; Mjrte; Sch P; 4H A; Type A; Outst Musician A; Talent Contest Win; Band Schol; High HR A; *Ricks Col; Mus.*

PARKER, Autyr James Jr
Wooddale HS; Memphis, TN; A Cap Choir; Chor; Hmrm; Lat C; Math C; Mu Alpha Theta; SC.

PARKER, Barbara Ann
John F Kennedy HS; Suffolk, VA; Chor; 4H; Hmrm; Span C; Sftbl; 4H A; Hon Prog; Most Out; Sci A; Type A; Yth Fel; Co-Ed-Hi-Y; VP, Pom-Pom Sq; Span A; *Va Commonwealth Col; Dentistry.*

PARKER, Barbara Elaine
Washburn HS; Minneapolis, MN; Bkbl; Ftbl; Sftbl; Swim; Tr; COM; Comm Achv A; *U of Minn; Modeling.*

PARKER, Betty Ann
Loris HS; Loris, SC (53-150) Band; Bus C; FBLA; FHA; FTA; 4H; Mjrte; 4H A; Bus C; Cpt, Bkbl; Ftbl; COM; Hon Prog; Interlochen Ntl Mus; JA A; Lion A; Ntl Conf Chr & Jews; Spch A; WW; Pep C; *Benedict Col; Sociology.*

PARKER, Betty Louise
Sussex Central HS; Sussex, VA (1-186) Ed, Ann; BC; Drama; Secy, FHA; Hmrm; 4H; Hmrm; Sci C; Span C; Sftbl; COM; Hon Prog; Math A; Sci A; Type A; *Va Polytechnic Inst; Computer Sci.*

PARKER, Brenda Lee
McCurtain HS; McCurtain, OK (10%-11) Chldr; 4H; Sftbl.

PARKER, Bruce Edward
Fairmont East HS; Kettering, OH (32-561) Chor; NHS; Sch Achieve Tm; JV, Ftbl; JV, Tr; COM; Hist A; NEDT; Opt A; Eng A; *U of Cincinnati; Chem Engr.*

PARKER, Carol Jeanene
Fred Page HS; Franklin, TN (20-125) Chor; FHA; Rptr, 4H; 4H A; Piano; *Legal Secy.*

PARKER, Cathy Roena
Edgewood HS; Edgewood, TX (1-53) Pres, Band; Span C; Tres, SC; Pres, Jr Cl; Secy, Soph Cl; Beauty; COM; NEDT; *Tyler Jr Col; Acct.*

PARKER, Cecelia Ann
Madison Acad HS; Huntsville, AL (6-43) Ann; BC; Cpt, Chldr; FHA; Math C; Monogram; Var C; Beauty; COM; Cl Fav; Hist A; HQn; HCt; Hon Prog; Most Out; Star Student; Type A; Jr Civitan; Bible A; Jr Chor; *Harding Col.*

PARKER, Cindy Ann
Empire HS; Duncan, OK (8-32) Secy, FHA; 4H; Bkbl; Tr; COM; 4H A; Outst Tr; Sch Record, Tr Relay; Soph BB Qn Cand; Cpt, Drill Tm; *Murray St Col; Bus.*

PARKER, Craig Alan
Sam Houston HS; Arlington, TX; AFS; Ann; Band; Chor; Rptr, City Conf; Ensm; HiY; F-Ed, Lit Mag; NHS; Order/Arrow; Sch Achieve Tm; SC; Ftbl; MVP, Soccer; Sftbl; COM; God & Country A; Hon Prog; Most Out; Order/Arrow A; Yth Fel; Yth Foundation; Yth Leg; Eagle Sct; *Dallas Baptist Sr Col; Med.*

PARKER, Cynthia Denise
MacKenzie HS; Detroit, MI (6-352) NHS; Citz A; Hon Prog; JA A; *Mich St U; Nurs.*

PARKER, David Alan
Columbia HS; Columbia, IL (19-134) Band; NHS; SC; Var C; Bsbl; Ftbl; HCt; Opt A; Yth Foundation A; *SE Mo St U; Archt.*

PARKER, Debra Rae
Benton HS; St Joseph, MO (1-276) A-Ed, Ann; NHS; COM; Citz A; ROTC A; Yth Fel; School Achv A; *NW Mo St Col; Home Ec.*

PARKER, Della Denise
Etowah HS; Attalla, AL; Chldr; FHA; Sftbl; Tr; *Ala Col; Nurs.*

PARKER, Denise Antoinette
Frederick Douglass HS; Baltimore, MD (5%-400) Chess C; NHS; Mgr, Swim; COM; Hon Prog; JA A; ARC A; Pres, Travel C; Church Yth Choir; Summer Schol, Md Inst of Art; Pres, Jr Missionary Soc; Secy, Layman's Organization; *U of Md; Ed.*

PARKER, Donald D
Christian HS; El Cajon, CA (47-107) Cpt, Bkbl; Cpt, Ftbl; Tr; *Pepperdine U; Bus Adm.*

PARKER, Donna Suzette
Hanceville HS; Hanceville, AL; Band; Math C; *Samford U; Sociology.*

PARKER, Douglas Andrew
Grove City Area HS; Grove City, PA (40%-250) Chess C; Fr C; Math C; Model UN; Orch; ARC; Sci C; Ski C; Bsbl; Swim; God & Country A; *Grove City Col.*

PARKER, Edward McDonald
Hale HS; Raleigh, NC (1-23) Pres, Jr Cl; Bsbl; MVP, Soccer; Bio A; Pres A; Eng A; All-St Soccer; Fr A; Hon Stu; *Mass Inst of Technology; Design.*

PARKER, Gaylen Weston
Dekalb HS; De Kalb, IL; FFA; Green Hand, FFA A; Industrial Coop Ed; *Kishwaukee Col.*

PARKER, George Ashley
Ballou Sr HS; Washington, DC; Chor; Bsbl; Bkbl; Ftbl; Sftbl; Citz A; *Morehouse Col; Photography.*

PARKER, Gregory Scott
John Jay HS; San Antonio, TX (67-639) JETS; Mu Alpha Theta; NHS; Bsbl; Bkbl; Co-Cpt, Ftbl; Drafting, Ath, A's; *San Antonio Col; Archt.*

PARKER, Jacqueline
Thornridge HS; Dolton, IL; *Pepperdine U; Inhalation Therapy.*

PARKER, Jay Norris
Lutheran HS S; St Louis, MO (50-159) Hmrm; Bsbl; JV, Bkbl; JV, Ftbl; Off, Yth Group; Yth Worship Committee; *Valpariso U; Bus Adm.*

PARKER, Jeffrey Mark
Shabbona HS; Shabbona, IL (8-42) Pres, Chor; FFA; Madrigal; Var C; Bsbl; Co-Cpt, Bkbl; JV, Tnns; All-Conf Bkbl; *Kishwaukee Col; Med.*

PARKER, Jeffrey Wayne
Crittenden Co HS; Marion, KY (8-116) Ann; Band; BC; Drama; Secy, Fr C; Lat C; St Stu Congress; Pres, SC; Pres, Sr Cl; Ftbl; Wrest; *Murray St U; Computer Sci.*

PARKER, Jennifer Lea
Headland HS; Headland, AL (20-85) JV, Chldr; VP, FBLA; FHA; FTA; 4H; DARGCA; Hon Prog; Hospital Vol; Fin, Miss Farm Bureau; *U of Ala; Consumer Affairs.*

PARKER, Julie Faith
Lawrence HS; Cedarhurst, NY (31-512) Secy, AFS; Drama; NHS; Hon Prog; Host Sister, AFS; *Duke U; Sociology.*

PARKER, Karen Lea
North HS; Omaha, NE (71-413) Ed, Ann; Secy, FNA; Lat C; Sch P; *Nebr Methodist Nurs Col; Nurs.*

PARKER, Karen Michelle
South HS; Springfield, OH; FHA; NHS; Ed, Sch P; Span C; Up Bound; Most Out; *North Carolina A&T Col; Engr.*

PARKER, Kevin Ralph
Hobbs HS; Hobbs, NM (2-419) CYO; City Conf; NHS; Cpt, Sch Achieve Tm; Ed, Sch P; SC; COM; Journ A; Sal; *U of Tex at Austin; Archaeology.*

PARKER, Kim Renee
Scarborough Jr-Sr HS; Houston, TX (80-310) Drama; Rptr, Ger C; Thes; B Crocker A; Best Actress UIL Contest Play; All-Star Cast UIL Contest Plays; Outst Performer.

PARKER, Kurt Arnold
Ben Davis HS; Indianapolis, IN; A Cap Choir; Tres, Chor; Dbte Tm; Drama; 4H; Hmrm; F-Ed, Sch P; Cr-Ctry; Tr; Amer Leg A; 4H A; Pres A; Puts Christ First A; Jr St Muzzleloading Champ; FCC Radio Oper Endorsement License; *Ministry.*

PARKER, Laura Grace
Hobart HS; Hobart, OK (14-52) FTA; S-T, Sr Cl; VP, Soph Cl; Rptr, Pep C; Art C; 1st Americans-Tomorrow's Engr, WW; *Southwestern Okla St U; Bus.*

PARKER, Linda Annette
O D Wyatt HS; Fort Worth, TX (97-300) *Bishop Col; Elem Ed.*

PARKER, Lowery Kinlock
Oak Ridge Sr HS; Orlando, FL; Band; Civitan C; *Sweet Briar Col; Hist.*

PARKER, Lynne Nannette
O D Wyatt HS; Fort Worth, TX (2-434) *Tarrant Co Jr Col; Elem Ed.*

PARKER, Mark Allan
Lanesboro HS; Lanesboro, MN (11-33) Fin, BS; Bsbl; Ftbl; *Bus.*

PARKER, Michael Earl
Waukegan E HS; Waukegan, IL (210-503) *Lake Co Col; Auto Mech.*

PARKER, Michael Lee
Cherryville Sr HS; Cherryville, NC (2-136) A-Ed, Ann; Band; Chor; NHS; MLS; Opt A; Sal; St Mus As, Hons; St Pythians Bicen Essay, Win; *Oberlin Conservatory of Mus; Mus.*

PARKER, Michele Cheketalee
Merganthaler HS; Baltimore, MD; Chor; FHA; Lit Mag; Mod Mus Mas; ARC; Soccer; Sftbl; Swim; Tnns; Path Finders; Usher; Bible Stu; *Morgan Col.*

PARKER, Pamela Cordelia
Montclair HS; Montclair, NJ (138-485) SC; Secy, Y-Tns; Tres, Sr Cl; Tres, Jr Cl; Tnns; Bsbl; Sftbl; Tr; COM; Yth Fel; Asst Secy Service A; Co-ordinator, Women's Day Prog; *Hampton Inst; Nurs.*

PARKER, Patricia Ann
Seward Park HS; New York City, NY (46-617) Cum Laude Soc; VFW A; *Brown U; Bio.*

PARKER, Patricia Carol
New Caney HS; Porter, TX (1-300) A-Ed, Ann; Secy, Band; Ensm; JETS; NHS; Hon Prog; Type A; All-Dist & All-Region Bands; WW-BAND; Outst Bandsman; WW-ENG; St Solo & Ensm; UIL Regional Shorthand Contestant; *U of Colo Boulder; Bus Mgt.*

PARKER, Patricia Dominici
Proviso E HS; Maywood, IL; Chldr; Chor; Var C; PTA A; Pray Group; Girls Glee C; Mixed Chor; *Baptist Bible Col; Elem Ed.*

PARKER, Patricia Kay
John F Kennedy Mem HS; Seattle, WA; Co-Cpt, Chldr; Rainbow; Cr-Ctry; Mgr, Wrest; Semi-Fin, Prom Ct; Pres, Church Yth; Church Coun; *Highline Comm Col; Med.*

PARKER, Philip Duwayne
Iroquois Sr HS; Louisville, KY (10%-470) Co-Ed, Ann; Chess C; Chor; Drama; Hmrm; NHS; ARC; SC; Alg A; Hist A; Hon Prog; Math A; Sci A; F-Ed, Annual; Fr A; *Bus Adm.*

PARKER, Phyllis Elaine
Kernersville Wesleyan Acad; Kernersville, NC (22-43) Ann; Chldr; Dbte Tm; Drama; Ensm; Spch C; Secy, SC; VP, Sr Cl; Sftbl; HCt; 1st Pl, Art As; 1st Pl, Vocal; Most Athletic; *Marion Col; Art.*

PARKER, Ramona Laurie
Headland HS; Headland, AL; Secy, FBLA; FHA; Yth Fel; *U of Ala.*

PARKER, Renee Avis
Spring Brook HS; Silver Spring, MD; Chor; JV, Hmrm; MVP, Bkbl; MVP, Sftbl; MVP, Tr; Beauty; Citz A; Child Care A; GSct A; Yth Participation A; Jr Charities A; *Bradford Col; Med.*

PARKER, Rhonda Jean
Fowler HS; Fowler, CO (33%-53) Chor; Dbte Tm; FHA; NFL; SC; Thes; Mgr, Bkbl; Mgr, Tr; Mgr, Vlbl; Stu Ath Trainer; *Hastings Col; Phys Therapy.*

PARKER, Richard George
Booker T Washington HS; Houston, TX; JETS; Pres, NHS; Co-Cpt, Bkbl; Bio A; Chem A; Hist A; *Brown U; Biol.*

PARKER, Robin Michelle
Chester HS; Chester, PA; Chor; *Bus Adm.*

PARKER, Ronald Kent
Empire HS; Duncan, OK (20-36) FFA; Ftbl; COM; *Murray St U; Drafting.*

PARKER, Sammy Chason Jr
Port St Joe Jr-Sr HS; Port St Joe, FL (3-121) Pres, Band; Pres, Drama; VP, Key C; NHS; Pres, Sr Cl; Pres, Jr Cl; Tnns; Cl Fav; DARGCA; H of F; Hist A; John Philip Sousa A; *Auburn U; Engr.*

PARKER, Sheila Maria
Nerinx Hall HS; Webster Groves, MO; A Cap Choir; Y-Tns; Candystriper A; *Bradley U; Anesthesiology.*

PARKER, Sheila Marie
Chester HS; Chester, PA; Recordkeeping A; *Bus.*

PARKER, Stanley Maurice
Junipero Serra HS; Gardina, CA; VP, Chess C; Math C; Sch P; Tres, Spch C; Var C; Cpt, Cr-Ctry; Tr; JA A; Lion A; Spch A; VofDEM; *Pol Sci.*

PARKER, Teresa Faye
Franklin Co HS; Frankfort, KY; Chldr; Chor; Drama; Ensm; 4H; Sci C; Spch C; Ftbl; Church Bkbl & Sftbl; *U of Ky; Ed.*

PARKER, Teri Lynn
Abilene HS; Abilene, TX (50%-540) A Cap Choir; Chor; Tr; Cert of Appreciation; *Abilene Christian U; Nurs.*

PARKER, Timothy Brian
Fulton HS; Knoxville, TN (50-306) Chor; Ensm; Key C; Madrigal; NHS; Bsbl; Cpt, Bkbl; Cpt, Ftbl; Cl Fav; HKg; Yth Fel.

PARKER, Timothy David
T Wingate Andrews HS; High Point, NC (45-327) Hmrm; Bsbl; Bkbl; Ftbl; Golf; Sftbl; *Western Carolina U; Radiology.*

PARKER, Vanessa Charmayne
Lynwood HS; Lynwood, CA (50-460) Cpt, Chldr; Drama; GS; NHS; Sch P; SC; Pres, Jr Cl; CSF; HCt; Hon Prog; Math A; Phy A; Sci A; Type A; Yrbk; Stu Coun Cert of Service; Dodger A' Stu; Alumni o-t Pres Clrm; *UCLA; Pre-Med.*

PARKER, Wanda Yvette
Engleside Christian Sch; Alexandria, VA (3-4) Ann; Chor; Cpt, Dbte Tm; Drama; A-Ed, Sch P; Pres, Sr Cl; Sci A; Type A; *Dartmouth Col; Eng.*

PARKER, William Michael
Tallulah HS; Tallulah, LA (4-55) Bus C; Rptr, FBLA; Rptr, 4H; Hmrm; NHS; Ed, Sch P; SC; Y-Tns; *Miss Col; Bus.*

PARKER, William Neil
Sullivan Central HS; Blountville, TN (10%-476) BC; Chess C; 4H; Var C; Bkbl; Ftbl; Tr; 4H A; Hon Prog; FCA; Best Def Back, Ftbl; Explorer Sct; Tr Ribbon As; Tr Coaches A; Tr Trophy As; Bkbl, All Trophy; *NC U; Bus Adm.*

PARKES, Gary Wayne
Battle Ground Acad; Franklin, TN (2-98) Lat C; Order/Arrow; Cr-Ctry; Tr; NEDT; *U S Military Acad.*

PARKEY, Jacqueline Renee
Purcell HS; Purcell, OK; Bus C; FHA; St Hon Soc; *Gateway Bible Col; Bus.*

PARKINSON, Jane Evelyn
Edmeston Central Sch; Edmeston, NY (1-45) Ed, Ann; Band; Chor; Ensm; Fr C; NHS; Amer Leg A; COM; Chem A; Regent Schol; Val; Fr A; *Cornell U; Horticulture.*

PARKS, Alvin Leo
East St Louis Lincoln Sr HS; E St Louis, IL (1-350) A Cap Choir; Drama; Fr C; Math C; NHS; Spch C; Pres, Soph Cl; Bsbl; Ftbl; Citz A; Elk A; Hon Prog; Opt A; Spch A; 3rd Pl, Kappa's Spch Contest; Soph Ath Schol; Rptr, Jack & Jill Tn Regional; *Pediatrics.*

PARKS, Barry Timothy
Harrisburg HS; Harrisburg, IL (29-158) Band; Chess C; Key C; Rptr, Sch P; Var C; Bsbl; JV, Bkbl; Ftbl; JV, Wrest; Spch A; Soccer C; Amer Legion Bsbl; *SE Jr Col; Sci.*

PARKS, Calvin Lawrence
Mendel Cath Prep HS; Chicago, IL (11-148) CYO; Chess C; 4H; Key C; Sch P; Ski C; Span C; Var C; Mgr, Bsbl; Tnns; Hon Prog; MLS; Knights of Augustine; Excel A; WW; *Air Force Acad; Engr.*

PARKS, Carl Orlando
Montgomery Co HS; Mount Sterling, KY; Spch C; Tr; Star Student.

PARKS, Cheryl Darline
Lexington Sr HS; Lexington, NE (5-133) Chor; 4H; Hon Prog; Academic Distinction; Lexington Cosmos Schol; All-A HR; Top 5% of Cl; *Midwestern Sch of Evangelism; Pre-Med.*

PARKS, D Joan
Flemington HS; Flemington, WV (4-43) Secy, FHA; Secy, FTA; Secy, Rainbow; *Fairmont St Col.*

PARKS, Dale Esther
Eddyville HS; Eddyville, OR (2-11) Chldr; Rptr, FFA; 4H; SC; Pres, Soph Cl; Cpt, Bkbl; Tr; 4H A; HCt; Vlbl; Child Growth & Development A; Outst Phys Ed Stu; Valentines Day Dance Qn.

PARKS, Deborah Ann
Canton Pub HS; Canton, MS; FBLA; Spch C; Pres, Sr Cl; Math A; *U of Sou Miss; Biol.*

PARKS, Dennis Keith
Willamette HS; Eugene, OR; Band; BS; Math C; Tres, NHS; Orch; Order/Arrow; Tnns; Elk A; Order/Arrow A; Computer Sci A; Eagle Sct; *Oreg St Col; Computer Sci.*

PARKS, Derek Novarro
Benedictine HS; Cleveland, OH (29-115) Swim; Tr; Hon Prog; *Engr.*

PARKS, Greta
Hope HS; Hope, AR (30-200) BC; Chldr; FTA; Ger C; Sftbl; Swim; Nike C; Leo C; *Liberty Bapt St Col; Psych.*

PARKS, Jacqueline Ann
South Side HS; Memphis, TN (78-355) VP, Band; Tres, Hmrm; H of F; 1st Alt, Miss Yrbk; Most Stu; *Memphis St U; Acct.*

PARKS, Karen Denise
Mumford HS; Detroit, MI; NHS; Y-Tns; Citz A; Yth Fel; Fin, Sci A; *Morehouse Col; Acct.*

PARKS, Keith Tyus
Cairo HS; Cairo, GA; Cpt, Band; Chor; Ensm; InterAct C; Lit Ral; Hon Prog; John Philip Sousa Band A; Rotary Schol; Lit Rally A; Outst Service Band A; *Valdosta St Col; Mus.*

PARKS, Kevin Wayne
Eaton HS; Eaton, OH; A Cap Choir; Co-Ed, Ann; Band; Chor; Tres, Drama; Ensm; Fr C; Pres, FTA; 4H; Tres, HiY; Order/Arrow; Sch Achieve Tm; SC; MVP, Swim; JV, Tnns; Mgr, Wrest; Hon Prog; Del, St Rep Conv; Pres, Church Group; Pres, Young Republicans; Mus As; *Drake U; Pol Sci.*

PARKS, Linda Gail
Fuller Normal HS; Greenville, SC; *Psych.*

PARKS, Lisa Kay
El Dorado HS; El Dorado, AR (8%-357) Anchor C; Co-Cpt, Chldr; Chor; Ensm; VP, FBLA; Madrigal; Tres, NHS; Tres, SC; Tres, Soph Cl; HCt; Hon Prog; Key C Calendar Girl; Jr Civitan C; Wearer o-t Gold; Schol, U of Ark Schol Soc.

PARKS, Lynn Alfred
Midland HS; Midland, TX (9-587) Band; NHS; Hon Prog; Acad A; *Tex Tech U; Law.*

PARKS, Myra J
N Gwinnett HS; Suwanee, GA (5%-120) Chor; FHA; COM; Gov Honor Prog; Type A; Shorthand A; Most Talented; FHA Jr Achv; Filing A; Outst Choral A.

PARKS, Penny Sue
Marion Harding HS; Marion, OH (1-466) FTA; Ed, Lit Mag; NHS; Ed, Sch P; Span C; Val; WW; *Ohio St U; Pre-Law.*

PARKS, Robin Kay
Bryan Adams HS; Dallas, TX (50-800) Drama; NHS; Span C; Hon Prog; *Abilene Christian U; Bus.*

PARKS, Sharon Kay
Breckinridge Co HS; Harned, KY (10%-250) Chor; Ensm; FHA; Sci C; Span C; SC; Tnns; Outst Stu, Home Ec; *U of Ky; Math.*

PARKS, Terry James
University HS; Spokane, WA (20-500) Chess C; FTA; NHS; Order/Arrow; Swim; JV, Tr; Alg A; Chem A; Hon Prog; Math A; NMS; Order/Arrow A; Phy A; ARC A; Sci A.

PARKS, William Henry
Ironton HS; Ironton, OH (10-191) Band; Demolay; NHS; Order/Arrow; Bkbl; Tr; Eagle A, Scts; *U of Cincinnati; Engr.*

PARLANGE, Angele Maltby
Episcopal HS; Baton Rouge, LA; VP, BC; Chor; Drama; Fr C; InterClub Coun; Lit Mag; NHS; Sch P; Hon Prog; Ch, Homecoming; Fr A; Excellence in Fr A; *La St U; Geology.*

PARMALEE, Brenda Lee
NE HS; Oakland Park, FL (332-568) Spch C; Bkbl; *SE Bible Col; Elem Ed.*

PARMAN, Vickie Ann
Oviedo HS; Oviedo, FL (40-245) Band; Drama; Ensm; Sftbl; COM; Secy, Church SC.

PARMELEE, Barit Lynn
Matawan Regional HS; Matawan, NJ (147-480) Band; Orch; *Mus.*

PARMENTER, Phyllis Diane
West HS; Columbus, OH; Band; Chor; Ensm; Y-Tns; Hon Prog; PTA A; Type A; *N Central Bible Col; Mus.*

PARMER, Katherine Marie
Mangum HS; Mangum, OK (1-65) F-Ed, Ann; Band; Chor; Ensm; FHA; Alg A; Hist A; Eng A; *Okla Baptist U.*

PARNELL, Cynthia Rene
El Dorado HS; El Dorado, AR; BC; Chor; NHS; Sci C; *Ouachita Baptist U; Nurs.*

PARNELL, Denise Darlene
E Richland HS; Olney, IL (35-272) Band; Chldr; Chor; Semi-Fin, Jr Miss Pa; Lat C; Madrigal; SC; 4H A; Swim Teacher; Ntl Champ Bible Quiz Tm; *Greenville Col; Secy.*

PARNELL, Joe Lynn
Cambridge HS; Cambridge, OH; InterClub Coun; Key C; SC; Var C; Pres, Soph Cl; Bkbl; Tnns.

PARNELL, Larry Thomas
Cambridge HS; Cambridge, OH (39-280) Key C; VP, NHS; Tnns; Most Improved, Tnns; *U of Cincinnati; Engr.*

PARNELL, Ray Forest
Topeka HS; Topeka, KS (175-511) Ger C; Model UN; Thes; COM; Tsar, Russian C; *Washburn Col; Linguistics.*

PAROLINI, Stephen Paul
W Aurora HS; Aurora, IL (16-760) A Cap Choir; Chor; NHS; Hon Prog; Yth Fel; All St Choir; Crimi Schol; Lead, Choir Shows; 1st, Dist Mus Festival; *Aurora Col; Ed.*

PARR, Cheri Lynn
Salina HS Central; Salina, KS; Chor; Tnns; Yth Fel; Pom Pon Squad.

PARR, Lois Ruby
Hiram W Johnson HS; Sacramento, CA (300-874) Hmrm; *UC Berkley; Archt.*

PARR, Treva Dian
Ninnekah HS; Ninnekah, OK (1-54) Chor; Rptr, FHA; 4H; NHS; Pres, SC; S-T, 4H; Amer Leg A; Citz A; Crisco A; DARGCA; 4H A; Hist A; Hon Prog; Math A; Val; Eng A; Art A; Home Ec A; Gen Bus A.

PARRETT, Martha Jane
Rowan Center HS; Hattiesburg, MS; Y-Tns; Piano A; *William Carey Col; Mus.*

PARRIS, Pamela Jo
Terrell Acad; Dawson, GA (10-35) Fr C; FTA; Secy, 4H; Lat C; Tri-HiY; 4H A; VP, 4-H C; *Ga SW Col.*

PARRISH, Cheryl Annette
Beaver Dam Sr HS; Beaver Dam, WI (27-388) Cpt, Chldr; Tres, Chor; Ensm; Fin, GS; Hmrm; Madrigal; NHS; Orch; Ski C; VP, SC; Var C; JV, Bkbl; Pres A; Sci A; Vlbl; Schol Achv, Art, Sci Fair, A's; Prom Qn; *Math.*

PARRISH, Gary Leavano
W Side Sr HS; Gary, IN (9-700) Band; Chess C; Hmrm; Lat C; NHS; Bkbl; Cr-Ctry; Citz A; Hon Prog; Ntl Sci Symposium; Win, Hon's Abroad to Italy Stu Prog; *Princeton U; Law.*

PARRISH, Gregory Stanley
Ft Pierce Central HS; Fort Pierce, FL (91-582) A Cap Choir; BC; VP, Chor; Ensm; Hmrm; SC; Co-Cpt, Wrest; H of F; Hon Prog; Most Out; St Sup Soloist; *Bethune-Cookman Col; Social Sci.*

PARRISH, Jean Gladys
Bible Baptist Sch; Savannah, GA (25%-54) F-Ed, Ann; Chldr; ARC; Tres, Sr Cl; Tres, Jr Cl; Sftbl; Cl Fav; ARC A; *Armstrong St Col; Art.*

PARRISH, Jeffery Ferrell
Medina HS; Medina, TN (3-23) F-Ed; Ann; BC; BS; Tres, FHA; Var C; Cpt, Bkbl; MLS; Most Popular; Mr MHS; *U of Tenn; Math.*

PARRISH, John Alvin
Thomasville HS; Thomasville, GA (5%-200) All Amer Yth; BC; Key C; Co-Cpt, Ftbl; Prep All Amer; WW; WW, Ath; Col Schol; *U of Ga; Pre-Med.*

PARRISH, Kathy Lynn
Greencastle HS; Greencastle, IN (28-155) Pres, Span C; Swim; Yth Fel; Church A; Academic A; Swim A; WW, Foreign Lang; *Ind St U; Med Tech.*

PARRISH, Thomas Maynard Jr
Jeff Davis HS; Hazlehurst, GA (36-169) Chess C; Literary One Act Play A; Chess Cert; Oral Interpretation A; *Social Studies.*

PARROTT, Jacki Kay
Broken Arrow HS; Broken Arrow, OK; Band; Tres, Fr C; Tres, FTA; Sftbl; COM; Citz A; Spelling A; Church Attendance A; *Okla Baptist U; Nurs.*

PARROTT, Kathryn Alice
Fallbrook Union HS; Fallbrook, CA; A Cap Choir; Chor; Madrigal; Citz A; Mus A; Poetry A; *Keypunch.*

PARROTT, Kirk Elder
Claremont HS; Claremont, CA (60-576) Drama; Ger C; Swim; CSF.

PARROTT, Lester
Academy HS; Temple, TX;

PARROTT, Lois Ann
Goodlettsville HS; Goodlettsville, TN (1-159) Band; Chor; VP, Lat C; Lat NHS; Pres, NHS; Alg A; Bio A; COM; Math A; MLS; NEDT; Opt A; Sci A; Val; Band Schol; *Tenn Tech U; Computer Sci.*

PARROW, Donna Marie
HS of Commerce; Springfield, MA (5-400) Commercial C; Hmrm; NHS; ARC; Span C; Hon Prog; Yth Fel; *Springfield Tech Comm Col; Acct.*

PARRY, Martha Catherine
James I O'Neill HS; Highland Falls, NY; Band; Drama; ARC; Hon Prog; Yth Fel; Comm Band; GSct; Church Sch Teacher; *Med.*

PARSEGHIAN, Gregory John
Upper Darby Sr HS; Upper Darby, PA (13-1000) Sch Achieve Tm; Ed, Sch P; Math A; Sci A; *U of Pa; Bus Adm.*

PARSELLS, Brian Clifford
Wellsboro Are Sr HS; Wellsboro, PA (62-219) CYO; Tres, Ger C; Var C; JV, Bkbl; Ftbl; Tr; COM; ARC A; Pres, NJHS; All Star Ftbl; *Mansfield St Col; Criminal Justice.*

PARSHALL, Diana Elizabeth
Santa Monica HS; Santa Monica, CA (415-850) Fr C; Adm Board; Co-Ch, MYF; Sunday Sch Teacher; Hon Qn, Intrntl Ord Job's Daughters; *Nurs.*

PARSLEY, Bernadette Louise
Verdi Pub Sch; Verdi, MN (2-11) Pres, Chor; Drama; Tres, SC; Co-Cpt, Bkbl; Tr; Spch A.

PARSLEY, Elizabeth Charleen
Pine Bluff HS; Pine Bluff, AR; Alg A; Math A; Most Out; Sci A; Chldr A; Schol A; Eng A; *U of Central Ark; Acct.*

PARSLEY, Kerri L
Norfolk Sr HS; Norfolk, NE; Pep C; Panther o-t Wk; *York Col; Eng.*

PARSLEY, Mark Joseph
Verdi Pub HS; Verdi, MN; Chor; Drama; VP, Soph Cl; Bkbl; Cr-Ctry; Ftbl; Tr; Hon Prog; *Law.*

PARSLEY, Mona Jane
Verdi HS; Verdi, MN (1-9) Ann; Band; Drama; Sch P; Spch C; Pres, SC; Pres, Sr Cl; Secy, Jr Cl; Pres, Soph Cl; Bkbl; Sftbl; Tr; B Crocker A; HQn; Spch A; MVP, Vlbl; *Granite Falls Col; Bus.*

PARSON, Naida Marie
Valley HS; Las Vegas, NV (70-535) Bus Mgr, Band; NHS; SC; Bkbl; Hon Prog; Gov Coun On Children & Yth; Sun Yth Forum; WW; *U of Calif at Riverside; Psych.*

PARSONS, Carmen Annette
Sch Without Walls; Washington, DC; F-Ed, Ann; Chldr; Rptr, Lit Mag; *Photojourn.*

PARSONS, Christy Lynn
John Marshall HS; San Antonio, TX (5%-765) A-Ed, Ann; Dbte Tm; Fr C; Math C; Mu Alpha Theta; SC; 1st Best Opening Section; SHSU Communications Workshop; Sr Play Choreographer; Tres, Yth Group 1st Cl, GSct; *Math.*

PARSONS, David Lynn
Scott Preparatory Sch; Opelika, AL (15%-29) Anchor C; Chess C; Demolay; Hmrm; SC; Var C; Pres, Sr Cl; VP, Jr Cl; Bsbl; Co-Cpt, Bkbl; HCt; Leo C; FCA; *Huntingdon Col; Bus Adm.*

PARSONS, Delwyn Aaron
Burnsville HS; Burnsville, MS; Tres, FFA; 4H; Cpt, Ftbl; H of F; *Northeast Miss Jr Col; Heavy Mach.*

PARSONS, John Douglas
Canton S HS; Canton, OH (1-273) BS; Chor; Pres, Drama; FTA; VP, Hmrm; Lat C; Pres, Math C; Pres, NFL; NHS; Sch P; Pres, Sci C; Pres, Spch C; Pres, Thes; VP, Sr Cl; Ftbl; God & Country A; Spch A; VofDEM; St, Ntl Qualifier, NFL; Tn o-t Mo; *Med.*

PARSONS, John Mark
Seymour HS; Seymour, TN (21-90) Pres, Key C; SC; Pres, Var C; Secy, Sr Cl; Secy, Jr Cl; Cpt, Bkbl; Cpt, Ftbl; Cl Fav; HCt; Hon Prog; Yth Fel; MVP, Ftbl; All-Co MVP Ftbl; FCA.

PARSONS, Judi A
Oxford HS; Oxford, KS (3-45) Band; Chor; Ensm; Sftbl; Tr; COM; 4H A; VP & S-T, 4-H C.

PARSONS, Kathleen Joy
Lely HS; Naples, FL (20-230) Chor; Drama; Ensm; Madrigal; Hon Prog; JA A; Yth Fel; Pres, Jr Achv Co; Pres, MYF; Pres, Z C; *U of Fla; Nurs.*

PARSONS, Leigh Ann
Goodlettsville HS; Goodlettsville, TN (23-159) Chor; Ensm; FHA; GS; Pres, Lat C; NHS; ARC; Var C; Mgr, Bkbl; Tnns; ARC A; Sci A; Hist, Swtht, Lat C; Candystriper; *Dental Hygiene.*

PARSONS, Loretta Jean
Highland HS; Sparta, OH (2-127) Pres, Bus C; Bkbl; Sal; *Ohio St U; Bus Adm.*

PARSONS, Mark Alan
Edison Sr HS; Stockton, CA; NHS; JV, Bkbl; Sftbl; Citz A; Hon Prog; Yth Fel; *U of Calif at San Diego; Marine Bio.*

PARSONS, Maxie Howard
Walhalla Sr HS; Walhalla, SC (10%-160) Tr; Pres, Yth Fellowship; *Clemson U; Elec.*

PARSONS, Myra Lee
Burnsville HS; Burnsville, MS (5-43) Ann; Band; VP, BC; FHA; 4H; Sch P; Bkbl; Tr; Beauty; Most Beautiful; Qn of Fair; *Freed-Hardeman Col; Bus.*

PARSONS, Nancy Frances
Mullens HS; Mullens, WV (7-115) Band; BC; Chess C; Drama; Pres, FBLA; HiY; Semi-Fin, Jr Miss Pa; NHSt; Tres, Pol Sci C; Ed, Sch P; Span C; Tri-HiY; Tnns; Journ A; Q&S A; Yth Leg; WW; Most Talented; *Concord Col; Bio.*

PARSONS, Nick Alan
Mena HS; Mena, AR (1-140) A-Ed, Ann; Band; Chem C; Ensm; NHS; Phys C; Pres, Jr Cl; Alg A; Yth Fel; Most Talented; Mus Camps Schol; Ntl Trumpet Symp; *Mus.*

PARSONS, Sharon Ann
Burnsville HS; Burnsville, MS (1-46) Ed, Ann; BC; Chldr; Chor; FHA; Ed, Sch P; Pres, Jr Cl; Pres, Soph Cl; Beauty; Cl Fav; H of F; HCt; MLS; Friendliest; Miss BHS; *Northeast Jr Col.*

PARSONS, Shonda Lynn
Battiest HS; Battiest, OK (1-45) Chor; Rptr, FHA; Bkbl; Sftbl; *Bus.*

PARSONS, Tammy Renee
Springville HS; Springville, AL (5%-50) Pres, BC; FHA; 4H; Hmrm; Sch P; Spch C; Beauty; 4H A; Hist A; Hon Prog; Eng A; Miss Springville; FFA Best Mod; Ala Christian Endeavorer o-t Yr; *Southeastern Bible Col; Teacher's Ed.*

PARTIN, Harold Allison Jr
Camden Co HS; St Marys, GA (4-200) BC; BS; Hmrm; Pres, Span C; SC; Ftbl; COM; DARGCA; Pres, Art; Art A; Parl, Span C; *Brunswick Jr Col; Bus Adm.*

PARTIN, Phillip Edward
S Dade Sr HS; Homestead, FL (60-850) MIT; Digital Elec Engr.

PARTON, Joel Dean
Harrison-Chilhowee Baptist Acad; Seymour, TN (7-46) F-Ed, Ann; BC; Chor; Madrigal; Sci C; SC; Pres, Sr Cl; I Dare You; Excel A; Del, St Republic Convention; Top 10; *Tenn Tech U.*

PARTON, Maureen Kay
Sacred Heart Acad; Salem, OR (10%-55) NHS; Sch P; Secy, SC; Cpt, Bkbl; Rotary A; Yth Leg; Bkbl, Vlbl, A's; *U of San Francisco; Law.*

PARTRIDGE, Charlotte
Northside HS; Atlanta, GA; Chldr; Tres, Chor; Attendance A's; *Fla A&M U; Phys Ed.*

PARTRIDGE, Micheal Reed
Springfield HS; Springfield, OR (10%-282) Chess C; Chor; Ed, Sch P; Elk A; VFW A; VofDEM; *Pepperdine U; Journ.*

PARTRIDGE, Paul Anthony
Seekonk HS; Seekonk, MA (7-224) Band; NHS; Orch; Var C; MVP, Golf; Hockey; ROTC Fin; *U of Notre Dame; Civil Engr.*

PARTRIDGE, Roselle Joy
Southport HS; Indianapolis, IN (1-499) Secy, Band; Ensm; FTA; 4H; Span C; Golf; Swim; Alg A; COM; Citz A; Cl Fav; 4H A; Math A; Pres A; Yth Fel; Cand, Hugh O'Brien Ldrshp A; *Ind Central U; Bus.*

PARTRIDGE, Stanley Mark
W Holmes HS; Millersburg, OH (7-200) A Cap Choir; Band; Drama; FTA; Lat C; NHS; Order/Arrow; Sch Achieve Tm; Sci C; God & Country A; Spch A; Alt, BS; Eagle Sct; Lat A; *Math.*

PARTYKA, Stan Frank
Driscoll HS; Addison, IL (12-144) NHS; Rptr, Sch P; Tres, Sr Cl; Bsbl; Chem A; *Elmhurst Col; Pre-Law.*

PASBRIG, Randall Scott
Horicon HS; Horicon, WI (12-110) FFA; NHS; Var C; Bsbl; Ftbl; JV, Golf; *Pre-Vet Col; Vet.*

PASBY, Garry Edward
Elk City HS; Elk City, OK; A Cap Choir; Ann; Rptr, Bus C; Chor; Dbte Tm; Rptr, Drama; Ensm; FBLA; FFA; FHA; 4H; Sch P; Spch C; Mgr, Bsbl; Bkbl; Mgr, Ftbl; Mgr, Tr; Citz A; Spch A; Outst FHA Member; Mus Schol; WW; *Southwestern Okla St Col; Mus.*

PASCHAL, Eunice Lee
Colonel White HS; Dayton, OH (140-201) A Cap Choir; Chldr; Chor; Drama; VP, Miss Pagent; Cpt, Sftbl; Cl Fav; Type A; Yth Fel; Mus A; *Montgomery Jr Col; Secretarial.*

PASCHAL, Gary Dean
LaPorte Sr HS; LaPorte, TX; Rptr, Sch P; Journ A; Q&S A; *San Jacinto Jr Col; Journ.*

PASCUAL, Jody Oliveros
Sylvan Hills HS; Atlanta, GA (9-160) BC; NHS; Soccer; Math A; *Ga Inst of Tech; Civil Engr.*

PASLAY, Ramona Kay
Tower Hill HS; Tower Hill, IL (3-30) Band; Chor; VP, FHA; Rptr, Sch P; S-T, SC; S-T, Jr Cl; Sftbl; Type A; Vlbl; Pep C; PA.

PASQUALE, Joseph Anthony
Chester HS; Chester, PA (20-680) *Widener Col; Elec.*

PASS, Connie Sue
N Gwinnett HS; Suwanee, GA (10%-120) Ed, Ann; BC; Dbte Tm; Secy, FHA; 4H; VP, SC; Secy, Sr Cl; Secy, Jr Cl; Chem A; HCt; Poet A; Sci A; Swtht; *Gainesville Jr Col; Early Childhood Ed.*

PASS, Jeffrey Alan
N Gwinnett HS; Suwanee, GA (1-150) Pres, BC; Dbte Tm; Math C; Fin, Wrest; Alg A; Hist A; Hon Prog; Math A; Type A; Eng A; PE A; TV Energy Pomel; *Emory U; Med.*

PASS, Michael Christopher
College Park HS; Pleasant Hill, CA; Band; COM; *Calif Maritime Acad; Nautical Engr.*

PASSARELLA, Barbara Jean
St Joseph HS; Hammonton, NJ (7-48) Co-Cpt, Chldr; Chor; Secy, Drama; Secy, Fr C; Hmrm; Jr Miss Pagent; Ed, Sch P; Sci C; VP, Jr Cl; MVP, Sftbl; HCt; WW; Principal's HR; Valentine Qn; *Camden Co Col; Dental Hygiene.*

PASSERINI, Carla Marie
Our Lady of Good Counsel HS; Newark, NJ (8-17) Chldr; Drama; Co-Ed, Sch P; Hon Prog; Dance Comm; Yrbk Staff; Lib Aid; *Montclair St Col; Pol Sci.*

PASSKIEWICZ, Cynthia Ann
Our Lady o-t Lakes; Waterford, MI (2-55) VP, NHS; Pres, Ski C; VP, Soph Cl; Type A; Ski Tm; *Baker's Jr Col; Secretarial.*

PASSMORE, Cynthia Jeannette
Mtn View HS; Mtn View, AR; BC; Chldr; FBLA; FHA; FTA; Sch P; Citz A.

PASSMORE, Deborah Ruth
John T Hoggard HS; Wilmington, NC (170-600) Drama; VP, Thes; Cpt, Bkbl; Sftbl; Tr; MVP, Bkbl; *W Carolina U; Journ.*

PASTER, Angela Konora
Carroll HS; Monroe, LA; Fr C; Hmrm; Phys C; VP, SC; Hon Prog; *Sou U; Nurs.*

PASTERNAK, Kathleen Jane
Goodman HS; Goodman, WI (1-23) Co-Ed, Ann; Band; Chldr; Chor; Drama; Ensm; S-T, NHS; Rptr, Sch P; Pres, SC; Pres, Sr Cl; JV, Bkbl; Alg A; Hon Prog; Sci A; Spch A; Val; Secy, SC; Civil Defense A; WW; Prom Court; *Fox Valley Tech Inst; Interior Decorator.*

PATCH, Becky Jo
John Marshall HS; San Antonio, TX (33%-746) FHA; Span C; Campus Life; Pres, Luther League; *Psych.*

PATCH, Margaret Elizabeth
Lewiston-Porter Central HS; Youngstown, NY (3-350) Chor; Ger C; NHS; NMS; Ntl Sci Found; *U of Buffalo; Nurs.*

PATE, Amy Elizabeth
Hardaway HS; Columbus, GA; Chor; Fr C; Mjrte; Hon Prog; *Fr.*

PATE, Cheryl Lynn
Edgewood HS; Trenton, OH (86-244) Chor; FNA; ARC; COM; *Miami U; Nurs.*

PATE, Glenda Gay
Sam Houston Sr HS; Houston, TX; Bus C; Pres, Hmrm; NHS; SC; *U of Houston.*

PATE, Kathy Diane
Riverside HS; Avon, MS; Cpt, Chldr; Drama; Secy, Hmrm; Lit Ral; SC; HCt; *Moorehead Col; Elem Ed.*

PATE, Manuel Franklin
Putnam City W HS; Oklahoma City, OK; Hockey; Soccer; Swim; Tr; Tr A, Copper Plaque; Eng A; St Yth Impach Tm; Fr Outst Achv Cert; Pres, Church Yth Soc; *Religion.*

PATE, Marcia Winona
Villa Rica HS; Villa Rica, GA; A-Ed, Ann; Secy, Band; BC; Chor; Hmrm; VP, Lat C; Lit Ral; Sci C; SC; WW; *Ga St U; Respiratory Therapy.*

PATE, Michael Victor
Osceola HS; Kissimmee, FL (8-350) BS; Thes; Bsbl; Ftbl; *Math.*

PATE, Raymond Martin Jr
Iroquois HS; Louisville, KY (40-470) Bsbl; *U of Louisville; Aerospace Sci.*

PATE, Regina Lynn
Villa Rica HS; Villa Rica, GA; Ann; Band; Chor; Fr C; Sci C; Mgr, Bkbl; Sftbl; *W Ga Col; Nurs.*

PATE, Thomas Edward
Poteau HS; Poteau, OK (50%-110) NHS; Sci C; SC; COM; VICA; *Carl Albert Jr Col; Auto Mechanics.*

PATEL, Hamant Jay
Los Angeles Lutheran HS; Burbank, CA; NHS; Bsbl; JV, Bkbl; CSF; *UCLA; Med.*

PATELSKI, Steven Robert
Palm Bay HS; Palm Bay, FL; Ftbl; *US Air Force; Mech.*

PATENT, Kevin R
Randolph Public Sch; Randolph, NE; Bkbl; MVP, Ftbl; All Conf Hon, Ftbl; *Wayne St U; Bus Adm.*

PATERSON, Cheryl Lynn
Oak Lawn Comm HS; Oak Lawn, IL (10-697) VP, A Cap Choir; Math C; Pres, NHS; Sci C; St Stu Congress; Tnns; Hon Prog; Kiwanis A; Yth Leg; Ed, Church Newspaper; *U of NM; Law.*

PATERSON, Virginia Bergen
Blacksburg HS; Blacksburg, VA (58-300) Band; Chor; Ensm; Fr C; Pres, Hmrm; Mjrte; NHS; Vlbl; All Regional Band; *U of Kans; Mus.*

PATH, Bill Rocklyn
A&M Consolidated HS; College Station, TX; A Cap Choir; JV, Bkbl; Bkbl & Vlbl Intramural Coach; 1st Pl, Trophey Bible Bowl.

PATIN, Dennis Joseph
Trinity Prep Sch; Orlando, FL (2-58) VP, Cum Laude Soc; Key C; Model UN; Co-Ed, Sch P; Span C; Swim; Hist A; Sal; Sci A; NMS Commended Stu; Sewanee A for Excellence; Traylor Found Schol; *Vanderbilt U; Environmental Engr.*

PATMORE, Daniel Ross
Winner Sr HS; Winner, SD (70-105) Band; Chor; Drama; Ensm; Thes; Bkbl; Ftbl; Tr; Outst Thespian A; Ltr, Band & Chorus; *Mitchel Va Tech; Elec.*

PATRICK, Barry Alan
Pleasant Grove HS; Pleasant Grove, AL (1-150) Chem C; NHS; Cpt, Golf; Val; *U of Ala; Bus Mgr.*

PATRICK, Bridgitte Michelle
Ragsdale HS; Jamestown, NC (147-385) Bkbl; Sftbl; *Art Inst of Atlanta; Fine Arts.*

PATRICK, Donald Anthony
Puckett HS; Brandon, MS; FFA; Bsbl; MVP, Sftbl; COM; Citz A; Cl Fav; HCt; MLS; Yth Fel; Most Dependable; *Clarke Col; Bus Adm.*

PATRICK, Gary James
Wallace Sr HS; Wallace, ID (37-108) Ann; Dbte Tm; Drama; Fr C; Key C; NHS; Order/Arrow; Rptr, Sch P; Ski C; Span C; Fin, Spch C; Fin, Thes; Bkbl; Spch A; WW; *Idaho St U; Communications.*

PATRICK, Glen Evan
Lindale HS; Lindale, TX (1-103) Band; BC; Dbte Tm; Math C; NFL; Span C; Pres, Spch C; Tnns; Rotary A; Spch A; St Dbte Champ; UIL St Soloist; Drafting A; *SMU; Law.*

PATRICK, Irish Frenett
Sebastopol HS; Sebastopol, MS (4-38) Rptr, Band; Chldr; Chor; Drama; FHA; VP, SC; Var C; Bkbl; Tr; Beauty; PA; Schol A; *Hinds Jr Col; Med Record Tech.*

PATRICK, Jacoby
Hirsch HS; Chicago, IL (28-210) Chess C; Chor; Swim; Yth Fel; *NW U; Law.*

PATRICK, Linda Ann
Carsonville-Port Sanilac HS; Carsonville, MI (10-67) Ann; Band; NHS; Sch P; Tres, Sr Cl; Bkbl; MVP, Sftbl; COM; Hon Prog; Magna Cum Laude; Ntl Achv Schol; NMF; NMS; St Scholar; Acad Schol Mich Competative Fin; *Grand Rapids Sch o-t Bible & Mus; Mus.*

PATRICK, Lola Dean
Waynesboro Central HS; Waynesboro, MS (25%-99) BC; Sch P; WW; *St Dominic Col; Nurs.*

PATRICK, Richard Carl
Puckett Attendance Center; Brandon, MS; All Amer Yth; Band; Chor; Pres, FFA; VP, 4H; Math C; Sch P; SC; Pres, Jr Cl; Bsbl; Bkbl; Cr-Ctry; Cpt, Ftbl; Cpt, Sftbl; Tr; Bio A; Citz A; Cl Fav; 4H A; HKg; HCt; Math A; Most Out; PTA A; Yth Fel; MVP, Ftbl; Yth Pastor; *Miss Col; Religous Ed.*

PATRICK, Rick Joe
Reeds Spring HS; Reeds Spring, MO (6-75) BC; Bkbl; Ftbl; Tr; Citz A; *Art.*

PATRICK, Rochelle Denise
MacKenzie HS; Detroit, MI (7-352) Secy, Bus C; NHS; BOEC Ldrship Conf A; *Bus.*

PATRICK, Scott Alan
Winnfield Sr HS; Winnfield, LA (18-116) Band; BC; Bus C; Dbte Tm; VP, Fr C; FBLA; 4H; Lit Ral; Rptr, Spch C; Citz A; DARGCA; Hist A; Sci A; Pres, Hist, Jr Amer Citizen; Masque & Gavel; *NW St U; Spch Ed.*

PATRICK, Sheila Maria
Cass Technical HS; Detroit, MI; SC; *Mich St U; Law.*

PATRIE, Stephanie Kathryn
J Graham Brown HS; Louisville, KY (5-80) Chor; Dbte Tm; 4H A; Hon Prog; NMS.

PATSCHKE, Priscilla Renee
Cy-Fair HS; Houston, TX; Band; FHA; Ger C.

PATSEY, John Drew
Somerset HS; Somerset, KY (40-180) God & Country A; *Engr.*

PATTEE, John Wallace
Avoha Comm HS; Avoca, IA (4-43) Hmrm; NHS; Pres, SC; Var C; Pres, Sr Cl; MVP, Bsbl; Cpt, Ftbl; Cpt, Wrest; Cl Fav; HCt; Most Out; *Drake U; Acct.*

PATTEN, Cheryl Marie
Boulder HS; Boulder, CO (250-500) CYO; 4H; Wrest; 4H A; JA A; Opt Out Tn; Scorekeeper, Wrest; *Parks Col; Med Tech.*

PATTEN, Linda Joyce
Southwest Sr HS; Miami, FL; Rptr, Sch P; Yth Fel; EAG C; VP, Yth Fel; *Jones Co Jr Col; Child Psych.*

PATTEN, Phil Andrew
Watson Green Christian HS; Seattle, WA (1-33) Hmrm; Sch P; Soph Cl; Cpt, Bkbl; Cpt, Cr-Ctry; Cpt, Tr; COM; Hon Prog; Ntl Sci Found; NEDT; Co-Cpt HS Super Star; *U of Wash; Math.*

PATTERSON, Anna Marie
Connellsville Area Sr HS; Connellsville, PA (10%-676) Chor; Sch P; Hon Prog; *Oral Roberts U; Med.*

PATTERSON, Betsy Lee
Lexington HS; Lexington, TN (1-200) BC; City Conf; Ensm; FTA; Semi-Fin, GS; Sch P; Sci C; Hon Prog; Most Intellectual; Most Stu; 1st Pl, Sci Fair; *Union U; Bus.*

PATTERSON, Bruce Wayne
Anna-Jonesboro Comm HS; Anna, IL (6-95) Band; FTA; Lat C; Orch; *NY U; Econ.*

PATTERSON, Cathy Leigh
Jackson Prep; Jackson, MS (50%-100) Chor; Ensm; Fr C.

PATTERSON, Cecil Dwayne
Hobbs HS; Hobbs, NM (10-570) Demolay; *Jr Col; Real Estate.*

PATTERSON, Cheryl Jean
Green Bay Preble HS; Green Bay, WI (190-496) Band; InterAct C; Fin, Lit Mag; ARC; Sci C; Swim; Ch, GSct; Fin, Preble Mus; Literary Contest; *U Wisc Eau Claire; Special Ed.*

PATTERSON, Christine Kay
Whitehall Mem HS; Whitehall, WI (12-85) Chor; NHS; Sch P; Span C; Pres, Soph Cl; Hon Prog; *Bethel Col; Dental Hygiene.*

PATTERSON, David James
Western Hills HS; Fort Worth, TX (40-620) Mgr, Bkbl; *Howard Payne U; Baptist Ministry.*

PATTERSON, Dawn Elizabeth
West Linn HS; West Lunn, OR; *OSU; Broadcasting.*

PATTERSON, Deborah Ann
Mt Carmel HS; Mt Carmel, IL (1-172) Ed, Ann; Band; Chor; VP, Lat C; Pres, NHS; DARGCA; Elk A; Kiwanis A; NMF; NEDT; St Scholar; Val; All St Band; WW; *N Ill U; Computer Sci.*

PATTERSON, Diana Faye
Springfield HS; Springfield, LA; Band; VP, BC; Chldr; Pres, FHA; Tres, 4H; Hmrm; Mod Mus Mas; NHS; Rainbow; Secy, Jr Cl; Citz A; 4H A; Band A; Ldrship A; *SE La U; Med.*

PATTERSON, Don Alan
Slaton HS; Slaton, TX (1-100) Ftbl; Tr; Hon Prog; Val; Highest Grade Point Avg; *Tex A&M U; Med.*

PATTERSON, Don Neal
Mt Carmel HS; Mt Carmel, IL (1-200) Chess C; Key C; Span C; Kiwanis A; NEDT; *Ga St U; Actuarial Sci.*

PATTERSON, Donald Matthew
Babylon Jr-Sr HS; Babylon, NY (2%-200) Chor; Var C; Ftbl; Tr; Wrest; Hon Prog; Suffolk Co Math Contest; *Engr.*

PATTERSON, Frances Ann
Tuscaloosa HS; Tuscaloosa, AL (1-561) Pres, Hmrm; InterClub Coun; Pres, Lat C; Mu Alpha Theta; NHS; SC; Mgr, Bkbl; Golf; Cl Fav; Math A; MLS; *U of Ala; Mech Engr.*

PATTERSON, Jana Stone
Eastern Hills HS; Fort Worth, TX; S-T, Fr C; *Religion.*

PATTERSON, Jeffrey Alan
S Mecklenburg HS; Pineville, NC; Span C; *U of NC at Wilmington; Environmental Studies.*

PATTERSON, Jimmy
Terrell Co HS; Dawson, GA (10%-112) Co-Cpt, Bkbl; MLS; *Fort Valley St Col; Bus Mgr.*

PATTERSON, John Clay
Hinsdale Central HS; Hinsdale, IL (22-650) Math C; NHS; Orch; JV, Cr-Ctry; JV, Tr; Hon Prog; Dean's List; Church Bell Choir; *U of Ill-Urbana; Engr.*

PATTERSON, Judith Ann
Metlakatla Jr-Sr HS; Metlakatla, AK; *Sheldon Jackson Col; Social Work.*

PATTERSON, June Diane
Florence Twp Mem HS; Florence, NJ (3-117) Cpt, Chldr; Pres, FBLA; GS; NHS; Var C; Type A; Co Cpt, March of Dimes; Bookkeeping A; Fin, Ntl Secy Schol; *Burlington Co Comm Col; Med Secy.*

PATTERSON, Kathryn Jo
Hood River Valley HS; Hood River, OR (50-185) Band; Bus C; FHA; VP, 4H; Hmrm; 4H A; Masonic A; Past Hon Qn, Jobs Daughters; Tres, Service C; *Oreg St U; Home Ec.*

PATTERSON, Kathy Gail
Dunedin Comprehensive HS; Dunedin, FL (10-840) Chor; Hmrm; NHS; Span, Lat, A's; Pom-Pon; Health Careers C; St Petersburg Jr Col; Dental Hygienist.

PATTERSON, Keith Joseph
Ramey Jr-Sr HS; Ramey, PR (2-22) Band; Chor; Sch P; Secy, Soph Cl; JV, Bkbl; Golf; Mgr, Wrest; Alg A; COM; Hist A; Math A; Sci A; Eng Merit A; Band Merit A; Coast Guard Acad; Math.

PATTERSON, Kelly Lee
Eastern Guilford HS; Gibsonville, NC (10%-175) Monogram; NHS; Bkbl; Cr-Ctry; Golf; Coaches' A; NC St U; Engr.

PATTERSON, Kirk Charles
Highland Park HS; Dallas, TX; MVP, Bkbl; FCA; Young Life.

PATTERSON, Laura Lee
Glendale HS; Springfield, MO (50%-460) A Cap Choir; Anchor C; Chor; Ensm; Fr C; Madrigal; Baylor U.

PATTERSON, Leigh Ann
Alamance Christian HS; Graham, NC (3-32) Ann; Chor; NHS; Hist A; Vlbl; Eng A; HR; Jr Marshal; UNC-Chapel Hill; Med.

PATTERSON, Lenore Elizabeth
Collinsville HS; Collinsville, OK (8-138) Chor; Drama; Spch C; SC; COM; Hon Prog; OBU Acad Prog; Okla Hon Soc; Okla Baptist U; Bus Ed.

PATTERSON, Lisa Carol
Hall HS; Little Rock, AR; A Cap Choir; Co-Cpt, Chldr; Y-Tns; Tnns; Beauty; Citz A; VP, Soph Cl; Psych.

PATTERSON, Lisa Jane
Sumter HS; Sumter, SC (56-750) Band; Ensm; Fr C; Hmrm; Lit Mag; Rainbow; SC; Bkbl; Swim; Beauty; COM; Citz A; Hon Prog; Masonic A; PTA A; ARC A; VFW A; Yth Fel; Coun of Ministries; Church Choir; YWCA A; Secy, Leaders C; AAU Swim; Group For Mentally Retarded; Med U of SC; Phys Therapist.

PATTERSON, Lori
Briarcrest Baptist HS; Memphis, TN; FHA; Span C; Co-Cpt, Bkbl; Memphis St U.

PATTERSON, Margot Anne
Kubasaki HS; Okinawa, JAPAN (4-271) Chor; VP, City Conf; FNA; Hmrm; Ch, NHS; ARC, Secy, Span C; SC; Sftbl; Alg A; COM; God & Country A; MLS; ARC A; Yth Fel; Span A; VP, Med Explorers; Yth Organization; Johns Hopkins U; Nurs.

PATTERSON, Marguerite
Marion HS; Marion, IN (106-706) Chor; Ensm; Fin, GS; NHS; Y-Tns; Tr; Hist A; HQn; HCt; Marion Col; Foreign Lang.

PATTERSON, Mark Alan
Pleasant Grove HS; Pleasant Grove, AL (10-150) Chem C; NHS; COM; U of Ala; Acct.

PATTERSON, Mark Robert
Mercer HS; Mercer, PA (65-184) Drama; Sftbl; Art Inst of Pittsburgh; Photography.

PATTERSON, Mary Annette
Trotwood Madison City Sch; Trotwood, OH (20-435) Band; Ensm; Secy, 4H; Hmrm; Orch; SC; Citz A; 4H A; Ntl Conf Chr & Jews; NEDT; Pres A; Yth Fel; Stu Ombudsman; Instr Solo & Ensms; Bus.

PATTERSON, Maurice
Saginaw HS; Saginaw, MI; Tnns; Art A; Attendence A; Var Ltr; Aviation.

PATTERSON, Melodie Louise
Elk Grove Sr HS; Elk Grove, CA (18-524) Band; Cpt, Chldr; Chor; Ensm; Secy, Sci C; Bkbl; Sftbl; Tr; COM; Citz A; Hon Prog; Sci A; Spch A; UCLA; Phar.

PATTERSON, Micah Denise
Crossville HS; Crossville, IL (5-25) F-Ed, Ann; Chldr; FHA; Thes; Tr; ISUE Evansville; Dental Lab.

PATTERSON, Michael David
Boulevard Bap Christian HS; Burleson, TX; A-Ed, Ann; F-Ed, Sch P; Pres, Span C; Sftbl; COM; Sal; Most Friendliest; Hon A for Node Merits; PA; 500 Merit C; Arlington Baptist Col; Evangelism.

PATTERSON, Nancy Carol
E Hardin HS; Glendale, KY (9-180) Ann; Secy, BC; Chldr; FBLA; FTA; Math C; Secy, Jr Cl; Cl Fav; DARGCA; HCt; WW; Hon Stu; Western Ky U; Elem Ed.

PATTERSON, Pamala June
Munford HS; Munford, AL; Chldr; Rptr, Sch P; Beauty; HQn; HCt; Ayers Trade Sch; Cosmetology.

PATTERSON, Pamela Diahonne
Dupont Park HS; Washington, DC (5-21) Chldr; Secy, Chor; Dbte Tm; Drama; FFA; Hmrm; Jr Miss Pagent; A-Ed, Sch P; Sci C; Span C; SC; Bsbl; Cpt, Bkbl; MVP, Swim; Tnns; Tr; Oakwood Col; Psych.

PATTERSON, Patricia Lucille
Stevenson HS; Stevenson, AL (25%-100) BC; Chldr; FHA; 4H; Bkbl; 4H A; NE St Jr Col; Acct.

PATTERSON, Patti Jean
Chester Co HS; Henderson, TN (8-147) Ann; Commercial C; Pres, FHA; FTA; SC; Most Cooperative; Communications.

PATTERSON, Richard Mark
Babylon Jr-Sr HS; Babylon, NY (95-200) Semi-Fin, BS; Hmrm; NHS; SC; Var C; Bsbl; Ftbl; Cpt, Wrest; Acolyte; Most Ath, Sr Cl; Championship Little League Coach; The Citadel; Bus Adm.

PATTERSON, Robbie
Kim HS; Kim, CO (2-7) FBLA; FFA; Pres, 4H; Sci C; SC; Var C; VP, Soph Cl; Bsbl; Cpt, Bkbl; Tr; Citz A; Elk A; 4H A; Sal; Sci A; Ntl Finals, Little Britches Rodeo.

PATTERSON, Robin Hope
Reid Ross Sr HS; Fayetteville, NC (3-250) Ed, Ann; Chor; Ensm; Pres, FHA; InterClub Coun; NHS; Alg A; Beauty; Citz A; Crisco A; Type A; Shorthand A; Eng A; Methodist Col; Bus Adm.

PATTERSON, Robin Lynn
Cottage Grove HS; Cottage Grove, OR (13-225) F-Ed, Ann; Chor; Semi-Fin, GS; NHS; SC; Pres, Soph Cl; Bkbl; Hockey; Tnns; COM; Elk A; Vlbl; Oreg Col of Ed; Elem Ed.

PATTERSON, Ruth Ann
Nevada Union HS; Grass Valley, CA (40-500) A Cap Choir; AFS; Chor; Ensm; Jr Miss Pagent; Madrigal; Thes; Arch; Bsbl; Yth Fel; Sierra Col; Nurs.

PATTERSON, Shelly Lynne
Clarke Comm HS; Osceola, IA (8-118) Band; Tres, FTA; Pres, 4H; 4H A; Band A; AIB Col; Legal Secy.

PATTERSON, Susan Elizabeth
Bryan HS; Bryan, TX (25%-500) MVP, All Dist, Vlbl; Tex A&M U; Biol.

PATTERSON, Teresa Susan
Osseo HS; Osseo, MN (100-500) Band; Drama; Fr C; Pres, FHA; Ski C; Ch, UN Council; Swim; COM; NMS; Pres A; ARC A; Spch A; Type A; Yth Fel; Co-Cpt, Dance Line, Rainbow Girls; Pres, UMYF; Hamline Col; Pub Broadcasting.

PATTERSON, Thomas James Jr
St Joseph HS; Jackson, MS; Sch P; Sci C; Up Bound; Bkbl; Tr; Church Yth Choir; Spirit Squad; Jackson St U; Sci.

PATTERSON, Vanessa Anna
Roosevelt HS; Minneapolis, MN (99-597) Ann; VP, 4H; Citz A; 4H A; Hon Prog; Pres A; Yth Fel; Pres, Church Chor; SW St Col; Hospital Adm.

PATTERSON, William Mark
Goreville HS; Goreville, IL (10-30) Ann; Band; Chor; Drama; FFA; Sch P; VP, Jr Cl; Sftbl; Tr; COM; Citz A; Type A; FFA Sentinial; Eng, Bachelor Foods, A's; Grain Judging A; Logan Col of Chiropractic; Chiropractor.

PATTESON, Karen Lynn Anne
Southeast HS; Lincoln, NE (22-565) JV, Dbte Tm; NHS; Var C; Sftbl; JV, Tnns; Tr; Hon Prog; Opt A; Spch A; FCA; Job's Daughters; Cpt, Vlbl; Sertoma A; U of Nebr; Med.

PATTILLO, Lynn Howell
Lowndes HS; Valdosta, GA; Key C; Sci C; Bkbl; MVP, Ftbl; Golf; Tr; Citz A; Most Out; Most Valuable Back A; Back o-t Week A.

PATTISON, Roberta Ruth
Warrensburg HS; Warrensburg, MO (23-197) A Cap Choir; Band; Chor; Ensm; Rptr, FHA; NHS; A-Ed, Sch P; Span C; Secy, Jr Cl; Journ A; Regent Schol; Central Mo St U; Mass Communications.

PATTISON, Stephen Robert
Warrensburg HS; Warrensburg, MO (87-224) A Cap Choir; Band; Chor; Ensm; Orch; Thes; Type A; Central Mo St U; Art.

PATTON, Betty Sue
Richardson HS; Richardson, TX (85-980) FHA; Sch P; SC; Pres, Tri-HiY; Tr; Hon Prog; Gym; Vlbl; Hon Camp Coun; Service Aide A; Baylor U; Sociology.

PATTON, Carol Jean
Powell Valley HS; Speedwell, TN (4-99) BC; FFA; Secy, FHA; Mu Alpha Theta; SC; Tres, Tri-HiY; DARGCA; Cumberland Col; Nurs.

PATTON, Christopher Neal
Virgie HS; Virgie, KY; Ann; Chess C; Demolay; 4H; Key C; Sci C; Bsbl; Mgr, Bkbl; Ftbl; 4H A; Sci A; U of Ky; Engr.

PATTON, Cynthia Maria
Notre Dame Acad; Staten Island, NY; Chldr; Chess C; Chor; Drama; FHA; SC; COM; Citz A; PTA A; William A Morris A.

PATTON, Dennis Don
Sam Houston HS; Arlington, TX; Stu Ath Trainer, All Sports; U of Ala; Phys Ed.

PATTON, Ellen Anne
Ysleta HS; El Paso, TX (23-650) FHA; NHS; SC; Secy, Sr Cl; WW; Ysleta Chpt, WW; Jr Ntl Hon Soc; U of Tex at El Paso; Nurs.

PATTON, Frank Caldwell
Freedom HS; Morganton, NC (10-450) AFS; Dbte Tm; Fr C; Hmrm; Pres, Key C; NHS; SC; Golf; NMS; Governor's Sch of NC; Duke U.

PATTON, Helen Elizabeth
Ysleta HS; El Paso, TX (10%-650) FHA; NHS; SC; WW; Ysleta Chpt, WW; VP, Jr Ntl Hon Soc; U of Tex at El Paso; General.

PATTON, Jack Robert
Capital HS; Helena, MT (25-380) Hmrm; JETS; Lat C; ARC; SC; Jr Cl; Hon Prog; ARC A; Church Yth Group; Forestry.

PATTON, Joe Lain
Jackson Central Merry HS; Jackson, TN (20-497) Math C; Mu Alpha Theta; Span C; U of Tenn; Chem Engr.

PATTON, John Russell
Natrona Co HS; Casper, WY (214-600) BS; Drama; Spch C; Thes; Pres, Var C; Cpt, Ftbl; Tr; Cpt, Wrest; Cl Fav; H of F; HKg; Most Out; NCAA Schol; WW; Pres, FCA; U of Wy; Zoology.

PATTON, Kimberly Jean
Coatesville Area HS; Coatesville, PA (30-650) A Cap Choir; Chor; Community Yth Symph; VP, Ger C; NHS; Orch; JV, Tnns; COM; Mus Ldrship A; Ger A; Academic A; Col of William and Mary; Law.

PATTON, Kristin Anne
Ashland Sr HS; Ashland, OR (8-250) Band;. Drama; Fr C; NHS; Amer Leg A; Hon Prog; Amer Heart, Lung Assn, Poster A; Actress, Dancer St Shakespearean; Cottey Col; Theater Arts.

PATTON, Lawrence Eugene
Marian HS; Tamaqua, PA; French NHS; SC; JV, Bsbl; JV, Bkbl; Hon Prog; NEDT; Attendance, Spelling, A's; Activities, Ath, Certs.

PATTON, Mark E
Warrior Run Sr HS; Turbotville, PA (1-179) AFS; Hmrm; SC; Pres, Soph Cl; Bkbl; Tr; Amer Leg A; Elk A; Hist A; Val; Penn St Schol; Penn St U; Engr.

PATTON, Mary Jane
John Shaw HS; Mobile, AL (20-468) Bus Mgr, Ann; Band; Ensm; NHS; Samford U; Med Tech.

PATTON, Maurice Emil
Cairo HS; Cairo, IL (22-80) Band; Mod Mus Mas; Monogram; SC; Bsbl; Hon Prog; SE Mo Col; Radiology.

PATTON, Patricia Ann
Howland HS; Warren, OH (25-437) A Cap Choir; Ensm; VP, FNA; NHS; ARC; Sftbl; COM; Hon Prog; Trumbull Mem Sch of Nurs; Nurs.

559

PATTON, Randall Lee
Ensley HS; Birmingham, AL (1-340) Pres, Hmrm; Math C; Pres, NHS; Bausch & Lomb A; Cl Fav; Math A; Most Out; Rensselaer A; Val; Top 5% Jefferson Co Stu; Amer Inst of Industrial Engrs A; Exchange C Yth o-t Mo; *U of Ala; Engr.*

PATTON, Sandra Kay
Bokchito HS; Bokchito, OK (4-22) Co-Ed, Ann; Band; Pres, FHA; VP, 4H; NHS; Co-Ed, Sch P; Secy, SC; S-T, Sr Cl; S-T, Jr Cl; S-T, Soph Cl; Mgr, Bkbl; Beauty; Chem A; Cl Fav; Hon Prog; Masonic A; Okla Hon Soc; Home Ec A; Ed A; Yrbk A; *Southeastern Okla St U; Med.*

PATTON, Stuart Freeman
Indian Springs Sch; Helena, AL (15-54) Demolay; Fr C; Soccer.

PATTON, Vickie Sue
McMinnville Sr HS; McMinnville, OR (15-225) A Cap Choir; Ensm; Hon Prog; Kiwanis A; Most Out; WW, Mus Stu; Pag Sound Col o-t Bible Alumni Sch; *Puget Sound Col of The Bible; Bible.*

PATZER, Faye Grace
Gillett Pub HS; Gillett, WI (3-80) *Liberty Baptist Col; Hist.*

PAUESE, Michael Gerard
Bishop Klonowski HS; Scranton, PA; Chor; Drama; Hmrm; NHS; Rptr, Sch P; Spch C; *Wilkes Col; Theater.*

PAUL, Amy Jo
Green Bay E HS; Green Bay, WI (125-477) Bkbl; Hon Prog; *Secy.*

PAUL, Cheryl Lee
Peabody HS; Pittsburgh, PA (213-479) Mgr, Mjrte; ARC A; Tres, Church Yth Group; Stu Security Aide; Service C; *U of Pittsburgh; Photography.*

PAUL, Cheryl Renee
Cresbard HS; Cresbard, SD; Ann; Band; Chor; Pres, 4H; Ed, Sch P; Var C; Bkbl; Sftbl; Tr; 4H A; Journ A; Phy A; Type A; All-St Band; Drill Tm; *Social Worker.*

PAUL, Daniel William
Chartiers Valley Sr HS; Bridgeville, PA (50-590) A Cap Choir; AFS; Chess C; Chor; Drama; Ger C; Hmrm; Pres, Order/Arrow; Var C; Bsbl; Ftbl; Order/Arrow A; Eagle A; Vigil Hon; WW; *Capital U; Bus.*

PAUL, Darlene Louise
Harold L Richards HS; Oak Lawn, IL (2-645) GS; InterAct C; Mu Alpha Theta; Pres, NHS; Sal.

PAUL, David Scott
McCluer N HS; Florissant, MO (220-782) Cpt, Ftbl; Cpt, Tr; JV, Wrest; MVP, Ftbl; Col Ftbl Schol; *Sou Ill U; Pre-Med.*

PAUL, Douglas Ray
Goddard HS; Goddard, KS (40-170) NHS; Bsbl; JV, Cr-Ctry; *Colo St Col; Forestry.*

PAUL, Jimmie
Baylor HS For Health Professions; Houston, TX (30-174) Pres, Band; Hmrm; ARC; SC; Up Bound; COM; Citz A; Journ A; MLS; Sci A; *U of Houston; Biol.*

PAUL, John David
Holland HS; Holland, MI (10%-300) Ger C; NHS; SC; Swim; Coun For The Arts School; Spect Found Schol; Wis Art Assn Schol; *Hope Col; Med.*

PAUL, Jospeh Michael
Elder HS; Cincinnati, OH (20-410) A-Ed, Ann; CYO; Lat C; Ski C; Soccer; Chem A; Hon Prog; *Pre-Med.*

PAUL, Noily III
Frances T Nicholls Sr HS; New Orleans, LA; Chor; NHS; Hon Prog; *UNO; Law.*

PAUL, Rosalind Louise
O D Wyatt HS; Ft Worth, TX (55-200) Band; Tr; Varsity Girls Tr; *Baylor U; Nurs.*

PAUL, Sandra Kay
Limestone Comm HS; Bartonville, IL; A Cap Choir; Chor; Drama; Madrigal; Spch C; *Methodist Sch of Nurs; Nurs.*

PAUL, Susan Lyndall
J W Robinson HS; Fairfax, VA (200-500) Model UN; ARC; Tri-HiY; Hon Prog; *Radford Col; Nurs.*

PAUL, Theodore Franklin Jr
Williamson Jr And Sr HS; Tioga, PA; Chor; Ensm; Soccer; Tr; Ath, Chess, A's; *Tech Work.*

PAUL, Vera Kimberley
John Adams HS; Cleveland, OH (100-600) Co-Ch, CYO; Hmrm; Ski C; Span C; SC; Tnns; COM; Cl Fav; Sci A; Type A; *Ohio U; Med.*

PAULBECK, Christopher Alan
Aitkin Pub HS; Aitkin, MN; *Hist.*

PAULBECK, Nancy Jean
Aikin HS; Aitkin, MN (22-135) Band; Secy, Bus C; Secy, FHA; Sch P; Spch C; Secy, SC; Pres, Sr Cl; Pres, Jr Cl; Tnns; HCt; Spch A; WW; *St Cloud St U; Bus.*

PAULETTE, Laura Uldene
Alexander Galt HS; Lennoxville, CANADA (5-439) Band; Community Yth Symph; Orch; Bkbl; Soccer; Hon Prog.

PAULETTE, Lynwood Eric
Alexander Galt Regional HS; Lennoxville, CANADA (7-539) Co-Ch, Band; Community Yth Symph; Secy, Hmrm; Lat C; Orch; Bkbl; Cpt, Soccer; Hon Prog; Yth Fel; MVP, Soccer; Badminton; Moral, Social Development A.

PAULEY, Donna Mae
Sissonville HS; Charleston, WV (3-195) Chor; Community Yth Symph; Ensm; Fr C; GS; NHS; Orch; Alg A; Hon Prog; Math A; MLS; *Brigham Young U; Mus.*

PAULEY, Jay Randall
Chadwick HS; Chadwick, IL (18-26) Band; Pres, Chor; Cpt, Dbte Tm; Drama; Ski C; Spch C; Pres, Jr Cl; Arch; Cr-Ctry; Semi-Fin, Tr; Citz A; HCt; All St Chor; Summer Stock, Playhouse; *W Ill Col; Theatre.*

PAULEY, Marie Antonette
Sunset HS; Hayward, CA (25-300) Chldr; Chor; Hmrm; Rptr, Lit Mag; Rptr, Sch P; SC; COM; St Scholar; Close- up Schol; *Azusa Pacific Col; Nurs.*

PAULEY, Regina Gail
Cache HS; Cache, OK (6-46) BC; NHS; WW; *Cameron U; Math.*

PAULEY, Susan Leigh
Scott HS; Madison, WV; Secy, Band; Semi-Fin, GS; Pres, Hmrm; Lat C; NHS; SC; Mgr, Bkbl; Bio A; VP, Pep C; WW; Pep & Jazz Band; *Marshall Col; Eng.*

PAULIN, Kathleen Mary
Lancaster Sr HS; Lancaster, WI (2-135) Pres, AFS; Ann; VP, Band; Chor; Ensm; 4H; Math C; Secy, NHS; Orch; Co-Ed, Sch P; Secy, Sr Cl; Secy, Jr Cl; Secy, Soph Cl; Bkbl; Sftbl; Mgr, Tr; NMS; *Northland Col; Environmental Bio.*

PAULS, Dennis Ray
Glasco HS; Glasco, KS; Band; NHS; Var C; VP, Sr Cl; Bsbl; Bkbl; Co-Cpt, Ftbl; Tr; Citz A.

PAULS, Scott William
Naperville Central HS; Naperville, IL (18-460) Semi-Fin, NHS; Co-Cpt, Wrest; Chem A; Hon Prog; NMS; Phy A; St Scholar; Yth Fel.

PAULSEN, Karla Janine
Avoha Comm HS; Avoca, IA (5-49) Band; Cpt, Chldr; VP, Chor; GS; NHS; Co-Ed, Sch P; VP, SC; VP, Thes; Pres, Y-Tns; Bkbl; Tr; COM; HCt; Journ A; Q&S A; Cert of Excel, St Sci Fair; Worthy Advisor, Rainbow Girls; *Bus.*

PAULSEN, Richard Raymond
St Mary's HS; Stockton, CA (60-204) CYO; Hmrm; Key C; Bsbl; Co-Cpt, Bkbl; HCt; Hon Prog; MVP, Bkbl League; Top Scorer, Area Bkbl; *Phys Ed.*

PAULSON, Barbara Ellen
Ripon Sr HS; Ripon, WI (3-175) VP, AFS; Secy, Band; Chldr; GS; Secy, 4H; Mjrte; NHS; ARC; Rptr, Sch P; Bkbl; Tr; 4H A; NMS; Pres A; ARC A; Rotary A; Ch, Jr Prom; Co Cpt, Pom Pon; Mus Band As; *Gustavus Adolphus Col; Nurs.*

PAULSON, Cindy Lee
Wasco Co Union HS; Maupin, OR (1-40) Ann; Band; Chem C; Chor; Drama; NHS; Bkbl; Tr; COM.

PAULSON, Diane Sheree
Rider HS; Wichita Falls, TX (57-513) FTA; Sftbl; Tnns; MYF; Church Choir; HR; *Midwestern Col; Interior Decorating.*

PAULSON, LeAnn Marie
Rider HS; Wichita Falls, TX (60-513) FTA; Sftbl; Tnns; MYF; Church Choir; HR; UIL Typing Contest; *Midwestern Col; Teaching.*

PAULSON, Mark John
Dassel-Cokato HS; Cokato, MN; BS; Chor; Fr C; Order/Arrow; Var C; Bsbl; Bkbl; Eagle Sct A; *St Cloud U.*

PAULUS, Mark Cornelis
E Hartford HS; E Hartford, CT; Lat C; DARGCA; Pres A; Yth Fel; *U of Conn; Bio.*

PAULY, Mary Page
N Shore HS; W Palm Beach, FL (5-353) Span C; COM; *Dance & Theater.*

PAUPE, Carla Jean
Fort Hill HS; Cumberland, MD (25%-342) Chor; Hmrm; SC; Tri-HiY; COM; Secy, Explorers.

PAVA, Susan Margaret
The MacDuffie Sch; Springfield, MA (6-50) Cum Laude Soc; Hmrm; Key C; A-Ed, Lit Mag; SC; Var C; Hockey; Tnns; Cum Laude; *St Lawrence Col; Psych.*

PAVEL, DeAnne Joy
Roosevelt HS; Minneapolis, MN (61-602) Bus C; Chor; NHS; Tri-HiY; Hon Prog; *Concordia Col; Mus Therapy.*

PAVELITZ, Steven Daniel
John S Fine HS; Nanticoke, PA (12-350) Amer Leg A; COM; Lion A; NEDT; PTA A; Phys Ed A; *Aerospace.*

PAVEY, Cynthia Kathleen
Saint Joseph Acad; Columbus, OH (1-16) Ensm; Fr C; French NHS; NHS; Val; Vlbl; GAA; *Ohio St U; Broadcasting.*

PAVLECHKO, Thomas John
Chaney HS; Youngstown, OH; Band; Sch Achieve Tm; Tr; COM; Hon Prog; Opt A; Sci A; Spch A; Industrial Arts A; *Archt.*

PAVLEROS, Pamela
Saint Angela Hall Acad; Brooklyn, NY (10-85) Drama; Math C; Bkbl; COM; Folk Group; Sunday Sch Teacher; GOYA; *Brooklyn Col; Health Sci.*

PAVY, Paula Sue
Switzerland Co HS; Vevay, IN (13-108) Band; FHA; NHS; Sftbl; Tr; HCt; Eng, Cl, A's; *Spencerian Col; Med Asst.*

PAWLIK, Joseph Richard
St Anthony HS; Minneapolis, MN (1-192) Dbte Tm; Drama; NFL; Order/Arrow; Sci C; Span C; Spch C; Tnns; Bio A; COM; Cl Fav; H of F; Order/Arrow A; ARC A; Sci A; Spch A; Dgre of Distin, Ntl Forensic League; *Marine Biol.*

PAWLOWSKI, Katherine Elizabeth
Smithfield-Selma Sr HS; Smithfield, NC; Band; CYO; Fr C; NHS; Orch; Sci C; WW; *NC St U; Microbiol.*

PAWSON, Debra Sue
Ramey HS; Ramey, PR (2-21) Ann; Chor; Pres, Drama; Pres, NHS; VP, SC; VP, Jr Cl; Pres, Soph Cl; Mgr, Bkbl; Tr; Bio A; Hist A; Sci A; Type A; Vlbl; Jim Brown Fresh Eng A; Soph Eng A; Drama A; Geom A; *Corporate Law.*

PAXTON, Billy Todd
Levelland HS; Levelland, TX (10%-250) VP, Chor; Pres, NHS; SC; Cpt, Bkbl; Tnns; Pres, Stu Christian Assn; FCA; Gano Tubb Mem A; WW; Stu o-t Mo; *W Tex St U; Acct.*

PAXTON, Clara Valeria
Tallulah Acad; Tallulah, LA (2-30) F-Ed, Ann; Cpt, Chldr; 4H; Lit Ral; NHS; F-Ed, Sch P; Spch C; Bkbl; Tr; Beauty; Cl Fav; 4H A; Hist A; Spch A; Yth Fel; Most Ath; *Miss St U; Spch.*

PAXTON, James Ann
Pisgah HS; Canton, NC (22-310) Band; Tres, Chor; French NHS; Monogram; NHS; Orch; Ski C; SC; Mgr, Wrest; WW; *St Mary's Col; Nurs.*

PAXTON, Jeffrey Clark
Valley Forge HS; Parma, OH (231-897) Span C; Fin, Bkbl; Tnns; Win, Church League Bkbl; *Bolling Green St U; Pre-Law.*

PAXTON, Lori Lynn
Zion Benton HS; Zion, IL (99-458) Chor; Ger C; Hmrm; SC; Tnns; Sunshine A; *Northern Ill U; Ed.*

PAXTON, Sara Jane
Mercer Area HS; Mercer, PA (4-188) Chor; Drama; Pres, 4H; NHS; Span C; 4H A; *Nutrition.*

PAXTON, Shari Ann
Clarenceville HS; Livonia, MI (8-175) Chor; NHS; Citz A; Magna Cum Laude; Jr NHS; Accompanist, Sch Choir; Secy, Yth Fel; Pianist, Church Choir.

PAYNE, Adrienne Evelyn
G W Carver Sr HS; New Orleans, LA (30-400) Chor; FNA; Sch P; Tr; Type A; Nurs Asst A; *Southern U; Nurs.*

PAYNE, Barbara Ellen
Belle Vernon Area HS; Belle Vernon, PA (6-238) Pres, Hmrm; NHS; B Crocker A; Lang Arts A; *Oral Roberts U; Christian Ed.*

PAYNE, Candace Renee
Saints Acad; Lexington, MS; Band; Chem C; Chor; VP, Lit Ral; VP, Sr Cl; Bsbl; Sftbl; *Tuskegee U; Med.*

PAYNE, Carl Anthony
Los Angeles HS; Los Angeles, CA; *San Diego St Col; Soc.*

PAYNE, Carmen Denise
C E Byrd HS; Shreveport, LA (236-400) Band; DECA; Jr Med League; *Sou U; Med Tech Lab.*

PAYNE, Carol Marie
Maine N HS; Des Plaines, IL (10%-360) Band; Community Yth Symph; Mod Mus Mas; NHS; Orch; Thes; Tnns; Yth Fel; All-St Orch; IMEA Dist Orch; Ntl Sch Orch; Assn Orch A; *Butler U; Mus Ed.*

PAYNE, Cathy Lynn
Fort Worth Christian HS; Fort Worth, TX (8-32) Secy, A Cap Choir; Chldr; Secy, Chor; Secy, Sr Cl; Secy, Jr Cl; Tres, Soph Cl; MVP, Bkbl; Swim; Beauty; Cl Fav; HQn; Most Out; Cpt, Vlbl, Bkbl; WW; Most Athletic; Most Spirited; Best All Around; *Harding Col; Ed.*

PAYNE, Cheryl Denise
Mumford HS; Detroit, MI; Bus C; Type A; Booster C; Extemporaneous Verbal A; Parl Procedure A; *Oakland Comm Col; Bus Mgt.*

PAYNE, Eugene J
Brother Rice HS; Chicago, IL (13-470) Ann; NHS; A-Ed, Sch P; Var C; Cpt, Cr-Ctry; Cpt, Tr; COM; Hon Prog; Journ A; St Scholar; MVP, Cr-Ctry; Gold Medalist Ath Schol; Chick Evans Caddy Schol; *U of Ill at Champaign; Chem Engr.*

PAYNE, Eugenia Collette
Inkster HS; Inkster, MI; Bus C; Chldr; Dbte Tm; Var C; Tnns; HCt; Spch A; Secy, Yth Fel; *Cleary Bus Col; Acct.*

PAYNE, Janice Denice
E Burke HS; Icard, NC (27-362) FBLA; Hmrm; InterAct C; NHS; Spirit C; Sou Assn Coun of Stu; FBLA Schol; *Western Peidmont Comm Col; Bus.*

PAYNE, John Alan
Effingham HS; Effingham, IL (1-201) Band; Chor; St Scholar; Val; Soc For Acad Achv; NML; *Rose-Hulman Inst of Tech; Engr.*

PAYNE, Kay Ann
Columbia HS; Decatur, GA (14-312) BC; FTA; NHS; COM; Drill Tm; VP, Kappa C; *U of Ga; Pre-Med.*

PAYNE, Kimberly K
Pattonville Sr HS; Maryland Heights, MO (18-895) NHS; Hon Prog; JA A; *Bus Adm.*

PAYNE, Margaret Andrea
Warren Central HS; Indianapolis, IN (50-1200) S-T, Band; French NHS; NHS; S-T, Christian Yth Fel; 1st Pl, Band Contest; Advanced Life Saving, Red Cross; WW; *Sci.*

PAYNE, Mary Catherine
Girls' Preparatory Sch; Chattanooga, TN (13-95) Drama; Fr C; Tnns; *Bio.*

PAYNE, Melissa Karen
Homewood HS; Homewood, AL (1-235) Chor; Secy, Hmrm; Mu Alpha Theta; NHS; Span C; Span NHS; Secy, SC; Most Out; *Samford U; Mus.*

PAYNE, Monica Vin
N Union HS; Richwood, OH; Band; Span C; Pres, Jr Cl; S-T, Soph Cl; Bkbl; Mgr, Tr; Yth Fel.

PAYNE, Natalie Yvonne
Inkster HS; Inkster, MI (10%-200) NHS; SC; Var C; Tnns; Hon Prog; Yth Fel; WW; *Howard U; Med Tech.*

PAYNE, Paula Elizabeth
Robert L Osborne HS; Marietta, GA; Cpt, Chldr; HCt.

PAYNE, Randy Eugene
Highland HS; Albuquerque, NM; Band; Fr C; ARC; SC; Citz A; *E NM U; Religion.*

PAYNE, Rodney Neal
Corsicana HS; Corsicana, TX (67%-300) A Cap Choir; Chor; VP, Hmrm; Key C; MVP, Ftbl; Sftbl; Co-Cpt, Tr; Cl Fav; Opt A; Opt Out Tn; Yth Fel; Yth Foundation; WW; Pres, MYF; Runner Up, Mr CHS; Hon Men, All District Ftbl; *Tarleton St U; Phys Ed.*

PAYNE, Sandra Jean
Inkster HS; Inkster, MI (43-195) Y-Tns; *Lawrence Inst Tech; Engr.*

PAYNE, Sara Ruth
Hopewell Valley Central HS; Pennington, NJ (52-280) AFS; Chor; Pres, Hmrm; Ch, SC; *Communications Film.*

PAYNE, Stephen Gregory
Millville Sr HS; Millville, NJ (150-550) Cpt, Bkbl; Tr; COM; Christian Ath A; HS All Amer, Bkbl; *Computer Sci.*

PAYNE, Steve Richard
Maine N HS; Des Plaines, IL; Band; Chor; Bkbl; Ftbl; Bio A; Sci A; Yth Fel; *Bus.*

PAYNE, Susan Luanne
Eastern Guilford HS; Gibsonville, NC (10%-164) Ann; Co-Cpt, Chldr; FHA; Hmrm; Monogram; NHS; Span C; SC; Pres, Soph Cl; HCt; Yth Foundation; *Appalachian Col; Spch Pathology.*

PAYNE, Teresa
Spalding HS; Chicago, IL (20-100) A Cap Choir; Chor; Hmrm; Co-Ed, Sch P; VP, SC; Executive Court; Prom Committee; *Roosevelt U; Acct.*

PAYNE, Thomas Brick
N Union HS; Richwood, OH (40-120) Band; 4H; JV, Wrest; Sr Patrol Ldr, BSct; *Ohio St U; Engr.*

PAYNE, Tony I
Kiser HS; Dayton, OH (11-175) Bkbl; Tnns; DECA; *Pepperdine U; Bus.*

PAYNE, Tracie Lynne
Checotah HS; Checotah, OK (13-117) Band; Chor; NHS; Bkbl; Tr.

PAYNE, Twyla Ann
Coronado HS; Colo Springs, CO (21-400) Chor; Interlochen Ntl Mus; 250 Hr Hospital Vol; Off Worker; Arrow Soc, A; Spirit, Super Outst, A's; *Westmar Col.*

PAYNE, Wilma Joyce
Classen HS; Okla City, OK (28-175) Rptr, Ann; Secy, NHS; Rptr, Sch P; Var C; Bkbl; Sftbl; Tr; Badminton; Vlbl; *Okla St U; Phys Ed.*

PAYOR, Susan Margaret
Lakewood Sr HS; St Petersburg, FL (25-560) Band; Tres, Ger C; Hmrm; InterClub Coun; ARC; SC; Var C; Swim; Mgr, Tr; Yth Fel; VP, NJHS.

PAYSOUR, Douglas Beam
Lord Botetourt HS; Daleville, VA (12-163) BS; Hmrm; S-T, Key C; Lit Mag; NHS; SC; Pres, Sr Cl; Bkbl; *Pfeiffer U; Christian Ed.*

PAYTON, Frederick James
Salem Acad; Salem, OR (20%-85) Ensm; SC; Bsbl; Bkbl; Ftbl; *San Jose Bible Col; Biblical Stu.*

PAZARY, Scott William
E Hartford HS; E Hartford, CT (22-360) BS; Pres, NHS; Cr-Ctry; Tr; Hon Prog; St Scholar; Gov Yth Action Conf; Dollars For Schol; Pres, Pilgrim Yth Fel; All Star Cr-Ctry Tm; *Colgate U; Law.*

PEABODY, Kathleen Marie
Whitman-Hanson Regional HS; Whitman, MA (17-328) Math C; NHS; Hon Prog; Math A; *Bentley Col; International Bus.*

PEACE, Larry Michael
Buffalo HS; Buffalo, MO (10%-160) Co-Cpt, Bkbl; Ftbl; Tr; *Rolla School of Engineering; Elec.*

PEACE, Robbin Michelle
Kensington HS; Philadelphia, PA; *Cushing Jr Col; Social Service.*

PEACH, Mark Allen
Mt Carmel HS; Mt Carmel, IL (105-178) Sch P; SC; Cpt, Bkbl; Cr-Ctry; *ITT; Elec.*

PEACH, Toya Kim
Manchester HS; Richmond, VA; Arch; Band; Co-Cpt, Chldr; Ensm; Arch; MVP, Bkbl; MVP, Soccer; Sftbl; Citz A; Cl Fav; Most Out.

PEACHEY, Keith Eugene
Galesburg Sr HS; Galesburg, IL (1-650) NHS; Bsbl; Bkbl; Ftbl; Amer Leg A; *Sci.*

PEACOCK, Dorothy Jean
Highland HS; Ewing, MO (7-130) NHS; Sci C; Bio A; COM; Ntl Sci Symposium; Sci A; Art C; Cert of Recognition Schol; WW; Home Ec Acad A; *NE Mo St U; Med Tech.*

PEACOCK, Eva Mae
Temple HS; Des Moines, IA; Orch; *Drake Col; Teaching.*

PEACOCK, Joseph Christopher
Lufkin HS; Lufkin, TX (350-592) SC; Up Bound; *Sam Houston St Col; Photography.*

PEACOCK, Karen Ann
Highland HS; Ewing, MO (3-130) Ch, CYO; Secy, Sci C; SC; Var C; Cpt, Bkbl; Tr; Hist A; Hon Prog; Math A; Type A; Parl, FHA; WW; *U of Mo; Computer Sci.*

PEACOCK, Kenneth DeWayne
Burkeville HS; Burkeville, TX (7-47) FFA; SC; Bsbl; Co-Cpt, Ftbl; Tr; COM; Cl Fav; Salta Hon Soc; *Pra View Col; Archt Engr.*

PEACOCK, Ronda Lowery
Jefferson Davis HS; Montgomery, AL; Band; VP, FBLA; Secy, NHS; *Troy St U; Med.*

PEACOCK, Suzanna Marie
Chrysler HS; New Castle, IN; Chor; JA A; Pom Pom Corp.

PEAK, Alda Eugenia
Greenwood HS; Lemon Springs, NC (18-77) Band; BC; Fr C; Co-Ed, Sch P; VofDEM; 3rd Pl, V of Dem; Miss Teenage Sanford; Yth VCE; *NCCU at Durham; Nurs.*

PEAK, Cynthia Kay
Bishop Carroll HS; Wichita, KS (2-211) NHS; Span C; Swim; COM; Hon Prog; Sal; Most Outst Swimmer; *U of Nor Colo; Sociology.*

PEAK, Tina May
Ingelwood HS; Inglewood, CA; Band; Chor; S-T, Fr C; Madrigal; SC; Mgr, Tnns; CSF; COM; Hon Prog; Masonic A; Math A; NEDT; Val.

PEAKE, Anthony Delann
Marion Sr HS; Marion, VA (10-351) Chor; God & Country A; Harvard Book A; Pres A; *Tenn Temple Col; Bible.*

PEAKE, David William
Benson Polytechnic HS; Portland, OR (20-285) Key C; NHS; Bsbl; Cpt, Bkbl; COM; Math A; MVP, Bkbl; *Lewis & Clark Col; Bus.*

PEAKE, Gerald Alton
Murphy HS; Mobile, AL (175-620) Hmrm; InterClub Coun; VP, Key C; Bsbl; Ftbl; Citz A; Cl Fav; Yth Fel; Pres, Usher C; FCA; Sch Santa Claus; *U of Ala; Pre-Law.*

PEARAH, Paul John
St Charles HS; St Charles, IL (8-514) Chess C; Fr C; Ftbl; *Law.*

PEARCE, Alice J
Mount Saint John Acad; Gladstone, NJ (1-27) Ed, Ann; Chor; Secy, 4H; NHS; Ed, Sch P; Ski C; Pres, Sr Cl; Secy, Jr Cl; Mgr, Bsbl; Mgr, Sftbl; B Crocker A; Citz A; DARGCA; Elk A; Hon Prog; Val; Cpt, Sftbl; *Boston Col; Pol Sci.*

PEARCE, Caroline Barnard
Nightingale Bamkor Sch; New York, NY; Citz A; 1st Cl GSct; Rep, Worship Coun; Sch Teaching Asst; *Hist.*

PEARCE, Cecil Lamar
Brunswick HS; Brunswick, GA (50%-459) FBLA; Sci C; Yth Fel; *U of Ga; Sci.*

PEARCE, Dana Lynne
Mecklenburg Acad; Chase City, VA (14-32) Ann; Chldr; FHA; Lat C; Monogram; Bkbl; Community Mem Hospital; Nurs.

PEARCE, James Wesley
Col Zadok Magruder HS; Rockville, MD; Ger C; SC; Soccer; NEDT; NML; Archt.

PEARCE, Karee Ann
Kim HS; Kim, CO (1-12) Ann; Chldr; Pres, FBLA; FFA; Pres, 4H; Sch P; S-T, Sci C; VP, SC; VP, Sr Cl; Pres, Jr Cl; Secy, Soph Cl; MVP, Bkbl; Semi-Fin, Tr; B Crocker A; 4H A; HCt; Math A; Swtht; Val; MVP, Vlbl; Panhandle St U; Acct.

PEARCE, Kimberly Inez
Silver HS; Silver City, NM (2-225) Secy, 4H; VP, NHS; SC; Var C; Tr; Amer Leg Orator A; DARGCA; Elk A; 4H A; MLS; Rotary A; Sal; Spch A; Grant Co 4-H Qn; Rodeo & Horse Show Trophies; 2nd Run-Up, Century III Ldrship; NM St U; Bus Adm.

PEARCE, Pamela Starr
Bertie Sr HS; Windsor, NC (15-335) Chldr; Chess C; Hmrm; Rptr, Monogram; F-Ed, Sch P; Rptr, SC; Citz A; MVP, Chldr; Appalachian Col; Graphics.

PEARCE, Patsy Louise
Millbrook HS; Raleigh, NC; Rainbow; Acct.

PEARCE, Ricky Lee
Centralia HS; Centralia, IL; Ftbl; High HR.

PEARCE, Robert Randolph
Wakulla HS; Crawfordville, FL (10%-182) Pres, NHS; Bsbl; Cpt, Ftbl; Wrest; FCA; U of Fla; Law.

PEARCE, Ronald Dale
Jordan Matthews HS; Siler City, NC (34-205) FFA; Soccer C; JV, Ftbl; Yth Fel; Life Sct; Explorers; Pep C; Royal Ambassadors; Vet Med.

PEARCE, Vicki Sue
Lakeland Sr HS; Lakeland, FL; Chldr; Outst Young Citz A; A of Valor.

PEARCE, Wendy Lynne
Cheraw HS; Cheraw, SC (9-259) Ann; Sci C; Thes; Sftbl; Clemson U; Zoology.

PEARCEY, Vickie Raeann
Sarasota Sr HS; Sarasota, FL (4-700) Hmrm; NHS; SC; VP, Jr Cl; Counteract; Purdue U; Math.

PEARL, Jeffrey Howard
New Albany HS; New Albany, IN; Hmrm; Order/Arrow; Tnns; Order/Arrow A; NAHS Athletic A; Purdue U; Engr.

PEARLE, Margie Louise
Muhlenberg HS; Laureldale, PA (34-360) Pres, Chor; Hmrm; Ski C; JV, Bkbl; Mus, Lat, GAA, A's; Ed, Christian Echo; Widener Col; Nurs.

PEARLMAN, David Ari
El Camino Real HS; Woodland Hills, CA (1-1095) Chem C; VP, Chess C; Ed, Lit Mag; VP, Math C; Model UN; Ed, Sch P; Sr Cl; Alg A; Bank Of Amer A; Bio A; CSF; COM; Chem A; Coun of Teach A; Hist A; Hon Prog; Math A; NMF; NMS; Sci A; St Scholar; Alumni Schol; MAA HR; Occidental Math Field Day A; Ntl Coun of Tchrs of Eng, Writing A; Stanford U; Engr.

PEARRE, Bonnie Susan
Parkville Sr HS; Baltimore, MD; A Cap Choir; Chor; ASC; SC; Swim; COM; JA A; Sci A; Yth Fel; Gym; HR; JA off; Church Tn Choir; Shenandoah Col; Mus.

PEARROW, William Glenn
Harlingen HS; Harlingen, TX (25-700) NHS; ROTC A; Air Force Acad; Aerodynamics.

PEARS, Kahle Daniel
Greenville HS; Greenville, PA; Chess C; Ger C; Mgr, Tr; Yth Fel; VICA C; Cpt, Bowl; Machinist.

PEARSON, Arthur M Jr
Homewood-Flossmoor HS; Flossmoor, IL (150-903) A Cap Choir; Parl, SC; Pres, Jr Cl; Bkbl; Golf; 1st, St Solo Contest; 2nd, St Duet Contest; Stu Choir Director; Applied Voice.

PEARSON, Cindy Leigh
First Assembly Christian Sch; Memphis, TN (20-32) Chor; A-Ed, Sch P; Bkbl; Sftbl; Tr; Memphis St U; Phys Ed.

PEARSON, Curtis Leonard
E St Louis Sr HS; East Saint Louis, IL (20-145) Chess C; Ftbl; Tr; Wrest; Fla U; Hist.

PEARSON, Debra Lou
Pinellas Park HS; Largo, FL; Secy, Jr Cl; Hon Prog; JA A; Q&S A; ARC A; Certs of A; Outst Bus Stu; St Petersburg Jr Col; Executive Secy.

PEARSON, Edna Marilea
Heidelberg American HS; Heidelberg, GERMANY (11-170) Co-Ed, Ann; BC; Dbte Tm; Drama; VP, Fr C; Pres, FBLA; NHS; Phys C; Rainbow; Sch P; Up Bound; Cr-Ctry; Swim; Tr; COM; Hist A; Hon Prog; Eng A; Queens Col; Marine Bio.

PEARSON, Gerald Andre
Hamilton HS; Memphis, TN; Bkbl; Tr; Tex A&M U; Math.

PEARSON, John Michael
New Providence HS; New Providence, NJ (15-338) Chem C; Drama; NHS; Sci C; Cpt, Hockey; Soccer; Duke U; Engr.

PEARSON, Joyce
Beaumont HS; St Louis, MO (20-569) CYO; Tres, Chor; NHS; Hockey; Hon Prog; JA A; Math A; Yth Foundation; U of Mo; Elec Engr.

PEARSON, Kenneth Martin
Dobyns-Bennet HS; Kingsport, TN; Fr C; VP, InterAct C; SC; Cpt, Ftbl; Tr; Wrest; COM; Hon Prog; U of Tenn; Dentistry.

PEARSON, Linnea Ann
Glenbrook HS; Glenview, IL (134-600) AFS; Chor; Dbte Tm; Ensm; Hmrm; Lit Mag; NHS; Orch; Sch P; Sci C; COM; Citz A; Hon Prog; Journ A; Q&S A; Sci A; Yth Fel; North Park Col; Geology.

PEARSON, Marlene
MacKenzie HS; Detroit, MI (40-352) Tres, Bus C; Chor; Mjrte; NHS; Hon Prog; Mich St U; Bus Adm.

PEARSON, Michael
Auburn HS; Rockford, IL (152-283) AFS; Hmrm; Kiwanis A; Most Out; ROTC A; Yth Fel; Lib Asst A; Rock Valley Col; Bus.

PEARSON, Mona Denise
Cloverdale HS; Cloverdale, IN (20%-110) F-Ed, Ann; Rptr, 4H; NHS; Sci C; Span C; Cpt, Bkbl; FCA; Bus.

PEARSON, Nae Hugh III
Virginia Episcopal Sch; Lynchburg, VA (12-51) Chor; Ensm; Fr C; Mgr, Cr-Ctry; Ftbl; Golf; Tr; Mgr, Wrest; 4H A; Ntl Conf Chr & Jews; Semi-Fin, 4-H C A; Church Choir; Ntl Piano Playing Auditions; Church Organist; Co Hunt Pony C; Yth Co-ordinator, UMYF; Vet Med.

PEARSON, Patricia Ann
Many HS; Many, LA; CYO; Chldr; Fr C; Secy, FHA; 4H Ltl Ral; NHS; Rptr, SC; Sftbl; HCt; Pres A; Miss MHS; NW La Col; Nurs.

PEARSON, Paul Alan
E Peoria Comm HS; E Peoria, IL (6-391) Chem C; Community Yth Symph; Pres, Dbte Tm; Ensm; Ger C; Tres, NFL; NHS; Tres, Orch; Order/Arrow; Opt A; Order/Arrow A; Spch A; St Scholar; Cpt, Debate Tm; Eagle Sct; Sterling Merit A; Cornell Col; Pol Sci.

PEARSON, Roselyn Denise
Takoma Acad; Takoma Park, MD; Drama; SC St U; Drama.

PEARSON, Sarajane
Mt Vernon Twp HS; Mt Vernon, IL; HiY; Fin, Lit Mag; Sci A; Ed.

PEARSON, Sharon Marie
Monta Vista HS; Cupertino, CA (41-590) Chor; Ensm; Span C; Spch A; Biola Col; Nurs.

PEARSON, Tamarind Ruth
Hillsdale HS; San Mateo, CA; Col of San Mateo; Fashion Design.

PEARSON, Victor Glenn
Reidsville Sr HS; Reidsville, NC (39-385) Hmrm; Order/Arrow; Span C; Order/Arrow A; Yth Fel; Eagle Sct A; U of NC; Chem.

PEART, Karen Ruth
Kewanee HS; Kewanee, IL (22-180) AFS; Pres, Dbte Tm; Fr C; Ger C; S-T, Hmrm; NFL; Ed, Sch P; Pres, Spch C; SC; Bkbl; Cpt, Tr; COM; Journ A; Spch A; St Scholar; Yth Leg; Exchange Stu Netherlands for AFS; U of Mo-Columbia; Journ.

PEASE, Donna Marie
Ellet HS; Akron, OH; FHA; ARC; PA; FHA Hero A; Akron U; Child Development.

PEASE, Joy Ann
Riverside-Brookfield HS; Riverside, IL (89-464) Chor; Drama; Ensm; Fr C; FBLA; Lit Mag; Sci C; SC; VP, Var C; Cpt, Tnns; MVP, Tr; COM; DARGCA; HQn; Journ A; Lion A; Most Out; Hon Prog; Pres, Ecology C; Gym C; Vocal Mus A; GAA; Badminton Tm As; All-St Choir; Pres, Grls Tnns As; 1st Pl, Var Shw; Pres, Fresh Cl; S-T, Point Sec; Principia Col; Conservation & Wildlife Mgt.

PEASE, Michael Murray
Crystal Lake Comm HS; Crystal Lake, IL (240-450) Band; Ch, Order/Arrow; Amer Leg A; Order/Arrow A; Eagle Sct; Rock Valley Col; Wildlife Specialist.

PEASTER, Sharon Raye
R Nelson Snider HS; Fort Wayne, IN (90%-600) A Cap Choir; Bus C; Chor; Commercial C; Ensm; FBLA; COM; Hon Prog; Spch A; Type A; Bus.

PECA, Mary Catherine
Firestone HS; Akron, OH (80-400) A Cap Choir; Chor; Ensm; Fr C; Hmrm; NHS; Pres, Sr HS Yth Ministry; Ch, Mock HS Election; Mary Washington Col; Hist.

PECHTEL, Darla Jean
St Joseph Sr HS; St Joseph, MI (40-350) Band; Chor; Drama; Hmrm; Orch; COM; 4H A; Band Executive Board; JV Vlbl; Band & Chor Schol; Mus.

PECK, Arnita Marie
Jane Addams Voc HS; Cleveland, OH; Chor; Ensm; Sch Achieve Tm; Tnns; Tr; COM; Citz A.

PECK, Beverly Marie
North Hall HS; Gainesville, GA (25%-196) Secy, FBLA; Gold Cert, Bus Machines; Gainesville Jr Col; Bus.

PECK, Catherine Mae
Normal Comm HS; Normal, IL (91-491) Span C; Tr; Pres, Church Yth; Pres, Lib C; Concordia Teachers Col; Social Work.

PECK, James Wesley
Mt Greylock Regional HS; Williamstown, MA (3-165) NHS; Sch P; Var C; MVP, Bkbl; MVP, Soccer; Tnns; Hon Prog; NEDT; Star Student; Yth Fel; Dartmouth Col; Pol Sci.

PECK, Joe Page Jr
Kubasaki HS; Okinawa, JAPAN (6-271) Chldr; VP, Chor; Drama; Ensm; Ger C; Madrigal; Mu Alpha Theta; NHS; VP, Thes; Golf; Yth o-t Chapel; Ger A; Ensm A; NML; Church Choir; Forklty Bowl; Ger.

PECK, Kevin Earl
San Pedro HS; San Pedro, CA (168-900) JV, Ftbl; Wrest; LA Harbor Jr Col; Bus.

PECK, Laurie Ann
Marissa Jr-Sr HS; Marissa, IL (7-79) FBLA; Math C; NHS; VP, Sci C; Span C; NEDT; Co- cpt, Drill Tm; Church Sch Teacher.

PECK, Penelope Juanita
Lake Placid Central HS; Lake Placid, NY (10%-90) Secy, FHA; FNA; NHS; Sftbl; Type A; Shorthand A; Bookkeeping A.

PECK, Robert Chapman
Mt Greylock Regional HS; Williamstown, MA (3-200) Hmrm; NHS; ARC; Ski C; Co-Ch, SC; Var C; Co-Cpt, Soccer; Tr; COM; Citz A; Hon Prog; Magna Cum Laude; NEDT; Rotary A; MVP, Soccer; Schol Fund Drive; Sum Soccer Camp Counselor; Cpt, Vlb; Pol Campaigner, Sch Commi Candidate; Vietnam Orphanage Fund Drive; Amherst Col; Philosophy.

PECKENPAUGH, Stephen Paul
Southside HS; Fort Smith, AR; Drama; Pres, Soph Cl; Bsbl; Co-Cpt, Ftbl; FCA; Jr Optimist; Hugh O'Brien Leadership A; Westark U; Acct.

PECKER, Claire Joy
Bruriah HS; Elizabeth, NJ (4-33) NHS; Hon Prog; Pre-Med.

PECORARO, Gerald John
Power Mem Acad; NY, NY (60-198) Sch P; Bkbl; Cl Fav; MLS; Photography, Computer, A's; Data Processing.

PECSOK, Thomas Richard
George Washington HS; Charleston, WV (6-350)
Key C; Math C; Mu Alpha Theta; Hon Prog; JA A;
Math A; Phy A; *U of Va; Engr.*

PECUCH, Gary Michael
Neshaminy Maple Point HS; Langhorne, PA
(26-429) Pres, Band; NHS; Var C; Cpt, Tnns; Citz
A; *Pa St U; Human Development.*

PECUNIA, Edgar
Jose de Diego HS; Mayaguez, PR (5-276) Pres,
Hmrm; Phys C; Magna Cum Laude; Math A; Sci A;
U of Puerto Rico at Mayaguez; Civil Engr.

PECUNIA, Richard Alan
Brother Martin HS; New Orleans, LA (48-315)
Band; NHS; SC; ROTC A; Band As; Lang As; *LSU;
Pre-Med.*

PEDEN, Ginger Ann
Whiteface HS; Whiteface, TX; Band; FFA; FHA;
Mjrte; Bkbl; Tnns; Tr; *S Plain Col; Airline Hostess.*

PEDEN, Linda Lou
Deshler HS; Tuscumbia, AL; Bus C; FHA; Tri-
HiY; *U of N Ala.*

PEDERSEN, Andrew Soren
Montclair Kimberley Acad; Montclair, NJ
(25-100) Pol Sci C; Sch P; SC; Ch, Var C; Bsbl;
Bkbl; MVP, Ftbl; Civics Day; *Jacksonville U.*

PEDERSEN, Birgitte Langberg
Tompkins HS; Savannah, GA; BC; Chor; Fr C;
NHS; ARC; Co-Ed, Sch P; Swim; Tnns; Fr A; *Den-
tistry.*

PEDERSEN, Eric David
Loch Raven Sr HS; Towson, MD (10%-247)
Drama; Hmrm; Co-Ed, Lit Mag; NHS; Ski C; Co-
Cpt, Ftbl; Tr; All Co Defensive End; Best Actor o-t
Yr; *Geology.*

PEDERSEN, Heidi Wathne
Edmonds Sr HS; Edmonds, WA (5-368) Chor; Fr
C; French NHS; Hmrm; Var C; Sftbl; Tnns; Citz A;
Elk A; Hon Prog; Col School; *Seattle Pacific U; Sci.*

PEDERSEN, Leslie Craig
Meriden-Cleghorn HS; Cleghorn, IA (7-35) Band;
Chor; FFA; Rptr, 4H; Pres, Soph Cl; Bsbl; Bkbl;
Ftbl; Tr; *Amer Inst of Bus; Computer Program-
ming.*

PEDERSEN, Mary Helen
Luverne HS; Luverne, ND (3-11) Bus Mgr, Band;
Cpt, Chor; Cpt, 4H; Secy, Sch P; Tres, Jr Cl; VP,
Soph Cl; Bkbl; Tres, Tr; Citz A; 4H A; Star Student;
ND St U; Lit.

PEDERSEN, Melanie Christine
Melodyland HS; Anaheim, CA (1-18) Co-Ch,
Hmrm; SC; Val; Wo He Lo Medallion; *Santa Ana
Col; Child Ed.*

PEDERSON, Julie Ellen
Prosser HS; Prosser, WA (10%-180) Band; FHA;
Var C; Hon Prog; Ntl Achv Schol; Pres A; Gym;
Off Practice A.

PEDERSON, Julie Renee
Hatton Pub HS; Hatton, ND (10-31) Ann; Band;
Chldr; Chor; VP, FHA; SC; Mgr, Ftbl; Lib A; *May-
ville St U; Bus Mgt.*

PEDERSON, Lisa Anne
Ed W Clark HS; Las Vegas, NV (5%-650) Ger C;
Ski C; SC; COM; Secy, Stu Senate; Jr NHS; A of
Recognition.

PEDERSON, Ruth Caroline
Lake Park HS; Lake Park, MN; FFA; 4H; Swim;
Tr.

PEDERSON, Sandra Jean
Loyalton HS; Loyalton, CA (12-42) Chldr; Secy,
Drama; FBLA; 4H; Spch C; Sftbl.

PEDOWITZ, Robert Alan
El Camino Real HS; Woodland Hills, CA
(10-1075) BS; Cpt, Chldr; Hmrm; Ski C; SC; Tres,
Sr Cl; Tres, Jr Cl; JV, Bkbl; JV, Tnns; Amer Leg A;
CSF; COM; Hist A; Hon Prog; NMS; Ntl Sci
Found; Alumni Schol; *UCLA; Math.*

PEDRAZA, Gloria Milo
Deming HS; Deming, NM (86-210) VP, CYO;
Chor; FHA; Hmrm; Span C; Up Bound; *Western
NM St U; Special Ed.*

PEEBLES, Henry Gregory
Spring HS; Spring, TX (26-495) JETS; Lat C; Lat
NHS; NHS; JV, Tr; NMF; Sci A; *Rice U; Pre-Med.*

PEEBLES, Natalie Louise
Middletown HS; Middletown, OH (25-500) VP,
Bus C; Chldr; Chor; Co-Cpt, Drill Tm; Ch, Church
Choir; *Ohio St; Med Secy.*

PEEK, David Grant
Smith HS; Atlanta, GA (4-135) F-Ed, Ann; Model
UN; Pres, NHS; Pol Sci C; ARC; Rptr, Sch P; Pres,
Sci C; Amer Leg A; COM; Chem A; Hist A; Math
A; MLS; Most Out; ROTC A; Sci A; Sci Congress;
Ga St Col; Chem.

PEEK, John Wayne
Robert E Lee Inst; Thomaston, GA (18-113) Ed,
Ann; Monogram; Span C; SC; Tri-HiY; Pres, Sr Cl;
Bsbl; Ftbl; HQn; ROTC A; Bsbl Coach's Trophy;
1st Lt, ROTC; Ftbl Sr A; *Pre-Med.*

PEEK, Megan Lynn
Plano Sr HS; Plano, TX (1-850) Pres, A Cap Choir;
Chor; Drama; Ensm; Pres, Fr C; Hmrm; Lit Mag;
Madrigal; NHS; SC; Thes; COM; Hon Prog; Journ
A; Val; Voice; Lib, A Cappella Choir; WW; Secy,
Fr C; Most Intellectual; JV Vlbl; Semi-Fin, All St
Choir; All Region Choir; *N Tex St U; Voice.*

PEEK, Susan Annette
Smith HS; Atlanta, GA (1-200) Bus C; Dbte Tm;
Pres, FBLA; FHA; Math C; VP, NHS; Rptr, Sch P;
Sci C; Gov Honor Prog; Hon Prog; Math A; Sci A;
Spch A; Val; Ntl HS A for Excellence; Black Hist
Essay A; Lib A; *Med.*

PEEKE, Christopher
Roseburg Sr HS; Roseburg, OR (5-490) Band; Demolay; Hmrm; NHS; Sci C; Tr; COM; Sal; St
Scholar; President Entrance Hons, Pacific U; *Pacific U; Optometry.*

PEEL, Lisa Anne
Sparks HS; Sparks, NV (6-290) Drama; VP, FHA;
Ger C; GS; 4H; Hmrm; Jr Miss Pagent; Ed, Lit
Mag; NHS; ARC; Sci C; Secy, Ski C; SC; VP, Var
C; Cpt, Golf; Tr; Alg A; Amer Leg A; 4H A; Hon
Prog; Most Out; Secy, VC; Candystriper; Ski Tm;
Outst Soph & Jr, Drill Tm; VP, Pep C; Cpt, YMCA
Swim Tm; Chch Yth Grp Adv; Jr Golf PGA Chmp;
U of Nev; Civil Engr.

PEEL, Lisa Mae
Jessamine Co HS; Nicholasville, KY (5-25) JV,
Chldr; Dbte Tm; Fr C; 4H; Rptr, Hmrm; SC; Var C;
Bsbl; Sftbl; Chldr A; A & B HR; *Georgetown Col;
Recreation.*

PEELE, Tim Edward
Mabank HS; Mabank, TX (3-144) NHS; JV, Ftbl;
Tr; Bio A; *Biol.*

PEELER, Dorothy Elizabeth
Salisbury HS; Salisbury, NC (33-234) AFS; Band;
Secy, Hmrm; Hon Prog; Poet A; SPEC Prog; *Ca-
tawba Col; Math.*

PEELER, John Talmadge
Cedar Shoals HS; Athens, GA; HR; *U of Ga; Agr.*

PEELER, Merrill Katherine
Burns Sr HS; Lawndale, NC; FBLA; Hmrm; Lit
Mag; Sch P; *Cleveland Tech Inst; Med.*

PEELER, William Royce
Blacksburg HS; Blacksburg, SC; FFA; FTA; Bsbl;
Ftbl; Pres A.

PEEPLES, William Dewey III
Homewood HS; Birmingham, AL (13-229) Band;
Chor; Ensm; Fr C; Mu Alpha Theta; Rptr, NHS;
Orch; Thes; Bkbl; Tr; WW; Top 10, Asst Drum
Major, Band; All St, All Amer, Band; *Samford U.*

PEERY, Kimberly Anne
Hickman Co HS; Clinton, KY (5-105) BC; FHA;
Hmrm; Ntl Yth Conf; Sci C; SC; Pres, Soph Cl; *U of
Ky; Commercial Art.*

PEET, Helen Marie
Paint Branch HS; Burtonsville, MD (11-355)
Montgomery Col; Acct.

PEETZ, Sally A
Grand Blanc HS; Grand Blanc, MI (352-666) A
Cap Choir; Chor; Ensm; Spch A; Pres, Jobs Daugh-
ters; St Win, Keyboard Solo; *Mott Comm Col;
Nurs.*

PEGARIDO, Enrico Vencer
George Washington Sr HS; Mangilao, GUAM;
NHS; *U of Hawaii.*

PEGLER, Duane Allen
Wadsworth Sr HS; Wadsworth, OH (150-268)
Band; Bus C; Orch; *Bowling Green St U; Mus.*

PEIFFER, Diane Kay
Blue Mountain HS; Schuylkill Haven, PA (89-237)
Band; Chor; Rainbow; Tr; COM; Commercial Art;
Drill Tm; Cert of Achv; Tres, Yth Fel; Church Bowl
Tm; Secy, Church Sftbl; Comm Beautification A;
Phys Ed A; *Commercial Art.*

PEIFFER, Jeffrey Lee
Twin Valley HS; Elverson, PA; Dbte Tm; Hmrm;
Sch P; Bsbl; Tr; Hon Prog; Journ A.

PEIFFER, Matthew Douglas
Charles H Milby HS; Houston, TX (1-600) BS;
Rptr, FFA; Ger C; InterClub Coun; JETS; Tres,
Math C; Tres, Mu Alpha Theta; Parl, NHS; Order/
Arrow; Sch Achieve Tm; Sci C; Ch, SC; Swim;
COM; Chem A; Hon Prog; NEDT; Order/Arrow
A; Phi Beta Kappa; Rotary A; Sci A; Eagle Sct;
Pres, Ger Hon Soc; Exchange C Yth of Month;
WW; *U of Tex; Engr.*

PEIFFLE, Steven James
Waukegan E HS; Waukegan, IL (15-495) Lit Mag;
VP, NHS; Soccer; JV, Tnns; Commended Stu; Com-
mended Stu; AAL All Col Schol; *Valparaiso U; Bus
Adm.*

PEIRCE, Susan Lynn
Central HS; Omaha, NE (9-577) A Cap Choir; Hon
Prog; Semi-Fin, NCTE; Young People's Choir;
Church Yth Coun; *Nebr Weslyan Col; Math.*

PEISINGER, Suzanne
Douglas MacArthur HS; San Antonio, TX
(23-610) AFS; Band; VP, CYO; Secy, Drama;
NHS; COM; Hon Prog; Band-UIL Solo Highest
Rating; Beauty San Antonio; VP, Explorer Post
840; *Southwest Tex St U; Mus.*

PEITZ, Charles Frederick
Hunterdon Central HS; Flemington, NJ; Chess C;
Chor; MVP, Bsbl; Hockey; Sftbl; Swim; *Art.*

PEKAREK, Gary Ray
Longmont HS; Longmont, CO (7-510) Ed, Ann;
BS; Dbte Tm; NFL; NHS; Order/Arrow; Rptr, Sch
P; Span C; Spch C; Tri-HiY; Order/Arrow A; Spch
A; Yth Leg; WW; *U of Colo; Engr.*

PEKAS, Darlene Joy
Mott Lincoln HS; Mott, ND (30-66) Ann; Band;
Chor; Drama; Ensm; Pres, FHA; Sci C; Spch C;
Mgr, Bkbl; Sftbl; Tr; GAA A; FHA A; Band A; *Ntl
Col of Bus; Airline Stewardess.*

PEKCHAM, Sherry Lynn
Liberty HS; Bedford, VA (52-257) BC; Drama; Fin,
Jr Miss Pagent; Lat C; Sci C; Bio A; COM; Math A;
Sci A; Chaplain, Tr-Hi-Y; SPCA Sci A; Mgr, Vlbl;
March of Dimes Schol; Pres, Yth Fel; 4th, Reg Sci
Fair; Gifted Stu; 1st Pl, Local Sci Fair; *VPI; Phys
Therapy.*

PELHAM, William Stacy
Rossville HS; Rossville, GA (15-225) Chess C;
Wrest; Alg A; COM; Chem A; Gov Honor Prog;
Math A; Ntl Sci Found; *U of Tenn at Chatt; Math.*

PELKEY, LeAnne
Ft Lauderdale HS; Ft Lauderdale, FL (10%-600)
Chor; Madrigal; Rainbow; Ch, Y-Tns; *Penn St U;
Lang Arts.*

PELLEGRINI, Cindy Darlene
Amos Alonzo Stagg Sr HS; Stockton, CA (10-692)
Chess C; NHS; Span C; Sftbl; Citz A; Vlbl; Bowl;
Hon Stu; Tutor, Children; *Calif Baptist Col; Sci.*

PELLERITO, Carolyn Laraine
Beth Haven Christian Sch; Greenville, MI; A Cap
Choir; Best Christian Character; Memorization;
Tenn Temple; Liberal Arts and Bible.

PELLETIER, Barbara Marie
St Dominic Regional HS; Lewiston, ME; Band; Fr
C; COM; Hon Prog; Sci A; Art, Composition, A's;
Mid-St Bus Sch of Commerce; Bus.

PELLETIER, Celine
College De Ste Anne De La Pocatiere; La Pocatiere, CANADA (3-29) Vlbl; *Adm.*

PELLETIER, Pauline
College De Ste Anne De La Pocatiere; La Poca-
tiere, CANADA (1-29) Pres, Hmrm; VP, Var C;
Bkbl; Swim; *Universite Laval; Sci De La Sante.*

PELLICCIONE, Lisa Anne
Notre Dame HS; Salinas, CA (17-95) NHS;
Beauty; Cl Fav; HCt; Secy, Pep C; *Foothill Col-Los
Altos; Dental Hygenist.*

PELLIKAN, Donald Robert
Jersey Comm HS; Jerseyville, IL (23-315) 4H; Math C; NHS; Bsbl; Bkbl; Cr-Ctry; Tr; 4H A; I Dare You; Pres, Sub-Dist Yth Fel; 12 Yr Church Sch Attendance Pins; *U of Ill; Statistics.*

PELLNAT, John Arthur
Hutchinson Central Tech HS; Buffalo, NY (12-212) Chor; NHS; ARC; SC; Var C; Cpt, Ftbl; *St U of NY; Computer Sci.*

PELLNITZ, Susan Elizabeth
Nutley HS; Nutley, NJ (25-500) Ger C; Math C; Tres, NHS; Tnns; Church Yth; Girls Wrest Auxillary; Vlbl; Ger A; *Math.*

PELO, Myra June
Lordstown HS; Lordstown, OH (2-55) Band; Chor; Co-Cpt, Bkbl; Sftbl; Tr; Hon Prog; Tres, JA; Co-Ch, Ways & Means Committee.

PELOUBET, Patricia Ann
John Jay Sr HS; Hopewell Jct, NY (120-560) Chor; Order/Arrow; Tr; Order/Arrow A; *The King's Col; Nurs.*

PELTON, Pamela
West Branch Jr-Sr HS; Morrisdale, PA (16-130) Chldr; Drama; Lit Mag; NHS; Rainbow; Spch C; Var C; Sftbl; Yth Fel.

PELTON, Penelope
West Branch Jr Sr HS; Morrisdale, PA (11-130) Chldr; Fr C; NHS; Rainbow; Var C; Sftbl; HQn; HCt; Yth Fel.

PEMBERTON, Teri Ann
Capital Hill Sr HS; Oklahoma City, OK; Band; OCPD Law Enforcement Explorer Lt; Band Ltr; *OSU Tech; Police Sci.*

PENA, Patricia Ann
Pacific HS; San Bernardino, CA (50%-600) CYO; Hmrm; SC; Arch; COM; Citz A; Leadership; Fr Artist; Outst Service; PTA Schol; *Art.*

PENAGARICANO, Dora Matilde
Colegio Puertorriquento de Ninas; Caparra Heights, PR (5-48) Dbte Tm; Secy, Hmrm; Ed, Lit Mag; VP, NHS; Sch P; Bio A; COM; Chem A; Hon Prog; Sci A; Val; Yrbk Ed; Best Over All Film Strip A; First Hon; *U of Mayaguez; Orthodontics.*

PENCE, Heidi Lynn
The Buckley Sch; Sherman Oaks, CA; Co-Ed, Ann; Secy, NHS; COM; Chem A; NEDT; *UCLA; Cinema.*

PENCHI, Gladys
Lola Rodríguez de Tio; San German, PR (22-350) Pres, FHA; Pres, ARC; Sci C; Pres, Span C; COM; Hon Prog; Magna Cum Laude; Summa Cum Laude; *Recinto Univ Mayaguez; Geol.*

PENDER, Barbara Ann
Dallas Christian HS; Mesquite, TX (14-53) Secy, A Cap Choir; Chldr; FHA; NHS; HCt; *Harding Col.*

PENDERGRASS, Carmen Dianne
Fyffe HS; Fyffe, AL; BC; Chor; FHA; FTA; Rptr, Sch P; COM; 4H A; Spch A; Star Student; Chor A; Most Talented A; FHA Art A; Sch Talent A; *NE Jr Col; Elem Ed.*

PENDERGRASS, Joann
Overton HS; Nashville, TN; *MTSU; PDA Nears.*

PENDERGRASS, William Bradley
T R Miller HS; Brewton, AL (3-98) Chess C; NHS; F-Ed, Sch P; SC; Var C; Bsbl; Ftbl.

PENDLETON, Carrie Jean
Box Elder HS; Brigham City, UT (3%-423) Chor; Fr C; NHS; ARC; Span C; Masonic A; Hon Qn, Job's Daughters; *Westminster Col; Nurs.*

PENDLETON, Edward Rhead
Box Elder HS; Brigham City, UT (62-468) Demolay; Fr C; Order/Arrow; Span C; SC; Var C; Bkbl; Ftbl; Sftbl; Tr; *Westminster Col; Religion.*

PENDLETON, Henry David
Caney Valley HS; Caney, KS (4-68) Ann; BS; CYO; NHS; Ed, Sch P; SC; Alg A; Journ A; Math A; *U of Kans; Journ.*

PENELTON, Teresa Eileen
Crispus Attucks HS; Indianapolis, IN (15-250) Ed, Ann; Bus C; Tres, Ger C; GS; NHS; Var C; Bkbl; Tr; COM; Hon Prog; Journ A; Most Out; Vlbl; Outst, Ger; *Ohio St U; Acct.*

PENFIELD, Patricia Ann
Bowman HS; Bowman, ND (3-63) Band; Rptr, FBLA; S-T, FHA; Sch P; Tr; FHA' ER o-t Yr; *Bio.*

PENICK, Leona Sue
Switzerland Co Jr Sr HS; Vevay, IN (15-108) Band; Chor; Drama; Mod Mus Mas; Rptr, Sch P.

PENLAND, Michael Eugene
Lenoir HS; Lenoir, NC (6-105) Band; Ensm; Rptr, Hmrm; InterAct C; Parl, Lit Mag; F-Ed, Sch P; Ski C; COM; Hon Prog; Opt A; PTA A; Spch A; Yth Fel; Yth Foundation; All St Band; *NC St U; Acct.*

PENLEY, Carol Rae
Elk Grove HS; Elk Grove Village, IL (101-625) Arch; Chor; Ensm; NHS; Ski C; Span C; SC; Var C; Arch; Swim; Hon Prog; *Central Mo St U; Nurs.*

PENLEY, Jeffrey Harper
York Comp HS; York, SC (8-240) Cpt, Hmrm; Ntl Teachers Coun; S-T, Soph Cl; Gr Marshal; Hon Prog; VP & Secy, Demolay DAR US Hist A; *USC-COLUMBIA; Engr.*

PENLEY, Stephen Holloway
York Comp HS; York, SC (16-240) Demolay; Fr C; *U of S Carolina at Columbia; Bus.*

PENLEY, Sue Ellen
E Mecklenburg Sr HS; Charlotte, NC (20%-744) Chor; Drama; Ensm; VP, Hmrm; SC; Sftbl; COM; Citz A; JA A; Sr Lifesaver; Sch Projects Comm; Choir; Project Aries; MYF; Cafeteria Advisory Board; Secy, Jr Achv; *U of NC; Law.*

PENN, Pamela
Monticello HS; Monticello, MS; Ann; Band; S-T, BC; GS; WW; *Acct.*

PENN, Robin Michelle
John Ehret HS; Marrero, LA (6-480) VP, Fr C; GS; Hmrm; Semi-Fin, Lit Ral; Lit Mag; Math C; Mu Alpha Theta; VP, NHS; A-Ed, Sch P; SC; Chem A; Hon Prog; PTA A; Century III Ldrship A; *U of New Orleans; Pre-Med.*

PENN, Vincent Orlando
Merced HS N; Merced, CA (75%-1000) All Amer Yth; Bsbl; MVP, Ftbl; Tr; Coun of Teach A; Most Out; Yth Fel; Ch, Jr Deacons; Mus; *Linfield Col; Dentistry.*

PENNE'S, David Israel
Juan Jose Osuna HS; Hato Rey, PR (8-150) Chldr; Hmrm; Math C; ARC; SC; Bsbl; Bkbl; Alg A; Hon Prog; Math A; MLS; Ping Pong; Nu Sigma Beta; *U of Puerto Rico; Engr.*

PENNELL, John Roddy
James F Byrnes HS; Duncan, SC (70-400) Fr C; FFA; Pres, Hmrm; InterAct C; Lat C; SC; JV, Bkbl; Yth Fel; DR Hill A; Sportsmanship A; *Furman U.*

PENNELL, Sara Anita
Hibriten HS; Lenoir, NC; Chldr; Chor; Fr C; Hmrm; Secy, InterAct C; Monogram; HCt; May Day Qn; Christmas Court; Valentines Court; *Pheiffer Col; Sociology.*

PENNER, David Damon
Southwest HS; Kansas City, MO (20%-500) Pres, Chor; Ger C; Order/Arrow; Var C; Cr-Ctry; JV, Ftbl; Swim; Tr; Eagle Sct; Soph of Yr, Tr A; Hon Sct A.

PENNER, Scott D
Sierra Joint Union HS; Tollhouse, CA; Hmrm; NHS; CSF; *Reedley Col; Elec Engr.*

PENNER, Susan Marie
Mt Morris HS; Mt Morris, IL (2-68) AFS; Band; Chor; Ensm; Madrigal; NHS; Span C; Thes; COM; Sal; St Scholar; Pres, Yth Fel; Manchester Schol; John Philip Sousa Band A; Hon Thespian; Attendance A; *Manchester Col; Mus Ed.*

PENNER, Vickie Ann
Sierra Joint Union HS; Tollhouse, CA (3-190) Chor; NHS; CSF; Pres A; HR; WW; Bible Memory Assn; *Biola Col; Bible.*

PENNEY, Susan Elizabeth
Pinellas Park HS; Largo, FL (25%-558) *St Petersburg Jr Col; Nurs.*

PENNIE, Vincent
Concordia HS; Oakland, CA; *Calif Col of Arts & Crafts; Art.*

PENNINGER, Lisa Ann
Breckinridge Co HS; Harned, KY (1-207) Ann; Band; Ensm; FTA; Tres, Math C; NHS; Cpt, Sch Achieve Tm; Tres, Jr Cl; Tnns; Lat A; WW; All Dist Band; Sup Rating, Solo & Ensm; *MIT; Math.*

PENNINGTON, Ann Marie
Wm Byrd HS; Vinton, VA (24-263) BC; Drama; Lit Mag; Span C; Mgr, Tr; Secy, New Life C; Secy, SODA; Outst Sr, Eng & Soc Studies Dept; *Virginia Polytechnic Institute; Elem Ed.*

PENNINGTON, Carla Annette
Malvern HS; Malvern, AR (14-198) FBLA; NHS; *Henderson St U; Bus.*

PENNINGTON, Donna Kay
Corsicana HS; Corsicana, TX (25%-375) A Cap Choir; Band; Secy, 4H; Mjrte; *Sam Houston St U; Home Ec.*

PENNINGTON, Ginger Deloris
Stephens Co HS; Toccoa, GA; VP, FHA; Ch, FTA; 4H; S-T, Span C; Missionettes Trophy; *U of NC; Elem Ed.*

PENNINGTON, James Barry
Marion Co HS; Lebanon, KY (30-324) Fr C; NHS; Bkbl; Tr; Hon Prog; Mr Soph; *E Ky U; Acct.*

PENNINGTON, Nancy Lee
Northside Christian HS; Pasadena, FL; Band; Bus C; Ensm; Pres, Orch; Sftbl; Cl Fav; Band, Ensm, Marching, A's; *Mus.*

PENNINGTON, Nancy Sheila
Marion Co HS; Guin, AL (10-29) Band; Tres, BC; FHA; Sch P; Bkbl; Sci A; Oboe Medalist; Band Section Ldr & Lib; *Brewer Jr Col; Early Childhood Dev.*

PENNY, Cynthia Anne
Mt Airy Sr HS; Mt Airy, NC (28-190) Chor; Tri-HiY; *Surry Comm Col; Eng.*

PENNYMAN, Carla Inez
B T Washington HS; Atlanta, GA (11-345) Ann; Band; Secy, NHS; Y-Tns; COM; Hon Prog; Yth Fel; *Law.*

PENTECOST, Teresa Renee
Elbert Co Comprehensive HS; Elberton, GA; Anchor C; Chldr; Fr C; Hmrm; Key C; Math C; Sci C; SC; Bkbl; Sftbl; Swim; Tnns; Beauty; Cl Fav; Key C Swtht; *Med Tech.*

PENTICOFF, Luanne R
Freeport Sr HS; Freeport, IL (70-515) A Cap Choir; Band; Chor; Drama; Ensm; Ger C; SC; Thes; Pres, Sr Cl; 1st Pl, St Solo & Ensm; *Ill St U; Special Ed.*

PENTICOFF, Rita Mae
Hampton Comm HS; Hampton, IA (14-115) Ann; Band; Chor; Dbte Tm; FBLA; FTA; Model UN; NHS; VP, Soph Cl; Hon Prog; Spch A; March of Dimes Merit A; Gold Cert, Organ Mus; Clarinet, Mus Contest A; *U of Northern Iowa; Special Ed.*

PENTZ, Dennis Allen
Arapahoe Pub Sch; Arapahoe, NE (1-32) Band; Chess C; Chor; Ensm; Order/Arrow; Var C; JV, Ftbl; Wrest; COM; Hon Prog; Order/Arrow A.

PENTZ, Gabrielle Antoinette
Clear Fork HS; Bellville, OH (1-157) S-T, Chor; Lit Mag; Secy, NHS; Ed, Sch P; Pres, Span C; Secy, Jr Cl; Bkbl; HQn; Journ A; Q&S A; Val; *U of Notre Dame; Eng.*

PEOPLES, Antionette Denise
Charleston HS; Charleston, SC; FTA; Co-Cpt, Bkbl; Delta Sigma Theta A; Secy, JA; *Johnson C Smith Col; Secondary Ed.*

PEOPLES, Kim Ann
NW HS; St Louis, MO; Hmrm; SC; Type A; *Forest Park Col; Clerk-Typist.*

PEPE, Shirley Diane
Kubasaki HS; Okinawa, JAPAN (8-421) Span C; JV, Tr; *Sweet Briar Col; Law.*

PEPMILLER, Diana Louise
Southwest HS; St Louis, MO (171-500) *Psych.*

PEPPER, Lisa Sue
Grosse Pointe N HS; Grosse Pointe Woods, MI (17-600) Band; Ensm; A-Ed, Lit Mag; NHS; Orch; Secy, SC; COM; Hon Prog; Journ A; Phi Beta Kappa; Poet A; Sunday Sch Teacher; Deaconess; Gov Board; SE Mich Pres, Christian Yth Fel; *Bethel Col; Psych.*

PEPPERS, Harold Lee
Logan Sr HS; Logan, OH (138-282) Bsbl; Co-Cpt, Ftbl; Outst Sr Ftbl; Most Popular Sr; All-Seol & All-Dist, Ftbl; All-League & All-Dist, Bsbl; *David Lipscomb Col; Bus Adm.*

PEPPLE, Linda Elisabeth
Melbourne HS; Melbourne, FL (6%-600) Ed, Ann; Chldr; FHA; NHS; Sch P; SC; COM; JA A; Yth Fel; Civitan A; MYF.

PEPPLER, Jeanne Louise
Luther N HS; Chicago, IL (27-219) A Cap Choir; Model UN; Span C; Pres, SC; *Valporaiso U; Art.*

PERALDO, George Harry
Bluefield HS; Bluefield, WV (25-375) Fr C; Inter-Act C; Spch C; JV, Golf; Hon Prog; Pres Summit Chapter, Jr NHS; *U of Va; Law.*

PERALEZ, Richard Daryl
Oak Ridge HS; Orlando, FL (6-800) Band; Math C; NHS; Order/Arrow; Sci C; Span NHS; Var C; Cr-Ctry; Cpt, Tnns; Eagle Sct; *Emory U; Chem.*

PERANSKI, Joann Marie
John S Fine HS; Nanticoke, PA (23-300) Chldr; Chor; Drama; FTA; Sch P; SC; Tri-HiY; Amer Leg A; NMF; Swtht; *Wilkes Col.*

PERAZZO, John Arthur
Western HS; Las Vegas, NV (150-750) Fin, BS; Pres, Mu Alpha Theta; Order/Arrow; Rptr, Sch P; VP, Sci C; VP, Sr Cl; Soccer; Amer Leg A; COM; NEDT; Order/Arrow A; Sci A.

PERCIVAL, Hisman Habili
Central HS; San Juan, PR (25-300) Bkbl; Sftbl; Wrest; COM; Math A; *US Air Force Acad; Aeronautical Engr.*

PERCIVAL, Regina Loretta
Wade Hampton HS; Greenville, SC; Ch, CYO; Chor; Hmrm; Y-Tns; Sftbl; Swim; Tnns; Tr; Religious A; *U of SC; Bus.*

PERCIVAL, Rhonda Jean
Bryan Sr HS; Omaha, NE (25%-350) Chor; COM; Swing Choir; Mus Ltrs; Sch Musicals; Concert Choir; Stage Band; Mixed Chor; Church Choir; Choir Coun; *U at Omaha; Fine Arts.*

PERCIVAL, Suzanne D
New Dorp HS; Staten Island, NY (23-727) Co-Ed, Ann; Chor; Hmrm; NHS; Orch; Span NHS; Tr; COM; Hon Prog; Sci A; Hon Key; Christian Fel; Ldrs C; Stu Sen; Usher Sq; VP, Church Yth Group; *Muhlenberg Hosp Sch of Nurs; Nurs.*

PERCLE, Susan Elizabeth
Archbishop Blenk HS; Gretna, LA (53-153) CYO; Chor; Math C; Hon Prog; Math A; Guitar C; Bowl Tm; Eucharistic Minister; Lector & Commentator; *Med.*

PERCOWYCZ, Barbara Ann
Immaculate Conception HS; Hamtramck, MI (12-42) Cpt, Chldr; Chor; Secy, Hmrm; NHS; Rptr, Sch P; SC; Secy, Jr Cl; Hon Prog; Ukrainian GSct A; *Wayne St U; Police Work.*

PERCY, Amy Lynn
Connellsville HS; Connellsville, PA (10%-620) Chldr; Chor; VP, Hmrm; NHS; Span NHS; SC; Tres, Tri-HiY; Swim; Most Congenial A, Sr Cl; *Acct.*

PERDUE, Kathryn Marie
Clarendon HS; Clarendon, TX (10%-60) A Cap Choir; Band; FHA; FTA; NHS; Eng A; 3rd Poetry, UIL Dist; *Hardin-Simmons U; Elem Ed.*

PEREBOOM, Wayne Edwin
Marina HS; Huntington Beach, CA; A Cap Choir; Madrigal; Spch A; *Mus.*

PEREIRA, Gerald
Mission HS; San Fernando, CA; Ann; Hmrm; Sch Achieve Tm; SC; Arch; Bsbl; JV, Ftbl; Citz A; Star Student; *Los Angeles Valley Col.*

PEREIRA, Sonia Ivette
Juan Jose Osuna HS; Baldrich, PR (13-101) Chldr; FHA; Pres, Hmrm; ARC; Secy, Sr Cl; COM; Chem A; Hon Prog; Sci A; *U of Cayey; Natural Sci.*

PEREYRA, Rosalia Noemi
Fort Hamilton HS; Brooklyn, NY; A Cap Choir; Span C; Span NHS; Co-Cpt, Bsbl; Alg A; Most Out; Phy A; Val; Yth Fel; Econ, Span, A's; *Computer Sci.*

PEREZ, Anita Elaine
Lakeview HS; Lakeview, MI (10%-140) Band; Chldr; Chor; FTA; NHS; Secy, Span C; Spch C; SC; Var C; Tr; HCt; Hon Prog; Spch A; Yth Fel; All Conf, Tr Tm; *Marion Col; Eng.*

PEREZ, Debra Jean
Willows HS; Willows, CA (7-130) Band; Chldr; 4H; JV, Sftbl; HCt; *Santa Rosa Jr Col; Nurs.*

PEREZ, Henrietta
Crystal City HS; Crystal City, TX (3-107) Co-Ed, Ann; Ensm; Tres, FHA; NHS; Sch P; Cl Fav; MLS; Drum Major, Band; *Incarnate Word Col; Nurs.*

PEREZ, Irma Gladys
Juan Jose Osuna HS; Hato Rey, PR (8-101) Band; Chldr; Chor; 4H; Hmrm; Mjrte; ARC; Sch P; SC; Swim; Beauty; Cl Fav; Hon Prog; Opt A; Star Student; Swtht; Cl Hon; *Universidad de Puerto Rico; Contabilidad.*

PEREZ, Jeannette
Francisco Mendoza HS; Isabela, PR; Chor; Commercial C; Dbte Tm; Drama; Fr C; FBLA; Pres, Hmrm; Spch C; Bkbl; Sftbl; Alg A; COM; Hon Prog; Math A; Spch A; Dramatic Art A; Eng A; Fr A; Cert of Advance; Scholastic Achv A; Spelling Cert.

PEREZ, John Anthony
Tampa Cath HS; Tampa, FL (50%-305) CYO; Rptr, Sch P; Cpt, Bkbl; One On One Bkbl A; *U of Fla; Journ.*

PEREZ, Juanita
Woodlake Union HS; Woodlake, CA (14-143) Band; Chldr; Drama; FHA; Pres, Hmrm; Sch P; S-T, SC; Var C; Pres, Jr Cl; Sftbl; Tnns; *Col of Sequoias.*

PEREZ, Julio Marcelo
Dr P Perea Fajardo Voc HS; Mayaguez, PR; Hon Stu; *Agr Sci.*

PEREZ, Lisa Virginia
George Washington Sr HS; Mangilao, GUAM; Cpt, Chldr; VP, NHS; VP, SC; Journ A; Most Out; Sal; *U of Calif; Hist.*

PEREZ, Lizzie Socorro
Maria Reina Acad; Rio Piedras, PR (15-58) Chor; Drama; *U of Puerto Rico; Bus Adm.*

PEREZ, Luis Enrique
Juan Jose Osuna HS; Hato Rey, PR (1-101) VP, A Cap Choir; Band; CYO; Chor; Drama; Hmrm; ARC; Sch P; SC; Bausch & Lomb A; COM; Citz A; Hon Prog; Math A; MLS; Most Out; Val; High Hon; *Universidad de Puerto Rico; Acct.*

PEREZ, Maria C
Antonio S Pedreira HS; Moca, PR (5-36) FBLA; FHA; FTA; COM; *UPR-RECINTO; Eng Ed.*

PEREZ, Maria Emily
William A Bass HS; Atlanta, GA (2-30) COM; Crisco A; Gov Honor Prog; Most Out; ROTC A; Top 10%; *Bus.*

PEREZ, Maribel
Francisco Mendoza HS; Isabela, PR; 4H; Rptr, Sch P; Bkbl; *Aguadilla-Cora Regional Col; Social Sci.*

PEREZ, Marisol
Adolfo Grana Rivera HS; Penuelas, PR (6-342) Band; FHA; GS; 4H; Secy, Hmrm; Mjrte; Pres, ARC; COM; Hon Prog; *Cath U of Puerto Rico; Sci.*

PEREZ, Milagros
St Jean the Baptiste HS; NY, NY (20-105) Cpt, CYO; Chldr; Pres, SC; Pres, Soph Cl; Bkbl; Cpt, Sftbl; COM; 2nd Merit Medal; *Bradford Col; Psych.*

PEREZ, Norma I
Academia Santa Monica; Santurce, PR; Ann; Chor; NHS; *Bus Adm.*

PEREZ, Oscar
Jose de Diego HS; Mayaguez, PR; Alg A; COM; Magna Cum Laude.

PEREZ, Susan Therese
John F Kennedy HS; Tumon, GUAM (4-511) Tres, NHS; Tnns; Type A; Art As; Eng A; Civics A; *Wash St U; Art.*

PEREZ, Zelideth Arabell
Colegio Santa Rita; Bayamon, PR (3-33) Chor; Pres, Sr Cl; COM; JA A; Phy A; *U of Puerto Rico; Med Technology.*

PERFECT, Paul Louise
Fairhope HS; Fairhope, AL (68-367) Chem C; Secy, FHA; 4H; Secy, Hmrm; Secy, Lat C; Sch P; SC; Citz A; JA A; Yth Fel; *Zoology.*

PERGEORELIS, Ruby Johanne
Melbourne HS; Melbourne, FL; Secy, Ger C; Apollo 16 Trophy; Secy, Jr Deputies; Law Day Parade.

PERI, Elizabeth Carol
Dexter HS; Dexter, KS (1-13) Ed, Ann; Band; Chldr; Chor; FHA; NHS; SC; Secy, Jr Cl; Pres, Soph Cl; Tr; Most Out; Spch A; Type A; Val; *Cowley Co Comm Col; Bus.*

PERKINS, Alan Luther
N Union HS; Richwood, OH (1-124) Ann; Band; Chess C; Chor; NHS; Ski C; Span C; SC; JV, Bkbl; Cr-Ctry; VofDEM; Span, Geom, A's.

PERKINS, Charles Theodore
Adlai E Stevenson HS; New York, NY (57-788) Chem C; Chor; Dbte Tm; FTA; Hmrm; VP, Inter-Club Coun; Sch Achieve Tm; VP, UN Council; Tr; COM; Citz A; Hon Prog; JA A; Homework Helper A; *US Military Acad; Military Sci.*

PERKINS, Cynthia
Peach Co HS; Fort Valley, GA (10-180) Band; BC; FBLA; Tr; COM; Ntl Achv Schol; NMF; NMS; *Ga Inst of Tech; Elec Engr.*

PERKINS, Deborah Kay
Montabella HS; Edmore, MI; Band; Ski C; *Montcalm Comm Col; Bus.*

PERKINS, Diana Elaine
Middletown HS; Middletown, OH (70-610) Chor; Ensm; FNA; Ger C; Pres, Rainbow; ARC; COM; Citz A; Hon Prog; Opt A; Spch A; Drill Tm; Career Testing Prog; Secy, Church Yth; Explorers; *Nurs.*

PERKINS, Henry
George Washington Carver HS; New Orleans, LA; Brick Masonry.

PERKINS, Janice
Comm HS; Houston, TX; A Cap Choir; Chor; Spch C; Bio A; JA A; MLS; Most Out; Mus A; Top 10, Yng Women Christian Coun; *Westminster Col; Bio.*

PERKINS, Janice Marie
Arlington HS; Indianapolis, IN (71-344) Chess C; Community Yth Symph; Fr C; Orch; Bkbl; Tnns; *Butler U; Mus Ed.*

PERKINS, Karen Louise
Jacksonville Sr HS; Jacksonville, NC; F-Ed, Ann; Chldr; Secy, Span C; Mgr, Bkbl; Sal; Candystriper; Vlbl; HR; Superior Stu Prog, W Carolina U; *Psych.*

PERKINS, Kathy J
Chester HS; Chester, PA; Chor; *Philadelphia Col of Phar; Phar.*

PERKINS, Laurie Rene
Chillicothe HS; Chillicothe, TX; Drama; 4H; 4H A; Historian, FHA; *Vernon Jr Reg Col; Home Ec.*

PERKINS, Lou Anne
E Rutherford HS; Forest City, NC; Chldr; Fr C; Monogram; SC; Leo C; *Bus.*

PERKINS, Maribeth Jane
Franklin Acad HS; Malone, NY (25%-265) Chor; NHS; Epsilon; Tres, Phi-Sigma; *Mohawk Comm Col; Acct.*

PERKINS, Mark Thomas
Bremen HS; Bremen, IN (59-170) *Bradley U; Police.*

PERKINS, Sheila Ann
George Washington HS; San Francisco, CA; A Cap Choir; Dbte Tm; VP, Hmrm; Ntl Yth Conf; SC; Tr; Cl Fav; I Dare You; JA A; Masque & Gavel A; ROTC A; Spch A; *Bishop Col; Psych.*

PERKINS, Sheri Amy
C C Raymond HS; LeCompte, LA (33%-30) Drama; FBLA; FHA; 4H; Sec C; Golf; Sftbl; Tnns; 4H A; Hist A; S-T, Missionettes; 3 P'S C; Ca's C; *Bus.*

PERKINS, Tab E
Sulphur HS; Sulphur, LA (170-433) Pres, FFA; 4H; 4H A; Ntl Del, FFA Convention; U of SW La; Elec Engr.

PERKINS, Teresa Lynn
Elgin HS; Elgin, OK (8-81) Chess C; Dbte Tm; NHS; Co-Ed, Sch P; Alg A; Bio A; Hist A; Masonic A; Type A; Southwestern Okla St U; Art.

PERKINS, Veronica Cecile
Petersburg HS; Petersburg, VA; Chor; Hist.

PERKINS, Vickie Lynn
Douglass HS; Douglass, TX (2-12) F-Ed, Ann; Cpt, Chldr; Tres, FHA; S-T, 4H; Fin, Jr Miss Pagent; F-Ed, Lit Mag; SC; Cpt, Bkbl; Tr; Cl Fav; PTA A; Poet A; Swtht; PA A; Eng Achv; Art Achv; Steven F Austin Col; Bookkeeping.

PERKINS, Wendy Sue
Canton S HS; Canton, OH; Band; FTA; Hmrm; Tri-HiY; COM; Ohio St U; Med.

PERKINSON, Theresia Kathleen
Calhoun HS; Hardin, IL (7-59) Drama; NHS; Rptr, Sch P; Spch C; Pres, SC; DARGCA; Art A; 2nd Pl, Amer Leg Orator; Eastern Col; Law.

PERKY, Robin Sue
Keyes HS; Keyes, OK (2-20) Band; NHS; S-T, SC; Bkbl; Alg A; H of F; Panhandle St U; Bus.

PERMAN, Valerie Lanette
Bowdle Pub HS; Bowdle, SD (10-32) Ann; Chldr; Chor; Ensm; Pres, 4H; Sch P; Var C; Bkbl; Sftbl; MVP, Tr; Beauty; B Crocker A; Cl Fav; 4H A; HQn; HCt; Type A; Yth Fel; SD Wheat Qn; Miss Bowdle Snow Qn; Drill Tm Cpt; SD St U; Registered Nurs.

PERRAULT, Lori Jean
Pinole Valley HS; Pinole, CA (50-700) AFS; Secy, Key C; NHS; JV, Swim; U of Calif; Acct.

PERRIGIN, Kathy Ann
Shades Valley HS; Homewood, AL (1-278) JV, Chldr; InterAct C; Fin, Jr Miss Pagent; Lat C; Mu Alpha Theta; NHS; Secy, SC; Secy, Soph Cl; Citz A; Cl Fav; MLS; Rotary A; Val; Samford U; Nurs.

PERRILL, Julie Ann
Gilmer Co HS; Glenville, WV (9-94) Band; Chor; Pres, Drama; Fr C; SC; Type A; W Va U; Gen Stu.

PERRIN, David Scott
St Joseph Regional HS; Lowell, MA; Chess C; Hmrm; Pres, NHS; Secy, SC; Bsbl; Bkbl; Tnns; U of Lowell; Chem Engr.

PERRIN, James Robert
Lake Highlands HS; Dallas, TX (139-701) Span C; JV, Bsbl; Dallas Area Assn, Christian Yth; U of Tex at Austin; Insurance.

PERRIN, Susanna
Bartow Sr HS; Bartow, FL (25-300) Anchor C; CYO; Drama; Tres, FHA; Semi-Fin, GS; Tres, NHS; Hon Prog; Yth Fair Tri-Color Ribbon; DAR Essay A; FSU; Home Ec.

PERRINE, Beth Rene
Newton Falls HS; Newton Falls, OH (4-170) A-Ed, Arch; Semi-Fin, GS; NHS; Rptr, Sch P; Sci C; Span C; JV, Bkbl; Sftbl; JV, Tr; Hon Prog; St Scholar; Ath A; Ohio St U; Conservation.

PERRINE, Jeffery Allen
Garden City HS E; Garden City, MI; MVP, Cr-Ctry; Tr; JA A; All Area Cr-Ctry Tm.

PERRINE, Kimberly Susan
Uniontown Area Sr HS; Uniontown, PA; CYO; Chor; Fr C; Secy, Hmrm; Co-Cpt, Mjrte; NHS; Sch P; Ski C; SC; Tnns; Citz A; VP, JA; Eng A; Bus Adm.

PERRINO, Thomas Vincent
Elder HS; Cincinnati, OH (40-386) CYO; NHS; SC; Xavier U; Hist.

PERRITT, Roslyn Jill
Glenmora HS; Glenmora, LA (4-46) FHA; Lit Ral; Bkbl; Alg A; Hon Prog.

PERRON, Susan Muriel
St Dominic Regional HS; Lewiston, ME (6-78) Ann; Tres, CYO; Tres, FHA; COM; Hon Prog; Sci A; Type A; Journ Sch Page; WW; Extra-Curricular Activity Trophy A; E Maine Voc-Tech Inst; Med Lab Tech.

PERRY, Allison
Shawl HS; Cleveland, OH; Band; Chor; Citz A; Hon Prog; Most Out; Attendance Banner; Pepperdine U; Mgt.

PERRY, Blanche Cecile
Austin HS; Decatur, AL; Math C; Mu Alpha Theta; Tres, Span C; Sci A; U of Ala; Sci.

PERRY, Charles Houston Jr
Grove HS; Grove, OK (10-100) BC; FBLA; NHS; Pres, SC; Cpt, Arch; Cpt, Bsbl; Cpt, Ftbl; Tr; Cl Fav; HCt; Hon Prog; Masonic A; Most Out; MVP, Bsbl; MVP, Ftbl; Cpt, FCA; All-Conf Ftbl Linebacker; Hon Men, All-St Linebacker; All-Conf Ftbl Linebacker; Northeastern Okla A&M U; Bus Adm.

PERRY, Chell Annette
Castlemont HS; Oakland, CA (20-600) Dance C; U o-t Pacific; Eng.

PERRY, Dale Cunningham
Clifton Forge HS; Clifton Forge, VA (25%-84) BC; Order/Arrow; Var C; Ftbl; JV, Tnns; Tr; Wrest; God & Country A; Eagle Sct; Phar.

PERRY, Darlene Elaine
Hammondsport Central Sch; Hammondsport, NY (1-100) Band; Chldr; Chor; Ensm; Hmrm; NHS; F-Ed, Sch P; Secy, Jr Cl; Sftbl; Drum Mjrte; All St, All Co, Band; Alt, GS; Qn & Princess, Yth Group; Ldrs C; Fin, Miss Tween Camp Qn; I Ratng, Chrch Dist & Zone Tal Con; Sociology.

PERRY, David Raymond
Danville HS; Danville, KY (60-230) Band; Order/Arrow; Mgr, Bkbl; Hon Prog.

PERRY, Deborah Yvonne
Eastmoor Sr HS; Columbus, OH (107-397) Sftbl; Citz A; Elk A; Math A; Type A; Shorthand A; Outst Yth A; OEA A; Loyalty A; PA A; Spelling A; Bowling Green U; Bus Adm.

PERRY, Delores Vondell
Berkeley HS; Moncks Corner, SC (50%-250) VP, FHA; 4H; 4H A; WW; SC St Col; Bus.

PERRY, Diane Lynette
Clayton Valley HS; Concord, CA (35-524) AFS; CSF; S-T, Yth Fel; CSF Seal Bearer; Cert of Proficiency, Secy Prog; Warner Pacific Col; Bus.

PERRY, Donald Eugene Jr
Champion HS; Warren, OH; Band; Chor; Demolay; Orch; Order/Arrow; God & Country A; Order/Arrow A; Yth Fel; Ntl Eagle Sct Assn.

PERRY, Drew Ann
Alma J Brown HS; Grambling, LA (8-48) Rptr, FBLA; Secy, FTA; 4H; Fin, Jr Miss Pagent; Secy, NHS; SC; VP, Sr Cl; Secy, Jr Cl; Sftbl; Hon Prog; Secy, Hon Prog; Outst Personality; Achv in Sci; Grambling Col; Early Childhood Ed.

PERRY, Emily Anne
Nyack HS; Nyack, NY (1-300) Chor; Ensm; Fr C; French NHS; Hon Prog; Harry Barnes Mem Sci A; 1st Hon's Fr, Lang Day Contest; NCTE Candidate; St John's Col.

PERRY, Jacqueline Zenobia
Homer L Ferguson HS; Newport News, VA (81-482) A Cap Choir; Band; Pres, Chor; Fr C; VP, FHA; FNA; FTA; Hmrm; NHS; Secy, Sci C; SC; Va Commonwealth U; Social Work.

PERRY, Jasper Deron
Hardaway HS; Columbus, GA; Columbus Col; Phar.

PERRY, Jeanette
Alexander HS; Starkville, MS (3-28) Rust Col; Bus.

PERRY, Joseph William
Stephens Co HS; Toccoa, GA; BS; Chor; Ensm; HiY; Ch, Key C; Ftbl; Wrest; Ga U; Air Force.

PERRY, Judy Ann
N Platte HS; N Platte, NE (1-376) Chor; Ensm; Madrigal; Pres, Orch; COM; NMS; Val; WW; U of Tulsa; Special Ed.

PERRY, Julie Kay
University HS; Waco, TX (109-350) A Cap Choir; Chor; S-T, Hmrm; Sci C; SC; MCC.

PERRY, Kama Joan
Escondido HS; Escondido, CA; A Cap Choir; Chor; Ger C; Jobs Daughters; NJROTC; Sch Mus; Mus.

PERRY, Karen Sue
W Carter HS; Olive Hill, KY (15%-174) BC; Chldr; FBLA; Hist A; Morehead St U; Bus.

PERRY, Kenny Gene
Lamar Sr HS; Houston, TX; Hmrm; SC; Bkbl; Ftbl; Tr; COM; Citz A.

PERRY, Kimberly Diane
Commerce HS; Commerce, OK (5%-60) Band; FHA; Bkbl; Sftbl; Sal; St Hon Soc; N Eastern A&M U.

PERRY, Leon
Chicago Voc HS; Chicago, IL (370-800) A Cap Choir; Chor; Ensm; 4H; Madrigal; Pres, Ntl Yth Conf; COM; Citz A; 4H A; Hon Prog; Ntl Conf Chr & News; Q&S A; Spch A; Yth Fel; Bishop Col; Theology.

PERRY, Mark Richard
Papillion HS; Papillion, NE (17-400) Band; MVP, Tr; Pres, Yth Fel; Minister.

PERRY, Mary Lynn
Raleigh HS; Raleigh, MS (20%-74) Ann; Band; Chldr; Rptr, Chor; Math C; NHS; Sci C; Spch C; Amer Leg Orator A; Cl Fav; Spch A; FFA Swtht; U of Sou Miss; Phar.

PERRY, Melody Sue
Clinton Sr HS; Clinton, TN; AFS; Chor; Carson Neman Col; Eng.

PERRY, Michael David
Shaler Area HS; Glenshaw, PA; Band; Ensm; Orch; Cpt, Cr-Ctry; Swim; Tr.

PERRY, Michael Lynn
Columbian HS; Tiffin, OH; VP, Bus C; Order/Arrow; Eagle Sct.

PERRY, Monette
Halter HS; Wellston, MO (3-150) Chldr; Sch P; SC; Secy, Soph Cl; Sftbl; Hon Prog; Type A; Bus Off Ed.

PERRY, Pamela Doris
L V Berkner HS; Richardson, TX (12-82) Chor; Model UN; NHS; Tres, Span C; Baylor U; Nurs.

PERRY, Pattie Will
Motley HS; Columbus, MS; FHA; Sci C; Secy, SC; Tri-HiY; Bkbl; Swtht; Valley St Col.

PERRY, Paul Stephen
Man HS; Man, WV (20-180) Tres, Band; MVP, Chess C; Ensm; InterAct C; NHS; ARC; Sci C; Span C; Var C; Ftbl; Wrest; Amer Leg A; VFW A; VofDEM; Yth Fel; All Co Band; W Va U; Biol.

PERRY, Rebecca Suzanne
Cumberland Valley Christian Sch; Chambersburg, PA (1-13) Cpt, Chldr; Chor; VP, Soph Cl; Sftbl; Schol A.

PERRY, Renee Denise
Sylva-Webster HS; Sylvia, NC; Band; Hmrm; Span C; SC; Citz A.

PERRY, Rodney Scott
Columbian HS; Tiffin, OH; VP, Bus C; Order/Arrow; Eagle Sct.

PERRY, Sandra Faye
Smithfield-Selma HS; Smithfield, NC (43-350) Ann; Chor; FHA; 4H; NHS; Sch P; Bkbl; Sftbl; 4H A; Rptr, Secy, Span C; Lacedaemon Court; NC St U; Animal Sci.

PERRY, Sharon Cely
Washington Avenue Christian HS; Greenville, SC (10%-15) Chor; Tres, Key C; Rainbow; Rptr, Sch P; Ntl Fed of Mus C; Musical Guild; Anderson Col; Fashion Merchandising.

PERRY, Shirley Deloris
Alma J Brown HS; Grambling, LA (20-54) Band; Chem C; VP, FHA; Sci C; Tres, SC; WW, Band; WW; HR; Grambling St U; Data Processing.

PERRY, Susan
Grissom HS; Huntsville, AL; Chldr; Chor; Hmrm; ARC; SC; Pres A; ARC A; Swtht; Auburn U; Acct.

PERRY, Susan Elizabeth
Milo Adventist Acad; Days Creek, OR (3-66) A Cap Choir; Chor; Drama; Sch P; Semi-Fin, Cr-Ctry; Cpt, Sftbl; Walla Walla Col; Nurs.

PERRY, Susan Rebecca
Nyack HS; Nyack, NY (1-300) Band; Ensm; Fr C; French NHS; Lit Mag; NHS; Orch; B Crocker A; COM; DARGCA; Hon Prog; NMF; Regent Schol; Val; Vassar Book A; Morning Mus C Prize; Pickwick Book A; Marion Haynes Legion of Hon A's; *Williams Col; Mus.*

PERRY, Tyrus Allen
Humboldt HS; Humboldt, TN (10-226) BC; Hmrm; Var C; Pres, Soph Cl; Bkbl; Ftbl; Tr; Cl Fav; ESAA Committee.

PERRY, Valorie Anne
Southport HS; Indianapolis, IN; Bus Mgr, Ann; Semi-Fin, Chldr; Ger C; Fin, Hmrm; ARC; A-Ed, Sch P; SC; Journ A; Q&S A; Gym; *Anderson Col; Bus.*

PERRY, Willie Lee
Navasota HS; Navasota, TX; Band; FHA; Rptr, Sch P; Sci C; Up Bound; Ftbl; Cpt, Tr; Yth Fel; *Sam Houston St U; Law Enforcement.*

PERRYMAN, Cynthia Louise
L'Anse Creuse HS N; Mt Clemens, MI; Co-Ed, Ann; F-Ed, Sch P; Sftbl; Eng Recognition A; Baptist Yth Fel Pres; *Macomb Co Comm Col; Social Services.*

PERRYMAN, Donna Jo
Yukon HS; Yukon, OK (30-248) FHA; Span C; Cr-Ctry; Sftbl; Tr; Kiwanis A; Most Out; Pres, 'Y' C; FCA; Vlbl; *Central St U; Special Ed.*

PERRYMAN, Kevin Grey
Lexington Sr HS; Lexington, NC; Band; Fr C; Key C; Most Improved, Band A; *Computer Prog.*

PERRYMAN, Stacey Ann
Livingston HS; Livingston, CA; *Pepperdine U; Beautician.*

PERRYMAN, Vanessa Gail
W Fulton HS; Atlanta, GA; Chor; Drama; HCt; ROTC A; ROTC Sponsor.

PERRYMAN, William Henry Jr
Granite Hills HS; El Cajon, CA; Bsbl; MVP, Ftbl; Cpt, JV Ftbl; *Pepperdine U; Math.*

PERSELL, Judy Ann
Edison HS; Minneapolis, MN (44-511) AFS; CYO; Dbte Tm; VP, Key C; NFL; Spch C; Spch A; 'A' HR; *St Mary's Jr Col; Nurs.*

PERSHERN, Patricia Leah
Gilbert HS; Gilbert, MN (10-76) Chldr; Chor; FHA; Ski C; Thes; Bkbl; Tr; HCt; Vlbl; *Col of Saint Benedict; Bio.*

PERSHING, David Edgar
Aurora Central HS; Aurora, CO (21-465) Band; Amer Leg A; Math A; ROTC A; Cpt, AFJROTC; SAR Leadership; Outst Cadet, ROTC; Ldrshp & Sedastic Longevity, ROTC.

PERSON, Cheryl I
Elk Grove HS; Elk Grove Village, IL; Chor; Ensm; Mod Mus Mas; Schol, Pres, Job's Daughters; Hon Pin; *William Rainey Harper Col; Math.*

PERSON, Peter William
George J Penney HS; E Hartford, CT (65-360) Band; Pres, Order/Arrow; Cr-Ctry; Order/Arrow A; *U of Conn; Lib Arts.*

PERSON, Phillip Ward
Detroit Lakes Sr HS; Detroit Lakes, MN (40-255) VP, FFA; Pres, 4H; Span C; Bkbl; Cr-Ctry; Co-Cpt, Ftbl; Tr; FFA Chapter Schol, St Blue Ribbon; *US Air Force Acad; Aeronautics.*

PERSON, Toby Scott
Cashmere HS; Cashmere, WA (30-90) Mgr, Bkbl; Cr-Ctry; Tr.

PERSONETTE, Suzanne Lynn
Independence Sr HS; Charlotte, NC (95-700) Ann; Ch, Drama; Hmrm; Bus Mgr, Sch P; Span C; Co-Ch, Spch; Civinettes; GAA; Fine Arts Hon Soc; Span A; *W Carolina Col; Television Broadcasting.*

PERSONS, Debra Kay
Antioch HS; Antioch, CA (5-500) Secy, Span C; Hon Prog; S-T, GSct; *Humboldt St Col; Psych.*

PERSSON, Nina Jean
Simi Valley HS; Simi Valley, CA (81-829) Hmrm; Bkbl; Bkbl Statistician; *Calif Lutheran Col.*

PESA, Susan Marie
Ursuline HS; Youngstown, OH; Ski C; ARC A; Spelling A; HR; *Med Asst.*

PESHEK, Ramona Kay
Sandy Creek Jr-Sr HS; Fairfield, NE (10%-48) Band; Chor; Tres, Soph Cl; Sftbl; Alg A; Bio A; Math A; Sci A; Type A; DAR A; Hist Excellence; Top 10%; *Kearney St Col; Sci.*

PETECKI, Adrienne Irene
Katella HS; Anaheim, CA (450-532) A Cap Choir; Chor; Drama; Madrigal; Swim; Tnns; Amer Leg A; COM; Cpt, Drill Tm; Best Dressed; Most Inspirational; *Biola Col; Nurs.*

PETERD, Tanya Denise
U S Grant HS; Van Nuys, CA; Jr Miss Pagent; A-Ed, Sch P; Tr; Hon Prog; Journ A; Follower of God; Cl Participation; *Cal St Dominguez; Criminology.*

PETEREIT, Anne Christine
Pinole Valley HS; Pinole, CA (85-600) Band; Ensm; NHS; Orch; ARC; Swim; COM; Citz A; Hon Prog; Explorer Search & Rescue; Most Improved Mus; Outst Mus Sch; Outst Perform, Yrbk; Daughters o-t Amer Revolution A; *Berklee Col; Mus.*

PETERKIN, Pamela Delores
Blenheim HS; Blenheim, SC (18-41) Band; Co-Cpt, Chldr; Dbte Tm; FHA; 4H; Mjrte; Sch P; Bio A; 4H A; Band A; *Benedict Col; Elem Ed.*

PETERMAN, Elizabeth Ann
Bishop Carroll HS; Wichita, KS (4-211) Chor; 4H; Madrigal; NHS; ARC; Sci C; SC; 4H A; HCt; Hon Prog; *Kans St U; Bio.*

PETERMAN, Karen Sue
C Leon King HS; Tampa, FL (186-619) A Cap Choir; Chor; Drama; Ensm; Madrigal; NHS; Spch A; *U of S Fla; Corporate Law.*

PETERMAN, Mark Bradford
Memorial Sr HS; Houston, TX (23-640) Hmrm; Ch, InterClub Coun; NHS; Order/Arrow; SC; Swim; JV, Tnns; CSF; Hist A; Hon Prog; Magna Cum Laude; Water Polo; Archt Drafting A; Eagle Sct; *Rice U; Engr.*

PETERMANN, Donna Doris
Sheboygan S HS; Sheboygan, WI (100-500) A Cap Choir; Band; Drama; Lit Mag; Fin, NFL; Orch; Thes; Spch A; St Mus A's; Outst, Crew; Stage Mgr; Thespian A; *Concordia Col; Elem Ed.*

PETERMANN, Julie Eann
Mandan Sr HS; Mandan, ND (55-313) Band; Pres, Chor; NHS; Tres, SC; Tri-St, All St, Mus Hon Prog; Tech Asst A, Broadway Mus; *Moorhead St Col; Elem Ed.*

PETERS, Becky Jane
Effingham HS; Effingham, IL (42-218) Band; Drama; Ensm; Fr C; Rainbow; Spch C; *Spch.*

PETERS, Calvin Michael
Everett HS; Everett, MA (70-375) Chem C; Order/Arrow; Tr; God & Country A; Pres, Yth Group; Church Usher; Coordinator, Hunger Walkathon; Church Trustee; Bicentennial Comm; Sec, Ecumen Com; Abrm Lincoln Schol; *Forestry.*

PETERS, Caroline N
Waterford Kettering HS; Drayton Plains, MI; Band; Tr; *Nurs.*

PETERS, Claudia Irene
Howe HS; Howe, OK (2-34) S-T, Ann; FHA; Secy, Hmrm; S-T, SC; Secy, Soph Cl; Cl Fav; Masonic A; Val; *Dental Aid.*

PETERS, Colleen Kay
Brownton Pub Sch; Brownton, MN (7-20) Ed, Ann; Band; Chor; FHA; Secy, Sr Cl; Hon Prog; Graduation Attendant; *Willmar Vo Tech Col; Cosmotology.*

PETERS, Darlene Gay
Northeastern HS; Detroit, MI; Secy, CYO; 4H; NHS; SC; Y-Tns; COM; Citz A; NHS; Star Student; Type A; Modern Dance; *Detroit Col of Bus; Executive Secy.*

PETERS, Debra Elsbeth
Richardson HS; Richardson, TX (56-888) NHS; Span C; VP, Tri-HiY; Tnns; *Tex A&M U; Acct.*

PETERS, Dennis Ray
Grand Co HS; Moab, UT; Chor; Ger C; NFL; Spch C; SC; Soccer; Tnns; Spch A; *Bethany Bible Col; Bible.*

PETERS, Diane Marie
Central Heights HS; Richmond, KS (3-54) Ed, Ann; NHS; Alg A; COM; Hon Prog; Math A; St Scholar; *Kans St Col of Pittsburg; Sociology.*

PETERS, Douglas James
Rossville Comp HS; Rossville, GA (12-212) Ann; BC; VP, Key C; Pres, Jr Cl; JV, Bsbl; Bkbl; COM; Gov Honor Prog; Math A; Key Clubber o-t Month; SOA A; Geom A; Ga Inst of Tech, Distin Sci Schol; *Dalton Jr Col; Pre-Phar.*

PETERS, Elsie
Abbotsford Jr Secondary HS; Abbotsford, CANADA; Ed, Ann; Hon Prog; Ger A; Duke of Edinburgh A.

PETERS, Glenn Allan
Dowagiac Union HS; Dowagiac, MI (22-315) Band; Band As; *Computer Programming.*

PETERS, Jacque Marie
Middleton HS; Charleston, SC (23-263) Chor; Ensm; Jr Miss Pagent; Madrigal; All St Choir; HR; WW; Charleston's Jr Miss; *Okla Baptist U; Mus Ed.*

PETERS, Jan Marie
Lexington HS; Lexington, MO (20-100) Band; Tres, Soph Cl; Tr; Vlbl; Fin, Homecoming Court.

PETERS, Janice Lynn
Inola HS; Inola, OK (10%-80) Band; Chldr; Pres, Chor; Ensm; VP, FHA; Mjrte; NHS; Spch C; Hist A; Hon Prog; Spch A; Band A; *OU; Nurs.*

PETERS, Joy Lee
Monroe Area Comprehensive HS; Monroe, GA (25%-300) Anchor C; Band; Chor; Ensm; Rptr, FTA; Hmrm; Lit Ral; SC; Tri-HiY; Var C; Gov Honor Prog; Hon Prog; Most Out; Sci A; *Mus.*

PETERS, Lenita Jeanine
J C Fremont HS; Los Angeles, CA; Band; Chldr; Chor; Orch; Tr; Alg A; Citz A; Math A; *Math.*

PETERS, Lou Rashelle
College View Acad; Lincoln, NE; A Cap Choir; VP, Band; Chor; Drama; Ensm; NHS; Ski C; Tres, Sr Cl; Ftbl; Swim; Citz A; Hon Prog; Singing Group; *Sou Miss Col; Nurs.*

PETERS, Nancy Jean
Badger HS; Lake Geneva, WI (38-228) Band; JV, Chldr; Chor; Ensm; Mjrte; Tr; Hon Prog; Sportsmanship A; *Olivet Nazarene Col; Bus.*

PETERS, Nathaniel II
Fern Creek HS; Louisville, KY (4-300) BC; Math C; Pres, NHS; VP, Sr Cl; JV, Bsbl; COM; Harvard Book A; Math A; MLS; NMF; Math League; Hi-Q Tm; U of Ky Merit Schol; WW; *U of Ky; Archt.*

PETERS, Richard Kevin
Benton HS; St Joseph, MO (31-248) Drama; NHS; Regent Schol; ROTC A; *Mo W St Col.*

PETERS, Robert Dale
New Caney HS; Porter, TX (25%-280) Bsbl; JV, Bkbl; Ftbl; *U of Houston; Bio.*

PETERS, Robert Otto
Clarkstown HS S; W Nyack, NY; Drama; JV, Tnns; Amer Leg A; Law Explorers; Yrbk Staff; *U of Nev at Las Vegas; Bus.*

PETERS, Robin Lori
John Charles Fremont HS; Los Angeles, CA; Band; Chldr; Chor; Orch; Tr; Alg A; Citz A; Math A; Type A; *Bus.*

PETERS, Sharon Gayle
Dothan HS; Dothan, AL (200-632) Tn Vol; Vlbl; Yth Assn for Retarded Children; *U of Ala; Phys Therapy.*

PETERS, Sheila Diane
Southeast of Saline HS; Assaria, KS (10%-57) Band; Chor; Ensm; Pres, 4H; Madrigal; NHS; 4H A; *Kansas St U; Elem Ed.*

PETERS, Sheila Renee
Elmer H Garinger HS; Charlotte, NC (20-626) Co-Ed, Ann; JV, Chldr; Tres, Ger C; Pres, Hmrm; NHS; SC; Delta Sigma Theta A; HCt; Hon Prog; I Dare You; Swtht; Top 10 Sr's; Ntl Brd of Church & Soc Nom, Gov Sc; *U of NC; Psych.*

PETERS, Stephen LeRay
Rusk HS; Rusk, TX; Band; FFA; 4H A; Yth Fel; Rodeo; Horse Show; Church As; *Tyler Jr Col; Criminology.*

PETERS, Timothy Douglas
Central HS; Omaha, NE (7%-546) A Cap Choir; Chor; Drama; Ensm; Mu Alpha Theta; Thes; Hon Prog; Rotary A; Mus Production Lead.

PETERS, William Joseph
Bolton HS; Alexandria, LA (6-350) Bus Mgr, Ann; Chess C; Drama; Fr C; French NHS; Key C; Fin, Lit Ral; Lit Mag; Ed, Sch P; COM; Hist A; Hon Prog; NEDT; Sci A; *LSU; Archt.*

PETERSEN, Dawn Adaire
Mucla HS; Nucla, CO (1-77) Ed, Ann; Band; Dbte Tm; Drama; Model UN; Rptr, NHS; Sch P; Ski C; Pres, Span C; Spch C; Mgr, Tr; Alg A; Journ A; Sci A; Spch A; Val; Yrbk Ed A; Hon Band A; *Colo U; Dietetics.*

PETERSEN, Eugenia Kay
Garner-Hayfield HS; Garner, IA (15-63) Ann; Band; Chor; Dbte Tm; Drama; Ensm; FNA; Sch P; Spch C; Thes; Golf; Spch A; WW; *U of N Iowa; Ed.*

PETERSEN, Gayle Laurene
Flagler Pub Sch; Flager, CO (8-18) Chldr; Chor; FHA; FTA; Secy, Soph Cl; Bkbl; Tr; COM; Pres A; Type A; Art A; *Phys Ed.*

PETERSEN, Katherine Ann
Washington HS; Fremont, CA (1-375) Chor; CSF; *W Baptist Bible Col.*

PETERSEN, Lawrence Doyle
Burkburnett HS; Burkburnett, TX; Band; Bkbl; *US Marines.*

PETERSEN, Lois Ann
Permian HS; Odessa, TX; Chem C; JETS; NHS; Sci C; Secy, Span NHS; Top Ten; *Tex Tech U; Acct.*

PETERSEN, Marla Gay
Valley HS; Hazelton, ID; Chor; Drama; FHA; Spch C; Sftbl; Swim; Tr; *Sci.*

PETERSEN, Renee Christine
Waverly-Shell Rock Sr HS; Waverly, IA; Chor; Drama; Ger C; Co-Ch, Sci C; Thes; COM; Spch A; Yth Fel; Art, Modern Dance, C'S; Mus, Art, A's; *Hawkeye Inst of Tech; Commercial Art.*

PETERSEN, Richard Lewis
Elk Point HS; Elk Point, SD (40-58) Chor; 4H; Bkbl; Mgr, Ftbl; *Vet.*

PETERSEN, Robert Anthony
Western Hills HS; Ft Worth, TX (20-600) CYO; Order/Arrow; Rptr, Sch P; SC; Wrest; Journ A; MLS; Opt Out Tn; Pres A; *N Tex St U; Bus.*

PETERSEN, Sherry Lynn
Spring HS; Spring, TX (25%-639) Mu Alpha Theta; JV, Bkbl.

PETERSEN, Stewart D
Cokeville HS; Cokeville, WY; Band; VP, SC; Pres, Jr Cl; Bkbl; Ftbl; Co-Cpt, Wrest; Movie Star-Where The Red Fern Grows; Seven Alone, Against A Crooked Sky; Express Rider; *Ricks U.*

PETERSEN, Tracey Linn
Holstein HS; Holstein, IA (15-64) A Cap Choir; Ann; Band; Chor; Ensm; Secy, Hmrm; Madrigal; NHS; Sch P; Bkbl; All St Chor; *Mus.*

PETERSEN, Wayne Thomas
Cokeville HS; Cokeville, WY; Band; 4H; Pres, SC; VP, Jr Cl; Bkbl; Tr; 4H A; MLS; Order/Arrow A; Type A; *Brigham Young U; Med Technology.*

PETERSON, Amy Lynn
Clark HS; Las Vegas, NV; Band; Chor; Madrigal; Orch; COM; Citz A; Pres, Church Bell Choir; Hon Band; All St Band; GSct; *U of Nev; Mus.*

PETERSON, Angela Crystal
Cass Tech HS; Detroit, MI; Hon Prog; Yth Fel; HR; *Mich St U; Bus Adm.*

PETERSON, Anita Faye
Rice Lake Sr HS; Rice Lake, WI (45-262) Band; Chor; Fr C; Ch, Ger C; VP, 4H; Mgr, Bkbl; Golf; 4H A; Hon Prog; Solo & Ensm, Band; Best Dressed Girl, Sr Cl; Ath A; Choral A; *U Minn Duluth; Med Tech.*

PETERSON, Anita Kathryn
Northgate HS; Walnut Creek, CA; Semi-Fin, Jr Miss Pa; gent; Pres, Sr League; Pres, Worship Choir; *Diablo Valley Col; Computer Training.*

PETERSON, Bernard Leo
Marion Co HS; Lebanon, KY (45-324) Co-Ed, Ann; BS; Hmrm; NHS; Rptr, Sch P; Sci C; Var C; Ftbl; *U of Ky; Vet Sci.*

PETERSON, Beth Ann
Sweeny HS; Sweeny, TX; A Cap Choir; Band; Ensm; Madrigal; SC; Citz A; FFA Swtht; *Tex Lutheran Col; Sociology.*

PETERSON, Beverly Ann
Abingdon HS; Abingdon, IL (2-120) Ed, Ann; Chor; Drama; Ensm; FTA; Pres, 4H; Lit Mag; Rptr, Sch P; Secy, Span C; Spch C; Pres, Jr Cl; Tres, Soph Cl; JV, Tr; Amer Leg A; 4H A; Hon Prog; Rotary A; Spch A; *U of Ill; Med.*

PETERSON, Bobbie Jean
Peoria HS; Peoria, IL; *Bus Acct.*

PETERSON, Bonita Faye
DuPont Manual HS; Louisville, KY; Fr C; Hon Prog; Excel Cert; *W St Col; Bus Ed.*

PETERSON, Brian Keith
Wanamingo Pub HS; Wanamingo, MN (2-40) Band; Drama; NHS; Pres, SC; Pres, Sr Cl; VP, Jr Cl; Tr; Declam; *Augustana Col; Religion.*

PETERSON, Brian Lee
Neshannock HS; New Castle, PA (28-150) Fr C; Hmrm; Math C; NHS; Sci C; SC; Bkbl; JV, Cr-Ctry; Tr; Bio A; Hon Prog; NEDT; Jr Acad of Sci; *Pa St U; Biol.*

PETERSON, Bruce Donald
Westview Sr HS; Braham, MN (10-86) Ann; Band; BS; Chor; Ensm; Sci C; Tres, Jr Cl; Co-Cpt, Bkbl; Cpt, Golf; Cl Fav; MLS; Pres, Photo C; Del, St Baptist Conf; Christian Service Brigade; Christian Yth Fellowship; Church Choir; *Bethel Col.*

PETERSON, Bruce L
Bismarck HS; Bismarck, ND (220-432) A Cap Choir; Band; Chor; *BJC; Bus Adm.*

PETERSON, Carol Louise
Los Altos HS; Hacienda Heights, CA; A Cap Choir; Chor; Sci C; Ski C; Swim; VP, Pioneer Girls; *Med.*

PETERSON, Carrie
Russell HS; Hurtsboro, AL (8-56) Chor; FHA; 4H; Sci C; Bkbl; Sftbl; COM; Citz A; 4H A; Hon Prog; JA A; ROTC A; *Albany U; Home Ec.*

PETERSON, Celia Ann
Duncanville HS; Duncanville, TX (49-482) Band; Ger C; Secy, 4H; Span C; *U of Tex; Foreign Lang.*

PETERSON, Cheryl Elizabeth
McGregor HS; McGregor, MN (7-66) Ed, Ann; Band; Chor; Drama; FHA; GS; Pres, 4H; Jr Miss Pagent; NHS; Rptr, Sch P; Thes; Var C; Cpt, Bkbl; Tr; COM; 4H A; H of F; HCt; Pres A; Yth Fel; Vlbl; *St Scholastica Col; Nurs.*

PETERSON, Clark Alan
Ottumwa HS; Ottumwa, IA (33%-565) A Cap Choir; Band; Chor; Drama; Ensm; Madrigal; Span C; Amer Leg A; Best Marcher, Band; Madrigal; *Simpson Col; Mus.*

PETERSON, Connie Jo
Claremore HS; Claremore, OK; FHA; 4H; Var C; Bkbl; Mgr, Tr; 4H A; HQn; Hon Prog; Swtht; Yth Fel; Treas, 4H; Leo C; Senate Page; *OSU; Dental-Hygiene.*

PETERSON, Coral Ann
Thomas Stone HS; Waldorf, MD (5%-365) F-Ed, Ann; Cpt, Chldr; Chor; Hmrm; Jr Miss Pagent; NHS; Ski C; SC; Mgr, Bsbl; Swim; Tr; COM; Citz A; Gov Honor Prog; Hon Prog; ARC A; WW; *Salisbury St Col; Psych.*

PETERSON, Craig Madson
Pawnee HS; Pawnee, TX (6-13) Ann; BS; Chem C; FFA; Span C; Spch C; Cpt, Bkbl; Cpt, Ftbl; Tnns; Tr; Amer Leg A; Cl Fav; Sci A; *Bee Co Col; Ath Trng.*

PETERSON, Cynthia Lynn
Tidewater Acad; Wakefield, VA (1-58) NHS; VP, SC; MVP, Bkbl; Sftbl; MVP, Tnns; Hon Prog; Ath o-t Yr; Schol A; Co-Cpt, Bkbl; Cpt, Tnns; *Richard Bland Col; Ed.*

PETERSON, Dana Kay
Mabel-Canton HS; Mabel, MN (11-50) All Amer Yth; Ed, Ann; Band; Cpt, Chldr; Chor; Chor; Ensm; FHA; Madrigal; NHS; Ed, Sch P; Spch C; SC; Tres, Sr Cl; Tres, Jr Cl; Tr; Spch A; Swtht; Vlbl; 1st Cl GSct; Phi Beta Mu; Dorian, Hon's Bands; Dorian Choir; *Nurs.*

PETERSON, Daniel Neil
Parkview HS; Orfordville, WI (50-142) BS; Chess C; Chor; FFA; SC; Attendance A; *Blackhawk Tech Col; Gen.*

PETERSON, Daphne Ann
Merrill Sr HS; Merrill, WI (65-300) Band; Ch, Ensm; Lit Mag; Rptr, Sch P; Ski C; SC; Bsbl; Tnns; Tr; Mus Camp Schol; Dist Tn Talent; Solo Ensm Cl A; *Central Bible Col; Elec Engr.*

PETERSON, Darcy Lynne
Park Center Sr HS; Brooklyn Park, MN; JV, Bkbl; JV, Sftbl.

PETERSON, Daryl Robin
River Valley HS; Three Oaks, MI (10%-195) Band; Chor; Drama; NHS; Tr; Citz A.

PETERSON, David A
Joliet Township W HS; Joliet, IL (100-540) Rptr, Sch P; SC; Bkbl; Ftbl; *U of Ill; Agr Engr.*

PETERSON, David L
Twin Falls HS; Twin Falls, ID (20%-500) Band; Pres, 4H; NHS; F-Ed, Sch P; Wrest; 4H A; NMS; *Journ.*

PETERSON, Dawn Karen
Gaylord Pub Sch; Gaylord, MN (2-88) Ann; Chor; FHA; Ger C; Sch P; Hon Prog; Yth Fel; Ger A; *Normandale Comm Col; Gen.*

PETERSON, Deborah Carol
N Shore HS; W Palm Beach, FL (37-266) Chldr; Chor; 4H; Hmrm; Key C; Var C; Swim; Alg A.

PETERSON, Debra Ann
Dugway HS; Dugway, UT (1-45) Band; Bus C; Tres, Hmrm; Model UN; COM; Most Out; PTA A; Type A; Vlbl; Ltr- ettes; HR; Bus A; *Secretarial Training.*

PETERSON, Diana Jo
San Carlos HS; San Carlos, CA; Band; Ensm; Orch; Swim; CSF; Commnd Perfor & Sup Ratng, Solo.

PETERSON, Diane Sue
Harold L Richards HS; Oak Lawn, IL (22-645) VP, Band; Mod Mus Mas; NHS; Bkbl; Tr; Hon Prog; *Mus.*

PETERSON, Donna Jean
Musselman HS; Bunker Hill, WV (1-92) Band; NHS; Tres, Sci C; Co-Cpt, Bkbl; COM; Citz A; MLS; Rensselaer A; *W Va U; Forensic Chem.*

PETERSON, Donna Joyce
Powers Lake Pub HS; Powers Lake, ND (2-25) Ann; Chor; Drama; Rptr, FHA; Mod Mus Mas; Sch P; Mgr, Bkbl; Tr; Sal; *Concordia Col.*

PETERSON, Donna Ruth
Reading Mem HS; Reading, MA; AFS; Drama; Pres, Hmrm; Rainbow; SC; Yth Fel; Gym C; Ch, Dance Group; *Framingham St Col; Home Ec.*

PETERSON, Dorcas Emily
Hope HS; Hope, AR (15-222) Cpt, Band; BC; FTA; Tres, Ger C; Co-Cpt, Mjrte; Nike C; All-St Band Tryouts; Ntl Mus Guild 0280000; *U of Ark; Occupational Therapy.*

PETERSON, Elisabeth May
Richwoods HS; Peoria, IL (207-463) Rptr, Sch P; Tr; Fin, Schol Art A; *Kans St U; Archt.*

PETERSON, Elizabeth Ann
Century HS; Bismarck, ND (11-200) Chldr; Orch; Span C; SC; *Bismarck Jr Col; Humanities.*

PETERSON, Eric Jon
Highland Pub Sch; Highland, WI (6-48) FFA; Pres, 4H; SC; Bsbl; JV, Bkbl; JV, Ftbl; Sftbl; 4H A; Hon Prog; Tres, Luther League.

PETERSON, Heidi Jo
Richfield Sr HS; Richfield, MN (130-800) Rptr, Ann; Chor; Community Yth Symph; Fr C; Orch; Sftbl; *NW Bible Col; Christian Ed.*

PETERSON, Holt Alexander
Hastings Sr HS; Hastings, MN (20-540) Band; Co-Cpt, Bkbl; Ftbl; Soccer; Tnns; Hon Prog; *Med.*

PETERSON, Jadeane Kay
Columbia HS; Richland, WA; FHA; Outst Achv A, Foreign Lang; *Bethany Bible Col; Ed.*

PETERSON, Jamie Lynne
Sweeny HS; Sweeny, TX (20-137) A Cap Choir; Chor; FFA; NHS; Co-Ed, Sch P; Beauty; HCt; Journ A; Ftbl Swtht; FFA Swtht; All St Choir; *Tex Lutheran Col; Mus.*

PETERSON, Jerome Renee
Richmond Acad; Augusta, GA; MVP, Bsbl; MVP, Bkbl; MVP, Ftbl; MVP, Tr; Hon Prog; Outst Art Stu; Phys Ed; *Morehouse Col; Religions.*

PETERSON, Jill Carol
Ottawa Hills HS; Grand Rapids, MI; Chor.

PETERSON, Jill Diane
Woodrow Wilson HS; Portland, OR (126-475) A Cap Choir; Chor; Drama; Ensm; Madrigal; Thes; Oreg Fed Mus C A; *U of Oreg; Psych.*

PETERSON, Jill Jane
Enid HS; Enid, OK (73-488) VP, Hmrm; NHS; Span C; SC; Tnns; *U of Okla; Chem Engr.*

PETERSON, Jill Kristi
Burke HS; Omaha, NE (101-871) Chor; Fr C; *Bethel Col; Ed.*

PETERSON, Joan Justine
Ansley Pub Sch; Ansley, NE (17-48) Tres, Band; Chor; Madrigal; Mgr, Bkbl; Tr; Pom Pon; *Mid-Plains Comm Col; Dentist Tech.*

PETERSON, Joan Lelie
Horseheads HS; Horseheads, NY (30-535) Band; Chldr; Chor; Lat C; NHS; *Phys Therapy.*

PETERSON, Joanne
Hyde Park HS; Boston, MA (10-24) Bkbl; COM; Cl Fav; Pres, Choir; Tres GScts; *Boston St Col; Mus.*

PETERSON, John Vernon
Ardmore HS; Ardmore, OK (25-250) Chor; Madrigal; NHS; Var C; Golf; *Tex Christian U; Spec Ed.*

PETERSON, John Westerfield
Watchung Hills Regional HS; Warren, NJ (32-450) Ed, Ann; Math C; Order/ Arrow; Sci C; Emergency Med Tech; Hospital Vol; NML; WW; *Rutgers Col; Pre-Med.*

PETERSON, Julie Denise
Coon Rapids Sr HS; Coon Rapids, MN; CYO; FHA; Swim; COM; Photography A; *Moorehead St U; Photography.*

PETERSON, Julie Ilene
Cardio HS; Carpio, ND; Band; Chor; Ensm; Ed, Sch P; Var C; Co-Cpt, Bkbl; Hon Prog; Type A; MVP, Co-Cpt, Tr; *Minot St Col; Bus Ed.*

PETERSON, Kamilee Faith
Ingraham HS; Seattle, WA (25%-400) Band; Drama; Key C; Environmental C; *Wash St U.*

PETERSON, Kari Marie
Holstein HS; Holstein, IA (9-66) Ed, Ann; Co-Ch, Band; Cpt, Chldr; Chor; Mjrte; F-Ed, Sch P; Spch C; SC; Golf; COM; Spch A; Pep C; Sup, St Sci Fair, Sr Chrch C; Best Support Actrs; Chambr Choir; Stage Band; Tres, Luther League; Best Upcoming Actress; Swing Choir; *Dietitian.*

PETERSON, Kathleen Louise
Soap Lake Sr HS; Soap Lake, WA (5-30) FBLA; Pres, FHA; Secy, NHS; Rptr, Sch P; Secy, Jr Cl; Cr-Ctry; Tr; Odd Fellow Fin; Swtht Princess; *Sci.*

PETERSON, Kenneth LaVerne
Oakridge HS; Oakridge, OR (41-89) Band; 4H; SC; Bkbl; JV, Cr-Ctry; JV, Golf; Tnns; *Northwest Nazarene Col; Pre-Seminary.*

PETERSON, Kenny Joe
York Comp HS; York, SC (5-240) Wrest; Jr Marshal; Auto Mech C; *York Tech Col; Computers.*

PETERSON, Kim Clores
Continued Ed Project; St Louis, MO; Citz A.

PETERSON, Kim Louise
Wethersfield HS; Kewanee, IL (33%-90) Ed, Ann; Band; Chldr; Drama; Spch C; *U of Ill; Med.*

PETERSON, Kimberly Ann
Valley City HS; Valley City, ND (14-156) F-Ed, Ann; Drama; GS; Hmrm; NHS; Mgr, Bkbl; *Valley City St Col.*

PETERSON, Kristine Elizabeth
Denfeld HS; Duluth, MN (15%-450) Chor; VP, 4H; *St Lukes Nurs Sch; Med.*

PETERSON, Layna Lee
Bay City Western HS; Auburn, MI; MVP, Bkbl; HCt; Vlbl; Pres, Mat C; *Psych.*

PETERSON, Leah Ann
Pittsburg HS; Pittsburg, KS (12-181) Band; Community Yth Symph; Ensm; Lat C; Orch; St Orch; *Wichita St U; Mus.*

PETERSON, Leslie Ann
Phila HS for Girls; Philadelphia, PA (82-392) Dbte Tm; Ch, Hmrm; Beauty; COM; 1st Prize, Black Hist Essay; Human Rights A; Yth Day A; 1st Prize, Victoms Rght Essay Cont; *U of Penn; Bus Adm.*

PETERSON, Linnea Alice
Amundsen HS; Chicago, IL; Hmrm; NHS; Span C; Pres, SC; Hon Prog; Tres, Luther League; *Acct.*

PETERSON, Lori Ann
Duluth E HS; Duluth, MN; Band; Orch; Pres, Span C.

PETERSON, Lori Kay
Northwood-Kensett HS; Northwood, IA (29-68) Ann; Band; Chldr; VP, Chor; Drama; Ensm; Fr C; Pres, 4H; Madrigal; Co-Ed, Sch P; Spch C; Secy, Sr Cl; Sftbl; Tr; 4H A; HCt; Spch A; Hayseeder's Ct; Top in St Presentation, 4-H; Chldr o-t Yr; Piano A; *U of Northern Iowa.*

PETERSON, Lynn Marie
Encino HS; Sacramento, CA (10%-500) A Cap Choir; Chor; ARC; CSF; COM; Citz A; MGM; *Med.*

PETERSON, Marji A
Ashland Sr HS; Ashland, OR (45-230) Band; Dbte Tm; Drama; Fr C; ARC; Bkbl; Swim; Tr; ARC A; *U of Oreg; Speical Ed.*

PETERSON, Mary Ann
Yankton HS; Yankton, SD; Band; Chor; Orch; Spch C; Var Gym; *Sioux Falls Col; Mus.*

PETERSON, Mary Beth
Manhattan HS; Manhattan, KS (238-425) Chor; VP, FHA; FTA; WW; *Kans St U; Bus Adm.*

PETERSON, Mary Kristin
Aurelia Comm Sch; Aurelia, IA; Band; VP, Chor; FHA; S-T, Jr Cl; Bkbl; DARGCA; Hist A; *Augustana Col; Sociology.*

PETERSON, Mary Lynn
Leilehua HS; Wahiawa, HI (10%-500) Pres, FFA; NFL; Cr-Ctry; Swim; Cl Fav; St Star Farmer; Outst Poultry Stu; Prom Court; *Calif Poly-Tech St U; Poultry Sci.*

PETERSON, Mary Susanne
Mechanicsburg Sr HS; Mechanicsburg, PA (90-360) Fr C; VP, Hmrm; JV, Bkbl; Tr; Spch A; Yth Fel; Cand, DAR A; Semi-Fin, Spch A; Semi-Fin, Radio Broadcasting; Sr Advisory Coun; VP, Yth Fel; *Central Penn Bus Sch; Executive Secy.*

PETERSON, Matthew David
Monte Vista HS; Danville, CA (148-381) Band; HCt; Yth Fel; Ldr, Ensm; *Pepperdine U; Psych.*

PETERSON, Miri Kay
Holstein Comm HS; Holstein, IA (8-47) A Cap Choir; Ann; VP, Chor; Madrigal; NHS; Sch P; Tres, Jr Cl; Golf; Sch Musical; Luther League Pres; Church Choir; Accompanist; *Luther Col; Bus.*

PETERSON, Nancy Alice
Two Harbors HS; Two Harbors, MN (21-174) Band; JV, Bkbl; Tnns; *U of Minn.*

PETERSON, Nancy Ann
Waialua HS; Waialua, HI (44-179) Fr C; Rptr, Sch P; *U of Puget Sound; Lib Arts.*

PETERSON, Nancy Elizabeth
Leilehua HS; Wahiawa, HI (25-600) Tres, 4H; Tr; 4H A; Sci A; *Animal Sci.*

PETERSON, Randall Dwight
S St Paul Sr HS; St Paul, MN; A Cap Choir; Chor; Var C; Bkbl; JV, Cr-Ctry; Tr; V Sports Ltrs; *U of Minn; Med.*

PETERSON, Rebecca Deanne
Twin Falls HS; Twin Falls, ID (10%-500) Band; Rptr, 4H; Sch P; Cpt, Bkbl; Tr; 4H A; VP, Kayettes; Tr As; Optimist C, Spch Contest; *Phillips U; Ed.*

PETERSON, Sandra Lynn
Granada HS; Livermore, CA (135-377) Co-Ed, Ann; Chor; 4H; S-T, Rainbow; Semi Fin, Maid of Livermore; *Chabot Jr Col; Bus.*

PETERSON, Sharon Lynn
M B Smiley HS; Houston, TX (2-461) Band; Ensm; Fr C; FTA; Math C; Mu Alpha Theta; NHS; SC; Up Bound; Parl, Soph Cl; Alg A; Bio A; Hist A; Type A; Eng, Phar, A's; *U of Houston; Computer Sci.*

PETERSON, Sherry Gayle
E Greene HS; Grand Junction, IA (2%-34) Band; Chor; NHS; Bkbl; Sftbl; Tr; Type A; *Iowa St U; Landscape Architecture.*

PETERSON, Suzanne Carolina
Minneapolis Lutheran HS; Minneapolis, MN (16-36) Chess C; NHS; Sch P; *Concordia Col St Paul; Elem Ed.*

PETERSON, Timothy Richard
Abraham Lincoln HS; Council Bluffs, IA (33%-450) Band; Chor; Ensm; Madrigal; Tnns; Drum Major; Distinguished Mus Cert; *Iowa St U; Meterology.*

PETERSON, Todd Gerard
McVille Pub HS; McVille, ND (10-19) Band; CYO; Chor; Ensm; Orch; Bkbl; Ftbl; Golf; Tr; *Valley City St Col; Mus.*

PETERSON, Todd Gregory
Forest Lake Sr HS; Forest Lake, MN; A Cap Choir.

PETERSON, Vytas Richard
Kelly HS; Chicago, IL (5-476) Chess C; Tres, NHS; Bkbl; Hon Prog; Math A; NMF; St Scholar; *Yale U; Physics.*

PETERSON, Walter Ray
Perkins Co HS; Grant, NE (50%-33) FFA; 4H; UN Pilgrimage; *Engr.*

PETERSON, Wayne Melvin
Santa Teresa HS; San Jose, CA (40-490) Co-Ch, Ger C; Model UN; Ski C; JV, Bsbl; H of F; *San Jose St U; Eng.*

PETERSON, Wendy Fern
Oak Park River Forest HS; Oak Park, IL (90-1057) CYO; Math C; Ski C; Hon Prog; NMS; 3rd Prize, IIT Archt Drawing Cont; *U of Ill; Archt.*

PETERSON, William Lee
Montabella HS; Edmore, MI (23-168) *Mich St U; Agr.*

PETIT, Gail Ann
W Jefferson HS; W Jefferson, OH (1-118) A-Ed, Ann; Band; Bus C; CYO; Chor; Secy, Drama; Fr C; Pres, 4H; Mjrte; NHS; Sch P; Span C; DARGCA; MLS; Poet A; Val; Domestic Sci C A; *Mount Carmel Sch of Nurs; Nurs.*

PETKAC, Eva
Highland HS; Medina, OH (10-250) A Cap Choir; Secy, Band; Chor; Ger C; Swim; Tnns; COM; Hon Prog; Band A; *Med.*

PETNIC, James Keith
Joppatowne Jr-Sr HS; Joppa, MD (10%-180) Chor; Fr C; NHS; Var C; Tnns; JV, Soccer; Tres, Explorers; BSct; Tres, Presbyterian Yth Group; *Sci.*

PETREE, Pamela Denise
McKinley Tech HS; Washington, DC; Secy, Hmrm; Citz A; Hon Prog; *St Augustine Col; Pre-Med.*

PETRICH, Brian Keith
Worthington Sr HS; Worthington, MN (90-280) Chor; Drama; Ensm; Pres, Hmrm; Key C; Ski C; SC; Ftbl; Tr; COM; HCt; Pres A; Snow Wk Court; Vocal Solo Regional, Drama, A's; *Mass Communications.*

PETRICH, Julie Kay
W Linn HS; W Linn, OR (40-260) AFS; Chor; FFA; 4H; *Judson Baptist Col; Home Ec.*

PETRIE, Brett Cameron
Southwestern Central HS; Jamestown, NY (41-195) All Amer Yth; Dbte Tm; Ger C; Hmrm; NFL; Var C; Pres, Soph Cl; Bsbl; All Conf, Bsbl; *Ariz St U; Bio Sci.*

PETRIE, Toby Ray
DeKalb HS; DeKalb, IL (86-550) Bsbl; Wrest; Hon Prog; Yth Fel.

PETRO, Gayle Lynne
Grand Blanc HS; Grand Blanc, MI (66-636) Band; NHS; ARC; Tr; Mich Competitive School; *Grand Rapids Baptist Col; Eng.*

PETROCCHI, Anthony Alan
Nolan HS; Fort Worth, TX (3-168) CYO; Chor; Drama; Pres, Hmrm; Parl, Math C; Pres, SC; Tnns; Bio A; Chem A; Hon Prog; WW; *St Mary's in San Antonio; Law.*

PETROFF, Bryan James
Temple Acceterated Christian HS; La Puente, CA; Ann; Band; Bus C; Chor; Bsbl; Bkbl; Ftbl; Sftbl; Tr; Wrest; Pacific Coast Baptist Bible Col; Missions.

PETROFF, John Henry
Marion HS; Marion, IN (25-750) Chess C; Model UN; SC; Y-Tns; JV, Tnns; JV, Tr; Taylor U; Pol Sci.

PETSCHKE, Dana Jill
Ceylon Pub Sch; Ceylon, MN (2-28) Bus Mgr, Ann; Band; Chor; FFA; NHS; Bkbl; Sftbl; Tr; Vlbl; Gustavus Adolphus Col; Mus.

PETTEE, Julie Gayle
Princeton HS; Princeton, IL (75-190) VP, Chor; Drama; Bradley U; Law.

PETTEWAY, Lovie Annell
Wilby HS; Waterbury, CT; Ntl Yth Conf; Span C; Tres, SC; Bsbl; Bkbl; Sftbl; Tnns; Yth Fel; 25 Dollars Bond A; Talent Show; Debutante; Nurs.

PETTEY, Mark Earl
Austin HS; Decatur, AL (10%-420) Band; Community Yth Symph; Ensm; Rptr, Lit Mag; Orch; McDonald's All-Amer HS Band; Ntl HS Hon Band; All-St Band; Solo & Ensm As.

PETTIE, Curtis Michael
Marvell HS; Marvell, AR (2-118) Co-Ed, Ann; Rptr, Band; VP, BC; SC; Cl Fav; Type A; Eng, Band, A's; Harding Col; Bus.

PETTIJOHN, Lori Lea
Justin Ford Kimball HS; Dallas, TX; Chor; Drama; NHS; Span NHS; S-T, Thes; Lion A; Spch A; Tex Tech U; Pre-Law.

PETTIT, Alisa Joy
Plant City HS; Plant City, FL; Band; Drama; Hmrm; SC; Vlbl; Hillsbourgh Comm Col; Special Ed.

PETTIT, Barbara Ann
Winnebago Pub HS; Winnebago, MN (2-44) Band; Chor; Ger C; Madrigal; Tres, Soph Cl; Tr; Co-Cpt, MVP, Gym; Vlbl.

PETTIT, Denise Michelle
South HS; Bakersfield, CA; Tnns; CSF; Hon Prog; Secy, Girls C; Outst Eng A; Med.

PETTIT, Gregory Lynn
Castleberry HS; Fort Worth, TX; Key C; Math C.

PETTIT, Lark Luanne
Lewis Central HS; Council Bluffs, IA (15-200) A Cap Choir; Band; Chor; Drama; FBLA; Madrigal; NHS; S-T, Span C; SC; Thes; Mgr, Bkbl; Tnns; Citz A; Opt A; Spch A; Pom Pon Squad; Secy, Jobs Daughters; Mus A's; U of Nebr; Mass Communications.

PETTIT, Renee Suzanne
Oswego Comm HS; Oswego, IL (20-360) Ann; Chor; Span C; VP, Art C; Chor, Schol Art Assn, A's; McPherson Col; Pre-Vet.

PETTIT, Taryn Jeanne
Flathead Co HS; Kalispell, MT (90-494) Chor; Ensm; Secy, Mjrte; NHS; Span C; Tnns; Pres, Jobs Daughters; U of Mont; Elementary Ed.

PETTUS, Cornelius Aaron
Alain LeRoy Locke HS; Los Angeles, CA (21-650) Band; City Conf; Dbte Tm; Pres, Hmrm; InterClub Coun; Key C; NHS; Rptr, Sch P; Pres, Span C; Parl, SC; JV, Bkbl; JV, Ftbl; JV, Tr; Bank Of Amer A; CSF; COM; Citz A; Hon Prog; Journ A; Most Out; ROTC A; Spch A; Yth Leg; Forestry; Rptr, Church Paper; Pres, Choir; USC; Pol Sci.

PETTWAY, Geraldine
Mattie T Blount HS; Prichard, AL; PA; Twentieth Century Bus Col; Bus.

PETTWAY, Jerlean
Mattie T Blount HS; Prichard, AL (12-400) Chor; Pres, Hmrm; Hon Prog; Jr Cl Officer; Les Femelles Elite; U of Ala; Acct.

PETTWAY, Josclyn
South HS; Columbus, OH (87-356) ARC; Span C; Tr; Type A; Philo C; Ohio St U; Bus.

PETTY, Anthony Edwin
Ritenour Sr HS; St Louis, MO (33%-908) Chor; Hmrm; Ntl Yth Conf; SC; Ftbl; Semi-Fin, Tr; Pres, Yth Fel; UCLA; Archt.

PETTY, Cheryl Lynn
Jamestown HS; Jamestown, NY (28-498) Band; Drama; Pres, 4H; NHS; Orch; VP, Span C; SC; 4H A; Regent Schol; Yth Fel; Future Family Ldr of Tomorrow; Most Artistic; Painting Exhibit, NY HS Arts A; Jamestown Comm Col; Vet Med.

PETTY, Debra Ann
Irvin HS; El Paso, TX; Ann; Chldr; Sch P; Golf; U of Tex at El Paso; Secretarial.

PETTY, Ed E
E Prairie HS; E Prairie, MO (13-140) NHS; Span C; JV, Bkbl; Soph Pilgrimage; Coaching.

PETTY, Felisa Gaye
John Motley Morehead HS; Eden, NC (10-30) Chor; 4H; Bkbl; Tr; Delta Sigma Theta A; 4H A; Pres A; ROTC A; Nurs.

PETTY, Paul Edward
Carver HS; Memphis, TN (76-298) Drama; Fr C; Hmrm; NHS; ARC; COM; Hist A; ARC A; Drama A; Black Hist A; Animal Sci.

PETTY, Sabrina Faye
Dupont Sr HS; Hermitage, TN (28-323) FHA; NHS; Sch Achieve Tm; JV, Bkbl; Talent C; Top 10%, Cl; Tenn Tech U; Bus.

PETTY, Steve R
Greenwood Comm HS; Greenwood, IN (76-254) Band; VP, Chess C; Ensm; Orch; Bsbl; Bkbl; Ftbl; Kiwanis A; Ball St U; Bus.

PETTY, Susan Elaine
Jamestown HS; Jamestown, NY; F-Ed, Ann; Band; Ger C; Ski C.

PETTY, Trent Olen
Levelland HS; Levelland, TX (10%-275) JV, Bkbl; JV, Ftbl; Semi-Fin, Tr; FCA; Tex A&M U; Vet Med.

PETTY, Wanda Jean
Savannah Central HS; Savannah, TN; Chor; FHA; 4H; Bkbl.

PETTYGROVE, Luanne Lynn
Upper Moreland Sr HS; Willow Grove, PA (178-465) A Cap Choir; Secy, Chor; FBLA; Sch P; Mgr, Hockey; Mgr, Tr; Yth Fel; Yth Foundation; Oral Roberts U; Social Work.

PETUSKEY, Mary Jo
Wellsboro Area Sr HS; Wellsboro, PA (33%-180) Band; Chldr; Chor; Fr C; Cpt, Mjrte; NHS; SC; Bkbl; Sftbl; Tr; Yth Fel; Tr Ltr; Chldr Ltr; Gold, Silver, Bronze Pins for HR; Bkbl Ltr; Hon Soc A; U of Pittsburg; Phys Therapy.

PETYAK, Mary Ann
G A R Mem HS; Wilkes-Barre, PA (8-186) Ann; NHS; Secy, SC; Hon Prog; NEDT; Communications.

PEURA, Robin Elayne
Ashtabula HS; Ashtabula, OH (15-265) Band; Ensm; Secy, FTA; Lat C; NHS; Sci C; Swim; COM; Hon Prog; VP, Lib C; Med.

PEVARNIK, Priscilla Ann
Carmichaels Area HS; Carmichaels, PA (2-83) NHS; Co-Ed, Sch P; Span C; DARGCA; Sal; Oct Girl o-t Month; WW; Penn St U.

PEWITT, Charles Stephen
Ellington HS; Ellington, MO (3-35) Band; Pres, BC; Chem C; Drama; Math C; Order/Arrow; Bsbl; Cpt, Bkbl; Hockey; Sftbl; Tr; Citz A; Cl Fav; Most Out; Order/Arrow A; ROTC A; Sal; Sci A; Drum Major; Eagle Sct; Psych, Band, A's; U of Mo; Engr.

PFADENHAUER, Glenn Jerold
Col Zadok Magruder HS; Rockville, MD (15%-425) Drama; Hmrm; ARC; SC; Bus Mgr, Sr Cl; Bus Mgr, Jr Cl; VP, Soph Cl; COM; Jr Chamber of Com A; NEDT; PTA A; ARC A; Spch A; Co Yth Commission; Church Appreciation Cert; AV A; Elizabethtown Col; Psych.

PFAFF, Sandra Jean
Westview HS; Braham, MN; 4H; COM; 4H A.

PFAHLER, Kimberly Rae
Goshen HS; Goshen, IN; Co-Ed, Ann; Bus C; Rptr, 4H; NHS; Yth Fel; Sunshine Soc.

PFANNENSTIEL, Shirley Ann
Immaculata HS; Leavenworth, KS; Chor; Bkbl; Tr; PE A; Phys Ed.

PFEFFER, Rosemary Martha
Evanston Township HS; Evanston, IL; Arch; Ski C; Tr; N Ill U; Photography.

PFEIFER, Susan Elizabeth
Loch Raven Sr HS; Baltimore, MD (20%-450) FBLA; Essex Comm Col; Dental Asst.

PFEIFFER, Donald Clark
Adelphian Acad; Holly, MI (11-53) Mgr, Band; Ed, Sch P; Ski C; Fr C; NHS; Soccer; Sftbl; Hon Prog; Swtht; Pastor Jr Cl; Mich Cert of Recognition, ACT; Family Living A; U of Mich; Bio.

PFEIFFER, Melinda Carol
Bolton Sr HS; Alexandria, LA; FBLA; FTA; LSU; Bus.

PFEIL, Michael Henry
Worthington Sr HS; Worthington, MN (112-280) Band; FFA; VP, 4H; 4H A; FFA St Band; Pres, VICA C; Church Executive Yth; Canby Vo Tech Col; Farm Equipment.

PFERDEHIRT, Judith Ann
Seneca Valley HS; Harmony, PA (20%-450) Chor; Drama; Semi-Fin, Jr Miss Pa; Secy, NHS; SC; Thes; COM; Edinboro St Col; Nurs.

PFIRRMAN, Steven John
Badin HS; Hamilton, OH (30-188) CYO; Bowl Tm; WW; Miami-U; Bus Adm.

PFISTER, Brenda Lee
Lancaster HS; Lancaster Co, VA (10-200) Band; Bus C; Crown & Scepter; FBLA; Hmrm; Sci C; Span C; HCt; Flag Tm A; Rappahanock Comm Col; Bus Adm.

PFLUGRAD, Cynthia Mae
Milo Adventis Acad; Days Creek, OR (4-66) Band; Bkbl; Umpqua Comm Col; Dental Hygiene.

PFOSER, Steven Eugene
Carmel HS; Carmel, IN (240-598) Band; Community Yth Symph; Ger C; Madrigal; Hon Prog; Interlochen Ntl Mus; 1st, Solo Contest; Ind U; Instrumental Mus.

PFUND, David Richard
Oswego HS; Oswego, NY (2-450) Pres, NHS; Order/Arrow; SC; Tnns; Amer Leg A; Bausch & Lomb A; COM; Elk A; Regent Schol; Rensselaer A; Sal; Outdoor C; US Power Squadron; BSct; Sch Service, Eagle Sct, A's; Pa St U; Archt Engr.

PHALO, Mamie Marie
Mattie T Blount HS; Prichard, AL (30-400) Ann; VP, Chor; VP, Hmrm; InterClub Coun; Parl, SC; Secy, Sr Cl; Secy, Jr Cl; Sftbl; Hon Prog; Promotion, Appreciation, PA, A's; U of Ala; Bus Adm.

PHAM, Lan-Anh Thi
Community HS; Houston, TX (10%-98) NHS; U of Houston; Acct.

PHAM, Phuong-Anh
Community HS; Houston, TX (10%-98) NHS; U of Houston; Computer Sci.

PHARES, Debra Kaye
South HS; Denver, CO (75-500) Band; Candystriper; Job's Daughters; JA.

PHARES, Lori Jo
El Dorado HS; El Dorado, AR; Chor; Ensm; Ouachita Baptist U; Nurs.

PHARES, Sheba Lorraine
Gilmer Co HS; Glenville, WV (20-94) VP, 4H; JV, Bkbl; Tr; 4H A; WW; Glenville St Col; Med Lab Tech.

PHARIS, Susan Patricia
Noble Central Sch; Nobleford, CANADA (3-16) SC; Col of Idaho; Ed.

PHELPS, Ann Marie
St Stephen HS; Saginaw, MI (6-109) Ann; Drama; NHS; SC; PTA A; Summa Cum Laude; Pres, Pep C; WW; Alma Hon School; Rose Watson Schol; Ntl Merit Ltr; Alma Col; Pre-Med.

PHELPS, Arthur A
Emsley A Laney HS; Castle Hayne, NC; Span C; Tnns.

PHELPS, Arthur Ashworth
Emsley A Laney HS; Castle Hayne, NC; Span C; Tnns.

PHELPS, Cynthia Anne
Hardaway HS; Columbus, GA;

PHELPS, David Hall
Rogers HS; Michigan City, IN (134-470) Ann; Monogram; Cpt, Swim; MVP, Swim; All Amer St Champion.

PHELPS, Debbie Leigh
Springboro HS; Springboro, OH; *Nurs.*

PHELPS, Deborah Mailin
Jonesboro-Hodge HS; Jonesboro, LA; Band; Chess C 4H; Sch P; SC; Bkbl; Sftbl; DARGCA; 4H A; Poet A; Outst Band; 1st, Dist Solo Festival; *La Tech U; Mus.*

PHELPS, Kimberly Ann
Lakeview HS; Battle Creek, MI (33%-350) JV, Chldr; Fr C; Hmrm; Ski C; *Special Ed.*

PHELPS, Lavella Fae
John Marshall HS; Indianapolis, IN; FHA; 4H; Var C; Y-Tns; Tr; 4H A.

PHELPS, Margo Lynne
Victory Christian HS; Carlsbad, CA (4-12) Ann; Co-Cpt, Chldr; Secy; Drama; Hmrm; NHS; SC; Citz A; Cl Fav; Hist A; Hon Prog; JA A; Math A; Type A; Chldr A; Handbell Choir; *Drama.*

PHELPS, Pamela Darlene
W Morgan HS; Trinity, AL (5%-62) Ed, Ann; Band; BC; SC; Bkbl; WW; HR; All-St Band; *Calhoun Jr Col; Sociology.*

PHELPS, William Calvin
Winnfield Sr HS; Winnfield, LA (20-120) Ann; BC; Drama; Ensm; FBLA; FTA; 4H; Lit Ral; NHS; Secy, Spch C; Masque & Gavel A; Spch A; Civics C; Mus A; *La Tech U; Med.*

PHIFER, Vickie Rae
Shelby Sr HS; Shelby, NC (60%-499) Band; Fr C; Rainbow; Past Worthy Advisor, Rainbow Girls; *W Carolina U; Mus.*

PHILBROOK, Kristin Alane
Stratford Sr HS; Houston, TX (50%-435) A Cap Choir; Band; Chldr; Fin, Chor; Drama; Madrigal; Span C; Thes; Bkbl; Soccer; Swim; Tr; Beauty; COM; HCt; Powder Puff Ftbl; Pres, Yth Fel; Sang Anthem at Graduation; Outst Choir Stu; Most Interesting, Versalite Sr; *U of Houston; Communication.*

PHILLABAUM, Carla
Hot Springs Co HS; Thermopolis, WY (10-79) Chldr; Fr C; Ger C; JV, Bkbl; Faculty Ind Stu Seminar; Sch Hon A.

PHILLABAUM, Mark Hanson
Hot Springs Co HS; Thermopolis, WY (15-100) Band; Chess C; Ger C; Pres, Ski C; Var C; Ftbl; Wrest; *U of Wy; Pre-Med.*

PHILLIPICH, Luann Marie
Gilbert HS; Gilbert, MN (3-76) CYO; Chor; Dbte Tm; Ensm; Sch P.

PHILLIPPI, Ginny
Mountain Brook HS; Birmingham, AL (25%-406) AFS; Chor; Fr C; Arch; Bkbl; Soccer; Yth Del, B'Ham Presbytery; *Special Ed.*

PHILLIPPY, Robert James
Clearwater HS; Clearwater, FL; Dbte Tm; Demolay; Lat C; NFL; Var C; Cr-Ctry; Tr.

PHILLIPS, Alice Rachelle
Greensburg HS; Greensburg, LA (25%-55) Band; VP, BC; Chldr; Chor; Lit Ral; SC; Bkbl; Sftbl; Puppet Tm; *Southeastern La U; Nurs.*

PHILLIPS, Angela Marie
Central Union HS; El Centro, CA; Cpt, Bkbl; Beauty; COM; Cl Fav; *Imperial Valley Col; Nurs.*

PHILLIPS, Beverly Kay
W Mecklenburg HS; Charlotte, NC; Hmrm; InterAct C; MVP, Sftbl; Mgr, Wrest; *Phys Ed.*

PHILLIPS, Brenda Eva
Fowler HS; Fowler, CO (25%-68) Band; Chldr; Chor; FFA; Madrigal; Pres, Rainbow; Bkbl; Tr; *Fort Collins Col; Agr.*

PHILLIPS, Brett Edward
Benjamin Franklin HS; New Orleans, LA (10-150) Lat C; Lit Ral; Rptr; Sch P; Bsbl; Journ A; Q&S A; Superior, Foreign Lang Festival; *Harvard Col; Law.*

PHILLIPS, Bruce George
Fort Madison HS; Fort Madison, IA; Band; JV, Ftbl; JV, Tr; COM; NEDT; *Iowa St U; Chem Engr.*

PHILLIPS, Bryan Lynn
Guymon HS; Guymon, OK; Band; Ensm; Tres, Math C; VP, NHS; Pres, Sci C; JV, Bkbl; Ftbl; Tr; Bio A; Chem A; Citz A; MLS; Most Out; St Scholar; Val; FCA, ESA Outst Yth; St Hon Soc; Outst, Hon Soc; *Okla Christian Col; Conservation.*

PHILLIPS, Camille June
Fairmont Sr HS; Fairmont, WV (40-240) Band; Secy, Chor; Key C; *Broadfording Christian Col; Secondary Ed.*

PHILLIPS, Cary Don
Putnam City HS; Okla City, OK (550-1049) Hmrm; Bkbl; MVP, Ftbl; Sftbl; *Baylor U; Bus.*

PHILLIPS, Charles Edmond
Fairborn Baker HS; Fairborn, OH (150-305) Band.

PHILLIPS, Charles Edward
Edisto HS; Cordova, SC (2-120) FFA; Tres, NHS; Order/Arrow; Sch P; SC; Pres, Jr Cl; Bsbl; Ftbl; Interlochen Ntl Mus; Order/Arrow A; Sci A; *Clemson U; Agr.*

PHILLIPS, Charles Edward Jr
Lakeshore HS; College Park, GA (10%-180) BC; BS; InterClub Coun; NHS; Ntl Yth Conf; A-Ed, Sch P; Span C; Span NHS; Pres, SC; Bkbl; COM; NMF; Rotary A; WW; Outst Sr; Ga Tech 'Mite' Prog; *Air Force Acad; Computer Sci.*

PHILLIPS, Clifford Douglas
Elkins HS; Elkins, WV (3-250) Ann; BS; Secy, Key C; NHS; SC; Var C; Mgr, Bsbl; Ftbl; Tr; Type A; St Math Field Day Fin; Exchange Stu; *US Air Force Acad; Math.*

PHILLIPS, Darrell Kay
Fredericktown HS; Fredericktown, OH (13-124) Rptr; FFA; Pres, 4H; Tres, NHS; Sch Achieve Tm; SC; Var C; Tnns; Soph Cl; JV, Bkbl; Ftbl; Sftbl; Co-Cpt, Tr; Alg A; 4H A; *N Central Tech Col; Computer Prog.*

PHILLIPS, David Alan
N Gaston HS; Dallas, NC (20-265) InterAct C; InterClub Coun; Key C; VP, Monogram; VP, Span C; Cpt, Bkbl; Cr-Ctry; Cpt, Tr; H of F; HCt; Most Out; Pres A; MVP, Bkbl; Most Ath; Sportsmanship A; *Appalachian St U; Pol Sci.*

PHILLIPS, Denise Gale
Lexington HS; Lexington, NE (30-160) Chor; Dbte Tm; Drama; FHA; 4H; Thes; Tr; *Grande Island Beauty Sch; Cosmotology.*

PHILLIPS, Denise Ranea
Lincoln HS; Dallas, TX; Model UN; Most Out; Yth o-t Yr; Angelic Qn; Principal's A.

PHILLIPS, Diana
Northwest HS; St Louis, MO (250-450) *Flossant Valley Col.*

PHILLIPS, Dianna Lynn
Carver HS; Columbus, GA (5%-350) F-Ed, Ann; Hmrm; Math C; NHS; Secy, Sci C; Tnns; COM; Chem A; Hon Prog; Most Out; Jr Adv Coun; Gov Hon Prog; WW; DAHSS; *Ill Inst of Tech; Chem Engr.*

PHILLIPS, Donald Craig
Geronimo HS; Geronimo, OK (10%-29) FFA; Span C; Span NHS; Bsbl; Bkbl; Amer Leg A; COM; HCt; Math A; MLS; Star Greenhand; *Cameron U; Engr.*

PHILLIPS, Donna Faye
Hart Co HS; Munfordville, KY (5-140) Band; Drama; VP, FHA; VP, 4H; Cpt, Mjrte; NHS; Spch C; Type A; Historian, Beta C; Historian, FBLA; *Western Ky U; Bus.*

PHILLIPS, Dorinda Jeanette
Roosevelt HS; Gary, IN (15-720) Community Yth Symph; Fr C; FTA; Math C; NHS; Orch; Sci C; Y-Tns; Citz A; Hon Prog; *Howard U; Sociology.*

PHILLIPS, Dottie Lyn
Smithfield-Selma Sr HS; Smithfield, NC; Ann; Chor; Fr C; FHA; NHS; Co-Ed, Sch P; Juliet Harris Schol Fin; Mus Talent Schol Fin; *Meredith Col; Applied Music.*

PHILLIPS, Douglas Paul
Wilmington HS; Wilmington, OH (4-301) Band; VP, Chor; InterAct C; 4H A; NEDT; Phi Delta Sigma; *Teaching.*

PHILLIPS, Doyle Claude
Henderson Co HS; Henderson, KY (20-650) A Cap Choir; Chess C; Chor; NHS; NMS; All Star, Champ Tm, E Coast Bible; *Oral Roberts U; Sci.*

PHILLIPS, Elizabeth Annis
Ironton HS; Ironton, OH (10%-225) Ann; Band; Tres, Fr C; Hmrm; Sch Achieve Tm; Tres, Soph Cl; Band Achv, Fresh Schol, A's.

PHILLIPS, Gary Anthony
Monterey HS; Lubbock, TX; A Cap Choir; Ensm; HiY; Madrigal; JV, Ftbl; *Tex Tech U; Dental.*

PHILLIPS, Glenda May
Fairborn Baker HS; Fairborn, OH (126-320) Band.

PHILLIPS, Jack Delotch
Lexington Sr HS; Lexington, NC; Chess C; Chor; Key C; Monogram; Span C; Bkbl; Ftbl; Tnns; *Bus.*

PHILLIPS, Jackie Diane
Stamps HS; Stamps, AR (8-62) Band; Cpt, Chldr; Crown & Scepter; Fr C; Secy, FBLA; VP, FHA; GS; Hmrm; Secy, Mu Alpha Theta; VP, NHS; F-Ed, Sch P; Sci C; Secy, SC; Bkbl; Tr; Bio A; COM; Chem A; FHA A; *Sou Ark U; Nurs.*

PHILLIPS, Jacqueline Patrice
Beaumont HS; St Louis, MO (98-638) Drama; Sch P; Up Bound; Tnns; *Bradley U; Anesthesiology.*

PHILLIPS, James Alan
Temple Heights Christian HS; Tampa, FL (1-30) Chess C; Bkbl; Ftbl; Wrest; Bio A; *Air Force Acad; Optometry.*

PHILLIPS, James Lee
Lincoln Comm HS; Lincoln, IL (60-350) A Cap Choir; Chor; Ensm; Hmrm; Span C; SC; Var C; Cr-Ctry; Tnns; Co-Cpt, Wrest; Citz A; DARGCA; Hon Prog; *Lincoln Christian Col; Missions.*

PHILLIPS, Jarvis Roosevelt
Ala Lutheran Acad; Selma, AL (3-12) Pres, Chess C; Chor; JV, Bkbl; COM; Hist A; Hon Prog; Sal; *Morehouse Col; Pol Sci.*

PHILLIPS, Jenny Marie
Clay Co HS; Ashland, AL (25%-65) Ann; BC; JV, Chldr; Chor; FHA; FTA; 4H; Hmrm; Var C; Tres, Sr Cl; Secy, Jr Cl; VP, Soph Cl; Chem A; Cl Fav; HCt A; Semi-Fin, Qn of Hearts; PA; Miss CCHS; *Auburn U; Legal Secy.*

PHILLIPS, Jill Elizabeth
Greater Atlanta Christian Sch; Norcross, GA (25-72) Co-Ed, Ann; Pres, Fr C; Semi-Fin, Hmrm; Secy, NHS; HCt; *David Lipscomb Col; Social Work.*

PHILLIPS, John Milton
Frazier HS; Perryopolis, PA; Band; Chor; Ensm; Tres, 4H; SC; Bsbl; Sftbl; 4H A; Bsbl All Stars; Square Dance Tm; *Air Cond & Refrigeration.*

PHILLIPS, Johnny Jr
Lincoln HS; San Diego, CA (9%-80) A Cap Choir; FFA; Key C; Sci C; Var C; Co-Cpt, Bsbl; CSF; MLS; Most Out; Booster C; *Southwestern Col; Bus Mgt.*

PHILLIPS, Juanita Faye
Riverdale HS; Jefferson, LA (33%-800) Band; FNA; Sci A; Yth Fel; Performing Arts Abroad Band A; Sch Band A; *SW Assembly of God Col; Bus.*

PHILLIPS, Karen Lariah
Lincoln HS; Dallas, TX; Band; FHA; Hmrm; Math C; ARC; Sci C; Span C; SC; Y-Tns; Bsbl; COM; Citz A; Cl Fav; Spch A; Yth Fel; 1st Prize, Yth Dist & St Orator; Alpha Kappa Alpha; Encounter A; *U of Houston; Psych.*

PHILLIPS, Keith Coleman
Forest Park Sr HS; Forest Park, GA (50-650) Chor; Ensm; 4H; HiY; Span C; Sftbl; Tr; Pres, Yth Legislature; All St Ch; Yth Pastor; *Clayton Jr Col; Religion.*

PHILLIPS, Keith David
Clark Co R-1 HS; Kahoka, MO (3-96) Band; Chor; Ensm; Pres, FFA; NHS; Pol Sci C; Sci C; Mgr, Ftbl; COM; Most Out; *Hannibal La-Grange Col; Agr.*

PHILLIPS, Kenneth Marion
St Ignatius HS; St Ignatius, MT (1-60) SC; Var C; Cpt, Bsbl; Bkbl; Ftbl; MVP, Tr; Wrest; NEDT; Pres A; Type A; Drafting A; *U of Mont; Forestry.*

PHILLIPS, Lauren Leigh
Southwood HS; Shreveport, LA; InterAct C; Lat C; NHS; Y-Tns; *Cosmetology.*

PHILLIPS, Lauri Gail
Palo Duro HS; Amarillo, TX; Chldr; Chor; FBLA; NHS; HCt; *Amarillo Col; Secy.*

PHILLIPS, Laurie Ann
Denair HS; Denair, CA (10-46) Chldr; VP, SC; Var C; Tr; H of F; HQn; HCt; Yth Leg; *Modesto Jr Col; Criminology.*

PHILLIPS, Leanne Kay
Jackson Central Merry HS; Jackson, TN (20-494) *U of Tenn; Sci.*

PHILLIPS, Lesa Gaye
Stanton HS; Stanton, NE (4-46) Band; JV, Chldr; Chor; FHA; 4H; Orch; S-T, Soph Cl; JV, Bkbl; JV, Golf; Tr; *Wayne St U; Teaching.*

PHILLIPS, Linda Ann
Motley HS; Columbus, MS (1-81) BC; Sci C; Bkbl; Alg A; Bio A; Sci A; Eng A; *Miss St U; Math.*

PHILLIPS, Linda Faye
Fayette-Ware HS; Somerville, TN;

PHILLIPS, Lisa Kay
Oak Ridge Acad; Oak Ridge, NC (2-30) Bus Mgr, Ann; Chor; NHS; Rainbow; Rptr, Sch P, VP, Sr Cl; Citz A; Hon Prog; ROTC A; Jr Marshal; *U of NC at Greensboro; Pre-Law.*

PHILLIPS, Lynette Ruth
Cottage Grove HS; Cottage Grove, OR (39-240) NHS; Tr; *George Fox Col; Phys Ed.*

PHILLIPS, Marla Regina
E St Louis Sr HS; E St Louis, IL (10%-600) Lat C; NHS; Hon Prog; *Pepperdine U; Pre-Law.*

PHILLIPS, Melissa Jean
Bethany HS; Reidsville, NC; Secy, Anchor C; BC; Fr C; FHA; Sch P; SC; Pres, Sr Cl; MLS; Hist, Jr Cl; WW; *Rockingham Comm Col; Secy Sci.*

PHILLIPS, Melvin Eugene
Stanley HS; Logansport, LA (1-16) Drama; Secy, FFA; 4H; Ed, Sch P; Ski C; Spch C; Pres, SC; Pres, Soph Cl; Bsbl; Bkbl; 4H A; Pres, Baptist Yth Organization; Early Col Admission; *LSU at Shreveport; Archt.*

PHILLIPS, Michael Harry
Forest Park HS; Forest Park, GA; Band; Ensm; Fr C; French NHS; COM; *Emory U; Med.*

PHILLIPS, Michael Ray
Calvary Christian Acad; Midland, MI; Anchor C; Chess C; Chor; Ski C; Pres, SC; Co-Cpt, Bkbl; Cr-Ctry; Co-Cpt, Soccer; Sftbl; MVP, Soccer; *Bob Jones U; Law.*

PHILLIPS, Michael Rhonde
Northwest HS; St Louis, MO (200-522).

PHILLIPS, Mitchell Lynn
Highland HS; Ewing, MO (17-130) BS; FFA; Hmrm; NHS; Sci C; SC; Var C; Pres, Sr Cl; Pres, Jr Cl; Co-Cpt, Ftbl; Ntl Sci Symposium; Sci A; WW; Win, Interntl Sci & Engr Fair; Ovral Win, Jr Sci, Engr & Human Sym; *U of Mo; Pre-Med.*

PHILLIPS, Naomi Leugenia
Western Sr HS; Baltimore, MD (296-765) Bus Mgr, Ann; Chor; COM; Yth Fel; Semi- fin, Declamation Contest; *Drexel U; Bus.*

PHILLIPS, Pamela Michelle
Kernersville Wesleyan Acad; Kernersville, NC (3-50) Pres, BC; Chor; Drama; Sch P; Secy, Jr Cl; Sftbl; *Chem.*

PHILLIPS, Perry Joyce
Klein HS; Spring, TX; Secy, Community Yth; Dbte Tm; VP, FHA; VP, Model UN; Spch C; Tnns; Beauty; B Crocker A; Most Outst, COOP; *U of New Orleans; Fashion Designing.*

PHILLIPS, Philip Perry
Putnam City W HS; Oklahoma City, OK (42-680) Band; Mu Alpha Theta; NHS; Sci C; Outst St Mus; St Mus Cont, Dist Mus Cont, A's; *Tex A&M U; Sci.*

PHILLIPS, Rebecca Joan
Westside HS; Omaha, NE (543-795) Band; Pres, 4H; Swim; Yth Fel; Explorer Scts; Explorer Olympics; Marching Band; Royal Ballet Acad; *Commercial Arts.*

PHILLIPS, Regina Ann
Broad Ripple HS; Indianapolis, IN; Chor; Secy, FHA; Methodist Hospital Service A; 100 Hour Pin A; *IUPUI; Bus Adm.*

PHILLIPS, Rethea Jean
Wilcox Co HS; Rochelle, GA (10-97) Ann; BC; Chor; FBLA; Lit Mag; Sch P; *Tift Col; Med.*

PHILLIPS, Richard James
Lakeview HS; Battle Creek, MI (5%-450) NHS; God & Country A; Eagle Sct; 1st Pl, Yth Talent; St Champ, Archery; *Bradley U; Solar Energy.*

PHILLIPS, Robert James
Milan C 2 HS; Milan, MO; Ann; Band; Chor; FBLA; FFA; 4H; Co-Ed, Sch P; Bsbl; Bkbl; MVP, Ftbl; Golf; Tr; COM; 4H A; HKg; Yth Fel; All Conf Ftbl; IFYE Tr; All Conf Chor; WW; PA; *NE Mo St U; Agr Sales.*

PHILLIPS, Robert Walter
E Mecklenburg HS; Charlotte, NC (109-550).

PHILLIPS, Robert Wayne
Coquille HS; Coquille, OR (100-128) Drama; Bsbl; Cr-Ctry; Wrest; Most Out; *Acct.*

PHILLIPS, Robyn Sherree
W Lincoln Sr HS; Lincolnton, NC (27-150) A Cap Choir; BC; Bus C; Cpt, Chldr; FBLA; Pres, FHA; NHS; Sftbl; Most Sch Spirited; Christmas Qn Rep; *Lees McRae Col; Ed.*

PHILLIPS, Robyn Sue
St Ignatius HS; St Ignatius, MT (4-42) Ann; Band; Chldr; Hmrm; Sch P; SC; VP, Jr Cl; Cpt, Bkbl; Cpt, Sftbl; Cpt, Tr; Pres A; *U of Mont.*

PHILLIPS, Rosemary
Geroge Washington Carver Sr HS; New Orleans, LA (25%-500) Hmrm; NHS; ARC; Tri-HiY; COM; Citz A; Hist A; Math A; Ewettes; GScts; Highest Avg Plaque; *Tulane U; Nurs.*

PHILLIPS, Sheila
Martin Luther King HS; Philadelphia, PA; VP, Hmrm; Mjrte; Pres, NHS; Pol Sci C; Service A; Pol A; PE Achv A; *Temple U; Nurs.*

PHILLIPS, Sheila Sue
Revere C-3 HS; Revere, MO (12-24) Chor; 4H; 4H A; Yth Fel; *SE Comm Col; Secy.*

PHILLIPS, Susan Elaine
El Dorado HS; El Dorado, AR (10%-300) Chldr; FHA; Hmrm; SC; Tr; *U of Tex; Fr.*

PHILLIPS, Tammy Lois
Calhoun HS; Calhoun, GA; Secy, Band; Chor; FBLA; 4H; Mjrte; Span C; Tri-HiY; Swim; Tnns; COM; Journ A; Math A; Yth Fel; Swim A; 4-H C A; Reading Skill A; Twirling A; *Shorter Col; Bus.*

PHILLIPS, Terresa Rae
Greenland HS; Greenland, AR; FHA; Bkbl; Tr; Home Ec A; *Med.*

PHILLIPS, Tina
Arkadelphia HS; Arkadelphia, AR (2-169) Chldr; V-Ch, GS; Cpt, InterClub Coun; NHS; VP, SC; Pres, Soph Cl; Chem A; HCt; Eng A; Kiwanis Acad Outst Stu; *U of Ark; Engr.*

PHILLIPS, Wendell Stephen
Battle Ground Acad; Franklin, TN (6-64) VP, Key C; NHS; SC; Var C; Bsbl; Ftbl; Tr; Alg A; HCt; Yth Fel; *Vanderbilt U; Biomedical Engr.*

PHILLIPS, Willie Steven
Mary Brantley Smiley HS; Houston, TX (50-400) Pres, A Cap Choir; Pres, Chor; Pres, FTA; Sci C; SC; Pres, Sr Cl; Cpt, Bkbl; COM; Cl Fav; Order/ Arrow A; *N Tex St U; Engr.*

PHILLIS, Vicki Lyn
Collinwood HS; Cleveland, OH; Bus C; COM; ODEA A; *General Clerical.*

PHILPOT, Bret Kim
Moreno Valley HS; Sunnymead, CA (72-470) Ann; Drama; Thes; Mgr, Ftbl; JV, Swim; Church Chor; *Col o-t Desert; Architecture.*

PHILPOT, Lloyd Reece
Forest Park HS; Beaumont, TX (25%-400) Ftbl; Sftbl; God & Country A; Del, Ntl Conf FCA; Pres Elect, FCA; 1st Cl BSct; YMCA; *Engr.*

PHILPOT, Michael McCreery
Vestavia Hills HS; Vestavia Hills, AL; Pres, Hmrm; InterClub Coun; Pres, Key C; SC; Cpt, Ftbl; Most Out; Most Friendliest; Most Improved Defensive Player; Ch, Sr Project Comm; *Harding Col; Bus.*

PHILPOT, Victor Lester
Forest Park HS; Beaumont, TX (50%-425) Ftbl; Sftbl; Swim; Wrest; God & Country A; Cl Pres, Sch; Life Guard; BSct Starr Rank; FCA; Day Camp Coun & Bus Driver; Water Safety Instructor Red Cross; *Lamar U; Phys Ed.*

PHILPOTT, Joan Michell
Heidelberg American HS; Heidelberg, GERMANY (5-175) Drama; Tres, FHA; Lit Mag; Ch, Model UN; NHS; Ed, Sch P; Pres, Span C; Parl, SC; UN Council; Secy, Sr Cl; God & Country A; Journ A; NMS; Q&S A; Span As; Hist A; *Emory U; Pre-Law.*

PHILPOTT, Karen Lynne
Andrew Lewis HS; Salem, VA; Span C; *Hallins Col; Mus.*

PHINNEY, Kurt Werner
Winchester HS; Winchester, MA (40-450) Band; Hmrm; Orch; Span C; SC; Tr; Most Musical; Most Talented; *Pol Sci.*

PHIPPEN, Teri Lin
Cut Bank HS; Cut Bank, MT (5-110) Secy, Band; Hmrm; VP, NHS; Rainbow; Span C; SC; Tnns; *Eastern Mont Col; Ed.*

PHIPPS, Anna Catherine
Elkins HS; Elkins, WV (5-224) Ann; Chor; GS; 4H; Co-Ed, Lit Mag; NHS; 4H A; Kiwanis A; Pres, Keywanettes; WW; *Davidson Col; Eng.*

PHIPPS, Carrie Lynn
Peoria HS; Peoria, IL (15%-490) Chor; Semi-Fin, GS; 4H; Key C; SC; JV, Bkbl; Fin, Tr; 4H A; HCt; Hon Prog; *Math.*

PHIPPS, Karen Denise
Red Bud HS; Calhoun, GA; Ann; Chldr; FHA; Ed, Sch P; Sftbl; COM; Cl Fav; Journ A; Sci A; Shorthand A.

PHIPPS, Kevin Russell
Bedford-N Lawrence HS; Bedford, IN (50-425) Ann; Band; S-T, Dbte Tm; Drama; Ger C; Math C; Spch C; Thes; God & Country A; *Ind U.*

PHIPPS, Lisa Diane
Everett HS; Maryville, TN (111-296) AFS; Drama; FHA; Rptr, Ger C; 4H; NFL; NHS; Secy, ARC; Spch C; Y-Tns; Sftbl; Tr; *U of Tenn; Elem Ed.*

PHIPPS, Melody Jenise
Dallas Christian HS; Mesquite, TX (8-43) A Cap Choir; FHA; NHS; Sci C; *Okla Christian Col; Phys Therapy.*

PHIPPS, Ruth Ellen
Weatherford HS; Weatherford, TX (8-252) NHS; Span C; *Tenn Temple Col; Bus.*

PHIPPS, Tom Mack
Sherman HS; Sherman, TX (24-404) BS; Mu Alpha Theta; NHS; SC; Pres, Sr Cl; Mgr, Ftbl; Cl Fav; Yth Fel; *Sou Methodist U; Bus.*

PHISTER, Jacquie Lynn
McKinley Sr HS; Canton, OH; Chor; Drama; Fr C; Lit Mag; NFL; Spch C; DARGCA; *Akron U; Law.*

PHLEGAR, Sharon Beth
Blacksburg HS; Blacksburg, VA (70-300) Band; Cpt, Chldr; Chor; Drama; Fin, GS; 4H; Pres, Hmrm; Monogram; NHS; Span C; SC; Pres, Soph Cl; Beauty; Citz A; DARGCA; HCt; *VPI; Elem Ed.*

PHOX, Zanita
Lutheran HS; Los Angeles, CA; *El Camino Col; Acct.*

PHTHISIC, Nancy Denise
John A Holmes HS; Edenton, NC (4-130) Ann; Co-Cpt, Chldr; Chor; VP, NHS; Sci C; Bio A; Type A; Marshal; Pres, Health Careers; *E Carolina U; Phys Therapy.*

PIANTANIDA, Suzette Marie
Althoff Cath HS; Belleville, IL (125-301) CYO; Chor; Lat C; Tnns; Amer Leg A; Hon Prog; *Sou Ill U; Law.*

PIAZZA, Judy
Carmel HS; Carmel, NY; Orch; Church Bell Choir; Pop Strings Group; Mus Production Workshop; *Alfred Col; Secy.*

PIAZZA, Shelly Lynn
Oak Harbor HS; Oak Harbor, OH (20-169) JV, Chldr; ARC; Rptr, Sch P; SC; Secy, Soph Cl; Yth Fel; Meth Yth Organization; MVP, Co-Cpt, Vlbl; *U of Sou Calif; Photography.*

PICCOLINO, Alberta Jean
West Haven HS; W Haven, CT (22-610) Co-Ch, A Cap Choir; AFS; CYO; Drama; Fr C; French NHS; Ger C; Hmrm; Madrigal; NHS; NEDT; St Scholar; Jaycee's Ten Outst Sr; Jr Women's A; Mothers C A; Alliance Francais Book A; All-St Choir; *Manhattanville Col; Voice.*

PICHAJ, Mark Adolf
McDowell Sr HS; Erie, PA (16-758) Band; Chess C; Chor; Community Yth Symph; Ensm; JETS; Madrigal; Orch; Sch P; Mgr, Bsbl; JV, Soccer; Hon Prog; NMS; Chess C Champion; HR Cert; *Math.*

PICKARD, Ernest L Jr
Fitzgerald HS; Fitzgerald, GA (10%-250) BC; Pres, 4H; HiY; A-Ed, Sch P; Var C; Ftbl; Sftbl; Tr; Wrest; COM; Math A; *U of Ga; Computer Programming.*

PICKARD, Joseph C
Syosset HS; Syosset, NY (19-720) Band; Dbte Tm; Order/Arrow; Tr; *Sci.*

PICKEN, Cindy Ann
Morton W HS; Berwyn, IL (20%-605) HiY; Ski C; SC; VP, Sr Cl; Hockey; Wrest; Hon Prog; *Northland Col; Forestry.*

PICKENS, Angela Renee
A C Reynolds HS; Asheville, NC (50-250) FHA; VP, Hmrm; NHS; JA A; Poetry Writing A; *Winston Salem St Col; Special Ed.*

PICKENS, Cheryl Lynn
Huntington E HS; Huntington, WV; A Cap Choir; Ann; Chor; Madrigal; Span C; Lib Asst A; *Bethany Col.*

PICKENS, Denise Renee
St Thomas Apostle HS; Chicago, IL (10-42) A Cap Choir; Chor; Pres, Drama; Hmrm; ARC; F-Ed, Sch P; Tres, SC; Tnns; COM; Hon Prog; Spch A; Type A; Yth Foundation; Drama A; Forensics A; Choir A; *Mundelein Col; Pol Sci.*

PICKENS, Joseph Edward Jr
Seminole HS; Sanford, FL (5%-750) Chor; Inter-Act C; InterClub Coun; VP, Math C; VP, Mu Alpha Theta; NHS; Ski C; Span C; SC; Var C; JV, Bsbl; Ftbl; Soccer; Tr; Amer Leg A; Citz A; Hon Prog; Math A; NEDT; ARC A; Sci A; Sr Calendar; Christian Influence; Pres, FCA; *Emory Col; Dentistry.*

PICKENS, Shelia Dianne
J M Tate HS; Gonzales, FL (60-570) BC; Chor; FHA; Spch A; A & B HR; Beta A; *Miss U For Women; Dietician.*

PICKEREL, Kevin Lee
Martinsville HS; Martinsville, VA (176-275) Bus C; ARC; Pres A; Co-Ed & F-Ed, Lit Mag; WW.

PICKERING, Elizabeth Ann
Middle Twp HS; Cape May Court House, NJ (10%-250) A Cap Choir; Chor; Drama; PTA A; NJ All St Choir; *Psychiatry.*

PICKERING, Mary Jane
Parkwood HS; Joplin, MO; Chor; Drama; Madrigal; Co-Ed, Sch P; Thes; Journ A; Most Outst; *Southwest Baptist Col; Religious Ed.*

PICKERRELL, Shelley Gay
Jeffersonville HS; Jeffersonville, IN (50-1000) Parl, FHA; NHS; Opt, Sftbl; Pres A; Eng A; Humanities A; Tr A; *Bradley U; Bus.*

PICKERT, Adele Hope
Newark Valley HS; Newark Valley, NY (50-185) Secy, Chor; VP, 4H; Hmrm; Ski C; SC; Var C; Bkbl; Hockey; Tr; Beauty; 4H A; Type A; Pres, Yth Fel; *Ithaca Col; Lit.*

PICKETT, Earl Norman
Spencer HS; Spencer, WI (4-59) Band; BS; CYO; Drama; Ensm; Math C; NFL; Sch P; Var C; Ftbl; Tr; Co-Cpt, Wrest; Masque & Gavel A; Math A; Spch A; Bauble A; Determination A; *St Joseph's Hospital; X-Ray Tech.*

PICKETT, Gina Eileen
National Trail HS; New Paris, OH (15-130) Semi-Fin, GS; NHS; Pres, Jr Cl; Pres, Soph Cl; Tr Statistician; Super A, Loc, Cty & Dist Sci Fairs; *Ind U; Bus Ed.*

PICKETT, Nancy Ann
Coronado HS; Colo Springs, CO (25-394) Chor; Pres, FBLA; NHS; Hon Prog; *Colo St U; Bus.*

PICKETT, Ruth Lynette
Thompson HS; Alabaster, AL; Ann; BC; Chor; NHS; Sci C; Hon Prog; Bus A.

PICKETT, Theodis
Bullock Co HS; Union Spring, AL; Pres, FFA; 4H; VP, Jr Cl; 4H A; *Art Inst; Industral-Art.*

PICKHARDT, Deborah Susan
Rhinebeck Central HS; Rhinebeck, NY (1-110) AFS; Chldr; Chor; Drama; Fr C; Hmrm; NHS; Var C; Secy, Jr Cl; VP, Soph Cl; Hockey; Sftbl; Amer Leg Orator A; NEDT; Regent Schol; Sportmanship A; Communications A; *Cornell U; Bio.*

PICKLE, Bruce Henry
Coral Gables Sr HS; Coral Gables, FL (130-700) Band; Chem C; Chor; Ensm; Ger C; Pres, Hmrm; Rptr, Key C; Mod Mus Mas; Phys C; ARC; Cr-Ctry; Tr; Citz A; Odd Fellow Fin; Sch Sen; All Co Chor; Law Day A; Ch, Instructor, Grand Cotillion; *Fla St U; Pre-Law.*

PICKLESIMER, Amy Gail
Virgie HS; Virgie, KY (10-110) BC; FTA; 4H; Pres, Hmrm; Rptr, Sch P; Sci C; Spch C; Bkbl; 4H A; Hon Prog; Lion A; Spch A; Principal A; DAHSS; *U of Ky; Psych.*

PICKRELL, Diane Laurie
Old Forge HS; Old Forge, PA (1-134) Band; Drama; Ch, FNA; NHS; Rptr, Sch P; Ski C; Span C; Thes; Chem A; Hon Prog; Lion A; Summa Cum Laude; Schol Achv, Hospital Vol, A's; Pa St U Schol; *Pa St U; Nurs.*

PICKRELL, Janice Irene
Churchland HS; Portsmouth, VA (7-250) AFS; Ann; Tres, BC; Dbte Tm; Pres, Fr C; GS; Hmrm; Jr Miss Pagent; Tres, NHS; Sch Achieve Tm; Pres, Tri-HiY; Most Dependable; WW; *William and Mary Col; Pre-Law.*

PICOU, Pamela Kay
Aransas Pass HS; Aransas Pass, TX (5-121) Secy, Ann; Band; Pres, Hmrm; Mjrte; Math C; NHS; Secy, Span C; Parl, SC; Pres, Soph Cl; Feature Twirler; *U Tex; Acct.*

PICTON, Tammi Leigh
Russell HS; Russell, KY; Drama; Fr C; Secy, HiY; Lat C; Model UN; Pres, SC; Ch, UN Council; VP, Sr Cl; DARGCA; Semi-Fin, DAR Good Citizenship A; *Transylvannia Col; Med Illustrator.*

PIECUCH, Maureen Kathryn
Dover HS; Dover, NH (63-465) Fr C; NHS; COM; *U of NH; Health Stud.*

PIEH, Tracy JoAnn
E L Bowsher HS; Toledo, OH; Parl, FHA; Rptr, Span C; JA A; Yth Fel; *Art.*

PIEL, Loren Allen
Perry HS; Perry, OK (10%-120) Chor; Ensm; NHS; Mgr, Ftbl; FCA; Pres, Church Yth Fel.

PIEPER, David Matthew
DeLand HS; DeLand, FL; Band; MYF; Weight Lifting; *Daytona Beach Comm; Machine Shop.*

PIEPER, Douglas Paul
Lutheran HS W; Rocky River, OH (10-106) Chor; Bkbl; COM; *Communications.*

PIEPER, Ellen Jane
Lutheran HS W; Rocky River, OH (25-90) A Cap Choir; Co-Cpt, Chldr; NHS; *Bowling Green St U; Clothing & Textiles.*

PIEPER, Janice Sue
Pearl City HS; Pearl City, IL (5-60) Band; FBLA; FHA; FTA; 4H; 4H A; Type A; Shorthand A; Band A.

PIEPER, Kim Marie
Lake of the Woods HS; Baudette, MN (13-88) Band; Pres, Bus C; Cpt, Chldr; VP, 4H; NHS; A-Ed, Sch P; 4H A; I Dare You; Vlbl; Potato Day Qn; 4-H Key A; *Alexandria Area Voc Inst; Law Enforcement.*

PIEPER, Linda Kay
Pearl City HS; Pearl City, IL (2-54) Ed, Ann; Band; Tres, FHA; Tres, FTA; Pres, 4H; Pres, NHS; Sci C; SC; Amer Leg A; B Crocker A; Elk A; 4H A; Hist A; Sal; St Scholar; Yth Fel; Secy, 4-H C; *Valparaiso U; Math.*

PIERCE, Ann
J F Kennedy HS; Barstow, CA; Chor; Ensm; Sch P; Secy, Sodality; SC; Citz A; Pres A; Yth Fel; Art A; Attendance A; *Pepperdine U; Art.*

PIERCE, Carl Hugh
Surry Co HS; Surry, VA; FHA; 4H; Ftbl; Wrest; *Tidewater Comm Col; Mus.*

PIERCE, Carol Ann
Millbrook Sr HS; Raleigh, NC (12-500) A Cap Choir; Chor; NHS; Span C; Y-Tns; Hon Prog; Raleigh Alumnac Schol; *Meredith Col; Home Ec.*

PIERCE, Charlotte Elaine
Snyder HS; Snyder, TX; Drama; FHA; F-Ed, Lit Mag; F-Ed, Sch P; Sftbl; COM; Journ A; Most Out; *Tex Tech U; Health Professions.*

PIERCE, Dan Craig
Irving HS; Irving, TX (95-800) Chor; Fr C; *Abilene Christian U; Pre-Dental.*

PIERCE, David Charles
Watson Chapel HS; Pine Bluff, AR (21-305) Band; BC; Orch; All Region Band Clinic; *U of Ark at Little Rock; Med.*

PIERCE, Debra Ann
Bellevue HS; Bellevue, MI (13-102) NHS; *Kellogg Comm Col; Registered Nurs.*

PIERCE, E Keith
Yukon HS; Yukon, OK (10%-388) Chor; NHS; JV, Cr-Ctry; Tr; Hon Prog; Sci A; Outst Tr Performer A; Mus A; Ltrmans A; *Bethany Nazarene Col; Bus.*

PIERCE, Elizabeth Danise
Irving HS; Irving, TX (53-600) Fr C; FHA; FTA; Ger C; NHS; SC; *Abilene Christian U; Philosophy.*

PIERCE, Elizabeth Jo
Carterville Comm HS; Carterville, IL; Tres, Band; Chor; Ensm; FHA; 4H; Sch P; Tr; HCt; Hon Prog; Mus A's; Best Personality; *Mus.*

PIERCE, Emily Katharine
Days Creek HS; Days Creek, OR (5-18) F-Ed, Ann; Chldr; Chor; Drama; FFA; Sch P; SC; Thes; Var C; VP, Sr Cl; Bkbl; Tr; HQn; Q&S A; Vlbl.

PIERCE, Frederick Scott
George C Marshall HS; Falls Church, VA (94-450) Pres, A Cap Choir; Pres, Chor; Tres, Drama; Madrigal; Mod Mus Mas; NHS; Cl Fav; Spch A; Best Actor As; Most Outst Madrigal As; *U of Cincinnati; Mus Theatre.*

PIERCE, Jerry Thomas
Suffolk HS; Suffolk, VA; BS; Chess C; Drama; Fr C; HiY; Hmrm; Pres, InterAct C; Lat C; Monogram; Tres, NHS; ARC; Thes; Bkbl; Tnns; HCt; Hon Prog; Yth Fel; Tres, Inter- act C; *William & Mary Col; Finance.*

PIERCE, Kay
N Gwinnett HS; Suwanee, GA (10%-120) Ann; Drama; Rptr, FBLA; FHA; Tres, SC; Tres, Var C; Tres, Sr Cl; Bkbl; Tnns; Tr; COM; HCt; Type A; *Gainesville Jr Col.*

PIERCE, Kenneth B
Cristobal Jr Sr HS; Coco Solo, CANAL ZONE (3-148) Band; Ensm; FTA; Hmrm; Order/Arrow; SC; Co-Cpt, Ftbl; JV, Tnns; COM; Hon Prog.

PIERCE, Kimberly Kay
Sooner HS; Bartlesville, OK (23-280) AFS; Secy, Bus C; Fr C; Secy, FBLA; NHS; Hon Prog; Bus Communications A; *Ozark Bible Col; Secy.*

PIERCE, Lisa Marie
Bend HS; Bend, OR; A Cap Choir; AFS; Chor; Drama; Hmrm; Span C.

PIERCE, Loren Lee
Cumberland Valley Sr HS; Mechanicsburg, PA (12-650) S-T, 4H; Hmrm; Lat C; NHS; SC; Tres, Jr Cl; Hockey; JV, Tr; Alg A; Math A; NEDT; Yth Fel; *Pre-Law.*

PIERCE, Marla Fae
Yukon HS; Yukon, OK (10%-300) Pres, Chor; Ensm; FBLA; FHA; NHS; Amer Leg A; Hon Prog; Vocal Belle; All-St Choir; *Bethany Nazarene Col; Bio.*

PIERCE, Mary Esther
Mount Miguel HS; Lemon Grove, CA (393-506) Chor.

PIERCE, Mary Ruth
Destrehan HS; Destrehan, LA (3-168) BC; Fr C; FHA; Fr, Eng, A's; Highest Rank, Jr; *SE La U.*

PIERCE, Melanie Elise
Rossville HS; Rossville, GA (6-212) Ch, Ann; Pres, BC; Ensm; Hmrm; SC; Y-Tns; Alg A; COM; Gov Honor Prog; Hist A; Hon Prog; Math A; Star Student; Type A; Yth Fel; Sgt, Band; Yth Choir ; Pep C; Eng A; Presbyterian Col Jr Fellow; Span A; All-Dist Band; Cpt, Pom Pom Sq; Pres, Yth Coun; Beta C Swtht; *Jacksonville State Univ; Early Childhood Ed.*

PIERCE, Nancy Elaine
Charlottesville HS; Charlottesville, VA (45-363) Band; FBLA; Span C; Drill Tm; Church Choir; Accompanist, Chor Ensm; Church Yth Coun; Handbell Chor.

PIERCE, Patricia Ann
Treadwell HS; Memphis, TN; F-Ed, Ann; VP, Chem C; Drama; FHA; Pres, Hmrm; Secy, Lat C; Math C; NHS; ARC; Sci C; JV, Bkbl; Magna Cum Laude; Type A; *U of Tenn; Anesthesiology.*

PIERCE, Patsy Luann
Northeastern HS; Elizabeth City, NC (5-400) Ann; Secy, Drama; VP, Fr C; Hmrm; Key C; Pres, NHS; SC; DARGCA; Hon Prog; Rotary A; Yth Fel; VP, S-T, Christian Yth Fel; S-T, Young Amers; Dramatics A; Stu Adv Comm; Bst Support Actress A; Jr Sci & Humanities Symp; *U of NC at Greensboro; Spch Pathology.*

PIERCE, Paula Sue
Chilton Co HS; Clanton, AL; Band; BC; Drama; FHA; Hmrm; Lit Mag; Cpt, Mjrte; Rainbow; Beauty; Yth Fel; Beauty Contest Schol; Most Talented; 1st Alt, Sch Swtht; *U of Ala; Social Work.*

PIERCE, Penny Elizabeth
Eldorado HS; Albuquerque, NM (136-744) Chldr; Chor; Drama; NHS; Thes.

PIERCE, Rhonda Lee
Plano HS; Plano, TX (33%-1200) Semi-Fin, Chor; FHA; Span C; Tr; Comm Drill Tm; Fin, St Bible Quiz; Gov Phys Fitness, A; Piano Recital, A; *Oral Roberts U; Med.*

PIERCE, Ronald D
Cristobal HS; Coco Solo, CANAL ZONE (7-124) Ann; Pres, Band; Ensm; FTA; NHS; Sch P; Pres, SC; Thes; Var C; Ftbl; Tnns; Tr; COM; Hon Prog; *Engr.*

PIERCE, Sandra Lynn
Charlottesville HS; Charlottesville, VA (30-540) Band; HiY; NHS; Span C; Sftbl; Citz A; *Mary Washington Col; Psych.*

PIERCE, Susan Elaine
Cartersville HS; Cartersville, GA (16-160) Band; BC; Pres, Chor; Ensm; FTA; Fin, Lit Ral; Madrigal; Mu Alpha Theta; Tres, Tri-HiY; Math C; Secy, Ch, Tri-Hi-Y; Jr Marshal; All St Chor; *Jacksonville St U; Vocal Mus.*

PIERCE, Susan Rhea
Holston HS; Damascus, VA (7-70) Ann; Chor; Rptr, FHA; FTA; Secy, 4H; Hmrm; InterClub Coun; NHS; Ed, Sch P; SC; S-T, Tri-HiY; Beauty; 4H A; Hist A; Hon Prog; MLS; Spch A; Yth Fel; Yth Leg; Lt Gov, St Stu Cong; *Hiwassee Col; Journ.*

PIERCEY, Lisa Marche
Temple Baptist Acad; Denver, CO (6-53).

PIERINGER, Peggy Anne
Auburndale Sr HS; Auburndale, FL (5%-538) BC; Orch; Span C; Math A; Pres A; Type A; All St, Mus; *U of S Fla; Mus.*

PIERRE, Barbara Jean
Clintonville Sr HS; Clintonville, WI (12-174) AFS; Ann; Dbte Tm; Drama; NFL; NHS; Bkbl; Rotary A; *U of Wis; Criminal Justice.*

PIERRE, David Dean
Clintonville Sr HS; Clintonville, WI (20-230) Fr C; Mgr, Wrest; COM; Pres A; *U of Wis; Law.*

PIERREPONT, Sarah Katherine
St Cloud HS; St Cloud, FL; Ann; Band; Secy, Drama; FBLA; Pres, 4H; Pres, Rainbow; A-Ed, Sch P; Thes; Secy, Soph Cl; 4H A; I Dare You; Fin, Miss Ntl Tn; *Interior Decorating.*

PIERSON, Amanda Weaver
Princeton HS; Princeton, NJ (84%-250) A Cap Choir; InterAct C; Rptr, Sch P; SC; Secy, Cl; Cpt, Hockey; Lacrosse; Candystriper; *Dartmouth Col.*

PIERSON, Catherine Rae
Lyons Township HS; LaGrange, IL; Chor; Ch, Board, Girls C.

PIERSON, Donna Marie
Meridian HS; Meridian, TX (1-36) Bus Mgr, Ann; Pres, Band; VP, BC; Chor; Ensm; Tres, FHA; Mjrte; Rptr, Sch P; Bkbl; Golf; Tnns; Cl Fav; HQn; Pres, Beta C; WW; 1st VP, Secy, FHA; Slide Rule & Number Sense; Jr Hist; *Tarleton Col; Bus.*

PIERSON, Edward Donahue IV
David Brearley HS; Kenilworth, NJ (20%-220) Chor; Mgr, Bkbl; Tnns; *Kean Col; Mus.*

PIERSON, James Graydon
Charleston HS; Charleston, IL (35-275) A Cap Choir; AFS; Band; Chor; Drama; FTA; Rptr, 4H; Madrigal; Orch; Spch C; Spch A; Art A; Mus A; *E Ill U; Theatre Arts.*

PIERSON, Kathryn Francine
Monroe Acad; Forsyth, GA (10%-43) Cpt, Chldr; Fin, Hmrm; SC; Cl Fav; HCt; Yth Fel; WW; *Gordon Jr Col.*

PIERSON, Kelly John
Winthrop HS; Winthrop, MN; Band; Rptr, FFA; SC; Wrest; HCt; Spch A; Yth Del, Farm Co-Op St Convention.

PIERZCHANOWSKI, Philip Anthony
Mercy HS; Riverhead, NY (13%-170) Co-Cpt, Bsbl; Co-Cpt, Ftbl; Publicity C; *US Air Force; Commercial Art.*

PIETERS, John Martinus
South Pasadena HS; South Pasadena, CA; CSF; *CSPU; Chem.*

PIETERS, Rosemary Constance
S Pasadena HS; South Pasadena, CA; A Cap Choir; Chor; Fr C; CSF; Drill Tm; *USC; Phys.*

PIETIG, Dawn Michelle
Kuemper HS; Carroll, IA (10%-270) A Cap Choir; Chor; Fr C; Hmrm; Madrigal; Monogram; SC; Golf; Sftbl; COM; All St Choir; *Fine Arts.*

PIETRANTONI, Julio Luis
Our Lady of Pilar HS; Rio Piedras, PR (1-150) Chem C; Hmrm; Pres, Model UN; NHS; Sch P; Ski C; Pres, SC; COM; Chem A; Hon Prog; MLS; Mod UN As; General Excellence; *Harvard U; Pol Sci.*

PIETROK, Gary Allan
Regis HS; Stayton, OR (4-61) NHS; Co-Cpt, Bkbl; Co-Cpt, Ftbl; Hon Prog.

PIETRONICO, Ann Marie Christine
Acad of Saint Aloysius; Jersey City, NJ (9-127) Chor; NHS; Ch, SC; Pres, Soph Cl; Hist A; Hon Prog; Math A; NEDT; Type A; SC A; *Wm Paterson Col; Nurs.*

PIGAGA, Janice Ann
Harry A Burke HS; Omaha, NE (20%-800) Chor; FHA; NHS; Rptr, Sch P; *U of Nebr Lincoln; Home Ec.*

PIGEON, Judy May
Crystal River HS; Crystal River, FL (1-254) Pres, BC; CYO; 4H; Hmrm; VP, InterAct C; InterClub Coun; Math C; SC; Alg A; Bio A; COM; Chem A; Citz A; 4H A; Hist A; Hon Prog; Lion A; Math A; Pres A; Rotary A; Sci A; Star Student; Type A; Val; Pres, Chapter & Dist DECA; St DECA Grl; Beta C A; Stu o-t Yr; Epsilon Sigma Alpha Intrntl A; Ntl Fin, DECA Girl Stu o-t Yr; *Central Florida Comm Col; Bus Mgt.*

PIGG, Karen Elaine
Pattonville Sr HS; Maryland Hts, MO (10%-877) Chor; Drama; Ensm; NHS; Thes; S-T, Soph Cl; Citz A; Hon Prog; Outst Art Stu; *Freelance Art.*

PIGGEE, Daphne Elizabeth
Cottonwood HS; Salt Lake City, UT (15%-800) Dbte Tm; Fr C; Model UN; Secy, Pep C; *Westminster Col; Med.*

PIHLSTROM, Denise Esther
Post Falls HS; Post Falls, ID (13-154) Spch C; Bkbl; JV, Sftbl; Tnns; B Teacher A; Hon Prog; Spch A; VFW A; VFW Orator Win; VofDEM; *Comm Chapel Bible Col; Bible.*

PIKE, Janine Marie
Grant HS; Portland, OR; Chor; Rainbow; Golf; Mgr, Soccer; Sftbl; Pep C; JA.

PIKE, Lee Anne
W Memphis Christian Sch; W Memphis, AR (10%-25) Cpt, Chldr; Fr C; FHA; Bkbl; Sftbl; Tr; Cl Fav; HQn; Swtht; St Mission Tm; Delta Beta Sigma Sorority; *Harding Col.*

PIKE, Richard Allen
Hogansville HS; Hogansville, GA (2-79) BC; VP, Chess C; Hmrm; JETS; Pres, Key C; VP, Span C; SC; Var C; Pres, Sr Cl; VP, Jr Cl; Ftbl; Alg A; Bio A; COM; Math A; NEDT; Phy A; Regent Schol; Sal; Sci A; Spch A; Hatton-Lovejoy Schol; EL Daniel Schol; *Ga Inst of Techology; Ceramic Engr.*

PIKE, Tony Lee
Hogansville HS; Hogansville, GA (6-83) Band; BC; Co-Ch, Chess C; FFA; FTA; Secy, Key C; SC; Mgr, Bkbl; Golf; Tnns; H of F; Hist A; Hon Prog; Type A; U of Tenn Hon Band; District Hon Band; *Troy St U; Mus.*

PILA, Elvis Rickey
Marist Brother' HS; Pago Pago, AMERICAN SAMOA (1-50) Dbte Tm; Rptr, Sch P; Spch C; COM; Hon Prog; Math A; Sci A; Spch A; *Pepperdine U; Law.*

PILCHER, Sheila Denice
Grand Ridge HS; Grand Ridge, FL (3-52) BC; FTA; VP, Hmrm; Sci C; Cl Fav; HCt; Sci A; *Chipola Jr Col; Secondary Ed.*

PILEGARD, Lynn Marie
Sanger HS; Sanger, CA (38-520) Chor; Ensm; 4H; Hmrm; NFL; Spch C; CSF; COM; Citz A; 4H A; Lion A; Pres A; Sci A; Spch A; Dist Creative Writing A.

PILGRIM, Barbara Ann
Columbia HS; Columbia, IL (47-127) Ann; Arch; Dbte Tm; Fr C; FHA; MVP, GS; 4H; ARC; Var C; MVP, Arch; Swim; Tr; Most Out; Yth Fel; St Archery; Swim Tm A; *Mo Baptist Col; Gen Courses.*

PILGRIM, Barbara Ann
Northside Sr HS; Ft Smith, AR; Tres, Chor; Ensm; Rptr, Sch P; Secy, SC; Bkbl; Type A; Drill Tm A; *Mus.*

PILGRIM, David Alan
Thomson HS; Thomson, IL (3-51) A Cap Choir; F-Ed, Ann; Pres, Band; Cpt, Chess C; Chor; Cpt, Dbte Tm; Drama; Rptr, FFA; Hmrm; Madrigal; Math C; NHS; Pol Sci C; Co-Ed, Sch P; Thes; Parl, Sr Cl; Parl, Jr Cl; Parl, Soph Cl; Alg A; Amer Leg A; COM; Citz A; Journ A; Math A; PTA A; Spch A; St Scholar; Type A; Yth Fel; Solo, Ntl FFA Band; 3rd St, FFA Home, Farmstead Imp; FFA St Farmer Degree; 1st Alt, IMEA All St Mus; *Ill St U; Mus Ed.*

PILGRIM, Janice Kay
Thomson Comm HS; Thomson, IL (1-44) Ann; Band; Chor; Ensm; FHA; Madrigal; NHS; Amer Leg A; COM; Hon Prog; *Ill St U; Mus.*

PILKER, Debora Lee
Lake Clifton Sr HS; Baltimore, MD (10%-500) Secy, NHS; Hist A; Hon Prog; Foreign Lang A; *Towson St Col; Span.*

PILKINGTON, Bradley Edward
McCluer N HS; Florissant, MO (40-788) Ann; JV, CYO; Chem A; Hon Prog; Math A; *Ouachita Baptist U; Mus.*

PILLOW, Brenda Lee
Central HS; Columbia, TN; FBLA; FHA; *Columbia St Comm Col; Marketing.*

PILLOW, David Randall
N Mesquite HS; Mesquite, TX (28-452) Lat C; COM; Semi-Fin, Spch Contests; *Eastfield Jr Col; Psych.*

PILON, Janine Alaine
Warwick Sr HS; Lititz, PA (7-260) Co-Cpt, Band; Chor; *Juniata Col; Med Technology.*

PILOSI, Lori Ann
N Pocono HS; Moscow, PA; Lat C; Lit Mag; Spch C; Cpt, Bkbl; Sftbl; Tnns; Pres A; Type A; Cpt, Vlbl; Sftbl League Champ; *Med.*

PILSON, Nevin Dale
Robert E Lee HS; Staunton, VA; Lit Mag; Mgr, Ftbl; Journ A; NEDT; Sci A; Ntl Jr Hon Soc.

PIM, Louise Frances
Washington-Lee HS; Arlington, VA (72-485) BC; Secy, Hmrm; Math C; Model UN; NHS; Tnns; Tr; Hon Qn, Job's Daughters; VP, Methodist Yth Group; *Old Dominion U; Dental Hygiene.*

PINA, Maria Da Luz Araujo
Acad o-t Holy Family; Baltic, CT; Chldr; Madrigal; SC; VP, Jr Cl; Bskl; Bkbl; Soccer; Sftbl; Tr; Hon Prog; Drama A; Mus A; *Eastern Conn St U; Math.*

PINCHOT, Bronson Alcott
Pasadena HS; South Pasadena, CA (1-312) Chor; Pres, Fr C; Madrigal; Bank Of Amer A; CSF; COM; Harvard Book A; Hon Prog; NMF; WW Among Amer HS Mus Stu; Art Dept Cert of Hon; *Yale U; Art.*

PINCKNEY, Donna Maye
H E McCracken HS; Bluffton, SC (2-77) A Cap Choir; Ed, Ann; Arch; Band; VP, BC; Pres, Bus C; CYO; Co-Cpt, Chldr; Chor; Fr C; FHA; 4H; Hmrm; Sch P; Hockey; Tr; Bio A; Sal; *Bus Adm.*

PINCKNEY, Elaine Gail
Brewster HS; Brewster, NY (25-294) Band; Chor; Mus.

PINDER, Deborah Ann
Deerborne HS; Coral Gables, FL (5-80) NHS; Bio A; Citz A; Homemaking, Golden Book, A's; *W Carolina Col; Vet.*

PINEDA, Hector
Colo HS; Colo City, TX (4-115) SC; VP, Soph Cl; Star Student; *Angelo St U.*

PING, Jami Lynn
Moreno Valley HS; Sunnymead, CA; Drama; Ger C; Spch C; Amer Leg A; COM; Hon Prog; Isomata Schol; 1st & 2nd Art A'S; Festival; *Pepperdine U; Art.*

PINGREE, Diane Elise
Post Falls HS; Post Falls, ID; Band; 1st Chair of Amer, Band A; *U of Wash; Computer Sci.*

PINGSTERHAUS,
Sharon Geralyn
Central Comm HS; Breese, IL (17-157) FBLA; FHA; Tres, 4H; 4H A; Pres A; Eng A; Clothing A; Spelling A; REA Essay A.

PINKARD, Kenneth Mack
Lancaster HS; Lancaster, VA; Chess C; Chor; Rptr; Model UN; Sch P; SC; Q&S A; Yth Fel; Span A; *Rappahannock Comm Col; Bus Mgt.*

PINKARD, Sylvester
Stewart Co HS; Lumpkin, GA; Tres, FFA; Var C; Pres, Jr Cl; Bkbl; Tr; COM; NEDT; 4 0 Hon Stu; *Fla A&M U; Computer Programing.*

PINKARD, Vanessa Yvonne
Lancaster HS; Lancaster, VA; Chldr; Chor; 4H; Sci C; Yth Fel.

PINKERTON, Donna Rae
Hinton Comm Sch; Hinton, IA (4-50) Ann; Band; Chor; 4H; NHS; Ed, Sch P; Art A; Vocal Mus A; Win, Bicen Cont, Tchr's As, ISEA; Church Soloist; Pres, MYF; *Morningside Col; Vocal Mus.*

PINKERTON, Grady E
Baton Rouge HS; Baton Rouge, LA; Chess C; Chor; Drama; Lit Mag; Thes; NEDT; *LSU; Performing & Visual Arts.*

PINKERTON, Julie Ann
Baton Rouge Magnet HS; Baton Rouge, LA (10%-123) Chor; Drama; Mu Alpha Theta; S-T; Thes; Sftbl; Swim; Tnns; Member, Keyetts; *LSU; Math.*

PINKERTON, Katharine Ray
Pace Acad; Atlanta, GA (15-70) JV, Chldr; Chor; Drama; Ensm; Fr C; 1st Pl, St Lit Meet; Fin, Gov's Hons Prog A; *Vanderbilt U; Nurs.*

PINKHAM, Stephen Craig
Boothbay Region HS; Boothbay Harbor, ME (20%-70) Chess C; Cum Laude Soc; Cr-Ctry; Tr; Math A; Sci A; Math Tm; *Le Tourneau Col; Aeronautics.*

PINKSTON, Helen
Jefferson Davis HS; Montgomery, AL (47-740) BC; Tres, 4H; Lat C; NHS; Span C; Span NHS; Tres, Tri-HiY; Pres, Soph Cl; 4H A; NEDT; *LSU; Acct.*

PINKSTON, Tammie Rene
Mansfield HS; Mansfield, LA (1-100) Band; BC; Span C; Pres, Soph Cl; Type A; *LSU; Med.*

PINN, Deborah Ann
Springfield SE HS; Springfield, IL (153-510) Citz A; Superior HR; PA; *Sou Ill U; Nurs.*

PINNOCK, Barbara Jean
Springfield HS; Springfield, PA (20%-440) *W Chester St U; Social Work.*

PINO, Donna Marie
Highland HS; Highland, IN (8-538) Chor; Ensm; Ger C; Star Student; Ger NHS; Hobbyist A; Nisbova A, Piano, Singing & Accomp.

PINO, Hector Carlos
Pater Noster HS; Los Angeles, CA; Pres, Christian Service; *Peperdine U; Elec Engr.*

PINSON, Daisy Mae
Laurens Dist 55 HS; Laurens, SC; Chor; Sftbl; All St Hons Chor; *Columbia Col; Mus.*

PINTER, Annette Marie
LaMoille Comm HS; LaMoille, IL (2-38) Ann; Pres, Band; Chor; Secy, Fr C; NHS; Pres, Jr Cl; Tnns; Sal; John Philips Sousa A; *Ill St U; Bus Adm.*

PINTER, Garry Wilbur
Princeton HS; Princeton, IL (10-200) NHS; Sch Achieve Tm; Var C; Ftbl; Tr; Sal; St Scholar; Engr Explorers; WW; Tres, Church Yth Group; Religious Singing Group; *Augustana Col; Chem.*

PINTER, Kevin Eugene
LaMoille Comm HS; LaMoille, IL (17-39) A-Ed, Ann; Secy, Band; Chor; Drama; Fr C; Sch P; Pres, SC; Var C; Cpt, Golf; Yth Fel; Gospel Group; *Ill Valley Comm Col; Lib Arts.*

PINTER, Larry John
Princeton HS; Princeton, IL (4-200) NHS; Sch Achieve Tm; Var C; Ftbl; Tr; St Scholar; Val; Highest Schol Avg, Jr Ltrman A; Secy, Church Yth; Religious Singing Group; WW.

PIOCH, David Allen
N Central HS; Indianapolis, IN (210-1255) Hmrm; NHS; JV, Bkbl; *Miami U of Ohio; Acct.*

PIONTEK, David James
Colegio San Antonio Abad; Humacao, PR (3-72) Chem C; Math C; NHS; Pres, Sci C; Var C; Ftbl; Chem A; HS Service A; 1st Pl, Chem Contest; Historian, NHS Carrib; *US Air Force Acad; Aeronautical Sci.*

PIPARO, Anthony Lawrence
St Peters Prep HS; Jersey City, NJ (23-259) Hmrm; SC; Var C; Hockey; Alg A; Hon Prog; Math A; *Rutgers U; Math.*

PIPENBERG, Paul Kenneth
Delaware Co Christian Sch; Newtown Square, PA (15-50) Tres, Jr Cl; VP, Soph Cl; Mgr, Bkbl; Tr; *Weidner Col; Pre-Med.*

PIPER, Alan David
Twin Valley HS; Elverson, PA (8-199) Band; Ensm; NHS; Order/Arrow; Var C; Cr-Ctry; Tnns; COM; God & Country A; Rotary A; *Pa St U; Civil Engr.*

PIPER, Dennis Lynn
Brookville HS; Brookville, OH (33%-185) Ann; Chor; Demolay; VP, Var C; Tres, Jr Cl; Tres, Soph Cl; Mgr, Bsbl; Mgr, Ftbl; Tnns; Mgr, Wrest; COM; Archt Drafting.

PIPER, Edward Lyon
Milo Adventist Acad; Days Creek, OR (3-66) *Umpqua Comm Col; Math.*

PIPER, Kadene Sue
Celina Sr HS; Celina, OH (39-279) Co-Cpt, Chldr; City Conf; Ch, Fr C; Ski C; Thes; Bkbl; Cr-Ctry; Golf; Swim; Tnns; Tr; Wrest; I Dare You; Yth Fel; Campus Life; GAA; Nurs.

PIPER, Karen Elizabeth
SW HS; Flint, MI; Band; Community Yth Symph; Ensm; Ski C; Semi-Fin, Golf; Hon Prog; Most Out; Church Chor; Pres, Church Yth Fel.

PIPER, Kimberly Ann
Cedarburg HS; Cedarburg, WI (13-350) A Cap Choir; Ch, Ann; Chor; Dbte Tm; Drama; Ch, Ger C; Fin, GS; Ch, Hmrm; NHS; Ch, Sch P; SC; VP, Sr Cl; VP, Jr Cl; VP, Soph Cl; JV, Bkbl; Tr; Q&S A; Yth Fel; FCA; ICS A; Blue Ribbon & Gold Key Scholastics; WW; Kodak Medallion, Scholastic Excel A; *U of Minn at Minneapolis; Bus.*

PIPER, Lisha Gail
Humansville HS; Humansville, MO; Band; Chldr; Chor; FHA; Jr Miss Pagent; Pres, Soph Cl; Bkbl; Sftbl; Citz A; Type A; Cpt, Vlbl; Bkbl Special A; Sftbl Special A; 1st Run-Up, Ms Merry Christmas; 1st Run-Up, Ms Merry Christman; *SWBC Bolivar Mo; Business.*

PIPERATA, Denise
St Joseph Sch; Hammonton, NJ (6-48) Drama; FTA; Secy, NHS; Sci C; Mgr, Hockey; WW; Immaculata Col; Mus.

PIPHER, Paul David
Tioga Central HS; Tioga Center, NY (25-95) Var C; Bsbl; Ftbl; Pres, Sr Young People; Industrial Arts Shop Achv A; *Nuclear Physics.*

PIPKIN, Leslie Ann
Southeast HS; Oklahoma City, OK; SC; *Okla St U; Psych.*

PIPPIN, Lauren Lee
Paw Creek Christian Acad; Charlotte, NC (3-11) Ed, Ann; Cpt, Chldr; Chor; Pres, Sr Cl; Bkbl; Sftbl; Type A; Most Sch Spirit; *Lee Col; PE.*

PIPPINS, Cassandra Delise
Lanier Sr HS; Jackson, MS (30-240) NHS; F-Ed, Sch P; Journ A; Q&S A; ROTC A; Bookkeeping A; *Jackson St U; Eng.*

PIPPINS, Jesse Lawrence
Vienna HS; Vienna, IL; Band; Span C; Pres, Jr Cl; JV, Bsbl; Bkbl; *U of Ill; Law Enforcement.*

PIPPINS, Vanessa Michelle
W H Canier HS; Jackson, MS; Bkbl; Sftbl; Tr; Ath As.

PIRATZKY, Patti Anne
S Hunterdon Regional HS; Lambertville, NJ (12-111) Chldr; Hmrm; NHS; SC; Mgr, Bsbl; Mgr, Ftbl; Hockey; Sftbl; Sch Play; Cpt, Gym; DAHSS; *Kutztown St Col; Bus.*

PIRIE, Elizabeth Lynn
Clinton HS; Clinton, MS (30-337) BC; Drama; Rainbow; Span C; Spch C; Y-Tns; Sftbl; Top Ten Beauty; 3rd Pl, Library Wk Essay; *Millsaps Col; Bio.*

PIRKLE, Denna Lavada
Oregon-Howell R-3 HS; Koshkonong, MO (2-22) F-Ed, Ann; Arch; Cpt, Chldr; Chor; FHA; Lit Mag; Rptr, Sch P; SC; Arch; Bkbl; Sftbl; Cl Fav; HQn.

PIRO, James Joseph
R H A M HS; Hebron, CT (56-190) A Cap Choir; AFS; Arch; CYO; Drama; Fr C; 4H; Hmrm; Rptr, Sch P; Sci C; Ski C; St Stu Congress; Pres, SC; Tnns; Tr; Bio A; Ntl Sci Symposium; Sci A; Yth Fel; Cr Cultural Exchange A; Hospital Vol; Ntl Sci Symp; *MCC; Occupational Therapy.*

PIRRIE, Gwendolyn Sue
Mercer Island HS; Mercer Island, WA; Hon Qn, Job's Daughters; Ski Instructor; Yacht C; *Mont St Col; Home Ec.*

PIRTLE, Clayton
Whittier HS; Flint, MI; Sci.

PIRTLE, Traci Leanne
Central HS; Tulsa, OK; A Cap Choir; Band; Ensm; Orch; Church Camp, Top Camper A; 2nd Pl Mus Duet, Ntl Church; Mus.

PISANI, Judy Lee
Jefferson Twp HS; Jefferson Twp, NJ (20-264) Chor; Semi-Fin, GS; Pres, NHS; Span C; SC; Var C; Tres, Sr Cl; Soccer; JV, Sftbl; Tr; Hon Prog; Sewing, Drafting, Woodworking, A's; WW; *Pa St U; Archt.*

PISANO, Mark Charles
Lumberton Sr HS; Lumberton, NC (38-320) Band; Chem C; Tres, Hmrm; Sci C; Span C; Var C; Cpt, Ftbl; Cpt, Golf; Bio A; Most Out; MVP, Golf; Champion, Golf St Conf; All Co Ftbl; Master Acolyte; *Furman U; Biol.*

PISCZOR, Christine Mary
Goodman HS; Goodman, WI (5-23) Bus Mgr, Ann; Band; Cpt, Chldr; Chor; Ensm; Sch P; Bkbl; HCt; Cpt, Vlbl; *Marian Col; Nurs.*

PITCHER, Tina Louise
Waynoka HS; Waynoka, OK; VP, Band; Chldr; Dbte Tm; FHA; GS; Spch C; Tres, Sr Cl; Bkbl; Sftbl; Swim; Tnns; Tr; Spch A; Type A; Band Qn; *NW Okla St U; Secy.*

PITCHERS, Danny Ray
Virden HS; Virden, IL (43-82) Chor; Drama; Madrigal; Pres, Var C; Bsbl; Bkbl; Ftbl; Best Rebounder; Highest Scorer, Bkbl; Lead, Musical; *U of Cincinnati; Phys Ed.*

PITCHFORD, Janet Eileen
Franklin HS; Franklin, IL (2-41) Pres, Band; CYO; Chor; FHA; Pres, 4H; Secy, NHS; Span C; Amer Leg A; Bio A; DARGCA; 4H A; St Scholar; Type A; Val; *Acct.*

PITCOCK, Cindy Lee
Panhandle HS; Panhandle, TX (19-59) Band; Drama; FHA; FTA; Spch C; Bkbl; Tr; Math A; Pres A; HS Rodeo A's; *Panhandle St U; Secondary Ed.*

PITEL, Stephanie Jane
McHenry Comm HS; McHenry, IL (10-485) Band; Mod Mus Mas; Span C; Var C; Bkbl; MVP, Tnns; Tr; COM; *McHenry Co Col; Nurs.*

PITMAN, Loretta
Nederland HS; Nederland, TX (54-480) Pres, Drama; Span A; VofDEM; Hon Men; Ntl Forensic League; NHS; Trophies, Spch & Poetry; Best Actress; Hon Thes; *Dramatics.*

PITMAN, Ruth Anne
Brentwood HS; Brentwood, MO (10-100) Ed, Ann; Chor; Madrigal; NHS; Rptr, Sch P; Span C; Secy, SC; Var C; VP, Soph Cl; Journ A; Vlbl; *Wheaton Col; Eng.*

PITNEY, Jerrine Lea
N Love Christian HS; Rockford, IL (1-4) Chor; 4H; Rptr, Sch P; Span C; Sftbl; Tnns; 4H A; Spch A; VofDEM; *Liberty Baptist Col; Elem Ed.*

PITT, Carol Elizabeth
Acad of Our Lady of Mercy; Milford, CT (2-86) Chldr; Lat C; Ski C; JV, Bkbl; Sftbl; NEDT; Fr A; Lat A.

PITT, Susan Margaret
Jamestown Sr HS; Jamestown, NY (50%-500) Rptr, Ann; Secy, Chor; Drama; SC; *Jamestown Comm Col; Elem Ed.*

PITTARD, Carol Alice
Eastside HS; Gainesville, FL (2-280) AFS; BC; Chor; Fr C; *Andrew Jr Col; Mus.*

PITTARD, Catherine Annette
Burkburnett HS; Burkburnett, TX (10-268) VP, Drama; FHA; Ed, Lit Mag; NHS; F-Ed, Sch P; VP, Thes; Hist A; Journ A; Spch A; Rptr, Yth For Christ; Eng A; Best Actress; Poetry A; *Midwestern St U; Psych.*

PITTENGER, Valerie Kay
Yreka Union HS; Yreka, CA; A Cap Choir; Band; Chor; Drama; Spch C; Thes; Swim; *San Diego Sch of Bus; Bus.*

PITTMAN, Bernard Wilmer
Southampton Acad; Courtland, VA (14-31) BC; Var C; Bsbl; Bkbl; Ftbl; Sftbl; *NC St U; Agr.*

PITTMAN, Briane
St Marys HS; Raleigh, NC (15-103) Chem C; French NHS; NHS; ARC; COM; Citz A; Hon Prog; Yth Fel; Yth Leg; Nom, Morehead Schol; St Yth Coun; Raleigh Yth Coun; *Wake Forest U; Pre-Med.*

PITTMAN, Bryan Steve
Columbia Acad; Columbia, MS (17-37) Drama; Sch P; Pres, SC; Mgr, Bsbl; Mgr, Bkbl; Mgr, Ftbl; HCt; I Dare You; Most Dependable; 1st Pl Dist, 5th St, ABC Gov Comp; *Pearl River Col; Bus.*

PITTMAN, Cheryl Gwenette
United Township HS; E Moline, IL (58-798) Ann; NHS; Sch P; Var C; Bkbl; JV, Hockey; Co-Cpt, T; COM; 4H A; Hon Prog; JA A; *Advertising.*

PITTMAN, Danny Bryan
Harrah HS; Harrah, OK (20%-119) FFA; Phys C; Bsbl; Ftbl; Wrest; Math A; St Scholar; FFA A; *Okla St U; Aeronautical Tech.*

PITTMAN, Darla Naomi
Chester HS; Chester, PA (57-680) Band; Chldr; Chor; FNA; Hmrm; NHS; Up Bound; Cr-Ctry; Hockey; Swim; Cpt, Tr; Alg A; B Crocker A; Hon Prog; Math A; HR; HR; Sewing A; Hist A; Georgraphy A; *Special Ed.*

PITTMAN, Elisabeth Ann
Wister HS; Wister, OK; FHA; Secy, Sci C; MLS; Val; *Carl Albert Jr Col.*

PITTMAN, Gregory Ross
Bixby HS; Bixby, OK (7-156) Chem C; Hmrm; Pres, NHS; SC; Bsbl; Cpt, Bkbl; HKg; Pres, FCA; Drafting A; Best Personality; Stu o-t Mo; *Okla St U; Pre-Med.*

PITTMAN, Kelvin Carter
Simon Gratz HS; Philadelphia, PA (15-375) FTA; Pres, Sr Cl; Cpt, Ftbl; Tr; Co-Cpt, Wrest.

PITTMAN, Lawrence William
Hardaway HS; Columbus, GA (100-450) Sftbl; *Columbus Col; Acct.*

PITTMAN, Lisa Suzanne
Heritage Acad; Birmingham, AL; 2nd Pl, Co Art A; *Law Enforcement.*

PITTMAN, Paula Elaine
Evan E Worthing Sr HS; Houston, TX (25-500) VP, Bus C; FHA; FTA; NHS; Bio A; Hist A; Eng A; *NTSU; Bus.*

PITTMAN, Scott Andrew
Cheyenne Mtn HS; Colo Springs, CO; A Cap Choir; Band; Chor; Ensm; Ski C; Ftbl; *Adam St Col; Mus Ed.*

PITTMAN, Wilda Faye
Scott Preparatory Sch; Opelika, AL (10-27) Tres, Anchor C; BC; Tres, Chem C; Hmrm; Math C; NHS; Pres, Span C; Secy, SC; VP, Y-Tns; COM; Hon Prog; Type A; Yth Fel; *Auburn U; Ed.*

PITTMON, Vickie Lynn
Kendrick HS; Columbus, GA; Chldr; Hmrm; Span C; *U of Ga; Social Worker.*

PITTS, Christina Marie
Glenwood HS; Phenix City, AL (10%-78) Band; Chor; FHA; Orch; Span C; A-B HR; Gov Phys Fitness A; *Birmingham Sou Col; Ecology.*

PITTS, Eugene
G W Carver HS; Birmingham, AL (20-237) Bus C; FBLA; Pres, Sr Cl; Bkbl; Cr-Ctry; Tr.

PITTS, Eva DeLois
Jess Lanier HS; Bessemer, AL; ARC; Sftbl; *Morehouse Col; Phys Ed.*

PITTS, Justine Denise
Overbrook HS; Philadelphia, PA (98-800) ARC; Hon Prog; *Penn St U; Psych.*

PITTS, Katherine Marie
Kickapoo HS; Springfield, MO (144-288) Chor; Var C; Sftbl; Tr; Pep C; Intermurals; *Baptist Bible Col.*

PITTS, Michael Kirk
Aiken HS; Aiken, SC (33%-700) Demolay; Sci C; *U of SC; Bus Adm.*

PIWONKA, Nancy Marie
Bishop Byrne HS; Memphis, TN (2-190) VP, Band; Community Yth Symph; NHS; Hon Prog; NEDT; HR; Band A; All St Band; WW; All West Tenn Band; Semi-Fin, Miss Teenage Memphis; Sewanee Summer Mus Center Schol; *Syracuse U; Mus.*

PIXLEY, Mark Randall
Sentinel HS; Sentinel, OK (17-33) BC; Pres, Chess C; Chor; Tnns; JV, Wrest; Citz A; Most Talented; *SW St U; Fine Arts.*

PIZOR, Jane Ann
Lake HS; Uniontown, OH (56-224) Tnns; Yth Fel; Alt, GS; *Akron U; Receptionist.*

PIZZURRO, Carol Virginia
Lutheran HS E; Harper Woods, MI; Chor; Drama; Hmrm; SC.

PLACE, Cheryl Ann
Pinckneyville Comm HS; Pinckneyville, IL (31-155) Band; Chldr; FHA; NHS; ARC; S-T, Sci C; Spch C; Mgr, Bkbl; Tr; ARC A; Swtht; *Eastern U.*

PLACE, Donna Yvonne
Sequoia HS; Redwood City, CA; FBLA; COM; *Canada Col; Secretarial.*

PLACKE, Jeffrey Dean
Oakville Sr HS; St Louis, MO; Tres, CYO; Bsbl; Golf; Soccer; COM; Hon Prog; JA A; Poet A; *Bus.*

PLAIN, Patrick Kent
Ballard HS; Louisville, KY; VP, Ann; Pres, Ensm; Fr C; Ed, Sch P; Tres, Sci C; Mgr, Tnns; I Dare You; JA A; Yth Fel; Bus Mgr, Sch P; *Communications.*

PLAKAKIS, Susan Gaye
Thomasville Sr HS; Thomasville, NC (50%-195) Chor; Commercial C; Ensm; Pres, Hmrm; Inter-Club Coun; Rainbow; Pres, Tri-HiY; Tri-Hi-Y Schol in Hon; *Davidson Co Comm Col; Religion.*

PLANCK, Leann
Bethel-Tate HS; Bethel, OH (39-133) Band; Chor; Madrigal; SC; Var Show A; Lead Role, Play; Jr Achv; *Acct.*

PLANER, William Robert
Hartland Arrowhead HS; Hartland, WI (60-180) Cr-Ctry; Tr; Yth Fel; Pres, Christian Yth Organization.

PLANK, Bruce Lee
Southeast HS; Wichita, KS; *Wichita St U; Bus Adm.*

PLANT, William Alfred
Castro Valley HS; Castro Valley, CA; Var C; Semi-Fin, Bkbl; Cpt, Ftbl; Fin, Sftbl; Co-Cpt, Wrest; All Stars, Church Bsbl & Sftbl; *Chabot Jr Col; Phys Ed.*

PLANTE, Elizabeth Grace
Stillwater Sr HS; Stillwater, MN; A Cap Choir; Chor; Drama; Ensm; Lit Mag; Madrigal; Ntl Yth Conf; Ed, Sch P; Spch C; SC; Thes; Citz A; Journ A; Spch A; Mus A, St Contest; Theater A; *U of Wis; Psych.*

PLASHINSKI, Kristin Elizabeth
Dallas Sr HS; Dallas, PA (121-244) Ed, Ann; Band; Chor; Hmrm; Rainbow; ARC; DARGCA; Dist IV Chor; Reg IV Chor; *U of Pittsburg; Pre-Phys Therapy.*

PLASHINSKI, Marilyn Ruth
Dallas Sr HS; Dallas, PA (33%-260) Band; Chor; Key C; Rainbow; Swim; Hon Prog; NEDT; Yth Fel; *Pediatric Nurs.*

PLASSMANN, Rebecca Joan
Los Alamos HS; Los Alamos, NM (10%-459) Band; Ensm; JV, Hockey; Publication in YOUTH; *Environmental Sci.*

PLATE, Karen Irene
Susan E Wagner HS; Staten Island, NY (60-682) *Missions.*

PLATFOOT, Melody Anne
Piqua Central HS; Piqua, OH (18-395) Band; Drama; Fr C; NHS; SC; Pres, Jr Cl; Pres, Soph Cl; Swim; COM; H of F; Hon Prog; Opt A; Scuba Diver Cert; Lifeguard; *Annapolis Acad; Oceanagraphy.*

PLATT, Anthony Dean
Crockett HS; Crockett, TX (10%-140).

PLATT, Brenda Kay
Limestone HS; Bartonville, IL (12-378) Tres, A Cap Choir; Chor; Drama; Ensm; FHA; Madrigal; NHS; Ski C; Secy, SC; Thes; Tr; Hon Prog; St Scholar; Yth Fel; WW; Gloria Schmidt Schol; 1st Pl, St Piano Solo; YL Work Crew; *Ill St U; Mus Ed.*

PLATT, Daniel Barry
Everglades City HS; Everglades City, FL (77%-27) Drama; Bkbl; *Math.*

PLATT, Guy Edwin Jr
Hudson Sr HS; Hudson, FL (100-300) BC; Pres, Hmrm; InterAct C; SC; MVP, Bsbl; Ftbl; MVP, Golf; COM; Citz A; Hon Prog; Pres A; *St Petersburg Jr Col; Bus.*

PLATT, James William
Catawba Acad; Rock Hill, SC (3-23) A-Ed, Ann; Hmrm; Key C; VP, NHS; Rptr, Sr Cl; Mgr, Bkbl; Tnns; Bio A; Chem A; Diligence A; HR; Bible A; *Presbyterian Col; Math.*

PLATT, Kay Lynn
Polytechnic HS; Ft Worth, TX (70-400) Band; Chem C; FHA; Math C; Math A; ARC A; WW; *U of Tex; Math.*

PLATT, Lisa Fay
Charleston HS; Charleston, IL (3-248) A Cap
Choir; Rptr, AFS; Chor; Pres, Fr C; 4H; Math C;
Model UN; NHS; Orch; SC; UN Council; COM;
Coun of Teach A; 4H A; Hon Prog; Math A; Vlbl;
Co-Ch, Yth For Easter Seals; E III U; Financing.

PLATT, Mary Lynn
Everglades City HS; Everglades City, FL (4-42)
Chldr; MVP, Band; Mus.

PLATT, Mary Margaret
Bothell HS; Bothell, WA (195-400) F-Ed, Ann;
Band; VP, Chor; Cpt, Dbte Tm; Drama; Semi-Fin,
GS; Hmrm; NFL; Rptr, Sch P; SC; Thes; Bus Mgr,
Sr Cl; Sftbl; Mgr, Tr; COM; Citz A; Spch A; Vof-
DEM; GSct; Most Talented Girl, Sr Cl; Drama,
Debate, G Sct 10 Yr, A's; Phi Kappa Delta Merit,
A; Cornish Inst o-t Arts; Theatre Arts.

PLATT, Michelle Susan
Sooner HS; Bartlesville, OK (10%-289) JV, Tnns.

PLATT, Steve Alan
Weed HS; Weed, CA (10-62) Band; BS; Drama;
VP, 4H; Madrigal; SC; Pres, Sr Cl; JV, Ftbl; CSF;
Cal Poly at San Luis; Elec Engr.

PLATT, Vicki Lynn
Borger HS; Borger, TX (18-200) Secy, Band; FHA;
Pres, Thes; Tex Tech U; Fashion Merchandising.

PLATTE, Thomas Emil
Crestwood HS; Cresco, IA (28-150) Band; Chess C;
FFA; NHS; Var C; Co-Cpt, Bsbl; Bkbl; MVP, Bsbl;
N Iowa Area Comm Col; Law Enforcement.

PLATTER, David Mark
Northgate HS; Walnut Creek, CA; SC; Var C; Bsbl;
JV, Swim; Tnns; CSF; COM; Hon Prog; MLS; Yth
Foundation A; Young Amer A; Stanford U; Med.

PLATTOR, Shelley Sue
Artesia HS; Artesia, NM; Band; Ensm; Rptr, Rain-
bow; Rainbow Girl o-t Yr; Band Festival A; Church
Coun On Ministries & Yth.

PLATZER, Debra Maureen
Proctor HS; Proctor, MN; Tres, FHA; Copywriter,
Yrbk; Church Yth Group; Tres, Sr GSct; Librarian,
Job's Daughters; Sunday Sch Teacher; Law.

PLAUTZ, Lori Lynn
Merrill Sr HS; Merrill, WI (48-324) Chor; Spch C;
Tr; Spch A; Type A; Yth Fel; Ath Ltr.

PLAYER, Karen Lee
Pomona Sr HS; Arvada, CO (126-456) Chor;
Ensm; Sr Rep, SC; Color Guard; VP, Health Ca-
reers C; U of Colo; Nurs.

PLAYER, Mary Elizabeth
Columbus HS; Columbus, GA; Chor; Secy, 4H;
Hmrm; Secy, NHS; Hon Prog; Most Out; Page One
A; Win, Art; Art-Commerical.

PLAYLE, Penny Lu
Austin HS; Austin, MN; Bus C; Chor; 4H; Tr;
COM; Hon Prog; Mgr, Vlbl; St Mary's Sch of
Practical Nurs; Nurs.

PLAYLE, Scott William
Austin HS; Austin, MN (65-514) Chess C; Drama;
NHS; Ed, Order/Arrow; Golf; Sftbl; JA A; NMS;
Order/Arrow A; Pres, Yth Group; Mankato St U;
Acct.

PLEASANT, N Paul
Pasadena HS; Pasadena, TX (64-570) A Cap Choir;
Semi-Fin, BS; Chor; Key C; Madrigal; NHS; Mgr,
Ftbl; Co-Cpt, Sftbl; Alt, Region Choir; DECA; Solo
Contest; Sounds of Saluation; Stephen F Austin
Col; Bus Adm.

PLEMMONS, Patricia Lynn
Asheville HS; Asheville, NC; Chor; Most Out; Star
Student; Type A; Most Cooperative; Outst Schol.

PLEMONS, Heidi Jamesa
Guilderland Central HS; Guilderland Center, NY;
Alg A; COM; Sci A; Yth Fel; Sceptre Service; So-
cial Work.

PLESKO, Jeffrey Joseph
Notre Dame-Bishop Gibbons HS; Schenectady,
NY (60-181) Band; Chor; Orch; Sch Mus & Plays;
WW; Church Mus; HR; Hudson Valley Col; Lib
Arts.

PLETCHER, Dianne Lynn
Spring-Ford Sr HS; Royersford, PA; Secy, Band;
Chor; Drama; Pres, FTA; Hmrm; Ntl Yth Conf;
Rainbow; Sch P; VP, Span C; SC; Sftbl; Cpt, Tnns;
Yth Fel; FTA A; Calif St Col; Elem Ed.

PLETSCHER, Petra Briggitte
Westfield HS; Westfield, NJ (300-660) Ger C; Ski
C; GScts; Sch Win, Home Ec Contest; God &
Comm A; U of Vt; Dietetics.

PLETTNER, Glenda Marie
Lakeview HS; Columbus, NE (9-72) Ann; Chldr;
GS; Pres, 4H; VP, NHS; Spch C; S-T, SC; Tr; 4H A;
HCt; Opt A; Sertoma A, Vlbl; Platte Tech Comm
Col; Spec Ed.

PLOEGER, Rebecca Catherine
Fraser HS; Fraser, MI (160-700) Band; Chor; I,
Ensm Solo Festival; Mich St U; Bus Adm.

PLOMBON, Michelle Ann
Coon Rapids Sr HS; Coon Rapids, MN (16-667)
Band; CYO; NHS; Orch; MMTA Theroy A; Solo,
Ensm A; Mus.

PLOOF, Mark Robert
St John's Prep Sch; Collegeville, MN (5%-60)
NHS; Ftbl; Tnns; Adv Ger Cl; Little League Bsbl;
Doubles Champ, Raquetball; Exchange Stu, Melk,
Austria.

PLOSS, Andrea Elizabeth
Woodmere Acad; Woodmere, NY; Fr C; Rptr, Sch
P; Secy, Sci C; SC; Hockey; Bio A; Vlbl.

PLOTSKY, Bruce Daniel
Liberty Central HS; Liberty, NY; Ann; Ski C;
Wrest; Cortland Col.

PLOTT, Linda Kay
Riverdale HS; Mt Blanchard, OH (44-119) Ann;
Band; Bus C; Chor; Ensm; FBLA; 4H; Sch P; Span
C; COM; 4H A; Type A; Yth Fel; Most Shy; Nea-
test; Teacher Secy; Findlay Col; Bus.

PLOUGH, Chris Allen
Ridgedale HS; Morral, OH (40-87) Ann; Band;
Chor; Pres, Sr Cl; Ftbl; Golf; Tr; Photographer, Sch
Paper; Homecoming Escort; Cl Comedian; U of
Akron; Bio.

PLUGGE, Christine Adele
Stanton HS; Stanton, NE (13-54) Band; Chor;
Drama; NHS; Wayne St Col; Mus.

PLUGGE, Guy Alan
Ralston HS; Ralston, NE (12-331) NHS; Var C;
Bkbl; Tnns; Math.

PLUHM, Faye Cristine
Litchfield Comm HS; Litchfield, IL (7-143) BC;
4H; NHS; 4H A; Hon Prog; Sunday Sch Teacher;
Pub Lib Aide; Bible Sch Helper; WW; Lincoln
Land Comm Col; Bus Adm.

PLUIMER, Kevin James
Lodi HS; Lodi, CA (10%-520) Ger C; Ed, Sch P;
CSF; Quill & Scroll; UCLA; Dentistry.

PLUMER, Clarissa Arleen
Ogemaw Heights HS; W Branch, MI; Span C;
Church Chor; Lay Reader; Albion Col; Span.

PLUMER, Marshall Wellington
Ogemaw Heights HS; West Branch, MI; Band;
Span C; Mgr, Bkbl; Cr-Ctry; Ftbl; Swim; Tr; Life-
guard C; Church Choir; Altar Boy; U of Mich; Sci.

PLUMLEE, Cathie Ann
Duncan HS; Duncan, OK; Okla Christian Col; Bus.

PLUMLEY, Patricia Jean
Landrum HS; Landrum, SC; Ann; BC; Jr Usher;
Spartanburg Tech Col; Acct.

PLUMMER, Angela Juanita
W Charlotte Sr HS; Charlotte, NC (125-638) A
Cap Choir; Ann; Band; Chldr; Pres, Chor; City
Conf; Dbte Tm; Drama; Ensm; Tres, FBLA; Secy,
FHA; FTA; GS; Hmrm; InterAct C; InterClub
Coun; Lit Mag; Mjrte; VP, Mod Mus Mas; B
Crocker A; COM; Citz A; Coun of Teach A;
DARGCA; Delta Sigma Theta A; HCt; Journ A;
MLS; ARC A; Swtht; Yth Foundation; Order o-t
Lion; Distinguished Mus Achv; Good Neighbor A;
Sister of Leonesde Grande; Central Peidmont Col;
Correctional Sci.

PLUMMER, Deborah Katherine
New Haven HS; New Haven, MO (13-41) Chor;
Ensm; 4H; Mjrte; SC; Golf; Cpt, Soccer; Sftbl;
Swim; Tnns; Journ A; E Central Jr Col; Eng Lit.

PLUMMER, Doris Dianne
N Natchez Adams HS; Natchez, MS (15%-220)
BC; Alcorn St U; Secretarial Sci.

PLUMMER, Duane Daniel
Center Grove HS; Greenwood, IN (33%-250) Pro-
Marksman, Ntl Rifle Assn; Purdue U; Agr.

PLUMMER, Lori Denise
Clinton HS; Clinton, MS; Chor; Sftbl; Tr; Hinds Jr
Col.

PLUMMER, Mary Jane
Wallace HS; Wallace, ID (50-95) FHA; Drill A;
Airlines.

PLUMMER, Terry Ann
Fremont HS; Oakland, CA; Chldr; Chor; Up
Bound; Cl Fav; ROTC A; Gym; Eng A; Annapolis
Naval Acad.

PLUNKETT, Mary Kathryn
Patrick Henry HS; Roanoke, VA (14-500) Ann;
BC; Fr C; Pres, Hmrm; Lat C; NHS; SC; COM;
Hon Prog; NEDT; Most Dependable; Randolph-
Macon Wmn's Col Distin Sch; Randolph-Macon
Woman's Col.

PLUNKETT, Timothy Arthur
Heidelberg American HS; Heidelberg, GER-
MANY (32-170) Band; NHS; Orch; Amer Leg A;
Math A; ROTC A; ROTC Battalion Commander;
Trinity U; Engr.

PLYMALE, Charles Evan
Anthony Wayne HS; Whitehouse, OH (80-380)
FFA; 4H; Sci C; SC; Var C; Cpt, Bsbl; Ftbl; Wrest;
4H A; Bowling Green Col; Vet.

PLYMIRE, Donald Bret
Highland HS; Ewing, MO (12-132) NHS; Var C;
Bsbl; Co-Cpt, Bkbl; Ftbl; Tr; WW; All Conf, Ftbl; U
of Mo; Arts.

POCHAP, Mike Louis
Gregory HS; Gregory, SD (20-61) Band; Orch; Var
C; JV, Bsbl; Ftbl; Tr; Wrest.

POCHE, Chet Gerard
St Martin HS; St Martinville, LA; CYO; 4H;
Bsbl; Pres, Industrial Arts C; Welding.

POCOCK, Cheryl Marie
Chillicothe HS; Chillicothe, OH (2%-400) Band;
Dbte Tm; NFL; Sci A.

POCTA, Sharon Lyn
Braddock Pub Sch; Braddock, ND (2-8) Ed, Ann;
Chldr; Chor; 4H; F-Ed, Sch P; Secy, Sr Cl; Rptr, Jr
Cl; Rptr, Soph Cl; Bkbl; 4H A; Sal; ND St U; Bus
Adm.

PODEHL, Lynn Marie
Spring Lake HS; Spring Lake, MI (8-235) Band;
Chor; GS; NHS; Bkbl; Mgr, Tr; Yth Foundation; U
of Mich; Med.

PODLEWSKI, Denise Ann
Michigan Center HS; Michigan Center, MI
(20%-155) Community Yth Symph; NHS; COM;
Citz A; Mus Ed.

PODNORSZKI, Teri Anne
Glens Falls Sr HS; Glens Falls, NY (4-292) Band;
Chor; FTA; GS; Pres, NHS; Pres, Orch; SC; HiY;
Amer Leg A; Citz A; DARGCA; Hon Prog; Most
Out; Opt Out Tn; PTA A; Regent Schol; AH; 1st
Pl, Co Bicentennial Essay; Eng Prize; Ntl Fr Con-
test; Jenkns Mem Life.

PODPESKAR, Karol Lynne
Gilbert HS; Gilbert, MN; Band; CYO; Chor;
Drama; FHA; GS; Orch; S-T, SC; Thes; Bkbl; Tr;
Cpt, Vlbl; Tri-St Bkbl Tm; Mesabi Jr Col; Phys Ed.

PODRAZA, Kathleen Annette
Holy Cross HS; Riverside, NJ (29-394) Secy, CYO;
NHS; Pres, Sodality; Tnns; JV, Tr; Amer Leg A;
COM; Hon Prog; K of C A; PTA A; Sci A; Ed.

PODRUCH, Lucy Catherine
Newman HS; Wausau, WI (12-136) Chldr; Tres, Fr
C; JETS; Math C; NHS; Sci C; Secy, SC; Cpt, Tr;
Kiwanis A; Opt A; Marquette U; Engr.

PODRUCHNY, Brenda Lea
Max Pub HS; Max, ND; Ann; Chor; Ensm; 4H;
Mgr, Tr; Math A; NW Bible Col; Math.

POE, Jennifer Ann
Cedar Bluff HS; Cedar Bluff, AL; BC; Chldr; Fin,
GS; Math C; Co-Ed, Sch P; VP, SC; Var C; Tres, Jr
Cl; Pres, Soph Cl; Beauty; HQn; MLS; Jacksonville
St U.

POE, Jerry Allen
Town East Christian Sch; San Antonio, TX (1-9) JV, Bkbl; JV, Ftbl; Song Ldr, Yth Group; *U of Ala; Mus.*

POE, Marjorie Lee
S Mecklenburg HS; Charlotte, NC; Hmrm; NHS; Secy, Span C; Span NHS; Swim; Yth Fel; Horsebackriding; Acolyte; Young Life; *William & Mary Col; Special Ed.*

POE, Nancy Janice
E Randolph HS; Ramseur, NC (25-265) Band; BC; Fr C; FHA; *U of NC; Health.*

POE, Robert Wayne
Lamar R-I HS; Lamar, MO (96-150) Var C; Bkbl; Cr-Ctry; Ftbl; Tr; *Ozark Bible Col; Ministry.*

POE, Vicki Anne
Tallapoosa Acad; Dadeville, AL (5-27) Ann; Band; VP, BC; B Crocker A; *Auburn U; Wildlife Mgr.*

POEHLER, Linda Susan
Reading Mem HS; Reading, MA (100-450) A Cap Choir; Band; Chor; Drama; Hmrm; Sch P; SC; Bsbl; Bkbl; Sftbl; COM; Yth Fel; Yth Leg; *North Shore Comm Col; Childhood Development.*

POEHLS, Lana Kaye
Blackwell Rural HS; Blackwell, TX; Ann; Secy, FHA; Cpt, Bkbl; Cpt, Tr; Cl Fav; Yth Fel; *Tarleton St Col; Phys Ed.*

POELKING, Thomas Francis
Glenbrook S HS; Glenview, IL; JV, Ftbl; JV, Tr; Bio A; Hist A; Hon Prog; *Social Sci.*

POERSCHKE, Carol Ann
Niagara Wheatfield Sr HS; Sanborn, NY (40-420) Chor; NHS; MVP, Bkbl; Cpt, Sftbl; Alg A; Bio A; Math A; Yth Fel; Ger A; Eng A; Co-Cpt, Bkbl; Vlbl.

POETTER, Royce Lyn
Crow HS; Crow, OR; Ann; NHS; Rptr, Sch P; SC; Pres, Var C; Bsbl; Bkbl; Cr-Ctry; Tr; COM; HCt; Sal; Yth Fel; WW; *Navy; Acct.*

POFF, William Robert
Columbia HS; Columbia, PA; Band; Span C; *Penn St U; Bus.*

POGORZELEC, Regina Rose
LaBrae HS; Leavittsburg, OH (9-176) JV, Chldr; Chor; Ensm; Secy, FTA; VP, Ger C; 4H; Hmrm; Secy, NHS; Bus Mgr, Sch P; Semi-Fin, GS; 4H A; JA A; *Youngstown St U; Med Tech.*

POGUE, Michelle Renee
Piggott HS; Piggott, AR (54-84) Ann; FHA; Sci C; Bkbl; Tr; HCt; Bkbl A; All Dist, Bkbl; 1st Alt, Miss Piggott; 4th Alt, Miss Clay Co; *U of Central Ark; Dental Hygiene.*

POGUE, Patricia Lynne
Pattonville Sr HS; St Louis, MO (300-900) Chldr; Chor; Ensm; NHS; Swim; Tr; *Bus.*

POHL, Christine Joy
Valley HS; Eden, ID (19-42) VP, FHA; Ger C; 4H; 4H A; JA A; *Cosmotology.*

POHL, David Harold
Neshaminy Maple Point HS; Langhorne, PA (9-415) JV, Ftbl; JV, Soccer; Swim; Tnns; Hon Prog; Chldr, Gymnight; *Engr.*

POHL, Kris Stanley
Adrian HS; Adrian, MI (9-491) Chor; SC; JV, Cr-Ctry; Tr; Yth Fel; Yth Leg; *U of Mich; Law.*

POHLMAN, Kent D
Stanton Comm Sch; Stanton, NE (2-55) Ann; Band; BS; Chor; Ensm; FFA; S-T, Ger C; NHS; Orch; Order/Arrow; VP, SC; Pres, Var C; COM; HKg; Hon Prog; Order/Arrow A; Sal; Spch A; Star Student; VofDEM; *Iowa St U; Animal Sci.*

POHORSKI, Alexandra Janine
Watsonville HS; Watsonville, CA (8-570) Math C; Var C; Co-Cpt, Swim; Tr; Amer Leg A; CSF; Math A; Sci A; Vlbl; *Art.*

POILLON, Denise Suzann
St Brendan's HS; Brooklyn, NY; Tres, SC; Cpt, Bkbl; Sftbl; Cpt, Swim; *Med.*

POINDEXTER, Latasha Louise
Douglass HS; Memphis, TN (25%-180) *U Tenn at Martin; Acct.*

POINDEXTER, Michael Kelly
Marine Military Acad; Harlingen, TX (1-57) Demolay; Tres, NHS; Span C; Bkbl; JV, Ftbl; JV, Tr; Alg A; Amer Leg A; COM; DARGCA; Hist A; JA A; ROTC A; Span A; PA; *Annapolis Naval Acad; Off.*

POINDEXTER, Robert William
George Washington Jr HS; Alexandria, VA (49-1040) Ftbl; Soccer; Cpt, Wrest; COM; Hist A; Hon Prog; Math A; Most Out; Sci A; Coache's, Eng, Wrest, Soccer, A's; *Bradford Col; Computer Field.*

POINTER, Barbara Carlene
Robert W Johnson HS; Gainesville, GA; Chor; Fr C; VP, FNA; Sci C; Choral A; *Nurse.*

POINTER, Carolyne Delores
Dobbins Tech HS; Philadelphia, PA (31-526) *Computer Sci.*

POINTER, Isaac Benjamin
W B Saul HS; Philadelphia, PA (44-125) Arch; BS; Chess C; FFA; Sch P; Bsbl; Bkbl; Golf; Sftbl; Tr; Citz A; MLS; *The Col of Idaho; Agr.*

POITIER, Reginald Vincent
Miami Jackson HS; Miami, FL (100-500) Band; InterClub Coun; NHS; JV, Wrest; Citz A; Hon Prog; Star General; Silver Knight Nom; Band A; Art A; *Jarvis Christian Col; Radiology.*

POITRAS, Yvan
College De Sainte; La Pocatiere, CANADA (1-28) VP, Drama; Cpt, 4H; Pres, Hmrm; Phys C; Ski C; Var C; Bkbl; Hockey; Cpt, Soccer; Swim; Tnns; COM; 4H A; ARC A; Spch A; Vlbl; Karate; Photo A; *CEGEP La Pocatiere; Ingenior.*

POKALSKY, Teresa Ann
Neshaminy Maple Point HS; Langhorne, PA (7-415) Band; Ensm; NHS; Orch; Tr; COM; Hon Prog; Co,dist, Orch; *Eastman Sch of Mus; Mus.*

POKLEMBO, Michelle Ann
Greater Latrobe Sr HS; Latrobe, PA (16-518) Ch, AFS; French NHS; NHS; Ch, Sci C; NMS; *U of Pittsburgh; Pre-Med.*

POKORNY, David James
Herricks Sr HS; New Hyde Park, NY (103-500) Orch; Order/Arrow; Var C; JV, Bkbl; JV, Soccer; Cpt, Swim; Regent School; MVP, Swim; Lacrosse; *Villanova U; Acct.*

POKRYWKA, Mark Benedict
Loyola HS; Towson, MD (10-134) Band; Ger C; Rptr, Lit Mag; Math C; Order/Arrow; Co-Cpt, Bkbl; Semi-Fin, Tnns; Ntl Achv Schol; NMS; NEDT; Order/Arrow A; *VPI; Aerospace Engr.*

POLACEK, Adrienne Sue
Brooklyn HS; Brooklyn, OH (3-190) Band; Ensm; Hmrm; Tres, Mu Alpha Theta; Pres, NHS; Orch; Sch Achieve Tm; Pres, SC; JV, Cr-Ctry; Tnns; Tr; Alg A; COM; Hon Prog; Math A; Type A; Girl's C; Eng Hon; Amer Soc of Women's Accts Schol; Acad Challenge; Panhellenic Schol A; *Miami U; Acct.*

POLANCHIK, Daria
Old Forge HS; Old Forge, PA (4-121) FHA; FNA; Hmrm; NHS; Ski C; SC; *Marywood Col; Dietitics.*

POLANCHIK, Paul
Old Forge HS; Old Forge, PA (15-121) NHS; Sci C; Hon Prog; *Pa St U; Computer Sci.*

POLAND, Stanley Eugene
Sam Houston HS; Arlington, TX (34-640) A Cap Choir; Band; Chor; Ger C; NHS; Rotary A; VFW A; *U of Tex; Computer Sci.*

POLAND, Toni Lee
Macon HS; Macon, IL (2-70) S-T, NHS; ARC; Rptr, Sch P; JV, Sftbl; Pres, MYF; Pep C; Coun On Ministries; *Millikin U; Forestry.*

POLCA, Cheryl Lynn
Midpark HS; Middleburg Heights, OH (25-500) Chor; NHS; Bio A; Hon Prog; Fundamentals of Writing A; HR.

POLCA, Cindy Lou
Midpark HS; Middleburg Heights, OH (35-600) Hon Prog; HR; *Vet.*

POLCYN, Barbara Jean
Corona HS; Corona, CA (20-568) A Cap Choir; Chor; Hmrm; Madrigal; NHS; Ski C; Amer Leg A; CSF; *Pasadena City Col.*

POLE, Gigi Louise
Notre Dame HS; Crowley, LA (2-120) Anchor C; BC; VP, CYO; Ch, Chor; GS; Rptr, SC; Alg A; 4H A; NEDT; Spch A; WW; *Clemson U; Ed.*

POLING, Bill Alan
Southeast HS; Bradenton, FL (20-246) Chess C; Hmrm; NHS; Co-Ed, Sch P; SC; Amer Leg A; Journ A; Q&S A; *Trevecca Nazarene Col; Communications.*

POLING, Cathy Sue
Windham HS; Windham, OH (5-120) Secy, Chor; VP, SC; Hon Prog; Librarian, Band; Band A; Choir A; *Ohio Valley Col; Mus.*

POLING, George Anton
Frankfort HS; Ridgeley, WV (5-151) Band; BS; Ensm; Tres, NHS; Tres, SC; Tnns; VofDEM; *W Va U; Mus Ed.*

POLIS, Gloria Jean
Struthers HS; Struthers, OH (9-275) NHS; NEDT; Type A; Pres, VP, Bus Off Ed C; Proficiency A, Bookkeeping; Outst Stu Cert, Bus Off Ed; 3rd Reg, 6th St, Gen Clerical; *Youngstown St Col; Off Mgr.*

POLITE, Georgetta
Savannah HS; Savannah, GA (64-371) BC; Bus C; FHA; Hmrm; SC; Up Bound; COM; MLS; Pres A; ROTC A; Sci A; ROTC Drill Tm; Reading A; Alpha Beta A; *Spelman Col; Bus Ed.*

POLIVKA, Richard Carl
Morton W HS; Berwyn, IL (50%-1200) Golf; Tnns; Tr; Bowl; St Bowl A; *Morton Jr Col; Engr.*

POLK, Brenda Denise
Columbia HS; Columbia, MS (14-170) Ann; Band; Drama; NHS; SC; Tnns; *U of Miss; Phar.*

POLK, Donna Louise
Kinston HS; Kinston, NC (10%-340) Ann; Secy, Dbte Tm; Secy, Fr C; Rptr, Sch P; Historian, Jr Tarheels; Yth Choir; VP, District CYF; Bellchoir; Co Cpt, Vikingnettes; *U of NC.*

POLK, Joyce Voncile
Skyline HS; Dallas, TX (12-850) Bus C; Chor; Drama; Secy, FHA; Bkbl; *E Tex St U; Bus Adm.*

POLK, Julie Marijean
Prescott HS; Prescott, AZ (15-390) CYO; Drama; InterAct C; Lat C; NHS; ARC; Spch C; Var C; Tnns; COM; Citz A; Hon Prog; ARC A; Hospital Auxillary; Lib Service A; YMCA Service A; *Stanford U; Computer Prog.*

POLK, Melanie Claire
Ed W Clark HS; Las Vegas, NV (18-815) F-Ed, Ann; Dbte Tm; Mu Alpha Theta; VP, NHS; Thes; Alg A; COM; Masonic A; Worthy Adv, Rainbow Girls; *Communications.*

POLK, Shelia Cherie
T R Miller HS; Brewton, AL (5-95) Sch P; Secy, SC; Tres, Jr Cl; Secy, Soph Cl; Hon Prog; *Gen Ed.*

POLK, William Lamar III
Starkville HS; Starkville, MS (25%-230) Ann; Band; FFA; Key C; VP, VICA; Dist & St VICA Ldrship Contest; *Miss St U; Horticulture.*

POLLACK, Eileen
Gloucester Cath HS; Gloucester, NJ (1-200) Ann; Chor; Mod Mus Mas; Ed, Sch P; Ld Play; Nom, NHS; *Social Work.*

POLLAR, Pamela Karen
John F Kennedy HS; New Orleans, LA; Band; BC; Rptr, Span NHS; Tri-HiY; Math A; *Loyola U; Pre-Law.*

POLLARD, Connie Suzanne
Snyder HS; Snyder, TX; 4H; Rptr, Jr Cl; Bkbl; Sftbl; Tr; 4H A; Type A; Yth Fel; Vlbl; *Baylor U; Acct.*

POLLARD, Curtis D
Peabody HS; Pittsburgh, PA (46-579) Chess C; Chor; Fr C; Bio A; Chem A; Hon Prog; Math A; Ntl Achv Schol; Opt A; Sal; St Scholar; Yth Fel; Chess Tourn; *MIT; Sci.*

POLLARD, Herbert L Jr
Pathfinder Regional Voc Tec HS; Palmer, MA; BS; Pres, FFA; Pres, 4H; JV, Bkbl; COM; 4H A; Dekalb Agr Research A; Dairy Judging Tour Jr Win; Green Thumb A; *Stockbridge Sch of Agr; Animal Sci.*

POLLARD, Mary Sue
Terrell Co HS; Dawson, GA (10%-112) BC; FBLA; FHA; HCt; *Fort Valley St Col; Bus Adm.*

POLLARD, Michael Irvin
Union Co HS; Morganfield, KY; Chor; Drama; Fr C; NFL; Pres, Thes; Spch A; Spch As, Trophies; Best Actor; One Act Play Contest; *Northwestern U; Drama.*

POLLARD, Michael LeVaughn
Locke HS; Los Angeles, CA; *U of Sou Calif; Elec.*

POLLARD, Steve Russell
Martin Co HS; Stuart, FL (50-500) Cpt, Band; BC; BS; Bsbl; *Indian River Comm Col; Math.*

POLLARD, Tanice Anita
N Fulton HS; Atlanta, GA (61-198) Chldr; FHA; Sch P; Span C; HCt; *Savannah St Col; Computer Prog.*

POLLARD, Wilton Scott
Pembroke HS; Hampton, VA (33%-383) A Cap Choir; Drama; Ensm; Key C; Order/Arrow; SC; Thes; Tr; Order/Arrow A; Eagle Sct; *Va Commonwealth U; Commercial Art.*

POLLEMA, Steven Craig
West Lyon Comm Sch; Inwood, IA (15-100) Chor; NHS; Ftbl; Tr; *U of N Iowa.*

POLLEY, Steven Earl
Oblong HS; Oblong, IL (1-82) Ann; Pres, Fr C; NHS; Ed, Sch P; Sci C; SC; Pres, Jr Cl; Eng A; Fr A; *Eastern Ill U; Physics.*

POLLEY, Suzanne Lorraine
Cumberland Valley HS; Mechanicsburg, PA (19-625) Chor; Tres, Fr C; NHS; COM; Hon Prog; NEDT; *Ohio St U; Special Ed.*

POLLEY, Tammy Ann
Alsea HS; Alsea, OR (1-30) Chldr; Chor; NHS; Secy, Soph Cl; Sci A; *Linn Benton Col.*

POLLEY, Terri Lynn
Alsea HS; Alsea, OR (1-20) Ann; Lit Mag; NHS; Sch P.

POLLINA, Susan Mary
Collegiate Sch; Passaic, NJ (2-23) Chldr; NHS; Sci C; Span C; SC; Co-Cpt, Sftbl; Tnns; COM; DARGCA; Hon Prog; Most Out; Vlbl; WW; *Col of St Elizabeth; Med.*

POLLMANN, David Lee
Valmeyer HS; Valmeyer, IL (4-46) Chor; Math C; NHS; SC; Bkbl; Math A; *Purdue U; Elec Engr.*

POLLOCK, Curt John
Reeds Spring HS; Reeds Spring, MO (10%-80) Band; Chor; Order/Arrow; ARC; Ski C; Secy, SC; Bsbl; Tr; Order/Arrow A; ARC A; Eagle Sct; *Oral Roberts U; Journ.*

POLLOCK, David Garnet
Mullens HS; Mullens, WV (1-115) BC; Chess C; HiY; Hmrm; NHS; JV, Ftbl; Hon Prog; Math A; MLS; Val; *VPI; Engr.*

POLLOCK, Deborah Kathryn
Mullens HS; Mullens, WV; BC; Chess C; HiY; Alg A; Hist A.

POLLOCK, Deborah Lee
Nathan Hale HS; Seattle, WA (23%-488) Hmrm; NHS; Acct Statement of Proficiency; *Seattle Pacific U; Nurs.*

POLLOCK, Julie Elizabeth
Carter HS; Knoxville, TN (8-310) Tres, FHA; GS; NHS; Ed, Sch P; V-Cht, SC; Bkbl; MVP, Tr; *U of Tenn; Communications.*

POLLOCK, Paula Kay
E Hills HS; Fort Worth, TX; Pres, Chor; Fr C; Rainbow; Pres, SC; Bsbl; Hon Prog; Pres A; Phys Fitness A; *Tex A&M U; Archt.*

POLLOCK, Phillip Dee
Parkrose Sr HS; Portland, OR (152-398) Chor; Var C; Golf; Tr; Order/Arrow A; Gym; Phys Fitness; All-Amer, Vault Gym; Oreg St Vault S; *U of Wash; Sci.*

POLLOCK, Theresa Ann
Irvin HS; El Paso, TX (50%-630) Band; CYO.

POLOWY, Marlene Jeanne
New Bloomfield HS; New Bloomfield, MO; Ann; Pres, Fr C; NHS; Rptr, Sch P; Bkbl; *William Woods Col; Eng.*

POLSEAN, Jill Mary
Freeport Sr HS; Freeport, IL (156-558) Citz A; Choir; Company Comm; Awana Leader; Sextet; Taught, Back Yard Bible C; Quiz Tm.

POLSON, Cheryl Marthelen
Columbus Sr HS; Columbus, NE (33%-250) AFS; F-Ed, Ann; Band; Chor; Demolay; Orch; Sch P; Span C; Tres, St Stu Congres; Pres, SC; Tnns; Tr; Citz A; Elk A; Masonic A; Opt Out Tn; Q&S A; Vlbl; Superior, District Mus; Mus As; Athletic As; Young Nebr; *Cotley Col; Child Psych.*

POLSON, Jan Marie
Texhoma HS; Texhoma, OK; Chldr; NHS; VP, Jr Cl; S-T, Soph Cl; Mgr, Bkbl; Cl Fav; *Panhandle St U; Acct.*

POLSON, Lori Kay
Texhoma HS; Texhoma, OK; Pres, Band; Chor; Ensm; Mjrte; VP, NHS; Co-Ed, Sch P; Bkbl; Tr; Alg A; Cl Fav; HQn; Math A; Regent Schol; Sal; Yth Fel; Pres, Pep C; Bicentennial Girl; Pres Clrm Sem; Aggie Princess Pageant; *Okla St U; Acct.*

POLZIEN, Julie Ann
Ardmore HS; Ardmore, OK (30-280) Band; Semi-Fin, GS; Math C; Mu Alpha Theta; NHS; Sci C; SC; Type A; Yth Fel; Cand, Band Qn; *Okla St U; Bus Adm.*

POLZIN, Priscilla Kay
Shawano HS; Shawano, WI (8-250) A Cap Choir; FHA; NHS; JV, Golf; JV, Tr; *U of Wis; Acct.*

POLZIN, Timothy Frank
Luverne HS; Luverne, MN (33-138) Rptr, A Cap Choir; Band; Rptr, Chor; Madrigal; SC; Bsbl; Bkbl; Ftbl; Cpt, Golf; MPV, Golf; All St Band; *Bemidjii St U; Mus.*

POMMER, Jeannie Lynn
Central Comm HS; Breese, IL (2-157) Ann; FHA; Secy, Math C; Sal; St Scholar.

POMPEO, Frank Louis
St Peters Prep Sch; Jersey City, NJ (12-250) Band; Orch; Hon Prog; Span A; Band Signal Service A; *Steven's Tech Col; Chem.*

POMPILI, Karen Ann
Cardinal Mooney HS; Youngstown, OH (108-307) Ed, Ann; Band; CYO; Lat C; Orch; Sodality; Hon Prog; *Youngstown St U; Nurs.*

POMROY, Katherine Ann
Park Center Sr HS; Brooklyn Park, MN (65%-648) Band; Ensm; Fr C; Semi-Fin, GS; Orch; Co-Ed, Sch P; Hon Prog; Yth Fel; Mgr, Danceline; All-St Band; Summer Hon Prog, Talented Musicians; *St Olaf Col; Journ.*

POMYKAL, Melenda Melea
Troy HS; Troy, TX (11-46) A-Ed, Ann; Band; BC; FHA; 4H; JV, Bkbl; Tr; St Competition, Piano; 1st St, Beta C Talent Tm; Grand Champ, Jr Fair & Livestock; *Tarleton Jr Col; Drama.*

PONCE, Patrick Ridge
Vanguard HS; Ocala, FL (13-350) CYO; Hmrm; Secy, Mu Alpha Theta; NHS; Bsbl; Bkbl; Golf; Most Out; Sci A; *U of Fla; Bus.*

PONCE de LEON, Linda Cristal
Goddard HS; Roswell, NM (23-310) Chor; Hmrm; NHS; Span C; Secy, Span NHS; SC; Mgr, Tr; Stenographic A; Span Hon Soc Cert; Chor Cert & Medal; Tr Ltr; *Eastern NM U at Roswell; Bus Adm.*

POND, Alan Wayne
Liberty Comm Unit Dist 2 HS; Liberty, IL (10-46) Ensm; NHS; Sci C; VP, Var C; Bsbl; Bkbl; MVP, Tr; Cpt, Tr Tm; SAA; *Bradley U; Elec Engr.*

POND, Stanley Ray
Robert E Lee HS; Midland, TX (343-632) Mgr, Bkbl; *E Tex Baptist Col; Acct.*

POND, Steven Roy
Robert E Lee HS; Midland, TX (373-632) Mgr, Bkbl; *E Tex Baptist Col.*

PONDER, Bonnie Joan
Petaluma HS; Petaluma, CA; Chor; Rptr, Sch P; Ski C; Span C; CSF; *La Jr Col; Eng.*

PONDER, Debra Karlene
Bibb Co HS; Centreville, AL (20-112) VP, Anchor C; Ann; Band; Chem C; Mjrte; Secy, Soph Cl; Band Ltr.

PONDER, Janice Lynn
Hendersonville HS; Hendersonville, NC (5-172) Ann; Band; Drama; Fr C; Hmrm; Fin, Jr Miss Pagent; Mjrte; NHS; ARC; Secy, SC; Secy, Thes; COM; Hon Prog; Hon Block Graduate; SC St Workshop Counselor; Loc Jr Ms Pagent Poise Ap Yth Ft Wn; *U of NC; Phys Therapy.*

PONDER, Jo Ann
Kirksville Sr HS; Kirksville, MO (27-232) A Cap Choir; Bus Mgr, Ann; Chor; Secy, Drama; FTA; Secy, Hmrm; ARC; Pres, Thes; COM; Hon Prog; ARC A; Regent Schol; Type A; Nom, Com, Betrmnt For Yth Ldrship; *NE Mo St U; Mus Ed.*

PONDER, Terry Lamar Jr
Lafayette HS; Lafayette, LA (33%-500) Hmrm; Key C; Cpt, Swim; NEDT; Photographer, Yrbk; *La Tech; Engr.*

PONDER, Thomas Brady
Los Alamos HS; Los Alamos, NM (4-445) Band; Mgr, Bkbl; Tnns; COM; Math A; Yth Fel; Yth Del, Church; Mus A; Comm Band; *NM St U; Dentistry.*

PONS, Patricia Louise
Brandon HS; Brandon, FL; Chor; *Hillsbourgh Col; Bus.*

PONT, Carmen Ana
Santa Rita HS; Bayamon, PR (1-33) Chor; NHS; Pres, SC; Tnns; COM; Excellence A; Principals A; *U of Puerto Rico; Pre-Med.*

PONTIA, Jeanette Leigh
Buckeye S HS; Tiltonsville, OH (3-150) Band; Cpt, Chldr; Dbte Tm; Hmrm; Pres, NHS; Sch Achieve Tm; Spch C; SC; Y-Tns; Alg A; H of F; HCt; Hon Prog; MLS; VofDEM; Tn o-t Wk; Essay A; *W Liberty Col; Math.*

PONTIER, Rose Mary
Nitro HS; Nitro, WV (25-310) Chor; Drama; GS; VP, Hmrm; Model UN; ARC; Sci C; Span C; SC; Thes; Bkbl; Tr; Amer Leg A; *Berea Col.*

PONTIOUS, Kristy Kaye
Nathan Hale HS; Tulsa, OK (27-800) NHS; Hon Prog; St Mus A; *Okla St U; Math.*

PONTIUS, James Ernest
Parkway HS; Rockford, OH (20-87) Co-Ed, Ann; Band; BS; Chor; Demolay; Ensm; VP, Span C; SC; Var C; Bkbl; Cr-Ctry; Mgr, Ftbl; Pres, FCA; Superior, Trumpet Ensm; *Journ.*

PONTIUS, Jon Brewster
Niskayuna HS; Schenectady, NY (40%-450) Ann; Band; Ensm; Order/Arrow; Rptr, Sch P; Soccer; Order/Arrow A; *Siena Col; Bus Adm.*

PONTIUS, Kristina Marie
Federal Way HS; Federal Way, WA; Chor; NHS; Var C; Swim; Hon Prog; NEDT; Co-Cpt, Swim C; Inspirational A; Swimmer o-t Yr; Personal Best A; Most Outst Achv, Home Ec, Phys Ed; *Whitworth Col; Sports Med.*

PONTNACK, Lori Elizabeth
Ashton Westview HS; Ashton, IL (12-56) Chldr; Chor; VP, FHA; NHS; SC; Var C; Pres, Jr Cl; Secy, Soph Cl; Tr; Hon Prog; *Oral Roberts U; Psych.*

POOL, Bobbi Faye
Lyon Co HS; Eddyville, KY (11-70) Band; Secy, BC; Chor; Ensm; VP, FHA; 4H; NHS; Rptr, Sch P; Spch C; SC; 4H A; Parl, FHA; *Murray St U.*

POOL, Joe Curtis
Bryan Adams HS; Dallas, TX (35-800) Pres, Key C; Lat C; VP, NHS; Order/Arrow; SC; Cr-Ctry; Cpt, Ftbl; Cpt, Tr; COM; Citz A; Cl Fav; God & Country A; Hon Prog; Kiwanis A; Most Out; Order/Arrow A; PTA A; Yth Fel; Young Life; Tutoring Prog; WW; Sadie Hawkins Kg; *Southwestern U; Lib Arts.*

POOL, Sylvia Jean
Northwest HS; St Louis, MO; *Hickey Sch of Bus; Secretarial.*

POOLE, Alice Jean
Simon Gratz HS; Philadelphia, PA (4-450) Chldr; FBLA; Tres, Hmrm; Pres, Mjrte; NHS; VP, Sr Cl; Sftbl; Ntl Sci Found; Sci A; Yth Fel; Yth Foundation A; Yth Leg; *U of Pittsburgh; Bs Nurs.*

POOLE, Dana Lloyd
Warren HS; Monmouth, IL (30-60) A Cap Choir; Band; Chor; Math C; Var C; Y-Tns; Bkbl; Cr-Ctry; Ftbl; Soccer; MVP, Sftbl; Tr; Wrest; Yth Fel; *Carl Sandburg Col; Building Trades.*

POOLE, Ellen Kennedy
Yorktown Sr HS; Arlington, VA; Chess C; Chor; Sftbl; Tr; Bio A; Sci A; *Westminster U; Special Ed.*

POOLE, Ellen Margaret
Ralph L Fike HS; Wilson, NC; Rptr, Hmrm; Rainbow; Rptr, SC; JV, Bkbl; JV, Sftbl; JV, Tr; Citz A; DARGCA; Most Out; *NC St U; Bio.*

POOLE, Felecia Michelle
Southwestern HS; Detroit, MI; Chor; F-Ed, Sch P; Bus Ed A; *Saginaw Val St; Nurs.*

POOLE, Jacquelyn Cecelia
Eastwood HS; El Paso, TX; FHA; Semi-Fin, Hmrm; Beauty; Delta Sigma Theta A; HCt; Lion A; OEA; DECA; *U of Houston; Bus.*

POOLE, Keith Lavern
Winyah HS; Georgetown, SC (30-128) Chess C; Phys C; Sci C; JV, Ftbl; God & Country A; Phy A; *U of SC; Chem.*

POOLE, Kevin Carl
West HS; Madison, WI (25%-700) Ski C; Span C; Ftbl; *U of Wisc; Med Tech.*

POOLE, Nathan Stan
Jena HS; Jena, LA (1-128) MVP, Band; BS; Rptr, Drama; Lit Ral; NHS; A-Ed, Sch P; Hon Prog; Masque & Gavel A; Val; VofDEM; Gen Mills Family Ldr of Tomorrow; *La Col; Speech Ed.*

POOLE, Peter Knox
Brunswick HS; Brunswick, GA (41-420) Band; BS; Chess C; Ensm; Hmrm; NHS; Sci C; SC; Tnns; COM; *St Andrews Presbyterian Col; Sci.*

POOLE, Ranae Louise
Winnebago HS; Winnebago, MN; Band; Chor; *Rocester Voc Tech Inst; Nurs.*

POOLE, Regina Renae
Century HS; Ullin, IL (3-64) Secy, BC; Co-Cpt, Chldr; FHA; 4H; Span C; SC; HCt; Swtht; Driver Ed A; *Off Work.*

POOLE, Robert Neil
Woodward Acad; College Park, GA (20-215) Order/Arrow; Sch P; Cr-Ctry; Hon Prog; NEDT; Jr Civitan; Silver Eagle A; Star Sct; *Forestry.*

POOLE, Sharon Marie
Central HS; Crookston, MN (9-189) A Cap Choir; Ann; Chor; Spch C; COM; Spch A; Active Christian Tns; Annual A; *Minot St Col; Ed.*

POOLE, Tamsie Marie
C H Darden Jr HS; Wilson, NC (25%-540) FHA; NHS; JV, Sftbl; Swim; Hist A; Ntl Piano Auditions; Church Yth Coun.

POOLE, Valerie Estelle
Surry HS; Dendron, VA (10-125) Band; Chldr; Secy, Drama; Secy, 4H; NHS; Rptr, Sch P; Secy, Span C; Secy, Soph Cl; Citz A; Journ A; *Va Union Col; Fashion Designer.*

POOLE, Venita Darlene
Anna-Jonesboro Comm HS; Anna, IL; FHA; Span C; *Cape Bus Col; Secy.*

POOR, Kimberely Teresa
Farmington HS; Farmington, NM; Chldr.

POORE, William Arthur
Arapahoe HS; Littleton, CO (25%-600) Chor; Ensm; ARC; JV, Bsbl; JV, Soccer; Most Out; ARC A; Star Student; Yth Fel; *Med.*

POPE, Benjamin James
Ripley HS; Ripley, TN (44-310) BC; Var C; Bsbl; Ftbl; Tr.

POPE, Charles Brian
North HS; Nashville, TN; SC; Bsbl; Bkbl; Ftbl; Tr; Alg A; Bio A; Swtht.

POPE, David John
Mission HS; St Ignatius, MT (5-32) Band; CYO; Drama; 4H; Hmrm; VP, SC; Pres, Sr Cl; Bsbl; Bkbl; Co-Cpt, Ftbl; Tr; 4H A; Type A; WW; *Carroll Col; Vet Med.*

POPE, Donald Ray
Hanceville HS; Hanceville, AL; Ann; FTA; NHS.

POPE, Dora Lynn
Grand Ridge Sch; Grand Ridge, FL (9-49) F-Ed, Ann; Tres, BC; Cpt, Chldr; Chor; FFA; VP, Jr Cl; Tres, Soph Cl; Sftbl; Cl Fav; MVP, Vlbl; Chor A; *Chipola Jr Col; Chem.*

POPE, Harold Andre
Christian Brothers Acad; Albany, NY (79-105) VP, 4H; Bsbl; Bkbl; Ftbl; Sftbl; Tr; 4H A; Hon Prog; *Farmingdale Ag Tech Col; Aerospace.*

POPE, Harriet Joy
Independence HS; Coldwater, MS (15%-106) BC; Chldr; FHA.

POPE, Jerry E
E Atlanta HS; Atlanta, GA (12-142) Span C; Pres, SC; Ftbl; Cpt, Soccer; *Morehouse Col; Engr.*

POPE, Kay Ann
Cedar Shoals HS; Athens, GA (50%-425) 4H; Span C; Tnns; 4H A; Jr Civitan C; *U of Ga; Sci.*

POPE, Lisa Michelle
Cardozo HS; Washington, DC (1-750) Chem C; CSF; COM; Pres A; Fr Plaque; PA; Highest Soph Avg; *Bradford Col; Pediatrician.*

POPE, Lori Sue
N Salinas HS; Salinas, CA (10%-400) AFS; Bus C; Chess C; Pres, FBLA; Ger C; Hmrm; NHS; Ski C; SC; CSF; Chem A; Type A; Secy, Backpacking C; Candystriper; Gym; Best Speller; Best Counselor For Retarded; *Hartnell Jr Col; Special Ed.*

POPE, Lyndon Dion
Inglewood HS; Inglewood, CA; Ed, Ann; Var C; Co-Cpt, Ftbl; Co-Cpt, Tr; PTA A; Stu o-t Mo; *Acct.*

POPE, Marilyn Lynn
Quitman HS; Quitman, MS (2-150) Ann; Band; BC; Chldr; Sch P; Span C; Pres, SC; Secy, Tri-HiY; Alg A; Beauty; COM; H of F; Hist A; Hon Prog; I Dare You; Math A; MLS; Sal; Sci A; Miss AHS; Senate Page; Co-Pres, SC; *U of Sou Miss; Acct.*

POPE, Patty Helen
Shawnee Mission Nw HS; Shawnee Mission, KS (70-740) Pres, CYO; Hmrm; NHS; Sci C; Pres, SC; Thes; Mgr, Cr-Ctry; Mgr, Sftbl; Tr; Bio A; COM; Citz A; Cl Fav; DARGCA; Sci A; Qn of Courts; Prom Personality Court; Conservation A; *Johnson Co Jr Col; Agr.*

POPE, Rae Ann
Cooper HS; New Hope, MN (390-732) Sftbl; Hon Prog; ARC A; Co Vol A; *Bethel Col; Psych.*

POPE, Reginald Sylvester
Kashmere Sr HS; Houston, TX; FHA; Cpt, Bkbl; ROTC A; *Tex A&M; Data Processing.*

POPE, Stuart L
Cowan HS; Muncie, IN (1-92) Chem C; Order/Arrow; VP, Span C; Mgr, Bkbl; JV, Golf; God & Country A; Order/Arrow A; Skill Bowl Tm; Eagle Sct; *Purdue U.*

POPEK, Diane
South HS; Omaha, NE (10%-550) Ann; Band; NHS; Orch; Tr; COM; Hon Prog; FOE Recognition; Pres, Yth Fel.

POPENFOOSE, Joel Dee
Wawasee HS; Syracuse, IN (59-293) VP, Chor; Drama; Madrigal; Var C; MVP, Ftbl; Tr; HCt; Pres, FCA; V Singers; *Butler U; Mus Ed.*

POPOVICH, Annette Kathleen
Bowman HS; Canyon Country, CA; *COC; Art.*

POPP, Kathryn Jane
Fairport Harding HS; Fairport Harbor, OH (12-56) Pres, Fr C; Semi-Fin, GS; NHS; Bus Mgr, Jr Cl; Secy, GAA; Secy, Yth Fel; *Cleveland St U; Bus Adm.*

POPPE, Maria Emma
Perkins Co HS; Grant, NE (5-36) Band; Chldr; Chor; Tres, 4H; Bkbl; Sftbl.

POPPE, Molly Ann
Tecumseh Sr HS; Tecumseh, MI (7-263) Band; NHS; ARC; VP, Span C; I Dare You; Schol, Medical Careers C; *Mich St U; Vet Med.*

POPPE, Zada Mae
LaKota Cons HS; Lakota, IA (4-20) Ann; Band; Bus C; Drama; Sch P; Secy, Sr Cl; Chor; Mgr, Bkbl; Mgr, Tr; HCt; Journ A; Type A; Mus A; *Waldorf Col; Social Services.*

POPPENS, Alexander Charles
Princeton HS; Princeton, IL (96-175) Lat C; Tnns; Cl Off; *U of Colo; Forestry.*

POPPENS, Anthony John
Aplington HS; Aplington, IA (10-45) Band; Chor; Rptr, FFA; JV, Bkbl; Golf; FCA; Record Book Proficiency A; *Hawkeye Tech Col; Animal Sci.*

POPPKE, Theodore Thomas
Bismarck HS; Bismarck, ND (8-435) Band; VP, Lat C; NHS; VP, Order/Arrow; Pres, Sci C; Mgr, Wrest; NMF; NMS; Eagle Sct; Fin, Inter-Ntl Sci Fair; *U of ND; Med.*

POQUETTE, Rita Marie
University of San Diego HS; San Diego, CA (25-311) Cum Laude Soc; NHS; CSF; Vlbl; Point Loma Col; Nurs.*

PORCELLIO, Nancy Jean
Mount Mercy Acad; Buffalo, NY (8-220) Band; Pres, Math C; Pres, NHS; A-Ed, Sch P; NEDT; Q&S A; Regent Schol; *U of Rochester; Physiological Psych.*

PORGES, Janet Ruth
Harold L Richards HS; Oak Lawn, IL (6-1045) Chor; Pres, Fr C; Hmrm; Math C; VP, Mu Alpha Theta; VP, NHS; Sci C; Spch C; COM; Hon Prog; St Scholar; Ed, Church Newspaper; Badminton; *Ill Wesleyan U; Bus Adm.*

PORMAN, Tamela Lynne
Fenton Sr HS; Fenton, MI (208-280) A Cap Choir; Fr C; *Alma Col; Child Development.*

PORTA, Tracy Sue
Riverside HS; Dearborn Heights, MI; Band; Fr C; Hmrm; NHS; Var C; Swim; Mus, Health, Church, A's; *U of Mich; Med.*

PORTALIS, Richard Charles
Lafayette HS; Lafayette, LA (10-23) Chor; Dbte Tm; 4H; Spch C; Bsbl; Bkbl; Ftbl; 4H A; *USL; Law.*

PORTER, April Denise
Martin Luther King Acad; Gary, IN (3-50) Bus Mgr, Bus C; Chor; Rptr, Sch P; VP, SC; Mus A; *Purdue U; Nurs.*

PORTER, Charles Donald Jr
Churchland HS; Portsmouth, VA (75-240) Chor; Drama; Ensm; COM; NMS; Pres, Church Yth; All Region, All St, Chor; *Old Dominion U; Mus Ed.*

PORTER, Charles Gregory
Elmer H Gaviner HS; Charlotte, NC (23-626) Band; Fr C; Hmrm; InterClub Coun; Key C; NHS; Orch; Rptr, Sch P; Pres, Ski C; SC; Tr; Journ A; Attendance A; NHS Schol; NMSC Ltr of Commendation; TV Schol o-t Month; *NC at CH; Chem.*

PORTER, Debra Charlette
Rowan HS; Hattiesburg, MS (5%-500) Band; Fr C; *Howard U; Psychiatry.*

PORTER, Debra Kim
Pittsburg HS; Pittsburg, KS (22-260) Band; Hmrm; NHS; SC; Tnns; Tr; Bio A; Sci A; *Pre-Med.*

PORTER, Derwin Darnell
Independence HS; Charlotte, NC (100-650) Key C; Monogram; Bsbl; Ftbl; *Wingate Col; Bus Adm.*

PORTER, Dianna Elizabeth
James A Shanks HS; Quincy, FL (10%-397) Ann; NHS; Q&S A; Sci A; Yth Fel; Academic Achv A; WW in Span; Span HR; 1st Pl, Regional Sci Fair; *Med.*

PORTER, Douglas Rayford
Plant City HS; Plant City, FL (15%-600) Ann; Band; Co-Ch, Model UN; Orch; ARC; UN Council; Cr-Ctry; Swim; *Hillsborough Comm Col; Bus.*

PORTER, Eileen Marie
Alcee Fortier HS; New Orleans, LA; FBLA; Hmrm; NHS; Swim; VP, Yth Group; Spelling A; Open Door C; *Dillard Col; Secy.*

PORTER, Eric Gene
Waseca HS; Waseca, MN (17-198) Span C; Bsbl; Bkbl; Ftbl; *Engr.*

PORTER, James Robert
Highlands HS; Natrona Heights, PA (20-420) Order/Arrow; Hon Prog; Order/Arrow A; Yth Fel; Jr NHS; Eagle Sct; Schol Achv; YMCA; *Westminster Col; Bus Mgt.*

PORTER, Jean E
Bellmont HS; Decatur, IN (19-267) Chldr; Chor; Fr C; GS; NHS; Spch C; SC; Var C; Pres, Span Cl; Sunshine Soc; Gym; *International Bus Col; Fashion Merchandising.*

PORTER, Jeanne Ann
Ross S Sterling HS; Baytown, TX (10%-600) Bus Mgr, Ann; Band; NHS; Yth Fel; Vlbl; Eng A; Soc Stu A; Outst Schol Achv A; *Law.*

PORTER, Jed Ira
Marist Brother's HS; Pago Pago, AMERICAN SAMOA (3-50) Dbte Tm; Spch C; COM; Hon Prog; Math A; Sci A; *Pepperdine U; Bus.*

PORTER, Joanie Carol
J O Johnson HS; Huntsville, AL; Future Secy's of Amer; Media C; Secy, Christ Ambassador; *N Ala Bus Col; Bus.*

PORTER, Joe Martin
Trinity HS; Louisville, KY (20%-250) CYO; Fr C; Tr; Hon Prog; NEDT; Cert of A, Art Contest; Cert d'honneur; Concours Ntl de Francais; *Pre-Law.*

PORTER, John David
S Albany HS; Albany, OR (10-280) Bus C; FBLA; Bkbl; JV, Tr; Masonic A; 1st Pl, FBLA Dist Data Processing; 3rd Pl, FBLA Dist Acct; HR; *Oreg St U; Bus Adm.*

PORTER, John Erwin
Baptist Acad; Grand Rapids, MI (12-40) Ann; Hmrm; Pres, SC; Var C; Bsbl; Bkbl; Soccer; HCt; *Taylor Col; Med.*

PORTER, Katherine Arnette
West HS; Denver, CO; A Cap Choir; Chor; City Conf; Drama; Ensm; Madrigal; St Stu Congress; Pres, SC; Thes; Pres, Sr Cl; Pres, Jr Cl; VP, Soph Cl; COM; Citz A; Cl Fav; HCt; Kiwanis A; ROTC A; Prom Qn; Most Friendly; *Tex Sou U; Mus.*

PORTER, Kathy Ann
Lawrence HS; Lawrence, KS (15-650) Band; Secy, Ger C; Key C; Hon Prog; *Kans U; Computer Sci.*

PORTER, Kelly Faith
Owen J Roberts HS; Pottstown, PA; Bus C; Chor; Arch; MVP, Hockey; Swim; Tr; Yth Fel; Tr Ribbons; *Vet.*

PORTER, Kern Lane
Orleans HS; Orleans, NE; Band; JV, Bkbl; Church Choir; *Agr.*

PORTER, Kirk Dell
Bethany HS; Reidsville, NC (4-60) Ann; BC; Fr C; FFA; Bkbl; C; Monogram; Forestry, Chapter, Greenhand, A's; *NC St U; Agr.*

PORTER, Lianne Lorraine
Los Alamitos HS; Los Alamitos, CA (30-700) A Cap Choir; Chor; Ensm; Ger C; Madrigal; NHS; Bank Of Amer A; CSF; Home Ec A; Fin, Miss Teenage Amer; Valentine Princess; Pres, Church Yth Board; *Point Coma Col; Social Sci.*

PORTER, Martin Wesley
New Bern HS; New Bern, NC (130-450) Ann; Hmrm; Span C; JV, Bkbl; Cr-Crtry; Tr; NEDT; Tres, Tri-Chi; *E Carolina U; Bus Adm.*

PORTER, Mary Kay
Burroughs HS; Ridgecrest, CA (10-413) AFS; Band; Fr C; Var C; Cpt, Swim; CSF; CIF Relay Fin; *Seattle Pacific Col; Bus.*

PORTER, Myra Dawn
Mona Shores HS; Muskegon, MI; Citz A; Sci A; Type A; Cooking A; *Hackley Sch of Nurs; Nurs.*

PORTER, Peter Bennett
Alcoa HS; Alcoa, TN (15-110) Band; Ch, Hmrm; Key C; NHS; Spch C; JV, Ftbl; Cl Fav; Photographer, Sch P; *Tenn Tech U; Plant and Soil Sci.*

PORTER, Randall
Shannon HS; Shannon, MS (10%-185) Chess C; Math C; Phys C; Mgr, Ftbl; Tr; *Delta St U; Ed.*

PORTER, Raymond Anderson
Spearman HS; Spearman, TX (1-84) Tres, FFA; Pres, NHS; Span C; Co-Cpt, Bkbl; Tnns; Alg A; Bio A; Phy A; Val; NML; *Wheaton Col; Sci.*

PORTER, Rena Marleen
Palo Duro HS; Amarillo, TX (120-285) A-Ed, Ann; Bus C; Drama; FBLA; Blue Ribbons, Tri-St Fair Cooking; *Amarillo Col; Mus.*

PORTER, Rhonda Gail
Fayetteville HS; Fayetteville, AR (221-352) AFS; Fr C; FHA; FTA; Sci C; Pep C; *Harding Christian Col; Elem Ed.*

PORTER, Robbie LaNiece
Crockett HS; Crockett, TX (10%-140) Secy, FHA; Tres, SC; HCt; Most Out; Eng A; Homemaking A; *Rice U.*

PORTER, Robert Glynn
Thomasville Sr HS; Thomasville, NC (10-250) Band; Chor; Fr C; NHS; Orch; Phys C; Var C; JV, Bkbl; JV, Ftbl; MVP, Golf; JV, Tnns; Hon Prog; ROTC A; Morehead Nom; ROTC Schol; *U of Notre Dame; Engr.*

PORTER, Sandra Denise
Northwest HS; St Louis, MO (2-433) Fr C; NHS; Curator A; HQn; Spch A; Type A; Yth Foundation A; *U of Mo; Bus Adm.*

PORTER, Scott Carter
Purcell HS; Cincinnati, OH; *U of Cincinnati.*

PORTER, Sharon Denise
Hopkinsville HS; Hopkinsville, KY; *W Ky U; Home Ec.*

PORTER, Sharon Gaye
Sooner HS; Bartlesville, OK; AFS; Band; NHS; COM; Hon Prog; Yth Fel; Drum Major; VP, Da Capo Mus C; Flag Tm; Shorthand A; Candystriper; Girls Service C; *Okla St U; Acct.*

PORTER, Thomas Josh
Avondale HS; Avondale Estates, GA; Hmrm; ARC; Span C; SC; JV, Bkbl; Ftbl; Tr; *Ga Tech; Bus.*

PORTER, Valerie Sue
S Albany HS; Albany, OR (24-274) Secy, FBLA; 4H; NHS; Tres, Span C; SC; Citz A; Masonic A; WW; FBLA, Shorthand, A's; Span, Russian, A's; *Linn Benton Comm Col; Secy.*

PORTERFIELD, Daniel Ryan
Loyola HS; Towson, MD; CYO; JV, Bsbl; JV, Cr-Ctry; NEDT.

PORTERFIELD, Lisa Kay
Sunset HS; Dallas, TX (25%-450) Chor; Drama; Ensm; Lat C; Rainbow; Hon Prog; Fin, Col Piano Auditions; Young Life; Top Rating, Ntl Piano Guild Aud; *Tex Tech U; Mus Theater.*

PORTERFIELD, Lori Ann
Pleasant HS; Marion, OH (11-150) Ann; Band; Chldr; Chor; Drama; Ensm; Pres, Fr C; NHS; Tr; Chem A; Q&S A; ARC A; Yth Fel; WW; Fr A; U for Young Amers; *Bowling Green St U; Spch & Hearing Therapy.*

PORTICE, Elden Webster
Benton Harbor HS; Benton Harbor, MI (7-450) A Cap Choir; Band; Chor; Pres, Ensm; Key C; Madrigal; Math C; Mu Alpha Theta; NHS; St Scholar; NML; Rotarian Mus Schol; *Anderson Col; Mus.*

PORTIER, Patty Anne
Landmark Christian Sch; Cincinnati, OH (3-60) A-Ed, Ann; COM; Bible A; Quiz Tm A; Camper o-t Wk A; *Teaching.*

PORTUONDO, Gloria Maria
Academia Maria Reina; Rio Piedras, PR (3-58) CYO; Chldr; Drama; Pres, Fr C; Pres, French NHS; Secy, NFL; NHS; SC; VP, Jr Cl; VP, Soph Cl; COM; Hon Prog; NEDT; Spch A; Bowl; PA; First, Second Hons; *U of Puerto Rico; Econ.*

PORTWOOD, Leesa Louise
Southside HS; Gadsden, AL (50-200) Chem C; Fr C; FHA; 4H; HiY; Jr Miss Pageant; VP, Math C; Sci C; 4H A; *U of Ala.*

PORUSH, Larry
El Camino Real HS; Woodland Hills, CA; Band; Hmrm; Ski C; Director, SC; *Stanford U; Law.*

POSEY, Bebe Teresa
Woodward Acad; College Park, GA (51-175) Key C; Secy, Bkbl; Soccer; Sftbl; Swim; Tnns; DARGCA; Kiwanis A; Yth Fel; FCA; Bus Ministry; *Ga Sou Col; Lib Sci.*

POSEY, Bridget R
Serramonte HS; Daly City, CA; Dbte Tm; Bkbl; *San Meteo Col; Computer Operater.*

POSEY, Janet Christine
Circleville HS; Circleville, OH; Band; Chor; Ensm; Rainbow; Bus Ministry; 2nd, Dist Comp; *Mus.*

POSEY, Jenny Lea
Channelview HS; Channelview, TX (10%-320) A Cap Choir; Ensm; Madrigal; Cl Fav; 1 Rating, 1st Div Singing Ensm.

POSEY, Julie Johnette
Southwood HS; Shreveport, LA; Orch; Sch P; Sftbl; COM; ARC A; *North East Col; Phar.*

POSEY, Kathy Sue
Channelview HS; Channelview, TX (10%-193) A Cap Choir; Chldr; Ensm; NHS; SC; Pres, Jr Cl; Pres, Soph Cl; Tr; Cl Fav; Hon Prog; 1 Rating, 1st Div Singing Ensm.

POSEY, Kenneth Richard
Channelview HS; Channelview, TX (30-254) Parl, A Cap Choir; Chor; Drama; Ensm; FTA; Madrigal; Thes; Most Out; All Region, All Area Choir; Pres, MYF; *Sacred Mus.*

POSEY, Robert Patrick
Kingsway Regional HS; Swedesboro, NJ (6-163) Band; Fr C; Key C; NHS; Sci C; Co-Ed, Sch P; COM; *Fairleigh Dickinson U; Biochem.*

POSEY, Roxie Jean
Dolores Co HS; Dove Creek, CO (1-38) Band; VP, NHS; Pres, Sci C; Cpt, Bkbl; Chem A; Masonic A; Outst Fresh Band; Directors A; Presidential Phys Fitness A; *Colo St U; Plant Sci.*

POSKEY, Michael Anthony
Nederland HS; Nederland, TX; CYO; Arch; Bsbl; JV, Ftbl; *Tex A&M U; Engr.*

POSPISIL, Sandra Jean
Flatonia HS; Flatonia, TX (6-39) Ann; Band; Pres, FHA; GS; Rptr, Sch P; SC; Tres, Sr Cl; Tres, Jr Cl; Tnns; Tr; Cl Fav; HQn.

POSSON, Steve Kenyon
Tuscaloosa Acad; Tuscaloosa, AL (1-25) Key C; Pres, NHS; SC; Bkbl; Tnns; Math A; Sci A; Val; Faculty A; Board of Trustee A; Sr Schol A; *U of Ala; Physics.*

POSSON, Steven Kenyon
Tuscaloosa Acad; Tuscaloosa, AL (1-25) Key C; Pres, NHS; SC; Var C; Bkbl; Tnns; Hon Prog; Math A; Sci A; Val; Faculty A; Board of Trustees A; Sr Schol A; *U of Ala; Geology.*

POST, Bradley Alan
Sutter Union HS; Sutter, CA (9-98) BS; Ski C; Span C; VP, SC; Tres, Var C; VP, Jr Cl; Pres, Soph Cl; JV, Bsbl; Bkbl; Co-Cpt, Ftbl; Tr; Amer Leg A; Amer Leg Orator A; CSF; Cl Fav; HKg; Spch A; Vof-DEM; *U o-t Pacific; Law.*

POST, Denise Aileen
Fairmont Sr HS; Fairmont, WV (16-230) Chor; Span C; SC; HCt; Highest Hon Graduate; *W Va U; Med Tech.*

POST, Michele Louise
Easton Area HS; Easton, PA (120-659) Yth Fel; Yth Leg; Church Choir; *Social Sci.*

POST, Sheryl Lynn
Sandy Creek HS; Fairfield, NE (50%-54) Band; Drama; Ensm; Pres, 4H; Span C; Bsbl; Sftbl; Swim; Tnns; Tr; COM; 4H A; Type A; VP, 4-H C; Pep C; Vocal A; Phys Fitness A; *Bethany Nazarene Col.*

POSTEMA, James Arthur
Grand Haven Sr HS; Grand Haven, MI (26-380) Tnns; Mich Comp Schol Win; *Northern Mich U; General Conservation.*

POSTON, Angela Kay
Dorman HS; Spartanburg, SC; BC; Hmrm; COM; Hon Prog; Yth Fel; Beta C; Tres, Civitan.

POSTON, Frances Jan
Paul M Dorman HS; Spartanburg, SC (12-551) BC; Drama; Cpt, Hmrm; NHS; *Wofford U; Bus.*

POTE, Corey James
Penns Grove HS; Penns Grove, NJ (40-200) Band; Chess C; Co-Ed, Sch P; Bsbl; Mgr, Bkbl; Ed, Yrbk; *Washington Col; Med.*

POTEET, Sherry Lynn
Clarksville HS; Clarksville, TN (10-132) Band; FHA; Secy, FTA; SC; Sftbl; Yth Fel; Drum Major; GSct; *Ed.*

POTEETE, James Alan
South HS; Bakersfield, CA; Chor; NHS; Tr; Co-Cpt, Wrest; Most Out; Russian C; Marine Phys Fitness Prog; *U S Air Force Acad; Phys Ed.*

POTEETE, Renee
S Bakersfield HS; Bakersfield, CA (15-400) Chor; Madrigal; NHS; Tr; Hon Prog; Russian C; *Astronomy.*

POTESTA, Robert Henry
Leetonia HS; Leetonia, OH (33%-100) Band; Span C; All Co Band; *Ohio Northern U; Pre-Med.*

POTHAST, Grant Earl
Terril HS; Terril, IA (1-30) FFA; NHS; Bsbl; Bkbl.

POTILLO, Carol Beth
Granite City HS; Granite City, IL (2-560) Band; Secy, Mod Mus Mas; Pres, NHS; NEDT; Cl Schol; 1st Pl, ISHS Mus Contest; *Millikin U; Mus.*

POTTER, Bradley Ryan
Ladysmith HS; Ladysmith, WI (1-107) BS; Chess C; Math C; NHS; Sch P; Cpt, Bsbl; Cpt, Bkbl; Ftbl; COM; NMS; Val; HR; *U of Wisc; Math.*

POTTER, Cathy Evelyn
Norte Del Rio HS; Sacramento, CA (50%-800) Span C; Church Choir; *Mus.*

POTTER, Cynthia Kay
Granger HS; Salt Lake City, UT; *Biola Col; Religion.*

POTTER, Fred K
Norwich Regional Voc-Tech Sch; Norwich, CT (120-180) Attendance A; *Automotive.*

POTTER, Jane Ann
Bismarck-Henning HS; Bismarck, IL; Band; Chor; FHA; 4H; Tr; 4H A; *Art.*

POTTER, Janet Lee
Thomas HS; Thomas, OK (4-34) Ann; FHA; NHS; Sch P; *OSU.*

POTTER, Karen Elaine
Susquehanna Comm HS; Susquehanna, PA (10%-120) Band; Bus C; Chor; Ensm; Pres, 4H; Rptr, Sch P; Ski C; Arion Found A; Prom Ct; *Robert Packer Sch of Nurs; Nurs.*

POTTER, Kevin Donald
Wisconsin Lutheran HS; Milwaukee, WI; Ski C; Wrest; Wrest A; *Bradley U; Archt.*

POTTER, Kimberly Marie
Winfield HS; Winfield, KS (25%-200) Ann; Chldr; NHS; Pres, Rainbow; SC; Golf; *Kans St U.*

POTTER, Lori Dawn
Grossmont HS; La Mesa, CA (115-600) Chldr; Hmrm; Cl Fav; HCt; Bat Girl; Sr Senate; Daisy Chain A; Hi-Fiette Board; Girl o-t Mo; Election Board; Campus Life; *Grossmont Jr Col; Bus.*

POTTER, Mark Kenneth
Patrick Henry HS; San Diego, CA; CSF; NML; Acad Distinction A; *Point Loma Col; Chem.*

POTTER, Nancy Lynn
Jefferson City HS; Jefferson City, MO (28-553) AFS; A-Ed, Ann; Chor; Lat C; NHS; Span C; Hon Men, Ntl PTA Poetry Contest; *Drama.*

POTTER, Paula Denese
Virgie HS; Virgie, KY; Chldr; Tres, Chem C; Ger C; 4H; Rainbow; Sci C; Var C.

POTTER, Pennie Sue
Galion Sr HS; Galion, OH (78-275) Co-Ch, Chldr; Chor; ARC; Ed, Sch P; Span C; Tri-HiY; Sftbl; Co-Ch, Tr; HCt; *Patrica Stevens Col; Fashion.*

POTTER, Phil Neale
Hudson HS; Hudson, MI (29-105) Band; Drama; Cr-Ctry; Co-Cpt, Tr; Wrest; Sr o-t Mo; *Grand Rapids Sch o-t Bible; Bible.*

POTTER, Robert Eugene
Salem HS; Salem, IN; HiY; Bsbl; Bkbl; Ftbl; Sports Trophies; *Conservation.*

POTTER, Suzanne Michelle
Arcadia HS; Arcadia, CA (250-2900) A Cap Choir; Hmrm; InterClub Coun; NHS; Tres, SC; Sr Hon Girls; Friendliest Girl; *Calif Polytech St U; Home Ec.*

POTTHOFF, Susan Ann
St Bede Acad; Peru, IL (12-130) Chldr; Chor; Madrigal; SC; Tnns; Hon Prog; Sci A; Mus; *Phar.*

POTTS, Cynthia Elaine
Hatley HS; Hatley, MS (8-138) Co-Ed, Ann; BC; Chor; Ensm; FHA; *Itawamba Jr Col; Acct.*

POTTS, Dean Roger
LaMoure HS; LaMoure, ND (4-40) Drama; Pres, FFA; Pres, 4H; Spch C; SC; Ftbl; Tr; Wrest; Citz A; *ND St U; Agr Engr.*

POTTS, Diana Lynn
Franklin HS; Franklin, TN; Band; BC; Crown & Scepter; NHS; Church Bkbl; *Med.*

POTTS, Donna Marie
Barnwell HS; Barnwell, SC (6-200) Chldr; Chor; Drama; Fr C; Hmrm; NHS; VP, Sch P; Bkbl; Co-Cpt, Sftbl; MVP, Swim; COM; Pres A; Jr Marshal; Bkbl Acad A; *U of SC; Law.*

POTTS, Janet April
W Essex HS; N Caldwell, NJ; Band; Bkbl; Sftbl; Methodist Yth Organization; *Kean Col; Architecture.*

POTTS, John Edward
W Essex HS; N Caldwell, NJ (220-415) Chess C; *Co Col of Morris; Engr.*

POTTS, Joyce Monica
Barnwell HS; Barnwell, SC (5-136) A-Ed, Ann; VP, CYO; Pres, Drama; NHS; Co-Ed, Sch P; Thes; Bkbl; COM; Hon Prog; Pres A; Jr Marshal; Hon Graduate; WW; Furman Schol; *Clemson U; Med Tech.*

POTTS, Larry Dale
Johnston City HS; Johnston City, IL (24-84) Mgr, Band; Mgr, Chor; Drama; Thes; Pres, Sr Cl; Cl Fav; Hon Prog; VP, Fresh Cl; Creative Arts A; *Comm Col o-t Air Force; Med.*

POTTS, Melissa Kay
Nitro HS; Nitro, WV (10%-250) Band; Chor; NHS; Co-Ed, Sch P; Tr; *David Lipscomb Col; Nurs.*

POTTS, Rodney Lafayette
Jamesville-DeWitt HS; Dewitt, NY (50-400) 4H; Tnns; Jr Methodist Yth Fellowship; J R Edwin Groom A; *Med.*

POTTS, Virginia Lynne
Lincoln Ne HS; Lincoln, NE (38-550) Bus Mgr, Sch P; JA A; *Lincoln Sch of Commerce; Legal Secy.*

POU, Dori Annette
Hillcrest HS; Jamaica, NY; ARC; Var C; Mgr, Bkbl; Mgr, Sftbl; ARC A; GScts; Vlbl; Tres, Qns Sounding Board; Church Yth Choir; Secy, Church Sch; *FIT; Art-Fashion Designing.*

POULOS, Cynthia Wills
Lincoln HS; Manitowoc, WI (60-607) Ensm; Pres, Ger C; NHS; VP, Orch; Swim; JV, Tr; Civic Orch; Graduation Violinist; Peter Quince Performing Co Orch; Masquers, In Or; Ger Flk Danc Grp; Bnd & Orch Parnts As Sum Mus Cmp Sc; *U of Wis at Stevens Point; Mus.*

POULSEN, Juliana Clair
Ft Walton Beach HS; Fort Walton Beach, FL (1-610) BC; CYO; FHA; Pres, Ger C; Hmrm; Inter-Club Coun; Lit Mag; Math C; Mu Alpha Theta; ARC; Ed, Sch P; Secy, Sci C; SC; Bkbl; JV, Sftbl; Amer Leg A; Beauty; COM; Citz A; DARGCA; H of F; Hon Prog; Journ A; Math A; NEDT; Sci A; Val; Scholastic A; Outst Ger Stu; Hon C Pres of Yr; WW; *New Col of U S Fla; Pre-Med.*

POULTER, Jeffrey Scott
Belvidere HS; Belvidere, IL (2-366) A Cap Choir; Chor; Madrigal; NHS; SC; Var C; Ftbl; DARGCA; St Scholar; First Tm All-Conf Ftbl; NHS Schol; First Tm All-Area Ftbl; Ntl Ath Hon Soc; Vetrans Schol; Dist Chor; *U of Ill; Bio.*

POUMELE, Faamafi T
Vista HS; Vista, CA (10-28) Band; Chor; FTA; Phys C; Rptr, Y-Tns; JV, Ftbl; JV, Tr; CSF; Chamber of Comm A; Citz A; Elk A; 4H A; Hist A; Journ A; Ntl Achv Schol; Ntl Conf Chr & Jews; PTA A; ARC A; Yth Fel; *Palomar Col; Law.*

POUMELE, Samuel Talo
Vista HS; Vista, CA (6-21) All Amer Yth; Band; Chor; Dbte Tm; VP, Y-Tns; Ftbl; Amer Leg A; Elk A; God & Country A; Gov Honor Prog; Ntl Conf Chr & Jews; NMF; NMS; Type A; Yth Foundation; Yth Leg; VP, Yth Fel; *Palomar Col; Commercial Arts.*

POUNDERS, Belinda Gail
Phil Campbell HS; Phil Campbell, AL (2-76) FNA; Pres, 4H; NHS; 4H A; JA A; Sal; Spch A; Pres, HOECA; Pres, Lib C; Del, Farm Bureau Yth Ldrship Conf; Jr Ldrship; S-T, Jr Civitan; *NW Al St Jr Col; Nurs.*

POUNDS, Phillip Linn
Huntington HS; Shreveport, LA (20%-400) Chem C; Secy, Key C; Bsbl; *U of Houston; Law.*

POVERSKI, Jayne Mary
Newman HS; Wausau, WI (21-134) HCt; Pep C; Top Typing Stu; *U of Wis; Acct.*

POWE, James
Quitman HS; Quitman, MS; FFA; Alg A; Bio A; COM; *Jackson St Col; Engr.*

POWE, Nikita Antonniette
Stone HS; Wiggins, MS; Chor; Bsbl; Bkbl; Cl Fav; *St Mary's Dominican Col; Law.*

POWELL, Arlene Sue
Shenandoah HS; Sarahsville, OH; Bus Mgr, Ann; Bus C; Chor; FHA; S-T, 4H; Tr; 4H A; Lion A; Yth Fel; Vlbl.

POWELL, Barry LaMont
Middlesex HS; Saluda, VA (10-101) AFS; Band; Dbte Tm; Fr C; ARC; Sch P; Sci C; SC; Bkbl; Cpt, Ftbl; Cpt, Soccer; Citz A; DARGCA; Hist A; Math A; Sci A; Article Published by Essay Press; Original Oratory; Co Bicentennial; BSct; Pres, Jr Missionary Circle; Church Organist; Tres, Yth Choir; *UCLA; Sci.*

POWELL, Bart L
Peru HS; Peru, IN (46-281) Chem C; Commercial C; Hmrm; Span C; Var C; Bsbl; Ftbl; COM; JA A; Sci A; Type A; *Ind St U; Pre-Med.*

POWELL, Beverly Diane
Westminster Christian Sch; Gadsden, AL (19-50) Band; Sci C; Hon Prog; Sci A; Acteens; Yth Choir; 1st Pl Sch, 2nd Pl Reg, Sci Fair; *Auburn U; Hist.*

POWELL, Brenton Craig
Forrest City HS; Forrest City, AR (66%-328) A Cap Choir; Chor; Dbte Tm; Drama; Ensm; 4H; Hmrm; Madrigal; Spch C; SC; Thes; JV, Soccer; JV, Wrest; Kiwanis A; Spch A; Mid So Chor; Hist C; Mr 1st Bapt Ch; All Region Choir; Der Singkries; Amer Choral Director's Assn; Barbershop Quartet; Church Choir; *Wayland Baptist Col; Voice Mus.*

POWELL, Carol Lynn
Moline Sr HS; Moline, IL; Lat C; Y-Tns; Sftbl; Swim; MVP, Tr; *Black Hawk Col; Eng.*

POWELL, Chanda Lou
Henderson Co Sr HS; Henderson, KY (139-550) S-T, A Cap Choir; Band; Chor; Ensm; 4H; Jr Miss Pagent; 4H A; Hon Prog; Most Talented; Amer Yth in Concert; All Dist, All St, Quad St, Chor; *E Ky U; Bus.*

POWELL, Cheryl Anita
Rocky Mount Sr HS; Rocky Mount, NC; Band; 4H; Hmrm; SC; Up Bound; Band A; *A&T U; Bus Adm.*

POWELL, Christain Dale
Franklin Co Sr HS; Rocky Mount, VA; FFA; Art A's.

POWELL, Christie Lynn
Butler Area Sr HS; Butler, PA (195-990) Chor; Hmrm; Yth Fel; Usher's C; *Anderson Col; Mus.*

POWELL, Christine Ann
Wheatland-Chili HS; Scottsville, NY; Ann; Band; Chor; Drama; Ensm; Fr C; Mjrte; Sch P; Sodality; Hon Prog; Yth Fel; Cpt, Bowl; All Co, All St, Choirs.

POWELL, Christy Jo
Hanceville HS; Hanceville, AL; Ann; Band; FHA; Math C; *Math.*

POWELL, Cindi Lou
Las Vegas HS; Las Vegas, NV; Pres, A Cap Choir; Pres, Chor; Ski C; Span C; Pres, SC; Var C; VP, Soph Cl; Cpt, Bkbl; Cpt, Sftbl; COM; Citz A; Swtht; Type A; Yth Fel; Vlbl; High Score, Vlbl; VP, MYF; MVP, Bkbl; MVP, Sftbl; *Phys Ed.*

POWELL, Cindy Lee
Magnolia HS; Anaheim, CA; Ann; VP, Band; Community Yth Symph; Pres, Ensm; Hmrm; InterClub Coun; NHS; Orch; Ski C; Secy, Var C; Tr; Hist A; Hon Prog; Interlochen Ntl Mus; Sci A; Gym; Tr Sch Records; CIF Runner; Flute Section Ldr; Sussie Sentinel A; Girls Ath A; *Cypress-USC; Dental Hygiene.*

POWELL, Clifford Eugene
George Henry Corliss HS; Chicago, IL (21-726) Band; Chor; SC; Ftbl; Alg A; COM; Citz A; Hon Prog; Math A; Sci A; *NW Ill U; Computer Sci.*

POWELL, Debora Joyce
Pass Christian HS; Pass Christian, MS (5-110) BC;
Fr C; ARC; NMS; ARC A; Yth Fel; *Tex Christian
U; Psych.*

POWELL, Deborah Lynn
Guymon HS; Guymon, OK (1-180) Band; Chor;
Dbte Tm; 4H; NFL; NHS; F-Ed, Sch P; Sci C;
Swim; 4H A; Sci A; Spch A; Val; WCTU A; *Ocean-
ography.*

POWELL, Diana Lynn
Minnehaha Acad; Minneapolis, MN (20%-154) Fr
C; Ski C; Pres, Jr Cl; HR.

POWELL, Douglas James
Crockett HS; Crockett, TX (16-108) Band; Ensm;
FTA; VP, Span C; Tnns; Hon Prog; *Tex A&M U;
Nuclear Engr.*

POWELL, Eleanor Elizabeth
E Mecklenburg HS; Charlotte, NC; Secy, Rainbow;
Art C; Candystriper; Tres, Church Yth Fel.

POWELL, Felicia Yvonne
Echols Co HS; Statenville, GA (1-40) BC; FHA;
4H; Hmrm; Fin, Jr Miss Pagent; MVP; Bkbl; Alg A;
Citz A; Cl Fav; Type A; Outst Attitude A, Bkbl.

POWELL, James Dean
Magnolia HS; Anaheim, CA (5%-430) Dbte Tm;
Order/Arrow; ARC; Spch C; Alg A; Amer Leg A;
CSF; COM; Citz A; God & Country A; Lion A;
Math A; Order/Arrow A; ARC A; Spch A; Yth
Fel; Eagle Sct; *Biola Col; Christian Ed.*

POWELL, James Stephen
Walker HS; Atlanta, GA (5%-180) NHS; COM;
Type A.

POWELL, Jan Rene
Coronado HS; Lubbock, TX; Band; Hmrm; SC; Tri-
HiY; Orch; Citz A; *Tex Tech U; Dentistry.*

POWELL, Jana Michelle
Findlay HS; Findlay, OH; Drama; Ensm; Fr C; Sci
A; Yth Fel; *Mus.*

POWELL, Jeff Lee
Savannah HS; Savannah, GA; A Cap Choir; Bus C;
Chor; Ensm; Order/Arrow; Mgr, Bsbl; JV, Ftbl; JV,
Tr; Citz A; MLS; Most Out; ROTC A; Yth Fel;
Goodwill A; DECA; *Ga Sou Col; Mus.*

POWELL, John Mark
Clinton HS; Clinton, MS (34-310) BC; SC; Pres, Sr
Cl; Cl Fav; HKg; HCt; Jr Cl Senator; *Miss Col;
Med.*

POWELL, John R
Chester HS; Chester, PA;

POWELL, Joseph Renard
Northeastern HS; Detroit, MI; *Eastern Mich St;
Elec Engr.*

POWELL, Kaiwen Marie
Pike HS; Indianapolis, IN (90-291) Ann; Chor;
Rptr, FBLA; FTA; A-Ed, Sch P; Sftbl; Tr; HCt;
Most Improved, Vlbl; Mgr, Gym; *Milligan Col; Ed.*

POWELL, Karen Ann
J L Mann HS; Greenville, SC; Bus C; VP, Hmrm;
Greenville Tech Col; Nurs.

POWELL, Katharyn JoAnn
Dan River HS; Ringgold, VA (4-238) Ed, Ann;
Band; BC; Drama; Fr C; Hmrm; Lit Mag; JV, Bkbl;
Beauty; Gov Honor Prog; Hon Prog; Q&S A; Semi-
Fin, St Forensics League; *VPI; Journ.*

POWELL, Kathy
The Cecilian Acad; Philadelphia, PA; Secy, CYO;
Chor; Fr C; 4H; Hmrm; Lat C; NFL; SC;
World Affairs C; Pres, Soph Cl; Hon Prog; NEDT;
U of Pa; Math.

POWELL, Kenneth Wayne
Brookhaven Acad; Brookhaven, MS; Ann; Pres,
BC; Fr C; Hmrm; Pres, SC; Pres, Sr Cl; Rptr, Jr Cl;
Bsbl; Co-Cpt, Bkbl; MVP, Ftbl; Tr; Alg A; Bio A;
Sci A; Star Student; Soph Rep; Mr Brookhaven
Acad; Most Dependable; Most Stylish; Most Intel-
lectual.

POWELL, Kenneth Wayne
Halifax Co Sr HS; S Boston, VA (5-550) Ann; BS;
Lit Mag; VP, NHS; A-Ed, Sch P; Bus Mgr, Span C;
COM; Sci A; Eagle Sct; *MIT; Engr.*

POWELL, Laura Gaye
Los Altos HS; Hacienda Heights, CA (100-680)
JV, Swim; Principal's HR; PA; *Journ.*

POWELL, Lesli Jennifer
Lampeter-Strasburg HS; Lampeter, PA (16-211)
Cpt, Chldr; Chor; Hmrm; Tres, NHS; Span C; Var
C; MVP, Chldr; *Albright Col; Social Sci.*

POWELL, Linda Sue
Moulton-Udell HS; Moulton, IA (2-45) A-Ed,
Ann; Band; Cpt, Chldr; Pres, Fr C; Tr; Hon Prog;
Sal; St Scholar; *U of Iowa; Lib Arts.*

POWELL, Linnie Darlene
Milford HS; Milford, TX (1-11) Pres, BC; Chor;
Drama; Pres, FHA; Pres, Jr Cl; Cl Fav; HCt; HR;
Pres, ESAA Comm; *E Tex St U; Bus Adm.*

POWELL, Lorenzo X
Dorsey HS; Los Angeles, CA; Swim; Sunday Sch
Teacher.

POWELL, Lori Yvette
Cherryville Sr HS; Cherryville, NC (13-136) Band;
Drama; Ensm; Fr C; Jr Miss Pagent; Sci C; SC;
Acteens; Rep, Stu Coun, Homecoming; *Social
Work.*

POWELL, Mark Andrew
Lansing E HS; Lansing, MI; Parl, Hmrm; SC; Bkbl;
Co-Cpt, Ftbl; Sportsmanship A; Sarah Hinman A;
Grace Col; Phys Ed.

POWELL, Martha Virginia
Hampton Roads Acad; Newport News, VA (15-52)
Drama; S-T, Fr C; Semi-Fin, GS; Thes; Hon Prog;
HR; *Wake Forest U; Bus.*

POWELL, Mary Frances
New Hanover HS; Wilmington, NC; A Cap Choir;
Chor; Ensm; Ch, Hmrm; Madrigal; NHS; Qn's
Court, Summer Camp; Church Choir; Kiwanette;
Emmanuel Col; Ed.

POWELL, Patricia Jeanne
Mecklenburg Acad; Chase City, VA (1-29) Hmrm;
Pres, Lat C; Pres, Monogram; VP, SC; VP, Sr Cl;
Pres, Soph Cl; Co-Cpt, Bkbl; MVP, Sftbl; Bio A; Gr
Marshal; *NC St U; Agr Sci.*

POWELL, Patrick Scott
Paducah Tilghman HS; Paducah, KY (18-375) A
Cap Choir; Chess C; Chor; Madrigal; Orch; VP,
Span C; Var C; Ftbl; Tnns; Wrest; Opt A; FCA;
Duke of Paducah; Orquestra A; *Abilene Christian
U; Personal Relations.*

POWELL, Philip Greg
John L McClellan HS; Little Rock, AR; Band;
Chor.

POWELL, Phillip Ray
Ballard Mem HS; Barlow, KY (1-102) Pres, BC;
FFA; Co-Cpt, Bsbl; Bio A; COM; MLS; Val; Geom
A; Mr BMHS; Bkbl Kg Court; Presidential Schol;
Murray St U; Pre-Vet.

POWELL, Rhonda Elaine
Celina Sr HS; Celina, OH (8-275) A Cap Choir;
Chem C; Chor; Fr C; FTA; 4H; Lat C; NHS; Thes;
JV, Tr; COM; 4H A; Campus Life; GAA; Vlbl;
Bowling Green St U; Acct.

POWELL, Ronnie Carroll
Greenwood HS; Greenwood, SC (515-570) Chor;
4H; *Lander Col.*

POWELL, Sandra Diane
Bond Co Comm Unit 2 HS; Greenville, IL; Band;
JV, Chldr; Chor; Ensm; Hmrm; Span C; SC; GAA;
HR; *Ozark Bible Col; Mus.*

POWELL, Scharlanne
Robert E Lee HS; Tyler, TX (33%-650) FHA; Fin,
Lit Mag; Secy, SC; Sftbl; Tyler Art League; Artist,
Civic Chorale; Art As; *Tex A&M U; Archt.*

POWELL, Scott David
Ellensburg HS; Ellensburg, WA; Band; Ski C; JV,
Bsbl; JV, Bkbl; JV, Soccer; Sftbl; COM.

POWELL, Sharon Ann
Brookhaven Acad; Brookhaven, MS; Band; BC;
FHA; F-Ed, Sch P; SC; Bkbl; Sftbl; Tr; Beauty; Cl
Fav; Miss Hustle; Most Ideal; Most Energetic;
Miss St U; Phys Sci.

POWELL, Sherilyn
Corsicana HS; Corsicana, TX (33%-310) A Cap
Choir; NEDT; Ntl Guild Exams; Tex St Theory
Exams; *Baylor U; Mus.*

POWELL, Sherri Anne
Clinton HS; Clinton, NC (25-250) BC; Chor;
Drama; Secy, 4H; Span C; 4H A; Chor A; *Meredith
Col; Mus.*

POWELL, Tammie Jo
Levelland HS; Levelland, TX (36-192) Tres, A Cap
Choir; Chor; Ensm; Tres, FHA; FTA; Bkbl; Lion A;
MLS; Most Out; Swtht; Yth Fel; WW, Mus Stu;
San Marcos Col; Mus.

POWELL, Taphas Corette
Hueytown HS; Hueytown, AL; Jr Miss Pagent;
Herzing Inst; Med Secy.

POWELL, Teresa Fern
Columbine HS; Littleton, CO (9-525) A Cap Choir;
Ensm; *Lubbock Christian Col; Elem Ed.*

POWELL, Terri Lorraine
Maud HS; Maud, OK (4-34) BC; FBLA; Tres,
FHA; Co-Ch, Model UN; Rainbow; SC; B Crocker
A; Sci A; Outst FHA Stu; Okla HS Hon Soc; Home
Ec A; *U of Sci and Arts of Okla; Home Ec.*

POWELL, Thomas Glen
N Augusta Sr HS; N Augusta, SC (100-390)
Hmrm; Section Coun; Lit Mag; NHS; SC; Bkbl;
COM; NEDT; *Clemson U; Engr.*

POWELL, Vernell
Galena Park HS; Galena Park, TX (171-303).

POWELL, Virginia May
Terril Comm Sch; Terril, IA (2-30) Co-Ed, Ann;
Band; Chor; S-T, NHS; S-T, Jr Cl; Tr.

POWELL, Walter Carroll
Lake Clifton Sr HS; Baltimore, MD (10%-315)
Chor; Hmrm; NHS; Phys C; Soccer; Swim; Alg A;
Bio A; COM; Chem A; Citz A; Hist A; Hon Prog;
Math A; Sci A; *U of Md at Col Park; Elec Engr.*

POWELL, William Clyde
Marked Tree HS; Marked Tree, AR (3-75) VP, BC;
Drama; FFA; NHS; Order/Arrow; Thes; Ftbl; Citz
A; Sci A; *Ark St U; Phar.*

POWER, Nicky Dale
Weir HS; Weir, MS; BC; Chor; Secy, FFA; 4H; VP,
Soph Cl; Bkbl; Ftbl; Tr; H of F; *Miss St U; Wild-
Life Mgr.*

POWER, Patricia Lynn
Acad o-t Holy Names; Tampa, FL (13-68) CYO;
Cpt, Chldr; Drama; Hmrm; NHS; Sci C; Span C;
Span NHS; SC; Pres, Sr Cl; Pres, Jr Cl; Pres, Soph
Cl; HCt; Hon Prog; Christman Formal Qn; *U of S
Fla; Law.*

POWERS, Ann Marie
St Mary's HS; Lynn, MA (19-129) JV, Chldr; SC;
Swim; Tr; Alg A; COM; Citz A; Hon Prog; Math A;
Sci A; Eng, Religion, A's; *Sci.*

POWERS, April Lee
Lake Clifton Sr HS; Baltimore, MD (10%-315)
Chor; Drama; FHA; Hmrm; JETS; Bus Mgr, NHS;
Ch, Up Bound; Tnns; COM; Hist A; Hon Prog; JA
A; Art A; Extra Curr A; Outst Tutor; Mayor Ltr of
Commendation; *Temple U; Visual Communica-
tion.*

POWERS, Charles Bryan Jr
Laurel Co HS; London, KY (90-350) Ann; BC;
Drama; Fr C; Key C; Spch C; Ftbl; Tr; Spch A;
Eastern Ky U; Plumbing.

POWERS, Craig Alan
South HS; Bakersfield, CA (171-363) 4H A; *Sou
Calif Col; Psych.*

POWERS, Debra Lynn
Gainesville HS; Gainesville, GA (38-205) Chldr;
Chor; Drama; Beauty; Citz A; Hon Prog; BPW Yth
Conf; *Western Carolina U; Sociology.*

POWERS, Elinda Jean
Hays HS; Hays, KS; Chor; Orch; Span C; Hon
Prog; *Ft Hays St Col; Eng.*

POWERS, Eugene Scott
Proctor HS; Proctor, MN (10%-250) Fr C; Tr; SC
A; *Golden Valley Lutheran Col; Theology.*

POWERS, James Joseph
Glenbrook S HS; Glenview, IL; Ski C; Var C; Pres,
Y-Tns; Bsbl; Co-Cpt, Ftbl; Bio A.

POWERS, Jeff Lynn
Comm Preparatory Acad; Erie, PA (6-12) F-Ed,
Ann; F-Ed, Sch P; COM; Hon Prog.

POWERS, Kimberle Lynette
Centennial Sr HS; Compton, CA (10%-700) Rptr,
Ann; Chldr; Chess C; Hmrm; ARC; Rptr, Sch P;
Span C; SC; COM; Citz A; Journ A; Schol A; *Pep-
perdine U; Professional Counseling.*

POWERS, Lucy Carol
Rossville Comp HS; Rossville, GA (14-225) BC; Chor; Drama; Lit Mag; Span C; Y-Tns; Sftbl; Math A; Yth Leg; Scholastic As; *U of Ga; Lang.*

POWERS, Margie
Alexander HS; Starkville, MS (30-60) Cpt, Chor; Pres, Y-Tns; Pres, Sr Cl; *Miss St U; Journ.*

POWERS, Matthew Dennis
Columbiana HS; Columbiana, OH (33-101) Chor; Co-Cpt, Bkbl; Co-Cpt, Ftbl; Tr; MVP, Bkbl; Special Men, All St Bkbl; Hon Men, All St Ftbl; *Harding Col; Bus.*

POWERS, Maurice Phillip
Bell Voc HS; Washington, DC; *NC St U; Bus Math.*

POWERS, Nancy Elizabeth
Danville Comm HS; Danville, IN (24-170) Secy, Band; Drama; Fr C; Mjrte; Orch; Tri-HiY; Swim; Hon Prog; St Scholar; Yth Fel; *Ind U; Elem Ed.*

POWERS, Rhonda Ann
Pawhuska HS; Pawhuska, OK (13-84) Ed, Ann; Band; Chor; Drama; GS; Hmrm; Mjrte; NHS; Rptr, Sch P; Span C; *Okla St U; Mus.*

POWERS, Rodney Lee
Frankfort HS; Ridgeley, WV (10%-149) Band; FTA; Mgr, Ftbl; *W Va U; Math.*

POWNALL, Michael Joseph
St Marys Manor Marist Prep; Penndel, PA (1-21) CYO; Chldr; Chor; Drama; Thes; VP, Jr Cl; Mgr, Bkbl; Alg A; Bio A; COM; Citz A; Hist A; Hon Prog; Math A; NEDT; Phy A; Sacristan; Sci A; Span A; Theology A; Lat A; Earth Sci A; *Loyola U; Eng.*

POY, Iris Yuk Ling
Laupahoehoe HS; Laupahoehoe, HI (6-41) F-Ed, Ann; Secy, SC; Mgr, Tr; Vlbl; *Hawaii Comm Col; Airline Receptionist.*

POY, Tom Chong
Laupahoehoe HS; Laupahoehoe, HI (10-39) Ann; FHA; Tres, Sci C; VP, SC; Secy, Soph Cl; Bsbl; Bkbl; Cr-Ctry; HCt; Lettermen C; VP, Pacific Asia Affairs Coun; Co- cpt, Vlbl & Bowl; St Stu Conf.

POYER, Beth Lynn
Berea HS; Berea, OH (20-700) F-Ed, Ann; Chor; Drama; Ensm; NHS; Thes; Math A; Choir Outst Underclman; *Drama.*

POYNTER, Thomas L
N Montgomery HS; Crawfordsville, IN (110-220) Chor; Key C; Span C; Bsbl; Bkbl; Ftbl; Tr; *Ball St U; Communications.*

POYNTER, Wayne Marion
Mooresville HS; Mooresville, IN (150-350) JV, Bsbl; JV, Bkbl; *Archt Tech.*

POZO, Aaron Linn
San Pasqual Acad; Escondido, CA; A Cap Choir; Chor; Lat C; Span C; Bsbl; Cpt, Bkbl; Ftbl; Soccer; Sftbl; Swim; Tnns; Wrest; Sergeant-At-Arms; *La Sierra Col; Bio.*

PRAGDAT, Mahandra
Eastside HS; Paterson, NJ (3-519) Tnns; Hon Prog; Hospital Vol A; *NY U; Med.*

PRAGDAT, Prema Carol
Eastside HS; Paterson, NJ; Tres, Drama; NHS; Thes; Zonta C; Horseback Riding C; *Commercial Design.*

PRAIRIE, Joy Marie
Momence HS; Momence, IL (40-140) CYO; Secy, Span C; Spch C; Thes; Secy, Jr Cl; Bkbl; Spch A; *Ill St U; Social Work.*

PRANKE, Kristi Ann
Maddock Pub Sch; Maddock, ND (5-23) Band; Chor; FHA; GS; SC; Var C; Tres, Soph Cl; Co-Cpt, Bkbl; Golf; Sftbl; Tr; Bio A; NMS; Bkbl A; Tr A; Band A; *ND St U; Med.*

PRASTON, Suann Marie
Southside HS; Elmira, NY (9-470) Hon Prog.

PRATER, Alison Ann
Bellefontaine HS; Bellefontaine, OH (1-227) VP, Band; Chem C; VP, Ger C; Semi-Fin, GS; Cpt, Mjrte; VP, NHS; Orch; Phys C; Cpt, Sch Achieve Tm; Secy, Sr Cl; Swim; Alg A; Amer Leg A; Bio A; COM; Hon Prog; Math A; Sci A; Val; Yth Fel; Band A; Snowball Qn Ct; *Kenyon Col; Pre-Med.*

PRATER, Marcia Kay
Brighton HS; Salt Lake City, UT (20%-613) Chor; Span C; COM; Hon Prog; *Hardin-Simmons U; Math.*

PRATER, Raymond Douglas
Westminster HS; Westminster, SC; Chess C; FFA; Pres, Hmrm; Ftbl; Tr; Hist A; *Clemson U; Bus Adm.*

PRATHER, Cecelia Ann
Thornwell HS; Clinton, SC; Bus Mgr, Ann; BC; Fr C; Var C; Bkbl; MVP, Tnns; COM; NEDT; Furman Schol; Presbyterian Col Jr Fel; Newberry Schol; WW; *Ed.*

PRATHER, Linda Gail
Sheffield HS; Memphis, TN (3-160) Ann; FHA; Tres, Mu Alpha Theta; NHS; Sch P; Tr; Math Art A; *Memphis St Col; Engr.*

PRATHER, Nancy Leigh
Tallapoosa Acad; Dadeville, AL (2-27) Ann; Band; Pres, BC; Semi-Fin, GS; Cpt, Mjrte; Beauty; B Crocker A; MLS; Sal; Graduation Monitor; *Auburn U; Acct.*

PRATT, Ernest Eller
Wm Monroe HS; Stanardsville, VA (25%-129) FFA; *U of Va.*

PRATT, Jerri Lynn
Sierra Joint Union HS; Tollhouse, CA; Math C; NHS; CSF; HR; *Humbolt Col; Forestry.*

PRATT, Judith Rebecca
El Dorado HS; El Dorado, AR (5%-370) Anchor C; Secy, BC; S-T, Chor; Hmrm; Lit Mag; NHS; Orch; SC; Hon Prog; 1st, Jobs Daughters St Essay; *Lit.*

PRATT, Kathy Marie
Parkrose Sr HS; Portland, OR; Drama; Ski C; Secy, Thes; Yth Fel; *U of Oreg; Psych.*

PRATT, Linda Lee
St Joseph Sr HS; St Joseph, MI (3-347) Pres, Chor; Drama; Fr C; SC; Var C; Bkbl; VofDEM; Thespian Drama Assn; NHS; Tres, Yth Commission; Yth Choir; Asst Sunday Sch Teacher; *Concordia Luth Jr Col; Teaching.*

PRATT, Madonna Denise
Rose Bud HS; Rose Bud, AR (1-36) Ed, Ann; Tres, BC; FHA; NHS; Co-Ed, Sch P; Hist A; Sci A; Most Studious; *Harding Col; Med.*

PRATT, Mary Agnes
Dobyns-Bennett HS; Kingsport, TN (50%-420) VP, CYO; Bkbl; Tnns; *E Tenn St U; Social Worker.*

PRATT, Robin Lee
Sterling HS; Somerdale, NJ (215-310) Band; Chor; Parl, Drama; FBLA; VP, Hmrm; InterAct C; Jr Miss Pagent; St Stu Congress; SC; De A; Modeling A; Band-Choral A; *Morgan St Col; Social Worker.*

PRATT, Ronnie Eugene
Horace Maynard HS; Maynardville, TN; BC; Sci C; SC; Var C; Bsbl; Cpt, Bkbl; Ftbl; *Lincoln Mem U; Engr.*

PRATT, Vicki Lynn
Live Oak HS; Morgan Hill, CA; Chor; JV, Swim; Hon Prog; *U of Calif; Med.*

PRAY, Christopher Allen
Milford HS; Milford, OH (49-474) JV, Bsbl; JV, Bkbl; JV, Golf; Jr Hon Soc; *Bus Adm.*

PREAU, Dennis Richard
Brother Martin HS; New Orleans, LA (4-315) Tres, Key C; NHS; Cpt, Cr-Ctry; Tr; Lykes Bros Schol; *LSU; Dentistry.*

PRECHT, David James
Lakota HS; West Chester, OH (13-450) Ger C; Secy, Key C; NHS; Alg A; COM; Chem A; Hist A; Hon Prog; Math A; Debate A; Ntl Merit Commended Stu; *Miami U; Bus.*

PREECE, George Stanley
Round Rock HS; Round Rock, TX (10%-400) A Cap Choir; Chor; Ensm; Madrigal; *U of Tex; Pre-Med.*

PREECE, Gladys Louise
Scott HS; Madison, WV; Ed, Ann; Cpt, Chldr; Semi-Fin, GS; 4H; NHS; SC; Pres, Var C; VP, Sr Cl; Tr; Bio A; Most Out; *W Va Tech Col.*

PREECE, Melanie Carmel
Kermit HS; Kermit, WV (1-35) Band; Cpt, Chldr; Chor; VP, FHA; GS; 4H; VP, Hmrm; Span C; SC; VP, Jr Cl; Bkbl; *Lee Col.*

PREKELAZAJ, Lisa
Aquinas HS; Bronx, NY (45-200) *Manhattan Col; Bus.*

PREKELEZAJ, Prena
Aquinas HS; Bronx, NY (78-200).

PREKOPA, David Phillip
Marian Cath HS; Hometown, PA (4-173) French NHS; Tres, NHS; A-Ed, Sch P; Co-Cpt, Bsbl; Co-Cpt, Bkbl; NMS; NEDT; *Mount St Mary's Col; Journ.*

PRELOW, Sepora Diane
Allen HS; Robeline, LA (1-27) Parl, FBLA; VP, Hmrm; Pres, Math C; COM; HCt; *Northwestern St U; Psych.*

PREMAZA, Joyce Edith
Southampton HS; Courtland, VA (10-220) Ed, Ann; Drama; 4H; Hmrm; NHS; F-Ed, Sch P; Ch, Span C; SC; Tri-HiY; Mgr, Bkbl; COM; 4H A; I Dare You; Math A; Span A; *Smithdeal-Massey Bus Col; Acct.*

PREMER, Jacki Lynne
Batavia HS; Batavia, IL (6-224) VP, AFS; Drama; Orch; Span C; SC; Thes; Hon Prog; Dist Mus; Span A; *Journ.*

PREMO, Laurie Jean Marie
John Marshall HS; Rochester, NY (79-283) A-Ed, Ann; Fr C; Hmrm; ARC; Ed, Sch P; SC; Hockey; Hon Prog; ARC A; Tn Sem; 'Yth Cares' A; Nurs Home Birthday C; Yth Tn Ministry; Candystriper; *St U of NY; Nurs.*

PREMO, Tracey Ellen
John Marshall HS; Rochester, NY (66-283) Ed, Ann; Fr C; ARC; Ed, Sch P; SC; Hon Prog; Journ A; ARC A; Yth Tn Ministry; Nurs Home Birthday C; Candystriper; Yth Cares A; *St U of NY; Nurs.*

PRENDERGAST, Susan Pace
Garinger HS; Charlotte, NC (120-650) F-Ed, Ann; ARC; VP, Ski C; Tnns; *W Carolina U; Ed.*

PRENTICE, Cynthia Anne
Gates-Chili HS; Rochester, NY (13-620) Chor; NHS; Hon Prog; Pres, Church Yth Group; Sunday Sch Teacher; Piano Stu; *Houghton Col; Missionary Nurs.*

PRENTICE, F Steven
Willows HS; Willows, CA (12-130) FFA; Tr; *Christian Heritage Col; Natural Sci.*

PRENTICE, Gregg Olain
Fort Pierce Central HS; Fort Pierce, FL (10%-549) Ed, Ann; 4H; HiY; Pres, Key C; NHS; Var C; Ftbl; Hon Prog; NEDT; Photo C; *Med.*

PRENTICE, James Alexander
Granville HS; Granville, OH (44-126) Chor; Secy, Key C; Order/Arrow; Cr-Ctry; Tr.

PRENTICE, Jody Lynn
Mascoutah Comm HS; Mascoutah, IL (32-288) Co-Ed, Ann; BC; NHS; Sch P; Field Hockey; *FSU; Social Work.*

PRENTIS, Julie Ann
Ottumwa HS; Ottumwa, IA (50-600) Band; Fr C; Orch; Ed, Sch P; Amer Leg A; COM; Hon Prog; Mus A; *Iowa St U; Optometry.*

PRESCOTT, Diana Lynne
Sidney HS; Sidney, OH (51-290) A Cap Choir; Chor; Ensm; 4H; Secy, NHS; Secy, Y-Tns; 4H A; Hon Prog; *Nurs.*

PRESCOTT, James Raymond
Oak Park-River Forest HS; Oak Park, IL (475-950) Monogram; Cpt, Golf; *Ill St U; Bus.*

PRESCOTT, Jeff Reid
Carey HS; Carey, OH (12-106) Co-Ed, Ann; BS; Chor; HiY; Key C; NHS; F-Ed, Sch P; Var C; Co-Cpt, Ftbl; COM; Val; *Kent St U.*

PRESCOTT, Karen
Ben C Rain HS; Mobile, AL (10%-238) Ed, Ann; NHS.

PRESCOTT, Karen Denise
Cumberland Valley HS; Mechanicsburg, PA (3-585) Chldr; Chor; Hmrm; NHS; Ski C; SC; Swim; Tnns; Dist & Regional Choirs; *Cornell U; Human Ecology.*

PRESCOTT, Leslie Faydra
Miramar HS; Miramar, FL (42-657) Band; FBLA; NHS; *LSU; Acct.*

PRESCOTT, Sharon
Ben C Rain HS; Mobile, AL (10%-238) Ed, Ann; Tres, NHS.

PRESGROVE, Steve Lane
R L Osborne HS; Marietta, GA; BC; Lat C; Math C; NHS; VP, Jr Cl; Bkbl; Tr; VP, FCA; *Computer.*

PRESLEY, Christine L
Utica Sr HS; Utica, OH; Band; Chor; Drama; Ensm; 4H; Sch P; Ftbl; Sftbl; Tr; COM; 4H A; Sci A; Yth Fel; *Art.*

PRESLEY, Debra Ann
Daniel Webster HS; Tulsa, OK (10%-350) A Cap Choir; Band; Chor; FNA; Lat C; Lat NHS; Pres, Math C; NHS; Orch; ARC; Sci C; Bkbl; Sftbl; COM; Citz A; Cl Fav; Elk A; Hist A; Hon Prog; Masonic A; Math A; Summa Cum Laude; Sch Spelling Bee Champ; Hon Men, City Sci Fair; Church Pianist; Fin, Orch; *Medically Related.*

PRESLEY, Emelia Elizabeth
Bishop Byrne HS; Memphis, TN (30-231) Drama; Lat C; Swim; NEDT; Sch Ltr; Chorister Guild A; *Med.*

PRESLEY, Jefferson Stephen
Rossville HS; Rossville, GA (2-212) BC; Bkbl; Ftbl; Wrest; DARGCA; Sal; *Fla Col; Graphic Design.*

PRESLEY, Lance Cooper
Rolling Fork HS; Rolling Fork, MS (2-79) Ann; Band; 4H; NHS; Rptr, Sch P; 4H A; *LSU; Vet Sci.*

PRESLEY, William James
W Philadelphia HS; Philadelphia, PA; Hon Prog; *Harvard U; Social Sci.*

PRESNELL, Gail Lorraine
Penncrest HS; Media, PA (10%-500) Band; Chor; Madrigal; SC; HR; Academically Talented Prog; Secy, Yth Fel; Liturgical Dance Group; *Art.*

PRESSLEY, Aline
Seward Park HS; New York City, NY (75-40) Chldr; Hmrm; COM; Curator A; Yth Fel; Fr A; Eng A; Character A; *Orangeburge Col; Nurs.*

PRESSLEY, Brenda Faye
Robert E Lee HS; Montgomery, AL (150-706) Chem C; Pol Sci C; Bus Mgr, Sch P; Sci C; 4H A; Troy St U; *Nurs.*

PRESSLEY, Kevin Ray
Pisgah Sr HS; Canton, NC (1-313) Pres, Band; Demolay; Fr C; Hmrm; NHS; Order/Arrow; Co-Ch, ARC; Pres, SC; Alg A; COM; Citz A; DARGCA; God & Country A; HCt; MLS; Order/Arrow A; VofDEM; Yth Fel; Secy, Fr Hon Soc; Jr Civitan C; *Davidson Col; Pre-Med.*

PRESSLEY, Mark Walden
Salisbury HS; Salisbury, MO (22-87) Band; City Conf; Cpt, Dbte Tm; FBLA; NHS; Order/Arrow; Var C; JV, Bsbl; Mgr, Bkbl; Co-Cpt, Ftbl; Tnns; JV, Tr; Bio A; Citz A; DARGCA; Sftbl; Yth Leg; Eagle Sct; *Northeast Mo St at Kirksville; Med.*

PRESSLEY, Tara Elizabeth
Thomas Jefferson HS; Tampa, FL; Sch P.

PRESSLY, Diana Elaine
Belton Sr HS; Belton, MO (12-314) GS; NHS; Span C; COM; Hon Prog; *Longview Comm Col; Bus Adm.*

PRESSLY, Robert Bruce
Belton HS; Belton, MO; Span C; Var C; JV, Bsbl; Ftbl; Hon Prog; Math A; *Math.*

PRESSLY, Sally White
Seneca Valley HS; Germantown, MD (40%-364) Chldr; Chor; Drama; 4H; Hmrm; NFL; SC; Thes; 4H A; HCt; Spch A; Yth Fel; Outst Drama Performance; *Catawba Col; Drama.*

PRESSNELL, Ricky Lynn
W Morgan HS; Trinity, AL (20-63) BS; Hmrm; SC; Sch Spirit; *Samford U; Religion.*

PRESSON, Dawn Monisa
N Co Christian HS; Ferguson, MO (1-18) Co-Cpt, Chldr; Chor; Co- cpt, Vlbl; *Mid-America Nazarene Col; Mus.*

PRESTBY, Mary Beth
Hamilton HS; Milwaukee, WI; VP, CYO; Sftbl; Citz A; JA A; *Marquette Col; Sociology.*

PRESTON, Allison Jocasta
E St Louis Sr HS; E St Louis, IL; Chess C; Mjrte; Secy, Sunday Sch; Pres, Choir; Church Usher; Runner-Up, Church Qn; *SIU-Edwardsville; Bus.*

PRESTON, Brian Kurt
San Angelo Central HS; San Angelo, TX; Order/ Arrow; Sci A.

PRESTON, Julie Ann
Hoopeston E Lynn HS; Hoopeston, IL (7-150) Ed, Ann; Arch; Band; Chor; Drama; Ensm; Pres, 4H; Sch P; Span C; Arch; Swim; Tr; Cl Fav; 4H A; HCt; Hon Prog; Pres A; *U of Ill; Law.*

PRESTON, Kimberly Anne
Charleston HS; Charleston, IL;

PRESTON, Lisa Sue
Elk Grove HS; Elk Grove Village, IL (70-600) Band; Chldr; Ski C; Tr; Yth Fel; Campus Life; Spring Play; *Ariz St U; Mus.*

PRESTON, Steve Caldwell
Pleasant Grove HS; Pleasant Grove, AL; JV, Bsbl; JV, Bkbl; Ftbl.

PRESTON, Steven Ray
Madison HS; Madison, WI (10%-700) Fr C; Hmrm; Bsbl; Bkbl; Ftbl; Citz A; Hon Prog; Pres A; *U of Wis; Bus.*

PRESTON, Tammy Jean
Gosnell HS; Blytheville, AR (20%-104) Chor; Fr C; Ed, Sch P; Bkbl; *Ark St U; Journ.*

PRESTRIDGE, Kimberly Anne
Pleasant Grove HS; Pleasant Grove, AL (4-145) Band; Pres, FTA; NHS; COM; NEDT; *U of Ala; Elem Ed.*

PRESTRUD, Paul Richard
Summit HS; Frisco, CO (3-88) Chor; Hmrm; SC; Cpt, Bkbl; Citz A; Yth Fel; MVP, Bkbl; Sch Mus; Solo, Ensm A; *Grand Canyon Col; Ed Bible.*

PRESZLER, Sheila Renee
Braddock Pub HS; Braddock, ND (1-8) Co-Ed, Ann; Chldr; Chor; GS; Tres, 4H; F-Ed, Sch P; Tres, Sr Cl; Pres, Soph Cl; Bkbl; 4H A; Val; Fr, Soc Stu, Art, Eng, Phys Ed, A's; Co 4-H Qn; Gen Mills Family Ldr of Tomorrow A; *ND St U; Special Ed.*

PRETTYMAN, Marcena Jo
Tecumseh Sr HS; Tecumseh, MI (4-244) Bus Mgr, Ann; Tres, FNA; GS; NHS; Span C; Secy, SC; Regent Schol; Type A; Yth Convention; FNA Schol; Bsbl, Ftbl & Wrest Statistician; Bookkeeping A; St Competition Schol; *U of Mich; Nurs.*

PREUSSER, Sandra Jane
New Braunfels HS; New Braunfels, TX (10-310) Band; Ensm; Theta Epsilon Nu; Solo & Ensm A.

PREVATT, Harry Robert Jr
St Augustine HS; St Augustine, FL (20-400) Drama; *U of Fla; Med.*

PREVATTE, Kenneth Deryl
Mouldin HS; Mauldin, SC (4-250) Chess C; JETS; NHS; JV, Bsbl; Co-Cpt, Ftbl; Tr; Wrest; COM; Hon Prog; *Engr.*

PREVATTE, Pamela Annette
W Columbus HS; Cerro Gordo, NC (10%-200) BC; Fr C; FHA; Church Choir; Yth Coun; Lib C; Jr Civitans C; *U of NC; Art.*

PREVOST, Joel Mark
Bordelonville HS; Bordelonville, LA; Pres, BC; CYO; VP, Chem C; Chess C; Pres, Fr C; Tres, FFA; VP, 4H; Pres, Hmrm; Lit Mag; Pres, Math C; Phys C; ARC; Sch P; Sci C; VP, SC; VP, Jr Cl; Pres, Soph Cl; Bkbl; Tr; Alg A; 4H A; Math A; ARC A; Sci A; Spch A; Val; Knights o-t Altar; Agr A; *LSU; Agr.*

PREVOST, Pamela Joy
Bridgeport HS; Bridgeport, TX (25%-104) Drama; Rptr, Sch P; *U of Tex at Arlington; Eng.*

PREWITT, Cynthia Ann
Belton HS; Belton, TX; Band; Lat C; NHS; Orch; Rptr, Sch P; Yth Leg; UIL Essay Writing; *Eng.*

PREWITT, Fenton Claude
Jessamine Co HS; Nicholasville, KY (120-256) Drama; Tres, FFA; SC; Ftbl; Tr; Wrest; *Georgetown Col; Hist.*

PREWITT, Joan Marie
Seymour HS; Seymour, IN; FTA; Span C; Var C; Pres, NVI Tn Cl; Pin, NYI Talent; Semi-Fin, FFA Swtht; *Olivet Nazarene Col; Ed.*

PREWITT, Timothy William
Weir HS; Weir, MS (3-53) VP, Chor; VP, Soph Cl; JV, Cr-Ctry; Hist A; Chor A; *Miss St U; Elec Engr.*

PRIBBLE, Rebecca Susan
Arlington HS; Indianapolis, IN; *Teaching.*

PRICE, Angelia Renee
Tuscaloosa Co HS; Northport, AL (25%-530) BC; FHA; NHS; COM; Stu Lib; Pep C; *U of Ala; Acct.*

PRICE, Bettie Catherine
Warren Central HS; Vicksburg, MS (160-350) Lat C; Parl, Spch C; Thes; Bkbl; Golf; *U of Miss; Spch.*

PRICE, Billy Warren II
Kosciusko HS; Kosciusko, MS (20%-160) Band; Chor; Dbte Tm; Ensm; Orch; Lion A; Yth Fel; Yth Foundation; Yth Leg; Chaplain, Police Explorers; Co Yth Ldr; License to Preach; All St, Clinic, Band Rep.

PRICE, Charles Randall
Shawnee HS; Louisville, KY; Cpt, Band; BC; Ensm; Fr C; Hmrm; NHS; Pres, SC; Bsbl; Co-Cpt, Ftbl; Tnns; JV, Wrest; Bio A; Hon Prog; *Purdue U; Elec Engr.*

PRICE, Claricea Elizabeth
Hyde Park Acad; Chicago, IL (50%-187) Band; Chor; Ensm; Hmrm; Span C; SC; Soccer; Sftbl; Tr; COM; Hist A; Tr A; Special Services A; *Computer Data.*

PRICE, Cynthia
Shawnee HS; Louisville, KY; *Ky St U; Eng.*

PRICE, Cyril Marlon
Miami Central HS; Miami, FL (5-30) FBLA; Inter-Act C; Key C; Var C; JV, Bsbl; JV, Ftbl; Alg A; *Phys Ed Teacher.*

PRICE, Daniel Scott
Landmark Christian HS; Cincinnati, OH (15-48) Band; Ed, Sch P; *Liberty Baptist Col; Bible.*

PRICE, David Bryan
Lawrence N HS; Indianapolis, IN (50-410) NHS; Var C; Tnns; Tr; Guitar C; *Ind U; Law.*

PRICE, Deanne Michelle
Scranton Central HS; Scranton, PA (60%-600) Chor; Pol Sci C; Span C; Sftbl; JA A; Type A; Piano; GSct; *Nurs.*

PRICE, Debbie Lynn
Whiteville HS; Whiteville, NC (47-187) Band; Drama; Span C; *E Carolina U; Nurs.*

PRICE, Deborah Annette
Adair Co R II HS; Brashear, MO (10%-17) Chor; 4H; Tres, NHS; Tres, SC; Tres, Soph Cl; Bkbl; Sftbl; Tr; COM; Type A; VofDEM; WW; Soph Pilgrimage; *NMSU; Coaching.*

PRICE, Deborah Elizabeth
Oakwood HS; Dayton, OH (26-150) AFS; Orch; Rainbow; Span C; Sftbl; Yth Fel; *U of Tenn.*

PRICE, Diane Margaret
Ft Pierce Central HS; Ft Pierce, FL (10%-1086) BC; Chldr; 4H; Key C; NHS; SC; Swim; NEDT; Pres, Yth C; Explorers; V Ltr, Swim; *Ed.*

PRICE, Elisabeth Carmichael
Durham Acad; Durham, NC (6-46) AFS; Pol Sci C; Cpt, Bkbl; Sftbl; Hist A; Cpt & MVP, Vlbl; Fin, Ntl German Test; Ap Hist; DAHSS; *Williams Col; Amer Stu.*

PRICE, Frances Lynn
Tuscaloosa Co HS; Northport, AL (30%-450) BC; DECA C; *U of Ala; Med.*

PRICE, Garth Edwin
Washington HS; Phoenix, AZ (70-500) Bsbl; Ftbl; Golf; Wrest; *U of Ariz; Acct.*

PRICE, Gary Andrew
W Hills HS; Cincinnati, OH (10%-1000) Cpt, Band; Chess C; Pres, Demolay; Ensm; HiY; Hmrm; NHS; Orch; ARC; Tres, SC; Var C; VP, World Affairs C; Co-Cpt, Ftbl; Cpt, Sftbl; Amer Leg A; COM; Citz A; Masonic A; ARC A; VFW A; Yth Foundation; Drum Major; Blue Hon Key, DeMolay; *Harvard U; Law.*

PRICE, Helen Jeanne
Highland HS; Salt Lake City, UT; Chor; Ger C; JA A; ARC A; Church Organist.

PRICE, Hunter Jr
Skyline HS; Dallas, TX; SC; JV, Ftbl; JV, Tr; COM; God & Country A; JA A; Eagle Sct; Cert of Appreciation; *US Air Force; Aviation.*

PRICE, Jane Wetherill
Patrick Henry Acad; Estill, SC (2-19) Ann; BC; Chldr; Chor; Sch P; SC; S-T, Jr Cl; Pres, Soph Cl; Beauty; Cl Fav; Sal; Baptist Col at Charleston; Mus Ed.

PRICE, Janet Lee
Hazen HS; Hazen, AR (1-50) Co-Ed, Ann; Band; BC; FFA; VP, FHA; Sci C; SC; Pres, Soph Cl; Cl Fav; Hist A; HCt; MLS; Sci A; Eng A; PA, Church; Home Ec A; Band As; Band Medals; U of Ark; Merchandising.

PRICE, Janet Marie
Spencer HS; Spencer, IA; Drama; NHS; VP, Span C; Fin, Spch C; Hon Prog; Most Out; Spch A; Yth Fel; ILCC; Bus Adm.

PRICE, Jody Lynn
Lakota Consolidated HS; Lakota, IA (13-20) Chor; 4H; SC; Cpt, Bkbl; Cr-Crty; Cpt, Sftbl; Tr; 4H A; HCt; Type A; Pres A of Phys Fitness; Hamilton Bus Col; Legal Secy.

PRICE, John Michael
Flint N HS; Flint, MI (10%-700) Band; Ensm; NHS; Orch; Order/Arrow; Span C; Swim; Tr; Yth Fel; Drum Major; Nom, Regent's Schol; U of Mich; Geol.

PRICE, Julie Marie
Hilbert HS; Hilbert, WI (6-89) Chor; Drama; Madrigal; SC; COM; Pom-Pon Squad.

PRICE, Karen Sue
Cory-Rawson HS; Rawson, OH (10%-78) A Cap Choir; Ann; Chor; Drama; Ensm; Co-Ed, Sch P; Sci.

PRICE, Larry Robert
Harrison HS; Colo Springs, CO (1-420) Pres, Band; BS; Hmrm; NHS; JV, Cr-Crty; COM; Yth Fel; US Air Force Acad; Aviation.

PRICE, Linda Carole
Reeds Spring HS; Reeds Spring, MO (33%-82) AFS; BC; Pres, Chor; Dbte Tm; Drama; Ensm; FFA; FHA; Madrigal; Math C; Sci C; Spch C; Thes; JV, Tr; Hon Prog; Spch A; Mus As; Harding Col; Drama.

PRICE, Lisa M
Nurnberg Amer HS; Apo New York, NY (1-148) CYO; NHS; Var C; MVP, Bkbl; Tr; Co-Cpt, Bkbl; Swtht Qn; 7th, All-Ger Triple Jump; Govt A; Best Personality; Graduation Speaker; Va Polytechnic Inst; Civil Engr.

PRICE, Lori Jean
Wayne Co HS; Jesup, GA (5%-370) Ann; Band; BC; S-T, 4H; Hmrm; Lat C; Span C; Tres, Y-Tns; Sftbl; COM; 4H A; Hon Prog; NEDT; Ch, Beta C Schol Committee; Alt, Gov Hon; Sunday Sch Teacher; Beta Cert; Church Pianist; U of Ga; Phys Therapy.

PRICE, Mary Catherine
Patrick Henry HS; Glade Spring, VA (25-140) Bus C; Cpt, Chldr; FTA; GS; Ch, NHS; Var C; Citz A; Pres Clroom; Acad Ltr; Extracurricular Ltr; Va Highlands Comm Col; Bus Adm.

PRICE, Nora Lee
Villa Christian HS; Broadview, IL (2-6) A-Ed, Ann; Ensm; Secy, Ger C; COM; Journ A; Highest Pace Avg; Scripture Memorizer A; Scripture & Bible Stu; Most Paces Per Quarter & Completed; Baptist Bible Col; Elem Ed.

PRICE, Patricia Athena
Castlemont HS; Oakland, CA; Model UN; NHS; CSF; The Silver 'F' Pin; HR; Oakland Ath League Block C; Marcus A Foster Educational Achv A; U of Calif at Los Angeles; Biological Sci.

PRICE, Paula Elaine
Dan River HS; Ringgold, VA (8-238) BC; Guilford Col; Vet.

PRICE, Rhonda Kay
West HS; Bakersfield, CA; Hmrm; COM; Citz A; PTA A; Drill Tm; Art C A's; Yth Coun, Church.

PRICE, Robert Allen
Robert E Lee HS; Jacksonville, FL (10%-475) HiY; NHS; Bkbl & Sftbl Church Tm; Acad HR; Touring Yth Choir; U of Ga; Agr.

PRICE, Ronald Robert
Durand HS; Durand, IL; Band; Orch; Bsbl; Sftbl; Tr; SME Drawing Contest Win.

PRICE, Ryan Jay
Saint Francis HS; Saint Francis, WI (29-175) Band; VP, Bus C; Drama; NFL; Ftbl; Swim; Tnns; JA A; Spch A; Hastings Col; Mus.

PRICE, Sandra A
S Vigo HS; Terre Haute, IN (105-625) Chess C; FTA; Ger C; 4H; Orch; Y-Tns; Mgr, Tnns.

PRICE, Sherrill Kathleen
Lompoc Sr HS; Lompoc, CA; Most Out; S-T, Pep C; Allen Hancock Col; Acct.

PRICE, Stephanie Sue
Durand HS; Durand, IL; Semi-Fin, Prom Court; Class Play; Rockford Mem Hosp; X-Ray Tech.

PRICE, Teresa Charmaine
Bladenboro HS; Bladenboro, NC (18-100) Chor; Fr C; 4H; Ftbl; Sftbl; Sci A; Jr Homemaker Degree; SE Comm Col; Automotive Mech.

PRICE, Teresa Dawn
Reidsville Sr HS; Reidsville, NC (15-344) Chldr; Fr C; Hmrm; NHS; Tnns; Hon Prog; NC St U; Chem.

PRICE, Teresa Diana
Powell Valley HS; Speedwell, TN; Tres, BC; Co-Cpt, Chldr; S-T, SC; Tres, Soph Cl; COM; Cl Fav.

PRICE, Thelbert Louis
Tallulah HS; Tallulah, LA (2-66) 4H; SC; Bsbl; Ftbl; Tr; Alg A; Cl Fav; Math A; Naval Acad.

PRICE, Timothy Scott
Tyner HS; Chattanooga, TN (1-261) BC; Pres, NHS; SC; COM; Hon Prog; MLS; Star Student; Val; U of Tenn; Elec Engr.

PRICE, Tricia M
Arroyo Grande HS; Arroyo Grande, CA (84-499) Pres, A Cap Choir; Chor; Bank Of Amer A; HCt; WW; Most Talented Sr Girl; Continental Singers; Cuesta Col; Social Service.

PRICE, Veronica LaShal
Baker Sr HS; Baker, LA (15%-374) BC; Secy, Fr C; FTA; Tri-HiY; Tulane U; Med.

PRICE, Vicki Ann
Hatboro-Horsham Sr HS; Horsham, PA (69-420) Band; Chor; Mjrte; A-Ed, Sch P; Excel A; Old Dominion U; Marine Biol.

PRICE, Viviree Lugia
Jordan-Matthews HS; Siler City, NC; Chor; FBLA; VP, FTA; SC; Tr; HCt; NCCU; Acct.

PRICE, Wanda Gail
Lincoln HS; Dallas, TX; Band; Secy, Hmrm; Key C; Tres, Math C; NHS; VP, ARC; Sci C; Cl Fav; Sci A; Band A; E Tex St U; Acct.

PRICE, Wanda Lisa
Johnson Co HS; Wrightsville, GA (15-89) Ann; Band; FBLA; FHA; FTA; Sch P; Tri-HiY; Flag Corp; Family Living A; Ga Tech; Med Secy.

PRICE, Yvonne Elaine
German Sr HS; Mc Clellandtown, PA; Chor; Ensm; COM; PA.

PRICKETT, Debbie Ann
Polytechnic HS; Sun Valley, CA; Citz A; Hon Prog; Valley Col; Nurs.

PRICKETT, Kenneth Wayne
Fairfield HS; Fairfield, AL (25%-180) Ann; Band; Order/Arrow; ARC; Sch P; Order/Arrow A; Yth Fel; Eagle Sct; Church Singing Group; Pres, Sunday Sch; Sch Plays; Auburn U; Vet Med.

PRICKETT, Kerry Alan
Fairfield HS; Fairfield, AL (25%-180) Ann; Band; Order/Arrow; ARC; Sch P; Order/Arrow A; Yth Fel; Eagle Sct; Church Singing Group; Pres, Church Yth Fel; Sch Plays; Auburn U; Vet Med.

PRICKETT, Sharon Pauline
Polytechnic HS; Sun Valley, CA; CSF; Citz A; Cal St U of Northridge.

PRIDDY, Barbara Jean
T Wingate Andrews HS; High Point, NC (30-300) Ann; BC; Fr C; French NHS; ARC; Sci C; Hon Prog; Keyettes; Acteens, Cert of Appreciation; Chapel Hill U; Nurs.

PRIDDY, Melinda Lee
Big Spring HS; Big Spring, TX (9-600) Chor; Golf; Yth Fel; Ntl Piano Playing Auditions; Tex Tech U; Ed.

PRIDDY, Tracie
Chattanooga Central HS; Harrison, TN (30-285) Ann; Bus C; Chor; Ensm; FBLA; FHA; Hmrm; NHS; ARC; Sftbl; Bible A; Schol A; Service A.

PRIDE, John Wayne
Union Co HS; Morganfield, KY; VP, BC; Fr C; 4H; Math C; NHS; VP, SC; VP, Sr Cl; Bkbl; Ftbl; Cl Fav; Hon Prog; Gen Bus A; Oral Roberts U; Bus Adm.

PRIDE, Matthew Lane
Union Co HS; Morganfield, KY; BC; Fr C; 4H; Math C; NHS; SC; Pres, Sr Cl; Bkbl; Ftbl; Cl Fav; Hon Prog; Oral Roberts U; Bus Adm.

PRIEBE, Malinda Diann
Putnam City HS; Oklahoma City, OK (325-850) A Cap Choir; Chor; Drama; Ensm; Ger C; Hmrm; Rainbow; SC; Mus As; E Central Col; Ed.

PRIEBE, William Paul
Benjamin Franklin Sr HS; New Orleans, LA; Demolay; Lat C; JV, Bkbl; JV, Sftbl; MIT; Aerodynamic Engr.

PRIER, Cheryl DeAnn
Pineville HS; Pineville, LA (6-231) Ann; FHA; FNA; Hmrm; Lit Ral; Secy, NHS; Rptr, Sch P; Y-Tns; Crisco A; Hon Prog; Cpt, Booster C; WW; Alumni Schol; Pastor's A Schol; La Col; Ed.

PRIEST, Cheryl Lynn
Redlands Sr HS; Redlands, CA (25%-950) F-Ed, Ann; Hmrm; SC; God & Country A; 1st Cl GSct; San Bernardino Valley Col; Sci.

PRIEST, Eric Paul
Paint Valley HS; Bainbridge, OH (11-88) Fin, BS; Chor; Drama; Ensm; Lat C; NHS; Sci C; JV, Bsbl; Amer Leg A; Sci A; Utah U; Metorology.

PRIEST, Mark Steven
Heritage HS; Monroeville, IN (50-190) Band; JV, Ftbl.

PRIEST, Michelle Elaine
Redlands Sr HS; Redlands, CA (25%-950) Chldr; Hmrm; Swim; CSF; God & Country A; Gym; Diving; 1st Cl GSct; Chldr Mascot; Phys Therapy.

PRIEST, Philip Andrew
Taft HS; Chicago, IL (84-840) Band; Community Yth Symph; Bus Mgr, Hmrm; NHS; VP, Orch; Soccer; NEDT; St Scholar; Yth Fel; U of Ill at Champaign; Pre-Law.

PRIESTER, Reeder
Scott Preparatory Sch; Opelika, AL (10%-27) Ch, Anchor C; BC; Chldr; VP, Hmrm; Var C; VP, Soph Cl; Beauty; COM; Hon Prog; NEDT; Bat Girl; Auburn U; Eng.

PRIETO, Maria Josefina
Colegio Universit Sagrado Corazon; San Juan, PR (1-25) Drama; NHS; Alg A; Bio A; COM; Hist A; Religion A; Eng A; Span A; Good Conduct A; Pre-Med.

PRIEVE, Beth Anne
Hutchinson HS; Hutchinson, MN (10-205) Band; Chor; Cpt, Mjrte; NHS; SC; Thes; Hon Prog; Opt A; Spch A; Sup Solo Voice; Augsburg Col; Spch Pathology.

PRIGMORE, David Bristow
Lake Highlands HS; Dallas, TX; A Cap Choir; Chor; Key C; Lat C; Madrigal; SC; Var C; Bsbl; Cpt, Bkbl; Cl Fav; Hon Prog; Star Student; Swtht; Church Choir; Pres, Royal Ambassadors; St Champs, Church Bkbl Tm; Baylor U; Archt.

PRIME, Charles Kevin
McGavock HS; Nashville, TN (206-836) Bkbl; Citz A; Home Ec A; Tenn St U; Home Ec.

PRINCE, Ella Denise
Denbigh HS; Newport News, VA (166-488) Tres, Band; Drama; Semi-Fin, GS; Hmrm; Tres, St Stu Congres; SC; Rptr, Soph Cl; Miss Peninsula Baptist Union; Goddess of Good Cheer; Va Commonwealth U; Nurs.

PRINCE, James Jarrell
Palestine HS; Palestine, TX (4-400) InterAct C; Sch P; SC; Bsbl; JV, Ftbl; Tres, FCA; Baylor U; Law.

PRINCE, Jimmy
Charles B Glenn HS; Birmingham, AL; Ann; Chem C; Chess C; Cr-Crty; Cpt, Tnns; Tuskgee Inst; Engr.

PRINCE, Kenneth Joseph
Briarcrest Baptist HS; Memphis, TN (25%-400)
Band; JV, Bsbl; JV, Bkbl; Jazz Band; Church Yth
Choir; Med Explorers; *U of Tenn; Med.*

PRINCE, Mollie Bell
Highland HS; Bakersfield, CA; Bus C; Rainbow;
Bank Of Amer A; *N Central Col; Missionary Field.*

PRINCE, Philip Alan
Woodrow Wilson HS; Beckley, WV (150-539)
Band; Ensm; Fr C; 4H; Tres, Mod Mus Mas;
DARGCA; God & Country A; JA A; Sci A; Yth
Leg; *W Va Wesleyan Col; Hospital Adm.*

PRINCE, Philip B
Shawnee HS; Shawnee, OK (1-350) Band; Ensm;
Fr C; Order/Arrow; NMF; NMS; Val; Most Intelligent Sr; *Vanderbilt Col; Eng.*

PRINCE, Tara Lee
Quincy HS; Quincy, MA; Bkbl; Colorguard; *Art.*

PRINCE, William Jr
Glenn Hills HS; Augusta, GA; SC; Bsbl; Bkbl; Ftbl;
Tr; Cl Fav; Most Out; Ftbl, Bkbl, Tr, Bsbl, A's;
Morehouse Col; Med.

PRINCIPE, Caleb Moises
Central HS; Santurce, PR (1-300) COM; *University of PR; Engr.*

PRINDLE, Warren Brown
Ft Pierce Central HS; Fort Pierce, FL (118-582) Lit
Mag; Sch P; Span NHS; JV, Bsbl; JV, Ftbl; JV,
Wrest; Tres, Christian Yth Fel; Photography C; Bi-Racial Committee; *Moody Bible Inst; Bible.*

PRINE, Mark Anthony
Eastern Local HS; Macon, OH (10-85) Fr C; FTA;
4H; NHS; Sch Achieve Tm; F-Ed, Sch P; 4H A;
Sou St Col.

PRINGLE, Charles Lawrence
Hightstown HS; Hightstown, NJ; Hon Prog; *Rutgers U; Forrestry.*

PRINGLE, Kristal Michelle
Highland Park HS; Dallas, TX (19-421) Math C;
Mu Alpha Theta; NHS; Orch; Cr-Ctry; Tr; Hon
Prog; Cpt, Vlbl; *Tex A&M U; Elec Engr.*

PRINGLE, Lonnie Ray
New Lexington HS; New Lexington, OH (53-178)
Y-Tns; Swim; Citz A; *Hocking Tech Col; Police
Sci.*

PRINGLE, Terry Lorraine
Science HS; Newark, NJ; Chor; Fr C; JETS; COM;
Citz A; MLS; Most Out; Pres, Yth Coun; Young
Adult Choir; Sch Rep, St Ed Meeting; Trip to Paris
As Top Fr Stu; Church Deconess; *UCLA; Law.*

PRINTY, Ronnie Ray
Harlingen HS; Harlingen, TX (45-600) Fr C; Key
C; Bsbl; Bkbl; Ftbl; Sftbl; Swim; Tr; Pres A; Ftbl,
Bsbl, Tr, Bkbl, A's; *Tex A&M U; Oceanography.*

PRINZING, Debra Kay
U S Grant HS; Portland, OR (52-300) AFS; Band;
Fr C; Hmrm; SC; Sftbl; Tr; Rose Festival Court;
Seattle Pacific U; Clothing-Textiles.

PRITCHARD, Cindy Gay
Mountain View HS; Mountain View, OK (1-31)
Ann; FHA; 4H; Bkbl; Sftbl; Bio A; Hist A; HCt; St
Hon Soc; Academic Achv A, OSU; Bkbl Ltr A;
Southwestern St U; Sci.

PRITCHARD, Joan Kay
Fredericktown HS; Fredericktown, OH; Band;
Chldr; Chor; 4H; Orch; Rainbow; Sch P; 4H A;
Drill Tm; Statistician; Tr & Bkbl.

PRITCHARD, Leonard Leon
Cambridge S Dorchester HS; Cambridge, MD
(20-360) AFS; MLS; Yth Fel; *Chesapeake Col;
Law.*

PRITCHARD, Nancy Louise
Milo Adventist Acad; Days Creek, OR (1-50)
ARC; VP, Soph Cl; *Oreg St U; Mus.*

PRITCHARD, Philip McAulay
Oak Ridge Acad; Oak Ridge, NC (5-30) Chor;
Drama; Var C; Bsbl; Bkbl; Soccer; Citz A; Military
HR; *Elon Col; Phys Ed.*

PRITCHETT, Annie Lois
Bullock Co HS; Union Springs, AL; Chor; Hmrm;
Jr Miss Pagent; NHS; Sch P; Sftbl; Bio A; Cl Fav;
Hist A; HQn; Sal; *U of Ala; Psych.*

PRITCHETT, Debra
Jefferson HS; Los Angeles, CA; NHS; Citz A; Sci
A; Vlbl; *Loyola Col; Bus.*

PRITCHETT, Michael Eugene
Vandalia-Farber Sr HS; Vandalia, MO; NHS; Hist
A; Soph Pilgrimage; Schol A; Schol Quiz Tm; FFA
Creed Speaker; *Stephen's Col; Sci.*

PRITCHETT, Patti Laverne
Willows HS; Willows, CA (17-130) Chldr; FHA;
Semi-Fin, GS; 4H; InterClub Coun; Sch P; SC;
Bank Of Amer A; 4H A; HCt; Pres A; Songleading
Ribbons; *American River Jr Col; Bus.*

PRITCHETT, Theresa Ann
Prague HS; Prague, OK (1-72) Ann; Tres, Band;
CYO; Dbte Tm; VP, FHA; GS; Pres, NFL; Pres,
NHS; Bkbl; Bio A; Gov Honor Prog; Masonic A;
MLS; Odd Fellow Fin; Spch A; Val; Jr Counselor,
GS; UN Pilgrimage for Yth; OU Achv A; St Sen
Page; *The U of Okla; Microbio.*

PRITTEN, Kenneth Lee
Luther Burbank HS; Sacramento, CA (175-614)
Band; Ensm; COM; *San Jose Bible Col; Religion.*

PRITZLAFF, Edward Philip
St Peters Prep Sch; Jersey City, NJ (16-250) Bsbl;
JV, Bkbl; Ftbl; COM; Hon Prog; All-Co & Fifth
Quarter C Ftbl Hons; *Ed.*

PRITZLAFF, Philip Edward
St Peters Prep HS; Jersey City, NJ (3-260) Band;
Var C; Bsbl; Alg A; Hon Prog; Math A; Eng A; *NJ
Inst of Tech; Engr.*

PRIVETT, Patricia Ann
Campbell HS; Fairburn, GA (10-125) BC; Chor;
VP, FTA; Hmrm; Lat C; Math C; Mu Alpha Theta;
NHS; SC; COM; Hon Prog; NEDT; Yth Fel; Lt,
Drill Tm; Tres, Jr Civitans; DECA; De District
Contestant A; Outst Jr Civitan; *Bio.*

PRIVETT, Roger Edwin
Palmdale HS; Palmdale, CA; Chor; JV, Ftbl; Wrest.

PRIVOTT, Karen Kay
Yukon HS; Yukon, OK (10%-388) Drama; FHA;
NHS; SC; Bkbl; Christian Fel; Eng A; *Okla U;
Journ.*

PROBERT, Laurine Lynn
Austintown Fitch HS; Youngstown, OH (245-741)
A Cap Choir; *Mobility Specialist.*

PROBST, Deborah Christine
Brady HS; Brady, TX (4-97) Band; FTA; 4H; NHS;
Lion A; Band Swtht; *Tex A&M U; Phys Therapy.*

PROBST, Donald Albert
JTHS East Campus HS; Joliet, IL (85-472) A Cap
Choir; Chor; Ensm; Ch, Hmrm; ARC; F-Ed, Sch P;
Amer Leg A; COM; Citz A; ARC A; ROTC A; Val;
VFW A; *Bradley U; Mus.*

PROBSTFIELD, Theresa Ann
Sunset HS; Beaverton, OR (33%-475) Band; Open
Door Tm; *Lewis and Clark Col; Advertising.*

PROCHNOW, Glenn Russell
Seguin HS; Seguin, TX (4-320) BS; Drama; Key C;
NHS; Order/Arrow; Bkbl; JV, Tr; Cl Fav; God &
Country A; NMF; NMS; Opt A; Order/Arrow A;
Eagle Sct; 1000 Gen Dynamics Schol; Most Intelligent; *Tex Lutheran Col; Acct.*

PROCHNOW, Tom James
Wausau W HS; Wausau, WI; *Heavy Machinery
Operation.*

PROCTOR, Juanita
Frost Independent HS; Frost, TX (4-15) Ann;
Drama; VP, FHA; Hmrm; SC; Cl Fav; 4H A; *Navarro Col; Ed.*

PROCTOR, Michael L
Roosevelt HS; Gary, IN; All Amer Yth; Cpt, Band;
VP, Chor; Fin, Ensm; HiY; NHS; Orch; Sci C; SC;
Up Bound; Bsbl; Bkbl; Sftbl; COM; Hon Prog;
MLS; Most Out; Sci A; Type A; Jr Schol A; Outst
Band; *Purdue U; Elec Engr.*

PROCTOR, Paul D Jr
Brazil HS; Brazil, IN (33-192) Hmrm; Key C;
NHS; Ed, Sch P; Span C; Tri-HiY; VP, Var C;
Co-Cpt, Ftbl; Co-Cpt, Wrest; HCt; Q&S A; Key to
the City; *Ind St U; Industrial Arts.*

PROCTOR, Thomas Alvis
Kinston HS; Kinston, NC (35-337) AFS; BC; Cpt,
Bkbl; Golf; Ntl Sci Found; *U of NC; Bio.*

PRODAN, Karen Ruth
El Camino Real HS; Woodland Hills, CA
(25%-1300) *Calif Baptist Col; Art.*

PROFFITT, Francine Delaine
Bob Jones HS; Madison, AL (15%-114) BC; JV,
Chldr; Rptr, FHA; Hmrm; Rainbow; Span C; Secy,
Jr Cl; Beauty; HCt; Spch A; Pres, FHA; *Emmanuel
Col; Nurs.*

PROFFITT, Katie Anne
Buckley HS; Sherman Oaks, CA; NHS; Bio A; Hist
A; Hon Prog; Math A; Sci A; *UC at Irvine; Allied
Health.*

PROKARYM, Lisa Anne
Old Forge HS; Old Forge, PA (21-121) Secy, Band;
FNA; Hmrm; NHS; Secy, Orch; Sci C; *Wilkes Col;
Bus.*

PROKOP, Rosemary
The Immaculata HS; Chicago, IL (2-157) Pres, Fr
C; French NHS; Pres, NHS; Pres, Soph Cl; COM;
Hon Prog; JA A; St Scholar; VofDEM; *Loyola U;
Sci.*

PRONGER, Timothy Albert
Adams Friendship HS; Adams, WI (85-177) Band;
Hmrm; Orch; SC; Cr-Ctry; Ftbl; Tr; Ftbl, Tr, A's;
Purdue U; Drafting.

PRONK, Hollyn Diane
Edgerton Pub HS; Edgerton, MN (2-31) Band; JV,
Chldr; Chor; NHS; JV Vlbl; *Med.*

PROPES, Gregory Charles
Grissom HS; Huntsville, AL; Yth Fel; Church Mus
Tours; Fraternity; Jr Church Deacon; Big Brothers;
Jacksonville St U; Bus.

PROPHET, Victoria
Seward Park HS; New York, NY (150-650) A Cap
Choir; Yth Choir; Secy, Women's Guild; Sunday
Sch Teacher; *Hunter Col; Mus.*

PROPP, Michael Steven
Salina S HS; Salina, KS (20-367) Ann; Chess C;
Hmrm; NHS; SC; Bkbl; Tnns; HCt; Hon Prog; Yth
Fel; KU Hon Prog; Principal's HR; WW; *Wichita St
Col; Math.*

PROPPS, Kim Lavita
Central HS; St Paul, MN; Chor; Bkbl; Kiwanis A;
Most Out; *Concordia Col; Ed.*

PROPST, Robin Leigh
Joppatowne HS; Joppatowne, MD (18-202) AFS;
Secy, Band; Chor; Ensm; F-Ed; Hmrm; NHS; Orch;
Rainbow; SC; Hon Prog; Star Student; Golden Anchor A; Best Dressed Sr; *Juniata Col; Pre-Med.*

PROSISE, Trina Lynell
Las Plumas HS; Oroville, CA (7-184) Band; Ensm;
NHS; SC; Mgr, Bkbl; CSF; COM; Lion A; Rifle &
Pistol C; Secy, Pro-tns; Ntl Rifle Assn; Pep Band;
Top 10; Earthquake Research; Outst Ac; Executive
Coun Rep, GAA; *Calif St U; Lib Stu.*

PROSSER, Roy Eugene
DeKalb HS; Auburn, IN; Pres, 4H; Wrest; 4H A;
Rptr, 4-H Jr Ldr; REMC Washington Trip.

PROTZMAN, Charissa Lynn
Nathan Hale HS; Tulsa, OK; Band; Community
Yth Symph; Ger C.

PROTZMANN, William Lee
Valley Christian HS; Saratoga, CA (25%-120)
Band; Co-Cpt, Chess C; Community Yth Symph;
4H; Hmrm; Orch; SC; Bkbl; Ftbl; Soccer; CSF; Citz
A; Hon Prog; Adventure Unlimited Tn Coun; 1st
Pl, Jr Woman's C, Piano; Win, UNICEF Mus Concerts; *Oral Roberts U; Bus Adm.*

PROUT, John Shepherd
N Salem HS; Salem, NY (15-110) Chess C; Drama;
Order/Arrow; Bsbl; Cr-Ctry; Tnns; Wrest; Regent
Schol; Eagle Sct; Pres, Loc Adventure Unlimited
Captr; *Eisenhower Col; International Relations.*

PROUTY, Alan Leslie
Walla Walla HS; Walla Walla, WA (15-550) Soccer; Citz A; Hist A; Sci A; 3rd Pl Sci Fair; Microbio
And Pathology A; *Washington St U; Nuclear
Chem.*

PROVINCE, Paul Ray
Cottage Grove Union HS; Cottage Grove, OR
(15-260) A Cap Choir; Chor; Drama; NHS; Tres,
SC; Thes; COM; *U of Oreg; Bus.*

PRUDE, Kelley Nelson
Robert E Lee HS; Midland, TX; A Cap Choir; Chor; Ensm; Madrigal; Math C; NHS; Alg A; COM; Hon Prog; JA A; Math A; Sci A; Choir A; *Tex Tech Col; Geol.*

PRUEFER, Debbie Sue
Port Washington HS; Port Washington, WI (99-334) Ski C; Tnns; Tr; 1st Pl Mile Relay, Conf; Tr A; Tnns Ltr; *Madison Col; Human Relations.*

PRUELL, Gail Diane
Alhambra HS; Martinez, CA; Ann; Drama; FHA; Sch P; JV, Bsbl; Ftbl; JV, Sftbl; Cl Fav; Type A; Rally C; Choir, Shorthand, A's; *Warner Col; Court Stenographer.*

PRUET, Kelli Denise
Duncanville HS; Duncanville, TX (19-400) Ann; Lit Mag; SC; Tr; COM; Hon Prog; Bible A; UIL Essay; Literary Magazine; Vol, X-Ray, Hospital; *Abilene Christian U; Bible.*

PRUETER, David Michael
Glendale HS; Springfield, MO (10-400) AFS; Hmrm; Key C; Order/Arrow; Span C; SC; Bsbl; Co-Cpt, Ftbl; Wrest; Curator A; Order/Arrow A; Principal's HR; *U of Mo; Chem Engr.*

PRUETT, David Craig
Gainesville HS; Gainesville, TX (36-184) Band; Span C; HR; Teacher's Aide; Church Yth Choir; *Cooke Co Col; Engr.*

PRUETT, Douglas Andrew
Burns Sr HS; Lawndale, NC (32-280) Ann; Drama; InterAct C; InterClub Coun; Key C; Span C; Gov Honor Prog; Governor's Sch of NC.

PRUETT, Melanie Starr
Resource Learning Center; Birmingham, AL; Band; Chldr; Dbte Tm; Drama; NHS; Span C; Span NHS; SC; Pres A; *Harding Col; Bus.*

PRUETT, Norma Ann
Burns HS; Lawndale, NC (30-270) Band; SC; Pres, Soph Cl.

PRUETT, Susan Kay
Princeton HS; Princeton, TX; *Social Work.*

PRUFERT, Leslie Eileen
Germantown HS; Germantown, TN; BC; Chor; Fr C; Lit Mag; Math C; NHS; Rptr, Sch P; Phy A; *Southwestern at Memphis; Med.*

PRUITT, Brenda Leigh
Jayhawk-Linn HS; Mount City, KS (2-48) Rptr, Ann; Cpt, Chldr; Chor; Secy, Drama; VP, FHA; GS; Parl, 4H; NHS; Rptr, Sch P; Secy, Spch C; SC; Bkbl; Sftbl; Tr; 4H A; HQn; Spch A; Rptr, 4-H C; FFA Swtht; HR; *Kans St Col; Phys Therapy.*

PRUITT, Carol Lynn
Klein HS; Houston, TX; FHA; COM; 3rd Pl, Art Ribbon; 1st Pl, VICA Ribbon; 4th Pl, Dist VICA Ribbon; *Commercial Art.*

PRUITT, Daryl Sheroid
Charles Lincoln Harper HS; Atlanta, GA; Rptr, Ger C; Pres, Hmrm; VP, InterAct C; Bus Mgr, Sch P; Co-Ch, SC; Tnns; Bio A; COM; Citz A; Hist A; Math A; ROTC A; Sci A; *Med.*

PRUITT, Dena Lorraine
Ruffin HS; Ruffin, NC (16-86) FTA; *Danville Comm Col; Elec.*

PRUITT, Gregory Don
Hickman Co HS; Clinton, KY (1-80) Pres, BC; BS; Chor; Math C; SC; Var C; Cpt, Bsbl; Bkbl; Hist A; Type A; Val; *Murray St U; Pre-Law.*

PRUITT, Hasan
Jamaica Plain HS; Jamacia Plain, MA; Drama; NHS; SC; Var C; Ftbl; Tr; *U of Calif; Math.*

PRUITT, Jean Ann
Eminence Consolidated HS; Eminence, IN (1-43) Secy, NHS; *Phys Ed.*

PRUITT, Joanna Michele
Alleghany Co HS; Covington, VA (5%-267) Bus C; Chor; Tr; Pres A; *Math.*

PRUITT, Penny Ann
Central HS; Memphis, TN; A Cap Choir; Bus C; Chor; Drama; Ensm; Fr C; NFL; Spch C; Thes; VP, Sr Cl; COM; Yth Fel; Ntl Piano Cert; Ntl Jr Hon Soc; PA A; *Clark Col; Computer Programming.*

PRUITT, Theresa Joy
Merryville HS; Merryville, LA (1-58) Band; Semi-Fin, Lit Ral; Sci C; Bkbl; Tr; Sci A; Ath Scholastic A; 3rd Pl, Regional Sci Fair; Best Stu; Regional Hon Band; *McNeese Col; Physics.*

PRUITT, Thomas Brian
David Crockett HS; Jonesboro, TN (10%-370) Bsbl; JV, Bkbl; UMYF at Church.

PRUITT, Tina C
Shawnee Sr HS; Louisville, KY; Co-Cpt, Chldr; Hmrm; HCt; Sci A; *Col of Modeling; Mod.*

PRUITT, Valarie Devonne
Wade Hampton HS; Greenville, SC (33%-553) Chor; Tres, Hmrm; F-Ed, Sch P; HCt; Pres, Choir; 'P' C; Central Spirit, Pep C; *Johnson C Smith Col; Bus Adm.*

PRUITT, Vera Irene
Pendleton HS; Pendleton, SC (9-133) Band; BC; Pres, Chor; Fr C; FHA; 4H; InterClub Coun; Sci C; All-St Hon Chor; *Anderson Jr Col; Mus.*

PRUNTY, Sandra Kim
East HS; Columbus, OH (8-350) Yth Ldrship A; *U of Mich; Marketing.*

PRUSS, Rox Ann Helen
Crescent HS; Joyce, WA (3-18) Ann; Band; Hmrm; NHS; VP, SC; Mgr, Bkbl; Mgr, Ftbl; HCt; *Hico Col; Phys Ed.*

PRUZAN, Marion Moore
Washington HS; Washington, NC (51-290) S-T, Band; Chor; Drama; Tres, Fr C; Hmrm; SC; Tnns; Yth Fel; All St Band; Nom, McDonalds All Amer Band; *St Andrews Presbyterian Col; Pre-Law.*

PRYDE, Craig Randolph
Elgin HS; Elgin, IL (113-1011) A Cap Choir; Chor; Madrigal; Ski C; Mgr, Bkbl; Golf; Tnns; Gr Marshal; Hon Prog; VP, Yth Fel; *Archt Engr.*

PRYER, Gregory Lee
Del Rio HS; Del Rio, TX (20-400) Yth Fel; *U of Tex; Phar.*

PRYER, Linda Kay
Del Rio HS; Del Rio, TX; Band; Chor; Ensm; Hmrm; Semi-Fin, Lit Ral; God & Country A; Math A; Most Out; Yth Fel; *U of Tex; Computer Sci.*

PRYJMA, Marta Anna
Immaculate Conception Ukrainian HS; Hamtramck, MI; CYO; Chor; NHS; Hon Prog; *U of Mich; Chem.*

PRYMA, Leo George
St Patrick HS; Chicago, IL (13-342) Chor; MVP, Bsbl; JV, Bkbl; JV, Cr-Ctry; WW; *Bradley U.*

PRYOR, Elizabeth Jane
McMinn Co HS; Athens, TN (31-276) Semi-Fin, Jr Miss Pa; Mu Alpha Theta; NFL; NHS; Bus Mgr, Sch P; SC; Thes; Tri-HiY; Hon Prog; Spch A; Vof-DEM; Yth Leg; Stu Govt Co Coun; Rotarian Exchange Stu to Mexico; *U of Tex at Arlington; Pre-Med.*

PRYOR, Leolla
DeVilbiss HS; Toledo, OH; Fr C; Semi-Fin, Jr Miss Pa; COM; Citz A; Cl Fav; Hon Prog; *Secy.*

PRYOR, Monica Arlene
Short Ridge HS; Indianapolis, IN; 4H; Cr-Ctry; Tr; Var Tr; *Math.*

PRYOR, Robert Frank
Texas City HS; Texas City, TX; Drama; Key C; Pres, SC; JV, Bsbl; JV, Bkbl; JV, Ftbl; Fin, Tr; Cl Fav; FCA.

PRYSTUPA, Ruth
Hollywood HS; Hollywood, CA; Hmrm; SC; COM; Citz A; *L A Valley Col; Cosmetology.*

PRZYBYCIEN, Robert William
Burnt Hills-Ballston Lake HS; Burnt Hills, NY (19-350) Bus Mgr, Ann; Hmrm; Lit Mag; Ed, Sch P; Mgr, Bsbl; MVP, Bkbl; Journ A; Regent Schol; *Union Col; Sociology.*

PRZYBYLSKI, Lisa
Holy Cross HS; Delran, NJ (21-394) CYO; JV, Chldr; FFA; Hmrm; NHS; Pol Sci C; Ski C; Span C; Span NHS; SC; JV, Swim; Cl Fav; Hon Prog; Chldr Trophy; Swim Medal; *Villanova Col; Pol Sci.*

PRZYBYLSKI, Theresa
Holy Cross HS; Riverside, NJ (10-360) Chldr; FFA; FTA; NHS; Span C; Span NHS; SC; Mgr, Bkbl; Amer Leg A; Hon Prog; *Cook Col; Horticulture.*

PUCHATY, Suzanne
Satellite HS; Satellite Beach, FL; CYO; Swim; Swim As; *Modeling.*

PUCILOWSKI, Lynne Marie
Riverside Jr Sr HS; Taylor, PA (2-186) Chldr; Chor; Drama; Secy, FTA; Ger C; NHS; Sch P; Sodality; SC; Hon Prog; NEDT; *Communications.*

PUCKETT, Donna Jean
Taylor HS; N Bend, OH; Co-Ed, Ann; Bus C; Cpt, Mjrte; Sch P; Past Hon Qn, Job's Daughters; Ohio Rep to Ky, Job's Daughters; *Court Rptr.*

PUCKETT, Jacqueline Yvette
Laurel Sr HS; Laurel, MD (35-500) NHS; Var C; Cpt, Sftbl; Sci A; Ath Ltr; Recreation Director,; Ping Pong C; Sftbl Tm Church; Vlbl; VP, Church Yth Coun; Photography C; Vacation Bible Sch; *Prince Georges Comm Col; Recreation.*

PUCKETT, Melissa Jayne
Loudon HS; Loudon, TN (9-150) JV, Chldr; FHA; Lat C; NHS; ARC; Sci C; *U of Tenn; Nurs.*

PUCKETT, Pamela Kaye
Weatherford Sr HS; Weatherford, TX (11-252) Ensm; FTA; Tres, NHS; Citz A; Hon Prog; MLS; Opt A; Choirster o-t Yr; Girl o-t Yr; *Phar.*

PUCKETT, Randal Gene
Koshkonong HS; Koshkonong, MO (2-21) Chor; Bsbl; Co-Cpt, Bkbl; Cr-Ctry; Bio A; Citz A; Elk A; Sal; Bookkeeping A; Mus A; Psych A; *Evangel Col; Acct.*

PUCKETT, Roger Daniel
Oregon-Howell R-3 HS; Koshkonong, MO (10%-20) Ann; Chor; Rptr, Sch P; Bsbl; Bkbl; Cr-Ctry; Type A.

PUDAS, Jeanette Ruth
Park Center Sr HS; Brooklyn Park, MN; Chor; Rptr, Lit Mag; Rptr, Sch P; COM; Journ A; Type A; Church Yth Coun; Church High League & Choir; 'A' HR; 'B' HR; *N Hennepin Comm Col; Nurs.*

PUDER, Janet R
Burkburnett HS; Burkburnett, TX; NHS; Yth for Christ; *Mid-W St U.*

PUDER, Sharon Ann
MacArthur HS; Irving, TX (5-365) SC; Hist, Drill Tm; *Stephen F Austin Col; Math.*

PUDLO, Luanne Marie
Lyman Memorial HS; Lebanon, CT; Chor; Fr C; Span C; Type A; Bus A; *Secretarial.*

PUDWILL, Tamara Lea
Lincoln E HS; Lincoln, NE (4-456) Chldr; Hon Prog; Pom Pon Sq; *U of Nebr; Phys Therapy.*

PUENTE, Ivan
Academia Sagrado Corazon; San Juan, PR (5-90) ARC; Sci C; SC; VP, Soph Cl; Cpt, Bsbl; Alg A; Math A; Phy A; Span A; Eng A; Geography A; *Westminster Col; Med.*

PUENTE, Miguel Angel
Paint Rock HS; Paint Rock, TX; BC; Rptr, FFA; Ftbl; *ASU; Engr.*

PUESCHNER, Maree Jo
Newman HS; Wausau, WI (35-136) Chldr; Hmrm; *U of Wis; Special Ed.*

PUETT, Peggy Ann
N Gaston HS; Dallas, NC (11-294) BC; Key C; Secy, Monogram; Span C; Bkbl; Tr; Pres A; *NC St U; Natural Sci.*

PUFKO, Ann Marie
Mount Vernon HS; Alexandria, VA; Band; Secy, CYO; Tr; Pres A; Var Ltr; Cpt, Drill Tm; *Elem Ed.*

PUFKO, Cathleen Marie
Mount Vernon HS; Alexandria, VA (10%-560) S-T, Band; Pres, CYO; Hmrm; S-T, Mod Mus Mas; NHS; Span C; SC; S-T, Sr Cl; Rptr, Jr Cl; Tr; Pres A; Band A; Drill Tm Ltr; *VPI; Mus.*

PUGH, Ann Marie
Wade Hampton HS; Greenville, SC (100-385) Secy, Fr C; S-T, Hmrm; Rptr, Sch P; *Winthrop Col; Bus Adm.*

PUGH, Beth Marie
Havre HS; Havre, MT; A Cap Choir; Pres, MYF; Church Adm Board; *Rocky Mountain Col; Psych.*

PUGH, Brian Conway
Royal Oak Kimball HS; Royal Oak, MI; Band; Community Yth Symph; Orch; Thes; Yth Fel; Sunday Sch Teacher; Church Choir; *Albion Col.*

PUGH, Karen Eileen
Neptune Sr HS; Neptune, NJ (25-550) CYO; GS; Lit Mag; NHS; Sch P; Tres, Sr Cl; COM; Hon Prog; NMS; Omega Psi Phi A; GAA; *Pratt Inst; Art & Design.*

PUGH, Karen Foster
Royal Oak Kimball HS; Royal Oak, MI; Band; Thes; Var C; Yth Fel; Co-Cpt, Gym; Sunday Sch Teacher; Church Choir; *Albion Col; Broadcasting.*

PUGH, Michael John
Fort Osage HS; Independence, MO (44-370) A Cap Choir; Chor; Drama; Hmrm; NFL; NHS; Spch C; Var C; Mgr, Ftbl; Mgr, Tr; Citz A; Hon Prog; *U of Mo; Arts.*

PUGH, Pamela Lynn
Texhoma HS; Texhoma, OK (2-30) Band; Chor; Ensm; NHS; Rptr, Sch P; S-T, Jr Cl; Bkbl; Alg A; Masonic A; Math A; Star Student; Yth Fel; *Computer Data Processing.*

PUGH, Sandra Renee
Killeen HS; Killeen, TX (50-900) Drama; FHA; FTA; Hmrm; Jr Miss Pagent; NFL; Spch C; Spch A; *Central Tex Col; Advertising.*

PUGH, Susan Catherine
W End Acad; Texhoma, LA (4-10) Chor; Hmrm; Rainbow; Pres, SC; Rptr, Jr Cl; Rptr, Soph Cl; Cpt, Bkbl; Yth Fel; Spring Ct; Bkbl A; Rptr, Tres, Secy, Historian, Chrch; Board Member, Councilion, Chrch; Rptr, Tres, Secy, Church; *U of Southwestern La; Ed.*

PUGSLEY, Mary Elizabeth
Msgr Ryan Mem HS; Dorchester, MA; Chor; Drama; Pres, Hmrm; Lit Ral; Spch C; S-T, SC; Swim; Hon Prog; VofDEM; *NE U; Nurs.*

PUIG, Carmen M
Academia Ntra Sra Providencia; Rio Piedras, PR (2-58) Chor; Drama; Fr C; Math C; Sch P; Var C; Tr; COM; Hon Prog; Lion A; Math A; Star Student; *Tampa U; Bus Adm.*

PUIG, Gilberto
Notre Dame HS; Caguas, PR (1-140) CYO; City Conf; Hmrm; COM; Cl Fav; High Hon; *U of Puerto Rico at Rio Piedras; Med.*

PUIG, Rosa Enid
Notre Dame HS; Caguas, PR (28-140) Drama; NHS; COM; Hon Prog; Excellence A; *Quimica.*

PULFER, Kathy Rose
Valley HS; Elgin, IA (24-64) Ann; Chor; 4H; Sch P; Tr; Amer Leg A; 4H A; *Kirkwood Comm Col; Med Asst.*

PULKOSKI, Diane Lois
St Angela Hall Acad; Brooklyn, NY (8-79) Chor; NHS; Tr; Hon Prog; Jr Math League Cert; *Pre-Med.*

PULLEN, Deborah Fannette
Bellevue HS; Nashville, TN; Chor; Tr; *Martin Col; Bus.*

PULLEN, Debra Colleen
Iroquois HS; Louisville, KY; NHS; Sftbl; Yth Fel; *U of Ky; Psych.*

PULLEN, Joseph Wright
Emma Sansom HS; Gadsden, AL (40-253) NHS; Span C; SC; Var C; Cpt, Ftbl; Cpt, Wrest.

PULLEN, Kim Ann
Allentown HS; Allentown, NJ (11-262) AFS; Band; Chldr; SC; Sftbl; *Berkley Col; Med Secy.*

PULLEN, Michael Dean
Norlina HS; Norlina, NC; Chor; Mu Alpha Theta; Bsbl; Ftbl; Tr; Math A; *Vance Granville Comm Col; Law Enforcement.*

PULLEN, Rhonda Jean
Rolling Meadows HS; Rolling Meadows, IL (108-631) Var C; Bkbl; Hockey; Mgr, Soccer; Sftbl; Alg A; Hon Prog; Co-Cpt, Vlbl; Hon Pin; *Abilene Christian U; Phys Ed.*

PULLEN, Sandra Kay
Broadway Baptist Sch; Houston, TX; Sci C; Secy, Church SC; Drill Tm; Art C; Vlbl, Pep Squad, A's; *Interior Decorator.*

PULLEN, Sarah Grace
Kirkwood HS; Kirkwood, MO (30-588) A Cap Choir; Chor; Drama; Ensm; Rptr, Sch P; Top 5% Score on PSAT-NMSQT Test; *Meramec Col; Social Work.*

PULLEN, Tacy Elizabeth
Putnam City HS; Oklahoma City, OK; A Cap Choir; Pres, Chor; Ensm; FBLA; NHS; Span C; COM; Citz A; Yth Fel; NHS, A, Camp Fire Girls; Hospital Vol A; *SW Okla St U; Home Ec.*

PULLEY, Barbara Ann
Isle of Wight Acad; Isle of Wight, VA (9-50) F-Ed, Ann; Chor; Fin, Jr Miss Pagent; NHS; A-Ed, Sch P; SC; Beauty; COM; Hon Prog; Sci A; Sch Emblem; Newspaper Participation Cert; *Old Dominion U; Ed.*

PULLEY, Linda Gail
Jonesboro Christian Sch; Jonesboro, AR; Chldr; Chor; Dbte Tm; Ensm; A-Ed, Sch P; S-T, SC; Cpt, Bkbl; Sftbl; Home Ec; Choir; Most Courteous; *Bob Jones U; Spch Ed.*

PULLIAM, Pamela Aube
Roosevelt HS; Gary, IN (11-555) Pres, Fr C; French NHS; Pres, NHS; Y-Tns; COM; Citz A; *Purdue U; Civil Engr.*

PULLIAM, Ronald Lee
Kenmore HS; Akron, OH (6-380) Lit Mag; NHS; Bsbl; Sftbl; Tr; COM; Citz A; Hon Prog; MLS; Christian Stu A; *Kent St U; Archt.*

PULLIAM, Ronald Lee
Kenmore HS; Akron, OH (5-400) Lit Mag; NHS; Bsbl; Sftbl; Tr; COM; Citz A; Hon Prog; MLS; *Kent St U; Archt.*

PULLIAM, Terri Dawn
Broken Arrow Sr HS; Broken Arrow, OK (44-446) Cpt, Band; Bus C; Chldr; FBLA; NHS; Ski C; SC; Sftbl; Masonic A; OSU Hon Soc A; *Okla St U; Home Ec.*

PULLIN, David Ian
Sunset HS; Beaverton, OR (120-540) Band; Sch P; Bkbl; Ftbl; Tr; WW; HS All-Amer Tr; *Lewis & Clark Col; Bus.*

PULS, Sherry Ann
Battle Mountain HS; Minturn, CO (11-68) Ann; Tres, FBLA; Sch P; VP, SC; Pres, Var C; VP, Sr Cl; Cpt, Bkbl; Tr; COM; Most Out; MVP, Bkbl; Cpt & MVP, Vlbl; S-T, SC.

PULSIFER, Donna Lynne
Livermore Falls HS; Livermore Falls, ME (11-94) FNA; Hmrm; SC; Co-Cpt, Bkbl; Hockey; Sftbl; *Springfield Col; Med Tech.*

PUMAREJO, Francisco A
Fernando Suria Chaves HS; Barceloneta, PR; Band; JV, Bsbl; JV, Bkbl; JV, Sftbl; COM; Lion A; Magna Cum Laude; Ch, Peer Counseling; *U of Puerto Rico; Psych.*

PUMPHREY, Annette
Rufus King HS; Milwaukee, WI; Hmrm; *Marquette Col; Med.*

PUMPHREY, Robert Marion
Orange HS; Orange, CA (363-600) Rptr, Hmrm; Bsbl; Ftbl; Tr; Yth Fel; *Santa Ana Jr Col; Gen Stu.*

PURCELL, Howard Balsdon
Cashmere HS; Cashmere, WA (20-125) Ann; Band; Chor; Dbte Tm; Ftbl; Golf; *Bio.*

PURCELL, Janet Elaine
Hauppauge HS; Hauppauge, NY (112-600) Sch P; Regent Schol; Yth Fel; St George Assn Schol; Acolyte, Sunday Sch Teacher; GSct; *Cortland Col; Lib Arts.*

PURCELL, John Michael
Warsaw Comm HS; Warsaw, IN (53-410) Band; Dbte Tm; NFL; F-Ed, Sch P; Bsbl; COM; JA A; Solo & Ensm A's; *Ball St U; Archt.*

PURCELL, Susan Kaye
Breckinridge Co HS; Harned, KY (30-200) Ed, Ann; Secy, Band; Pres, FTA; NHS; Secy, Sci C; Pres, Var C; Pres, Jr Cl; Semi-Fin, Tnns; H of F; HQn; HCt; Yth Fel; WW; *Lexington Tech Inst; Dental Hygiene.*

PURCELL, Sylvia Annette
Suitland Sr HS; Suitland, MD; FTA; ARC; Span C; Bio A; Math A; Most Out; Sci A; Secy, Jr Usher Board; Patrol Ldr, GSct; Vlbl; Home Ec, Span, GSct, A's; *Morgan St U; Ed.*

PURCELL, William Lloyd III
Crater HS; Central Point, OR; FFA; F-Ed, Sch P; Mgr, Ftbl; *Psych.*

PURCELL, Wilma Vernell
Suitland Sr HS; Suitland, MD; Pres, FBLA; Lat C; Secy, SC; Mgr, Tr; Hon Prog; Journ A; Most Out; Sci A; Pres, GSct Cadettes; Bus Mgr, Tr; Jr NHS; Vlbl; Drill Tm; Yrbk C; FBLA, Sch Safety Patrol, A's; Superintendent, G Sct, A's; *Morgan St Col; Elem Ed.*

PURCHASE, Carole Lynn
Wellsboro Area HS; Wellsboro, PA (50-285) AFS; Band; Chor; Pres, Drama; Fr C; Ed, Lit Mag; Ed, Sch P; Pres, Thes; Tnns; NEDT; AFS Schol; Religion Hon; AFS; De Witte Wallace Readers Dig AA; *Helene Fulch Sch of Nurs; Nurs.*

PURCHASE, Ruth Ann
Wellsboro Area Sr HS; Wellsboro, PA (33%-200) AFS; Band; Chldr; Chor; Drama; Ger C; HQn; Yth Fel; Sch Play; Church Folksingers; Sr Life Sav; Art C; Chrch Drma Grp; Trs, Forgn Stu C; Rotary Exchng Sch; Dist Rep, St Baptist Yth Fel; *Helene Fuld Sch of Nurs; Nurs.*

PURDIE, Joseph Alexander
Butler HS; Butler, NJ; A Cap Choir; Band; Chor; Drama; Ensm; Orch; Hist A; *Archt.*

PURDIMAN, Elmo Worsham
Cotton Plant HS; Cotton Plant, AR (1-46) BC; Chor; Pres, Drama; Pres, Fr C; FBLA; Sci C; VP, SC; Pres, Jr Cl; Pres, Soph Cl; Bkbl; Ftbl; Tr; COM; MLS; *Henderson St U; Interior Decorating.*

PURDOM, Carol Lynn
Washington Co HS; Springfield, KY (4-211) BC; S-T, FHA; *Acct.*

PURDY, Daniel Mark
Earl L Vandermeulen HS; Port Jefferson, NY (39-240) Var C; Cr-Ctry; Tr; JV, Wrest; 4H A; ARC A; Best Sr Life Saver; Running A's; *Engr.*

PURDY, Greg Allen
Bowling Green Sr HS; Bowling Green, OH; JV, Wrest; Type A; Stage Band; Yth Rep, Church Pulpit Comm; *Entertainment.*

PURDY, Jeffrey Earl
Dupont Sr HS; Hermitage, TN; Hmrm; JV, Wrest; Most Out; Star Student; Graphic Arts A.

PURDY, Sharon Lynne
Castle Park HS; Chula Vista, CA (1-426) Chldr; Drama; GS; Hmrm; A-Ed, Sch P; SC; Thes; CSF; COM; Val; Drill Tm; Girl's League Qn; Drama As; *San Diego St U; Dramatics.*

PURIFOY, Gina Marie
Beaumont Sch For Girls; Cleveland Heights, OH; FNA; FTA; VP, Lat C; Bkbl; Latin As; *Sci.*

PURIFOY, Janet Marie
Gurdon HS; Gurdon, AR (15-90) Band; FHA; Type A; Band Medals & Ltrs; *Ouachita Baptist U; Mus.*

PURINTON, Debra Ann
Lamar R-1 HS; Lamar, MO (19-150) AFS; Chor; Drama; Ensm; Tres, 4H; NFL; Spch C; Sftbl; Swim; Tnns; COM; 4H A; ARC A; Spch A; Type A; Swim Tm Ribbons; Mus, Pep C, GAA, Ltrs; *Ozark Bible Col.*

PURINTUN, Micheal Wayne
Forest Park HS; Forest Park, OH (110-475) Chor; Drama; Fr C; Cert of A.

PURKEY, Lois Marie
Carlisle Sr HS; Carlisle, OH (9-208) VP, Bus C; Cpt, Chldr; NHS; SC; VP, Sr Cl; Pres, Jr Cl; Tnns; HCt; Carlisle Ed Recognition Assn; *Miami Bus Col; Bus.*

PURKEY, Vance LaRue
N Mesquite HS; Mesquite, TX; A Cap Choir; Band; Span C; *Eastfield Col; Mus.*

PURNELL, Pamela Jo
Percy L Julian HS; Chicago, IL (11-175) Chldr; Dbte Tm; Drama; Hmrm; Lat C; Lit Mag; NHS; Sch Achieve Tm; Ed, Sch P; VP, SC; Up Bound; VP, Soph Cl; COM; Citz A; Journ A; Most Out; *Ill St U; Communications.*

589

PURPERO, Lisa Louise
Bayview HS; Milwaukee, WI (90-656) A Cap Choir; Band; Chor; Hmrm; Madrigal; Mjrte; Rptr, Sch P; Twirl Sabre Mjrte; Usher C; X-C; Finanical Affairs Comm, SGA; Job's Daughters.

PURRINGTON, Robyn Beatrice
Humansville HS; Humansville, MO (20%-30) Bus Mgr, Drama; 4H; St Scholar; Librarian Pins; *Dr Martin Luther Col; Ed.*

PURSCELL, Dave Keith
Spencer HS; Spencer, IA; Band; Chor; Ensm; Thes; Yth Fel; I Rating, Solo, Trio & Ensm Percus; *Computer Prog.*

PURSLEY, David Ray
Antelope Valley HS; Lancaster, CA; JV, Bsbl; JV, Bkbl; JV, Tr; *Art.*

PURVIS, Alan Clay
Rock Hill Acad; Charlottesville, VA (4-15) BC; Chess C; Drama; Tres, Hmrm; Lat C; Monogram; Rptr, Sch P; SC; Bsbl; Tr; NEDT; *John Tyler Comm Col; Mortuary Sci.*

PURVIS, Amy Kathleen
Fremont HS; Fremont, MI (40-250) Dbte Tm; NHS; VP, SC; Var C; Swim; *Hope Col; Bus.*

PURVIS, Cindy Sue
Cross Plains HS; Cross Plains, TX (8-26) Band; Drama; Secy, FHA; Cpt, Mjrte; Spch C; Secy, SC; Thes; Bkbl; Tnns; Tr; Cl Fav; Swtht; *Nurs.*

PURVIS, Derrick Martin
Anderson HS; Anderson, IN (20%-550) Pres, Chor; Tres, Drama; Fr C; Pres, Hmrm; Tres, Thes; Ftbl; *Ind U; Mus.*

PURVIS, Frances Joy
Bay Ridge HS; Brooklyn, NY (23-197) Band; Chor; COM; Type A; *NYCCC; Comm Service.*

PURVIS, John Leslie
Harlingen HS; Harlingen, TX (114-800) Bsbl; Ftbl; Tr; COM.

PURVIS, Thomas Cole
Checotah HS; Checotah, OK (20-120) Band; Chem C; Chess C; Chor; FFA; Math C; Bio A; Math A; Sci A; Secy of St, Okla Hist; *U of Okla; Engr.*

PUSEY, Frank Olin Jr
Summerville HS; Summerville, SC (15-550) BC; Chess C; NHS; JV, Ftbl; Tr; Wrest; *Col of Charleston; Pre-Med.*

PUSKARICH, Annette
North HS; Bakersfield, CA; Sftbl; CSF; VFW A; Principal's Scholastic Hon A; *Bakersfield Col; Acct.*

PUSTKA, Jeffrey Wayne
Belton HS; Belton, TX (25%-249) Band; CYO; FFA; *Tex Tech U; Acct.*

PUTMAN, Lani Jean
Palmetto Sr HS; Miami, FL; Chor; Semi-Fin, Cr-Ctry; 1st Pl, Sonnet Comp; *Mus.*

PUTMAN, Aileen Frances
Crescent HS; Joyce, WA (1-26) Tres, 4H; NHS; SC; Secy, Var C; Bkbl; MVP, Vlbl; *U of Wash; Ed.*

PUTMAN, Annette Irene
York Comp HS; York, SC (21-240) Band; Fr C; WW; All-Amer Band; Interntl Relations A; *Winthrop Col; Elem Ed.*

PUTNAM, Debbie Jane
Wahconah Regional HS; Dalton, MA (50%-350) A Cap Choir; Chor; Drama; Hmrm; Madrigal; Cpt, Mjrte; Arch; Swim; Mgr, Tnns; Ski As; Camp Coun; Vol, Nurs Home; Skate As; Bell Choir; Leo C; *Early Childhood Development.*

PUTNAM, Julie Kay
Monroe Sr HS; Monroe, WI (3-246) Ann; Band; Chor; Ensm; FHA; Ch, SC; COM; Type A; *U of Wis; Social Work.*

PUTNAM, Karen Sue
Pinole Valley HS; Pinole, CA (89-430) ARC; Tres, Church Yth; Head Ftbl Statistician; *Diablo Valley Col; Real Estate.*

PUTNAM, Linda Jean
Bremerhaven American HS; Bremerhaven, GERMANY (1-20) Cpt, Chldr; Chor; Tres, Soph Cl; Sftbl; Cpt, Tr; Alg A; Citz A; God & Country A; *Ed.*

PUTNAM, Lisa Maye
Bremerhaven American HS; Bremerhaven, GERMANY (2-31) Band; CYO; NHS; SC; Tres, Var C; VP, Sr Cl; Cpt, Bkbl; Cpt, Sftbl; Tr; God & Country A; Pres A; Female Athlete o-t Yr; All Conf, Bkbl; *U of Tex; Guidance and Counseling.*

PUTNAM, Michael Lee
Albia Comm HS; Albia, IA (10-148) Ann; Band; BS; Chess C; Chor; Drama; NHS; Spch C; *U of Iowa; Phar.*

PUTNAM, Rebecca Gayle
Carey HS; Carey, OH (8-106) All Amer Yth; Chor; Lat C; NHS; Sch Achieve Tm; Span C; Var C; Co-Cpt, Bkbl; MVP, Tr; COM; Hist A; Magna Cum Laude; MVP, Bkbl; Cl Top 10; All St Bkbl A; WW, Ath; *Heidelberg Col; Phys Ed.*

PUTNEY, Alice Joyce
Sawyer Pub Sch; Sawyer, ND (4-20) Drama; Y-Tns; Tr; Citz A; Outst Home Ec Stu; *Mid-Amer Nazarene Col; Teaching.*

PUTNEY, Michael Everett
Eastwood HS; El Paso, TX; NHS; Var C; Co-Cpt, Bkbl; Co-Cpt, Tr; COM; *Rice Col; Med.*

PUTTIE, Karen Dawn
Temple Christian HS; Redford, MI; Co-Cpt, Chldr; Chor; Ensm; Sch P; Var C; Tres, Jr Cl; Bkbl; Sftbl; Alg A; Amer Leg A; Citz A; HCt; Bible A; *Bob Jones U; Bus.*

PYATT, Timothy Dwight
W Forsyth Sr HS; Clemmons, NC (29-487) Band; Chor; Key C; NHS; Sci C; Sftbl; Nom, NC Gov's Sch; WW; Hi IQ Tm; Chem Symp; Most Outst Stage Bandsman; *Duke U.*

PYCHA, Sheri Lynn
Greeneville HS; Greeneville, TN (78-200) Chor; FBLA; Secy, UN Council.

PYE, Robert Wesley
Eau Claire HS; Columbia, SC (8-312) Chess C; NHS; Hon Prog; MLS; Cpt, Bowl; Nom, Gov Sch; Furman Schol; *U of SC; Bus Adm.*

PYE, William Keith
Cartersville HS; Cartersville, GA (25-160) BC; Hmrm; Math C; Mu Alpha Theta; Ed, Sch P; SC; S-T, Jr Cl; Tres, Soph Cl; Co-Cpt, Cr-Ctry; Tr; Elk A; *Ga Tech.*

PYEATT, Linda
Dondero HS; Royal Oak, MI (16-500) Chem C; Drama; Tres, Fr C; Hmrm; NHS; Secy, SC; B Crocker A; COM; Hon Prog; Math A; Phi Beta Kappa; Q&S A; Regent Schol; Sci A; Runnerup, Century III; Stu Senate; *Col of William & Mary; Chem.*

PYKARE, Jill Marie
Champion HS; Warren, OH (21-219) Cpt, Chldr; NHS; Ski C; Span C; SC; Secy, Sr Cl; Secy, Soph Cl; *Kent St U; Secy Stu.*

PYLAR, Janet Eileen
D D Eisenhower HS; Washington, MI (188-588) Fr C; Hmrm; SC; Writing A; Fr Dance C; *Western Mich U; Occupational Therapy.*

PYLE, Donna Catherine
Greenwood HS; Midland, TX (2-13) Ed, Ann; Chldr; Chor; VP, FHA; Pres, Hmrm; Math C; S-T, Sci C; SC; Pres, Sr Cl; Pres, Jr Cl; Cpt, Bkbl; Fin, Tr; COM; Cl Fav; Math A; MLS; Type A; Miss Greenwood; Most Friendly; *Midland Col; Bus.*

PYLE, Jeffrey Carlton
Hopkinsville HS; Hopkinsville, KY; Ann; Chem C; Chess C; VP, Hmrm; Order/Arrow; Sch P; SC; Ftbl; Wrest; COM; JA A; Order/Arrow A; ARC A; WW; *Hopkinsville Comm Col; Data Processing.*

PYLE, Martin Wayne
McGavock HS; Nashville, TN (20%-850) Band; Chess C; Dbte Tm; Drama; Ger C; Math C; Mu Alpha Theta; NFL; Order/Arrow; Ed, Sch P; Spch C; Amer Leg Orator A; God & Country A; Hist A; Journ A; NEDT; Order/Arrow A; Spch A; *U o-t South; Law.*

PYLES, Edythe Annette
Valencia HS; Placentia, CA; Chor; Ensm; Spch C; JA A; Med OCC A; *Point Loma Nazarene Col; Mus.*

PYLES, Robert Craig
E Mecklenburg HS; Charlotte, NC (80-700) Chess C; Chor; Drama; ARC; Span C; JV, Bsbl; Co-Cpt, Ftbl; Sftbl; Citz A; NEDT; Yth Fel; VP, UMYF; Board of Ministries; Phi Omega Beta; *Mercer U; Health.*

PYLES, Robert David
Wheelersburg HS; Wheelersburg, OH (60-134) Lat C; Bkbl; Ftbl; Tr; *Industry.*

PYLES, Tamela Sue
Frankfort HS; Ridgeley, WV (10%-139) Chldr; Chor; FHA; NHS; Secy, SC; Var C; *Potomac St Col; Communications.*

PYNNONEN, Ruth Arlene
Flambeau HS; Tony, WI (3-86) Band; Chor; Ensm; Ger C; Madrigal; NFL; NHS; Hons Chor; *U of Wisc; Computer Engr.*

PYOTT, Patricia Lynn
Sacred Heart HS; Vineland, NJ; Chor; Drama; NHS; F-Ed, Sch P; Sci C; Bkbl; JV, Sftbl; Amer Leg A; COM; PTA A; Photographer; Ann; Pres, Hist C; Special Constitutional Convention; Historian, Health C; Miss Spirit, Bkbl Tm; *Sci.*

Q

QUA, Sharon Margaret
Arcadia HS; Arcadia, CA (35-900) AFS; Band; Hmrm; NHS; CSF; Hon Prog; Tall Flag; Church Ushering Tm; *U of Calif; Health Sci.*

QUACKENBUSH,
Raymond Melvin
Southside HS; Elmira, NY; Chess C; 4H; JETS; JV, Ftbl; JV, Tr; JV, Wrest; 4H A; Hon Prog.

QUADE, Susan Lucille
Verona R-VII HS; Verona, MO (7-30) Band; Chor; Ensm; FBLA; GS; 4H; NHS; Mgr, Bkbl; Amer Leg A; 4H A; Hon Prog.

QUADY, Thomas James
Buffalo Sr HS; Buffalo, MN (33%-219) Chor; Var C; Ftbl; Tr; Wrest; Cl Fav; HCt; Pres, Yth Fel; *U of Minn-Duluth; Psych.*

QUALLS, Brenda Diane
Savannah Central HS; Savannah, TN (12-250) FHA; FTA; 4H; Stu For Christ; Lib C; DECA.

QUALLS, Kathy Marian
Dyer Co HS; Newbern, TN (2-105) VP, Fr C; Lat C; NHS; Sci C; SC; Bio A; Cl Fav; *Freed-Hardeman Col; Secondary Ed.*

QUALLS, Teresa Lynn
Frayser Baptist Sch; Memphis, TN; BC; Chor; FHA; Sftbl; Cl Fav; HQn; HCt; *Memphis St U; Nurs.*

QUAM, Joel Eric
Marshall Sr HS; Marshall, MN (1-251) Band; Chor; Bkbl; Ftbl; Math A; NMF; Val; *St Olaf Col; Math.*

QUAM, Kent Duane
S Hamilton HS; Jewell, IA (3-86) Band; Chor; SC; Bsbl; Bkbl; Ftbl; Golf; *Iowa St U; Pre-Med.*

QUAM, Lois Elaine
Marshall HS; Marshall, MN (12-265) Band; Chor; Dbte Tm; NFL; Rptr, Sch P; Spch C; Spch A.

QUAMME, David Mark
Seneca HS; Seneca, WI (10-45) Band; Ensm; Secy, FFA; Var C; Bkbl; Hon Prog; *U of Wis; Agr.*

QUARLES, Eugene Edison
Marvell HS; Marvell, AR (15-120) FFA; Ger C; Spch C; SC; Bsbl; Cpt, Ftbl; Tr; Cl Fav; Most Outst; All St; All Amer; *U of Central Ark; Bus Adm.*

QUARLES, John Cobb
Dalton HS; Dalton, GA (33-275) Band; HiY; Span C; Hon Prog; *Auburn U; Civil Engr.*

QUARLES, Lillian Marlene
Grace King Sr HS; Metairie, LA; Lit Ral; Mu Alpha Theta; NHS; Hon Prog; *Med.*

QUARLES, Tina Louise
Patrick Henry HS; San Diego, CA (464-1106) Bus C; Secy, Chor; VP, 4H; NHS; ARC; Sci C; Sftbl; Tr; Vlbl; Rptr, Church Paper; *SD Col of Bus; Courtroom Rptr.*

QUARNSTROM, Jackie
Fulda Jr Sr HS; Fulda, MN (8-75) Ed, Ann; Band; Ensm; NHS; Spch C; SC; S-T, Sr Cl; HCt; Hon Prog; Spch A; Minn All-St Band; *Concordia Col; Communications.*

QUARTERMAN, Virginia Cleo
James Island HS; Charleston, SC; Hmrm; NHS; Pres, Rainbow; ARC; SC; Pres, Y-Tns; Opt Out Tn; ARC A; Grand Cross of Color; Graduation Usher.

QUATTLEBAUM, Donna Lee
Pendleton HS; Pendleton, SC (25%-136) Fr C; FHA; 4H; *Winthrop Col; Special Ed.*

QUATTLEBAUM, Tammy Jean
Pendleton HS; Pendleton, SC; Chldr; Fr C; Pres, Hmrm; Lit Mag; A-Ed, Sch P; SC; 4H A; Eng A; *Furman U; Art.*

QUATTRONE, Anthony Daniel
Marian HS; Tamaqua, PA (24-175) Pres, French NHS; Secy, NHS; Co-Ed, Sch P; JV, Bsbl; What Is An American Essay Contest; *Bio.*

QUAYHAGEN, Victoria Leigh
Many HS; Many, LA; CYO; Chldr; FHA; Sch P; Sftbl; *LSU; Nurs.*

QUEEN, Clifford Wayne
North HS; Omaha, NE (150-400) Rptr, Bus C; Chor; Parl, Var C; Bsbl; Bkbl; Ftbl; COM; Cl Fav; HCt; *U of Nebr; Teaching.*

QUEEN, Diana Kay
Columbia HS; Columbia, IL (36-127) Arch; Bus C; FBLA; FHA; Arch; Sftbl; Pres A; *Bellville Area Col; Bus.*

QUEEN, Lois Aelisa
Springbrook HS; Silver Spring, MD; Secy, Lat C; Ballet Co; Church Acolyte; *Med.*

QUEEN, Patty Jean
N Natchez HS; Natchez, MS (15%-220) A Cap Choir; BC; Chor; Fr C; NHS; Sci C; Pres, Soph Cl; Bio A; COM; Cl Fav; DARGCA; H of F; Hist A; Hon Prog; Math A; NMS; Sci A; Star Student; Type A; *Miss St U; Chem Engr.*

QUEEN, Richard Gene
Columbia Unit 4 HS; Columbia, IL; Bkbl; Chem A; God & Country A; JA A; MLS; Ntl Sci Found; Yth Fel; *Archt.*

QUEEN, Suzanne Mellisa
Rhinebeck Central HS; Rhinebeck, NY (29-110) AFS; Pres, Fr C; Cr-Ctry; Swim; Tr; Swim A; *SUNY; Horticulture.*

QUEEN, Wesley Gerald
Pflugerville HS; Pflugerville, TX (8-76) Pres, Band; Tres, BC; Ensm; Math C; VP, NHS; SC; Bsbl; Co-Cpt, Bkbl; Hon Prog; Math A; Type A; All District, All Tourney, Bkbl; Sweepstakes Band; UIL Number Sense; Band Favorite; *Lubbock Christian Col; Bus Adm.*

QUEENER, Lori Ann
Howe HS; Howe, OK (1-35) A-Ed, Ann; Cpt, Chldr; Rptr, FHA; Pres, 4H; Rptr, Hmrm; Rptr, Sch P; SC; Cpt, Bkbl; Cpt, Sftbl; Cpt, Tr; Cl Fav; 4H A; Most Out; Sal; Talent Show; Ltr A; WW; St of Okla Citation; *N Eastern St U; Med.*

QUELLAND, Elizabeth Lynne
R L Turner HS; Carrollton, TX (10%-800) Fr C; FHA; InterAct C; Drill Tm.

QUENZER, Barbara Ann
Pierre Riggs HS; Pierre, SD; Band; Yth Fel; *Jamestown Col; Acct.*

QUESENBERRY, Larry Wayne
Herndon HS; Herndon, WV (2-37) VP, FBLA; Secy, 4H; Pres, NHS; Sci C; SC; Bio A; 4H A; Hist A; Type A; *Concord Col; Acct.*

QUESENBERRY, Tony
N Gwinnett HS; Suwanee, GA (15%-120) Var C; Bkbl; Tr; HCt; Bkbl HS All Amer; Most Popular; Co Tm o-t Month.

QUEVEDO, Elizabeth
Jose de Diego HS; Mayaguez, PR (5-276) CYO; ARC; Sci C; COM; Magna Cum Laude; C de Becarios; *U of Puerto Rico at Mayaguez; Math.*

QUICK, Diane Marie
St James Pub Sch; St James, MN (19-153) *Iowa Lakes Comm Col; Nurs.*

QUICK, Gretchen Eileen
Monte Vista HS; Danville, CA (97-357) Chor; VP, 4H; Key C; Sch P; 4H A; Yth Fel; Red Ltr of Acclaimation; *U of Calif; Communications.*

QUICK, Wilma Ruth
Hanceville HS; Hanceville, AL (3-106) Secy, Band; Chldr; 4H; SC; VP, Sr Cl; Secy, Jr Cl; 4H A; MLS; Pres A; Co-Cpt, Dance Tm; Marshal; *U of S Ala; Oceanography.*

QUIGG, Kathy Anne
The Cecilian Acad; Philadelphia, PA; Chldr; Fr C; Lat C; Hon Prog; NEDT; Lat A; *Chestnut Hill Col; Ed.*

QUIGG, Pamela Sue
Jefferson City HS; Jefferson City, MO (30-487) Secy, Band; Chor; Fr C; NHS; Amer Leg Orator A; NMS; NEDT; Social Sci A; *Southern Methodist U; Econ.*

QUIGLEY, Cynthia Marie
Roxborough HS; Philadelphia, PA; Hmrm; Citz A; Hon Prog; Most Out; PTA A.

QUIGLEY, Patricia
Notre Dame HS; Chicago, IL; JV, Chldr; Drama; Hmrm; Hockey; Sftbl; Swim; Fin, Tr; Sci A; Christian Service Prog; Sch of Dance; *Columbia U; Dramatic Arts.*

QUIGLEY, Tammy Lynn
Elmira HS; Elmira, OR (7-147) Pres, Band; Chor; S-T, NHS; Hon Prog; Geography A.

QUIGLEY, Tom Merrill
Castleford HS; Castleford, ID (1-23) Band; Drama; FFA; Hmrm; Order/Arrow; Spch C; SC; JV, Bkbl; Ftbl; *Lawyer.*

QUILL, Timothy Gerard
Notre Dame HS for Boys; Niles, IL (86-275) Order/Arrow; Ski C; Y-Tns; Bsbl; Ftbl; Co-Cpt, Sftbl; JV, Tr; COM; Citz A; Order/Arrow A; ARC A; Sacristan; Yth Leg; *St Joseph-Rensaller Col; Bus Adm.*

QUILLEN, Cecelia Anne
Prospect HS; Mt Prospect, IL (125-600) Band; Chor; Ensm; Sftbl; Alg A; Vlbl; 1st Pl, St Solo & Ensm; Cpt A, Band; *E Ill U; Social Work.*

QUILLEN, Ira Marshall
Hargrave Military Acad; Chatham, VA (5-54) BC; Bsbl; Squadman o-t Yr; HR; *Wash and Lee U; Economics.*

QUINLAN, Ann Marie
Brady HS; W St Paul, MN (6-150) Ann; Chor; VP, Drama; Ensm; Mjrte; NHS; VP, Thes; Pres, Sr Cl; VP, Jr Cl; COM; Hon Prog; Interlochen Ntl Mus; Kiwanis A; Magna Cum Laude; St Star Mus Rating; *St Benedicts Col; Med Technology.*

QUINLAN, Margaret Mary
N Shore HS; W Palm Beach, FL (10-353) Chor; Fr C; Key C; COM.

QUINLEY, Ernest Luther
Byram HS; Jackson, MS; Band; BC; Chem C; Ensm; Bsbl; Bkbl; Ftbl; *U of S Ala; Med Tech.*

QUINN, Anne Marie
W Philadelphia Girls HS; Philadelphia, PA (23-388) CYO; Fr C; Hmrm; Lat C; COM; *Drexel U; Chem Engr.*

QUINN, Cynthia Ann
DeLand HS; DeLand, FL; Span C; Art C; *Art Inst of Ft Lauderdale; Advertising Design.*

QUINN, Daryl Clifton
N Kansas City HS; North Kansas City, MO (38-431) Chess C; Dbte Tm; Key C; NFL; NHS; Ed, Sch P; VP, Sci C; God & Country A; *U of Mo-Rolla; Chem.*

QUINN, Debbie Lee
Franklin Regional HS; Murrysville, PA (30%-401) Fr C; Ski C; ARC A; *Westminster Col; Law.*

QUINN, Elaine Ann
Salisbury R-IV HS; Salisbury, MO; Band; Pres, Bus C; Chldr; Chor; City Conf; Drama; Pres, FBLA; FHA; NHS; Pres, Span C; SC; Thes; Var C; Pres, Sr Cl; VP, Soph Cl; Bkbl; Sftbl; Tr; HCt; Inspirational Sftbl A; *Stephens Col; Bus.*

QUINN, Joanne Mary
St Mary's HS; Lynn, MA (13-117) Ed, Ann; CYO; Drama; Hmrm; Rptr, Sch P; Span C; Hist A; Emmanuel Col School; WW; Marian Medal; *Boston Col; Journ.*

QUINN, Julie Ann
Garden City Sr HS; Garden City, KS (33%-371) A Cap Choir; Chor; Type A; HR; Amer Col of Mus 8 Yr A; *Mid Amer Nazarene Col; Mus.*

QUINN, Karen Jo
Tuscola HS; Tuscola, IL (12-122) Ann; Fr C; FTA; Semi-Fin, GS; Rainbow; VP, Sr Cl; Tres, Soph Cl; NEDT; *Eastern Ill U; Elem Ed.*

QUINN, Kathleen Ann
Dr J J Hogan Shs; Vallejo, CA; Pres, Ger C; NFL; NHS; Spch C; Bank of Amer A; Hon Prog; Spch A; Tres, 'S' C; YF Tres, YF Executive Coun; *U of Calif; Vet.*

QUINN, Marguerite Marie
St Mary's Acad; Alexandria, VA (5-70) Chldr; French NHS; Pres, Key C; Tres, Mu Alpha Theta; NHS; Cpt, Swim; Hist A; NEDT; WW; HR; Sportsmanship A; Tnns; *St Mary's Col; Fr.*

QUINN, Michael J
Loyola HS; Towson, MD (6-134) Ed, Ann; Fr C; Hmrm; Rptr, Sch P; Cr-Ctry; Tr; COM; NEDT; *Amherst Col; Biol.*

QUINN, Mitzi Dawn
E Central Sr HS; Tulsa, OK (33%-650) Chem C; NHS; *Med.*

QUINN, Patricia Kathleen
Los Alamos HS; Los Alamos, NM (20%-440) NHS; Ski C; SC; JV, Bkbl; Hockey; Soccer; Sftbl; Type A.

QUINN, Retta Kathryn
J W Hallahan HS; Philadelphia, PA (99-404) CYO.

QUINN, Thomas Francis Jr
Andrew Jackson HS; Jacksonville, FL (33%-400) Bus Mgr, Ann; Drama; Span C; Bsbl; Bkbl; *Eng.*

QUINN, Valerie
Northwest HS; St Louis, MO (24-433) Bus C; FBLA; Hmrm; SC; COM; Citz A; Hon Prog; Type A; Sewing, Keypunch, A's; *Stephen Col; Bus Adm.*

QUINONES, Agnes
Academia Sagrado Corazon; Santurce, PR (3-92) Tres, Drama; NHS; ARC; Span C; Spch C; Alg A; COM; Math A; Cooperation A; Mus A; Religion A; *ETSU; Architecture.*

QUINONES, Agnes
Jose de Diego HS; Mayaguez, PR; Band; Chem C; Dbte Tm; Pres, FHA; 4H; Mgr, Orch; Sci C; Pres, SC; Bio A; COM; Magna Cum Laude; Sci A; Star Student; C de Becarios; Behavior A.

QUINONES, Iris
Consuelo Escalona Private Sch; Carolina, PR (2-56) Chor; Rptr, Sch P; Rptr, SC; COM; Hon Prog; Co-Ed, Sch Paper; *U of PR; Phys Therapy.*

QUINONES, Rebecca
Consuelo Escalona Private Sch; Carolina, PR (6-56) Band; Cpt, Chldr; Chor; Dbte Tm; Drama; Semi-Fin, Jr Miss Pa; S-T, ARC; Span C; Secy, SC; MVP, Tnns; COM; Hist A; JA A; ARC A; Spch A; Type A; *U of Puerto Rico; Pre-Medics.*

QUINONES, Sandra Damaris
Dra Maria Cadilla HS; Arecibo, PR (58-429) BS; Chem C; Phys C; Sci C; JV, Swim; COM; Hon Prog; Sci A; *Universidad de Puerto Rico; Ciencias Naturales.*

QUINONES, Velez Rafael A
Francisco Mendoza HS; Isabela, PR; AFS; Tres, BS; CYO; Chldr; Chem C; Chor; City Conf; Drama; Order/Arrow; ARC; Sch P; Sci C; Span C; Bsbl; MVP, Bkbl; Cpt, Sftbl; Bio A; COM; Citz A; Cl Fav; Order/Arrow A; ARC A; Sci A; Star Student; Summa Cum Laude; Sports A; Instructor A; Ldrship A; *St Benedict Col; Social Sci.*

QUINTANA, David Lawrence
Eldorado HS; Albuquerque, NM (86-744) Ed, Ann; BS; Tres, Chess C; Chor; Key C; NHS; Order/Arrow; Spch C; Span NHS; VofDEM; Salute to Tnagers; *Claremont Col; Pre-Law.*

QUINTANA, Elena Teresa
Richard Montgomery HS; Rockville, MD; Chor; Cpt, Color Guard.

QUINTANILLA, Sandra Eileen
McMullen Co HS; Tilden, TX; Co-Ed, Ann; Ch, Chldr; Rptr, FFA; 4H; VP, Soph Cl; Bkbl; Tnns; Tr; Beauty; COM; 4H A; Mus, Bkbl, A's; *U of Tex; Mus.*

QUINTERO, Isabel
Colegio Puertorriqueno de Ninas; Caparra Heights, PR (3-70) Band; Drama; Pres, Math C; NHS; Secy, UN Council; COM; Social Action C; Activity C; Second Hon A; *Publicity.*

QUINTERO, Rebecca S
Colegio Universit Sagrado Corazon; Santurce, PR (2-25) Dbte Tm; Hmrm; NHS; Alg A; COM; Citz A; Hist A; Magna Cum Laude; *U of Puerto Rico; Acct.*

QUINTO, Gina
Long Beach HS; Long Beach, NY (31-435) Ed, Ann; Bus C; NHS; Regent Schol; DECA A; Chairperson, Prom Comm; Sunday Sch Teacher; *SUNY at Binghamton; Acct.*

QUINTON, Karla Marie
Peru HS; Peru, IN (13-256) Fr C; NHS; Var C; Bkbl; Co-Cpt, Tnns; Tr; St Scholar; Sch Service A; *Ind U; Med.*

QUIRK, Susan Alice
Silver Creek HS; San Jose, CA; F-Ed, Ann; SC; Tres, Jr Cl; CSF; Secy, Baptist Yth Fel; Black Stu Union; *Tuskegee Inst; Nurs.*

QUIROS, Delba Eunice
Adolfo Grana Rivera HS; Penuelas, PR (8-342) COM; Hon Prog; *Universidad Catolica; Farmaceutica.*

QUIROS, Orengo Madeline
Adolfo Grana Rivera HS; Penuelas, PR (4-263) Parl, FHA; Tres, Sci C; SC; COM; Hon Prog; *U of Puerto Rico; Sci.*

QUIROZ, Cristina
Jefferson Davis HS; Houston, TX (40-312) Tres, Bus C; Secy, CYO; Up Bound; COM; *Tex Women's U; Special Ed.*

QUISENBERRY, John William
Clover Park HS; Tacoma, WA; Dbte Tm; Tr; Spch A; Yth Fel; Cert of Appreciation, ROTC; *Religion.*

QUISENBERRY, Sarah Jane
Valley Forge HS; Parma Heights, OH (120-800) Chess C; Fr C; Ski C; COM; *Ariz St U; Zoology.*

QUITUQUA, Evangeline Rose
George Washington Sr HS; Mangilao, GUAM (19-740) Band; Chldr; Chor; SC; Tnns; *U of Oreg; Psych.*

QUOOS, Charles Richard
Minnetonka Sr HS; Minnetonka, MN (75-638) Chess C; Spch C; Bsbl; Ftbl; Swim; ARC A; *Med.*

QUOW, Alson Essels
Hillside HS; Hillside, NJ; Chess C; Fr C; JV, Bkbl; Cpt, Soccer; Yth Fel; Yth Foundation; Industrial Arts A; *Elec Tech.*

QUOW, Ulric Leon
Hillside HS; Hillside, NJ; Soccer; Yth Fel; Industrial Arts A; *Elec Tech.*

R

RAAB, John Howard
Heritage HS; Littleton, CO (74-466) Hmrm; Sci C; SC; Bsbl; Bkbl; Ftbl; Sftbl; Swim; Tnns; Tr; COM; Citz A; Most Out; *Engr.*

RAAB, Katherine Elaine
Wayne HS; Dayton, OH (69-622) Chor; VP, Drama; 4H; Hmrm; Bkbl; Tr; *Wright St U; Phys Therapy.*

RAAK, Gene Irwin
Jasper HS; Jasper, MN (5-51) Band; Tres, FFA; 4H; NHS; Orch; Thes; JV, Tr; Star Greenhand; *Northwestern U-Orange City.*

RABASCA, Carol Jeanette
Scotch Plains-Fanwood HS; Scotch Plains, NJ (390-600) FNA; InterAct C; Orch; Ski C; Yth Fel; HR; Orch A; Vol, Hospital; *Kean Col; Occupational Therapy.*

RABATIN, Annette Marie
Uniontown Area Sr HS; Uniontown, PA; Ed, Ann; JV, Chldr; FNA; NHS; HQn; *Nurs.*

RABB, Ozella Elaine
HS for Performing And Visual Arts; Houston, TX (88-173) Chor; Ensm; Madrigal; *Tex Sou U; Bus.*

RABE, DeAnn Verda
Wyanet HS; Wyanet, IL (1-31) Band; Cpt, Chldr; NHS; Span C; Yth Fel; *IVCC; Secretarial Sci.*

RABE, Mark Luther
Crystal Lake Comm HS; Crystal Lake, IL (1-550) Lat C; SC; Bsbl; Cr-Ctry; Swim; Tr; *U of Ill; Med.*

RABIONET, Juan Carlos
Consuelo Escalon Private Sch; Villa Carolina, PR (2-38) Chess C; Hmrm; Model UN; Sci C; SC; COM; Hon Prog; PTA A; *U of PR; Social Sci.*

RABON, Donna Bennette
Aynor HS; Aynor, SC (5%-85) Pres, All Amer Yth; Co-Ed, Ann; Secy, BC; Chem C; Chor; 4H; Sci C; Span C; 4H A; Opt A; Spch A; Mus A; *Coastal Carolina Col; Elem Ed.*

RABON, Thomas Richard
Waccamaw Acad; Whiteville, NC (6-15) Ed, Ann; Chor; NHS; UN Council; Citz A; PA; *Duke U; Med.*

RABORN, Wayne Harry
Bogalusa HS; Bogalusa, LA (48-289) BS; Drama; Rptr, Sch P; *SE La U; Bio.*

RABUN, Daniel Ivey
Thomson HS; Thomson, GA; F-Ed, Ann; BC; InterAct C; F-Ed, Sch P; Span C; Ftbl; Tr; Nom, Gov Hon; Art, Hustle, A's; FCA.

RACE, Donna Lynne
Westfield Acad; Westfield, NY; Band; Chor; Pres, Key C; Span C; Yth Fel; Amer's Yth in Concert; Venture '77; Co Mus Festival; Church Sr Choir; Conductor, Church Jr Choir; Altar Guild; *Eastman Col; Mus.*

RACEY, Linda Susan
Kingsway Regional HS; Swedesboro, NJ; Chor; Mjrte; NHS; *Newberry Jr Col; Interior Design.*

RACHAL, James Gregory
La Porte HS; La Porte, TX; Chor; Fr C; Thes; Golf; Mus A; *Baylor U; Banking.*

RACHAL, Walter Jay
St Matthew HS; Melrose, LA (12-47) FFA; Sch P; Cpt, Bkbl; Sftbl; Most Dependable.

RACINE, Maggie
Springbrook HS; Silver Spring, MD; Co-Cpt, Chldr; SC; Jr Cl; Bkbl; Sftbl; Tr; HCt; *Penn St U; Law.*

RACKER, Barbara Diane
John Ehret HS; Marrero, LA (1-500) Band; Lit Ral; Bio A; Chem A; Hon Prog; PTA A; Sci A; Mus A; Span A; Lit A; Art A; *La Tech U; Fine Arts.*

RACKLEY, Audette Marshelle
Amarillo HS; Amarillo, TX; A Cap Choir; Chor; Ensm; Lat C; Lat NHS; Madrigal; JV, Cr-Ctry; Tr; Alg A; COM; Gov Honor Prog; Most Out; Sci A; Math.

RACKLEY, Douglas Kelly
Carrollton Sr HS; Carrollton, MO (10-136) A Cap Choir; Chor; Drama; Ger C; Key C; Madrigal; Sci C; Spch C; Thes; Bsbl; Mgr, Bkbl; Ftbl; Mgr, Tr; Citz A; DARGCA; God & Country A; People to People Ambassador; Eagle Sct; *U of Mo-Rolla; Engr.*

RACKLEY, Leicia Leann
Amarillo HS; Amarillo, TX (109-602) Chor; Ensm; FHA; Span C; JV, Cr-Ctry; Tr; Gov Honor Prog; *Amarillo Col; Home Ec.*

RACKLEY, Renee
Amarillo HS; Amarillo, TX; Band; FHA; Orch; Span C; Gov Honor Prog; Pres A; Most Improved; Miss Trinity.

RACZKOWSKI, Kathy Ann
Boulder HS; Boulder, CO (43-663) A Cap Choir; CYO; Chor; Drama; Hmrm; Madrigal; SC; Thes; Theater A's; *Colo St U; Theater.*

RADA, Liliana
Colegio Puertorriqueno de Ninas; Caparra Heights, PR (2-70) Band; Chor; Fr C; Math C; Secy, NFL; NHS; Tres, Sci C; Spch C; COM; Social Action C; First Hon A.

RADACK, Todd Graham
Thomas A Edison HS; Tulsa, OK (26-483) Band; Demolay; Ensm; NHS; Orch; Hon Prog; Math A; *Principia Col; Physics.*

RADCLIFFE, Ellen Joy
Schafer HS; Southgate, MI; Ann; Chor; Drama; Yth Fel; VP, Church Yth Group; *Psych.*

RADCLIFFE, LeAnn Sue
Aloha HS; Aloha, OR (10%-450) Band; Ensm; Ger C; Orch; COM; Citz A; Hon Prog; Sup Mus Achv A; Hon Band; *Warner Pacific Col; Mus.*

RADDUE, Diana Elizabeth
J F Kennedy HS; Richmond, CA; A Cap Choir; Fr C; Hon Prog; *U of Calif; Social Welfare.*

RADEBAUGH, Belinda Rene
Independence HS; Independence, MS (15%-106) Ann; BC; Chor; FBLA; FHA; Math C; Sch P; Sftbl; *Memphis St U.*

RADELT, Michael William
Imlay City HS; Imlay City, MI (9-156) VP, FFA; VP, Sci C; Var C; Cpt, Ftbl; Hon Prog; Magna Cum Laude; ROTC A; Spch A; Co- cpt, Ftbl; FFA Ldrship A; Forensics A; V- ch, Co Republicans; *U of Mich.*

RADER, Brian Douglas
Aledo HS; Aledo, IL (20%-113) FFA; 4H; Span C; Bkbl; Mgr, Ftbl; FFA Creed A.

RADFORD, Al Wettstein
Christian Co HS; Hopkinsville, KY (22-350) BC; Pres, Hmrm; NHS; SC; Cpt, Swim; *Centre Col; Bus.*

RADFORD, Helen Patricia
Mansfield HS; Mansfield, LA (1-90) Band; BC; VP, FBLA; Lit Ral; Cpt, Mjrte; Span C; *La Tech U.*

RADFORD, James Ray
Octavia HS; Colfax, IL (20-60) Band; Chor; Secy, Drama; 4H; Hmrm; Rptr, Sch P; Tr; Wrest; Amer Leg A; 4H A; *Freed-Hardeman Col; Art.*

RADI, Brenda Lanae
Crookston Central HS; Crookston, MN (16-225) Band; Cpt, Mjrte; Orch; COM; Vlbl.

RADICCHI, Sharon Ann
Susquehanna Comm HS; Susquehanna, PA (2-120) Band; Cpt, Chldr; Chor; Ski C; VP, Jr Cl; Bkbl; Sftbl; Tr; Bausch & Lomb A; HCt; ARC A; Type A; Feature Twirler, Mjrte; Co-Ed, Yrbk Staff; *Penn St U at Park; Phys Ed.*

RADICH, Karen Lynn
E Detroit HS; E Detroit, MI (17-940) A Cap Choir; Chor; Dbte Tm; Drama; Ensm; Lit Mag; NHS; Rptr, Sch P; Spch C; Thes; COM; Journ A; Phi Beta Kappa; Sci A; Spch A; Secy & VP, Yth Group; A-Ed, Yrbk Staff; All-A Stu A; Mich Stu Merit Schol; Comm Relations A; *Mich St U; Vet Med.*

RADIL, Shari Lynn
Oak Harbor HS; Oak Harbor, WA (10%-330) Chor; NHS; S-T, SC; Tr; Bus Wk Schol; *Skagit Valley Comm Col; Secretarial.*

RADOCAJ, Stephanie Ann
Wellsboro Sr HS; Wellsboro, PA (30-250) Band; Chor; Drama; Ger C; Sch P; SC; Bsbl; Bkbl; Sftbl; Tr; NJHS; *Sci.*

RADOMSKY, Ann Elizabeth
Philipsburg-Osceola Area HS; Philipsburg, PA (86-231) Pres, FHA; FTA; Hmrm; Rainbow; Ch, Ski C; SC; Yth Fel; *Penn St U; Pre-Sch Ed.*

RADOSEVICH, Scott Gregory
Thoreau HS; Thoreau, NM (6-73) Band; NHS; SC; Bkbl; Ftbl; Alg A; Bio A; COM; Cl Fav; Hist A; HCt; Hon Prog; Math A; St Scholar; All Dist Bkbl; Coaching.

RADOVICH, Stephanie Michelle
Albuquerque HS; Albuquerque, NM (15%-600) CYO; Chor; Ensm; Citz A; *Marine Bio.*

RAEBURN, Debbie Louise
Octavia HS; Colfax, IL (13-65) Band; Co-Cpt, Chldr; NHS; Pres, SC; *Secretarial Work.*

RAEDEKE, Gary F
Worthington Sr HS; Worthington, MN (26-265) Arch; FFA; Ger C; Ch, Hmrm; NHS; Order/ Arrow; Sci C; Arch; Cr-Ctry; Ftbl; Swim; Cpt, Wrest; Bio A; Citz A; Hist A; Hon Prog; Order/ Arrow A; ARC A; Sci A; Lutheran Yth; Cl Project A; Ducks Unlimited; Eagle Sct; FFA A; *Worthington Comm Col; Hist.*

RAESZ, Cristi Lynn
E Central HS; Tulsa, OK (200-1000) A Cap Choir; Chor; Ensm; FTA; Madrigal; Math C; SC; Tnns; Hon Prog; Spch A; Yth Fel; *W Tex St U; Math.*

RAFAIL, Frank Elias
Uniontown Area Sr HS; Uniontown, PA; Band; Ensm; Pres, Hmrm; Key C; Tres, NHS; Orch; Sch P; Sci C; Span C; Alg A; Hist A; Hon Prog; Kiwanis A; Math A; Sci A; 2nd Pl, Art Contest; *Calif St U; Dentistry.*

RAFAIL, Paul Elias
Uniontown Area HS; Uniontown, PA (20-400) Band; Key C; Math C; VP, NHS; Orch; Sci C; *Calif St U; Bio.*

RAFTER, Diana Louise
Richmond Hill HS; Richmond Hill, NY (181-657) Tnns; COM; Type A; HR; Scholastic Achv; Typing Hon; Off Skill A; *Plaza Bus Sch; Collegiate Secy.*

RAFTER, Sivert David Erik
Richmond Hill HS; Richmond Hill, NY; BS; Dbte Tm; Rptr, Sch P; Sci C; Cpt, Sftbl; Swim; Co-Cpt, Wrest; Hon Prog; Sci A; Spch A; Schol A; Ltr, Swim; Ltr, Wrest; *Oral Roberts U; Sci.*

RAFTERY, Kelly Marie
Pathway HS; Savannah, GA (1-15) Ed, Ann; BC; Co-Cpt, Chldr; Dbte Tm; Drama; Ger C; Secy, SC; Bkbl; Sftbl; Alg A; Citz A; HQn; Hon Prog; Journ A; Type A; *Armstrong St Col; Pre-Med.*

RAGAN, Terry Douglas
Milburn HS; Milburn, OK (1-20) Pres, 4H; VP, Hmrm; NHS; Pres, SC; Pres, Soph Cl; Co-Cpt, Bkbl; Gov Honor Prog; 4H A; Hist A; Most Out; Sal; Spch A; Yth Fel; Best Personality; Most Attractive; Most Stu; *SE U; Law.*

RAGASA, Alejandrino Andy
Kohala HS; Kohala, HI (1-68) FFA; Hmrm; SC; Pres, Soph Cl; Greenhand A; Filipino CA; PAAC; Landscaping Box A; *U of Hawaii at Manoa.*

RAGGO, Valerie Lynn
Farmington HS; Farmington, MO (44-257) A Cap Choir; Ann; Band; Bus C; Cpt, Chldr; Drama; VP, Hmrm; Mod Mus Mas; NHS; Orch; Pres, ARC; Span C; SC; Hon Prog; Hons Band; Bus C; Swtht Qn Cand; *Mineral Area Col; Dental Asst.*

RAGIN, Debra Lynn
Myrtle Beach HS; Myrtle Beach, SC (27-240) F-Ed, Ann; Cpt, Chldr; Model UN; Secy, SC; Var C; VP, Sr Cl; VP, Jr Cl; Secy, Soph Cl; Hon Prog; Civinettes; Furman Schol; Qn of Heart; *Georgetown U; Hist.*

RAGLAND, Carol Yvette
Northwest HS; Indianapolis, IN (85-541) Chldr; Sci C; Tnns; COM; Hon Prog; Span A; Type A; HR; Mus A; *Morehouse Col; Bus Adm.*

RAGLAND, Patricia Ann
B T Washington HS; Atlanta, GA; Band; Chor; FHA; Cpt, Bsbl; Cpt, Sftbl; Cpt, Swim; Cl Fav; Most Out; Lib As.

RAGLAND, Sherry Ann
Briarfield Acad; Lake Providence, LA (8-60) Ann; BC; Ensm; 4H; Lit Ral; Sci C; Span C; Mgr, Bkbl; COM; 4H A; *LSU; Early Childhood Ed.*

RAGLIN, Leonard Dean
Harlan HS; Harlan, KY; Band; Chor; Ensm; Fr C; Orch; Sci C; Var C; Cpt, Bsbl; Bkbl; Ftbl; Swim; Tr; COM; Most Out; All Star Tm; Mus A; Section Ldr; Asst Secy.

RAGOOPATH, Samdai
Germantown HS; Philadelphia, PA; Badminton; Meritorious A; *U of Pa; Bio.*

RAGSDALE, Kevan Ray
Century HS; Ullin, IL (15%-52) Chor; VP, FFA; Bsbl; Phys Ed A; HS Industrial Occup; *US Army; Military Police.*

RAGSDALE, Rebecca Rose
Matoaca HS; Ettick, VA; Fr C; French NHS; Key C; Secy, NHS; Tres, SC; 4H A; *William & Mary Col; Dentistry.*

RAGSDALE, Tia Lynn
Daniel Webster HS; Tulsa, OK (2%-350) Hmrm; Math C; COM; Secy of St A; *Okla U; Med.*

RAHE, James Dean
Salina S HS; Salina, KS; Drama; F-Ed, Sch P; CYF; *Kans St U; Archt.*

RAHE, James Edward
Linn HS; Linn, KS (23-46) FFA; *Beloit Vo-tech Col; Carpentry.*

RAHLF, Charlane Debra
Merrill Sr HS; Merrill, WI (80-350) A Cap Choir; Band; Chor; Hmrm; Madrigal; SC; Amer Leg A; VFW A; VofDEM; Mus As; Regional Talent Comp A; *Central Bible Col; Mus.*

RAHMANN, Patricia Ann
Franklin HS; Franklin, PA (77-307) Hmrm; SC; Sftbl; Candystriper; Dist Yth Coun; *Nurs.*

RAHN, Cary L
Weston-McEwen HS; Athena, OR (4-39) Band; FFA; NHS; Rptr, Sch P; Span C; Tres, SC; Thes; VP, Var C; VP, Jr Cl; Tres, Soph Cl; Bsbl; Bkbl; Ftbl; Hon Prog; Star Student; Photography C; *BMCC.*

RAHN, Laura Jean
Madeira HS; Madeira, OH (6-208) Band; Chor; Lat C; NHS; SC; Tr; Hon Prog; Math A; NEDT; Hist, AFS; Siefert A; *Sci.*

RAILEY, Karen Lee
Roma HS; Roma, TX (1-130) F-Ed, Ann; Band; Chldr; Chor; Ensm; Tres, FHA; Pres, 4H; Hmrm; Mjrte; NHS; ARC; Secy, Sci C; Spch C; SC; Tres, Sr Cl; Tres, Jr Cl; Parl, Soph Cl; COM; 4H A; Hon Prog; Sal; Sci A; Spch A; S-T 4-H C; WW; Best Actress; FHA A; *Engr.*

RAIMER, Richard Allan
Saranac Comm HS; Saranac, MI (21-76) Band; Ski C; Var C; Co-Cpt, Bkbl; Cpt, Ftbl; *Ferris St Col; Plastic Technology.*

RAINACH, Lori Leanne
Claiborne Acad; Haynesville, LA (4-32) JV, Bkbl; *La Tech U.*

RAINBOLT, Judy Ann
Eminence R-I HS; Eminence, MO (11-37) Bkbl; Sftbl; *Central Christian Col of The Bible.*

RAINER, Richard Carroll
Hattiesburg HS; Hattiesburg, MS; Key C; Lat C; Var C; Mgr, Ftbl; Mgr, Tr; Citz A; Hist A; *U of Sou Miss; Health Ed.*

RAINES, Darrel Gene Jr
Levelland HS; Levelland, TX (1-207) VP, Band; Chess C; Dbte Tm; Ensm; Tres, Math C; NHS; A-Ed, Sch P; Tres, Sci C; Alg A; Bio A; Hon Prog; Math A; Ntl Sci Found; Type A; Drafting, St Ensm, HR, A's; Bicentennial Essay, A; *S Plains Col; Engr.*

RAINES, Donna Jean
Wayne Mem HS; Wayne, MI (20%-800) Dbte Tm; Fr C; Orch; Span C; Attendance A; Pres, Secy, Baptist Yth Group; *Perdue U; Secretarial.*

RAINES, Elizabeth Ann
Hardaway HS; Columbus, GA (42-407) VP, Anchor C; Dbte Tm; Hmrm; Fin, Model UN; NHS; Sch P; Pres, SC; Pres, Jr Cl; Secy, Soph Cl; COM; Gov Honor Prog; Hist A; NMS; Outst Social Sci Stu; Outst Acad Jr; Page 1 Social Stu A; Win, Ga Alumni Schol.

RAINES, Kathryn Denise
Engleside Christian Sch; Alexandria, VA (2-22) Co-Ed, Ann; Bus Mgr, Band; Bus Mgr, Ensm; Secy, SC; Pres, Jr Cl; Sci A; Cert of Hon; *Missions.*

RAINES, Rodney Reece
Woodsboro HS; Woodsboro, TX; Band; Industrial Arts C; 1st Pl, St Indust Arts Wood Working; *Bee Co Col; Computer Programmer.*

RAINEY, Glenda Faye
Jefferson Davis HS; Montgomery, AL (134-700) Ann; Fr C; French NHS; Ed, Sch P; Tri-HiY; Sftbl; *Auburn U; Sci.*

RAINEY, Kenneth Wayne
Oak Grove HS; Hattiesburg, MS; BC; Secy, Hmrm; *U of Sou Miss; Psych.*

RAINEY, Michelle Lee
Clewiston HS; Clewiston, FL (9-149) F-Ed, Ann; Band; BC; Hmrm; Ch, SC; Pres, Jr Cl; Mgr, Bsbl; Cl Fav; HCt; Pres, MYF; Cpt, Powder Puff Ftbl; Secy, Pep C; Tigerettes; Candystriper; Most Dependable; Pres, Explorers; *U of Fla; Interior Design.*

RAINGE, Lance Lovell
Corliss HS; Chicago, IL (51-776) *Ill St U at Circle Campus; Sci.*

RAINIER, Kimberly Jean
Terre Haute S Vigo HS; Terre Haute, IN (60-625) Band; Pres, 4H; Hmrm; SC; Y-Tns; Sci A; Fr A; *Ohio St U; Nurs.*

RAINS, Eugene Todd
Seneca HS; Louisville, KY (33-363) BC; Drama; JV, Bkbl; Ftbl; HKg; Most Versatile; FCA; Pep C; Human Relations C; *U of Ky; Civil Engr.*

RAINS, Mary Ann
Litchfield HS; Gadsden, AL (6-144) BC; VP, FHA; VP, Span C; COM; VFW A; *Gadsden St Jr Col.*

RAINS, Mary Beth
Clarksville HS; Clarksville, TX (10-120) Band; FTA; Fin, Jr Miss Pagent; Mjrte; Span C; Hon Prog; Yth Fel; Pres, Yth Fel; WW; *Tyler Jr Col; Dental Hygiene.*

RAINS, Richard Alan
Clarksville HS; Clarksville, TX; Bus Mgr, Ann; FTA; Key C; Order/Arrow; Span C; Order/Arrow A; Yth Fel; Eagle Sct; Ideal Sct A; *Baylor U; Dentistry.*

RAINS, Scott Alan
S Dade HS; Homestead, FL (10%-750) Band; Chem C; Chess C; Math C; SC; Soccer; *U of Fla; Engr.*

RAINWATER, Curtis James
Civic Mem HS; Bethalto, IL (100-225) Ftbl; *SE Mo Col; Sci.*

RAINWATER, Elizabeth Anne
Palmetto HS; Palmetto, GA (3-100) Chor; FBLA; *Atlanta Area Tech Sch; Nurs.*

RAINWATER, Linda Kay
Southside HS; Fort Smith, AR (57-435) Drama; FBLA; VP, Y-Tns; S-T, Christ Ambassadors; Fin, Tn Talent; St, Ntl, Ntl Guild Piano Tchrs; *Westark Jr Col; Bus.*

RAKER, Sue Ellen
Liberty Jr-Sr HS; Liberty, PA; Band; Ensm; Ger C; Bkbl; Tr; Jr Dist Soloist; 1st Ch Sr Dist; 2nd Ch, Regionals; Outst Jr Musician.

RAKESTRAW, Jill Lorraine
Waverly HS; Lansing, MI (45-450) Chor; Ensm; Secy, Madrigal; HCt; Hon Prog; Most Talented; MSVA Hon Choir; Semi-Fin, Solo Ensm; *Mus.*

RAKOCZY, Dorothy Jean
Central Valley Pub Sch; Buxton, ND; Ann; Band; FHA; 4H A; Sci A; Jr Degree.

RALEIGH, Anita Faye
Highland HS; Ewing, MO; Band; CYO; Ensm; FHA; NHS; Bkbl; Sftbl; HCt; Type A; *Nurs.*

RALEY, Barbara Christine
Frankfort HS; Ridgeley, WV (10%-139) Band; Chor; FHA; NHS.

RALEY, Ralene Denise
Hardee HS; Wauchula, FL (28-264) JV, Chldr; Ensm; Rptr, FFA; FTA; Pres A; Chapter Farmer Degree; 4 H A; Lionettes; Yth Choir; *Gurpton Jones Col; Mortuary Sci.*

RALMUTO, Mitch Wayne
Tomball HS; Tomball, TX; Pres, Band; Chor; NHS; COM.

RALPH, Doug Calvin
N Salinas HS; Salinas, CA; JV, Wrest; 3rd Pl, Bay Area Wrest Tourn; *Hartnell Jr Col; Carpentry.*

RALPH, Julie Diane
Warren Co Sr HS; McMinnville, TN (43-400) Semi-Fin, GS; NHS; Sci C; VofDEM; Caney Fork Essay Contest; *David Lipscomb Col; Bus.*

RALPH, Portia Yvonne
Piscataway HS; Piscataway, NJ (240-497) VP, Chor; Up Bound; Co-Cpt, Tnns; Opt A; Type A; *Morgan St U; Speech Ed.*

RALPH, Susan Kay
Delmar HS; Delmar, De (8-100) NHS; VP, Var C; Cpt, Bkbl; Cpt, Hockey; Cpt, Sftbl; MVP, Bkbl & Sftbl; *Salisbury St Col; Bus Adm.*

RALPH, Thomas Peter
Lorain HS; Lorain, OH (96-380) *Computer Prog.*

RALSTON, Belinda Jo
Ephrata Sr HS; Ephrata, WA; FHA; Pres, Rainbow; F-Ed, Sch P; Spch A; *Spokane Comm Col; Police Sci.*

RALSTON, Bryan Lee
Orleans HS; Orleans, NE; Band; Chor; NHS; Bkbl; Ftbl; HCt; *U of Nebr; Bus.*

RALSTON, Donald Peter
Lansdowne-Aldan HS; Lansdowne, PA (5-230) Chor; Mgr, Bkbl.

RALSTON, George Albert
Robert E Lee Sr HS; Jacksonville, FL; Drama; Hmrm; Soccer; Outst Member, Children o-t Confede; Jefron Davis Med, Child o-t Confed; *Newbery Col; Law.*

RAMAGE, David Edward
Mt Carmel Area HS; Mt Carmel, PA (4-212) Ann; Chem C; Chess C; Chor; Ger C; Hmrm; Sch P; Sci C; Span C; JV, Bkbl; Tnns; COM; Hon Prog; Yth Fel; Yth Leg; Penn District Chor; *Bucknell U; Marine Bio.*

RAMAGE, Pamela Jane
Scottsboro HS; Scottsboro, AL; Anchor C; Ann; Band; Mjrte; Mu Alpha Theta; Tres, Art C; Rptr, Pep C; *Auburn U; Elem Ed.*

RAMAGE, Russell Stuart
Scottsboro HS; Scottsboro, AL; Ed, Ann; Band; Mu Alpha Theta; Rptr, NHS; Sci C; Span C; Art-Ed, Lit Mag; Art C; Lit Mag Art As; Yrbk A; *Auburn U; Pre-Dentistry.*

RAMANAUSKAS, Diane Marie
John W Hallahan HS; Philadelphia, PA (13-431) Pres, NFL; NHS; Ed, Sch P; Pres, Spch C; Sci A; Spch A; Val; Eng A; Lat A; *Temple U; Spch Therapy.*

RAMBO, C Blake
Plant City HS; Plant City, FL (86-805) Band; UN Council; MLS; Yth Fel; Yth Leg; Drum Major; Stage & Concert Bands; Tns for Christ C; Band Medals; *Fla St U; Mus.*

RAMBO, James Alan
Harlingen HS; Harlingen, TX (5%-850) Demolay; NHS; Hon Prog; Type A; Span A; *Tex A&M U; Mech Engr.*

RAMBO, Kathleen Karen
Butte Falls HS; Butte Falls, OR (10-25) Ch, FTA; Ed, Sch P; B Crocker A; Citz A; Journ A; Sal; Sci A; Type A; Val; *Sou Oreg St Col; Med Secy.*

RAMER, Faith
Cushing HS; Cushing, OK; A Cap Choir; Ann; Chor; Ensm; FHA; Orch; ARC; Most Out; *Moody Bible Inst; Mus.*

RAMER, Toni Lynn
Pinole Valley HS; Pinole, CA (38-661) Citz A; Nurs.

RAMES, Wayne Dale
Yankton HS; Yankton, SD; Sftbl.

RAMEY, Carol Anne
East Central HS; Hurley, MS (13-115) VP, Band; BC; Chor; Ensm; S-T, Sci C; Ntl Sci Symposium; Yth Fel; *Ole Miss; Math.*

RAMEY, Claire Martin
Robert E Lee HS; Tyler, TX (10%-700) FHA; Span C; Beauty; Hon Prog; Scholastic A; Drill Group.

RAMEY, Marcia Renee
Greenland HS; Greenland, AR; Fr C; Parl, FHA; ARC; Var C; Bkbl; Sftbl; Citz A; Math A; PTA A; Sci A; Eng A; *U of Ark; Bus.*

RAMEY, Richard Anthony
Stone HS; Wiggins, MS (33%-32) FFA; 4H; Sci C; Tr; *Morehouse Col; X-Ray Tech.*

RAMEY, Vicki Diane
Brawley Union HS; Brawley, CA (25-341) AFS; CSF; St Scholar; 'S' C; Tres, Fresh Cl; Venture C; Loma Linda Col; *Phys Therapy.*

RAMIREZ, Cecilia Irene
John O'Connell HS; San Francisco, CA; Band; Secy, Hmrm; NHS; Ed, Sch P; Secy, SC; *San Francisco St U; Nurs.*

RAMIREZ, Cindia L de Lourdes
Academia Santa Monica; Santurce, PR (10-53) Drama; NFL; Sch P; Span C; Spch C; SC; Var C; World Affairs C; Tnns; SC A; *Tulane U; Med.*

RAMIREZ, Diana Rae
O W Holmes HS; San Antonio, TX (155-600) CYO; Key C; Span C; SC; COM; *Southwest Tex St; Nurs.*

RAMIREZ, Lizette
Luis Munoz Rivera HS; Lajas, PR; Drama; FFA; FHA; Hmrm; Mjrte; Sch P; Swim; Tnns; Poet A; *U of PR; Psych.*

RAMIREZ, Maria Celina
Academia Maria Reina; Rio Piedras, PR; Chor; Drama; Fr C; NHS; Sci C; Hon Prog; *U of Mass; Ecology.*

RAMIREZ, Maria Eloisa
Colegio Puertorriqueno de Ninas; Rio Piedras, PR (4-61) Ann; Chor; Pres, Math C; NFL; NHS; Sftbl; COM; Sci A; *Bradley Col; Hist.*

RAMIREZ, Mary Agnes
St Augustine HS; Laredo, TX (10%-70) Ann; Secy, FHA; GS; NHS; Lib A; Pep Sq Cert; HR; *Laredo Jr Col; Special Ed.*

RAMIREZ, Norma Jean
Luis Munoz Marin HS; Cabo Rojo, PR (2-200) Chldr; Chor; Drama; FHA; Hmrm; Lit Ral; Lit Mag; ARC; SC; Swim; COM; Chem A; Cl Fav; H of F; Hon Prog; Masonic A; Most Out; Poet A; Sci A; Star Student; Summa Cum Laude; *U of PR; Med.*

RAMIREZ, Orlando
Jose de Diego HS; Mayaguez, PR (18-276) VP, Chem C; Pres, Chess C; VP, Chor; Commercial C; Hmrm; Pres, InterAct C; Lit Mag; NHS; Pres, Phys C; ARC; VP, Sch Achieve Tm; Pres, Sci C; SC; COM; Chamber of Comm A; Chem A; Citz A; Cl Fav; Hist A; Hon Prog; JA A; Jr Chamber of Com A; Lion A; Ntl Sci Found; Phy A; Pres A; Sci A; Yth Foundation; Yth Foundation A; Pres, Leo C; Ntl Distrophy Assn A; *U of Puerto Rico at Mayaguez; Nuclear Physics.*

RAMIREZ, Wally
Herbert H Lehman HS; New York City, NY (440-1255) Chor; Secy, Hmrm; Citz A; *Drew U; Foreign Lang.*

RAMM, Mary Beth
Fremont HS; Fremont, MI; Drama; Ger C.

RAMOS, Debbie Jean
Memorial HS; San Antonio, TX (6-300) Co-Ed, Ann; Secy, FBLA; FTA; NHS; Span C; Pres, Span NHS; COM; Eng A; Span A; *Rice U; Creative Writing.*

RAMOS, Elisa Elia
Roma HS; Roma, TX (4-144) Ch, Ann; Chor; FHA; 4H; Hmrm; NHS; S-T, Spch C; Ch, SC; Nurs.

RAMOS, Filipina Fallejo
George Washington Sr HS; Mangilao, GUAM (20-600) NHS; Secy, SC; *U of Guam; Lib Arts.*

RAMOS, Jose Luis
Manuela Toro HS; Caguas, PR; *U of Puerto Rico; Law.*

RAMOS, Martinez Carlos
Dr Pedro Perea Fajardo Voc HS; Mayaguez, PR; Bkbl; Sci A; Hon Stu; *Elec Engr.*

RAMOS, Sonia Marta
Consuelo Escalona Private Sch; Carolina, PR (1-56) Chldr; Chor; Dbte Tm; Drama; Hmrm; Lit Mag; NHS; Secy, ARC; Sci C; Secy, SC; Swim; Tnns; COM; Citz A; Hon Prog; JA A; Summa Cum Laude; *U of PR; Med.*

RAMOS, Sylvia
Jose de Diego HS; Mayaguez, PR; Phys C; SC; COM; Magna Cum Laude.

RAMP, Angel Marie
Glen Oak HS; Canton, OH; Interpreter for Deaf; Singing Group; Bible Bowl Tm; *Malone Col; Ed.*

RAMP, Jane Louise
Claymont HS; Claymont, DE (1-265) Band; Co-Cpt, Chldr; Chor; FTA; GS; Hmrm; NHS; Bus Mgr, Sch P; Pres, SC; Tri-HiY; Tres, Jr Cl; Citz A; Cl Fav; *Madison Col; Home Ec.*

RAMP, Norman Charles III
Glenoak W HS; Canton, OH; Band; Chor; Bsbl; Ftbl; Tr; Wrest; COM; Citz A; Math A; ARC A.

RAMPELLO, Karen Lynn
Central Baptist HS; Cincinnati, OH; Ed, Ann; Cpt, Chldr; Chor; Secy, Hmrm; SC; Secy, Jr Cl; Pres A; Yth Fel; *Special Ed.*

RAMSAY, Jennifer Lynn
H L Pardin Elsberry HS; Elsberry, MO (12-63) Band; Chor; Bkbl; Sftbl; Tr; *USC; Sci.*

RAMSAY, Melinda Ann
Carlsbad HS; Carlsbad, CA (100-400) Chor; *Pacific Christian Col; Mus.*

RAMSAY, Page Lee
Sumter HS; Sumter, SC (29-753) Rptr, Ann; Chldr; Drama; Fr C; HiY; F-Ed, Lit Mag; NHS; SC; Bkbl; Swim; Yth Fel; VP, District Yth Coun; Coun On Ministry; 2nd Pl, Optimist Oratorial; Del, District Yth Annual Conf; *Law.*

RAMSDALE, Donna May
Kingman HS; Kingman, KS (4-130) Band; Ensm; Hmrm; Sci C; Pres, Span C; Span NHS; SC; Var C; Y-Tns; Tr; Hon Prog; Yth Fel; *Sci.*

RAMSDALE, Lori Ann
Kingman HS; Kingman, KS; A Cap Choir; Chor; Drama; Pres, Sci C; Pres, Span C; Span NHS; Var C; Y-Tns; Tr; Hon Prog; St Scholar; *Southwestern Col; Bio.*

RAMSDALE, Samuel John
Kingman HS; Kingman, KS (5-111) FFA; Sci C; Hon Prog; Yth Fel; *Kans St U; Engr.*

RAMSEY, Debbie Ann
Harmony Grove HS; Benton, AR (3-25) Band; Chor; Orch; Sftbl; HQn; *Ouachita Col.*

RAMSEY, Debbie Lee
Crockett HS; Crockett, TX; Band; Co-Cpt, Chldr; NHS; SC; Tnns; *Tex A&M U; Pol Sci.*

RAMSEY, Delores Yvette
Biloxi Sr HS; Biloxi, MS (100-500) Chor; Sftbl; *Perkinston Jr Col.*

RAMSEY, Gerald Lynn
Oglesby HS; Oglesby, TX (2-12) Ann; Bsbl; Bkbl; Ftbl; Hon Prog; *Baylor U; Elem Engr.*

RAMSEY, Guy Myers
P C West HS; Oklahoma City, OK (50%-500) Art A; *Okla St U; Art.*

RAMSEY, Jan Carol
Homestead HS; Mequon, WI (150-400) Band; *Carthage Col; Elem Ed.*

RAMSEY, Johnny Ray
N Little Rock Ole Main HS; N Little Rock, AR (34-431) Mu Alpha Theta; NHS; ACT Schol; *U of Ark; Archit.*

RAMSEY, Lisa Gayle
Central HS; Louisville, KY (50%-400) Rptr, Sch P; PA; *W Ky U; Social Worker.*

RAMSEY, Michael Dan
Prairiland HS; Pattonville, TX; VP, FFA; Phys C; Sch Achieve Tm; Var C; Co-Cpt, Ftbl; Tr.

RAMSEY, Nedia Faye
Carolina HS; Greenville, SC (12-150) I Dare You; Most Out; Type A; *Eckerd Col.*

RAMSEY, Paige Ayran
Watkins Mem HS; Pataskala, OH (22-203) Secy, Band; Chor; Pres, Drama; Ensm; Tres, Fr C; Tres, FTA; Rptr, 4H; Tres, NHS; Tres, Jr Cl; COM; 4H A; B-1 Cl, Piano Solo; *Elem Ed.*

RAMSEY, Phyllis Jane
Clarkrange HS; Clarkrange, TN; BC; Chor; Drama; FHA; Hmrm, 4H; VP, Sci C; Spch C; Co-Cpt, Bkbl; Bio A; 4H A; Yth Fel; Miss Hustle; Best Offensive, All Region, Bkbl; Hist, Home Ec; *Tenn Tech U; Bus.*

RAMSEY, Robert Mark
Salisbury R IV HS; Salisbury, MO; Band; Parl, FBLA; NHS; A-Ed, Sch P; Pres, SC; Var C; Bsbl; Co-Cpt, Ftbl; *Moberly Jr Col; Bus.*

RAMSEY, Ronald Dean
Charleroi Sr HS; Charleroi, PA (100-340) Order/Arrow; Order/Arrow A; Stage Crew; *Calif St Col; Lib Arts.*

RAMSEY, S'Neta Marie
Rogers HS; Toledo, OH; A Cap Choir; Bus C; FHA; Model UN; Arch; Bsbl; Bkbl; Sftbl; Swim; Tnns; Tr; SC; Most Out; Type A; Cl Historian; *Ohio U; Bus Adm.*

RAMSEY, Tami Sue
Centerville Sr HS; Centerville, IN (70-177) Cpt, Chldr; Hmrm; Sch P; Var C; Y-Tns; Mgr, Bsbl; Cpt, Gym; Fresh & Jr Princess; Jr NHS; HR; *Ball St U; Bus.*

RAMSLAND, Mark Alden
Johnson HS; St Paul, MN; Semi-Fin, Golf; *Archt.*

RAMSOUR, Carol Ann
Hickory HS; Hickory, NC (39-360) AFS; Secy, Band; Pres, FBLA; Secy, InterClub Coun; Math C; NHS; Span C; Crisco A; Type A; Bowl A; FBLA A; *Appalachian St U; Bus.*

RAMSOUR, Paul Dailey
Hickory HS; Hickory, NC (52-380) Band; BC; FBLA; Band A; Pres, Sr High Yth Ministry; *ASU; Bus.*

RAMSTEAD, Julie Ann
N Kitsap Sr HS; Poulsbo, WA (24-186) AFS; Chor; Hmrm; NHS; VP, SC; Bkbl; Tnns; DARGCA; H of F; HCt; MLS; VP, Secy, Church Yth; GPA A, Bkbl; Most Inspiration, Tnns; Girl o-t Mo; Girl o-t Semester; *Wash St U; Phys Therapy.*

RAMUS, Lori Marie
Batavia Sr HS; Batavia, IL (5-211) AFS; Band; Community Yth Symph; Drama; Orch; Thes; Tr; Amer Leg A; Mus As; *Mus.*

RANALLO, Deanna Elizabeth
Hartshorne HS; Hartshorne, OK (5-70) FHA; Bkbl; Citz A; *Bus.*

RANALLO, Roxanne Marie
St Anthony Village HS; St Anthony, MN (92-200) AFS; FHA; Mgr, Tnns; JA A; *Col of St Thomas; Bus Adm.*

RAND, Helen Leigh
Antelope Valley HS; Lancaster, CA (307-654) AFS; Chor; Hmrm; Ski C; Span C; SC; Y-Tns; Tr; *Antelope Valley Col.*

RAND, Janice Lynn
Reidsville Sr HS; Reidsville, NC (20-344) Drama; Fr C; NHS; Bkbl; Yth Fel; *Appalachian St U; Home Ec.*

RAND, Valarie Joyce
Willibrord Cath HS; Chicago, IL (8-79) Math C; NHS; Pol Sci C; Sci C; Span C; Span NHS; Secy, SC; Tres, Jr Cl; Bio A; Sci A; GSct; Mus A; *U of Ill; Psych.*

RANDALL, Alison Leigh
Muskogee HS; Muskogee, OK (65-575) AFS; Band; Ger C; NHS; Sci C; Alg A; Bio A; NMF; Opt A; *Rice U; Biological Sci.*

RANDALL, Christina Marie
Martin Co HS; Stuart, FL (95-500) BC; City Conf; GS; Hmrm; InterClub Coun; Ed, Sch P; Span C; SC; Pres, Sr Cl; VP, Jr Cl; Arch; Sftbl; Tnns; Amer Leg A; Bio A; Citz A; Elk A; HCt; Most Out; Pres A; Span A; Tn o-t Mo; *U of Notre Dame; Communications.*

RANDALL, Cindy Diane
McRae HS; McRae, AR (2-19) Ann; BC; Pres, FBLA; *Ark St U; Drama.*

RANDALL, Daryl Robert
Coon Rapids Sr HS; Coon Rapids, MN (12-700) BS; NHS; Pres, SC; Var C; Pres, Sr Cl; Pres, Jr Cl; Ftbl; MVP, Hockey; Sftbl; Tnns; Amer Leg A; Citz A; Hon Prog; Sci A; Cpt, Hockey; Citz Spkr; Homecoming Emcee.

RANDALL, Deanna Kaye
Monroe Union HS; Monroe, OR (1-65) Chor; Pres, Jr Cl; JV; Bkbl; Vlbl; *Oreg St U; Animal Sci.*

RANDALL, Donald Glenn
Thurston Sr HS; Springfield, OR; Tres, Ger C; *U of Oreg; Law.*

RANDALL, Hattie Mae
Terrell Co HS; Dawson, GA (6-200) BC; 4H A; Hon Prog; Sci A; PA, Eng, Gen Bus, A's; *Bus Adm.*

RANDALL, Joyce Jill
Dunlap Comm Sch; Dunlap, IA (1-57) Ann; Chor; Fr C; FHA; Monogram; NHS; Rptr, Sch P; SC; Var C; Co-Cpt, Bkbl; Tr; B Crocker A; Citz A; St Scholar; Val; Yth Fel; Sr Prom Qn; *Iowa St U; Interior Design.*

RANDALL, Nicolette Louise
McCluer N HS; Florissant, MO (45-799) Chor; COM; Hon Prog; Math A.

RANDALL, Philip Edward
Brazil Sr HS; Brazil, IN (21-203) Rptr, Ann; Pres, Band; Ensm; Pres, Fr C; Model UN; NHS; Pres, Orch; SC; UN Council; Var C; Co-Cpt, Bkbl; Golf; Tnns; HCt; Hon Prog; Most Out; Ntl Achv Schol; St Scholar; Yth Leg; Cpt, FCA; FCA A; Thomas Schol; *DePauw U; Law.*

RANDALL, Roderick Kirkland
Andrews HS; High Point, NC (37-298) Co-Cpt, Band; BC; Monogram; Ftbl; Tr; Wrest; Chem A; Jr Patricans; VP, Coed C; WW; US Naval Acad, Engr, Sci Workshop; *Ga Tech; Elec Engr.*

RANDALL, Sandra Elizabeth
Central Acad; Macon, MS (20%-44) Tres, Anchor C; Ann; Mgr, Band; Chor; SC; S-T, Soph Cl; HCt; Type A; Asst Brownie Ldr; Sr GSct; Stu Director, Jr Play; Eng A; *Miss St U; Interior Design.*

RANDALL, Sandra Lynn
El Segundo HS; El Segundo, CA (1-250) AFS; Band; Secy, Fr C; FHA; Hmrm; Orch; Bkbl; Amer Leg A; CSF; Spch A; Drill Tm; Paramedic Training Schol; Vlbl; Fr A; Principal's Trophy; Mus A; *Brigham Young U; Foreign Lang.*

RANDALL, Trina Renee
David Starr Jordan HS; Los Angeles, CA; Hmrm; SC; COM; Citz A; Hon Prog; Tutoring C; Cert of Recognition; Service A; Cert of Promotion; *Cal St at Long Beach; Nurs.*

RANDALL, Wendy Sue
Scott Comm HS; Scott City, KS (13-135) A Cap Choir; Chldr; Chor; SC; Y-Tns; Tr; Most Out; Yth Fel; Cpt, Gym; 1st, St Gym; Outst Chldr; Horsemanship A; *Kans St U; Phys Ed.*

RANDLE, Catherine Louise
The Bolles Sch; Jacksonville, FL (73-158) Best Actress As; Headmasters List; Service A; *FSU; Spch Pathology.*

RANDLE, Paul Barton
Foothill Sr HS; Sacramento, CA (26-400) Chem C; Community Yth Symph; Pres, Drama; Ensm; Orch; Ski C; Pres, Span C; Var C; Mgr, Soccer; Tnns; Bio A; COM; Chem A; Elk A; NEDT; St Scholar.

RANDLE, Sonja LaNell
S P Waltrip Sr HS; Houston, TX (1-654) FTA; Hmrm; Semi-Fin, Jr Miss Pa; NHSt; Sci C; Span C; Parl, SC; Tres, Up Bound; Tr; Amer Leg A; Hon Prog; JA A; Pres A; Rotary A; Sci A; Human Relations A; PA; Social Sci Dept A; *Tex Women's U; Phys Therapy.*

RANDOL, Mary Kaye
Maysville HS; Maysville, OK; Ann; Band; FHA; GS; Mjrte; Rainbow; Sch P; Cl Fav; Most Out; Drum Major, Outst, Band; Band Qn Attendant; *Central St U; Bus.*

RANDOLPH, Belinda Catherine M
Sumter HS; Sumter, SC; Pres, NHS; Pres, SC; Pres, Soph Cl; Bkbl; Tr; Opt A; Hon Men, Actress & Playwriting.

RANDOLPH, Gloria Jean
Livingston HS; Livingston, CA (11-300) Chor; MVP, Bkbl; Sftbl; Tr; Hon Prog; Yth Pres; Asilomar Conf; *Pepperdine U; Bus.*

RANDOLPH, Lisa Marie
Saint Ursula Acad; Cincinnati, OH (14-108) CYO; Chldr; Chor; K of C; Span C; Span NHS; SC; Alg A; COM; Math A; Most Out; Squirrettes Drill Tm; Vlbl Tm; Attendance A; Straight 'A' Stu; *Broadcasting.*

RANDOLPH, Nathaniel Garfield
Bell Voc HS; Washington, DC; Bsbl; Cpt, Ftbl; Tr; Citz A; *U of Md; Mech Engr.*

RANDOLPH, Patricia Faye
Springfield Gardens HS; Springfield Gardens, NY (406-793) Chor; Hmrm; Ntl Yth Conf; ARC; Sci C; Secy, Soph Cl; Sftbl; Tnns; Citz A; Hist A; Math A; ARC A; Sci A; Yth Fel; Hospital Cert of Appreciation; Church Cert of Appreciation; *Howard U; Food and Nutrition.*

RANDOLPH, Patrick David
Lubbock Christian HS; Lubbock, TX (10-56) A Cap Choir; Chor; Drama; Spch C; Bsbl; JV, Bkbl; Ftbl; Tr; Spch A; *Harding Col; Bible.*

RANDOLPH, Wendy Kay
Tallapoosa Acad; Dadeville, AL (5-24) Band; BC; Bio A; HCt; Mardi Gras Court; *UCLA; Med.*

RANDON, Lennox Wayne
Smiley HS; Houston, TX (4-400) Bus Mgr, Mu Alpha Th; Ed, Sch P; Tr; Citz A; Hist A; Journ A; Math A; NMF; NMS; Type A; Eng A; *U of Houston; Engr.*

RANES, Susan Leigh
Madisonville N Hopkins HS; Madisonville, KY; Band; BC; Chor; 4H; Mjrte; Tri-HiY; COM; 4H A; Hon Prog; Secy, Tns Who Care C; Glee C; DAR Essay; *Madisonville Comm Col; Elem Ed.*

RANESTORE, Angel Denet
Mattie T Blounx HS; Prichard, AL; Chor; Hmrm; Sci C; Vlbl; Span, Cert; PA; *U of S Ala; Bus.*

RANEY, Douglas Karl
Coppell HS; Coppell, TX; Pres, Band; Bsbl; JV, Bkbl; JV, Ftbl; Swim; Tr; *Mus.*

RANFTLE, Gary Peter
Hauppauge HS; Hauppauge, NY (175-700) JV, Ftbl; Tr, Wrest; *Suffolk Comm Col; Computer Sci.*

RANGE, Dale Joseph
New Athens HS Unit 60; New Athens, IL (6-400) Band; CYO; Chess C; VP, FFA; Tres, NHS; Orch; Spch C; Pres, Jr Cl; Pres, Soph Cl; Co-Cpt, Bsbl; Bkbl; Amer Leg A; Spch A; VFW Orator Win; *VofDEM; Bus.*

RANGE, Tammy Lynn
Joliet Central HS; Joliet, IL (66-555) A Cap Choir; Chor; Fr C; Hmrm; Madrigal; NHS; SC; *Judson Col.*

RANGEL, Felipe Jr
Hayden HS; Topeka, KS (29-165) A Cap Choir; Chldr; Chor; NHS; Bsbl; Bkbl; Cn-Ctry; Ftbl; Sftbl; Tnns; Tr; NHS A; *Benedictine Col; Med.*

RANGEL, Francisco Mario
New Caney HS; Porter, TX; CYO; Pres, Chess C; Dbte Tm; Drama; Hmrm; JETS; NHS; Ed, Sch P; Spch C; Rptr, SC; Thes; Ch, Sr Cl; JV, Ftbl; Journ A; Q&S A; *Tex A&M U; Civil Engr.*

RANGEN, Kristin Kay
Maddock Pub HS; Maddock, ND (14-28) VP, Band; Chldr; Chor; Secy, FHA; Rptr, 4H; Sch P; 4H A; FHA Hon A; All-Star Stu Selection; Ntl Chldr; *Lake Region Jr Col; Fashion Merchandising.*

RANHEIM, Joanna Lynn
Willow Glen HS; San Jose, CA (10%-600) Band; Chor; Ensm; Fr C; Hmrm; NHS; SC; Cpt, Bkbl; Cpt, Hockey; JV, Soccer; Cpt, Sftbl; COM; Hon Prog; Ntl Achv Schol; Yth Leg; CSF; Mus A; Sports A; Cpt, Vlbl; MVP, Sftbl; *St Olaf Col; Sci.*

RANKIN, David Mark
Highlands Intermediate HS; Natrona Heights, PA; Chor; Ntl Jr Hon Soc; Pres, Audio-Visual C; *Penn St U; Elec Tech.*

RANKIN, Deborah Karen
Montrose Acad; Montrose, AR (11-42) Band; SC.

RANKIN, Theresa R
Poughkeepsie HS; Poughkeepsie, NY; Chor; Fr C; Pres, 4H; Arch; Bsbl; Bkbl; Sftbl; Swim; Tnns; Tr; COM; 4H A; *Fashion Inst of Tech; Retailing Bus Mgt.*

RANKIN, Venus Elvira
Western HS; Baltimore, MD (86-764) Span C; Sign Lang C; Senatorial Schol; W Md U Schol; *W Md U; Sociology.*

RANKIN, William Michael
Montrose Acad; Montrose, AR (11-32) Band;
Chem C; Secy, FFA; 4H; Sci C; Bkbl; Ftbl; 4H A;
HCt; *Ark St U.*

RANKINS, Anthony
Withrow HS; Cincinnati, OH;

RANKINS, Raymond Lynell
St Helena HS; Greensburg, LA; A Cap Choir; FFA;
Arch; Bkbl; Cpt, Ftbl; *Agr.*

RANNEY, Amy Elizabeth
E Hartford HS; E Hartford, CT; Band; Hmrm; SC;
Bkbl; Sftbl; JV, Swim; Yth Fel; St All Star, Sftbl;
Executive Board, Yth Fel.

RANNEY, Christine Marie
Bishop Mark K Carroll HS; Wichita, KS (29-211)
Dbte Tm; NHS; Sftbl; *Kans Newman Col; Ed.*

RANSOM, Brian Anthony
N Nashville HS; Nashville, TN;

RANSOM, Jayne
Conestoga Sr HS; Berwyn, PA (5%-600) Chor;
Drama; Ensm; NHS; Span C; COM; Projects Ch,
Church Yth Fel; GSct; Piano Quartet; *Lib Arts.*

RANSOM, Leah Loraine
Crestview Sr HS; Crestview, FL (10%-300) JV,
Chldr; Drama; Chldr Ltr; *Ohio St U.*

RANSOM, Ralph Clark
San Angelo Central HS; San Angelo, TX; Band;
Orch; F-Ed, Sch P; SC; *U of Tex at Austin; Bus.*

RANSOM, Vivian Kay
N Nashville HS; Nashville, TN; FHA; Bowl; *Pepperdine Col; Eng.*

RANSOM, Wanda Anita
Whetstone Sr HS; Columbus, OH; Band; Bsbl;
Bkbl; Sftbl; Yth Fel; VP, Jr Achv; *Howard U; Social
Psych.*

RANSON, James Edward Jr
S Dade HS; Homestead, FL (15%-860) Key C;
Secy, Model UN; Monogram; Order/Arrow; Var
C; Bsbl; JV, Bkbl; Cpt, Ftbl; Soccer; Cpt, Tr; COM;
Elk A; God & Country A; HKg; Order/Arrow A;
ROTC A; Yth Fel; MVP, Ftbl; Band A; Silver
Knight A; Eagle Sct; WW; Ath Schol; Ath Vs MS;
Duke U.

RANURO, Steven Joseph
Secaucus HS; Secaucus, NJ (11-164) Key C; NHS;
VP, SC; Cpt, Bkbl; Co-Cpt, Ftbl; Swtht; *NE U;
Acct.*

RANZENBERGER, Robert John
Highlands HS; N Highlands, CA; 4H; 4H A; US
Army, Sci Fair, Sch Achv, A's; *Pepperdine U; Elec.*

RAO, Suzanne Lynn
Uniontown Area Sr HS; Uniontown, PA (16-435)
Secy, Arch; Band; F-Ed, Lit Mag; NHS; Orch; Ski
C; Alg A; Hon Prog; Penn Mus Ed As Western Dist
Band A; *Penn St U; Forestry.*

RAPALJE, Beth Ann
Lewis Central HS; Council Bluffs, IA; Chor; Swim;
Tr; Kiwanis A; Type A; Drill Tm; Pom Pon A;
Swim A; Stu Teacher A; *Photography.*

RAPER, Cynthia Caldwell
Avery HS; Amory, MS; Bus C; Drama; Pres, Fr C;
FBLA; HiY; Thes; Swim; *U of Miss; Marine Bio.*

RAPER, Randy Lee
Phil Campbell HS; Phil Campbell, AL (1-95) VP,
FFA; FTA; Secy, 4H; Pres, NHS; Var C; Secy, Jr
Cl; Ftbl; 4H A; Spch A; Stu o-t Month; *NWASJC;
Agr Engr.*

RAPER, Steven Michael
Cedartown Comprehensive HS; Cedartown, GA
(20-325) Key C; NHS; Sci C; Hist A; Hon Group;
Floyd Jr Col; Elec.

RAPILLARD, Elaine Ann
Sw Miami Sr HS; Miami, FL (44-992) Ann; GS;
Hmrm; InterClub Coun; NHS; Tres, SC; Pres, Jr Cl;
Hon Prog; 'Miss Southwest'; Smith Co Book A; Co
Stu Traffic Safety Coun; *Miami-Dade S Col; Bus
Mgr.*

RAPISTA, Suzette Villa
George Washington Sr HS; Mangilao, GUAM
(43-740) NHS; *U of Hawaii; Med.*

RAPPA, Theresa Marie
Qn o-t Rosary Acad; Amityville, NY (2-68) Chldr;
NHS; ARC; Tres, SC; Alg A; COM; Math A; *Adel-
phi U; Lang.*

RAPPOLD, Sandra Patricia
Luther HS; Chicago, IL (18-289) NHS; Mgr, Tr;
Girl's Service C; *Bus.*

RAPPOPORT, Randee Lynn
Hebrew Acad HS; Yonkers, NY (1-15) Chess C;
Drama; Hon Prog; Val.

RARDIN, Pamalla Sue
Charleston Sr HS; Charleston, IL (89-240) Drama;
Rptr, 4H; Spch C; SC; Tres, Yth for Easter Seals;
Bat Girl; Dance Concert; Cinderette; Scho Musi-
cal.

RARICK, Sherry Lynne
Fleetwood Area HS; Fleetwood, PA (17-149) A
Cap Choir; Band; Chor; FTA; Co-Ch, Hmrm; Lit
Mag; NHS; Orch; God & Country A; *Lebanon Val-
ley Col; Mus.*

RASALAN, Cynthia Agudong
John F Kennedy HS; Tumon, GUAM (10-511)
Chor; City Conf; FNA; Madrigal; NHS; HR; Eng
A; WW; Chor A; Pep C; *Berlin Col; Mus.*

RASBERRY, Debra Ann
Second Ward HS; Gloster, LA; Bus C; FHA; Math
C; Sci C; SC; Sftbl; Hon Prog; *Sou U at Baton
Rouge; Engr.*

RASBERRY, Renata Denise
Luther Burbank Sr HS; Sacramento, CA (275-700)
A Cap Choir; Secy, Chor; Dbte Tm; Orch; Y-Tns;
Semi-Fin, Jr Cl; Mgr, Tr; Citz A; Miss Personality;
Most Likeable; Participant, 1st Black Hist Wk; *San
Francisco St Col; Social Worker.*

RASCH, Juanita Rose
Shawano HS; Shawano, WI (2-239) Band; Fr C;
FHA; Semi-Fin, GS; Math C; NHS; Sch P; VP, Sr
Cl; MLS; Sal; Intern, NJ Congress; Washington
Workshops I & II; Century IV Ldr A; Alt, St Hon
Band; *Boston Col; Pol Sci.*

RASCHKE, Mary Jo
Cedar Shoals HS; Athens, GA (10%-300) 4H;
COM; 4H A; Yth Fel; Gym As; *Home Ec.*

RASCO, Clarence Elzy
Dell City HS; Dell City, TX (3-21) Ann; FFA;
NHS; Pres, Jr Cl; Tres, Soph Cl; Ftbl; Chamber of
Comm A; Math A; Star Greenhand A; Outst Stu A;
FFA; Eng A; Sheepman's A.

RASH, Erin Ruth
St Mary's Central HS; Bismarck, ND (17-171)
Chor; Ensm; Bkbl; Inter-Ntl Mus Camp Schol; Yth
Choir; Ntl Piano Playing Auditions Cert; *Moor-
head St U; Mus Ed.*

RASHLEY, Lura Kay
Citrus HS; Inverness, FL (7-250) Band; 4H; Hmrm;
NHS; Span C; VP, Jr Cl; COM; 4H A; H of F; HCt;
Pasco-Hernando Comm Col; Bus.

RASKI, Marion Joann
John S Fine HS; Nanticoke, PA (22-340) Chor;
Hmrm; ARC; Tri-HiY; COM; *Allentown Hospital
Sch of Nurs; Nurs.*

RASMUSSEN, Daniel Dean
Warren Central HS; Indianapolis, IN; Band; 4H;
Hmrm; Bsbl; Cr-Ctry; ARC A; Yth Fel; Pres, My
Group; Yth Del, Methodist Conf; Yth Camp Coun-
selor; *Ind Central U; Religion.*

RASMUSSEN, Jon Charles
Big Bay de Noc HS; Cooks, MI; Cr-Ctry; Ftbl; Tr;
Math A; *Mich Tech U; Engr.*

RASMUSSEN, Rik Lorin
Benicia HS; Benicia, CA; Drama; Am Iris Soc;
Bishop Personal Page; S-T, Bridge C; Interntl C;
Head Acolyte & Lector; 2nd Pl, Nation Yth Achv
A; *Solano Jr Col; Botany.*

RASMUSSEN, Scott Kendall
Clintonville Sr HS; Clintonville, WI (50%-189)
NHS; Var C; Bkbl; Ftbl; Tnns; Tr; *Fox Valley Tech
Sch; Police Sci.*

RASMUSSEN, Sharon Linn
Robert E Lee HS; Montgomery, AL (40-706)
CYO; Math C; NHS; NEDT; Art C; Craft C; 2nd
Pl, Art Exhibit; Win, LIFE Event Logo Contest;
Auburn U; Visual Arts.

RASMUSSEN, Tom Niel
Baltimore Lutheran HS; Baltimore, MD (33%-60)
Bsbl; Cpt, Bkbl; Cpt, Soccer; PA; HR; No Tardy
Cert.

RASMUSSON, Patricia Ann
Lincoln Jr HS; Jamestown, NY (25%-300) Pres,
Band; Chor; Ensm; Hmrm; Orch; Rptr, Sch P; Pres,
Mozart C; Most Mus; All St Sect; *Oral Roberts U;
Med.*

RASNAKE, Anita Blanche
Garden HS; Oakwood, VA; BC; Cpt, Chldr; Chem
C; 4H; Hmrm; Model UN; Monogram; Secy, SC;
VP, Tri-HiY; UN Council; Var C; Sftbl; Beauty; 4H
A; HQn; HCt; Pres A; Spch A; Bulletin Board
Comm; Chldr A; Prom Comm; Phys Ed A; Span A;
St Forensic A; *Designing.*

RASNER, Kathie Jo
Hillcrest HS; Country Club Hills, IL (63-342)
Chor; Secy, Fr C; Hmrm; Math C; A-Ed, Sch P;
Spch C; Pres, SC; Tnns; Tr; Alg A; Amer Leg A;
Amer Leg Orator A; COM; Citz A; Hon Prog;
Journ A; Math A; MLS; Poet A; Q&S A; Sci A;
Spch A; VFW A; VFW Orator Win; VofDEM; *Sou
Ill U; Elec.*

RASNER, Terri Lane
Ben Davis HS; Indianapolis, IN (50-900) Band;
NHS; Thes; Tr; Pres A; Mus A's; *Ind U; Ed.*

RASPBERRY, Rosalind Denise
Fairfield HS; Fairfield, AL (25%-160) Cpt, Chldr;
Fr C; InterClub Coun; Sch Achieve Tm; SC; HCt;
Hon Prog; Yth Speaks Out; *U of Ala; Biol.*

RASSKE, Jane Elizabeth
Ripon HS; Ripon, WI (63-170) AFS; Chldr; Chor;
Ger C; NFL; ARC; Tr; ARC A; Forensics, GAA,
A's; Pom Pon, Chldr, A's; *Mercy Med Sch of Nurs;
Nurs.*

RAST, Laura Marie
Huntsville HS; Huntsville, AL; Chor; Drama; Sci
A; Church Choir; Drill Tm; Dance Tm; Gym Tm;
Auburn U; Home Ec.

RATAIC, Joan Susan
E Cath HS; Manchester, CT (41-335) CYO; Cpt,
Chldr; VP, Chor; Dbte Tm; Drama; Pres, Fr C;
Hmrm; ARC; Ed, Sch P; SC; Pres, Soph Cl; Span A;
Bkbl; Soccer; Cpt, Sftbl; Swim; Tnns; Tr; COM;
Citz A; Cl Fav; Hon Prog; Journ A; MLS; Most
Out; Opt A; Pres A; Spch A; Church Lector; Solo-
ist; Tutor; Ballet A's; Lead, Mus; Chor A's; *Saint
Joseph Col; Mus Ed.*

RATCLIFF, Roselyn Annette
Holly Springs HS; Holly Springs, MS (50-165) F-
Ed, Ann; Secy, Band; Drama; Bus Mgr, Hmrm; Sch
P; Beauty; Cl Fav; Hon Prog; Most Out; Swtht;
Type A; Yth Fel; *Grambling St U; Bus Adm.*

RATERMANN, Elizabeth Mary
Central Comm HS; Breese, IL (4-157) Ann; Bio A;
HCt; Hon Prog; Type A; WW; Hist A; Eng A;
Typing A; *Kaskaskia Jr Col; Executive Secy.*

RATH, Susan Lynn
McCluer N HS; Florissant, MO; IOJD.

RATH, William Charles III
McCluer N HS; Florissant, MO (35-764) NHS; *U
of Mo; Bus.*

RATHBONE, William Alfred Jr
The Balles Sch; Jacksonville, FL (10-160) Ann;
Chess C; Drama; Co-Ed, Lit Mag; Math C; NHS;
Order/Arrow; F-Ed, Sch P; Mgr, Bsbl; Hon Prog;
Journ A; Math A; Order/Arrow A; ARC A; Ntl
Merit Ltr of Commendation; NROTC Schol; Nav
Acad Engr-Sci Sem & Workshop; *MIT; Elec Engr.*

RATHBUN, Janet Henry
National Cathedral School for Girl; Washington,
DC (10%-71) Drama; Var C; Most Out; *Psychol-
ogy Speech.*

RATHERT, Bryan Dean
Steeleville Comm Unit HS; Steeleville, IL (2-67)
Pres, NHS; Pres, Span C; JV, Bkbl; Golf; Amer Leg
A; Cl Fav; MLS; Sal; Ill St Schol; Sou Ill Soc for
Achv; *U of Mo at Rolla; Elec Engr.*

RATHERT, Sharon Ann
Chester HS; Chester, IL (18-96) Pres, Band; FHA;
SC; Sftbl; Tr; Pres, Church Yth Group; Church
Chor; Vlbl; *SE Mo St U; Gen.*

RATHGABER, Scott William
New Haven HS; New Haven, IN (2-384) Chor; Ensm; Hmrm; JV, Bsbl; Bkbl; Ftbl; Hon Prog; FCA; Ind U; Med.

RATHKE, Robin Lea
Cedarburg HS; Cedarburg, WI (62-360) Band; Secy, Span C; Bkbl; Swim.

RATLIEF, Myra Annette
Flagstaff HS; Flagstaff, AZ; Hmrm; God & Country A; ARC A; Office Service; Bowl Trophy; PA; CYC As; N Ariz U; Bio.

RATLIFF, Carolyn Gail
The Cecilian Acad; Philadelphia, PA; Chor; Lat C; NFL; ARC; COM; Hon Prog; ARC A; Dietetics.

RATLIFF, Christopher Wendell
Proviso E HS; Maywood, IL (40%-620) Chor; Community Yth Symph; Dbte Tm; Drama; Ensm; Var C; Ftbl; Tr; COM; Citz A; Hon Prog; Interlochen Ntl Mus; Yth Fel; Sunday Sch Teacher; Comm Choir A; Choir; Ftbl A; Tr A; Bradley U; Archt Engr.

RATLIFF, Danny Lee
Lawton HS; Lawton, OK (100-537) Pres, Club Procedure; VICA; Asst Coach, Little League Bsbl; Okla St U; Archt Engr.

RATLIFF, David Summers
Ironton HS; Ironton, OH (4-185) Model UN; NHS; Tres, Jr Cl; JV, Bsbl; Golf.

RATLIFF, Gladys Marie
T L Weston HS; Greenville, MS (14-700) Chor; Pres, FHA; Secy, 4H; Rptr, Sch P; Bus Mgr, SC; Crisco A; Eng A; Typing A; Bio A; Home Ec A; SC A; 2nd, Miss Tl Weston; Miss Valley St U; Pre-Sch Ed.

RATLIFF, James Brian
Pikeville HS; Pikeville, KY (6-85) Band; NHS; All Co Band; Eastern Ky U; Acct.

RATLIFF, Janet Lee
Amarillo HS; Amarillo, TX (30-700) Lat C; Lat NHS; JV, Cr-Ctry; Tr; Amer Leg A; Bio A; COM; Pres A; Ken C, AHS Hon C; Golden Key A, Art; U of Tex; Pre-Med.

RATLIFF, Mary Joyce
Allen HS; Robeline, LA (3-27) Chldr; FBLA; Secy, Hmrm; Secy, Math C; NHS; Tr; HQn; Hon Prog; Bus Adm.

RATLIFF, Terri Michele
Robert E Lee HS; Montgomery, AL (200-700) Ann; BC; Ensm; Glee C; Choralees; Triple Quintet; Phys Ed Ldrship C; Church Pianist; Mus Appreciation C; Devotional C; Samford U; Early Childhood Ed.

RATTAN, Christopher Bradley
Bishop McGunness HS; Oklahoma City, OK (65-135) Order/Arrow; ARC; Sci C; Soccer; JV, Tr; Order/Arrow A; ARC A; Cent St Col; Bus.

RATTERMAN, Scott Curtis
Cleveland HS; Cleveland, TN (37-242) VP, CYO; Span C; Var C; Bsbl; Ftbl; Wrest; COM; Hon Prog; Church Yth Coun; Ind U; Bus.

RATTI, M Luisa
Notre Dame HS; Salinas, CA (11-105) Model UN; NHS; Rptr, Sch P; Span C; SC; Pres, Soph Cl; JV, Bkbl; NHS Seal Bearer; Calif St Schol; Semi-Fin, Bank of Amer A; U of Calif at Los Angeles; Pre-Med.

RATTO, Margaret Mary
St Joseph's Notre Dame HS; Alameda, CA (6-56) NHS; Ski C; Pres, Var C; Bkbl; MVP, Sftbl; CSF; Hon Prog; Math A; Ath Director, SC; UC-DAVIS; Math.

RATTRAY, Richard Scott
Chillicothe HS; Chillicothe, OH (60-300) Sch P; Cr-Ctry; Tr; U of Cincinnati; Graphic Design.

RATZLAFF, Durward Delane
Highmors HS; Highmore, SD (10-56) Drag Racing; Voc.

RATZLAFF, Lucille Mae
Highmore HS; Highmore, SD (50%-64) Band; VP, Chor; 4H; Madrigal; Bethany Fel Col; Bible.

RAU, Jennifer Faye
Leola HS; Leola, SD (6-40) Ann; Band; Bus C; Chldr; Chor; Ensm; FBLA; Rptr, FHA; 4H; SC; Bkbl; Sftbl; Amer Leg A; Citz A; 4H A; Swtht; Type A; Swing Choir; Northern St Col; Special Ed.

RAU, Kimberly Ann
York Suburban HS; York, PA (40-300) Mjrte; Tr; Liberal Arts.

RAUCH, Douglas Paul
Cedar Crest HS; Lebanon, PA (16-389) Drama; Fr C; NHS; Var C; JV, Soccer; Co-Cpt, Swim; Pres, Tn Democrats; Hon Banquet; WW; Widener Col; Philosophy.

RAUDABAUGH, Tracy Lee
Van Wert HS; Van Wert, OH (26-210) A Cap Choir; Chor; Secy, Ger C; Y-Tns; JA A; Ohio N U; Phar.

RAUNIKAR, Marji Lynn
Muskogee HS; Muskogee, OK (16-575) AFS; Chess C; Chor; Fr C; Hmrm; NHS; Sci C; Bio A; Sci A; VFW A; Okla St U; Math.

RAUP, Timothy Christopher
Seekonk HS; Seekonk, MA (14-224) Ann; Band; Chor; Community Yth Symph; Drama; Ensm; Orch; NMS; NEDT; U of NH; Forestry.

RAUSAW, Marva Rechelle
Sharpstown Sr HS; Houston, TX; Band; Ensm; Fr C; Pres, Hmrm; InterAct C; Swim; Tnns; Tr; Mus A; N Tex St; Engr.

RAUSCH, Beth Ellen
Watertown Sr HS; Watertown, WI (27-355) AFS; Ann; Chor; Drama; Ensm; Ger C; Lat C; NHS; Thes; Var C; MVP, Golf; Hon Prog; Domestic Exchange Stu; Fin, Amer Abroad; Carrol Col; International Relations.

RAUSCH, Laura Anne
Cedar Falls HS; Cedar Falls, IA (25%-500) Band; Chldr; Drama; Fr C; Hmrm; Lit Mag; Rainbow; Sch P; SC; Bkbl; Tr; Pres, Guild Girls; Ldr, Worship Service; Lead Role, Summer Theater; U of Iowa; Law.

RAUSCH, Nancy Jo
Guttenberg HS; Guttenberg, IA (9-89) Ann; Chor; NHS; Naval Sch; Data Processing.

RAUSHER, Mark Loren
Skyline HS; Salt Lake City, UT; Bsbl; Bkbl; Citz A; Span A; Outst Scholastic Achv; Aeronautical Engineering.

RAVAN, Darlene Anita
Landrum HS; Landrum, SC; Bus Mgr, Ann; VP, BC; Pres, FBLA; Hmrm; SC; Type A; Secy.

RAWLINGS, Betty Lynn
Greenville Sr HS; Greenville, TX (50%-315) A Cap Choir; Chor; FFA; Madrigal; Tri-HiY; Equestrian Tm; All Dist, Choir; Young Tx Tn Board; FFA Achv A; E Tex St U; Hist.

RAWLINGS, Kathleen Ann
Franklin HS; Franklin, IL (3-44) Ann; Chor; ARC; Bkbl; Cr-Ctry; Sftbl; Tr; Bio A; Sci.

RAWLINS, Joseph William
Stone Mountain HS; Stone Mountain, GA (15%-275) BC; Ger C; Sci C; Cr-Ctry; Tr; Hist A; Freedom Foundation at Valley Forge; West Point Acad; Sci.

RAWLINS, Sue Ellen
Wilmot Union HS; Wilmot, WI (3-235) Band; Chldr; Chor; Dbte Tm; Hmrm; NHS; SC; Yth Fel; U of Wisc; Interior Design.

RAWLS, Janet Verona
Wilcox Co HS; Rochelle, GA (10-97) Ann; Cpt, Band; Tres, BC; Chldr; Ensm; FBLA; FHA; S-T, FTA; 4H; Hmrm; Mjrte; NHS; Sch P; Pres, SC; Tres, Soph Cl; COM; Cl Fav; HCt; Hon Prog; Type A; PA; Ga SW Col; Elem Ed.

RAWLS, Jeffrey Lynn
Huntington HS; Shreveport, LA; Key C; Spch C; Bsbl; Sailor with Spirit; La Tech U; Biol.

RAWSON, Penelope Louise
Oak Park-River Forest HS; Oak Park, IL (65-1047) Secy, CYO; Hmrm; SC; Swim; Hon Prog; Secy, Angelo Yth Organization; U of Ill; Bus.

RAWSON, William Otis
Oak Park-River Forest HS; Oak Park, IL (445-1042) Pres, Demolay; Hmrm; Monogram; Cpt, Ftbl; Swim; Tr; Pres, Angelo-Cath Yth Organization; Demolay Ath; Demolay Visitation; U of Ill; Hist.

RAXTER, Tracy William
Crestview Sr HS; Crestview, FL (6-250) BC; Chor; Drama; Acct.

RAY, Amy Ann
Morristown HS E; Morristown, TN; BC; FHA; Tres, Lat C; Walters St Col; Med.

RAY, Avery Brant
Bethany HS; Reidsville, NC (3-60) BC; Fr C; FFA; Guilford Tech Inst; Computer Prog.

RAY, Bruce Elliott
La Jolla HS; La Jolla, CA (20-500) Hmrm; Key C; Co-Ed, Lit Mag; Bsbl; Hockey; Co-Cpt, Sftbl; Tnns; Yth Fel; All Star Bsbl; Acolyte o-t Yr A; Williams Col; Lib Arts.

RAY, Bruce Robert
Episcopal HS; Baton Rouge, LA (7-62) Ann; Fr C; Lit Ral; NHS; Sci C; Bio A; COM; Chem A; Hon Prog; NMF; NMS; NEDT; ROTC A; Sci A; Fr A; Lit Rally; Lang Festival; Mech Drawing A; Rose-Hulman Inst of Tech; Mech Engr.

RAY, Bryan Russell
S Grand Prairie HS; Grand Prairie, TX (78-377) Bkbl; UN-Washington Seminar.

RAY, Carolyn Marlette
Rankin Acad; Star, MS; BC; Chor; Rptr, Hmrm; Bkbl; Sftbl; Tr; COM; Lib C; Absent Nor Tardy A; Hinds Jr Col; Phys Ed.

RAY, Cathy Lynn
West Point HS; West Point, MS; Chor; FBLA; Bkbl; Sftbl; COM; WW; 4th, St FBLA Off Procedures; Art C; Miss St U; Elem Ed.

RAY, Cheri Ann
Faith Christian Acad; Milwaukee, WI; Chor; Timothy A; Meritorious A; Olympic A; UWM; Child Development.

RAY, Cheri Anne
Faith Christian Acad; Milwaukee, WI; Chor; Timothy & Meritorious A'S; Awana; U of Wis; Mus.

RAY, Christie Denita
Shelbyville Central HS; Shelbyville, TN; Fr C; FHA; HiY; Hmrm; Key C; Middle Tenn St U; Dental Hygienist.

RAY, Connie Louise
Hyde Park Career Acad; Chicago, IL (100-244) Cl Fav; Loop Col; Sociology.

RAY, Deborah Lynn
Goodlettsville HS; Goodlettsville, TN (2-159) F-Ed, Ann; Chor; FTA; GS; InterClub Coun; Lat C; Lat NHS; Pres, NHS; Sec; VP, Soph Cl; Balfour A; Bio A; Cl Fav; H of F; Sal; Swtht; VP, SC; W Ky U; Elem Ed.

RAY, Flora Mae
Carver HS; Birmingham, AL; ROTC A; Alabama A&M Col; Bus.

RAY, Gina Marie
Opelousas Cath HS; Opelousas, LA (16-99) BC; Chor; NHS; Sch P; Spch C; COM; Fr A; U of SW La; Radio and Television.

RAY, Greg Paul
Beaumont-Charlton-Pollard HS; Beaumont, TX (45-350) Key C; Math C; Tnns; COM; Tex A&M U; Phys Ed.

RAY, Jennifer Faye
Leola Ind HS; Leola, SD (7-40) Ann; Band; Chldr; Chor; FBLA; Pres, FHA; 4H; SC; Bkbl; Sftbl; Amer Leg A; Citz A; 4H A; Swtht; Type A; FHA A.

RAY, Jenny Lynn
North Side HS; Fort Wayne, IN (290-499) Lat C; Orch; Olivet Nazarene Col; Med.

RAY, Jodie Carol
Del City HS; Del City, OK (50%-600) Chor; Hmrm; Tri-HiY; Mgr, Tr; Type A; Yth Leg; S-T, MYF; Off Aid A; Pep C; Jr Executive Board; Gold Medal, Del Aires; Central St U; Med Therapy.

RAY, Keith Mark
Newnan HS; Newnan, GA; W Ga Col; Mech Engr.

RAY, Lisa Jo
Palmer HS; Palmer, TX (2-21) Bus Mgr, Ann; Chldr; FHA; Lit Ral; SC; Rptr, Soph Cl; HQn; UIL Poetry Interpretation; Eng A; Health A; *Tex A&M U; Eng.*

RAY, Lisa Maureen
Worth R-III HS; Grant City, MO (6-53) Co-Ed, Ann; Band; Bus C; Ensm; Rptr, FTA; 4H; NHS; Pres, Rainbow; Co-Ed, Sch P; Sci C; Mgr, Bkbl; Golf; Journ A; Q&S A; Yth Fel; Yth Leadership A; *Columbia Col; Journ.*

RAY, Lynnette Carol
Green Forest HS; Green Forest, AR; BC; FHA; Sci C; Bkbl.

RAY, Mitchell Brent
Potosi R-3 HS; Potosi, MO (53-271) Sci C; Var C; Cr-Ctry; Tr; *U of Mo; Metalurgy.*

RAY, Nancy Rebekah
Blair HS Rowah Center; Hattiesburg, MS (20%-499) A-Ed, Ann; Band; Drama; ARC; Secy, SC; Swim; Hon Prog; Sci A; Chrch Yth Choir; Band A; Jr Hist Soc; Q&S; Sup Rating, Hymn Festival; 1st Pl, St Hist Soc Essay Cont; Mus C; 2nd P, Drug Ed Spch Contest.

RAY, Phillip Anthony
Chase HS; Forest City, NC (28-141) Band; BC; Lat C; Monogram; Bsbl; JV, Bkbl; Cr-Ctry; Tnns; *Appalachian St U; Physics.*

RAY, Robert Douglas
Haltom HS; Haltom City, TX (40-625) Band; Chor; NHS; Sci C; Hon Prog; ROTC A; BSct 'Jr Ldr'; Gifted Stu Found; *Tex A&M U; Chem.*

RAY, Robert Henry
Shawnee HS; Louisville, KY (173-203) Hmrm; VP, Sr Cl; Cpt, Bkbl; Cpt, Cr-Ctry; Cl Fav; HCt; MLS.

RAY, Sammy Lee
Buena Vista HS; Imperial, TX (1-18) Ann; Band; Dbte Tm; Ensm; FFA; Pres, NHS; Pres, Jr Cl; JV, Ftbl; Tnns; COM; Citz A; Type A; John Philip Sousa A; Star Greenhand A; Band Ltr Jacket; *Hardin-Simmons U; Mus.*

RAY, Steven Wayne
Hart Co HS; Hartwell, GA; Fr C; *Mercer U; Law.*

RAY, Susan Regina
McMinn Co HS; Athens, TN; Fr C; NFL; Tri-HiY; Mgr, Bkbl; Sftbl; Tnns; Poet A; Pres A; Yth Fel; *Middle Tenn St U; Health & PE.*

RAY, Tiani Gayle
Woodham HS; Pensacola, FL (29-530) Fr C; NHS; *Pensacola Jr Col; Bus.*

RAY, Timothy Wade
George H Corliss HS; Chicago, IL (200-300) Drama; Pol Sci C; Ski C; Co-Cpt, Bkbl; Ftbl; Alg A; PA; Best Dressed; *North Central Col; Bus Adm.*

RAYBORN, Sherrod Mitchell
Monticello HS; Monticello, MS (10-100) BC; Bsbl; Bkbl; Ftbl; Tnns; HCt; *U of Sou Miss; Engr.*

RAYE, William Robert
Crystal Lake Comm HS; Crystal Lake, IL (50-570) NHS; St Scholar; SDAHSS; WW; *Augustana Col; Bus.*

RAYER, Mark Alan
Richmond Hts HS; Richmond Heights, OH (45-125) Band; JV, Ftbl.

RAYFIELD, Reginald R
Penn Career Center; Washington, DC; Swim; Tnns; Composition.

RAYGOZA, Arturo
Valley HS; Sanders, AZ (5-70) Drama; FFA; Spch C; SC; Var C; Bsbl; JV, Bkbl; Tr.

RAYMER, Kathleen Sue
St Joseph HS; St Joseph, MI; Band; Fr C; *Central Mich U; Commercial Art.*

RAYMOND, Alain
College De Ste Anne De La Pocatiere; La Pocatiere, CANADA (1-30) Drama; Phys C; Var C; Bkbl; Hockey; Soccer; Swim; Tnns; COM; ARC A; Spch A; Vlbl; Karate; *Med.*

RAYMOND, Denis
College De Ste Anne De La Pocatiere; La Pocatiere, CANADA (2-30) Drama; Var C; Bsbl; Bkbl; Hockey; Sftbl; Swim; *U Laval; Med.*

RAYMOND, Julie Frances
Wasson HS; Colorado Springs, CO (5-514) Band; NHS; ARC; COM; Citz A; Hon Prog; Lion A; Mus A; Fr A.

RAYMOND, Karen Lynn
Mounds View HS; St Paul, MN (5%-550) AFS; NHS; SC; Swim; HCt; *St Olaf Col; Bus.*

RAYMOND, Katharine S
Morenci HS; Morenci, MI (1-80) Band; Chor; VP, NHS; Sch P; Var C; Cpt, Bkbl; Cpt, Sftbl; Kiwanis A; MLS; Most Out; Val; Cpt, Vlbl; Church Organist; Stu o-t Yr; Sr o-t Mo; *Adrian Col; Phys Ed.*

RAYMOND, Laura Marguerite
Reynolds HS; Greenville, PA (2-212) AFS; NHS; Ed, Sch P; Span C; SC; Thes; Tri-HiY; VofDEM; Del, World Affairs Coun; VP, Sr Planning Board; GSct; Lib C; *Clarion St Col; Span.*

RAYMOND, Mark Alan
Lancaster HS; Lancaster, OH (150-600) A Cap Choir; Chor; Sci C; Pres, Luther League; *Ohio U; Communications.*

RAYMOND, Michael
Vashon HS; St Louis, MO (75-324) *U of Mo; Bus Adm.*

RAYMOND, Ronald Allen
Fulton HS; Knoxville, TN (8-306) Pres, Key C; NHS; Tnns; Alg A; Hon Prog; Math A; *U of Tenn; Civil Engr.*

RAYMOND, Ronald Keith
Northwestern Sr HS; Albion, PA; Math C; Bsbl; JV, Bkbl; Pres A; Bsbl Tm Trophy; Jr Church Pianist; Talent Musical A; Church Radio Prog; Jr Staff, Yth Center; Piano Duet, Sr High Tn-Talent Musi; *Edinboro St Col.*

RAYMOND, Sharon Mae
Wayne Memorial HS; Wayne, MI; Band; Fr C; Span C; Secy, Church Yth Group; *Bus.*

RAYMOND, Tamarah Lee
Valley HS; Albuquerque, NM (30-740) Chor; Rptr, Hmrm; NHS; Ski C; St Stu Congress; SC; Tres, Sr Cl; Tnns; COM; Math A; Yth Fel; Piano Performing A; Prom Comm; Homecoming Comm; *U of Colo; Bio.*

RAYNER, Leslie Millicent
John Marshall HS; Okla City, OK (16-470) NHS; Church Sftbl; GSct; Pep C; VP, Yth Coun; Vlbl; *Sou Methodist U; Computer Sci.*

RAYNOR, Carol Jean
Simi Valley HS; Simi Valley, CA; Ch, Band; NHS; Tres, Sr Cl; Tr; Hon Prog; *Calif Lutheran Col; Primary Ed.*

RAYNOR, Michael Joseph
Whiteville HS; Whiteville, NC (39-189) Band; Hmrm; SC; Tr; Lit Guild; Bus Driver's C; Lib A-V C; Jr-Sr Steering Comm; *Southeastern Comm Col; Computer Sci.*

RAYSON, Annette
Banning HS; Banning, CA (50-153) Chldr; Span C; Var C; Bank of Amer A; Citz A; *Calif St U; Bus Adm.*

RAZO, Ramon David
Hutchinson Sr HS; Hutchinson, KS (131-430) A Cap Choir; Chor; Ensm; Madrigal; Orch; Span C; Hutchinson Symph Orch; Kans Mus Ed Assn; All St Choir; *Hutchinson Comm Jr Col; Pre-Phar.*

REA, Carla Sue
Amer Christian Acad; Pomona, CA (4-21) Chor; Hmrm; Citz A; Hon Prog; *Bob Jones U; Elem Ed.*

REA, Carol Linn
Houston HS; Houston, MO (30-125) Christian Fel C; *Sch o-t Ozarks; Elem Teacher.*

REA, Dawna Kim
Vega HS; Vega, TX (10%-34) Band; Ensm; Mjrte; Bkbl; Tr; WW; *W Tex St Col; Acct.*

REA, Jenifer Lou
Westmont Hilltop Sr HS; Johnstown, PA (127-211) FTA; Orch; Ski C; Swim; Mgr, Tr; COM; Citz A; Yth Fel; *Mercyhurst Col; Dental Hygiene.*

REA, Lisa Ann
Salem Sr HS; Salem, OH (100-299) S-T, AFS; FHA; Yth Fel; *Aultman Hospital; Nurs.*

REA, Woodrow Hamilton
Albemarle HS; Charlottesville, VA (290-750) Chor; Bkbl; Cpt, Sftbl; Citz A; Schol A; Leadership A; Honesty Hon; PA; *VPI; Forestry.*

READ, Andy Thomas
Brethren HS; Paramount, CA (20-86) Hmrm; SC; Pres, Sr Cl; VP, Jr Cl; Co-Cpt, Ftbl; CSF; HCt; Type A; Semester Schol's; *Biola Col; Bio Ed.*

READ, Cheryl Faye
Prairie View Acad; Bastrop, LA (6-40) Ann; Band; Lit Ral; NHS; Rptr, Sch P; Tres, Sr Cl; Tres, Jr Cl; Pres, Soph Cl; MVP, Bkbl; Cl Fav; Most Ath; All Dist, Bkbl; *NE La U; Nurs.*

READ, Janice Diane
Silsbee HS; Silsbee, TX (10-265) A Cap Choir; Chor; Fr C; VP, FTA; JETS; NHS; SC; Tr; Tex All-St Choir; Choir A; Outst Soloist; WW Among Mus Stu; *Lamar U; Mus.*

READ, Paul Wayne
Silsbee HS; Silsbee, TX (15-295) Fr C; JETS; JV, Bkbl; Tr; *Lamar U.*

READ, Robin Kathleen
Niskayuna HS; Schenectady, NY (20%-380) Band; Drama; Hmrm; Lit Mag; Girl's Service C; JV Ski Tm; VP, Church Yth Group; Alt, Regent's Schol; Modern Dance C; Church Yth Choir; *Syracuse U; Fine Arts.*

READ, Tobyn Arnel
Fountain Valley HS; Fountain Valley, CA; Key C; Gym; Prin HR; *Mechanics.*

READE, Michael Allen
Benkelman HS; Benkelman, NE (3-32) SC; VP, Soph Cl; Golf; Hon Prog; Golf Ltr; Luther League; WW; Gen Mills Family Ldr of Tommorow; *Wichita St Col; Optometry.*

READER, Bettie Arlene
First Colonial HS; Virginia Beach, VA (25%-541) Chor; Secy, Fr C; 4H; Sch P; 4H A; Ed, Church News Paper; Pres, Church Yth Coun; Tres, Church Yth Coun; *Va Commonwealth U; Sociology.*

READING, Russell Vivian
Van-Far HS; Vandalia, MO (12-70) Bkbl; Cr-Ctry; *Moberly Jr Col; Phys Ed.*

READINGER, Teresa Ann
Fleetwood Area HS; Fleetwood, PA (14-130) A Cap Choir; Chor; Hmrm; NHS; VP, Jr Cl; Mgr, Hockey; *Eng.*

READY, David Warren
Monticello HS; Monticello, MS; Band; BC; Chor; Ensm; *USM.*

READY, Dennis Ray
Sam Houston HS; Arlington, TX (250-650) *U of Tex; Bookkeeping.*

READY, Kevin Alan
E Richland HS; Olney, IL (1-271) Var C; Cr-Ctry; Tr; *Math.*

READY, Pam Jean
Miramonte HS; Orinda, CA (5%-400) A Cap Choir; Hmrm; Ski C; CSF; Hon Prog; Type A; JV Vlbl; Span A; *U of Calif.*

READY, Scott William
Miramonte HS; Orinda, CA (20-400) Mgr, Band; Span NHS; Var C; Bsbl; Cpt, Bkbl; JV, Golf; MVP, Soccer; CSF; COM; Math A; *Calif Polytech Inst; Math.*

REAGAN, Julie Karin
Seminole HS; Sanford, FL (150-479) Anchor C; Cpt, Chldr; InterAct C; InterClub Coun; Ski C; SC; Swim; Tnns; HQn; Swtht; Secy, WW; FCA; Class Rep; Class Chaplain; *Jackson Sch of Nurs; Nurs.*

REAGAN, Maryanne
Holy Cross HS; Riverside, NJ (1-350) Band; CYO; Drama; Bus Mgr, Lit Mag; NHS; SC; Hon Prog; Val; Yrbk A; Most Quiet; *St Joseph Col; Interntl Relations.*

REAGANS, Elliott
Crockett HS; Crockett, TX (3-127) Band; Secy, FFA; SC; Pres, Jr Cl; Bsbl; Bkbl; Cpt, Ftbl; Tr; COM; Math A; *US Naval Acad; Engr.*

REAGINS, Markus Aaron
Banning HS; Banning, CA (34-218) Fin, BS; Drama; Span C; Up Bound; CSF; Yth Fel; Pres, Stu Union; *U of Sou Calif; Med.*

REAGINS, Marsha Leonette
Banning HS; Banning, CA (32-207) Span NHS; Up Bound; Var C; Sftbl; CSF; Yth Fel; Stu Union; GSct; *U of Sou Calif; Bus.*

REALE, Cynthia Ann
Seekonk HS; Seekonk, MA (23-224) *Green Mt Col; Recreation.*

REAM, Douglas Ralph
Porterville HS; Porterville, CA; Band; Most Out; Co Sr Hgh Hon Bnd; Co Yth Symh Orch; St Bicen Band Fabulous Studio Band; John Philip Sousa Band A; La Sierra Mus Camp Schol; *Mus.*

REAM, Elizabeth Grace
Northeast HS; St Petersburg, FL (50-800) Band; Ger C; Secy, SC; NJHS; *Bethany Nazarene Col; Law.*

REAMES, Brenda Kay
North Union Sr HS; Richwood, OH; 4H; Math A; Sci A; Cpt, Vlbl; 100 Hrs Vol Hospital Work; *Ohio St U; Journ.*

REANEY, Byron Burdette
Clark HS; Las Vegas, NV (100-600) Drama; Order/Arrow; Mgr, Bkbl; Citz A; God & Country A; Order/Arrow A; Eagle Sct; *Scripps Inst; Oceanography.*

REASER, Ann Marie
Los Angeles Lutheran HS; Burbank, CA (1-68) A Cap Choir; AFS; Pres, Band; Hmrm; NHS; SC; Bkbl; Tr; CSF; Citz A; Co-Cpt, Vlbl; *Engr.*

REASEY, Elizabeth Ann
Chambersburg Area Sr HS; Chambersburg, PA (50%-600) Chess C; Ecolo-Kind; *Acct.*

REASON, Deborah Ellen
Elston Sr HS; Michigan City, IN; Band; Drama; Fr C; Hmrm; Rainbow; Ski C; Swim Timer A.

REASONER, Anita Kay
Gordon HS; Gordon, TX (4-14) FHA; Tnns; Cl Fav; *Tarleton St U; Bus.*

REASONS, Helen Jean
Harrisburg HS; Harrisburg, IL; FHA.

REASOR, Brian Lloyd
Tahlequah HS; Tahlequah, OK (150-250) Band; Chor; Sftbl; Tnns; *NE Okla St U; Mus.*

REAT, Bonnie Elaine
Lubbock Christian HS; Lubbock, TX (15-55) A Cap Choir; Madrigal; NFL; Tres, NHS; Church Chor; WW, Mus; Amer Heritage A; *Lubbock Christian Col; Spch Therapy.*

REAVES, Anthony
Miami Jackson HS; Miami, FL; Ftbl.

REAVES, Carolyn Bernice
Miami Jackson Sr HS; Miami, FL (4-600) NHS; Most Intellectual; Outst Stu, Superstar, Eng, A's; *U of Fla; Bus Adm.*

REAVES, Cheryl Lavonne
William Cullen Bryant HS; Woodside, NY; *Queensboro Comm Col; Nurs.*

REAVES, Debby Louise
Cibola HS; Albuquerque, NM; FFA; Pres, 4H; Tr; 4H A; Most Out; VP, 4-H C; Gym; *Denver U.*

REAVES, Elizabeth Anne
Lake Highlands HS; Dallas, TX; Fr C; Tres, Lit Mag; Spch C; SC; Hon Prog; Essay A; *Baylor U; Pol Sci.*

REAVES, Pamela Verenda
Asbury Park HS; Asbury Park, NJ; NHS; Bkbl; Tnns; Cl Fav; HCt; *U of Md; Journ.*

REAVES, Robert Addam
Magnolia HS; Magnolia, AR (3-222) A Cap Choir; Ann; Math A; Most Out; Span A; *NE La U; Phar.*

REAVIS, Becky
Campslindo HS; Moraga, CA; AFS; HiY; NHS; CSF; Jr HS Coun; Yth Comm; Fast-A-Thon; Peer Coun Group.

REAVIS, Carol Sue
Tahlequah Sr HS; Tahlequah, OK (25-242) Band; FTA; Mjrte; NHS; Rainbow; Span C; *NE Okla St U; Law.*

REB, Catherine Irene
Hot Springs HS; Truth Or Consequences, NM (2-110) Ann; Chor; NHS; Span C; Spch C; SC Var C; JV, Bkbl; Golf; Swim; COM; Citz A; MLS; Sal; *McMurry Col; Journ.*

REBAUDO, Lisa Rita
Acad of Our Lady of Mercy; Milford, CT (11-93) Arch; Chor; Fr C; Co-Ed, Lit Mag; NHS; Sch P; Hon Prog; Poet A; *Journ.*

REBER, Connie Lee
Schuylkill Haven Area HS; Schuylkill Haven, PA (20-116) FNA; Hmrm; Tres, Sci C; SC; Arch; JV, Sftbl; Tr; HQn; WW; Co-Cpt, Color Guard; *Pa St U; Mortuary Sci.*

REBER, Lisa M
Hemet HS; Hemet, CA (75-425) *Sci.*

REBHOLZ, Raymond John
Copiague Sr HS; Copiague, NY (9-399) Ann; Co-Ed, Lit Mag; Math C; NHS; Hon Prog; Regent Schol; *Adelphi U; Ed.*

REBILLARD, John Leslie
Torrington HS; Torrington, CT (33%-350) Demolay; *NEDT A; Acct.*

REBMAN, Marcia Kay
Tulpehocken HS; Bernville, PA (15-100) Secy, Band; Pres, Chor; Pres, 4H; NHS; Secy, Sci C; JV, Bkbl; Hockey; Tr; 4H A; Yth Fel; WW Among Mus Stu in Amer; *Elizabethtown Col; Med Tech.*

RECER, Carol Ann
Cleburne HS; Cleburne, TX; Ann; Band; FHA; FTA; Hmrm; Mjrte; NHS; Ski C; St Stu Congress; SC; Tri-HiY; Hon Prog; Yth Fel; Soph Rep, Band; Bus.

RECHE, Daniel Henry
Paul Harding HS; Ft Wayne, IN (25-289) NHS; Var C; Cpt, Ftbl; Cpt, Wrest; Rotary A; Kg of Sr Prom; *Ball St U; Social Stu.*

RECIO, Michael Thomas
Huntsville HS; Huntsville, AL (100-500) Dbte Tm; Hmrm; InterAct C; Span C; SC; JV, Bkbl; Part-time job; *Bus.*

RECK, Sandra Jean
Rockford E HS; Rockford, IL (63-510) AFS; NHS; Orch; F-Ed, Sch P; Co-Ch, SC; Hon Prog; Q&S A; Ch, Tn Hospital Vol; *Wheaton Col; Elem Ed.*

RECKARD, Vickie Ann
Albert Lea Sr HS; Albert Lea, MN (63-575) Chess C; Chor; Span C; JA A; Jr Achv; Citz A; *Austin Comm Col; Nurs.*

RECTOR, Darlene Kay
Crawford Co R II HS; Cuba, MO (10%-90) Band; Chor; Pres, NHS; SC; VP, Sr Cl; Pres, Jr Cl; Freedom Forum; *Baptist Col; Mus.*

RECTOR, Donna Kay
Mehlville Sr HS; St Louis, MO (158-500) Chor; Bible C; Bus Cpt; HR; Special Chor A; Christ Ambassador's; *Evangel Col; Psych.*

RECTOR, Jay William
Carmi Comm HS; Carmi, IL (20-140) Key C; NHS; Rptr, Sch P; Pres, Var C; Bsbl; Co-Cpt, Bkbl; Co-Cpt, Ftbl; Fin, Tr; HCt; *E Ill U; Pre-Optometry.*

RECTOR, Richard Paul
Loyola HS; Towson, MD (7-134) Bus Mgr, Drama; NHS; Sch P; Tres; Bsbl; Bkbl; Hon Prog; Frisbee Tm; WW; *U of Md.*

RECTOR, Robert Reid
Okeene HS; Okeene, OK (4-39) Ann; Pres, Band; BS; Dbte Tm; NHS; Sci C; Spch C; Var C; Pres, Sr Cl; Pres, Jr Cl; Rptr, Soph Cl; Bkbl; Ftbl; Tr; Cl Fav; Masonic A; MLS; Sci A; All-St Band; SWOK Hon Band; NWOK Hon Band; Photography A.

REDBAND, JoAnne Beth
Fredonia HS; Fredonia, NY; Chor; Drama; Span C; Pres, Church Yth Group; *Physicians Asst.*

REDBURN, Doug Wayne
Will Rogers HS; Tulsa, OK (95-800) Band; Chess C; Key C; Orch; Bkbl; Sftbl; Tnns; Alg A; COM; Math A; Yth Fel; *OSU; Math.*

REDD, Brenda Joyce
Calhoun Co HS; Edison, GA (2-107) Co-Ed, Ann; Band; Rptr, BC; JV, Chldr; Chor; Pres, Drama; Ensm; Pres, FTA; Hmrm; Rptr, Lit Mag; Pres, Thes; COM; Cl Fav; Gov Honor Prog; Gr Marshal; HCt; Math A; Sal; Nat Merit Commended Stu; Best Thespian; 4th, St Lit, Piano; 2nd, St Lit, Trio.

REDD, Kirt Douglas
Lakeview HS; Cortland, OH (43-152) 4H; InterAct C; ARC; Var C; Bsbl; Bkbl; Ftbl; Sftbl; Tr; COM; Citz A; Hon Prog; Star Student; *Kent St U; Archt.*

REDD, Penelope Michelle
St Aquinas HS; Southgate, MI; *U of Mich; Psych.*

REDD, Victoria Ann
Eau Gallie HS; Melbourne, FL (50-600) FBLA; Secy, Sch P; COM; Citz A; Fla Camp Keystone A; Jr Hon Soc; Church General Secy; Sunday Sch Teacher; *Brevard Comm Col; Physics.*

REDD, Yvette Marcel
E St Louis Sr HS; E St Louis, IL; NHS; MLS; Star Student; Sunday Sch Attendance A; *Belleville Area Col; Phys Therapy.*

REDDEN, Deborah Faye
Mount Vernon Acad; Mount Vernon, OH; Chor; 4H; Mod Mus Mas; Bsbl; Sftbl; Tr; Bio A; ARC A; Art As; Worker o-t Month; *Sou Missionary Col; Med.*

REDDEN, Nathan Neal
Manila HS; Manila, UT (3-14) BS; Pres, Hmrm; Sch P; SC; Pres, Sr Cl; Bsbl; Cpt, Bkbl; Tr; COM; Hist A; HKg; Hon Prog; MVP, Bkbl; Sct, Art, A's; *Ricks Col.*

REDDEN, Pamela Michelle
Temple Sch; Des Moines, IA; Band; Cpt, Chldr; Chor; Pres, Dbte Tm; 4H; Mjrte; Co-Ed, Sch P; Pres, SC; Bsbl; Bkbl; JV, Ftbl; Sftbl; Swim; Tr; Citz A; Cl Fav; HQn; Hon Prog; MLS; Pres A; S-T, SC; *Areall Comm Col; Sociology.*

REDDICK, Charles
G W Carver Sr HS; New Orleans, LA; *U of New Orleans; Acct.*

REDDICK, Deborah Lynn
Denison Sr HS; Denison, TX (5%-436) FTA; Secy, NHS; Sci C; Tnns; Span C; Rptr, Y-Tns; COM; Hon Prog; PA; *Tex Tech U.*

REDDICK, Lisa Gayle
Pattonville Sr HS; Maryland Heights, MO; Chor; Span C; *Ed.*

REDDIN, Bennett Marshall
Yuma HS; Yuma, AZ (12-348) Chess C; Drama; NHS; Sch P; Sci C; Pres, Spch C; Span NHS; JV, Tr; Alg A; COM; Hon Prog; Math A; Opt A; Opt Out Tn; VFW Orator Win; 1st Pl, St Preacher-Boy Contest; *Pacific Christian Col; Preaching.*

REDDING, Elizabeth Jane
Hunter Huss HS; Gastonia, NC (29-495) Anchor C; Band; BC; Rainbow; Span C; Hon Prog; Colorguard; Tutor Prog; *U of NC; Home Ec.*

REDDING, Melissa Terrell
Suda E Butler HS; Louisville, KY; Pres, Band; BC; Ensm; GS; Hmrm; Math C; NHS; ARC; Tres, SC; *David Lipscomb Col; Health Sci.*

REDDING, Rachel Ann
Greater Atlanta Christian Sch; Norcross, GA (50-71) Drama; Fr C; Ed, Lit Mag; 2nd Pl, Region Home Ec; *Mercer U; Sociology.*

REDDING, William Christopher Jr
Sanford Central HS; Sanford, NC (80-350) WW; Pres, Knights of Pythagoras; Pres, Church Usher Board; Pres, Yth Fel; Steward Board; Yth Choir; *A&T U; Bus Adm.*

REDDISH, Lanita Carol
Wayne Co HS; Jesup, GA (15%-350) Ann; FHA; Secy, Span C; Bsbl; COM; Jr Homemaker Degree.

REDDY, Carla Joy
Neshaminy Maple Point HS; Langhorne, PA (8-429) Band; NHS; Swim; *Millersville St Col; Med Tech.*

REDECKER, Walter Joseph
Flat River-Central HS; Flat River, MO (22-140) A Cap Choir; Madrigal; NHS; Pres, SC; Var C; Cpt, Bkbl; Tr; HCt; *Mineral Area Col.*

REDFEARN, Janet Catherine
Mt Pleasant HS; Mt Pleasant, TX (26-213) Ann; Bus C; Chldr; Chor; Pres, FHA; Fin, Jr Miss Pagent; Math C; Mu Alpha Theta; NHS; Span C; Beauty; Lion A; Most Out; Yth Fel; 1st Runner-up, Jr Miss; WW; Lions C Swtht; Outst Young Tn of Amer; Rotaryettes; *Stephen F Austin St U; Bus Mgt.*

REDFERN, Katherine Luvenia
Waynesboro Central HS; Waynesboro, MS (10%-115) FHA; Y-Tns; Pres, Jr Cl; *Jones Co Jr Col; Math.*

REDFERN, Matt David
Clyde HS; Clyde, OH (50%-201) Pres, A Cap Choir; Chor; Var C; Bsbl; Bkbl; Cpt, Ftbl; Tr; Wrest; Citz A; Most Imp Stu; Outst Ftbl Player; U of Toledo; Engr.

REDFOOT, Marcia Ann
Sharpsville Area HS; Sharpsville, PA (7-157) Secy, Band; Chor; FNA; NHS; Opt Out Tn; Mat Maid; Penn St U; Nurs.

REDIC, Cedric L
Roth HS; Dayton, OH; A Cap Choir; Chor; FBLA; Sch P; COM.

REDIC, Cheryl Diane
Paul Lawrence Dunbar HS; Fort Worth, TX; Chor; Mod Mus Mas; NHS; Orch; U of Tex at Arlington; Nurs.

REDICK, Darren Vern
Service HS; Anchorage, AK; NHS; VP, SC; Bsbl; Bkbl; COM; Math A; Spirit Week Kg; Ariz St U; Civil Engr.

REDINBAUGH, Cindy Ann
Tomball HS; Tomball, TX (4-138) NHS; Ed, Sch P; Hist A; Overall Excellence As.

REDINBO, Julia Ann
Sidney HS; Sidney, OH (10-200) Ger C; 4H; NHS; Orch; Y-Tns; Sftbl; Pres A; Co- cpt, Gym; Ohio St U; Phys Therapy.

REDING, Theresa Marie
Springfield HS; Springfield, OR; Pres, Band; Pres, NHS; SC; Tnns; COM; HCt; Lane Comm Col; Bus.

REDINGTON, Cindy Roseanne
Sequoia HS; Redwood City, CA (5%-500) A Cap Choir; Chor; Hon Prog; Yth Fel; CMEA Chor Festival.

REDINGTON, Linda Ruthanne
Sequoia HS; Redwood City, CA (5%-520) Pres, A Cap Choir; Chor; Ensm; Ch, InterClub Coun; Tnns; CSF; COM; Citz A; Hist A; Hon Prog; Math A; Yth Fel; Solo & Ensm A; CMEA Chor Festival; Canada Col; Lib Arts.

REDMAN, Bonnie Lou
Du Quoin HS; Du Quoin, IL (33%-175) Chor; FNA; FTA; Secy, Mjrte; Citz A; Type A; Pep C; Stu Teaching A; Candystriper; Treas, Social Stu C; S Ill U; General Law.

REDMAN, Gerald William
Edgewood HS; Edgewood, TX (10-70) Chor; Drama; F-Ed, Sch P; SC; Bkbl; Ftbl; Tnns; Tr; Cl Fav; All-Star Cast, One Act Play; Lee Col; Bus Mgt.

REDMAN, Mark Alan
Joliet Township HS; Joliet, IL (118-543) Pres, HiY; Yth Fel; Yth Leg; Honorary Big Brother.

REDMAN, Pamela Ann
Plant City HS; Plant City, FL; Model UN; Sch P; MVP, Swim; Vlbl.

REDMAN, Susan Lynn
Plant City HS; Plant City, FL (56-600) Model UN; NHS; Bus Mgr, Sch P; Var C; Cpt, Swim; Amer Leg A; DARGCA; Tres, Civinettes; VP, Hospitality Girls; Tns for Christ; Cpt, Vlbl; Reign & Shine Court; Stetson U.

REDMOND, Charley Lester
Mt Brook HS; Birmingham, AL; Commercial C; Co-Cpt, Ski C; Var C; World Affairs C; Bkbl; Cr-Ctry; Sftbl; Swim; Tnns; Tr; COM; Citz A; Type A; Church Choir; Samford U; Aviation.

REDMOND, John Garner Jr
Winchester HS; Winchester, MA; Pres, S-T, Church Yth Fel; Hotel Mgt.

REDMOND, Lee Ann
Whispering Hills Christian Acad; Nashville, TN; Ann; Chldr; Chor; Drama; Sch P; Spch C; Mgr, Bkbl; Sftbl; Spch A; Vlbl; Acteen Qn; Soph Rep, Qn of Carnival; Belmont Col; Med.

REDMOND, Paul Joseph
Saint Thomas More Sch; Colchester, CT (2-30) Ed, Ann; Co-Ed, Sch P; Hockey; Tnns; Syracuse U; Pre Law.

REDMOND, Timothy Matthew
Union HS; Tulsa, OK (15-275) Cr-Ctry; Tr; Wrest; Alg A; Bio A; Math A; MLS; Most Out; All Stars, Wrest; Yth Counselor, Full Gospel Yth Fel; Oral Roberts U; Chem.

REDMOND, Wanda Elizabeth
Detroit Central HS; Detroit, MI (100-563) Chldr; Span C; SC; Tr; COM; Citz A; Cl Fav; Opt A; Yth Fel.

REDUS, Samual Jack
Pampa HS; Pampa, TX (150-300) Drama; Key C; SC; Thes; VP, Soph Cl; Golf; Tnns; Sci A; Spch A; Hon Thespian; Best Actor.

REDWINE, Nancy Lois
N Salinas HS; Salinas, CA (20%-340) A Cap Choir; Band; Chldr; Chor; Ensm; Hartnell-Pepperdine Col; Ed.

REDWING, Michael Duane
Castlewood HS; Castlewood, SD (11-26) Ann; Chor; Var C; Mgr, Bkbl; Co-Cpt, Cr-Ctry; Ftbl; Tr; SD Sch of Mines & Tech; Mech Engr.

REEBE, Caryl Jean
Tottenville HS; Staten Island, NY (204-1191) Yth Fel; Sr GSct; Col of Staten Island; Math.

REECE, Charlotte Yvette
Tex Sr HS; Texarkana, TX; Band; ARC; Secy, FHA; Ms St Paul, Church; Francis Marion Col; Nurs.

REECE, Clara Lou
Pisgah Sr HS; Canton, NC; Chor; Fr C; Pres, 4H; 4H A; Jr Ldr, Co-4-H; Co Exchange C; Win, Co Dress Revue; Church Choir; Haywood Tech Inst; Secretarial.

REECE, Evangeline Carole
Mira Loma HS; Sacramento, CA (20-400) Chor; NHS; Sch Achieve Tm; SC; COM; Yth Leg; F-Ed, Sch Yrbk; HR; Rep, St Test of Academic Achv; NHS A.

REECE, Katrina Orelette
Jesse Jones Vanguard HS; Houston, TX (15%-710) All Amer Yth; Hmrm; Math C; NHS; ARC; Sch P; Sci C; Pres, SC; Amer Leg A; COM; Cl Fav; Hist A; Math A; Most Out; Sci A; Star Student; Yth Fel; Sci Fair A; Excellent Schol A; Service A; U of Houston; Law.

REECE, Kevin Antoine
Phineas Banning HS; Wilmington, CA; Y-Tns; Bsbl; Bkbl; Ftbl; Briar Cliff Col; Dramatic Art.

REECE, Sheila Jean
Tryon HS; Tryon, NC (4-28) Ann; BC; Co-Cpt, Chldr; Fr C; Bkbl; Dental Tech.

REECE, Tim Wayne
South Page Comm Sch; College Springs, IA (4-33) Chor; Drama; FFA; NHS; Spch C; Tr; Hon Prog; Math A; Spch A; Iowa St U; Agr.

REECE, Wanda Elaine
Walhalla Sr HS; Walhalla, SC (20-190) Citz A; PA.

REED, Andy Mark
Allison HS; Allison, TX (4-10) Ann; FFA; Bkbl; Clarendon Jr Col; Agr.

REED, Angelina Germaine
Sch o-t Performing Arts; Washington, DC; A Cap Choir; Mgr, Chldr; Chor; Madrigal; Citz A; Mus A.

REED, Anthony Leon
Halter HS; St Louis, MO (4-58) Hon Prog; JA A; Art.

REED, Becky Sue
Ritenour Sr HS; Overland, MO (50%-904) Ensm; VP, SC; Tr; Tr A.

REED, Beverly Ann
Peebles HS; Peebles, OH (1-118) Band; Cpt, Chldr; Chor; Drama; 4H; Tres, Lat C; Sch Achieve Tm; Rptr, Soph Cl; Tr; 4H A; St Scholar; Yth Fel; Vlbl Tm; 4-H Jr Ldr; Mus.

REED, Brett Lamar
Canyon HS; Anaheim, CA (6-519) InterClub Coun; Pres, Key C; NHS; SC; Amer Leg A; CSF; ASB Ch of Justice; U of Calif-Berkeley; Bus Admin.

REED, Brian Buford
N Miami HS; Denver, IN (5-114) BS; Drama; NHS; Pres, Sci C; Var C; VP, Jr Cl; Cpt, Bkbl; JV, Cr-Ctry; COM; Cl Fav; MLS; Purdue U; Biological Sci.

REED, Carol Jeanette
Soldan HS; St Louis, MO; Med.

REED, Cathy Ann
Greenville HS; Greenville, IL (161-193) Chor; Sch P; Missionettes A; 1st Prizes and 2nd Prize; Secy.

REED, Chandra Janine
Clinton HS; Clinton, MS; Chor; FHA; Span C; Tr; Jackson St U; Bus.

REED, Charles Frederick
Evangelical Christian Sch; Memphis, TN (9-57) VP, Chess C; NHS; Pres, Order/Arrow; VP, Sci C; SC; Mgr, Bsbl; Ftbl; Chem A; Order/Arrow A; 3rd Runnerup, Co Spelling Bee; Eagle Sct; Congressional Nom, US Naval Acad; Christian Brothers Col; Sci.

REED, Charles Wayne Jr
Starkville HS; Starkville, MS (25%-200) Chem C; Key C; Var C; Bsbl; Mgr, Bkbl; Mgr, Ftbl; Miss St U; Pre-Dental.

REED, Cheryl Lynn
Tippecanoe Valley HS; Mentone, IN (35-130) A Cap Choir; Ann; Chor; Pres, 4H; Span C; 4H A; Pom Pon Squad; Ind U; Mus.

REED, Clarence Bernard
J C Fremont HS; Los Angeles, CA (20-600) NHS; Bsbl; Alg A; Citz A; Hon Prog; Math A; Attendance A; Eng A; Sports A; USC; Law.

REED, Colette Gwyn
Mansfield HS; Mansfield, LA (14-90) Band; BC; Ensm; FBLA; Lit Ral; Span C; Alg A; Math A; HR; Nom, GS; La Tech U; Math.

REED, Connie Annette
Rossville Comp HS; Rossville, GA (8-225) BC; Chldr; Secy, VP, Y-Tns; Secy, Soph Cl; Alg A; Gov Honor Prog; Dalton Jr Col; Dental Hygiene.

REED, Crystal Cassandra
Christian Fenger HS; Chicago, IL (5-646) Chor; Fr C; SC; Hon Prog; Prncpl's Schol A; St Xavier Col; Nurs.

REED, Cynthia Ann
Clinton HS; Clinton, MS; FHA; Y-Tns; Art.

REED, Danny Lamar
Walnut HS; Walnut, MS (1-50) FFA.

REED, David C
Lake Clifton HS; Baltimore, MD (10%-500) Ch, NHS; COM; Hist A; Hon Prog; Phys Ed A; Extra Curr A.

REED, Deborah Lynn
Sheffield HS; Memphis, TN (10%-214) Mu Alpha Theta; NHS; Span C; Christian Brothers Col; Math.

REED, Debra Lynn
Mangum HS; Mangum, OK (5-60) Chor; Ensm; FHA; HCt; St Hon Soc; JNHS; Okla Baptist U; Mus Ed.

REED, Denise Elaine
St Matthias Cath Girls HS; Huntington Park, CA; Attendance A; Los Angeles City Col; Bus.

REED, Denise Marie
Conecuh Co HS; Castleberry, AL (5%-21) Ed, Ann; BC; Cpt, Chldr; FHA; 4H; Var C; B Crocker A; 4H A; Hist A; HCt; Most Out; Val; Ntl Observer A; Jefferson Davis St Jr Col; Bus.

REED, Derlene
Manila HS; Manila, UT (1-19) Band; Chldr; 4H; Secy, Hmrm; Bkbl; Tr; Alg A; COM; Cl Fav; 4H A; Hist A; Hon Prog; Math A; Sci A; Piano, Band, A's; Horse Training.

REED, Erika Lynne
Vanguard HS; Ocala, FL (13-350) Bus Mgr, Ann; FBLA; FHA; NHS; Santa Fe Comm Col; Nurs.

REED, Harley Duane Jr
Edgeley HS; Edgeley, ND (2-59) Band; Chor; Bsbl; Bkbl; Ftbl; ND St U; Elec Engr.

REED, Jean Dorothy
Penncrest HS; Media, PA (36-480) Mu Alpha Theta; NHS; SC; COM; Hon Prog; Elizabethtown Col; Occupational Therapy.

REED, Jeffery Allen
Fruitport HS; Fruitport, MI (50-300) NHS; Cpt, Bkbl; Hockey; Lion A; MVP, Bsbl; Hope Col; Bus.

REED, Jody Lynn
Warren Central HS; Indianapolis, IN (27-791) S-T, A Cap Choir; Chor; Drama; Hmrm; S-T, Madrigal; Monogram; NHS; Ed, Sch P; Pres, Sci C; SC; Var C; Bkbl; Tr; Citz A; Journ A; Kiwanis A; Most Out; Ntl Sci Found; ARC A; Sci A; Accompanist, Service, WW; A's; *U of Ala; Sociology.*

REED, John Taylor
First Assembly Christian Sch; Memphis, TN (20-32) A Cap Choir; Rptr, Sch P; Co-Cpt, Bkbl; Golf; Sportsmanship A; *U of Tenn; Dentist.*

REED, Linda Sue
Bellmont HS; Decatur, IN (31-300) Band; Chor; JV, Tr; Yth Group; Campus Life; *Special Ed.*

REED, Lynda Lee
Oak Ridge HS; Orlando, FL (5-780) Ed, Ann; French NHS; NHS; COM; 1st Cl, GSct; Teenboard; Schol Certs; Quiz Bowl Tm; Cagers; *Lib Sci.*

REED, Mark Allen
Pascagoula HS; Pascagoula, MS (56-460) F-Ed, Ann; Pres, Hmrm; Key C; Tr; Elk A; WW; *US Ala; Med.*

REED, Matthew Edward
Hemet HS; Hemet, CA; Chor; Order/Arrow; Phys C; Citz A; Health A's; *Berkshire Christian Col.*

REED, Melinda Von
Lafayette HS; Lexington, KY; Chor; Ensm; Spch C; COM; Spch A; Mus A; Superior Spch A; Dist NFSM; 66 C; *Mus.*

REED, Pamela Faye
Melrose Sr HS; Memphis, TN (12-380) Mu Alpha Theta; NHS; F-Ed, Sch P; Span C; Hon Prog; *Memphis St U; Med.*

REED, Patricia Ann
Manchester HS; Manchester, OH; Band; Chor; Ensm; FHA; 4H; Span C; SC; Tr; Cl Fav; 4H A; Drill Tm; *Elem Ed.*

REED, Renae Marie
Albert Lea Sr HS; Albert Lea, MN (227-559) Band; Chor; Tr; *St Paul Bible Col; Missionary.*

REED, Scott Wagoner
James Ford Rhodes HS; Cleveland, OH (33-450) A Cap Choir; Pres, AFS; Band; Chor; NHS; Orch; SC; *U of Cincinnati; Archt.*

REED, Sherrill Ann
Columbia HS; W Columbia, TX (5-180) AFS; S-T, Band; Ensm; FTA; Secy, NHS; SC; Cl Fav; HCt; Rotary A; Band Swtht; *Baylor U; Math.*

REED, Tammy Dawn
River Forest HS; Hobart, IN; Cum Laude Soc; FNA; ARC; God & Country A; Harvard Book A; ARC A; Yale Book A.

REED, Terrence Maurice
Williamson HS; Mobile, AL (10-300) BS; Chor; Hmrm; Pres, Key C; NHS; Pres, SC; Up Bound; JV, Bsbl; Sftbl; Tr; Amer Leg A; Chamber of Comm A; Hon Prog; Most Out; ROTC A; Sci A; *Math.*

REED, Terry Leonard
Jordan HS; Los Angeles, CA (3-32) A Cap Choir; Dbte Tm; *Pepperdine U; Counselor.*

REED, Tracy Alan
Pasadena HS; Pasadena, TX; A Cap Choir; JV, Bsbl; Cpt, Bkbl; Co-Cpt, Ftbl; Tr; *Sam Houston St Col.*

REED, Vivian Dawn
Vicksburg HS; Vicksburg, MS (13-244) JV, Chldr; 4H; Key C; Lat C; Math C; Bkbl; JV, Tnns; Beauty; 4H A; HCt; Page, St Capital; *Miss St U; Math.*

REED, William Robert
Warren Central HS; Indianapolis, IN (90-1125) Key C; Math C; Order/Arrow; Mgr, Bsbl; Golf; Cpt, Hockey; JV, Swim; Alg A; Kiwanis A; Math A; Order/Arrow A; Fin, Hockey; Eagle Sct; *Butler Col; Computers.*

REEDER, John Milton
Henderson Co Sr HS; Henderson, KY (30-674) A Cap Choir; Chor; Ensm; Pres, Hmrm; NHS; SC; Bkbl; Ftbl.

REEDER, Scott Lendon
Vestavia Hills HS; Vestavia Hills, AL; AFS; Sci C; MVP, Swim; Church Choir; Royal Ambassadors; Pep C; Ntl Record, 200 IM, Swim; *Oceanography.*

REEDER, Wendy Anne
Champion HS; Warren, OH (13-233) Band; Drama; Tr; Alg A; Hon Prog; Math A; Yth Fel; Piano A; *Carnegie-Mellon U; Engr.*

REEL, David Robin
Lakeshore HS; College Park, GA (5-120) BC; Fr C; French NHS; NHS; Order/Arrow; Sch Achieve Tm; Co-Cpt, Wrest; COM; Citz A; DARGCA; Hon Prog; JA A; Pres A; Schol, Six Flags; Cert of Acad Achv; Cert of A; PC Jr Fellow; *Ga Inst of Tech; Bio.*

REEP, Daniel Mark
Marion L Steele HS; Amherst, OH (29-315) Band; BS; NHS; Var C; Co-Cpt, Bkbl.

REEP, Dave James
Northmor HS; Galion, OH (20%-145) Semi-Fin, BS; Chor; Var C; Bkbl; Tr; God & Country A; Poet A; Yth Fel; Eagle Sct; *Moody Bible Inst; Sociology.*

REEP, Walter Paul
Paris HS; Paris, TX (8-268) VP, Ger C; HiY; Pres, Key C; Parl, NHS; Cpt, Golf; COM; Hon Prog; Rotary A; Permanent Cl Pres; *U of Tex; Bus Adm.*

REERINK, Judy Ann
Central HS; Omaha, NE (5%-570) A Cap Choir; Band; Chor; Hon Prog.

REES, Dean Orval
Glenwood Springs HS; Glenwood Springs, CO (5-137) A Cap Choir; Band; Chor; Kiwanis A; Pres, MYF; European Tour.

REES, Jane Anne
Episcopal HS; Baton Rouge, LA (11-61) BC; Pres, Drama; Tres, Fr C; 4H; InterClub Coun; Lit Mag; NHS; Sch P; Sci C; Rptr, Thes; Sftbl; Hon Prog; ROTC A; Spch A; VFW A; Superior, Foreign Lang Festival; *Centenary Col; Computer Sci.*

REESE, Bonita Trina
Devilbiss HS; Toledo, OH;

REESE, Brian Dale
Crenshaw HS; Los Angeles, CA; Chor; JETS; Spch C; Bkbl; JV, Cr-Ctry; MVP, Tnns; JV, Tr; COM; JA A; Most Out; Tr Ltr; *Morehouse Col; Archt Engr.*

REESE, Charles Martin
Dadeville HS; Dadeville, AL (4-72) F-Ed, Ann; Co-Cpt, Band; BC; Rptr, Fr C; Ed, Sch P; Amer Leg Orator A; Hist A; Spch A; WW; All St Chor; Asst Concert Conductor; *Samford U; Mus Ed.*

REESE, Cynthia Louise
N Pocono HS; Moscow, PA; Cpt, Mjrte; Tnns; Law Day A; *Elizabethtown Col; Med Technology.*

REESE, Edgar Joseph Jr
Jordan Voc HS; Columbus, GA; Key C; Model UN; Var C; Bsbl; Ftbl.

REESE, Gary Steven
Mecklenburg Acad; Chase City, VA (13-32) Fr C; FFA; Rptr, Sr Cl; Co-Cpt, Bsbl; Bkbl; Co-Cpt, Ftbl; *Longwood Col; Phys Ed.*

REESE, Jeanese Cynthia
Sol C Johnson; Savannah, GA; Fr C; 4H; Span C; Math A; ARC A; *Spellman Col; Secondary Ed.*

REESE, John Earl
G W Carver Area HS; Chicago, IL; Chor; Drama; NHS; SC; COM; Citz A; Phi Beta Kappa; *Moody Bible Inst; Bible Theology.*

REESE, Joy Ann
Norwayne HS; Creston, OH (14-126) Band; Pres, 4H; *Secy.*

REESE, Julie Ann
Jordan Voc HS; Columbus, GA; Hmrm; Key C; Model UN; Span C; SC.

REESE, Kathryn Lee
Healdsburg HS; Healdsburg, CA (14-200) Band; Fr C; NHS; Bank of Amer A; Gym; Band Schol; Anita Alexander Mus A; Ntl Presbyterian Schol; *Col of Idaho; Med Techonology.*

REESE, Kathy Gayle
Jones Co HS; Gray, GA; F-Ed, Ann; Pres, BC; FHA; GS; Math C; SC; Secy, Sr Cl; COM; Crisco A; 4H A; NEDT; *LaGrange Col; Math.*

REESE, Kenneth Charles
Jones Co HS; Gray, GA (10%-250) BC; Math C; Pres, Sci C; Gov Honor Prog; Math A; NEDT; Sci A; Type A; *Math.*

REESE, Rebecca Ann
Fairview HS; Fairview, PA (40-200) Band; Chor; S-T, Drama; MVP, Orch; Most Outst Sr, Mus; WW in Amer Mus; Orch A; *St Vincent Sch of Nurs; RN Nurs.*

REESE, Rickey Lynn
Calumet HS; Gary, IN (100-263) FBLA; Key C; Up Bound; Data Process A, Computer Emphasis; *Purdue U; Industrial Mgt.*

REESE, Ronald William
Sandy Valley HS; Magnolia, OH (48-155) *NW Bus Col; Auto-Diesel Tech.*

REESE, Scott Mitchell
Wilmington HS; Wilmington, IL (2-143) VP, Band; Madrigal; Math C; VP, NHS; Span C; Pres, SC; Gr Marshal; Hon Prog; Sal; VofDEM; Yth Fel; All St Repertoire Band; Band Achv A; *Eastern U; Mus.*

REESE, Shirley Ann
Wasatch HS; Heber City, UT (10-200) Band; JV, Chldr; Chamber of Comm A; 4H A; Type A; *Snow Col.*

REESE, Stewart III
Columbia HS; Decatur, GA (100-400) Band; Community Yth Symph; Ensm; VP, Hmrm; Mod Mus Mas; Jr Cl; JV, Ftbl; Tr; JA A; Gold & Silvr Med, Solo & Ensm Fest; *GA St U; Acct.*

REESE, Tom William
Kirkwood HS; Kirkwood, MO (30-650) Ger C; Cpt, Order/Arrow; Ed, Sch P; SC; Tr; Citz A; Hon Prog; Journ A; Order/Arrow A; Q&S A; Mo Stu Journ o-t Yr; Eagle Sct; Cert of Recognition; Photo A; Writing A; *U of Mo at Columbia; Journ.*

REESE, William Kirk
Southwest HS; Atlanta, GA (57-200) Band; BC; Secy, Hmrm; Sci C; Tr; ROTC A; *N Ga Col; Bio.*

REESER, Patricia Anne
Mason HS; Mason, MI (10%-318) Chor; Secy, 4H; NHS; SC; 4H A; Kiwanis A; S-T, High Tn Church; Tres, 4-H C; *John Wesley Col; Vet Sci.*

REEVE, Laura Ellen
Centaurus HS; Lafayette, CO; JV, Chldr; 4H; Math C; Ski C; Tr; MLS; NML; Coach's A, Gym; *Colo St U; Bio.*

REEVES, Anne Whitfield
Bowie Sr HS; Bowie, MD (28-930) Span C; Schol Achv A; Outst Art Ability A; Job's Daughters; Tn Mission Tm; Secy, Jr UMYF; *Span.*

REEVES, Barbara Ann
Greencastle-Antrim HS; Greencastle, PA (129-177) Band; Chor; Ensm; Var C; VP, Y-Tns; Mgr, Sftbl; Tnns; Mgr, Tr; Sci A; Statistician, Bsbl & Soccer; Band A; Choir A; *Horticulture.*

REEVES, Brigitte Marcia
Northeast HS; Philadelphia, PA (625-1159) Band; Tres, Chor; Tres, Hmrm; *Pa St U; Human Development.*

REEVES, Charles Gregory
Bogue Chitto HS; Bogue Chitto, MS (5-32) Co-Ed, Ann; Tres, BC; Parl, Bus C; Dbte Tm; Drama; Parl, FBLA; FFA; Sch P; COM; FFA As; St Mus A; *Copiah-Lincoln Jr Col; Bus Adm.*

REEVES, Cindy Joy
Reeds Spring HS; Reeds Spring, MO; AFS; Ann; Band; BC; Cpt, Chldr; FBLA; Jr Miss Pagent; Sci C; Span C; SC; Secy, Var C; Bkbl; Tr; Citz A; HQn; HCt; Sci A; *Columbia U; Sci.*

REEVES, Darrell Ray
Kountze HS; Kountze, TX; Band; Math C; Sci C; *Lamar U; Bus.*

REEVES, David Norman
Haralson Co HS; Tallapoosa, GA (5-137) BC; COM; Gov Honor Prog; Most Out; *Ga Tech; Elec Engr.*

REEVES, Debbie Lynne
Greenway HS; Phoenix, AZ (60-456) NHS; Yth Fel; Shorthand A; Vogue Sewing A; *Glendale Comm Col; Bus.*

REEVES, Debra Susan
McDermitt HS; McDermitt, NE (10%-16) *Acct.*

REEVES, Gary Dwayne
Eunice HS; Eunice, LA (20-290) F-Ed, Ann; FBLA; Secy, Key C; NHS; Span C; Tnns; *LSU; Law.*

REEVES, Gary Michael
Marion HS; Marion, VA (32-210) Ann; FBLA; Hmrm; Span C; Geo A; Span A; Sweet Briar Col; Bus.

REEVES, James Richard
Monticello HS; Monticello, MS; Band; BC; Pres, FFA; Lat C; Order/Arrow; Sch P; Mgr, Bsbl; MLS; Order/Arrow A; Eagle Sct; WW; Co-Lin Jr Col; Archt.

REEVES, Kelli Renee
Ole Main HS; N Little Rock, AR; Drill Tm Lieutenant; Colo Inst of Ar; Interior Design.

REEVES, Laura Kathleen
Arlington HS; Arlington Heights, IL; Tres, Fr C; Magna Cum Laude; Photography.

REEVES, Linda Sue
Castleberry HS; Fort Worth, TX; FBLA; Secy, FHA; Span C; Tarrant Co Jr Col.

REEVES, Lisa Daun
Bradley-Bourbonnais HS; Bradley, IL; Fr C; Olivet Col; Home Ec.

REEVES, Pamela Sue
Hammond Christian Acad; Griffith, IN (1-11) Chor; Drama; Ensm; Pres, 4H; Pres, SC; 4H A; Pres A; Choir A.

REEVES, Shawn Kay
Buena HS; Sierra Vista, AZ (300-495) Rptr, FHA; Tnns; VP, NAACP; VP, Minority Stu Union; Cochise Col; Nurs.

REEVES, Sylvia Monice
East St Louis Sr HS; E St Louis, IL (2-650) Chem C; Tres, Drama; Fr C; Hmrm; Secy, Math C; VP, Mu Alpha Theta; Rptr, NHS; Spch C; Tres, SC; Tnns; Alg A; Bausch & Lomb A; Beauty; Elk A; HCt; Hon Prog; JA A; Math A; MLS; Opt A; ROTC A; Sal; Sci A; Spch A; Most Polite; Alpha Kappa Alpha; WW; Physics.

REGAN, Charles Nelson
Hawaii Baptist Acad; Honolulu, HI (54-85) Demolay; Hmrm; SC; Bsbl; Ftbl; Swim; Campus Life; VP, Church Yth Group; Pepperdine U; Aeronautical Engr.

REGAN, Ellen Gail
Maple Shade HS; Maple Shade, NJ (16-241) Bus Mgr, Ann; GS; Hmrm; VP, Key C; Lit Mag; NHS; Pep C; Jr Hon Soc; Lib Aid; Bowl C; Asst Ed, Annual; Legal Secy.

REGAN, John F
St Mary's Prep; Orchard Lake, MI (10-44) Ski C; Bsbl; Ftbl; Hon Prog; Polish Oratorical Contest Semi-Fin; 2nd Hon; U of Detroit; Architecture.

REGAN, Rosemary
Clark Co R-I HS; Kahoka, MO (3-92) Band; Bus C; Chldr; Chor; Drama; FBLA; NHS; Thes.

REGAN, William Bates
Tallulah Acad; Tallulah, LA (25%-39) Tres, SC; Secy, Soph Cl; Bkbl; Golf; Tnns; Cl Fav.

REGER, Timothy Allen
Hemet HS; Hemet, CA (30-500) FFA; CSF; Rotary A; Yth Fel; FFA A; Daise Chaine Hon Escort; John Brown U; Broadcasting.

REGIER, Dale Randal
Yukon HS; Yukon, OK (64-246) Span C; Art C; Principal's HR; WW; Pres, MYF; World Hunger Seminar; United Methodist Yth Coun; Skiing; Legislative Affairs Seminar; El Reno Jr Col; Forestry.

REGISTER, Chandler
Echols Co HS; Statenville, GA (6-37) Tres, BC; FFA; 4H; Hmrm; InterAct C; InterClub Coun; SC; Pres, Sr Cl; Cl Fav; DAHSS.

REGISTER, Chester
Echols Co HS; Statenville, GA (5-38) Pres, BC; Tres, FFA; 4H; InterAct C; InterClub Coun; Cl Fav; Mech A.

REGOR, Nina Dierdre
Mainland Sr HS; Daytona Beach, FL (5%-250) NHS; Eng.

REHBEIN, Brian Jay
O'Fallon Township HS; O'Fallon, IL (100-200) Band; Span C; Bsbl; Bkbl; Ftbl; Golf; Tnns; Tr; SIU-Edwardsville.

REHBEIN, Rachel Marie
Mpls Lutheran HS; Minneapolis, MN (6-37) Chldr; Chor; Drama; GS; Co-Ed, Lit Mag; Madrigal; NHS; A-Ed, Sch P; SC; Valparaiso U; Special Ed.

REHM, Stephanie Louise
Orrville HS; Orrville, OH (102-187) Band; Drama; Rptr, 4H; Thes; COM; 4H A; Type A; Yth Fel; Bus.

REHNBORG, Steven Radley
Horseheads Sr HS; Horseheads, NY (45-588) Pres, 4H; 4H A; NMS; Regent Schol; Col Schol; Essay Published, Amer Essay Press; Essay Published, Ntl Essay Press; David Lipscomb Col; Psych.

REHRING, Kathy Roxanne
Hixson HS; Hixson, TN; Band; Bio.

REICH, Arthur Lee
Wheatland HS; Wheatland, WY; VP, 4H; Rptr, Hmrm; Rptr, Sch P; Bsbl; JV, Bkbl; JV, Ftbl; 4H A; Star Student; Yth Fel; Awana Trophies; Bob Jones U; Bus.

REICHARD, Brenda Sue
Reynolds HS; Greenville, PA (1-183) AFS; Chldr; Chor; Ensm; FTA; Math C; VP, Span C; Secy, SC; Tri-HiY; HCt; Graceland Col; Psych.

REICHELT, Debra Ann
Oconomowoc Sr HS; Oconomowoc, WI; AFS; Mgr, Bkbl; JV, Tr; Pep C; MVP, Bkbl; Vlbl; Schol A's; Lou Keller Acad Ath A's; Phys Ed.

REICHENBACH, Eric Paul
White Plains HS; White Plains, NY (60-555) Band; Ensm; Ger C; JV, Tnns; Rotary A; Ger, Mus, A's; Chem Engr.

REICHENBACH, Jean Marie
Pike Central HS; Petersburg, IN (1-176) Band; NHS; Orch; ARC; Sci C; Tr; DARGCA; Hist A; NMF; NMS; Val; VP, Sr GSct Troop; Purdue U; Vet Med.

REICHERT, Ann Louise
Lutheran HS E; Harper Woods, MI (61-150) A Cap Choir; Hmrm; ARC; SC; Sftbl; Tr; Semi-Fin, St Tr; Coun.

REICHERT, Margaret Ann
Central Dauphin E HS; Harrisburg, PA (28-375) Drama; Fr C; NHS; Bauder Fashion Col; Fashion Merchandising.

REICHERT, Mark Allan
Hazelwood Central Sr HS; Florissant, MO (53-1045) Mgr, Bsbl; Math A; PTA A; Sci A; Math.

REICHL, Betty Jean
Parkville Sr HS; Baltimore, MD; A Cap Choir; Hon Prog; Yth Fel; Oral Roberts U; Nurs.

REICHLE, John Andrew Jr
Parkway W Sr HS; Chesterfield, MO (33%-608) A Cap Choir; Chor; Ensm; Math C; Ftbl; Hockey; Cl Fav; Yth Fel; SE Mo St U.

REICHLEIN, Pamela Gae
Myrtle Point HS; Myrtle Point, OR (5-125) Band; Ger C; NHS; 4H A; Type A; Counselor A, Best Musicianship; Fresh Band Cup; Secy, Camera C.

REID, Alvin Garner
HS of Art and Design; New York, NY; A Cap Choir; Band; Pres, Chess C; Chor; Pres, Sch P; Pres, Thes; Pres, Bkbl; Coun of Teach A; Sci A; Advertising.

REID, Barbara Jean
Westfield HS; Westfield, NJ; ARC; JV, Hockey; JV, Sftbl; VFW A; Yth Fel; DAR Sewing A; Radford Col; Home Ec.

REID, Cynthia Marie
Acad of Notre Dame; Washington, DC (50-74) COM; Sch Mascot; Pres, Pep C; U of Md; Bus Mgt.

REID, Deborah June
Central Bucks HS W; Doylestown, PA (5-522) Ann; Chor; Drama; Hmrm; Madrigal; NHS; SC; Thes; Amer Leg A; Math A; MLS; Most Out; Val; VFW A; Equity Comm; Outs Stu o-t Yr; Church Yth Group; Girl o-t Month; Co Chor; Yth Ed Assn; Sexette; Presbyterian Nurs Sch; Nurs.

REID, Ellen Sandra
Rufus King HS; Milwaukee, WI; Bus C; Chor; City Conf; Hmrm; SC; Pres, Jr Cl; Bkbl; Cpt, Tr; Attendance A; Sports As; Tr Medals; Hon Pin; Iowa St U; Vet.

REID, Gary Don
Henryetta HS; Henryetta, OK (50%-90) HKg; HCt; Kiwanis A; MLS; Okla St U; Psych.

REID, Jon Kevin
Liberty HS; Clarksburg, WV (28-351) Chess C; Drama; 4H; Tres, Var C; Bsbl; JV, Bkbl; Ftbl; JV, Tr; Wrest; MLS; Sci A; WVA U; Elec Engr.

REID, Kimberly Renee
Kubasaki HS; Okinawa, JAPAN (9-280) Secy, Fr C; FNA; FTA; Hmrm; Math C; Secy, Mu Alpha Theta; NHS; Span C; Mgr, Bkbl; Swim; JV, Tr; Beauty; Gym; Homecoming Comm; Clown, Parade; Photo C; Eng A; Phys Fitness A; Secy, Explorer; Prom Comm; U of Wash; Ed.

REID, Latisha Anne
Rock Hill HS; Rock Hill, SC; JV, Chldr; Chor; VP, Hmrm; Rainbow; F-Ed, Sch P; SC; Tri-HiY; Dental Hygiene.

REID, Lloyd Eugene
New Hanover HS; Wilmington, NC (82-537) Chor; Hmrm; SC; MVP, Ftbl; MVP, Tr; Citz A; Cl Fav; Gov Honor Prog; Most Out; Star Student; Beautiful Person A; Sch Spirit C; Yth Adv, Bd of Ed; Tenn St U; Hist.

REID, Robert Stephen
New Caney HS; Porter, TX (5-220) Band; Ensm; Hmrm; VP, JETS; Tres, NHS; SC; Co-Cpt, Sftbl; JV, Tr; Drum Major; Outst Bandsman; All-Dist & All-Region Bands; Tex A&M U; Nuclear Engr.

REID, Sarah Joanne
Brandon HS; Brandon, MS (58-135) Chor; Hinds Jr Col; Elem Ed.

REID, Sheila La Verne
Dunbar Comm HS; Baltimore, MD (250-500) Co-Cpt, Chldr; Chor; Sch P; Var C; Hist A; HCt; Chldr A; U of Md; Sociology.

REID, Shirley Ann
Zanesville HS; Zanesville, OH (89-356) Band; Fr C; Tr; Ntl Essay Contest; Shorthand A; Secy.

REID, Trica Rosheda
Middleton HS; Charleston, SC (88-304) U of SC; Computer Sci.

REIDY, Patrick Gerard
Fordham Preparatory HS; New York, NY (14-200) CYO; Key C; JV, Ftbl; COM; Hon Prog; Val; HS Schol; Mile Swim; BSct; Savings Bond A; Columbia Col; Journ.

REIDY, Sharon Ann
St Mary's Acad; Englewood, CO (3-54) VP, CYO; VP, Fr C; VP, French NHS; Lat C; Co-Ed, Lit Mag; NHS; SC; Hon Prog; Math A; Ntl Merit Commended Schol; Notre Dame U; Bio Chem.

REIDY, William Harwood
Sacred Heart HS; Kingston, MA (2-85) Band; Chess C; Chor; NHS; Rptr, Sch P; Hon Prog; Ger A; Meteorology.

REIER, Rhonda Jean
Putman City W HS; Oklahoma City, OK (377-603) Hmrm; Span C; Sftbl; WW.

REIERSON, Jeffrey Robert
Belvidere HS; Belvidere, IL (12-434) Band; Var C; Cr-Ctry; Tr; Timothy, Hon, A's.

REIERSON, Timothy James
Belvidere HS; Belvidere, IL (1-370) Pres, Band; NHS; SC; Var C; MVP, Cr-Ctry; Tr; Alg A; Hon Prog; Math A; MLS; Val; WW; Meritorious, Timothy, A's; Outst Newspaper Carrier, A; U of Ill; Pre-Law.

REIF, Renee Marie
Bernie Sr HS; Bernie, MO (22-70) CYO; FHA; Jr Miss Pagent; Thes; Mgr, Sftbl; COM; Jr Chamber of Com A; Lion A; Civic C A; 1st Cl GSct A; Vlbl; Nurs.

REIF, Rhonda Ann
Bernie Sr HS; Bernie, MO (8-32) CYO; Chor; FHA; Semi-Fin, Jr Miss Pa; Sodality; Thes; Sftbl; Vlbl; Tr A; Badminton A; Phys Fitness; Southeast Mo St; Pre-Vet.

REIFF, Burt Hunter
Rio Hondo HS; Rio Hondo, TX (5-95) Band; BS; Pres, Key C; NHS; Sci C; SC; JV, Bkbl; Ftbl; Yth Fel; Section Ldr, Band; Jr Cl Rptr; Most Popular.

REIFF, Teri Diane
Twin Lakes HS; Monticello, IN (21-216) Fr C; 4H; COM; Secy, Pep C; Secy, Sunshine Soc; *Bus.*

REIFSCHNEIDER, Janet Ruth
Bismarck HS; Bismarck, ND (10%-534) Band; Chldr; Lat C; *Vet.*

REIGN, Jonathan Richard
Citrus HS; Inverness, FL (16-250) Chor; Ensm; Key C; Ed, Lit Mag; VP, NHS; Span C; Wrest; ROTC A; 1st Lt, Band; WW; *US Air Force Acad; Aeronautics.*

REILLY, John Francis
Don Bosco Tech HS; Boston, MA (6-222) CYO; Pres, Order/Arrow; ARC; Order/Arrow A; *U of Lowell; Elec Engr.*

REIMER, David Alvin
Eisenhower HS; Saginaw, MI; Chess C; Drama; Hon Prog; Yth Foundation A; Staff Asst; *Delta Col; Bus.*

REIMERS, Paul Timothy
Lutheran HS; Los Angeles, CA (10%-100) A Cap Choir; Key C; NHS; MVP, Bkbl; CSF; MLS; ROTC A; St Scholar; *U of So Cal; Elec Engr.*

REIMERS, Timothy Wayne
Agawam HS; Agawam, MA (100-426) Band; 4H; Sftbl; Audio Visual C&A; *Drafting.*

REIMNITZ, Ruth Annette
Bismarck Sr HS; Bismarck, ND (480-539) Var C; Swim; MVP, Gym; Ltrman's A; Cert of A; *ND St U; Lang.*

REIMOLD, Wendy Sue
Reynolds HS; Greenville, PA (6-212) Ger C; Rptr, 4H; Lat C; Lit Mag; Math C; Bus Mgr, Sch P; Sci C; Tri-HiY; B Crocker A; 4H A; *Penn St U; Environmental Resource.*

REINARTZ, Gretchen Anne
Virgil I Grissom HS; Huntsville, AL (10%-575) Secy, SC; Bkbl; Tr; All-City Vlbl Tm; Statistics Girl Bkbl.

REINARTZ, Karen Elizabeth
Grissom HS; Huntsville, AL (10%-575) Tres, SC; Bkbl; Tr; Vlbl; Statistics Girl Bkbl.

REINE, Cynthia Lee
Jefferson City HS; Jefferson City, MO; AFS; Chor; *Baylor U.*

REINECKE, Bryan William
Shawnee Mission W HS; Overland Park, KS (30-600) Band; Dbte Tm; NHS; SC; Hon Prog; NMS; V-Ch, Church Yth; *Kans St U; Civil Engr.*

REINEKE, Caryn Donna
Secaucus HS; Secaucus, NJ (6-162) Chldr; Chor; Hmrm; NHS; A-Ed, Sch P; Cr-Ctry; Sftbl; Spch A; *Montclair St Col; Spch Therapy.*

REINER, Susan Kay
Goshen HS; Goshen, IN (15-250) Ann; Chor; Ensm; Hmrm; Madrigal; NHS; Span C; SC; COM; Magna Cum Laude; St Scholar; *Ball St Col; Ed.*

REINERT, Carol Ann
Hazelwood E Sr HS; St Louis, MO (21-455) Secy, Band; Drama; VP, NHS; SC; VP, Thes; Gym; Unsung Hero A; *Kans City Art Inst; Visual Arts.*

REINERT, MaryJo
Holy Rosary Acad; Louisville, KY; NHS; ARC; PA; *Jefferson Comm Col; Bus.*

REINERTSEN, Paul Edward
Centennial HS; Champaign, IL; Regent, Acolytes; Eagle Sct; Explorer Sct; *Augustana Col; Aviation.*

REINHARD, Tony Kim
Callaway HS; Callaway, NE; Ann; Chor; VP, 4H; ARC; Sch P; Thes; Var C; Secy, Sr Cl; Secy, Jr Cl; Secy, Soph Cl; Bkbl; Ftbl; Tr; Amer Leg A; COM; Elk A; Pres A; Spch A; WW; Tn-Ager o-t Mo; Amer Yth Symph & Chor; *Wayne St Col; Broadcast Communications.*

REINHARDT, Andreas Ferdinand
Newark Sr HS; Newark, NY; JV, Soccer; MVP, Tnns; *Rochester Inst of Tech; Criminal Justice.*

REINHARDT, Dawn Janese
Shawano HS; Shawano, WI (22-240) A Cap Choir; Band; Chor; Drama; Ensm; NFL; NHS; Ed, Sch P; *U Wis-Eau Claire; Mus.*

REINHARDT, Ellen Lea
Hickory HS; Hickory, NC (51-340) F-Ed, Ann; Rptr, FBLA; InterClub Coun; NHS; Pres, Span C; FCA; Q&S; *Appalachian St U; Special Ed.*

REINHARDT, Kathy Sue
Spring Branch HS; Houston, TX; FHA; Ger C; NHS; Bkbl; Cpt, Sftbl; Tr; Type A; *Concordia Teachers Col; Hist.*

REINHARDT, Patty Lynn
Althoff Catholic HS; Belleville, IL; CYO; Chor; Fr C; Hmrm; NHS; Sftbl; Amer Leg A; COM; 4H A; Hon Prog; Sci Fair A; *ACHS Prin A.*

REINHARDT, Ronald Craig
Tates Creek Sr HS; Lexington, KY (25%-550) BC; Key C; Mu Alpha Theta; Opt Out Tn; Table Tnns; *U of Ky; Math.*

REINHOLD, Donald Frank
Valmeyer Community Unit 3 HS; Valmeyer, IL (10-36) CYO; Chess C; Drama; VP, Math C; Bsbl; Cpt, Bkbl; MVP, Bkbl; Co Free-Throw A; Post Dispatch Schol Ath; *Eastern Ill U; Engr.*

REINISCH, Duane Allen
Valley City Sr HS; Valley City, ND (24-162) Chor; 4H; Order/Arrow; Ftbl; Wrest; COM; Yth Fel; Eagle Sct A.

REINOEHL, Amy Ann
Muncie Central HS; Muncie, IN (23-379) Chor; Dbte Tm; Drama; Ensm; NFL; Orch; Span C; Thes; Tnns; Mgr, Tr; COM; *Ball St U; Sci.*

REINSCHMIDT, Richard Paul
Fontana HS; Fontana, CA (27-621) VP, A Cap Choir; Pres, Chor; VP, Madrigal; Model UN; Orch; VP, Thes; CSF; Best Actor; Graduation Usher; *U o-t Pacific; Mus Theory.*

REINSEL, Tom Edwin
Lutheran HS; St Louis, MO (12-158) VP, NHS; Bsbl; Ftbl; Soccer; *Pre-Med.*

REISCHMAN, Susan Faye
Coventry HS; Akron, OH (9-225) Band; Tres, Fr C; Scroll C; *Akron U; Mus.*

REISER, Anita Susan
Westlake Sr HS; Westlake, OH (40-314) V-Ch, A Cap Choir; Chor; COM; Hon Prog; Interlochen Ntl Mus; Val; Asst Teacher, Ger Sch; Church Yth Group; Ger A; 1st Cl G Sct; Jr NHS; Vice- ch, Ger Yth Choir; *Bowling Green St U.*

REISER, Kimberly Anne
Ithaca Sr HS; Richland Center, WI (15-40) F-Ed, Ann; Chor; Ger C; NFL; Sch P; Soccer; Sftbl; Tr; Asst Ed, Ed, Annual; *Professional & Commerical Art.*

REISER, Susan Ann
Secaucus HS; Secaucus, NJ (11-185) Chor; Hmrm; NHS; Sch P; SC; Var C; Hon Prog; Bowl Tm.

REISIG, Sherri Renee
San Marcos HS; Santa Barbara, CA; A Cap Choir; 4H; ARC; Spch C; CSF; 4H A; ARC A; Vol, Humane Soc; *Biola Col; Elem Ed.*

REISINGER, Susan Patrice
Corning Comm HS; Corning, IA (13-70) Chldr; Chor; Drama; ARC; Pres, SC; Thes; Ch, Y-Tns; Secy, Jr Cl; JV, Bkbl; Sftbl; Tr; HCt; Hon Prog; Yth Fel; Secy, SC; HR; Co-Ch, Y-Tns; FFA Qn; Tr Hon's; *Creighton U; Nurs.*

REISNER, Kenneth Neal
Hood River Valley HS; Hood River, OR; Ger C; Var C; JV, Ftbl; Wrest; *Law.*

REISS, Heidi Anne
Watertown HS; Watertown, CT (14-302) Hmrm; St Scholar; Sunday Sch Teacher; GSct; WW; Church Yth Group; Co-Ch, Teacher Evaluation Stu Comm; Albright Col; *Home Ec.*

REISS, John Charles
Melbourne HS; Melbourne, FL (380-645) Pres, CYO; Chor; Ger C; Madrigal; God & Country A; Yth Fel; Jr Civitan; *Teaneck Col; Hist.*

REIST, Peter Michael
Badin HS; Hamilton, OH (40-195) CYO; JV, Bsbl; Bkbl; Golf; COM; Prom Court; *Miami U; Bus.*

REITER, Annette Clair
Holdrege HS; Holdrege, NE (50-143) Band; Chor; VP, 4H; Rptr, Sch P; Thes; Sftbl; Swim; Tnns; Tr; 4H A; Band A; *Kerney St U; Nurs.*

REITER, Jolene Renae
Lincoln Sr HS; Sioux Falls, SD; Chor; Tres, Soph Cl; Cpt, Bkbl; Ldr, Y-Tn; Vlbl.

REITER, Lynnette Ann
Lincoln Sr HS; Sioux Falls, SD; NHS; Sch P; Q&S A; *U of SD.*

REITH, Kenneth Douglas
Ithaca HS; Ithaca, WI (19-40) FFA; 4H; Bsbl; Co-Cpt, Bkbl; Ftbl; Tr; HCt; Bkbl, Tr, Ltrs; *U of Wis; Phys Ed.*

REITZ, Diane Louise
Charles H Roth HS; Henrietta, NY (25%-250) Demolay; Hmrm; Lit Mag; NHS; SC; Pres, MYF; Schol Ltr; Swtht, Demolay; Beloved Qn of Fidel Triangle No 4; *Business Adm.*

REITZEL, Vera Elizabeth
Hickory HS; Hickory, NC; AFS; Chor; Hmrm; S-T, InterClub Coun; Jr Miss Pagent; Span C; Phys Ed A; VP, Yth Group; Co Ch, Parent-Teacher-Stu Assn; Pres, Sub Jr Women's C; Jr Civitan C; *UNC; Elem Ed.*

RELATOR, Pearla Maureen
Maryknoll HS; Honolulu, HI (2-115) Chor; Math C; NHS; Spch C; VP, Soph Cl; JV, Bkbl; Math A; NEDT; Japanese Lang A; *U of Hawaii; Math.*

RELF, Kimberley Jean
Arlington HS; Arlington, MA (100-650) A Cap Choir; Chor; Drama; Fr C; Madrigal; A-Ed, Sch P; SC; DAHSS; Sunday Sch Teacher; 1 Hosp Vol; Sch Mus Production C; Jr Nurse Aide; Mus Group; Ldr, Children's Choir; *Salem St Col; Nurs.*

RELF, Scott Bradley
Claremont HS; Claremont, CA (14-486) Dbte Tm; VP, Key C; NFL; NHS; ARC; F-Ed, Sch P; Spch C; JV, Bkbl; Cpt, Cr-Ctry; JV, Tr; CSF; COM; Citz A; Hon Prog; Spch A; *Princeton U; Chem.*

RELJIC, Susan
Northeastern HS; Detroit, MI; Tnns; Bio A; Citz A; *Brigham Young U; Archaeology.*

RELPH, Bernard Dwaine
Wayne Comm Sch Dist; Corydon, IA (17-65) Band; Pres, Chor; Pres, FFA; VP, 4H; Madrigal; Tres, NHS; Thes; JV, Tr; JV, Wrest; Co-Cpt, Chor; St, Ntl, FFA Bands; *Iowa St U; Vet Med.*

RELPH, Darla Kay
Wayne Comm HS; Corydon, IA (48-75) Band; Chldr; Chor; Drama; Ensm; Tres; Spch C; Thes; Tr; *Kirkwood Col; Mental & Phys Disorder.*

REMALEY, Kevin Steele
Kiskiminetas Springs Sch; Saltsburg, PA (10-51) JV, Bsbl; JV, Bkbl; JV, Soccer.

REMEDIES, Pamela Retha
Many HS; Many, LA; CYO; FHA; NHS; Var C; COM; Pres A; *Westmar Col; Bus.*

REMME, Mark Andrew
Luverne Jr Sr HS; Luverne, MN; Ed, Ann; Bsbl; Ftbl; Golf; Wrest; *Law.*

REMMERS, Lori Sue
Johnson-Brock HS; Johnson, NE (25%-34) F-Ed, Ann; Band; Cpt, Chldr; Chor; Mjrte; Secy, Jr Cl; Bkbl; Sftbl; Hon Prog; Journ A; Most Out; Type A; Vlbl; Phys Fitness A; Secy, Fresh Cl; Co Govt Day; Sch Play; Most Outst Yth, Church; *Lincoln Sch of Commerce; Secy.*

REMMERS, Marcia Diane
Johnson-Brock HS; Johnson, NE (5-24) Ann; Band; Chor; Ensm; 4H; JV, Bkbl; Sftbl; 4H A; Spch A; JV Vlbl; Pep C; HR; *U of Nebr; Hist.*

REMSHARD, Lynne Marie
Immaculata HS; Philadelphia, PA (6-432) Dbte Tm; Pres, Fr C; NFL; NHS; Sch P; Sci C; World Affairs C; Hon Prog; Spch A; Excel Rating, Ntl Forensic League; Treasury's Wash Medallion A; Bicentennial Yth Debates; *Chestnut Hill Col; Biochem.*

REMUND, Charles Paul
Wilmot Pub 54-7 HS; Wilmot, SD (2-27) Band; Chor; 4H; NHS; Bsbl; Ftbl; Alt, BSct; *SD St U.*

RENARD, Keith Raleigh
Watkins Overton HS; Memphis, TN (50-244) F-Ed, Ann; Band; Key C; SC; Mgr, Tnns; Q&S A; *Memphis St U.*

RENCKEN, Valori Lynn
Weston McEwen HS; Athena, OR (7-41) Band; Chldr; Chor; VP; Drama; FHA; 4H; NHS; ARC; A-Ed, Sch P; SC; Secy, Soph Cl; Sftbl; Mgr, Tr; Vlbl; *Eastern Oreg St Col; Bio.*

RENDAHL, Kirsten Elizabeth
Denfeld HS; Duluth, MN; A Cap Choir; Band; Chor; Model UN; Orch; Girl's C Cabinet; Denfeld Hon 'D'; City Hon Choir; *Bethel Col; Elem Ed.*

RENDER, Angeila Renee
Kensington HS; Buffalo, NY (11-25) Chor; Hmrm; Bus.

RENDER, Sheila
Bennett HS; Buffalo, NY (10-28) Tr; *Dental Asst.*

RENECKER, Wanda Jean
Leesville HS; Leesville, LA; Band; Sftbl.

RENEGAR, Lori Ann
Mid-High HS; Shawnee, OK; Band; Ensm; Span C; Masonic A; Sci A; *Okla Baptist U; Math.*

RENFRO, Alan Daniel
Topeka HS; Topeka, KS (41-500) Chor; Madrigal; JV, Bkbl.

RENFRO, Ann Margaret
Bishop Carroll HS; Wichita, KS (1-211) VP, NHS; Ed, Sch P; Sci C; Span C; SC; Journ A; *U of Kans; Nurs.*

RENFRO, Dean Howard
Topeka HS; Topeka, KS (100-500) Chor; Madrigal; Thes; Mgr, Bkbl; *Washburn Col; Mus.*

RENFRO, Sarah L
Maryville HS; Maryville, TN; AFS; Band; NHS; Tnns.

RENFROE, Carolyn
Terrell Co HS; Dawson, GA (10%-112) Ed, Ann; BC; Drama; Parl, FHA; Cpt, Bkbl; Hist A; Hon Prog; Most Out; *Law.*

RENFROE, Debra Jane
G W Carver Sr HS; Montgomery, AL (1-400) Chess C; Chor; Ensm; FTA; Madrigal; Math C; Mu Alpha Theta; Secy, NHS; Val; All St Chor; Jacksonville St School; Outst Singer; *Jacksonville St U; Sci.*

RENFROE, Yana Sue
Miss Baptist HS; Jackson, MS; Co-Cpt, Chldr; Chor; Sftbl; Macette; Hon Stu; *Hinds Jr Col; Dental Asst.*

RENFROW, Beverly Simone
Overbrook HS; Philadelphia, PA (209-750) Chldr; Chor; Hmrm; Semi-Fin, Jr Miss Pa; SCnt; Var C; Yth Fel; *W Chester St Col; Elem Ed.*

RENFROW, Julia Flythe
W Guilford HS; Greensboro, NC (1-240) Band; BC; Ensm; Tnns; Alg A; Citz A; Sci A; Yth Fel; Jr Jaycettes; Schol Ltr; Nom, Gov Sch; *U of NC; Law.*

RENICK, Cheri Alice
Mannington HS; Mannington, WV; VP, FFA; Hmrm; VP, SC; Bkbl; Tr; Hist A; Spch A; 1st Pl Tm in St, FFA Land Judging; 1st Pl Spkr, St FFA Ldrshp Camp; *W Va U; Agr Ed.*

RENKOSKI, Luke Martin
Wheaton HS; Wheaton, MO (4-36) CYO; FFA; Agr Tm; *U of Mo; Agr Sci.*

RENN, Cynthia Lynne
Red Lion Area Sr HS; Red Lion, PA (64-516) Band; Ensm; Pres, Rainbow; Tnns; Yth Fel; *Ind U of Pa; Mus.*

RENN, Donald W
Pleasure Ridge Park HS; Pleasure Ridge Park, KY; Band; Sftbl.

RENNARD, Karen Edele
Central HS; Thomasville, GA; FHA; Tri-HiY; *Legal Secy.*

RENNER, Ann Elizabeth
Orange HS; Pepper Pike, OH (34-280) Chor; Model UN; NHS; ARC; Co-Ch, Ski C; Span C; Thes; Hon Prog; NHS; *Liberal Arts.*

RENNER, Barbara Joyce
Mainland Sr HS; Daytona Beach, FL (4-425) Tres, Anchor C; Band; Ensm; NHS; COM; Citz A; Elk A; Hon Prog; Math A; NEDT; Summa Cum Laude; St Excel, Super Dist, Solo & Ensm; *Mercer U; Math.*

RENNER, Daniel Walter
Mission Bay HS; San Diego, CA (25-400) Hmrm; JV, Ftbl; Tr; CSF; St Scholar; Most Talented; Outst Achv, Phys Ed; *Biola Col; Biblical Stu.*

RENNER, Denise Ann
Stafford HS; Fredericksburg, VA; Chor; FHA.

RENNER, Elaine Ruth
Hannibal Sr HS; Hannibal, MO; A Cap Choir; Chor; Drama; Ch, Madrigal; Pres, Rainbow; Sch P; Sci C; Bsbl; Bkbl; Ftbl; Sftbl; Interlochen Ntl Mus; Pres A; Sci A; Home Ec Sewing A; *NE Mo St U; Theater.*

RENNER, Lynn Dee
Granite Hills HS; El Cajon, CA (33%-400) *Biola Col; Nurs.*

RENNER, Marcia Jane
Jefferson HS; Rockford, IL (7-390) Band; VP, 4H; NHS; 4H A; Hon Prog; St Scholar; Vlbl; *N Park Col; Nurs.*

RENNINGER, Peggy Lynn
Fremont Sr HS; Fremont, NE (30-530) F-Ed, Sch P; Span C; Q&S A; *Saint Paul Bible Col; Journ.*

RENNOCK,
Michael Joseph William
Beaver Dam HS; Beaver Dam, WI (1-331) Co-Ed, Ann; BS; Chess C; Dbte Tm; FBLA; Pres, SC; VP, Var C; Pres, Jr Cl; Bkbl; Co-Cpt, Cr-Ctry; Tnns; NMS; Val; VofDEM; Director of Operette, Chor; MVP, Cr-Ctry; VP, SC; *Harvard Col; Law.*

RENO, Frank R
Tascosa HS; Amarillo, TX (50%-800) Span C; Ftbl; *Tex A&M U; Vet Med.*

RENSBERGER, Sharon Kay
Goshen HS; Goshen, IN (33-233) Ann; Band; Sch P; Span C; Bkbl; COM; VP, Sunshine Soc; Mus A; Pep Band; Sunshine A; Cheerblock; Shorthand A.

RENTAS, Mireya
Adlai E Stevenson HS; Bronx, NY; Band; COM; Citz A; Math A; Sci A; Type A; *Med.*

RENTZ, Dennis Leslie
Jeff Davis HS; Hazlehurst, GA (33-162) Chess C; FFA; FTA; Pres, 4H; Rptr, Sch P; SC; Y-Tns; Bsbl; Mgr, Ftbl; Tnns; 4H A; I Dare You; WW; Chapter Farmer; *Ga Sou Col; Hist.*

RENTZ, Rhonda Denise
Jeff Davis HS; Hazlehurst, GA; Chor; Drama; FHA; FTA; 4H; Hmrm; Sch P; SC; Tri-HiY; Y-Tns; Sftbl; FHA Degree; Sch Beauty Court; S-T, Bible C; S-T, Church Yth for Christ C; Yth Group Pianist; *Brewton Parker Col; Mus.*

RENTZEL, Mona Linn
Irvington HS; Fremont, CA (10%-500) JV, Bkbl; Tnns; CSF; COM; Citz A; Yth Fel; Interntl C; *Calif St U; Gen.*

REPKA, Suzanne Bozena
Billings W HS; Billings, MT; SC; Bkbl; Ftbl; Sftbl; Swim; Tr; *Mont St U; Forestry.*

REPLOGLE, Alice Irene
Waynoka HS; Waynoka, OK (4-35) Band; FHA; FTA; 4H; St Hon Soc.

REPNOW, Charles Llody
Underwood Pub HS; Underwood, ND (9-22) Ann; Bus C; Chor; Drama; Co-Ed, Sch P; Soccer; Sftbl; Swim; Tnns; Journ A; Swing Choir; *Minot St U; Journ.*

RESETAR, Ruth
Gaithersburg HS; Gaithersburg, MD (10%-452) Chor; NHS; Bkbl; Hockey; Sftbl; *Okla Baptist U.*

RESH, Connie Jo
Essex Comm HS; Essex, IA (12-35) Band; Cpt, Chldr; SC; Tres, Sr Cl; JV, Bkbl; Tr; HQn; Type A.

RESH, Susan Marie
Windom Area HS; Windom, MN (2-138) Pres, Band; Chor; Ensm; GS; Madrigal; NFL; NHS; Sch P; SC; Secy, Sr Cl; Amer Leg A; COM; Citz A; DARGCA; HCt; NMF; VFW Orator Win; VofDEM; Fin, Outst Young Adult; Applicant, NHS Schol; *Bethel Col; Spch Therapy.*

RESINA, Debra Jo
Leto Adult and Comm Sch; Tampa, FL (4-200) FHA; Citz A; Type A.

RESSLER, Christie Ann
St Mary's Central HS; Bismarck, ND (30-180) Band; Drama; Swim; *Bismarck Jr Col; Bus.*

RESZ, Martha Leigh
Raytown S HS; Raytown, MO (20-550) Madrigal; Orch; Tres, SC; Gl C; Ntl Piano Guild; Dist, St Voice Solo A; *Baylor U; Nurs.*

RETALLACK, Cynthia Sue
Scarsdale HS; Scarsdale, NY (5-425) AFS; Cpt, Mjrte; Span C; VP, Yth Fel Group Church; 1st Cl GSct; *Wheaton Col; Psych.*

RETHERFORD, Michael Wayne
Raytown S HS; Raytown, MO (20-583) Dbte Tm; Tres, Drama; Model UN; NFL; NHS; Tres, Spch C; St Stu Congress; UN Council; Spch A; Ntl Stu Cong; Dist Stu Sen; *William Jewell Col.*

RETHMAN, Ann Barbara
Fort Loramie Local HS; Ft Loramie, OH; Bus Mgr, Ann; Band; Pres, FHA; FTA; 4H; Pres, Span C; JV, Bkbl; Tr; God & Country A; HCt; *Col of Mount St Joseph; Nurs.*

RETHORST, Mariann Gail
Wichita HS E; Wichita, KS; Rptr, Sch P; Hon Prog; Golden Key Art A; Outst Achievement; 1st Cl GSct; *Art.*

RETTIG, Ranae Marie
Lourdes Central HS; Nebraska City, NE (2-33) Band; Chor; Mu Alpha Theta; Spch C; Tr; *Med.*

RETTKE, Kesse Heidi
San Pedro HS; San Pedro, CA; Ger C; Citz A; Pres A.

RETZ, Celia Elaine
E Greene Comm HS; Grand Junction, IA (2-34) A-Ed, Ann; Band; Chor; Drama; NHS; Rptr, Sch P; Spch C; Q&S A; *Pre-Law.*

RETZER, Chris Lester
Buena Park HS; Buena Park, CA (60-500) Chess C; Ger C; Span C; Var C; Cr-Ctry; Tr; *Calif St Col; Elec.*

RETZER, James Everett Jr
Calhoun HS; Hardin, IL (1-59) Pres, Chor; Pres, NHS; VP, SC; Pres, Soph Cl; Tr; B Crocker A; NMF; NMS; Sci A; Val; Ntl Sch Choral A; *U of Ill; Engr.*

RETZER, Mary Lou
Steubenville HS; Steubenville, OH (33%-256) A Cap Choir; FTA; Madrigal; Rainbow; Sch P; VP, Span C; Y-Tns; Niki C; Campus Life; *Ky Christian U; Missionary.*

RETZKE, Joan Marie
Manawa Little Wolf HS; Manowa, WI (10%-89) A Cap Choir; Band; CYO; Chor; Community Yth Symph; Hmrm; Madrigal; Orch; Ski C; Spch C; SC; Var C; Sftbl; Tr; Citz A; Vlbl; Hon Orch; Hon Band; Swing Choir; *Stevens Point Col; Mus.*

REUSCHLING, Cathy Ann
Jefferson Area HS; Jefferson, OH (19-213) AFS; S-T, Band; FTA; VP, 4H; Hmrm; NHS; Orch; Tres, SC; Y-Tns; VP, Jr Cl; Stu o-t Mo; *U of Akron; Med.*

REUTER, Ray L
Kuemper HS; Carroll, IA (10-280) Ann; Chor; Fr C; Key C; Madrigal; Monogram; Sci C; Tnns; *St John's U; Acct.*

REVEL, Maryanne Bernadette
Acad of St Aloysius; Jersey City, NJ (18-104) Chldr; Hmrm; NHS; Secy, SC; Mgr, Bkbl; Math A; Media A; Stu Service; *Montclair St Col; Math.*

REVEL, Robert Douglas
El Reno HS; El Reno, OK; Bsbl; Bkbl; *Okla U; Law.*

REVELL, Michael Dean
Luther Burbank HS; Sacramento, CA; Tr; *Elec.*

REVELS, Jackie Ann
Williamston HS; Williamston, NC (24-179) BC; Drama; Pres, FHA; FTA; Monogram; SC; Drum Major, Color Guard; Statistician, Bsbl & Bkbl; *Meredith Col; Hist.*

REVIS, Donna L
Hubbard HS; Hubbard, OH; Span C; Tri-HiY; Octagon C; Vlbl; *Milligan Col; Drama.*

REVIS, Robert William
Sylva-Webster HS; Sylva, NC (50-185) Band; Drama; Ski C; Span C; *W Carolina Col; Biol.*

REVORD, Janie Marie
Marillac HS; Northfield, IL (14-222) Hmrm; NHS; SC; Citz A; Opt A; St Scholar; WW; *St Mary's Col of Notre Dame; Sociology.*

REY, Elizabeth Ann
L A Webber HS; Lyndonville, NY (4-68) Ann; GS; Fin, Jr Miss Pagent; NHS; SC; Var C; Secy, Jr Cl; Secy, Soph Cl; Bkbl; Cpt, Soccer; Sftbl; COM; HCt; Yth Fel; MVP, Vlbl; On the Go; Coaches A; Sibleys Art As; WW; *Nazareth Col; Art.*

REY, Gladys Rosa
Los Angeles Baptist HS; Sepulveda, CA; *Whitworth Col; Special Ed.*

REYERING, Sally Ann
St Ursaul Acad; Cincinnati, OH (1-84) Hmrm; Lit Mag; NHS; S-T, Sodality; SC; Tnns; Alg A; Bio A; Chem A; Hon Prog; Vlbl; *Med.*

REYES, Angeles Margarita
Centro Oportunidad Educativas B HS; Guaynabo, PR; Chldr; FHA; COM; *U of Puerto Rico; Social Worker.*

REYES, James
Robinson Sch; Santurce, PR (1-52) Band; Hmrm; Math C; NHS; VP, SC; JV, Bkbl; Cpt, Cr-Ctry; JV, Tr; COM; Hon Prog; NEDT; Math Fair Win; *Harvard U; Engr.*

REYES, Judy Ann
Cupertino HS; Cupertino, CA (45-697) All Amer Yth; Band; Pres, Fr C; Pres, Soph Cl; Ftbl; CSF; COM; Most Out; Gym; Superintendent's HR; *UC Berkeley; Pre-Med.*

REYES, Leticia
St Augustine Sch; Laredo, TX; CYO; City Conf; Span C; Spch C; Hon Prog; VofDEM; Cooking A; *LJC; Policewoman.*

REYES, Mary
Dra Cadilla de Martinez HS; Arecibo, PR (76-480) *Universidad de Puerto Rico; Medicina.*

REYES, Ramon E
Centro Oportunidad Educativas HS; Guaynabo, PR; *Regional Bayamon Col; Tegnology Electronic.*

REYES, Ruiz Lydia
Dra Maria Cadilla de Martinez HS; Arecibo, PR (23-480) FBLA; ARC; Most Out; *Colegio Regional; Contabilidad.*

REYES, Susana
Parlier HS; Parlier, CA; Chor; FHA; Tres, Hmrm; CSF.

REYNERTSON, Richard Paul
Laurens-Marathon Comm Sch; Laurens, IA (15-76) Band; Ensm; Ger C; JV, Golf; Wrest; Citz A; Hon Prog; Yth Fel.

REYNOLDS, Amy Louise
Cleveland HS; Cleveland, TN (40-250) Bus C; Chldr; Drama; Fr C; FBLA; FTA; Hmrm; Bus Mgr, Sch P; Spch C; SC; Tri-HiY; Swim; Tnns; Journ A; Spch A; Art A's; *Auburn U; Art Ed.*

REYNOLDS, Amy Louise
Spartanburg HS; Spartanburg, SC (10%-800) Band; BC; Ensm; Fr C; Bus Mgr, Hmrm; Orch; Hon Prog; Yth Fel; Jr Hs, Hon 'E'; Jr West Reg Band; 5 Sup Ratings, St Solo & Ensm Con.

REYNOLDS, Anne Louise
Sidney Lanier HS; Montgomery, AL; Drama; FTA; Co-Ch, ARC; Rptr, Sch P; Span C; Spch C; NEDT; Spch A; Acteens; Qn Regent; *Judson Col; Drama.*

REYNOLDS, Arlene Mitsu
Mililani HS; Mililani Town, HI (103-266) Secy, Drama; Eng A; *Leeward Comm Col.*

REYNOLDS, Barbara Ann
Laurel Park HS; Martinsville, VA (21-173) Chor; Drama; Fr C; FBLA; 4H; 4H A; Spch A; Mus A; *Howard U; Bio.*

REYNOLDS, Beverly Renea
Bullock Co HS; Union Springs, AL (3-150) FBLA; Hmrm; Rptr, NHS; Co-Ed, Sch P; SC; Secy, Sr Cl; COM; Hist A; HCt; Hon Prog; Sci A; Service, A's, Schol Achv, A's; *U of Ala; Acct.*

REYNOLDS, Brad Alan
Wilmington Sr HS; Wilmington, OH (25%-300) 4H; PA; *Liberty Baptist Col; Radio TV Communications.*

REYNOLDS, Bradley M
Rutledge HS; Rutledge, TN (10%-125) Chem C; Span C; Ftbl; *Walters St Jr Col; Bus.*

REYNOLDS, Carolyn Rae
Manila HS; Manila, UT (2-19) Band; Drama; Tnns; Alg A; COM; Math A; Band A.

REYNOLDS, Cedric
Compton HS; Compton, CA (17-800) NHS; JV, Bsbl; JV, Bkbl; CSF; COM; Opt Out Tn; *U of Calif; Adm Stu.*

REYNOLDS, Colettia
Dilce Combs Mem HS; Jeff, KY (1-156) BC; *Sci.*

REYNOLDS, Dale Matthew
Panhandle HS; Panhandle, TX (8-65) Band; BS; Tres, FTA; VP, Span C; Pres, SC; Pres, Jr Cl; Bkbl; Co-Cpt, Ftbl; Golf; Alg A; Cl Fav; *Baylor U; Bus.*

REYNOLDS, Danny Eugene
Ilion Central HS; Ilion, NY (14-176) AFS; F-Ed, Ann; S-T, BC; Chor; City Conf; Drama; Pres, Fr C; Monogram; NHS; Bus Mgr, Sch P; Sci C; SC; Pres, Y-Tns; Mgr, Bkbl; Soccer; Tr; Cl Fav; HCt; Hon Prog; Sci A; Yth Fel; Fin, JC Outst Tn o-t Yr; *U of Miss; Vet Med.*

REYNOLDS, Darlene Yvonne
Thayer R-2 HS; Thayer, MO; Band; BC; Chldr; FHA; Fin, Jr Miss Pagent; Cpt, Mjrte; Sch P; Bkbl; Sftbl; Tr; Pres A; MVP, Vlbl; Phys Ed A; *Phys Ed.*

REYNOLDS, Debbie Lynne
Field Kindley Mem HS; Coffeyville, KS; Chldr; FHA; 4H; Span C; 120 C; *Ozark Bible Col; Christian Ed.*

REYNOLDS, Donna Susan
W J Woodham HS; Pensacola, FL (32-530) JV, Chldr; Chor; FBLA; Ger C; Fin, Jr Miss Pagent; NHS; Co-Ed, Sch P; Exchange C, Home Ec, A's; Am Experien, Dist Shorthand, A's; *Harding Col; Bible.*

REYNOLDS, Douglas Oxton
Beverly HS; Beverly, MA (34-530) Order/Arrow; Co-Cpt, Bsbl; MVP, Bkbl; Cr-Ctry; NMS; Yth Fel; Eagle Sct; Ind Ins Agents of Mass, 1000 Schol; *Syracuse U; Insurance Mgt.*

REYNOLDS, Grady Edward II
Dupont Sr HS; Hermitage, TN (33%-375) *Tenn Tech U; Bus.*

REYNOLDS, Ingrid Ann
Page HS; Greensboro, NC; Civinettes C; Pres, Yth Church Group; *Converse Col; Sociology.*

REYNOLDS, Ivory Vertrina
Arlington HS; Indianapolis, IN (33%-420) Band; FNA; Hmrm; Mjrte; Secy, Span C; Hon Prog; HR; Human Relations A; SC A; *Howard U; Law.*

REYNOLDS, James David
Cross Plains HS; Cross Plains, TX (5-49) Dbte Tm; Drama; Tres, FFA; Pres, 4H; Hmrm; NFL; NHS; Spch C; Pres, SC; Thes; Pres, Jr Cl; Spch A; FFA A; *Law Enforcement.*

REYNOLDS, Jane Lynn
Pamlico Comm Sch; Washington, NC (5-12) Ann; Chor; Sch P; VP, Jr Cl; *St Andrews Col; Ed.*

REYNOLDS, Janie Sue
Thayer R II HS; Thayer, MO (25%-70) Ann; Band; BC; Chldr; Chor; Ensm; FHA; Madrigal; Sftbl; COM; Vlbl; Attd, Miss Merry Christmas; Secy, CFC; *SMS; Home Ec.*

REYNOLDS, Jean Marie
Walton Central HS; Walton, NY (15-145) VP, FFA; Citz A; Hist A.

REYNOLDS, Joe David
Blacksburg HS; Blacksburg, SC; Drama; Pres, FFA; 4H; Tres, Hmrm; Rptr, Sch P; Spch C; Ftbl; Sftbl; Tr; Journ A; Best Actor; Drama A; *Navy.*

REYNOLDS, Julie Anna
Bethel-Tate HS; Bethel, OH (6-132) Fr C; NHS; Sch Achieve Tm; Co-Cpt, Bkbl; Pres A; Star Student; Mgr, Vlbl; All Star, Bkbl.

REYNOLDS, Julie Melanie
John T Hoggard HS; Wilmington, NC; Band; All St Symph Band; *Mus.*

REYNOLDS, Kevin Micheal
Petaluma Sr HS; Petaluma, CA; FFA; JV, Cr-Ctry; Ftbl; Tr; *Architecture.*

REYNOLDS, Kimberly J
Robert E Lee HS; Montgomery, AL; Band; Ensm; Thes; Tr; COM; NEDT; Pres A; Tres, Yth Group; Yth Alive C; Gym; Hospital Vol; Speedball; Mus Apprec C; All Co & St Bands; Hist C; Phys Fitness Tm.

REYNOLDS, Linda Louise
Pattonville Sr HS; Maryland Heights, MO (16-884) Pres, AFS; GS; Secy, NHS; Secy, SC; Hist A; Hon Prog; WW; Acteens; AFS Exchange Stu; *William Jewell Col; Mission Work.*

REYNOLDS, Mark Robert
Cottage Grove HS; Cottage Grove, OR (13-240) Band; Hmrm; NHS; SC; Var C; MVP, Ftbl; MVP, Tr; Elk A; *George Fox Col.*

REYNOLDS, Mark Wayen
Field Kindley HS; Coffeyville, KS; Ftbl; Tr.

REYNOLDS, Mary Lois
Virgie HS; Virgie, KY; FHA; FTA; SC; *Eastern U; Psych.*

REYNOLDS, Melinda Marcel
Christian Co HS; Hopkinsville, KY (10-370) BC; Pres, FFA; 4H; Hmrm; Ch, NHS; SC; MLS; NEDT; Spch A; Ch, Tres, Region Tres, FFA; *Brigham Young U; Eng.*

REYNOLDS, Michael Alan
Washington Co HS; Springfield, KY; DECA; *E Ky U; Acct.*

REYNOLDS, Monty Weldon
Azle HS; Azle, TX; Chem C; Span C; Bkbl; Hist A.

REYNOLDS, Myletia
Dilce Combs HS; Jeff, KY (6-110) BC.

REYNOLDS, Pamela Ruth
Grand Prairie HS; Grand Prairie, TX (15%-450) FTA; Sup, Dallas Mus Teacher's Assn; UIL, 1st Pl Medal; Sup, Guild Auditing; *N Tex St U; Mus.*

REYNOLDS, Reid Alan
S Grand Prairie HS; Grand Prairie, TX (15%-350) Tn Jury; Outst Newspaper Boy; *Baylor U; Bus.*

REYNOLDS, Ricky Joe
Bokchito HS; Bokchito, OK (5-24) Ed, Ann; Bus C; Math C; Ed, Sch P; Span C; Hist A; Hon Prog; Journ A; MLS; Sal; Type A; Val; Amer Lit A; Eng Grammar A; Bookkeeping A; General Bus A; *Southeastern St U; Acct.*

REYNOLDS, Rita Frances
Destrehan HS; Destrehan, LA (6-168) BC; *LSU; Social Working.*

REYNOLDS, Robert Alan
Purcell HS; Cincinnati, OH (10-225) A Cap Choir; Band; Orch; SC; Tres, Soph Cl; Swim; 1st Pl, 1 Yr HS Schol.

REYNOLDS, Ronald Wade
Sam Houston Sr HS; Houston, TX; VP, Hmrm; NHS; Bsbl.

REYNOLDS, Sandra Lynn
Penn Hills Sr HS; Pittsburgh, PA (20%-1150) ARC; Tr; *Sci.*

REYNOLDS, Shawn Andrew
Valparaiso Sr HS; Valparaiso, IN (64-464) Pres, FTA; Ftbl; JV, Tr; *Valparaiso U; Eng.*

REYNOLDS, Sheila Ann
Columbia HS; Columbia, NC (10-67) Ann; Band; BC; Chor; FBLA; FTA; 4H; Lit Mag; Mjrte; Sch P; SC; Tri-HiY; 4H A; Masonic A; Marshall; Hon Graduate; WW; WW, Mus; *Freewill Baptist Bible Col; Mus.*

REYNOLDS, Sheila Jean
Englewood Sr HS; Jacksonville, FL; FBLA; Inter-Club Coun; Yth Fel; VP, DECA; 1st Pl, Dist Comp, Gen Merchand; *Jones Col; Fashion Merchandising.*

REYNOLDS, Timothy Lynn
Martinsville HS; Martinsville, VA (65-250) Band; Chor; Drama; SC; *Central Wesleyan Col; Elem Ed.*

REYNOLDS, Violet Renee
Palm Beach Gardens HS; Palm Beach Gardens, FL; Bus C; Hmrm; Ntl Yth Conf; SC; Arch; Bsbl; Ftbl; Sftbl; Tnns; Tr; B Crocker A; Citz A; Cl Fav; Delta Sigma Theta A; Ntl Achv Schol; Pres A; Attendant A; Tr & Field A; *FAMU.*

REYNOSO, Francisco Javier
Woodlake Union HS; Woodlake, CA (4-120) Ann; Drama; Sch P; CSF; *Humboldt St U; Bus Adm.*

RHAME, William Van
Texas City HS; Texas City, TX (25-600) FFA; NHS; Bsbl; Ftbl; Tr; VP, FCA; *Baylor U.*

RHEA, Brian Charles
Cubberley HS; Palo Alto, CA (20%-324) Rptr, Ann; Band; Community Yth Symph; Ensm; Order/ Arrow; JV, Bkbl; Ch, Yth Comm; VP, Adventure Unlimited Tn Coun; Savoyards; *Foothill Col; Communications.*

RHEA, David Keith
Milburn HS; Milburn, OK (3-18) All Amer Yth; Chem C; Chor; Dbte Tm; Drama; Pres, 4H; Math C; NHS; Sch Achieve Tm; Sch P; Sci C; Var C; Pres, Sr Cl; VP, Jr Cl; Bsbl; Bkbl; Citz A; Cl Fav; Gov Honor Prog; 4H A; MLS; Most Out; *Wildlife Mgr.*

RHEA, Stacy Denise
Robert E Lee HS; Midland, TX (76-649) FHA; NHS; JA A; Art A; Co Ch, Art C; Cpt, OEA; YOE; *Midland Jr Col; Art.*

RHEA, Teresa Carol
Holston HS; Knoxville, TN (23-209) FHA; NHS; Y-Tns; Amer Leg A; ROTC A; PTSA Pin & Sch Ltr Win; *Wildlife & Fisheries Sci.*

RHEA, Tony Joseph
John Marshall HS; Indianapolis, IN; Band; Bsbl; *Southwestern Christian Col.*

RHEE, Anna
Teaneck HS; Teaneck, NJ; A Cap Choir; Lit Mag; Hon Prog; Yth Fel; Gold Cup Win; Ntl Fed of Mus C; *Harvard U; Law.*

RHEE, Deborah S
The Masters Sch; Dobbs Ferry, NY; Sch P; Yth Fel; Ch, Interntl C; Master's Glee C.

RHEE, Roy Buk
Reseda HS; Reseda, CA (1-750) Chess C; Math C; Pres, NHS; Sch Achieve Tm; Sch P; SC; InterAct C; Swim; JV, Tnns; CSF; Citz A; Hon Prog; Math A; Spelling A; *UCLA; Pre-Med.*

RHEUDASIL, Penny Reene
Lewisville HS; Lewisville, TX (30-361) FHA; NHS; Sch P; SC; Pres, Sr Cl; S-T, Jr Cl; Bkbl; MVP, Tr; Beauty; HQn; Yth Fel; FCA o-t Yr; Stu Action Committee; Best All Around; *Tex Tech U; Med.*

RHEW, Deborah Lynn
Eastern Guilford HS; Gibsonville, NC (10-164) Chor; Drama; Ensm; Fr C; FHA; French NHS; Hmrm; Tres, NFL; NHS; Co-Ed, Sch P; SC; B Crocker A; Nom, Gov Sch; *U of NC; Math.*

RHINE, Debbie Lou
Salina Central HS; Salina, KS (11-300) A Cap Choir; Pres, Bus C; JV, Chldr; Chor; Ensm; Fin, FBLA; Pres, Hmrm; Semi-Fin, Bkbl; Sftbl; COM; Spch A; Vlbl; Stu of Yr, DECA; *Bethany Col; Phys Ed.*

RHINEHARDT, Darren Gerald
Tascosa HS; Amarillo, TX; Dbte Tm; Drama; Tres, Spch C; Pres, Thes; Sr Cl; S-T, Jr Cl; Bsbl; Cpt, Swim; MVP, Tnns; Citz A; Cl Fav; ROTC A; Spch A; Choir A.

RHINEHART, Ruth Ann
St Mary's Acad; Englewood, CO (2-58) Bus Mgr, Ann; CYO; Ch, Chldr; Chor; Hmrm; Lat C; Tres, NHS; Ski C; Span C; Span NHS; SC; Var C; Pres, Sr Cl; Tres, Jr Cl; Tres, Sodl; Cl; Bkbl; Tnns; Tr; Citz A; DARGCA; Hon Prog; NMS; Vlbl; Good Sportsmanship A.

RHOADES, Bobby Evans II
Booker HS; Sarasota, FL; Shop A; President's A; Mus A; *Manatee Jr Col; Elec.*

RHOADES, Kathy Jo
Heritage Christian Acad; Ravenswood, WV (6-58) Band; Chldr; Chor; Dbte Tm; Ensm; S-T, SC; Sftbl; Vlbl; *Liberty Baptist Col; Elem Ed.*

RHOADES, Patrice Annetta
Parkway Prog Beta HS; Philadelphia, PA; Dbte Tm; Ch, Yrbk Comm; Tutor; *U of Pittsburgh; Pre-Med.*

RHOADES, Perian
York HS; York, NE (33%-134) A Cap Choir; F-Ed, Ann; Chor; SC; Bkbl; Golf; Sftbl; Swim; Jobs Daughters; *Nebr Wesleyan U; Counseling.*

RHOADES, Randall Bruce
Asheville Christian Acad; Asheville, NC (7-9) Ann; Order/Arrow; ARC; COM; Order/Arrow A; ARC A; Eagle Sct; *SW Tech Col; Environmental Sci.*

RHOADES, Regina Ann
Bellmont HS; Decatur, IN (52-234) A Cap Choir; HR; *Anderson Col.*

RHOADES, Carmen Denise
Richland HS; Ft Worth, TX; Band; Chldr; FHA; Sftbl; Presidential A; *Baylor U; Special Ed.*

RHOADS, Jeffrey Flynn
Robert E Lee HS; Midland, TX (825-950) Chldr; NHS; 4 Point Grade Avg, Soph; *Harding Christian Col; Elec.*

RHOADS, Kenny Claude
Cache HS; Cache, OK (2-65) VP, Band; Ensm; 4H; Mod Mus Mas; Span C; Pres, SC; VP, Soph Cl; COM; Citz A; Curator A; Masonic A; Pres A; Yth Fel; Yth Leg; SW Okla Hon Band; Band Top 10; Superior, Dist Solo; *Okla St U; Psych.*

RHOADS, Linda Kaye
NE HS; N Little Rock, AR (95-450) AFS; BC; Chor; FBLA; Sci C; Span C; Chamber of Comm A; Special Mus A's; *Okla St U; Bus Adm.*

RHOADS, Robert James
Cache HS; Cache, OK (2-46) VP, Band; BC; Tres, 4H; Hmrm; NHS; SC; Var C; VP, Sr Cl; Bsbl; Co-Cpt, Ftbl; Tr; COM; 4H A; Sal; Star Student; Co-Scholar; Yth Fel; WW; Secy of St A; *U of Okla; Hist.*

RHOADS, Teri Lyn
Traverse City Sr HS; Traverse City, MI; Band; Chor; Drama; VP, 4H; Thes; Tr; 4H A; *Central Mich U.*

RHODA, Devin Todd
Centerville HS; Centerville, IN (10%-160) Chess C; Drama; VP, Fr C; Hmrm; Order/Arrow; VP, Span C; SC; Var C; VP, Soph Cl; Cpt, Cr-Ctry; Cpt, Tr; Hist A; Hon Prog; Order/Arrow A; Pres A; Yth Fel; Yth Leg; Outst Male, Model Legislator; *Notre Dame U; Pol Sci.*

RHODEN, Alan Joseph
John F Kennedy HS; La Palma, CA; JV, Bkbl.

RHODEN, Donis Ray
Tivy HS; Kerrville, TX; VP, 4H; JETS; Mgr, Bkbl; Mgr, Ftbl; Mgr, Tr; 4H A; *Tex A&M U; Archt.*

RHODES, Angela Maria
Westside HS; Anderson, SC (24-305) NHS; FSA; *Tri-County Tech Col; Secy Sci.*

RHODES, Catherine Marie
Natrona Co HS; Casper, WY (122-550) Band; Chor; 4H; F-Ed, Sch P; 4H A.

RHODES, Gail Yvonne
Buena HS; Sierra Vista, AZ (173-505) Chor; Hmrm; Mjrte; ARC; Mgr, Tr; COM; Citz A; Masonic A; Type A; NCO Schol A; St Fin, VICA; *N Ariz U; Nurs.*

RHODES, Jacqueline
Simon Grate HS; Philadelphia, PA (25%-600) 4H; Journ A; *U of Pa; Journ.*

RHODES, Janice
Wellston HS; Wellston, OH; Band; Chldr; 4H; Mjrte; COM; 4H A; Most Out; Poet A; Sal; *Ohio U; Spch Therapy.*

RHODES, Jim Leroy
Northbrook Sr HS; Houston, TX; Chor; Bkbl; Fin, Cr-Ctry; Ftbl; Fin, Sftbl; MVP, Swim; Fin, Tr; Fin, Swim; *U of Houston; Phys Ed.*

RHODES, John Stephen
Robert E Lee HS; Tyler, TX (10%-650) Lat C; Ftbl; Tr; VP, Ltrmans Assn.

RHODES, Laura Lee
Morristown W HS; Morristown, TN; BC; FHA; ARC; F-Ed, Sch P; Span C; Tri-HiY; Amer Leg A; Art C; *Carson Newman Col.*

RHODES, Lisa Christine
Strong Vincent HS; Erie, PA (81-213) Tres, Bus C; City Conf; Hmrm; COM; Math A; Yth Fel; Hon Men Graduate; Piano Cert of A; Cert of Apprec, Project Share; *Mercyhurst Col; Secy Sci.*

RHODES, Nancy Annette
Abilene HS; Abilene, TX; Tri-HiY; Tnns; COM; Phys Ed.

RHODES, Phyllis Diane
St Elmo HS; St Elmo, IL (14-46) Ed, Ann; Band; S-T, Chor; Ensm; Pres, 4H; Mjrte; NHS; Sch P; Span C; SC; Pres, Sr Cl; Tr; COM; Citz A; 4H A; Hon Prog; I Dare You; Pres, Lib C; Pres, MYF; Vlbl; Sch Musical; Yth to Wash Essay Contest Win; All-St Jazz Choir; *Eastern Ill U; Home Ec.*

RHODES, Rebecca Lynn
Christian Sch of Fine Arts 2; Bradenton, FL (2-5) Pres, A Cap Choir; Ch, Ann; Chor; Hmrm; Sch Achieve Tm; Co-Ed, Sch P; Pres, SC; Pres, Sr Cl; COM; Cl Fav; God & Country A; Star Student; Yth Fel.

RHODES, Robin Joy
Ralph L Fike HS; Wilson, NC (85-400) Drama; Key C; NHS; Sci C; Health Careers C; *Meredith Col; Nurs.*

RHODES, Russell Scott
Paris HS; Paris, TX (50-250) Band; BS; Pres, Chor; Pres, FTA; Ger C; HiY; Secy, Key C; Madrigal; NHS; Best All Around Stu; FTA Distinguished Service A; Outst Choir; *Paris Jr Col; Mus.*

RHODES, Sabrina Carole
E Davidson HS; Thomasville, NC (5%-224) Co-Ed, Ann; BC; Hmrm; Pres, Span C; Mgr, Bkbl; Tnns; Scholastically Exceptional; *Meredith Col; Mus.*

RHODES, Sharon
John F Kennedy HS; Bronx, NY; Co Cpt, Badminton; *Law.*

RHODES, Steven Robert
Exeter Pub Sch; Exeter, NE (10%-33) Band; Chor; Secy, FFA; Sci C; Spch C; Bkbl; Ftbl; COM; Yth Fel; *U of Nebr; Agr.*

RHODES, Teresa Annette
Browstown HS; Brownstown, IL (7-40) Chor; Fr C; Pres, FHA; Sch Achieve Tm; Sch P; Pres, SC; B Crocker A; Cl Fav; HQn; HCt; MLS; *Kaskaskia Jr Col; Mus.*

RHODES, Tina Diane
Tate HS; Pensacola, FL; Co-Cpt, Chldr; Chor; Drama; 4H; NHS; SC; MLS; Most Out; *Eng.*

RHYNE, James Michael
W Lincoln HS; Lincolnton, NC (10-150) Chem C; Fr C; Ftbl; Tr; Wrest; Church Yth Coun; Top 5% in Nation SAT & PSAT Tests; *Wake Forest U; Lit.*

RHYNER, George Anthony
Newman HS; Wausau, WI; Band; BS; Math C; NHS; Sci C; Ftbl; Cpt, Wrest; Math A; NMF; Opt Out Tn; Rotary A; Sci A; Pres, Explorers; Explorer A; *Marquette U; Engr.*

RHYNES, Stephanie Yolanda
George Washington HS; Los Angeles, CA (10%-850) Chor; Hmrm; Pres, InterAct C; Pres, InterClub Coun; Sch Achieve Tm; Span C; SC; Sftbl; Bank Of Amer A; CSF; Cl Fav; God & Country A; I Dare You; JA A; MLS; Spch A; Yth Foundation; Acad Advancement A; *UCLA; Sci.*

RIBAR, Louis John
Northrop HS; Fort Wayne, IN (3-680) Rptr, Ann; Band; Fr C; Rptr, Sch P; SC; Pres, Soph Cl; Tr; Citz A; Hon Prog; Math A; Opt A; Citz Champ, High Jump; McMillen A; Top 10 Schol; *Photojourn.*

RIBAS, David Scott
Knob Noster HS; Knob Noster, MO (40-118) Sci A; *Central Mo St U.*

RIBBLE, Lorri Jo
Ogallala HS; Ogallala, NE (10%-170) Chor; Drama; Span NHS; JV, Bkbl; Mgr, Ftbl; Tr; Yth Fel; *U of Nebr; Psych.*

RIBEIRO, Monica Aquiar
St Cecilia Acad; Nashville, TN (4-55) Ed, Ann; CYO; Chor; NHS; Rptr, Sch P; Sodality; SC; *Vanderbilt Col; Psych.*

RIBOT, Gracy
Jose de Diego HS; Mayaguez, PR; Dbte Tm; Drama; C; Sci C; *UPR at Mayaguez; Pre-Med.*

RICCIO, Dolores Ann
Archbishop Kennedy HS; Conshohocken, PA (2-161) CYO; Math C; Pres, NHS; Span C; COM; Hon Prog; K of C A; *Penn St U; Pre-Med.*

RICE, Amy Lauren
Clifton Forge HS; Clifton Forge, VA; Band; Chor; 4H; Hmrm; SC; Tri-HiY; Sftbl; Tr; Vlbl; Chaplain, Tri Hi Y; *Emory And Henry Col; Special Ed.*

RICE, Belinda Elizabeth
Westwood HS; Atlanta, GA (15-130) A Cap Choir; Band; Chor; Pres, 4H; Hmrm; Madrigal; SC; COM; Citz A; 4H A; All St Choir; WW; Ga Baptist Hospital Sch of Nurs; Nurs.

RICE, Brenda Lynn
Clay Sr HS; Oregon, OH; Chor; Rainbow; ARC; COM; Citz A; Yth Fel; Hospital Vol A; Toledo U; Mental Health.

RICE, Christine Lynn
Nucla HS; Nucla, CO (3-78) Band; Model UN; Secy, NHS; Pres, Jr Cl; Secy, Soph Cl; JV, Bkbl; Citz A; Crisco A; 4H A; Hist A; Masonic A; Most Out; Regent Schol; Pres, VP, Secy, 4-H C; All St Hon Bnd; Western St Hon Bnd; All St Hon Band; Top o-t Nation Hon Band; U of Northern Colo; Elem Ed.

RICE, Cynthia Renee
Mtn View HS; Mtn View, AR (18-60) Rptr, Band; Pres, BC; FHA; Rptr, FTA; GS; 4H; Rptr, SC; 4H A; Sci A; Bicentennial Yth Ral; Outst Bicentennial Activities; U of Central Ark; Bio.

RICE, Dale Emmett Jr
Crestview HS; Crestview, FL; VP, Key C; SC; Var C; VP, Sr Cl; Bsbl; Bkbl; Co-Cpt, Ftbl; Cpt, Ftbl; U of Ala; Law.

RICE, David A
Cumberland Valley HS; Mechanicsburg, PA (4-564) Band; Community Yth Symph; Math C; NHS; Orch; Sci C; Soccer; Bausch & Lomb A; COM; Pa St U; Biophysics.

RICE, David Byron
Newburgh Free Acad; Newburgh, NY (41-850) Drama; Key C; NHS; A-Ed, Sch P; Regent Schol; NML; Columbia Col; Journ.

RICE, Deborah Draves
Hershey Sr HS; Hershey, PA (40-265) Cpt, Band; Chor; Pres, Drama; S-T, Fr C; Hmrm; VP, NHS; A-Ed, Sch P; SC; Bkbl; Tr; Yth Fel; Elem Ed.

RICE, Delores Jean
Motley HS; Columbus, MS (8-101) Band; FHA; Rptr, Sch P; Sci C; Sci A; Valley St Col.

RICE, Delphime
Motley HS; Columbus, MS (2-101) Band; Sci C; Spch C; Tri-HiY; Pres, Soph Cl; Beauty; COM; Hist A; Hon Prog; MUW; Fashion Designer.

RICE, Donna Marie
Patrick Henry HS; Roanoke, VA (111-500) Pres, FBLA; ARC; Pres, Church Yth Group; Drill Tm; Va Western Comm Col; Secretarial Sci.

RICE, Edwin Stewart
Scott Preparatory Sch; Opelika, AL (5%-25) VP, BC; SC; Cpt, Bkbl; Cpt, Ftbl; Cpt, Golf; Cpt, Swim; COM; MVP, Bkbl; Auburn U; Construction.

RICE, Elizabeth Ann
Warrensburg HS; Warrensburg, MO; A Cap Choir; Band; Chor; Tres, Fr C; Orch; Span C; Type A; Ed, Church Yth Paper; Central Mo St U; Spec Ed.

RICE, Elizabeth Ann
Woodrow Wilson; Dallas, TX (59-292) Chldr; Chor; ARC; Sftbl; Cl Fav; HQn; HCt; 'B' HR; Fin, Cl Fav; Fin, HQn; Fin, Homecoming Ct; Baylor U; Special Ed.

RICE, Eugene Allbritton Jr
Warrior HS; Warrior, AL (25%-63) Bus Mgr, Ann; 4H; Pres, InterClub Coun; Rptr, Sch P; Bus Mgr, Sci C; SC; Bkbl; Ftbl; 4H A; Journ A; Sci A; All Co, Ftbl; 1st Pl, St Poetry Soc; WW; 1st, St, Ntl, Tn Talent Poetry; U of Ala; Bus Adm.

RICE, Frank Oliver
East Central HS; Hurley, MS (10-115) BC; Var C; Ftbl; Tr; U of Miss; Radio TV Broadcasting.

RICE, Hughes Hamilton III
Apollo HS; Owensboro, KY; BC; Hmrm; Span C; SC; Cpt, Swim; Tnns; VP, Young Democrats; WW; Young Historians; MVP, Swim; Presidential Clrm For Young Amer; US Military Acad.

RICE, James A
Amos Alonzo Stagg HS; Palos Hills, IL (85-590) JV, Golf; Architectural Engr.

RICE, Janet Elizabeth
Denison HS; Denison, TX (10%-340) Chor; FTA; Hmrm; NHS; Ch, Sci C; VP, Span C; SC; Y-Tns; Tr; WW; Runnerup, Most Humorous; Ntl HS Bio Hon Soc; Grayson Co Col; Lib Arts.

RICE, Janet Lynn
Rio Americano HS; Sacramento, CA (75-370) NHS; Sftbl; Calif St U; Phys Ed.

RICE, Jennifer Lynn
Peninsula HS; Gig Harbor, WA (8-350) Model UN; Tres, Span C; Past Worthy Advisor, Rainbow Girls; Sunday Sch Teacher; Acolyte; U of Wash.

RICE, Jenny Sue
Graham HS; St Paris, OH; Secy, Bus C; Chor; FHA; 4H; Sftbl; 4H A; Mt Vernon Col; Pre-Law.

RICE, Joan Marie
Springfield HS; Springfield, MI (13-116) Band; NHS; Tnns; Tr; HR A; Band Festival A; Pep Band A; Solo Ensm A.

RICE, John Burton
Newburgh Free Acad; Newburgh, NY (17-1000) Band; Math C; NHS; UMYF; David B McKeever A.

RICE, Kathleen Sue
Austin HS; Austin, MN (27-539) Band; Chor; 4H; NHS; Swim; 4H A; NMS; Westmar Col; Sociology.

RICE, Kathy Ann
Welch HS; Welch, WV (33%-200) Band; FHA; Mjrte; Orch; Rainbow; Sch P; Tnns; Tr; All Co, Jr HS Band; Home Ec C; All Co, Sr HS Band; GSct; All Area, Band; VP, Yth Group; Pep C; Med.

RICE, Kimberly Jean
Redmond HS; Redmond, OR (35-250) Co-Ch, AFS; Chor; 4H; Hmrm; Secy, InterAct C; NHS; Ski C; SC; COM; Chldr Mascot; Campfire Girls, 10 Yrs; Oreg St U; Ed.

RICE, Kimberly Joan
Redmond HS; Redmond, OR (34-250) AFS; Chor; 4H; Hmrm; Secy, InterAct C; NHS; Bus Mgr, Sch P; Ski C; SC; COM; Mascot; Highest A, Camp Fire Girls; Oreg St U; Teaching.

RICE, Lee Ann
Robert W Groves HS; Garden City, GA; Chor; Ensm.

RICE, Lois Earlene
Skyline HS; Dallas, TX; Chor; Ensm; Unity A; St Assn of Health Occupations Stu; W Tex St U; Psych.

RICE, Lorie Ann
Southwest HS; St Louis, MO; Chor; Math C; COM; Citz A; Hon Prog; NHS; Most Out; Bookkeeping A; Running A; Oral Roberts U; Bus.

RICE, Mark Edward
Boyd Co HS; Ashland, KY (26-315) BS; Key C; SC; Bkbl; Ftbl; MVP, Tr; HCt; Liberty Baptist Col; Bus.

RICE, Mary Beth
Aropahoe HS; Littleton, CO; A Cap Choir; Band; Chldr; Key C; SC; Swtht; GSct; VP, Pep C; Morehead St U; Counseling.

RICE, Michael Anthony
Duncanville HS; Duncanville, TX (50%-535) Model UN; JV, Ftbl.

RICE, Michael Paul
Herbert H Dow HS; Midland, MI; Tr; Wrest.

RICE, Michele
Nucla HS; Nucla, CO (1-70) Band; Chldr; Mjrte; NHS; VP, Jr Cl; Hist A; Masonic A; Soil Conservation Essay A; WAA, Rainbow Girls; U of Colo; Med.

RICE, Patricia Jane
Oak Grove HS; Oak Grove, MO (24-111) AFS; Band; Chor; Ensm; Fr C; FHA; FTA; Madrigal; SC; Sftbl; Central Mo St U; Art.

RICE, Paul Norman
Clifton Forge HS; Clifton Forge, VA; Band; 4H; HiY; Hmrm; Key C; SC; Mgr, Bkbl; Mgr, Ftbl; Tr; Wrest; Yth Fel; Art.

RICE, Rebecca Ernestine
Patrick Henry HS; Roanoke, VA; JV, Chldr.

RICE, Ricky Lee
Wilson HS; Wilson, TX (3-27) Pres, Band; BS; Pres, FFA; Tres, Sr Cl; Pres, Jr Cl; Secy, Soph Cl; Bkbl; Cpt, Ftbl; Golf; Tr; Citz A; Cl Fav; HKg; Yth Foundation A; FHA Beau; Family Life, Outst Eng, A's; Outst Agr, A; Tex A&M U; Agr Ed.

RICE, Robert Edwin
Andress HS; El Paso, TX (49-524) Math C; Order/Arrow; Order/Arrow A; Nuclear Physics.

RICE, Ronda Loyce
Watson Chapel HS; Pine Bluff, AR (25-250) Ann; BC; NHS; Rptr, Sch P; U of Ark at Conway; Med.

RICE, Ronda Lynn
G W Carver Sr HS; Montgomery, AL (5-400) Chor; Math C; Mu Alpha Theta; NHS; Span C; Span NHS; SC; Ambassador Col; Bus Adm.

RICE, Sheryl Lyn
Whispering Hills Christian Acad; Nashville, TN; Chor; 4H; Rptr, Sch P; Bkbl; Sftbl; Vlbl; Fin, St Cecilia Mus Soc A; Fin, TACS St Span A; Semi-Fin, 4-H A; Calvin Col.

RICE, Spencer D
Guthrie HS; Guthrie, OK; Chem C; VP, FFA; NHS; Sci C; Math C; Cl Fav; Sal; Central St U; Bus.

RICE, Teresa Ann
Northbrook Sr HS; Houston, TX (75-592) Voc Christian Service.

RICE, Terry Lynn
New Caney HS; New Caney, TX (25%-360) JV, Bkbl; Tr; Hon Prog.

RICE, Wayne David
W Jones HS; Laurel, MS (25%-173) Chess C; Chor; Fr C; Sci C; Jones Co Jr Col; Chem.

RICH, Charles Douglas Jr
Wade Hampton HS; Greenville, SC (45-400) Co-Ed, Ann; Band; Ensm; Pres, JETS; NHS; Church Bktbl Tm; Oral Roberts U; Chem.

RICH, Charles S
Paramus HS; Paramus, NJ (27-600) BS; Hmrm; Lit Mag; Math C; VP, NHS; Sch P; Parl, SC; Ch, Soph Cl; JV, Soccer; COM; Hon Prog; USY A; Bnai Hon Soc; Princeton U; Pol Sci.

RICH, Dennis Clifton
Cairo HS; Cairo, GA (20%-225) Bsbl; Ftbl; Sftbl; Valdosta St Col.

RICH, Gregory Lee
Texas City HS; Texas City, TX (100-443) Pres, AFS; VP, Chor; InterAct C; Thes; Swim; ALSG Fel, Europe; Col Level Organ Stu; Tex Lutheran Col; Communication Arts.

RICH, James Oliver
Jefferson City HS; Jefferson City, MO (20%-600) Span C; Bkbl; Ftbl; Tr; Amer Leg A.

RICH, Jean Pierre Michel
J Graham Brown Sch; Louisville, KY (10-75) Chor; Dbte Tm; Fr C; ARC; Sch P; Pres, Soph Cl; COM; Citz A; Val; F-Ed & C-Ed, Yrbk; Yrbk Theme A; Special Ed.

RICH, Nancy Jean
Immaculate Heart of Mary HS; Westchester, IL; F-Ed, Ann; Ger C; Hmrm; NHS; Ski C; VP, SC; Hon Prog; NEDT; Ntl Merit Commended Stu; Loyola U; Pol Sci.

RICH, Randy Ray
S Sioux City HS; S Sioux City, NE (11-205) A Cap Choir; Tres, BS; Span C; JV, Bkbl; JV, Tr; Outst Yth A; Yth Pres; Theology.

RICH, Reid Harlen Jr
Randleman HS; Randleman, NC (24-124) F-Ed, Ann; Band; BC; Fr C; Pres, FTA; Lit Mag; Monogram; Bsbl; Ftbl; Citz A; Gov Honor Prog; Sousa Band A; All Co & All Amer Bands; Band Service A; E Carolina U; Bus.

RICH, Robin Elaine
Westminster Christian HS; Gadsden, AL (4-56) BC; Ensm; Sci C; Span C; COM; Hon Prog; Math A; Pep C.

RICHARD, Anthony Keith
Jonesboro-Hodge HS; Jonesboro, LA (25-150) A-Ed, Ann; 4H; Span C; Mgr, Bsbl; Mgr, Bkbl; Mgr, Cr-Ctry; Mgr, Ftbl; Mgr, Sftbl; Mgr, Tr; Cl Fav; Attendance A; NE La U; Journ.

RICHARD, Deborah Lynne
Everett HS; Lansing, MI; Chor; Ensm; NHS; Citz A; Hon Prog; Journ A; Ed & Rptr, Sch Paper; Jr Hon Soc; Everett Chorale; Central Mich U; Psych.

RICHARD, John Victor
Sandy Valley HS; Magnolia, OH (50-200) A Cap Choir; Chor; HiY; Span C; Ftbl; Cpt, Sftbl; Tr; MLS; Sci A; Lee Col.

RICHARD, Kathy Dianne
Cass Tech HS; Detroit, MI; COM; WW; NAS
Commended Stu; St Comp Schol; Schol A; U of
Mich; Dentistry.

RICHARD, Lawrence
Tilden HS; Chicago, IL (3-408) City Conf; NHS;
Pres, SC; Alg A; Yth Foundation A; Ill Inst of Tech;
Bus Adm.

RICHARD, Lisa Anne
McKinley Sr HS; Baton Rouge, LA (1-250) Hmrm;
Lit Ral; Cpt, Mjrte; Pres, Math C; Pres, Mu Alpha
Theta; NHS; Up Bound; Alg A; COM; Chem A; Cl
Fav; Hon Prog; Journ A; Math A; MLS; Ntl Achv
Schol; Ntl Sci Found; NEDT; Phy A; Sci A; Val;
Soc of Women Engr A; Alpha Kappa Alpha Schol;
Leg Schol; Tulane U Academic Schol; Tulane U;
Chem Engr.

RICHARD, Robin Renay
Rogsdale HS; Jamestown, NC; Fr C; Pres, Hmrm;
COM; Sci A; UNC-Chapel Hill; Acct.

RICHARD, William Clark
Lynbrook HS; San Jose, CA (200-650) Chess C;
Key C; Bkbl; Soccer; Tnns; Alg A; De Anza Col.

RICHARD, Winifred Inell
E Bakersfield HS; Bakersfield, CA; All Amer Yth;
Chldr; Dbte Tm; FBLA; Sch Achieve Tm; Var C;
Cpt, Bkbl; Tr; Pepperdine U; Probation Off.

RICHARDS, Ann Lynn
Riverside Jr Sr HS; Taylor, PA (5-190) Chor;
Drama; FNA; Hmrm; Mjrte; NHS; Span C; Chem
A; Hon Prog; Yth Fel; Drama A; Phys Therapy.

RICHARDS, Bernice Louise
Largo Sr HS; Largo, FL (29-825) NHS; Civinettes;
Pep C; Lenoir Rhyne Col; Deaf Ed.

RICHARDS, Brenda Lee
Parkersburg South HS; Parkersburg, WV; Sftbl;
DECA C; Gym; Lib Asst A; B-HR, Gym A; Par-
kersburg Comm Col; Interior Decorating.

RICHARDS, Carol E
Santa Monica HS; Santa Monica, CA (15%-1100)
Chor; Madrigal; Kiwanis A; Yth Fel.

RICHARDS, Carolyn Sue
Marina HS; Huntington Beach, CA; Co-Ch, AFS;
Cpt, Chldr; Chor; Hmrm; Lat C; Bkbl; Citz A; Vol
Hospital Duty A; Church Secy; HR; Long Beach St
U; Med.

RICHARDS, Cheryl Kay
Newton Comm HS; Newton, IL (35%-200) Band;
Bus C; Chor; Rptr, 4H; NHS; Golf; Swim; Tnns; 4H
A; NEDT; Eastern Ill U; Bus.

RICHARDS, Curtis Linn
Eastern HS; Lansing, MI; A Cap Choir; Chor;
Ensm; Hmrm; Madrigal; Mod Mus Mas; MVP, So-
dality; SC; Thes; Up Bound; Arch; Golf; Hockey;
Swim; Personality A; Short Story Creative Writer;
Religious A; Navy; Chaplain.

RICHARDS, Darcy Lynn
Shenandoah Valley Acad; New Market, VA
(10%-98) Band; Chor; Dbte Tm; Spch C; SC; Arch;
Sftbl; Swim; Tr; Hon Prog; JA A; Opt A; Spch A;
Newcomer's C; Theology.

RICHARDS, Elizabeth Louise
Petaluma Sr HS; Petaluma, CA (4-400) Chor; Secy,
Fr C; Secy, 4H; NHS; Orch; Secy, SC; Sftbl; Tr;
COM; 4H A; Pres A; Star Student; Candystriper;
S-T, Yth Fel; Gym; U of Calif; Sociology.

RICHARDS, Gay Kane
Moanalua HS; Honolulu, HI; Chldr; Chor; Drama;
Pres, 4H; Secy, HiY; Hmrm; Madrigal; Sch P; Thes;
Sftbl; Tr; 4H A; Pres A; Yth Fel; VP, 4 H C; Dra-
matic Art.

RICHARDS, George Thomas Jr
W Haven HS; West Haven, CT (13-600) Chem C;
Hmrm; Math C; NHS; Span C; VP, Span NHS;
NEDT; Tn o-t Mo.

RICHARDS, Greg Allen
Alton Sr HS; Alton, IL; Band; Chor; Ensm; Bkbl;
Sftbl.

RICHARDS, Janice Lea
John McEachern HS; Powder Springs, GA; Co-Ed,
Ann; HiY; Mgr, Cr-Ctry; Mgr, Soccer; HCt; FCA.

RICHARDS, Julie Ann
Papillion HS; Papillion, NE (104-366) Grace Col
o-t Bible; Missions.

RICHARDS, Michael Rodney
Towering Oaks Baptist HS; Memphis, TN; BS; Key
C; NHS; Pres, SC; Cpt, Ftbl; Cl Fav; H of F; Tnager
o-t Mo, Exchange C; Memphis St U; Forestry.

RICHARDS, Nancy Kaye
Dollar Bay HS; Dollar Bay, MI (5-30) Band; FNA;
Secy, 4H; 4H A; VofDEM; Mich Tech U; Med
Tech.

RICHARDS, Raymond A Jr
H W Schroeder HS; Webster, NY; Chess C; Chor;
Fr C; Hmrm; Orch; Sci C; SC; Var C; Cr-Ctry; Tr; U
of Va; Law.

RICHARDS, Rebecca Ann
Tabernacle Christian Sch; Greenville, SC (3-18)
Bus Mgr, Ann; Chor; FHA; Pres, Hmrm; Sch P;
Bkbl; Sftbl; Co-Cpt, Quiz Tm; Pennsicola Christian
Col; Missions.

RICHARDS, Roman Edward
Adlai E Stevenson HS; Bronx, NY (7-788) Band;
Chem C; NHS; Phys C; Mgr, Ftbl; Bio A; COM;
Chem A; Gov Honor Prog; Hon Prog; Sci A; Col-
umbia U; Physics.

RICHARDS, Steve Earl
Post Falls HS; Post Falls, ID (16-154) Ann; Pres,
4H; SC; Pres, Soph Cl; Co-Cpt, Wrest; Spch A; N
Idaho Col; Engr.

RICHARDS, Suzanne Marie
St Regis Falls Central Sch; St Regis Falls, NY
(10-37) Band; Cpt, Chldr; Chor; FHA; Hmrm; Co-
Ed, Sch P; Sci C; VP, SC; Soccer; Sftbl; Art & Mus
A's; Potsdam St Col; Elem Ed.

RICHARDS, Theresa Jean
Monroe Union HS; Monroe, OR (1-41) Band; 4H;
Tres, Sr Cl; Tres, Jr Cl; Bio A; MVP, Vlbl; WW;
Social Sci A; Linn-Benton Comm Col; Computer
Programming.

RICHARDS, Timothy Allen
Chase HS; Forest City, NC (17-147) BC; Fr C; Key
C; Monogram; MVP, Tnns; Engr.

RICHARDS, Tommy David
Granite City HS N; Granite City, IL (82-485)
NHS; Sci C; Span C; VP, SC; VP, Jr Cl; Bkbl; Tnns
Stu Advisory Board, Red Cross; Acct.

RICHARDSON, Allison Meddie
W Craven HS; Vanceboro, NC (10%-213) F-Ed,
Ann; Band; BC; Co-Cpt, Chldr; Chor; Hmrm;
NHS; Rptr, Sch P; Sci C; Pres, Span C; SC; VP, Jr
Cl; COM; Citz A; NEDT; Principal's, Chldr, A's;
Meredith Col; Math.

RICHARDSON, Angela Lynn
Berea HS; Greenville, SC; Bsbl; Ftbl; Cpt, Sftbl;
MLS; Most Out; MVP, Vlbl.

RICHARDSON, Arthur Lee
Lincoln HS; Dallas, TX; Pres, A Cap Choir; A-Ed,
Ann; Bus C; Pres, Chor; Dbte Tm; Drama; Ensm;
Pres, Key C; Math C; Parl, NHS; Ch, SC; Up
Bound; Var C; Pres, Sr Cl; Pres, Jr Cl; Pres, Soph
Cl; Bkbl; Co-Cpt, Ftbl; Cpt, Tnns; Tr; Citz A; Cl
Fav; DARGCA; Hist A; Hon Prog; Kiwanis A;
MLS; Most Out; Star Student; Sou Methodist U;
Law.

RICHARDSON, Barbara Ann
Cainhoy HS; Huger, SC (3-62) Secy, FHA; Secy,
Hmrm; Math C; Span C; HQn; HR; Eng, Sci,
A's; Winthrope Col; Interior Designer.

RICHARDSON, Beverly Ann
Southland HS; Arbyrd, MO (2-44) Band; FHA;
Hmrm; SC; Tres, Jr Cl; Pres, Soph Cl; Cl Fav;
Swtht; Homecoming Candidate; Gold Medal,
Driver's Ed.

RICHARDSON, Brent David
Gulf Comprehensive HS; New Port Richey, FL
(22-321) Band; Chor; Ensm; Pres, Ntl Prayer
Breakfast; St Petersburg Jr Col; Mus.

RICHARDSON, Carrie Lynn
Harding Acad; Memphis, TN (75-150) Chor; Dbte
Tm; Spch C; Memphis St Col; Social Work.

RICHARDSON, Cindy Ann
Vernon HS; Vernon, TX; Rptr, Band; U of Ark;
Bus.

RICHARDSON, Cindy Anne
Puyallup HS; Puyallup, WA (15-426) A Cap Choir;
AFS; Ed, Ann; Band; Chor; Drama; Ensm; Fr C;
Hmrm; InterClub Coun; NHS; Rptr, Sch P; Ski C;
SC; Thes; Secy, Sr Cl; VP, Soph Cl; Bkbl; Amer Leg
A; COM; Citz A; Hon Prog; Journ A; MLS; Sr
Recognition Stu; All NW Choir; Inspirational A;
Viking Lady; Warner Pacific Col; Mus.

RICHARDSON, Connie Sue
Clear Lake HS; Clear Lake, IA (28-170) AFS;
Chldr; Chor; 4H; SC; Pres, Soph Cl; Tnns; 4H A;
Spch A.

RICHARDSON, Cynthia Kay
Arlington HS; Arlington Heights, IL; Chor; Fr C;
Hon Prog; JA A; Summa Cum Laude; Sci.

RICHARDSON, Darryl Toby
James Island HS; Charleston, SC (5-150) BC; Math
C; Mu Alpha Theta; NHS; JV, Ftbl; Tr; Wrest;
Howard U; Architecture.

**RICHARDSON,
David Alexander**
Abraham Lincoln HS; San Francisco, CA; A Cap
Choir; Pres, BS; Chor; Ftbl; Tr; City Col of San
Francisco; Mach.

RICHARDSON, Debra Ann
Jane Adams HS; Cleveland, OH; Chor; NHS; Alg
A; Bio A; Citz A; HR; Cuyahoga Comm Col; Legal
Secy.

RICHARDSON, Debra Renee
Manual Arts HS; Los Angeles, CA; Pres, Sci C;
CSF; Hon Prog; Achv Cert; First HR; Jep Mural
Painting; Law.

RICHARDSON, Derrick D
DeLand Sr HS; DeLand, FL; Band; ROTC A;
Emery Riddles Col; Aeronautics.

RICHARDSON, Ellie Catherine
Havana HS; Havana, FL; Hmrm; NHS; PA; U of
Fla; Phys Ed.

RICHARDSON, Gary
Rebecca Comer HS; Eufaula, AL (2-64) Chor;
FFA; 4H; Math C; NHS; Sch Achieve Tm; Bsbl;
Bkbl; Ftbl; Tr; 4H A; Hon Prog; Sci A; Spch A;
Math A; Bsbl A; Athletic Achv; Eckerd Col; Ftbl.

RICHARDSON, George
Bell Voc HS; Washington, DC; Cleveland Inst;
Diesel Mechanic.

RICHARDSON, Greg Howard
Spruce Creek HS; Port Orange, FL (45-450) BC;
Pres, Chess C; NHS; VP, Order/Arrow; Sci C;
Bkbl; JV, Ftbl; Order/Arrow A; Yth Fel; BSct;
Vigil Hon, Order o-t Arrow; Daytona Beach Comm
Col; Sci.

RICHARDSON, Gregory Doane
Haure HS; Havre, MT (21-376) VP, Chess C; Dbte
Tm; Fr C; Hmrm; InterAct C; NFL; SC; JV, Ftbl;
JV, Tnns; Spch A; Whitman Col; Law.

RICHARDSON, Jacqueline Lita
New Rochelle HS; New Rochelle, NY; Tr; Morehouse Col; Ed.

RICHARDSON, Janet Kay
Homewood-Flossmoor HS; Flossmoor, IL
(15-903) A Cap Choir; Chor; Ensm; NHS; Hon
Prog; Swtht; Accompanist; Chor, Ensm; NHS
Highest Character A; WW; Fin, NCTE Achv A in
Writing; U of Tex; Nurs.

RICHARDSON, Janis Renee
Madison Park HS; Boston, MA; Chor; Drama; 4H;
HR; New England Deaconess Col; Registered
Nurs.

RICHARDSON, Jeanne Marie
Thomas Jefferson HS; Council Bluffs, IA (1-495)
Ensm; Fr C; Orch; Sch P; Bkbl; Tr; Pres A.

RICHARDSON, Janis
Springfield HS; Springfield, LA (1-53) BC; Pres,
FBLA; Lit Ral; Secy, Sr Cl; Sftbl; Amer Leg A;
Chem A; Hist A; Masonic A; MLS; Sci A; Val; Eng
A; Bus A; SE La U; Med Sci.

RICHARDSON, Jo Ann
Pike Central HS; Petersburg, IN (17-255) Band;
Pres, FHA; NHS; SC; Most Out; Soph A; VofM-
DEM; Pres, Job's Daughters; 1st Pl, Band Contest;
HR; Ind St U; Home Ec.

RICHARDSON, Johnny Mack
Fort Pierce Central HS; Fort Pierce, FL; Bkbl; Ftbl.

RICHARDSON, Joseph Scott
Bethel Christian Sch; Ruston, LA (5-12) SC; VP, Jr Cl; VP, Soph Cl; Bsbl; Bkbl; Cl Fav; PA; *Ariz St U; Forestry.*

RICHARDSON, Karen Ann
Monette HS; Monette, AR (1-40) F-Ed, Ann; Chor; Ensm; VP, Fr C; FTA; Hmrm; Jr Miss Pageant; Madrigal; Tres, Math C; NHS; F-Ed, Sch P; Sci C; Secy, SC; Rptr, Jr Cl; Tnns; Tr; COM; Citz A; Cl Fav; DARGCA; Elk A; HCt; Hon Prog; MLS; Spch A; Type A; Val; Dist Secy, FBLA; NEA Hon Solo; St VP, FHA; Most Talented; Hist, Sr Cl; Most Stu; Home Ec A; *U of Central Ark; Acct.*

RICHARDSON, Kathryn Ann
Western Hills HS; Fort Worth, TX (29-613) Hmrm; Orch.

RICHARDSON, Kristi Jan
Oconomowoc Sr HS; Oconomowoc, WI; 4H; Hon Prog; Active Christian Tns; HR; MVP; Scts of Glory Choir; Vlbl; Asst Chldr Coach; Statistician, Grade Sch Bkbl Tm; *Concordia Col; Ed.*

RICHARDSON, Laurie Ann
Wasatch HS; Heber City, UT (2-135) A Cap Choir; FHA; NFL; NHS; Phys C; Spch C; B Crocker A; Bio A; Journ A; MLS; Spch A; Type A; Val; Brigham Young U Trustees Schol; *Brigham Young U.*

RICHARDSON, Lonnie Jay
Little Miami HS; Morrow, OH; Bsbl; Bkbl; Sftbl; Tnns; Pres A.

RICHARDSON, Mark Alan
Norlina HS; Norlina, NC; Chess C; Chor; Bsbl; Ftbl; *Auto Mech.*

RICHARDSON, Mark Lynn
Augusta Sr HS; Augusta, KS (1-125) Band; BS; Dbte Tm; Key C; NHS; Order/Arrow; SC; Thes; God & Country A; NMS; St Scholar; *U of Kans; Biol.*

RICHARDSON, Mary Suzanne
Marion C Moore HS; Louisville, KY; BC; Chor.

RICHARDSON, Melanie Aneatha
Saints Acad; Lexington, MS; Chor; Drama; Hmrm; Bkbl; Hockey; Sftbl; HCt; MLS; Ntl Achv Schol; Star Student; Yth Fel; Sports As; *UCLA; Mus.*

RICHARDSON, Michele
Cecilian Acad; Philadelphia, PA; Chldr; Chor; 4H; Pres, Hmrm; Lat C; NFL; SC; Hon Prog; WW; *Stanford U; Pre-Med.*

RICHARDSON, Norman
Gainesville HS; Gainesville, TX (36-241) Ann; 4H; Ftbl; Tr; *U of Okla; Biol.*

RICHARDSON, Pamela Sue
Ritenour Sr HS; Overland, MO (15%-800) A Cap Choir; Chor; NHS; Hon Prog; Pres A; Type A; Rhythmettes; Mo Sch-Col Relations Commission.

RICHARDSON, Paul D
Kashmere Sr HS; Houston, TX; Hmrm; Sch P; Span C; SC; Cpt, Bsbl; Cpt, Ftbl; Career Day Activities Achv As; *U of Houston; Printing.*

RICHARDSON, Peggy
Bentworth Area HS; Bentleyville, PA; Band; Ski C; Campus Life; Vol to Elderly; Yth Traffic Safety Coun.

RICHARDSON, Peggy Olivia
Williamson HS; Mobile, AL (26-230) JV, Chldr; Chor; Key C; NHS; Pres, ARC; Y-Tns; Pres, Sr Cl; Cl Fav; HCt; Hon Prog; ROTC A; Swtht; Econ A; ROTC; Commander, Girls Drill Team; Ed, Yrbk; Hist A; Home Ec; Sch Qn; *Tex Southern U; Fashion Designing.*

RICHARDSON, Ralph Edward Clenton
Oregon Episcopal Sch; Portland, OR (70%-32) Ann; Chor; Bkbl; JV, Soccer; JV, Tnns; COM; Citz A; Yth Fel; Acolyte Merit A; Art A; Pres, Church Group; Readers Digest Schol; *Stanford U; Bus Adm.*

RICHARDSON, Randy Kent
Union HS; Union, MS (10%-50) F-Ed, Ann; BC; Hmrm; Sci C; Pres, SC; COM; MLS; Yth Fel; St Col Chem Cert; Del, St Yth Gov Affairs; *E Central Jr Col; Pre-Med.*

RICHARDSON, Ricky Lee
Perry Co HS; Linden, TN; BC; VP, Math C; Sci C; Pres, Soph Cl; Bsbl; Bkbl; Most Studious; *Vanderbilt U; Engr.*

RICHARDSON, Ronald David
H E McCracken HS; Bluffton, SC; BC; CYO; VP, 4H; Hmrm; Bsbl; Wrest; 4H A; Jr Marshal; Top 10, Sr; *Clemson U; Agr.*

RICHARDSON, Sally Lynn
Charleston HS; Charleston, WV; Band; MVP, Tnns; Pres A; *Fairmont St Col.*

RICHARDSON, Sandra Delee
Centerville Sr HS; Centerville, IN (2-180) Ed, Ann; Chor; Ensm; VP, NHS; Orch; Tres, SC; Y-Tns; Sftbl; Alg A; Bio A; 4H A; Hon Prog; Journ A; Math A; Swtht; *Ind U; Nurs.*

RICHARDSON, Selena
Terrell Co HS; Dawson, GA (5-200).

RICHARDSON, Susan Eve
N Augusta Sr HS; N Augusta, SC; Band; Ensm; Hon Prog; NEDT; Corresponding Secy, Hospital Vol; U of Tenn Hon Band; Regional, All St, Bands.

RICHARDSON, Susan Leigh
Sooner HS; Bartlesville, OK (4-290) Fr C; Secy, Lat C; NHS; Tr; Bio A; Math A; *S Western U; Phar.*

RICHARDSON, Venus Rochelle
MacKenzie HS; Detroit, MI (40-352) NHS; Ntl Teachers Coun; Hon Prog; *Highland Park Col; Social Worker.*

RICHARDSON, Verda Marie
Green Oaks HS; Shreveport, LA; VP, Band; Chem C; Dbte Tm; Lit Ral; Math C; Sch P; Sftbl; Swim; Rptr, Secy, Stu Coun; Band A; Dbte A; *Vo Tech Trade School; X-Ray Tech.*

RICHBURG, Douglas
Frederick Douglass HS; Baltimore, MD (3-35) Band; Ftbl; Wrest; *Mus.*

RICHBURG, Jerry Lee
Southwestern Sr HS; Baltimore, MD (7-29) AFS; Arch; HiY; Pol Sci C; Var C; JV, Bsbl; Cr-Ctry; JV, Ftbl; Mgr, Swim; JV, Tr; Wrest; Bio A; COM; Interlochen Ntl Mus; Sports As; *RETS; Elec.*

RICHBURG, Larry
Harlem Park Jr HS; Baltimore, MD (5-20) Band.

RICHERT, Steven Carl
Kingman HS; Kingman, KS (15-96) Band; BS; Pres, Chor; Drama; Ensm; Pres, Key C; Tnns; Yth Fel; Drama A; Band A; Chor A; Hon Stu A; *Tabor Col; Car Restoration.*

RICHEY, Amy Elizabeth
Dayton Christian HS; Dayton, OH; Chor; HCt; Hon Prog; Candystriper; Sch Mus; Mus, Bible Verses, A's; *U of Cincinnati; Med.*

RICHEY, Jane N
Andrew J Terrell HS; Blanchard, OK; Co-Ed, Ann; Pres, BC; Chldr; Parl, FHA; 4H; Hmrm; Math C; Model UN; NHS; Ntl Yth Conf; ARC; Sch P; SC; Var C; Co-Cpt, Bkbl; Co-Cpt, Sftbl; Swim; Tr; Alg A; COM; Citz A; Cl Fav; Gov Honor Prog; Hist A; HCt; Hon Prog; Journ A; Type A; Yth Fel; Yth Leg; MVP, Bkbl & Sftbl; Fresh Rptr; Home Ec, Lit A's; Recreation Ldr, FHA; WW; *Okla St U; Ed.*

RICHEY, Kelly Dennise
Spruce Creek HS; Port Orange, FL; Band; Key C; Fin, Tnns; *Scripp's Inst of Oceanography; Marine Bio.*

RICHEY, Pamela Renee
Compton HS; Compton, CA (46-800) CSF; Hon Prog; *Long Beach Col; Elem Ed.*

RICHEY, Roy Max
Lead Hill HS; Lead Hill, AR (3-25) FBLA; VP, FFA; Key C; Sch P; SC; Bsbl; Bkbl; Cl Fav; HCt; Sci A; Free Throw A, Bkbl; All-Dist Tm, Bkbl; *U of Ark; Agr.*

RICHICHI, Kimberly Diane
Amos Alonzo Stagg HS; Stockton, CA; *Delta Col; Policewoman.*

RICHICHI, Kristine Louise
Amos Alonzo Stagg HS; Stockton, CA; *Delta Col; Pathologist.*

RICHIE, Lisa Ann
Lafayette HS; Lafayette, LA (10%-565) Band; FBLA; Math C; NHS; S-T, Rainbow; Span NHS; COM; Grand Cross of Color, Rainbow Grls; *NW St U; Law.*

RICHIGER, Christina Dee
Grand Blanc HS; Grand Blanc, MI (185-595) Band; Ntl Fed Mus C; Mi Sch Band & Orch Assn Dist & St; *Mott Comm Col; Mus.*

RICHMAN, Carol Joan
Salem HS; Salem, NJ (11-275) Band; Ensm; 4H; Secy, Lat C; NHS; Co-Ch, SC; Pres, Jr Cl; Pres, Soph Cl; Amer Leg A; Chamber of Comm A; Citz A; Crisco A; 4H A; Hon Prog; Yth Fel.

RICHMAN, Gary Dean
N Mercer R III HS; Mercer, MO; Chor; Bkbl; Sftbl; Tr; HR; Cl Pres, Soph.

RICHMOND, Michaela Denise
Salina Central HS; Salina, KS (43-330) Semi-Fin, AFS; Chor; Fin, GS; Lat C; SC; Sci A; Red Cross Vol; Red Cross & YMCA Lifeguard; Candystriper; *Kans U; Elem Ed.*

RICHMOND, Percy Otis
M B Smiley HS; Houston, TX (5-461) A Cap Choir; Ger C; Hmrm; Math C; Mu Alpha Theta; NHS; SC; MVP, Bsbl; Bkbl; Cr-Ctry; Ftbl; Tr; Alg A; Bio A; Cl Fav; Hist A; Math A; Most Out; Sci A; DAR Research A; *Air Force Acad; Astronautic Engr.*

RICHMOND, Richard Verner
Tallulah HS; Tallulah, LA (15-56) VP, Bus C; VP, FBLA; 4H; *NE La U; Computer Secy.*

RICHMOND, Stefanie Angela
Emil G Hirsch HS; Chicago, IL; City Conf; FNA; Sch P; Tr; Cl Fav; Journ A; Modern Dance; Best Manners; Good Social Graces; *UCLA; Journ.*

RICHMOND, Steven Brett
Midland HS; Midland, TX (171-692) Co-Ed, Ann; Hmrm; Order/Arrow; Bkbl; Order/Arrow A; Ntl Rifle Assn; Eagle Sct; 1st Pl, Interntl Sct Photo Contest; *Tex Tech U; Journ.*

RICHOUX, Cynthia Mary
John Ehret HS; Marrero, LA (5-450) A Cap Choir; Pres, BC; CYO; Cpt, Chldr; Cum Laude Soc; Hmrm; Jr Miss Pagent; Lit Ral; Math C; Mu Alpha Theta; NHS; Parl, SC; Bsbl; COM; Hon Prog; Math A; WW; *La Tech U; Elec Engr.*

RICHOUX, Kathleen Mary
John Ehret HS; Marrero, LA (5-450) A Cap Choir; Tres, BC; CYO; Cum Laude Soc; Hmrm; Jr Miss Pagent; Lit Ral; Mjrte; Math C; Mu Alpha Theta; NHS; Tres, SC; MVP, Bsbl; MVP, Sftbl; COM; Hon Prog; Math A; WW A; *La Tech U; Art Ed.*

RICHTER, Janeil Christina
Blue Valley HS; Randolph, KS (3-18) S-T, Band; Cpt, Chldr; Chor; Ensm; Tres, FHA; 4H; Secy, SC; VP, Jr Cl; Bkbl; Sftbl; Tr; Lion A; Type A; All League, Vlbl; All League Hon Men, Bkbl; *Kans St U; Dental Health.*

RICHTER, Noreen Louise
Port Jefferson HS; Port Jefferson, NY (100-375) Band; Bus C; SC; Sftbl; Tr; *LI Bus Inst; Secy.*

RICHTER, Randall Howard
Shawano HS; Shawano, WI (80-239) Band; Tres, FBLA; *U of Wis; Bus Mgt.*

RICHTER, Robin Suzanne
Monroe Union HS; Monroe, OR (1-63) Cpt, Chldr; Chor; VP, SC; Tr; Soc Sci A; Tr Records; Chldr As; *U of O; Secretarial.*

RICHTER, Roger Kyle
Pflugerville HS; Pflugerville, TX; VP, Band; Dbte Tm; Drama; Co-Ed, Sch P; Span C; Cr-Ctry; Tr; General Mills Family Leadership A; Sch Govt A; *Abilene Christian U; Computer Sci.*

RICHTER, Sandy Ruth
Shawano Sr HS; Shawano, WI; Band; FBLA; Pres, 4H; Jazz Band; Vlbl; Ftbl Frosh A; *Legal Secy.*

RICHTER, Timothy Alan
Wauwatosa W Sr HS; Wauwatosa, WI (124-444)
Band; Drama; Tri-HiY; VP, Var C; Y-Tns; Mgr,
Tnns; COM; HCt; Poet A; Yth Fel; Yth Leg; Cpt, 4
Yr Ltr, Vlbl; 4 Yr HR; FCA; *George Williams Col;
Applied Behavorial Sci.*

RICHTER, Timothy Allan
Wauwatosa W Sr HS; Wauwatosa, WI (122-438)
Band; Drama; HiY; Lit Mag; Var C; Mgr, Tnns;
COM; HCt; Poet A; Yth Fel; Yth Leg; Cpt, Vlbl;
FCA; 4 Yr HR; 4 Yr Ltrman; VP, Ltrman's C;
George Williams Col; Applied Behavorial Sci.

RICHTER, William T
Robert E Lee HS; Tyler, TX (66%-600) Fr C; VP,
Key C; NHS; SC; Var C; Pres, Soph Cl; Co-Cpt,
Bkbl; Tr; Amer Leg A; COM; Hon Prog; Spch A;
Yth Fel; Cpt, Cannon Crew; Presidential Class-
room; *Southwestern U; Communications.*

RICHTMAN, Jewel
Jewish Educational Center HS; Elizabeth, NJ; A
Cap Choir; Cpt, Chldr; Chess C; Chor; Co-Cpt,
Dbte Tm; Ch, Drama; VP, Hmrm; Math C; Secy,
NHS; Ntl Yth Conf; Sch Achieve Tm; F-Ed, Sch P;
Span C; Tnns; Hon Prog; Most Out; Ntl Achv
Schol; Ch, Acrobatics; Ch, Dance C; Co-Cpt, To-
rah Hon Soc; Mother Daughter Luncheon; Ch, Gift
& Programming.

RICHWAGEN, Dorothy Jo-Ellen
Wissahickon HS; Ambler, PA (10%-400) 4H; Var
C; World Affairs C; JV, Hockey; Soccer; Sftbl; 4H
A; Hon Prog; Pres A; FCA; JV, Lacrosse; VP, Jr
Historians; *Pol.*

RICICAR, Sandra Jean
Hitchcock HS; Hitchcock, TX (4-130) Pres, Bus C;
FHA; NHS; Alg A; Elk A; Math A; Type A; Vof-
DEM; Tres, Bus C; Most Promising Future; Most
Scholarly; Phys Ed, Ldrship, A's; *Col o-t Mainland;
Bus.*

RICK, Mary Eileen
Bellingham HS; Bellingham, WA (15-320) Secy,
CYO; Chor; NHS; ARC; Swim; *W Wash Col; Soci-
ology.*

RICKARD, Janis Denise
First Assembly Christian Sch; Memphis, TN (5-32)
Chldr; Chor; Cum Laude Soc; Secy, Hmrm; VP,
Lat C; Lat NHS; Math C; Secy, Soph Cl; Mgr, Bkbl;
COM; Cl Fav; Magna Cum Laude; *U of Tenn;
Med.*

RICKARD, Linda Kay
East HS; Cheyenne, WY (54-440) Band; Chor;
Ensm; FHA; Secy, 4H; Orch; Swim; Citz A; 4H A;
Outst Musician; Band Performance A; *John Brown
U; Mus.*

RICKARDS, Lynn Carol
Springfield HS; Springfield, PA (33%-440) Chor;
ARC; Hockey; Hon Prog; ARC A; Yth Fel; Sea
Explorers; Young Life; Bowl; Stage Crew; Hist C;
Goldey Beacom Col; Legal Secy.

RICKAWAY, Penny
Columbia HS; W Columbia, TX; AFS; Ann; Band;
FHA; FTA; Model UN; NHS; Span C; SC; *Brazos-
port Col; Elem Ed.*

RICKER, Cheryl Lynne
Bad Axe HS; Bad Axe, MI (2-170) Chor; Dbte Tm;
Drama; Pres, NHS; Secy, Sci C; Secy, SC; Tres, Jr
Cl; Sal; Mich St Forensics League; *Alma Col.*

RICKER, Shirley Ann
Ft Jennings HS; Ft Jennings, OH; Band; JV, Chldr;
Chor; JV, Sftbl; Sci A; Co-Cpt, Vlbl.

RICKER, Stephanie Anne
Greeneville HS; Greeneville, TN (10%-223) Band.

RICKETT, Craig Steven
Aloha HS; Beaverton, OR (29-573) Bkbl; Golf;
Tnns; Opt A; Opt Out Tn; *NW Nazarene Col; Res-
taurant Career.*

RICKETTS, Kenneth Michael
Valley Forge Military Sch; Wayne, PA; Bsbl; Co-
Cpt, Ftbl; Best Cadet in Cl A; *Bus Adm.*

RICKETTS, Mary Jane
SW Central HS; Jamestown, NY (10-200) AFS;
Ann; Chldr; Chor; Drama; Ensm; Tres, Ger C;
NFL; NHS; Rptr; Sch P; Ski C; Spch C; Math C;
Sci A; Spch A; Yth Fel; Pep C; Eng A.

RICKETTS, Pamela Jean
Pinellas Park Sr HS; Largo, FL; F-Ed, Ann; Chor;
Pres, Crown & Scepte; Secy, Fr C; SC; VP, Jr Cl;
Bkbl; Sftbl; Beauty; Pres, Pep C; Burdines Tnboard;
Jr Cl VP A; *St Pete Jr Col; Fashion Co-Ordinator.*

RICKEY, Frederick James
Seekonk HS; Seekonk, MA (5-224) Chess C; Math
C; NHS; St Stu Congress; Ch, Stu Govt Day; Ed,
Yrbk; 2nd Pl, Sci Fair; Ntl Merit Hon Men; *Brown
U; Lib Arts.*

RICKEY, Robert Bruce Jr
Van Horn HS; Independence, MO (87-415) Band;
Fr C; Order/Arrow; Co-Cpt, Cr-Ctry; Co-Cpt, Tr;
Wrest; *Central Mo St U; Bio.*

RICKLEFF, Kathy Lee
Naperville N HS; Naperville, IL; A Cap Choir;
Chor; Ch, Drama; Ensm; Fr C; Madrigal; Mjrte;
Summer Place Theater; Benedictine Col Musicals;
Ill Wesleyan Col; Mus Theater.

RICKLEFS, Debra Sue
Anamosa Sr HS; Anamosa, IA (3-150) Band; Chor;
Sci C; SC; Var C; VP, Soph Cl; JV, Bkbl; JV, Cr-
Ctry; Tr; COM; Math A; NEDT; Sci A; *U of
Northern Iowa; Secondary Ed.*

RICKS, Alanda Rena
Crenshaw HS; Los Angeles, CA; *Pepperdine U;
Bus.*

RICKS, Barbara Ann
I C Norcom HS; Portsmouth, VA (67-183) Chor;
FBLA; 4H; Sftbl; Citz A; 4H A; Type A; Chorus A;
Tidewater Comm Col; Mus.

RICKS, Janet Faxon
Bible Baptist HS; Savannah, GA (4-39) Ntl Fr Contest.

RICKS, Kelley Jean
Bible Baptist Day Sch; Savannah, GA (5-54) Hon
Prog; Ntl Fr Contest; *Ga Sou Col; Interior Design.*

RICKS, Vera Elaine
Claxton HS; Claxton, GA (25%-116) FHA; Hmrm;
Jr Miss Pagent; Sci C; Tr; PE Cert; Home Ec A;
Fashion Designer.

RICORD, Charles David
Comeaux HS; Lafayette, LA; Key C; Ftbl; 'C' A; *U
of Sou La; Engr.*

RIDAUGHT, Paul Leslie
Dixie Co HS; Cross City, FL (20-95) FFA; Ftbl;
Star Chapter Farmer, FFA; *Abraham Baldwin Agr
Col; Agr.*

RIDDELL, Diane Margaret
N Salinas HS; Salinas, CA (22-400) Sftbl; Bank of
Amer A; Sr for Disneyland; Most Artistic; *Art Sch;
Art.*

RIDDELL, Kent Ernest
Eureka HS; Eureka, IL (15-110) AFS; Band; Ensm;
JV, Bkbl; Ftbl; Tr; Citz A; Most Out; Pres A; Outst
Fresh Athlete; Mr Hustle; *Northwestern U; Hist.*

RIDDER, Daniel Mark
Thornton Fractional S HS; Lansing, IL (28-609)
Band; Orch; JV, Bkbl; Amer Leg A; NEDT; *Whea-
ton Col; Mus.*

RIDDICK, Cherrivance Londell
Camden HS; Camden, NC; BC; Chor; 4H; Mgr,
Bkbl; Cpt, Ftbl; Tr.

RIDDICK, Leonard Patches
Croft HS; Waterbury, CT; All Amer Yth; Chor;
Drama; Pres, Ntl Yth Conf; Pres, Sci C; Bkbl; Sftbl;
Tr; Hist A; I Dare You; MLS; Ntl Sci Found; Ntl
Sci Symposium; Sci A; *US Army; Diesel Mach.*

RIDDICK, Ronnie Lee
Northeastern HS; Elizabeth City, NC (50%-368)
Band; Tr; *Elizabeth City St U; Hist.*

RIDDLE, Cynthia Jane
Fairfield Sr HS; Fairfield, OH (50-522) Chor; Fr C;
NHS; VP, Secy, Pres, Russian C; Outst Russian
Hon A; *Ohio St U; Russian.*

RIDDLE, Emily Irene
N Fla Christian Sch; Tallahassee, FL (10%-67) 4H;
4H A; Hon Prog; MLS; Yth Fel; WW; Church
Choir; Bell Choir; Art C; Vlbl; Pres, Yth Fel; *Tallahassee Comm Col; Home Ec.*

RIDDLE, James Anthony
John Marshall HS; Indianapolis, IN;

RIDDLE, Susan Carole
Baptist Temple Sch; Orlando, FL (4-13) Chor; Pup-
pett Ministry; Bus Ministry; *Criminology.*

RIDDLE, Terry Wayne
Reeds Spring HS; Reeds Spring, MO (11-75) BC;
Sci C; Span C; Var C; Bkbl; JV, Tr; COM; Citz A;
Hist A; Hon Prog; Sci A; Co-Ed, Yrbk; Cpt, Tourn
of Knowledge; *Drury Col; Bus.*

RIDENOUR, Jeffrey Robert
Canyon HS; Canyon Country, CA (60-500) Var C;
MVP, Bkbl; Elk A; *Pepperdine U; Sci.*

RIDENOUR, Kimberly Jean
Canyon HS; Canyon Ctry, CA (15-625) Secy,
NHS; SC; Tres, Sr Cl; VP, Jr Cl; JV, Bkbl; Semi-
Fin, Frontier Belle; Screening Greenies C; MIP;
Pepperdine U; Sci.

RIDEOUT, Mark Steven
Haskell HS; Haskell, OK (2-78) BS; Chor; Ed, Sch
P; Hon Prog; Art A; Drama A; Eng A; Span A; *U of
Tulsa; Drama.*

RIDER, Carol Ann
E Hardin HS; Glendale, KY (52-180) Ann; FBLA;
FTA; Math C; Swthr; *W Ky U; Elem Ed.*

RIDER, Martha Priscilla
Dongola Unit Sch; Dongola, IL (3-28) Tres, BC;
VP, FHA; Pres, 4H; SC; Tres, Jr Cl; Tres, Soph Cl;
4H A; Hon Prog; I Dare You; Type A; Home Ec A;
Co-Ed Correspondent; Co 4-H Qn; *Shawnee Jr
Col; Secy.*

RIDER, Russell David
Upper Columbia Acad; Spangle, WA (3-75) Arch;
Tres, BS; Cum Laude Soc; Ger C; NHS; Ski C; SC;
Arch; Bsbl; Cpt, Bkbl; Cpt, Ftbl; Golf; Hockey;
Sftbl; Tnns; Tr; Citz A; Hon Prog; Sanctuary Soc;
Star Student; Pres, Fresh Cl; *Bus.*

RIDGE, Kimberly Anne
Belton-Honea Path; Honea Path, SC (3-315) Band;
Drama; Fr C; Hmrm; SC; COM; *Col of Charleston;
Mus.*

RIDGEWAY, Deborah Jean
Hinsdale Township HS Central; Hinsdale, IL
(33%-668) Band; Sch P; Ski C; Sftbl; Hon Prog;
Hon Men, N Ill Industrial Ed; Co-Moderato,
Church Yth Group; Work-Tour; *U of Ill; Architec-
ture.*

RIDGEWAY, Debra Ann
Burkeville HS; Burkeville, TX (4-47) Chor; FHA;
French NHS; FTA; NHS; Bkbl; Tr; Hon Prog; Jr Cl
Play; *Lamar U; Home Ec.*

RIDGEWAY, Joan Marie
John T Hoggard HS; Wilmington, NC (247-590)
Miss Yth; Best Personality; *East Coast Bible Col;
Bible Stu.*

RIDGEWAY, Mary Elizabeth
Greenville Sr HS; Greenville, SC (4-229) Chor;
NHS; PC Jr Fel; *Clemson U; Bus.*

RIDGLE, Patricia Ann
C E Murray Elem And HS; Greeleyville, SC (9-28)
4H; Sci A; *Francis Marion Col; Nurs.*

RIDGWAY, Teresa Leann
Hallsville R-IV HS; Hallsville, MO (1-46) Ed, Ann;
BC; Chor; Pres, FHA; Pres, 4H; S-T, NHS; SC; Var
C; Secy, Jr Cl; Bkbl; Tr; Amer Leg A; 4H A; MLS;
Most Out; Pres A; Type A; Val; VFW A; Ann Staff
A; Art A; Shorthand A; Gen Fees Schol; 4-H Key
A; Eng A; *Northeast Mo St U; Home Ec.*

RIDINGER, Robin Ann
Glenbard W HS; Glen Ellyn, IL (63-519) Chor;
Hmrm; Mu Alpha Theta; Ski C; Swim; WW; *U of
Iowa; Nurs.*

RIDLEY, Barbara Renee
Jeb Stuart HS; Falls Church, VA (80-428) Drama;
Fr C; Madrigal; NHS; VP, Soph Cl; Mgr, Tnns;
COM; Drill Tm; *U of Va.*

RIDLEY, Carolyn Laverne
Chamberlain HS; Tampa, FL (110-680) Drama;
Pres, Fr C; NHS; Rptr, Sch P; Thes; Kiwanis A;
Asbury Col.

RIDLEY, Mary Robin
J E B Stuart HS; Falls Church, VA (68-481) Hmrm;
Model UN; NHS; Tri-HiY; Tres, Jr Cl; VP, Soph
Cl; COM; Citz A; DARGCA.

RIDLEY, Vernon Lee
Patterson Cooperative HS; Dayton, OH (222-500) Tri-HiY; Up Bound; Bkbl; Cr-Ctry; Ftbl; Swim; Tr; Master Hon A, Newspaper Carrier; *Math.*

RIEBEL, G Kevin
Glendale HS; Springfield, MO (25%-400) *Drury Col; Instrumental Mus.*

RIEBEN, Andrea Kay
Franklin Co HS; Winchester, TN (5%-430) Ann; Chldr; NEDT; Scholastic Achv A; Jr BC.

RIEBEN, Karen Michele
Franklin Co HS; Winchester, TN (1-310) Ed, Ann; BC; Secy, Dbte Tm; Drama; Rptr, FHA; Hmrm; VP, NHS; COM; Crisco A; NEDT; Most Involved Sr Girl; Hon Stu; *King Col; Occupational Therapy.*

RIECHMANN, Eric John
Valmeyer Community Unit 3 HS; Valmeyer, IL (7-38) Band; CYO; Pres, Chess C; Chor; Pres, FFA; Math C; NHS; Orch; Sch P; Var C; MVP, Bsbl; Co-Cpt, Bkbl; HCt; I Dare You; Spch A; VofDEM; Most Ath; Dramatics A; DeKalb; St Farmer Degree; *Belleville Area Col; Journ.*

RIECK, Linda Marie
Brookings HS; Brookings, SD (5-200) Secy, Band; Co-Cpt, Chldr; Chor; Ensm; Secy, FHA; Semi-Fin, GS; Secy, 4H; Madrigal; Secy, NFL; NHS; Orch; Secy, SC; Secy, Thes; Secy, Jr Cl; Swim; 4H A; JV Gym; St Piano A; *Home Ec.*

RIECKMAN, Pamela Ann
Cedar Springs HS; Cedar Springs, MI (10%-140) Band; Chldr; 4H; NHS; 4H A; *Moody Bible Inst; Christian Ed.*

RIED, Mike Lynn
Mason City HS; Mason City, IA (92-491) Chess C; Math C; Order/Arrow; JA A; Ntl Sci Symposium; Order/Arrow A; Eagle Sct; *U of N Iowa; Math.*

RIEDLING, Lynn Carol
Waggener HS; Louisville, KY; BC; Pres, Chor; NHS; ARC; 1st, Ntl Guild, Piano Playing; *Jefferson Comm Col; Elem Ed.*

RIEHART, Sara Jane
Pampa HS; Pampa, TX (3-308) Rptr, A Cap Choir; Rptr, Drama; Pres, Hmrm; Key C; Pres, Lat C; NHS; SC; Thes; Golf; MLS; Opt A; NMS Commended Stu; Lat A; WW in Eng; *Cottey Col; Eng.*

RIEKE, Nan Elizabeth
Fairmont HS; Fairmont, MN (10%-210) Band; Chor; Community Yth Symph; Ensm; Ger C; Madrigal; Orch; Ski C; Var C; Bkbl; Golf; Sftbl; Swim; JV, Tnns; Sunday Sch Teacher; 1st Chair A; Church Choir; HR A; Band Camp A; Church Yth Coun; All St Band.

RIEKER, Walter Charles
Archmere Acad; Claymont, DE (5-90) BS; NHS; ARC; Sci C; Span NHS; Cr-Ctry; Tr; JV, Wrest; Hon Prog; Spch A; CAP; *Engr.*

RIEKHOF, Laurie Jo
Lexington HS; Lexington, MO (6-105) Ann; Band; Chor; Ensm; 4H; NHS; Orch; Thes; 4H A; Regent Schol; Yth Fel; Women's C Girl o-t Mo; *Central Mo St U; Vocal Mus.*

RIEMAN, Monti Curtis
El Camino Real HS; Woodland Hills, CA (10%-1039) Bus C; Fr C; Hmrm; Math C; Ski C; Spch C; JV, Swim; *U Calif at Irvine; Information.*

RIES, Cheryl Ann
Chaska Sr HS; Chaska, MN (24-268) CYO; Chor; Ensm; NHS; *Normandale Col; Nurs.*

RIES, Donita Elizabeth
Immaculata HS; Chicago, IL (10-157) Ch, Chess C; NHS; Span NHS; SC; Amer Leg A; COM; Hon Prog; St Scholar; *Creighton U; Pre-Phar.*

RIES, Steve Blaine
Bellflower HS; Bellflower, CA (130-400) Rptr, Sch P; Ftbl.

RIESE, Johnny Erwin
Bladen Pub Sch; Bladen, NE (6-18) Band; Chor; Drama; Madrigal; SC; Bsbl; Bkbl; Co-Cpt, Ftbl; Tr; Amer Leg A; Spch A; *Archt.*

RIESSEN, Joan Marie
Spencer HS; Spencer, IA (10%-200) Rptr, Ann; Chor; Dbte Tm; NHS; Span C; Spch C; Thes; Spch A; Church Organist; *Home Ec.*

RIESSEN, Mark James
Spencer Pub HS; Spencer, IA (25%-200) Golf; COM; Jr Bowl Tm.

RIESTER, Amy Jo
Roy J Wasson HS; Colorado Springs, CO (82-580) Band; Community Yth Symph; Drama; *Home Ec.*

RIESZ, Nancy Diane
Victoria HS; Victoria, TX; Anchor C; Fr C; NHS; Hon Prog; Drill Tm; *Tex Tech U; Sci.*

RIETH, David Allen
River Valley HS; Three Oaks, MI (21-175) Ger C; F-Ed, Sch P; Ski C; SC; VP, Soph Cl; Bkbl; MVP, Cr-Ctry; Cpt, Tr; Cl Fav; Most Out; Spch A; Marine A; All Conf Tr HR; *Central Mich U; Phys Ed.*

RIETHMILLER, Marilyn
Buffalo Sr HS; Buffalo, MN (11-214) Band; Chldr; H of F; Regent Schol; Yth Fel; Hon Stu; *Augustana Col; Special Ed.*

RIETMAN, Sandra Ann
Temple Heights Christian Sch; Tampa, FL (1-62) AFS; NHS; Span C; World Affairs C; Alg A; NMF; NEDT; Val; *Art.*

RIFFE, Linda Jan
Mountain View HS; Mountain View, OK; Chldr; Rptr, FFA; FHA; Yth Foundation; *Okla U; Nurs.*

RIFFEL, Kathleen Alice
Immaculata Acad; Hamburg, NY (8%-76) CYO; Chor; Span C; SC; COM; *Bible Stu.*

RIFFLE, Cindy L
Frankfort HS; Ridgeley, WV (10%-151) Band; Chor; Fr C; NHS.

RIFFLE, Renee Elizabeth
Clark Co R-I HS; Kahoka, MO (6-92) CYO; Chldr; FFA; 4H; NHS; Sci C; JV, Cr-Ctry; Bio A; 4H A; Sci A; *U of Mo at Columbia; Vet Med.*

RIFNER, Vollie Brian
John Marshall HS; Indianapolis, IN (102-463) Ger C; Key C; Sci C; SC; Thes; VP, Radio C; VP, Church Yth Fel; Industrial Arts A; *Ind St U; Elec Tech.*

RIGBY, Julie Ann
Silver Creek HS; San Jose, CA; COM; HCt; Math A; *San Jose St U; Eng.*

RIGDON, Cynthia Cheryl
Kemper Acad; DeKalb, MS (9-42) Chldr; Pres, Jr Cl; MVP, Bkbl; Beauty; Cl Fav; Eng A; *Meridian Jr Col; Radiologic Tech.*

RIGDON, Jeffery Wayne
Rockville HS; Rockville, IN (19-82) BS; Fr C; Sci C; Var C; VP, Soph Cl; Cpt, Bsbl; Co-Cpt, Bkbl; Co-Cpt, Ftbl; Kappa Kappa Kappa; *Purdue U; Engr.*

RIGGAN, Russell Craig
Monterey HS; Lubbock, TX;

RIGGINS, Marvelyn Denise
Gordon HS; Decatur, GA; BC; 4H; Hmrm; NHS; Span C; COM; Star Student; HR A; Beta Qn; Kappa A; Off A; *Spelman Col; Secy.*

RIGGINS, Norbert Thilenius
Walker HS; Decatur, GA; Chor; ARC; Span C; Co-Cpt, SC; Co-Cpt, Bsbl; Cr-Ctry; Cpt, Ftbl; MVP, Tr; Wrest; Math A; *U of Ga; Math.*

RIGGINS, Obera Lynne
Pendleton HS; Pendleton, SC (8-133) BC; Fr C; FHA.

RIGGINS, Vickie Lynn
South HS; Springfield, OH; *Ohio St U; Math.*

RIGGINS, Wynne Renee
George C Marshall HS; Falls Church, VA (25-479) Chor; Model UN; NHS; Secy, World Affairs; Journ A; *Madison Col; Eng.*

RIGGS, Bruce
Russell HS; Russell, KY (17-250) BC; Chor; HiY; *U of Ky; Med.*

RIGGS, David Lee
W Aurora Sr HS; Aurora, IL (60-650) NHS; Thes; Bkbl; Ftbl; Tr; St Scholar; Yth Fel; *Engr.*

RIGGS, Debbie
Fayetteville HS; Fayetteville, AR; Band; Chor; *U of Ark; Sci.*

RIGGS, Debra Ann
White Oak HS; Jacksonville, NC; Bus C; Secy, FBLA; Parl, FHA; *Sweet Briar Col; Bus.*

RIGGS, James Strowd Jr
Nw Cabarrus HS; Concord, NC (75-290) Band; Drama; Fr C; Order/Arrow; ARC; A-Ed, Sch P; Sci C; Bkbl; Cr-Ctry; Tr; God & Country A; Gov Honor Prog; Hon Prog; Order/Arrow A; Q&S A; Yth Foundation A; Gov Page; Eagle Sct; Sch Bus Driver; *U of NC; Mech Engr.*

RIGGS, Janelle Evelyn
Oregon City HS; Oregon City, OR (10%-450) AFS; Chor; GS; NHS; Var C; Tr; Pres A; Vlbl; Disc; Dist Champ ; HR, Tr; Oreg AAU Champ; Pioneer Dad's C A; League All Star A; *Dental Hygienist.*

RIGGS, Louis Wayne
Hannibal Sr HS; Hannibal, MO (27-342) Band; Dbte Tm; Drama; Secy, Order/Arrow; Co-Ed, Sch P; JV, Cr-Ctry; Order/Arrow A; Spch A; Top 10%; Bicentennial Essay A; Prose Fin, Mahan Minor Div; Runner Up, Spell Bee; *U of Mo; Journ.*

RIGGS, Marissa Louise
DuPont Manual HS; Louisville, KY (72-375) Band; NHS; Span C; Tr; COM; Citz A; Sci A; Band, Reading, A's; *U of Louisville; Journ.*

RIGGS, Paulette Elizabeth
Claremore HS; Claremore, OK; Chor; S-T, Yth Fel; *Claremore Jr Col; Secy.*

RIGHTMYER, Gerald Rush
McLean Co HS; Calhoun, KY (2-156) BC; S-T, Chess C; Order/Arrow; S-T, Sci C; SC; VP, Jr Cl; Bkbl; JV, Tr; Alg A; Bausch & Lomb A; Math A; Sal; Eagle Sct; Psych A; Ath Academic A; W Hewitt Young Merit A; *U of Ky; Pre-Phar.*

RIGHTS, Roberta Lee
Ft Pierce Central HS; Fort Pierce, FL; Hmrm; NHS; Secy, SC; Keyettes; *Teacher.*

RIGNEY, Regina Ann
Buckatunna HS; Buckatunna, MS; BC; FHA; *Jones Co Jr Col; Med.*

RIGSBY, Paul Michael
Central HS; Tulsa, OK (69-372) Band; Pres, Hmrm; JV, Bsbl; JV, Bkbl; Ftbl; HCt; Pres, Distributive Ed C; *ORU; Religion.*

RIKARD, Rosanna
Lanier HS; Montgomery, AL (1-500) Chldr; Drama; Hmrm; Lat C; Lat NHS; NHS; Spch C; Pres, Thes; COM; MLS; NEDT; Opt A; Spch A; Drill Tm; Play Cast; Most Talented; Cl Pres Cand; Friendliest; Academic A; VIVA School; *Dramatics.*

RILES, Karen Denise
Sou Baptist Educational Center; Memphis, TN (6-129) BC; NHS; *Union U; Acct.*

RILEY, Cheri Lynn
Howard-Lake Waverly HS; Howard Lake, MN (25%-120) Band; Tr; JV, Vlbl; *Col of Saint Benedict; Eng.*

RILEY, Deborah Ann
Rockledge HS; Rockledge, FL (20%-295) Bus C; Chor; FBLA; Hmrm; SC; Coun of Teach A; HCt; Most Out; Achv A; Most Faithful; Shorthand A; Most Improved; Yth Coun; Talent A; Most Dedicated; *U of Fla; Bus Ed.*

RILEY, Elizabeth Carol
Lancaster HS; Lancaster, VA (30-150) Drama; Tres, Fr C; Model UN; *Va Intermont Col; Fashion Merchandising.*

RILEY, Garrett Paul
Sacred Heart HS; Kingston, MA (40-54) Co-Cpt, Bkbl; Cooperation & Effort A; Star Player o-t Week; *Dartmouth Col; Econ.*

RILEY, Jerry Lee
Goshen HS; Goshen, IN (60-200) SC; Bsbl; Bkbl; Ftbl; Theatre Arts.

RILEY, Joe Brett
Palo Duro HS; Amarillo, TX (9-320) Chor; Hmrm; Madrigal; SC; Cl Fav; *Dentistry.*

RILEY, Jonathan Mark
Millville HS; Millville, NJ; All Amer Yth; Chor; Co-Ch, Hmrm; Var C; Cpt, Bkbl; Yth Fel; MVP, Bkbl; All Conf; All Area; All Amer; *U of Md; Phys Ed.*

RILEY, Judith Diane
Gainesville HS; Gainesville, TX; Pres, FHA; Hmrm; SC; Most Out; Pres A; *Cooke Co Col; Secy.*

RILEY, Karen Marie
Shawnee Mission NW HS; Shawnee, KS (33%-700) Fr C; *Kan U; Teacher.*

RILEY, Kevin Daniel
Nordonia HS; Macedonia, OH; Chor; Math A.

RILEY, Laura Lea
Jackson Central Merry HS; Jackson, TN; Ann; Chor; Fr C; Hmrm; Beauty; Hon Prog; Kappa Beta Chi; *Law.*

RILEY, Mark P
Taylor HS; N Bend, OH (50-200) Demolay; SC; Var C; VP, Jr Cl; JV, Ftbl; MVP, Swim; *Ariz St U; Bus Law.*

RILEY, Mary Josephine
Glenbard W HS; Glen Ellyn, IL (206-488) CYO; Semi-Fin, Chldr; Chor; Drama; Hmrm; InterAct C; Sch Achieve Tm; Ski C; Span C; Tres, SC; Thes; Pres, Y-Tns; Tres, Jr Cl; Bsbl; Sftbl; Tnns; Amer Leg A; Gov Honor Prog; *Ill St; Nurs.*

RILEY, Maureen Anne
Glenbard W HS; Glen Ellyn, IL (125-500) G-Tn; VP, Pep C; *U of Ill; Ed.*

RILEY, Pamela Sue
Oak Hill HS; Converse, IN (6-180) Band; Chor; Pres, Drama; Ensm; FHA; Secy, Ger C; Pres, 4H; Madrigal; NFL; NHS; Orch; Rptr, Sch P; Spch C; Pres, Thes; Pres, Tri-HiY; Y-Tns; Secy, Sr Cl; Co-Ch, Jr Cl; COM; 4H A; Yth Fel; Hon Bar Thespians; Ger NHS; Best Actress; *Ind U; Pre-Med.*

RILEY, Paula Gail
Buckhorn HS; Buckhorn, KY (3-63) BC; Rptr, FHA; Bkbl; HQn.

RILEY, Ralph Patrick Jr
Ramey Jr-Sr HS; Ramey, PR (1-22) Ann; Band; Tres, Sci C; Pres, Soph Cl; JV, Tr; JV, Wrest; Hist A; HQn; NJHS; Algebra Merit; Pres, Fresh Cl; Span A; Eng A; *Auburn U; Vet.*

RILEY, Rebecca Ann
Regina HS; Cincinnati, OH (65-116) CYO; JV, Chldr; Hmrm; SC; Bsbl; Bkbl; *Phys Therapy.*

RILEY, Sharon Lynn
Person Sr HS; Roxboro, NC (22-430) JV, Chldr; NHS; Span C; *Atlantic Christian Col; Ed o-t Deaf.*

RILEY, Tana Lou
Madison C-3 HS; Madison, MO (6-29) Ann; BC; Cpt, Chldr; Chor; FHA; 4H; Rptr, Sch P; Sci C; VP, SC; Var C; Pres, Sr Cl; Sftbl; Tr; Cl Fav; DARGCA; 4H A; Drama A; Yrbk Qn, 1st Attendant; WW; WW Among Amer HS Stu in Mus.

RILEY, Terry Cathleen
John Burroughs HS; St Louis, MO (62-81) Band; Drama; Pres, Hmrm; Model UN; Orch; Span C; SC; S-T, Sr Cl; Mgr, Tr; *Drake U; Bus.*

RIMAC, Rita Therese
Driscoll HS; Addison, IL (8-144) Chor; Lit Mag; NHS; St Scholar; *Interntl Mgt.*

RINALDI, Joni Lynn
Glen Oak HS; N Canton, OH; A Cap Choir; Band; Chor; Lat C; JA A; Yth Fel; WW; Pres, Yth Group; Accompanist, All Choirs; Chldr Adv; *Kent St U; Mus Ed.*

RINALDO, Laurel Ann
Jamestown HS; Jamestown, NY (10%-540) Tres, Band; Fr C; NHS; Span C; SC; Squad Ldr, Marching Band; 1st Chr, Al St Wind Ensm & Concert; *Onondaga Col; Nurs.*

RINDSIG, Steve Jay
Spencer HS; Spencer, IA (5-224) Band; Chess C; Ensm; Phys C; Pres, Span C; Var C; Golf; JV, Wrest; Hon Prog; Solo, Ensm, A's; Hon Band; *Iowa St U; Construction Engr.*

RINEHART, Harry Winston
Northside HS; Fort Smith, AR; Ann; Fr C; SC; Tnns; *U of Ark; Med.*

RINEHART, Susan Gail
Valdosta HS; Valdosta, GA; Band; Mjrte; Pres, Tri-HiY.

RINEHART, Victoria Lynn
Albia Comm HS; Albia, IA (35-148) Band; Chor; Mjrte; Rainbow; Rptr, Sch P; S-T, SC; Var C; Golf; Mgr, Sftbl; Type A; WW; Worthy Adv, Rainbow Girls; Rainbow Service A; *NE Mo St U; Bus Adm.*

RINELLA, James Martin
H L Richards HS; Oaklawn, IL (155-600) Co-Cpt, Ftbl; JV, Wrest; HCt; Hon Prog; Founder, Bible Stu Group; *Psych.*

RINESMITH, David W
Worthington Christian Sch; Worthington, OH (5-10) Chor; Drama; Hmrm; SC; Co-Cpt, Bkbl; Cpt, Soccer; Sftbl; Cpt, Tr; Daniel A; MVP, Tr & Soccer; *Ohio St U; Law Enforcement.*

RINEY, Lois Jean
Clark Co R-I HS; Kahoka, MO (4-92) Band; Chor; Ensm; Pres, 4H; Mjrte; NHS; Sch Achieve Tm; COM; 4H A; ARC A.

RING, Vickie Sue
Metamora Township HS; Metamora, IL (4-200) Band; Chor; Ensm; 4H; NHS; Ntl Yth Conf; Span C; Y-Tns; COM; 4H A; Hon Prog; Ntl Achv Schol; Pres A; Sci A; Spch A; St Scholar; Yth Fel; Ntl Spch Contest; St Quiz Tm A; Ntl Quiz Tm; Yth o-t Yr A; *Ill Central Col.*

RINGER, Lisa A
Kountze HS; Kountze, TX; Chem C; Math C; Bus Mgr, Sch P; Sci C; Bkbl; Alg A; Bio A; Hist A; Math A; Sci A; Type A; *Lamar U; Med Tech.*

RINGGENBERG, Thomas Dean
Robbinsdale Sr HS; Robbinsdale, MN (61-676) Ann; Chor; Madrigal; NHS; A-Ed, Sch P; Bsbl; NML; Co-Cpt, Cr-Ctry Skiing; *U of Minn; Chem.*

RINGGOLD, Patricia Lynn
Wichita N HS; Wichita, KS; Chor; Ensm; Mgr, Sftbl; *Wichita St U; Mus.*

RINGLER, Cindy Nadine
Salisbury-Elklick HS; Salisbury, PA (10-45) Ann; Sch P; Mgr, Bkbl; Mgr, Sftbl; Type A; Yth Fel; *Frostburg St Col; Secondary Ed.*

RINGOEN, John Richard
Northside HS; Muncie, IN (30-283) Dbte Tm; Ensm; Span C; Tnns; JA A; Opt A; Spch A; Yth Fel.

RINGOLD, Edward Morgan
Huntingdon HS; Huntingdon, TN (30-105) BC; Math C; MVP, Ftbl; *US Air Force Acad; Elec.*

RINGS, Mary Elizabeth
Canton Acad; Canton, MS (33%-120) Rptr, Ann; Band; Chor; Chldr; Mjrte; Rptr, Sch P; Bkbl; Sftbl; Swim; Tnns; Tr; Bio A; Chem A; Cl Fav; HCt; Sci A; Dixie Debs; *Miss St U.*

RINKER, Cynthia Lynn
Frankfort HS; Ridgeley, WV (25%-151) Chor; NHS.

RINKER, Karen Elizabeth
Clarke Co HS; Berryville, VA; Bus C; Fr C; 4H; Hmrm; Semi-Fin, Jr Miss Pa; Ch,tTri-HiY; Math A; Pres, Yth Fellowship; Job's Daughters; Runner Up, Miss Clarke Co; *Ferrum Col; Art.*

RINKS, John Lloyd
Brethren HS; Paramount, CA (5-105) Ed, Lit Mag; Pres, SC; Pres, Var C; Pres, Sr Cl; Pres, Jr Cl; Pres, Soph Cl; Bsbl; Cpt, Bkbl; Cr-Ctry; CSF; COM; HCt; Hon Prog; Type A; MVP, Bkbl; Bible A; WW; Archt A; Eng A; *Bus Adm.*

RINNERT, Susan Elizabeth
Fayetteville HS; Fayetteville, AR (10%-390) Ann; Chor; Drama; Ensm; Fr C; FBLA; FHA; A-Ed, Sch P; *Auburn U; Elem Ed.*

RIORDAN, Carolyn
Rhinebeck Central HS; Rhinebeck, NY (13-110) AFS; Band; Tres, Chor; NHS; Span C; SC; Var C; VP, Soph Cl; Bkbl; Hockey; Tr; Regent Schol; *US Coast Guard Acad; Ocean Engr.*

RIORDAN, James Joseph
St Anthony's HS; Smithtown, NY (86-200) CYO; Chor; ARC; Co-Ed, Sch P; Var C; Bsbl; Mgr, Bkbl; Mgr, Ftbl; Mgr, Soccer; Sftbl; Tr; ARC A; Dun Scotus Cert; *St Johns U; Ath Adm.*

RIORDAN, Rosemary Teresa
Rhinebeck Central HS; Rhinebeck, NY; AFS; CYO; Chldr; Chor; *Nursing.*

RIOS, Elvira
Central HS; Santurce, PR; CYO; Chldr; VP, FHA; Pres, Hmrm; Semi-Fin, Jr Miss Pa; SCnt; COM; Hon Prog; Spch A; *U of PR; Sci.*

RIOS, Lourdes R
Academia Santa Monica; Santurce, PR (11-25) Ann; Tres, InterAct C; Tres, Lit Ral; NHS; Sch P; SC; Tnns.

RIPLEY, Brian Dale
Winnebago HS; Winnebago, MN (3-50) Band; Chor; Pres, FFA; 4H; Pres, SC; Pres, Soph Cl; Cr-Ctry; Tr; *U of Minn; Law.*

RIPLEY, Cynthia Ann
Norwayne HS; Creston, OH (20-153) MVP, Band; Chldr; Chor; Drama; Tr; Yth Fel; PA; Flag Girl; Pom Pon Girl; Statistician; *Bowling Green St U; Home Ec Teacher.*

RIPLEY, Debbie Kay
Sonner HS; Bartlesville, OK (20-280) Pres, AFS; Fr C; NHS; Span C; Span NHS; Bkbl.

RIPLEY, Jenice Elaine
S Page Comm Sch; College Springs, IA; Band; JV, Chldr; Chor; Drama; FHA; Co-Ed, Sch P; Spch C; Y-Tns; 4H A; Spch A; *William Woods Col; Equestrian Stu.*

RIPLEY, Michael Charles
Luverne HS; Luverne, MN (35-140) Cpt, Bsbl; Bkbl; JV, Ftbl; Tnns; MVP, All Conf, Bsbl; *Mankato St U; Bus.*

RIPLEY, Theresa K
Norwayne HS; Creston, OH (5-103) Band; Chldr; Chor; Fin, GS; NHS; Bkbl; Tr; Amer Leg A; *Wayne Col; Executive Secy.*

RIPPE, Jayne Rae
Bruning HS; Bruning, NE (1-16) Band; Chor; Fin, GS; 4H; Alg A; Bio A; Math A; Spch A; Eng A; Hist A.

RIPPEL, Linda Jean
Rudyard HS; Rudyard, MI; MVP, Band; Bkbl; Sftbl; Sci A; *Lake Superior Col; Math.*

RIPPEL, Linda Kay
Normal Comm HS; Normal, IL (110-510) Bus C; 4H A.

RIPPEL, Sheryl Rene
Warren Township HS; Gurnee, IL (150-300) Prom Ct; Vlbl; Devillettes, Pom-Pon Girl.

RIPPELMEYER, Ken Robert
Valmeyer HS; Valmeyer, IL (1-38) Band; Pres, Chess C; FFA; Tres, 4H; Pres, Math C; Pres, NHS; Tres, SC; Bsbl; Math A; MLS; St Scholar; Val; *U of Ill; Sci.*

RIPPENTROP, Alan Wayne
Lakota Consolidated Sch; Lakota, IA (3-15) Ann; Bsbl; Bkbl; Tr; Type A; *Iowa Lakes Comm Col; Agr.*

RIPPY, Michael Don
Northside Christian Sch; St Petersburg, FL (9-35) Pres, Band; Span C; Bkbl; Ftbl; Swim; Sci A; HR; Dean's List; *St Pete Jr Col; Bus.*

RIPPY, Paul Willis
Shelbyville Central HS; Shelbyville, TN; HiY; Yth Leg; Yth Leg A; Leo C.

RIPPY, Ruby Jane
Shelbyville Central HS; Normandy, TN; FHA; Secy, Sunshine Band; Leo C; Jr & Sr Choir.

RIPSOM, Jonathan Clark
William Allen HS; Allentown, PA (24-778) NHS; Order/Arrow; COM; Summa Cum Hon; Eagle Sct; *Lehigh Col; Chem.*

RISBERG, Donna Arlene
Grissom HS; Huntsville, AL (200-600) Anchor C; JV, Chldr; Hmrm; SC; Hon Prog; Pres, Church Choir & Yth Group; VP, Yth Group; Projects Ch; *Birmingham Sou Col.*

RISK, Danella Marie
Miami Christian HS; Miami, FL (15%-53) A Cap Choir; Chem C; Chor; NHS; Sch Achieve Tm; Swim; Tr; Alg A; Amer Leg A; Hist A; Hon Prog; Journ A; Ntl Achv Schol; Spch A; Yth Fel; *Eng.*

RISLEY, Belinda Rene
Kelso HS; Kelso, WA; FHA; NHS; Pep C Serv A; Pep C; VP, International Relations C; *Calif Bap Col; Pre-Sch Ed.*

RISLEY, John Arthur
St Joseph-Ogden HS; St Joseph, IL (1-100) Band; NHS; SC; Co-Cpt, Ftbl; Tr; Co-Cpt, Wrest; COM; HKg; Hon Prog; St Scholar; Interntl C; MVP, Ftbl; Lettermen's C; SAR Good Citz A; VP, FCA; MVP, Wrest; U of Ill; Engr.

RISLEY, John Phillip
Bolles Sch; Jacksonville, FL (18-156) BC; Chor; Hmrm; Math C; SC; Bsbl; JV, Bkbl; Ftbl; Hon Prog; President's Phys Fitness A; VP, JA; Semi-Fin, Math A; Fin, Hist A; Vanderbilt U; Bus.

RISNER, Brenda
Jackson Co HS; McKee, KY (21-120) Ed, Ann; BC; Fr C; 4H; Cl Fav; 4H A; Hist A; HCt; Yth Fel; VP, Yth Fel; Most Stu; 4h A of Excel; PA; U of Ky; Textiles Clothing.

RISNER, Pamela Renea
Mtn View HS; Mtn View, AR; Tres, BC; VP, FBLA; FTA; GS; SC; Bkbl; Cl Fav; Hist A; Short-hand A.

RISNER, Stanley Ray
Hart Co HS; Hartwell, GA; VP, Chess C; Tnns; Math A.

RISON, Mary Annette
Waukegan W HS; Waukegan, IL; Tres, A Cap Choir; Chor; Rptr & Bus Mgr, Sch Paper; Cosmetology.

RIST, Roxanna
Nathan Hale HS; Tulsa, OK (20%-700) Band; Chldr; City Conf; Hmrm; NHS; SC; Tres, Sr Cl; VP, Jr Cl; MVP, Golf; Alg A; HCt; Math A.

RISTVEDT, Cynthia Gail
Littlefield HS; Littlefield, TX (63-90) Band; JV, Bkbl; Tr; Beauty; COM; Yth Fel; Court of Hon; All Region Band; Region Qualifier, Tr; Sch Spirit A; Concordia Col; Med.

RITCH, David Kyle
Eastern Randolph HS; Ramseur, NC (30-230) Hmrm; Monogram; SC; Ftbl; Tr; Health C; UNC-G; Pre-Med.

RITCHEY, Theresa Ann
Zanesville HS; Zanesville, OH (33%-500) Beauty; HCt; Drill Tm; Neatness A; Ohio St U; Bus.

RITCHEY, Tom Alan
Zanesville HS; Zanesville, OH (33%-500) Band; Orch; Bkbl; Ohio St U; Radio Broadcasting.

RITCHIE, Anne Kathryn
Radford HS; Honolulu, HI (30-508) Chldr; U of Hawaii; Journ.

RITCHIE, Diana Lynn
Celina Sr HS; Celina, OH (10-275) Fr C; FTA; Ger C; NHS; COM; Hon Prog; GSct; U of S Fla; Elem Ed.

RITCHIE, John Adrian
Parkview HS; Little Rock, AR (21-478) BC; BS; Dbte Tm; FBLA; InterClub Coun; Key C; NHS; Sci C; Ch, St Stu Congress; Pres, SC; Cl Fav; H of F; Hon Prog; I Dare You; Opt A; Spch A; Amer Govt A; US Sen Yth Prog; 1st Pl, Key C Dist Orator; Outst SC Pres A; Vanderbilt U; Pol Sci.

RITCHIE, Pamela Carol
S H Rider HS; Wichita Falls, TX; Tri-HiY; Type A; Hospital Vol; Church Choir & Yth Coun; Baylor U; Bus.

RITCHIE, Viola Patricia
Melbourne HS; Melbourne, FL (10%-703) Band; Mu Alpha Theta; Health Careers C; Young Churchmen; Astronomy C; Jr Civitan; VP, Explorers; Duke U; Med.

RITTALL, Susan Marilyn
Boothbay Region HS; Boothbay Harbor, ME (33%-45) Pres, AFS; Band; Cpt, Chldr; Chor; Pres, Hmrm; Lat C; Rptr, Sch P; Ski C; SC; Pres, Sr Cl; Secy, Soph Cl; Pres A; Gym A; Top Three, Athletic Stu; Cpt, Gym; Central Maine Med Center; Nurs.

RITTENHOUSE, Barbara Ann
Uniontown Area Sr HS; Uniontown, PA; Band; Chldr; Secy, Fr C; Pres, Hmrm; Pres, NHS; Sci C; Ski C; SC; COM; Math A; Stu ot Month; Jr Acad of Sci; Carnegie-Mellon U; Art.

RITTENHOUSE, Kerry Ray
Wm James Jr HS; Statesboro, GA (7-320) Band A; Ga Southern Col; Med.

RITTENHOUSE, Lorrie Ann
Uniontown HS; Uniontown, PA; 4H; NHS; Ski C; Span C; Alg A; Amer Leg A; Hist A; Math A; Sci A; Yrbk; Bio.

RITTER, Diane Lynn
Pomona HS; Arvada, CO (5-410) Chor; Secy, Dbte Tm; Drama; NFL; NHS; Alg A; DARGCA; Elk A; Hist A; Hon Prog; Opt Out Tn; Regent Schol; Spch A; Yth Foundation; JA A; Tres, GSct; Cpt, Vlbl; Colo Energy Research Inst Schol; Colo Sch of Mines; Chem.

RITTER, Josh Leigh
Carlsbad HS; Carlsbad, CA (125-425) AFS; Drama; Ensm; Mgr, Ftbl; Mgr, Tr; San Diego St U; Geol.

RITTER, Julienne Cecile
Sacred Heart Acad; Salem, OR (8-32) Drama; NHS; Cpt, Bkbl; Tr; Pres, Sports C; Cpt, Vlbl; Vlbl A; Oreg St U; Biol.

RITTER, Mairon
Westmont Hilltop Sr HS; Johnstown, PA (30-135) Band; Tr; Hon Prog; Sci A; Med Explorers C; Andrews U; Med.

RITTER, Marlene Grace
Bishop Klonowski HS; Scranton, PA; NHS; Spch C; Hon Prog; Engr.

RITTER, Robin Gail
Kohala HS; Kapaau, HI (1-68) AFS; Band; Hmrm; Span C; SC; Tnns; Instructor, Stwide Marine Sci Prog; Del, Hawaii Conf On Aging; Chem Oceanography.

RITTSCHER, Peggy Sue
Elkhorn Valley HS; Tilden, NE; Band; Chldr; Chor; Bkbl; Vlbl; U of Nebr; Pub Relations.

RITZ, Frederick
Livonia Stevenson HS; Livonia, MI (181-803) Co-Cpt, Bsbl; Ftbl; Hon Prog; Schoolcraft Col; Engr.

RIVALTO, Lisa Ann
Bishop Byrne HS; Memphis, TN; Ann; Co-Cpt, Chldr; FBLA; Beauty; H of F; HQn; HCt; Short-hand A; All-Dist Vlbl.

RIVERA, Alma Milagros
Colegio Espiritu Santo; Hato Rey, PR; Tres, Hmrm; Semi-Fin, Jr Miss Pa; Lit Mag; Tulane U; Occupational Therapy.

RIVERA, Bellia Ann
Laupahoehoe HS; Laupahoehoe, HI (1-24) CYO; FHA; FTA; Tres, Lit Ral; Monogram; NHS; Secy, Sci C; SC; Secy, Y-Tns; Pres, Soph Cl; Cpt, Tnns; COM; Cl Fav; HCt; Pres A; SBG A; U of Hawaii; Med.

RIVERA, Berrios Israel
Dr Pedro Perea Fajardo Voc HS; Mayaguez, PR; Hon Stu; Elec Engr.

RIVERA, Bethzaida
Adolfo Grana HS; Penuelas, PR (5-263) CYO; Chor; Drama; FHA; COM; Cl Fav; University of Puerto Rico.

RIVERA, Blanca Margarita
Notre Dame HS; Caguas, PR (30-136) NHS; VP, Sch P; SC; Bsbl; Bkbl; COM; Phy A; Q&S A; San Juan Board of Realtors Schol; Excellence Medals; Hon Medals; WW; Tulane U; Pre-Med.

RIVERA, Daniel Eduardo
Wesleyan Acad; Guaynabo, PR (1-32) Chor; Drama; NHS; Rptr, Sch P; SC; NEDT; HR; U of Puerto Rico; Engr.

RIVERA, Esther Annette
Belton HS; Belton, TX; Band; CYO; VP, Drama; GS; Hmrm; Span C; SC; Amer Leg A; Baylor U; Law.

RIVERA, Frances Rafaela
Colegio Espiritu Santo; Hato Rey, PR (6-96) Ann; Chor; Drama; Math C; Spch C; SC; Ch, Var C; Secy, Jr Cl; COM; Hon Prog; Secy, Ecology C; Vlbl; U of Puerto Rico; Sci.

RIVERA, Hilda M
Consuelo Escalona Private Sch; Carolina, PR (4-56) Co-Cpt, Chldr; Chor; Fr, Dbte Tm; Drama; FTA; Rptr, Sch P; SC; Swim; COM; Hon Prog; Magna Cum Laude; Sci A; Hon Medal Loyalty Medal; Drew U; Med.

RIVERA, Jorge J
Notre Dame HS; Caguas, PR (9-128) Chem C; Chess C; VP, Hmrm; JETS; Sch Achieve Tm; VP, Sci C; Alg A; Bio A; COM; Chem A; Math A; Sci A; Philately C; Monacillo A; Philately A; Engr.

RIVERA, Lillian Annette
Our Lady of Pilar HS; Rio Piedras, PR (20%-166) Chem C; VP, Model UN; NFL; Span A; Pepperdine U; Interntl Law.

RIVERA, Luis Alberto
Jose De Diego HS; Mayaguez, PR (7-276) Sci C; Bsbl; Bkbl; Sftbl; Magna Cum Laude; C Becarios; U of Puerto Rico at Mayaguez; Med.

RIVERA, Luis Alberto
Central HS; Santurce, PR (16-300) U of Puerto Rico; Bus Adm.

RIVERA, Maribel
Escuela Superior Dr Pila HS; Ponce, PR; Chor; Tres, Hmrm; Bkbl; Lion A; Volibol; UPR-PONCE; Administracion Comercial.

RIVERA, Maritza Haydee
Luis Munoz Marin HS; Cabo Rojo, PR (3-200) Band; Chem C; FHA; FTA; 4H; Pres, Hmrm; Lat C; Math C; Span C; SC; Alg A; Bausch & Lomb A; Bio A; COM; Chem A; DARGCA; Hon Prog; Math A; Phy A; Sci A; Spch A; UPR-RECINTO de Mayaguez; Med.

RIVERA, Miguel Ramon
Herrin HS; Herrin, IL; Bsbl; Naval Acad; Oceanography.

RIVERA, Mildred Elisa
Yauco HS; Yauco, PR; FHA; Pres, Hmrm; Bradley U; Bio.

RIVERA, Nancy
A E Stevenson HS; New York, NY (49-788) Bus C; FBLA; Hmrm; InterClub Coun; NHS; Sch Achieve Tm; SC; COM; Citz A; Baruch Col; Acct.

RIVERA, Noemi
Central HS; Santurce, PR (15-300) Pres, Sr Cl; COM; Ldrship A; U of Puerto Rico; Med.

RIVERA, Ramos Evelyn
Adolfo Grana Rivera; Penuelas, PR (2-336) Secy, FHA; Pres, Hmrm; ARC; COM; Hon Prog; Universidad Catilica; Sci.

RIVERA, Rosalina
Adolfo Grana Rivera HS; Penuelas, PR (2-263) FBLA; FHA; Sftbl; COM; Hon Prog; Math A; Sci A; Star Student; Cath U; Nurs.

RIVERA, Sally Diane
Jose de Diego HS; Mayaguez, PR; Chem C; Sch Achieve Tm; Secy, Sci C; Span C; COM; Phy A; Summa Cum Laude.

RIVERA, Samuel E
Wesleyan Acad; Guaynabo, PR (2-29) Chor; Pres, NHS; Sch P; Bsbl; JV, Bkbl; Bausch & Lomb A; NEDT; Cl Win, Essay Contest; U of Puerto Rico; Pre-Med.

RIVERA, Santos
Jose de Diego HS; Mayaguez, PR (12-276) Drama; InterAct C; Lit Ral; Phys C; ARC; Span C; SC; Bio A; COM; Cl Fav; Magna Cum Laude; ARC A; Sci A; Adv Span Group; U of Puerto Rico at Mayaguez; Med Technology.

RIVERA, Steven
Harry S Truman HS; Bronx, NY (447-923) A Cap Choir; Co-Cpt, All Amer Yth; Chor; Drama; Madrigal; Sc C; Bsbl; Soccer; Swim; Bio A; Sci A; Madrigal; Northland Col; Forestry.

RIVERA, Wanda Ivelisse
Dr Pila HS; Ponce, PR (26-703) Chem C; Pres, Hmrm; Math C; NHS; ARC; Pres, Sch P; Span C; SC; Secy, Sr Cl; Beauty; COM; Citz A; Cl Fav; H of F; Hon Prog; MLS; Most Out; Star Student; Type A; Lib Asst A; Cath U of PR; Med.

RIVERA, William Xavier
Santa Barbara HS; Santa Barbara, CA; Rptr, Sch P; Cal Poly; Archt.

RIVERO, Jorge Osmar
Miami Springs Sr HS; Miami Springs, FL (39-816) Hon Prog; JA A; Foreign Lang Hon Soc; Miami Dade Col; Engr.

RIVERO, Manuel Quirino
H B Plant HS; Tampa, FL (150-500) Cpt, Church Bkbl; Church Newspaper; Church Ftbl& Sftbl; Civitan C; Bible Quizzer; *U of Ala; Med.*

RIVERS, Jeffrey Lawrence
Cotter HS; Winona, MN (23-105) Rptr, Sch P; Span C; Bkbl; Ftbl; Hon Prog; *St Mary's Col; Bus.*

RIVERS, Steven Paul
John F Hodge HS; St James, MO; Band; Demolay; Pres, Sci C; JV, Bkbl; Ftbl; Golf; Pres A; Drivers Ed A; 1st & 3rd Pl, Region Sci Fair; 2 rating, St Mus Contest; WW.

RIVERS, Valerie Dorice
E Atlanta HS; Atlanta, GA (9-175) Hmrm; Mjrte; Sch P; HQn; Most Out; Band, Mjrte, Achv, Attendence, A's; *Interior Decorator.*

RIVERS, Willa Mae
McIntosh HS; McIntosh, AL; *Livingston U; Sociology.*

RIVOIRE, Rory Diwaine
Gainesville HS; Gainesville, TX; Band; Pres, FFA; Ch, Hmrm; Key C; Math C; NHS; Phys C; Pres, SC; Citz A; DARGCA; MLS; Opt A; Rotary A; Ceramic As; Sheep Prod, Star Chapter Farmer; Star Greenhand Farmer; *Tex A&M U; Agr.*

RIXIE, Cynthia Diane
Walnut HS; Walnut, MS (5-55) Tres, BC; Tres, Sr Cl; Rptr, Jr Cl; Eng A; Most Intellectual; *Jackson Col of Ministries; Dactylology.*

RIXIE, Valarie Cheryl
E Ridge HS; E Ridge, TN (60-300) Ed, Ann; BC; Pres, Crown & Scepte; Hmrm; NHS; SC; Tri-HiY; Bkbl; Tr; Yth Foundation; Vlbl; Ch, Handbook Comm; FCA; Letterettes C; Sr Coun; Most Improved, Bsbl; S-T, Ecology C; *Carson-Newman Col; Sci.*

RIXSE, James Scott
Yorktown HS; Arlington, VA (5%-450) Secy, Key C; NHS; Sch Achieve Tm; F-Ed, Sch P; JV, Bsbl; Hon Prog.

RIZEK, Lisa Ann
North Liberty HS; North Liberty, IN (20%-125) Band; Chor; Span C; SC; Citz A; Hurdle Honey; Bus.

RIZEK, Susan Mary
St Joseph's o-t Palisades HS; W New York, NJ (10-225) NHS; Span NHS; Hon Prog; NEDT; *Fairleigh Dickenson U; Dental Hygiene.*

RIZER, Eric Stephen
Helena Sr HS; Helena, MT; A Cap Choir; Chor; Ger C; Bsbl; Bkbl; Ftbl; Swim; Wrest; Starlighters; *N Seattle Comm Col; Math.*

RIZZO, Edward Kevin
Don Bosco Tech HS; Boston, MA (2-211) CYO; NHS; Bkbl; Hon Prog; Pres A.

RIZZO, Tina Louise
Weed HS; Weed, CA (6-58) Chldr; Sch P; S-T, Jr Cl; CSF; HQn; Type A; HR; *Col o-t Siskiyou; Bus.*

ROACH, Edward Guy
Cache HS; Cache, OK; Pres, Jr Cl; Bsbl; Ftbl.

ROACH, Grace Anne
St Aloysius HS; Jersey City, NJ (2-110) Ann; Chor; Rptr, Hmrm; Pres, NHS; Ed, Sch P; Swim; Cpt, Tnns; Bio A; COM; Chem A; MLS; Phy A; Sci A; Most Versatile; Hon A; *U of Ut; Bio.*

ROACH, Ivee Jo
W Beaver HS; Industry, PA; Band; Chor; Ensm; FHA; Orch; Type A; Mus Ltr; Co Bicentennial Cert; *Duffs Bus Inst; Secy Sci.*

ROACH, Kathryn Sue
Manual HS; Peoria, IL (4-434) Span C; Cl Fav; Hon Prog; MLS.

ROACH, Kelley Dupree
Colo HS; Colo City, TX (5-126) Pres, FHA; FTA; WW; Top 5, Soph; Chem, Eng, Bio As; *Angelo St Col; Homemaking.*

ROACH, Kirwin Marlo
Christian Brother's Col; St Louis, MO (27-130) Chor; Spch C; SC; Cpt, Cr-Ctry; ROTC A; Spch A; *Saint Louis U; Bus Adm.*

ROACH, Mark Stuart
Sussex Central HS; Sussex, VA (3-200) BC; Chess C; Span C; VP, Tri-HiY; Bsbl; Ftbl; Wrest; Phys Fitness A; 2nd Pl, Wrest A; 2nd Pl, RA Church Tr; *Wildlife Mgt.*

ROACH, Peggy Henderson
River Rouge HS; River Rouge, MI (52-178) A Cap Choir; Chor; Ensm; Fr C; Hmrm; Madrigal; Sci C; Ski C; Secy, Span C; SC; COM; Hon Prog; MLS; Mus A; House of Rep Cert, Outst Acad Achv; Sch Art A; *Detroit Inst of Tech; Court-Rptr.*

ROACH, Richard Lee
Eldorado HS; Albuquerque, NM (299-744) BS; Hmrm; Key C; Ch, SC; Ftbl; Twirp Cand; Optimist Yth Appreciation A; *Denver Diesel & Automotive Col; Diesel Mech.*

ROACH, Vanessa Renee
John Jay HS; San Antonio, TX; Chor; Tr; COM; Art.

ROACHE, Linda Susann
Savannah HS; Savannah, GA (6-400) BC; Chem C; FBLA; Math C; Secy, NHS; Ed, Sch P; COM; Hist A; Hon Prog; Journ A; JA A; Q&S A; Regent Schol; Sci A; *U of Ga; Pub Relations.*

ROADS, Peggy Jane
Hillsboro HS; Hillsboro, OH (7-180) VP, Band; Cpt, Chldr; Chor; Drama; Ensm; GS; 4H; Hmrm; Lat C; NHS; SC; VP, Tri-HiY; S-T, Jr Cl; JV, Bkbl; Sftbl; Swim; Tr; Alg A; Bio A; 4H A; Hon Prog; Math A; Sci A; High HR; Lat C A; *Otterbein Col; Pre-Law.*

ROANE, Leslie Kyle
St Joseph HS; Jeanerette, LA (6-29) Ann; Sch P; Span Cert; *USL; Acct.*

ROANSAVILLE, Steven Donnell
Kodiak HS; Kodiak, AK (21-97) Cpt, Wrest; Rotary A; MVP, Wrest; Robin Harvey Mem Schol A; *Willamette Col; Bio.*

ROARK, J Scott
Bridgeport HS; Bridgeport, TX; FFA; Math C; NHS; Sftbl; Tnns; Phys Ed A; *Draftsman.*

ROARK, Janie Christine
Koshkonong HS; Koshkonong, MO (10-21) Chor; VP, FHA; Cl Fav; HQn; Most Out; Type A.

ROARK, Vickie Lynn
Fairview HS; Ashland, KY (7-100) Co-Ed, Ann; VP, FHA; GS; Secy, NHS; Type A; WW; *Ashland Comm Col; Nurs.*

ROBB, Catherine Anne
Northwest HS; Omaha, NE (33%-496) A Cap Choir; Chor; Ensm; Type A; Yth Fel; HR; Sunday Sch Teacher; Vacation Church Sch Teacher; Church Yth Group; *Wayne St Teachers Col; Home Ec.*

ROBB, Celestene
Sussex Central HS; Sussex, VA (2-186) Band; Secy, BC; Chess C; Dbte Tm; Fr C; NHS; SC; Pres, Tri-HiY; Chem A; Gov Honor Prog; Hist A; MLS; Sci A; Val; Band Jacket; Fr Medal; WW; Chor Pin; *U of Va; Acct.*

ROBB, Cheri Lynn
Nordonia HS; Macedonia, OH (9-439) BC; Drama; Hmrm; NHS; Ski C; Swim; Tnns; COM; Hon Prog; Yth Fel; 1st Cl GSct; Drill Tm; Church Choir; Presbyterian Yth Group; *Nurs.*

ROBB, Lisa Ann
Guide Rock Pub HS; Guide Rock, NE; S-T, Band; Chldr; Rainbow; Spch C; Mgr, Bsbl; Bkbl; Sftbl; Tr; Spch A; Type A; *Spch.*

ROBB, Michele Marie
Se Whitfield HS; Dalton, GA (5-234) Band; BC; Chess C; Ensm; Math C; NHS; Sci C; Alg A; COM; Hist A; Dist Band; Jr Beta C; Highest Score PSAT; *Berry Col.*

ROBB, Sharon Sue
Pinckneyville Comm HS; Pinckneyville, IL (13-155) Bus C; Chor; Fr C; FHA; Pres, 4H; Co-Ch, Key C; NHS; Sftbl; COM; Citz A; 4H A; Hon Prog; I Dare You; Most Out; St Scholar; Yth Fel; Lib Staff; 4-H Ill Outst; Vlbl; GAA; 4-H Key C; *Covanant Col; Bus.*

ROBBEN, Edward James
Southside HS; Fort Smith, AR (20%-490) Key C; Bsbl; Ftbl; *Okla St U; Sci.*

ROBBINS, Charles Edward
Jesse H Jones Sr HS; Houston, TX (82-347) City Conf; Pres, Span C; SC; Citz A; ROTC A; *Prairie View A&M U; Elec Engr.*

ROBBINS, Dana Royce
Milford HS; Milford, UT (1-39) Var C; Bkbl; *U of Ariz; Archt.*

ROBBINS, Daniel Stephen
W Chicago Comm HS; W Chicago, IL; A Cap Choir; Band; Chor; Drama; Madrigal; Mod Mus Mas; Orch; A-Ed, Sch P; Spch C; Rptr, Sch Paper; NIGSOA Mus Medal; St Mus Medals; Band-Mus Camp Schol; Mod Mus Master Mus Camp Schol; *Mus.*

ROBBINS, Diane
Richmond Sr HS; Rockingham, NC (30-600) Ann; Span C; Citz A; 4H A; ROTC A; *Dental Technician.*

ROBBINS, James Luther
Charleroi Area Jr Sr HS; Charleroi, PA (40-240) Chor; Demolay; NHS; Sch P; COM; Past Master Coun, Demolay A Pin; *Inst of Computer Management; Computer Prog.*

ROBBINS, Karen Ann
Blanchet HS; Seattle, WA (42-285) CYO; Fr C; Rptr, Sch P; Cpt, Vlbl; *Shoreline Col; Law.*

ROBBINS, Kimberly Gail
Oak Harbor HS; Oak Harbor, WA (70-350) Span C; Secy, SC; Sftbl; Swim; Academic Schol; *Northwestern Col; Bus.*

ROBBINS, Lynne Dianne
Marianapolis Prep Sch; Thompson, CT (7-24) Chldr; Pres, 4H; Ski C; 4H A; *Eng.*

ROBBINS, Mark Bruce
Searcy HS; Searcy, AR; BC; BS; VP, Key C; NHS; SC; Pres, Jr Cl; Pres, Soph Cl; Ftbl; WW; Lt Gov, Key C; *U of Ark; Med.*

ROBBINS, Mark David
Westfield Sr HS; Westfield, NJ (33%-650) Chor; Bus.

ROBBINS, Neil Frederick
Trinity Sch; New York, NY (36-92) Dbte Tm; JV, Bsbl; Bkbl; Tr; NMS; Ntl Sci Found; NEDT; *Nuclear Sci.*

ROBBINS, Nickie Dewayne
Lake HS; Uniontown, OH; JV, Ftbl; JV, Wrest.

ROBBINS, Paul David
A E Beach HS; Savannah, GA (1-275) Band; VP, BC; Tres, Fr C; Key C; Lat C; Pres, Mu Alpha Theta; NHS; Order/Arrow; Alg A; Bausch & Lomb A; Bio A; COM; Chem A; Gov Honor Prog; Hist A; Math A; NMF; NMS; NEDT; Order/Arrow A; Sci A; Star Student; Summa Cum Laude; Century III Ldrs, St Semi-Fin; Savannah Sci Seminar; WW; Most Intellectual.

ROBBINS, Randall Eugene
Allen Jay HS; High Point, NC (22-100) Band; Fr C; Hmrm; Monogram; SC; Rptr, Jr Cl; Pres, Soph Cl; Bkbl; Ftbl; Tr; Sports Ltr; *ASU; Computer Sci.*

ROBBINS, Richard Damon
Ensley HS; Birmingham, AL; Secy, Math C; Order/Arrow; Ftbl; *Birmingham Sou Col; Math.*

ROBBINS, Sandra Faye
Chester HS; Chester, PA; *Temple U; Bus Ed.*

ROBBINS, Sandra Lea
Manchester HS; Akron, OH (100-300) Ann; Sch P; Secy, JA; Future Secy's of Amer; *Secy.*

ROBBINS, Sherry Louise
Springdale HS; Springdale, AR; Dbte Tm; FHA; FTA; Span C; Golf; Tnns; Valentine Qn; Pres, VP, Church Yth Group; *U of Ark; Elem Ed.*

ROBBINS, Trudy Gale
E Ascension Acad; Gonzales, LA; Cpt, Chldr; FBLA; VP, SC; Pres, Jr Cl; Pres, Soph Cl; Cl Fav; Fresh Maid; Miss EAA; Homecoming Maid of Hon.

ROBENALT, Anita Elizabeth
Belaire HS; Baton Rouge, LA (25%-403) Cpt, Chldr; Secy, FBLA; Tnns; Hist A; Asst Drum Major; HR; Shorthand I; Outst Soph Musician; Outst Phys Ed A; *LSU.*

ROBER, Paul Ewald
Temple Christian HS; Redford Twp, MI (4-60)
Chor; VP, Jr Cl; Bsbl; Co-Cpt, Bkbl; JV, Ftbl; Cpt,
Hockey; Soccer; Alg A; Chem A; Math A; MLS;
Sci A; *U of Mich; Med.*

ROBERSON, Barbara Diane
F O Alexander HS; Starkville, MS (30-59) Fin,
Hmrm; *Miss St U; Spch Ed.*

ROBERSON, Darrell Keith
Homewood HS; Homewood, AL (20%-283) Fr C;
A-Ed, Sch P; JV, Bkbl; JV, Ftbl; Hon Prog; Q&S A;
Samford U.

ROBERSON, Debora Denice
Wilburton HS; Wilburton, OK (3-62) FHA; NHS;
Span C; Span NHS; Var C; Bkbl; Tr; Alg A; Bio A;
Gov Honor Prog; Hon Prog; Sci A; Yth Fel; *Okla
City U; Religion.*

ROBERSON, Gary Charles
Hazlewood HS; Town Creek, AL (3-50) Pres, BC;
Drama; Secy, FFA; Sci C; Secy, SC; Pres, Sr Cl;
Bkbl; Ftbl; Lion A; Spch A; Schol Bowl Tm; *U of
Ala; Commerce.*

ROBERSON, George Franklin
Hazlewood HS; Town Creek, AL (5-50) F-Ed,
Ann; Band; Parl, BC; Chor; Drama; Ensm; Tres,
FFA; VP, 4H; NHS; Sci C; SC; Var C; Bsbl; Bkbl;
Ftbl; Spch A; 1st Tm, All-St Ftbl; Schol Bowl Tm;
U of Ala; Bus Adm.

ROBERSON, Gregory Alan
Homewood HS; Homewood, AL; Band; Chor;
Drama; Fr C; Thes; WW Among Mus Stu in Amer
HS; Cl Musician; Most Outst Male Choral Member; *Samford U; Mus.*

ROBERSON, Jan Marie
Glendale Acad; Glendale, CA (10-68) A Cap
Choir; Band; Chor; JV, Bkbl; JV, Soccer; Sftbl; Tr;
Pres A; Pathfinder; *La Sierra U; Bio.*

ROBERSON, Marion Shevette
Northeastern HS; Elizabeth City, NC; Ch, Ann;
Band; Drama; Rptr, Fr C; Key C; SC; Secy,
Tri-HiY; COM; Citz A; Delta Sigma Theta A; Elk
A; Journ A; Yth Fel; AKA' S 2nd Pl A, Fashion;
AKA' S 3rd Pl A, Talent; GS Coun Hon; *U of NC
at Greensboro; Psych.*

ROBERSON, Phyllis Anita
Northwest HS; St Louis, MO (2-728) SC; Tnns;
COM; Citz A; *Sci.*

ROBERSON, Shari Lynn
Homewood HS; Homewood, AL; Bus C; Chor;
FBLA; Cpt, Swim; Yth Coun; *U of Montevallo;
Secy Sci.*

ROBERSON, Tina Renee
Hewitt-Trussville HS; Trussville, AL (5%-280)
Tres, Band; Mu Alpha Theta; NHS; Orch; COM;
Ed.

ROBERT, Mary Catherine
Colegio Ntra Sra de la Merced; Hato Rey, PR
(5-92) Band; VP, Chem C; Chor; Lit Mag; Math C;
Model UN; Secy, Phys C; VP, Pol Sci C; Sci C;
Span C; Spch C; Semi-Fin, Tr; Alg A; Bio A; COM;
Chem A; Hist A; Hon Prog; Math A; Phy A; Sci A;
Star Student; Type A; Art A; *Vet Med.*

ROBERT, Robin Paula
Destrehan HS; Destrehan, LA (2-200) BC; Chldr;
Co-Ed, Sch P; SC; Tres, Jr Cl; *Oeshner Sch; Surgical Tech.*

ROBERT, Todd Arthur
Glenbard E HS; Lombard, IL (55-647) Band; NHS;
Var C; Ftbl; Co-Cpt, Wrest; NMS; *Valdoraiso Col;
Med.*

ROBERTI, David Gene
Loyalton HS; Loyalton, CA (33%-42) Band; BS;
4H; Ch, SC; Ch, Soph Cl; Bsbl; Bkbl; Ftbl; 4H A;
Yth Fel; Comm Yth Choir; Church Choir.

**ROBERTO,
Therese Anne Pereira**
George Washington Sr HS; Mangilao, GUAM;
NHS; SC; Class Coun; *Solano Col; Special Ed.*

ROBERTS, Anna Laura
Bible Baptist Day Sch; Savannah, GA (5-54) Chor;
Most Academic; *Armstrong St Col; Bus Adm.*

ROBERTS, Anna Louise
Virgie HS; Virgie, KY (3-112) Ann; Rptr, FTA; Sci
C; Spch C; Friendliest; Co-Ed-Y; Pep C.

ROBERTS, Benjamin Daryl
Harriman HS; Harriman, TN (9-149) Ann; Cpt,
Band; BC; InterAct C; Key C; Pres, SC; Bsbl; Bkbl;
HCt; Rotary A; *Bryan Col; Bus Acct.*

ROBERTS, Beth Ann
Norwood HS; Norwood, OH;

ROBERTS, Bonita Lovella
Mifflin Sr HS; Columbus, OH; Cpt, Mjrte; Rptr,
Sch P; Tres, Jr Cl; Bkbl; Sftbl; COM; Journ A; ARC
A; Vlbl; Treas, OEA C Cl.

ROBERTS, Bradley Ray
Odessa HS; Odessa, TX; NHS; Sch P; SC; MVP,
Bsbl; Bkbl; MVP, Ftbl; Cl Fav; Hon Prog; Most
Out; FCA; *Tex Tech Col; Archt.*

ROBERTS, Brenda Gail
Valdosta HS; Valdosta, GA;

ROBERTS, Brenda Joyce
S Jones HS; Ellisville, MS; FHA; Spch C; Phys Ed
A; *Jones Jr Col; Bus Adm.*

ROBERTS, Brenda Lee
Hoehne HS; Hoehne, CO; Chldr; FHA; Pres, 4H;
NHS; Secy, SC; Pres, Jr Cl; VP, Soph Cl; MVP,
Bkbl; Swim; Tnns; Fin, Tr; DARGCA; 4H A; Hist
A; HQn; Most Out; Poet A; Cpt, Bkbl; Rodeo Qn;
WW; Bkbl Princess; Fresh Qn.

ROBERTS, Carl Lewis
Central HS; Little Rock, AR (75-554) FBLA; Span
C; Ntl Achievement Semi-Fin; KLRA Yth Ldrship
A; *U of Ark at Fayetteville; Architecture.*

ROBERTS, Carol Ann
Daviess Co HS; Owensboro, KY (225-300) Band;
Ky Wesleyan Col; Art.

ROBERTS, Carol Elizabeth
Ashbrook HS; Gastonia, NC (35-450) AFS; Band;
V-Ch, Drama; Ensm; Fr C; NHS; 4H A; Keyette C;
Appalachian St U; Fr Ed.

ROBERTS, Carol Jean
Dunlap Comm HS; Dunlap, IA (20-57) Ann; Chor;
Drama; VP, Fr C; FHA; FTA; Pres, 4H; F-Ed, Sch
P; SC; Bus Mgr, Bkbl; Beauty; B Crocker A; Cl Fav;
4H A; HCt; Yth Fel; S-T, Church Yth Fel; SC Rep;
Journ.

ROBERTS, Carolyn Ann
Madison HS; Madison, TN; FHA; ARC; Sftbl;
Nurs.

ROBERTS, Carolyn Jean
Virgie HS; Virgie, KY; Band; BC; Chor; Ger C; 4H;
4H A; Cpt, Drill Tm; Spelling A; *Morehead Col;
Journ.*

ROBERTS, Chris Edwin
Greenville HS; Greenville, MS (7-569) Lat C; Pres,
NHS; Sch Achieve Tm; Spch C; Sftbl; COM; Hon
Prog; Math A; NMS; NEDT; Opt Out Tn; *Mich St
U; Physics.*

ROBERTS, Christopher Jon
Kalamazoo Central HS; Kalamazoo, MI (7%-460)
A Cap Choir; Band; Lat C; Madrigal; NHS; Ski C;
Cpt, Swim; COM; Citz A; Hon Prog; St Scholar;
MVP, Swim; Neill Schol; Merit A; Schol A; *Kalamazoo Col; Sci.*

ROBERTS, Colleen Andra
Northport Pub HS; Northport, MI (1-18) Ann;
Pres, Band; NHS; HCt; Val; FOREST Rep; *U of
Mich.*

ROBERTS, Connie Kay
Bradleyville Sch; Bradleyville, MO (7-30) Chor;
Sch o-t Ozarks.

ROBERTS, Cynthia Diane
Fosdick Masten U HS; Buffalo, NY (2-110) Bus C;
CYO; Chor; Pres, Drama; Ensm; FNA; Cpt, Mjrte;
NHS; Sch P; SC; Alg A; COM; Cl Fav; Hon Prog;
MLS; Most Out; Spch A; Dancing A; Sewing A;
Hons A; Art A; *Harvard U; Law.*

ROBERTS, Cynthia Jane
Quabbin Regional HS; Barre, MA (24-151) A Cap
Choir; Band; Community Yth Symph; Ensm; Semi-
Fin, GS; 4H; Lat C; Tri-HiY; 4H A; Math A; *Lyndon St; Special Ed.*

ROBERTS, Cynthia Lea
Lawrenceville HS; Lawrenceville, IL (5-179) Chem
C; NHS; Span C; SC; *Psych.*

ROBERTS, David Eugene
Cleburne HS; Cleburne, TX (44-386) Band; HiY;
Tres, Key C; NHS; Ski C; Span C; Golf; Hon Prog;
Church Sftbl Tm; Pres, Yth Fel; *Tex Tech U; Bus
Adm.*

ROBERTS, David Lee
Grove HS; Grove, OK (19-90) BC; 4H; Bsbl; Ftbl;
Tr; 4H A; Hist A; FCA; Secy of St A; Hist; *Northeastern A&M U; Pre-Law.*

ROBERTS, David Wayne
LaFarge Pub Sch; LaFarge, WI (25-42) Bus Mgr,
Ann; Var C; Mgr, Bsbl; JV, Bkbl; Mgr, Ftbl; Tr;
Army; Military Police.

ROBERTS, Debbie Jeanne
Broadview Acad; Lafox, IL; Band; Chor; Ski C; SC;
VP, Girls C; Band A; *Andrews U.*

ROBERTS, Deborah Ruth
Lubbock Christian HS; Lubbock, TX; Band; Chor;
NHS; All Region Band; Bus Ministry Work; *Lubbock Christian Col.*

ROBERTS, Dinah Elizabeth
Kountze HS; Kountze, TX (5-84) Secy, NHS; St
Stu Congress; Tres, SC; Bkbl; H of F; Hon Prog;
Vlbl; All Dist Bkbl.

ROBERTS, Donald Scott
A Crawford Mosley HS; Panama City, FL (4-600)
VP, BC; VP, Chess C; Ensm; Mu Alpha Theta;
NHS; Span C; Citz A; MLS; *Astronomy.*

ROBERTS, Douglas Earl
Maranatha HS; Arcadia, CA (18-65) Chor; Pres,
Hmrm; Ski C; JV, Bsbl; JV, Ftbl; JV, Tnns; Eagle
Sct; *Biola Col; Bus.*

ROBERTS, Douglas Lee Jr
Churchland HS; Portsmouth, VA; Pres, Bus C; S-T,
CYO; Dbte Tm; HiY; Hmrm; Lat C; SC; JV, Ftbl;
Tnns; Alg A; COM; Chem A; Citz A; Hon Prog;
Opt A; Sci A; Coastal Canoeists; Va Phar Assn;
Tidewater Sci Congress; Jr NHS; *U of Va; Med.*

ROBERTS, Elizabeth Ann
Virgie HS; Virgie, KY (11-103) Ann; BC; FHA;
FTA; Good Schol A; *Prestonsburg Col; Acct.*

ROBERTS, Elizabeth Anne
Barboursville HS; Barboursville, WV (33%-500)
Lat C; Art C; Art Exhibit; *W Va U; Spch Pathology.*

ROBERTS, Emily Diane
Ritenour HS; Overland, MO (150-800) A Cap
Choir; Band; Chor; Fr C; Hmrm; NHS; SC; Tr; *U of
Mo; Special Ed.*

ROBERTS, Freda Ann
Cache HS; Cache, OK; BC; S-T, FHA; 4H; Tres, Jr
Cl; Opt A; *Cameron U; Tech.*

ROBERTS, Freddy Dean
Cache HS; Cache, OK; BC; Secy, FFA.

ROBERTS, Gloria Jeannette
Alfred E Beach HS; Savannah, GA; BC; Chor; 4H;
Hmrm; Lat C; Lat NHS; NHS; SC; COM; 4H A;
Hist A; Lat Hon Soc; Lat Achievement; Eng A;
Med.

ROBERTS, Gynell Katherine
Memphis HS; Memphis, TX; FHA; Swim; Tnns;
Swtht, Church; PA; Tres, Home Ec Relative Occupations; *TSTI.*

ROBERTS, Ingrid Louise
Lumen Cordium HS; Bedford, OH; Chor; Drama;
FHA; Mjrte; Ntl Yth Conf; ARC; Span C; Spch C;
Y-Tns; Co-Cpt, Sftbl; Co-Cpt, Tnns; COM; Citz A;
Yth Fel; *Nurs.*

ROBERTS, Jackson James
Clyde A Erwin HS; Asheville, NC (125-250) Bus
C; Hmrm; Span C; Up Bound; Swim; COM; Span
A; *Oral Roberts U; Bus Adm.*

ROBERTS, Jacquelyn Yvonne
Vicksburg HS; Vicksburg, MS; Band; NHS; H of F;
Jackson St U; Acct.

ROBERTS, James Edward
Northwest HS; St Louis, MO (10-642) NHS; Hon
Prog; VICA; *Kans U; Archt.*

ROBERTS, Janice Lynne
Shades Valley HS; Birmingham, AL (16-278) Tres,
Lat C; Math C; Mu Alpha Theta; NHS; COM; Yth
Fel; Parl, Ala Jr Classical League; Usher's C; Lat
HR; All A's Cert; Pres, Church Yth Group; Hon
Graduate; *U of Montevallo; Med Technology.*

ROBERTS, Jerri Rea
Vanguard HS; Ocala, FL (1-350) FHA; NHS; Phys Fitness A.

ROBERTS, Jerry
Columbia HS; Columbia Station, OH; Fr C; SC; Bkbl; Tr; Math.

ROBERTS, Jerry Shane
Pleasant Grove HS; Pleasant Grove, AL (6-150) VP, Chem C; Tres, NHS; VP, Phys C; Cpt, Var C; Pres, Sr Cl; Cpt, Ftbl; Cl Fav; Most Out; Yth Fel; MVP, Golden Helmet, Ftbl; Talent Search; U of Ala; Dentistry.

ROBERTS, Joanne Louise
Philadelphia HS for Girls; Philadelphia, PA; Chldr; Drama; Hmrm; Model UN; Swim; Sci A; Yale Book A; U of Pa; Law.

ROBERTS, Joy Norma
Prospect HS; Mount Prospect, IL (150-593) Chor; Ntl Yth Conf; Sftbl; Yth Fel; Campfire Girls; Vlbl; Sunday Sch Teacher; Secy, Church HS League; Harper Jr Col; Executive Secy.

ROBERTS, Judy Anne
Willows HS; Willows, CA (17-130) Sci A.

ROBERTS, Julia Taylor
Orangeburg-Wilkinson HS; Orangeburg, SC (10%-500) Cpt, Chldr; GS; SC; VP, Sr Cl; Beauty; DARGCA; HCt; Most Sch Spirit; May Court; Wofford Schol; Clemson U; Sociology.

ROBERTS, Julie Karen
Lakewood HS; St Petersburg, FL (7-349) Fr C; Pres, French NHS; Secy, NFL; NHS; Spch C; COM; VFW Orator Win; St Pete Jr Col; Med Tech.

ROBERTS, Karen Ann
Madison HS; Richmond, KY; BC; Fr C.

ROBERTS, Karen Denise
Brandon HS; Brandon, MS (36-136) FHA; Shorthand A; Miss Col; Bus.

ROBERTS, Karen Dianna
E St Louis Sr HS; E Saint Louis, IL (120-647) Drama; Hmrm; Lat C; Ntl Yth Conf; Spch C; Beauty; Hon Prog; Spch A; Yth Fel; Sigma Gamma Rho; Miss Wesley-Bethel; Secy, Pom-Pom Sq; Church Yth Choir; Acct.

ROBERTS, Katherine Elizabeth
Joseph Kershaw Acad; Camden, SC (2-30) BC; Bus Mgr, Lit Mag; Rainbow; Bus Mgr, Sch P; Bio A; Gr Marshal; Hon Prog; Sal; WW; Winthrop Col; Mus.

ROBERTS, Kathy
Elbert Co Comprehensive HS; Elberton, GA; Chor; Hmrm; SC; Bkbl.

ROBERTS, Kathy Jean
Bakersfield R-4 HS; Bakersfield, MO (1-16) Ed, Ann; Pres, Band; Chldr; Chor; FHA; 4H; Pres, NHS; Ed, Sch P; SC; VP, Jr Cl; VP, Soph Cl; Bkbl; Sftbl; Journ A; MLS; Regent Schol; Type A; Val; Eng A; Yrbk Ed; Band A; HS Schols; SMSU.

ROBERTS, Kathy Lee
E Longmeadow HS; E Longmeadow, MA (25-269) Drama; Fr C; Rptr, Lit Mag; NHS; Sci C; Sftbl; Tr; Bausch & Lomb A; Bio A; Citz A; Hon Prog; Yth Fel; Director-Producer, Drama C; Commencement Spkr; Springfield Col; Therapeutic Recreation.

ROBERTS, Kevin Jerome
N Hollywood HS; N Hollywood, CA (35-650) Band; Hmrm; Mod Mus Mas; Cpt, Cr-Ctry; Cpt, Tr; Ntl Assn of Negro Mus; St Church Brotherhood Union; BSct; Tutorial Service A; Hoyla Marymount U; Mech Engr.

ROBERTS, Larry Dale
Kountze HS; Kountze, TX; FFA; Tex A&M Col; Vet.

ROBERTS, Laura Lynn
Quincy Notre Dame HS; Quincy, IL; SC.

ROBERTS, Lee
S Jones HS; Ellisville, MS (9-27) Band; FFA; COM; HKg; Jones Jr Col; Aeronautic Tech.

ROBERTS, Leigh Anne
Briarcrest HS; Memphis, TN; Co-Cpt, Chldr; Chor; FHA; GS; VP, Hmrm; Tnns; COM; Citz A; Cl Fav; HCt; Hon Prog; Kiwanis A; ARC A; Decem C; Jaycettes; Soc Secy & Hist, Chi Sigma Omega So; U of Miss; Med.

ROBERTS, Lew Anthony
Balaton HS; Balaton, MN (25%-33) Ann; Band; Chor; Drama; Ensm; Madrigal; Spch C; Thes; Var C; Fin, Bsbl; Bkbl; Ftbl; Golf; Sftbl; JV, Tr; COM; ARC A; Spch A; Champion Ftbl Tm; Three Trophies Bsbl; Golden Valley Lutheran Col; Spch.

ROBERTS, Lisa Clair
Crestview Sr HS; Crestview, FL (55-240) Pres, A Cap Choir; Band; Pres, Chor; Ensm; VP, InterClub Coun; Madrigal; Cpt, Mjrte; Orch; VP, SC; VP, Sr Cl; Pres A; Achv A; Fin, Beauty; Tallahassee Barber Col; Hair Stylist.

ROBERTS, Lizabeth Dawn
E Pennsboro Area HS; Enola, PA (9-230) Chor; Drama; Ger C; Hmrm; Madrigal; NHS; Best Bible Stu; Run-Up, Bst Cmpr Pa Christian Camp; Bucknell U; Bus Adm.

ROBERTS, Lois Jean
Man HS; Man, WV (8-180) Bus C; Commercial C; FBLA; FHA; NHS; Hon Prog; Type A; Shorthand, Bookkeeping, A's.

ROBERTS, Lorinda Lee
Rolling Hills HS; Rolling Hill Est, CA (20-700) Fr C; Ski C; CSF; Hospital Vol; Pres Clrm; Social Ch, Church HS Department; Secy, Church Yth; Pastor's Yth Board; Westmont Col; Nurs.

ROBERTS, Lucinda Ruth
Virgie HS; Virgie, KY; Ann; Chldr; Ch, Dbte Tm; FTA; 4H; Sci C; Sftbl; Tr; 4H A; Sci A; Type A; Hon A; U of Ky; Law.

ROBERTS, Mari Jon
Sublette HS; Sublette, KS (25-45) Ch, Ann; Band; Dbte Tm; Ensm; GS; Pres, 4H; Bkbl; Sftbl; Tr; 4H A; VP, S-T, Rptr, Parl, 4-H C; U of Kans; Psych.

ROBERTS, Mark David
Friendly Sr HS; Oxon Hill, MD; Ger C; Silver Stars, Military Acad; Embry-Riddle U; Aviation.

ROBERTS, Mark Gregory
Pattonville Sr HS; Maryland Heights, MO (21-855) BS; Ger C; NHS; Bkbl; Cpt, Golf; Curator A; MVP, Golf; Westminster Col.

ROBERTS, Mark Lawrence
Fayette Co HS; Fayette, AL (23-150) Band; VP, Mu Alpha Theta; Sci C; Span C; Bsbl; Cl Fav; Hon Prog; Brewer St Jr Col.

ROBERTS, Meredith Ann
Mt Blue Jr HS; Farmington, ME (2%-265) Band; Chor; Orch; Sftbl; Pres, Stage Band.

ROBERTS, Meredith Jan
Tar Heel HS; Tar Heel, NC; BC; FBLA; Span C; Marshal; WW; Bladen Tech Inst; Bus Adm.

ROBERTS, Michael Charles
Royal Oak Dondero HS; Royal Oak, MI (82-510) Co-Ch, Chess C; Ger C; NHS; Sci C; Ftbl; Tnns; Yth Fel; MHEAA Schol; W Mich U; Chem.

ROBERTS, Patricia Ann
S R Butler HS; Huntsville, AL (10%-600) BC; Co-Cpt, ARC; ARC A; Auburn U; Vet Med.

ROBERTS, Patti Beth
Grove HS; Grove, OK (5-136) Band; BC; Dbte Tm; Drama; Rptr, FHA; VP, 4H; Mjrte; NHS; Spch C; Soph Cl; Bkbl; Sftbl; Citz A; 4H A; Most Out; Odd Fellow Fin; Sci A; Spch A; Yth Fel; Odd Fellow UN Trip Spch Win; Dist, Regional & St Spch Contest; Supt HR; Spch Fin, Farmers Union; Northeastern Okla Jr Col; Spch.

ROBERTS, Patty Lynn
Cache HS; Cache, OK (3-46) VP, BC; Pres, FHA; VP, 4H; NHS; Pres, Jr Cl; B Crocker A; Cl Fav; FFA Swtht; Cameron U; Home Ec.

ROBERTS, Paul Walter
Hampton HS; Hampton, VA (25-587) Tres, A Cap Choir; Chem C; VP, Chess C; Fr C; Co-Ch, Key C; NHS; Phys C; Tnns; Hon Prog; Yth Fel; Va Polytech Inst St U; Mech Engr.

ROBERTS, Paul William
Central Bucks W HS; Doylestown, PA (150-550) JV, Soccer; Tr; Meteorology.

ROBERTS, Rachel Ann
E Gaston HS; Mount Holly, NC (10%-301) Band; VP, BC; Drama; Hmrm; VP, Span C; Rptr, SC; Hon Prog; Nom, Gov Sch.

ROBERTS, Randy Glen
Hutsonville HS; Hutsonville, IL (16-44) Chor; FFA; Var C; Bsbl; JV, Bkbl; Cr-Ctry; COM; 4H A; Lincoln Trail Jr Col; Industrial Art.

ROBERTS, Rebecca Ruth
Shenendoah Vally Acad; New Market, VA (2-110) Band; Chor; Secy, 4H; Span C; Fin, Tr; COM; 4H A; HR; Cl Pastor; Sou Missionary Col; Home Ec.

ROBERTS, Reginald
Amite Co Attendance Center; Gloster, MS (1-220) Band; BC; FFA; 4H; Hmrm; Orch; Secy, Soph Cl; Alg A; COM; Citz A; 4H A; MLS.

ROBERTS, Richard Coyd
Southside HS; Gadsden, AL; JV, Bkbl; Art C.

ROBERTS, Robin Renee
Fairfield Local HS; Leesburg, OH (4-42) Ann; Pres, Drama; Pres, FTA; NHS; Sch Achieve Tm; VP, Span C; VP, Sr Cl; Cl Fav; Type A; FTA Schol; Kettering Col of Med Arts; Radiology.

ROBERTS, Roderick Abel
Redlands Sr HS; Redlands, CA (15%-850) Chor; Fr C; InterClub Coun; Madrigal; Pres, Order/Arrow; Co-Ed, Sch P; SC; Pres, Sr Cl; Pres, Jr Cl; MVP, Cr-Ctry; Co-Cpt, Tr; CSF; Citz A; Journ A; Most Out; Rotary A; St Scholar; Bus Mgr, Sch Paper; U of Calif at Riverside; Humanities.

ROBERTS, Sadie Renee
Roosevelt HS; Gary, IN (4-555) Band; FTA; Lit Ral; Math C; NHS; VP, SC; COM; Hon Prog; Math A; Yth Fel; Ind U; Bus.

ROBERTS, Samuel Powell
Marked Tree HS; Marked Tree, AR (2-110) Ann; Chor; Drama; NHS; Sch P; Thes; Pres, Soph Cl; Bsbl; JV, Bkbl; Alg A; Bio A; Hon Prog; PTLC; Geom A; Art A; Civics A; Pres Fresh C; Best Actor; All-Region Choir; Win, Sci Fair; Highest GPA; Best Supporting Actor; Ouachita Baptist U; Bus Adm.

ROBERTS, Sharon Barbara
El Camino Real HS; Woodland Hills, CA (18-1095) Chor; Drama; Ch, Hmrm; Ski C; Thes; CSF; Hon Prog; U of Calif at Los Angeles; Liberal Arts.

ROBERTS, Sheila Anne
Shenendoah Valley Acad; New Market, VA (2-77) NHS; Ed, Sch P; Ski C; NMF; Excel A; Sou Missionary Col; Eng Ed.

ROBERTS, Steve Alan
Crittenden Co HS; Marion, KY (20-116) BC; BS; Drama; 4H; Tres, SC; Tres, Sr Cl; Pres, Jr Cl; Secy, Soph Cl; Bkbl; Cr-Ctry; Ftbl; Cpt, Tr; 4H A; Hon Prog; Math A; Most Out; 100 Point C, Tr; 1st Pl Woodworking, Murry St; Murray St U; Pre Phar.

ROBERTS, Susan Alice
S R Butler HS; Huntsville, AL (100-627) Chor; Fr C; Math C; Mu Alpha Theta; Sci C; Alg A; Mu Alph Theta; Auburn U; Archt.

ROBERTS, Susan Ann
Western Grove HS; Western Grove, AR (1-15) Bus Mgr, Ann; F-Ed, Sch P; Pres, Sr Cl; VP, Soph Cl; Cpt, Bkbl; Sftbl; COM; 4H A; Hist A; HCt; Hon Prog; Val; U of Central Ark; Psych.

ROBERTS, Tammy Marie
Cumberland Valley Christian Sch; Chambersburg, PA (1-11) Pres, Hmrm; Pres, Jr Cl; Hon Prog; Pres A; Secretarial.

ROBERTS, Theresa Evelyn
Loup City HS; Loup City, NE (25-82) Band; Chor; PTA A; JV, Vlbl; Nom, GS; Hastings Col; Acct.

ROBERTS, Thomas Eugene
Tillamook HS; Tillamook, OR (19-180) A Cap Choir; Ed, Ann; Pres, Demolay; Drama; Hmrm; InterClub Coun; Key C; VP, Mod Mus Mas; NHS; SC; Thes; Mgr, Ftbl; Tnns; Citz A; DARGCA; H of F; NEDT; Q&S A; All NW, All St, Choir; Ldrship Contest; Linfield Col; Bus Mgr.

ROBERTS, Wanda Annette
Acadiana HS; Lafayette, LA (30%-400) Fr C; Rainbow; U of SW La; Bus Adm.

ROBERTS, Wanda Gail
N Gwinnett HS; Suwanee, GA (10%-150) Band; Chldr; FHA; 4H; Mgr, Golf; Gov Honor Prog; 4H A; Journ A; Creative Writing A.

ROBERTS, William Allen
S R Butler HS; Huntsville, AL (25-650) BC; Pres,
Mu Alpha Theta; NHS; Order/Arrow; *Auburn U;
Law.*

ROBERTS, William Wade
Walter Hines Page HS; Greensboro, NC; ARC;
Yth Fel; Jr NHS; Law Explorers; *U of NC; Law.*

ROBERTSON, Brenda Jo
Plano Sr HS; Plano, TX (40%-1500) Chor; Sftbl;
Solo-Ensm A.

ROBERTSON, Charles Ricky
Goodlettsville HS; Goodlettsville, TN (53%-145)
Pres, Chor; Dbte Tm; Ensm; ARC; Bkbl; Sftbl;
Swim; Tnns; Tr; Cl Fav; Most Talented; Cl Offices;
Trevecca Nazarene Col; Mus.

ROBERTSON, Chonita
Pershing HS; Detroit, MI; Chldr; Asst Director,
Church Choir; *E Mich U; Pre-Med.*

ROBERTSON, Cindy Sue
Queen City HS; Queen City, TX (1-44) Ann; FHA;
Pres, NHS; Ed, Sch P; Span C; Cpt, Bkbl; Tr;
DARGCA; Type A; 1st Pl, Ready Writing; All-
Dist Bkbl; Regional Fin, Tr; *Texarkana Col; Ed.*

ROBERTSON, Dale Lee
F L Schlagle HS; Kansas City, KS (33-423) BS;
Hmmr; Order/Arrow; Rptr, Sch P; SC; Ftbl; Tr;
Wrest; *Med.*

ROBERTSON, Dana Lou
Ritenour Sr HS; Overland, MO (39-400) Var C;
Bkbl; Sftbl; Tnns; Hon Prog; Top 15%; *U of Mo;
Med Tech.*

ROBERTSON, Darice Ann
Reeds Spring HS; Reeds Spring, MO (9-75) Ann;
Chor; Secy, FHA; Span C; *Crowder Col.*

**ROBERTSON,
Deborah Roxanne**
Classical HS; Providence, RI (136-224) Citz A;
Mount Ida Jr Col; Interior Design.

ROBERTSON, Debra Lee
Dorman HS; Spartanburg, SC (1-425) Anchor C;
FHA; Ger C; NHS; COM; Sci A; S-T, Drill Tm;
Presbyterian Col Jr Fel; Jr Marshal; Top 10; *Winth-
rop Col; Early Childhood Ed.*

ROBERTSON, Denise Marie
Winnebago HS; Winnebago, MN (1-35) A-Ed,
Ann; JV, Chldr; Chor; Drama; FHA; Madrigal;
Rptr, Sch P; SC; HCt; Swtht; Type A; Gym; Merit
Achv A; WW; FFA Swtht; *Mankato St U; Bus
Adm.*

ROBERTSON, Donald Lee
Centerburg HS; Centerburg, OH (5-75) Pres, NHS;
A-Ed, Sch P; Span C; SC; VP, Var C; Co-Cpt, Cr-
Ctry; Co-Cpt, Ftbl; Tnns; Elk A; Journ A; Q&S A;
Public Relations.

ROBERTSON, Donna Machelle
St Elizabeth Acad; St Louis, MO; Chldr; Span C;
SC; *Marquette U; Med.*

ROBERTSON, Edith
Rufus King HS; Milwaukee, WI; Hmmr; NFL;
NHS; Swtht; PA A; Bus A; Phys Fitness A; Bus
Day A; *U of Wisc; Bus Adm.*

ROBERTSON, Jannette Lynn
Woodlawn HS; Baton Rouge, LA (150-300) Chldr;
Drama; FHA; Hmmr; SC; Thes; Swtht, Church Yth
Group; Contestant, Sch Beauty Pageant; All
Around Bstr; Missionette Qn; *LSU; Social Welfare.*

ROBERTSON, John David
Sooner HS; Bartlesville, OK (1-289) Lat C; SC; JV,
Bsbl; JV, Bkbl; Okla Hon Soc; *Okla U; Law.*

ROBERTSON, John Donald Jr
Central Baptist HS; Hampton, VA (2-21) Ger C;
VP, SC; Co-Cpt, Bsbl; Ftbl; Sftbl; COM; Phys Ed
Medal; *Archt.*

ROBERTSON, Joseph Claude
Norcross HS; Norcross, GA (33%-244) Demolay;
4H; Mgr, Bkbl; Mgr, Ftbl; Sftbl; Mgr, Tr; 4H A; JA
A; RD Rep, Demolay Highest Hon; *Ga Inst of
Tech; Computer Programming.*

ROBERTSON, Kathleen Marie
Ilion Jr Sr HS; Ilion, NY (10-180) Chor; NHS;
Orch; Secy, Y-Tns; *Nurs.*

ROBERTSON, Kathy Lynn
Olathe HS; Olathe, KS (17-460) Dbte Tm; NHS;
Swim; COM; Citz A; 4H A; Hon Prog; Math A;
Pres, Church Yth Group; *Kans St U; Acct.*

ROBERTSON, Kenneth Lee
Permian HS; Odessa, TX; Band; Fr C; *Tex Tech U.*

ROBERTSON, Letitia Annette
Carver Sr HS; Montgomery, AL; S-T, Chor; Span
C; Tr; COM; Type A; Acteens, Qn Regent in Serv-
ice; *U of Miss; Ed.*

ROBERTSON, Lou Ida
Norte Del Rio HS; Sacramento, CA (30-394) *San
Franciso St Col; Bus Adm.*

ROBERTSON, Mica Raelene
Spring Woods Sr HS; Houston, TX (10%-510)
AFS; GS; JETS; Math C; Mu Alpha Theta; NHS;
Sci C; Alg A; Pres, Explorer Post; Association Ch,
Explorer Pres; *Texas A&M U; Engr.*

ROBERTSON, Patrick Wayne
Herrin HS; Herrin, IL (22-200) Ann; Ger C; Key C;
Rptr, Sch P; SC; Var C; Pres, Jr Cl; Bkbl; Co-Cpt,
Cr-Ctry; Ftbl; Tr; COM; HCt; Faculty List; Tr &
Field HR; *US Naval Acad; Engr.*

ROBERTSON, Regina Mary
S F Austin HS; Austin, TX; Dbte Tm; Drama; F-
Ed, Sch P; SC; Citz A; Sci A; Spch A; Drill Tm;
City Swim League; Vlbl; Fin, Optimist Oratorial
Contest; *Sweet Briar Col; Law.*

ROBERTSON, Rosa Lee
St Helena HS; Greensburg, LA; Cpt, Chldr; FBLA;
Shorthand A; Most Female Ath; Miss Chldr; Miss
FBLA; *Sou U; Bus.*

ROBERTSON, Stephen Wayne
Kaufman HS; Kaufman, TX (20-120) Band; Bsbl;
Mgr, Ftbl; *Tex A&M U; Bus.*

ROBERTSON, Susan Elizabeth
Hickman Mills HS; Kansas City, MO; A Cap
Choir; Band; Chldr; S-T, Chor; VP, Drama; Ensm;
Pres, NHS; Orch; Spch C; SC; Sftbl; Tnns; Hon
Prog; Journ A; Spch A; Yth Fel; Creative Writing
A.

ROBERTSON, Tommy Lee
Risco HS; Risco, MO; Ann; FFA; NHS; Ed, Sch P;
Pres, Sr Cl; Pres, Jr Cl; Pres, Soph Cl; Tr; Cl Fav;
DARGCA; Type A; Friendliest; Prom King; Most
Artistic; Barnwarming King; *Southeast Mo St U.*

ROBERTSON, Vernon LaMarr
Risco HS; Risco, MO; FFA; Pres, Soph Cl; MVP,
Bsbl; Bkbl; Tr; Alg A; Math A; MLS; Sci A; *U of
Mo; Math.*

ROBERTSON, William Marion
Fuquay Varina Sr HS; Fuquay-Varina, NC; BC; Lat
C; Sci C; Drafting A; 3rd Pl, Dist Drafting Contest;
U of Va; Archt.

ROBESON, Kathleen Louise
Reseda HS; Reseda, CA (168-658) Nom, May
Court; Gym Tm; No 1 Dist, Drill Tm; *Pierce Col.*

ROBICHAUD, Robin Cathleen
Upperman HS; Baxter, TN; BC; CYO; Chldr;
Drama; FHA; NHS; Thes; Pres, Soph Cl; Sftbl;
Rptr, TOEC; Civinette o-t Yr; Princess of Personal-
ity; Best Personality; Most Sch Spirit; *Tenn Tech
U; Bus.*

ROBINS, Debbie Annmarie
St Catharine Acad; Bronx, NY (76-199) Chor;
COM; Sci A; *Drew U; Acct.*

ROBINS, Rodney Selwyn
NW HS; St Louis, MO (52-325) SC; Soccer; Tr; JA
A; Spch A; HR; *U of Mo; Elec Engr.*

ROBINSON, Addie Elizabeth
Plano Sr HS; Plano, TX (5-850) Secy, Ger C; Jr
Miss Pagent; NHS; Hon Prog; Accompanist, Con-
cert Choir; Rotary C Swtht; Church Organist; *Tex
Woman's U; Mus Therapy.*

ROBINSON, Adrian Gleen
Merced HS; Merced, CA (10%-800) Var C; JV,
Bkbl; Ftbl; *Bishop Col; Psych.*

ROBINSON, Angela Lee
Jones HS; Lynnville, TN (1-22) Ed, Ann; Tres, BC;
Bus C; Chldr; Drama; FHA; 4H; Ed, Sch P; Spch C;
SC; Var C; Pres, Sr Cl; Bkbl; Sftbl; Alg A; Beauty;
Chem A; 4H A; Hist A; HCt; Hon Prog; Math A;
Sci A; Spch A; Val; VofDEM; Sch Win, DREMC;
Shorthand A; WW; *Columbia St Comm Col; Med-
Lab Tech.*

ROBINSON, Angela Marie
George Wythe HS; Wytheville, VA (25-143) Band;
Co-Cpt, Chldr; Drama; Sci C; Secy, SC; Bkbl;
Chaplin, NHS & Mu Alpha Theta; Jr Princess,
Job's Daughters; GAA; Friendliest; Vlbl; Ldrship &
SCA Activity As, SC; *Emory & Henry Col; Vet Sci.*

ROBINSON, Anita Ann
Ebbert L Furr HS; Houston, TX (73-211) Bus C;
Rptr, Drama; Pres, FHA; Hmmr; Rptr, Spch C; SC;
Yth Fel; Pres, Christian Stu Union; FHA A; *San
Jacinto Col; Commuter Sci.*

ROBINSON, Ann Elizabeth
Hoopeston-E Lynn HS; Hoopeston, IL (1-150)
Ann; Band; Chldr; Chor; FTA; Secy, 4H; Cpt,
Hmmr; Math C; NHS; Span C; SC; Tr; 4H A; Hist
A; Hon Prog; I Dare You; Val; Band A; St 4-H Key
C; Ntl Citizenship Short Course; WW; *U of Ill;
Econ.*

ROBINSON, Anna Jane
Benton Co R-1 HS; Cole Camp, MO; Rptr, FFA;
FHA; NHS; Bkbl; FFA Schol; Growth Encounter,
FHA; *St Fair Comm Col; Animal Husbandry.*

ROBINSON, Bill Edward
Gumberry HS; Gumberry, NC; Fr C; 4H; Sch P;
Ftbl; 4H A; *A&T St U; Elec.*

ROBINSON, Boni S
Cleveland HS; Seattle, WA (84-269) NHS; ARC;
Journ A; Pres, Church Yth; Church Yth Choir; Pub
Sch Work Trng Prog; Nurses Aid; *Shoreline Comm
Col; Nurs.*

ROBINSON, Brenda Jean
Smyrna HS; Smyrna, DE (50-225) S-T, Chldr;
Hmmr; SC; Var C; Secy, Jr Cl; Gym; Tres, Church
Yth ; Ch, Mayday; YMCA Gym Instructor; Gym
Show; Church Pianist; Sunday Sch Teacher; *Ed.*

ROBINSON, Brenda Kay
Northeastern HS; Detroit, MI; NHS; Y-Tns; Bkbl;
Citz A; Schol; PA; *U of Detroit; Phys Ed.*

ROBINSON, Brian Damone
Canisius HS; Buffalo, NY (54-160) CYO; Ftbl;
Wrest; COM; Math A; *UCLA; Law.*

ROBINSON, Burma Joan
Virgie HS; Virgie, KY (1-103) Ann; Pres, BC; FTA;
Ger C; Co-Ed, Sch P; Spch C; SC; Cl Fav; Ntl Achv
Schol; Tres, Co-Ed-Y; Miss Jr; Miss Sr; Schol A.

ROBINSON, Carla S
Raytown HS; Raytown, MO (60-503) Chor; NHS;
Cert of Achv; Cert of Recognition; *Longview
Comm Col; Bus Adm.*

ROBINSON, Carol Ann
Lyons Township HS; LaGrange, IL (93%-1207)
NHS; Orch; Phys C; Tres, Sci C; St Scholar; *Gusta-
vus Adolphus Col; Biol.*

ROBINSON, Carolyn Celestine
Surry Co HS; Dendron, VA (9-125) Chldr; Chor;
Fr C; FHA; Secy, Hmmr; Mjrte; Swim; Piano Cert
of A; Ntl Fr Competition A; Salvation Army A;
Homecoming Trophy; *Va St U; Counseling Psych.*

ROBINSON, Charles Marion
Ruston HS; Ruston, LA (2-257) VP, Band; Dbte
Tm; Lit Ral; NFL; NHS; Orch; VP, Sci C; Spch C;
Tr; Alg A; Bio A; COM; Chem A; Gov Honor Prog;
Hon Prog; Math A; NMF; NMS; Ntl Sci Found;
Ntl Sci Symposium; NEDT; Phy A; Sal; Sci A;
Spch A; Type A; VofDEM; Yth Fel; WW; Outst
Stu in Statistics; Bell Telephone Sci A; La Engr
Soc; All St Band; Sch Ltr A; Army Sci Med; Stu
Cond & Asst Drm Mj; *La Tech U; Elec Engr.*

ROBINSON, Charlie III
Pontiac Central HS; Pontiac, MI; Dbte Tm; Hmmr;
Spch C; SC; Tnns; COM; Citz A; Cl Fav; Hon Prog;
JA A; Math A; Executive, Outst Salesman, A's;
Mich St U; Bus Adm.

ROBINSON, Cherrel Ann
Whitehouse HS; Whitehouse, TX (4-99) BC; FHA;
NHS; SC; Sal; Homemaking; Eng; VOE, Art, A's;
Top 10; *Tyler Jr Col; Legal Secy.*

ROBINSON, Cheryl Marie
Holt HS; Holt, MI; NFL; Thes; Pres, Soph Cl; SG A; Forensics A; *Psych.*

ROBINSON, Christina Marie
Mayo HS; Darlington, SC (2-113) Secy, Band; VP, Drama; Parl, FHA; Pres, FTA; NHS; SC; Pres, Jr Cl; Hist A; Sal; Sci A; Type A; Most Stu; Most Concerned; Eng A; Jr Marshall; *U of SC; Psych.*

ROBINSON, Christopher Nelson
Duluth Central HS; Duluth, MN; Chor; Drama; Model UN; *U of Minn at Duluth; Geol.*

ROBINSON, Cynthia Lowe
Springville HS; Springville, AL (10-54) Ann; BC; Sch P; Var C; S-T, Sr Cl; Bkbl; Tr; Gov Honor Prog; Pres A; All-Co Girls Bkbl; Sr Cl Best A; Fin, Beauty A; Fin, Homecoming Court; *Jeff St Jr Col; Phys Ed.*

ROBINSON, Debra Ann
Second Ward HS; Gloster, LA; Bus C; Parl, FBLA; Parl, FHA; Math C; Sci C; SC; Bkbl; Sftbl; Hon Prog; *Sou U; Sci.*

ROBINSON, Derrick Keith
Inkster HS; Inkster, MI; Band; Orch; Var C; Co-Cpt, Tnns; Citz A; Hon Prog; V Ltr; Dist Band Medal; *Morehouse Col; Engr.*

ROBINSON, Dirk Irl
Salem Acad; Salem, OR (1-95) SC; Pres, Soph Cl; JV, Bkbl; JV, Ftbl; *George Fox Col; Med.*

ROBINSON, Donell Jr
Central HS; W Helena, AR; Band; Chess C; Tnns; *U of Ark; Sci.*

ROBINSON, Donna Lois
Llano HS; Llano, TX (1-80) VP, NHS; Tres, Sr Cl; Tres, Jr Cl; Tres, Soph Cl; Cpt, Bkbl; Tr; Cl Fav; Sci A; Swtht; Best All Around.

ROBINSON, Elise
Tilden HS; Chicago, IL (74-408) Band; Bkbl; Sftbl; Achv Dinner; *Ill St U; Med Tech.*

ROBINSON, Ellena Marie
Herbert Hoover HS; San Diego, CA; CYO; Chor; SC; Tr; Tr Medals; *UCLA; Child Psych.*

ROBINSON, Elma Lee
St Matthew HS; Natchitoches, LA; Ann; Fr C; Rptr, FHA; Lit Ral; VP, Jr Cl; VP, Soph Cl; Alg A; Amer Leg A; B Crocker A; COM; Citz A; Cl Fav; Crisco A; Hist A; Hon Prog; JA A; MLS; Most Out; Opt Out Tn; Sal; Val; Yth Fel; Yth Foundation A; *Northeast U; Sociology.*

ROBINSON, Felicia Joy
Unity HS; Chicago, IL (54-145) Co-Cpt, Chldr; Ntl Yth Conf; *U of Chicago; Pre-Med.*

ROBINSON, Felicia Karen
Lincolnton HS; Lincolnton, NC (1-247) JV, Chldr; Fr C; FTA; Hmrm; NHS; Ed, Soph P; SC; HCt; Journ A; Q&S A; Sci A; Fr A; *Eng.*

ROBINSON, Frank Charles
Park Center HS; Brooklyn Park, MN (225-575) Band; Orch; ARC; Ski C; SC; Ftbl; Tnns; HKg; Cabinet; Best Personality; *U of Wis; Voc Rehabilitation.*

ROBINSON, Gary DeWayne
H Grady Spruce HS; Dallas, TX; Band; Chor; Ensm; *Tex A & M U; Plumbing.*

ROBINSON, Gerrilyn Dennise
Marvell HS; Marvell, AR (6-118) Band; Tres, BC; FBLA; FHA; Mjrte; SC; HCt; Most Out; Type A; *Rust Col; Med.*

ROBINSON, Glenda Ann
El Segundo HS; El Segundo, CA; VP, Chor; Secy, Ensm; Fr C; Semi-Fin, GS; Hmrm; *Brigham Young U; Child Developement.*

ROBINSON, Henry G
Murrah HS; Jackson, MS (75-260) Spch C; Bkbl; Cpt, Ftbl; Cl Fav; *Hinds Jr Col; Phys Therapy.*

ROBINSON, Jacqueline Yavette
Ross Shaw Sterling Sr HS; Houston, TX (48-400) Cum Laude Soc; Pres, FHA; HiY; Hmrm; ARC; Y-Tns; COM; Hon Prog; MLS; Most Out; RT Fr A; *Prairie View A&M U; Bus Adm.*

ROBINSON, James Terry
Elyria W HS; Elyria, OH; Tnns; HiY; Rptr, Hmrm; Math C; Span C; Up Bound; JV, Bkbl; Co-Cpt, Ftbl; Tr; COM; Hon Prog; Rptr, Church Newsltr; Hon Grades; *Case Western Reserve U; Health.*

ROBINSON, Jamie Michael
Fountain Central HS; Veedersburg, IN (40-120) SC; Var C; Bsbl; JV, Bkbl; Tnns.

ROBINSON, Jan
Star Valley HS; Afton, WY; Chldr; Chor; 4H; Ski C; 4H A; HCt; Scholastic As; Secy, SAE; *Brigham Young U.*

ROBINSON, Jo Ann
Paschal HS; Fort Worth, TX (51-725) Chor; Community Yth Symph; Mgr, Drama; Fr C; Orch; ARC; Tnns; Yth Fel; Ballet Concerto; *Psych.*

ROBINSON, Joel David
Northwestern HS; Rock Hill, SC (85-380) Demolay; Fr C; Order/Arrow; Cr-Ctry; Tr; *U of SC; Computer Sci.*

ROBINSON, Jon Tracy
Elyria W HS; Elyria, OH; HiY; Span C; Pres, SC; Up Bound; JV, Bkbl; Co-Cpt, Ftbl; Fin, Tr; COM; Pres A; Asst Superintendent, Sunday Sch; *Case Western Reserve U; Health.*

ROBINSON, Karen Denise
Nw Cabarrus HS; Concord, NC (15-251) Ann; Band; BC; Chor; Pres, Hmrm; Pres, SC; Pres, Tri-HiY; Cpt, Bkbl; Sftbl; HCt; Rifle Squad; Lady of Troy; Tres, Chi Alpha C; *Gardner Webb Col; Nurs.*

ROBINSON, Karrie Jo
MacKenzie HS; Detroit, MI (1-352) Band; Chldr; Secy, NHS; ARC; Secy, Sci C; Tr; Amer Leg A; MLS; Sci A; *Clemson U; Microbio.*

ROBINSON, Kenneth Wayne
Hogansville HS; Hogansville, GA (20-79) Co-Cpt, Sch Achieve; Pres, Jr Cl; S-T, Soph Cl; Cl Fav; H of F; MLS; Most Out; Cpt, MVP, Bkbl; Cpt, MVP, Ftbl; *U of Louisville; Acct.*

ROBINSON, Kent Lyle
Park Center HS; Brooklyn Park, MN (115-575) A Cap Choir; Chor; Ensm; Hmrm; Ski C; Ftbl; Golf; Tr; JA A; Most Out; Pres A; Yth Fel; City Win, Fire Prevention Poster; Pres, JA; *Archt.*

ROBINSON, Laura Lee
East St Louis Sr HS; E St Louis, IL (1-1033) Band; Chldr; Chem C; Pres, Fr C; Hmrm; NHS; Sch P; Pres, Span C; SC; Sci A; Prelude Regional Ballet Co; Cecchetti Ballet Coun of Amer; Classical Sch of Dance; *Sou Ill U at Edwardsville.*

ROBINSON, Leslie Craig
Lincoln HS; Wisconsin Rapids, WI (33%-600) Band; 4H; Var C; Cr-Ctry; Tr; *U of W Stout; Ind Ed.*

ROBINSON, Lillie Vianna
Cass Tech HS; Detroit, MI (400-890) A Cap Choir; Band; Chor; Community Yth Symph; Ensm; Orch; COM; Citz A; *Berkley Col of Mus; Arranging & Composition.*

ROBINSON, Linda Sue
Wilmington Sr HS; Wilmington, OH (5-301) Band; BS; JV, Chldr; 4H; Lit Mag; SC; Tnns; 4H A; NEDT; Phi Delta Sigma; Band Librarian; *Social Stu.*

ROBINSON, Lisa Ann
Germantown HS; Germantown, TN (89-404) BC; Bus C; Chem C; Chor; Math C; Sci C; Span C; Hon Prog; 4th St, DECA A; *Memphis St Col; Journ.*

ROBINSON, Lisa Rene
Valley View HS; Germantown, OH (33%-185) Chor; Fr C; Bkbl; Tr; Drill Tm; Fr C COM; MVP, Vlbl; St Schol Test; PA Cert; Chor COM.

ROBINSON, Lori Ann
Pima Pub Sch; Pima, AZ (4-35) Band; Chldr; Chor; FHA; Hmrm; NHS; SC; Bio A; Sci A; Cpt, Vlbl; Eng A; Hon Stu; *Ariz St Col; Psych.*

ROBINSON, Lori Ann
Hebert HS; Beaumont, TX; Bkbl; Tr; Cpt, JV Vlbl; *Tex A&M U; Nurs.*

ROBINSON, Louis James
St Matthew HS; Melrose, LA (38-43) Band; Pres, Soph Cl; JV, Bkbl; Sftbl; Alg A; HCt; Hon Prog; Math A; Sci A; *Northeast U; Med.*

ROBINSON, Louise Owens
George Washington HS; New York, NY (5-40) Pres, A Cap Choir; Cpt, Chldr; Ch, Chor; Drama; Sci C; Bsbl; Bkbl; Swim; Tr; COM; Citz A; Hist A; Sci A; Spch A.

ROBINSON, Lucinda Sue
Fremont Comm HS; Fremont, IA (2-15) Band; VP, Chor; Ensm; 4H; Bkbl; Sftbl; Tr; 4H A; Sal; Carnival Qn; 2nd Tm, Hon Men; Best in Cl, Art; Empire Conf; Phys Ed As; Bkbl As.

ROBINSON, Marcia Jan
Levelland HS; Levelland, TX (10%-210) Pres, Band; Chor; Fin, Ensm; VP, FHA; Secy, 4H; Inter-Club Coun; Fin, Mjrte; NHS; Span C; Bkbl; Sftbl; Swim; Hon Prog; Pres A; ARC A; Vlbl; Twirling As; Chaplain, Vlbl Tm; All Star Bkbl & Sftbl; *Texas A&M U; Med.*

ROBINSON, Mark Curtis
Douglass HS; Oklahoma City, OK (58-260) Math C; Mu Alpha Theta; Bsbl; Math A; Math Outst Stu; *Central St Col; Math.*

ROBINSON, Mary Ann
Proviso E HS; Maywood, IL (151-1039) Band; Co-Cpt, Chldr; Fin, Jr Miss Pagent; SC; Alg A; Sci A; Gym Ldrs; *Triton Col; Radio & Television.*

ROBINSON, Mary Ann
Levelland HS; Levelland, TX (10%-210) Secy, Band; Chor; Fin, Ensm; Fin, FHA; 4H; Secy, Inter-Club Coun; Fin, Mjrte; NHS; Span C; Bkbl; Sftbl; Swim; Alg A; COM; Hist A; Hon Prog; Math A; Most Out; Pres A; ARC A; Sci A; Type A; Vlbl; Stage Band; Drum Major; WW in Band; All Star Bkbl, Sftbl; JP Sousa A; Stu Christian Assn; *Texas A&M U; Math.*

ROBINSON, Mary Beth
Douglas Co HS; Douglasville, GA; Chldr; Secy, Fr C; NHS; Secy, Jr Cl; Tnns; COM; Gov Honor Prog; HCt; *Emory U; Med.*

ROBINSON, Melissa Ann
Dobyns-Bennett HS; Kingsport, TN (33%-500) Band; BC; 4H; ARC; Co-Cpt, Bkbl; Ftbl; COM; Pres A; Pres, Phi-Delta-Kappa; VP, JA; *Tenn Tech U; Special Ed.*

ROBINSON, Melzie Lee
Eau Claire HS; Columbia, SC (8-312) Hmrm; NHS; A-Ed, Sch P; Ch, SC; Var C; JV, Bkbl; Co-Cpt, Cr-Ctry; Tr; COM; Citz A; Gov Honor Prog; Hist A; Hon Prog; Pres A; Jr Civitan C; *Phar.*

ROBINSON, Michelle Elaine
Northeastern HS; Detroit, MI (10%-250) NHS; *U of Detroit; Archt.*

ROBINSON, Millie Rea
Springdale HS; Springdale, AR (10%-561) CYO; ARC; Soph Maid, Color's Day Court; TV Production C; Tn Involvement; *Math.*

ROBINSON, Nancy Marie
Wister HS; Wister, OK (10-40) Tres, FHA; Bkbl; Sftbl; 4H A; HQn; HCt; JA A; Pres A; 4-H A; Jr Rodeo; Improvement A; 9th Cl Qn; *Dentistry.*

ROBINSON, Nancy May
W Bridgewater HS; W Bridgewater, MA (18-120) Ann; FTA; Ger C; Rainbow; Sch P; Span NHS; Sftbl; Ella J Brown Schol Fund; Tres, Baptist Yth Fel; Grange; *Bridgewater St U; Elem Ed.*

ROBINSON, Nora Louise
McMinnville HS; McMinnville, OR; Key C; Tr; Sci A.

ROBINSON, Pamela Roxanne
E Orange HS; E Orange, NJ (65-417) Chor; Bio A; Chem A; Citz A; Cl Fav; Hist A; HKg; HQn; MLS; Most Out; Order/Arrow A; Sci A; Type A; Yth Fel; *Rutgers St Col; Bus Adm.*

ROBINSON, Paula
University City Sr HS; University City, MO (136-465) Cpt, Chldr; Cpt, Gym Tm; Girls Ath A; *U of Mo-Columbia; Fashion Design.*

ROBINSON, Peggy Lynne
Shenandoah HS; Sarahsville, OH (2-111) Band; VP, 4H; Mu Alpha Theta; NHS; VP, SC; Bio A; 4H A; Good Grooming, OMEA, A's; *Med.*

ROBINSON, Raleigh Marie
Burnsville Sr HS; Burnsville, MN (132-750) Ethnic Awareness Committee Pres; Stu Govt; *U of Minn; Math.*

ROBINSON, Rhonda Gail
Ross Shaw Sterling HS; Houston, TX; FTA; Hmrm; NHS; Sci C; Amer Leg A; COM; Nom, Amer Leg A; *U of Houston; Law.*

ROBINSON, Roberta Lynn
Rio Linda HS; Rio Linda, CA (5%-500) A Cap Choir; Chor; Drama; Hmrm; F-Ed, Sch P; SC; Var C; Cpt, Bkbl; Sftbl; HCt; MVP, Bkbl; Cpt, Vlbl; Fin, Amer Leg A; *Pepperdine U; Hist.*

ROBINSON, Robin Elaine
Warren Central HS; Indianapolis, IN (220-863) Rptr, 4H; Sftbl; Swim; Citz A; Pres A; Vlbl; *Childhood Ed.*

ROBINSON, Russell Louis
Southside HS; Gadsden, AL (9-124) HiY; Pres, Math C; NHS; Sch Achieve Tm; VP, Sci C; Cl Fav; *Jacksonville St U; Pol Sci.*

ROBINSON, Sharon Denise
Fairfield HS; Fairfield, AL (28-160) Chor; FHA; S-T, Y-Tns; HCt; *U of Ala; Bus.*

ROBINSON, Sheila Diane
Rock Hill HS; Rock Hill, SC (151-425) Rptr, Sch P; HCt; *SC Med U; Nurs.*

ROBINSON, Sheri Ann
Penns Grove Regional HS; Penns Grove, NJ (29-230) Chess C; VP, Ger C; Rptr, Sch P; Co-Cpt, Bkbl; Mgr, Hockey; Mgr, Sftbl; Mgr, Tnns; Hon Prog; Pres A; Yth Fel; Home Ec Cooking & Sacrament & Services Committee; *Drew U; Forestry.*

ROBINSON, Stephen Andrew
Farragut HS; Knoxville, TN (10%-466) Hist A; Math A; Piano A; *Harding Col; Math.*

ROBINSON, Steven Daniel
Hermon Christian Sch; Hermon, ME; Chor; Ensm; Fr C; VP, SC; Co-Cpt, Bkbl; Sftbl; *Bob Jones U.*

ROBINSON, Susan Marie
Hitchcock HS; Hitchcock, TX (16-130) Band; Chess C; Drama; Ensm; Pres, Ger C; VP, NHS; Tr; Bio A; Hist A; Hon Prog; VofDEM; Yth Fel; HR A; Head Drill Ldr; *Sci.*

ROBINSON, Teresa Anne
Broadview Acad; La Feria, IL (60%-80) Ski C; Co-Cpt, Bkbl; Co-Cpt, Sftbl; *Pepperdine U; Art.*

ROBINSON, Terri Lynn
Mosley HS; Panama City, FL; BC; Chess C; Inter-Club Coun; Mu Alpha Theta; NMS; *Troy St U; Religion.*

ROBINSON, Timothy John
North Comm HS; Minneapolis, MN; Chor; Ftbl; Tnns; Tr; *U of Minn; Hospital Adm.*

ROBINSON, Wanda Joy
Richmond HS; Augusta, GA; Ann; Band; Tres, Hmrm; Tr; Beauty; COM; Most Out; *Morehouse Col; Bus.*

ROBINSON, William Davis
Permian HS; Odessa, TX (69-691) BS; NHS; JV, Cr-Ctry; JV, Tr; Lion A; NMS; Candidate, Air Force Acad; Merit Schol, Col; Jr Ldr, Wilderness Back-Pack Trips; *Odessa Jr Col; Computer Sci.*

ROBINSON, William Joseph
Archmere Acad; Claymont, DE (5%-77) Pres, BS; VP, NHS; Rptr, Sch P; Span SC; Span NHS; Pres, SC; Jr Cl; Pres, Soph Cl; JV, Ftbl; Amer Leg A; COM; Century III Ldr; *Georgetown U; Foreign Service.*

ROBINSON, William Russell
Christian Brothers HS; Memphis, TN (30-230) Ann; Chor; Demolay; Drama; Span C; NMF; NMS; NEDT; *Southwestern Col; Pre-Med.*

ROBINSON, Willie Claire
Jack Yates Sr HS; Houston, TX; *Tex Sou Col; Phar.*

ROBIRDS, Stephen Ray
McGavock HS; Nashville, TN; Math C; Ntl Yth Conf; Y-Tns; Co-Cpt, Bkbl; Soccer; Sftbl; *Hillsdale Baptist Col; Commercial Art.*

ROBISON, Cherie Ann
Nettleton HS; Jonesboro, AR (18-150) Band; Chor; Madrigal; Mjrte; VP, Sci C; VP, Yth Fel; All St, Regional, Choirs; *Ark St U; Mus.*

ROBISON, James Frederic
Glendale Acad; Glendale, CA (3%-65) Bus Mgr, Ann; Band; Ensm; Pres, Math C; Phys C; Ski C; VP, SC; Var C; Tres, Sr Cl; Cpt, Bsbl; Bkbl; Ftbl; Cpt, Soccer; Tr; Bank Of Amer A; Math A; *UCLA; Bus.*

ROBISON, Jan Estelle
Gainesville HS; Gainesville, TX (10%-250) A Cap Choir; Band; Chor; FHA; 4H; Hmrm; NHS; Rainbow; SC; Parl, Soph Cl; Sftbl; Citz A; Yth Fel; Yth Leg; 2nd Lt, Drill Tm; *Baylor U; Psych.*

ROBISON, Julie Lynne
Thomasville HS; Thomasville, AL; BC; Chldr; Chor; Drama; FHA; Lat C; Vlbl; Outst Sr; All St Chldr; *Auburn U; Phys Therapy.*

ROBISON, Robert William
Highlands HS; San Antonio, TX (2-600) BS; Tres, Ger C; JETS; Pres, Math C; Pres, Mu Alpha Theta; NHS; Soccer; Hon Prog; Math A; Sal; Cpt, Math Tm; *Rice U; Elec Engr.*

ROBISON, Timothy Lane
St Elmo Comm HS; St Elmo, IL (20-55) Bkbl; *Anderson Col; Pastor Ministry.*

ROBJAK, Michael Simon
Salpointr HS; Tucson, AZ (80-170) Pres, Band; Key C; Ftbl; COM; Most Out; Pres A; Asst Director Band A; Bandsman A; Sch Off Cert; *U of Ariz; Bus Adm.*

ROBLENSKI, David John
Rutherford HS; Springfield, FL; Drama; ARC; Fin, Cr-Ctry; Golf; Cpt, Wrest; St Fin & MVP, Wrest; HS All Amer; First Aid Achv A; *U of Fla; Forestry and Conservation.*

ROBLES, Carmen Ivelisse
Dra Maria Cadilla de Martinez HS; Arecibo, PR (63-636) Alg A; COM; Kiwanis A; Lion A; Most Out; Highest Score, Econ Domestic Tutory.

ROBLES, Lisa Nan
Stuart HS; Louisville, KY; Chor; Fr C; *U of Louisville; Nurs.*

ROBLES, Margaret Diane
Jessie Stuart HS; Louisville, KY (65-360) Pres, A Cap Choir; Superior A, Choir Competition; Church Sftbl; Gospel Group; *Jefferson Comm Col; Social Work.*

ROBLES, Miguel Angel
Dra Maria Cadilla de Martinez HS; Arecibo, PR (38-636) COM; Hist A; Kiwanis A; Most Out.

ROBLES, Olga Iris
Eastside HS; Paterson, NJ (8-519) NHS.

ROBNETT, Deborah Marie
Albia Community HS; Albia, IA (22-148) FTA; Var C; Mgr, Bkbl; Sftbl; Jr Chamber of Com A; VP, Girls Recreation; Pep C; Hon Banquet; *Centerville Col; Elem Ed.*

ROBSON, Beth Anne
Mt Vernon HS; Mt Vernon, OH (175-400) Band; FHA; Secy, 4H; 4H A; *Mt Vernon Nazarene Col; Child Evangelism.*

ROBY, Desiree Kay
Zanesville HS; Zanesville, OH (102-356) Band; Chldr; Chor; JV, Bkbl; S-T, GAA; Tanker Timer; *Ohio U.*

ROCCAFORTE, Theresa Lynn
Nederland HS; Nederland, TX (15%-461) Band; NHS; 1st Pl Solo Medals, Band; 1st Pl Ensm Medals Band; All Region Band; *Lamar Col; Deaf Ed.*

ROCHE, Raydene
Highland HS; Pocatello, ID (1-400) 4H; NHS; SC; Secy, Jr Cl; Swim; 4H A; Spch A; Drill Tm; Mat Maid; *Idaho St U; General.*

ROCHE, Thomas Joseph
Dover HS; Dover, NH (41-396) BS; Key C; Mu Alpha Theta; NHS; Var C; Bkbl; Cr-Ctry; Tr; Harvard Book A; WW; Yth o-t Mo; *Dartmouth Col; Acct.*

ROCHELL, Debra Lynn
John Overton HS; Nashville, TN (34-442) Band; Fr C; FFA; Hmrm; NHS; COM; Hon Prog; NEDT; Tres, VICA; Pres, Civitans; *David Lipscomb Col; Pre-Vet.*

ROCHELLE, David James
New Hanover HS; Wilmington, NC; Chor; SC; Yth Fel; Pres Yth Coun; VP, Wilderness C; Bus Driver C; VP, Azalea Festival Yth Division; *U of NC; Psych.*

ROCHEN, Jeffrey Lynn
Spring Woods Sr HS; Houston, TX (5%-625) JETS; Lat C; Orch; Bio A; Hist A; Hon Prog; Math A; Sci A; Eng As; Computer A; Mus A; *Trinity U; Med.*

ROCHESTER, Donald Ray
Tabernacle Christian Day Sch; Greenville, SC; Ed, Ann; Pres, Sr Cl; Pres, Jr Cl; VP, Soph Cl; Bkbl; Mr TCS; *Bob Jones U; Art.*

ROCHESTER, Linda
Montevallo HS; Montevallo, AL (5-98) A-Ed, Ann; NHS; Span C; *U of Montevallo; Sci.*

ROCHET, Christian Louis
Acad Ntra Sra Providencia; Rio Piedras, PR (14-58) Cum Laude Soc; Drama; Order/Arrow; Bus Mgr, Sch P; Sci C; Tres, SC; Rptr, Bsbl; Rptr, Bkbl; Swim; Hon Prog; Sci A; Conduct A; *U of Puerto Rico; Sci.*

ROCK, Cheryl Lynn
Westmont Hilltop HS; Johnstown, PA (50-200) Chor; Ensm; Vlbl Tm; HR; Secy, Pep C; Church Tn C; *Ind U of Penn; Elem Ed.*

ROCK, Connie Lynne
Washington HS; Kansas City, KS; *KCK Comm Col; Nurs.*

ROCK, Garry Richard
Lord Botetourt HS; Daleville, VA (38-163) Chor; Key C; NHS; Mgr, Bkbl; Golf; *Va Tech U; Mech Engr.*

ROCK, Mary Louise
Sahuarita HS; Sahuarita, AZ (20-127) Band; Chor; Dbte Tm; 4H; Model UN; NFL; VP, Sci C; Spch C; Ch, St Stu Congress; Tr; COM; NEDT; Yth Leg; Pom Pons; *Northern Ariz U; Special Ed.*

ROCK, Michael Russell
St Edward HS; Lakewood, OH (170-300) Ann; Pres, CYO; Dbte Tm; Pres, Hmrm; Rptr, Sch P; Spch C; SC; Secy, Soph Cl; Soccer; COM; Cl Fav; MLS; Pres A; Ed o-t Yr, Holy Name Soc Newsltr; Outst Yth, CYO Pres; *Niagra U; Pol Sci.*

ROCK, Olympia Charmaine
Leesville HS; Leesville, LA; FHA; Pep Sq; *Northwestern Col; Sci.*

ROCK, Virginia Sue
Sahuarida HS; Sahuarita, AZ (10-145) Chor; Model UN; NHS; Tres, Sci C; SC; Mgr, Tr; Journ A; Yth Fel; Yth Leg; Co-Ed, Ann; Mod Leg St Comm; Outst Sen; *Northern Ariz U; Nurs.*

ROCKER, Brenda Dianne
Mattie T Blount HS; Prichard, AL; Pres, FHA; Pres, Hmrm; SC; Cl Fav; Hon Prog.

ROCKER, Gwendolyn
M T Blount HS; Prichard, AL (20-388) Chor; FHA; Hmrm; NHS; COM; Cl Fav; Hon Prog; Social Stu A; Most Ladylike; *Computer Sci.*

ROCKEY, Cheryl Lee
Lutheran HS E; Harper Woods, MI (10-143) Band; *Alma Col.*

ROCKEY, Marsha Lynne
Homestead HS; Fort Wayne, IN (4-256) Band; Chor; NHS; Orch; Hon Prog; NMS; Sci A; *Ind Purdue U; Mus Therapy.*

ROCKHILL, Ronna Marie
St Regis Falls Central HS; St Regis Falls, NY (6-30) Rainbow; Sch P; *Mount Ida Jr Col; Fashion Illustration.*

ROCKHOLT, Jeffrey Scott
Arvin HS; Arvin, CA (2%-300) Mgr, Band; NHS; Ftbl; *Point Loma U; Theology.*

ROCKHOLT, Jennifer Lynn
Arvin HS; Arvin, CA (2%-300) Band; Dbte Tm; Math C; NHS; Ski C; Span C; Span NHS; SC; Tnns; CSF; Math A; Sci A; Home Ec A; Eng A; *Med.*

ROCKWELL, Jay Thomas
Mt Diablo HS; Concord, CA; Band; MVP, Swim; *Col o-t Redwoods; Wedding Tech.*

ROCKWELL, Kristina Marie
Omaha S HS; Omaha, NE (51-660) Chor; NEDT; Yth Fel; *U of Nebr; Social Services.*

ROCKWELL, Marie Louise
J T Wright HS; Mobile, AL (40%-59) Yth Fel; Yth Fel; *U of Ala; Med.*

ROCUSKIE, Karen Ann
Tamaqua; Tamaqua, PA (19-153) CYO; Chldr; Dbte Tm; Hmrm; NHS; SC; Bkbl; Tr; COM; Citz A; Hon Prog; JA A; St Art Contest; Best Camper, YMCA.

ROCUSKIE, Kelly Marie
Marian HS; Tamaqua, PA (30-173) CYO; Cpt; Chldr; Chess C; Drama; FNA; Hmrm; Sch P; SC; Sftbl; HCt; Miss Christmas Seal, Central Penn; *Bloomsburg St Col; Nurs.*

RODAK, Renee Ruth
Louisville Sr HS; Louisville, OH (20%-380) Bus Mgr, Ann; Drama; NFL; Spch C; 4H A; Spch A; *Baptist Bible Col; Elem Ed.*

RODDEY, Connie Frances
W Charlotte HS; Charlotte, NC; FBLA; *Central Piedmont Col; Computer Operations.*

RODDEY, Elizabeth Jenkins
Hammond Acad; Columbia, SC; Ann; VP, Community Yth Sy; Drama; Hmrm; ARC; SC; Up Bound; Swim; Tnns; NEDT; Chrch Lector; Camp Coun; Chrch Yth Chor; GSct; Civinettes; VP, Pres, Church Yth Group; Symph Belles; *Converse Col; Psych.*

RODELL, Janet Dolore
Centerville HS; Centerville, TX (1-36) Ed, Ann; Pres, Band; FFA; Secy, FHA; 4H; VP, NHS; Tnns; 4H A; HCt; Hon Prog; Type A; Val; 4-H Gold Star; *Tex A&M U; Elem Ed.*

RODELL, Marilyn
Centerville HS; Centerville, TX (15-47) Pres, A Cap Choir; VP, Band; Pres, Chor; FHA; 4H; Bsbl; Sftbl; Tnns; 4H A; Type A; Miss CHS; Tres, Rodeo Tm; Band A; Church Organist; Drum Major; *Sam Houston St U; Elem Ed.*

RODELL, Mark Donald
Aurora HS; Aurora, OH (32-164) Mu Alpha Theta; Ski C; JV, Tnns; Hist A; Ctry C Swim Tm; Fr Schol Test Tm; *Pre-Law.*

RODEN, Angela Claudette
Tyner HS; Chattanooga, TN (1-261) Rptr, BC; Chor; Drama; Fr C; VP, NHS; Co-Ed, Sch P; SC; Cl Fav; DARGCA; Hon Prog; Most Out; PTA A; Sci A; Star Student; Val; Tres, Civinettes; Bicentennial Stu o-t Yr; CC Burgner, Principal's Sch, A's.

RODENBIKER, Darcy Allen
Rock Lake Pub HS; Rock Lake, ND (1-24) Ann; Band; BS; Chor; Tres, FFA; S-T, 4H; Hmrm; Fin, JETS; Pres, Var C; Bkbl; Ftbl; Elk A; 4H A; PTA A; Sci A; Val; VofDEM; S-T V C; St Star Mus Rating; European Good Will Tour Choir.

RODENBIKER, Eric Von
Rock Lake Pub HS; Rock Lake, ND (20%-24) Ann; Band; Chor; 4H; Hmrm; SC; Pres, Jr Cl; Ftbl; COM; 4H A; PTA A; Sci A; Star Vocal Rating; *U of ND; Elec.*

RODERICK, Susan Lynn
Kennedy Sr HS; Cedar Rapids, IA (37-533) Chor; Drama; Ski C; Span C; Thes; JV, Tr; *U of N Iowa; Ed.*

RODGERS, Antoinette Yvetta
King William HS; King William, VA; BC; Rptr, Fr C; Ed, Lit Mag; *U of Pittsburgh; Sci.*

RODGERS, Deborah Kathleen
Foreman HS; Chicago, IL (15-373) Ann; Chor; Hmrm; S-T, Madrigal; Ann; Hon Prog; Journ A; Foreman Ldrs; Explorers; Hon Pin; *DePaul U; Acct.*

RODGERS, Gloria Ann
Pascagoula HS Annex; Pascagoula, MS (32-765) 4H; Tres, Hmrm; Bkbl; Cpt, Tr; Amer Leg A; Cl Fav; 4H A; VFW A; Phys Fitness A; Phys Ed A.

RODGERS, Helen Dianne
T L Hanna HS; Anderson, SC; Band; Ger C; VP, Hmrm; Co-Cpt, Mjrte; Monogram; NHS; Orch; Sch P; COM; Drum Mjrte; Mus Ed A; *Anderson Jr Col; Med.*

RODGERS, John Aaron
W Middlesex Area HS; W Middlesex, PA (7-146) Band; Pres, NHS; SC; Pres, Sr Cl; VP, Jr Cl; Semi-Fin, Tr; NMS; NEDT; 2nd, Co Essay Contest; *Westminster Col.*

RODGERS, Joy Ann
Riverside HS; Avon, MS; Ann; Band; SC; Var C; Rptr, Sr Cl; Pres, Soph Cl; Co-Cpt, Bkbl; Hist A; MVP, Bkbl; Bus A; Occupational Orientation A; Most Improved Player, Bkbl; *Delta St U; Bus.*

RODGERS, Karen Lynn
Stafford Sr HS; Falmouth, VA (35-400) Pep C; Rep, Jr Cl; Home Ec C; *Delaware Valley Acad; Dental Asst.*

RODGERS, Karen Ruth
T R Miller HS; Brewton, AL (24-110) Co-Cpt, Chldr; Chor; Rptr, FHA; FTA; SC; Var C; Sftbl; Journ A; Pres A; Sci A; Yth Fel; Most Spirited Chldr; *Auburn U; Med Tech.*

RODGERS, Kimberly Dawn
Northside HS; Columbus, IN; Ann; Band; Chldr; 4H; Tr; COM; 4H A; *Olivet Col.*

RODGERS, Lawrence Richard
Norman HS; Norman, OK (22-665) A Cap Choir; Fr C; Hmrm; SC; JV, Bkbl; Tnns; St Scholar; Eagle Sct; Wash Workshops Congressional Sem; *Eng.*

RODGERS, Lewis Edward
Lutheran HS W; Rocky River, OH (40-90) Chor; Hmrm; SC; Ftbl; Sftbl; Tr; Wrest; Pres A; Most Helpful; *Concordia Col.*

RODGERS, Lewis Edward III
Lutheran HS W; Rocky River, OH (40-94) Chor; Hmrm; Parl, SC; Ftbl; Tr; Mgr, Wrest; Pres Schol A; *Concoradia Col; Teacher Ed.*

RODGERS, Lucy Gail
Bethany HS; Reidsville, NC; Anchor C; Ann; Chldr; Fr C; Rptr, FHA; Hmrm; Monogram; SC; HCt; WW; *U of NC; Mus.*

RODGERS, Philip Dean
Crystal Lake Comm HS; Crystal Lake, IL (26-585) Band; NHS; Orch; Chem A; Hon Prog; St Scholar; Cadet Teacher, SAE; *Sou Ill Col; Biol.*

RODGERS, Robin Lisa
Rocky Grove HS; Franklin, PA (57-140) Chor; Ensm; Mgr, Bkbl; *Slippery Rock St Col; Communications.*

RODGERS, Sharon Elaine
Trenton HS; Trenton, FL (6-78) Band; Rptr, BC; FBLA; Pres, Jr Cl; Pres, Soph Cl; Tr; *U of Fl; Mus.*

RODGERS, Wesley Alvin
Stockton R-1 HS; Stockton, MO (44-79) S-T, Var C; Ftbl; Tr; Ftbl A; All Conf; All Dist; Hon Mem All St; *U of Ark; Phys Ed.*

RODGIGUEZ, Patricia
Will C Crawford HS; San Diego, CA; Bus C; COM; Hon Prog; Type A; *San Diego St Col; Acct.*

RODIER, Anne Elizabeth
Jeb Stuart HS; Falls Church, VA (44-462) Band; S-T, Chor; Ensm; NHS; Orch; Ch, SC; Rptr, Sr Cl; Soccer; Bio A; All-Island Band; Keyettes; Pres, VP, NJHS; *U of Va; Bio.*

RODMAN, Gloria S
Greenville Sr HS; Greenville, TX (10%-350) Ann; NHS; F-Ed, Sch P; *U of Tex; Eng.*

RODOLPH, Gwen Ellen
Hobbs HS; Hobbs, NM (2-496) Band; Chor; Tres, FTA; Rainbow; Amer Leg A; Hon Prog; 1st Cl GSct; *McMurray Col; Pre-Sch Ed.*

RODRIGUE, Carol Ann
St Dominic Regional HS; Lewiston, ME; CYO; Chor; Fr C; Ed, Sch P; Pres, SC; Pres, Sr Cl; Citz A; DARGCA; Type A; Fr, Sewing, PA, A's; *St Mary's Sch of Nurs; Nurs.*

RODRIGUE, Caroline Mary
Destrehan HS; Destrehan, LA (5%-200) BC; Hmrm; COM; Sci A; Eng, Attendance, Mus, A's; Bathing Suit, Swim, A's; *LSU; Mus.*

RODRIGUEZ, Ana Sofia
Academia Sagrado Corazon; Santurce, PR (4-65) Fin, Lit Ral; Co-Ch, Madrigal; NHS; ARC; Co-Ed, Sch P; Spch C; *U of Puerto Rico; Phar.*

RODRIGUEZ, Anamary
Dra Maria Cadilla de Martinez HS; Arecibo, PR (1-429) A Cap Choir; FHA; Hmrm; Ed, Sch P; Span C; SC; Y-Tns; Bio A; COM; Cl Fav; Hon Prog; Rotary A; Sci A; *Universidad de Puerto Rico.*

RODRIGUEZ, Angel Candido
Dra Maria Cadilla de Martinez HS; Arecibo, PR (47-429) Tres, Commercial C; Pres, Hmrm; Tres, Sch Achieve Tm; MVP, Bkbl; Fin, Cr-Ctry; JV, Sftbl; Alg A; COM; Cl Fav; Hist A; Math A; ACAA A; *Mayaguez Col; Elec Engr.*

RODRIGUEZ, Angel Luis
Our Lady of Pilar HS; Rio Piedras, PR (20%-166) CYO; Chem C; Drama; Hmrm; VP, NFL; NHS; Span C; Spch C; Tnns; Alg A; Bio A; COM; Hist A; Math A; Sci A; Spch A; Fin, Ntl Forensics League; Lib C; Fin, Paradise Bowl Tm; Span Forensic C; Marine Bio C; Newspaper Rptr; Fin, Mod UN; *Yale U; Laws.*

RODRIGUEZ, Antonia
Central HS; Santurce, PR; CYO; Span C; COM; Citz A; *U of PR; Eng Ed.*

RODRIGUEZ, Arlene Ivette
Lola Rodriguez de Tio; San German, PR (25-350) Secy, FHA; 4H; Math C; ARC; Span C; COM; Hon Prog; Magna Cum Laude; Math A; Pres A; ARC A; Star Student; Summa Cum Laude; *Univ Catolica Ponce; Med Technology.*

RODRIGUEZ, Augustine
Detroit Western HS; Detroit, MI; A-Ed, Sch P; Up Bound; Ftbl; Opt A; *U of Mich; Law.*

RODRIGUEZ, Carmen Waleska
Jose de Diego HS; Mayaguez, PR; Pres, CYO; VP, FHA; VP, 4H; Phys C; ARC; Sci C; Secy, Span C; COM; Summa Cum Laude.

RODRIGUEZ, Cecilia Ann
Providence HS; San Antonio, TX (10%-100) A Cap Choir; CYO; Chldr; Drama; FHA; FTA; Hmrm; SC; Beauty; HCt; Fin, Miss Tex Teen-Ager Pageant; Miss Photogenic; Parish Qn; WW; Fin, Teena Tex Board Comp; 2nd/drill Tm; Marian Choristersan; *Fashion Design.*

RODRIGUEZ, Consuelo
Colegio Puertorriqueno de Ninas; Rio Piedras, PR (4-48) Math C; NHS; COM; Hon Prog; *Med.*

RODRIGUEZ, Daniel Antonio
Yauco HS; Yauco, PR; Bsbl; Bkbl; *Bradford Col; Acct.*

RODRIGUEZ, David
Kelvyn Park HS; Chicago, IL; Span C; Span NHS; Sch Service; *N Park Col; Psych.*

RODRIGUEZ, Elida
Yauco HS; Yauco, PR; *UPR Regional; Math Ed.*

RODRIGUEZ, Ezequiel
Chino HS; Chino, CA; Var C; Co-Cpt, Cr-Ctry; Tr; Cl Fav; *Seattle Pacific U; Phys Ed.*

RODRIGUEZ, Gregoria
Crystal City HS; Crystal City, TX (5-107) Ann; Drama; Ensm; Cpt, Mjrte; NHS; Ed, VP, SC; Hist A; Swtht; Eng A; Jr Dutchess; *U of Tex at Austin; Law.*

RODRIGUEZ, Hetty Milagros
Jose de Diego HS; Mayaguez, PR; Chem C; Math C; Spch C; Alg A; COM; Hist A; Phy A; Summa Cum Laude.

RODRIGUEZ, Irma
Oak Grove HS; San Jose, CA; *Pre-School Ed.*

RODRIGUEZ, Ivette
Saint Aloysius HS; Jersey City, NJ (2-129) NHS; Chem A; Hon Prog; *Christ Hospital Nurs Sch; Nurs.*

RODRIGUEZ, Joe I
Bowman HS; Canyon Country, CA; Tnns; *Col o-t County; Data Processing.*

RODRIGUEZ, Jorge Luis
St Patrick HS; Chicago, IL (20-350) Chess C; Chor; VP, Hmrm; NHS; Rptr, Sch P; Ski C; Span C; Tres, SC; Tres, Jr Cl; Tr; Amer Leg A; Citz A; Hon Prog; St Scholar; Evans Schol Win; *U of Ill at Urbana; Archt.*

RODRIGUEZ, Jose Daniel
Smithtown HS W; Smithtown, NY (15%-550) Band; Chor; Order/Arrow; Pres, Span NHS; Ftbl; Tr; Wrest; Nom, US Air Force Acad; *US Air Force Acad; Aero-Space Engr.*

RODRIGUEZ, Jose Francisco
Dra Maria Cadilla de Martinez HS; Arecibo, PR (33-429) Chem C; Phys C; Bkbl; COM; Hon Prog; *Colegio de Mayaguez; Elec Engr.*

RODRIGUEZ, Jose Luis
Luis Munoz Marin HS; Cabo Rojo, PR (6-200) Dbte Tm; Lit Mag; Alg A; COM; Cl Fav; H of F; Hon Prog; Math A; MLS; Most Out; Opt A; Spch A; Star Student; Summa Cum Laude; *CAAM; Engr.*

RODRIGUEZ, Lisa Margaret
Scotch Plains-Fanwood HS; Scotch Plains, NJ (20%-650) A Cap Choir; Band; Chor; Drama; Rptr, Sci C.

RODRIGUEZ, Lorna Lizzette
Colegio Puertorriqueno de Ninas; Rio Piedras, PR (1-61) Math C; NFL; NHS; Sch P; COM; Sci A; Spch A; Bradley U; Sci.

RODRIGUEZ, Lourdes Ivette
Luis Munoz Marin HS; Cabo Rojo, PR (1-200) Chldr; Dbte Tm; Hmrm; Alg A; Bio A; COM; Chem A; Hist A; Hon Prog; Magna Cum Laude; Math A; Sci A; CAAM; Phar.

RODRIGUEZ, Lourdes T
Dr Pila HS; Ponce, PR; A Cap Choir; CYO; Chor; Hmrm; ARC; SC; Sftbl; Bio A; COM; Hon Prog; ARC A; Sci A; Cath U of PR; Med.

RODRIGUEZ, Luis Ernesto
Yauco HS; Yauco, PR; BS; Bkbl; COM; Citz A; UPR-MAYAGUEZ; Engr.

RODRIGUEZ, Luis Jr
Cardinal Spellman HS; Bronx, NY (25-555) Band; Chess C; Orch; Y-Tns; COM; JA A; Cpt, Bowl; Band Medal; Manhattan Col; Bus Mgr.

RODRIGUEZ, Luis Ramon
Academia Sagrado Corazon; Santurce, PR (5-92) Drama; NHS; ARC; Var C; Bsbl; MVP, Bkbl; MVP, Tr; Alg A; Bio A; Hon Prog; Phy A; Geography A; Espanish A; Eng A; Bradley U; Med.

RODRIGUEZ, Luisa Maria
MacDuffie Sch; Springfield, MA; SC; 90% Grade Avg A; Rollins Col; Bus Adm.

RODRIGUEZ, Magda Ivette
Dr P Perea Fajardo Voc HS; Mayaguez, PR; COM; Sci A; Hon Stu; Ex Hon Stu; Med Technology.

RODRIGUEZ, Marc Angelo
Central Cath HS; San Antonio, TX (1%-212) CYO; Chor; Dbte Tm; Hmrm; NHS; Spch C; SC; Bsbl; Bkbl; COM; Ntl Achv Schol; NEDT; Sci A; Spch A; Eng A; Med.

RODRIGUEZ, Maria Elizabeth
Wesleyan Acad; Guaynabo, PR (2-32) Cpt, Chldr; Chor; Co-Ch, Drama; Tres, Hmrm; NHS; PA; Escuela de Medicina U PR; Pediatrician.

RODRIGUEZ, Mariluisa
Colegio San Antonio HS; Rio Piedras, PR; Chor; Drama; Hmrm; Math C; Pres, NHS; Spch C; SC; Var C; Pres, Sr Cl; Parl, Jr Cl; Parl, Soph Cl; Bkbl; Sftbl; Tnns; Beauty; COM; Hon Prog; MLS; Spch A; Yale Book A; Drama A; Bradford Col; Laws.

RODRIGUEZ, Marisel
Adolfo Grana Rivera HS; Penuelas, PR (4-336) Chor; ARC; Bsbl; COM; Hon Prog; Sci A; Universidad de PR; Ciencia.

RODRIGUEZ, Mary Angela
Ross S Sterling HS; Baytown, TX (25%-620) Key C; Secy, Orch; SC; Pres, Soph Cl; Swim; Cl Fav; Governor & 1st Lady Court; Star Drill Tm; Tex Women's U; Nurs.

RODRIGUEZ, Nitza Enid
Dra Maria Cadilla de Martinez HS; Arecibo, PR (46-429) CYO; Chem C; Chor; 4H; Pres, Hmrm; Phys C; Sci C; Alg A; COM; Chem A; 4H A; Hon Prog; Sci.

RODRIGUEZ, Oscar David
Luis Munoz Marin HS; Cabo Rojo, PR (3-150) Chor; Dbte Tm; Drama; Sci C; Span C; Bio A; COM; Cl Fav; Hon Prog; Pres A; Sci A; Col Agricultura y Artes Mechnicas; Med.

RODRIGUEZ, Patricia Ann
Crockett HS; Austin, TX; CYO; CCD A; Bus.

RODRIGUEZ, Rachel H
David Crockett HS; Austin, TX (30%-650) CYO; Rptr, FHA; SC; Secy, Sr Cl; Beauty; Rank Ldr, Drill Tm; Del Mar Col; Dental Hygiene.

RODRIGUEZ, Rafael Juan
Colegio Nuestra Sra de la Merced; Hato Rey, PR (3-92) Tnns; Chem C; Pres, Chess C; Cpt, Dbte Tm; Drama; VP, Hmrm; Ed, Lit Mag; VP, Math C; Model UN; Pres, Phys C; Tres, Pol Sci C; Sci C; Secy, Span C; Pres, Spch C; Tres, Sr Cl; Alg A; Bio A; COM; Chem A; Hist A; HKg; Hon Prog; I Dare You; Journ A; Math A; MLS; Most Out; Opt A; Phy A; Spch A; Star Student; Semi-Fin, C-6 A; Arts A; Computer Sci.

RODRIGUEZ, Wanda Leticia
Dr Pila HS; Ponce, PR; Cpt, CYO; Co-Ch, Chem C; Pres, Hmrm; Math C; Secy, Sch Achieve Tm; Secy, Sch P; Cl Fav; Lion A; Cath U; Sci.

RODRIGUEZ, Yolanda
Passaic HS; Passaic, NJ; Span C; Art & Health Ed Certs of Achv; HR; Cl Pal Trophy; William Paterson Col; Nurs.

RODRIGUEZ, Elizabeth
Miami Springs Sr HS; Miami Springs, FL; Math C; COM; Hon Prog; Miami Dade Col; Phar.

RODSTROM, Joan Louise
Morgan Park HS; Chicago, IL (75-556) A Cap Choir; Ann; Fr C; InterClub Coun; Ski C; Tri-HiY; Swim; Hon Prog; Opt A; Sci A; Bethel Col; Econ.

ROE, Andrew Grant
Brookings HS; Brookings, SD (40-202) Band; Sch P; VP, Soph Cl; Bsbl; JV, Bkbl; Ftbl; Tr; Type A; Lions Good Citz A; SDSU; Engr.

ROE, David Hamer
Bennington HS; Bennington, NE; Band; Chor; S-T, Var C; Bkbl; Ftbl; BS Alt; Drama A; Jazz Band; U of Nebr-Lincoln.

ROE, Karen Jane
Lewisville HS; Lewisville, TX (8-570) A Cap Choir; Band; Chor; Ensm; Pres, FHA; Math C; NHS; Orch; Pres, Rainbow; Masonic A; Band A; Nurs.

ROE, Leslie Joan
Bennington HS; Bennington, NE (7-67) F-Ed, Ann; Tres, Band; Chor; Ensm; Math C; Bkbl; Sftbl; Tr; COM; Vlbl; GAA; Jazz Band; All Conf Hon Band.

ROE, Pamela Ann
Bowling Green HS; Bowling Green, OH; Chor; FHA; 4H; Hmrm; Sch P; Tr; HCt; Type A; Semi-Fin, HQn; Milligan Col; Bus.

ROE, Tana Jean
Duncan HS; Duncan, OK (48-350) Chor; Mgr, Bkbl; Sftbl; Mgr, Tr; Citz A; JA A; Kiwanis A; Sci A; Okla Christian Col; Elem Ed.

ROEBUCK, Martha Sue
Wooster HS; Wooster, OH (69-375) Ger C; Tres, 4H; Math C; Span C; Tnns; 4H A; Aquacade; 1st Cl A, GSct; Wittenberg U; Special Ed.

ROEDER, Terri Ann
Weldon Valley Sch; Weldona, CO (1-12) Band; Secy, FBLA; Secy, FFA; GS; Pres, 4H; Pres, NHS; Secy, Sch P; Secy, Sci C; Ski C; Span C; SC; Pres, Soph Cl; Co-Cpt, Bkbl; Tr; DARGCA; 4H A; Masonic A; Sci A; Type A; Val; U of Northern Colo; Home-Ec.

ROEDL, Mark Douglas
Beaver Dam Sr HS; Beaver Dam, WI (40-317) CYO; Chor; Ensm; Hmrm; Madrigal; Ski C; SC; Var C; Pres, Jr Cl; Arch; Bsbl; Bkbl; Ftbl; Golf; Tr.

ROEFS, Rhobbi Lynn
California HS; Whittier, CA; Band; Chldr; Dbte Tm; Drama; InterClub Coun; Co-Ch, Model UN; NFL; NHS; Span C; Spch C; SC; Thes; Secy, Sr Cl; VP, Soph Cl; Chamber of Comm A; Cl Fav; Opt A; Spch A; Athenas; Ind Mime Finals; Sou Calif Original Oratory Semis; Girls League Outst A; Biola Col; Communications.

ROEGGE, Mary Elizabeth
Minneapolis Lutheran HS; Minneapolis, MN (7-48) Band; Chldr; Chor; Model UN; Rptr, Sch P; Ski C; Cr-Ctry; Tr; U of Minn; Occupational Therapist.

ROEGGE, Sarah Jane
Minneapolis Lutheran HS; Minneapolis, MN (5-45) Ann; Band; Chldr; Chess C; Chor; Model UN; Secy, SC; VP, Soph Cl; Cr-Ctry; Mgr, Ftbl; Tr; Hon Prog; VP, Mus A; U of Minn.

ROEGLIN, Andrea Sue
Burnsville Sr HS; Burnsville, MN (30-765) Chor; NHS; Ski C; Math.

ROEGLIN, Douglas Paul
Keokuk Sr HS; Keokuk, IA (70-225) Bsbl; Bkbl; JV, Golf.

ROEHL, Janice Blaine
Thomas Jefferson HS; Portland, OR (2%-250) Tnns; S-T, Yth Fel; Yth Adv Comm, Metropol Yth Coun; Taylor U; Elem Ed.

ROEHL, Janice Elaine
Thomas Jefferson HS; Portland, OR (2%-250) Tnns; Tres, S-T, Yth Fel; Metropolitan Yth Commission; Taylor U; Elem Ed.

ROEHLKE, Wendy Louise
Richfield Sr HS; Richfield, MN (21-732) Ann; Community Yth Symph; NHS; Orch; Co-Ed, Sch P; Wartburg Col; Mus Performance.

ROEHR, Gerald Allen
Hopkinsville HS; Hopkinsville, KY (10-450) FFA; Church Usher; Rabbit A's.

ROELING, Christopher Nilson
De La Salle HS; New Orleans, LA (88-265) Drama; Parl, Hmrm; Lit Mag; NHS; St Stu Congress; Thes; NEDT; Tulane U; Archt.

ROENKER, Timothy Andrew
Princess Anne HS; Virginia Beach, VA (116-592) Sci C; Span C; Var C; Ftbl; Tr; Wrest; Old Dominion U; Acct.

ROEPKE, Kevin Douglas
Hillcrest HS; Springfield, MO (5%-375) Hmrm; SC; Bsbl; Bkbl; Ftbl; Kiwanis A; Best Camper; Bus.

ROEPKEN, Stephen Francis
Westminster Christian Sch; Miami, FL (77-103) Pres, Chor; Lat C; Order/Arrow; Cpt, Cr-Ctry; Cpt, Soccer; God & Country A; Yth Fel; Eagle A; Yth Pres; Yth Board; Capital U; Ministry.

ROESCH, Robbi Deborah
Bishop Verot HS; Fort Myers, FL (20-104) Pres, 4H; Hmrm; NHS; Citz A; 4H A; Spch A; Miss Fla Fancy Poultry; WW; Lee Co Bicentennial; Page, Fla House of Rep; Agri-Bus.

ROESER, Mark David
Brookville HS; Brookville, OH (25-185) Var C; Tres, Sr Cl; Bsbl; Tnns; COM; Hist A; MVP, Tnns; Sinclair Col; Bus Adm.

ROESKE, Michael Jerome
Ridgewood HS; Ridgewood, NJ (20%-600) A Cap Choir; CYO; Chor; Drama.

ROESKE, Sandra Rae
Jamestown HS; Jamestown, ND; Tres, FBLA; Tres, Ger C; 4H; Fin, Jr Miss Pagent; NHS; Spch C; Mgr, Bkbl; Concordia Col; Communications.

ROESNER, Michele Lynn
Kewanee HS; Kewanee, IL; AFS; Chem C; Pres, Dbte Tm; Drama; FTA; Ger C; VP, 4H; Hmrm; Phys C; Rptr, Sch P; Sci C; Spch C; SC; Pres, Sr Cl; 4H A; Spch A; Debate A; U of Ill; Fine Arts.

ROESSLER, Susan Elizabeth
S San Antonio HS; San Antonio, TX; Tnns.

ROETSCHKE, Terry Lee
Lake Worth HS; Fort Worth, TX (15-100) NHS; Var C; Bkbl; Sftbl; Tr; All Dist Bkbl; Stu Adv Committee; Cpt, Vlbl; Pres, Yth Fel; Most Ath.

ROFFMANN, Amy Elizabeth
Mt Vernon Township HS; Mt Vernon, IL (75%-400) Chor; Rptr, Lit Mag; Rainbow; Law.

ROFFMANN, Jennifer Lee
Mt Vernon Township HS; Mt Vernon, IL (31-389) F-Ed, Ann; Rainbow; St Scholar; Senate Rep, Yth in Gov't; GSct; Tres, JA; Operetta; Pres, Westminister Fel; Pep C; Rend Lake Jr Col; Acct.

ROGALSKI, Kim Ann
Old Forge HS; Old Forge, PA (12-121) VP, FTA; Hmrm; NHS; Ski C; Chem A; Pa St U; Med Tech.

ROGAN, Elfleta Rowlon
Mt Clemens HS; Mt Clemens, MI; Chldr; Chor; Semi-Fin, City Conf; Fr C; Ntl Yth Conf; Tr; COM; Star Student; Vlbl; Mus A; Semi-Fin, DAR Good Citz A; Eng A; Social Stu A; Wayne St U; Law.

ROGAN, Lloyd William
Tallulah HS; Tallulah, LA (18-105) 4H; HiY; Sch P; Var C; Cr-Ctry; Ftbl; Tnns; Tr; Cpt & MVP, Band; Northeast La U; Mus.

ROGER, Ivelisse
Cristobal HS; Coco Solo, CANAL ZONE (16-130) Chor; Fr C; FNA; Foreign Lang.

ROGERS, Alan Shane
Stafford HS; Fredericksburg, VA; Band; Fr C; Swim; Tr; COM; BSct; Tr, Swim, Cert of A; Air Force Acad; ROTC.

ROGERS, Barbara Ellen
Petersburg HS; Petersburg, VA (10%-565) Fr C;
NHS; Va St Col; Computer Programmer.

ROGERS, Beth Ann
Irving HS; Irving, TX (70-596) A Cap Choir; Chor;
Drama; Ensm; NFL; NHS; SC; Tres, Tri-HiY; Hon
Prog; Spch A; Yth Fel; Best Supporting Actress;
Abilene Christian U; Bio.

ROGERS, Carla Jaye
Wheeler Co HS; Alamo, GA (8-50) Ann; BC;
Chldr; Chor; JV, 4H; JV, Hmrm; NHS; Tri-HiY;
JV, Bkbl; Sftbl; Valdosta St Col; Math.

ROGERS, Carol Denese
Claxton HS; Claxton, GA; Rptr, BC; Cpt, Chldr;
4H; Sch P; Tres, SC; Tri-HiY; Chem A; Citz A;
Hon Prog; JA A; Eng A; Home Ec A; Drivers Ed
A; Chem A; U of Ga.

ROGERS, Catherine Pate
Scotland HS; Laurinburg, NC; Chor; FFA.

ROGERS, Cathy Lynette
Hazen HS; Hazen, AR (4-45) VP, Band; BC; Pres,
Chor; Secy, FBLA; FHA; GS; Madrigal; Cpt,
Mjrte; Ed, Sch P; Secy, Sci C; Rptr, SC; Cl Fav;
HCt; Journ A; Miss Hazen; Neatest; U of Ark;
Health-Related Field.

ROGERS, Celia A
W Henderson HS; Hendersonville, NC (21-178)
Lib Sci A; Tenn Temple Col; Christian Ed.

ROGERS, Charles Allen Jr
Hickory HS; Hickory, NC (20-350) Drama; Key C;
NHS; Order/Arrow; Tnns; Hon Prog; Jr Marshal;
U of NC Chapel Hill; Bus Adm.

ROGERS, Cherie Linda
Wilson HS; Easton, PA (13-195) Drama; NHS;
Bkbl; Sftbl; Hon Prog; Yth Fel.

ROGERS, Cheryl Lynn
Thornwell HS; Clinton, SC (4-20) BC; Co-Cpt,
Chldr; Chor; Drama; Secy, Fr C; FBLA; InterAct
C; SC; Secy, Sr Cl; Beauty; JA A; Sci A; Presby-
terian Col; Drama.

ROGERS, David Alan
Brandon Sr HS; Brandon, FL (25-901) VP, Band;
Pres, BC; Demolay; NHS; World Affairs C; U of S
Fla; Chem.

ROGERS, David George
Cashmere HS; Cashmere, WA (80-100) Chor;
FFA; Rptr, Sch P; Var C; MVP, Cr-Ctry; JV, Golf;
Wrest; 4H A; JA A; Central Wash St Col; Agr.

ROGERS, Debbie Diane
N Mecklenburg HS; Huntersville, NC (150-498)
Band; Span C; U of NC; Elem Ed.

ROGERS, Debbie Sue
El Cajon Valley HS; El Cajon, CA (10%-300) Band;
Ger C; Bank Of Amer A; Hon Prog; Mus.

ROGERS, Edward Morris
Cartersville HS; Cartersville, GA (1-135) A Cap
Choir; BC; Chor; Ensm; FTA; HiY; Hmrm; Lit Ral;
Mu Alpha Theta; Order/Arrow; SC; JV, Ftbl; Ga
Tech; Industrial And Systems Engr.

ROGERS, Evelyn Deorlean
Clark HS; Las Vegas, NV; Drama; Bsbl; Comm Col;
Nurs.

ROGERS, G Stuart
Kimberton Farms Sch; Phoenixville, PA (2-16)
Chor; Madrigal; JV, Bkbl; Soccer; NEDT.

ROGERS, Gordon Dean
Hillcrest HS; Dallas, TX; A Cap Choir; Band; Chor;
Hmrm; Bsbl; Citz A; Lone Star HS Rodeo Assn;
Tex Tech U; Voice.

ROGERS, James McClain
Pisgah HS; Canton, NC (190-310) Bus C; Ch, De-
molay; Drama; FBLA; 4H; InterClub Coun; Key C;
Lat C; Phys C; Ch, ARC; Ski C; Ch, SC; Co-Cpt,
Bsbl; Co-Cpt, Sftbl; Citz A; PTA A; ARC A; Spch
A; Yth Fel; Yth Foundation A; Pres, Church Yth
Coun; Best Actor A; Friendliest, Sr Cl; Campbell
Col; Bus Law.

ROGERS, James Ronald
Appalachian HS; Oneonta, AL (9-38) Ed, Ann;
Pres, BC; Pres, FFA; 4H; Sch P; Pres, Sr Cl; Bsbl;
Cpt, Bkbl; Cpt, Ftbl; Cl Fav; 4H A; Auburn U.

ROGERS, James Tracey
Robert E Lee HS; Midland, TX (40%-700) VP, Key
C; NHS; Bsbl; Co-Cpt, Ftbl; Amer Leg A; Spch A;
FCA; Church Bkbl; Tn Rep, Church Gen Nom
Committee; Tex A&M U.

ROGERS, Jane Buchanan
Grissom HS; Huntsville, AL; Cpt, Chldr; Pres,
Drama; SC; Pres, Soph Cl; MLS; Most Out; Pres,
Tn Board; Little Theatre; Comm Chor; Director,
Angel Choir; U of Ala; Drama.

ROGERS, Jeanne Marie
Mountain Brook HS; Mountain Brook, AL; Band;
Chldr; Fr C; Lat C; Thes; VP, Tri-Ettes Service C;
Explorers C; Auburn U; Med.

ROGERS, John William III
Columbus HS; Columbus, GA (2%-325) CYO;
Math C; Mu Alpha Theta; Sch Achieve Tm; Gov
Honor Prog; JA A; Math A; ROTC A; Civitan A;
Air Force Acad; Aerospace Engr.

ROGERS, Joyce Cathlyn
Alexandria Sr HS; Alexandria, LA (20-450) Ann;
Bus C; S-T, FBLA; Hmrm; Lit Ral; Lit Mag; Sci C;
SC; Y-Tns; Hon Prog; LSU; Nurs.

ROGERS, Karen Marie
Crescent HS; Crescent, OK (15-41) Ed, Ann; Band;
Chor; Ensm; Ch, FTA; Rainbow; F-Ed, Sch P; Yth
Fel; AAUW, Crescent Outst Sr Girl; FTA Schol;
FTA Qn; Ann Staff Qn; Central St U at Edmond;
Special Ed.

ROGERS, Karen Michelle
Brandon HS; Brandon, FL; BC; Hon Prog; Dancerette; U of S Fla; Nurs.

ROGERS, Kathy Levon
Wendell Phillips HS; Chicago, IL (9-320) Ann;
NHS; ARC; VP, SC; Cpt, Bkbl; Cpt, Tr; Iowa Wes-
leyan Col; Phys Ed.

ROGERS, Kelley Ann
Headland HS; East Point, GA (10%-150) S-T,
AFS; BC; Drama; S-T, Fr C; Math C; Rptr, Sch P;
SC; Mgr, Bsbl; Hon Prog; NEDT; St Cert of Merit,
Fr; Co Schol Achv; Hon Page, St House of Rep;
Lang.

ROGERS, Kim Alan
Lakeview HS; Battle Creek, MI; Bsbl; Co-Cpt, Ftbl;
Co-Cpt, Wrest; MVP, Ftbl; Wrest Record; Albion
Col; Computers.

ROGERS, Lamar E Jr
River Oaks Sch; Monroe, LA (25-39) Bus C; VP,
Key C; Spch C; NE La U; Bus Adm.

ROGERS, Laura Carole
Williamston HS; Williamston, NC (13-219) Band;
BC; Fr C; HCt; Pres, Keywanettes.

ROGERS, Lisa Ann
Sto-Rox Sr HS; McKees Rocks, PA (32-35) Band;
Pres, FBLA; FNA; Mjrte; Y-Tns; Bkbl; Cr-Ctry;
Sftbl; Tr; Bio A; Citz A; Cl Fav; Pepperdine U;
Med.

ROGERS, Margaret Michelle
Belton Honea Path HS; Belton, SC; Cpt, Chldr; Ntl
Yth Conf; Bkbl; Sftbl; Piano; Academics; Excell-
ence Girls League Sftbl; Christian Charm Course;
PA A; Mus.

ROGERS, Martin Randy
Rutledge HS; Rutledge, TN (6-124) Band; BC; Bus
C; Chem C; VP, FFA; 4H; Pres, Math C; St Stu
Congress; SC; Var C; Cr-Ctry; Ftbl; Tr; Hist A; Star
Student; Yth Fel; U of Tenn; Acct.

ROGERS, Mary Lynn
Hall HS; Little Rock, AR; Band; BC; Tres, FBLA;
Y-Tns; Bus.

ROGERS, Michelle Louise
M B Smiley Sr HS; Houston, TX (6-400) Band;
Chldr; Ensm; Tres, Fr C; Hmrm; Mu Alpha Theta;
Ch, NHS; Sci C; Span C; SC; VP, Soph Cl; Bio A;
COM; Citz A; Cl Fav; Magna Cum Laude; Type A;
Band, Shorthand Medal; Bicentennial Yth Fair;
Advanced Composition; San Jacinto Col; Phys Ed.

ROGERS, Neal Francis
Paw Paw HS; Paw Paw, IL (1-31) Band; VP, FFA;
NHS; Tres, Sr Cl; Bkbl; Golf; HCt; Val; DeKalb
Agr A; Bradley U; Mech Tech.

ROGERS, Neva Lee
Ocean Springs HS; Ocean Springs, MS (6-260) A-
Ed, Ann; BC; Fr C; VP, FHA; SC; Cpt, Bkbl; Sftbl;
Tnns; Pres A; Auburn U; Nurs.

ROGERS, Nina Yulanda
Big Sandy HS; Big Sandy, TX (5-42) Ann; Chor;
Ensm; FHA; Secy, NHS; Orch; Sch P; Bkbl; Citz
A; MLS; Vlbl; Eng A; Most Intellectual; Key,
Scroll & Torch A, FHA; Ambassador Col; Oral
Communications.

ROGERS, Pamela Lou
Lansing Everett HS; Lansing, MI (15-531) Cpt,
Chldr; Pres, City Conf; Ensm; InterAct C; Inter-
Club Coun; NHS; Parl, SC; Var C; Pres, Sr Cl; Pres,
Jr Cl; Tres, Soph Cl; Cpt, Bkbl; Sftbl; Cpt, Swim;
Bio A; Citz A; Hon Prog; MLS; Most Out; Ntl Sci
Found; Star Student; MSU Hon Schol; NSF HS
Hon Sci Prog; Alma Hon Schol; St Hon Schol; Sci.

ROGERS, Peter Todd
Warren Central HS; Vicksburg, MS (1-340) Band;
Dbte Tm; Fr C; Hmrm; Math C; Order/Arrow; Sci
C; SC; Alg A; Bio A; God & Country A; Sci A;
Eagle Sct; Fr A; Yale U; Math.

ROGERS, Regina Susan
Dublin HS; Dublin, GA; Ga Sou Col.

ROGERS, Rena Kathleen
Center HS; Center, TX (14-160) VP, FTA; Rptr,
NHS; Rptr, Soph Cl; JV, Bkbl; Co-Cpt, Ftbl; B
Crocker A; Bio A; Colo St U; Biomed Sci.

ROGERS, Richard Leonard
Moanalua HS; Honolulu, HI (14-236) Band; NHS;
Ftbl; Co-Cpt, Tr; God & Country A; US Air Force
Acad; Engr.

ROGERS, Richard Leonarrd
Moanalua HS; Honolulu, HI (14-236) Band; NHS;
Ftbl; Co-Cpt, Tr; God & Country A; Appointment,
US Air Force Acad; US Air Force Acad; Engr.

ROGERS, Robert Allen
Houston Sr HS; Houston, MO (7-117) Semi-Fin,
FBLA; Monogram; Secy, NHS; VP, SC; Var C;
Ftbl; Tr; MLS; Most Out; Regent Schol; VP,
FBLA; WW; SW Mo St U; Market & Mgt.

ROGERS, Robyn Lyn
Perry HS; Perry, OK (26-88) Ann; Band; FHA;
FTA; Mjrte; Rainbow; ARC; Tres, Soph Cl; Ma-
sonic A; Most Popular; Miss PHS Nom; Pep Coun;
FTA Schol; Okla St U; Home Ec.

ROGERS, Sandra Lee
Burke HS; Charleston, SC (2-210) Band; Drama;
NHS; VP, Y-Tns; Gov Honor Prog; Hist A; Hon
Prog; Most Out; US Armed Forces Bicentennial
Band; WW Among Mus Stu in Amer HS; WW;
Charleston Co Bicentennial Band; U of SC; Mus.

ROGERS, Sara Lynne
Briarcrest Baptist HS; Memphis, TN; Chor; Pres,
Lat C; Lit Mag; Mu Alpha Theta; NHS; Soccer;
Aux Lat; NEDT; Med.

ROGERS, Sherry Lynn
DuVal Sr HS; Lanham, MD (90-650) A Cap Choir;
Band; NHS; Sftbl; Mgr, Tr; Hon Prog; Vlbl; An-
nouncer A; Annoucer C; U of NC; Phys Ther.

ROGERS, Steven Murray
Brockport HS; Brockport, NY (25-275) Ed, Ann;
Chess C; Dbte Tm; Drama; Ger C; Math C; VP,
Order/Arrow; Ftbl; Tr; Bio A; COM; Hon Prog;
Order/Arrow A; Bradford Col; Bio.

ROGERS, Steven Wayne
N Natchez Adams HS; Natchez, MS; Band; BC;
Math C; NHS; VP, Sci C; Miss St U; Acct.

ROGERS, Stewart Wesley
Houston HS; Houston, MO (15-153) Band; Chor;
FFA; Ftbl; Tr; US Air Force; Mech.

ROGERS, Susan Lynn
Campbell HS; Smyrna, GA (20%-390) BC; Chor;
Ensm; FBLA; Hmrm; SC; Sftbl; COM; Citz A; Ki-
wanis A; Sci Fair; GSct; Ga St U; Guidance Coun.

ROGERS, Tanya Dalzell
University City HS; Philadelphia, PA; A Cap
Choir; Chor; Dbte Tm; Drama; Ensm; Hmrm; SC;
Citz A; Bowl.

ROGERS, Teresa Ann
New Palestine HS; New Palestine, IN (11-165) F-
Ed, Ann; Chor; Madrigal; NHS; Span C; SC; Thes;
Tr; Tres, Yth Fellowship; Dragon Dozen; WW;
Outst Chor Stu; Taylor U; Physics.

ROGERS, Theresa Lucille
Columbia HS; Decatur, GA (10-375) BC; Fr C;
Chem A; Hon Prog; Vlbl; Eng A; DeKalb Jr Col;
Criminology.

ROGERS, Thomas Foster
Bath Co HS; Owingsville, KY (1-123) A-Ed, Ann; Parl, BC; Chor; Pres, 4H; F-Ed, Sch P; SC; Cpt, Tnns; Alg A; 4H A; I Dare You; Sci A; Photography, Eng, Piano, A's; Tech Drawing, Chor, A's; *E Ky U.*

ROGERS, Tina Rene
Maysville HS; Maysville, OK (10%-40) Band; FHA; NHS; Bkbl; Amer Leg A; Bio A; COM; Citz A; Cl Fav; Hist A; Kiwanis A; Math A; Sci A; Spch A; Type A; Band As; Vocal As; Okla HS Hon Soc; *Okla U.*

ROGERS, Todd Alan
Petal HS; Petal, MS (8-240) Chor; Fr C; SC; Bible C; Civics A; Span A; *U of Sou Miss; Mus.*

ROGERS, Wanda Ellen
Model HS; Shannon, GA (10%-200) Band; Bus C; Bus Mgr, Commercial; Cr-Ctry; Sftbl; COM; JA A; Sci A; *Berry Col; Chem.*

ROGERS, Wanda Jean
Lyons Sr HS; Lyons, GA; *Arlington Baptist Col; Bible.*

ROGERSON, Kristi Lynn
Williamston HS; Williamston, NC (10-189) Fr C; Rptr, FHA; Key C; Monogram; NHS; SC; Mgr, Bkbl; Sftbl; Tnns; *E Carolina U; Child Development.*

ROGOFF, Joseph Aaron
Calif Preparatory Sch; Encino, CA; SC; VP, Sr Cl; Bsbl; Bkbl; *U o-t Redlands; Bus.*

ROGSTAD, Elizabeth Maude
Detroit Lakes HS; Detroit Lakes, MN; Pres, AFS; Band; Span C; Spch C; Golf; Co-Cpt, Swim; Snowball Princess; Best Sense of Humor; Hardest Worker Swim A; *Wells Col; Ed.*

ROGUE, Noel
Juan Jose Osuna HS; Rio Piedras, PR (6-150) Band; CYO; Chor; Dbte Tm; JETS; Rptr, Lit Ral; Lit Mag; Span C; Bsbl; Semi-Fin, Bkbl; COM; Lion A; Phy A; Sci A; *U of Puerto Rico; Computer Programming.*

ROHAN, Margaret Mary
St Angela Hall Acad; Brooklyn, NY (5-82) Math C; Alg A; Bio A; Math A; Sci A; *Bus.*

ROHDE, Harry John
Lyons Township HS; La Grange, IL (100-1200) Co-Ed, Ann; Chor; Ensm; Var C; Hon Prog; NEDT; Radio Station; Semi-Fin, Mus Composition; Semi-Fin, Area Mus Camp; *Bus.*

ROHE, Kathryn Mary
Morristown Hamblen HS; Morristown, TN (27-294) Band; Chor; Ensm; Madrigal; Thes; Cr-Ctry; Swim; Best Actress; Most Outst Sr Choir Member; *U of Tenn at Knoxville; Theatre.*

ROHLFING, Jane Delores
Gasconade Co R-1 HS; Hermann, MO (5-97) Band; Chor; Rptr, Drama; Mjrte; Pres, NHS; Sch P; COM; God & Country A; Yth Fel; GSct; Flag Corps; Outst Eng Stu; City Band; All Conf Band; Church Choir; Secy, Art C; Bicentennial Courier, Belgium; *Eng.*

ROHLFING, Susan Marie
Valmeyer HS; Valmeyer, IL (8-40) Co-Ed, Ann; Band; Tres, CYO; Chor; Ensm; FBLA; VP, FHA; GS; S-T, 4H; VP, Math C; NHS; Orch; Ed, Sch P; Mgr, Tr; 4H A; Math A; St Scholar; Type A; Vlbl; Shorthand A; Amer Legion Auxiliary; District Mus Fest; WW; *Eastern Ill U; Journ.*

ROHLMANN, Michael Scott
Oakville Sr HS; St Louis, MO; VP, Band; CYO; Soccer; *St Louis U; Sales and Managing.*

ROHM, Kevin Lee
N Gaston Sr HS; Dallas, NC (25-250) MVP, Band; MVP, BC; MVP, Chess C; V-Ch, Hmrm; MVP, Monogram; MVP, Span C; MVP, Bsbl; Mgr, Tr; Sci A; *U of NC; Arch.*

ROHNER, Lisa Mary
Boulder HS; Boulder, CO (53-507) 4H; Cpt, Tr; 4H A; H of F; *Colo St U; Vet Med.*

ROHR, Barbara Jean
Elizabeth Ann Johnson HS; Mt Morris, MI (41-239) Co-Ed, Ann; NHS; Cpt, Bkbl; Tr; MVP, Bkbl; *Jackson Comm Col; Teaching.*

ROHR, Janel Rose
Cunningham HS; Cunningham, KS (3-21) Band; Pres, CYO; Chldr; Chor; Ensm; GS; Mjrte; Pres, Sr Cl; Cpt, Bkbl; Sftbl; Tr; Vlbl; Kayette Board; Band A; All League Bkbl; All League Vlbl; *St Mary's o-t Plains; Elem Ed.*

ROHRBAUGH, Pamela Joy
George C Marshall HS; Falls Church, VA (47-471) Chor; Semi-Fin, Jr Miss Pa; Ski C; Sftbl; Drill Tm; *Madison Col; Elem Ed.*

ROHRBERGER, Robert Jay
Paramus HS; Paramus, NJ (58-580) Lit Mag; NHS; Ch, St Stu Congress; Tri-HiY; COM; Yth Leg; Social Stu A; *U of Pa.*

ROHRER, Lisa Ann
Cross Keys HS; Atlanta, GA (10%-200) Band; Ger C; NHS; SC; *U of Ga; Law.*

ROHRER, Melanie Sue
Leetonia HS; Leetonia, OH (12-100) Ann; Band; GS; Span C; Tri-HiY; Bio A; 4H A; Span, Home Ec, PA, A's; HR; *Youngstown St Col; Nurs.*

ROHRING, Rebecca Louise
St Joseph HS; St Joseph, MI (1-370) Pres, Chor; Hmrm; NHS; Orch; Pres, Pol Sci C; Pres, SC; Bausch & Lomb A; COM; NMF; NMS; Phy A; Outst Fresh A; NML; Col Merit A; Cert of Recog; St Comptetive Sch Prog; *Kalamazoo Col; Med.*

ROHRS, Kirby Ray
Auburn HS; Auburn, NE (54-92) Cr-Ctry; Wrest; Chamber of Comm A; *W Nebr Tech Col; Heavy Equipment Operation.*

ROIDT, Julie Ann
Montello HS; Montello, WI (4-71) Band; Ensm; Sch P; SC; *U of Wis; Psych.*

ROIGER, Beth Ann
Kuemper HS; Carroll, IA (50%-280) MVP, Band; CYO; Chldr; FHA; VP, 4H; Rptr, Hmrm; Inter-Club Coun; Model UN; Orch; Span C; Golf; Sftbl; Swim; COM; 4H A; Hon Prog; Interlochen Ntl Mus; MLS; Ntl Cath Mus Ed Asn; Poet A; Band Cert; PA; *Benedictine Col; Sociology.*

ROLAND, Bert Lee
Asheville HS; Asheville, NC (23-375) Band; Co-Cpt, Chldr; Hmrm; NHS; SC; HQn; *U of Tenn; Computer Sci.*

ROLAND, Katherine Lucille
Rockford E HS; Rockford, IL (64-607) Sftbl; Pres A; JV, Vlbl; *Bethel Col; Phys Ed.*

ROLAND, Ricardo Montalban
Asheville HS; Asheville, NC; Band; *US Armed Forces; Elec.*

ROLE, Richard B
Driscoll HS; Addison, IL (6-144) Lit Mag; NHS; Golf; St Scholar; *U of Notre Dame; Architecture.*

ROLEN, Rene Annette
Ritenour HS; St Louis, MO (75-825) A Cap Choir; Drama; NHS; Swim; *Harding Col; Nurs.*

ROLFE, Kevin Bruce
Crenshaw HS; Los Angeles, CA; Band; *Bell and Howell Sch; Elec Tech.*

ROLLE, Tara Denise
Palm Beach Gardens HS; Palm Beach Gardens, FL (150-450) Chldr; Hmrm; SC; *U of Fla; Dentistry.*

ROLLE, Tyrone M
John F Kennedy HS; New York, NY; Alg A; Phy A; Foreign Lang A; Attendance A.

ROLLER, Jennifer Jayne
Maumee HS; Maumee, OH (36-361) Band; VP, Dbte Tm; Fr C; Mjrte; NFL; Tr; COM; Citz A; Hon Prog; NFL Excel; Most Improved, Debate; Band A; Bowling Green St U; Radio-tV Broadcasting.*

ROLLIN, Patricia Lynn
Warwick Sr HS; Lititz, PA (3-277) Band; Orch; SC; Secy, Jr Cl; Secy, Soph Cl; Tr; Amer Leg A; NEDT; Yth Fel; *Psych.*

ROLLINS, Christi Ann
Oakland Comm HS; Oakland, IA (5-46) Bus Mgr, Ann; Band; Chldr; Chor; Pres, FHA; NHS; Rptr, Sch P; Tres, Var C; S-T, Sr Cl; Bkbl; Tr; HCt; WW; St Tr Meet; Best Cl Leadership; *NW Mo St U; Elem Ed.*

ROLLINS, Darrell Gene
Tivy HS; Kerrville, TX; Co-Ch, Band; JETS; SC; Tnns; *Baylor U; Law.*

ROLLINS, Patricia Ellen
Amite Sch Center; Liberty, MS (4-44) Sch P; *SW Miss Jr Col; Biol.*

ROLLINS, Shenell Annette
Paw Creek Christian Acad; Charlotte, NC (1-12) A-Ed, Ann; Chor; Star Student; Type A; Val.

ROLLINS, Starla Ann
Berea HS; Greenville, SC (30-250) Chor; Ensm; FBLA; Semi-Fin, Hmrm; COM; Cl Fav; Hon Prog; *Secy Sci.*

ROLSMA, Daniel Joseph
Norco HS; Norco, CA;

ROMAN, Angel Luis
Antonio S Pedreira HS; Moca, PR (2-29) COM; Hon Prog; *UPR-AGUADILLA; Pol Sci.*

ROMAN, Anthony
The Stony Brook Prep Sch; Stony Brook, NY (25-78) Chess C; Dbte Tm; Drama; Mgr, Bsbl; Ftbl; Wrest; COM; Four Way Test A; *Geneva Col; Hist.*

ROMAN, Carmen M
Antonio S Pedreira HS; Moca, PR (2-38) Chor; Span C; Hon Prog; *Colegio de Mayaguez; Nurs.*

ROMAN, Dennis Rafael
Dra Maria Cadilla de Martinez HS; Arecibo, PR (28-429) Arch; Pres, BS; Chem C; Drama; Order/ Arrow; Phys C; VP, ARC; Sci C; Fin, Arch; Swim; COM; Chem A; Hon Prog; Sci A; *U of Md; Sci.*

ROMAN, Gilberto Aviles
Dra M Cadilla HS; Arecibo, PR (55-482) Chor; Drama; Lit Mag; Math C; Sci C; Span C; Swim; Tnns; Alg A; Bio A; COM; Math A; Ntl Sci Found; Sci A; Contific Ferie; *Universidad de Puerto Rico; Med.*

ROMAN, Maria C
Antonio S Pedreira HS; Moca, PR (3-48) Chor; Span C; Hon Prog; *Colegio de Mayaguez; Nurs.*

ROMAN, Maria N
Antonio S Pedreira HS; Moca, PR (2-49) Chor; Span C; COM; Cl Fav; *UPR-AGUADILLA; Sci.*

ROMAN, Myrna Belen
Academia Santa Monica; Santurce, PR; CYO; Chor; Secy, FBLA; NHS; COM; Hon Prog; *U of Puerto Rico; Chem.*

ROMAN, Reinaldo
Francisco Mendoza HS; Isabela, PR; CYO; Dbte Tm; Rptr, Sch P; COM; Citz A; DARGCA; *U of Puerto Rico; Phar.*

ROMANELLI, Stephen Nicholas
Cold Spring Harbor HS; Cold Spring Harbor, NY (80-200) Chor; Ensm; Rptr, Sch P; Pres, Sr Cl; Mgr, Bkbl; MVP, Ftbl; Amer Leg A; Kiwanis A; Rotary A; LaCrosse; *Gettysburg Col; Bus.*

ROMANI, Paula Ann
Northgate HS; Walnut Creek, CA (1-400) CYO; NHS; Span C; Bank Of Amer A; CSF; Val; *Stanford U; Med.*

ROMANIK, George Joseph
West Haven HS; W Haven, CT (1-573) CYO; Chem C; Pres, Chess C; Ger C; Pres, Math C; NHS; Pres, Phys C; Sch P; Bausch & Lomb A; COM; Chem A; Elk A; H of F; Harvard Book A; Jr Chamber of Com A; Math A; NEDT; St Scholar; Summa Cum Laude; Val; St Andrews Sci School; Ger A; WW; Yth Day A; *Lehigh U; Chem Engr.*

ROMANO, Evelyn Anne
West Phila Cath Girls HS; Philadelphia, PA (9-388) Mjrte; NHS; Sch P; COM; Type A; Alpha Filing Cert; *Peirce Jr Col; Automation Bus Mgt.*

ROMANOWSKY, Kathy Ann
R J Reynolds HS; Winston-Salem, NC (246-900) Anchor C; Chor; Drama; Ensm; Lat NHS; Rainbow; Pep Board Coun; *UNC; Communications.*

ROME, Jo Ann
Garfield HS; Hamilton, OH; Chldr; VP, Chor; Fr C; SC; Pres, Soph Cl; Opt Out Tn; *Anesthesiology.*

ROME, Marina Jeanne
Burbank HS; Burbank, CA (10-750) Semi-Fin, Chldr; MVP, Bkbl; CSF; Citz A; Pres A; Fin, Amer Leg A; VP, UMYF; VMA; JV, Vlbl; DCYM; SC; Barbershop; Pep C.*

ROMEO, Dominic Joseph
Ursuline HS; Youngstown, OH (169-600) Carpentry.*

ROMERDAHL, Eric Thomas
Everett HS; Everett, WA (30-400) A Cap Choir; Fin, Hmrm; Math C; NHS; Parl, Soph Cl; Alg A; Bio A; COM; Cl Fav; Hon Prog; Math A; Best Baker; *Gonzaga Col; Law.*

ROMERO, Charlotte Ann
L D Bell HS; Hurst, TX (35-900) CYO; Span C; Bkbl; Sftbl; *Tex Tech; Math.*

ROMERO, Christopher Alex
Albuquerque HS; Albuquerque, NM; Band; CYO; Bsbl; Ftbl; Soccer; *St Michaels Col; Priesthood.*

ROMERO, Jerome Martin
Alamosa HS; Alamosa, CO; Band; CYO; Bsbl; Bkbl; Ftbl; Swim; Tr; COM; Cl Fav; Most Out; *Ft Collins Col; Vet Med.*

ROMERO, John N
Albuquerque HS; Albuquerque, NM; A Cap Choir; Band; CYO; Chor; Bkbl; Ftbl; Swim; Tnns; Tr; Citz A; *UNM; Mus.*

ROMERO, Kathi Louise
Albuquerque HS; Albuquerque, NM; CYO; Chor; Hmrm; NHS; Span C; SC; Bkbl; Sftbl; Vlbl; Pom Pon Girl A; *U of NM; Bus.*

ROMICH, Robyn Elaine
Chenango Valley Jr-Sr HS; Binghamton, NY; Chor; Hon Prog; NJHS; *Secretarial.*

ROMICK, Eliza Ann
Sunset HS; Beaverton, OR (45-502) Band; FPC Dearons Schol; *Oreg St Col.*

ROMINE, Fonda Lynne
Franklin Co HS; Frankfort, KY (10%-400) BC; Hmrm; Span C; Span NHS; SC; 1st Pl, Sch Art Contest; *U of Ky; Archt.*

ROMINE, Jennifer Lou
Franklin Co HS; Frankfort, KY (200-450) Chor; 4H A; Hon Prog; *Georgetown Baptist Col; Elem Ed.*

ROMNEY, Patricia Charlotte
Skyline HS; Salt Lake City, UT (5%-700) Ed, Ann; ARC; Sch P; COM; Citz A; Kiwanis A; Outst Schol Achv A; *Brigham Young U; Linguistics.*

ROMO, Nelson Oscar
Shamrock HS; Decatur, GA (10%-360) Chor; Span C; Soccer; Best Defense Trophy, Soccer; All St Chor; *Mus.*

ROMO, Refugio Carlos
St Augustine HS; Laredo, TX; Bus Mgr, Ann; Dbte Tm; Drama; Hmrm; Spch C; VP, SC; Tres, Soph Cl; Cl Fav; NEDT; Opt A; Spch A; *Interntl Bus Adm.*

ROMSEY, Paul Elbert Jr
Madison Acad HS; Huntsville, AL (3-43) BC; Math C; Monogram; NHS; ARC; Sci C; Var C; Mgr, Bkbl; Cr-Ctry; Bio A; COM; Hon Prog; Sci A; Star Student; Bus Law A; Eagle Sct; *UAH.*

RONALD, Meachele Angelica
Benhaven HS; Olivia, NC; BC; Fr C; 4H; Sci C; Alg A; Math A; Fr A; *Sandhills Comm Col; Ed.*

RONALD, Richard Hale
Oak Hills HS; Cincinnati, OH (205-845) Rptr, Sch P; Sci C; Var C; Mgr, Bsbl; Mgr, Ftbl; Mgr, Swim; *Ohio U; Ath Training.*

RONAN, Patricia Josephine
W Philadelphia Cath Girls HS; Philadelphia, PA (30-389) Ann; Cum Laude Soc; Hmrm; Lat C; NHS; Span C; Journ A; Semi-Fin, Journ A; *Hahnemann Col; Radiology.*

RONE, Rodney Tobe
Bolton HS; Alexandria, LA; FBLA; Lit Rel; Swim; COM; Math A; NEDT; Type A; Yth Fel; Coach's A, Swim; *Miss St U; Acct.*

RONEY, Terry Jean
Glenwood HS; Phenix City, AL; Band; BC; Chor; Ensm; Ch, Mjrte; Tnns; *Auburn U; Mus.*

RON FORNES, Gloria Mirta
St Joseph's o-t Palisades HS; W New York, NJ (2-225) Pres, Fr C; French NHS; Hmrm; NHS; Hon Prog; *Stevens Inst of Tech.*

RONNFELDT, Julia Ann
John Marshall HS; San Antonio, TX; Band; Ensm; Math C; Mu Alpha Theta; Rainbow; Span C; Hon Prog; Interschol League A; *Ed.*

RONNING, Paul Allen
Columbus HS; Columbus, ND (3-18) Band; Pres, Soph Cl; Bkbl; Ftbl; Tr; Pres, Yth League; Co Hon Band; PA; HR; *Jamestown Col.*

ROOD, Cindy Kay
Holy Cross HS; Marine City, MI (4-54) Chor; FNA; Ski C; Span C; Hon Prog; Pres A; *Western U; Bus.*

ROOD, Darlene Donna
Lower Dauphin Sr HS; Hummelstown, PA (35-300) 4H; Rptr, Span C; JV, Bkbl; JV, Hockey; JV, Sftbl; *Phys Therapy.*

ROOD, Nelson Wiley
Jupiter Christian Sch; Jupiter, FL (4-29) Pres, Band; BS; Chor; Ensm; Pres, Jr Cl; Pres, Soph Cl; MVP, Bsbl; Bkbl; Ftbl; Soccer; Tnns; Mr Offense; Band Medal; Leading Hitter; Piano Playing Auditions; Band, Span, A'S; PA; *Agr.*

ROOK, Terri Lynn
L A Webber HS; Lyndonville, NY (19-70) AFS; Opt, Chldr; Chor; Jr Miss Pagent; Tres, Var C; Pres, Yth Fel; Miss Congeniality; All-Star Chldr; WW; *Daemen Col; Phys Therapy.*

ROOKER, Mary Helen
John Graham HS; Warrenton, NC (1-145) BC; Fr C; FHA; NHS; Sch P; Secy, Soph Cl; Bio A; COM; Gov Honor Prog; Gr Marshal; HQn; HCt; Gov Sch; Cert of Hon; Off Asst; *Meredith Col; Home Ec.*

ROOKS, Jonathan Melton
Mt Carmel HS; San Diego, CA (73-505) A Cap Choir; Chor; Ensm; Madrigal; JV, Bsbl; *San Diego St Col.*

ROOKS, Priscilla Anne
Citrus HS; Inverness, FL (26-250) FTA; HCt; Best Dressed; Kiwanettes.*

ROOKS, Sharon Elizabeth
Newton Co Comp HS; Covington, GA; *Morehouse Col.*

ROOME, Mark Scott
Rio Linda Sr HS; Rio Linda, CA (37-295) COM; Hist A; Hon Prog; Sci A; Merit A; *Trinity Sch o-t Bible; Ministerial Arts.*

ROONEY, Michael Bernard
Don Bosco Tech HS; Boston, MA (7-222) NHS; VP, SC; Bsbl; Ftbl; Co-Cpt, Swim; *Harvard U; Engr.*

ROONEY, Patti Anne
Acad of Our Lady of Mercy; Milford, CT (7-88) Chldr; Chor; Drama; Key C; NEDT; *Math.*

ROOP, Barbara Ann
Elida HS; Elida, OH (48-190) Band; FTA; Sch P; Bkbl; Sftbl; COM; Type A; Phys Ed A; Band A; GAA A; *Ohio St; Phys Ed.*

ROOPER, Nancy Lee
Redmond Sr HS; Redmond, OR (30-200) GS; 4H; NHS; VP, Span C; Bus Mgr, SC; 4H A; Hon Qn, Job's Daughters; WW; *NW Bus Col; Fashion Merchandising.*

ROORDA, Douglas Lawrence
New Monroe Comm HS; Monroe, IA (2-57) Band; Secy, Chor; FFA; NHS; Tres, SC; Thes; JV, Ftbl; Wrest; NMF; NMS; Sal; Spch A; St Scholar; Yth Fel; All St Band; *Iowa St U; Farm Operation.*

ROOS, Donna Joy
Worthington Sr HS; Worthington, MN (76-265) Band; Chor; Ensm; Orch; *Tabor Col; Special Ed.*

ROOS, Kristine Louise
Acalanes HS; Lafayette, CA; Secy, AFS; Chor; Ger C; MVP, Cr-Ctry; Tr; WW A; Co-Ch, Rally; *Oregon St U; Ecologist.*

ROOSA, Elizabeth Anne
John Jay Sr HS; Hopewell Junction, NY (47-551) Drama; Hmrm; NHS; Rptr, Sch P; Tres, Jr Cl; Tres, Soph Cl; Mgr, Cr-Ctry; Mgr, Tr; Hon Prog; Ch, Valentine-O-Grams; The Comm; Sunday Sch Tchr & Pianist; Stu-Faculty Game Comm; Ed, Jr Prom; Sr Prom Comm; Law Off Asst; *Vassar Col; Pol Sci.*

ROOSA, Marlene Elaine
Astoria HS; Astoria, IL; Band; Chor; Span C; Tr; *Ozark Bible Col.*

ROOSA, Nancy Marion
John Jay Sr HS; Hopewell Junction, NY; Lat C; Pres, Soph Cl; Hon Prog; Yth Fel; Pres, Ring Comm; Pol Campaign Asst; Tres, John Jay Pep Sq; Cpt, Almost Anything Goes; JV, Vlbl.

ROOSEN, Margaret Mary
Holy Cross HS; Marine City, MI (4-41) Chldr; NHS; Var C; COM; *Bus.*

ROOT, Jeffrey Ronald
Arkadelphia HS; Arkadelphia, AR; Band; Dbte Tm; Hmrm; SC; Pres, Soph Cl; Church Yth Coun; Outst Bandsman; Schol, Band Camp; *Ouachita Baptist U.*

ROOT, Randal William
Stinnett HS; Stinnett, TX (8-50) Band; Drama; Pres, NHS; VP, Soph Cl; Tnns; *Frank Phillips U; Mus.*

ROOT, Susan Rene
Wakulla Co HS; Crawfordville, FL; FHA.

ROOTS, Stefan Eric
Chester HS; Chester, PA (20-680) Key C; Bkbl; *Chem Engr.*

ROPEL, Lori Ann
Andrew Jackson HS; Jacksonville, FL; Chor; NHS; Alg A; Sci A; Fr A; *Arlington Baptist Col; Bible.*

ROPER, Claudia Diane
Argenta-Oreana HS; Argenta, IL; AFS; Chor; FHA; Sftbl; Tr; 4H A; GAA A; Phys Fitness A; *Mich Christian Col; Sci.*

ROPER, Dianne Lynn
Tallapoosa Acad; Dadeville, AL (4-27) Ann; Band; Tres, BC; *Troy St U; Nurs.*

ROPER, Mildred Arleit
Independence HS; Charlotte, NC; Band; Drama; Hmrm; ARC; Up Bound; Project Aries A; Children's Theatre; Pres, Explores; Secy, Jr Choir; COO; VP, Jr Usher Board; Sue C; VP Yth Movemnt; Jr Misson; *NC Central U; Bus Ed.*

ROPER, Nettie Marie
Compton Sr HS; Compton, CA (25%-850) Drama; Hmrm; Span C; CSF; *Berkely U; Psych.*

ROPER, Rodney Brent
Broken Arrow HS; Broken Arrow, OK (20%-600) Mgr, Bkbl; Co-Cpt, Soccer; Tr; Yth Fel; Art A; Outst Drafting Stu; *Engr.*

ROPPOLO, Pamela Marie
John Ehret HS; Marrero, LA (1-450) Lit Ral; Mu Alpha Thes; NHS; Bio A; Hon Prog; Math A; Sci A; Val; WW; NMS Commendation; St Lit Ral Hon; Acad Achv Ltrs; Presidential Schol of Excellence; Prep Quiz Bowl Tm; *UNO; Med Tech.*

RORIE, Darline Bonita
Cardinal McCloskey HS; Albany, NY; Chor; Secy, Lat C; NHS; Hon Prog; Ntl Achv Schol; Excel A; *Rensselaer Polytech Inst; Bio.*

RORIE, David Markham
Bowman Sr HS; Wadesboro, NC; Band; VP, Chess C; *Duke U; Religion.*

RORVIK, Ellen
Westlake HS; Thornwood, NY (7-227) Tres, NHS; SC; Hockey; Tnns; Hist A; Hon Prog; Math A; Opt A; Opt Out Tn; Regent Schol; Houghton Col Fresh Schol; *Houghton Col; Psych.*

ROS, Karen Elizabeth
Franklin HS; Franklin, VA (2-170) Band; BC; VP, Fr C; Tri-HiY; Secy, Sr Cl; NMF; Sal; VA Gov Sch for the Gifted; *Bryn Mawr Col; Archaeology.*

ROSA, Cynthia Lynn
Quincy Sr HS II; Quincy, IL (100-785) Fr C; Rainbow; SC; Hon Prog; *Math.*

ROSA, Sheryl Ann
Fairmont HS; Fairmont, MN; Band; Chor; Hon Prog; *Math.*

ROSADO, Carlos Saul
Wesleyan Acad; Guaynabo, PR (4-31) Chor; NHS; Pres, Jr Cl; Bkbl; NEDT; HR.

ROSADO, David Alejandro
Wesleyan Acad; Caparra Heights, PR (5-29) Ed, Ann; Chor; NHS; Sch P; Tres, SC; Hypertension Clinic Service A; PR Rep, 20th Celebration; Thomas A Edison Found A; *U of Mich; Bio.*

ROSADO, Deborah
Yonkers Prep Sch; Yonkers, NY; Pres, A Cap Choir; Pres, All Amer Yth; Chldr; Chor; Ch, Dbte Tm; Ensm; Hmrm; Key C; Span NHS; Co-Ch, SC; World Affairs C; Bio A; COM; Citz A; God & Country A; Hist A; Hon Prog; Most Out; Spch A; Yth Fel; Yth Foundation; Yth Foundation A; Yth Leg; *Wellesley Col; Religion.*

ROSADO, Elizabeth Elaine
Aquinas HS; Bronx, NY; CYO; Chor; World Affairs C; Swim; COM; Catechist; *St Thomas Aquina Col; Bilingual Secondary Ed.*

ROSADO, Francisco Miguel
Academia Discipulos de Cristo; Bayamon, PR (10-122) A Cap Choir; Chem C; Chess C; Dbte Tm; Drama; Pres, Hmrm; Pres, NHS; Orch; VP, Phys C; ARC; Ed, Sch P; Span C; Pres, Sr Cl; Pres, Jr Cl; Pres, Soph Cl; Co-Cpt, Bkbl; Alg A; Bio A; COM; Chem A; Hist A; Math A; Phy A; Sci A; Spch A; *U of Wis; Astronomy.*

ROSADO, Wanda Denise
Aquinas HS; Bronx, NY (5-200) CYO; World Affairs C; Swim; COM; Hon Prog; Ntl Cath Mus Ed Asn; Teaching, Writing, A's; *Elizabeth Seton Col; Gen.*

ROSADO, Zoraida Socorro
Colegio Santa Rita; Bayamon, PR (1-40) CYO; COM; *U of Puerto Rico; Med.*

ROSALES, Annamarie
Thomas A Edison HS; San Antonio, TX (1-690) CYO; Dbte Tm; Drama; Hmrm; VP, Lit Mag; Math C; NFL; Spch C; Thes; COM; Citz A; Hon Prog; Spch A; Pep Squad; *Rice U; Med.*

ROSALES, Jacqueline Jean
Thomas Edison HS; San Antonio, TX; Bus C; CYO; Chor; Hmrm; SC; COM; Citz A; Hist A; Journ A; Kiwanis A; Sci A; Spch A; *Trinity U; Sociology.*

ROSAMOND, Carla Sue
Springdale HS; Springdale, AR (3-540) Sch P; Tr; COM; Drill Tm; *U of Ark; Bus.*

ROSAMOND, Troy Michael
St Joseph HS; Jeanerette, LA (4-28) Band; Lit Ral; JV, Bkbl; Tnns; Tr; COM; Math A; Type A; *LSU.*

ROSANE, Britt Alan
St Edward Pub Sch; St Edward, NE (15-30) Var C; Bkbl; Ftbl; Tr; HCt; Yth Fel; *Coaching.*

ROSARIO, Maria Margarita
Dra Maria Cadilla de Martinez HS; Arecibo, PR (53-429) CYO; Hmrm; COM; *Universidad de Puerto Rico; Ciencias Sociales.*

ROSARIO, Maricruz Blanca
Colegio San Antonio Abad; Humacao, PR; Chem C; Fr C; VP, Hmrm; Semi-Fin, Jr Miss Pa; Secy, NHS; Sch P; Mgr, Swim; COM; Chem A; Cl Fav; HQn; Journ A; Lion A; ARC A; Type A; Span A; Fr A; Mus A; *Universidad de Puerto Rico.*

ROSAS, Janise Marie
Adlai E Stevenson HS; Bronx, NY (3-800) City Conf; NHS; Sch Achieve Tm; Alg A; Bio A; COM; Citz A; Gov Honor Prog; Hon Prog; Math A; Ntl Achv Schol; Phy A; Regent Schol; Service A; *Pace U; Bus Adm.*

ROSAS, Rebecca Lynn
Del Norte HS; Albuquerque, NM (170-610) Pres, Bus C; SC; *Abilene Christian Col; Bus Ed.*

ROSATI, Donna Irene
McNally HS; Costa Mesa, CA; Hmrm; Co-Ed, Sch P; SC; Sch Spirit A; *Orange Coast Col; Ed.*

ROSCOE, Marilyn Louise
Custer Co HS; Westcliffe, CO (2-18) Ed, Ann; Band; NHS; Sch P; Spch C; Bkbl; Tr; Hist A; Journ A; *U of Northern Colo; Journ.*

ROSCUM, David Allen
Burlington Comm HS; Burlington, IA (220-406) Demolay; Order/Arrow; Ftbl; Sftbl; Tr; God & Country A; Eagle Sct; *U of Iowa; Bus Adm.*

ROSE, Anne
Robinson Sch; Santurce, PR (5-38) Ed, Lit Mag; NHS; Ed, Sch P; COM; Hist A; Hon Prog; Most Out; Co-Ed, Yrbk; Eng A; Religion A; *Journ.*

ROSE, Cynthia Gail
Falls Church HS; Falls Church, VA; Band; NHS; Span NHS; Church Crown & Sceptor; Eng A; Church Orch; All Reg Band; Torch & Banner Soc; U of W Va Summer Band Camp; *Mus.*

ROSE, Donald David
N Shore HS; W Palm Beach, FL (1-266) Band; Chess C; Community Yth Symph; InterClub Coun; NHS; Var C; Bkbl; Golf; Alg A; Bio A; COM; Hist A; Hon Prog; Math A; NMS; Sci A; *Lib Arts.*

ROSE, Dwane Lee
Tahlequah Sr HS; Tahlequah, OK (1-300) Math C; Bio A; Hist A; Val; Govt A; Civics A; *Okla U; Sci.*

ROSE, Grant Eugene
David Crockett HS; Austin, TX (5%-900) NHS; Span NHS; VP, SC; Co-Cpt, Gym; Trustee's Schol A; *Air Force Acad; Aeronautics.*

ROSE, Janice Marie
Zebulon HS; Zebulon, NC (19-40) *Wake Tech Col; Secy.*

ROSE, Jeffrey Stuart
N Plainfield HS; N Plainfield, NJ (16-269) BS; VP, Chor; VP, Ger C; Hmrm; Key C; Ntl Yth Conf; VP, Sci C; SC; JV, Ftbl; Co-Cpt, Tnns; COM; Cl Fav; Hon Prog; Star Student; Yth Fel; Yth Leg; Best Dressed; *Penn St U; Elec Engr.*

ROSE, Joseph Udell
Attica HS; Attica, IN (8-98) Drama; NHS; *Ind St U; Acct.*

ROSE, Kevin David
Warren Central HS; Indianapolis, IN (165-863) Madrigal; *Judson Col; Human Relations.*

ROSE, Kevin Scott
Marysville-Pilchuck HS; Marysville, WA (18-389) BS; Ger C; Hmrm; Key C; NHS; SC; Var C; Pres, Sr Cl; Bsbl; Ftbl; Swim; JA A; Jr Chamber of Com A; *Wash St U; Med.*

ROSE, Lisa Joan
Decatur HS; Decatur, AL (100-416) Cpt, Chldr; FTA; SC; VP, Soph Cl; Cl Fav; Most Out; *U of Tenn; Art.*

ROSE, Melinda Marie
Montgomery HS; San Diego, CA; Chor; Ger C; Hmrm; InterClub Coun; Citz A; Bio-Med C; *Med.*

ROSE, Nancy Kay
Alliance HS; Alliance, NE (95-153) Chor; FFA; VP, 4H; Y-Tns; MLS; *Sch of Tech Agr; Vet Tech.*

ROSE, Nancy Lee
Decatur HS; Decatur, AL (120-331) FHA; Inter-Act C; Var C; Swim; *U of Tenn; Recreation.*

ROSE, Nichole Celeste
Immaculate Conception Acad; San Francisco, CA (20%-74) Fr C; Span NHS; CSF; Calif St Schol; Ch, Jr Sr Farewell; *San Francisco St U; Bio.*

ROSE, Robert Allen
New Testament Christian Sch; Norton, MA; Chor; Pres, Jr Cl; Cpt, Bkbl; *Pastorate.*

ROSE, Robert Joseph
Coldwater HS; Coldwater, OH (55-168) Chor; Parl, FFA; Pres, 4H; 4H A; FFA Schol; Stu Advisor, FFA; *Agr.*

ROSE, Robert Russell
Kim HS; Steamboat Springs, CO (57-93) A Cap Choir; Band; Chor; 4H; Hmrm; Key C; Sch P; SC; Var C; Bkbl; Ftbl; Tr; 4H A; HCt; *Lubbock Christian Col.*

ROSE, Sandra Jane
Kenmore W Sr HS; Kenmore, NY (5%-800) A Cap Choir; Chor; Drama; VP, Fr C; Thes; Tnns; Hon Prog; Horsebackriding C; HR; Jr NHS; Best Dancer o-t Yr A; Pres, Triangle; Lead, Sch Mus; Russian C.

ROSE, Sarah Patricia
Adlai E Stevenson HS; Bronx, NY; NHS; Var C; Hon Prog; *Ambassador Col; Mass Communication.*

ROSE, Teresa Beth
Hickman Mills HS; Kansas City, MO (13-577) Chor; Pep C; Drill Tm; Letter of Achv; Senator Manford; Jr NHS; Principal HR; *Acct.*

ROSE, Timothy Edward
Hazlewood HS; Town Creek, AL (4-40) Band; BC; 4H; Math C; Cl Fav; 4H A; Schol Bowl; *U of Ala; Med Sci.*

ROSE, Walton Hurst
Adli E Stevenson HS; New York, NY (300-788) *Atlantic Union Col; Bio.*

ROSEBERRY, Diana June
Carlsbad HS; Carlsbad, CA; JV, Chldr; S-T, Chor; Drama; Madrigal.

ROSEBERRY, Marcia Melinda
S H Blair HS; Hattiesburg, MS (1-395) Co-Ed, Ann; Chor; Ensm; Semi-Fin, Jr Miss Pa; Lat C; Lit Mag; SC; Tres, Jr Cl; Q&S A; Summa Cum Laude; 2nd Pl, Ntl Span; Eng A; Lat A; *U of Ala; Communications.*

ROSEBORO, Anthony Michael
Columbus E HS; Columbus, OH (3-350) Band; BS; Dbte Tm; Hmrm; NHS; Orch; SC; Y-Tns; Pres, Jr Cl; Golf; Amer Leg A; COM; Hon Prog; Kiwanis A; NEDT; Rotary A; *Ohio St U; Vet Med.*

ROSECRANS, Christopher Jude
Keveny Mem Acad; Cohoes, NY (4-72) Hmrm; Pres, Ski C; Span C; Mgr, Bkbl; Co-Cpt, Soccer; Tnns; General Bus A; Phys Sci A; Health A; *Rensselaer Polytechnic Inst; Mech Engr.*

ROSEL, James Michael
San Marcos HS; San Marcos, CA (60-300) Order/Arrow; Soccer; Swim; Order/Arrow A; Pro Dev Et Patria; Jr Asst Sct Master.

ROSEL, Tammy Lynn
San Marcos HS; San Marcos, CA (105-210) Chor; Fr C; Bsbl; *Design.*

ROSELLI, Sarah Lou
Blanchet HS; Seattle, WA (62-285) Swim; HQn; *U of Wash; Health Sci.*

ROSEMAN, Patricia Ann
Hoggard HS; Wilmington, NC; *Campbell Col.*

ROSEN, Carolyn Margaret
Westview Sr HS; Braham, MN (13-85) Band; Bkbl; Tr; B Crocker A; Vlbl; *U of Minn; Phys Therapy.*

ROSENAU, Pamela Lee
York HS; York, NE (3-156) Chldr; Chor; Drama; NHS; Pres, SC; Sunday Sch Tchr; Copy-Ed, Yrbk; Job's Daughters; Secy-Treas, Swing Choir; Most Outst Female Voice; *U of Nebr at Lincoln.*

ROSENAU, Patricia Lynn
York HS; York, NE (7-156) F-Ed, Ann; Chldr; Pres, Chor; Drama; NHS; Part, SC; Job's Daughters; Swing Choir; *U of Neb; Dental Hygienist.*

ROSENBAUM, Mark Edward
Dobyns-Bennett HS; Kingsport, TN (115-520) Bsbl; Co-Cpt, Ftbl; Tr; Wrest; MVP, Ftbl; *U of Tenn; Bus Mgr.*

ROSENBAUM, Rachel
Hebrew Acad of Nassau Co; Uniondale, NY; Chldr; Chor; Dbte Tm; Hmrm; NHS; Sch P; SC; Bkbl; Tr; COM; Faculty A; Poetry A.

ROSENBERGER, Richard Guy
T L Hanna HS; Anderson, SC; Chor; VP, Hmrm; NHS; COM; Gov Honor Prog; Math A; Pres A; Mus A; PA A; *U of Ga; Math.*

ROSENBLUETH, Jeffrey
Hebrew Acad of Nassau Co; Uniondale, NY (4-25) Dbte Tm; Drama; Hmrm; Ch, InterClub Coun; Co-Ed, Lit Ral; NHS; JV, Bkbl; Tr; COM; Hon Prog; MLS; *Columbia U; Med.*

ROSENBROCK, Patricia Lynn
Fort Lupton HS; Fort Lupton, CO (5-100) Ann; Band; FTA; GS; Pres, 4H; Mjrte; Math C; NHS; Sci C; Tres, Spch C; Var C; Tr; COM; 4H A; Hon Prog; Masonic A; Spch A; VofDEM; Yth Fel; VP, 4-H C; Pep C; Ushers C; Leo C; GAA; Statistician, Boys Bkbl; *Colo St U; Pre-Vet Med.*

ROSENHOOVER, Bernice Adair
Eldorado HS; Albuquerque, NM; Chldr; Fin, Crown & Sceptor; FBLA; Co-Ch, Key C; Ntl Yth Conf; COM; Citz A; H of F; Opt A; Swtht; DECA Ntl A; St DECA A; Stu o-t Yr; St Chldr As; *Parks Col; Fashion Merchandise.*

ROSENKRANZ, Pnina Gail
Paramus HS; Paramus, NJ (1-591) AFS; Secy, Dbte Tm; GS; Lit Mag; Secy, NFL; Pres, NHS; Rptr, Sch P; Sci C; Secy, SC; Tri-HiY; Bio A; COM; Citz A; Coun of Teach A; MLS; Most Out; Sci A; Star Student; St Scholar; Val; VofDEM; Ntl Merit Ltr of Commendation; Fr A; AAUW A; NCET Essay Contest Win; NC Fr Teacher's Contest Win; Princeton U; Biochem.

ROSENQUIST, Russell Melvin
Stamford HS; Stamford, TX (2-67) Tres, FFA; Lat NHS; Pres, NHS; SC; Bkbl; Co-Cpt, Ftbl; Tnns; Alg A; Bio A; Chem A; Hist A; Math A; Phy A; Sal; Sci A; Type A; Best All-Around Sr; Tex Tech U; Optometry.

ROSENTHAL, Mary Patricia
Twenty Nine Palms HS; Twentynine Palms, CA; CYO; Chldr; Hmrm; SC; JV, Bkbl; Swim; COM; Citz A; DARGCA; Type A; Vlbl; Teenage Citizen A; TAC Camp Schol; Jr HS Ann Staff.

ROSENTHAL, Paulette Esther
Heidelberg American HS; Heidelberg, W GERMANY; Band; Chess C; Swim; Tnns; CSF; COM; GAA; Florence Caylor A; U of Calif; Sci.

ROSENTHAL, Peggy Ann
29 Palms HS; Twenty Nine Palms, CA; AFS; Bus C; VP, CYO; Hmrm; Cpt, Mjrte; SC; Swim; Cl Fav; San Diego Col of Bus; Bus.

ROSENTHAL, Ralph David
Charlevoix HS; Charlevoix, MI (150-175) Band; Agr.

ROSER, Joyce Anne
Lafayette HS; Lexington, KY (50%-650) BC; Mgr, Bkbl; Golf; Hon Prog; Yth Fel; U of Ky; Athletics.

ROSICH, Desiree Marleine
Dr Pila HS; Ponce, PR; GS; Tres, Hmrm; Fin, Swim; Fin, Tr; COM; Lion A; JV Vlbl; Colegio de Mayaguez; Engr.

ROSINE, William Douglas
Ft Myers HS; Ft Myers, FL; Band.

ROSING, Lisa Jill
Grant Comm HS; Fox Lake, IL; A Cap Choir; Madrigal; HCt; Moody Bible Inst; Vocal Mus.

ROSKAM, Peter James
Glenbard W HS; Glen Ellyn, IL; Chor; Hmrm; Mu Alpha Theta; Span C; SC; Pres, Jr Cl; Hon Prog; Cpt, Gym; Best Routine, Gym Tm; US Coast Guard Acad; Officer Training.

ROSMAN, Debra Janine
North HS; Omaha, NE (2-430) Band; Chor; Community Yth Symph; GS; Pres, Lat C; NHS; Orch; Sch P; Chamber of Comm A; U of Nebr at Lincoln; Psych.

ROSOL, Annette Rose
Grant Comm HS; Fox Lake, IL (27-271) A Cap Choir; Band; Madrigal; SC; Thes; Tr; Pres A; Art.

ROSPLOCK, Linda Ann
Beaver Dam Sr HS; Beaver Dam, WI (27-331) Co-Ed, Ann; CYO; JV, Chldr; Chor; Ensm; Hmrm; Sch P; Ski C; SC; Tnns; Tr; HCt; Hon Prog; Carroll Col; Liberal Arts.

ROSS, Autry Wayne
Irwin Co HS; Ocilla, GA (2-125) Ann; Tres, BC; Dbte Tm; Drama; Secy, 4H; Lit Ral; Model UN; Co-Ed, Sch P; Pres, SC; COM; 4H A; I Dare You; Ntl Sci Found; Win, St Extemporaneous Speaking.

ROSS, Barbara Kim
W Seneca W Sr HS; W Seneca, NY (200-600) Chor; NHS; Bio A; Cum Laude, Lat; Nurs.

ROSS, Barri Lynne
William Allen HS; Allentown, PA; Sacred Heart Nurs Col; Nurs.

ROSS, Brian Howard
W Linn HS; W Linn, OR (17-235) Bus Mgr, Ann; Band; NHS; Sch P; SC; Ftbl; Citz A; Cl Fav; Elk A; Hon Prog; MLS; Most Out; St Scholar; Judson Baptist Col; Theology.

ROSS, Bruce Lindsay
Independence HS; Charlotte, NC (82-597) Rptr, Hmrm; NC St U; Acct.

ROSS, Catherine Louise
Yorkwood Jr-Sr HS; Monmouth, IL (4-44) A-Ed, Ann; Tres, Band; NHS; Rptr, Sch P; Span C; SC; DARGCA; Hon Prog; Journ A; HR; Band A.

ROSS, Charles Edward
Redlands HS; Redlands, CA (33%-1000) Band; CSF; YMCA; Pres, Jr High; Church Yth Group; Dentistry.

ROSS, Christopher Darnell
Cathedral HS; Los Angeles, CA; Drama; Key C; VP, Spch C; JV, Bkbl; Ftbl; MLS; Spch A; Type A; Ohio St U; Psych.

ROSS, Cindy Gail
Crescent HS; Crescent, OK (35-60) Chor; FHA; Pres, FTA; Rainbow; Mgr, Bkbl; Okla St U; Journ.

ROSS, Craig Myron
Mendota HS; Mendota, IL (25%-220) Bkbl; Mus A; Bkbl A; IVCC; Drafting.

ROSS, Craig William
Nevada Union HS; Grass Valley, CA (25-450) A Cap Choir; Band; Chor; Community Yth Symph; Drama; Hmrm; Madrigal; Mod Mus Mas; Ntl Teachers Coun; Orch; Sci C; Ski C; VP, SC; VP, Soph Cl; Ftbl; CSF; 4H A; Hon Prog; Most Out; Yth Fel; All St Hon Choir; Concert Master; Barbershop, Dixieland Band; Westmount Col; Mus.

ROSS, Cynthia Ann
Cardinal Stritch HS; Oregon, OH (2-170) Pres, Fr C; Hmrm; VP, NHS; Tres, Spch C; Alg A; COM; Chem A; Hon Prog; Pres, Quiz Tm; Full Col Schol; U of Toledo; Elec Engr.

ROSS, Debra Janette
W Seneca W Sr HS; W Seneca, NY (29-687) AFS; Chor; Ensm; NHS; Tnns; Bio A; Cum Laude, Lat; D'Yooville Col; Nurs.

ROSS, Debra Leigh
Southern HS; Durham, NC (14-300) Chor; NHS; HR; Jr Marshal; WW; Durham Tech Inst; Computer Programming.

ROSS, Dennis Ray
Manassas HS; Memphis, TN (15-150) Bus C; VP, Lat C; Mu Alpha Theta; Pres, Jr Cl; COM; JA A; Job Readiness A; Memphis St U; Bus Adm.

ROSS, Donald Lee
Academia Sagrado Corazon; Santurce, PR (5-92) Ann; Tres, NHS; ARC; Sch P; Pres, Sci C; Spch C; SC; Bio A; Hist A; Hon Prog; Sci A; Eng A; Geography A; Dickinson Col; Bio.

ROSS, Elizabeth Ann
Eau Claire HS; Columbia, SC; VP, FBLA; Hmrm; Pres, NHS; S-T, SC; COM; Crisco A; Rptr, DECA; Civinettes; Pep Squad; Howard U; Bus Adm.

ROSS, Glenda
Ole Main HS; Little Rock, AR; Drama; Hmrm; Spch C; Beauty; Delta Sigma Theta A; MLS; Sanctuary Soc; Memphis St U; Eng.

ROSS, Jacob Carl
Tuscola HS; Waynesville, NC; Chor; Ski C; Span C; Var C; Cpt, Ftbl; Tr; Ftbl, Tr As; Audio Visual.

ROSS, Jacqueline LaRue
Killeen HS; Killeen, TX;

ROSS, James David
East HS; Columbus, OH (14-350) WW; All A's Yrbk Staff; Bk C; U of Denver; Communications.

ROSS, Janeen Kay
Buckeye Central HS; New Washington, OH (17-92) Band; FBLA; VP, FHA; VP, 4H; Bowl.

ROSS, Karl Clifton
Kenwood HS; Chicago, IL (25-350) Rptr, Sch P; Ski C; Hon Prog; Q&S A; St Scholar; Northwestern U; Econ.

ROSS, Katharine Kay
Worth County R-14; Grant City, MO (20-57) Ann; Band; Bus C; FHA; FTA; GS; 4H; Rainbow; Sch P; Cpt, Golf; HCt; Journ A; NW Mo St U.

ROSS, Keith Erwin
Hutchinson Central Tech HS; Buffalo, NY (66%-210) Band; Bus C; CYO; Chor; Drama; Pres, Hmrm; Orch; Sch P; Fin, Spch C; Ftbl; Tr; Alg A; Elk A; Hon Prog; MLS; Pres A; Spch A; Most Talented; US Marines; Intelligence.

ROSS, Kimberly Camille
Miami Jackson Sr HS; Miami, FL (10%-500) FHA; COM; Hon Prog; Bowl; Span A; Acct.

ROSS, Linda L
Gulf Comprehensive HS; New Port Richey, FL (25%-353) Band; Secy, NHS; Amer Leg A; Hist A; Tres, Yth Group; Bryan Col.

ROSS, Linda Louise
Coatesville Area Sr HS; Coatesville, PA (250-650) FBLA; ARC; Span C; 1st Cl GSct A; Goldey Beacon Col; Secretarial.

ROSS, Lora Jean
Springdale HS; Springdale, AZ; A Cap Choir; U of Ariz; Social Worker.

ROSS, Lucy Elaine
China Spring I S D HS; China Spring, TX (20-56) Band; BC; Drama; Hmrm; FHA; Rainbow; Sci C; Spch A; Agape' Force III; Morehouse Col; Lib Sci.

ROSS, Mary Kathryn
Warren HS; Warren, AR (40-136) Chor; 4H; Sch P.

ROSS, Michael Edmund
Albuquerque HS; Albuquerque, NM (63-614) Chor; Drama; Swim; God & Country A; NM St U; Forestry.

ROSS, Pamela Darlene
George Henry Corliss HS; Chicago, IL (5-256) Pres, Band; Pres, NHS; Co-Ed, Sch P; SC; Pres, Sr Cl; COM; Cl Fav; Hon Prog; Journ A; MLS; NEDT; Spch A; IIT; Mgt.

ROSS, Randall Charlton
Plano Sr HS; Plano, TX (5-850) A Cap Choir; Chor; Drama; Pres, FTA; Lat C; NHS; Order/Arrow; ARC; Pres, SC; Bkbl; Ftbl; Citz A; Cl Fav; Coun of Teach A; DARGCA; God & Country A; Hon Prog; Order/Arrow A; Swtht; Fin, Mr FTA Tex; Eagle Sct; WW; Hon Graduate; Baylor U; Religious Ed.

ROSS, Rani Vanessa
West Charlotte Sr HS; Charlotte, NC; Project Aries; Bus.

ROSS, Renee Denise
Del Valle HS; Del Valle, TX (10-254) Band; Secy, FTA; Rptr, Hmrm; I Ratng, Solo & Ensm Flute Trio, Qt; U of Tex; Bus.

ROSS, Richard Edward
Nevada Union HS; Grass Valley, CA (42-545) A Cap Choir; Band; Chess C; Chor; Drama; FFA; VP, 4H; Hmrm; Madrigal; Orch; Order/Arrow; Sci C; Ski C; Mgr, Bkbl; Tnns; Bio A; Order/Arrow A; U of Calif; Zoology.

ROSS, Richard McNeil Jr
Miami Jackson Sr HS; Miami, FL (3-585) BS; Dbte Tm; VP, Key C; Rptr, Lit Mag; NHS; Phys C; Sch Achieve Tm; Rptr, SC; Co-Cpt, Tnns; COM; H of F; Hon Prog; Ntl Achv Schol; NMF; Ntl Sci Symposium; NEDT; Phy A; Pres A; Sci A; Spch A; Star Student; Stu Ldrship; Duke U; Pre-Med.

ROSS, Roger C
Troy HS; Troy, KS (10%-39) FFA; Rptr, 4H; SC; Bkbl; Ftbl; Tr; COM; 4H A; Lion A; Animal Sci.

ROSS, Ron Duane
Lincoln HS; Wis Rapids, WI (75-600) VP, A Cap Choir; Band; Chor; Ensm; Madrigal; Ski C; Var C; Ftbl; Tr; Cl Fav; Interlochen Ntl Mus; Northwest Bible Col; Mus.

ROSS, Sandy Gail
Wilmington Sr HS; Wilmington, OH (94-360) Band; Chldr; Ensm; Church Choir; Christ Ambassador A; Band A; Pres, Yth Group; Phys Ed A; South Eastern Bible Col; Mus.

ROSS, Suricia Ann
Shaw HS; E Cleveland, OH; Hon Prog; PA; Morehouse Col; Med.

ROSS, Suzanne Louise
Jesse H Jones HS; Houston, TX (1-950) A Cap Choir; Mgr, Chor; Hmrm; Pres, InterAct C; Model UN; NHS; F-Ed, Sch P; SC; Alg A; COM; Hist A; Journ A; Math A; Sci A; 1st Pl, Sci Fair; 1st Pl, Law Day Essay Contest; 3rd, Fr Poetry Cont; Phys Ed As; Milligan Bible Col.

ROSS, Tammy Renee
Leesburg HS; Leesburg, FL (1-298) AFS; Ed, Ann; Chldr; Hmrm; InterClub Coun; Lat C; VP, NHS; Sch P; Tres, SC; VP, Sr Cl; Mgr, Swim; COM; Cl Fav; Hon Prog; Journ A; Math A; Type A; Val; Tres, Triad Service C; Lat A's; David Lipscomb Col; Math.

ROSS, Teresa Dianne
Cainsville Ri HS; Cainsville, MO (25%-18) Chldr; Chor; Bkbl; Sftbl; 4H A; JA A; Type A; Trenton Jr Col; Bus.

ROSS, Tom Edward
Grand Co HS; Moab, UT; Band; Ftbl; Pres, Church Yth Group; Asst Sunday Supt; 3rd Pl, St HS Woodshop Contest; *Northwest Col; Religion.*

ROSS, Tracy Loreen
Columbia HS; Columbia, PA (13-150) Drama; FHA; Hmrm; SC; Art C; Intramurals; 1st Pl, Spelling A; 1st Pl, Sci Fair.

ROSSE, Kathryn Jo Ann
Hart HS; Hart, MI (12-185) Band; Drama; Ski C; Thes; Band A's; Essay A; *Pyschatric Social Work.*

ROSSER, Pamela Sue
Benhaven HS; Olivia, NC (7-84) BC; Sci C; SC; VP, Jr Cl; *Campbell Col; Optometry.*

ROSSI, Denise Gayle
Weed HS; Weed, CA (4-72) JV, Chldr; S-T, Jr Cl; HCt; HR; *Heald's Bus Col; Bus.*

ROSSI, Laura Jean
Benjamin N Cardozo HS; Bayside, NY (111-1109) Yth Fel; Sunday Sch Teacher; *Adelphi Col; Law.*

ROSSITER, Christine Lynne
Shenandoah HS; Sarahsville, OH; Band; Chor; Cpt, Ensm; VP, 4H; Orch; Bkbl; Ftbl; Soccer; Sftbl; Bio A; Cl Fav; 4H A; MLS; Type A; *Central Bible Col; Mus.*

ROSSITER, Darlene Rae
Immanuel Baptist Christian Sch; Menomonie, WI (1-4) Co-Ed, Ann; Band; Chldr; Chor; SC; Citz A; Hon Prog; Sci A; *Pillsbury Bible Col; Vet Med.*

ROSSMAN, David Wayne
Hartley Comm HS; Hartley, IA (6-58) Band; Pres, FFA; Ger C; NHS; Ftbl; JV, Golf; COM; Yth Fel; Iowa Farmer Degree; *Iowa St U; Engr.*

ROSSOW, Nancy Lillian
Payson HS; Payson, AZ; JV, Chldr; FHA; Sftbl; HCt; Secy, Hero Chapter, FHA.

ROSTEK, Wayne Frederick Jr
St Charles HS; St Charles, MO (80-646) A Cap Choir; ARC; Bsbl; Cr-Ctry; Swim; *Meteorology.*

ROSVOLD, Rochelle Ann
Simley Sr HS; Inver Grove Heights, MN (12-279) Secy, Band; Ensm; NHS; F-Ed, Sch P; COM; Journ A; Co-Cpt, Vlbl; *Dakota Co AVTI; Visual Merchandising.*

ROTENBERGER, Scott Jon
Detroit Lakes Comm HS; Detroit Lakes, MN (33%-291) Tres, Chess C; Ger C; 4H; Math C; Bkbl; Golf; 4H A; *Math.*

ROTH, Alison Jean
Penn Manor HS; Millersville, PA (19-395) Pres, Chor; Community Yth Symph; Drama; Ensm; NHS; Orch; Thes; Pres, Sr Cl; Pres, Jr Cl; NMS; Gov Sch for the Arts; Chor A; Most Mus; Co, Dist, Reg, St Chor; Co, Dist, Reg, St, Al E St's Chor; *Mich St U; Mus.*

ROTH, Bette Bob
Rock Island Sr HS; Rock Island, IL (13-610) Band; Chess C; 4H; NHS; COM; Hon Prog; NML; *U of Ill; Engr.*

ROTH, Carolyn Lee
Othello HS; Othello, WA; Ann; Hmrm; Sch P; Ski C; SC; HCt; *Eastern Wash St Col; Secy.*

ROTH, Cristie Kay
Faith Christian Acad; Adrian, MI (1-4) Chor; SC.

ROTH, James Douglas
Crestview Christian Acad; O'Fallon, MO (2-3) Band; Chor; Drama; Orch; Pres, SC; Table Tnns; Scholastic Quiz Tm; First Pl, Trumpet Solo.

ROTH, Janet Lynn
Viroqua HS; Viroqua, WI (25-152) Ann; Band; Chor; FHA; 4H; Orch; Sch P; 4H A; *U of Wis; Home Ec.*

ROTH, Kay Louise
Marysville-Pilchuck HS; Marysville, WA (25%-532) Ann; Band; Community Yth Symph; 4H; Hmrm; Span C; Var C; Tr; 4H A; Vlbl; *Everett Comm Col; Food Tech.*

ROTH, Laurel Jean
Tucker HS; Tucker, GA (150-450) Chor; Drama; Sci A; *Bus.*

ROTH, Laurie Joanne
Walla Walla HS; Walla Walla, WA (10%-600) Chor; Drama; Ensm; 4H; NHS; Orch; Bkbl; JV, Sftbl; Type A; Carneigie Art A; City Symph; Family Mus Group; Pres, Church Yth Fel; *Olivet Nazarene Col; Mus.*

ROTH, Lori Jane
Washington HS; Washington, IA (25%-170) Ann; Cpt, Chldr; Chor; Fr C; Hmrm; Madrigal; SC; Y-Tns; Bkbl; Tr; Spch A; Semi-Fin, Drill Tm; Outst Performer, St Spch Contest; *Ed.*

ROTH, Lori Jolene
Perry HS; Perry, OK (4-115) Band; Chor; FHA; NHS; VP, Soph Cl; Amer Leg A; Hist A; Masonic A; *Okla St U; Pre-Med.*

ROTH, Madalene Suzan
W Philadelphia Cath Girls HS; Philadelphia, PA (4-488) Secy, A Cap Choir; All Amer Yth; Bus Mgr, CYO; Chem C; Chor; Dbte Tm; Drama; Fr C; French NHS; Rptr, Lit Mag; Math C; VP, NHS; Phys C; Rptr, Sch P; Sci C; World Affairs C; Soccer; Bio A; COM; Chem A; HQn; Hon Prog; MLS; PTA A; Hon Men, Alg 2-Trig A; Prom Qn; Semi-Fin, Journ A; 'Big Smile' A; *Chestnut Hill Col; Chem.*

ROTH, Nancy Aleen
Chardon HS; Chardon, OH; A Cap Choir; Chor; Drama; Ensm; ARC A; Quartette; Church Choir; *Psych.*

ROTH, Pamela Renae
Goshen HS; Goshen, IN (77-263) Band; Chor; Pres, 4H; Hmrm; Ntl Yth Conf; SC; COM; 4H A; Yth Fel; Church Mus Group; GAA; Vlbl; Ch, Homecoming Comm Sunshine Soc; Gifts For Life of Christian Serv; *Secy.*

ROTH, Thomas King
Fremont HS; Fremont, MI (67-247) Var C; Ftbl; Swim; Young Life; *Central Mich U; Engr.*

ROTH, Tom King
Fremont HS; Fremont, MI (67-247) Ski C; Var C; Ftbl; Swim; Young Life; *Central Mich U; Eng.*

ROTHFIELD, Linda Cheryl
Canarsie HS; Brooklyn, NY (8-945) Band; Pres, Drama; NHS; Co-Ed, Sch P; Amer Leg A; COM; Hon Prog; Regent Schol; *Brooklyn Col; Performing Arts.*

ROTHFORK, Theresa Ann
Foley HS; Foley, MN; Semi-Fin, Tr; Mgr, Wrest; Pom-Pom; *Phys Ed Teacher.*

ROTHFUSS, Melanie Rene
Iroquois Central HS; Elma, NY; Chldr; Chor; NHS; SC; Pres, Sr Cl; VP, Jr Cl; VP, Soph Cl; Swim; HCt; *Interior.*

ROTHFUSZ, Craig Edward
Ashley Pub HS; Ashley, ND (2-41) A Cap Choir; Band; BS; Chor; Drama; Var C; Secy, Soph Cl; Tr; Co-Cpt, Wrest; Hon Prog; Pres A; Sal; *Concordia Col; Bio.*

ROTHGERBER, Daven Elaine
Ahrens HS; Louisville, KY; BC; Cpt, Chldr; Drama; FBLA; Ger C; Hmrm; NHS; SC; Tres, Soph Cl; HCt; Type A; *U of Ky; Art.*

ROTHSCHILD, John Lowenberg
Columbus HS; Columbus, GA (5%-350) BS; Tres, Key C; Math C; Mu Alpha Theta; NHS; Sci C; Mgr, Soccer; COM; NML; *Wash U; Math.*

ROTHSCHILLER, David D
Rugby HS; Rugby, ND (31-110) Band; BS; Chor; Drama; Madrigal; Monogram; Order/Arrow; Bsbl; Bkbl; Ftbl; Cpt, Golf; Amer Leg A; HCt; Hon Prog; Order/Arrow A; *Concordia Col; Vet Sci.*

ROTHSTEIN, Paul
Woodmere Acad; Woodmere, NY (2-55) Band; Chor; Cum Laude Soc; Pres, Drama; Fr C; Math C; Bio A; Chem A; Hist A; Regent Schol; NMS Ltr of Commendation; *Yale U; Pol Sci.*

ROTHWELL, Julia Ann
Mainland Sr HS; Daytona Beach, FL (122-507) Anchor C; Chldr; Ch, Fr C; Fin, Jr Miss Pagent; Opt A; Miss ROTC Qn Fin; Miss Mainland Fin; 2nd Pl, Talent Contest; SG; *U of Mass; Fine Arts.*

ROTONDI, Anthony James
St Peters Prep Sch; Jersey City, NJ; CYO; Drama; NHS; COM; Hon Prog; Pres A; Pres Phys Fitness A; Dramatics Ltr; Religious Ed A.

ROTRAMEL, Andrew Mark
Carbondale Comm HS; Carbondale, IL; Chess C; Demolay; 4H; Orch; Order/Arrow; Cr-Ctry; Tr; 4H A; Hon Prog; Order/Arrow A; Fire Crafter; *Physics.*

ROTZ, Joseph Samuel IV
James Buchanan HS; Mercersburg, PA (94-224) Band; FFA; Percussion Ensm; Outdoors C; FFA; Swine A.

ROUBINEK, Mark Eugene
Pine City HS; Pine City, MN (12-144) Band; Bkbl; Cr-Ctry; Golf; MVP, Amer Legion Bsbl.

ROUCKUS, Randy John
Los Lunas HS; Los Lunas, NM (18-240) Ann; Hmrm; Sci C; Hon Prog; Sci A; Best Sci Paper o-t Yr; NCHO; *NM St U; Pre-Med.*

ROUGHTON, Venisha Grace
Cambridge HS; Cambridge, OH (10%-261) Fr C; French NHS; Hmrm; NHS; Span C; Thes; Excellent Rating, St Acad of Sci; Sup Ratng, Sci Day; Chrch Bell Chor; Pres, MYF; Area Yth Choir; Cert of A; Fr, St Tests Acad Achv; *Oral Roberts U; Law.*

ROULLIER, Amy Lou
St Ignatius HS; St Ignatius, MT (2-37) Ann; Band; CYO; Chor; Tres, Jr Cl; 4H A; Type A; Alt, GS; Bookkeeper A; Bus Mgr & Rptr, Sch Paper; HR A; Most Improved Band Player; *Journ.*

ROUNDS, Cynthia Marie
Berea HS; Berea, OH (50%-300) Band; Cpt, Ensm; NHS; Orch; Swim; Alg A; COM; Hon Prog; Math A; Type A; Service A; Mus A; *Fairview General Hospital; Nurs.*

ROUNDS, Iris Yolanda
N Natchez Adams HS; Natchez, MS (15%-220) BC; CYO; Chess C; Semi-Fin, Jr Miss Pa; Ed,tLit Mag; Model UN; NHS; Span C; Beauty; COM; Cl Fav; H of F; Type A; *Tex Sou U; Pre-Law.*

ROUNDS, Kenny Wayne
Leedey HS; Leedey, OK; Drama; VP, FFA; Var C; VP, Sr Cl; VP, Jr Cl; Bsbl; Bkbl; COM; Hon Prog; Banquet Sg; St Farmer A, FFA; Grand Champion Steer; St Horse Judg; 1st Tm Horse Judging; Ntl Livestock Show; *Okla St U; Animal Sci.*

ROUNDS, Phyllis Gail
Douglass HS; Memphis, TN; Ann; FHA; 4H; Hmrm; Jr Miss Pagent; Bkbl; Cl Fav; HCt; *Tenn St U; Nurs.*

ROUNDTREE, Charmaine
Simon Gratz HS; Philadelphia, PA (25-703) Hmrm; Model UN; Pol Sci C; SC; World Affairs C; Citz A; Hon Prog; Yth Leg; *Temple U; Pre-Med.*

ROUNDTREE, Karen Elise
Hughes HS; Cincinnati, OH (26-377) Chldr; Sftbl; VICA; WW; Grant, Ohio St U; *Ohio St U; Pre-Med.*

ROUNDTREE, Katherine Elaine
Hughes HS; Cincinnati, OH (21-377) Co-Cpt, Chldr; Sftbl; Beauty; Citz A; VICA Competition A; *Columbus Col of Art & Design; Commercial Art.*

ROUNTREE, Elizabeth Ann
York Central Sch; Retsof, NY; NHS; *US Navy.*

ROUSE, Beth LuDean
Grundy Center Comm HS; Grundy Center, IA (20-80) Band; Chor; Drama; Ensm; FBLA; Thes; JV, Golf; Spch A; Win, FBLA St Contest; Indiv Outst Performance, IHSSA; Duet Outst Performance, IHSSA.

ROUSE, Matthew Scott
Parkwood HS; Joplin, MO (83-330) Bkbl; 2nd Pl Art, SW Baptist Col; *Mo Sou St Col; Art.*

ROUSE, Rebecca Lenore
Eldorado HS; Albuquerque, NM (14-746) GS; Hmrm; NHS; Ski C; Secy, SC; Pres, Sr Cl; VP, Jr Cl; S-T, Soph Cl; Off Scorekeeper & Timer, Swim; *U of NM;; Sociology.*

ROUSE, Renee
East HS; Cleveland, OH; Ger C; Bkbl; *Howard U; Law.*

ROUSEY, Lynda Lee
S H Rider HS; Wichita Falls, TX (20%-400) Lat C; Rainbow; Tri-HiY; *Texas A&M U; Veterinary.*

ROUSEY, Sharon Annette
S H Rider HS; Wichita Falls, TX (20%-400) Lat C; Rainbow; Tri-HiY; Golf; *U of Tex; Med.*

ROUSEY, Sherry Annette
Danville HS; Danville, KY; VP, FHA; Span C; Y-Tns; Secy, Yth Rally; Church Sftbl; Home Ec, Cecilia Fowler, A's.

ROUSH, Douglas Robert
Van Buren Comm HS; Keosauqua, IA (38-80) 4H; Var C; Tr; Wrest; *Northeast Mo St Col.*

ROUSH, Randall Keith
Truman HS; Independence, MO (124-575) Band; Ensm; InterAct C; Orch; VP, SC; Var C; Cpt, Tnns; Fin, Tnns; *U of Mo; Bus Adm.*

ROUSH, Vicky Lynn
Anderson Sr HS; Anderson, IN (50-494) JA A; Church Chor; Vlbl; Home Ec, Special Men, A; Gov Essay, A; *Purdue U; Home Ec.*

ROUSH, Vyanne Jennelle
Claxton HS; Claxton, GA; Band; Hmrm; Var C; Cpt, Bkbl; Sftbl; Tnns; Most Outt; *PE.*

ROUSON, Avis Belinda
Oxon Hill Sr HS; Oxon Hill, MD; Bus C; FBLA; Tres, Hmrm; Tres, Mjrte; Sch P; FBLA A; *Md U.*

ROUSSEL, Jeffrey Alan
Parkview HS; Little Rock, AR (20%-503) BC; BS; FBLA; Hmrm; Key C; NHS; Order/Arrow; SC; Order/Arrow A; Eagle Sct; *U of Ark; Engr.*

ROUTH, Susan Patricia
Eisenhower HS; Lawton, OK (110-560) Chldr; FHA; HiY; Hmrm; NHS; Span C; SC; Tri-HiY; Tnns; Yth Leg; Bsbl Qn; Stu o-t Mo; Pom-Pon Drill Tm; *Cameron U; Spch Pathology.*

ROUTHIER, Christine Ann
Alexander Galt Regional HS; Lennoxville, CANADA (1-539) Band; Community Yth Symph; Dbte Tm; Hmrm; SC; UN Council; Hockey; HR; MSD A; Coun A

ROUTON, Denice Rene
MacArthur HS; San Antonio, TX (10%-750) Band; Fr C; Mjrte; Hon Prog; *LSU; Math.*

ROW, Richard Jay Jr
Dauphin Co Tech HS; Harrisburg, PA (25%-300) Drama; SC; *Penn St U; Meteorology.*

ROWE, Carrlon Louise
Hanceville HS; Hanceville, AL; Chor; FTA; 4H; Rptr, Sch P; *Wallace Jr Col; Clerical.*

ROWE, Cynthia Ruth
Cache HS; Cache, OK (5-46) Ann; Tres, BC; FFA; GS; 4H; NHS; Sch P; Span C; Rptr, SC; Rptr, Var C; Rptr, Jr Cl; Secy, Soph Cl; Cpt, Bkbl; Tr; Cl Fav; Hist A; HQn; Masonic A; Spch A; Type A; *Okla St U; Agr.*

ROWE, Dee M
Lancaster Sr HS; Lancaster, WI (5-139) AFS; Band; Ensm; FFA; Pres, 4H; Math C; NFL; Sch P; Span C; Var C; Bkbl; Golf; Tr; 4H A; Hon Prog; JA A; Pres A; Spch A; Yth Fel; VP, Helicopter Rescue, Law Enf Ex; Discus Rec; Dist Yth Coun On Minist; Co, Dist & St 4-H Livstock Judg Con; St P, Soil & Wtr Cons, Jr Brd Supr.

ROWE, John Dewitt
NW Acad; Houston, TX (13-63) AFS; Bsbl; Cpt, Ftbl; Outst HS Stu, Houston; All St Ftbl; Guitarist, Mus Group; VP, FCA; Mus.

ROWE, Karen Lynn
Belvidere HS; Belvidere, IL (99-350) AFS; Band; Ensm; VP, Ger C; GS; NHS; Ski C; Hockey; Tr; Stu Director, Band; Pres, GAA; *Ill St U; Med Tech.*

ROWE, Linda Carol
Mason HS; Mason, MI (33%-283) Chor; Secy, FFA; 4H; Var C; Sftbl; Cpt, Swim; Mgr, Wrest; JV Vlbl; FFA Knowledge A; *Mich St U; Phys Ed.*

ROWE, Mary Ann
Kings Park Sr HS; Kings Park, NY; Band; Co-Cpt, CYO; Chor; Ensm; Fr C; NHS; SC; COM; Hon Prog; NY St Sch of Mus Solo Medals; *Mus Ed.*

ROWE, Robert Mark
Duluth Central HS; Duluth, MN (33%-442) Co-Ed, Ann; *NC St U; Pre-Med.*

ROWE, Steven James
Calumet HS; Calumet, MI (35-150) Band; VP, Sr Cl; Pres, Soph Cl; Ftbl; Co-Cpt, Hockey; Co-Cpt, Tr; Most Popular; *Central Mich U; Bio.*

ROWELL, Barbara Kaye
Central HS; Memphis, TN; Chor; ARC; SC; Bkbl; Sftbl; COM; HCt.

ROWELL, Diwana Daphene
Pine Bluff HS; Pine Bluff, AR (10%-500) A Cap Choir; Madrigal; Y-Tns; Bkbl; Citz A; MLS; Pres, Jr Soc C; *U of Miss; Art.*

ROWELL, Lisa Ann
Huntsville HS; Huntsville, AL (15%-454) JV, Chldr; Hmrm; Span C; SC; Beauty; Cl Fav; Sr Adv Board; Pep C; *Auburn U; Forestry.*

ROWLAN, Michele Louise
U S Grant HS; Oklahoma City, OK; Lat C; NHS; Var C; Cpt, Bkbl; Lion A; WW; *Okla City SW Col; Phys Therapy.*

ROWLAND, Ann Karin
Grace Davis HS; Modesto, CA (10%-500) AFS; Ensm; Madrigal; NHS; Orch; Swim; COM; *Stanislaus St Col; Bus.*

ROWLAND, Betty Marie
Mt Ida HS; Mt Ida, AR (12-35) BC; Cpt, Chldr; VP, FHA; 4H; F-Ed, Sch P; Secy, SC; Beauty; HCt; Swtht; WW.

ROWLAND, Cynthia Lee
Godley HS; Godley, TX (1-24) Ann; FHA; Ed, Sch P; SC; Jr Cl; Secy, Soph Cl; Mgr, Bkbl; Mgr, Tr; Citz A; Hon Prog; *Tarleton St U.*

ROWLAND, Gina Renee
Sou Baptist Ed Center; Memphis, TN; Hmrm; Co-Ed, Sch P; VP, Span C; *Eckerd Col; Respiratory Therapy.*

ROWLAND, Jerri Ann
Johnson Co HS; Wrightsville, GA (10%-120) Pres, BC; FBLA; Secy, FHA; FTA; Tri-HiY; COM; Yth Fel; Cl Ed, Ann; Soc Ed, Sch P; Hon Guard; St Lib Assn; *Ga Sou Col; Journ.*

ROWLAND, Mark Eugene
Jones Co HS; Gray, GA; FFA; Order/Arrow; Sftbl; Eagle Sct; *Macon Jr Col; Criminal Justice.*

ROWLAND, Sandra Lea
Switzerland Jr Sr HS; Vevay, IN (3-137) Band; 4H; Span C; JV, Bkbl; Tr; 4H A; Sci A; Span A; *Ind U; Med.*

ROWLAND, Thomas
E Laurens HS; Dublin, GA; Rptr, Span C; COM; Math A; Sci A; PC Jr Fel; Span A; *Swainsboro Area Vo-tech Sch; Elec.*

ROWLAND, Timothy
E Laurens HS; Dublin, GA (10%-85) FBLA; COM; JA A.

ROWLAND, Tokunboh Iyamu
Springfield Gardens HS; New York, NY (116-962) Mgr, Band; Ensm; Fr C; Sch Achieve Tm; Span C; Alg A; Bio A; Citz A; Hist A; Math A; Spch A; Gym Competitor A; *NY City Col; Engr.*

ROWLAND, Tonia Anna
Springfield Garden HS; Queens, NY; Dbte Tm; Tres, Tr; *Queens Col; Med.*

ROWLANDS, Janet Elizabeth
Center Sr HS; Kansas City, MO (5%-423) A Cap Choir; Band; Chor; Community Yth Symph; Dbte Tm; Drama; Sch P; Phy A; *Pre-Med.*

ROWLEN, Mary Evelyn
Mathiston HS; Mathiston, MS (25%-29) Ann; BC; Chldr; FHA; 4H; A-Ed, Sch P; Sftbl; Tr; Cl Fav; 4H A; I Dare You; Journ A; *Wood Jr Col; Vet Med.*

ROWLES, Roger Dean
E Green Comm HS; Grand Junction, IA (1-28) Band; Chor; Demolay; Tres, FFA; 4H; VP, NHS; Mgr, Bkbl; Ftbl; Val; *Iowa St U; Agr-Bus.*

ROWLETT, Alvous Warren
Swifton Pub HS; Swifton, AR (1-23) Band; FFA; Bsbl; Bkbl; Star Student; *Ark St U; Pol Sci.*

ROWLETT, Anita Lynne
Treadwell HS; Memphis, TN (16-174) Chem C; Drama; Cpt, Mjrte; NHS; ARC; Sch P; Span C; Spch C; Span NHS; Pres, SC; VP, Soph Cl; Mgr, Bkbl; Mgr, Tr; Cl Fav; HQn; Ntl Conf Chr & Jews; ARC A; Spch A; Miss Treadwell; *Memphis St U; Nurs.*

ROWLETT, Katherine Wood
Henrico HS; Richmond, VA (10%-400) Lat C; SC; Pres, Y-Tns; Bkbl; Sftbl; Swim; Nom, Gov Sch for the Gifted; *Law.*

ROWLEY, Daniel Robert
Apollo Ridge HS; Spring Church, PA (1-204) Chor; Math C; NHS; VP, Var C; Co-Cpt, Bkbl; Co-Cpt, Cr-Ctry; Co-Cpt, Tr; HCt; Lion A; Math A; NEDT; PTA A; Val; Bstr C Sports Schol; Nelson Mem Schol; *Grove City Col; Engr.*

ROWLEY, Kathleen Louise
Tisdale Unit Composite Sch; Tisdale, CANADA (1-97) Sch P; Bkbl; Yrbk, Typing, Geography, C'S; Fr A; Legion Poem Contest A; *U of Regina; Psych.*

ROWLEY, Nancy Jane
Kiski Area Sr HS; Vandergrift, PA (135-507) Lit Ral; Rainbow; Ski C; Appreciation A; *Clarion St Col; Bus Adm.*

ROY, Cheryl Ann
Western Hills HS; Cincinnati, OH (40-900) Hmrm; Secy, Span C; SC; Cpt, Tnns; Tr; COM; Citz A; Daisy Chain; *U of Cincinnati; Acct.*

ROY, Dominic
College De Ste Anne De La Pocatiere; La Pocatiere, CANADA (1-28) Ftbl; *CEGEP La Pocatiere; Med.*

ROY, Sheryl Ann
Hobart Sr HS; Hobart, IN (85-406) Chldr; Fr C; 4H; ARC; SC; JV, Tnns; St Scholar; *Purdue U; Communications.*

ROY, Tina Dimitri
Jesse H Jones HS; Houston, TX (12-347) Cum Laude Soc; FNA; Hmrm; Math C; Tres, Mu Alpha Theta; NHS; St Stu Congress; Tres, Sr Cl; COM; Hon Prog; Journ A; Most Outt; Q&S A; ARC A; Type A; WW; Les Dix; Most Outst Foreign Lang Stu; *U of Tex at Austin; Med.*

ROY, Ty Scott
Ark Sch for the Deaf; Little Rock, AR; Drama; Key C; Bkbl; Ftbl; Tr; COM; Cl Fav; Tres, Explorers; *Galladet Col; Dentistry.*

ROYAL, Alan Bradley
Tift Co HS; Tifton, GA (150-300) Span C; *Christian Ed.*

ROYAL, Jonathan Mark
Apollo HS; Owensboro, KY (33%-390) BC; Chess C; Hmrm; Lat C; SC; Bsbl; JV, Bkbl; Ftbl; Swim; Pres A; *U of Ky; Law.*

ROYAL, Joy Anne
Brewer HS; Brewer, ME (116-284) Chor; Orch; Rptr, Sch P; Tr.

ROYAL, Judy Ann
Hoquiam HS; Hoquiam, WA (33-194) AFS; FBLA; 4H; NHS; WW; Acct A; *W Wash St Col; Bus Adm.*

ROYAL, Linda Kay
T Wingate Andrews HS; High Point, NC (43-298) Ed, Ann; BC; Span C; Hon Prog; Yth Fel; WW; Acteens; Ed, Church Newspaper; Tres, Church Yth Coun; Keyettes; *Mars Hill Col; Ed.*

ROYALL, Sarah Elizabeth
Green Mtn HS; Lakewood, CO (1-350) A Cap Choir; Chor; Madrigal; NHS; COM; NMF; Regent Schol; Val; *U of Colo; Mus.*

ROYCE, Vicki Lynn
Bowsher HS; Toledo, OH; Band; Orch; Rainbow; *Toledo U; Radiology.*

ROYER, Susanne Elizabeth
Telstar Regional HS; Bethel, ME (13-77) Chor; Co-Ch, Drama; GS; NHS; SC; DARGCA; WW; *Gordon Col; Eng Lit.*

ROYSE, Mark Edward
Ottawa HS; Ottawa, KS (44-192) SC; VP, Sr Cl; Bkbl; Work-Stu Trip, Haiti; Most Inspirational Player A, Bkbl; *Wichita St U; Adm of Justice.*

ROYSTER, Debbie Ann
Southern HS; Durham, NC; Drama; Span C; SC; Pres, Soph Cl; Bkbl; Sftbl; *U of NC; Nurs.*

ROYSTER, Larry Darnell
Northwestern Comm HS; Flint, MI (167-498) Ftbl; Explorers; *Morehouse Col; Bus Adm.*

ROZELL, Rex Lee
Rockdale HS; Rockdale, TX (80-135) BS; Chem C; Math C; Tnns; Amer Leg A; *Sam Houston St U; Social Work.*

628

ROZELLE, Lorna Grace
Riverside Jr Sr HS; Taylor, PA (1-184) Chess C; Chor; NHS; Span C; Chem A; Hon Prog; NEDT; Yth Fel; Triboro Banner A; *Astronomy.*

ROZEMAN, Paul Anthony
Northwood HS; Shreveport, LA (25%-180) BS; Pres, Key C; Fin, Lit Ral; SC; Pres, Sr Cl; Pres, Jr Cl; VP, Soph Cl; Bsbl; Ftbl; Opt A; All Dist Ftbl; Jr Sr Prom Prince; Pres, FCA; Ldrship A; Top 20 Sr; Challenger A; Comm Drug Abuse Control; *La Tech U; Bus.*

ROZENDAAL, James Paul
Aplington Comm Sch; Aplington, IA (8-50) Band; Chor; Ensm; NHS; Mgr, Bkbl; Cr-Ctry; Tr; NMS; Spch A; Yth Fel; *Iowa City Col; Med.*

ROZICH, Diane Elizabeth
St Mary's Acad; Englewood, CO (3-60) Chor; Community Yth Symph; Secy, NHS; Orch; ARC; SC; ARC A; *Colo St U; Math.*

ROZIER, Janet Muriel
Cape Fear HS; Fayetteville, NC (199-345) Chldr; FBLA; FHA; Tri-HiY; *Fayetteville Tech Inst; Dental Asst.*

ROZIER, Patricia Elaine
Eastside HS; Paterson, NJ; *Drew U; Bus Adm.*

ROZMANIK, Ann Marie
Warren HS; Warren, MI (35-300) Ed, Ann; CYO; Chldr; Sch P; Span C; Bkbl; Journa A; Vlbl; HR; *Math.*

ROZMUS, Melody Lane
Port Chester Sr HS; Port Chester, NY; A Cap Choir; AFS; Cpt, CYO; Chor; Sch P; Pres, Church Yth Fel; *CCYM.*

RUARK, Karen Marie
Uniontown Area Sr HS; Uniontown, PA (15-435) Band; Fr C; NHS; Sci C; Ski C; Swim; Amer Leg A; Kiwanis A; Sci A; Pony C Stable Mgt A; Most Enthusiastic Rider A, Pony C; *U of Penn; Vet Med.*

RUARK, Terry Lynn
Loganville HS; Loganville, GA (6-265) BC; VP, Hmrm; Span C; Tri-HiY; Bkbl; Tr; Gov Honor Prog.

RUBACH, Ellen K
Ionia HS; Ionia, MI; Band; NHS; Var C; Bkbl; MVP, Sftbl; Tr; *Eng.*

RUBECK, Janet Lynn
MacArthur HS; Irving, TX (100-580) Cpt, Band; Lat C; ARC; Bkbl; Sftbl; Citz A; Yth Fel; Jr Historians; All Region Band; Ecology C; Coun on Ministries; GSct; Yth Ministry Coun; Key Link; All Star Sftbl; *Stephen F Austin St U; Psych.*

RUBERTI, Lisa Kay
LaGrande HS; LaGrande, OR; Chor; Ensm; SC; VP, Sr Cl; Hist, Girl's League; Bible C; St Rep, Yth Ministry Congress; *Columbia Christian Col; Geology.*

RUBIN, Sherry Lee
Mainland Sr HS; Daytona Beach, FL; S-T, Ger C; Tres, Keyettes C; *Art.*

RUBLE, Donald Nathan
Emmanuel Baptist Sch; Hartsville, SC (1-13) Band; Chor; Ensm; Bsbl; Bkbl; Co-Cpt, Soccer; COM; Citz A; Hist A; Ntl Achv Schol; NEDT; *Tenn Temple Col; Bible.*

RUBLE, Douglas Eugene
Glendale HS; Springfield, MO (9%-415) Key C; JV, Bkbl; Hon Prog; *US Air Force Acad; Aeronautics.*

RUBLE, Gloria Lea
Kermit HS; Kermit, WV (4-35) Secy, Band; FHA; Span C; Type A; Band A; Hon Stu; *Marshall U.*

RUBLE, John Edward
Powell Valley HS; Speedwell, TN (10-95) Mu Alpha Theta; *W Va U; Elec Engr.*

RUBLE, Linda West
Winyah HS; Georgetown, SC; Chldr; Hmrm; SC; Bkbl; *Limestone Col; Child Ed.*

RUBLE, Lisa Ann
Kermit HS; Kermit, WV (3-40) Band; VP, FHA; Pres, Hmrm; Cpt, Mjrte; Span C; Pres, Soph Cl; All-Co Band; *Marshall U; Bus.*

RUBLE, Stacy Renea
Hoover HS; N Canton, OH (25%-552) A Cap Choir; Chor; Rptr, 4H; Citz A; 4H A; *David Lipscomb Col; Acct.*

RUCCI, Corey
Forest View HS; Arlington Heights, IL (10%-747) Band; NHS; Bsbl; Bkbl; Hon Prog; *U of Ill; Bus.*

RUCH, Kenneth Russell
N Penn HS; Lansdale, PA (15-872) Bkbl; Ping Pong; Pres, Yth Fellowship; *Pinebrook Jr Col; Lib Arts.*

RUCHTI, Linda Lou
Ker Khoven HS; Kerkhoven, MN; FFA.

RUCKER, Debby Contreta
South Side HS; Memphis, TN (10%-370) Chldr; Pres, Hmrm; Span C; *Memphis St Col; Acct.*

RUCKER, James Myron
Hopkinsville HS; Hopkinsville, KY; FFA; VP, Order/Arrow; Eagle A; *U of Ky; Agr.*

RUCKER, Lloyd Dwayne
Statesville Sr HS; Statesville, NC (3-30) Chor; Drama; 4H; Hmrm; COM; Citz A; Cl Fav; Hon Prog; Belmont Singers of Faith; PA; Lib C; Monogram A; Safe Boating A; Parl, VICA; Sports A; Kg Boy o-t Yr; *NC St U; Textiles.*

RUCKER, Peggy Juanita
South Side HS; Memphis, TN (10%-370) Chldr; Span C; Cl Fav; MS Soph; Eng Achv; *Memphis St U; Industrial Engr.*

RUCKER, Richard Mabry
Fair Park HS; Shreveport, LA; BS; Demolay; NHS; ROTC A; *La Tech U; Mech Engr.*

RUCKMAN, Linda Carol
Lookeba-Sicles HS; Lookeba, OK (1-24) Bus Mgr, Ann; S-T, FHA; GS; NHS; S-T, Sr Cl; S-T, Jr Cl; Chem A; Masonic A; MLS; Type A; Val; *Okla St U; Bus.*

RUDANSKY, Samuel R
Hebrew Acad of Nassau Co; Uniondale, NY; Dbte Tm; French NHS; Hmrm; InterClub Coun; Rptr, Sch P; Pres, SC; Bsbl; Cpt, Bkbl; Bsbl; Sftbl; Tnns; Tr; COM; Hon Prog; Sal; Spch A; Sport A; General Stu A; Hon Soc; *Yeshiva U; Law.*

RUDD, Ivora Regina
E N Woodruff HS; Peoria, IL (83-286) Ann; Bus C; VP, Hmrm; Span C; JA A; ARC A; Type A; Lib Asst A; PA; Pom Pom Squad; Ed, Talisman; *Ill St U; Psych.*

RUDD, Linda
Green HS; Uniontown, OH (16-300) S-T, Band; Chor; Tres, Drama; Ensm; Semi-Fin, GS; NHS; Sch Achieve Tm; Ski C; Y-Tns; JA A; GSct; Secy, GAA; *Miami U; Ed.*

RUDD, Margaret Ann
Richmond Sr HS; Rockingham, NC; Ann; Drama; FHA; Hmrm; Span C; Hon Prog; Pep C; Sub Jr Women's C.

RUDD, Mary Elizabeth
Richmond Sr HS; Rockingham, NC; Ann; BC; Chor; Ensm; Hmrm; Sch P; Span C; Chor A; PA; Pep, Sprtsmnshp, Sub-Jr Women, C'S; *Duke U; Med Tech.*

RUDD, Ronald Aaron
Edisto HS; Cordova, SC (2-88) BS; VP, FFA; A-Ed, Lit Mag; Secy, NHS; Order/Arrow; Sch P; Pres, SC; Var C; Ftbl; HKg; Journ A; Opt Out Tm; Order/Arrow A; Spch A; Pub Speaker; Marshal; Star FFA; Chapter Farmer; Furman Wofford & Presbyterian Schol; *Clemson U; Agronomy.*

RUDD, Suzanne
Bryan Adams HS; Dallas, TX (10%-850) Band; Ensm; Lat C; NHS; SC; Y-Tns; Hon Prog; Sci A; *Abilene Christian U; Med.*

RUDDICK, Lori Grace
Fort Scott HS; Fort Scott, KS (23-160) Bus Mgr, Ann; Chldr; Drama; Hmrm; Mjrte; Math C; Span C; VP, SC; Alg A; Pres A; Geo A; *Kans U; Psych.*

RUDE, Craig Steven
Norte Del Rio HS; Sacramento, CA (1-500) Band; Chess C; NHS; Rptr, Sch P; Ftbl; MVP, Swim; Alg A; Bank Of Amer A; Bio A; CSF; Chem A; Hist A; Math A; Phy A; Sci A; Math Conf; Nom, Stu o-t Mo; Hon Band; *Sacramento St Col; Math.*

RUDE, Peter Heinz
Anoka Sr HS; Anoka, MN; AFS; Drama; Ger C; Secy, 4H; Rptr, Sch P; Ski C; SC; Tnns; 4H A; Sci A; St Jr Trapper o-t Yr; Play A; *U of Minn; Wildlife.*

RUDE, Richard Wayne
Columbus HS; Columbus, ND (14-20) Band; S-T, BS; 4H; 4H A; *ND St Sch of Sci; Machine Tooling.*

RUDEK, Timothy Joseph
Harrah HS; Harrah, OK (12-118) Band; MVP, Bsbl; Ftbl; *Central St U.*

RUDGINIS, Susan Diane
Whitney Point Sr HS; Whitney Point, NY (12-161) Band; Chor; Pres, Drama; NHS; Amer Leg A; COM; God & Country A; *Ithaca Col; Phys Therapy.*

RUDINOFF, John Jeffrey
Pennsville Mem HS; Pennsville, NJ (52-285) A Cap Choir; Band; Chor; Community Yth Symph; Ensm; Hmrm; InterAct C; Orch; Drum Major; Stage, Pit, Co Bands; Co Chor; *Glassboro St Col.*

RUDMAN, Marion
Gilbert HS; Gilbert, MN; Band; CYO; Rptr, Sch P; Bkbl; Ftbl; Mgr, Tnns; Mgr, Tr; *Col of Saint Benedict; Photography.*

RUDOLPH, Annette
Anniston HS; Anniston, AL (150-400) Secy, BC; Secy, FHA; Pres, Hmrm; VP, SC; Tr; B Crocker A; Cpt, Vlbl; Pres, Amer Legion; Phys Ed Cert of A; 1st Pl, St Dist & Ntl Cooking Cont; *Gadsden St Jr Col; Food Service.*

RUDOLPH, Charlotte Ruth
Normal Comm HS; Normal, IL (47-508) AFS; Secy, 4H; Orch; ARC; Tr; 4H A; Vlbl; Med Explorers; Home Ec A; Ecology C; GAA; VP, Yth Group; *Med Sci.*

RUDOLPH, Gordie Raymond
Duncan MacMillan HS; Sheet Harbour, CANADA (7-24) Bkbl; Hockey; Sftbl; Tr; Chem A; Sci A; *Acadia Col; Chem.*

RUEB, Mary Jean
Herreid HS; Herreid, SD (6-28) Ann; Band; Chor; Drama; Ensm; Orch; Sch P; Hon Prog; Declamation Tm; Flute A; Piano A; Pres, Missionettes; Comm Choir; Pres, Yth Fel; *Trinity Bible Inst; Bible.*

RUEDE, Brian Joseph
Colonie Central HS; Albany, NY (90-765) NHS; Co-Cpt, Soccer; Swim; *Paul Smith's Col; Ecology.*

RUEDEBUSCH, Susan Mary
Wapakoneta Sr HS; Wapakoneta, OH; Band; FNA; Span C; JV, Bkbl; Tr; Bio A; *Nurs.*

RUEFF, James Russell Jr
Jeffersonville HS; Jeffersonville, IN (4%-800) Chor; Drama; Bkbl; *Asbury Col; Fine Arts.*

RUEHL, Kathleen Anne
Joel E Ferris HS; Spokane, WA (40-388) Chldr; NHS; Cl Fav; Lilac Princess; Top Sr Home Ec Stu; Bon Marche Fashion Acad; Church Yth Coun.

RUEHMANN, Roger Arden
Mabel-Canton HS; Mabel, MN (10-60) Band; Ensm; Var C; Bkbl; Ftbl; Pres A.

RUEN, David Charles
Lanesboro HS; Lanesboro, MN (1-35) A-Ed, Ann; Band; Chor; Commercial C; Ensm; Rptr, FFA; 4H; Spch C; Bkbl; COM; 4H A; Sptr A; Yth Leg; Nom, Ntl FFA Show; FFA Profic & Livestock Show, A's; *U of Minn; Pol Sci.*

RUEN, Joyce Ilene
Lanesboro HS; Lanesboro, MN (7-37) Band; Chldr; Chor; Commercial C; Ensm; FHA; 4H; Sftbl.

RUEST, Ann
College Ste Anne De La Pocatiere; La Pocatiere, CANADA (2-34) CYO; Pres, Hmrm; SC; Soccer; Swim.

RUETER, Susan Carol
Hazelwood E HS; St Louis, MO (1-445) Band; Ensm; Jr Miss Pagent; NHS; Orch; F-Ed, Sch P; COM; Curator A; PTA A; Val; All-Suburban Band; *Sou Ill U at Edwardsville; Mus Ed.*

RUFF, Barbara Ann
Kelso HS; Kelso, WA; FHA; Tres, Ski C; SC; Pres, Soph Cl; Cr-Ctry; Tr; Amer Leg A; Outst Girl.

RUFF, Bryan Eugene
Oswego HS; Oswego, IL (35-333) Ftbl; Wrest; *Concordia Lutheran Col; Theology.*

RUFFIN, Belinda
Chocowinity HS; Chocowinity, NC; Monogram; Bkbl.

RUFFIN, Milton
Churo HS; Chocowinity, NC; Monogram; Bkbl.

RUFFOLO, Daria Christina
J Sterling Morton E HS; Cicero, IL (219-798) U of Ill; Nurs.

RUFI, Debi Jean
Hartford HS; Hartford, WI (15%-425) NHS; Ed, Sch P; Hon Prog; NEDT; Q&S A; UW-Milwaukee; Journ.

RUGER, Dale Lee
Hughson HS; Hughson, CA; FFA; Sch P; Bsbl; JV, Bkbl; Ftbl; Wrest; Cl Fav; Automotive.

RUGGIERO, Andrea Julia
Hightstown HS; Hightstown, NJ (59-253) Band; Chor; Drama; Semi-Fin, GS; NHS; Rptr, Sch P; Sci C; Citz A; Hon Prog; Drama A; Mercer Co Comm Col; Secy.

RUGGLES, Ann
Quabbin Regional Jr-Sr HS; Barre, MA; Band; Chor; Community Yth Symph; Drama; 4H; Lat C; NHS; Rainbow; 4H A; Yth Fel; Librarian; Grand Cross of Color; Hardwick Fair A; Mus.

RUGGLES, Martha Armistead
Norfolk Collegiate Sch; Norfolk, VA (33%-69) Fr C; Monogram; NHS; Secy, Jr Cl; Co-Cpt, Bkbl; MVP, Sftbl; Tnns; MVP, Bkbl; Westhampton Col; Bus Adm.

RUGGLES, Marvin Alan
Lutheran HS W; Rocky River, OH; Kent St U; Agr.

RUHL, Brenda Sue
Kreamer Christian Acad; Kreamer, PA; Chldr; Ensm; Pres, SC; God & Country A; Vlbl; Eng Lit Composition A; Stu o-t Yr; Christian A; Missionary A; Mus A; Hyles-Anderson Col; Elem Ed.

RUHL, Christopher Daniel
Mayo Sr HS; Rochester, MN (19-611) Dbte Tm; NHS; Spch C; Sftbl; Tr; Spch A; Astronomy C; Century III Ldr A; U of Minn; Pre-Theology.

RUHLAND, Lynn Marie
Hilbert HS; Hilbert, WI (4-81) Chor; Drama; Ensm; Madrigal.

RUHLAND, Roger A
Eden Valley Watkins HS; Eden Valley, MN; Band; Ensm; Orch; COM; Elec.

RUHLIG, Patricia Sally
Lakeview HS; Battle Creek, MI (27-416) Band; Ensm; Fr C; NHS; Orch; Span C; COM; Interlochen Ntl Mus; St Competitive A; Lakeview Ed Schol; Mich St.

RUIZ, Barbara Margarita
L C Anderson HS; Austin, TX (380-620) CYO; Span C; COM; Hon Prog; Dallas Fashion Merchandising Col; Fashion Merchandising.

RUIZ, Carmen N
Fernando Suria Chaves HS; Barceloneta, PR; Pres, FHA; Ed, Sch P; COM; Lion A; Magna Cum Laude; U of Puerto Rico; Phar.

RUIZ, Elizabeth Ogaz
George Miller Schurr HS; Montebello, CA; Type A; Service C; PA A; Campus Life; JV Vlbl; HR; Calif St U; Bus.

RUIZ, Jorge Alberto
Academia Ntra Sra Providencia; Rio Piedras, PR (5-32) CYO; Span C; VP, Jr Cl; Bsbl; Soccer; COM; Conduct A; Archt.

RUIZ, Marcelino Gonzalez Jr
Bell Voc HS; Washington, DC; Mgr, Bkbl; Mgr, Tr; Machine Shop Co- op Prog; Wash Tech Col.

RUIZ, Sheyla Providencia
Nuestra Sra de la Merced HS; Hato Rey, PR (5-108) CYO; K of C; Swim; Tnns; Alg A; Bio A; Chem A; Hist A; Hon Prog; Most Out; Phy A; Sci A; 9th Grade Hon Graduate; Span A; Eng A; Med.

RUKAVINA, Peter James
Homestead HS; Mequon, WI (10-390) Band; NHS; Tres, SC; Cr-Ctry; Sftbl; Cpt, Wrest; COM; NMF; NMS; Purdue U; Chem Engr.

RULE, Chris Allen
Sooner HS; Bartlesville, OK; Demolay; FHA; NHS; Orch; Span C; Span NHS; SC; Pres, Sr Cl; JV, Ftbl; COM; Elk A; Kiwanis A; Sci A; Val.

RULEY, Douglas Avery
Parkersburg HS; Parkersburg, WV (15-750) Bsbl; Wrest; MLS; Med.

RULLAN, Marisa
Sacred Heart Acad; Santurce, PR (9-65) Chor; Madrigal; Secy, NHS; Secy, ARC; Sch P; Alg A; B Crocker A; COM; Hist A; Hon Prog; Math A; Dickinson Col; Math.

RULLMAN, Janet Sue
Benton HS; St Joseph, MO (15-350) Bus C; Chor; Hmrm; InterAct C; NHS; SC; Hon Prog; JA A; Winter Soph Princess; Young Life; Lead, All Sch Play.

RULON, Donald Scott
Haddon Township HS; Haddon Township, NJ;

RUMANCIK, Nancy
Carmichaels Area HS; Carmichaels, PA (1-83) Band; 4H; Cpt, Mjrte; NHS; Span C; Val; Vof-DEM; Girl o-t Month; Pennsylvania St U; Pol Sci.

RUMBAUGH, Nancy Irene
Eldorado HS; Albuquerque, NM (19-744) Ed, Ann; NHS; Rptr, Sch P; Q&S A; WW; Baylor U; Journ.

RUMMEL, Daniel Edward
Northeast HS; St Petersburg, FL (20-614) Chem C; InterAct C; JETS; Lat C; NHS; Sci C; Cpt, Cr-Ctry; Tr; All-Amer Cr Ctry; Clemson U; Elec Engr.

RUMPF, Tina L
Penncrest HS; Media, PA (225-463) Chldr; Drama; Hmrm; Span C; Foreign Exchange Stu to Mexico; Lib Aide; Keystone Jr Col; Child Development.

RUMSEY, Vanessa Kay
Stephens Co HS; Toccoa, GA (15%-255) Co-Cpt, Chldr; Rptr, 4H; Hmrm; NHS; Var C; Tr; Cl Fav; Yth Fel; Jr HS Homecoming Qn; Most Courteous; Sr HS Homecoming Ct; Libby Graves Mem A For Chldr; Piedmont Col; Mus.

RUNAGER, Jane
Orangeburg-Wilkinson HS; Orangeburg, SC; Chldr; Fr C; Hmrm; NHS; JV, Bkbl; Sftbl; Beauty; COM; Citz A; U of SC; Phys Ed.

RUNDLETT, Larry Roland
Flint Central HS; Flint, MI (17-400) A Cap Choir; Madrigal; NHS; COM; Yth Fel.

RUNGE, Alan Lambert
Glendale HS; Springfield, MO; A Cap Choir; Drama; Ensm; Pres, Hmrm; Key C; Madrigal; Thes; Bsbl; JV, Bkbl.

RUNION, Terry Alan
Herndon HS; Herndon, WV (11-37) Pres, FBLA; Pres, 4H; HiY; NHS; VP, Sci C; SC; Mgr, Bkbl; 4H Yth Fel; Yth Leg; Concord Col; Bus Adm.

RUNION, Thomas Richard
John T Moggard HS; Wilmington, NC; Ftbl; Tr; Pres, Yth Coun; Church Coun; FCA; Yth Choir; U of NC at Wilmington; Bus Adm.

RUNKLE, Catherine Ann
Reynolds HS; Greenville, PA (10-183) Chor; FNA; Lat C; VP, Thes; Tri-HiY; Villa Marie Col; Nurs.

RUNKLE, Peggy Ann
Douglas HS; Douglas, AZ (135-310) AFS; Pres, Chor; Pres, Ensm; FBLA; 4H; InterClub Coun; Rainbow; Citz A; 4H A; Mus A; Sci Fair A; Pepperdine U; Acting.

RUNNELS, Jeffrey Paul
Anna-Jonesboro HS; Anna, IL (5-150) Ann; JV, Bsbl; Ftbl; Tr; Cl Fav; HCt; Hon Prog; Art C.

RUNNING, Phyllis Joan
Custer HS; Custer, SD (50%-60) Band; Chor; 4H; Tr; 4H A; All-Hon & All-St Choirs; Black Hills St Col; Mus.

RUNYEN, Scott Kevin
Argenta-Oreana HS; Argenta, IL (2-105) Band; Cpt, Dbte Tm; NHS; Order/Arrow; SC; Var C; Ftbl; Tr; BSct; Eureka Col; Physics.

RUNYON, Ellen Elizabeth
Logan HS; Logan, WV (131-367) Band; BC; Chess C; FFA; Math C; ARC; Swim; COM; ARC A; Sci A; Yth Fel; Keyette C; 1st Cl GSct; Sou Sem Jr Col; Equitation.

RUNYON, Gina Carol
Madison HS; Richmond, KY; Band; BC; Band Ltr A; Sup A, Ky Mus Ed Assn.

RUNYON, Michelle Lea
Clay City HS; Clay City, IN (1-80) Bus Mgr, Ann; Band; GS; Secy, 4H; Cpt, Mjrte; Pres, Math C; NHS; Secy, SC; Sftbl; DARGCA; 4H A; HCt; Math A; Sci A; St Scholar; Val; Yth Fel; Cpt, Vlbl; Most Studiest; Eng A; FFA Chapter Swtht; Co Stu o-t Month; Prom Qn Attendant; Indiana U; Phys Therapy.

RUNYON, Thomas Edward
Paris HS; Paris, IL (19-235) Chem C; VP, Key C; NHS; Var C; Mgr, Bsbl; JV, Bkbl; Ftbl; JV, Tr; Wrest; Barnes Hospital Sch of Nurs; Anesthesia.

RUNYON, Timothy Joseph
Paris Comm HS; Paris, IL (43-225) Chem C; Key C; Ftbl; Tr; Wrest; Yth Fel; St Louis Col of Phar; Phar.

RUOF, Anne Tracy
Cortland Sr HS; Cortland, NY (15-300) Chor; Y-Tns; Hon Prog; Yth Fel; Pres, Church Yth; Yrbk Photographer; Anthropology.

RUPEL, Kirsten Louise
Lincoln HS; Stockton, CA; Community Yth Symph; Cum Laude Soc; Orch; CSF; Math A; Ger A; McPherson Col; Lang.

RUPEL, Wesley Ogden
Lincoln HS; Stockton, CA (8-373) Band; Semi-Fin, Chess C; Pres, Math C; Pol Sci C; Sci C; S-T, Var C; Ftbl; Alg A; CSF; Chem A; Hon Prog; Most Valuable Lineman, Ftbl; Geom A; Trigonometry A; Semi-Fin, Math As of Amer; Manchester Col; Chem.

RUPERT, Beth Ann
Cedarburg HS; Cedarburg, WI (16-330) Co-Ed, Lit Mag; NHS; Span C; Hon Prog; Marion Col; Eng.

RUPERT, Susan Jean
Cedarburg HS; Cedarburg, WI (36-375) Drama; Fr C; Co-Ed, Lit Mag; Hon Prog; Spch A; Rptrs, F-Ed, Sch Paper; Wisc Solo Ensm; Marion Col of Fonddulac Wis.

RUPINSKI, Marie Christine
Mont Pleasant HS; Schenectady, NY; Hon Prog; S-T; Folk Group; Lector; Teacher's Aide; Teaching.

RUPINSKI, Sharon Dawn
Riverside Jr Sr HS; Taylor, PA (2-185) Drama; NHS; Co-Ed, Sch P; Span C; SC; Chem A; Hon Prog; NEDT; U of Pa; Acct.

RUPLE, Robert Mark
Southside HS; Ft Smith, AR (33%-465) Bsbl; Ftbl; U of Ark; Bus.

RUPNOW, Gregory Donald
Oconomowoc Sr HS; Oconomowoc, WI (183-249) MVP, Bsbl; Cpt, Bkbl; Pres, ACT Yth C; YMCA Church League Bkbl & Bsbl.

RUPP, Rodney Lynn
Montpelier HS; Montpelier, OH (36-102) Arch; BS; FFA; 4H; Fin, Arch; 4H A; Sci A; Arch A; Toledo U; Med.

RUPPE, Sharon Marie
Terry Sanford Sr HS; Fayetteville, NC (30-370) VP, Hmrm; Semi-Fin, Jr Miss Pa; NHSt; Rptr, Sch P; Span C; Hon Prog; VP, Scottish Dancer; Keywanettes.

RUPPRECHT, M Jeffrey
C H Spurgeon Acad; Memphis, TN (3-18) Ann; Pres, Chor; Co-Ed, Sch P; Var C; Pres, Soph Cl; Bsbl; MVP, Bkbl; MVP, Soccer; HCt; Memphis St U; Engr.

RUPRECHT, James Theodore
Stephen Hempstead HS; Dubuque, IA (2-528) Chess C; NHS; Order/Arrow; Co-Cpt, Ftbl; Bkbl; Tr; God & Country A; Hon Prog; NMF; NMS; Order/Arrow A; St Scholar; 1st Tm, All-Conf Ftbl; Engr.

RUPRIGHT, Greg Jon
Homestead HS; Fort Wayne, IN (96-252) Band; Hope Col; Ministry.

RURA, Barbara
Uniontown HS; Uniontown, PA (109-435) A-Ed, Ann; Band; Fr C; FTA; Pres, Hmrm; Mjrte; NHS; Orch; Secy, Sci C; Ski C; SC; Sci A; WW; Hon Men, Miss Tnage Amer; Duquesne U; Phar.

RUSAK, Jo Jeen Marie
Central of Lunenburg HS; Victoria, VA (13-142) Cpt, Chldr; 4H; InterClub Coun; Jr Miss Pagent; Monogram; NFL; NHS; Span C; Tri-HiY; Chldr A; Win, Miss Victoria Title; *U of Va; Spch Pathology & Audiology.*

RUSCHE, Raymond Edward
Herricks Sr HS; New Hyde Park, NY (143-500) Cr-Ctry; Tr; Yth Fel; *Embry-Riddle Aeronautical U; Aeronautical Sci.*

RUSERT, David Gene
Lafayette Sr HS; Ellisville, MO (30-503) Hist A; Hon Prog; Bus,a; Ongoing Ambass For Christ; Ppes, Yth Group; Evangelism Group; Yth Del, Mo Dist LCMS Conv; Coach, Bkbl & Soccer Tms; *Concordia Teachers Col; Ed.*

RUSH, Carol Renee
Columbus Sr HS; Columbus, NE (4-290) Band; Chor; Dbte Tm; Ensm; 4H; NFL; ARC; Swim; Chem A; 4H A; Most Improved, Swim; Debate A; 100 Hr Candystriper A; Chem Schol; *Med Research.*

RUSH, Cynthia Anne
Conway HS; Conway, SC (3-700) Anchor C; Ed, Ann; JV, Chldr; Chor; Fr C; FTA; NHS; Pres, SC; VP, Jr Cl; Pres, Soph Cl; Bkbl; Tnns; Beauty; Most Out; *Converse Col; Special Ed.*

RUSH, Debbie Lynn
Connersville HS; Connersville, IN (35-398) Ger C; NHS; *Vocational Col; Cosmetology.*

RUSH, Deborah Susan
Bloom Trail HS; Chicago Hts, IL; 4H A; *Ill St U; Bus.*

RUSH, Jeri Jo
Harris-Lake Park Comm HS; Lake Park, IA (15%-38) Chor; GS; VP, 4H; Madrigal; NHS; Co-Cpt, Var C; Bkbl; MVP, Sftbl; Tr; 4H A; Secy, Tres, 4-H C; All St Mus; All Conf Bkbl; *Wartburg Col; Phys Therapy.*

RUSH, Keith Lamont
U City HS; U City, MO; Bsbl; Bkbl; *Contracting.*

RUSH, Lauri Lisa
Ramona HS; Riverside, CA (10%-400) Chor; Bkbl; *U of Calif at Riverside; Med.*

RUSH, Pamela Ann
Ramona HS; Riverside, CA (5-350) Bkbl; Swim; CSF; Coaches A; Schol Ath; Amer Bus Women's Schol; *U of Calif at Riverside; Bio-Med.*

RUSH, Randye Lee
John Ehret HS; Marrero, LA (5-470) 4H; Hmrm; InterClub Coun; Lit Ral; Pres, Math C; Mu Alpha Theta; Pres, NHS; SC; Chem A; Hist A; Hon Prog; PTA A; Sci A; WW; *Tulane U; Computer Engr.*

RUSH, Sondra Jean
Abilene HS; Abilene, TX; Band; FFA; Secy, 4H; NHS; Tri-HiY; Alg A; God & Country A; 4H A; Math A; *Bible Baptist Col.*

RUSH, Teri Lorraine
Tyler Street Christian Acad; Dallas, TX; A Cap Choir; MVP, Band; Chor; Orch; Secy, SC; Golf; Swim; Select A; Beauty; Instrumental A; Fin, Cl Fav; Fin, HCt; UIL St Comp, Mus; *Oral Roberts U; Mus.*

RUSHEFSKI, Marie Elaine
Old Forge HS; Old Forge, PA (9-121) Cpt, Mjrte; NHS; Chem A; *Comm Med Center; Nurs.*

RUSHIN, Janet Lynne
Watson Chapel HS; Pine Bluff, AR; Dbte Tm; VP, Drama; Fr C; FBLA; FHA; Thes; *Ark St U; Special Ed.*

RUSHIN, Linda Jo
Watson Chapel HS; Pine Bluff, AR (10%-308) BC; FBLA; *U of Ark, Fayetteville; Math.*

RUSHING, Deborah Jean
Granite City HS S; Granite City, IL; VP, Hmrm; Sci C; Achv A; Pres Phys Fitness A; *Belleville Area Col; Health.*

RUSHING, Donna Lee
McComb HS; McComb, MS (125-250) Band; Drama; Yth Fel; Church Chor & Ensm; *SW Jr Col; Bookkeeping.*

RUSHING, Michael Wayne
Independence HS; Charlotte, NC; Chess C; Fr C; *U of NC at Charlotte; Elec Engr.*

RUSHTON, Nanette Cecile
Hibbing HS; Hibbing, MN (233-431) Co-Ed, Sch P; Job's Daughters; *Augsburg Col; Elem Ed.*

RUSING, Randall James
Prescott HS; Prescott, AZ (98-442) CYO; VP, Key C; Ski C; Var C; Bkbl; Ftbl; Sftbl; Cpt, Tr; COM; Kiwanis A; Most Out; MVP, Tr; Vlbl; Schol A; *Bus.*

RUSK, Donna Dean
Niagara Falls HS; Niagara Falls, NY; Band; Chor; Drama; Orch; Rptr, Sch P; SC; Thes; Lion A; Swth; Lead, Play; *Anderson Ind Col; Mus.*

RUSLAND, Janet Fern
Harlingen HS; Harlingen, TX (50-629) Ann; Q&S; Leo C; *Tex A&I U; Med Tech.*

RUSNAK, Anna Maria
Riverside Jr Sr HS; Taylor, PA (8-190) Chor; Drama; Mjrte; NHS; Span C; VP, SC; Sftbl; Tr; Chem A; Hon Prog; NEDT; Drama, SC, A's; *U of Scranton; Banking & Finance.*

RUSNAK, Robert
Torrington HS; Torrington, CT (120-394) Fr C; Chaplin, VP & Tres, Yth Fel; *Mattatuck Comm Col; Med.*

RUSS, Jeanette Lynn
San Diego HS; San Diego, CA; A Cap Choir; Chldr; Chor; Drama; SC; Cpt, Tr; Cl Fav; Most Out; Yth Fel; Drill Tm; Good Citz A; *Morehouse Col.*

RUSSELL, Amy Jean
Eastern HS; Lansing, MI; Chor; Community Yth Symph; NHS; SC; COM; MVP, Co- cpt, Ten; Vlbl; *U of Mich; Pol Sci.*

RUSSELL, Amy Lynn
George Washington Sr HS; Cedar Rapids, IA (109-533) Arch; Chor; Spch C; Secy, SC; Tnns; Tr; Choir; Swimtimers; I Rating, Dist & St Spch Contest; PTSA; Iowa Naturalist; *U of Mont; Forestry.*

RUSSELL, Cathy Ann
Post Falls HS; Post Falls, ID (3-154) Chldr; SC; Pres, Jr Cl; Tr; HQn; Sal; Spch A; *N Idaho Col; Nurs.*

RUSSELL, Charmaine Dianne
Mendenhall Jr HS; Greensboro, NC (5%-400) Ann; Chldr; Co-Ed, Sch P; Citz A; Hon Prog; Opt A; Spch A; Val; Jr NHS; Stu Affairs; Film C; *Law.*

RUSSELL, Christina Fay
Potosi R-3 HS; Potosi, MO (21-211) A Cap Choir; Band; Drama; Ensm; FTA; Madrigal; NHS; Rainbow; S-T, Thes; COM; Type A; St Mus Contests; Chor; All Dist Choir; Mus Achv; *Central Methodist Col; Instrumental Mus.*

RUSSELL, Cynthia Annette
Dixon R-1 HS; Dixon, MO (17-86) Ann; Band; BC; Chor; FHA; FTA; 4H; Mod Mus Mas; Sch P; SC; 4H A; Hon Prog; Fair of Dixon; HR; *Draughon Bus Col; Med Secy.*

RUSSELL, Cynthia Elaine
Louisville HS; Louisville, OH (25%-380) Band; Dbte Tm; Ensm; FNA; NFL; Tri-HiY; Sftbl; *Baptist Bible Col; Missions.*

RUSSELL, Cynthia Louise
Tishomingo HS; Tishomingo, MS (1-33) VP, BC; Pres, Chor; Pres, FBLA; FHA; S-T, Sr Cl; B Crocker A; MLS; Val; Most Dignified Sr; Most Intellectual; Miss FBLA; 4th, St FBLA Spch; *Freed-Hardeman Col.*

RUSSELL, Cynthia Lynn
W Mid High Sch; Norman, OK; Band; Ger C; Sergeant, Police Explorer Post; 150 Hours, Hospital Auxilary; Church Chapel Choir; Jr Choir Asst; *Okla U; Law.*

RUSSELL, Dana Lynn
Mazon-Verona-Kinsman Dist 2 HS; Mazon, IL (25%-55) A-Ed, Ann; Chess C; Drama; Math C; Sch P; *Journ.*

RUSSELL, Daniel Joseph
St Peters Prep Sch; Jersey City, NJ (58-277) CYO; Cum Laude Soc; Drama; Pres, Pol Sci C; Co-Ed, Sch P; Var C; Cr-Ctry; Golf; Co-Cpt, Tnns; Tr; Cl Fav; Hist A; Most Out; NEDT; Sch Hon Pin; *Holy Cross Col; Pol Sci.*

RUSSELL, David Wayne
Memorial HS; Joplin, MO (89-245) A Cap Choir; Band; Chor; Ensm; Madrigal; Ntl Yth Conf; Bsbl; Regent Schol; Director; Yth Choir; Drum Major; Tres, Nazarene Young Peoples Soc; Cpt, Mem Yth, Christ; Quartet; *Mo Sou St Col; Mus.*

RUSSELL, Deborah Jean
Oceanside HS; Oceanside, CA (27-181) Band; Model UN; F-Ed, Sch P; Secy, Ski C.

RUSSELL, Dianne
Norwood HS; Norwood, OH (25%-500) A Cap Choir; Bus C; Chor; Swim; Tr.

RUSSELL, Elisa Jean
N Chicago Comm HS; Chicago, IL; Band; Drama; *Devry Inst; Elec.*

RUSSELL, Elizabeth Hope
Enid HS; Enid, OK (190-500) Hmrm; Span C; SC; Thes; Church Administrative Board; Cpt, Drill Tm; Offical Scorekeeper, Bkbl; *Okla St U; Fashion Merchandising.*

RUSSELL, Francis Penrose
St James Sch; St James, MD (2-30) Ski C; Ftbl; Tr; Sacristan; *Reed Col; Eng.*

RUSSELL, Gina Marie
Charlotte HS; Charlotte, MI; Ch, Band; Chor; JV, Golf; Citz A; Hon Prog; Yth Fel; *Ferris St Col; Phar.*

RUSSELL, Harlow Garfield
Neshaminy Maple Point HS; Langhorne, PA (10-413) Chess C; Chor; NHS; COM; Hon Prog; *U of Sou Calif; Archt.*

RUSSELL, Jody Lynn
S Park HS; Library, PA (6-158) Ed, Ann; Chor; Drama; Pres, Hmrm; NHS; Rptr, Sch P; Sci C; SC; Mgr, Tr; Blackbelt, ASP Soc; WW; *Calif St U; Bio.*

RUSSELL, John Cyrus
Flint Southwestern HS; Flint, MI (271-564) Chor; Var C; Bsbl; Ftbl; Superint, Sundy Sch; Vespor Choir; Pres, CYM; Soloist, Yth Choir; Del, Dist Christian Ed Conf; All-Cty 1st Tm, Hon Men, Al-Conf Fb; *Central Mich U; Communications.*

RUSSELL, Julia Morgan
Harrodsburg HS; Harrodsburg, KY (3-80) Ann; BC; Co-Cpt, Chldr; GS; Math C; NHS; DARGCA; HCt; *Centre Col; Med Field.*

RUSSELL, Julie Ann
Industry HS; Industry, IL (12-33) Band; Chldr; Chor; Drama; Fr C; SC; Secy, Soph Cl; HQn; Chldr A; WW; *W Ill U; Bus.*

RUSSELL, Karen Monica
John Marshall HS; Okla City, OK (150-480) VP, Chor; Ensm.

RUSSELL, Kathy Meshele
Geronimo HS; Geronimo, OK (6-31) FHA; Rptr, Sch P; SC; Rptr, Jr Cl; Secy, Soph Cl; COM; HQn; HR.

RUSSELL, Kimberly Ann
Chanute Sr HS; Chanute, KS; Chor; Mjrte; Bkbl; JV, Tr; Type A; HR; Drum Corps.

RUSSELL, Lamar Alan
Pass Christian HS; Pass Christian, MS (25%-110) BC; Bsbl; Ftbl; Industrial Art A; *Miss St U; Marine Bio.*

RUSSELL, Lisa Marie
Woodrow Wilson HS; Long Beach, CA (10%-750) Cpt, Chldr; InterClub Coun; Ski C; VP, SC; CSF; Hon Prog; Dance; Sycronized Swim; *Long Beach St; Criminilists.*

RUSSELL, Michael William
Pittsburgh Learning Lab Cntr; Pittsburgh, PA (2-127) All Amer Yth; Chor; Dbte Tm; Pres, Hmrm; F-Ed, Lit Mag; Pres, Math C; Co-Ch, Sch Achieve T; Arch; Co-Cpt, Ftbl; Tr; Wrest; Alg A; Bio A; Hon Prog; Journ A; Yth Foundation A; *Carnegie Mellon U; Elec.*

RUSSELL, Randy Michael
Greater Latrobe HS (7-518) NHS; Ski C; Tnns; Bausch & Lomb A; Bio A; Math A; Rensselaer A; *U of Rochester; Astrophysics.*

RUSSELL, Rebecca Pearl
Springfield S HS; Springfield, OH (30-275) Band; 4H; Orch; Swim; Symph Choir; Lib C; Lib Aide; Sr Booster Hmrm; *Clark Tech Col; Nurs.*

RUSSELL, Richard Michael
College Park HS; Pleasant Hill, CA; Order/Arrow; ARC; Sch P; Bsbl; Bkbl; Ftbl; Golf; Sftbl; Swim; Tnns; Wrest; COM; Sch Dist Camp Counselor; Bowl Tm; Teacher's Aid; Tres, Sunday Sch; S-T, Church Yth Group; Diablo Valley Col; Recreation.

RUSSELL, Robin Kelly
Lodi HS; Lodi, CA; A Cap Choir; Fin, GS; CSF; Calif Mus Ed Assn A's; San Francisco St U; Mus.

RUSSELL, Ruth Ann
Ephrata Sr HS; Ephrata, WA (11-168) Chor; Hmrm; Semi-Fin, Jr Miss Pa; NHSt; VP, Rainbow; Ch, SC; Rptr, Jr Cl; JV, Bkbl; Pres, Campfire; Pres, UMYF; U of Wash; Med.

RUSSELL, Sandra Denise
Lincoln HS; Dallas, TX; Tr; Cl Fav; Crisco A; UIL Bulletin Board; N Tex St Col; Law.

RUSSELL, Sarah Moss
Winnfield Sr HS; Winnfield, LA; Anchor C; Chldr; Dbte Tm; Fr C; FBLA; GS; Lit Ral; Spch C; Masonic A; Masque & Gavel A.

RUSSELL, Sherrie Gayle
Powell Valley HS; Speedwell, TN; VP, Band; BC; Secy, FHA; Mu Alpha Theta; Sch P; SC; Tri-HiY; Crisco A; Yth Fitness Achv A; Lincoln Mem U; Sci.

RUSSELL, Susan Virginia
Evergreen Sr HS; Evergreen, CO; Band; NHS; Orch; Colo St U; Zoology.

RUSSELL, Teresa Lee
Deshler HS; Tuscumbia, AL; Band; FBLA; FHA; Rptr, Tri-HiY; U of N Ala; Bus Ed.

RUSSELL, Terri A
N Central HS; Indianapolis, IN (802-1262) Ntl Yth Conf; Tr; IUPUI; Bus.

RUSSELL, Theresa Dianne
Union HS; Union, MS (10%-47) A-Ed, Ann; Band; BC; FHA; Rptr, Jr Cl; COM; Secy, Band Coun; Flag Corp; 1st Chair Player; Miss St U.

RUSSELL, Tim Alan
Putnam City W HS; Oklahoma City, OK; Band; Tnns; U of Tex; Bus.

RUSSELL, Travis Earl
Royal Oak HS; Covina, CA; Ski C; Cert Landscaper, A; Cert Horticulturist, A; Mount San Antonio Col; Mus.

RUSSELL, Valle Rodene
Dixon HS; Dixon, MO (3-101) Band; BC; Chldr; Chor, Secy, FHA; FTA; Fin, GS; 4H; Parl, Mod Mus Mas; SC; VP, FHA; Home Ec A'S; Band A's; FHA Christmas Qn; PA; Hon Stu; Cosmetology.

RUSSELL, William Brent
Porter HS; Maryville, TN (1-70) A-Ed, Ann; Pres, BC; Pres, 4H; Secy, Key C; Math C; Monogram; SC; Tres, Soph Cl; Bsbl; JV, Bkbl; Ftbl; 4H A; Hist A; Most Out; Sci A; Eng, Schol, A's; U of Tenn; Phar.

RUSSELL, William Elie
Northwestern HS; Rock Hill, SC (51-355) Chor; ROTC A; Winthrop Col; Bus Adm.

RUSSELL, William Roger
Powell Valley HS; Speedwell, TN; FFA; SC; Bkbl; UCLA; Communications.

RUSSELL, Yvonne Dennette
Warrensburg-Latham HS; Warrensburg, IL; FHA; Ntl Yth Conf; Var C; Tr; IUPUI Sftbl; Church Valentine Qn; Declamation, Crusader Group; First Free Will Baptist Col; Missionary.

RUSSO, Bernadette Vivian
Eastside HS; Paterson, NJ (2-850) S-T, Chess C; VP, Math C; Sci C; Brown U; Cardiovascular Surgery.

RUSSO, Glenn Mark
Holy Cross HS; Delran, NJ; Bsbl; Ftbl; Tnns; Amer Leg A; Eng Achv A; PTA General Excellence A; U of Mich; Med.

RUSSO, Ines Maria
Nuestra Senora de la Merced HS; Hato Rey, PR (5-108) Arch; Chldr; Chor; Drama; FHA; Secy, Hmrm; Arch; Alg A; Bio A; COM; Chem A; Citz A; Hist A; Hon Prog; Lion A; Math A; Most Out; Phy A; Sci A; Val; Art A; Span A; U of Puerto Rico.

RUSSO, Maria Liliana
Colegio La Merced; Hato Rey, PR (5-108) Arch; Chldr; Chor; Drama; Hmrm; SC; Arch; Bkbl; Bio A; COM; Chem A; Citz A; Hist A; Hon Prog; Lion A; Math A; Most Out; Phy A; Sci A; Spch A; Val; First A, Art Competition.

RUSSOM, Jeffery Dillion
Pattonville HS; Bridgeton, MO (5%-800) Pres, A Cap Choir; All Amer Yth; BS; Dbte Tm; Drama; Ensm; Math C; NHS; Thes; Bkbl; Tr; Most Outst Vocalist; Drawing A; Rolla Sch of Mines; Mech Engr.

RUSSOW, Lynn Ann
Cache HS; Cache, OK (20-46) Band; Rptr; BC; Rptr, FHA; Opt A; Cameron U; Elem Ed.

RUST, Christopher Vail
Enloe HS; Raleigh, NC (33%-250) Drama; Tres, VICA; Appalachian St U; Art.

RUST, Kristi Lee
Arvada HS; Aruada, CO (64-630) A Cap Choir; Chor; Thes; Choral Accompanist, Sch Musical; Sunday Sch Teacher; Manhattan Christian Col; Vocal Mus.

RUST, William Douglas
Calvin Coolidge HS; Washington, DC; Chess C; WW; George Washington U.

RUSTELKA, Stephen Frank Jr
Don Bosco Tech HS; Boston, MA (12-223) CYO; Ntl Conf Chr & Jews; NE U; Civil Engr.

RUSTIN, James Dickerson
Circleville HS; Circleville, OH; Band; Key C; Lat C; VPI; Engr.

RUSTIN, Janice Kay
Bible Baptist HS; Savannah, GA (3-34) Tres, Hmrm; Bus Mgr, Sch P; Sftbl; Armstrong St Col; Med.

RUSTIN, Jim Dickerson
Circleville HS; Circleville, OH; Band; Key C; Lat C; VPI; Engr.

RUSTIN, Mark Anderson
Circleville HS; Circleville, OH (10-206) Key C; Lat C; Lat NHS; NHS; Lt Gov Sr Yr; U of Tenn; Chem.

RUTAN, Deanna Beth
Columbus E HS; Columbus, IN; House of James Col; Beautician.

RUTH, Loranne
Sidney Comm HS; Sidney, IA (1-48) Drama; VP, FHA; Pres, 4H; Math C; SC; Bkbl; Sftbl; Tr; 4H A; HCt; I Dare You; Math A; Sftbl As; Tr As; Iowa St U; Sci.

RUTH, Tamela
Sidney Comm HS; Sidney, IA (2-47) Bus C; Chor; Pres, FHA; Pres, 4H; VP, Hmrm; Math C; Secy, NHS; VP, Sr Cl; Secy, Jr Cl; VP, Soph Cl; Cpt, Bkbl; Co-Cpt, Sftbl; Mgr, Tr; COM; Citz A; St Scholar; Type A; NW Mo St U; Acct.

RUTHART, Brenda Lee
Amarillo HS; Amarillo, TX; FHA; SC; Bkbl; Hon Prog; Rptr, Stu Body; Vlbl; Outst A, SC; Elem Ed.

RUTHERFORD, Beverly Sue
Southport HS; Indianapolis, IN (50%-500) Band; NFL; Orch; Spch C; Thes; Golf; Hon Prog; S-T, Stagecrafter; IUPUI; Bus.

RUTHERFORD, Jo Lynn
Tucker HS; Tucker, GA (30-401) Ch, Anchor C; BC; Chor; Hmrm; NHS; Gov Honor Prog; Lion A; Jr Civitan; Fin, All St Chor; Ga Tech; Industrial Mgt.

RUTHERFORD, John Steven
Robert E Lee HS; Midland, TX (180-450) Band; Ensm; Ger C; Order/Arrow; Hon Prog; Order/Arrow A; Theology.

RUTHERFORD, Julie Anne
Tucker HS; Tucker, GA (50-440) Chor; Ensm; Civitan Rep; Civitan Pageant.

RUTHERFORD, Mark David
N Ridgeville HS; N Ridgeville, OH (260-347) A Cap Choir; Chor; Cr-Ctry; Sftbl; Tr; Wrest; JA Off o-t Yr; US Air Force Acad; Elec.

RUTHERFORD, Pam
Belle Vernon Area HS; Belle Vernon, PA; Chor; Yth Fel; Pres Phys Fitness A.

RUTHERFORD, Tamela Gayle
DeRidder HS; DeRidder, LA; F-Ed, Ann; Chor; Fr C; Lit Ral; Sch P; Spch C; Lit Ral A; Computer Sci.

RUTHFORD, Ronda Rena
Steven's HS; Rapid City, SD (190-415) Ger C; Black Hills St Col; Social Work.

RUTLAND, Beverly Myran
Muscle Shoal HS; Muscle Shoals, AL; Chor; Drama; Span C; SC; Sftbl; PA; Pres Phys Fitness A; Med Training A; U of Ala; Bus.

RUTLAND, J Allison
DeLand HS; DeLand, FL (2-691) Band; Fr C; Sci C; Amer Leg A; Hon Prog; Sci A; Med.

RUTLEDGE, Billy J
Marshall HS; Marshall, MO (35-189) Sch P; Span C; SC; Var C; Cpt, Bsbl; Cpt, Bkbl; Cpt, Cr-Ctry; Tr; Pres A; Yth Fel; MVP, Bsbl; Cr-Ctry; Artist, Sch P; Hist.

RUTLEDGE, Karen Lee
W J Woodham HS; Pensacola, FL (3-530) Band; CYO; Dbte Tm; Ger C; Secy, Mu Alpha Theta; Secy, NHS; Orch; Bkbl; NEDT; Girl o-t Mo; Sewanee, Ger, A's; NC St U; Pulp & Paper Tech.

RUTLEDGE, Kimberly Jo
Mt Zion HS; Mt Zion, IL (50-300) A Cap Choir; Fin, AFS; Fin, Band; Chem C; Fin, Chor; Fin, Dbte Tm; Drama; FBLA; Fin, 4H; Fin, Madrigal; Fin, Mjrte; Sch P; Thes; Mgr, Cr-Ctry; Mgr, Tr; Chem A; 4H A; Spch A; Yth Fel; Tres, Hospital Vol; 500 Hrs, Hospital Nurs Home; Bradley U; Nurs.

RUTLEDGE, Linda Jane
Lowell HS; Lowell, MA (33-650) Chor; Fr C; Lat C; NHS; Hon Prog; Yth Fel; U of Lowell; Med.

RUTLEDGE, Lisa Carol
Franklin Road Christian Sch; Murfreesboro, TN; F-Ed, Ann; Band; BC; Chldr; Chor; Ensm; Orch; Var C; Most Out; Swtht; Yth Fel; Straight 'A' As; PA; Tenn Temple Col; Mus.

RUTLEDGE, Susan Robb
Trinity Valley Sch; Fort Worth, TX (1-28) A Cap Choir; Pres, SC; Soccer; Val; Excellence A; Service A; Newcomb Col; Mus.

RUTLEDGE, Teresa Carol
Glendale HS; Springfield, MO (64-411) SW Mo St U; Acct.

RUTZ, Joy Elaine
San Benito Joint Union HS; Hollister, CA (275-350) Chor; FHA; Pres, 4H; Sftbl; Tnns; 4H A; Sportsmanship A; CAL Ploy Col; Home Ec.

RUVARAC, Heidemarie Victoria
York Comm HS; Elmhurst, IL; Co-Ch, Drama; Semi-Fin, Bkbl; Fin, Sftbl; Northeastern U; Elem Ed.

RUZICKA, Christopher Alan
Livermore HS; Livermore, CA (75-596) Band; Fr C; Hmrm; Order/Arrow; Var C; Swim; CSF; Order/Arrow A; Eagle Sct; Optometry.

RYABIK, Jessica Marie
George C Marshall HS; Falls Church, VA (14-459) Chor; Drama; S-T, Ger C; NFL; Tres, NHS; Ski C; JV, Bkbl; Bausch & Lomb A; U of Va; Med.

RYALLS, Constance Lynn
Abington Sr HS; Abington, PA (177-893) Church Yth Group; Lib Aid; Church Girls Group; Church Singing Group; Church Activities Coun; Peirce Jr Col; Acct.

RYAN, Annie Artrue
Mount Pleasant HS; Mount Pleasant, TX (2-205) FHA; NHS; Span C; Chamber of Comm A; DARGCA; Hon Prog; Sal; Tex St Teachers Assn Schol; Coun of Church Related Sch Schol; Nike C, Girl o-t Month; Presidential Clrm; Baylor U; General Stu.

RYAN, Beth Anita
Elston Sr HS; Michigan City, IN (165-375) A Cap Choir; Chor; Ensm; Hmrm; Rptr, Sch P; SC; Thes; Bkbl; Sftbl; Win, Girls Sports Letter; Swim Timer; Acct.

RYAN, Carolyn Jean
Peebles HS; Peebles, OH (1-90) Band; Chldr; Drama; Sch Achieve Tm; Co-Ed, Sch P; Rptr, SC; Sftbl; Tr; COM; Q&S A; Type A; Pep C; Vlbl; Spelling Bee A; WW.

RYAN, Catherine Joyce
H V Jenkins HS; Savannah, GA (25-322) BC; Span
C; SC; Span A; Adult Choir; Yth Choir; Candystri-
per; Most Dependable; Best Christian Examp;
Most Talented; Handbell Choir; Friendliest; *Mus
Ed.*

RYAN, Connie Jo
Peebles HS; Peebles, OH (1-109) VP, Band; Sch
Achieve Tm; Sch P; Tres, Sr Cl; Secy, Jr Cl; Cpt,
Bkbl; Co-Cpt, Sftbl; Cpt, Tr; Beauty; COM; H of F;
Most Out; Val; Cpt, Vlbl; All League Bkbl; Chieftan
Qn; Women Sports Athlete o-t Yr; All Amer Tr A;
Morehead St U; Phys Ed.

RYAN, Deborah Anne
Clyde Sr HS; Clyde, OH; A Cap Choir; Ann; Band;
Co-Cpt, Chldr; Chor; Ensm; 4H; Var C; Tr; Pres,
Luther League; Teen Tuners; Pep Band; Wind
Symph; Stage Band; Lib C.

RYAN, Della Mary
Thomas Kelly HS; Chicago, IL (17-485) Chor;
Drama; Model UN; NHS; *Writing.*

RYAN, James A
Ft Pierce Central HS; Ft Pierce, FL (18-520) *Automotive Engr.*

RYAN, James C
Southside HS; Elmira, NY (5%-450) Band; NHS;
Pres, Order/Arrow; Parl, Jr Cl; Parl, Soph Cl; Or-
der/Arrow A.

RYAN, Joseph Michael
Brooke HS; Wellsburg, WV (13-500) Tres, Hmrm;
Ski C; Span C; SC; *W Va U.*

RYAN, Judy Ann
McHenry HS W; McHenry, IL (54-584) A Cap
Choir; Band; Drama; Ensm; Mod Mus Mas; Span
C; Jazz Band; *Drama.*

RYAN, Kathleen Ann
Msgr Ryan HS; Dorchester, MA; Tres, Chor; Pres,
Lit Ral; SC; Bkbl; Hon Prog; *Thomas Col; Acct.*

RYAN, Kathy Ann
Seton HS; Cincinnati, OH; F-Ed; Ann; Hmrm;
ARC; Sci C; SC; Soccer; Hon Prog; *U of Cincinnati;
Nurs.*

RYAN, Lisa Anne
Coventry HS; Coventry, RI (5-400) Band; Secy,
NHS; SC; Sftbl; Tnns; COM; Hon Prog; Church
Choir & Teacher; Span A; *Pre-Med.*

RYAN, Mary Pat
Mercy HS; Albany, NY (20-108) CYO; Hmrm;
InterAct C; Lat C; SC; Sftbl; Hon Prog; Regent
Schol; Ntl Essay Contest; 20 Mile Walkathon;
Maua Col; Occupational Therapist.

RYAN, Matthew Victor
Prescott HS; Prescott, AZ (1-462) InterAct C; JV,
Bkbl; JV, Ftbl; Alg A; Bio A; Lion A; Math A; Sci
A; Outst Fresh Acad Ath A.

RYAN, Michael Patrick
Washington HS; Massillon, OH (5%-612) A Cap
Choir; Chor; Pres, Ger C; Pres, Soph Cl; *Kent St U;
Law Enforcement.*

RYAN, Susan Frances
Spring Woods Sr HS; Houston, TX (10%-510)
Chldr; NHS; SC; Miss Jr Cl; Safari Spotlight; *U of
Texas.*

RYAN, Thomas Wellington
S Charleston HS; S Charleston, WV (50-294) ARC;
Span C; Bus Mgr, SC; Bkbl; Ftbl; Tnns; God &
Country A; VP, JA; Grand Prize, Arts & Craft Fair;
W Va U; Civil Engr.

RYBERG, Mary Jane
N Shore HS; W Palm Beach, FL (2-353) Fr C;
InterClub Coun; Key C; Alg A; COM; *Forestry.*

RYDE, Thomas Carl
Robinson HS; Santurce, PR (3-38) Pres, Math C;
Pres, Mu Alpha Theta; NHS; Pol Sci C; SC; Parl, Sr
Cl; Tres, Soph Cl; Bsbl; Ftbl; Wrest; Hon Prog;
Math A; NEDT; Yth Fel; *Elec Engr.*

RYDEN, Thomas Harald
Andover HS; Andover, MA (74-529) Co-Ch, AFS;
Sch P; Pres, Photography C; *Rensselaer Polytech
Inst; Engr.*

RYDER, Christopher John
Dover HS; Dover, NH (1-397) Ed, Ann; BS; Chess
C; Secy, Key C; Mu Alpha Theta; NHS; Order/
Arrow; SC; Cr-Ctry; Tr; COM; MLS; Most Out;
Ntl Sci Found; Order/Arrow A; High Scorer, St
Math Contest; *Biol.*

RYDING, Jeanette Marie
Havre HS; Havre, MT (50-250) A-Ed, Ann; Chess
C; Chor; Drama; A-Ed, Sch P; Spch C; Thes;
Northern Mont Col; Secretarial.

RYDING, Mark Allen
Havre HS; Havre, MT (50-257) Band; Order/
Arrow; Thes; *Mont St U; Elec Engr.*

RYE, Melanie Dawn
Bartlett HS; Bartlett, TN (90-280) Bus C; Span C;
Y-Tns; Most Outst Bus Stu; *Miller Hawkins Col;
Bus.*

RYGH, Shereen Rae
Turtle Lake-Mercer HS; Turtle Lake, ND (8-30)
Ann; Band; Chem C; Chor; Ensm; FHA; JETS; Sch
P; Var C; Co-Cpt, Bkbl; Mgr, Tr; Hon Prog; Sci A;
Yth Fel; *ND St U; Psych.*

RYLEE, Terry Steven
Fitzgerald HS; Fitzgerald, GA; Chor; All St Chor;
Ga Tech; Acting.

RYMER, Diane Kay
Bradshaw Mountain HS; Dewey, AZ (2-60) Secy,
Band; Chor; NHS; Span C; Secy, SC; Mgr, Sftbl;
COM; Hon Prog; Poet A; Type A; VFW A; Vof-
DEM; Cpt, Vlbl; Pom-Pon; Band, Vlbl, A's; *Vet
Sci.*

RYNELL, Terri Lane
John H Reagan HS; Houston, TX (10-350) Co-Ch,
Hmrm; SC; VP, Soph Cl; COM; Most Out; *U of
Houston; Nurs.*

RYOR, Katherine Anne
Winston Churchill HS; Potomac, MD (10%-576)
Chldr; NHS; ARC; Tri-HiY; Secy, Soph Cl; *U of
Md; Nurs.*

RYPCHINSKI, Polli Joan
Bayshore HS; Bradenton, FL (32-250) Anchor C;
Band; Drama; Tres, NHS; *Trevecca Nazarene Col;
Special Ed.*

RYPKEMA, Yon Peter
Northstar Christian Acad; Rochester, NY (3-6)
Pres, Chor; Pres, Hmrm; Rptr, Sch P; Ski C; Pres,
Sr Cl; Most All Around; Most Improved; *Massillon
Baptist Col; Ministry.*

RYSAVY, Robin Marie
Raytown S HS; Raytown, MO (45-583) A Cap
Choir; Band; Chor; Ensm; Madrigal; NHS; Orch;
Sch P; Sftbl; PTA A; Regent Schol; Type A; WW;
Mus Schol; Church Campus A; Academic Schol;
SW Baptist Col; Ed Mus.

RYSTROM, Marcia Lynn
Columbus Sr HS; Columbus, NE (40-275) Chor;
JV, Bkbl; JV, Tnns; *U of Nebr; Med Tech.*

RYU, Wang Yong
Fort Lee HS; Fort Lee, NJ; Wrest; Bio A; Citz A;
Hon Prog; Math A; *Columbia Col; Bus.*

RZESZUTKO, Rhonda Marie
Kelly HS; Chicago, IL (6-689) Band; Chor; Drama;
Ensm; Math C; NHS; Orch; Span NHS; Thes;
Tnns; Hon Prog; Journ A; Q&S A; Yrbook Publica-
tions; WW; Mus Solo, Ensm As; Tnns A; *DePaul
U; Math.*

S

SAAB, Albert Jr
Canton Acad; Canton, MS (2-100) Pres, BC; Ch,
CYO; Pres, NHS; Sci C; Span C; Pres, Soph Cl;
Ftbl; Alg A; COM; Hist A; Math A; Sal; Lion's
Honoree; Beau; *Miss St U; Pre-Med.*

SAAB, Joseph Girard
Canton Acad; Canton, MS (28-85) CYO; 4H; JV,
Bkbl; JV, Ftbl; Tnns; HCt; *U of Miss; Bus Mgt.*

**SAALMAN,
Jacqueline Sue Grace**
Coldwater HS; Coldwater, OH (20-165) Band;
CYO; Chor; Drama; Ensm; FTA; Orch; F-Ed, Sch
P; Span C; Spch C; Var C; Tnns; Mgr, Tr; God &
Country A; HCt; Journ A; Opt Out Tn; PTA A;
VofDEM; Piano Solo A; Miami U; Eng.

SAAVEDRA, Ivan Miguel
Colegio San Antonio; Isabela, PR (8-33) Band;
Dbte Tm; Drama; Orch; Span C; Bsbl; Fin, Bkbl;
Sftbl; Swim; COM; Hon Prog; *U of Puerto Rico.*

SABACKY, Julie Ann
Litchfield Sr HS; Litchfield, MN (33%-200) Band;
Ger C; Secy, SC; Candy Striper.

SABANSKI, Karen Lynn
Eastbrook HS; Marion, IN (35-200) Band; Hmrm;
Mjrte; SC; Rptr, Jr Cl; JV, Tr.

SABATELLI, Frank Willard
Notre Dame HS; Clarksburg, WV (3-63) Band;
Dbte Tm; Drama; Ensm; VP, Fr C; FBLA; Key C;
Pres, Lat C; Lat NHS; Lit Mag; Secy, Math C;
Secy, Sci C; Tres, Spch C; Ch, SC; Pres, Jr Cl; Pres,
Soph Cl; Cpt, Tnns; Sacristan; Sci A; VFW A; Vof-
DEM; Best, Acting A; Lat A; Semi Fin, Performing
Arts; Semi Fin, St Cath Forensic.

SABATINI, Pamela Kay
Saint Joseph's Notre Dame HS; Alameda, CA
(3-55) Chor; NHS; ARC; Sci C; VP, Span C; CSF;
COM; Citz A; Hist A; Hon Prog; NEDT; Religion
A; Span A; *Calif St U at Chico; Hist.*

SABBATH, Marjorie Ann
Sumner HS; Saint Louis, MO; *Maryville Col; Elec
Cordic Tech.*

SABIN, Kathleen Eleanor
Kingsway Regional HS; Swedesboro, NJ (25-165)
Arch; NHS; Yth Fel; Yrbk Staff; WW; *The King's
Col.*

SABLAN, Rose Borja
Castle Park HS; Chula Vista, CA (108-400) Ed,
Ann; Chldr; Pres, Hmrm; ARC; SC; Y-Tns; Citz A;
HCt; JA A; Kiwanis A; Masonic A; Pres A; WW; *U
of Hawaii; Spch Pathology.*

SABO, Dave C
Chardon HS; Chardon, OH; 4H; Hmrm; Order/
Arrow; Ski C; SC; Bsbl; Bkbl; Ftbl; Soccer; Tr; Jr
Deacon; Umpire, Little League.

SABO, Dusty E
Chardon HS; Chardon, OH (2-250) Band; Drama;
4H; Hmrm; Order/Arrow; Ski C; SC; Bsbl; Ftbl;
Soccer; Tr; Wrest; Jr Deacon; Life Sct; Staff, BSct
Camp; Little League Umpire.

SACCA, Thomas George
Callaway HS; Jackson, MS (50%-450) A Cap
Choir; Chor; Drama; Ensm; Thes; Bsbl; Cl Fav;
HCt; *Miss St U; Law.*

SACHS, Joan Adele
Perry Meridian HS; Indianapolis, IN (1-546) Secy,
Band; Ensm; Lat C; NHS; Orch; Phys C; Swim;
NEDT; Phi Beta Kappa; ARC A; Rotary A;
Summa Cum Laude; Val; Yth Fel; *Ind Central U.*

SACHS, Meredith Anne
Central HS; Springfield, MO (4-307) Chor; Com-
munity Yth Symph; Drama; Ensm; Fr C; Hmrm;
Madrigal; Math C; Orch; SC; Thes; Citz A; Inter-
lochen Ntl Mus; Kiwanis A; Math A; VFW A;
VofDEM; Yth Leg; Yth Talent Auditions Win;
HR; Symph Orch; Drum Corps; 1st, Mus Festival;
World Yth Orch; Ntl Piano Guild; *U of Mich; Mus.*

SACKETT, Sally Jean
Tehachapi HS; Tahachapi, CA (10-180) Ch, Model
UN; Ski C; Cpt, Bkbl; MVP, Vlbl; Outst Fresh A,
Eng, Math. Home Ec.

SACKS, Suzanne Carol
N Harford Sr HS; Pylesville, MD; Ger C; Pres, 4H;
Ed, Sch P; Parl, SC; Stu Coun A; *U of Md; Studio
Art.*

SADBERRY, Eva Janece
Salinas HS; Salinas, CA; A Cap Choir; Chor; Hon
Prog.

SADIK, Tracey Blair
Watertown HS; Watertown, CT (61-313) AFS;
Band; Secy, Church Yth Group; *Journ.*

SADLER, Cynthia Lorraine
Antelope Valley HS; Lancaster, CA (71-700) NHS; Span C; *Merit Col of Court Reporting; Court Reporter.*

SADLER, Donald Paul
Vicksburg HS; Vicksburg, MS (10-244) AFS; Lat C; Math C; NHS; Math A; NEDT; Opt A; *U of Sou Miss; Pol Sci.*

SADLER, Rory Dee
Anna-Jonesboro Comm HS; Anna, IL (4-150) Ed, Ann; BC; Drama; Fr C; FTA; Key C; NFL; NHS; Ed, Sch P; COM; Hon Prog; Q&S A; Excel, Prose; Prom Decorating Committee; Excel, Reader's Theater; *U of Hawaii; Law.*

SAENZ, Minerva
Whiteface HS; Whiteface, TX; Ann; Band; Ensm; FHA; VP, Jr Cl; Bkbl; Tr; Amer Leg A; A-HR; Scholastic Fav; Soph Schol; *S Plains Jr Col; Secretarial Work.*

SAENZ, Roel Armando
Roma HS; Roma, TX (12-180) Band; NHS; SC; Pres, Soph Cl; COM; MLS; *U of Tex; Law.*

SAENZ, Virginia Diane
Dwight D Eisenhower HS; Rialto, CA (1-808) InterClub Coun; SC; Pres, Sr Cl; Tnns; Alg A; Amer Leg A; CSF; Elk A; Hon Prog; Masonic A; St Scholar; Val; All CBL Stu; Calif St Senate Yth Program; VP, Sobobans; Statistician, Bkbl.

SAFFELL, Glenna Jean
New Lexington Sr HS; New Lexington, OH (63-178) Band; Chor; Ensm; Fr C; Pres, 4H; Orch; Rainbow; ARC; Amer Leg A; COM; 4H A; Masonic A; ARC A; Yth Fel; *Ohio U; Nurs.*

SAFFELL, Kent Leon
A C Davis Sr HS; Yakima, WA (9-552) Band; BS; Chor; NHS; Sch P; COM; Masonic A; Outst, Mus; Eng Achv A; *NW Nazarene Col.*

SAFFELL, Lusty Ann
Sanger HS; Sanger, CA; Rptr, Sch P; Pres, Church Yth; Jr Schol; *Bus.*

SAFFELL, Montey Ray
Sanger HS; Sanger, CA; FFA; *Reedley Jr Col; Forestry.*

SAFFORD, Annella Marie
Ogemaw Heights HS; W Branch, MI; JV, Chldr; Chor; NHS; S-T, Soph Cl; S-T, Var C; Cpt, Bkbl; Sftbl; Tr; MVP, All Conf, All St, Bkbl; All Conf Sftbl & Vlbl; *Mich St U.*

SAFLEY, Brian William
Cottage Grove HS; Cottage Grove, OR (12-225) A Cap Choir; Chor; NHS; Var C; Bkbl; Ftbl; Golf; Tr; Ldrship, Underclman, A's; Co-Cpt, Outst Sr, A's; *U of Oreg; Elem Ed.*

SAFREND, Casey Douglas
Amador Valley HS; Pleasanton, CA (1-414) CYO; Chess C; Pres, 4H; Math C; Model UN; NHS; Ski C; Span C; VP, SC; Var C; VP, Sr Cl; VP, Soph Cl; Fin, Arch; Cr-Ctry; Tr; Alg A; Bank Of Amer A; CSF; Cr-Ctry; Coun of Teach A; 4H A; HCt; Hon Prog; Math A; MLS; Most Out; Ntl Achv Schol; Phy A; Pres A; Rotary A; Val; Yth Leg; Math Excellence; Cr-Ctry A; Most Outst Sr; Gabrillo C A; *Stanford U; Econ.*

SAFRENO, Casey Douglas
Amador Valley HS; Pleasanton, CA (1-414) CYO; Pres, 4H; Ski C; Span C; VP, SC; Var C; VP, Soph Cl; Arch; Cr-Ctry; Tr; Bank Of Amer A; CSF; COM; Cl Fav; 4H A; Hon Prog; Math A; MLS; Most Out; Rotary A; Val; Cabrillo Civics C A; Jr Ldr, 4-H; *Stanford U; Econ.*

SAFSTROM, Richard Paul
Niles W HS; Skokie, IL (50%-550) Band; Chor; Fr C; SC; Var C; Bkbl; Cpt, Tr; Amer Leg A; COM; Tr A; Bkbl Ltr; 2nd Male Voice, Talents for Christ; Co Championship Monogram; Mus A for Band; *Faith Baptist Bible Col; Bible.*

SAGA, Lorene Carol
Mentor Pub HS; Mentor, MN (4-19) Band; Chldr; Chor; FHA; NHS; Sch P; Pres, SC; Pres, Jr Cl; Mgr, Bkbl; *Bemidji St U; Law Enforcement.*

SAGE, Debrah Ann
Buena HS; Sierra Vista, AZ (126-515) A Cap Choir; Tres, Chor; Ensm; Model UN; Bkbl; *San Jose Bible Col; Mus.*

SAGEN, Lisa Renee
Eastern Hills HS; Ft Worth, TX (1-480) Ann; NHS; Sftbl; COM; Hon Prog; Summa Cum Laude; Amer Assn of U Women A; Eng A; *Stephen F Austin St U; Eng.*

SAGER, Daniel Swink
Ashland Sr HS; Ashland, OR (10%-250) Band; Demolay; Fr C; Hmrm; NHS; Var C; JV, Bkbl; Soccer; JV, Tnns; Most Out.

SAGER, Harold J
Port HS; Port Washington, WI (18-250) Chor; Drama; Orch; *Julliard Col; Mus.*

SAGER, Vicky Jean
Kalama HS; Kalama, WA (30-60) Ann; Chldr; Chor; Spch C; Var C; Cpt, Bkbl; Sftbl; HCt; Pep C Ltr; Bkbl Ltr; *Bus.*

SAGER, William Jeffrey
New Miami HS; New Miami, OH (8-73) FFA; Span C; Tr; Cl Fav; *Muskingum Area Tech Col; Conservation.*

SAGERS, Veronica Yvette
Southwest HS; Atlanta, GA; BC; Dbte Tm; Mjrte; Hon Prog; Gifted Cl EIE; Yth Choir.

SAGESER, Lee Ann
Cotton Center HS; Cotton Center, TX (1-16) Chldr; Dbte Tm; Pres, FHA; Secy, 4H; Rainbow; SC; VP, Jr Cl; VP, Soph Cl; JV, Bkbl; Cl Fav; 4H A; Type A; Yth Fel; *Tex Tech U.*

SAGESTER, Terri Lynne
Lake Taylor Sr HS; Norfolk, VA; F-Ed, ·Ann; FBLA; FHA; Hmrm; S-T, NHS; Sch P; Tres, SC; VP, Soph Cl; Tnns; COM; H of F; Sci A; Yth Fel; Keyettes; Placement, Health Fair; Hermitage A; Cl Off; SCA; Art.

SAGLIOCCO, Joseph Giulio
St Peters Prep HS; Jersey City, NJ (24-259) Pres, Hmrm; SC; Soccer; Hon Prog; Silver Medal Italian A; *Rutgers U; Engr.*

SAHLBERG, Jeffrey Lee
Chrysler HS; New Castle, IN (14-390) BS; Chess C; Lat C; NHS; Cpt, Swim; JV, Tnns; Sal; *Miami U; Bus.*

SAHLIE, Virginia
The Montgomery Acad; Montgomery, AL (30-45) Rptr, Ann; Hmrm; S-T, Span C; Mgr, Bkbl; HCt; Vlbl; *Miss U For Women; Fashion Merchandising.*

SAHMS, Diane Lynne
Roxborough HS; Philadelphia, PA (10-450) Chor; FTA; Hmrm; NHS; Pres, Rainbow; Pres, Var C; Co-Cpt, Hockey; JV, Sftbl; COM; Citz A; HCt; Hon Prog; Most Out; PTA A; Pres A; Yth Fel; Photographer, Sch Paper; Cpt & MVP, Gym; City Coun Cert; Ath Ldrship; Miss Roxborough; Outst Accomplishments; *E Stroudsburg St U; Phys Ed.*

SAHR, Jean Marie
Newman HS; Wausau, WI; Band; Ger C; *Photography.*

SAHR, Michael James
Dixie Hollins HS; Pinellas Park, FL; JV, Bsbl; *Pensacola Christian Col; Coaching.*

SAIKI, Linda Naomi
Maryknoll HS; Honolulu, HI (20-110) Chldr; S-T, Hmrm; NHS; Tnns; JA A; Pres, Japanese C; Japanese A; Intersch; Bowl; *U of Hawaii; Nurs.*

SAILER, Cynthia Ann
Stanton HS; Stanton, ND; Band; Chldr; Chor; Ensm; S-T, Soph Cl; Bkbl; Hon Prog; Band As; Chor As; Chldr As; *SD Col; Airline Stewardist.*

SAILER, Paul Andrew
Patterson HS; Patterson, CA (33%-190) Band; Ensm; Bsbl; Ftbl; MVP Trophy, Bsbl; *Calif Lutheran Col; Phys Ed.*

SAILER, Sharon Rae
Hazen Pub HS; Hazen, ND; Band; Chor; Ensm; VP, FHA; GS; Tres, 4H; 4H A.

SAILORS, Donna Lynn
Shamrock HS; Decatur, GA (25-310) BC; Chldr; FBLA; S-T, FHA; Pres, Hmrm; Sch P; Span C; Span A; All St, Drill Tm; Swtht, Home Room; Civitan C; Drill Tm; Office, Interntl Activities; *Sociology.*

SAIN, Kathryn Ann
W Lincoln HS; Lincolnton, NC (7-120) A Cap Choir; Band; BC; Chor; Hmrm; Cpt, Mjrte; Sftbl; Chor Merit A; *Marhill Col; Mus.*

SAINE, Deborah Jean
W Lincoln Sr HS; Lincolnton, NC (1-150) Pres, BC; Co-Ed, Lit Mag; Sci C; Q&S A; Val; Yth Fel; Most Intellectual; Schol A; *Appalachian St U; Special Ed.*

SAINT, Barbara Faye
Carrollton HS; Carrollton, GA (23-130) A Cap Choir; Ann; Band; BC; Chor; Dbte Tm; Secy, FTA; Lit Mag; Sch P; Sci C; Spch C; Hon Prog; Ga Sci Sym; *W Ga Col; Mus.*

SAINT PAUL, Nanette Paulette
Adlai Stevenson HS; New York, NY; Band; Orch; Tnns; Hon Prog; *Psych.*

SAINT PAUL, Odette
Adlai E Stevenson HS; New York, NY; Cpt, Chor; Law.

SAINZ de la PENA,
Lourdes Maria
Academia Maria Reina; Rio Piedras, PR; Chldr; Chor; Drama; Pres, Hmrm; ARC; Sci C; Span C; SC; Pres, Sr Cl; Swim; COM; Hon Prog; *Universidad de Puerto Rico; Sci.*

SAITO, Steven Manabu
Payette HS; Payette, ID (13-108) Band; BS; Chem C; Chess C; JETS; Key C; Math C; Sci C; Ski C; Var C; Bkbl; Tnns; John Philip Sousa Band A; *Oreg St U; Agr.*

SAITO, Valaine Naru
Kubasaki HS; Okinawa, JAPAN (8-355) Mgr, Bkbl; Math A; Eng A; *Computer Sci.*

SAKAI, James J
Kubasaki HS; Okinawa, JAPAN (20-271) Hmrm; NHS; SC; Ftbl; MVP, Soccer; MVP, Wrest; Cl Fav; *Calif; Aviation.*

SAKALA, James Mark
Manchester HS; Manchester, GA; Chor; *Upson Tech U.*

SAKALES, Stephanie Olga
Packer Collegiate Inst; Brooklyn, NY (10-50) Sch P; Sci C; Span C; JV, Bkbl; Sftbl; *Fordham U; Child Study.*

SAKAMOTO, Steve Masaru
Kohala HS; Kapaau, HI (1-76) Chess C; Tres, FFA; Hmrm; Model UN; NHS; Tres, SC; *U of Hawaii; Computer Programming.*

SAKATA, Ross Sakae
Kailua HS; Kailua, HI; HiY; SC; Tri-HiY; Y-Tns; Pres, Jr Cl; Tnns; Tr; COM; MLS; Most Out; Yth Leg; Vlbl; Hugh O'Brien Nom.

SAKRISMO, Stephen Jon
Ulen-Hitterdal HS; Ulen, MN (3-46) Pres, FFA; NHS; SC; Ftbl; Tr; Writing A; HR; St FFA Judging Tm; Hog Production; Regional FFA A; *Bemidji U.*

SALA, Beth Ann
Kinnelon HS; Kinnelon, NJ; Band; Chor; Ensm; Lit Mag; Sch P; Mgr, Cr-Ctry; Tr; COM; Congressional Intern; High Hons; *Law.*

SALANDY, Sherill Ann
Greater New York Acad; Brooklyn, NY (46-73) A Cap Choir; Sch P; Bkbl; *Oakwood Col; Secretarial Sci.*

SALAS, Cynthia Martinez
Millbrook Sr HS; Raleigh, NC; MVP, Vlbl; VP, Church Yth Fel; *Wake Tech Col; Art.*

SALATA, Debbie Ann
St Pius X HS; Albuquerque, NM (80-205) Band; CYO; Chldr; Chor; Secy, Hmrm; SC; Cpt, Bkbl; Cl Fav; Hon Prog; Pres A; JV, Vlbl; MVP, Bkbl; *Phys Ed.*

SALAY, Gene Paul
Arlington HS; Pleasant Valley, NY (520-950) Hon Prog; Cpt, Semi- fin, Bible Quiz Tm; Top Quizzer, Bible Quiz League; Hon Men, Co Sci Fair; *Sci.*

SALAY, Valerie Jeanne
Arlington Sr HS; Poughkeepsie, NY (20%-200) A-Ed, Lit Mag; Hon Prog; NMS; Regent Schol; *Oral Roberts U; Biol.*

SALAZAR, Juaquin Larry
Holbrook HS; Holbrook, AZ (21-200) Band; CYO; Chor; Math C; Mgr, Bkbl; Hon Prog; Type A; *Engr.*

SALAZAR, Loyda A
Music and Art HS; New York, NY (243-512) Chldr; MVP, Chor; Fr C; Secy, Hmrm; Semi-Fin, Jr Miss Pa; Rptr, Mjrte; Secy, Span C; Spch C; Rptr, Sr Cl; Bsbl; Cpt, Sftbl; MVP, Swim; Fin, Tr; Beauty; Cl Fav; God & Country A; I Dare You; MLS; Most Out; Odd Fellow Fin; Swtht; *The City Col of New York; Ed.*

SALAZAR, Mary Lisa
Holbrook HS; Holbrook, AZ (42-214) Bus C; VP, CYO; FBLA; Type A; HR; *Pepperdine U; Bus Mgt.*

SALAZAR, Paula Sue
Santa Fe HS; Alachua, FL (10%-175) BC; FBLA; FFA; *Santa Fe Comm Col; Bus.*

SALCHLI, Stanley Agee
Franklin Co HS; Frankfort, KY; Band; Ensm; 4H; Key C; Span C; 4H A; *U of Ky.*

SALCIDO, Albert Ivan
San Jose HS; San Jose, CA; SC; VP, Soph Cl; *San Jose City Col; Bus Adm.*

SALEH, Magda Gabra
Hillcrest HS; Dallas, TX; Chor; FHA; VP, Span C; Sftbl; Sportsmanship A; *Computer Tech.*

SALES, Lisa VeAnne
Westinghouse HS; Pittsburgh, PA (28-302) Chor; FHA; Secy, ARC; Rptr, Sch P; Hon Prog; Pride Contest; *Fisk U; Child Psych.*

SALETT, Kim Yvette
Jane Adams HS; Cleveland, OH;

SALGE, Dawn Marie
Canyon HS; New Braunfels, TX; Band; Ger C; 4H; Ski C; Bsbl.

SALHA, Rhett Herman
Los Banos HS; Los Banos, CA (30-230) Ch, Band; CYO; Ensm; Orch; Bsbl; Cpt, Bkbl; Sftbl; Bank Of Amer A; HKg; Kiwanis A; Lion A; *Fresno St U; Acct.*

SALINA, Deborah Arlene
Indian Valley Jr HS; Midvale, OH; Band; Bus C; Chor; Ensm; FTA; Span C; *Jefferson Tech Inst; Dental Asst.*

SALINAS, Alma Jean
Ingleside HS; Ingleside, TX (9-76) Pres, Band; CYO; Ensm; Tres, NHS; Sch P; John Philip Sousa A; All-Dist Band; LULAC Schol A; *Del Mar Jr Col; Mus.*

SALINAS, Blanca Estela
St Augustine Sch; Laredo, TX (8-68) Ann; Drama; Tres, NHS; Cpt, Bkbl; MVP, Bkbl; Most Ath; WW; Presidential Clrm For Young Amer; *UT at Austin; Architecture.*

SALINAS, Leticia Marie
Mem HS; San Antonio, TX (4-300) VP, NHS; Rptr, Span NHS; *St Phillips Col; Retarded Ed.*

SALISBURY, Jeffrey Dean
Campbell Central Sch; Campbell, NY; VP, Var C; Cpt, Bsbl; Cr-Ctry; Soccer.

SALISBURY, Vicki Sue
Putnam City HS; Oklahoma City, OK (50%-1135) Band; Drama; SC; Thes; World Affairs C; Touring Choir; Flute Talent Contest; Officer, Sunday Sch; *U of Tex; Child Psych.*

SALJIAN, George Vincent
American HS; Fremont, CA (180-365) Var C; Cpt, Bsbl; Bkbl; MVP, Bsbl; Phys Ed A; *Ohlone Jr Col; Bus.*

SALLADE, Mendy Renee
The Andrews Sch; Willoughby, OH (15-45) Fr C; A-Ed, Sch P; Hon Men, Co Schol Art A's; *Moody Bible Inst; Communications.*

SALLEE, Donald Bruce
Winona HS; Winona, MO (2-23) Co-Ed, Ann; BC; FBLA; Hon Stu; *Southwest Mo St U; Phar.*

SALLENAVE, Rossana Mary
Alexander Galt Regional HS; Lennoxville, CAN-ADA (8-539) Co-Ch, Band; Hmrm; Lat C; NHS; SC; Bkbl; Cr-Ctry; Hockey; Swim; Tr; Hon Prog; Jr Eng A.

SALLEY, Kathy Colleen
Rivers HS; Charleston, SC; SC; 1st Pl, Miss Yrbk; Baptist Col; Elem Ed.

SALLSTROM, Steven Allen
Winthrop Comm Sch; Winthrop, MN (2-66) Band; Chor; Drama; Ensm; FFA; Pres, 4H; Madrigal; NHS; Cpt, Bkbl; Ftbl; Tr; B Crocker A; 4H A; Hon Prog; NMS; Sal; Dist & St Stars, Mus; Player o-t Wk, Ftbl; *Carleton Col; Math.*

SALMEN, Joseph Claire
Columbiana HS; Columbiana, OH; Ann; Fr C; ARC; Sch P; Bkbl; Ftbl; Tr; *Youngstown St U; Phar.*

SALMESTRELLI, Bruce Paul
St Marys Manor Marist Prep; Penndel, PA (1-13) CYO; Chor; Hist A; Hon Prog; Math A; Sci A; Eng A; Dramatics A; Stu Librarian A; Stu Service A; *Loyola U; Hist.*

SALMON, Brent Dale
Pontotoc HS; Pontotoc, MS (10-150) BC; Pres, Span C; Citz A.

SALMON, James Frederick
Mt Whitney HS; Visalia, CA; A Cap Choir; Chor; Ensm; *Mus.*

SALMONS, Beth Ann
Grove City HS; Grove City, OH (240-500) A Cap Choir; Band; Chor; FTA; Ger C; SC; Y-Tns; *Ohio St U; Mus Ed.*

SALMONS, Richard Waring Jr
St James Sch; St James, MD (6-26) Ann; Dbte Tm; Pres, Drama; Pres, Lit Ral; Pres, SC; Var C; Pres, Sr Cl; Soccer; Sacristan; Hon Coun; Noble C Powell Prize; Co-Cpt, La Crosse; 'Willingness to Serve' A; Excel in Sacred Stu Prize; *Washington And Lee U; Law.*

SALMONS, Susan Joy
Stanton HS; Stanton, NE (1-46).

SALPINI, Kirk Alan
Oakton HS; Vienna, VA (136-522) Band; Hmrm; Key C; Model UN; JV, Bkbl; Tnns; Tr; BSA; Graduation Comm; Independent Stu in Eng; All Star Bkbl Trophy; *James Madison U; Bus Mgt.*

SALTARELLI, Mario David
E Peoria Comm HS; E Peoria, IL (2-512) AFS; Chem C; Chess C; Fr C; Hmrm; InterClub Coun; Lat C; Order/Arrow; ARC; Ed, Sch P; St Stu Congress; VP, SC; Y-Tns; Pres, Jr Cl; Pres, Soph Cl; Hon Prog; Order/Arrow A; Yth Foundation A; Eagle Sct; Ad Altare Dei; *U of Ill; Med.*

SALTARELLI, Matthew Gerard
Cleveland Hill HS; Cheektowaga, NY (16-242) VP, NHS; Bsbl; Bkbl; Ftbl; Hockey; A of Excellence; High Scholastic Rating; Latin, Classic As of Westrn NY Hon; *Med.*

SALTER, Carol Jean
Aiken Sr HS; Cincinnati, OH (1-13) Band; Chem C; NHS; Sch Achieve Tm; Span C; Triple A; Sr Mo; 1st Pl, VICA; *Med Lab Tech.*

SALTER, Charles Theodore Jr
Cathedral Prep Sem; Ny, NY (3-20) CYO; Chor; Dbte Tm; Drama; Ensm; NFL; Sch P; Span C; SC; Cpt, Bkbl; Ftbl; Hockey; Cpt, Tr; COM; Hist A; Hon Prog; Journ A; PTA A; Sacristan; Spch A; Instructional TV; Lat, Eng, A's; Marine Corps Phys Fitness, A; *Dickinson Col; Hist.*

SALTER, Darryl Wesley
West Side HS; Gary, IN (50-700) Band; Fr C; French NHS; NHS; COM; Citz A; JA A; Most Out; BSct; *Purdue U; Engr.*

SALTER, Mary Linden
Nevada HS; Nevada, MO (21-164) Band; Chor; Semi-Fin, GS; NHS; Rainbow; Ed, Sch P; Thes; Hon Prog; NMS; Regent Schol; GSct; SB Ex-Offio, City Planning Comm; *Kans U; Archt.*

SALTER, Todd Michael
Fremont Christian Acad; E Syracuse, NY (1-3) Ch, Ann; Chor; Drama; Rptr, Sch P; VP, SC; Var C; Bkbl; Ftbl; Sftbl; COM; Citz A; Journ A; Yth Fel; St Realtors Citz A; St Talents for Christ; 2nd Pl, Boys Pub Speaking; 2nd Pl, St ACE Convention; *Grand Rapids Baptist Col; Hist.*

SALTON, Beverly Jean
S Clay HS; Gillett Grove, IA (12-24) Ann; Chor; Tres, 4H; Spch C; 4H A; Journ A; Spch A; Yth Fel; *Westmar Col; Home Ec.*

SALTZMAN, Jane B
Eastside HS; Paterson, NJ (1-520) Dbte Tm; Drama; Ch, NHS; Thes; Ch, Y-Tns; Hon Prog; Hospital Vol; VP, United Synogogue Yth; Schol A to Israel; *Rutgers Col; Pre-Med.*

SALVANT, Roxanne Edwina
Lyndon Baines Johnson HS; Austin, TX (15-349) NHS; Co-Ed, Sch P; Most Out; Q&S A; Trustee A; Cpt, Drill Tm; *Zoology.*

SALVO, Lisa Marie
James Island HS; Charleston, SC; Fr C; Mu Alpha Theta; Bkbl; Tr; Elk A; Opt A; Job's Daughters; Vlbl Tm.

SALYER, Cindy Jo
NW Classen HS; Oklahoma City, OK (5%-500) Tres, NHS; Span C; Citz A; Secy, Pep C; Advanced Modern Dance Company; Courtesy C; *Okla St U; Psych.*

SALYER, Mary Jean
Oak Grove RVI HS; Oak Grove, MO (13-103) AFS; Chor; *U of Calif; Soc & Psych.*

SALYER, Peggy Ann
Oak Grove R-6 HS; Oak Grove, MO (11-112) Ann; Band; Chor; Secy, Fr C; Regent Schol; *SW Mo St U; Fr.*

SALYERS, Carolyn Marie
Lakeview HS; Battle Creek, MI (1-416) A Cap Choir; Chor; Lat C; Tres, NHS; Beauty; COM; Hon Prog; MLS; Val; Yth Fel; Top 10 Schol A; Most Admired; Win, St Competitive Schol; *Calvin Col; Nurs.*

SALZMANN, Philip Emanuel
Hightstown HS; Hightstown, NJ (42-253) Ger C; Math C; NHS; Ski C; *Stevens Inst of Tech; Elec Engr.*

SALZWIMMER, Leisa Darlyn
Kenmore Sr HS; Akron, OH (28-383) Chor; Drama; Hmrm; NHS; Advertising Mgr, Sch Paper; *Mt Vernon Nazarene Col; Commercial Art.*

SAMANO, Isaias Pimental
Apollo HS; Simi Valley, CA (10%-150) Tres, Span C; Asst Director, Video Cl.

SAMDAHL, Lori Marie
Osnabrock Pub HS; Osnabrock, ND (3-10) Ann; Drama; Ed, Sch P; Pres, SC; Mgr, Bkbl; Hon Stu; *Trinity Med Center; Nurs.*

SAMEK, Gary Eldon
Dallas Christian HS; Dallas, TX; Ann; Dbte Tm; NHS; Order/Arrow; Sci C; Var C; Bsbl; Ftbl; Tr; Math A; Order/Arrow A; Eagle Sct; Eng A; Soph Distinguished HS Stu; *Tex Tech U; Math.*

SAMMIS, Jennifer Ann
W Springfield HS; Springfield, VA (202-528) Ann; Chor; Tres, Fr C; Hmrm; SC; Tri-HiY; COM; ARC A; Sci A; NJHS; Wash Jr Acad of Sci.

SAMMONS, Scott A
Early Co HS; Blakely, GA (10%-30) Parl, BC; Drama; FFA; 4H; Span C; Ftbl; Golf.

SAMOILOFF, Patricia Carlene
Winchester HS; Winchester, MA (33-430) NHS; Sch P; Span C; Hockey; Tnns; Tr; *U of Maine at Orono.*

SAMOLINSKI, Thomas James
Wausau E HS; Wausau, WI (66%-372) CYO; Ski C; *Saint Francis de Sales Col; Psych.*

SAMPLE, Edith Ann
Hazen HS; Hazen, AR; Chor; FBLA; FHA; Sci C; *Pulaski Voc Tech Col; Dental Asst.*

SAMPLE, Suzanne Dorothea
Brazoswood HS; Clute, TX; A Cap Choir; Lat C; Sftbl; Homemaking Merit A; *Med.*

SAMPLES, Jaril Van
N Gwinnett HS; Suwanee, GA (15%-190) Chess C; Dbte Tm; Key C; Fin, Lit Ral; NHS; Var C; Bsbl; Bkbl; Ftbl; 2nd, Region 8-A Debate; *U of Ga; Debate.*

SAMPLES, Russell Max
Buford HS; Buford, GA (11-67) BC; Chor; Drama; VP, Key C; Thes; Bkbl; MVP, Tnns; HCt; I Dare You; *Young Harris Col; Med.*

SAMPSON, Beth Ellen
Point Pleasant Boro HS; Point Pleasant, NJ (20-309) Band; NHS; Orch; 1st Cl Sct; Choir; Plays; Sunday Sch Teacher.

SAMPSON, Carlton Bernard
Pine Forge Acad; Pine Forge, PA (4-80) A Cap Choir; Chor; Ensm; VP, SC; Var C; Pres, Soph Cl; Bkbl; COM; Citz A; Hon Prog; Fr School; Attendance A; Oakwood Col; Chem.

SAMPSON, Debra Gay
Logan HS; Logan, OH; Rainbow; Span C; Y-Tns; 4H A; Yth Fel; Eng Schol Tm; Ohio U; Sci.

SAMPSON, Gregory Lynn
Delphos Jefferson Sr HS; Delphos, OH (4-95) Band; BS; Rptr; Chor; Drama; Ensm; Madrigal; Math C; Pres, NHS; Sch Achieve Tm; Sch P; Sci C; Span C; SC; Alg A; COM; Math A; Sci A; Ntl Choral A; Cincinnati U; Pre-Med.

SAMPSON, Jacqueline Gail
Killeen HS; Killeen, TX; Band; Chor; Ensm; FHA; FTA; Tex Sou U; Eng.

SAMPSON, Laura Ann
Holly Sr HS; Holly, MI (30-353) Band; Drama; Fr C; 4H; Ski C; Mich St U; Teaching.

SAMPSON, Mary Kate
Oakmont Regional HS; Ashburnham, MA (1-160) A Cap Choir; Chldr; Chor; Drama; Ski C; League & Dist Hon Chor; Chem.

SAMPSON, Scott David
Austin HS; Decatur, AL; Band; Math Tm; Math Medal; U of Ala; Physics.

SAMS, Kathleen Valorie
Weston-McEwen HS; Athena, OR (1-35) Ann; GS; Co-Ch, 4H; NHS; F-Ed, Sch P; Var C; Bkbl; Tnns; Hon Prog; Journ A; Pres A; Vlbl; Most Respected; Blue Mountain Comm Col; Acct.

SAMS, Sandra Iona
Antelope Valley HS; Lancaster, CA (140-575) Secy, Fr C; GS; HiY; Hrmr; InterClub Coun; Pres, SC; Y-Tns; VP, Jr Cl; HCt; Hon Prog; Yth Fel; VP, SC; Yth o-t Mo; Alt, GS; Sr Guide; Grossmont Jr Col; Criminology.

SAMSON, Elizabeth Maria
East HS; Erie, PA (30-222) Band; Ensm; Secy, Ger C; Orch; ARC; Y-Tns; Spelling Bee Win; Quartermaster, Band; Mercyhurst Col; Ed.

SAMSON, Lawrence Joseph
Immaculata HS; Leavenworth, KS (10-75) A Cap Choir; CYO; Chor; Bsbl; Bkbl; Chem A; Hon Prog; Outst Photographer, Yrbk; Math.

SAMSON, Torelang
Marshall Islands HS; Majuro, MARSHALL ISLANDS; Secy, SC; Bsbl; Hon Prog; Most Out; Sci A; Star Student.

SAMUEL, Alvin Jerome
Friendly HS; Oxon Hill, MD; Va St Col; Bus Mgt.

SAMUEL, Janet Renee
Russell HS; Hurtsboro, AL (2-56) Chor; FHA; FTA; 4H; Secy, NHS; Sci C; Bkbl; COM; Citz A; 4H A; Hist A; Hon Prog; JA A; ROTC A; Sal; Spch A; Spelman Col; Bus Adm.

SAMUEL, Mendal Anne
Paisley HS; Winston-Salem, NC (25-400) Fr C; Hon Prog; Yth Fel; Girls C; 1st Cl GSct; UNC-Chapel Hill; Ed.

SAMUELS, Thomas William II
Myers Park Sr HS; Charlotte, NC; Pres, Chor; JA A; Teachers Aid; Central Piedmont Comm Col; Tech.

SAMUELS, Vicki Elaine
B T Washington HS; Tulsa, OK; Bus.

SAMUELSEN, Chandra Joan
Spring Woods Sr HS; Houston, TX (2-510) Band; JETS; Math C; Mu Alpha Theta; NHS; Sci C; Alg A; Bio A; Math A; Sci A; Eng As; U of Colo; Chem Engr.

SAMUELSON, Glenn Curtis
Montville Twsp HS; Montville, NJ (5%-320) Band; NHS; Hon Prog; Stevens Inst of Tech; Engr.

SAMUELSON, Paul Frederick
Winthrop HS; Winthrop, MN (26-70) Band; VP, Chor; Drama; Ensm; Co-Ed, Sch P; Var C; Bsbl; Bkbl; Ftbl; Tr; U of Sou Miss; Oceanography.

SAMUELSON, Thomas William
Duluth E HS; Duluth, MN (80-535) NHS; JV, Bsbl; Hockey; Math A; NHS A; HR; Concordia Col; Bus.

SANASARIAN, Paula Jean
Waltham Sr HS; Waltham, MA; Chor; Drama; Sch P; Swim; Mass Col of Phar; Phar.

SANCHEZ, Aida Margarita
Colegio Puertorriqueno de Ninas; Caparra Heights, PR (2-61) Tres, NFL; Secy; NHS; Sch P; Bkbl; COM; Cornell U; Bachelor Natural Sci.

SANCHEZ, Anne Louise
Jesus And Mary HS; El Paso, TX; Ed, Ann; NHS; Rptr, Sch P; Secy, SC; MVP, Soccer; Journ A; Poetry A; Art.

SANCHEZ, Carlos Eduardo
Deerborne HS; Miami, FL (18-72) Soccer; Eckerd Col; Engr.

SANCHEZ, Catalina
Yauco HS; Yauco, PR; Westminster Col; Med Technology.

SANCHEZ, Cindy Ann
Goddard HS; Roswell, NM (136-300) Band; Chor; Fr C; VP, Office Ed Assn; Centaur; Beauty Pageant; E NM U; Bus.

SANCHEZ, Cynzia Matilde
Colegio Universit Sagrado Corazon; Santurce, PR (2-25) Tres, Hrmr; NHS; Tres, SC; Bio A; Chem A; Hist A; Col Uni de Mayaguez; Optometry.

SANCHEZ, Diana
Sw HS; San Antonio, TX (5%-275) A Cap Choir; Chor; Ensm; FTA; NHS; Tres, SC; COM; Fr C; Y-Tns; HCt; Spch A; Vlbl; Solo Mus Medal; Trinity Col; Sci.

SANCHEZ, Giovanna Mercedes
Colegio Santa Rita; Bayamon, PR; Val; Excellence A; U of Puerto Rico; Psych.

SANCHEZ, Imilsa
Dra Maria Cadilla de Martinez HS; Arecibo, PR (72-429) Drama; Pres, Hrmr; COM; St Scholar; Colegio Regional; Enfermeria.

SANCHEZ, Karen Elaine
PaloDuro HS; Amarillo, TX (13-285) CYO; Pres, FHA; Hrmr; NHS; Mgr, Tr; Journ A; Q&S A; Fin, Cl Fav; Amarillo Col; Social Working.

SANCHEZ, Laura Estella
William H Wells HS; Chicago, IL (33-300) Secy, Hrmr; MVP, Bsbl; COM; Yth Fel; MVP, Vlbl; Awana A; Vlbl A's; Tn Missions Certs; Trinity Col; Creative Writing.

SANCHEZ, Lisa Marie
Greater New York Acad; Woodside, NY; Fin, NHS; Pres, Jr Cl; Bkbl; Sftbl; Alg A; Chem A; Citz A; Cl Fav; Eng A; Fine Arts A; Columbia Union Col; Lab Tech.

SANCHEZ, Maria Diliana
Roma HS; Roma, TX (7-130) Chor; FHA; Laredo Jr Col; Nurs.

SANCHEZ, Mary Louise
Springdale HS; Springdale, AR; A Cap Choir; Secy, CYO; Chor; Fr C; GS; Hrmr; Span C; JV, Tr; Hon Prog; U of Ark; Foreign Lang.

SANCHEZ, Migdalia
Adlai E Stevenson HS; New York, NY (15-814) Band; Hon Prog; Regent's Schol Alt; New York City Col; Engr.

SANCHEZ, Roberta JoAnn
Eldorado HS; Albuquerque, NM (19-780) Band; Chor; Community Yth Symph; NHS; Orch; U of NM; Applied Mus.

SANCHEZ, Salvador
Consuelo Escalona Private Sch; Carolina, PR (4-28) Tres, Hrmr; Bsbl; COM; JA A; Weight Lifting; U of PR at Mayaguez; Civil Engr.

SAND, Dusteen Ann
Paradise HS; Paradise, CA (1-252) Band; Ger C; Pres, 4H; Y-Tns; Sftbl; Bank Of Amer A; CSF; COM; 4H A; Shorthand, Acct, A's; Butte Jr Col; Bus Adm.

SANDBACH, Patricia Jane
Floyd Central HS; New Albany, IN (1-336) A Cap Choir; Ed, Ann; Drama; Pres, NHS; A-Ed, Sch P; Co-Ch, Soph Cl; DARGCA; Journ A; NMF; Val; Ind U; Telecommunications.

SANDBERG, Wendy Anne
Jamestown HS; Jamestown, NY (2%-516) A Cap Choir; Band; NHS; Ski C; Swim; NEDT; Regent Schol; U of Rochester; Math.

SANDBURG, Denise Jeanne
Marina HS; Huntington Beach, CA (10%-850) NFL; NHS; Spch C; CSF; Hist A; Spch A; NCTE Essay Contest; Religion.

SANDBURG, James Bradley
Victoria HS; Victoria, TX (288-548) Parl, Key C; Cpt, Bkbl; JV, Tr; Cl Fav; Coach's HS All Amer; All District, All Region, Bkbl; Angelo St U; Bus.

SANDE, Linda Rae
Bemidji HS; Bemidji, MN (26-384) F-Ed, Ann; Parl, FHA; NHS; Phys C; Pres, Sci C; Spch C; H of F; Spch A; WW; Northern Ariz U; Astronomy.

SANDEFUR, Mary Pearl
Nordhoff HS; Ojai, CA (53-315) Band; Ensm; Christ Col; Teacher.

SANDEFUR, Patrice Donelle
Southeast HS; Wichita, KS (143-651) Chor; VP, Ensm; Abilene Christian U.

SANDEN, Christopher Joel
Annandale HS; Annandale, VA (40%-500) Hrmr; Ski C; Ftbl; Gym; Bus.

SANDEN, Dawn Louise
Kennedy Sr HS; Cedar Rapids, IA; JV, Bkbl; COM; 4H A; Health Careers C; JV Vlbl; St Lukes Sch of Nurs; Nurs.

SANDEN, Kelly Sue
Winona Sr HS; Winona, MN (25-500) Dbte Tm; NHS; Sci C; Span C; Winona Vo Tech; Civil Engr.

SANDEN, Sherry Lynn
J F Kennedy HS; Cedar Rapids, IA; Band; CYO; Health C; MVP, Vlbl; Sci.

SANDERS, Angela Gaile
Palm Beach Gardens HS; Palm Beach Gardens, FL; Drama; Hrmr; Spch C; SC; Cl Fav; Spch A; Xavier Col; Spch Pathology.

SANDERS, Annette Renee
Freeburg Comm HS; Freeburg, IL (1-160) Ann; Arch; Band; Drama; Tres, FHA; Var C; Arch; Schol A; Sci Army A.

SANDERS, Catherine Claire
Beaufort Acad; Beaufort, SC (6-38) Ann; Chor; Drama; NHS; Rptr, Sch P; Var C; Bkbl; Hon Prog; May Day Court; Converse Col; Ed.

SANDERS, Cheryl Louise
James Campbell HS; Ewa Beach, HI (25-370) Chldr; Drama; Ensm; Pres, 4H; VP, Soph Cl; Bkbl; Tr; Cl Fav; 4H A; Spch A; Religious Ed.

SANDERS, Crystal Lynn
Columbus E Sr HS; Columbus, OH; A Cap Choir; Band; Mgr, Chldr; Chor; Community Yth Symph; Drama; Orch; SC; Mgr, Tr.

SANDERS, Cynthia Ann
George Washington Carver HS; Montgomery, AL (15-400) Co-Cpt, Chldr; Chor; Ensm; Madrigal; Math C; Secy, Mu Alpha Theta; NHS; All St Chor; WW; Auburn U; Sci.

SANDERS, Debbie Faye
N Charleston HS; N Charleston, SC (35-135) Chor; 4H; Hrmr; InterClub Coun; Rptr, Sch P; SC; Y-Tns; COM; JA A; Opt A; Yth Fel; U of SC; Law.

SANDERS, Dinah Lynn
Jesup W Scott HS; Toledo, OH (40-499) VP, BC; Secy, Chor; Hrmr; Var C; Bkbl; Sftbl; Tr; COM; Cl Fav; Tenn St U; Fashion Design.

SANDERS, Dolores Renae
Ecorse HS; Ecorse, MI (2-200) Ann; Wayne St U; Sci.

SANDERS, Don M
S R Butler HS; Huntsville, AL; Drama; Pres, SC; Thes; Pres, Soph Cl; NMF; NMS; Best Thespian; Bst Solo Actor, Al St Thespian Conv; Birmingham-Sou Col; Spch and Drama.

SANDERS, Dorothy Elberta
Murphy HS; Mobile, AL (10-550) Tres, Chor; NHS; Rptr, Sch P; Span C; Hon Prog; Pres Clrm; Span A; Chor A; Journ.

SANDERS, Edna Anita
Wando HS; Mt Pleasant, SC (33-383) Chldr; 4H; Semi-Fin, Jr Miss Pa; NHSt; Rptr, Sch P; Span C; Mgr, Bkbl; COM; 4H A; HR; Phys Ed A; Miss A's; U of SC; Pediatrics.

SANDERS, Etta Rose
William Marion Raines Sr HS; Jacksonville, FL; Chor; Fr C; COM; Chor Most Outst Service A; *Fla A&M U; Sociology.*

SANDERS, Gail Elizabeth
Northwestern Sr HS; Hyattsville, MD; Band; Var C; Alg A; Math A; Sch, Yrbk; Vlbl; Phi Beta Nu; Edith Orem A; *U of Md; Phys Ed.*

SANDERS, Gina Marie
Chadwick HS; Palos Verdes Peninsula, CA (10%-46) JV, Bkbl; Tr; Hon Prog; Acting Ct; Lit Magazine; *Stanford U; Astronaut.*

SANDERS, Glenn Edward
Diamond Hill-Jarvis HS; Fort Worth, TX (1-140) Band; BS; Pres, Drama; Pres, Hmrm; Math C; NHS; Order/Arrow; Pres, Spch C; Pres, SC; Pres, Thes; Pres, Sr Cl; COM; Citz A; DARGCA; Math A; Opt A; Spch A; WW; Ntl HS A of Excel; Regional Bands; *Baylor U.*

SANDERS, Harvey David
Murry Wright HS; Detroit, MI; All Amer Yth; JETS; Var C; Bsbl; Bkbl; Cr-Crtry; Ftbl; Tr; *Wyane St U; Elec.*

SANDERS, Jerry Raymond
Hubbard HS; Hubbard, OH (59-375) Chess C; Fr C; Sftbl; Hist A; Hon Prog; *Ky Christian Col; Ministry.*

SANDERS, Joe William
Del Rio HS; Del Rio, TX; A-Ed; Ann; Band; Span C; SC; *U of Tex; Med.*

SANDERS, John Christopher
Daviess Co HS; Owensboro, KY (42-320) Band; Orch; Tnns; NML; *Georgetown Col; Applied Mus.*

SANDERS, John Kevin
Gallatin Sr HS; Gallatin, TN (52-300) Band; Chem C; Dbte Tm; Ensm; Tres, HLY; Math C; Phys C; Span C; Spch C; Co-Cpt, Ftbl; Golf; God & Country A; Explorer A; *Ohio Wesleyan Col; Law.*

SANDERS, Joseph Edward
Tahlequah HS; Tahlequah, OK (33%-272) Band; 4H; *Tulsa U; Bus.*

SANDERS, Julie Renee
Central HS; Springfield, MO; Band; FHA; *Burge Sch of Nurs; Nurs.*

SANDERS, Karen Louise
Shawnee Mission Nw HS; Shawnee Mission, KS; Co-Ed, Ann; CYO; NHS; Rptr, SC; COM; Hon Prog; Opt A; Q&S A; Spch A; Rep, Parish Liturgy; Lector; Walk for Mankind; *U of Kansas; Bio-Chem.*

SANDERS, Kathy Isabel
Robinson Sch; Santurce, PR (5-39) Co-Cpt, Chldr; NHS; Span C; Type A; *Math.*

SANDERS, Kyle William
Sky-View Baptist Acad; Memphis, TN (11-101) A-Ed, Ann; BC; BS; Hmrm; Pres, Sci C; Pres, SC; VP, Jr Cl; Soph Cl; Bsbl; Bkbl; Golf; Cl Fav; MLS; Most Out; PTA A; Mr Sky View; Memphis Press Scimitar A; *Memphis St U; Animal Husbandry.*

SANDERS, Lanita Renee
George Henry Corliss HS; Chicago, IL (1-485) NHS; Rptr, Sch P; VP, Span C; COM; Citz A; Hon Prog; Math A; NEDT; PA; HR; *Chicago Circle Campus U; Phar.*

SANDERS, Laura Dianne
Litchfield HS; Gadsden, AL (26-144) S-T, ARC; Rptr, Span C; COM; ARC A; Attendence A; Ntl Jogging Day A; *Gadsden St Jr Col; Bus.*

SANDERS, Lauren Elizabeth
Lufkin HS; Lufkin, TX (5%-520) Band; Chor; Drama; Ger C; Rptr, Mu Alpha Theta; A-Ed, Sch P; NEDT; *Baylor U.*

SANDERS, Lowell Jeffery
Springfield Sr HS; Springfield, OR; Chor; Ger C; Tres, SC; JV, Bkbl; Tnns; *Oreg Col of Ed; Ed.*

SANDERS, Marion Keith
Spartanburg HS; Spartanburg, SC; Hmrm; SC; Cpt, Bkbl; Cpt, Ftbl; Cpt, Tr; Amer Leg A; COM; Citz A; Most Out; Pres, Explorers; *Clemson U; Archt.*

SANDERS, Mary Jane
Franklin Co HS; Frankfort, KY; Band; BC; Fr C; French NHS; Hmrm; *Georgetown Col; Ed.*

SANDERS, Myra Frances
Lake Clifton HS; Baltimore, MD (10%-315) Hmrm; JETS; NHS; ARC; Hist A; *U of Pittsburgh; Med Technology.*

SANDERS, Patricia Leigh
Northside Christian Sch; Charlotte, NC (6-40) Chor; Pres, FHA; NHS; Var C; Sftbl; Citz A; HCt; Yth Fel; *Tenn Temple Col; Acct.*

SANDERS, Robert James
Shawnee Mission Northwest HS; Lenexa, KS (5-675) Ed, Ann; NHS; Tres, SC; Hon Prog; Math A; Q&S A; St Scholar; *U of Kans; Mech Engr.*

SANDERS, Rosemary Ellen
Birmingham HS; Van Nuys, CA (810-860) A Cap Choir; Secy, Band; VP, Chor; Drama; Ger C; Tres, Madrigal; Orch; Beauty; Yth Fel; *Calif Baptist Col; Mus.*

SANDERS, Scott Bradley
Circleville HS; Circleville, OH (10%-200) Band; Key C; Sch Achieve Tm; SC; Bsbl; Golf; Alg A; COM; *Miami U; Tech Acct.*

SANDERS, Shari Loraine
Millikan HS; Long Beach, CA; Commercial C; Sch Achieve Tm; MVP, Swim; Math A; Pres A; *Pepperdine U; Health.*

SANDERS, Sharon Lee
Alton Sr HS; Alton, IL (25%-7) Silver Alpha; *La St U; Pre-Med.*

SANDERS, Stefan Shejuon
Sheffield HS; Memphis, TN (15%-214) NHS; F-Ed, Sch P; SC; Thes; Pres, Soph Cl; JV, Bkbl; Cl Fav; Lion A; *U of Ind; Law.*

SANDERS, Stephen Craig
Millikan HS; Long Beach, CA (825-900) A Cap Choir; Chldr; Chor; City Conf; Drama; Hmrm; InterAct C; NHS; ARC; F-Ed, Sch P; Pres, SC; Swim; CSF; *Biola Col; Bus.*

SANDERS, Susan Lynn
Northwestern HS; Hyattsville, MD; Band; Cpt, Chldr; Hmrm; Lit Mag; Orch; Alg A; Sci A; *U of Md.*

SANDERS, Teresa Arlene
St Francis DeSales Central HS; Morgantown, WV (1-68) Ann; Band; Chor; VP, Drama; Secy, GS; Math C; Mu Alpha Theta; NHS; VP, SC; Tr; HCt; Hon Prog; NEDT; Rotary A; Val; Outst Citizen, GS; Religion A; Mem Schol; Prom Qn; *W Va U; Elec Engr.*

SANDERS, Teri Lee
Temple Christian Sch; Redford, MI (9-60) Chor; Sftbl; *U of Mich; Law.*

SANDERS, Tina
Murry Wright HS; Detroit, MI; Dance Stu; Sch Secy; *Wayne St U; Secy.*

SANDERS, William Alan
Wooddale HS; Memphis, TN (44-325) ARC; Spch C; *Baylor U; Humanities.*

SANDERSON, Dana Kay
Hastings Sr HS; Hastings, NE (117-302) Co-Ed, Ann; Chldr; Chor; Drama; Ch, Hmrm; Ch, SC; Y-Tns; Tnns; Spch A; Jobs Daughters; Intramural Sports; Tutor; Chldr A; Tigerette; *Carroll Col.*

SANDERSON, Debbie Lynette
Dunbar Voch HS; Chicago, IL (6-512) NHS; COM; Math A; MLS; Star Student; Engr C; Industrial Arts A; Engr Found; Ill Inst of Tech Drawing Comp A; *Illinois Institute of Tech; Mechanical Engineering.*

SANDERSON, Donna Lou
Lindbergh HS; Renton, WA (21-375) Band; Chor; Ensm; SC; Most Out; NW Dist Yth Choir; Historian, Girl's C; Cabinet, Girl's C; Yth Coun; *Northwest Col; Liberal Arts.*

SANDERSON, Juanita Gale
Oakdale HS; Oakdale, LA; Ann; Cpt, Band; FBLA; Pres, FHA; Pres, 4H; Mjrte; NHS; ARC; SC; Co-Cpt, Bsbl; Sftbl; Beauty; COM; Cl Fav; 4H A; H of F; HQn; HCt; Hon Prog; JA A; FFA Qn; Most Ath Girl; *Northeast La St U; Bus.*

SANDERSON, Karen Elizabeth
Waynesboro-Central HS; Waynesboro, MS (25%-99) Ann; BC; Drama; Ger C; Semi-Fin, Jr Miss Pa; F-Ed, Sch P; Y-Tns; COM; NEDT; Ch, Stu Drug Coun; *U of Sou Miss; Engr.*

SANDERSON, Linda Jean
Hamden HS; Hamden, CT; Band; Drama; Y-Tns; Hon Prog; YMCA Vol; *Bus.*

SANDERSON, Lynn Elizabeth
Northgate HS; Walnut Creek, CA; Mgr, Swim; CSF; Jobs Daughters.

SANDERSON, Rebecca Alene
E Central HS; Pascagoula, MS; VP, Sci C; SC; Mgr, Tr.

SANDERSON, Rebecca Alene
East Central HS; Hurley, MS (9-115) VP, Sci C; SC.

SANDERSON, Susan Camille
DeKalb HS; DeKalb, IL (88-360) A Cap Choir; Band; MVP, Chor; Madrigal; Thes; Cpt, Sftbl; Tnns; Tr; Interlochen Ntl Mus; PTA A; All St & Dist Choir; *Mt Vernon Bible Col; Mus.*

SANDERSON, Vickie Lynn
Montgomery Co HS; Mt Sterling, KY (25%-290) Band; FBLA; FHA; Hmrm; Young Republicans; Pres, Church Yth Fel; Jr, Chapter & St Degrees, FHA; *Lindsey Wilson Col; Sociology.*

SANDGREN, Laurie Beth
Stoneham HS; Stoneham, MA (67-394) Band; Secy, Chor; MVP, Ensm; GS; Madrigal; Mus A; *U of Lowell; Mus Ed.*

SANDHOP, John Riley Jr
Robert E Lee HS; Baytown, TX; Tres, InterAct C; Parl, Lat C; Lat NHS; Pres, NHS; Golf; Amer Leg A; Opt Out Tn; NML; WW; *Tex A&M U; Mech Engr.*

SANDIDGE, Anita
South Side HS; Memphis, TN (10%-370) Tres, Tr; *U of Tenn-Knoxville.*

SANDIDGE, Cynthia Ann
Daviess Co HS; Owensboro, KY; Co-Cpt, Chldr; Fr C; SC; JA A; Type A; *Murray Col; Social Services.*

SANDIDGE, Horace Thomas Jr
Withrow HS; Cincinnati, OH (8-642) Chor; Drama; VP, Ensm; NHS; Ch, SC; World Affairs C; Ch, Sr Cl; *U of Cincinnati; Acct.*

SANDIDGE, Tamara Sue
Fort Madison Sr HS; Fort Madison, IA; Rptr, Sch P; Sci C; Span C; JV, Bkbl; Tnns; Tr.

SANDIDGE, Thomas Evans II
Daviess Co HS; Owensboro, KY; A Cap Choir; Chor; Ger C; Citz A; JA A; Ky Colonel; Yth Traffic Safty Conf; *Ind U; Bus.*

SANDLIN, Novalene
Buckhorn HS; Buckhorn, KY (4-36) A-Ed, Ann; VP, BC; Chor; Tres, FHA; Math A; Hmrm; F-Ed, Sch P; Pres, SC; MVP, Bkbl; Sftbl; DARGCA; HQn; HCt; *Hazard Comm Col.*

SANDLIN, Valerie Hope
Buckhorn HS; Buckhorn, KY (1-63) Secy, BC; VP, FHA; Bkbl; *Biol.*

SANDOVAL, Lia Therese
Mercy HS; Red Bluff, CA (4-28) JV, Chldr; Drama; Fin, GS; S-T, 4H; Hmrm; Model UN; Sci A; SC; Pres, Sr Cl; VP, Jr Cl; Pres, Soph Cl; MVP, Bsbl; MVP, Bkbl; MVP, Sftbl; MVP, Tr; Amer Leg A; Bank Of Amer A; B Crocker A; CSF; Citz A; DARGCA; 4H A; HQn; Hon Prog; Kiwanis A; NEDT; Sci A; Spch A; Co-Cpt, Bkbl; Shakespeare C; PG&E Schol Fin; Math & Sci A, Bank of Amer; *UC at San Diego; Bio.*

SANDOWICH, Linda
Nichols Christian Acad; Trumbull, CT; Chor; Fr C; Swim; Tnns; Type A; Church Yth Group; Fr As; Good Sports A.

SANDRITTER, David Allen
Hoisington HS; Hoisington, KS (15%-82) Band; Dbte Tm; NFL; SC; Tr; *Washburn U; Law.*

SANDS, Cecile Marie
Marillac HS; Northfield, IL (19-222) NHS; NMS; *Ind U; Anthropology.*

SANDS, Gary Lynn
John F Kennedy Sr HS; Sacramento, CA; Band; Tr; Alg A; CSF; Citz A; Cl Fav; DARGCA; Hon Prog; JA A; MLS; Most Out; Ntl Achv Schol; Ntl Conf Chr & Jews; NMF; NMS; Opt Out Tn; Star Student; Yth Fel; *U of Calif; Math.*

SANDS, Sandy Jo
Athens HS; The Plains, OH; Bus C; FHA; Y-Tns; Hocking Tech Col; Bus.

SANDSTROM, Brian David
Wheaton Central HS; Wheaton, IL (131-345) Ed, Sch P; Pres, SC; VP, Jr Cl; Pres, Soph Cl; Sch Spirit A; Eng.

SANDSTROM, Carolyn Elaine
Robbinsdale Sr HS; Robbinsdale, MN; Chor; Orch; JV, Tr; Nurs.

SANDUE, Allison Jane
Spring Valley Sr HS; Spring Valley, WI (4-67) Band; Drama; NFL; Rptr, Sch P; Ski C; Spch A; All Sch Play.

SANDVIG, Laurie Catherine
Lindbergh HS; Minnetonka, MN (198-433) Ger C; SC; Swim; Honored Qn, Job's Daughters; Yth Ministry Coun; Church Task Force; AFS C; St Olaf Col; Psych.

SANDY, Mike Roy
Herndon HS; Herndon, WV (9-58) Bsbl; Bkbl; Mus.

SANER, Amy Sue
Parma HS; Parma, ID (17-62) Band; Community Yth Symph; Fr C; 4H; Orch; Sftbl; Appreciation A.

SANETRO, Terri Ann
Simi Valley HS; Simi Valley, CA (116-829) Key C; Calif Lutheran Col; Med.

SANFORD, Brenda Joyce
Robert L Osborne Sr HS; Marietta, GA (50%-365) BC; Chor; Drama; Thes; Hon Prog; Hon Prog.

SANFORD, David Harding
Harry A Burke HS; Omaha, NE; Fr C; Mgr, Bkbl; Mgr, Ftbl; Yth Fel; Yth Foundation; Amer Yth Found; Social Work.

SANFORD, David Roy
Inglemoor HS; Bothell, WA (15-340) Chess C; Ed, Lit Mag; NHS; Ed, Sch P; Journ A; Quzzing A; Pres, Yth Group; WW; Bell Essay A; Shoreline Comm Col; Communications.

SANFORD, Faye Lynn
Temple Heights Christian Sch; Tampa, FL (9-62) Ann; MVP, Chldr; Chor; Drama; Ensm; NHS; Sch P; Mgr, Sftbl; Yth Fel; Tenn Temple Col; Psych.

SANFORD, Kaye Helen
Temple Heights Christian Sch; Tampa, FL (6-62) Ann; Cpt, Chldr; Chess C; Chor; Drama; Ensm; NHS; Mgr, Sftbl; Most Spiritual; Baptist Christian Col; Bible.

SANFORD, Lyle Joseph
Lake Charles HS; Lake Charles, LA (27-270) Band; Bus C; HiY; Lit Ral; NHS; Ftbl; Daughter of Revolution; A of Merit; Cert of Recognition; LSU; Acct.

SANFORD, Marshall Clement
Westminster Acad; Fort Lauderdale, FL (15-62) Order/Arrow; MVP, Cr-Ctry; Soccer; Tr; Citz A; HCt; Order/Arrow A; Outst Sct A; Eagle Sct A; Agr.

SANFORD, Sharon Nadine
Jimtown HS; Elkhart, IN (1-94) Band; Chor; Pres, Drama; Ensm; Fr C; 4H; Jr Miss Pagent; NHS; Rainbow; Thes; Tnns; 4H A; Hon Prog; St Scholar; Type A; Val; St Vocal & Instrumental Contests; Olivet Nazarene Col; Nurs.

SANFORD, Stephanie Lynne
Glasco HS; Glasco, KS (3-23) Ed, Ann; Chldr; FHA; Jr Miss Pagent; NHS; A-Ed, Sch P; Ch, Y-Tns; Sftbl; St Scholar; Vlbl; Kans St U Engr A; WW; Kans Hon Soc; U of Kans; Elem Ed.

SANFORD, Steven Reed
Glasco HS; Glasco, KS (2-28) BS; SC; Pres, Soph Cl; Bsbl; JV, Bkbl; Tr; U of Kans; Law.

SanGIOVANNI, Paul Louis
N Shore HS; W Palm Beach, FL (38-336) A Cap Choir; Tres, Chor; VP, Drama; Ensm; Fr C; InterClub Coun; Tres, SC; VP, Soph Cl; COM; Best All Around, Choir; Best Actor; Superiors, St Ensm; Med.

SANGREE, Paul Huyett
Holliston HS; Holliston, MA (12-257) Chor; Drama; NHS; Sch P; Cr-Ctry; Co-Cpt, Tnns; Tr; NMF; VP, Yth Fel; Brown U; Pre-Law.

SANGSTER, Brenda Elaine
Guysborough Municipal HS; Guysboro, CANADA (1-33) Chem C; Chem A; Hist A; Hon Prog; Math A; Fr A; Econ A; Eng A.

SANGSTER, Ruth Yvonne
Brunswick HS; Brunswick, GA; Chor; Ensm; Semi-Fin, 4H; Tnns; Hist A; Poet A; Ntl Piano Auditions; Ntl Fraternity of Stu Mus; Piano Hobbists o-t World; Stu Division, Amer Col of Mus; NY Col of Mus; Mus.

SANGSTER, Timothy Britt
Stephens Co HS; Toccoa, GA (50%-325) Chor; Secy, 4H; Pres, HiY; InterAct C; InterClub Coun; Pres, Soph Cl; Bsbl; Sftbl; Tr; VP, Hi-Y; Dist VP, Hi-Y; Atlanta Boys Choir; VFW St Tnage Driving Contest Scho; Aviation.

SANGSTER, Vanessa Rachel
Oak Park And River Forest HS; Oak Park, IL (347-936) Trinity Christian Col; Religion.

SANICH, Stephanie Anne
Gilbert HS; Gilbert, MN (8-64) Co-Ed, Ann; Band; CYO; Chor; Community Yth Symph; Ensm; FHA; Orch; Sch P; B Crocker A; Most Imaginative; Mesabi Jr Col; Hist.

SANNER, Eric Monroe
Bishop Walsh HS; Cumberland, MD (60-190) JV, Ftbl; JA A.

SANNER, Gregory Paul
Duncan HS; Duncan, OK; Band; Pres, Span C; Bsbl; Wrest; WW; OCC.

SANNER, Pamela Sue
Rockwood Area HS; Rockwood, PA (20-116) Pres, Fr C; Pres, Ger C; Hmrm; Sch P; SC; Jr Cl; NEDT; Type A; Scholastic A; Animal Sci.

SANSOM, Felecia Carol
David W Carter HS; Dallas, TX; TAHOS A; VP, TAHOS; Med Career.

SANSOM, La Juan
David W Carter HS; Dallas, TX (271-599) Drama; Fr C; Pres, FHA; ARC; Spch C; Y-Tns; Bishop & Atlanta U; Math.

SANSON, Floyd Andrew
McCullough HS; Woodlands, TX; Bsbl; Bkbl; Sftbl; Tnns; Spch A; Yth Coun; Minister.

SANSONE, Anthony Frank
Chaminade HS; St Louis, MO; BS; CYO; Hmrm; Ntl Yth Conf; ARC; VP, SC; Ftbl; Golf; Cpt, Hockey; Tr; Hon Prog; St Mary's U; Bus Adm.

SANSREGRET, Anne Aileen
Gresham Union HS; Gresham, OR; Band; Community Yth Symph; Ger C; ARC; Ski C; U of Oreg Med Sch; Nurs.

SANTANA, Elva I
Manuela Toro Morice HS; Caguas, PR; CYO; Chldr; Chem C; Chor; FTA; Secy, Hmrm; Chem A; Hist A; Math A; U of Humacao; Chem.

SANTANA, Jose Carlos
St Augustine HS; Laredo, TX (15%-70) Chor; Hmrm; F-Ed, Sch P; Spch C; SC; Bkbl; Citz A; HR; Guitar A; WW; Hon Guard; Laredo Jr Col; Elec.

SANTANA, Maria Elena
Nuestra Senora de la Merced HS; Hato Rey, PR (4-92) Chem C; VP, Chess C; Lit Mag; S-T, Phys C; Tres, Sci C; Span C; Spch C; Alg A; Bio A; COM; Chem A; Hist A; Hon Prog; Journ A; Math A; MLS; Most Out; Phy A; Sci A; Star Student; Art A; Med.

SANTANA, Maria Eugenia
Academia Sagrado Corazon; Santurce, PR (2-65) Drama; FHA; VP, NHS; ARC; Span C; Spch C; SC; COM; Citz A; Spch A; Stu o-t Month A; Cooperation A; Sch Spirit A.

SANTANA, Teresa
St Genevieve HS; Panorama City, CA; CYO; Secy, Span C; SC; JV, Sftbl; COM; Citz A; Math A; Most Out; Yth Fel; CYO Tn Qn A; Achv A; Century Acct A; Religion A; USC; Med.

SANTIAGO, Angel G
Adolfo Grana Rivera HS; Penuelas, PR (2-342) Drama; 4H; Span C; COM; Chem A; Cl Fav; Hon Prog; Spch A; Spelling Eng Cert; Oral Reading Cert; High Proficiency Cert; Cath U of Puerto Rico; Sci.

SANTIAGO, Hector Francisco
Richmond Hill HS; Richmond Hill, NY; Span NHS; Bio A; COM; Hon Prog; Span A; HR; Scholastic Achv A; Architectural Drawing.

SANTIAGO, Ivette Maria
Colegio Santa Rita; Bayamon, PR (4-33) Chor; Co-Ed, Sch P; Bkbl; U of Puerto Rico; Sci.

SANTIAGO, Jorge Luis
Academia Discipulos de Cristo; Bayamon, PR (10-122) Chor; Cpt, Bsbl; MVP, Bkbl; Mgr, Swim; Alg A; Bio A; COM; Chem A; Hist A; Magna Cum Laude; Math A; Phy A; Universitad Puerto Rico.

SANTIAGO, Jose Juan
Colegio Universitario Corazon; Santurce, PR (4-37) Model UN; Sch P; Sci C; Soccer; U of Calif at Berkeley; Nuclear Research.

SANTIAGO, Nicholas
Dra Maria Cadilla de Martinez HS; Arecibo, PR (10-429) A Cap Choir; CYO; Chor; Drama; VP, Hmrm; Phys C; Arch; Semi-Fin, Swim; MVP, Tnns; COM; Chem A; Hon Prog; Most Out; Phy A; Pres A; Sci A; Penn St U; Sci.

SANTIAGO, Sylvia Esther
Colegio San Antonio Abad; Humacao, PR (7-72) Fin, Chem C; Hmrm; Pres, NHS; SC; Var C; Tnns; MVP, Vlbl; Col Archt of Puerto Rico; Archt.

SANTILLO, Victor
St Edward HS; Lakewood, OH (50%-450) VP, CYO; Chem C; Secy, Hmrm; Phys C; Span C; Bsbl; Bkbl; Cpt, Ftbl; Sftbl; COM; Cl Fav; Pres A; U of Cincinnati; Archt.

SANTO, Paul Victor
Hopkins Eisenhower HS; Hopkins, MN (20-430) A Cap Choir; Chor; Drama; Fr C; Madrigal; NHS; Thes; COM; Spch A; Sch Rep, Century III Ldrship A; St Olaf Col; Math.

SANTOORJIAN, Gary George
Minnehaha Acad; Minneapolis, MN (15-120) Order/Arrow; ARC; Ski C; Hockey; Soccer; Hon Prog; Engr.

SANTORA, Gregory Alan
St Peters Prep HS; Jersey City, NJ (30-260) Band; Drama; ARC; Ftbl; Tnns; Hon Prog; Hon Pins; Rutgers Col; Pre-Med.

SANTORA, Victoria Anne
Country Day Sch o-t Sacred Heart; Philadelphia, PA (2-10) Chor; Drama; Fr C; NHS; Ski C; Pres, Soph Cl; Bkbl; JV, Hockey; COM; Hon Prog; PA; Math.

SANTOS, Ana Hilda
Centro Oportunidades Edu Buc HS; Guaynabo, PR; Chor; Aprovechamexto; U of Puerto Rico; Acct.

SANTOS, Ana Lourdes
Academia Ntra Sra Providencia; Rio Piedras, PR (1-64) Bus C; CYO; Bkbl; Tnns; COM; Summa Cum Laude; Vlbl; Conduct A; Sci.

SANTOS, Annie Flores
John F Kennedy HS; Tumon, GUAM (8-511) CYO; NHS; Bio A; COM; Hon Prog; Most Out; Sci A; Type A; HR; Span A; Pepperdine U; Bus Adm.

SANTOS, Antonio Manuel
Central HS; Philadelphia, PA (135-400) Bkbl; COM; Lion A; Ntl Achv Schol; Fla A&M U; Acct.

SANTOS, Arlene Pijuan
Bishop Conaty HS; Los Angeles, CA (8-124) NHS; Control Data Inst; Computer Programming.

SANTOS, Jane Marie
William Byrd HS; Vinton, VA (1-246) BC; FBLA; 4H; Hmrm; Co-Ed, Lit Mag; Pol Sci C; Span C; Bausch & Lomb A; COM; Gr Marshal; Math A; Sci A; Val; Gov's Sch for Gifted; Eng A; Eng Mem Schol; NMS Commended Stu; VPI; Biological Sci.

SANTOS, Juana Elizabeth
Tabernacle Christian Acad; San Diego, CA (2-7) Fin, All Amer Yth; Drama; Math C; Sci C; Cpt, Sftbl; Cpt, Tnns; Tr; Bio A; Citz A; Cl Fav; MLS; Most Out; Ntl Achv Schol; Sci A; Oral Roberts U; Med Tech.

SANTOS, Lauralie F
Tri-Co Christian HS; Mechaniesburg, PA (10-35) Chor; Ger C; Orch; SC; Co-Cpt, Bkbl; Sftbl; Fin, Tr; Christian Ath; Spelling & Art A's; Baptist Bible Col; Elem Ed.

SANTROCK, Anne Janine
Nitro HS; Nitro, WV (10%-310) Secy, AFS; Chor; Secy, NHS; Ed, Sch P; Pres, Sci C; Sci A; All St Chor; *W Va U.*

SANZOTTO, Marcia Joann
Cumberland Valley HS; Mechanicsburg, PA (6-622) Band; Community Yth Symph; Math C; NHS; Orch; Tr; Regional & Dist Bands; *Pa St U; Math.*

SAO, Henry Taufoina
Lynwood HS; Lynwood, CA (25%-350) Chor; Drama; Pres, Hmrm; Cl Fav; HKg; Most Out; Phy A; Yth Fel; Photo C; *Pepperdine U; Physics.*

SAPALA, Rose Mary
Renolds HS; Greenville, PA (7-183) FBLA; Math C; Rptr, Sch P; Tri-HiY; GAA; *Secy.*

SAPAYO, Jacobo
Amer Military Acad; Guaynabo, PR (1-36) JV, Ftbl; JV, Soccer; Fin, Swim; Most Out; *MIT; Engr.*

SAPER, Lisa Lehrer
Pass Christian HS; Pass Christian, MS (5-110) F-Ed, Ann; Band; BC; Ensm; Pres, Fr C; Pres, Hmrm; Sch P; SC; Amer Leg Orator A; COM; Hist A; Hon Prog; Sci A; VFW Orator Win; VofDEM; Civics A; Home Ec A; Hon Men, Dist Sci Fair; Eng A; *U of Tex; Pol Sci.*

SAPP, Daniel Edward
Cascade HS; Turner, OK (1-223) Band; Chor; Ensm; NHS; Orch; Rptr, Sch P; Golf; Hon Prog; Scuba Diving C; Hon Cert; *Oral Roberts U; Sci.*

SAPP, Kathy H
Lawrence HS; Lawrence, KS; Band; Flag Corps; Soph Choir; Pres, Dist Coun On Yth Ministries; Conf Coun On Yth Ministries.

SAPP, Kelli Lyn
Putnam City HS; Oklahoma City, OK (10%-1000) Chor; Ensm; Fr C; Ger C; Hmrm; NHS; Co-Ed, Sch P; SC; COM; Type A; Piano A, Guild Audit, Mus Festival; *U of Okla; Mus.*

SAPP, Mary Elizabeth
Dalton HS; Dalton, GA (18-266) Drama; NHS; Sch P; Thes; Tri-HiY; Hon Prog; NEDT; WW; *Journ.*

SAPP, Merrilly Ann
Montgomery HS; San Diego, CA; Chor; Ensm.

SAPP, Patricia Lee
Miramar HS; Miramar, FL (16%-489) S-T, Band; Chor; Ensm; Tres, FBLA; Madrigal; Most Out; Yth Fel; Girls Ftbl; DAHSS; Outst Fresh, Soph & Jr, Band; *Broward Comm Col; Mus Therapy.*

SARCHET, Kimberley Jeanne
Twentynine Palms HS; Twentynine Palms, CA (1-153) Pres, Sci C; Tr; CSF; Elk A; MLS; Phy A; Regent Schol; Sci A; Val; Soroptimist A; Bank of Amer A; CSF Seal Bearer; *U of Calif Riverside; Biomed Sci.*

SARCHET, Marisa Jayne
Twentynine Palms HS; Twentynine Palms, CA (1-153) Sci C; CSF; Drama C; Elk A; NMS; Regent Schol; Val; Calif St Schol; USMC Wive's C A; Soroptomist A; *U of Calif at Riverside; Sociology.*

SARDO, Debbie Lynn
Exeter Township Sr HS; Reading, PA (10-235) Tres, BC; Pres, FTA; Hmrm; Pres, Lat NHS; NHS; A-Ed, Sch P; SC; Hist A; MLS; Summa Cum Laude; Announcement Reader; WW; Lat A; Win, Sertoma-Freedom Essay; *W Chester St Col; Secondary Ed.*

SARDYNSKI, Michael Paul
Mohonasen HS; Schenectady, NY (114-256) CYO; Bsbl; Bkbl; Ftbl; COM; *Hudson Valley Comm Col; Construction Technology.*

SARGEANT, Jill Kathryn
Northern Burlington Co HS; Columbus, NJ (18-255) French NHS; FNA; Hmrm; NHS; Var C; Hockey; Mgr, Tnns; *Lancaster Bible Col; Bible.*

SARGENT, Alana Dean
Colombia HS; Maplewood, NJ; FTA; Vol, Zoo Work; *Art.*

SARGENT, Cindy Ann
Centralia HS; Centralia, IL (12-364) NHS; Span C; Span NHS; SC; VP, Jr Cl; *Sou Ill U; Special Ed.*

SARGENT, Lennie Gaye
Uniontown Area Sr HS; Uniontown, PA; Cpt, Chldr; Drama; Tres, FNA; Pres, Hmrm; SC; Pres, Jr Cl; Stu Communicating Comm; Sch Board Stu Director; Jr-Sr Jr Attendant; *Carnegie Mellon Col; Art.*

SARGENT, Nancy Laurine
Homewood HS; Homewood, AL (35-229) Bus Mgr, Ann; Fr C; French NHS; VP, Lit Ral; Lit Mag; F-Ed, Annual; *U of Montevallo; Ed.*

SARGENT, Nell Alison
Columbia HS; Maplewood, NJ; Arch; Band; CYO; Chor; Drama; Sch P; Cl Fav; PTA A; Best Liked; PTA Mus A; *Social Worker.*

SARGENT, Verleta Rose
Waynoka HS; Waynoka, OK (12-29) Secy, FHA; 4H; Ed, Sch P; Spch C; SC; Co-Cpt, Ftbl; COM; 4H A; Type A; VP, S-T & Pres, Co 4-H C; PA; Co Meat Judging Tm; Leisure Lab; NW Ldrship Conf; VP, Pep C; 4-H Citz Seminar; Okie Cert.

SARIAN, Carol Ronda
Upper Merion HS; King of Prussia, PA (50-600) Chor; Drama; Orch; Pres, Thes; COM; Hon Prog; Yth Fel; Lit Ed, Yrbk; Vlbl; Gov's Sch o-t Arts; Ballet School; *International Law.*

SARJENT, Laura Elizabeth
Warren Central HS; Indianapolis, IN (37-863) Ann; CYO; Chess C; NHS; Tres, Sci C; Tr; Alg A; COM; Math A; Sci A; *DePauw U; Nurs.*

SARK, Daniel Dean
Fairfield Jr-Sr HS; Goshen, IN; VP, Math C; VP, Sci C; *Math.*

SARMIENTO, Julio Cesar
Jefferson Comp HS; Tampa, FL (8-575) Chess C; VP, Dbte Tm; Pres, Fr C; Pres, French NHS; VP, NFL; VP, NHS; VP, Spch C; St Stu Congress; Bsbl; Bkbl; COM; Citz A; Hist A; Hon Prog; Math A; Sci A; Spch A; Tres, Jr Jaycees; *Tulane U; Med.*

SARMIENTO, Margarita
Thomas Jefferson HS; Tampa, FL (15-701) Ann; Fr C; French NHS; Alg A; COM; Citz A; Hon Prog; Math A; Sci A; *Fla St U; Fine Arts.*

SARNA, Angelo Joseph
Carmel HS; Carmel, NY (13-300) Pres, Band; Chor; Ensm; K of C; Math C; NHS; Var C; Bsbl; Hon Prog; *Regent Schol; NYIT; Engr.*

SARRATT, Susan Renae
Ringgold HS; Ringgold, GA (1-290) Band; BC; Rptr, FHA; Hmrm; Rptr, SC; COM; Hon Prog; PC Jr Fel A; Calendar Girl A; *U of Ga; Law.*

SARTEN, Herbert Dexter
Lenoir City HS; Lenoir City, TN; BS; Pres, Drama; Pres, Hmrm; InterAct C; SC; Mgr, Bsbl; Co-Cpt, Ftbl; All Co, Ftbl; *Engr.*

SARTOR, Cyril Ephraim
Neptune Sr HS; Neptune, NJ (1%-650) Cpt, Chess C; Dbte Tm; Natnl U; COM; Hon Prog; Kiwanis A; Math A; MLS; Opt A; Spch A; Summer Sci Prog; Omega Sci Phi A; Best All Around Speaker & Debator; Scarlet Key A.

SARVER, Hillard Leroy Jr
Shippensburg Area Sr HS; Shippensburg, PA (194-250) Tape & Bus Ministries; Church; Bible, Astronomy, C'S; Art, Cave Exploring, C'S; *Pensacola Jr Col; Bible.*

SARVER, Robert Charles
Taft HS; Chicago, IL (20-804) NHS; Bsbl; Amer Leg A; COM; Hon Prog; NEDT; Advanced Placement; Span Lang A; *U of Ill; Ind Engr.*

SASSE, Ann Maria
Gordon HS; Gordon, NE (20-76) VP, CYO; Chor; FHA; Ger C; Pres, 4H; NHS; Tres, SC; Tr; DARGCA; Elk A; HCt; VofDEM; Fin, GS Attendent; Pres, Pep C; Vlbl; Semi-Fin, V of D; *Nebr Methodist Hosp Sch of Nurs; Nurs.*

SASSE, John Carl
Gordon HS; Gordon, NE (3-93) CYO; Parl, FBLA; NHS; SC; Var C; JV, Bkbl; Ftbl; Alg A; Bio A; Outst Fresh Boy; *U of Nebr; Med.*

SASSE, Teri Annette
McArthur HS; Hollywood, FL; Band; Key C; NHS; Span NHS; Mgr, Tr; COM; Opt A; Span Hon's; *Nurs.*

SASSER, J Yvonne
Permian HS; Odessa, TX; Chldr; Dbte Tm; FHA; Hmrm; Spch C; SC; Tri-HiY; COM; Citz A; Sci A; Spelling A; *Odessa Col; Eng.*

SASSER, Pamela Tamar
Jamaica HS; Jamaica, NY; Chldr; Chor; Drama; Orch; Sch P; Y-Tns; Arch; Bsbl; Bkbl; Sftbl; Swim; Tnns; God & Country A; VFW A; Yth Leg; VP, Yth Fel; Sr GSct; Girl's League; Attendance A; Creative Arts Soc; *Queens Col; Child Psych.*

SASSER, Tracey Lynn
Martin Van Buren HS; New York, NY; Band; Chldr; Chor; Drama; Y-Tns; Bsbl; Bkbl; Ftbl; Sftbl; Swim; Tr; COM; Cl Fav; Hon Prog; Math A; Yth Fel; Cpt, Gym; Pres Coun On Phys Fitness; PA; Tr & Field A; Obstacle Course.

SASSOON, Clare Penelope Mary
Sandy Spring Friends Sch; Sandy Spring, MD; Chor; Drama; Ger C; Hockey; Swim; Tnns; I Dare You; Swtht; Nurdleybawl; Frazlee & Ham; Hoop-e- doop; Friedlefrapp; *Arts.*

SATCHWELL, DeImna Christine
Post Falls HS; Post Falls, ID (8-151) Co-Ed, Ann; VP, Band; Chor; 4H; Spch C; SC; JV, Tr; 4H A; Spch A; Mus A; *U of Idaho; Mus Performance.*

SATHRUM, David Howard
West Concord HS; West Concord, MN (26-52) Band; Drama; VP, FFA; Spch C; Bkbl; Theater; FFA A; *Northwestern Bible Sch.*

SATOR, Linda Ann
Villa Park HS; Villa Park, CA (19-631) Pres, GS; NHS; Parl, Sr Cl; Tnns; Amer Leg A; CSF; Hon Prog; *Calif St U; Bio-Chem.*

SATOR, Lori Lynn
Villa Park HS; Villa Park, CA (26-400) Fr C; Ski C; JV, Bkbl; JV, Ftbl; JV, Sftbl; Tnns; JV, Tr; Pres A; *Stanford U; Law.*

SATORIE, Greogry Merle
N Bend Central Jr Sr HS; North Bend, NE (3-68) Ann; Band; Chor; Drama; Ensm; Madrigal; NHS; Spch C; Math A; All St Choir.

SATTERFIELD, Ginger Michele
Loganville HS; Loganville, GA; Ann; Band; Chor; Fin, Jr Miss Pagent; Lit Ral; Mjrte; Tres, Span C; Secy, SC; Tres, Tri-HiY; Sftbl; Beauty; HCt; *Mus.*

SATTERFIELD, Lynette Leanne
Eastwood HS; El Paso, TX (25%-750) Band; FHA; NHS; Rainbow; Outst Span Lang Stu; Eng Stu o-t Week; Band As; Ballet Schol; *Tex Tech U; Phys Therapy.*

SATTERFIELD, Marianne
Warner Acad; S Daytona, FL (3-11) Co-Ed, Ann; Band; Chldr; Chor; Drama; Semi-Fin, GS; Secy, Hmrm; A-Ed, Lit Mag; Co-Ed, Sch P; Span C; S-T, SC; Var C; Secy, Jr Cl; Secy, Soph Cl; Cpt, Bkbl; Cr-Ctry; Cpt, Sftbl; Tnns; Citz A; Cl Fav; HCt; Most Out; VFW A; VFW Orator Win; Yth Bicentennial A; *Daytona Beach Comm Col; Child Development.*

SATTERFIELD, Melanie Farrell
Lumpkin Co HS; Dahlonega, GA (10%-150) Pres, FHA; 4H; Hmrm; SC; Bkbl; COM; JA A; Sch Safety Patrol; FHA Jr Homemaker; Jr Missionary Vol; *N Ga Col; Pre-Med.*

SATTERFIELD, Pamela Ruth
Walhalla Sr HS; Walhalla, SC (6-138) VP, Anchor C; Ann; BC; Chldr; VP, FTA; Lat C; Secy, SC; Beauty; Cl Fav; Hon Prog; Journ A; VFW A; Best All Around; *U of SC; Chem.*

SATTERTHWAITE, Patricia Ann
St Mary's Acad; Alexandria, VA (3-64) Ann; Fr C; VP, Mu Alpha Theta; VP, NHS; SC; Tres, Jr Cl; Mgr, Tr; Bio A; COM; Hon Prog; NEDT; *U of Pa; Acct.*

SATTERWHITE, David Jerome
Lafayette HS; Buffalo, NY (101-300) MVP, Band; MVP, Chor; Hmrm; Ntl Yth Conf; Orch; ARC; SC; Var C; Ftbl; Tnns; Tr; Cl Fav; I Dare You; *U of Buffalo; Law.*

SATTLER, Melody Ann
Norfolk Sr HS; Norfolk, NE (81-345) *Evangel Col; Hist.*

SAUD, Abel
St Joseph's o-t Palisades HS; W New York, NJ (4-232) Drama; Pres, K of C; NHS; Span C; Span NHS; Swim; H of F; Hon Prog; MLS; *Sci.*

SAUDER, Elisabeth Ann
Wheeling Park HS; Wheeling, WV (33%-800) Chldr; Chor; Drama; Fr C; Hmrm; NFL; ARC; Spch C; Thes; Hockey; Spch A; Bishop's Prayer Book; Bishop's Good Samaritan Cross; Candystriper; *Juilliard Col; Dance.*

SAUDER, Nancy Grimm
Wheeling Park HS; Wheeling, WV (33%-800) VP, Drama; Fr C; GS; NFL; Cpt, Spch C; Thes; COM; Spch A; Bishop's Prayer Book; Thespian A's; NFL Degree of Distinction; *Syracuse U; Drama.*

SAUER, Audrey Donna
Eden Central Sr HS; Eden, NY (20-219) AFS; Band; Chor; Ensm; Ger C; NHS; Regent Schol; PA; *Concordia Col; Botany.*

SAUER, Curtis Alan
Cherokee Washington HS; Cherokee, IA (55-133) Var C; Bsbl; MVP, Ftbl; Co-Cpt, Wrest; HCt; *Wartburg Col; Math.*

SAUER, Ellen M
Manalapan HS; Englishtown, NJ (36-306) Pres, Chor; Drama; Semi-Fin, Jr Miss Pa; SCnt; Secy, Thes; Alg A; HCt; Math A; WW; WW, Mus Stu; Eng A; Most Dramatic; *Douglass Col; Theatre Arts.*

SAUER, Timothy James
Springfield HS; Springfield, MI (66%-80) SC; Ftbl; Golf; Co-Cpt, Tr; Wrest.

SAUER, Wayne Allen
Secaucus HS; Secaucus, NJ (2-164) Band; Fin, BS; Chor; Hmrm; Pres, Key C; NHS; Orch; Pres, Sci C; SC; VP, Soph Cl; JV, Bkbl; Cr-Ctry; Cpt, Tnns; Tr; Amer Leg A; COM; Citz A; God & Country A; Kiwanis A; Order/Arrow A; Pres A; Sci A; Yth Fel; Eagle Sct; PTSA; All Conf, Cr-Ctry; Hornaday Medal; WW; Hon Men, All Co Cr-Ctry; 1st Aid Squad; *US Military Acad; Sci.*

SAUERER, Elizabeth Marie
Cotter HS; Winona, MN (26-99) Ann; CYO; Drama; Ger C; VP, Sodality; COM; Yrbk Cert A; Sch Ldrship Medals; Sch Play Dramatics As; Sch Service Medal; *Col of St Teresa; Nurs.*

SAUERS, Joni Gay
Lakewood HS; Lake Odessa, MI (33%-200) Chldr; Hmrm; SC; Citz A.

SAULS, Angela Danene
Baldwin HS; Milledgeville, GA; Children's Church Helper; Ldr, Daisy's; Highest Cert Hon, Bible Course.

SAULS, Kathy JoAnn
Wenatchee HS; Wenatchee, WA; Tr; Hon Prog; Journ A; VP, Art C; *Journ.*

SAULSBURY, Ann Webb
Morristown Hamblen HS W; Morristown, TN (1-380) VP, Lat C; VP, SC; Tres, Tri-HiY; Pres, Soph Cl; Bkbl; Tr; Yth Foundation; Church Yth Council; *E Tenn St U; Dentistry.*

SAUM, Marjorie Marie
Fort Jennings HS; Fort Jennings, OH; Band; Chor; Fr C; Sch Achieve Tm; VP, Jr Cl; Sftbl; NEDT; *St Vincent's Sch of Nurs; Registered Nurs.*

SAUNDERS, Colleen Rene
Venice HS; Venice, FL; *Marshall U; Ed.*

SAUNDERS, Donald Gerald
Chester HS; Chester, PA (60%-625) Band; Chor; Drama; Ensm; Orch; Cl Fav; WW; *Cumberland Col; Mus.*

SAUNDERS, James Donovan
E Union Acad; Marion, LA (5-21) Chor; VP, Hmrm; Bsbl; Bkbl; Cr-Ctry; Sftbl; Cl Fav; Best Sch Spirit.

SAUNDERS, Jamie Lynne
Franklin Co HS; Frankfort, KY; Band; Co-Cpt, Chldr; Chor; Secy, FHA; Rptr, 4H; Secy, Mjrte; Sci C; SC; *U of Ky; Bio.*

SAUNDERS, Karen Renee
Saline HS; Saline, MI (25%-256) Band; Chor; FHA; Y-Tns; Sftbl; Church Choir; Chirst Ambassadors; Ldr, Children's Choir; Vol, Christian Sch; Tn Talent; Young Women's Mission Prog; *Southeastern Bible Col; Mus.*

SAUNDERS, Kimberley Ann
Lexington Sr HS; Lexington, NC (10-260) AFS; Band; Fr C; Chief Alt Marshal; *Converse Col; Vet Med.*

SAUNDERS, Phillip Lee
Suffolk HS; Suffolk, VA; Drama; HiY; InterAct C; VP, Lat C; NHS; Order/Arrow; Thes; Tri-HiY; Golf; God & Country A; Order/Arrow A; *Va Military Inst; Civil Engr.*

SAUNDERS, Raymond Martin Jr
Sunbright HS; Sunbright, TN (3-63) A-Ed, Ann; Band; BC; Chor; Drama; Pres, 4H; Rptr, Sch P; Sci C; SC; 4H A; MLS; Q&S A; Century III Ldrship Schol; 4-H A's; *U of Tenn; Pre Law.*

SAUNDERS, Richard Llewellyn
Pine Bluff HS; Pine Bluff, AR; Schol Achv A; *U of Ark; Engr.*

SAUNDERS, Sandra Kay
Ashland Sr HS; Ashland, OR (2-230) Band; Ger C; Math C; NHS; Chem A; Ntl Sci Found; WW; Nom, US Band; Yth for Understanding; *Oreg St U; Oceanography.*

SAUNDERS, Scott Alan
Peninsula HS; Gig Harbor, WA (71-330) Pres, Band; Dbte Tm; Ger C; Math C; NFL; Spch C; Bkbl; Ftbl.

SAUNDERS, Stephen Wayne
Douglas Southall Freeman HS; Richmond, VA (19-32) Sftbl; *Bluefield Col; Minister.*

SAUNDERS, Tim Mark
Venice HS; Venice, FL (73-388) Band; *Manatee Jr Col; Finance.*

SAUR, Charles Curt
Canyon HS; New Braunfels, TX; FFA; Mgr, Bkbl; Ftbl; Amer Leg A; *Tex A&M U.*

SAUSEN, Diane Jeanette
Forest Lake Sr HS; Forest Lake, MN (2-424) Drama; A-Ed, Lit Mag; NFL; NHS; Spch C; Spch A; Val; VofDEM; *U of Minn; Spch Pathology.*

SAUTER, Heidi Susan
John Jay Sr HS; Hopewell Jct, NY; Lat C; Tres, Soph Cl; Hon Prog; Yth Fel; *Law.*

SAVAGE, Bill Lowell
Fairfield Comm HS; Fairfield, IL (1-200) VP, Band; BS; Drama; FTA; Parl, JETS; Math C; NHS; Sci C; Span C; SC; Amer Leg A; DARGCA; NMS; *Sou Ill U; Pre-Med.*

SAVAGE, Connie Elizabeth
Franklinton HS; Franklinton, LA; Chor; Ensm; FBLA; Rptr, Sch P; Sftbl; Flag Corp; Drill Tm; *SE U; Ed.*

SAVAGE, Darcel Lorraine
Chester HS; Chester, PA; Co-Cpt, Chldr; FBLA; Record Keeping A; *Goldey Beacom Col; Executive Secy.*

SAVAGE, David Cabe
Pisgah HS; Canton, NC (10%-300) Bus Mgr, Ann; Fr C; French NHS; Monogram; Cr-Ctry; MVP, Tr; *NC St U; Forestry.*

SAVAGE, Douglas Hamilton
Westfield Sr HS; Westfield, NJ (21-660) F-Ed, Ann; Chor; Fr C; NHS; Rptr, Sch P; Sci C; Swim; Hon Prog; Inco Schol; NML of Commendation; *MIT; Mgt.*

SAVAGE, Jay Dee
Tahlequah Sr HS; Tahlequah, OK; Pres, Dbte Tm; VP, Hmrm; Key C; Pres, NHS; A-Ed, Sch P; SC; Pres, Soph Cl; Ftbl; Mgr, Tr; Cl Fav; Hist A; Math A; Shop A; St Hon Soc; PA; Cl King.

SAVAGE, Merrie Kay
Tahlequah Sr HS; Tahlequah, OK (46-250) A Cap Choir; Band; Chor; Drama; FHA; FTA; 4H; Bus Mgr, Hmrm; Sch P; Cpt, Swim; Tr; Hist A; Most Out; Spch A; 'S' C; Bible C; *Lubbock Christian Col; Art.*

SAVAGE, Robert Mark
Centerville HS; Centerville, OH (57-616) NFL; NHS; Spch C; Hon Prog; Spch A; Hon Recital, Piano; Hon A, Wittenberg U; Acad Schol, Butler U; Admission with Dist, Butler U; *Butler U; Law.*

SAVAGE, Sonya Lee
Greenup Co HS; Greenup, KY (11-250) BC; Chldr; 4H; Var C; 4H A; Eng A; *U of Ky; Med.*

SAVANNAH, Emmitt Alfonza Jr
O D Wyatt HS; Fort Worth, TX (27-500) Cpt, Cr-Ctry; Co-Cpt, Tr; Hon Prog; *Morehouse Col; Engr.*

SAVANT, Mike Lee
Bolton HS; Alexandria, LA (75-450) InterAct C; Key C; Mgr, Ftbl.

SAVARY, Mary Elizabeth
Riverview HS; Sarasota, FL (5%-780) JV, Chldr; Chor; Ensm; Fr C; Hmrm; Mod Mus Mas; NHS; Order/Arrow; Tri-HiY; Beauty; COM; Citz A; Hon Prog; JA A; Most Out; Order/Arrow A; Secy, Jr Cl; Phi Beta Chi, Sci Hon; Secy, St Jr Mus Assn; Chldr Qn; VP, Co Jr Mus Assn; Gold Cup, Piano Solo; *Law.*

SAVILLE, Steven Thomas
Hemet HS; Hemet, CA; A Cap Choir; Chor; Order/Arrow; Bsbl; Ftbl; Eagle Sct; Mus A; *Mt San Jacinto Jr Col; Engr.*

SAVILLE, Zina Annette
Northeast HS; N Little Rock, AR; Chor; Fr C; FBLA; Tr; Most Out; Yth Fel; Puppeteer, Children's Bible Hour; Monitor-Media Center A; Sign Lang Course; *Ed, Church Newspaper; Nurs.*

SAVITSKY, Michael Thomas
Bishop Klonowski HS; Scranton, PA (2-110) Lat C; Ed, Lit Mag; NHS; Rptr, Sch P; Span C; Tres, SC; Amer Leg A; COM; Hon Prog; *U of Scranton; Pre-Law.*

SAVOIE, Warren Luke Jr
Hahnville HS; Boutte, LA (110-215) CYO; Chor; VP, Key C; VP, Var C; Bsbl; Ftbl; Ftbl & Bsbl A's; *Nicholls St U; Gen.*

SAVRAMIS, Nicholas George
Dover HS; Dover, NH (60-400) BS; Demolay; Key C; NHS; Pres, Var C; Pres, Jr Cl; Ftbl; Tr; Hon Prog; All Tri-City Ftbl; Outst Lineman; *Pre-Law.*

SAWICKI, Doreen Marie
Mattituck HS; Mattituck, NY; Band; Fr C; Sch P; St Mus Comp Festival A; *Mt St Mary Col; Nurs.*

SAWIN, John Deibler III
Fruitport HS; Fruitport, MI (63-319) Band; Semi-Fin, BS; Chor; NHS; Span C; Lion A; HR; *Oral Roberts U; Mus.*

SAWIN, Nancy Ruth
Our Lady of Victory HS; Dobbs Ferry, NY (80-125) Chor; Span C; Hon Prog; GSct; Candystriper; Bicent Historic Restoration Comm; Exchange Prog, Fr GSct; Finance Comm Yrbk; *Mercy Col; Sociology.*

SAWYER, Bryan Lee
Estherville HS; Estherville, IA (5%-215) Var C; Bsbl; JV, Bkbl; JV, Ftbl; Golf; DARGCA; HCt; *Archt Engr.*

SAWYER, Cynthia Ellen
Quincy Sr HS II; Quincy, IL (10-760) A Cap Choir; Tres, Band; Ensm; NHS; Church Choir; Allerton Park Symp; Church Sch Tchr; Concert Band Hon A; City Band; Soc For Academic Achv A; Exchange Stu to Germany; *Knox Col; Bio.*

SAWYER, David Wayne
Washington HS; Washington, NC (83-290) Bus C; Span C; Proficiency A, DECA; *Bus Adm.*

SAWYER, Deanna Marie
Moreno Valley HS; Sunnymead, CA (4-460) Band; NHS; A-Ed, Sch P; Span C; Rptr, Sch Paper; *Journ.*

SAWYER, George Bernard
Alfred E Beach HS; Savannah, GA; Ann; Tres, Band; Tres, Chess C; Hmrm; Key C; VP, Mu Alpha Theta; NHS; Pres, Sr Cl; Tnns; Bio A; COM; Citz A; Math A; Sci A; Ntl Ach Semi-Fin; WW; Presbyterian Col Jr Fellow; *Ga Inst of Tech; Chem Engr.*

SAWYER, Jacqueline Elaine
Mayo HS; Darlington, SC; Secy, Band; FTA; NHS; VP, Sci C; Secy, SC; Alg A; HR; Tn Peer-Counseling; Ger A; *Psych.*

SAWYER, Jay Michael
LaMarque HS; La Marque, TX (56-351) Chor; Drama; Ensm; Thes; VofDEM; *Col o-t Mainland; Oceanographic Instrumentation.*

SAWYER, Jean Marie
Lawrence HS; Lawrence, KS (125-528) Chor; Q&S A; Pres, Yth Fel; Ed, Quill & Scroll; *Southwest Mo St U; Interior Design.*

SAWYER, Pam Dian
Reagan HS; Austin, TX (100-500) Ger C; JA A; *Special Ed.*

SAWYER, Richard Allen
Troup HS; Lagrange, GA; Band; Parl, FFA; 4H; 4H A; Del, St FFA Convention; Study & Tour Group, Italy; Del, St Soil Conserv Workshop.

SAWYER, Teresa Darleen
Edgewood HS; W Covina, CA (20-500) Chldr; VP, Chor; Bank Of Amer A; Yth Fel; Pres, Art C; Mus C; 1st Cl GSct; Church Choir; *Mt San Antonio Col; Home Ec.*

SAWYER, Timothy Kenneth
Eden Prairie HS; Eden Prairie, MN (92-230) A Cap Choir; Band; Chor; Drama; Ensm; Ski C; Span C; Ch, SC; Soccer; COM; Most Out; Fin, Natl Span Comp; All St Choir; *Bethel Col; Bus.*

SAWYERS, Jacqueline Sue
Clinton Co HS; Albany, KY (1-138) Ann; Band; Rptr, BC; Ensm; FHA; FTA; 4H; Pres, Math C; COM; 4H A; School Pins; *U of Ky; Med.*

SAWYERS, Larry Dale
El Dorado HS; El Dorado, AR; Ann; NHS; St Win, NSPE Schol; *La Tech U; Elec Engr.*

SAXE, Virginia
Minnechaug Regional HS; Wilbraham, MA (40-450) A Cap Choir; Ed, Ann; Chor; Drama; 4H; Hmrm; S-T, Lat C; Lit Mag; Madrigal; NHS; Ntl Yth Conf; F-Ed, Sch P; SC; Mgr, Tr; COM; Journ A; Magna Cum Laude; Q&S A; Yth Fel; Eng A; Home Ec A; Dist & All St Chor; *Bay Palm Jr Col; Legal Secy.*

SAXION, Nancy Elizabeth
Manasquan HS; Manasquan, NJ (63-362) Fr C; FNA; FTA; Hmrm; Key C; Ed, Lit Mag; Mjrte; Rptr, Sch P; Span C; Tres, Jr Cl; COM; Coun of Teach A; Woman's C Schol; Most Literary, Cl; *W Md Col; Fr.*

SAXON, William Hollis
S R Butler HS; Huntsville, AL (10%-700) Hmrm; Key C; VP, NHS; SC; MVP, Ftbl; Tr; Alg A; All City, All Tenn Valley, Ftbl; Rebel A, Ftbl; St Fin, Tr; *U of Ala; Bio.*

SAXTON, Barbara Ann
San Diego HS; San Diego, CA; All Amer Yth; Drama; Sch P; Sftbl; Type A; Stu Govt; William J Oak A; Health Professional A; *Oral Roberts U; Nurs.*

SAXTON, Nena Loice
Bentonia HS; Bentonia, MS (1-52) Cpt, Dbte Tm; Secy, FHA; 4H; S-T, Hmrm; Y-Tns; Co-Cpt, Sftbl; Hon Prog; Journ A; Star Student; Swtht; Yth Fel; MVP, Sftbl; Hon Stu A; *Miss Col; Computer Prog.*

SAYABOC, Simplicia Corazon
Molokai HS; Hodehua, HI; Band; CYO; Tres, FTA; Pres, NHS; Sci C; Ch, SC; Sci A; Ntl Hon A; Essay A; *U of Hawaii; Ed.*

SAYDAH, Donna Marie
Plainview-Old Bethpage HS; Plainview, NY (20%-326) Pres, FBLA; Type A; Foreign Lang Festival Committee; Outst Bus Stu A; *St U of NY; Secy Sci.*

SAYER, Craig Alan
Carrollton HS; Saginaw, MI (37-156) Dbte Tm; Drama; Thes; Pres, Soph Cl; Opt A.

SAYERS, Cheri Jayne
Andover HS; Bloomfield Hills, MI (34-435) Chldr; Chem C; Ger C; NHS; Ski C; Tr; Most Out; MVP, Cpt, Ski Tm; Hon Men, St Skiing; All Conf Skiing; *Mich St U; Vet Med.*

SAYERS, Cynthia Louise
Greenon HS; Springfield, OH; Ann; Chldr; FTA; VP, 4H; Hmrm; SC; Sftbl; 4H A; HCt; Yth Fel; Vlbl; Bowl; *Wright St U; Phys Ed.*

SAYES, Judy Kay
Glencliff HS; Nashville, TN (2-190) BC; S-T, Phys C; VP, Span C; SC; Alg A; Math A; Phy A; Sal; Spch A; NSF-SST Participant; Sci Chair; *Nashville Tech; Data Processing.*

SAYLER, Shelly Kay
Hartley Comm HS; Hartley, IA (6-71) Band; Chldr; VP, Chor; Drama; Tres, NHS; Secy, Jr Cl; HQn; Miss Congeniality; Yrbk Attendant; *Drake U; Med Tech.*

SAYLES, Ellen Morrow
Joliet W HS; Joliet, IL (2-603) Band; Ensm; Fr C; Orch; VP, Soph Cl; Hon Prog; Kiwanis A; NSOA Orch A; *Northwestern U; Mus.*

SAYLES, James Watson
Fairview HS; Boulder, CO; Eagle Sct; *Mo Sou St Col.*

SAYLOR, Judie Ann
Polk Pub HS; Polk, NE (7-19) Band; Drama; FBLA; GS; Tr; Spch A; Yth Fel; Hon Band; Vlbl; *Grand Island Sch of Bus; Acct.*

SAYLOR, Kay Elizabeth
N Mecklenburg HS; Charlotte, NC (71-350) Sch P; Span C; *U of NC at Chapel Hill; Communications.*

SAYLOR, Kimberly Dianne
Aiken HS; Cincinnati, OH (75-680) Fr C; Orch; Soccer; Sftbl Umpire.

SAYLOR, Sandra Elizabeth
Daniel Boone HS; Jonesboro, TN (30-320) BC; Chor; Ensm; Key C; 4H A; Type A; *Milligan Col; Acct.*

SAYLOR, Wendy Jo
Grundy Center Comm HS; Grundy Center, IA (52-75) Band; Chor; Thes; Spch A; Mus Contest Medals; *Westmar Col.*

SAYNE, Brian Lee
Richmond Sr HS; Richmond, IN; Chor; Ftbl; *Sci.*

SAYNE, Brice Eugene
Richmond Sr HS; Richmond, IN; Chor; Ftbl; Wrest.

SCAGGS, Angela Kay
LeRoy HS; LeRoy, IL (6-91) AFS; Band; Spch C; Var C; Pres, Soph Cl; Tr; Kiwanis A; *U of Ill; Bio.*

SCALESE, Cheryl Ann Lorraine
Riverside Jr-Sr HS; Taylor, PA (17-193) CYO; Chldr; Chor; FTA; Hmrm; NHS; Sch P; Pres, SC; Pres, Sr Cl; Pres, Jr Cl; Coun of Teach A; Hon Prog; Prom Court; WW; SC Service A; Driving Cert; *Wilkes Col; Math.*

SCALFANO, Jimmy George
Bolton HS; Alexandria, LA (7-200) Lit Ral; NHS; Span C; NMF; NEDT; *La Tech U; Physics.*

SCALISE, Judith Marie
Weed HS; Weed, CA (13-58) Chldr; Sch P; Ski C; Pres, Jr Cl; CSF; HQn; Hon Prog; *Col-o-t Siskiyous; Nurs.*

SCAMBLER, Sherrie Lynn
Fort Pierce Central HS; Fort Pierce, FL (32-500) Band; NHS; Commander, Rifle Corp; WW; PA; Band A; Grand Cr, Rainbow; *Indian River Comm Col; Pol Sci.*

SCAMMAN, Judith Lee
Wahconah Regional HS; Dalton, MA (40-240) Band; 4H; F-Ed, Lit Mag; Rainbow; Art Major Prog; *Berkshire Comm Col; Art.*

SCANLON, Candy Lee
Argenta-Oreana HS; Argenta, IL (5-105) Band; Chldr; Chem C; Chor; FHA; NHS; Citz A; Chor A; *Millikin U; Biochem.*

SCANLON, Eileen Gallagher
Acad of Saint Aloysius; Jersey City, NJ (4-127) A Cap Choir; Chor; Drama; Fr C; Hmrm; Lat C; Math C; NHS; Span C; SC; JV, Bkbl; COM; Hist A; Hon Prog; NEDT; Opt A; Sci A; Hon Men, US Naval A; Hon Men, 2nd Pl, St Paul Sch Sci.

SCANLON, Kerry Ann
Hinsdale Central HS; Hinsdale, IL; Chldr; Chor; Secy, SC; Var C; Secy, Jr Cl; Chem A; HCt; Hon Prog; Pres Clrm; Chem Qn; Pres Coun; Cpt, Pom Pon Squad; Sr Ldr, Phys Ed; *Trinity Col; Lib Arts.*

SCANNELL, Dana William
Kearsarge Regional HS; N Sutton, NH (10%-140) VP, AFS; Ed, Ann; Band; Chor; Drama; Tnns; Secy General, Mod UN, UN Coun.

SCARA, Susan Margaret
Manasquan HS; Manasquan, NJ (18-362) CYO; Hmrm; NHS; SC; Cpt, Bkbl; Hon Prog; Kiwanis A; Pres, Keyette C; Most Resourceful; Kiwanis Stu o-t Mo; *Pol Sci.*

SCARBORO, Rebecca Anne
Ahrens HS; Louisville, KY; Secy, NHS; Alg A; Chem A; Hist A; *U of Ky; Med Technology.*

SCARBOROUGH, Kamala Nanette
Estill HS; Estill, SC (25%-175) Ann; Drama; Math C; Sci C; Span C; *U of SC; Mus.*

SCARBOROUGH, Karol Ruth
Hazelwood Central HS; Florissant, MO (15%-800) Secy, A Cap Choir; Chor; Drama; Ensm; F-Ed, Sch P; Mus Schol, SW Baptist Col; Outst Vocal A; *Applied Voice.*

SCARBOROUGH, Suzanne Lewis
Phoebus HS; Hampton, VA (60-275) Chor; Pres, FBLA; Hmrm; Rptr, Sch P; SC; Y-Tns; Cl Fav; Journ A; Pres A; Q&S A; Bus Mgr, Sch P; Pres, Job's Daughters; *Thomas Nelson Comm Col; Bus Adm.*

SCARBOROUGH, William Bradley
Hattiesburg HS; Hattiesburg, MS; A Cap Choir; Bsbl; Bkbl; Ftbl; FCA.

SCARBOROUGH, Debora Lee
Plano Sr HS; Plano, TX (15-950) NHS; VP, Historian, VICA; Dist VP, VICA; *Tex A&M U; Bus.*

SCARBOROUGH, Ella Louise
Stone HS; Wiggins, MS; Fr C; Y-Tns; Sftbl; Tr; Telephone A; Explorer's C.

SCARLETT, James Sandford
S Bend Jr Acad; S Bend, IN (4-13) Bkbl; Ftbl; Sftbl; Tnns; *Andrew U.*

SCARNATO, Theresa Marie
Madison Acad HS; Huntsville, AL (7-43) BC; NHS; Ed, Sch P; Ski C; Mgr, Bkbl; COM; Hist A; Hon Prog; Math A; Sci A; Star Student; Bible A; Jr Chor; Psych A; Sociology A; *Abilene Christian U.*

SCARRY, Joseph Patrick
St Joseph's o-t Palisades HS; W New York, NJ (3-232) CYO; NHS; Rptr, Sch P; Span NHS; Secy, SC; Cpt, Cr-Ctry; Tr; Amer Leg A; Hon Prog; NEDT.

SCARRY, Kathleen
St Joseph's o-t Palisades; W New York, NJ (18-225) NHS; Span NHS; Hon Prog; WW; Dance As; *Montclair St U.*

SCATES, Penny Gail
Bryan Adams HS; Dallas, TX (50-756) FHA; NHS; ARC; Span C; Bkbl; Yth Fel; Homemaking A; *Dallas Baptist Col; Nurs.*

SCHAAL, Dave Wayne
Wm Kelley HS; Silver Bay, MN (8-160) AFS; Band; Chem C; Chor; Drama; NHS; Sci C; Ski C; SC; Var C; VP, Jr Cl; Semi-Fin, Bkbl; Cpt, Ftbl; Tnns; Bio A; HCt; NMS; Sci A; *U of Minn at Duluth; Spch Therapy.*

SCHAAL, Jeannine Lynn
Littleton HS; Littleton, CO (84-507) Chor; Ensm; JV, Bkbl; *Colo St U; Home Ec.*

SCHAAP, Susan Lynne
Waverly HS; Lansing, MI; Co-Ed, Ann; Hmrm; NHS; Rptr, Sch P; Sci C; Span C; SC; Secy, Sr Cl; Cpt, Pom Pom; Cadet Teacher; *W Mich U; Special Ed.*

SCHABACKER, Dawn Lee
Rochelle Township HS; Rochelle, IL; Band; Var C; Bkbl; Sftbl; Tnns.

SCHACHTSICK, Gina Marie
Regis HS; Stayton, OR (6-56) Co-Ed, Ann; NHS; Rptr, Sch P; Tres, SC; Hon Prog; *Oreg St U; Computer Sci.*

SCHAEDEL, James Douglas
Macomb HS; Macomb, IL; Chor; Drama; Ensm; Madrigal; Thes; *W Ill U; Drama.*

SCHAEDEL, Joanna
N Plainfield HS; North Plainfield, NJ (42-260) Chor; Drama; HCt; Yth Fel; Russian C; Church Choir.

SCHAEFER, David Edwin
Polo HS; Orient, SD (3-11) Rptr, Ann; Chem C; Chor; Drama; Rptr, Sch P; Pres, Var C; VP, Jr Cl; Pres, Soph Cl; Co-Cpt, Bkbl; Co-Cpt, Ftbl; Tr; COM; Cl Fav; Most Out; *SD St U; Civil Engr.*

SCHAEFER, Diane Marie
Shelter Island HS; Shelter Island, NY (4-19) Band;
CYO; Chldr; Chor; Community Yth Symph; FNA;
Hmrm; Mjrte; Math C; NHS; Orch; Sci C; Hockey;
Soccer; Sftbl; Tnns; COM; DARGCA; Math A; Sci
A; Mus, Ath, A's; GSct; *Baylor U; Sci.*

SCHAEFER, Donald Scott
Waukegan E HS; Waukegan, IL (146-629) Ger C;
Ski C; Mgr, Bkbl.

SCHAEFER, Joseph Patrick
Notre Dame HS; Portsmouth, OH (40-65) Chor; K
of C; Math C; Sci C; Span C; Secy, Sr Cl; Bsbl; Ftbl;
Tr; *Cincinnati Col; Acct.*

SCHAEFER, Karen Sandra
Von Steuben HS; Chicago, IL (12-333) F-Ed, Ann;
Chor; Ensm; VP, Hmrm; NHS; Span NHS; Hon
Prog; Sci A; Cpt, Bowl; *U of Ill; Computer Sci.*

SCHAEFER, Michael Harrison
Northgate HS; Walnut Creek, CA (25-413) Model
UN; NHS; Thes; CSF; *UCLA; Dramatics.*

SCHAEFER, Patrick Paul
Flatonia HS; Flatonia, TX (4-39) Co-Ed, Ann; BS;
FFA; Sch P; Pres, SC; Var C; Pres, Soph Cl; Tr;
DARGCA; *Blinn Jr Col; Med.*

SCHAEFFER, Robert Joseph
Oakville Sr HS; Mehlville, MO (20-350) AFS;
Tres, CYO; NHS; Co-Ed, Sch P; Bsbl; Co-Cpt,
Hockey; Amer Leg A; Journ A; Q&S A; Corona-
tion King; *U of Mo; Journ.*

SCHAFALE, Connie Beth
Freeburg Comm HS; Freeburg, IL (3-160) Ann;
Arch; Band; Chor; Drama; FHA; FTA; Sci C; Spch
C; JV, Arch; Mgr, Tr; Amer Leg A; DARGCA; Gr
Marshal; Sci A; Spch A; Church Yth Group; Art A;
Scholastic A; 1st Pl Mus A.

SCHAFER, Ann Louise
Southwestern HS; Piasa, IL (16-163) Band; Ch,
FBLA; Secy, 4H; NHS; Tr; 4H A; Hon Prog; I Dare
You; Hons Seminar; *Eastern Col; Bus.*

SCHAFER, David Clinton
Wyoming Sem; Kingston, PA (15-69) Chem C;
Chess C; Ger C; JV, Ftbl; NEDT.

SCHAFER, Lorrie Elizabeth
Spencer HS; Spencer, WI (10-83) Band; CYO;
Chldr; Drama; Ensm; FHA; 4H; Math C; Mod Mus
Mas; NFL; Span C; Mgr, Bsbl; Bkbl; 4H A; Vlbl;
Band A; *U Wis Marshfield; Conservation.*

SCHAFER, Tammy Ann
Spencer HS; Spencer, WI (6-65) Ann; Band; CYO;
Chldr; Chor; VP, Drama; FHA; Secy, 4H; Mod
Mus Mas; NFL; Spch C; 4H A; Band A; Best of
Yth; Vlbl; Chor A; Prom Ct; Drama A; *UW Marsh-
field; Child Care.*

SCHAFFER, John Scott
Benhaven HS; Olivia, NC; BC; Pres, FFA; Mono-
gram; Bsbl; JV, Bkbl; High Avg, FFA, Health, Phys
Ed; Fr A.

SCHAFFER, Michael Fred
Java Pub HS; Java, SD (7-15) Ann; Sch P; Var C;
Bkbl; Cr-Ctry; Ftbl; Hon Men, Conf Ftbl; *Black
Hills St Col; Wildlife Mgt.*

SCHAFFER, Sherri Lillian
Herreid HS; Herreid, SD (1-30) A Cap Choir; Ann;
Band; Chor; Ensm; Sch P; *Presentation Col; Med
Lab Technician.*

**SCHAFFHAUSER,
Charles Thomas**
Marvell HS; Marvell, AR (1-151) Ann; BC; FFA;
Civics A.

SCHAFFNER, Janis Mae
Leola HS; Leola, SD (13-43) Ann; CYO; Chor;
Parl, FBLA; Tres, FHA; 4H; Sch P; S-T, Var C;
Bkbl; Tr; 4H A; Hon Prog; MLS; Most Out; Type
A; Outst Sr Bus Stu; St Parl Procedure Tm; WW;
Ntl Col of Bus; Acct.

SCHALEGER, Paul Conrad
Honolulu Jr Acad; Honolulu, HI; Cpt, Band; Chor;
Community Yth Symph; Pres, Drama; Orch; Mus,
Drama, A's; *San Francisco St Col; Mus.*

SCHALLER, Hope
Bridgman HS; Bridgman, MI (10-75) JV, Chldr; Fr
C; Ger C; Fin, GS; Hmrm; SC; Cpt, Bkbl; Co-Cpt,
Sftbl; Pres A; All-St Vlbl; Cpt, Vlbl; *Special Ed.*

SCHALLER, Mary Lisa
Erie Comm HS; Erie, IL (3-103) 4H; Rptr, Sch P;
Sftbl; MVP, Tr; Lion A; Pres A; Yth Fel; Superior
HR; HR; Lion's C A; Pres Phys Fitness A; *Moline
Pub Sch of Nurs; Nurs.*

SCHALLOM, James Gerard
Oakville Sr HS; St Louis, MO (65-504) CYO; SC;
JV, Soccer; *Air Force Acad; Aviation.*

SCHALLOM, Roger David
Oakville Sr HS; St Louis, MO (221-445) CYO;
Mgr, Chldr; Soccer; Hon Men All Suburban W; St
Champs, Soccer; *McKenoree Col; Bus.*

SCHALOW, Scott Alan
Capitol City Baptist Sch; Lansing, MI (1-6) Ann;
Chor; Hmrm; NHS; Sch P; Pres, Sr Cl; Co-Cpt,
Bkbl; Tr; COM; Cl Fav; HCt; Magna Cum Laude;
Val; Pres, Yth Fel.

SCHANCK, Bruce Alan
Kingsway R HS; Swedesboro, NJ; Band; SC; JV,
Bkbl; JV, Tnns.

**SCHAPERKOTTER,
Nancy Jane**
Ottawa Hills HS; Grand Rapids, MI; A Cap Choir;
NHS; Cl Secy; Yth Group; Service A; Girls League;
Church Choir; *Central Michigan U; Social Work.*

SCHAPPERT, Steven Gerard
St Anthony's HS; Smithtown, NY (60-183) NHS;
Bkbl; Sacristan; Sanctuary Soc; Lector; Dun Scotus
Soc; *St U of NY; Horticulture.*

SCHARFE, Carol Suzanne
Oakton HS; Vienna, VA (50%-600) Chor; Hmrm;
Sch P; Hon Prog; *Old Dominion Col; Zoology.*

**SCHARLEMANN,
Daniel Andrew**
Carlyle HS; Carlyle, IL (10-125) Chess C; Ger C;
Kaskaskia Col.

SCHARLEMANN, Nancy Sue
Carlyle HS; Carlyle, IL (8-138) Co-Cpt, Chldr;
Drama; Secy, FBLA; NHS; Tr; HQn; HCt; St
Scholar; *Kaskaskia Col.*

SCHARN, Nancy Ann
Minn Lake Ind Dist 223 HS; Minnesota Lake, MN
(33%-31) Band; Chldr; Chor; Ensm; Secy, FHA;
GS; Madrigal; Mjrte; Monogram; NHS; Sch P; S-T,
SC; Tres, Soph Cl; Bkbl; Co-Cpt, Tr; Vlbl; *Mankato
St U; Mus Therapy.*

**SCHARNHORST,
Bruce DeWayne**
Hillsdale HS; San Mateo, CA (195-429) Drama;
Soccer; Swim; Tr; Wrest; COM; Pres A; *San Fran-
cisco St Col; Photography.*

SCHATH, Karen Rose
Tift Co HS; Tifton, GA (10%-450) A Cap Choir;
Band; Chor; Secy, 4H; Tri-HiY; Swim; Tr; 4H A;
Hon Prog; All-St Chor; *Recreation.*

SCHATZ, Anne Catherine
University HS; San Diego, CA (24-311) CYO;
Math C; NHS; Ed, Sch P; Bkbl; COM; Hon Prog;
CSF; Candystriper; Med Explorers; Badminton
Tm; *U of Calif; Med.*

SCHATZMAN, Robert William
Manasquan HS; Manasquan, NJ (27-371) CYO;
Pres, Key C; NHS; Ski C; SC; JV, Bsbl; Cpt, Ftbl; Cl
Fav; Kiwanis A; MLS; Rotary A; Star Student;
Vince Lombardi Outst Lineman A; *Wake Forest U;
Law.*

SCHAUB, DiAnna Maria
Samnorwood HS; Samnorwood, TX (1-12) Ed,
Ann; Pres, Chor; Ensm; Secy, FHA; GS; VP, SC;
Pres, Sr Cl; Pres, Jr Cl; Pres, Soph Cl; MVP, Bkbl;
Beauty; DARGCA; Most Out; FFA & Bkbl Swtht;
Best All Around; Secy, SC; 1st Runner-Up, Ctry
Qn; Miss Samnorwood; Farm Bureau Qn; Farm
Bureau Citz Seminar; *Wayland Baptist Col; Eng.*

SCHAUB, Diana Jo
Celina Sr HS; Celina, OH (10-275) Dbte Tm; FTA;
Pres, Ger C; Semi-Fin, GS; NHS; Bkbl; Sftbl; JV,
Tnns; COM; Math A; Vlbl; NML; WW; *Kenyon
Col; Pol Sci.*

SCHAUB, James Bryan
Pampa Sr HS; Pampa, TX; Bkbl; Octagon C.

SCHAUB, Karen Elaine
Bellevue Comm HS; Bellevue, IA (8-100) Band;
Chor; NHS; Secy, Yth Fel; Sunday Sch Teacher;
Secy, Yth Group; Piano Accompanist; *Finley Med
Col; Med.*

SCHAUB, Lawrence William
Hall HS; Spring Valley, IL; Bkbl; Power Mech C.

SCHAUB, Stephen Paul
Fremont HS; Fremont, MI (15-236) Community
Yth Symph; Dbte Tm; Orch; JV, Tnns; COM;
NMS; Spch A; Bicentennial Yth Debates; St Span
Contest; *Data Processing.*

SCHAUB, Susanna Charlotte
Hall HS; Spring Valley, IL (65-129) *IVCC; Acct.*

SCHAUER, Karen Jane
Ashley HS; Ashley, ND (5-40) Bus Mgr, Band;
Chor; Drama; Ensm; FHA; NHS; Rptr, Sch P; Mgr,
Bkbl; Alg A; Citz A; Hon Prog; Journ A; Pres A;
Spch A; Pilot A; Schol A; *UND; Med Tech.*

SCHAUER, Rita Mae
Monte Vista HS; Spring Valley, CA (121-476)
Chor; SC; Ftbl; COM; Hon Prog; Type A; Co-Cpt,
Vlbl; Cert of Common Core; Vlbl Ltr A; *Grossmont
Col; Bus.*

SCHAUF, Steven Lee
Blanchet HS; Seattle, WA (123-285) Chess C; Co-
Ed, Sch P; Span C; Ftbl; Wrest; *U of Santa Clara;
Pol Sci.*

SCHAUREN, Elaine Marie
Columbia HS; Columbia, PA (1-109) Band; Chor;
Drama; Math C; Secy, NHS; Orch; SC; Secy, Sr Cl;
Rotary A; NH Merit Ltr of Commendation; Aca-
demic Schol, Elizabethtown Col; *Elizabethtown
Col; Mus.*

SCHAUT, Michael Thomas
Beverly Hills HS; Beverly Hills, CA (10%-500)
Chess C; Dbte Tm; Fr C; French NHS; NFL; Cr-
Ctry; Ftbl; Soccer; Tr; *UCLA; Econ.*

SCHAVEY, Deborah Lynn
Hobart Sr HS; Hobart, IN (3-406) Pres, Ger C; Fin,
GS; Hmrm; Fin, Jr Miss Pagent; NHS; SC; JV,
Bkbl; Tnns; Sci A; Most Outst Adv Ger Stu; Schol
A; Outst Adv Art Stu; Jaycee Jr Miss; WW; Activi-
ties A; Foreign Lang; *Purdue U; Vet Med.*

**SCHEAFNOCKER,
Robin Lynne**
Karlsruhe Amer HS; Karlsruhe, GERMANY; JV,
Chldr; Drama; Ger C; Tr; Hon Prog; *Med.*

SCHEEL, Margaret Jane
Rocky River HS; Rocky River, OH (74-332) AFS;
Band; Hmrm; Orch; Rainbow; VP, Span C; Amer
Leg A; COM; Citz A; Hon Prog; Secy, Span C;
Sunday Sch Teacher; VP, Swim Tm Timers; Tutor;
Tr Tm Asst; Highest HR; *Slippery Rock St Col;
Special Ed.*

SCHEEL, Rian J
Hinsdale S HS; Darien, IL (10%-450) SC; Bkbl;
Ftbl; Tr.

SCHEEL, Valyn
New Braunfels HS; New Braunfels, TX (26-300)
FTA; Ger C; NHS; Theta Epsilon Nu; Outst Dan-
cer; Lt, Drill Tm; Qn of Hearts; Rep, Jr Cl; *Fine
Arts.*

SCHEELS, Beverly Louise
Pewaukee HS; Pewaukee, WI (1-135) A Cap Choir;
AFS; F-Ed, Ann; Chor; NHS; Rptr, Sch P; Pres,
Span C; Pres, Span NHS; Mgr, Bkbl; COM; Hon
Prog; WW Span Stu; 3rd Pl in Level; 3rd Pl Span
Pronunciation Contest; 1 in St Span Pronunciation
Contest; 5th Pl in Level II Span Contest; *Bus Adm.*

SCHEELS, Christine Anne
Pewaukee HS; Pewaukee, WI (2-125) A Cap Choir;
Band; Drama; Cpt, Math C; NHS; Span C; Span
NHS; Var C; Golf; Amer Leg A; Hon Prog; Math
A; Sci A; Type A; VP, Home Ec C; Fed Women's C
A; Math & Sci Excel A; Soc Women Engr; Wauke-
sha Mem Hospital Schol A; Milwaukee Sch of Engr
A;; *U of WI Eau Claire; Nurs.*

SCHEETZ, Connie Sue
Parkston Pub HS; Parkston, SD (39-83) Band;
FHA; Ger C; Mus As; *Eng.*

SCHEETZ, David Andrew
Lewis C Obourn HS; E Rochester, NY (6-168)
Band; Drama; Math C; NHS; Order/Arrow; Rptr,
Sch P; Tnns; COM; Hon Prog; Math A; Regent
Schol; NMSQT Commended Stu; Cornell U; Engr.

SCHEETZ, David Ernest Jr
Parkston HS; Parkston, SD; JV, Bkbl; JV, Tr; U of
SD; Mech Engr.

SCHEETZ, Mavis Jean
Parkston Pub HS; Parkston, SD (15-85) Band; Pres,
Dbte Tm; Ger C; NFL; Spch C; St Stu Congress;
Amer Leg A; Spch A; Fin, Miss United Tnager;
Math.

SCHEETZ, Michael Alan
Lewis C Obourn; E Rochester, NY (10-170) Band;
Drama; NHS; Order/Arrow; Rptr, Sch P; Tnns;
Hon Prog; Magna Cum Laude; Regent Schol; Syra-
cuse U; Computer Sci.

SCHEFF, Laura Suzanne
Chaska Sr HS; Chaska, MN (12-263) Band;
Drama; Fr C; Ger C; Jr Miss Pagent; NHS; Ski C;
SC; Tres, Jr Cl; Cr-Ctry; Golf; Hon Prog; Spch A; U
of Minn; Modern Lang.

SCHEFF, Marta Deanne
Chaska Sr HS; Chaska, MN (5-263) Band; Drama;
Fr C; Ger C; Fin, Jr Miss Pagent; NHS; Ski C; VP,
SC; 4H A; Hon Prog; Cr-Ctry Skiing; U of Minn;
Lang.

SCHEFFLER, Erich
Campbell Central Sch; Campbell, NY (11-60)
Chor; VP, Fr C; Ski C; Soccer; Tr; COM; Hon Prog;
Corning Comm Col; Archaeology.

SCHEFFLER, Jan Michelle
Okeene HS; Okeene, OK; Band; Tres, FHA; Bkbl;
Tr; Band Princess.

SCHEIBE, Randy Lee
Valmeyer HS; Valmeyer, IL (1-46) Chor; FFA;
Secy, 4H; Math C; NHS; Bsbl; Bkbl; 4H A.

SCHEIBEL, Laura Lee
H L Richards HS; Oak Lawn, IL (40-645) Band;
Mu Alpha Theta; NHS; Spch C; Tr; Spch A; U of
Ill; Engr.

SCHEIDEL, Jennifer Ann
Salem Acad; Salem, OR; 4H; Span C; Secy, Soph
Cl; Tnns.

SCHEIDERER, David Jacob
Boardman HS; Youngstown, OH (19-557) Pres,
Chor; HiY; NHS; Bkbl; Cr-Ctry; Cpt, Tr; HKg;
Hon Prog; Swtht; Hon Schol; Mem Schol; All-Conf
Tr & Bkbl; Kent St U; Bus.

SCHEIL, Charles David
Lenoir HS; Lenoir, NC (1-120) Secy, Band; Chor;
Hmmr; NHS; Rptr, Sch P; Ski C; Tres, SC; VP, Jr
Cl; Bsbl; Ftbl; Golf; Cpt, Swim; Tnns; Outst Civics
A; Hon Prog; Opt A; Opt Out Tn; Yth Fel; Yth
Foundation; Yth Leg; Swim, Ftbl, Band Contest,
A's; Duke U; Pre-Med.

SCHELL, Barbara Jean
Northfield Jr-Sr HS; Northfield, VT (10-93) A Cap
Choir; Band; JV, Chldr; Chor; Drama; Rptr, FHA;
Orch; Sci A; Ntl Piano Guild.

SCHELL, Deborah Ann
E Aurora HS; E Aurora, NY (25-269) Chor; NHS;
Regent Schol; Roberts Wesleyan Col; Math.

SCHELL, Kevin Thomas
Charlotte Cath HS; Charlotte, NC (5-101) Ed,
CYO; Chess C; Fr C; Key C; NHS; Sci C; Mgr,
Bsbl; Math A; Ntl Sci Found; Sci A; NC St U;
Textile Chem.

SCHELL, Margaret Ann
Moorefield HS; Moorefield, WV (8-85) Cpt, Chldr;
Chor; FBLA; 4H; NHS; Var C; VP, Sr Cl; MVP,
Bkbl; Sftbl; Tr; Master Coun, Dist Gov, Demolay;
St Jr Coun, Demolay; Hist Coloquiem; Meritorious
Service A; 2nd Pl Essay Contest; W Va U;
Math.

SCHELL, Thomas Jefferson
La Vega HS; Waco, TX (3-126) JETS; Tres, NHS;
Citz A; H of F; Hist A; Sci A; Health A; Elem
Analysis A; MCC; Real Estate.

SCHELLENGER, Carol Nadine
Sutter Union HS; Sutter, CA (6-101) Band; Chor;
Ensm; Pres, FHA; Ed, Sch P; Hockey; Kiwanis A;
Healds Bus Sch; Legal Secy.

SCHELLER,
Walter Jennings III
Connellsville Area HS; Connellsville, PA
(10%-700) Bkbl; Ftbl; W Va U; Law.

SCHELLHASE, Brian Douglas
Chambersburg Area Sr HS; Chambersburg, PA;
Area Sr HS Rifle Tm; Church Chimer; Area Sr HS
Glee C; Law Enforcement Prog; Joyful Noise Sing-
ing Group; Law Enforcement.

SCHELLPEPER, Nancy Ann
Stanton Pub HS; Stanton, NE (5-45) Co-Ed, Ann;
Band; Chor; Community Yth Symph; FHA; Pres,
4H; NHS; Sch P; S-T, SC; 4H A; Hon Prog; Vof-
DEM; Mus Ltr; NE Nebr Tech Col; Bus.

SCHENCK, Penny Sue
Moravia Central HS; Moravia, NY (2-100) Band;
Chldr; Chor; NHS; HCt; Hon Prog; Regent Schol;
Sal; Yth Fel; Cayuga Co Comm Col; Bio.

SCHEPERS, Thomas Joseph
Chaminade Col Prep; St Louis, MO (6-128) CYO;
NHS; F-Ed, Sch P; Alg A; Bio A; Hist A; Hon Prog;
Math A; Ntl Sci Symposium; NEDT; Sci A; Type
A; Fr A; Phys Sci A; U of Mo at Rolla; Nuclear
Engr.

SCHER, Timothy R
Carmel HS; Carmel, IN (121-658) CYO; Drama;
Thes; COM; Sci A; Hon Carrier, Indpls News; Ball
St U; Bio.

SCHERER, Edgar Dale
Argo Comm HS; Summit, IL (35-564) Ski C; Tnns;
U of Ill; Biol.

SCHERFF, Brad Dean
Parkview HS; Springfield, MO (60-420) Band; Mo
U; Phys Sci.

SCHERLER, Margot Elise
Geronimo HS; Geronimo, OK (2-35) Fr C; NHS;
Co-Ed, Sch P; Pres, Span C; Span NHS; SC; VP,
Soph Cl; DARGCA; HCt; Sal; VofDEM; Cameron
U; Journ.

SCHERLING, Victoria Lynn
St Benedict Acad; Pittsburgh, PA (1-65) NHS; A-
Ed, Sch P; Sci C; Amer Leg A; COM; MLS;
NEDT; Sci A; Val; Louis Caplan Human Relations
A; Vol Action Center Cert of Achv; U of Pitts-
burgh; Phys Therapy.

SCHERMERHORN,
Diane Marie
Louis E Dieruff HS; Allentown, PA; Mjrte; COM;
H of F; Hon Prog; MLS; Spelling A; Lang A; Outst
Achv, Span; Vlbl A; Diplomatic Service.

SCHERMERHORN,
Jeffrey Wade
Westminster HS; Atlanta, GA (50-100) Band; Or-
der/Arrow; Ftbl; Cpt, Swim; Citz A; ARC A; Black
Belt Karate; Outst Bible Stu; Eagle Sct; Duke U;
Bio.

SCHEUER, Kenneth David
Neshaminy-Langhorne; Langhorne, PA
(20%-700) Cpt, Bkbl; HKg; Ursinus Col; Econ.

SCHEUERMANN, Janet Marie
St Elizabeth HS; Pittsburgh, PA (7-102) Chor;
Drama; Ed, Lit Mag; Alg A; COM; NEDT; Pres,
Zonta C; Eng.

SCHEUNEMANN, Alice Louise
York Comm HS; Elmhurst, IL (400-925) A Cap
Choir; Chor; Ensm; Sup, IHSA Choir Contest; Ill St
U; Mus.

SCHEXNAYDER, Karen Benita
Lake Charles HS; Lake Charles, LA; Chldr; Secy,
FBLA; Pres, FHA; Secy, FTA; Alg A; Secy, Jr
Chapter Zeta Phi Beta; Outst Civics A; St Patricks
Sch of Radiology; Radiology.

SCHEXNEIDER,
Malton Anthony
Comeaux HS; Lafayette, LA (15%-266) VP, Chess
C; Sci C; JV, Ftbl; Hon Prog; Opt A; Sci A; S-T,
Chess C; U of Southwestern La; Phys Therapy.

SCHIBLEY, Laurie Ann
De Sales HS; Geneva, NY (10-50) NHS; Var C;
Bkbl; Soccer; Sftbl; Vlbl; Block D As.

SCHICK, Kimberly Anne
Denison HS; Denison, TX (25-500) Chor; Ch, Lat
C; Y-Tns; Hon Prog; Geom Ltr; Tex Women's U;
Nurs.

SCHICK, Pat Eileen
Denison HS; Denison, TX (20%-400) VP, Chor;
Lat C; Sci C; Swtht; Pres, Lib C; Bible C; Grayson
Jr Col; Ed.

SCHICKE, Mary Kathleen
Thomas Kelly HS; Chicago, IL (7-661) Chor;
Drama; Math C; Citz A; Kiwanis A; Most Out; Eng
A; Art Contest; PA; Kelly Hon Soc; Circle Campas
Col; Journ.

SCHIEFELBEIN, Kenneth Allen
Downers Grove HS N; Downers Grove, IL
(25%-850) Yth Fel; BSct; Cpt, Bowl Tm; PA A;
Bowl A; Col of DuPage; Marketing.

SCHIEFELBEIN,
Michele Marie
Austintown Fitch HS; Austintown, OH (1-717)
AFS; Band; FTA; Ger C; Tres, 4H; Hmrm; NFL;
NHS; ARC; Sch Achieve Tm; Sci C; Span C; Spch
C; SC; Swim; Bio A; COM; 4H A; Math A; Most
Out; NMF; Rotary A; Spch A; Val; VP, 4-H C; All
Col Schol; Amer Med Soc A; WW; Foreign Ex-
change, Columbia; Youngstown U; Med.

SCHIEFER, John Norman
Wynford HS; Bucyrus, OH (54-105) Co-Ed, Ann;
Band; Chor; Pres, 4H; Key C; Var C; JV, Bsbl; Mgr,
Bkbl; JV, Ftbl; 4H A; Stu Advisor, FFA; Agr.

SCHIEVELBEIN, Brenda Sue
Sequin HS; Seguin, TX (95-375) Ann; Band;
Drama; Ch, Ensm; Rptr, FTA; Rptr, Ger C; 4H;
Hmrm; Lit Mag; Rptr, Sch P; Sci C; SC; Swim;
Tnns; Tr; COM; Cl Fav; Hon Prog; Type A; Yth
Fel; SW Tex St U; Med.

SCHIEWE, Dianna Rae
Weston-McEwen HS; Athena, OR (1-61) Hmrm;
NHS; Span C; Bkbl; JV, Tnns; Hon Prog; JV, Vlbl;
Pioneer Princess of City; Med.

SCHIFERL, David Eugene
Abbotsford HS; Abbotsford, WI (4-56) BS; CYO;
Tres, Math C; VP, SC; Var C; Tres, Sr Cl; Pres,
Soph Cl; Bkbl; Elk A; Math A; MLS; VFW A; U of
Wis; Math.

SCHIFFER, Ilene
Kingsway Regional HS; Swedesboro, NJ (3-166)
Secy, NHS; Type A.

SCHILDGEN, Virginia Joyce
Lancaster Sr HS; Lancaster, WI (18-131) AFS;
Chldr; Chor; FHA; Hmrm; Lat NHS; NFL; NHS;
Span C; VP, SC; Pres, Soph Cl; Mgr, Bkbl; Tr; Citz
A; HCt; Duluth Voc-Tech Col; Broadcasting.

SCHILDKAMP, Donald Edwin
Iroquois Central Sch; Elma, NY (8-360) AFS; Or-
der/Arrow; JV, Soccer; Order/Arrow A; Med.

SCHILLER, Mary Ann
Plainview-Old Bethpage HS; Plainview, NY
(25%-326) VP, FBLA; Type A; Foreign Lang Festival Committee; Nurs Home Vol; Achv Cert, Lib
Vol; St U of NY; Secy Sci.

SCHILLER, Michael James
Raleigh-Egypt HS; Memphis, TN (1-255) Ed, Ann;
Fin, BS; Chem C; Key C; Lat C; Math C; Mu Alpha
Theta; NHS; Phys C; Sci C; Co-Cpt, Bsbl; Amer
Leg A; COM; Citz A; Hon Prog; Journ A; Lion A;
MLS; Opt A; Q&S A; ROTC A; Val; Fla Inst of
Tech; Ocean Sci.

SCHILLER, Susan Deborah
Tecumseh HS; Tecumseh, MI; Band; Span C; Bio
A; 4H A; Missionary.

SCHILLER, Vicki Lilien
The Buckley Sch; Sherman Oaks, CA (10-68) Ann;
Community Yth Symph; NHS; Orch; JV, Bkbl; Alg
A; Bio A; Hist A; Hon Prog; Math A; NEDT; Sci
A; Type A; Copy-Ed, Yrbk; Span Lang A; Hebrew
A; Hon Musician A; Mus Service A; USC; Bio.

SCHILLING, Bryan Glen
Wausau W HS; Wausau, WI (25%-456) Dbte Tm;
Bsbl; Bkbl; JV, Ftbl; U of Wisc; Law.

SCHILLING, Linda
El Camino Real HS; Woodland Hills, CA
(150-1076) Fin, GS; Pres, Hmrm; Parl, SC; Ch, Sr
Cl; COM; Chem A; Citz A; Hon Prog; Most Outst
Member, Girls League; Outst Member, SC; U of
Calif at Berkeley; Nutrition.

SCHILLINGER, Corinne Ann
Campbell-Tintah HS; Campbell, MN; Band; Ensm;
COM; Type A; HR; Attendance A.

SCHILLINGER, Jean Marie
Campbell-Tintah HS; Campbell, MN (10-45) Band; Ensm; COM; Attendance A; HR; Drum Ensm; First Aide A.

SCHILLINGER, Karen Ruth
Wausau E HS; Wausau, WI; Drama; Hmrm; ARC; ARC A; Prom Court; Cpt, MVP, Vlbl; S-T, VP, GAA; *St Joseph's Sch of Nurs; Nurs.*

SCHILLINGER, Rhonda Mae
Campbell-Tintah HS; Campbell, MN (4-39) Band; Chor; Ensm; Sch P; Bkbl; COM; HR; Clarinet Ensm A; Acct A; Bkbl A; Dist & Regional Solo A; Choir A; Band A; *Alexandria Voc Col; Clerical.*

SCHILREFF, Gregory Scott
Sidney HS; Sidney, NE; Band; HiY; Bsbl; Bkbl; Ftbl; Tr; Yth Fel; Nebr Shrine Bowl Ftbl Game; Sport Ltrs; Swtht Court; Bkbl Full Schol; S-C; *York Col; Recreation.*

SCHILTHUIS, Susan Ann
Salem HS; Salem, NJ; Band; Thes; Candystriper; Contact; Band A.

SCHIMMELPFENNIG, Cindi Sue
Morton HS; Morton, IL (73-298) Band; FHA; Pres, 4H; Orch; Var C; Co-Cpt, Bkbl; Sftbl; Tnns; 4H A; All Star Quiz Tm; Cpt, Vlbl; *Olivet Nazarene Col; Elem Ed.*

SCHIMPF, Cathy Jo
Arthur Hill HS; Saginaw, MI (33%-623) Orch; COM; Hon Prog; Yth Fel; Mus A; *Saginaw Valley St Col; Bus Adm.*

SCHIMPF, Sandra Lynn
Jackson Prep HS; Jackson, MS; Chor; Alpha Sigma Omega.

SCHIMPF, Susan Annette
Jackson Prepratory HS; Jackson, MS (25-180) A-Ed, Ann; Chor; Ensm; Lat C; NHS; Sci C; COM; Hon Prog; Magna Cum Laude; Alpha Sigma Omega; Cpt, Flag Corps; *Baylor U; Med Tech.*

SCHINDEHETTE, Marc Clarence
Reidsville Sr HS; Reidsville, NC (4-324) BS; Fr C; Math C; Ftbl; Tnns; JV, Wrest; Gr Marshal; *GMI; Engr.*

SCHINDLER, Kathryn Nannette
John F Kennedy Sr HS; New Orleans, LA (2-415) Band; BC; Pres, FBLA; Lit Ral; Mu Alpha Theta; Secy, NHS; Sci C; Var C; Bio A; COM; Hon Prog; Math A; Sal; FCA; Eng A; Beta A; Trig Medal; Young Life; Top 10 Srs; Church Yth Group; Band Librarian; *U of New Orleans; Phys Therapy.*

SCHINSKE, Diana Lynn
Grace Baptist Sch; South Bend, IN (1-23) Band; Chldr; Chor; Drama; 4H; Cpt, Mjrte; Thes; 4H A.

SCHIONNING, Michael William
Oak Ridge HS; Orlando, FL (14-720) Ger C; Math C; NHS; Sci C; JV, Ftbl; JA A; Math A; *Notre Dame U; Math.*

SCHIPPERS, Jan Carol
Adrian HS; Adrian, MI (25-430) Band; NHS; Orch; Phys C; Bkbl; Swim; COM; NMF; Art Cert; Drafting A; Varsity Letter; *U of Mich; Archt.*

SCHIRARD, Joseph Brantley Jr
Fort Pierce Central HS; Fort Pierce, FL (45-700) BC; Key C; Pres, Lat C; NHS; Var C; Co-Cpt, Bsbl; Ftbl; Citz A; *Oceanography.*

SCHIRBER, Richard Francis
St Mary's Central HS; Bismarck, ND (15-165) A Cap Choir; Chor; Drama; Ensm; Order/Arrow; Span C; Bkbl; Ftbl; Golf; Tr.

SCHIRMER, Donna Marie
Notre Dame HS; St Louis, MO (30-104) Ann; Secy, CYO; Chor; Hmrm; Sch P; SC; VP, Sr Cl; Co-Cpt, Ftbl; Soccer; Sftbl; Sch Rep, Vianney HS; *Barnes Hospital Sch of Nurs; Nurs.*

SCHIRO, Phillip Mack
Merryville HS; Merryville, LA (5-50) Parl, Fr C; Parl, Key C; Sci C; VP, Sr Cl; Cpt, Bsbl; Cpt, Bkbl; Cpt, Ftbl; Co-Cpt, Tr; Amer Leg A; COM; Citz A; Cl Fav; Most Out; NEDT; Sci A; VFW A; Vof-DEM; *McNeese St U; Civil Engr.*

SCHJENKEN, Sandra Gail
Grand Rapids Sr HS; Grand Rapids, MN (22-401) Arch; FHA; Arch; COM; Hist A; Hon Prog; JA A; Sci A; *Itasca Comm Col; Acct.*

SCHLADENSKY, Pamela Leigh
Hardaway HS; Columbus, GA (10%-400) Hmrm; SC; Tnns; Yth Fel; Dancing Company; Secy, Sorority; Gayfer's Tn Board; *Fashion Merchandising.*

SCHLAFER, Rachel Elisabeth
Harrison-Chilowee Baptist Acad; Seymour, TN (1-50) A-Ed, Ann; Band; Pres, BC; Co-Cpt, Chldr; Chor; Fin, Jr Miss Pagent; Orch; Secy, SC; Secy, Sr Cl; Secy, Jr Cl; Alg A; Balfour A; Bio A; COM; Cl Fav; Hist A; Opt A; Type A; Val; Miss Chilhowee; Natl HS Excellence A; Downing Trophy; *U of Tenn; Deaf Ed.*

SCHLAMB, Nathan Curtis
Albemarle HS; Charlottesville, VA (60-700) Tres, Ger C; NHS; Thes; Math A; NMS; *Chem.*

SCHLANGE, Howard D
Auburn HS; Auburn, NE (27-100) Band; JV, Golf; *Drafting.*

SCHLANT, E Stephanie
Westminster Girls' Sch; Atlanta, GA (13-91) AFS; Ann; Ger C; Lat C; Mgr, Soccer; Goete Inst A; Sunday Sch Teacher; Vol Action; Amer Hist A; Bible C; *Jackson Col; Humanities.*

SCHLAPPI, Shelley Anne
El Dorado Union HS; Placerville, CA (74-474) MGM; Heritage As; Alt, Al-Str Sftb; 2nd, Mason Lodg Essay Contest; Bobby Sox Girls Sftbl Tm; Pres, Trs, First Mother Lode Puppets.

SCHLASSA, Reinhard
Brecksville Sr HS; Brecksville, OH (39-363) Ger C; NHS; Sci C; Rogue & Peasant Slave A; *Case Western U; Pre-Med.*

SCHLATHER, Denise Ann
Thomas Jefferson HS; Tampa, FL; Ann; Fr C; French NHS; Civinettes C; *FSU; Fashion.*

SCHLATTMAN, Linda Marie
Blanchet HS; Seattle, WA (38-308) VP, CYO; Var C; Swim; *Med.*

SCHLEBECKER, Laura Catherine
Thomas Carr Howe HS; Indianapolis, IN (157-423) Drama; Ensm; Pres, 4H; Orch; ARC; Thes; Pres, Y-Tns; Mgr, Tr; 4H A; Best Thes; *Ind Central U; Pre-Med.*

SCHLECHT, Tamara Lee
Lutheran HS; Burbank, CA (2-84) Hmrm; CSF; *Ed.*

SCHLEICHER, Sandy Jane
Fremont Sr HS; Fremont, NE (15%-450) Span C; Yth Fel; Drill Tm; *Lang.*

SCHLEITWEILER, Patrick Marvin
Blanchet HS; Seattle, WA (33-308) CYO; Bsbl; JV, Bkbl; Elk A; H of F; Spch A; VFW A; Yth Ldrship A; Hon Camper; *Bus.*

SCHLEMMER, Kris L
Anamosa Comm HS; Anamosa, IA (50%-140) Bkbl; Golf; *Kirkwood Col; Acct.*

SCHLEMMER, Michelle Joanne
Newbury Park Adventist Acad; Newbury Park, CA; Chor; Ski C; Tnns; Tr; Pres A; *Pacific Union Col; Dental Hygiene.*

SCHLENKER, Gaye Lynn
Spring Vale Acad; Owosso, MI (15-31) Ann; Band; Chor; Ensm; Sftbl; Hon Prog; Stu o-t Mon; *Jamestown Col; Nurs.*

SCHLENSKER, David Richard
Lakewood HS; St Petersburg, FL (20-500) VP, French NHS; Jr NHS.

SCHLESENER, Nancy Lee
Kingman HS; Kingman, KS (4-96) Band; Chldr; Fr C; 4H; SC; Secy, Y-Tns; Cpt, Tnns; Tr; Citz A; 4H A; HCt; Hon Prog; St Scholar; Swtht; Ed, Yrbk; *U of Ala; Arts.*

SCHLESINGER, Kathy Louise
Miller Co R-III HS; Tuscumbia, MO (2-18) Ann; Chor; Pres, 4H; NHS; Sch P; SC; Tr.

SCHLESINGER, Ronald Terry
Paw Paw HS; PawPaw, IL (12-34) Chor; VP, FFA; 4H; SC; Var C; Bsbl; MVP, Bkbl; Cr-Ctry; Tr; 4H A; *Farmer.*

SCHLETER, Lisa Anne
Zion-Benton Township HS; Zion, IL (7-458) Fr C; Hmrm; NHS; Ski C; Golf; COM; NEDT; Yth Foundation A; Pom Pon Squad; Fr A; *Ed.*

SCHLETT, Ronald Allan
De Soto Sr HS; De Soto, MO; VP, Band; Chor; Bkbl; Tr; Bkbl Ltr; Band Ltr; Jr Band Rep; Tr Ltr.

SCHLICHTENMYER, Steven Vaughn
Samuel F B Morse HS; San Diego, CA (4-500) Chess C; Model UN; NHS; SC; Soccer; CSF; Hon Prog; Sci A; Sci Fair Stu Adv Board; *Pepperdine U; Fine Arts.*

SCHLICHTING, Carol Anne
Mankato W HS; Mankato, MN (86-321) Drama; Hmrm; Orch; Thes; Horse C; *Mankato St U; Art.*

SCHLITT, Cindy
Northbrook HS; Houston, TX; AFS; Swim; *Tex A&I U; Bio.*

SCHLOM, Ann Mary
Waupun HS; Waupun, WI (28-280) Ann; Band; Secy, Hmrm; Ski C; SC; Tr; GGAA; Hiker's C; *U of Wis; Dietetics.*

SCHLORFF, David Emerson
Hatboro-Horsham HS; Horsham, PA; Band; Tnns; Citz A.

SCHLUTER, Barbara Jean
Springfield HS; Springfield, IL (141-478) Pres A; *Lincoln Christian Col.*

SCHLUTER, Don Wayne
Dongola HS; Dongola, IL (1-28) Ann; Band; BC; Chor; Tres, FFA; Rptr; 4H; Sci C; Var C; Bsbl; Bkbl; Cr-Ctry; Amer Leg A; 4H A; HCt; Hon Prog; I Dare You; Sci A; *Shawnee Jr Col; Agr.*

SCHLUTER, Jane Marie
St Joseph HS; Kenosha, WI (10-226) GS; NHS; Ski C; SC; VP, Sr Cl; Bkbl; First Hon; *Notre Dame U; Sci.*

SCHMAL, Kristine Kay
St Joseph HS; St Joseph, MI (25%-372) Ann; Chor; Drama; Hmrm; Secy, Treas, Stu Coun; Office Monitor; Ed, Bus Mgr, 8th Grade Yrbk; Soloist, Christmas Pageant; *Performing Arts.*

SCHMALJOHN, Ginger Ann
Mt Vernon Township HS; Mt Vernon, IL (50-428) A Cap Choir; Ann; Chor; Drama; Ensm; Madrigal; Secy, Mod Mus Mas; Rainbow; F-Ed, Sch P; Span C; Journ A; Mus Ltr; *Sou Ill U; Marketing.*

SCHMALZ, Michael John
Hutchinson HS; Hutchinson, MN (80-200) Band; Order/Arrow; Co-Ed, Sch P; Tres, SC; Thes; Bsbl; Bkbl; Ftbl; Sftbl; Tnns; Tr; COM; Hon Prog; Order/Arrow A; Yth Fel; Distinguished Mus Stu A; *Vo-tech Col; Mech.*

SCHMATZ, Kathryn Lynn
Crestwood HS; Dearborn Heights, MI (7-357) VP, Band; Ger C; NHS; SC; COM; Most Out; Phi Beta Kappa; Mus A; *Kalamazoo Col; Math.*

SCHMATZ, Linda Marie
Crestwood HS; Dearborn Hgts, MI; Band; Chor; Ski C; Span C.

SCHMAUTZ, Tamara Kim
Flathead HS; Kalispell, MT (85-540) A Cap Choir; AFS; Dbte Tm; Ensm; Ger C; Key C; NFL; NHS; Ski C; Spch C; St Stu Congress; Tres, SC; Thes; Soph Cl; Cpt, Sftbl; Tnns; Spch A; St Spch Meet; *Engr.*

SCHMELING, Dean Lyle
Cherry Creek HS; Englewood, CO (22-700) Ann; Band; Bkbl; Flight Commander, Civil Air Patrol; Best Defensive Player, Summer Camp; *Air Force Acad; Aerospace Engr.*

SCHMELING, Dorothy Jo
Martin Co HS; Stuart, FL (8-500) GS; VP, NHS; Amer Leg A; Chem A; Hist A; *U of S Fla; Engr Sci.*

SCHMELING, Linda Sue
Century HS; Bismarck, ND (36-244) Fr C; Sch P; Span C; *Eng.*

SCHMELZER, Todd Eric
Maumee HS; Maumee, OH; Golf; U of Toledo; Bus Adm.

SCHMICK, Kristi Lynn
Corona Sr HS; Corona, CA; Chor; 4H; 4H A; HCt; Math A; Drill Tm; MVP, Vlbl; Fullerton Col; Ed.

SCHMID, Joni Sue
Warrensburg-Latham HS; Warrensburg, IL (10-101) AFS; Chldr; Chor; FHA; 4H; 4H A; Mich Christian Col; Bus.

SCHMID, Patricia Ann
Pine Bluff HS; Pine Bluff, AR; U of Ark; Bus.

SCHMID, Peter John
Pine Bluff HS; Pine Bluff, AR (5%-700) Band; Order/Arrow; Span C; Life Sct; Hon Stu.

SCHMID, Robert Edward
Poland Seminary HS; Poland, OH (100-350) Chor; Bsbl; Youngstown St U; Criminology.

SCHMID, Russ Lynn
Oxford HS; Oxford, KS (2-40) NHS; Tr; Kans Wesleyan Col; Hist.

SCHMIDT, Beth Leigh
Kingsway HS; Swedesboro, NJ; Tres, Arch; Band; Pres, Fr C; Tres, Key C; NHS; Sch P; Thes, Mgr, Bkbl; COM; Ottawa Col; Ed.

SCHMIDT, Catherine Austin
Gallia Acad HS; Gallipolis, OH; Co-Ed, Ann; Band; Fr C; FTA; Sci C; Tri-HiY; VP, GSct; GSct Wider Opportunity A.

SCHMIDT, Cecil
Thomas More Prep HS; Hays, KS (20-115) 4H; Ftbl; Tr; Wrest; 4H A; Kans St U; Med.

SCHMIDT, Cindy L
Central HS; Scranton, PA (50-400) Chor; Rptr, 4H; NHS; Rainbow; Sch P; Ski C; Span C; Swim; Hon Prog; JA A; Yth Fel; U of Scranton; Dental Hygiene.

SCHMIDT, Dave Arlan
Maddock Pub HS; Maddock, ND (10-23) Co-Ed, Ann; BS; Drama; Sch P; VP, SC; Var C; Pres, Jr Cl; Ftbl; Golf; Swim; Tnns; Tr; Eastman Kodak Photography A; Ftbl As; Sch of Mod Photography; Photography.

SCHMIDT, David Carl
Brookfield Central HS; Brookfield, WI (8-523) Rptr, Ann; Lit Mag; Math C; NHS; Order/Arrow; Wrest; Math A; NMF; Order/Arrow A; Sci A; Vilas Merit Schol; Pres, Yng Christians for Christ; U of Wis; Engr.

SCHMIDT, Denise Annette
Chester Area HS; Chester, SD (4-40) Ann; Band; FHA; GS; 4H; NHS; Rptr, Sch P; Amer Leg A; GS A; WW; U of Sd; Special Ed.

SCHMIDT, Eloise Lucille
Luverne Jr Sr HS; Luverne, MN; A Cap Choir; Band; Chldr; Chor; FHA; 4H; Hmrm; Madrigal; Sch P; SC; Yth Fel; Westmar Col; Home Ec.

SCHMIDT, Eric William
Argo Comm HS; Summit, IL (6-540) Model UN; Pres, NHS; Orch; Pres, SC; Hockey; Swim; Cpt, Tnns; Creighton U; Pre-Med.

SCHMIDT, Gretchen Marie
Berea HS; Berea, OH; Band; Timer's C; Prom Server; Early Childhood Ed.

SCHMIDT, Jacqueline D
Arlington HS; Arlington Hts, IL (33%-572) Chor; DECA; Trinity Col; Early Childhood Ed.

SCHMIDT, Jaimie Susan
Batavia HS; Batavia, IL (2-214) Band; Chor; Madrigal; Math C; NHS; Ski C; Tnns; COM; Hon Prog; Math A; Sal; Star Student; St Scholar; WW; St Summer Yth Mus Camp; HR; Woman's C Mus Schol; Wmn's C Mus Sch; Spec Mus Dept; DAHSS; Paul Peeples A; Lawrence U; Lib Arts.

SCHMIDT, Jay A
Benson HS; Portland, OR (100-407) Secy, Band; Order/Arrow; JV, Ftbl; Tr; Eagle Sct; Mus.

SCHMIDT, Jim Thomas
Wauconda HS; Wauconda, IL; BS; Pres, Var C; Co-Cpt, Ftbl; Tr; MVP, Ftbl; Sports A; Col of Lake Co; Bus.

SCHMIDT, Julie Beth Marie
Maine Township HS N; Des Plaines, IL (33%-400) Chor; Bkbl; Sal; Sci A; Concordia Col; Nurs.

SCHMIDT, Karen Lee
Spotswood HS; Spotswood, NJ (2%-114) Tres, AFS; Ann; Fr C; GS; Tres, Lat C; Lit Mag; Hon Prog; Library Sci.

SCHMIDT, Karen Marie
Marissa Jr-Sr HS; Marissa, IL (2-73) Chor; Ensm; 4H; NHS; Sci C; Amer Leg A; Sci A; SAE.

SCHMIDT, Karla Marie
Marissa Jr-Sr HS; Marissa, IL (1-73) Chor; Ensm; 4H; NHS; Sci C; Amer Leg A; Sci A; SAE.

SCHMIDT, Kathy Emery
Blytheville Sr HS; Blytheville, AR (160-285) Ann; BC; Bus C; Chor; Ensm; FBLA; FHA; 4H; Madrigal; ARC; ARC A; All Region Choir.

SCHMIDT, Katrina Lynn
Hickory HS; Sharon, PA (24-272) Bus C; Ger C; NHS; Sch P; Journ A.

SCHMIDT, Kent Christopher
Pueblo Co HS; Pueblo, CO; Ftbl; Tr; Wrest; Weight Lifting.

SCHMIDT, Kurt Wilson
Lincoln HS; Stockton, CA (50-350) Chor; Order/Arrow; JV, Ftbl; Citz A; Order/Arrow A; Yth Leg; Pres, Yth Cabinet; Backpacking C; Campus Life; Phys Ed A; U of Calif; Pre-Med.

SCHMIDT, Laurie Jean
River Valley Sr HS; Spring Green, WI (13-167) Band; Chor; Ensm; Mjrte; NFL; Orch; Ski C; SC; Secy, Jr Cl; Chor Directors A; Combined Band-Chor A.

SCHMIDT, Lawrence Franklin
Niagara Wheatfield HS; Sanborn, NY (30-453) Pres, A Cap Choir; Drama; NHS; SC; JV, Bkbl; Cr-Ctry; Ftbl; JV, Wrest; Cl Fav; Jazz Band; All St, All Conf, Choirs; Ithica Col; Mus Ed.

SCHMIDT, Lewis Lloyd
Gallia Acad HS; Gallipolis, OH; Band; Chem C; Chess C; Chor; FNA; 4H; Madrigal; NHS; Rptr, Sch P; Sci C; Span C; SC; Thes; Var C; Ftbl; Tr; Hon Prog; Chem.

SCHMIDT, Lisa Dawn
Whitehouse HS; Whitehouse, TX (13-99) Rptr, Band; BC; FHA; Mjrte; Fin, SC; Bkbl; Tr; Hon Prog; Hon Men, Vlbl; Tyler Jr Col; Sociology.

SCHMIDT, Lynn Ann
River Valley Sr HS; Spring Green, WI (15-156) Tres, Band; Chldr; Secy, Chor; Community Yth Symph; Madrigal; NHS; Q&S A; Band Directors A; Outst Musician A; UW at Eau-Claire; Mus.

SCHMIDT, Mark Steven
Thornton Twp HS; Harvey, IL (6-893) BS; Math C; NHS; Cr-Ctry; Swim; Cpt, Tr; COM; Hon Prog; St Scholar; Co-Cpt & Fin, Tr; General Assembly Schol NHS; U of Ill Urbana; Elec Engr.

SCHMIDT, Mary Jo
Kaukauna HS; Kaukauna, WI; A-Ed, Ann; Ski C; Pres, Span C; Q&S A; Rotary A; Excellence in Span; Yth Tutoring A; UW Whitewater; Span.

SCHMIDT, Raymond Joseph
Valmeyer HS; Valmeyer, IL (5-45) FFA; NHS.

SCHMIDT, Robert John
Skyline HS; Salt Lake City, UT (33%-800) Bus C; FBLA; Sci A; Yth Fel; Win, Marketing Research Manual; U of Utah; Bus.

SCHMIDT, Sandra Lee
Fern Creek HS; Louisville, KY (21-264) BC; Fr C; Rainbow; Mus A; Hospital Vol A; Church Pianist Cert of Appreciation; Ky Baptist Hospital Sch of Nurs; Registered Nurs.

SCHMIDT, Schuyler N
Lakeshore HS; Stevensville, MI (33%-336) Band; Ger C; Key C; Mgr, Tr; Jun Achv.

SCHMIDT, Susan Lynn
Pewaukee HS; Pewaukee, WI (21-159) Bus C; Var C; Co-Cpt, Bkbl; Cr-Ctry; Sftbl; Tr; Vlbl All Amer; Art A; All Conf, Vlbl & Bkbl; All Star Sftbl; U of Wis; Phys Therapy.

SCHMIDT, Theresa Allyson
Spotswood HS; Spotswood, NJ (20%-137) Sci A; Colorguard; Social Stu A.

SCHMIDTENDORFF, Rochelle Jan
Constantine HS; Constantine, MI (11-112) Ed, Ann; VP, Bus C; GS; Secy, NHS; Rptr, Sch P; VP, Jr Cl; Tres, Soph Cl; DARGCA; HCt; Most Out; Stu o-t Month; Southwestern U; Bus.

SCHMIDTKE, Todd Howard
St James Sr HS; St James, MN (35-130) Bsbl; Bkbl; Ftbl; Tr.

SCHMIEL, Peter George
Edina W HS; Edina, MN (275-550) Band; Ger C; Ftbl; Sftbl; Tnns; COM; Cr-Ctry, Slalom, Skiing; Concordia Col; Sociology.

SCHMIT, Deanna Marie
Cody-Kilgore Unified Sch; Cody, NE (3-16) CYO; Chor; Drama; Parl, FHA; Fin, GS; Pres, Mjrte; Secy, Sr Cl; Secy, Jr Cl; Tr; HCt; Math A; Val; Vlbl; Mus As; Secy Assistant, Work-Study Prog; Pep C As; Aux Legion GS A; Secretarial.

SCHMITT, Albert John
Columbia HS; Columbia, PA (2-121) CYO; Hmrm; VP, NHS; Span C; Tres, Sr Cl; Tr; Pres A; Rotary A; Co-Ed, Yrbk; Penn St U; Pre-Dental.

SCHMITT, Janet Mary
Mabel-Canton HS; Mabel, MN (2-52) Band; Chor; FHA; GS; Sch P; Up Bound; Mgr, Vlbl; All-St Band; Ntl Merit Commended Stu; Col of St Catherine.

SCHMITT, Joseph Gene
Guttenberg Comm HS; Guttenberg, IA (13-89) Bus Mgr, Ann; Band; Pres, Chor; Madrigal; Bsbl; Golf.

SCHMITT, Lori Ellen
Limestone Comm HS; Bartonville, IL (35-430) NHS; Span C; Span NHS; SC; Sftbl; Hon Prog; Span A; Ill Central Col; Science.

SCHMITT, Sherry Jean
Scott Comm HS; Scott City, KS (8-135) Band; Chor; Dbte Tm; Ensm; NFL; Var C; Tnns; Tr; HCt; Most Out; Mus.

SCHMITZ, Carl David
Bainbridge-Guilford HS; Bainbridge, NY (77-112) FFA; Ftbl; Tr; Yth Fel; Varsity & JV Ltrs; Heavy Equipment.

SCHMITZ, Carla Jean
Highland HS; Ewing, MO (10-126) CYO; VP, FHA; NHS; Sci C; Span C; Secy, Sr Cl; Hon Prog; Regent Schol; WW; Del, St FHA Conf; Pep C; Culver-Stockton Col; Bus.

SCHMITZ, John Eugene
Tower Hill HS; Tower Hill, IL (3-23) NHS; Pres, Soph Cl; Citz A; Hist A; Hon Prog.

SCHMITZ, Nancy Annette
Mansfield HS; Mansfield, LA; Chldr; City Conf; FBLA; Ch, Hmrm; Span C; SC; Beauty; Yth Fel; La Tech U; Phys Therapy.

SCHMITZ, Nancy Kay
Horton HS; Horton, KS (2-60) Band; Pres, CYO; Chldr; Chor; Ensm; VP, FHA; NHS; Sch Achieve Tm; Pres, SC; Alg A; Math A; Type A; Val; Kans St U; Home Ec.

SCHMITZ, Sharon Ann
Spring Woods Sr HS; Houston, TX; CYO; Span C; Bio A; Hist A; Eng A; Span A; Texas A&M U; Math.

SCHMUCKER, Cindy Lou
Greater Latrobe HS; Latrobe, PA (71-560) Pres, AFS; Secy, Ger C; NHS; Ed, Sch P; Q&S A; Pa St U; Elem Ed.

SCHNABEL, Leslie Grace
Lincoln E HS; Lincoln, NE (125-504) Secy, 4H; Community Playhouse; Nebr Summer Repertory Theatre; U of Nebr; Dance.

SCHNAIDT, Kristie Ann
Leola HS; Leola, SD (5-43) Band; Chor; Rptr, FBLA; Rptr, FHA; Pres, 4H; 4H A; Hon Prog; I Dare You; Type A; Army.

SCHNECK, Glenn Alan
Bonner Springs HS; Bonner, KS (31-200) Order/Arrow A; Eagle Sct; HR; Agr.

SCHNEIDER, Cheryl Ann
Lakeview HS; Battle Creek, MI (10%-350) A Cap Choir; Band; Fr C; NHS; Ski C; Var C; Swim; Tnns; COM; U of Mich; Law.

SCHNEIDER, Cynthia Elaine
Concordia HS; Oakland, CA; Citz A; *UC Santa Barbara;* Art.

SCHNEIDER, Cynthia Lynn
L W Higgins HS; Marrero, LA (3-341) Mu Alpha Theta; Pres, NHS; SC; DARGCA; Hon Prog; *U of New Orleans.*

SCHNEIDER, David Allen
Crestwood HS; Montua, OH; Bsbl; Bkbl; Ftbl; Tr; HR; *Math.*

SCHNEIDER, Debbie Joy
N Augusta Sr HS; N Augusta, SC (137-391) Bus Mgr, Ann; InterClub Coun; NHS; Future Secy's; Worth Adv, Grnd Cross of Clr, Rainb; *Legal Secy.*

SCHNEIDER, Gayle Lynn
Fairborn Baker HS; Fairborn, OH (15%-340) A Cap Choir; Ensm; Alg A; Drill Tm; *Defiance Col; Social Work.*

SCHNEIDER, Kimberly Anne
Argenta-Oreana HS; Argenta, IL; Chor; Ensm; Fr C; Ch, FHA; NHS; Ed, Sch P; SC; Sftbl; *U of Ill; Med.*

SCHNEIDER, Laura Ann
Plattsmouth HS; Plattsmouth, NE (4-164) Band; Chor; Fr C; Secy, Math C; NHS; Parl, Ski C; Secy, SC; Pres, Sr Cl; Tres, Jr Cl; Prom Ct; Graduation Speaker; *U of Ariz; Med.*

SCHNEIDER, Loren James
St Mary's Prep; Orchard Lake, MI (20-44) Chldr; Chess C; Ensm; Rptr, Sch P; Var C; Cr-Ctry; Tr; Hon Prog; ROTC A; 2nd Hon; *U of Mich; Bio-Chem.*

SCHNEIDER, Lori Kay
Wapello Comm HS; Wapello, IA (2-66) Ann; Band; Chor; Drama; Ensm; Pres, FHA; NHS; Orch; Thes; VP, Soph Cl; Mgr, Bkbl; NHS; Pres, Yth Fel; *Math.*

SCHNEIDER, Lynda Denise
Jefferson HS; Edgewater, CO (33%-367) A Cap Choir; Bus C; Chor; Ensm; FBLA; Fin, Jr Miss Pagent; Beauty; Spch A; Fin, Miss Colo; Win, Colo-Wyo Tn Talent; Fashion Model; Sunday Sch Teaching A.

SCHNEIDER, Marc Earl
Pewaukee HS; Pewaukee, WI (20-130) Band; Tres, Fr C; Cr-Ctry; Cpt, Hockey; Soccer; Tnns; Wrest; COM; Most Out; Yth Leg; Civil Air Patrol A's; USAF A; Flight School; Interntl Air Cadet Exchange; Cadet Commander; *U of Wis; Aeronautics.*

SCHNEIDER, Marie Bernadette
Berkley HS; Berkley, MI (39-571) VP, A Cap Choir; Madrigal; NHS; Magna Cum Laude; Ensm o-t Yr; Ntl Sch Choral A; Jr Deaconess; *U of Mich; Nurs.*

SCHNEIDER, Mary Lynn
James A Madison Sr HS; Houston, TX (80-530) Co-Ch, Chor; Hmrm; NHS; SC; Thes; COM; Citz A; Yth Fel; 3 Ntl Piano Cert and Pins; Vlbl; 4 Houston Mus Teachers Assn Cert; Gold Medal, UIL Solo Contest; Outst Reserve; Campus Life; *U of Tex; Mus.*

SCHNEIDER, Paula Marie
Chaska HS; Chaska, MN (4-244) NHS; Sftbl; HCt; DECA; *U of Minn at Duluth.*

SCHNEIDER, Richard Gregory
S Broward HS; Hollywood, FL (25-258) Band; Chor; NHS; Orch; COM; Sci A; Pres, UMYF; Church Organist; *U of Miami; Mus.*

SCHNEIDER, Rick Ken
Gasconade Co R-1 Sch; Hermann, MO (30-100) A Cap Choir; Ann; Band; Chor; Madrigal; Pres, SC; Co-Cpt, Bkbl; Bkbl; Fin, Cr-Ctry; Fin, Tr; Cl Fav; Math A; VP, SC; Math Assn of Amer A; *U of Mo; Engr.*

SCHNEIDER, Robert Kevin
Nordonia Hills HS; Northfield, OH (69-429) Pres, Band; Drama; NHS; Ski C; Thes; Hon Prog; Yth Fel; *Akron U; Engr.*

SCHNEIDER, Scott Lawrence
Nordonia HS; Macedonia, OH (94-518) Band; Drama; Order/Arrow; ARC; Ski C; JV, Cr-Ctry; Tr; Hon Prog; Order/Arrow A; ARC A; Yth Fel.

SCHNEIDER, Steven William
Saline HS; Saline, MI; ARC; Var C; Ftbl; Wrest; COM; ARC A; Health Occupations; *US Navy; Med.*

SCHNEIDER, Teresa Fay
Huntsville HS; Huntsville, AL (40-520) Band; Dbte Tm; Drama; Lat C; NFL; Spch C; Swim; Spch A; Scholastic Honorary C; U of Ala Schol; *U of Ala; Spch & Mus.*

SCHNEIDEWIND, Gail Linda
W J Woodham HS; Pensacola, FL (27-530) Band; Ger C; Bkbl; Sftbl; Vlbl; Ger A; *U of Vt; Math.*

SCHNELL, Jeffrey Lee
Potter HS; Potter, NE (1-17) Band; BS; NHS; Var C; VP, Jr Cl; Cpt, Bkbl; Ftbl; Amer Leg A; NEDT; Typing Pin; Chadron School Contest.

SCHNELL, Karen Elizabeth
Oak Hall Private Sch; Gainesville, FL (2-19) Ann; Chldr; Fr C; French NHS; Lat C; Lat NHS; Bkbl; Hon Prog; Highest Cl Schol As; Most Improved, Bkbl; Outst Fr A; Outst Lat A.

SCHNELL, Shirwin Shane
San Dimas HS; San Dimas, CA; Cr-Ctry; Ftbl; Tr; COM; Citz A; Most Out; Church Chor; Pres, Rock Climbers C; Sct o-t Yr, Best Worker, A's; V Ltr; Minister of Yth.

SCHNELLER, Benjamin Don
Middle Park HS; Granby, CO (2-76) All Amer Yth; Band; Bkbl; Cr-Ctry; Sftbl; Most Out; *Colo St U; Elec Engr.*

SCHNIEDERJAN, Helen Ann
Gainesville HS; Gainesville, TX; CYO; Chem C; Drama; Rptr, FTA; NHS; Ed, Sch P; Secy, Spch C; Secy, SC; MLS; Opt A; Spch A; VFW Orator Win; VofDEM; Dist Best Actress; Yth Dbte Win; 1st Pl Prose Reader; Dist All Star Cast; *N Tex St; Speech.*

SCHNIRRING, Susan Kay
Hastings Sr HS; Hastings, MN (90-430) AFS; Ann; Band; NFL; Spch C; Tnns; Spch A; *U of Wis; Pol Sci.*

SCHNITTGER, Becky Lemay
Hazelwood Central HS; St Louis, MO (262-1045) Drama.

SCHNITTGER, Mary Elizabeth
Hazelwood Central Sr HS; Florissant, MO (505-879) Chor; Drama; Nurs.

SCHNITZER, Diana Lynn
Rancho Alamitos HS; Garden Grove, CA (50-450) Co-Cpt, Band; NHS; SC; Citz A; Hon Prog; Yth Fel; Homecoming Som; Prom King Escort; *Pepperdine U; Social Sci.*

SCHNITZER, Sonja Kaye
Highland HS; Ewing, MO; Secy, Fr C; NHS; Sci C; VP, Soph Cl; JV, Bkbl.

SCHNOKE, Kenneth Scott
Lebanon HS; Lebanon, PA; Key C; Bsbl; Soccer; Type A; Bus.

SCHNORENBERG, Julie Beth
Hillsboro Sr HS; Hillsboro, OR (16-595) Parl, Fr C; Hmrm; Ed, Lit Mag; NHS; Tr; COM; Hon Prog; Sci A; St Scholar; Poetry As; Sch Literary Mag; Best Fr Stu; 3rd Pl, Shrt Stry, Sch Literary Mag; *Portland St U; Eng.*

SCHNORENBERG, Molly Marie
Hillsboro Sr HS; Hillsboro, OR (6-672) Ger C; Fin, GS; 4H; NHS; Tr; COM; 4H A; Nom, NCTE Writing Contest.

SCHNUIT, Nancy Carol
North East HS; Pasadena, MD; Band; Orch; SC; Commercial Art.

SCHNURMAN, Joanna Bennett
Wethersfield HS; Wethersfield, CT; Drama; Rptr, Sch P; Hockey; NEDT; High HR; *Law.*

SCHNURPEL, Jon Allen
Brazil HS; Brazil, IN (40-180) Key C; NHS; SC; Pres, Var C; Co-Cpt, Ftbl; Tr; Co-Cpt, Wrest; HCt; Pep C; MVP, Ftbl; MVP, Wrest; Key to The City A; Engr.

SCHOBER, Bethanne Jean
Plantation HS; Plantation, FL (5%-656) Mu Alpha Theta; NHS; COM; Jr Sinawiks; WW; *Oral Roberts U; Acct.*

SCHOBER, Suzanne Jane
Plantation HS; Plantation, FL (5%-650) Mu Alpha Theta; NHS; NEDT; *Oral Roberts U; Bus Adm.*

SCHOCK, Judy Kay
Leola HS; Leola, SD; Chor; FHA; Hon Prog; Type A; *Watertown Voc Sch; Childcare.*

SCHOCKE, Gary Lynn
Salem HS; Salem, IN (40-120) HiY; Hmrm; Lat C; Lit Mag; Bkbl; Spch A; *Cambellsville Col; Bible.*

SCHOEDEL, Peter Michael
Lutheran HS S; Afton, MO (5-187) Ger C; SC; Bkbl.

SCHOEFFLER, Micki Lane
Pasadena HS; Pasadena, TX (20-530) Hmrm; InterAct C; Mu Alpha Theta; Rptr, NHS; SC; Sftbl; Opt A; WW; Academic Excellence; *Tex Tech U; Math.*

SCHOEN, Craig Scott
Edgewater HS; Orlando, FL (80-650) Ger C; Bsbl; FCA; All Metro Bsbl; *Furman U; Bus.*

SCHOEN, Kelvin Lee
Mount Vernon HS; Mount Vernon, MO (3-105) Chor; VP, FFA; VP, 4H; Math C; SC; VP, Sr Cl; COM; Citz A; Curator A; 4H A; *U of Mo; Agr Mech.*

SCHOEN, Peggy Ann
Monett HS; Monett, MO (1-125) Chldr; Dbte Tm; Pres, FHA; FTA; GS; Pres, 4H; S-T, NFL; NHS; Sch Achieve Tm; Span C; SC; Tres, Soph Cl; Tnns; Amer Leg A; COM; 4H A; I Dare You; Journ A; Spch A; Type A; Hist, SC; Outst, FHA; GAA; VP, Yth League; 4-H Key A; *U of Mo; Journ.*

SCHOEN, William Ross
Sooner HS; Bartlesville, OK (7-300) Band; Ensm; NHS; Orch; Rptr, Sch P; Rptr, Sci C; JV, Golf; Masonic A; Math A; Yth Fel; All-Dist, All-St & All-Tri Bands; Spelling A; *Chem Engr.*

SCHOENER, Anthony Paul
Wethersfield HS; Wethersfield, CT; Band; Chess C; Orch; Ski C; JV, Soccer; Hon Prog; NEDT; Yth Fel; *Dartmouth Col; Math.*

SCHOENFELD, Frederick Carl
George J Penney HS; E Hartford, CT (15-400) Chess C; Bkbl; Sftbl; *Computer Sci.*

SCHOENFUSS, Michael David
Abbotsford HS; Abbotsford, WI (5-60) Band; CYO; Ensm; Math C; Tres, NHS; Rptr, Sch P; Elk A; Type A; NHS Schol; Abbotsford St Bank Schol; Part A in the 1977 NCTI; *DeVry Inst of Tech; Elec Tech.*

SCHOENHALS, Kristina Marie
William C Hinkley HS; Aurora, CO (17-548) A Cap Choir; Ed, Ann; Chor; Secy, FHA; Semi-Fin, GS; Madrigal; Math C; NHS; Rptr, Sch P; SC; Hon Prog; Hon Engr Inst; Quill & Scroll; Outst Sr; SG; *Colo St U; Engr.*

SCHOENHERR, Mark Wayne
Merrill Sr HS; Merrill, WI (36-345) Band; Ensm; Ger C; Bkbl; Ftbl; Tr; *Archt.*

SCHOENHOFEN, Lisa Kaye
Chippewa Falls Sr HS; Chippewa Falls, WI (25%-300) Chor; Span C; A-B HR; *Computer Technology.*

SCHOENLAUB, Paul Edward
Central HS; St Joseph, MO; Chem C; Chor; Ger C; Hon Prog; Eagle Sct; Mic-O-Say; Inter-Serv; Christian Ed Board; *William Jewell Col; Forestry.*

SCHOENROCK, Tracy Allen
Winnebago Lutheran Acad; Fond Du Lac, WI (1-75) Bkbl; Golf; Solo Flight On 16th Birthday; Private Pilots License; Prs, Winnebago Co Aviation Exp Grp; Over 100 Hours Flight Time; *Auburn U; Aviation.*

SCHOENTAG, Lisa Ann
Parkway N Sr HS; St Louis, MO; Cpt, Chldr; NHS; Math A; Art A; Jr NHS; *Sci.*

SCHOESLER, Gail Ann
Ritzville HS; Ritzville, WA (5-38) Ann; Band; Co-Cpt, Chldr; FFA; VP, FHA; 4H; NHS; Sch P; Secy, SC; VP, Jr Cl; Citz A; 4H A; Type A; Adams Co Wheat Qn; Win; Dist 4 Wheat Qn; Wash St Wheat Princess; Hon Band.

SCHOFIELD, Karen Kay
Parsons Sr HS; Parsons, KS (25%-200) Community Yth Symph; S-T, Orch; VP, Soph Cl; Bsbl; Type A; Pom Pons; Orch A; *Psych.*

SCHOFIELD, Linda Lee
Monte Vista HS; Danville, CA (25-350) Chor; Key
C; SC; Secy, Sr Cl; Secy, Jr Cl; CSF; *Biola Col;
Nurs.*

SCHOFIELD, Michael J
Crestview Sr HS; Crestview, FL (10%-215) A Cap
Choir; Anchor C; Band; Chor; Key C; Madrigal;
Orch; Golf; COM; Hon Stu; *U of Fla; Med.*

SCHOFIELD, Scharon Lynn
Hamburg Comm Jr-Sr HS; Hamburg, IA (10-45)
Ann; Chor; Sch P; Secy, Sci C; Spch C; Mgr, Bkbl;
Spch A; Art A; Poppy Qn Lg Aux; HR; *Drama.*

SCHOKMAN, Jeremy Keith
Ossinins HS; Ossining, NY; Co-Cpt, Soccer; Tnns;
Bus.

SCHOLAND, Steve Robert
Central Valley Pub Sch; Buxton, ND; FFA; Tr.

SCHOLEN, Barbara Joanne
Kentridge HS; Kent, WA (10%-579) Band; Drama;
NHS; Thes; Outst Social Studies Stu; *U of Wash;
Theatre Arts.*

SCHOLES, Ronald Scott
John F Kennedy HS; Denver, CO; Pres, Band;
Pres, SC; JV, Bsbl; Golf; City Band; *Colo St U; Vet
Med.*

SCHOLL, Dennis Lee Jr
Yorktown Sr HS; Arlington, VA; Order/Arrow;
Cpt, Ftbl; Sftbl; Tr; HCt.

SCHOLL, Penny Sue
Jackson Co Western HS; Parma, MI (19-145)
Band; Chor; Secy, NHS; Orch; Span C; Pres, Yth
Fel; *Jackson Comm Col; Nurs.*

SCHOLTEN, Mark Allen
Crystal Lake Comm HS; Crystal Lake, IL
(122-505) Ski C; *Purdue U; Chem Engr.*

SCHOLZ, Charisse Melanie
Heidelberg American HS; Heidelberg, GER-
MANY (16-173) F-Ed, Ann; Chor; Pres, Fr C;
Secy, Ger C; Hmrm; Ch, Model UN; NHS; ARC;
VP, SC; COM; NMS; PTA A; Daughters of Pa-
triots, Founders A; Soc Stu Achv A; Advanced
Placement A; Service Ac; *U of Va; Pol Sci.*

SCHOLZ, Janet Katherine
Brookville HS; Brookville, OH (5-178) A Cap
Choir; Band; GS; 4H; Lat C; VP, NHS; Sch
Achieve Tm; Secy, Sci C; SC; Bio A; 4H A; Opt
Out Tn; Chopin Piano A; Buckeye GS; WW; Hons
Seminars; *Sci.*

SCHOLZ, Jean Elizabeth
Ashley Hall HS; Charleston, SC; Pres, Ann;
Drama; Fr C; COM; Current Events, Lib, Sailing,
C'S; Pres, Art C; Ch, Church Yth Commission; Art
A; *Skidmore Col.*

SCHOLZ, Jennifer Lynn
Staunton River HS; Moneta, VA; Chldr; Lat C;
Math C; Monogram; Tr.

SCHOLZ, Sherri Rae
N Miami Sr HS; N Miami, FL (6-628) Band; BC;
Chor; Ensm; InterClub Coun; Pres, NHS; COM;
Hon Prog; Principal's List; Para-Med; Honoria,
Girl's Service C; *U of Fla; Pre-Vet Med.*

SCHOMBURG, Gretchen Marie
Kirkwood HS; Kirkwood, MO (4-587) Ed, Ann;
Ger C; GS; Secy, Tri-HiY; Var C; Tres, Sr Cl;
Tres, Jr Cl; Tres, Soph Cl; Cpt, Bkbl; Sftbl; Citz A;
Journ A; Q&S A; Coronation Qn; Gold 'K' & Gold
'N'; Sftbl Ltr; Christmas Maid; *U of Kans; Archt.*

SCHOMER, Timothy Edward
Pinellas Park Sr HS; Largo, FL (156-367) Ski C;
Soccer; Wrest; Pres A; Yth Fel; Church Scripture
Reader; Human Relations & Bi-Racial Commi; Co-
Ch, Principles Advisory Commi; Co-Ch, Bi-Racial
Committee; *U of Sou Calif; Oceanography.*

SCHONERT, Steven Paul
Bryan Sr HS; Omaha, NE; Order/Arrow; JV, Bsbl;
Ftbl; JV, Wrest; *W Point Military Acad; Computer
Sci.*

SCHONSHECK, Kathleen Kay
Spruce Creek Sr HS; Port Orange, FL (7-800) BC;
Fr C; COM; Civics A; *Mod Lang.*

SCHOOLER, Emily Jane
Winyah HS; Georgetown, SC (20%-145) Span C;
SC; JV, Bkbl; JV, Sftbl; Jr Civinettes; Pres, Soph C;
U of SC; Acct.

SCHOOLER, Judy Kay
Snyder HS; Snyder, TX (33-203) Pres, Pep C; *Midwestern St U; Dental Hygiene.*

SCHOOLER, Krista Annette
Colonel White HS; Dayton, OH (14-160) Chor; Fr
C; Choir A; *Ky St U; Mus.*

SCHOOLER, Raymond Reed
Winyah HS; Georgetown, SC (23-126) Ann; Fr C;
F-Ed, Sch P; VP, Var C; Mgr, Bsbl; Mgr, Ftbl; Hon
Prog; Journ A; *U of SC; Journ.*

SCHOOLFIELD, Cheryl Ann
Granite City N HS; Granite City, IL (85-455)
Band; Chor; Mod Mus Mas; NHS; VP, SC; Var C;
Cpt, Bkbl; Hockey; Cpt, Sftbl; GAA; *Phys Ed.*

SCHOONMAKER, John David
Newburgh Free Acad; Newburgh, NY (200-830)
Order/Arrow; Rptr, Sch P; Regent Schol; *Syracuse
U; Journ.*

SCHOONOVER, Linda Ann
Frankfort HS; Ridgeley, WV (10%-151) Band;
FTA; NHS; Bkbl; Tr; Co-Cpt, Vlbl; *Potomac St
Col; Photography.*

**SCHOONOVER,
TerryLee Sandy**
Sussex Co Voc-Tech HS; Sparta, NJ (20%-227) JV,
Hockey; COM; Journ A; Type A; Sunday Sch
Teacher; HR; *E Stroudsburg Col; Journ.*

SCHOPF, Nancy Jane
Momence HS; Momence, IL (50%-155) Chor; 4H;
Pres, Span C; Spch C; SC; Bkbl; Sftbl; Tnns; Amer
Leg A; *Kankakee Comm Col; Phys Ed.*

SCHORKEN, Susanna Maria
Moreau HS; Hayward, CA; Swim.

SCHORR, Jenny Marie
Westminster Christian Sch; Miami, FL; Band;
Chor; Ensm; ARC; Rptr, Sch P; Sftbl; Q&S A; Bus
Mgr, Sch P; *Purdue U; Interior Design.*

SCHORSCH, Paula Jean
Jamestown HS; Jamestown, ND (30-300) Chor;
Drama; Ensm; GS; Pres, NHS; Secy, Jr Cl; Co-Cpt,
Swim; Elk A; Most Out; Spch A; Cpt, Drill Tm;
MVP, Swim; 1st Pl, Dist Spch; *U of ND; Bus Adm.*

SCHORZMAN, Brenda Lea
Lamar R-1 HS; Lamar, MO (20-83) Band; Chor;
Tres, FTA; Madrigal; Mjrte; Jr Play Day; Jr-Sr
Banquet; Schol Bowl; Outst Mus Service A; *Secy.*

SCHOTT, Dennis Paul
Whitman-Hanson Reg HS; Whitman, MA (4-328)
Commercial C; NHS; Bkbl; COM; Hon Prog; MLS;
Syracuse U; Acct.

SCHOTT, Pamela Ann
Greater Latrobe Sr HS; Latrobe, PA (14-518) AFS;
Dbte Tm; Ger C; NFL; Hist A; NMS; Spch A;
Essay A; Exchange Stu; *Pa St U; Engr.*

SCHOTT, Randall James
Mandan Sr HS; Mandan, ND (14-313) Band; BS;
Chor; Ensm; Madrigal; Model UN; NHS; SC;
COM; Elk A; Most Out; Spch A; Cpt, Drill Tm; City
Sftbl League; Star Rating, St Mus Festival; Band A;
Louis Armstrong Jazz A; *Seattle Pacific U; Vocal
Mus.*

SCHOTT, Stephen Charles
Radford HS; Honolulu, HI (29-508) Pres, Y-Tns;
Hon Prog; 3rd Pl, School Magazine Contest; Pres,
Church Yth; NMS Commended Stu; *Bradley U;
Engr.*

SCHOWALTER, Steven Scott
Gillett HS; Gillett, WI (30-95) Bus C; FBLA; Ger
C; Var C; Ftbl; *NE Wis Tech Inst; Med Off Mgt.*

SCHOWE, Donna Sue
New Haven HS; New Haven, MO (2-41) Ann;
Pres, Band; Ensm; FTA; VP, NHS; Sch P; Beauty;
COM; Cl Fav; HCt; Hon Prog; Sal; Type A; Yth
Fel; Vlbl; Mus As; *U of Mo; Nurs.*

SCHRADER, Ann Esther
Unity HS; Mendon, IL (16-83) Ann; Chor; Secy,
4H; Co-Ed, Sch P; Sftbl; 4H A; Pres, Yth Fel; Parl,
Art C; Yth Choir; *Beautician.*

SCHRADER, Debbie Elizabeth
Briarcliff HS; Briarcliff Manor, NY (13-127) Chldr;
Chor; NHS; JV, Bkbl; Hockey; Academic A; Sch
Yrbk; *Bucknell U; Math.*

SCHRADER, Kathie Marie
Freeport Sr HS; Freeport, IL (110-449) A Cap
Choir; Chor; Ensm; Secy, Thes; Secy, Tres, Church
Yth; Mus A; Church Choir; Chor Soc; Sunday Sch
Teacher; *Concordia Teachers Col; Mus.*

SCHRADER, Kathryn Ann
Charter Oak HS; Charter Oak, CA (104-414) Ann;
Fr C; Sch P; Citz A; Math A; *Mount San Antionio
Col; Bus.*

SCHRAM, Nancy Rose
Detroit Lakes Sr HS; Detroit Lakes, MN (7-259)
AFS; Ann; Secy, Band; Ensm; Ger C; A-Ed, Lit
Mag; NHS; St Stu Congress; COM; Yth Leg; Secy,
Camp Fire Girls; Wohelo A; Rep, St Govt Seminar;
MMTA A, Piano; Reg & St Mus Cont Win, Flute;
Elem Ed.

SCHRAMER, Timothy George
Batavia HS; Batavia, IL (3-211) COM; Hon Prog;
Ill St U; Engr.

SCHRAMM, Steven Wayne
Chamberlain HS; Grassy Lake, CANADA (1-16)
Parl, 4H; Co-Cpt, Bkbl; 4H A; Vlbl; *Rick's Col;
Agr.*

SCHRAMM, Theodore Fred
University HS; San Diego, CA (29-315) Hmrm;
Var C; Ftbl; All League; *UCLA; Criminal Law.*

SCHREFFLER, Vivian Elizabeth
Halifax Co Sr HS; S Boston, VA (6-750) Tres, Fr C;
NHS; St Stu Congress; VP, Tri-HiY; Swim; Yth
Fel; Yth Leg; WW; *Col of William & Mary.*

SCHREIB, Kim Shirley
Henry P Becton HS; E Rutherford, NJ; SC; Hon
Prog; Co-Cpt, Flag Sq.

SCHREIBER, Hardy
Driscoll HS; Addison, IL (1-144) NHS; Bausch &
Lomb A; Hon Prog; St Scholar; *Ill Inst of Tech;
Mech.*

SCHREIBER, Nora Joan
Bensalem HS; Cornwells Hgts, PA (82-710) Band;
Chldr; Hmrm; SC; Hon Prog; Gifted Stu Program.

SCHREIN, Christina Gail
Cedar Falls HS; Cedar Falls, IA (160-450) Chldr;
SC; S-T, Sr Cl; *Iowa St U; Int Design.*

SCHREINER, Barbara Jean
Holy Cross HS; Marine City, MI (3-41) Chor;
NHS; Ski C; Secy, Jr Cl; VP, Soph Cl; Tr; HCt;
Dental Hygiene.

SCHREINER, Katherine J
Rib Lake HS; Rib Lake, WI (25%-62) Rptr, AFS;
Band; Chor; 4H; Mjrte; Co-Ed, Sch P; Secy, SC;
Var C; Pres, Jr Cl; Bkbl; Sftbl; All Conf Bkbl & Vlbl;
AFS Schol; AFS Host Sister; *Psych.*

SCHREINER, Nancy Lou
Newman HS; Wausau, WI (3-135) Math C; Co-Ch,
NHS; Rptr, Sch P; Tr; NEDT; *Special Ed.*

SCHREINER, Scott Alan
Jackson HS; Jackson, MO (43-267) Chess C; Chor;
Drama; NHS; Ed, Sch P; Bkbl; COM; Var C; Mgr, Bkbl;
Mgr, Tr; 3rd Pl, St Bookkeeping Tm; 4th Pl, Indi-
vidual St Bookkeeping; *SE Mo St U; Acct.*

SCHREPEL, Douglas Gene
Ulysses HS; Ulysses, KS (2-106) Band; BS; Chor;
Ensm; Madrigal; NHS; Span C; Var C; JV, Bkbl;
Ftbl; Tnns; Amer Leg A; Hon Prog; Yth Fel; BS;
Kans U; Engr.

SCHREPPEL, Julee Elaine
Oswego HS; Oswego, KS (10-40) Chldr; Chor;
FHA; Spch C; St Mus A.

SCHREY, Charles M Jr
Grand Island HS; Grand Island, NY (15-360)
Drama; NHS; Order/Arrow; Golf; NEDT; Regent
Schol; *Miami U; Systems Analysis.*

SCHRIDER, Carol Rose
Montgomery Blair HS; Silver Spring, MD; CYO;
Chor; Bkbl; Sftbl; Swim; Diving; Chor A; Drill Tm;
Glee C; Sftbl A; *Md U; Teacher.*

SCHRIER, April Lynn
Pennsville Mem HS; Pennsville, NJ (33-284) Band;
Chor.

SCHROCK, Valerie Jane
Harrisburg HS; Harrisburg, IL (11-196) Ann; 4H;
Christian Ed.

SCHRODER, Bryan Douglas
Eldorado HS; Las Vegas, NV (2-370) VP, Band; BS; Pres, Fr C; VP, NHS; Pres, Ski C; Golf; JV, Soccer; JV, Tnns; DARGCA; God & Country A; MLS; Order/Arrow A; Sal; WW; Eagle Sct; Pres, Explorer Post; *US Coast Guard Acad; Law.*

SCHRODER, Dee K
Orleans HS; Orleans, NE (25%-27) Chor; 4H; NHS; HCt; Fr A.

SCHRODER, Loretta Kay
Bennington Public HS; Bennington, NE (5-43) Ann; VP, Band; Chor; VP, 4H; NHS; Mgr, Bkbl; 4H A; All-Conf Vocalist; All-Conf Band Mem; *Midland Lutheran Col; Teacher.*

SCHROEDER, Arlene
Yorktown HS; Yorktown, TX (5-67) Band; NHS; God & Comm A; *U of Tex; Eng.*

SCHROEDER, David Greg
New Life Christian Sch; Bridgeton, MO; Ed, Ann; Chor; ACE Regional Convention; 1st, St Table Tnns; 3rd, Relay Tm; *U of Mo; Mus.*

SCHROEDER, Edward
Bridgman HS; Bridgman, MI (1-80) NHS; Sci C; Var C; VP, Jr Cl; Bkbl; Golf; *Valparaiso U; Bus.*

SCHROEDER, Fred William
Dwight Eisenhower HS; Utica, MI; Band; CYO; SC; Cr-Ctry; Tr; Prayer Group; VP, Ushers C.

SCHROEDER, Jeffrey Allen
Richwoods HS; Peoria, IL (9-517) Hon Prog.

SCHROEDER, Jil Denise
Fairmont Sr HS; Fairmont, MN (33%-200) Ann; Chor; Pep C; Gym; VP, St Off Ed Assn.

SCHROEDER, Kerry Lynne
Worthington Sr HS; Worthington, MN (7-265) Band; Chor; Ensm; Pres, FHA; Ger C; VP, 4H; 4H A; Hon Prog; Runnerup, Crailsheim Exchange; *Green House Mgr.*

SCHROEDER, Loretta Kay
Bennington Pub HS; Bennington, NE (5-43) Ann; VP, Band; Chor; Ensm; VP, 4H; Math C; NHS; Mgr, Bkbl; 4H A; All Conf Vocalist; All Conf Band; *Midland Lutheran Col; Teacher.*

SCHROEDER, Lynn Ann
Richwoods HS; Peoria, IL (190-512) Chldr; Chor; WW; *Ill St U; Home Ec.*

SCHROEDER, Pamela Lynn
Robert M LaFollette HS; Madison, WI (5-520) Pres, A Cap Choir; Band; Chor; Madrigal; Math C; Pres, NHS; Secy, Jr Cl; Amer Leg A; Citz A; DARGCA; Hon Prog; Kiwanis A; Vlbl; UW Alumni Schol; *UW Madison; Mus Ed.*

SCHROEDER, Rick Alan
Edgerton Sr HS; Edgerton, WI (10%-200) JV, Math C; SC; Pres, Soph Cl; JV, Bkbl; Co-Cpt, Ftbl; JV, Golf; Stu Faculty Coun; *Law.*

SCHROEDER, Robert
Lodi HS; Lodi, CA (100-500) AFS; Chldr; Chess C; FBLA; Key C; SC; Var C; JV, Bkbl; Tnns; CSF; Yth Fel; *U of Calif; Med.*

SCHROEDER, Robin Lee
Edgerton Sr HS; Edgerton, WI (10%-200) Chldr; Drama; Fr C; SC; VP, Jr Cl; Alg, GS; Stu Faculty Coun; Gym; Winterfest Court; *U of Wis; Journ.*

SCHROEDER, Ronald Alan
Burrell Sr HS; Lower Burrell, PA (125-350) Chor; Hmrm; Key C; Order/Arrow; Span C; Co-Cpt, Sftbl; Wrest; God & Country A; Order/Arrow A.

SCHROEDER, Ronda Lynne
Lewiston Cons HS; Lewiston, NE; FHA; Pres, 4H; Cpt, Bkbl; MVP, Bkbl; VP, Secy, Tres Rptr, 4-H C; 4-H C As.

SCHROEDER, Sandra Lynn
Gainesville HS; Gainesville, TX; CYO; FHA; NEDT; 2 Ceramics A; NJHS; *Cooke Co Col; Bus.*

SCHROEDER, Sarah Jeanne
Valparaiso HS; Valparaiso, IN; Band; Ski C; V-Tns; Foreign Exchange C; Jr NHS; *Valparaiso U; Pre-Med.*

SCHROEDER, Susan Barbara
W Bend E HS; W Bend, WI (145-318) Chor; Hmrm; NFL; *Moody Bible Inst; Bus.*

SCHROEDER, Terri Renae
Gackle Pub HS; Gackle, ND (10-23) Chor; GS; 4H; Tr; 4H A; VP, FHA; Tres, FYC; *Moorhead St U; Elem Ed.*

SCHROER, Joseph William
Potosi Sr HS; Potosi, MO (14-160) Pres, Band; Ensm; Pres, NHS; SC; Tr; I Dare You; MLS; Phy A; Rotary A; Band A; *Mineral Area Jr Col; Engr.*

SCHROER, Mary Ann
Hannibal Sr HS; Hannibal, MO; Band; Dbte Tm; Drama; Ensm; Secy, Fr C; 4H; Mjrte; Pres, SC; Swim; COM; Spch A; *U of Mo; Med.*

SCHROTT, Jeffrey William
The Park Sch of Buffalo; Snyder, NY; Soccer; Cpt, Lacrosse; *Canisus Col in Buffalo; Bus Adm.*

SCHROYER, Kathy Jo
Celina Sr HS; Celina, OH; A Cap Choir; Chor; Lat C; Yth For Christ; Wrest Chldr; *Mus.*

SCHRUMPF, Raymond Albert
Father Judge HS; Philadelphia, PA (15-630) CYO; Chldr; Cpt, Math C; NHS; Span C; Amer Leg A; Hon Prog; *Saint Joseph's Col; Food Marketing.*

SCHRUPP, Lisa Joy
Winthrop Comm HS; Winthrop, MN (10%-60) Chor; VP, Drama; Ensm; FHA; NHS; Sch P; SC; VP, Sr Cl; VP, Jr Cl; Hon Prog; Prom Royalty; Cl Attendant; *Vet Med.*

SCHRYBER, Richard Eppel
John Jay Sr HS; Katonah, NY (10%-300) Band; Ensm; Orch; Soccer; Mus A; Archt A; Sportsmanship A; Social Stu A; *Princeton U; Archt.*

SCHUBERT, Lisa Karen
Central Dauphin HS; Harrisburg, PA (20%-500) Ch, Hmrm; Co-Ch, SC; Tr; *Lehigh U; Computer Sci.*

SCHUCH, Connie Delois
Gibbon Pub HS; Gibbon, MN; Cpt, Chldr; JV, Chor; FFA; FHA; 4H; Spch C; 4H A; Spch A; Lib C; Ltrman's C.

SCHUCH, Julie Kay
N Mesquite HS; Mesquite, TX (10%-705) A Cap Choir; NHS; Div I Rating, Solo & Ensm Contest; *Baylor U; Voice.*

SCHUCK, Daniel Duane
New Hartford Community HS; New Hartford, IA (15-45) SC; VP, Var C; Bsbl; MVP, Bkbl; Ftbl; Bkbl Dove A.

SCHUCK, Kimberly Kaye
New Hartford HS; New Hartford, IA (5-36) Band; Chor; Pres, NHS; Rptr, Sch P; Span C; SC; Var C; Bkbl; Sftbl; WW; *Elem Ed.*

SCHUDDE, Albert Mark
Tillamook HS; Tillamook, OR (14-200) Band; Key C; NHS; A-Ed, Sch P; St Stu Congress; SC; Var C; JV, Cr-Ctry; JV, Tnns; Tr; *Concordia Portland Col; Wildlife Sci.*

SCHUEHLER, Diane Elise
Neshaminy Langhorne HS; Langhorne, PA (60-700) JV, Chldr; Chor; Drama; NHS; Tnns; HQn; Semi-Fin, HQn; *U of Del; Bus.*

SCHUETZ, Maria Louise
Stanton HS; Stanton, NE (3-45) Chor; *Bob Jones U.*

SCHUETZ, Steven Edward
George S Parker Sr HS; Janesville, WI (47-491) NHS; Order/Arrow; Pres, Var C; Ftbl; Co-Cpt, Wrest; BSct Eagle A; All-Conf Ftbl; *U of Wis; Bus.*

SCHUETZ, William John
George S Parker Sr HS; Janesville, WI (9-608) NHS; Order/Arrow; Ski C; Var C; Swim; Eagle BSct; *U of Wis; Engr.*

SCHUETZE, Steven Mark
Grace M Davis HS; Modesto, CA (2-425) BS; Chess C; Key C; Bank of Amer A; CSF; *UC at Berkeley; Physics.*

SCHUHMACHER, Randy Alan
Albert Lea Sr HS; Albert Lea, MN (315-575) BS C; Ftbl; Cpt, Wrest; *Makato St Col; Bus.*

SCHUHMANN, Karen Jean
Atlanta HS; Atlanta, TX (10%-220) Band; FTA; Rainbow; Sci C; Tnns; COM; Star Student; Yth Fel; *Baylor U; Med.*

SCHUITTER, Susan I
Chitenango HS; Chittenango, NY; AFS; Band; Orch; Amer Leg A; *Bus.*

SCHULER, Dawn Irene
Mckinleyville HS; McKinleyville, CA; Sr ASB Secy; Stu Govt, Fresh Rep; Forensics A's; Soph, Jr, Sr ASB Tres; Merit A; 4-H; *Point Loma Nazarene Col; Pre-Law.*

SCHULER, Lori Alice
Corona Ind HS; Corona, SD (3-10) Band; Co-Cpt, Chldr; Chor; A-Ed, Sch P; VP, Soph Cl; Bkbl; Tr; Journ A; Type A.

SCHULLER, Dean Alan
Austintown Fitch HS; Youngstown, OH (62-875) VP, Bus C; Ger C; NHS; Tnns; COM; Hon Prog; JA A; Most Out; Opt A; Sci A; VP, Art C; Cpt, Bowl; Children's Theater; Pres, Luther League.

SCHULLER, William Jeffrey
Spring Woods Sr HS; Houston, TX (3-510) CYO; JETS; VP, Mu Alpha Theta; VP, NHS; Sci C; Tres, SC; JV, Swim; JV, Tr; Hist A; Bill Archer Stu Intern; *Texas A&M U; Elec Engr.*

SCHULT, Dennis Timothy
S St Paul Sr HS; S St Paul, MN; Dbte Tm; NFL; Math A; *U of Minn; Math.*

SCHULTE, Mary Beth
Central Comm HS; Breese, IL (12-157) Secy, 4H; 4H A; Sacristan; Type A; WW; General Bus A; Eng A; Geography A; *Kaskaskia Jr Col; Executive Secy.*

SCHULTE, Michael James
Charlotte Valley Central Sch; Davenport, NY (2-44) Band; NHS; Var C; Bsbl; Bkbl; Golf; Soccer; Alg A; Hist A; Math A; Eng, Span, Mus, A's; *Acct.*

SCHULTE, Tom Dean
Wheelersburg HS; Wheelersburg, OH (6-134) NHS; Pres, Soph Cl; JV, Bkbl; Ftbl; Tr; Bio A; COM; HCt; Rotary A; Certified Lifeguard; *U of Ky; Sci.*

SCHULTZ, Anita Beth
Central Campus HS; Waukesha, WI; Chor; Span C.

SCHULTZ, Beverly Jean
New Bern Sr HS; New Bern, NC (154-436) Cpt, Chldr; Fr C; Hmrm; Secy, Sci C; HCt; MVP, Chldr; Jr Civitan; Girls Tri Chi; *E Carolina U; Dance.*

SCHULTZ, Cynthia Denise
Wyoming HS; Cincinnati, OH (9-25) Occupational Work Adjustment A.

SCHULTZ, Duvall Clark
Beaufort Acad; Beaufort, SC (1-43) Co-Cpt, Chldr; Var C; Tres, Soph Cl; JV, Bkbl; MVP, Tnns; HCt; Hon Prog; Headmasters A; *St Mary's Col; Math.*

SCHULTZ, Frank Mark
Westbury HS; Houston, TX (80-400) InterAct C; Order/Arrow; Bkbl; Pilgrim Lutheran Yth Group; *U of Houston; Elec.*

SCHULTZ, Jack David
Trinity Jr-Sr HS; Washington, PA (25%-450) Band; Dbte Tm; Pres, Hmrm; Key C; Co-Cpt, Bsbl; Ftbl; Wrest; HCt; MLS; Yth Fel; *US Air Force Acad; Engr.*

SCHULTZ, Jo Ann
Northeast Comm HS; Goose Lake, IA (14-104) Chor; FBLA; Madrigal; NHS; COM; 4H A; Spch A; Type A; Pres, Tres, Secy, Historian, 4-H C; Wrestlerette; Spch Contest; *Wartburg Col; Bus.*

SCHULTZ, Karen Aleise
Aiken HS; Aiken, SC (40%-600) Bus Mgr, Ann; Var C; Tnns; Hon Prog; *Speech Therapy.*

SCHULTZ, Lorie Ann
W Allis Central HS; West Allis, WI; *Teacher of Deaf.*

SCHULTZ, Micki Lynn
Oak Harbor HS; Oak Harbor, OH; Chor; Drama; Ensm; Thes; 4H A; Creative Writing A; Solo & Ensm Contest; *Lit.*

SCHULTZ, Nancy Marie
Oconomowoc Sr HS; Oconomowoc, WI (50-250) Ger C; Hon Prog.

SCHULTZ, Pamela Marie
La Salle-Peru Township HS; La Salle, IL (43-480) Chor; Fr C; NHS; Tnns; Chopin A; *IVCC; Med Records.*

SCHULTZ, Paul Victor
Clintonville Sr HS; Clintonville, WI (25-120) FFA; NHS; Ftbl; Tr; Wrest.

SCHULTZ, Sally Jane
Hortonville HS; Hortonville, WI (2-158) Secy, AFS; F-Ed, Ann; Secy, Band; Chor; Ensm; FHA; VP, 4H; VP, NHS; Sch P; Span C; Tr; 4H A; Journ A; MLS; Sal; Gym; Vlbl; Secy, Photo C; High Quiz Bowl Tm; *U of Wisc; Nurs.*

SCHULTZ, Sue Ann Holly
Hortonville HS; Hortonville, WI (1-158) AFS; Ed, Ann; Band; Ensm; FHA; 4H; NHS; Sch P; B Crocker A; 4H A; Journ A; Math A; Val; Mgr, Gym Tm; Most Intelligent; Secy-Treas, GAA; Photo C; Hi Quiz Bowl Tm; *U of Wisc; Actuarial Sci.*

SCHULTZ, Tamera Lynn
Tripp Pub HS; Tripp, SD (3-35) Pres, Chor; Ensm; Secy, FHA; VP, NHS; B Crocker A; Yth Fel; *Dakota Wesleyan U; Med Lab Technician.*

SCHULTZ, Tammy Lynn
Lakewood HS; Lakewood, CA (127-789) NHS; CSF; Drill Tm; Handbell Choir; Yth Choir; Sr Choir; *Long Beach City Col; Med.*

SCHULZ, Bradley Nicholas
Smithfield-Selma Sr HS; Smithfield, NC (20-355) Band; Bs; Drama; Hmrm; Secy, Key C; NHS; Orch; Span C; SC; Bsbl; JV, Soccer; JV, Wrest; Amer Leg A; Amer Leg Orator A; COM; Citz A; Hon Prog; Kiwanis A; VFW A; VofDEM; Yth Fel; Pep C; Key C Pres A; U of Tenn Hon Band; Schol, Wake Forest U; *Wake Forest U; Pol Sci.*

SCHULZ, Debbie Jean
New Haven HS; New Haven, MI; ARC; Var C; Sftbl; Yth Fel; Vlbl; Pres, Church Yth Fel; Church Choir; *Macomb Comm Col; Crime Prevention.*

SCHULZ, Debra Jean
New Haven HS; New Haven, MI (56-150) Sftbl; Vlbl; Pres, Yth Group; *Tenn Tech Col; Crime Prevention.*

SCHULZ, Diane Kay
New Haven HS; New Haven, MI; ARC; Var C; Bkbl; Sftbl; Sci A; Yth Fel; Church Choir; *Nurs.*

SCHULZ, Gregory Delmer
West Fargo HS; West Fargo, ND (31-166) Band; Chor; Tres, FFA; Pres, 4H; NHS; SC; JV, Cr-Ctry; JV, Tr; JV, Wrest; Cl Fav; 4H A; Math A; *ND St U; Agr.*

SCHULZ, Jayne Carol
John Marshall Jr-Sr HS; Milwaukee, WI; Chor; Math C; NHS; Orch; Ski C; Span C; SC; COM; Hon Prog; Church A's; NHS A; *U of Wis; Ed.*

SCHULZ, Karen Gayle
Parkston Pub HS; Parkston, SD (12-95) Band; Drama; FHA; Fin, GS; Bkbl.

SCHULZ, Karen Margaret
N Royalton HS; N Royalton, OH (147-304) Band; Chor; Drama; Ensm; Orch; Ski C; Yth Fel; Dance Group; Church A's; *Akron U; Nurs.*

SCHULZ, Mark Andrew
Spring HS; Houston, TX (15%-500) Chess C; Community Yth Symph; Orch; Golf; Cpt, Bowl Tm; *Tex A&M U; Law.*

SCHULZ, Pat Josephine
Lenoir HS; Lenoir, NC (17-110) F-Ed, Ann; Bus C; FBLA; Hmrm; Rptr, Lit Mag; Monogram; NHS; Span C; SC; Secy, Jr Cl; Pep C; Vlbl; *UNC-G; Psych.*

SCHULZ, Paul David
Montevideo Sr HS; Montevideo, MN (10-150) AFS; Band; Chor; Ensm; Madrigal; Orch; Order/ Arrow; Ed, Sch P; SC; Pres, Sr Cl; Pres, Jr Cl; Pres, Soph Cl; Tnns; Kiwanis A; Masonic A; Order/ Arrow A; Spch A; VFW Orator Win; VofDEM; Eagle Sct; Outst Tn A; *Concordia Col; Pre-Dentistry.*

SCHUMACHER, Valerie Beth
Gurley Pub HS; Gurley, NE (4-12) Ann; Band; SC; Var C; Cpt, Bkbl; Tr; Hist A; HCt; Cpt, Vlbl; HR; All Around Girl Ath; All Conf and All St Bkbl; All Conf Vlbl.

SCHUMAKER, Michael Burnell
Sycamore HS; Sycamore, IL (120-262) Bus C; Hmrm; Ski C; Var C; Bsbl; Co-Cpt, Cr-Ctry; Golf; Hockey; Tnns; Tr; Prom Ct; *Kishwakee Comm Col; Bus.*

SCHUMANN, Ann Marie
Brazoswood HS; Clute, TX (10%-500) Ger C; NHS; COM; Sci A; Art A; Cpt, Drill Tm; Tnns, GSct; VP, Episcopal Young Church; *N Tex St U; Psych.*

SCHUMANN, Kathy
Clarkstown S HS; W Nyack, NY; Span C; Bsbl; Bkbl; Soccer; Sftbl; Pep C; Interntl C; Horseback Riding C.

SCHUMANN, Sara Christine
New Braunfels HS; New Braunfels, TX (60-300) Band; Ensm; FTA; Ger C; Mjrte; Rptr, Sch P; Sci C; Soccer; Fin, Swim; Yth Fel; Twirler; Church Comm; Tres, Young Republicans; *U of Tex; Occupational Therapy.*

SCHUNDLER, Bret Davis
Westfield Sr HS; Westfield, NJ (160-670) CYO; Drama; Ger C; Ski C; MVP, Ftbl; Alg A; COM; Hist A; Hon Prog; Yth Fel; Cpt, Ftbl; Eng, Drama, A's; Church Deacon; All St Ftbl; Golden Book A; *Harvard U; Sociology.*

SCHUNTER, Randall Leigh
Longmont HS; Longmont, CO (56-485) Band; Chor; NHS; Bkbl; Cr-Ctry; JV, Tnns; Tr; Pres A; FCA; Ed, Tn Republicans; *Bus Adm.*

SCHURR, Barry Dean
East HS; Wichita, KS; *Law Enforcement.*

SCHUSS, Pamela Joan
Western Hills HS; Fort Worth, TX; Community Yth Symph; Orch; Rainbow; *Tex Christian U; Spch Pathology.*

SCHUSSLER, Henry William III
Hopewell Valley Central HS; Pennington, NJ (41-309) Chor; Secy, 4H; NHS; Sch P; 4H A; Yth Fel; *U of Ill; Chem Engr.*

SCHUSTER, Carla Rosann
Alameda HS; Lakewood, CO (210-627) Band; Secy, CYO; VP, FBLA; Citz A; Tres, FBLA; *Bus.*

SCHUTE, Carol Marie
Webster Groves HS; Webster Groves, MO (109-489) Chldr; Fin, Jr Miss Pagent; HCt; Gym Tm; Pep C.

SCHUTT, Lori Lynn
Columbus Sr HS; Columbus, NE (8-295) A Cap Choir; Ann; Sch P; Flag Carrier, Marching Band; Ed.

SCHUTTEMEIER, Elizabeth Jean
Cashton HS; Cashton, WI (13-81) Co-Ed, Ann; Band; Secy, Chor; Drama; Pres, FHA; Fin, GS; Madrigal; NHS; Secy, Sr Cl; DARGCA; HCt; Spch A; VofDEM; Forensics Spch C; Badger GS; Fall Festival Court; *U of Wis-Lacrosse; Elem Ed.*

SCHUTZ, Connie Anne
Findlay Sr HS; Findlay, OH; Chor; Amer Leg A; Citz A; HCt; Star Student; Yth Fel; Pepper C; Candystriper; *Psych.*

SCHUTZ, Thomas Nick
Eden Valley-Watkins Pub HS; Eden Valley, MN (4-100) BS; FFA; NHS; A-Ed, Sch P; H of F; *U of Minn; Hist.*

SCHUYLER, Tammy Marie
Oppenheim Ephratah Central Sch; St Johnsville, NY (32-38) Chor; Fr C; Soccer; Spch A; Vlbl; *Fulton Montgomery Comm Col.*

SCHWAB, Carlene Kay
Canyon HS; New Braunfels, TX (1-153) Band; Chor; Ensm; Pres, Ger C; GS; 4H; Jr Miss Pagent; Mjrte; NHS; Orch; Sci C; Mgr, Bsbl; JV, Bkbl; Sftbl; Amer Leg A; Elk A; Most Out; Rotary A; Val; *Tex A&M U; Wildlife Sci.*

SCHWAB, Susan Marie
Memorial Sr HS; Houston, TX (139-640) Chor; NHS; Span C; Span NHS; Bio A; Cpt, Drill Tm; *Trinity Col; Mus.*

SCHWALENBERG, Sue Ann
Kaukauna HS; Kaukauna, WI; Sftbl; Pom Pom; Sftbl; Pep C; Gym; *Poet.*

SCHWALL, Jeff Allen
Ontario HS; Ontario, OH (70-190) Var C; Ftbl; Wrest; Yth Fel; 3rd Sectionals, Dist, Wrest; *Baldwin-Wallace Col; Math.*

SCHWAN, William Charles Jr
James A Garfield HS; Garrettsville, OH (33%-137) Ann; Sci C; Span C; Superior, Excel, Sci Fairs; *Phys Sci.*

SCHWANKE, Gerald Arthur
Morristown HS; Morristown, MN (12-42) Band; NHS; SC; Var C; Pres, Soph Cl; Ftbl; Tr; Wrest; *Coaching.*

SCHWANKE, Randy Alfred
Morristown HS; Morristown, MN (14-38) Band; Chor; SC; Var C; VP, Sr Cl; Ftbl; Cpt, Swim; Cpt, Tr; Cpt, Wrest; HS All Amer; *Phys Ed.*

SCHWARTAU, Cheryl Ann
S H Rider HS; Wichita Falls, TX; Span C; UMYF; Coun on Ministries; *Midwestern St U.*

SCHWARTING, Kevin D
Williamsburg Comm HS; Williamsburg, IA (10%-103) Band; FFA; NHS; Var C; Co-Cpt, Ftbl; Wrest.

SCHWARTZ, Chet Marlow
Leander HS; Leander, TX (22-160) FFA; NHS; SC; Bkbl; Ftbl; Tr; COM; *Tex A&M U; Vet Med.*

SCHWARTZ, Daniel Albert
N Lebanon HS; Fredericksburg, PA (16-240) Band; Chor; NHS; Orch; Citz A; *Engr.*

SCHWARTZ, Darene
Palmer HS; Palmer, TX (10-28) Dbte Tm; Tres, FHA; Hmrm; Sch P; VP, SC; Cpt, Bkbl; Sftbl; Cpt, Tnns; Cpt, Tr; MVP, Bkbl; Best Female Ath; Fin, Tnns; Health A; Semi-Fin & Fin, Tr; Sch Brd A of Mt; Tn Magazine Super Sport o-t Month.

SCHWARTZ, Janice Rae
Belle Vernon Area HS; Belle Vernon, PA; Band; Span C; *Nurs.*

SCHWARTZ, Joel Andrew
Seguin HS; Seguin, TX; Band; Drama; Ensm; Best Supporting Actor; Outst Jazz Combo, Sam Houston Fest; *N Tex St U; Mus.*

SCHWARTZ, Lawrence Marc
Hightstown HS; Hightstown, NJ (9-308) F-Ed, Ann; Math C; F-Ed, Sch P; Cr-Ctry; Tr; Hist A; *Princeton U; Sci.*

SCHWARTZ, Lynn Diann
Martin Co HS; Stuart, FL (53-500) Hmrm; Var C; Cr-Ctry; Ftbl; Tr; Pres A; Jr Civitans; Mech Draw A; WW; *Indian River Comm Col; Law Enforcement.*

SCHWARTZ, Rebecca Maree
Steubenville HS; Steubenville, OH; Band; FNA; Hmrm; Secy, Lat C; Orch; Rainbow; *Nurs.*

SCHWARTZ, Robert Michael
Hinsdale Township HS Central; Hinsdale, IL (34-626) Order/Arrow; Swim; Hon Prog; Guard Organization; *Biol.*

SCHWARTZ, Suzanne Beth
Academia Maria Reina; Rio Piedras, PR; CYO; Hmrm; Lit Mag; NHS; SC; Co-Cpt, Var C; Swim; Tnns; COM; Hon Prog; Cert of Service, Stu Coun.

SCHWARTZ, Varian Phillip
Western Grove HS; Western Grove, AR (2-27) Order/Arrow; Pres, Jr Cl; Bsbl; Bkbl; *N Ark Comm Col; Park & Recreation.*

SCHWARZ, Carrie Lynn
Fort Pierce Central HS; Fort Pierce, FL; BC; Chldr; Parl, Key C; NHS; Var C; Tnns; Tr; Distinguished HS Ath; WW.

SCHWARZ, Catherine Joanne
Wellcome Mem HS; Garden City, MN (20-58) S-T, Ann; Band; Chor; Drama; FFA; FHA; 4H; 4H A; HCt; WW; *Mankato St U; Clothing and Textiles.*

SCHWARZ, Daniel Charles
Fairfield Sr HS; Fairfield, OH (30-735) CYO; NHS; Sacristan; Explorers; Career GE Group; Industrialarts A; *Trade.*

SCHWARZ, Daniel Leland
William Henry Harrison HS; W Lafayette, IN (1-340) Band; Ger C; Order/Arrow; Amer Leg A; Yth Fel; Tres, Jr Achv; *DePauw U; Med.*

SCHWARZ, Diane Patricia
Lomega HS; Omega, OK; Chldr; Hmrm; Rptr, SC;
Pres, Soph Cl; Bkbl; Sftbl; Tr; 4H A; Sal; *South-western U.*

SCHWARZ, Gretchen Eve
Shenendehowa Central Sch; Clifton Park, NY
(71-675) Band; Cpt, Chldr; Chor; Drama; Lat C;
VP, NHS; Ski C; SC; Var C; JV, Hockey; Tr; Citz
A; NEDT; Regent Schol; *Union Col.*

SCHWARZ, Janet Lyn
Park Center Sr HS; Brooklyn Park, MN (11-600)
F-Ed, Ann; Ger C; NHS; JV, Bkbl; Tnns; Tr; Hon
Prog; Pres A; ARC A; *Forestry.*

SCHWARZ, Julie Ann
Valley HS; Hazelton, ID (1-42) Band; Chor; FHA;
GS; VP, Mod Mus Mas; NHS; Ed, Sch P; Secy, Sr
Cl; Val; Vlbl; Drill Tm; Pep C; Sch Play; *U of Idaho;
Communications.*

SCHWARZ, Paula Ann
McCluer HS; Florissant, MO; A Cap Choir; Hmrm;
SC; Most Out; *Teacher.*

SCHWARZ, Rebecca Lyn
Wellcome Mem HS; Garden City, MN; Chldr;
Chor; Ger C; 4H; Math C; Sci C; Spch C; SC; 4H A;
HR A; Cl VP A; PA A; SC A; *Rochester Jr Col;
Nurs.*

SCHWARZ, Tonjia Sue
Valley HS; Hazelton, ID (3-46) Ann; 4H; NHS; JV,
Bkbl; Tr; *Gym.*

SCHWARZ, Wendy Lynelle
Valley HS; Eden, ID (4-45) 4H; Rptr, Sch P; SC;
Bkbl; Sftbl; Tr; 4H A; Pres A; Yth Fel; Tres, Yth
Group; Gym; Fin, St Tr; Semi- fin, St Gym; *U of
Idaho; Forestry.*

SCHWARZBACH,
James Edward
El Paso HS; El Paso, TX (25%-340) Co-Ed, Ann;
Tnns; *U of Tex; Photography.*

SCHWARZENBERG, Lori Deen
Orchard View HS; Muskegon, MI; Chldr; Swim;
Citz A.

SCHWEDE, Mark Phillip
Norfolk Sr HS; Norfolk, NE (26-300) NHS; Var C;
Ftbl; Tr; Wrest; Hist A; NMS; *U of Neb; Phys
Therapy.*

SCHWEER, Kellie Jo
S Park HS; Fairplay, CO; Ann; Drama; S-T, 4H; Sci
C; SC; Var C; Tr; COM; 4H A; HCt; Hon Prog; Sal;
Drama C A; *Lorretto Heights Col; Theater.*

SCHWEHR, Michael W
Medina Sr HS; Medina, NY (7-190) A Cap Choir;
VP, Band; Ensm; Hmrm; VP, NHS; VP, Order/
Arrow; SC; JV, Ftbl; JV, Wrest; NEDT; Regent
Schol; *Clemson U; Engr.*

SCHWEIGER, James
Gilbert HS; Gilbert, MN (2-65) CYO; NHS; Sch P;
Sci C; Ftbl; Mgr, Hockey; NMF; NMS; Sal; *U of
Minn; Pre-Dentistry.*

SCHWEIHOFER, Sharon Marie
Holy Cross HS; Marine City, MI (5-41) NHS; Ski
C; Hon Prog; Type A; *St Clair Co Comm Col;
Secretarial.*

SCHWEIHOFER, Susanne Mary
Holy Cross HS; Marine City, MI; NHS; Hon Prog;
St Clair Co Comm Col; Bus.

SCHWEINFURTH,
William Robert
Howland HS; Warren, OH (50-489) Band; Fin, BS;
S-T, Chess C; Ensm; Fr C; Hmrm; NHS; Orch;
Co-Ch, Order/Arrow; Sch Achieve Tm; Rptr, Sch
P; Tres, SC; Tres, Sr Cl; Secy, Jr Cl; OS, Soph Cl;
Citz A; God & Country A; Hon Prog; Math A;
Order/Arrow A; Pres A; Eagle Sct A; Rifle Tm A;
World Conservation A; *Ohio St U; Engr.*

SCHWEITZER, Cynthia Ann
Dra Maria Cadilla de Martinez HS; Arecibo, PR
(40-429) CYO; Chor; Drama; FHA; Pres, Hmrm;
Pres, SC; Tres, Sr Cl; Bkbl; Sftbl; Swim; Tnns;
COM; Cl Fav; Hon Prog; Math A; Opt A; Sci A;
Star Student; *Universidad de Rio Piedras; Law.*

SCHWEITZER,
Michael Theodore
Bowman HS; Wadesboro, NC; VP, Band; Lat C; Sci
C; SC; JV, Bkbl; Cr-Ctry; Cpt, Tnns; Sci A; All-St
Band; HR; Lt Gov Civitan; Pres, Dist SC; *Carolina
at Chapel Hill; Bus Adm.*

SCHWEIZER, Caren Faye
Dublin HS; Dublin, CA (10%-300) F-Ed, Sch P;
CSF; Del, Girl's Ldrship; *U of Calif; Sociology.*

SCHWELLENBACH,
Marilyn Renee
Durand HS; Durand, WI (1-146) Chor; Dbte Tm;
NFL; NHS; Sodality; Secy, Soph Cl; Sftbl; Sacris-
tan; Spch A; Debate A; Ntl Ed Development Cert;
Drafting A; Degree of Excel & Distn; 1st Pl, Fire
Prevention Art Cont; 2nd Pl, Helen Mears Mem
Art Cont.

SCHWENK, Gilbert Lee
Hastings Sr HS; Hastings, NE (38-289) Band;
Hmrm; NFL; Sch P; SC; Dbte Tm; God & Country
A; Sci A; *Mid-America Nazarene Col; Religion.*

SCHWENK, Michelle Anne
Harvard Pub Sch; Harvard, NE (9-41) A Cap
Choir; Chor; Ensm; Semi-Fin, GS; Madrigal; NHS;
Var C; Hon Prog; Yth Fel; *Mid-America Nazarene
Col; Bus.*

SCHWERIN, Karen Elizabeth
Wells-Easton HS; Wells, MN (2-100) A Cap Choir;
Ann; Band; Chor; Drama; Ensm; FHA; Semi-Fin,
GS; Fin, Jr Miss Pageant; Cpt, Mjrte; Spch C; Bkbl;
Tnns; Amer Leg A; B Crocker A; Sal; Spch A;
VofDEM; Vlbl; All St Choir; Dist Select Band &
Chor; *Concordia-Moorhead Col.*

SCHWERTNER, June Catherine
Wilson HS; Wilson, TX (1-26) CYO; FHA; Fin, Lit
Ral; Pres, Soph Cl; JV, Bkbl; Tr; Alg A; COM; Hist
A; Sci A; Type A; Val; Home Ec A; S-T, Fresh Cl.

SCHWING, Herbert James
Hackley Sch; Tarrytown, NY (15-55) Band;
Drama; Orch; Sch P; Bkbl; Cr-Ctry; Hist A; NMF;
William A Small A; All Co Band; Deacon, Church;
Dartmouth Col; Pol Sci.

SCHWINN, Mary Elizabeth
Immaculata HS; Leavenworth, KS (20%-60) A Cap
Choir; VP, Band; Chor; Secy, 4H; NFL; ARC; Spch
C; Mgr, Tnns; 4H A; Spch A; Type A.

SCHWOCHOW, Loren Leland
Fremont Ross HS; Fremont, OH; All Amer Yth;
Band; Drama; Tres, FFA; Secy, 4H; NHS; Orch;
4H A; All Amer Hall of Fame; Band Hons; *May
Terra Tech; Engr.*

SCISM, Carmen D
Doane Stuart Sch; Albany, NY (10-42) Chor; Sal;
Brown Book A; *Brown U; Fr.*

SCISM, Loretta Jane
New Life Christian Sch; Bridgeton, MO (1-7)
Chor; Ensm; Ntl Piano Playing Auditions Cert.

SCISSONS, Amelia Ann
Owyhee HS; Owyhee, NV (4-25) VP, FBLA;
Mjrte; Bkbl; Tr; Alg A; Type A; FHA A; *Photogra-
phy.*

SCOFIELD, Charles William
Providence HS; Providence, KY (15-57) Band; BC;
NHS; Hon Prog; Band A; *Western U; Archt.*

SCOFIELD, Paula Ann
McDermitt HS; McDermitt, NV (2-14) Chor;
Drama; Spch C; Swim; *Boise St U; Registered
Nurs.*

SCOFIELD, Robin Ann
Lewisville HS; Lewisville, TX (12-400) Band; VP,
Drama; Hmrm; Ed, Lit Mag; NHS; Co-Ed, Sch P;
COM; Hon Prog; Journ A; MLS; Sr Play; Daily
Newspaper A; WW; NMS Commended Stu; 3rd Pl,
Dist UIL, Journ.

SCOFIELD, Shelly Denise
Providence HS; Providence, KY (5-51) Band; BC;
Chldr; Drama; Secy, FHA; NHS; Tres, Sci C; Tr;
Hon Prog; *Murray St U; Teacher.*

SCOGGINS, Emily Ann
Sooner HS; Bartlesville, OK (8-290) Tres, Fr C;
Span C; Bkbl; Tr; COM; Fr Service A; St Hon Soc;
Oral Roberts U; Phys Ed.

SCOGGINS, Mark Orlando
Inglewood HS; Inglewood, CA; Chor; Madrigal;
SC; Var C; Pres, Jr Cl; Pres, Soph Cl; Bsbl; Ftbl; Cl
Fav; Pres A; Vlbl; Mr Above & Beyond; Stu o-t Mo;
Most Inspirational Player; Most Dedicated.

SCOGGINS, Mitzi Nell
Morton HS; Morton, TX (6-53) Ann; Chor; Ch,
FHA; S-T, FTA; Pres, NHS; Math A; MLS; Chor
Pianist; WW; *S Plains Jr Col; Math.*

SCOGIN, Cheryl Ann
Cave Spring HS; Roanoke, VA (185-500) Chor;
MVP, Bkbl; Pres A; Co-Cpt, Bkbl; *Va Western
Comm Col.*

SCONYERS, George Walter
Highland HS; Highland, IL (12-170) Band; 4H;
Tres, NHS; Tr; *U of Ill; Elec.*

SCOTT, Alan Douglas
Palo Verde HS; Tucson, AZ (5-550) Model UN;
NHS; Order/Arrow; A-Ed, Sch P; VP, SC; Var C;
Cr-Ctry; Tr; Bausch & Lomb A; COM; Eagle Sct;
All City, All St Cross Ctry; *Rice U; Elec Engr.*

SCOTT, Angela Ray
Wakulla HS; Crawfordville, FL (10%-117) Cpt,
Chldr; Drama; Secy, 4H; Secy, Sci C; Secy, SC; VP,
Sr Cl; Secy, Jr Cl; 4H A; Hist A; Sci A; WW; *FSU;
Teaching.*

SCOTT, Anthony Mark
Tecumseh HS; New Carlisle, OH; *Baptist Bible
Col; Missions.*

SCOTT, Arnold Weldon
Central Comm HS; Flint, MI; Band; Chor; Orch;
Sci C; Var C; Bkbl; Tr; COM; *Vet Med.*

SCOTT, Arthur Charles Jr
Lutheran HS; Burbank, CA; Band; Hmrm; NHS;
Var C; Cpt, Bsbl; Bkbl; Cpt, Ftbl; CSF; H of F;
MVP, Ftbl; All CIF, All League, Ftbl; All Central
Cty & All Amer, Ftbl; *Ariz U; Engr.*

SCOTT, Aubrey Dennis
Trinity Presbyterian Sch; Montgomery, AL (4-42)
BC; InterClub Coun; S-T, Key C; Lat C; Math C;
NHS; Sci C; Var C; Pres, Soph Cl; Ftbl; Wrest; Sci
A; *Auburn U; Med.*

SCOTT, Barbara Ann
Halter HS; Wellston, MO (6-58) FHA; NHS; Sch
P; JA A; *Forest Park Col; Radiology Technician.*

SCOTT, Barbara Jeanne
Northwest HS; Jackson, MI; A Cap Choir; CYO;
Chor; 4H; Swim; Tnns; Math A.

SCOTT, Bonnie Jean
Arnold HS; Arnold, NE (10-23) Band; Drama;
FHA; GS; S-T, 4H; VP, Hmrm; Secy, Var C; Co-
Cpt, Bkbl; Tr; 4H A; HCt; Rotary A; Spch A; Parl,
4-H C; Co-Cpt, Vlbl; *Sioux Falls Col; Elem Ed.*

SCOTT, Calvin Lewis
Rufus Icing HS; Milwaukee, WI; Band; City Conf;
Hmrm; Math C; NHS; Sci C; Span C; JV, Bsbl; JV,
Bkbl; JV, Tr; Chem A; Citz A; Math A; Sci A; Achv
A; Elec Safety A; *Va St U; Med.*

SCOTT, Calvin Lorenzo
Second Ward HS; Gloster, LA (3-46) *Grambling
Col; Bus Adm.*

SCOTT, Carlee Regina
Dunbar Voc HS; Chicago, IL (200-670) Secy, Span
C; *U of Calif; Pre-Law.*

SCOTT, Charles Glen
Ft Smith Northside HS; Ft Smith, AR; BS; Fr C;
Pres, FTA; Math C; Bsbl; Bkbl; Co-Cpt, Ftbl; Alg
A; H of F; Crime Prevention Workshop; *U of Ark;
Psych.*

SCOTT, Charles Thomas
Fort Payne HS; Fort Payne, AL (10-120) Chor;
Drama; Pres, HiY; Lit Mag; NHS; Order/Arrow;
Sch Achieve Tm; F-Ed, Sch P; Tres, Span C; Pres,
SC; Var C; Bkbl; Co-Cpt, Tnns; Tr; Balfour A; HCt;
Journ A; Most Out; Spch A; Yth Leg; Jr Marshal;
Eng A; Civics A; NEA-AEA Bicen Contest St A;
Most Talented; *U of Tenn at Chattanooga; Eng.*

SCOTT, Colleen Kae
Wauseon HS; Wauseon, OH (47-148) Ann; Band;
Chor; Drama; Ensm; Secy, Fr C; VP, FTA; Mjrte;
Sch P; Thes; Y-Tns; Sftbl; Drama A; *Taylor U; Sci.*

SCOTT, David Russell
Druid Hills HS; Atlanta, GA (40%-172) Chor; Ger C; Hmrm; Key C; SC; Cr-Ctry; Tr; Most Improved A, Cr-Ctry; *Journ.*

SCOTT, Debbie Lynn
Pearland HS; Pearland, TX; Ensm; Pres, FHA; Pol Sci C; SC; Pres, FHA; 2nd VP, FHA; *Sam Houston St U; Home Ec.*

SCOTT, Deborah Suzanne
St Albans HS; St Albans, WV (2%-480) Band; Mjrte; Mu Alpha Theta; Span C; NHS; Cpt, Mjrte Corp; Top Span A; Outst Jr Ldrship A; *Marshall U; Home Ec.*

SCOTT, Deborah Yvonne
Roosevelt HS; Gary, IN (24-560) Fr C; Lat C; Lit Ral; Secy, Math C; NHS; Sci C; Alg A; COM; Citz A; Journ A; Band Cert; *Purdue U; Pharmacy.*

SCOTT, Dennis Eugene
David Mackenzie HS; Detroit, MI; Chess C; Bkbl; Co-Cpt, Cr-Ctry; Tnns; Tr; Yth Fel; Ath A, Bkbl; *Tenn St U; Eng.*

SCOTT, Derallin Denise
Woodmont HS; Piedmont, SC (12-160) Ann; Secy, BC; Chor; Sci C; Secy, SC; Tr; Hist A; Hon Prog; Math A; Drum Mjrte; Outst Band Soph; Semi-Fin, Miss Woodmont Pageant; Miss Congeniality; WW; *Lander Col; Nurs.*

SCOTT, Dianna Althea
Destrehan HS; Destrehan, LA (5-200) BC; Cpt, Bkbl; Sci A; Bkbl A; *Grambling St U; Computer Sci.*

SCOTT, Donald Keith
Waukomis HS; Waukomis, OK (3-35) Band; BC; Drama; FFA; SC; Ftbl; Tr; Bio A; HCt; Math A; *Okla St U; Biological Sci.*

SCOTT, Donna J
Switzerland HS; Vevay, IN (3-108) Drama; Secy, FHA; Fin, GS; NHS; SC; Amer Leg A; VFW A; VofDEM.

SCOTT, Donna Jean
Butler Area Sr HS; Butler, PA (108-990) FBLA; Cert of Achv Quality Point Average; Cert of A Lester Hill Corporation; Most Valuable Mgr Simulated Off.

SCOTT, Douglas Jerome
M B Smiley HS; Houston, TX (5-461) NHS; Cr-Ctry; Hockey; Tr; Citz A; Hist A; Sci A; VFW A; *U of Tex; Med.*

SCOTT, Ellen Jo
Festus R-6 Sr HS; Festus, MO (5-163) A Cap Choir; Band; Chor; Dbte Tm; Drama; Ensm; FHA; Hmrm; Madrigal; Cpt, Mjrte; VP, NHS; Sch Achieve Tm; Secy, SC; Pres, Sr Cl; VP, Jr Cl; COM; Chamber of Comm A; Citz A; DARGCA; Regent Schol; Rotary Stu o-t Mo; Tommy Alexander A; *SE Mo St U; Math.*

SCOTT, Frances N
Sweet Home HS; Buffalo, NY; Model UN; Sci C; Bus Mgr, JA; Art, GAA, Mus, A's; Cpt, MVP, Vlbl; *Psych.*

SCOTT, Gayle Ann
Maplewood HS; Nashville, TN; Hon Prog; Spch A; Star Student; *Bradley U; Spch Pathology.*

SCOTT, Grata Anne
Warren Co Sr HS; McMinnville, TN (10%-419) Chem C; Fr C; FHA; Sci C; Sftbl; *Middle Tenn St U; Pre-Phar.*

SCOTT, Gregory Allan
Roswell Sr HS; Roswell, NM (103-382) Band; Commercial C; Dbte Tm; Drama; Ensm; NFL; Order/Arrow; ARC; Span C; Spch C; Tnns; Mgr, Wrest; Citz A; God & Country A; Order/Arrow A; Pres A; Q&S A; ARC A; Spch A; Yth Fel; Instrumental Solo & Ensm; Eagle Sct; *Bus Adm.*

SCOTT, Gregory James
Inkster HS; Inkster, MI (5-30) Band; Chem C; Chor; Drama; Rptr, Up Bound; Bsbl; Bkbl; Ftbl; Swim; COM; Hon Prog; Bowling.

SCOTT, Harvey James III
Central HS; Little Rock, AR (220-666) BS; Demolay; Bus Mgr, Hmrm; Tres, Key C; Var C; Ftbl; Sftbl; Most Out; ROTC A; Civil Air Patrol; *US Air Force Acad; Aeronautics.*

SCOTT, Jamie Dee
NE HS; N Little Rock, AR; Chor; FBLA; FHA; NHS; Span C; SC; Citz A; Hon Prog; Pep C; VP, Pres, NIKE; Pres, Secy, S-T, Church Yth; *U of Central Ark; Off Adm.*

SCOTT, Jeffrey Allen
Spruce Creek HS; Port Orange, FL (37-450) Cpt, Band; Cum Laude; Mus A; WW, Mus; Outst Co Mus Stu; *U of Fla; Dentistry.*

SCOTT, John Keith
Tarrant HS; Tarrant, AL (15-105) Pres, Band; BS; InterClub Coun; VP, NHS; Tres, SC; Parl, Sr Cl; VP, Jr Cl; Amer Leg A; Cl Fav; Most Dependable; *U of Ala.*

SCOTT, Jonathan M
Blanchard HS; Blanchard, OK; A Cap Choir; F-Ed, Ann; BC; Chor; Hmrm; Madrigal; Model UN; NHS; SC; VP, Var C; VP, Sr Cl; VP, Jr Cl; Bkbl; Co-Cpt, Ftbl; Tr; Alg A; Citz A; Cl Fav; Gov Honor Prog; HCt; Hon Prog; Journ A; MLS; Most Out; NMS; PTA A; Star Student; St Scholar; Summa Cum Laude; Yth Leg; 4 Yr Schol; Eng, Bookkeep; Ser, Secy of St, A's; *U of Okla; Engr.*

SCOTT, Joyce Faye
Blue Ridge HS; Blue Ridge, TX (1-20) Ann; Tres, BC; VP, FHA; Hist A; Math A; MLS; Sci A; Val; *E Tex St U; Photography.*

SCOTT, Julie Ann
Rockville HS; Rockville, IN (7-85) Chldr; Pres, 4H; NHS; Rainbow; ARC; Sch P; Secy, Sci C; Span C; SC; VP, Var C; VP, Sr Cl; VP, Jr Cl; VP, Soph Cl; Cpt, Bkbl; Cpt, Sftbl; MVP, Tnns; Tr; Yth Fel; MVP, Bkbl; Cpt, MVP, Vlbl; Pres, FCA; *Purdue U; Sci.*

SCOTT, June Marie
Mt Ida HS; Mt Ida, AR (1-35) A-Ed, Ann; VP, BC; VP, FHA; Lit Mag; Ed, Sch P; MLS; S-T, Lib C; Geom A; *U of Central Ark; Bus Adm.*

SCOTT, Karen Ann
Martin Luther King HS; Philadelphia, PA (8-692) NHS; Pres, World Affairs; C; Eng A; Span A; Distinguished Hon; *LaSalle Col; Med Technology.*

SCOTT, Karen Denise
William M Raines HS; Jacksonville, FL; Secy, Chor; COM; Hon Prog; Miss Mus A; Ribbon, Math Tutor; Chor Trophies; *Fla Jr Col; Basic Ed.*

SCOTT, Kelly Joseph
St Anthony HS; St Anthony, MN; Mgr, CYO; Hmrm; SC; Pres, Soph Cl; Bkbl; Tnns; H of F; MLS.

SCOTT, Kenneth Andrew
W End HS; Birmingham, AL; Ftbl; *US Navy; Elec.*

SCOTT, Linda Carol
Booker T Washington HS; Tulsa, OK; Chor; Ch, Hmrm; ARC; SC; Up Bound; Tr; JA A; ARC A; Yth Fel; *Cental St Col; Bus Communication.*

SCOTT, Linda Lee
Richfield HS; Waco, TX; Rptr, FHA; Span C; Spirit C.

SCOTT, Loretta
Lake City Sr HS; Lake City, SC (5%-225) VP, BC; Chldr; Fr C; FHA; Hmrm; SC; Bkbl; Sftbl; *SC St Col; Elem Eng.*

SCOTT, Lorie Dawn
Amarillo HS; Amarillo, TX (25%-800) Secy, Chor; FHA; Pres, Hmrm; MVP, Cr-Ctry; Tr; Miss PBC; FCA; Church Yth Coun.

SCOTT, Marcia Kay
Kingman HS; Kingman, KS; A Cap Choir; Chor; Ensm; Pres, Fr C; Madrigal; Y-Tns; Tr; Amer Leg A; COM; Citz A; Hist A; Hon Prog; Journ A; Yth Fel; Vlbl; Pres, BYF; *Emporia Kans Col; Foreign Lang.*

SCOTT, Margaret Dow
St Mary's Jr Col; Raleigh, NC; Chor; Ensm; NHS; Sch P; Bkbl; Sftbl; Swim; Co-Cpt, Tnns; Tr; Beacon-St Mary's Hon Soc; *Biological Sci.*

SCOTT, Margie Jean
Jamaica HS; Jamaica, NY (250-1102) Secy, Chor; Drama; Hmrm; Secy, NHS; SC; Bkbl; Swim; Tr; COM; Citz A; Hon Prog; Mus A; *Stony Brook Col; Psych.*

SCOTT, Marianne Elizabeth
St Ursula Acad; Cincinnati, OH (2-75) Chor; Pres, Fr C; Hmrm; Secy, NHS; Ed, Sch P; SC; DARGCA; Poet A; Fr A; Ohio Cert of A; St Board of Ed A of Distinction; U of Cin Admission With Distin; *U of Cincinnati; Liberal Arts.*

SCOTT, Mark David
Hopewell Sr HS; Aliquippa, PA (200-500) Band Ltr; Adv Math Courses; High Sales A; *Penn St U; Horticulture.*

SCOTT, Mark Edward
Wallace Sr HS; Wallace, ID (6-99) Band; Chor; Lat C; Lat NHS; NHS; B Crocker A; MLS; NMF; NEDT; *Computer Sci.*

SCOTT, Mark Lyndon
Hart Co HS; Hartwell, GA; Chess C; FFA; 4H; HiY; VP, Hmrm; SC; SC; Golf; Sftbl; Tnns; Tr; COM; *Tri-Co Tech; Bus Adm.*

SCOTT, Mark McKay
Oroville HS; Oroville, CA (13-250) Fin, BS; NHS; Bsbl; Bkbl; JV, Ftbl; CSF; MC; Homecoming; Block 'O' Soc; Top 10, Soph; NHS A; *U o-t Pacific; Math.*

SCOTT, Marquis
Proviso E HS; Maywood, IL (113-1000) Ftbl; Tr; HR; *Archt.*

SCOTT, Martin Ray
Keokuk Sr HS; Keokuk, IA (50-250) JV, Golf; *Engr.*

SCOTT, Mary Ellen
Charleston HS; Charleston, SC; Chor; *Rice Bus Col; Bus.*

SCOTT, Michael Eric
Alfred Ely HS; Savannah, GA; FFA; Cr-Ctry; Tr; Friendliest; Most Attractive; *Atlanta Area Tech Col; Computer Programming.*

SCOTT, Michael Patrick
Foley HS; Foley, MN (15-161) Chor; 4H; NHS; SC; Var C; Co-Cpt, Bsbl; Co-Cpt, Bkbl; Cr-Ctry; Tr; 4H A; JA A; Most Out; All-Amer A; All-Conf A; George M Palmer Schol; *Carleton Col; Med.*

SCOTT, Michele Elizabeth
Central Comm HS; Breese, IL (8-157) CYO; FHA; Span C; VP, FSA; Span Achv As; *Eastern Ill U; Foreign Lang.*

SCOTT, Norman Bruce
E Syracuse Minoa HS; E Syracuse, NY (25-487) BS; Dbte Tm; Tres, Drama; NFL; NHS; Order/Arrow; Sci C; Spch C; St Stu Congress; Thes; Hon Prog; JA A; Order/Arrow A; Yth Fel; Eagle Sct; WW; *Pre-Med.*

SCOTT, Pamela Louise
Sooner HS; Bartlesville, OK (1-300) Band; Ensm; Orch; Rainbow; S-T, Sci C; Span C; COM; Citz A; Hon Prog; Band Ldrship A; *U of Okla; Chem.*

SCOTT, Patricia Leslie
St Anthony HS; St Anthony City, MN (65-209) A Cap Choir; AFS; CYO; Chor; Cpt, St Stu Congress; Cpt, SC; Bkbl; Cpt, Tr; Hon Prog; Ath A; *Stout Col; Home Ec.*

SCOTT, Radina Kim
N Mercer R-3 HS; Mercer, MO (1-13) Ann; Band; JV, Chldr; Chor; JV, 4H; Jr Miss Pagent; JV, Mjrte; Sch P; SC; Sftbl; B Crocker A; WW; *Platt Col; Banking and Acct.*

SCOTT, Randall Harold
Del City HS; Del City, OK (50%-2000) Hmrm; Pres, Key C; VP, SC; VP, Soph Cl; Ftbl; Cpt, Tr; Citz A; Cl Fav; Most Out; Regent Schol; Swtht; Blue Chipper; Tr & Field Ath o-t Yr '76; Sons of Amer Revolution A; *Okla Christian Col; Bus.*

SCOTT, Rebecca Louise
Carlsbad Mid HS; Carlsbad, NM; FHA; 4H; Swim; COM; 4H A; Spch A; 4-H Ribbons; Horsemanship As; *Tex Tech U; Phys.*

SCOTT, Renee Jeannette
Windsor Forest HS; Savannah, GA; Band; BC; Parl, SC; Tnns; Ntl Beta C; *U of Ga; Psych.*

SCOTT, Rhonda Davonne
Westburg HS; Houston, TX (93-614) Band; Hmrm; Mjrte; WW; Church Yth Group; *Ohio St U; Acct.*

SCOTT, Robin Elaine
W Mecklenburg HS; Charlotte, NC; 4H; InterAct C; InterClub Coun; SC; Co-Cpt, Bkbl; Ntl Conf Chr & Jews; Ch, Election Comm; Acteens; Pep C; Project Aries; Phys Ed A; Pres, Jr Usher Board; Pres, Comm NAACP.

SCOTT, Robin Terry
George Wythe HS; Wytheville, VA (18-143) Band; Hmrm; Math C; Mu Alpha Theta; Sch P; Sci C; Most Improv; All Reg, All Co, Band; *Wytheville Comm Col; Gen Stu.*

SCOTT, Rosemary Delores
Carver HS; Birmingham, AL (10-237) Band; NHS; Tri-HiY; Hon Prog; ROTC A; *Fla A&M U; Nurs.*

SCOTT, Rosie Lee
Motley HS; Columbus, MS (3-81) BC; Hmrm; Sch P; Sci C; SC; Bkbl; Alg A; Sci A; SC; Eng A; *Miss Valley St U; Math.*

SCOTT, Shawn Ann
Ribault Sr HS; Jacksonville, FL; Secy, Yth Dept; Sunday Sch Teacher; *Ga St U; Med.*

SCOTT, Shelia Fae
Claxton HS; Claxton, GA (25%-110) FBLA; Pres, FHA; SC; Tr; Hist A; Math A; Type A; Girls Phys Ed As; WW; PA; *Savannah St U; Math.*

SCOTT, Steven Sorrells
Cedar Shoals HS; Athens, GA; Band; BC; Lat C; Math C; Sci C; All St Jazz Ensm; *Ga Inst of Tech; Engr.*

SCOTT, Susan Elizabeth
Hall HS; Spring Valley, IL; Chldr; Drama; FTA; Secy, Sci C; Wrest; Hist A; Sci A; Pom Pom Squad; Art & Writing A; Tn Ldr; *Ill St U; Elem Ed.*

SCOTT, Susan Lynn
Crawford Co R-III; Cuba, MO; Band; FTA; Rainbow; *SW Mo St U.*

SCOTT, Terry Gene
Madison Acad HS; Huntsville, AL (2-51) BC; Dbte Tm; Hmrm; Math C; Monogram; NHS; Sci C; SC; Var C; JV, Bsbl; Mgr, Bkbl; Cr-Ctry; Ftbl; Alg A; Bio A; COM; Cl Fav; Hon Prog; Math A; NEDT; Sci A; Star Student; *UA; Med.*

SCOTT, Traci Jo
Chateaugay Central HS; Chateaugay, NY (25%-92) Chor; Drama; GS; NHS; SC; Sci A; Type A; Fr Contest; Lib C; *Med.*

SCOTT, Virgil Miguel
Frederick Douglass HS; Atlanta, GA (34-427) Band; Pres, Chess C; Ensm; Pres, Hmrm; JETS; Math C; NHS; Bsbl; Bkbl; COM; ROTC A; PA; Ldrship A; Hon Stu; *Clark Col; Engr.*

SCOTT, Wayne DuMetz
Aquinas HS; Augusta, GA (49-130) A Cap Choir; Chor; Ensm; Up Bound; Tnns; High Hon & Outst Achv, Health; *Morehouse Col; Biol.*

SCOTT, Wayne William
Valley Forge HS; Parma Hts, OH; Band; Ger C; *Ohio St U; Acct.*

SCOTT, Wesley Robert
Valley Forge HS; Parma Hts, OH (98-880) A Cap Choir; Band; Chor; Drama; Madrigal; Orch; Thes; Cr-Ctry; Tr.

SCOVEL, Karen Lynn
Derby Sr HS; Derby, KS (11-388) Chor; Ensm; Math C; NHS; Span C; Golf; Math A; Yth Fel; Mus Cast; Solo, St Mus Contest; Dist & All St Choirs; NML; S-T GSct; God & Comm A; *U of Mo; Mus.*

SCOVILLE, Janet Kay
Naperville Central HS; Naperville, IL (113-417) Chor; Var C; Yth Fel; Candystriper; Young Life; Gym; Pres, Yth Fellowship; *Phys Ed.*

SCRANAGE, Sharon Marie
LeLycee Francais HS; Culver City, CA (8-19) CYO; Chor; Semi-Fin, Dbte Tm; MVP, Drama; Sch P; MVP, Thes; Soccer; Hon Prog; HR; Choir A; *Howard Col; Acting.*

SCRANTON, Charles Michael
Marion HS; Marion, IN (100-700) A Cap Choir; Chor; Demolay; Drama; Pres, Ensm; NHS; Phys C; Sci C; Bsbl; Bkbl; Ftbl; Swim; Tr; Mem Thespian; Hon Thespian; *Ind U; Physics.*

SCRANTON, Mark Allen
Marion HS; Marion, IN; Chor; Ensm; Pres, Sci C; Cr-Ctry; JV Vlbl; *Ind U; Mus Theory.*

SCREWS, Michael Anthony
Dublin HS; Dublin, GA (20%-150) Band; Bus C; Drama; Ensm; FBLA; Hmrm; Semi-Fin, Lit Ral; Orch; Tri-HiY; Tnns; Tr; COM; Hist A; Hon Prog; Yth Ldr of Church; Pianist & Organist; Church Mus; Asst Sunday Sch Teacher; *Ga Col; Hist.*

SCRIPPS, Nancy Jill
Hesperia Comm Sch; Hesperia, MI; WW Among Amer Mus Stu; *Grand Rapids Sch of Bible & Mus; Mus Ed.*

SCRIPTER, Susan Beth
Superior HS; Superior, NE (18-72) Ann; Cpt, Chldr; NHS; F-Ed, Sch P; SC; Y-Tns; Secy, Jr Cl; VP, Soph Cl; Hon Prog; *Lincoln U; Special Ed.*

SCRIPTURE, Reba Ferne
Encina HS; Sacramento, CA (33%-390) Tres, Band; Fin, Spch C; Sftbl; CSF; Spch A; *Amer River Col; Nurs.*

SCRIVNER, Paula Lynn
Edwin G Foreman HS; Chicago, IL (59-373) ARC; Secy, SC; Dad's C A; *Faith Baptist Bible Col.*

SCROGGINS, Kimberley Sue
Ottawa Sr HS; Ottawa, KS; A Cap Choir; Chor; Ensm; Rptr, Hmrm; ARC; Swim; Tr.

SCROGGINS, Mark Timothy
Mark Morris HS; Longview, WA (50-300) A Cap Choir; Bus C; Chor; Community Yth Symph; Ensm; Madrigal; Mod Mus Mas; Arch; Bkbl; Soccer; Sftbl; Tr; HKg; Most Out; All NW Choir; Calif Mus Schol; Bicentennial Soloist; *AZUSP; Bus.*

SCROGGINS, Stephanie Lynn
John Ehret HS; Gmarrevo, LA (9-550) FHA; Hmrm; Math C; Mu Alpha Theta; NHS; Co-Cpt, Bkbl; Sftbl; Tr; COM; Hon Prog; PTA A; Yth Fel; Yth, Worship Choirs; VP, Church Yth Coun; 1st Pl St, Social Stu Fair; *NW St U; Phys Therapist.*

SCROGGINS, Stuart Lawrence
Canadian HS; Canadian, TX; BS; Drama; FFA; Span C; JV, Bkbl; JV, Ftbl; *Tex Tech U; Elec Engr.*

SCROGGS, Gerald Leon
Parker HS; Greenville, SC (50%-200) Var C; Bkbl; Ftbl; Cpt, Golf; Golf Ltr; Ftbl Ltr; Bkbl Ltr; *N Greenville Jr Col.*

SCRUGGS, Christine May
Pennsville Memorial HS; Pennsville, NJ; Band; Hmrm; SC; Secy, Soph Cl; Mgr, Bsbl; Hockey; Mgr, Tnns; Fr A.

SCRUGGS, Henry Lee
Polytechic HS; Ft Worth, TX (59-300) JA A; *TCJC; Auto Mech.*

SCRUGGS, LaVicki
Thornton Township HS; Harvey, IL; Secy, Chor; Drama; SC; Citz A; Cl Fav; Cert of Recognition, Lib Asst; Attendance A; *Eastern U; Acct.*

SCRUGGS, Matthew Samuel
Pennsville Mem HS; Pennsville, NJ (18-250) Band; BS; Secy, InterAct C; NHS; Orch; Thes; Rotary A; Star Student; Ntl Merit Ltr of Commendation; Director's A, Band; All Co Band; WW; Concert & Marching Band; Stage Band; *Mich St U; Physics.*

SCRUGGS, Vanessa Lynn
Thornton Township HS; Harvey, IL (25%-650) Chldr; Citz A; Hist A; Hon Prog; Math A; Sci A; Badminton; *U of Ill; Acct.*

SCUDDER, Amy Leigh
Goodlettsville HS; Goodlettsville, TN (10-159) VP, Band; Tres, Lat C; Lat NHS; NHS; Alg A; Bio A; *DARGCA; Tenn Tech U; Acct.*

SCUDDER, Edson F
Fieldston Sch; Bronx, NY (5-120) Bkbl; Soccer; Tr; Yth Fel; Pres, Church Yth Group; Christian Ed Comm; *Phys Ed.*

SCUDDER, Susan Selena
Mt Juliet HS; Mt Juliet, TN (16-277) VP, Band; BC; Chor; Ensm; NHS; Type A; Keyettes; *Middle Tenn St U; Ed.*

SCUDERI, Robert John
Dugway HS; Dugway, UT (3-45) CYO; Dbte Tm; Fin, Drama; Model UN; UN Council; Golf; COM; Cl Fav; 2nd Degree Brown Belt Cert; DYA Bkbl Trophy; Skiing; *U of Utah; Art.*

SCULLY, William Aylward
Archmere Acad; Claymont, DE; CYO; Dbte Tm; NHS; Span NHS; JV, Bsbl; JV, Bkbl; JV, Soccer; NEDT; Sci A; Star Student; Most Promising Fresh Eng Stu; Mark Vanderbrach Mem Schol; *Princeton U; Pol Sci.*

SCURRY, Jennifier Arlene
Saluda HS; Saluda, SC (75-184) Band; BC; Chor; Pres, FTA; Rptr, 4H; Jr Miss Pagent; Lit Mag; Bus Mgr, Sch P; Bio A; Citz A; Gov Honor Prog; 4H A; Hist A; Journ A; Spch A; *Lander Col; Elem Ed.*

SCYOC, Kelly Jo
Hannibal Sr HS; Hannibal, MO (30-350) Drama; Sodality; Span C; Iowa Tests A; *U of Mo; Law.*

SEABOCK, Elizabeth Lynn
Hickory HS; Hickory, NC (23-365) AFS; Band; FBLA; Math C; NHS; Jr Marshal; Confirmation Schol A; *Appalachian St U; Early Childhood Ed.*

SEABORN, Doris Marie
Petersburg HS; Petersburg, VA (13-600) Bus Mgr, Ann; Band; JV, Chldr; Chess C; Chor; Fr C; Ger C; GS; NHS; Spch C; VP, Jr Cl; Jr Miss Pagent; Cr-Ctry; Tr; Amer Leg A; Amer Leg Orator A; COM; Cl Fav; Elk A; HCt; Spch A; VFW A; VFW Orator Win; VofDEM; Versatile; Sr Cl; Mod Dance Group; Miss Loyalty Day Pageant; Miss Mocha Temple.

SEABORN, Frances Louise
Central Sr HS; Victoria, VA (1-130) Ann; Pres, FHA; InterClub Coun; Lit Mag; VP, NHS; Span C; Tres, SC; Pres, Tri-HiY; Tnns; *Math.*

SEABROOK, Kathryn Marie
Oakland Tech HS; Oakland, CA (75-650) Swim; Tnns; Hon Prog; *Sou St U.*

SEABROOK, Konstane Gwen
Oak Tech HS; Oakland, CA; Dbte Tm; Ensm; JETS; NHS; *UC at Davis.*

SEAFORD, Michael Patrick
Benjamin Franklin HS; Los Angeles, CA (40%-750) CYO; Order/Arrow; Ed, Sch P; Cpt, Bkbl; Journ A; Most Inspirational, Bkbl; Coach's A, Bkbl; League Bkbl Champs; *UCLA.*

SEAGLE, Nicky Reeves
Fred T Foard HS; Newton, NC; Tres, FFA; Span C; Var C; JV, Bsbl; Bkbl; Golf; Tnns; Citz A; Lion A; Opt A; Pres A; Yth Fel; *W Carolina Col; Phys Therapy.*

SEAGO, Debra Lynne
Burnsville HS; Burnsville, MS; BC; FHA; *Northeast Col; Acct.*

SEAGO, Michael Davis
Bowman HS; Wadesboro, NC (10%-310) Band; Pres, Lat C; Sci C; *Pol Sci.*

SEAGO, Pamela Kaye
John H Reagan HS; Austin, TX (10%-460) Chor; Ensm; SC; Trustee Schol A; Cert of A in Piano; Yth Church Choir; Secy, Ecology C; *U of Tex in Austin; Mus.*

SEAGREN, Heide
Barrington HS; Barrington, IL (25%-900) A Cap Choir; Fr C; Sci C; SC; Mgr, Swim; Tnns; Tr; Citz A; Hon Prog; *Gym.*

SEAGREN, Johan-Carl Eric
Parkway North Sr HS; Creve Coeur, MO (48-519) Ger C; NHS; Ch, Order/Arrow; Var C; MVP, Ftbl; Tr; Fin, Wrest; Order/Arrow A; *US Naval Acad; Marine Biochem.*

SEAL, Jefferson Daniel
Eastwood HS; El Paso, TX (55-706) Pres, Chess C; Chor; Dbte Tm; Demolay; Ger C; NHS; Ski C; Sr Cl; S-T, Jr Cl; Tres, Soph Cl; Bkbl; Cr-Ctry; Ftbl; Soccer; Tr; Math A; Most Out; ROTC A; Sci A; *US Air Force Acad; Aerospace Engr.*

SEALES, James Porter III
McColl HS; McColl, SC; Fr C; Key C; NHS; Bsbl; Ftbl; NEDT; *Florence-Darlington Tech Col; Police Sci.*

SEALS, Brenda
Martin Luther King HS; Chicago, IL (59-297) Drama; Fr C; Pres, SC; Pres, Sr Cl; Cpt, Bkbl; Bio A; COM; Hon Prog; Pres A; *George Williams Col; Psych.*

SEALS, Charlotte Jean
Jess Lanier HS; Bessemer, AL (114-250) FTA; Lit Mag; COM; *U of Ala; Art.*

SEALS, Denise Ann
Highland HS; Ewing, MO (2-160) Chor; FHA; NHS; Sch Achieve Tm; Hon Prog; NE Mo St U; Vet Asst.

SEALS, Janet Kay
Hobart HS; Hobart, OK (1-52) JV, Chldr; VP, FTA; Hmrm; NHS; Span C; Pres, SC; S-T, Var C; Mgr, Bsbl; Bkbl; Sftbl; Tr; COM; Masonic A; Val; Yth Fel; All-Sports Qn; WW; All-Area & All-Conf Bkbl; Cand, Miss HHS; Best All Around Sr Girl; Okla St U.

SEALS, Jeffery Carl
Springs Valley HS; French Lick, IN (1-88) Chess C; Fr C; NHS; Var C; Co-Cpt, Bsbl; Ftbl; Math A; Phy A; Sci A; St Scholar; Val; Alt, BS; Highest 4-Yr GPA; Habig Mem Sch; U of Evansville; Engr.

SEALS, Valorie Lynn
Paris HS; Paris, TX (4-267) Chess C; Chor; VP, FHA; NHS; Rptr, Sch P; Sci C; Tri-HiY; Bkbl; Hon Prog; Chaplain, Fr C; FTA; E Tex St U; Math.

SEALY, Lori Ann
Randolph Co Comm HS; Cuthbert, GA; Chldr; Drama; Fr C; Secy, FBLA; Rptr, FHA; Lit Ral; Grad Usher; Vacation Bible Sch Vol; Fr A; Church Pianist; Choir Director, Children's Choir; 1st Run-Up, Ms Ga Tn-Ager Pag; Auburn U; Fashion Merchandising.

SEAMAN, Kenneth Wade
Yukon HS; Yukon, OK; Mu Alpha Theta; NHS; Sci C; Span C; Bio A; Math A; Sci A; St Hon Soc; Eng, Swim, A's; Okla St U; Bus.

SEAMAN, Margaret
Menlo-Atherton HS; Atherton, CA (20%-500) Ger C; Gym; U of Calif, Davis; Foreign Lang.

SEAMAN, Susan Elaine
Wadley HS; Wadley, GA; Ann; 4H; Sch P; Journ A; Reading A.

SEAMAN, Virginia Lyn
Wheaton Warrenville HS; Wheaton, IL (50%-275) Chor; Horse Back Riding; Church Yth Group; Church Nursery; Church Choir; Church Acolyte; Mus.

SEARCY, Bryan Dale
Freedom HS; Morganton, NC (150-675) AFS; Drama; Tres, InterAct C; Order/Arrow; SC; Jr Cl; Ftbl; Tr; Order/Arrow A; Yth Fel; Yth Leg; Eagle Sct; Western Piedmont Col.

SEARCY, Scott William
Lyons Township HS; La Grange, IL (91-1235) Band; Math C; Bsbl; COM; Hon Prog; JA A; NEDT; Ed, Bus C Newspaper; Christian Ed Committee; Swim Guard C; Math.

SEARD, Melvin Leon II
Takoma Acad; Takoma Park, MD (2-140) Band; Chor; NHS; Orch; Bkbl; Citz A; NMF; NMS; Sal; WW; Oakwood Col; Pre-Med.

SEARLE, Suzanne
Harlingen HS; Harlingen, TX (104-609) A Cap Choir; Cpt, Drill Tm; VP, Oceanography; Cardinale Chorale; HPE.

SEARS, David Alton
T Wingate Andrews HS; High Point, NC (21-279) Cpt, Band; BC; Ensm; Fr C; French NHS; Hmrm; Sftbl; Hon Prog; S-T, Jr Jaycees; Outst, Band; Stu Group, Journeyed to France; NC St U; Acct.

SEARS, Glen Richard II
Punahou Sch; Honolulu, HI; Band; Ger C; ROTC A; Pres, Yth of Unity; ROTC Battalion Commander; Riflery; Naval Acad Preperatory Sch; Naval Archt.

SEARS, Jon
Calif Preparatory Sch; Encino, CA (1-33) Ann; VP, SC; Bsbl; Bkbl; Math A; MLS; U of Calif; Marine Stu.

SEARS, Patricia Lynn
Claxton HS; Claxton, GA (25%-116) Cpt, Chldr; Sch P; Var C; Most Out; Ga Sou Col.

SEARS, Sarah Elizabeth
George Washington Sr HS; Cedar Rapids, IA; Band; Chor; Drama; Mgr, Bkbl; Handicapp Teaching.

SEASTRUNK, Mary Claire
Lutcher Stark HS; Orange, TX (39-196) A Cap Choir; Chor; Fr C; French NHS; NHS; PTA A; Star Student; Most Rep, Sr Cl; Abilene Christian U; Eng.

SEAU, David Tiaina
Oceanside HS; Oceanside, CA (9-181) Sch Achieve Tm; Cpt, Bkbl; Cpt, Ftbl; Most Out.

SEAY, JacQue
Lebanon HS; Lebanon, TN; 4H; Rptr, Hmrm; SC; 4H A; Cumberland Col; Phys Ed.

SEAY, Jane Karen
Dorman HS; Spartanburg, SC (65-631) NHS; Bio A; NEDT; Sci A; Church Bkbl & Sftbl; Gardner Webb Col; Religious Ed.

SEAY, Leisa Lynne
Swain Co HS; Bryson City, NC (6-131) S-T, Chess C; Secy, Fr C; FHA; NHS; VP, Sci C; JV, Bkbl; Star Student; Homemaker; Chief Marshal; Med.

SEAY, Mark Anthony
Berea HS; Greenville, SC; BC; FFA; Bkbl; Cr-Ctry; Tr; MVP, Cross Ctry.

SEBASTIA, Tony Elutario
A E Stevenson HS; Bronx, NY; Chess C; Sch P; Foreign Lang, Span A; Baruch Col; Acct.

SEBASTIAN, Cindy Lynn
Mansfield HS; Mansfield, LA (1-104) Band; VP, BC; Secy, FBLA; Jr Miss Pagent; Mjrte; Sch Achieve Tm; Pres, Span C; Rptr, Soph Cl; Hist A; HCt; Spch A; Val; Alt, GS; LSU Fresh Hons A; Miss FBLA; Miss Mansfield HS; Most Intellectual.

SEBASTIAN, Julie Anne
Mansfield HS; Mansfield, LA (8-80) Band; BC; Lit Ral; Mjrte; Span C; Tres, Soph Cl; Bkbl; Sftbl; Cl Fav; Vlbl.

SEBESTA, Kelli Ann
Skyline HS; Salt Lake City, UT (10%-600) NHS; Fin, Tr; Pep C; Cpt, MVP, Tr; U of Utah.

SEBREN, Jack William
Little Rock Central HS; Little Rock, AR; Westminster Col.

SEBRING, Denise Lynn
Watsonville HS; Watsonville, CA (70-700) A Cap Choir; Chldr; Ch, Hmrm; SC; Hist A; Sci A; Secy, Hmrm; Cabrillo Jr Col; Sci.

SEBURG, James Allen
Minnehaha Acad; Minneapolis, MN (10-150) Band; NHS; Orch; Chem A; Phy A; GPA, Highest Hon; Stage Band; Star Rating, Concert Band; Omaha Lutheran Bible Sch.

SECAUR, Jeffrey Brent
Brethren Christian HS; Osceola, IN (5%-30) A Cap Choir; Ann; Drama; Pres, Sr Cl; Pres, Soph Cl; Bkbl; Soccer; Grace Col; Mus.

SECAUR, Terri Lynn
Bellmont HS; Decatur, IN; Span C; Tnns; Mgr, Tr; DARGCA; Tnns A; Ath A; Saint Francis Col; Art.

SECONE, Theresa Ann
Marian HS; Tamaqua, PA (3-152) Chldr; NHS; Span NHS; JV, Golf; Hon Prog; NEDT; Bowl Tm; WW; JC Bowl Tourn Trophy; Jaycees Bowl Tourn Trophy; Math.

SECOR, Kristy Marie
Bedford Comm HS; Bedford, IA (33%-69) Band; Bus C; NHS; Span C; Yth Fel; Vennard Col; Christian Ed.

SECORD, Jacqueline Kaye
Chittenango Central HS; Chittenango, NY; FBLA; Pres, FHA; 4H; NHS; Span C; 4H A; BYF; Pres, Guild; Sports Advisor, Yrbk; Bus.

SECORD, Tammy Jean
Roy C Start HS; Toledo, OH (93-408) Co-Ch, Hmrm; Sci C; Co-Ch, Sr Cl; Tres, Service C; Anderson Col; Ed.

SECOY, Jacqueline Rene
E Prairie HS; E Prairie, MO (8-106) Band; Cpt, Chldr; Rptr, Chor; Tres, FHA; Madrigal; NHS; Ed, Sch P; SC; MVP, Sftbl; Alg A; HCt; Type A; Soph, Jr, Sr, Cl Rep; Hon Men, Geom; Yth For Comm Betterment; Vlbl; WW; SE Mo St U.

SECREST, Pamela Ann
McArthur HS; Hollywood, FL (50-500) Lat C; NHS; Rainbow; Bio A; Mercer U; Microbio.

SECREST, Paula Michele
Meadowbrook HS; Byesville, OH; FHA; 4H; Sci C; 4H A; HCt; Ohio St U; Child Psych.

SECRIST, Becky Lynn
North HS; Oildale, CA; VP, Bus C; Cpt, Chldr; GS; Hmrm; Ski C; Span C; SC; Pres, Sr Cl; MVP, Sftbl; Tr; Amer Leg A; Citz A; St Scholar; Val; Optimist Ldrship A; Chldr o-t Yr; Most Inspirational Dancer; Most Creative Dancer; Cal Poly at San Luis; Phys Ed.

SEDA, Laurietz
Luis Munoz Marin HS; Cabo Rojo, PR (4-150) Band; Chldr; Chor; FHA; Hmrm; Tres, SC; COM; Hon Prog; Recinto U Mayaguez; Pediatria.

SEDA, Nilda
Antilles HS; Fort Buchanan, PR (16-124) Chor; Drama; Hmrm; Pres, NHS; Secy, Soph Cl; Secy, Drill Tm; Keyettes; Span Hon; Bradford Col; Law.

SEDGASS, Dana Howard
Ark Sr HS; Texarkana, AR (8-420) A-Ed, Ann; BS; Fr C; Key C; NHS; A-Ed, Sch P; Sci A; Photo A; Texarkana Col; Engr.

SEDGWICK, Arlene Renee
Hampton HS; Hampton, VA (104-600) Band; Hmrm; Tr; Band Medals; U of Md; Mus.

SEDLACEK, Russell Alan
Prague Pub Sch; Prague, NE (5-19) Band; Chor; Var C; Bkbl; Ftbl; Tr; COM; Photo-Ed, Ann; Jr Carrier A; Cert of Recogn, Wahoo Newspaper; U of Nebr.

SEDLAK, Sandra Ann
Springfield Local HS; Petersburg, OH (23-135) Fr C; FTA; Tres, 4H; Hmrm; NHS; SC; H of F; Bowling Green St U; Acct.

SEDMAN, Joy Lynn
Hamill Road Christian Sch; Hixson, TN; Bus Mgr, Ann; BC; Cpt, Chldr; Ftbl; FHA; 4H; Cpt, Hmrm; SC; Co-Cpt, Bkbl; Sftbl; JV, Tr; 4H A; Math A; Most Out; Poet A; Swtht; MVP, Bkbl; Fin, Soccer Qn, Swtht Qn, Eng A; Hist.

SEDOR, Paul
Wellsboro Sr HS; Wellsboro, PA (24-216) CYO; Ger C; NHS; SC; Ftbl; Tnns; COM; Hon Prog; MLS; Mansfield Col; Hist.

SEE, Edward Alan
Delmar Jr-Sr HS; Delmar, De (3-102) Pres, Band; BS; Chor; VP, Key C; Pres, NHS; SC; Bsbl; Glassboro St Col; Mus.

SEE, Lucille Marie
Kountze HS; Kountze, TX (7-92) Band; Drama; FHA; Pres, FTA; SC; Pres, Jr Cl; Alg A; Bio A; Hist A; Math A; Sci A; Type A; All Dist Band; Lamar U; Psych.

SEE, Tonya D
Ainsworth HS; Ainsworth, NE (7-80) Ann; Chor; Pres, Fr C; Sch P; VP, Sr Cl; Hon Qn, Jobs Daughters.

SEEDS, Linda Jo
Western Reserve HS; Berlin Center, OH; Band; FHA; NHS; Tres, Jr Cl; Cpt, Bkbl; Sftbl; Tr; Hon Prog.

SEEFELDT, Kathryn Lorainne
Birmingham HS; Van Nuys, CA (10%-3000) A Cap Choir; Mgr, Soccer; Citz A; Pres, GSct; Great Books C; Psych.

SEEFERT, Alison Lynn
Frank B Kellogg HS; St Paul, MN (39-508) Secy, Band; Ensm; NHS; Bkbl; Sftbl; COM; Hon Prog; Star Student; Yth Fel; Vlbl; Ltr, Sftbl; Band A; Pres Phys Fitness A; 2nd Pl, Sftbl Trophy; Phys Ed.

SEEGER, Betty Nadine
Putnam City W HS; Oklahoma City, OK; Fr C; Bkbl; Opt A; Yth Fel; OSU; Art.

SEEGER, Kim Renee
Malden HS; Malden, MO (80-150) Chor; Sch P; Beauty; Legal Secy.

SEEGERS, Douglas Alexander
Carroll HS; Monroe, LA; Band; Key C; Lat C; Crisis Center Adv Board; NE La U; Phar.

SEEKMAN, Roger A
Spring Lake HS; Spring Lake, MI (7-185) Tres, NHS; F-Ed, Sch P; Mgr, Bkbl; Mgr, Ftbl; MLS; Muskegon Comm Col; Engr.

SEELAND, Cynthia Louise
Toms River HS N; Toms River, NJ; Band; Chldr; Tres, Chor; Drama; Lit Mag; F-Ed, Sch P; Pres, SC; Thes; Wrest; Chor Accompanist; Accompanist A Off, Church Group; Church Choir; Rep, Operation Friendship; Westminster Col; Church Mus.

SEELER, Evelyn Harrison
The Kew-Forest Sch; Forest Hills, NY (12-40) A Cap Choir; Span C; SC; S-T, Var C; Bkbl; Hockey; Sftbl; Tnns; DARGCA; Hist A; GAA; Sportsmanssip A; Tn A; GAA Service A.

SEELEY, Mary Lyn
Susquehanna Comm HS; Susquehanna, PA (10%-120) Band; Bus C; Chldr; Chor; Ensm; Hmrm; Cpt, Mjrte; NHS; Rptr, Sch P; Ski C; SC; Type A; Nurs.

SEELEY, Susan Marie
Orofino HS; Orofino, ID (1-90) Ann; CYO; Dbte Tm; GS; NHS; Sftbl; Citz A; Most Spirited; U of Idaho; Phys Ed.

SEELIGER, Jeff Clair
Perry HS; Perry, OK (8-115) BS; NHS; Pres, Soph Cl; Bsbl; Bkbl; Ftbl; Tr; Hon Prog; Masonic A; Off, FFA; Okla Hon Soc; Pep Coun; Engr.

SEELKE, Mark Dale
Okeene HS; Okeene, OK; Band; FFA; Scrapbook A; Farming.

SEELOW, Timothy Allen
Taylor Center Baptist Acad; Taylor, MI (1-11) Band; Ensm; Fr C; Order/Arrow; Var C; Tres, Soph Cl; Bkbl; Soccer; Order/Arrow A; Sci A; Art A; US Naval Acad; Physics.

SEEMANN, Eunice Marie
Notre Dame Acad; Toledo, OH (12-140) A Cap Choir; Drama; NHS; ARC; COM; MLS; Sal; Ohio St U; Occupational Therapy.

SEEMANN, Gaylord William
St John's Cath HS; Toledo, OH (20-200) Chor; Drama; Mgr, Ftbl; Sftbl; COM; JA A; Cl Hon; 1st Hon; Toledo U; Bus Adm.

SEERY, Deborah Ann
St Ignatius HS; St Ignatius, MT (3-37) Ann; Band; CYO; Ensm; GS; NHS; Tres, SC; Bkbl; Amer Leg A; Hon Prog; All-Conf 1st Tm, Bkbl.

SEESHOLTZ, David Neil
Battle Ground HS; Battle Ground, WA (20%-560) Dbte Tm; Cr-Ctry; Co-Cpt, Soccer.

SEESHOLTZ, Suzanne Lorraine
Battle Ground HS; Battle Ground, WA (202-404) AFS; FHA; Semi-Fin, GS; Cr-Ctry; Mgr, Soccer; Stu Store; Counseling Off; Carolyn Hansen Col; Fashion.

SEEVERS, Boyd Vernon
O'Neill Pub HS; O'Neill, NE (1-82) Ann; 4H; VP, NHS; Order/Arrow; SC; Var C; VP, Jr Cl; Pres, Soph Cl; Bkbl; Cr-Ctry; MVP, Swim; Tr; Alg A; B Crocker A; Bio A; COM; Chem A; God & Country A; 4H A; Hist A; HCt; Hon Prog; Math A; MLS; Phy A; Regent Schol; Val; Eagle Sct; Most Stu; Sioux Falls Col; Ministry.

SEEVERS, Jodi Leanne
Argenta-Oreana HS; Argenta, IL (1-100) Chldr; Chor; Ensm; FHA; NHS; Secy, Sch P; HCt; Yth Fel; Scholastic Bowl; Essay Contest Win; Tres, UMYF; Pres, UMYF; Parkland Col; Criminalistics.

SEFCIK, Patricia Ann
Ridgewood HS; Ridgewood, NJ (173-608) K of C; Hockey; Tr; Schol Achv A; Cath U; Bus Adm.

SEFFENSE, Carol Ann
Northeast HS; N Little Rock, AR (15-495) Chor; Fr C; FBLA; Mu Alpha Theta; NHS; Y-Tns; Hon Prog; Outst Girl's Choir Stu; Vol Service A, Vet Adm; Nurs.

SEGAL, Tracie Flynne
Richfield HS; Waco, TX; Secy, Hmrm; Key C; V-Ch, ARC; Spch C; Secy, SC; Var C; Secy, Jr Cl; Secy, Soph Cl; Tnns; Citz A; Spch A; Rep to ESSA; Spch A; Citz A; Member, Art C; U of Tex; Fashion Design.

SEGANISH, Julie Lynn
Potomac Sr HS; Oxon Hill, MD; Ann; Span C.

SEGARRA, Edna Rosa
Academia San Jorge; Santurce, PR (10-75) 4H; VP, Sr Cl; Bio A; Universidad Puerto Rico; Biological Sci.

SEGARRA, Enrique Valois
Juan Jose Osuna HS; Rio Piedras, PR (1-150) BC; Dbte Tm; Fr C; Hmrm; Lit Mag; ARC; JV, Bsbl; JV, Bkbl; JV, Soccer; JV, Sftbl; COM; Hist A; Hon Prog; Lion A; Magna Cum Laude; Most Out; Nu Sigma Beta Cert; Dept of Ed Cert; Cert of Good Behavior; US Naval Acad; Chem.

SEHORN, Nancee Othelia
Concord HS; Concord, NC (142-220) AFS; Band; Span C; Tres, VICA C; Brevard Col; Mus.

SEHRINGER, Diane Lynn
Owego Free Acad; Owego, NY (38-350) Ch, AFS; Secy, Chor; Fr C; 4H; Hmrm; Madrigal; Cpt, Mjrte; Ski C; SC; Tnns; Tr; COM; Hon Prog; Yth Fel; JV Bowl; St Mus Assn Solo A; Cornell U; Interior Design.

SEIBEL, Alan Eugene
Lamar R-1 HS; Lamar, MO; FFA; Bsbl; Bkbl; FFA Schol A; Ind Arts A; Welding.

SEIBEL, Cynthia Lou
Bloomer HS; Bloomer, WI (23-145) AFS; Ann; Band; Bus C; Pres, CYO; Secy, FHA; Pres, 4H; Ch, Hmrm; NHS; Sch P; SC; Secy, Cl; Bkbl; COM; 4H A; HQn; Most Out; Pres A; Swtht; Val; Vlbl; Win, Soc of Foresters Schol; District One Tech Inst; Radiologic Tech.

SEIBEL, Janet Marie
Morristown Pub Sch; Morristown, MN (12-42) Ann; Chldr; Chor; Pres, FHA; Sch P; Sftbl; Vlbl; Nurs.

SEIBEL, Sherene Lynne
Lodi HS; Lodi, CA; Hmrm; Co-Ed, Sch P; SC; Delta Col; Psych.

SEIBEL, Timothy Joel
Lamar R-1 HS; Lamar, MO; Fin, BS; FBLA; FFA; Var C; Bkbl; Ftbl; Tr; Coaching.

SEIBERT, Magdaline
Skyline HS; Oakland, CA (3-500) Tres, Chor; Rptr, Hmrm; SC; COM; Kiwanis A; Tutor; Co-Ch, Gospel Choir; Yth Fel; Guild Girls; Achiev A; Med Explores; Pres, Eastern Star; Pres, Black Stu Union; Merritt Col; Radiologic Technology.

SEIBERT, Marl Leslie
Manteca HS; Manteca, CA; A Cap Choir; Band; Chor; Ger C; Madrigal; Bsbl; Hon Prog; Sci A; WW, Mus; Bethany Bible Col; Mus.

SEIBERT, Omer Lee
S Spencer HS; Rockport, IN (40-163) Chor; Thes; Opt A; Spch A; Solo A; Outst Mus A; Ky Wesleyan Col; Acct.

SEIBERT, Shelley Lynne
Mechanicsburg Sr HS; Mechanicsburg, PA (71-388) Co-Ed, Lit; Sch P; Hon Prog; Liberty Baptist Col; Sociology.

SEIBOLD, Julene Anne
Will C Crawford HS; San Diego, CA (40-600) Ger C; NHS; Ski C; Swim; CSF; U of Calif; Bio.

SEID, Deann
Buckley Sch; Sherman Oaks, CA (10-64) NHS; ARC; Alg A; Bio A; COM; NEDT; Sci A; Equestrian; Stanford U.

SEIDEL, Sharla Mae
Havre HS; Havre, MT (59-270) Chor; Pres, 4H; NFL; Sch P; Spch C; JV, Tr; 4H A; Vlbl; Mont St U; Sociology.

SEIDELL, Cheryl Mae
Imlay City HS; Imlay City, MI; Bus Col; Secy.

SEIDLER, Connie Jane
Bismarck-Henning HS; Bismarck, IL; A-Ed, Ann; Chor; Drama; Secy, 4H; Spch C; Secy, SC.

SEIFERT, Christopher Paul
St Mary's Central HS; Bismarck, ND; Band; Chor; Choir Ensm A.

SEIFERT, John Gerard
Loyola HS; Mankato, MN (25-66) Rptr, Sch P; Var C; Bkbl; MVP, Ftbl; Tr; Sports Ltrs; Ftbl Player o-t Yr A; Bio.

SEIFERT, Keith George
Lakeview HS; Battle Creek, MI (1-400) Community Yth Symph; Orch; Ski C; Tnns; Kalamazoo Col; Health Care.

SEIFERT, Shelley Jean
Ladysmith HS; Ladysmith, WI (8-134) Secy, Chldr; Chor; NHS; SC; Heart o-t N Math Tm; Co Govt Day; Math.

SEIFFERT, Brenda Kay
Westview HS; Braham, MN (5-100) Tres, FFA; Tr; Co-Ch, Christian Yth Fel; Vlbl; Marine Phys Fitness A; Scholastic A; Bethel Col.

SEIFRIED, Debra Lynn
Naperville N HS; Naperville, IL (40-466) Band; Tr; Hon Prog; Yth Fel.

SEIGENFUSE, Jackie
Marian Cath HS; Hometown, PA (78-172) CYO; Chldr; Chor; Hmrm; Fin, Jr Miss Pageant; Rptr, Sch P; Mgr, Bsbl; JV, Hockey; Tnns; Beauty; COM; Hon Prog; Most Out; Sacristan; Girl o-t Mo; Clarion St Col; Eng.

SEIKEN, David Jay
Wm J Woodham HS; Pensacola, FL (7-530) BS; Dbte Tm; Math C; Mu Alpha Theta; Tres, NHS; Span C; Alg A; Amer Leg A; JA A; NEDT; Georgetown U; Pre-Law.

SEILER, Ellen Marie
Hazelwood Central HS; Florissant, MO (200-600) Soccer; Sftbl; Tr; Close-Up Found.

SEILS, Roy Allen
Luther HS S; Chicago, IL (1-160) NHS; Rptr, Sch P; COM; Hon Prog; VofDEM; Bowl Tm; Concordia Col; Math.

SEIM, Ruth Esther
Bison HS; Bison, SD; Ann; Band; Chor; FHA; Tr; Oral Interpretation C; Forestry.

SEITTER, Colleen Ann
New Haven HS; New Haven, MO (2-42) Band; Chldr; Ensm; FTA; NHS; Sftbl; Alg A; Yth Fel; Acad A; E Central Jr Col

SEITTER, Grace Elizabeth
New Haven HS; New Haven, MO (6-40) Band; Cpt, Chldr; Chor; Ensm; FTA; NHS; Sch P; VP, Sr Cl; Sftbl; Type A; Yth Fel; Acad A; E Central Jr Col; Health.

SEITTER, Karen Kay
New Haven HS; New Haven, MO (2-59) Band; Ensm; FTA; NHS; Sftbl; Yth Fel; E Central Jr Col.

SEITTER, Linda Ann
Winyah HS; Georgetown, SC (20%-170) Drama; Fr C; Bio A; Hon Prog; Yth Fel; Secy.

SEITZ, Anneliese
Poughkeepsie HS; Poughkeepsie, NY (25-264) Pres, AFS; Band; Chor; Fr C; VP, Ger C; Orch; Sch P; Tres, SC; Mgr, Ftbl; Ger Teachers A; Chor A; 1st Run-Up, JC Outst Yng Wmn o-t Y; Russell Sage Col; Sociology.

SEITZ, April Elizabeth
Wapakoneta Sr HS; Wapakoneta, OH; Band; VP, Bus C; Rainbow; VP, OEA; Past Worthy Advisor, Rainbow Girls; Ohio St U; Bus.

SEITZBERG, Carol Anne
Siren HS; Siren, WI (2-48) Ed, Ann; Chldr; Chor; Fin, NFL; SC; Pres, Jr Cl; Tr; Bio A; Thes; Alg A; SHE C; Forensics A; U of Minn-Minneapolis; Nurs.

SEITZINGER, Mitchell Scott
Monroe Union HS; Monroe, OR (3-48) Cpt, Bkbl.

SEIVERS, Cheryl Ann
Clinton Sr HS; Clinton, TN (50%-350) VP, Bus C; Sftbl; Type A; Shorthand A; Church Swtht; Acteens Swtht; Bus.

SEJBA, Lynda Rae
Sheboygan Falls HS; Sheboygan Falls, WI (125-165) Secy, AFS; Chor; Tutor; Chor A.

SEJDA, Carmel Mary
St Joseph Acad; McSherrystown, PA (2-12) Chor; Dbte Tm; FHA; Pres, Hmrm; NHS; Pres, SC; Var C; Pres, Jr Cl; Cpt, Bkbl; Hockey; Sftbl; Hon Prog; Stu o-t Wk.

SEKERES, Cecelia Ann
Clairton HS; Clairton, PA; Ann; Fr C; Secy, SC; Pres, Jr Cl; Penn St U.

SELAN, Susan Marie
Reynolds HS; Greenville, PA (1-207) Chldr; Chor; Span C; Rptr, SC; HCt; Hon Prog; Gym; Vlbl; Lib C; Piano, Organ C; Penn St U; Recreation & Mgt.

SELBY, Halbert Ray Jr
Bentonia HS; Bentonia, MS (4-55) FBLA; Bkbl; Amer Leg A; Most Ath; Holmes Jr Col; Phys Therapist.

SELBY, Jeffrey Dale
Bellevue Sr HS; Bellevue, NE (128-841) U of Nebr; Archt.

SELBY, Jennifer Ann
Tara HS; Baton Rouge, LA (8-377) BC; GS; Hmrm; VP, Mu Alpha Theta; NHS; Tri-HiY; I Dare You; Most Out; NEDT; Yth Leg; Wash U; Fine Art.

SELBY, Pamela Rose
Hicks HS; Hicks, LA; Chor; FBLA; 4H; Lit Ral; Cl Fav; 4H A; Type A; Most Dependable; Henderson St Teachers Col; Ed.

SELBY, Robert Brett
Capitol Hill HS; Okla City, OK (2-450) Hmrm; Lat C; Math C; NHS; SC; Bsbl; Bkbl; Cr-Ctry; COM; Rotary A; Alt, BS; Okla St U; Engr.

SELDON, Evelyn Joyce
Smiths Station HS; Smiths, AL (10%-180) F-Ed, Ann; Band; BC; Drama; 4H; Hmrm; Lit Mag; Math C; Mu Alpha Theta; Sch P; Sci C; VP, SC; Beauty; COM; 4H A; Most Out; Outst Young Amer; Auburn U; Med.

SELEMAN, Teresa M
St Paul Cath HS; Bristol, CT (25%-300) Chor; Span C; Hockey; Swim; Art, Mus, A's.

SELENSKY, Laura Ann
Ross S Sterling HS; Baytown, TX (10%-564) Band; CYO; Tex A&M U; Animal Sci.

SELF, Celeste Marie
Kofa HS; Yuma, AZ (4%-650) A Cap Choir; Bus C; Secy, Chor; Cpt, Ensm; FBLA; Madrigal; NHS; ARC; Ftbl; COM; Citz A; Stenography, Solo & Ensm A's; Pacific Christian Col; Mus.

SELF, Elizabeth Ann
Denton HS; Denton, TX (20%-565) Hmrm; Span C; SC; Tres, Soph Cl; Yth Fel; Drill Tm Off; Runnerup, Valentine Swtht; Tex Tech U; Phys Therapy.

SELF, James Mark
Watonga HS; Watonga, OK (75-100) Band; Key C; Bsbl; Sr Patrol Ldr, BSct; Band Kg; Sup, Solo Band As; Sup, Vocal Solo A; Okmulgee Tech U; Elec.

SELF, John Christopher
Decatur HS; Decatur, AL; Band; Bkbl; Golf; Alg A; NEDT; Math Tm; BSct, St Wide Drum & Bugle Corps; U of Ala; Bus.

SELF, Karen Ruth
Roane Co HS; Kingston, TN (31-177) A-Ed, Ann; Chldr; Key C; Sch P; Span C; SC; Pres, Soph Cl; Cl Fav; HCt; Church Yth Choir; Sr Cl High Hon's; Tenn Tech U; Bus Adm.

SELF, Kimberly Faye
Hardaway HS; Columbus, GA (10%-377) AFS; Hmrm; NHS; SC; Cpt, Tnns; MVP, Fin, Semi-Fin, Tnns; Outst Tnns Player A; Auburn U; Special Ed.

SELF, Monica Nan
Warrensburg HS; Warrensburg, MO (71-224) Secy, Band; JV, Chldr; Dbte Tm; Drama; Mjrte; NFL; Sch Achieve Tm; Spch C; Thes; COM; Hon Prog; JA A; Poet A; Pres A; Spch A; Type A; Yth Leg; Law.

SELF, Monty Craig
N Gaston Sr HS; Dallas, NC; Fr C; InterClub Coun; Key C; Tres, SC; Wrest; COM; Pres A; U of NC; Criminal Law.

SELFA, Lance Albert
Moreau HS; Hayward, CA (1-383) CYO; Ski C; Bkbl; JV, Ftbl; COM; Hist A; Hon Prog; Math Tutor; Retreat Ldr; Columnist, Local Newspaper; Eng A; Stanford U; Bio.

SELL, Alan Craig
Hillsdale HS; Hillsdale, MI (3-190) Band; Chor; Key C; NHS; SC; Bkbl; Ftbl; Tr; Kiwanis A; Sal; Western Mich U; Mus.

SELL, Judith Anne Elizabeth
Thornton Township HS; Harvey, IL; Ann; Span C; JV, Tnns; Girl's C; Lat Tourn Hon A; Historian, Mat-Mates; Kappa Alpha Tau; T-Pin A; The Art Inst; Art Historian.

SELLARS, Crystal Lynn
Snyder HS; Snyder, TX (61-209) Chor; FHA; Bkbl; Crisco A; Phys Therapy.

SELLARS, Kimberly Kay
Frontenac HS; Frontenac, KS; Drama; Tres, FHA; Spch C; Bio A.

SELLARS, Laura Sue
Bartow Sr HS; Bartow, FL; Chor; Ensm; FHA; NHS; Golf; COM; Sup, Chor St Contest; Sup, Piano Solo, St Contest; U of Fla; Med Sci.

SELLARS, Stephanie G
New Brunswick Sr HS; New Brunswick, NJ; AFS; FBLA; Hon Prog; Rider Col; Bus Adm.

SELLERS, David Prentiss
Bremerhaven American HS; Bremerhaven, GERMANY (4-24) Order/Arrow; Soccer; Kans St U; Med.

SELLERS, Doyle Allen
Cottonwood HS; Cottonwood, AL (10-70) BC; FFA; Sci C; Bsbl; Bkbl; Ftbl; Sftbl; Cl Fav; Yth Fel.

SELLERS, George D
Fairdale HS; Louisville, KY; Bkbl.

SELLERS, Gregory Lee
Cleburne HS; Cleburne, TX (65-375) NHS; Pres, VICA; Abilene Christian U; Phar.

SELLERS, Janet Beall
Brookwood Sch; Thomasville, GA (7-24) Ed, Ann; JV, Chldr; Span NHS; Secy, SC; VP, Sr Cl; VP, Jr Cl; Co-Cpt, Bkbl; Beauty; Math A; Headmaster's A; Sr Superlative; Yrbk A; Headmaster's List; St Win, 1-Act Play; Auburn U; Spch Pathology.

SELLERS, Joannah Marie
Terrell Acad; Dawson, GA (25%-59) Pres, Drama; Ensm; Pres, Fr C; VP, 4H; Lit Ral; Secy, SC; Tri-HiY; Secy, Soph Cl; Bkbl; Beauty; Cl Fav; 4H A; I Dare You; Yth Fel; Messenger, House Yth Assembly; Biol.

SELLERS, June Katherine
Our Lady of Fatima HS; Lafayette, LA (1-67) A Cap Choir; F-Ed, Ann; BC; CYO; Chor; Drama; Fr C; Ger C; GS; Lit Ral; Math C; Mu Alpha Theta; NHS; Spch C; Pres, SC; Pres, Thes; Pres, Jr Cl; Pres, Soph Cl; COM; Cl Fav; NEDT; Opt A; Spch A; Swtht; Northwestern U; Zoology.

SELLERS, Marcia Ann
La Salle HS; South Bend, IN; S-T, Band; Chor; Ensm; Orch; Citz A; Sci.

SELLERS, Mary Anna
Oak Grove HS; Hattiesburg, MS (1-160) S-T, Band; BC; FHA; Sch P; Alg A; Flag Corp.

SELLERS, Ronald Leland
Xenia HS; Xenia, OH (349-700) Fr C; Key C; Up Bound; Ftbl; Central St U; Bus.

SELLERS, Sheryl Louise
Lehighton Area HS; Lehighton, PA (4-220) A-Ed, Ann; Band; Chor; Pres, 4H; Mjrte; NHS; SC; JV, Bkbl; 4H A; NEDT; Secy, 4-H C; U of Del; Marine Bio.

SELLERS, Terry Ray
Bradford HS; Bradford, TN (7-46) Ann; Pres, FFA; 4H; Mgr, Var C; Pres, Sr Cl; Pres, Jr Cl; Pres, Soph Cl; Bkbl; Star Student; FFA St Farmer; U of Tenn at Martin; Agr.

SELLIN, Arlan Lee
Norfolk Sr HS; Norfolk, NE (40-350) Chess C; Chor; Dbte Tm; Parl, FFA; Pres, GS; Pres, 4H; 4H A; FFA Chapter Farmer; FFA Diary A; U of Nebr; Voc Agr.

SELLMAN, Elizabeth Jane
Corona Sr HS; Corona, CA (33%-800) Band; JV, Chldr; Amer Leg A; COM; Sal; Type A; Gym.

SELLNER, James Clifton
Hastings Sr HS; Hastings, MN (10%-430) NHS; Ski C; Co-Cpt, Cr-Ctry; Tr; Co-Cpt, Cr Ctry Ski; Rosmount Vo-tech; Graphic Arts.

SELLNER, Jerrold Louis
Hastings Sr HS; Hastings, MN (10%-430) NHS; Cpt, Cr-Ctry; Tr; MVP, Cr Ctry; Most Outst, Cr Ctry; VICA St Contest; Rosemont Area Vo-tech; Graphic Communications.

SELLON, Roberta Jane
Randolph Public HS; Randolph, NE (22-70) S-T, Band; S-T, Chor; Drama; Ensm; Parl, FBLA; Secy, 4H; ARC; Tr; 4H A; Mus Camp Court; Chor Accompanist; Med Explorers; Swing Choir; Red Cross Lifeguard; Church Organist; U of Nebr; Nurs.

SELLS, Debra Kay
Benton Harbor HS; Benton Harbor, MI (4-416) Tres, Chor; Secy, Madrigal; NHS; Hon Prog; NMS Commended Stu; Mich Competitive Schol; Panhellanic Schol; Rotarian Schol.

SELLS, Karen Renee
T W Andrews HS; High Point, NC (48-327) BC; Drama; Span C; Sftbl; Art A; Art.

SELLS, Nora Elizabeth
Grace Baptist Sch; South Bend, IN (1-30) Meteorology.

SELVAGE, Vivian Denise
Crestview Sr HS; Crestview, FL (10%-270) BC; PA; Phys Ed A; Pensacola Jr Col; Registered Nurs.

SELVEY, Edward Don
Vashon HS; St Louis, MO (94-295) Ftbl; Tr; Black Stu Union; DOE; Architectual A; Ftbl; U of Mo at Columbia; Law.

SELVEY, Kimberly Ann
Vashon HS; St Louis, MO (64-465) Drama; Pres, Hmrm; SC; Thes; Jr Cl; ARC A; Pres, Black Stu Union; Pom-Pom Sq.

SELZER, Jay Alan
Spencer HS; Spencer, IA; Band; Demolay; FFA; Hmrm; SC; Var C; Bsbl; Cr-Ctry; Ftbl; Tr; Co-Cpt, Wrest; FFA A; FCA.

SEMIEN, Wilton Joseph Jr
Oakdale HS; Oakdale, LA (4-140) NHS; JV, Bkbl; Ftbl; Tr; Alg A; COM; Hon Prog; VofDEM; Industrial Arts A; Phys Ed A; Jr Beau; Mech Drawing A; McNeese St U; Engr.

SEMINARIO, Mitchell
Cardinal Spellman HS; Bronx, NY; Pres, CYO; Chor; Lat C; Span C; Cpt, Var C; Bsbl; Co-Cpt, Cr-Ctry; Co-Cpt, Ftbl; Co-Cpt, Swim; Co-Cpt, Tr; Wrest; COM; JA A; Bus Law.

SEMMEL, Beth Ann
Neshaminy Maple Point HS; Langhorne, PA (1-415) Pres, Chor; NHS; SC; Var C; Hockey; Tr; Type A; Gym; Schol Service A; Fr A; All Around Ath A's; Math.

SEMONES, Claudia Marie
Butler HS; Shively, KY (50-453) Chor; Ger C; Mod Mus Mas; F-Ed, Sch P; Cpt, Bkbl; Golf; Sftbl; JA A; JA; Journ.

SENECHAL, Edward Charles
Preble HS; Green Bay, WI (25-600) Band; Community Yth Symph; Mildred Havelik A; Mus Sch Schol Soc; HR; Wisc St Hon Band; U of Wisc Green Bay; Flute.

SENECHAL, Edward Charles Jr
Preble HS; Green Bay, WI (50-611) Band; Community Yth Symph; Ger C; Hmrm; SC; Hon Prog; Jr Symph Musician A; St Hons Band; St Mus Assn Schol; Pi Sigma Sigma; Mus.

SENEKER, Carl Allen
Katella HS; Anaheim, CA (25%-500) Band; MVP, Tnns; Type A; MVP, Tnns; Point Loma Col.

SENGER, Cheryl Lee
St Mary's Central HS; Bismarck, ND (9-166) Cpt, Chldr; Fr C; SC; Tr; Math A; 1st Cl GSct.

SENGER, Mary Beth
Girard HS; Girard, PA (33%-164) Chor; NHS; Rainbow; Secy, Sr Cl; Amer Leg A; Hon Prog; St Vincent Hlth Ctr Sch of Nurs; Registered Nurs.

SENGSTACKE, Daniel Nicholas V
Osceola HS; Kissimmee, FL (20%-283) Pres, Chor; Key C; SC; Thes; Pres, Sr Cl; Ftbl; Swim; Sup & Excellent St Chor Medals; Outst New Male, Drama; Troy St U.

SENKYR, Sandra JoLynn
Coon Rapids Sr HS; Coon Rapids, MN (31-676) CYO; Chor; NHS; F-Ed, Sch P; Spch C; SC; Church Yth Coun; Staff Yth Retreats; St Thomas Col.

SENN, Angela Lenora
Chipley HS; Chipley, FL (60-112) Gulf Coast Comm Col; Child Psych.

SENN, Mary Amy
Atherton HS; Louisville, KY (2%-350) Co-Ed, Ann; Chor; Fr C; Co-Ch, ARC; Rptr, Sch P; Spch C; SC; Bkbl; COM; Hon Prog; Math A; ARC A; Pres, Pep C; Vlbl; Ed.

SENN, Troy Von
Magnet Cove HS; Malvern, AR; BC; Bus C; FFA; Hmrm; SC; Bsbl; Bkbl; Ftbl; Tr.

SENOR, Herman Alphonse
Springfield HS; Springfield, IL (50%-500) Cpt, Bsbl; Cpt, Bkbl; Ftbl; Tr; *Sci.*

SENSENBRENNER, Cynthia Nadine
Whetstone HS; Columbus, OH (63-587) Pres, Bus C; FHA; FTA; NHS; Rainbow; Span C; COM; Citz A; Type A; Yth Fel; Cpt, MVP, Drill Tm; DeMolay Swtht; *Miami U; Bus Adm.*

SENSENY, Brent Nolan
Chambersburg Area Sr HS; Chambersburg, PA (10%-750) Band; Lat C; Order/Arrow; Cr-Ctry; Tr; Amer Leg A; God & Country A; *Dartmouth Col; Civil Engr.*

SENTENO, Cheryl Lynn
Parlier HS; Parlier, CA; Chor; Fin, GS; HiY; SC; Tnns; Tr; Alg A; Bio A; COM; Hon Prog; Math A; Ger A; *Acct.*

SEPPELER, Daniel Raymond
Marion Central Sch; Marion, NY (10-100) Band; Chess C; Ger C; Pres, 4H; Var C; Co-Cpt, Cr-Ctry; Tr; Alg A; 4H A; Math A; Best Mus; All Co Band; *U of Mich; Elec Engr.*

SEPULVEDA, Florence
Lola Rodriguez de Tio; San German, PR; ARC; COM; Vlbl; High Hon; *RUM at Mayaguez; IBM.*

SERGENT, Gayla Sue
Landmark Christian HS; Glendale, OH (10-36) Band; Drama; Secy, Fr C; 4H; Hmrm; Orch; Var C; Pres, Y-Tns; Bsbl; Cpt, Cr-Ctry; Sftbl; Cpt, Tr; COM; 4H A; Pres A; Mgr, Tr; Band Solo; *Tenn Temple; Dectalogy.*

SERICH, Scott Thomas
Springfield Local HS; Petersburg, OH (1-140) BS; Pres, NHS; Span C; Pres, Jr Cl; JV, Bkbl; Ftbl; JV, Tr; HCt; Math A; NMS; Rensselaer A; Cl Best All Around; Prom Kg; Math Assn of Amer A; *Rensselaer Inst; Engr.*

SERIE, Cynthia Rose
Jasper HS; Jasper, MN (17-52) Band; CYO; Chor; Ensm; FHA; 4H; Var C; Bkbl; 4H A; Outst Minn Farm Yth; *Mt Marty Col; Nurs.*

SERIZAWA, Rodney Keiji
Sacred Heart HS; San Francisco, CA (1-178) Chess C; S-T, Math C; S-T, Sci C; Cr-Ctry; Alg A; Bank Of Amer C; Bio A; CSF; Chem A; Hist A; Math A; NMF; NMS; NEDT; Sci A; *Engr.*

SERMENO, John Lee
Hiram Johnson HS; Sacramento, CA; Band.

SERMENO, Judith Marlene
Alliance HS; Alliance, NE; AFS; Thes; Y-Tns; Pep C; Am Field Serv, Interntl Schol; *Med.*

SERNA, Jill Ann
Reynolds HS; Greenville, PA (20-212) CYO; Chor; FTA; S-T, 4H; Lat C; SC; Tri-HiY; 4H A; Hon Prog; NEDT; Art C As; *Edinboro St Col; Art Ed.*

SERRAL, Amie Carol
Greeneville HS; Greeneville, TN (65-193) Ann; Chor; Drama; Pres, Fr C; VP, FHA; Ed, Sch P; Ski C; SC; Thes; Cl Fav; Gr Marshal; Yth Fel; *U of Tenn; Lib Arts.*

SERRANO, Carmen Celia
Academia Ntra Sra Providencia; Rio Piedras, PR (3-32) Secy, CYO; Chor; 4H; InterAct C; ARC; Sci C; Tres, Jr Cl; COM; Rotary A; Sci A; Conduct A; Fidelity A; *Universidad de Puerto Rico; Med.*

SERRANO, Isaias
Aca Ntra Sra Providencia; Rio Piedras, PR (5-58) Dbte Tm; Drama; Lit Ral; Rptr, Sch P; Span C; Spch C; Tres, Sr Cl; VP, Soph Cl; COM; Hon Prog; Sci A; Summa Cum Laude; Conduct A; *U of Puerto Rico; Phar.*

SERRANO, Joel Soto
Dra Maria Cadilla HS; Arecibo, PR (32-636) MVP, Bsbl; Alg A; COM; Math A; Sci A.

SERRANO, Judith Esther
Manuela Toro HS; Caguas, PR; *U of Puerto Rico; Executive Secy.*

SERRANO, Lourdes
Dra Maria Cadilla de Martinez HS; Arecibo, PR (18-429) Pres, CYO; FHA; FTA; GS; Pres, Hmrm; ARC; SC; Sertoma's A; *Universidad de Puerto Rico.*

SERRANO, Pedro Luis
La Crosse HS; LaCrosse, KS (7-50) Ann; Pres, Span C; Tr; *Kans St U; Engr.*

SERRIO, Marc Thomas
Monte Vista HS; Danville, CA (8-381) Key C; Ski C; Spch C; Pres, CSF; Most Intelligent; Fr Dept A; Social Stu Dept A; Principals HR; *USC; Bus Adm.*

SERVAES, Linda Joyce
Fremont HS; Sunnyvale, CA (1-713) Band; Ensm; Fr C.

SESBERRY, Shirley Ann
Terrell Co HS; Dawson, GA (10%-147) Chor; Tr; Hon Prog; Sci A; Type A; Lib Sci, Eng, A's; *Morris Brown Col; Home Ec.*

SESLER, Tracy Ann
Cleveland HS; Cleveland, TN (14-220) Anchor C; Band; CYO; Chor; Drama; Ensm; Fr C; NHS; SC; Secy, Soph Cl; Alg A; Elk A; Art C; NML; Mus A; Super, Chattanooga Mus Tchrs As Aud; *U of Tenn; Mus.*

SESS, Sheri Lynn
Colerain Sr HS; Cincinnati, OH; JV, Chldr; Chor; Ger C; Hmrm; Tr; HQn; *Evangel Col; Mus.*

SESSAMEN, Harry Dean
Shades Valley HS; Birmingham, AL; Band; Order/Arrow; Thes; Mgr, Bsbl; Tr; Presidential Sports A; Civitan Citz Seminar A; Carrier of Quarter A; *Auburn U; Mus.*

SESSER, Susan Jeanine
Modesto HS; Modesto, CA (41-300) A Cap Choir; Ed, Ann; Band; Chor; Ensm; Tres, Fr C; Pres, 4H; Madrigal; Ntl Yth Conf; Orch; Ski C; JV, Cr-Ctry; Bank Of Amer A; 4H A; Journ A; Chrldr Mascot; WW, Mus; Sen, Hmrm; Sr Rep, SC; President's Phys Fitness A; *UC Santa Barbara; Spch Therapy.*

SESSION, James Henry
U of Detroit HS; Detroit, MI (30-200) Band; Var C; Bsbl; Bkbl; Hon Prog; *Northwestern U; Med.*

SESSION, Keith Duane
Manual Arts HS; Los Angeles, CA; Band; Chess C; Hmrm; JETS; Bsbl; Ftbl; Tr; Coun of Teach A; HCt; *Calif St U Fullerton; Sociology.*

SESSOM, Anne
Independence HS; Independence, MS (10%-118) BC; FBLA; FHA; Cpt, Sftbl; Beauty; *Eckerd Col; Social Sci.*

SESSOMS, Robin Carol
McGavock HS; Nashville, TN; Band; BC; Hmrm; Mu Alpha Theta; SC; Mgr, Bkbl; Bio A; Yth Choir; Church Puppets; *U of Tenn; Vet.*

SETHER, Dianna Lynn
Alexander Ramsey Sr HS; Roseville, MN (80%-555) Chor; 4H; NHS; Citz A; 4H A; 4-H St Comp Achv, Ldrshp & Ctznshp; *U of Minn; Home Ec.*

SETHRE, Robert Thomas
Mounds View HS; Arden Hills, MN (2-630) Chor; InterClub Coun; SC; Tr; Choir Accompanist; Most Talented; Schubert C; Hons Concerts; MMTA Mus Hons; *Duke U; Psych.*

SETIAN, Ann
Siloam Springs HS; Siloam Springs, AR (1-150) S-T, Band; Chem C; Dbte Tm; Drama; FTA; Mod Mus Mas; NHS; Phys C; Sch P; Sci C; Span C; Bkbl; Cr-Ctry; Yth Fel; Piano Guild Audit; All Reg, Band; All St Band; Miss December; Sup, Piano Jr Fest; 1st Pl, Cross Ctry; *Mus.*

SETSER, James Mark
Plainview HS; Plainview, TX (65-327) Pres, SC; Pres, Jr Cl; Pres, Soph Cl; Bsbl; JV, Bkbl; Ftbl; Lt Gov, BS; Pres, FCA; WW; Best All Around; *Hardin-Simmons U; Psych.*

SETSOR, Kyna Lynne
Sidney HS; Sidney, OH (50-300) Band; Cpt, Chldr; Semi-Fin, GS; 4H; Pres, InterClub Coun; NHS; Orch; Pres, Rainbow; Pres, SC; Secy, Sr Cl; Secy, Jr Cl; Sftbl; Tr; HCt; Kiwanis A; Outst Recognition Stu; *Ohio St U; Phys Therapy.*

SETTERLUND, Scott Steven
Galt HS; Galt, CA (22-165) Drama; Fr C; Ger C; Sch Achieve Tm; Span C; VP, SC; Thes; MVP, Var C; VP, Jr Cl; Cpt, Bkbl; Co-Cpt, Ftbl; Golf; Citz A; Cl Fav; HKg; Hon Prog; Opt A; Co-Cpt, JV Bkbl; Full Schol; *U of Oreg-Eugene; Bus Adm.*

SETTERSTROM, Bruce Daniel
Orangeville HS; Orangeville, IL (1-73) NHS; Var C; Pres, Soph Cl; Bkbl; *Agr Tech.*

SETTERSTROM, Paul Henry
Bacon Acad; Colchester, CT; Drama.

SETTLE, Iris Willette
Holly Hill HS; Holly Hill, SC (6-145) S-T, Band; BC; Hmrm; Sch P; SC; Ch, Var C; Bkbl; *Drew U; Mus.*

SETTLE, James Russell
Northwest HS; Clarksville, TN (20%-400) S-T, FFA; *Austin Peay U; Agr.*

SETTLE, Joy Lynn
Hixson HS; Hixson, TN; FBLA; Span C; *U of Tenn; Elem Ed.*

SETTLE, Randy Douglas
Palo Duro HS; Amarillo, TX (56-285) Pres, Band; Drama; Pres, Key C; Orch; Thes; Ftbl; Tr; Citz A; God & Country A; Kiwanis A; Band King; Fav, Key C; *Angelo St Col; Engr.*

SETTLES, Bradley Wayne
Washington Co HS; Springfield, KY (1-177) BC; Chem C; Drama; 4H; Hmrm; Math C; NHS; Phys C; Co-Ed, Sch P; Sci C; Spch C; Var C; Bsbl; Bio A; Hon Prog; ARC A; Sci A; Val; *U of Ky; Civil Engr.*

SEUNTJENS, Debra A
Vanguard HS; Ocala, FL (5-350) Pres, FHA; NHS; Math C; Mu Alpha Theta; NHS; Rainbow.

SEVEREID, Sharen Kim
Clear Lake HS; Lakeport, CA (5-95) Band; Rptr, 4H; NHS; ARC; Secy, SC; Cpt, Cr-Ctry; Swim; Tnns; Cpt, Tr; Citz A; 4H A; HCt; ARC A; MVP, Cr-Ctry & Tr; *ASU; Eng.*

SEVERNS, Jerri Lynn
Abingdon HS; Abingdon, IL (22-120) Band; Chldr; SC; Citz A; Hon Prog; Kiwanis A; Vlbl; *ISU; Med.*

SEVERSON, Joey Tilman
Parkview HS; Orfordville, WI (1-138) Band; Chess C; Co-Ch, Community Yth; Ensmph; NHS; SC; Var C; Bsbl; Bkbl; Ftbl; Tr; Dist & St Mus A; Gold Cup Mus A; Ltrman; *U of Wis-Madison.*

SEWALL, Diane Claire
Southport HS; Indianapolis, IN (127-433) Bus Mgr, Anchor C; Bus Mgr, Ann; FHA; Ch, Hmrm; VP, Mjrte; ARC; Rptr, SC; Var C; Parl, Sr Cl; Parl, Jr Cl; Parl, Soph Cl; Bus Mgr, Sch P; Co-Cpt, Swim; Journ A; Q&S A; Swtht; Yth Fel; S-T, Fresh Cl; Yng Life; *Purdue U; Psych.*

SEWALL, Janice Arline
Boothbay Region HS; Boothbay Harbor, ME; Chor; Secy, Lat C; S-T, Var C; Mgr, Bkbl; Hockey; Mgr, Sftbl; Journ A; VofDEM; *U of Maine; Lib Arts.*

SEWALL, Mary Kathryn
Harrington HS; Harrington, WA (5-13) Ann; Band; Cpt, Chldr; Chor; Drama; Jr Miss Pagent; Mjrte; Rptr, Sch P; Secy, SC; Secy, Y-Tns; Tnns; HQn; Secy, Pep C; Girl's League; Vlbl; Spirit Girl; *Spokane Comm Col; Cosmetology.*

SEWARD, Lynda Carole
Benedictine Acad; Elizabeth, NJ (14-33) Chldr; 4H; Hmrm; NHS; Pres, Soph Cl; Beauty; Journ A; Swtht; *Howard U; Communications.*

SEWELL, Deatria Lynne
Wilmington Sr HS; Wilmington, OH (25-339) Chldr; Vlbl; *Morehouse Col; Bus Mgt.*

SEWELL, Sandra Lee
Wm A Russell HS; E Point, GA (26-149) Anchor C; Band; Cpt, Chldr; FBLA; Hmrm; Span C; SC; Pres, Y-Tns; VP, Sr Cl; VP, Soph Cl; Bkbl; Sftbl; HCt; Opt A; PTA A; Type A; Fire Marshall.

SEXTON, Bradley Booth
Levelland HS; Levelland, TX (21-212) Band; NHS; Co-Ch, Span C; Mgr, Bkbl; NMS; Stu o-t Mo; WW; *Tex Tech U; Med.*

SEXTON, Charlene Dale
Sunbright HS; Sunbright, TN (2-63) Band; BC; FHA; 4H; Tres, Rainbow; Bkbl; 4H A; Sal; E Tenn Baptist Hospital Sch of Nur; Nurs.

SEXTON, Cindy Amanda
Ala Christian HS; Montgomery, AL (27-40) Chor; Pres, FHA; Secy, SC; Swtht; Most Spirited; WW; Home Ec Achv A; Troy St U; Psych.

SEXTON, Gary Edward
Huffman HS; Birmingham, AL; A Cap Choir; Pres, Hmrm; Sftbl; Auburn U; Drafting.

SEXTON, Marlene Gale
Sunbright HS; Sunbright, TN (5-63) Band; FHA; 4H; Rainbow; Sci C; Var C; Co-Cpt, Bkbl; 4H A; Faculty Schol; Tenn Tech U; Phys Therapy.

SEXTON, Patricia Trotter
Decatur HS; Decatur, AL (27-291) FHA; FTA; Hmrm; Mu Alpha Theta; NHS; Sci C; Span C; U of Ala; Biochem.

SEXTON, Sandi Sue
Union Grove HS; Union Grove, WI (25%-250) Drama; Secy, SC; Union U; Sociology.

SEYBOLD, Mark Alan
Rockville HS; Rockville, IN (5-82) Pres, Chem C; Fr C; NHS; Phys C; Sci C; Var C; Bsbl; JV, Bkbl; Cr-Ctry; Golf; St Scholar; Dr Basil Merill Ath Schol A; BS Alt; Ind U; Dentistry.

SEYBOLD, Thelma May
Centennial HS; Pueblo, CO; A Cap Choir; Chor; Drama; Ensm; Pres, FBLA; NHS; Citz A; DARGCA; U Sou Colo; Bus Teacher.

SEYFRIED, Barbara A
Clarkstown HS; New City, NY (112-504) Bus C; FBLA; Span C; Rockland Comm Col; Bus.

SEYMOUR, Frances Jane
Chapel Hill Sr HS; Chapel Hill, NC (4-300) AFS; Band; Co-Cpt, Chldr; Community Yth Symph; Hmrm; NHS; Ski C; Span NHS; SC; COM; NMF; Pres A; Ch, Sr Cl Ball Comm; Gov Sch; Morehead Schol; Span A; Drama A; U of NC.

SEYMOUR, Herman Curtis
Hart Co HS; Hartwell, GA; A Cap Choir; Bus C; VP, FFA; Sftbl; COM; Spch A; FFA A's; Emmanuel Col.

SEYMOUR, John Taylor
Douglas Bryd Sr HS; Fayetteville, NC (73-374) Ger C; Order/Arrow; Sci C; Ftbl; Wrest; God & Country A; ROTC A; Eagle Sct; NC St U; Mech Engr.

SEYMOUR, Pamela Gail
Wayne Co HS; Jesup, GA (5%-400) Ann; BC; Span C; COM; HR; Gov Hon Nom; Ga Sou Col; Acct.

SEYMOUR, Ronda Denice
North Hall HS; Gainesville, GA (120-240) JV, Bkbl; Outst Wrk A; Stop Drugs at Source.

SEYMOUR, Yvonne Maybeth
Taft HS; Hamilton, OH (20%-499) Chor; MVNC.

SHABLOM, Harold Clayton
Elmira Southside HS; Elmira, NY; JV, Bkbl; JV, Ftbl; Tr; Hon Prog; Yth Leg.

SHACKELFORD, Brenda Lee
Heritage Baptist HS; Sand Springs, OK; Cpt, Chldr; Secy, SC; Bkbl; Sftbl; Outst Stu A; Baptist Bible Col.

SHACKELFORD, Diane Renee
Hardee Co HS; Wauchula, FL; BC; FHA; FHA; Rptr, FTA; Span C; Inter-C A.

SHACKELFORD, Elizabeth Lee
Hahnville HS; Luling, LA (45-520) A Cap Choir; Chor; Drama; Ensm; FHA; COM; Cl Fav; Columbia Bible Col; Religious Ed.

SHACKELFORD, Joel Wayne
East Lake N HS; East Lake, OH (118-778) A Cap Choir; Chor; Ensm; HR; COM; Pres, Church Yth Dept; Tn o-t Yr; Church Chorale; Ensm Medal; Church Pianist; Solo, Choir, A's; JA; Bible Baptist Col; Mus.

SHACKELFORD,
Patrick Raymond Brown
Central HS; Tulsa, OK; Thes; Swim; Okla St U.

SHACKLETON, Barbara Kay
Menomonie HS; Menomonie, WI (90-225) Chor; Vlbl; N Central Bible Col.

SHACKLETT, Leslie Hart
Joseph Wheeler HS; Marietta, GA; FHA; Hmrm; NHS; Sch P; Span C; SC; Tr; Mgr, Wrest; Jr Civitan C; Harding Col.

SHACKLETT, Tracy Lou
Joseph P Wheeler HS; Marietta, GA (20-423) F-Ed, Ann; BC; Fr C; NHS; SC; Pres, Soph Cl; Mgr, Bsbl; S-T, Flag Corps; Jr Civitan; VP, Fresh Cl; Foreign Lang Coun; Lynchburg Col; Foreign Lang.

SHADDEN, William Neal III
Cartersville HS; Cartersville, GA (3-146) Band; BC; Math C; Mu Alpha Theta; Pres, Order/Arrow; Tres, Sci C; Tnns; Eagle Sct; Jr Cl Marshall; U of Ga; Sci.

SHADDOCK, Martha Lynn
Canyon HS; New Braunfels, TX (25%-145) Co-Ed, Ann; Chor; FFA; Semi-Fin, Jr Miss Pa; gent; SW Tex St U; Commercial Art.

SHADDOX, Suzy Cain
Whitehouse HS; Whitehouse, TX (9-99) FHA; NHS; Beauty.

SHADDOX, Terry Joe
Acadiana HS; Lafayette, LA (34-443) Fr C; Secy, Key C; S-T, Var C; Ftbl; COM; Hon Prog; Secy, FCA; Fr A; Acad Schol; Player o-t Wk, Ftbl; U of SW La; Chem Engr.

SHADID, Deana Christine
Clarksville HS; Clarksville, TX; Parl, FTA; Var C; Bkbl; Sftbl; Tr; Yth Fel; Vlbl A; Paris Jr Col; Horti-culture.

SHADIOW, Bruce James
Thomas Carr Howe HS; Indianapolis, IN (28-691) CYO; Chess C; Chor; 4H; Hmrm; NHS; SC; Var C; Pres, Soph Cl; Cpt, Bsbl; JV, Bkbl; JV, Cr-Ctry; Cpt, Ftbl; Sftbl; COM; Citz A; 4H A; Hon Prog; Math.

SHADLEY, Camilla Lynne
NW HS; Jackson, MI; VP, 4H; Bkbl; Cpt, Sftbl; Bio A; 4H A; Yth Fel; Mech Drawing A; Straight 'A'S'; Mich U; Drafting Tech.

SHAFER, Carole Jean
Holbrook Pub Sch; Holbrook, NE; Ann; Band; Chor; Drama; Pres, FHA; Pres, 4H; Ed, Sch P; Var C; Secy, Soph Cl; Bkbl; Ftbl; Tr; Alg A; 4H A; U of Nebr; Bus Ed.

SHAFER, Charles Welsh
Fort Myers HS; Fort Myers, FL (8%-1800) BS; Pres, Hmrm; InterClub Coun; Pres, SC; Var C; Bsbl; Bkbl; Cpt, Ftbl; Amer Leg A; COM; Cl Fav; Elk A; H of F; Kiwanis A; Most Out; Pres A; Star Student; Yth Fel; Pres, Fresh Cl; Christmas Dnce Cort; All-Amer Bkbl Tm; Hgh Spirit A; Valentine Dnce Cort; Pres, Church Yth Group; Edison Comm C; Law.

SHAFER, Christopher Robert
Spencer HS; Spencer, IA (70-240) Chem C; Chess C; Sch P; SC; Y-Tns; MVP, Bsbl; JV, Bkbl; JV, Cr-Ctry; Cpt, Ftbl; MVP, Sftbl; JV, Swim; Tr; JV, Wrest; Spch A; Chess Champ; U of Northern Iowa; Sci.

SHAFER, Douglas Charles
Aloha HS; Aloha, OR (50-540) JV, Bsbl; Phi Beta Kappa; Pres A; NW Nazarene Col; Bus Adm.

SHAFER, James Milton
Horace Maynard HS; Maynardville, TN (1-127) Co-Ed, Ann; Pres, BC; Pres, Sci C; Span C; Secy, SC; Var C; Tres, Sr Cl; Cpt, Ftbl; MLS; Val; WW; Tenn Tech U; Engr.

SHAFER, Mary Rehnea
Forest Park HS; Beaumont, TX (12-435) Chor; Ensm; Semi-Fin, GS; InterClub Coun; Madrigal; NHS; Tr; COM; Magna Cum Laude; WW; Sr Mbr, Drill Tm; Chor A; WW Forest Park Sr; Lamar U; Marketing.

SHAFER, Renee Sue
Moanalua HS; Honolulu, HI (30-231) Lat C; HR; Med Asst Sch of Hawaii; Med Asst.

SHAFER, Robin Lynne
Spencer HS; Spencer, IA (25%-200) Band; Drama; Ensm; Span C; Spch A; VP, Span Cl; Jr NHS; Secy, Christian Yth Fel; Iowa St U; Psych.

SHAFER, Valerie Jean
Eleanor Roosevelt HS; Greenbelt, MD (15%-300) Chldr; 4H; Sr Cl.

SHAFFER, Beth Ann
Ben Davis HS; Indianapolis, IN (5%-900) A Cap Choir; Band; Chor; NHS; Bus.

SHAFFER, Diana Margaret
Hempfield Area Sr HS; Greensburg, PA (10%-750) Lat C; NHS; Hon Prog; Seton Hill Col; Vet Med.

SHAFFER, Donna Lynn
Springfield Sr HS; Springfield, OR (15%-322) A Cap Choir; Chor; Dbte Tm; NHS; Rptr, Sch P; Hon Prog; Journ A; Spch A; U of Oreg; Mus.

SHAFFER, Judith Ann
S Charleston HS; S Charleston, WV; Band; Rainbow; Span C; Spch A; Yth Fel; Tres, Sunday Sch; Span Dancers; Color Guard; Marshall U; Nurs.

SHAFFER, Lisa Marie
Bishop Byrne HS; Memphis, TN (20-192) Chldr; Pres, FBLA; VP, NHS; Span C; Beauty; COM; H of F; HCt; Swtht; Vlbl; Fin, Executive Secy Contest; Miss FBLA for Tenn; Memphis St U; Secy Sci.

SHAFFER, Melinda Jane
Titusville Sr HS; Titusville, PA (24-233) NHS; Sch P; Hon Prog; Yth Fel.

SHAFFER, Randall Alan
Safford HS; Safford, AZ (4-228) Pres, Band; Chor; Ensm; Order/Arrow; Sci C; Ftbl; Elk A; Hist A; Outst Boy Camper A; U of Ariz; Elec.

SHAFFER, Sherri Kay
Lampeter-Strasburg HS; Lampeter, PA (11-211) AFS; Co-Cpt, Chldr; Chor; Fr C; Secy, Var C; Yth Fel; Outst Newspaper Carrier; Drew U.

SHAFFERMAN, Joanna Susan
Frankfort HS; Ridgeley, WV (10%-139) Band; NHS; Var C; Bkbl; Tr; Pep Band; Pep C; Vlbl; Shepherd Col; Recreation.

SHAFFNER, Paul Raymond
Lancaster Central Sr HS; Lancaster, NY (167-603) Order/Arrow; Var C; Bkbl; Co-Cpt, Ftbl; Order/Arrow A; Yth Fel; Eagle Sct; Phys Ed.

SHAKE, Ralph Tom
Henryville HS; Henryville, IN (5-65) Rptr, FFA; VP, NHS; VP, Jr Cl; Cr-Ctry; Tr; Amer Leg A; Geom A; Span A; Elec Engr.

SHALANDER, Sandra Jean
Forest Lake Sr HS; Forest Lake, MN (78-511) Chldr; Ski C; JV, Tr; Phys Fitness A; Explorers; Mankato Col; Photography.

SHALLCROSS, Jason Stuart
Smithfield-Selma Sr HS; Smithfield, NC (35-355) CYO; VP, Key C; NHS; Ftbl; Tr; MVP, Wrest; NC St U; Textiles.

SHAMBAUGH, Shawn C
Wasco Union HS; Wasco, CA (5-146) BS; Ch, Hmrm; Math C; SC; Pres, Var C; Pres, Sr Cl; Pres, Soph Cl; Bkbl; Cr-Ctry; Ftbl; Swim; Tr; Bank Of Amer A; CSF; Hon Prog; Sci A; WW; Fresno St U; Med Tech.

SHAMBERGER, Carla Jean
Wenatchee HS; Wenatchee, WA (14-397) Ann; Chor; Hmrm; Madrigal; NHS; Orch; ARC; Ski C; St Stu Congress; Y-Tns; Pres, Sr Cl; Hist A; Wash St U; Ed.

SHAMBLEY, Linda Annette
Cresset Christian Acad; Durham, NC; Ed, Ann; Chor; Drama; SC; Best Desk A; Mus A; Scripture Memory A; Courtesy A; Liberty Baptist Col; Ed.

SHAMBLIN, Douglas Allan
Doyle HS; Knoxville, TN (25-360) Band; U of Tenn; Elec Engr.

SHAMBURGER, Mark Douglas
Bolton HS; Alexandria, LA (2-435) Parl, Chess C; Hmrm; Semi-Fin, Lit Ral; S-T, Span C; LSU; Law.

SHAMEY, Janine Ann
Richland Sr HS; Gibsonia, PA; AFS; Band; Pres, 4H; Mjrte; NFL; Orch; 4H A; Mus; Candystriper; Girl's Ldr C; Lib Arts.

SHAMMASH, Deborah Susan
MacDuffie Sch; Springfield, MA (3-50) Cum Laude Soc; Drama; Math C; VP, Sr Cl; Pres, Jr Cl; S-T, Soph Cl; Hockey; Tnns; Jewish Yth Coun; Co-Cpt, Ski Tm; Biol.

SHANAHAN, Bridgid Joan
Bishop Watterson HS; Columbus, OH; Social Work.

SHANAHAN, James Michael
Axtell HS; Axtell, NE (50%-30) Pres, 4H; Sch P; Var C; Ftbl; Tr; Wrest; 4H A.

SHANAHAN, Sheila Marie
Winston Churchill HS; Livonia, MI (19-678) CYO; Chor; Hmrm; Lit Mag; Ed, Sch P; Ski C; Mgr, Swim; Citz A; Sci A; Corresponding Secy, SC; Art A; HS Hons Sci Prog; Scholastic Achv A; CCD Teacher; Art C; Secy, Church Yth Group; *Sci.*

SHANE, Scott Robert
Springfield Local HS; Petersburg, OH (15-150) Fr C; HiY; Bsbl; Bkbl; Ftbl; HCt; Hon Prog; Best All Around; Ltrman; VP, Hist C; Prom Court; *Forestry.*

SHANELEC, Abby Gail
Kingman HS; Kingman, KS (15-111) Band; JV, Chldr; Chor; Drama; Secy, 4H; Fin, Jr Miss Pagent; Mjrte; Var C; Y-Tns; Tres, Soph Cl; Tnns; Tr; 4H A; Pres A; Fin, Hugh O'Brien Ldrship Sem; *Kansas St Col; Home Ec.*

SHANK, Cheryl Ruth
Parkwood HS; Joplin, MO (15%-150) VP, BC; Tres, NHS; Regent Schol; WW; Nom, Amer HS Stu; *Baylor U; Developmental Therapy.*

SHANK, Eric Todd
Trotwood-Madison HS; Trotwood, OH (150-450) *Ariz St U; Agr.*

SHANK, Kim Marie
S Park HS; Fairplay, CO; Ed, Ann; Drama; Pres, Sr Cl; Pres, Jr Cl; Bkbl; Tr; *Bauder Fashion Col; Fashion Merc.*

SHANK, Thomas Carl
Greenville HS; Greenville, IL; Hmrm; VP, Lat C; Var C; Cpt, Bkbl; Ftbl; Cpt, Tr; Cl Fav; MLS; Yth Fel; *Ill W U; Pre-Law.*

SHANKEL, Kymbria Lanette
Fort Scott Sr HS; Fort Scott, KS (3-150) All Amer Yth; Band; Chldr; Chor; Drama; Ensm; HiY; Rainbow; Span C; SC; Bsbl; Bkbl; MVP, Sftbl; HQn; Yth Fel; Span A; Sch Play; Cpt, Pom Pon; Mus A; *Kans St Col; Span.*

SHANKEL, Lynda Lee
Breckenridge Jr-Sr HS; Breckenridge, MI; Chldr; Drama; SC; Sftbl; Tr; Math A; Most Out.

SHANKLES, Susan Carol
Collinsville HS; Collinsville, AL (11-60) Ann; Band; FHA; Secy, 4H; Sftbl; Swim; Tnns; 4H A; *U of Ala; Psych.*

SHANKLIN, Richard Allen
Eureka HS; Eureka, IL (60-130) Band; FFA; VP, 4H; Bsbl; Bkbl; Ftbl; 4H A; *ICC; Agr.*

SHANKLIN, Sharon Lee
Eureka HS; Eureka, IL (15-129) A Cap Choir; Band; Chor; FHA; FNA; Pres, 4H; Madrigal; ARC; Arch; Bkbl; Tr; 4H A; I Dare You; St Scholar; *Ill St U; Med Tech.*

SHANKS, Phyllis Kay
Long Beach HS; Long Beach, NY (150-400) Chor; Drama; Hmrm; Fin, Arch; Mgr, Sftbl; *Okla St U; Sci.*

SHANNON, Bonnie Lavaine
Permian HS; Odessa, TX; Band; Dbte Tm; Ensm; FHA; Hmrm; COM; Type A; Vocational Office; Ed Officer; *Bible Baptist Col; Secy.*

SHANNON, Colleen Ann
Perry Hall Sr HS; Baltimore, MD; Chor; Tr.

SHANNON, Diane
Olney HS; Philadelphia, PA (160-879) Kiwanis A; Off Monitor; Span A; Human Relations Comm; Black Stu League; Eng A; *Temple U; Lib Arts.*

SHANNON, George William
SE HS; Springfield, IL (294-557) Tr A; *Bradley U; Med.*

SHANNON, Gregory Edward
West Sr HS; Iowa City, IA (10%-350) Band; BS; CYO; Dbte Tm; Orch; *U of Iowa; Chem.*

SHANNON, James W
Nevada HS; Nevada, MO (5-210) Band; NHS; Tr; Drum Major; Soph Pilgrim.

SHANNON, James William
Starkville HS; Starkville, MS (25%-245) Band; Chem; 4H; Lat C; Sftbl; *Miss St U; Chem Engr.*

SHANNON, Kerry Wayne
Central HS; La Crosse, WI (33%-534) A Cap Choir; Band; Chor; Demolay; Secy, Drama; *U of Wisc; Engr.*

SHANNON, Kimberley Sue
Southside HS; Elmira, NY; Band; Chor; Hmrm; Span C; SC; Off Girl; HR; VP, Secy, Church Yth Group.

SHANNON, Kimmie Lynn
Andrew J Terrell HS; Blanchard, OK; BC; Bus C; Chor; Ensm; Secy, FBLA; FHA; 4H; Bkbl; Sftbl; Bus.

SHANNON, Michael Douglas
Robert E Lee HS; Montgomery, AL (190-740) Band; JA A; *Auburn U; Bus.*

SHANNON, Patrice Diane
Notre Dame-Bishop Gibbons HS; Schenectady, NY; CYO; NHS; Tnns; Hon Prog; *Siena Col; Math.*

SHANNON, Sherman
Leesville HS; Leesville, LA; Black Heritage C; *Sou U; Bus.*

SHANNON, Susan Elizabeth
St Marys Girls HS; Manhasset, NY (33%-180) CYO; Chor; Drama; ARC; Var C; Cpt, Swim; COM; Hon Prog; Yth Fel; Swim Schol, St John's U; *St John's U; Med Tech.*

SHANNON, Willis James
Eastside HS; Paterson, NJ (19-600) Cpt, Cr-Ctry; Cpt, Tr; Citz A; Most Out; Mite A; *Drew U; Pre-Med.*

SHAPIRO, Ephraim Avraham
Hebrew Acad HS; Yonkers, NY (1-16) Chess C; Fr C; Co-Ch, Math C; Rptr, Sch P; SC; Tr; *Brown U; Pol Sci.*

SHAPIRO, Karen Eileen
Maple Shade HS; Maple Shade, NJ (10-241) Chor; Drama; Key C; NHS; Bowl C; *Psych.*

SHAPLEIGH, Susan Gayle
Ysleta HS; El Paso, TX (71-650) Swim; Citz A; Hon Prog; Gym; *Northern Arizona U.*

SHAPLEY, Phyllis Ruth
Hickman Mills HS; Kansas City, MO (26-488) Chor; Ensm; FHA; Math C; NHS; Orch; Sci C; Span C; Hon Prog; Regent Schol; Med Careers C; Outst Academic Achv Certs; *UMKC.*

SHARETTE, Denise Suzanne
N Farmington HS; Farmington, MI (164-454) A Cap Choir; Chor; Madrigal; Hon Graduate; WW; *Calvin Col; Mus.*

SHARKEY, Keith Charles
Hannibal HS; Hannibal, NY; Band; Drama; Thes; Cr-Ctry; Tr; COM; Drama A; *Carpentry.*

SHARKEY, Lori Jo
Burlingame HS; Burlingame, CA (10%-400) Band; Chor; Ensm; Orch; Bkbl; Ftbl; Sftbl; Tnns; Mus A's; Block B, Ath; *UCLA; Oceanography.*

SHARKEY, Scott Allen
Barberton HS; Barberton, OH (12-515) Demolay; Tres, Ger C; Hmrm; Key C; NHS; Sch Achieve Tm; Rptr, Sch P; Ftbl; Tr; Q&S A; Huddle Con-Cpt, FCA; NML; Acad Challenge Quiz Show; *Wittenberg U; Bio.*

SHARP, Barry Joseph
Princeton HS; Cincinnati, OH (3-607) VP, Band; Dbte Tm; FBLA; Hmrm; Math C; NFL; NHS; Orch; Co-Cpt, Sch Achieve; MVP, Golf; Chem A; JA A; Yale Book A; Cpt, Golf Tm; Win, Acct Contest; Top 10, 3yrs; NML; *William & Mary Col; Acct.*

SHARP, Carl Joseph Jr
Union Co HS; Liberty, IN (10-131) FFA; 4H; NHS; Order/Arrow; Ftbl; Wrest; 4H A; JA A; Order/Arrow A; Sci A; Yth Fel; Alt, BS; Explorers Off; ESct; Firecrafter; St Fin, Century III Ldrs Schol.

SHARP, Carol Ann
Kingsway Regional HS; Swedesboro, NJ; Band; GS; Semi-Fin, Hmrm; Key C; NHS; Ski C; Bkbl; Hockey; Sftbl; *Gettysburg Col.*

SHARP, Charles Eugene
Mountain Brook HS; Mountain Brook, AL (33%-360) BS; Pres, InterClub Coun; Order/Arrow; VP, SC; Var C; Ftbl; Cl Fav; *Med.*

SHARP, David Keith
Inglemoor HS; Seattle, WA (21-348) Ch, Hmrm; NHS; Tnns; Hon Prog; *U of Wash; Engr.*

SHARP, Derrel Lynn
New Caney HS; Porter, TX (25%-230) NHS; SC; Pres, Soph Cl; Bsbl; JV, Bkbl; Ftbl; Cl Fav; WW in Geom; Okla NHS; *Engr.*

SHARP, Eric Thomas
Sandy Valley HS; Magnolia, OH (66-167) Band; Pres, Chess C; Life Sct; *Math.*

SHARP, Heather Jo
Alameda Sr HS; Lakewood, CO (10-620) Band; Ensm; Orch; Alg A; Coun of Teach A; Hist A; Hon Prog; Math A; Opt A; Sci A; Spch A; Russian C; Gym; Mus A.

SHARP, Jenny Christina
Wenatchee HS; Wenatchee, WA (78-400) A Cap Choir; Chor; Community Yth Symph; Parl, FBLA; NHS; Orch; Bus Mgr, Sch P; SC; Sftbl; Most Out; Star Student; All St, All NW Pacific, Orch; Stu Teacher, Piano, Cello; Most Inspirational, Orch; *Wash St U; Med Tech.*

SHARP, Karen Ann
Covington HS; Covington, LA (4-273) Band; BC; Secy, FTA; Hmrm; NHS; Span C; SC; VP, Sr Cl; Kiwanis A; Academic Schol; *Southeastern La U; Ed.*

SHARP, Kathy Marie
Covington HS; Covington, LA (5-273) Band; BC; FTA; Lit Ral; NHS; Span C; SC; Kiwanis A; Academic Schol; *Southeastern La U; Bus.*

SHARP, Lisa Kay
Pisgah Sr HS; Canton, NC; VICA Graphics C; Planning Comm, Health Careers C; *Haywood Tech Inst; Nurs.*

SHARP, Lori Grace
Clarence M Kimball HS; Royal Oak, MI (10%-650) Ann; NHS; Swim; *Med Tech.*

SHARP, Marianne Faneuil
Webb Sch of Knoxville; Knoxville, TN (43-83) Tnns; *Bus Adm.*

SHARP, Mark David
Milford HS; Milford, OH (49-364) Band; Tres, Chor; Ensm; Lat C; Span C; Sftbl; Pol Campaign Worker; *Oral Roberts U; Mus.*

SHARP, Mark Wayne
Springdale HS; Springdale, AR (275-500) Chor; Span C; Y-Tns; *U of Ark; Bus Mgt.*

SHARP, Mark Wayne
Central HS; Columbia, TN (69-381) Math C; Alg A; Hist A; Math A.

SHARP, Michael Burton
Ross S Sterling HS; Houston, TX (8-400) Chldr; Chem C; FTA; Hmrm; NHS; Sch P; Sci C; Span C; Spch C; Span NHS; SC; Tr; COM; Rotary A; DECA A; Display A; *UCLA; Bus Admin.*

SHARP, Michael Drake
Hardaway HS; Columbus, GA (20%-450) Band; ARC; Ski C; Yth Fel; Art A; Tres, Yth Fel.

SHARP, Randall David
Dos Pueblos HS; Goleta, CA (25%-671) Band; Chor; Drama; NHS; Orch; JV, Cr-Ctry; JV, Tnns; JV, Tr; Handbell Choir; Life Rand; Sr Patrol Ldr, BScts; *Santa Barbara Jr Col; Mech Engr.*

SHARP, Sharon Kay
Bethany HS; Reidsville, NC (6-64) Anchor C; Ann; Fr C; FHA; 'B' HR; *Rockingham Comm Col; Secy Sci.*

SHARP, Susan Marie
Webb Sch of Knoxville; Knoxville, TN (20%-83) Lat C; Tnns; NEDT; Yth Fel.

SHARP, Thomas Andrew
Battle Ground Acad; Franklin, TN (2-64) Chldr; Pres, Key C; Tres, NHS; Pres, SC; Var C; Pres, Sr Cl; VP, Jr Cl; VP, Soph Cl; Bsbl; Ftbl; Most Out; NEDT; Sewanee C A; *U of Ky; Dentistry.*

SHARP, Trendy Leigh
Eula HS; Clyde, TX (1-22) Co-Ed, Ann; Cpt, Chldr; Pres, FHA; VP, SC; Tres, Jr Cl; Secy, Soph Cl; Bkbl; Tr; Amer Leg A; Cl Fav; HCt; MLS; Lions C Swtht; Fin, Miss Teenage Abilene; One Act Play; Miss Eula HS; *McMurry Col; Eng.*

SHARP, Tunene Jane
W Memphis Christian Sch; W Memphis, AR; Ann; Chor; Fr C; VP, FHA; S-T, Jr Cl; VP, Soph Cl; JV, Bkbl; JV, Sftbl; Tr; Citz A; Cl Fav; HCt; Math A; Sci A; *Harding Col; Bible.*

SHARPE, Donetta Sue Smith
LaVeta HS; LaVeta, CO (1-22) VP, BC; Drama; VP, FBLA; S-T, NHS; Rainbow; Tres, SC; Bkbl; Alg A; Bio A; COM; HQn; Math A; MLS; Sci A; Spch A; Type A; Val; Pep Band; Most Humorous; Eng A; Vlbl; Creative Writing A; Stu Asst; Better Homes & Gardens A; General Mills A; *Creative-Writing.*

SHARPE, Gerald Doyle
H V Jenkins HS; Savannah, GA (15-360) Sch P; Co-Cpt, Bsbl; Co-Cpt, Bkbl; Mgr, Ftbl; COM; Hist A; Hon Prog; Outst Sr; *Recreation.*

SHARPE, Joy Renee
Swansboro HS; Swansboro, NC (4-138) Ed, Ann; Secy, BC; Cpt, Chldr; GS; InterClub Coun; Monogram; SC; Chem A; Citz A; Cl Fav; DARGCA; Hist A; HQn; VFW A; VofDEM; Outst Sr; Span, Home Ec, A's; Best All Around; *U of NC.*

SHARPE, Ronald Owen
Holston HS; Knoxville, TN (40-209) AFS; Chor; Drama; Ensm; Pres, Fr C; Madrigal; Thes; All-St Chor; WW; Amer Abroad.

SHARPLEY, Mavis Elaine
Corsicana HS; Corsicana, TX (25-275) Secy, A Cap Choir; Hmrm; SC; Hon Prog; Opt A; All-Region Choir; All-Dist Choir; Psych C; *Tex Tech U; Bus Adm.*

SHARPNACK, Irene Marie
Del Oro HS; Loomis, CA; Bus C; Cum Laude Soc; Phys Fitness, Acad Excel, A's; *Nurs.*

SHARUM, Wayne Patrick
Southside Sr HS; Fort Smith, AR (1-435) BS; Inter-Act C; NHS; COM; Hon Prog; NMF; NMS; Opt A; ROTC A; Cpt, ROTC Rifle Tm; Robert Sherman-Lazenby Schol; Jr Asst Sct-Master, BSct.

SHATSWELL, Dawn Elesa
Oak Valley Christian Sch; Oakdale, CA (1-18) 4H; Tr; *The Col of Idaho; General Ed.*

SHATTO, Nancy Lynn
Memorial Sr HS; Houston, TX (20-640) Band; Math C; Model UN; Mu Alpha Theta; NHS; Secy, Span C; Secy, Span NHS; Citz A; God & Country A; Hon Prog; Magna Cum Laude; 1st Cl GSct; Secy, Amigos; Church Choir; *Baylor U; Bus.*

SHATTO, Rosalynda Diane
DeKalb HS; Waterloo, IN (152-326) Band; Chor; Ger C; 4H; Bkbl; Tr; *Purdue U; Sci.*

SHATTO, Stephen Marshall
Memorial Sr HS; Houston, TX (30%-640) Band; Dbte Tm; Order/Arrow; ARC; Bkbl; Citz A; God & Country A; Order/Arrow A; Yth Fel; Eagle Sct; Sportsmanship A; *Tex A&M U; Vet Med.*

SHATTUCK, John Hunt
Battle Mountain HS; Vail, CO; Ann; Chor; SC; Var C; Ftbl; Tr; Wrest; *Pepperdine U; Bus.*

SHAUD, Patty Anne
W Springfield HS; Springfield, VA (25-585) A Cap Choir; Secy, Key C; Monogram; JV, Cr-Ctry; Tr; Jr NHS; FCA; *Ed.*

SHAUM, Raymond Warren
Del Norte HS; Albuquerque, NM (1-605) NHS; Span C; Span NHS; COM; Citz A; I Dare You; Math A; NMS; NEDT; Sci A; Val; Century III Ldrs A; Span A; *U of NM; Chem.*

SHAUNFIELD, Julie Kay
Richardson HS; Richardson, TX (625-946) FHA; *Richland Col; Elem Ed.*

SHAVER, Gloria Ann
Macomb HS; Macomb, IL (10%-250) Bus C; Chor; Ensm; 4H; NHS; ARC; Pom Pom; Soc for Acad Achv; *Animal Med.*

SHAVER, Warren Boyd
Lanien HS; Montgomery, AL; Lat C; Math C; Mu Alpha Theta; Sch Achieve Tm; Math A; *Ga Tech; Aero Space Engr.*

SHAVERS, Alvis Wesley
Midway HS; Waco, TX (50%-185) Band; FFA; Bsbl; Bkbl; Ftbl; Sftbl; Tnns; Citz A; FFA Achv & Ldrship A's; *McLennan Comm Col; Phar.*

SHAW, Barbara Ellen
Sacred Heart HS; Vineland, NJ (1-56) Fin, Jr Miss Pagent; Mjrte; S-T, NHS; Ed, Sch P; Bus Mgr, Sci C; S-T, Span C; COM; Kiwanis A; *Georgetown U; Med.*

SHAW, Brian Douglas
Henderson Co Sr HS; Henderson, KY; Band; BC; Fr C; Hmrm; NHS; Pres, SC; Bkbl.

SHAW, Carol Dawn
John Shaw HS; Mobile, AL (80-430) Secy, Fr C; Var C; Swim; Tr; Hon Prog; Gym, Ballet, Phys Ed, Swim, A's; *U of S Ala; Nurs.*

SHAW, Charles Lamar
Ponchatoula HS; Ponchatoula, LA (5-200) VP, Key C; F-Ed, Sch P; Tr.

SHAW, Colleen Mae
Guide Rock HS; Guide Rock, NE (5-8) Chor; 4H; F-Ed, Sch P; Tres, Soph Cl; JV, Bkbl; Sftbl; Tr; Amer Leg A.

SHAW, Della Joy
Kerwin Christian HS; Kernersville, NC; Nurses Asst; *Bob Jones U; Teaching.*

SHAW, Demetria
Corliss HS; Chicago, IL (3-215) Chess C; Drama; VP, Fr C; NHS; COM; Hon Prog; Math A; *Chicago Circle U; Bus.*

SHAW, Eric Jon
Virgil I Grissom HS; Huntsville, AL (25-500) Band; Ensm; Sch Achieve Tm; Alg A; Math A; NEDT; *U of Ala-Huntsville; Mus.*

SHAW, Gregory Brent
Elmore Co HS; Eclectic, AL (1-89) BC; Chor; Hmrm; SC; Var C; Bsbl; 4H A; *Communications.*

SHAW, James Clark
Midland HS; Midland, TX (59-640) NHS; A-Ed, Sch P; Golf; *Tex A&M U; Marine Engr.*

SHAW, Janet Ellen
Bonneville HS; Ogden, UT (16-490) AFS; Model UN; Secy, NHS; Ch, ARC; Span C; COM; Hist A; Hon Prog; Masonic A; Math A; NMS; NEDT; St Scholar; Yth Fel; Jobs Daughters; 1st Cl GSct; Ci-tation, Vol Service; Pres, Hospital Yth Vol Organ; *Westminster Col; Nurs.*

SHAW, Jill Elizabeth
Mt Clemens HS; Mt Clemens, MI (98-324) A Cap Choir; Chor; *Detroit Bible Col; Mus.*

SHAW, Julie Anne
Havre HS; Havre, MT; SC; Var C; Bkbl; Sftbl; Tr; Hon Prog.

SHAW, Kelly Jean
Parkway N Sr HS; Creve Coeur, MO; Chor; Secy, Lat C; Lat NHS; A-Ed, Sch P; Kiwanis A; Jr NHS; Church Pianist; Piano Teacher; Professional Dog Groomer; Candystriper; Church Yth Group; *Med.*

SHAW, Kenneth Lyle
Little Rock Central HS; Little Rock, AR (171-543) F-Ed, Sch P; Cr-Ctry; Ftbl; Tr; Journ A; Most Out; *U of Ark at Little Rock; General Bus.*

SHAW, Kim Lynae
Heidelberg American HS; Heidelberg, GER-MANY (14-170) Chor; Hmrm; Tres, NHS; ARC; 1st Cl, Cadette, GSct; Hon Men, Amer Writing Contest; Cert of Achv, Sociology, Ger; *Seattle Pa-cific Col; Home Ec.*

SHAW, Kirby Donetta
Woodrow Wilson HS; Dallas, TX; F-Ed, Ann; Band; Fin, Chldr; Fr C; Mjrte; Sci C; Span C; Mgr, Swim; DARGCA; Most Out; *Psych.*

SHAW, Linda Janette
Kingstree Sr HS; Kingstree, SC (22-197) Ann; BC; SC; Chem A; Phy A; Sci A; Furman Schol; *U of SC; Engr.*

SHAW, Loretta Amelia
Newnan HS; Newnan, GA; BC; Chor; Dbte Tm; Drama; Ensm; 4H; Hmrm; ARC; SC; 4H A; Hon Prog; Opt A; Drama A; *Mercer Col; Med.*

SHAW, Marisa Louise
Towers HS; Decatur, GA (20%-35) Bus C; FBLA; Sftbl; Tr; Tr A; *Dekalb Jr Col; Bus Ed.*

SHAW, Marjorie Lynn
South Side HS; Memphis, TN (5%-320) Chess C; Fr C; Math C; Mu Alpha Theta; Bus Mgr, NHS; *Washington U; Math.*

SHAW, Marlene Patricia
Sandusky HS; Sandusky, OH; Hmrm; Lat C; Cpt, Bkbl; Bkbl A; Tr A; *Law.*

SHAW, Maureen Ann
R L Turner HS; Carrollton, TX (123-743) A Cap Choir; Chor; Drama; InterAct C; Madrigal; *N Tex St U; Mus.*

SHAW, Michele Annette
Jefferson HS; Cedar Rapids, IA (42-573) Ch, Band; Chor; NHS; JV, Tnns; Mgr, Tr; JA A; 1st Cl GSct; Forest Resource Career Workshop; *Iowa St U; For-estry.*

SHAW, Monique Vena
St Nicholas HS; Brooklyn, NY (85%-35) A Cap Choir; Chor; Secy, Hmrm; SC; Secy, Soph Cl; Bkbl; COM; Math A; Sci A; Seminary Recreation Com-mittee; Dance Comm; All Tchrs Helper; Sch Moni-tor; Cafeteria Clean-Up; Cl Decoration Comm; Tutor; *Stonybrook Col; Specialized Ed.*

SHAW, Pamela Louise
Vicksburg HS; Vicksburg, MS (25-244) Chldr; Drama; Lat C; NHS; Cl Fav; H of F; HCt; *Sou U; Pol Sci.*

SHAW, Rachel Donna
Owyhee HS; Owyhee, NV (2-22) Chldr; Secy, FFA; S-T, Soph Cl; Tr; Alg A; *Ariz St U; Dietetics.*

SHAW, Reginald Bernard
Douglass HS; Memphis, TN; VP, Hmrm; Pres, Span C; Bus Mgr, SC; VP, Sr Cl; COM; HKg; ROTC A; *Memphis St Tech Col; Elec.*

SHAW, Rickey Leon
Rossville HS; Rossville, GA (36-211) Key C; Math A; *Dalton Jr Col; Phar.*

SHAW, Robin Allen
Jefferson HS; Cedar Rapids, IA (133-609) Band; Chor; Drama; Orch; JV, Tnns; Mgr, Wrest; Kiwanis A; *Hawkeye Tech Col; Elec.*

SHAW, Rosa Marie
Waterproof HS; Waterproof, LA; BC; *Sou U; Art.*

SHAW, Sandra Lee
John Marshall HS; Indianapolis, IN (50-500) Band; Pres, Chor; Ensm; Madrigal; NHS; SC; Thes; Thes A; *Ball St U; Art.*

SHAW, Simone Drea
Bishop Ford HS; Brooklyn, NY; A Cap Choir; Chess C; Secy, Hmrm; Spch C; Bkbl; Tr; Journ A; Sci A; Spch A; Yth Foundation; Teacher's Helper; Seminarian; Sch Monitor; Tutor; *Stonybrook Col; Corporate Law.*

SHAW, Sonya Jean
Samuel J Tilden HS; Brooklyn, NY (100-855) A Cap Choir; Secy, CYO; VP, Chor; Pres, Hmrm; NHS; Pol Sci C; SC; Tr; Citz A; Hon Prog; Inter-lochen Ntl Mus; MLS; Pres A; ARC A; *St U of NY; Eng.*

SHAW, Tracy Denise
Compton HS; Compton, CA (46-800) Chldr; Chor; City Conf; Dbte Tm; Pres, Ger C; Hmrm; Math C; NHS; S-T, Ntl Yth Conf; Span C; Spch C; St Stu Congress; SC; VP, Jr Cl; CSF; Hon Prog; Spch A; Yth Fel; Yth Foundation; Yth Leg; Psych, Spch Reading, A's; *U of Calif; Biol.*

SHAWK, Dale Herman
Colonel Crawford HS; N Robinson, OH (30-155) Band; Pres, FFA; Tres, 4H; 4H A; *Ohio St U; Agr.*

SHAWL, James Wallace
McKeesport Area Sr HS; McKeesport, PA (120-653) Band; NHS; Orch; MVP, Ftbl; Tr; Yth Fel; Sportsmanship A, Ftbl; *Bethany Col; Ed.*

SHAWL, Timothy Fred
McKeesport Sr HS; McKeesport, PA (21-653) Band; NHS; Orch; Wrest; Yth Fel; *Waynesburg Col; Med Tech.*

SHAWVER, Judy Ann
W Middlesex Sr HS; W Middlesex, PA (3-158) AFS; Chor; Co-Ch, Hmrm; Span C; Span NHS; Swim; Tnns; HR Cert; Job's Daughters; *Youngs-town St U; Med Lab Tech.*

SHAWVER, Tracy JoAnn
Timberline HS; Weippe, ID (3-47) Chem C; Fr C; Pres, NHS; Hon Prog; *Kinman Bus U; Acct.*

SHAY, Barry Dean
Campbell HS; Smyrna, GA (33%-393) Chor; Dbte Tm; Drama; Ensm; Mgr, Bkbl; All St Chor; *Mus.*

SHAY, Carolyn Wilma
Big Walnut HS; Sunbury, OH (33-212) Span C; Yth Fel; Ntl Mus Guild; *Denison U; Law.*

SHAY, John William
Wood River HS; Hailey, ID (14-60) BS; Ger C; NHS; Order/Arrow; Ski C; Span C; SC; Pres, Var C; Bsbl; Cr-Ctry; Ftbl; Tr; Cpt, Wrest; Citz A; H of F; MVP, St Champ, Wrest; *Miami U of Ohio; Phys Ed.*

SHAY, Russ T
Moniteau HS; West Sunbury, PA (20-104) Chess C; Drama; Hmrm; Var C; Bsbl; Sftbl; Tr; *Elec.*

SHAY, Tamara Louise
Moniteau HS; West Sunbury, PA; Chor; FHA; Hmrm; Mjrte; Sch P; SC; *Bus.*

SHAY, William Bradford
Clark Co R-I HS; Kahoka, MO (9-92) NHS; Ed, Sch P; Co-Cpt, Bkbl; Ftbl; MVP, Golf; Citz A; Type A; Fin, Conf Medalist, Golf; Journ & Typing Academic Contests; *Mo Western St U; Chem.*

SHEA, Dawn LuAnn
Benson HS; Omaha, NE; *U of Nebr.*

SHEA, John Edward
George W Hewlett HS; Hewlett, NY (75-375) Drama; Math C; SC; Thes; *Art.*

SHEA, Lark A
J H Rose HS; Greenville, NC (10-450) Ed, Ann; S-T, Fr C; Key C; *Law.*

SHEALY, Charlie Jacob
Saluda HS; Saluda, SC; FFA; JV, Bkbl; JV, Ftbl; *Midland Tech Col; Keypunch.*

SHEALY, Richard Allen Jr
Memphis Prep Sch; Memphis, TN (50%-125) Chess C; Order/Arrow; Bkbl; Ftbl; Tr; Math A; Yth Fel; Photo C; Current Affairs C.

SHEARD, Bridgette Marie
Inglewood HS; Inglewood, CA (12-495) Ann; Chldr; Chor; Fr C; Hmrm; Model UN; Sch P; Spch C; SC; Bkbl; Cpt, Sftbl; Alg A; CSF; Citz A; Cl Fav; Hon Prog; Journ A; MLS; Most Out; Spch A; Yth Fel; *UCLA; Phys Therapy.*

SHEARD, Melonie Ann
Centennial HS; Pueblo, CO (24-450) Fr C; Hmrm; NHS; JV, Bkbl; Cr-Ctry; Tr; Citz A; God & Country A.

SHEARD, Patricia Ann
Terrell Co HS; Dawson, GA (10%-112) BC; VP, Fr C; Bio A; COM; Citz A; Hon Prog; Math A; Fr A; *Albany St Col.*

SHEARER, Becky Lynne
Glendora HS; Glendora, CA; NHS; Span C; Beauty; Sci A; *Fashion.*

SHEARER, Christopher Alan
Claremore HS; Claremore, OK; Bsbl; Ftbl; Golf; Swim; Tnns; *Or U; Phar.*

SHEARER, Diane Lynn
South HS; Omaha, NE; Chor; Fr C; *Omaha Col of Health Careers; Dental Asst.*

SHEARER, John Claude
Baylor HS; Chattanooga, TN (35-120) Lat C; Sch P; Ftbl; Golf; Tr.

SHEARER, Randall L
Jackson HS; Jackson, MI (15-400) Bus C; Ger C; Pres, Hmrm; Tnns; Sci A; VP, NHS; Scholastic Hon A; *Olivet Col; Chem.*

SHEARER, Shelly Lyn
Alisal HS; Salinas, CA (5%-360) VP, Bus C; Drama; Bank Of Amer A; S-T, Christ's Ambass; VP, FSA C; FSA Sch; Church Newspaper Typing; Sunday Sch Teacher; *Hartnell Jr Col; Bus Mgt.*

SHEARIN, Suellen
Parkway W Sr HS; Manchester, MO; Semi-Fin, Chldr; Chor; Hmrm; Sch P; SC; MVP, Hockey; MVP, Sftbl; MVP, Swim; Mgr, Tr; Talent Show; Dance Group; Dance Instructor; *SW Mo U.*

SHEARRER, Kathleen Ann
Normandy Sr HS; St Louis, MO (5-565) Ensm; Fr C; FBLA; French NHS; Madrigal; NHS; *Mid-America Nazarene Col; Ed.*

SHEASLEY, Alan Craig
Northern Chester Co Tech; Phoenixville, PA (10%-192) Chess C; Hmrm; Pres, NHS; Order/Arrow; Pres, SC; Var C; VP, Sr Cl; Tres, Jr Cl; Tres, Soph Cl; Cr-Ctry; Tr; Co-Cpt, Wrest; God & Country A; HCt; Hon Prog; MLS; Order/Arrow A; Eagle Sct; Stu o-t Mo.

SHEDD, Vickie Lorene
Portageville HS; Portageville, MO (9-90) Band; FBLA; FHA; FNA; FTA; NHS; Citz A; Hon Prog; *Ark St U; Bus.*

SHEDRICK, Gail Marie
Gardendale HS; Gardendale, AL; Span C; Bkbl; Sftbl; Tr; Beauty.

SHEEHAN, Judy Anne
MacDuffie Sch for Girls; Springfield, MA (7-47) Cum Laude Soc; Key C; NEDT; St Schol; NML; Cum Laude; *Pol Sci.*

SHEEHAN, Margaret Louise
Clear Creek HS; League City, TX; AFS; Ann; Band; CYO; Chor; Ensm; Key C; Lat C; NHS; *U of Tex at Austin; Hist.*

SHEEHAN, Michael Ryan
Tabernacle Baptist HS; Va Beach, VA (3-24) Tres, FTA; 4H; Sci C; Span C; Bkbl; Cpt, Sftbl; 4H A; Sci A; *Law.*

SHEEHAN, Stuart Lee
Wade Hampton HS; Greenville, SC (90-400) A Cap Choir; Pres, Chess C; VP, Chor; Ensm; Hmrm; Madrigal; Orch; Thes; COM; Hist A; Phy A; Sci A; *Clemson U; Mechanical Engr.*

SHEELEN, John Francis
Huntington HS; Huntington, NY (50%-619) AFS; Chess C; Bsbl; Soccer; Intramurals, Wrest, Soccer; Sftbl, Hockey; Bkbl; *Bus.*

SHEEN, Cynthia Gail
Colo HS; Colo City, TX (2-115) Rptr, FTA; JV, Bkbl.

SHEEN, Susan Diane
Colo HS; Colo City, TX (3-126) Bkbl; Tr; *Engr.*

SHEESLEY, Beverly May
Glen Burnie Sr HS; Glen Burnie, MD (36-587) Ann; Chor; Fr C; V-Ch, Hmrm; F-Ed, Sch P; SC; Ftbl; Hon Prog; Journ A; Masonic A; Q&S A; Yth Fel; Cl Ed, Annual; Pres, Yth Fel; Pep Squad; *U of Md; Journ.*

SHEETS, Colleen Diane
Allegany HS; Cumberland, MD; AFS; Chor; Tres, Fr C; Tr; GAA; Nurs Explorers VP; Candystripers; Mgr, Drill Tm; *Columbia Union Col; Nurs.*

SHEETS, John Foxe
Laupahoehoe HS; Laupahoehoe, HI (1-24) Band; Hmrm; NHS; Sci C; *Yale U; Theatre.*

SHEETS, Kimberly Kelly
Portsmouth HS; Portsmouth, OH (23-263) Chor; VP, Drama; Ensm; Fr C; 4H; Secy, Rainbow; ARC; Sch Achieve Tm; Span C; VP, Thes; Arch; Hon Prog; Masonic A; VofDEM; WW; Span, Biol, Amer Gov, Schol Tms; *Ohio N U; Pol Sci.*

SHEETS, Rebecca Sue
Adams Central HS; Monroe, IN (1-107) Rptr, Ann; Band; Chldr; Tres, Chor; GS; Hmrm; NHS; Rptr, Sch P; SC; Mgr, Tr; Elk A; Most Out; NEDT; Val; Yth Fel; WW; WW, Chldrs; *Purdue U; Acct.*

SHEETS, Zenda Kay
Buchanan HS; Troy, MO (10%-200) Band; Fr C; NHS; Sch P; Tres, Sci C; Tnns; Citz A; Soph Pilgrimage; *Mo U; Med Lab Tech.*

SHEFFER, Keith Allen
Rolling Meadows HS; Rolling Meadows, IL (212-643) *Bradly U; Engr.*

SHEFFEY, Denise Renee
St Pauls Cathedral HS; Pittsburgh, PA (40%-90) Hmrm; Fin, Jr Miss Pagent; NFL; VP, Spch C; SC; Gov Honor Prog; Secy, Spch C; Fin, Ms Black Tnage Pagent; Fin, Ms US Tn Pagent; *Carnegie-Mellon U; Mus.*

SHEFFIELD, Beth Louise
Thomas A Edison HS; Elmira Heights, NY (1-140) Ann; Chldr; Chor; GS; Jr Miss Pagent; Madrigal; NHS; Ski C; Amer Leg A; Bausch & Lomb A; Chem A; Hon Prog; Lion A; Regent Schol; Rensselaer A; Val; Yth Fel; Chor Accompanist; Yth Co; Hist C; Lead, Sr Mus; Gym; All Co Choir; People to People; WW; *Duke U; Pre-Med.*

SHEFFIELD, Jesse David
Loraine HS; Loraine, TX (1-20) Rptr, Band; FFA; Mod Mus Mas; NHS; Span C; Pres, Jr Cl; VP, Soph Cl; Bkbl; Tnns; Citz A; Cl Fav; Sal; Type A; Chaplain, SC; Best Bandsman.

SHEFFIELD, Wendy Lee
Denison Sr HS; Denison, TX (25%-400) Chor; Drama; FHA; Fin, Hmrm; Rainbow; Y-Tns; Co-Cpt, Sftbl; Swim; Vol, Hospital; Art C; HR; Tres, Printing C; Drill Tm; Candystriper; *Grayson Jr Col; General.*

SHEHORN, Cari Ruth
Pekin Comm HS; Pekin, IL (150-807) Chor; Drama; Fr C; Pres, SC; Pres, Soph Cl; Mgr, Bkbl; Most Out; Yth Foundation A; *Ariz St Col; Law.*

SHEHORN, Cathy Ann
Pekin Comm HS; Pekin, IL (9-702) A Cap Choir; Chor; Ensm; Fr C; French NHS; NHS; B Crocker A; COM; NEDT; Top Ten, Sr Cl; WW, Mus Stu; *Moody Bible Inst; Sacred Mus.*

SHELBURNE, Linda Carol
Snyder HS; Snyder, TX (45-209) A Cap Choir; Drama; FTA; 4H A; *Howard Payne U; Elem Ed.*

SHELBY, Cindy Lee
Kalama HS; Kalama, WA (10-65) Band; Chor; Drama; Pres, NHS; Pres, Rainbow; SC; Secy, Jr Cl; HCt; *Lower Columbia Col; Med Tech.*

SHELBY, Dorothy Ellen
A E Beach HS; Savannah, GA; BC; Secy, Fr C; FBLA; NHS; Rainbow; A-Ed, Sch P; COM; Hist A; Quill & Scroll C; *U of Ga; Bio.*

SHELBY, Judy Sue
Kalama HS; Kalama, WA (30-60) Chor; 4H; Spch C; Tres, SC; Var C; Bkbl; Sftbl; COM; Hon Soc; *Longview Bus Col; Legal Secy.*

SHELDON, Cheryl Lynn
Tecumseh HS; Tecumseh, MI (63-263) Chor; Rptr, Sch P; Secy, Sr Cl; JV, Tr; Modern Dance C; Pep C; VP, Med Careers C; *Hope Col; Biol.*

SHELDON, Curtis Lee
Lincoln HS; Park Falls, WI (25-140) A Cap Choir; Chor; Drama; Ensm; Pres, Madrigal; Order/Arrow; JV, Bkbl; Co-Cpt, Ftbl; Tr; HCt; NEDT; Eagle Sct; *U of N Colo; Bus.*

SHELDON, Jill Ann
James I O'Neill HS; Highland Falls, NY; *Secretarial Work.*

SHELDON, Les Brian
Edinburg HS; Edinburg, IL; Tres, FFA; Bsbl; Bkbl; Cr-Ctry; Tr; COM; MVP Trophy; Mr Hustle; PA Cert.

SHELL, Lori Lee Ann
Karlsruhe Amer HS; Karlsruhe, GERMANY (3-35) Band; Chor; 4H; Tnns; JV, Tr; COM; Citz A; Hon Prog; Sci A; *LSU; Nurs.*

SHELL, Mary Jane
Fountain Lake HS; Hot Springs, AR (7-36) Ann; BC; FHA; Sch P; VP, Span C; SC; Thes; Bkbl; Tnns; *Braniff Ed Systems; Airlines Reservations Agent.*

SHELL, Susan Elise
Winnfield Sr HS; Winnfield, LA (7-122) Anchor C; Pres, BC; Fr C; FBLA; Lit Ral; Sch P; Spch C; SC; *Centenary Col.*

SHELLEY, Tammie Sue
Sebastopol Attendance Center; Sebastopol, MS; Ann; Band; BC; Chor; Drama; Ensm; Hmrm; Orch; SC; Bio A; Yth Fel; Yth Foundation Impr; Mus; Friendliest Fresh; *U of Sou Miss; Psychiatry.*

SHELLEY, Valerie Kay
Eastern Hills HS; Fort Worth, TX (100-487) Bus Mgr, Lit Mag; Span C; Sftbl; Mgr, Swim; Citz A; *Trinity U; Deaf Ed.*

SHELLHAMMER, Pamela Jean
Connellsville Area HS; Connellsville, PA (10%-700) Band; French NHS; *Alderson-Broadus Col; Physicians Asst.*

SHELLNUTT, Christopher Bryant
Campbell HS; Fairburn, GA; F-Ed; Ann; Co-Ch, Drama; NHS; Sch P; Span NHS; Hon Prog.

SHELT, Cindy Ann
Campbell HS; Fairburn, GA (10%-149) Anchor C; Hmrm; Jr Miss Pagent; Mu Alpha Theta; NHS; Span NHS; Beauty; Cl Fav; Hon Prog; Jr Civitans; *Ga St Col; Phys Therapy.*

SHELTON, Albert Andrew
Lebanon Sr HS; Lebanon, MO (26%-210) AFS; F-Ed, Ann; Band; Hmrm; InterAct C; Key C; SC; Pres, Sr Cl; Pres, Soph Cl; JV, Bsbl; Ftbl; Tnns; Tr; VofDEM; *SW Mo St U; Med.*

SHELTON, Alex Dale
Ainsworth HS; Flint, MI (10-285) NHS; JV, Tnns; Hon Prog; Mich Competitive Schol; *Harding Col; Acct.*

SHELTON, Ava Renee
Hugo HS; Hugo, OK (2-84) Ed, Ann; Band; VP, Drama; Ensm; GS; Hmrm; Math C; NHS; Pres, Sci C; Pres, Span C; S-T, SC; Most Out; Sal; Type A; Drum Major; *Southeastern Okla St U; Math.*

SHELTON, Brent W
Wichita W HS; Wichita, KS (15%-650) Band; Dbte Tm; NFL; VP, SC; COM; St Ensm Medal; *Wichita St Col; Pol Sci.*

SHELTON, Christina L
W T Woodson HS; Fairfax, VA (500-749) Chor; Span C; Chem A; Sci A; Sword & Feather; Pres, Church Yth Group; *Animal Sci.*

SHELTON, Dolly Ethel
Patrick Henry HS; Roanoke, VA; Chor; 4H; ARC; Sftbl; Choir A; *Sweet Briar Col; Mus.*

SHELTON, Donna Kay
Southland HS; Southland, TX; Band; 4H; Secy, NHS; Pres, Jr Cl; Bkbl; Tr.

SHELTON, Emily Gordon
Lufkin HS; Lufkin, TX (25%-250) A Cap Choir; Chor; Dbte Tm; Rptr, Drama; Span C; Secy, SC; Thes; *Baylor U; Dramatics.*

SHELTON, Emmett Lavelle
McMullen Co HS; Tilden, TX (6-6) FFA; 4H; Tres, SC; Tres, Sr Cl; Bkbl; Tr; COM; 4H A; Ntl Pres, Yth Range Forum; Star Farmer; WW; High Point Area, Range Judging; *Tex A&M U; Range Sci.*

SHELTON, Eric Jonathan
Lord Botetourt HS; Daleville, VA; Chor; *Va Tech U; Engr.*

SHELTON, Frankie Lee
Winnfield Sr HS; Winnfield, LA; Anchor C; FFA; Mgr, Bsbl; Ftbl; *Tyler Jr Col; Respiratory Therapy.*

SHELTON, Gibb Lawrence
East HS; Salt Lake City, UT; Arch; Fr C; Bus Mgr, Key C; Tnns; Pres, Church Yth Group; St Ch, Tn March of Dimes.

SHELTON, Janice Carol
Vienna HS; Vienna, IL (45-102) Drama; Thes; Cl Fav; *SIU.*

SHELTON, Joan Elizabeth
Vienna HS; Vienna, IL; FHA; FTA; 4H; Sch P; *Sou Ill U; Eng.*

SHELTON, Julie Lynn
Lafayette HS; Ellisville, MO (33-440) A Cap Choir; Chor; FTA; Mjrte; NHS; Arch; Bsbl; Citz A; Regent Schol; Mus A; Church As; Scholastic As; *Southeast Mo St U; Elem Ed.*

SHELTON, Marc Wesley
Ontario HS; Ontario, OH (100-206) Band; Ensm; Ftbl; Most Out; Outst Rookie Band; *Anderson Col; Industrial Engr.*

SHELTON, Marguerite Lenora
Forest HS; Ocala, FL; Band; FHA; FBLA; *Airline Sch.*

SHELTON, Rosa Marie
Montrose Acad; Montrose, AR (10-40) Band; FHA; Semi-Fin, Jr Miss Pa; NHSt; Sci C; Tr; *NE La U; Med.*

SHELTON, Sheri Dee
Seneca HS; Louisville, KY; BC; Chor; *Harding Christian Col; Children.*

SHELTON, Tamye Lynn
Lafayette HS; Ellisville, MO;

SHEMBOR, Lilli Ann
Thomas Kelly HS; Chicago, IL (13-629) Chor; Hmrm; NHS; VP, ARC; HCt; Hon Prog; Kiwanis A; *Loyola U; Med.*

SHEMORY, Kathleen Grace
Middleburg HS; Middleburg, PA (4-134) Chor; Hmrm; NHS; Alg A; DARGCA; Math A; NEDT; Acct.

SHEN, Andrew
Jackson Mem HS; Jackson, NJ (2-385) FBLA; Hmrm; Pres, NHS; F-Ed, Sch P; Pres, SC; Tr; Bio A; COM; Hon Prog; MLS; NEDT; Rotary A; Sal; NJ Mr FBLA A; Art Show A; Mod Congress A; Most Talented; *Harvard U; Bus.*

SHENEMAN, Carol Diane
Green HS; Greensburg, OH (50-312) Band; Drama; Ski C; Tr.

SHENNING, David Arnold
Brandon Sr HS; Brandon, FL (100-1100) Band; Ensm; Citz A; *U of S Fla.*

SHEPARD, Carrie Darlene
Sheffield HS; Memphis, TN; Rptr, Fr C; Math C; NHS; Gym; *Oral Roberts U.*

SHEPARD, Dana Jolene
Caney Valley HS; Caney, KS (5-66) Bus Mgr, Ann; Drama; FBLA; FHA; NHS; WW; St Hon Stu; *Independence Comm Jr Col; Art-Applied Design.*

SHEPARD, David Eglin
Marine Military Acad; Harlingen, TX (1-46) CYO; Drama; Ftbl; Swim; Tr; Hon Prog; Journ A; Most Out; ROTC A; Spch A; VofDEM; DAC A; Eagle Sct; *US Coast Guard Acad; Nuclear Engr.*

SHEPARD, Denise Renee
Zion Benton Township HS; Zion, IL (5%-450) Band; Secy, Chor; Dbte Tm; Ger C; NHS; ARC; Secy, Jr Cl; Swim; Amer Leg A; Citz A; Hist A; Sci A; Vlbl; Meritorious A; Ger A; Eng A; Superior HR A; *Wheaton Col; Elem Ed.*

SHEPARD, Harold Leigh
Rockdale HS; Rockdale, TX (75-123) BS; JV, Bkbl; Ftbl; Tr; Stage Band; *Engr.*

SHEPARD, Naomi Sue
Huntington HS; Huntington, WV (20%-350) Band; Hmrm; Lat C; NHS; SC; *W Va Career Col; Med Secy.*

SHEPARD, Ruth Elaine
Fort Scott Sr HS; Fort Scott, KS (14-156) Band; Chor; Community Yth Symph; Fr C; Hmrm; Pres, Rainbow; SC; S-T, Soph Cl; Yth Fel; WW; St Piano A; St Vocal A; Demolay Swtht; Ntl Fed of Mus A; District Choir.

SHEPARD, Sandra Kay
Rye Cove HS; Clinchport, VA; Mgr, Ann; VP, BC; VP, FBLA; Hmrm; Bio A; COM; Sal; Sci A; Type A; Ad-Mgr, Ann; PA; Production Mgr, Sch Paper; Arithmetic Proficiency A; Spelling Proficiency A; *MECC; Bus.*

SHEPARD, Sherrie Dalynne
Sheffield HS; Memphis, TN; Parl, Fr C; Math C; NHS; Secy, ARC; Gym; *Oral Roberts U; Art.*

SHEPERD, Sherri Lynn
Glendale Acad; Glendale, CA (10%-68) Band; Ski C; Var C; Bkbl; Ftbl; Sftbl; Pres A; Type A; *La Sierra Col; Nurs.*

SHEPHERD, Barry Todd
Carroll Co HS; Carrollton, KY (3-125) Chess C; Fr C; Pres, NHS; SC; Pres, Sr Cl; Tnns; DARGCA; MLS; Sci A; Stu o-t Mo; HR; *U of Ky; Entomology.*

SHEPHERD, Chandra Yvette
Inglewood HS; Inglewood, CA; Chess C; Swim; *El Camino Jr Col; Sociology.*

SHEPHERD, Juanita Lee
Newton Comphensive HS; Covington, GA; Coun of Teach A; *W Ga Col; Elem Ed.*

SHEPHERD, Kevin Dale
Dixon HS; Dixon, MO; Arch; BC; Drama; JETS; Ski C; Span C; Var C; Pres, Jr Cl; Bsbl; Bkbl; Cr-Ctry; Sftbl; Tr; HKg; HQn; Sci A; Yth Fel; *Refrigeration.*

SHEPHERD, Laverne
Pennsville Mem HS; Pennsville, NJ; SC; Bkbl; Hockey; Sftbl; *Fashion Designer.*

SHEPHERD, LeeAnn Mildred
Davison Sr HS; Davison, MI; A Cap Choir; Chor; Drama; Fr C; FNA; Sch P; Thes; JA A; *Matt Comm Col; Journ.*

SHEPHERD, Linda Ann
Copiague HS; Copiague, NY (3-399) A-Ed, Ann; GS; Hmrm; Cpt, Math C; VP, NHS; SC; Hon Prog; Math A; MLS; Ntl Achv Schol; Regent Schol; *U of Pa; Bus Adm.*

SHEPHERD, Mattie Doris
Choctawhatchee HS; Fort Walton Beach, FL; FHA; Asst Sergeant, ROTC; *Okaloosa Walton Jr Col; Bus Adm.*

SHEPHERD, Nancy Jean
Normandy Sr HS; St Louis, MO (30-500) Chor; NHS; *SW Baptist Col; Art.*

SHEPHERD, Wendy Elizabeth
New Canaan HS; New Canaan, CT (25%-450) Fr C; NHS; F-Ed, Sch P; MLS; Most Friendly; *Biochem.*

SHEPHERD, William Alan
Dilce Combs Mem HS; Jeff, KY (1-156) Band; BC; Demolay; Ger C; 4H; 4H A; *Cumberland Col; Sci.*

SHEPLEY, Craig Stephen
Strong Vincent HS; Erie, PA (161-214) Band; Orch; *Mercyhurst Col; Mus.*

SHEPPARD, David Allan
Viroqua HS; Viroqua, WI (7-149) Ann; Fin, BS; 4H; Rptr, Sch P; Pres, Sci C; Tr; Spch A; *Computers.*

SHEPPARD, Diane Marie
Manasquan HS; Manasquan, NJ (7-371) Mjrte; NHS; Ski C; Secy, Span C; Sftbl; Hon Prog; Kiwanis A; *Acct.*

SHEPPARD, John Wilbur
Hickory Sr HS; Hermitage, PA (1-283) Chor; Orch; Sci C; *Case Western Reserve Col; Med.*

SHEPPARD, Jonathan William
Warren HS; Monmouth, IL (25%-40) Ftbl; HR; Christian Yth Fel; Sr Choir; Church Deacon; Ldr, Lay Witness; Radio C; Technician, Cl Plays; *Carl Sandburg Jr Col; Elec.*

SHEPPARD, Kenda Sue
Levelland HS; Levelland, TX (42-200) A Cap Choir; Mgr, Ann; Chor; Ensm; VP, FHA; FTA; Semi-Fin, GS; Madrigal; NHS; F-Ed, Sch P; Span C; Thes; *South Plains Col; Law Enforcement.*

SHEPPARD, Martha Ruth
Sunset HS; Dallas, TX (10-375) A Cap Choir; F-Ed, Ann; Band; Fr C; VP, FHA; Hmrm; Pres, NHS; ARC; Spch C; Parl, SC; Secy, Jr Cl; Bio A; Cl Fav; Hon Prog; MLS; Q&S A; VofDEM; Sen, Sr Cl; TACT Tn Citz Fin; Secy, Woods and Waters C; Lab-Stage Band; FHA Outst Stu; Quill and Scroll; Jr Hon Guard; *Tex A&M U; Pre-Med.*

SHEPPARD, Veronica Ann
Ferguson HS; Newport News, VA (340-482) Amer Leg A; Citz A; DARGCA; Hon Prog; MLS; Most Out; *Drew U; Nurs.*

SHEPPERSON, Patricia
Paterson Cath HS; Paterson, NJ (79-250) Co-Cpt, Chldr; Tr; Best Attendance; *Fla St U; Psych.*

SHERBURNE, Lynne Darling
Hillsboro HS; Nashville, TN; Anchor C; Chldr; Chor; Dbte Tm; NFL; Ed, Sch P; Cr-Ctry; NEDT; Opt A; *Vanderbilt U.*

SHERBURNE, Nancy Elizabeth
Hillsboro HS; Nashville, TN (2-280) A Cap Choir; Anchor C; Ann; Hmrm; NHS; SC; Bio A; COM; Math A; NEDT; Sal; Vlbl Tm; Karate Tm; St Mus A; *Vanderbilt U; Philosophy.*

SHERBURNE, Richard Lester
Arlington HS; Arlington, MA (25%-800) Band; Chor; Drama; Hmrm; Madrigal; Thes; Ftbl; Wrest; Spch A; *Tufts U; Behavorial Sci.*

SHERE, Carla
Grandview Heights HS; Columbus, OH (25-142) Band; FTA; Ski C; Var C; Tnns; *U of Cincinnati; Art.*

SHERER, Lesa Jo
Brazil HS; Brazil, IN (45-200) Cpt, Chldr; FHA; FTA; Model UN; VP, NHS; Thes; Tri-HiY; Co-Cpt, Bkbl; Secy, Cr-Ctry; Cpt, Golf; Tnns; MVP, Bkbl; *Vincennes U; Psych.*

SHERER, P LeAnn
Thompson HS; Alabaster, AL (10%-280) NHS; Hist A; Hon Prog; PA; *U of Montevallo; Pol Sci.*

SHERICK, Philip Lyle
Fremont Ross HS; Fremont, OH (35-527) AFS; Ann; Pres, Band; BS; Drama; Ensm; Rptr, 4H; NHS; Pres, Orch; Sch P; Amer Leg A; COM; 4H A; Hist A; Rotary A; VofDEM; OMEA St Band; WW; Purdue Band Hons; *Bowling Green St U; Ger.*

SHERIDAN, Mary Susan
Holy Cross HS; Delran, NJ; CYO; Hon Prog; Piano Teacher A; Chldr Coach; *Westchester St Col; Mus.*

SHERK, Jacob Mario
Donegal HS; Mount Joy, PA (1-200) Chem C; Hmrm; NHS; Span NHS; Var C; Soccer; Wrest; Chem A; DARGCA; NEDT; Rensselaer A; Rotary A; Sci A; Amer Chem Soc A; 27th Interntl Sci Fair; *Juniata Col; Chem.*

SHERK, Tammie Lynne
Rocky Mount Sr HS; Rocky Mount, NC (75-553) *E Carolina U; Bus.*

SHERMAN, Angela Eloise
Alexander HS; Starkville, MS (5-25).

SHERMAN, Anne Marie
Antilles HS; Fort Buchanan, PR (22-124) Cpt, Chldr; Chor; Drama; Rptr, Hmrm; NHS; Secy, SC; Secy, Jr Cl; Rptr, Soph Cl; Tnns; Hon Prog; JA A; Pres, Keyettes; DAHSS; *Mass Inst of Tech; Architecture.*

SHERMAN, Beatrice Ellen
Balaton Pub Sch; Balaton, MN (16-33) Band; Chess C; Chor; FHA; 4H; Spch C; Arch; 4H A; Foreign Exchange; FHA & 4-H Mus Ldr; Choir Ltr; Co 4-H Share The Fun; Farmers Union Yth A; *Art.*

SHERMAN, Deborah Dianne
North Toole County HS; Sunburst, MT (1-35) Band; Chor; Drama; Ensm; Hmrm; Fin, Jr Miss Pagent; Math C; Ed, Sch P; Sci C; SC; Amer Leg A; COM; Citz A; Cl Fav; Elk A; Journ A; NMS; NEDT; Val; Secy, Saddle C; WW; Shorthand A; Wash Workshop Found; *U of Mont; Journ.*

SHERMAN, Debra Anne
New Hartford Central HS; New Hartford, NY; Band; Chor; Drama; Hmrm; Lit Mag; Thes; Mgr, Bkbl; Hon Prog; Journ A; Most Out; Poet A; Yth Fel; Tres, Baptist Yth Organization; Highest Hons; Ross Hoyt A; *Psychiatry.*

SHERMAN, Denise Carol
Community HS; Houston, TX (10%-98) Chldr; Sch P; SC; COM; Hist A; *Tyler Jr Col; Psych.*

SHERMAN, Georgia Jean
Brown HS; Sturgis, SD (42-196) Band; Chor; FBLA; FTA; Ger C; Pres, 4H; Hmrm; Madrigal; NHS; S-T, SC; Thes; Golf; Wrest Statistician; Drill Tm; Pres, Interdenomintl Yth; St Planning Comm, Drugs; *Augustana Col; Nurs.*

SHERMAN, Glenn Richard
Mt Greylock Regional HS; Williamston, MA; Band; Ensm; Lat C; Lit Mag; Ed, Sch P; Ski C; JV, Cr-Ctry; Hon Prog; NEDT; Ntl Mass Jr Classical League; *Williams Col; Bio.*

SHERMAN, James William
W Reserve HS; Collins, OH; BS; Pres, 4H; Pres, Sr Cl; JV, Ftbl; Tr; Amer Leg A; 4H A; *Bus.*

SHERMAN, Linda Ellen
Bainbridge-Guilford Central Sch; Bainbridge, NY (10-125) Chor; Ensm; NHS; Alg A; Yth Fel; MVP, Bowl; Span A; Sunday Sch A; Church Choir; *Phys Therapy.*

SHERMAN, LouAnn Lamar
Brown HS; Sturgis, SD (130-223) Band; Chldr; Chor; 4H; Span C; Tres, Jr Cl; Bkbl; MVP, Golf.

SHERMAN, Lynden Craig
Herculaneum HS; Herculaneum, MO (33%-194) Band; Chess C; Ensm; Sci C; Bsbl; Tr; Highest Hon Ratings, St Mus Fest.

SHERMAN, Randall Dean
Herculaneum HS; Herculaneum, MO (4-160) Band; Pres, Chess C; Fr C; NHS; Rptr, Sch P; VP, SC; Mgr, Tr; Hon Ratings, St Mus Contest; *U of Mo; Journ.*

SHERMAN, Richard Lee
John C Fremont HS; Los Angeles, CA (1-300) NHS; Sch P; Ftbl; CSF; Journ A; Pres A; Yth Fel; PA; *USC; Math.*

SHERMAN, Robert Stephen
Brandon Sr HS; Brandon, FL; Cr-Ctry; Yth Fel; Christian Fel; Yth Coun A; Co-Ch, Yth Choir Social Comm.

SHERMAN, Sara Ellen
N Shore HS; W Palm Beach, FL (14-266) Drama; Fr C; NHS; Orch; COM; Hon Prog; NMS.

SHERMAN, Sharon Amelia
Marianapolis Prep Sch; Thompson, CT; Chess C; 4H; Ski C; JV, Bkbl; JV, Soccer; COM; 4H A; Yth Fel; Tres, St Quarter Horse Yth Assn; Quarter Horse Shows; St Yth Tm; St A's; *Sci.*

SHERMAN, Susan Noel
James Bowie HS; Arlington, TX (51-300) Chldr; Chor; Ensm; Ger C; Tr; Most Talented; SG Day; *UTA-Arlington; Mus.*

SHERO, John Christopher
Wilburton HS; Wilburton, OK (15-62) Arch; Band; BC; BS; Chem C; Chess C; Dbte Tm; Drama; FFA; 4H; Math C; NHS; Order/Arrow; Phys C; Sci C; Span C; Spch C; Arch; JV, Ftbl; Bio A; 4H A; Sci A; FFA A; *Okla St U; Vet Med.*

SHERRELL, Robin Sue
Parkrose HS; Portland, OR (77-457) A Cap Choir; Ann; Band; Chor; NHS; Cr-Ctry; Tr; Cl Fav; Spch A; Star Student; *Eng.*

SHERRER, Elizabeth Ann
Southeast Whitfield HS; Dalton, GA (28-175) Anchor C; Ann; Band; Chldr; Drama; FBLA; Secy, FHA; Hmrm; Cpt, Mjrte; Sch P; SC; Tri-HiY; Mgr, Bkbl; Twirling A; Drama A; IOP A; Bus A; *Dalton Jr Col; Secretarial Adm.*

SHERRER, Kathy Marie
N Augusta Sr HS; N Augusta, SC (20-394) F-Ed, Ann; BC; Drama; Pres, FHA; InterClub Coun; Mu Alpha Theta; NHS; H of F; Yth Fel; Miss FHA; Most Outst Home Ec Stu; Hon Grad; *Auburn U; Nurs.*

SHERRILL, Nancy Leigh
Paw Creek Christian Acad; Charlotte, NC (1-7) Chldr; Chor; VP, Hmrm; Monogram; Rptr, Sch P; Bkbl; Sftbl; *Pensacola Christian Col; Phys Ed.*

SHERRILL, Natalyn Minnette
Mooresville Sr HS; Mooresville, NC (3-170) BC; Dbte Tm; Hmrm; Monogram; SC; Bkbl; Arts A; *UNC-Chapel Hill; Dentistry.*

SHERROD, Cathy Lynn
Llano HS; Llano, TX (8-77) Band; Dbte Tm; FTA; Mjrte; Secy, NHS; Tres, SC; Bkbl; Tr; WW; Jr-Sr Banquet Server; Jr Play; *Tex Tech U; Interior Design.*

SHERROD, Stephen Ray
Hubbard HS; Hubbard, OH (21-375) Sftbl; COM; Hon Prog; HR; *Ky Christian Col; Ministry.*

SHERROD, Terri Sabrina
Hammond HS; Hammond, IN; Drama; Tr; Miss Black Amer Pageant; *Savannah St Col; Social Sci.*

SHERRY, Kathleen Patricia
Elizabeth Seton HS; Pittsburgh, PA (14-88) CYO; Chor; NHS; Rptr, Sch P; Span C; Span NHS; Amer Leg A; Type A; Shorthand A; *U of Pittsburgh; Elem Ed.*

SHERWOOD, Julie Louise
Sidney Comm HS; Sidney, IA (4-45) Chor; FHA; VP, 4H; Secy, NHS; MVP, Bkbl; Sftbl; Tr; 4H A; Most Out; Girls C.

SHERWOOD, Mary Etta
Clinton Sr HS; Clinton, TN (97-326) Pres, Bus C; Pres, Chor; FHA; 4H; Rptr, Sch P; Bkbl; *Tenn Tech U; Psych.*

SHERWOOD, Ross Lynn
Sidney Comm HS; Sidney, IA (5-40) Band; BS; 4H; Pres, SC; Secy, Jr Cl; Pres, Soph Cl; Bsbl; Bkbl; MVP, Ftbl; 4H A; *Iowa St U; Pol Sci.*

SHERWOOD, Tressa Rae
Moses Lake HS; Moses Lake, WA; SC; Y-Tns; Tnns; Tr; Soccer A; *Kinman Bus Col; Bus.*

SHERWOOD, William Matthew
Whitney Point HS; Whitney Point, NY (5-160) Chess C; Pres, Chor; Drama; FTA; Lit Mag; NHS; Ed, Sch P; Span C; Var C; JV, Ftbl; Tnns; COM; Regent Schol; *Broome Comm Col; Sociology.*

SHEW, Glenda
McAdory HS; Mc Calla, AL (26-190) Cpt, Band; Chldr; Secy, Chor; Ensm; FHA; FNA; 4H; Sci C; SC; Tri-HiY; COM; 4H A; HCt; Spch A; Yth Fel.

SHEW, Glenda Jo
McAdory HS; Bessemer, AL (31-190) Cpt, Band; Chldr; Secy, Chor; Ensm; FHA; FNA; 4H; Hmrm; SC; Tri-HiY; Sftbl; COM; 4H A; HCt; Spch A; VofDEM; Yth Fel.

SHEW, Virginia Louise
Thomas Jefferson HS; Pittsburgh, PA; Band; Drama; NHS; Rainbow; Spch C; Thes; Hon Prog; Kiwanis A; Yth Fel; *Communications.*

SHEWMAKE, Julia Ann
Paris HS; Paris, IL (24-235) Band; NHS; Span C; Hon Prog; St Scholar; *Ind St U; Nurs.*

SHICK, Barry Headley
Harbor HS; Ashtabula, OH (23-181) Chess C; Chor; Var C; VP, Sr Cl; Bsbl; Co-Cpt, Ftbl; Wrest; Sci A; Star Student; Yth Fel; 2nd Tm, All Co; *Air Force Acad; Engr.*

SHIELDS, Carol Ann
Raytown S HS; Raytown, MO (124-583) A Cap Choir; Secy, Chor; Drama; Ensm; Madrigal; Thes; WW; *SW Bapt Col; Drama.*

SHIELDS, Lori Ann
Capitol HS; Boise, ID (43-594) A Cap Choir; Chor; Drama; NHS; Secy, SC; COM; Hon Prog; PA; Del, Nazarene St Yth Conf; *NW Nazarene Col.*

SHIELDS, Rhonda Elise
Bluefield HS; Bluefield, WV (30-350) Band; Chor; Drama; Hmrm; Span C; SC; Yth Fel; Bible C; Pres, Tres, Yth Group; Mascot; *Concord Col; Med Tech.*

SHIELDS, Timothy Arthur
Atholton HS; Simpsonville, MD (10%-270) Band; Drama; Sci C; Ski C; SC; Thes; Ftbl; God & Country A; Yth Fel; PTSA; Bstr C; Young Life.

SHIELDS, Vivian
Lake Wales Sr HS; Lake Wales, FL (8-250) Ann; Secy, Band; Tres, Drama; Ensm; Parl, FHA; Hmrm; InterClub Coun; Secy, Math C; NHS; Sch P; Sci C; SC; Up Bound; Sftbl; COM; Hon Prog; Math A; Sci A; District VP, Achv, FHA; Poetry A; Fin, NROTC Schol; Win, Math, Sci Fair; Hon Stu; *Polk Comm Col; Mus.*

SHIFFER, John Lawrence
Conestoga Valley Sr HS; Lancaster, PA (9-324) Chess C; Hmrm; NHS; Bus Mgr, Sch P; SC; COM; Hon Prog; Rotary A; *U of Pa; Anthropology.*

SHIFFLETT, Sherry Lynn
William Monroe HS; Stanardsville, VA; Ann; Band; BC; Chldr; Drama; FBLA; 4H; NHS; VP, SC; HCt; Math A; Yth Fel; WW; FBLA Spelling A; *VPI; Psych.*

SHIFLEY, Melinda Jane
Colonel Crawford HS; North Robinson, OH (5%-160) Ann; Band; Chor; Ensm; Secy, Fr C; Tres, FTA; GS; Tres, 4H; NHS; F-Ed, Sch P; VP, Soph Cl; Bkbl; All Ohio St Fair Yth Band; YF Pres; Candy Striper; *Wheaton Col; Special Ed.*

SHIFLEY, Tennyson Calvin
Colonel Crawford HS; N Robinson, OH (10-160) Band; Chor; Drama; Ensm; VP, FTA; NHS; Co-Ed, Sch P; Bowl; *Mus.*

SHIKLES, Victoria Lynn
Loy Norrix HS; Kalamazoo, MI; Chor; Ski C; *Mich St U; Nurs.*

SHIKUMA, Lois Reiko
Laupahoehoe HS; Laupahoehoe, HI (3-40) FHA; FTA; Secy, NHS; VP, Sci C; Ch, SC; B Crocker A; *U of Hawaii; Med.*

SHILDMYER, Cindy Ann
Shawnee Mission S HS; Overland Park, KS (25%-800) NFL; Semi-Fin, NHS; Orch; Bus Mgr, Sci C; Hon Prog; Spch A; Schol Pin; Ch, Church Yth Group; Drill Tm; Pep C; Orch A; *Biol.*

SHILEY, Donna Mae
Eastern HS; Middletown, KY; Chldr; Chem C; Hmrm; F-Ed, Sch P; SC; Var C; Pres, Jr Cl; VP, Soph Cl; *Ind U; Journ.*

SHILLING, Steven Lee
Arlington HS; Arlington, TX (5%-450) Ger C; NHS; Golf; Soccer; Alg A; Hon Prog; Type A; Ntl Piano Guild A; Camp Coun; *Med.*

SHILLINGLAW, Scott Donnan
Permian HS; Odessa, TX (28-799) Band; BS; VP, Chem C; Ger C; Orch; VP, SC; Bkbl; Cr-Ctry; Mgr, Ftbl; Sftbl; Swim; *US Air Force Acad; Aeronautical Engr.*

SHILTZ, Sharon Ann
Garfield HS; Akron, OH (147-500) A Cap Choir; Chor; Secy, Ensm; Fr C; NHS; ARC; SC; COM; Most Out; Secy, JA; *Asbury Col.*

SHIMEL, Julie Eileen
Niwot HS; Longmont, CO (4-317) Pres, NHS; Span C; Mgr, Swim; Vlbl; Photographer, FBLA; WW; *Denver U; Acct.*

SHIMIZU, Kathy Mitsue
Pasadena HS; Pasadena, CA; VP, Band; Orch; Bank Of Amer A; CSF; COM; Cert for Mus; John Philip Sousa A; Outst Soph Girl, PHS Band & Orch; Faculty Hon; Achv & Ciz; WW; Outst Stu Mus Dept; *Pasadena City Col; Bus.*

SHIMKO, Sheryl Lynne
Westlake HS; Westlake, OH; Chor; Secy, ARC; F-Ed, Sch P; SC; JV, Tr; Pres A; Church A.

SHIMOTA, Mark Joseph
Foley HS; Foley, MN (34-166) BS; Chor; Ger C; 4H; NHS; Var C; Co-Cpt, Cr-Ctry; Co-Cpt, Tr; Amer Leg A; 4H A; H of F; MVP, Cr-Ctry; Svihel-Shaefer Ath A; WW; *St John's U; Pre-Med.*

SHIMOZONO, Michele Michi
Christian HS; El Cajon, CA (2-149) CSF; Hon Prog; Sci A; Yth Fel; Red Cross Sr Life-Saving Cert; 2nd Pl Tourn, Judo; *Christian Heritage Col; Home Ec.*

SHIMPOCK, Ray Daniel
Thomasville Sr HS; Thomasville, NC; 4H; JETS; Var C; JV, Bsbl; Tnns; *Davidson Co Comm Col; Drafting.*

SHIMSHOCK, Mary Ellen R
Uniontown Area Sr HS; Uniontown, PA; Band; Pres, 4H; Orch; Alg A; 4H A; Hist A; Sci A; Stu o-t Month; *Math.*

SHIMSHOCK, Pamela Josephine
Uniontown Area Sr HS; Uniontown, PA (14-435) 4H; 4H A; Hon Prog; WW; *Nurs.*

SHINABERY, Kimberly Ann
Bluffton HS; Bluffton, OH (16-85) Band; Chor; Drama; Ensm; Fr C; VP, Ger C; 4H; Orch; Spch C; Opt A; Spch A; God & Comm A; Comm Chor; GSct; Dist Band; Christian Ed Committee; Sundy Sch Tchr; Chrch Chor; Stu Action For Ed; Pres, Yth Fel; *Ohio St U.*

SHINES, Ruby Faye
Chicago Voc HS; Chicago, IL (432-1563) Chor; Mus A; Chor A; *Anderson Col; Nurs.*

SHINGLER, Lisa Marie
Hannibal HS; Hannibal, MO (83-292) Chor; Drama; Fr C; Sch P; Q&S A; News Ed, Sch Paper; *NE Mo St Col; Journ.*

SHINKLE, Greg Louis
Peoria HS; Peoria, IL (150-500) Key C; Rptr, Sch P; Jim Dischert A; *Ill Central Col; Diesel Elec.*

SHINKLE, Lois Jeanne
Mt Healthy HS; Healthy, OH (125-496) Band; Drama; Ensm; FBLA; *N Ky U; Commercial Art.*

SHINN, Charles Milton III
Winter Haven HS; Winter Haven, FL (25%-700) Band; Semi-Fin, BS; Order/Arrow; God & Country A; *U of Fla; Audio Tech.*

SHINN, David Wayne
Rockdale HS; Rockdale, TX (10-130) Band; Orch; Tnns; Alg A; Sci A; *U of Tex; Computer Sci.*

SHINN, Diane Jeannette
Roosevelt HS; Seattle, WA; Tres, Jr Cl; Crew; 1st Cl, GSct; Actv Coordinator, Church Yth Group; *Col of Idaho; Interior Design.*

SHINTANI, Rachel Jane
Permian HS; Odessa, TX; Co-Ed, Ann; FHA; NHS; SC; Tri-HiY; Bkbl; Tr; Beauty; Most Out; Art A; *Dental Hygiene.*

SHINTON, Christine Louise
Edward H White HS; Jacksonville, FL (171-646) Band; Secy, Ger C; Lat C; Rainbow; COM; *Dental Lab Tech.*

SHIPE, Debbie Lee
Angola HS; Angola, IN (50%-157) Cpt, Chldr; 4H; ARC; Var C; Y-Tns; Tnns; Mgr, Wrest; 4H A; HCt; Yth Fel; *Olivet Nazarene Col; Phys Therapy.*

SHIPE, Paul Campbell
Sheffield HS; Memphis, TN (1-160) VP, Mu Alpha Theta; Parl, NHS; Rptr, Sch P; Golf; *U of Tenn; Med.*

SHIPLET, Kathleen Gene
Pomona HS; Arvada, CO (150-470) Chor; Swim; Tr; Swim A; *St Paul Bible Col; Elem Ed.*

SHIPLEY, Elizabeth Jane
Edward H White Sr HS; Jacksonville, FL (1-695) Band; Community Yth Symph; Ensm; Lat C; NHS; MLS; Val; Outst Marcher, Band; Eng A; All St Reading Orch; Jacksonville U Pres Schol; *Jacksonville U; Mus Ed.*

SHIPLEY, James Weldon
Port Neches-Groves HS; Port Neches, TX; Band; Ftbl; Tr; Cl Fav; Most Attractive, Jr Cl.

SHIPLEY, John Paul
Beaver Local HS; Lisbon, OH (15-210) A Cap Choir; Band; Chem C; Chor; Drama; Ensm; Mjrte; NHS; SC; Secy, Thes; Asst Director, A Cappella Choir; Drum Major; Jazz Band.

SHIPLEY, Molly Bett
Crandall HS; Crandall, TX (1-24) Band; BC; Secy, FHA; Spch C; Secy, SC; Secy, Sr Cl; Bkbl; Tnns; Tr; COM; Cl Fav; HCt; Spch A; Swtht; Val; Eng A; Stu Recognition; *Kilgore Jr Col; Liberal Arts.*

SHIPLEY, Peggy Zoe
Philipsburg-Osceola HS; Philipsburg, PA (4-256) S-T, Band; Pres, Chor; Dbte Tm; Drama; FTA; GS; Hmrm; Mjrte; NHS; Rainbow; SC; Amer Leg A; Rotary A; WW; Regional, District, Chor, Band; *Penn St U; Mus Ed.*

SHIPMAN, Karen Sue
Wister HS; Wister, OK (2-34) Chor; Pres, FHA; 4H; Pres, Jr Cl; S-T, Soph Cl; Bkbl; Sftbl; 4H A; Hist A; Val; Secy, St A; OSU Acad Achv A's; *Carl Albert Jr Col; Phys Therapy.*

SHIPMAN, Pamela Kay
Immaculata HS; Leavenworth, KS; CYO; FBLA; Mgr, Bkbl; Sftbl; Tnns; COM; Type A; Shorthand A; Pep C; *Bus.*

SHIPMAN, Sadie Francis
New Bloomfield HS; New Bloomfield, MO; Ann; Chor; Sch P; Tres, SC; Citz A.

SHIPMAN, William David
Leavenworth Sr HS; Leavenworth, KS; CYO; ARC; Mgr, Ftbl; ROTC A; Automotive Cert; *Achison Voc Tech Col; Automotive Mech.*

SHIPP, Denice Lynn
Elston Sr HS; Michigan City, IN (24-365) 4H; Hmrm; NHS; SC; COM; Rotary A; *Purdue U; Elem Ed.*

SHIPP, Douglas William
Fort Payne HS; Fort Payne, AL (3-117) Fr C; Pres, HiY; InterClub Coun; NHS; Order/Arrow; VP, SC; Bsbl; JV, Bkbl; God & Country A; Order/Arrow A; Yth Fel; Yth Leg; Eagle Sct; Dist Sct o-t Yr; *U of Ala; Med.*

SHIPP, Paula Ann
Upper Scioto Valley HS; McGuffey, OH (10-60) Chor; Pres, 4H; Span C; SC; Co-Cpt, Bkbl; Tr; 4H A; Type A; Yth Fel; Cpt, Vlbl.

SHIPPY, Cheryl Ann
Venice HS; Venice, FL (85-355) Drama; FHA; Rptr, Lit Mag; Ed, Sch P; Sftbl; Journ A; Press A; Creative Writing A; HR; *Valencia Jr Col; Journ.*

SHIPTON, Elizabeth Ann
Delavan HS; Delavan, IL (1-64) Co-Ed, Ann; Band; Chor; Drama; InterClub Coun; NHS; SC; Thes; NEDT; Stu o-t Mo; Civil Defense Essay Contest; 1st Pl, IHSA Mus Contest; St 4-H Project Hon A; *Math.*

SHIRER, Kayla Marie
Hoisington HS; Hoisington, KS (8-91) Band; Chldr; Chor; Ensm; Model UN; Pres, NHS; Tr; HCt; Hon Prog; *Forst Hays St Col; Radiologic Tech.*

SHIRER, Michael Robert
Belmond Community HS; Belmond, IA (3-81) A-Ed, Ann; BS; Chor; Hmrm; Madrigal; Pres, NHS; Order/Arrow; St Stu Congress; Pres, SC; Thes; Var C; Pres, Soph Cl; Cpt, Bkbl; Cpt, Cr-Ctry; Ftbl; Cpt, Tr; COM; Most Out; NMS; Order/Arrow A; St Scholar; MVP, Bkbl, Cr-Ctry & Tr; St Tr Champion; *MacAlester Col; Math.*

SHIREY, Lori Sue
Pottstown Sr HS; Pottstown, PA (36-285) Chldr; NHS; HCt; Lacrosse; *Phys Therapy.*

SHIREY, Wayne Samuel
Harry Hill HS; Lansing, MI; Bsbl.

SHIRLEY, Carl Dean
Francisco Mendoza HS; Isabela, PR; Chess C; Sch P; Bkbl; Cr-Ctry; Tr; COM; Math A; Phy A; Sci A; *Recinto Universitario Mayaquez; Civil Engineering.*

SHIRLEY, Darla Sue
LaVille Jr And Sr HS; Lakeville, IN (5-148) Band; Ensm; GS; 4H; Pres, NHS; Rainbow; Var C; Cpt, Bkbl; Tr; Bausch & Lomb A; Chem A; Gov Honor Prog; Co-Cpt, Vlbl; Social Stu A; Lang Arts A; *Ind U at S Bend; Chem.*

SHIRLEY, Elizabeth Ann
Wade Hampton HS; Greenville, SC (12-371) FHA; NHS; Span NHS; Bkbl; Sftbl; Tr; Jr Marshall; *Columbia Col; Math.*

SHIRLEY, Harry Alvin
Lincoln HS; Midland, PA (15-66) Lat C; Bkbl; Ftbl; COM; JA A; Ftbl Ltrs; OUC First Tm All-Star; *Computer.*

SHIRLEY, Kathie Vannette
Lincoln HS; Midland, PA; Band; Chor; Fr C; Bkbl; Beauty; Citz A; H of F; Harvard Book A; Type A; Yth Fel; Band A; *Med.*

SHIRLEY, Laura Jane
Pendleton HS; Pendleton, SC (1-145) Band; BC; JV, Chldr; Pres, Fr C; FHA; Pres, Hmrm; InterClub Coun; Cpt, Bkbl; COM; HCt; Hon Prog; Lion A; MLS; Val; Fr A; Furman, Wofford, Schol; *Winthrop Col; Fr.*

SHIRLEY, Mark Harper
Westminster HS; Atlanta, GA (9-101) Band; Chess C; Chor; Fr C; VP, Math C; Order/Arrow; Soccer; Alg A; Hon Prog; Math A; Phy A; Sci A; Eagle Sct.

SHIRLEY, Melody Lynn
Baker HS; Columbus, GA (33%-400) FTA; HR; Jr Achv; Delta C; *Columbus Col; Ed.*

SHIRLEY, Samuel Otis
Warren Central HS; Vicksburg, MS (106-387) Co-Cpt, Band; Ensm; Order/Arrow; Sci C; Superior Stars, Bach Festival; Dist Win, Church Tn Talent Mus; *NE La U; Piano Mus.*

SHIRLEY, Teresa Louise
Cumberland HS; Toledo, IL (25-121) Chor; Pres, FBLA; 4H; Sch P; Tr; HQn; GAA.

SHIVELER, Donna Lynn
Kingsway Regional HS; Swedesboro, NJ (16-160) Cpt, Chldr; NHS; Ski C; SC; Citz A; DARGCA; HCt; *Elizabethtown Col; Bus.*

SHIVELY, Carolyn Frances
Caney Valley HS; Caney, KS (10%-70) S-T, Band; S-T, CYO; VP, Drama; FBLA; FHA; GS; Mjrte; Secy, Jr Cl.

SHIVELY, David Jonathan
Canyon HS; Anaheim, CA (148-592) AFS; Fr C; Ger C; Key C; Rptr, Sch P; Spch C; Hon Prog; *Annapolis Naval Acad; Nuclear Physicist.*

SHIVELY, Sherry Leigh
John D Bassett HS; Bassett, VA (78-150) AFS; Chor; Drama; Ensm; Ntl Yth Conf; *Radford Col; Nurs.*

SHIVER, Anthony Paul
Terry Parker HS; Jacksonville, FL; Ftbl; Tnns; *Eckerd Col; Acting.*

SHIVERDECKER, Dawn
Van-Far R-1 HS; Vandalia, MO (1-66) VP, FHA; Pres, NHS; Tres, Soph Cl; B Crocker A; Bio A; Curator A; Courtesy A; BPW Career Girl; *Mid-America Nazarene Col; Biol.*

SHIVERS, Jewel Regena
St Mary's HS; Jersey City, NJ (10-30) Math C; Sch P; Span C; Soccer; Sftbl; Tnns; Alg A; Bio A; Math A; HR; *St Joseph's Col; Acct.*

SHIVERS, Marcia Denise
Northwestern Comm HS; Flint, MI (20%-636) Secy, Chor; Hmrm; NHS; Pres, SC; Tr; Hon Prog; Journ A; Secy, VICA; MIES; Ch, CEPD; LIT Design Comp; Pres, Jr Nurs Guild; Secy, Explorers Post; *Lawrence Inst of Tech; Archt.*

SHIVERS, Reginald
St Peter's Prep HS; Jersey City, NJ (8-20) Bsbl; Ftbl; Citz A; *Acct.*

SHIVERS, William E Jr
Centerville HS; Centerville, TX (10%-39) FFA; 4H; NHS; Bsbl; Ftbl; Golf; Tnns; 4H A; Type A; *Sam Houston St U; Pre Law.*

SHOBE, Phillip Lorenza
N Central HS; Indianapolis, IN (600-1200) *Minister.*

SHOBER, Edward Charles
Marian Cath HS; Tamaqua, PA (20-180) JV, AFS; Ann; Hon Prog; NEDT; Sacristan; Ath & Academic Achievement; WW; *Civil Engr.*

SHOCKEY, Charles Herschel
King George HS; King George County, VA (1-160) Bus Mgr, Ann; Band; Chess C; Pres, Fr C; 4H; Hmrm; NFL; Rptr, NHS; Sch P; SC; Var C; Pres, Y-Tns; JV, Bkbl; Co-Cpt, Ftbl; Tr; Wrest; Citz A; Gov Honor Prog; 4H A; Hist A; Hon Prog; PTA A; Val; Chenille A; WW; Win, Dist-Regional Forensics; *Ga Tech; Engr.*

SHOCKLEE, David Randol
Medowbrook HS; Richmond, VA; Band; Bsbl; Bkbl; Sftbl; *Bethany Nazarene Col; Sci.*

SHOCKLEE, Mark John
Meadowbrook HS; Richmond, VA (15%-350) Key C; Span C; JV, Bsbl; Bkbl; Ftbl; Tr; COM; HCt; *Va Tech U; Archt.*

SHOCKLEY, Gerald Lynn
Oregon City HS; Oregon City, OR; *Cabinet Making.*

SHOEMAKE, Jeffrey Donald
Lewisville HS; Lewisville, TX; A Cap Choir; Chor; NHS; SC; Ftbl; Tr.

SHOEMAKER, Donna Lynn
East HS; Wichita, KS; FHA; Ger C; ARC; *Wichita St U; Nurs.*

SHOEMAKER, Evelyn Marie
D D Eisenhower HS; Yakima, WA (2-325) Ger C; NHS; VP, Rainbow; Sci C; COM; Sal; *Yakima Valley Comm Col; Math.*

SHOEMAKER, Frank Lyle
Hillcrest HS; Cuba, KS (1-17) A Cap Choir; Band; Bus C; Chem C; Chor; Ensm; VP, 4H; Math C; Sci C; Var C; Pres, Jr Cl; Co-Cpt, Bkbl; Ftbl; Fin, Tr; 4H A; *Kans St U; Agr.*

SHOEMAKER, Jan Robyn
Franklin Co HS; Frankfort, KY (70-475) Band; FBLA; VP, FHA; 4H; Hmrm; S-T, SC; SC; Sftbl; Sci A; *Home Ec.*

SHOEMAKER, Jane Lynn
Southfield-Lathrup Sr HS; Southfield, MI (100-650) Ger C; GS; ARC; Swim; HR; High Hon; *Mich St U; Ed.*

SHOEMAKER, Kimberly Ann
Lakewood HS; Lake Odessa, MI (42-184) Band; VP, Hmrm; Sci C; VP, SC; VP, Jr Cl; Sftbl; Swim; Tnns; Tr; Yth Fel; Lifeguard; Vlbl; *Ferris St Col; Psych.*

SHOEMAKER, Naomi Jeanne
Waynesboro HS; Waynesboro, VA; Band; BC; Drama; Key C; Lat C; Sci C; COM; Citz A; NEDT; 1st Pl, St Lat A; *UVA; Med.*

SHOEMAKER, William Meier
Ottawa Hills HS; Grand Rapids, MI (40-530) Band; Ensm; Tres, NHS; Orch; Order/Arrow; SC; Var C; JV, Bsbl; MVP, Ftbl; Tr; MVP, Wrest; Co-Cpt, Ftbl; Cpt, Wrest; Ath o-t Yr; Cl Brain; *Alma Col; Chem.*

SHOFFNER, David Lynn
Silver Creek HS; San Jose, CA; JV, Bsbl; JV, Ftbl; *California Baptist Col; Wood Working.*

SHOFNER, Deborah Lee
Harlingen HS; Harlingen, TX (3-609) FHA; B Crocker A; 1st Alt, DECA, Merchandising; *Tex A&I U; Interior Design.*

SHOLL, Ruth Lee
East Central HS; Hurley, MS (1-115) Ann; Band; Pres, BC; FBLA; FHA; Jr Miss Pagent; Cpt, Mjrte; Rainbow; Sci C; Tres, SC; Most Out; Val; Miss Personality; Scholastic Achv A; Essay A; *Perkinston Jr Col; Journ.*

SHOLLENBERGER, Ronald R
Reynolds HS; Greenville, PA (11-212) Band; Chor; Ensm; HiY; Ch, Lat C; Math C; Order/Arrow; VP, Sci C; Mgr, Wrest; *U of Pittsburgh; Phar.*

SHOLTZ, Darcie Jo
Guide Rock HS; Guide Rock, NE (4-8) Chor; GS; 4H; Ed, Sch P; Spch C; Secy, Jr Cl; Secy, Soph Cl; JV, Bkbl; Tr; Amer Leg A; 4H A; Spch A; Vlbl; Pep C A.

SHON, Michael James
Elmira Southside HS; Elmira, NY (10-500) Parl, UN Council; Hon Prog; MES; NMS; Regent Schol.

SHOOK, Brenda Gayle
Walnut Hills HS; Cincinnati, OH (20%-497) A Cap Choir; Chor; Drama; Rainbow; *Miami U; Psych.*

SHOOK, Kathy Louise
Tishomingo HS; Tishomingo, MS; Ed, Ann; BC; Co-Cpt, Chldr; Chor; Drama; FBLA; Bus Mgr, FHA; 4H; VP, Soph Cl; Sftbl; Beauty; Cl Fav; HCt; Lib, Chor; Songleader, FHA; S-T, Lib C; Runner Up, Miss FBLA; 4th Parl Procedures, St; *Northeast Miss Jr Col; Secy Sci.*

SHOOK, Robert Edgar
Crown Point HS; Crown Point, IN (25-530) Ann; Band; Drama; Lat C; Lit Mag; Sch P; Thes; DARGCA; Yth Fel; Vol; Handicapped Children; *Milligan Col; Special Ed.*

SHOOK, Shaay Leigh
Clyde A Erwin HS; Asheville, NC (50-285) BC; FHA; Mgr, Tr; Beta C A; PA; Acteen Qn; *Mars Hill Col; Elem Ed.*

SHOOK, Sherry Lynn
Clyde A Erwin HS; Asheville, NC (50-285) BC; Mgr, Tr; PA; Acteen Qn; Beta A; *Mars Hill Col; Psych.*

SHOOKE, Donald P
Gainesville HS; Gainesville, GA (6-195) Cpt, Chess C; Dbte Tm; Tnns; COM; NMS; Sci A; Acad Letter; NCTE Comp; Debate Letter; Cert of Schol; *Duke U; Physics.*

SHOOS, Kenneth John Jr
Shaker Hts HS; Shaker Hts, OH (50%-503) A Cap Choir; Drama; SC; Bkbl; MVP, Ftbl; Sftbl; Tr; Most Valueable Back, Ftbl; All League, Ftbl; *Syracuse U.*

SHOOT, Melanie
Middletown Twp HS S; Middletown, NJ (20%-500) NHS; *Oral Roberts U; Elem Ed.*

SHOPIS, Karen Ann
Acad of Our Lady of Mercy; Milford, CT (6-88) CYO; Drama; Tres, Fr C; Key C; Ski C; NEDT; DAR Sci A.

SHOPTAW, Margaret Rose
Dublin HS; Dublin, GA (26-192) Ann; Band; Orch; SC; Drum Major; Director's A, Band; *Auburn U.*

SHORE, Donna Sue
Starmount HS; Boonville, NC (3-204) Band; Drama; Ch, FFA; VP, 4H; Monogram; Orch; Ed, Sch P; COM; 4H A; I Dare You; Spch A; Yth Fel; Best Actress; 2nd Pl, St Elec Essay; *NC St U; Vet Med.*

SHORE, Jeannie Ann
Herbert Hoover HS; Glendale, CA; Cpt, Chldr; Amer Leg A; Cpt, Drill Tm; *Calif Lutheran Col; Philosphies.*

SHORE, Susan Linn
Ulysses HS; Ulysses, KS (7-109) Band; Bus C; Chor; Ensm; FBLA; 4H; Madrigal; Co-Cpt, Mjrte; NHS; Pres, Rainbow; Co-Ch, Y-Tns; Mgr, Bkbl; Co-Cpt, Golf; Swim; Hon Prog; Most Out; Yth Fel; *Kans U; Med Technology.*

SHORE, William Lee
Starmount HS; Boonville, NC (2-155) Pres, FTA; Mu Alpha Theta; Pres, NHS; Mgr, Bkbl; Mgr, Ftbl; Tnns; Gov Honor Prog; Jr Marshal; Morehead Nom; Pep C; *NC St U; Bio.*

SHORT, David Darrell
Springfield HS; Springfield, OR; A Cap Choir; Band; Ensm; Co-Cpt, Bkbl; *Oregon Col; Math.*

SHORT, Deloris
Soldan HS; St Louis, MO (35-450) Mjrte; *Stephens Col; Social Worker.*

SHORT, John Daniel Jr
Whitmer HS; Toledo, OH; Order/Arrow; Order/Arrow A; Eagle Sct; *Apprentice Machinist.*

SHORT, Kay Ann
Greeley W HS; Greeley, CO (8-270) VP, Ger C; NHS; Orch; F-Ed, Sch P; Bio A; COM; Hon Prog; Masonic A; Pres A; VP, DECA; Excellent Rating, St Mus Contest; Ntl Merit Schol Prog Ltr of Commend; *Colo St U; Microbio.*

SHORT, Michael Lee
Warrensburg Sr HS; Warrensburg, MO; A Cap Choir; Band; Dbte Tm; Fr C; NFL; Thes; COM; Spch A; Type A; Pres, Church Yth Fel; *Central Mo St U; Bus.*

SHORT, Robin Lynnette
Adlai E Stevenson HS; Bronx, NY; Band; Ensm; Orch; COM; Hon Prog; *Md U; Mass Communications.*

SHORT, Ted Bruce
Fountain Lake HS; Hot Springs, AR (4-50) Ann; BC; BS; Ftbl; Tnns; Type A; *Math.*

SHORT, Tracy Alberta
Chichester Jr HS; Boothwyn, PA; Band; *Math.*

SHORT, William Robert
Reeds Spring HS; Reeds Spring, MO; AFS; BC; Math C; Sci C; Span C; Ftbl; Math A; Opt A; Sci A; Sci A; *Ark U; Bus Adm.*

SHORTER, Pamela Kaye
Galena Park Sr HS; Galena Park, TX (37-269) A Cap Choir; Cpt, Chldr; FHA; Hmrm; SC; Sr Cl; Outst Homemaker o-t Yr; *Prairie View A&M U; Home Ec.*

**SHORTHOUSE,
Daniel George Jr**
McKinley HS; Buffalo, NY; Band; Drama; Orch; Span C; *Carson Newman Col; Sci.*

SHORTHOUSE, Marjorie Lee
Kensington HS; Buffalo, NY; *US Air Force.*

SHORTS, Brigetta Carlinda
Castlemont HS; Oakland, CA; Drama; Model UN; Co-Ch, Sci C; VP, SC; COM; ARC A; CJSF Seal Bearer; *Med.*

SHORTSLEF, Donna Marie
Hannibal Central Sch; Hannibal, NY; Chor; Pres, 4H; NHS; 4H A.

SHORTT, Mary Jane
Ogemaw Heights HS; W Branch, MI (20-240) Band; Orch; Ski C; Swim; Tr; Yth Fel; *Saginaw Valley Col; Nurs.*

SHOTTS, Tammy Diane
Weld Central HS; Keenesburg, CO (14-105) Band; Chor; Ensm; Secy, FBLA; Ger C; NHS; SC; JV, Bkbl; Sftbl; Tr; MVP, Vlbl; *York Col; Psych.*

SHOULDERS, Marcie Marie
Henryetta HS; Henryetta, OK (10-65) FHA; NHS; Bkbl; Swim; Tr; *Okla St U; Phys Therapy.*

SHOUP, Cindy Louise
Orrville HS; Orrville, OH (5-186) Band; Ensm; VP, FTA; S-T, 4H; Lat C; Mjrte; Tres, NHS; 4H A; Hon Prog; *Canton Timkern Mercy's Sch Rdolgy; Radiology.*

SHOUP, Lane D
Montpelier HS; Montpelier, OH (56-120) Demolay; Pres, 4H; SC; Var C; Bkbl; Cr-Ctry; Tnns; 4H A; Yth Fel; *Agr.*

SHOUSE, Danny Scott
Franklin Co HS; Frankfort, KY; S-T, Drama; Fr C; VP, Key C; Sci C; COM; Hon Prog; *Eastern Ky U; Communications.*

SHOUSE, Shawn Carroll
Gladbrook Comm HS; Gladbrook, IA (2-32) Ann; Band; BS; 4H; Model UN; NHS; SC; JV, Wrest; MLS; NMS; St Scholar; Lions C Schol; Admission with Recogn & Sch A, Col; *Iowa St U; Engr.*

SHOVEY, Kenneth David Jr
Pacific HS; San Bernardino, CA (2-535) AFS; Drama; Secy, InterAct C; NFL; NHS; Sch P; Spch C; Thes; CSF; Spch A; *U of Calif, Redlands; Drama.*

SHOWALTER, David L
Ainsworth HS; Ainsworth, NE (7-80) Rptr, Ann; Band; Fin, BS; Chor; Tres, Monogram; SC; VP, Thes; Tres, Var C; Bsbl; Bkbl; Ftbl; Golf; Elk A; Hon Prog; Yth Fel; *Kearney St Col; Art.*

SHOWELL, Jeffrey Alan
Glen Ridge HS; Glen Ridge, NJ (24-175) A Cap Choir; Band; Orch; Co-Ed, Sch P; Arch; Mgr, Tr; Journ A; NMS; *Hampshire Col; Pol Sci.*

SHOWERS, Carole Ann
Alton Sr HS; Alton, IL (22-776) AFS; Band; Chor; Drama; Math C; Secy, NHS; Orch; Sci C; Span C; St Scholar; AFS Schol.

SHOWERS, Robert Gerard
Waupun HS; Waupun, WI (30-300) Ann; Band; Chess C; Ensm; VP, 4H; NHS; Sci C; Spch C; NMF; Spch A; Civil Air Patrol; *Col of St Thomas; Theology.*

SHOWLER, James Douglas
Imlay City Comm HS; Imlay City, MI (11-170) Band; Bsbl; Bkbl; Ftbl; Tr; HCt; *U of Mich; Med.*

SHOWMAN, Linda Sue
Connellsville Area HS; Connellsville, PA (110-700) Band; FNA; Marching Band; Pep Band; Lib Aide; Sq o-t Yr; *Alderson-Broaddus Col; Nurs.*

SHOWS, Barbara Speed
Crenshaw Christian Acad; Luverne, AL (2-30) Band; Chldr; Chor; 4H; Math C; Phys C; Var C; Bkbl; Beauty; Sci A; Hon Soc; Talent, Band, A's; All Star Chldr; *U of Ala; Phys Therapy.*

SHOWS, Paula Renee
Hattiesburg HS; Hattiesburg, MS; Rptr, Sch P; Span C; God & Country A; 1st Cl, GSct; God & Comm A; *U of Sou Miss.*

SHPAKOVSKY, Tammy Lynn
N Schuylkill Jr-Sr HS; Fountain Springs, PA (2-295) Hist A; Math A; Sci A; Type A; Bowl; Eng A; PA; Scoring A, SRA Assessment.

SHRECKENGAST, Mark Eric
Richland HS; Gibsonia, PA; Band; Order/ Arrow; Bsbl; Bkbl; Cr-Ctry; JV, Ftbl; Tr; Order/ Arrow A.

SHRECKENGAST, Scott Evan
Richland Sr HS; Gibsonia, PA; Band; Pres, Hmrm; NFL; NHS; Ntl Yth Conf; Order/Arrow; A-Ed, Sch P; SC; Bsbl; Mgr, Ftbl; Swim; Tr; Yth Guidance Conf; *Archt.*

SHREDER, Lisa Ann
Wilburton HS; Wilburton, OK (15-62) Ann; Secy, Band; CYO; Chem C; Chor; Dbte Tm; Pres, Drama; Ensm; Rptr, FHA; GS; VP, 4H; Math C; NHS; Phys C; Ed, Sch P; Sci C; Span C; VP, Spch C; Pres, SC; Alg A; Amer Leg A; Amer Leg Orator A; Bio A; Chem A; Citz A; Gov Honor Prog; 4H A; Hist A; Hon Prog; Journ A; Lion A; Masonic A; Math A; Most Outst; Ntl Sci Found; Ntl Sci Symposium; Sci A; Spch A; Star Student; Type A; *U of Okla; Geo Engr.*

SHREINER, Deborah Louise
Warwick Sr HS; Lititz, PA (23-275) Band; Chor; Early Bach A; *Penn St U; Phys Therapy.*

SHRIEVES, Deborah Lynn
John Yeates HS; Suffolk, VA (10%-155) Ann; Secy, BC; Drama; Pres, FHA; VP, Sr Cl; Secy, Jr Cl; Chamber of Comm A; HCt; WW; *Old Dominion U; Dental Asst.*

SHRIVER, Francine
S Charleston HS; South Charleston, WV (10-240) Lit Mag; NHS; Span NHS; Most Studious; *Marshall U.*

SHROCK, Michael Mathew
Davis Douglas HS; Portland, OR (90-530) Chor; Dbte Tm; Drama; NFL; Spch C; Pres, SC; Thes; Pres, Sr Cl; Pres, Jr Cl; Pres, Soph Cl; JV, Ftbl; Amer Leg A; COM; Elk A; Opt A; Spch A; Citizen's Advisory Committee; Sch Board; Win, US Senate Yth Prog; Ldrship A.

SHROPSHIRE, D Garrett
Howe Military Sch; Howe, IN (3-52) A Cap Choir; Ed, Ann; Band; Chor; Cum Laude Soc; Drama; Ensm; NHS; Order/Arrow; Ed, Sch P; Thes; Var C; Ftbl; Cpt, Swim; JV, Tr; Hist A; Order/Arrow A; Pres A; Q&S A; ROTC A; MVP, Swim; Ath o-t Yr; Eagle Sct; WW; Alpha Delta Tau; *U of Ky; Engr.*

SHROPSHIRE, Josetta Calvene
Roosevelt HS; Gary, IN; Community Yth Symph; Drama; Fr C; Orch; Citz A; Hon Prog; Yth Fel; GSct; Urban League; Lit C; NAACP.

SHROPSHIRE, Nathan James
Druid Park Baptist HS; Satsuma, AL; Chor; Key C; SC; Bsbl; Cpt, Bkbl; Ftbl; Chamber of Comm A; Cl Fav; Hon Prog; *Fla Col.*

SHROPSHIRE, Reginald Carlisle
Andrean HS; Gary, IN (155-287) Order/Arrow; Tr; Order/Arrow A; Yth Fel; Tres, Urban League; NAACP; Kappa League; Jr Usher Board; Cpt, CYO Bkbl; *Howard U; Archt.*

SHRULL, Randall Dean
Rock Bridge HS; Columbia, MO (100-300) A-Ed, Ann; Band; Rptr, Sch P; Var C; Tr; Wrest; *U of Mo at Columbia; Architecture.*

SHRULL, Richard Gene
Rock Bridge HS; Columbia, MO (60-280) A-Ed, Ann; Chor; Rptr, Sch P; *U of Mo; Engr.*

SHRUM, Pamela Sue
Hendersonville Sr HS; Hendersonville, TN (55-468) BC; Bus C; VP, FBLA; Lit Mag; NHS; ARC; Band; Rptr, Sch P; Sci C; Sftbl; Beauty; 4H A; Hon Prog; Journ A; Q&S A; Spch A; Type A; Bus Filing A; Acct A; Bible Quiz A; Exchange Ed, Star News.

SHRUMM, Donald Arthur
Bellevue Sr HS; Bellevue, WA (99-475) Band; Chor; Dbte Tm; NHS; Hockey; Senate Page; Mgt A; *Whitworth Col; Philosophy.*

SHRYOCK, Betsy Ann
Donald E Cavit Jr-Sr HS; Hammond, IN (24-312) SC; Tri-HiY; COM; *Mich U; Phys Therapy.*

SHUDA, Lester John
Neshaminy Maple Point HS; Langhorne, PA (2-413) NHS; Ski C; Ftbl; Tr; JV, Wrest; Amer Leg A; Hon Prog; Wrest Tourn Champ; All Area Ftbl; Cpt, Gymnight; *Sci.*

SHUEMAKER, Tanya Rene
Washington HS; Los Angeles, CA; *Trade-Tech Col; Bus Ed.*

SHUEY, Keith Alan
Hershey Sr HS; Hershey, PA (1-260) A-Ed, Ann; Band; Chess C; Ensm; Tres, NHS; Orch; Mgr, Swim; MLS; Rotary A; Val; Pres, Curling; *Susquehanna U; Finance.*

SHUGAR, Dana Renee
Geneva Comm HS; Geneva, IL (10-224) AFS; Band; Dbte Tm; Pres, Fr C; 4H; Bkbl; Sftbl; JV, Tnns; Amer Leg A; COM; 4H A; Hist A; Opt A; Pres A; ARC A; Sci A; Spch A; Yth Deacon; *Biol.*

SHUGREN, Neil Brian
Cambridge Sr HS; Cambridge, MN; Chor; Tres, 4H; 4H A; Treas, DECA.

SHULL, Denise K
Cuyahoga Valley Christian Acad; Cuyahoga Falls, OH (6-32) Cpt, Chldr; Chor; Drama; Ski C; SC; VP, Jr Cl; COM; Citz A; HCt; NEDT; News-Ed, Sch Paper; Chaplin, Soph Cl; Soph Bible Outst Stu A; *Wheaton Col; Med Tech.*

SHULL, Douglas Arthur
East Noble HS; Kendallville, IN (16-291) Chess C; 4H; Bkbl; Golf; Amer Leg A; *Rose Hulman Int of Tech; Chem Engr.*

SHULT, Mindy Marie
Doland Ind HS; Doland, SD (4-31) Chor; Ensm; Rptr, Fr C; FNA; St Stu Congress; Coun of Teach A; JA A; Yth Fel; *SD St U; Acct.*

SHULTE, Vickie Jo
Waterford Township HS; Pontiac, MI (24-440) Summa Cum Laude; VofDEM; Adv Scot Hghland Dance; Chrch Tchr; Chrch Mission Brd; Hon Men Lit Con; Outst Tchr Aid o-t Yr; Sr GSct; Oper Sunshine Staf; SF St Brd Ed; *Kalamazoo Col; Special Ed.*

SHULTZ, Darla Dee
Big Walnut HS; Sunbury, OH (12-209) Band; Cpt, Chldr; Chem C; Fr C; FFA; FTA; Secy, 4H; 4H A; Bsbl Statistician; Runnerup, FFA Qn; Miss Hartford Fair Qn; *Ohio St U.*

SHULTZ, Dell Ann
Big Walnut HS; Sunbury, OH (20-209) Chldr; Chem C; FFA; Pres, FHA; Pres, 4H; Span C; VP, 4H A; Yth Fel; Bsbl Statistician; FFA Qn; Fin, Miss Ohio FHA; Co Fair Princess; Hartford Fair Princess; *Career Acad; Dental Hygienist.*

SHULTZ, Sherry Rayne
Clovis HS; Clovis, NM; Chldr; 4H; Pres, Hmrm; NHS; Bkbl; Tr; Alg A; Citz A; 4H A; Ntl Rifle Assn; Vlbl; Sch Ltr, Gym; Sportsmanship, Depart, Gym, A's; *Lubbock Christian Col; Ed.*

SHUMA, Roger Edward
Morton W HS; Berwyn, IL (10%-780) Tr; Amer Leg A; Pres, Church Yth Fel; *Morton Jr Col; Engr.*

SHUMACHER, Julie Elaine
Broken Bow HS; Broken Bow, OK; Cpt, Band; Chor; Drama; Ensm; FHA; NHS; Secy, Span C; Spch C; Ch, SC; Beauty; Hon Prog; Spch A; Swtht; Yth Fel; St Scholar; Solo Vocal A; Flag Corps Cpt; St Forensic Spch A; *Special Elem Ed.*

SHUMAKE, William Stephen
Campbell HS; Smyrna, GA (10%-326) Band; BC; Chor; Hmrm; NHS; Order/Arrow; SC; Pres, Sr Cl; VP, Jr Cl; Mgr, Bkbl; JV, Ftbl; Tnns; Elk A; Order/ Arrow A; Rotary A; Yth Fel; All St Band & Chor; WW; *Shorter Col; Church Related Mus.*

SHUMAKER, Mark Alan
Warren Central HS; Indianapolis, IN (50%-600) IUPUI; Arch.

SHUMAN, Scott Kenneth
Mohlenberg HS; Laureldale, PA (23-321) A Cap Choir; Chess C; Chor; Hmrm; Rptr, Sch P; Sci C; SC; COM; Cl Offices; *Messiah Col; Radio-t V-Film.*

SHUMATE, Audrey
Doherty HS; Colorado Springs, CO (200-600) Chldr; Sci C; Ski C; SC; Swim; *El Paso Comm Col; Dental Hygiene.*

SHUMATE, Belinda Ann
Salisbury HS; Salisbury, NC; Band; Secy, Lat C; SC; Tnns; *Appalachianor St U; Bus.*

SHUMATE, Kimberly Smith
Columbus HS; Columbus, GA; Band; Orch; Gov Honor Prog; Symph Orch; All St Orch; Columbus Col Symph; Cpt, Flag Corp; Pres, Mus Stu C; Lib, Band; *Mus.*

SHUMATE, Robert Bradley
Virgie HS; Virgie, KY (11-103) Bus Mgr, Ann; Band; BC; Spch C; SC; Pres, Sr Cl; Hist A; Hon Prog; *U of Ky; Med Tech.*

SHUPE, James Grant
Sky View HS; Smithfield, UT (1%-610) Pres, 4H; Ski C; Var C; JV, Bsbl; JV, Golf; Fin, Wrest; Alg A; Amer Leg A; Citz A; God & Country A; 4H A; Math A; Duty to God A; *Utah St U; Med.*

SHUPE, Mary Ann
West HS; Davenport, IA (33%-825) A Cap Choir; Chor; Community Yth Symph; ARC; Swim; ARC A; Yth Fel; VP, Candystripers; Vol Worker, Retarded Children; Vol Worker, Nurs Home.

SHUPERT, Cynthia Jean
Arapahoe HS; Littleton, CO (112-583) *N Ariz Col; Lang.*

SHUPING, Kristen Elizabeth
Moultrie Sr HS; Moultrie, GA; Band; Math C; Orch; Sci C; Stu Assn for Ga Ed; Special A, Math Exam; Section Ldr, Band & Orch.

SHUPING, Lisa Lane
Kernersville Wesleyan Acad; Kernersville, NC (20-50) Span C; Beauty; HQn; HCt; Pres, Yth Fel; *U of NC at Greensboro; Nurs.*

SHUPP, Kathi Jo
Garden Spot HS; New Holland, PA (24-283) AFS; Chor; Drama; Ger C; NHS; WW in Foreign Languages; *Mus.*

SHUPP, Lori Ann
Dallastown HS; Dallastown, PA; Band; Colorguard Ltr; Rifle Head Pin; *Journ.*

SHURTE, Julia Kay
Flint Northern HS; Flint, MI (5%-700) Band; Chor; Community Yth Symph; Ensm; NHS; Orch; Hon Men, Story Writing; *U of Utah; Dance.*

SHUSTER, Paul Johann
Las Cruces HS; Las Crucas, NM (10%-800) Pres, Band; Chess C; Chor; Ensm; Key C; Orch; ARC; Spch C; SC; Thes; Opt A; Opt Out Tn; ARC A; Yth Fel; Outst Soloist; Drum Major; Outst Ensem; Charles A Lindbergh Assn; Terpsichorean Tn; *NM St U; Mus.*

SHUTES, Polly Ann
Coronado HS; El Paso, TX (35-300) A Cap Choir; Chor; Yth Fel; Yth Off; *Nurs.*

SHUTT, Dana Kee
Mullens HS; Mullens, WV; BC; Chess C; FBLA; Hmrm; Tres, Rainbow; Rptr, Sch P; SC; Alg A; Sci A.

SHUTTLESWORTH, David Lee
Belton HS; Belton, TX (20-220) Drama; VP, FFA; Hmrm; NHS; Tres, SC; Bsbl; Ftbl; Amer Leg A; Cl Fav; Pres, FCA; VP, Fresh Cl off; *Temple Jr Col; Health & Ed.*

SHUTZ, Daniel Paul
Chickasaw Acad; Satsuma, AL; Math C; Pres, Pep C.

SHY, David Edward
Antelope Valley HS; Lancaster, CA (50-700) A Cap Choir; Chor; Pres, Fr C; Tnns; Gym; Fr A; *Hope Col; Chem.*

SHY, Pamela Jean
Sou Reynolds R II HS; Ellington, MO (2-87) Band; BC; Cpt, Chldr; Chor; Mjrte; VP, Jr Cl; S-T, Soph Cl; Sftbl; Tr; Alg A; Hist A; HCt; Math A; MLS; Yth Fel; Vlbl; Span A; *SE Mo U.*

SHY, Pepper Giles
Northeastern HS; Detroit, MI (5-200) NHS; VP, SC; Bsbl; Hon Prog; MLS; Sci A; Spch A; Cl Brain; *U of Mich; Engr.*

SHYNE, Patricia Ann
Minden HS; Minden, LA; Chor; Math C; Sftbl; Math A; *Grambling Col; Social Worker.*

SIAS, David Glenn
Lake Charles HS; Lake Charles, LA; Band; FTA; Lit Mag; NHS; Rptr, Sch P; Rptr, Span C; SC; Bkbl; Ftbl; Tr; Alg A; COM; HCt; Hon Prog; Secy, Sunday Sch; Lib C; FCA; *U of New Orleans; Elec Engr.*

SIBLEY, Cynthia Lea
Central HS; W Helena, AR (10-350) Ann; VP, BC; Co-Cpt, Chldr; GS; Hmrm; Model UN; VP, NHS; Tres, Span C; SC; Tnns; COM; H of F; HCt; Hon Prog; Kiwanis A; Yth Fel; Pres, UMYF; Church Adm Board; Dist Yth Coun; *Sou Meth U; Sci.*

SIBLEY, Louise Delorese
Monroe HS; Albany, GA (6-329) Chldr; GS; Secy, Hmrm; SC; Amer Leg A; COM; Citz A; Cl Fav; Gov Honor Prog; HQn; *Albany St Col; Bus Adm.*

SIBLEY, Maresa Dean
Grace Christian HS; Prattville, AL (3-11) Ann; Chor; Ensm; HQn; Hon Prog; *Bob Jones U; Sacred Mus.*

SIBLEY, Mary Frances
Fairless HS; Navarre, OH; Pres, Bus C; NHS; Var C; Y-Tns; Cpt, Bkbl; MVP, Bkbl; *U of Akron; Bus.*

SIBLEY, Shawn Carol
Cary Sr HS; Cary, NC (17-600) Pres, BC; Drama; Ger C; GS; InterClub Coun; Pres, Lat C; Tr; B Crocker A; Gov Honor Prog; Hon Prog; Yth Fel; Jr Marshall; HR; NC Repretory Ballet Company; *U of NC; Vet Med.*

SIBLI, Dewi Liz
Consuelo Escalona Private Sch; Carolina, PR (2-38) Chor; ARC; COM; Hon Prog; Loyalty A; *Duquesne Col; Phar.*

SIBURG, Daniel Reay
St John's Military Sch; Salina, KS (3-38) BS; Dbte Tm; Fr C; VP, Key C; Tres, NHS; SC; Var C; Ftbl; Tr; Wrest; God & Country A; Hon Prog; ROTC A; Sci A; Drill Tm; Debate A; Shark Prize; Faculty Merit A; NBA Star Spangled Stu; *W Point Military Acad; Engr.*

SICKELS, LuAnn Marlee
Loup City HS; Loup City, NE (27-70) Ann; Band; Chor; FHA; Hon Chor; All St Singers; Stu Director,band.

SICKING, Helen Mae
Gainesville HS; Gainesville, TX (9-184) Pres, Bus C; CYO; VP, Fr C; FHA; Tres, FTA; Pres, 4H; Hmrm; NHS; Spch C; SC; Citz A; Hon Prog; NEDT; Soroptomist A; Schol A; *Cooke Co Col; Bus.*

SICKLER, Eric Douglas
Corning Comm HS; Corning, IA (3-88) A Cap Choir; F-Ed, Ann; Band; Chor; Ensm; Madrigal; ARC; Pres, SC; Thes; JV, Ftbl; Golf; Spch A; Yth Fel; Yth Foundation A; Yth Leg; Trainer, Bsbl & Bkbl; Semi-Fin, Hugh O'Brien Found A; *Drake U; Phys Therapy.*

SIDDOWAY, Tom Benedict
Sidney Sr HS; Sidney, MT (15-120) AFS; Band; BS; CYO; Chor; S-T, Drama; Ensm; Fr C; Secy, Key C; S-T, Spch C; Swim; Spch A; *Bus.*

SIDES, David Lee
Elmore Co HS; Eclectic, AL; Band; BC; Orch; *Auburn U; Law.*

SIDES, Melinda Anne
E Mecklenburg HS; Charlotte, NC (99-650) A Cap Choir; BC; Hmrm; InterClub Coun; A-Ed, Sch P; Span C; SC; Hon Prog; VP, Jr Civinettes; Sch Musicals; Chor; Stu Cong Rep; Yth Adv Board; Spch & Hearing Center Intern; Assoc Ed, Newspaper Staff; *U of Tenn; Spch Pathology.*

SIDES, Terri Lou
Dora HS; Dora, AL (90-130) Ann; Band; JV, Chldr; Secy, Chor; Drama; Pres, Hmrm; Beauty; Top 8, Miss Walker Co; Win, Miss Dora High; Most Popular; Walker Co Ideal Miss.

SIDLO, Lynn Marie
Park Center Sr HS; Brooklyn Park, MN (30-545) NHS; H of F; Math A; *Vermillion Comm Col; Forestry Technology.*

SIDLOWSKI, Paula Ann
Lake Clifton Sr HS; Baltimore, MD (10%-315) NHS; Math A; *Essex Comm Col; Radiologic Technology.*

SIDLOWSKI, Stephen Frank
Carl Sandburg HS; Orland Park, IL (30-750) VP, Bus C; VP, CYO; Drama; Mu Alpha Theta; NHS; Order/Arrow; Ed, Sch P; Span C; Cr-Ctry; Tr; Amer Leg A; Hon Prog; Order/Arrow A; Q&S A; St Scholar; Conservation Schol A, Women's C; *Loyola U; Pol Sci.*

SIDMON, Janet Marie
Mt Vernon HS; Mt Vernon, MO (25-105) AFS; Band; Secy, BC; Chor; Drama; Secy, FHA; FTA; Ed, Sch P; VP, SC; Thes; Pres, Soph Cl; COM; Spch A; Rptr, Parl, FHA; Early-Out Sr; Courier Schol; Acteen Schol; Acct Department Schol; *SW Baptist Col; Acct.*

SIDWELL, Barbara Emily
Wood River HS; Hailey, ID; F-Ed, Ann; VP, Fr C; NHS; Ski C; St Stu Congress; Secy, SC; Thes; Secy, Soph Cl; Tnns; JV, Tr; Citz A; Ntl Sci Symposium; Spch A; Outst Soph; Ceramics Sch, Creative Art Center; *Archt.*

SIEBENAHLER, Kathy Jo
Luverne Jr Sr HS; Luverne, MN; Chor; *Bookkeeping.*

SIEBERN, Peggy Anne
E Brunswick HS; E Brunswick, NJ; Chor; *Pre-sch Ed.*

SIEBERS, Carl Edwin
Northview HS; Grand Rapids, MI (20-331) NHS; JV, Ftbl; Hon Prog; *U of Mich; Bio Sci.*

SIEBERT, Barbara Lynn
W Holt HS; Atkinson, NE (5-58) Ed, Ann; Chldr; Chor; Drama; Madrigal; Mjrte; NHS; Rptr, Sch P; SC; JV, Bkbl; JV, Tr; Amer Leg Orator A; Regent Schol; Spch A; Prom Qn; Mgr, Tr; Superior, One Act Play; Superior, Drama Reading; Drill Tm; *U of Nebr; Journ.*

SIEBERT, Sandra Joan
Reeds Spring HS; Reeds Spring, MO; A Cap Choir; VP, BC; Chor; Drama; Secy, FHA; Sci C; VP, Sr Cl; Chamber of Comm A; HCt; Math A; Opt A; Sci A; Spch A; *U Mo at Kansas City; Med Technology.*

SIEBLER, Jenette Angelli
LaCenter HS; La Center, WA (10-34) Band; Chor; FHA; Pres, 4H; NHS; Mgr, Bkbl; 4H A; JA A; WW; PA; *Psych.*

SIECK, Mary Aline
Malcolm HS; Malcolm, NE (10-43) Ann; Band; JV, Chldr; Drama; 4H; Sch P; Spch C; JV, Bkbl; Sftbl; Semi-Fin, Tr; COM; 4H A; *Journ.*

SIEDLECKI, Andrew Joseph
Medina Sr HS; Medina, NY (3-175) A Cap Choir; Band; Chess C; Chor; Ensm; Hmrm; K of C; NHS; A-Ed, Sch P; SC; Var C; Pres, Sr Cl; Cpt, Bsbl; Co-Cpt, Bkbl; Co-Cpt, Ftbl; Golf; B Crocker A; COM; Citz A; Cl Fav; Hon Prog; NEDT; Regent Schol; Sci A; Star Student; PA; All League, Golf; Schol A; *Dartmouth Col; Med.*

SIEGEL, Craig Stephen
Maple Shade HS; Maple Shade, NJ (6%-241) Band; Bkbl; Col Schol; *Geneva Col; Chem.*

SIEGEL, Michael Wayne
Smithton R VI HS; Smithton, MO (20%-47) Rptr, CYO; Chor; Rptr, FFA; Cr-Ctry.

SIEGEL, Steven Bennett
Batavia HS; Batavia, IL (5-224) Lat C; Math C; Bkbl; Tr; Hon Prog; JA A; Math A; VofDEM; *Air Force Acad; Aeronautics.*

SIEGELIN, Cindy Lynn
Clearwater HS; Clearwater, FL; AFS; A-Ed, Ann; Y-Tns; Keyettes; *Fla St U; Mass Comunications.*

SIEGLE, Mary Beth
Russell HS; Russell, KY; BC; CYO; Chor; Madrigal; Mod Cert; *U of Louisville; Elem Ed.*

SIEGMANN, Eric Todd
Niagara Wheatfield HS; Sanborn, NY (128-435) Arch; MVP, Cr-Ctry; Tr; Citz A; *Northland Col; Environmental.*

SIEKIERSKI, Marzanna Ludmila
Acad of Our Lady of Mercy; Milford, CT (1-88) CYO; Chor; Ski C; Span C; NEDT.

SIELING, Andrew William
Lyons Central HS; Lyons, NY (19-113) A Cap Choir; Band; Chor; Ensm; Pres, 4H; Orch; *Agr.*

SIEMBORA, Teresia Marie
The Cecilian Acad; Philadelphia, PA; Bus C; Chor; Fr C; Lat C; Secy, Sodality; Eng A; *RI Sch of Design; Arch Design.*

SIEMIATKOWSKI, Ann Irene
St Angela Hall Acad; Brooklyn, NY (8-82) Chldr; Drama; Citz A; Journ A; Best Composition A; *Dance.*

SIEMSEN, Keith Allen
Manhattan HS; Manhattan, KS (23-431) Band; Tres, 4H; Math C; Sci C; 4H A; *Kans St U; Geol.*

SIENKIEWICZ, Laura Jeanne
Bishop Klonowski HS; Scranton, PA (10-105) Drama; Co-Ed, Lit Mag; NFL; NHS; Mgr, Bkbl; Amer Leg A; COM; NEDT; Sci A; Eng A; *Mansfield St U; Math.*

SIERRA, David W
Ysleta HS; El Paso, TX (250-800) Band; Ensm; Louis Armstrong Jazz A; *Lubbock Christian Col; Mus.*

SIERRA, Milagros
Miguel Melendez Munoz; Bayamon, PR; Drama; Pres, Hmrm; ARC; SC; Bsbl; Alg A; COM; Hon Prog; Sci A; *U of Puerto Rico; Nurs.*

SIESS, Paul Frederick
Langley HS; McLean, VA (200-544) Chess C; *VPI; Mech Engr.*

SIEVERS, Carole Lynne
Newell-Providence Comm HS; Newell, IA (1-36) Ann; Band; Co-Cpt, Chldr; Chor; VP, FFA; VP, 4H; Ed, Sch P; Spch C; SC; Var C; Sftbl; Tr; COM; Cl Fav; 4H A; Lion A; Spch A; Librarian, FHA; Co 4-H Coun; *Acct.*

SIEVERS, Patrick Bernard
Brussels Comm HS; Brussels, IL (8-26) CYO; VP, FFA; 4H; Var C; VP, Sr Cl; Pres, Soph Cl; Bsbl; Cpt, Bkbl; Cl Fav; HKg; Most Ath; Best Looking.

SIEVERS, Wendy Anne
Normal Comm HS; Normal, IL (50-500) AFS; Chor; Bkbl; Amer Leg Orator A; Ecology C; *Psych.*

SIFFORD, Debra Kay
Lord Botetourt HS; Daleville, VA (19-163) Dbte Tm; GS; NFL; NHS; Pres, SC; Thes; Pres, Jr Cl; Pres, Soph Cl; Spch A.

SIFRE, Lyda Maribel
Santa Rita HS; Bayamon, PR (1-40) CYO; Sch P; COM; *U of Puerto Rico; Phar.*

SIGGERS, Lynda Louise
Old Mill Sr HS; Glen Burnie, MD; Chor; Ensm; *Morgan St U; Social Worker.*

SIGLER, Letetia June
Fairfield HS; Fairfield, AL (25%-186) FHA; *U of Ala; Obstetrics.*

SIGLER, Pamela Kay
Thomson HS; Thomson, GA; BC; Chor; FHA; Hmrm; St Stu Congress; NEDT; Upper 10% of Cl A; *Berry Col.*

SIGMAN, Daniel Edward
Brown HS; Sturgis, SD (85-194) Bsbl; Ftbl; Cpt, Wrest; *Black Hills St Col; Natural Sci.*

SIGMON, Amy Leigh
William Byrd HS; Vinton, VA (3-228) Ann; BC; Lit Mag; COM; Yth Fel; Yth Leg; VP, New Life C; *Ntl Bus Col; Acct.*

SIGMON, Brian Clifford
William Byrd HS; Vinton, VA (60-260) BC; Fin, BS; Sci C; JA A; *Ntl Bus Col; Bus.*

SIGMON, Elizabeth Rene
St Stephens HS; Hickory, NC (11-265) AFS; F-Ed, Ann; Band; Tres, BC; FHA; GS; Key C; Secy, Rainbow; Ed, Sch P; Sci C; Pres, Span C; Bkbl; Alg A; Hist A; HCt; MLS; Co Trs, Beta C; Prs, Art C; Span A; Sndv Sch Tchr; Sub-Jr; Health A; Pep Squad; Trs, Biol C; Phys Ed A; Q & S; Jr Marshall; Home Ec A; *U of NC; Ed.*

SIGMON, Margaret Ann
Hickory HS; Hickory, NC; Band; Chldr; Span C; Most Outst, Chldr; Most Outst, Band Stu; *UNCC; Health Field.*

SIKES, Jon Brian
Del City HS; Del City, OK (5%-615) BS; Demolay; NHS; Pres, SC; Var C; Bsbl; Ftbl; *Southwestern Col; Phar.*

SIKES, Mary Alicia
West Point HS; West Point, VA (3-61) Ann; Band; Span C; Thes; Hon Prog; Historian, Drama C; *Engr.*

SIKES, Michael June
Loganville HS; Loganville, GA (20%-138) BS; Parl, FTA; Lit Ral; Sch P; Mgr, Bkbl; Tr; *De Kalb Col; Ed.*

SIKES, Penny Lisa
SW HS; Macon, GA; Chor; Ensm; Pres, FHA; Math A; Ga Jubilee; Ga Social Sci Fair; *Interior Design.*

SIKES, Teresa Gale
Northern Nash Sr HS; Rocky Mount, NC; FBLA; FHA; Pres, FNA; Sftbl; *Kings Col; Med Secy.*

SIKKEMA, Martha Sue
Fulton HS; Fulton, IL (99-115) Pres, AFS; Chor; Ensm; Fr C; NHS; Thes; Hon Prog; Outst Alto; *NW Col; Bus.*

SILAS, Steven Lee
St Joseph HS; Jeanerette, LA (1-19) 4H; Hmrm; Fin, Lit Ral; Bkbl; Tr; COM; Hist A; HCt; Math A; Sci A; Social Stu A; Fr A; Religion A; 1st, World Geography, Lit Ral; *LSU; Med.*

SILBERNAGEL, Donna Nadeane
St Mary's Central HS; Bismarck, ND; A Cap Choir; Band; Chem C; Chor; Drama; Ensm; 4H; K of C; Madrigal; Mardi Grau Candidate; 1st & 2nd Pl, Talent Show; 4-H Ribbons; *Mus.*

SILBERNAGEL, Randall Joseph
Regis HS; Stayton, OR (2-56) BS; Chem C; Drama; Math C; NHS; Sci C; VP, SC; Bsbl; Bkbl; Ftbl; Hon Prog; Math A; NML; Most Inspirational, Bkbl; *Oreg St U; Engr.*

SILBERT, Lee Anne
Colonial HS; Orlando, FL; Lit Mag; Rainbow; *Art.*

SILCOTT, Janelle Lynn
Mormon Trail Comm HS; Garden Grove, IA (8-36) Cpt, Chldr; Chor; Pres, FHA; Madrigal; ARC; Rptr, Sch P; St FHA Mus; Dist FHA Pres; I Rating, Mus Solo Contest; *Amer Inst of Bus; Secy.*

SILCOX, Deborah Ann
Norwalk HS; Norwalk, OH; Fr C; JA A; COE.

SILER, Darell Vern
Pleasant Plains HS; Pleasant Plains, AR (10-30) Band; FFA; 4H; SC; Bsbl; Bkbl; Sftbl; 4H A; *Archt.*

SILER, Laurie Lowe
Western Guilford HS; Greensboro, NC (70-200) S-T, Band; Var C; MVP, Bkbl; MVP, Swim; Vlbl; Band Coun; Civinettes; *GTI; Lab Technician.*

SILER, Pamela June
Landmark Christian HS; Cincinnati, OH (11-90) Ann; Chldr; Drama; Hmrm; Span C; SC; Bkbl; Sftbl; Tr; Pianist; *Teacher.*

SILK, Richard Carl
Oakland HS; Murfreesboro, TN; Band; BC; Chess C; Chor; Drama; *Middle Tenn St U; Computers.*

SILLIMAN, Scott A
Cassadaga Valley Central HS; Sinclairville, NY (40-150) NHS; Mgr, Bsbl; Mgr, Bkbl; *Math.*

SILLS, Norma
Martin Luther King Acad; Gary, IN (5-50) SC; Bkbl; Sftbl; Hon Prog.

SILSLEY, Vicki Lynn
Southmoreland Sr HS; Alverton, PA; Span C; COM; Sci A; *Palmer Col; Chiropractor.*

SILVA, Colleen Faye
South HS; Pueblo, CO (100-300) Chor; FBLA; 4H; Hmrm; ARC; Ski C; JV, Swim; *U of Sou Colo; Gen.*

SILVA, Joseph Michael
J F Kennedy HS; La Palma, CA (31-641) Semi-Fin, BS; Ger C; Hmrm; VP, Key C; Sci C; CSF; Emerald Chain; *UC Berkeley; Engr.*

SILVA, Juan
Luis Munoz Marin HS; Cabo Rojo, PR (7-200) Hist A; Math A; Sci A; *Col de Agr y Artes Mecanicas; Fisica.*

SILVA, Kathleen
Hitchcock HS; Hitchcock, TX (13-130) Tres, Band; S-T, Chess C; Ensm; Mjrte; NHS; Sch P; Secy, Jr Cl; Hon Prog; VofDEM; HR A; *Col o-t Mainland; Nurs.*

SILVA, Mark Anthony
Los Banos HS; Los Banos, CA (50%-220) Bus C; Pres, FBLA; FFA; FFA A; *Merced Jr Col; Bus.*

SILVA, Marleen Elizabeth
Maryknoll HS; Honolulu, HI (14-115) CYO; Pres, Hmrm; Pres, Jr Cl; Pres, Soph Cl; Mgr, Bkbl; Cpt, Sftbl; HCt; K of C A; Spch A; Ldrship A; Cl Spirit A; *U of Hawaii; Nurs.*

SILVA, Michael Ben
Memorial Sr HS; Houston, TX (50-640) Chem C; Cum Laude Soc; Pres, InterClub Coun; JETS; Key C; Pres, Math C; Pres, Mu Alpha Theta; Co-Ch, NHS; Order/Arrow; Phys C; Sch P; Pres, SC; Bkbl; Ftbl; Bio A; COM; God & Country A; Hon Prog; Magna Cum Laude; NMS; Opt A; Order/Arrow A; Yth Leg; Graduation Commencement Address; Eagle Sct; *Rice U; Med.*

SILVA, Michael Ben Jr
Memorial Sr HS; Houston, TX (52-640) Chem C; Cum Laude Soc; Hmrm; Pres, InterClub Coun; JETS; Key C; Pres, Mu Alpha Theta; Co-Ch, NHS; Order/Arrow; Phys C; Sch P; Pres, Sci C; Pres, SC; JV, Bkbl; Ftbl; Sftbl; Tr; Bio A; COM; God & Country A; Hon Prog; Magna Cum Laude; NMS; Opt A; Order/Arrow A; Yth Fel; Yth Leg; Eagle Sct; Graduation Commencement Speaker; Pres, Stu Body; *Rice U; Pre-Med.*

SILVEIRA, Deborah Ann
University HS; San Diego, CA (59-311) A Cap Choir; CYO; Chor; Cum Laude Soc; Hmrm; Ch, InterClub Coun; Sch P; St Stu Congress; Ch, Secy, Soph Cl; Hon Prog; *Eaton Col; Legal-Secy.*

SILVER, Antonio James
Loup City HS; Loup City, NE (7-70) Band; NHS; SC; Bkbl; COM; Hist A; Sci A; *U of Nebr; Computer Sci.*

SILVER, Laurel Lynne
Robert A Waller HS; Chicago, IL (33-105) Math C.

SILVERBERG, Annie Juniper
Apollo HS; Simi Valley, CA (2-90) Ed, Sch P; COM; Journ A; F-Ed, Co-Ed, Asst Ed, Sch P; *Moorpark Col; Art.*

SILVERMAN, Fayge
Yeshiva o-t South HS; Memphis, TN; Co-Ed, Ann; Ch, Chor; Fr C; NMS; NEDT; *Barnard Col; Journ.*

SILVERS, Michael Dwayne
Anderson HS; Anderson, IN; Bus C; *Bus.*

SILVESTRI, Joseph G
Chester HS; Chester, PA; Arch; *Drafting Tech.*

SILVIS, Debbie Kay
Washington Sr HS; Sioux Falls, SD (33%-780) Ann; Span C; Q&S A; *Ntl Col of Bus; Travel.*

SILVIS, Sandy Lynn
Miami Springs Sr HS; Miami Springs, FL (11-816) Anchor C; CYO; FNA; InterAct C; Pres, Var C; Cpt, Tnns; Hon Prog; Opt A; Spch A; Swtht; Cpt, Vlbl; Cpt, MVP, Badminton; Semi-Fin, HCt; Opt Qn; *U of Fla; Dentistry.*

SIMACEK, Mark J
Hastings Sr HS; Hastings, MN (10%-450) NHS; Order/Arrow; SC; Bkbl; Order/Arrow; Amer Leg A; Order/Arrow A; Eagle Sct; Jr Asst, Scoutmaster of Troop; Explorer Post; Hastings Natural Resources Comm; *U of Wis at Stout; Industrial Ed.*

SIMANSKY, Shelley Ann
Wasson HS; Colo Springs, CO (47-569) A Cap Choir; Band; VP, Chor; Drama; Ensm; Madrigal; Swim; JV, Tr; COM; *Med Tech.*

SIMARD, Lorraine Janet
St Mary's HS; Lynn, MA (15-146) Chldr; Ftbl; Sftbl; Swim; Alg A; Bio A; *Salem St Col; Acct.*

SIMBARI, Judy Ann
Amphitheatre HS; Tucson, AZ (128-400) Chor; Drama; Ensm; Ski C; Thes; Most Out; Choral Mus Outst Achv A; Gym JV Ltr; *U of Ariz; Fashion Merchandising.*

SIMCAK, Deborah Marie
Cy-Fair HS; Houston, TX (157-564) Parl, FHA; Ger C; *Sam Houston St U.*

SIMEONE, Mary Ann Judith
Acad of St Joseph; Brentwood, NY (10-100) CYO; Chor; Ensm; Sodality; Span C; Sftbl; COM; *St Johns U; Criminal Justice.*

SIMKINS, Lori Dale
Kickapoo HS; Springfield, MO; FHA; Pres, Span C; Alg A; COM; Math A; Drum & Bugle Corp; *Bradford Col; Bus.*

SIMKOVICH, Tamara
Belle Vernon Area HS; Belle Vernon, PA (18-338) A Cap Choir; Chor; Pres, Fr C; FBLA; NHS; Rptr, Sch P; WW; Pres, Jr Russian C; *Bauder Col; Fashion Merchandising.*

SIMMERS, Scott Phillip
Canton HS; Canton, OH (1-308) HiY; NHS; Order/Arrow; Bkbl; Golf; Sftbl; Pres A; Yth Fel; Sup, Co Sci Fair; *Cincinnati U; Chem Engr.*

SIMMET, Becky Sue
Everett HS; Lansing, MI (25%-500) Citz A; Hon Prog; Outst Tn Vol; Chor; GScts; Sch Aide, Lib; VP, Yth Fel; *Lansing Comm Col; Nurs.*

SIMMONS, Andre Jon
Humboldt HS; Humboldt, TN (20-186) *U of Tenn; Phys Ed.*

SIMMONS, Annette
Shaw HS; East Cleveland, OH (104-522) Bus C; *Youngstown U; Bus Adm.*

SIMMONS, Audrey Francylle
Norman HS; Norman, OK (80%-600) Tres, A Cap Choir; Band; Tres, Chor; Ensm; Hmrm; Orch; Sodality; Span C; SC; Cl Fav; Hist A; Most Outst; *Gen.*

SIMMONS, Barbara Ann
Kensington HS; Philadelphia, PA; MVP, Sch Achieve Tm; MVP, Tr; Dancing A; *Comm Col; Eng.*

SIMMONS, Brad Lee
Palmer HS; Palmer, TX (3-40) FFA; Bsbl; Mgr, Bkbl; Mgr, Ftbl; Bio A; *UTA; Archeology.*

SIMMONS, Brenda Lee
Eastside HS; Paterson, NJ; Mjrte; NHS; Hon Prog; High Hon Achv A; *U of SC; Nurs.*

SIMMONS, Cathy Renee
R E Lee Inst; Thomaston, GA; Band; Pres, HiY; Hmrm; Ed, Lit Mag; Cpt, Mjrte; SC; Tri-HiY; Var C; Tnns; *Fashion Merchandising.*

SIMMONS, Cheryl Bernice
Shaker Hghts HS; Shaker Heights, OH (2%-575) Band; ARC; ARC A.

SIMMONS, Chris Howard
Bullitt Central HS; Shepardsville, KY (16-125) Drama; MVP, Ftbl; Sftbl; Tr; *David Lipscomb Col; Elec Engr.*

SIMMONS, Christy Lynne
Floyd E Kellam HS; Virginia Beach, VA; Co-Ed, Lit Mag; Tri-HiY; Pres, Yth Fel; Deaconess; V-Ch, World Outreach & Comm Serv; VP, Dist Yth Fel; Nominating Comm.

SIMMONS, Clara Mae
Tilden HS; Chicago, IL (19-408) Secy, FHA; Math C; NHS; Pres, Sr Cl; VP, Jr Cl; Hon Prog; Afro C; Service C; Afro Qn; *Sou Ill U; Computer Sci.*

SIMMONS, Dana Christina
Miller Co R III HS; Tuscumbia, MO (1-28) Band; Chor; FTA; NHS; Bkbl; Sftbl; Band A; *Conservatory of Mus; Mus.*

SIMMONS, Darlene
Big Valley Jr-Sr HS; Bieber, CA (1-27) Chldr; Chor; Drama; Sch P; Spch C; Tres, SC; Bkbl; Ftbl; Sftbl; Mgr, Tr; CSF; Hist A; Lion A; Spch A; VFW A; VofDEM; Big Valley Days Princess; Swtht Swing Qn; *Nurs.*

SIMMONS, David Allan
Mt Zion HS; Mt Zion, IL (12-200) AFS; Band; Chor; Fr C; FBLA; Madrigal; Math C; NHS; Orch; St Scholar; *Millikin U; Engr.*

SIMMONS, Debra Kay
Ellet HS; Akron, OH (68-376) FHA; Span C; COM; Hon Prog; Yth Fel; Close Up Recognition Schol; *Akron U; Dietetics.*

SIMMONS, Denise Darlene
Seward Park HS; New York, NY; Band; Bio A; Citz A; Yth Fel; *Secy.*

SIMMONS, Earl Dennis
Spingarn HS; Washington, DC (17-718) Bsbl; Soccer; Tr; *Archt Drafting.*

SIMMONS, Edward Earl
F O Alexander HS; Starkville, MS; Cpt, Ftbl; *United Elec Inst; Elec.*

SIMMONS, Emet Holt
Wayne Co HS; Jesup, GA (5%-322) BC; VP, FBLA; Ski C; Bsbl; Mgr, Ftbl; COM; Chamber of Comm A; Hon Prog; Kiwanis A; NEDT; Rotary A; Star Student; *U of Ga; Pre-Med.*

SIMMONS, Freddy
Wayne Co HS; Jesup, GA; ROTC A.

SIMMONS, Gwendolyn Dolores
W Craven HS; Vanceboro, NC; BC; Fr C; FBLA; FHA; 4H; Hmrm; NHS; SC; Bible C; Fr A; Jr Civitan; DECA Stu o-t Yr Trophy; 1st & 2nd Pl Trophies, Sci Fair; *U of NC.*

SIMMONS, Hyattye Oresyua
Burkeville HS; Burkeville, TX (1-47) Chor; Dbte Tm; Drama; Pres, FFA; Hmrm; Rptr, SC; Mgr, Bsbl; Mgr, Bkbl; Mgr, Ftbl; Mgr, Tr; COM; Hist A; Math A; MLS; Mr FFA; Sch Hon Soc; PA A; Salta Hon Soc; *Pre-Law.*

SIMMONS, James Mark
Westside HS; Anderson, SC (20%-500) F-Ed, Ann; Span C; Spch C; SC; Var C; Y-Tns; Bkbl; Ftbl; *Anderson Jr Col; Forestry & Conservation.*

SIMMONS, James Reno
Gainesville HS; Gainesville, GA (10%-200) Chess C; Chor; Fr C; Key C; Sci C; Span C; Span NHS; VP, SC; Ftbl; Tr; Wrest; Cl Fav; Hist A; WW; *US Naval Acad; Engr.*

SIMMONS, Janice Kay
Pattonville Sr HS; Maryland Heights, MO (36-895) Citz A; Hon Prog; *Apostolic Bible Inst; Bible.*

SIMMONS, Jody Grant
Vancleave HS; Vancleave, MS (3-90) BC; 4H; Span C; SC; Tres, Soph Cl; Ftbl; VFW A; 2nd Pl, St Math & Sci Competition; St Stu Gov Conf; WW; *U of S Fla; Mass Communications.*

SIMMONS, Karen
Northwest HS; St Louis, MO (80-600) JA A; Math A; Type A; *Washington U; Acct.*

SIMMONS, Kimberly Ann
Richmond Sr HS; Rockingham, NC (97-585) BC; Chldr; FHA; A-Ed, Sch P; Tri-HiY.

SIMMONS, LaQuine
Miami Jackson Sr HS; Miami, FL; S-T, FBLA; F-Ed, Sch P; Opt A; Secy, Opti-Miss; Vp, JA; Yrbk; *Sou Methodist U; Film Media.*

SIMMONS, Lisa Inez
Humboldt HS; Humboldt, TN; Chldr; Chor; VP, FHA; 4H; Jr Miss Pagent; Rainbow; Tr; 4H A; VofDEM; Yth Fel; Chldr A; Secy, Church Yth Choir & Yth Fel; *Tenn St U; Home Ec.*

SIMMONS, Lula Marie
Shaw Sr HS; East Cleveland, OH (130-500) AFS; Math C; Secy, Sr Cl; Cl Fav; Most Friendliest; *Ohio U; Zoology.*

SIMMONS, Marlene
Big Valley Jr-Sr HS; Bieber, CA (4-27) Band; Chldr; Drama; Sch P; SC; Cpt, Bkbl; Ftbl; MVP, Sftbl; Tr; Journ A; Swtht; *Secretarial.*

SIMMONS, Mary Elizabeth
Reynolds Sr HS; Winston-Salem, NC (10%-750) A Cap Choir; Chldr; Hmrm; Mjrte; SC; Hon Prog; Yth Foundation; Yth Leg; Pres, Yth Fel; Dramatic Productions; Hon Ct; Girl's Coun; Yth Coun.

SIMMONS, Merrian Lee
Lake HS; Lake, MS (5-40) Band; BC; FBLA; FHA; Mjrte; Band A; District FBLA Poster Contest; Band Coun; *East Central Jr Col; Lib Arts.*

SIMMONS, Pamela Denise
Huntingdon HS; Huntingdon, TN (17-100) Co-Ed, Ann; BC; Drama; Secy, FHA; FTA; Hmrm; Span C; VP, Soph Cl; 4H A; *Nurs.*

SIMMONS, Patricia Yvette
Louis D Brandeis HS; New York, NY; Chldr; Hmrm; Bkbl; *Psychoanalyst.*

SIMMONS, Renee Denise
Wagner Jr HS; Philadelphia, PA; SC; Pres, Jr Cl; Bkbl; COM; MLS; Cpt, Kickball; Seminar Cert; VBS Cert; *Cheyney St Col; Med.*

SIMMONS, Rita Dalene
Fruitdale HS; Fruitdale, AL (10-31) BC; Chor; Sftbl; HQn; Miss FHS; Wittiest; *Nurs.*

SIMMONS, Roy Elworth
Silsbee HS; Silsbee, TX (18-241) Band; JETS; NHS; SC; JV, Bkbl; COM; Commended Stu, PSAT Scores; WW; Most Promising Future; Hon Graduate; *Lamar U; Industrial Engr.*

SIMMONS, Russell Nathaniel
South Garland HS; Garland, TX (50-750) Band; Secy, Chem C; Key C; Orch; Secy, Sr Cl; Bkbl; Most Out; Type A; Yth Fel; Yth Leg; Most Ludicrous; Pres Puerile Behaviorist Assn; *Air Force Acad; Elec Engr.*

SIMMONS, Sonya Lynne
Andress HS; El Paso, TX (30%-565) Cpt, Chldr; SC; Tr; Vlbl; Semi-Fin, Cl Fav; Semi-Fin, HCt; *U of Tex-Houston; Phys Ed.*

SIMMONS, Tarristine
Southfield Sr HS; Southfield, MI; All Amer Yth; Rptr, Sch P; JV, Bkbl; Journ A; Sci A; *Wayne St U; Food and Nutrition.*

SIMMONS, Terry Lynn
Tioga HS; Tioga, LA (22-190) Secy, BC; Chor; Ensm; FHA; VP, FNA; Lit Ral; Hon Prog; S-T, Pep C; *La Col; Archt.*

SIMMONS, Tyrone
Northeastern HS; Detroit, MI (10%-260) Pres, Hmrm; NHS; SC; Up Bound; Amer Leg A; Citz A; Hon Prog; *Engr.*

SIMMONS, Valerie Deanna
Roxana Comm HS; Roxana, IL; FBLA; Ntl Yth Conf.

SIMMONS, Venetia Evette
James Island HS; Charleston, SC (77-165) Ann; Chor; Sodality; *Col of Charleston; Pre-Med.*

SIMMONS, Wanda Lee
Muscle Shoals HS; Muscle Shoals, AL; Pres, Chor; 4H; InterClub Coun; Most Out; All St, Quad Cities, Choir; Quad City, Ensm; Superior, Solo Comp; *Muscle Shoals Tech Inst; LPN Training.*

SIMMS, Anne Woodruff
Westminster Sch; Atlanta, GA (11-90) AFS; Chor; Cum Laude Soc; Pres, Fr C; NHS; Tnns; Bio A; Chem A; Hist A; Math A; Q&S A; Pres, Bible C; Atlanta Vol Action Tutor; Art Ed, Ann; *Duke U; Math.*

SIMMS, Bill R
Nacogdoches HS; Nacogdoches, TX (50-300) Band; Ntl Yth Conf; Span C; JV, Ftbl; COM; Semi-Fin, Tex A&M Archt; UIL Ensm Medal; *Stephen F Austin St U; Engr.*

SIMMS, Laura Siling
University HS; Baton Rouge, LA (7-62) F-Ed, Ann; Band; FBLA; Hmrm; A-Ed, Lit Mag; Orch; SC; Y-Tns; Rptr, Soph Cl; Hon Prog; JA A; NEDT; Q&S A; *LSU; Natural Sci.*

SIMMS, Raymond III
Stafford HS; Falmouth, VA; FFA; Lit Mag; Sch P; Cr-Ctry; Cpt, Tr; 1st Cl BSct; Sr Patrol Ldr, BSct; Quarter Master Patrol Ldr, BSct; *Frostburg State College; Forestry.*

SIMMS, Steven Terrell
Franklin Co HS; Winchester, TN; *Motlow St Comm Col; Computer Sci.*

SIMNING, Patrick Lance
Tahoe-Truckee HS; Truckee, CA (2-75) Dbte Tm; Drama; Math C; Ski C; Spch C; SC; VP, Sr Cl; Ftbl; Soccer; Bank Of Amer A; Bausch & Lomb A; Bio A; CSF; COM; Cl Fav; Hon Prog; Lion A; Math A; MLS; Sal; Sci A; Spch A; Eagle Sct; *U of Rochester; Pre-Med.*

SIMON, Almer
Marshall Islands HS; Majuro, MARSHALL ISLANDS (22-103) Sch P; Star Student; *NW Mich Col; Nurs.*

SIMON, Barbara Anne
Calhoun Unit 40 HS; Hardin, IL (1-75) Pres, Drama; Secy, FHA; GS; NHS; Pres, Spch C; Secy, Sr Cl; Secy, Jr Cl; Arch; Amer Leg A; 4H A; JA A; FHA A; Hon A; *Med.*

SIMON, Bruce Lawrence
Chetek HS; Chetek, WI (20-80) Band; NHS; Orch; JV, Bsbl; JV, Bkbl; Mgr, Ftbl; *U of Minn; Nuclear Engr.*

SIMON, Corinne Anita
Glenbard W HS; Glen Ellyn, IL (63-488) Band; Ger C; Model UN; COM; *Northern Ill U; Bus.*

SIMON, Deborah Marie
Sullivan Co HS; Laporte, PA (116-141) Var C; Bowl Tm; Vlbl; JV & V Ltrs; *Williamsport Area Comm Col; Nurs.*

SIMON, Karen Elizabeth
Nederland HS; Nederland, TX (113-480) Anchor C; Secy, CYO; FTA; Vlbl; HR; *Lamar U; Secretarial Sci.*

SIMON, Linda Angela
Destrehan HS; New Sarpy, LA (5-227) Ann; VP, BC; Sch P; Secy, Bkbl; HCt; *U of New Orleans; Computer Sci.*

SIMON, Lisa Ilene
The Altamont Sch; Birmingham, AL (10-41) Ann; Chor; Drama; Pres, Fr C; French NHS; Hmrm; Lat C; Co-Ed, Lit Mag; NHS; ARC; Sci C; SC; Thes; COM; Magna Cum Laude; NEDT; 7th Pl, Ntl Fr Concourse; Fin, Poetry Contest; *Brown U; Eng.*

SIMON, Marta Sue
Fairmont Sr HS; Fairmont, MN (7-200) A Cap Choir; Ger C; Madrigal; Orch; Tnns; Hon Prog; *Gustavus Adolphus Col; Ed.*

SIMON, Mary Beth
Chetek HS; Chetek, WI (13-100) Tr; Hon Prog; *U of Wis-Eau Claire; CPA.*

SIMON, Michael Robert
Chetek HS; Chetek, WI (6-106) Chor; Hmrm; Model UN; SC; Bsbl; JV, Bkbl; Ftbl; *UW Platteville; Civil Engr.*

SIMON, Patricia Ann
South Park HS; Beaumont, TX (81-170) Tnns; Bio A; *Lamar U; Bus Adm.*

SIMON, Perry Elliot
Hebrew Acad HS; Yonkers, NY (1-16) Rptr, Sch P; Regent Schol; Val; *Journ.*

SIMONDS, Shawn Kathleen
Middle Park HS; Granby, CO (11-78) Band; 4H; Bkbl; *Colo U; Med Sci.*

SIMONE, Jill Marie
El Dorado Springs HS; El Dorado Springs, MO (8-156) Cpt, Chldr; Secy, Drama; Fr C; Hmrm; NHS; Rptr, Rainbow; Sci C; Spch C; SC; Thes; Var C; COM; HCt; Hon Prog; Sci A; Spch A; Vlbl; WW, Chldr; Best Dressed; *U of Mo; Sci.*

SIMONEAU, Betty Jean
Nashua Sr HS; Nashua, NH (100-800) VP, Fr C; Hmrm; NHS; WW; Four Agency Cert, Nurses Aide; Head Start; *E Nazarene Col; Nurs.*

SIMONETTI, Elizabeth Mary
Acad of Our Lady of Mercy; Milford, CT (12-92) Cpt, Chldr; Chor; Pres, Drama; Fr C; GS; Secy, NHS; Pres, Ski C; SC; Amer Leg A; NEDT; Holy Cross Bk A; Fr A; *Yale U; Pre-Law.*

SIMONETTI, Simone Marie
New Caney HS; Porter, TX (10%-215) NHS; Geom A; *U of Houston; Acct.*

SIMONS, Alana Gail
Robinson HS; Waco, TX; Chor; *Baylor U; Law.*

SIMONS, Larry Cecil
Bellevue Comm HS; Bellevue, IA (1-65) VP, Band; BS; Chor; Demolay; Ensm; Pres, NHS; Order/ Arrow; Span C; SC; Var C; VP, Sr Cl; Tnns; Jr Cl; Pres, Soph Cl; Bsbl; Bkbl; MVP, Ftbl; JV, Golf; Tnns; Tr; DARGCA; HCt; Yth Fel; *Wartburg Col; Bus Adm.*

SIMONS, Mark Alan
Jeffersontown HS; Louisville, KY; BC; Tres, Key C; JV, Bsbl; JV, Golf; *U of Louisville; Med.*

SIMONS, Scott William
Owyhee HS; Owyhee, NV (1-25) Ann; FFA; Sch P; SC; Var C; Pres, Sr Cl; Tres, Jr Cl; Bkbl; Tr; COM; Hon Prog; Val; Outst Eng Stu; *Col of Idaho.*

SIMONSICK, William Joseph
Maple Shade HS; Maple Shade, NJ (3-243) BS; NHS; SC; Bsbl; Bkbl; MLS; *Seton Hall Col; Sci.*

SIMONSON, Jean Marie
Estherville Sr HS; Estherville, IA (16-180) Chor; Semi-Fin, Dbte Tm; 4H; NFL; A-Ed, Sch P; Y-Tns; Ntl Forensics League A's; *Iowa Lakes Comm Col; Bus.*

SIMONSON, John Joseph
Estherville Sr HS; Estherville, IA (37-154) Fin, BS; CYO; Chor; Dbte Tm; NFL; Spch C; JV, Golf; Spch A; *Bus Adm.*

SIMONSON, Terri Lee
Cunningham HS; Cunningham, KS (1-21) A-Ed, Ann; Band; Chor; Ensm; Madrigal; SC; Pres, Jr Cl; HQn; St Scholar; *Pratt Jr Col.*

SIMPKINS, Rodney Michael
George Washington HS; Charleston, WV; Bkbl; Ftbl; *Marshall U; Law.*

SIMPKINS, Sharon Kay
McCluer N HS; Florissant, MO (18-796) A Cap Choir; Co-Ed, Ann; Chor; Hmrm; Orch; Hon Prog; Stu o-t Day; Top Ten; Puppetry A; *Okla Baptist U; Sociology.*

SIMPSON, Andrea Kay
Kirkwood HS; Kirkwood, MO; Hmrm; Lat C; Ch, SC; Sci A; Yth Fel; *Concordia Col; Deaconess.*

SIMPSON, Carol Marie
Southport HS; Indianapolis, IN (100-425) Fr C; FNA; Sftbl; Type A; *Ind St U; Bus Mgt.*

SIMPSON, Christine Denise
Moore HS; Moore, OK; A Cap Choir; Chor; Drama; S-T; Bio A; Yth Fel; VP, Pep C; *Colo U; Med Tech.*

SIMPSON, Constance Joann
Carver HS; Columbus, GA (5%-318) Pres, CYO; FHA; Lit Mag; Outst, Fresh; *Eng.*

SIMPSON, Daphne Kay
Marked Tree HS; Marked Tree, AR (5-75) GS; 4H; Jr Miss Pagent; Lit Mag; NHS; Span C; Thes; 4H A; Hon Prog; Art A; WW; *Ark St U; Archt Engr.*

SIMPSON, David Roy
Robert E Lee HS; Montgomery, AL (300-750) Band; Chor; Bsbl; Gov Honor Prog; Solo, Ensm Metal; *Auburn U; Bus Adm.*

SIMPSON, Deborah Elaine
Southwest Ga Acad; Damascus, GA (18-26) Chor; Drama; FHA; S-T, 4H; Sch P; Spch C; Sftbl; *Young Harris Col; Dental Hygiene.*

SIMPSON, Donald Richard
Highland HS; Albuquerque, NM (42-695) Hmrm; NHS; Rptr, Sch P; SC; Yth Fel; Col Schol; VP, Sub-Dist Yth Coun; *U of NM; Sci.*

SIMPSON, Edith Melinda
Tupelo HS; Tupelo, MS; Anchor C; Band; Chor; Community Yth Symph; Ensm; 4H; Mjrte; Orch; Span C; VP, Thes; Y-Tns; Bkbl; Sftbl; Tr; Foreign Culture League; Tres, Jr Civitan; St, Mid-S, Hon Bands; Band A; *Miss Sou Col; Span.*

SIMPSON, Elizabeth Jane
Columbus HS; Columbus, GA; Band; NHS; COM; Gov Honor Prog; Hon Prog; Sci A; *Troy St U; Art.*

SIMPSON, Henry Joseph
Durand Sr HS; Durand, WI (1-106) Cpt, Dbte Tm; Pres, NHS; SC; Tnns; COM; Most Out; NEDT; Spch A; Dbte Trophies; Extemporaneous A; *Med.*

SIMPSON, Jane Kathleen
Montrose Acad; Montrose, AR (2-40) Band; Bus C; Chem C; Ensm; Fr C; GS; NHS; SC; Sftbl; Tr; NEDT; Church Organist; Eng A; *U of Central Ark; Occupational Therapy.*

SIMPSON, Jari Annette
Mt Carmel HS; Mt Carmel, IL (3-195) A Cap Choir; Ed, Ann; Band; Chor; Community Yth Symph; Pres, Fr C; Hmrm; 4H; Mjrte; NHS; Orch; Swim; 4H A; Hon Prog; Kiwanis A; NEDT; WW; GAA; Girl's Sextet; Pres, Girls Board; GSct; *Ind U; Mus Ed.*

SIMPSON, John Eugene
Judge Mem Cath HS; Salt Lake City, UT (71-137) Model UN; Soccer; Citz A; Schol A; *U of Utah; Math.*

SIMPSON, John Worthington
Salina Central HS; Salina, KS; Span C; JV, Bkbl; Church Deacon; *Kans U; Law.*

SIMPSON, Kathryn Elaine
John F Kennedy HS; Tumon, GUAM (15-511) NHS; Alg A; Math A; Geom A.

SIMPSON, Marjorie Becky
Cartersville HS; Cartersville, GA; Band; Thes; Tri-HiY.

SIMPSON, Mark Alan
Parkview HS; Orfordville, WI (64-158) 4H; Thes; JV, Ftbl; *Ohio St U; Solar Engr.*

SIMPSON, Mark Keith
Ballard R-2 HS; Butler, MO (1-23) Band; 4H; Var C; Pres, Soph Cl; Bsbl; JV, Bkbl; Tr; Alg A; Bio A; 4H A; HCt; Math A; Sci A; Type A; Yth Fel; VICA; *Rolla U; Mech Engr.*

SIMPSON, Mark Robert
Martin Co HS; Stuart, FL (9-500) BC; Key C; Hon Prog; Star Student; WW; *U of S Fla; Hist.*

SIMPSON, Melinda Susan
Mainland Sr HS; Daytona Beach, FL (9-718) VP, FHA; Math C; NHS; Span C; SC; Chamber of Comm A; Citz A; Kiwanis A; Pres A; Span A; *Stetson U; Elem Ed.*

SIMPSON, Michael Maurice
Reidsville Sr HS; Reidsville, NC (33-324) Pres, Band; BS; Chess C; Hmrm; Key C; SC; JV, Bkbl; WW Among HS Band Members A; *NC St U; Engr.*

SIMPSON, Sarita Carole
Irving HS; Irving, TX (4-678) A Cap Choir; VP, Mu Alpha Theta; NHS; Span C; Citz A; Coun of Teach A; Hon Prog; PTA A; *Sou Methodist U; Math.*

SIMPSON, Scott Raymond
Mason City HS; Mason City, IA (275-495) Band; 4H A; Eagle Sct; *Iowa St U; Eng.*

SIMPSON, Sheila Larain
Bryant HS; Bryant, AR (4-201) Chor; Fr C; Rptr, Hmrm; NHS; Bio A; Hon Prog; Opt A; Run-Up, Best Al Around; Schol; Bio C; 1st, Earth & Sci IV Fair; Pep C; Brown Achv Schol; NJHS; KLRA Yth Ldrship Salute; *U of Ark For Med Sci; Nurs.*

SIMPSON, Steven Riley
Spruce Creek HS; Port Orange, FL (20%-749) F-Ed, Ann; Key C; Rptr, Sch P; Ftbl; Soccer; Cartoonist, Sch P; Beach Lifeguard; *U of Fla; Bio.*

SIMPSON, Suzanne Ruth
Paducah Tilghman HS; Paducah, KY (1-375) Band; Fr C; *Okla Christian Col; Phar.*

SIMPSON, Tammi Lynn
Gainesville HS; Gainesville, GA (33%-200) Chor; Drama; FNA; 4H; Lit Mag; ARC; Sal; *Hall Sch of Nurs; Nurs.*

SIMPSON, Thomas Edwin
Briarwood Acad; Thomson, GA (6-23) Band; Chess C; Drama; Ensm; Hmrm; Key C; Lit Ral; NHS; Orch; Order/Arrow; SC; Var C; Bkbl; Ftbl; Tr; COM; Citz A; Hon Prog; Order/Arrow A; Sci A; FCA; Eagle Sct; Friendship A; *US Military Acad; Pol Sci.*

SIMPSON, Timothy Douglas
Southport HS; Indianapolis, IN (23-501) Pres, Ger C; NHS; Tnns; Alg A; Math A; Type A; Yth Fel; *UCLA; Engr.*

SIMPSON, Tracy Marie
N Beach HS; Moclips, WA (50-60) Band; JV, Chldr; Chor; HCt; Fin, Miss SOS; *DeWitt Beauty Sch; Beauty Culture.*

SIMPSON, Wilfred Willie
Judge Mem Cath HS; Salt Lake City, UT (121-163) Dbte Tm; Bkbl; Tr; Citz A; JA A; Kiwanis A; Most Out; *U of Utah.*

SIMS, Boyce Griffin
Westminster HS; Atlanta, GA (59-100) Chor; Pres, InterAct C; Rptr, Sch P; Bsbl; Ftbl; Rotary A; Co-Cpt & MVP, Soccer; Pres, Charles Wesley Yth Choir; All-St Soccer Tms; *James Madison U.*

SIMS, Brittetta
Susan Miller Dorsey HS; Los Angeles, CA; *Bus.*

SIMS, Brittoris
Susan Miller Dorsey HS; Los Angeles, CA; Chor; Hmrm; Bank Of Amer A; Citz A; Hon Prog; *Childhood Aide.*

SIMS, Cathy Sue
Ainsworth HS; Flint, MI (36-291) Band; Chor; Ensm; Orch; Cpt, Bkbl; JV, Sftbl; JV, Tnns; JV, Tr.

SIMS, Charles Rodney
Columbus E HS; Columbus, OH; Chem C; Bsbl; Golf; Wrest; WW; FCA; *Ohio St; Bus Mgt.*

SIMS, David Anthony
St Martin HS; Biloxi, MS (1-186) Rptr, Sch P; Val; VFW A; Most Dependable; *Jackson Co Jr Col.*

SIMS, Deborah Elaine
N Cobb HS; Acworth, GA; *Queens Bus Col; Bus.*

SIMS, Dora Lee
Hiram W Johnson HS; Sacramento, CA (318-653) Chldr; *American River Col; Acct.*

SIMS, James Allen
Yough Sr HS; Hermine, PA; BS; CYO; Chor; Co-Ed, Sch P; Sci C.

SIMS, Joel Nathan
Edgewood HS; Edgewood, TX (18-39) Band; FFA; Span C; Cl Fav; WW; WW, Band; WW, DECA; Good Guy Band A.

SIMS, John Collins Jr
Hall HS; Little Rock, AR (35-432) A Cap Choir; Band; BC; Fr C; VP, Math C; NHS; VP, Sr Cl; Cr-Ctry; Tnns; Golf; Cl Fav; H of F; MLS; WW; *Baylor U; Math.*

SIMS, Karl Anthony
Gates Co HS; Gatesville, NC (21-137) BC; Chor; Fr C; Sci C; Pres, SC; DARGCA; SC A; Best All Around Boy A; Chor A; *Lenoir-Rhyne Col; Sci.*

SIMS, Lori Lee
Scott Comm HS; Scott City, KS (1-125) Band; Ensm; ARC; SC; Var C; Golf; Lion A; Yth Fel; Yth Rep, Church Adm Board; Off, MYF; *Bible.*

SIMS, Marcia Jane
Reading Mem HS; Reading, MA; Chor; Drama; Rainbow; Tr; HR; *Katharine Gibbs Col; Bus.*

SIMS, Martha Susan
Jones Co HS; Gray, GA; Ed, Ann; VP, BC; Fr C; COM; Gov Honor Prog; HCt; NEDT; *Macon Jr Col; Acct.*

SIMS, Marva Dean
Sunnyvale HS; Sunnyvale, CA; De Anza Col; Phys Therapist.

SIMS, Mary Christina
Waldwick Jr Sr HS; Waldwick, NJ (20%-256) AFS; Band; Chor; COM; N Jersey JR H Chorus; Bergen Co Chorus; Child Care.

SIMS, Mary Nelle
Smiths Station HS; Smiths, AL (11-147) Parl, BC; FHA; SC; VP, Jr Cl; Most Out; WW; Spelman Col; Econ.

SIMS, Melanie A
E Rowan HS; Salisbury, NC (46-230) Ann; Band; Hmrm; Mjrte; Monogram; Span C; Tnns; Pres, Church Jr League; Church Coun; Pastoral Nom Committee; NC St U; Park Adm.

SIMS, Michele Renee
Holly Grove HS; Holly Grove, AR (1-80) VP, BC; Bus C; Chldr; Chor; VP, FHA; 4H; Co-Ed, Sch P; Tres, SC; COM; Citz A; Cl Fav; 4H A; HCt; JA A; Phy A; Q&S A; Swtht; Type A; Val; Ark St U; Law.

SIMS, Monica
Thomasville HS; Thomasville, AL; BC; Co-Cpt, Chldr; Chem C; FHA; Ch, Hmrm; Sftbl; Swim; Auburn U; Phar.

SIMS, Penny M
Cross Key S HS; Atlanta, GA; Chldr; Chor; Fr C; Rptr, Sch P; SC; Belhaven Col; Sociology.

SIMS, Peter Morris
Mountain Brook HS; Birmingham, AL (69-365) Band; Community Yth Symph; VP, Fr C; InterAct C; Orch; SC; All St Band; Wittiest; 5th in St, Ntl Fr Exam; Med Win, Solo & Ensm Band Comp; Spartan Crest Hons A; Samford U; Nurs.

SIMS, Rita Louise
Gladewater HS; Gladewater, TX (11-125) Band; FHA; NHS; Spch C; COM; Spch A; Kilgore Jr Col; Elem Ed.

SIMS, Stefanie Shea
Tyner HS; Chattanooga, TN; A Cap Choir; BC; Chor; FHA; Hmrm; Lat C; Pres, Y-Tns; Hon Stu; Belmont Col; Eng Ed.

SIMS, Tamara Anita
Oregon-Howell R-3 HS; Koshkonong, MO (3-20) Ed, Ann; Arch; FHA; Lit Mag; Rptr, Sch P; Arch; Cpt, Bkbl; Sftbl; COM; Cl Fav; HCt; Journ A; Type A; Shorthand Merit; Miss KHS; Most Ath; SMSU at Res Center; Bus.

SIMS, Walter Lee
E Kemper HS; Scooba, MS (3-24) Math C; Pres, Sr Cl; Hon Prog; MLS; Jackson St U; Math.

SIMS, Wanda Vivian
Grand Ridge HS; Grand Ridge, FL (9-68) Chldr; Sci C; Sftbl; Chldr As; Sftbl Trophy; Vlbl As; Bkbl Cert; Chipola Jr Col; Special Ed.

SIMS, William Henry
Howe HS; Howe, OK (5-17) SC; Bsbl; Bkbl; MLS; Eastern U; Ed.

SINATRA, Melody H
Elmira HS; Elmira, OR (9-147) Co-Ed, Ann; NHS; Rptr, Sch P; SC; Co-Cpt, Bkbl; Tr; Hon Prog; Vlbl; MVP, Bkbl; Span A; Outst Player; OSU; Dental Hygiene.

SINCLAIR, Charles Albert
Watson Chapel HS; Pine Bluff, AR (13-306) Key C; JV, Ftbl; Cpt, Tr; COM; U of Ark; Bus Mgt.

SINCLAIR, Deborah Gay
Plano Sr HS; Plano, TX (50%-1150) Fr C; FHA; Art Cl Merit A; Tex Tech Col; Commercial Art.

SINCOX, Eddie Charles
Haynesville HS; Haynesville, LA (6-83) Dbte Tm; FFA; Fin, Lit Ral; Tres, Soph Cl; Bkbl; Ftbl; Tnns; Tr; La Tech U; Petroleum Engr.

SINDLINGER, Cindy Elaine
Dallastown Area HS; Dallastown, PA (10-400) AFS; Band; Cpt, Chldr; ARC; Tnns; Amer Leg A; Hon Prog; Val; Yth Fel; Pres, Yth Fel; Sch Ltr & Pin; Sunday Sch Teacher & Pianist; Colorguard; U of Md; Nurs.

SINDORF, Robin Elaine
Llano HS; Llano, TX (15-77) Chldr; Chor; FHA; FTA; SC; Var C; JV, Bkbl; Tr; HCt; Pres A; Swtht; Pres, Pep C; Dist Ldrship, VICA; Fin, Ntl Co-Ed Magazine Cover Girl; Nom, Homecoming 4 Yr's; Valentine Swtht; Bauder Fashion Col; Fashion Merchandizing.

SINER, Pamela Rose
W Vigo HS; W Terre Haute, IN (4-187) A Cap Choir; Chor; VP, FTA; Semi-Fin, GS; NHS; Secy, SC; Secy, Sr Cl; Secy, Jr Cl; DARGCA; HCt; Opt Out Tn; Sal; Type A; Grand Rapids Sch o-t Bible & Mus.

SINES, Cathy Lynn
Flemington HS; Flemington, WV (1-43) Band; Drama; Ensm; Secy, Fr C; Parl, FHA; Rptr, FTA; Pres, 4H; Orch; Sch P; Bio A; 4H A; Hist A; Worthy Adv, Rainbow Girls; Golden Horseshoe A; Alderson Broaddus Col.

SINES, Steve Mitchell
Park Center Sr HS; Brooklyn Park, MN (10%-607) A Cap Choir; Chor; Dbte Tm; Drama; Hmrm; NFL; Spch C; SC; Ftbl; Tr; Drew U; Law.

SINGER, Kendra Nicole
Edmond Mem HS; Edmond, OK (25%-601) Band; Chor; Drama; Ensm; FBLA; NHS; Thes; Spch A; Yth For Understanding; Foreign Exchange Stu; Biol.

SINGH, Surinder
Imperial HS; Imperial, CA (2-90) Ann; Band; Chldr; 4H; SC; Pres, Sr Cl; Pres, Jr Cl; Alg A; Bank Of Amer A; CSF; HCt; Math A; Most Out; PTA A; Sal; Imperial Valley Col; Bus.

SINGLETARY, Elise Renee
Starkville HS; Starkville, MS (14-250) F-Ed, Ann; Band; Rptr, Chem C; Community Yth Symph; Fin, Jr Miss Pagent; Lat C; Cpt, Mjrte; NHS; Y-Tns; Bkbl; Bio A; Kiwanis A; Miss St U; Elec Engr.

SINGLETARY, Linda Jane
McMinnville HS; McMinnville, OR (10%-200) A Cap Choir; Band; Drama; Ensm; Key C; NHS; Thes; WW, Mus; U of Oreg; Mus Ed.

SINGLETARY, Patricia Ann
Permian HS; Odessa, TX (295-668) Band; Bus C; COM; Odessa Jr Col; Ed.

SINGLETARY, Randall Craig
Hononegah Comm HS; Rockton, IL (24-288) Arch; Drama; Ntl Yth Conf; Tr.

SINGLETARY, Robyn Paulette
Forest Hills HS; Forest Hills, NY (500-1500) Chor; Pres, Hmrm; SC; COM; Hon Prog; Math.

SINGLETON, Ann Elizabeth
Hoopeston-East Lynn HS; Hoopeston, IL (7-130) Ann; Band; Chor; Ensm; VP, FTA; NHS; Sci C; Span C; Pres, SC; Thes; VP, Soph Cl; Amer Leg A; Sci A; Purdue U; Communications.

SINGLETON, Catherine Lynne
Harlem HS; Harlem, GA (5-160) BC; Hmrm; Tres, Math C; SC; Bio A; COM; HCt; Sci A; Anatomy & Physiology A; Cert of Achv; Med Col of Ga; Nurs.

SINGLETON, David Lee
Harlem HS; Harlem, GA (2-140) VP, Chess C; Math C; Parl, SC; Tnns; Bausch & Lomb A; Bio A; COM; Hist A; Phy A; Sci A; Anatomy & Physiology A; Eng A; Young Harris Col; Vet.

SINGLETON, Donald Earl
David Starr Jordan HS; Los Angeles, CA (25%-320) Chess C; U of Sou Calif; Math.

SINGLETON, John Scott
Stevenson HS; Stevenson, AL (2-63) F-Ed, Ann; Band; BC; Chor; Ch, Order/Arrow; Sftbl; God & Country A; Order/Arrow A; Eagle Sct; Auburn U; Textiles.

SINGLETON, Kerwin Christopher
St Louis Ctry Day Sch; St Louis, MO (40%-52) Chor; Dbte Tm; Drama; Mgr, Soccer; JV, Tnns; JV, Tr; Lacrosse; Livingston Col Mus A; Chem.

SINGLETON, Pamela Eileen
Madison HS; Richmond, KY; Ann; BC; Chor; Ensm; Fr C; SC; Tres, Jr Cl; Bio A; COM; Journ A; Opt A; Fr A; Eng A; Miss Vocal Mus.

SINGLETON, Rickie Bernard
Cairo HS; Cairo, GA (20-250) 4H; Bkbl; JV, Ftbl; Tr; Hon Prog; MLS; Most Out; Sci A; Yth Fel; Tres, Jr Mission; Yth o-t Yr A; Church Choir; Pres, Usher Board; HR; U of Ga; Pschiatry.

SINGLETON, Roy Dale
El Dorado HS; El Dorado, AR; H of F; Babe Ruth Bsbl; Church Bkbl; All Star Bkbl; La Tech U; Acct.

SINGLETON, Sharon Ruth
John F Kennedy HS; New Orleans, LA; BC; HiY; Tnns; SE La U; Communication.

SINGLETON, Timothy Ray
S Lake HS; St Clair Shores, MI (20%-600) Tr; Bethel Col.

SINGLETON, William Quentin
St Louis Ctry Day Sch; St Louis, MO (29-51) Band; Secy, Chor; Dbte Tm; Drama; Model UN; A-Ed, Sch P; Thes; Bsbl; Mgr, Ftbl; Mgr, Soccer; COM; Curriculum Committee; Co-Cpt, Lacrosse; BSct; WW; U of Mo; Bus.

SINGLEY, Kathleen Ann
Valencia HS; Placentia, CA (65-355) Chor; Cpt, Bkbl; Sftbl; Swim; Co- cpt, MVP, Vlbl; Ed.

SINISI, Daniel Theodore
Pennsbury HS; Fairless Hills, PA (90-1030) Chor; Dbte Tm; Hmrm; JETS; NFL; ARC; Co-Ed, Sch P; Co-Ch, SC; Golf; Hockey; Tnns; COM; Citz A; Hon Prog; Lion A; Math A; ARC A; Sci A; Spch A; Yth Fel; NFL A; Drexel U; Elec Engr.

SINK, Amanda Leigh
Thomasville Sr HS; Thomasville, NC (1-250) Band; Dbte Tm; Ensm; NFL; Pres, NHS; Var C; Bkbl; Tnns; Gr Marshal; Spch A; Band A; Gov's Sch Nom; U of NC at Chapel Hill; Pol Sci.

SINK, Kelley Jo
Lexington Sr HS; Lexington, NC; Chor; Community Yth Symph; Drama; Span C; SC; Mgr, Tnns; Mgr, Wrest; HCt; Yth Fel; Yth Coun; Tres, Travel C; Senator; Photography.

SINK, Patti Ann
Penns Manor Jr-Sr HS; Clymer, PA (3-106) A Cap Choir; Bus Mgr, Ann; Band; Chor; Ensm; FTA; Cpt, Mjrte; NHS; Rptr, Sch P; NEDT; Ind U of Pa; Nurs.

SINK, Ralph Merritt
Cedar Shoals HS; Athens, GA (30-300) Band; BC; Chor; Fr C; Hmrm; Sci C; U of Ga; Chem.

SINKOVEC, Audrey Lynn
Yough Senior HS; Herminie, PA (15-293) Ann; NHS; Hon Prog; Type A; Shorthand A.

SINLEY, Christine Louise
Manchester HS; Akron, OH; Co-Cpt, Bkbl; Sftbl; MVP, Bkbl; Akron U; Phys Ed.

SINN, Leslye Marie
Albemarle HS; Charlottesville, VA (10%-750) Drama; Rptr, 4H; Hmrm; NHS; Pol Sci C; Sci C; Span C; Span NHS; Thes; COM; Gov Honor Prog; 4H A; Hon Prog; I Dare You; Math A; NEDT; Sci A; Spch A; Hon Thespian; 4-H All Star; Wellesley Col; Sci.

SINQUEFIELD, Gary Keith
Columbus HS; Columbus, GA; Golf; U of Ala; Med.

SINZ, Eduardo J
Amer Military Acad; Guaynabo, PR (5-30) Band; Math C; VP, Sr Cl; Tres, Jr Cl; Cr-Ctry; Tr; Alg A; Hon Prog; Math A; Phy A; MIT; Engr.

SIPE, David Michael
Goldendale HS; Goldendale, WA (4-97) NHS; Var C; Co-Cpt, Ftbl; Tr; Cpt, Wrest; HCt; Most Out; St Champ, Wrest; 3rd Sch, Ntl Math Test; Stanford U; Bio Sci.

SIPIORSKI, Connie Rae
Clintonville Sr HS; Clintonville, WI (1-200) Secy, AFS; Ed, Ann; Band; CYO; Cpt, Dbte Tm; Drama; Ensm; Fr C; SC; Mjrte; Monogram; NHS; Thes; JV, Bkbl; Sftbl; Hon Prog; Spch A; GSct; Gym.

SIPOS, Marybeth
El Camino Real HS; Woodland Hills, CA; GS; Ch, Hmrm; Model UN; Co-Ed, Sch P; Ch, Jr Cl; Ch, Soph Cl; CSF; Hist A; Hon Prog; Opt A; Yth Leg; Nom, Hugh O'Brien Ldrship Found; Producer, Television News Show; Ntl Coun of Tea; UCLA Hon Prog; Am As of Tchrs of Fr Cont 1st Pl; Princeton U; Fr.

SIPPEL, Kevin Jon
Brookings HS; Brookings, SD (3-215) A Cap Choir; Pres, Band; BS; Drama; Secy, Ensm; Madrigal; NHS; Orch; Pres, Sci C; SC; Elk A; *SD St U; Mus.*

SIRAY, Barbara Ruth
Noble Central HS; Nobleford, CANADA (4-28) Chldr; Chor; Fr C; VP, Ski C; Cr-Ctry; Tnns; Tr; Co Cpt, Vlbl; Acad A; Tr-Field A; Best Salesman A; *Col of Idaho; Bio Sci.*

SIRES, Clare Rebecca
Shaker Heights HS; Shaker Heights, OH (33%-500) A Cap Choir; *Ohio St U; Bus Adm.*

SIRES, Teresa Ann
Central HS; Pageland, SC; All Amer Yth; Ann; Band; BC; Chor; Drama; Secy, 4H; Hmrm; Spch C; SC; Bkbl; Tr; Deca Display A; WW; Beta Cert; *U of SC; Computer Sci.*

SIRMANS, Stephanie Joyce
Queen City HS; Queen City, TX (10%-41) Ann; Pres, Band; Ensm; VP, FHA; NHS; Sci C; Secy, Soph Cl; WAA Rainbow Girls; Drum Major 028000; Band Medals; Band Outst Service A; *Texarkana Comm Col.*

SIROCKI, Steve Jeffery
G A R Mem HS; Wilkes-Barre, PA (17-200) NHS; Ftbl; JV, Tr; *Wilkes Col; Chem.*

SIRYJ, Stephan Jaroslaw
St Peters Prep Sch; Jersey City, NJ (4-252) Band; Ensm; Lit Mag; Soccer; Tr; COM; Citz A; Hon Prog; NEDT; Summa Cum Laude; Val; Ger A; Lat A; *US Military Acad; Engr.*

SISEMORE, Leigh Anna
Girls' Prep Sch; Chattanooga, TN (10%-90) Drama; Fr C; Span C; Tnns; Chem A; Hist A; Math A; Sci A; Star Student; Fr A; *Med Research.*

SISEMORE, Russell Dane
Kress HS; Kress, TX (1-31) Ann; FTA; Bkbl; Cpt, Ftbl; Tr; Citz A; Lion A; Math A; Most Out; Val; Industrial Arts A; Govt Civics A; Mr KHS; FHA Swtht of Yr; *W Tex St U; Industrial Tech.*

SISK, Catherine Esther Louise
Eastwood HS; El Paso, TX (700-900) Fr C; Pres, 4H; ARC; SC; Citz A; 4H A; ARC A; ROTC A; Yth Fel; *Sul Ross St U; Eng.*

SISK, Deborah Denise
Breckinridge Co HS; Harned, KY; Secy, Band; 4H; Cpt, Mjrte; Tres, Soci C; *Owensboro Bus Col; Secy.*

SISK, Martha Ann
Franklin Co HS; Winchester, TN; BC; CYO; Chor; Fr C; Hist A; Type A; *U of Tenn; Law.*

SISK, Robert Glen
Union Co HS; Morgonfield, KY (4-275) Chor; Co-Cpt, Dbte Tm; Drama; Fr C; 4H; NFL; Spch C; Hon Prog; Spch A; Outst Stu; Most Talented; Soph Cl Officer.

SISK, Tim Wade
Oil Trough HS; Oil Trough, AR (3-25) Ann; VP, FFA; Pres, FTA; Secy, 4H; NHS; SC; Cpt, Bkbl; Tr; Citz A; 4H A; HCt; I Dare You; Lion A; MLS; Spch A; Type A; Ath A; FFA Pub Speaking; Offense & Sportsmanship A'S, Bkbl; *U of Central Ark; Med.*

SISK, Vicki Lynne
Scottsboro HS; Scottsboro, AL; Anchor C; FTA; Jr Miss Pagent; Sci C; DARGCA; *U of N Ala; Nurs.*

SISK, William Mark
Scottsboro HS; Scottsboro, AL (10%-245) Secy, FFA; Mu Alpha Theta; NHS; Span C; SC; St Semi-Fin, FFA Speaking Contest; Sup Rating, Solo & Ensm; Hon Men, Sci Fair; Star Greenhand; *Archt.*

SISSOM, Sherry Sue
Crockett HS; Crockett, TX (2-120) FBLA; NHS; Alg A; Hist A; Geom A.

SISSOM, Stacey Ellen
Southland HS; Arbyrd, MO (8-38) Chldr; FHA; FTA; Rptr, SC; Bio A; HCt; *Fashion.*

SISSON, Charles Augustus
Amory HS; Amory, MS (10-175) Bsbl; Tr; *Ole Miss; Bus.*

SISSON, Thomas Fielding
Mansfield HS; Mansfield, LA (23-99) BS; Tres, FBLA; Hmrm; Secy, Order/Arrow; VP, SC; Bkbl; Co-Cpt, Ftbl; Cl Fav; Most Friendly; *La St U; Engr.*

SISTARE, Joyce Kay
Cherryville Sr HS; Cherryville, NC (18-147) FBLA; FHA; *Gaston Col; Acct.*

SISTI, Rosemarie Christine
Manasquan HS; Manasquan, NJ (5-371) Ann; CYO; Secy, FNA; FTA; Hmrm; Pres, NHS; Span C; SC; Hon Prog; Kiwanis A; MLS; Bowl; Kiwanis Stu o-t Mo; Keyettes; Board of Ed A; Drum Mjrte; Cl Schol; *Seton Hall U; Nurs.*

SITGRAVES, April Michelle
The Frankliw Sch; New York, NY (3-21) Ger C; Pres, Hmrm; NHS; Secy, SC; Tr; Hon Prog; Sci A; Tr A; *Med.*

SITTERSON, Susan Byrd
Roanoke HS; Robersonville, NC (5-160) A Cap Choir; Co-Ed, Ann; Band; Secy, BC; Chem C; Fr C; FHA; InterClub Coun; Cpt, Mjrte; Math C; Phys C; Sci C; Secy, SC; Pres, Sr Cl; Secy, Soph Cl; Bio A; HCt; Most Out; Sci A; Band A's; *U of NC; Phar.*

SITTON, Janet Elaine
Dalton HS; Dalton, GA (16-325) Band; NHS; Span C; Tri-HiY; Swim; Hon Prog; NEDT; Pep C; Yth Coun; Co-Ch, Mission Action Committee; Church Singing Group; F-Ed, Church Newspaper.

SITTON, Larry Kyle
Layton HS; Layton, UT; Band; Chor; Ensm; Arch; Tr; COM; Citz A; Pres PE A; Ltrman Tr.

SITTON, Louise Irene
Northside HS; Fort Worth, TX (2-180) Band; Chor; NHS; Orch; SC; Bausch & Lomb A; HCt; Math A; PTA A; Sal; *Tex Wesleyan Col; Mus Ed.*

SITZ, Joan Elizabeth
Marked Tree HS; Marked Tree, AR (1-110) A Cap Choir; Band; BC; Secy, Chor; FHA; Mjrte; Thes; Bkbl; HCt; Hon Prog; Type A; Art A; *U of Ark.*

SIVERTSEN, LeAnn Rae
Miller HS; Miller, SD (30-88) Ann; Chldr; Chor; Madrigal; Sftbl; 4H A; St Pres, FHA; *Ntl Col of Bus; Bus.*

SIX, Jamie Lynn
Butler HS; Butler, MO (6-90) Band; Chldr; Fr C; Secy, FBLA; NHS; WW; 4th Pl Shorthand, St FBLA; *Central Mo St U; Secy.*

SIZEMORE, David Russell
Crawford Co R II HS; Cuba, MO (1-115) Band; Chess C; Chor; Demolay; Ensm; Parl, 4H; NHS; Var C; Bsbl; JV, Bkbl; JV, Tnns; HCt; Opt A; Opt Out Tn; Pres, Pioneers; Co-Star, Mus; Church Yth Choir & Yth Coun; Comm Choir; PA.

SIZEMORE, Gregory Kent
Laurel Co HS; London, KY (12-360) Band; BC; Tres, Drama; Hmrm; Key C; Sci C; Tres, Spch C; Ftbl; Tr; *U of Ky.*

SIZEMORE, Melanie Sue
Paisley HS; Winston-Salem, NC (50-350) Band; 4H; 4H A; Mus; Piedmont Princess Mus; Win, Brevard Mus Center; Win, Northwest Dist 4-H Talent.

SIZEMORE, Sherry Kay
Pass Christian HS; Pass Christian, MS (25%-110) Cpt, Band; BC; Pres, Hmrm; Fin, Jr Miss Pagent; SC; Tnns; Alg A; Beauty; HCt; Math A; Phys Ed A; *Pensacola Jr Col; Computor Sci.*

SIZEMORE, Velda Regina
Harrison Chilowee Baptist Acad; Seymour, TN (8-48) Chor; Madrigal; *Georgetown U; Med.*

SJOGREN, Loriann
Verona HS; Verona, NJ (90-250).

SJOGREN, Wade Richard
Verona HS; Verona, NJ (100-265) CYO; Hmrm; Ski C; Span C; Var C; Ftbl; Swim; Tr; *Acct.*

SJOLIE, John Martin
Montevideo Sr HS; Montevideo, MN (20-193) Band; Dbte Tm; Drama; Ger C; 4H; Orch; Co-Ed, Sch P; Spch C; Swim; Hon Prog; Journ A; Spch A; BSct; Swim A; Newspaper A's; *St Olaf Col; Bio.*

SJOLIE, Sarah Elaine
Montevideo HS; Montevideo, MN; Band; Chor; Drama; Ensm; FHA; Madrigal; Orch; *St Olaf Col; Eng.*

SKAANNING, Jodi Elizabeth
Foxboro HS; Foxborough, MA (40-275) A Cap Choir; Sch P; SC; Tnns; *Framingham St Col; Home Ec.*

SKAAR, Alfred Arnold
Bible Baptist HS; Savannah, GA (25%-54) Band; 4H; Rptr, Sch P; Hon Prog.

SKAAR, Kris Kelly
Bible Baptist HS; Savannah, GA (2-39) Band; Chess C; Demolay; Fr A; *Ed.*

SKABLA, Diana Lynn
Hayward Jr HS; Springfield, OH (10-196) Co-Ch, Hmrm; NHS; SC; Jr HS School; Ohio Test of Schol Achv; *Clark Tech Col; Horticulture.*

SKAGGS, Cynthia Lou
Lee-Davis HS; Mechanicsville, VA (2-450) Pres, BC; Co-Cpt, Chldr; Pres, Chor; Hmrm; NHS; Span C; SC; Tr; HCt; Sal; *Col of William And Mary; Span.*

SKAGGS, Dixie Lee
E Prairie HS; E Prairie, MO (25-117) Band; Chor; Ensm; FBLA; FHA; Madrigal; NHS; Rptr, Sch P; Type A; Band, Choir As; *SE Mo St U; Nurs.*

SKAGGS, Esther Elaine
Greenwood HS; Greenwood, AR (10-121) A Cap Choir; Ed, Ann; Secy, BC; Pres, Chor; Cpt, Ensm; Secy, Fr C; GS; 4H; Sch P; Secy, Sr Cl; Secy, Jr Cl; H of F; Cpt, Chor; Most Talented A; Choir A; Secy, Pep C; Yrbk A; Home Ec A; Pres & VP, FHA; Girl o-t Yr A; Best All Around A; *West Ark Comm Col; Bus.*

SKAGGS, John Milton
Lee-Davis HS; Mechanicsville, VA (50-600) A-Ed, Ann; Chess C; A-Ed, Lit Mag; A-Ed, Sch P; Span C; Hist A; Journ A; Pres A; Sci A; *VPI; Sci.*

SKAGGS, Kimberly Jane
Howland HS; Warren, OH (112-560) InterAct C; COM; Word of Life C; Off Aide; *Youngstown St U; Lab Tech.*

SKAGGS, Linda Sue
Springfield HS; Springfield, IL (42-487) A Cap Choir; Fr C; Ger C; NHS; COM; St Scholar; WW; *Ill Wesleyan U.*

SKAGGS, Mary Alesia
Greenwood HS; Greenwood, AR (14-200) A Cap Choir; Ann; BC; Chor; VP, FHA; Sch P; Tnns; COM; HCt; Choir A; *Art.*

SKAGGS, Randall Darell
Lone Grove HS; Lone Grove, OK (3-42) SC; Pres, Sr Cl; Pres, Jr Cl; Bsbl; Bkbl; Tnns; Cl Fav; Hist A; Most Out; Sal; Eng A; Acad Achv A; *Elec.*

SKAGGS, Samuel Russell
Pojoaque HS; Pojoaque, NM (23-96) BS; FFA; Math A; Sci A; Ntl Ski Patrol; *NM St U; Engr.*

SKAGGS, Steven Jeffrey
Highland HS; Pocatello, ID (1-550) NHS; Var C; Golf; Hon Prog; Yth Fel; Eagle Sct; *Acct.*

SKAGGS, Teresa Lynn
N Co Sr HS; Desloge, MO (23-180) Band; Secy, NHS; Sch P; Span C; Tnns; Tnns School; *SE Mo U; Med Tech.*

SKAGGS, Terry Lynn
Lyon Co HS; Eddyville, KY (05-70) Ann; VP, Band; Ch, BC; Chor; Ensm; Orch; F-Ed, Sch P; Bsbl; Most Out; Outst, Mus; Top 12; Most Talented; *Murray St U; Acct.*

SKAPURA, Cynthia Ann
Meadowbrook HS; Byesville, OH (6-160) Band; Chor; VP, Math C; NHS; Sch P; Pres, Span C; Amer Leg A; Cl Fav; Hon Prog; Most Out; Type A; John P Sousa A; *Ohio St U; Computer Math.*

SKARE, Pamela Jane
Park Center Sr HS; Brooklyn Park, MN (71-501) Fr C; Orch; Hon Prog; Vlbl; Statistician, Bkbl; *Luther Col; Nurs.*

SKARPHOL, Randy Allen
Souris Pub HS; Souris, ND (4-11) Ann; Band; BS; Chor; SC; Bsbl; Bkbl; Tr; Math A; Drama A; Eagle Sct A; *U of ND; Bus.*

SKARR, Paul Joseph
Oak Park River Forest HS; Oak Park, IL (25%-1015) Pres, Madrigal; Orch; Bsbl; Golf; Swim; Tnns; Tr; COM; Cl Fav; JA A; Outst Bkbl Shooting Trophy A; *Acct.*

SKEEN, Kimberly Ray
Chilhowie HS; Chilhowie, VA; FHA; *Tenn Temple Col; Child Evangelism.*

SKEEN, Tara April
Model HS; Rome, GA (10%-180) Chldr; Pres, FBLA; 4H; NHS; Var C; Bkbl; Sftbl; Tnns; 4H A; Type A; FCA; Lit A; *Shorter Col; Mus.*

SKELLY, Mitchell James
Oak Lawn Comm HS; Oak Lawn, IL (7-850) Band; Order/Arrow; COM; Order/Arrow A; Yth Fel; Outst, Band; Top Olympian, Dist Spring Olympics; *The Sorbonne; Fr Lang & Culture.*

SKELTON, Alice Marie
Washington HS; Greenville, MS (11-100) BC; Lat C; Bkbl; Hist A; *U of Miss; Pol Sci.*

SKELTON, Kelly Jean
Middleton HS; Middleton, ID (2-90) Ed, Ann; Pres, Band; Drama; S-T, NHS; F-Ed, Sch P; Secy, Jr Cl; Secy, Soph Cl; Bkbl; MVP, Cr-Ctry; Hockey; Tr; Alg A; DARGCA; Spch A; Type A; *Columbia Christian Col; Eng.*

SKIDMORE, Kimberly Ann
Jordan Voc HS; Columbus, GA (20%-250) Fr C; Hmrm; SC; *Columbus Col; Elem Ed.*

SKIDMORE, Letitia Ellen
Mount Tahoma HS; Tacoma, WA (42-383) Chor; Ger C; NHS; Var C; Sftbl; Tr; *Calif Baptist Col; Mus.*

SKIDMORE, Samuel Allan
Peebles HS; Peebles, OH (8-109) Band; Sci C; Co-Cpt, Ftbl; COM; *U of Cincinnati; Nuclear Engr.*

SKILES, Gaye LeAna
Dexter HS; Dexter, KS (2-19) Band; Chldr; Chor; Ensm; Secy, FHA; VP, 4H; NHS; Secy, SC; Bkbl; Alg A; COM; Cl Fav; 4H A; Hist A; JA A; Math A; Type A; Vlbl; Secy, Pep C; *SW Col; Bus.*

SKILES, Mark Anthony
Dexter HS; Dexter, KS (3-13) Pres, 4H; NHS; Pres, SC; Bsbl; Bkbl; Ftbl; Alg A; 4H A; HCt; Type A; *Coffeyville Jr Col; Agr.*

SKINKLE, Linda Ann
Mercy HS; Albany, NY (4-108) F-Ed, Ann; Drama; Ski C; Tr; COM; NEDT; Regent Schol; WW; *Architecture.*

SKINNER, Becky Lynn
Gilmer HS; Gilmer, TX (10-140) Band; FTA; Math C; NHS; Secy, Sci C; Span C; *Tyler Jr Col; Med Lab Tech.*

SKINNER, Clyde Jerome
Lakeshore HS; College Park, GA; Band; BC; Chor; Fr C; Hmrm.

SKINNER, Cynthia Sue
Boardman HS; Youngstown, OH (5-14) A Cap Choir; Chor; Ensm; NHS; Pres, Span C; Foreign Lang Declam Contest A's; *E Tex Baptist Col; Bus.*

SKINNER, David Benson
Aiken HS; Aiken, SC (44-640) S-T, Band; Demolay; Hmrm; Mu Alpha Theta; NHS; Order/Arrow; Sch P; COM; H of F; Opt A; All St Band; AAUW Mus A; *U of SC; Computer Sci.*

SKINNER, Dorothy Marie
Wellsboro Area Sr HS; Wellsboro, PA (10%-500) Drama; Ger C; NHS; Ski C; SC; Tr; Hon Prog; Vlbl; Adv Math A; Ntl HS A for Excellence; *Purdue U; Phar.*

SKINNER, Kimberly Ann
Northeast HS; Oakland Park, FL; Chldr; Chor; Hmrm; Lit Mag; SC; Tres, Pep C; Juniorettes; Hurricane Court; *Phys Therapy.*

SKINNER, Linda
Immanuel HS; Reedley, CA (4-83) CSF; COM; Jr Festival.

SKINNER, Patricia Mary
Forest Ridge Sch; Bellevue, WA; CYO; Fr C; Pres, French NHS; NHS; Ski C; SC; Swim; Bio A; Citz A; Hist A; Hon Prog; Phy A; Eng A; Service A; Christian Ldrship A; Religion A; *U of Wash; Law.*

SKINNER, Sherrie Lynn
Ponder Isd HS; Ponder, TX (3-14) Bus Mgr; Ann; VP, FHA; VP, SC; Co-Cpt, Bkbl; Sftbl; Tr; Alg A; Type A; PA; Phys Sci A; *Cooke Co Col; Bus.*

SKINNER, Valerie Jurae
Christian HS; El Cajon, CA; Band; Drill Tm; *Sou Calif Col; Psych.*

SKIPPER, Debra LaVern
Clarksdale HS; Clarksdale, MS (4-32) Band; Chldr; FHA; SC; Citz A; Hist A; Hon Prog; Math A; Band A; HR; Chldr A; *Memphis St U; Archeologist.*

SKIPPER, Lawton Lamar
Sarasota HS; Sarasota, FL (140-615) InterAct C; *Harding Col; Sci.*

SKJOITEN, David Paul
Hatton HS; Hatton, ND (5-31) A-Ed, Ann; Band; BS; Chor; Ensm; 4H; VP, SC; Tres, Jr Cl; Tres, Soph Cl; Bsbl; Ftbl; Co-Cpt, Wrest; COM; 4H A; I Dare You; *ND St U; Home Ec.*

SKJOITEN, Karen Louise
Hatton Pub Sch; Hatton, ND (8-20) A Cap Choir; Chldr; Chor; Drama; Pres, FHA; GS; VP, Hmrm; SC; Bkbl; Tr; FHA' ER o-t Yr; *NDSU; Home Ec.*

SKLENAR, Beth Ann
Lakewood HS; St Petersburg, FL; NHS; Rainbow; Var C; Sftbl; Tr; Yth Fel; GAA; Cpt, Vlbl; *Stetson U; Recreation.*

SKLENAR, Paula Lynn
Lakewood Sr HS; St Petersburg, FL (25%-550) Secy, Rainbow; Sftbl; Tr; GAA; Excellence A.

SKLENICKA, Jeffrey Scott
Staples HS; Staples, MN (133-166) FFA; JV, Bsbl; Bkbl; Ftbl; Mgr, Wrest; *Staples Voc-Tech; Heavy Equipment.*

SKODA, Sandra Marie
Palmer HS; Palmer, TX (3-28) Sch P; Secy, Jr Cl; Secy, Soph Cl; Bkbl; Sftbl; Tr; COM; Spch A; Type A; UIL Prose Reading; UIL Typing Tm; HR; Ath o-t Yr; *U of Tex in Arlington; Art.*

SKOGEN, Kevin Dale
Othello HS; Othello, WA; Chor; Bkbl; Ftbl; Citz A.

SKOGLUND, Donna Jean
Roosevelt HS; Fresno, CA (25%-700) A Cap Choir; Band; Fr C; Co-Cpt, Mjrte; COM; VP, Sr HS Group; *Chiropractic.*

SKOLAUT, Susan Lee
Hoisington HS; Hoisington, KS (31-93) Band; Chor; Ensm; Model UN; Pres, Jr Cl; Bkbl; Tr; HQn; Hon Prog; Vlbl; GAA; All St Choir; *Barton Co Comm Col; Mus.*

SKOLD, Steven Mitchell
Hopkins Eisenhower HS; Hopkins, MN (89-400) Order/Arrow; JV, Soccer; Swim; Order/Arrow A; Hugh O'Brien Yth Ldrship A; Eagle Sct A; Amer Wilderness Ldrship Sch; St Capital Page; *Bus.*

SKORINKO, Sharon Kay
Philipsburg-Osceola HS; Philipsburg, PA (12-241) Fr C; FHA; NHS; A-Ed, Sch P; Fr A; Semi-Fin, Rotarian A; Fin, COM; Fin, DAR Good Citz A; Fin, NEDT Cert.

SKOYLES, Judith Eleanor
Vincent Massey Secondary Sch; Windsor, CANADA; Band; Math C; Orch; Mgr, Bkbl; Ftbl; Tr; Pres A Committee; Mus o-t Yr; Badminton; Mgr, Vlbl; *U of Windsor; Math.*

SKRELJA, Lena
Aquinas HS; NY, NY (31-231) CYO; Hon Prog; Good Conduct A; *Fordham U; Lab-Tech.*

SKUBICH, Kimberly Ann
Hubbard HS; Chicago, IL (53-449) Ann; Bus C; CYO; Chldr; Chor; Drama; Hmrm; InterClub Coun; NHS; Sch P; Span C; SC; Var C; VP, Jr Cl; Ftbl; HCt; Hon Prog; Most Out; Yth Fel; Yth Leg; Bat Girl, Bsbl; Outst Chldr o-t Yr; *Northern Ill U; Phys Therapy.*

SLABACH, Ruth Alyce
Halifax Co Sr HS; S Boston, VA; Fr C; Pres, FTA; Pres, Hmrm; Pres, NHS; SC; COM; DARGCA; NMS; Delta Kappa Gamma; Fr Stu o-t Yr; Most Courteous; WW; *Eastern Mennonite Col; Elem Ed.*

SLACK, Brian Dale
Trott Voc HS; Niagara Falls, NY (4-143) NHS; Cpt, Bsbl; Cpt, Wrest; Cl Fav; Lion A; Realtor's A; Thomas E Hewitt A; Nom, WW; *NY St U; Engr.*

SLACK, Sue Ellen
Refugio HS; Refugio, TX (1-120) S-T, Band; Cum Laude Soc; Dbte Tm; Pres, FTA; Pres, NHS; Rptr, Sch P; Tres, SC; Secy, Sr Cl; Pres, JV, Tnns; Alg A; Magna Cum Laude; Summa Cum Laude; Val; VFW A; VofDEM; Vlbl; Region All Star Vlbl Tm; Valentine Court; Region Band; St Qualifier, Solo & Ensm; *Tex A&M U; Child Development.*

SLACK, Velma Lee
John F Kennedy HS; New Orleans, LA (40-350) Dbte Tm; Hmrm; Lit Ral; ARC; Rptr, Sch P; Span C; VP, Span NHS; SC; COM; Citz A; Hon Prog; Most Out; Eng & Span A's; *Law.*

SLADE, Debbie E
Holbrook HS; Holbrook, AZ (10-150) CYO; Cpt, Chldr; FHA; FTA; Semi-Fin, GS; InterAct C; Model UN; Sec; Var C; Tres, Jr Cl; Tres, Sr Cl; Tres, Jr Cl; Tres, Soph Cl; Tr; Amer Leg A; Bio A; Cl Fav; Elk A; HCt; Hon Prog; Most Out; Cpt, Vlbl; MVP, Vlbl; *Central Ariz Col; Mental Retardation.*

SLADE, Julia Annette
Saginaw HS; Saginaw, MI; Tr; Type A; Yth Fel; *Ferris St Col; Algebra.*

SLAMA, Erline Rae
Immanuel Baptist Christian Sch; Menomonie, WI; Ann; Band; Chor; Bkbl; *Hyles-Anderson Col; General Bible.*

SLANE, Craig Jonathan
Trumbull HS; Trumbull, CT (33%-780) Sch P; MVP, Bsbl; Soccer; Yth Fel; Semi-Fin, Table Tnns; Pres, Yth Found; Church Choir; *Nyack Col; Mus.*

SLANE, Julia Ann
Peoria Central HS; Peoria, IL (127-481) All Amer Yth; Pres, CYO; Pres, FBLA; Mjrte; Phys C; JA A; ARC A; *Bradley U; Computer Sci.*

SLATE, David Arthur
Crescent City Jr Sr HS; Crescent City, FL (10-150) Band; BC; Dbte Tm; Ensm; Orch; Spch C; Bkbl; Tr; COM; Hist A; Spch A; *U of Fla; Ed.*

SLATE, Kellie Alison
Elmhurst HS; Fort Wayne, IN (51-348) Band; Chor; SC; Bkbl; Tnns; Tr; Type A; *Ball St U; Phys Ed.*

SLATE, Vern Orville
Mozelle HS; Gouldbusk, TX (2-9) Ann; BC; FFA; Bkbl; Ftbl; Tr; *Tarleton St U; Agr.*

SLATER, Bennie Earl
Jim Hill HS; Jackson, MS (50-200) Up Bound; Cpt, Bkbl; Ltr, Jacket, Bkbl; *Jackson St U; Bus Mgr.*

SLATER, Darla Jean
Marion Franklin HS; Columbus, OH (65-365) FHA; FTA; Hmrm; NHS; SC; Cl Fav; MLS; Most Out; Child Care A; *Bowling Green Col; Child Development.*

SLATER, Gary Donald
Clay Center Pub Sch; Clay Center, NE (3-32) Drama; Pres, 4H; Var C; VP, Jr Cl; Bsbl; Bkbl; Ftbl; Tr; 4H A.

SLATER, Linda Ann
Blanchet HS; Seattle, WA (16-308) All Amer Yth; Cpt, Bkbl; Soccer; Hon Prog.

SLATER, Sandy Sue
Clay Center Pub Sch; Clay Center, NE (1-32) Band; Chor; Drama; Secy, 4H; NHS; Spch C; Secy, Y-Tns; 4H A; Journ A; Spch A; Vlbl; *Doane Col; Journ.*

SLATER, William Thomas
Milford Mill Sr HS; Baltimore, MD; Chor; Drama; Spch C; Var C; Bsbl; Bkbl; Ftbl; Cpt, Tr; JA A; Yth Fel; Black Stu Union; Acolyte; Ntl Fraternity of Stu Musicians; St Win, Ntl Piano Play Auditions; *Morehouse Col; Communications.*

SLATES, Kevin Robert
Pewaukee HS; Pewaukee, WI (12-128) AFS; Fr C; French NHS; Math C; NHS; Var C; Ftbl; Kiwanis A; *Marquette U; Engr.*

SLATON, Deirdre Lynn
Canton Acad; Canton, MS (13-95) Ann; BC; Co-Cpt, Chldr; Chor; 4H; Span C; Spch C; SC; Y-Tns; Secy, Sci C; Lion A; Yth Fel; *Miss St U; Lib Arts.*

SLATON, Jim C
Fairview Alpha HS; Coushatta, LA (1-31) Pres, 4H; Pres, Hmrm; Fin, Lit Ral; JV, Bkbl; Tr; Bio A; Chem A; 4H A; MLS; *La Tech Col; Engr.*

SLATTERY, Kevin Timothy
Ojai Valley Sch; Ojai, CA; Drama; SC; Bsbl; Cr-Ctry; Cpt, Soccer; Opt A; *Pitzer Col; Pre-Med.*

SLATTON, Patricia Margaret
E Ridge HS; Chattanooga, TN (31-288) Ann; BC; Hmrm; NHS; Pres, ARC; *Middle Tenn St U; Animal Sci.*

SLAUGHTER, Brian Stuart
Wetumpka HS; Wetumpka, AL (33%-190) BC; Drama; FFA; Sci C; SC; Parl, Jr Cl; Bsbl; Mgr, Bkbl; Ftbl; Tnns; Tr; *Auburn U; Archt Design.*

SLAUGHTER, Jacques Wayne
John Marshall Harlan HS; Chicago, IL (167-700) Chor; Bkbl; *Olive Harvey Col; Mus.*

SLAUGHTER, Jimmy Leon Jr
Fenger HS; Chicago, IL (383-732) All Amer Yth; Pres, Chor; Fr C; Bsbl; Sftbl; *Olive-Harvey Col; Physcian.*

SLAUGHTER, Kate Pelot
Bartow Sr HS; Bartow, FL; Pres, Drama; InterClub Coun; Star Stu A, Piano; *Furman U; Elem Ed.*

SLAUGHTER, Marion Gail
Daviston HS; Daviston, AL; BC; Co-Cpt, Chldr; 4H; Beauty; Cl Fav; Hist A; Sal; *Sou Union Col; Computer Prog.*

SLAUGHTER, Mary Ellen
Bremen HS; Bremen, GA (13-77) Drama; FBLA; Ch, FHA; VP, 4H; S-T, NHS; 4H A; JA A; Cpt, Drill Tm; Key A; Jr Leadership; *Auburn U; Clothing & Textiles.*

SLAUGHTER, Pamela Gene
Harlan HS; Chicago, IL; Hon Prog; Fashion Clinic; *Bus.*

SLAVENS, Beverly Jene
San Juan HS; Blanding, UT (7-100) Drama; FHA; 4H; Semi-Fin, Jr Miss Pa; NHSt; SC; Bkbl; Golf; Tnns; Beauty; COM; Citz A; 4H A; Hon Prog; Spch A; Vlbl; Powder Puff Ftbl; Pres, Drill Tm; Jr Prom Royalty; HR; Spirit C; *BYU; Phys Therapist.*

SLAVIC, Andrea Helen
Reynolds HS; Greenville, PA; AFS; FBLA; Co-Cpt, Mjrte; Tri-HiY.

SLAYBAUGH, Lisa Diane
Littlestown Sr HS; Littlestown, PA (18-150) Chor; FHA; NHS; Hon Prog; Opt A; S-T, GSct; *Computer.*

SLAYTON, Wanda Terese
Hazlewood HS; Town Creek, AL (5-53) Pres, Band; BC; FHA; Pres, Soph C; Cl Fav; 4H A; HCt; Pres, Yth Rally; Secy, Acteens; Stu o-t Mo; All St Band Tryouts; *Calhoun Col.*

SLECHTA, Ginger Michelle
Lake Highlands HS; Dallas, TX (150-750) AFS; Hon Prog; Yth Fel; *Abilene Christian U; Med.*

SLEDD, Margaret Westray
Slippery Rock Area HS; Slippery Rock, PA; AFS; Band; Fr C; Rainbow; Yth Fel; Rotary Exchange Stu; *Lang.*

SLEDGE, Patricia Dianne
S Cobb HS; Austell, GA; Ann; BC; Secy, FBLA; Type A; Shorthand A; *Marietta Cobb Voc-Tech Col; Bus Ed.*

SLEDGE, Robert Owen Jr
Indianola Acad; Indianola, MS (14-85) A Cap Choir; Band; BC; Chor; Madrigal; *Miss St U; Elec.*

SLEPPY, Patricia Lynne
Valley HS; New Kensington, PA (1-384) Chldr; Chor; Drama; Key C; NHS; Span C; Var C; Hon Prog; St Scholar; SC At; Dist I & Region Chor; *Pa St U; Pre-Vet Med.*

SLETTEN, Danette Mae
Two Harbors HS; Two Harbors, MN (70-175) Band; Chldr; Chor; Community Yth Symph; Fr C; Sch Achieve Tm; SC; Sftbl; Tr; Gym; *Golden Valley Col; Secy.*

SLICIS, Michael Anthony
Warren Central HS; Indianapolis, IN; Pres, CYO; Pres, K of C; Mgr, Ftbl; Mgr, Tr; *Fla St U; Aeronautics.*

SLIGER, Timmy Tye
Hobbs Sr HS; Hobbs, NM (270-497) Band; *Acct.*

SLIMON, Heather Marina
Cristobal Jr Sr HS; Coco Solo, CANAL ZONE (2-158) Band; Chldr; Fr C; FNA; FTA; Hmrm; NHS; SC; VP, Jr Cl; Swim; COM; Hon Prog; JA A; Spch A; *Stanford Col; Bio.*

SLIMP, Kevin Kent
University HS; Johnson City, TN (27-61) Band; Sftbl; Tnns; Jr Civitan; Karate; *East Tenn St U; Engr.*

SLINGSBY, Dean Gerald
Ansley Pub HS; Ansley, NE (40-48) Band; Chor; Pres, FFA; Madrigal; Bsbl; JV, Bkbl; Ftbl; Tr; Wrest; Pres A; Star Student; *Northeast Tech Col; Agr.*

SLOAN, Corinne Kay
Midway HS; Waco, TX; VP, Span C; Bkbl; JV, Tnns; JV, Tr; *Tex A&M U.*

SLOAN, Gary Wayne
DeSoto HS; DeSoto, MO (93-230) A Cap Choir; Drama; Hmrm; *Jefferson Col; Ed.*

SLOAN, Lynn Anne
Midway HS; Waco, TX (10%-180) Chor; Ensm; Madrigal; VP, Mu Alpha Theta; NHS; COM; Hon Prog; WW; *Tex A&M U; Archt.*

SLOAN, Steven LaRoy
Halter HS; Wellston, MO (1-110) Chor; Hmrm; NHS; Ntl Yth Conf; SC; Var C; Tres, Jr Cl; Co-Cpt, Bkbl; Hon Prog; Type A; Bkbl A; *Alcorn U; Natural Sci.*

SLOAN, Teresa Jean
Tullahoma HS; Tullahoma, TN (33%-317) BC; Chldr; Chor; FHA; VP, Hmrm; Var C; MVP, Tr; MVP, Church Bkbl; MVP, City Sftbl League; DAR Essay Contest; *Middle Tenn St U; Ed.*

SLOAT, Laurie Ann
Lawrence Vo-tech HS; New Castle, PA (10-430) Chor; Ensm; ARC; Sci C; Y-Tns; Hon Prog; NEDT; Sci A; Yth Fel; Sch Musicals; Med Explorers; *St Jr Acad of Sci; Art.*

SLOCUM, Debra Mae
Batavia Sr HS; Batavia, IL; AFS; Drama; Hmrm; Math C; Tnns, NHS; Secy, SC; Secy, Soph Cl; JV, Bkbl; Sftbl; Alg A; Hon Prog; Math A; St Scholar; Pom Pon Girl; *DePauw Col; Art.*

SLOCUM, James Sidney
Pine HS; Franklinton, LA (8-58) Pres, BC; VP, FFA; Fin, Lit Ral; NHS; MLS; Beta C A; Agr A; *Southeastern U; Computor Sci.*

SLOCUMB, Jonathan Bernardo
Frederick Douglass HS; Atlanta, GA (36-350) Chor; FBLA; NHS; Rptr, Sch P; Pres, SC; Pres, Jr Cl; COM; WW; *Oakwood Col; Acct.*

SLONAKER, David Martin
Sci Hill HS; Johnson City, TN (20%-441) A Cap Choir; Chor; Ftbl; Tr; COM; *E Tenn St; Mech Engr.*

SLONE, Cherie Jo
Wilson HS; Wilson, TX (3-14) Band; Drama; Rptr, FHA; Parl, FTA; GS; 4H; Mjrte; Bkbl; Tnns; Tr; Cl Fav; 4H A; ARC A; All Dist Guard; Co Harvest Festival Qn; All Tourn, Bkbl; *Tex Tech U; Med.*

SLONESKI, Steven Clement
St Augustine Prep Sch; Richland, NJ (10%-50) Pres, Band; Chem C; Chess C; Pres, Chor; Dbte Tm; Demolay; Drama; VP, Hmrm; Lat C; Lit Ral; Lit Mag; NHS; Sch P; Sci C; VP, SC; Thes; Tnns; Wrest; COM; Hon Prog; HR Cert; Mus A; Hon Soc A; Piano Accomp A; *Villanova Col; Med Sci.*

SLOOTMAKER, Henry Densel
Clifton Sr HS; Clifton, NJ (40%-1000) Band; Hmrm; SC; Wrest; ARC A; *Pace Col; Acct.*

SLOOTMAKER, Kevin Peter
Manchester Regional HS; Haledon, NJ (50%-225) JV, Bsbl; Bowling; *Bus Adm.*

SLOPER, Beth Jan
LaFayette Central HS; La Fayette, NY (11-93) Band; Chor; NHS; Span C; Regent Schol; Yth Fel; Sou All Co Band; NYSSMA; Gen Mills Family Ldr of Tomorrow; *SUNY; Sociology.*

SLOPER, Kitt Shirley
Lafayette HS; La Fayette, NY; Band; 4H A; Yth Fel.

SLOSTED, Norman Wayne
Aptos HS; Aptos, CA; Ensm; H of F; HCt; St Scholar; Cpt & MVP, Bsbl & Ftbl; Block 'A'; *Azusa Pacific; Physical Education.*

SLOVENSKI, Thomas Joseph
W Chester Christian Sch; W Chester, PA (4-25) Ann; Chor; Var C; Bkbl; Soccer; COM; Hon Prog; WW; *Bob Jones U; Religion.*

SLOVER, Jacquelyn Sue
Jackson HS; Jackson, MO (23-267) Ann; Band; Bus C; Chor; FHA; Sch P; Secy, SC; Bowl Tm; HR; SC A; *U of Denver; Social Work.*

SLUDER, Thomas Jefferson III
Plant City Sr HS; Plant City, FL (100-550) FFA; Ftbl; *Agr.*

SLUMPFF, Wendy Louise
Port Huron HS; Port Huron, MI (25-350) Band; NHS; Span C; JV, Tr; Past Worth Adv & Grnd Rep, Rainbow; *St Clair Co Comm Col; Nurs.*

SLUSS, Stephen Craig
Frankfort HS; Ridgeley, WV (10%-151) BS; NHS; Order/Arrow; SC; Var C; Pres, Jr Cl; Pres, Soph Cl; JV, Bkbl; Co-Cpt, Cr-Ctry; Tnns; Tr; *W Va U; Law.*

SLUSSER, Amy Lynne
Cuyahoga Falls HS; Cuyahoga Falls, OH; Sunday Sch Teacher; Church Yth Group; Puppets; *Kent St U; Sociology.*

SLUTZ, James Allen
Sandy Valley HS; Magnolia, OH (17-160) Ann; BS; Bus C; Tres, HiY; NFL; NHS; Sci C; SC; Thes; Pres, Jr Cl; Cr-Ctry; Ftbl; *Ohio St U; Med.*

SLY, Albert Lawrence
Antilles HS; Fort Buchanan, PR (5-124) Ann; Chess C; Drama; Tres, Key C; NHS; Sch P; Hon Prog; DAHSS; *Ga Inst of Tech; Engr.*

SLYKHOUSE, John Edward
Ottawa HS; Grand Rapids, MI (26-500) NHS; Var C; NMS; Co-Cpt, MVP, Swim; *U of Mich; Bus Adm.*

SMAAGE, Cheryl Susan
Lincoln Comm HS; Lincoln, IL; Chor; Fr C; *Lincoln Christian Col; Psych.*

SMADES, Jean Marie
Rapid City Central HS; Rapid City, SD (192-575) *Bus.*

SMALL, Charles Jeff
Hamden HS; Hamden, CT (50-700) Math C; Mu Alpha Theta; NHS; Chem A; Hon Prog; Math A; NMS; Sci A.

SMALL, Deborah Denise
Blacksburg HS; Blacksburg, SC (20%-96) Chor; Drama; FTA; 4H; Pres, Hmrm; Jr Miss Pageant; A-Ed, Sch P; SC; Journa A; 1st Runnerup, 'Miss BHS' Contest; *Coker Col; Voice.*

SMALL, Douglas Clifton
A&M Consolidated HS; College Station, TX (75-205) Ch, A Cap Choir; Band; Ch, Chor; Madrigal; Mgr, Bkbl; Cr-Ctry; Tr; All Region, All St, Choirs; Amer Yth Symph & Chor; *Abilene Christian U; Bible.*

SMALL, Kathy Ann
Washburn HS; Minneapolis, MN; Hmrm; SC; Interlochen Ntl Mus; *Luther Col; Pre-Med.*

SMALL, Kimberly Joyce
Kermit HS; Kermit, WV (1-30) Ann; Band; Chldr; S-T, Chor; Pres, FHA; 4H; S-T, SC; S-T, Jr Cl; S-T, Soph Cl; KHS Qn; Rep, Know St Govt Day; WW; *Marshall U; Pre-Law.*

SMALL, Peter McMichael
P K Yonge Lab Sch; Gainesville, FL (10%-94) Ftbl; Tnns; Ntl Sci Found; Ntl Merit Comm; Graduation Speaker; *Princeton U; Engr.*

SMALL, Robin Cheryl
Community HS; Houston, TX (10%-98) Chor; NHS; Alg A; COM; First Aid A; Drama A; *U of Houston; Govt.*

SMALL, Susan Claire
John A Holmes HS; Edenton, NC (8-184) Ann; Chor; FHA; Sci C; *Meredith Col.*

SMALL, Terry Ray
Bloomfield HS; Bloomfield, IN (20-120) Band; FFA; NHS; Pres, Soph Cl.

SMALL, Valerie Ann
San Roman Valley HS; Danville, CA (30-336) Ski C; Span C; SC; Outst Jr Stu, Social Stu; St, CSF; Pep C; Service C; *U of Oslo-Norway.*

SMALLCOMBE, Carol
Hollywood Professional Sch; Hollywood, CA; NHS; Jr Cl Officer; *UCLA; Med.*

SMALLS, LaWanda Yvette
W Charlotte Sr HS; Charlotte, NC; Chor; Fr C; Rptr, Hmrm; ARC; SC; Driver's Ed A; Bible Sch Teacher; *NC Central Col; Bus Adm.*

SMALLS, Pamela Veronica
Berkeley HS; Moncks Corner, SC; Chor; SC; *Spelman Col;; Econ.*

SMALLS, Queen Angela
Cainhoy HS; Huger, SC (5-84) Band; Co-Cpt, Chldr; FHA; 4H; Phys C; Span C; 4H A; HQn; *U of SC; Eng.*

SMALLWOOD, Cheryl Lee
Tallmadge HS; Tallmadge, OH; Band; Chor; Dbte Tm; NHS; *Akron U; Ed.*

SMALLWOOD, Kevin William
Carlisle Intermediate HS; Carlisle, PA (20%-575) Band; Chess C; Tr; Dist & Co Band; *Temple Col; Med.*

SMALLWOOD, Molly Ethel
Martin Luther King Sch; Philadelphia, PA (3-750) NHS; Tres, World Affairs; Hon Prog; Most Out; *U of Penn; Psych.*

SMALLWOOD, Sandra Sue
Kiski Area Sr HS; Vandergrift, PA (25%-530) Ann; Band; NHS; Ski C; Span C; *Slippery Rock St Col; Med Records Adm.*

SMART, Alicia Lynn
Latexo HS; Latexo, TX (10%-16) Ann; Chldr; Rptr, FHA; Secy, SC; S-T, Sr Cl; Pres, Jr Cl; Pres, Soph Cl; Bsbl; Cpt, Bkbl; JV, Sftbl; JV, Tr; COM; Cl Fav; DARGCA; Hon Prog; Most Out; Val; MVP, All Dist, All Tourn, Bkbl; *Angelina Col; Bus.*

SMART, Allan C
Sky View HS; Smithfield, UT (11-611) Key C; Var C; Ftbl; Tr; *Utah St U; Computer Sci.*

SMART, Clifton Murray III
Fayetteville HS; Fayetteville, AR; Band; Chess C; Key C; Span C; *U of Ark; Law.*

SMART, Larry Wesley
Winnfield Sr HS; Winnfield, LA (3-123) Ch, Band; FBLA; Lit Ral; Fin, Wrest.

SMART, Loraine Andrea
E Orange HS; E Orange, NJ (15-300) FNA; Hon Prog; *Rutgers U; Nurs.*

SMARTT, Lucy Moore
George Mason Jr-Sr HS; Falls Church, VA (20%-130) Tres, AFS; Ann; GS; Key C; NHS; Ski C; SC; Bkbl; MVP, Soccer; Tnns; All Dist Soccer; Schol Cert; Ger NHS.

SMATHERS, Deirdre Lee
Oswego Comm HS; Oswego, IL; Band; Chor; Sftbl; Tnns; COM; Most Out; Yth Fel; Yth Leg; *NW Col; Drama.*

SMEALLIE, Terri Lynn
Mentor HS; Mentor, OH (10%-916) Ann; Band; Drama; 4H; NHS; Rptr, Sch P; Secy, Ski C; Tr; Vol A; *Ohio St U; Advertising.*

SMEDLEY, Donna Lee
Kountze HS; Kountze, TX (3-92) Co-Ed, Ann; Pres, Band; Bus C; Ensm; FTA; 4H; Cpt, Mjrte; Math C; Orch; Sci C; Type A; *Lamar U; Health.*

SMEDLEY, James Robert Jr
Poteau HS; Poteau, OK (25%-110) Band; Chor; Community Yth Symph; Drama; Fin, Ensm; 4H; Key C; NHS; Orch; Sci C; Bsbl; Bkbl; Ftbl; Tnns; Tr; Sci A; Bus.

SMEDLEY, Julie Anne
Kountze HS; Kountze, TX (3-88) Band; Chem C; Ensm; FHA; FTA; Math C; Tres, NHS; Orch; Sch P; Span C; H of F; *E Tex Baptist Col; Social Psych.*

SMELCHER, Tamera Elaine
Central HS; Knoxville, TN; BC; Rainbow; Span NHS; Masonic A; NHS; Nurs Explorers; Law Enforcement Explorers; *U of Tenn; Med.*

SMELKO, Laurie Sue
Upper St Clair HS; Pittsburgh, PA (61-491) AFS; Band; Bus C; Chor; NHS; Thes; Tr; COM; Vars Ltr; Phys Fitness A; *Robert Morris Col; Secretarial Sci.*

SMELKO, Linda Ann
Upper St Clair HS; Pittsburgh, PA; Span C.

SMESTAD, Rebecca Jewel
Fordville Pub Sch; Fordville, ND (40%-22) Bus Mgr, Ann; Band; Chor; 4H; Sch P; Hon Prog; Pres, Luther League; Pep C; Curling; Vlbl; *NDSU; Home Ec.*

SMETANA, Susan Marie
St Elizabeth HS; Pittsburgh, PA; Drama; Model UN; Sci C; Ski C; Sodality; Span C; Alg A; Chem A; NEDT; Yrbk; Lib Service A; Geom A; Mus Appreciation A; *U of Pittsburgh; Pre-Med.*

SMIDDY, Randall Lee
PaloDuro HS; Amarillo, TX (9-285) Drama; FBLA; Lat C; NHS; Spch C; Thes; Tnns; COM; Citz A; Hon Prog; Spch A; Type A; Gen Mills Family Ldr of Tomorrow; NML.

SMIDT, Darla Ann
Shawnee Mission N HS; Shawnee Mission, KS (39-611) A Cap Choir; Drama Crews; Choir Ltr; *Bethany Col; Pre-Med.*

SMILEY, Garett
Garfield Sr HS; Hamilton, OH; Bkbl; Ftbl; Tr; Bkbl Champship Tm; Ch, Yth Group; *USC; Hist.*

SMILEY, Malinda Elizabeth
Dixie Hollins HS; St Petersburg, FL; *St Petersburg Jr Col; Dental Asst.*

SMILEY, Richard Lee
Ralph L Fike Sr HS; Wilson, NC (10-475) NHS; Span C; DARGCA; NMS; *U of NC; Bus.*

SMILEY, Sandra Louise
Garfield Sr HS; Hamilton, OH; Sunday Sch Teacher; *Miami U; Elem Ed.*

SMILING, Al Nathaniel
E D Byrd Sr HS; Fayetteville, NC (99-600) BC; Bus C; Fr C; Hmrm; SC; Bsbl; Bkbl; Type A; Yth Fel; *Campbell Col; Pre-Law.*

SMIRCICH, Douglas Mark
Hanford HS; Richland, WA (10-240) Band; Chor; Ensm; Band A; Choir A; *Columbia Basin Jr Col.*

SMIT, Julie Anne
Central HS; Davenport, IA; AFS; Band; Chem C; Sci C; *U of Iowa; Math.*

SMIT, Kathy Ann
Montevideo Sr HS; Montevideo, MN (40-160) Ed, Ann; Bus C; Chor; Madrigal; Type A; Head Usher, Ushers C; St & Regional OEA A's; *Presentation Col; Nurs.*

SMITH, Adrian Lawrence
York Central HS; Retsof, NY (2-86) Band; Community Yth Symph; Drama; NHS; Orch; Swim; *Cornell U; Archt.*

SMITH, Alan Gerard
Holy Family HS; Birmingham, AL (5-41) Band; Fr C; Pres, Hmrm; NHS; Sci C; SC; Mgr, Var C; Pres, Jr Cl; Cpt, Tr; Hon Prog; *Fisk U; X-Ray Technology.*

SMITH, Albert Paul Jr
Lumberton Sr HS; Lumberton, NC; Bsbl; Tr; Royal Ambassadors Phys Fitness A.

SMITH, Aldan Randolph
Tipton HS; Tipton, OK (17-45) Chor; Drama; VP, 4H; ARC; Spch C; Var C; Bsbl; Bkbl; Ftbl; Wrest; Citz A; Cl Fav; 4H A; HCt; Spch A; *OSU; Athletics.*

SMITH, Alfred Lowell Jr
Glenbard N HS; Carol Stream, IL (150-400) Mgr, Bkbl; *DeVry Inst of Tech; Computer Prog.*

SMITH, Alfredo Alverez
Immaculata Conception HS; Clarksdale, MS; Chor; Drama; Pres, 4H; SC; Bio A; Citz A; Elk A; 4H A; Hist A; Most Out; Sci A; Val; Phillips Acad Schol; Bio A; Troop Ldr A, BSA; Health & PE A; Eng Hon Cert; Cl Ldr A; Mus Hon Cer; Sup Rating, Oratorical Contest; *Columbia U; Pre-Med.*

SMITH, Alice Maria
Northwest HS; St Louis, MO (17-433) FHA; NHS; ARC; *Fontbonne Col; Special Ed.*

SMITH, Alicia Renee
S Choctaw Acad; Taxey, AL (1-26) Ann; BC; Chldr; Chor; Tres, Soph Cl; Cl Fav; MLS; Most Beautiful; Best Dressed; PA.

SMITH, Alison Renee
River Forest HS; Hobart Township, IN; Mjrte; SC; JV, Vlbl; Attendance A.

SMITH, Allison
N Gwinnett HS; Suwanee, GA (15%-120) Pres, FBLA; St Win, FBLA.

SMITH, Allison Marie
Spring Woods HS; Houston, TX (50%-550) Chor; Tres, FTA; Yth Fel; *Tex A&M U; Acct.*

SMITH, Amy Armistead
Dobyns Bennett HS; Kingsport, TN (10-450) BC; Fr C; InterClub Coun; Pres, Lat C; NFL; VP, NHS; DARGCA; VFW Orator Win; VofDEM; Attended Amer Acad of Achvs; NMS Commended Stu; St Win, Tenn Acad of Sci Comp; Del, Tenn Sci & Humanities Symp; *U of Va; Pre-Law.*

SMITH, Amy Elizabeth
W A Berry HS; Birmingham, AL; Anchor C; Ensm; SC; HCt; Candystriper; Badminton Tm; Chaplain, Sorority; *Auburn U; Phys Therapy.*

SMITH, Andrea LaClaire
Belton HS; Belton, TX (65-220) Ann; Dbte Tm; Hmrm; Lit Mag; Sch P; Spch C; SC; *U of Ala; Law.*

SMITH, Angela
Hancock Central HS; Sparta, GA; 4H; Sci C; SC; Home Ec A; *Atlanta Med Col; Med.*

SMITH, Angela Dee
Cherryville Sr HS; Cherryville, NC (91-136) Math C; Sci C; SC; Los Amigos; Disciples; Pep C; Qn, Qn with Septor As; Church Yth Choir; Acteens; *Gardner Webb Col; Lib Sci.*

SMITH, Angela Margurite
Hillside HS; Durham, NC; Lat C; *Howard U; Med.*

SMITH, Angela Mechele
Marshall HS; Marshall, TX (31-449) A Cap Choir; Chor; FTA; VP, Hmrm; Mod Mus Mas; Campfire Girls Wohelo Medallion; WW; *E Tex Baptist Col.*

SMITH, Anita Ann
DeLand Sr HS; DeLand, FL (33%-600) Tres, FBLA; Pres, Yth Fel; *Daytona Beach Comm Col; Bus.*

SMITH, Ann Mary
Central Dauphin E HS; Harrisburg, PA (64-358) Band; Tres, CYO; ARC; Span C; Co-Cpt, Bkbl; Schol & Ath Achv A; *Harrisburg Area Comm Col; Nurs.*

SMITH, Anna Marie
Arapahoe HS; Littleton, CO (48-585) Band; SC; Sftbl; Tnns; Hon Prog; *Baylor U; Elem Ed.*

SMITH, Anne Elizabeth
Trinity Christian Acad; Dallas, TX (7-42) NHS; Secy, Sr Cl; MVP, Bkbl; MVP, Tnns; Seventeen Mag A; Sportsmnshp A; Mary Lowdon A, Outst Jr Girl in Te; Most Promising Jr Grl Tnns Plyr US; *Trinity U; Psych.*

SMITH, Annette Neomi
Jesup W Scott HS; Toledo, OH; Drama; Pres, Hmrm; Cl Fav; Type A; Yth Fel; *Data Acct.*

SMITH, Anthony Edward
Jess Lanier HS; Bessemer, AL; Key C; Mgr, Ftbl; Tnns; *Oceanography.*

SMITH, Anthony John
Randolph HS; Randolph, WI (33%-60) Band; Chor; Cr-Ctry; Hon Prog; Sch Play; *VW at Stevens Point; Paper Sci.*

SMITH, Anthony Paul
Shaker Hts HS; Shaker Heights, OH (20%-400) A Cap Choir; Chess C; Fr C; Ger C; Hon Prog; 2nd Pl Trophy, Chess Tourn; *Wheaton Col; Physics.*

SMITH, Antionette
Lakewood HS; St Petersburg, FL; Chor; NHS; Bkbl; Hon Prog; Piano A's.

SMITH, Anya Eden
Martin Luther King HS; Philadelphia, PA (18-692) NHS; Tnns; Art A; Fr A; Phys Ed A; Health A; *Penn St U; Med Tech.*

SMITH, Arleta Louise
Lowell Sr HS; San Francisco, CA (50%-900) Pres, Hmrm; Var C; Sftbl; Fin, Gym; *U of Calif, San Diego; Bio.*

SMITH, Arthur Lee
Corliss HS; Chicago, IL (8-726) COM; Stu Recognition A; Bus.

SMITH, Barbara Jean
Douglass HS; Memphis, TN (3-150) Lat C; NHS; Secy, Span C; Tr; MLS; *Computer Programming.*

SMITH, Barbara Lynn
Sullivan Central HS; Blountville, TN (25%-350) Band; Chor; Ensm; ARC; Bkbl; Tr; ARC A; Jazz Band; Most Dependable; Sch Store Worker; All Co Band; Sr Rep, Band; E Tenn Ed Assn Chor; All St Chor; *E Tenn St U; Mus.*

SMITH, Barbara Susette
Plainfield Jr-Sr HS; Plainfield, IN (19-304) Band; Rptr, 4H; NHS; Sch P; Tres, Span C; SC; 4H A; Regional Sci Fair; *Milligan Christian Col; Eng.*

SMITH, Becky Ann
Valley City HS; Valley City, ND (65-130) Pres, FBLA; Ski C; Pep C; Pom Pon Tm; Gym; *Elem Ed.*

SMITH, Benjamin Ralph
Big Sandy HS; Big Sandy, TX; Band; Chess C; Sch P; Y-Tns; Arch; Bsbl; Bkbl; Tnns; Wrest; Citz A; ARC A; Yth Fel; Yth Foundation; *Kilgore Col; Diesel Mech.*

SMITH, Betsy Gwynne
Lincoln Co Central HS; Fayetteville, TN (10%-300) BC; Rainbow; Sci C; Span C; Eng A; *U of Tenn; Vet Med.*

SMITH, Betty Lou
Osbourn Park HS; Manassas, VA; FBLA; NHS; Social Work.

SMITH, Beverly Anne
Randolph HS; Randolph, WI (33%-64) AFS; A-Ed, Ann; Band; Tres, Chor; Ensm; FHA; Model UN; Semi-Fin, NFL; Semi-Fin, NHS; A-Ed, Sch P; Mgr, Bkbl; Tr; HCt; Hon Prog; Spch A; Prom Court; *U of Wis; Elem Ed.*

SMITH, Beverly Joy
Shelton HS; Shelton, CT (10%-520) 4H; NHS; Tres, Ski C; Bsbl; Co-Cpt, Soccer; Sftbl; 4H A; Hon Prog; Gym A; *Nurs.*

SMITH, Billy Wayne
South San W Campus; San Antonio, TX (50-300) JV, Ftbl; Hon Prog; *U of Ala; Mech.*

SMITH, Blake Edwin
Northbrook HS; Houston, TX (71-561) NMS; *Baylor U; Pre-Med.*

SMITH, Bobby Wayne
Highland HS; Albuquerque, NM; Band; Chess C; NHS; SC; Hon Prog; Star Sct, BSA; Outst Schol A; *Hardin-Simmons U; Physics.*

SMITH, Bonnie Eloise
Soldan HS; St Louis, MO; Chor; *Secy.*

SMITH, Bonnie Jo
Bowdon HS; Bowdon, GA (3-100) Band; BC; Chess C; FHA; 4H; Span C; Tri-HiY; Secy, Sr Cl; Tres, Soph Cl; Tnns; Hon Prog; WW; WW, Mus; Miss Bohian; *W Ga U; Math.*

SMITH, Bradley Harrison
LaFayette Central HS; La Fayette, NY (25%-122) Ann; Chor; Order/Arrow; Alg A; Math A; Order/Arrow A; Sci A; *Med.*

SMITH, Brenda Ann
Newport Harbor HS; Newport Beach, CA; *Biola Col.*

SMITH, Brenda Dee
Denair HS; Denair, CA; Span C; CSF; Eng A.

SMITH, Brenda Evonne
Hollywood Professional Sch; Hollywood, CA; Ann; Band; Cpt, Chldr; Chor; Ftbl; Drama A.

SMITH, Brenda Leneice
Sibley HS; Sibley, LA (4-55) Ann; Band; FHA; 4H; Span C; Up Bound; *Grambling St U; Bus Mgt.*

SMITH, Brenda Sue
McNeil HS; McNeil, AR (4-33) Pres, Hmrm; Math C; Sci C; Pres, Soph Cl; Mgr, Bkbl; Alg A; Hist A; HCt; Sci A; Eng A; *Henderson St U; Psych.*

SMITH, Brenda Sue
Lubbock Christian HS; Lubbock, TX (25%-45) Chor; NHS; *Lubbock Christian Col.*

SMITH, Bryant Rene
Watsonville HS; Watsonville, CA; Hmrm; SC; Var C; Bsbl; MVP, Bkbl; Ftbl; Swim; Tnns; COM; HCt; Yth Fel; Most Improved, Ftbl; Sour-Tart, Bkbl; Talent A; *Cabrillo Col; Archt.*

SMITH, Bryce Malcolm
Lutheran HS; Los Angeles, CA (8-84) Rptr, Ann; CSF; *UC at San Diego; Engr.*

SMITH, Buster DeAngelo
Simon Gratz HS; Philadelphia, PA (42-450) Inter-Act C; Pol Sci C; *Cheyney St Col; Bio.*

SMITH, Calvin Neal
Smyrna HS; Smyrna, TN (87-326) VP, 4H; Inter-Act C; S-T, Key C; SC; JV, Wrest; *U of Tenn; Archt Engr.*

SMITH, Camilla Leann
Crockett HS; Crockett, TX (7-106) Ed, Ann; Pres, Band; Secy, Bus C; Fin, Ensm; Secy, FTA; Cpt, Mjrte; NHS; SC; Tnns; Citz A; Hist A; HCt; Twirling Trophies & Medals; SDJST Twirling St Talent; Miss Sr; *Tyler Jr Col; Registered Nurs.*

SMITH, Carla Janell
South Side HS; Counce, TN; BC; Chldr; FHA; Sci C.

SMITH, Carol Ann
Justin F Kimball HS; Dallas, TX (10-700) Ger C; Math C; Secy, Orch; Hon Prog; Bible Credit A; Math Tm; European Study Group; *Harding Christian Col; Acct.*

SMITH, Carol Lynn
Charlottesville HS; Charlottesville, VA (20-380) Band; Secy, Chor; Crown & Scepter; Ensm; FBLA; Hmrm; Secy, NHS; COM; Citz A; DARGCA; Tres, Keyette; 1st Pl Steno, St FBLA Comp; Band A; *U of Va; Spch Therapy.*

SMITH, Carolyn Denise
Killeen HS; Killeen, TX (798-963) Cpt, Bkbl; *Baylor U; Psych.*

SMITH, Casey A
Elk City HS; Elk City, OK (1-132) BS; Drama; FBLA; Hmrm; Secy, Key C; SC; Bkbl; Ftbl; Tr; Elk A; Jr Chamber of Com A; Lion A; Math A; Phy A; Val; U School; Pres's Man, Key C; *Okla U; Elec Engr.*

SMITH, Catherine Anne
Telstar Regional HS; Bethel, ME (4-76) Pres, Band; Chor; Ensm; Ger C; Math C; VP, NHS; Ed, Sch P; Bio A; Hist A; Journ A; Eng, Ger, A's; Blessed Hearts; *U of Maine; Forest Engr.*

SMITH, Catherine Robin
Trinity HS; High Point, NC; Fr C; FHA; FTA; ARC; Tutoring A; *Ed.*

SMITH, Cathy Ann
Breckinridge Co HS; Harned, KY (30%-200) Ann; Chldr; Chor; Drama; FBLA; VP, FFA; FTA; 4H; VP, SC; Var C; Secy, Soph Cl; Cr-Ctry; Sftbl; Tnns; Cl Fav; H of F; HCt; Spch A; Ky Pork Qn; FFA Ldrship A; Food- a- rama Conf; U of Ky, Col of Agr Schol; *U of Ky; Agr.*

SMITH, Cathy Jean
Mt Vernon HS; Mt Vernon, OH (5%-387) Fr C; Solo, Church Choir; WW in Lang Stu; Church Yth Group Tn Rep.

SMITH, Cecilia Ann
Ole Main HS; N Little Rock, AR; Band; Hmrm; NHS; ARC; Span C; Citz A; Hon Prog; MLS; Most Out; Yth Fel; Adm Board; *Okla U; Med.*

SMITH, Charlann Carole
Morrisville HS; Morrisville, PA (2-190) Band; FTA; InterAct C; NHS; Tres, Sch P; Mgr, Hockey; Hon Prog; Poet A; *Bus Mgt.*

SMITH, Charlene Beth
Eagle Mtn HS; Eagle Mountain, CA (10-61) Co-Ed, Ann; Band; Ensm; F-Ed, Sch P; Span C; SC; Pres, Jr Cl; Secy, Soph Cl; Bkbl; Sftbl; Bank Of Amer A; Cl Fav; Journ A; Mus A, Schol to Workshop; Rep, Board of Ed; Daisy Chain; WW; *Pepperdine U; Journ.*

SMITH, Charles William
Shawnee Mission W HS; Overland Park, KS (50%-694) A Cap Choir; Chor; Bio A; COM; *Auto Mech.*

SMITH, Charlotte Ann
Hazlewood HS; Town Creek, AL (12-47) BC; FFA; 4H; Hmrm; SC; Span C; Beauty; Cl Fav; MLS; Swtht; *Calhoun Jr Col; Animal Sci.*

SMITH, Cheryl Ann
Skyline HS; Dallas, TX (20%-800) Pres, Bus C; Fr C; FBLA; Hmrm; ARC; Var C; Bsbl; Bkbl; Tr; COM; Cl Fav; Hon Prog; JA A; MLS; Spch A; Type A; *E Tex St U; Special Ed.*

SMITH, Cheryl Ann
Whitehouse HS; Whitehouse, TX (2-140) Band; FTA; Alg A; *Tyler Jr Col; Mus.*

SMITH, Cheryl Anne
Newark HS; Newark, DE (30-400) Sch P; Hockey; *Geneva Col; Eng.*

SMITH, Cheryl Denise
Carl Brablec HS; Roseville, MI (60-500) Chor; NHS; Sci C; Co-Cpt, Sftbl; JV Vlbl; Art A; *Concordia Col; Deaconess.*

SMITH, Cheryl Vernice
East St Louis Sr HS; East St Louis, IL (40-1000) COM; 4H A; Most Out; Most Creative; *SIU; Mus.*

SMITH, Christina Judith
DuQuoin HS; DuQuoin, IL (2-179) Ann; Band; Chor; Drama; FHA; Key C; F-Ed, Sch P; Spch C; Journ A; Opt A; Spch A; *Sou Ill U; Law.*

SMITH, Christina Marie
Vandercook Lake HS; Jackson, MI (56-121) Maranatha Col; Teaching.

SMITH, Christine Jill
Hendersonville HS; Hendersonville, TN (18-438) BC; Hmrm; NHS; SC; WW.

SMITH, Christopher Owen
Thornwood HS; S Holland, IL (167-1015) Chor; Bsbl; Ftbl; Wrest; FCA; *Notre Dame U; Pre-Law.*

SMITH, Cindy DeAnne
Thomas Jefferson HS; Council Bluffs, IA (1-495) Band; NHS; Orch; COM; Citz A; Jazz Band; Talent Show, Piano Solo.

SMITH, Cindy Lesia
Wren HS; Piedmont, SC; Band; Commercial C; Mjrte; DECA C; Homecoming Sponsor; *Tri-Co Tech Col; Secretarial Sci.*

SMITH, Cindy Ruthenia
Cainhoy HS; Huger, SC (1-84) Cpt, Chldr; FHA; Phys C; Span C; SC; Bio A; 4H A; HCt; Sci A; Type A; *U of SC.*

SMITH, Clark Owen
Pickens HS; Pickens, WV (4-15) Drama; 4H; Hmrm; VP, NHS; Pres, SC; Pres, Soph Cl; Cpt, Bkbl; Alg A; COM; Gov Honor Prog; 4H A; I Dare You.

SMITH, Clipper Leeon
Elbert Co Comprehensive HS; Elberton, GA (170-343) Chess C; Fr C; FBLA; Hmrm; Ftbl; Tr; S-T, Social Stu C; Weightlifting; ROTC Rifle Tm Expert; ROTC Drill Tm.

SMITH, Colleen Marie
Greenfield HS; Greenfield, IL (5-90) Chldr; Chor; Ensm; Spch C; Semi-Fin, Var C; VP, Soph Cl; Tr; Citz A; Most Friendly.

SMITH, Connie Doreen
Monticello HS; Monticello, MS; Ann; BC; Sch P; Beauty; *Co-Lin Jr Col; Data Processing.*

SMITH, Craig Steven
Clifford J Scott HS; E Orange, NJ (50%-222) Aviation.

SMITH, Curtis Dean
Athens HS; Athens, AL (19-273) Ed, Ann; Bio A; Cl Fav; ROTC A; *Ala U; Bus Ed.*

SMITH, Cynthia
Villa Maria Acad; Buffalo, NY; All Amer Yth; Chor; ARC; Swim; Hist A; ARC A; *Bryant Statton Col; Bus.*

SMITH, Cynthia Darlene
Bible Baptist HS; Savannah, GA (10%-54) Chor; Dbte Tm; Fr C; Span C; COM; Hon Prog; *U of Ga; Spch Pathology & Audiology.*

SMITH, Cynthia Denise
Barringer HS; Newark, NJ; Chor; Hmrm; SC; Hist A; Attendance A; *Communications.*

SMITH, Cynthia Elaine
Howard D Woodson HS; Washington, DC (25%-616) Hmrm; NHS; ARC; F-Ed, Sch P; Tres, Span C; SC; Tr; Hon Prog; Type A; Val; Yth Fel; Jr Citz A; GSct; Careers C; Pres; NJHS; Board of Ministries; Afro-Amer Bicentennial Corp Outst; Ntl Tech Assn A; *Harvard U; Law.*

SMITH, Cynthia Ferne
Van-Cove HS; Cove, AR (4-28) F-Ed; Ann; Chldr; VP, FHA; 4H; VP, SC; Cpt, Bkbl; Sftbl; Alg A; Beauty; B Crocker A; 4H A; Math A; Sci A; Yth Fel; Hon Men, All Dist Bkbl; Eng A; *Sou Ark U.*

SMITH, Cynthia Louise
N Platte HS; N Platte, NE; Chor; Drama.

SMITH, Cynthia Marie
Bishop Byrne HS; Memphis, TN (1-190) Secy, Band; Tres, CYO; Chor; NHS; Span C; Alg A; Bio A; COM; NMS; NEDT; VP, CYO; Eng A; *U of Va; Pre-Med.*

SMITH, Dale Ann
Thomson HS; Thomson, GA; 4H; ARC; *Augusta Col; Psych.*

SMITH, Dale Marie
Eupora HS; Eupora, MS; Ann; BC; Cpt, Chldr; Chor; Ensm; FHA; FTA; VP, 4H; Hmrm; SC; VP, Jr Cl; 4H A; Farm Bureau Qn; *Ole Miss; Social Work.*

SMITH, Danette
Acalanes HS; Lafayette, CA; A Cap Choir; Chor; Ensm; Hon Choir; *Universal Beauty Sch; Cosmotology.*

SMITH, Daniel Lee
Norfolk Sr HS; Norfolk, NE (50-320) Band; BS; Ntl Yth Conf; Wrest; Lion A; *Embry Riddle Aeronautical U; Aeronautical Sci.*

SMITH, Daniel Philip
Elyria HS; Elyria, OH (33%-780) FFA; Yth Fel; FFA A's; *Hocking Tech Inst; Agr.*

SMITH, Danny Eugene
Noxubee Co HS; Macon, MS (10-200) Hmrm; Cpt, Bsbl; Yth Fel; *Wood's Jr Col; Phys Ed.*

SMITH, Darlene Dee
W Carteret HS; Morehead City, NC; A Cap Choir; Chor; Fr C; Hmrm; SC; Tr; Gym; Fr A; *ECU; Med.*

SMITH, Darryl Jerome
Cubberley Sr HS; Palo Alto, CA; Bsbl; Cpt, Ftbl; Wrest; Hist A; MVP, Ftbl; *Foothill Jr Col; Pol Sci.*

SMITH, David Alan
McMinn Co HS; Athens, TN; HiY; Order/Arrow; Span C; Ftbl.

SMITH, David Allen
Goshen HS; Goshen, IN (23-289) Band; Chess C; NHS; Orch; SC; Hon Prog; *Bethel Col; Chem.*

SMITH, David Daniel
Bladensburg Sr HS; Bladensburg, MD; Band; Sch P; Ftbl; Alg A; Hist A; I Dare You; Math A; Sci A; *NC A&T Col; Elec.*

SMITH, David Junior
Saddleback HS; Santa Ana, CA; A Cap Choir; Chor; Cpt, Bkbl; Citz A; Elk A; Yth Fel; *U of Calif; Law.*

SMITH, David Kelly
Calhoun HS; Calhoun, GA (5-275) Bus Mgr, Band; Chor; Co-Cpt, Dbte Tm; Drama; Fr C; VP, HiY; InterClub Coun; Key C; NFL; NHS; Spch C; St Stu Congress; VP, Tres; Gov Honor Prog; Hon Prog; Opt A; Opt Out Tn; Spch A; VFW A; VFW Orator Win; VofDEM; Yth Leg; Co-Cpt, Vlbl Tm; St Boy's Quartet; St Dbte Champions; *Yale U; Pre-Med.*

SMITH, David Lee
Burnsville HS; Burnsville, MS (2-46) Pres, BC; SC; Bsbl; Bkbl; Tr; Alcorn Spelling Champion; Most Dependable; Most Intellectual; *Northeast Jr Col; Sci.*

SMITH, David Michael
Crown Point HS; Crown Point, IN (20-570) Band; Chem C; Lat C; Amer Leg A; Most Out; Gym; Med.

SMITH, David Paul
Whiteface HS; Whiteface, TX (12-24) Band; BS; Dbte Tm; Tres, FFA; 4H; SC; VP, Sr Cl; VP, Jr Cl; Tres, Soph Cl; Bsbl; Bkbl; Ftbl; JV, Tnns; Tr; Amer Leg A; Cl Fav; *Tarleton St U; Geol.*

SMITH, David Robert
Fayetteville-Manlius HS; Marlius, NY (66-430) A Cap Choir; Chor; Community Yth Symph; Ch, Ensm; Madrigal; NHS; Ch, Orch; Rptr, Sch P; JV, Cr-Ctry; JV, Tr; COM; Hon Prog; NMS; Regent Schol; Yth Fel; Foreign Lang A; *Mus Ed.*

SMITH, Dawn Renee
Barnesville HS; Barnesville, OH (10-140) Band; InterAct C; Sftbl; COM; 4H A; HCt; Hon Prog; Sci A; Writing, Band, A's; *Ohio Valley Nurs Sch; Nurs.*

SMITH, DeAnna
Kingsbury HS; Memphis, TN (20%-300) Y-Tns; JA A; *St Tech Inst; Acct.*

SMITH, Debbie Lynn
Newark HS; Newark, DE (10-400) AFS; Bus Mgr, Ann; Chor; Dbte Tm; GS; Jr Miss Pagent; NHS; Rptr, Sch P; Span C; St Stu Congress; Secy, SC; COM; Pres & Secy, Hmrm Rep; Ballet As; *U of Del; Bus Adm.*

SMITH, Debbie Jean
Battle Ground HS; Battle Ground, WA; Band; Pres, 4H; Orch; COM; Citz A; *Mus.*

SMITH, Debora Lynn
St Stephens HS; Hickory, NC; Fr C; FHA.

SMITH, Deborah Jeanette
Irvin HS; El Paso, TX (10%-550) Chor; Rptr, Lit Mag; NHS; Span C; Span NHS; Type A; Art A; MVG, Gym; UTEP-SUMMER; Orient Eng; Gym Schol; *U Tex at Austin; Archt Engr.*

SMITH, Deborah Lee
New Bern Sr Sch; New Bern, NC (33-500) Chor; Fr C; NHS; Sci C; Tr; NEDT; J-Sr Pagette; *UNC at Chapel Hill; Zoology.*

SMITH, Deborah Lynn
Jefferson HS; Los Angeles, CA; Chldr; Chor; Semi-Fin, Jr Miss Pa; Hon Prog; Kiwanis A; MLS; Type A; Eng As; Homemaking As; Spelling As; *Cal St at Long Beach; Bus Law.*

SMITH, Deborah Lynne
Robert E Lee HS; San Antonio, TX (25-750) FBLA; JV, Vlbl; *Phys Ed.*

SMITH, Deborah Lynne
New Haven HS; New Haven, MO (5-45) Band; Chldr; NHS; SC; Secy, Jr Cl; Secy, Soph Cl; HCt; Yth Fel; Mus, Ath, Acad, A's; *Elem Counseling.*

SMITH, Deborah Ruth
Irving HS; Irving, TX (25-805) Ed, Ann; Band; Mu Alpha Theta; Rainbow; ARC; Sch P; Tnns; Citz A; DARGCA; Pres A; Yth Fel; Jr Hist; 1st, Poster Contest; 1st Cl GSct; Evangelism Comet; 1st, UIL Solo & Ensm; 1st, Hobie 10 Sailing; *Stephen F Austin St U; Forestry.*

SMITH, Deborah Susan
Carencro HS; Lafayette, LA;

SMITH, Debra Darlene
Bridgeport; Bridgeport, OH; *Ohio U Branch; Phys Therapy.*

SMITH, Debra Kay
Plano Sr HS; Plano, TX (5%-1000) Chor; NHS; Ed, Sch P; Sup Rating, UIL Solo; *Howard Payne Col; Med.*

SMITH, Debra Sue
Winnetonka HS; Kansas City, MO (70-600) VP, A Cap Choir; Cpt, Chldr; Pres, Chor; Drama; Ensm; Hmrm; SC; Tres, Thes; All St Choir; Lead, HS Mus; *Theatre.*

SMITH, Delia Renee
Lanier HS; Jackson, MS (25%-299) Ann; Chldr; Chor; Model UN; Mgr, Bkbl; Mgr, Sftbl; Tnns; Beauty; HCt; *Tenn St U; Biol.*

SMITH, Delores
Dunbar Voc HS; Chicago, IL; Secy, Chor.

SMITH, Denise Gayle
Heritage HS; Littleton, CO (165-467) FBLA; Tr; FCA; Job's Daughters; *Harding Christian Col.*

SMITH, Denny Leland
Shenandoah Valley Acad; New Market, VA (10-77) Cpt, Bkbl; Cpt, Ftbl; Hon Prog; *Va Tech U; Archt.*

SMITH, Dewey Ray
Tyner HS; Chattanooga, TN (39-261) VP, BC; Pres, Hmrm; SC; Var C; VP, Sr Cl; Bsbl; Co-Cpt, Ftbl; Soccer; Most Out; CC Burgner Loyalty A; Bachelor o-t Yr; *U of Tenn; Psych.*

SMITH, Diane Marie
Southside HS; Memphis, TN (15%-370) *St Tech Inst; Nurs.*

SMITH, Diane Michele
Kentridge Sr HS; Kent, WA (33%-560) Band; FBLA; Elk A; *Seattle Pacific U; Bus.*

SMITH, Dianna Jo
Eastern HS; Lansing, MI (150-500) Tres, Sr Cl; *Lansing Comm Col; Corrections.*

SMITH, Don Wilson
Southside HS; Counce, TN; Ann; FFA; *NE Miss Jr Col; Art.*

SMITH, Donald Ashley
W Union Pinola HS; Simpson County, MS (15-60) FFA; 4H; Sci C; Bsbl; Ftbl; HCt; *Copiah-Lincoln Jr Col; Vocational.*

SMITH, Donald Dean Jr
Cashmere HS; Cashmere, WA (33%-100) BS; Chor; Drama; Pres, NHS; Span C; Pres, SC; Ftbl; Tr; Wrest; JA A; Masonic A; Pres, Fresh Cl; *U of Wash; Ed.*

SMITH, Donald Durain
Marshall HS; Chicago, IL (100-250) MVP, Band; Bsbl; Bkbl; MVP, Ftbl; Swim; Cpt, Tr; COM; Sports A; *Eastern Ill; Sport.*

SMITH, Donald Person Jr
Lumberton Sr HS; Lumberton, NC; Lat C; JV, Ftbl; Sci A.

SMITH, Donna Ann
Eastside HS; Gainesville, FL (8-100) Band; Bus C; FHA; NHS; Swim; JV, Tr; Hist A; JA A; *U of Fla; Pre-Med.*

SMITH, Donna Earl
Monticello HS; Monticello, MS (25%-140) Ann; Cpt, Band; BC; FHA; Pres, Hmrm; SC; Beauty; Cl Fav; *Copiah-Lincoln Jr Col; Secretarial.*

SMITH, Donna Gail
Temple Heights Christian Sch; Tampa, FL (10-54) Ann; Chor; NHS; Co-Ed, Sch P; Spch C; Semi-Fin, Sci A; *U of Ga; Journ.*

SMITH, Donna Gayle
Chester Co HS; Henderson, TN (11-126) Band; Commercial C; FTA; Rptr, Hmrm; Mjrte; Bus Mgr, Sch P; SC; H of F; Hon C; Sch Lib Asst A; Schol; *Sou Ala; Bus.*

SMITH, Donna Jean
E Laurens HS; Dublin, GA; FBLA; Tres, FHA; Medal, Cert, Home Ec; Bookkeeping Hon; *Swainsboro Tech Col; Nurs.*

SMITH, Donna Marie
Savannah HS; Savannah, GA; Band; 4H; Pres, Hmrm; Mjrte; S-T, SC; COM; HCt; *Ga Sou Col; Mus.*

SMITH, Doreen Ann
Hope HS; Hope, AR (27-220) Band; BC; FTA; NHS; Span C; *U of Ark at Little Rock; Nurs.*

SMITH, Dorothy Roberta
Heritage Christian Sch; Indianapolis, IN (6-38) F-Ed; Ann; Cpt, Chldr; Secy, Jr Cl; VP, Soph Cl; Q&S A; Sch Hon Soc; WW; *IU; Nurs.*

SMITH, Douglas Eric
E Ridge HS; Chattanooga, TN (43-288) BC; Hmrm; Key C; NHS; SC; Tr; JV, Wrest; Amer Leg A; NEDT; FCA A; *Annapolis Naval Acad; Engr.*

SMITH, Douglas Faamalufanua
Marist Brothers' HS; Pago Pago, AMERICAN SAMOA (4-50) Ed, Ann; Dbte Tm; Rptr, Sch P; Spch C; COM; Hon Prog; Journ A; Spch A; *Col of Idaho; Journ.*

SMITH, Douglas Parker
Kirkwood HS; Kirkwood, MO (94-590) Drama; ARC; SC; Thes; Citz A; Journ A; Opt A; Meritouious Skier; Mediator A; *Creighton U Sch of Med; Med.*

SMITH, Douglas Wilson
John Glenn HS; New Concord, OH (52-210) Tres, A Cap Choir; Chess C; Pres, Drama; Fr C; Lat C; Madrigal; Var C; Bsbl; Co-Cpt, Cr-Ctry; Yth Fel; Tres, Media C; Arion A; *Muskingum Col; Life Sci.*

SMITH, Dwayne Oliver
Rio Lindo Acad; Healdsburg, CA; Sch P; Ftbl; Soccer; *Pacific Union Col; Commercial Art.*

SMITH, Edgar Eugene
Madison Acad HS; Huntsville, AL (1-51) A-Ed, Ann; BC; Dbte Tm; Hmrm; Math C; Monogram; Pres, NHS; SC; Var C; Bsbl; JV, Bkbl; JV, Cr-Ctry; Ftbl; COM; Hist A; Hon Prog; Math A; Sci A; Star Student; Type A; Bible A; Fr A; Jr Civitan; PA; *David Lipscomb Col; Law.*

SMITH, Edson McIntyre
Herbert Hoover HS; Glendale, CA; Pres, Band; Chess C; Community Yth Symph; Drama; Ger C; V-Ch, Lat C; Orch; CSF; Hon Prog; NEDT; PTA A; Mus Schol; Bandsman o-t Yr; *UCLA; Pre-Med.*

SMITH, Edward Lee
Druid HS; Tuscaloosa, AL; *Eckerd Col; Bkbl.*

SMITH, Edward Lee
Hume Fogg Tech HS; Nashville, TN; Up Bound; Cpt, Ftbl.

SMITH, Edward Robin
Smiths Station HS; Smiths, AL (10%-188) Key C; Math C; Mu Alpha Theta; Sci C; Math A; *Auburn U; Engr.*

SMITH, Elizabeth Anne
Guilford HS; Rockford, IL (100-650) Fin, NHS; Hockey; Mgr, Sftbl; Tr; Beauty; Hon Prog; Fin, Dist Tr Meet; Fine Arts A; *N Park Col; Pol Sci.*

SMITH, Ellen Marie
Qn o-t Rosary Acad; Amityville, NY (12-68) CYO; Cpt, Chldr; Hmrm; NHS; Co-Ed, Sch P; St Stu Congress; SC; Alg A; Math A; Ldrs C; Pub Relations; CCD Teacher; Parish Coun; *Boston Col; Pol Sci.*

SMITH, Ellen Marie
Elizabeth Seton HS; Pittsburgh, PA; CYO; Chor; Fr C; Hmrm; NFL; NHS; Sch Achieve Tm; F-Ed, Sch P; SC; JV, Bkbl; Sftbl; Alg A; COM; Hist A; Hon Prog; Math A; NEDT; Sci A; Spch A; Star Student; 1st Cl GSct A; Pro-Life Group; Eng A; Yrbk Staff; Stage Crew; Religion A; Photography C; Vlbl; Runnerup, Press Spelling Bee; *U of Pgh; Journ.*

SMITH, Emma Joyce
St Matthew HS; Melrose, LA; Tres, Chor; Drama; Fr C; FBLA; Secy, FHA; 4H; Bio A; Hon Prog; Home Ec A; Eng A; *U of Houston; Bus Mgt.*

SMITH, Eric Edward
Westside HS; Omaha, NE (350-787) Demolay; ARC; Yth Rep, Church Coun; Off, Order of St John; *St Olaf Col; Drama.*

SMITH, Eric Quenton
Mount Mansfield Union HS; Jericho Ctr, VT; Order/Arrow; Span C; Order/Arrow; Yth Fel.

SMITH, Eugene
Bainbridge HS; Bainbridge, GA (10-300) COM; Hon Prog; *Metalwork.*

SMITH, Eugene Sidney III
Justin F Kimball HS; Dallas, TX (10-700) Chor; Ensm; Ger C; Pres, Math C; Hon Prog; Math A; Bible Credit A; Dal-Hi Orch; Math Tm; European Study Group; *Harding Col; Pre-Med.*

SMITH, Evelyn Mae
Gridley Union HS; Gridley, CA (35-167) Ger C; 4H; Ski C; Bkbl; Sftbl; Sci A; Bowl; *Butte Jr Col; Ass't Phys Therapist.*

SMITH, Felicia Germaine
Eastern Guilford HS; Gibsonville, NC (10%-164) Ann; Fr C; FHA; FTA; GS; Rptr, Hmrm; NHS; Sci C; SC; COM; WW; Hostess, Jr Sr Prom; 1st Runner Up, Sorority Ball; *U of NC; Psych.*

SMITH, Ferne Anthea
Wheaton HS; Wheaton, MD (7-300) Hon Prog; *Montgomery Col; Phys Science.*

SMITH, Francina Kaye
Alcee Fortier Sr HS; New Orleans, LA; Mjrte; *Nurse RN.*

SMITH, Francis Wellington Jr
Winston Churchill HS; Potomac, MD (9-1200) 4H; Bsbl; Bkbl; Ftbl; Tr; H of F.

SMITH, Gabrielle Ruth
Murdock Pub Sch; Murdock, MN (1-35) Ann; Band; Chor; Drama; Rptr, Sch P; Span C; Pres, Jr Cl; Secy, Soph Cl; Bkbl; Hon Prog; VofDEM; *Vet Med.*

SMITH, Gaila Jan
Appalachian HS; Oneonta, AL (4-37) Ann; BC; Sch P; Tres, Sr Cl; Rptr, Jr Cl; Most Studious.

SMITH, George Edward
Dunbar Voc HS; Chicago, IL (30-328) Merit A; Employee o-t Month; Solo Comp A; *Chicago St U; Carpentry.*

SMITH, Giner Arlene
Oakdale HS; Oakdale, LA (3-129) Chor; Secy, FHA; Semi-Fin, Lit Ral; VP, NHS; Spch C; H of F; Hon Prog; Home Ec A; Eng A; Most Civic Minded Girl A; *LSU at Alexandre; Elem Ed.*

SMITH, Glen Castle
Harrah HS; Harrah, OK (10-125) Chor; NHS; SC; Var C; VP, Soph Cl; Bsbl; Bkbl; Co-Cpt, Ftbl; COM; Citz A; Hist A; Hon Prog; Sci A; Cpt, Ftbl; Industrial Arts A; Eng A; *Okla Baptist U; Minister of Mus.*

SMITH, Glenwood Eugene Jr
Kinston HS; Kinston, NC (42-331) Chess C; Hmrm; Pres, Order/Arrow; Pol Sci C; Ftbl; God & Country A; Eagle Sct; *NC St U; Textile Tech.*

SMITH, Gordon Brian
Glenbard W HS; Glen Ellyn, IL; Radio Station Mgr; VP, Church Tn C; *Col of Dupage; Elec Tech.*

SMITH, Gregory Brian
Pattonville Sr HS; Hazelwood, MO (13-1000) Band; Dbte Tm; NFL; NHS; COM; Hon Prog.

SMITH, Gregory Valdemar
All Saints Cathedral Sch; St Thomas, VI (2-28) Dbte Tm; Span C; SC; Bkbl; Tnns; COM; Hon Prog.

SMITH, Gretchen Elaine
Wm Penn Sr HS; York, PA (73-564) Band; Vlbl; Jr NHS; GAA; Secy, Pastor's Yth Organization; *York Col; Legal Secy.*

SMITH, Gwendolyn Denise
Clements HS; Athens, AL (10-50) F-Ed, Ann; BC; Chldr; FHA; 4H; F-Ed, Sch P; Bkbl; Cpt, Tr; Citz A; Gov Honor Prog; HCt; Hon Prog; Journ A; Pres A; Vlbl; Youthpoll Amer; Most Ath; St Champ Tr, 100 Yd Dash; *Ala St U; Biol.*

SMITH, Heather Sue
Marion HS; Marion, IN (64-750) Co-Ed, Ann; Arch; S-T, SC; Pres, Soph Cl; Young Life; *Purdue U; Sci.*

SMITH, Heidi Lyman
Andover HS; Andover, MA (28-510) NMS; Type A; VFW A; Ntl Coun of Eng Teachers A; Townwide Essay Contest; *Lewis and Clark Col; Psych.*

SMITH, Heidi M
Spring Valley HS; Spring Valley, WI (15-85) NFL; Tr; Pres A; Vlbl; *Viterbo Col; Nurs.*

SMITH, Heldise Annette
Thornton HS; Harvey, IL (103-839) A Cap Choir; Drama; Ensm; HS; Hmrm; NHS; SC; COM; Most Out; PTA A; T-Ettes; *Prarie St Col; Law.*

SMITH, Ileta Faye
United Township HS; E Moline, IL (201-792) Drama; Span C; *Bus Adm.*

SMITH, Irving Lee III
Roanoke HS; Robersonville, NC (24-145) Band; FFA; Hmrm; SC; Bsbl; Co-Cpt, Ftbl; Jr Cl Band A; *E Carolina U.*

SMITH, J Frazier
Walnut Hills HS; Cincinnati, OH; A Cap Choir; Chor; Ensm; JV, Bkbl; Ftbl; COM; Most Out; *Ohio St U; Journ.*

SMITH, Jack Darrel
Compton HS; Compton, CA (4-895) Dbte Tm; Span C; Spch C; Bkbl; Co-Cpt, Ftbl; Tr; Cpt, Wrest; CSF; Hon Prog; *U of Sou Calif; Bus.*

SMITH, Jacqueline Annette
Seton HS; Baltimore, MD (39-154) Chor; Secy, Drama; Yth Fel; WW; Yr Day Skit Writer; Dance C; VP Sr Yth Fel; Soc of Creative Arts; Acolyte; *U of Md; Bus Adm.*

SMITH, Jacqueline Kay
Gordon HS; Gordon, NE (43-88) Band; Chor; Drama; Thes; Golf; Citz A; Job's Daughters; Gym Tm; *Home Ec.*

SMITH, Jacquelyn Elaine
Joppatowne Jr-Sr HS; Joppatowne, MD (33%-150) Band; Chor; Black Hist Art A; GScts; 1st Pl, Co Art Show; Jr Olympics A; Artist, Poet, Sch P; Chrch Yth Chor; 1st Pl, Jr Bowling League; *U of W Va; Commercial Art.*

SMITH, James Albert
East HS; Denver, CO; JV, Bkbl; JV, Tr; COM; Most Out; *Langston U; Computer Sci.*

SMITH, James Allen
Chicago Voc HS; Chicago, IL (127-965) Bsbl; *Ill Inst of Tech; Engr.*

SMITH, James Byron
Marvell HS; Marvell, AR (12-120) All Amer Yth; FFA; Bsbl; Co-Cpt, Bkbl; Co-Cpt, Ftbl; Tr; MLS; *Henderson St U; Phys Ed.*

SMITH, James Edwin
Hoisington HS; Hoisington, KS; Var C; VP, Soph Cl; Bsbl; JV, Bkbl; Ftbl; Tr; FCA; *Okla U; Phys Ed.*

SMITH, James Gregory
Raleigh Egypt HS; Memphis, TN (21-255) Chem C; Fr C; VP, Mu Alpha Theta; NHS; Sci C; SC; *Southwestern at Memphis; Math.*

SMITH, James H
Harry S Truman HS; Bronx, NY (671-923) Band; *Drew U; Pilot.*

SMITH, James Ora
Layton HS; Layton, UT (13-454) Chess C; Dbte Tm; Math C; Model UN; NFL; NHS; Sci C; COM; Hist A; Hon Prog; Math A; Sci A; Spch A; *Southwest Baptist Col; Ministry.*

SMITH, James Wiley Ross
Cath HS; Little Rock, AR (50-180) MVP, Chess C; MVP, Soccer; MVP, Tr; *Hendrix Col; Med.*

SMITH, Jamie Lee
Commerce HS; Commerce, OK (21-55) Band; Chor; Drama; Ensm; FHA; Pres, 4H; Jr Miss Pageant; Key C; ARC; Co-Ed, Sch P; Spch C; Rptr, Sr Cl; Ftbl; Sftbl; Chamber of Comm A; 4H A; ARC A; Spch A; Pub Speaking A; Sunday Sch Teacher; Co 4-H Off & Songleader; Rptr, Pep C; Church Choir; *NEO Jr Col; Journ.*

SMITH, Jana Leigh
Bend Sr HS; Bend, OR (22-459) Chor; Ensm; Hmrm; NHS; ARC; Span C; ARC A; Type A; *George Fox Col.*

SMITH, Jane Ellen
Grandview Hts HS; Columbus, OH (8-130) VP, Band; Chor; Ensm; NHS; Tnns; Hon Prog; Pres, GAA; Fred Waring Mus Workshop Schol; *Ohio St U; Floriculture.*

SMITH, Janelle Marie
Auburn Sr HS; Auburn, NE (24-92) Band; Chldr; FHA; Pres, 4H; Math C; Sci C; Pres, Span C; Mgr, Bkbl; Swim; 4H A; S-T, 4-H C; *NW Mo St U; Elem Ed.*

SMITH, Janet Catherine
Lincoln Sr HS; Bloomington, MN; Orch; Ski C; SC; Y-Tns; Pres, Sr Cl; Pres, Jr Cl; Co-Cpt, Bkbl; Sftbl; Tr; MVP, Bkbl; All Conf, Bkbl; *Normandale Jr Col.*

SMITH, Janet Elaine
T L Hanna HS; Anderson, SC (6-315) GS; Pres, Lat C; Monogram; Pres, NHS; Bkbl; Tnns; Beauty; NEDT; Rensselaer A; Commencement Marshal; Lat A; Furman Schol; Wofford Schol; Win, Declamation Contest; USC Schol; *Anderson Col; Phar.*

SMITH, Janet Kay
Cooperstown HS; Cooperstown, ND (5-40) Band; Chldr; Chor; Rptr, Sch P; S-T, SC.

SMITH, Janet Lee
Waverly HS; Lansing, MI; Band; Hmrm; Pres, Soph Cl; JV, Bkbl; Sftbl; JV, Swim; COM; Hist A; HCt; Hon Prog; Opt A; Spch A; Type A; Pres & VP, SC; Ath As; SC As; *U of Colo; Creative Writing.*

SMITH, Janet Leigh
Beech Hill HS; Pulaski, TN (3-27) Ann; BC; FHA; VP, Sr Cl; Cl Fav; Sci A; WW; *Martin Col.*

SMITH, Janet Marie
St Joseph-Ogden HS; St Joseph, IL (13-120) Chor; Ensm; Fin, GS; NHS; Span C; SC; Secy, Thes; Var C; Secy, Jr Cl; Mgr, Tr; *Milligan Col; Hist.*

SMITH, Janice Anne
Truman HS; Independence, MO (93-663) CYO; Fr C; FTA; A-Ed, Lit Mag; NFL; A-Ed, Sch P; COM; Opt A; Q&S A; Spch A; Lit Arts Sem C; Cream o-t Crop; *Eng.*

SMITH, Janice Leslie
Alexander Galt Regional HS; Lennoxville, CAN-ADA (17-539) Chor; Hmrm; SC; Hockey; Hon Prog; Ch, Prom Comm; Cpt, MVP, Vlbl; *Champlain Col; Psych.*

SMITH, Janice Ruth
Boulevard Baptist Sch; Burleson, TX; Chldr; Chor; Ed, Sch P; Sftbl; Tr; HQn; Most Stu.

SMITH, Janie Elaine
Sullivan Central HS; Blountville, TN (4-400) Bus Mgr, Ann; BC; Chor; NHS; Span C; Span NHS; Hist A; Wesley Found Schol; Emory & Henry Schol List; *Emory & Henry Col; Ministry.*

SMITH, Janis Lea
Pleasanton HS; Pleasanton, TX (50%-151) Band; Chor; FHA; FTA; Madrigal; Mjrte; Golf; *Southwest Tex St U; Commercial Art.*

SMITH, Jason
Russell HS; Hurtsboro, AL; Chem C; FTA; Pres, 4H; Lit Mag; NHS; Sci C; Pres, Jr Cl; Bkbl; COM; Citz A; Hist A; Hon Prog; ROTC A; Eng A.

SMITH, Jay Roger
Speedway HS; Speedway, IN (22-190) NHS; Var C; Bsbl; Ftbl; JV, Wrest; Pres A; Type A; *Ball St U; Archt.*

SMITH, Jean Laslon
Tyner HS; Chattanooga, TN; Anchor C; BC; *Chatt St U; Secretarial Sci.*

SMITH, Jeffery Jay
Mount Si HS; Shoqualmie, WA (8-208) Math C; Mu Alpha Theta; Pres, Sci C; Var C; Wrest; JA A; Math A; NMF; *Annapolis; Aeronautical Engr.*

SMITH, Jeffery Lynn
Thornton Township HS; Harvey, IL; Chor; Hmrm; Spch C; SC; MVP, Ftbl; MVP, Wrest.

SMITH, Jeffrey Allen
Tahlequah Sr HS; Tahlequah, OK; Chor; Fr C; Span C; Arch; Bsbl; Ftbl; Soccer; Swim; *NE Okla St U; Bio.*

SMITH, Jeffrey Donnell
Eupora HS; Eupora, MS; VP, BC; Dbte Tm; 4H; Pres, Soph Cl; MVP, Ftbl; St Champ, 4-H C; Election Commissioner, SC; Ch, Church Clean-Up Committee; Mile Swim, BSct; *Miss St U; Acct.*

SMITH, Jeffrey Gene
Fairmont E HS; Kettering, OH (100-800) NFL; Span C; Var C; Bsbl; Spch A; *Wright St Col; Acct.*

SMITH, Jeffrey Lee
Cumberland Valley HS; Mechanicsburg, PA (11-585) NHS; Cpt, Bsbl; MVP, Bkbl; Cpt, Ftbl; Amer Leg A; COM; Hon Prog; Math A; Pres A; Cpt, Bkbl; Project Concern; WW; *Engr.*

SMITH, Jeffrey Lynn
Sunbright HS; Sunbright, TN (12-63) Band; VP, Drama; Secy, FFA; Pres, 4H; Rptr, Sch P; 4H A; *U of Tenn; Agr.*

SMITH, Jeffrey Wheaton
Westboro HS; Westboro, MA (10-250) Secy, Band; Demolay; NHS; Orch; Ski C; St Stu Congress; Co-Cpt, Soccer; Tnns; Alt, BS; A-Ed, Yrbk; Church Bkbl; *Brown Col; Econ.*

SMITH, Jeffrey Willard
Lake Forest HS; Lake Forest, IL (68-465) Ger C; *Col of Lake Co; Hist.*

SMITH, Jeffrey William
Tulpehocken HS; Bernville, PA; Band; Chor; Pres, 4H; SC; Bkbl; Soccer; Tnns; COM; 4H A; *Elim Bible Inst; Ministry.*

SMITH, Jennifer Kaye
George Washington Carver HS; Montgomery, AL; FHA; Hmrm; Mu Alpha Theta; ARC; Sci C; Span C; Secy, SC; MLS; ARC A; Homemaker o-t Yr; *Auburn U.*

SMITH, Jennifer Marie
London HS; London, OH (2-164) Chldr; Drama; Secy, 4H; Hmrm; NHS; A-Ed, Sch P; Tres, SC; Tr; 4H A; Kiwanis A; JV, Vlbl; Top Twenty; *Wittenburg Col; Art.*

SMITH, Jenny C
Gadsden HS; Gadsden, AL; Pres, Chor; Ensm; InterClub Coun; DECA C; Chaplin, SC; Pres, Phi Omega Phi Social Sorority; *Phys Therapy.*

SMITH, Jerome Elmer
August Martin HS; New York, NY; Band; Chor; SC; Ftbl; Tr; *Auto Mech.*

SMITH, Jethro Kevin
Blue Mountain Acad; Hamburg, PA (15-100) Band; Chor; Bkbl; Ftbl; Sftbl; Swim; Hon Prog; *Loma Linda U; Bio.*

SMITH, Jimmie Marquette
Sw HS; Atlanta, GA (3-240) Band; BC; NHS; Orch; Pres, Sci C; Alg A; Citz A; Hon Prog; Math A; Most Out; ROTC A; Sci A; *Morehouse Col; Sci.*

SMITH, Joan Marie
Lincoln HS; Portland, OR; Y-Tns; Gym; *Portland St U; Art.*

SMITH, Joann Kay
Maddock Pub HS; Maddock, ND (5-28) Ed, Ann; Secy, Band; Chor; SC; Pres, Sr Cl; Rptr, FHA; Math A; John Philip Sousa Band A; All-St Band; Chor A; *Moorhead St U; Elem Special Ed.*

SMITH, Jocelyn Rene
Golden Gate Acad; Oakland, CA (5-22) A Cap Choir; Parl, Anchor C; Chor; FNA; Co-Ed, Lit Mag; Bsbl; Sftbl; Tnns; Bio A; Citz A; Journ A; MLS; *Loma Linda U; Nurs.*

SMITH, John Harley
Claremore HS; Claremore, OK; Ftbl; FCA; *Bus.*

SMITH, John Mark
W E Stebbins HS; Dayton, OH (20-460) SC; Thes; Bio A; DARGCA; HCt; Opt A; NCTE Writing A; Ntl Merit Commended Stu; *Wright St U; Eng.*

SMITH, John Michael
Washington Co HS; Springfield, KY (8-175) BC; BS; Drama; Hmrm; F-Ed, Sch P; Span C; Pres, SC; Var C; Bsbl; Bkbl; Ftbl; HCt; ROTC A; 4-H Ky Yth Sem; ROTC Region Stu Ldrship Wk; *Vanderbilt U; Molecular Bio.*

SMITH, John Nickolas
F Douglas Byrd Sr HS; Fayetteville, NC (132-432) BC; Sch P; SC; DECA C; Short Story As; *Campbell Col; Religion.*

SMITH, John Paul
Beeson Acad; Hattiesburg, MS (18-32) Hmrm; Sch P; SC; Pres, Sr Cl; Bsbl; Ftbl; Cl Fav; Spch A; *Miss St U; Mech Engr.*

SMITH, John Wayne
Wadley HS; Wadley, GA; Secy, FFA.

SMITH, Jonathan Cedric
Thornton Township HS; Harvey, IL (80-892) Chor; Drama; NFL; NHS; Pres, SC; Thes; Ntl Achv Schol; Spch A; St Scholar; Alpha Kappa Psi Schol; Foreign Exchange; *Princeton U; Pol.*

SMITH, Joni Allison
Newton Co Comprehensive HS; Covington, GA (25%-300) Band; Bus C; Chor; FHA; 4H; Hmrm; InterClub Coun; Lit Mag; Ed, Sch P; Span C; St Stu Congress; SC; Tri-HiY; Ch, Y-Tns; Bio A; COM; Citz A; DARGCA; Hon Prog; Journ A; Yth Fel; Yth Leg; *N Ga Col; Bio.*

SMITH, Joseph David
Ashville HS; Ashville, AL (10%-70) BC; NHS; Cl Fav; Math A; Pres A; Sci A; *Engr.*

SMITH, Joseph Ray
Thomas Carr Howe HS; Indianapolis, IN (181-720) Hmrm; SC; Var C; Bsbl; Ftbl; Cpt, Golf; COM; Kiwanis A; MVP, Golf; City Stu Congress; *Ball St U; Archt Design.*

SMITH, Joyce Ann
Wendell Phillips HS; Chicago, IL (20-398) SC; Bkbl; Cpt, Tr; COM; *Bradley U; Bus.*

SMITH, Judith Carol
Elyria HS; Elyria, OH (6-640) Band; NHS; Orch; Scholastic Ltr; Band Ltr; Bowling Green St U; *Chem.*

SMITH, Judy Ann
John F Kennedy Sr HS; Bloomington, MN; NHS; Sftbl; Bowling.

SMITH, Judy Elaine
Steubenville HS; Steubenville, OH (43-186) F-Ed, Ann; Ger C; Co-Ed, Sch P; Bkbl; Tnns; Journ A; Photography A; *Chatham Col; Journ.*

SMITH, Judy Linn
Hutchinson HS; Hutchinson, MN (6-211) AFS; Band; F-Ed, Sch P; Thes; Hon Prog; Journ A; *U of Minn at Minneapolis; Phar.*

SMITH, Julia Anita
Compton HS; Compton, CA (20%-850) Chor; Drama; Spch C; CSF; Spch A; *UCLA; Law.*

SMITH, Julia Diane
Whiteface HS; Whiteface, TX; Band; FFA; FHA; Mjrte; Bkbl; Tnns; Tr; Cl Fav; Swtht; *S Plains Col; Lab Technology.*

SMITH, Julia Marie
Fort Jennings HS; Fort Jennings, OH; Band; Chldr; Chor; Bkbl; Golf; Sftbl; Tr; Amer Leg A; MLS; NEDT; Sci A; Schol Tm; Sr Musical Play; Art C; Computer Games; *U of Dayton; Pre-Law.*

SMITH, Julie Agnes
Tylertown HS; Tylertown, MS (20%-118) Hon Prog; Hospital Tn Vol; VP, Acteens; Church Yth Choir; *SW Miss Jr Col; Nurs.*

SMITH, Julie Rene
D Perry Walker HS; New Orleans, LA; Bus C; Chor; Ensm; Fr C; NHS; COM; Jr Chamber of Com A; *U of New Orleans; Med Tech.*

SMITH, Justin Jay
Hicks HS; Hicks, LA; Bkbl; Kiwanis A; Yth Fel; Stu Lib; *Drafting.*

SMITH, Karen Elaine
Hanceville HS; Hanceville, AL (6-104) VP, Band; VP, Ensm; FTA; NHS; *Jefferson St Jr Col; Computer Sci.*

SMITH, Karen Jenean
Kenwood HS; Chicago, IL; Chldr; Span C; Citz A; Swtht; Yth Fel.

SMITH, Karen Jo
Hobbs HS; Hobbs, NM (22-400) A Cap Choir; Secy, Bus C; Chor; Ensm; NHS; Off Ed Service A; WW; *NM Jr Col; Bus.*

SMITH, Karen Louise
Cairo HS; Cairo, IL (1-79) Co-Ed, Ann; GS; Pres, NHS; Sch P; SC; Elk A; Hon Prog; Journ A; MLS; St Scholar; Val; WW; *Sou Ill U.*

SMITH, Karen Lynn
Abbeville HS; Abbeville, LA; Band; BC; Hmrm; Bkbl; Sftbl; Tr; Pres A; *U of Sou La; Ed.*

SMITH, Karen Suzette
Franklin Co HS; Winchester, TN (86-310) Chor; FBLA; Sftbl; WW; *Motlow St Com Col; Acct.*

SMITH, Karla Jean
Quitman HS; Quitman, TX (16-77) Chor; Drama; FHA; Span C; COM; Yth Fel; S-T, Church Yth Organization; JV, Vlbl; Church Organist; *N Tex St U; Journ.*

SMITH, Kathleen Beth
Monterey HS; Lubbock, TX; Fr C; NHS; Tri-HiY; COM; Hon Prog; *Baylor U; Med Sci.*

SMITH, Kathleen Elizabeth
St Joseph HS; Camden, NJ (35-111) CYO; Chldr; Fr C; Hmrm; Hon Prog; *Special Ed.*

SMITH, Kathleen Verle
S R Butler HS; Huntsville, AL; SC; Swim; Most Improved, Swim; Swim Medals.

SMITH, Kathy Dean
Evadale HS; Evadale, TX (2-40) Ann; Band; Drama; FHA; Math C; Spch C; Bkbl; Sftbl; Tr; COM; Sal; Spch A; *Lamar U.*

SMITH, Kathy Lynn
E Central HS; Tulsa, OK (10%-600) A Cap Choir; Band; Chor; Ensm; FBLA; Hmrm; NHS; Orch; ARC; Span C; Bkbl; Ftbl; Sftbl; Swim; COM; Citz A; Most Out; Yth Fel; Yth Leg; *Oral Roberts U; Secy.*

SMITH, Kathy Lynn
Eastern Guilford HS; Gibsonville, NC (25%-177) F-Ed, Ann; Sci C.

SMITH, Kathy Swan
Haltom HS; Fort Worth, TX (10%-450) S-T, A Cap Choir; Chor; Drama; Ensm; NHS; Choir Jr Fav; *Baylor U.*

SMITH, Keith Dale
Elkins HS; Elkins, WV (4-240) Band; Ensm; Key C; NHS; Bausch & Lomb A; Hon Prog; Math A; *W Va U; Mining Engr.*

SMITH, Keith Elliot
Amphitheater HS; Tucson, AZ (99-398) Bus C; Model UN; Sch P; 4H A; Q&S A; *Pepperdine U; Theology.*

SMITH, Kelly Anne
Ojai Valley HS; Ojai, CA; Ed, Ann; Chor; Drama; Fr C; Span C; SC; Sftbl; Swim; Tnns; Alg A; Hist A; *Loyola Marymount Col; Psych.*

SMITH, Kelly Marie
Springfield Sr HS; Springfield, OR (5-296) Chor; NHS; Var C; Bkbl; Sftbl; Tr; MVP, Vlbl; *Eastern Oreg St Col; Health.*

SMITH, Kelmer Ray Jr
Brookhaven Acad; Brookhaven, MS; BC; COM; Hist A.

SMITH, Kenneth Dean
St Joseph-Ogden HS; St Joseph, IL (6-98) Ann; Chor; Ger C; NHS; Bsbl; Cpt, Bkbl; Ftbl; Tr; Amer Leg A; HCt; St Scholar; Pres, FCA; *Ozark Bible Col; Bible.*

SMITH, Kenneth Lee
New Caney HS; New Caney, TX (4-223) Demolay; NHS; F-Ed, Sch P; Span C; SC; Hist A; *Stephen F Austin St U.*

SMITH, Kenneth Sims
Beaumont HS; St Louis, MO; Work Stu A; *Northwestern U; Archt.*

SMITH, Kevin Dwight
Oak Ridge HS; Orlando, FL (40-1200) Band; Lit Mag; NHS; Var C; Tr; Pres A; FCA; Tr A; All Conf Tr Tm; *U of Fla; Biol.*

SMITH, Kevin Laine
Suffolk HS; Suffolk, VA (11-118) Pres, Band; Inter-Club Coun; Key C; NHS; Golf; *Va Tech U; Aerospace Engr.*

SMITH, Kevin Lamont
Mt Clemens HS; Mt Clemens, MI; Chor; Drama; InterAct C; Hon Prog; COM; Pres, SC; VP, Soph Cl; Cpt, Bkbl; Ftbl; Co-Cpt, Tr; Citz A; DARGCA; Hon Prog; Kiwanis A; Pres A; *Pepperdine U; Law.*

SMITH, Kevin Lee
Sacred Heart Acad; Salem, OR (5-33) Chess C; NHS; Ed, Sch P; Pres, SC; Bsbl; JV, Bkbl; Soccer; Elk A; Regent Schol; Rotary A; *St Martin's Col; Ed.*

SMITH, Kim Bryant
Normandy HS; St Louis, MO; Bus C; Dbte Tm; Ch, FBLA; Hmrm; Spch C; SC; JV, Tnns; Citz A; NMS; Spch A; Outst Yth A; Public Speaking; FBLA, MC; *U of Mo-St Louis; Law.*

SMITH, Kim Clarice
Southwest HS; Atlanta, GA (16-270) BC; CYO; Chldr; Tnns; Bio A; COM; HCt; Hon Prog; *Pepperdine U; Bio.*

SMITH, Kimberly J
Cadiz HS; Cadiz, OH (2-100) Band; Chem C; GS; Lat C; Phys C; Span C; Hist A; Sci A; Eng Lit A; *Muskingum Col; Engr.*

SMITH, Kimberly Louise
Olmsted Falls HS; Olmsted Falls, OH (59-265) A-Ed, Ann; Chor; Ensm; F-Ed, Sch P; Sftbl; Tnns; Rptr, Sch P; Pres, Church Yth; Amer Yth in Concert; Candystriper; St Bicentennial Choir; Mus A; *Bethel Col; Sci.*

SMITH, Kirk Linwood
Highlands HS; N Highlands, CA; Band; Drama; Rptr, Sch P; SC; Pres, Jr Cl; Bkbl; Ftbl; Soccer; Sftbl; Tr; *Commercial Art.*

SMITH, Kristi Lynn
Irving HS; Irving, TX (5-590) A Cap Choir; Secy, Chor; Drama; Fr C; Secy, Math C; Secy, Mu Alpha Theta; NHS; St Stu Congress; Pres, SC; Thes; Y-Tns; COM; Citz A; DARGCA; Hon Prog; Opt A; Fin, TACT; Tr Swtht; Top Tiger o-Wk; *Sou Methodist U; Mus.*

SMITH, Kyda Ann
Springfield HS; Springfield, OR; Band; NHS; Ed, Sch P; JV, Tr; Type A; 1st Cl, GSct; God & Comm A; *Pepperdine U; Journ.*

SMITH, Kym Clarice
Southwest Atlanta HS; Atlanta, GA (16-270) BC; CYO; Co-Cpt, Chldr; Pres, Hmrm; Tnns; Bio A; HCt; Sci A; *Pepperdine U; Bio.*

SMITH, Lance Clay
Jefferson HS; Los Angeles, CA; A Cap Choir; Chor; Drama; InterClub Coun; Ntl Yth Conf; Bsbl; Co-Cpt, Bkbl; Co-Cpt, Ftbl; Tr; Church Choir; Usher Board; Most Inspirational, Ftbl; *Long Beach City Col; Psych.*

SMITH, Lanor
Mount Olive HS; Ft Mitchell, AL (2-63) Secy, 4H; NHS; Sch P; SC; Bkbl; Ftbl; Bio A; 4H A; Hon Prog; ROTC A; Sci A; Spch A.

SMITH, Larry Gene
Brownstown HS; Brownstown, IL (4-36) Pres, FFA; Pres, 4H; NHS; Tres, Var C; Bsbl; Bkbl; Tr; HCt; *Lake Land Jr Col; AG Mech Tech.*

SMITH, Larry Walter Jr
Picayune Mem HS; Picayune, MS; DECA; *Pearl River Jr Col; Animal Sci.*

SMITH, Laura Elaine
Lyons Sr HS; Lyons, GA (30-100) FBLA; VP, FTA; Bkbl; Sftbl; Hon Prog; FCA; FCA A; PE A; Ltr C; *Special Ed.*

SMITH, Laura Lee
Richland HS; Richland Hills, TX (25%-575) Tres, FTA; Ger C; Lit Mag; NHS; Cpt, Bkbl; Sftbl; Tnns; Hon Prog; Swtht; Bkbl Swtht; Poet Hon; *N Tex St U; Bus.*

SMITH, Laura Lou
Perry HS; Massillon, OH; *Cosmetology.*

SMITH, Laura Lynn
Highland Park HS; Dallas, TX (101-392) AFS; Tres, Chor; Fr C; Thes; Tri-HiY; Y-Tns; MVP, Soccer; Yth Fel; Ballet A; Piano Ribbons; *Math.*

SMITH, Laurie Ann
Overbrook HS; Philadelphia, PA; Chor; Drama; Hmrm; Ntl Yth Conf; COM; Citz A; Hon Prog; TS Medley A; PA; Fr A; SG Conf Ldr; *Penn St U; Pediatrics Asst.*

SMITH, Lavonna Ann
John Marshall HS; Indianapolis, IN (100-250) Drama; *Ind U; Nurs.*

SMITH, Lawrence Edward
T R Miller HS; Brewton, AL; Band; Ensm; Order/ Arrow; ARC; Spch C; Bkbl; Order/Arrow A; Bkbl Ltr; *Navy; Radar Operator.*

SMITH, Lee Norman
Antilles HS; Ft Buchanan, PR (7-124) Ed, Ann; Band; Pres, Key C; NHS; Orch; SC; VP, Soph Cl; JV, Golf; NMS; Ntl Sci Found; NEDT; DAHSS.

SMITH, Leigh Anne
First Baptist Church Sch; Charleston, SC (2-44) Semi-Fin, GS; Pres, NHS; Pres, Jr Cl; Citz A; Gov Honor Prog; NEDT; Furman Schol; Presbyt Col Jr Fel; *Eng.*

SMITH, Leland Alan
Cheraw HS; Cheraw, SC; Key C; Thes.

SMITH, Lesa Faye
Olustee HS; Olustee, OK (6-20) Cpt, Chldr; Chor; Rptr, FHA; Rptr, GS; 4H; Rptr, Sch P; SC; Rptr, Sr Cl; Rptr, Jr Cl; Tres, Soph Cl; Cpt, Bkbl; Amer Leg A; Citz A; HCt; Lion A; Masonic A; Most Outst; MVP, Bkbl; Amer Bus Women Schol; Scottish Rights Schol; Miss OHS; *W Okla St Col; Child Care Adm.*

SMITH, Lesha Sue
North Hall HS; Gainesville, GA; BC; Chldr; FBLA; FHA; Fin, GS; Fin, Hmrm; ARC; SC; COM; Citz A; Fav; Opt A; Lang A; Church Yth Group; Eng Academics A.

SMITH, Leslie Karen
Hiram Johnson HS; Sacramento, CA (200-853) Rptr, Sch P; *Sacramento St U; Counselor.*

SMITH, Leslie Laurelle
Whetstone Sr HS; Columbus, OH; MLS; Yth Fel; Jr NHS; *Oral Roberts U; Nurs.*

SMITH, Lethara
Havana HS; Havana, FL; Rptr, NHS; Rptr, Jr Cl; Spelling A; Phys Fitness A; Pen Pals; *FSU; Advertising.*

SMITH, Letitia Rae
Kubasaki HS; Okinawa, JAPAN (8-421) Chldr; Chor; *Auburn U; Vet Med.*

SMITH, Lewis John
Harlingen HS; Harlingen, TX;

SMITH, Lillian Rachel
University Sch of Nashville; Nashville, TN (50%-84) AFS; Fr C; SC; Secy, Jr Cl; Hockey; *Horticulture.*

SMITH, Linda Drunell
Jones Co HS; Gray, GA; Fr C; FBLA; Model UN; VP, NHS; COM; Morris Brown Col Schol; Shorthand A; *Morris Brown Col; Sociology.*

SMITH, Linda Elaine
Maplewood HS; Cortland, OH (7-96) BC; Drama; Fr C; FTA; NHS; Sch P; Sftbl; Math A; Sci A; Pres, Bible C; Fr A; Eng A; *Ashland Col; Religion.*

SMITH, Linda Kay
Richmond Sr HS; Rockingham, NC (5-730) BC; Hmrm; Pres, Span C; Span Highest Achv A; *Bus Adm.*

SMITH, Linda Louise
Corinth Christian Acad; Kinsman, OH (2-6) Band; Cpt, Chldr; Secy, Chor; Secy, Rainbow; ARC; Ski C; Cpt, Bkbl; Sftbl; Cl Fav; God & Country A; MLS; Ntl Achv Schol; NMS; *Brescia Col; Spch & Hearing Therapy.*

SMITH, Linda Sue
New Hartford HS; New Hartford, IA (3-32) Co-Ed, Ann; Chor; Pres, 4H; Sch P; Bkbl; Tr; B Crocker A; Sup Academic Achv A; Ntl Assn of Math A.

SMITH, Lindon Carl
Thomas Jefferson HS; Council Bluffs, IA (6-498) Chess C; Chor; Demolay; Ensm; Hi-Y; NHS; Orch; Ed, Sch P; St Stu Congress; SC; Bkbl; Ftbl; Tnns; COM; Citz A; Journ A; JA A; Kiwanis A; Opt A; Pres A; Spch A; *Math.*

SMITH, Linn Marie
Dillingham HS; Dillingham, AK (2-27) Co-Cpt, Bkbl; Sal; Attendance A; Lang Arts A; *Northwest Christian Col.*

SMITH, Llorre B
Northrop HS; Fort Wayne, IN (111-671) Art A; Nisbova A; *Art.*

SMITH, Lori Annette
Sonoma Valley HS; Sonoma, CA (100-175) Citz A; Choir Pianist; Church Organist; *Santa Rosa JC; Banking.*

SMITH, Louanne
New Bern Sr HS; New Bern, NC; Bus C; Chor; Drama; FBLA; FTA; *Craven Comm Col; Nurs.*

SMITH, Louise Christine
Manley HS; Chicago, IL (7-443) Chor; VP, NHS; SC; Bkbl; Soccer; Tnns; COM; Citz A; Hon Prog; Math A; Most Out; Ntl Achv Schol; Sci A; Type A; Rotary C; Chor A; SC A; Cowhide C; Most Outst Gym Stu; Service A; Art A; *U of Ill; Computer Data.*

SMITH, Luann
Secaucus HS; Secaucus, NJ (49-164) Cpt, Bkbl; Sftbl; Tr; Kiwanis A; Cl Ath; All Tri-Co Bsbl, Sftbl & Bkbl.

SMITH, Lydia Renay
Bennett HS; Buffalo, NY; Chldr; Math C; Span C; SC; Soph Cl; Swim; Alg A; Bio A; COM; Citz A; Hon Prog; Math A; Regent Schol; AKA Debutante; *GMI; Math.*

SMITH, Machelle Eilene
George Washington HS; Los Angeles, CA; Chldr; Chor; FBLA; Sftbl; Tr; Sci A; Yth Fel; Bowl A; Marthonian C; *Cal St Long Beach; Child Development.*

SMITH, Marcia Arlene
Frontenac HS; Frontenac, KS (1-43) Ed, Ann; Dbte Tm; VP, FHA; GS; Math C; Orch; Sch P; Secy, Spch C; VP, SC; Pres, Sr Cl; Tres, Jr Cl; Secy, Soph Cl; Alg A; Citz A; HQn; Hon Prog; I Dare You; Math A; Opt A; PTA A; Spch A; St Scholar; Val; Yth Fel; Jr Diaconate, Interntl Affairs Sem; *Pittsburg St U; Bus.*

SMITH, Marcia Christine
Kentridge Sr HS; Kent, WA (25%-600) A Cap Choir; Chor; Drama; Ensm; NHS; *Seattle Pacific U; Interior Decorating.*

SMITH, Margaret Elizabeth
Tylertown HS; Tylertown, MS (5%-120) Band; BC; Fr C; FHA; 4H; S-T, SC; Sftbl; COM; 4H A; PTA A; Type A; Rep, PTA; *Miss St U.*

SMITH, Margaret Lundie
Beaufort Acad; Beaufort, SC (2-38) Co-Ed, Ann; Ed, Sch P; *Purdue U; Zoology.*

SMITH, Marietta Jean
Central Comm HS; Breese, IL (3-157) Drama; FHA; Math C; Span C; Alg A; Amer Leg A; DARGCA; Hist A; St Scholar; VP, FSA; Span A, Eng As; VP, Cath Yth Organization; Yrbk Staff; Candystriper; *Kaskaskia Col; Ed.*

SMITH, Mark Alan
Princeton HS; Princeton, TX; Band; Mgr, Bkbl; N Tex Hon Band; Band Rep; *Mech.*

SMITH, Mark Darrell
Southport HS; Indianapolis, IN (100-433) A Cap Choir; Band; Chor; Dbte Tm; Drama; Ensm; Secy, Ger C; VP, 4H; Hmrm; NFL; Spch C; SC; Thes; Amer Leg Orator A; God & Country A; 4H A; Hon Prog; Spch A; VofDEM; Gov A of Excel, Art; *Ind U; Journ.*

SMITH, Mark Stanton
Douglas MacArthur HS; San Antonio, TX (25%-625) Chess C; Rptr, Sch P; St Stu Congress; Co-Ch, SC; COM; NEDT; *U of Tex; Law.*

SMITH, Marlin Don
Shelby Co HS; Columbiana, AL (80%-101) Band; Ensm; 4H; Sci C; Spch A; Yth Fel; Yth Leg; Yth Asst Pastor; Nom Comm; *Samford U.*

SMITH, Marlin Hamilton
St Mary's HS; Harlingen, NC (4-103) A-Ed, Ann; Chldr; Drama; Fr C; Lit Mag; NHS; F-Ed, Sch P; Pres, Jr Cl; Bsbl; NMF; *Sweet Briar Col; Art Hist.*

SMITH, Martha Ellen
Harlingen HS; Harlingen, TX; Band; Rainbow; UIL Gold, Silver Medals; *Computer Programmer.*

SMITH, Martha Jill
Fairview HS; Sherwood, OH; Band; Chor; Secy, 4H; VP, Span C; Var C; Bkbl; Sftbl; Tr; 4H A; MVP, Vlbl; *Toledo U; Med Tech.*

SMITH, Martin Lee
Aledo HS; Aledo, IL (10%-135) Key C; Var C; Bkbl; Ftbl; Tr; Amer Leg A; VofDEM.

SMITH, Marty Loyd
Cleburne HS; Cleburne, TX (33%-260) Span C; Ftbl; HR.

SMITH, Mary Beth
Cleveland HS; Cleveland, TN (15%-250) Band; CYO; Chldr; Fr C; VP, Sci C; Tri-HiY; Bkbl; Tnns; Hon Prog; Acad Excellence A.

SMITH, Mary Elizabeth
Citrus HS; Inverness, FL (3-250) 4H; NFL; Tres, NHS; Span C; JV, Tnns; 4H A; Hon Prog A; NMS Commended Stu; WW; *U of Fla; Fine Art.*

SMITH, Mary Jacquelyn
Litchfield HS; E Gadsden, AL (20-149) Chor; Fr C; ARC; Span C; Swim; ARC A; *U of Ala; Phys Therapy.*

SMITH, Mary Jayne
Fairview HS; Sherwood, OH (10-110) Band; Chor; Ensm; Pres, FTA; Semi-Fin, GS; Pres, 4H; NHS; Sch Achieve Tm; Span C; Var C; Pres, Soph Cl; Bkbl; Sftbl; Swim; Tr; 4H A; Hist A; Hon Prog; Yth Fel; Vlbl; *Social Work.*

SMITH, Maryann
Jefferson HS; Los Angeles, CA; Dbte Tm; Drama; Bkbl; Sftbl; Alg A; Citz A; Hist A; Hon Prog; Math A; Schol A; Achievement A; Ath Schol A; *Calif St U at L A; Phys Ed.*

SMITH, Maurice Wayne
John F Kennedy HS; Richmond, VA (32-309) ARC; Var C; Cpt, Ftbl; Tr; Wrest; Tr & Ftbl Meriterious A; *Accountant.*

SMITH, Melanie Louise
Whetstone HS; Columbus, OH (50%-549) Mjrte; Orch; Mgr, Ftbl; Mgr, Tr; Citz A; PTA A; Church Choir; Jr NHS; Drill Tm; Off Aid A; *Otterbein Col; Special Ed.*

SMITH, Melinda Kay
Irving HS; Irving, TX (30-850) A Cap Choir; Rptr, Chor; Drama; Hmrm; Mus C; SC; PTA A; Var C; Secy, Y-Tns; VP, Jr Cl; Secy, Soph Cl; Cpt, Soccer; Tr; Yth Fel; FCA; 1st Pl, Dist High Jump; 6th Pl, Regional High Jump; Top Attitude, Tr Tm.

SMITH, Melinda Sue
Charleston Sr HS; Charleston, IL; *E Ill U; Elem Ed.*

SMITH, Melissa Jane
Marion HS; Marion, IN; Co-Cpt, Swim; Tnns; 4H A; *Marine Bio.*

SMITH, Melissa Jo
Fairfax HS; Fairfax, VA; Pres, Band; InterClub Coun; COM; Most Out; MYF; Pastor-Parish Relations Comm; Yth Choir; Pres, Choir; Administration Board; *Ferrum Col; Environmental Stu.*

SMITH, Melissa Lea
Polo HS; Polo, MO (2-40) Co-Ed, Ann; Chor; Pres, FHA; Madrigal; Cpt, Mjrte; NHS; A-Ed, Sch P; Span C; SC; Tr; B Crocker A; MLS; Sal; Sci A; Outst, Eng Stu; Outst Span Stu; Outst Home Ec Stu; *Stephens Col; Fashion.*

SMITH, Meredith Elizabeth
Wade Hampton HS; Greenville, SC; Chor; Ensm; Bkbl; Swim; Yth Fel; *Clemson U; Arch Engr.*

SMITH, Merry Helen
Leeton HS; Leeton, MO; Chor; Orch; Sch P; SC; JV, Sftbl; Sci A; Court Warming Princess; *Horticulture.*

SMITH, Michael Allan
Southwestern Comm HS; Flint, MI; NHS; Cr-Ctry; Tr.

SMITH, Michael Anthony
Smithfield-Selma Sr HS; Smithfield, NC (1-355) Band; 4H; Hmrm; Rptr, Key C; NHS; Span C; Pres, SC; Pres, Soph Cl; COM; Gov Honor Prog; Gr Marshal; 4H A; Hist A; Kiwanis A; Ntl Achv Schol; Val; Human Relations Coun; *Duke U; Chem.*

SMITH, Michael Cline
Elyria HS; Elyria, OH (73-465) A Cap Choir; Band; Chor; Madrigal; Band A; Choir A; Soph Octet.

SMITH, Michael Dwain
Papillion-Lavista Sr HS; Papillion, NE (17-365) Span C; JV, Ftbl; Swim; Hon Prog; *NW Okla St U; Med.*

SMITH, Michael Glenn
Princeton HS; Princeton, TX (1-50) Band; Ensm; VP, NHS; VP, Sci C; Alg A; Bio A; COM; Chem A; Cl Fav; Math A; MLS; NMF; Phy A; Sci A; Val; Eng A; Attendance A; Grand Prize, Regional Sci Fair; John Philip Sousa A; 1st Pl, St Sci UIL; *Tex A&M U; Chem Engr.*

SMITH, Michael Ray
New Braunfels HS; New Braunfels, TX (40%-265) Fr C; Golf; *Concordia Lutheran Col; Statistician.*

SMITH, Michele Jean
Huntington HS; Huntington, NY; Bkbl; Hockey; Sftbl; Tnns; *Katherine Gibbs Col; Legal Secy.*

SMITH, Michelle Denise
Edward Tilden HS; Chicago, IL (4-408) Band; Pres, Math C; NHS; Rptr, Sch P; Secy, Sr Cl; *Roosevelt U; Computer Sci.*

SMITH, Millicent Denise
N Natchez Adams HS; Natchez, MS; S-T, BC; Fr C; NHS; Bio A; Chem A; Cl Fav; DARGCA; H of F; Hon Prog; *U of Miss; Acct.*

SMITH, Minnie Leeann
Lyons Sr HS; Lyons, GA (20-135) Band; FTA; Mjrte; Bkbl; Sftbl; Tnns; Math A; Ltr C; FCA; *Brewton Parker Col; Elem Ed.*

SMITH, Mitzi Gay
Eastern Randolph HS; Ramseur, NC (72-232) JV, Chldr; Ensm; Tres, FTA; JV, Monogram; Span C; Mgr, Wrest; 3rd Pl, Sch Sci Fair; Pres, Acteens; 4th Pl, Dist Sci Fair; Acteen's Schol; Secy, VP, Hist C; Mental Health Vol; *Wingate Col; Acct.*

SMITH, Myron Spencer
Land O'Lakes Jr And Sr HS; Lando'lakes, FL (63-140) Tres, Chor; FBLA; Ftbl; Tr; Wrest; FBLA A.

SMITH, Nancy Elizabeth
Jones HS; Lynnville, TN (4-22) Ann; Pres, BC; Chldr; F-Ed, Sch P; Bkbl; Ftn, Tr; 4H A; Hon Prog; VofDEM; *Columbia St Col; Med Lab.*

SMITH, Nancy Kaye Campbell
Justin F Kimball HS; Dallas, TX; Chor; Ensm; Fr C; COM; *Tex Tech U; Elem Ed.*

SMITH, Nancy Lee
Sunbright HS; Sunbright, TN (9-63) Band; Secy, BC; Cpt, Chldr; Secy, FHA; Secy, 4H; Var C; Cpt, Bkbl; Sftbl; *Lincoln Mem Col; Hist.*

SMITH, Nancy Lee
Valley HS; Lucasville, OH (1-103) Band; Chor; FTA; Alg A; Alg Schol Tea; *Ohio St U; Psych.*

SMITH, Nancy Lynn
Bellflower HS; Bellflower, CA (18-382) A Cap Choir; Chor; Commercial C; Ensm; VP, FHA; InterClub Coun; Phys C; Ski C; Beauty; CSF; JA A; 1st Cl GSct; *Brook's Fashion Col; Merchandising.*

SMITH, Nancy Lynn
Raytown S HS; Raytown, MO (25-572) Ann; Secy, Drama; Fr C; Ed, Sch P; Thes; Y-Tns; Journ A; NJHS; Fr A; Best Actress; *SW Baptist Col; Church Recreation.*

SMITH, Nathan
Smith HS; Atlanta, GA (22-285) Fr C; Pres, Var C; Bsbl; Bkbl; Ftbl; Tnns; JA A; ARC A; ROTC A; *Northern Ky St Col; Bus Mgt.*

SMITH, Nathan Clark
Adrian Sr HS; Adrian, MI (174-437) Bus Mgr, A Cap Choir; Ann; Arch; Band; Chor; 4H; Ltr C; Orch; SC; Cadet Commander, Civil Air Patrol; Asst Coach, Gym; Ldrship, Mitchell A's; Civil Air Patrol A; *Adrian Col; Mus.*

SMITH, Nathaniel
Bloomfield HS; N Bloomfield, OH (7-40) BC; Chor; 4H; Sch Achieve Tm; Rptr, Sch P; SC; Bkbl; COM; 4H A; Opt A; Spch A; VFW A; VofDEM; *Selma U; Religious Studies.*

SMITH, Neil Morgan
Putnam Co HS; Cookeville, TN (75-350) F-Ed, Ann; BC; InterAct C; Span C; Tr; *Tenn Tech Col; Marketing.*

SMITH, Niki Lynn
Tower Hill Comm HS; Tower Hill, IL (2-23) Chldr; Chor; S-T, Drama; FHA; Ed, Sch P; Pres, Span C; SC; Tr; Hist A; Type A; VofDEM; WW; *Lakeland Comm Col; Bus Adm.*

SMITH, Nita Gail
Independence HS; Charlotte, NC (155-600) Tnns; S-T, DECA; *King's Col; Secy.*

SMITH, Ortega Darryl
Plymouth HS; Plymouth, NC (5-192) Ann; Drama; Math C; NHS; Ed, Sch P; Sci C; Span C; Mgr, Bsbl; Mgr, Bkbl; Mgr, Ftbl; Tnns; COM; Gov Sch Nom; *UNC-CH; Pol Sci.*

SMITH, Pamela Darlene
Wakefield HS; Arlington, VA (84-256) FHA; SC; Hist A; Most Out; Geog, Home Ec, A's; *Va Commonwealth U; Sociology.*

SMITH, Pamela Jane
Pascagoula HS; Pascagoula, MS; Band; Chor; Ensm; FHA; NHS; Rainbow; Sftbl; Hon Prog; *U of Miss; Religious Ed.*

SMITH, Pamela Jo
Irvin HS; El Paso, TX; Band; Chor; Ger C; Orch; Tri-HiY; Swim; Math Hon Prog; Parl, NJHS; Whitlock Theory Piano; 1st Div Flute Solo; 3rd, Piano Tx Mus Tchrs As HS Div; *Gynocology.*

SMITH, Pamela Joyce
Statesville Sr HS; Statesville, NC (22-256) Band; BC; Fr C; Lit Mag; Math C; Mod Mus Mas; Jr Marshal; *Harding Col; Nurs.*

SMITH, Pamela Louise
El Camino HS; Oceanside, CA (215-500) Tr & Tnns A's; *Mira Costa Col; Secy.*

SMITH, Pamela Rae
Fletcher Sr HS; Neptune Beach, FL (11-700) Phys Fitness A; *Baptist Bible Col; Teaching.*

SMITH, Pamela Sue
West HS; Columbus, OH (3-500) Band; Bkbl; Sftbl; Yth Fel; Bell Choir; Vlbl.

SMITH, Pamela Valda
Carol W Hayes HS; Birmingham, AL (4-190) VP, Band; Ensm; VP, Hmrm; ARC; Pres, Yth Choir; Secy, Church Department; WW; Top 5%, Co Stu; Nurs.

SMITH, Patricia Ann
Princeton HS; Princeton, NC (10-73) Ed, Ann; BC; Bus C; Secy, Chor; Ensm; FHA; FTA; Hmrm; Monogram; Bkbl; Sftbl; Gr Marshal; HCt; Poet A; Stu o-t Mo; *E Carolina U; Bus Ed.*

SMITH, Patricia Ann
Saint Joseph Acad; McSherrystown, PA (1-12) Ann; Chor; NHS; Sch P; SC; VP, Jr Cl; DARGCA; Hon Prog; *Bloomsburg St Col; General Studies.*

SMITH, Patricia Jean
Nw Classen HS; Okla City, OK; Chor; Ger C; Hmrm; ARC; SC; COM; Citz A; VP, Lib C; Courtesy, Pep, C'S; Secy, JA; Safety Coun; *Central St Col; Secy.*

SMITH, Patricia Kay
Kenowa Hills HS; Grand Rapids, MI (10%-300) Band; 4H; NHS; Spch C; COM; Spch A; *Grand Rapids Baptist Col; Communications.*

SMITH, Patricia Maureen
James Island HS; Charleston, SC; Ann; BC; Cpt, Chldr; Mu Alpha Theta; NHS; Span C; SC; Alg A; COM; Math A; Span A; *Wofford Col; Math.*

SMITH, Patty Diane
Blackwell HS; Blackwell, OK (10%-150) A Cap Choir; Band; Chldr; Chor; Ensm; GS; Jr Miss Pageant; Madrigal; NHS; Sch P; Secy, SC; Y-Tns; Pres, Sr Cl; Sftbl; Amer Leg A; COM; Cl Fav; Elk A; HCt; Rotary A; Yth Fel; Powder Puff Ftbl; All-St Choir; WW; Washington Crossing Essay Win; B & PW A; Miss BHS; *Okla St U.*

SMITH, Paula Beth
Church Hill HS; Church Hill, TN (20%-140) Chldr; Beauty.

SMITH, Penny Joy
Jackson HS; Jackson, MI (60-490) Band; Bkbl; Sftbl; *Theology.*

SMITH, Penny Lynn
Stone Mountain HS; Stone Mountain, GA (2-335) BC; Drama; Fr C; FHA; Hmrm; NHS; Mgr, Bkbl; COM; St Sci Fair; Co Sci Fair.

SMITH, Peter Percival
Denton Pub HS; Denton, MT; FFA; VP, Sr Cl; Wrest; *N Mont Col; Farm and Ranch Mgr.*

SMITH, Phillip Dwayne
London Christian Acad; London, KY (2-35) A-Ed, Ann; Ch, Band; Chor; VP, Drama; Ensm; Secy, Fr C; 4H; Pres, Hmrm; Ch, InterClub Coun; SC; Bsbl; MVP, Bkbl; Tr; Citz A; Superior Ratings, Mus; *Pensicola Christian Col; Mus.*

SMITH, Phillip Taylor
Fort Payne HS; Fort Payne, AL (10-140) FTA; Pres, HiY; Hmrm; Pres, InterClub Coun; NHS; Order/Arrow; Ch, Sci C; Span C; VP, SC; Bkbl; Amer Leg Orator A; COM; Cl Fav; HCt; Hon Prog; Spch A; Yth Leg; *Auburn U; Med.*

SMITH, Portia Belinda
West Point HS; West Point, VA; Band; Chor; FHA; Co-Cpt, Mjrte; Sftbl; *Telephone Operation.*

SMITH, Portia Renee
Immanuel HS; Reedley, CA (7-83) A Cap Choir; CSF; *Point Loma Col; Bus.*

SMITH, Raejeana Gale
Glenn HS; Birmingham, AL; Band; Drama; Mjrte; NHS; Secy, SC; Tnns; *UCLA; Med.*

SMITH, Ralph Allen
Mosley HS; Panama City, FL (5%-550) Fin, BS; Mu Alpha Theta; NHS; Ftbl; Co-Cpt, Wrest; Jaybees; *Auburn U; Math.*

SMITH, Randy Oneal
Pickwick South Side HS; Counce, TN (5-33) Pres, FFA; 4H; Pres, Jr Cl; Pres, Soph Cl; Bsbl; Cl Fav; 4H A; MLS; Most Intellectual; *Memphis St Col; Bus.*

SMITH, Raymond G
St Joseph-Ogden HS; St Joseph, IL (3-118).

SMITH, Rebecca Blanche
Johnson Co HS; Wrightsville, GA (10%-123) Ed, Ann; Band; Tres, BC; Tri-HiY; Bkbl; HCt; Ath A; *Young Harris Col.*

SMITH, Rebecca May
New Hope Solebury HS; New Hope, PA (33%-62) Band; Chor; VP, Ski C; Hockey; *Landscape Design.*

SMITH, Rebecca Sue
Lake Worth HS; Lake Worth, FL; Chldr; Hmrm; ARC; Ski C; SC; Sftbl; Tnns; HCt; *Med.*

SMITH, Rene Jean
Dos Pueblos HS; Goleta, CA; FHA; 4H; ARC; Interior Decorating A; Forerunners Choir; *UCSB; Interior Decorating.*

SMITH, Reve Marie
Portsmouth HS; Portsmouth, OH (2%-300) Chor; Drama; Sch Achieve Tm; Span C; Schol Avg A; Eng A; WW, Foreign Lang.

SMITH, Rhetta Jane
Dodge Co HS; Eastman, GA; FBLA; FHA; 4H; Middle Ga Col; Bus Ed.

SMITH, Rhonda Joyce
Fitzgerald HS; Fitzgerald, GA; Tri-HiY; Math A; Eng A; *Valdosta St Col.*

SMITH, Richard Hugo Jr
Strake Jesuit Coll Prep HS; Houston, TX (50%-455) Chess C; Sci C; Eagle Sct; *Tex A&M U; Elec Engr.*

SMITH, Richard Melvin
Greenwich HS; Greenwich, CT (69-974) Chess C; Drama; Golf; Hon Prog; *Physics.*

SMITH, Richard Wesley
Capitol Hill HS; Oklahoma City, OK; Pres, Band; Chor; Hmrm; SC; Pres, Sundy Sch Dept; Pres, Yth Ral; Distin Mus Cert, US Marines; Pres, St Yth Camp; Lys, Central Ok BMA Churches; *Jacksonville Baptist Col; Mus.*

SMITH, Robert Boulware IV
Henderson HS; Chamblee, GA (175-400) Band; Ger C; VP, Sr High MYF; *Emory U; Pre-Med.*

SMITH, Robert David
T R Miller HS; Brewton, AL (2-95) Ann; Math C; NHS; Sci C; Tnns; Sci A; *Auburn U; Computer Sci.*

SMITH, Robert H
Central Valley HS; Spokane, WA (75-400) Co-Cpt, Dbte Tm; NFL; Order/Arrow; COM; Hon Prog; Order/Arrow A; Spch A; Eagle Sct A; Chapter Chief, Order of Arrow; *Spokane Falls Comm Col; Hist.*

SMITH, Robert Leon
N Platte HS; N Platte, NE (33%-500) Order/Arrow; *Auto Mechanics.*

SMITH, Robert Steve
South San W Campus; San Antonio, TX (2-165) Hmrm; JETS; Math C; NHS; Order/Arrow; ARC; SC; Ftbl; Tr; COM; Hon Prog; Order/Arrow A; Spch A; *Howard Payne Col; Math.*

SMITH, Robin Benjamin
Franklin Co HS; Winchester, TN; BC; Chor; Drama; Parl, Math C; Sftbl; Hist A; PA; Lead, HS Mus; US Senate Race Worker; *U of Tenn; Bus.*

SMITH, Robin Elaine
El Cerrito HS; El Cerrito, CA; Secy, A Cap Choir; *Cal St U at Hayward; Child Development.*

SMITH, Robin L
Highlands HS; Norths Highlands, CA; A Cap Choir; Cpt, Chldr; Chor; Madrigal; Bkbl; Hockey; Sftbl; Tr; B Crocker A; Citz A; ARC A; Miss Amer '1976' Australia; Sftbl Championship; Spell A; *Mus.*

SMITH, Robin Lynn
Bentworth HS; Bentleyville, PA (5-144) Band; Drama; Pres, Hmrm; Ski C; SC; Tres, Jr Cl; Pres, Soph Cl; HCt; NHS; Art A; *U of Pittsburgh; Engr.*

SMITH, Rodney Lynn
Eastern Guilford HS; Gibsonville, NC (10-175) Fr C; NHS; WW; *NC St U; Elec.*

SMITH, Roger Allen
L B J HS; Austin, TX;

SMITH, Roger Mark
Eastside HS; Taylors, SC; Chess C; JV, Ftbl; *Clemson U.*

SMITH, Roger Roy
Murphysboro Township HS; Murphysboro, IL (51-263) Band; Order/Arrow; ARC; NEDT; Order/Arrow A; Eagle Sct; *Theol.*

SMITH, Ronald Dean
Clarke Central HS; Athens, GA (12-410) BC; Chor; Fr C; NHS; Tres, SC; Soccer; COM; Hon Prog; *U of Ga; Archaeology.*

SMITH, Ronald H
West HS; Waterloo, IA (21-539) NFL; Span C; Cr-Ctry; Tnns; Tr; VP, JA.

SMITH, Ronald James
Palm Beach Gardens HS; Palm Beach Gardens, FL (125-500) Pres, Chor; Dbte Tm; Drama; VP, Ensm; VP, FNA; Pres, Hmrm; Model UN; Pres, ARC; Sftbl; Swim; B Crocker A; COM; Cl Fav; ARC A; Spch A; Star Student; Yth Fel; VP, Chor; Pres, Annual Yth Prog; PA; Oratorical Contest A; Gospel Choirs; *U of Hawaii; Law.*

SMITH, Ronnie Wayne
Coffee Co HS; Manchester, TN (1-357) VP, BC; Ed, Sch P; Bkbl; Civics A; *Vanderbilt U; Law.*

SMITH, Ronny
Noxubee HS; Macon, MS (20-180) FFA; Cpt, Bkbl; Yth Fel; *Wood's Jr Col; Phys Ed.*

SMITH, Rosa Lee
Scotland HS; Laurinburg, NC (4-442) FBLA; NHS; Span C; Secy, SC; Math A.

SMITH, Rosalind Denise
Newtown HS; Elmhurst Queens, NY (258-1112) Queens Col; Secondary Ed.

SMITH, Rose Janette
Walbrook HS; Baltimore, MD (55-1000) Chor; VP, City Conf; Drama; Pres, SC; Var C; Swim; Tr; Amer Leg A; Bowl, Achv, A's; *Catonsville Comm Col; Data Processing.*

SMITH, Roy Joseph
Eastern HS; Lansing, MI (10-470) Chess C; Fr C; NHS; Tnns; COM; NMF; NMS; WW; *Oakland U; Computer Sci.*

SMITH, Roy Richmond Jr
Lebanon HS; Lebanon, VA (1-175) A-Ed, Ann; BS; FTA; Tres, HiY; Hmrm; Model UN; Pres, NHS; Span C; SC; Var C; Secy, Soph Cl; Bsbl; MVP, Bkbl; Ftbl; Tnns; Tr; DARGCA; HKg; Val; WW; Wash Workshop Participant; *Va Polytechnic Inst; Math.*

SMITH, Rufus Derayn
Forest Brook Sr HS; Houston, TX (10%-584) COM; Citz A; Hon Prog; Magna Cum Laude; Most Out; Spch A; Academic Schol; *Pepperdine U; Theology.*

SMITH, Russell Craig
Middle Park Jr Sr HS; Granby, CO (2-78) Band; Dbte Tm; Secy, SC; Cpt, Bkbl; Cpt, Ftbl; Spch A; *Colo Sch of Mines; Math.*

SMITH, Ruth Elaine
Northglenn HS; Northglenn, CO (144-750) F-Ed, Sch P; Q&S A; *Journ.*

SMITH, Sandi Lynn
N Pocono HS; Moscow, PA (30-268) Chldr; NHS; COM; JV, Vlbl.

SMITH, Sandra Jean
Hathaway Brown HS; Shaker Heights, OH; Drama; Hmrm; Lit Mag; NHS; Sch P; Alg A; Bio A; COM; Citz A; Hon Prog; Type A; ABC Schol; *Case Western Reserve U; Med.*

SMITH, Sandra Lou
Milano HS; Milano, TX (2-25) Chldr; FFA; Pres, FHA; NHS; Bkbl; Tr; Amer Leg A; Bio A; Hist A; Sal; Home Mgt; PA; HE II A; Chldr Medal; *Blinn Col; Phys Ed.*

SMITH, Sandra Lynn
Bethel Christian Sch; Ruston, LA (10%-15) Chldr; 4H; S-T, Hmrm; S-T, Sr Cl; Secy, Soph Cl; Bkbl; Sftbl; COM; Citz A; Cl Fav; DARGCA; HCt; Yth Fel; Most Improved, All Dist Bkbl; Outst Defensive, Bkbl; *La Tech U; Bus.*

SMITH, Sandra Renee
Blairsville Sr HS; Blairsville, PA (11-150) Chor; Hmrm; NHS; Sch P; SC; Pres, Var C; VP, Sr Cl; VP, Soph Cl; Cpt, Bkbl; Co-Cpt, Sftbl; DARGCA; Pres A; Cpt, Vlbl; Most Involved; Cl Friendliest; *Ind U of Pa; Health.*

SMITH, Sandy Ellen
Ritenour Sr HS; Overland, MO (5-950) A Cap Choir; NHS; Secy, Orch; Citz A; Math A; *Harding Col; Bus Adm.*

SMITH, Sarah Joy
Blair HS; Hattiesburg, MS (1%-380) Ann; Pres, Hmrm; Rptr, Lat C; Secy, Mu Alpha Theta; Schol A Win, Jr Miss Pageant; Lat A; Special Hons Graduate; *U of Ala; Math.*

SMITH, Sarah Lee
Commerce HS; Springfield, MA; Mus.

SMITH, Scott Marion
Bolton HS; Alexandria, LA; FBLA; Secy, Key C; Pres, SC; Theology.

SMITH, Scott Russell
Newman Smith HS; Carrollton, TX (80-320) Ann; Chor; Drama; Fr C; Math C; Thes; Citz A; Hon Prog; Journ A; ROTC A; Yth Fel; Yth Foundation; Excellent Rating at UIL; Pres Phys Fitness A; Oral Robert's U; Law.

SMITH, Selvin Lewis III
Frederick Douglass HS; Atlanta, GA (3-343) FBLA; NHS; Soccer; COM; Cl Fav; ROTC A; PC Jr Fel; Outst Work Performance; Ga Inst of Tech; Industrial Engr.

SMITH, Sharon Ann
Melville HS; Melville, LA; BC; Chldr; FBLA; Lit Ral; Bio A; Math A; Sci A; Type A; U of Sou La; Phar.

SMITH, Sharon Denice
Normandy Sr HS; St Louis, MO (215-565) Bkbl.

SMITH, Sharon Elaine
Forest Glen HS; Suffolk, VA (20-145) BC; Span C; WW; 1st Pl, Physics Sci Fair; VPI; Vet Med.

SMITH, Sharon Kay
Brookhaven Acad; Brookhaven, MS; BC; Chess C; FHA; Tr; COM; NEDT; Most Intellectual; Miss St U; Journ.

SMITH, Sharon Lee
Pasco Sr HS; Pasco, WA; Fr C; VP, FHA; Hmrm; JV, Bkbl; JV, Tnns; U of Wash; Anthropology.

SMITH, Sharon Louise
Tara HS; Baton Rouge, LA (10-378) BC; CYO; VP, Fr C; Mu Alpha Theta; NHS; Tri-HiY; Tres, Jr Cl; Hon Prog; Yth Leg; Fr Rally A; Straight A's A; LSU; Med.

SMITH, Sharon Patricia
Russell HS; Hurtsboro, AL (1-56) Chor; FHA; FTA; 4H; Pres, NHS; Pres, Sci C; Alg A; Citz A; 4H A; Hist A; Hon Prog; Math A; ROTC A; Spch A; Type A; Val; Yth Fel; Clothing Achv; Ala A&M U; Med.

SMITH, Sharon Ruth
E Ridge HS; Chattanooga, TN (54-284) BC; Chor; Ensm; Hmrm; Madrigal; NHS; SC; Tri-HiY; Lee Col.

SMITH, Sharron Denice
Liberty-Eylau HS; Texarkana, TX (58-170) Chem C; FHA; Cl Fav; Swtht; 2nd Runner-Up, Missle; E Tex St U; Modeling.

SMITH, Sharry Lynn
Crestview Sr HS; Crestview, FL (10%-247) Anchor C; Band; SC; Sch P; Beauty; Cl Fav; HQn; Deserving Dozen; Okaloosa-Walton Jr Col; Acct.

SMITH, Shellie Sue
Benson HS; Omaha, NE (68-439) Chor; Hon Prog; Ntl Achv Schol; Yth Fel; Omaha Symph; Col Mus Schol; Church Choir; Ntl Federation of Mus C; Dana Col; Ed.

SMITH, Shelly Jeannine
Roswell HS; Roswell, NM (1-400) Ann; Band; Dbte Tm; Drama; NHS; Sci C; VP, Spch C; SC; VofDEM; Win, Optimist Oration; Tex Tech U; Psych.

SMITH, Sheral Willette
Theodore HS; Theodore, AL; 4H; Cpt, Sftbl; Cpt, Tr; Walkathon; Driver's Ed, PA, Bible Sch, A's; Nurs.

SMITH, Sherrie Ann
Douglas Byrd Sr HS; Fayetteville, NC (40-384) BC; Tri-HiY; DECA C; Campbell Col; Spec Ed.

SMITH, Sherrill Lucille
Lafayette HS; Lafayette, LA (10%-900) Band; Dbte Tm; Ensm; Fr C; Ch, Hmrm; S-T, Lat C; SC; Cpt, Arch; Bsbl; Bkbl; Cpt, Ftbl; Sftbl; Swim; Tnns; Tr; COM; Cl Fav; Most Out; NEDT; Swtht; Type A; Yth Fel; Pep Sq; Church Membership Ch; FMLA; Pres, Jr MYF; LMTA; Piano A; La Tech U; Dentistry.

SMITH, Sheryl Lynn
Westchester Sr HS; Houston, TX (53-520) Cum Laude Soc; Dbte Tm; FTA; Secy, JETS; Ed, Lit Mag; Math C; Tres, Mu Alpha Theta; NHS; ARC; A-Ed, Sch P; Sftbl; Hon Prog; God & Comm A; U of Tex at Austin; Ed.

SMITH, Shirley Anne
Cushing Acad; Ashburnham, MA (24-77) Ann; Cpt, Chldr; Chor; Drama; Lit Mag; Var C; VP, Soph Cl; Cpt, Bkbl; Cpt, Hockey; Cpt, Tr; HCt; Hon Prog; Most Out; Church Orch; VP, Fresh Cl; MVP, Tr; Sou Vt Col; Dramatic Arts.

SMITH, Sidonia Marie
Rugby HS; Rugby, ND (14-110) Band; Chor; Pres, FHA; Madrigal; NHS; Hon Prog; Masonic A; Swtht; WW; Jamestown Col; Nurs.

SMITH, Sonja Jean
Rugby HS; Rugby, NY; Band; Chor; Drama; Ensm; FHA; Ger C; GS; Golf; Church Hi-League; Pon-Pom Girl; Minn Sch of Bus; Fashion Merchandising.

SMITH, Staci Anne
Northmont HS; Clayton, OH (30%-498) Band; Drama; 4H; Mgr, Wrest; HCt; Ball St U; Fashion Merchandising.

SMITH, Stacia Anne
Bay HS; Panama City, FL; Anchor C; Fr C; Mu Alpha Theta; Rainbow; DARGCA; Hon Prog; Sci A; DeMolay Swtht; U of Fla; Sci.

SMITH, Stanley Patrick
Northwestern HS; Rock Hill, SC; A Cap Choir; Chor; Drama; Fr C; Sch P; Var C; Mgr, Ftbl; Mgr, Wrest; All St Hon Chor A; All St Regional Chor A; Winthrop Col; Mus.

SMITH, Stanley Stephen
Denton Pub HS; Denton, MT (1-24) VP, FFA; Ger C; Pres, NHS; Pres, SC; Pres, Soph Cl; Ftbl; Tr; Cpt, Wrest; Amer Leg Orator A; Hon Prog; Math A; Spch A; Val; Del, BS; Rocky Mountain Col; Engr.

SMITH, Stefan Alan
LaQuinta HS; Westminster, CA; Bsbl; Bkbl; Vlbl.

SMITH, Stephanie Ann
Manheim Central HS; Manheim, PA (58-261) Band; Orch; Hockey; Co Band; Med Careers C; Penn St Field Hockey Tm.

SMITH, Stephanie Ann
Kirkwood HS; Kirkwood, MO (150-529) AFS; Tres, Tri-HiY; Hon Prog; Environmental Sci Comm; Pep C; Secondary Stu Trng Prog; South Co Yth Govt; Church Choir; Intrntl Christian Yth Exchange.

SMITH, Stephanie Jannene
Knob Noster Sr HS; Knob Noster, MO; Chldr; Span C; SC; Var C; Bkbl; Co-Cpt, Tr; COM; Tex A&M U; Phys Ed.

SMITH, Stephanie Lorraine
A H Parker HS; Birmingham, AL; Chor; Drama; Swim; Cl Fav; Mus Contribution; Gaston Jr Col; Stenography.

SMITH, Stephanie Lynn
Oxford HS; Oxford, KS (2-44) Band; Chor; Type A; Art A; Kayettes; Jr Grad Attendant; Art.

SMITH, Stephen Craig
E L Furr Jr-Sr HS; Houston, TX (10-220) Pres, A Cap Choir; Chess C; Chor; Madrigal; NHS; Cr-Ctry; Cpt, Tnns; All-Region Choir; Baylor U; Mus Ed.

SMITH, Stephen Gregory
Bay HS; Panama City, FL (15-416) Pres, Demolay; Fr C; Key C; Mu Alpha Theta; Bsbl; Ftbl; Sftbl; Hon Prog; Kiwanis A; Masonic A; U of Fla; Pre-Med.

SMITH, Stephen Lloyd
Archbishop Curley HS; Miami, FL (3-128) Ed, Ann; Mu Alpha Theta; Sci C; Bio A; Chem A; Hon Prog; NMS; NEDT; Rensselaer A; Type A; Century III Runner-Up; Rensselaer Polytechnic Inst; Nuclear Chem.

SMITH, Stephony Ellen
Harding Acad; Memphis, TN; A Cap Choir; Chor; Drama; NFL; Thes; Bkbl; Golf; Chor, Drama Back Stage, A's; Abilene Christian Col; Mus.

SMITH, Steve Warren
Thomas Jefferson Sch; Natchez, MS (1-35) Ann; BS; Chem C; Ch, Dbte Tm; FTA; Ch, Hmrm; Co-Ed, Sch P; SC; Parl, Sr Cl; Parl, Jr Cl; COM; HCt; Hon Prog; Star Student; Type A; Val; General Mills A; Eagles Nest A; Sr Eng A; Millsaps Col; Pol Sci.

SMITH, Steven Allen
Deer Creek Sch; Arcola, MS (9-33) BC; Chor; Ensm; Rptr; Sch P; Citz A; Dist & St Sci Fairs; Moorehead Delta Jr Col; Drafting.

SMITH, Steven Andrew
Columbus E HS; Columbus, OH (2-350) BS; Drama; French NHS; NHS; Sch P; Cpt, Bsbl; Cpt, Ftbl; Cl Fav; Hon Prog; MLS; PTA A; Sal; Yale U; Archt.

SMITH, Steven Gregory
William Fleming HS; Roanoke, VA (32-402) Tres, BC; Sch P; Tres, Var C; VP, Jr Cl; Cpt, Ftbl; MVP, Ftbl; Appalachain St U.

SMITH, Susan Ann
John T Haggard HS; Wilmington, NC (7-590) Math C; NHS; U of NC; Forestry.

SMITH, Susan Ann
W Monroe HS; W Monroe, LA (30%-471) Anchor C; Ann; Drama; InterAct C; NHS; Spch C; Thes; Rptr, Y-Tns; Ch, Soph Cl; Spch A; Christmas Court; Rebel Raider; Dance Instructor; Best Supporting Actress; NE La Ly; Spch Thrapy.

SMITH, Susan Jane
Saranac HS; Saranac, MI (4-76) Band; NHS; PA; Davenport Col; Legal Secy.

SMITH, Susan Lynn
N Fort Myers Sr HS; Fort Myers, FL; Chor; Lang Arts; PA; Bible Sch; Interior Designer.

SMITH, Susan Margaret
Big Sandy HS; Big Sandy, TX (2-42) Ann; Band; Sch P; Sal; Vlbl; Band Jacket; Ambassador Col; Computer Sci.

SMITH, Susan Marie
Cristobal HS; Coco Solo, CANAL ZONE (9-113) Cpt, Chldr; Pres, Chor; FNA; FTA; Hmrm; SC; Secy, Sr Cl; VP, Jr Cl; Secy, Soph Cl; Mgr, Bsbl; Bkbl; Mgr, Swim; Mgr, Tnns; HCt; GAA; Nurs.

SMITH, Suzanne
Bible Baptist HS; Savannah, GA (7-34) SE Col.

SMITH, Suzanne
Dunbar HS; Dayton, OH; Cpt, Swim; Tr; Central St U; Beautician.

SMITH, Suzanne Lois
Lansdowne-Aldan HS; Lansdowne, PA (3-237) Chldr; UN Council; Odd Fellow Fin; Yth Fel; Drexel U; Home Ec.

SMITH, Sylvia Elane
Gretna Sr HS; Gretna, VA (25%-290) VP, BC; JV, Chldr; Fr C; Rptr, FHA; Secy, 4H; Hmrm; Monogram; Secy, SC; Ch, Tri-HiY; Mgr, Bkbl; St Homemaker Degree, FHA.

SMITH, Tamara Beth
Tuscaloosa HS; Tuscaloosa, AL; Chor; Ensm; FHA; Hmrm; Sftbl; Brewer Jr Col; Spec Ed.

SMITH, Tammara Faye
Goodlettsville HS; Goodlettsville, TN (26-155) F-Ed, Ann; Chor; FTA; Secy, Lat C; Lat NHS; ARC; SC; Var C; Bkbl; Mgr, Cr-Ctry; Tnns; U of Tenn; Marketing.

SMITH, Tammy Kay
Mountain View Jr And Sr HS; Mountain View, OK (4-33) Chldr; Chor; Ensm; FHA; 4H; Bkbl; Bio A; 4H A; HQn; Co Spelling Bee Champ.

SMITH, Tammy Leigh
Elbert Co Comprehensive HS; Elberton, GA (15-262) Anchor C; Band; BC; Bus C; Chor; VP, FBLA; Hmrm; NHS; Spch C; SC; Alg A; COM; Gov Honor Prog; Cpt, Flag Corps; WW; Pres, Voc Off Trng C; Sigma Alpha Kappa; VOT Sut o-t Yr; La Grange Col; Bus Ed.

SMITH, Tammy Lynn
Casa Roble HS; Orangevale, CA; Chor; Drama; Vlbl; Amer River Col; Bus.

SMITH, Tammy Sue
Jonesboro HS; Jonesboro, AR; Band; Hmrm; Mod Mus Mas; SC; Cl Fav; MLS; Opt A; Band A.

SMITH, Teresa Anne
Monta Vista HS; Cupertino, CA (18-600) Dbte Tm; Ensm; NFL; CSF; COM; Hon Prog; JA A; *Ed.*

SMITH, Teresa Lynn
Dryden HS; Cortland, NY; *Med.*

SMITH, Teresa Sue
Perry HS; Massillon, OH; *Photography.*

SMITH, Teri Lee Ann
Holy Cross HS; Marine City, MI; Co-Cpt, Chldr; Sftbl; Social Stu; *St Clair Co Comm Col.*

SMITH, Teri Lynn
Hewitt Trussville HS; Trussville, AL (2-269) Tres, Chor; Ensm; Math C; NHS; Secy, Y-Tns; Tnns; Beauty; COM; Citz A; Hon Prog; Lion A; Sal; Bible Schol; WW; *Samford U; Ed.*

SMITH, Terry Dean
Union HS; Roosevelt, UT; Ftbl; Friendship C.

SMITH, Terry Lynn
LaMarque HS; LaMarque, TX (27-450) Chor; Mod Mus Mas; NHS; Mgr, Tr; Hist A; Sci A; FCA; PA; Ntl Reading A; Eng A; Vlbl; Top Notcher-Tri-M; Reading A; Hon Choir; Choir A; Phys Fitness A; *Baylor U; Nurs.*

SMITH, Terry Randall
Burkeville HS; Burkeville, TX (5-36) Band; FFA; 4H; SC; Bsbl; Sal.

SMITH, Theresa Elaine
East Ridge HS; Chattanooga, TN (37-288) Band; Model UN; ARC; Tres, Span C; COM; NEDT; *U of Tenn at Chattanooga; Phys Therapy.*

SMITH, Thomas Everett
Barton Sr HS; Barton, FL; Var C; Co-Cpt, Cr-Ctry; Tr; Amer Leg A; ROTC A; *US Military Acad; Computer Tech.*

SMITH, Thomas Herrold
W Muskingum HS; Zanesville, OH (18-195) Pres, Band; Pres, Chor; Community Yth Symph; FTA; Hmrm; Key C; Math C; NHS; Sci C; MLS; Ntl Merit Commended; Ohio Power Schol; St Bicentinnial Sch; 3 5 Banquet; *Ohio St U; Pol Sci.*

SMITH, Thomasina
Independence HS; Charlotte, NC (126-641) Band; Pres, FNA; Mjrte; Sftbl; HCt; Health Careers; *Eckerd Col; Nurs.*

SMITH, Thresa Joann
Loraine HS; Loraine, TX (2-20) VP, FHA; 4H; Mod Mus Mas; NHS; SC; Jr Cl; Secy, Band; FFA; FTA; Bkbl; Tnns; Tr; Val.

SMITH, Tim Al
S Gwinnett HS; Snellville, GA; Band; Orch; Band Med Solo & Ensm, Super & Excel; *Oral Roberts U; Religion.*

SMITH, Tim Wayne
Cheyenne Mt HS; Colorado Springs, CO (75-200) Ski C; JV, Golf; Stu Ambassador; *Friends U; Acct.*

SMITH, Timothy Duane
Sumner HS; Sumner, WA (65-320) A Cap Choir; Band; Ger C; ARC; SC; Soccer; Tr; Wrest; *Pacific Coast Baptist Bible Col; Bible.*

SMITH, Timothy Eugene
Rev; Graber Fort Smith, AR (25%-300) FBLA; John Brown U; Religion.

SMITH, Timothy Glyn
Lexington HS; Lexington, AL (10-30) FFA; 4H; 4H A; Hon Prog; *UNA.*

SMITH, Timothy Joel
Sumter HS; Sumter, SC (355-753) Ann; Chess C; VP, Hmrm; Rptr, Sch P; SC; *U of SC; Psych.*

SMITH, Timothy Marcus
Salisbury HS; Salisbury, NC (1-250) AFS; Fr C; Hmrm; Secy, Var C; NHS; SC; Var C; Pres, Soph Cl; Bkbl; Ftbl; Tr; Gov Honor Prog; Hon Prog; *Pre-Med.*

SMITH, Tina Lou
Parkersburg South HS; Parkersburg, WV (164-510) Chor; FHA; 4H; Tr; Sci A; Hon A; *Marshall U; PE Coordinator.*

SMITH, Tina Louise
Chamberlain HS; Tampa, FL (110-671) Chor; Tres, FTA; InterClub Coun; NHS; Sftbl; COM; Hon Prog; VP, Exchangettes; JFMM Mus Schol; Pres, Fla Federation of Mus C; Jr Musicale; 1st Pl, Talent Show; Ntl Bicentennial Handbell Choir; *U of S Fla; Mus Ed.*

SMITH, Tometta Diane
Sumner HS; Kans City, KS (5%-193) A Cap Choir; Cpt, Chldr; Chor; FHA; Fin, Jr Miss Pagent; rigal; NHS; Hon Prog; St Hon Sr A; *Pepperdine U; Mus.*

SMITH, Tommy Gene
Madison Heights HS; Anderson, IN (45-375) Ann; Var C; Pres, Sr Cl; JV, Bkbl; Ftbl; Sftbl; Q&S A; Yth Fel; FCA; Campus Life; *Taylor Col; Phys Ed.*

SMITH, Tracey Lynne
Xenia HS; Xenia, OH; Fr C; Tr; COM; Congeniality A; *Mus.*

SMITH, Trieste
Covert HS; Covert, MI (1-39) Arch; Chldr; Chor; FHA; NHS; Span C; Tnns; Tr; Beauty; COM; Hon Prog; Val; MSU A For Academic Excellence; Sl Cl Play; Miss Covert Un Contest; 3rd Pl, Bicen Essay Contest; *Mich St U; Acct.*

SMITH, Usana Victoria
Berkeley HS; Berkeley, CA; GS; *Armstrong Bus Col; Bus.*

SMITH, Valerie Denise
Pershing HS; Detroit, MI; Co-Cpt, Chldr; FNA; FTA; ARC; Sch P; SC; Y-Tns; Swim; Tnns; B Crocker A; Citz A; Cl Fav; HQn; MLS; *Oakland Co Comm Col; Nurs.*

SMITH, Valerie Irmaneice
Minden HS; Minden, LA (30-270) Band; Hmrm; Cpt, Mjrte; HCt; Hon Prog; Type A; Drum Mjrte; Pres, Church Yth Fel; Band A; Sci Cert; *Grambling St U; Pol Sci.*

SMITH, Valli Jeanenne
Spruce Creek Sr HS; Port Orange, FL; Ann; Band; BC; Secy, Chor; Ensm; 4H; NHS; Sch P; Span C; Bkbl; Soccer; COM; Cl Fav; Sci A; Type A; Span, Band; Chor, Merit A's; *Daytona Beach Comm Col.*

SMITH, Vernon Gregory
Isabella HS; Maplesville, AL (1-27) Ed, Ann; VP, BC; BS; Secy, FFA; F-Ed, Sch P; Var C; Pres, Jr Cl; Pres, Soph Cl; MVP, Bsbl; Bkbl; Cpt, Ftbl; Tr; Amer Leg A; Citz A; Cl Fav; Val; All-St Ftbl; *Auburn U; Ed.*

SMITH, Vicki Sue
Pekin Comm HS; Pekin, IL (33%-850) S-T, 4H; Candystriper; *Ed.*

SMITH, Vickie Lynn
Robert Nelson Snider HS; Ft Wayne, IN; Ann; Ensm; Secy, 4H; Rptr, Sch P; Pres, Church Yth Organization; 1st Pl, St Tn Talent Search; *Oral Roberts U; Bus.*

SMITH, Victoria Lynn
Camden HS; Camden, NJ; Chor; VP, Dbte Tm; Hon Prog; Mus A; *U of Pa; Mus.*

SMITH, Vida Lenora
John S Shaw HS; Mobile, AL; Secy, Chor; Span C; Cl Fav; Hon Prog; MLS; Opt A; Spch A; *U of S Ala; Journ.*

SMITH, Virginia Ann
Lincoln HS; Dallas, TX; Co-Ed, Ann; Band; Pres, Hmrm; Secy, Key C; Model UN; SC; Hist A; HCt; Kiwanis A; Sci A; Type A; *N Tex St U; Fashion Designer.*

SMITH, Wanda Selina
Dothan HS; Dothan, AL (7-500) FBLA; FHA; FTA; Hmrm; Lit Mag; NHS; Span C; SC; MVP, Bkbl; Sftbl; Hon Prog; Yth Fel; Creative Writing C; Pep C; WW; *Auburn U; Computer Prog.*

SMITH, Warren Lee
Lomega HS; Omega, OK; Chor; Ensm; Bsbl; Bkbl; *Okla St U; Elec Engr.*

SMITH, Wendy Anne
Delavan-Darien HS; Delavan, WI; Dbte Tm; FBLA; SC; Var C; Co-Cpt, Tnns; Tr; Yth Fel; *Coun Psych.*

SMITH, William Henry
All Hallows Inst; Bronx, NY (55-177) Band; Hmrm; Orch; SC; Cpt, Bsbl; Mgr, Bkbl; Tr; Hon Prog; 12 Yr A; *Fairfield U; Bus Mgt.*

SMITH, William Michael
Fitzgerald HS; Fitzgerald, GA (10%-250) Band; BC; Chor; HiY; Tnns; COM; WW; *Ga Sou Col; Bus Mgt.*

SMITH, Wilma K
Ravenna HS; Ravenna, OH (45-344) Band; Tres, Bus C; Chor; Drama; FBLA; NHS; Orch; Rainbow; Var C; Cpt, Bkbl; Sftbl; Tr; Type A; *Psych.*

SMITH, Yvon Rochelle
Golden Gate Acad; Oakland, CA (2-15) Pres, A Cap Choir; Pres, Chor; Secy, Span C; A-Ed, World Affairs; CSF; MLS; Most Out; Yth Fel; *Loma Linda U; Psych.*

SMITH, Yvonne Louise
Cambridge High and Latin Sch; Cambridge, MA (20%-499) Drama; Hmrm; Span C; COM; Hon Prog; Eng A, Lang Arts; *Bus Adm.*

SMITHEE, Derek Ron
Harrah HS; Harrah, OK; VP, 4H; Order/Arrow; JV, Bkbl; Ftbl; Tr; 4H A; Order/Arrow A; Eagle Sct; *Zoological Sci.*

SMITHERMAN, Robin Regina
Fairhope HS; Fairhope, AL (20-400) A-Ed, Ann; Chess C; Hmrm; NHS; SC; Q&S A; Jr Civitan; *U of S Ala; Acct.*

SMITHERS, Roy Kevin
W Memphis Sr HS; W Memphis, AR (73-394) BC; Fr C; Key C; Mgr, Ftbl; Tr; Harding Schol; *Harding Col; Acct.*

SMITHEY, Tammy Lynn
Lindale HS; Lindale, TX; Rptr, Ann; Ch, Chldr; Drama; Golf; Swim; Tnns; Chamber of Comm A; Cl Fav; HCt; Jr Chamber of Com A; Swtht; Most Sch Spirit; Sr Play; Lifeguard; *Tyler Jr Col; Bus.*

SMITHGALL, William Todd
Leesburg HS; Leesburg, FL (1-400) Mod Mus Mas; NHS; Sci C; Secy, Experiment Aircraft As Chpt; *MIT; Chem.*

SMITH HAMILTON, Jerry
Castlemonte HS; Oakland, CA; Bkbl; *Laney Col; Elec.*

SMITHPETERS, Velvet Kay
Gurdon HS; Gurdon, AR (10-96) Band; BC; FHA; Pres A; Art A; Band Medals & Ltrs; Home Ec A.

SMITHSON, Alesia Loy
St Elmo Community HS; St Elmo, IL (7-56) Ann; Band; Chor; Pres, FFA; Pres, 4H A; NHS; SC; Secy, Jr Cl; Tr; 4H A; I Dare You; Spch A; Pres, Christian Yth; Ntl FFA Ldrship Schol; *SIU at Carbondale; Agr.*

SMITHSON, Michael Kevin
York Pub HS; York, NE; Band; Pres, Chess C; Drama; Orch; Yth Fel; Dist Yth Coun; Drama A; Art Designer, Gym Mural; Chess Prize; *Kearney St Col; Drama.*

SMITHSON, Norman Dean
Vian HS; Vian, OK; BS; Hmrm; NHS; Sch P; SC; Bsbl; Ftbl; Sftbl; Swim; Tr; Amer Leg A; COM; Citz A; Hon Prog; Math A; Sci A; FCA; *Naval Acad; Law.*

SMITHSON, Sonia Celeste
DuPont Sr HS; Hermitage, TN (2-323) Band; NHS; Bio A; Chem A; Citz A; NEDT; Sal; PA; Middle Tenn Math Contests; Signal Mjrte; Top 10 A; Tenn Tech Work Schol; Rotary C Schol; *Tenn Tech U; Pre-Dentistry.*

SMITLEY, Philip Alan
East HS; Sioux City, IA; Band; Chor; Orch; *Evangel Col; Acct.*

SMITS, Susan Kay
Lincoln HS; Wisconsin Rapids, WI (135-563) Chor; FBLA; *N Central Bible Col; Mus.*

SMOAK, Caroline Gordon
Wilkes Central HS; Wilkesboro, NC (30-325) Band; Hmrm; Key C; COM; NEDT; Yth Fel; Poetry A; St Fin, Spelling Bee; *Vet Med.*

SMOCK, Pamela Sue
Paris HS; Paris, IL (3-235) A Cap Choir; Chem C; Chor; Ensm; Madrigal; NHS; Span C; SC; Golf; St Scholar; Type A; Sci Yrbk; Yrbk A; Tiger Relay Court; Holiday Tourn Court; GAA A; *Med.*

SMOCK, Susan Ann
Crockett HS; Crockett, TX (3-120) 4H; NHS; Span C; Alg A; Hist A; *Tex A&M U; Liberal Arts.*

SMOLINSKI, Michael Glen
Timberline HS; Weippe, ID (10-47) Chem C; French NHS; Var C; Bsbl; Co-Cpt, Bkbl; Ftbl; Beauty; Cl Fav; HKg; Most Out; Odd Fellow Fin; Star Student; Swtht; Hall A.

SMOOTS, Joscelyn Kassandra
Compton Sr HS; Compton, CA (50%-950) Up Bound; CSF; Calif St U; Marketing.

SMOTT, Kenneth James
Glenbrook S HS; Glenview, IL (64-597) CYO; NHS; Ski C; JV, Bsbl; JV, Ftbl; Hon Prog; Span A; Graphic Arts A; Graphic Arts.

SMOTT, Suzanne Lynn
Glenbrook S HS; Glenview, IL (96-600) CYO; Key C; NHS; Ski C; SC; Secy, Sr Cl; Hon Prog; Phy A; Sci A; Cpt, Pom Pon; Art A; Prom Ct; U of Ill; Chem Engr.

SMYRE, David Alan
Reidsville Sr HS; Reidsville, NC (17-344) VP, AFS; VP, Chess C; Fr C; Tnns; NEDT; Stu Rotarian; Stu Rep, AFS Adult Chapter; UNC-Greensboro; Math.

SMYTH, Pamela Jean
Tyner HS; Chattanooga, TN (85-261) Bus Mgr, Ann; Pres, BC; Chldr; Semi-Fin, GS; Hmrm; SC; Pres, Tri-HiY; Tnns; Citz A; HCt; Most Sch Service; Miss Spirit; U of Tenn; Special Ed.

SMYTH, Sallee Sinclair
Robert E Lee HS; Tyler, TX (25%-685) Ed, Sch P; Span C; Arch; Journ A; Spch A; Drill Tm; Foreign Lang Festival; HR; U of Tex; Phys Ed.

SMYTH, Scott Edward
White Plains HS; White Plains, NY; SC; Golf; Hon Prog; Bus Adm.

SNAPP, Glyna June
Lakeland Sr HS; Lakeland, FL (29%-750) Lat C; VP, Lionettes; Lionette o-t Yr; Secy, Chaplain, CYF; Bethany Col; Special Ed.

SNARGRASS, Marsha Danette
Central HS; Minneapolis, MN; Chldr; Chor; Hmrm; ARC; SC; Sftbl; Pres A; Shorthand A; Spellman Col; Bus.

SNEAD, Edward Paul
Goddard HS; Roswell, NM (79-301) Band; Community Yth Symph; Pres, Order/Arrow; Cr-Ctry; God & Country A; Order/Arrow A; Eagle Sct; Conquistador Coun; Jr Asst Sct-Master; Stage Band; Rep, Eagle Sct Bicentennial Cel; Children o-t Amer Revolution; NM Military Inst; Law Enforcement.

SNEAD, Sandra Austin
Watauga HS; Boone, NC; Cpt, Chldr; Ensm; FTA; Hmrm; SC; Sftbl; Appalachian St U; Deaf Ed.

SNEAD, Sharon Christine
North Olmsted Sr HS; North Olmsted, OH (52-683) AFS; Hmrm; NHS; Secy, Sr Cl; COM; Hon Prog; Pres, Church Yth Group; Drill Tm; Cpt, Bible Quiz Tm; Church Zone Coun; Olivet Nazarene Col; Social Work.

SNEARLY, William Norman
Southside HS; Elmira, NY (3-425) A Cap Choir; Chor; Marshal; NHS; Order/Arrow; Var C; Swim; Amer Leg A; Citz A; Elk A; Hon Prog; Math A.

SNEED, Amy Elizabeth
Eupora HS; Eupora, MS (6-84) Ann; Band; VP, BC; Ensm; FTA; Cpt, Mjrte; Ed, Sch P; Ole Miss; Acct.

SNEED, Carol Vanessa
Warren G Harding Sr HS; Warren, OH; A Cap Choir; Chor; Ensm; FHA; GS; Lat C; Madrigal; ARC; Sch P; Sci C; Sftbl; Tr; Hugh O'Brien Campaign; Cleveland St U; Phys Therapy.

SNEED, Mary Lynn
Russell HS; Russell, KY (15-280) BC; Chor; Drama; Lat C; Madrigal; Hon Prog; St, FCA; Gym; Lat A; Phys Ed A; Eastern Ky U.

SNEED, Michael Robert
Carlisle Sr HS; Carlisle, PA; JV, Cr-Ctry; Tr; 1000 Mile C Trophy; U of Md; Engr.

SNEED, Patty Ann
Heritage Hall Upper Sch; Oklahoma City, OK (25%-80) A-Ed, Ann; Ski C; Y-Tns; Bkbl; SC Rep; Secy, Art C; Vlbl; Badminton; Okla U; Dance.

SNELBAKER, Beth Ann
Cumberland Valley HS; Mechanicsburg, PA (1-585) Ed, Ann; Dbte Tm; Hmrm; NHS; Ed, Sch P; Secy, Ski C; St Stu Congress; Alg A; COM; NMS; NEDT; Cornell U; Biometry.

SNELBOROUGH, Wilhemina W
Vailsburg HS; Newark, NY (3-250) Drama; Fr C; Hmrm; NHS; Bkbl; Tr; Alg A; COM; Most Out; Ntl Achv Schol; Mus A; Bkbl A; Tr A; Rutgers Col; Chem.

SNELL, Angie Felicia
Leesville HS; Leesville, LA (74-360) Chldr; Chor; Drama; Bus Mgr, 4H; Hmrm; Fin, Jr Miss Pagent; Spch C; SC; Var C; MVP, Tr; Beauty; Cl Fav; HCt; JA A; Yth Fel; Pres, Fresh Cl; Lib C; Gym C; Church Usher; Bradley U; Govt.

SNELL, Paul William
Garnet Valley HS; Concordville, PA (23-163) Span C; Tr; COM; Widener Col; Mech Engr.

SNELLING, Marybeth
Sumner HS; Sumner, WA (25%-325) Chess C; Fr C; Sch P; Spch C; Yth Fel; Church Deacon; Church Nom Committee; Green River Comm Col.

SNELLING, Taressa Lynn
Caney Valley HS; Caney, KS (10%-70) Pres, Drama; Span C; Bkbl; Tr; Phys Therapy.

SNELLING, Warren Mark
Caney Valley HS; Caney, KS (5-70) Band; Bus C; Fr C; FBLA; JV, Bkbl; Golf; Okla St U; Sci.

SNELLINGS, Eric David
Andrew Lewis HS; Salem, VA (35-350) Mgr, Bkbl; Mgr, Tr; VPI; Archt.

SNELSON, Robert Otis
Burges HS; El Paso, TX; BS; Lat C; Ntl Conf Chr & Jews; Pres, CYF; Baylor U; Med.

SNELSON, Sheila Jean
Niantic-Harristown HS; Niantic, IL (7-55) All Amer Yth; Secy, Band; Chldr; Chor; Community Yth Symph; Drama; ARC; Sch P; Span C; SC; Var C; Sftbl; Tr; Q&S A; ARC A; Spch A; Cpt, Vlbl; Amer Yth Band European Tour; WW, Mus; E Ill U; Social Work.

SNELSON, Sherry Twanette
Niantic-Harristown HS; Niantic, IL (42-69) Band; Chor; FHA; ARC; Sftbl; Swim; Tr; Vlbl.

SNETHEN, Nancy Lea
Moore HS; Moore, OK (125-844) Band; Fr C; Yth Fel; Secondary Teacher.

SNEYERS, Jacqueline
St Joseph's o-t Palisades HS; W New York, NJ (12-232) CYO; Chldr; Hmrm; Sch P; Span NHS; Hon Prog; NEDT; Lib Arts.

SNIDER, Amy Louise
Saks HS; Anniston, AL; Secy, Chor; Ensm; Tri-HiY; Cl Fav; HCt; Jacksonville U; Ed.

SNIDER, Belinda Sue
Williamston HS; Williamston, MI (25%-167) AFS; Madrigal; Mgr, Tr; Yth Rep, Church Coun of Ministries; Church Yth Group & Mus Group; 1st Cl GSct; U of Mich; Med.

SNIDER, Bradley Frank
Jonesboro HS; Jonesboro, AR; A Cap Choir; Drama; Thes; Ftbl; Tr; ASU.

SNIDER, Brian Alan
Ottawa Hills HS; Grand Rapids, MI (5%-450) Dbte Tm; NHS; Bsbl; Mgr, Hockey; COM; Hon Prog; Math A; Jr Review; St Sen Resol Sr Ltl League Wrld Ser; U of Mich; Med.

SNIDER, Bruce Russell
Middletown HS; Middletown, RI (5%-250) Math C; Bsbl; Bkbl; Sci.

SNIDER, Frances Leigh
Greeneville HS; Greeneville, TN; Band; Hmrm; SC; Bkbl; Sftbl; Tnns; HCt.

SNIDER, Kenneth Randal
Amos Alonzo Stagg HS; Stockton, CA (40-700) Var C; Co-Cpt, Bsbl; Ftbl; Kiwanis A; CIF Section Championship Tm; All City-All Stars; Chrch Sftbl, Bkbl & Ensm; Delta Jr Col; Bus.

SNIDER, Ramona Dianne
Pathway HS; Savannah, GA (5-15) Band; Hmrm; Sch P; SC; Bkbl; COM; Type A; Secretarial.

SNIDER, Teri Lynne
Pathway Day Sch; Savannah, GA (3-18) Ann; Band; Chor; Secy, Hmrm; Sch P; SC; Bkbl; Tnns; COM; Secretarial.

SNIPE, Monique Lorraine
Middleton HS; Charleston, SC (219-280) Chldr; Y-Tns; Claflin Col; Stewardess.

SNIPES, Robin Lance
Paxon Sr HS; Jacksonville, FL (1-384) Anchor C; Band; Tres, Chem C; Chor; Pres, Dbte Tm; Ensm; Rptr, Hmrm; S-T, InterClub Coun; Tres, Key C; Math C; VP, NHS; Orch; Rptr, Sch P; Sci C; Parl, SC; Rptr, Sr Cl; Rptr, Jr Cl; Cr-Ctry; Golf; Tr; COM; Citz A; H of F; Hon Prog; Math A; Most Out; Poet A; Sci A; Star Student; Val; VFW A; Yth Fel; Boy o-t Yr; Chaplain, Soph Cl; Phi Kappa Phi; Calendar; Schol; FSU; Bus.

SNIPES, Teri Lynne
Woodward HS; Woodward, OK (20-185) A Cap Choir; Band; BC; Chor; Dbte Tm; Drama; NHS; Secy, Sci C; Tr; Drama A; St NHS A; SW Okla St U; Phys Therapy.

SNIPES, Wayne Bruce
Aiken High Schofield Campus; Aiken, SC; F-Ed, Ann; BC; Demolay; Drama; Rptr, Sch P; SC; Fashion.

SNIVELY, John Wesely
Montabella HS; Edmore, MI (25-110) BS; Drama; Parl, NHS; Ski C; Pres, SC; JV, Bkbl; Co-Cpt, Cr-Ctry; JV, Ftbl; JV, Golf; Tr; Industrial Arts A; Alma Col; Biol Sci.

SNIVELY, Naomi Irene
Vandalia Butler HS; Vandalia, OH; Band; FFA; Rotary A; Ohio St Col; Horticulture.

SNODERLY, Donna Kaye
Jupiter Christian Sch; Jupiter, FL (3-29) CYO; Chor; Fr C; Math C; MVP, Bkbl; Sftbl; Bus Adm.

SNODGRASS, Brenda Lee
Southside HS; Elmer, OK (1-11) Ann; FHA; 4H; NHS; VP, Soph Cl; Bkbl; Alg A; Bio A; Chem A; Gov Honor Prog; Hon Prog; Math A; Phy A; Sci A; St Hon Soc; Ath Ltr; Southwestern Okla St U; Sci.

SNODGRASS, Carole Denise
Trinity Heights Christian Acad; Shreveport, LA (2-50) F-Ed, Ann; Lit Ral; Math C; Mu Alpha Theta; Secy, NHS; Sci C; SC; Pres, 'Z' C; Cpt, Drill Tm; Fin, Beauty Pageant; La Tech U; Math Ed.

SNODGRASS, Jeane Micheal
Maries R-L HS; Vienna, MO (3-70) Ed, Ann; Tres, FBLA; Tres, FHA; FTA; GS; MVP, Tr; Eng A; Southwest Baptist Col; Elem Ed.

SNODGRASS, John Ross
Valley HS; Pine Grove, WV (2-78) BS; NHS; Pres, SC; Thes; Var C; VP, Jr Cl; VP, Soph Cl; Bkbl; Co-Cpt, Ftbl; Tr; Fairmont St Col; Chem.

SNODGRASS, Michael Roy
Texico HS; Texico, NM (19-38) FFA; 4H; Sch P; Bkbl; Amer Leg A; COM; NM St U; Agr Bus.

SNODGRASS, Susan Lynn
Price Lab HS; Cedar Falls, IA; Band; Chor; Drama; Orch; Secy, Soph Cl; JV, Bkbl; Soccer; Sftbl; Tnns.

SNODGRASS, Susan Lynn
Texico HS; Texico, NM (4-38) Band; FFA; VP, FHA; Secy, French NHS; S-T, 4H; VP, NHS; Ed, Sch P; Bkbl; Tr; Journ A; Most Out; Sci A; All Dist Bkbl A; Sociology WW; Hon Men, Texas Tech Yrbk Workshop; FFA Horse Proficiency; FFA Schol A; Sociology Outst Stu; Colo St U; Vet Med.

SNODY, Susan Eileen
O D Wyatt HS; Fort Worth, TX (1-435) Bus Mgr, Ann; Ensm; NHS; Hon Prog; Summa Cum Laude; People HS Hon; TCJC.

SNOOR, Robert Paul Jr
Utica HS; Utica, MI (90-280) Band; ARC; Golf; Cpt, Wrest; Sci A; Macomb Co Comm Col; Bus.

SNOW, Albert David
St Charles HS; St Charles, MI (32-140) Pres, Band; Chor; NHS; Orch; Sch P; Cr-Ctry; St Scholar.

SNOW, Barry Alan
W A Berry HS; Birmingham, AL; Archt.

SNOW, Elaine Joyce
Mainland Sr HS; Daytona Beach, FL; BC; Chor; VP, Ger C; Fin, Sftbl; Fin, Tnns; Alg A; Citz A; Math A; PTA A; VP, Keyette C; Attendance A; *DBCC; Computer Programming.*

SNOW, Gina Marie
Orofino HS; Orofino, ID; CYO; Fr C; Tr; 4-H Horse Tn Ldr; Soph Service C.

SNOW, Sherry S
Skyline HS; Dallas, TX (30%-1000) Chor; NHS; Bkbl; Sftbl; Hon Prog; Yth Fel; WW; NJHS; Yth Rep, Church Adm Board; *N Tex St U.*

SNOW, Teryl Lee
Garfield HS; Hamilton, OH (57-445) Band; Chor; Drama; Orch; Sch P; Span C; Thes; Tr; Citz A; Hon Soc; Lib, Mus, Merit, A's; *Ohio U; Journ.*

SNOW, Theresa Ann
Mormon Trail HS; Garden Grove, IA (23-45) Chor; Chor A; *Des Moines Area Col; Developmental Disabilities.*

SNOW, Wanda Sue
Mt Ida HS; Mt Ida, AR (15-47) Ann; Band; FHA; Sftbl; COM; *Ark Tech Univ; Mus.*

SNOWDEN, Brenda S
Fitzgerald HS; Fitzgerald, GA (29-250) Pres, 4H; Tri-HiY; MYF; *N Ga Col; Phys Ther.*

SNOWDEN, Jan Neal
Putnam City HS; Oklahoma City, OK; *U of Mo; Bus Adm.*

SNOWDEN, Kenneth Scott
Santa Fe HS; Alauchua, FL; BC; FFA; Ftbl; Tr; Military.*

SNOWDEN, Monty LaRue
Lomega HS; Omega, OK; Chor; Parl, FFA; Bsbl; Bkbl; Citz A; Hist A; HCt; Masonic A; Sci A; Val; Ind Arts A.

SNYDER, Annette
Lewiston Con HS; Lewiston, NE (6-31) Band; Chldr; Chor; Drama; Ensm; Ch, FHA; 4H; Madrigal; Ntl Yth Conf; VP, Jr Cl; Pres, Soph Cl; JV, Bkbl; 4H A; Yth Fel; Mus As; *McPherson Col; Mus.*

SNYDER, Betty Ann
Chatham HS; Chatham, VA; Rptr, FHA; FTA; 4H; Tres, Lat C; Span C; Tri-HiY; Church Swtht; Stu o-t Day; *Lynchburg Col; Law.*

SNYDER, Bradley Grant
Ridgeway HS; Memphis, TN (65-110) A-Ed, Ann; Band; Chor; Orch; ARC; Sci C; Bsbl; MVP, Ftbl; Sftbl; Tr; COM; Citz A; Most Out; ROTC A; Yth Leg; Big Brothers Organization; *Evangel Col; Bus.*

SNYDER, Carl Robert
Dobyns Bennett HS; Kingsport, TN; Tnns; Yth Fel; JA; Cpt, Church Acolyte; *U of Tenn; Aviation.*

SNYDER, Christal Ann
Pennsville Mem HS; Pennsville, NJ (36-240) Hmrm; Cpt, Mjrte; NHS; SC; JV, Sftbl; JV, Tnns; Bio A; *E Orange Gen Hospital Nurs Sch; Nurs.*

SNYDER, Cynthia Alice
Moon Sr HS; Coraopolis, PA; Band; Rainbow; Var C; Sftbl; Type A; 1st Cl, Sct; UMY Coun; Pres Phys Fitness A; *Slippery Rock Col; Ed for Exceptional Children.*

SNYDER, David Scott
Ottawa Sr HS; Ottawa, KS (4-190) Cpt, Dbte Tm; NHS; Orch; Bkbl; Golf; Tnns; *Bus.*

SNYDER, David Wells
Lehighton HS; Lehighton, PA (11-226) NHS; Pres, SC; Var C; Pres, Sr Cl; Pres, Jr Cl; Pres, Soph Cl; Cpt, Ftbl; MVP, Tr; Wrest; *US Military Acad.*

SNYDER, Debbie Jean
Covina HS; Covina, CA; Chldr; Chor; *Citrus Col; Sci.*

SNYDER, Debra Ann
Garden Spot HS; New Holland, PA (25-220) AFS; Chor; Co-Ch, Drama; Pres, Fr C; NHS; Orch; Mgr, Bkbl; JV, Tnns; *Millersville St Col; Elem Ed.*

SNYDER, Denise Ann
Notre Dame HS; Clarksburg, WV (4-63) Band; Bus C; Chldr; Chess C; Drama; FBLA; S-T, FTA; Ger C; Hmrm; VP, Lat C; Lit Mag; Math C; NFL; NHS; Ch, ARC; SC; Math A; NEDT; Poet A; *W Va U.*

SNYDER, Donna Lynn
Victoria HS; Victoria, TX (10%-750) Fr C; NHS; *U of Tex.*

SNYDER, Felecia Ann
Tulpehocken HS; Bernville, PA; Band; Chor; 4H; Hmrm; Hockey; JV, Sftbl; 4H A; A Cappella Quartet; *Fine Arts.*

SNYDER, Gary Lee
Lancaster HS; Lancaster, OH (250-600) Bus C; *Mount Vernon Nazarene Col; Bus Adm.*

SNYDER, Glenn Reverdy
Owen J Roberts HS; Pottstown, PA (4-324) Chem C; 4H; NHS; SC; Soccer; Swim; Tr; 4H A; Hon Prog; *US Naval Acad; Engr.*

SNYDER, Jack David
Mark Morris HS; Longview, WA (10%-350) Band; Pres, Bus C; Dbte Tm; Hmrm; NHS; ARC; SC; Cpt, Ftbl; Elk A; Top St Bible Quizzer; *Jackson Col of Ministries; Theology.*

SNYDER, James Martin
Glenbrook N HS; Northbrook, IL (300-670) Citz A; Raquet Ball; *Enviromental Sci.*

SNYDER, Karen Louise
Central Dauphin HS; Harrisburg, PA (40%-500) Cpt, Band; Secy, Ger C; ARC; SC; Tr; ARC A; Yth Fel; Bandfront As; Church Yth Pres A; Sftb Trophies; *Pottsville Hospital Sch of Nurs; Nurs.*

SNYDER, Karen Louise
Central York HS; York, PA (119-294) AFS; Ann; 4H; Bus Mgr, Sch P; Mgr, Bsbl; Mgr, Bkbl; VP, Arts & Crafts C; Ch, Pep C; Art A's; Fin, 4-H C A; *Bloomsburg St U; Art.*

SNYDER, Keith Alan
Lincoln Comm HS; Lincoln, IL (40-290) Band; NHS; Mgr, Bkbl; Golf; Math A; St Scholar; WW; *N Ill U; Pol Sci.*

SNYDER, Kimberly Ralene
Belle Plaine HS; Belle Plaine, KS (15-68) Ann; Chor; Ensm; VP, Fr C; Pres, FHA; 4H; Pres, Rainbow; SC; Secy, Var C; Sftbl; Tr; Odd Fellow Fin; Spch A; Yth Fel; Dist Pres, FHA; Rainbow Girls A's; WW; *Fort Hays St Col; Bus.*

SNYDER, Laura Lynn
Booker T Washington HS; Tulsa, OK; Band; *Tulsa U; Criminal Law.*

SNYDER, Lee Ann
Freeport Sr HS; Freeport, IL (27-553) A Cap Choir; Chor; Madrigal; Ski C; Span C; Tnns; Pres A; Yth Fel; Cr-Ctry Skiing; Span, Art, Mus, A's; *Nurs.*

SNYDER, Linda Marie
Cumberland Valley HS; Mechanicsburg, PA (8-627) NHS; JV, Hockey; *Shippensburg St Col; Elem Ed.*

SNYDER, Lora Jean
Smiths Station HS; Smiths, AL (5%-190) BC; Drama; FHA; 4H; Mu Alpha Theta; *Auburn U; Zoology.*

SNYDER, Maida Patricia
Bentworth HS; Bentleyville, PA (1-160) Band; NHS; Sftbl; MLS; Val; Semi-Fin, Secy, Bowl; Pa St Schol Prog; *Gannon Col; Med.*

SNYDER, Mary Elizabeth
Winyah HS; Georgetown, SC (50%-150) Chldr; Mu Alpha Theta; *Francis Marion Col; Social Services.*

SNYDER, Michele Dee
Bluffton HS; Bluffton, OH (1-99) Band; Lat C; Orch; NEDT; SAE; Eng A; Hospital Vol Cert; OMEA Solo; *Cedarville Col.*

SNYDER, Pamela Dee
Belle Vernon HS; Belle Vernon, PA; Chor; FBLA; Span C; Swim; Tr.

SNYDER, Pamela Sue
Clinton Sr HS; Clinton, MO (63-180) Span C; *SW Baptist Col; Secy.*

SNYDER, Randy Lee
Allen Jay HS; High Point, NC (30-100) Band; Fr C; Ftbl; Band & Ftbl Ltrs; *U of NC; Mus.*

SNYDER, Raymond Davis
Methacton HS; Fairview Village, PA (8%-426) Band; Hmrm; Order/Arrow; SC; JA A; NEDT; Eagle Sct; HR; Pa Bicentennial Comm A; *Law.*

SNYDER, Sara Anne
Lincoln HS; Lincoln, IL; Band; Fr C; VP, Lib C; Candystripers; S-T, Explorers; *Nurs.*

SNYDER, Sharon Ann
Bellwood-Antis HS; Bellwood, PA (20-116) Drama; Sch P; Secy, Var C; Tres, Sr Cl; Tres, Jr Cl; Co-Cpt, Hockey; HCt.

SNYDER, Susan Alice
Eastwood HS; Pemberville, OH (11-150) Chor; FHA; FTA; GS; Madrigal; NHS; Secy, ARC; Span C; FTA Schol; *Bowling Green St U; Ed.*

SNYDER, Susan Lynn
Freeport Sr HS; Freeport, IL (72-558) SC; JV, Tnns; Pres, Yth Fel; Pom Pon Squad; JV Vlbl; Badminton; *Ed.*

SNYDER, Susan Marie
John W Hallahan HS; Philadelphia, PA (23-432) *Penn St U; Pol Sci.*

SNYDER, Susan Rebecca
Huntingdon Area HS; Huntingdon, PA (10-221) Ed, Ann; Band; Chor; Hmrm; NHS; Var C; Hockey; Tr; Hon Prog; Pres A; Dance C; Mayor's Yth Coun; *Nurs.*

SNYDER, Terri Lisa
Waynesboro Central HS; Waynesboro, MS (25%-119) Drama; FHA; 4H; Pres, Hmrm; ARC; Sch P; Y-Tns; Bkbl; Tnns; Amer Leg A; Cl Fav; 4H A; Most Out; *Miss St U; Pre-Med.*

SNYDER, Vicki Lynn
N Side HS; Ft Wayne, IN (140-501) Chor; Dbte Tm; Drama; Lat C; NFL; Rptr, Sch P; Pres, Spch C; Thes; Citz A; Hon Prog; Spch A; Ltr Spch; Ltr Drama; *Purdue U; Aviation.*

SNYDER, William Mark
Hutchinson HS; Hutchinson, MN (10-219) BS; Demolay; NHS; Var C; Swim; House of Rep Page Prog; FCA; *Engr.*

SOARD, Deborah Jean
Bellflower HS; Bellflower, CA; Chor; FNA; God & Country A; Sci A; Yth Fel; *Cerritos Col; Sci.*

SOARDS, Barbara Elaine
Tuscola HS; Tuscola, IL (48-118) Chor; Fr C; FHA; Tres, 4H; Rainbow; Rptr, Sch P; 4H A; Co-Ch, 4-H C; Mgr, Vlbl; *Parkland Jr Col; Secy Sci.*

SOBALVARRO, Ivania M
Inglewood HS; Inglewood, CA; Fr C; ARC; CSF; COM; Citz A; Type A; Art A; Fr A; *USC; Art.*

SOBERS, Rogelio Valentino
Rainbow City Jr Sr HS; Rainbow City, CANAL ZONE; Band; Dbte Tm; Bkbl; Soccer; Tr; Alg A; Chem A; Math A; Sci A; Mus A; *Canal Zone U; Engr.*

SOBEY, Janet Denise
Richardson HS; Richardson, TX (1-954) Lat C; NHS; Orch; Pres, Tri-HiY; COM; Coun of Teach A; Schol Sweater A.

SOBIERAJ, Maria Theresa
St Angela Hall Acad; Brooklyn, NY (1-82) Math C; Rptr, Sch P; Alg A; Bio A; Hist A; Hon Prog; Math A; NEDT; 2nd Hon, Fr Contest; *St John's U; Pre-Med.*

SOBOLEWSKI, Annette Marie
Mannington HS; Mannington, WV (4-111) Band; JV, Chldr; GS; 4H; Hmrm; NHS; Pres, SC; Amer Leg A; Bio A; Elk A; HCt; VofDEM; Stu o-t Yr; Prom Qn; *W Va U; Pre-Bio.*

SOCIA, Debbie Dawn
Roseville HS; Roseville, MI; Ann; Drama; Tres, Lat C; NHS; Ski C; Sftbl; Hon Prog; Acteens.

SOCKWELL, Mary Beth
Woodrow Wilson HS; Dallas, TX; A Cap Choir; CYO; Chor; Ensm; Fr C; FHA; Hmrm; SC; Tri-HiY; Tnns; *E Tex St U; Elem Ed.*

SODERQUIST, Cheryl Dawne
Southwestern Central HS; Jamestown, NY (26-200) AFS; Chldr; Hmrm; NHS; Ski C; Span C; Swim; Hon Prog; *Augustana Col; Med Technology.*

SODERQUIST, Denise Therese
Alvernia HS; Chicago, IL (3-240) Co-Ed, Ann; Chor; Drama; NHS; Hon Prog; St Scholar; Schol Art A; WW; *DePaul U; Liberal Arts.*

SODERQUIST, Jill Ann
Columbus Pub HS; Columbus, ND (2-21) Ann; Band; Chor; Drama; Ensm; Fin, GS; Rptr, Sch P; Amer Leg A; Hon Prog; Yth Fel; GAA; Pom Pon; Math.

SODERSTROM, Ryan Whitney
Fridley Sr HS; Fridley, MN (163-481) Drama; Co-Ed, Sch P; Ski C; Bkbl; Tr; Hon Prog; Rptr, Sch P; Brown Inst For Broadcasting; TV & Radio Broadcasting.

SODINI, Gregg Steven
Manasquan HS; Manasquan, NJ; Kiwanis A; Harvard U; Law.

SOEBBING, Mary Elizabeth
Quincy Notre Dame HS; Quincy, IL (14-161) Chor; Ensm; Hmrm; SC; Hon Prog; Forestry.

SOEFFNER, Lori Anne
Bible Baptist HS; Savannah, GA (5-34) Ann; Chldr; Secy, Hmrm; HCt.

SOETER, Mary Esther
Preble HS; Green Bay, WI; Band; Hmrm; NHS; Orch; SC; Soccer; JV, Tr; COM; Type A; All St Band; Mus Camp Schol; All St Orch; St Mus Contest A; Ntl Jr Hon Soc; Phi Sigma; All Star Soccer; Hope Col.

SOFIO, Mark Gerard
Hastings Sr HS; Hastings, MN (25%-560) Band; Chor; Drama; Thes; Soccer; Superior, St Solo.

SOHN, Bruce
Herrin HS; Herrin, IL; Ann; Band; Ensm; Pres, Key C; Sch P; Hon Prog.

SOISSON, Valerie Ann
Stow HS; Stow, OH (26-485) NHS; JA A; Cl Offices; Kent St U; Nurs.

SOLA, David Mark
New Providence HS; New Providence, NJ (2-300) Chess C; Math C; Var C; Cr-Ctry; Tr; Hon Prog; Princeton U; Physics.

SOLAZZO, Thomas James
University HS; San Diego, CA (1-315) VP, Drama; NHS; Thes; Swim; CSF; Hon Prog; Most Out; Waterpolo; Outst Actor; Fresh, Soph, Achv A's; U of Calif; Sci.

SOLBERG, Donald Paul
N Crawford HS; Gays Mills, WI; Band; Math C; Tres, NHS; Order/Arrow; SC; Var C; Pres, Soph Cl; JV, Bsbl; Bkbl; JV, Ftbl; MLS; NEDT; Order/Arrow A; U of Wis; Bus Adm.

SOLBERG, Fran Elizabeth
Wells-Easton HS; Wells, MN (54-110) A Cap Choir; Chor; Drama; Ensm; Pres, FHA; Secy, SC; Swim; Tnns; Tr; Pres A; Home Ec.

SOLBERG, John Thomas
Tyler HS; Tyler, MN; A Cap Choir; Band; Chor; Ensm; Madrigal; Order/Arrow; Spch C; SC; Var C; Pres, Jr Cl; Pres, Soph Cl; Bsbl; Cpt, Bkbl; Cpt, Ftbl; Tr; Order/Arrow A; Pres A; Star Student; Yth Fel; Pres, FCA; Minneapolis Tribune Schol A; Best Paper Boy A; Augustana Col; Elem Ed.

SOLBERG, Mary Kay
Central Valley HS; Buxton, ND (2-33) Ann; Band; Drama; Pres, FHA; GS; 4H; Ed, Sch P; SC; Pres, Sr Cl; Secy, Jr Cl; Co-Cpt, Bkbl; Sftbl; 4H A; NDSU; Phar.

SOLDNER, David Weldon
Adams Central HS; Monroe, IN (20-104) Hmrm; NHS; Span C; VP, SC; Bsbl; Bkbl; Ftbl; Yth Fel; FCA; Mech.

SOLER, Chris
Colegio San Antonio HS; Rio Piedras, PR; VP, Hmrm; NHS; Var C; VP, Sr Cl; JV, Bsbl; JV, Bkbl; COM; Hon Prog; MLS; Hist C; Ciclism C; Silva Mind Control Course; Intramural Ping-Pong Champion; Intrmural, Vlbl; George Washington U; Econ.

SOLER, Maricelis
Academia Ntra Sra Providencia; Rio Piedras, PR (12-58) Band; CYO; Chor; Dbte Tm; GS; Sch Achieve Tm; Sch P; Var C; VP, Sr Cl; Secy, Jr Cl; COM; Hon Prog; JA A; Rotary A; Jr Cath Daughters of Amer; Sports A; Conduct A; University of Fla at Gainesville; Med Technology.

SOLES, Mary Ann
Caney Valley HS; Caney, KS (20-70) Ann; Chor; FHA; NHS; SC; Var C; Bkbl; Tr; Tri Valley League Vlbl A; Independence Jr Col; Phys Ed.

SOLHEIM, Jeffery Arthur
Redfield HS; Redfield, SD; Ann; BS; Chem C; Chor; Drama; FFA; 4H; Lat C; Math C; Monogram; NHS; Var C; Bsbl; JV, Bkbl; Ftbl; JV, Golf; JV, Tr; Alg A; Amer Leg A; COM; 4H A; Hon Prog; Journ A; Math A; VFW A; Yth Fel; Star Greenhand, FFA; Superior, St FFA Crops Judging; Hon Stu; Geometry.

SOLIMINE, Diane Jane
St Mary's Regional HS; Lynn, MA (8-129) CYO; JV, Chldr; Sftbl; Swim; Alg A; COM; Hon Prog; NEDT; Sci A; Phys Ed, Art, Eng, A's; PA, Span, Sewing, A's; Sci.

SOLIS, Diana
Mission HS; Mission, TX (52-387) Tres, CYO; VP, FHA; Rptr, FTA; Sci C; Span C; SC; H of F; Lion A; Rotary A; Rptr, FHA; Pan American U; Nurs.

SOLLARS, Teresa Ann
Blanchet HS; Seattle, WA (1-308) CYO; NHS; Var C; Swim; Tr; Hon Prog; JA A; Ed.

SOLLARS, Valerie Ann
Robert E Lee HS; Tyler, TX (70-650) Math C; Span C; U of Tex at Austin; Acct.

SOLLMAN, June Marie
Memorial HS; St Marys, OH (46-217) Band; Chor; FTA; Rptr, 4H; Mod Mus Mas; ARC; Thes; Y-Tns; God & Country A; ARC A; Yth Fel; Pres, Summer Mus On Campus; Hospital Vol; Pulpit Comm; 4-H Counselor; Perfect Church Attendence; Lima Tech; X-Ray.

SOLODYNA, E Lin
Kailua HS; Kailua, HI (7-570) NHS; A-Ed, Sch P; Span C; Ch, SC; Journ A; VFW A; VFW Orator Win; VofDEM; Northwestern U-NHSI, Journ Div; Bicentennial Essay A; St Bus Law A; Grinnell Col; Pol Sci.

SOLOMON, Anthony
John F Kennedy HS; Richmond, VA (246-309) Pres, Chor; Drama; Math C; ARC; Sch P; Cr-Ctry; Tr; Interlochen Ntl Mus; Longwood Col.

SOLOMON, George Gregory
G A R Mem HS; Wilkes-Barre, PA (2-186) Co-Ed, Ann; Key C; NHS; Tres, SC.

SOLOMON, Janice Dale
Central HS; Phenix City, AL; FBLA; NHS; Type A; 'Speak Up for Young Amer'; WW.

SOLOMON, Lana Kay
Jefferson City Sr HS; Jefferson City, MO; Band; Drama; SW Mo St U.

SOLOMON, Mary Kay
Ringgold Monongahela HS; Monongahela, PA (36-368) A Cap Choir; Bus C; Chor; Drama; FBLA; S-T, Hmrm; Madrigal; NHS; Hon Prog; Spch A; SOYO.

SOLOMON, Melodie Lashawn
Carver HS; Birmingham, AL (10%-240) FBLA; Sftbl; ROTC A; Sou Bus Col; Eng.

SOLTERMANN, Scott Morris
Shortridge HS; Indianapolis, IN (18-350) Pres, A Cap Choir; Ann; Band; Chem C; Dbte Tm; Drama; Ensm; Fr C; Pres, Key C; Madrigal; NHS; Orch; Sch Achieve Tm; Rptr, Sch P; SC; Thes; Var C; Ftbl; Hon Prog; PTA A; Q&S A; St Scholar; Mus A; Ball St U; Mus.

SOLTYS, Paul Mark
Christopher Dock Mennonite HS; Lansdale, PA (19-70) Ann; Drama; JV, Bkbl; JV, Soccer; Yth Fel; Pinebrook Jr Col; Eng.

SOLUM, Cindy Fawn
Warren Township HS; Gurnee, IL; Band; Ensm; NHS; Bkbl; Sftbl; Historian, Var C; Phys Ed.

SOMERS, Dorothy Colleen
Reidsville Sr HS; Reidsville, NC (10-344) AFS; Pres, Band; Hmrm; Secy, NHS; S-T, Span C; Hon Prog; Yth For Understanding Bicen Courier; 2nd Pl-Local, Women's C Lit As; 3rd Pl-Dist, Women's C Lit As; U NC at Greensboro; Span.

SOMERVILL, Barbara Veronica
Chopticon HS; Morganza, MD (12-289) NHS; Secy, Span C; Math A; WW; March of Dimes Schol; Merit A, St Mary's Co Film Festival; Medix Sch; Paramed.

SOMERVILLE, Charlotte Denise
Messick HS; Memphis, TN; Chldr; FHA; Hmrm; ARC; SC; Bsbl; Bkbl; Sftbl; Tr; Shelby St Comm Col; Ed.

SOMMER, Linda Jean
Celina Sr HS; Celina, OH (14-275) Tres, CYO; Tres, FBLA; NHS; VP, Cath Yth; Pep C; Fresh Choir; WW.

SOMMER, Scott William
Peoria HS; Peoria, IL (1-437) Pres, Fr C; JETS; Pres, Key C; NHS; Sci C; SC; JV, Bkbl; JV, Tnns; COM; Citz A; Gr Marshal; Hon Prog; Kiwanis A; Math A; Most Out; Opt A; St Scholar; Val; Sterling Merit A; WW; U of Ill; Biochem.

SOMMERS, Daniel Lee
Wonderview HS; Hattieville, AR; BS; Pres, FFA; Pres, Sr Cl; Pres, Jr Cl; Bsbl; Bkbl; Cl Fav; Hist A; HCt; MLS.

SOMMERS, Laurie Matile
Wasson HS; Colo Springs, CO (67-450) NHS; Tres, SC; Swim; JV, Tnns; Hockey Statistician; Pres, Sr High Yth; Soc, Pub, Tres, Stu Rel, Comm; Colo St U; Med Tech.

SOMMERS, Paula Jean
Stonington HS; Pawcatuck, CT (50%-246) 4H; Hmrm; Tnns; Tr; 4H A; HQn; HCt; Sci A; Jr Prom Court; SG A; Central Conn St Col; Special Ed.

SOMMERS, Stephanie Ann
Montezuma Cortez HS; Cortez, CO (13-253) Band; Hmrm; NHS; Pres, SC; JV, Bkbl; Cpt, Sftbl; JV, Tnns; Alg A; COM; Kiwanis A; Job's Daughters; VIP o-t Day; Mesa Col.

SOMMERVILLE, Mark Anthony
William M Raines HS; Jacksonville, FL (3-29) Math C; Orch; Wrest; Alg A; Bio A; Citz A; Math A; Engr.

SOMSEN, Shirley Lois
Courtenay Pub Sch; Courtenay, ND (5-7) Ed, Ann; Cpt, Chldr; Chor; Drama; GS; Ed, Sch P; Sftbl; Tr; St Sch of Sci; General Office.

SONDEEN, Peggy Ann
Fremont HS; Fremont, MI (13-247) NHS; Magna Cum Laude; 2nd Pl, St Art Show; Ferris St Col; Off Adm.

SONE, Paul M
Hicksville Sr HS; Hicksville, NY (56-954) NHS; BSct; St U of NY; Med.

SONES, Susan Michelle
Vicksburg HS; Vicksburg, MS (5-250) AFS; F-Ed, Ann; Co-Cpt, Chldr; Drama; FBLA; 4H; Lat C; NHS; Mgr, Bsbl; Beauty; 4H A; H of F; HCt; Math A; Sci A; Swtht; Key C Swtht; Art A; Mac-Ette; Sub-Deb; Hinds Jr Col; Secondary Ed.

SONNENBURG, Carole Lynn
Champaign Centennial HS; Champaign, IL (6-300) Band; Nom, NHS; Abilene Christian Col; Computer Sci.

SONNIER, Clayton
Forest Brook HS; Houston, TX (25%-480) Fr C; VP, JETS; Mu Alpha Theta; Parl, NHS; Alg A; COM; Citz A; VFW A; U of Houston; Engr.

SONNTAG, Larry Chester
W Mesa HS; Albuquerque, NM (32-400) BS; Pres, Chor; Demolay; Lat NHS; NHS; Order/Arrow; ARC; Spch C; MVP, Bsbl; Cpt, Cr-Ctry; God & Country A; Hon Prog; JA A; Masonic A; Most Out; Order/Arrow A; Spch A; Yth Fel; Eng A; U of NM; Recreation Mgt.

SONNY, Carolyn Annette
Rufus King HS; Milwaukee, WI; Tres, Drama; Hmrm; Math C; NHS; Span C; SC; Schol Plaque; Drama Cert; Milwauke Sch of Engr.

SOPINSKI, Michael Gerard
Bishop Klonowski HS; Scranton, PA (2-110) BS; Hmrm; NHS; SC; JV, Bsbl; Bkbl; Hon Prog; Math A; NEDT.

SOPKO, Jean Marie
Washington Sr HS; Sioux Falls, SD (280-622) Secy, Chor; Dbte Tm; Drama; NFL; ARC; JA A; Spch A; *Northern St Col; Social Work.*

SOPTELEAN, Janet
Jewett-Scio HS; Scio, OH; Bus Mgr, Ann; SC; A of Distinction; Ohio Off Ed Assn; *Secy.*

SORENSEN, Christian Charles
N Hollywood HS; N Hollywood, CA (100-600) BS; VP, SC; JV, Tnns; Amer Leg A; COM; VP, Ldrship Cl; Sunday Sch Teacher; Parl, SB; Drama A; Amer Leg Rep, BS; Asst Coach, Hockey Tm; *Law.*

SORENSEN, David Paul
Roosevelt HS; Minneapolis, MN (99-542) NHS; Ftbl; Sftbl; *U of Minn; Bus.*

SORENSEN, Diana Lee
Fruitport HS; Muskegon, MI (141-358) Ski C; Pep C; *Mich St U; Vet Med.*

SORENSEN, Diane Kay
Galva Comm HS; Galva, IA (3-23) Band; Chem C; Chor; Model UN; Cpt, Bkbl; Sftbl; Tr; 4H A; HCt; Type A; Yth Fel; St Tr; Augusta Band Festival; All Conf Sftbl, Bkbl; Church Organist; NW Iowa Band; *Morningside Col; Nurs.*

SORENSEN, Jana Dawn
Sierra Joint Union HS; Tollhouse, CA (2-168) Chor; Ger C; Hmrm; Math C; NHS; JV, Tnns; COM; Math A; MIP, Tnns; Girls' League; *U of Calif; General Ed.*

SORENSEN, Jennifer Louise
Logan HS; Logan, UT; Drama; Rptr, Sch P; Masonic A; Spch A; Marshall, Job's Daughters; Pep C; *Utah St U; Eng.*

SORENSEN, Karen Lee
Dover HS; Dover, NH (25%-392) Secy, Band; Chor; Span C; Tr; Mission & Action Board Schol; *U of NH; Nurs.*

SORENSEN, Mark Bruce
Immanuel HS; Reedley, CA (5-83) Bsbl; Ftbl; Most Out; *Farming.*

SORENSON, David Andrew
Robert M LaFollette HS; Madison, WI (6-557) A Cap Choir; Madrigal; Math C; NHS; Tres, SC; JV, Bkbl; JV, Ftbl; Tnns; *U of Wis; Bus.*

SORENSON, Mary Jean
Little Wolf HS; Manawa, WI (10-95) Band; Cpt, Chldr; Chor; Drama; Ensm; Hmrm; ARC; SC; Var C; Pres, Soph Cl; Bkbl; Sftbl; Tr; COM; Citz A; Cl Fav; Elk A; Hon Prog; Interlochen Ntl Mus; Kiwanis A; Pres A; Star Student; *Eng.*

SORENSON, Michael Robert
Sheboygan S HS; Sheboygan, WI; Order/Arrow; JV, Cr-Ctry; JV, Tr; Order/Arrow A; *Math.*

SORENSON, Vicki Lynn
Lake of The Woods HS; Baudette, MN (17-89) Band; MVP, Chldr; Fr C; FHA; NHS; VP, Soph Cl; Bkbl; HQn; Yth Fel; Vlbl; Outst Chldr; *U of ND; Nurs.*

SORENSSON, Charles Ture
Niwot HS; Niwot, CO (10-350) S-T, Band; Secy, BS; Chor; Semi-Fin, Dbte Tm; Madrigal; NHS; Order/Arrow; Spch C; VP, Sr Cl; Cr-Ctry; Tr; Order/ Arrow A; Spch A; Dist Creative Writing A; Eagle Sct; *Cornell U; Entomology.*

SORG, Kenneth Edward
Bishop Luers HS; Fort Wayne, IN (45%-250) Band; Community Yth Symph; Orch; Hon Prog.

SORG, Lisa Rae
St Elizabeth HS; Pittsburgh, PA (4-101) Ann; Drama; Model UN; Phys C; B Crocker A; Hon Prog; Math A; NEDT; WW; Ntl *hs A For Excellence; Duquesne U Chem Lecture Series Cer; *Gannon Col; Med Asst.*

SORRELL, Debbie Lynn
Man HS; Man, WV (9-180) Band; Bus C; Commercial C; FBLA; FHA; FNA; Secy, Hmrm; Mjrte; NHS; Hon Prog; Type A; Bookkeeping, Shorthand, A's; *Marshall U; Acct.*

SORRELL, Samuel Scott
The Kinkaid Sch; Houston, TX (48-100) Hmrm; Cpt, Bkbl; *Baylor U; Bus.*

SORRELLS, Belinda
Franklin HS; Somerset, NJ; CYO; Hmrm; Up Bound; Bkbl; *Livingston Col; Bus Adm.*

SORRELLS, Susan
Trinity Prep Sch; Orlando, FL (1-63) Rptr, Ann; Secy, Cum Laude Soc; Ed, Lit Mag; Model UN; F-Ed, Sch P; COM; Val; Top Schol As; UDC Ntl Schol; Scoville Fr A; *U of Fla; Dentistry.*

SORROW, Reny John
Towers HS; Decatur, GA (50-400) Ensm; Var C; Mgr, Ftbl; Wrest; *Communication.*

SORSBY, Dayton Phillip III
Homewood HS; Homewood, AL; Chor; Span C; Ftbl; Life Sct; *Auburn U.*

SORTOR, Jane Elaine
Pennington Sch; Pennington, NJ (9-45) Band; Cpt, Chldr; Chor; NHS; Thes; Bkbl; Hon Prog; Fr A; Mus.

SORTORE, Dahle Lynn
LaSalle Sr HS; Niagara Falls, NY (230-493) AFS; Band; Secy, Chor; Drama; Hmrm; Secy, Madrigal; Kiwanis A; NYS Rating, Voice; *Appalachian Bible Inst; Bible.*

SOSA, Howard Charles
Babylon Jr-Sr HS; Babylon, NY (50%-200) JV, Wrest; Newspaper Boy; Stock Boy, Hardware Store; Second Mate, Fishing Boat; Alter Boy,bSct; *Suffolk Co Comm Col.*

SOSA, Jaime Cruz
St Augustine HS; Laredo, TX (7-67) Ann; Math C; Pres, NHS; Bsbl; Bkbl; Alg A; COM; Chem A; Math A; Ntl Sci Symposium; Nom, WW; Geom A; DAHSS; *St Mary's Col; Med.*

SOSA, Nereida
A S Pedreira HS; Moca, PR (5-39) Commercial C; FBLA; Pres, Hmrm; Lit Mag; Span C; COM; Hist A; Journ A; Star Student; Cooperation Assistence A; *CAAM; Acct.*

SOSEBEE, Leslie Claire
Stephens Co HS; Toccoa, GA; Chor; Ensm; Hmrm; Lit Ral; Tri-HiY; Hon Prog; All-St Chor; 1st Pl Trio, St Lit Meet; Women's C Schol; Mus Workshop; *Shorter Col; Mus.*

SOSNIN, Julie Ruth
Iroquois HS; Louisville, KY (4-460) NHS; Span C; *U of Louisville; Lib Arts.*

SOSSKO, Vera
Woodrow Wilson HS; Youngstown, OH (1-356) Secy, Ger C; Key C; COM; Spch A; VFW A; Vof-DEM; PA Announcer; Cert of Service; Luther League; Ntl Slovak Soc; Jednota; *Sci.*

SOSTER, Sharon Lynne
Deer Lakes Sr HS; Cheswick, PA; Ann; Chor; Sch P; Var C; JV, Bkbl; Tnns; Yth Fel; Pres, Yth Group.

SOTELO, Eva Marie
Alpine HS; Alpine, TX (5-73) Band; Parl, CYO; NHS; St Stu Congress; Pres, SC; Bio A; Hist A; Pol Sci Dept Sul Ross Schol; Diocesan Coun Board of Dir Hon Grad; *Sul Ross St U; Pol Sci.*

SOTELO, Ingrid Maria
Notre Dame HS; Caguas, PR (1-128) Fr C; NHS; JA; Hon A; Excellence A; VP, Lib C; Secy, Philatelic C; Lit Circle; *U of Puerto Rico at Mayaguez; Sci.*

SOTERO, Domingo
Samuel Gompers Vths; Bronx, NY (5%-210) Ann; CYO; Math C; Tres, NHS; Ed, Sch P; Swim; COM; Photograph C; Altar Server; HR; MIT Prog; Phys Fitness Merit A; Ed, Church Yth Group Newspaper; Karate C; BSct; *Rochester Inst of Tech; Physics.*

SOTO, Carlos G
Dr Pedro Perea Fajardo Voc HS; Mayaguez, PR; Exc Hon; *Elec.*

SOTO, Judith G
Antonio S Pedreira HS; Moca, PR (5-38) Chor; Tres, Lat C; Bkbl; Swim; ARC A; Type A; *Colegio de Mayaguez; Nurs.*

SOTO, Marc Anthony
St Augustine Sch; Laredo, TX; Mgr, Ann; Chor; Tres, SC; Hon Prog; VFW A; HR; *U of Tex at Austin; Bus.*

SOTO, Maria Del Rosario
Consuelo Escalona Private Sch; Carolina, PR (1-30) Chess C; Chor; Dbte Tm; Pres, Model UN; NHS; ARC; Hist A; Hon Prog; Summa Cum Laude; *Eckerd Col; Med Technology.*

SOTO, Mayra Liz
Juan Jose Osuna HS; Hato Rey, PR (11-101) Chldr; Drama; GS; ARC; Swim; Tnns; Alg A; COM; Hon Prog; Lion A; Sci A; Hon Cl; *U of Puerto Rico; Bus Adm.*

SOTO, Nancy
Dr Pedro Perea Fajardo Voc HS; Mayaguez, PR; FHA; COM; *Bradford Col; Arts.*

SOTO, Philip Lee
Los Altos HS; Hacienda Heights, CA (8-500) Pres, A Cap Choir; BS; Chess C; Chor; Hmrm; Pres, Key C; Madrigal; Tres, Model UN; Tnns; CSF; Most Out; WW; *Stanford U; Pol Sci.*

SOTO, Providencia
Antonio S Pedreira HS; Moca, PR (1-49) CYO; FHA; Span C; SC; Alg A; COM; Cl Fav; Math A; High Hon A; *UPR-AGUADILLA; Sci.*

SOTOLONGO, Jorge Felix
Central HS; Santurce, PR; CYO; SC; VP, Sr Cl; VP, Jr Cl; Bkbl; Cpt, Swim; Alg A; Chem A; Hist A; Hon Prog; Sci A; Spch A; *U of PR; Engr.*

SOTOMAYOR, Janet Ann
Norman Thomas HS For Comm Ed; New York, NY; FBLA; Type A; Future Secy's Assn; Steno Cert; FBLA Spec Achv Cert & Medalion; *Secy Sci.*

SOUCEK, Sandra Jean
William J Palmer HS; Colorado Springs, CO (137-452) A Cap Choir; Band; Chor; Community Yth Symph; Ensm; Madrigal; Orch; Rptr, Sch P; WW, Mus; All St Orch; *Ariz St U; Mus.*

SOUGSTAD, Timothy James
Jefferson-Moore HS; Waco, TX; Span C; NMS; DECA; *McLennan Comm Col; Marketing.*

SOULE, David Michael
University HS; San Diego, CA (18-311) NHS; Rptr, Sch P; Cpt, Cr-Ctry; Tr; CSF; Hon Prog; Church Lector; *U of Calif; Sci.*

SOULEN, Richard Kendall
The Open HS; Richmond, VA (1-28) Band; Dbte Tm; Drama; Ger C; Hmrm; Key C; Ed, Lit Mag; NHS; Ed, Sch P; SC; UN Council; COM; Gov Honor Prog; H of F; Journ A; NMF; NMS; Poet A; Co-Cpt, Frisbee Tm; Public Poetry Readings; Poetry & Prose Published; Bar Assn Law A; *Yale U; Creative Writing.*

SOUTH, Jo Ann
Northern Burlington Co Reg HS; Columbus, NJ; Tres, Christian Yth in Action; Steno A; *Rider Col; Bus.*

SOUTH, Laurie Ann
Lawndale HS; Lawndale, CA (33%-339) AFS; Band; Hon Prog; Pres, Christian C; Job's Daughters; *Pacific Christian Col; Christian Ed.*

SOUTH, Wesley Willis
Katy HS; Katy, TX; Band; JV, Bkbl; JV, Ftbl; Band A; Ath Achv A, Bsbl and Ftbl; *Tex A&M U; Archt.*

SOUTHARD, Brian Dale
Shelton HS; Shelton, CT; Chess C; Lat C; Order/ Arrow; Var C; Swim; Tr; Order/Arrow A; Life Sct; *Phar.*

SOUTHARD, Richard Byrd
Oak Ridge Military Acad; Oak Ridge, NC (7-30) Ann; Band; Chor; Dbte Tm; Ensm; 4H; Monogram; Bsbl; Mgr, Bkbl; Soccer; Citz A; Hon Prog; ROTC A; Morehead Schol Nom; Marksmanship A; *U of South at Sewanee; Med.*

SOUTHERLAND, Terry Dale
Campbell HS; Smyrna, GA; Ftbl; Tr; FCA; Lettermen's C.

SOUTHERN, Craig Elijah
Apostolic Christian Sch; Jonesboro, GA; Band; 4H; Ed, Sch P; Pres, SC; Cr-Ctry; Ftbl; Soccer; Hist A; Hon Prog; PTA A; Sci A; Jr Deputy A; Yth Choir; HR; Pub Relations,; Bus Ministry; Soo Sci Fair; Ann Cover Designer; Rel Radio & TV; *Ga St U; Advertising.*

SOUTHERTON, Patricia Mary Ann
Blanchet HS; Seattle, WA (31-285) NHS; Soccer; Hon Prog; *U of Wash; Natural Sci.*

SOUTHWICK, Laura Lee
Butler Area Sr HS; Butler, PA (260-1000) Ger C; Hmrm; ARC; Sci C; Ski C; SC; Cpt, Swim; COM; MVP, Swim; *Mount Holyoke Col; Sociology.*

SOUTHWICK, Michelle Renee
Union HS; Union, MO (8-180) A-Ed, Ann; Chldr; Ger C; NHS; SC; Tr; COM; HCt; NEDT; Snow Qn Court; FFA Qn Court; Highest Scorer, NEDT, PSAT; Harding Col; Mass Communications.

SOUTHWICK, Trudy Anne
Villa Maria HS; Villa Maria, PA (20-40) CYO; Chor; Fr C; Math C; Swim; Wheelock Col; Psych.

SOUTHWORTH, Denise Ray
Reading HS; Reading, MI (20-65) Pres, FTA; NHS; Tr; Tres, Yth Group; Jr Church Teacher; St Off, FTA; Ed.

SOUTHWORTH, Lou Wana
Yukon HS; Yukon, OK; Chor; Drama; Ensm; FHA; St & Dist Jazz Chor & Ensm Cont; Bethany Nazarene Col; Social Work.

SOUTHWORTH, Steven Harry
Arlington Sr HS; Poughkeepsie, NY; Bsbl; Bkbl; Soccer; Drew U; Pre-Law.

SOUTO, Yolina C
Academia Maria Reina; Rio Piedras, PR; Ann; Pres, CYO; Chldr; Chor; Drama; Fr C; French NHS; Pres, InterClub Coun; NFL; NHS; Span C; Spch C; SC; Swim; COM; Hon Prog; Ntl Achv Schol; NEDT; Spch A; French C Pin; Span, Drama Pin; Veteran's Hosp Pin.

SOVEREIGN, John Michael
Monterey HS; Monterey, CA (10%-525) Chess C; Demolay; Ch, InterClub Coun; Key C; Ch, Sci C; SC; CSF; Citz A; Hon Prog; U of Calif/ Biochem.

SOVEREIGN, Susie Jane
Monterey HS; Monterey, CA; Band; Rainbow; Citz A; Hon Prog; U of Calif/ Vet Med.

SOWA, Christine Ann
Thomas A Edison HS; Elmira Heights, NY (90-140) Band; Orch; Span C; God & Country A; Yth Fel; Pres, GSct.

SOWDER, Julie Lynne
Southeastern HS; Augusta, IL (33%-50) Band; Chldr; Pres, Chor; Drama; Pres, NHS; Pres, Sr Cl; Tres, Jr Cl; Beauty; DARGCA; Gr Marshal; HQn; Hon Prog; Swtht; Type A; Lincoln Christian Col; Christian Ed.

SOWELL, Alan Mark
Goodlettsville HS; Goodlettsville, TN (10%-185) Fr C; Bsbl; Bkbl; Ftbl; JV; Tr; Order/Arrow A; Eagle Sct; Multimedia 1st Aid; Advanced Lifesaving; Vanderbilt U.

SOWER, Brenda Lee
East Noble HS; Kendallville, IN (39-253) Ann; S-T, FHA; Pres, 4H; 4H A; JA A; Tres, JA; Scholastic A; Bus.

SOWERBY, Julie Ann
Canyonville Bible Acad; Canyonville, OR (3-24) CYO; Bkbl; Tr; U of NH; Med.

SOWERS, Cary Charles
Anaheim HS; Anaheim, CA; Fr C; HiY; Ski C; Y-Tns; JV, Bkbl; Ftbl; Tnns; JV, Tr; Wrest; Citz A; Pepperdine U; Law.

SOWERS, Deanna Gaye
Henry Grady HS; Atlanta, GA; S-T, BC; S-T, Fr C; Ch, Hmrm; Hist.

SOWERS, Gary Allen
Cumberland HS; Toledo, IL (31-94) Secy, FFA; 4H; Bkbl; Ftbl; Ind Arts A; Carpentry.

SPACKMAN, Paul Ernest
Sky View HS; Smithfield, UT (11-611) A Cap Choir; Pres, Jr Cl; Bsbl; Ftbl; Citz A; Eagle Sct A; Utah St U; Ed.

SPADAFINA, Linda Marie
St Angela Hall Acad; Brooklyn, NY; All Amer Yth; CYO; Pres, Hmrm; NHS; Sch P; SC; Cpt, Sftbl; COM; Hon Prog; Math A; Cpt, MVP, Vlbl; Stu Faculty Advisory Coun; St Francis Col; Phys Therapy.

SPADAFINO, Geralyn Theresa
Secaucus HS; Secaucus, NJ (4-200) Hmrm; SC; Pres, Soph Cl; Bkbl; JV, Sftbl; JV, Tnns; Hon Prog; K of C A; Jr NHS; Executive Stu Coun; Secy, PTA.

SPAEDY, Kerry Lynn
St Mary's Central HS; Bismarck, ND (10%-180) Ann; Chem; Drama; Fr C; Hmrm; Spch C; S-T, SC; Secy, Soph Cl; Mgr, Bkbl; Lion A; Spch A; Mardi Gras Court; Stephens Col; Communications.

SPAEDY, Melanie Ann
St Mary's Central HS; Bismarck, ND (1-180) Ann; Chor; Mgr, Drama; Pres, 4H; NHS; Sci C; Ski C; SC; Co-Cpt, Bkbl; Sftbl; 4H A; Hon Prog; Val; Piano C; Mus A's; Spelling A; Creighton U; Pre-Med.

SPAIGHTS, Lauren Renee
Arts HS; Newark, NJ (22-175) Band; Community Yth Symph; Ensm; Orch; Sci C; Var C; Tnns; NJ Mus Ed Mus Auditions; Future Physicians C; Syracuse U; Bio.

SPAIN, Carcill
Loris HS; Loris, SC (18-150) Ann; Pres, Band; Pres, Chor; VP, 4H; Ch, Mjrte; Sch P; Sci C; Cpt, Var C; Cpt, Bkbl; Ftbl; Cl Fav; 4H A; HCt; Hon Prog; Interlochen Ntl Mus; JA A; MLS; Most Out; Ntl Conf Chr & Jews; S-T, Band; Secy, Chor; Secy, 4-H C; Benedict Col; Pol Sci.

SPAIN, Cari Ann
Frederick HS; Frederick, OK (13-60) Ed, Ann; Secy, Bus C; Chldr; Chor; Ensm; GS; Hmrm; Math C; Rptr, Sch P; Sci C; SC; Var C; Bkbl; Cl Fav; HCt; Most Popular; Colo St U; Bus.

SPAIN, Carolyn Jo
Robert E Lee HS; Tyler, TX (40-610) Ann; Chem C; Chor; Drama; Madrigal; NHS; Span C; SC; Yth Fel; Off, Dist Church Yth; Baylor U; Psych.

SPAIN, Shannon Marie
Valentine HS; Valentine, NE (10-66) Ann; Chldr; Drama; FTA; GS; Var C; Mgr, Tr; Schol, Spch, Contests; Psych.

SPAINE, Marsha Lynn
W Mecklenburg HS; Chalotte, NC (20%-352) NHS; Span C; SC; Hon Prog; Pres, Church Yth Fel; Civinettes; 1st Cl GSct; U of NC; Guidance & Counseling.

SPALTENSPERGER, Margaret
E Detroit HS; E Detroit, MI (9-900) NHS; Hon Prog; Fashion & Design.

SPANE, Suzanne Griffith
Conestoga HS; Berwyn, PA (33%-600) Band; Chldr; Chor; Drama; Pres, Hmrm; SC; U of Richmond; Mus.

SPANG, Vickie Lynne
Cedar Crest HS; Lebanon, PA (20-389) A-Ed, Ann; Cpt, Band; Drama; FTA; Co-Ed, Lit Mag; NHS; Rptr, Sch P; Sftbl; Citz A; Q&S A; Rotary A; Soroptimist A; Ursinus Col; Psych.

SPANGENBURG, Gary Lee
Warwick Sr HS; Lititz, PA (140-220) Pres, Bus C; Order/Arrow; JV, Ftbl; Williamsport Area Comm Col; Graphic Arts-Trade.

SPANGENBURG, Scott Douglas
Warwick HS; Lititz, PA; A Cap Choir; Chor; Drama; Ftbl; COM; Citz A; Yth Fel; Pa St U; Phys Ed.

SPANGLER, Elizabeth Anne
Manhattan HS; Manhattan, KS (30-400) Chor; Community Yth Symph; Span C; Kiwanis A; NMF; NMS; St Scholar; Northwestern U; Biochem.

SPANGLER, Kim Michele
Stuarts Draft HS; Stuarts Draft, VA (20%-180) Chldr; Chor; Drama; Fr C; FHA; Hmrm; Sci C; Thes; Rptr, Jr Cl; Secy, Soph Cl; Tr; Citz A; HCt; Drama A; Essay Contest A; Old Dominion U; Dental Hygiene.

SPANGLER, Otto Maurice Jr
Gainesville HS; Gainesville, FL (85-465) JV, Bkbl; Ftbl; Tr; Pres, FCA; Schol, Sportsmanship A, Ftbl; U of Fla; Archt.

SPANGLER, Peggy Louise
Guilford HS; Rockford, IL (14-725) Pres, 4H; 4H A; I Dare You; Med.

SPANKE, Mary Ellen
Our Lady of Grace Acad; Beech Grove, IN (20-47) VP, CYO; Chor; Tres, Deanery; Vlbl; Purdue U; Dentistry.

SPANKOWSKI, Debbie Marie
Los Banos HS; Los Banos, CA (3-277) A Cap Choir; AFS; Ed, Ann; CYO; Chess C; Chor; Dbte Tm; FFA; Madrigal; ARC; Mgr, Tnns; CSF; K of C A; ARC A; Spch A; San Jose St Col; Mus.

SPANN, Alaina Hollis
Berkeley HS; Berkeley, CA (25%-580) Band; Chor; Ensm; Rptr, Sch Newspaper; Badminton Tm; Merrit Col; Journ.

SPARACINO, Linda Marie
Old Forge HS; Old Forge, PA; Band; FHA; Mjrte; NHS; Sci C; Ski C; Hon Prog; Pa St U; Bus Ed.

SPARKES, David Charles
Ayer Jr Sr HS; Ayer, MA (10-250) Mu Alpha Theta; NHS; Rptr, Sch P; Bsbl; Hon Prog; Math A; Yth Fel; Church Board of Christian Ed; Ch, Church Ushers; PA; High Hon A; Math.

SPARKMAN, Nancy Carol
Kemper Acad; DeKalb, MS (5-42) Ed, Ann; Pres, BC; Chor; 4H; Fin, Jr Miss Pagent; F-Ed, Sch P; Sftbl; Bio A; Chem A; Citz A; Sci A; Miss U For Women.

SPARKMAN, Timothy Alan
Laurel Co HS; London, KY (5-360) Ann; BC; Hmrm; Pres, Lat C; VP, Sr Cl; JV, Bkbl; Tnns; Al; A; Bio A; COM; Citz A; Math A; Spch A; Star Student; Dist Top Quizzer; Regional Bible Quizzer; Mount Vernon Nazarene Col.

SPARKS, Brenda Delois
Napa Sr HS; Napa, CA; FBLA; Sch Achieve Tm; Bank Of Amer A; Type A; Shorthand A; Key C Schol; Okla Jr Col; Bus.

SPARKS, Doug Calen
Willows HS; Willows, CA (7-136) Band; Ensm; Hmrm; SC; Bsbl; Bkbl; Engr.

SPARKS, Ellen Mary
Haddon Township HS; Westmont, NJ (20%-225) Semi-Fin, GS; Lat C; Secy, NHS; Messiah Col; Eng.

SPARKS, Fenton Ernest
N Chicago Comm HS; N Chicago, IL (172-320) Band; Ensm; Ftbl; Tnns; Jazz Band A; Gym; Morehouse Col; Mus.

SPARKS, Karen Leslie
Tuttle HS; Tuttle, OK (12-80) Chor; FHA; Mgr, Bkbl; Mgr, Tr; COM; Gen Mills Family Ldr of Tomorrow A; Okla St U; Home Ec.

SPARKS, Kathy Gayle
W Carter HS; Olive Hill, KY (6-130) Ann; BC; FBLA; Rptr, 4H; Tr; WW; Morehead St U.

SPARKS, Kimberly Sheryl
Briggs HS; Columbus, OH; Drama; Fr C; Secy, Sr Cl; Sftbl; Yth Fel; Rep, Briggs Stu Forum; Bowling Green Col.

SPARKS, Lea Alison
Mem Sr HS; Houston, TX; AFS; Chor; Corresponding Secy, SC; Day Camp CIT; Hospital Vol; Corr Secy, Fresh Cl; Princeton U; Hist.

SPARKS, Martin Allen
James Monroe HS; Fredericksburg, VA (43-145) Key C; Span C; Thes; Pres, Var C; Ftbl; WW; Va Tech U; Building Construction.

SPARKS, Mike Waldon
Loganville Jr-Sr HS; Loganville, GA (8-120) VP, BC; BS; Span C; Amer Leg Orator A; COM; Photography, Sch Paper; PC Jr Fellow A; Arts.

SPARKS, Tony L
Fairfield HS; Fairfield, AL; Ann; Band; Chor; Sch P; SC; Thes; COM; Poet A; Sci A; Pres, Yth Found; Career Achv A; U of Ala, Birmingham; Mus.

SPARLING, Linda Lee
Marshall Sr HS; Marshall, MN (40-256) Band; Chor; Dbte Tm; Drama; VP, 4H; NFL; Ed, Sch P; Tr; COM; 4H A; Magna Cum Laude; Spch A; NFL Degree of Distinction; St Olaf Col; Eng.

SPARLING, Patricia Lynn
Marshall HS; Marshall, MN (53-250) A Cap Choir; Band; Chor; Drama; Ensm; NFL; Rptr, Sch P; Spch Mus A's; All St Band; Luthe Col; Mus.

SPARR, Julie Ann
Meyersdale Area HS; Meyersdale, PA (20-128) Cpt, Chldr; Chor; Hmrm; Tres, SC; Tres, Jr Cl; Bkbl; Sftbl; Cl Fav; Lion A; Most Out; Pres A; Tutoring A; Hire The Handicapped Essay A; Shippensburg St Col; Elem Ed.

SPARROW, Hilburn II
Montclair HS; Montclair, NJ (216-485) Orch; Bsbl; Bkbl; Yth Fel; Yth Leg; NC Central U; Pol Sci.

SPARROW, Steven Pettus
Choctaw Co HS; Butler, AL (20-110) FHA; Ftbl; Sci A; Samford U; Chem.

SPARS, Donna Jean
Beaver Dam Sr HS; Beaver Dam, WI (9-331) VP, AFS; A-Ed, Ann; NHS; Span C; Hon Prog; Type A; U W at Eau Claire.

SPATHAS, Thomas John
Ulysses S Grant HS; Portland, OR; Pres, AFS; Ann; Band; BS; Chor; Hmrm; JETS; Model UN; Sch P; Pres, SC; UN Council; Pres, Jr Cl; Parl, Soph Cl; Cpt, Bkbl; Pres, Church Yth; Gym; Greek Folk; Oreg St U; Engr.

SPATHELF, Christopher Lawrence
Bishop Klonowski HS; Scranton, PA; NHS; COM; Hon Prog; NEDT; Geom, Fr & Lat Cert As; Phila Col of Phar & Sci; Phar.

SPAULDING, Jacqueline Kate
Freehold HS; Freehold, NJ (1-200) Band; Chem C; Math C; Mod Mus Mas; NHS; Orch; Var C; Cr-Ctry; Tr; Alg A; Hon Prog; Math A; Ntl Sci Found; Ntl Sci Symposium; Q&S A; Val; Bucknell U; Bio.

SPAULDING, Karen Lynne
Bowling Green Sr HS; Bowling Green, VA (4-135) Ed, Ann; Co-Cpt, Chldr; Dbte Tm; FBLA; French NHS; Hmrm; NFL; NHS; Sch P; SC; Tres, Sr Cl; Tres, Jr Cl; Tres, Soph Cl; Bkbl; Sftbl; Tr; Gov Honor Prog; Scorekeeper & Announcer, Bkbl; Most Intelligent; Sports Ltrs; MVP, Sftbl; U of Tenn; Phys Ed.

SPAULDING, Kimberly Francine
Clinton HS; Clinton, NC; Ann; BC; JV, Chldr; Chor; Ch, Hmrm; NHS; VP, SC; VP, Jr Cl; Mgr, Bkbl; Alg A; COM; Hon Prog; Math A; Most Out; Gov Sch M; VP, Stu Body; Ntl Piano Auditions A; Phar.

SPAULDING, Scott Andrew
Nitro HS; Nitro, WV; Band; BS; Chor; Drama; Hmrm; Cr-Ctry; Tr; Wrest; The Bible Speaks Col; Ministry.

SPAVENTA, Daniel Joseph
Malvern Prep HS; Malvern, PA (4-80) NHS; JV, Bsbl; Tr; COM; NEDT; Span A; 1st Hons; Law.

SPEAK, Ann Patrice
Lexington Sr HS; Lexington, NE (15-144) Chor; S-T, FTA; Fin, GS; NHS; Thes; Var C; Tr; Yth Fel; 1st Pl, Fr A; Teach, Sun Sch; Pep C; Church Choir; Co Govt Day; Kearney St Col; Elem Ed.

SPEAKS, Clint Leon
Fredonia HS; Fredonia, KS; Cpt, Bkbl; Mgr, Ftbl; Tr; Vocal Mus; YCF; Maranatha Choir.

SPEAKS, Mitchell Van
Plainfield HS; Plainfield, IN;

SPEAKS, Shelley Lynne
Fredonia HS; Fredonia, KS (33%-93) Band; Chldr; Chor; FHA; NHS; Tres, SC; VP, Sr Cl; Pres, Jr Cl; Pres, Soph Cl; HCt; Hon Prog; Yth Fel; Vlbl; Pep C; Pom Pon Girls; Emporia St U; Phys Ed.

SPEAKS, Sonya Jeanne
Fredonia HS; Fredonia, KS (15%-95) Vlbl; Friends U; Religion.

SPEARMAN, Vicki La Nae
Haralson Co HS; Tallapoosa, GA; Ann; 4H; Sch P; HQn; HCt; W Ga Col; Off Adm.

SPEARS, Amanda Gail
Grace Baptist HS; Decatur, AL; Ed, Ann; Band; Cpt, Chldr; Chor; Rptr, Hmrm; Math C; Secy, NHS; Rptr, Sch P; Span C; Secy, Sr Cl; Secy, Jr Cl; Bkbl; Cl Fav; HCt; Vlbl; Miss GBS; Assn of Distinguished Young Amer; WW; Bob Jones U; Art.

SPEARS, April Dawn
Maryville HS; Maryville, TN (20%-248) BC; FHA; Lat C; Sch P; Y-Tns; Cpt, Swim; Tnns; Citz A; Hon Prog; Most Out; ARC A; Cum Laude, Lat A; PA; Swim As; Tnns As; U of Tenn; Phys Ed.

SPEARS, Barbara Ruthene
Ethel HS; Ethel, MS (50%-52) Band; BC; FHA; 4H; Sci C; SC; Holmes Jr Col; Math.

SPEARS, Leslie Jo
Bentworth Sr HS; Bentleyville, PA (50-170) Drama; Drill Tm; Campus Life; Calif St Col; Computer Sci.

SPEARS, Linda Kay
Garden City E HS; Garden City, MI (7-495) Ger C; NHS; Semi- fin, St Competitive School; Bus.

SPEARS, Sherry Lynn
Virgie HS; Virgie, KY (8-112) Bus Mgr, Ann; BC; Chor; Pres, Jr Cl; Yth Fel; Sr Superlative; Morehead St U; Bus Adm.

SPEASE, Randall Jon
Luverne HS; Luverne, MN (13-134) A-Ed, Ann; Chor; NHS; SC; Pres, Sr Cl; Pres, Jr Cl; VP, Soph Cl; Bsbl; Ftbl; Amer Leg A; HCt; St Cloud St U; Bus.

SPECHT, Rebecca Claire
Sprague HS; Salem, OR (180-450) Chldr; Chor; Drama; Y-Tns; Tnns; U of Oreg; Lib Arts.

SPECK, Rhonda Renee
De Anza HS; El Sobrante, CA (10-500) Secy, Chor; NHS; Span C; Tnns; CSF; Hon Prog; Kiwanis A; Most Out; Pres A.

SPEDDING, Ben Scutt
Neshaminy Maple Point HS; Langhorne, PA (11-400) Band; Chor; NHS; Soccer; Cpt, Swim; Tr; US Air Force Acad; Areonautic Engr.

SPEECH, Roderick
Argo Comm HS; Argo, IL (40-460) MVP, Bsbl; Bkbl; Ftbl; Co-Cpt, Wrest; COM; Trustee, Mayor's Hon Prog A; BSct; Tres, Sunday Sch; Advertising Salesman.

SPEED, Dorothy Ruth
Kathleen Sr HS; Lakeland, FL; Band; FHA; Math C; Pres, Soph Cl; Sftbl; HCt; Math A; Fla St U; Bus Ed.

SPEED, Thomas Eugene Jr
Crestview HS; Crestview, FL (10%-200) Ftbl; HR; FCA; Rod & Gun C; Pep C; U of S Ala; Acct.

SPEER, Kathryn Mae
Hobart Sr HS; Hobart, IN (10-406) Pres, A Cap Choir; Secy, Chor; Drama; VP, Fr C; Hmrm; Fin, Jr Miss Pagent; S-T, Madrigal; NHS; SC; Thes; Bio A; Citz A; Hon Prog; Interlochen Ntl Mus; Most Out; Sci A; Outst, Choir; Ball St U; Nurs.

SPEER, Linda Elaine
Haltom HS; Fort Worth, TX (63-453) Secy, FNA; NHS; Hon Prog; Stephen F Austin St U; Pediatrics.

SPEERSCHNEIDER, Anne Kathryn
Minnetonka HS; Minnetonka, MN (2-633) Cpt, Orch; Hon Prog; Sal; Secy, Saber Soc; Jobs Daughters; St Mus Contest A; NSOA Orch A; Lawrence Col; Hist.

SPEERSCHNEIDER, Karen Elizabeth
Minnetonka HS; Minnetonka, MN (1-633) Fr C; French NHS; Orch; Hon Prog; Math A; Val; Jobs Daughters; Tres, Saber Soc; NSOA Orch A; Most Intelligent; St Olaf Col; Bio.

SPEH, Stephanie Joan
Kinnelon HS; Kinnelon, NJ (51-224) SC; WW; Concordia Col; Elem Ed.

SPEHR, Martha Jean
Batavia HS; Batavia, IL (7-214) AFS; Band; Chor; Dbte Tm; Fin, GS; Hmrm; Pres, NHS; P-S-T, SC; Amer Leg A; Hon Prog; Ntl Sci Found; Sci A; Spch A; VofDEM; Yth Foundation A; Art C; Northern Ill U; Fine Arts.

SPEIDEL, Craig Thomas
Edgeley Pub HS; Edgeley, ND (21-56) Bus Mgr, Ann; Chor; FBLA; VP, Sr Cl; Ftbl; Co-Cpt, Wrest; Alt, BS; Whapeton Sch of Sci; Elec Tech.

SPEIDEL, Curtis Charles
Edgeley Pub HS; Edgeley, ND (3-56) Ann; BS; Chor; FBLA; Order/Arrow; SC; Bsbl; Co-Cpt, Bkbl; Cpt, Ftbl; Tr; HKg; Order/Arrow A; U of ND; Med Tech.

SPEIGHT, William III
The Buckley Sch; Sherman Oaks, CA (4-52) NHS; JV, Ftbl; Tr; Alg A; Bio A; COM; Citz A; Math A; NEDT; Sci A; Harvard Col; Biomed Sci.

SPEIGHTS, Don Cameron
John F Kennedy HS; Bronx, NY; MVP, Tr; Yth Fel; Baruch U; Acct.

SPEIGHTS, Pamela Jo
Brook Haven Acad; Brook Haven, MS; BC; Fr C; Bio A; COM; Lion A.

SPEIGNER, Stanley Warren
New Brockton HS; New Brockton, AL; Ed, Ann; Pres, BC; BS; VP, FBLA; Sci C; Pres, Sr Cl; Cl Fav; MLS; Troy St Col; Pre-Med.

SPELL, Gregory Edward
Wayne Co HS; Jesup, GA; Band; Pres, 4H; Hmrm; Citz A; VICA C; Pres, Rifle C; Hon Soc; Railroad.

SPELLMAN, Beth Davene
Stafford HS; Stafford Springs, CT (59-144) Chor; Drama; Span C; E Conn St Col; Psych.

SPELLMAN, Valencia
Great Bridge HS; Chesapeake, VA (82-489) Monogram; Sftbl; COM; Dist Sftbl; Voc Sch of Bus; Bus.

SPELLS, Ina Ruth
Denbigh HS; Newport News, VA; Co-Cpt, Chldr; Community Yth Symph; Ensm; 4H; Hmrm; Orch; 4H A; Most Out; Teachers Choice, Solo & Ensm, A's; All City Orch Schol; All St Orch; Sociology.

SPELLS, Winona Delphine
Wm Penn Sr HS; York, PA; Band; Hmrm; NHS; Sch P; Bkbl; Pres A; Ath, Bkbl, Mus; Computer Sci.

SPENA, Mark Steven
Raymore-Peculiar HS; Peculiar, MO (12-180) Band; Chor; Ensm; Math C; NHS; Var C; Bsbl; Ftbl; COM; Citz A; Soph Pilgrimage; Musicals; William Jewell Col; Bus Mgt.

SPENCE, Daniel Lee
E Jordan HS; E Jordan, MI (13-100) Band; VP, Hmrm; Bsbl; Bkbl; Golf; Tnns; Co-Ch, Yth Fel; Jr Rotarian; Jr Play; Lake Superior Col; Elec.

SPENCE, Dawn Yvette
Travelers Rest HS; Travelers Rest, SC (10%-300) Ann; Lat NHS; NHS; Sch P; Hon Prog; Chem.

SPENCE, James Kelly
Valentine HS; Valentine, NE (20-75) 4H; Var C; Cpt, Ftbl; Tr; HR; Sports As; Cl Offices; Lincoln Sch of Commerce; Professional Acct.

SPENCE, Karen Yolanda
SW HS; Baltimore, MD; Drama; Bsbl; Outst Achv; Modeling; Coppin St Col; Early Childhood Ed.

SPENCE, Kevin Guy
Clark Co R-I HS; Kahoka, MO (5-92) Band; S-T, FFA; 4H; NHS; Thes; Cr-Ctry; Tr; All-Conf Bands; Proficiency A; Mus Ed.

SPENCE, LaBarre Burkhardt
Frontier Central HS; Hamburg, NY (5-560) Band; Ensm; NHS; JV, Ftbl; Hon Prog; NEDT; Regent Schol; Case Western Reserve U; Chem Engr.

SPENCE, Myron Kent
Valentine HS; Valentine, NE (20%-69) Chess C; 4H; Var C; Pres, Jr Cl; JV, Ftbl; COM; 4H A; Yth Fel.

SPENCE, Reubena Lavern
Absegami HS; Mayslanding, NJ (20-350) Fr C; NHS; Ed, Sch P; SC; Sftbl; Tr; Citz A; Hon Prog; Drew U; Psych.

SPENCE, Robin Elizabeth
Wheaton HS; Wheaton, MD; Lit Mag; ARC; Hon Prog; Journ A; Judo C; Young Life; Mus As; U of Md; Spch Pathology.

SPENCE, Wayne Allen
Colonel Crawford HS; N Robinson, OH (5-140) VP, Fr C; Var C; Bsbl; JV, Bkbl; Ftbl; Tr; Alg A; Amer Leg A; Sci A; Yth Fel; Computer Tech.

SPENCER, Alan Jeffery
Clearwater HS; Clearwater, FL (75-800) Chess C; Community Yth Symph; 4H; Orch; Order/Arrow; SC; Cr-Ctry; 4H A; Order/Arrow A; Chess A; Sci.

SPENCER, Amy Elizabeth
Farragut HS; Concord, TN (4-30) Chor; Drama; FHA; Lat C; Co-Ed, Lit Mag; NHS; Hon Prog; U of Tenn; Lib Arts.

SPENCER, Andrea Lee
Monmouth Reg HS; Tinton Falls, NJ (10%-300) Chor; Drama; Ensm; Hmrm; Pres, InterClub Coun; Madrigal; Model UN; Orch; VP, SC; Hon Prog; Economic Resolution a; Model UN; Hon Cham Tm; Cent Reg NJ Orch & All-St Orch; Pol Sci.

SPENCER, Anita Beth
Tyner HS; Chattanooga, TN (15-261) BC; Ch, Chor; Drama; Ensm; NHS; SC; Tri-HiY; Tnns; U of Tenn; Bus.

SPENCER, Arthur Finis
Cass HS; Cassville, GA; BC; Fr C; Hmrm; Tres, Math C; Sci C; SC; Cpt, Bkbl; MVP, Ftbl; MVP, Tr; HCt; Oglethorpe U; Bus Adm.

SPENCER, Barbara Jean
Taylor Center HS; Taylor, MI (35-250) Chor; Sch P; Span C; Tr; Tres, Afro-Amer C; Sr Varsity Show; Pepperdine Col; Social Work.

SPENCER, Daniel Theodore
E Ridge HS; Chattanooga, TN (15-300) BC; NHS; Mgr, Bsbl; Hon Day; U of Tenn; Engr.

SPENCER, Deborah Ann
La Salle Sr HS; Niagara Falls, NY (35-494) Arch; Hmrm; NHS; SC; Arch; Bkbl; Sftbl; Most Out; Martin Luther King A; Niagara U; Bus.

SPENCER, Don A
Union HS; Tulsa, OK (40%-200) Tulsa U; Photography.

SPENCER, Dwayne Curtis
Bell Voc HS; Washington, DC; NHS; Var C; Bkbl; Ftbl; Tr; Citz A; Most Out; Woodward Found; WW in Voc Sch; Outst PE A; Wash Col; Diesel Mechanic.

SPENCER, Eutha Mae
Terrell Co HS; Dawson, GA (10%-147) Hist A; Hon Prog; Eng A; Ga SW Col; Home Ec.

SPENCER, Gene David Jr
Walnut HS; Walnut, MS (3-65) Rptr, BC; Pres, Jr Cl; MVP, Bsbl; Bkbl; Cpt, Ftbl; Alg A; Citz A; Hist A; Sci A; Eng A; U of Miss; Dentistry.

SPENCER, Ginny Lee
Drury Sr HS; N Adams, MA (10%-280) JV, Sftbl; Citz A; Church Choir; Sci Fair A; Sr Life Saving; Academic Achv A; Best Camper A.

SPENCER, Jacki Lee
Morton HS; Morton, WA (3-45) JV, Chldr; Chor; Ensm; FHA; VP, NHS; Pres, Rainbow; Ski C; Span C; JV, Bkbl; Sftbl; Tr; Lion A; NEDT; WW; Pacific Luthern U; Bus Adm.

SPENCER, James Anthony
Greencastle HS; Greencastle, IN (5%-170) Pres, Soph Cl; Bkbl; Tr; H of F; Cumulative HR.

SPENCER, Julie Lois
Wichita HS S; Wichita, KS (47-592) Chldr; Ensm; Ger C; NHS; SC; Tres, Soph Cl; Mgr, Bsbl; Mgr, Bkbl; Mgr, Ftbl; Tr; Oral Roberts U; Pre Med.

SPENCER, Katherine Charlotte
Almont HS; Almont, MI (10-110) Band; Chor; Ensm; 4H; NHS; Tres, Jr Cl; Sftbl; NEDT; Med.

SPENCER, Kathy Lynn
Belle Plaine HS; Belle Plaine, KS (20-61) Foreign Lang C; Adm Band; Cowley Co Comm Col; Phys Therapy.

SPENCER, Kendra Mae
Oxford HS; Oxford, KS (6-46) Ann; Band; Chor; Drama; Ensm; A-Ed, Sch P; Spch C; Var C; Co-Cpt, Bkbl; COM; HCt; Spch A; Co-Cpt, Vlbl; K-ST U; Fine Art.

SPENCER, Kimberly Jane
Warren Area HS; Warren, PA (29-438) A Cap Choir; Drama; FNA; Madrigal; NHS; Ski C; Span C; Tr; Silver B A; Ind U of Penn; Med.

SPENCER, Kimberly Kay
Mt Carmel HS; Mt Carmel, IL; Arch; Sftbl; Swim; GAA; Wabash Valley Col; Math.

SPENCER, Laura Kay
Mem HS; St Marys, OH (18-218) Band; Chldr; Chor; Rptr, 4H; NHS; A-Ed, Sch P; Y-Tns; Swim; Yth Fel; Ntl Gym; Fin, Citz A; Fin, God and Co A; Journ.

SPENCER, Laurie Anne
Dunkirk Sr HS; Dunkirk, NY (150-250) Band; Drama; Sch P; Sci C; Ski C; Swim; HQn; HCt; Jr Cl Play; VP, Church Yth Group; Med.

SPENCER, Lisa Kay
R J Reynolds HS; Winston-Salem, NC; Fr C; Bkbl; Sftbl; Bio A; Citz A; Sci A; Ch, Hospitality Comm; Vlbl; Top Schol A.

SPENCER, Lucinda Katherine
Herscher HS; Herscher, IL (36-188) Chor; Ensm; 4H; Madrigal; Yth Fel; Ntl Piano Playng Aud, Am Col of Mus; Mus.

SPENCER, Ronda Rae
Northland HS; Columbus, OH (25%-538) GS; Bkbl; Sftbl; Vlbl; Rep, Camp Enterprise; Ohio St U; Math.

SPENCER, Star Angela
Cooley HS; Detroit, MI (12-34) Chor; Y-Tns; Bsbl; Co-Cpt, Bkbl; Sftbl; Tnns; B Crocker A; Mich St U; Psych.

SPENCER, Steven Thomas
Amer Christian Acad; Pomona, CA (1-32) Chem C; Fr C; Math C; Phys C; Sci C; Span C; Secy, SC; Ftbl; Soccer; Alg A; Hist A; Math A; Sal; Sci A; Principals A; Timothy A; Eng A; Bible A; Nucleonics.

SPENCER, Susan Kay
Lyons Jr-Sr HS; Lyons, NY (20-110) Ski C; Vet Asst.

SPENCER, Susan Kaye
Nevada HS; Nevada, MO (68-160) Chldr; Rptr, FHA; FTA; 4H; Lat C; NHS; Rainbow; Tres, Span C; Secy, Sr Cl; Secy, Jr Cl; Tres, Soph Cl; JV, Bkbl; Tr; Type A; Shorthand A; Span A; SW Mo St U; Sociology.

SPENCER, Susan Leigh
Huntsville HS; Huntsville, AL; Pres, Drama; Inter-Club Coun; Rptr, Sch P; SC; Pres, Thes; NEDT; Birmingham Sou Col; Communications.

SPENCER, Teresa Ann
Sandy Valley HS; Magnolia, OH (28-167) A Cap Choir; Ann; Chldr; Chor; Drama; Ensm; Hmrm; NFL; NHS; Spch C; SC; Thes; Tr; HCt; Poet A; Spch A; Star Student; Tres, Yth Fel; Singing competition Medals; Fin, St Spch Tourn; Alt, GS; The William and Mary Col; Voice.

SPENCER, Terri Lea
Central HS; Knoxville, TN (36-349) NHS; Bus Mgr, Sch P; COM; VOEC; Wittiest; U of Tn; Bus Adm.

SPENCER, William Wayne
New Brockton HS; New Brockton, AL; BC; FFA; NHS; Sci C; Span C; SC; Cl Fav; Hon Prog; Enterprise St Jr Col.

SPENCER, Yvette
Phillips HS; Birmingham, AL (2-200) Chem C; Chor; Fr C; SC; COM; Birmingham Sou Col; Bio.

SPENGIER, Tammy Diane
Fleetwood Area HS; Fleetwood, PA (10-122) Ann; Band; Chor; Pres, FTA.

SPENGLER, Catherine Louisa
Liberty HS; Bethlehem, PA (300-794) Chor; Shorthand A.

SPENNEBERG, Melody Ann
Grant Co HS; Dry Ridge, KY (9-129) F-Ed, Ann; Model UN; NHS; Sch P; Tri-HiY; Y-Tns; Bio A; Hon Prog; Journ A; Q&S A; WW; Art A; Yrbk; Schol; Florence Sch of Hair Design; Cosmetology.

SPENNER, Pauline Jane
Regis HS; Stayton, OR (5-61) NHS; JV, Bkbl; Hon Prog.

SPENO, Sandra Michele
Saint Joseph HS; Camden, NJ (9-111) Fr C; NHS; Pres, Jr Cl; Citz A; Hon Prog; Peace Day Art A; SG Day; Bus.

SPERLAK, Frank John
Leo HS; Chicago, IL (1-140) Hmrm; NHS; Bsbl; JV, Cr-Ctry; U of Ill; Phar.

SPERLE, Gregory James
Napoleon HS; Napoleon, ND (1-56) A Cap Choir; Band; BS; CYO; Chor; Ensm; Madrigal; SC; Pres, Jr Cl; Co-Cpt, Ftbl; Wrest; Lion A; Val; ND St U; Computer Prog.

SPERLING, Edwina Diane
Gordon HS; Gordon, TX (4-14) Ann; BC; FHA; Mgr, Bkbl; DARGCA; Coun of Ministries; Pres, Pep Squad; Mgr, Drill Tm; Oral Roberts U; Deaf Ed.

SPERLING, John Howard
Northgate HS; Walnut Creek, CA; Orch; CSF; Hon Prog; UCLA; Aeronautics.

SPERLING, Linda Rae
Bowman HS; Canyon Country, CA; Beautician.

SPERRY, Donna Jean
Sentinel HS; Missoula, MT (17-453) NHS; Cpt, Drill Tm; U of Mont; General Stu.

SPERRY, Terry John
29 Palms HS; Twenty Nine Palms, CA; Dbte Tm; Ftbl; Spch A; Pepperdine U; Automotive Mech.

SPERRY, William Bart
Denham Springs HS; Denham Springs, LA (20-226) FBLA; Secy, Key C; NHS; Bsbl; Hon Graduate; LSU; Civil Engr.

SPESS, Lisa Ann
Cleveland HS; Cleveland, OK; Tres, Jr Cl; Bkbl; HCt; Bkbl A; S-T, Church Yth Group; Okla U.

SPETSERIS, Maria Patricia
James Island HS; Charleston, SC (1-200) Ann; Ch, BC; Pres, NHS; Sch P; Bkbl; Tr; Citz A; Gr Marshal; Math A; Opt A; Pres A; Sci A; Vlbl; Col of Charleston; Med.

SPETSERIS, Theodora
James Island HS; Charleston, SC; Ann; Tres, BC; Chor; Hmrm; Pres, NHS; Ed, Sch P; Span C; SC; Bkbl; Tr; Hist A; Math A; Opt A; Pres A; Spch A; Vlbl; Col of Charleston.

SPICE, Brian David
St Joseph HS; Toms River, NJ (17-190) CYO; Hmrm; Hon Prog; Bowl C; Humanities A; Va Commonwealth U; Dentistry.

SPICER, Lola Jean
N Division HS; Milwaukee, WI (3-20) JV, Chldr; Fin, Jr Miss Pagent; Mjrte; MVP, Tnns; Beauty; COM; Elk A; HCt; Off Monitor; HR; U of Wis-Milwaukee; Lab Tech.

SPICER, Virden Gerome Jr
Sunbright HS; Sunbright, TN (1-65) Band; BC; 4H; F-Ed, Sch P; Sci C; Hon Prog; Math A; Sci A; Val; Most Studious; Tenn Tech U; Pre-Med.

SPICKNALL, Kimberly Ann
Highland HS; Ewing, MO; Band; Mjrte; NHS; Var C; JV, Bkbl; Sftbl; Math A; Type A; Bus.

SPICKNALL, Renae Sue
Akron HS; Akron, CO (1-42) Band; Bus C; Chor; Ensm; FBLA; Tres, FHA; Semi-Fin, GS; Pres, 4H; Hmrm; Mjrte; Bus Mgr, NHS; Sci C; VP, SC; VP, Jr Cl; Secy, Soph Cl; Mgr, Bkbl; Mgr, Tr; Amer Leg A; COM; Citz A; Cl Fav; 4H A; HCt; Hon Prog; K of C A; Lion A; Pres A; Rotary A; Swtht; Val; VFW A; VofDEM; ESA Outst Yth A; WW; Band Letter; FFA Swtht Court; U of N Colo; Elem.

SPIDEL, Barbara Jo
Winfield Sr HS; Winfield, KS; Band; Dbte Tm; Parl, 4H; 4H A; Flagbearer; Horsemanship A; Debate Letter; Kans Ntl Fed of Mus; Horticulture Champion; Colby Comm Jr Col; Horsebreeding.

SPIEGEL, Jay Philip
Central Dauphin E HS; Harrisburg, PA; Band; Order/Arrow; God & Country A; Hon Prog; BSct; HACC; Hist.

SPIEGELBERG, Faith Dorothy
Lutheran HS W; Rocky River, OH (40-87) Drama; Thes; Best Actress; Kent St U; Drama.

SPIELBERGER, Gail Teresa
Acad o-t Holy Names; Tampa, FL; Ann; InterClub Coun; Mjrte; NHS; Span NHS; U of Miami; Econ.

SPIERS, Mary Virginia
Westside HS; Omaha, NE (48-795) Fr C; Model UN; NHS; Orch; Ch, Coun On Yth Ministries; Nebr Wesleyan U; Social Work.

SPIKES, Janet Elaine
East Rome HS; Rome, GA (42-115) Drama; Sch P; Parl, Tri-HiY; Shorter Col; Ed.

SPIKES, Patricia Anne
Will C Crawford HS; San Diego, CA (115-576) Bus C; NHS; Y-Tns; Pres, Yth Fel; Principal's HR; U of Calif; Bus Adm.

SPILKER, Catherine Lynn
Fairfield HS; Leesburg, OH; Band; FHA; 4H; St Stu Congress; Sftbl; 4H A; Yth Fel; All Co Band; Dist Yth Coun On Ministry.

SPILKER, Gregg Anthony
Clio HS; Clio, MI; Band; Dbte Tm; Drama; Ensm; Fr C; 4H; 4H A; Tn Talent Hon Cert; Central Bible Col; Mus.

SPILLER, Ricky Wayne
Tascosa HS; Amarillo, TX; Drama; Secy, Order/Arrow; Spch C; Order/Arrow A; ROTC A; Rifle Tm; Colorguard; W Tex St U; Advertising.

SPILLING, Elly A
Fremont HS; Sunnyvale, CA;

SPILLMAN, Catherine Fairley
Forsyth Ctry Day Sch; Lewisville, NC (2-43) NHS; Hist A; NMF; Span A; Gold Key Art A; Duke U; Pol Sci.

SPILMAN, William Benson
Harlingen HS; Harlingen, TX (10%-800) Demolay; Key C; Ski C; SC; JV, Bkbl; MVP, Ftbl, MVP, Tr; COM; Cl Fav; HCt; PTA A; Yth Fel; Peacemakers; Best Blocker, Ftbl; High Point, Tr; U of Tex; Bus Adm.

SPINDLER, Mark Stephen
McCluer N Sr HS; Florissant, MO (200-800) VP, Chor; Madrigal; Bkbl; Cr-Ctry; Tr; U of Missouri; Construction Engr.

SPINK, Jane Elizabeth
Coventry HS; Coventry, CT (13-129) Ann; Band; Cpt, Chldr; Fr C; NHS; SC; Cpt, Soccer; MVP, Tr; COM; Gr Marshal; Hon Prog; Spch A; Type A; MVP, Soccer; Ch, Fund Raising; Brd of Christian Ed; Sch Superstr A; Soccer Tourn, Wash DC; Ch, Comm Food & Clothing Drive; Johnson & Wales Col; Culinary Arts.

SPINK, Janet Lynn
Wellsboro HS; Wellsboro, PA (33%-210) Band; Pres, Chor; Drama; Ger C; Hmrm; Ski C; Pres, SC; Pres, Var C; Mgr, Bsbl; JV, Bkbl; Sftbl; Tr; Pres A; Vlbl.

SPINK, Karen Elaine
Wellsboro Sr HS; Wellsboro, PA (12-220) Band; S-T, Chess C; Ger C; Hmrm; Key C; Model UN; NHS; ARC; SC; UN Council; Pres, Soph Cl; Bkbl; Tnns; Tr; Amer Leg A; Journ A; NEDT; Spch A; VofDEM; Ntl Ath Schol Soc; HR; Bus & Prof Wmn's Girl o-t Month; St Bonaventure Col; Journ.

SPINK, Ronald Francis
Lyons Central Sch; Lyons, NY (30-110) Lat C; JV, Bsbl; Bkbl; Cr-Ctry; Ftbl; Tr; Math.

SPINKS, Edwina
Bishop Noll Inst; Hammond, IN (158-351) Chor; Hmrm; Up Bound; Y-Tns; MLS; Chor A; GSct.

SPINKS, Kathy Sue
Warren Central HS; Indianapolis, IN (50-950) Chor; Ger C; 4H; NHS; COM; Citz A; 4H A; Math A; Most Out; ARC A; Yth Fel; 1st Cl, GSct; NHS; Purdue U; Vet Med.

SPINNER, Lyndon Paul
Broken Bow HS; Broken Bow, OK (40%-250) A Cap Choir; Chor; Ensm; Madrigal; Ftbl; Tr; E Central U; Acct.

SPINOSI, Kolleen Marie
Delsea Regional HS; Franklinville, NJ (10-225) Chor; FTA; 4H; NHS; Rptr, Sch P; JV, Bkbl; Hockey; Alg A; Hon Prog; W Jersey Hospital; Nurs.

SPITLER, Laurie Shannon
Mt Whitney HS; Visalia, CA;

SPITZER, David Martin II
Trotwood-Madison HS; Trotwood, OH (15-384) Pres, A Cap Choir; Chor; Band; Pres, Chor; Community Yth Symph; Ensm; NHS; Orch; ARC; SC; Pres, Sr Cl; VP, Jr Cl; VP, Soph Cl; HCt; ARC A; Comm Band; Director, Church Choir; WW, Mus; Mich Hon Choir; Bowling Green St U; Mus.

SPITZER, Eleanor Jean
Scott Comm HS; Scott City, KS (3-125) Band; GS; Rptr, 4H; Var C; Tnns.

SPIVEY, Delilah Delphene
MacKenzie HS; Detroit, MI (4-352) NHS; Detroit Col of Bus; Secretarial.

SPIVEY, Donna Lynn
Johnson HS; Gainesville, GA; Chor; Ensm; FHA; PA Cert; Lee Col; Mus.

SPIVEY, Gail Wanda
E Laurens HS; Dublin, GA (10%-90) Cpt, Band; BC; Chldr; Secy, NHS; Secy, Span C; Tri-HiY; COM; WW; Sr Superlative; Shorter Col; Bus Adm.

SPIVEY, Kevin Scott
Westview HS; Kankakee, IL (85-200) Chor; Drama; Hmrm; Rptr, Soph P; SC; Bsbl; Cr-Ctry; Tr; COM; Citz A; Olivet Col; Mus.

SPIVEY, Mark Anthony
Lyndon Baines Johnson HS; Austin, TX (68-350) A Cap Choir; Chor; SC; Cpt, Bkbl; Ftbl; Tr; Jr Chamber of Com A; WW; SW Tex St U; Engr.

SPLAN, Claire Anne
St Joseph's Notre Dame HS; Alameda, CA (6-72) NHS; Sch P; Bio A; CSF; Hist A; Hon Prog; NEDT; Outst Service of Hrs, Yrbk A; Religion A; U of San Francisco; Journ.

SPLAWN, Michael Duane
William Workman HS; Valinda, CA (100-500) Bkbl; CSF; Math A; US Air Force Acad; Math.

SPLETH, Martha Jean
Hillcrest HS; Dallas, TX; A Cap Choir; Chor; Ensm; S-T, Fr C; VP, French NHS; NHS; Mu Alpha Theta; NHS; Orch; COM; Hon Prog; Ntl Piano Guild; Tex Christian U; Religion.

SPOEHR, Eugene John
Unionville HS; Unionville, PA (40-200) Mu Alpha Theta; NHS; Bsbl; Soccer; Amer Leg A; Gettysburg Col; Bus Adm.

SPOFFORD, John Rawson
University HS; Chicago, IL (15-120) Phys C; Tr; Carleton Col; Math.

SPOHRER, Dawn Marie
Bishop Klonowski HS; Scranton, PA; CYO; Chldr; Chor; Span C; Hon Prog; Art.

SPOLARICH, Robin Sue
Man HS; Man, WV (24-180) MLS.

SPOND, Kimberly Kae
Washington HS; Washington, IN; JV, Chldr; Fr C; SC; Tres, Jr Cl; Swtht; WW; Nurs.

SPONSEL, Lisa Carol
Richmond Sr HS; Richmond, IN (97-775) Chor; Drama; Secy, 4H; NHS; Rainbow; A-Ed, Sch P; Span C; Bkbl; Sftbl; COM; 4H A; NEDT; ARC A; Yth Fel; Secy, Church Luther League; Tex Lutheran Col; Span.

SPOO, Anne Linder
Eastern HS; Louisville, KY (10-300) Chem C; Ensm; Fr C; FBLA; NHS; ARC; Jr Beta C; U of Ky; Phar.

SPOONER, John Dennis
Willows HS; Willows, CA (15-130) CYO; Var C; Bsbl; Bkbl; JV, Ftbl; Pres A.

SPOONER, Keith DeCoursey
Greater New York Acad; Woodside, NY (15-46) Co-Ed, Sch P; SC; Cpt, Sftbl; Citz A; Ath A; Atlantic Union Col; Med.

SPORRI, Joanne Marie
Haralson Co HS; Tallapoosa, GA (6-143) Ann; Secy, BC; Chldr; 4H; SC; 4H A; WW; COM, U of Ga; W Georgia Col; Lang.

SPORT, Terry Leigh
Jeff Davis HS; Montgomery, AL; Co-Ed, Ann; Chldr; Sch P; Span C; Ch, Tri-HiY; Ldr C; Sci.

SPORTSMAN, Sharon Gayle
McKinney HS; McKinney, TX; F-Ed, Ann; Chldr; Pres, Chor; Pres, FTA; Span C; SC; Tr; Citz A; Cl Fav; Pres, Church Choir; Th Coun Church; Most Spiritual, Drill Tm; Ouchitia Baptist U; Ed.

SPOTTEN, Derry Jeanne
Ravena Coeymans Selkirk HS; Ravena, NY; Chor; Ger C; Hmrm; Soccer; Alg A; Hon Prog; VP, Yth Fel; Central Col; Lib Arts.

SPOTTS, Donna Kay
Highland HS; Bakersfield, CA (1-362) Dbte Tm; NFL; CSF; COM; Sou Calif Col; Ed.

SPRADLEY, Jacqueline Evette
Eisenhower HS; Houston, TX; A Cap Choir; FHA; Tr; U of Houston; Data Processing.

SPRADLIN, John Louis
McNeil HS; McNeil, AR (1-33) VP, Hmrm; Bkbl; Alg A; COM; Citz A; Cl Fav; HKg; Hon Prog; Math A; Sci A; Sou Ark U; Architecture.

SPRADLIN, Linda Diann
Hogansville HS; Hogansville, GA (20-83) Band; Chldr; FBLA; FHA; 4H; MVP, Bkbl; JA A; Bus.

SPRADLIN, Russell Alan
J F Kennedy HS; La Palma, CA (44-640) Band; Var C; Wrest; Emerald Chain; Biola U.

SPRADLING, Annette Carroll
Arlington HS; Indianapolis, IN (33-350) A Cap Choir; Band; Chor; Madrigal; Mjrte; NHS; Mgr, Bsbl; Hon Prog; F-Ed, Yrbk; Purdue U; Nurs.

SPRADLING, Cindy Kay
Richland HS; Ft Worth, TX (93-600) NHS; SC; Cpt, Bkbl; MVP, Sftbl; Tr; Hon Prog; Secy, Tex Girl's Choir; Spirit C; Vlbl; Outst Tr A; U of Tex; Phys Ed.

SPRADLING, Cris Ellison
Herbert Hoover HS; Clendenin, WV; Band; NHS; Sch P; W Va Tech Col; Engr.

SPRADLING, Dana Sue
Spur HS; Spur, TX (1-33) S-T, Band; FHA; Pres, NHS; Sci C; SC; Bkbl; Homemaking A; WW; San Angelo Col; Bus Adm.

SPRAGENS, Marcia Lynn
Oak Hills HS; Cincinnati, OH (22-840) Ann; NHS; Var C; Hon Prog; Sci A; Type A; Gym; NML; Child's Intl Summer Swedish Exch; Miami U; Art Mgt.

SPRAGUE, Lanette Lea
Sharpstown Sr HS; Houston, TX (25%-695) FHA; Span C; Keyette C; Special Interest A; Close Up; Bicentennial A; Pres, VP, Secy, Tres, Campfire Grl; Outdoor Progress A; Baylor U; Arts.

SPRAGUE, Ralph Edward
Bentonia HS; Bentonia, MS (4-50) Bus C; FBLA; VP, FFA; 4H; Co-Ed, Sch P; Bkbl; Cpt, Ftbl; Holmes Jr Col.

SPRATLEY, Sabrina Gai
Petersburg HS; Petersburg, VA (10%-595) Ann; Chor; Drama; Ensm; Fr C; Math C; NHS; Sci C; SC; Mus A; Mus.

SPRATLEY, Selma Lynee
Surry Co HS; Dendron, VA; Cpt, Chldr; City Conf; Pres, Fr C; FBLA; Pres, FHA; Semi-Fin, Hmrm; Secy, Jr Cl; Secy, Soph Cl; Miss FHA, Homecoming; Pres, Mt Nebo Yth Dept; Norfolk St Col; Fashion Designing.

SPRATLING, Reginald
Mackenzie HS; Detroit, MI (134-304) Bus C; Bsbl; Bkbl; Ftbl; Sftbl; Tr; Elec.

SPRATT, Anna Marie
Hatley HS; Hatley, MS (1-40) BC; Chor; 4H; Span C; MVP, Tr; Alg A; Itawamba Jr Col; Acct.

SPRAY, Deanna Leigh
Caprock HS; Amarillo, TX (45-280) Chor; FHA; VP, FTA; Math C; Sci C; Tri-HiY; Most Out; Encounter A; Motivation of People; W Tex St U; Interior Design.

SPRAY, Richard Gage
Granville HS; Granville, OH (47-139) Chor; Mgr, Bkbl; Ftbl; Ohio U; Phys Ed.

SPRENGER, Karmen Joy
North Fargo HS; Fargo, ND (151-380) A Cap Choir; Ed, Creative Writing Annual; Jamestown Col; Nurs.

SPRENGER, Keith Bryan
Bear Creek HS; Lakewood, CO (201-400) Band; JV, Bkbl; Golf; Co-Cpt, Tr; Phys Ed.

SPRENGER, Mary Joan
Polo HS; Orient, SD (1-11) Ed, Ann; Chem C; Chor; Drama; GS; Co-Ed, Sch P; SC; Tres, Sr Cl; Pres, Jr Cl; S-T, Soph Cl; Mgr, Bkbl; Tr; HQn; Journ A; MLS; Val; N St Col.

SPRIGGS, JoAnn
Bishop Conaty HS; Los Angeles, CA; Mgr, Chldr; Chor; Dbte Tm; Drama; Ch, Hmrm; Span C; Spch C; Bsbl; Bkbl; Soccer; Sftbl; Mgr, Swim; Tr; UCLA; Modeling.

SPRIGGS, Mark Clayton
Grapevine HS; Grapevine, TX; FFA; JV, Ftbl; Tex Reader A; Med.

SPRIGGS, Mark Clayton
Grapevine HS; Grapevine, TX; FFA; JV, Ftbl; Med.

SPRING, Janet Lee
West HS; Billings, MT; Chor; Fr C; Ski C; SC; Sftbl; Tr; Most Out; Yth Fel; Yth Leg; Vlbl; Tr & Field A; Missoula U; Social Worker.

SPRING, Jeffrey Chapline
Plain Dealing Acad; Plain Dealing, LA (5-48) Drama; Fin, Lit Ral; Math C; Mu Alpha Theta; NHS; Spch C; Pres, SC; Cpt, Ftbl; Tnns; Tr; Spch A; Rodeo Fin; Mus Group; *Texas A&M U; Vet Med.*

SPRING, Keith Mitchell
Sou HS; Durham, NC (28-295) NHS; Tnns; COM; Pres, Yth Fel; WW; HR; *Durhams Tech Inst; Archt.*

SPRING, Leslie Claire
Plain Dealing Acad; Plain Dealing, LA (1-45) Chldr; Drama; Semi-Fin, Lit Ral; Math C; NHS; Spch A.

SPRING, Vicky Lynn
Cass Tech HS; Detroit, MI (40-853) Drama; NHS; NMF; NHS; Phi Beta Kappa; VofDEM; WW; Performing Arts Guild; *Marygrove Col; Theatre.*

SPRINGER, Angle M
Letsche Alternative HS; Pittsburgh, PA;

SPRINGER, Daniel Joseph
Roosevelt Sr HS; Gary, IN (10%-450) Chor; FTA; VP, Madrigal; Alg A; COM; Math A; NISBOVA A; *Elec Engr.*

SPRINGER, David Donald
Monroe HS; Monroe, WI (70-246) A Cap Choir; Band; Chor; Ensm; Key C; Sch P; Yth Fel; *Wheaton Col; Biol.*

SPRINGER, Deborah Lynn
Celina Sr HS; Celina, OH (84-200) Pres, 4H; Sch P; Arch; Swim; Tnns; Tr; 4H A; Sci A; Excellent Rating, Local Sci Fair; Bible Quiz Tm; Interntl Field Stu; Pres, MYF; Campus Life; *Sci.*

SPRINGER, Donna Jean
St John Lutheran HS; Ocala, FL (1-24) NHS; S-T, Jr Cl; VP, Soph Cl; MVP, Bkbl; Sftbl; MVP, Vlbl.

SPRINGER, Joannie Susan
Jersey Comm HS; Jerseyville, IL (97-315) *Lewis & Clark Comm Col; Acct.*

SPRINGER, Karen Renee
Many HS; Many, LA; FHA; NHS; Bus.

SPRINGER, Lester Davis
Mount De Sales HS; Macon, GA (42-103) Drama; Elem Ed.

SPRINGER, Linda Sue
St John Lutheran HS; Ocala, FL; Cpt, Chldr; NHS; Pres, Sr Cl; Pres, Jr Cl; VP, Soph Cl; Bkbl; Sftbl; HQn; Swtht; Demolay Swtht; All-Amer Chldr; *U of Miss Med Center; Dental Hygiene.*

SPRINGER, Nancy Ann
Jayhawk Linn HS; Mound City, KS (1-51) Band; Chldr; Drama; Ensm; FHA; GS; Rptr, 4H; NHS; Span C; Spch C; Secy, Jr Cl; VP, Soph Cl; Cpt, Bkbl; Sftbl; Tr; Amer Leg A; 4H A; Type A; Cpt, Vlbl; *Otawa Col; Med.*

SPRINGER, Shelby Ann
St John Lutheran HS; Ocala, FL (2-30) Chldr; SC; Bkbl; Sftbl; Vlbl; *Palm Beach Jr Col; Dental Hygiene.*

SPRINGER, Vicki Elda
Prague HS; Prague, OK (10%-115) Chor; FHA; Lion A; Home Ec A; *Seminole Jr Col; Secy Sci.*

SPRINGHART, Vanessa Gaye
Berkeley Sr HS; Berkeley, MO (16-260) Chor; Ch, Fr C; NHS; SC; *Central Baptist Col; Spec Ed.*

SPRINGMAN, Vicki Jo
N Liberty HS; N Liberty, IN; Bus.

SPRINGMANN, Laura Ellen
Tottenville HS; Staten Island, NY; Chor; Madrigal; Swim.

SPRINGMEYER, Susan Elizabeth
Miami Killian Sr HS; Miami, FL (58-1182) Ensm; Pres, Ger C; InterClub Coun; NHS; Orch; Alg A; Bio A; COM; Citz A; H of F; Hon Prog; Most Out; NMF; Nom, Silver Knight; CUM Laude; WW; *Ohio Wesleyan U; Acct.*

SPRINGS, Clara Jane
Central HS; Memphis, TN (66-266) Hmrm; SC; *Memphis St U; Fashion Designing.*

SPRINGS, Gina Suzanne
Lewisville HS; Lewisville, TX; 4H; Rodeo Tm; *Tex Tech U; Elem Ed.*

SPRINGS, Marilyn Sue
Mt Carmel HS; Mt Carmel, IL (30-180) FTA; Span C; Voc Secy; Off Worker; Koinonia Yth Group; *Wabash Valley Col; Bus.*

SPROCH, James David
Cumberland Valley Sr HS; Mechanicsburg, PA (19-564) NHS; Orch; Rptr, Sch P; Hon Prog; Rensselaer A; *RPI; Elec Engr.*

SPROULE, Thomas Morris
George Wythe HS; Wytheville, VA; BS; Key C; Mu Alpha Theta; NHS; Order/Arrow; Sci C; Bkbl; Ftbl; Tnns; Tr; Order/Arrow A; Yth Fel; *Washington and Lef U; Law.*

SPROUSE, Terry Lynn
William Monroe HS; Stanardsville, VA (10-78) FBLA; Citz A; Sci A; Type A.

SPROW, Kelly Claudette
F D Roosevelt HS; Hyde Park, NY; Band; Nurs.

SPROWLS, Dana Ellen
Park Center HS; Brooklyn Park, MN (115-597) A Cap Choir; Synchronized Swim Tm; Piano A; Sunday Sch Teacher; Church Worship Commission.

SPROWLS, Elizabeth Louise
Park Center HS; Brooklyn Park, MN (25%-597) A Cap Choir; Ensm; JV, Swim; Synchronized Swim Tm; Sunday Sch Teacher; Secy, Chu Discipleship Commission.

SPRUILL, Rhonda Leigh
Gurdon HS; Gurdon, AR (10-75) FHA; Alg A; Eng A; *Ouachita Baptist Col; Nurs.*

SPRY, J Frank
Memphis HS; Memphis, TX (3-45) VP, Band; BC; Ensm; Lit Ral; Math C; Order/Arrow; Co-Ed, Sch P; Spch C; Citz A; Cl Fav; HKg; Order/Arrow A; Band, We Care, A's; WW; *W Tex St U; Mus Ed.*

SPRY, Sharon Kay
Oconto HS; Oconto, NE; Ed, Ann; Chor; Drama; Pres, 4H; SC; VP, Sr Cl; Pres, Soph Cl; Sftbl; Bio A; 4H A; HCt; Hon Prog; Math A; Co-Cpt, Vlbl; Eng A.

SPRYSZAK, Suzanne Marie
Alexander Hamilton HS; Milwaukee, WI (40-860) Ann; CYO; Hmrm; Pres, Span C; SC; Math A; Teacher & Vol, CCD Yth Ministry; Span & Eng A's; Silver Cord; *U of Wis; Psych.*

SPURGEON, Deana Kay
Southport HS; Indianapolis, IN (156-482) Chor; FNA; ARC; Span C; Golf; Nurs.

SPURGEON, Mark Lynn
Lufkin HS; Lufkin, TX (25%-515) Band; Chor; Ensm; Order/Arrow; BSA Rifle Tm; All Reg, 1st Div, St Ensm, Percus; *Stephen F Austin Col; Forestry.*

SPURGIN, Louis Kent
McKinney HS; McKinney, TX; Key C; Lat C; NHS; Cpt, Bkbl; MLS; *U of Tex at Arlington; Archt.*

SPURGIN, Timothy Dewayne
Albia Comm HS; Albia, IA (40-145) NHS; Pres, Var C; Bsbl; Bkbl; Co-Cpt, Ftbl; Fin, Tr; Hon Prog; Outst Ftbl & Tr Ath; WW in HS Ath.

SPURLIN, Timothy Ray
Gosnell HS; Gosnell, AR; Key C; Bkbl; Best Free Throw Shooter; Phys Ed.

SPURLING, William James
Stone Mountain HS; Stone Mountain, GA; NHS; Bsbl; Cr-Ctry; Cpt, Wrest; COM; Type A; Jr Beta C; *Dekalb Comm Col; Math.*

SPURLOCK, Derrell Ray
Claiborne Acad; Homer, LA; Ann; Pres, 4H; Lit Ral; NHS; Spch C; Pres, Var C; Pres, Sr Cl; VP, Jr Cl; Bsbl; MVP, Bkbl; Ftbl; Cl Fav; 4H A; Mr Claiborne Acad; Best All Around; All Dist Bkbl; *La Tech U; Aviation.*

SPURLOCK, Karen Marie
Bayside HS; Bayside, NY; Chor; MLS; *Fashion Inst of Tech; Fashion Design.*

SPURR, John William
King's Garden HS; Seattle, WA (1-60) Pres, Band; Ensm; Hmrm; NHS; Rptr, Sch P; SC; Tres, Sr Cl; Tres, Soph Cl; Cpt, Cr-Ctry; COM; HCt; Type A; Val; *Christian Heritage Col; Ed.*

SQUEO, Paul Ben
Venice HS; Venice, FL (50-250) Band; NHS; Orch; SC; Bsbl; Tr; Sci A; Boxing; Schol Achv, Band, SC, A's; Lang Arts, Service, Attend, A's.

SQUIRES, Alice Marie
Breckinridge Co HS; Harned, KY (10%-207) Rptr, Chess C; Chor; Ensm; FBLA; FTA; 4H; Math C; Rainbow; Span C; 4H A; Span A; *U of Evansville; Span.*

SQUIRES, Anna Marie
Glendale HS; Springfield, MO (5%-432) AFS; Drama; Fr C; NFL; Spch C; Thes; Fin, Dist Spch A; Glendale Thes A; Springfield Little Theater; Spkr, Yth Sunday Church; 3rd, Humorous Interpret Spch Tour; *Spch.*

SQUIRES, Jennifer Elaine
Aynor HS; Aynor, SC (2-85) Ann; BC; Secy, Fr C; Co-Ch, Hmrm; SC; Var C; Co-Ch, Jr Cl; Bkbl; Gov Honor Prog; Hon Prog; Furman Schol; Presbyterian Schol; *Clemson U; Bio.*

SQUIRES, Kay Ellen
Warren Central HS; Indianapolis, IN (1-791) Ensm; Ger C; Secy, NHS; Orch; Math A; Phi Beta Kappa; VP, Yth Fel; Ntl Sch Orch Assn A; NML; *Purdue U; Math.*

SQUIRES, Lee Ann
Dan River HS; Ringgold, VA (14-238) Chldr; Drama; FBLA; Monogram; Sch P; Jr Marshal; Hon Graduate; *VPI; Acct.*

SROF, Jana Eilene
Perryton HS; Perryton, TX (52-111) Secy, A Cap Choir; Secy, Chor; SC; Cl Fav; HCt; Cpt, Vlbl; U Interschol League Mus A; Miss PHS; *Hesston Col; Phys Ed.*

SROF, Jody Lane
Perryton HS; Perryton, TX (15-115) VP, A Cap Choir; Band; FTA; Madrigal; VP, Jr Cl; JV, Tnns; *Hesston Col; Secondary Ed.*

SROKA, Janet Marie
Auburn Comp HS; Auburn, NY; Pep C; Yrbk C; GSct; Cadettes.

STAATS, Sandra Jayne
Moore HS; Moore, OK; A Cap Choir; Band; Chor; Swim; *Oscar Rose Jr Col; Phys Ed.*

STAATZ, Shelly Mae
King's Garden HS; Seattle, WA (2-64) Ed, Ann; NHS; Rptr, Sch P; Secy, SC; Secy, Soph Cl; Bio A; COM; Journ A; Type A; 1st Pl, Bible Quiz Tm; Camp Counselor; Lit Critic A; *Religion.*

STABEL, Lori Kris
Booker HS; Booker, TX (18-28) F-Ed, Ann; Band; Chor; Ensm; FHA; FTA; JV, Bkbl; JV, Golf; Tnns.

STABLER, Steven Roy
William Tennent HS; Warminster, PA;

STACEY, Kathleen Mary
Valley Central HS; Montgomery, NY (27-330) A Cap Choir; F-Ed, Ann; Chor; Drama; Lit Mag; F-Ed, Sch P; Pres, Soph Cl; Mgr, Bkbl; Jim Brown Eng A; Service A; Fin, Regent's Schol; Drama A; Fin, Cert of Merit; *John Hopkins U; International Affairs.*

STACEY, Vivian Saletha
W Catholic Girls HS of Philadelphia; Philadelphia, PA (112-479) Chor; Community Yth Symph; Orch; Span C; Bkbl; Tnns; Tr; Star Student; Stu Hon; Art Hon; Hand Writing Hons; *U of Penn; Art.*

STACHE, Judy Ann
Hilbert HS; Hilbert, WI (7-89) Ger C.

STACK, Marie Elena
Susquehanna Comm HS; Susquehanna, PA (3-120) Cpt, Chldr; Secy, Ski C; Tres, Thes; Ch, Jr Cl; Tr; DARGCA; HQn; Hon Prog; *U of Pittsburgh at Bradford; Social Sci.*

STACK, Patricia Ann
Susquehanna Comm HS; Susquehanna, PA (6-110) Chldr; Drama; Ski C; Co-Cpt, Bkbl; Tr; *Law.*

STACK, Timothy David
Littleton HS; Littleton, CO (160-600) Chess C; FBLA; Rptr, Lit Mag; Ski C; Span C; Bkbl; Tr; JA A; Pres A; Type A; Yth Fel; Yth Foundation; *Elec.*

STACKHOUSE, Lisa Helen
Walter P Chrysler Mem HS; New Castle, IN; Secy, SC; Swim; Hist A; Pep C; *Purdue U; Pre-Med.*

STACKHOUSE, Lisa Kay
Springs Valley HS; French Lick, IN (1-86) Ed, Ann; Chldr; Fr C; GS; NHS; Var C; Cpt, Bkbl; Sftbl; Cpt, Tr; Math A; Most Out; Sci A; St Scholar; Val; MVP, Vlbl; Ind U; Phys Ed.

STACKHOUSE, Stephen Morton
Norfolk Collegiate HS; Norfolk, VA; Drama; Pres, Key C; Monogram; F-Ed, Sch P; Span C; Mgr, Soccer; MVP, Wrest.

STACKS, Regina Jo
Herrin HS; Herrin, IL; Chor; Pres, Hero C; John A Logan Col; Bus.

STACKS, Scott Alan
Herrin HS; Herrin, IL;

STACY, Debra Lou
Howe HS; Howe, OK (6-17) Carl Albert Jr Col.

STACY, Joan Edney
Lumberton HS; Lumberton, NC (10%-250) Cpt, Chldr; Fr C; Tri-HiY; Sub Jr C; Acolyte; Jr Recreation Coun.

STACY, Lisa Marie
McCluer N Sr HS; Florissant, MO (25-792) Pres A; 1st Cl, GSct; Candystriper; HR; FCA; Secy, UMYF.

STACY, Robin Purser
Lumberton HS; Lumberton, NC (5-280) Co-Cpt, Chldr; VP, Fr C; GS; Hmrm; S-T, NHS; Rptr, Sch P; Co-Ch, SC; Tri-HiY; Pres, Sr Cl; Gr Marshal; VP, Yth Fel; U of NC.

STADELMAN, Bernard Edward
Fremont Christian HS; Fremont, CA; A-Ed, Ann; Drama; Ensm; Sch P; Span C; JV, Bsbl; Bkbl; Cr-Ctry; Soccer; JV, Tr; Cl Fav; Spch A; Type A; Yth Leg; Best Camper A; Bethany Bible Col; Ministerial.

STADLER, Kathy Sue
Wm M Kelley HS; Silver Bay, MN (10-150) AFS; Ann; Cpt, Chldr; FHA; NHS; Sci C; Ski C; Swim; Tr; Amer Leg A; Citz A; HCt; Hon Prog; JA A; MLS; Sci A; Gym; WW A; Frank Rukovina Schol; Power & Light Schol; St Cloud St U; Mass Communications.

STADTMUELLER, Lisa
Star Valley HS; Afton, WY; Chor; Pres, 4H; Secy, SC; Cl Fav; 4H A; Type A; Brigham Young U; Art.

STADTMUELLER, Lori
Star Valley HS; Afton, WY; Chor; Pres, 4H; Secy, SC; Bsbl; Bkbl; Sftbl; 4H A; Brigham Young U; Art.

STAFFANSON, K Craig
LaConner HS; LaConner, WA (2-52) S-T, Chem C; Chess C; Drama; Pres, Math C; VP, Phys C; Ski C; VP, Span C; Skiing; Drama A; Wash St U; Agr.

STAFFORD, Carla Jo
South Side HS; Ft Wayne, IN (144-500) Band; Chor; Hmrm; Orch; Y-Tns; VP, Jr Cl; All City Choir; Ind St Solo & Ensm Comp; Assembly of God Talent Comp; Jazz Band Comp; Oral Roberts U; Mus Ed.

STAFFORD, Chris
W Memphis HS; W Memphis, AR; JV, Bkbl; US Air Force Acad.

STAFFORD, DeNorah Leigh
Sophronia M Tompkins HS; Savannah, GA; Secy, FBLA; WW; Armstrong St Col; Acct.

STAFFORD, Joseph Eric
W Charlotte HS; Charlotte, NC; Central-Piedmont Comm Col; Elec.

STAFFORD, Kimberly Ann
Cleveland HS; Cleveland, OK; NHS; Sci C; Var C; Bkbl; Pres, VICA C; St Hon Soc; Fin, St VICA; Pep C; Central AVTS Col; Nurs.

STAFFORD, Lisa Linnea
Tartan Sr HS; Oakdale, MN (37-483) Band; Hon Prog; U of Minn; Bio.

STAFFORD, Loretta Alisha
Siena HS; Chicago, IL (79-90) Chor; Community Yth Symph; Sch P; SC; Cr-Ctry; Sftbl; Swim; Journ A; Loyola U; Philosophy.

STAFFORD, Reba Jewell
Bradleyville HS; Bradleyville, MO (1-30) Band; VP, BC; Chldr; Pres, Drama; S-T, FHA; Pres, 4H; Bus Mgr, Math C; F-Ed, Sch P; NHS; Bsbl; Sftbl; Alg A; 4H A; HCt; I Dare You; Type A; Co-Cpt, Vlbl; Drafting A; Drury Col; Lit.

STAFFORD, Robin Linn
Grover Cleveland HS; Reseda, CA (778-900) St Scholar; BEOG Grant; Stu Life; Biola Col; Missions.

STAFFORD, Rodney Alan
Lodi HS; Lodi, CA (5-490) Pres, Model UN; Pres, NHS; SC; Pres, World Affairs; Wrest; Bank Of Amer A; CSF; HCt; Hon Prog; Most Out; U of Calif; Chem Engr.

STAGER, Mark Phillip
San Carlos HS; San Carlos, CA; Band; Pres, Hmrm; Key C; NHS; ARC; Bkbl; Ftbl; Hockey; MVP, Swim; Water Polo; Davis Col; Engr.

STAGG, John Wayne
Tioga HS; Tioga, LA; Band; BC; Key C; COM; Hon Prog; La Tech U; Sci.

STAGGS, Jacqueline Elaine
Chapman HS; Inman, SC (65-268) Pres, Hmrm; SC; Bkbl.

STAGGS, Mark Andrew
Marion HS; Marion, IL (25%-283) All Amer Yth; BS; Var C; Bkbl; Co-Cpt, Ftbl; Cpt, Tr; Lion A; Swtht; Yth Fel; MVP, Ftbl & Tr; Leo C; Strength & Health C; Most Dedicated Ath A; NE La U; Acct.

STAGGS, Vicky Darlene
New Palestine HS; New Palestine, IN (15-47) Chor; NHS; Amer Leg A; COM; St Scholar; Vol A; Convalescent Center; Shorthand A; Co Spelling Champ; Mus Service, Writing, A's; Butler U; Mus.

STAGNER, Anne Revis
Huntsville HS; Huntsville, AL (3%-400) Band; Chem C; Ger C; MVP, Swim; NEDT; Med.

STAGNER, Sheri Lynne
L C Anderson HS; Austin, TX (5%-675) Band; Ensm; Orch; Twirling A; Trustee Schol A; Band A; All-Dist Band; Excel Ratngs; Tx St Solo & Ensm Con; Abilene Christian U; Mus.

STAHL, James Louis
Liberty Sr HS; Bethlehem, PA (205-800) Soccer; Co-Cpt, Swim; Hon Prog; Yth Fel; St Soccer Champ; United Wesleyan Col; Missions.

STAHL, Kathleen J
Santa Rita HS; Tucson, AZ (45-617) NHS; Ski C; U of Denver; Spec Ed.

STAHL, Maynard Scott
Montpelier HS; Montpelier, OH (47-92) Bus Mgr, Ann; BS; FFA; Sch P; SC; Var C; Pres, Sr Cl; Pres, Jr Cl; Co-Cpt, Bkbl; Co-Cpt, Ftbl; Tr; Hist A; MVP, Bkbl & Ftbl; League A, Bkbl & Ftbl; NW Tech Col; Tool and Die Engr.

STAHL, Rebecca Gale
Rockwood Area HS; Rockwood, PA (20-116) Band; Hmrm; Co-Cpt, Mjrte; Rainbow; SC; VP, Jr Cl; Buhl Planetarium Schol; Achievement A; Scholastic A; Allegany Comm Col; Dental Hygienist.

STAHL, Rochelle Kay
Galva Comm Sch; Galva, IA (33%-23) Band; Chor; Ensm; Bkbl.

STAHL, Sandra Jean
Iroquois Central HS; Elma, NY; Chor; Ensm; Secy, Orch; Mus.

STAHLE, Carl Landis II
Hershey Sr HS; Hershey, PA (100-250) Band; Chess C; Chor; Drama; Ensm; Ger C; Hmrm; InterClub Coun; Orch; Phys C; SC; Var C; Bsbl; W German Govt A; Outst Achv in Mus; Mansfield St Col; Mus.

STAHLE, Janice Lorraine
The Christian Acad; Chester, PA (6-30) Chor; Tres, Y-Tns; Hon Prog.

STAHLECKER, Alan Roy
Rangely HS; Rangely, CO (10-55) Ann; Chor; Tres, NHS; Ed, Sch P; St Stu Congress; Pres, SC; Cpt, Bkbl; Cr-Ctry; Ftbl; Tr; Cl Fav; Elk A; HKg; Masonic A; MLS; Pres, Photo C; Co-Cpt, FCA; Act A; MVP, All Conf, Bkbl; All St Hon Men, All Amer, Bkbl; All Conf, All St, All Amer, Ftbl; Adams St Col; Acct.

STAHLER, Miriam Elizabeth
Wenatchee HS; Wehatchee, WA (18-397) Hmrm; NHS; Pol Sci C; SC; Secy, Sr Cl; Secy, Soph Cl; Yth Leg; Comm Involvement Commissioner; Sch Board Rep; Pres Pro-tem of Senate, Yth Legis; Pacific Lutheran U.

STAINBACK, Kari
Greenville Sr HS; Greenville, TX (7-345) A Cap Choir; Cpt, Chldr; Chor; VP, Fr C; NHS; Ed, Sch P; SC; Amer Leg A; COM; Cl Fav; HCt; I Dare You; Journ A; Miss GHS; Top Ten; Chldr A; Academic Excellence; Baylor U; Bus.

STAIR, Tracy Allyn
J J Pearce HS; Richardson, TX (400-1000) Arch; Bkbl; Sftbl; Hon Prog; Yth Fel; Rodeo Tm; UTD; Anthropology.

STAKELIN, Jeffrey Alan
Lafayette HS; Lexington, KY; SC; Bsbl; Bkbl; Ftbl.

STAKER, Frederick George III
Kermit HS; Kermit, WV (1-35) Pres, Band; Tres, Span C; Pres, Jr Cl; Bsbl; Amer Leg A; DARGCA; I Dare You; Math A; Val; Eng A; Span A; All-Area Band; All-Co Band; W Va U; Pol Sci.

STAKER, Lant Robert
Kermit HS; Kermit, WV (3-31) Band; Span C; Bsbl; Karate Green Belt; Ky Colonel; W Va U; Med.

STALDER, Connie Sue
River Local HS; Hannibal, OH (36-170) Chor; Parl, FHA; FTA; Pres, 4H; Sci C; Bkbl; 4H A; VP, Ldrship C; Pres, Yth Fel; Fin, Co Fair Health Qn; Col C; W Liberty St Col; Elem Ed.

STALEY, Amber Ellen
Allen Jay HS; High Point, NC (25-115) Chor; V-Ch, City Conf; Fr C; FHA; FTA; Hmrm; SC; Yth Leg; Appalachain St Col; Psych.

STALEY, Anita Gayle
Little Rock Central HS; Little Rock, AR (50-546) BC; Chldr; Tres, FBLA; VP, Hmrm; InterClub Coun; NHS; Y-Tns; WW; Ouachita Baptist U; Special Ed.

STALEY, Ruth Ellen
C L McLane HS; Fresno, CA (27-800) Pres, Math C; ARC; Tres, SC; Tres, Jr Cl; Cpt, Swim; CSF; Yth Fel; Pres, Hi-Group; VP, FCA; Yth For Christ; Water Polo; Calif St U; Hist.

STALEY, Timothy Robert
Kings Academy; W Palm Beach, FL (10-60) Crown & Scepter; Drama; NHS; JV, Bkbl; JV, Ftbl; Most Inspirational Christian; Fla Inst of Tech; Computer Sci.

STALLARD, Dana Jolene
Engleside Christian Sch; Alexandria, VA (1-22) Ed, Ann; Co-Cpt, Chldr; Chor; SC; Tres, Jr Cl; Bkbl; Sftbl; Alg A; Hist A; Washington Bible Col; Mus Ed.

STALLARD, David Frederick
Civic Memorial HS; Bethalto, IL; Band; 4H; JV, Bsbl; Bkbl; Sftbl; SonShine Celebration; Ushering Staff; Tres, Sr Walther League; Ch, Wheat Ridge Seal Campaign; Law.

STALLARD, Gary John
Seekonk HS; Seekonk, MA (18-224) NHS; Computer Sci.

STALLARD, Mark Dayton
Lake City HS; Lake City, TN (1-110) Ann; Pres, BC; Parl, Span C; Hist A; MLS; Val; Geom, Civics, A's; WW; Tenn Tech U; Computer Sci.

STALLINGS, Darrell Patterson
William M Raines HS; Jacksonville, FL (3-28) Orch; JV, Ftbl; Tr; COM; Yth Fel; Archt.

STALLINGS, John Carl Jr
Stevenson HS; Stevenson, AL (5-90) BC; FFA; 4H; JV, Bkbl; U of Ala; Elec.

STALLINS, Wendy Lynn
Mayfield HS; Mayfield, KY (19-158) A-Ed, Ann; BC; JV, Chldr; Secy, Chor; Ensm; Rptr, Fr C; Ger C; VP, Hmrm; Pres, Span C; VP, SC; Secy, Jr Cl; VP, Soph Cl; Cl Fav; All St; Murray St U; Mus.

STALLONS, Kenneth Ray
East HS; Sioux City, IA; Bsbl; JV, Ftbl; JV, Tr; WIT; Acct.

STALLWORTH, Deborah Ann
St Ursula Acad; Toledo, OH (21-115) All Amer Yth; CYO; Chldr; Chor; Commercial C; Drama; 4H; Mod Mus Mas; Rainbow; ARC; Span C; Cpt, Bkbl; Cpt, Tnns; 4H A; Hon Prog; ARC A; Yth Fel; King-Qn Contest; Ohio St U; Law Enforcement.

STALLWORTH, Sandra Louise
MacKenzie HS; Detroit, MI (12-352) Bus C; Fr C; VP, FTA; Mjrte; Math C; NHS; Sch P; St Stu Congress; SC; Alg A; Citz A; Hon Prog; JA A; Math A; Type A; HR A; Mjrte A; Eng A; *Detroit Bus Inst; Bus.*

STALNAKER, Cathy Leana
Orofino HS; Orofino, ID (6-96) Band; CYO; Pres, 4H; NHS; 4H A; Band Trophy; Dist Hon Band; WW; *U of Idaho; Civil Engr.*

STALNAKER, Phillip Lowell
Gilmer Co HS; Glenville, WV (3-122) NHS; Var C; Bsbl; Ftbl; Tr; Co-Cpt, Wrest; *W Va U; Engr.*

STALNAKER, Roberta Louise
Orofino HS; Orofino, ID (7-135) Band; CYO; VP, 4H; JV, Bkbl; Tr; 4H A; *U of Idaho.*

STALVEY, Ellen Dunning
Winyah HS; Georgetown, SC (25%-170) A-Ed, Ann; Fr C; Tres, Hmrm; NHS; Bio A; Hon Prog; *Col of Charleston; Art.*

STALVEY, Rex Hilton
Brunswick HS; Brunswick, GA (79-380) Hmrm; Bsbl.

STAMAS, George Dennis
Central HS; Waterloo, IA; Arch; Band; S-T, Bus C; Ed, Sch P; Ski C; Span C; Arch; *W Wash St U; Journ.*

STAMBAUGH, Deborah Lynn
Ray Dist HS; Kearny, AZ (14-97) Drama; FHA; 4H; Key C; NHS; SC; Var C; Pres, Sr Cl; JV, Tnns; Beauty; DARGCA; 4H A; Most Out; Rotary A; ROTC A; Yth Leg; Jr & Sr Cl Senator; Color Guard; JV Vlbl; Prom Princess; Career Ed A; *Baylor U; Home Ec.*

STAMBAUGH, Lisa Faye
W York Sr HS; York, PA; Chess C; ARC; Y-Tns; Hon Prog; *York Col.*

STAMBAUGH, Nancie Carol
Cresset Christian Acad; Durham, NC (1-2) Chor; Drama; Sch P; Bkbl; Alg A; Christian Ldrship A; Highest Overall Avg; Courtesy A; Chorale; *U of NC; Eng.*

STAMBAUGH, Teena Marie
Peebles HS; Peebles, OH (5-109) Fr C; FTA; Lat C; Sci C; Mgr, Bkbl; Ohio U Fresh Schol; Dist Bio Schol Tm; Win, Soil & Water Conserv Essay; *Ohio U.*

STAMBAUGH, Tom Lee
Minnetonka Sr HS; Minnetonka, MN (100-700) Ger C; Var C; MVP, Cr-Ctry; Tr; Hon Prog; Most Out; Yth Fel; All Conf; *U of Minn; General Ed.*

STAMBERGER, Kathleen Marie
Tippecanoe Valley HS; Mentone, IN (75-160) FHA; Tres, 4H; 4H A; S-T, Church Yth Fel.

STAMLER, Janet Ellen
Normandy HS; Parmo, OH (455-770) *Baldwin Wallace Col; Art.*

STAMLER, Sharon N
Canarsie HS; Brooklyn, NY (12-950) Chldr; Cum Laude Soc; Ch, Hmrm; Alg A; COM; Hon Prog; Magna Cum Laude; Sci A; Summa Cum Laude; District Attorney A; *Boston U; Phys Therapy.*

STAMM, Rachel Ellen
Bellaire Sr HS; Bellaire, TX (1-735) AFS; Span C; Drill Squad; Monopoly C; Schol, PA, A's.

STAMPER, Pamela Susan
Homer L Ferguson HS; Newport News, VA (79-482) Secy, FBLA; FTA; Hmrm; Key C; NHS; Drill Tm; FTA Swtht; *Tomlinson Col; Bus Adm.*

STAMPER, Suzan Elizabeth
Greencastle Sr HS; Greencastle, IN (34-187) Chor; Secy, 4H; NHS; S-T, Span C; Semi-Fin, Spch C; Thes; 4H A; St 4-H Chor; Art, Spch, Mus, A's; Co-Ch, Bible C; Outst Jr; Pres, Christian Yth Fel; Vlbl; *Ball St U; Ed.*

STAMPS, Teresa Faye
Maplewood HS; Nashville, TN (20%-336) Band; Mjrte; Journ A; JA A; Type A; Teacher's Aid; FSA; Qn Regent, Girl's Acteens; Church Pianist; Pres, Yth Coun; *U of Tenn; Legal Secy.*

STAMPS, Vicki Kae
New Market HS; New Market, IA (10-23) Band; Chor; Drama; Pres, 4H; NHS; Ed, Sch P; SC; Tres, Var C; Mgr, Bkbl; Tr; 4H A; I Dare You; Band Qn; VP, Secy, Tres, 4-H C; Historian, FHA; Pres, Lib C; Statistician, Sftbl; *Mt View Bible Col.*

STANBACK, Bradford Graham
Salisbury HS; Salisbury, NC (12-220) AFS; Pres, Fr C; Hmrm; NHS; SC; Var C; Amer Leg A; Bausch & Lomb A; Hon Prog; VP, Jr Civitan C; Jr Rotarian; Jr Marshal; All Conf, Tnns; *Duke U.*

STANCIELL, Trina Marie
James Madison HS; Houston, TX; COM; Citz A; Drill Tm; DECA; Miss Madison; *Baylor U; Nurs.*

STANCIK, Cheryl Lynn
Oroville HS; Oroville, CA (37-243) Ch, Hmrm; Var C; Nom, GS.

STANCIL, Ronald Edward
Jones Co HS; Gray, GA (10%-250) BC; Chess C; NHS; VP, Sci C; Bio A; *Ga Tech; Solar Engr.*

STANCILL, Tina Raye
Suffolk HS; Suffolk, VA; Drama; *Old Dominion Col; Bus.*

STANDARD, Richard Maurice
Groves HS; Garden City, GA; Band; Sci C; *Ga Col; Mus.*

STANDBRIDGE, Keith Alan
Barrington Comm HS; Barrington, IL (80-700) NHS; SC; Pres, Sr Cl; Fin, Bsbl; Secy, Ftbl; HCt; *Lafayette Col; Law.*

STANDEFER, John Paul
Wilburton HS; Wilburton, OK (15-62) Band; BS; Bus C; Chem C; 4H; Math C; NHS; Orch; Phys C; Sci C; SC; 4H A; Ntl Sci Found; Sci A; Ntl World Champion; Drum Major; Bus A; *Okla U; Bus.*

STANDIFER, Dorothy Joanette
Richwood HS; Monroe, LA; Fr C; Bsbl; Swim; Citz A; Most Out; Yth Fel; Sunday Sch Teacher; Church Secy; *Pepperdine U; Nurs.*

STANDLEY, Cheryl Ann
LeRoy HS; LeRoy, KS (4-27) Band; Chor; NHS; Ed, Sch P; Pres, Jr Cl; Tr; B Crocker A; St Scholar; Alt, GS; WW; *Emporia St U; Secondary Ed.*

STANDRIDGE, Andrew Max
Wilcox Co HS; Rochelle, GA (10-97) BC; Chor; Dbte Tm; 4H; Lit Mag; Ed, Sch P; Span C; COM; 4H A; Hist A; Sci A; 4-H Key A; *Brewton-Parker Col; Religion.*

STANDRIDGE, Gloria Ann
Lexington HS; Lexington, OK; Band; Chor; Ensm; FHA; 4H; Secy, SC; 4H A; *Mus.*

STANDRIDGE, Melanie Ann
Mount Ida HS; Mount Ida, AR (15-33) VP, Band; BC; FHA; 4H; F-Ed, Sch P; Bkbl; Type A; WW; Mus Stu; Distinguished Musician A; *Ark Tech U; Mus.*

STANEK, Scott Alan
Heidelberg American HS; Heidelberg, GERMANY (19-170) Arch; NHS; Arch; Amer Leg A; ROTC A; *Tulane U; Pre-Med.*

STANFIELD, Henry Christopher
Bennettsville Sr HS; Bennettsville, SC (25-275) Band; Ensm; FHA; Hmrm; Ntl Teachers Coun; Sch P; SC; Cpt, Ftbl; Tr; Sci A; Yth Fel; MVP, Ftbl; Mus, Tr, Ftbl, A's; *U of NC; Military Sci.*

STANFIELD, Perry Hugh
Coupeville HS; Coupeville, WA (12-50) BS; 4H; Tres, NHS; Pres, Jr Cl; Bsbl; *Wash St U; Vet Med.*

STANFORD, Alfred Young
The Auburndale HS; Cordova, TN (5-70) A Cap Choir; Chor; Dbte Tm; Hmrm; SC; Mgr, Bkbl; Tnns; Citz A; Hon Prog; Eagle Sct; Art A; *Memphis St U; Ed.*

STANFORD, Frederick Cossitt
Auburndale HS; Memphis, TN; Tres, Chess C; Dbte Tm; Ch, Hmrm; Order/Arrow; ARC; Bus Mgr, SC; Var C; Bsbl; Cr-Ctry; Tr; COM; Cl Fav; H of F; Order/Arrow A; Pres A; Eagle Sct; Executive A; Bsbl Ltr; Bkbl Ltr; *Memphis St U; Journ.*

STANFORD, Mary Alice
Western Hills HS; Ft Worth, TX (93%-600) FHA; NHS; Sch P; Sch Mag.

STANFORD, Sheila Denise
Kendrick HS; Columbus, GA (11-350) Band.

STANFORD, Sheryl Lynn
Bayless HS; St Louis, MO (3-183) Band; Pres, Fr C; Tres, FHA; Secy, FTA; Hmrm; NHS; Tres, Sci C; SC; Secy, Sr Cl; Secy, Jr Cl; Span C; Field Hockey; Job's Daughters; Pom Pom Girl; Pep C; *St Louis U; Nurs.*

STANFORD, Stephen H
Kofa HS; Yuma, AZ; Ann; Tres, 4H; Rptr, Hmrm; Key C; Span C; Spch C; Ch, St Stu Congress; S-T, SC; Var C; Cpt, Bkbl; Cpt, Ftbl; Golf; 4H A; Most Out; Ntl Conf Chr & Jews; Spch A; Weight-Lifting; Most Outst Fresh; Bkbl, Most Rebnd; Ntl Rifle Assn Cl; Ftbl, Most Tackles; *Okla St U; Phys Ed.*

STANG, Richard Cameron
Col Zadok Magruder HS; Rockville, MD (85-400) Var C; Bsbl; Bkbl; Cpt, Ftbl; Yth Fel; MVP, Ftbl; *Frostburg St Col; Bus Adm.*

STANG, Sharon Lee
La Crosse HS; LaCrosse, KS (2-50) Chldr; Secy, Chor; Dbte Tm; Ensm; Madrigal; Model UN; Pres, NFL; St Stu Congress; SC; Sftbl; B Crocker A; Bio A; COM; Math A; NMS; Spch A; St Scholar; VFW Orator Win; VofDEM; WW; AAU Mo Valley Off; *U of Kans; Biol.*

STANGER, Martha Sue
Thomas Jefferson HS; Alexandria, VA (1-840) Mgr, Band; Community Yth Symph; GS; NHS; Orch; Pres, Span C; Gov Sch for the Gifted; All-St Orch; *Col of William & Mary; Foreign Service.*

STANGL, Kim Elizabeth
Kuemper HS; Carroll, IA (21-275) Ann; CYO; Chor; Monogram; ARC; Sch P; Sci C; Mgr, Tr; Bio A; COM; Journ A; Q&S A; ARC A; Sci A; Spch A; Amer Legion Auxilary; GSct Ldr; Kodak Medallion of Excel; *Iowa St U; Psych.*

STANGROOM, James Ray
Greensburg-Salem HS; Greensburg, PA (60-400) Archt Design.

STANIFORD, Joy Beth
Collinsville HS; Collinsville, OK (3-137) Chor; Dbte Tm; GS; Tres, Jr Cl; Span; Sch Pl; Amer Leg A; Hon Soc; Legal Secy Schol; Press C; Most Intellectual; Fin, Miss Tulsa; Jr, Sr Plays; St Chmps, Drvr Ed Pro; Drill Tm; Attendent, Rptr, Chor; *Tulsa Jr Col; Legal Secy.*

STANISLAWSKI, Susan
Clintonville Sr HS; Clintonville, WI (60-200) A Cap Choir; CYO; Chor; Secy, FBLA.

STANLEY, Anthony Joe
Henderson Co Sr HS; Henderson, KY (96-546) Band; Pres, Chess C; Math C; Orch; High Scorer, Bible Quiz Clinic; *Oral Roberts U; Ministry.*

STANLEY, Cynthia Ann
Daniel Boone HS; Birdsboro, PA; Cosmetology.

STANLEY, Dale Arthur
Newton Falls HS; Newton Falls, OH; Var C; Golf; HCt; *Kent St U; Bus Adm.*

STANLEY, Denise Elaine
A H Parker HS; Birmingham, AL; Band; Drama; Math C; Mu Alpha Theta; VP, NHS; Co-Ed, Sch P; Sci C; SC; COM; Hist A; WW; *U of Ala; Bus Adm.*

STANLEY, Diane Sue
Newton Falls HS; Newton Falls, OH (1-197) Band; Drama; Hmrm; Rptr, Sch P; Span C; Citz A; *Social Counseling.*

STANLEY, Janet Sue
North Co R-1 HS; Desloge, MO (10-175) A Cap Choir; Band; Co-Cpt, Chldr; FHA; Madrigal; NHS; Var C; Secy, Sr Cl; Crisco A; WW; Cand, Santa Dreamgirl Coronation; *SMS; Acct.*

STANLEY, Jerry Allen
Park Center HS; Brooklyn Park, MN (25%-600) A Cap Choir; All Amer Yth; Band; Chor; Community Yth Symph; Mod Mus Mas; Ntl Yth Conf; VP, Orch; Ch, Y-Tns; Swim; Ntl Mus A; All St Orch; Sup, St Contests 0280000; *Concordia-Moorehead Col; Mus.*

STANLEY, Juanita Kay
Wingfield HS; Jackson, MS; FHA; *Hinds Jr Col; Bus Ed.*

STANLEY, Kari Denise
Princeton HS; Sharonville, OH; Chor; French NHS; Hmrm; NHS; *E Ky U; Elem Ed.*

STANLEY, Katherine Lynne
Thomasville HS; Thomasville, AL (4-130) BC; Chem C; FHA; Span C; *Auburn U; Interior Design.*

STANLEY, Lorna Sue
Daniel Boone HS; Birdsboro, PA (20-156) Ensm; Fr C; FTA; InterAct C; NHS; Ed, Sch P; Y-Tns; *Long Beach St Col; Phys Therapy.*

STANLEY, Paul Michael
North Co HS; Desloge, MO; Band; Chess C; Chor; Sch P; Mgr, Bkbl; Cr-Crtry; JV, Tr; Journ A.

STANLEY, Rena Sue
St Elmo HS; St Elmo, IL (2-54) Band; Chldr; Dbte Tm; Ensm; Tr; Beauty; COM; HCt; Hon Prog; *Modeling.*

STANLEY, Rhonda Gayle
Wade Hampton Acad; Orangeburg, SC (18-73) Chor; Pres, Drama; Lit Mag; Madrigal; NHS; A-Ed, Sch P; Sci C; Y-Tns; Hon Prog; Pres A; Sci A; HR; Attendance A; *Fla St U; Bio.*

STANLEY, Sherry Lea
Boyd Co HS; Cannonsburg, KY; FBLA; FHA; Sch P; Hon Prog; Jr Homemaker Degree; *Ashland Comm Col; Bus.*

STANSBURY, Kathy Ann
David Lipscomb HS; Nashville, TN (20-125) A Cap Choir; Chor; Drama; Ensm; Lat C; NHS; Sch P; Alg A; Citz A; Hon Prog; Math A; *David Lipscomb Col; Health Occupations.*

STANTON, Clinton Jr
Woodside HS; Woodside, CA; Chess C; Ravenswood School; *San Francisco St U; Med Lab Tech.*

STANTON, Frederick George
Honesdale HS; Honesdale, PA; V-Ch, Band; Chess C; Chor; Ensm; Order/Arrow; Var C; Golf; Tr; Co-Cpt, Wrest; MVP, Wrest; Explorers Sct; HR; Pres, BYF; Wrest Medals; Most Versitile, Sr Cl; *Penn St U; Bus Mgt.*

STANTON, Jeannie Lynn
Upperman HS; Baxter, TN; Ann; BC; Bus Mgr, Sch P.

STANTON, Kathryn Jeanne
Crown Point HS; Crownpoint, IN (20%-500) A Cap Choir; Band; Chor; Community Yth Symph; Ensm; Fr C; Madrigal; *Milligan Col; Deaf Ed.*

STANTON, Kimberly Jo
Norwood Sr HS; Norwood, OH; NHS; VP, Span C; Span NHS; *Bus.*

STANTON, Lori Elizabeth
Chillicothe HS; Chillicothe, OH; Band; Chor; Drama; Fr C; Mjrte; NFL; NHS; Spch C; Spch A; St Champion in Duo- acting; Leads in Musicals; Church Choir; Leads in Dramas; Swing Choir; *U of Akron; Theatre and Communications.*

STANTON, Naomi Louise
Brookhaven HS; Brookhaven, MS (10-30) Chldr; Drama; FHA; 4H; Y-Tns; Bkbl; Sftbl; Tr; *Jackson St U; Interior Decorating.*

STANTON, Randall Wayne
Silsbee HS; Silsbee, TX (10-290) A Cap Choir; Band; S-T, Chess C; Ensm; JETS; Math C; NHS; Sch P; Hon Prog; Journ A; Star Student; WW; Young Amer Speaks; DAHSS; TMEA All-Region Choir; Ntl Essay Press; *U of Tex at Austin; Elec Engr.*

STANTON, Sandra Dee
Northwest HS; St Louis, MO (49-600) FBLA; Hon Prog; JA A; Type A; Drill Tm; *Sou Calif U; Secy.*

STANTON, Terrance Ward
Collegiate HS; New York, NY (10%-44) Lit Mag; A-Ed, Sch P; Soccer; MLS; NMS; Regent School; *Eng.*

STANYARD, Geormine Deweya
C A Brown HS; Charleston, SC (1-175) Band; Secy, BC; GS; 4H; Hmrm; Mu Alpha Theta; NHS; SC; Alg A; COM; Sci A; Star Student; Miss C A Brown HS; All Co & Bicentennial HS Band; WW; Civic Ballet Co; *U of NC; Math.*

STAPERT, Jane Ann
John S Fine HS; Nanticoke, PA (16-350) Chldr; Chor; *Bloomsburg St Col; Ed.*

STAPLES, Christine Ann
Holliston HS; Holliston, MA (5%-250) AFS; Chor; Drama; Fr C; Lat C; Ed, Lit Mag; Span C; COM; Hon Prog; Yth Fel; Schol Merit A; *Boston Col; Drama.*

STAPLES, Denise Renee
S Hamilton Comm Sch; Jewell, IA (8-84) A Cap Choir; Band; Chor; Madrigal; Math C; Spch A; Piano & Harp Festvals; Girls Trio; IMTA St Auditions; Clarinet Choir; IMTA Theory HR; Girls Quartet; Dorian Young Artists Recital; HR.

STAPLES, Janice Marie
Saginaw HS; Saginaw, MI; Chldr; Chor; Drama; 4H; Jr Miss Pagent; NHS; Sch P; Spch C; SC; Bsbl; Bkbl; Sftbl; Tr; Citz A; 4H A; Hon Prog; Most Out; Type A; Ntl Hons A; Service Hours A; Sports A; Gold Pin A; *Mich St U; Photo.*

STAPLES, Kathryn Lynn
NW Classen HS; Okla City, OK (36-460) Pres, Band; Chor; Ensm; NHS; Orch; A-Ed, Sch P; Span C; Sftbl; COM; Citz A; Hon Prog; Type A; Cert of Acad Achv, Okla St U; *Mus.*

STAPLES, Larry Howard
LaPorte HS; LaPorte, IN (30-600).

STAPLES, Malcolm Bryan
Saginaw HS; Saginaw, MI; Chor; Pres, SC; Var C; Soph Cl; JV, Bkbl; Ftbl; Tr; Alg A; Cl Fav; Math A; MLS; Ntl Achv Scrol; NEDT; Pres A; Star Student; Sports A; *U of Mich; Computers.*

STAPLES, Maurice Bryce
Saginaw HS; Saginaw, MI (10-800) Hmrm; NHS; SC; Bsbl; Bkbl; Ftbl; Tr; Alg A; COM; Citz A; *U of Calif; Bus Mgt.*

STAPLETON, Brian Gerard
Don Bosco Tech HS; Boston, MA; CYO; Dbte Tm; Sftbl; Swim; Hon Prog; Math A; MLS; *U of Mass; Bus Mgr.*

STAPLETON, Derrick Eugene
Southeast HS; Springfield, IL; Tr; *Lincoln Land Col; Drafting.*

STAPLETON, James Randal
Elder HS; Cincinnati, OH (50%-387) Ann; Chldr; SC; Pres, Poster C; *Hocking Tech Col; Broadcasting.*

STAPLETON, Laura Sue
Washington HS; Kansas City, KS (12-595) Chldr; ARC; Concerned Girl's School; *Kans City Comm Jr Col; Nurs.*

STAPLETON, Loretta Diane
Copeland HS; Copeland, KS; Chor; SC; VP, Var C; Bkbl; Sftbl; Swtth; Vlbl.

STAPP, John Phillip
Dallas Christian HS; Dallas, TX (6-55) Ann; Lat C; NHS; Spch C; Var C; Bsbl; Cpt, Bkbl; Ftbl; Tr; Spch A; *Abilene Christian U; Bible.*

STARC, Miriam Dolores
Saint Mary's HS; Stockton, CA (1-256) Band; CYO; Dbte Tm; Lit Mag; NFL; NHS; Span C; Spch C; CSF; Hon Prog; NEDT; Poet A; Star Student; Sci Camp Counselor; SDAHSS; Committee On World Hunger; Eng, Span, A's; GAA.

STARE, James Marlin
Plant City HS; Plant City, FL; Band; Demolay; Phys C; Bsbl; Bkbl; Ftbl; Type A; *Engr.*

STARE, Raymond Lee
Zion Benton HS; Zion, IL (240-495) Band; Pres, Chess C; Ger C; Bkbl; Golf; Tr; Phys Fitness A; *Bethel Col; Mus.*

STARGELL, Bruce Peyton
Arlington Heights HS; Ft Worth, TX (25-650) Ftbl; NHS; *U of Tex; Aerospace Engr.*

STARK, Gregory Lewis
Clay Center HS; Clay Center, NE (5-33) Band; BS; 4H; VP, NHS; Spch C; Var C; Secy, Sr Cl; Bsbl; Bkbl; Co-Cpt, Ftbl; Tr; COM; Spch A; MVP, Ftbl; WW; *U of Nebr; Engr.*

STARK, Raymond
Flushing HS; Flushing, NY (367-706) InterAct C; Bkbl; Attendance As; *Queensborough Col; Bus Adm.*

STARK, Ron David
Hughson HS; Hughson, CA; Ch, Key C; Ski C; Var C; Cpt, Bsbl; Cpt, Bkbl; Ftbl; All-League, Sr Ftbl; Hon Men, Bkbl & Bsbl; *MTC; Phys Ed.*

STARK, Sheri Diane
Bond Co Comm Unit 2 HS; Greenville, IL (70-180) Chor; FHA; Hmrm; Span C; Arch; *Kaskaskia Col.*

STARK, William Robert
Prospect HS; Mt Prospect, IL (44-587) VP, HiY; Semi-Fin, NHS; Bsbl; Bkbl; Sftbl; COM; St Scholar; *Iowa St U; Computer Engr.*

STARKEBAUM, Linda Lea
Cass HS; Cassville, GA (10%-190) Band; Math C; Span C; Type A.

STARKEY, Sheri Leigh
Robert E Lee; Baytown, TX; Band; FHA; Key C; NHS; Drill Tm; St Readers Cert; PA; *Lee Col; Bus.*

STARKS, Angela
E Atlanta HS; Atlanta, GA (4-142) Tusk U; Pre-Med.

STARKS, Bernita Lavelle
Carolina HS; Greenville, SC; VP, CYO; FBLA; SC.

STARKS, Brent Alan
Southport HS; Southport, IN (60-490) Band; Ger C; 4H; Mgr, Bsbl; 4H A; Yth Fel; Eagle Sct; *Purdue U; Pre-Vet.*

STARKS, Charles Ansel
Portageville HS; Portageville, MO (14-90) Band; Chess C; Key C; Ftbl; Swim; *Memphis St U; Law.*

STARKS, Edward
Richwoods HS; Peoria, IL; Bkbl; Sftbl; Swim; Tnns; Tr; Wrest; *Bradley U; Bus Mgt.*

STARKS, Francine Elizabeth
Lutheran HS; Burbank, CA; Fr C; Span C; VP, Soph Cl; CSF; COM; Hon Prog; Handbell Choir; Guest Soloist, Comm Yth Symp; 1st Pl Win, Bach Festival; 2nd Pl Win, Talent Show; *USC; Sci.*

STARKS, Jerald Howard
Mazon Verona Kingman HS; Mazon, IL (8-62) Band; Chess C; Chor; Drama; Golf; Wrest; Interntl C; Mus As; Sports As; *Ill St Col; Elec.*

STARKS, Kenley Andrea
Fairview HS; Dayton, OH (30-232) VP, Hmrm; Span C; Cpt, Bsbl; Mgr, Bkbl; Cpt, Ftbl; Fin, Tr; Cl Fav; HCt; Hon Prog; Most Out; Star Student; VP, Yth Chapter NAACP; Spokesman, Sch Affairs; *Morehouse Col; Foreign Lang.*

STARKS, Thomas Ray Jr
Mason HS; Mason, TX (10%-44) Band; FFA; Sch P; Mgr, Bkbl; JV, Ftbl; Tnns; COM; Life Sct; *U of Tex; Elec Engr.*

STARKWEATHER, Alisa Ann
Waterford Township HS; Pontiac, MI; SC; Scorekeeper, Bsbl; *West Mich U; Art.*

STARLEY, Richard Lawrence
Box Elder HS; Brigham City, UT (15%-390) Pres, City Conf; Ch, Commercial C; Ch, Dbte Tm; Drama; Parl, FBLA; Model UN; NFL; Ski C; Thes; S-T, UN Council; Spch A; Pres, Young Democrats; Pol Envolv A; Adv Col Placement; Outst Debator; *U of U Spch School; U of Utah; Law.*

STARLING, Deborah Ann
Andrew Jackson HS; Cambria Heights, NY (50-527) Cum Laude Soc; Drama; Hmrm; SC; Secy, Ftbl; Booster; Martin Luther King Fund Comm; Secy, Sunday Sch; Yth Coun, Sunday Sch Day Camp; *Baruch Col; Acct.*

STARLING, Joy Marie
Citrus HS; Inverness, FL (13-250) Band; Chor; FFA; Pres, FTA; Mjrte; NHS; Sch P; COM; H of F; *Anthropology.*

STARLING, Virginia
Randolph Sou Sch; Shellman, GA (1-17) Bus Mgr, Ann; BC; Dbte Tm; Ensm; Pres, Fr C; Hmrm; Fin, Jr Miss Pagent; NHS; F-Ed, Sch P; SC; Tri-HiY; Pres, Sr Cl; Rptr, Soph C; Tnns; COM; DARGCA; Hist A; Rotary A; *Auburn U; Mus Theory.*

STARNES, Bill Allen
Clarksdale HS; Clarksdale, MS (14-28) Cpt, Bsbl; Ftbl; Tr; Photo C; Bkbl, Ftbl, Shop, Band, Tr As; *Saint Mary's Col; Photo.*

STARNES, Darlene Paula
LaBrae HS; Leavittsburg, OH (90-174) Band; Ensm; Pres, Ger C; Orch; COM; Blossom Festival; *Youngstown St U; Mus.*

STARNES, Francina
York Comp HS; York, SC (14-240) Band; FBLA; Hmrm; NHS; Rptr, Sch P; Span C; Spch C; WW; Columbia Col; Journ.

STARR, Amanda Lynne
S Charleston HS; S Charleston, WV (25%-300) A Cap Choir; Ann; Chor; GS; Hmrm; Mjrte; F-Ed, Sch P; Span C; Thes; Tr; Yth Fel; Tn Board; Drama.

STARR, Sherian Denise
John Marshall HS; Okla City, OK (25%-535) Chor; Ensm; Cosmetology A; Okla St U; Archt Engr.

STARR, Wanda Ann
Bakersfield HS; Bakersfield, CA; Bakersfield Col; Secy.

STARTZELL, Linda Joyce
Penns Manor HS; Kenwood, PA (12-160) Chor; Hmrm; SC; NEDT; Yth Fel; Asbury Col; Psych.

STARY, Randall Lee
Abbot Pennings HS; De Pere, WI (6-104) Chldr; Chor; Drama; Key C; NHS; Sch P; Tres, SC; Drama A; Chor A; Marquette U; Pre-Med.

STASHIK, Theresa Ann Marie
John S Fine Sr HS; Nanticoke, PA (1-347) Sch P; Pres, Sodality; Amer Leg A; K of C A; Lion A; NEDT; VFW A; Soc Stu A; Law.

STATEN, Dolly Jean
Waynesboro Central HS; Waynesboro, MS (25%-99) Jackson St U.

STATEN, Jeffery Paul
Carroll HS; Monroe, LA; Bsbl; Ftbl; Sou U; Engr.

STATEN, Roddy
Miami Killian HS; Miami, FL (199-1100) Journ Cert of A; Fla A&M U; Archt.

STATON, Beth
Forest Glen HS; Suffolk, VA (1-151) BC; Drama; FBLA; InterClub Coun; SC; Gov Honor Prog; Val; Yth Fel; WW; Project MORE; Old Dominion U; Med Tech.

STATON, Lois Irene
B T Washington HS; Norfolk, VA; Drama; Pepperdine U; Drama.

STATON, William Richard
Mullens HS; Mullens, WV; A-Ed, Ann; Pres, BC; Chess C; FBLA; Pres, HiY; InterClub Coun; NHS; Sci C; Var C; Pres, Soph Cl; Mgr, Bkbl; Cpt, Tnns; Yth Leg; W Va U; Bio.

STATZER, Misty Ann
Tuscola Comm HS; Tuscola, IL (30-110) A Cap Choir; Band; Chor; Pres, 4H; Lat C; Madrigal; Order/Arrow; 4H A; Hon Prog; Order/Arrow A; Yth Fel; Swing Choir; E Ill U; Sci.

STAUB, Glenn
W Allis Central HS; West Allis, WI (200-500) Pres, Ski C; Var C; Ftbl; Sftbl; Tnns; Wrest; Sadie Hawkins, 3rd Pl A; Var Ltr, Ftbl; Milton Col; Acct.

STAUDENMAIER, Shelly Kay
Troy HS; Troy, KS; CYO; Chor; Pres, Hmrm; SC; Var C; Pres, Jr Cl; Tr; Alg A; Amer Leg A; Citz A; Hist A; PTA A; Pres A; Yth Foundation A; Math A; Hugh O'Brian A; FFA Swtht Cand; Kayette Off; Secy, Pep C; Home Ec.

STAUDINGER, Mark
Martin Luther HS; Maspeth, NY (10-100) Chem C; Ger C; Var C; Bsbl; JV, Bkbl; Tr; Amer Leg A; COM; Hon Prog; JA A; Ariz St U; Sci.

STAUDT, Debbie Suzanne
Meridian HS; Meridian, TX (3-36) Ann; Band; Tres, BC; Ensm; Secy, FHA; Mjrte; Rptr, Sch P; Bkbl; Fin, Tr; St Qualifier, UIL Typing; Halloween Qn; Jr Hist; Baylor U; Pediatrics.

STAUFFER, Carla Jane
Garden Spot HS; New Holland, PA (2-220) AFS; Band; Chor; Secy, Drama; Ensm; Secy, Ger C; Secy, 4H; Secy, NHS; Orch; Hon Soc Schol; Lebanon Valley Col; Mus Ed.

STAUFFER, Lee Ann
E Clinton HS; Lees Creek, OH (12-137) Band; Chldr; Chor; NHS; Mus C A; Prom Qn; Miami U; Retailing.

STAUFFER, Ronald Gene
Monroe HS; Monroe, WI (50-245) Band; Ensm; FFA; Yth Fel; HR; Stu Exchange; U of Wis; Agr.

STAUSS, Karen Lynn
Hazelwood E HS; St Louis, MO (1-700) Cpt; Chldr; Chor; NHS; WW; Co Yth Ldrship Coun A; Nurs.

STAVELY, Linda Marie
Northwestern Sr HS; Hyattsville, MD (1-673) Tres, Hmrm; Sci C; Span C; COM; Rotary A; Val; U of Md; Med Technology.

STAVEM, Nancy Lynn
Westview Sr HS; Braham, MN (33%-102) Band; Chor; Ensm; Sch P; 4H A; Vlbl; 4-Star A, GMG; Bethel Col; Bio.

STAVES, Debra Ann
W O Boston HS; Lake Charles, LA; Secy, Band; Chor; FHA; Hmrm; Bsbl; Sftbl; Swim; Cl Fav; HQn; Swtht; Band, Vlbl, A's; McNesse Col; Nurs.

STAYMAN, Veronica Edith
King's Acad; W Palm Beach, FL (5-49) CYO; Chor; NFL; NHS; Rptr, Sch P; Hon Prog; VofDEM.

STAYTON, Barbara G
Cherry Hill HS E; Cherry Hill, NJ; Church Yth Choir; Church Yth Coun.

STAYTON, Beverly G
Cherry Hill HS E; Cherry Hill, NJ; Church Yth Choir; Church Yth Coun.

ST CHARLES, Valerie Ann
Joseph Samuel Clark Sr HS; New Orleans, LA; Southern U; Law.

ST CLAIR, Christina Addison
Cheyenne Central HS; Cheyenne, WY (4-462) Chor; Ensm; Fr C; Hmrm; Key C; NFL; Secy, Soph C; VP, St Stu Congress; Secy, SC; Spch A; VofDEM; Yth Fel; Yth Foundation A; Yth Leg; Win, Hugh O'Brian A; All St Choir; Lead in 'Oklahoma'; Superior, Mus Festival.

ST CLAIR, Harry Lance
Brozosport HS; Freeport, TX (9-227) JETS; Mu Alpha Theta; NHS; Orch; Tnns; Citz A; Pres A; COM; All St Orch; Baylor U; Mus.

ST CLAIR, Jill Caroline
W A Berry HS; Birmingham, AL; Band; Ensm; Fr C; Orch; Bkbl; Sftbl; Alg A; Chem A; Yth Fel; Ed, Church Yth Newsletter; Christian C; VP, UMYF; Solo, Ensm Band Comp; U of Ala; Psych.

ST CLAIR, Kimberly Vernice
Shaw HS; East Cleveland, OH; Ohio St; Psych.

ST CLAIR, Michael Wayne
Somerset HS; Somerset, KY (30-180) Ann; Chess C; Pres, Hmrm; Order/Arrow; Bkbl; Sftbl; Citz A; God & Country A; Order/Arrow A; Del, Church Conf; Duke U; Med.

ST CYR, Carol Lynn
Wethersfield HS; Wethersfield, CT; Chor; Ski C; Mgr, Swim; Mgr, Tr; ARC A; Bio.

ST CYR, Karen Patricia
Springfield HS; Springfield, LA (1-54) BC; Cpt; Chldr; Pres, FHA; 4H; Fin, Lit Ral; Cl Fav; 4H A; 4th Pl, St Eng Lit Rally; SE La U; Bio Sci.

STEARNS, Betsy Jeanne
Long Beach Poly HS; Long Beach, CA; A Cap Choir; Chor; Fin, Pursuit of Excel A; Mus.

STEARNS, Kathleen Marie
Bayshore Methodist Christian Sch; Tampa, FL (1-6) Ann; CYO; Hmrm; Sch P; Pres, SC; Sftbl; COM; Val; Yth Fel; Parl, Self-Defense C; Christian Prayer C; Mgr, Vlbl; Principal's Hon A; Fla St U; Biol Oceanography.

STEBBINS, David Allen
Fruitport HS; Fruitport, MI; Band; 4H; Yth Fel; Ferris St; Automotive Engr.

STEBLIN, Mary Ann
Notre Dame HS; Springfield, MA (1-86) CYO; Chor; Drama; NHS; NFL; NHS; Ed, Sch P; Spch C; Amer Leg Orator A; St Choir A; Spch A; Val; VFW Orator Win; VofDEM; Most Studious; Secy, JA; Arts & Crafts C; Nursing Home Vol; Family Ldrs of Tomorrow; Bio C; Young Christian Stu C; Saint Joseph Col; Nurs.

STECK, Eric William
Nutley HS; Nutley, NJ (30-493) Cpt, Band; Community Yth Symph; Fr C; NHS; Ski C; Tnns; NMS; WW; Pres, MYF; Lafayette Col; Bus.

STEDMAN, Barbara Devere
Mount Rainier HS; Des Moines, WA; NHS; Var C; Bkbl; Cr-Ctry; Tr.

STEDMAN, Gilbert R
Chittenango Central HS; Chittenango, NY (77-201) Var C; Ftbl; Tr; WW; Prep Tr & Field Athlete o-t Yr; Herkimer Co Comm Col; Forestry.

STEDMAN, Roger Warren
Upper Scioto Valley HS; McGuffey, OH; BS; Chem C; FFA; Pres, 4H; Math C; VP, NHS; Phys C; Sch P; Var C; Bkbl; Cr-Ctry; Tr; Cl Fav; HKg; Hon Prog; Math A; Phy A; Ohio St U; Acct.

STEDWILL, Mary Susan
Bowsher HS; Toledo, OH (31-472) Band; Cpt, Mjrte; NHS; Rptr, Span C; SC; VP, Jr Cl; Sftbl; Tr; Symph Band A; Acad A's; Bowling Green St U; Med.

STEED, Alan Craig
Bowdon HS; Bowdon, GA (15-95) BC; 4H; HiY; Span C; Tnns; Sci A; WW; U of Ga; Phar.

STEED, Lisa Margaret
Cleburne HS; Cleburne, TX (9-283) Secy, Band; Ensm; FHA; Pres, FTA; Lat C; NHS; VP, Sch P; DARGCA; MLS; Alumni Schol; Eunice Buchanan Schol; Austin Col; Elem Ed.

STEEL, Sharon
Manhattan Acad; Jackson, MS (25%-92) Co-Cpt, Chldr; NHS; Soph Cl; Bkbl; Alg A; Beauty; Cl Fav; HCt; Math A; Ole Miss; Phar.

STEELE, Brad Lyle
Valentine HS; Valentine, NE (16-68) Ann; VP, Band; SC; Var C; JV, Bkbl; Ftbl; JV, Golf; Sup A'S, Trumpet, Brass, March Band; Kearney St U; Mus.

STEELE, Bruce Carl
Northview HS; Grand Rapids, MI (1-256) Demolay; Drama; NHS; Ed, Sch P; Pres, Span C; SC; Tres, Sr Cl; COM; Hon Prog; NMS; Val; Foreign Lang A; Fin, St Math Competition; U of Ala; Span.

STEELE, Carla Kaye
Franklin Co HS; Meadville, MS (10-140) VP, BC; Chldr; SC; Math A; St Bible Drill; Miss Col; Med.

STEELE, Charles Edward
Midway HS; Waco, TX (36-181) Math C; Phys C; Sci C; Citz A; Math A; McLennan Comm Col; Acct.

STEELE, Colleen DeArcy
Bonanza HS; Bonanza, OR (10%-35) Chor; Secy, FHA; Secy, NHS; Var C; Bkbl; Tr; Most Ath, Sr Cl; Oreg St U; Registered Nurs.

STEELE, Daniel Emery
N Bullitt HS; Shepherdsville, KY (3%-200) Band; Sci C; Var C; Ftbl; Band As; U of Ky; Law.

STEELE, Denise Marie
Gloucester HS; Gloucester, VA (10%-300) AFS; Ann; Band; Cpt, Chldr; Dbte Tm; FTA; Hmrm; InterAct C; Madrigal; Ed, Sch P; SC; HCt; Swtht; Yth Fel; VPI; Biol.

STEELE, Desiree Rachell
Kubasaki HS; Okinawa, JAPAN (19-271) Ed, Ann; Pres, CYO; Hmrm; NHS; ARC; SC; Co-Cpt, Bkbl; MVP, Sftbl; Mgr, Wrest; COM; Hist A; Ariz St U; Engr.

STEELE, Eileen Ann
Douglas HS; Douglas, AZ (112-287) Secy, 4H; Pres, Rainbow; Secy, ARC; 4H A; ARC A; Type A; Fashion Board; Walk-A-Thon.

STEELE, Gary Alan
Fremont HS; Fremont, IA (5-20) Var C; Pres, Jr Cl; Cpt, Bsbl; Cpt, Bkbl; Cr-Ctry; Tnns; Cpt, Tr; MVP, Bsbl; Centerville Col; Building Trades.

STEELE, Jackie Lynn
Central Baptist Sch; Hampton, VA (4-21) Chldr; Chor; FHA; Sftbl; Bus.

STEELE, Jill Elaine
Yorkwood Jr-Sr HS; Monmouth, IL; S-T, 4H; Span C; Lib Asst A.

STEELE, Karen Jayne
Lakeville Mem HS; Otisville, MI (40-250) Semi-Fin, Arch; NHS; Pres, Ski C; Pres, Jr Cl; Sftbl; Hon Prog; U of Mich; Sci.

STEELE, Lawanda Rose
Reeds Spring HS; Reeds Spring, MO (5-75) BC; FHA; FNA; Math C; ARC; Sci C; Span C; Math A; U S Navy; Elec.

STEELE, Linda DeAnn
Maryville R-II HS; Maryville, MO; Band; Chor; Ensm; Span C; JV, Bkbl; Type A; *Stephens Col; Bus.*

STEELE, Loretta Lyn
Chewelah Jenkins HS; Chewelah, WA (10%-100) Secy, Band; Pres, 4H; Pres, Y-Tns; *Portland Bible Col; Mus.*

STEELE, Mark O
Northwest HS; Omaha, NE; Bsbl; Bkbl; Sftbl; Swim; *Milford Col; Building Construction.*

STEELE, Moxie Ilene
Gilmer Co HS; Glenville, WV (21-94) Drama; NHS; SC; Pres, Sr Cl; *W Va U; Spch Pathology.*

STEELE, Nancy Ann
Los Alamitos HS; Los Alamitos, CA (103-450) Chor; Dbte Tm; Drama; Swim; Citz A; Lion A; Ntl Achv Schol; Spch A; St Scholar; Val; Yth Fel; Lions C Speaker; WW; *Long Beach St U; Bus.*

STEELE, Norene Claire
Nathan Hale HS; Seattle, WA; Band; Ensm; Hmrm; NHS; Hon Prog; Type A; Church Sftbl; Ch, Church Yth; Statement of Proficiency; Cpt, Colorguard; Rep, Yth Convention; *N Seattle Comm Col; Commercial Art.*

STEELE, Valeria Dale
Oak Ridge HS; Oak Ridge, TN (145-519) Chor; Ensm; Secy, Sunday Sch; Rptr, Off Ed C; Tn Board; Tres, Yth Group; Vocal Clinic; *Berea Col; Sociology.*

STEELE, Valeria Larraine
Concord Sr HS; Concord, NC (60-225) FBLA; ARC; Sci C; Span C; SC; Bkbl; Cl Fav; *U of NC; Pol Sci.*

STEELMAN, Dixia Danette
Starmount HS; Boonville, NC (1-155) Chor; FHA; Fin, Jr Miss Pagent; Mu Alpha Theta; Span C; Pres, SC; Tnns; HCt; Jr Marshall; Moorehead Nom; *Lenoir Rhyne Col; Deaf Ed.*

STEELMAN, Harold Danny
Starmount HS; Boonville, NC (32-151) Band; FFA; SC; VP, Sr Cl; JV, Bkbl; Co-Cpt, Ftbl; Cpt, Golf; MVP, Golf; Pres Phys Fitness A; All Conf, Golf; *NC Stu; Engr.*

STEELY, Brian Duane
Eldorado HS; Albuquerque, NM (90-744) NHS.

STEELY, Kathy Leigh
Eastern HS; Louisville, KY; Ann; Chor; VP, FTA; Secy, ARC; Opt A; Opt Out Tn; *Eastern Ky U; Spec Ed.*

STEEN, William Baxter
Hueytown HS; Hueytown, AL; Band; Drama; Span C; Swim; Tnns; Yth Fel; *UAB; Ed.*

STEER, Robert Lawrence
Shawnee Mission NW HS; Shawnee, KS; CYO; Cum Laude Soc; Ski C; Ftbl; Cl Fav; Hon Prog; ARC A; HR; Red Cross Instructor; *Kan U; Pre-Law.*

STEER, Rodney James
Cottage Grove HS; Cottage Grove, OR (5-260) AFS; NHS; Thes; *U of Oreg; Bus.*

STEFANAK, Denise Lynne
W Middlesex HS; W Middlesex, PA (9-146) Bus C; Co-Cpt, Chldr; Chor; FBLA; FNA; Tres, FTA; NHS; Co-Ed, Sch P; Co-Ed, Sr Cl; A-Ed, Jr Cl; VP, Soph Cl; HCt; Journ A; Q&S A; Jr Deb; *U of S Fla; Bio.*

STEFANEK, Lillian Eleanor
Marian Cath HS; Tamaqua, PA (45-177) Cpt, Chldr; FNA; Tr; HCt; WW, HS Stu; WW, Chldrs; *U of Pittsburgh; Phys Therapy.*

STEFANO, Julianne Marie
Swissvale Area HS; Pittsburgh, PA (1%-187) Secy, Band; CYO; Chor; Fr C; F-Ed, Sch P; VP, Y-Tns; Alg A; DARGCA; Sci A; Schol, Band, Chor, Newspaper, A's; *Pitt U; Sci.*

STEFANOV, Steve Allen
Greater Latrobe HS; Latrobe, PA; Ger C; Hmrm; SC; Var C; Pres, Soph Cl; Tr; JV, Wrest; Outst, Tr; *Entomology.*

STEFANSKI, Patrick Wayne
Wichita N HS; Wichita, KS (150-750) Band; Ensm; ARC; Bkbl; Ftbl; Tr; St Mus A; *Mus.*

STEFFAN, Ann Louise
Michigan Pub HS; Michigan, ND (1-30) Co-Ed, Ann; Band; Chor; Ensm; GS; 4H; Pres, Jr Cl; Mgr, Tr; 4H A; *General.*

STEFFEE, Amy Jane
Wellesley Sr HS; Wellesley, MA (10-400) AFS; Lat C; Orch; Swim; JV, Tr; COM; Citz A; Hon Prog; Sci A; Church Choir; Hon's Pin; Var Ltr; MYF; LaCrosse; *Gym.*

STEFFEE, Linda Sue
Wellesley Sr HS; Wellesley, MA (9-466) AFS; Band; NHS; Citz A; Hon Prog; Interlochen Ntl Mus; Globe Scholastic Art A; NHS A; Dance; *Princeton U.*

STEFFEK, Kathy Elizabeth
Kelly HS; Chicago, IL (26-485) NHS; ARC; Sci C; Hon Prog; ARC A; Sci A; Type A; Service A.

STEFFEN, Barbara Jane
Rocky River HS; Rocky River, OH (50%-300) Band; Citz A; Solo, Ensm Contest; *Valpairaiso U; Guidance Coun.*

STEFFEN, Mark William
Aiken Sr HS; Cincinnati, OH (25-544) Chor; Drama; Ensm; Ger C; Hmrm; Lit Mag; Model UN; Rptr, Sch P; SC; Amer Leg A; Eagle Sct; *Wittenberg U; Pre-Med.*

STEFFY, Dawn Elaine
Warwick HS; Lititz, PA (21-282) Chldr; NHS; Secy, Var C; *Lancaster General Sch of Nurs; Nurs.*

STEGALL, Donna Elizabeth
Norlina HS; Norlina, NC (5-90) Ann; BC; Chldr; Chor; Pres, Hmrm; *U of NC; Mus.*

STEGEMAN, Jane Ellen
Maries R-1 HS; Vienna, MO (13-69) CYO; Chor; FNA; Sci A; General Bus A; Acct II Trophy; Attendance A; *Nurs.*

STEGEN, Kathryn Marie
Woodburn HS; Woodburn, OR (1-131) A Cap Choir; Ensm; Jr Miss Pagent; NHS; Orch; COM; Chem A; Elk A; Masonic A; NMF; Rotary A; Val; Yth Fel; St Off, Rainbow Girls; Federation of Mus C Schol; St Hon, Federated Mus C Festival; *Colo St U; Zoology.*

STEGER, Richard Rian
Texas HS; Texarkana, TX; Chess C; Demolay; JV, Ftbl; *SW Col; Archt.*

STEHL, Joan Ann
Qn o-t Rosary Acad; Amityville, NY (3-68) Ann; CYO; Hmrm; Bkbl; *Le Moyne Col; Med Technology.*

STEHL, Mark Alan
New Athens Comm HS; New Athens, IL (11-65) Pres, NHS; SC; Mgr, Bkbl; DARGCA; HKg; *S Ill U; Acct.*

STEHR, Krista Sue
Downers Grove HS N; Downers Grove, IL (89-787) AFS; Ger C; Co-Ed, Lit Mag; Hon Prog; *Newspaper Editing.*

STEIGER, Michael Joseph
Hall HS; Little Rock, AR (15-435) Ann; NHS; Ftbl; NEDT; Outst Lineman, Ftbl; *Baylor U; Mass Communications.*

STEIL, Lisa Marie
Estherville Sr HS; Estherville, IA (11-175) GRA; Vlbl; *Iowa City Col; Med.*

STEIL, Marueen Kay
Beaver Dam Sr HS; Beaver Dam, WI (78-331) Ski C; Secy, Var C; Cpt, Bkbl; Sftbl; Tnns; HCt; *U of Wis-LaCrosse; Recreation & Parks.*

STEIMEL, Beth Ellen
W Holmes HS; Millersburg, OH (15-197) Band; Chor; 4H; NHS; Sci C; Secy, Span C; Secy, SC; JV, Bkbl; Sftbl; Tr; Bio A; Hon Prog; Sci A; Hist C; Church Choir; GAA; Dist Sci Fair; FCA; Musicals; Presbyterian Deacon; *Wooster Col; Vet Med.*

STEIMLING, Deanna Kay
Middleburg Joint HS; Middleburg, PA; FBLA; SC; HQn; HCt; VP, Tres, VICA; Executive Committee.

STEIN, James Wilfred
Premontre HS; Green Bay, WI (36-154) Key C; Ftbl; Hon Prog; Serra C Servers A; *St Norbert's Col; Theology.*

STEIN, Susan E
Tuscaloosa HS; Tuscaloosa, AL; A-Ed, Ann; Band; Hmrm; Math C; Mu Alpha Theta; NHS; Orch; SC; Beauty; Cl Fav; Swtht; Yth Fel; Chaplain, Civinettes; Vol Action Coun; Tn Board; *U of Ala.*

STEINBACH, Michael William
Albia Comm HS; Albia, IA (37-155) Mgr, Wrest; Hon Prog; Math A; *Indian Comm Col; Marketing.*

STEINBACH, Paul Alan
Medina Sr HS; Medina, OH (200-335) Ftbl; Tnns.

STEINBAUGH, Mark Allen
Bismarck-Henning HS; Bismarck, IL (8-90) Band; Chor; FTA; NHS; Sci C; Span C; SC; Var C; Pres, Sr Cl; Bsbl; Bkbl; Ftbl; Golf; Tnns; MVP, Tr; Citz A; Effort A, Bkbl; SDAHSS; Sch Play A.

STEINBECK, Allen Louis
Paso Robles HS; Paso Robles, CA (10-190) Math C; Phys C; Var C; Wrest; CSF; *Questa Col; Math.*

STEINBECK, Rise Fern
Hartley HS; Hartley, IA (50%-55) FHA; Tres, Rainbow; Swim; Tr; Yth Fel; *Sci.*

STEINBERG, Karla Sue
Lincoln HS; Lincoln, KS (5-66) A Cap Choir; Band; Chor; Ensm; Ger C; Madrigal; COM; Hon Prog; NEDT; 1st Bandsman; *Kans St U; Mus.*

STEINBERG, Robyn Anne
Civic Mem HS; Bethalto, IL (5-275) Ann; FHA; Ger C; Rainbow; Sci C; Ftbl; St Scholar; Yth Fel; Drill Tm; Prom Committee; SDAHSS; Pom pon Girl; GAA; Sou Ill Conf Yth Coun; Church Children's Choir Director; *Sci Research.*

STEINBERG, Steven Louis
El Camino Real HS; Woodland Hills, CA; A Cap Choir; Chor; Drama; Ensm; Madrigal; Model UN; Thes; Bank Of Amer A; CSF; COM; Hon Prog; PTA A; Dance; Thespian A; *UC of Los Angeles; Theater Arts.*

STEINBERGER, Lance Theodore
St Ignatius HS; St Ignatius, MT (4-32) Ann; NHS; Pres, SC; Var C; VP, Jr Cl; Mgr, Bkbl; Ftbl; *Bozman Col; Acct.*

STEINER, Alan David
NorthWood HS; Nappanee, IN (20-260) Band; Drama; SC; Thes; Bkbl; Ftbl; FCA; Campus Life.

STEINER, Dirk Douglas
Wapakoneta Sr HS; Wapakoneta, OH (1-360) Chor; Demolay; Ensm; Fr C; Pres, Lat C; Math C; NHS; Co-Ed, Sch P; Bio A; Journ A; *Ohio St U; Psych.*

STEINER, Jolinda
Jeannette Sr HS; Jeannette, PA (6-164) AFS; Lat C; Pres, Rainbow; Mgr, Sftbl; Yth Fel; Pres, Yth Fel; Med Explorers C; *U of Pittsburgh; Med.*

STEINER, Mark Alan
Hemet HS; Hemet, CA (200-500) A Cap Choir; Band; Chor; Community Yth Symph; Orch; Jazz Ensm; *Calif Lutheran Col.*

STEINER, Mark David
Suffolk HS; Suffolk, VA (18-125) Ann; Chess C; Dbte Tm; Tres, Drama; Fr C; Ger C; HiY; InterAct C; Math C; NHS; Tres, Thes; JV, Ftbl; Golf; Yth Fel.

STEINER, Susan Jean
Piqua Central HS; Piqua, OH (9-395) Chor; Community Yth Symph; Drama; Ensm; Fr C; Parl, GS; Secy, 4H; NHS; VP, Orch; Sch Achieve Tm; Chamber of Comm A; NEDT; Mus Boosters Orch A; *Mus Ed.*

STEINER, Toni Yvette
George Washington HS; San Francisco, CA; A Cap Choir; Up Bound; Type A; *San Francisco U.*

STEINHARDT, Norma Jean
Bad Axe HS; Bad Axe, MI (2-164) Band; Cpt, Chldr; Drama; Fr C; NFL; NHS; Tres, Sci C; COM; Hist A; HCt; NMS; Sal; Spch A; Yth Fel; Eng Hons; 4 0 Hons; Presidential Recognition A; *Albion Col; Bio.*

STEINHART, Richard Thomas
Mt Carmel Area Sr HS; Mt Carmel, PA (62-212) Band; Chem C; Chor; Dbte Tm; Drama; Hmrm; Lit Mag; NHS; ARC; Sch P; Sci C; Span C; SC; VP, Soph Cl; Bkbl; COM; Cl Fav; Hon Prog; ARC A; Yth Fel; District Chor; *Penn St U; Vet Med.*

STEINIGER, Kimberly Ann
Smithtown HS W; Smithtow, NY (60%-600)
Hmrm; Ski C; Yth Fel; JA; Candystriper; Sunday
Sch Teacher; Legal Secy.

STEINKAMP, Ellen Javais
Madison HS; Madison, KS (10-41) Band; Ger C;
All St Band; Kans St U; Mus Theory.

STEINKAMP, Joann Marie
Quincy Notre Dame HS; Quincy, IL (2-140) F-Ed,
Ann; Co-Cpt, Chldr; Chor; Fr C; Secy, 4H; Hmrm;
Pres, NHS; SC; Secy, Soph Cl; DARGCA; 4H A;
Hon Prog; NEDT; Opt Out Tm: Sal; St Scholar;
SAA As; WW; U of Ill; Math.

STEINKE, Steve Russel
Fountain Valley HS; Fountain Valley, CA
(271-950) Ski C; Span C; Var C; Ftbl; Soccer; JV,
Tr; Citz A; Hon Prog; Pre-Dentistry.

STEINKUEHLER, Janet Kay
Santa Fe HS; Alta Loma, TX (25-300) Band; Secy,
Drama; FHA; Secy, 4H; Jr Miss Pagent; Mjrte; JV,
Tr; 4H A; De A; Church Choir; Fashion Merchandising.

STEINMETZ, Edward Joseph
Bishop Klonowski HS; Scranton, PA (3-105)
Hmrm; Lit Mag; NHS; Order/Arrow; Sch P; Span
C; SC; Mgr, Bkbl; Amer Leg A; Hon Prog; NEDT;
Sci A; U of Scranton; Bus Adm.

STEINMETZ, JoAnne Marie
Holy Cross HS; Marine City, MI (16-54) Chor; Ski
C; Span C; Bkbl; Sftbl; Mich St U; Phys Therapy.

STEINMETZ, Zoe Marie
Holy Cross HS; Marine City, MI; Chor; Pres, NHS;
Sch P; Ski C; Tres, Jr Cl; Hon Prog; Central Mich
U; Med Tech.

STEKLINE, Cindy Elizabeth
Palo Duro HS; Amarillo, TX (1-285) A Cap Choir;
Secy, Band; Chor; Ensm; Fr C; FBLA; FTA; Madrigal; NHS; Orch; Secy, Sr Cl; Outst Girl o-t Mo;
Outst Fr; All St Choir; W Tex St U; Mus.

STELLA, Charles Robert
Red Lion Area Sr HS; Red Lion, PA (100-375)
Chess C; Var C; Cr-Ctry; Tr; Pres Sports A; Pres,
Yth Fellowship; York Col of Penn; Police Sci.

STELLA, Donna Lynn
Hightstown HS; Hightstown, NJ (45-354) AFS;
Hmrm; NHS; SC; Pres, Sr Cl; Bkbl; Co-Cpt,
Hockey; Co-Cpt, Sftbl; Citz A; HCt; Hon Prog;
Schol Hon A; Douglass Col; Lang.

STELTZ, Lynda Maria
S Saint Paul Sr HS; South Saint Paul, MN (29-464)
A Cap Choir; AFS; Drama; Ger C; NHS; Lawrence
U; Vocal Performance.

STELZNER, Janet Dorothy
St Joseph's Notre Dame HS; Alameda, CA (10-55)
Sci C; Ski C; Bio A; Chem A; Hist A; Span Cert; UC
at Berkeley; Botany.

STEMLE, Cara Maria
Springs Valley HS; French Lick, IN (1-90) Band;
CYO; Chldr; Fr C; Var C; Pres, Soph Cl; Bkbl; Tr;
Vlbl; Cpt, Flags; Ind U.

STEMLE, Julia
Martin Co HS; Stuart, FL (14-500) Secy, Anchor
C; BC; U of Fla; Med.

STEMPLE, Peggy Louise
Aurora HS; Aurora, WV (1-40) Band; Secy, FHA;
GS; NHS; Sci C; Secy, Jr Cl; Hist A; Hon Prog;
VFW A; FHA St Commitment Degree; Lena
Charter Ldrship A; FHA Member o-t Yr; Fairmont
St Col; Nurs.

STENBERG, Kathleen Marie
Mountlake Christian HS; Mountlake Terrace, WA
(1-21) Cpt, Chldr; Drama; Orch; Bkbl; HCt; Val;
Girl o-t Yr; Seattle Pacific Col; Bio.

STENBERG, Lynne Ellen
Rhinebeck Central HS; Rhinebeck, NY (1-100)
Band; Pres, 4H; VP, NHS; Var C; Tres, Jr Cl; Cpt,
Bkbl; Hockey; Sftbl; Citz A; NEDT; Pres, Church
Yth Group; Co All-Star Sftbl; Sci.

STENBOL, Carl William
Port Washington HS; Port Washington, WI
(26-400) Bus C; Chor; Demolay; FBLA; Tr; Hon
Prog; Yth Fel; DeMolay Merit Bars; Founders A; U
of Wisc; Bus Adm.

STENDERUP, Kent Kresten
Arvin HS; Arvin, CA (10-270) BS; VP, Chess C;
FFA; Model UN; Ski C; SC; VP, Var C; Pres, Sr Cl;
Bsbl; Bkbl; MVP, Ftbl; MVP, Tr; CSF; Lion A;
Stanford U; Ec.

STENGEL, Miriam Ruth
Cambridge HS; Cambridge, MN (57-273) AFS;
Chor; Secy, 4H; 4H A; Bethel Col; Bus.

STENGEL, Naomi Joy
Cambridge Sr HS; Cambridge, MN; Chor; VP, 4H;
4H A; St Cloud Beauty Col; Cosmetologist.

STENSGARD, Peter Craig
Detroit Lakes HS; Detroit Lakes, MN; Bkbl; N
Central Bible Col; Social.

STENSGARD, Rachel Joy
Senior HS; Detroit Lakes, MN; Chor; Secy, Pep C;
S-T, CA' S, Church Yth Group; Missionette Hon
Star.

STENSON, Dana Lynn
Superior HS; Superior, NE (33%-80) Chor; 4H; Y-
Tns; Photography.

STENSRUD, David Bartholomew
St James Sr HS; St James, MN (95-142) Ann; Chor;
Sch P; Ftbl; Golf; Tr; Wrest; Wilmar Voc Col; Photography.

STEPHAN, Daniel David
Valley City Sr HS; Valley City, ND (60-180) Ch,
Pol Sci C; HR; U of ND; Law.

STEPHAN, Lori Jean
Franklin Comm HS; Franklin, IN (8-260) Band;
Chor; Secy, Lat C; NHS; Tri-HiY; Magna Cum
Laude; Sci A; Prom Ct; Swtht Ct; U of Evansville;
Nurs.

STEPHANS, Michael Edward
Leo HS; Chicago, IL (42-152) Band; Drama; COM;
Lion A; Sci A; Yth Bowl Assn; Art A; Med.

STEPHEN, Diana Lynne
Canton S HS; Canton, OH (1-270) A Cap Choir;
Co-Ed, Ann; JV, Chldr; Chor; Drama; Ensm; GS;
Hmrm; Math C; NHS; Phys C; ARC; Sch Achieve
Tm; Sch P; Span C; Spch C; Thes; Tri-HiY; Amer
Leg A; Elk A; Math A; Most Out; ARC A; Sci A;
Spch A; Val; Teenager o-t Mo; Super Sr; Lead in
Musicals; Ga Inst of Tech; Mech Engr.

STEPHEN, Dianna Lee
Westfield HS; Westfield, IL (1-16) Ann; Secy,
Band; Chor; Pres, NHS; SC; Secy, Sr Cl; Tres, Jr Cl;
Secy, Soph Cl; Tr; Bausch & Lomb A; Hist A; Hon
Prog; Ind St U; Life Sci.

STEPHEN, James Robert
John Foster Dulles HS; Stafford, TX (25%-800)
AFS; Ger C; Mu Alpha Theta; DARGCA; Abilene
Christian U; Bible.

STEPHENS,
Alexander Hamilton
MacKenzie HS; Detroit, MI (3-352) Pres, NHS;
ARC; JV, Tr; Hon Prog; Sci A; U of Mich; Natural
Resources.

STEPHENS, Alicia
Fairview HS; Boulder, CO; A Cap Choir; Chor;
FBLA; Madrigal; SC; S-T, Soph Cl; U of Colo;
Arts.

STEPHENS, Alicia Hermine
St Angela Hall Acad; Brooklyn, NY; A Cap Choir;
Chor; Drama; Tr; JA A; Yth Fel; Bowl Tm; Neighborhood Yth Groups; Morgan St U; Law.

STEPHENS, Allen Jackson
Rossville HS; Rossville, GA (1-212) BC; NHS; Order/Arrow; SC; Pres, Sr Cl; VP, Jr Cl; Ftbl; Alg A;
COM; Chem A; Gov Honor Prog; Math A; NEDT;
Sci A; Star Student; Val; Yth Fel; Pres, Jr Exchange
C; Barrett A; Dalton Jr Col; Med.

STEPHENS, Brenda Jean
Wakulla HS; Medart, FL; Band; Chor; Mod Mus
Mas; Alg A; Opt A; Chor A; FSU; Mus.

STEPHENS, Cheryl Denise
Wm J Woodham HS; Pensacola, FL (34-530) Secy,
BC; Tr; Phys Ed Achv A; U of Fla; Dentistry.

STEPHENS, Cindy Sanland
Rossville Comp HS; Rossville, GA (4-212) Ed,
Ann; BC; SC; Y-Tns; Alg A; Hon Prog; Journ A;
NEDT; Eng A; Social Stu Cert; Dalton Jr Col; Bio.

STEPHENS, David King
James Monroe HS; Fredericksburg, VA (16-155)
Chor; Key C; Ski C; NMS; U of Richmond; Acct.

STEPHENS, Denise Darnell
Lutheran HS W; Detroit, MI; Yth Fel; Pep C; Eastern Mich U; Ed.

STEPHENS, Diana Linne
Lawrence HS; Lawrence, KS (114-689) Band; JV,
Tnns.

STEPHENS, Donna Lynn
Fairview HS; Boulder, CO (450-700) U of Colo.

STEPHENS, Douglas Lyle
Lawrence HS; Lawrence, KS (80-550) Band; BS;
Ensm; Orch; Order/Arrow; SC; VP, Sr Cl; Amer
Leg A; Order/Arrow A; Gym; WW; U of Kans.

STEPHENS, Kathy Sue
Dothan HS; Dothan, AL (5%-550) Chor; Madrigal;
NEDT; George C Wallace Jr Col; Bus.

STEPHENS, Linde Jay
Goodlettsville HS; Goodlettsville, TN (10%-185)
Band; FTA; Hmrm; Lat C; NFL; ARC; SC; Bkbl;
MVP, Cr-Ctry; Tnns; Spch A; Hon Squad.

STEPHENS, Lisa Kay
Springfield S HS; Springfield, OH (25-425) Band;
Co-Cpt, Chldr; Chor; Hmrm; Secy, Orch; Pres, SC;
COM; Drill Tm; Gym Tm; Psych.

STEPHENS, Lori Ann
Lakota HS; Westchester, OH (108-533) Span C;
Bkbl; Soccer; Eng A; Bus.

STEPHENS, Marilyn Elyse
Cairo HS; Cairo, GA (20-250) Ann; FHA; Rptr,
Sch P; Bkbl; COM; Hon Prog; Yth Fel; Bkbl A; Ga
Sou Col; Phys Therapist.

STEPHENS, Mark Ellis
Seaside HS; Seaside, CA (60-600) Band; Church
Orch Director; Church Camp Kg; Westminster
Col; Mus.

STEPHENS, Melvin Edward
John Jay HS; San Antonio, TX; Band; Chor; Madrigal; Order/Arrow; Bio A; All Region Choir; U of
Tex; Mus.

STEPHENS, Robin Lea
Huntington Beach HS; Huntington, CA; Dbte Tm;
Model UN; Eng.

STEPHENS, Russell Hamrick
Petaluma Sr HS; Petaluma, CA (151-260) A Cap
Choir; Chldr; Chor; Dbte Tm; Drama; FBLA; Ger
C; 4H; Hmrm; Ntl Yth Conf; Span C; Thes; 4H A;
Hist A; Spch A; Local School; St Rep, Ntl Bible
Bowl; Church Yth Spiritual Ldr; Song Ldr, 4-H C;
Calif Christian Col; Bible.

STEPHENS, Ruth Valerie
Halifax Co Sr HS; South Boxton, VA (10%-850)
Bus C; Chor; FBLA; FHA; 4H; NHS; Sci C; Secy,
SC; 4H A; Choral A; Span A; All A's A; Va Commonwealth U; Acct.

STEPHENS, Sonya Renee
Darby Township HS; Glenolden, PA; Band; 4H;
Lit Mag; Bkbl; Tnns; Spch A; Temple U; Journ.

STEPHENS, Terri Lynn
Diamond Hill-Jarvis HS; Ft Worth, TX;

STEPHENS, Terri Lynne
Woodrow Wilson HS; Washington, DC (46-500)
Hmrm; Ski C; SC; Hon Prog; Superintendent's HR;
Pre-Med.

STEPHENS, Terry Lee
Baker HS; Columbus, GA;

STEPHENS, Tracy Edgar
Channel Island HS; Oxnard, CA (6-20) A Cap
Choir; Chor; Bsbl; Co-Cpt, Bkbl; Cr-Ctry; JV, Ftbl;
Swim; Tr; Oxnard Jr Col.

STEPHENSON, Ceonta
Franklin HS; Somerset, NJ; Kean Col; Phys Therapist.

STEPHENSON, Cindi Kae
Ralston HS; Ralston, NE (100-300) AFS; Band;
Ntl Yth Conf; ARC; COM; Yth Fel; U of Nebr at
Omaha; Bus.

STEPHENSON, Connie Sue
Pawhuska HS; Pawhuska, OK (17-121) Chor; Ensm; Rptr, FHA; 4H; Hmrm; Lit Mag; ARC; Tr; COM; 4H A; Hon Prog; ARC A; Yth Fel; Yth Against Communism; Tnns, Achv, Yth Fitness, A's; *Animal Husbandry.*

STEPHENSON, Crystal Yvonne
Columbus E HS; Columbus, IN (42-420) Band; Hon Prog; Band A; *Olivet Col; Mus.*

STEPHENSON, James Edward
Sheffield HS; Memphis, TN (13-142) Ann; BS; Hmrm; InterClub Coun; Mu Alpha Theta; Pres, NHS; Order/Arrow; SC; Tres, Jr Cl; Cpt, Ftbl; H of F; Order/Arrow A; ROTC A; Exchange C Yth o-t Month; Scripps Howard Tnage o-t Week; *Christian Brothers Col; Elec Engr.*

STEPHENSON, Julie Lynn
Roosevelt HS; Portland, OR; COM; Citz A; *Art.*

STEPHENSON, Karen Diane
Girls' Prep Sch; Chattanooga, TN (10-100) Chor; Fr C; Madrigal; Rptr, Sch P; Span C; Tr; COM; NEDT; Poet A; Vlbl; Acad Excel A; Cpt, Church Bkbl; Glee C A; Sch Distinguished List; *U of Tenn; Pre-Med.*

STEPHENSON, Kyle Ray
Eula HS; Clyde, TX (1-32) Secy, FFA; Bkbl; Tr; Sci A; FFA Schol; One Act Play, Dist All Star Cast; *Tex A&M Col; Meteorology.*

STEPHENSON, Nancy Sue
Madison Acad HS; Huntsville, AL (2-42) BC; Math C; NHS; Alg A; COM; Hist A; Hon Prog; Math A; NEDT; Sci A; Star Student; Eng A; Home Ec A; *David Lipscomb Col.*

**STEPHENSON,
Phillip Raymond**
Guthrie HS; Guthrie, OK; BS; Math C; NHS; Bsbl; Bkbl; Ftbl; HCt; Masonic A; *PE.*

STEPHENSON, Ruthie Dorraine
Weir HS; Weir, MS (1-53) Hist A; Eng, Mus, A's; *Miss St U; Lab Tech.*

STEPHENSON, Sharon Lynn
East Central HS; Hurley, MS (6-115) BC; FHA; Sci C; WW; *Journ.*

STEPHENSON, Sigrid Charlene
Levelland HS; Levelland, TX (50%-300) Rptr, A Cap Choir; UIL 1st Division; *S Plains Col; Mus.*

STEPHENSON, Teri Lynn
Van Buren Comm HS; Keosauqua, IA (1-80) Pres, NHS; Pres, Rainbow; A-Ed, Sch P; Span C; Var C; Bkbl; Cr-Ctry; Tr; COM; *Iowa St U.*

STEPHENSON, Tina Jerene
Mt Pleasant HS; Mt Pleasant, TX (20-213) Bus C; NHS; SC; Co-Cpt, Bkbl; Tr; Rotaryettes; MVP, Bkbl; Cpt, Vlbl; Womens Sports Mag HS All-Star A; *Paris Jr Col; Phys Ed.*

STEPHENSON, Tonya Jayne
Goddard HS; Goddard, KS (12-165) Band; NHS; Sci C; Bkbl; Tr; St Scholar; Type A; *Kans St U; Vet Med.*

STEPIEN, Linda Marie
Miami Springs Sr HS; Miami Springs, FL (26-800) Anchor C; Lat C; Span NHS; COM; Hon Prog; Type A; *Miami Dade Jr Col; Nurs.*

STEPLETON, Theodore Paul
Lima Sr HS; Lima, OH (75-550) A Cap Choir; Chor; Tnns; Alg A; Math A; *Purdue U; Landscape Archt.*

STEPP, Brian Arnold
Lindblom Tech HS; Chicago, IL (10-613) A Cap Choir; Chor; Ger C; Madrigal; Math C; NHS; Var C; Swim; COM; Hon Prog; Math A; Ntl Sci Found; ROTC A; Swim Ltr; Sr Boy's Coun; *Ill Inst of Tech; Engr.*

STEPP, James Harlan Jr
Kermit HS; Kermit, WV (3-25) Chor; FBLA; Hmrm; Span C; Bsbl; Bkbl; Hon Prog; Yth Fel; All Star Babe Ruth Tm; Alt, BS; *Marshall U.*

STEPP, Karen Anita
Lindblom Tech HS; Chicago, IL (30-433) Ger C; Model UN; NHS; Pres, Sci C; COM; VofDEM; Amer Cancer Soc Summer Schol; Golden Eagle for Sch Service; *Eastern Ill U; Zoology.*

STEPP, Linda Gail
Crispus Attucks HS; Indianapolis, IN (10%-430) NHS; Rptr, Sch P; JV, Bkbl; Sftbl; Tr; Type A; *IUPUI-INDIANAPOLIS U; Health & Phys Ed.*

STEPP, Susan Elise
Naperville Central HS; Naperville, IL; *Chem.*

STEPP, Timothy Edward
Buffalo Sr HS; Buffalo, MN (16-240) BS; Fr C; Secy, FFA; Pres, 4H; Ftbl; Co-Cpt, Hockey; HCt; Yth Fel; MVP, Hockey; *U of Minn at Duluth.*

STEPP, Willard Thomas Jr
Kermit HS; Kermit, WV (2-34) Band; BS; Order/ Arrow; Pres, Span C; Bsbl; God & Country A; Math A; Sal; *Boston U; Pre-Med.*

STEPTOE, Sonja Renece
Lutcher HS; Lutcher, LA (1%-247) Ed, Ann; Rptr, BC; FTA; Semi-Fin, GS; 4H; Rptr, Mu Alpha Theta; Sci C; Rptr, SC; COM; Journ A; Math A; VofDEM; 1st Pl, St Sci Fair; Miss FTA; Win, Americansm Vs Communsm Essay; *U of Mo at Col; Journ.*

STERETT, Tamee Kay
Union HS; Biggsville, IL; Ann; Cpt, Chldr; Ch, FHA; S-T, SC; Mgr, Tr; HR; Faculty List.

STERKEL, Jon Michael
Los Altos HS; Hacienda Heights, CA (78-605) Var C; Cpt, Swim; St Scholar; Co-Cpt, Waterpolo; 2nd Tm, Waterpolo; *Pepperdine U.*

STERLING, Dana Lynne
Charles C Mason HS; Tulsa, OK (26-260) Drama; Hmrm; Lit Mag; SC; Hon Prog; Spch A; Pres, Russian C; Mime Repertory; *Communications.*

STERLING, David Arthur
Elston Sr HS; Michigan City, IN (29-359) Chess C; NHS; JV, Cr-Ctry; JV, Tr; Ensm A, Sch Band & Orch Vocal Assn; Elston Schol A; *Valparaiso U; Ministry.*

STERLING, Inga Alison
Eleanor McMain Magnet Sec HS; New Orleans, LA; Band; Chor; NHS; Sch P; Citz A; PA; *Tulane U; Engr.*

STERLING, Ruby Lee
McKinley Sr HS; Baton Rouge, LA (2-217) Math C; Tres, Mu Alpha Theta; NHS; SC; COM; Cl Fav; Hon Prog; ARC A; Sal; Sci A; Spch A; Star Student; Eng A; Geography A; WW; *LSU; Acct.*

STERN, Steve Kent
Geneva Comm HS; Geneva, IL (6-217) Co-Ed, Ann; Hmrm; InterClub Coun; VP, Key C; Pres, NHS; Parl, SC; JV, Bkbl; Ftbl; JV, Golf; Cpt, Tr; Amer Leg A; COM; HKg; NMS; St Scholar; Deacon, Church; *Purdue U; Bio-Med Engr.*

**STERNBERGER,
Michael Gerard**
Bishop Luers HS; Fort Wayne, IN; Fr C; Tnns; COM; Minstrels Swing Choir; *US Navy; Aerographer's Mate.*

STERNER, Mary Suzanne
Kingsway Reg HS; Swedesboro, NJ (14-166) Band; Chor; Fr C; NHS; *Messiah Col; Dietetics.*

STERNS, Mark Jeffrey
Indianapolis Baptist HS; Indianapolis, IN (35-52) Television Sound.

STERRITT, Mark Alan
Mount Gilead HS; Mt Gilead, OH; Yth Fel; Art C; Industrial Arts C; BSct.

STETKEWYCZ, Oksana
Immaculate Conception Ukr Cath HS; Hamtramck, MI; JV, Chldr; Chor; Bkbl; Hon Prog; *Wayne St Col; Med Lab Technology.*

STETLER, Cynthia Ann
Coatesville Area Sr HS; Coatesville, PA (136-600) Chor; JV, Tnns; *Psych.*

STETLER, Laurie Ann
Coatesville Area Sr HS; Coatesville, PA (3-600) Chor; Fr C; NHS; Secy, Jr Cl; JV, Tnns; NEDT; Lukens Conf; *Math.*

STETTLER, Peggi Wynn
Coronado HS; Colorado Springs, CO (23-395) NHS; Secy, Span C; JV, Tnns.

STETTNER, Lisa Gail
Harrison HS; Harrison, NY (21-290) Ann; Chor; Fr C; Mjrte; NHS; Var C; Mgr, Tr; Hon Prog; *U of Pa; Mus Theater.*

STEUCK, Larry Dean
David Starr Jordan HS; Long Beach, CA (45-600) InterAct C; InterClub Coun; Key C; Secy, SC; Var C; Cpt, Ftbl; Swim; Wrest; Bank Of Amer A; Hist A; Kiwanis A; MLS; Brd of Realtors, Ctzn of Tmrow A; *US Air Force Acad; Social Stu.*

STEVEN, Darlene P
Midpark HS; Middleburg Hts, OH; A Cap Choir; Chor; Drama; Ensm; 4H; Hmrm; Ntl Yth Conf; Thes; 4H A; Pres, VP, GSct; Junior League; Planner, SW Yth Days; Area & Sr Planning Boards, GSct; *Stephens Col; Mus.*

STEVENS, Alexander Jr
Spingarn HS; Washington, DC; Chess C; V-Ch, Commercial C; FBLA; Citz A; Coun of Teach A; DARGCA; Hist A; Most Out; Phy A; Sci A; Jr Litho C; Printing; *Offset Printing.*

STEVENS, Betsy A
Emerson HS; Emerson, AR (3-30) Fin, FHA; Secy, SC; Pres, Jr Cl; Bkbl; Beauty; Cl Fav; HCt; Eng; Most Talented; Best Dressed; Straight 'A' A; *Sou Ark U; Nurs.*

STEVENS, Bonnie Faye
Verdi HS; Verdi, MN; Ann; Chldr; Chor; 4H; Sch P; Tres, Jr Cl; Vlbl.

STEVENS, Brad B
Cleburne HS; Cleburne, TX; Chor; Madrigal; Mgr, Ftbl; COM; Outst Choir Stu; *Abilene Christian U; Bible.*

STEVENS, Brenda Kay
Pacifica HS; Garden Grove, CA (10%-714) A Cap Choir; Chor; Drama; Span C; SC; COM; Most Out; Swtht; Church Rep Yth; *Pepperdine U; Drama.*

STEVENS, Brian Edward
Lodi HS; Lodi, CA (11-480) FBLA; Key C; Tres, SC; Bsbl; Ftbl; CSF; Rotary A; *San Joaquin Delta Col; Acct.*

STEVENS, Bruce
Mountain View HS; Mtn View, AR (7-68) VP, Band; VP, BC; Chem C; VP, Chor; Dbte Tm; Drama; Pres, Ensm; Hmrm; Lit Ral; Lit Mag; Math C; ARC; Sci C; Spch C; Pres, SC; VP, Jr Cl; Bkbl; Ftbl; Sftbl; Hon Prog; Opt A; Pres A; Pres, St SC Assn; Top 10% Sr; Stage Band; Church Organist; Sunday Sch Tchr & Superintendent; *Ark Col; Sci.*

STEVENS, Carla Michelle
Hapeville HS; Hapeville, GA; BC; Ensm; Span C; Y-Tns; PTA A; Type A; *Sci.*

STEVENS, Crystal Elizabeth
Post Falls HS; Post Falls, ID (12-154) Ann; Pres, Band; Chor; Drama; Fr C; NHS; Spch C; S-T, SC; Mgr, Tr; Spch A; WW; 1st Chair of Amer; *U of Idaho; Mus Composition.*

STEVENS, Dave A
Randolph Pub Sch; Randolph, NE; Band; Chess C; Chor; FBLA; VP, 4H; Order/Arrow; Var C; Ftbl; Tr; Wrest; Citz A; Order/Arrow A; 1st, Boys Glee C; 2nd, Cornet Solo; *Law Enforcement.*

STEVENS, David Wayne
Mountain View HS; Mountain View, AR (25-58) BC; Bus C; FFA; FTA; Drivers Ed A; Attendance A.

STEVENS, Deborah Jean
Grove City HS; Grove City, OH (44-488) Band; Chor; NHS; SC; *Mount Carmel Sch of Nurs; Nurs.*

STEVENS, Donna Marie
Yukon HS; Yukon, OK; FHA; Yth Fel; Drill Tm; Yth Coun; Comm On Ed; Church Sch Teacher; *El Reno Jr Col.*

STEVENS, Elizabeth Ann
Bridgeport HS; Bridgeport, TX (25%-77) Ann; Band; Cpt, Chldr; Chem C; FBLA; Math C; NHS; Sch P; Sci C; Bkbl; Tr; Cl Fav; HCt; Journ A; Most Friendly; *Tex A&M U; Journ.*

STEVENS, Ellen Kaye
Hartshorne HS; Hartshorne, OK; VP, Drama; NHS; Span C; Spch C; VP, SC; VP, Sr Cl; Bkbl; Tr; Alg A; Bio A; Hist A; MLS; Sci A; Val; *U of Okla; Dentistry.*

STEVENS, Gina Lynne
McKinley Tech HS; Washington, DC; Citz A; Hon Prog; MLS; *Fed City Col; Journ.*

STEVENS, Gloria Ann
John H Reagan HS; Austin, TX (10%-300) Band; Bus C; Secy, Chor; Ensm; JETS; Lit Mag; Madrigal; Math C; NHS; Orch; Sci C; SC; Alg A; COM; Magna Cum Laude; Math A; Type A; WW; All St Baptist Yth Choir; All Region, Choir; Hardin-Simmons U; Bus Law.

STEVENS, Gordon Curtis
Greeley Central HS; Greeley, CO (30-390) A Cap Choir; Parl, BS; Chor; Pres, Drama; Ensm; VP, Ger C; Hmrm; Madrigal; SC; Pres, Thes; JV, Bsbl; Hon Prog; Yth Fel; U of Northern Colo; General Stu.

STEVENS, Holly Scott
Chamberlain HS; Tampa, FL (95-671) Band; Chor; Drama; NHS; Orch; Thes; Golf; Fla St U; Mass Communications.

STEVENS, James Darryl
Palestine HS; Palestine, TX (4-380) Chor; Pres, Hmrm; Tnns; Bio A; Hist A; Math A; All St Choir; Eng A; Tex A&M Col; Med.

STEVENS, James Edward Jr
Lee Acad; Clarksdale, MS (10%) Secy, Band; Math C; Mu Alpha Theta; NHS; Secy, Sci C; Mgr, Bkbl; Hist A; 5th Dist, Academic Betterment Comp; Med.

STEVENS, James Ernest
Hillcrest HS; Jamaica, NY (49-667) Bsbl; Hockey; Regent Schol; Yth Fel; NJHS; CYO Bsbl All-Star; St U of NY at Albany.

STEVENS, John Kirwin
Chaminade Col Prep; St Louis, MO (5-118) NHS; F-Ed, Sch P; Pres, SC; JV, Bkbl; Co-Cpt, Cr-Ctry; Swim; Tr; Hon Prog; NEDT; Washington U; Pre-Med.

STEVENS, John Lawrence
E Forsyth HS; Kernersville, NC (150-630) FFA; Sch P; Bsbl; Sftbl.

STEVENS, John Mark
Garfield Hts HS; Garfield Hts, OH (3-407) Drafting.

STEVENS, Joyce Purdell
Clinton HS; Clinton, NC (10-275) Band; BC; Drill Tm; Secy, TAYJ; PA; 'A' Stu; U of NC; Med.

STEVENS, Judith Louise
Sou Wayne Sr HS; Dudley, NC (80-400) AFS; Cpt, Chldr; Hmrm; InterClub Coun; ARC; Span C; Tnns; ARC A; Swtht; Lifeguard; U of NC; Phys Ed.

STEVENS, Judy Leigh
Norco Sr HS; Norco, CA (50-400) Chldr; Fullerton Jr Col; Dance.

STEVENS, Karen Donna
Hopewell HS; Hopewell, VA (62-354) BC; FHA; Span C; Tri-HiY; Richard Bland Col; Secy.

STEVENS, Karen K
Randolph HS; Randolph, NE (24-65) Chldr; Chor; Drama; Ensm; VP, FBLA; Pres, 4H; Mgr, Tr; 4H A; Spch A; SC; Secy, 4-H C; Tr Record Setter; 1st Runnerup, Dairy Princess; I Rating, Dist Mus Contest; 3 Rating, Dist Solo; Wayne St Col; Recreation.

STEVENS, Kate Marie
Sunset HS; Dallas, TX; A Cap Choir; JV, Chldr; Chor; Lat C; SC; Bkbl; Soccer; Swim; Citz A; DARGCA; Hon Prog; Opt A; Opt Out Tn; PTA A; Yth Fel; Life Ldrship A; U of Tex; Pub Relations.

STEVENS, Kathleen Louise
Alameda Sr HS; Lakewood, CO (50-620) Chldr; NHS; Mgr, Tr; Hon Prog; U of Northern Col; Bio.

STEVENS, Kathryn Joy
Beaman-Conrad-Liscomb HS; Conrad, IA (5%-60) Band; Chor; NHS; Tres, SC; Mgr, Sftbl; Mgr, Tr; Worthy Adv, Rainbow Girls; St Exex Comm, Rainbow; Med.

STEVENS, Kimberly Ann
Clara HS; Clara, MS (17-50) VP, Chess C; FHA; Tr; Sch Beauty Pageant; Jones Jr Col; Secy.

STEVENS, Leonora Jean
George Henry Corliss HS; Chicago, IL (4-485) Ensm; NHS; Secy, Span C; COM; Citz A; Hon Prog; Type A; Vlbl; Bradley U; Med.

STEVENS, Linda Sue
San Jacinto HS; San Jacinto, CA (38-77) Pres, Band; Secy, FTA; Span C; COM; Hon Prog; Republican's Womens Schol; Ldr, Girls in Action; Qn Regent in Service, Acteens.

STEVENS, Lisa Frances
Wetumpka HS; Wetumpka, AL (1-205) BC; Chldr; FTA; Ski C; SC; Tres, Soph Cl; Swim; Cl Fav; FCA; Tres, Christian Yth Assn; Hon Stu; 'Smartest', Soph Cl; Auburn U; Special Ed.

STEVENS, Lisa Gaye
River Forest HS; New Chicago, IN (4-200) NHS; Hon Prog; Bus.

STEVENS, Lori Suzanne
Spartanburg HS; Spartanburg, SC; Chldr; 4H; VP, Hmrm; Rainbow; Ski C; Beauty; HCt; Civinettes C; Tres, Art C; Art A; Spencer C; Spartanburg Methodist Col; Fashion Merchandising.

STEVENS, Maris Ann
Germantown HS; Philadelphia, PA (42-551) Drama; NHS; Citz A; Hist A; Math A; Sci A; Star Student; Type A; Yth Fel; Young Adult Choir; Providence Bus C; Social Concerns Comm; Temple U; Communications.

STEVENS, Mark Peter
Owatonna HS; Owatonna, MN (4-420) Secy, Band; Chor; Ensm; Orch; SC; Cr-Ctry; MLS; Gustavus Adolphus Col; Sci.

STEVENS, Melissa Ann
Meadowbrook HS; Byesville, OH (25-160) Ann; Chor; FTA; GS; 4H; Math C; Lat A; Ohio St U; Horticulture.

STEVENS, Mindi
Meadowbrook HS; Byesville, OH (5-200) Band; Rptr, 4H; Math C; Sci C; Lat A; Band A; Malone Col; Pre-Med.

STEVENS, Penni Renee
Fairfield Union HS; Lancaster, OH (3-200) Chor; Ensm; Rptr, Sch P; Spch A; Ohio U; Nurs.

STEVENS, Roderick William
Forest Hill HS; W Palm Beach, FL; Chor; Ensm; Span C; Span NHS; Citz A; Exchange C; Chaplain, Church Yth Chor; Director, Yth Choir; Mortuary Sci.

STEVENS, Ross William
Huntington N HS; Huntington, IN (140-614) Chess C; Chor; Demolay; Ger C; Order/Arrow; F-Ed, Sch P; Swim; Journ A; Order/Arrow A; Rotary A; Eagle Sct; Purdue U; Mech & Elec Engr.

STEVENS, Scott H
S Houston HS; South Houston, TX; HiY; Hmrm; JETS; Mu Alpha Theta; NHS; SC; JV, Bsbl; JV, Bkbl; Ftbl; Amer Leg A; Chamber of Comm A; Citz A; Acad Excel; Tex A&M U; Law.

STEVENS, Susan Hope
Elmira Southside HS; Elmira, NY (3-435) Band; Chor; Ensm; Hmrm; Lat C; NHS; Pres, Rainbow; Co-Ed, Sch P; Bsbl; COM; Regent Schol; Yth Leg.

STEVENS, Susan Marie
Elmira HS; Elmira, OR (6-192) Prof Photography.

STEVENS, Valerie Anne
Vicksburg HS; Vicksburg, MS (1-244) AFS; JV, Chldr; GS; Lat C; Secy, Math C; VP, NHS; Sch Achieve Tm; Bkbl; Elk A; H of F; Hist A; Star Student; Val; U of Miss; Engr.

STEVENSON, Bradley Scott
Union HS; Biggsville, IL (2-90) JV, Bkbl; Ftbl; Hon Prog.

STEVENSON, Douglas Reed
Spencer HS; Spencer, IA (20-210) NHS; Cpt, Bkbl; Cpt, Ftbl; Tr; COM; Hon Prog; Iowa St U; Engr.

STEVENSON, Earnest
Martin Luther King HS; Chicago, IL (6-210) Pres, FBLA; Tr; JA A; FBLA A; Schol A; Computer Sci.

STEVENSON, Elizabeth Ann
Santa Barbara HS; Santa Barbara, CA; A Cap Choir; Band; Madrigal; NHS; S-T, SC; DARGCA; Type A; Most Inspirational, Mus; Bethel Col; Elem Ed.

STEVENSON, Elizabeth Leigh
Patrick Henry HS; San Diego, CA (1-1054) Math C; SC; CSF; Math A; NMF; Val; Fr, Span, A's; Stanford U; International Relations.

STEVENSON, Jeana Alene
El Dorado Springs HS; El Dorado Springs, MO (31-126) Band; Secy, Chor; Dbte Tm; Drama; Secy, FHA; Secy, Hmrm; ARC; A-Ed, Sch P; Semi-Fin, SC; Citz A; Cl Fav; Most Out; ARC A; Photography C; Safety Merit A; Chor A, Most Outst Vocalist; U of Mo; Special Counseling for Yth.

STEVENSON, Jeffrey Alan
East HS; Corning, NY; JV, Tr; Yth Fel; YMCA Bkbl; Forestry.

STEVENSON, Joanie Evette
Temple HS; Temple, TX; Tr; Secy, Church Chor; Vlbl; Phys Ed A; Nurs.

STEVENSON, Julie Gay
W Tredell HS; Statesville, NC (73-173) Band; Chor; FHA; Span C; SC; VP, Sr Cl; Crisco A; HCt; Most Out; Yth Fel; MIP; FHA Swtht; Wingate Col; Home Ec.

STEVENSON, Karen Annette
Henry Ford HS; Detroit, MI (200-458) Chor; Rptr, Sch P; SC; Tnns; Citz A; Val; Yth Fel; Mich St U; Pre-Law.

STEVENSON, Lisa Meyers
Winn Acad; Winnfield, LA (3-18) S-T, Chldr; 4H; Lit Ral; Pres, Rainbow; F-Ed, Sch P; Bkbl; Sftbl; 4H A; HQn; NHS; Lit Fel; Miss Winn Acad; WW; Off, Yth Choir; La Tech U; Nurs.

STEVENSON, Mark Brian
Hazelwood Central Col; Florissant, MO (67-881) Bkbl; Citz A; Film Making A; Parks Col; Pro Pilot-Math.

STEVENSON, Martha Yvette
Fort Walton Beach HS; Fort Walton Beach, FL (2-630) Anchor C; BC; Chldr; Rptr, Sch P; SC; Var C; Tr; ROTC A; Keyettes; WW; Academic Achv, AF Assn; Fla St U; Computer Tech.

STEVENSON, Mary Yvonne
Fort Walton Beach HS; Fort Walton Beach, FL (50-670) Anchor C; Band; Parl, BC; Chor; SC; ROTC A; Bus Adm.

STEVENSON, Monica Mary
George O Robinson HS; Santurce, PR (1-48) F-Ed, Lit Mag; Secy, Math C; Mu Alpha Theta; NHS; Pres, Jr Cl; NEDT; Math Fair Semi-Fin; Photojourn.

STEVENSON, Rebecca Lynn
N Mesquite HS; Mesquite, TX; Tres, FHA; Span C; E Tex St U; Bus.

STEVENSON, Roslyn Roberta
Cardinal Spellman HS; New York, NY; Hmrm; SC; COM; Sal; Afro-Amer C; Social Committee; Sociology.

STEVENSON, Samuel F
Crenshaw HS; Los Angeles, CA; Dbte Tm; Drama; Orch; Spch C; St Stu Congress; MVP, Tnns; Spch A.

STEVENSON, Sara Lynn
Chantilly Secondary Sch; Chantilly, VA (43-333) Drama; NHS; SC; Thes; VP, Y-Tns; Sftbl; COM; Vlbl; Drama Medal; Acad Schol, Stephens Col; Stephens Col; Early Ed.

STEVENSON, Simone Paris
Walt Whitman HS; Bethesda, MO; SC; 8 Yrs, Wash Dance Center; Duke U; Counscling.

STEVENSON, Virginia Dianne
Weir HS; Weir, MS (2-50) Bus Mgr, Ann; S-T, BC; Chor; Rptr, Jr Cl; S-T, Soph Cl; Bio A; H of F; Swtht; Gen Bus A; Most Dignified Sr; Miss St U; Med Tech.

STEVENSON, William Alan
Clarence Kimball HS; Royal Oak, MI (41-678) COM; Yth Fel; Mich St U; Bus Adm.

STEVERS, Karla Jo
Newell Providence HS; Newell, IA (9-29) Ann; Cpt, Chldr; Chor; Rptr, FHA; Pres, 4H; Sch P; Tres, SC; VP, Sr Cl; 4H A; HQn; Lion A; WW; Des Moines Area Comm Col; Dietetic Tech.

STEVES, Daniel Martin
Glens Falls HS; Glens Falls, NY (50-286) Chor; InterClub Coun; Sch P; Sci C; Parl, SC; Regent Schol; Yth Fel; Regional Win, Ntl Fr; Clarkson Col of Tech; Elec Engr.

STEWARD, Jaleena Kay
North HS; Omaha, NE (120-430) Choir; Lat C; Rainbow; VP, Church Yth Group; Past Advisor, Rain Bow for Girls; Grand Rep, ND Rain Bow; Grnd Flag Bearer for Nebra Rainbow; *Northeast Tech Col; Deaf Ed.*

STEWARD, James Edward Jr
Denison HS; Denison, TX (50%-450) Choir; Bsbl; Bkbl; Ftbl; Golf; Tr; Yth Fel; *SE St U; Bus.*

STEWARDSON, Judy Lynn
Virgie HS; Virgie, KY (5-100) BC; VP, Chem C; Choir; FTA; Ger C; 4H; VP, Hmrm; Math C; Secy, SC; VP, Jr Cl; Sftbl; COM; 4H A; Hon Prog; Sci A; Swtht; Type A; *U of Ky; Pre-Law.*

STEWART, Alphonse Jennings
University City Sr HS; University City, MO (66-450) Mgr, Bsbl; School A; Dual Degree Prog Schol; Full Tuition Sch, Morris Brown Col; *Morris Brown Col; Civil Engr.*

STEWART, Becky Lynn
Georgia Christian HS; Dasher, GA; Band; BC; 4H; 4H A.

STEWART, Ben Hayden
Sidney Lanier HS; Austin, TX (120-476) Ftbl; Tr; *Abilene Christian U; Engr.*

STEWART, Brenda Gail
Eupora HS; Eupora, MS (3-85) A-Ed, Ann; BC; Rptr, FBLA; FTA; VP, FTA; Hmrm; SC; Star Student; *Wood Jr Col; Bus.*

STEWART, Bryan Douglas
Northwest Classen HS; Oklahoma City, OK (1%-500) Chess C; Ger C; VP, Key C; Tres, Math C; Tres, Mu Alpha Theta; NHS; Tres, Span C; Var C; Co-Cpt, Tnns; Math A; *Okla U; Meteorology.*

STEWART, Carolyn Elizabeth
N Augusta Sr HS; N Augusta, SC; InterClub Coun; Bus Mgr, Lit Mag; NHS; A-Ed, Sch P; Q&S A; *Baylor U; Religious Ed.*

STEWART, Christopher Mark
Dover HS; Dover, OK (1-23) Semi-Fin, BS; CYO; Secy, FFA; NHS; SC; Pres, Jr Cl; Tres, Soph Cl; Bkbl; HCt; Okla Hon Soc; Supt HR; Cl Scholastic A; *Okla St U; Agr.*

STEWART, Clay Lynn
Beach Sr HS; Savannah, GA (1-325) Math C; NHS; Sci C; Tnns; Alg A; Bio A; COM; Cl Fav; Gov Honor Prog; Hist A; Hon Prog; Sci A; Industrial Arts A; WW; *West Point Acad; Sci.*

STEWART, David Bryan
Kellogg Sr HS; Little Canada, MN (229-527) Band; Drama; Span C; Thes.

STEWART, David Byron
Rundlett Jr HS; Concord, NH (10%-422) Ski C; Soccer; Tnns; *Archt.*

STEWART, Debra Ann
Kingsbury HS; Memphis, TN (91-210) VP, FHA; S-T, Hmrm; InterClub Coun; *Kingsbury School; Secy.*

STEWART, Debra Kay
Portageville HS; Portageville, MO (3-76) Ed, Ann; Band; Fr C; Rptr, FNA; Pres, FTA; Cpt, Mjrte; Secy, NHS; Rptr, NHS; WW; WW, Mus; Top 10; Photographer, Sch P; All Division Band; Band A; *SE Mo St U; Eng.*

STEWART, Dedra Kay
Theodore F Riggs HS; Pierre, SD (7-260) Choir; Ensm; Monogram; F-Ed, Sch P; Span C; Tnns; COM; Q&S A; *Stetson U; Med Tech.*

STEWART, Dennis D
South Plainfield HS; South Plainfield, NJ (50-350) Band; Ger C; NHS; Orch; Order/Arrow; ARC; Sch P; Hist A; Pres, Treas, Explorer Post 10; MYF; Eagle Sct with Palm; Tres, Luth Yth Leg; Expl Post 108; Pres, VP, Tres, Jerseymn Hist Soc; *Rutgers Col; Pol Sci.*

STEWART, Donald Dean
South Plainfield HS; South Plainfield, NJ (70-347) Band; Ger C; Orch; Secy, Order/Arrow; Eagle Sct; Explorer's Pres Assn; Towtown Jerseymen Hist Soc; S Plainfield Hist Soc; S-T, Lutheran Yth Organization; *Rutgers Col; Econ.*

STEWART, Donna Elaine
Lake Clifton Sr HS; Baltimore, MD (1-350) Chem C; Lit Mag; NHS; Sci C; Span C; VP, SC; COM; Hon Prog; Ntl Achv Schol; *Chatham Col; Chem.*

STEWART, Elizabeth Anne
Keyser HS; Keyser, WV (6-242) Pres, Lat C; NHS; F-Ed, Sch P; DARGCA; Hist A; Yth Fel; *Potomac St Col; Secondary Ed.*

STEWART, Elizabeth Jane
Woodsboro HS; Woodsboro, TX (1-70) Rptr, Ann; Band; Ensm; FTA; NHS; Sch P; SC; Band A; NMS; UIL Solo & Ensm; TMEA All St, Dist, Reg, Area Bands; All Star Cust, UIL; *Baylor U; Mus.*

STEWART, Elizabeth Jane
Carlisle HS; Carlisle, OH (10%-200) A Cap Choir; Band; Choir; NHS; VP, SC; Tnns; Pres, GSct; Band, Choir A's; 1st Cl GSct; *Wooster Col; Environmental Stu.*

STEWART, Ellen Patrice
Mercy HS; Albany, NY (2-135) Chldr; Drama; InterAct C; Lat C; Sftbl; Tnns; Hon Prog; Prom Comm.

STEWART, Gregory Bryan
Robert E Lee HS; Tyler, TX; Hmrm; Order/Arrow; Span C; SC; JV, Bkbl; Hon Prog; Order/Arrow A; Hon Stu; Eagle Sct; *Tex Christian U; Ed.*

STEWART, Gwendolyn Elizabeth
Marion HS; Lake Charles, LA; Band; Bus C; FBLA; Cpt, Mjrte; Tr; Delta Sigma Theta A; HCt; Spch A; Swtht; Type A; *Sou La U; Early Childhood.*

STEWART, James Thompson
Donald E Gavit HS; Hammond, IN (24-245) Hmrm; NHS; Sch P; Sci A; St Scholar; ISU Academic Schol; Graphic Arts C; WW; Teacher's Asst; *Ind St U; Printing Mgt.*

STEWART, Jan Leslie
E Peoria Comm HS; E Peoria, IL (5-400) Tres, Chem C; Pres, Fr C; NHS; Sch P; COM; JA A; St Scholar; *Augustana Col; Sci.*

STEWART, Janice Barron
Tift Co HS; Tifton, GA (5%-400) Band; Pres, BC; Drama; Fr C; French NHS; Fin, GS; InterClub Coun; NHS; COM; Hon Prog; *Berry Col; Special Ed.*

STEWART, Jeanne Ellen
Pinckneyville Comm Col; Pinckneyville, IL (8-161) Chldr; Fr C; Ch, FHA; NHS; Spch C; Var C; Bkbl; MVP, Sftbl; Tnns; Tr; Hon Prog; Most Out; ARC A; Spch A; Drama A; *Nurs.*

STEWART, Jerilyn Jo
Valentine HS; Valentine, NE; Chldr; FTA; Var C; Tres, Soph Cl; Tr; Yth Fel; Vlbl; *Dental Asst.*

STEWART, Karen Arlene
Hitchcock HS; Hitchcock, TX (2-130) Band; Chess C; Drama; Ensm; Secy, Ger C; Mjrte; Sal; Spch A; Yth Fel; Ger, HR, A's; Drum Major; *Sam Houston St U; Elem Ed.*

STEWART, Karen Elizabeth
Doss HS; Louisville, KY; Drama; Orch; JV, Ftbl; Tr; Church Sftbl; *Jefferson Comm Col; Sociology.*

STEWART, Karen Lynn
Upperman HS; Baxter, TN; Ann; BC; Dbte Tm; Drama; Fr C; FHA; 4H; Math C; NFL; ARC; Sch P; Spch C; Thes; Amer Leg Orator A; COM; Citz A; 4H A; Hist A; Q&S A; Spch A; VFW A; *Tenn Tech U; Phar.*

STEWART, Kathryn Rose
Sooner HS; Bartlesville, OK (48-280) A Cap Choir; Band; Community Yth Symph; Ensm; FBLA; Madrigal; Orch; COM; Citz A; Yth Fel; John P Sousa A; *U of Okla; Mus Ed.*

STEWART, Kathy Jo
Winfield HS; Winfield, KS (15-180) Band; Ensm; Tres, Orch; S-T, Sr Cl; S-T, Soph Cl; Bkbl; Hon Prog; *Emporia Kans St U; Acct.*

STEWART, Kimberly Anne
Parsons Sr HS; Parsons, KS (30-202) NHS; *Tulsa U; Psych.*

STEWART, Lisa Joy
Jackson Central Merry HS; Jackson, TN (124-494) Band; BC; Choir; Ensm; Mjrte; Sftbl; Math A; Type A; *U of Tenn; Med.*

STEWART, Malcolm Alexzander
Benedictine HS; Cleveland, OH (30-114) Cr-Ctry; Hockey; Tr; *Wheeling Col; Clinical Sci.*

STEWART, Marcus Anthony
E E Smith Sr HS; Fayetteville, NC; Band; Choir; Tres, Fr C; Key C; Cr-Ctry; Sftbl; Tr; COM; ROTC A; VFW A; VofDEM; Semi-Fin, COM; Fin, Mus A; Semi-Fin, VFW A; Semi-Fin, V of D; Fin, ROTC A; *McNeese St U; Mortuary Sci.*

STEWART, Margaret Ann
Northern Heights HS; Allen, KS (1-45) Pres, 4H; Model UN; NHS; Alg A; Bio A; Chem A; Citz A; 4H A; Hist A; Math A; PTA A; Sci A; Spch A; Type A; VFW A; VFW Orator Win; VofDEM; Yth Fel; Jr Acad of Sci; Americus Days 77 Board; Sci Fair As; United Presbyterian Yth Pres; *Home Ec.*

STEWART, Mark Edward
S Choctaw Acad; Toxey, AL (2-26) BC; Pres, Jr Cl; Ftbl.

STEWART, Mark Sheldon
Plant City HS; Plant City, FL (74-527) Tres, Band; Ensm; NHS; Orch; Bkbl; Golf; Sftbl; Swim; Wrest; *U of S Fla; Bus.*

STEWART, Martha Lear
Union Co HS; Morganfield, KY (6-213) Band; BC; Chldr; Drama; Fr C; FHA; 4H; Fin, Jr Miss Pagent; S-T, Math C; NHS; SC; MLS; Spch A; Type A; Band, Outst Fresh, A's; *Lambuth Col; Bus.*

STEWART, Mary Lynn
Banks HS; Birmingham, AL; Chor; FBLA; Orch; Bus Mgr, Sch P; Q&S A; Chaplain, Band; *Samford U; Bus.*

STEWART, Michael Warden
Winston Churchill HS; Potomac, MD (8-588) Bkbl; Ftbl; Tr; 4H A; Sch A's.

STEWART, Micheah Warden
Winston Churchill HS; Potomac, MD; Var C; Bkbl; JV, Ftbl; Tr; 4H A; Pres A; 4-H Safety A; MVP Sftbl.

STEWART, Michele Robin
Castlemont HS; Oakland, CA; Chor; NHS; Bkbl; Sftbl; CSF; Yth Vol; *UC Davis; Med.*

STEWART, Monica Faye
Woodlawn HS; Shreveport, LA (3-450) Dbte Tm; Ch, Sftbl; Swim; Tnns; *Fisk U; Model.*

STEWART, Nancy Ann
Plant City HS; Plant City, FL; ARC; COM; Citz A; Hon Prog; Tns for Christ; Bible Sch Teacher; *Eckerd Col; Child Psych.*

STEWART, Patricia Gail
Osceola HS; Kissimmee, FL (90-260) Mgr, Chldr; Drama; Ensm; Span C; SC; Thes; Tri-HiY; Cpt, Ftbl; Sftbl; Yth Fel; Yth Leg; Yth Coun; *U of S Fla; Elem Ed.*

STEWART, Peter Jackson
Richard J Reynolds HS; Winston-Salem, NC (125-830) Lat C; Bsbl; Ftbl; Swim; Wrest; Good & Country A; Yth Fel; 1st Pl, NC Archt Drafting A; Outing C; *Archt.*

STEWART, Reagan Alan
Winnfield Sr HS; Winnfield, LA; Anchor C; Band; BC; Pres, FBLA; FFA; 4H; Math C; VP, Sch P; SC; Pres, Var C; Bsbl; Bkbl; Ftbl; Tr; Hist, FTA; Beau; WW; Outst Forester, FFA; *LSU; Commercial Banking.*

STEWART, Regina Grace
N Hall HS; Gainesville, GA (100-200) Band; Chor; 4H; Mjrte; WW; Chor Off.

STEWART, Robert Daniel
Florence HS; Florence, MS; Ann; Chem C; Chess C; Drama; FFA; 4H; Sci C; Bsbl; Cpt, Ftbl; Tr; Cl Fav; 4H A; *Miss St U; Forestry.*

STEWART, Robert Stanley
Bethel Sr HS; Spanaway, WA (10%-600) Band; Chess C; Tnns; Tnns, Most Improved; *Central Wash St; Mus.*

STEWART, Ronda Dee
Monterey HS; Lubbock, TX (25%-689) Band; Bus Mgr, Chor; FHA; Type A; *Tex Tech U; Elem Ed.*

STEWART, Sandra Lynn
Hattiesburg HS Rowan Center; Hattiesburg, MS (5%-500) Band; Mu Alpha Theta; SC; Alg A; Hon Prog; *William Carey Col; Math.*

STEWART, Shiela Lynn
Osceola HS; Kissimmee, FL; Band; Cpt, Chldr; Drama; Ensm; Thes; Tri-HiY; Amer Leg A; COM; Yth Fel; Superior Band A; Yth Coun.

STEWART, Shirley Genese
W Morgan HS; Trinity, AL (10%-59) BC; Tres, FHA; Tres, Jr Cl; Home Ec A; PA; *Calhoun Comm Col; Home Ec.*

STEWART, Susan Kay
Cadiz HS; Cadiz, OH (14-136) Band; 4H; Span C; Co-Cpt, Bkbl; Hist A; Modern Authors A; *Jefferson Co Tech Col; Acct.*

**STEWART,
Susan Mary Elizabeth**
Kearsarge Regional HS; South Sutton, NH (98-150) Fr C; FNA; Hmrm; Sch P; Ski C; Cr-Ctry; JV, Hockey; Sftbl; JV, Tnns; Pres, VP, Sec, Tres, Rainbow Grls.

STEWART, Susan Patricia
Thomas Jefferson HS; Pittsburgh, PA; Band; NHS; Bkbl; Ftbl; Golf; Sftbl; Swim; Tnns; Hon Prog; *Bus.*

STEWART, Teresa Kathleen
Lanier HS; Austin, TX; FHA; Mgr, Bkbl; *Abilene Christian U; Homemaking.*

STEWART, Terrie Lynn
Butler RV HS; Butler, MO (4-90) AFS; VP, CYO; Fr C; Tres, FBLA; S-T, 4H; Rptr, NHS; Tres, Span C; Secy, Sr Cl; Tr; Alg A; Bio A; DARGCA; 4H A; HCt; Hon Prog; Parl, FBLA; Soph Pilgrim; *Central Mo St U; Bus.*

STEWART, Terry Gaye
Temple Baptist Acad; Denver, CO (4-11) Ed, Ann; Cpt, Chldr; Chor; Ensm; NHS; Sftbl; HCt; Pres A; Cpt, MVP, Vlbl; Asst Teacher; *Pacific Coast Baptist Bible Col; Christian Ed.*

STEWART, Teryl L
Gadsden HS; Gadsden, AL (50-350) A Cap Choir; Ann; Tres, Band; Fr C; HiY; Church Jr Choir Director; *Art.*

STEWART, Walter Mark
Cuyahoga Valley Christian Acad; Cuyahoga Falls, OH (1-31) Band; Orch; SC; VP, Sr Cl; Tr; Amer Leg A; Hist A; NEDT; Sal; Chrysler A; WW; Eng A; *Oral Roberts U; Med.*

STEWART, Wendy Sue
Cary-Grove HS; Cary, IL; Band; NHS; Sch P; Span C; Hon Prog; *Northern U; Dietetics.*

STEWMAN, Janet Louise
Patten Acad of Chris Ed; Oakland, CA (2-11) A Cap Choir; Chem C; Chor; Community Yth Symph; Dbte Tm; Drama; Madrigal; Orch; Spch C; Tres, SC; Bsbl; Soccer; Sftbl; Citz A; Silver 'A'; *Ed.*

ST GERMAIN, Leonard Carlton
Sanford Acad; Sanford, MS (33%-11) Ann; BC; FFA; 4H; Pres, Hmrm; Sch P; VP, SC; Pres, Jr Cl; Bkbl; Ftbl; Tr; HCt; Most Valuable Back; *LSU; Elec.*

STIANCHE, Thomas Joseph
Marian Cath HS; Tamaqua, PA (52-176) Bsbl; Bkbl; Ftbl; Varsity Ltrs; Ftbl Specialist A; 1st Hon; *Williamsport Area Comm Col; Elec Construction.*

STIANSEN, Gregg Martin
Tottenville HS; Staten Island, NY (115-1058) *Wagner Col; Bus Adm.*

STICE, Dianne Kay
E Peoria Comm HS; E Peoria, IL (17-450) AFS; FBLA; Lat C; Sch P; Type A; Shorthand Speedtakes A; *Ill St U; Secy.*

STICE, Ralph Warren
High Point HS; Beltsville, MD; Band; Soph Cl; Sftbl; Church Ensm; *U of Miami; Broadcasting.*

STICHAK, Mary Catherine
John S Fine HS; Nanticoke, PA (15-297) Co-Ed, Ann; Var C; Math A; *Luzerne Co Comm Col; Off Sci Tech.*

STICHNOTH, Carri Ann
Milford Township HS; Milford, IL (25%-75) *Danville Jr Col; Med Secy.*

STICKEL, Nancy Leigh
Durham Acad Upper Sch; Durham, NC (3-46) Chldr; Ed, Lit Mag; Rptr, Sch P; SC; Bkbl; MVP, Sftbl; Tnns; NMS; *Interntl Stu.*

STICKLER, Lisa Nanette
United Township HS; E Moline, IL (52-700) Drama; 4H; Tr; 4H A; Hon Prog; Close-Up; *U of Ill; Home Ec.*

STICKLER, Steven Lynn
Hazelwood Central HS; Florissant, MO;

STICKLES, Deborah J
James B Conant HS; Hoffman Estates, IL (33%-430) Chldr; Hmrm; SC; Secy, Sr Cl; COM; Pres A; *Palatue Sch of Beauty Culture; Cosmotology.*

STICKLIN, Michael J
Wellsboro Sr HS; Wellsboro, PA (15-219) Ger C; Pres, Hmrm; NHS; SC; JV, Bkbl; Cr-Ctry; Tr; Wrest; COM; Hon Prog; VFW A; *Mansfield St Col; Criminal Justice.*

STICKLIN, Michael Joseph
Wellsboro Sr HS; Wellsboro, PA (15-219) Ger C; Pres, Hmrm; NHS; SC; JV, Bkbl; Cr-Ctry; Tr; Wrest; Hon Prog; VFW A; *Mansfield St Col; Criminal Justice.*

STIDHAM, Jennifer Marie
Bartow Sr HS; Bartow, FL (7-300) Ch, Anchor C; Drama; Parl, FHA; Semi-Fin, GS; Hmrm; NHS; Span C; SC; Tnns; Beauty; Hon Prog; Pres Phys Fitness A; *Stetson U; Financing.*

STIEFEL, Cynthia Lane
Geraldine HS; Geraldine, AL; Band; BC; FTA; 4H A; VP, Lib C; *U of Ala; Med.*

STIEHL, James Edward
Wanamingo Pub HS; Wanamingo, MN (4-40) Band; Drama; Math C; NHS; Phys C; SC; Cpt, Bkbl; Ftbl; Tr; HCt; *Winona Voc Col; Aviation Mech.*

STIEMKE, David Walter
Watertown HS; Watertown, WI; Ger C; Var C; Ftbl; Swim; Tnns; Math A; Sci A; *Hist.*

STIER, Barbara Lynn
Rio Americano HS; Sacramento, CA (20-450) A Cap Choir; NHS; Ski C; SC; Sftbl; CSF; MGM; Powder Puff Ftbl; 'S' C; Stu Govt Board; Vlbl; *UC San Luis Obispo; Landscape Archt.*

STIER, Laura Jane
Central Jersey Christian Sch; Asbury Park, NJ; Cpt, Chldr; Chor; Hmrm; S-T, SC; Co-Cpt, Bkbl; Sftbl; Alg A; HCt; Math A; Sal; Tres, SC; Hiking C; Candystriper; *Nurs.*

STIERHOFF, Ron L
Norwalk HS; Norwalk, OH; A Cap Choir; Chor; Bkbl; Ftbl; Tres, Luther League; *Religion.*

STIERS, Lisa V'Lea
Hermann HS; Hermann, MO (32-125) Band; Secy, 4H; NHS; 4H A; Hon Prog; Pres A; Yth Fel; Candystriper A; *Nurs.*

STIFFLER, Ruth Marie
Field HS; Mogadore, OH (16-270) Ensm; 4H; NHS; Sftbl; 4H A.

STIFFLER, Terry Brian
Defiance HS; Defiance, OH (45-365) JV, Ftbl; Hon Prog; Bible Quiz Trophy; *U of Cincinnati; Law.*

STILES, Joe Alan
Wichita E HS; Wichita, KS (180-525) Fr C; SC; *Wichita St U; Psych.*

STILES, Lillian
W Carteret HS; Morehead City, NC; Band; Bus C; Chor; Drama; Span C; HCt; Most Out; Secy, Black Awareness; Secy, Crusaders for Christ; Candidate, Cotillion Qn; Cpt A, Flagcorp; Qn of Hearts A; *Durham Col; Med Lab.*

STILES, Myrna Jo
Broken Bow HS; Broken Bow, OK (4-140) Parl, FHA; Secy, NHS; B Crocker A; MLS; Yth Fel; Co-ed Correspondent; *E Central St U; Environmental Sci.*

STILES, Rebecca Joyce
N Gwinnett HS; Suwanee, GA (10%-190) BC; FHA; COM; Sci A; *Gainesville Jr; Science.*

STILES, Robert Louis
Hillcrest HS; Ctry Club Hills, IL (47-379) Sci C; Cr-Ctry; Tr; *Eastern Col; Bus.*

STILES, Syndee Kaye
Mineral Wells HS; Mineral Wells, TX (5%-340) Band; Drama; Sci C; SC; Bio A; DARGCA; Hist A; Math A; Sci A; Zee C; Lutheran Yth Organization; VP, Heart of Tex GSct Coun; Eng A; *Tex A&M U; Bio.*

STILL, Delise Kay
Lufkin HS; Lufkin, TX (110-500) Co-Ch, A Cap Choir; Chor; Drama; Span C; Writing A; *Baylor U.*

STILLER, Jon Paul
University HS; San Diego, CA (21-311) Rptr, Sch P; CSF; Hon Prog; Most Out; *San Diego St U; Hist.*

STILLER, Susan Leslie
Minnetonka HS; Minnetonka, MN; Chor; Orch; Comm Theatre; Puppetry; Coun, YMCA Camp Christmas Tree.

STILLEY, Ricky Dale
Vandalia Christian Sch; Greensboro, NC (3-14) Ann; Chem C; Chor; Rptr, Sch P; Bkbl; *UNGG; Photography.*

STILLIONS, Clarence Leonard
McDonald Co R-1 HS; Anderson, MO (21-180) Ed, Ann; Band; Drama; Ch, FTA; NHS; Sch P; Pres, Span C; Spch C; Rptr, SC; Thes; Bsbl; JV, Golf; JV, Tnns; JV, Tr; Bio A; Cl Fav; Hist A; Hon Prog; Journ A; Sci A; Spch A; Type A; FTA Stu Teacher; Weekly Columnist, Co Newspaper; *Crowder Col; Hospital Adm.*

STILLMAN, Allen Lynn
Lafayette HS; St Joseph, MO (150-290) Bkbl; Cr-Ctry; Co-Cpt, Tr; *NE Mo St U; Phys Ed.*

STILLS, Natalie Regenia
Smith HS; Atlanta, GA (10-145) Bus C; Chldr; Chess C; Dbte Tm; NHS; Secy, Sci C; Golf; Tr; HCt; JA A; Bus Ed A; Creative Dancing A; *Secretarial Sci.*

STILLWELL, Sylvia Jean
Central-Mid-Hi-Sch; Norman, OK; Band; Pres, Rainbow; Yth Fel; *Okla U; Writing.*

STILTNER, Sharon
Defiance Sr HS; Defiance, OH (81-365) Bible Quiz A; Stu o-t Wk; Art Project A; Art Crew, HS Play; *Advertising.*

STILWELL, Jill Renae
Viroqua Area HS; Viroqua, WI; Chor; Tres, FHA; 4H; Secy, Span C; Pres A; *Spch Pathology.*

STIMITS, Monica Ann
Evadale HS; Evadale, TX (2-30) Band; Chem C; Chess C; Drama; FHA; Math C; Spch C; Bkbl; Tr; Spch A; Type A; Twiler; Vlbl; *Lamar U.*

STIMITS, Roy Alan
Evadale HS; Evadale, TX (6-43) Band; Chess C; Drama; JV, Bkbl; JV, Ftbl; Drama A; *Lamar U.*

STIMSON, Harriet Anne
Central HS; Knoxville, TN (19-382) BC; Chor; Ensm; NHS; Sci C; Tri-HiY; Bio A; Citz A; *E Tenn St U; Environmental Health.*

STINCHCOMB, Bobby Lee
Webster HS; Tulsa, OK (7-243) Lat C; NHS; SC; Bsbl; Bkbl; Ftbl; PTA A; *Northeastern Okla A&M U; Engr.*

STINE, Bradley Joseph
Pinole Valley HS; Pinole, CA (22-500) AFS; Order/Arrow; Sci C; CSF; Order/Arrow A; Eagle Sct; Gen Mgr, Radio C; *U of Calif; Engr.*

STINE, Ellen Marie
Hershey Sr HS; Hershey, PA (30-275) Band; Chldr; Chor; Fr C; ARC; Rptr, Sch P; *Fr.*

STINE, Jeffrey Richard
Cumberland Valley HS; Mechanicsburg, PA (105-625) Pres, Demolay; VP, Order/Arrow; ARC; JV, Bsbl; JV, Swim; God & Country A; Exceptional Service A's; Police Dept; Bicentennial Service A's; *Shippensburg St Col; Law Enforcement.*

STINE, Karen Marie
Waynesboro Area Sr HS; Waynesboro, PA (90-365) Band; FTA; GS; Hmrm; SC; Tr; HCt; Wrest Qn; *Mont Alto Col; Elem Ed.*

STINES, Melody Jean
Potter Pub HS; Potter, NE (8-14) Band; Chor; Sch P; SC; S-T, Var C; Bsbl; Tr; HCt; MVP, All St, Vlbl; *Kearney St Col; Bus.*

STINGLEY, Michael Deprieste
Lanier HS; Jackson, MS; Var C; JV, Ftbl; Elk A; Star Grit Salesman; Elks Jr Exalter Ruler; Intern Breakfast C; *Jackson St U; Phys Ed.*

STINSON, David Allen
Stephen Decatur HS; Decatur, IL (31-340) Rptr, Sch P; Tnns; Mgr, Wrest; *Mich Christian Col; Acct.*

STINSON, Donna Jean
Ahrens HS; Louisville, KY; FBLA; Hmrm; NHS; SC; Type A.

STINSON, Duane Michael
Buffalo HS; Buffalo, OK (10-30) Band; FFA; Bkbl; Ftbl; Tr; COM; Cl Fav; Okla U; Aviation.

STINSON, Myron Alfred
Central HS; Flint, MI; Bsbl; Bkbl; Ftbl; Swim; Wrest.

STINSON, Pamela Faye
St Jude Cath HS; Montgomery, AL (9-52) 4H; NHS; Co-Ed, Sch P; Secy, SC; Sftbl; Hon Prog; Most Out; Sci A; Art A; Ala St U; Law.

STINSON, Pamela Gene
Beth Haven Christian Sch; Louisville, KY; Rainbow; Co-Cpt, Bkbl; Swim; Yth Fel; U of Louisville; Med.

STINSON, Steven Matthew
Salina HS S; Salina, KS (10%-300) Monogram; SC; Bkbl; JV, Ftbl; Tr; Varsity Tr Record; U of Kans.

STINSON, Vivian C
E Atlanta HS; Atlanta, GA (4-142) Fisk U; Nurs.

STIPANOVIC, Theodore Joseph
Chaminade Col Prep; St Louis, MO (44-128) Var C; Ftbl; Cpt, Tr.

STIPP, Teresa Elaine
Robert E Lee HS; Midland, TX; Fr C; FTA; NHS; Hon Prog; Spch A; Exporers; Abilene Christian Col.

STIRMELL, Donnette Patricia
Rolling Meadows HS; Rolling Meadows, IL (369-631) Chor; FTA; Rptr, Hmrm; SC; Var C; Swim; Yth Fel; Attendance off Guide & Aide; Church Acolyte; Church Choir; Christian Ed Comm.

STITELER, William Hughson
Dan River HS; Ringgold, VA (100-250) Pres, FFA; Span C; Parl, SC; FFA St Farmer Degree; FFA Chapter Ldrship A; Danville Comm Col; Elec.

STITES, Judy Ann
Foothill HS; Sacramento, CA; Band; Ch, Social, Publicity; American River Col; Bus.

STITES, Vicki Sue
Rantoul Township HS; Rantoul, IL (50-350) Chor; Hmrm; Span C; SC; Tres, Jr Cl; HCt; Pres, Jr Luther League; Parkland Col; Bus.

STITH, Kathleen Sue
Madison C-3 HS; Madison, MO (5-29) BC; Chor; FHA; 4H; Rptr, Sch P; Sci C; Pres, SC; Var C; Sftbl; Tr; HCt; Yrbk Qn.

STITH, Robert Glenn
Rosedale HS; Rosedale, IN (8-69) BS; Pres, 4H; Lat C; Model UN; NHS; VP, Sr Cl; Rptr, Jr Cl; Gr Marshal; 4H A; Math A; Head Var Mgr; Rose-Holman Col; Mech Engr.

STITLE, Mark David
Western Hills HS; Ft Worth, TX (119-547) Rptr, Ann; Ger C; Co-Cpt, Ftbl; Tr; Opt A; Tex Tech; Phys Ed.

STITT, Kathy Jo
Chadron HS; Chadron, NE (21-81) Pres, Band; Ch, Bus C; Cpt, Chldr; FTA; Fin, GS; NHS; Bkbl; Tr; HQn; VP, Luther League; Demolay Swtht; All Conf Vlbl; Outst Jr & Sr, Band; Jr Princess; Job's Daughters; Chadron St Col; Sci.

STITT, Shirley Marie
W Sr HS; Baltimore, MD (307-790) Tres, Drama; Hmrm; Jr Miss Pagent; SC; Up Bound; Cl A; Hon Prog; Ntl Conf Chr & Jews; St Ldrship Workshop; Va St Col; Special Ed.

STIVERS, Kimberly Diane
Eastern HS; Middletown, KY (33%-300) Ann; BC; Fr C; COM; Cl Fav; U; Presch Ed.

STJERNHOLM, Paul David
South HS; Pueblo, CO (4-527) Band; BS; Ftbl; Masonic A; Most Out; NMF; Regent Schol; Rotary A; Ldr, Young Life; St Olaf Col; Pre-Med.

ST JOHN, Robert William
James I O'Neill HS; Highland Falls, NY (23-149) Pres, Band; NHS; Span C; Soccer; Wrest; H of F; Regent Schol; Band, Mus Theory, A's; Co Mus Ed Assn Schol; US Collegiate Wind Band; Yth Soloist, Hudson Valley Philharm; St U of NY; Mus Performance.

ST LOUIS, Micheal Wayne
Norco Sr HS; Norco, CA; Calif St U; Sci.

ST MARIE, Peter Michael
Windham HS; Willimantic, CT; Band; Chem C; Drama; Orch; Thes; Computer Engr.

STOAKES, Carl Ralph
Rogers HS; Michigan City, IN; Band; Chor; Demolay; Drama; NHS; Swim; Jr Concessions; Outst Newspaper Carrier; Purdue N Central Col; Archt.

STOBER, Elaine Carol
Cleveland HS; Reseda, CA; Chor; 4H; Treas, GSct; Letter Girls; ISSO; Outst Achv, Horticulture I; C; Pierce Col Woodland Hills; Horticulture.

STOCK, Dana Christina
Centralia HS; Centralia, IL; Chor; Ensm; Ger C; Madrigal; Thes; 4H A; Pres, Yth For Christ; Tres, Choir Coun; F-Ed, Church Newsltr.

STOCK, Mark Allen
Troy HS; Troy, KS (7-40) F-Ed, Ann; Rptr, FFA; F-Ed, Sch P; S-T, SC; Pres, Soph Cl; Bkbl; Ftbl; Tr; Amer Leg A; FFA Star Greenhand.

STOCK, Paula Jean
Marysville-Pilchuck HS; Marysville, WA (3-385) GS; Hmrm; Secy, NHS; Rainbow; Var C; Tres, Jr Cl; Bkbl; Cr-Ctry; Soccer; Tr; Citz A; Hon Prog; Masonic A; Math A; NMF; Girl o-t Mo; Trustee Schol; U of Puget Sound; Phys Therapy.

STOCK, Ryan Lee
Meridian HS; Bellingham, WA (50%-100) Band; Var C; Cr-Ctry; Tr.

STOCKDALE, Lori Ann
John F Kennedy HS; Cedar Rapids, IA; Band; Drama; Rptr, Hmrm; Orch; Bkbl; Swim; Tnns; Citz A; Yth Fel; Phys Therapy.

STOCKDILL, Juli Beth
Northwood HS; Silver Spring, MD; Chldr; Drama; NHS; SC; COM; Hon Prog; 1st Cl, GSct; Cystic Fibrosis Service A; U of Colo; Dance Therapy.

STOCKDILL, Linda Lea
Norwin Sr HS; N Huntingdon, PA (308-780) Yth Fel; Bradford Sch; Acct.

STOCKHOUSE, Bruce Claar
Riverton HS; Riverton, WY (5-235) A Cap Choir; Band; BS; Chor; Demolay; Drama; Ensm; Madrigal; Pres, NFL; Pres, NHS; Order/Arrow; Ski C; VP, Thes; Order/Arrow A; Spch A; All St Choir; BSct World Jamboree; U of Wyom; Pre-Med.

STOCKHOUSE, Heidi Ann
Riverton HS; Riverton, WY (20-285) Band; Chldr; Chor; 4H; Hmrm; Madrigal; Ski C; Spch C; Thes; Secy, Jr Cl; SC; Cpt, Bkbl; Tr; Tres, Pep C; Vlbl; U of Wy; Ed.

STOCKIN, Daniel Gordon
San Marcos HS; Santa Barbara, CA (5%-650) Bkbl; CSF; COM; Sci A; Cpt, Vlbl; Westmont Col; Vet.

STOCKING, Karla Reed
Northwest HS; St Louis, MO; Drama; Tnns; Hon Prog; Yth Fel; Yth Choir; Stephens Col; Home Ec.

STOCKMAN, David Scott
Stevenson HS; Bronx, NY (28-814) FTA; NHS; COM; Hon Prog; Attendance A; Arista; Service A; Vol Tutor, Reading; Lehman Col; Lib Arts.

STOCKS, Gwendolyn
Aiken Sr HS; Cincinnati, OH (1-9) Band; Chor; Ger C; Secy, Jr Cl; Citz A; Drill Tm; Band A; Ger A; Clark Col; Bus.

STOCKS, Robert Howard
Mariner HS; Everett, WA; Band; Chor; Hmrm; Bsbl; Bkbl; COM; Cl Fav; Most Out; Star Student; Grand Rapids Sch o-t Bible & Mus; Music.

STOCKSLAGER, Sara Marie
Balaton Pub HS; Balaton, MN (21-42) Band; 4H; Vlbl; Health.

STOCKTON, Janet Eileen
Luther L Wright HS; Ironwood, MI (42-180) Secy, Fr C; Past Hon Qn, Jobs Daughters; William Woods Col; Secy.

STOCKWELL, Mark Robert
Wachusett Regional HS; Holden, MA; Fr C; Order/Arrow; JV, Ftbl; Tr; Order/Arrow A; Pres A; Yth Fel; Life Sct.

STOCKWELL, Mary Ann
Riverdale HS; Port Byron, IL (38-150) S-T, Ann; Cpt, Chldr; NHS; Ski C; S-T, SC; Var C; Sftbl; Tr; Amer Leg A; HCt; NE Mo St U; Spec Ed.

STODDARD, Stephanie Lea
Morrow Sr HS; Morrow, GA (8-385) BC; Hmrm; NHS; VP, SC; Bkbl; Tr; COM; Cl Fav; HCt; WSB Young Amer; Sci.

STODOLAK, Linda Sue
Wilmington Area HS; New Wilmington, PA (1-145) FTA; Lat C; Lat NHS; Cpt, Math C; NHS; WW; Most Scholarly; Penn St U; Acct.

STOECKER, Suzanne Louise
E Peoria Comm HS; E Peoria, IL (10-508) Tres, Chor; Ensm; Lat C; Madrigal; NFL; VP, Spch C; Pres, SC; Amer Leg Orator A; Citz A; Hon Prog; Opt A; Spch A; VFW Orator Win; VofDEM; U of Ill; Pre-Law.

STOECKLE, Diana Lee
Northgate HS; Pittsburgh, PA (22-160) Fr C; Hmrm; Pres, Span C; SC; VP, Jr Cl; Co-head, Drill Tm; Counselors A; Span-Fr Polyglot A; Allegheny Comm Col; Lang.

STOEL, Lorretta Grace
Luverne HS; Luverne, MN; Bookkeeping.

STOELKER, Dorothea Ann
Maple Shade HS; Maple Shade, NJ;

STOFFEL, Lynn Phyllis
Leesburg Sr HS; Leesburg, FL (33%-305) Band; 4H; Mjrte; Mod Mus Mas; Orch.

STOFFREGEN, Janice Carole
Litchfield HS; E Gadsden, AL (20-150) Ed, Ann; FHA; Hmrm; Sci C; SC; Explorers; Gadsden St Col.

STOFREGEN, Keith Gustave
Broken Bow HS; Broken Bow, OK (60-145) Band; Chor; Okla St U; Conservation of Resources.

STOGNER, Brian Lynn
Flint Central HS; Flint, MI (3-400) Band; Chess C; Pres, NHS; Bkbl; COM; Hon Prog; NMF; NMS; Drum Major; Hon Coun; WW; Mich Christian Col; Eng.

STOHS, Kristine E
LeRoy HS; LeRoy, KS (6-27) Ann; Band; Chor; Ensm; Secy, Sr Cl; Secy, Soph Cl; WW; Recognition A, Piano Accompanist; Emporia Kans St Col; Computer Sci.

STOHS, Linda J
LeRoy HS; LeRoy, KS (2-27) Bus Mgr, Ann; Band; Chor; Ensm; NHS; Pres, Sr Cl; Citz A; Hon Prog; Sal; St John's Col; Bus.

STOKES, Anne Lindsay
Central HS; Grand Cane, LA (3-15) Chldr; Lit Ral; NHS; Secy, SC; S-T, Jr Cl; Bkbl; Sftbl; Tr; Wittiest; All Dist Sftbl; NE La U; Phar.

STOKES, Brenda Faye
DuVal Sr HS; Lanham, MD (10%-600) Chor; Rptr, Hmrm; NHS; SC; Home Ec A; HR As; Med.

STOKES, Catherine Jeanette
D H Conley HS; Greenville, NC (1-223) Fr C; Rptr, FBLA; Hmrm; Mu Alpha Theta; Secy, NHS; Sci C; SC; Gr Marshal; Sci A; Accompanist, Choir; E Carolina U; Intermediate Ed.

STOKES, Evelyn Elaine
Rockdale Co HS; Conyers, GA (200-400) MVP, Band; Pres, FHA; Rptr, 4H; S-T, Span C; 4H A; Kiwanis A; MV Flag Corps Mem; Tift Col; Elem Ed.

STOKES, Gregory P
Marina HS; Huntington Beach, CA; Band; Fr C; Calif St Col; Ed.

STOKES, Jay Beauford
John Foster Dulles HS; Stafford, TX; Soccer; Livestock Show As; Rodeo Art A; Art.

STOKES, Linda
Star Valley HS; Afton, WY; Chem C; Chor; Drama; Fr C; FTA; Pres, Mjrte; Math C; NHS; Phys C; Sci C; Ski C; VP, 4H; 4H A; Hon Prog; NMF; Type A; Brigham Young U; Mech Engr.

STOKES,
Lisa Laine Oakdale Hs
Oakdale, LA; Chor; Ensm; FHA; 4H; Secy, NHS; H of F; Phys Ed A; Amer Hist A; Eng A; La St U; Ed.

STOKES, Ricky Lynn
N Pitt HS; Bethel, NC (20-300) Ann; Band; Ensm; FFA; Pres, Hmrm; Monogram; Rptr, NHS; Span C; Pres, Sr Cl; Bkbl; Ftbl; Co-Cpt, Wrest; Pres, Stu Govt; Pres, Stu Body; *NC St U; Elec.*

STOKES, Sunni Leigh
Madisonville N Hopkins HS; Madisonville, KY (1-296) BC; Swim; Tr; Bio A; Hon Prog; Val; Cl Marshal; *U of Ky; Phar.*

STOLL, Sarah Ruth
Northeastern HS; Elizabeth City, NC; Band; Drama; Fr C; Hmrm; Secy, NHS; Pres, SC; Bkbl; Sftbl; Tr; Hon Prog; Coach, Midget League Bkbl; Soph Senator, SC; *Engr.*

STOLL, Thomas Christopher
Oakville Sr HS; St Louis, MO; Band; CYO; Chess C; Hmrm; Orch; Order/Arrow; ARC; Sci C; Var C; Life Sct; Coronation Court; *US Coast Guard.*

STOLSIG, Jeff Alan
Lebanon Union HS; Lebanon, OR (52-235) Hmrm; Key C; NHS; SC; Pres, Var C; Bsbl; JV, Bkbl; Ftbl; Citz A; Jr Rotarian; Most Dependable, Sr Cl; *Oreg St U; Forestry Engr.*

STOLTENBERG, Todd Alan
W Holt HS; Atkinson, NE; Rptr, FFA; 4H; *Vet Asst.*

STOLZE, Anthony G
Alton HS; Alton, IL; Chess C; Math C; Bsbl; Cr-Ctry; DARGCA; *SIU; Elec Engr.*

STONE, Brenda Jane
Williamsville HS; Williamsville, IL (30-80) CYO; Secy, Chor; FHA; FTA; Spch C; Sftbl; Tnns; Spch A; Mus A; *Secy.*

STONE, Catherine Diann
Trinity Christain Sch; Chattanooga, TN (4-17) Ann; Band; Ensm; Sch P; Bkbl; Sftbl; *Memphis St U; Med.*

STONE, Cynthia Lynn
East HS; Pueblo, CO (2-384) Secy, Band; Community Yth Symph; Ensm; Ger C; NHS; Orch; Pres, Rainbow; COM; Most Outst Band Member; All-St Band; All-St Orch; Semi-Fin, Spencer Penrose Mus Comp; *U of Denver; Mus Performance.*

STONE, D Craig
S P Waltrip HS; Houston, TX (196-654) Drama; SC; Co-Cpt, Cr-Ctry; Co-Cpt, Tr; Q&s; Sales Mgr, Sch P; *SW Tex at San Marcies; Pre-Law.*

STONE, Danny A
Woodbridge Sr HS; Woodbridge, VA (6-600) Chess C; Fr C; NHS; Rptr, Sch P; *Lee Col; Eng.*

STONE, David Lee
Oak Hills HS; Cincinnati, OH (113-850) Pres, Fr C; Hmrm; SC; Tnns; Radio Broadcasting Tm; *Cincinnati Bible Col; Christian Ministry.*

STONE, Elizabeth Diane
New Caney HS; Porter, TX (25%-230) Secy, Bus C; Chor; Drama; FHA; Spch A; *N Harris Col; Bus.*

STONE, Ernest Leonard
A H Parker HS; Birmingham, AL (8-30) JETS; SC; Cpt, Bsbl; Cpt, Bkbl; Cpt, Ftbl; Cpt, Tr; Bio A; *UAB; Telecommunication.*

STONE, Gregory Alan
Rutherfordton-Spindale HS; Rutherfordton, NC (30-250) Band; Chor; 4H; VP, Hmrm; Lat C; Monogram; ARC; 4H A; *NC St U; Phys Sci.*

STONE, Ilaloa Naomi
Moreno Valley HS; Sunnymead, CA; Chor; Drama; Rptr, Sch P; Thes; *UCLA; Dramatics.*

STONE, Jacqueline Suzanne
Maine Township HS N; Des Plaines, IL (44-402) Chor; Ensm; Mod Mus Mas; Orch; Span C; Methodist Yth Tres; Co-Ed, Church P; Sunday Sch Teacher; *Northeastern U of Ill; Eng.*

STONE, Jeanette Gail
Chopticon HS; Morganza, MD (5-289) VP, Span C; Spch A; Lib C; St of Md Merit Scholastic A; WW; *Charles Co Comm Col.*

STONE, Jody Christine
Maine N HS; Des Plaines, IL; Chor; Ensm; Mod Mus Mas; VP, NHS; Opt A; Pres, Methodist Yth Group; *N Park Col.*

STONE, Jody Renea
Moultrie Sr HS; Moultrie, GA (10-500) A Cap Choir; Ann; Band; BC; Chor; FHA; Hmrm; SC; Tri-HiY; JV, Bkbl; JV, Sftbl; Sr All St Choir; HR; *Ed.*

STONE, Jonathan LeCount
Surrattsville HS; Clinton, MD (122-386) Band; NHS; *Md U; Acct.*

STONE, Jonmark
Cox HS; Va Beach, VA; Drama; Hmrm; InterClub Coun; SC; Pres, Soph Cl; Tr; MLS; *Phys Ed.*

STONE, Julie Irene
Suffolk HS; Suffolk, VA (6-110) Co-Ed, Ann; Drama; Semi-Fin, GS; NHS; F-Ed, Sch P; Thes; VP, Tri-HiY; Pres, Soph Cl; B Crocker A; Bio A; Citz A; *VPI; Psych.*

STONE, Karla Jean
Bellevue HS; Nashville, TN (20-250) BC; Chem C; Chor; Drama; Ensm; Pres, Lat C; Lat NHS; Sci C; SC; WW; Med A; *Med.*

STONE, Katherine Ann
Tupelo HS; Tupelo, MS (10%-381) Ann; BC; Ensm; Lit Mag; Tri-HiY; Hon Prog; JA A; NHS; Anchor C; Jr Civitan C.

STONE, Kimbra Leigh
Vines HS; Plano, TX; Chor; Ensm; Hmrm; NHS; Sch P; SC; Tr; Co-Cpt, Drill Tm; *Tex Tech; Hist.*

STONE, Marcia Sue
Hannibal Sr HS; Hannibal, MO (17-337) Band; Chor; NHS; Tnns; 2nd Pl, Mahan Poetry Contest.

STONE, Margo M R
E Peoria Comm HS; E Peoria, IL (4-508) A Cap Choir; CYO; Chor; Ensm; Fr C; GS; Madrigal; NFL; F-Ed, Sch P; S-T, Spch C; Amer Leg Orator A; COM; Hon Prog; Opt A; Spch A; *U of Notre Dame; Biol.*

STONE, Marilyn Frances
The Bishops Sch; La Jolla, CA (10%-76) Orch; Pres, Span C; Bkbl; JV, Swim; COM; HR; *Math.*

STONE, Martha Ann
Plain Dealing Acad; Plain Dealing, LA (5-50) Ann; GS; 4H; Mjrte; Mu Alpha Theta; Sch P; Span C; Spch C; JV, Bkbl; Tnns; JV, Tr; COM; Hon Prog; LISA Hon Soc; Miss Redbud Pageant; Chaplain, SC; Sch Photographer; Photographer, Math C; *NE La U; Pre-Vet.*

STONE, Merrill Rust
Battle Ground Acad; Franklin, TN (3-64) Key C; NHS; Cr-Ctry; Tr; Alg A; NEDT; *Vanderbilt U; Sci.*

STONE, Randall Craig
Cascia Hall Prep Sch; Tulsa, OK (5%-50) SC; Alg A; HR; Sch Schol; *Math.*

STONE, Rhonda Gayle
Poteau HS; Poteau, OK (15%-134) Band; Ensm; NHS; Orch; Sch P; Pres, SC; PA; Excellent, Ensm; Okla Hon Band; Principal's HR; Sup, Solo & Ensm; *Ark U; Sci.*

STONE, Risa D Ann
Anton HS; Anton, TX (1-40) Band; FHA; NHS; Bkbl; Sftbl; Tr; Cl Fav; Mascot; WW, Ath; Explorers; 3rd in St, 880 Relay.

STONE, Sharon Julienne
Wallace Sr HS; Wallace, ID (12-100) F-Ed, Ann; Chldr; Drama; FHA; Semi-Fin, GS; 4H; S-T, Lat C; Lat NHS; Math C; NHS; Pres, Rainbow; Ski C; Bkbl; Tr; Elk A; 4H A; Ntl Sci Symposium; Yth Fel; Campfire Wohelo Medallion; WW; *U of Mont; Phar.*

STONE, Shedrick Leaudis
Rayen HS; Youngstown, OH; Drama; Spch C; Ftbl; Tr; COM; Citz A; Poet A; *Law.*

STONE, Tammy Renee
Lyon Co HS; Eddyville, KY (9-70) Ann; Band; BC; Chldr; FHA; Rptr, Sch P; WW; Top 12; Best Dressed; *Paducah Comm Col; Bus.*

STONE, Valoree Sue
Hickman Mills Sr HS; Kansas City, MO (1-577) Chldr; Secy, Chor; Ger C; GS; NHS; Tr; Math A; Drill Tm; *Med.*

STONE, Vernon Ray
Anton HS; Anton, TX (2-40) VP, Band; Pres, NHS; Bkbl; Ftbl; Tr; Cl Fav; Hist A; VP, NHS; 1st Pl, Dist Tr.

STONE, Wendy Lelyn
SW Central HS; Jamestown, NY (10%-200) Band; Ger C; NFL; NHS; Spch C; Bkbl; *Med.*

STONE, William Malvin
Pendleton HS; Pendleton, SC (48-130) Best Dressed; *Limestone Col; Bus Adm.*

STONE, Zania Browning
Union Co HS; Morganfield, KY (10-310) Fr C; FHA; VP, 4H; Tres, Spch C; Mgr, Bkbl; COM; 4H A; HCt; ARC A; Spch A; Yth Fel; Most Dependable; Outst Stu o-t Mo; Service A; *Dental Hygienist.*

STONEBRAKER, Pamela Annette
El Camino HS; Oceanside, CA (66-355) Band; Ensm; Rptr, Hmrm; Model UN; Orch; Secy, Rainbow; SC; Tres, Jr Cl; Kiwanis A; Past Worthy Advisor, Rainbow Girls; *Westmont U; Ed.*

STONEBRAKER, Ruthann
Wickliffe Sr HS; Wickliffe, OH; Band; Ensm; Ski C; Fin, Tnns; COM; Hon Prog; Life Saving A.

STONEBRAKER, Stephanie Anne
Huntington N HS; Huntington, IN (1-590) Cpt, Chldr; Drama; FTA; Ger C; NHS; ARC; SC; Tres, Soph Cl; DARGCA; Kiwanis A; NEDT; Opt Out Tn; ARC A; Rotary A; St Scholar; Val; *Huntington Col; Bus Ed.*

STONEBURNER, Thomas Scott
Hibbing HS; Hibbing, MN (20%-450) Var C; Odd Fellow Fin; Yth Fel; Curling Tm; *Engr.*

STONEKING, James Bruce
Elkins HS; Elkins, WV (1-200) BS; VP, HiY; Pres, NHS; Wrest; Pres of Sen, W Va Yth in Govt; *W Va U; Pol Sci.*

STONEKING, Sally Ann
Moline Sr HS; Moline, IL (31-831) A-Ed, Ann; NHS; Span C; Span NHS; Q&S A; St Scholar; WW; *Bradley U; Marketing Research.*

STONEMAN, Daniel Jeffrey
Pennsville Mem HS; Pennsville, NJ (18-290) Band; Orch; Order/Arrow; Thes; *Engr.*

STONEMAN, Thomas Kevin
R L Tucker HS; Carronnton, TX (250-856) Band; Var C; Co-Cpt, Tnns; *N Tex St U; Mus.*

STONER, David Arnold
Hobart HS; Hobart, IN (23-405) AFS; Chess C; Fr C; NHS; Span C; Hon Prog; *Ind U; Acct.*

STONER, Eric Warren
Celina HS; Celina, OH (90-300) Hockey; Ski Tm; VP, Church Yth Group; *Miami U; Engr.*

STONER, Lloyd Wayne
Heritage Christian HS; Indianapolis, IN (1-38) Ed, Lit Mag; Hon Prog; WW; *Butler U; Dentistry.*

STONER, Mark Thomas
Ephrata Sr HS; Ephrata, PA (23-255) Band; Chem C; Chor; Dbte Tm; Drama; Ensm; Ger C; Hmrm; ARC; Ed, Sch P; SC; COM; Citz A; Journ A; Math A; NMF; Sci A; Yth Fel; *Pa St U; Biochem.*

STONER, Yvonne Marie
Mattoon Comm HS; Mattoon, IL (290-420) Band; Secy, Chor; Tres, FHA; Rptr, 4H; Yth Fel; Church Bkbl; Most Ath; Yrbk Cover Designer; Sportsmanship, Band, A's; *Lake Land Col; Secy.*

STOOKSBURY, Jo Ann
Sparta Highland HS; Sparta, GA (48-123) Band; Parl, Bus C; Rptr, 4H; JV, Bkbl; Sftbl; 4H A; Type A.

STOOPS, Kenneth Parker
King's Temple Christian Sch; Seattle, WA; Chess C; Chor; Orch; Soccer; COM; Hon Prog; Pres A; Yth Fel; *U of Wash; Engr.*

STOOPS, Patricia Ann
Smiths Station HS; Smiths, AL (2-148) BC; Chor; Drama; FHA; 4H; Math C; Mu Alpha Theta; Ed, Sch P; Sci C; Span C; Thes; COM; Hist A; Cl Fav; Sal; *Auburn U; Animal Sci.*

STOOTS, Cindy Anne
Evangelical Christian Sch; Memphis, TN; Chor; Fr C; Hmrm; SC; Var C; Bkbl; Cr-Ctry; Sftbl; Tr; Bio A; Sci A; Vlbl; Tr A; All Conf, Vlbl, Cr-Ctry, Tr; *Memphis St U; Phys Ed.*

STOPHER, Leslie Jean
Santa Ana HS; Santa Ana, CA (15-421) A-Ed; Ann; Chldr; Fr C; Fin, GS; MVP, Tnns; U of Calif; Bus Mgt.

STORJOHANN, Karla Dee
Brown HS; Sturgis, SD (50-194) A Cap Choir; Chor; Tres, FBLA; COM; Pom Pon Squad; Young Democrat; Amer Drill Tm; Cert of Achv; Pep C; Black Hills St Col; Secy.

STORK, Diane A
St Bernard HS; Breda, IA (1-32) Co-Ed; Ann; Chor; GS; Sch P; Spch C; Amer Leg Orator A; Bausch & Lomb A; COM; Sch A; St Scholar; Val; U of Nor Iowa; Elem Ed.

STORLIE, Bonnie Marie
Mabel-Canton HS; Mabel, MN (8-52) A Cap Choir; Band; Chor; Ensm; Pres, FHA; GS; Pres, 4H; Semi-Fin, Spch C; SC; Rptr, Sr Cl; VP, Jr Cl; Amer Leg A; 4H A; Spch A; Stu of Month; Phi Beta Mu; Ms Congen of Hespr-Mabl Stm Eng Dys.

STORM, Debbie Kay
Faith HS; Faith, SD (25-32) Ann; Band; Chor; Drama; Ensm; Fin, Jr Miss Pagent; Monogram; Sch P; Tres, Sr Cl; Tres, Soph Cl; Bkbl; Mgr, Tr; Hon Prog; Journ A; Ntl Col of Bus; Travel Agent.

STORM, Mark Allen
Merrill Sr HS; Merrill, WI; Band; BS; Sch P; VP, St Stu Congress; JV, Bkbl; Cr-Crty; JV, Ftbl; MVP, Tr; Oshkosh Col; Mental Retardation.

STORMO, James Alan
Monticello HS; Monticello, MS; FFA; Order/ Arrow; Ftbl; Tnns; Tr; Order/Arrow A; Cer of Acv, St Gme & Fsh Frest Mgmt; Miss St U; Engr.

STORMS, Kevin Mark
Melbourne HS; Melbourne, FL (20-740) Rptr, Ann; InterClub Coun; Rptr, Key C; Parl, SC; Cpt, Golf; VFW A; VofDEM; Furman U; Med.

STORRER, Bobbianne
Montpelier HS; Montpelier, OH (52-117) Band; Chldr; 4H; Rainbow; ARC; Var C; Bkbl; Sftbl; Swim; Tr; Yth Fel; Vlbl; DAR Hist A; U of Mich; Phys Ed.

STORRS, Kym Rae
Redmond HS; Redmond, OR (33%-237) Band; Chor; S-T, Fr C; FHA; French NHS; Pres, 4H; InterAct C; ARC; Co-Cpt, Sftbl; Cpt, Swim; Tnns; Cl Fav; St VP, FHA; Ad Hoc; Candystriper; Yth Coun; Swim Instructor; Home Ec St Adv Board; Pacific Lutheran U; Counseling.

STORY, Carolyn Annquinetta
A H Parker HS; Birmingham, AL; Chor; Dbte Tm; Drama; Secy, Hmrm; ARC; Rptr, Sch P; Secy, SC; Y-Tns; Secy, Soph Cl; Beauty; Hist A; HCt; NEDT; ROTC A; Yth Leg; Morehouse Col; Law-Enforcement.

STORY, Dennis
A H Parker HS; Birmingham, AL; Chor; Dbte Tm; COM; ROTC A; Battalion Commander; Art A; Eng Fair A.

STORY, Edward Lyn Earl
Carlisle HS; Price, TX (5-12) A Cap Choir; Band; Chor; FFA; Cl Fav; Tex Bible Col; Theology.

STORY, Kimberly Beth
Ebbert L Furr HS; Houston, TX (20-335) Sch P; Tr; Hon Prog; Journ A; Baylor Col of Med; Nurs.

STORY, Lee Eugene
Newton HS; Newton, IL (1-230) FFA; 4H; NHS; SC; S-T, Jr Cl; Pres, Soph Cl; NEDT; FFA Star Greenhand; Olney Central Col; Welding.

STORY, Lisa Kathryn
Washington Col Acad; Washington College, TN (5%-15) Anchor C; Bus Mgr, Ann; Chor; Drama; Fr C; Ed, Sch P; VP, Sci C; Spch C; Secy, SC; BC; Citz A; Hon Prog; Most Out; Spch A; Milligan Col; Bus.

STORZ, Michael David
Willows HS; Willows, CA (16-130) Ski C; JV, Bkbl; Ftbl; Tr; Bank Of Amer A.

STOTT, Edward Milton
Summerville Intermediate HS; Summerville, SC (50-780) Band; 'B' HR; Naval Acad; Sci.

STOTTS, Debra Inez
Bowling Green HS; Bowling Green, KY (15%-387) Bus C; JV, Chldr; FBLA; InterClub Coun; Jr Miss Pagent; NHS; SC; Pres, Tri-HiY; HCt; Hon Prog; Most Out; Secy, Tri-Hi-Y; Most Outst Young Bus Woman; 3rd, Region Ldrship Conf; Bus & Professional Women's C A; Stenotype Inst; Court Rptr.

STOTTS, Rick Coleman
Weld Central Jr-Sr HS; Keenesburg, CO (75-185) FFA; Tr; Denver Tech Sch; Gas & Diesel Mech.

STOUGH, Elaine Carol
High Point Sr HS; Beltsville, MD; Chor; Secy, Drama; Ensm; Semi-Fin, GS; 4H; Semi-Fin, NHS; Orch; ARC; SC; Sftbl; 4H A; Sci A; Church Choirs; Vol, Nursing Home; VBS Teacher; Basic Yth Seminar; VBS Backyard Stu; Co Orch; HR; Misson Frnds Tchr; Concert Choir; U of Md; Nurs.

STOUGH, Scott David
Central Dauphin HS; Harrisburg, PA (347-498) Order/Arrow; Ftbl; Wrest; Order/Arrow A; Eagle Sct; Millersville St Col; Industrial Arts Ed.

STOUGH, Sheryl Lucretia
Christian Sch of Fine Arts 2; Bradenton, FL (1-15) Ann; Band; Pres, Hmrm; Orch; Sch P; VP, SC; Sr Cl; COM; Cl Fav; Coun of Teach A; God & Country A; Val.

STOUGHTON, Joan Kathleen
Newark Valley HS; Newark Valley, NY; Chor; Pres, Ger C; Pres, 4H; 4H A; NEDT.

STOUGHTON, Nancy Katrine
Daniel Boone HS; Jonesboro, TN (17-300) BC; Chor; Ensm; NHS; Sci C; Beauty; HCt; Most Out; Drill Tm; E Tenn St U; Mus Ed.

STOUKY, Marjorie Lynn
Biggs HS; Biggs, CA (5-43) Ed, Ann; Drama; FHA; NHS; Sch P; Span C; HCt; Statist & Scorekeeper, Bsbl, Bkbl; Statist & Scorekeeper, Ftbl, Tr; San Joaquin Delta Col; Acct.

STOUT, Barbara Jean
Hampton Roads Acad; Newport News, VA; Chor; Drama; Thes; Hockey; Keyettes; VP, Candystripers; Madison U; Dietician.

STOUT, Debra Sue
Southgate HS; South Gate, CA; FHA; Pepperdine U; Psych.

STOUT, Deidre Ann
White Oak HS; Jacksonville, NC (1-250) CYO; NHS; Span C; Homemaking A; Nurs.

STOUT, Donald E
Council Rock HS; Newtown, PA (10-690) NHS; NMF; Intramurals; Houghton Col; Phys Sci.

STOUT, Kaye Diane
Shadle Park HS; Spokane, WA (24-640) Co-Ch, Band; Ensm; Hmrm; NHS; Eastern Wash U; Elem Ed.

STOUT, Lisa Carole
Bentworth HS; Bentleyville, PA (27-165) Band; Chldr; Chor; Hmrm; Span C; SC; Var C; VP, Soph Cl; Amer Leg A; DAR Essay A; May Court; Sch Spelling Champ; BVFD A; W Va U; Ed.

STOUT, Noell Eugenia
Odessa HS; Odessa, TX (1-550) Band; Community Yth Symph; Pres, Lat C; Secy, NHS; Orch; Tri-HiY; Hon Prog; Most Outst Sr Girl, Band; Tex Tech U; Acct.

STOUT, Pamela Yvonne
DuPont Sr HS; Hermitage, TN (25-350) Band; BC; FHA; NHS; ARC; COM; Hon Prog; Top 10%, Cl; Memphis St U; Nurs.

STOUT, Sandra Marie
Highland HS; Highland, IL (2-227) Sou Ill U; Communications.

STOVALL, Dorothy Turena
John D Bassett HS; Bassett, VA (15-180) VP, AFS; Band; Chor; S-T, Drama; Ensm; FHA; 4H; Hmrm; InterClub Coun; Madrigal; NFL; NHS; Ntl Yth Conf; Span C; Tr; COM; 4H A; JA A; Spch A; All St, Chor; Regional Forensics; Nurs.

STOVALL, Melinda
Thomas Jefferson HS; Richmond, VA; Va Commonwealth U; Computer.

STOVALL, Pamela Denise
Frederick Douglass HS; Atlanta, GA (100-344) Band; Co-Cpt, Chldr; Chor; Secy, Hmrm; Ntl Yth Conf; SC; Beauty; COM; Cl Fav; Most Out; Swtht; Yth Fel; Ntl Piano Mus A; Sch Achv A; Most Popular; GSct Part A; U of Ga; Journ.

STOVALL, Tanya Yvonne
Chicago Voc HS; Chicago, IL; NHS; Cpt, Church Vlbl; Gym Ldr A; SIU; Acct.

STOVER, Elizabeth Ann
Decatur HS; Decatur, AL (1-295) Ann; VP, Lat C; Mu Alpha Theta; Pres, Span C; SC; Bkbl; Sftbl; Tnns; MLS; NMS; NEDT; Piano Schol, U of Ala; 2nd Prize, Sch Lang Fair; Interntl Relations.

STOVER, Julie Anna
Millbrook HS; Raleigh, NC; Span C; COM; Citz A; Art.

STOVER, Kimberly Ann
Person Sr HS; Roxboro, NC (3-430) Drama; Ensm; Fin, Jr Miss Pagent; VP, NFL; NHS; COM; Cl Fav; Coun of Teach A; Gr Marshal; Spch A; 1st Runner Up Jr Miss; Miss Scholastic; Best Actress Featured Role; Dram, Best Sound Achv; U of Tenn; Eng.

STOVER, Linda Gail
Bakersfield R-4 HS; Bakersfield, MO (2-16) Ann; Secy, Band; FHA; 4H; Secy, NHS; Sch P; Secy, SC; Bkbl; Sftbl; Hist A; HQn; Sal; SMSU at Springfield.

STOVER, Martha Ellen
Danville HS; Danville, IL (4-604) A Cap Choir; Co-Ed, Ann; Chor; Community Yth Symph; Drama; Ensm; Fr C; Madrigal; NHS; Orch; Thes; COM; Citz A; Hon Prog; Math A; Rotary A; St Scholar; Ind U; Pre-Law.

STOVER, Ronald H
Grace M Davis HS; Modesto, CA; Band; Chor; Madrigal; Orch; St Hon Band; 1st Pl St, 'Talents For Christ'; 2nd Pl Ntl, 'Talents For Christ'; U of Redlands; Mus.

STOWE, Cindy Lou
Ladywood HS; Livonia, MI (33-130) A Cap Choir; Tres, CYO; FHA; FNA; Orch; ARC; Tr; COM; Citz A; ARC A; Yth Leg; U of Mich; Med.

STOWE, Cynthia Joyce
Crockett HS; Crockett, TX; San Jacinto Col; Bus.

STOWE, Donald Benjamin
Greenville HS; Greenville, IL (15-200) Ann; Fr C; U of Ill; Art.

STOWE, Marilyn Ann
Greenville HS; Greenville, IL (1-200) FTA; GS; NHS; Pres, Span C; F-Ed & C-Ed, Ann; U of Ill; Biological Sci.

STOWE, Selina Jewel
S Point Sr HS; Belmont, NC; Hmrm; Monogram; SC; Bkbl; Sftbl; Tr; 1st Cl, GSct; Presidential Phys Fitness A; Church Rep, UN; Lawyer.

STOWELL, Valerie Ann
Oppenheim-Ephratah HS; St Johnsville, NY (1-49) AFS; Fr C; NHS; Sftbl; Sci A; Eng A; Health A; Cornell U; Vet Asst Biology Teacher.

STOWERS, Richard Ward Jr
Robert E Lee HS; Montgomery, AL; SC; Var C; Cpt, Bsbl; Cr-Crty; Tr; Bio A; MLS; Sci A; Church Bkbl; Hitchcock, Outst School, A's; Samford U; Religion.

STOWERS, Vicki Lynn
Sentinel HS; Sentinel, OK (1-32) BC; Cpt, Chldr; Chor; Ensm; FHA; Semi-Fin, GS; NHS; Tnns; SC; S-T, Jr Cl; Bkbl; COM; Gov Honor Prog; 4H A; HCt; Hon Prog; NEDT; Val; Yth Fel; Okla U; Fashion Merchandising.

ST PIERRE, Yvonne Marie
Livermore Falls HS; Livermore Falls, ME (4-94) Commercial C; Pres, FHA; GS; NHS; VP, Jr Cl; MLS.

STRAATMEYER, Cynthia Jean
Lathrop HS; Fairbanks, AK; Pres, AFS; Ann; Ger C; Hmrm; NHS; ARC; Ed, Sch P; SC; Journ A; Service A, Ger C; Outst Sr High Yth, Church; Whitworth Col; Math.

STRAATSMA, Tracy Marie
Midwest HS; Midwest, WY (5-21) Band; NHS; Bkbl; Tr; Type A; Sheridan Col; Bus.

STRACENER, Karen Sue
Sheffield HS; Memphis, TN (20-142) Ed; Ann; Fin, Jr Miss Pagent; Secy, Math C; Citz A; H of F; Q&S A; WW.

STRACENER, Shelia Dianne
Central HS; Savannah, TN; Hist, FHA; *U of N Ala.*

STRACENER, Troy Kendall
Farmerville HS; Farmerville, LA (10-160) 4H; Hmrm; NHS; Rptr, SC; Bsbl; Bkbl; Ftbl; Cl Fav; 4H A; Yth Fel; *La Tech Col; Bus Adm.*

STRACHAN, Davia Donna
Adlai E Stevenson HS; Bronx, NY (6-788) Band; Chem C; HiY; NHS; Tr; Gov Honor Prog; Regent Schol; *Med.*

STRACK, James Donald
Catholic Central HS; Troy, NY; Sci C; Citz A; Audio-Visual C; Sch Spirit A; *Hudson Valley Comm Col; Bio.*

STRACKE, Edward Alan
Ygnacio Valley HS; Concord, CA (10%-475) Tnns; CSF.

STRADWICK, Anthony James
Wheeling Park HS; Wheeling, WV (89-690) HiY; NHS; Pres, Up Bound; Var C; Co-Cpt, Ftbl; Co-Cpt, Tr; COM; Citz A; DARGCA; Elk A; Stifel Schol; Ath Schol; Ath As; *Marshall U; Pre-Law.*

STRAEFFER, Greg Scott
Rogers Sr HS; Michigan City, IN (13-586) A Cap Choir; Band; Chor; JV, Tnns.

STRAFER, Audrey Dale
Mineola HS; Garden City Park, NY (165-411) GS; *Nassau Comm Col; Bus.*

STRAFER, John Thomas
Mineola HS; Mineola, NY (250-475) *Farmingdale Col; Elec Engr.*

STRAIGHT, Sharon Ellen
Scotch Plains-Fanwood HS; Scotch Plains, NJ (5%-613) Chor; Drama; Secy, Fr C; Lit Mag; Orch; Rptr, Sch P; SC; Hist A; Hon Prog; Trinity Mus A; Musical C; Sunday Sch Teacher; *Law.*

STRAIGHT, Terri Lynn
Glenbard E HS; Lombard, IL; Chor; Rptr, Sch P; Span C; JV, Tnns; Hon Prog; Sci A; *Botany.*

STRAIN, Susan Elizabeth
Cabrillo Sr HS; Lompoc, CA (363-390) Band; Ensm; JV, Bkbl; Sftbl; Most Out; Yth; 3-A CIF Sftbl Champs; *Cal Poly San Luis Obispo; Phys Ed.*

STRAIT, Karl Murray
Del City HS; Del City, OK (5%-600) Chor; Fr C; NHS; Thes; Sftbl; Alg A; Amer Leg A; Sci A; All St Choir; Brain-Bowl; Outst Actor; Outst Soph Thespian.

STRAIT, Mary Esther
Van Buren Comm HS; Keosauqua, IA (12-89) Band; Chldr; Drama; Ensm; FHA; 4H; NHS; ARC; Var C; Sftbl; Tr; Mgr, Wrest; Rotary A; Runner- up, Co Fair Qn; *Indian Hill Comm Col; Secy.*

STRALEY, Mary Colleen
Illinois Valley HS; Cave Junction, OR (2-90) Ann; CYO; Chor; Drama; FHA; 4H; NHS; Orch; Ed, Sch P; Pres, Span NHS; SC; Tres, Jr Cl; Tres, Soph Cl; Hon Prog; Sal; *Willamette U; Mus.*

STRAMMIELLO, Elizabeth Ann
W Babylon Sr HS; West Babylon, NY; Band; JV, Chldr; Drama; Fr C; Hmrm; Lit Mag; Ski C; Secy, SC; Citz A; Ntl Fr Contest; Outst Stu A; Miss Tn Amer Pageant; James Street Players; Eng Hon Soc.

STRAND, Charles Robert
Luther L Wright HS; Ironwood, MI; Chor; Dbte Tm; ARC; Rptr, Sch P; Ski C; SC; Swim; Tr; Swing Choir; Skiing; Ntl Ski Patrol; *Med.*

STRAND, Joan Marie
Rice Lake HS; Rice Lake, WI (60-285) Ch, A Cap Choir; Chor; *Health.*

STRAND, Krai Lynn
Juanita HS; Kirkland, WA (18-340) NHS; Gospel Singing Group; Pres, Church Yth Group; Yth Choir; *Oral Roberts Northwest Bible Col; Elem Ed.*

STRANGE, David Gerard
Loogootee HS; Loogootee, IN (4-120) BS; Fr C; SC; Bsbl; Co-Cpt, Bkbl; Alg A; Amer Leg A; Bausch & Lomb A; Hist A; Math A; Phy A; St Scholar; MVP, Bkbl; *Rose Hulman Inst of Tech; Engr.*

STRANGE, Janet Marie
Vicksburg HS; Vicksburg, MS (2-244) AFS; Pres, Lat C; Math C; NHS; Secy, SC; Tnns; DARGCA; H of F; NEDT; Sal; *Miss Col; Math.*

STRANGE, Kent Gerard
Loogootee HS; Loogootee, IN; Fr C; Bsbl.

STRANLUND, John Kevin
Brawley Union HS; Brawley, CA; JV, Ftbl; Swim.

STRANO, Michael Anthony
St Joseph HS; Hammonton, NJ (1-78) Chess C; Mgr, Bsbl; Tr; Ecology C; Service A; *US Naval Acad at Annapolis; Ocean Engr.*

STRASESKI, Jane E
Waupun HS; Waupun, WI (147-300) Ann; Chor; *Fon du Lac Tech Col; Child Care.*

STRASLER, Jerri Lyn
Big Bay de Noc HS; Cooks, MI; Chldr; Chor; Pres, FHA; 4H; Secy, Jr Cl; Secy, Soph Cl; Tr; 4H A; HCt; Hon Prog; Home-Ec A; *N Mich U; Home Ec.*

STRATTON, Douglas Ray
Glenwood HS; Chatham, IL (5%-200) A Cap Choir; Band; Ensm; Fr C; NHS; Cr-Ctry; H of F; *Judson Col; Religion.*

STRATTON, Henrietta Phillips
Columbus HS; Columbus, GA; JV, Chldr; NHS; Var C; Secy, Sr Cl; Tnns; Most Out; *Clemson U; Conservation.*

STRATTON, Rob Alan
Mt Blue HS; Farmington, ME (10%-175) Chess C; NHS; Cr-Ctry; Cpt, Wrest; COM; Most Out; Art Contests; *Presque Isle Col; Art.*

STRATTON, Robert Lee
Santa Rosa HS; Santa Rosa, CA (52-367) F-Ed, Ann; Pres, Band; Chor; Orch; COM; Mus Achv A; *Santa Rosa Jr Col; Fire Sci.*

STRATTON, Robin Kathleen
Temple Christian HS; Detroit, MI (5%-57) Ed, Ann; Co-Cpt, Chldr; Ensm; SC; Bkbl; Cpt, Sftbl; Citz A; *Tenn Temple Col; Elem Ed.*

STRATTON, Sandy Irene
Princeton HS; Princeton, NJ; Ger C; Sch P; Co-Cpt, Bkbl; Hockey; Soccer; JV, Sftbl; Swim; Fin, Tnns; ARC A; Yth Fel; Pep C; Sftbl & Swim A'S; V&JV Ltrs; Christian Ed; Lacrosse; Soccer & Tnns Trophies; Sr Citizen Aid; *Eng.*

STRAUB, Jane Arlene
Shenandoah Valley HS; Shenandoah, PA; Band; Chor; Cpt, Sftbl; Co Chor; Sftbl A; PA A; *Northampton Comm Col; Med Secy.*

STRAUB, Kathy Adele
Healdsburg HS; Healdsburg, CA;

STRAUB, Kathy Ann
River HS; Hannibal, OH (1-180) VP, 4H; NHS; 4H A; Kiwanis A; Scholastic Achv Test, Fr; *Ohio St U; Med.*

STRAUB, Linda Louise
Alton HS; Alton, IL (536-738) Chor; St Stu Congress; SC; COM; *Lewis & Clark Col; Dental Asst.*

STRAUB, Nancy Ann
Centaurus HS; Lafayette, CO (30-280) Lit Mag; Sch P; Sci C; Span C; Arch; Bkbl; Swim; Tnns; Best in Span A; *Psych.*

STRAUB, Teresa Joyce
Joseph Badger HS; Kinsman, OH (25-120) Chor; NHS; Pres, Span C; Cl Fav; *Nurs.*

STRAUBE, Peggy
Robinson Sch; Santurce, PR (5-39) Chldr; Drama; Math C; Ch, NHS; Secy, Soph Cl; NEDT.

STRAUCH, Lindy Sue
Chadwick HS; Chadwick, IL (6-23) Ann; Pres, Band; Pres, FHA; Sftbl; Tnns; HCt; Yth Fel; Vlbl; WW; *Sauk Valley Col; Mus.*

STRAUSER, Carmen Dell
Bunker R 3 HS; Bunker, MO (33%-48) Band; Band A; *Kansas City Col; Dental Asst.*

STRAUSS, Bonnie Sue
Central Dauphin HS; Harrisburg, PA; *Central Pa Bus Sch; Legal Secy.*

STRAUSS, Michael Joseph
Woodland Hills Baptist Acad; Jackson, MS (20%-54) BC; Bsbl; NEDT; Jolliest Jr; Most Intellectual; Challenge Show; *Miss St U; Chem Engr.*

STRAUSS, Richard
Liberty Jr-Sr HS; Liberty, NY (10-130) Band; InterAct C; NHS; Sch P; SC; Pres, Jr Cl; Cpt, Golf; Hon Prog; NEDT; Regent Schol; *Union Col; Med.*

STRAWDER, James Earl
Waterproof HS; Waterproof, LA (2-55) Band; BC; Semi-Fin, Lit Ral; Bsbl; Bkbl; Ftbl; *Sou U; Elec.*

STRAWN, Karen Kay
Hutchinson HS; Hutchinson, KS; Hon Prog; Star Student; Type A; Yth Fel; *Hutchinson Jr Col; Airline Hostess.*

STRAWSER, Kathy Lynn
Aurora HS; Aurora, WV (6-32) Band; JV, Chldr; Rptr, FHA; 4H; Pres, Hmrm; Mjrte; Rptr, NHS; Secy, Sci C; SC; Pres, Sr Cl; Secy, Soph Cl; COM; VofDEM; Participation A.

STRAYER, Trevor Darton
Harrison HS; Harrison, NY; Tres, Band; Sch P; Cr-Ctry; Tr; Hon Prog; Life Sct; Alt, Regent's Schol; *Bucknell U; Mech Engr.*

STRAYHORN, Don Diego
Loris HS; Loris, SC (54-123) Tres, FFA; Cpt, Bkbl; Cpt, Ftbl; Most Out; Phy A; Regent Schol; Cpt, Co-Cpt & MVP, Varsity C; Cpt, Co-Cpt & MVP, Physics C; Co-Cpt, Bkbl; MVP, Ftbl; *Lenior-Rhyne Col; Coach.*

STREAM, Darryl Theodore
Chisago Lakes Sr HS; Lindstrom, MN; Chor; Mgr, Wrest; *Mus.*

STRECKER, Cheri Lynn
Salina HS S; Salina, KS; Ann; Chor; Community Yth Symph; Ensm; 4H; Hmrm; Orch; SC; Sftbl; Hon Prog; Hon Stu; *Fort Hays St Col; Phys Therapy.*

STREED, Laurie Joan
Waukegan E HS; Waukegan, IL; A Cap Choir; Band; Mod Mus Mas; Tr; *Ed.*

STREET, Pamela Joyce
Maplewood HS; Nashville, TN; Ann; Chor; SC.

STREET, Wiley Dewitt
Treadwell HS; Memphis, TN (9-176) Ann; Pres, Chem C; Lat C; Ch, Math C; Mu Alpha Theta; NHS; Sch P; Ch, Sr Cl; Bsbl; Bio A; Citz A; H of F; Sci A; *Memphis St U; Acct.*

STREETE, Carol Ann
Booker Tea Washington HS; Tulsa, OK (50%-395) Chor; Ensm; 4H; Hmrm; SC; Soph Cl; Bkbl; Hockey; Sftbl; COM; Cl Fav; 4H A; Hon Prog; Ja A; MLS; Best Dressed; *Clarmore Jr Col; Med Lab Tech.*

STREETER, Chyrel
Toulminville HS; Mobile, AL;

STREETER, Marilyn Theresa
University City HS; Philadelphia, PA; *Drew U; Law Enforcement.*

STREETER, Susan Mary
Cherry Creek Sr HS; Englewood, CO (350-700) Var C; Big Sisters; Gym; Tres, Yth Group Board; *Col of St Teresa; Nurs.*

STREETMAN, Robert Oliver Jr
Columbus HS; Columbus, GA (1%-379) JV, Band; Hon Prog; *U of Ga; Dentistry.*

STREFF, Laura Marie
Holdrege Sr HS; Holdrege, NE (29-129) Band; Chldr; Chor; Dbte Tm; FBLA; 4H; Sch P; SC; Thes; Tres, Sr Cl; Spch A; Miss Congen, Harvest of Harmony Par; *U of Northern Colo; Spch Therapy.*

STREICH, Jeanne Gerette
Pacific HS; San Leandro, CA (14-317) Band; InterAct C; Pres A; Band A; Span A; Sci A; CJSP Gold Seal A.

STREICH, Patricia Jo
Jefferson HS; Jefferson, WI (15-180) Band; Ensm; JV, Tr; Hon Prog; PA; Top 10, Soph.

STREID, Mark B
Chatsworth HS; Chatsworth, CA; Ftbl; Tr; Wrest; Schol-Ath A; *Sci.*

STREIT, Susan Janet
Chicopee Comprehensive HS; Chicopee, MA (7-650) FTA; Hmrm; NHS; VP, SC; Hon Prog; Yth Fel; Colleen Court; *Holyoke Comm Col; Legal Secy.*

STREJC, Leonard Paul
John F Kennedy HS; Chicago, IL; JV, Bsbl; Cpt, Ftbl; Yth Ldr; Camp Counselor; Church Choir; Asst Choir Director; *Wheaton Col; Ed.*

STRENGTH, Rebecca Lynn
Enterprise HS; Enterprise, AL; Chor; FBLA; NHS; *Mac Arthur Technical Col; Bus.*

STREVEL, Howard Samuel
Ensley HS; Birmingham, AL (10%-340) Chor; Pres, Hmrm; NHS; Rptr, Sch P; SC; WW; DECA C; Ch, Patriotic Committee; *U of Ala; Math.*

STREY, Theresa Ann
Spencer HS; Spencer, WI (15-75) Ann; Band; Chldr; Chor; Drama; 4H; Mod Mus Mas; Co-Ed, Sch P; Secy, Soph Cl; Mgr, Tr; *Art.*

STRIBLING, Andrea Lee
Moss Point HS; Moss Point, MS; Band; Chor; Ensm; Fr C; Orch; Y-Tns; Most Out; Ensm Accompanist; Chor A; Amer Lit A; Piano Playing Festival A; *U of Sou Miss; Ensm Accompaniment.*

STRICKER, Michael Christopher
Mercy HS; Red Bluff, CA (3-27) CYO; Tres, Drama; Model UN; Rptr, SC; Secy, Soph Cl; JV, Bkbl; Bank Of Amer A; CSF; *U of San Francisco; Bio.*

STRICKLAND, Alesia
Estill HS; Estill, SC (25%-50) Ann; Chor; Secy, TAPS; *Secy Sci.*

STRICKLAND, Alice Lynn
Herbert Hoover HS; Clendenin, WV (75-275) Pres, DECA.

STRICKLAND, Amy Louise
Jenkins County HS; Millen, GA (6-100) Secy, BC; Sch P; Sci C; SC; Pres, Tri-HiY; Art A; Secy A; Secy SE Dist St YMCA; *Ga Col; Criminal Justice.*

STRICKLAND, Brenda Louise
Kenton Ridge HS; Springfield, OH (5%-200) Band; Ensm; VP, FHA; Mgr, Vlbl; FHA Qn, St Local Cand; *Mt Vernon Col; Home Ec.*

STRICKLAND, Bruce Alan
Dothan HS; Dothan, AL; Friendliest; WW; Yrbk; Most Christ-Like; *Drafting.*

STRICKLAND, Cynthia Kay
Watulla HS; Crawfordville, FL (1-117) Pres, FBLA; VP, NHS; Secy, Sr Cl; Alg A; COM; Chamber of Comm A; Citz A; Math A; NMS; Sci A; Star Student; Type A; Eng A; Pub Speaking A; WW; DAHSS; *FSU; Bus.*

STRICKLAND, David Richard
Franklin Co HS; Carnesville, GA (20-210) Ann; Band; Chem C; Ensm; Fr C; FFA; 4H; Hmrm; Sch P; Tri-HiY; Golf; JV, Swim; COM; 4H A; Hist A; Hon Prog; ARC A; Yth Fel; Pres, Secy, Sun Sch; Secy, Training Union; *Emmanuel & U of Ga; Law.*

STRICKLAND, Elaine Jeannine
Reid Ross Sr HS; Fayetteville, NC (20%-255) Ed, Ann; Chess C; Chor; City Conf; Drama; Ensm; Fr C; Hmrm; Pres, InterClub Coun; Lit Mag; Pres, NHS; Ed, Sch P; Pres, Sci C; Pres, SC; Parl, Tri-HiY; Pres, Sr Cl; Bkbl; COM; Citz A; Hist A; Hon Prog; Journ A; MLS; Sci A; Eng, Fr, Service As; *NC St U; Chem.*

STRICKLAND, Kenneth Lamar
Echols Co HS; Statenville, GA (5-37) BC; VP, FFA; InterAct C; InterClub Coun; NHS; Secy, Sr Cl; VP, Jr Cl; Bkbl; 4H A; Math A; MLS; Star Student; Schol A; *Abraham Baldwin Agr Col; Bus.*

STRICKLAND, Kenneth Micheal
Ritenour HS; Overland, MO (180-889) A Cap Choir; Chor; Drama; Hmrm; SC; Hon Prog; *Mus.*

STRICKLAND, LaVada Annette
Canton Pub HS; Canton, MS; Chldr; Chor; Drama; FHA; Secy, Hmrm; Math C; Secy, Mu Alpha Theta; Sci C; Spch C; Up Bound; Secy, Jr Cl; Amer Leg Orator A; HCt; Hon Prog; *Bus.*

STRICKLAND, Lex William Jr
Claxton HS; Claxton, GA (25%-110) BC; Rptr, 4H; 4H A; Hon Prog; Sci A; *Abraham Baldwin Agr Col; Agr Engr.*

STRICKLAND, Lila Yvonne
B T Washington HS; Atlanta, GA (21-360) Cpt, Mjrte; NHS; COM; Hon Prog; Math A; *U of Ga; Pol Sci.*

STRICKLAND, Lynn Marie
Illiana Christian HS; Lansing, IL (6-150) A Cap Choir; Lit Mag; Madrigal; NHS; Span C; St Scholar; Pioneer Girl's Prog Graduate; *Wheaton Col; Mus Ed.*

STRICKLAND, Mack III
Columbus HS; Columbus, GA (15%-33) Band; Chor; Ensm; COM; Hon Prog; Yth Fel; Hon Band & Choir; Chor, Church & Yth Choir Pianist; Mus Guild; *Emory U; Dentistry.*

STRICKLAND, Martha Jean
Illiana Christian HS; Lansing, IL (1-170) Ann; Band; Lit Mag; NHS; Hon Prog; St Scholar; St Solo & Ensm; Pioneer Girls; *Wheaton Col; Elem Ed.*

STRICKLAND, Martha Lane
Pine Forest Sr HS; Fayetteville, NC; Sch P; Tri-HiY; *Appalachian St U.*

STRICKLAND, Roderick Derrick
Booker T Washington HS; Atlanta, GA (32-345) Band; FBLA; Pres, Hmrm; Model UN; NHS; Ntl Yth Conf; Span C; SC; Rptr, Sr Cl; Rptr, Jr Cl; Pres, Soph Cl; Tr; COM; Hon Prog; NEDT; ROTC A; WW; *Boston U; Theater Arts.*

STRICKLAND, Thomas Jesse
Flushing HS; Flushing, MI; Cr-Crty; JV, Tnns; Tr; Cr-Crty Ltr Win; *Central Mich U; Industrial Arts.*

STRICKLAND, Tony Baxter
Hendersonville HS; Hendersonville, NC (40-172) Chor; Fr C; NHS; Bkbl; Cpt, Ftbl; Amer Leg A; FCA; Worker YMCA; Christian in Action; Semi-Fin, Amer Leg A; *UNC.*

STRICKLAND, Wallis Elaine
Tarboro Sr HS; Tarboro, NC (2%-250) Chor; Drama; Ensm; VP, FHA; Fin, GS; Hmrm; Monogram; NHS; Sci C; SC; Tnns; Sportsmanship A; Outst Alg Stu; All St Chor; Marine Bio Workshop; VP, Sub Jr Wmn's C; Jr Men Health; Fin, Woman's C Lit Contest; *UNC-Chapel Hill; Sci.*

STRICKLAND, Wendy Barry
Suffolk HS; Suffolk, VA (3-150) InterClub Coun; NHS; Span C; *Roanoke Bible Col; Psych.*

STRICKLER, Donita Lynn
Ontario Sr HS; Ontario, OH (1-220) Ann; Chldr; 4H; SC; Y-Tns; Sftbl; Swim; Tr; Hon Prog; Yth Fel; Co-Cpt Gym.

STRICKLER, Jeffrey Max
Ontario HS; Ontario, OH (13-205) BS; NHS; Bsbl; Bkbl; MVP, Ftbl; Swim; Tr; Amer Leg A; DARGCA; Ontario Teachers Fed School; Outst Ath; *Anderson Col; Sec Ed.*

STRICKLIN, Alice Carolyn
Obion Co HS; Troy, TN (6-178) Pres, Band; BC; Tres, Chor; Ensm; Hmrm; Math C; NHS; Co-Ed, Sch P; Sci C; Span C; Cr-Crty; COM; MLS; NEDT; Q&S A; Amer HS A For Excel; WW; Most Intelligent; *Murray St U; Engr.*

STRICKLIN, Charles Walter
C E Byrd HS; Shreveport, LA; Chess C; 2nd Pl Mech Draw, Indust Arts Fair; *La St U; Archt.*

STRICKLIN, Randal Lee
Bethel Baptist HS; Memphis, TN (6-26) Chor; Sch P; Bsbl; Bkbl; Ftbl; Soccer; Hist A; Most Out; Mr D L Moody A; Friendliest; Unlimited Yth o-t Yr; All Star, Ftbl; *Hyles Anderson Col; Bible.*

STRIEDL, Tamara Ann
Batavia Sr HS; Batavia, IL (5-211) AFS; Band; Chldr; *Phys Ed.*

STRINGER, Cynthia Kaye
Clifton HS; Clifton, TX (10%-53) A-Ed, Ann; Band; Ensm; NHS; Rptr, Sch P; Journ A; *Tex Tech; Journ.*

STRINGER, Eva Luan
Goodrich HS; Goodrich, TX (1-30) BC; FHA; Cl Fav; Val; Homemaking A; Reader's C; *Angelina Jr Col.*

STRINGER, Tony Patten
Walthall Acad Inc; Tylertown, MS (10-25) BC; Bsbl; JV, Bkbl; Ftbl; Sftbl; Cl Fav; Hist A; HCt; Math A; *Southwest Miss Jr Col.*

STRINGFELLOW, John William
Ashford HS; Ashford, AL (5-89) Ann; Parl, BC; Pres, Key C; Co-Ed, Sch P; Outst A, Key C; Art Show A's; Teamsters Schol Fund; *The Memphis Acad of Arts; Art.*

STROBEL, Diane Elizabeth
Norton HS; Norton, OH (4-325) Chr, Band; Chor; Community Yth Symph; FTA; GS; Secy, Lat C; Fin, NFL; NHS; SC; Thes; Math A; Spch A; *Mus.*

STROBEL, Karen Ann
Norton HS; Norton, OH (29-252) VP, Band; Pres, FTA; VP, Lat C; Lit Mag; NHS; SC; Citz A; WW; *Miami U Oxford; Elem Ed.*

STROBEL, Roddy Marlene
E Chambers Co Consd Ind Sch; Winnie, TX (1-102) Ann; Band; JV, Chldr; FHA; NHS; Rainbow; Mgr, Bsbl; Co-Cpt, Bkbl; Tr; Alg A; NEDT; Past Worthy Advisor, Rainbow Girls; 1st Pl, Finger Furniture Design; Pres, Jr NHS; 2nd Pl, Dist Essay Contest; *A&M U; Ed.*

STROCIAK, Andrew Henry
St Mary's Prep; Detroit, MI (16-345) Ensm; Bsbl; Hon Prog; Magna Cum Laude; Second Hon; *Oakland U; Psych.*

STRODE, Cheryl Ann
Arlington HS; Indianapolis, IN (75-344) Chor; Hmrm; SC; Ftbl; Type A; VP, Pep C; Parl, COE; *Ind U; Law.*

STROEBEL, Karen Jean
Juneau HS; Milwaukee, WI (54-200) Band; Ger C; VP, 4H; 4H A; *UW-BARABOO.*

STROH, Steven Lymoine
Columbia HS; Columbia, IL (50%-113) Band; SC; Bsbl.

STROHMEYER, Celeste Marie
Mineral Ridge HS; Mineral Ridge, OH (29-81) A-Ed, Ann; Drama; Home Ec C; Lenox China Contest; *YSU; Nurs.*

STROHMEYER, Lorraine Jean
Mineral Ridge HS; Mineral Ridge, OH; Lib; *Youngstown Bus Col; Acct.*

STROLE, Gregory Scott
Quartz Hill HS; Quartz Hill, CA (18-420) Pres, Band; Pres, 4H; Math C; Span C; Wrest; CSF; 4H A; ROTC A; *Rensselaer Poly Ins; Nuclear Engr.*

STROM, Jeffrey Thomas
St Edward HS; Lakewood, OH (9-410) Band; CYO; Ensm; Bsbl; Bkbl; Ftbl; Soccer; Sftbl; Wrest; COM; Hon Prog; Sci A; Stage Band; Stu o-t Yr; 2nd Pl, NE Ohio Sci Fair; Acad Schol; *Engr.*

STROM, Randi Barbara
Preble HS; Green Bay, WI (1-400) A Cap Choir; Chor; Ensm; Hmrm; Madrigal; Span C; SC; Alg A; Bio A; Citz A; Hon Prog; MLS; Most Out; Pres A; *Mus A.*

STROM, Randy Charles
Booker-Bay Haven HS; Sarasota, FL (6-40) Band; Chor; *Manatee Jr Col; Religion.*

STROMAN, Patricia Carmel
Tex Sr HS; Texarkana, TX (5%-465) Band; Ensm; Fr C; FTA; NHS; Sci C; 1st Division Medal; *Baylor U; Hist.*

STROMBERG, William Joseph
Loyola HS; Baltimore, MD; NHS; Bsbl; Ftbl; *Design.*

STROMGREN, Leanne
Newport Harbor HS; Newport Beach, CA; Secy, Girls League; Most Sincere; Most Innocent; Drill Tm; *Biola Col; Nurs.*

STROMME, Karen Louise
Duluth Central HS; Duluth, MN; Pres, Chor; NHS; Sch P; SC; Cpt, Bkbl; Golf; Swim; Tr; Amer Leg A; HCt; All Conf Bkbl & Swim; Hugh O'Brien Ldrship; *Bio.*

STROMMEN, Gregory Guy
Huron Sr HS; Huron, SD (12-262) BS; Pres, Hmrm; S-T, Key C; Pres, NHS; Ed, Sch P; Span C; VP, SC; Bkbl; JV, Ftbl; Golf; Amer Leg A; DARGCA; Hon Prog; Q&S A; Type A; Yth Leg; Ntl Merit Commended Stu; *U of SD; Law.*

STROMOWSKY, Jay
Robert E Peary HS; Rockville, MD (200-500) Band; Ensm; Orch; COM; Yth Fel; Montgomery Col; Computer Sci.

STROMQUIST, Brian Dean
Braham HS; Braham, MN (33-100) A Cap Choir; Band; Chess C; Chor; Ensm; Cr-Ctry; Golf; Hamlin Col; Bus.

STRONG, Barbara Ruth
S Hadley HS; South Hadley, MA; Band; Drama; Sftbl; Westfield St Col; Criminal Justice.

STRONG, Jacqueline
South-Side HS; Memphis, TN (15%-370) Band; Chor; FHA; Hmrm; Lat C; Mjrte; Tres, Spch C; Bkbl; Tr; Beauty; COM; Kiwanis A; Math A; Opt A; ROTC A; Spch A; Camper o-t Yr; Miss KT; All W Tenn Chor; Oratorical A; Tex St U; Spch.

STRONG, Myra Lynn
Berleley Sr HS; Berkeley, MO; Chldr; Orch; Orchestra A; Med.

STRONG, Nathan Antonio
Westwood HS; Memphis, TN; Band; Chor; ARC; Bsbl; MVP, Ftbl; Tr; Math A; ARC A; Mus; Ftbl & Bsbl A; Tenn St U; Mus.

STRONG, Stephanie Lynn
Paisley HS; Winston-Salem, NC (80-400) Yth Fel; PSGC; Academically Talented; 1st Cl GSct; Wake Forest U; Psychiatry.

STRONG, William Earl
Mineral Wells HS; Mineral Wells, TX (2-296) Pres, Hmrm; Key C; Span C; SC; Pres, Soph Cl; Co-Cpt, Bkbl; Ftbl; Golf; DARGCA; Hist A; Opt A; Opt Out Tn; VP, Church Yth Fel; Eng Blanket; Highest Eng Rank; Air Force Acad; Banking.

STROOPE, Jim Lester
Mt Ida HS; Mt Ida, AR (15-33) Band; FFA; 4H; Hmrm; Pres, SC; Bkbl; Ftbl; Tr; Yth Fel; Dekalb Agr Accomplishment; Most Handsome; Most Valuable; U of Ark; Agr Engr.

STROUD, Paul Joseph Jr
Euclid Sr HS; Euclid, OH (200-850) Ann; Band; Community Yth Symph; Hmrm; Key C; Mod Mus Mas; Pres, Orch; SC; Var C; Cr-Ctry; Tnns; Citz A; JA A; Q&S A; Master Mus; 1st Pl, St Solo Contest; Baldwin Wallace Col; Mus Performance.

STROUD, Raymond Shane
McGavock HS; Nashville, TN (286-836) CYO; Hmrm; VP, SC; Pres, Jr Cl; Pres, Soph Cl; Bsbl; Mgr, Bkbl; Ftbl; Tr; Citz A; Cl Fav; Most Talented; Christian Ath o-t Yr; Pres, FCA; Sr Superlitivie; Tenn Tech.

STROUD, Steven Johnson
R S Central HS; Rutherfordton, NC (20-260) BS; Hmrm; Key C; Monogram; St Stu Congress; Pres, SC; Pres, Sr Cl; Pres, Jr Cl; Co-Cpt, Ftbl; Cpt, Tnns; HKg; Nom, Morehead Schol; Clemson U; Civil Engr.

STROUD, Susan Shayne
Carroll HS; Ozark, AL; Span NHS; U of Ala; Spch Pathology.

STROUP, Gerald Leroy
Carson HS; Carson City, NV (11-400) NHS; USC; Engr.

STROUP, Paulene Cora
Orion HS; Orion, IL (10-130) Band; Chor; Drama; Ensm; FHA; Tres, 4H; Madrigal; NHS; Thes; 4H A; JA A; Most Out; Cl Offices; Black Hawk Col; Engr.

STROZIER, James Roy
Glenmora HS; Glenmora, LA (1-35) Ann; BS; Pres, FBLA; Lit Ral; NHS; Sch P; Sci C; SC; Pres, Jr Cl; Mgr, Bkbl; Alg A; Bio A; COM; Cl Fav; Hist A; English A; Geom A; Most Ambitious; Most Courteous; La Tech; Engr.

STRUBHAR, Kim Louise
Pine Grove Area HS; Pine Grove, PA (36-153) A Cap Choir; Band; Chem C; Chor; Drama; FTA; Ger C; Sch P; Bkbl; God & Country A; Pres A; Sci A; Via-Veritas-Vita; 1st Cl Sct; Pa St U; Elem Ed.

STRUBHAR, Lisa Ann
Pine Grove Area HS; Pine Grove, PA (4-150) Arch; Chor; FNA; Hmrm; Cpt, Mjrte; NHS; SC; Var C; Arch; Reading Hospital Sch of Nurs; Nurs.

STRUCK, Dawn Edythe
Pewaukee HS; Pewaukee, WI (16-127) Tres, Bus C; Semi-Fin, Jr Miss Pa; NHSt; Ski C; Span C; SC; Var C; Secy, Sr Cl; Tres, Jr Cl; Mgr, Bsbl; Mgr, Bkbl; JV, Tr; HQn; Hon Prog; Kiwanis A; Type A; Semi-Fin, Span Pronunciation; Ftbl Statistician; Prom Court; Vlbl Statistician; S-T Bowl League; U of Wis; Acct.

STRUCKMEYER, Alan Dean
Navasota HS; Navasota, TX (5-125) Dbte Tm; Drama; Hmrm; Key C; NHS; Sci C; Tres, Span C; VofDEM; Tex Lutheran Col; Theology.

STRUTHERS, Charity Ann
Washington HS; Cedar Rapids, IA; A Cap Choir; Co-Cpt, Chldr; Dbte Tm; Drama; Fin, GS; Hmrm; VP, NFL; Orch; SC; Spch A; All St Chor; Mayor's Yth Coun; Tres, MYF; Pol Sci.

STRUVE, David Michael
Downers Grove S HS; Downers Grove, IL (5%-1500) Ftbl; Computer C; Yth Fellowship; U of Nebr; Med.

STRYD, Lori Lee
Hanford Joint Union HS; Hanford, CA; A Cap Choir; Chor; Sci C; Tr; CSF; Pres, Young Peoples Soc; MVP, Vlbl; Fin, Miss Kings Co; Col o-t Sequoias; Nurs.

STRYKER, Tad LaVern
Callaway HS; Callaway, NE (2-23) Band; Chor; 4H; Y-Tns; Bkbl; Ftbl; Tr.

STUART, Andrea Lynn
Maryville R-II HS; Maryville, MO (30-120) Ann; Chor; FBLA; GS; NHS; Span C; Q&S A; Type A; WW; NW Mo St U; Bus.

STUART, Cindy Joann
Kings Acad; West Palm Beach, FL (8-60) Ann; Chor; Drama; Hmrm; NHS; SC; Var C; Cpt, Bkbl; Sftbl; Citz A; Hon Prog; Sal; VofDEM; Most Sch Spirit; Most Improved, Vlbl, Bkbl; Samford U; Pre-Med.

STUART, Deanna Lynn
Naperville Central HS; Naperville, IL (33%-450) Chor; SC; Mont St U; Horticulture.

STUART, Glen Raymond
Henderson Sr HS; W Chester, PA (2-450) Hmrm; SC; Pres, Sr Cl; Pres, Soph Cl; JV, Bsbl; Co-Cpt, Soccer; COM; MLS; NMF; Sal; U of Pa; Pol Sci.

STUART, Lois Jo
San Jacinto HS; San Jacinto, CA; Fine Arts.

STUART, Mark Anthony
Calhoun Co HS; Edison, GA (1-139) BC; Chor; Dbte Tm; FTA; Var C; Bsbl; Ftbl; Tnns; Tr; COM; 4H A; US Naval Acad; Engr.

STUART, Walter Houston
East Central HS; Hurley, MS; BC; BS; Sci C; Pres, SC; Pres, Var C; VP, Sr Cl; Pres, Jr Cl; Pres, Soph Cl; Bkbl; Cl Fav; Yth Fel; Ole Miss; Pol Sci.

STUBBLEFIELD, Hurley Archie
Westview HS; Kankakee, IL (135-238) Commercial C; MVP, Ftbl; Tr; Wrest; H of F; Grambling St U; Creative Arts.

STUBBLEFIELD, Jeffrey Robert
Peoria HS; Peoria, IL (50%-500) Var C; Bsbl; Graphic Arts.

STUBBLEFIELD, Sheri Lynn
Odell Comm HS; Odell, IL (5-34) Chor; Drama; Fr C; FHA; S-T, 4H; Var C; Golf; HCt; S-T, Fresh Cl; WW; ISU; General.

STUBBS, Beverly Elaine
McColl HS; McColl, SC;

STUBBS, Daniel James
Wilcox Co HS; Rochelle, GA (5-110) 4H; Ftbl; COM.

STUBBS, Jim M
Edison HS; Tulsa, OK (10%-450) Pres, SC; JV, Bsbl; JV, Ftbl; Citz A; Hon Prog; Masonic A; MLS; Principal's HR; Boy o-t Mo.

STUBBS, Kevin Charles
Garner Hayfield HS; Garner, IA (17-73) Band; BS; Order/Arrow; Ftbl; Tnns; Tr; Wrest; Order/Arrow A; Yth Fel; Iowa St U; Bio.

STUBBS, Kirk Howard
Garner-Hayfield HS; Garner, IA (12-74) Band; Chor; Madrigal; Span C; Var C; JV, Ftbl; Tr; Wrest; Yth Fel; U of Iowa; Elec.

STUBBS, Susan Gail
Grants HS; Grants, NM (5-329) Ed, Ann; Band; Semi-Fin, Jr Miss Pa; NHSt; Secy, Sci C; SC; Bio A; H of F; AAUW A; St Sci Fair A; McMurry Col; Bus.

STUBER, Patricia Ann
Southwest Christian Sch; Oswego, NY; Chldr; Chor; Ed, Sch P; Pres, SC; Pres, Sr Cl; COM; Citz A; Cl Fav; Hist A; Most Out; Christian Ldrship A; Highest Avg; Bob Jones U; Mus Ed.

STUBLI, Marilyn Kathleen
Addison Comm HS; Addison, MI (60-102) Chor; Ger C; 4H; SC; DARGCA; 4H A; Mich St U; Horticulture.

STUCHELL, Patricia Mary
Penn Hills Sr HS; Pittsburgh, PA (40%-1252) AFS; Drama; Hmrm; Sch P; SC; Tr; Journ A; NEDT; W Liberty St Col; Dental Hygiene.

STUCK, Gretchen Louise
Centerville Sr HS; Centerville, IN (5-186) Ann; Fr C; Hmrm; Var C; Y-Tns; Tres, Jr Cl; VP, Soph Cl; Bkbl; MVP, Sftbl; MVP, Tr; WW, St HS Fr Stu; Outst Fr Stu; All St Sftbl A; Pre-Law.

STUCKART, Roberta Ann
Regis HS; Stayton, OR (2-60) NHS; Hon Prog; Pep C; Roustabout; Jr Cheerette C.

STUCKENBRUCK, Loren Theo
University HS; Johnson City, TN; BC; BS; Chor; Community Yth Symph; Ger C; Orch; Bsbl; Citz A; Cl Fav; Milligan Col; Theology.

STUCKEY, Sandra Carol
Antioch HS; Antioch, CA (154-574) A Cap Choir; Ch, Band; Chor; Drama; Ensm; Pres, Orch; Pres, Span C; JV, Tnns; CMEA As; Summer RMC Schol; Hayward St U; Mus.

STUCKY, William Vincent
Dearborn HS; Dearborn, MI (10%-550) NHS; MVP, Bkbl; Tr; Hon Prog; Co-Cpt, Bkbl; Vanderbilt U; Bio Med Engr.

STUDER, Sara Lynn
Elston Sr HS; Michigan City, IN; Ann; Chor; Drama; SC; Amer Leg A; Citz A; Hon Prog; Pres A; Sci A; Superior, Vocal; Tr & Field A.

STUDNICKA, Linda Jean
Tuscola HS; Tuscola, IL (44-108) Band; Chor; Spch C; E III U; Mus.

STUDSTILL, Gordon Anthony
Wilcox Co HS; Rochelle, GA (1-116) BC; Lit Mag; Span C; SC; Alg A; Bio A; COM; Gov Honor Prog; Hon Prog; Math A; Ga Tech; Math.

STUDSTILL, Joseph Woodrow
Wilcox Co HS; Rochelle, GA (5-110) Band; BC; FFA; 4H; Hmrm; Span C; Hist A; Hon Prog; Eng A; Agr.

STUDY, Melinda Jane
Grosse Pointe N HS; Grosse Pointe Woods, MI (40%-600) Fin, AFS; Chor; Fr C; Pres, Hmrm; NHS; Ski C; Swim; HQn; HCt; Hon Prog; Pianist for Church Choir; Mich St U; Engr.

STUEWE, Robert Brian
Salina HS S; Salina, KS (1-367) Band; Dbte Tm; Drama; Hmrm; NFL; Order/Arrow; Wrest; NMS; St Scholar; Most Outst HS Sr in Sci & Math; Kans St U; Nuclear Engr.

STUFFT, Grant Edwin
Bridgeport HS; Bridgeport, OH (5-121) Band; BS; Tres, Lat C; NHS; Orch; Sch Achieve Tm; Span C; Pres, SC; Bkbl; Tnns; Amer Leg A; Math A; Sci A; Eng A; Ohio St U; Pre-Med.

STUKE, Deborah Jeanne
Palm Valley HS; Ponte Vedra Beach, FL; Chldr; Bsbl; Bkbl; Hon Prog; Sci A; Yth Fel; Blue Belt; Karate; Acolyte; Jacksonville U; Ed.

STULL, Christine Lynn
South Central HS; Union Mills, IN (1-73) Co-Ed, Ann; VP, Band; Chor; Drama; Ger C; Hmrm; NHS; Thes; Mgr, Bkbl; Mgr, Tr; B Crocker A; 4H A; Yth Fel; Vlbl; Ind Central Col; Acct.

STULL, Jean Ann
Springfield HS; Springfield, IL (91-500) Band; Ger C; Pres, 4H; Orch; 4H A; Big 12 Band Contest; *St Johns Nurs Sch; Nurs.*

STULL, Mark Douglas
S Central HS; Union Mills, IN (10-80) 4H; Ski C; Ftbl; Tr; VofDEM; *Purdue U; Agr.*

STULTS, Andrew Gordon
W Holmes HS; Millersburg, OH (10-200) Chor; FTA; NHS; Order/Arrow; Sch Achieve Tm; Rptr, Sch P; Sci C; VP, Span C; Secy, Spch C; Arch; Alg A; Math A; Order/Arrow A; Sci A; St Scholar; *Bowling Green St U; Econ.*

STULTS, Clifford Clairton III
Bellevue E HS; Bellevue, NE (29-777) Chess C; Math C; Order/Arrow; Swim; Citz A; Order/ Arrow A; Eagle Sct; HR; High Achv Program.

STULTS, Susan Dorre
Bellevue E HS; Bellevue, NE (180-800) Fr C; Mgr, Swim; JV, Tr; Yth Fel.

STULTZ, Dawn LuAnn
Washington HS; Washington, IA (10%-100) Band; Chldr; VP, 4H; Tr; 4H A; *Bethal; Mathmetics.*

STULTZ, Glenda Ann
Norlina HS; Norlina, NC (7-102) BC; Chor; *U of NC; Mus.*

STULTZ, Shawn Rene
Washington HS; Washington, IA; COM; *U of Iowa; Writing.*

STUMBAUGH, Michaelle Ann
J Frank Faust Jr HS; Chambersburg, PA; Chor; 4H; JV, Hockey; Church Choir; Audio Visual C.

STUMHOFER, Richard John
Columbus HS; Columbus, GA (10%-700) Key C; NHS; Ftbl; COM; *U of Ga.*

STUMP, Alton Chris
Northridge HS; Middlebury, IN (40-120) Band; 4H; Ftbl; JV, Tr; JV, Wrest; HR; *Lincoln Tech; Auto Mech.*

STUMP, Elizabeth Ann
George Wythe HS; Wytheville, VA (5-136) FHA; Mu Alpha Theta; NHS; Tri-HiY; *Radford Col; Acct.*

STUMP, Karla Louise
Robert E Lee HS; Midland, TX (225-700) A Cap Choir; Hmrm; Fin, Jr Miss Pagent; SC; Beauty; COM; Chamber of Comm A; Citz A; JA A; MLS; Pres A; *Midland Col; Bus Adm.*

STUMP, Kevin Douglas
Boca Ciega HS; Gulfport, FL; Band; Span C; JV, Wrest; *Eckerd Col; Religion.*

STUMP, Leigh Ann
Trotwood-Madison Sr HS; Trotwood, OH; Band; Orch; Pres, Span C; Octagon C; Drill Tm Ltr; Band Ltr.

STUMP, Tammy Jean
Permian HS; Odessa, TX; Pres, A Cap Choir; NHS; Bkbl; Hon Prog; UIL Vlbl; *Phys Ed.*

STUNTZ, Karen Joy
Lake Braddock HS; Burke, VA; Bus C; Chor; Fr C; Sftbl; Type A; Pep C A; *Nova Col; Lib Arts.*

STURCH, Cheryl Lynn
Delavan HS; Delavan, IL; Band; Ensm; Ch, 4H; 4H A; Lib A; Band Medals; *ICC; Lib Sci.*

STURDEVANT, Cheryl Ann
Wauconda HS; Wauconda, IL (6-230) Band; Ch, 4H; Span C; Sftbl; 4H A; FCYF; V-P, JNHS; *Northwestern U; Med.*

STURDIVANT, Genise
Eastside HS; Paterson, NJ; Chldr; Chor; Swim; Tnns; HQn.

STURGEON, Lisa Marie
River Valley HS; Marion, OH (50%-250) Chor; Lat C; Yth Fel; Candystriper; Med Explorers; Sunday Sch Song Ldr; *Nurs.*

STURGEON, Marilyn Diana
Brown Co HS; Nashville, IN (7-156) Ed, Ann; Pres, 4H; NHS; 4H A; Journ A; Q&S A; St Scholar; Type A; Secy, 4-H C; Psi Iota Xi Schol A; Yrbk Staff A; *Ind U; Psych.*

STURGES, Virginia Lynn
Hopkinsville HS; Hopkinsville, KY (20-400) Rptr, BC; Drama; Ed, Lit Mag; Co-Ed, Sch P; Thes; Poet A; Q&S A; *Centre Col; Eng.*

STURGILL, Judy Blair
San Mateo HS; San Mateo, CA (5%-500) Sftbl; Pres A; Girl's Flagball; *San Francisco St Col; Med.*

STURGIS, Howard Dee
Chatsworth HS; Chatsworth, CA; Semi-Fin, Chess C; City Conf; Ch, Hmrm; Ntl Yth Conf; ARC; Rptr, Sch P; Ch, SC; Thes; Bsbl; Bkbl; COM; Co-Ed, Sch P; *Hyles & Anderson Col; Ed.*

STURM, Laura Ann
Fairview HS; Boulder, CO; CYO; Key C; SC; Y-Tns; Bkbl; Tr; *Pepperdine U; Psych.*

STURM, Susan Elizabeth
Lawrence Central HS; Indianapolis, IN (64-737) Band; BC; 4H; VP, Hmrm; Cpt, Mjrte; NHS; VP, SC; Tri-HiY; VP, Jr Cl; Bio A; Hon Prog; Most Out; Pres A; Yth Leg; MVP, Mjrte; *Ind U; Recreational Therapy.*

STURM, Trudy Louise
Crossville HS; Crossville, IL (1-24) Co-Ed, Ann; Pres, Band; Pres, BC; Tres, FHA; Pres, 4H; Pres, Math C; Secy, SC; VP, Thes; Tres, Sr Cl; Tres, Jr Cl; Tres, Soph Cl; Amer Leg A; Cl Fav; DARGCA; 4H A; HCt; I Dare You; Math A; MLS; Rotary A; St Scholar; Type A; Val; John Phillip Sousa Band A; *U of Ill; Agr.*

STURTEVANT, Cynthia Marie
Kewanee HS; Kewanee, IL; Chldr; Dbte Tm; FTA; Span C; Spch C; *Bradley Col; Math.*

STURTEVANT, Patricia Joan
Freeport Sr HS; Freeport, IL (19-523) A Cap Choir; Math C; Mgr, Tr; St Scholar; *Rockford Mem Hospital; X-Ray Tech.*

STURTZ, Steve Charles
Lake HS; Uniontown, OH (174-224) Chess C; De-molay; Rptr, Sch P; Tres, Sr Cl; Bsbl; Bkbl; Ftbl; *US Air Force; Elec.*

STYLES, Jeffery Owen
Bowdon HS; Bowdon, GA (7-106) BC; Chem C; Fr C; 4H; HiY; Secy, Hmrm; Key C; Math C; Sci C; Pres, Span C; SC; Ftbl; Golf; Citz A; Gov Honor Prog; HCt; Yth Leg; Spelling A; Ga Hi-Y Yth Assm; Ind Stu; *W Ga Col; Forestry.*

STYNES, James Orean
Tuscaloosa HS; Tuscaloosa, AL; Cr-Ctry; Tr; *U of Ala; Commercial Art.*

STYRON, Joseph Brantley
Mendenhall Attendance Center; Mendenhall, MS (12-65) V-Ch, BC; Math C; Mu Alpha Theta; Bsbl; Ftbl; MLS; Christian Ath A; Acad, Mus, Schol; *Clarke Jr Col; Mus.*

STYRON, Kimberly K
Westbury HS; Houston, TX; FHA; Westbury Re-belettes; *Harding Col; Drama.*

STYSKAL, Shelly Jean
Perkins Co HS; Grant, NE (7-32).

SUAREZ, Angela Elena
Academia San Jorge; Santurce, PR (3-75) Tres, In-terAct C; NHS; Secy, Sr Cl; Chem A; Hon Prog; Sci A; PA; *Seaton U; Biological Sci.*

SUAREZ, Jose Ramon
Cristobal HS; Coco Solo, CANAL ZONE (1-107) Band; Fr C; FTA; Hmrm; Span C; Amateur Boxing; *MIT; Engr.*

SUAREZ, Yvette Marie
Academia Ntra Sra Providencia; Rio Piedras, PR (2-64) Bus C; CYO; Sftbl; Semi-Fin, Tr; COM; Summa Cum Laude; Vlbl; *Sci.*

SUBER, Sarah Elizabeth
Laurens Dist 55 HS; Laurens, SC (10-206) Fr C; FHA; NHS; *Greenville Tech Col; Secy Sci.*

SUBLETT, Katherine Elizabeth
Edward H White Jr HS; Jacksonville, FL; Pres, BC; Pres, Drama; Fr C; Hmrm; Citz A; Most Out; *New-berry Col; Med.*

SUBLETT, Steve Corken
Lawrence HS; Lawrence, KS (142-668) Band; BS; Demolay; Gym; *Air Force ROTC.*

SUBLETT, Susan Anne
Lawrence HS; Lawrence, KS (9-551) A Cap Choir; Drama; Orch; Secy, Span C; SC; Secy, Sr Cl; Secy, Jr Cl; Presidential Schol Baker U; *Baker U; Early Childhood Ed.*

SUBLETT, Tracy Louise
Fern Creek HS; Louisville, KY; Fr C; Bible Forensics; *Freed Hardeman Christian Col; Child Psych.*

SUBRAHMANYAM, Lakshmi
Hightstown HS; Hightstown, NJ (23-300) Band; Fr C; Hon Prog; Math A; Russian C; Classical Indian Dancing; *Princeton U; Social Sci.*

SUCCO, Julie Ann
Taylors Falls HS; Taylors Falls, MN; Ann; Band; Chor; Ensm; Ger C; Tres, 4H; 4H A; *Anoka Voc Tech Inst; Med Receptionist.*

SUDBRINK, Faye Marie
Western HS; Baltimore, MD; Hmrm; Yth Fel; Weight Control C; *Western Md Col; Sci.*

SUDBURY, Deborah Ann
Rochelle Township HS; Rochelle, IL (6-220) S-T, AFS; Band; Chor; Ensm; Pres, SC; Tres, Sr Cl; Tres, Soph Cl; COM; Citz A; Hon Prog; NEDT; St Scholar; Yth Fel; Century III Ldrs A; All Dist, All Conf, All St, Bands; Tres, Church Yth Fel; Amer Mus Ambassadors European Tour; *Ill Wesleyan U; Pre-Med.*

SUDDERTH, Del Ray
Bovina HS; Bovina, TX (29-45) Band; Secy, FFA; SC; Pres, Soph Cl; Bkbl; Ftbl; Golf; Tr; Cl Fav; Hustler A, FFA; Swine Prod A, FFA; *Tex Tech U; Bus.*

SUDER, Billie Jo
Uniontown Area Sr HS; Uniontown, PA (1-435) Ann; Arch; Chor; Ger C; Hmrm; Math C; Pres, NHS; Rptr, Sch P; Sci C; Span C; Arch; Alg A; COM; Chamber of Comm A; Citz A; Cl Fav; Hist A; Hon Prog; Math A; MLS; Rotary A; Sci A; WW; *Alderson-Broaddus Col; Pre-Med.*

SUDLOW, Leland Clark
Brookings HS; Brookings, SD; Ann; Chor; Dbte Tm; Drama; Ensm; Fr; 4H; NFL; NHS; Sch P; Thes; NMF; *S D St U; Entomology.*

SUDMANN, Terri Kay
Treynor Comm Sch; Treynor, IA (11-48) Co-Ed, Ann; Band; Chor; 4H; Madrigal; NHS; Co-Cpt, Bkbl; Sftbl; Tr; HCt; Hon Prog; Type A; Mus A; Outst Girl Ath; *Midland Lutheran Col; Elem Ed.*

SUEDA, Alison Akie
McKinley HS; Honolulu, HI (37-848) Band; NHS; *U of Hawaii; Sci.*

SUEDA, Joyce N
Laupahoehoe HS; Laupahoehoe, HI (8-39) F-Ed, Ann; Mgr, Wrest; *Hawaii Comm Col; Acct.*

SUFFICOOL, Steven Orrin
Crofton HS; Crofton, NE (11-67) A Cap Choir; Band; BS; Chor; Drama; Ensm; Ger C; Madrigal; NHS; Spch C; SC; Cr-Ctry; Tr; Hon Prog; Spch A; Mus A; Swing Choir; Acting A; HR; Boys Quartet; *Med.*

SUGAR, Karen J
The Buckley Sch; Sherman Oaks, CA (6-52) NHS; Pres, SC; Tnns; MLS; NEDT; *Pol Sci.*

SUGG, Mildred Diane
Houston Co HS; Erin, TN; Ann; Band; 4H; Cl Fav; Yth Fel; Pres, Church Yth; Statistition, Bkbl.

SUGGS, Cheryl Lynn
Baker HS; Columbus, GA (50-300) Hmrm; Span C; Sftbl; Delta Sigma Theta Sorority; *Criminal Justice.*

SUGGS, Lora Ann
Washington HS; Milwaukee, WI; Cpt, Chldr; Ger C; JV, Tr; *U of Milw; Med Work.*

SUGGS, Phyllis Ellen
Belleville HS; Belleville, AR (2-17) Ann; Chor; Pres, FHA; GS; NHS; ARC; Bkbl; Sftbl; Hon Prog; MLS; *Ark Valley Voc Tech Sch; Off Occupation.*

SUGGS, Shelby Jean
Live Oaks Cdc HS; Milford, OH (7-257) Bus C; VP, Jr Cl; Sftbl; Hon Prog; *Cincinnati Tech Col; Data Processing.*

SUGIKAWA, Wane M
Laupahoehoe HS; Laupahoehoe, HI (6-39) NHS; *Hawaii Comm Col; Liberal Arts.*

SUHR, Cynthia Anne
Friendly Sr HS; Oxon Hill, MD (25-550) AFS; Chlr; Drama; Madrigal; Math C; Math A; *William & Mary Col; Law.*

SUITOR, James Edward
Alexander Galt HS; Lennoxville, CANADA (6-439) Band; Hon Prog.

SUKENIS, Carole Jean
Hartshorne HS; Hartshorne, OK; S-T, Drama; NHS; S-T, Thes; S-T, Jr Cl; Bkbl; Alg A; Bio A; COM; Hist A; HCt; Math A; Odd Fellow Fin; Sci A; Type A; VFW A; FCA; Stu o-t Yr; 3rd Oratory, Curriculum Contest; 3rd Prose Interp, Curriculum Con.

SULLENGER, Venessa Jane
Bradleyville HS; Bradleyville, MO (1-20) Co-Cpt, Chldr; Chor; Pres, Fr C.

SULLIVAN, Anita Rose
Craigmont HS; Memphis, TN (25%-500) DAR Essay A; *Memphis St U; Psych.*

SULLIVAN, Beth Ann
St Louise de Marillac HS; Northfield, IL (1-175) Ann; Chldr; InterClub Coun; SC; JV, Bkbl; Tnns; Math A; Spch A; Fr A; Bkbl Trophies; *U of Notre Dame; Math.*

SULLIVAN, Betty Sue
Battiest HS; Battiest, OK (4-24) F-Ed, Ann; Chor; *Southeastern Okla St U; Secretarial.*

SULLIVAN, Catherine Ann
Archbold Area Sch; Archbold, OH; A Cap Choir; Band; Chor; Ensm; Bsbl; Tnns; *Bowling Green St U; Phys Ed.*

SULLIVAN, Colby Corrin
Summit HS; Frisco, CO (1-85) A Cap Choir; F-Ed, Ann; Chldr; Chor; Pres, FHA; Secy, InterAct C; Bkbl; HCt; Hon Prog; MLS; Val; *Southwest Baptist Col; Occupational Therapy.*

SULLIVAN, Cynthia Denise
S Grand Prairie HS; Grand Prairie, TX; Chor.

SULLIVAN, Danette Ruth
Auburn HS; Auburn, NY (4-615) Math C; NHS; Rptr, Sch P; Tres, Sci C; Hon Prog; NMS; Regent Schol; Star Student; WW; *Biol.*

SULLIVAN, Davis Paul
Portsmouth HS; Portsmouth, OH (18-263) Band; Bkbl; MVP, Sftbl; Tr; Hon Prog; Grade Spelling Champ Schol; Fresh Distinction; *Mount Vernon Nazarene Col; Religion.*

SULLIVAN, Glenna Faye
Burnside HS; Burnside, KY (3-70) Tres, BC; Alg A; Poet A; Eng A; Beta o-t Yr.

SULLIVAN, Jack
John Adams Sr HS; Cleveland, OH (135-658) VP, Chor; Drama; Ensm; Parl, Hmrm; Madrigal; Ed, Sch P; SC; JV, Ftbl; COM; Citz A; Journ A; Most Out; Q&S A; Rotary A; Yth Fel; VP, Radio C; Solo Contest; WW; Cleveland Orch Stu Chorale; Mr John Adams HS; All City Chor; Comm Pageant King; *Ohio U; Communications.*

SULLIVAN, Kathleen Anne
Norwood HS; Norwood, CO (2-33) Ann; Band; Chldr; Chor; Drama; NHS; Spch C; Tres, Soph Cl; Tr; NMS; NEDT; Spch A; Type A; *Mesa Col; Bus.*

SULLIVAN, Kathleen Marie
St Mary's HS; Lynn, MA (5-117) Chor; Span C; Bkbl; Co-Cpt, Ftbl; Tres, Photography C; Most Talented; Outing C; Yrbk Photographer; SIGN A; *U of Maine; Span.*

SULLIVAN, Kathy Jean
Taylorville HS; Taylorville, IL; Band; Drama; Hmrm; Rptr, Sch P; SC.

SULLIVAN, Kelley Ann
Metropolis Comm HS; Metropolis, IL (18-172) Mu Alpha Theta; Secy, NHS; S-T, Sci C; St Scholar; VP, Pep C; Jr Civitan; Hi-Tri; *Murray St U; Lib Sci.*

SULLIVAN, Kelly Ann
Clay Center Pub Sch; Clay Center, NE (2-34) Chor; Drama; Ensm; NHS; Span C; Spch C; Y-Tns; Sftbl; Tr; Pres A; Pep C; Jr Amer Legion Auxiliary; Vlbl; 1st Pl, Tnns; Sch Evaluation Comm; *U of Nebr; Pre-Med.*

SULLIVAN, Laura Ellen
Hillcrest HS; Dallas, TX (70-350) Lat C; Mgr, Swim; *Austin Col; Religion.*

SULLIVAN, Laurie R
St Joseph HS; Ogden, UT (1-36) Model UN; NHS; Tnns; COM; NEDT; Pres A; VP, Fresh Cl; Vlbl; Fr A.

SULLIVAN, Linda Carol
Freedom HS; Morganton, NC; Chor; *Randolph Tech Col; Interior Design.*

SULLIVAN, Lisa Anne
Hightstown HS; Hightstown, NJ; Band; Chldr; Chor; Drama; Ger C; 4H; Hmrm; Mjrte; Sch P; Ski C; Var C; Pres, Soph Cl; Bkbl; Hockey; Sftbl; Tr; HCt; Spch A; *Princeton U; Sci.*

SULLIVAN, Mary Loretta
Gridley Union HS; Gridley, CA (131-164) CYO; FNA; Ger C; JV, Bkbl; Swim; JV, Tnns; *U of Santa Clara; Sci.*

SULLIVAN, Melony Jean
Washington HS; Washington, NC (48-280) Chor; NHS; Span C; Span NHS; Acteens A; Church Yth Coun; *E Carolina U; Early Childhood Development.*

SULLIVAN, Neil Scott
Stafford Sr HS; Falmouth, VA (35-470) BS; Hmrm; InterClub Coun; Pres, Key C; Lat C; NHS; Ski C; Tnns; HCt; Phy A; Jaycees Oustt Stu o-t Month; *U of Va; Architecture.*

SULLIVAN, Patricia Carolyn
Woodward Sch For Arts; Quincy, MA (3-11) Chor; Madrigal; VP, SC; Pres, Sr Cl; Pres, Jr Cl; Pres, Soph Cl; Citz A; Hist A; Hon Prog; Pres A; Pres, Fresh Cl; WW; SG; VP & Secy, Yth Fel; Fr A; Mus A; *Eastern Nazarene Col; Special Ed.*

SULLIVAN, Patrick Brian
Falls Church HS; Falls Church, VA (140-450) Drama; JV, Cr-Ctry; Tr; *Va Tech U; Forestry.*

SULLIVAN, Paul Clayton
Ulysses HS; Ulysses, KS (2-97) Band; Dbte Tm; Ensm; NFL; NHS; Var C; Mgr, Bkbl; Mgr, Ftbl; Tr; Spch A; Band A; Ath A; *Fort Hays Kans St Col; Chem.*

SULLIVAN, Peggy Kathleen
Clay Center Pub Sch; Clay Center, NE (6-33) Ed, Ann; Band; CYO; Cpt, Chldr; Chor; Fin, Drama; Ensm; Jr Miss Pagent; Mjrte; Rptr, NHS; Span C; Spch C; SC; Var C; Pres, Y-Tns; Sftbl; Tr; DARGCA; Most Out; Pres A; Spch A; Vlbl; St Spch Champ; Jr Amer Legion; Sch Evaluation Comm; *U of Nebr; Creative Writing.*

SULLIVAN, Robert Dean
G W Carver Sr HS; Montgomery, AL; Band; Ensm; Fr C; Orch; Ch, ARC; ARC A; Pres, Mac Dowell Jr Mus C; Sup Musician, Mus Festival; Mus Workshop Schol; Handbell Choir; Church Organist; *U of Sou Miss; Church Mus.*

SULLIVAN, Sharon Ann
Raleigh HS; Raleigh, MS (33%-75) Ann; BC; Chldr; FHA; Rptr, Hmrm; Sch P; Sci C; Span C; Tri-HiY; Amer Leg A; Ann Staff A; Paper Staff A; 3rd Pl, Sci Fair; *Jones Co Jr Col; Nurs.*

SULLIVAN, Tammy Gayle
Harlingen HS; Harlingen, TX (20%-657) FHA; Mjrte; Sch P; Span C; SC; Leader, Drill Tm; Excel A, Outst; *Tyler Jr Col; Gen Bus Adm.*

SULLIVAN, Tracy Elizabeth
Summit HS; Frisco, CO (25%-80) A Cap Choir; Bkbl; Sftbl; Tnns; Bsbl A; Bkbl A.

SULLIVAN, Van Albert
Tullahoma HS; Tullahoma, TN (3-300) BC; Lat C; Math C; NHS; Tr; Hist A; *U of Tenn; Vet Med.*

SULLIVAN, Virginia Marie
Dwight D Eisenhower HS; Washington, MI (20-350) Secy, CYO; NHS; Tres, Span C; Hon Prog; *Mich St U; Med.*

SULLIVAN, Wendy Ann
Colonial HS; Orlando, FL (20%-1000) Bus C; GS; Hmrm; InterClub Coun; NHS; Sch P; Span C; Span NHS; SC; Tri-HiY; COM; Hon Prog; Yth Fel; Dade Co Vol; Prs Pryr Breakfast Cong Invitation; *Gardner-Webb Col; Psych.*

SULLIVAN, William Timothy
Big Sandy HS; Big Sandy, TN (8-25) Ann; BS; Bsbl; Bkbl; Cr-Ctry; Tr; Yth Fel; Yth Leg; Parl, VICA C; *U of Tenn; Soc.*

SULLIVAN, Winfrey
Westwood HS; Memphis, TN (3-212) Hmrm; Lit Mag; VP, Math C; NHS; A-Ed, Sch P; Sci C; Span C; Tnns; Alg A; Cl Fav; Hon Prog; MLS; NMS; Yth Fel; Civitan C A; *Ga Inst of Tech; Chem Engr.*

SULLIVANT, Edwin Randall Jr
Ganesha HS; Pomona, CA (40-400) Secy, Key C; Ftbl; COM; I Dare You; Pres A; *Calif Poly Tech U; Bio.*

SULLIVANT, Patti Lynn
Franklin Road Christian Sch; Murfreesboro, TN (2-7) A Cap Choir; F-Ed, Ann; Cpt, Chldr; Drama; Spch C; Bkbl; Sftbl; COM; Most Out; Co-Cpt, Chldr; Church Sports Qn; *Hyles Anderson Col; Ed.*

SULLY, Mary Frances
Blair Sr HS; Blair, NE (100-175) Co-Cpt, Band; CYO; Chldr; JV, Chor; S-T, Dbte Tm; Drama; Drama; FBLA; FHA; FNA; FTA; Fin, GS; Pres, 4H; Hmrm; ARC; A-Ed, Sch P; SC; Thes; Bkbl; Sftbl; COM; Citz A; Cl Fav; 4H A; Co-Cpt, Pom Pom; Comm Theater; Pres, Pep C; Lector; Glee C; GSct; Merit Stu; Mascot; Drill Tm; Stu Director, Contest Play; *Pol Sci.*

SULZBY, Steven Frazee
Fountain Valley HS; Fountain Valley, CA; Bkbl; Hon Prog; *UCLA; Engr.*

SUMBRY, Fredrick
Mount Olive HS; Seale, AL; Ann; Rptr, 4H; Pres, NHS; Pres, Sr Cl; Bkbl; 4H A; Hon Prog; ROTC A.

SUMMERALL, Kandi Lynn
Riverdale HS; Ft Myers, FL (8-350) Secy, BC; Chor; Ensm; Madrigal; NHS; Math A; Spch A; *Edison Comm Col; Ed.*

SUMMERLIN, David Jeffrey
Emma Sansom HS; Gadsden, AL (15%-260) Band; Pres, Hmrm; Span C; JV, Bkbl; Church Orch; Rep, Mayor's Yth Coun; *U of Ala.*

SUMMERLIN, William Gregory
Emma Sansom HS; Gadsden, AL (10%-223) Band; Hmrm; Secy, Math C; NHS; Sch P; Sci C; Span NHS; SC; Var C; Span C; Co-Cpt, Bkbl; Cl Fav; *U of Ala; Bus.*

SUMMERS, Bobbie Jo
Glen Oak HS; Canton, OH (184-730) A Cap Choir; Chor; Drama; Y-Tns; Vlbl; *Oral Roberts U; Psych.*

SUMMERS, Frank Donald
Hamilton HS E; Trenton, NJ (171-755) COM; Yth Fel; Yth Leg; Church Bkbl; VP, Yth Advisory Coun; Corporal, Christian Serv Brigade; *Mercer Co Comm Col; Auto Mech.*

SUMMERS, James Alan
E Hills HS; Ft Worth, TX (17-455) Lat C; NHS; Ftbl; Soccer; Hist A; Summa Cum Laude; N Tex Yth Sem; *U of Tex; Engr.*

SUMMERS, James Craige
Salisbury HS; Salisbury, NC (24-234) AFS; Band; VP, Hmrm; Key C; NHS; Sch P; Tres, Span C; VP, SC; Hon Prog; Jr Rotarian; NC Sen Page; Ed Consortium; Yth in Industry Prog; *Duke U; Bus.*

SUMMERS, James Keith
O D Wyatt HS; Ft Worth, TX; Bsbl; Ftbl; JV, Tr; Math A; Opt A; Gold R A; *N Tex St U; Ind Arts.*

SUMMERS, Jean Denise
Cleveland HS; Cleveland, OK (10%-140) Secy, FHA; Bkbl; Tr; *Okla St U; Eng.*

SUMMERS, Lori Anne
Eldorado Comm HS; Eldorado, IL; Ger C; NHS; Sch P; HR; *Sou Ill U; Phys Therapy.*

SUMMERS, Mary Louise
Valparaiso HS; Valparaiso, IN; Band; TMI; Secy, Yth Group; League Winning Quiz Tm; HR; *Baptist Bible Col of Pa.*

SUMMERS, Sherri Lynn
Gilmer Co HS; Glenville, WV (10-122) Chldr; ARC; Var C; Ch, Y-Tns; Bkbl; Tr; *Parkersburg Comm Col; Bus.*

SUMMERS, Stephanie Ann
Logan Elm HS; Circleville, OH; Band; Tres, 4H; Beauty; 4H A; Pep C; GSct; Band A; *Warner Sou Col; Eng.*

SUMMERS, William Kermig Jr
John S Shaw HS; Mobile, AL (49-415) Chess C; Co-Ch, Ensm; Tres, Key C; NHS; Citz A; Hon Prog; Pres A; *U of S Ala.*

SUMMERTON, Ann Marie
Telstar Regional HS; Bethel, ME; U of Maine.

SUMMEY, Gary Neil
Robert S Tower HS; Warren, MI; Band; Chor; Ensm; Hmrm; Bsbl; Bkbl; Ftbl; Sftbl; COM; Citz A; Hon Prog; Journ A; Yth Fel; Arrow of Light, The Ath, A's; Drama, 1st Aid, Sct A's; U of Mich; Math.

SUMMEY, Rebecca Deniese
Wade Hampton HS; Greenville, SC (127-400) Bus Mgr, Ann; Chor; Ensm; FHA; Hmrm; Lit Mag; SC; Sftbl; Swim; Sr Lifesaver; Sr Couns & Unit Ldr, Church Camp; Winthrop Col; Food & Nutrition.

SUMNER, Darla Kathleen
Tuscaloosa HS; Tuscaloosa, AL; Drama; MLS; VICA; Candy Striper; Civitan; Swtht, Drama C; Art C; Blue Ribbons, Art; U of Ala; Commercial & Fine Arts.

SUMNER, Dennis Wayne
Ramey HS; Ramey, PR (1-21) A-Ed, Ann; Hmrm; NHS; Sci C; SC; Bsbl; JV, Cr-Ctry; Alg A; Bio A; Hist A; Sci A; Eng A; Typing A; Physics A; Span A; Geom A; U S Coast Guard Acad; Engr.

SUMNER, Karie Lynn
Eastern Hills HS; Fort Worth, TX (1-458) Cum Laude Soc; NHS; Sftbl; Tr; Summa Cum Laude; NHS; 100 wpm Shorthand; Ch, Lassie Pep Squad; Tarelton St U; Acct.

SUMNER, Robert Fredrick
Palm Beach Gardens HS; Palm Beach Gardens, FL; Bsbl; Bible Quiz Tm; Eckerd Col; Bus.

SUMNER, Susan
Castleberry HS; Fort Worth, TX; FHA; Math C; NHS; Baylor U; Art.

SUMRALL, Annette Lee
Long Beach Polytechnic HS; Long Beach, CA (100-500) Chldr; Ch, InterAct C; Ski C; SC; Hon Prog; Press, GSct; Cor Sec, Scarabs Sorority; Dance Productions A; Jane Harnett Schol; USC; Bio.

SUMRELL, James Keith
Brookstone Sch; Columbus, GA (25-70) Chor; Drama; Cpt, Bkbl; Ftbl; Tr; U of Ga; Conservation.

SUMRELL, Patricia Glenn
Brookstone Sch; Columbus, GA (2-38) Cpt, Chldr; Chor; Cum Laude Soc; French NHS; Secy, Math C; Mu Alpha Theta; Bkbl; Cpt, Soccer; Cpt, Tr; COM; Gov Honor Prog; Hon Prog; Math A; NEDT; Pres A; Col Trustee Merit Schol; Converse Col; Mus.

SUN, Mary Houn
George Washington HS; Denver, CO (2-693) Chor; Community Yth Group; NHS; Hmrm; Pres, NHS; Orch; Ch, SC; Tnns; COM; Hon Prog; Most Out; Opt Out Tn; GAA; JV, Vlbl; Jr Escort; VP, Tres, Church Yth Group; Campus Life; All St Orch; Ch, Caduceus C; Northwestern U; Pre-Med.

SUND, Marilyn Jean
Braham HS; Braham, MN (3-87) Ann; FHA; 4H; NHS; Span; Secy, SC; Secy, Jr Cl; Tr; Cl Fav; Vlbl; Bemidji St U; Social Work.

SUNDBERG, Brent Alan
Mason Sr HS; Mason, MI (5%-388) Band; VP, Fr C; NHS; SC; JV, Ftbl; JV, Wrest; 1st Pl, Creative Writing; Computer Engr.

SUNDBERG, Patricia Ann
Westside HS; Omaha, NE (130-787) AFS; Chor; Fr C; SC; Hon Prog; Yth Fel; U of Nebr; Psych.

SUNDBERG, Sherryl Anne
Mason Sr HS; Mason, MI (10%-275) Band; Jr NHS; 1st Division, St Solo & Ensm; Pensacola Christian Col; Bio.

SUNDELL, Cynthia Lee
Rutherford HS; Rutherford, NJ (10-237) VP, Key C; NHS; Sch P; Tnns; COM; Bronze Key A; Silver Key A; Gold Key A; Douglass Col; Bio.

SUNDERLAND, Debra Kay
Cumberland Valley HS; Mechanicsburg, PA (11-564) A Cap Choir; Band; Chor; Math C; NHS; VP, Span; NHS; Cl Pres; Yth Fel; 1st Cl Sct; Dist Band & Choir; Bridgewater Col; Psych.

SUNDERMANN, Susan Beth
Treynor Comm HS; Treynor, IA (8-48) Band; Drama; Pres, 4H; Semi-Fin, Jr Miss Pa; NHSt; Bkbl; Swim; Beauty; 4H A; Spch A; Type A; St Achv A; Ntl Ldrship Conf; General Mills Ldr of Tomorrow; Park Princess; Miss Ldrship; Iowa St U; Sci.

SUNDLOFF, Mark Douglas
Eau Gallie HS; Melbourne, FL; Ann; BC; BS; Dbte Tm; NHS; Span NHS; Bsbl; Cr-Ctry; Swim; U of Fla; Journ.

SUNDQUIST, Kathleen April
New Buffalo HS; New Buffalo, MI (10-100) Band; Chor; Drama; Secy, Ski C; VP, Thes; U of Mich; Law.

SUNDRY, Craig Alan
Wanamingo Pub Sch; Wanamingo, MN (15-41) Band; Chor; Drama; Ensm; VP, Soph Cl; Co-Cpt, Bsbl; Bkbl; Co-Cpt, Ftbl; HCt; Acct.

SUNDSTEDT, Sonia Lyn
Davenport W HS; Davenport, IA; A Cap Choir; Co-Ed, Ann; Band; Chor; Drama; Ensm; Fr C; Rptr, 4H; Orch; Rptr, Sch P; Thes; COM; Citz A; Pep C; GAA; Church Tres; Iowa City Col; Eng.

SUNDWALL, Joan Terri
Pekin Comm HS; Pekin, IL (142-807) Band; St Grand Rep, Job's Daughters; Bradley U.

SUNESON, Ann Marie
Oregon HS; Oregon, IL (1-110) AFS; Band; Ensm; NHS; Co-Ed, Sch P; Span C; HCt; Hon Prog; Pom Pon Squad; U of Wisc; Phys Therapy.

SUNGALA, Carol Marie
Brashear HS; Pittsburgh, PA (4-177) NHS; Co-Ed, Sch P; Tnns; Hon Prog; Journ A; Type A.

SUNICH, Mary Anne
Driscoll HS; Addison, IL (5-144) Chor; Lit Mag; NHS; Span C; Tnns; Tr; Hon Prog; St Scholar; U of Ill; Biomed Engr.

SUNNARBORG, Bev A
Hibbing HS; Hibbing, MN (5%-450) Chor; Math C; NFL; Spch C; COM; Hon Prog; Math A; Spch A; Yth Foundation; Yth Foundation A; JA; Med Explorer's Post; NFL, Degree of Merit; NFL, Degree of Honor; St Olaf Col; Med.

SUNNARBORG, David Earl
Hibbing HS; Hibbing, MN (13-431) Chor; NFL; NHS; Sch P; Sci C; Spch C; COM; Spch A; Natl Fed Mus C; St Paul Bible Col; Bible.

SUNSHINE, Bettyann
Woodrow Wilson HS; Washington, DC; A Cap Choir; Religion.

SUNTKEN, Donna Lee
Triad HS; St Jacob, IL (11-212) Chor; Dbte Tm; Ger C; Model UN; NHS; Co-Ed, Sch P; Dist Bicentennial Yth Debate; Chor Ltr; Journ.

SUNTKEN, Gloria Ann
Belmond HS; Belmond, IA (11-76) Band; Chor; NHS; SC; Var C; VP, Sr Cl; Co-Cpt, Bkbl; MVP, Sftbl; Co-Cpt, Tr; Citz A; Hon Prog; Yth Fel; MVP, Bkbl & Tr; Winter Sports Qn; All-St Sftbl & Bkbl; U of SD; Therapeutic Recreation.

SUPKOSKI, Elaine Marie
John S Fine HS; Nanticoke, PA; Band; Drama; Hmrm; Key C; NEDT; PTA A; Sci A; Art A's; Wilkes Col; Nurs.

SUPKOSKI, Karen Anne
John S Fine HS; Nanticoke, PA (9-297) Band; Chor; Hmrm; Var C; COM; NEDT; PTA A; Sci A; Art A; Wilkes Col; Nurs.

SURGENT, Paul Gerard
Riverside HS; Taylor, PA (6-196) Pres, CYO; Ger C; Hmrm; NHS; Rptr, Sch P; Ski C; VP, Sr Cl; Co-Cpt, Ftbl; Co-Cpt, Tr; NEDT; Sacristan; Agr.

SURGEON, Gary Alan
Springfield Sr HS; Springfield, OR (10%-300) Hmrm; Sch P; Co-Cpt, Soccer; U of Oreg; Med.

SURGES, Michael James
Joliet Cath HS; Joliet, IL (34-194).

SURGES, Robert Lee
Joliet Cath HS; Joliet, IL (48-178) Hon Cert; Schol A; Joliet Jr Col; Acct.

SURLES, Jason Matthew
James Monroe HS; Fredericksburg, VA (15-165) Bus Mgr, Ann; Band; BS; Demolay; Secy, Fr C; Hmrm; Mod Mus Mas; Secy, NHS; Orch; Ski C; Thes; Hon Prog; Q&S A; U of Richmond; Bus Adm.

SURNEY, Michael Lawrence
Pittsburg HS; Pittsburg, CA; Band; FFA; Co-Cpt, Bkbl; Ftbl; Hon Prog; Los Medanas Col; Computer Tech.

SURRENCY, Kimberly Denise
Wayne Co HS; Jesup, GA; Ann; Gov Honor Prog; Hon Prog.

SURRETT, Douglas Mark
Louden HS; Loudon, TN (30-125) Rptr, FFA; InterAct C; NHS; Sci C; SC; Bkbl; E Tenn St U; Acct.

SURRY, George Frank
Foley HS; Foley, AL; CYO; Fr C; Key C; Order/ Arrow; Ftbl; Spch A; Life Sct; Challenger A; Pres, Explorer Post; Most Dedicated, Ftbl; Bio.

SUSLECK, Dacy Carol
Shenandoah Valley Acad; New Market, VA (10-77) Ed, Ann; Sou Missionary Col; Office Mgr.

SUSMAN, Robert Michael
Waukegan E HS; Waukegan, IL (98-498) A Cap Choir; Chor; Ensm; Ed, Lit Mag; Madrigal; Pres, Mod Mus Mas; NHS; Debate Participation; Bradley U.

SUSONG, Martha Lane
Greeneville HS; Greeneville, TN; Pres, Anchor C; Fr C; FBLA; Mgr, Bkbl; U of Tenn.

SUTCLIFFE, Carolyn
Highland HS; Pocatello, ID (37-466) Dbte Tm; Fr C; Pres, Lat C; NHS; A-Ed, Sch P; Ski C; Tr; Spch A; Publicity Ch, Secy, TORCH; VP, Church Yth; Sunday Sch Teacher; Stu Del, PTA; Idaho St U; Hist.

SUTER, Dirk Lyon
Montpelier HS; Montpelier, OH (33%-100) BS; Chor; Var C; JV, Ftbl; Swim; Tr; Amer Leg A; Citz A; God & Country A; Pres, Yth Fel; Mus A.

SUTER, Karen Bertha
Morton Jr Sr HS; Morton, WA; Chor; Ensm; FFA; FHA; Semi-Fin, GS; NHS; Span C; Tres, SC; Var C; Bkbl; Tr; Citz A; Lion A; Cpt, Vlbl; Centralia Col; Med.

SUTHERIN, Paige Lynne
Toronto HS; Toronto, OH (33-143) Chldr; Chor; Fr C; Bkbl; Mgr, Sftbl; Tr; Citz A; Ohio Valley Sch of Nurs; Nurs.

SUTHERLAND, Ann Cox
McLean HS; McLean, VA (11-430) Chor; Drama; Fr C; French NHS; Hmrm; InterClub Coun; VP, Madrigal; Mod Mus Mas; NHS; Thes; COM; Gov Honor Prog; VP, Booster C; Church Yth Group; Fairfax Hosp Auxiliary; Piano Solo A; Ntl Fedof Mus C.

SUTHERLAND, James Brooks
George Wythe HS; Wytheville, VA (5-143) Band; Hmrm; Mu Alpha Theta; NHS; Order/Arrow; Sci C; SC; Tr; VPI; Math.

SUTHERLAND, Jeffrey Wayne
Williams HS; Plano, TX (10%-1000) Band; Band King; Harding Christian; Mus.

SUTHERLAND, Karie Lee
Landmark Christian Sch; Evendale, OH; Chldr; Chor; Mus A; Gym; Co-Cpt, Spirit C; Church Pianist; Secy, Crusaders; Mus.

SUTHERLAND, Sally Elaine
LeRoy HS; LeRoy, KS (5-27) Bus Mgr, Ann; NHS; Rptr, Sch P; Tr.

SUTHERLAND, Suzette Hope
Patrick Henry HS; Glade Spring, VA; Band; 4H; Tri-HiY; Gov Honor Prog; 4H A; Lat A; All Co, All Regional Band; 4-H All St Band; Emory & Henry Col; Med.

SUTHERLIN, Brenda Kaye
Chickasaw Acad; Prichard, AL; F-Ed, Ann; BC; NHS; Pres, Sr Cl; Tres, Jr Cl; Beauty; Cl Fav; HCt; Hon Prog; Best All Around; Mobile Col; Psych.

SUTLER, Diana Lee
Stonewall Jackson HS; Charleston, WV (10%-275) F-Ed, Ann; 4H; Pres, Hmrm; Lat C; F-Ed, Sch P; VP, Sci C; Tres, SC; Y-Tns; Mgr, Bkbl; COM; Citz A; Pres A; Yth Fel; Pres, DECA; JCL; *Commercial Photography.*

SUTPHIN, David William
Duval Sr HS; Seabrook, MD; Chess C; Hmrm; Lat C; Math C; SC; Bsbl; Bkbl; Ftbl; COM; Hon Prog; Math A; *Law.*

SUTPHIN, Vicki Lynn
Duval Sr HS; Seabrook, MD; FTA; Hmrm; Span C; SC; Bsbl; Bkbl; Sftbl; Swim; Amer Leg A; COM; Hon Prog; Pres A; Spch A; Yth Fel; Boys C; Jim Evans A; *U of Md; Christian Ed.*

SUTTER, Beth Ann
Laurel Valley Jr Sr HS; New Florence, PA (36-126) AFS; Bus Mgr, Ann; Band; Tres, FBLA; Ch, Hmrm; NFL; Spch A; *Bus.*

SUTTER, Jennifer McCune
Thomas Jefferson HS; Jefferson, PA (40%-380) A Cap Choir; Chor; Drama; Co-Ed, Lit Mag; Rainbow; Ski C; SC; Hon Prog; Yth Fel; Ordained Elder; Choir; Voice; Tutor; Creative Writing A; Art A; Drama A; *Christian Ed.*

SUTTER, Richard Donald
Thomas Jefferson HS; Jefferson Borough, PA (40%-400) A Cap Choir; Chor; Golf; Tr; Athletic Letters; Top Salesman; *Bus.*

SUTTLE, Jenifer Ann
Pampa HS; Pampa, TX (195-350) Bus C; FHA; ARC; Cr-Ctry; Tr; Tr; *W Tex St U; Secy.*

SUTTLE, Kelli Sue
Attica HS; Attica, IN (2-98) Ed, Ann; Drama; Pres, FTA; NHS; A-Ed, Sch P; Span C; SC; Tr; Sal; GAA; Best Server, Vlbl; *Ind U; Phys Therapy.*

SUTTLE, Myra Jo
Druid HS; Tuscaloosa, AL; Secy, Ann; Band; Fr C; NHS; Ntl Yth Conf; Secy, SC; Alg A; Sci A; *NC A&T St U; Engr.*

SUTTLES, Shirley Jean
Jasper Co Comp HS; Monticello, GA (4-65) FHA; SC; Outst Jr; *Lee Col; Bus.*

SUTTON, Bobby Derrell Jr
First Baptist Church HS; Shreveport, LA (18-46) Band; Chem C; VP, 4H; Sci C; Ski C; SC; Bkbl; Ftbl; COM; Chem A; 4H A; Sci A; Spch A; *La Tech U; Pre-Med.*

SUTTON, Derek Leigh
Bainbridge HS; Bainbridge Island, WA (20-180) BS; Pres, Dbte Tm; Hmrm; NFL; NHS; Parl, SC; JV, Bkbl; Soccer; Tnns; DARGCA; Spch A; St Debate A; *U of Wash; Bus Law.*

SUTTON, Dixie Byrd
Wilcox HS; Rochelle, GA (8-97) Ann; VP, BC; Cpt, Chldr; VP, FHA; Pres, 4H; Sch P; SC; Var C; Pres, Jr Cl; Rptr, Soph Cl; Cpt, Bkbl; Cl Fav; 4H A; HQn; Hon Prog; Yth Leg.

SUTTON, Donna Lucille
W Craven HS; Vanceboro, NC (2-160) Dbte Tm; Fr C; Pres, NHS; Sci C; Bio A; Hist A; HCt; Sal; *U of NC at Chapel Hill; Ed.*

SUTTON, Elizabeth Kay
Washington Co HS; Springfield, KY (1-211) Band; BC; 4H; Sci A; 4th Dist Sr HS Band; *Stephens Col; Sci.*

SUTTON, James Philip
Garner HS; Garner, NC (90-520) Drama; Cr-Ctry; Tr; Math A; Ntl Math Exam Achv A; *U of NC; Math.*

SUTTON, Katherine Hines
Sou Wayne Sr HS; Dudley, NC (10%-461) Ann; Band; BC; Chor; FHA; FTA; Secy, 4H; 4H A; *U of NC; Computer Processing.*

SUTTON, Kimberly Ball
John F Kennedy HS; Cleveland, OH; Fin, Hmrm; SC; COM; Citz A; HQn; *Bishop Col; Systems Analyst.*

SUTTON, Kristi Kay
Royal HS; Simi Valley, CA (81-846) NHS.

SUTTON, Pam Irene
Amer Christian Acad; Pomona, CA (1-31) Chor; Citz A; Hon Prog; *Pacific Christian Col; Ed.*

SUTTON, Pamela Irene
American Christian Acad; Pomona, CA; Ann; Chor; Math C; COM; Citz A; Yth Fel; Sunday Sch Teacher; *Pacific Christian Col; Elem Teacher.*

SUTTON, Pamela Jane
Irwin Co HS; Ocilla, GA (2-120) Ann; BC; Dbte Tm; Fin, GS; 4H; Tres, SC; Thes; Secy, Tri-HiY; Tnns; COM; Gov Honor Prog; 4H A; I Dare You; JA A; Yth Leg; Ga Key A; WW; Hon Stu; *Valdosta St Col; Bus.*

SUTTON, Paula Ann
Centennial HS; Gresham, OR; Band; Ed, Sch P; Tnns; Val; *Lewis & Clark Col; Ed.*

SUTTON, Randy James
Temple Baptist Acad; Denver, CO (10%-54) NHS; Bsbl; Bkbl; Ftbl; Tr; *Bible.*

SUTTON, Richard Evans
Hemet HS; Hemet, CA; A Cap Choir; Band; Ch, Order/Arrow; JV, Bsbl; Order/Arrow A; Eagle Sct; Ch, Order o-t Arrow A.

SUTTON, Sandi Gail
Malvern Sr HS; Malvern, AR (46-269) Secy, A Cap Choir; Ann; BC; 4H; Sch P; Journ A; Q&S A; *Ouachita Baptist U; Nurs.*

SUTTON, Stephanie Georjette
Kingsway Regional HS; Swedesboro, NJ (22-170) NHS; SC; Hockey; HCt.

SUTTON, Susan Delaine
Houston HS; Houston, MO (8-122) Band; VP, Chor; Drama; Ensm; Pres, NHS; Spch C; Pres, SC; HCt; Math A; Spch A; Drama A; Miss Talent; Fr A; Miss Merrie Christmas; Band A; Fin, Miss Mo Ntl Teenager; *Joplin Col; Mus.*

SUTTON, Wanda Lynne
Russellville HS; Russellville, AL (19-170) Band; Chor; FHA; Monogram; Mu Alpha Theta; Sch P; Top 10%; *U of N Ala; Eng.*

SUTTON, Willard Timothy
Greenville Christian Acad; Greenville, NC (1-12) Ann; Chor; Drama; Pres, Hmrm; SC; Var C; Cpt, Bkbl; Cl Fav; *Tenn Temple Col; Math.*

SUTTON, William Robert
Danville Comm HS; Danville, IN (2-157) Band; Parl, BS; Chor; Drama; Ger C; NFL; Parl, NHS; Pres, Spch C; Pres, SC; Thes; NMF; Spch A; Vof-DEM; Eagle Sct; *Rose-Hulman Inst; Physics.*

SUVER, Linda Kay
Johnstown-Monroe HS; Johnstown, OH (6-134) Ann; Band; Drama; Pres, 4H; Hmrm; Secy, NHS; A-Ed, Sch P; Span C; VP, SC; COM; 4H A; Math A; NEDT; *Ohio St U; Adm Sci.*

SVALSTAD, Gregg Brian
Fountain Valley HS; Fountain Valley, CA (19-1005) Bkbl; CSF; Summa Cum Laude; Campus Life; Vlbl.

SVANDA, Cauleen Rene
Ogallala Sr HS; Ogallala, NE (13-147) Band; NHS; Var C; Tr; *Health Sci.*

SVOBODA, Charles Martin
Apollo HS; Simi Valley, CA; Drama; Hmrm; Inter-Act C; ARC; Sch P; Ski C; Pres, SC; Bkbl; *U of Calif; Vet.*

SVOBODA, James Kelly
Nederland HS; Nederland, TX (200-489) Ch, CYO; Co-Cpt, Ftbl; Cl Fav; All Dist, All Area Ftbl; Ftbl Schol; *U of Tex; Phar.*

SVOBODA, Robin Kim
Cloverleaf HS; Lodi, OH (10-265) Band; Chor; Drama; Ensm; 4H; NHS; Thes; Sftbl; COM; 4H A; Hist A; Vlbl; S-T, Luther League; Eng, Fr, Schol A's; *Kent St U; Foreign Lang.*

SWABY, Susan Nadine
Stranahan Sr HS; Fort Lauderdale, FL (9-450) Secy, 4H; Secy, NHS; DARGCA; 4H A; Hon Prog; Drill Tm; Varsity Ltr; Jr Exchangettes A; WW; HR; AAL All-Col Schol Prog Semi-Fin; *Florida Southern College; Psychology.*

SWADLEY, Rick
Richardson HS; Richardson, TX (25%-1000) Band; NHS; Sftbl.

SWADLEY, Steven Howard
Richardson HS; Richardson, TX (25%-975) A Cap Choir; Chor; Madrigal; Co-Cpt, Ftbl; Sftbl; *Baylor U; Mus.*

SWAFFER, Regina Louise
Campus HS; Wichita, KS; Bible Quiz A; *Okla City Col; Elem Ed.*

SWAFFER, Veronica Arlette
Campus HS; Wichita, KS; COM; Spch A; Explorers C; Bible Quiz.

SWAFFORD, Bradley Scot
Smackover HS; Smackover, AR (8-55) Rptr, Anchor C; Band; FTA; Math C; Span C; Bsbl; Bkbl; Ftbl; Golf; Sftbl; Tnns; Tr; All Co & All Dist Ftbl; *Tex A&M U; Marine Biol.*

SWAFFORD, Janet Ann
Smackover HS; Smackover, AR (10-59) Anchor C; Ann; Band; Tres, FBLA; FTA; Pres, Spch C; COM; HCt; Math A; Q&S A; *Ouachita Baptist U; Special Ed.*

SWAFFORD, Linda Diane
Fairdale HS; Fairdale, KY; FBLA; Soccer; *U of Louisville; Art.*

SWAFFORD, Patricia Ann
Sam Houston HS; Arlington, TX; A Cap Choir; FTA; *UTA; Art.*

SWAFFORD, Robert Ralph
Odessa HS; Odessa, TX (25%-700) A Cap Choir; Chor; Semi-Fin, Dbte Tm; VP, Demolay; Drama; FTA; NFL; Order/Arrow; Thes; Ftbl; Swim; Hist A; Opt A; Order/Arrow A; Spch A; Win, St DAR Essay Contest; Ntl Eagle Sct Assn; *U of Tex; Law.*

SWAIM, Rebecca Ann
Rockville HS; Rockville, IN (10-83) Band; Chor; FHA; Tres, 4H; NHS; Pres, Rainbow; 4H A; God & Comm A; *Ind Bus Col; Adm Secy.*

SWAIN, Barbara Joan
Kenwood HS; Chicago, IL (45-450) Span C; Swim; Math A; Val.

SWAIN, David Gibson
Middleton HS; Charleston, SC (100-325) Band; Band A's & Ltr's; *U of SC; Dentistry.*

SWAIN, Jane Morgan
Plymouth HS; Plymouth, NC (30-200) Chldr; Drama; Fr C; Math C; Monogram; Sci C; Tnns; Rifle Corps; Concert Band; Senate Pagette, St Gen Assembly; Secy, FCA; *U of NC; Pol Sci.*

SWAIN, Susan Gaynell
Bethany HS; Reidsville, NC; Anchor C; BC; Tres, FHA; Sch P; Math A; Hist A; WW; *Rockingham Comm Col; Secy.*

SWAMY, Edgar Udaya
Lakeview HS; Battle Creek, MI (20%-400) Band; Ensm; Ch, Hmrm; NFL; NHS; SC; Soccer; Sftbl; MAIG & AIG Mu A; Major Fred Beech Mem A; Outst CAP Cadet; CAP Drill Tm; *Western Mich U; Flight Tech.*

SWAN, Bryan Edward
Claremore HS; Claremore, OK; NHS; Cpt, Bsbl; Ftbl; Pres, FCA; *Tulsa U; Engr.*

SWAN, Cindy Lou
Sahuaro HS; Tucson, AZ (54-685) A-Ed, Ann; Chor; Ensm; Hmrm; NHS; COM; Hon Prog; Poet A; Sup, St Solo & Ensm; All St Choir; Female Lead, Sch Play; *U of Ariz; Mus.*

SWAN, Cindy Lou
Horseheads Sr HS; Horseheads, NY (23-573) Chor; Drama; Fr C; NHS; Tres, Ski C; UN Council; Regent Schol; Sr Ball Court; *St U of NY; Psych.*

SWAN, Ingrid
Mahar Regional HS; Orange, MA; Band; Fr C; Hmrm; NHS; Mgr, Bkbl; Hockey; Sftbl; Yth Fel.

SWAN, Julie Lynn
Bloomington HS; Bloomington, IL (10-450) Co-Ed, Ann; Band; Secy, Drama; Ensm; Fr C; NHS; Orch; Cpt, Spch C; Pres, Thes; Spch A; St Scholar; Drum Major; St Fin, Spch; Best Actress A; *Harding Christian Col; Spch & Drama.*

SWAN, Lesa Ann
Balaton Pub HS; Balaton, MN; Band; Chor; VP, Hmrm; Bkbl; Golf; COM; Type A; Bkbl & Vlbl Ltr As; *Handicap Therapy.*

SWAN, Thomas Brian
Lompoc Sr HS; Lompoc, CA (20%-200) Band; Bkbl; Golf; *Allan Hancock Col.*

SWAN, Virginia Layne
Thomson HS; Thomson, GA (10%-280) BC; FHA; Cert of Achv; Pres, MYF; Chapter Homemakers Degree; Govs Hon Prog Nom; Activities Ch, Campus Life; *Ga Col.*

SWANHORST, Wendy J
Cresbard HS; Cresbard, SD; Bus Mgr, Ann; Band; Chor; Bus Mgr, Sch P; SC; Pres, Var C; S-T, Soph Cl; MVP, Bkbl; Sftbl; Tr; Journ A; Type A.

SWANIGAN, Camille Ruth
Buffalo HS; Buffalo, MO (10-180) A Cap Choir; Band; Chor; Ensm; Fr C; FHA; Spch C; Alg A; Hon Prog; Math A; Type A; Piano Guild; St Mus Festival; *SW Baptist Col; Mus.*

SWANK, Jamie Diane
Miami HS; Miami, OK (3-216) Band; Bus C; CYO; Drama; Fr C; Hmrm; Math C; Mu Alpha Theta; NHS; Thes; COM; Hon Prog; Stu o-t Mon; *Northeastern A&M Col; Bus Adm.*

SWANK, Stuart Oscar
Waukegan E HS; Waukegan, IL; Hockey.

SWANK, Susan Jessie
Waukegan E HS; Waukegan, IL (174-629) Kans City U of Art School; *Art.*

SWANKE, Susan M
Lakota HS; Lakota, ND (3-43) Ann; Band; Chldr; Chor; Ensm; FHA; GS; Madrigal; Secy, NHS; Sch P; Tres, SC; Bkbl; B Crocker A; HCt; I Dare You; Lion A; ROTC A; Sal; *ND St U; Pharmacy.*

SWANLUND, Jean Ann
Tartan Sr HS; Oakdale, MN; Band; Chor; Ski C; Sftbl; Swim; JA A; *U of Minn; Law.*

SWANN, Steve Philip
Temple Christian Sch; Rockville, MD (5%-5) Ed, Ann; Chor; Ensm; VP, SC; VP, Jr Cl; Co-Cpt, Bkbl; Co-Cpt, Ftbl; Sftbl; Hon Prog; Journ A; Math A; Bkbl Trophy; Ftbl Trophy; *Bob Jones U; Communications.*

SWANNER, James Lanny Jr
Slaton HS; Slaton, TX (25%-95) Ann; BS; VP, FFA; Sch Achieve Tm; SC; Ftbl; FFA As; *Tex Tech U; Agr.*

SWANSON, Allan David
Batavia HS; Batavia, IL; Hmrm; Math C; NHS; SC; Bsbl; Hon Prog; Math A; St Scholar; *Northern Ill U; Acct.*

SWANSON, Bernice Patrica
Chester HS; Chester, PA (3-680) Hon Prog; *Law Enforcement.*

SWANSON, Cathy Jean
Chaney HS; Youngstown, OH; VP, Hmrm; Mjrte; VP, SC; Y-Tns; VP, Jr Cl; Yth Fel; V-Tn Cand For Winterformal; Action Coun; Yrbk Staff; Sunday Sch Teacher; *Eckerd Col; Med.*

SWANSON, Charles Edward
Liberty HS; Youngstown, OH; Order/Arrow; Ftbl; *Youngstown St Univ; Criminology.*

SWANSON, David Carl
San Bernardino HS; San Bernardino, CA; Band; NHS; Orch; Bsbl; Bkbl; Soccer; Sftbl; Tnns; CSF; Bowling; Church Yth Ldr.

SWANSON, David James
Maddock Pub HS; Maddock, ND (6-23) Band; FFA; 4H; SC; Var C; Ftbl; 4H A; Hist A; HCt; Sci A; Drivers Ed A; FFA A; Farmers Union A; *NDSU; Agr.*

SWANSON, David Robert
Lexington HS; Lexington, MA (70-700) AFS; Ski C; Swim; Hon Prog; Stamps & Coins C; HR; *Archt.*

SWANSON, Diane Victoria
Wachusett Regional HS; Holden, MA (299-525) Band; Citz A; Dance Tm; *Phys Therapy.*

SWANSON, Doreen Kaye
East HS; Rockford, IL (14-607) NHS; *Wheaton Col; Bio.*

SWANSON, Duane Walter
Benson HS; Omaha, NE; Arch.

SWANSON, Eileen Anne
Mason City HS; Mason City, IA (33%-457) HR; *NIACC; Forestry.*

SWANSON, Gary Wayne
Oxford HS; Oxford, KS (6-40) Ann; Rptr, Sch P; Pres, Span C; SC; Ftbl; Industrial Arts A; Dramatics A; *Okla St Tech; Diesel Mech.*

SWANSON, Janice Ann
Traverse City HS; Traverse City, MI (350-800) Band; Ensm; GS; Hmrm; Ntl Teachers Coun; Secy, SC; Secy, Jr Cl; Citz A; Cl Fav; MLS; Most Out; *Pol Sci.*

SWANSON, Jon Arthur
Prague HS; Prague, NE; Chor; FFA; 4H; Bkbl; Ftbl; Tr; *Agr.*

SWANSON, Karen Ruth
Schuyler Central Sch; Schuyler, NE (3-117) Band; Cpt, Chldr; Chem C; Math C; VP, NHS; Rainbow; Sci C; Var C; Tr; COM; HQn; Masonic A; Sunday Sch Teacher; Off Girl; Prom Server; Co Govt Day; Ch, Prom Comm; *Elem Ed.*

SWANSON, Karl Edward
Kickapoo HS; Springfield, MO (16-397) Band; BS; Community Yth Symph; Orch; Order/Arrow; Ftbl; Order/Arrow A; Eagle Sct; Yth Talent Win, Mus; *Mo U; Engr.*

SWANSON, Kathy Helen
LuVerne Comm HS; LuVerne, IA (33%-16) Ann; Band; Chor; Bkbl; Tr; *Iowa St U; Interior Design.*

SWANSON, Kirk Charles
Los Angeles Baptist HS; Sepulveda, CA (50%-200) Band; Ftbl; *Cal St U-Northridge; Dentistry.*

SWANSON, Kristin Sigrid
Harold L Richards HS; Oak Lawn, IL (43-796) Ann; Cpt, Chldr; Ensm; Secy, Fr C; InterClub Coun; NHS; Secy, SC; Hon Prog; *U of Ill; Pol Sci.*

SWANSON, Laurel Ann
Vallejo HS; Vallejo, CA (33%-490) Chess C; *Solano Col; Bus.*

SWANSON, Laurie Denise
Whitesboro Sr HS; Whitesboro, NY (9-465) Oral Roberts U; *Med.*

SWANSON, Lori Ann
Prague Pub HS; Prague, NE (1-19) Ann; Band; Chldr; NHS; Pres, Jr Cl; Bkbl; Tr.

SWANSON, Melody Elizabeth
Rockford E HS; Rockford, IL (80-510) NHS; Stu Ldrship; *Rockford Col; Psych.*

SWANSON, Michael Lee
Fulton HS; Fulton, IL (20%-150) Chor; Span C; Thes; Faculty Hon; PA; *NW Col; Chem.*

SWANSON, Russell Arthur
Luther S HS; Chicago, IL (71-145) Co-Cpt, Bkbl; Cr-Ctry; Tr; *MacMurray Col; Psych.*

SWANSON, Sandy Lynne
Ralston HS; Ralston, NE (1-300) AFS; Chor; NHS; S-T, Ski C; Var C; Chamber of Comm A; Hon Prog; Regent Schol; Val; WW; Drake Pres Schol; Creighton Pres Schol; *U of Nebr-Lincoln; Health Professions.*

SWANSON, Stephanie Gail
Cushing HS; Cushing, OK (7-143) Chor; Rptr, 4H; NHS; Bkbl; Sftbl; Tr; Cl Fav; 4H A; HCt; DeMolay Swtht; *Okla St U; Fashion Merchandising.*

SWANSON, Tamra Diane
Brawley Union HS; Brawley, CA (10-350) A Cap Choir; AFS; Ann; Chor; Key C; VP, Madrigal; NHS; SC; JV, Tr; CSF; Cl Fav; *U of Sou Calif; Bus Adm.*

SWANSON, Wanda Louise
Industry HS; Industry, IL (5-30) Bus Mgr, Ann; Band; Pres, Fr C; Pres, 4H; Secy, Sci C; Sftbl; Tnns; 4H A; Type A; *U of Iowa; Nurs.*

SWANZY, Cheryl Ann
Lawrence D Bell HS; Hurst, TX (58-800) Pres, Band; Secy, CYO; Drama; Pres, FHA; Mjrte; NHS; Secy, SC; *St Mary's U; Med.*

SWARINGEN, Donna Lynn
Brownfield HS; Brownfield, TX; A Cap Choir; 4H; Madrigal; St Solo & Ensm Contest; *Tex Tech U; Mus.*

SWARTHOUT, Janet Kay
Pearl City HS; Pearl City, HI (60-686) Ger C; *N Va Comm Col; Bus.*

SWARTWOUT, Linda Carol
Cincinnati Christian HS; Fairfield, OH (20%-40) Christian Character A; Secy, Family Training Prog; Choir Soloist; Asst Pianist; *E Coast Bible Col; Religion.*

SWARTZ, Ann
Marion Harding HS; Marion, OH (283-446) Yth Fel.

SWARTZ, Robert Eugene Jr
Edgewood HS; Trenton, OH (48-261) NHS; Pres, Span C; SC; Pres, Soph Cl; Cpt, Bkbl; Cpt, Cr-Ctry; MVP, Bkbl; *Lebanon Valley Col; Bus.*

SWARTZ, Sharon Joy
Buchanan HS; Troy, MO (10%-160) Band; Chor; Ensm; Math C; Sci C.

SWARTZBECK, Carole Marie
Greenville Sr HS; Greenville, PA; Chor; *Mercer Co Vo-tech Col; LPN.*

SWARTZENDRUBER, Sandra Sue
S Albany HS; Albany, OR (30-245) A Cap Choir; Ensm; GS; Secy, NHS; Amer Leg A; Chamber of Comm A; WW; *U of Oreg; Nurs.*

SWARTZFAGER, Kathleen Marie Henrietta
Buckeye Central HS; New Washington, OH (18-99) Ann; Band; HS; Sch P; Span C; Secy, SC; Tr; Yth Fel; Health Careers C; WW; SC A; Candystriper; Vlbl; Top Tm, Top 5, Run-Up Co Tm, Bowl; Marching, Concert, Stge & Pep Bnds; *Capital U; Social Work.*

SWARTZLANDER, Kirk Joseph
Dubois Area HS; DuBois, PA (59-375) NHS; Yth Fel.

SWATEK, Catherine Mary
John S Fine HS; Nanticoke, PA (6-347) NEDT; Eng A; *Eng.*

SWATERS, Mark Joseph
Montrose R-14 HS; Montrose, MO (4-26) BS; CYO; 4H; NHS; MVP, Bkbl; Cr-Ctry; Alg A; Cl Fav; 4H A; Regent Schol; Industrial Arts A; MFA Schol; *Central Mo St U; Ag Bus.*

SWAYNE, Jeannette Marie
Harrison HS; Colorado Springs, CO (119-450) VP, Fr C; Executive HS Intern; *Med.*

SWAYNE, Kimberly Dawn
Peebles HS; Peebles, OH (4-92) Band; Chor; Fr C; 4H; Sch Achieve Tm; Pep Band; Pep C.

SWAYZE, Glenda Sue
N Park HS; Walden, CO; Ann; Chor; Drama; Pres, FBLA; 4H; Ski C; Bkbl; Tr; VFW A; Yth Fel; Co Cpt, Vlvl; Rodeo Qn; *Col of St Benedict; Phys Ed.*

SWEARINGEN, Beth Ann
Plainfield HS; Plainfield, IN (195-295) A Cap Choir; Band; Chor; Swim; Type A; Ind Mus Aud; 1st Pl & 2nd Pl Piano; *Med Records.*

SWEAT, Sylvia Sabrina
Pickwick Southside HS; Counce, TN (3-32) Pres, FHA; VP, 4H; Hmrm; Sci C; Var C; S-T, Soph Cl; Mgr, Bsbl; MVP, Bkbl; Beauty; Cl Fav; 4H A; HQn; Most Out; Star Student; Yth Fel; FHA Sub-Region Off; Eng A; Acteens; Girl Sct; *NE Miss Jr Col; Eng Ed.*

SWEATMAN, Charlene Kae
N Salinas HS; Salinas, CA (20%-400) A Cap Choir; Chor; Yth Co- ordinator, Church Projects; Publicity Ch, Co Baptist Yth Assn; Church Budget Committee; *Cardio Pulmonary.*

SWEATMAN, Kent Ellis
Atlanta HS; Atlanta, TX (25%-160) Ann; Cpt, Band; Chor; Ensm; Q&S A; *Ouachita Baptist U.*

SWEAZY, Kathleen Diane
Ulysses HS; Ulysses, KS (10-106) Band; Cpt, Chldr; Ensm; FBLA; Ger C; 4H; Secy, NHS; Rainbow; SC; Y-Tns; Bkbl; Cpt, Golf; HCt; Pres A; St Scholar; *Tex Tech; Pre-Dental.*

SWEDIEN, Betsy Anne
Sw Secondary Sch; Minneapolis, MN; Chor; *Home Ec.*

SWEDLUND, Sid
Abingdon HS; Abingdon, IL (39-81) Cpt, Bkbl; Ftbl; Tr; HKg; Rotary A; SAR A; High Hon; *W Ill Col; Bus Mgr.*

SWEEDEN, Judith Anne
Union HS; Union, OR (4-50) Ed, Ann; Band; Chldr; Chor; 4H; Pres, Hmrm; Pres, NHS; SC; Var C; Cpt, Bkbl; Tr; HQn; HCt; Q&S A; Type A; MVP, Bkbl; MIP, Tr; Tm Spiker A; District All Star Tm, Bkbl; Sou Oreg St Col; Bus.

SWEENEY, Carroll Elizabeth
Saint Elizabeth Seton HS; South Holland, IL (112-249) Pres, A Cap Choir; Pres, Chor; Drama; Rptr, Hmrm; InterAct C; Pres, InterClub Coun; Spch C; Pres, Soph Cl; Ftbl; Soccer; Sftbl; Alg A; Cl Fav; Coun of Teach A; Hon Prog; Math A; MLS; Most Out; Pres A; Spch A; Outst Sr; Spirit As; Northern U; Theatre.

SWEENEY, Donna Beth
Daviess Co HS; Owensboro, KY (10-385) Band; Fr C; VP, Lat C; Mgr, Cr-Ctry; Mgr, Ftbl; Mgr, Tr; Cl Fav; Hist A; Hon Prog; JA A; Middlebury Col; Lang.

SWEENEY, Donna Kay
HS for Health Professions; Houston, TX (80-139) A Cap Choir; Chess C; Chor; Ntl Yth Conf; COM; Cl Fav; Type A; Ntl Piano Playing Guild A; U of Houston; Bus.

SWEENEY, Kelly Ann
Elizabeth Seton HS; South Holland, IL (105-215) Chor; Lat C; Tnns; St Mary's Col.

SWEENEY, Laura Marie
Holy Rosary Acad; Louisville, KY (18-86) Bus Mgr, Ann; Chess C; Drama; Fr C; Fin, Jr Miss Pagent; Co-Ed, Sch P; HCt; SC Executive A; Bellarmine Fr A; U of Louisville; Home Ec.

SWEENY, Pamela E
Arlington Sr HS; Arlington, MA (110-630) Co-Ed, Ann; Chor; Drama; Lit Mag; Co-Ed, Sch P Span C; JV, Sftbl; Sou Methodist U; Eng.

SWEET, Donald Alvin
Charles H Roth HS; Henrietta, NY (25-214) S-T, 4H; VP, Order/Arrow; Tr; God & Country A; 4H A; Hon Prog; Order/Arrow A; Pres A; ARC A; VP, Secy & Ch, Order o-t Arrow; United Methodist Yth Group; NJHS; Monroe Co Sheepherd; Eagle Sct A; Ntl Eagle Sct Assn; Project Soar; NY-SUNY; Agr.

SWEET, Pamela Ann
Las Plumas HS; Oroville, CA (33-360) A Cap Choir; Cpt, Chldr; Sch P; SC; Swim; Point Loma Col; Mus.

SWEET, Trancell
W Side HS; Gary, IN; Chor; Meritorious A; NJHS; Hon Stu; Recognition Certs; Straight A HR; Sch Service Lang Arts Mert Cert; Instrum Mus Achv Cer; Pge, St H Rep.

SWEETEN, Gary Ross
Kingsway Reg HS; Swedesboro, NJ; Pres, Band; Key C; NHS; Ski C; Tnns; H of F; Best Musician; Wheaton Col; Engr.

SWEETEN, Michael Wayne
New Bloomfield R III Sch; New Bloomfield, MO (6-40) Ann; Chor; Parl, SC; Pres, Soph Cl.

SWEETING, Christine Avis
Luther Burbank Sr HS; Sacramento, CA (20-680) AFS; VP, Chor; Span C; COM; Ntl Merit Schol Commended Stu; U of Calif-Davis; Span.

SWEGLE, James Hugh
Crescent HS; Joyce, WA (2-18) Pres, NHS; Rptr, Sch P; Pres, SC; Var C; VP, Sr Cl; VP, Jr Cl; Bkbl; Co-Cpt, Ftbl; MVP, Bkbl; Tr; HCt; WSU; Agr.

SWEIGART, John Lowell
Annville-Cleona HS; Annville, PA (7-170) JV, Cr-Ctry; Tr; JV, Wrest; Franklin Col; Pre-Med.

SWEISFORT, Audrey Jean
Cave Spring HS; Roanoke, VA (112-500) Chor; Tres, FHA; Span C.

SWENSEN, Paul Daniel
Montgomery HS; Santa Rosa, CA (80-700) A Cap Choir, Band; VP, Chor; Community Yth Symph; S-T, Drama; Ch, Hmrm; Madrigal; SK; SC; Sr Cl; Jr Cl; Soph Cl; HKg; Most Out; CMEA, Command Performance Solo; Director, Mus Church; Stu Conductor Sch; Outst Musician; Calif St Hon Choir; UC Northridge; Mus.

SWENSON, Cheryl Lyn
Crystal Lake Comm HS; Crystal Lake, IL (118-500) Chldr; Gym; Cl Flirt; HR; Homecoming Qn; Eastern Ill U; Bus.

SWENSON, Lisa Anne
Washington HS; Sioux Falls, SD (50%-800) Band; Pres, Hmrm; COM; Poet A; Eng.

SWENSON, Luther Gaylord
Two Harbors HS; Two Harbors, MN (8-174) Band; Tres, NHS; Order/Arrow; SC; Var C; Tres, Jr Cl; Ftbl; MVP, Swim; Tnns; Tr.

SWENSSON, Kurt Dickenson
Battle Ground Acad; Franklin, TN (1-76) Dbte Tm; Key C; NFL; NHS; Spch C; St Stu Congress; Ftbl; Swim; Tr; Math A; NEDT; Spch A; Art A.

SWERTFEGER, Lance Scott
Rhinebeck Central Sch; Rhinebeck, NY (25-115) Band; Chor; Ensm; Fr C; Orch; Order/Arrow; Golf; JV, Soccer; Wrest; Citz A; God & Country A; Order/Arrow A; Area, Co, St, Orch; 1st Pl Area, Part Ntl, Tetrathlon.

SWETT, Brian Lee
Bentley Sr HS; Burton, MI (30-220) Pres, Bus C; NHS; JV, Golf; JV, Wrest; E Mich U; Computer Sci.

SWICEGOOD, Lisa Michele
T C Roberson HS; Skyland, NC (52-240) Fr C; Pres, SC; Tr; Citz A; Civitan A; V Gym; Miss Aries Court; Outst Sr; EYC Pres; Pies, YMCA Ldrs C; U of NC; Pre-Law.

SWICKARD, Laura Sue
Charleston HS; Charleston, IL (11-248) AFS; Chor; Dbte Tm; 4H; Orch; Spch C; SC; 4H A; Hon Prog; Type A; Chor A; Mus Camp Schol; Med.

SWICKLIK, Cynthia Marie
John S Fine HS; Nanticoke, PA (8-347) Band; Sodality; Var C; MVP, Hockey; Nurs.

SWICKLIK, Susan Ann
John S Fine HS; Nanticoke, PA; CYO; 4H; Co-Cpt, Mjrte; Var C; Hockey; Sftbl; 4H A; E Stroudsburg St Col; Math.

SWIDERSKI, Frank Joseph
Leavenworth Sr HS; Leavenworth, KS (70-374) CYO; NEDT; Kansas U; Engr.

SWIDERSKI, Patti Jo
Luther HS; Chicago, IL (182-275) A Cap Choir; Span C; Canoe C; Lib C; Triton Col; Psych.

SWIFT, Glenn Baxter
Nicholas Blackwell HS; Bartlett, TN; Key C; Span C; SC; Ftbl; Cl Fav; Ole Miss.

SWIFT, Richard LeRoy
Queen Anne HS; Seattle, WA (187-388) Sunday Sch Teacher; Pres, Yth Group; Church Bkbl & Choir; NW Col; Theology.

SWIFT, Shaune Patrick
Secaucus HS; Secaucus, NJ (23-185) Pres, Soph Cl; Ftbl; JV, Tr; Wrest; Marine Phys Fitness A.

SWIFT, Teresa Gail
Eastland HS; Eastland, TX (20-60) Bus Mgr, Band; Chldr; Chem C; Drama; Ensm; FFA; FHA; Pres, Mjrte; ARC; Spch C; Thes; Var C; Bsbl; Bkbl; Sftbl; Swim; Tnns; Tr; ARC A; Swtht; FFA Swtht; Tyler Jr Col; Dental Hygiene.

SWIGGUM, Peter
N Crawford HS; Gays Mills, WI (26-75) Band; Order/Arrow; Var C; Bsbl; Bkbl; Ftbl; Tr; Eagle Sct; MVP, Band; U of Wisc; Parks Adm.

SWIHART, Sharon Ruth
Robert E Lee HS; Midland, TX (101-649) A Cap Choir; NHS; Midland Col; Mus.

SWIHART, Steven Farrell
Goshen HS; Goshen, IN (40-325) Ed, Ann; Band; Secy, Demolay; Ensm; Fr C; Sch P; SC; Cpt, Bsbl; Ftbl; Intramural Bkbl; Park Dept Staff; Ariz St U; Engr.

SWIM, Betty May
Boyd H Anderson HS; Lauderdale Lakes, FL; Pres, Chor; Pres, Ensm; FNA; SC; Bkbl; Tr; Outst Chor A; Broward Comm Col; Phys Therapy.

SWIMS, Jametra
Northwestern; Flint, MI (50%-300) JV, Chldr; Chor; Hmrm; Sch P; Y-Tns; Citz A; Most Pleasing Personality; Friendliest; Academic Achv; Eng.

SWINDALL, Maggie Susie
Tallapoosa Acad; Dadeville, AL (5-23) Band; BC; Cl Fav; Sci A; U of Ala.

SWINDELL, Ricky Franklin
Scotland HS; Laurinburg, NC; VICA; US Army; Communications.

SWINDELL, Terry Lynn
Bradford HS; Bradford, TN (10%-63) Ann; VP, BC; FFA; 4H; Hmrm; Monogram; Var C; Bkbl; Homecoming Escort; Union U; Acct.

SWINDLE, Carla Jo
Abilene HS; Abilene, TX (94-550) VP, Bus C; Hmrm; Sch P; SC; Tri-HiY; Type A; Yth Leg; Angelo St U; Marketing.

SWINDLE, Deborah Kay
Mathiston HS; Mathiston, MS (33%-29) Ann; BC; FHA; F-Ed, Sch P; Bkbl; MVP, Sftbl; HCt; Hon Sr; Academic Schol; Most Talented; Wood Jr Col; Bus.

SWINDLER, Robert Austin
Eastern HS; Middletown, KY; Chor; Madrigal; Ed, Sch P; Pres, Sci C; Span C; SC; JV, Bkbl; JV, Ftbl; Alg A; COM; NEDT; Sci A; Star Student; Val; US Army, Sci A; Span Leadership A; Transylvania U; Med.

SWINEY, Cynthia Ann
Loudon HS; Loudon, TN (25-143) Ann; Band; Fr C; FHA; GS; Hmrm; Lat C; NHS; ARC; Sci C; Tres, SC; VP, Jr Cl; Cl Fav; ARC A; Yth Fel; Bio Sci.

SWINEY, Lindel Mark
Fulton HS; Fulton, MO; Lat C; Bkbl; Tr; SW Baptist Col; Church Recreation.

SWINEY, Valithia Latrice
Justin F Kimball HS; Dallas, TX; FHA; Bus.

SWINFORD, Robin Elizabeth
Patten Acad of Christian Ed; Oakland, CA (4-11) A Cap Choir; Chem C; Chor; Community Yth Symph; Dbte Tm; Cpt, Drama; Ensm; Fr C; Math C; Orch; Sci C; Ski C; Spch C; Pres, SC; Pres, Jr Cl; Bsbl; Bkbl; MVP, Cr-Ctry; Ftbl; Soccer; Swim; Tnns; MVP, Tr; Citz A; Pres A; Fin, Cr-Ctry; Silver 'A' A; Patten Bible Col; Mus.

SWINGLE, Millard Raymond
Oxon Hill Sr HS; Oxon Hill, MD; Bsbl; Bkbl; Ftbl; Soccer; Fin, Wrest; Engr.

SWINK, Sandra Dee
Macon HS; Macon, IL (27-64) Band; Ensm; FHA; Sftbl; Tr; Richland Comm Col; Social Work.

SWINT, Debbie Joy
Augusta Christian Acad; Augusta, GA (1-40) U of Ga; Math.

SWINT, Tamela Renee
S Phila HS; Philadelphia, PA; Bsbl; Sftbl; 4H A; Morehouse Col.

SWISHER, Lisa Anne
Lake City HS; Lake City, TN (5-155) F-Ed, Ann; Band; BC; Orch; Rptr, Soph Cl; Alg A; Bio A; Ed.

SWITALSKI, Debra Ann
S Moreland HS; Scottdale, PA; Band; Yth Fel; Greensburg Bus Inst; Commercial.

SWITZER, Kevin James
Ottawa HS; Ottawa, KS; Band; BS; Fr C; Bsbl; Mgr, Ftbl; Mgr, Wrest; WW; 'O' C.

SWITZER, Ronda Lynn
Hutchinson HS; Hutchinson, KS (10%-500) AFS; Chor; Span C; Span NHS; Hon Prog; McPherson Col; Nurs.

SWOFFORD, Donald Dudley Jr
Derby Sr HS; Derby, KS (150-350) Chor; Tres, Order/Arrow; Rptr, Soph P; JV, Tnns; Order/Arrow A; Yth Fel; Most Valuable, BSct Camp.

SWOFFORD, Tracy Karen
Green Forest HS; Green Forest, AR (7-74) Bus Mgr, Ann; Band; Tres, BC; Pres, FHA; Ed, Sch P; SC; S-T, Jr Cl; Citz A; Math A; Q&S A; VP, FHA; Eng A; PA; Sch o-t Ozarks.

SWOPE, Kevin Roger
Ritenour Sr HS; St John, MO; A Cap Choir; Band; Wrest; Mo Baptist Col; Mus.

SWOPE, Natalie Jane
Shaler Area HS; Glenshaw, PA (10%-900) Band; Mjrte; Ntl Yth Conf; Orch; Sch P; Ski C; Span C; Span NHS; Amer Leg A; Drum Mjrte; Gym; Band Festival; HR; *Grove City Col; Pre-Law.*

SWOPES, Danny Fredrick
N Chicago HS; North Chicago, IL (53-256) Band; NHS; Pres, Var C; Cpt, Cr-Ctry; Cpt, Tr; Wrest; *Ill St U; Bus Adm.*

SWOPES, Dierdra Letitia
N Chicago Comm HS; North Chicago, IL; Chldr; FHA; Var C; Cpt, Tr; HCt.

SWORDS, Andrew Rigby
Ossining HS; Ossining, NY (9-356) A Cap Choir; Band; Chess C; A-Ed, Lit Mag; NHS; Orch; Sch P; SC; Regent Schol; Ntl Merit Ltr of Commendation; Secy, Yth Fel; *Hamilton Col; Engr.*

SWOVERLAND, Leslie Lynn
Flambeau HS; Tony, WI (11-83) Chldr; VP, Chor; FNA; NFL; NHS; Spch C; Tres, SC; Var C; Tres, Sr Cl; Tres, Jr Cl; HCt; NEDT; Spch A; 'A' Ratings, St Forensics; *Col of St Scholastica; Respiratory Therapy.*

SWYERS, John Clarence
St Francis HS; Athol Springs, NY; CYO; FTA; Lit Mag; Ntl Yth Conf; Orch; Sch P; Golf; Soccer; Tnns; *Theology.*

SWYERS, Vicki Jo
Pattonville Sr HS; Bridgeton, MO; Co-Cpt, Chldr; HCt; *Stephens Col; Hist.*

SWYSTUN, Nancy Elaine
Harpeth Hall HS; Nashville, TN (5%-85) AFS; Ed, Ann; Cum Laude Soc; Fr C; Lat C; Lit Mag; Mu Alpha Theta; F-Ed, Sch P; COM; Coun of Teach A; NMF; NEDT; Star Student; Sewanee C A; Fin, Presidential Schols; *Rice U; Engr.*

SYBOUTS, Mark Lawrence
Goldendale HS; Goldendale, WA (1-74) Ann; Band; BS; NHS; Tres, SC; Tres, Jr Cl; Tres, Soph Cl; JV, Bkbl; COM; Val; *Central Wash St Col; Acct.*

SYDBOTEN, Kymbal Rai
Ballard Mem HS; Barlow, KY; BC; Chldr; Tres, FHA; FTA; Ch, Hmrm; Orch; SC; Golf; Fin, Beauty; Yth Choir; 1st Run-Up, Miss Ky Ntl Teenager; Historian, Band; All St Orch; *Fashion Merchandising.*

SYKES, Gregory Eugene
Kankakee Westview HS; Kankakee, IL (18-256) BS; City Conf; A-Ed, Sch P; Ski C; Sptn C; Thes; Amer Leg A; Spch A; VofDEM; Tres, District Stu Congress; Drama A; Cert of Merit; Dist Win Bicen Yth Debates; Amer Assn of Fr; *Bradley U; International Stu.*

SYKES, Lacy Kirk
Proviso E HS; Maywood, IL (310-964) Chor; Bkbl; Tr; *Aeronautics.*

SYKES, Mary Ann
North Co HS; Desloge, MO; Band; FBLA; FNA; 4H; NHS; Span C.

SYKES, Melvin
Holy Family HS; Birmingham, AL (1-42) Bkbl; *Alcorn St Col; PE.*

SYKES, Suzanne Ashley
Roxborough HS; Philadelphia, PA; Chor; Dbte Tm; Hockey; Mgr, Sftbl; Tnns; Citz A; Hon Prog; Most Out; *Temple U; Journ.*

SYKES, Tamra Denise
Proviso E HS; Maywood, IL (204-712) Ch, Chor; Semi-Fin, Jr Miss Pa; ARCt; Ski C; COM; Hon Prog; Most Out; ARC A; Sci A; 1st Runner- up, Pageant; Win, Talent Show; *Sou Ill U; Modern Dance.*

SYLVESTER, Elizabeth Ann
Tewksbury Mem HS; Tewksbury, MA (19-444) Chor; NHS; Sch P; Yth Fel; 1st Cl GSct; God & Comm A; *Foreign Lang.*

SYLVESTER, Ronald Charles
Parkview HS; Springfield, MO (25-390) Rptr, Ann; Dbte Tm; NFL; As-Ed, Sch P; Var C; JV, Wrest; TP; COM; Journ A; Q&S A; Spch A; Conf Tr A; Dist Tr A; Tr High Point A; *U of Mo; Journ.*

SYLVESTER, Rosie Lee
Marvell HS; Marvell, AR (5-120) BC; Pres, FHA; Spch C; COM; Citz A; Math A; Gov A; WW; *U of Ark; Elem Ed.*

SYMONS, Lee Rae
Sewickley Acad; Sewickley, PA (10%-70) Chor; Lat A; HR; Piano Playing As; Yrbk Staff A.

SYMONS, Robert Allen
Central HS; Woodstock, VA (15-110) Semi-Fin, BS; FFA; Ch, Hmrm; NHS; SC; MVP, Bsbl; Ftbl; Cpt, Tr; Most Out; Yth Fel; *Math.*

SYMOSH, Michele Maria
Old Forge HS; Old Forge, PA (5-121) Tres, FTA; Tres, NHS; ARC; Cpt, Bkbl; Sftbl; Chem A; Pres A; HS All Am Sports, Sftbl Super Star; *E Stroudsburg St Col; Phys Ed.*

SYMULESKI, Joseph Stephen
Riverside Jr-Sr HS; Taylor, PA (8-196) NHS; Span C; Bkbl; Hon Prog; Bkbl Ltr.

SYNEK, Oylen Daniel
Sidney Sr HS; Sidney, MT (57-150) Band; BS; CYO; Chor; Ensm; K of C; Key C; Madrigal; Orch; Order/ Arrow; Var C; Bkbl; Ftbl; Tr; *Mont St U; Automobile Mech.*

SYNOVEC, Robert Eugene
Canby HS; Canby, MN (10-120) Band; Chor; Sci C; Var C; Bsbl; JV, Bkbl; JV, Cr-Ctry; Golf; *Bethel Col; Math.*

SYPHER, Kathryn Elizabeth
John Glenn HS; Westland, MI (65-700) Bus C; Cum Laude Soc; Yth Organization; Clerk, District Court; *Taylor U; Ed.*

SYPOLT, Jeffrey Steven
Milton Hershey Sch; Hershey, PA (50-142) Arch; Chor; Ger C; Arch; Soccer; Swim; Tr; Citz A; V Ltr, Swim & Glee C; V 'H' Pin; *U of Pittsburgh; Elec Engr.*

SYSLO, Lynne Ann
Taft HS; Chicago, IL (88-825) Chor; Hmrm; Key C; Span C; COM; Hon Prog; NMS; NEDT; VFW A; Yth Fel; Span A; *U of Ill-Champaign; Zoology.*

SYTSMA, Wendi Colleen
Hutchinson HS; Hutchinson, MN (33-218) Ann; Secy, Bus C; Chor; Sftbl; Type A; Sftbl A; *Hutchinson Area Voc Tech Inst; Secy.*

SYVERSON, Jay Steven
Wanamingo HS; Wanamingo, MN (8-40) Band; Pres, Drama; NHS; Ftbl; Cpt, Tr; *Mankato St U; Phys Therapy.*

SYVERSON, John Arthur
Harrison HS; Harrison, NY (39-300) Tres, Chor; VP, Drama; Ensm; Sch P; VP, Thes; JV, Ftbl; Golf; JV, Tnns; Hon Prog; Alt, Regent's Schol; *Econ Sci.*

SYVERSON, Mark Douglas
Rochelle Township HS; Rochelle, IL (37-217) Chess C; Community Yth Symph; Math C; VP, Orch; Var C; Co-Cpt, Cr-Ctry; Hon Prog; NEDT; Yth Fel; All St Orch; *U of Ill; Commerce.*

SYX, Terressa Jean
Hueytown HS; Hueytown, AL (169-350) Band; Mjrte; Tnns; Drill Tm; *Nurs.*

SZABAT, Mary Margrethe
Mercy HS; Riverhead, NY (2-130) CYO; Cpt, Chldr; Chor; Hmrm; NHS; Pol Sci C; Secy, Sodality; Secy, SC; Hon Prog; Ntl Sci Found; Parish Lector; CCD Teacher; Runnerup, LI Spelling Bee.

SZABO, Carolyn Joan
Westlake HS; Westlake, OH (10%-315) Chor; ARC; Jr NHS; Off, Yth Group; Church Orch; Missionette Star & Hon Star; St Qn Missionette.

SZABO, Susan May
Roeper City and Ctry Sch; Bloomfield Hills, MI; Chldr; Chor; Drama; Soccer; Ntl Sci Found; S-T, Church Yth Group; *Kalamazoo Col; Bio-Chem.*

SZEPESI, Diane Carole
Uniontown Area Sr HS; Uniontown, PA; Band; Chor; Drama; VP, Fr C; Pres, Hmrm; NFL; Pres, NHS; ARC; Sch P; Sci C; SC; Alg A; Amer Leg A; MLS; Amer Leg Co-Best Girl; NOW Essay Contest; *George Washington U; Foreign Service.*

SZOBONYA, Gayle Anne
Trenton HS; Trenton, MI (38-573) Fr C; NHS; Var C; Coaches A, JV Vlbl; Vlbl Ltr; *Ferris St Col; Dental Hygiene.*

SZUMIGALA, David James
St Frances de Sales HS; Toledo, OH (18-242) NHS; Rptr, Sch P; Var C; Cr-Ctry; Swim; Tr; Hon Prog; Ntl Merit Commendation; *Geol.*

SZYMANSKI, Deborah Lynn
Fox Lane HS; Bedford, NY; Band; Ensm; Fr C; Hmrm; Orch; SC; World Affairs C; Citz A; Fr A; *Pace U; Bus.*

T

TABB, Otis Gene
Marvell HS; Marvell, AR (1-120) Ann; Band; Ch, BC; Pres, FBLA; Ger C; Hmrm; Ed, Sch P; SC; Pres, Sr Cl; Pres, Jr Cl; Bio A; Hist A; Math A; Ntl Sci Found; Sci A; Val; WW; Ger C A; *U of Ark; Biol.*

TABER, Evan Beth
Forest Ridge HS; Bellevue, WA (2-50) Secy, Chor; Hmrm; NHS; Span C; Alg A; Amer Leg A; COM; Mus A; WW; Religion A; *Stanford U; Biological Sci.*

TABER, Ken John
Twin Lakes HS; W Palm Beach, FL (150-500) Arch; Band; Bus C; Chess C; Drama; Math C; Span C; Arch; Bsbl; Ftbl; Soccer; Sftbl; Swim; Tnns; Wrest; Interlochen Ntl Mus; JA A; Ntl Achv Schol; Yth Fel; Interntl Guild of Piano Auditions; *Bethany Col; Bus Adm.*

TABIANDO, Hertchel Carolino
George Washington Sr HS; Mangilao, GUAM; Band; NHS; *ORU; Mus.*

TABLERIOU, Cynthia Ann
Kelly HS; Chicago, IL; VP, Band; Hmrm; NHS; Pres, Sci C; Span NHS; SC; VP, Jr Cl; Hon Prog; Vlbl; Stu Exec Bd; Eng A; Band Letter; *Daley Col; Bus.*

TABLERIOU, Susan Marie
Kelly HS; Chicago, IL; Ed, Ann; Secy, Band; Hmrm; Math C; NHS; SC; Tr; Bio A; COM; Hon Prog; Journ A; NEDT; Q&S A; Recognition A; Division Secy; Eng A; Art A; Band A; *Daley Col; Bus.*

TABOR, Angela Kay
Rossville HS; Rossville, GA (9-211) BC; Fr C; Math A; Sci A; Star Student; *Berry Col; Psych.*

TABOR, John D
Milford Area Sr HS; Milford, NH (15-300) Band; *E Nazarene Col; Math.*

TABOR, Whitmell Martin
Baton Rouge HS Magnet; Baton Rouge, LA; A Cap Choir; Drama; Fr C; Thes; *LSU; Mus.*

TABORSKY, Patricia Ann
Lake Co Baptist Sch; Waukegan, IL (2-6) Co-Cpt, Ann; Chldr; Chor; Cpt, Vlbl; *Bob Jones U; Ed.*

TABRON, Michele Andrea
Chester HS; Chester, PA (5-673) Ed, Ann; NHS; Sci A; Star Hon; *Widener Col; Nurs.*

TACKEBERRY, Patty Sue
North Love Christian Sch; Rockford, IL (2-20) Chldr; Chor; *Ed.*

TACKETT, Amy Arlene
Pampa HS; Pampa, TX; Span C; JV, Bkbl; Tr; Keywanette C; Phys Ed A; *Marine Bio.*

TACKETT, Michael
Virgie HS; Virgie, KY; Band; BC; Ger C; Sci C; *U of Ky; Mus.*

TADA, Ichiro
Kubasaki HS; Okinawa, JAPAN (14-271) Ann; Chess C; Hmrm; Tres, SC; Bsbl; Bkbl; Soccer; HCt; Vlbl; Photo C; *USC; Engr.*

TADLOCK, Martha Rebecca
Parkview Sr HS; Little Rock, AR (8-400) AFS; Tres, BC; GS; Hmrm; InterClub Coun; VP, Mu Alpha Theta; VP, NHS; Sci C; Secy, Span C; Secy, SC; Y-Tns; DARGCA; Hon Prog; Math A; NEDT; Sergeant, Drill Tm; *Centenary Col; Computer Sci.*

TAGAWA, Michele Kiku
Maryknoll HS; Honolulu, HI (6-110) Co-Ed, Ann; Pres, Bus C; Fr C; S-T, Hmrm; Key C; Secy, NHS; Mgr, Tr; JA A; Math A; VP & Tres, Bus C; JV Bowl; VP, Japanese C; Adv Design A; Spirit Comm; Employee o-t Month; Pep C; Employee o-t Month; *U of Hawaii.*

TAGERT, Bert Edwin
St Augustine HS; St Augustine, FL (8-250) Drama; HiY; Pres, InterClub Coun; NHS; VP, Order/ Arrow; Pres, SC; VP, Sr Cl; Pres, Soph Cl; JV, Ftbl; Tnns; Tr; Elk A; MLS; Yth Leg; Eagle Sct; Bicentennial Yth Debates; *Millsaps Col; Pol Sci.*

TAGERT, Lisa Karen
Columbia HS; Columbia, MS; Band; 4H; Sftbl; Sci A; Most Improved Bandsman; HR; *U of Miss.*

TAGG, Rondi Jeannette
Peabody HS; Pittsburgh, PA (21-579) A Cap Choir; Chor; Pres, Dbte Tm; Ensm; Ger C; Madrigal; NHS; Hon Prog; JA A; Pres A; *Pre-Med.*

TAGGART, David John
S Page Comm HS; College Springs, IA (3-42) Band; Chor; Drama; FFA; Rptr, 4H; Spch C; Bsbl; JV Bkbl; Mgr, Ftbl; 4H A; ARC A; Spch A; Yth Fel; FFA Dist C A.

TAGGART, Debbie Lynn
Perry Meridian HS; Indianapolis, IN (62-560) Chem C; Fr C; FBLA; S-T, 4H; NHS; St Scholar; Ball St Schol; Hoosier Schol; Cl Hon; *Ball St U; Bus.*

TAGGART, Elizabeth Lee
S Page Comm HS; College Springs, IA (9-32) Ann; Band; 4H; NHS; Y-Tns; Sftbl; Citz A; 4H A; Sterling Col Mus A; *Sterling Col; Lib.*

TAGTMEYER, Kristine Jo
Northrop HS; Fort Wayne, IN (11-630) Alg A; COM; Eng A; Ger A; *Purdue U; Psychology.*

TAGUE, Mark Alan
Carlsbad HS; Carlsbad, CA (23-464) Chor; Drama; Tr; *San Diego St Col; Law.*

TAICLET, Lynne Marie
St Benedict Acad; Pittsburgh, PA (9-65) Pres, Band; Rptr, Drama; NHS; COM; Hon Prog; JA A; Girl o-t Month A; Band A; WW Nom; Highest Hon, Soc of Women Engr; *Allegheny Col in Meadville; Bio-Chem.*

TAINTER, Anthony Robin
Sergeant Bluff-Luton HS; Sergeant Bluff, IA (2-52) Dbte Tm; VP, SC; Ftbl; Tr; St Scholar; Val; *Iowa St U; Econ.*

TAINTER, Kristine Ann
Port Washington HS; Port Washington, WI (62-256) Fin, AFS; Band; Chor; Drama; Ensm; COM; Yth Fel; VP, Job's Daughters; Homemaker A; Performing & Visual Arts Soc; Masonic Yth Review.

TAIT, James Olin
Austin HS; Decatur, AL; Band; *U of Ala; Law Enforcement.*

TAIT, Joseph Randall
Abraham Lincoln HS; Council Bluffs, IA (150-400) Chor; Pres, Demolay; Rptr, Hmrm; JV, Tnns; Bowl; Rep, Demolay; *Iowa Western Comm Col; Acct.*

TAIT, Melody Dawn
Lindbergh HS; Renton, WA; *U of Wash; Childcare & Child Abuse.*

TAJIMA, Wendy Sue
John Muir HS; Pasadena, CA (16-527) Tres, AFS; Hmrm; Pres, Lat C; Pres, Mod Mus Mas; Orch; SC; Tres, Sr Cl; CSF; NMS; Opt A; *Yale U; Pol Sci.*

TAKARA, Kaoru
Macarthur HS; San Antonio, TX; A Cap Choir; Spch C; *San Antonio Col; Lang.*

TAKATA, Katherine Yoshiko
Beverly Hills HS; Beverly Hills, CA (20%-576) S-T, AFS; Mu Alpha Theta; NFL; Spch C; SC; S-T, Jr Cl; CSF; COM; Hon Prog; PTA A; Spch A; Comm Internship A; Hospital Vol Emblem; Individual Excellence, Forensics; *UCLA; International Relations.*

TAKEUCHI, Elizabeth Fay
Kubasaki HS; Okinawa, JAPAN (20-271) F-Ed, Ann; NHS; Span C; *Vet Med.*

TALBERT, Jeanine Elizabeth
McClellan HS; Little Rock, AR; Chor.

TALBERT, Robert Walker
Aiken HS; Aiken, SC (16-640) BC; BS; Pres, Ger C; InterClub Coun; Tres, Key C; Mu Alpha Theta; VP, NHS; SC; Var C; Ftbl; DARGCA; Hon Prog; Opt Out Tn; Rotary A; Yth Fel; Benjamin Wofford Schol; Hiking C; SC Exec Comm; Best Defensive Back A; Scholastic A, Bkbl; *Baylor U.*

TALBOT, Alan Richard
Holliston HS; Holliston, MA;

TALBOT, Mark Harold
Holliston HS; Holliston, MA; Band; Chor; VP, Drama; Thes; Wrest; *Zoology.*

TALBOT, Robin Lynn
Glen Oaks HS; Baton Rouge, LA; Ann; BC; Pres, FHA; Key C; Secy, SC; Secy, Sr Cl; Secy, Jr Cl; Tres, Soph Cl; Sftbl; Citz A; Cl Fav; Crisco A; *Southeastern U; Nurs.*

TALBOTT, Charles Wayne
Palisade HS; Palisade, CO (2-68) Band; COM; Type A; Eagle Sct; HR.

TALBOTT, Harry Bruce
Palisade HS; Palisade, CO (3-69) Band; NHS; Var C; Wrest; COM; DARGCA; Lion A; MLS; Opt A; Sal; Eagle Sct; *Ottawa U; Math.*

TALBOTT, Norbert Drew
Warren Central HS; Indianapolis, IN (3-650) Order/ Arrow; Soccer; Order/ Arrow A; Soccer C; Eagle Sct; *U of Evansville; Bus.*

TALBOTT, Rita Kathlene
Rifle HS; Rifle, CO (12-86) Drama; Secy, Fr C; Ski C; Drum Major; Swing Choir; *Ottawa U; Mus.*

TALBOTT, Sherry Ann
Halifax Co Sr HS; S Boston, VA (10%-500) Bus C; Lat C; NHS; Sch P; *Va Polytechnic Inst; Home Ec.*

TALEVICH, Sheri Louise
Hitchcock HS; Hitchcock, TX (2-132) A Cap Choir; Ensm; FFA; Mjrte; Pres, Span C; Tr; 1st Pl Ensm.

TALIAFERRO, Michael Clark
Washington Lee HS; Arlington, VA (50-443) Drama; NHS; Ski C; Mgr, Bkbl; Swim; Hon Prog; Rowing Crew; *U of Tex; Engr.*

TALISON, Calvin
Pershing HS; Detroit, MI (26-450) NHS; Sch P; COM; Cum Laude; Kappa Alpha Psi; *Wayne St U; Med.*

TALKMITT, Brenda Sue
Wilson HS; Wilson, TX (7-25) Ann; Dbte Tm; Drama; FFA; VP, FHA; VP, Sr Cl; S-T, Soph Cl; Mgr, Bkbl; Tr; Cl Fav; Yth Fel; Homemaking A; Miss WHS; WW; *Voc Trng Sch; Nurs.*

TALLENT, Cathy Ann
Carlmont HS; Belmont, CA (1%-567) A Cap Choir; Band; CSF; COM; Church Bell Choir; Yth Chor; for A Cappella Choir; 1st Clarinet Duet at Festival; Piano Accompanist for A Cappella; *Simpson Col; Mus.*

TALLENT, Tim Arnold
Robert E Lee HS; Tyler, TX (20-675) Pres, Bus C; Pres, FBLA; ARC; Var C; Golf; Amer Leg A; Chamber of Comm A; ARC A; Spch A; Yth Fel; St Champion Golf Tm; *Okla St U; Bus.*

TALLERICO, Betty Louise
Thomas Jefferson HS; Pittsburgh, PA (10%-450) Band; Chem C; Hon Prog; 1st Cl GSct; *Chem.*

TALLEY, Anna Marie
North Hall HS; Gainesville, GA (20%-210) Pres, Chor; Tres, FHA; ARC; DARGCA; Gov Honor Prog; *Shorter Col; Elem Ed.*

TALLEY, Brenda Leigh
A C Jones HS; Beeville, TX; A Cap Choir; Chor; Sci A; Eng A.

TALLEY, Deborah Dee
Scottsboro HS; Scottsboro, AL; Anchor C; FHA; Pres, Jr Miss Pagent; Sci C; World Affairs C; *U of N Ala; Med.*

TALLEY, Debra Lynn
Chelan HS; Chelan, WA (10-50) FHA; NHS; Ski C; Tres, SC; Bkbl; Sftbl; Most Dependable Girl o-t Month; Sportsmanship Bkbl Camp; Bkbl Varsity Ltr; *Wenatchee Valley Col; X- ray Technician.*

TALLEY, Paul Stemmons
Skyline HS; Dallas, TX (50%-890) Band; Pres, Chor; Demolay; Key C; Hon Prog; WW; Pride A; *E Tex St U; Photography.*

TALLEY, Thomas Curtis
Emerson HS; Emerson, AR (1-31) F-Ed, Ann; VP, FFA; F-Ed, Sch P; Pres, Sr Cl; Tnns; Tr; B Crocker A; Hist A; Magna Cum Laude; Math A; Val; *Sou Ark U; Elec Engr.*

TALLEY, Twylla Marie
Broad Ripple HS; Indianapolis, IN (25%-300) Chor; Rptr, Sch P; SC; Bkbl; Sftbl; MVP, Tr; Amer Leg A; COM; Citz A; Journ A; Most Out; ROTC A; Methodist Yth Organization; Healthy Hearts, Baking Contest A; Leg of Hon & Merit; *Butler U; Home Ec.*

TALLEY, Vanessa
Baker HS; Columbus, GA; Drama; Fr C; MVP, Sftbl; *Columbus Col; Sociology.*

TALLMAN, David Alexander
Bishop Ryan HS; Minot, ND (15-95) Bus Mgr, Ann; Bus Mgr, Band; Dbte Tm; Ch, Drama; NHS; Orch; Sci C; Bkbl; COM; Most Out; Sacristan; Sci A; F-Ed, Annual; Best Dramatist; Com Thtre Civ Opera Mgr, Light Dir.

TALLMAN, Edwinna Lou
Lawrence HS; Lawrence, KS; Band; Bible Quiz Tm; Flag Corps; Secy, VP, Pres, Christ Ambassadors; Marching Lion Band; Historian, OEA C; *Christ For The Nations Inst; Deaf Ed.*

TALLMAN, Janet Katherine
Los Alamos HS; Los Alamos, NM (15-405) Pres, A Cap Choir; Chor; Drama; GS; Hmrm; Lit Mag; NFL; Pres, NHS; SC; Pres, Jr Cl; COM; Phi Beta Kappa; Rotary A; Hist, Drama C; WW; Bkstore Ch, SC; All St Mixed Chor; Jr-Sr Prom Court; 1st Alt, Girls Nation; Outbound Exchange Prog; *U of Calif; Cellular Biol.*

TALLMAN, Karen Anne
Cath Central HS; Troy, NY;

TALLY, Tom Lee
Carson HS; Carson, CA (100-1000) Bkbl; Ftbl; Citz A; Principal's List; Art A's; *Long Beach St Col; Art.*

TALMADGE, Paula Renee
Sandia HS; Albuquerque, NM; Band; Chor; Drama; Ensm; Pres, Hmrm; Lit Mag; Sch P; Ski C; Fin, Spch C; SC; COM; Opt A; Spch A; Star Student; Yth Fel.

TALOFF, Mary Beth
W Platte HS; Weston, MO (20-80) AFS; Ann; JV, Chldr; VP, FHA; FTA; 4H; NHS; Order/ Arrow; Rainbow; COM; Citz A; Hist A; Order/ Arrow A; Sci A; Outst Girl; Eng A; Vlbl; *Baker U; Pol Sci.*

TALOFF, Shirley Ann
W Platte R-2 HS; Weston, MO (25%-78) AFS; Ann; Chor; Secy, FHA; FTA; NHS; Rainbow; Span C; *Mo Western Col; Social Work.*

TALTON, Wanda Carol
Maypearl HS; Maypearl, TX (1-18) Ann; BC; Pres, FHA; Pres, SC; Pres, Sr Cl; Pres, Jr Cl; Co-Cpt, Bkbl; Tnns; Tr; MLS; Ntl Achv Schol; NMF; NMS; Val; VFW A; VofDEM; Brigman A for Excellence; *Mary-Hardin Col; Math.*

TAMASHIRO, Celia Lai Lan
Roosevelt HS; Honolulu, HI (69-591) HiY; Pres, Soph Cl; Bkbl; *U of Hawaii; Health.*

TAMAYO, Jeannette Patricia
Saint Benedict HS; Chicago, IL (20-227) Chor; Drama; Fr C; Ger C; Pres, Hmrm; Orch; ARC; Ski C; SC; Hon Prog; HS Scholastic Schol; Excellence A, Fr I; Red Cross Tutor; Co-teacher, Span Cl; *Loyola Col; International Diplomacy.*

TAMI, Steven Michael
Northgate HS; Walnut Creek, CA; Chess C; Drama; Ski C; Parl, SC; Thes; S-T, Jr Cl; Mgr, Ftbl; CSF; *Berkeley Col; Bus.*

TAMMARO, Tammy Jean
Wheeling Park HS; Wheeling, WV; Hmrm; Pres A; *Belmont Tech Col; Bus.*

TAMPLIN, Eddie Frank
Miami Norland Sr HS; Miami, FL (245-650) Ed, Ann; Bus C; Drama; FBLA; FFA; Sci C; Thes; Up Bound; Bus Mgr, Bkbl; Bio A; COM; Hist A; Journ A; Sci A; Black Amer A; *Calarts Col; Drama.*

TANALLON, Dionelia Diones
John F Kennedy HS; Tumon, GUAM (1-511)
NHS; Tres, SC; Alg A; Chem A; Hist A; Math A;
Phy A; Sci A; Type A; Top Ten; HR; Candystriper;
U of Wash; Engr.

TANDE, Lori Clareen
Souris HS; Souris, ND; Band; Chldr; Chor; Drama;
Ensm; Sch P; S-T, Jr Cl; Hon Prog; Type A; Miss
Ntl Tnager Pageant; Tutor A; *Bus.*

TANGEN, Janice Helen
Tottenville HS; Staten Island, NY; Chor; Citz A;
Down St Med Col; Phys Therapist.

TANKERSLEY, Angela Marie
Gainesville HS; Gainesville, GA (30-200) S-T,
Band; Chor; Hmrm; Thes; Tres, Jr Cl; *Gainesville
Jr Col; Ed.*

TANKSLEY, Kevin
Cardinal McCloskey HS; Albany, NY (135-159)
Chor; Bkbl; *Stoney Brook Col; Sociology.*

TANKSLEY, Ronnie Marvin
Cardinal McCloskey HS; Albany, NY (79-159)
Drama; Hmrm; Phys C; Cpt, Bkbl; COM; Most
Out; *U of Pittsburgh; Bus Adm.*

TANN, Amanda Carol
Aldine Sr HS; Houston, TX (214-537) Sftbl; Rptr,
VICA; Notebook, VICA, A's; *Cosmetology.*

TANNER, Brenda Sue
Morton HS; Morton, TX (12-56) Band; Ch, FHA;
Parl, FTA; NHS.

TANNER, Glen William
Grapevine HS; Grapevine, TX (25-200) InterAct
C; Lat C; Ch, SC; Pres, Jr Cl; Ftbl; Golf; Tnns;
Teacher Schol A; *Tex Tech; Phar.*

TANNER, Gwendolyn
Humphrys Co HS; Belzoni, MS (6-125) BC; FHA;
4H; Math C; Hon Prog; *Grambling St U; Psych.*

TANNER, Isao
Kubasaki HS; Okinawa, JAPAN (8-271) Hmrm;
VP, Mu Alpha Theta; NHS; Soccer; VP, Photo C;
Ch, Tech Crew; Vlbl; Racial Inter Act C; *U of Tex;
Archt.*

TANNER, Kristy Lynne
Attica HS; Attica, IN (11-115) Chldr; Pep C; FFA
Swtht; *Ind Voc Tech Col; Dental Asst.*

TANNER, Michael DeWayne
Jesuit HS; Shreveport, LA (5-97) BS; Pres, CYO;
Chldr; Dbte Tm; Drama; Key C; Math C; NFL;
NHS; A-Ed, Sch P; Pres, Sodality; Pres, SC; Amer
Leg A; Elk A; Most Out; Opt Out Tn; Outst Citzen,
BS; *U of Notre Dame; Pre-Med.*

TANNER, Nancy Louise
Murphy HS; Mobile, AL (29-550) Drama; NHS; Cl
Fav; Yth Choir; Azalea Trail Maid; Church Yth
Coun; Girl's Service C; Holme's Tn Board; *U of
Ala; Primary Ed.*

TANNER, Pamela Michele
Monroe Comprehensive HS; Monroe, GA (2-300)
S-T, BC; JV, Chldr; Chor; FBLA; Pres, Tri-HiY;
Crisco A; Gov Honor Prog; Kiwanis A; NEDT;
HR.

TANNER, Renee Frances
Saint Joseph's HS; W New York, NJ (29-225)
Mjrte; Secy, Span NHS; Cpt, Bkbl; Cpt, Cr-Ctry;
Secy, Sftbl; Secy, Swim; Tres, Tr; Hon Prog; *Upsala
Col; Vet.*

TANNER, Richard Coe
Perimeter S Christian Acad; Conley, GA (1-26)
Chor; Hmrm; InterClub Coun; Monogram; Ski C;
SC; Bsbl; Bkbl; Ftbl; Sftbl; Citz A; Cl Fav; Coun of
Teach A; H of F; Hon Prog; Most Out; Star Stu-
dent; Discipleship A; *Ga Tech; Computer Sci.*

TANNER, Steven Gregory
Marion HS; Marion, IA (80-206) Band; Tres, 4H;
4H A; Secy, 4-H C; Tres, Church Yth Fel; *Iowa St
U; Agr.*

TANNER, Tara Lisa
Richland HS; Fort Worth, TX; Ann; FTA; Ger C;
N Tex St U; Radio and Television.

TANNER, William Fred
Pinellas Park HS; St Petersburg, FL; Band; Chor;
Orch; MVP, Bkbl; MVP, Ftbl; Swim; MVP, Tr;
Glee C, Band, Outst Religious A's; *Mus.*

TANOUE, Cherril Yuri
John F Kennedy HS; Agana, GUAM (24-511) Ed,
Ann; NHS; Rptr, Sch P; VP, SC; *U of Hawaii.*

TANT, Allison Elizabeth
Fletcher Sr HS; Jacksonville Beach, FL (25%-300)
Pres, A Cap Choir; Ann; Co-Ch, Chor; Community
Yth Symph; Ensm; VP, Span C; Most Out; Chor A;
Local & Dist Piano A's; Omega C; Yth Adv Board;
Pennsacola Christian Col; Psych.

TAPELBAND, Gerda Ellen
John Marshall HS; Los Angeles, CA (30-625) Fr C;
Pres, Hmrm; A-Ed, Sch P; Swim; MVP, Tr; Citz A;
Hon Prog; Ntl Sci Symposium; Pres A; Yth Leg;
Jobs Daughters; Co-Cpt, Badminton; Gold Crown,
Star, A's.

TAPELBAND, Karen Estelle
John Marshall HS; Los Angeles, CA (30-600) Fr C;
Semi-Fin, GS; Hmrm; InterAct C; NHS; Sci C; Var
C; CSF; Hon Prog; MVP, Badminton; Jewel &
Gold Crowns, Star, A's; *U of Calif; Computer Sci.*

TAPLEY, Bruce Allen
Atwater HS; Atwater, CA; Church Kg; *Calif Polytechic Inst; Poultry Sci.*

TAPLEY, Rhonda Sue
Hermon Christian Sch; Hermon, ME; Cpt, Chldr;
Chor; Drama; Ensm; S-T, InterClub Coun; S-T, SC;
Bkbl; Sftbl; Pastor's A; Eng A; *New Brunswick
Bible Inst; Bible.*

TAPLEY, Theresa
Brandon Sr HS; Brandon, FL (107-850) Anchor C;
Bus C; FBLA; NHS; Yth Choir; *Eckerd Col; Pup-
pet Ministry.*

TAPP, Sandra Jean
Wade Hampton HS; Greenville, SC (155-371) A
Cap Choir; AFS; Chor; Fr C; Pol Sci C; JA A;
Furman U; Mus.

TAPP, Timothy Alan
Ballard HS; Louisville, KY (19-400) A Cap Choir;
BC; BS; Drama; Math C; Mu Alpha Theta; NHS;
Pres, Sci C; Span C; Tr, JA A; Jr Chamber of Com
A; Spch A; Boys Nation; Outst Young Kentuckian;
Whitehouse Conf On Yth Technology; *Purdue U;
Engr.*

TAPSCOTT, Katharine Caroline
Columbus HS; Columbus, GA; NHS; Sr Cl; *Dance.*

TARDI, Marilyn
Yauco HS; Yauco, PR; Commercial C; FBLA;
Bradley U; Computers Programming.

TARGETT, Larry E
Greenfield Central HS; Greenfield, IN; Ger C; 4H;
Math C; NHS; Tres, Order/Arrow; SC; Pres, Jr Cl;
Wrest; Hon Prog; Order/Arrow A; Yth Fel; Eagle
Sct; Firecrafter; *Purdue U; Engr.*

TARPLEY, Teresa Jan
Ensley HS; Birmingham, AL; BC; Chor; Fr C; Sftbl;
JA A.

TARR, Cami Annette
Auburn HS; Auburn, WA (43-574) NHS; *UPS Tacoma.*

TARR, Darrell Lavon
Robert Lindblom Tech HS; Chicago, IL (52-617)
Pres, Dbte Tm; NHS; Amer Leg A; Hon Prog;
ROTC A; *Pre-Med.*

TARR, Kathleen L
Cuyahoga Valley Christian Acad; Cuyahoga Falls,
OH (4-56) Chor; Ensm; Ger C; Ski C; Alg A; Bio A;
Citz A; Math A; NEDT; Piano Solo; Ntl Fed of
Music Fest; *Med.*

TARR, Zelda Renee
George Henry Corliss HS; Chicago, IL (15-30)
Chor; Span C; Citz A; *Morehouse Col; Bio.*

TARTER, Tamara Beth
Goddard HS; Roswell, NM (34-300) Secy, Chor;
Ensm; Fr C; NHS; Rainbow; Sci C; SC; WW;
WTSU; Elem Ed.

TARVER, Cynthia Anita
Smith HS; Atlanta, GA (5-264) Fr C; NHS; Secy,
SC; Gov Honor Prog; Hon Prog; *Grady Hosp Sch
of Nurs; Nurs.*

TARVER, Dorothy Ann
Wadley HS; Wadley, GA (11-85) Chldr; Chor; Fr
C; FHA; VP, 4H; Sch P; 4H A; HQn; Sci A; Read-
ing, Phys Ed, A's; *Paine Col; Social Worker.*

TARVID, Russell Justin
Quigley S HS; Chicago, IL (59-260) Chor; SC; Mgr,
Bkbl; Amer Leg A; *NW Col; Journ.*

TASABIA, Ezequiel
Luther Burbank Sr HS; Sacramento, CA (248-702)
Band; Most Out; *Pepperdine U; Ed.*

TASSIE, Carrie Jane
Redmond HS; Redmond, OR (3-250) Band; NHS;
Tr; Social Stu Stu o-t Mo; *Central Oreg Comm Col;
Sci.*

TASSIN, Gerard Bennett
Brother Martin HS; New Orleans, LA (1-330) Pres,
Chess C; VP, Dbte Tm; Lit Ral; NHS; VP, Spch C;
Alg A; Bio A; Chem A; Hon Prog; Math A; NEDT;
ROTC A; Sci A; Spch A; Ntl Academic Games
Olympic Champ; Yrbk Staff; Debate A; WW; *Tu-
lane U; Med.*

TASSIN, Stephen Allen
Baker HS; Baker, LA; BC; BS; Mu Alpha Theta; Tr;
LSU; Engr.

TASZAREK, Roxane T
Edgeley HS; Edgeley, ND (10%-56) A Cap Choir;
F-Ed, Ann; Band; Cpt, Chldr; Chor; Ensm; Secy,
FBLA; Tres, FHA; SC; Var C; Mgr, Bkbl; Tr; HCt;
St Rptr, FBLA; District Secy, Church Zone;
Church Organist; *U of ND; Phys Therapy.*

TATE, Celia Mae
Dan River HS; Ringgold, VA; FBLA; FHA; Sch P;
Span C; Tri-HiY.

TATE, Cynthia D
Papillion-LaVista Sr HS; Papillion, NE (110-368)
FBLA; FTA; ARC; Mgr, Bkbl; Mgr, Soccer;
Beauty; COM; Pres A; WW; *U of Nebr; Elem Ed.*

TATE, Debra Ann
Booker T Washington HS; Memphis, TN; *Morehouse Col.*

TATE, Glenda Ruth
Newton Co Comprehensive HS; Covington, GA
(35-340) Merit, Principal, HR'S; Golden Ray A;
Morris Brown Col; Biol.

TATE, Harold Nelson
Lee HS; Montgomery, AL (25%-800) Band; BC;
Hmrm; NHS; Order/Arrow; SC; Mgr, Ftbl; Tr;
Most Out; Symph, Stage, Bands; Sct Patrol A;
Hon Men, Art Fair; Tot & Tn's, Inc; Den Chief,
Scts; *Tuskegee Inst.*

TATE, James Wilson
Ashbrook HS; Gastonia, NC (40-562) Chor; Fr C;
Rptr, Sch P; VP, TAPS; Yth o-t Yr; JAL; Mus
Camp School; March of Dimes A; PA; *Acct.*

TATE, Juanita
Eastside HS; Paterson, NJ; A-Ed, Sch P; VP, Sr Cl;
HR; *Eng.*

TATE, Patricia Anne
LaMarque HS; La Marque, TX (10%-400) Anchor
C; Band; Mjrte; Tres, NHS; Swim; Alg A; Tres,
FCA; Water Polo; Most Improved Swimmer; *Tex
A&M U.*

TATE, Penny Claretha
John McDonogh HS; New Orleans, LA; Band; *U of
New Orleans; Math.*

TATE, Rebecca Annette
First Assembly Christian Sch; Memphis, TN (1-30)
Ed, Ann; Tres, Hmrm; Lat C; Math C; Mgr, Bkbl;
Alg A; COM; H of F; HQn; Math A; Most Out; Sci
A; Yth Fel; *Evangel Col; Acct.*

TATE, Rozetia Marieia
McLain Sr HS; Tulsa, OK; Chldr; Var C; JV, Swim;
Hon Prog; VFW A; VofDEM; *Kans Wesleyan Col;
Acct.*

TATE, Sarah Elizabeth
Reidsville Sr HS; Reidsville, NC (42-344) AFS;
Ann; Ch, Fr C; Hmrm; Ed, Sch P; SC; HCt;
Bible C; Ch, Jr-Sr Prom; *The U of NC at Greens-
boro; Nurs.*

TATE, Sheryl Lynn
Winner HS; Winner, SD (20-115) Band; 4H; Bkbl;
Sftbl; Yth Fel; Explorer; *Child Development.*

TATE, Valerie Jewel
Roosevelt HS; Gary, IN (32-555) Fr C; FHA; FTA;
NHS; Ch, Up Bound; NAACP A; *U of San Fran-
cisco; Sociology.*

TATE, Willie Regina
Marvell HS; Marvell, AR (9-118) MVP, Band; BC;
Hon Prog; Yth Fel; U of Colo; Law.

TATHAM, David Lee
Pisgah HS; Canton, NC (10-30) FFA; Sftbl; Co-
Cpt, Wrest; Most Out; NC St U.

TATLOCK, Donald Robert
Woodrow Wilson HS; Dallas, TX; Band; VP, Fr C;
Butler U; Religion.

TATRO, Donna Ellen
Huntington HS; Huntington, NY (15%-600) AFS;
Band; Chor; Ensm; NJHS; Band A; Engr.

TATRO, Lisa Ann
Huntington HS; Huntington, NY (10%-618) A Cap
Choir; Mgr, Chor; Secy, Drama; Rptr, Sch P; SC;
Hockey; Regent Schol; Span, Choir, Drama, A's;
Allegheny Col; Span.

TATUCH, Dennis Leon
Immaculate Conception HS; Hamtramck, MI
(7-29) Bsbl; Ftbl; NMS; Mich St U; Forestry.

TATUCH, Martin Borys
Immaculate Conception HS; Hamtramck, MI
(9-39) Chor; Rptr, Sch P; Bsbl; JV, Bkbl; Ftbl; Ecology.

TATUM, Conrad Ray
Cartersville HS; Cartersville, GA; F-Ed, Ann; BC;
Dbte Tm; Drama; FTA; Hmrm; SC; Thes; Tri-HiY;
VP, Sr Cl; MVP, Drama; Cl Fav; HCt; Yth Leg; Jr
Marshall; 5 Yr Pin, Church Attendence; 3 Yr 1-Act
Cast; Page; Sou Baptist Convention; Journ.

TATUM, Demetris Michelle
Saint Mary's Acad; Inglewood, CA (10-200)
Drama; ARC; Span C; Spch C; Span NHS; CSF;
Eng, Spch, Typing As; Pepperdine U; Med.

TATUM, Latynia Denice
Gardena HS; Gardena, CA (650-1300) Los Angeles SW Col; Nurs.

TATUM, Michael Warren
Central HS; Memphis, TN (40-250) Hmrm; Order/
Arrow; Bkbl; Opt Out Tn; Memphis St U; Acct.

TATUM, Myra Denice
Hillwood HS; Nashville, TN (49-170) Chor; ARC;
Span C; Up Bound; HCt; PA; Gym; Friendship A;
Nashville-Tech Col; Bus Ed.

TATZ, Victoria Lynn
Naperville N HS; Naperville, IL (55-400) Pres,
Band; Ger C; NHS; John Phillip Sousa Band A;
Northern Ill U.

TAUER, Michelle Sue
S San Antonio HS; San Antonio, TX (10-255)
Chldr; Cl Fav; Hon Prog; Fresh Cl Swtht; Med.

TAUMAOE, Lelia Salley
Vista HS; Vista, CA (765-854) Palomar Col; Clerical Typist.

TAUNTON, Carole Marie
Robert E Lee Inst; Thomaston, GA; Span C; Vet
Med.

TAUNTON, Lisa Jeanne
Quartz Hill HS; Quartz Hill, CA; Rptr, 4H; SC; 4H
A; Drill Tm; Lawton Dental Asst Trade Sch; Den-
tal Asst.

TAUNTON, Marion Scott
Robert E Lee HS; Tyler, TX (75%-685) Pres, Yth;
Most Inspirational, Sftbl; Tex A&M Col; Banking
& Finance.

TAUTFEST, Janette Marie
Centennial HS; Gresham, OR (10%-500) Band;
Ger C; 4H; Hmrm; Secy, SC; Citz A; Lib Service A;
Whitworth Col; Lib.

TAUVELA, Hana
Carson HS; Carson, CA; JV, Sftbl; Tr; Calif St U;
Bio Sci.

TAVAREZ, Luis
Colegio San Antonio; Isabela, PR (4-33) Pres,
CYO; Chor; Drama; Fin, Spch C; Bsbl; Sftbl; Tr;
COM; U of Puerto Rico; Med.

TAVENNER, John Stephen
Slaton HS; Slaton, TX (2-98) Ann; NHS; Span C;
SC; Cpt, Bkbl; Sci A; VP, Yth Fel; Tex Tech Col.

TAVENNER, Sharon Lynne
Slaton HS; Slaton, TX (25%-150) Band; Chldr;
FHA; Span C; SC; Bkbl; Tnns; Tr; Most Talented;
Tex Tech U.

TAVERNIER, Benjamin Ivan
Patten Acad of Christian Ed; Oakland, CA (2-13)
A Cap Choir; Band; Chem C; Chor; City Conf;
Community Yth Symph; Cpt, Dbte Tm; Drama;
Ensm; Lit Ral; Madrigal; Orch; Ed, Sch P; Spch C;
Tres, SC; Pres, Jr Cl; MVP, Bsbl; Cr-Ctry; Cpt,
Ftbl; Cpt, Soccer; MVP, Sftbl; Semi-Fin, Swim; JV,
Tnns; Bio A; COM; Chem A; Citz A; JA A; Ki-
wanis A; Most Out; WW; Semi-Fin, Yth Mus Com-
petition; Mus.

TAVES, Rick Jay
Camden HS; San Jose, CA; Bus C; Tres, Chor;
Cr-Ctry; Swim; JV, Tr; San Jose U; Bus.

TAVITIAN, Susan Araxie
Whitman-Hanson Regional HS; Whitman, MA;
Band; Chor; Drama; Key C; NHS; SC; Bkbl; Sftbl;
Tnns; Hon Prog; V Ltrs; Win, Spellman Essay;
Bridgewater St Col; Special Ed.

TAY, Michael Edward
Cumberland Valley HS; Mechanicsburg, PA
(12-650) CYO; K of C; NHS; JV, Bsbl; Ftbl; JV, Tr;
Bucknell Col; Biol.

TAYLOR, Amanda Rae
Sam Barlow HS; Gresham, OR; Band; Chldr; Chor;
Sch P; Swim; Journ A; Pres A; Gym; HR A; Pep-
perdine U; Journ.

TAYLOR, Andrew Warren
Bellevue HS; Bellevue, WA (67-486) NHS; Eagle Sct; Pacific Lutheran U; Communications.

TAYLOR, Angela Gae
Greenville HS; Greenville, SC (37-256) Chor; SC;
Secy, Jr Cl; Gr Marshal; Pres, DECA; Samford U;
Psych.

TAYLOR, Ann Charlotte
Richfield HS; Richfield, MN (67%-734) Rptr, Sch
P; Span C; Normandale Comm Col; Eng.

TAYLOR, Anthony Octavius
Plymouth HS; Plymouth, NC (19-192) Ann; Math
C; NHS; Rptr, Sch P; Pres, Jr Cl; Pres, Soph Cl;
Ftbl; Tnns; UNC; Journ.

TAYLOR, Ardene
Mercy Acad; Louisville, KY; ARC; JA A; ARC A;
Bowl A; Pep C; Licensed Model; Patsy Bloor Dan-
cers; Jefferson Comm Col; Bus.

TAYLOR, Arline Johnson
W Charlotte Open HS; Charlotte, NC; Cpt, Chldr;
FHA; Ger C; Ntl Yth Conf; Sftbl; Yth Fel.

TAYLOR, Becky Jane
Emerson HS; Emerson, AR; Chor; Alg A; Bio A;
COM; Hon Prog; Math A; Sou Ark U; Math.

TAYLOR, Belinda Mae
Crestview HS; Crestview, FL (10%-250) Anchor C;
BC; Dbte Tm; Drama; FBLA; FHA; GS; Hmrm;
Pol Sci C; ARC; Parl, SC; Citz A; Hist A; JA A;
Spch A; Page at Capitol; Wash Congressional
Workshop; Columbia Col; Pol Sci.

TAYLOR, Ben Richard
Weatherford HS; Weatherford, TX (10-252) De-
molay; FBLA; FTA; NHS; Golf; Tnns; HCt; Tex
Tech Col; Bus.

TAYLOR, Betty Marie
Williamsburg HS; Andrews, SC (20-59) SC; Pres,
Soph Cl.

TAYLOR, Beverly Ann
Boone HS; Orlando, FL (5%-600) BC; FHA; Hon
Prog; Pres A; Yth Fel; Jr NHS; Civitan; Torch Soc;
Gym; Teaching.

TAYLOR, Beverly Denise
Humboldt HS; Humboldt, TN (10%-200) A Cap
Choir; Cpt, Band; BC; Cpt, Chldr; Chor; Pres,
FHA; Madrigal; Span C; VP, Soph Cl; HQn; Yth
Fel; U of Tenn; Law.

TAYLOR, Billy Edwin Jr
Central HS; Thomasville, GA; FFA; Key C; NHS;
Order/Arrow; Bsbl; COM; Eagle Sct.

TAYLOR, Brooks Edward
Baylor Sch for Boys; Chattanooga, TN; Ann; Ger
C; Mgr, Ftbl; Wrest; Drama A; Engr.

TAYLOR, Cara Lynette
Carrollton HS; Carrollton, MO (9-88) Band; Cpt,
Chldr; Dbte Tm; FHA; FTA; Secy, 4H; NHS; Pres,
Rainbow; Sci C; Pres, SC; Secy, Sr Cl; B Crocker A;
Cl Fav; HCt; Regent Schol; U of Mo-Columbia;
Home Ec.

TAYLOR, Carol Sue
Plant City HS; Plant City, FL; Chor; FBLA; Citz A;
Type A; Eckerd Col; Working with Children.

TAYLOR, Carrie Ann
Bay HS; Panama City, FL; Anchor C; Gulf Coast
Comm Col; Phys Ed.

TAYLOR, Cheryl Ann
Reynoldsburg HS; Reynoldsburg, OH (21-350) VP,
Bus C; Secy, NHS; Y-Tns; Hon Prog; Yth Fel;
Church Choir; Sr Cl Play; Col Hon Schol; Mount
Vernon Nazarene Col; Psych.

TAYLOR, Christine Ann
Southside HS; Elmira, NY; Band; Chor; COM.

TAYLOR, Cindy Lou
Exeter Pub HS; Exeter, NE (19-32) Ann; Drama;
Pres, 4H; Math C; Mu Alpha Theta; S-T; Var C;
Y-Tns; Bkbl; Citz A; 4H A; Spch A; Band Rep;
Tres, Yth Fel; VP, Pep C; U of Nebr; Secy.

TAYLOR, Cindy Michelle
S Chodaw Acad; Toxey, AL (1-26) Ed, Ann; BC;
Chor; Hmrm; Cpt, Mjrte; NHS; SC; Tres, Soph Cl;
MVP, Bkbl; Sftbl; Beauty; Cl Fav; HCt; Most Out;
Sci A; Best Personality; Best Dressed; Most Beauti-
ful.

TAYLOR, Claudia Jeanne
Northside HS; Fort Smith, AR (10-250) Hmrm;
Math C; Mu Alpha Theta; NHS; Rptr, Sch P; Span
C; Span NHS; Citz A; Hon Prog; PTA A; Eng,
Character, A's; U of Tex; Med.

TAYLOR, Clementine
Yoxubee Co HS; Macon, MS (16-170) Cpt, Band;
Drama; FHA; Phys C; Tres, Y-Tns; Bkbl; Sftbl;
Citz A; H of F; Hist A; Hon Prog; Journ A; MLS;
Type A; Yth Fel; US Army; Clerk Typist.

TAYLOR, Clinton Eugene Jr
Troy HS; Troy, TX (1-49) Ann; Band; BC; Drama;
Rptr, Sch P; Bsbl; JV, Bkbl; Mgr, Ftbl; Tnns; COM;
1st Pl, Bsbl.

TAYLOR, Colleen Adanan
New Bloomfield R III HS; New Bloomfield, MO;
Co-Ed, Ann; Band; Chldr; Chor; Fr C; 4H; NHS;
Co-Ed, Sch P; Sci C; SC; Var C; Bsbl; Bkbl; 4H A;
Foley Foods A; Drivers Ed A; Lincoln U; Bus.

TAYLOR, Curtis Walter
Klamath Union HS; Klamath Falls, OR (140-496)
Band; Order/Arrow; Golf; BSct Life Rank; Cand,
Eagle Sct; Carpentry.

TAYLOR, Cynthia Alyne
Norton Comm HS; Norton, KS (50%-88) A-Ed,
Ann; FFA; Rptr, FHA; 4H; F-Ed, Sch P; Sci C;
Span C; Bkbl; MVP, Tnns; Tr; 4H A; Hist A; HCt;
Journ A; Sci A; Runner-Up, FFA Swtht; Home-
coming Duchess; Ath A; Hays U; Acct.

TAYLOR, Cynthia Rena
Green Oaks HS; Shreveport, LA (10-20) Y-Tns;
Sftbl; Swim; Sci A; Yth Fel; Math A; Nurs.

TAYLOR, Damon Turone
Lincoln HS; Dallas, TX; Hmrm; NHS; Bkbl; JV,
Ftbl; Tr; Cl Fav; Hon Prog; Eng A; Aeronautical
Engr.

TAYLOR, Dana Claire
Jefferson Davis HS; Montgomery, AL (25%-800)
BC; FHA; Home Ec.

TAYLOR, Dana Jewell
Tollesboro HS; Tollesboro, KY (1-75) BC; Tres,
FHA; 4H; Sci A; Eng A; U of Ky; Med.

TAYLOR, Darleen Lannette
Tulare Union HS; Tulare, CA; Church Qn; Secy,
Yth Group.

TAYLOR, David Gray
Choctawhatchee Sr HS; Fort Walton Beach, FL
(45-700) Tres, BC; Chor; Sci C; Ch, Church Yth
Coun; Okaloosa-Walton Jr Col; Computer Programming.

TAYLOR, Debbie Ann
Sooner HS; Bartlesville, OK (22-280) F-Ed, Ann;
Hmrm; NHS; Span C; SC; Hist A; St Scholar; Yth
Fel.

TAYLOR, Debbie Clare
Bryan Sr HS; Omaha, NE; Span C; JV, Tnns; Type
A; U of Nebr; Worldstu.

TAYLOR, Debbra Jean
Yorkwood HS; Monmouth, IL (1-44) Chor; NHS; Span C; Pres, Soph Cl; St Scholar; Val; *Monmouth Col; Hospital Adm.*

TAYLOR, Deborah Louise
Pewaukee HS; Pewaukee, WI (99-127) A Cap Choir; Chor; Drama; Spch C; Midwest Shrine Qn; *WCTI; Data Processing.*

TAYLOR, Debra Kay
Bay HS; Panama City, FL; Anchor C; Beauty; Swtht; Contestant, Miss Photogenic; *Gulf Coast Comm Col; Fashion Designing.*

TAYLOR, Deena Rae
Concord HS; Concord, CA (6-430) Band; Model UN; Bkbl; Sftbl; Swim; CSF; Hon Prog; *Seatle Pacific Col; Phys Ed.*

TAYLOR, Denise Adele
Houston Tech Inst; Houston, TX; Bus C; FBLA; VP, Hmrm; ARC; Up Bound; Arch; Cpt, Bkbl; Co-Cpt, Ftbl; Golf; Swim; Semi-Fin, Tnns; COM; Citz A; Hist A; JA A; ARC A; Swtht; Type A; Shorthand, Inter Decorating, A's; *U of Houston; Bus Adm.*

TAYLOR, Derek John
Springbrook HS; Silver Spring, MD; Key C; Bkbl; Golf; Tnns; *Md U; Psych.*

TAYLOR, Diann
St Matthew HS; Melrose, LA; A Cap Choir; Pres, Chldr; Chor; Hmrm; Sftbl; Alg A; Bio A; Cl Fav; Hon Prog; Ldrship A.

TAYLOR, Don E
Hammond Christian Acad; Griffith, IN (1-25) Ann; Band; Chor; Drama; JETS; Orch; Cpt, Ftbl; MVP, Ftbl; *Ind Central Col; Phys Ed.*

TAYLOR, Donn Nicholas
Crestview HS; Crestview, FL (40%-300) Order/ Arrow; Sci C; Span C; COM; Order/Arrow A; ARC A; ROTC A; Battered Boot A; Yth Fitness Achv A; *Okaloosa Walton Jr Col; Engr.*

TAYLOR, Donna Lynn
Winona Acad; Winona, MS (10-30) Ann; Chor; 4H; Sch P; Var C; Co-Cpt, Bkbl; Sftbl; Tr; COM; HCt; Sci A; PA; *Pharmacy.*

TAYLOR, Dorothy Ann
Allen HS; Robeline, LA (2-27) Secy, FBLA; Pres, Hmrm; VP, Math C; NHS; Spch C; Pres, Sr Cl; Pres, Jr Cl; VP, Soph Cl; HQn; Sal; *Northwestern St U; Bus Adm.*

TAYLOR, Edward Brent
Bel Aire HS; Baton Rouge, LA; *USL; Civil Engr.*

TAYLOR, Elizabeth Lynette
Pine Forest Sr HS; Fayetteville, NC (33%-530) Chor.

TAYLOR, Ellen Walker
Summerville Acad; Summerville, SC (3-8) Bus Mgr, Ann; Cpt, Chldr; Drama; Hmrm; VP, SC; Bio A; Chem A.

TAYLOR, Emarilyn
W End HS; Birmingham, AL (77-236) Secy, Chor; Secy, FHA; VP, Hmrm; SC; Outst Part A, Sch Activities; Pep Sq Ldrship A; SGA Cert; Church Yth o-t Yr; *Ala A&M U; Bus Ed.*

TAYLOR, Eric Scott
Wm R Boone HS; Orlando, FL; Mgr, Band; Ger C; Order/Arrow; God & Country A; Order/Arrow A; Eagle Sct; *Fla Tech U; Bus Adm.*

TAYLOR, Eva Colline
Zion Benton HS; Zion, IL; VP, Chor; Drama; Ger C; VP, Lit Ral; Lit Mag; Math C; NHS; Sch P; SC; Thes; Tnns; Bio A; COM; Citz A; Gov Honor Prog; HCt; Hon Prog; Math A; Poet A; Sci A; Cpt, Flag Drill Tm; PA; Social Stu A; *Ohio St U; Vet.*

TAYLOR, Evelyn Renee
Asbury Park HS; Asbury Park, NJ (27-300) Tr; Type A; *N Taylor Bus Inst; Legal Secy.*

TAYLOR, Evie Anita
South Side HS; Memphis, TN (10%-370) Band; Pres, Hmrm; Math C; NHS; ARC; Sci C; Span C; Spch C; SC; Pres, Jr Cl; COM; Citz A; Hon Prog; Sci A; Mus, Achv, A's; Phys Ed School; *Oral Roberts U; International Relations.*

TAYLOR, Frank Issac
Montclair HS; Montclair, NJ; Bsbl; Ftbl; Mgr, Chmpnship Little Lge Bsbl Tm; *Ariz St U; Pre-Law.*

TAYLOR, Freida Adele
Shortridge HS; Indianapolis, IN (1-450) Ann; Fr C; Ger C; Bus Mgr, Sch P; Tres, Soph Cl; Soccer; DARGCA; Math A; Sci A.

TAYLOR, Frieda Adele
Shortridge HS; Indianapolis, IN (1-300) Ann; Fr C; Ger C; Bus Mgr, Sch P; Tres, Soph Cl; Soccer; DARGCA; Math A; Sci A; Star Student.

TAYLOR, Gloria
Terrell Co HS; Dawson, GA (10%-112) FHA; *Albany St Col; Bus Adm.*

TAYLOR, Glynise Ann
Granger HS; Salt Lake City, UT; Band; Chor; Citz A; Hon Prog; Mus A; *Rockmont Col; Mus.*

TAYLOR, Greg Eugene
Gold Coast Christian HS; Ft Lauderdale, FL (12-31) *Grace Col.*

TAYLOR, Harriet Carol
Columbia Acad; Columbia, MS; A Cap Choir; Anchor C; Ensm; FHA; Hmrm; VP, Sci C; SC; Beauty; Drill Tm; FHA A.

TAYLOR, Herman Ivan Jr
Savannah HS; Savannah, GA (53-371) Fr C; Math C; ROTC A; Pres, Off C; Cpt, Drill Tm; Explorers; *Fla A&M U; Archt.*

TAYLOR, Izora Lynn
Overbrook HS; Philadelphia, PA (20%-700) Chor; Community Yth Symph; MVP, Ensm; MVP, Orch; COM; Hon Prog; Most Out; *W Va U; Mus.*

TAYLOR, Jacqueline Ann
Ballard HS; Seattle, WA (10%-350) Ensm; NHS; Semi-Fin, Swim; Tr; Most Out.

TAYLOR, Jacquelyn
W S Creecy HS; Rich Square, NC (3-42) Secy, BC; Hon Prog; WW; *NC Central U; Bus Adm.*

TAYLOR, James Ashley Jr
White City Baptist HS; Ft Pierce, FL (6-18) MVP, Bsbl; Babe Ruth Ath o-t Yr; All Stars.

TAYLOR, James Harold
Benjamin Bosse HS; Evansville, IN (50-380) Band; BS; Hmrm; NHS; Pres, SC; Ftbl; Tr; Chamber of Comm A; Citz A; Cl Fav; HCt; Opt A; Summa Cum Laude; Future Ldr of Tomorrow; *Ind U; Bus.*

TAYLOR, James Mark
Putnam City HS; Oklahoma City, OK (85-970) A Cap Choir; Pres, Chor; Ensm; Co-Ch, FTA; Ger C; Madrigal; NHS; Thes; COM; Swtht; All St Chor; Pearl Coffy School; ACDA Conv; Outst Mus Theory Stu; Ntl Win, Boy's Voc Solo & Ensm; Most Talented Sr Boy; *Oral Roberts U; Vocal Mus Ed.*

TAYLOR, Jay Scott
Arkadelphia HS; Arkadelphia, AR (15-200) Chem C; Chess C; Fr C; FFA; 4H; Tnns; Citz A; 4H A; Yth Fel; *Henderson St U; Sci.*

TAYLOR, Jeanette Eileen
Holy Names HS; Oakland, CA; SC; HCt; Hon Prog; Yth Fel; Yth Leg; Phi Delta Kappa; *The Fashion Inst of Des and Merch; Fashion Coordinator.*

TAYLOR, Jo Lynn
Brookwood Sch; Thomasville, GA; AFS; F-Ed, Ann; Chldr; Drama; Pres, Hmrm; Secy, SC; Pres, Soph Cl; Bkbl; Tnns; COM; Math A; Swtht; Eng A; *U of Ga; Elem Ed.*

TAYLOR, Joanne Elizabeth
W Philadelphia HS; Philadelphia, PA; Pres, A Cap Choir; All Amer Yth; Chldr; Hmrm; NHS; Span C; World Affairs C; MVP, Bkbl; MVP, Sftbl; MVP, Swim; Tr; *Drew U; Med.*

TAYLOR, John Byron II
E Hills HS; Fort Worth, TX (96%-540) Band; Cum Laude Soc; Demolay; Ensm; Hmrm; NHS; Bsbl; Golf; Bio A; Chem A; Hon Prog; Sci A; Summa Cum Laude; Sci Fair; *Tex Christian U; Pre-Med.*

TAYLOR, Johnnie Rue
Western Grove HS; Western Grove, AR (1-25) Cpt, Chldr; 4H; SC; VP, Jr Cl; VP, Soph Cl; Bkbl; Sftbl; Cl Fav; Coun of Teach A; 4H A; HQn; Hon Prog; Lib Staff; All Co, Bkbl; *N Ark Comm Col.*

TAYLOR, Joni Elaine
Norwell HS; Ossian, IN; Band; Chor; Ensm; 4H; Swim; 4H A; PTA A; Sci A; *Fort Wayne Bible Col; Arts.*

TAYLOR, Joyce Dalphine
Lake Clifton Sr HS; Baltimore, MD (10%-315) NHS; Hist A; Math A; Ntl Achv Schol; Type A; Eng As; *U of Md in Balto Co; Acct.*

TAYLOR, Julie Ann
Sheffield HS; Memphis, TN (7-142) Mu Alpha Theta; NHS; ARC; HCt; WW; *Liberal Arts.*

TAYLOR, Julie Ann
J R Tucker HS; Richmond, VA (94-419) Chldr; SC; Y-Tns; Gym; *Radford Col; Recreation.*

TAYLOR, Julie Anne
Fairview HS; Boulder, CO; CYO; Chor; Hmrm; Hockey; COM; Pres A; Pres, GSct; Gym; Ntl Yth Phys Fitness A; Cert of Achv; *Teaching.*

TAYLOR, Karen Rochelle
Rockdale HS; Rockdale, TX (2-133) NHS; Sal.

TAYLOR, Katherine Yvette
McDonogh 35 Sr HS; New Orleans, LA (76-306) Chldr; Chor; SC; Y-Tns; Chldr A; Chor A; Sch Service A; *UNO; Computer Technology.*

TAYLOR, Kathryn Lynn
Sequin HS; Sequin, TX (25%-372) Band; Drama; Ensm; Rptr, Hmrm; NHS; Sequin League Arts & Crafts Schol; *Texas Lutheran Col; Art.*

TAYLOR, Kathy Jean
Bourbon County HS; Paris, KY; FHA; Bsbl; Bkbl; Cl Fav; ROTC A; VFW A; Powder Puff Ftbl; Art A; *Lexington Voc Sch; Nurs.*

TAYLOR, Kevin Charles
Putnam City W HS; Bethany, OK; Chess C; Span NHS; *Sci.*

TAYLOR, Kevin Scott
Raytown S HS; Raytown, MO (33-585) A Cap Choir; Chor; Semi-Fin, Ensm; Madrigal; COM; Citz A; Math A; CMSU Schol; CBC Schol; 2nd Pl, Regional Vocal Ensm; 1st Pl, Keyboard Solo; *Central Bible Col; Mus.*

TAYLOR, Kristi Lee
Othello HS; Othello, WA (4-135) F-Ed, Ann; Band; Dbte Tm; Secy, Drama; Ensm; NHS; VP, Ski C; Spch C; JV, Golf; Citz A; Hon Prog; Masonic A; Spch A; Type A; Beta Sigma Phi Bi-Cent Essay Con; *Wash St U; Bus.*

TAYLOR, Kristin Anne
Champaign Central HS; Champaign, IL (27-408) A Cap Choir; CYO; Chor; Drama; Ensm; Fr C; French NHS; Madrigal; NHS; Rptr, Sch P; NMF; NMS; St Scholar; Ntl Exchange C A; Pom- pon Girl; Sch Mus; All St Choir; *U of Ill; Bus Adm.*

TAYLOR, Larry Joe
Wakulla HS; Crawfordville, FL (10%-117) FFA; Sci C; Cpt, Bsbl; Cpt, Bkbl; Co-Cpt, Ftbl; FFA A; *FSU; Elec.*

TAYLOR, Leanda Jean
Dyer Co HS; Newbern, TN; Bus Mgr, Ann; Band; Chldr; Chor; Ensm; Secy, FHA; 4H; Lat C; NHS; Cl Fav; 4H A; *Marketing.*

TAYLOR, Lee Frederic
Thornwood HS; S Holland, IL (44-970) Order/ Arrow; Mgr, Swim; Tnns; VP, Explorer Post; Pres, Bicentennial Park Project; *Ill Inst of Tech; Chem.*

TAYLOR, Leslie June
Clovis HS; Clovis, NM; Span C; Mus A; Schol A; *Lubbock Christian Col; Spec Ed.*

TAYLOR, Leslie Marie
Hemet HS; Hemet, CA; Tres, A Cap Choir; AFS; VP, Chor; Swim; *Calif Lutheran Col; Psych.*

TAYLOR, Linda Ann
Laurel Highlands HS; Uniontown, PA (17-451) Ann; Band; Chor; Hmrm; Mjrte; NHS; Pres, Rainbow; Sch P; Ski C; Tri-HiY; *Ind U of Pa; Home Ec.*

TAYLOR, Lisa Ruth
Winyah HS; Georgetown, SC (50-129) F-Ed, Ann; Co-Cpt, Chldr; Fr C; Pep C; Most Sch Spirited; Jr Civinetes; Frosh C; Soph Board; *Col of Charleston; Nurs.*

TAYLOR, Lou Ellen
Central HS; Phoenix, AZ (127-527) Pres, FHA; SC; Tri-HiY; 1st Pl, HERO St Convention; Semi-Fin, HERO School; *Phoenix Col; Special Ed.*

TAYLOR, Mark Alan
Broken Arrow HS; Broken Arrow, OK (10%-200)
Band; Dbte Tm; Drama; VP, Hmrm; Model UN;
Order/Arrow; Spch C; UN Council; Ftbl; Wrest;
COM; Order/Arrow A; Wrest A's; U of Tulsa;
Med.

TAYLOR, Martha Ruth
Monticello Ind HS; Monticello, KY (5-45) Chldr;
Drama; Tres, Fr C; FHA; Pres, FTA; Pres, NHS;
Tres, Sr Cl; VP, Jr Cl; VP, Soph Cl; H of F; Math A;
U of Ky; Math.

TAYLOR, Mary Ellen
Green Oaks HS; Shreveport, LA; Chor; Drama;
Bkbl; Sftbl; Cl Fav; Spch A; Yth Fel; Dance A;
Bethany Col; Dramatics.

TAYLOR, Mary Jo
Wynford HS; Bucyrus, OH (24-108) S-T, Band;
VP, Chor; VP, FHA; Pres, 4H; NHS; SC; Thes; 4H
A; Secy, Tres, Rptr, 4-H C; Scribe, Thespian; Otter-
bein Col; Home Ec.

TAYLOR, Mary Katherine
Niles Sr HS; Niles, MI (27-377) Cpt, Chldr;
Drama; Sftbl; Tnns; MLS; Most Out; Women's C
Schol; U of Mich; Nurs.

TAYLOR, Michael Anthony
Palm Beach Gardens HS; Palm Beach Gardens,
FL; BS; Chldr; Drama; Order/Arrow; SC; Tr;
Amer Leg A; Friendliest; Civitans; CHO; Tuskegee
Inst; Vet Med.

TAYLOR, Nelson Lewis
Saluda HS; Saluda, SC (20-115) FFA; Midlands
Tech Col; Diesel Mech.

TAYLOR, Nick Scott
Lubbock Christian HS; Lubbock, TX (10-50) A
Cap Choir; BS; Chor; Ensm; VP, NHS; Pres, SC;
Rptr, Sr Cl; Lubbock Christian Col; Yth Ministry.

TAYLOR, Otis Edward III
Hyeneme HS; Hueneme, CA; Hmrm; SC; Ftbl;
Cert A for Teaching; Cert of Attendance; Oxnard
Col; Banking.

TAYLOR, Patricia Ann
Bartlett HS; Anchorage, AK (47-478) Chor;
Hmrm; NHS; Bkbl; ROTC A; St Win, Abilty
Counts A; NM U; Special Ed.

TAYLOR, Paula Lynn
Cherryville Sr HS; Cherryville, NC (98-126) Band;
Bus C; Chldr; Fr C; Hmrm; Lit Mag; Sch P; Sci C;
SC; Tnns; Pres, Jr Heart Board; Gaston Col; Secy
Stu.

TAYLOR, Phyllis Jean
Treadwell HS; Memphis, TN; Mus.

TAYLOR, Portia Renee
White Station HS; Memphis, TN (198-233) Mus.

TAYLOR, Randall Jack
Overton HS; Nashville, TN (30-400) BC; Cr-Ctry;
Tenn Tech U; Engr.

TAYLOR, Rebecca Ann
Hooper Acad; Hope Hull, AL (15%-68) BC; Chor;
Drama; Ensm; JV, 4H; Math C; Sci C; Tres, Var C;
Tres, Jr Cl; Sftbl; Citz A; Vlbl; Good Sportsmanship
A; Auburn U at Montgomery.

TAYLOR, Rex Kendall
Llano HS; Llano, TX (10-105) FHA; Hon Prog.

TAYLOR, Rex L
Louisville HS; Louisville, MS; BC; Bus Mgr,
Hmrm; St DECA; E Central Jr Col; Elec.

TAYLOR, Rhonda Jo
Lakeland HS; LaGrange, IN (30-175) Chor; Secy,
4H; Span C; Y-Tns; Tr; Hon Prog; Yth Fel; Yth
Fitness A; Conservation Essay; Art.

TAYLOR, Richard Jay
Concord HS; Concord, CA (43-450) Band; Var C;
Cpt, Swim; Citz A; Hon Prog; NEDT; ARC A;
Newspaper Super Sport o-t Wk, Swim; Wheaton
Col; Econ.

TAYLOR, Robert Bruce
Sam Barlow HS; Gresham, OR (33-300) A Cap
Choir; Dbte Tm; Ensm; Hmrm; NFL; Sch P; Pres,
SC; Pres, Jr Cl; Pres, Soph Cl; Swim; COM; Law.

TAYLOR, Ronnie Eugene
Groveton HS; Groveton, TX (4-53) Sch P; SC;
Bsbl; Bkbl; Ftbl; Attendance A; Cl Rptr; Pepper-
dine U; Acct.

TAYLOR, Samuel Arthur
Wilburton HS; Wilburton, OK (4-63) Math C;
NHS; Phys C; SC; S-T, Var C; Bkbl; Co-Cpt, Ftbl;
Tr; Alg A; Chem A; Cl Fav; Eastern Okla St Col;
Psych.

TAYLOR, Sandra Jeannette
Clovis HS; Clovis, NM; Drama; Tres, Hmrm;
ARC; Spch C; Tr; Spch A.

TAYLOR, Seth Michael
Charlotte Valley Central Sch; Davenport, NY
(4-44) VP, NHS; Tres, Var C; JV, Soccer; Tr; Math
A; Sci A; Med.

TAYLOR, Sheri Lyn
Oakhaven Baptist Acad; Memphis, TN (7-64) Ann;
Band; VP, Span C; Sftbl; Religion A; Band A; Li-
brarian, Chor; Memphis St U; Elem Ed.

TAYLOR, Sherry Luann
Ainsworth HS; Flint, MI (16-234) S-T, A Cap
Choir; Chor; Madrigal; Pres, NHS; SC; Thes; Miss
Teenage Amer Pageant; Miss Mich Ntl Teenage
Pageant; WW; Mich Christian Col; Eng.

TAYLOR, Skip
Homewood HS; Homewood, AL (50-220) InterAct
C; Span C; Var C; Bsbl; Ftbl; Yth Fel; WW; Auburn
U; Engr.

TAYLOR, Stacy Maria
Sumner HS; St Louis, MO (57-459) Chldr; FBLA;
Citz A; Type A; Fla St U; Law.

TAYLOR, Stephen Paul
Putnam City W HS; Bethany, OK; Lang.

TAYLOR, Susan Ann
Williamston HS; Williamston, NC (26-179) BC;
Chor; Secy, Drama; Fr C; FBLA; Hmrm; Semi-Fin,
Mus Talent Schol; Meredith Col; Mus.

TAYLOR, Susan Lee
Moorefield HS; Moorefield, WV; Tres, 4H; SC; VP,
Soph Cl; Beauty; Cl Fav; Swtht; Yth Foundation;
W Va Weslyan Col; Nurs.

TAYLOR, Teresa Darlene
W Carteret HS; Morehead City, NC; VP, Band;
FNA; FTA; ARC; Sftbl; Tr; A&T St U; Nurs.

TAYLOR, Thomas Clyde
Smackover HS; Smackover, AR (2-70) Band;
FBLA; FTA; Math C; Mu Alpha Theta; NHS; Or-
der/Arrow; VP, Span C; Pres, SC; Pres, Soph Cl;
Ftbl; Tr; Alg A; Bio A; COM; Math A; MLS;
NEDT; Order/Arrow A; US Air Force Acad; Biol
Sci.

TAYLOR, Thomas Floyd Jr
Peoria Central HS; Peoria, IL (50%-452) Drama;
SC; Mgr, Swim; Tr; Grace Col o-t Bible; Spch.

TAYLOR, Timothy O
Mississinewa HS; Gas City, IN (21-211) F-Ed;
Ann; MVP, Band; Semi-Fin, BS; Community Yth
Symph; VP, Drama; NHS; VP, Thes; JV, Cr-Ctry;
Amer Leg A; Lion A; John Philip Sousa A; Louis
Armstrong Jazz A; Brian Wright Mem A; Butler U;
Telecommunications.

TAYLOR, Torey Jean
Russellville HS; Russellville, AL (15-150) F-Ed;
Ann; FHA; VP, Mu Alpha Theta; NHS; Sch P;
Secy, SC; Pres, Jr Cl; Most Out.

TAYLOR, Vanessa Maddlean
Sussex Central HS; Sussex Co, VA (6-200) BC;
Cpt, Chldr; Cpt, Chor; Cpt, 4H; Sci C; Span C; SC;
4H A; Hist A; Math A; MLS; Sci A; Eng A; PA;
Outst Service A; Smithdeal Massey Col; Acct.

TAYLOR, Vannester
Second Ward HS; Gloster, LA (5-46) Bus C; Chldr;
Pres, FHA; Sci C; Pres, Sr Cl; Pres, Jr Cl; Pres,
Soph Cl; Northwestern La St U; Nurs.

TAYLOR, Varnie Tyrone
Allen HS; Robeline, LA (5-27) Chor; FFA; FHA;
4H; Pres, Hmrm; Lit Ral; Pres, SC; Pres, Sr Cl;
Pres, Jr Cl; Cpt, Bkbl; Sftbl; Tr; COM; Armed
Forces.

TAYLOR, Veronica Lee
Willows HS; Willows, CA (17-130) Ann; CYO;
Cpt, Chldr; SC; HCt; Heald's Bus Col; Bus.

TAYLOR, Vickie Juanita
Clements HS; Athens, AL; Ann; BC; FTA; Secy,
Sch P; Cl Fav; Journ A.

TAYLOR, Victoria Elizabeth
Sussex Central HS; Sussex, VA (14-186) Chldr;
Chem C; FHA; Pres, 4H; HiY; NHS; Sci C; Span C;
SC; Tri-HiY; Mgr, Tr; Beauty; COM; 4H A; Hon
Prog; Type A; Chldr A; Tr A; Petersburg General
Sch of Nurs; R N Nurs.

TAYLOR, Virginia Diane
Bluefield HS; Bluefield, WV (5%-500) JV, Chldr;
Secy, Community Yth; Fr Ch; Hmrm; Ntl Yth
Conf; Y-Tns; Fin, Tr; Citz A; Cl Fav; Hist A; Yth
Fel; Eng A; Laurel Leaves; Marshall Col; Anesthe-
tist.

TAYLOR, Wanda Denise
John F Kennedy HS; Richmond, VA (41-309) Ann;
Fr C; FBLA; Cpt, Mjrte; SC; S-T, Sr Cl; Mgr, Tr;
Hon Prog; JA A; Madison Col; Ed.

TAYLOR, William Anthony
S Shore HS; Chicago, IL (69-575) Band; Chem C;
Sci C; Bio A; Chem A; Sci A; Spch A; Creighton U;
Nurs.

TAYLOR, William Heilard
Kinston HS; Kinston, NC (76-331) FBLA; JV, Ftbl;
A&T St U; Bus Adm.

TAYLOR, William Ramsey
Hazlewood HS; Town Creek, AL (2-45) Band; BC;
Ensm; FFA; FHA; Rptr, Sch P; Sci C; 4H A; Star
Student; U of N Ala; Mus.

TAYLOR, Wona Lorena
A C Reynolds HS; Asheville, NC (42-272) A B
Tech Col; Bus Adm.

TAYLOR, Yolanda Lynn
Roosevelt HS; Gary, IN (94-565) VP, FTA; SC;
Pres, Y-Tns; Secy, Jr Cl; Swim; Tr; Citz A; MLS;
Most Out; St Scholar; Evan H J Redd School; Pur-
due U; Fashion Retailing.

TAZUMI, Kathleen Takako
Heidelberg American HS; Heidelberg, GER-
MANY (6-170) A Cap Choir; Chor; Madrigal;
NHS; Hist A; Hon Prog; HR; Stu Vol A; Syracuse
U; Pre-Med.

TEACHWORTH, Gladys Lynn
Woodlawn HS; Birmingham, AL; Chor; COM;
Most Out; MVP, Vlbl; Teaching.

TEAGLE, Lola Renee
Simon Gratz HS; Philadelphia, PA (22-500) FTA;
Hon Prog; U of Pitt at Brad; Life Sci.

TEAGLE, Phil Ray
N Mesquite HS; Mesquite, TX; A Cap Choir; Rptr,
Hmrm; Madrigal; NHS; Sch P; Pres, SC; Bkbl;
MVP, Ftbl; MVP, Tr; Amer Leg A; Pres A; Sci A;
Yth Foundation; Pepperdine U.

TEAGUE, Andrew Leo
Jones Co HS; Gray, GA (10%-250) NHS; Sci C;
Mgr, Bsbl; Mgr, Bkbl; Ftbl; NEDT; Type A.

TEAGUE, Donna Elaine
Glendale HS; Springfield, MO; AFS; F-Ed, Ann;
FHA; Ger C; NFL; Sftbl; Journ A; Q&S A; Opti-
mist Spch Contest; 1st Pl Writ Con, Ntl Bapt Yth
Mag; Baylor U; Journ.

TEAGUE, Johnnie Mae
McAdams HS; McAdams, MS; Bus Mgr, Band;
Fin, FFA; Data Processing.

TEAGUE, Nancy Elizabeth
Stamps HS; Stamps, AR (12-71) FHA; Sch P; Sci
C; S Ark U; Secy.

TEAGUE, Stewart Daniel
Starkville HS; Starkville, MS; Band; Church Choir;
Miss St U; Agr.

TEAGUE, Timothy Walter
S Gwinnett HS; Snellville, GA (91-256) Tnns;
Chess C; SC; Yth Fel; DECA; Pres, Yth Fel; De-
kalb Tech Col; Elec.

TEAKELL, Randolph Paul
Permian HS; Odessa, TX (30-650) Madrigal; Pres,
NHS; Sci C; SC; Cpt, Ftbl; Tr; Citz A; Cl Fav; Hist
A; Hon Prog; Opt Out Tn; Chaplin, A Cappella
Choir; Most Conscientious Player A, Ftbl; Most
Dependable Sr; Pres, FCA; Rice U; Bus.

TEAL, Brenda Diann
Atlanta HS; Atlanta, LA (1-28) A-Ed; Ann; Chor; Ensm; FBLA; FHA; FTA; Lit Ral; Sch P; Pres, SC; Tres, Sr Cl; Cpt, Bkbl; Sftbl; Beauty; 4H A; Hon Prog; Journ A; Most Out; Type A; Val; Yth Fel; Distinguished Schol A; 1st, FBLA Spell; All District, Bkbl; *La Col; Math.*

TEAL, Sherrie Lynn
Wilcox Co HS; Rochelle, GA (5-116) BC; Co-Cpt, Chldr; Chor; FBLA; VP, FTA; Tres, 4H; Hmrm; Ed, Lit Mag; Sch P; Tres, Var C; Bio A; COM; Gov Honor Prog; 4H A; Hist A; Hon Prog; JA A; Math A; Sci A; Eng A; *U of Ga; Secondary Ed.*

TEAM, David O Brian
Lexington Sr HS; Lexington, NC (11-300) AFS; BC; Dbte Tm; Key C; Monogram; A-Ed, Sch P; Span C; Var C; Bkbl; Ftbl; Golf; Chem A; NEDT; Order/Arrow A; Tres & VP, FCA; Best Blocker & All-Conf, Ftbl; *Wake Forest U; Med.*

TEARS, Nadine Faith
Marcus Whitman HS; Rushville, NY (30-145).

TEATER, Barry David
Jessamine Co HS; Nicholasville, KY; VP, BC; Spch C; Pres, Soph Cl; JV, Bkbl; *U of Ky; Communications.*

TECKLENBURG, Davi
Valley HS; Sanders, AZ (8-49) Pres, Chldr; Drama; Hmrm; Model UN; Spch C; Pres, SC; Rptr, Jr Cl; Citz A; *NAU; Journ.*

TEDFORD, Kent Alan
George J Penney HS; E Hartford, CT (12-378) Bus C; Chess C; FBLA; Hmrm; NHS; SC; JV, Bkbl; JV, Golf; DARGCA; Hon Prog; Math A; St Scholar; *U of Mich; Actuarial Sci.*

TEDFORD, Kris Michael
Lakewood HS; Lakewood, OH (25%-900) Chess C; Chor; Drama; Ensm; Hmrm; SC; Alg A; COM; Hist A; Hon Prog; Math A; Ger A; *Sterling Col.*

TEED, Eleanor Walker
William Monroe HS; Stanardsville, VA (10-90) Band; BC; Drama; FTA; 4H; Monogram; SC; Bkbl; MVP, Tr; Type A; Gifted Stu Prog; All Dist, Bkbl; Schol, Bkbl Camp; *Madison Col; Phys Ed.*

TEEHEE, Cyndi Ann
Broken Arrow HS; Broken Arrow, OK (30-590) Ensm; Fr C; FHA; FHA Swtht Attendant; *Okla Baptist U.*

TEEL, Lora May
East Jackson HS; Jackson, MI; Band; 4H; 4H A; Hon Prog; *Horticulture.*

TEEMER, Marilyn L
Monroe HS; Albany, GA (25-265) Secy, Span C; Tres, Sr Cl; COM; Hon Prog; *Brenau Col; Biol.*

TEEPLE, Katherine Lynne
Jackson HS; Massillon, OH (80-417) Band; Chor; Ensm; Fr C; 4H; Orch; Swim; 4H A; ARC A; Church Yth Fel; Good News C; 1st Cl Cadette, GSct; Sup Rating, Flute Solo & Ensm; *Mus.*

TEESLINK, Lynn G
Central HS; Springfield, MO; Anchor C; Band; Bus C; Chem C; Fr C; FHA; Mjrte; Orch; SC; *Sou Mo St U.*

TEETER, Laura Lou
S Bend Jr Acad; S Bend, IN (1-12) Chor; *Andrews U; Ed.*

TEETS, Robin Ann
Aurora HS; Aurora, WV (9-32) Band; Co-Cpt, Chldr; Parl, FHA; 4H; Mjrte; SC; Var C; Pres, Soph Cl; Bkbl; Cpt, Chldr; FHA A; *Garrett Comm Col; Children.*

TEGNELL, Elizabeth Haas
Venice HS; Venice, FL (100-360) A Cap Choir; Chor; Ensm; FHA; Hmrm; Madrigal; SC; Sftbl; Jr Boosters; HR; GAA; Mus A's; 1st Pl Medals, Mus Festival; *Manatee Jr Col; Lib Arts.*

TEGTMAN, LeLanie Renee Hope
Weld Central HS; Keenesburg, CO; Tres, Chldr; 4th, Cl Decathelon; *Highland Beauty Sch; Cosmetology.*

TEI, Fugalei Talafatu
El Camino HS; Oceanside, CA; MLS; Most Out; Ntl Achv Schol; *Mira Costa Col; Bus Adm.*

TEIBEL, Suzanne Kaiulani
Our Redeemer Lutheran HS; Honolulu, HI (10-60) Chor; Mgr, Bkbl; JV, Bkbl; Mgr, Cr-Ctry; Sftbl; Pres, Tres, Church Yth Group; St o-t Mo.

TEICHER, Miriam Wendy
Hebrew Acad of Nassau Co; Uniondale, NY; Chor; NHS; Ed, Sch P; SC; NEDT; Eng Faculty A; Essay Contest A; Fr Excellence A; *Stern Col in Yeshiva U.*

TEICHERT, Mark Lucian
Cokeville HS; Cokeville, WY (2-12) Ann; Band; BS; Chor; Ensm; Pres, 4H; NHS; SC; VP, Sr Cl; VP, Jr Cl; Bkbl; Ftbl; 4H A; Type A; Eagle Sct; *Ricks Col; Agr.*

TEICHMEIER, Ronald Lee
Ravenna Sr HS; Ravenna, NE; Pres, FFA; Cpt, Bkbl; Ftbl; Tr; Hon Soc; *Pepperdine U; Archt.*

TEIGE, Valerie Joy
E Peoria Comm HS; E Peoria, IL (8-400) F-Ed, Ann; Ensm; Secy, Fr C; Co-Ed, Lit Mag; Madrigal; NHS; Pres, Orch; COM; Hon Prog; NMS; St Scholar; Rptr, Annual; Secy, Orch; WW; Sterling Merit, Top 10, Excel, A's; *Rockford Col; Art Therapy.*

TEIGELER, Dawn Margriet
SW Central HS; Jamestown, NY (25-112) Chldr; Ger C; Ski C; Tres, Jr Cl; MVP, Tr; COM; Cl Fav; Regent Schol; Type A; Sports, Chldr, A's; *Bus.*

TEIGEN, David Curtis
Rugby HS; Rugby, ND (15-104) BS; VP, FFA; Tres, 4H; S-T, SC; Bkbl; Ftbl; Swim; Tnns; Tr; 4H A; ARC A; Yth Leg; *Pub Relations.*

TEISL, Christine Marie
Clarkstown S HS; W Nyack, NY (34-513) Chor; NHS; JV, Bkbl; Soccer; Tr; *Cornell U; Environmental Stu.*

TEITELBAUM, Jeanne Elizabeth
Westfield Sr HS; Westfield, NJ; Chor; Ensm; Hmrm; Orch; Vlbl; *Madison Col; Special Ed.*

TEIXEIRA, Richard Paul
DeKalb HS; Waterloo, IN (66-320) BS; Cr-Ctry; Tr; Citz A; *Harding Col; Bus Mgt.*

TELESFORD, Christopher Alexander
Thornridge HS; Dolton, IL; Co-Cpt, Ftbl; Tr; *Bradley U.*

TELESKO, Rebekah Marie
Taylor Allderdice HS; Pittsburgh, PA; JA A; Hospital Vol, 100 Hr Pin; 25 & 50 Hr Patches; *U of Pittsburgh; Dental Hygiene.*

TELFORD, David Eugene
Salem Comm HS; Salem, IL (25%-300) Band; SC; MVP, Bsbl; Ftbl; Swim; Amer Leg A; HCt; Opt A; *Mortuary Sci.*

TELKAMP, Janelle Fay
Armour HS; Armour, SD; A-Ed, Ann; Band; JV, Chldr; Chor; Ensm; V-Ch, FHA; 4H; SC; JV, Bkbl; Sftbl; Tr; *SD St U; Home Ec.*

TELOTTA, Kieran Marie
St Joseph HS; Jeanerette, LA (5-30) NHS; Sch P; Sftbl; *Nurs.*

TELSCHOW, Sandra June
Valparaiso HS; Valparaiso, IN (101-460) Chor; Ensm; Fr C; Orch; Yth Fel; *Valparaiso U; Social Work.*

TEMMER, Nancy Lynn
Arapahoe HS; Littleton, CO (33%-620) Sch P; Cpt, Soccer; Citz A; *Colo St U; Fine Arts.*

TEMPAS, Daniel Alan
Richwoods HS; Peoria, IL (48-462) Band; Chess C; Dbte Tm; Fr C; NHS; Order/Arrow; Co-Cpt, Soccer; Tnns; Tr; Chem A; God & Country A; NMS; Order/Arrow A; *U of Ill; Med.*

TEMPLE, Jane Elizabeth
Sevier Co HS; Sevierville, TN (10%-300) Rptr, AFS; F-Ed, Ann; Band; BC; Fr C; Rptr, Hmrm; InterAct C; Orch; Tn Board; Ed, Sch Paper in Jr HS; Hon Men, Poetry Contest; *U of Tenn; Liberal Arts.*

TEMPLE, Linda Fay
Tallapoosa Acad; Dadeville, AL (3-27) Ed, Ann; BC; Chldr; Semi-Fin, GS; Spch C; Var C; Secy, Sr Cl; Pres, Soph Cl; Beauty; HCt; WW; Best Dressed; *Auburn U; Lab Tech.*

TEMPLE, Michele Mary
Celina Sr HS; Celina, OH (17-275) A Cap Choir; VP, CYO; Fr C; SC; Ensm; Pres, Madrigal; NHS; F-Ed, Sch P; SC; VP, Thes; Tnns; WW; *Ashland Col; Broadcast Journ.*

TEMPLE, Patricia Anne
Geneva Comm HS; Geneva, IL (40-202) A-Ed, Ann; Chor; Fr C; Hmrm; Pres, InterClub Coun; Lit Ral; NHS; Sch P; Pres, SC; Pres, Jr Cl; MVP, Swim; Fin, Tnns; HCt; Cpt, Swim; SC A; *Albion Col; Merchandising.*

TEMPLEMAN, Derrel Eugene
Princeton HS; Princeton, TX; FFA; Bsbl; Cpt, Bkbl; JV, Ftbl; HCt; Soph Cl Off; Stock Show As; *A&M U-Tarleton; Vet.*

TEMPLER, Rebecca Lynne
Albia Comm HS; Albia, IA; Band; Chor; Drama; Ensm; Mus A; Drama Ltr; *NWMSU.*

TEMPLETON, Alice Jane
Sunnyside HS; Tucson, AZ; A Cap Choir; Chldr; Chess C; Chor; Ensm; FHA; Hmrm; VP, Lat C; NHS; ARC; Span C; Secy, SC; V-Ch, Soph Cl; Ftbl; Sftbl; Beauty; HCt; MLS; Levy's Hi Band Win; Modeling; *U of Ariz; Psych.*

TEMPLETON, Jon Brooks
Potosi R-3 Sch; Potosi, MO (33-156) A Cap Choir; Band; Bus C; Chor; Pres, Demolay; Drama; Ensm; FBLA; Madrigal; Order/Arrow; Thes; A Cappella A; *Jacksonville Col; Mus.*

TEMPLETON, Rexanne
DeSoto HS; De Soto, TX (30-200) Band; Ensm; FNA; VP, Span C; Span NHS; All Region Band; Co-Cpt, Flag Corps; *Baylor U; Dental-Asst.*

TEMPLETON, Sandra Ann
Valley HS; Albuquerque, NM (10%-700) Fr C; NHS; SC; Yale Book A; *Sci.*

TEMTE, Gary Wayne
Roosevelt HS; Minneapolis, MN (14-600) A-Ed, Ann; Band; NHS; *U of Minn; Bus Adm.*

TENDALL, Jacqueline Denise
E E Smith Sr HS; Fayetteville, NC (33%-250) Chor; FHA; Pom Pom Sq; *A&T St U; Phys Therapy.*

TENER, Mark Alan
Greenon HS; Springfield, OH; Var C; Bsbl; JV, Bkbl; JV, Ftbl; Golf; JV, Wrest; *Rio Grande Col; Bus.*

TENGESDAL, Daniel Scot
N Kitsap HS; Poulsbo, WA; Band; Chess C; Math C; Orch; Bsbl; Soccer; Type A; Good Guy A; *Pacific Lutheran U; Sci.*

TENGESDAL, Mark Owen
N Kitsap HS; Poulsbo, WA (13-250) Band; NHS; Orch; Soccer; Pres A; Best Cinematography; *Pacific Lutheran U; Communication Arts.*

TENHOLDER, Kimberly Rachelle
Montrose Pub HS; Montrose, MO (1-25) CYO; Chor; S-T, 4H; NHS; Mgr, Bkbl; Sftbl; 4H A; Hist A; HCt; Math A; Home Ec A.

TENNANT, Kurt Hiatt
Humansville HS; Humansville, MO (2-30) Chor; *SW Mo St U; Bus.*

TENNANT, William James
Northwestern HS; Baltimore, MD (10-30) Bsbl; Ftbl; COM; Cl Fav; God & Country A; Gov Honor Prog; H of F; Harvard Book A; HKg; Hon Prog; I Dare You; Math A; MLS; Most Out; Odd Fellow Fin; Pres A; ARC A; Sacristan; Star Student; Yale Book A; *Pepperdine U; Phys Ed.*

TENNEBOE, Jim L
Royal HS; Simi, CA (23-647) Band; Ensm; Orch; Bsbl; Ftbl; COM; Win, Bach Festival; *Calif St-Northridge; Mus.*

TENNEY, Cherie DeAnn
St Albans HS; St Albans, WV (33%-400) Band; Mjrte; Span NHS; *W Va Wesleyan Col; Nurs.*

TEOTICO, Melissa Gaye
Castle Park HS; Chula Vista, CA (20-425) GS; Hmrm; Secy, SC; CSF; COM; MLS; UC at San Diego; Med.

TERCERO, Lily Frances
Balmorhea HS; Balmorhea, TX (2-18) Co-Ed, Ann; Pres, Band; Dbte Tm; Drama; FHA; NHS; Ed, Sch P; VP, SC; Rptr, Jr Cl; Hist A; MLS; Most Out; Sal; Sci A; Bus Admn A; Span A; Miss BHS A; Eng A; 1st Soil Conservation Essay Cont; 1st, Dist Ready Writing; Sol Ross St U.

TERENZI, Sandra Marie
Liggett HS; Grosse Pointe Woods, MI (1-74) Cum Laude Soc; Drama; Rptr, Sch P; Sftbl; Hon Prog; NMF; U of Notre Dame; Law.

TERIFAY, Robert Joseph
Archmere Acad; Claymont, DE; Ed, Ann; Band; Drama; Fr C; VP, French NHS; Pres, NFL; NHS; ARC; Sch P; Pres, Spch C; Thes; Swim; COM; Journ A; Ntl Sci Symposium; NEDT; ARC A; Spch A; Ntl Fr Contest A; U of Notre Dame; Pre-Med.

TERKHORN, Pamela Jean
Madison E HS; Madison, WI (141-540) Ann; JV, Chldr; Drama; Fr C; Hmrm; Ski C; SC; S-T, Sr Cl; S-T, Jr Cl; Gym; Service 'E' A; U of Wis; Bus.

TERLOUW, Pamela Sue
New Monroe Comm HS; Monroe, IA (16-58) Ann; Band; VP, Chor; Drama; Ensm; Tres, 4H; Madrigal; ARC; Thes; 4H A; Spch A; Type A; Amer Inst of Bus; Acct.

TER MAAT, Michael Andrew
Forest View HS; Arlington Hts, IL (100-700) Bkbl; Ftbl; Tr; Hon Prog; Math A; Hon Men, Math Contest; Math.

TERNES, Barbara Lynn
Bishop Carroll HS; Wichita, KS (14-211) CYO; Pres, Chor; Madrigal; NHS; ARC; Spch A; St Scholar; EKSC Schol; St Mus Festival A; WW-MUS Stu; PA; Emporia Kans St Col; Spch.

TERNSTROM, Ingrid Beth
Bennington Pub HS; Bennington, NE; Band; Chor; Ensm; Bkbl; Interior Decorating.

TERPSTRA, David John
Northfield Sr HS; Northfield, MN (34-287) Chor; NHS; Bkbl; Hon Prog; Bethel Col; Philosophy.

TERPSTRA, Michael James
Ogilvie Pub HS; Ogilvie, MN; Band; Chor; Ensm; Madrigal; Ski C; Bsbl; Ftbl; Tr; Elec.

TERPSTRA, Randy Jay
Ogilvie Pub HS; Ogilvie, MN (15-50) Chor; Ensm; NHS; Ski C; Bsbl; Co-Cpt, Ftbl; Co-Cpt, Wrest; U of Minn at Crookston; Agr Bus Mgt.

TERRANO, Mark Allen
Benjamin Franklin HS; New Orleans, LA; Arch; Hmrm; Lat C; Sci C; Swim; Sci A; Sci.

TERRAS, Lynn
S Lake HS; St Clair Shores, MI; Chor; Med Research.

TERRELL, Ava Marie
Elida HS; Elida, OH (2-200) Ann; Band; Chor; Drama; FFA; Pres, 4H; NHS; Bio A; 4H A; Sci A; Star Chapter Farmer, FFA; YFU; Str Greenhand, FFA; YFU; Co Beef; Ohio Synod Yth Min Task Force; Highest Sch Score, PSAT- NMSQT; Ohio St U; Vet Med.

TERRELL, Brenda Kay
Dover HS; Dover, OK (2-24) Chor; FHA; GS; NHS; Tres, SC; Bkbl; HQn; Type A; Tri-St Hon Chor; Northwestern St U; Bus.

TERRELL, Jonathan Dailey
Mars Area HS; Mars, PA; NHS; Order/Arrow; Thes; Var C; Soph Cl; Ftbl; Tr; Order/Arrow A; NHS A; Tex A&M U; Marine Bio.

TERRELL, Lisa Ann
Prague HS; Prague, OK (13-70) FHA; NHS; Okla St U; Floristry.

TERRELL, Pamela Arden
Smithtown HS W; Smithtown, NY (65%-534) Chor; Ski C; Tres, Span NHS; Secy, SC; JV, Sftbl; Hon Prog; ARC A; Type A; Vlbl; Badminton; Span Hon; Wesley Touring Choir; Oneonta St U; Pol Sci.

TERRELL, Ralf D
Karlsruhe Amer HS; Karlsruhe, WEST GERMANY; A-Ed, Ann; Ger C; Sch P; SC; Pres, Sr Cl; Cr-Ctry; Soccer; Ind St U; Med Tech.

TERRELL, Rose Marie
Waynesboro Central HS; Waynesboro, MS (25%-119) Band; BC; Drama; VP, FHA; 4H; S-T, Hmrm; Mjrte; Y-Tns; Church Ensm; Jones Jr Col; Eng.

TERRELL, Stephanie Janine
East Union HS; Manteca, CA (84-335) Band; Chor; Drama; Fr C; Madrigal; Hon Prog; Interntl C; Point Loma Col; Mus.

TERREY, John Douglas
Rogers Sr HS; Michigan City, IN (80-560) Chor; Rptr, Demolay; Drama; Madrigal; NHS; Valpariso U; Bus Adm.

TERRICOLA, Toni Ann
Oppenheim-Ephratah HS; St Johnsville, NY (5-49) Band; VP, Hmrm; NHS; Bus.

TERRILL, Kimberly Sue
Bear Creek Sr HS; Lakewood, CO (50-400) A Cap Choir; Band; Chor; Ensm; NHS; Orch; Thes; Hon Prog; Bartlesville Wesleyan Col.

TERRILL, Sharon Mae
Fountain Lake HS; Hot Springs, AR (12-42) Chor; FNA; ARC; Spch C; Thes; Sftbl; WW; Col of The Ozarks; Med Tech.

TERRY, Audrey Lynn
Jim Hill HS; Jackson, MS (50%-199) Band; Chor; ARC; Tres, Soph Cl; Bkbl; Tr; PA; Gym A; Jackson St U; Photography.

TERRY, Barbara Jo
Woodford Co HS; Versailles, KY (20-275) Ann; BC; Secy, Fr C; FBLA; Hmrm; Pres, InterClub Coun; Lit Mag; Math C; Sch P; VP, SC; Secy, Jr Cl; Mgr, Bsbl; Mgr, Bkbl; Mgr, Ftbl; Yth Fel; Yth Foundation; All Yr HR; Ntl Fr Contest; Special Ed.

TERRY, Bobby Keith
Hazlewood HS; Town Creek, AL (10-65) BC; Drama; VP, FFA; Sci C; Spch C; Var C; Bsbl; Bkbl; Ftbl; Hon Prog; U of N Ala; Bus Adm.

TERRY, Claude Thomas
High Point Central HS; High Point, NC; Band; Tnns; Sweet Briar Col; Sci.

TERRY, Edward S
McDonogh 35 HS; New Orleans, LA; Xavier Col; Acct.

TERRY, Edwina Beverly
George Henry Corliss HS; Chicago, IL (5-32) Hon Prog; Morehouse Col; Hist.

TERRY, Evelyn Kay
Whitehouse HS; Whitehouse, TX (1-99) Ann; Secy, Band; S-T, Math C; S-T, Mu Alpha Theta; NHS; A-Ed, Sch P; SC; B Crocker A; Outst Bandsman & Marcher; Band Qn; Tyler Jr Col; Med Tech.

TERRY, Julie Marie
Clearlake HS; Lakeport, CA; Ski C; Pres, SC; Bsbl; Bkbl; Sftbl; Vlbl.

TERRY, Kay Lynn
Evadale HS; Evadale, TX (5-35) Cpt, Band; Chem C; Dbte Tm; Drama; GS; Hmrm; Math C; SC; Var C; Bkbl; Tr; COM; Cl Fav; HCt; Math A; Type A; Lamar U; Bus.

TERRY, Marilyn Lovejoy
Whitehouse HS; Whitehouse, TX (2-99) A-Ed, Ann; Secy, 4H; NHS; Sch P; SC; Bkbl; Sftbl; Cl Fav; HCt; Lion A; Tyler Jr Col; Interior Design.

TERRY, Melvina Sean
Wheelersburg HS; Wheelersburg, OH (5-130) Chor; VP, FHA; 4H; Rainbow; Sch Achieve Tm; Sch P; Span C; SC; COM; Ntl Achv Schol; NEDT; St Scholar; Yth Fel; Miss Portsmouth Pageant; Talent Contest A; Spelling Bee A's; Capitol Col; Nurs.

TERRY, Mike Eugene
Southside HS; Gadsden, AL (19-200) BC; Bus C; FBLA; HiY; Hmrm; Tri-HiY; Pres, Var C; Fin, Sr Cl; VP, Jr Cl; VP, Soph Cl; Bsbl; Bkbl; Cpt, Ftbl; Tr; Cl Fav; Pres, FCA; Jacksonville St U; Bus.

TERRY, Norman Dale
Gainesville HS; Gainesville, TX (140-184) Demolay; N Tex St U; Hist.

TERRY, Rhonda Frances
Hazlewood HS; Town Creek, AL (2-50) Band; BC; Chor; Pres, Crown & Scepte; Ensm; Secy, 4H; Secy, Hmrm; Rptr, Sch P; Bkbl; Sftbl; Coun of Teach A; 4H A; Hon Prog; Regent Schol; Yth Fel; Asst Pianist, Yth Rallies; Church Pianist; Pres, Acteens; John C Calhoun Col; Elem Ed.

TERRY, Richard Alan
Willis HS; Willis, TX (10%-100) A Cap Choir; Band; Chess C; Chor; Ensm; FTA; 4H; Madrigal; NHS; Phys C; Sci C; Span C; 4H A; Hist A; Hon Prog; Ntl Sci Found; Ntl Sci Symposium; ARC A; Tex A&M U; Computer Engr.

TERTOCHA, Polly Carmen
Herbert Hoover HS; Glendale, CA (10%-550) Chem C; Fr C; Ger C; Math C; Span C; Co-Cpt, Hockey; Sftbl; Swim; Tnns; 4H A; Ntl Sci Symposium; NEDT; Pres, Sportsmen C; USC; Chem.

TERTOCHA, Thomas Everett
Herbert Hoover HS; Glendale, CA (10%-500) Chem C; Key C; Math C; NHS; Phys C; Sci C; Bsbl; Cpt, Hockey; CSF; Hon Prog; Ntl Sci Symposium; NEDT; Pres, Sportsmens C; USC; Elec Engr.

TESCH, William Thomas
Ashwaubenon HS; Green Bay, WI (153-362) Swim; Spch A; Poetry Reading A; Yth Ministry Comm; Pres, Luther League; Puppet Show; Win, Forensics Tourn; Lector; Fin, One Act Play.

TESKE, Kurt Frederick
Bay Village HS; Bay Village, OH (10%-400) A Cap Choir; Ed, Ann; Band; Community Yth Symph; Hmrm; Lit Mag; NHS; Orch; Cpt, Sch Achieve Tm; Ed, Sch P; Sci C; SC; Pres, Thes; Citz A; I Dare You; Journ A; Kiwanis A; Math A; MLS; Ntl Achv Schol; NMF; NMS; NEDT; Phi Beta Kappa; Q&S A; Sci A; Yth Foundation A; Camp Miniwanca A; Musical Comp A; Pres, NOSPA; Drama As; NCTE Writing A; No Ohio Schol Press As of Kent St U; Harvard Col; Biol.

TESSENIAR, Carroll Dean
Shelby HS; Shelby, NC; Chor; Ensm; Span C; Gardner Webb Col; Mus.

TESSIN, Steven John
Eisenhower HS; Saginaw, MI; VP, Chess C; Chor; Ger C; Bkbl; Tr; Wrest; Delta Col; Sci.

TESSMAN, Terri Jean
Ventura Comm HS; Ventura, IA (16-35) Band; Chldr; Chor; FTA; 4H; JV, Bkbl; Str; 4H A; I Dare You; Pres, Yth Fel; Ntl Yth- power Conf; Navy; Air Control.

TEST, Christopher Anthony
L D Bell HS; Hurst, TX (150-760) CYO; NHS; Tnns; Pres; Church Yth Organization; Med.

TESTA, Donna Jean
Western Hills HS; Fort Worth, TX; SC; Tnns; Cl Fav; FCA; Public Relations, Sch Paper; Evangel Col; Journ.

TESTA, Paul Charles
Cardinal Stritch HS; Oregon, OH; Chor; Bkbl; Tnns; Tr; Bowling Green Col; Landscaping.

TESTEN, Martina Marie
Neshaminy Maple Point HS; Langhorne, PA (4-388) Band; Chor; Drama; Hmrm; Mjrte; NHS; Sr Cl; Jr Cl; Swim; Type A; E Stroudsburg St Col; Nurs.

TETER, Kenneth Scott
Elkins HS; Elkins, WV (1-230) Band; BS; Pres, 4H; Key C; NHS; Ed, Sch P; Var C; Pres, Jr Cl; Cpt, Cr-Ctry; Tr; B Crocker A; COM; Most Out; Val; Marshall U; Med Lab Technology.

TETER, Kennith Allan
Zanesville HS; Zanesville, OH; Chor; Ensm; Sci C; Sftbl.

TETRICK, Bruce Richard
Canby HS; Canby, MN; Chor; Drama; Pres, SC; MVP, Bsbl; Bkbl; Cr-Ctry; Ftbl; Bethel Col; Christian Service.

TEUBER, Rodney James
Hillcrest HS; Springfield, MO (9-315) AFS; Band; Key C; Math C; Sci C; SC; Mgr, Ftbl; Sftbl; Tnns; Alg A; Yth Fel; High Point Scoring Trophy; Evangel Col; Bus.

TEUBNER, Nancy Jo
Cando Pub HS; Cando, ND; Ed, Ann; Chldr; Chor; Drama; Ensm; GS; Secy, 4H; Sch P; Fin, Spch C; S-T, Jr Cl; Tr; 4H A; Hon Prog; Spch A; Hon Stu.

TEUNE, Kathryn Jane
Timothy Christian HS; Elmhurst, IL (20-90) A Cap Choir; Band; Chor; F-Ed, Sch P; Bkbl; Tr; *Dordt Col; Nurs.*

TEWKSBURY, Kathy Deann
Edgeley HS; Edgeley, ND (10-56) Band; Cpt, Chldr; Chor; Pres, FHA; Pres, 4H; Ed, Sch P; Secy, Sr Cl; Tr; Citz A; 4H A; *ND St U; Home Ec.*

THACKER, Beth Anne
Center Grove HS; Greenwood, IN; Span C; Sftbl; Sunshine & Pep C'S; *U of Evansville; Elem Ed.*

THACKER, Eunice Cassandra
John F Kennedy HS; Sacramento, CA; Chor; Pres, Ntl Teachers C; COM; Citz A; Most Out; GSct; YWCA; Yell; Charm Sch; *Bus Adm.*

THACKER, Leigh Anne
Chapman HS; Inman, SC (31-188) Ed, Ann; Band; VP, Hmrm; SC; Journ A; GS Alt; Pres, UMYF; Church Choir; *Columbia Col; Journ.*

THACKER, Lynette
Wasatch HS; Heber City, UT (5-138) JV, Chldr; Dbte Tm; GS; Hmrm; Co-Ed, Lit Mag; Spch C; VP, SC; Co-Cpt, Bkbl; Tnns; Tr; Stu o-t Wk; *Brigham Young U; Elem Ed.*

THACKER, Martha Sue
Feds Creek HS; Feds Creek, KY (2-120) Fr C; Hon Prog; Fin, Cl Fav.

THACKRAY, Todd Allen
Joel E Ferris HS; Spokane, WA (1-420) Band; Ger C; NHS; Order/Arrow; *Elec.*

THACKSTON, Ruby Virginia
Herchal Van Jenkins HS; Savannah, GA; Chor; S-T, Religious C; *Nurs.*

THAKOR, Michael Samir
St Mary's Central HS; Bismarck, ND (1-170) Hmrm; Pres, Soph Cl; Bkbl; Golf; Tnns; *MIT; Physics.*

THAL, Adelia Barbara
S Stokes HS; Walnut Cove, NC (15-250) Band; Secy, BC; Tres, FTA; GS; Math C; Mu Alpha Theta; NHS; Sci C; Hon Prog; All St Band; *Forsyth Tech Inst; Nuclear Med Tech.*

THALKEN, Curtis Larry
Columbus Sr HS; Columbus, NE (50-293) Ger C; Order/Arrow; JV, Wrest; *W Point Military Acad; Chem Engr.*

THALMAN, Ronald Lorin
Sky View HS; Smithfield, UT (403-573) A Cap Choir; Ski C; Var C; Hmrm; Tr; Cpt, Wrest; H of F; Most Out; HS All Amer; *Utah St U; Phys Ed.*

THAMES, Mary Anne
Lufkin HS; Lufkin, TX (10-520) Drama; VP, Fr C; Pres, Mu Alpha Theta; NHS; Span C; Tnns; WW; *Sou Methodist U; Math.*

THAMES, Michale Ruth
Minnetonka Sr HS; Minnetonka, MN (134-658) AFS; Yth Fel; Vlbl; Pres, Camp Fire Girls; Zone Yth; *U of Wisc; Phys Ed.*

THARP, Harry Cornelius Jr
Christian Brother's Military HS; Clayton, MO (56-132) Dbte Tm; Pres, Hmrm; SC; Bkbl; Ftbl; Tr; COM; JA A; NEDT; ROTC A; WW; Sup Jr ROTC Cadet; Jr Supt, Sunday Sch; *UCLA; Law.*

THARP, Jane Marie
De Soto HS; De Soto, MO (5%-250) Ed, Ann; Pres, Bus C; Chor; Drama; Ensm; Pres, FBLA; GS; Math C; NHS; SC; Pres, Sr Cl; Tr; Alg A; COM; Cl Fav; Math A; MLS; Most Intellectual; *U of Mo; Spec Ed.*

THARP, Janice Elizabeth
Charles Sumner HS; St Louis, MO; Band; GS; SC; VP, Jr Cl; Bkbl; Tr; HCt; JA A; Pres Phys Fitness; Mo St Tr A; Service A; *Bus.*

THARP, Katrina Diane
Fairdale HS; Fairdale, KY; *U of Ky; Social Work.*

THARP, Marlys Lee
Miami Palmetto Sr HS; Miami, FL (114-1075) Span C; JA A; Tres, Sailing C; VP Church Yth Group; VP, JA; Secy, Lutheran Yth Group; *Newberry Col; Acct.*

THARP, Martha Lanette
Grand Ridge Sch; Grand Ridge, FL (6-49) F-Ed, Ann; BC; Mgr, Bkbl; *Chipola Jr Col; Secy.*

THARP, Sharon Kay
William Penn Sr HS; York, PA (78-564) AFS; NHS; Hon Prog; Jr Hist Soc; PA; *Secy.*

THATCH, Carless Renee
Lincoln Sr HS; E St Louis, IL (2-200) VP, NHS; Sch P; VP, SC; S-T, Jr Cl; Hon Prog; Scholastic Achv A; PA; Lang Arts A; 2nd Pl, Spch Ribbon; *SIUE; Nurs.*

THATCHER, Lori Ann
Crestview HS; Convoy, OH (33%-80) Ann; Band; Chor; Rptr, FHA; Pres, 4H; VP, SC; Y-Tns; Secy, Soph Cl; COM; 4H A; Sci A; Yth Fel; 4-H Co As; Solo A; *Home Ec.*

THAYER, Alan Davenport
Valley Regional HS; Deep River, CT (16-180) Span C; *Pepperdine Col; Med.*

THAYER, James Elliott
Sweet Home Sr HS; Tonawanda, NY; Band; Community Yth Symph; Ensm; Orch; Wrest; COM; Most Out; NYSSMA Solo A's; 1st & 2nd Pl, Jazz Competition; *Fredonia Col; Mus.*

THAYER, Kevin Paul
Sublette HS; Sublette, KS (15-50) Band; BS; Ensm; Spch C; VP, SC; Golf; *Kansas St U.*

THAYER, Marcia Jean
Burlingame HS; Burlingame, CA; Chor; Secy, SC; Tnns; *UCLA; Econ.*

THAYER, Rebecca Sue
Foy H Moody HS; Corpus Christi, TX (4-397) Semi-Fin, GS; Lit Mag; Mu Alpha Theta; VP, NHS; Y-Tns; *Mid-Amer Nazarene Col.*

THAYER, Thomas Paul
Charles C Mason HS; Tulsa, OK; Ed, Ann; Mgr, Drama; Rptr, Hmrm; NHS; ARC; Sci C; Spch C; Var C; Ftbl; Golf; Masonic A; Ntl Sci Found; Sci A.

THEALL, David Andrew
Winter Park HS; Winter Park, FL (25%-805) Span C; Yth C; Weightlifting; Bible Sch Aide; Stu Pilot, Sailplanes; Camp Counselor; *US Air Force Acad; Aeronautical Engr.*

THEANDER, Cole Eugene
Clackamas HS; Milwaukie, OR; A Cap Choir; Hmrm; Sci C; Tres, Ski C; Ftbl; JV, Tr; *Sci.*

THEBERT, William Jeffrey
Dwight D Eisenhower HS; Washington, MI (2-593) BS; Dbte Tm; Ch, Model UN; Pres, NHS; A-Ed, Sch P; Ski C; SC; VP, Jr Cl; JV, Ftbl; Amer Leg A; COM; Hon Prog; Magna Cum Laude; NMF; NMS; Opt A; Opt Out Tn; Sal; *Mich St U; Pre-Law.*

THEE, John Henry Jr
Vineland Sr HS; Vineland, NJ (90-800) Ger C; Lat C; Bkbl; *US Air Force Acad; Psych.*

THEEL, Janice Rhoda
Paynesville HS; Paynesville, MN; Ann; Chor; Sch P; Mgr, Bkbl; *N Central Bible Col; Mus.*

THEIMER, Keith Edward
Mineral Wells HS; Mineral Wells, TX (2%-296) Bsbl; JV, Bkbl; Co-Cpt, Ftbl; Alg A; Tn Involvement Prog; *Coaching.*

THEIROFF, George Vieweg Jr
Linsly Military Inst; Wheeling, WV (4-65) NHS; A-Ed, Sch P; Band C; Span NHS; Var C; Ftbl; Tr; Hon Prog; *Washington & Jefferson Col; Med.*

THEIS, Lawrence Eugene
Immaculata HS; Leavenworth, KS (30-60) A Cap Choir; CYO; Chor; Ensm; 4H; Hmrm; Tres, Key C; Ftbl; COM; 4H A; HCt; Hon Prog; Type A; Acolyete; *Northeast Kans Vo-tech Col; Auto-Mech.*

THELANDER, Rodger Darwin
Superior HS; Superior, NE (21-81) Chor; Drama; Key C; Spch C; VP, SC; Var C; Bsbl; Co-Cpt, Ftbl; Tr; Amer Leg A; COM; HKg; *Phys Ed.*

THEMER, Kathy M
Kingfisher HS; Kingfisher, OK (5-92) Tres, Band; FBLA; GS; Pres, 4H; Hmrm; Model UN; NHS; Sch Achieve Tm; Secy, SC; Pres, Soph Cl; Citz A; 4H A; Lion A; NMS; Regent Schol; *Okla St U; Journ.*

THENELL, Julie Ann
Blanchet HS; Seattle, WA (30-383) CYO; SC; Secy, Soph Cl; Bkbl; Sftbl; Pres A; JV Vlbl; Order o-t Cross-Cup.

THEOBALD, Cynthia Caryl
Potsdam Central HS; Potsdam, NY (8%-205) Pres, 4H; Orch; COM; 4H A; Yth Fel; Home Ec, Pub Spch, 4-H A's.

THEOBALD, Scott Wade
Geneva HS; Geneva, NE (16-53) Chess C; Fin, FFA; 4H; Cpt, Bkbl; Cr-Ctry; Tnns; Tr; 4H A; HCt; Hon Prog; Pres A; MVP, Bkbl; All Conf Bkbl; *Bus.*

THEODORE, Cheryl Lisa
McDonogh 35 Sr HS; New Orleans, LA; Secy, CYO; Chldr; NHS; Spch C; COM; Service, Hon, A's; *Surgical Tech.*

THERIAULT, Rachel Marie
Saint Dominic Regional HS; Lewiston, ME (4-108) Chldr; Drama; NEDT.

THERRIEN, Kelly Sue
Saint Joseph's Regional HS; Lowell, MA; NHS; *Green Mountain Col; Special Ed.*

THERRIEN, Matthew Arthur
St Mary's HS; Lynn, MA (10-117) CYO; Drama; Fr C; Mgr, Ftbl; Hockey; Bio A; Chem A; SIGN A; Lat A; Eng A; *Merrimack Col; Med.*

THEUERKAUF, Krista Jane
North HS; Evansville, IN (56-395) Band; Community Yth Symph; Ensm; VP, Orch; Bkbl; Tr; Mgr, Wrest; Bio A; Hon Prog; Sci A; Yth Fel; Fin, Dist & St Mus; Sec & 1st Chr, Al Cty Bnd & Orch; *Marine Biol.*

THEURER, Kimberly Allyson
Gulf Comp HS; New Port Richey, FL; A Cap Choir; Band; Chor; City Conf; Drama; Ensm; Hmrm; InterClub Coun; Lat C; Tres, NHS; Ntl Yth Conf; Orch; SC; Tnns; Alg A; COM; Citz A; Hist A; Hon Prog; Math A; Pres A; Yth Fel; Yth Leg; Fla All St Band; Page; St House & Sen; *Harvard U; Law.*

THIBAULT, Elwin Rudolph II
Ramey HS; Ramey Base, PR (5-18) VP, Chess C; Pres, SC; Bsbl; Bkbl; Phy A; *Law.*

THIBODEAUX, Kathleen Marie
Church Point HS; Church Point, LA (2-120) A-Ed, Ann; Secy, CYO; Cpt, Chldr; Secy, FHA; GS; Pres, 4H; Fin, Lit Ral; NHS; Tres, Jr Cl; Tres, Soph Cl; 4H A; Most Out; *LSU; Nurs.*

THIBODEAUX, Keith Edward
St Martinville Sr HS; St Martinville, LA; Arch; Fr C; Rptr, 4H; JETS; NHS; Sci C; Ftbl; Swim; Citz A; 4H A; Hist A; Val; Woodmen o-t World A; 1st, Sci Fair-Botany; BSct Merit Badges.

THIBODEAUX, Phyllis Ann
Our Lady of Mercy HS; St Martinville, LA (1-19) CYO; Dbte Tm; Lit Ral; Math C; Pres, NHS; Phys C; Var C; Tres, Sr Cl; Tres, Jr Cl; Tres, Soph Cl; Mgr, Bkbl; Hon Prog; I Dare You; Math A; Rotary A; Val; Eng A; Bookkeeping A; *U of Southwestern La.*

THIEL, Jean Marie
Hilbert HS; Hilbert, WI (6-66) A-Ed, Ann; Secy, Band; Chldr; Chor; Ensm; GS; Madrigal; NHS; Spch C; Bkbl; Tr; DARGCA; Tres for Tomorrow; Prom Ct; St Tr Trophy; Solo & Ensm Medals.

THIEL, Kathryn Gail
Norwich Free Acad; Norwich, CT (20%-650) Band; Chor; Fr C; Hmrm; Madrigal; Mod Mus Mas; Orch; Bkbl; Sftbl; Hon Prog; Pres, VP & S-T, SC; Cl Musician; Glee C A; Prize Reading As; Cl Singer; *U of Conn; Fine Arts.*

THIELE, Jon David
Whitefish Bay HS; Whitefish Bay, WI (100-320) Ger C; Rptr, Sch P; SC; Sftbl; Yth Fel; Yth Leg; *U of Wisc; Econ.*

THIELMANN, Kathy Lynn
Chilton HS; Chilton, WI (1-120) AFS; Ann; CYO; NHS; Sch P; Span C; Type A; *Med.*

THIES, Debbie Lyn
Potter Pub HS; Potter, NE (4-14) Ed, Ann; Band; NHS; Sch P; Secy, Sr Cl; Secy, Jr Cl; Mgr, Bkbl; Most Valuable, Pep C Member; Home Ec A; *Lincoln Sch of Commerce; Acct.*

THIES, Susan Kay
Auburn Sr HS; Auburn, NE (9-109) A Cap Choir; Band; Chor; Math C; Sci C.

THIESEN, Ronald Joel
Immanuel HS; Reedley, CA (3-57) Tres, Chor; SC; Bkbl; Tr; CSF; HCt; MLS; WW; *Pacific Col; Ed.*

THIESSE, Lesli Inga
Springdale Sr HS; Springdale, AR (1%-427) GS; NHS; Sci C; Bausch & Lomb A; Bio A; H of F; Sci A; Food Service Schol; St Sci Fair, St Jr Acad of Sci, A's; *U of Ark; Food Sci.*

THIESSE, Lori Esther
Springdale HS; Springdale, AR (13%-427) Chldr; Chor; FHA; NHS; Sftbl; Sci A; Mus A; Pres, VICA-HOE C; *Nurs.*

THIESZEN, Charlotte Elaine
Holdrege Sr HS; Holdrege, NE (25%-125) Chor; Dbte Tm; Drama; 4H; Thes; Sftbl; Tr; Bio A; 4H A; Vlbl; *Westmar Col; Social Work.*

THIGPEN, Mary Emma
First Baptist HS; Charleston, SC (3-50) Band; GS; NHS; Tres, SC; Y-Tns; VP, Jr Cl; Pres, Soph Cl; Bkbl; HCt; Yth Fel.

THILL, Peggy Diane
Greeley W HS; Greeley, CO (14-290) NHS; Span C; Spch C; Hist A; Odd Fellow Fin; Span A; *U of N Colo; Biol.*

THISTED, Ellen Margaret
St George's HS; Spokane, WA (8-19) A-Ed, Ann; Bkbl; Vlbl; War Games C; Computer C; Fencing C; *Math.*

THODE, Nadine Marie
Hastings HS; Hastings, MN (5-484) AFS; Chor; Fr C; Orch; Rainbow; ARC; Thes; Swim; Job's Daughters; Fin, Beauty; *U of Minn; Med.*

THOE, Annie Rachel
Northwood-Kensett Comm HS; Northwood, IA; A Cap Choir; Band; Chor; Ensm; Fr C; Madrigal; NHS; Rptr, Sch P; SC; JV, Bkbl; Cr-Ctry; Sftbl; Tr; Secy, Luther League; Church Choir; Evangelism Comm; *Sci.*

THOES, Sally Diane
Guilford HS; Rockford, IL (211-683) JV, Chldr; Tr; *Taylor U; Social Work.*

THOGMARTIN, Greg
Princeton HS; Princeton, MO (5-60) Ed, Ann; NHS; Ed, Sch P; Span C; VP, Sr Cl; God & Country A; Regent Schol; Eagle Sct; Tribe Mic-O-Say; *Oral Roberts U; Ministry.*

THOLKES, Gregory James
Estherville HS; Estherville, IA (2-176) NHS; SC; Ftbl; Tr; Stu Rep, Chamber of Commerce; *U of SD; Bus.*

THOLKES, Lori Jean
Estherville HS; Estherville, IA (12-205) Ann; Cpt, Chldr; Chor; Sch P.

THOM, Deborah Jean
Centerville HS; Centerville, IA (50-139) Bus C; Chldr; Chor; Ensm; FHA; Type A; Vocal Citation A; *Indian Hills Comm Col; Bus.*

THOM, Gerald Robert
Redford Union HS; Redford, MI (6-650) BS; NHS; Bsbl; Cr-Ctry; Phi Beta Kappa; Rensselaer A; *U of Mich; Engr.*

THOMAS, Alvin Jeffrie
West Side HS; Gary, IN;

THOMAS, Andrew
Waterproof HS; Waterproof, LA (7-68) Cpt, Band; Parl, BC; Chor; Pres, Hmrm; Ed, Sch P; Pres, Sr Cl; Bkbl; Ftbl; COM; Cl Fav; HKg; Hon Prog; *NE La U; Bus Adm.*

THOMAS, Ann Loraine
Danville HS; Danville, IL (10-604) Band; Drama; Orch; Citz A; DARGCA; Hon Prog; Math A; Rotary A; St Scholar; Marine Band A; All St Band; Eng Hon's; *U of Ill; Gen.*

THOMAS, Anne Marie
Smithtown HS E; St James, NY (10%-690) Band; Chor; NHS; Tres, Sci C; Y-Tns; Hon Prog; Cpt, 1st Cl GSct; NY St Mus Assn A's; 100 Hr Pin, Hospital Vol; *Bethany Col; Nurs.*

THOMAS, April Nadine
Penncrest HS; Media, PA (162-500) Chldr; Chor; Drama; GS; Hmrm; Pres, Mjrte; Span C; Var C; MVP, Bkbl; Hockey; Tr; COM; Citz A; Cl Fav; Hon Prog; Most Out; Ntl Achv Schol; NMS; Essay Contest; Pres A; Bible Cl A; Cpt, Bkbl; *U of Pittsburg; Bus Adm.*

THOMAS, Arneither
Phila HS for Girls; Philadelphia, PA (200-395) Drama; Lit Mag; Certs of Service; *Wilberforce U; Theology.*

THOMAS, Arthur
Benhaven HS; Olivia, NC (2-84) Band; VP, BC; Chor; Pres, FTA; Sci C; SC; Bio A; Hist A; Fr A; *U of NC; Phar.*

THOMAS, Arthur R
Rogers Sr HS; Michigan City, IN (25-550) Math C; NHS; Tnns; *Acct.*

THOMAS, Ava Denise
M B Smiley HS; Houston, TX (11-461) Band; Drama; Fr C; Math C; Mu Alpha Theta; NHS; Thes; JV, Tnns; Alg A; Bio A; Sci A; Thespian, Drama, A's; *Med.*

THOMAS, Avery Leon
Surry Co HS; Dendron, VA; Wrest; *Advertising.*

THOMAS, Barbara Ann
Northwest HS; Jackson, MI; Chldr; Chor; Drama; 4H; Span C; Spch C; *Christian Teacher.*

THOMAS, Belinda Denise
Northwest HS; St Louis, MO (1-728) Bkbl; Tr; Citz A; Hon Prog; Sci A; Art A; *Fashion Designing.*

THOMAS, Betty Carol
Woodsboro HS; Woodsboro, TX (13-44) A Cap Choir; Ann; Band; Chor; Ensm; Tres, FHA; VP, FTA; Sch P; Pres, Sr Cl; Pres, Jr Cl; Bkbl; Cpt, Tr; Lion A; Rotary A; Yth Fel; One Act Play St Fin; *Tex Luthern Col; Phys Ed.*

THOMAS, Billy
John F Kennedy HS; Tumon, GUAM; Hmrm; NHS; Cpt, Soccer; Tr; ROTC A; Jr Achv; Guam Soccer Assoc; Soccer C; Guam Toc Kwon Ds C; *West Point Acad; Elec.*

THOMAS, Bonita Renee
Baker HS; Columbus, GA (54-260) Community Yth Symph; SC; Bkbl; Best Dressed; Bkbl A; *Howard U; Law.*

THOMAS, Bruce Howard
St James HS; St James, MD (1-30) Chess C; Lit Ral; JV, Cr-Ctry; Golf; JV, Soccer; Alg A; Hist A; Head Master's A; *Cornell U; Archaeology.*

THOMAS, Camelia Angela
Williamson HS; Mobile, AL (44-348) CYO; Chldr; Cpt, Cr-Ctry; Cpt, Tr; Hon Prog; Most Out; Most Ath; UA Ath Schol; *U of Ala; Ed.*

THOMAS, Carla Jean
Piqua Central HS; Piqua, OH (50-320) Band; Bus C; Chor; Drama; Tr; Mus A; *Bowling Green St U; Secretarial Sci.*

THOMAS, Charles David
Truman HS; Independence, MO (183-663) A Cap Choir; Chor; Hmrm; Math C; Span C; Bsbl; Ftbl; Sftbl; Tr; Sch Spirit; Cream of the Crop, TK Med & Rib; Bkbl & TK Cert for Records Set; *William Jewell Col; Math.*

THOMAS, Charles Eric
Kathleen Sr HS; Lakeland, FL (25%-560) Lat C; Pres, Up Bound; Sen, SC; *Fla St U; Pre-Law.*

THOMAS, Charles Jr
E Atlanta HS; Atlanta, GA; Hmrm; Span C; Ftbl; Cpt, Tr; Cl Fav; Hon Prog; Most Out; Tr Trophy & Medals; *Computer Sci.*

THOMAS, Cheri Lynn
Trinity Christian HS; Chattanooga, TN; Ed, Ann; Chldr; Ed, Sch P; SC; Rptr, Sr Cl; Secy, Jr Cl; Bkbl; Star Student; TACS Creative Writing A; *Chattanooga St Col; Advertising Arts.*

THOMAS, Cherri Gayle
Leesville HS; Leesville, LA (1-262) Band; Secy, BC; VP, FBLA; 4H; Lit Ral; Cpt, Mjrte; Cl Fav; MLS; Most Out; Val; *La Tech U; Pre-Optometry.*

THOMAS, Cheryl Marie
Northwest HS; St Louis, MO (6-433) Pres, Bus C; NHS; Y-Tns; Hon Prog; WW; HR; *U of Mo; Nurs.*

THOMAS, Christina Joann
Martinsville HS; Martinsville, IN (61-377) Band; Community Yth Symph; Pres, 4H; Orch; 4H A; Yth Fel; Alpha Tn Yth Competition, Mus, A's; *Fort Wayne Bible Col; Christian Ed.*

THOMAS, Christine Ann
The Key Sch; Annapolis, MD (1-25) Drama; Pres, Hmrm; A-Ed, Sch P; SC; Pres, Jr Cl; Hockey; High HR; Fr, Creative Writing, A's; *Lib Arts.*

THOMAS, Claudette
Banning HS; Banning, CA (41-207) *Grossmont Col; Orthodontist Asst.*

THOMAS, Connie Kaye
Pleasant Grove HS; Pleasant Grove, AL (8-150) NHS; Beauty; Dance, Pep, C'S; Top 5%, Co; Girl's Sports Assn; *Jefferson St Jr Col.*

THOMAS, David Ross
Benhaven HS; Olivia, NC; BC; Bkbl; Ftbl; Alg A; Hist A; Sci A; Fr A; *NC St U.*

THOMAS, David Wayne
St Joseph's HS; Camden, NJ (4-76) Fr C; NHS; Yrbk A; *Glassboro St Col; Art.*

THOMAS, Deborah
Monroe HS; Albany, GA (25-329) VP, Bus C; Cpt, Chldr; SC; Bkbl; Tr; *Albany St Col; Math.*

THOMAS, Debra Ann
Manley HS; Chicago, IL (9-443) Bus C; FBLA; NHS; Bkbl; Swim; Tr; Citz A; Hon Prog; Type A.

THOMAS, Debra Ann
Owensboro Cath HS; Owensboro, KY (66-231) Hon Prog; Opt A; Spch A; *U of Ky; Nurs.*

THOMAS, Dexter Stanley
Luther Burbank HS; Sacramento, CA; *Elec.*

THOMAS, Dorothy Elliott
Northeastern HS; Elizabeth City, NC (4-300) Ed, Ann; Chor; Drama; Fr C; FHA; Hmrm; Secy, NHS; Sci C; SC; Gov Honor Prog; Journ A; Magna Cum Laude; ARC A; Yth Fel; WW; Hon Marshall; Nom, Tngr o-t Yr; Carol Roberson A; *U of NC at Chapel Hill; Pre-Med.*

THOMAS, Earl David
R L Osborne HS; Marietta, GA; Chor; Madrigal; Thes; Soccer; Sci A; All St Chor.

THOMAS, Eddie Jr
Luther Burbank HS; Sacramento, CA (12-600) Chor; Drama; InterClub Coun; VP, SC; Thes; Secy, Sr Cl; Cpt, Bkbl; Cl Fav; MLS; Opt A; Type A; Best Actor; Most Humorous; Most Spirited Boy; YFU Schol; *Sacramento Col; Theater Arts.*

THOMAS, Elizabeth Elayne
Springfield Local HS; Bergholz, OH (13-97) BC; Drama; FTA; Sch P; Span C; SC; Yth Fel; Comm Bicentennial Spch A; Missionary Soc; Pres, Lib C; Secy, Yth Fel; *Col of Steubenville; Ed.*

THOMAS, Elizabeth Jean
Nutley HS; Nutley, NJ (200-500) Rptr, Sch P; SC; Tnns; *Moravian Col.*

THOMAS, Ethelyne Virginia
Jess Lanier HS; Bessemer, AL; *Airline Stewardess.*

THOMAS, Faye Carl
HS of Charleston; Charleston, SC (10-29) ARC; ARC A; *Nurs.*

THOMAS, Felicia Anne
Santa Fe HS; Alachua, FL; BC; FBLA; Sftbl; *Santa Fe Comm Col; Bus.*

THOMAS, Frank Almarine III
DeVilbiss HS; Toledo, OH (20-400) Dbte Tm; Drama; NHS; Span C; Hist A; Spch A; NML; *U of Toledo; Engr.*

THOMAS, Gary Eugene
Manual HS; Kansas City, MO (38-190) Dbte Tm; Drama; Sch P; Spch C; Spch A; Type A; Mr Theatre Trophy; *U of Mo; Spch.*

THOMAS, Gregory Lorenzo
Monroe HS; Albany, GA (12-265) NHS; Span NHS; COM; Gov Honor Prog; Hon Prog; Ntl Achv Schol; NMF; NMS; *U of Ga; Physics.*

THOMAS, Hattie Mae
Hancock Central HS; Sparta, GA; NHS; Hon Prog; Type A; Driver's Ed A; Acct A.

THOMAS, Howard
Charles E Hughes HS; New York, NY; Chor; JETS; Bsbl; Bkbl; Ftbl; Sftbl; Tr; COM; Achv A; *Steven Inst of Tech; Tech.*

THOMAS, Ida Mae
Grover Cleveland HS; Buffalo, NY; Chor; VP, Hmrm; InterClub Coun; SC; Bkbl; COM; Hon Prog; Spch A; Vlbl; *Child Stu.*

THOMAS, Jacqueline Faye
Soldan HS; St Louis, MO (100-600) Sch Achieve Tm; Hon Prog; *Bus.*

THOMAS, Jacquelyn Beatrice
Darby Township HS; Glenolden, PA (9-110) Band; Chldr; Chor; Ensm; Hmrm; NHS; Ntl Yth Conf; Sch P; SC; Hockey; Cl Fav; Hon Prog; Bulletin Schol Ath; Most Sch Spirited; Hon Stu; WW; *Widener Col; Nurs.*

THOMAS, James Lewis
Sheffield HS; Memphis, TN (15-160) Hmrm; Mu Alpha Theta; NHS; Bus Mgr, Sch P; SC; Thes; *Memphis St U; Law.*

THOMAS, Janet Lynn
Seminole HS; Sanford, FL (15%-495) Anchor C; Parl, Mu Alpha Theta; NHS; ARC; Var C; Bkbl; Sftbl; ARC A; Type A; Vlbl; *U of S Fla; Pre-Med.*

THOMAS, Jason Charles
Brazil HS; Brazil, IN (20-200) Var C; Bkbl; Ftbl; Wrest; *Ind U; Med.*

THOMAS, Jeffrey Scott
Ft Scott Sr HS; Fort Scott, KS; Dbte Tm; NFL; F-Ed, Sch P; Span C; SC; God & Country A; HKg; Yth Fel; *Law.*

THOMAS, Jerry Dean
Scott Comm HS; Scott City, KS (18-110) Band; Hmrm; Pres, InterClub Coun; Monogram; Ntl Yth Conf; Order/Arrow; Sch Achieve Tm; Spch C; SC; Cpt, Var C; Pres, Sr Cl; VP, Jr Cl; Cpt, Bsbl; Cpt, Bkbl; Cpt, Ftbl; Tr; COM; Citz A; HCt; Hon Prog; JA A; Order/Arrow A; Pres A; Type A; Yth Fel; MVP, Ftbl; Eagle Sct A; All-Conf Ach; *Southwestern Col; Pre-Law.*

THOMAS, Jill Elaine
Colton-Pierrepont Central Sch; Colton, NY (7-35) Band; Chor; Ski C; Span C; SC; Bkbl; Soccer; Sftbl; NEDT; Yth Fel; *Equestrian Comp.*

THOMAS, John Richard
Vicksburg HS; Vicksburg, MS (13-240) Key C; Lat C; NHS; Lat A; *NE La U; Phar.*

THOMAS, John Wesley
Abraham Lincoln HS; Denver, CO; Arch; Swim; Tnns; Sch Yrbk; Photography City A; *Art.*

THOMAS, Joseph Carl
Stone Mountain HS; Stone Mountain, GA (20%-300) Chor; Ger C; Bkbl; Ftbl; Gym; 1st Pl, Hon Chorale; All St Chor; Soloist, Atlanta Boy Choir; Dist Lit Meet; *Mus.*

THOMAS, Joseph Gabriel
Notre Dame-Bishop Gibbons HS; Schenectady, NY (2-158) NHS; Tres; SC; Bkbl; Tr; NEDT.

THOMAS, Joy
Winyah HS; Georgetown, SC; SC; NEDT; Yth Fel; Secy, EYC; Hon Men, Schol Art A; Jr Booster C; *Queens Col; Sociology.*

THOMAS, Julia Adeliade
E Providence Sr HS; E Providence, RI; Chor; Fr C; 4H; Tres, SC; Bkbl; Cr-Ctry; Beauty; JA A; Yth Fel; Miss Congeniality; Miss RI Ntl Teenage Comp; Tres, Yth Fel; Pres, JA; *Broadcasting Tech.*

THOMAS, Julia Ann
Festus R-6 Sr HS; Festus, MO (20-233) Band; Chor; Church Pianist; Cpt, Vlbl; Vol, Christian Child Care Center; Run-Up, Mod Woodmn Civ Oration Comp; *SE Mo St U; Early Childhood Ed.*

THOMAS, Karen Elaine
Lake HS; Uniontown, OH (102-210) Ann; Tres, SC; Sftbl; Pep C; Attendance A; Shorthand A; VP, S-T, Band; Yrbk Staff A; Jr Cl Play; Hon A; Office Aide A; Statistician, Tr.

THOMAS, Karin Kay
Bozeman Sr HS; Bozeman, MT (15-375) VP, Band; Chor; Model UN; NFL; NHS; Orch; Rainbow; Spch C; Rotary A; Mont U Hon Sch; MSU Eng Schol; *Mont St U; Eng.*

THOMAS, Karolyn Jeannie
Marlington HS; Alliance, OH (10-312) Chor; GS; NHS; MLS; VofDEM; Yth Fel; WW; *Massillon Baptist Col; Religion.*

THOMAS, Kay Ann
Bridgeport HS; Bridgeport, OH (5%-126) Drama; VP, Lat C; SC; Y-Tns; Type A; Col Careers C; Art C; 4 Point A; *Therapy.*

THOMAS, Keith Edward
Pike Central HS; Petersburg, IN (6-182) Pres, NHS; Sci C; Secy, Sr Cl; Cpt, Bkbl; Golf; Citz A; Yth Fel; Mental Attitude A, Bkbl; *DePauw U; Pre-Med.*

THOMAS, Keith Lenardo
Wakulla HS; Crawfordville, FL (10%-117) Semi-Fin, BS; Hmrm; Fin, Lit Mag; NHS; VP, SC; Up Bound; Pres, Sr Cl; Pres, Jr Cl; Bkbl; Co-Cpt, Ftbl; Citz A; Poet A; VofDEM; WW; *Fla A&M U; Journ.*

THOMAS, Kelli Alisa
Leesville HS; Leesville, LA (1-353) Band; FTA; Lit Ral; *LSU; Paleontology.*

THOMAS, Kelly Oneta
Pekin Comm HS; Pekin, IL (38-721) A Cap Choir; Chor; Ensm; Tres, 4H; NHS; A-Ed, Sch P; SC; COM; 4H A; Hon Prog; Cpt, Pom Pon Girls; *Ill Wesleyan U; Elem Ed.*

THOMAS, Kenneth Warren
Douglas Byrd Sr HS; Fayetteville, NC (100-450) Ann; Band; Bus C; Chor; Drama; InterClub Coun; Lit Mag; Order/Arrow; Sch P; Cpt, Ftbl; Wrest; Journ A; Order/Arrow A; Q&S A; ROTC A; Bus Driver of Month; Eagle Sct; 1st Pl, Photo Contest; Wona Dance Contest; *E Carolina U; Computer.*

THOMAS, Kevin Eugene
McKinley HS; Washington, DC (115-760) Citz A; Jr Litho C; *Wash Tech Inst; Offset Printing Mgt.*

THOMAS, Kurt Robert
Thornton Twp HS; Harvey, IL; Chess C; Chor; Dbte Tm; Spch C; SC; Cr-Ctry; Tr; COM; Spch A; *Lincoln Christian Col; Minister.*

THOMAS, Lauri Ann
Rapides HS; Lecompte, LA; HCt; Secy, Art C; Vlbl Tourn; *La Col.*

THOMAS, Lisa Marie
Mercy Acad; Louisville, KY (6-79) Drama; ARC; Alg A; Bio A; Hist A; Sci A; Zoology A; Physiology A; Fr A; Eng A; *Brescia Col; Pre-Med.*

THOMAS, Lori Ann
Sparta HS; Sparta, IL; Band A; VICA C.

THOMAS, Lucretia Elois
Ben L Smith HS; Greensboro, NC (85-418) Dbte Tm; Orch; JA A.

THOMAS, Lynnette Rochelle
Oakland Tech HS; Oakland, CA; SC; Sci A; Recognition A; *Stanford U; Med.*

THOMAS, Mardell Marie
Stanton HS; Stanton, NE (2-45) Band; Chor; 4H; SC; 4H A; Stage Band; Lib A; Swing Choir; Art A; Phys Fitness A; *The Col of Idaho; Fine Arts.*

THOMAS, Margaret Ann
Bridgeport HS; Bridgeport, OH (6-121) Ed, Ann; Cpt, Chldr; Drama; Pres, FHA; Fin, GS; VP, Lat C; Tres, NHS; Pres, Spch C; SC; Y-Tns; Tres, Jr Cl; Amer Leg A; Lat As; *Miami U; Pre-Law.*

THOMAS, Mark Jeffrey
Ritenour Sr HS; Overland, MO (100-826) NHS; Mus.

THOMAS, Martin William
Eastside HS; Paterson, NJ (17-519) COM; *Fairleigh Dickinson U; Acct.*

THOMAS, Mary Ann
Motley HS; Columbus, MS (4-70) BC; Chldr; 4H; Hmrm; F-Ed, Sch P; Sci C; SC; Tri-HiY; Tres, Jr Cl; VP, Soph Cl; Arch; Bio A; COM; Hist A; Math A; Sci A; Eng A; *Miss St U; Med.*

THOMAS, Maurice Carl
Northeastern HS; Detroit, MI; Chess C; *Wayne St U; Bus.*

THOMAS, Maxine
Chester HS; Chester, PA (219-673) Co-Ed, Ann; Chor; 4H; Key C; World Affairs C; Pres, Jr Cl; COM; Cl Fav; 4H A; Hon Prog; Ed A, GSct; Med Explorers; *Liberal Arts.*

THOMAS, MeLanie Denise
Goodlettsville HS; Goodlettsville, TN (30-171) Span C; Sftbl; *Treveca Col; Math.*

THOMAS, Nancy Katherine
Southview Acad; Wadesboro, NC (1-20) F-Ed, Ann; VP, BC; NHS; F-Ed, Sch P; SC; Pres, Soph Cl; Val; Scorekeeper, Bkbl; Erline Mayberry; Jr Marshal; Nom, Gov's Hon Prog; Hardee's Academic Excellence A; *Wingate Col Math Contest.*

THOMAS, Nedra Sue
Southwest HS; St Louis, MO (94-489) Tr; Alg A; COM; Citz A; DARGCA; Math A; Pres A; Type A; Yth Fel; *Math.*

THOMAS, Nicolaus August
University HS; Westwood, CA; Chor; Drama; Bsbl; *Sou Ill U; Law.*

THOMAS, Patrick M
Creighton Prep Sch; Omaha, NE (25%-198) NHS; Sci C; SC; UN Council; Hon Prog; NMF; NMS; NEDT; Summa Cum Laude; WW.

THOMAS, Phillip Terry
Lewisville HS; Lewisville, TX (25%-490) NHS; Ftbl; Yth Fel; *U of Tex; Mech Engr.*

THOMAS, Prindelle Anthony
Crenshaw HS; Los Angeles, CA (20-1500) Sch P; Bsbl; Cpt, Ftbl; God & Country A; Yth Participation A; Most Inspirational, Ftbl; *U of Sou Calif; Telecommunications.*

THOMAS, Randi Lynn
Chillicothe HS; Chillicothe, TX (2-33) Ann; Secy, FHA; SC; JV, Tr; Hist A; Sal; *W Tex St U; Photography.*

THOMAS, Randi Ruth
Owatonna HS; Owatonna, MN; Chldr; Chor; VP, FHA; MVP, Sftbl; Swtht; Vlbl; FFA Swtht.

THOMAS, Rebecca Dianne
Lakeside HS; Atlanta, GA (5-339) Anchor C; BC; Chor; Drama; Ger C; 4H; Math C; Mu Alpha Theta; NHS; SC; Tres, Soph Cl; COM; Gov Honor Prog; 4H A; Hon Prog; All St Chor; *U of Ga; Math.*

THOMAS, Ricardo Jeffrey
Portola Jr HS; San Francisco, CA (5-35) Pres, Hmrm; SC; MVP, Bsbl; Co-Cpt, Bkbl; Golf; Soccer; Sftbl; Cpt, Tnns; Tr; COM; Citz A; Pres A; Fin, Tnns; Phi Beta Sigma; Schol A; *South Western Christian Col; Theology.*

THOMAS, Richard Floyd
Fountain Valley HS; Fountain Valley, CA; Wrest; Pres A; Principles HR; *Orange Coast Col; Construction Tech.*

THOMAS, Robert Allen
Yucca Valley HS; Yucca Valley, CA (1-180) AFS; F-Ed, Ann; Model UN; NHS; Sci C; Mgr, Bkbl; Golf; Alg A; Amer Leg A; CSF; COM; Hon Prog; MLS; NMF; NMS; NEDT; UC Math A; *Stanford U; Pre-Law.*

THOMAS, Robert Ben Jr
Fort Mill HS; Fort Mill, SC (1-135) FFA; 4H; Cr-Ctry; Ftbl; Swim; Tr; *The Citadel; Bus.*

THOMAS, Robert Randall
Burkburnett HS; Burkburnett, TX (158-267) Band; Rptr, Drama; Rptr, Fr C; FFA; Lit Mag; NFL; Ed, Sch P; Rptr, Thes; JV, Ftbl; JV, Wrest; Amer Leg A; COM; Journ A; Spch A; Hon Thes; Photography A; *Midwestern St U; Hist.*

THOMAS, Roslyn Ann
Pontiac Central HS; Pontiac, MI (10%-525) Band; Hmrm; NHS; ARC; SC; Citz A; Solo & Ensm Medals; Band Prin; *Mich St U; Med.*

THOMAS, Ruth Loraine
McKinley Sr HS; Baton Rouge, LA (5-230) Co-Ed, Ann; VP, Math C; VP, Mu Alpha Theta; Pres, NHS; SC; Bus Mgr, Sr Cl; VP, Jr Cl; Alg A; B Crocker C; Cl Fav; Hon Prog; NEDT; *LSU; Chem.*

THOMAS, Sandra Leigh
St Mary's Col; Raleigh, NC (19-103) Ann; Chldr; Sch P; Sci C; SC; MVP, Tnns; *U of NC at Chapel Hill; Journ-Photography.*

THOMAS, Sandra Lynn
Muscle Shoals HS; Muscle Shoals, AL; VP, Chor; VP, Ensm; FBLA; Sup, St Solo Comp; *U of N Ala; Bus.*

THOMAS, Sandra Marie
Lake Taylor Sr HS; Norfolk, VA (40-511) VP, Chor; Secy, Ger C; Hmrm; Fin, Jr Miss Pagent; Secy, Madrigal; H of F; Lion A; Opt A; Hermatiage A; Bland A; Most Talented; Soropthomist; *E Carolina U; Voice Performance.*

THOMAS, Sheila Robynn
Nettie Lee Roth HS; Dayton, OH (10-200) Rptr, Sch P; SC; Bkbl; Swim; COM; Hon Prog; NEDT; Sup Rating, Piano; *Howard U; Communications.*

THOMAS, Summer Lee
Westridge Sch for Girls; Pasadena, CA; Pres, Drama; Co-Ch, Comm Service Coun; *Principia Col; Fine-Arts.*

THOMAS, Susan Ann
Miami Killian Sr HS; Miami, FL (41-1102) Ger C; Secy, Hmrm; NHS; Magna Cum Laude; *Miami Dade Comm Col; Bus.*

THOMAS, Susan Eileen
Newfane Central HS; Newfane, NY (32-185) Chor; Math C; NHS; Sch P.

THOMAS, Susan Frances
Independence Sr HS; Charlotte, NC (90-700) Cpt, Chldr; Fr C; Hmrm; Y-Tns; Beauty; HCt; Yth Fel; Carrousel Princess; Order o-t Patriot; Civinette; *Meredity Col; Bio.*

THOMAS, Susan Jane
Reseda HS; Reseda, CA (8-770) S-T, NHS; Ski C; Hon Prog; *U of Calif; Forestry.*

THOMAS, Terri Lynn
Morgan Co HS; Hartselle, AL (37-240) *Archt Engr.*

THOMAS, Terrince Arlette
Huntington HS; Shreveport, LA (4-200) Pres, Lat C; Lat NHS; Sch P; Y-Tns; *Oxford U; Communications.*

THOMAS, Terry
Russell HS; Hurtsboro, AL (3-60) FFA; 4H; Sci C; Bkbl; 4H A; Hist A; Hon Prog; ROTC A; *Hist.*

THOMAS, Timothy Astor
W Morgan HS; Trinity, AL (10%-60) BC; Span C; Pres, Jr C; Bsbl; Co-Cpt, Bkbl; Ftbl; Cl Fav; Hist A; MVP, Bkbl; Secy, FCA; All Co, Reg, Area, St, Bkbl; *U of Ala; Ath.*

THOMAS, Timothy Robert
Jamestown HS; Jamestown, NY (5-600) A Cap Choir; NHS; Rptr, Sch P; Span C; SC; Bkbl; Ftbl; Sftbl; Swim; NEDT; *Grove City Col; Bus Adm.*

THOMAS, Timothy Wayne
Caprock HS; Amarillo, TX (140-330) VP, Chor; Drama; Thes; Karate; VP, Yth Coun; *Baylor U; ROTC.*

THOMAS, Tina Theresa
Trott Vocational HS; Niagara Falls, NY; Secy, Chor; Bkbl; *Niagara U; Psych.*

THOMAS, Vickie Lorraine
Reid Ross HS; Fayetteville, NC (20%-220) Chor; Ensm; Fr C; FHA; *Fayetteville Tech Inst; Dental Asst.*

THOMAS, Virginia Ruth
Marion HS; Marion, IN; Ensm; Fr C; French NHS; Lat C; Lat NHS; Madrigal; NHS; Usher C; Sch Ambassador; Vlbl; *Foreign Lang.*

THOMAS, William Michael
A And M Con HS; College Station, TX; FFA; SC; Pres, Soph Cl; JV, Golf; Ldrship A; Pres, Fresh Cl; *Tex A&M U; Agr.*

THOMAS, Yvonne Renee
Second Ward HS; Gloster, LA (2-35) Scholastic Achievement; PA; *Grambling St U; Secretarial Sci.*

THOMASON, Crystal Lee
N St Francois R-I HS; Desloge, MO (1-188) A Cap Choir; Band; Madrigal; NHS; Var C; Tr; Curator A; Sci A; Val; VofDEM; Choreographer, Pom-Pon Sq; Co-Cpt, Vlbl; Miss Drill Tm; St Joe Minerals Schol; Top 10%; *U of Mo-Rolla; Chem Engr.*

THOMASON, Dennis Mark
Crestview Sr HS; Crestview, FL; Var C; Bkbl; Ftbl; *U of Fla; Wildlife Conservation.*

THOMASON, Joetta
Wakulla HS; Medart, FL; Band; FBLA; Hmrm; NHS; Hon Prog; Swtht; Church; *Lee Col; Elem Ed.*

THOMASON, L Kent
Union HS; W Plains, MO; Bkbl; ROTC A; *Phoenix Inst Tech Col; Auto Mech.*

THOMASON, Mike Edward
LaConner HS; LaConner, WA; Mgr, AFS; *Med.*

THOMASON, Neva Irene
Smiths Station HS; Smiths, AL (6-157) F-Ed, Ann; BC; Pres, Drama; FHA; 4H; Math C; Mu Alpha Theta; Bus Mgr, Sch P; Sci C; VP, Span C; Pres, Thes; Beauty; COM; Citz A; Hist A; Yth Fel; *Bauder Fashion Col; Fashion Merchandising.*

THOMASSON, Michael Robert
Mission San Jose HS; Fremont, CA (260-520) Chess C; Drama; FBLA; VP, Hmrm; Orch; Y-Tns; JV, Cr-Ctry; JV, Tr; CSF; COM; PTA A; Pres A.

THOMASTON, Karen Teresa
Columbus HS; Columbus, GA; Bus Mgr, Ann; Chor; Hmrm; *Columbus Col; Pre-Dentistry.*

THOME, Heidi Elizabeth
Karlsruhe Amer HS; Karlsruhe, GERMANY;

THOME, Marianna
Arvin HS; Arvin, CA; Chldr; S-T, Chor; S-T, Ensm; Fr C; 4H; Ski C; SC; Beauty; Crisco A; Swtht; Yth Fel; Soph Cl Princess; Head Varsity Songldr; Girl's League; RAH C.

THOME, Michelle Lee
Green Bay E HS; Green Bay, WI; Ann; CYO; Chor; Drama; Hmrm; ARC; SC; Bkbl; Ftbl; Sftbl; Tnns; Tr; JA A; ARC A; *Northeastern Wis Tech Inst; Fashion Merchandising.*

THOMISON, Lee
Robert E Lee HS; Baytown, TX (10%-400) AFS; Drama; French NHS; NHS; COM; Hon Prog; MLS; NMS; Odd Fellow Fin; NSPE Schol Cand; UN Pilgrimage; *Engr.*

THOMLINSON, Belinda Gail
George Washington HS; San Francisco, CA; B Crocker A; Beauty; HQn; JA A; *Pepperdine U; Air Stewardess.*

THOMLINSON, Nathaniel
George Washington HS; San Francisco, CA; Journ A; Ntl Cath Mus Ed Asn; ROTC A; Sci A; *Pepperdine U; Computer Sci.*

THOMPKINS, Laurie Denise
Seventy-First Sr HS; Fayetteville, NC (150-800) Band; BC; Sci C; MLS; Most Out; *UNC-Charlotte; Registered Nurse.*

THOMPKINS, Sandra Kaye
Lincoln HS; Dallas, TX; Key C; NHS; Alg A; Hon Prog; Math A; Type A; *Bus.*

THOMPKINS, Zonese Rose
Melbourne HS; Melbourne, FL; FHA; 4H; Hmrm; Model UN; Mgr, Tr; Bio A; COM; *Morris Brown Col; Criminology.*

THOMPSON, Alana Lynnette
Silsbee HS; Silsbee, TX (85-250) A Cap Choir; Bus C; S-T, Chess C; Drama; FHA; FTA; Hmrm; JETS; Spch C; SC; Thes; S-T, Jr Cl; S-T, Soph Cl; Golf; Interlochen Ntl Mus; Spch A; Yth Fel; Drill Tm; Miss Satsuma; Hon Men, FHA Wool Contest; *Lamar U; Off Adm.*

THOMPSON, Andrea Louise
Twin Lakes HS; W Palm Beach, FL (5%-500) Band; Chor; Dbte Tm; Key C; NFL; NHS; Span A; *St Olaf Col; Religion.*

THOMPSON, Art
Decatur HS; Decatur, AL; Key C; Mu Alpha Theta; Bkbl; Ftbl.

THOMPSON, Aubrey Wayne
Westminster Christian HS; Gadsden, AL (36-50) Demolay; Sci C; Var C; Mgr, Bkbl; Mgr, Ftbl; Math A; VofDEM; *Elec.*

THOMPSON, Becky Adel
Forest Park Sr HS; Forest Park, GA; Band; Secy, BC; Drama; Pres, 4H; HiY; Hmrm; SC; Tri-HiY; Beauty; 4H A; JA A; Yth Fel; Yth Leg; HR; *Ga Sou Col.*

THOMPSON, Benita Lynne
Burnside HS; Burnside, KY (4-70) BC; FTA.

THOMPSON, Betty Ilene
Lake City HS; Lake City, SC; A Cap Choir; Band; BC; Chor; Ensm; FHA; FNA; Hmrm; NHS; SC; COM; Most Out; Yth Fel; Eastern Dist Band; WW; Jr Marshal; Nurs C Schol; Sisters Book C Schol; Tenn All-Hon Band; WW Among Mus Stu; *Med U of SC; Nurs.*

THOMPSON, Beverly Gina
New Caney HS; Porter, TX (13-225) Band; Ensm; Hmrm; Pres, NHS; Rptr, Sch P; VP, Sr Cl; Cpt, Bkbl; Tr; Bio A; Sargeant- at-Arms; Sc; Vlbl; *Southwest Tex St U; Phys Ed.*

THOMPSON, Billy
Claxton HS; Claxton, GA (50%-110) FFA; VP, Hmrm; Tres, SC; Var C; VP, Jr Cl; Bkbl; Ftbl; Tr; Sci A.

THOMPSON, Brenda Kay
Lexington Sr HS; Lexington, NE (18-127) FBLA; COM; Type A; Spell A; Drill Tm; Vlbl.

THOMPSON, Brenda Lynne
Glendale HS; Springfield, MO (25%-438) A Cap Choir; AFS; Anchor C; Chor; Journ A; *Journ.*

THOMPSON, Bruce A
Richmond HS; Richmond, IN (240-696) *Archt.*

THOMPSON, Carole Ann
Cokeville HS; Cokeville, WY; A-Ed, Ann; Band; Chldr; Chor; VP, FHA; Pres, 4H; Hmrm; SC; Pres, Soph Cl; 4H A; Type A; SBR, Jr Cl; *Wyo U.*

THOMPSON, Carolyn Jane
Clear Lake HS; Lakeport, CA (4-110) Band; Chor; Drama; VP, 4H; Jr Miss Pagent; Pres, Rainbow; Span C; Swim; Tnns; CSF; COM; Citz A; 4H A; H of F; Yth Fel; Demolay Swtht; Outst Acad Achv; *Santa Rosa Jr Col; Mus.*

**THOMPSON,
Catherine Elizabeth**
Unicoi Co HS; Erwin, TN (33%-219) BC; Cpt, Chldr; SC; Cpt, Bkbl; Tr; HCt; Mus A; *Health.*

THOMPSON, Charles Jeffers
Bluefield HS; Bluefield, WV (48-311) BS; Hmrm; InterAct C; NHS; Span C; JV, Bkbl; VP, Yth Fel; *Ky U; Bus Adm.*

THOMPSON, Charles Kendrick
Hogansville HS; Hogansville, GA (1-65) Hmrm; VP, FFA; FTA; 4H; Pres, Key C; Sch P; Span C; Pres, Soph Cl; Bsbl; Golf; Tnns; Alg A; Bio A; COM; Math A; NEDT; Sci A; Type A; Presbyterian Col A; WW; Mr Hustle, Bsbl.

THOMPSON, Charolette Joy
Swifton HS; Swifton, AR; Rptr, FBLA; Secy, FHA; MLS; Rptr, Lib C; *U of Central Ark; Secondary Ed.*

THOMPSON, Cheryl Lynn
Greenville Sr HS; Greenville, PA; Chor; FHA; *Erie Beauty Acad; Cosmotology.*

THOMPSON, Clarence
Broad Ripple HS; Indianapolis, IN; Bkbl; Hon Prog; *Art.*

THOMPSON, Clifford Edwin
Beaumont HS; St Louis, MO (65-900) *U of Mo.*

THOMPSON, Colleen Kay
E Greene Comm HS; Grand Junction, IA; Chldr; Chor; FHA; 4H; Sci C; *DMACC in Boone; Secretarial.*

THOMPSON, Cynthia Lynne
Apollo HS; Owensboro, KY; SC; Chor; Drama; Fr C; FHA; F-Ed, Sch P; Best Supporting Actress; *U of Ky; Theatre Arts.*

THOMPSON, Cyril Vincent
Rossville HS; Rossville, GA (14-211) Band; COM; Gov Honor Prog; Star Student; Eng A; A-V A; *Lee Col.*

THOMPSON, David Anthony
Brandeis HS; NY, NY; Band; Drama; JV, Bkbl; MVP, Hockey; JV, Sftbl; 4H A; Most Out; *Eckerd Col; Mus.*

THOMPSON, David S
Manila HS; Manila, UT (2-19) Band; Chor; Drama; Rptr, Sch P; Span C; Mgr, Bkbl; COM; Hon Prog; Acct, Eng, A's; *Utah St U; Acct.*

THOMPSON, Deborah Sue
Pendleton HS; Pendleton, SC (6-133) Band; BC; Fr C; Bkbl; *Clemson U; Chem.*

THOMPSON, Della Virginia
Reidsville Sr HS; Reidsville, NC (26-344) Chor; Drama; Hmrm; NHS; Sch P; COM; Gov Honor Prog; Hon Prog; NEDT; *U of NC at Greensboro;; Drama.*

THOMPSON, Diana Marie
Hirsch HS; Chicago, IL; Chor; Sftbl; Swim; *U of Ill; Sci.*

THOMPSON, Diane Kay
Cumberland Valley HS; Mechanicsburg, PA (15-627) NHS; NEDT; *Pa Bus Sch; Acct.*

THOMPSON, Diane Lyn
Centerburg HS; Centerburg, OH (10%-82) Pres, Band; Dbte Tm; Drama; Fin, GS; Ed, Lit Mag; NHS; Ed, Sch P; Span C; Soph C; Pres, SC; Thes; Var C; Parl, Sr Cl; Pres, Jr Cl; Parl, Soph Cl; MVP, Bkbl; Tr; Amer Leg A; DARGCA; Elk A; HCt; Hon Prog; Journ A; MLS; Q&S A; Spch A; MVP, Vlbl; Creative Writing A; *Bethany Col; Communications.*

THOMPSON, Domonique Renette
East Sr HS; Buffalo, NY; Hmrm; SC; Var C; MVP; Tnns; *General Motors Inst; Drafting.*

THOMPSON, Donal Michael
Cleveland HS; Seattle, WA; *UCLA; Archt.*

THOMPSON, Donald Eugene
East HS; Columbus, OH (7-350) I N The Know Tm; Schol Ath; Top Tns of Amer; Sgt of Arms; *Ohio St U; Engr.*

THOMPSON, Donna Lynn
Washington and Lee HS; Montross, VA (10-205) Chldr; Drama; 4H; Tr.

THOMPSON, Douglas Warren
E Central HS; Tulsa, OK (75-600) Chem C; Ger C; NHS; *Okla St U; Sci.*

THOMPSON, Elaine Rene
Marion Co HS; Lebanon, KY (2-298) CYO; Drama; Tres, FBLA; Tres, FHA; FTA; Jr Miss Pagent; NHS; Spch C; Hon Prog; Math A; Regent Schol; Sci A; Spch A; Type A; Chapter, St Degrees, FHA; Acct A; Off Machine A; *W Ky U; Acct.*

THOMPSON, Elizabeth Lynne
Ritenour Sr HS; Overland, MO (131-826) A Cap Choir; Chor; Ensm; NHS; God & Country A; Hon Prog; Pom Pon Squad; *William Jewell Col; Nurs.*

THOMPSON, Eric Dewitt
Robichaud HS; Dearborn Heights, MI; Cr-Ctry; Tnns; *Lawrence Tech Col; Archt.*

THOMPSON, Floyd Gene
Marine Military Acad; Harlingen, TX; Ftbl; Hon Prog; *Nor Ariz U; Law Enforcement.*

THOMPSON, George Michael
Vestavia Hills; Vestavia Hills, AL (1-283) Chor; Ch, Ger C; Ed, Lit Mag; Math C; NHS; Hon Prog; Math A; NEDT; Val; Excel, MAA, A's; Wilkens Schol, U o-t South; Most Intellectual; *The U o-t South; Physic.*

THOMPSON, Gilbert Grant
Hillsboro HS; Hillsboro, OH (10-190) BS; Drama; Pres, Fr C; Pres, Lat C; NHS; Sch Achieve Tm; F-Ed, Sch P; Var C; JV, Bkbl; MVP, Tnns; ROTC A; VP, Yth Fel; Jr Chrch Director; Del, World Affairs Inst; Bicentennial Comm Prog; Fin, Hist Schol Test; *U of Notre Dame; Law.*

THOMPSON, Gloria Alice
Winter Haven HS; Winter Haven, FL (300-800) Secy, A Cap Choir; Arch; Secy, Chor; Ensm; 4H; Hmrm; Mjrte; ARC; Ski C; Beauty; 4H A; Chrch Yth Fel; Sup Solo, Chor Comp; Bar I, Ntl Rifle As; 400 Hr A; Adv, Ntl Watrski As; Outst Watrski; 4-H Horsemanship A'S; Hospital Vol; *Music Design.*

THOMPSON, Gregory Albert
Claxton HS; Claxton, GA (3-150) Tres, BS; Chess C; Sch P; Var C; Tres, Soph Cl; Fin, Tnns; COM; Hon Prog; Geography A; *U of Ga; Sci.*

THOMPSON, Gregory Leo
Lake Clifton Sr HS; Baltimore, MD (10%-500) JETS; NHS; Alg A; Hist A; Most Out; Historian, Jr Cl; Artistic As; *Engr.*

THOMPSON, Gregory Phillip
Monroe Area HS; Monroe, GA (30-180) Band; Key C; Tres, Jr Cl; Golf; Most Out; Yth Fel; Pres, Yth Fel; Yth Rep, Adm Board; Choir Tours; Director, Local Band; *U of Ga; Mus.*

THOMPSON, Gwendolyn Michele
Saginaw HS; Saginaw, MI (19-225) Cpt, Chldr; Chor; Ensm; Hmrm; NHS; SC; Secy, Jr Cl; COM; Type A; Academic Achievement; Mus A; Hon A; *U of Mich; Pre-Law.*

THOMPSON, Hal Martin
Ravenscroft HS; Raleigh, NC (40-100) Ftbl; Tr; Pres, FCA; Tres, MYF; Var Ltr; *Engr.*

THOMPSON, Helen May
Rockland Dist HS; Rockland, ME; AFS; Secy, Chor; Drama; Thes.

THOMPSON, Jack Alan
Rockdale HS; Rockdale, TX; Ann; Rptr, Sch P; SC; Pres, Sr Cl; Bsbl; Cpt, Bkbl; Fin, Ftbl; Pres A; Yth Fel; Most Ath; All Amer Ftbl; WW; *Sam Houston St U; Sociology.*

THOMPSON, Jacqueline Marie
Charles Sumner HS; Saint Louis, MO; Chldr; Dbte Tm; Hmrm; SC; Up Bound.

THOMPSON, James Edward
Johnson Sr HS; St Paul, MN (72-687) Ger C; NHS; Golf; *U of Minn; Forestry.*

THOMPSON, Janet Ann
Winston Churchill HS; Potomac, MD; Bkbl; Vlbl Cert of Participation; Bkbl Ltr; *Md U; Bus Mgt.*

THOMPSON, Janetta Kay
Sullivan Central HS; Blountville, TN (17-450) Tres, Band; BC; Community Yth Symph; NHS; *Mus.*

THOMPSON, Jeff Alan
Wheaton N HS; Wheaton, IL (175-357) Var C; Bkbl; MVP, Ftbl; Tnns; Tr; HKg; *Tulsa U; PE.*

THOMPSON, Jeffrey Lee
Kelly Walsh HS; Casper, WY (62-411) Pres, Chor; Tres, Drama; Sch P; Tres, Thes; Arch; Ftbl; Swim; Tnns; Tr; Wrest; Hon Prog; Kiwanis A; Thespian A; Nom, Wyo St Jr Arch A; Bible Quiz St High Scorer A; *Archt.*

THOMPSON, Jim Fletcher
Dorman HS; Spartanburg, SC (15%-900) Band; BC; Drama; Pres, SC; Pres, Jr Cl; Wrest; MLS; Best Actor; *William and Mary Col; Theater.*

THOMPSON, Joan Marie
Dunkirk Sr HS; Dunkirk, NY; Bus C; FBLA; DECNY A; *Bus.*

THOMPSON, Joel Charles
Atlanta HS; Atlanta, TX; Fr C; JETS; Sch P; Pres, SC; Pres, Jr Cl; Pres, Soph Cl; Bkbl; Ftbl; Cpt, Golf; Cl Fav; Journ A; Q&S A; *Baylor U; Pol Sci.*

THOMPSON, Joetta Marie
Fremont HS; Sunnyvale, CA; Rptr, Hmrm; SC; Bsbl; Bkbl; Swim; Hon Soc; HR; *Stanford U; Med.*

THOMPSON, John Vincent
N Penn HS; Lansdale, PA; JV, Bsbl; JV, Bkbl.

THOMPSON, Jonathan Lee
Glen Burnie HS; Glen Burnie, MD (33%-600) Fr C; Wrest; *Duke U; Med.*

THOMPSON, Joseph Charles
Central HS; Grand Rapids, MI; Ger C; Lat C; Cr-Ctry; Tr; *Elec.*

THOMPSON, Joy Lynn
Johnson HS; Gainesville, GA (20%-300) BC; Cpt, Chldr; Chor; Hmrm; Tri-HiY; VP, Jr Cl; VP, Soph Cl; Tnns; Beauty; HQn; WW.

THOMPSON, Joyce Ellen
Vian HS; Vian, OK (10-105) Band; NHS; COM; Yth Fel; *Northeastern Okla St Col; Sci.*

THOMPSON, Julia Kaye
Kinmundy-Alma HS; Kinmundy, IL (13-36) Rptr, Ann; Chldr; VP, FHA; 4H; VP, NHS; Pres, SC; Bkbl; Sftbl; 4H A; Pres A; Vlbl; Jr Carnival Court; GAA; Pep C; *St Louis Christian Col; Ed.*

THOMPSON, Julie Lynn
Poway HS; Poway, CA (7-300) Cpt, Soccer; MVP, Sftbl; Fin, Tnns; Tr; Athlete o-t Mo; *San Diego St Col; Phys Ed.*

THOMPSON, Karen Ann
Ashwaubenon HS; Green Bay, WI (20-360) Band; Chor; Ensm; Hmrm; NHS; SC; JV Vlbl; *St Olaf Col; Mus.*

THOMPSON, Karen Elaine
Menchville HS; Newport News, VA (180-563) Co-Cpt, Chldr; Drama; FBLA; Secy, FHA; Secy, FTA; Ch, Hmrm; Span C; Thes; Citz A; 4H A; Type A; *Va St Col; Bus.*

THOMPSON, Karen Frances
Booker T Washington HS; Atlanta, GA (20-345) Ed, Ann; Bus Mgr, Band; Rptr, Hmrm; NHS; Secy, Span C; COM; Citz A; HQn; HCt; Hon Prog; Journ A; NEDT; *Spelman Col; Eng.*

THOMPSON, Karen Renee
East HS; Cheyenne, WY (38-446) Chor; Ger C; NHS; *Laramie Co Comm Col; Child Psychiatry.*

THOMPSON, Karyn Lynn
Burnsville Sr HS; Burnsville, MN (303-765) Rptr, Ann; Band; Dbte Tm; Span C; SC; Secy, Soph Cl; JV, Sftbl; Swim; Tr; Candystriper; Teacher's Aide; Asst Sunday Sch Teacher; Fin, Dist Band.

THOMPSON, Kathy Lynn
Zion Benton Township HS; Zion, IL; Fr C; NHS; JV, Tnns; Art C; Acad Achv; Fr A; Outst Art St; *Mus Ed.*

THOMPSON, Kenneth Leon
Inglewood HS; Inglewood, CA; Band; Hmrm; Orch; Var C; Bkbl; Cpt, Ftbl; Tr; Cl Fav; Hist A; HCt; Most Out; Star Student; Swtht.

THOMPSON, Kim
Watson Chapel HS; Pine Bluff, AR (7-225) Ann; BC; FBLA; Rainbow; A-Ed, Sch P; HQn; Masonic A; Most Out; Q&S A; St Demolay Swtht; *Ark St U; Pol Sci.*

THOMPSON, Kristi Kay
Orleans Pub HS; Orleans, NE (25%-26) Band; Chldr; Chor; Pres, 4H; Monogram; NHS; SC; Var C; Co-Cpt, Bkbl; Sftbl; Tr; Alg A; Cl Fav; 4H A; HCt; Math A; Pres A; Yth Fel; Russian C; Co-Cpt, Vlbl; *Pepperdine U; Phys Ed.*

THOMPSON, Kristin Diane
Bartow Sr HS; Bartow, FL (2%-300) Anchor C; Drama; VP, FHA; GS; 4H; VP, NHS; Span C; Var C; Cpt, Swim; Mgr, Tnns; Tr; COM; H of F; Hon Prog; MVP, Swim; Secy, Tres, Lat C; Presidential Phys Fitness A; *Colo Col.*

THOMPSON, Kristy Lynn
Crawfordsville HS; Crawfordsville, IN; Band; Chor; FTA; Math C; Rainbow; Span C; Mgr, Bkbl; Tr; Pres A; Type A; Yth Fel; FCA; Pres, CYF; Vlbl; Swing Choir; Pep Block; Pres, Camp Fire Girls; Pom Pon Girls; Vlbl; Sunshine Soc; Swing Choir; *Purdue U; Math.*

THOMPSON, Lance Lyle
Napa HS; Napa, CA (1-444) Band; Chor; Bank Of Amer A; CSF; NMF; *U o-t Pacific; Mus Ed.*

THOMPSON, Leslie Dawn
Crestview HS; Crestview, FL (6-214) AFS; Ann; Band; BC; Secy, 4H; CSF; 4H A; Hon Prog; Reserve Hi- point; *U of Fla; Vet Med.*

THOMPSON, Linda Denise
W Charlotte Sr HS; Charlotte, NC (135-625) Bus Mgr, Ann; Pres, Band; Chldr; Mjrte; Mod Mus Mas; Orch; ARC; Secy, SC; Gov Honor Prog; Sci A; Head Drum Mjrte; Order of Lion; Pres, Explorers; Church Pianist; *E Carolina U; Phys Therapy.*

THOMPSON, Linda Faye
St John's HS; Darlington, SC; Lat C; Lat NHS; Rptr, Sch P; Journ A; Eng A; Schol A; *Pharmacology.*

THOMPSON, Linda Gail
Cainsville Ri Sch; Cainsville, MO (25%-13) F-Ed, Ann; Chldr; Fin, Chor; Dbte Tm; Fin, Ensm; Co-Ed, Sch P; Pres, Soph Cl; Bkbl; Tr; Citz A; Spch A; Type A; VP & Tres, FHA; 2nd Pl St Girl Sextet; Tr Ltr; Bkbl Ltr; *Interior Design.*

THOMPSON, Linsley Jeanne
The Lovett Sch; Atlanta, GA; Drama; Ger C; Span C.

THOMPSON, Lisa Carole
Oak Ridge HS; Orlando, FL (65-783) AFS; Chor; Ensm; Span C; *Stetson Col; Mus.*

THOMPSON, Lolita Lucille
Kennard Jr HS; Cleveland, OH (1-34) Bsbl; Math A; Phy A; Poet A; Art A; Book C; Kickball Tm; Hon Men A; *Secy.*

THOMPSON, Lori Jeanne
Superior Sr HS; Superior, WI (54-520) Band; Pres, GSct; VP, Church Yth; *U of Wisc; Special Ed.*

THOMPSON, Malinda Diane
Alma HS; Alma, AR; Band; JV, Chldr; Drama; FHA; InterClub Coun; Cpt, Mjrte; Co-Ed, Sch P; Rptr, SC; Bkbl; Golf; Tr; Beauty; WW; Jacettes 'Miss Merry Christmas'; Baton Talent A; *U of Ark; Elem Ed.*

THOMPSON, Marcia Elaine
Jamaica HS; Jamaica, NY (166-1102) Chor; Drama; Hmrm; NHS; Tres, Sr Cl; COM; Hon Prog; NMS; Creative Arts Soc; *NY St U; Theatre.*

THOMPSON, Margaret Jane
Rye Cove HS; Clinchport, VA (8-77) BC; Rptr, FBLA; F-Ed, Sch P; SC; HCt; Type A; Shorthand A; Reg FBLA Stenography II Win.

THOMPSON, Marian Ann
Baker Sr HS; Baker, LA; BC; VP, Hmrm; Alg A; Bio A; Hon Prog; Math A; Phys Ed A; *Sou U; Computer Sci.*

THOMPSON, Martan Louise
Bishop Dwenger HS; Fort Wayne, IN (1%-260) Sci C; Chem A; Hist A; Hon Prog; Span A; Tri-Kappa A; *Med.*

THOMPSON, Mary Beth
John Muir HS; Pasadena, CA (164-527) A Cap Choir; Chldr; Mod Mus Mas; VP, Ski C; Sodality; JV, Tr; CSF; Yth Fel; Yth Leg; Gym; *Pasadena City Col.*

THOMPSON, Mary Gail
Fort Payne HS; Fort Payne, AL (26-156) Band; Chldr; FHA; Hmrm; SC; Tri-HiY; Beauty; Colorguard; Pep C; Ecology C; Church Yth Choir; *Auburn U.*

THOMPSON, Michael Joseph
Stonewall Jackson HS; Charleston, WV; Dbte Tm; Drama; Key C; Math C; Mu Alpha Theta; NHS; Secy, Order/Arrow; Spch C; *W Va U; General.*

THOMPSON, Michelle Joyce
Sky View HS; Smithfield, UT (7-622) 4H; Hmrm; Citz A; Poet A; Schol A; *Brigham Young U.*

THOMPSON, Monisa Leola
River Oaks Sch; Monroe, LA (1-45) Ed, Ann; Bus C; Fr C; Fin, Lit Ral; Sch P; Spch C; Y-Tns; Journ A; Hon Stu; *Eng.*

THOMPSON, NanDora
New Hanover HS; Wilmington, NC (67-537) NHS; Health Careers C; Tres, Lib Media C; *U of NC at Wilmington; Nurs.*

THOMPSON, Norma Jean
Cainsville Ri Sch; Cainsville, MO; Co-Ed, Ann; Fin, Chor; Fin, Ensm; FHA; Sch P; Tr; Excellent Vocal Mus A; 2nd Pl A, Girls Sextet; *Trenton Col of Cosmetology; Cosmetology.*

THOMPSON, Ollie Caroline
Lawrence HS; Lawrence, KS; Band; Fr C; *Kans U; Mus.*

THOMPSON, Pamela Jeanne
N Clayton Sr HS; College Park, GA; Ann; BC; FBLA; Sci C; Super HR; *Tift Col; Elem Ed.*

THOMPSON, Pamela Lea
Pascagoula HS; Pascagoula, MS (42-453) BC; VP, Hmrm; S-T, JETS; Sci C; Sftbl; Hon Prog; Becky Bacot Nurs Schol; *Jackson Co Jr Col; Nurs.*

THOMPSON, Patricia Angella
Springfield Gardens HS; Springfield Gardens, NY; Chor; Citz A; Type A; Yth Fel; *Secy.*

THOMPSON, Patricia Ann
E Kemper HS; Scooba, MS (1-24) Ann; Bus C; Drama; FHA; Jr Miss Pagent; Secy, SC; Secy, Sr Cl; Pres, Jr Cl; S-T, Soph Cl; Cl Fav; HQn; Hon Prog; JA A; Val; *Jackson St U; Home Ec.*

THOMPSON, Patricia Annette
Loganville HS; Loganville, GA (3-90) Ann; Band; BC; Span C; Pres, Tri-HiY; Gov Honor Prog; Hon Prog; Solo & Ensm Band Medals; Band Trophy; Fin, Art Contest; Fin, Essay Contest; *Truett McConnell Col; Social Work.*

THOMPSON, Paul William
H D Woodson HS; Washington, DC; NHS; Soccer; *Howard Col; Architecture.*

THOMPSON, Peter Jared
Hoehne HS; Hoehne, CO; Chess C; Pres, Dbte Tm; Drama; A-Ed, Sch P; Spch C; Pres, Jr Cl; Bkbl; JV, Ftbl; Soccer; JV, Tnns; Alg A; COM; Hon Prog; Math A; *Princeton U; Hist.*

THOMPSON, Prentiss Lane
NY Sch of Printing; New York, NY (11-27) Chor; Hmrm; Chem A; Hist A; Hon Prog; Math A; Most Out; Phy A; Sci A; Attendance, Span, Mus, A's; Ath Accomplishment A; *Pepperdine U; Mus.*

THOMPSON, Rella Sue
Howe HS; Howe, OK; Pres, FHA; Secy, Hmrm; VP, SC; Secy, Jr Cl; Pres, Soph Cl; Bkbl; Sftbl; Cl Fav; Hist A; HCt; Val.

THOMPSON, Rhonda Fay
Greeley W HS; Greeley, CO (55-410) Chor; FHA; SC; Bkbl.

THOMPSON, Richard Lee
Carnegie HS; Carnegie, OK (20%-55) Band; Chor; Ensm; Tres, Order/Arrow; Var C; Bsbl; Bkbl; Ftbl; Co-Cpt, Sftbl; Tr; Co-Cpt, Wrest; Cl Fav; Hon Prog; Eagle Sct; All Region Concert Band; Arrow-of-Light A; *Okla Baptist U; Mus.*

THOMPSON, Richard Martin
N Rowan HS; Spencer, NC (1-193) Band; Pres, Fr C; Hmrm; Pres, Lat C; Monogram; Pres, NHS; Pres, SC; Var C; Bsbl; Cpt, Bkbl; Ftbl; Gr Marshal; Val; Lat A; Morehead Fin; All-Co Ftbl Tm; *UNC-Chapel Hill.*

THOMPSON, Rickie William
Inkster HS; Inkster, MI; Bus C; SC; Tr; *Engr.*

THOMPSON, Robert Carmon
Yankton Sr HS; Yankton, SD (90-250) Drama; Math C; NFL; Phys C; VP, Sci C; Thes; Drama C A; *SD Sch of Mines; Elec Engr.*

THOMPSON, Robert Earl II
Castlemont HS; Oakland, CA (10%-605) Chor; Drama; Tres, NHS; Pres, Var C; Cpt, Swim; Bio A; CSF; *Bus Adm.*

THOMPSON, Robert John
Lodi HS; Lodi, CA; Golf; *U of Calif; Bus.*

THOMPSON, Robin Deneen
Tremont HS; Tremont, IL (3-75) Band; Secy, Drama; Ger C; Cpt, Mjrte; NHS; Thes; Tres, Jr Cl; 4H A; Hon Prog; Type A; Ger, Band, A's; *Bradley U; Archaeology.*

THOMPSON, Ronald Dale
Pisgah Sr HS; Canton, NC (40%-375) Ann; Hmrm; SC; *W Carolina U; Eng.*

THOMPSON, Ronald Wayne
Laurel HS; London, KY; Chess C; Math C; Mu Alpha Theta; Bsbl; Sci A; *Architecture.*

THOMPSON, Rosemarie
Man HS; Man, WV (3-180) Bus C; Commercial C; FBLA; FHA; Co-Ed, Lit Mag; NHS; COM; Hon Prog; Type A; Bookkeeping, Shorthand, A's.

THOMPSON, Russell Devon
Amite Co Attendance Center; Gloster, MS; BC; Chem C; Drama; FFA; SC; Ftbl; Tr; Hon Prog; Most Out; *MSU; Elec Engr.*

THOMPSON, Russell Leroy
Roy HS; Roy, UT; FFA; Ski C; *Weber Col; Mech Engr.*

THOMPSON, Sallie Elizabeth
Emmaus HS; Emmaus, PA (100-500) Hmrm; SC; Var C; Swim; COM; Yth Fel; Keyette C; Vlbl; Service-Ldrship A; *Millersville St Col; Social Work.*

THOMPSON, Sandra Ellen
St Elizabeth HS; Pittsburgh, PA (7-103) Bus C; Drama; Span C; Bio A; NEDT; Pres A; Shorthand A; *Pittsburgh Beauty Acad; Cosmetology.*

THOMPSON, Sandra Jean
Thomas A Edison HS; Tulsa, OK; Chor; City Conf; Ensm; Rptr, Hmrm; Cpt, Mjrte; Hon Prog; JA A; Yth Fel; Yth Leg; *Okmulgee St Tech Col; Home Ec.*

THOMPSON, Sandra Jeanice
Beaumont HS; St Louis, MO (10-350) Chor; NHS; F-Ed, Sch P; Journ A; Q&S A; Secy, Ldrship C; *U of Mo; Journ.*

THOMPSON, Sandra Joy
E Brunswick HS; East Brunswick, NJ (40%-980) Band; 4H; Hmrm; Ski C; Tr; HQn; V-P, Treas, Church Yth Group; Vol Hospital Worker; Sunday Sch Teacher; 'Help in Hand' Carnival; *William Paterson Col; Speech Pathology.*

THOMPSON, Sarita Glenn
Germantown HS; Philadelphia, PA (89-398) Band; Dbte Tm; Mjrte; Ski C; SC; COM; Read Graduation Spch; Historial Hon Soc; *W Chester St Col; Criminal Justice.*

THOMPSON, Sharon Kaye
West HS; Salt Lake City, UT (50%-426).

THOMPSON, Sharon Lee
Palisades HS; Pacific Palisades, CA (35-749) Chldr; Chor; Drama; Jr Miss Pagent; Spch A; Yth Fel; Pres, Yth Fel; Outst Achv Trophy, Ballet; Dist Methodist Conf; *Santa Monica Col; Fine Arts.*

THOMPSON, Sheri Dawn
Harrah HS; Harrah, OK (10-124) Band; Cpt, Chldr; Chem C; Chor; FHA; Hmrm; Phys C; Secy, SC; Mgr, Bkbl; Tr; COM; HCt; Spch A; St Hon Soc; *Okla Baptist U; Child Psych.*

THOMPSON, Sherri Charissa
Rossville Comp HS; Rossville, GA (5-362) Sftbl; COM; *Lee Col.*

THOMPSON, Steven Wade
Southside HS; Memphis, TN (5%-370) Order/Arrow; ROTC A; Saber C; Rifle Tm; Superior Cadet; *US Air Force Acad; Acct.*

THOMPSON, Susan Denise
Washington HS; Washington, NC; Chor; FHA; Rptr, Sch P; Pep C; Qn, Qn With a Scepter, Acteens; *Wingate Col; Yth Worker.*

THOMPSON, Susan Joyce
Maryknoll HS; Honolulu, HI (13-110) CYO; Chldr; Chor; Drama; Fr C; Semi-Fin, Jr Miss Pagent; NHSt; Sch P; Spch C; VP, SC; VP, Sr Cl; Bkbl; Tnns; Hon Prog; VofDEM; Cpt, Vlbl; Ldrship A; *U of Hawaii; Communications.*

THOMPSON, Tammy Lee
Philadelphia HS for Girls; Philadelphia, PA; Drama; Secy, Hmrm; ARC; Secy, Sr Cl; *Pa St U; Child Psych.*

THOMPSON, Terri Lynn
Warren Central HS; Indianapolis, IN (161-952) Chor; Span C; Sftbl; *Taylor U; Social Work.*

THOMPSON, Terry Lynn
Lowndes HS; Valdosta, GA (98-470) Chldr; FHA; 4H; Sci C; Tri-HiY; Sftbl; 4H A; Most Out; Sci A; Spch A; Cpt, Powder Puff Ftbl; BatGirl, Bsbl; *Valdosta St Col; Criminology.*

THOMPSON, Therrall Jean
Mt Clemens HS; Mt Clemens, MI; A Cap Choir; Band; Cpt, Chldr; Chor; 4H; Cpt, Hmrm; Cpt, Mjrte; Fin, Ntl Yth Conf; Span C; Pres, SC; COM; DARGCA; 4H A; Hon Prog; JA A; Ntl Conf Chr & Jews; Star Student; Badminton; Dale Carneige Schol; Attendance Cert; *Southwestern Christian Col; Bus Adm.*

THOMPSON, Timothy James
Wheeling Park HS; Wheeling, WV (120-694) A Cap Choir; Chor; Drama; Pres, HiY; NFL; Spch C; Thes; Var C; Tres, Sr Cl; Bsbl; Bkbl; Co-Cpt, Ftbl; Spch A; 1st Tm, All St, All Valley, Ftbl; All OVAC, All Mountaineer, Ftbl; *Bethany Col; Communications.*

THOMPSON, Timothy Jay
H V Jenkins HS; Savannah, GA; Golf; Soccer; *Central Fla Bible Col; Ministry.*

THOMPSON, Timothy Paul
Montclair Col Prep Sch; Van Nuys, CA (3-50) Commercial C; NHS; CSF; *Calif Lutheran Col; Bio.*

THOMPSON, Tracy Yvette
Lynch HS; Lynch, KY (2-30) Ann; Secy, BC; NHS; Secy, Soph Cl; Cl Fav; Americanism A; Highest Avg A; Home Ec A; Nom, GS; *Acct.*

THOMPSON, Velma Jean
Inola HS; Inola, OK; *Mus.*

THOMPSON, Vicky Lynn
Plain Dealing Acad; Plain Dealing, LA; BC; JV, Chldr; Secy, FHA; 4H; Math C; Mu Alpha Theta; NHS; Spch C; Bkbl; Tr; Beauty; Cl Fav; HCt; Harvest Carnival Court; HR; May Pageant; Danceline; Headmasters List; *La Tech U; Bus Sci.*

THOMPSON, Virginia Ellen
Northwestern HS; Rock Hill, SC (18-388) BC; Drama; Ensm; Fr C; Semi-Fin, GS; NHS; Pres, Rainbow; F-Ed, Sch P; Sci C; Span C; Gym; Alt, GS; Order o-t Star; *Clemson U; Math.*

THOMPSON, Walter Edward
Ny Sch of Printing; New York, NY; Band; Drama; JV, Bsbl; JV, Bkbl; JV, Sftbl; Math A; Most Out; Phys Fitness A; *Pepperdine U; Printing.*

THOMPSON, Wendi Lynnette
East HS; Columbus, OH (14-200) Band; Chor; Drama; Ensm; Fr C; Hmrm; NHS; SC; *Broadcasting.*

**THOMPSON,
William Alexander III**
Vestavia Hills HS; Vestavia, AL; SC; Ftbl; *U of Ala; Med.*

**THOMPSON,
William Langham IV**
Charles Henderson HS; Troy, AL; BC; Drama; Sci C; Church Bkbl; *Chem.*

THOMSEN, Deborah Ann
Granville HS; Granville, OH; Band; NHS; Tres, Span C; Co-Cpt, Bkbl; HQn; Co-Cpt, Vlbl; *Rollins Col; Ed.*

THOMSEN, Lori Jean
Avo-Ha Comm HS; Avoca, IA (21-41) Band; Chldr; Chor; Drama; Thes; Y-Tns; Cl Fav; Thespian A; Band A; Chorus A; *Dana Col; Sociology.*

THOMSEN, Mary Michele
Escambia HS; Pensacola, FL; Most Out; *Pensacola Jr Col.*

THOMSON, Danie Marie
Owyhee HS; Owyhee, NV (4-25) Pres, FBLA; Pres, FHA; GS; Mjrte; SC; Bkbl; Tr; Hon Prog; Pres A; Type A; *Bus.*

THOMSON, David B
Los Alamos HS; Los Alamos, NM (15%-400) Band; Chor; NHS; Orch; Tnns; Tr; Hist A; Sinfoniette; Church Mission Coun; Bus Mgr, Yth Employment Service; VP, Tres, As For Retarded Citizens; *Eng.*

THOMSON, Janice Lynn
John Marshall HS; San Antonio, TX (45-715) Band; Chor; VP, Drama; FTA; Pres, ARC; VP, Thes; COM; Hist A; Hon Prog; ARC A; Drama A; Sch Service A; Band As; *Tex Lutheran Col; Psych.*

THOMSON, Karen Marie
Gaithersburg Sr HS; Gaithersburg, MD (40-385) Ann; Band; Chor; Cpt, Tr; Pres A; Yth Fel; Head, Acolyte-Ascension; MCR Rep; *Anderson Col; Nurs.*

THOMSON, Steven Eugene
Estes Park HS; Estes Park, CO (1-119) Co-Ch, Band; NHS; Orch; Var C; Bsbl; JV, Bkbl; Golf; COM; Citz A; *U of Colo; Aeronautical Engr.*

THORDARSON, JoAnn Evelyn
Post Falls HS; Post Falls, ID (2-154) Chldr; Chor; GS; SC; Co-Cpt, Bkbl; Tr; Hon Prog; Sal; Spch A; Pres, GAA; Drill Tm; Vlbl; *Pacific Lutheran U; Archt.*

THORELL, Mike Alan
Loomis Pub HS; Loomis, NE (5-28) Band; Chor; Order/Arrow; ARC; SC; VP, Var C; Bsbl; MVP, Bkbl; Ftbl; Tr; Alg A; COM; Citz A; Hon Prog; Math A; Most Out; Order/Arrow A; Pres A; ARC A; All Conf, All Area Ftbl; All Conf Bkbl.

THOREN, Carolyn Kay
New Berlin HS; New Berlin, WI (98-315) Band; Chor; ARC; Ski C; Swim; Phy A; Flag Corp; *U of Minn; Dental Hygiene.*

THOREN, Todd Brian
New Berlin HS; New Bevlin, WI (230-318) Chor; *Waukesha Tech Col; Auto-Mech.*

THORESON, Gloriann Mae
Blaine Sr HS; Blaine, MN; Band; Ed, Sch P; Bkbl; Pres A; Cpt, Vlbl; Fin, Pres A; *Superior St; Phys Ed.*

THORESON, Joan Marie
Cottage Grove HS; Cottage Grove, OR (33-260) Band; Chor; SC; Thes; VP, Jr Cl; Bkbl; Tr; HCt; Dance Tm; Swing Choir; *Audiology.*

THORINGTON, Debra Sue
Creston HS; Grand Rapids, MI (33%-400) Band; Lat C; DARGCA; ROTC A; ROTC Drill Tm; NRA Marksman; ROTC Outst Cadet; *Baptist Bible Col; Bible.*

THORN, Cynthia Lynn
F D Roosevelt HS; Hyde Park, NY; VP, 4H; 4H A; S-T, 4-H C.

THORN, Dean Dewey
Fred C Beyer HS; Modesto, CA (20%-800) Chess C; Hmrm; Golf; Tnns; Crisco A; Math A; *Cal Poly; Archt.*

THORN, Debbie Lynn
Fred C Beyer HS; Modesto, CA (35%-600) Chor; CSF; Co-Ch.

THORN, Mark Grayson
Zion-Benton Township HS; Zion, IL; Ger C; NHS; Order/Arrow; Ski C; SC; JV, Golf; JV, Tnns; COM; Hon Prog; NEDT; Yth Foundation; Eagle Sct; Soc Stu A; Eng A; Pres, Yth Fel.

THORNBURG, Theresa Dawn
Muskogee HS; Muskogee, OK (36-575) Ann; Cum Laude Soc; FBLA; Tres, Hmrm; NHS; ARC; SC; Hist A; Hon Prog; Sci A; Shorthand A; Bus Eng A; Okla Hon Soc; *Okla St U.*

THORNE, Carla Elizabeth
Wendell Phillips HS; Chicago, IL (12-752) A Cap Choir; Chem C; Chor; Drama; Fr C; Up Bound; Sci A; Ldrship A; *Bradley U; Med.*

THORNE, Denise Marie
Cold Spring Harbor HS; Cold Spring Harbor, NY (5-190) Drama; Rainbow; Mgr, Bkbl; Mgr, Sftbl; Hon Prog; Pep C; Bowl Tm; HR; *Nurs.*

THORNE, Jeffrey Alan
Mannington HS; Mannington, WV (15-109) BS; Pres, FFA; Var C; Ftbl; Elk A; WW; George Sharp A; FFA As.

THORNE, Nancy Ann
Wellston HS; Wellston, OH (12-135) NHS; Phys C; Rainbow; Tres, Tri-HiY; Alg A; Hist A; Ntl Achv Schol; Rotary A; Yth Fel; *Rio Grande U; Med Lab Tech.*

THORNE, Rhonda Louise
Santa Monica HS; Santa Monica, CA; CSF; COM; Spch A; 3rd Pl, Shakespearian Festival; *Point Loma Col; Theology.*

THORNE, Veronica Deen
Mercy HS; San Francisco, CA; Pres, Hmrm; Span C; SC; *San Francisco St U; Surgical Nurs.*

THORNE, William Douglas
Elkhart Mem HS; Elkhart, IN (100-460) Ed, Ann; Band; Ed, Lit Mag; Orch; Ed, Sch P; Journ A; Q&S A; Pres Classroom; *Hist.*

THORNHILL, Earlene Rose
Buchanan HS; Troy, MO (27-184) Chor; Secy, FHA; FTA; VP, 4H; NHS; Span C; Reg Schol; Cpt, Drill Tm; Barnwarming Qn, FFA; SC Rep; Church Pianist; *NE Mo St U; Med Secy.*

THORNHILL, Susan Lynn
Elkins HS; Elkins, WV (2-238) Pres, FFA; GS; NHS; Rainbow; Sci C; Pres, SC; Var C; VP, Jr Cl; Tnns; Amer Leg A; Chamber of Comm A; Citz A; DARGCA; 4H A; Most Out; Sal; Sci A; Spch A; Swtht; Yth Fel; Best Shorthand Stu; Most Outst FFA' ER; Rainbow Grand Off; *WV at Wesleyan; Special Ed.*

THORNSBURY, Brenda
Virgie HS; Virgie, KY; Sci C; Pres, Soph Cl; Bkbl; COM; Cl Fav; Swtht; *Pikeville Col; Math.*

THORNSBURY, Sandy
Virgie HS; Virgie, KY; BC; NHS; Tr; COM; Citz A; Hon Prog; *Pikeville Col; Nurs.*

THORNTON, Allison Brent
Bryan Adams HS; Dallas, TX (263-750) Chor; Ensm; Handbell Ensm; Church Yth Choir; Tahos C; *Tarrent Co Jr Col; Dental Hygiene.*

THORNTON, B W
Kermit HS; Kermit, WV (1-50) Band; VP, Span C; Bsbl; Bio A; Yth Fel; *W Va U; Forestry.*

THORNTON, Bryan Stanley
Independence HS; Independence, MS (10%-72) Ann; BC; Pres, FFA; Bsbl; Bkbl; Ftbl; Tr; *Northwest Jr Col; Agr.*

THORNTON, Carolyn Renee
Princeton HS; Princeton, NC (4-80) BC; FHA; Pres, 4H; NHS; JV, Bsbl; 4H A; MLS; PA Sunday Sch; Co Win Sewing; Co Win Art; *Cosmetology.*

THORNTON, Charles Harold
Indian Springs Acad; Jackson, GA; Pres, Key C; Pres, SC; *Gordon Jr Col; Bus Adm.*

THORNTON, Clayton Lenhart
Summerville HS; Summerville, SC; Band; Hmrm; Sci C; Fin, Bsbl; Bkbl; Ftbl; Swim; Tnns; ROTC A; Highest Batting Avg, Bsbl; *Clemson U; Engr.*

THORNTON, David Marshall
Overton HS; Memphis, TN (83-243) Band; Secy, Thes; COM; 1st Pl, Solo & Ensm; *Guilford Tech Inst; Automotive Mech.*

THORNTON, Deita Renee
Whitley Co HS; Williamsburg, KY; BC; Fr C; FHA; ARC; Opt A; *Cumberland Col; Nurs.*

THORNTON, Donna Nell
Copiah Acad; Gallman, MS; BC; Ensm; Sci C; Y-Tns; Most Intellectual; Church Pianist; *Miss Col; Church Mus.*

THORNTON, Gena Lynn
Athens HS; Athens, AL; FBLA; Hmrm; *Calhoun Comm Col; Denistry.*

THORNTON, Jeanie Lynn
Jones Co HS; Gray, GA (10%-250) Ann; BC; JV, Chldr; Hmrm; SC; Swtht.

THORNTON, Jennifer Kaye
Nathan Hale HS; Tulsa, OK (10%-700) NHS; COM; Hist A; Type A; Explorers; Acad Achv A; *Okla St U; Police Sci.*

THORNTON, Jennifer Kim
Rochelle Township HS; Rochelle, IL; Chor; Art A; *Kishwaukee Col; Art.*

THORNTON, Jerome Albert
Everman HS; Everman, TX (2-300) A-Ed, Ann; Bus C; Chor; InterClub Coun; Pres, Key C; Sch P; Co-Cpt, Ftbl; Sftbl; Kiwanis A; Church A's; BSct; Ftbl A; *N Tex St Col; Bus Adm.*

THORNTON, Leslie Anne
Arapahoe HS; Littleton, CO (42-583) Band; GS; Key C; Mjrte; Swtht; Rotary Exchange Stu.

THORNTON, Peggy Ellen
Empire HS; Duncan, OK (35%-30) Chldr; FHA; 4H; Rainbow; JV, Bkbl; 'E' A; VP, Soph Cl; Ann Qn Cand; *Okla St U; Interior Decorating.*

THORNTON, Rebecca Ruth
Shawnee Mission S HS; Johnson Co, KS; Dbte Tm; Fr C; ARC; Alg A; Math A; Sci A; *Med.*

THORNTON, Richard Neil
Aloha HS; Aloha, OR (15%-500) Cpt, Bkbl; *Pacific U; Phys Therapy.*

THORNTON, Teresa Faye
Monroe Area Comprehensive HS; Monroe, GA (50-250) Anchor C; 4H.

THORNTON, Vanesa Lynne
Evans HS; Orlando, FL; A Cap Choir; Band; Madrigal; Bkbl; Tr; Pres, Church Chor; Handbell Choir; Church SC; King's Daughters Ensm; Outst Camper; Bus Ministry; *Baylor U; Mus.*

THORNTON, Vicki Lynn
Lord Botetourt HS; Daleville, VA (13-163) Cpt, Chldr; GS; NHS; VP, Sr Cl; Scorer, Wrest; Outst Chldr As; *Madison Col; Legal Asst.*

**THOROUGHGOOD,
Miles Gerrold**
Wm Penn HS; Philadelphia, PA (45-1500) Drama; Pres, Hmrm; InterAct C; SC; COM; Type A; Val; Edelson A; *Advertisement.*

THORP, Rebecca Jean
Carpio HS; Carpio, ND (2-23) Band; Chor; Ensm; GS; 4H; NHS; A-Ed, Sch P; Bkbl; Tr; Hon Prog; VP, Church Yth Fel; *Phys Therapy.*

THORPE, Carol Ann
Pine Plains HS; Pine Plains, NY; JV, Chldr; Chor; Sch P; Var C; Secy, Sr Cl; Secy, Jr Cl; Bkbl; Mgr, Ftbl; Hockey; Sftbl; Tnns; Mgr, Tr; Bowl A; *Colorado Col; Bus.*

THORPE, Elizabeth Ann
Rocky Mount Acad; Rocky Mount, NC; Chor; Drama; Vlbl; Service to Sch A; *NC St U; Obstetrician.*

THORPE, Jerry Dean
Le Mars Comm HS; LeMars, IA (30-200) Tr; Co-Cpt, Wrest; Western Iowa Tech; Elec.

THORPE, Laura Elaine
Mt Vernon HS; Mt Vernon, OH; A Cap Choir; Chor; Ch, Dbte Tm; Ch, Drama; Spch C; SC; Swim; Tr; Ath A; Hon Mus & Spch; Mt Vernon Nazarene Col; Spch.

THORPE, Tyrone
Sol C Johnson HS; Thunderbolt, GA; Hmrm; Rptr, Sch P; Co-Cpt, Bsbl; Bbbl; Cpt, Ftbl; Fla A&M U.

THORSON, Karin Marie
Convent of Sacred Heart; Bellevue, WA (8-50) Ann; Semi-Fin, Chldr; Drama; Fr C; NHS; Alg A; Math A; Most Out; Fr A; Religion A; U of Wash; Engr.

THORSON, Kathy Gwen
Luverne HS; Luverne, MN (43-140) Cpt, Bkbl; Sftbl; All Conf, Bkbl; Vlbl; SW St Col; Bus.

THORSTENSON, Brian John
Cottage Grove HS; Cottage Grove, OR (7-260) AFS; Band; NHS; Spch C; VP, SC; S-T, Thes; Eng A; LCC; Theatre.

THORSTENSON, Janet Ruth
Cottage Grove HS; Cottage Grove, OR (10-300) AFS; Band; Chor; Drama; Span C; Thes; Dance.

THORSTENSON, Rene Aline
Century HS; Bismarck, ND (17-192) Chor; NHS; ARC; Pres, SC; JV, Tnns; DARGCA; Bismarck Jr Col; Psych.

THRASH, Andrea Leigh
Hope HS; Hope, AR (10-222) Band; BC; FTA; Ger C; Nike C; Ntl Mus Guild; All Religion Clinic; Yth Coun; Ouachita Baptist U.

THRASH, Jonna Sue
Keyes HS; Keyes, OK; Chldr; SC; Var C; Bkbl; Tr; H of F; Panhandle St Col; Bus.

THRASH, Katherine Eileen
Sweet Home HS; Sweet Home, OR (6-193) Band; Hmrm; NHS; SC; Bsbl; Elk A; Lion A; Yth Fel; Industrial Arts A; Chemeketa Comm Col; Law Enforcement.

THRASH, Keith Edward
Ouachita Parish HS; Monroe, LA; Band; Ensm; Pres, Sci C; Bsbl; Bkbl; Band A; La Tech U; Engr.

THRASHER, David Lloyd
Southside HS; Gadsden, AL (1-218) BC; Sci C; JV, Bkbl; Cl Fav; Gov Honor Prog; Hist A; Math A; Most Out; Sci A; Star Student; Auburn U; Engr.

THRASHER, Gregory Allen
Sturgis HS; Sturgis, MI; Demolay; Key C; Bkbl; Tr.

THRASHER, Martha Ruth
Sam Houston HS; Arlington, TX; A Cap Choir; Ensm; Sci A; Howard Payne U; Phys Therapy.

THREATT, Loretta Francine
Classen HS; Oklahoma City, OK; Chldr; FBLA; Hmrm; SC; VP, Jr Cl; SouthWestern Col; Archt.

THREATT, Sonya Belinda
Crenshaw HS; Los Angeles, CA; Drama; Hmrm; SC; Sftbl; Cpt, Tnns; Alg A; Bio A; COM; Cl Fav; HKg; HQn; HCt; Hon Prog; Journ A; Math A; MLS; Most Out; PTA A; Phy A; Pres A; ARC A; Sci A; Spch A; Star Student; St Scholar; Swtht; Type A; W Los Angeles Col; Bus Ed.

THREET, Toby Alaska
Moorcroft HS; Moorcroft, WY (1-26) Rptr, FTA; VP, NHS; Ed, Sch P; Pres, Span C; Rptr, SC; Pres, Var C; Tres, Jr Cl; Tres, Soph Cl; Mgr, Bkbl; Tr; Alg A; Bio A; COM; Chem A; Citz A; Hist A; Math A; MLS; NMF; Sci A; Spch A; Type A; Val; F-Ed, Sch Paper; Prom Kg; WW; Tr Ltr; Presidential School; Pres, Lib C; Brigham Young U; Pre Law.

THRELFALL, Jimmie Paul
Grace Baptist HS; Decatur, AL (5-10) Math C; Pres, NHS; Co-Ed, Sch P; Sci C; Ftbl; B Crocker A; Christian Character A; Bob Jones U; Bus.

THRELKEL, Kathryn Walker
Winter Haven HS; Winter Haven, FL (5%-1000) Anchor C; Fr C; Hist A; Math A; Sci A; GSet As; Bio.

THRESHER, Marva Jo
Central HS; Tulsa, OK; Band; Chor; Sch P; Sci C; COM; Hon Prog; Band A; HR; Pep C; Tulsa Jr Col; Computer.

THRIFT, Juanita Mae
S Carroll HS; Sykesville, MD (150-371) Hmrm; Jr Miss Pagent; Hockey; Tr; Bus Adm.

THRIFT, Walter Everett
S Carroll HS; Sykesville, MD (250-422) Chess C; 4H; JV, Ftbl; MVP, Wrest; Sergeant, Boy's Brigade; Plumber.

THROCKMORTON, Douglas Carl
Hastings Sr HS; Hastings, NE (15-325) Chor; Madrigal; Orch; Order/Arrow; JV, Cr-Ctry; Hon Prog; Regent Schol; Hastings Col; Pre-Med.

THROCKMORTON, Renet DeLea
Harding HS; Marion, OH (17-600) A Cap Choir; Chor; Drama; Lit Mag; Sch P; Span C; COM; 4H A; Sci A; Qn, Church Banquet; Secy, Church Yth; Tn Inst of Evangelism; Arlington Baptist Col; Religion.

THROWER, Cynthia Diane
Samuel Wolfson Sr HS; Jacksonville, FL; Band; Chor; Ensm; Fr C; Sch P; Fr C; Soph & Jr Girls C; Vol Aide; Comm Dance Guilds; Ballet Guild; Chrch Yth Actv; March Band As; Ecol C; Flute Trio As; Symp Band; FSU; Mus.

THROWER, Stacy Rene
Putnam City HS; Oklahoma City, OK; DECA; Okla St U; Med.

THUMBERGER, Greg Mathew
Spring Valley HS; Centerville, OH; Bsbl; Bkbl; Ftbl; Sftbl.

THUMMEL, Hans Peter
Niles N HS; Skokie, IL (10%-422) Soccer; COM; NEDT; Gym; Engr.

THURMAN, Bradley Joe
Enid HS; Enid, OK (5%-700) Hmrm; SC; Stage Crew; Okla St U.

THURMAN, Rachel Anne
Chapel Hill HS; Tyler, TX (25-190) Band; Ensm; Pres, FHA; FTA; Math C; Sci C; Span C; JV, Sftbl; Type A; Yth Fel; Top Tn of Amer; E Tex St U; Computer Sci.

THURMAN, Rhonda Michele
Catoosa HS; Catoosa, OK; Chor; Dbte Tm; FHA; 4H; NFL; Rainbow; Thes; Journ A; Spch A; Best Actress, Thespians; Fin, Regional & St Spch Tourn; Oral Roberts U; Theology.

THURMOND, Brent Xavier
Wakulla HS; Medart, FL; Ann; NHS; Mgr, Bkbl; JV, Ftbl; Tr; VofDEM; Yth Appreciation A.

THUROW, Lee Robert
Oconomowoc Sr HS; Oconomowoc, WI (80-530) Chor; Bkbl; Ftbl; MIP, Ftbl; HS Swing Choir; Bus.

THURSTON, Andrea Lynn
Central HS; Minneapolis, MN (32-400) Bus C; Cpt, Chldr; Secy, Chor; MVP, Drama; Ensm; 4H; Ed, Sch P; Secy, SC; Tres; Secy, Soph Cl; Bkbl; Tr; Beauty; HCt; Hon Prog; JA A; Most Out; Pres A; Yth Fel; Gym; Vol A; 1st Run-Up, Miss Mn Teenage Pageant; Laubach Lit Coun; City & Regional Gym Meets; Med Engr.

THURSTON, Debra Kay
Hillsboro HS; Hillsboro, KS; Chor; Dbte Tm; Drama; FHA; GS; 4H; Pres, NFL; Secy, SC; Spch A; Keyetts; UMYF; Lettered, Debate; NFL Degree of Excellence; Emporia St; Ed.

THURSTON, Ronda Kaye
Gainesville HS; Gainesville, TX; Band; Fr C; FTA; Rainbow; Flag Corps A; Biol.

THUSS, Robert Wilkey
The Westminster Sch; Atlanta, GA (37-99) Ger C; JV, Bkbl; Tr; Med.

THWAITES, George Alan Jr
Narrows HS; Narrows, VA; Band; Demolay; Fr C; JV, Ftbl; Tr.

THWEATT, Ray
Parkland HS; El Paso, TX (1-250) Chem C; Cum Laude Soc; FTA; Lat C; Math C; NHS; Sci C; Spch C; SC; Alg A; Aux Lat; Bio A; Chem A; Hist A; Hon Prog; Magna Cum Laude; Math A; Phy A; ROTC A; Sci A; Val; U of Tex; Chem.

TIBBETS, Carol E
John F Kennedy HS; Fremont, CA (75-500) Pepperdine U; Ed.

TIBBETS, Mike Neil
Gainesville HS; Gainesville, TX (8%-237) Band; Rptr, 4H; 4H A; NEDT; Ceramic A; Baylor U; Conservation.

TIBBETTS, Richard Philip
Boca Ciega HS; St Petersburg, FL (75-700) NHS; Ftbl; Co-Cpt, Soccer; Hon Prog; U of Fla; Med.

TIBBITS, Sheryl Ruth
Bruce HS; Bruce, WI (2-67) Band; FFA; 4H; Pres, Span C; Tr; Amer Leg A; Cl Fav; MLS; Sal; UW-EAU Claire; Nurs.

TICE, Jodi Rane
St Joseph Acad; St Augustine, FL (7-52) Ann; Jr Miss Pagent; NHS; Co-Ed, Sch P; VP, Sr Cl; Secy, Jr Cl; Tnns; COM; Elk A; Journ A; Spch A; VP, Yth Fel; Prom Qn; WW; Most Schol, Jr Miss Pageant; U of Fla; Law.

TICE, Laura Jean
Kingsway Regional HS; Swedesboro, NJ (10-136) Chor; Key C; Madrigal; NHS; Tres, Rainbow; Rptr, Sch P; NEDT; U of Wisc; Acct.

TICE, William Dean
Heidelberg American HS; Heidelberg, GERMANY (20-170) Band; Math C; VP, NHS; Ski C; Span C; Mgr, Bkbl; Cr-Ctry; Hist A; MLS; Sci A; Duke U; Pre-Med.

TICE, Willis Lourene
Miami Killian Sr HS; Miami, FL (425-1100) Chor; Bkbl; Sftbl; JA A; Pres A; Sportsmanship A; Ldrship A; Eckerd Col; Nurs.

TICHENOR, Carmen Kelly
Wheaton R-III HS; Wheaton, MO (9-31) Band; Cpt, Chldr; FHA; 4H; Rainbow; Bkbl; Golf; Sftbl; Tr; Cl Fav; 4H A; HQn; MLS; Swtht.

TICKLE, Linda Marie
Wm J Woodham HS; Pensacola, FL (21-530) Pres, BC; VP, CYO; InterClub Coun; Lat C; Math C; Mu Alpha Theta; COM; Russian C; Lang, Phys Ed, A's; Providence St U; Nurs.

TICKLE, Sharon Ann
Bethany HS; Reidsville, NC (2-60) Ann; BC; Fr C; Math C; Monogram; HCt; NEDT; Marshal; Miss BHS; NC St U; Math.

TIDRICK, Lee Edwin
Ilwaco HS; Ilwaco, WA; Lit Mag; Var C; Wrest; Wrest; Wash St U; Bus Mgt.

TIDWELL, Blanche Kay
Dothan HS; Dothan, AL (10%-600) JV, Chldr; FTA; Thes; Sftbl; COM; Pres A; Gym Tm; Ltr, Boy's C, Vlbl, A's; George C Wallace Col; Phys Ed.

TIDWELL, Carroll Belinda
Tuscaloosa HS; Tuscaloosa, AL (10%-450) Band; Hmrm; Lat C; Mu Alpha Theta; 1st Pl, Dist & St Social Stu Fair; 3rd Pl, Sch Sci Fair; U of Ala; Nurs.

TIDWELL, Richard John
Chaparral HS; Las Vegas, NV (144-643) BS; Var C; Co-Cpt, Soccer; Yth Fel; WW; UNLV; Archt.

TIEDE, Charles Eugene
Midwest City HS; Midwest City, OK (38-560) Demolay; Hmrm; VP, Lat C; NHS; Ed, Sch P; SC; JV, Bkbl; Ftbl; Tr; Citz A; Hist A; Hon Prog; Most Out; Spch A; Pres, UMYF; Jr Executive; Chem Engr.

TIEFENAUER, Steven Allen
North Co R-I HS; Desloge, MO (33%-200) Chor; Var C; Arch; JV, Bkbl; Cpt, Cr-Ctry; Tr; Citz A; Yth Coun; Auxiliary Fire Dept; Mineral Area Jr Col; Phys Ed.

TIEMANN, Judith Ann
Litchfield Sr HS; Litchfield, IL (4-153) Chor; Ensm; Span C; Bkbl; Hon Prog; VFW A; Chor Accompanist; GAA; HR.

TIEMANN, Tamara Jean
Salina HS S; Salina, KS (13-367) Band; Dbte Tm; Rptr, 4H; Parl, 4-H C; Kans St U; Dietetics.

TIERNEY, Patrick Thomas
Bishop Klonowski HS; Scranton, PA (7-110) NHS; Amer Leg A; COM; Hon Prog; Penn St U; Engr.

TIERNEY, Tresa Ann
Hillsboro Sr HS; Hillsboro, OR; CYO; Hmrm; Mgr, Soccer; Swim; JV, Tr; Church Folk Group; Portland Comm Col; Gen.

TIESWORTH, Kathy Mary
Winston Churchill HS; Livonia, MI (50%-650) Band; Chor; Hmrm; Sch P; VP, SC; Sftbl; Tr; Citz A; JA A; Opt A; Service A; Stu Gov A; Wayne St U; Ed.

TIETJEN, Cheryl Ann
Coatesville Area Sr HS; Coatesville, PA (48-600) Chor; 4H; Hmrm; Bkbl; Journ A; Hon Soc; Juniata Col.

TIGER, Donald Henry
Attica Jr Sr HS; Attica, IN (6-98) BS; Ger C; Ntl Yth Conf; Sci C; Pres, SC; Var C; Tres, Jr Cl; Mgr, Bsbl; Mgr, Bkbl; Mgr, Ftbl; Golf; Mgr, Tr; Elk A; Most Outst; Stu Coun; World Affairs Inst; Purdue U; Aeronautical Engr.

TIGHE, Maureen Ann
Kolbe-Cathedral HS; Bridgeport, CT; AFS; Ed, Ann; Co-Cpt, Chldr; S-T, Fr C; Secy, NHS; A-Ed, Sch P; Secy, Jr Cl; Journ A; Fr A; Soc of Women Engr, A; Excellence-Math & Sci A; U of Bridgeport; Med Technology.

TIGRETT, Tauni Denise
Franklin Heights HS; Columbus, OH (145-248) Chor; Tr; Drill Tm; Statistician, Tr; Southwestern Bible Col; Mus.

TILFORD, John Michael
Calumet Baptist HS; Griffeth, IN (8-45) Band; Chess C; 4H; Sci C; Co-Cpt, Bkbl; Soccer; Cedarville Col; Sci.

TILGHMAN, Hugh Francis
Eastern HS; Washington, DC (14-604) NHS; Bkbl; Alg A; Woodward Found; HR; Bkbl Ltr; Western Md Col; Bus.

TILL, William Jeffery
E Union Acad; Marion, LA (1-15) F-Ed, Ann; BS; Fin, Lit Ral; VP, NHS; Rptr, Sch P; Bkbl; Alg A; Amer Leg A; Bio A; Chem A; Cl Fav; Hist A; Math A; MLS; Sci A; Val; Eng A; PA; La Tech U; Acct.

TILLACK, Robert Harris
Millbrook HS; Raleigh, NC (10%-550) Chor; Ftbl; Tr; ARC A; Davidson Col; Med.

TILLAPAUGH, David Roy
James Madison HS; Vienna, VA (6-490) BS; NHS; Sci C; Sftbl; ROTC A; U of NC at Chapel Hill; Bio.

TILLAPAUGH, Susan Gail
James Madison HS; Vienna, VA (10-500) Drama; Sci C; Span C; JV, Bkbl; JV, Sftbl; Swim; Tnns; Tr; Pres A; Sci A; Yth Fel; Sftbl A; Pres Phys Fitness As; Tnns A; Bkbl; VPI; Bio.

TILLEN, Victoria Jane
Marianapolis Prep Sch; Thompson, CT; Chor; Drama; 4H; Co-Ed, Lit Mag; Madrigal; Secy, NHS; F-Ed, Sch P; Ski C; Secy, SC; JV, Swim; JV, Tnns; Hon Prog; NEDT; Yth Fel; Dance Tm; Pres, Yth Group; Director, Jr Choir; U of Conn; Eng.

TILLER, Eddie Lee
Dilce Combs Mem HS; Jeff, KY (5-84) Band; VP, BC; Chem C; Tres, Drama; 4H; F-Ed, Sch P; Sci C; Tres, Spch C; Tres, Thes; Co-Cpt, Bsbl; Bkbl; 4H A; Hon Prog; Spch A; Co- pres, Drama C; Most Talented; Co- pres, Spch C; Co- pres, Thespians; Drama A; Eastern U; Biol.

TILLEY, Janice Yvonne
Lake Charles HS; Lake Charles, LA; Semi-Fin, Lit Ral; Rptr, Lit Mag; Ed, Sch P; Span C; Tri-HiY; Citz A; La Col; Journ.

TILLEY, Jill
Arkadelphia HS; Arkadelphia, AR (1-165) Co-Ed, Ann; GS; Hmrm; NHS; Pres, SC; VP, Soph Cl; HCt; Journ A; Kiwanis A; Val; Boys, Girls Nation; Jr Eng A; Pre-Law.

TILLMAN, Earlene Jeanette
Lafayette HS; St Joseph, MO; Chldr; Hmrm; Tres, SC; Y-Tns; Citz A; Pres A.

TILLMAN, James Robert
W Aurora HS; Aurora, IL; Span C; MVP, Bkbl; Co-Cpt, Ftbl; Tr; COM; MLS; Yth Fel; Cpt, Bkbl; Most Ath.

TILLMAN, Laura Adams
Page HS; Greensboro, NC (5%-700) F-Ed, Ann; Hmrm; Lat C; NHS; SC; Secy, Jr Cl; Wake Forest U; Journ.

TILLMAN, Mark Edward
Sooner HS; Bartlesville, OK (7-290) Tres, CYO; Chess C; Hmrm; Lat C; NHS; VP, Order/Arrow; ARC; Ski C; COM; Citz A; Hon Prog; Order/Arrow A; ARC A; Summa Cum Laude; U of Mo at Rolla; Geological Engr.

TILLMAN, Patricia Ann
Suncoast HS; Rivier Beach, FL; FHA; Sci C; Palm Beach Jr Col; General Bus.

TILLMAN, Robert Jeffery
Mena HS; Mena, AR (20%-147) Pres, Soph Cl; Bkbl; Ftbl; U of Ark; Sci.

TILLMAN, Sandra Renee
Emerson Sr HS; Gary, IN (129-211) Chor; Orch; SC; COM; PTA A; ROTC A; Sci A; Schol Achv A; Ms Personality; Ind U; X-Ray Tech.

TILLMAN, Theresa June
Colerain Sr HS; Cincinnati, OH (183-630) St OEA; Tres, Yth Fel C; Fedder Strng Comp; Pres, Guild Grls; Ntl Assn F-T Adv of Colored People; Afro-Amer C; Pres, Sunshine Band; Ohio U at Athens; Bus Adm.

TILLY, Philip Reed
Doss HS; Louisville, KY; S-T, Chess C; Ger C; Rptr, Hmrm; Hrs; NHS; SC; Bio A; Hon Prog; Sci A; Geog A; Pres, Christian Yth Organization; U of Tex; Sci.

TILSTRA, Luanne Faith
Luverne Jr Sr HS; Luverne, MN (4-162) A Cap Choir; S-T, FHA; Ger C; Madrigal; NFL; A-Ed, Sch P; Spch C; Pres A; Spch A; Central Col; Med.

TIMAEUS, Rachel Kathleen
Port Neches-Groves HS; Port Neches, TX; Band; Ensm; FHA; NHS; Co-Ed, Sch P; COM; Lion's C Swtht; Asst Sunday Sch Teacher; Lamar U; Nurs.

TIMKO, Karen Sue
Bridgeport HS; Bridgeport, OH (8-108) Ann; Bus C; VP, FHA; Semi-Fin, GS; NHS; Tres, SC; Y-Tns; VP, Soph Cl; Cl Fav; H of F; HQn; Type A; Off Practice Service A.

TIMM, Harriet A
Clarke Central HS; Athens, GA; Drama; Ger C; Mjrte; Thes; Mgr, Soccer; B Crocker A; HS Soro Sec; Church Yth Coun; Church Admin Board; Northland Col; Game Mgt.

TIMM, Patricia Joan
Riverview HS; Sarasota, FL (55-700) Fr C; Inter-Club Coun; NHS; Pres, Tri-HiY; Secy, Sr Cl; Secy, Jr Cl; I Dare You Ldrship A; Paramed C; Nom, GS; Wittiest; Church; Deacon; Cover Design, Sch Directory; Tres, Keyettes; U of Fla; Med.

TIMMONS, Cathie Lynn
Grandview Heights HS; Columbus, OH (4-175) Ann; Chor; Ensm; FTA; Sch Achieve Tm; Hon Prog; Rotary A; Sch Achv Tm; Church Deacon; Co- ed C; Outst Co Jr; Ohio St U; Elem Ed.

TIMMONS, David Eugene
Jefferson Forest HS; Forest, VA (27-150) Band; BC; BS; Ger C; Hmrm; Lat C; Orch; SC; Ftbl; COM; Most Outst Sr Band Member; Lynchburg Col; Bus Adm.

TIMMONS, David Selkirk
London HS; London, OH (1-187) Band; Chess C; Fr C; JV, Ftbl.

TIMMONS, Gary Allen
Grandview HS; Columbus, OH (11-129) Sch Achieve Tm; JV, Tnns; Yth Fel; Schol Banquet A; Eckard Col; Math.

TIMMONS, Gregory Benet
Temple HS; Temple, TX (10%-400) Cpt, Band; Math C; Orch; Sci C; Dist, Regional, Area, Bands; All St Band Cert; All St Solo & Ensm; Mus School.

TIMMONS, Gregory Earl
Riverview HS; Sarasota, FL (97-600) FBLA; Ftbl; Cl Fav; Dist FBLA Fashion Show; Mr FBLA; Fla A&M U; Bus Adm.

TIMMONS, Joy Lynn
Teays Valley HS; Ashville, OH (33%-225) NHS; VICA Achv; Opening Closing Tm; Ohio St U; Vet.

TIMMONS, Kay Charlotte
Lakeshore HS; College Park, GA (1-250) AFS; Anchor C; Ann; Band; Secy, BC; French NHS; Hmrm; InterClub Coun; Math C; VP, NHS; Orch; Bkbl; Mgr, Tr; B Crocker A; COM; DARGCA; MLS; Most Out; Co-Cpt, Drill Tm; Eng A; Ga Inst of Tech; Engr.

TIMMONS, Stephen Andrew
London HS; London, OH (4-96) Band; BS; Pres, Chess C; Lat C; NHS; Cr-Ctry; Tr; Hist A; Jr Chamber of Com A; Kiwanis A; U o-t South; Hist.

TIMMONS, Timothy Nolen
Choctawhatchee HS; Fort Walton Beach, FL; SC; Hon Art C; Panama City Jr Col; Med.

TIMMS, Jennifer Sue
Odessa-Montour Central Sch; Odessa, NY (1-120) Band; Chor; Ensm; Fr C; Semi-Fin, GS; Secy, 4H; NHS; Orch; Sch P; 4H A; Regent Schol; Sch Board A; Layout Ed & Ed-In-Chief, Yrbk; Area All St Orch; Church Organist.

TIMMS, Sonja Machelle
Calhoun HS; Calhoun, GA (10%-250) Band; Cpt, Chldr; 4H; NHS; Span C; Tri-HiY; 4H A; Outst Chldr; Berry Col; Phys Therapy.

TIMON, Donna Marie
Leavenworth Sr HS; Leavenworth, KS; Yth Fel; New Way Singers, Church; Bradford Col; Social Worker.

TIMON, Esther May
Leavenworth Sr HS; Leavenworth, KS; Yth Fel; New Way Singers, Church; Bradford Col; Law.

TIMPE, Janice Elizabeth
Quincy Sr HS I; Quincy, IL (30-714) Cpt, Chldr; Chor; Ensm; Hmrm; Orch; SC; HR; Quincy Col; Bus.

TIMPE, Mark Theodore
Quincy Notre Dame HS; Quincy, IL; Band; Ger C; Ch, Key C; VP, NHS; Tnns; Mgr, Wrest; US Marines Outst Musicianship A; St Louis U; Bus Adm.

TIMS, Laura Elaine
Oak Ridge Sr HS; Orlando, FL (60-785) Band; NHS; Church Yth Choir; Span, Band, Church Mus A's; Band Medals; Valenica Jr Col; Math.

TINAPP, Barton Richard
Central HS; LaCrosse, WI; A Cap Choir; Chor; Drama; Hmrm; VP, SC; Tnns; 1 Rating, St Vocal; Ntl Mus Clinic; Fin, Ntl Assoc Teachers St Vocal; Most Outst, Actor, Singr, Dancer A; U of Colo; Mus.

TINCHER, Markus L
Somerset HS; Somerset, KY; Chor; Drama; Bsbl; Mgr, Bkbl; JV, Ftbl; Tr; JV, Wrest; Citz A; Sports As; Warner Sou Col; Mus.

TINCHER, Tammy Gayle
Taft HS; Hamilton, OH; Chor; Secy, Sr Cl; Sftbl; Swim; Type A; Shorthand A; Miami U; Nurs.

TINDALL, Ann Lucille
Queen Anne HS; Seattle, WA (15%-500) Chor; Drama; Span C; Home Ec.

TINDALL, Julie Ann
Richardson HS; Richardson, TX (9-908) Secy, NHS; Tri-HiY; Ntl Merit Commended Stu; Scholastic Sweater Win; U of Tex at Austin; Eng.

TINDALL, Leslie Letitia
Tupelo HS; Tupelo, MS (36-359) Anchor C; Chor; NHS; U of Miss; Med.

TINDALL, Linda Lou
Fremont HS; Fremont, MI (75-247) Chor; FTA; 4H; Choir; Campership A for Sports; Camp Schol; Pres, Christ Ambassadors Group.

TING, Benjamin Chan
Ingraham HS; Seattle, WA (70-450) Chess C; Chor; Soccer; U of Wash; Computer Sci.

TINGEN, Julius Marvin
E Forsyth Sr HS; Kernersville, NC (161-687) Nashville Auto and Diesel Sch; Mech.

TINGLEY, Michelle Ivamarie
Galesburg Sr HS; Galesburg, IL (5-1698) GAA; Bible Quizzer; Pom Pon Girl; Pres, Nazarene Tn Fellowship; Art C; Olivet Nazarene Col.

TINIACOS, Zoy
Cristobal Jr Sr HS; Coco Solo, CANAL ZONE (6-130) Pres, Fr C; Pres, FNA; FTA; Span C; SC; Thes; COM; Agnes Scott Col; Microbiology.

TINIUS, Julie Ann
Norfolk Sr HS; Norfolk, NE (10%-360) Span C; JV, Tnns; 4H A; Math A; Type A; *U of Nebr; Med.*

TINIUS, Mike Scott
Norfolk Sr HS; Norfolk, NE (40%-360) Pres, 4H; JV, Bkbl; 4H A; *NE Nebr Tech Col; Draftsmans.*

TINKEL, Deanna Kay
Northrop HS; Fort Wayne, IN (148-671) Band; Chor; Drama; Ntl Yth Conf; Mus A; *Mus.*

TINKER, Donna Jean
Switzerland Co Jr Sr HS; Vevay, IN (1-108) Secy, Band; Chor; Drama; NHS; Span C; Sci A; Yth Fel; *Good Samaritan Sch of Nurs; Nurs.*

TINKEY, Judy Rose
Lincoln HS; Ellwood City, PA (1-266) Band; ARC; Span C; NEDT; Yth Fel; Church Choir; Asst Sunday Sch Teacher; Achv A.

TINKEY, Rebecca Ruth
Lincoln HS; Ellwood City, PA; BC; Chor; Drama; Tres, 4H; Tres, Hmrm; NHS; Span C; 4H A; *Psych.*

TINKLER, Matthew Allen
N Fulton HS; Atlanta, GA (24-176) BC; Model UN; Order/Arrow; JV, Bkbl; Tnns; JV, Tr; H of F; ROTC A; Swtht; *U of Ga; Bus Adm.*

TINNEY, Ledford Scott
Clay Co HS; Ashland, AL (16%-74) BC; Chor; Ensm; Hmrm; Order/Arrow; Sci C; SC; Var C; Bsbl; Ftbl; *UAB of Bham; Phar.*

TINNEY, Pamela Kay
Mangum HS; Mangum, OK (3-72) Co-Cpt, Chldr; Chem C; Chor; Drama; Ensm; FHA; 4H; NHS; ARC; VP, Jr Cl; Pres, Soph Cl; Bkbl; Swim; Tr; Alg A; Bio A; COM; Chem A; Citz A; 4H A; Hon Prog; Masonic A; Stu of Today; St Hon Soc; NHS; *Okla St U; Floral Design.*

TINSLEY, Bobby Paul
Swifton HS; Swifton, AR (2-25) Band; Rptr, BC; Secy, FFA; Rptr, SC; Pres, Soph Cl; Bsbl; Bkbl; Cl Fav; HCt; Hon Prog; *Vanderbilt U; Law.*

TINSLEY, Cynthia Curine
Daviess Co HS; Owensboro, KY (33-316) A Cap Choir; Chor; Ensm; Bio A; Cl Fav; All St, Quad-St, All Dist, Chor; *W Ky U; Med Tech.*

TINSLEY, Holly Ann
Morehead HS; Eden, NC; *Rockingham Comm Col; Nurs.*

TINSLEY, Kim Leslie
Swifton HS; Swifton, AR; Ed, Ann; Band; Pres, BC; Cpt, Chldr; Pres, FBLA; VP, FHA; VP, SC; Tres, Soph Cl; Cpt, Bkbl; Sftbl; Chem A; Cl Fav; HQn; HCt; Hon Prog; Sal; Swtht; Type A; Most Popular; *Bus.*

TINSLEY, Kimberley Helene
Saginaw HS; Saginaw, MI (12-400) Chor; S-T, NHS; ARC; Hon Prog; ARC A; Type A; *Saginaw Valley St U; Nurs.*

TINSLEY, Margaret Jeanette
Greensboro Day Sch; Greensboro, NC; Ann; Drama; Lit Mag; Rptr, Rptr, SC; Ski C; Tres, Soph Cl; Hockey; Soccer; Hon Prog.

TINSLEY, William Daniel
Mayme S Waggener HS; Louisville, KY; Chor; Drama; Span C; SC; Bkbl; Pres A; *U of Louisville; Pol Sci.*

TINTINALLI, Connie Elizabeth
Vincent Massey HS; Windsor, CANADA; *U of Windsor; Fine Arts.*

TINTORRI, Joan Marie
LaSalle-Peru Township HS; LaSalle, IL (9-500) CYO; Chor; SC; JV, Tnns; Amer Leg A; COM; Sci A; Spch A; High School League; *Med.*

TIPPETT, Faye
Soldan HS; St Louis, MO (88-568) A Cap Choir; Band; Chor; Drama; Ed, Lit Mag; SC; JA A; Choir Ltr; SC A; *St Louis U; Chem.*

TIPPETT, Mike Scott
Devilbiss HS; Toledo, OH (52-375) A Cap Choir; Chor; Ensm; Hmrm; Madrigal; Ntl Yth Conf; Swim; COM; Star Student; Yth Fel; 1st Pl A, Chinese; *Toledo U.*

TIPPETT, Paula Marie
Smithfield-Selma Sr HS; Smithfield, NC (17-355) Band; Tres, BC; Cpt, Chldr; Drama; Monogram; NHS; Pol Sci C; Rptr, Sch P; Secy, Sci C; *Appalachian St U; Biol.*

TIPPIN, Don Eldean
Decatur HS; Decatur, AR (1-30) Secy, NHS; SC; Cpt, Bsbl; Cpt, Bkbl; Cpt, Ftbl; Val; MVP, Bkbl; Span A; Biggest Flirt; All-Dist D End; *U of Ark; Pre-Law.*

TIPPINS, Elizabeth Marie
Claxton HS; Claxton, GA (25%-110) Secy, BC; Chess C; Fin, Hmrm; S-T, Lit Mag; NHS; Sch P; SC; Bkbl; Tnns; COM; HCt; *Ga Sou Col; Med Technology.*

TIPPS, Christine Ruth
Crystal Lake Comm HS; Crystal Lake, IL (97-505) A Cap Choir; Band; Chor; FTA; Madrigal; Mjrte; NHS; Orch; Cpt, Bsbl; Cpt, Bkbl; Cpt, Sftbl; Tnns; Coun of Teach A; Hon Prog; Ath o-t Wk; *U of Wis; Elem Phys Ed.*

TIPTON, Donna Dee
Madison Acad HS; Huntsville, AL (4-42) A Cap Choir; BC; Chor; Math C; NHS; Alg A; COM; Hon Prog; Math A; NEDT; Star Student; *Vanderbilt U; Med.*

TIPTON, Kimberly Celeste
Van-Cove HS; Cove, AR (1-28) Cpt, Chldr; Secy, FHA; 4H; Co-Ed, Sch P; SC; Secy, Jr Cl; Bkbl; Sci A; Val; Yth Fel.

TIPTON, Mike David
Lake Howell HS; Maitland, FL (95-380) Hmrm; Order/Arrow; VP, Sci C; Span C; JV, Ftbl; COM; Gov Honor Prog; *U of Fla; Agr.*

TIPTON, Sandy Kay
Winston Churchill HS; San Antonio, TX (481-800) SC; *Tex St Tech Inst; Dental Asst.*

TIPTON, Thomas Mark
Field Kindley HS; Coffeyville, KS (37-260) Dbte Tm; VP, Key C; NHS; Ftbl; Cpt, Wrest; Hon Prog; Kiwanis A; Rotary A; 'V' Schol A; *Coffeyville Jr Col; Bus.*

TIPTON, Wayne
Central HS; St Louis, MO (13-290) Ann; Tres, Chor; SC; VP, Sr Cl; Soccer; Tnns; Wrest; Citz A; MLS; Princip Spec Stu Adv Com; BSct Mer; Concert Choir; Triple 'A' C; Cornation Win; 2nd Cl BSct; HR; 3rd, Mo Industrial Arts Comp; *U of Dayton; Journ.*

TIRADO, Elizabeth
Channel Islands HS; Oxnard, CA (178-402) Secy, A Cap Choir; Chor; Drama; 4H; Hmrm; Secy, Madrigal; SC; *Ventura Col; Law.*

TISCHBEIN, Linda Diane
Quakertown Comm Sr HS; Quakertown, PA (27-360) Band; Pres, FBLA; Hmrm; NHS; SC; Asst Dir, Drama; HR; Woman's C Service A; *Maryland Med Secretarial Sch; Med Secy.*

TISCHLER, Sandra Fay
Coronado HS; Lubbock, TX; Chor; FHA; Ger C; Arch; Bkbl; Hist A; *Lubbock Christian Col; Secy.*

TISDALE, Tammy Lee
Midway HS; Waco, TX (50%-375) Cpt, FHA; VP, FTA; Hmrm; SC; JV, Sftbl; JV, Tnns; Beauty; *Tex U.*

TISDALE, Wanda
Williamsburgh HS; Andrews, SC (5-59) 4H; SC; VP, Jr Cl; VP, Soph Cl; Bkbl; Home Ec A; Stu Adv Comm; 1st Runner Up HQn; *Florence-Darlington Tech Col; Med Lab Tech.*

TISDALE, Weldon Louis
Booker T Washington HS; Tulsa, OK; 4H; Hmrm; Bkbl; COM; 4H A; JA A; K of C A; Most Out; Opt A; Spch A; *Bus Adm.*

TISH, Diana Lynn
Lebanon Union HS; Lebanon, OR; *Forestry.*

TISHMAN, Virginia Denese
Connellsville Area HS; Connellsville, PA; Secy, Hmrm; Span C; Tri-HiY; VP, UN Council; Most Out; Outst Health Asst; 3rd Pl, Essay; *Pitt U; Dental.*

TITTLE, Gary Lynn
Bellaire HS; Bellaire, TX (298-717) Hmrm; Order/Arrow; Order/Arrow A; ROTC A; Pres, Christian Stu Union; Eagle Sct; *U of Tex; Engr.*

TITUS, Angela Lynn
Ferndale Union HS; Ferndale, CA (11-76) CYO; Chldr; Chor; Rptr, 4H; Span C; SC; Secy, Jr Cl; VP, Soph Cl; CSF; 4H A; HCt; Qn Attndnt, Portuguese Celebration; *Sacramento City Col; Dental Asst.*

TITUS, Cynthia Ann
Morristown-Hamblen HS E; Morristown, TN (54-290) FHA; Y-Tns; *Bradford Col; Bus Adm.*

TJARKS, Richard Dwane
Saybrook-Arrowsmith HS; Saybrook, IL (33%-36) FFA; VP, SC; S-T, Var C; Pres, Soph Cl; Bkbl; Tr; *Ill Wesleyan U; Archt.*

TO'AILOA, Sa
Vista HS; Vista, CA (382-854).

TOALSON, Chris Edward
Mexico Sr HS; Mexico, MO (75%-250) Band; Fr C; Bsbl; *CMSU; Acct.*

TOBECK, Kevin Lee
Galt Joint Union HS; Galt, CA; Rptr, Hmrm; SC; Bsbl; Cpt, Bkbl; MVP, Ftbl; Tr; Bank Of Amer A; H of F; Hist A; Sal; Pres, Ltrmans Hon Soc; Ath o-t Yr; Principal's HR; CSF Life Member; Full Ath Schol, UOP; *U o-t Pacific.*

TOBEY, Brooks Carl
Sylvan Hills HS; N Little Rock, AR; Band; Chess C; Dbte Tm; Drama; NFL; NHS; COM; Math A; Sci A; *U of Ark; Law.*

TOBEY, Mary Beth
Manistee HS; Manistee, MI (138-210) Band; Chldr; SC; Tri-HiY; Tres, Soph Cl; Sftbl; *Central Mich U; Mental & Handicap Ed.*

TOBEY, Pamela Ann
Silsbee HS; Silsbee, TX (8-231) Chess C; Fr C; French NHS; JETS; NHS; Rainbow NS; P; COM; Hon Prog; NMF; *Tex Woman's U; Fashion Design.*

TOBIAS, Robin Lynn
Ingleside HS; Ingleside, TX (3-80) Ann; Band; Ensm; Rptr, NHS; Mgr, Bkbl; Tnns; Poet A; Type A; St Fin, Shorthand; Outst Eng & Bus Stu; Dist UIL Ready Writing & Typing; Voice of Democracy; *Del Mar Col; Art.*

TOBIN, Allison Ann
Breckinridge Co HS; Harned, KY (11-200) F-Ed, Ann; Chldr; FBLA; FTA; Math C; Mu Alpha Theta; NHS; F-Ed, Sch P; Tres, Soph Cl; Tnns; H of F; *U of Ky; Bus.*

TOBIN, John Richard
Natrona Co HS; Casper, WY (88-569) Rptr, Ann; BS; Chor; Dbte Tm; Drama; 4H; Hmrm; Tres, Key C; NFL; NHS; Tnns; 4H A; Spch A; VFW Orator Win; Elder, Church; Win, Odd Fellow, UN Pilgrimage; *Law.*

TOBIN, Timothy Alan
Canby HS; Canby, MN (15-126) A-Ed, Ann; SC; Var C; Pres, Sr Cl; Co-Cpt, Bkbl; Ftbl; Golf; Tr; *U of Minn; Law.*

TOBIN, Veronica Ann
Our Lady of Mercy Acad; Syosset, NY (17-144) Tres, Hmrm; NHS; SC; VP, Sr Cl; Spch A; VP, Tn Activity Prog; Pep Squad; Ch, Soc Comm; HR; Soc Action C; Ldrs C; Cpt, Spirit Tm; Folk Group; Teacher, Exceptional Children CCD; *Ariz St U; Pol Sci.*

TOCCI, Pam Sue
Apollo HS; Simi Valley, CA; Ann; Dbte Tm; Pres, Drama; FHA; Hmrm; Secy, Ski C; SC; Var C; Bsbl; Sftbl; Tnns; Hist A; Opt A; Q&S A; Star Student; Yth Fel; *Moorpark Col; Vet.*

TODD, Beebe Darlene
Dothan HS; Dothan, AL (5%-625) NHS; Sch P; SC; Sftbl; COM; MLS; Pres A; Stu Action For Ed; Tn Vol; *Auburn U; Med.*

TODD, Candace Kay
Jefferson City HS; Jefferson City, MO (108-570) A Cap Choir; Chor; Drama; Orch; Vlbl; Art Hon C; Lettered Var B-Vlbl; HR; Orig Stry, Ann-Best Creat Writ; *U of Mo; Journ.*

TODD, Darlene Robin
Parkland Sr HS; Winston-Salem, NC (23-625) Anchor C; Hmrm; Monogram; NHS; VP, Span C; Bkbl; Sftbl; Tr; HCt; Hon Prog; Jr Marshal; Vlbl A; *Central Wesleyan Col; Hist.*

TODD, David Bernard III
McGavock Sr HS; Nashville, TN (106-836) Band; Chess C; Dbte Tm; Fr C; HiY; Hmrm; Math C; Mu Alpha Theta; SC; Swim; Alg A; Bio A; JA A; Math A; Q&S A; *Morehouse Col; Pre-Med.*

TODD, Jesse Turrentine Jr
Briarwood Christian HS; Birmingham, AL (10-60) Ann; BC; Lat C; Pol Sci C; Rptr, Sch P; Bio A; Chamber of Comm A; Academic Achv A; Hon Men, Ala Sen & St Militia; 1st, So As of Christian Sch Essay A; *Social Sci.*

TODD, Kimberly Ann
Marion HS; Marion, IN (75-850) Cpt, Chldr; Chor; Secy, Ensm; NHS; SC; Ambassador; Exchange C; Today's Tn; *Ariz U; Nurs.*

TODD, Leigh Alan
Tipton HS; Tipton, OK (1-37) Band; Drama; Tres, FFA; NHS; Spch C; I Dare You; Val; Outst Band Member; Star Farmer A; Outst Sr FFA; Band Kg; *Western Okla Col; Agr.*

TODD, Marty McClain
Claxton HS; Claxton, GA (25%-110) Bus C; Chess C; FBLA; Pres, FFA; 4H; Tr; COM; Hon Prog; WW; *ABAC; Agr.*

TODD, Mary Martha
Portland HS; Porland, MI (38-150) Band; Ed, Sch P; Span C; SC; Pres, Jr Cl; JV, Bkbl; Sftbl; Q&S A; Yth Fel; Vlbl; *Olivet Col; Spch Therapy.*

TODD, Peggy Lynn
Valentine HS; Valentine, NE; Drama; MVP, Bkbl; Pep C; *Patricia Stevens Col; Interior Decorator.*

TODD, Robert Morris
J R Tucker HS; Richmond, VA (20%-470) Alt, BS; *VPI; Engr.*

TODD, Russell Bryan
James Madison HS; Vienna, VA; Ftbl; Tr; Wrest; *Engr.*

TODD, Sherman Renard
Lindblom Technical HS; Chicago, IL (33-610) Chess C; Hmrm; NHS; SC; Cr-Ctry; COM; Citz A; Hon Prog; MLS; Sci A; Val; *IIT; Engr.*

TODD, Susan Kay
Haughton HS; Haughton, LA; Chor; FHA; *La Col; Office Work.*

TODD, Susan Louise
Odessa Sr HS; Odessa, MO (31-129) Chem C; Chor; FHA; NHS; ARC; Span C; JV, Tr; NHS A; Tr Ltr; Pep C Ltr; *Warrensburg CMSU; Nurs.*

TODD, Susan Lucinda
York Comm HS; Elmhurst, IL (87-973) Chor; Ensm; NHS; Span NHS; Thes; St Scholar; *N Ill U; Elem Ed.*

TODD, Terry Alan
Lewistown Comm HS; Lewistown, IL (50-145) A Cap Choir; Band; Chor; Drama; Fin, Ensm; Bus Mgr, Hmrm; Spch C; Thes; Mgr, Bsbl; Cpt, Ftbl; Tr; Citz A; DARGCA; Pres A; Yth Fel; 1st, St Mus; *Drama.*

TODD, Tracy Lynne
George Washington HS; Los Angeles, CA; *Harbor Col; Mus.*

TODD, Vicki Janette
Truman HS; Independence, MO (142-663) Fr C; Win, Mid Amer Mus Assn; Tickers; Art A; Hospital Vol; A-Ed, Church Paper; Pres, Tres, Christ Ambassador; *Art.*

TOELLE, Cynthia May
Campbell-Tintah HS; Campbell, MN (2-38) Ann; Band; Chor; Drama; Ensm; Secy, FHA; Mjrte; Co-Ed, Sch P; Spch C; Bkbl; Tr; B Crocker A; COM; Hon Prog; Sal; Spch A; *Bemidji St U; Art.*

TOELLE, Steven Dean
Campbell-Tintah HS; Campbell, MN (5-43) Band; Chor; FFA; Ftbl; MVP, Sftbl; JV, Tnns; A&B HR; *Agr.*

TOENJES, Rita Marie
Althoff Cath HS; Belleville, IL; VP, CYO; Chor; Var C; Sftbl; Hon Prog; JV, Vlbl; Religion A; *Secretarial.*

TOENNIES, Lorie Frances
Cresbard HS; Cresbard, SD (3-32) Ed, Ann; Band; Chor; Rptr, Sch P; VP, SC; Bkbl; Tr; Hon Prog; *Dakota Wesleyan U; Lab Tech.*

TOEPFERT, Terri Lynn
Colerain Sr HS; Cincinnati, OH (63-630) A Cap Choir; Chor; Drama; Ensm; Pres, Fr C; Hmrm; InterClub Coun; Madrigal; Tres, SC; Var C; HCt; Pres A; Gym; Most Reliable; *U of Cincinnati; Nurs.*

TOFT, Gregory Wayne
Norte Del Rio HS; Sacramento, CA; Band; Ensm; Orch; Arch; Ftbl; Tnns; *NW Bible Col; Ministerial.*

TOGIA, Fetoai F
Venice HS; Venice, CA; *UCLA; Math.*

TOIFEL, Ronald Charles
W J Woodham HS; Pensacola, FL (25-530) Pres, Chess C; Ger C; NHS; Ger A; *U of Fla; Engr.*

TOLBERT, Aaron Charles
Dunbar Voc HS; Chicago, IL (9-660) Ed, Ann; NHS; Sci C; Span C; COM; Hon Prog; Ntl Conf Chr & Jews; ROTC A; WW; *DePaul U; Acct.*

TOLBERT, Carla Gail
Pinckneyville Comm HS; Pinckneyville, IL (40-155) Band; Drama; Fr C; FHA; NHS; Orch; NEDT; St Scholar; *Barnes Hospital Sch of Nurs; Nurs.*

TOLBERT, Darryl Vincent
Smoky Hill HS; Denver, CO (45-460) Chor; Drama; Ski C; Var C; JV, Bkbl; Ftbl; Tnns; Co-Cpt, Tr; Cl Fav; HCt; JA A; BEU A; *Colo U; Bus Adm.*

TOLBERT, Dewayne Henry
Trenton Central HS; Trenton, NJ; Tres, Chor; JV, Soccer; Wrest; Citz A; Yth Fel; Dr Martin L King, Jr A; RCA MEP Cert; *Engr.*

TOLBERT, Geraldine
Jones Commercial HS; Chicago, IL (74-452) Chor; FBLA; SC; Citz A; Hon Prog; 2nd & 3rd Pl, FBLA City Contests; *W Ill U; Bus Adm.*

TOLBERT, James Edwin
Lindblom Tech HS; Chicago, IL (52-436) A Cap Choir; Chor; Hmrm; Math C; Bus Mgr, Model UN; NHS; VP, Sci C; VP, SC; Bio A; COM; JA A; WW; SC Patch & Pin; Sch P Pin; *Coe Col; Bus Adm.*

TOLBERT, Rondale Gail
Baker HS; Columbus, GA; *Clark Col; Criminal Law.*

TOLEDANO, Martha McCrary
Asheboro HS; Asheboro, NC (153-310) Chldr; Hmrm; Monogram; Span C; SC; HCt; Yth Fel; *Sweet Briar Col.*

TOLEDO, Alberto
Eastside HS; Paterson, NJ (10%-615) Mgr, Cr-Ctry; Tnns; Schol Achv A; *Yale U; Law.*

TOLEDO, Carmen Rosario
Academia Sagrado Corazon; Santurce, PR (4-92) Chor; Drama; Hmrm; NHS; ARC; Sci C; SC; Secy, Jr Cl; Alg A; Bio A; Hist A; JA A; Phy A; Eng A; Span A; *U of Puerto Rico; Phar.*

TOLEDO, Evelyn
Juan Jose Osuna HS; Hato Rey, PR (12-101) CYO; FHA; Tres, Hmrm; ARC; COM; Chem A; Hon Prog; MLS; Phy A; Sci A; Pres, GSct; Hon A; *Colegu U Sagrado Cerazon; Medical Technology.*

TOLEDO, Juan
Eastside HS; Paterson, NJ (15-550) Tnns; Tr; *Rutgers U; Pre-Med.*

TOLEN, William Edward Jr
SW HS; Saint Louis, MO; A Cap Choir; Bus C; Chor; Var C; Bsbl; Co-Cpt, Bkbl; Ftbl; Ntl Achv Schol; NMS; Pres A; ROTC A; WW; Bkbl & Ftbl Ltrs; Bsbl Trophies; *Bus Adm.*

TOLERICO, Ann Jude
Saint Rose HS; Carbondale, PA (9-53) Dbte Tm; Fr C; Ski C; Spch C; Hon Prog; JA A; NEDT; *Comm Med Center; Nurs.*

TOLIN, Dallas Tim
Sooner HS; Bartlesville, OK (18-260) Band; Pres, Key C; NHS; Bsbl; MVP, Bkbl; Ftbl; Elk A; *Wichita St U; Bus.*

TOLLEFSON, Cathy Ann
Fertile-Beltrami HS; Fertile, MN (33%-65) Band; Chor; Ensm; Madrigal; Ski C; Thes; Var C; Bkbl; Tnns; Tr; COM; Spch A; Type A; *Moorehead St U; Phys Ed.*

TOLLEFSON, Diane Lynn
Mabel-Canton HS; Prosper, MN (9-50) Band; Chor; Ensm; FHA; Sch P; Secy, SC; Thes; Pres, Sr Cl; Bkbl; Tr; *Rochester Col; Med Lab Technician.*

TOLLEFSON, Jan Erik
Escanaba Area Sr HS; Escanaba, MI; Band; VP, Order/Arrow; Order/Arrow A; Eagle Sct A; *Mich Tech U; Chem.*

TOLLEFSON, Susan Jo
Queen Anne HS; Seattle, WA (9-386) Band; Chor; Ensm; Citz A; Hon Prog; Star Student; Yth Fel; Young Artist Festival; Hon Soc; *Seattle Pacific U; Col Prep.*

TOLLETT, Patricia Ann
McCellan HS; Little Rock, AR; A Cap Choir; Band; Chor; Ensm; FBLA; NFL; All-Region & All-St Choirs; Amer Yth in Concert Choir; *Memphis St U; Mus.*

TOLLIE, Kimberlee June
Shawnee Mission S HS; Overland Park, KS (200-900) Band; FNA; Pres A; Anchorette; Lib A; *Nurs.*

TOLLIFERREO, Geneva Elizabeth
Germantown HS; Philadelphia, PA (51-531) Hmrm; Var C; Mgr, Tr; Citz A; Ch, Host & Hostess Comm; Stu Assn; Co-Ch, Assembly & Finance Comm; Sch Co-Announcer; Home & Sch Rep; Sch Mascot; Hist Hon Soc; SG; *W Chester St Col; Secondary Special Ed.*

TOLLIVER, Michael Anthony
John S Shaw HS; Mobile, AL (75-421) Band; Hmrm; Orch; *Mus.*

TOLLIVER, Sheila Ann
Powell Valley HS; Speedwell, TN; VP, BC; FHA.

TOLMAN, Pamela Sue
N Shore HS; W Palm Beach, FL (41-266) FBLA; Alg A; Jr NHS; Top 10% Cl.

TOLSTAD, Dwight Raymond
Souris Pub Sch; Souris, ND (2-7) Co-Ed, Ann; Pres, 4H; Co-Cpt, Bkbl; 4H A; Sal; Yth Foundation; Ed A; Shop A; *ND St Sch of Sci; Elec Tech.*

TOLSTAD, Laurie Kay
Souris Pub Sch; Souris, ND (8-11) Secy, 4H; Bkbl.

TOLZMAN, Kathleen Ann
Owatonna HS; Owatonna, MN; Chor; Cpt, Dancing; Fin, H Qn; *Minnesota Sch of Bus; Interior Design.*

TOM, George J
Immaculata HS; New York, NY (38-95) *Elec Repair.*

TOMA, Aleda Ann
Hobart HS; Hobart, OK (1-52) Ann; Chldr; VP, FHA; FTA; Hmrm; NHS; Span C; VP, SC; Secy, Var C; Bkbl; COM; Citz A; DARGCA; HQn; Val; Miss FTA; Cand Miss HHS; WW; All-Conf, Bkbl; *Okla U; Psych.*

TOMA, Cathy Michie
Waialua HS; Waialua, HI; Hmrm; Spch C; Cr-Ctry; *Leeward Comm Col; Clerical.*

TOMA, Gigi
Hobart HS; Hobart, OK (1-68) Chldr; Parl, FHA; Secy, FTA; NHS; SC; Citz A; *Okla U; Pre-Med.*

TOMAMICHEL, Nancy Jo
Southport HS; Southport, IN; FHA; FTA; Hmrm; Span C; Tr; Math A; VP, OEA.

TOMASI, Teresa Lynne
Greeley W HS; Greeley, CO (26-305) Swim; *Colo St U; Ed.*

TOMASIK, Deborah Ann
McArthur HS; Hollywood, FL (50%-630) Band; FNA; Pres, Hmrm; Sftbl; Opt A; Opt Out Tn; Yth Fel; Pres, Church Yth Fel; *Beoward Comm Col; Nurs.*

TOMASO, Tina Lynn
Redlands HS; Redlands, CA (13-778) Chor; Fr C; CSF; Daisy Chain; Vocal Mus Schol, Mus Tchrs Assn; Personal Mus Achv Hon; *Pepperdine U.*

TOMASZEWSKI, Thomas Edward
Manistee HS; Manistee, MI (12-200) Band; NHS; Bsbl; Bkbl; Ftbl; Summa Cum Laude; *Central Mich U.*

TOMAYKO, Louis
Westmont Hilltop HS; Johnstown, PA (60-200) Key C; Order/Arrow; Tr; Wrest; Alg A; Bio A; COM; HCt; Hon Prog; Math A; Eagle Sct; *Penn St U of Altoona; Engr.*

TOMBERLIN, Laura Jayne
Greater Atlanta Christian Sch; Norcross, GA (25%-150) Sci C; Bkbl; JV, Sftbl; *Ga St Col; Eng.*

TOMES, Michele Marie
Centennial HS; Utica, NE (7-63) Ann; Chldr; Chor; Semi-Fin, GS; NHS; S-T, Sci C; VP, Sr Cl; HQn; *U of Nebr; Child Care.*

TOMKO, Michal David
Beaver Dam HS; Beaver Dam, WI (60-350) *Genisis Col; Pastor.*

TOMLINSON, Dana John
Southeast HS; Ravenna, OH (12-150) Pres, 4H; 4H A; Stu Adv, FFA; FFA Sheep A; FFA Notebook A; *Ohio St U; Agr.*

TOMLINSON, Dawn Lorraine
West HS; Bakersfield, CA; A Cap Choir; Band; Pres, Chor; Lit Mag; Swim; *Bakersfield Jr Col; Nurs.*

TOMLINSON, Julie Ann
Trinity Heights Christian Acad; Shreveport, LA (25%-65) Band; Chldr; Chor; Dbte Tm; Drama; FFA; FHA; FTA; Pres, Span C; Spch C; Hockey; Soccer; Sftbl; Tnns; Tr; Beauty; Cl Fav; Jamboree Qn; Industrial Arts Stu Assn.

TOMLINSON, Julie Anne
Dothan HS; Dothan, AL; Band; Chor; Jr Miss Pagent; Swim; Tnns; Tr; Cpt, Flagcorp; Harmony C; *Chipola Col; Mus.*

TOMLINSON, Tammy Renee
Burnsville Sr HS; Burnsville, MN (4-777) Band; Chor; Quizzer o-t Yr; *Christian Ed.*

TOMLINSON, William Bradley
Pingry Sch; Hillside, NJ (75-119) Chor; Drama; F-Ed, Lit Mag; Orch; Span C; Var C; Mgr, Bkbl; Soccer; Var Ltr & Trophies; *Skidmore Col; Art.*

TOMMERAASEN, Debora Sue
Simley Sr HS; Inver Grove Heights, MN (30-350) Band; Semi-Fin, Ensm; NHS; Mgr, Tnns; Math A; Fin, Ensm; 150 Hr Jr Vol, Hospital; *U of Minn; Sci.*

TOMPKINS, Craig Jay
Glenbard W HS; Glen Ellyn, IL (22-488) Lat C; Rptr, Sch P; Bsbl; Bkbl; Ftbl; Alg A; Hon Prog; *Engr.*

TOMPKINS, Judith Suzanne
Forest View HS; Arlington Heights, IL (165-712) God & Country A; GSct; Vol Service; Cadette Ldr, Day Camp; Ntl Convention of GScts.

TOMPKINS, Lisa Gaye
Buena HS; Sierra Vista, AZ (131-500) Fin, GS; Hmrm; InterClub Coun; NHS; SC; Mgr, Bkbl; Sftbl; Mgr, Tr; Elk A; HCt; City Yth Coun; Keywannettes C; Mgr, Vlbl; Pres, Stu Body; *Ariz St U; Sociology.*

TOMPKINS, Lisa Jane
Eddyville HS; Eddyville, OR (1-17) Chldr; 4H; SC; Rptr, Jr Cl; Bkbl; Tr; COM; Hon Prog; Vlbl; Christmas Court; Attendance A; Attendance A; *Oreg St U; Phys Ed.*

TOMPKINS, Lori Gayle
Buena HS; Sierra Vista, AZ (60-500) Ann; NHS; Span C; Span NHS; Mgr, Bkbl; Q&S A; *Tex Southwest St U; Journ.*

TOMPKINS, Lynette Carol
The Brearley Sch; New York, NY (50%-57) Chor; Drama; Ensm; Sch P; Bkbl; Hockey; Sftbl; Swim; Tnns; Piano Lessons; Ballet Lessons; Inter Lochen Mus Comp; *Mus Dance.*

TOMPKINS, Pamela Mae
Sunbright HS; Sunbright, TN (10-66) BC; Cpt, Chldr; Tres, FHA; Secy, 4H; Rptr, Sch P; Secy, Soph Cl; Cpt, Bkbl; 4H A; Spch A; *Sou Missionary Col; Med Tech.*

TOMPKINS, Regina Faye
Lindblom Tech HS; Chicago, IL (169-789) Chldr; Mjrte; Sftbl; Tnns; COM; Citz A; Most Out; Sal; Attendance A; Vlbl; *Bradley U; Computer Programming.*

TOMPKINS, Thomas Jay
Zanesville HS; Zanesville, OH; Band; Chor; Community Yth Symph; Drama; Ensm; Pres, NHS; Orch; ARC; Sch P; VP, Sci C; COM; Hon Prog; OMEA A; *Psych.*

TOMPKINS, Wayne
Aurora Central HS; Aurora, CO; Chess C; Swim; Elec.

TOMSICH, Katherine Elaine
Staples HS; Staples, MN (1-150) A Cap Choir; Band; Chldr; Chor; Secy, Drama; GS; Madrigal; Model UN; NHS; Sch P; Ski C; Secy, SC; Thes; Cpt, Tr; Hon Prog; NMS; Val; *Carleton Col.*

TOMTEN, Roger Lloyd
Winona Sr HS; Winona, MN (24-530) Order/Arrow; JV, Tr; COM; Order/Arrow A; *Architecture.*

TONAK, Lori Kay
Clark Sr HS; Clark, SD (21-65) Band; FFA; Parl, FHA; Pres, 4H; Tr; 4H A; Miss Congeniality, Snow Qn; *SD St U; Dairy Sci.*

TONEY, Debra Denise
Douglas HS; Douglas, AZ (70-310) Rainbow; Tr; Advanced Bio Research Tm; *Med.*

TONEY, James Douglas
Melbourne HS; Melbourne, FL (50%-500) Key C; Order/Arrow; ARC; Order/Arrow A; ARC A; Yth Fel; Eagle Sct; Sportsmanship A; *Brevard Comm Col; Environmental Control Tech.*

TONEY, Michael Gene
E Henderson HS; E Flat Rock, NC (25%-323) Band; Chor; 4H; ARC; COM; Citz A; 4H A; ARC A; Sci A; Yth Fel; BSct A's; Young Action Ldr; Candystriper; *Brian Col; Biol.*

TONEY, Rosa Lee
Carver HS; Birmingham, AL; Math C; Sci C; ROTC A; *Bessemer St Tech Sch; Nurs.*

TONEY, Rosemari
E Rutherford HS; Forest City, NC (25-351) Span C; *NC St U; Aviation.*

TONG, Carol B
Lowell HS; San Francisco, CA (301-827) Swim; CSF; Hon Prog; Tutor; Teaching Asst; Chinese C; *U of Calif; Ed.*

TONG, Steve Ray
Queen City HS; Queen City, TX (10%-45) Pres, FFA; Hmrm; NHS; Order/Arrow; Span C; SC; Ftbl; JV, Tr; Cl Fav; Order/Arrow A; *Baylor U; Med.*

TONSING, Catherine Elizabeth
Parkway W Sr HS; Ballwin, MO (10-629) AFS; Chor; Dbte Tm; Model UN; NFL; St Stu Congress; Hon Prog; 1st Cl GSct.

TOODLE, Wanda Gayle
Glenn HS; Birmingham, AL; Ann; Band; Drama; Fr C; NHS; Sch P; SC; Bio A; COM; Poet A; Sci A; Art.

TOOGOOD, Jay Daniel
Mayo HS; Rochester, MN (45-650) Ann; Chor; Drama; NHS; Swim; Stage Mgr; Dist Luther League; YMCA Ldrs C; *Rochester Comm Col; Pre-Law.*

TOOLAN, John Anthony
Cardinal Hayes HS; Bronx, NY (74-370) Band; Orch; Swim; COM; Regent Schol; *Manhattan Col; Acct.*

TOOLE, Gayle Todd
Jessamine Co HS; Nicholasville, KY (76-290) Band; Chess C; Fr C; A-Ed, Sch P; JV, Cr-Ctry; Hist A; Radio A; *Georgetown Col; Law.*

TOOLES, Stephanie Elaine
Douglass HS; Memphis, TN; Fin, Crown & Scepter; SC; HQn; Miss Douglas; Miss Hist; Sr-Ed, Yrbk; Secy, TOEC; *Memphis St U; Nurs.*

TOOLEY, Richard Norman
Traverse City; Traverse City, MI; Band; Order/Arrow A; *Vet Sci.*

TOOLEY, Yvonne Zaida
Traverse City HS; Traverse City, MI; Band; SIU; Communications.

TOOMBS, Daniel Thurman
Geronimo HS; Geronimo, OK (2-31) Drama; Secy, FFA; Co-Ed, Sch P; Pres, Sr Cl; VP, Jr Cl; Co-Cpt, Bsbl; Bkbl; Alg A; Math A; MLS; Sal; HR; Drama A; *Cameron U.*

TOOMER, Anthony Laral
Charles L Harper HS; Atlanta, GA; Chor; Bsbl; Bkbl; Ftbl; Swim; Tnns; Alg A; Bio A; COM; Hon Prog; Math A; ROTC A; Sci A.

TOOMEY, Elizabeth Anne
Blanchet HS; Seattle, WA (38-285) CYO; Pres, Hmrm; NHS; Rptr, Sch P; SC; Secy, Jr Cl; Soccer; Co-Cpt, Tr; Elk A; Hon Prog; ARC A; Most Inspirational, Tr; Order o-t Cross; Co-Ch, Sch Majr Fund Raising Event.

TOOMEY, Shaun Joseph
Shawe HS; Madison, IN (1-25) Semi-Fin, BS; NHS; Rptr, Sch P; Bsbl; Mgr, Bkbl; Mgr, Cr-Ctry; Mgr, Tr; Alg A; Bio A; COM; Chem A; Hist A; HCt; Cramer Stu Trainer A; *Rose-Hulman Inst Tech; Elec Engr.*

TOONE, Kymmberlie
Weequahic HS; Newark, NJ (175-400) Hmrm; SC; Cpt, Sftbl; HCt; Ch, Sch Store; *Kean Col; Med Tech.*

TOPE, Anne Elisabeth
W Orange HS; Winter Garden, FL (25-400) Drama; Fr C; Hmrm; Pres, InterAct C; InterClub Coun; NHS; Mgr, Soccer; Swim; COM; *Queens College; History.*

TOPHAM, Ella Sue
Havre HS; Havre, MT; Ann; Band; Fr C; Hmrm; Var C; JV, Bkbl; Tr; Vlbl; WW; Superior, St Band; Mus Program, Church.

TOPHAM, Leslie Ann
East HS; Denver, CO; Chor; Drama; ARC; Ski C; Sftbl; Tnns; COM; Pres A; Secy, VP, Yth Group; *Seward Col; Christian Ed.*

TOPP, Becky Lynn
Pillager Pub HS; Pillager, MN (6-36) Bkbl; Tr; *Brainerd Comm Col.*

TOPP, David Allen
James W Robinson Jr Secondary Sch; Fairfax, VA (4-584) French NHS; Cr-Ctry; *Engr.*

TOPP, Monte Anne
Murray-Wright HS; Detroit, MI; Tr; Math A; *East Mich Col; Criminal Justice.*

TOPPEL, Fredrick Howard
Larkin HS; Elgin, IL (29-626) Golf; Rotary A; St Scholar; Russian C; *U of Mich; Econ.*

TOPPIN, Donna Marie
Adlai E Stevenson HS; Bronx, NY (2-822) Chem C; City Conf; Ch, Dbte Tm; Ch, Drama; Ch, Hmrm; InterClub Coun; Math C; NHS; Sch Achieve Tm; SC; VP, Sr Cl; Alg A; COM; Chem A; Citz A; Gov Honor Prog; H of F; Hon Prog; Math A; Most Out; NMS; Ntl Sci Symposium; Phy A; Regent Schol; Sal; Sci A; Homework Helpers; Geom; *Columbia U; Engr.*

TORBERT, Kathy Lynne
York Co Voc-Tech HS; York, PA; A Cap Choir; Band; Chor; S-T, Hmrm; S-T, SC; S-T, Soph Cl; Bkbl; Golf; Sftbl; Swim; Tnns; Tr; Most Out; ARC A; Peterson Penmanship; Chor; Lib Asst; *Cosmetology.*

TORGERSON, Neil Ecker
Stevens HS; Rapid City, SD (100-450) Dbte Tm; Drama; Fr C; Hmrm; NFL; Order/Arrow; SC; Bkbl; Golf; Soccer; Swim; Order/Arrow A; Spch A; Eagle Sct A; Special Service A, BSct; Ntl Forensics A.

TORNBERG, Karen Lynn
Lyons Township HS; La Grange, IL (66-1223) AFS; Drama; Hon Prog; NEDT; VP, Church Yth Group; Sunday Sch Teacher; *U of Ill; Law.*

TORNITO, Theresa Marie
John F Kennedy HS; Tumon, GUAM (35-511) NHS; Pres, SC; Secy, Jr Cl; Tnns; Sci A; *U of Hawaii; Special Ed.*

TORNQUIST, Gary Alan
Paso Robles HS; Paso Robles, CA (1-178) Band; Chess C; Secy, Lat C; Math C; Sci C; Var C; Cpt, Bkbl; CSF; Lion A; Math A; NMF; Val; MVP, Cpt, Waterpolo; *Calif Tech U; Sci.*

TORO, Ademar Martinez
Amer Military Acad; Guaynabo, PR (7-30) Chem
C; Math C; Span C; Bkbl; Hon Prog; Math A; *Col of
William And Mary; Banking.*

TORO, Zulma
Luis Munoz Marin HS; Cabo Rojo, PR (4-200)
Pres, FHA; Span C; VP, SC; Alg A; Beauty; COM;
Chem A; H of F; Hist A; Hon Prog; Masonic A;
Math A; Sci A; *Recinto Universitario Mayaguez;
Ingenieria.*

TORONJO, Jeffery Mark
Lamar HS; Houston, TX (326-526) Band; Fr C; Sci
A; Sup Rating, UBA Vocal Solo & Ensm; Stu Choir
Dir, Church; *Sci.*

TORRADO, Anali Ciencia
Acad of Our Lady of Guam; Agana, GUAM
(10-91) Band; Hmrm; NHS; VP, Jr Cl; JV, Sftbl;
Tnns; Hon Band; *U of Sou Calif; Med.*

TORRANCE, John Robert
Minto HS; Minto, ND; VP, Jr Cl; Bkbl; *Mankato St
U.*

TORRANCE, Susan Marie
Union HS; Biggsville, IL (1-72) Drama; NHS;
ARC; Vlbl; *Western Ill U; Pre-Dentistry.*

TORRENCE, Patricia Elaine
Martin Luther King HS; Chicago, IL (2-238) NHS;
Bkbl; COM; Hist A; Hon Prog; Sal; Eng A; *Wiley
Col; Acct.*

TORRES, Alexis Ramon
Colegio San Antonio Abad; Humacao, PR (1-86) A
Cap Choir; CYO; NHS; Order/Arrow; Tnns; Tres,
Caribbean NHS; *Princeton U; Pol Sci.*

TORRES, Angel Gabriel
Yauco HS; Yauco, PR; Bkbl; *Bradley Col; Acct.*

TORRES, Ayleen
Dra Maria Cadilla de Martinez HS; Arecibo, PR
(25-429) CYO; Chor; FTA; Tres, Hmrm; ARC; A-
Ed, Sch P; Sci C; Bkbl; Sftbl; COM; Hon Prog;
Most Out; Val; Ath A; *Penn St U; Med.*

TORRES, Brunilda
Greater New York Acad; Woodside, NY (9-73)
FNA; NHS; ARC; Sci C; Secy, SC; Alg A; Citz A;
Val; Semi-Fin, Courtesy Qn; *Antillian Col; Nurs.*

TORRES, Edith
Miguel Melendez Munoz; Bayamon, PR (1-290)
Secy, CYO; Chem C; Chor; Cum Laude Soc; Tres,
FHA; Pres, Math C; Orch; VP, Phys C; ARC; A-
Ed, Sch P; Span C; Spch C; SC; Pres, Soph Cl; Alg
A; Bio A; Chem A; Hist A; Phy A; ARC A; Sci A;
U of Puerto Rico; Med.

TORRES, Eiby Elizabeth
The Immaculata HS; Chicago, IL (20-157) CYO;
Chess C; Secy, Fr C; Hmrm; Mod Mus Mas; NHS;
Sch P; Pres, SC; COM; Hon Prog; Semi-Fin, CYO
Tnage Citzn o-t Mon; Designed, G Sct Patch;
Yrbk; ISLI Cert, Clarke Col; TISA Cert, North-
western U; *Northwestern U; Sci.*

TORRES, Evelyn
Luis Munoz Marin HS; Lajas, PR (6-170) Drama;
FHA; 4H; Hmrm; Lit Mag; *Interameri U; Bio.*

TORRES, Francisco Manuel
Our Lady of Pilar HS; Rio Piedras, PR (4-200)
Chem C; Hmrm; Lit Mag; Model UN; NHS; Tres,
Sci C; Alg A; Bio A; COM; Hist A; Hon Prog; Math
A; Sci A; Religion A; Span A; *Engr.*

TORRES, Hector
Jose de Diego HS; Mayaguez, PR (1-276) Drama;
Pres, Phys C; VP, SC; Alg A; JA A; Phy A; Summa
Cum Laude; Pres, C Becarios; Pres, JA; Pres,
JEPME; Pres, Cooperative C; *UPR at Mayaguez;
Med.*

TORRES, Isabelita
Luis Munoz Marin HS; Cabo Rojo, PR (7-200)
CYO; FHA; Hmrm; ARC; SC; Hon Prog; *CAAM-
UPR; Bus Adm.*

TORRES, Juan L
Our Lady of Pilar HS; Rio Piedras, PR (3-148)
Pres, Chem C; Lit Mag; Model UN; Secy, NHS; Sci
C; Tr; Alg A; Bio A; Hon Prog; Math A; Sci A;
Essay A; Span A; Religion A; Sci Fair A; *Chem.*

TORRES, Mary Helen
Incarnate Word Acad; Houston, TX; CYO; Bsbl;
Bkbl; Sftbl; Swim; Tnns; Good Attendance; *Eckerd
Col; Modeling.*

TORRES, Migdalia
Juan Jose Osuna HS; Hato Rey, PR (4-150) Chldr;
4H; Hmrm; ARC; Bsbl; Sftbl; Swim; COM; Hon
Prog; Lion A; Math A; Civic Act C; Lib C; Art A;
Vlbl; *U of PR; Sci.*

TORRES, Miriam Del Rosario
Academia Santa Monica; Santurce, PR; Chor; Tres,
Sch P; Pres, Jr Cl; Bsbl; Bkbl; Tnns; *Conservatorio
De Musica; Mus.*

TORRES, Noe
Presbyterian Pan American HS; Kingsville, TX
(3-53) Bkbl; Soccer; *A&M Col; Engr.*

TORRES, Pedro Angel
Yauco HS; Yauco, PR; *Drew; Engr.*

TORRES, Perfecto
Dra Maria Cadilla HS; Arecibo, PR (70-429) Alg
A; Hist A; Math A; NMF; DECA C; *University of
Puerto Rico; Phar.*

TORRES, Raymond
Dr Pila HS; Ponce, PR; CYO; Pres, Hmrm; Orch;
Rptr, Sch P; VP, Sr Cl; COM; JA A; *Astronaut.*

TORRES, Wanda Jeannette
Notre Dame HS; Caguas, PR (1-140) CYO; Fr C;
Pres, 4H; COM; 4H A; Phy A; Sci A; *U of Puerto
Rico; Sci.*

TORREY, David Alan
Plantation HS; Plantation, FL (180-540) ARC; SC;
JV, Cr-Cnty; JV, Soccer; JV, Tr; Yth Fel; Pres,
Prom Committee; Sr Cl Executive Board; *Presby-
terian Col.*

TORREZ, Elizabeth Ann
Roma HS; Roma, TX (3-130) Band; Mjrte; Tres,
NHS; ARC; Tres, Sci C; Spch C; Pres, Soph Cl; Tr;
Beauty; COM; Cl Fav; 4H A; Pres, VP & Secy,
FHA; Ath C; Tres & Parl, 4-H C; Pep Sq; Pres &
Tres, Sc; FFA Swtht; WW; *U of Tex; Law.*

TORREZ, Guadalupe Tomasa
Hayden HS; Topeka, KS; CYO; NHS; Co-Ed, Sch
P; COM; Hon Prog; Rptr, Sch P; Cert of Recognition; Bicen Mexican-Amer Qn of Topeka; *Washburn U; Acct.*

TORRILLO, Lina Maria
Acad of Saint Aloysius; Jersey City, NJ (6-104)
Chor; Fr C; Ger C; Hmrm; Lat C; Math C; NHS;
Rptr, Sch P; Span C; Stu Service Corp; 1st Prize,
Poster Contest; 1st Prize, Fire Prevention; *Bus.*

TORSON, Tamara Leigh
Bellmont HS; Decatur, IN; Chess C; Drama; Fr C;
ARC; ARC A; Art C; Sunshine Girls; Counselor,
Deaf Camp; Candystriper; *Saint Mary's Col; Law.*

TORY, Rhonda Rae
Foothill Sr HS; Sacramento, CA; Band; Ger C; 4H;
Secy, Lit Mag; Swtht; Banquet Qn; *U of Calif; Law.*

TOSTE, JoAnn Michelle
Ferndale Union HS; Ferndale, CA (35-52) Ch,
CYO; Chor; Drama; 4H; All Co Hon Choir; *Col o-t
Redwoods; Nurs.*

TOTARO, Maria
Old Forge HS; Old Forge, PA (10-134) Band;
Drama; NHS; Ski C; Chem A; Hon Prog; *Wilkes
Col; Med Tech.*

TOTH, Elizabeth Louise
Vanguard HS; Ocala, FL (16-350) Fr C; Rptr,
FBLA; Pres, Mu Alpha Theta; NHS; SC;
DARGCA; Hon Prog; Outst, Fr; *Central Fla
Comm Col; Elem Ed.*

TOTH, Susan Carol
Saline HS; Saline, MI (10%-268) Band; Drama;
Ensm; Fr C; NHS; Rptr, Sch P; SC; Thes; Journ A;
Eastern Mich U.

TOTTEN, Gracie Mae
Independence HS; Independence, MS (15%-106)
BC; FBLA; Beauty; *Jackson St U; Engr.*

**TOUCHSTONE,
Cynthia Vallette**
Adairsville HS; Adairsville, GA; FHA; Sci C; Bkbl;
Sftbl; Tr; Beauty; Interlochen Ntl Mus.

TOULOUMDJIAN, Lisa Marie
John F Kennedy HS; Willingboro, NJ (156-525)
Band; Hmrm; Lat C; Pres, Orch; Ski C; Hockey;
Swim; Cl Fav; Concert Mistress; *Marywood Col;
Hotel and Resort Industries.*

TOURDOT, Mary Catherine
Waupun Sr HS; Waupun, WI (31-237) Band; Ensm;
NFL; Ski C; Solo & Ensm A's.

TOURVILLE, Timothy Paul
De Soto HS; De Soto, MO (30-250) Band; Ensm;
Ftbl; Tr; Cl Fav; Most Out; *SW Mo St Col; Occupa-
tional Therapy.*

TOUTGES, Candace Faith
Sierra HS; Whittier, CA (20%-300) Ann; Chor; Ski
C; Span C; Q&S A; *LaVerne; Bible Study.*

TOW, Lucy Marie
Foreman HS; Chicago, IL (8-373) Band; Ger C;
Hmrm; Pres, Mod Mus Mas; VP, Mu Alpha Theta;
NHS; SC; Tres, Sr Cl; Tnns; Hon Prog; Band Ltr;
Tnns Ltr & Trophy; HR Pins; *U of Ill; Biol.*

TOWE, Edison Louis III
Plymouth HS; Plymouth, NC (31-242) Ann; VP,
Band; Most Out; *E Carolina U; Mus.*

TOWE, Marshall Jr
Luther HS N; Chicago, IL (33%-300) Band; Chor;
Bsbl; Bkbl; Ftbl; Soccer; Sftbl; Swim; Tr; COM;
Citz A; God & Country A; Hon Prog; Pres, Tres,
Yth Fel; VP, Yth Leg; H Coun, NSEC Summer
Camp; Explorer Post; Soc Ch, Bowl League; Neigh-
borhood Bsbl & Bkbl Coach Cou; *Judson Col; The-
ology.*

TOWER, Janet Elizabeth
Lakeview HS; Battle Creek, MI (20%-450) Band;
Chor; Yth Fel; Deaconess; Jr Choir Ldr; Campfire
Girls; 750 Hr Vol; *Kellogg Comm Col; Nurs.*

TOWLES, Vincent Bernard
Fairfield HS; Fairfield, AL; MVP, Ftbl; Most Out.

TOWN, Elizabeth Olive
Bartow Sr HS; Bartow, FL (10%-300) Chor;
Drama; Hmrm; NHS; F-Ed, Sch P; SC; Sftbl; Hon
Prog; WW; President's Phys Fitness A; *FSU.*

TOWNE, Carla Jo
Heritage HS; Littleton, CO (3%-434) Chor; Ensm;
4H; COM; Hon Prog; Gold Medals, Ntl Piano
Guild; Outst, St Mus Teachers Assn; *Mus.*

TOWNE, Vickie Louise
Weston McEwen HS; Athena, OR (7-41) Drama;
FHA; ARC; Co-Ed, Sch P; Secy, Span C; SC; Thes;
Var C; Sftbl; Tr; Prom Qn; *Eastern Oreg St Col;
Spch Therapy.*

TOWNE, William Allen
R A Millikan HS; Long Beach, CA; Hmrm; NHS;
Co-Ed, Sch P; Bsbl; Bkbl; JV, Ftbl; Tr; Wrest; CSF;
COM; Coun of Teach A; HKg; Ath o-t Yr; *Biola
Col.*

TOWNES, Dorothy Anne
Aiken HS; Aiken, SC (60-650) BC; Secy, Ger C;
Fin, Jr Miss Pagent; Key C; Pol Sci C; COM; HCt;
U of SC; Pre-Law.

TOWNES, Patrick Mark
Castle Heights Military Acad; Lebanon, TN (4-54)
Key C; Math C; Secy, Monogram; Tres, NHS; Phys
C; Secy, Var C; Cpt, Bkbl; Co-Cpt, Ftbl; Cpt, Tr;
COM; HKg; Most Out; ROTC A; Span Cup; Most
Valuable Ath; Most Versatile; Jr Hon Star; Cum
Hon; *Middle Tenn St U.*

TOWNES, Phenician DeLois
Eastside HS; Paterson, NJ (19-550) Hmrm; NHS;
New Jersey Inst of Tech; Bus Mgt.

TOWNES, Phenician Delois
Eastside HS; Paterson, NJ (19-519) Hmrm; NHS;
NJ Inst of Tech; Computer Sci.

TOWNLEY, Dana Rene
Big Walnut HS; Sunbury, OH (125-250) Band; 4H;
Span C; Sftbl; Tr; COM; 4H A; *Ohio St U; Nurs.*

TOWNSEND, Bonnita Louise
Beecher HS; Flint, MI; Secy, NHS; Citz A; Vlbl; *U
of Mich; Archt.*

TOWNSEND, Carolyn Elizabeth
Blacksburg HS; Blacksburg, SC (10%-96) S-T,
Band; Chor; Tres, Fr C; FTA; VofDEM; Most In-
tellectual; Jr Marshal; Furman School; Presbyterian
Col Jr Fel; *Winthrop Col; Bio.*

TOWNSEND, Cassie Muriel
Bullock Co HS; Union Springs, AL; *U of Ala; Law.*

TOWNSEND, David Stephen
Irondquoit HS; Rochester, NY (240-485) Chor;
Pres, Church Yth; Pres, HS Radio Station; *Commu-
nications.*

TOWNSEND, Deborah Delois
Brainerd HS; Chattanooga, TN (33%-275) Bus C; NHS; Bkbl; Q&S A; Alpha Kappa Alpha A; *Morris Town Jr Col; Social Sci.*

TOWNSEND, Dee Ann
Clarke Comm HS; Osceola, IA (17-116) AFS; Chldr; NHS; Secy, Jr Cl; VP, Soph Cl; Tnns; Secy, FCA; FFA Swtht.

TOWNSEND, Dennis Layton
Lake View HS; Lake View, SC (3-99) Ann; BS; Pres, Soph Cl; Bsbl; Ftbl; Marshal; *Clemson U; Bus.*

TOWNSEND, Hal Douglas Jr
Lake View HS; Lake View, SC (1-109) Chor; FFA; Citz A; Greenhand; Chpt Farmer; *Wake Forest U; Law.*

TOWNSEND, Henry Clay
Crestview HS; Crestview, FL (3-304) Band; BC; Orch; VP, Sci C; Golf; Tnns; *U of Fla; Pre-Med.*

TOWNSEND, Jerry Christopher
Swansboro HS; Swansboro, NC (8-150) Band; BC; Chor; Bsbl; JV, Ftbl.

TOWNSEND, John David
Las Cruces HS; Las Cruces, NM (33%-500) Ann; Band; Pres, Drama; Hmrm; NFL; NHS; ARC; Sch P; Pres, Spch C; SC; Pres, Thes; Masque & Gavel A; Rotary A; Spch A; AIT, BS; Rotary Foreign Prog; Spch Trophy; *NM St U; Econ.*

TOWNSEND, Judith Carol
Huntingdon HS; Huntingdon, TN (10-100) F-Ed; Ann; BC; FHA; FTA; VP, Span C; Most Out; Tn o-t Month, Church A; *Baptist Sch of Nurs; Nurs.*

TOWNSEND, Marie Therese
Willows HS; Willows, CA (8-136) Hmrm; Math C; Rptr, NFL; Ski C; Spch C; Tres, SC; Tnns; CSF; Hon Prog; JA A; *U of Nev; Art.*

TOWNSEND, Mark Harold
Episcopal HS; Baton Rouge, LA (3-61) BC; Chor; Drama; Pres, InterClub Coun; Key C; A-Ed, Lit Mag; NHS; Bsbl, Sch P; Pres, Sci C; Span C; Pres, SC; Cr-Ctry; Ftbl; Tr; B Crocker A; Chem A; Citz A; Journ A; Kiwanis A; NMF; Ntl Sci Found; ROTC A; Sct Alt, Century III; LSU Alumni Schol; *U of Chicago; Pre-Med.*

TOWNSEND, Mary Grace
Independence HS; Independence, MS (10%-73) Ann; BC; H of F; *U of Miss; Pre-Law.*

TOWNSEND, Randall Calvin
Temple Heights Christian Sch; Tampa, FL (16-62) Band; NHS; Orch; Ski C; Span C; Spch C; Ftbl; Yth Fel; Photographer, Ann; *U of S Fla; Law.*

TOWNSEND, Robert Toussiant
Beecher Sr HS; Mt Morris, MI (10-370) Band; NHS; Citz A; *U of Mich; Mus.*

TOWNSEND, Terri Lou
Fairfield HS; Fairfield, AL (25%-175) Chldr; Tres, SC; Tri-HiY; Y-Tns; Beauty; HCt; Hon Prog; Head Chldr, B-Tm; Key C Swtht; Tres, Dist SC.

TOWNSEND, Yolana Rene
Fremont HS; Los Angeles, CA; Chor; Tnns; B Crocker A; *Cal St U; Med.*

TOY, Ronald Griffith Jr
Richland HS; N Richland Hills, TX; Band; *Aviation.*

TOY, Tamara Grace
The Head-Royce Sch; Oakland, CA (25-43) F-Ed; Ann; Hmrm; Lat C; SC; *U of Calif; Obstetrics.*

TOYEN, Timothy Joseph
Cretin HS; St Paul, MN (147-239) CYO; ARC; Sch P; SC; Bkbl; Bsbl; Tnns; COM; Citz A; ARC A; Art A; Stage Crew; Altar Bay; *St Thomas Col; Theology.*

TRAAS, Robert Michael
Jesuit HS; Shreveport, LA; CYO; Dbte Tm; Drama; Key C; Math C; NHS; A-Ed, Sch P; Sodality; Span C; Spch C; COM; Spch A; *Stanford U; Psych.*

TRABUE, Robyn Lee
Van-Far Sr HS; Vandalia, MO (6-90) Chor; Ensm; Rptr, FHA; NHS; A-Ed, Sch P; JV, Bkbl; VP, FHA; Career C; JV Vlbl; Alt, Soph Pilgrimage; *Med.*

TRACY, Charles Alan
Webster Co HS; Upper Glade, WV (2-112) Pres, Chess C; Sch P; Sci C; Pres, SC; S-T, Var C; Mgr, Ftbl; Tr; Cpt, Wrest; MLS; Sal; Sci A; Ldrship A; WW; *Shepherd Col; Pre-Med.*

TRACY, Hugh Walter Jr
Savannah Co Day Sch; Savannah, GA (5-62) Band; Chor; Ensm; NHS; Sci C; Soccer; Tnns; Alg A; COM; *Chem Engr.*

TRACY, John Thomas
Marian HS; Tamaqua, PA (40-160) CYO; Hmrm; Bkbl; COM; Cl Fav; Sacristan.

TRACY, Keith Alan
Sanger HS; Sanger, CA (12-500) Ann; Chor; Ensm; Madrigal; Rptr, Sch P; Swim; Waterpolo; Top 25; Omicron Zeta; *Calif Polytechnical Inst; Architecture.*

TRACY, Lori Ann
Aledo HS; Aledo, IL (40-105) AFS; Chldr; Chor; Rptr, Sch P; Ch, SC; Var C; COM; HCt; Swtht; *Bus.*

TRACY, Thea Gay
Telstar Regional HS; Bethel, ME (8-69) Band; Chor; Pres, Drama; GS; Mjrte; NHS; Pres, Sr Cl; Secy, Jr Cl; Co-Cpt, Bkbl; Hockey; Sftbl; Amer Leg A; Citz A; Cl Fav; HCt; Poet A; Pres A; WW; All Amer, Bkbl; SDAHSS; *U of Maine; Phys Ed.*

TRACY, Tracy Lee
Granite City HS S; Granite City, IL (154-656) Mus.

TRADER, Ramona Marie
Cottage Grove HS; Cottage Grove, OR (8-200) Band; VP, 4H; NHS; Spch C; Soc Sci A; Fin, Essay Contest; *Pacific U; Legal-Gov Services.*

TRAEGER, Charles Edward
John Marshall HS; San Antonio, TX (150-627) Band; Ensm; Order/Arrow; SC; All-City Bicentennial Band; All-Dist, All Reg & All-Area Band; *Tex Tech U; Mus.*

TRAHMS, Timothy Robert
La Canada HS; La Canada, CA (15%-475) Bsbl; Ftbl; Wrest; *Med.*

TRAINOR, Michael Ott
Premontre HS; Green Bay, WI (12-154) Key C; Pres, NHS; Soccer; COM; Hon Prog; Outst HS Jr; *Engr.*

TRAMMEL, Danita Kay
Huffman HS; Birmingham, AL; Band; FHA; Bank Teller; Sunday Sch Teacher; Agape; S-T, Yth Group; Church Choir.

TRAMMELL, Marguretta
Troup HS; LaGrange, GA; Chor; Bsbl; Bkbl; Sftbl; Swim; Tnns; HCt; VP, Step C; *Morris Brown Col; Bio.*

TRAMMELL, Martin Gil
Inglemoor Sr HS; Bothell, WA (17-390) Pres, A Cap Choir; Ann; Ensm; Ger C; Co-Ed, Lit Mag; Pres, NHS; Rptr, Sch P; Rptr, SC; Citz A; God & Country A; Hon Prog; Journ A; Kiwanis A; Masonic A; Poet A; Spch A; Yth Fel; NHS Outst Stu A; *Western Baptist Bible Col; Ministry.*

TRAMMELL, Traci Lynn
Tallapoosa Acad; Dadeville, AL; Band; BC; Chor; Mjrte; Pres, Jr Cl; Beauty; Cl Fav; *Auburn U; Med.*

TRAMONTOZZI, Thomas Michael
Don Bosco Tech HS; Boston, MA (16-211) Band; NHS; ARC; Ski C; Hockey; Swim; Tnns; ARC A.

TRAN, Danh Uy
John F Kennedy HS; Tumon, GUAM; *Pepperdine U; Engr.*

TRAN, Huong T
Abraham Lincoln Comm HS; Houston, TX (10%-98) FNA; FTA; Orch; Tnns; Alg A; Ntl Cath Mus Ed Asn; Type A; *U of Tex City Col; Med.*

TRANA, Scott Arnold
Valley HS; Hoople, ND (10-26) Cpt, Bsbl; JV, Bkbl; Ftbl; Hockey; Soccer; Sftbl; Tnns; Chess A; *St Sch of Sci; Elec.*

TRANQUADA, Katherine Anne
South Pasadena HS; South Pasadena, CA (1-330) A Cap Choir; AFS; A-Ed, Ann; Mgr, Arch; Chor; Hmrm; Co-Ed, Lit Mag; Madrigal; Semi-Fin, NHS; Rptr, Sch P; Span C; Secy, SC; VP, Tri-HiY; VP, Soph Cl; Mgr, Arch; JV, Bsbl; JV, Hockey; JV, Sftbl; Bank Of Amer A; CSF; Citz A; NMS; PTA A; Essentier Creative Writing A; Soroptomist A; Sportmanship Service A; *Amherst Col; Liberal Arts.*

TRANTHAM, Rachel Ann
Arkadelphia Sr HS; Arkadelphia, AR; Band; Hon Prog; 1st Band; 2nd Chair, All Region, Band; *Ouachita Baptist U; Mus.*

TRAPHAGEN, Janis Ellene
Castleberry HS; Fort Worth, TX (10-218) FHA; Mu Alpha Theta; NHS; I Dare You; Chor, Art, A's; *Cedarville Col; Mus Ed.*

TRAUB, Niklas Gerard
John Muir HS; Pasadena, CA (10-530) Lat C; Lat NHS; CSF; Hon Prog; Pres, Fantasy-Gaming C; Ntl Merit Commended; *Caltech; Math.*

TRAUBE, Kevin Paul
St Albans HS; St Albans, WV (81-496) Chess C; InterAct C; Mu Alpha Theta; Span C; Sci A; *WVA U; Computer Engr.*

TRAUTLEIN, Marylu
Saint John HS; Ashtabula, OH (15-115) A Cap Choir; CYO; Chor; S-T, Fr C; Semi-Fin, GS; 4H; NHS; DAHSS; *Miami U; Arts.*

TRAUTMAN, Richard Michael
Wheaton-Warrenville HS; Wheaton, IL (50%-290) A Cap Choir; Band; Chor; Drama; NFL; Ski C; Spch C; Spch A; Church Bkbl; *Taylor U.*

TRAUTMAN, Vickie Lynn
Jamestown Sr HS; Jamestown, ND (157-300) Pres, 4H; Key C; JV, Bkbl; Tr; COM; 4H A; I Dare You; VP, Secy, Tres, Rptr, 4-H C; *Mary Col; Nurs.*

TRAUTMANN, Kenneth Robert
Winona Sr HS; Winona, MN (90-493) NHS; Var C; Bkbl; Co-Cpt, Cr-Ctry; Tr; HCt; *Med.*

TRAUTNER, Jeffrey Wayne
Park View HS; Sterling Park, VA (85%-240) Band; Chess C; Ger C; Sch P; Tnns; *US Air Force Acad; Pilot.*

TRAUTWEIN, Mara Adele
Ritenour Sr HS; Overland, MO; Band; Tr; Sch Record, Tr; PA; Run-Up, Best Long Distance Runner; *Mo Baptist Col; Social Work.*

TRAVAILLE, Laurel Lynn
E Waterloo HS; Waterloo, IA (12-275) A Cap Choir; Chor; Spch C; Hon Prog; *Bethel Col; Home Ec.*

TRAVER, Deborah Ann
Colonie Central HS; Albany, NY (1-698) Chor; Pres, Drama; Secy, NHS; Sch P; SC; DARGCA; Hon Prog; Val; *Maria Col; Occupational Therapy Asst.*

TRAVER, Paula Janelle
Lewiston Poter Sr HS; Youngstown, NY;

TRAVIS, David Robert
Campbell HS; Smyrna, GA (5%-384) Band; BC; Fr C; Soccer; Acad A; *Ga Sou Col; Wildlife.*

TRAVIS, Earl Allen
James Monroe HS; Fredericksburg, VA (15-150) Band; Pres, Key C; NHS; Orch; Ski C; Thes; Var C; Pres, Soph Cl; JV, Bkbl; JV, Ftbl; Tr; *Va Tech U; Computer Sci.*

TRAVIS, Janet Marie
Greensburg HS; Kentwood, LA; BC; Pres, Hmrm; Lit Ral; Secy, SC; Pres, Soph Cl; HCt; NEDT; 'A' HR; *La Col; Psych.*

TRAVIS, John Paul
Northport Pub Sch; Northport, MI (1-30) Band; NHS; Co-Cpt, Bkbl; Soccer; Tr.

TRAVIS, Lauren Beth
Pompano Beach Sr HS; Pompano Beach, FL (200-535) St Stu Congress; Tres, SC; Ftbl; Presidential Phys Fitness A; *Northwestern Nazarene Col; Biological Sci.*

TRAVIS, Michael Henry
Columbia HS; W Columbia, TX (16-250) Pres, AFS; Band; Tres, Drama; NHS; Orch; Thes; Chamber of Comm A; Gov Honor Prog; Lion A; Masonic A; *U of Tex; Law.*

TRAVIS, Stuart Alan
Akron HS; Akron, CO (1-50) Band; Fr C; Order/ Arrow; Sci C; SC; JV, Bkbl; JV, Golf; JV, Tr; Alg A; Sci A; *Colo Sch of Mines; Engr.*

TRAVIS, William Augustus III
Dillon HS; Dillon, SC (2-267) BC; Key C; SC; MVP, Tnns; NEDT; Furman & Wofford Schol's; Presbyterian Col Fel; *Clemson U; Civil Engr.*

TRAVITZ, Ronald Paul
Dauphin Co Tech Sch; Harrisburg, PA (25-351) Hmrm; Yth Fel; *Ind U; Bio.*

TRAVNICEK, Pam Simone
Clintonville Sr HS; Clintonville, WI (16-235) Band; Chldr; NHS; Yth Fel; Vlbl; Church Ed Comm.

TRAWICK, Terry W
Central HS; Phenix City, AL (29-349) VP, BC; BS; InterClub Coun; Model UN; Pres, NHS; SC; Cl Fav; *U of Ala; Law.*

TRAXLER, Marla Marie
Carey HS; Carey, OH (23-106) Co-Ed, Ann; Band; Tres, Chor; NHS; Orch; Rainbow; Y-Tns; *Bowling Green St U; Acct.*

TRAYLOR, Garret Eugene
Pine Forest Sr HS; Fayetteville, NC (200-580) Band; Chess C; Ensm; Orch; Mgr, Ftbl; Mgr, Tnns; Tr; Wrest; Type A; All Co, Hon's, Bands; Distinguished Mus Stu A; John Phillip Sousa A; *Appalachian St U; Mus Ed.*

TRAYLOR, Glenn Owen
Pine Forest Sr HS; Fayetteville, NC (90-580) Band; S-T, Chess C; Pres, FBLA; Mu Alpha Theta; Order/Arrow; Sci C; Span C; Wrest; Order/Arrow A; Eagle Sct; St Sci Fair; *NC St U; Mech Engr.*

TRAYLOR, Rebecca Edna
Harry P Harding HS; Charlotte, NC (197-423) Drama; Hmrm; Tres, Span C; *E Carolina U; Phys Therapy.*

TRAYLOR, Sondi Lynn
Bethel Christian Sch; Ruston, LA (10%-18) Lit Ral; SC; Pres, Soph Cl; JV, Bkbl; Citz A; DARGCA; PA; Schol A; *La Tech U; Phar.*

TRAYLOR, Walter Lanier
Newton Co Comprehensive HS; Covington, GA (20%-265) Chor; FBLA; Pres, 4H; HiY; Hmrm; InterClub Coun; Key C; Sch P; Span C; Parl, SC; JV, Bkbl; COM; 4H A; I Dare You; Kiwanis A; MLS; *Ga Tech; Engr.*

TRAYWICK, Connie Loueen
Southview Acad; Wadesboro, NC (3-28) Ann; Band; BC; Chldr; Chor; Hmrm; Monogram; Sch P; Sftbl; Alg A; HCt.

TRAYWICK, Debbie Lynn
Yukon HS; Yukon, OK (25%-250) Chor; Ensm; VP, FBLA; FHA; VP, Var C; JV, Bkbl; Sftbl; Tnns; Tr; Vlbl; Ltrman's A; 6th St Bus Law; *Central St U; Phys Ed.*

TRAYWICK, Donna Gail
Southland HS; Arbyrd, MO (5-38) VP, FHA; FTA; Rptr, NHS; Rptr, Soph Cl; Alg A; Bio A; COM; Hist A; HCt; Hon Prog; Math A; Phy A; Sci A; Gold Medal, Phys Ed; WW; Best Ath; 1st Pl, Regional Sci Fair; *Ark St U; Elec Engr.*

TRAYWICK, Ronald Lee
Southview Acad; Wadesboro, NC; Band; Chor; Monogram; Spch C; Bsbl; Co-Cpt, Bkbl; Most Desire; Most Improved; *Ed.*

TREADAWAY, John Craig
Northside Christian Sch; Charlotte, NC (4-45) Cr-Ctry; Ftbl; Tnns; Fin, Citz A; Outdoors C; *Miss St U; Dairy Production.*

TREADWELL, Debra Jean
Malcolm X Shabazz HS; Newark, NJ; Home Ec A; Span A; Trustee A; *Nurs.*

TREAKLE, Kathy Jean
York Acad; Shacklefords, VA; Chor; Lat C; Beauty; HCt; *Mus.*

TREDWAY, Linda Lee
Winfield HS; Winfield, KS (35-214) AFS; Chldr; Semi-Fin, GS; NHS; JV, Tnns; Hon Prog; *Kans St U; Journ.*

TREDWAY, Linda Marie
Washington HS; Cherokee, IA (25%-137) Chldr; Chor; FTA; 4H; Hmrm; Madrigal; NHS; JV, Tnns; HCt; Hon Prog; Sportsmanship A; *Iowa St U; Elem Ed.*

TREEN, Jane Alison
Jamesville Dewitt HS; Dewitt, NY (5%-360) Band; Co-Cpt, Tr; Hon Prog; Yth Fel; Var Ltrs, Tr; NYSSMA Solo Comp; Amer Assoc Fr Tchrs, Hon Men; *Sci.*

TREEND, Deborah Ann
Post Falls HS; Post Falls, ID; Dbte Tm; Tr; Hon Prog; VP, Yth Group; Semi-Fin, Miss Idaho Tn Pageant; *U of Idaho; Ed.*

TREER, Cathy Cay
Downingtown Sr HS; Downingtown, PA (51-512) A Cap Choir; NHS; Tres, Span C; Var C; Hockey; Sftbl; Amer Leg A; NEDT; Opt A; Spch A; Type A; HS All Amer, Field Hockey; WW; *Temple U; Spch Pathology.*

TREGEA, Gregg Douglas
Gates-Chili Sr HS; Rochester, NY (10%-600) Chess C; Ski C; Sftbl; JV, Wrest; *U of Pa; Bus Adm.*

TREGEAR, Kathleen Bernadette
W Philadelphia Cath Girls HS; Philadelphia, PA (5-352) Chldr; Chem C; Fr C; NHS; Sch P; World Affairs C; Hist A; Hon Prog; Fr A; Religion A; Lib Aid; Spirit C; *Thomas Jefferson U; Nurs.*

TREHEARNE, Todd Eugene
Cowan HS; Muncie, IN (1-57) Mgr, Band; Dbte Tm; Ensm; NHS; Tres, Sci C; Mgr, Bsbl; Mgr, Bkbl; Mgr, Cr-Ctry; Mgr, Tr; Alg A; COM; Math A; Sci A; Type A; Ath Directors A; Outst, Band.

TREICHLER, Dorothy McNitt
N Plainfield HS; N Plainfield, NJ (128-260) Church Fellowship Group; 1st Cl A, GSct; GAA.

TREIMER, Trent Douglas
Thomas Jefferson HS; Bloomington, MN (130-750) Band; Chor; Community Yth Symph; Orch; Ftbl; Tr; COM; Citz A; *Engr.*

TRELOAR, Kay Lynn
Ventura Comm HS; Ventura, IA (13-34) A Cap Choir; Band; Chldr; Chor; Ensm; FTA; Madrigal; Tres, Jr Cl; 4H A; Math A; Vocal, Band, Mus A's; Bus Sch; Secy.

TREMEWAN, Martha Joy
Overton HS; Memphis, TN; NHS; Rptr, Sch P; Span C; COM; *The U of Iowa; Creative Writing.*

TRENT, Joseph
Rogersville HS; Rogersville, TN (15-30) FFA; *Agr.*

TRENTHAM, Shellie L
Everett HS; Lansing, MI (113-531) Chor; Drama; NHS; Sch P; Ski C; Citz A; Powderpuff Ftbl; 'Best Actress in a Scene' A; 'Most Improved in Acting' A; *Lansing Comm Col; Secy.*

TRENTHEM, Steven Terry
Independence HS; Independence, MS (10%-73) BC; Math C; Sci C; *U of Miss; Sci.*

TRENTIN, Karla Angela
Our Lady of Good Counsel HS; Newark, NJ (1-76) NHS; Ed, Sch P; SC; Alg A; Bio A; Hist A; Math A; NEDT; General Excellence A; Span A; *Montclair St Col; Span.*

TREPTOW, Mary Catherine
Ada HS; Ada, MN (25-65) Ann; Dbte Tm; Pres, Drama; FHA; St Stu Congress; Pres, Thes; Secy, Sr Cl; HCt; Outst Thespian; *St Edwards U; Acting.*

TRESCA, Caroline Rita
Saint Joseph HS; Hammonton, NJ (3-67) Bus C; Drama; 4H; NFL; Sci C; Mgr, Bkbl; Principal's List; *Pre-Law.*

TRETHRIC, Carol Jean
Campolindo HS; Moraga, CA; Hmrm; Mgr, Swim; Tr; CSF; Hon Prog; Adv, Jr HS Hon Prog; First Cl A, GSct; Sr HS Fel; Vol, GSct Day Camp; Church Yth Comm; Worship Comm; *Pepperdine U; Bus Adm.*

TREU, Randolph David
Brookfield E HS; Brookfield, WI (117-530) Band; Drama; Key C; JV, Wrest; COM; 1st Arguer A; *Wheaton Col; Anthropology.*

TREUDE, Don Michael
Navasota HS; Navasota, TX (5-130) Tres, Key C; NHS; Sci C; Span C; Parl, SC; Co-Cpt, Ftbl; Math A; Most Dependable; *Tex A&M U; Civil Engr.*

TREVILLIAN, Barbara Lynn
Freeport Sr HS; Freeport, IL (1-516) Ger C; JETS; Math C; COM; Hon Prog; Val; *U of Ill; Industrial Engr.*

TREVINO, Elizabeth Ann
M B Smiley HS; Houston, TX (4-461) Mu Alpha Theta; Ch, NHS; Bio A; COM; Hist A; Eng Medal A.

TREVINO, Frank Gabriel
Holy Cross HS; Riverside, NJ (30-397) Fin, BS; CYO; Semi-Fin, NHS; JV, Cr-Ctry; JV, Tr.

TREVINO, Maria Olivia
Roma HS; Roma, TX (8-130) Band; Tres, FHA; Pres, 4H; Hmrm; NHS; SC; Var C; Pres, Sr Cl; VP, Jr Cl; Bkbl; 4H A; *U of Tex at San Antonio; Bio.*

TREVINO, Maria Virginia
St Augustine HS; Laredo, TX (10-70) F-Ed, Ann; Semi-Fin, GS; Hmrm; NHS; SC; Secy, Jr Cl; Sftbl; Cl Fav; Spch A; VFW A; Bowl; Phys Ed A; Hon Guard; WW; *Incarnate Word Col; Fashion Merchandising.*

TREVINO, Rene Luis
Crystal City HS; Crystal City, TX (2-107) CYO; Chess C; Drama; K of C; Math C; ARC; Span C; Pres, Sr Cl; Cpt, Bsbl; Bkbl; Cpt, Ftbl; Cl Fav; Hist A; HKg; Math A; MLS; Sal; *U of Tex at Austin.*

TREVINO, Ruben Jr
Harlingen HS; Harlingen, TX (25%-600) Sch P; Bkbl; *San Antonio Col; Meteorology.*

TREVITHICK, Beth Ann
Niwot HS; Longmont, CO (7-348) Chor; Pres, Fr C; NHS; Co- cpt, Mgr, Vlbl; Hon Men, All Conf Vlbl; Fencing Champ; HR; Pres Hon A, U of N Colo; *Bethel Col; Phys Ed.*

TREVITHICK, Rebecca Lynn
Niwot HS; Longmont, CO (1-345) Fr C; Ger C; SC; Bkbl; Jr NHS; Ntl Fraternity of Stu Mus; Piano Auditions; HR; *Phys Therapy.*

TREWYN, Donna Lee
Whitewater HS; Whitewater, WI; Ann; Band; Fr C; GS; NHS; Rainbow; Ski C; SC; Tr; Prom Court; Band, Solo, Ensm Metals; Yth Enabler, Lutheran Nlt Conv; *U of Wisc; Psych.*

TRIAY, Teresita de Lourdes
Academia Maria Reina; Rio Piedras, PR; CYO; Chor; Fr C; Pres, Math C; Model UN; NHS; COM; Hon Prog; Public Relations.

TRIBBLE, Beth Ann
Parkview HS; Little Rock, AR (5%-400) BC; Rptr, City Conf; GS; Hmrm; InterClub Coun; Co-Cpt, Mjrte; NHS; S-T, Span C; Spch C; SC; Secy, Sr Cl; COM; Citz A; Hon Prog; Ntl Activ Schol; NEDT; Spch A; Gym; Outst Stu Coun; Sch Band A; Ark Yth Coun Ldrship; KLRA Yth Ldrship; *Hendrix Col; Sociology.*

TRIBBLE, David Ray
Parkview HS; Little Rock, AR (10-350) Ger C; Hmrm; Key C; Order / Arrow; Sci C; Span C; SC; Pres, Jr Cl; Soccer; COM; God & Country A; Order/Arrow A; Eagle Sct A; *Marine Bio.*

TRIBBLE, Melissa Ann
John F Kennedy HS; Richmond, VA (47-310) Drama; FBLA; VP, Hmrm; Pres, Thes; JV, Tnns; HCt; WW; *Ricks Col; Childcare Specialist.*

TRIBBY, Ruth Ellen
Greenfield Central HS; Greenfield, IN (5-330) Fin, Hancock Bank & Trust A; *Secy Skills.*

TRIBLEY, Craig Gilbert
Joliet W Campus; Joliet, IL (155-490) Band; ARC; Ski C; Swim; Hon Prog; *Northern Ill U; Geology.*

TRICEBOCK, Valerie Jean
Myers Park HS; Charlotte, NC (12-547) Band; Community Yth Symph; French NHS; Math C; Mod Mus Mas; Mu Alpha Theta; NHS; Orch; Math A; NMS; St Scholar; *Valparaiso U; Elem Ed.*

TRICHE, Paul Michael
Destrehan HS; New Sarpy, LA (12-227) BC; BS; Hmrm; SC; Bsbl; Bkbl; Ftbl; COM; Math A; Service A; *LSU; Computer Sci.*

TRICHELL, Kim
Fairview Alpha HS; Coushatta, LA (3-26) Ed; Ann; Pres, FHA; 4H; Co-Ed, Sch P; VP, Jr Cl; MVP, Bkbl; H of F; HQn; HCt; MLS; All-Dist & All-Parish.

TRICHLER, Danise Ann
Peebles HS; Peebles, OH (6-109) F-Ed, Ann; Rptr, Band; Chem C; Community Yth Symph; Drama; FTA; Hmrm; VP, Lat C; Orch; Sch Achieve Tm; Sch P; Sci C; VP, SC; Bkbl; Alg A; Chem A; Hon Prog; Land of Grant Hon Band; *Art Inst of Ft Lauderdale; Photography.*

TRICKETT, Cathy Ann
Flemington HS; Flemington, WV (3-43) Band; Chor; Tres, FHA; Rptr, FTA; NHS; Gov Honor Prog.

TRICKETT, Janet Lea
Grafton HS; Grafton, WV; Band; FTA.

TRICKEY, Timothy Ray
Copeland Unified Sch 476; Copeland, KS; Chor; Bkbl; *Mech.*

TRIESCH, Mark A
Canyon HS; New Braunfels, TX (13-160) FTA; VP, Ger C; Pres, NHS; Sci C; SC; Bsbl; Ftbl; Opt A; Gen Mills Ldr of Tomorrow; *Tex A&M U; Phys Ther.*

TRIESTRAM, Deborah Lynn
Lawrence HS; Lawrence, MI (1-64) Band; Cpt, Chldr; Ensm; Mjrte; Ch, Sch Achieve Tm; Sch P; Secy, Soph Cl; Tnns; Tr; COM; Citz A; Hon Prog; *A Beauty Col; Cosmetology.*

TRIESTRAM, Kevin Richard
Lawrence HS; Lawrence, MI (2-60) Chor; NHS; Span C; Pres, SC; Var C; Bkbl; Co-Cpt, Ftbl; Tr; Hon Prog; Sal; Yth Fel; *Grand Rapids Sch o-t Bible & Mus; Bible.*

TRIETSCH, Susan Leigh
Will Rogers Sr HS; Tulsa, OK; Band; Secy, Hmrm; Orch; Ski C; Secy, SC; Secy, Soph Cl.

TRIETSCH, Suzie Leigh
Will Rogers Sr HS; Tulsa, OK (20%-545) Hmrm; Orch; SC; Secy, Soph Cl; Superior, St Mus Contest; *Law.*

TRIGG, Dale Allan
Highland HS; Salt Lake City, UT (25%-560) A Cap Choir; Fin, BS; Chor; Ensm; Cr-Ctry; Tr; COM; Eagle Sct A; *Bio.*

TRILLA, Luz Marina
Academia Maria Reina; Rio Piedras, PR; Ann; Pres, Hmrm; Hon Prog; *Bryn Mawr Col; Foreign Lang.*

TRIM, David Emerson
Big Spring HS; Big Spring, TX (20-420) A Cap Choir; Band; Chor; MVP, Drama; VP, InterClub Coun; Lat C; NHS; VP, SC; MVP, Thes; Hon Prog; All Star Cast, UIL; All Area Choir; Best Performer; *Loretto Heights Col; Mus Theater.*

TRIMBELL,
James John William
Sparks HS; Sparks, NV (6-380) Ski C.

TRIMBLE, Kim Eileen
Center Area HS; Monaca, PA (85-225) FBLA; NHS; Yth Group; Lib C; Campus Life C; Quiz Tm; Voices o-t Lord; Yth Drama; *Bus.*

TRIMBLE, Pamala Lynn
Colton HS; Colton, CA; Chor; FHA; *San Bernardino Valley College; Education.*

TRIMBLE, Patricia Sue
Ouachita Parish HS; Monroe, LA; Anchor C; Chldr; Chor; Ensm; Hmrm; SC; Secy, Sr Cl; Pres, Jr Cl; *NE La U; Acct.*

TRIMBLE, Peggy Lou
Ouachita Parish HS; Monroe, LA (33-341) Anchor C; Chldr; Chor; Ensm; VP, Hmrm; NHS; Y-Tns; HCt; *NE La U; Nurs.*

TRIMBLE, Penny Sue
Colton HS; Colton, CA; Pres, FHA; Hon Prog; *S Calif Col of Optometry; Optometry.*

TRIMBLE, Ray Jean
Carter G Woodson HS; Tullahassee, OK; Chldr; FHA; 4H; Bkbl; Sftbl; Tnns; 4H A; Hist A; HCt; Math A; Sci A; Type A; Bkbl A.

TRIMBLE, Terrell Wayne
C E Donart HS; Stillwater, OK; A Cap Choir; *Midwest Christian Col; Ministry.*

TRIMMER, Dianne Marie
Cumberland Valley HS; Mechanicsburg, PA; Ger C; NHS; Co-Ed, Sch P; *Nurs.*

TRIMMER, Sherry Lou
Holt Co R-II HS; Mound City, MO (2-29) Ed, Ann; Pres, FHA; 4H; Secy, Jr Cl; Citz A; 4H A; HQn; Poet A; Sal; Type A; Yth Fel; Freedom Forum; Del, Regents Schol; FHA St Ldrship Conf; Co-Op Camp; *U of Mo at Columbia; Nurs.*

TRINIDAD, Cynthia Luana
Western HS; Elon College, NC (72-239) Cpt, Chldr; Pres, Hmrm; VP, Jr Cl; Secy, Soph Cl; Hon Prog; Most Out; Yth Fel; Most Sch Spirit; *W Carolina U; Home Ec.*

TRIPLETT, David Ernest
Bryan Adams HS; Dallas, TX (300-900) A Cap Choir; Co-Ed, Ann; Fin, Chldr; Drama; Ensm; Thes; Regional All Star Cast A, Drama; WW; *Tex Tech U; Communications.*

TRIPLETT, Jeffrey Prescott
Jefferson Sr HS; Cedar Rapids, IA (30-648) Pres, Band; NHS; Orch; Thes; Math A; Star Student; Symph, Concert, Jazz & Pep Bands; Symph & Pit Orch; Band & Orch A's; *Mus.*

TRIPLETT, Tara Lee
Galion Sr HS; Galion, OH (65-275) VP, A Cap Choir; Rptr, All Amer Yth; F-Ed, Ann; VP, Chor; Ensm; ARC; Span C; Rptr, St Stu Congres; Tri-HiY; Secy, Jr Cl; Secy, Soph Cl; Sftbl; Tr; Cl Fav; HCt; MLS; ARC A; Yth Fel; Yth Leg; Ch, A Cappella Choir; Wrest Statistician; Fin, McDonald's All Amer Band; Med Ch, March of Dimes Walkathon; *Lenoir-Rhyne Col; Nurs.*

TRIPP, Andrew Robert
Highland HS; Salt Lake, UT; BS; Cr-Ctry; Tr; Eagle Sct.

TRIPP, Martha L
Dongola HS; Dongola, IL (1-23) Band; BC; Chor; Pres, FHA; NHS; VP, Sr Cl; Pres, Jr Cl; Amer Leg A; Hon Prog; Pres A; Sci A; Val; Home Ec A; *Shawnee Jr Col; Nurs.*

TRISLER, Lloyd Jr
Block HS; Jonesville, LA (5-125) Dbte Tm; Bkbl; Mu Sigma; *Northeast Col; Pharmacy.*

TRISSLER, Paula Ruth
Middleburg HS; Middleburg, PA (11-134) Chor; Secy, FNA; NHS; *Bloomsburg St Col; Nurs.*

TRITT, Virginia Ann
Hubbard HS; Hubbard, OH; A Cap Choir; CYO; Chor; *Home Ec.*

TRKULJA, Kimberly Renee
Hopewell HS; Aliquippa, PA (320-420) Hmrm; Mjrte; SC; Mjrte A; *Wheeler's Bus Col; Fashion Merchandizing.*

TRNKA, Debbie Ann
New Albany HS; New Albany, IN (58-600) Hmrm; NHS; Hon Prog; Yth Fel; Accompanist, Chor; WW; Off, Girls Glee C; VP, Booster C; Accompanist, Swing Choir; *U of Evansville; Nurs.*

TRNKA, John Edward
New Albany HS; New Albany, IN (25%-700) Chor; Drama; Ger C; Thes; Bsbl; Fin, Soccer; Wrest; God & Country A; Hon Prog; Yth Fel.

TROBAUGH, Ronald Eugene
Sw HS; Macon, GA (28-544) VP, Band; Chess C; Ensm; Hmrm; Orch; Bsbl; Golf; COM; MVP, Band.

TROCHE, Maribel
Jose de Diego HS; Mayaguez, PR; Chor; Sci C; COM; Hist A; Magna Cum Laude; Phy A; C Becarios.

TROCIN, Jeffrey Edward
Huntington HS; Huntington, WV (25-400) City Conf; Fr C; VP, Math C; VP, Mu Alpha Theta; NHS; Tri-HiY; Swim; Alg A; Math A; NMS; Pres A; Huntington Swim C, Hall of Fame; St AAU Swim Champ; *Bus Adm.*

TROHKIMOINEN, Susan Joy
Grover Cleveland HS; Seattle, WA (21-243) Band; Chor; Swim; COM; *U of Wash; Journ.*

TROISI, Gina Maria
Secaucus HS; Secaucus, NJ (10-181) MVP, Chldr; Chor; Ed, Sch P; Mgr, Sftbl; *Col o-t Holy Cross.*

TROJAN, Craig Lee
Centennial Pub HS; Utica, NE (35-62) CYO; City Conf; 4H; Var C; JV, Bsbl; JV, Bkbl; JV, Ftbl; Swim; Journ A; Ldrship & Willing A; *Farming.*

TROLINE, Mark Edward
Galva HS; Galva, IL (16-77) Ann; Fr C; NHS; Tres, SC; Var C; Bkbl; Co-Cpt, Ftbl; Tr; HCt; Hon Prog; Western Ill Sch Ftbl Tm; Tres, Luther League; *Ill St U.*

TRON, Vicki Lynn
Mt Vernon Sr HS; Mt Vernon, IN; Citz A; 4H A.

TRONCOSO, Mark Lawerce
Thoreau HS; Thoreau, NM (10-89) 4H; UN Council; Var C; Bsbl; Bkbl; Ftbl; Tr; Cl Fav; Ftbl A; *St Mary's Col; Phys Ed.*

TRONE, Stephen C
Astoria HS; Astoria, IL (2-37) FFA; NHS; Co-Cpt, Bkbl; Ftbl; Tr; Sal; St Scholar; WW; *Spoon River Col; Agr.*

TRONSTAD, Doris June
Simms HS; Simms, MT (8-68) Band; Chor; Rptr, Sch P; Heisey A; *Film Television Broadcasting.*

TRONSTAD, Russell Eli
Simms HS; Simms, MT (5-70) Band; BS; FFA; NHS; Sch P; Ftbl; Wrest; Alg A; Yth Fel; *Agr.*

TROOP, Leann
Hobbs HS; Hobbs, NM (5-400) GS; NHS; Co-Ch, Bkbl; Bio A; Hon Prog; Type A; Yth Fel; *Baylor U; Sci.*

TROST, Scott David
Paton-Churdan HS; Churdan, IA (7-37) Pres, Band; Chor; NHS; Sch P; SC; VP, Sr Cl; Bsbl; Bkbl; Ftbl; Golf; Tr; HCt; *Buena Vista Col; Bus.*

TROTIER, Phillip Bradley
Parkview HS; Springfield, MO (200-350) MVP, Sftbl; *Evangel Col; Hist.*

TROTT, Lydia Christine
White Oak High; Jacksonville, NC (13-300) FBLA; FHA; Hmrm; NHS; Sci C; SC; Mgr, Bsbl; Bkbl; Citz A; Hon Prog; Principal's A; Sunday Sch Attendance A; *Coastal Carolina Comm Col; Bus Secy.*

TROTT, Mary Elizabeth Gayle
Asbury Park HS; Asbury Park, NJ (33-346) Pres, Band; Chldr; Semi-Fin, GS; NHS; SC; Tr; Hon Prog; Kiwanis A; NMS; Omega Psi Phi A; *Philadelphia Col of Phar and Sci; Phar.*

TROTTER, Emily Anne
MVK HS; Mazon, IL (15-50) Ann; S-T, Band; Pres, 4H; Lat C; Tres, Math C; Secy, SC; B Crocker A; 4H A; I Dare You; Q&S A; VP, Secy, Tres, Rptr, 4-H C; *Millikin U; Phys Therapy.*

TROTTER, Marvin Maurice
Ocean Springs HS; Ocean Springs, MS (181-275) Bus C; Ed, JETS; ARC; Sftbl; Swim; ARC A; HR; Soc of Schols; Ath Achv A; Secy, BTU; PA A; Afro-Amer C; Swim A; Church Choir; BSct; *Alcorn St U; Industrial Tech.*

TROTTER, Melvin Marcus
Ocean Springs HS; Ocean Springs, MS; Chem C; Chor; JETS; ARC; Ftbl; Swim; ARC A; Publicity Ch, Shop C; NAACP; BSct; Pres, Chrch Dist Chor; Cert of Attn; Cert in Bible Study; Afro-Amer C; Cert, Christian Ed; Soc of Scholars; *Tougaloo Col; Med.*

TROTTER, Robert William Jr
McMinn Co HS; Athens, TN (58-300) HiY; Hmrm; Pres, Key C; SC; Tnns; Tr; *Bus.*

TROUBLEFIELD, Mari Frances
Palo Duro HS; Amarillo, TX (23-200) Chor; FHA; NHS; Tres, VOE; Co-Cpt, Vlbl; Sr Favorite; Choir.

TROUBLEFIELD, Vicki Lynne
Artesia HS; Artesia, NM (56-273) AFS; VP, Bus C; Pres, Hmrm; Secy, Ski C; Pres, SC; Tnns; Tr; Beauty; HCt; Type A; Yth Fel; Tres, Hmrm; All Sports Attendant; Bsbl Batgirl; Girl o-t Mo; VP, OEA; *Bauder Fashion Col; Fashion Merchandiser.*

TROUP, Nancy Lynn
Melodyland HS; Anaheim, CA; SC; Pres, Jr Cl; Art A's; *Oral Roberts U; Art.*

TROUP, Ronald Sterling
Melodyland HS; Anaheim, CA (3-20) Pres, Ski C; Pres, SC; Co-Cpt, Ftbl; Cpt, Tr; HKg; Type A; *Melodyland Sch of Theology; Theology.*

TROUSDALE, James Philip Jr
Richardson HS; Richardson, TX (212-954) Band; VP, Bus C; Ensm; Order/Arrow; Order/Arrow A; Campus Crusade for Christ; Devotional Ch, Chor; Service Aid A; Co-Ch, Discipleship Comm; Pres, Royal Ambassadors; *Baylor U; Acct.*

TROUT, Bruce Charles
N Penn HS; Lansdale, PA (53-797) Tres, Drama; Key C; NHS; Ftbl; Bus Mgr, Drama C; Most Dramatic; Spotlight A; *Philadelphia Col of Phar & Sci; Phar.*

TROUT, Sharon Ruth
The Christian Acad; Chester, PA (13-35) Chor; Span C; JV, Sftbl; Type A; Yrbk Typist; *Washington Bible Col.*

TROUTMAN, Ellen
Sycamore HS; Cincinnati, OH (15-400) Chor; Drama; Ensm; Lit Mag; Madrigal; NHS; Sch P; Thes; God & Country A; Hon Prog; JA A; NEDT; *Milligan Col; Nurs.*

TROUTMAN, Freeman
Wilcox Co HS; Rochelle, GA (5-110) FFA; SC; Cl Fav; Hon Prog; *Fort Valley St Col.*

TROUTMAN, Gearld Stevenson Jr
Druid Hills HS; Atlanta, GA; Chor; Fr C; HiY; Key C; Bkbl; Ftbl; Soccer; Tr; Wrest; VP, Outdoor Activities C; LCA Yth Consulting Comm; Eagle Sct.

TROWBRIDGE, Connie Lou
Wellsboro Area Sr HS; Wellsboro, PA; Band; Tres, Chor; Ger C; Hon Prog; Outst, Home Ec, Ger; *Mansfield St Col; Math.*

TROWER, Teresa Rose
Mount Tahoma Sr HS; Tacoma, WA (20-460) Chor; Ensm; FBLA; Math C; Ski C; Hon Prog; JA A; Math A; Drill Tm; Secy, JA; Pres, Tracketts; *Calif Baptist Col; Mus.*

TROXEL, Jan Elise
Bloomington HS; Bloomington, IL (10%-300) Drama; Mu Alpha Theta; Span C; Spch C; Spch A; *Ill St U; Acct.*

TROXEL, Julie Ann
Northglenn Sr HS; Northglenn, CO (95-755) NHS; Span C; *Colo Col of Med & Dental Assts; Dental Asst.*

TROXEL, Ronda Lynn
Covington HS; Covington, TN (19-217) NHS; *Memphis St Col; Archaeology.*

TROXELL, Patricia Ann
Westfair Christian Acad; Jacksonville, IL; Citz A; Miss WCA; *Baptist Bible Col; Elem Ed.*

TROY, Adam Kendall
Brookhaven HS; Columbus, OH; NHS; Cpt, Bkbl; COM; Most Out; Yth Fel; MVP, Bkbl; Yth Ldr; Meritorious A; *Morehouse Col; Bus Adm.*

TROY, Christine Melinda
Northeast Sr HS; N Little Rock, AR; FBLA; Pres, FHA; NHS; Secy, SC; Secy, Sr Cl; Pres, Jr Cl; HCt; Drill Tm; Hon Graduate; *U of Ark at LR; Bus.*

TROY, Deborah Lynn
Edward H White HS; Jacksonville, FL (490-646) Beauty; Modeling; *Fla Jr Col; Nurs.*

TROYER, Arlin Ray
Goshen HS; Goshen, IN (44-298) JV, Tnns; *Med.*

TROYER, David Otto
Hershey Sr HS; Hershey, PA (35-269) Band; Community Yth Symph; Ensm; Pres, Hmrm; Model UN; Orch; UN Council; Cr-Ctry; Ftbl; Sftbl; Mgr, Tr; Hon Prog; *U of Pittsburgh; Engr.*

TROYER, Renee Denise
Goshen HS; Goshen, IN (70-267) S-T, Chor; Ntl Yth Conf; Swing Choir; Leading Role, Mus; Planning Comm; *Bethel Col; Psych.*

TROYER, Teresa Elizabeth
Goshen HS; Goshen, IN (25%-252) Hon Prog; Yth Fel; OEA; Grapplerette; *Marion Col.*

TRUAX, Cynthia Lynn
W Hills HS; Ft Worth, TX (3-500) Ed, Ann; Hmrm; NHS; Span C; SC; Tri-HiY; Cpt, Bkbl; Cr-Ctry; Tr; Amer Leg A; Beauty; Citz A; Tr Ltrs; *SW U; Pre-Law.*

TRUAX, Douglas Reid
Tabernacle Christian Sch; Greenville, SC; Ann; Band; Chor; Cpt, Dbte Tm; Ensm; Rptr, Sch P; SC; Bsbl; Cpt, Bkbl; JV, Ftbl; WW; Ftbl A; MVP, All Star, All Tourn, Bkbl; Most Active Ldrship, Bkbl; Sports Ldrship, Bkbl; *Tenn Temple Col; Bible.*

TRUBISZ, Karen Theresa
Riverhead Sr HS; Riverhead, NY; CYO; Ski C; Sodality; VP, Span C; JV, Sftbl; COM; Hist A; Odd Fellow Fin; GSct A; *Bradford Col; Eng.*

TRUBLOOD, Cheryl Ann
Western Grove HS; Western Grove, AR (1-15) Ed, Ann; 4H; F-Ed, Sch P; SC; Pres, Sr Cl; Co-Cpt, Bkbl; Sftbl; 4H A; HCt; Hon Prog; MLS; Val; Hist A; *N Ark Comm Col; Bus.*

TRUCCO, Thomas Aloysius
Saint Patrick HS; Chicago, IL (29-342) CYO; Mgr, Bkbl; Amer Leg A; COM; St Scholar; A & B HRs; *Bradley U; Elec Engr.*

TRUCKENMILLER, Gary Edward
Warrior Run Sr HS; Turbotville, PA; AFS; Band; Demolay; Ensm; Pres, 4H; Tres, SC; Bkbl; Tr; 4H A; *Penn St; Agr.*

TRUE, Donald William
Thomas Jefferson HS; Louisville, KY (24-250) A Cap Choir; BC; Bus Mgr, Chor; Ensm; Ger C; Madrigal; NHS; Bsbl; COM; *U of Louisville; Elec Engr.*

TRUE, Robert Evan
Rossville Comp HS; Rossville, GA (39-212) BC; SC; Cpt, Bkbl; Pres, Pep C; VP, Jr Exchange C; Sr Cl Social Ch; *Dalton Jr Col; Communications.*

TRUE, Robin G
Homewood-Flossmoore HS; Flossmoore, IL (180-800) Band; Community Yth Symph; FNA; Orch; Russian C; Riding C; Vlbl; Schol to Wesleyan Mus Camp; Baptist General Conf String Solo; All St Orch.

TRUEBLOOD, Darleen
John F Kennedy Sr HS; New Orleans, LA; Inter-Club Coun; Rptr, Sch P; Span NHS; Bio A; Hist A; *Loyola U; Med.*

TRUELOVE, Betty Ann
Cary Sr HS; Cary, NC (117-518) Fr C; Hmrm; Bkbl; Sci A; Girls Scorekeeper, Bkbl; *E Carolina U; Criminology.*

TRUELOVE, Sherrie Denise
North Hall HS; Gainesville, GA (18-194) BC; Chor; ARC; Hon Prog; ARC A; Hon Graduate; WW; VICA; Nurse Aide; *N Ga Col; Pre-Med.*

TRUESDALE, Yvonne Denise
Murrell Dobbins Tech HS; Philadelphia, PA; Chor; Hmrm; SC; Var C; Bsbl; Sftbl; Tnns; B Crocker A; Most Intellectual; *Howard U; Psych.*

TRUETT, Amelia Lou
Clifton Forge HS; Clifton Forge, VA (10-75) Secy, BC; Chldr; NHS; SC; VP, Tri-HiY; Var C; Mgr, Bkbl; Tr; Hon Prog; Vlbl.

TRUITT, Shanta Dorthea
Salem HS; Salem, NJ (57-300) JV, Chldr; FTA; Pres, Hmrm; SC; JV, Bkbl; Hockey; Sftbl; Best All Around; *Brandywine Col; Acct.*

TRUJILLO, Raymond
Baldwin Park HS; Baldwin Park, CA; Band; Wrest; Most Improved, Choir; *Azusa Pacific Col; Law.*

TRUJILLO, Sergio Pavon
Amer Military Acad; Guaynabo, PR; Best Dress A; *Harvard U; Med.*

TRUJILLO, Shirley Ann
Chinle HS; Chinle, AZ (2-170) Chldr; Dbte Tm; Model UN; SC; Bkbl; Tr; Cl Fav.

TRUJILLO, Sonia Maria
Academia del Sagrado Corazon; Santurce, PR (5-90) ARC; Secy C; Math A; Phy A; Geography A; Span A; Eng A; Conduct A; *St Mary's Dominican Col; Med.*

TRULL, Virginia Ann
St Stephens HS; Hickory, NC (2-230) AFS; Ann; BC; Fr C; FHA; Hist A; Hon Prog; Poet A; *Pre-Med.*

TRUMBLE, Elaine
E Peoria HS; E Peoria, IL (4-400) Fr C; NHS; F-Ed, Sch P; Pres, SC; Tnns; Amer Leg A; COM; HCt; Hon Prog; St Scholar; Secy, SC; GAA; Badminton; Sterling Merit A; *Ill Central Col; Computer Sci.*

TRUMBO, Cheryl Dawn
Westside HS; Memphis, TN (1-76) Band; Chess C; Chor; Dbte Tm; FTA; Hmrm; Math C; Secy, NHS; ARC; Ed, Sch P; Sci C; Pres, Span C; S-T, Sr Cl; Sftbl; Citz A; Hon Prog; Most Out; Val; WREC Young Amer A; *Baptist Mem Hospital Sch of Nurs; Nurs.*

TRUMBULL, Tim T
Wallace Sr HS; Wallace, ID (2-103) Secy, Arch; Math C; Span C; Spch C; Secy, Arch; Bsbl; Cr-Ctry; Tr; JV, Wrest; COM; *Creative Writing.*

TRUMP, Drew Alan
Hershey Sr HS; Hershey, PA (111-255) Span NHS; Var C; Cr-Ctry; Tr.

TRUNKO, John L
Chaminade Col Prep; St Louis, MO (12-118) Band; Chess C; Pres, Dbte Tm; NFL; Pres, Spch C; St Stu Congress; Alg A; Hist A; Hon Prog; Math A; NMS; NEDT; Opt A; Sci A; Spch A; *Washington U; Archt.*

TRUSELL, Elaine Alice
Heritage HS; Littleton, CO (120-466) *Denver Metropolitan; Math.*

TRUSSELL, Gary Clinton
Tishomingo HS; Tishomingo, MS (33%-50) FFA; Rptr, Soph Cl; Bkbl.

TRUSSELL, Roy Kenneth
Brentwood Sch; Sandersville, GA (1-53) Ed, Ann; Pres, BC; Drama; Pres, Sr Cl; Mgr, Bkbl; Alg A; Bio A; COM; DARGCA; Gov Honor Prog; Hon Prog; Math A; Phy A; Sci A; Star Student; *Ga Inst of Tech; Elec Engr.*

TRUSTER, Thomas Leigh
Edgewood HS; Trenton, OH (4-270) BS; Tres, 4H; Hmrm; NHS; Sch Achieve Tm; Span C; SC; Y-Tns; Ftbl; Alg A; COM; 4H A; *Miami U; Applied Sci.*

TRUXTON, Kristen Michele
Parkview HS; Little Rock, AR; AFS; Band; Chor; Community Yth Symph; VP, 4H; Lat C; Madrigal; NHS; Co-Ed, Sch P; Y-Tns; VP, Jr Cl; Citz A; 4H A; NEDT; Spch A; Piano A; *U of Kans; Mus Therapy.*

TRYCIECKY, Diana Mary
Immaculate Conception HS; Hamtramck, MI (11-30) Chor; Ed, Sch P; VP, Jr Cl; Cpt, Bkbl; Rptr, Sch P; MVP, Bkbl; *Wayne St U; Lib Arts.*

TSAI, Lena
John Ehret HS; Marrero, LA (22-550) Chess C; Drama; Fr C; Math C; Mu Alpha Theta; NHS; SC; Thes; Pres, Soph Cl; Amer Leg A; Bio A; Chem A; Hist A; Hon Prog; JA A; Math A; PTA A; Sci A; VofDEM; Eng A; *U of New Orleans; Commercial Art.*

TSO, David Anthony
Newbury Park HS; Newbury Park, CA (17-609) Hmrm; NHS; Phys C; Sch Achieve Tm; Ski C; Span C; St Stu Congress; SC; Co-Cpt, Hockey; CSF; COM; Citz A; Hon Prog; Star Student; Type A; St Yth Newspaper Found; *UCLA; Biol.*

TSO, Paul Lu
High Point HS; Beltsville, MD; Orch; Alg A; Coun of Teach A; Hon Prog; *U of Md.*

TSOSIE, Susan A
Chinle HS; Chinle, AZ (9-120) Span C; Up Bound; Citz A; WW; *Yavapai Col; Law.*

TSOSIE, Willard Johnson
Valley HS; Sanders, AZ; Var C; Cpt, Ftbl; Tr; Cpt, Wrest; Alg A; Bio A; Math A; Sci A; Type A; *ASU.*

TSUHA, Millie Rumi
Kubasaki HS; Okinawa, JAPAN; Chor; Hmrm; NHS; SC; Tres, Tns for Christ; Mgr, Vlbl; Outst Stu A.

TSUI, Avery Joseph
Roosevelt HS; Honolulu, HI (250-400) Swim.

THE SOCIETY OF DISTINGUISHED AMERICAN HIGH SCHOOL STUDENTS

TUBB, Myra Joy
Fairfield HS; Fairfield, AL (25%-160) Ann; Chldr; FHA; InterClub Coun; Sch P; Y-Tns; Hon Prog; *U of Ala; Med.*

TUBBS, Jenny Lynn
Forest Park HS; Beaumont, TX (88-450) Fr C; VP, Math C; VP, Pol Sci C; Pres, Math C; *SW U; Behavioral Sci.*

TUBBS, Rebecca Suzanne Southwood Hs
Southwood HS; Shreveport, LA (12-528) Band; Chor; Community Yth Symph; Mod Mus Mas; Orch; All Star Orch; Secy, MYF; Longview Symph; ROTC Drill Tm; ROTC Clr Grd; Sup Ratng, Mus Fest; Secy, Sr HS Sunday Sch; *Centenary Col; Theatre.*

TUBERGEN, Paul Randall
Arthur Hill HS; Saginaw, MI (45-650) Band; Order/Arrow; Sftbl; COM; Hon Prog; Order/Arrow A; Metal Tech A; Woodwork A; *Calvin Col; Sci.*

TUCH, Julita Rae
Ralston HS; Ralston, NE (5%-300) Band; Chor; SC; God & Country A; Hist A; Fr A; *Med.*

TUCHMANN, Michael Ellsworth
Greenview HS; Greenview, IL (6-32) Bsbl; Wrest; *Memphis St Col; Solar Engr.*

TUCK, Ann Louise
Wynford HS; Bucyrus, OH; Chor; FHA; VP, 4H; 4H A; JA A; Bowl; 100 Hr Candystriper; *Nurs.*

TUCK, Bennie Frank
Forest Hills HS; Forest Hills, NY (200-650).

TUCK, Deena Marie
Morehead HS; Eden, NC; Band; ARC; Sch P; Swim; *Rockingham Comm Col; Gen.*

TUCK, Don Anthony
Lamar R-1 HS; Lamar, MO (35-88) Chem C; Chor; Pres, Demolay; Ensm; Tres, SC; Pres, Var C; Bsbl; Golf; Tr; COM; Sci A; Pres, FCA; MFA Schol; Ntl Chor A; Mem Schols; *Mo Sou St Col; Phys Ed.*

TUCK, Tamara DeAnne
Foothill HS; Sacramento, CA (62-528) Ensm; Orch; Span C; Drill Tm; Orch, Ensm; Hon Orch; Pres, Yth Choir; Cpt, Church Vlbl; Pres, Training Union; Semi Fin, Spch.

TUCK, Vanessa Rachel
John Bartram HS; Philadelphia, PA; Cum Laude Soc; Lat C; Lat NHS; Afro-Amer Hist C; *Howard U; Law.*

TUCKER, Alex Mare
Hillel Acad; Pittsburgh, PA (4-18) Chor; Rptr, Sch P; Bus Mgr, Sr Cl; Bkbl; Ftbl; Soccer; COM; Meritorious Ser Citation; *Duquesne U; Bus Adm.*

TUCKER, Andrew Morris
Paris HS; Paris, IL (22-270) Key C; NHS; SC; Var C; Bkbl; Golf; Amer Leg A; *U of Ill; Communications.*

TUCKER, Annette Veree
Shaker Heights Sr HS; Shaker Hts, OH (5%-535) A Cap Choir; Drama; Ensm; InterAct C; Lit Mag; Madrigal; Bus Mgr, Sch P; JV, Hockey; JV, Tnns; JV, Tr; Hon Prog; Lead, Sch Mus; Young Life; Campaigners; NML; *Duke U; Pre-Law.*

TUCKER, Ava Renee
Far Rockaway HS; Far Rockaway, NY (371-514) Chor; Drama; Bkbl; Spch A; *New Paltz St Col; Mus.*

TUCKER, Bobby Glenn
Charles Henderson HS; Troy, AL (5%-190) BC; InterClub Coun; Key C; SC; SC; Var C; Cr-Ctry; Ftbl; Tr; FCA; Twenty-One C; Brother Prep Bowl Tm; *Sci.*

TUCKER, Carolyn Kay
Flanagan HS Unit 4; Flanagan, IL (6-49) VP, Bus C; Chor; Ger C; Rptr, 4H; Madrigal; NHS; Sch P; Secy, Sr Cl; Bkbl; Tr; 4H A; *Illinois Central Col; Acct.*

TUCKER, Cheryln
Hancock Central HS; Sparta, GA; FHA; 4H; Hist A; *Clark Col; Data Processing.*

TUCKER, Cornelia Anne
Southview Acad; Wadesboro, NC (2-20) F-Ed, Ann; Pres, BC; Co-Cpt, Chldr; Drama; Secy, Monogram; NHS; F-Ed, Sch P; SC; Tres, Sr Cl; DARGCA; 4H A; HCt; Math A; *NC St U; Horticulture Sci.*

TUCKER, David Emerson
Reading HS; Reading, MA (25%-449) Cpt, Band; Chor; Drama; Co-Ch, Hmrm; Ski C; SC; JV, Ftbl; Soccer; Fin, Swim; JV, Wrest; COM; Hon Prog; *Boston U; Med.*

TUCKER, Debora Anita
Petersburg HS; Petersburg, VA; Up Bound; Citz A; DARGCA; MLS; Spch A; Yth Fel; Yth Foundation A; *Richard Bland Col; Elem Ed.*

TUCKER, Dennis Haden
Gretna Sr HS; Gretna, VA (75-250) Band; Wrest A; Stu Bus Driver; *Central Va Comm Col; Machine Tool.*

TUCKER, Dennis Ray
Richland Sr HS; Ft Worth, TX (20%-700) Ed, Ann; Drama; Thes; JV, Tnns; Spch A; Best of Show, Art A; *A&M U; Architecture.*

TUCKER, Ellyn Jeanette
John Motley Morehead Sr HS; Eden, NC (1-300) Ed, Ann; Chor; Ensm; Pres, Fr C; NHS; Rptr, Sch P; Tr; Pres, Sub-Jr Federated C; Co- chief, Colorguard; Fr A; *Greensboro Col; Eng.*

TUCKER, Erskine Ramsay
Univesity Sch of Milwaukee; Milwaukee, WI (73-90) AFS; Band; Chor; Drama; Ensm; Lit Ral; Madrigal; Model UN; Ski C; Bkbl; Soccer; Tr; Hon Prog; NEDT; *Med.*

TUCKER, Fredrick Marshall
James F Byrnes HS; Duncan, SC (11-264) Band; Pres, BC; VP, Drama; VP, Fr C; Tres, Hmrm; Secy, Lat C; A-Ed, Sch P; Sci C; Hon 'H' A; Wittiest; Graduation Usher; *Furman U; Drama.*

TUCKER, Greg Karl
Marianapolis Prep HS; Thompson, CT (6-33) Chess C; 4H; Hmrm; ARC; Ski C; Co-Cpt, Bkbl; Cr-Ctry; Cpt, Golf; 4H A; Pres A; ARC A; Sci A; *Biol.*

TUCKER, Gwendolyn
Lake Clifton Sr HS; Baltimore, MD (10%-500) FBLA; Hmrm; NHS; ARC; St Stu Congress; SC; Secy, Jr Cl; Math A; Type A; DECA; *Morgan St U; Bus Adm.*

TUCKER, Jacquelyn
Groves HS; Savannah, GA (35-300) Crown & Scepter; SC; Alg A; Math A; *Armstrong Col; Algebra.*

TUCKER, Janet Ellen
Civic Mem HS; Bethalto, IL; Pep C; Young Ladies Auxilary; *Lewis & Clark Col; Bus.*

TUCKER, Janet Leigh
Central HS; Thomasville, GA; A Cap Choir; Chor; Superior, Solo & Ensm.

TUCKER, Janice Michele
Springville HS; Springville, AL (25%-96) Band; BC; 4H; Hmrm; SC; Cl Fav; 4H A; Yth Fel; 2nd Pl, Qn of Hearts; Yth Choir; MYF; *Jefferson St Jr Col; Acct.*

TUCKER, Jantha Dianne
Harlingen HS; Harlingen, TX (24-700) A Cap Choir; Chor; Dbte Tm; Ensm; NHS; Swim; Citz A; DARGCA; Spch A; Vlbl; *Baylor U; Communications.*

TUCKER, Joanne Lucille
Glens Falls HS; Glens Falls, NY (11-298) AFS; Chor; Drama; FTA; HiY; Hmrm; Pres, InterClub Coun; Ch, Key C; Cpt, Mjrte; NHS; Orch; Ch, SC; Tr; Citz A; PTA A; Hess Schol; Broad St Formes Stu A; GF Activities Schol; *RIT; Computer Sci.*

TUCKER, John Cannon
John S Shaw HS; Mobile, AL; Ch, Drama; Hmrm; Key C; Rep, Church Yth Coun; *Wrangling Sch of Art; Commercial Design.*

TUCKER, Joyce Annette
Madison Acad HS; Huntsville, AL (1-43) Secy, A Cap Choir; Tres, Ann; BC; JV, Chldr; Secy, Chor; Dbte Tm; FHA; VP, Hmrm; Math C; Pres, NHS; ARC; Rptr, Sch P; VP, SC; Secy, Jr Cl; COM; Citz A; Cl Fav; DARGCA; HCt; Hon Prog; MLS; NEDT; ARC A; Star Student; Bible A; S-T, Jr Civitan; Amer Stu Prog; *Harding Christian Col.*

TUCKER, Julie Ann
Tuscola HS; Waynesville, NC (50%-450) Band; Chldr; Swim; Tnns; Yth Fel; Sub Deb C; FCA; Pres, Yth Fellowship; *Social Work.*

TUCKER, Karen Jo
Middletown Christian HS; Middletown, OH; A-Ed, Ann; Ensm; Hmrm; SC; *Arlington Baptist Col; Christian Ed.*

TUCKER, Kathlene Susan
W B Saul HS; Philadelphia, PA (35-101) Drama; FFA; Tres, Hmrm; Tres, SC; World Affairs C; Bkbl; Tr; Journ A; St Scholar; Vlbl; Dramatics A; *Harcum Jr Col; Retail Merchandising.*

TUCKER, Keith Donald
Elmira HS; Elmira, OR (7-192) Band; Ski C; Var C; Bkbl; Ftbl; Most Improved, Ftbl; *Oreg St U; Phys Therapy.*

TUCKER, Laura Elizabeth
Watkins Overton HS; Memphis, TN; Band; Orch; Sci C; COM; Astra; GSct; Pres, Yth Chor; Secy, UMYF; *Memphis St U; Med Sci.*

TUCKER, Linda Louise
Norwalk HS; Norwalk, OH (3-250) Band; 4H; Tr; Superior, Dist Sci Fair Project; Excel, St Sci Fair Project; Hghst Scre Jr Grl; Am Sch Hist Test; *Ohio St U; Vet Sci.*

TUCKER, Margaret Ann
Cleburne HS; Cleburne, TX (50%-269) Chor; Ensm; FHA; Madrigal; WW, Mus Stu; Most Outst Choir; Songbearer; FHA; Soloist, Choir & Madrigal; *Tarrant Co Jr Col; Teaching Mentally Retarded.*

TUCKER, Melanie Lynn
Jones Co HS; Gray, GA; Ann; Tres, BC; Hmrm; Math C; Model UN; VP, Span C; COM; NEDT; Sci A; Star Student; *Wesleyan Col; Psych.*

TUCKER, Michael Gregory
James Wood HS; Winchester, VA; JV, Wrest.

TUCKER, Michael Lee
Marion HS; Marion, IN (60-735) Demolay; NHS; Sci C; JV, Bkbl; JV, Ftbl; Tr; Yth Fel; *Purdue U; Engr.*

TUCKER, Rebecca Lea
Forest Park Sr HS; Forest Park, GA; 4H; Bkbl; Sftbl; 4H A; Pres Phys Fitness A; Goldmedal, Tr A; *U of Ga; Phys Ed.*

TUCKER, Rebeccah Rae
Seymour HS; Seymour, MO (20-65) Band; Rptr, Chor; Drama; Ensm; FHA; COM; Eng A; *Drury Col; Nurs.*

TUCKER, Robert H
Cleveland HS; Cleveland, TN (11-25) Bsbl; Bkbl.

TUCKER, Sharon Lynn
Picayune Mem HS; Picayune, MS; Chor; Ensm; FHA; NHS; Y-Tns; COM; Hon Prog; Chor A; *Miss Col; Nurs.*

TUCKER, Sheila Louise
John P Stevens HS; Edison, NJ; Band; Model UN; Span NHS; Var C; Tr.

TUCKER, Shelton Scot
Harlingen HS; Harlingen, TX; Key C; Var C; Bsbl; Swim; HCt; *Blinn Jr Col; Pre-Med.*

TUCKER, Sherri Diane
Shawnee HS; Louisville, KY; Chldr; Hmrm; Tres, Jr Cl; COM; HCt; *Phys Therapy.*

TUCKER, Sherri Lynne
Allen Jay HS; High Point, NC; Band; Ensm; Fr C; Monogram; NFL; ARC; Sci C; SC; Bkbl; Tr; COM; Cl Fav; *Nurs.*

TUCKER, Steve Andrew
Warren Area HS; Warren, PA (50-399) Band; Drama; Fr C; Ger C; Orch; Span C; Yth Leg; *Grove City Col; Communicative Arts.*

TUCKER, Steven Dale
E Peoria Comm HS; E Peoria, IL (6-515) Band; Chem C; Chess C; Hon Prog; NMS; Pres, Radio C; Win, Sch Math Contest; I Rating, Mus; *Sci.*

TUCKER, Tammy Elaine
W Monroe HS; W Monroe, LA; Anchor C; Band; Jr Miss Pagent; Thes; Y-Tns; Bsbl; Flag Corps; Congeniality A; *Northeast U; Teaching.*

TUCKER, Terri Leigh
Allen Jay HS; High Point, NC; Band; Ensm; Fr C; Monogram; NFL; ARC; Rptr, Sci C; SC; JV, Bkbl; Sftbl; Tr; COM; Most Out; Yth Coun; *Med Tech.*

TUCKER, William Bryan
Parklane Acad; McComb, MS (5%-34) BS; Hmrm; NHS; Span C; Pres, SC; Pres, Jr Cl; Ftbl; COM; Math A; Most Deserving; *Miss St U; Agr.*

TUCKER, William Lamar
DeLand Sr HS; Deland, FL; Chess C; Chor; Drama; Pres, 4H; Orch; Bsbl; Soccer; 4H A; Yth Fel; Best Dressed Guy, 50'S Dance; *DBCC; Mus.*

TUDOR, David James
Plano Sr HS; Plano, TX (200-800) A Cap Choir; Chor; Ensm; Madrigal; SC; Cpt, Golf; *David Libscombp Col; Bus.*

TUDOR, Karen Lynn
Bellevue HS; Nashville, TN (4-210) BC; FHA; Y-Tns; Cpt, Bkbl; Mgr, Cr-Crtry; Sftbl; Tr; Beauty; COM; Hon Prog; NEDT; Pres A; Yth Fel; WW; Striders; Yth Coun; Civinettes; FCA; GAA; *Auburn U; Bus.*

TUERS, Sharon Mae
Potomac Sr HS; Oxon Hill, MD; Chor; FNA; COM; DARGCA; Hist A; 1st Recipient, Freedom A.

TUFFIN, Trent Sheldon
Redford HS; Detroit, MI (50-175) Band; Chldr; Chor; Drama; Ensm; Sch Achieve Tm; Bkbl; Cpt, Golf; Tr; HKg; JA A; MLS; *Ky St U; Mus.*

TUFFY, Kimberly Ann
Lyons Jr-Sr HS; Lyons, NY (86-112) Bus Mgr, Ann; Band; Cpt, Chldr; Chor; Fr C; FTA; Stu Adv Comm; Musicals; *Elem Ed.*

TUGGLE, Christopher Keith
Stillwater Sr HS; Stillwater, MN (25-570) Chor; Drama; Ger C; Madrigal; NHS; Order/Arrow; Phys C; Soccer; Amer Leg A; COM; God & Country A; NMF; NMS; Out A; Order/Arrow A; Pres, Photography C; Eagle Sct; *St Cloud St U; Physics.*

TUGGLE, James Charles Jr
University City HS; University City, MO; Orch.

TUGGLE, Jeffery Newton
Dora HS; Dora, AL (2%-135) BC; Sci C; Pres, SC; Var C; Pres, Sr Cl; Ftbl; *Walker Jr Col; Engr.*

TUINSTRA, Laurie Ann
Harris-Lake Park Comm HS; Lake Park, IA (2-41) Band; Chor; Drama; FFA; Spch C; COM; Spch A; Type A; FHA A's; *Court Stenography.*

TULENKO, Edward P
Greater Latrobe HS; Latrobe, PA; SC; Bsbl; Bkbl.

TULIK, Margaret Mary
St Joseph HS; Chicago, IL (20-78) VP, Hmrm; SC; Type A; Cpt, Bowl; Service A; PA; *St Mary's Col; Interior Decorating.*

TULLAR, Susan Lynne
Batavia HS; Batavia, IL (13-214) Cpt, Chldr; Chor; Drama; Ger C; Hmrm; NHS; Rainbow; ARC; Tri-HiY; Co-Cpt, Tr; Citz A; DARGCA; HQn; Hon Prog; *DePauw U; Psych.*

TULLEY, Sherry Beth
Lake Taylor HS; Norfolk, VA; Band; Sftbl; Swim; Tnns; *Longwood Col.*

TULLIS, Toni Anita
N Gwinnett HS; Suwanee, GA (15%-120) Band; FHA; 4H; JV, Bkbl; Gov Honor Prog; Star Student; *Reinhardt Col; Pre-Med.*

TULLY, Joe Lee
Pleasant Grove HS; Pleasent Grove, AL; Order/Arrow; Bsbl; Bkbl; Ftbl; Soccer; Sftbl; Swim; Tnns; HCt; Church Bkbl & Sftbl.

TULS, Amy S
Quartz Hill HS; Quartz Hill, CA (5-500) AFS; Chor; Secy, Dbte Tm; NHS; VP, Span C; CSF; CASO A; Independent Schol; WW; *Westmont Col; Psych.*

TUMBLIN, Susan Regina
Mortimer Jordan HS; Morris, AL; NHS; *Jeff St Col; Secy Sci.*

TUNNICLIFF, Lilly Mae
Mtn View HS; Mtn View, AR (25-60) BC; Bus C; Chor; FBLA; FHA; Lit Mag; Spch C; Beta C A; HR; PA; Journ C; *Ark St U; Nurs.*

TUNSTALL, Cerelyn Joan
Northside HS; Atlanta, GA; Chldr; Chor; Drama; Ensm; Pres, FHA; Pres, Hmrm; ARC; Sch P; Cpt, Bkbl; Beauty; B Crocker A; COM; Hon Prog; Citz A; Attendance, Chldr, A's; *Phys Ed.*

TUPMAN, Kathryn Leigh
Plano Sr HS; Plano, TX (25%-950) Band; Chem C; Chor; Ensm; Fr C; FTA; Rainbow; Bkbl; COM; Church Yth Coun; *Baylor U.*

TUR, Ivette Milagros
Juan Jose Osuna HS; Hato Rey, PR (13-101) Band; Chldr; Dbte Tm; Drama; Lit Ral; Math C; ARC; Swim; Tnns; COM; Citz A; Hon Prog; MLS; Hon Medal; *U of Puerto Rico; Acct.*

TURANO, Betsy
Alamosa HS; Alamosa, CO (26-196) Chldr; Sch P; Ski C; SC; Pres, Jr Cl; Sftbl; Tr; MVP, Gym; Ldrship A; SC A; *Colo St U; Pre-Vet.*

TURBETT, Kay Johnna
Gaylord HS; Gaylord, MN; Band; Chor; Fin, Ensm; FHA; FNA; Pres, Jr Cl; Hon Prog.

TURBETT, Lynette Fay
Gaylord Pub HS; Gaylord, MN; Chor; Sch P; Var C; Cpt, Bkbl.

TURCIC, Diane Sue
Greenville Sr HS; Greenville, PA (20-205) Chor; Fr C; NHS; Sch P; Y-Tns; Cpt, Bkbl; Sftbl; NEDT; *Edinboro St Col; Spch Communications.*

TURCO, Beth
Edsel Ford HS; Dearborn, MI (25%-450) Chor; Community Yth Symph; Orch; Elk A; Interlochen Ntl Mus; Kiwanis A; Superior, Dist & St Mus Festivals; *Hope Col; Mus.*

TURCOTT, Scott Dennis
Pinkerton Acad; Derry, NH (17-550) Drama; 4H; Hmrm; NHS; ARC; Mgr, Bsbl; Ftbl; Hockey; Wrest; Hon Prog; Most Out; Co-Ch, Nazarene Young Peoples Soc; *Eastern Nazarene Col; Dentistry.*

TURCOTTE, James Carlton
Clinton HS; Clinton, MS; Ftbl; Tr; FCA; VP, HS Choir; Coun, Yth Coordinator, Retreats; HS Ensm; Best Christian Athlete A.

TUREK, Stephen Robert
Franklin Central HS; Indianapolis, IN (26-262) Chor; Drama; Fr C; NHS; F-Ed, Sch P; Sci C; Spch C; Thes; COM; Secy, Hmrm; VP; Ntl Audubon Soc; Book o-t Yr, Lib, Fr Merit, A's; Patriotic Committee; *Central Bible Col; Theology.*

TURETZKY, John Mark
Immaculate Conception HS; Hamtramck, MI (4-29) Drama; Fr C; C; S-T, NHS; Semi-Fin, Sch Achiev; Var C; NMS; Ntl Sci Symposium; PA; *Wayne St U; Pre-Med.*

TURK, Sharri Lynn
Ithaca HS; Ithaca, NY (8%-600) Chor; Ensm; *Airline Hostess.*

TURLEY, David Wayne
First Baptist Church Sch; Shreveport, LA (31-40) Jr Member NRA; Off Worker; VP, Sch Gun C; Asst to Librarian; *La Tech U; Agronomy.*

TURLEY, Irvine Allen III
Springfield SE HS; Springfield, IL (10-402) Ger C; NHS; St Schol; WW; *Lincoln Land Comm Col; Geog.*

TURLEY, Jeff R
Trigg Co HS; Cadiz, KY (15-140) BC; CYO; NFL; Spch C; SC; Spch A; 4V Debate Champ; 3rd Pl, JV Extemporaneous; Top Debate Speaker; *Broadcast.*

TURLEY, Wendal Ray
Paris HS; Paris, IL (49-200) Band; Tres, 4H; Pres, Key C; SC; Var C; Ftbl; Wrest; 4H A; Hon Prog; Pres, Yth Arc; *Rose-Hulman Col; Chem Engr.*

TURNAGE, Helen Elizabeth
Dillon HS; Dillon, SC; Band; Pres, BC; Mjrte; NEDT; Type A; Secy, Beta C; Church Yth Coun; Presbyterian Col Fel; Graduation Speaker; VP, Church Yth Choir; *Florence-Darlington Tech Inst; Bus.*

TURNAGE, James Louis
Columbia HS; Columbia, MS; Chess C; Drama; *Pearl River Jr Col; Audio Elec.*

TURNBEAUGH, Michelle Renee
A A Stagg HS; Stockton, CA; Chor; City Conf; Drama; Hmrm; NHS; Ntl Yth Conf; Sch P; Thes; Tnns; Tr; Most Out; Vlbl; Teacher Asst, Out Pep C Member; Special Olympics Helper; *Calif Baptist Col; Drama.*

TURNBOW, Lori Ann
Iroquois HS; Louisville, KY (17-425) A Cap Choir; Ed, Ann; Band; VP, Chor; NHS; Rainbow; All St Chor; *Spencerian Col; Fashion Merchandiser.*

TURNBOW, Paul Eugene
Bartlett HS; Bartlett, TN (50-300) A Cap Choir; Ann; Chess C; Chor; Community Yth Symph; Ensm; 4H; Key C; Orch; Sci C; Span C; SC; Swim; Tr; W Tenn, All St, Quad St, Chor's; Concert Master, Yth Symph; *Memphis St U; Mus.*

TURNBOW, Sherry Lynn
Marked Tree HS; Marked Tree, AR (4-110) Band; VP, BC; VP, Chor; FHA; 4H; Madrigal; Mjrte; Thes; Bkbl; HQn; Eng A; Home Ec A; Highest Cl Avg; All-St Chor; *Ark St U; Mus.*

TURNBULL, Michael Thomas
Hazen HS; Renton, WA (5-500) Bus C; VP, Dbte Tm; VP, Spch C; Pres, Church Yth Group; Church Usher; 3rd Pl, St Debate; Debate Cert of Excel.

TURNBULL, Sandra Colleen
Apple Valley HS; Apple Valley, MN; Band; Chor; Bkbl; Sftbl; Swim; Citz A; JA A; Pres A; *Oral Roberts U; Mus.*

TURNBULL, Stephen John
Herndon HS; Herndon, VA (40-725) Band; Ensm; Hmrm; NHS; SC; Bsbl; Cr-Crtry; Soccer; Swim; Tnns; Tr; *Bradford Col; Bus.*

TURNER, Andrew Kerns
Loyola HS; Towson, MD (1-134) NHS; Bsbl; Cpt, Bkbl; COM; NEDT; Sportsmanship A; *Cornell U; Engr.*

TURNER, Angela Faye
Winnfield Sr HS; Winnfield, LA (13-122) Anchor C; BC; Chldr; Tres, Fr C; Parl, FBLA; FHA; FTA; 4H; Lit Ral; Bkbl; Sftbl; Tr; Beauty; HCt; *Northwestern U; Nurs.*

TURNER, Anthony Ray
Tishomingo HS; Tishomingo, MS (4-33) BC; Bsbl; Bkbl; Ftbl; Math A; Hon Stu; Schol; Hi-Lo; *Northeast Miss Jr Col; Elec.*

TURNER, Ardene Patricia
N Natchez HS; Natchez, MS (15%-220) A Cap Choir; BC; Chem C; Chor; NHS; Sci C; Span C; COM; H of F; Hon Prog; Math A; *U of Miss; Pre-Nurs.*

TURNER, Brigetta Kay
Provine HS; Jackson, MS; Chem C; Drama; 4H; F-Ed, Lit Mag; S-T, Mu Alpha Theta; Rptr, NHS; Sch Achieve Tm; Bus Mgr, Sch P; Sci C; Span NHS; COM; Citz A; Coun of Teach A; 4H A; JA A; MLS; Attendance A; WW; Service A; *Howard U; Med.*

TURNER, Bruce Douglas
Pittsburg HS; Pittsburg, KS; Band; Demolay; Order/Arrow; God & Country A; Order/Arrow A; Eagle Sct; Jr Counselor, Demolay.

TURNER, Caleta Schele
Columbus HS; Columbus, GA (10%-379) Co-Cpt, Chldr; Hmrm; Var C; COM; Gov Honor Prog; Hon Prog; Most Out; Yth Adv Coun to Congress; *Med.*

TURNER, Caroline Frances
Donoho Sch; Anniston, AL (10-39) Fr C; Lat C; Lit Mag; Mu Alpha Theta; Ed, Sch P; NEDT; Yth Leg; Service Projects Ch, Tri-Hi-Y; Vlbl Official; Yth in City Govt; Pres, Church Yth Group; Yth Rep, No Alapresbytery; *Princeton U; Journ.*

TURNER, Carolyn Jo
Pascagoula HS; Pascagoula, MS (5%-450) Cpt, Band; FBLA; NHS; Span C; Tres, Span C; Band A; Bus A; Shorthand C; Span A; *U of S Ala; Bus Ed.*

TURNER, Charles Lowell
Georgetown HS; Georgetown, TX (30-200) Band;
Citz A; God & Country A; Hon Prog; Outst, Band;
U of Tex; Mus Ed.

TURNER, Charlotte Elaine
Hannah-Pamplico HS; Pamplico, SC; VP, FBLA;
FHA; S-T, Hmrm; *FWB Bible Col; Elem Ed.*

TURNER, Clyde Tab
Arkadelphia HS; Arkadelphia, AR (19-200) BS;
Bus C; Chem C; Pres, Key C; Var C; MVP, Bsbl;
Co-Cpt, Ftbl; Tr; Citz A; Hon Prog; All District,
Ftbl; Outst Lineman; Athletic Schol; *Ouachita
Baptist U; Phys Ed.*

TURNER, Cynthia Lynette
Northeastern HS; Detroit, MI; Chldr; SC; Tnns; Tr;
Citz A; Ntl Achv Schol; *Mich St U; Psych.*

TURNER, Dana Annette
Knob Noster Sr HS; Knob Noster, MO; Band;
Chor; FTA; 4H; Hmrm; SC; Opt Out Tn; Type A;
S-T, Church Sr High Yth Fel; Del, Ntl Stu Safety
Prog-Wash St; *Central Mo St U; Secy.*

TURNER, David Allan
N Ridgeville HS; N Ridgeville, OH; Band; Yth
Bible Stu Teacher; *Liberty Baptist Col; Theology.*

TURNER, David Anthony
Warren Central HS; Indianapolis, IN (425-800)
Cpt, Bsbl; Co-Cpt, Ftbl; Tnns; Semi-Fin, Tr; Bus
Mgr, Parl, CYO; *Ind U; Art.*

TURNER, David Dorian
Tivy HS; Kerrville, TX (20%-350) Band; Ensm;
FTA; JETS; SC; Math A; All Dist, All Region,
Band; *Math.*

TURNER, David Wayne
Pascagoula HS; Pascagoula, MS; Band; Order/
Arrow; Sci C; Swim; COM; Most Out; *Jackson Co
Jr Col; Sci.*

TURNER, Deborah Anne
Sultan Jr-Sr HS; Sultan, WA (8-89) Ch, CYO;
Chldr; Chor; Drama; FHA; NHS; Sch P; Var C; Tr;
Citz A; Lion A; Masonic A; Type A; *Phys Therapy.*

TURNER, Dolores Sofia
Howe HS; Howe, OK; Ann; Tres, Hmrm; Tres, Jr
Cl; Hist A; Val; Jr Olymics; *Law Enforcement.*

TURNER, Donna Mae
Scott HS; Madison, WV; FBLA; FHA; NHS;
Bookkeeping A; *Bus.*

TURNER, Doretha
E Atlanta HS; Atlanta, GA (2-175) Band; FHA;
SC; COM; Hon Prog; Swtht; PC Fellow; *Ga St U;
Eng.*

TURNER, Ellen Wease
Conroe Sr HS; Conroe, TX (672-814) FHA; Sftbl;
COM; Citz A; 4H A; Hon Prog; Ntl Achv Schol;
NMS; *N Harris Co Jr Col; Off Adm.*

TURNER, Ernest Alvin
Terrell Co HS; Dawson, GA (1-200) BC; FBLA;
Hon Prog; Sci A; Geography, Eng, Gen Bus, PA,
A's; *Acct.*

TURNER, Eugene Ray
Buckhorn HS; Buckhorn, KY (1-41) Hist A; Math
A; *U of Ky; Anthropology.*

TURNER, Geoffrey Allen
Kiskiminetas Springs Sch; Saltsburg, PA (31-72) A
Cap Choir; Chor; Fr C; Ski C; JV, Golf; JV, Soccer;
Sch Choral; *Engr.*

TURNER, Gregory Thomas
Newton-Conover HS; Newton, NC (2-196) AFS;
BC; BS; Drama; InterAct C; InterClub Queen; Rptr,
Sch P; Pres, Span C; JV, Tnns; COM; NEDT; Sal;
Sci A; Schol, US Air Force Acad; *US Air Force
Acad; Aerospace Engr.*

TURNER, Henry W
Pascagoula HS; Pascagoula, MS (25%-400) Demo-
lay; Pres, Hmrm; NHS; Order/Arrow; SC; VP, Jr
Cl; Secy, Soph Cl; Ftbl; Swim; Tr; HCt; Pres A; Yth
Leg; *Jackson Co Jr Col; Law.*

TURNER, Jackie Marie
S Choctaw Acad; Toxey, AL (2-26) Ann; BC; JV,
Chldr; Chor; Bkbl; Sftbl; Beauty.

TURNER, John Bruce
John Muir HS; Pasadena, CA; BS; Co-Cpt, Bkbl;
Amer Leg A; Church Sftbl; Tres, Yth Fel; *LSU;
Bus.*

TURNER, John Raymond
Mt View HS; Mt View, CA;

TURNER, Jolynn
Rockville HS; Rockville, MD; Sch P; Hon Prog;
Pep C; Outst Child Development A; *Montgomery
Col; Early Childhood Ed.*

TURNER, Judith Alene
Clarkrange HS; Clarkrange, TN; Ann; S-T, Band;
BC; Chor; FFA; FHA; Pres, 4H; Ed, Sch P; Sci C;
Spch C; Bkbl; 4H A; Sci A; Hon Page, Legislature;
Department of Interior A; *W Ky U; Vet Sci.*

TURNER, Karen Collette
Saint Joseph HS; Kenosha, WI; A Cap Choir; Chor;
4H; Madrigal; Bkbl; Tr; COM; Type A; Tr A; MVP.

TURNER, Kathleen Johnell
Clovis HS; Clovis, NM; Secy, Chor; Ensm; NHS;
Tr; Jr NHS; Sch Ltr, Choir; *Abilene Col; Data Au-
tomation.*

TURNER, Kelly Diane
Permian HS; Odessa, TX; Band; Chor; Ensm; Fr C;
Parl, FHA; Co-Ch, Hmrm; VP, Tri-HiY; Type A;
Secy, Rptr, Tri-Hi-Y; Band Solo & Ensm A's; Most
Dependable A; Most Enthusiastic A; *Oral Roberts
U; Art.*

TURNER, Kevin William
S Salem HS; Salem, OR (134-350) Parl, AFS;
Chess C; Dbte Tm; Span C; Spch C; JV, Bkbl; Yth
Fel; Cabinet, Oreg Baptist Yth Fel; *Willamette U;
Spch.*

TURNER, Larry Leo
Northeastern HS; Elizabeth City, NC (15%-300)
Fr C; Monogram; Co-Ed, Sch P; Sci C; Pres, SC;
Pres, Sr Cl; Parl, Jr Cl; Co-Cpt, Ftbl; Delta Sigma
Theta A; Gov's Page Prog; *U of NC at Chapel Hill;
Pol Sci.*

TURNER, Lisa Rene
Moberly HS; Moberly, MO (29-200) Secy, Span C;
Bkbl; Tnns; *SW Mo St U; Span.*

TURNER, Lori Lanette
Mattie T Blount HS; Prichard, AL (6-113) *Clark
Col; Creative Writing.*

TURNER, Lynn Nanette
Central HS; Camp Point, IL (48-86) Band; Chldr;
Chor; Drama; Rainbow; Spch C; Tr; Beauty;
DARGCA; HCt; *Quincy Beauty Acad; Beautician.*

TURNER, Margaret Lee
Whitehouse HS; Whitehouse, TX (3-106) NHS;
Alg A; Sci A; *Sci.*

TURNER, Mark A
Baker HS; Columbus, GA (10-25) Golf; *Columbus
Col; Pre-Law.*

TURNER, Martha Ann
Northwest Classen HS; Oklahoma City, OK
(1-400) Fr C; Mu Alpha Theta; NHS; Sftbl; Bio A;
Hist A; Fr A; *Austin Col; Eng.*

TURNER, Marvin Wentz
Lamberton HS; Philadelphia, PA (7-128) Drama;
Hmrm; NHS; VP, Sr Cl; JV, Bkbl; Alg A; Hon Prog;
Math A; NMF; Sch Vol Service A; *Howard U; Bus
Adm.*

TURNER, Mary Lynn
Cherryville Sr HS; Cherryville, NC (56-136) Band;
Fr C; Math C; Sci C; Candystriper; Cert of Excel,
Piano; *Mus.*

TURNER, Melanie Beth
E Jordan HS; E Jordan, MI (10-90) Band; VP, SC;
Tr; Yth Fel; Solo & Ensm Medals; Ribbon, 2 Mile
Tr Competition; Tr Ltr; *Bethel Col.*

TURNER, Michael Glen
Emerson HS; Emerson, AR (1-30) Rptr, FFA;
Span C; JV, Bkbl; Tr; Alg A; Citz A; Math A; Sci A;
Span, Eng, A's; Best All Around; *Colo Sch of
Mines; Geophysics.*

TURNER, Michael Wayne
James E Sperry HS; Rochester, NY; Lat C; Soccer;
JV, Tr.

TURNER, Michelle Dawn
Bedford HS; Bedford, PA (1-240) Ann; Band;
Chor; VP, Fr C; Hmrm; NHS; Ntl Yth Conf; Rptr,
Sch P; Elk A; Hon Prog; Val; VofDEM; Sunday
Sch Teacher; Chor Librarian; Dist Band; Varsity
Singers; Reg Bnd; Chrch Chor; Pres Yth Fel; Co-
Cpt, Marching Band; *Ind U of Pa; Mus Ed.*

TURNER, Nathan Shreve
Wakefield HS; Arlington, VA; Lat C; Order/
Arrow; Rptr, Sch P; JV, Wrest; Head Acolyte,
Church; Life Sct.

TURNER, Paul Eugene
Webster Groves HS; Webster Groves, MO; Co-
Cpt, Tr; Var Ltr, Var A; *Langston U; Phys Therapy.*

TURNER, Phyllis Elaine
Huffman HS; Birmingham, AL (15%-420) Bus C;
Chem C; Chor; Pres, Ensm; FBLA; FTA; Hmrm;
Sci C; Tri-HiY; JA A; VICA; *Auburn U; Med.*

TURNER, Ramona Maria
Cleveland HS; Cleveland, TN; Drama; FHA.

TURNER, Rischelle Denise
Harbor City Christian HS; Harbor City, CA (5-13)
Chldr; Chor; Drama; Chldr A; Choir A; *SW Col;
Pediatrician.*

TURNER, Rita Joyce
Jesse H Jones HS; Houston, TX; Arch; Fr C; FHA;
Arch; Tnns; COM; *Morehouse Col; Phar.*

TURNER, Robert Forest
Cherryville Sr HS; Cherryville, NC (20-135) Fr C;
InterAct C; Math C; Monogram; NHS; Sci C; Mgr,
Bkbl; Tnns; Hon Prog; WW; *Gaston Col; Elec Engr
Tech.*

TURNER, Russell William
Charles Roth HS; Rush, NY; Chor; Order/Arrow;
Cr-Ctry; Sftbl; Tr; Order/Arrow A; Pres A; Eagle
Sct; *Math.*

TURNER, Sandra Bell
Toulminville HS; Mobile, AL; NHS; Hon Prog;
Bishop St; Acct.

TURNER, Sandra Rena
McClymonds HS; Oakland, CA; Secy, FHA; NHS;
MVP, Tr; *UCLA; Pol Sci.*

TURNER, Sarah Ann
Belvidere HS; Belvidere, IL (120-439) Chldr; Tres,
4H; Key C; Ski C; Span C; SC; Ch, Sr Cl; Sftbl; Citz
A; 4H A; I Dare You; Sci A; Spch A; Ch, Yth Fel;
4-H Camp A; 1st, Pub Speaking; Chldr A; St 4-H
er; *Wesleyan Col; Nurs.*

TURNER, Tammy Lyn
Beverly HS; Beverly, MA; MVP, Bkbl; JV, Sftbl;
Tnns; Tr; Citz A; Flag Ftbl; *Springfield Col; Phys
Ed.*

TURNER, Teresa Deaun
Permian HS; Odessa, TX (38-668) A Cap Choir; Fr
C; Hmrm; NHS; SC; Tri-HiY; Outst Fr Stu; *Oral
Roberts U; Chem.*

TURNER, Terry S
Sweet Home HS; Sweet Home, OR (27-193) *Merritt Davis Col of Bus; Acct.*

TURNER, Theresa Ann
Shenandoah Valley Acad; New Market, VA
(10-77) NHS; *Columbia Union Col; Biol.*

TURNER, Thomas Lee
Eudora HS; Eudora, AR; Band; Bkbl; Ftbl; Tr; 4H
A; *USC.*

TURNER, Tina Lisa
United Township HS; E Moline, IL (25-11000)
Chor; SC; Sftbl; Sci A; Spch A; Art A; *Harding Col;
Bus.*

TURNER, Verna Lynn
Smithfield-Selma HS; Smithfield, NC (15-400)
Ann; Band; Pres, BC; Chor; Ensm; Fr C; Rptr,
Hmrm; NHS; Orch; SC; Yth Fel; Band A; *Salem
Col; Fine Arts.*

TURNER, Vickey Lenell
John Muir HS; Pasadena, CA (221-527) Chldr; Sch
P; Bsbl; Cpt, Bkbl; Secy, Sftbl; CSF; HCt; MLS; Yth
Fel; BSU; Fin, Miss BTU; *Pasadena City Col; Bus.*

TURNER, Vicki Starr
Queen City HS; Queen City, TX (10%-73) Band;
Ensm; NHS; Sci C; Span C; Cl Fav; St Hon Bands;
1st Pl, Band Medals; *Texarkana Col; Math.*

TURNER, Virginia Jeanette
Riverside HS; Greer, SC (60-220) Ed, Ann; Pres,
Hmrm; Span C; Secy, SC; VP, Jr Cl; *U of SC; Journ.*

TURNER, Virginia Sharman
Las Cruces HS; Las Cruces, NM; Band; Orch;
Tnns; *U of Ga; Mus.*

TURNER, Vivian Denise
Independence HS; Charlotte, NC (52-648) Bus C;
FBLA; Hmrm; InterClub Coun; NHS; Pres, Pep C;
WW; *King's Col; Acct.*

TURNER, Walter James
Mirabeau B Lamar HS; Houston, TX (200-512)
Bkbl; Cpt, Ftbl; Tr; Most Spirited & MVP, Ftbl;
Ranger Jr Col; Econ.

TURNER, William Timothy
Eldorado HS; Albuquerque, NM (26-744) Band;
NHS; Orch; Tnns; JA A; Presidential Schol, U of
NM; *U of NM; Electrical Engineering.*

TURNER, Yolanda Yvonne
Middletown HS; Middletown, OH (10%-700)
Chor; Ensm; Secy, FHA; Hmrm; Rptr, Sch P; Span
C; Span NHS; Tr; Hist A; Home Ec A; Ohio Test
Scholastic Achv; *Med.*

TURPIN, Debra Kay
Helena HS; Helena, MT;

TURVEY, Julie P
Christian HS; El Cajon, CA (88%-150) AFS; CSF;
COM; VP, Church Yth Group; Fin, Gym; *Christian Service.*

TUSA, Anne Marie
John Ehret HS; Marrero, LA (46-450) CYO; Cpt,
Chldr; 4H; Hmrm; SC; Chem A; 4H A; Eng A;
Chldr A; *LSU at Baton Rouge; Nurs.*

TUSCHOFF, Becky Jo
Leroy-Ostrander HS; LeRoy, MN (14-50) Band;
Chor; Ensm; FHA; 4H; Mgr, Bkbl; Vlbl; Sports,
Chor, A's; *Nurs.*

TUTCHKO, Mary Jo
Shaler Area HS; Glenshaw, PA; CYO; Chldr;
Hmrm; Math A; Pres A; Reading A; *St Francis Sch
of Nurs; Occupational Therapy.*

TUTEN, David Carlton
Wheeler Co HS; Alamo, GA (4-50) BC; Chor; Dbte
Tm; NHS; Rptr, Tri-HiY; Pres, Jr Cl; B Crocker A;
COM; MLS; NMS; Star Student; *Andrew Col;
Eng.*

TUTERAL, Sharon Renee
Muskogee HS; Muskogee, OK (4%-550) Chor;
Drama; Ensm; Spch C; Thes; Amer Leg A; COM;
Spch A; Vocal As.

TUTHEROW, Tammy Renee
W Lincoln HS; Lincolnton, NC; Band; Gifted &
Talented Eng; *Wake Forest U; Bus.*

TUTHILL, Brian Frank
Northwood-Kensett HS; Northwood, IA (35-71) A
Cap Choir; Chor; Drama; Ensm; Madrigal; JV, Cr-
Ctry; JV, Tr; JV, Wrest; COM.

TUTTEROW, Tammy Ann
N Gwinnett HS; Suwanee, GA (10%-120) Anchor
C; A-Ed, Ann; Secy, Band; Rptr, BC; Tres, Bus C;
Ch, Fr C; FHA; Parl, FTA; Hmrm; Fin, Jr Miss
Pagent; Co-Cpt, Mjrte; F-Ed, Sch P; VP, Jr Cl; Citz
A; Hon Prog; Yth Fel; Vlbl; Fr A; *U of Ga; Elem
Ed.*

TUTTLE, Heather Sue
Lansing E HS; Lansing, MI (41-479) Hmrm; NHS;
SC; Yth Fel; Bell Choir; Church Choir; *Mich St U;
Horticulture.*

TUTTLE, James Mason
Farmington HS; Farmington, NM; Secy, Band; BS;
Ensm; Orch; WW; Mus A; *U of NM; Mus.*

TUTTLE, Kim Denise
Richmond Sr HS; Rockingham, NC; Band; BC;
FHA; Mgr, Bkbl.

TVERBERG, Karis Lyn
Valhalla HS; El Cajon, CA; Semi-Fin, Chldr; Fr C;
Hmrm; CSF; Campus Life; VP, Hospital Jr Auxi-
lary; Powder Puff Ftbl; Cand, SC; Jr Auxiliary Cap
& Pen A; *UCSD; Molecular Bio.*

TWADDLE, Martha L
Buffalo Grove HS; Buffalo Grove, IL (1-525)
Drama; Ger C; A-Ed, Lit Mag; NHS; Swim; PTA
A; Q&S A; St Scholar; Val; Pres, Church Chor &
Church Yth; *Purdue U; Chem.*

TWEDT, Anthony Wayne
Maddock Pub HS; Maddock, ND (5-23) Var C;
Bkbl; Ftbl; Golf; Swim; Bkbl A; Ftbl A; PA; *Wahpe-
ton St Sch of Sci; Elec.*

TWEED, David Scott
Dundee Comm HS; Carpentersville, IL (7-353) Lat
C; Sci C; Var C; Mgr, Ftbl; Swim; Tr; Bio A; Hon
Prog; Sci A; Var Ltrs; *Carthage Col; Pre-Med.*

TWEED, Jody Lee
Coshocton HS; Coshocton, OH (22-222) Chor;
Hmrm; VP, NHS; F-Ed, Sch P; Span C; Tres, SC;
S-T, Var C; VP, Soph Cl; Co-Cpt, Bkbl; Co-Cpt, Tr;
HCt; GS Alt; Mascot; MVP, Co-Cpt, Vlbl; MVP,
Bkbl; *DePauw U; Phys Ed.*

TWEEDY, Coleen Claire
Cut Bank HS; Cut Bank, MT (3-101) A Cap Choir;
Ann; Chor; Pres, 4H; Hmrm; NHS; Pres, Rainbow;
ARC; Ski C; Span C; SC; Var C; JV, Cr-Ctry; Cpt,
Swim; Citz A; Elk A; 4H A; Fox Found Schol; Miss
Wrest; *U of Mont; Ed.*

TWEETEN, Roger Lynn
N Central HS; Manly, IA; VP, 4H; Mgr, Tr; Mgr,
Wrest; I Dare You.

TWENHAFEL, Lori Jane
Carlyle HS; Carlyle, IL (18-138) Ann; Bus C; Bus
Mgr, Drama; FBLA; Rptr, Sch P; Secy, SC; Var C;
Sftbl; Cl Fav; HCt; Hon Prog; Journ; Q&S A; 1st
Pl, Acct, FBLA; *Murray St U.*

TWENTER, Carol Christine
Otterville R6 HS; Otterville, MO (8-22) Co-Ed,
Ann; FBLA; Secy, 4H; Sch P; 4H A; Type A; *St
Fair Comm Col; Word Processing.*

TWENTER, Philip Edmund
Smith-Cotton HS; Sedalia, MO (97-324) A Cap
Choir; Band; CYO; Chor; Drama; Sch P; Span C;
Soccer; *St Fair Comm Col.*

TWILLMAN, Robert Keith
Laura Speed Elliott HS; Boonville, MO (2-153)
Band; Chor; Ensm; S-T, Fr C; Pres, 4H; JV, Bkbl;
JV, Cr-Ctry; Mgr, Ftbl; JV, Golf; Citz A; 4H A; I
Dare You; Vocal Mus A; *Med.*

TWILLMANN, Mike William
Centralia HS; Centralia, MO (74-109) Ch, FFA;
4H; Var C; Cpt, Ftbl; Tr; Wrest; 4H A; Most Out;
Rotary C.

TWINE, Janiene Marie
Alamosa HS; Alamosa, CO (10-186) Co-Ed, Ann;
Chldr; FBLA; Semi-Fin, GS; NHS; Ed, Sch P; Co-
Ch, Ski C; Rptr, SC; VP, Soph Cl; Mgr, Bkbl; COM;
Journ A; *Colo St U; Bus Mgt.*

TWINING, Missy Lee
Bellevue HS; Belleville, NE (206-859) Band; JV,
Swim.

TWITCHEL, David James
Bonneville HS; Washington Terrace, UT; Band;
Demolay; Span C; MVP, Soccer; MVP, Sftbl;
Swim.

TWYMAN, Michael Nathanal
Bell Voc HS; Washington, DC; Chor; FTA; SC;
Bsbl; Bkbl; *Baton Rouge U; Chem.*

TYBERENDT, Jodene Lynn
Carlyle HS; Carlyle, IL (58-138) Chor.

TYE, Karen Cecilia
Berea HS; Greenville, SC; Fr C; Beauty; 2nd
Runner-Up, HS Pageant.

TYISKA, Anita Colette
Flint Central HS; Flint, MI (33%-416) Cpt, Tr;
Vlbl; Art A; Three Yr Tr A; *U of Mich; Art.*

TYLER, Anne Elizabeth
Cedar Shoals HS; Athens, GA (1-382) Band; BC;
Chor; VP, Ensm; Fin, Jr Miss Pagent; Mjrte; Math
C; COM; DARGCA; Ga All St Choir; Schol A, Jr
Miss; *U of Ga; Dietetics.*

TYLER, Anne Sylvia
Litchfield HS; Litchfield, MN (14-183) Band;
Chor; Dbte Tm; Drama; Secy, Ger C; GS; Lit Mag;
Secy, NHS; Co-Ed, Sch P; Fin, Spch C; SC; Thes;
Var C; Bkbl; Tr; Journ A; Spch A; Star Student;
Bethel Col; Journ.

TYLER, Lamarr Bernard
Willibrord Cath HS; Chicago, IL (6-82) Chess C;
VP, 4H; VP, Hmrm; Key C; Ch, Math C; Mono-
gram; NHS; ARC; Sci C; Pres, Span NHS; SC;
Bkbl; Co-Cpt, Tnns; COM; Citz A; 4H A; Hon
Prog; JA A; Most Out; Sci A; Spch A; Most Im-
proved, All Conf, Bkbl; Co & St Outst 4-H Mem-
ber; Key A; *Loyola U; Bio.*

TYLER, Lamont Anthony
Willibrord Cath HS; Chicago, IL (3-91) VP, Chess
C; Pres, 4H; Hmrm; Ch, Math C; Monogram; Tres,
NHS; ARC; VP, Sci C; VP, Span NHS; SC; Bkbl;
Tnns; Bio A; COM; Citz A; 4H A; Hon Prog; JA A;
Math A; MLS; Most Out; ARC A; Sci A; *Loyola U;
Bio.*

TYLER, Marc Logan
Minnehaha Acad; Minneapolis, MN; Band; Bkbl;
Ftbl; Co-Cpt, Tr; Hon Prog; Most Out; Bible Quiz
Tm; Pres, Yth Group; *NW Col; Missionary Lingu-
ist.*

TYLER, Sharon Louise
Los Altos HS; Hacienda Heights, CA (200-600)
Band; Hmrm; SC; Ltrettes Squad; Principal's HR;
Campus Life; Secy, Wrest Statisticians; Bsbl Statis-
tician; *Sou Calif Col; Bible.*

TYLER, Stephen Douglas
Minnehaha Acad; Minneapolis, MN; Band; Mgr,
Tr; Wrest; Hon Prog; Span Tm; Off, Church Bible
Yth Group; *Moody Bible Col; Pastor.*

TYLER, Victor Christopher
Goodlettsville HS; Goodlettsville, TN (37-155)
Band; BS; Hmrm; Var C; Pres, Sr Cl; Ftbl; Tr; Amer
Leg A; Citz A; Eagle Sct A; WW; *U of Tenn; Civil
Engr.*

TYNAN, Kenneth Robert
Sayreville War Mem HS; Sayreville, NJ; Band;
Rutgers U; Elec Engr.

TYNDALL, Jennifer Lynn
Ayden-Grifton HS; Ayden, NC (3-224) Chldr;
Sftbl; Alg A; Bio A; Health, Phys Ed A; *Sci.*

TYNES, Ingram Dickinson
Mountain Brook HS; Mtn Brook, AL (33%-400)
VP, Demolay; Hmrm; VP, InterClub Coun; VP, SC;
Lat C; HCt; Most Out; Cpt, MVP, Golf; *Wake
Forest U; Law.*

TYNES, Wilma Eileen
Classical HS; Springfield, MA (400-517) Chess C;
Fr C; Hmrm; Orch; Pres, Up Bound; Var C; Bkbl;
Tr; Alg A; COM; Citz A; Math A; Most Out; Yth
Fel; Afro-Amer C; Appreciation A, Prom Commit-
tee; Ath Ltr; *U of Mass; Elem Ed.*

TYREE, Cecilia
Belmont HS; Dayton, OH (9-400) Hmrm; NHS;
Var C; Bkbl; Cpt, Tr; B Crocker A; Math A; Prom
Court; Engr Schol; Cincinnati Reds Strght 'A'
Tickets; *Ga Tech; Engr.*

TYREE, Mark Randall
Hillsborough HS; Tampa, FL (34-640) Key C;
Math C; Mu Alpha Theta; NHS; Pol Sci C; Kiwanis
A; Math A; ROTC A; *Ozark Bible Col; Christian
Ed.*

TYRELL, Marcia Jacqueline
Eastside HS; Paterson, NJ; Mjrte.

TYSOE, Barbara Lynn
B Cardozo HS; Bayside, NY (57-1117) Hmrm; Key
C; NHS; Ski C; COM; Citz A; Hon Prog; Most Out;
Pres A; Type A; *Queens Col; Ed.*

TYSON, Charles Todd
Moultrie Sr HS; Moultrie, GA; Key C; Y-Tns; Gov
Honor Prog; *Valdosta St Col; Art.*

TYSON, David Evans
Springfield HS; Springfield, PA (10%-440) NHS;
JA; Tres, Church Bowl League; Vlbl; S-T, Baptist
Yth Fel; Tres, Diaconate Board; *Widener Col;
Acct.*

TYSON, Mary Lynn
Savannah Ctry Sch; Savannah, GA (3-60) Pres,
Chor; Lit Mag; NHS; Sci C; Mgr, Bkbl; Bio A;
COM; Gov Honor Prog; Sci A; Sci Fair As; Air
Force As; Outst Achv A; 1st Pl Ribbons, Sci; Most
Outst Project; *U of Ga; Med.*

TYSON, Nancy Juliette
Bowman HS; Wadesboro, NC (16-360) Band;
Chor; Drama; Tres, FTA; 4H; Hmrm; Cpt, Mjrte;
Pres, NHS; SC; Bsbl; Coun of Teach A; 4H A; Yth
Fel; James M Johnston Schol; Bio C; Jr Marshal;
Tres, Yth Adv C; Hon Grad; Comm Theater;
Handbell Choir; Tres, Jr Civitan C; *1NCG; Home
Ec.*

TYSON, Paula Lynn
Savannah HS; Savannah, GA; Chor; Ensm; 4H;
Hmrm; SC; Bsbl; Bkbl; Sftbl; Swim; Tr; 4H A; Bsbl,
Bkbl, Swim, Tr, A's; *Ga Sou Col; Phys Ed.*

U

TYSOR, Gary Wayne
Chantilly HS; Centreville, VA; Lat C; Order/ Arrow; JV, Bkbl; JV, Cr-Ctry; Tr; Order/Arrow A; Yth Fel; Co-Cpt, Bkbl; *Med.*

TYUS, James Darryl
Ripley HS; Ripley, TN; Bsbl; Bkbl; *Memphis St U; Acct.*

TYUS, Karen Yvette
Peabody HS; Pittsburgh, PA (129-550) Tres, Hmrm; Secy, Y-Tns; Amer Leg A; COM; Citz A; Hon Prog; *Allegheny Comm Col; Nurs.*

UAINA, Helen Upufaitele
Carson HS; Carson, CA; *UCLA; Computer Pro.*

UBALDI, Suzanne Beth
New Rochelle HS; New Rochelle, NY; Hmrm; Choir; *Col of New Rochelle; Nurs.*

UBBELOHDE, Kevin K
Clear Lake Comm HS; Clear Lake, IA (11-150) Semi-Fin, BS; Tres, NHS; Order/Arrow; SC; Var C; Bkbl; Cr-Ctry; Tr; Eagle Sct; *Iowa St U; Teaching.*

UBBELOHDE, Nancy Jane
Sheboygan Falls HS; Sheboygan Falls, WI (16-150) 4H; NHS; Tres, Sr Cl; Sftbl; 4H A; Hon Prog; Q&S A; Tyh Tutor; *Yth Tutor.*

UBEL, Lorene Geri
Lake of the Woods HS; Baudette, MN (15-78) Ann; Band; Chldr; Chor; Ensm; Fr C; Pres, 4H; Sch P; S-T, Jr Cl; 4H A; HQn; HCt; Hon Prog; Type A; Chor Pianist; *Northland Comm Jr Col; Acct.*

UBINAS, Sofia Elena
Colegio Espiritu Santo; Hato Rey, PR (10-96) A-Ed, Ann; Chldr; Drama; VP, Hmrm; Math C; VP, NFL; Ch, NHS; Ed, Sch P; Sodality; Span C; VP, Spch C; SC Var C; Secy, Sr Cl; VP, Jr Cl; VP, Soph Cl; COM; Hon Prog; Lion A; Q&S A; Spch A; Vlbl; SC A; *Yale U; Hist.*

UDITIS, Daniel John
Neshaminy Maple Point HS; Langhorne, PA (25-400) Ski C; JV, Bsbl; HR; *Computer Sci.*

UDORVICH, Debbie Sue
Spencer HS; Spencer, IA; Band; Bkbl; Golf; Hon Prog; Off Ed A.

UDOUJ, Natalie Marie
Southside HS; Fort Smith, AR (67-491) Co-Cpt, Chldr; Fr C; GS; SC; Soph, Jr, Coun; HR; Drill Tm; Charity Sorority; Service Organization; Superior, Ntl Federation of Mus; *Mus Ed.*

UDOVICH, Jo Ann Kathy
Springfield Local HS; Petersburg, OH (8-136) NHS; Span C; MLS; Secy, Hist C; WW; Pep C; Dr Belinky Med A; Petersburg Fire Dept School; *St Elizabeth Hospital Sch of Nurs; Nurs.*

UEBELEIN, Kevin Charles
Ritenour HS; St Louis, MO (50-668) Pres, A Cap Choir; Pres, Chor; Drama; Hmrm; VP, NHS; Co-Ch, SC; Sftbl; COM; Citz A; Math A; Rotary A; 1st Pl, Talent Shows; Cast, Dramatic Shows; Lead, Mus; *Harding Col; Mus.*

UEBINGER, Brad Lee
Flora Township HS; Flora, IL; A Cap Choir; Band; Chor; Dbte Tm; Span C; Yth Fel; Sch Mus; *Sou Ill U; Mus.*

UFFELMAN, Mike Lynn
Chester Comm HS; Chester, IL (33%-100) Var C; MVP, Bsbl; Bkbl; Ftbl; Sci A; *Bus.*

UHL, David Thomas
Ft Pierce Central HS; Ft Pierce, FL (5-800) Band; BC; Ensm; Key C; SC; *Elec.*

UHL, Linda Marie
Ft Pierce Central HS; Ft Pierce, FL (15-600) Secy, BC; French NHS; NHS; Pres, Keyettes; *Ed.*

UHL, Richard James
Purcell HS; Cincinnati, OH (15-191) Ftbl; *Bus.*

UHLIR, Thomas Lester
Champaign Central HS; Champaign, IL (185-325) Cr-Ctry; Co-Cpt, Tr; *Parkland Col; Social Ministry.*

UIBEL, Ruth Elizabeth
Manheim Central HS; Manheim, PA (20-300) Band; Chor; Ensm; 4H; Hmrm; Orch; SC; *Sociology.*

UITHOVEN, Leanne Renae
Luverne Pub HS; Luverne, MN (120-145) F-Ed, Ann; Band; Cpt, Chldr; Chor; Drama; Ensm; FHA; FTA; Ger C; Madrigal; Cpt, Mjrte; F-Ed, Sch P; Spch C; SC; Cpt, Tr; COM; Pres A; Spch A; *Alexandria Vocational Col; Med Tech.*

UITTENBOGAARD, Joan Ruth
Sioux Valley HS; Lake Park, IA (3-23) A Cap Choir; Ann; Band; Chor; Drama; Ensm; Rptr, FHA; 4H; Pres, Hmrm; JV, Bkbl; Cpt, Sftbl; Tr; Amer Leg A; COM; HCt; Hon Prog; *Mus.*

ULDRICH, Mary DeAnn
Geneva Pub HS; Geneva, NE; Chor; Secy, FFA; Pres, 4H; ARC; Spch C; Var C; Secy, Soph Cl; Bkbl; Sftbl; Tnns; COM; 4H A; Spch A; Secy, 4-H C; Bicentennial '200' C; Vlbl; FFA A's; Dist Win, Funks 304 Bushel Challeng; Jr Cl Coun.

ULIBARRI, Frank Robert
Del Norte HS; Albuquerque, NM; Ftbl; Tr; *Abiline Christian Col; New Testament.*

ULLEN, Candy Diane
Anoka HS; Anoka, MN (62-733) MVP, Band; Chor; Community Yth Symph; Drama; Ensm; VP, Fr C; NHS; Orch; Spch C; COM; Hist A; Hon Prog; Journ A; Most Out; Spch A; Choir, Band, Fr, Drama & Spch As; USMC Distinguished Musician A; *Col of St Benedict; Mus.*

ULLIAN, Kimberly Denise
Joliet Township E HS; Joliet, IL (53-356) A Cap Choir; Bus C; Chor; Drama; Madrigal; NHS; Hon Prog; Rotary A; Spch A; VofDEM; *Joliet Jr Col; Secy Stu.*

ULLIMAN, David Michael
Bishop Watterson HS; Columbus, OH (50-245) Chor; JETS; Lat C; Soccer; Tnns; Hon Prog; Evans Schol Found Schol; Pianist, Glee C & Cl Play; *Ohio St U; Engr.*

ULLIMAN, Mark Eugene
Bishop Watterson HS; Columbus, OH (1-250) BS; Chor; Drama; A-Ed, Sch P; JV, Tnns; Alg A; Amer Leg A; COM; Hon Prog; Math A; NEDT; Sci A; *Wash U; Archt.*

ULLMAN, Cheryl Lynne
Hetting HS; Hettinger, ND (10%-67) Band; Chor; Tres, 4H; 4H A; *Mus.*

ULLMAN, Elizabeth Ann
Parma Sr HS; Parma, OH; Chor; COM; Hon Prog; NEDT; Yth Fel; Schol Art As; *Mount Union Col; Pre-Med.*

ULLMANN, Timothy Thomas
Arapahoe HS; Littleton, CO (399-600) Band; Ski C; Co-Cpt, Bkbl; Co-Cpt, Ftbl; Sftbl; Tr; JA A; Opt A; Opt Out Tn; *U of Colo; Elem Ed.*

ULLRICH, George Jackson
Shenandoah Valley Acad; New Market, VA; BC; Parl, SC; Pres, Soph Cl; *Columbia Union Col; Chem.*

ULLRICH, Richard G
Syosset HS; Syosset, NY; Cr-Ctry; Tr; Wrest; *Wittenberg U; Bus.*

ULMAN, Geoffrey Stephen
Coral Gables Sr HS; Coral Gables, FL (444-657) Tres, Hmrm; SC; Wrest; Yth Fel; Miami Boys Choir; *Miami Dade Jr Col; Art.*

ULMER, Edna Jane
Dunlap Comm Sch; Dunlap, IA; FHA; VP, UMYF; *Nurs.*

ULMER, Victoria Lynn
N E HS; North East, MD; Band; Chor; Hon Prog; *Mus.*

ULRICH, Carolyn Lee
Hermann HS; Hermann, MO; Chor; Sftbl; *Phys Therapy.*

ULRICH, Carrie Denise
Horicon HS; Horicon, WI (25%-126) Band; Chldr; Ensm; Mgr, Bsbl; Amer Leg A; Vlbl.

ULRICH, Daniel Warren
Turner Ashby HS; Dayton, VA (1-275) Chor; Dbte Tm; Drama; Tres, NHS; Ntl Yth Conf; Span C; Chamber of Comm A; Gov Honor Prog; Hon Prog; NMF; St Dbte Champion; Eagle Sct; All St Chor; *Bridgewater Col; Math.*

ULRICH, Kathryn Ann
Duluth E Sr HS; Duluth, MN (124-545) A Cap Choir; AFS; Chor; Drama; Ger C; Ski C; Thes; Ftbl; Sftbl; Tr; COM; JA A; Yth Fel; Ski Tm; Highest Point, Thespian; Broomball; Rep, Girl's C; Director, 1 Act Play; P A Announcer; *U of Minn; Bus.*

ULRICH, Rita Colleen
Minidoka Co HS; Rupert, ID (34-312) Chess C; Rptr, FFA; Ftbl; Tr; Choir; Wrest Mat Maid; Pres, Church Dist Yth; Dist Co-Op A; *U of Idaho; Plant Sci.*

UMBERGER, Karen Sue
Hickory HS; Hickory, NC (14-350) Fr C; FBLA; Ch, French NHS; Math C; NHS; Tr; HCt; Stu o-t Mo; Graduation Marshal; *Appalachian St U; Bus Adm.*

UMBERGER, Roxann
Greeley W HS; Greeley, CO (59-293) Drama; Fr C; FBLA; FHA; ARC; Spch C; ARC A; Spch A; Secy, Pep C; Qn, Acteens; *Barnes Bus Col; Clerk Typist.*

UMBERGER, Thomas Mark
Manheim Central Sr HS; Manheim, PA (30-300) Parl, BS; JV, Ftbl; JV, Wrest; Amer Leg A; Math A; *Penn St U; Computer Sci.*

UMFRESS, Samuel Ray
Burnsville HS; Burnsville, MS (33%-42) Band; BC; Pres, FFA; Pres, 4H; Sch P; SC; Pres, Sr Cl; VP, Jr Cl; Bsbl; Bkbl; Ftbl; 4H A; HCt; I Dare You; Jr Chamber of Com A; MLS; WW; St 4-H Off; *U of Miss; Law.*

UMIPEG, Roland Cortez
George Washington HS; Mangilao, GUAM; Chess C; Ensm; *Data Processing.*

UMPIERRE, Sharee Ann
Academia Del Sagrado Corazon; Santurce, PR (1-65) Chor; Drama; Madrigal; Pres, NFL; NHS; ARC; Rptr, Sch P; Span C; Secy, SC; Alg A; Bio A; Hist A; Hon Prog; Sci A; Sch Spirit A; Eng Forensic; Span Forensic; Exchange Talent Show; *Cornell U; Biochem.*

UMSTED, Scott Stewart
Kasson-Mautonville HS; Kasson, MN (33-101) AFS; Chor; Tr; Tr Ltr.

UNDERGAN, Gwen Louise
Mentor Pub Sch; Mentor, MN (7-23) Chldr; Chor; Ensm; Sch P; Spch C; SC; MVP, Bkbl; Mgr, Ftbl; Cpt, Sftbl; HQn; HCt; Journ A; Pres A; Spch A; Type A; FHA A; Ath o-t Yr; *Law Enforcement.*

UNDERDAL, Beth Annell
Rugby HS; Rugby, ND (4-110) Band; Chor; Ensm; 4H; Madrigal; Sci C; Mgr, Bkbl; Hon Prog; Dist Mus; St Mus; *U of ND; Phar.*

UNDERDOWN, Homer Jack Jr
McMinn Co HS; Athens, TN (31-270) Band; BC; FBLA; FFA; 4H; NHS; Sci C; SC; 4H A; I Dare You; Spch A; Swtht; *U of Tenn Knoxville; Med.*

UNDERDOWN, Patricia Ann
McMinn Co HS; Athens, TN; Band; FBLA; 4H; JA.

UNDERDUE, Bessie Jane
Gumberry HS; Gumberry, NC; Fr C; Hmrm.

UNDERDUE, Betty Jean
Gumberry HS; Gumberry, NC; Fr C.

UNDERHILL, Debbie Gail
Greenland HS; Greenland, AR (2-47) Ann; FHA; Rptr, Hmrm; Ed, Sch P; Var C; Rptr, Sr Cl; Secy, Soph Cl; Bkbl; Sftbl; COM; Citz A; Type A; Phys Ed, Eng, A's.

UNDERHILL, Lori Jane
Motley Public School; Motley, MN (4-45) Co-Ed, Ann; VP, Chor; Ensm; VP, FHA; Fin, GS; Pres, 4H; Fin, Jr Miss Pagent; Mjrte; NHS; Sch P; Tr; 4H A; HCt; Hon Prog; *Brainerd Comm; Interior Design.*

UNDERWOOD, Dalana Lea
McDonald HS; Anderson, MO (20%-204) FHA; FTA; 4H; Sftbl; Swim; Citz A; Pres A; *Mo Sou St Col; Bus.*

UNDERWOOD, Danita Elsie
Etowah HS; Attalla, AL; *Gadsden St Jr Col; Banking & Finance.*

UNDERWOOD, Dean Robert Jr
Memphis University Sch; Memphis, TN (33-89) Band; Lat C; Order/Arrow; JV, Cr-Ctry; JV, Tr; NEDT; Order/Arrow A.

UNDERWOOD, Dee Ann
S P Waltrip HS; Houston, TX (25%-800) Fin, Chldr; Chor; FNA; FTA; Hmrm; SC; COM; Most Out; Demolay Swtht; Off, Drill Tm; *Bus.*

UNDERWOOD, Dianna Lynne
Portageville HS; Portageville, MO (5-77) Ann; Secy, Band; Cpt, Chldr; FHA; Pres, FNA; FTA; NHS; Pres, Sr Cl; Tres, Soph Cl; Chem A; HCt; Powder Puff Ftbl; WW; *Memphis St U.*

UNDERWOOD, Edward John
Massapequa HS; Massapequa, NY (5-600) Ger C; NHS; Sci C; Pres, World Affairs; COM; Hon Prog; Ntl Conf Chr & Jews; *Cornell U; Life Sci.*

UNDERWOOD, Karen Joy
Blacksburg HS; Blacksburg, VA (55-280) Ger C, Ann; JV, Chldr; Chor; Pres, Hmrm; NHS; SC; HCt; Spring Festival Court; Art C; GAA; Pep C; *Va Tech; Sociology.*

UNDERWOOD, Mark Latey
Burroughs HS; Ridgecrest, CA (6-381) Chem C; Fr C; Key C; Math C; JV, Bsbl; Alg A; Bank Of Amer A; CSF; Ntl Sci Found; Pres, CSF; *UCLA; Chem.*

UNDERWOOD, Mary Carolynn
Palm Beach Gardens HS; Palm Beach Gardens, FL; Pres, Chldr; Chor; Rptr, Hmrm; Secy, SC; St SC; Church Beauty; SGA Achv; Cl Coun; *Mid-South Bible Col; Bible.*

UNDERWOOD, Robin Arthur
Woodrow Wilson HS; Long Beach, CA (64-864) NHS; Var C; CSF; COM; Lion A; Co-Cpt, Gym; MVP, Gym; Calif Interscholastic Fed; Principal's HR; *U of Calif at Davis; Pre-Med.*

UNDERWOOD, Tamara Teresa
Citizens Christian Acad; Douglas, GA; Chldr; Drama; 4H; Sch P; Sftbl; HCt; *S Ga Col; Bus Ed.*

UNDERWOOD, Valerie Dianne
Smith HS; Atlanta, GA; Band; Dbte Tm; NHS; Sch P; SC; VP, Sr Cl; VP, Jr Cl; Tr; COM; Citz A; HQn; ROTC A; *Ky St U; Nurs.*

UNGER, Douglas Harleth
John Marshall HS; San Antonio, TX (130-657) Band; Hmrm; JETS; Math C; Mu Alpha Theta; Order/Arrow; Span C; COM; 1977 Tourn of Roses Parade, Band; *Tex A&M U; Pre-Med.*

UNGER, Leslie Kay
Manheim Township HS; Lancaster, PA (154-400) Var C; Bkbl; Tr; Yth Fel; Superior Rating, Piano; Bkbl & Tr Ltrs; *Va Tech Col; Bus.*

UNGETHUM, Patricia Marie
Mount Vernon Sr HS; Mount Vernon, IN (8-245) AFS; Band; Ensm; Cpt, Mjrte; Tres, Mod Mus Mas; Secy, NHS; Rainbow; Type A; Yth Fel; Swtht, Demoley; WW; *Murray St U; Bus Data Processing.*

UNGS, Mark Thomas
Jesuit HS; Portland, OR (10-122) CYO; Chem C; Tres, Chess C; Fr C; NHS; Rptr, Sch P; Cpt, Soccer; COM; Sci A; *U of Portland; Bio-Chem.*

UNICE, Ronald Mark
Uniontown Area Sr HS; Uniontown, PA (40-435) Tres, Chess C; Key C; NHS; Sch P; Co-Cpt, Cr-Ctry; Hon Prog; Rotary A; WW; *Washington & Jefferson Col; Pre-Med.*

UNKE, Alyson Nadine
St Thomas Pub HS; St Thomas, ND (5-20) Ann; Band; Chldr; Chor; Ensm; Hmrm; Sch P; SC; Cpt, Bkbl; HQn; Type A; *Luth Deaconess Hosp Sch of Nurs; Nurs.*

UNRUH, Craig Alan
Jamestown HS; Jamestown, NY (450-500) Chor; SC; Bsbl; Bkbl; *Fredonia Col; Mus.*

UNRUH, Kathryn Ruth
Doherty HS; Colorado Springs, CO; A Cap Choir; *Bethany Nazarene Col; Home Ec.*

UNRUH, Lori Diane
Cherry Creek HS; Englewood, CO (335-690) Band; FBLA; Appreciation A; New Stu C; *Bus.*

UNTIET, Linda Lorraine
Winona Sr HS; Winona, MN (25-558) Band; Chor; Ger C; Orch; Most Valuable Actress; *Winona St U; Elem Ed.*

UNTZ, Gail Elaine
Nw Cabarrus HS; Concord, NC (15-225) Band; Rptr, BC; FNA; Secy, Hmrm; Math C; Co-Ed, Sch P; Mgr, Bkbl; HCt; Journ A; Pres A; Q&S A; Yth Fel; *Kings Col; Med Off Asst.*

UPCHURCH, Deborah Jeanette
Sherman HS; Sherman, TX (38-404) Ann; FTA; Span C; *N Texas St U.*

UPCHURCH, Gilbert Rivers
Reidsville Sr HS; Reidsville, NC (5%-375) Hmrm; Key C; Order/Arrow; Span C; JV, Ftbl; Tr; NEDT; Order/Arrow A; Eagle Sct; Scholastic Achv A; *U of NC At CH; Med.*

UPCHURCH, Pamela Jean
East Tech HS; Cleveland, OH (16-400) AFS; Band; Pres, Bus C; Pres, Chor; Hmrm; Mjrte; NHS; A-Ed, Sch P; Pres, SC; Tr; Citz A; Elk A; Hist A; Hon Prog; Ntl Achv Schol; Type A; Ch, Prom; Fin, Cleveland Schol; Mayor's A; WW; *Wilberforce U; Marketing.*

UPCHURCH, Patricia Ann
Muskogee HS; Muskogee, OK (46-575) AFS; Ed, Ann; Cum Laude Soc; NHS; Sci C; Span C; SC; Hon Prog; Journ A; MLS; Type A; Pres, Entre Nous; Showstopper; Okla Hon Soc; FJA Secy; *Okla St U; Bus.*

UPDEGRAVE, Darla Denise
Milo Adventist Acad; Days Creek, OR (4-50) Band; Chor; *Walla Walla Col.*

UPDIKE, Michael Duvall
Centerburg HS; Centerburg, OH (3-81) Ed, Ann; NHS; A-Ed, Sch P; Sci C; SC; Var C; Mgr, Bkbl; B Crocker A; Math A; Q&S A; Sci A; Powderpuff Kg; WW.

UPDIKE, Steven Richard
W S Neal HS; E Brewton, AL; Band; Chess C; Secy, Drama; VP, FFA; VP, 4H; Key C; Sci C; Rptr, Soph Cl; 4H A; *Welding.*

UPDYKE, Jay
Western Alamance HS; Elon College, NC (37-235) Band; Chess C; Pres, Hmrm; EMT Emergency Med Tech; Vol Firemen; *Rowan Tech Col; Fireman.*

UPHOLD, Bonnie Louise
Uniontown Area HS; Uniontown, PA (3%-510) Band; Chor; Fr C; 4H; NHS; Orch; Rainbow; Var C; Bkbl; Sftbl; Dist Chor.

UPP, Delana Jo
Lancaster HS; Lancaster, OH (100-546) Rainbow; Jr Schol; Big Sister; GAA; *Ohio U; General Secy.*

UPPGAARD, David Alan
Edina W Upper Division HS; Edina, MN (230-510) Ger C; ARC; Soccer; Tr; Most Out; Pres A; *U of Minn; Pre-Dental.*

UPSHAW, Ira Cordell
Leesville HS; Leesville, LA (115-266) Span C; Var C; Co-Cpt, Bkbl; Beauty; Most Improved, Bkbl; *NW St U; Phys Ed.*

UPSHAW, Nikki Vanessa
Cushing HS; Cushing, TX (2-32) Ed, Ann; FHA; NHS; Secy, SC; VP, Jr Cl; Bkbl; HCt; *Stephen F Austin U; Bus.*

UPSON, Marisa Lee
Patrick Henry HS; San Diego, CA (1-1173) NHS; Ski C; Tnns; Alg A; Hist A.

UPTON, Barbara Lynne
Green Ridge R Viii; Green Ridge, MO (3-36) Ann; Secy, FHA; Secy, 4H; Bkbl; Sftbl; Regent Schol; *Central Mo St U at Warrensburg; Elem Ed.*

UPTON, Dorothy Jean
Sacred Heart HS; Klamath Falls, OR (4-35) Chor; Ensm; Math C; NHS; Amer Leg A; Hon Prog; NEDT; *Oreg Inst; Bus.*

UPTON, Sandra Denise
Sanford Acad; Sanford, MS (1-12) Tres, Ann; BC; Cpt, Chldr; Chor; Secy, Sch P; VP, Soph Cl; Bkbl; Alg A; Beauty; Math A; MLS; Most Out; Most Courteous; Best Sch Spirit; *U of Sou Miss; Math.*

UPTON, Sherri Lynn
Dothan HS; Dothan, AL (5%-35) FBLA; *George C Wallace Jr Col; Bus.*

URBACH, LoAnn Marie
Callaway Public Sch; Callaway, NE (1-25) Band; Chldr; Chor; Rptr, FHA; 4H; NHS; Spch C; SC; Bkbl; Tr; Amer Leg A; Spch A; Yth Fel; Var, Vlbl; Pom Pon; C Club; Swing Choir; *Sci.*

URBACH, Raymond Leroy
Callaway HS; Callaway, NE (1-25) Band; Pres, NHS; SC; Var C; Pres, Sr Cl; Tres, Jr Cl; Co-Cpt, Bkbl; Ftbl; Tr; Amer Leg A; COM; Elk A; Most Out; Val; Yth Fel; *Wayne St Col; Bus Adm.*

URBAN, Donna Lynn
Half Hollow Hills HS E; Dix Hills, NY (10%-1000) Chor; Drama; Co-Ed, Lit Mag; Mod Mus Mas; NHS; Orch; Span NHS; Thes; Hon Prog; Masque & Gavel A; Sci A; Mus Medals; Sch Service A; *E Stroudsburg St Col; Spch & Hearing Therapy.*

URBAN, John David
Port Chester Sr HS; Port Chester, NY (35-320) Band; Sci A; Yth Fel; *Math.*

URBAN, Lisa Marie
Wichita HS N; Wichita, KS; Band; Ed, Sch P; Q&S A; Rptr, Sch P; *Kans Wesleyan Col; Journ.*

URBAN, Marisa Adella
Windham HS; Willimantic, CT (20%-360) Chldr; Hmrm; SC; VP, Soph Cl; Nurs A; Gym A; Home Ec A.

URDIALES, Thomas
Holgate HS; Holgate, OH (50%-65) Band; Span C; Var C; VP, Jr Cl; Bsbl; Co-Cpt, Bkbl; Cpt, Cr-Ctry; Tr; *Bus.*

URIARTE, Mienda Ann
Ilion Central Jr Sr HS; Ilion, NY (15-180) Chor; Drama; NHS; Orch; Rainbow; Sch P; Span C; Thes; God & Country A; Hon Prog; Swtht; Yth Fel; VP, Church Yth; DeMolay Swtht; Church Adm Board; *U of Calif; Humanities.*

URIBE, Becky
Ajo HS; Ajo, AZ (3-124) NHS; Rotary A; WW; Pom Pon; *Northern Ariz U; Finance.*

URIE, Terrie
James Island HS; Charleston, SC; Hmrm; Span C; SC; Pres, Sr Cl; Pres, Jr Cl; WW; *Palmer Col; Legal Secy.*

URMSON, Cindy Jean
Champion HS; Warren, OH (67-300) Co-Ed, Ann; Band; JV, Chldr; Chor; Ensm; Orch; Sch Achieve Tm; Ski C; SC; Y-Tns; Bkbl; Sftbl; Tr; Yth Fel; Schol Tm; Span A; Eng A; *Ohio St U; Genetics.*

URQUHART, Betsey Derr
St Mary's Jr Col; Raleigh, NC (5%-100) Chor; Fr C; VP, Hmrm; NHS; Sci C; Tnns; COM; *UNC; Eng.*

URQUHART, Sarah Jane
Melbourne HS; Melbourne, FL (25%-600) Band; Ensm; NHS; SC; COM; Keyettes; Band Soloist; *U of Fla; Pol Sci.*

URRY, Joni Dawn
Cottonwood HS; Salt Lake City, UT (10%-1000) Secy, Orch; Amer Leg A; COM; Kiwanis A; Masonic A; MLS; Sci A; Secy, Baptist Yth Fel; Dance C; Yth Symptm; Pres, Choir; Drill Tm; Best Achv A; Job's Daughters; *Dance.*

URRY, Mark Holden
Cottonwood HS; Salt Lake City, UT (15%-790) Band; Demolay; Ger C; Bkbl; Cr-Ctry; Sftbl; Tr; Citz A; Masonic A; Sci A; Tres, Baptist Yth Fel; Mus A; Jazz Band; Marksmanship A; Eagle Sct; Mus Schol.

URSCHEL, Mary Rose
Mercy HS; Albany, NY (7-115) CYO; Drama; InterAct C; NHS; SC; NEDT; Pres, Fresh Cl; Director, Winning Cl Play; *Albany Col of Phar; Sci.*

URSITS, Dara Lee
Belle Vernon Area HS; Belle Vernon, PA (18-235) Band; JV, Chldr; Chor; Fr C; Bus Mgr, FBLA; VP, Hmrm; NHS; Sch P; Bkbl; FBLA Schol; *Robert Morris Col; Bus Ed.*

URUENA, Maria Elena
Glendale Acad; Los Angeles, CA; *Cal State LA; Occupational Therapy.*

URUENA, Osvaldo
Glendale Acad; Glendale, CA; Chess C; Lat C; Span C; Bsbl; Bkbl; Cr-Ctry; Ftbl; Soccer; Sftbl; Swim; Tnns; Tr; *PUC; Dentist.*

URWICK, Richard Scott
Olympic HS; Charlotte, NC; SC; *U of NC; Dentistry.*

USHER, Jack Holmes
Savannah Ctry Day Sch; Savannah, GA (20-65) Ann; Cpt; Golf; Soccer; HR; *U of Ga; Bus Adm.*

USHER, Tammy Lanette
Jesse H Jones HS; Houston, TX; Mu Alpha Theta; *U of Houston; Engr.*

USHIGUSA, Kosaku
El Cerrito HS; El Cerrito, CA (20-492) Sci C; CSF; Los Sabios; Stu o-t Mo; *U of Calif; Engr.*

USHMAN, Peggy Sue
East HS; Madison, WI (11-540) Fr C; NHS; Hon Prog; PTA A; *U of Wisc at Madison; Nurs.*

USMILLER, Karen Rebecca
Tyner HS; Chattanooga, TN (8-261) BC; Chldr; Drama; Fin, GS; Model UN; NHS; Sch P; Pres, Sigma Phi Omega; Friendliest; Christmas Court; *U of Tenn.*

USRY, Tina Ann
Lake HS; Lake, MS (2-40) Band; Pres, BC; FHA; Ed, Sch P; B Crocker A; Sal; Eng, Best All Around, A's; *Matty Hersee Sch of Nurs; Nurs.*

USSERY, Mark Wayne
Seymour HS; Seymour, TN (1-90) BC; Key C; Var C; Pres, Jr Cl; Bsbl; Bkbl; Chem A; Cl Fav; MLS; Sal; Jr Yr A; *U of Tenn; Bus Adm.*

USSERY, Melody Dawn
Jones Co HS; Gray, GA (10%-250) Ann; Chldr; Hmrm; S-T, NHS; F-Ed, Sch P; Pres, Sci C; VP, SC; Var C.

UTECH, William George
Merrill Sr HS; Merrill, WI (17-323) A Cap Choir; Chor; Drama; Ensm; Ger C; Hmrm; Madrigal; Sch P; Spch C; Bkbl; Tr; Spch A; WW; *Concordia St Paul U; Ministerial.*

UTLEY, Saralyn
Woodrow Wilson HS; Camden, NJ; Band; Chor; Hmrm; InterAct C; SC; Humanitarian A; Glee C A; SG A; Cafeteria Helpers A; Mus A; Safety Sq A; *Trenton Col; Special Ed.*

UTSEY, Cynthia Maria
George Washington HS; Denver, CO (210-700) Chor; Citz A; Yth Fel; City-Wide Chor; Yth Ldrship A; *U of N Colo; Mus.*

UTSEY, Delbert Lewis
John Marshall HS; Milwaukee, WI; Band; Community Yth Symph; Bio A; Math A; *Mus.*

UTSMAN, Sanya Anne
Farragut HS; Concord, TN; Band; Sch P; *U of Tenn; Communications.*

UTTER, Andrew Marsh
S Plantation HS; Plantation, FL (8-660) Semi-Fin, BS; Ger C; InterAct C; NHS; SC; Tnns; Alg A; Elk A; Hon Prog; Math A; NEDT; Opt A; Opt Out Tn; Freedom's Found A; Ger A; *Wake Forest U; Pol Sci.*

UTTER, Dorothy Jean
Citrus HS; Inverness, FL (26-250) Chor.

UTTER, Karen Sue
Quincy Sr HS II; Quincy, IL (33%-700).

UYEDA, Steven Masaji
Luther Burbank HS; Sacramento, CA; Band; CSF; *Biological Sci.*

UYENO, Richard Akira
Reseda HS; Reseda, CA (1-640) Tres, InterAct C; NHS; S-T, SC; Tnns; CSF; Hon Prog; Regent Schol; Schol Ath; *UCLA; Biol.*

UYEUNTEN, Donne Mayumi
Roosevelt HS; Honolulu, HI (20-591) Span C; Pres, Y-Tns; Secy, Soph Cl; Most Out; *U of Hawaii; Fashion.*

V

VACCARIELLO, Patricia Mary
Mercy HS; Albany, NY (10-108) Hon Prog; NEDT; Regent Schol; Ntl Essay Press; *Siena Col; Psych.*

VACCARO, Theresa Joann
St Joseph HS; Hammonton, NJ (7-48) Cpt, Chldr; Chor; Fr C; FTA; Jr Miss Pagent; NHS; SC; Pres, Sr Cl; Secy, Jr Cl; Secy, Soph Cl; Bkbl; Co-Cpt, Hockey; HQn; Hon Prog; Principal's List; *Immaculata Col; Fr.*

VadeBonCOEUR, Andrew Mark
Bradley-Bourbonnzas Comm HS; Bradley, IL (79-402) Rptr, Sch P; Var C; JV, Bkbl; Cr-Ctry; *US Army; Phys Ed.*

VAGEDES, Frank Thomas
Coldwater HS; Coldwater, OH; CYO; VP, FFA.

VAHLE, Kurt Michael
Winter Haven HS; Winter Haven, FL (35-900) AFS; Chess C; Ger C; Secy, Key C; NHS; JV, Cr-Ctry; Faculty A; *Physics.*

VAIL, Evelyn Janice
Shawnee Mission Northwest HS; Shawnee Mission, KS (24-712) A Cap Choir; NHS; Orch; Tr; Yth Leg; KMEA Dist 1 Orch; KMEA St Orch; *Mid-Amer Nazarene Col; Sociology.*

VAIL, Trina Kay
Crothersville HS; Crothersville, IN (5-55) Chldr; NHS; Sch P; Hist A; HCt; St Scholar; Type A; VFW A; VofDEM; Yth Fel; Acct A; *Vincennes U; Bus Mgt.*

VAJDOS, Margaret Adelle
Douglas MacArthur HS; San Antonio, TX (59-610) Band; BC; Lat C; NHS; Ed, Sch P; Sci C; Region, Dist & Area Band; 2nd Pl, Jr Classical Art Contest; 1st Div, Solo & Ensm Contest; Bank Bicentennial Band; *St Mary's U; Bio.*

VAKAS, Linda Susan
T C Williams HS; Alexandria, VA (1-750) NHS; Orch; Rptr, Sch P; Bio A; COM; Hon Prog; Math A; Mus Camp Schol; Run-Up, Eng Composition Contest; *U of Va; Law.*

VALACH, Kenneth Joseph
Salem HS; Salem, OR (10%-300) VP, Fr C; Order/ Arrow; SC; Var C; Ftbl; JV, Tr; Wrest; Order/ Arrow A; Eagle Sct; *Law.*

VALCARCEL, Teresita J
Our Lady of Good Counsel HS; Newark, NJ (3-76) Secy, Sch P; *Rutger's St Col; Acct.*

VALDES, Maria Grace
Acad o-t Holy Names; Tampa, FL (7-68) Chess C; Pres, InterClub Coun; NHS; Ed, Sch P; Sci C; Span C; Span NHS; Pres, SC; Tnns; Hon Prog; Q&S A; Most Dependable; *Emory U; Law.*

VALDES, Raul
Juan Jose Osuna HS; Hato Rey, PR (11-101) CYO; VP; Lit Ral; Phys C; ARC; Sci C; Span C; Ftbl; Golf; Swim; Tnns; COM; Hon Prog; JA A; Lion A; Math A; Sci A; Cl Hon; *UPR; Acct.*

VALDEZ, David Lee
Holy Trinity HS; Chicago, IL (57-175) AFS; Var C; Cpt, Bsbl; Bkbl; COM; Citz A; Hon Prog; Most Out; *Goshen Col; Social Worker.*

VALENCIA, Norman De Jesus
Farrington HS; Honolulu, HI (46-700) Band; Cum Laude Soc; Ensm; Cr-Ctry; Outst Fr Stu; *Leeward Comm Col; Liberal Arts.*

VALENCIA, Ramona Haunani
Aiea HS; Aiea, HI; Bus C; Chldr; Tr; Hawaiian Lang Cert.

VALENTICH, Lynne Marie
Cleveland HS; Cleveland, TN (50-240) Anchor C; Ann; Band; CYO; Drama; Fr C; Hmrm; Span C; Swim; COM; Citz A; *St Mary's Col; Med.*

VALENTINE, Cheri Dawnette
Brethren HS; Paramount, CA (30-95) JETS; Span C; Tr; CSF; Spch A; Yth Fel; Most Inspirational, Vlbl; Ethics, Span, A's.

VALENTINE, Jacqueline Annette
Brethren Christian HS; Paramount, CA; Chor; Drama; Math C; Y-Tns; Sftbl; Swim; Math A; Most Out; Yth Fel; Ath, Charm C, A's; Lib Asst & Hostess A's; *El Camino Jr Col; Optometric Asst.*

VALENTINE, James Lloyd
N Hollywood HS; N Hollywood, CA (25%-700) Band; VP, Demolay; Ensm; HiY; Orch; JV, Bsbl; Hon Prog; Pres, Church Yth Group; Semi- fin, St DeMolay Bkbl; *Calif St U; Bus Adm.*

VALENTINE, John Babbage
Del Valle HS; Walnut Creek, CA (40-220) Band; Chess C; Hmrm; VP, Model UN; Rptr, Sch P; Span C; SC; Golf; CSF; Eagle Sct; *U of Calif.*

VALENTINE, Kimberly Sue
Lancaster Sr HS; Lancaster, WI (5-135) AFS; Ed, Ann; Band; Chldr; Chor; Ensm; Secy, 4H; Hmrm; Semi-Fin, Jr Miss Pa; Madrigal; NHS; Sch P; SC; Bkbl; 4H A; HCt; Hon Prog; Spch A; AFS Abroads Stu; St Secy, Jr Boards NACA; Jr Miss, Talent Schol Achiev As; *Valparaiso U; Spch.*

VALENTINE, Mary Jane
Barboursville HS; Barboursville, WV (7-447) Fr C; NHS; SC; VP, Soph Cl; Yth Fel; Art II A; *W Va U; Journ.*

VALENTINE, William Louis
Campbell HS; Fairburn, GA; Lat C; Var C; Cpt, Ftbl; Cpt, Wrest; 2nd Co Wrest Tournament; Local Region Tournaments, Wrest.

VALENTINI, Mary Elizabeth
Marian HS; Tamaqua, PA (30-150) Pres, Band; Hmrm; Orch; S-T, Span NHS; SC; Swim; *Phys Therapy.*

VALENZUELA, Dolores Ann
Riverdale HS; Riverdale, CA; Span C; Swim; Vlbl; Interntl Dancing Group; *Galen Col; Dental Asst.*

VALENZUELA, Elaine Valerie
James Lick HS; San Jose, CA; CYO; Crown & Scepter; Span C; Secy, SC; Bsbl; Sftbl; Coun of Teach A; Swtht; Mexican-Amer Yth; Cand, Qn; *Riverside Baptist Col; Bus.*

VALENZUELA, Lawrence Mitchell
San Jose HS; San Jose, CA (80-350) Band; A-Ed, Sch P; Span C; SC; Pres, Var C; Bsbl; Cpt, Bkbl; Cr-Ctry; Ftbl; CSF; Pres, Excalibur; *UCLA; Mus.*

VALERIO, Mark James
Deer Lakes HS; Cheswick, PA; Soccer; *Pittsburgh U; Bio.*

VALIN, Phillip Clay
Glen Oaks Sr HS; Baton Rouge, LA (6-349) VP, BC; BS; Cpt, Dbte Tm; Tres, Key C; NHS; ARC; SC; COM; Math A; Most Out; NEDT; Ldrship A; Cpt A, Quiz Bowl; *LSU; Vet Med.*

VALINO, Jardiolyn Navarro
Lake Clifton Sr HS; Baltimore, MD (10%-350) Band; Lit Mag; NHS; Phys C; COM; Citz A; Type A; Distinction A; Fr A; *U of Md.*

VALLE, Anna Idalia
Mem HS; San Antonio, TX (14-300) *San Antonio Col; Bus.*

VALMORE, Kim Allyson
Walnut Hills HS; Cincinnati, OH (44-550) Lit Mag; Orch; SC; COM; Yth Fel; NJHS; Cert of Achv; *Asbury Col; Theology.*

VALVO, Louis Albert
Fredonia HS; Fredonia, NY (25%-200) Tr; *Math.*

VAN't HOF, Barbara Jean
Edgerton Pub HS; Edgerton, MN (2-31) Chor; FHA; NHS; Pres, Soph Cl; Cpt, Bkbl; Tr; Yth Fel; Girl's League.

VanAGTMAEL, Lillian Lea
Regis HS; Stayton, OR (5-56) Ann; Chem C; Chor; GS; Math C; NHS; Sci C; Ski C; Secy, SC; Var C; Tr; Hon Prog; Ntl Sci Symposium; Mst Inspirational, Vlbl; Tr & Field; *U of Portland; Med Tech.*

VaN ALSTINE, Dale William
Hannibal Central Sch; Hannibal, NY; Math C; NHS; JV, Cr-Ctry; Tr; Regent Schol; *Penn St; Acct.*

VanAUKEN, David Pharr
Mooresville HS; Moonesville, NC; *Montreat Anderson Col; Phys Ed.*

Van BEBBER, Timothy Wayne
Greenview HS; Greenview, IL (2-27) Ensm; NHS; Secy, Jr Cl; Mgr, Bbkl; Cr-Ctry; Gr Marshal; NEDT; *Southwest Baptist Col; Theology.*

VanBOCHOVE, Carolyn Helen
Comstock HS; Comstock, MI (25-211) Bus Mgr, Band; Chor; NHS; VP, SC; Pres, Jr Cl; Pres, Soph Cl; Sftbl; DARGCA; HQn; GScts; Candystriper Lamp; SC A; *Vanderbilt U; Nurs.*

Van BRUNT, Dwight Steven
Chelan HS; Chelan, WA (9-49) Band; Hmrm; NHS; Order/Arrow; Var C; Bsbl; JV, Bkbl; Order/ Arrow A; Drum Major; Jr Asst Sct Master; Bus Mgr & Pres, Bus C; Eagle Sct; St DECA Off.

Van BUREN, David Hunter
Lakewood HS; Lake Odessa, MI (2-255) Chor; NHS; Ski C; SC; JV, Bkbl; Cr-Ctry; Mgr, Tr; *Math.*

VANCE, Debbie June
Washington HS; Washington, IN (50%-150) Band; Lat C; Dist Flute, John Wesley Hghst, A's; *Vincennes U.*

VANCE, Diana Kay
Alief Hastings HS; Houston, TX (30-518) Tres, NHS; Outst Girl, Drill Tm; *Tex A&M U; Math.*

VANCE, Ellen Marie
Evangelical Christian Sch; Cordova, TN (14-57) Chor; Drama; Pres, SC; Var C; Co-Cpt, Bkbl; Cpt, Tr; Bio A; Citz A; HCt; Sci A; PA; Co Cpt, Vlbl; VP, Stu Coun; Pres, Pep C; *U of Tenn Martin.*

VANCE, Ivy Bennett
Fletcher Sr HS; Neptune Beach, FL (20-545) VP, Fr C; NHS; COM; Hon Prog; *U of Fla; Systems Analysis.*

VANCE, Karen Doris
Garden HS; Oakwood, VA; Secy, 4H; Hmrm; NHS; Hist A; HCt; GAA; Club Coordinating Comm; *Nurs.*

VANCE, Randolph Ivan
Macomb HS; Macomb, IL (45-330) Band; Chor; Ensm; Fr C; Pres, 4H; Madrigal; Co-Cpt, Sftbl; 4H A; Yth Fel; Swing Choir; All-Dist Choir; All-St Choir; Jazz Band; *Western Ill U; Math.*

VANCE, Robert Allen
Harmony Comm HS; Farmington, IA (3-50) Tres, FFA; Schol A.

VANCE, Sherri Louise
Bonneville HS; Ogden, UT (50-535) Tres, Band; Community Yth Symph; Drama; Ensm; Co-Ed, Lit Mag; NHS; Orch; Alg A; COM; Hon Prog; PTA A; Poet A; Sci A; Yth Fel; All St Band; *Mus.*

VANCE, Thomas Joel
Ketron HS; Kingsport, TN (21-146) Ann; Pres, BC; Key C; NHS; Pres, SC; Pres, Sr Cl; Ftbl; Elk A; Hon Prog; Best All-Around, Sr Cl; *Tenn Tech U; Engr.*

VANCE, Valli Deanna
Shamrock HS; Decatur, GA (50-450) BC; Fr C; Hmrm; InterClub Coun; Mgr, Cr-Ctry; Co-Cpt, Soccer; COM; Cl Fav; *Ga St U; Hist.*

VANCIL, Douglas Wayne
Anna Jonesboro Comm HS; Anna, IL (65-144) VP, Band; Pres, Hmrm; Orch; VP, SC; Ftbl; HCt; Band A's; *Murry St U; Mus.*

VANCIL, Janis Lynn
W Monroe HS; W Monroe, LA (5-500) Tres, Anchor C; Chor; Ensm; GS; NHS; WW; *NE La U; Acct.*

VanCLEAVE, Timothy John
Bend Sr HS; Bend, OR; JV, Bkbl; Ftbl; Rodeo C; *Central Oreg Col of Ed.*

VanCORBACH, Willard Gerard
Timberline HS; Weippe, ID (7-47) Chem C; Community Yth Symph; Drama; Fr C; Parl, NHS; Pol Sci C; A-Sch P; Pres, Ski C; Spch C; SC; Var C; Bkbl; Ftbl; *U of Idaho; Communications.*

VANDAHL, Teresa Marie
W Platte HS; Weston, MO (34-85) AFS; Chor; FHA; 4H; Rainbow; JV, Bkbl; *Bus Adm.*

Van DAME, Annette Marie
Attica HS; Attica, IN (11-98) Ann; Band; CYO; Fr C; NHS; Sch P; Tres, Sr Cl; Bkbl; Tr; Citz A; Hon Prog; Vlbl; Vlbl Trophies; GAA; WW; Sunshine Qn; *Purdue U; Engr.*

VandeBERG, Jocelyn Kay
Blacksburg HS; Blacksburg, VA (3-300) Madrigal; Theatre Arts C; Energy Seminar; Mus C; Gym Tm; Mus Seminar; *Dartmouth Col; Psych.*

VandeGIESSEN, Cheryl Lynn
Gull Lake HS; Richland, MI (7-270) Band; Fr C; 4H; Orch; Ski C; Tr; Hon Prog; *Hope Col; Mus.*

Van DE HEY, Bruce Richard
Kaukauna HS; Kaukauna, WI (50%-450) Chor; JV, Bkbl; JV, Ftbl; *Northland Col; Bus.*

VANDE KOPPEL, Thom E
St Joseph HS; St Joseph, MI (64-367) Band; Chem C; Math C; NHS; Sci C; *U of Mich; Engr.*

VandenBERG, James Kent
Loy Norrix HS; Kalamazoo, MI (110-415) A Cap Choir; Chor; Tres, Sr Cl; Tres, Jr Cl; Mgr, Bsbl; Hockey; Swim; NMS; *Hope Col; Med.*

Van DENBURGH, Marylou L
Johnstown HS; Johnstown, NY (3-200) Ann; Chor; Drama; Ensm; NHS; ARC; Balfour A; B Crocker A; Bio A; ARC A; Regent Schol; Co Fireman's Assn Qn; Hon Men, St Betty Crocker; *Union Col; Pre-Med.*

VandenTOORN, Jeff
Godwin Heights HS; Wyoming, MI; Band; Chor; Up Bound; Var C; Ftbl; Cpt, Soccer; Sftbl; Co-Cpt, Tr; *Forestry.*

VanDERBEEK, Cynthia Jane
Watchung Hills Regional HS; Warren, NJ (92-472) Band; Chor; Ensm; Madrigal; Yth Fel; *Occupational Therapy.*

VANDERBROOK, Mark Raymond
Middle Park Jr Sr HS; Granby, CO (1-76) Band; Ed, Sch P; Masonic A; NMS; Regent Schol; Val; WW; Climax Molybdenum Schol; Ntl Assn of Jazz Ed A; *U of Colo; Psych.*

VANDERBURG, Joyce Ann
Champion HS; Warren, OH; Chor; Fr C; Madrigal; Y-Tns; COM; NEDT; *Kent St U; Mus.*

VaN dER HARST, Deborah Ann
Bentley HS; Livonia, MI (292-731) MVP, Band; Chldr; Chor; Community Yth Symph; Drama; Ensm; Hmrm; Orch; SC; Arch; Interlochen Ntl Mus; Cpt, Vlbl; Schol, Interlochen All St Band; Schoolcraft Comm Col; *Woodwind Instrument Repair.*

VANDERHIDER, Vicki Gay
Robert E Lee HS; San Antonio, TX (25%-515) FHA; Hmrm; Parl, Jr Cl; VP, Soph Cl; Amer Leg A; COM; Sq Ldr, Drill Lt, Lee-Ettes; Cpt Secy, Lee-Ettes; *Northwood Inst; Fashion Merchandising.*

VanDERHOEF, Kathryn Marie
Blanchet HS; Seattle, WA (32-383) VP, CYO; Var C; Hon Prog; Pres A; Spch A; Vlbl; Piano Schol; Marian A; Dean's List; *Mus Ed.*

VanDERHOEF, Philip John
Blanchet HS; Seattle, WA (7-285) Pres, CYO; Dbte Tm; Fr C; Pres, Hmrm; NHS; Spch C; Pres, SC; Amer Leg A; COM; Elk A; Hon Prog; NMF; NMS; Spch A; Debate A; Dean's List; Religion Schol; *U of Notre Dame; Lib Arts.*

VAN dER HOEVEN, Peter Howell
Ridgefield HS; Ridgefield, CT (100-490) NHS; Sch P; JV, Ftbl; 5th Pl Physics, Sci Fair; *Tex A&M U; Mech Engr.*

VANDER HORST, Karol Ann
Celina Sr HS; Celina, OH (47-275) CYO; Chor; FTA; Lat C; NHS; Sch P; Secy, Sr Cl; Secy, Jr Cl; Ftbl; Cpt, Tnns; Hon Prog; Bkbl Statistician; *Ohio St U; Dental Hygiene.*

VANDER KAY, Lisa Del
Downers Grove S HS; Downers Grove, IL (108-946) A Cap Choir; Chor; Community Yth Symph; Drama; Orch; Yth Fel; Mus Schol, Summer Mus Prog; *Northern Ill U; Acct.*

VANDERLAAN, Kathy Lynn
Mason Co Central HS; Scottville, MI (25-150) Co-Ed, Ann; Cpt, Chldr; Cum Laude Soc; Ski C; Span C; Var C; Mgr, Bkbl; Cl Fav; Hon Prog; *W Shore Comm Col.*

VANDERLIN, Kelly Elizabeth
Edison Sr HS; Lake Station, IN (28-170) Band; Cpt, Chldr; Fr C; VP, FTA; GS; Hmrm; Semi-Fin, Jr Miss Pa; Mjrte; NHS; SC; VP, Jr Cl; Hockey; *Valpariaso Col; Phys Ed.*

VANDERLIP, David Allen
Eisenhower HS; Saginaw, MI (200-325) Bsbl; Ftbl; Yth VP; *Saginaw Valley St Col; Phys Ed.*

VanderLUGT, D David
Grace Baptist HS; South Bend, IN (3-30) Bkbl; Soccer; Tr; HCt; *Ind U; Med.*

VANDER-MEULEN, Mary Lynn
Fulton Comm HS; Fulton, IL (11-125) AFS; Chor; Secy, FHA; FTA; Madrigal; Span C; Thes; Hon Prog; VofDEM; Yth Leg; FTA A; *Mt St Clare Col; Govt.*

VANDER MEYDEN, Marike
Santa Monica HS; Santa Monica, CA; Chor; JV, Swim; Lois Lind Mem Fund, Art, A's; *Santa Monica Col; Child Development.*

VANDERMOLEN, Andy Arthur
Tillamook HS; Tillamook, OR (1-189) A Cap Choir; Band; Chor; Ch, Demolay; Ch, Drama; FFA; Pres, FTA; Pres, 4H; InterClub Coun; Pres, Key C; Mod Mus Mas; NFL; NHS; Orch; Spch C; Ch, SC; Ch, Thes; Ch, Var C; Tres, Jr Cl; Bkbl; Cpt, Ftbl; Tr; COM; Elk A; 4H A; Hon Prog; NMF; NMS; NEDT; Val; VofDEM; St Fin, Century III Leadership; *U of Oreg; Bio.*

VANDER MOLEN, Carrie Frances
Newton Co Comp HS; Covington, GA (20%-325) BC; Fr C; Jr Miss Pagent; Tri-HiY; *Special Ed.*

VANDER MOREN, Karen Deanne
Immanuel HS; Reedley, CA (1-92) Chor; VP, 4H; Citz A; 4H A; Spch A; Val; Vlbl; Mus A; *Biola Col; Elem Ed.*

VANDERPAN, Dorthy Marie
Brookings HS; Brookings, SD (25%-202) Chor; Drama; Ensm; 4H; Hmrm; NFL; Span C; Spch C; St Stu Congress; JV, Bkbl; Tr; Citz A; Church Yth Board; Church Yth Task Force; Intramural, Sftb & Water Polo; Vlbl; *Concordia Col; Child Development.*

VANDER PLAATS, Barbara Kaye
Verdi Pub Sch; Verdi, MN (1-11) Co-Ed, Ann; Band; Chldr; 4H; Secy, SC; Pres, Jr Cl; Tr; Hon Prog; Spch A.

VANDER PLOEG, Phyllis June
Bridgman HS; Bridgman, MI (30-60) Sch P; Sci C; COM; *Nurs.*

VanderSCHEL, Debra Sue
Eureka HS; Eureka, IL (50%-150) AFS; Chor; FHA; Pres, 4H; Cpt, Bkbl; 4-H Hon; *Mennonite Hospital; Nurs.*

VANDER STELT, Ruth Ann
Immanuel HS; Reedley, CA (3-60) Chor; NHS; Span C; Y-Tns; Sal; Sci A; *Col of Sequoias; Art.*

VANDER STOEP, Sheryl Ann
Oak Harbor HS; Oak Harbor, WA (20-355) Chor; 4H; Madrigal; NHS; Var C; Cpt, Tr; Amer Leg A; Citz A; Hon Prog; Vlbl; Gym; Girls C Off; *Northwestern Col.*

VanderVEER, Eric John
Sylvania Northview HS; Sylvania, OH; Band; Ski C; Ftbl; Soccer; Wrest; *US Naval Acad; Engr.*

VANDERWENDE, Carla Ann
Woodbridge HS; Bridgeville, DE (11-111) Ann; Chldr; Chor; Ensm; Fr C; S-T, FFA; FNA; FTA; Pres, 4H; Hmrm; Fin, Jr Miss Pagent; NHS; SC; S-T, Var C; Pres, Jr Cl; VP, Soph Cl; JV, Bkbl; Hockey; Co-Cpt, Sftbl; Alg A; Beauty; Citz A; Cl Fav; 4H A; Hon Prog; Kiwanis A; Pres A; Spch A; Dela Ntl Tn; St FFA Swth; Agr; Miss Bridgeville; Outst Female Ath; *Phys Ed.*

VANDERWERF, Terry Scott
Waverly HS; Lansing, MI (3-400) Pres, Band; Chor; Community Yth Symph; Ensm; NHS; JV, Tnns; Pres, Church Sr HS Yth Group; VP, Sch Service C; Top Band A; Top Ten; All-St Orch; I Rating, Dist & St Mus Comp; *Lansing Comm Col.*

VanDEVENDER, Roy Oswald
Kemper Acad; DeKalb, MS (6-42) Rptr, Sch P; Pres, SC; Rptr, Jr Cl; Citz A; Phy A; Sci A; Most Dependable; Most Congenial; Halloween Kg; *U of Miss; Law.*

VANDEVENTER, Jana Larice
Taylorville Sr HS; Taylorville, IL (42-145) Band; Orch; Yth Fel; Fr A; Carillons; Church Babysitter; Off Asst; Mus A's; Chapel Choir; Church Organist & Pianist; *Eureka Col; Ed.*

VanDIBLE, Pretta LaFaye
Worthing Sr HS; Houston, TX (6-427) Chldr; Pres, Jr Cl; Tr; Bio A; COM; Hon Prog; Most Out; Ntl Sci Found; Sci A; Yth o-t Mo; *Rice U; Chem Engr.*

VANDIVER, Julie Lynne
E Mecklenburg HS; Charlotte, NC; Co-Ed, Ann; Fin, Crown & Scepter; Ch, ARC; Sch Achieve Tm; Co-Cpt, Bkbl; Sftbl; Tr; NEDT; Opt A; MVP, Bkbl & Vlbl; Fin, Memory Work; *Appalachian St Col; Ed.*

VANDIVER, Linda Kay
Sylvania Southview HS; Sylvania, OH; Chor; FHA; *Bus Ed.*

VANDIVER, Lisa Rachelle
Berkeley HS; Berkeley, CA; Chldr; Hmrm; Sch P; SC; *San Francisco St U; Broadcast Communications.*

VANDIVER, Mark William
Simi Valley HS; Simi Valley, CA; Soccer.

VanDIVIER, Randy Lee
Anaheim HS; Anaheim, CA; Hmrm; Tres, Var C; Cpt, Ftbl; Cpt, Tr; Cpt, Wrest; Prep All Amer; 1st Tm, Daily Pilot; Orange Co All-Star Game; Line Cpt; 1st Tm, Anaheim Bulletin; 1st Tm, All Leg; Player o-t Game; *U of Wash.*

VanDUZEE, Ellen Lesley
Oceanside HS; Oceanside, NY (125-900) Chldr; Chor; Ensm; NHS; Orch; ARC; Tr; COM; JA A; Kiwanis A; Explorers; Secy, Yth Fel; Baking, Mus Festival, A's; Bicentennial Participation, A; *St U of NY.*

Van DUZEN, Robert Mason
Pougekeepsie HS; Poughkeepsie, NY (100-200) Var C; Y-Tns; MVP, Bkbl; MVP, Ftbl; MVP, Tr; PA A; *Dutchess Comm Col; Social Work.*

Van DYCK, Karen Rhoads
Princeton HS; Princeton, NJ (25%-250) Chor; Drama; Fr C; InterAct C; Rptr, Sch P; Ski C; SC; Secy, Soph Cl; LaCrosse; *Mus.*

VanDYKE, Angela Renee
Model HS; Rome, GA (16-110) Ann; Secy, Band; Tres, FHA; 4H; NHS; Sci C; Sftbl; 4H A; 2nd Pl Piano, Lit Meet; *Dalton St Col; Bus Adm.*

VanDYKE, Harvey Reese Jr
Sullivan Central HS; Kingsport, TN; *U of Tenn; Engr.*

Van DYKE, Mary Rebecca
Vidalia HS; Vidalia, GA; Chldr; Chor; Drama; Ensm; Hmrm; Lit Ral; Rainbow; F-Ed, Sch P; Thes; Tri-HiY; Fin, Sftbl; Fin, Swim; Chor A; All-St Chor; *U of Ga.*

VanDYKE, Orla June
Castlewood Consolidated HS; Castlewood, SD (11-23) Ann; Chor; Drama; Ensm; Parl; FHA; B Crocker A; *Lake Area Voc Tech Sch; Dental Asst.*

VanDYKE, Ruth Ellen
Brookhaven HS; Columbus, OH (310-450) Chor; F-Ed, Sch P; Var C; Cpt, Tr; COM; Boxing Qn Contest; *Fort Wayne Bible Col; Missionary.*

Van DYKE, Vena Midori
Chichester Sr HS; Boothwyn, PA; Band; Chor; Span NHS; Secy, SC; *Morgan St Col; Social Work.*

VanEATON, Warren East Hs
Bowling Green HS; Bowling Green, KY (9-164) F-Ed, Ann; Pres, BC; Cpt, Chldr; Drama; VP, Fr C; Rptr, FTA; Ch, GS; Fin, Jr Miss Pagent; Math C; NFL; Ed, Sch P; Sci C; SC; S-T, Var C; Secy, Sr Cl; Mgr, Bsbl; Cpt, Ftbl; Alg A; COM; Cl Fav; DARGCA; Gr Marshal; HCt; Math A; Most Out; Opt A; Sci A; Spch A; Runner Up, Co Jr Miss; Alt, GS; Schol A; St Sci Symposium; Eng A; Best Actress, Sch Play; 2nd Pl, St Spch Tourn; *Abilene Christian U; Pre-Med.*

VANEK, Alison Marie
Binghamton N HS; Binghamton, NY (10-230) Fr C; Tnns; COM; Pres, Zonta C; Collier Fine Art A; VP, Art C; Zonta C A; Flag Sq A; Cpt, Flag Sq; Tres, Sorority; Woodrow Wilson Alumni A; *Harpur Col; Art.*

VANEK, Michael John
Prague Public HS; Prague, NE (2-20) Ann; Pres, Band; BS; VP, FFA; NHS; Tres, Jr Cl; Pres, Soph Cl; Mgr, Bkbl; H of F; FFA Proficiency A; Yrbk Photography; *Nebr Voc Tech Col; Mech Engr.*

VanELMENDORF, Leah Elizabeth
Ft Pierce Central HS; Ft Pierce, FL (20-586) Secy, Band; BC; Parl, NHS; Mgr, Tr; Keyettes; *Abraham Baldwin Agr Col; Bio.*

VANEPS, Jeffrey Charles
Grand Rapids Sr HS; Grand Rapids, MN (50%-450) A Cap Choir; Mgr, Bkbl; Cr-Ctry; Tr; Yth Fel; Yth Leg; Pres, Yth Fel; *Itasca Jr Col.*

VANERSTROM, Peggy Joan
Carpio HS; Carpio, ND (3-17) Band; Chor; Ensm; GS; Lit Mag; NHS; SC; Secy, Sr Cl; Bkbl; Sal; *U of ND; Nurs.*

VANETTA, Laura Ann
Blanchet HS; Seattle, WA (75-285) Cpt, Chldr; Tr; Chldr A; *U of Wash; Arts.*

Van FOSSON, Kim Marie
S Page Comm Sch; College Springs, IA (1-32) Bus Mgr, Ann; Pres, Band; Chor; Drama; Tres, FHA; Pres, 4H; Madrigal; NHS; Span C; Spch C; SC; VP, Sr Cl; Tres, Soph Cl; JV, Bkbl; DARGCA; HCt; Spch A; St Scholar; Val; St Off, FHA; Outst Performer A; *Des Moines Area Comm Col; Human Services.*

Van GALEN, Brenda Fay
Lawton HS; Lawton, OK (36-467) Band; NHS; Span C; Sftbl; Hon Prog; Pres, Church Yth Group; Campfire Girls; Band Ltr; Piano Solo A; *Hope Col; Social Work.*

VanGORDER, Sharon Louise
Lawrence Co Voc Tech HS; New Castle, PA (20-350) Chor; FHA.

VanGORDER, Susan Elaine
Lawrence Co Voc Tech HS; New Castle, PA (30-350) Chor; Rptr, Sch P; Math A; *Bus.*

Van HALM, Elizabeth Claire
Sehome HS; Bellingham, WA (54-338) Drama; Fresh Col Schol; *Calvin Col; Engr.*

VanHAMMEN, Stephen John
Grand Rapids Ottawa Hills HS; Grand Rapids, MI (50-600) A Cap Choir; Model UN; Order/Arrow; Sch P; SC; Var C; JV, Bsbl; JV, Bkbl; JV, Cr-Ctry; Mgr, Ftbl; JV, Tr; *Mich St U; Biological Sci.*

Van HEERDE, Douglas Glen
Luverne Jr Sr HS; Luverne, MN (7-160) Ed, Ann; Dbte Tm; NFL; Spch C; *Photography.*

Van HEMERT, Angela Ruth
Highland HS; Albuquerque, NM (40-695) Ger C; NHS; Sftbl; Sci A; Pres, Church Yth Forum; Asst Mgr, Sftbl; *Archt.*

VanHOOSE, Mark Kevin
Big Walnut HS; Sunbury, OH (61-170) Chor; FHA; Pres, 4H; F-Ed, Sch P; JV, Wrest; COM; Journ A; Chaplin, FFA; Bldg An Ameri Comm A, FFA; 1st Pl, FFA Meat Judging; *Ohio St U; Agr Ed.*

VanHOOSE, Michael Darren
Big Walnut HS; Sunbury, OH (60-200) Fr C; Tres, 4H; Var C; Ftbl; COM; Sectional VP, FFA; FFA Greenhand A; FFA Chpt Farmer A; *Miami of Ohio; Conservation.*

VanHORN, Debra Lou
Colonial Hills Christian HS; E Point, GA (4-36) BC; Chor; NHS; Ed, Sch P; Chaplain, Beta C & Soph Cl; *Tenn Temple Col; Home Ec Ed.*

VanHORN, Michael Joseph
Crystal Lake Comm HS; Crystal Lake, IL; Orch; Bkbl; Cr-Ctry; Tr; *U of Mich; Wildlife Mgt.*

VanHORN, Pamela Jane
U S Grant HS; Oklahoma City, OK (300-500) Drama; FBLA; SC; Pep C; *Central St U; Nurs.*

VanHORN, Richard Thomas
Highland HS; Ewing, MO (8-130) Chess C; Fr C; Tres, 4H; NHS; Cr-Ctry; Co-Cpt, Tr; COM; Hon Prog; Math A; Regent Schol; *Hannibal La Grange Col; Ed.*

Van HORN, Sharon Lynne
Friendswood HS; Friendswood, TX; Band; Secy, FTA; Sci C; Span C; Hon Prog; Band A; Eng A; Academic A; *Eng.*

Van HORNE, James B
Sandy Valley HS; Magnolia, OH (160-257) HiY; Bsbl; Bkbl; Cl Fav; *Bus.*

VANHOY, Denise Ann
S Stokes HS; Walnut Cove, NC; BC; Bus C; FBLA; FTA; Beta C Cert; HR; *Bus.*

VANHOY, Kevin Bruce
N Mecklenburg HS; Charlotte, NC (80-445) Band; Chess C; Lat C; JV, Ftbl; *UNCC; Sci.*

VanKERREBROOK, Joyce Cheryl
Gordon HS; Gordon, NE; Band; CYO; Chor; VP, Dbte Tm; Ensm; FHA; FTA; Fis, GS; Sch Achieve Tm; Ski C; SC; Pres A; Fin, Pres's A.

Van KLEECK, Clayton Robert
Kingston HS; Kingston, NY (140-719) F-Ed, Ann; Band; Bus C; Hmrm; Lit Mag; VP, Orch; Sftbl; Citz A; Lion A; Yth Fel; Co Band A; *Ulster Co Comm Col; Bus.*

VanLEIDEN, Timothy Edward
Ottawa HS; Ottawa, KS (25-200) Band; BS; JV, Tnns; COM; Hon Prog; Chor Accompanist; Church & Campus Schol; Mildred Stevens Mus Schol; *Ottawa U; Bus.*

VanLEIDEN, Timothy Edward
Ottawa HS; Ottawa, KS (50-200) Band; BS; Chor; JV, Tnns; Chor Accompanist; Church & Campus Schol; Mildred Stevens Mus Schol; *Ottawa U; Bus.*

Van MAREL, Jaylynn
Victoria HS; Victoria, TX (15-620) Anchor C; Fr C; FTA; NHS; Pres A; *SW Tex Col; Elem Ed.*

Van METER, Joan Peggy
Henryetta HS; Henryetta, OK (16-105) Rptr, FHA; NHS; Rptr, Sch P; Spch C; Bkbl; Sftbl; Tnns; Tr; Hon Prog; Journ A; *Okla St U.*

Van METER, Kellie Denise
Hobbs HS; Hobbs, NM (48-440) Ed, Ann; Parl, Commercial C; SC; Co-Cpt, Bkbl; Tr; Journ A; FCA; Most Ath; All Dist Vlbl; *NM St U; Bus.*

VANN, Angela Dell
Clinton HS; Clinton, NC (10%-275) Band; BC; Chldr; Chor; Drama; VP, Hmrm; SC; Bkbl; Beauty; Citz A; HCt; VP, Jr Cl; PA; *U of NC; Pediatrican.*

VANN, Debra Kay
Central HS; Woodstock, VA (10-155) Ann; BC; Bus C; FBLA; FHA; InterAct C; NHS; Sftbl; Hon Prog; Yth Fel; Top 10, Cl; *E Mennonite Col; Nurs.*

VANN, Kimberly Lavon
Staunton River HS; Moneta, VA (5-164) Chess C; Drama; Fr C; Math C; Monogram; Sci C; Bkbl; Geom A.

VANN, Lois Marie
Suffolk HS; Suffolk, VA (8-150) Tres, Lat C; NHS; Span C; Citz A; *Obicie Sch of Nurs; Nurs.*

VANN, Marjorie Ann
Skyline HS; Oakland, CA; Pres, Chor; COM; Citz A; Vol Tutor; Eastern Star; Guild Girls; Sci C; Ch, Yth Fel Refreshment Comm; Ch, Flower Arrangement Group; *Spelman Col; Early Childhood Ed.*

Van NAMEN, Beverly Ann
Callaway HS; Jackson, MS (60-530) Chor; Hmrm; SC; Hon Prog; *Hinds Jr Col; Med.*

VANNATTA, Louis Jay
Perry Comm HS; Perry, IA (7-145) BS; Drama; 4H; Hmrm; VP, Thes; Tr; Co-Cpt, Wrest; Amer Leg A; Citz A; Hon Prog; Kiwanis A; St Scholar; Schol-Ath; *Iowa St U; Engr.*

Van NATTA, Robert Lee
Marion HS; Marion, IA (138-202) A Cap Choir; Band; Chor; FTA; Hmrm; Madrigal; Order/Arrow; SC; Var C; God & Country A; Chor Accompanist; Pres A; Yth Fel; Pres, UMYF; Swing Choir; Win, MD Dance-A-Thon; Aggressive A; *Eng.*

VANNEST, Kelly Lee
Calvary Christian Acad; Midland, MI; Ann; Chor; Drama; SC; Principals A; Bob Jones U; Gen.

VANNIX, David Lee
Linda Vista Jr Acad; Oxnard, CA (1-13) A-Ed, Anchor C; La Sierra Col; Theology.

VanNORMAN, Karen Elaine
Woodbury Central Comm Sch; Moville, IA (1-55) Co-Ed, Ann; Band; Chor; Ensm; Fr C; NHS; Sch Achieve Tm; Pres, Spch C; Mgr, Bkbl; Sftbl; Regent Schol; Spch A; St Scholar; Val; Band & Choir A; WW; Augustana Col; Environmental Bio.

Van NOY, David Ellsworth
Williamson HS; Williamson, WV (7-155) BS; VP, NHS; SC; Var C; Bsbl; W Va U; Dentistry.

VanORDEN, Duane Delial
Howe Military Sch; Howe, IN (5-46) Drill Tm; Assn of Army Medal; 4H A; Radio C; Christian Courtesy Medal; Hist C; Best Drilled Cadet Medal; Alpha Del Tau Hon Soc; Manatee Jr Col; Pre-Med.

VanOSS, Mark Timothy
Arcadia HS; Arcadia, CA (38-806) Chor; Hmrm; NFL; NHS; Pres, Sch Achieve Tm; Tres, Spch C; Thes; CSF; COM; Citz A; Hon Prog; Most Out; Spch A; St Scholar; Exchange C A; Stanford U; Humanities.

Van PATTEN, Brenda Lois
Midway HS; Waco, TX; JV Vlbl.

Van PATTEN, Jeffery Wendell
Searcy HS; Searcy, AR (25-256) Pres, A Cap Choir; BC; BS; Chor; Dbte Tm; Pres, Demolay; Pres, Ensm; FBLA; Key C; NHS; SC; Thes; Golf; Masonic A; Demolay Rep; Ark St U; Bus.

Van PATTEN, Lynn Renae
Winner Sr HS; Winner, SD (1-105) Golf; Tr.

Van PATTEN, Russell LeRoy Jr
Willows HS; Willows, CA (4-136) Band; Chess C; Drama; 4H; Sch P; Pres, Ski C; Swim; MVP, Tr; CSF; MLS; Stanford U; Law.

Van PATTEN, Tamara Lou
Midway HS; Waco, TX (10%-180) Secy, Band; Chor; Ensm; FHA; Madrigal; Tres, Math C; Tres, Mu Alpha Theta; NHS; Hon Prog; U of Ark; Pre-Med.

VanPATTEN, Tracie Rae
Yamhill Carlton HS; Yamhill, OR; Band; Chor; FHA; Art C.

VanPATTER, Laurie Kathryn
Springfield HS; Springfield, PA; a Cap Choir; Fr C; Yth Fel; Sci A; Pop Singing Group; Sch Musical Production; Social Service; Ed.

Van PELT, Cynthia Ione
Danville HS; Danville, AR; Chldr; Tres, FHA; Sch P; Mgr, Bkbl; Sftbl; Tr; Journ A; Poet A; Best Ath; Morrilton Vo-tech Col; Bus Ed.

Van PELT, Wesley Herman
Kelly Walsh HS; Casper, WY; Chor; Ensm; 4H; Bsbl; Bkbl; Ftbl; Tr; Wrest; Gym; Alt, All NW, All St Chor; NW Bible Col; Mus.

VanPERNIS, James
Wheaton Central HS; Wheaton, IL (30-340) F-Ed, Ann; NHS; Order/Arrow; VP, Var C; Ftbl; Kiwanis A; Lion A; Rotary A; St Scholar; Gym; WW; FCA; Schol Art A; Cert of Merit, Photography; Rochester Inst of Tech; Graphic Arts.

Van REETH, Jack Russell
W Holmes HS; Millersburg, OH (7-180) A Cap Choir; Band; BS; Chess C; Chor; Drama; Lat C; NHS; Pol Sci C; Sci C; Pres, SC; COM; Hist A; Co Legal Soc A; Drama A; Malone Col; Psych.

Van₀RIS, Sally Georgina Olivia
R L Turner HS; Carrollton, TX; Orch; Span C; Section Ldr, Band; All Region Band; Stage Band; St Solo & Ensm; Church Choir; MYF; N Tex St U; Mus Ed.

VanROEKEL, Bradley Merritt
New Monroe Comm HS; Monroe, IA (20-73) Band; FFA; Bsbl; Bkbl; Ftbl; Tr; Hon Men, All Conf Bkbl.

VanROEKEL, Brian Wayne
New Monroe Comm HS; Monroe, IA (15-59) Band; Chor; FFA; VP, 4H; SC; Bsbl; Bkbl; Cr-Ctry; JV, Ftbl; Golf; Band Major; St Farmer Degree, FFA; All Conf Bsbl; Iowa St U; Agr.

VanRULER, Nancy Anne
Luverne Jr Sr HS; Luverne, MN;

VANSANT, John Herndon Jr
Norfolk Acad; Norfolk, VA (3-82) Cum Laude Soc; Pres, Ger C; Co-Ch, Model UN; Monogram; Sch Achieve Tm; Co-Ed, Sch P; S-T, SC; Co-Ch, World Affairs; JV, Bsbl; Ftbl; Soccer; JV, Tnns; Tr; B Crocker A; MLS; NMF; NMS; Dartmouth Col; Pol Sci.

VanSCHAICK, Ruth Carol
Pekin Comm HS; Pekin, IL (180-800) Chor; Ntl Yth Conf; Bkbl; Yth Fel; Secy, Yth Fel; Ill Central Col; Child Development.

Van SCHUYVER, Toni Gayle
Tahlequah HS; Tahlequah, OK; Ann; Band; Chor; FTA; Rainbow; Spch C; Bkbl; Tnns; 4H A; Poet A; Spch A; Green Co Singers; Secy; 1st United Methodist Church; U of Okla; Speech.

Van SLOOTEN, Denise Gail
Zeeland HS; Zeeland, MI (173-236) Band; Chor; Ftbl; Choir.

VANSOELEN, Linda Sue
Ames HS; Ames, IA; Span C; Iowa St U; Microbio.

Van SWERINGEN, Anne Elizabeth
Cleveland Heights HS; Cleveland Heights, OH; Future Scientists; Yth Conservation Corps; Vol, Cleveland Musem of Natrl Hist; Bio.

VANTASSEL, Philip David
Roger L Putnam Voc-Tech HS; Springfield, MA (1-315) NHS; Sch P; Tr; Val; Rochester Inst of Tech; Printing.

VanTATENHOVE, Kristina Lee
Mark Keppel HS; Monterey Park, CA (200-500) A Cap Choir; Tri-HiY; Arch; Living Word Bible Col; Bible.

VANTATENHOVE, Kristina Lee
Mark Keppel HS; Monterey Park, CA (200-450) A Cap Choir; Chor; Tri-HiY; Arch; Living Word Bible Col; Bible.

VantHOF, Dawn Faye
Luverne HS; Luverne, MN (13-133) Chor; Drama; NHS; Arch; Sftbl; Art A.

VANTHOURNOUT, Donald Brian
St Charles HS; St Charles, IL (4-482) Chess C; Math C; NHS; Sch P; VP, Span C; Spch C; SC; Bsbl; NMS; Spch A; St Scholar.

Van TRESS, Jon Roger
Abingdon HS; Abingdon, IL (33%-100) Band; Secy, FFA; VP, 4H; SC; Bkbl; Cr-Ctry; JV, Ftbl; JV, Tr; 4H A; HCt; Lincoln Arc Welding A; Kappa Delta Chi Fraternity; Tn Choir; U of Ill; Agr.

Van TREUREN, Bradford Gene
S Hunterdon Regional HS; Lambertville, NJ (19-109) A Cap Choir; Chor; Key C; Madrigal; NHS; ARC; Sch P; Ftbl; Golf; 1st, Preaching & Singing Contest; Corporal, Christian Serv Brigade; LeTourneau Col; Mech Engr.

VanWESTEN, Kevin Alan
Luverne Pub HS; Luverne, MN (20-164) Tres, FFA; 4H; Ftbl; Sftbl; 4H A; FFA A; Worthington Jr Col; Commercial Art.

Van WYCKHOUSE, Heidi
Hawthorne HS; Hawthorne, NJ; Bus C; Chor; SC; Swim; Cpt, Tnns; Tr; Kiwanis A; Most Out; GAA; Tres, Art C; JV Winter Tr; Swim, Tr, A's.

Van WYE, Shelly Jo
Montpelier HS; Montpelier, OH (11-96) Band; Chor; Rptr, FBLA; Semi-Fin, GS; NHS; Tr; Yth Fel; Acad Achv C; NW Tech Col; Acct.

Van WYHE, Harlan Jay
Luverne HS; Luverne, MN (1-130) Band; Ensm; NHS; Pres, SC; Pres, Jr Cl; Bsbl; Ftbl; Wrest; U of Minn; Tech.

Van WYNGARDEN, Cathy Lynn
New Monroe Comm Sch; Monroe, IA (8-55) Band; 4H.

Van ZANT, Janet Lynne
Buena Sr HS; Ventura, CA; Campfire Girls; Pepperdine U; Art.

VanZANT, Jay Kevin
Prague HS; Prague, OK (1-85) Rptr, Band; Tres, NHS; Bkbl; Golf; Hist A; Okla Central St U; Acct.

VanZYL, Jane Rochelle
Coronado HS; Colorado Springs, CO (1-331) Community Yth Symph; Ger C; InterClub Coun; Lat C; Math C; NHS; Orch; Swim; Tr; Hist A; Hon Prog; Math A; Rotary A; Val; Foreign Lang A; Eng A; Pres Schol Fin; Wash Crossing Found Essay Contest; US Naval Acad; Math.

VARCO, Theresa Camille
Mt Mercy Acad; Buffalo, NY; Band; CYO; Cpt, Chldr; Chor; Hmrm; VP, Math C; NHS; SC; Lion A; NEDT; Regent Schol; Marquette U; Phys Therapy.

VARDELL, Michelle Renee
Bryan Adams HS; Dallas, TX (25%-1000) NHS; Span C; Hon Prog; U of Tex at Austin; Law.

VARELA, Eddy Jr
Broward Christian Sch; Fort Lauderdale, FL; Chor; Math C; Bkbl; Cr-Ctry; Ftbl.

VARGA, Dara Marie
Sacred Heart HS; Vineland, NJ; Ann; JV, Chldr; Chor; Dbte Tm; NHS; Rptr, Sch P; VP, Sci C; VP, Span C; S-T, SC; S-T, Jr Cl; Sftbl; General Excellence A; Bio.

VARGAS, Abigail
Norman Thomas HS; New York, NY; Y-Tns; Cl Fav; Math A; Most Out; Sci A; Star Student.

VARGAS, Marilyn
Adolfo Grana Rivera HS; Penuelas, PR (2-336) FBLA; FHA; Hmrm; Bio A; COM; Hist A; Hon Prog; Span A; Cath U; Trabajodora Social.

VARGAS, Rosalinda
Bishop Conaty Mem HS; Los Angeles, CA (1-120) NHS; Span NHS; Tres, SC; Bank Of Amer A; Bausch & Lomb A; CSF; Chem A; Hist A; Hon Prog; Val; General Excellence; USC; Petroleum Engr.

VARGAS, Venietta Maria
Spruce Creek HS; Port Orange, FL (27-450) Cpt, Anchor C; Cpt, Band; BC; Mod Mus Mas; Magna Cum Laude; Sr Dir, Anchor C; WW; Daytona Beach Comm Col; Med Secy.

VARGO, Charles Richard
St Elizabeth HS; Pittsburgh, PA; Ed, Ann; Drama; Model UN; Phys C; Sch P; Sci C; Pres, Span C; Thes; Secy, Sr Cl; Alg A; NEDT; Sci A; Interntl Fel; Dorothy Lombardi Mem Schol A.

VARGO, William James
Coshocton HS; Coshocton, OH (3-240) A Cap Choir; All Amer Yth; A-Ed, Ann; Band; BS; Chor; Ensm; HiY; NHS; Order/Arrow; Span C; DARGCA; Eagle Sct; Edmont Achv A; Engr.

VARNADO, Denise
Locke Sr HS; Los Angeles, CA (13-575) Fr C; Span C; ROTC A; Val; Pre-Med.

VARNER, Kym D'Anne
Hobbs HS; Hobbs, NM (145-497) Bkbl; Co-Cpt, Sftbl; Tr; Masque & Gavel A; Yth Fel; Proficiency A; Wayland Baptist Col; Phys Ede.

VARNEY, John Robert
Manhattan HS; Manhattan, KS (25-500) Band; BS; Chem C; Chess C; Dbte Tm; Math C; NFL; NHS; Order/Arrow; Golf; Alg A; Citz A; Order/Arrow A; Spch A; Type A; Engr.

VARNON, Geneva
Hayes HS; Birmingham, AL; Secy, A Cap Choir; Rptr, Hmrm; Secy, Sch P; Rptr, SC; Citz A; Cl Fav; Hon Prog; Most Out; U of Ala; Nurs.

VARVALOUKAS, Ellen
Brooklyn Tech HS; Brooklyn, NY (5-40) Chldr; Secy, Hmrm; Mjrte; SC; Val; Yth Fel; Religion A; Nicholas W Scourby A; Amer Col in Greece; Graphic Communications.

VARY, Donna Emilie
Dearborn HS; Dearborn, MI (2%-560) A Cap Choir; Semi-Fin, AFS; NHS; Thes; Mgr, Bkbl; COM; Hon Prog; Phi Beta Kappa; Yth Fel; The Col of Idaho; Zoology.

VASBINDER, Julie Ann
Ellsworth J Wilson Sr HS; Spencerport, NY (10%-356) Drama; 4H; Lat C; Model UN; NHS; Ski C; Tnns; 4H A; Regent Schol; Pres, Explorers; Col of Environment Sci; Forest Engr.

VEGA, Victor Manuel
Adolfo Grana Rivera HS; Penuelas, PR (4-336) CYO; Dbte Tm; Lit Mag; Sci C; Bsbl; Bkbl; Swim; COM; Chem A; Hon Prog; Lion A; Mjrte A; Col Ingeniero de Maguez; Ingenieria.

VEGA, Wanda Ivette
Luis Munoz Marin HS; Cabo Rojo, PR (4-150) Dbte Tm; Secy, FHA; FTA; Mjrte; Mod Mus Mas; Secy, SC; COM; Hon Prog; Sci Fair A; Colegio Agri y Artes Mech; Computer Prog.

VEILLEUX, Elisabeth Reine
Wethersfield HS; Wethersfield, CT; Drama; 4H; Rptr, Sch P; Ski C; Swim; Tr; Pres A.

VEJRASKA, Beth Deanne
Alliance HS; Alliance, NE (15-150) Band; Ger C; Mjrte; Y-Tns; Hon Prog; Sci A; Ger A; Scholastic Contest; U of Nebr.

VEJRASKA, Mark Thomas
Alliance HS; Alliance, NE; Pres, Band; Community Yth Symph; Ensm; Hmrm; NHS; Fin, Sch Achieve Tm; SC; SC; Var C; VP, Sr Cl; Bsbl; Fin, Cr-Ctry; Fin; Tr; Fin, Wrest; Chem A; Hon Prog; Yth Fel; U of Nebr; Elec Engr.

VELASQUEZ, Indira Lillian
Adlai E Stevenson HS; Bronx, NY (37-788) Anchor C; InterClub Coun; Lit Mag; Secy, NHS; Sch Achieve Tm; SC; COM; Citz A; Hon Prog; Berkeley Bus Sch; Executive Secy.

VELAZQUEZ, Enid
Dr Pila HS; Ponce, PR (1-688) A Cap Choir; CYO; NHS; ARC; COM; Hon Prog; Lion A; U de PR; Med.

VELAZQUEZ, Goel A
Adolfo Grana Rivera HS; Penuelas, PR (5-342) Band; Drama; 4H; Bsbl; Bkbl; Sftbl; COM; 4H A; Hon Prog; Lion A; U of Puerto Rico; Med.

VELDKAMP, Jody Allen
Luverne Jr Sr HS; Luverne, MN (11%-135) Dbte Tm; NHS; Bemidji St U; Broadcasting.

VELDMAN, Meredith
Timothy Christian HS; Elmhurst, IL (1-90) Band; Hmrm; NHS; A-Ed, Sch P; Ski C; SC; Pres, Jr Cl; Secy, Soph Cl; Tr; Hon Prog; NMS; Amer Lit A; Graduation Marshal; Lat A; Hist.

VELEZ, Ana de los Angeles
Academia Discipulos de Cristo; Bayamon, PR (10-122) A Cap Choir; Chldr; Chem C; Chess C; Dbte Tm; Fr C; Tres, Hmrm; Pres, Sci C; Cpt, Tnns; Alg A; Beauty; Bio A; COM; Chem A; Hon Prog; Magna Cum Laude; Phy A; Sci A; Spch A; U of Puerto Rico; Law.

VELEZ, Axel
Yauco HS; Yauco, PR; Bkbl; Tr; Jamestown Col; Engeneering.

VELEZ, Carlos Arnaldo
Juan Jose Osuna HS; Hato Rey, PR (3-150) Band; Bus C; Chem C; Chor; Fr C; Hmrm; Lit Mag; Math C; Mod Mus Mas; Phys C; ARC; Sch P; Span C; SC; Ftbl; Golf; Swim; Bio A; COM; Chem A; Hon Prog; Journ A; JA A; Lion A; Math A; MLS; Poet A; Sci A; Fin, Ntl Eng Contest; U of Puerto Rico; Sci.

VELEZ, Emilio D
Francisco Mendoza HS; Isabela, PR; Secy, BS; CYO; Chor; 4H; Hmrm; Lit Mag; Mod Mus Mas; NHS; Order/Arrow; Ed, Sch P; Sci C; Span C; Spch C; Swim; Alg A; Bio A; COM; Citz A; Cl Fav; Hon Prog; Order/Arrow A; Pres A; Sci Swtht; Painting A; Poetry A; Col of Agr & Mech Arts; Bio.

VELEZ, Lissette
Antonio S Pedreira HS; Moca, PR (2-44) CYO; FHA; Tnns; Universidad de Puerto Rico; Ciencias Politicas.

VELEZ, Lizzette
Adolfo Grana Rivera HS; Penuelas, PR (7-342) CYO; Chldr; Chor; Drama; GS; S-T; Hmrm; Cpt, Mjrte; Span C; Alg A; COM; Cl Fav; Hon Prog; Lion A; Mjrte A; Cath U; Med.

VELEZ, Maria Theresa
Juan Jose Osuna HS; Hato Rey, PR (6-101) Chldr; Drama; FHA; ARC; Swim; Hon Prog; Spch A; U of Puerto Rico; Secretarial Sci.

VELEZ, Nancy
Dra Maria Cadilla de Martinez HS; Arecibo, PR (71-429) UPR-Regional.

VELEZ, Samuel
Doctor Pila HS; Ponce, PR; Pres, Hmrm; NHS; Swim; Alg A; Lion A; BSct; JV, Vlbl; Lib C; Mayaguez Col; Elec Engr.

VELEZ, Wanda
Luis Munoz Marin HS; Cabo Rojo, PR (10-200) 4H; Lit Mag; CAAM; Psych.

VELKY, Julia Ann
Grand Rapids Christian HS; Grand Rapids, MI (70-378) NHS; Span C; Hon Prog; Fine Arts A; U of Oreg; Computer Sci.

VELO, Tony
Belton HS; Belton, TX (8-276) VP, CYO; Bsbl; Ftbl; Baylor U; Law.

VELTRI, Gerard Anthony
Notre Dame HS; Clarksburg, WV; BS; Pres, CYO; Fr C; Hmrm; Key C; NHS; SC; Bsbl; Cpt, Bkbl; Ftbl; COM; Hon Prog; Sal; All St, All Co, Bkbl; Fairmont St Col; Dentistry.

VELTRI, Rebecca Anne
Notre Dame HS; Clarksburg, WV (11-54) CYO; Chldr; Drama; FBLA; Hmrm; NHS; F-Ed, Sch P; SC; VP, Jr Cl; Co-Cpt, Bkbl; COM; Cl Fav; Pres Phys Fitness A; W Va U; Radiology.

VELTRI, Rosemary
Notre Dame HS; Clarksburg, WV (3-63) Band; JV, Chldr; Drama; FBLA; VP, FTA; Math C; NHS; A-Ed, Sch P; Sci C; Spch C; Secy, SC; VP, Soph Cl; Bkbl; Swim; Bio A; Math A; Poet A; Pres Phys Fitness A; Ed.

VENABLE, Donna Sue
Springville HS; Springville, AL; Ed, Ann; Pres, BC; Tres, Rainbow; Rptr, Sch P; SC; Type A; Bus A; Jefferson St Jr Col; Bus.

VENABLE, Dorothy Winn
Columbus HS; Columbus, GA; NHS; A-Ed, Sch P; VP, Jr Cl; Hon Prog; Journ A; Q&S A; F-Ed, Sch P; 1st VP, St School Press Assn; Chapt & Convention Ch, Jr Civitan.

VENABLE, Eleanor Queenine
Sheffield HS; Memphis, TN (10%-214) Ann; Hmrm; NHS; SC; Lat A; Memphis St U; Bio.

VENABLE, Joyce Ann
Scott HS; Madison, WV; Chor; VP, Drama; Secy, FNA; VP, Hmrm; VP, Math C; VP, Mu Alpha Theta; Rptr, Sch P; SC; VP, Thes; Tnns; COM; Miss Scottonian; W Va U.

VENBURG, Gregory Dean
Lincoln NE HS; Lincoln, NE (1-514) Band; Dbte Tm; VP, Math C; NFL; NHS; Order/Arrow; Var C; Elk A; I Dare You; Regent School; Val; Gym; Elks Ntl Found Schol; Eagle Sct; Sertoma A; WW; U of Nebr; Dentistry.

VENCILL, Cherry Lee
Lee-Davis HS; Mechanicsville, VA; HiY; Sftbl; Tnns; HCt; Pres A; Art Cert of Achv & Cert of Part; Art.

VENEMA, Lynn Annette
Modesto Christian; Modesto, CA (11-28) Chldr; Fr C; Swim; HQn; Most Out; Modesto Junior College; Working With The Disabled.

VENEN, Susan L
Otsego HS; Otsego, MI (16-247) A Cap Choir; Chldr; GS; Hmrm; NHS; Secy, SC; Var C; Swim; Tnns; Tr; COM; Mich St U; Bus.

VENETTE, Robin Louise
Chateaugay Central HS; Chateaugay, NY;

VENIER, Debra Carol
Roosevelt HS; Wyandotte, MI (25-550) Bus C; FBLA; NHS; Hon Prog; Type A; Sports Announcer; Cpt, Vlbl; Muscular Distrophy Door to Door; Insurance Secy.

VENNERI, Christine Lynn
Bishop McDevitt HS; Harrisburg, PA (20-300) Ger C; NHS; SC; Swim; Hon Prog; Sci A; Ger Cl Achv A; Pa St U; Bus.

VENNING, Anna Maria
Burke HS; Charleston, SC (4-177) Bus C; NHS; COM; Delta Sigma Theta A; Hon Prog; Col of Charleston; Med.

VENTRCEK, Evelyn Ann
Pleasanton HS; Pleasanton, TX (10%-165) VP, Band; Pres, FHA; FTA; Jr Miss Pagent; VP, NHS; Sch P; St Stu Congress; Pres, SC; Var C; VP, Jr Cl; Bkbl; JV, Golf; COM; Citz A; Opt A; Opt Out Tn; Rotary A; Tres, Chaplain, Projects Ch, NHS; Artist, Sch P; Vlbl; Best Citizen; VP, SC; Exchange Stu, Australia; ST, Fresh Cl; Area Pres, FHA; Tex St Tech Inst; Advertising.

VENTRELLA, Michael George
Livermore Falls HS; Livermore Falls, ME (1-94) F-Ed, Ann; BS; Math C; Pres, NHS; SC; Var C; Pres, Sr Cl; Pres, Soph Cl; Bkbl; Ftbl; Alg A; Bio A; Hon Prog; Type A; S-T, Ecology C; Winter Carnival Kg; Most Dependable; Best Dressed; U of Maine; Chem Engr.

VERA, Kristi Marie
Washington-Lee HS; Arlington, VA (10%-513) GS; Pres, Hmrm; NHS; Span C; Span NHS; Bkbl; Sftbl; William & Mary Col; Law.

VERB, Andrea Rene
Clay Sr HS; Oregon, OH (12-350) Ann; Fr C; FHA; Pres, 4H; Mgr, Bkbl; Sftbl; Mgr, Tr; 4H A; Hon Prog; Sci A; Food & Nutrition.

VERCHEREAU, Victor Joe
Chelsea HS; Chelsea, MI (50%-225) Tres, FFA; Bsbl; Co-Cpt, Ftbl; Wrest; Bob Jones U; Sales.

VERDEYEN, David Michael
St Elmo HS; St Elmo, IL (6-56) Band; VP, CYO; Chor; Ensm; 4H; NHS; SC; Pres, Jr Cl; Pres, Soph Cl; JV, Bkbl; Citz A; 4H A; Hon Prog; Arch.

VERDREE, Stanley
Windsor Forest HS; Savannah, GA (20-250) St U of NY; Mech Engr.

VERDUIN, Pamela Anne
Pacific Grove HS; Pacific Grove, CA (6-215) AFS; Band; Chldr; Chor; Drama; Hmrm; Model UN; Orch; A-Ed, Sch P; Pres, SC; Pres, Sr Cl; Pres, Jr Cl; Pres, Soph Cl; Bkbl; Sftbl; Cpt, Swim; Bank Of Amer A; CSF; DARGCA; MLS; Yth Leg; Drama A; Monterey Peninsula Col; Journ.

VEREEN, Deborah Maurice
S Hills HS; Pittsburgh, PA (92-530) Lat C; Orch; ARC; Hon Prog; Yth Fel; All City Orch; W Va Weslyan Col; Home-Ec.

VEREEN, Donna
Parkway Prog Beta HS; Philadelphia, PA; Hmrm; Co-Ed, Sch P; SC; Amer Leg A; Fleischman Schol; MLS; Most Out; Columbia U; Pre-Law.

VEREEN, Sharon Rene
Palm Beach Gardens HS; Palm Beach Gardens, FL (285-560) Cpt, Bkbl; Ftbl; Sftbl; Swim; Cpt, Tr; Beauty; COM; Citz A; Cl Fav; Most Out; Pres A; Phys Ed A; PA; Most Courteous; Del St Col; Phys Ed.

VERELL, Jamie Jean
Houston HS; Houston, MS (10-150) Band; Chor; FHA; 4H; 4H A; Candystriper; Distinguished Stu A; Miss St U; Nurs.

VERESPEJ, Raymond Christopher
Lake Cath HS; Mentor, OH (39-284) Drama; NHS; Ed, Sch P; Thes; COM; Christian Life A; Service A; Marquette U; Journ.

VERFURTH, Francis Theodore
Carroll HS; Dayton, OH (2-265) Math C; NHS; Order/Arrow; Ski C; Pres, St Stu Congres; Var C; Soccer; God & Country A; Hon Prog; Sal; Statistician, Bkbl & Ftbl; Eagle Sct; AFROTC Schol; NROTC Schol; U of Notre Dame; Pre-Med.

VERHAGEN, Stacy Corneila
Tallulah HS; Tallulah, LA (3-80) Band; Chldr; VP, 4H; Hmrm; Lit Ral; NHS; Ed, Sch P; Secy, SC; Bio A; Cl Fav; HCt; Friendliest; Secy, Allied Yth; LSU; Bio.

VERHEECKE, Kathy Marie
N Gwinnett HS; Buford, GA (10%-190) Band; BC; Chldr; FHA; 4H; Sftbl; COM; Sci A; Tr As; Gainesville Jr Col; Ed.

VERKADE, Elaine Elizabeth
United Comm of Boone HS; Boone, IA (4-42) Band; Chldr; Chor; Pres, 4H; NHS; Sci C; Spch C; SC; Tr; COM; 4H A; Sci A; Spch A; Type A; NML; Iowa St U; Vet Sci.

VERKADE, Valerie Grace
Brethren HS; Paramount, CA (10-100) A Cap Choir; F-Ed, Ann; Ensm; FTA; NHS; CSF; Ldr, Drill Tm; Semi-Fin, Miss Teenage Amer; WW; GSct; *Westmont Col; Eng.*

VERKEN, William Carrol
Belvidere HS; Belvidere, IL (13-391) Band; Ger C; Ski C; SC; Var C; VP, Jr Cl; Tres, Soph Cl; Mgr, Bsbl; Mgr, Bkbl; Golf; Yth Fel; Jazz Band; Church Acolyte; Lutheran Young People; *Rock Valley Col.*

VERKLER, Darlene Kay
Cissna Park HS; Cissna Park, IL (2-39) Band; Chldr; FHA; SC; Pres, Jr Cl; Bkbl; Sftbl; *Acct.*

VERM, Charles Anthony
Brazos HS; Wallis, TX (10-69) Band; CYO; Dbte Tm; Ensm; FFA; SC; Bkbl; Ftbl; Tnns; HCt.

VERMAAT, Krisanne Kim
Batavia HS; Batavia, IL; Band; Ensm; Math C; NHS; Orch; Ski C; SC; Hon Prog; Math A; NMS; St Scholar; St Span Contest; *U of Ill; Engr.*

VERMEER, Kristi Jan
Excelsior HS; Norwalk, CA (90%-400) Ed, Ann; Chldr; S-T, Lat C; Pres, SC; Amer Leg A; CSF; COM; Masonic A; Math A; MLS; Most Out; Scorekeeper, Bsbl, Bkbl; Stu ot Quarter; Stu o-t Yr; Principal's HR; *Hope Col; Pre-Med.*

VERMEIRE, Daniel Roland
Farrell Sr HS; Farrell, PA (19-200) Band; VP, Demolay; Span C.

VERMILYEA, Gail
James W Robinson Secondary HS; Fairfax, VA (1-584) Ger C; Math C; Rptr; Sch P; Alg A; All A's; HR.

VERNARD, William Henry
New Haven HS; New Haven, IN (6-240) VP, Chess C; Dbte Tm; NFL; Sci C; COM; Chamber of Comm A; Hon Prog; Math A; Rotary A; Sci A; St Scholar; *Purdue U; Engr.*

VERNON, John Leroy Jr
Kernersville Wesleyan Acad; Kernersville, NC (20-45) Drama; Spch C; Pres, SC; Soccer; *Carolina Sch of Broadcasting; TV Broadcasting.*

VERNON, Linda Marie
Benson HS; Omaha, NE (146-450) AFS; Band; Chor; Ensm; Orch; Midland Col Schol; Christian Ed; Choir; Rep, Yth Fel; Bell Choir; Deacons; *Midland Col; Special Ed.*

VERNON, Robert Dale
Pacific Christian HS; Los Angeles, CA (25-37) A Cap Choir; Drama; Ensm; Rptr, Sch P; SC; Var C; Bkbl; MVP, Ftbl; Tr; HQn Escort; All League Linebacker; Allstar Tm; *Biola Col; Communications.*

VERNON, Sheila Diana
Steinmetz HS; Chicago, IL (49-618) A Cap Choir; Chldr; Chor; Key C; NHS; Orch; Hon Prog; Orch, Gym Ldrs, Sch Service A's; *Bradley U; Biol Sci.*

VERNON, Thomas Corbin
Marion HS; Marion, IA (13-222) Chor; Tres, Drama; Madrigal; Pres, Spch C; Tres, Thes; Pres, Soph Cl; JV, Bsbl; Ftbl; JV, Tr; Citz A; Math A; Most Out; Spch A; Yth Fel; Cert of Recognition, Thespian; Drama Recog A; Outst Performance; *Mus.*

VERSEMAN, Susan Jane
Crystal Lake Comm HS; Crystal Lake, IL (36-550) NHS; SC; Secy, Jr Cl; HCt; *Chicago Col of Commerce; Court Rptr.*

VERSER, Karen
Montrose Acad; Montrose, AR (25%-34) Ed, Ann; Band; Bus C; Ensm; Pres, Fr C; FHA; Hmrm; NHS; Orch; ARC; Sch P; SC; Var C; Ftbl; Co-Cpt, Sftbl; Tr; Beauty; Pres, Baptist Girls Organizations; Church Pianist; Most Talented A; Sch Photographer; WW; *Ouachita Baptist U; Dental Hygiene.*

VER STEEG, Kelly Anne
Mission Bay HS; San Diego, CA (27-433) MVP, Sftbl; Pres A; Breitbard; Prep, Most Ath, Ath A's; HR; Methodist Women A & Hon; *Point Loma Col.*

VERSWEYVELD, James John
Charlotte Valley Central Sch; Davenport, NY (3-44) VP, Band; Chor; Ch, 4H; Ch, Hmrm; NHS; SC; Var C; Tr; Bio A; 4H A; Industrial Arts A; *Animal Sci.*

VERTHEIN, Lyn Marie
McGregor HS; McGregor, MN (1-72) Chor; Drama; Tres, FHA; Mjrte; NHS; Sch P; Sci C; Span C; *U of Minn; Computer Prog & Tech.*

VESSEL, Laura Louise
Baymonte Christian HS; Scotts Valley, CA; Chldr; Chor.

VESSELLS, Brenda Sue
N Mesquite HS; Mesquite, TX (217-450) Band; Span C; *Tex Womens U; Nurs.*

VESSELS, Stephen Arthur
Richland HS; Ft Worth, TX (40%-500) F-Ed, Sch P; Span C; Tr; Wrest; Pres, Ntl Jr Hon Soc; Span A; Judo A; *Ministry.*

VESSELS, Yvonne Marie
King William HS; King William, VA; Co-Ed, Ann; JV, Chldr; Secy, Drama; FBLA; 4H; Co-Ed, Lit Mag; F-Ed, Sch P; Sci C; Tres, SC; Mgr, Tr; COM; HCt; Hon Prog; Q&S A; Spch A; Col Enrichment Prog; *Va St Col; Journ.*

VEST, Christine Lee
Great Bridge HS; Chesapeake, VA (47-518) Band; Chor; Ensm; Fr C; Tr; *Med.*

VEST, John Garret
Liberty HS; Bedford, VA (33%-250) Band; Chess C; HiY; Sci C; Geography A; Ntl Piano Playing Audition Certs.

VEST, Julie Ann
Oak Hills HS; Cincinnati, OH; Chor; *Miami U; Fashion.*

VEST, Melynda Lea
Claremore HS; Claremore, OK (1-270) Fr C; FHA; Tres, NHS; SC; Tnns; Crisco A; Hist A; Conf Champ, Tnns; Yrbk Qn; *Okla St U; Archt.*

VEST, Richard Earl II
Lenoir City HS; Lenoir City, TN; Chess C; 4H; Bsbl; Cpt, Ftbl.

VEST, Vickey Diane
Levelland HS; Levelland, TX (75-200) Band; Chor; Ensm; FHA; NHS; Yth Fel; *S Plains Col; Secy.*

VESTAL, Donna Lee
Rocky Mount Sr HS; Rocky Mount, NC (20-598) Band; Hmrm; Orch; SC; Citz A; Math A; Sci A; Faculty A; Outst Service; Marshal; Jr Alumnus; *Med.*

VESTAL, Donna Mae
Hubbard HS; Hubbard, OH (243-350) A Cap Choir; Chor; Rainbow; Swim; Star Student; Type A; Yth Fel; Line Officer, Rainbow; *Nurs.*

VESTAL, Mitzi Gayle
Starmount HS; Boonville, NC (5-151) Co-Cpt, Chldr; Chor; Ensm; FHA; Math C; Mu Alpha Theta; NHS; Span C; Mgr, Tr; 2nd Runner Up, Jr Miss Pageant; Statistician, Tr; Govn Sch Nom; Jr Marshal; *High Point Col; Theatre Arts Ed.*

VETSCH, Donna Mae
Napoleon HS; Napoleon, ND (7-72) FHA; NHS; Sci A.

VETTEL, Laurie Ann
Thompson Pub Sch; Thompson, ND (6-28) Ed, Ann; Chldr; Chor; Drama; Ensm; S-T, SC; Mgr, Bkbl; WW; Interntl Mus Camp Schol; *Navy; Communications.*

VETTER, Judy Marie
Notre Dame HS; Portsmouth, OH (19-45) Cpt, Chldr; Cl Fav; HCt.

VEZEY, Carol Lynn
Naperville Central HS; Naperville, IL; AFS; Ski C; Span C; *Foreign Lang.*

VIA, Victoria Glyn
Northside HS; Roanoke, VA; F-Ed, Ann; Fr C; NHS; Thes; Hist A; Hon Prog; Spch A; Chorale; Outst Cl Off; Super Piano Solo; Ntl Fed Mus Fest; *William and Mary Col; Hist.*

VICIANA, Enrique Jose
Miami Christian Sch; Miami, FL (3-53) Ed, Ann; Band; Lit Mag; NHS; Parl, SC; Bkbl; Cr-Ctry; Tr; B Crocker A; NMF; NEDT; *Baylor U; Premed.*

VICK, Regina Nicholette
Franklin Acad; Winnsboro, LA; Ann; BC; Fin, Lit Ral; SC; Bkbl; *NE La U; Eng.*

VICK, Rhonda Darlene
Central HS; Thomasville, GA; 4H; Sch P; Sci C; Tri-HiY; Bkbl.

VICK, Richard Nicholson Jr
Bertie Sr HS; Windsor, NC (5-340) BC; Chess C; FTA; Monogram; Sci C; Cpt, Bsbl; Hon Prog; WW; *E Carolina U; Phys Therapy.*

VICK, Robert Stephen
J H Rose HS; Greenville, NC (32-409) Monogram; NHS; Order/Arrow; Cr-Ctry; Tr; *Wake Forest U; Bio.*

VICKERS, DeLena Caye
Snyder HS; Snyder, TX (8-200) Band; Tres, FHA; Tres, Lat C; NHS; Swim; Bio A; Hist A; Hon Prog; NMS; Top 10, 4 Yrs; Eng A; *Tex Tech U; Biol.*

VICKERS, Mark Douglas
N Tonawanda Sr HS; N Tonawanda, NY (2-650) Band; Ensm; Hmrm; NHS; Sch Achieve Tm; SC; Golf; COM; Cl Fav; Hist A; Hon Prog; Most Out; Span, Mus, A's; *Med.*

VICKERS, Ron K
Starkville HS; Starkville, MS (25%-281) Band; BS; Chem C; FBLA; FTA; Hmrm; Key C; Math C; NHS; Phys C; Sci C; SC; Var C; Pres, Sr Cl; Pres, Jr Cl; Bkbl; JV, Ftbl; *Ole Miss; Law.*

VICKERS, Tanetta Gail
Coffee HS; Douglas, GA; *S Ga Col; Art.*

VICKERY, Donald Thurston
Hart Co HS; Hartwell, GA; FBLA; HiY; VP, Hmrm; InterAct C; Rptr, Sch P; Sci C; Tr; COM; HCt; Hon Prog; Journ A; SAGE C; VICA; Machine Shop A'S, Local & Area; St Machine Shop Contest.

VICKS, Sherell Denise
Mitchell Co HS; Camilla, GA (1-137) Secy, BC; Chldr; Secy, Drama; FBLA; Pres, FTA; Tnns; Beauty; COM; Hist A; Hon Prog; Math A; Phy A; Sci A; Type A; Val; AKA Schol; WW; Sr Superlative; Campus Hostess; *Morris Brown Col; Med Technology.*

VICTOR, Brian Joseph
Hall HS; Spring Valley, IL (1-154) Drama; FTA; Math C; Rptr, Sch P; Sci C; Span C; Spch C; Thes; Wrest; *U of Ill; Sci.*

VIDAL, Denise
Colegio San Antonio HS; Rio Piedras, PR (10-100) Chldr; NHS; Tres, SC; COM; Hon Prog; Sci A; Vlbl; WW; *Harvard U; Bus Adm.*

VIDAURRETA, Beverly L
Orangewood Acad; Garden Grove, CA (80%-70) Chor; Ger C; Ski C; Var C; Secy, Soph Cl; Co-Cpt, Bkbl; MVP, Ftbl; Co-Cpt, Soccer; JV, Sftbl; Co-Cpt, Tr; Hon Prog; Pres A; Vlbl Tm; Badminton; Ath o-t Month; HR; Presidential Phys Fitness A; *Loma Linda U; Psych.*

VIDAURRETA, Samuel Thomas
Orangewood Acad; Garden Grove, CA (10-70) Chem C; Chor; Math C; Phys C; Sch Achieve Tm; Ed, Sch P; Ski C; Pres, Span C; VP, St Stu Congress; Cpt, Var C; Bsbl; Bkbl; Ftbl; Golf; Hockey; Soccer; Sftbl; Tnns; Tr; Citz A; Hon Prog; Most Out; Pres A; Rptr, Sch P; Outst Stu A; Sports Invitational A's; *Loma Linda U; Dentistry.*

VIDAURRI, Jo Ann Garcia
Memorial HS; San Antonio, TX (10%-275) Ch, Hmrm; Secy, Span NHS; COM; Most Out; Jr Cl Officer; *Med.*

VIDLER, Floyd Edwin Jr
S Charleston HS; S Charleston, WV (10%-350) Band; Ensm; All Co Band; *Abilene Christian U; Mus.*

VIDRINE, Jame Emmett
Oakdale HS; Oakdale, LA (6-105) Band; CYO; 4H; Key C; NHS; Cpt, Bsbl; Ftbl; Tr; COM; H of F; Hon Prog; Spch A; *La Tech U; Civil Engr.*

VIDRINE, Patricia Ann
Wossman HS; Monroe, LA; Chor; Pres, FBLA; Semi-Fin, Jr Miss Pa; NHst; SC; Y-Tns; NHS A; WW; *NE La U; Bus.*

VIE, Elizabeth Kay
Klein HS; Spring, TX (5-620) A Cap Choir; Rptr, Drama; Ensm; Fin, GS; 4H; Madrigal; Math C; Mu Alpha Theta; NHS; Span C; Rptr, Thes; Chem A; Hon Prog; Regent Schol; Summa Cum Laude; Swtht, Thespian; U Interschol League As, Mus; Tex Lutheran Col; Mus Ed.

VIEBACK, Gina Linn
Tower Hill HS; Tower Hill, IL (1-23) Band; Cpt, Chldr; Chor; Drama; Span C; SC; Tr; HQn; Yth Fel; WW; WW Among Amer Chldr; WW Among Mus Stu in Amer HS; Lakeland Comm Col; Acct.

VIEBROCK, Pamela Jean
Parkview HS; Springfield, MO (25-405) Band; Fr C; French NHS; Orch; Fin, Swim; I Rating, Mus; Sou Mo St U; Sociology.

VIEHMANN, Laura Ruth
Phillips Acad; Andoven, MA (40%-345) Band; Chor; Hmrm; SC; All-Sch Social Functions Comm; W Quad S Charity Comm; Asst Bus Mgr, Yrbk; NMS Prog; Del, Blue Key Soc; Biological Sci.

VIEHMANN, Martha Lynn
Phillips Acad; Andover, MA; Chor; Hmrm; Lit Mag; SC; Yth Fel; Social Functions Committee; Washington Intern; 1st Cl Sct; Lib Arts.

VIELWEBER, Natalie Ann
Belleville E HS; Belleville, IL (20%-732) Chor; Drama; Thes; Bowl A; Pres, Yth Fel; BAC; Data Processing.

VIEN, Nancy Jo
Montevideo Sr HS; Montevideo, MN; AFS; FHA; Ger C; Span C; Special Ed.

VIERNES, Jay Leland
Kohala HS; Kapaau, HI (1-76) AFS; Band; VP, FFA; Hmrm; Model UN; NHS; Pres, SC; Secy, Var C; VP, Jr Cl; Vlbl; USC; Dentistry.

VIERNO, Jacqueline Marie
Antilles HS; Fort Buchanan, PR (7-118) Ann; Drama; Lit Mag; NHS; SC; Hon Prog; VP, Key-ettes.

VIETH, Christopher Gene
Fulton HS; Fulton, MO; A Cap Choir; Chor; Ensm; Hmrm; SC; Var C; Ftbl; Tnns; JV, Wrest; Hon Prog; All Dist & St Choir; NE Mo St U; Mus.

VIETH, Teri Lynn
Newbury Park HS; Newbury Park, CA (7-636) Semi-Fin, GS; Phys C; Ski C; Parl, SC; Bank of Amer A; CSF; Hon Prog; Campus Life; CPR, 1st Aid, Cert; Jr Hospital Vol; Alice B Tuohy A; Advanced Lifesaving; Math.

VIGANSKY, Gerald Lynn
Bridgman HS; Bridgman, MI (15%-100) SC; JV, Bsbl; JV, Bkbl; JV, Ftbl; Tr; Gov.

VIGGIANO, Margaret Mary
Acad of Saint Aloysius; Jersey City, NJ (10-127) Fr C; Ger C; Lat C; JV, Math C; NHS; Span C; Hon Prog; Special Ed.

VIGIL, Kenneth Mark
Bonneville HS; Ogden, UT (40-490) A Cap Choir; Band; BS; Chor; Order/Arrow; Cpt, Cr-Ctry; MVP, Ftbl; Cpt, Tr; Pres, VP, Secy, Boy's Assn; HR; Drum Major; HS All Amer, Cr Ctry; Sr Pat Ldr, BSct; Hon Bnd; Lifegrd; WW; Chief Justice of Sup Ct, BS; U of Idaho.

VIGOREN, Paul Christian
Miller HS; Aberdeen, WA; Band; Tr.

VIGSNES, Susan Anne
Mt Anthony Union HS; Bennington, VT (4-400) Band; NHS; Orch; Ski C; NEDT; Math.

VIGUE, Carol Ann
Sanford HS; Sanford, ME (10%-329) Bus Mgr, Sch P; Type A; Highest Ranking Undergraduate.

VIK, Timothy Douglas
Nathan Hale HS; Seattle, WA; Cr-Ctry; Hon Prog; Radio Communication Prog; Television Communications Prog; Station Engr; Civil Air Patrol; N Seattle Comm Col; Bio-Med.

VIKTORIN, Patricia Marie
E Bernard HS; East Bernard, TX (5-60) Ann; Band; CYO; Ensm; FHA; FTA; Math C; NHS; Sch P; Sci C; Q&S A; Swtht; Vlbl; Wharton Co Jr Col; Child Therapy.

VILES, Eric Andrew
Newton-Conover HS; Newton, NC; Band; BC; Chor; Hmrm; Orch; Order/Arrow; Bsbl; Ftbl; Tnns; NEDT; Davidson Col; Law.

VILLA, Donna Michel
Oakton HS; Vienna, VA (20%-600) Chor; Sci C; JA A; Secy, JA.

VILLA, Gonzalo Valdez Jr
Mem HS; San Antonio, TX (14-300) Pres, DECA; Saint Marys U; Bus Mgt.

VILLA, Susan Mary
St Joseph's Notre Dame HS; Alameda, CA (10-56) Hmrm; NHS; Phys C; Sci C; Span C; Alg A; Bio A; CSF; Chem A; Hist A; NEDT; Sci A; Co-Ed, Yrbk; U of Calif at Berkeley; Combined Sci.

VILLAFANE, Eileen Cristina
San Conrado HS; Ponce, PR (3-72) A Cap Choir; CYO; Chem C; Pres, Chor; Secy, Dbte Tm; Drama; Hmrm; Math C; NHS; ARC; Secy, Sci C; Pres, Span C; Sch C; SC; Var C; Bkbl; Swim; Tnns; Alg A; Bio A; COM; Chem A; Hon Prog; Math A; Sci A; Navy Sci A; Mayaguez Col; Pre-Med.

VILLAFANE, Juan A
Our Lady of Pilar HS; Rio Piedras, PR (10%-166) Chem C; Model UN; Hmrm; Span NHS; SC; JV, Cr-Ctry; Alg A; Bio A; COM; Hist A; Math A; Sci A; Merit Achievement A; Elec Engr.

VILLALOBOS, Cecilia
Gridley Union HS; Gridley, CA; Sch P; Span C; Vlbl; Vol Religious Teaching A; Butte Col; Lang.

VILLALOBOS, Diana
Garfield HS; Los Angeles, CA; Chldr; Chor; Pres, Hmrm; Sch Achieve Tm; Tnns; Cl Fav; Most Out; Med.

VILLALOBOS, Norma
Notre Dame HS; Salinas, CA (32-93) CYO; NHS; Var C; Bkbl; Hon Prog; San Jose St U; Bus.

VILLALPANDO, Ralph Villasenor
McCollum HS; San Antonio, TX (46-488) F-Ed, Ann; Drama; FTA; Sci C; Span C; Spch C; Thes; Secy, Sr Cl; Bkbl; COM; Span A; U of Tex SA; Bio.

VILLANJEVA, Michael J
Mercy HS; Red Bluff, CA (1-27) Rptr, Ann; BS; Chor; Pres, Drama; Hmrm; Model UN; Sch P; Tres, SC; S-T, Sr Cl; Amer Leg A; Bank Of Amer A; CSF; DARGCA; HKg; Kiwanis A; Regent Schol; Val; Badminton; U of Calif at Berkeley; Pre-Med.

VILLANUEVA, Carmen M
Francisco Mendoza HS; Isabela, PR; Chor; 4H; Hmrm; Span C; Alg A; Citz A; 4H A; Math A; Acct.

VILLANUEVA, Elsa Iris
Miguel Melendez Munoz; Bayamon, PR (1-290) Chem C; FHA; Pres, Rainbow; ARC; Secy, Sch P; VP, SC; Star Student; Eckerd Col; Pediatra.

VILLANUEVA, Gustavo
Francisco Mendoza HS; Isabela, PR; CYO; Drama; Bsbl; UPR-CAAM at Mayaguez; Acct.

VILLANUEVA, Jose Javier
Notre Dame HS; Caguas, PR (1-128) Chem C; Dbte Tm; JETS; Lit Ral; NHS; Sch P; Sci C; COM; Chem A; MIT; Physics.

VILLAR, Eve Carol
Roberto Clemente HS; Chicago, IL (83-453) A Cap Choir; Anchor C; Arch; Cpt, Chldr; Chor; Community Yth Symph; Drama; Ensm; Hmrm; Fin, Jr Miss Pagent; Bus Mgr, Sch P; Span C; St Stu Congress; SC; Thes; Cpt, Var C; Arch; Golf; Swim; Tnns; Cl Fav; Hon Prog; Jr Chamber of Com A; All City Chor; City Champ Chldr; N Park Col; Mus.

VILLAREAL, RoseMarie
Goddard HS; Roswell, NM (20%-389) Chldr; Chor; Span C; SC; JV, Bkbl; Sftbl; Tr; Citz A; MIP, Runner; Cl Swtht; Highlands U; Special Teaching.

VILLARINO, Laura
Col Nuestra Sra de la Merced; Hato Rey, PR (3-92) Cpt, Chldr; Secy, Chem C; Chess C; Pres, Hmrm; Lit Mag; Pres, Math C; Model UN; VP, Phys C; Secy, Pol Sci C; VP, Sci C; Tres, Span C; Spch C; World Affairs C; Pres, Sr Cl; Alg A; Bio A; COM; Chem A; Hist A; Hon Prog; Journ A; Math A; MLS; Most Out; Phy A; Sci A; Star Student; Arts A; Computer Sci.

VILLARS, Daphne Antoinette
Franklin HS; Seattle, WA; NHS; Cr-Ctry; Mgr, Sftbl; Tr; Yth Fel; Seattle Central Comm Col; Special Ed.

VILLEGAS, Stephanie
Montgomery HS; San Diego, CA (23-611) Rptr, Sch P; Journ A; Gym; Journ.

VILLEMARETTE, Brent Jude
Cottonport HS; Cottonport, LA (6-59) Pres, BC; Lit Ral; Pres, Sr Cl; Cpt, Ftbl; Alg A; Amer Leg A; Chem A; Math A; MLS; LSU; Engr.

VILLEMURE, Mary Ann
Englewood Christian Sch; Independence, MO (1-20) COM; Star Student; Type A; Asst VP, SC; Vlbl; Lang A; William Jewell Col; Secretarial.

VILSOET, Robert W
Glenbrook N HS; Northbrook, IL (158-718) Community Yth Symph; Orch; Bsbl; Bkbl; Amer Leg A; Computer Sci.

VINANSKY, Joseph James
Bishop Klonowski HS; Scranton, PA (4-110) CYO; Lat C; Lit Mag; NHS; Sch P; Span C; Bsbl; COM; Hist A; Hon Prog; NEDT; Phys Ed Instructor; Prom Ticket Ch; Boy's C Bkbl; U of Scranton; Journ.

VINCA, Dondi V
McKinley HS; Honolulu, HI (51-819) Band; Inter-Act C; NHS; Grievance Board; U of Hawaii; Eng.

VINCENT, James McKinley
Reidsville Sr HS; Reidsville, NC (3-344) Fr C; Hmrm; Key C; Pres, NHS; Bkbl; Ftbl; Gov Honor Prog; Most Out; Jr Marshal; Hon Stu; NC A&T St U; Elec Engr.

VINCENT, John Christian
Robert E Lee Sr HS; Jacksonville, FL (1-480) Pres, A Cap Choir; Pres, Chor; Drama; Ensm; Hmrm; Bus Mgr, Lat C; Madrigal; NHS; ARC; Alg A; Bio A; COM; Hist A; Hon Prog; Math A; Pres A; Sci A; Val; Mus A; Jacksonville U; Social Stu A; Solo Accompanist, Band; Jacksonville Symphony Orchestra; Fla St U; Mus.

VINCENT, Leatrice
Lefors HS; Lefors, TX (3-20) Chor; Pres, FHA; NHS; Thes; Co-Cpt, Bkbl; Tr; DARGCA; Spch A; Type A; WW; All Star Bkbl; All Star Cast, 1 Act Play; Clarendon Jr Col; Secy.

VINCENT, Melinda Naomi
Southmoreland Sr HS; Alverton, PA (2-285) Band; Ger C; Sch P; Computer Sci.

VINES, Darla Dee
Perry HS; Massillon, OH; A Cap Choir; Chor.

VINES, Debra Lynn
James River HS; Buchanan, VA (25%-145) FTA; 4H; Monogram; SC; Bkbl; Sftbl; Tr; Pres A.

VINES, Mark Lane
Homewood HS; Homewood, AL (10-240) A-Ed, Lit Mag; NHS; Order/Arrow; F-Ed, Sch P; Span C; Span NHS; God & Country A; Hist A; Hon Prog; Journ A; NMS; NEDT; Order/Arrow A; Q&S A; VP, Lit C; Congressional Yth Conf; Eagle Sct A; Phys Fitness; Scholastic Excellence A.

VINEYARD, Bryan Clay
Kress HS; Kress, TX (9-31) FFA; FHA; Tres, FTA; Cpt, Bkbl; Mgr, Ftbl; COM; Cl Fav; Swtht; Amarillo Col; Computer Info Systems.

VINING, Kim Ann
S R Butler HS; Huntsville, AL; Anchor C; Hmrm; SC; Tres, Soph Cl; HCt; Sub-Deb Sorority; David Lipscomb Col; Social Stu.

VINING, Timothy Paul
Thompson HS; Alabaster, AL; Phys C; Tr; Eckerd Col; Religion.

VINKLAREK, Patricia Frances
Flatonia HS; Flatonia, TX (3-39) Ann; CYO; Chldr; Rptr, FHA; Rptr, Sch P; JV, Tnns; Cl Fav; Type A; WW; Blinn Col; Bus.

VINKLAREK, Suzanne Gale
Flatonia HS; Flatonia, TX (8-39) Ann; Band; CYO; Tres, FHA; Hmrm; Co-Ed, Sch P; Rptr, SC; Mgr, Bkbl; Sftbl; JV, Tnns; WW; Sam Houston St U.

VINOLUS, Stacy Lee
Lakeview HS; Battle Creek, MI; Fr C; Hmrm; SC; VP, Jr Cl; Co-Cpt, Swim; Tnns; Secy, FCA; Pom Pon; Water Ballet; Best Sch Camper; *Fashion Designer.*

VINROE, Robert Ralph
Butler Area HS; Butler, PA (413-985) Rptr, Sch P; God & Country A; Yth Fel; *Pittsburgh Theological Seminar; Religion.*

VINSON, Christine Louise
Rincon Valley Christian Sch; Rincon Valley, CA (3-13) Chldr; Chor; Hmrm; SC; Cpt, Sftbl; *Azusa Pacific Col; Drama.*

VINSON, Jerry Deese Jr
W Florence HS; Florence, SC (15-296) Band; BC; BS; Drama; Ger C; NHS; *Clemson U; Hist.*

VINSON, Kay Frances
Burns Sr HS; Lawndale, NC (34-207) Hmrm; Inter-Club Coun; Tres, Span C; Span NHS; SC; VP, Sr Cl; Co-Cpt, Bkbl; MVP, Tr; HCt; *A&T St U; Elem Ed.*

VINSON, Lawrence Nathan Jr
Central-Hower HS; Akron, OH (37-334) VP, Hmrm; VP, SC; VP, Sr Cl; Cr-Ctry; JV, Ftbl; Cpt, Wrest; Alg A; Math A; MLS; Ntl Achv Schol; VICA; *Ga Tech; Computer Elec Engr.*

VINSON, Richard Mark
Woodrow Wilson HS; Dallas, TX; Pres, Band; Ensm; Orch; Cr-Ctry; Soccer; Tr; Most Intelligent; *Tex A&I U; Marine Biol.*

VINSON, Timothy William
S Eugene HS; Eugene, OR (85-550) A Cap Choir; Chor; Dbte Tm; Ensm; Hmrm; Madrigal; Thes; Wrest; Spch A; All Northwest Choir; *Pepperdine U; Mus.*

VINZANT, Suzanne
Robert E Lee HS; Tyler, TX; Span C; Hon Prog; NEDT; *Baylor U; Elem Ed.*

VIOLETT, Rhonda Kay
Mid-Buchanan R-V HS; Faucett, MO (4-80) Band; Chor; Drama; Pres, Fr C; Pres, NHS; Spch C; SC; Tres, Jr Cl; Golf; Alg A; Hist A; Math A; Poet A; Spch A; *Culver-Stockton Col; Remedial Reading.*

VIRGIL, Beverly
S Miami Sr HS; S Miami, FL; VP, Hmrm; VP, Jr Cl; PA; Yth & Jr Choir; Bible Cl; VP, Jr Mission; Jr Usher Board; VP, Yth for Christ; Gen Mission; Watu Wazuri; Chaplin, Yth Fel; *Albany St U; Spch Pathology.*

VISCUSI, David Peter
Frankford HS; Philadelphia, PA (23-1115) Chess C; Bkbl; Cr-Ctry; Golf; COM; *Engr.*

VITOR, Loreto Agot
John F Kennedy HS; Tumon, GUAM; Tnns; AIK-IDO C; *Engr.*

VITUCCI, William Michael
Carl Sandburg HS; Orland Park, IL (162-932) A Cap Choir; Band; CYO; Chor; Drama; Ensm; Lat C; Madrigal; NHS; Ski C; SC; Thes; Hon Prog; 1st, Solo & Ensm Contest; Choir Ltr; *Notre Dame U; Pre-Law.*

VIZCARRA, Nidza Margarita
Colegio Puertorriqueno de Ninas; Caparra Heights, PR (1-70) Fr C; Tres, FHA; Math C; NHS; Sci C; COM; Social Action C; First Hon A; *Psych.*

VIZZARD, Eileen Theresa
Holy Cross HS; Riverside, NJ (37-400) F-Ed, Ann; CYO; Chor; Fr C; FNA; Fin, GS; 4H; NHS; Hon Prog; Sci A; Principal's List; Candystriper A; Sch Ad Drive A; *Nurs.*

VIZZI, Rosalie Marie
Acad o-t Holy Names; Tampa, FL; Hmrm; VP, NFL; VP, NHS; Sci C; Span NHS; SC; VP, Jr Cl; Amer Leg Orator A; NFL Degrees of Merit; Hon Distinction & Excellance; *U of S Fla; Acct.*

VOELKER, Emilie Anne
Baltimore Lutheran HS; Towson, MD (2-80) CYO; Chor; Ger C; NHS; Bkbl; Cpt, Soccer; Sftbl; Tnns; Ger Hon Soc; *Math.*

VOELKER, Patrick John
Forest Lake Sr HS; Forest Lake, MN (15%-530) A Cap Choir; Drama; Ski C; *Lincoln Christian Col; Christian Ministry.*

VOELZ, Erick Charles
Paris HS; Paris, IL (105-220) Bsbl; Co-Cpt, Cr-Ctry; Tr; Wrest.

VOGE, Lori Jane
Oxford HS; Oxford, KS (5-45) VP, Span C; Alg A; Pep C; Kayette; *Acct.*

VOGEL, Dale Duane
Westfield HS; Westfield, WI (5-130) Chem C; Math C; Tres, NHS; Phys C; Sci C; SC; Var C; Wrest; *Engr.*

VOGEL, Danny Carl
Memorial HS; Saint Marys, OH (1-230) Band; BS; Pres, Bus C; Pres, Chess C; Chor; Ensm; Pres, FTA; NHS; Order/Arrow; Sch Achieve Tm; Sci C; Alg A; Amer Leg A; COM; JA A; Math A; NMF; NMS; Ntl Sci Found; Order/Arrow A; Eagle Sct; 1st in Cl; Gold Palm; Most Stu; *MIT; Elec Engr.*

VOGEL, Jane Elizabeth
Shanley HS; Fargo, ND (1-160) CYO; Chldr; Chor; Drama; Ensm; Fr C; GS; Pres, 4H; Hmrm; NHS; Rptr, Sch P; SC; S-T, Soph Cl; JV, Tnns; Tr; COM; Citz A; 4H A; Most Out; Rotary A; Spch A; Best Supporting Actress; Lead Role, Fall Drama; Ntl Piano Guild A; Shanley Schol; Ch, SC School Comm; *Col of St Catherine's; Nurs.*

VOGEL, Jeanette Kay
Weld Central Jr-Sr HS; Keenesburg, CO (12-130) Band; Chor; Ensm; 4H; NHS; Sftbl; Tr.

VOGEL, Jerry
Ritenour Sr HS; St Louis, MO (250-1000) Chor; Bkbl; Sftbl; Tr; Wrest; Rep, Yth Coun.

VOGEL, Kay Louise
Carlyle HS; Carlyle, IL (15-140) Band; Dbte Tm; Drama; Parl, FBLA; Mjrte; NHS; Spch C; Bkbl; Sftbl; HCt; Type A; Baton Trophies; Bkbl Trophies; Bowl Trophy; FBLA As; *U of Ill; Med Record Adm.*

VOGEL, Nancy Elizabeth
Oak Lawn Comm HS; Oak Lawn, IL (100-700) Ann; Chor; Y-Tns; ROTC A; Debutante; Candy Stripe A; *Concordia Teachers Col; Elem Ed.*

VOGEL, Peggy Jean
Gerard Cath HS; Phoenix, AZ (22-130) CYO; Pres, Drama; F-Ed, Sch P; Thes; COM; Outst Yth Ldr A.

VOGEL, Sandra Kay
Belleville W HS; Belleville, IL; Chor; *SIU Edwardsville Col; Nurs.*

VOGELPOHL, Sandy Sue
Rockdale HS; Rockdale, TX; Band; Drama; Pres, 4H; JV, Tnns; *Blinn Col; Elem Ed.*

VOGELSANG, Amy Margaret
Greater Latrobe Sr HS; Latrobe, PA (21-518) VP, AFS; VP, NHS; Outst Sr, Drama; *Bryn Mawr Col; Psych.*

VOGES, Valerie Lorelei
Mineola HS; Garden City Park, NY; SC; *Law.*

VOGGESSER, Judi Lynne
Maryville R-II HS; Maryville, MO; Band; JV, Bkbl; JV, Tnns; Hon Prog; Type A; *NW Mo St U.*

VOGGESSER, Judy Lynne
Maryville R-II HS; Maryville, MO; Band; JV, Bkbl; JV, Tnns; Hon Prog; Type A; *NW Mo St U.*

VOGHT, Jeffrey Alan
Marion HS; Marion, IN; Band; St Band A's; *Purdue U; Engr.*

VOGT, Eric Alan
Bend Sr HS; Bend, OR (14-375) A Cap Choir; Band; Chor; Ensm; NFL; NHS; Ski C; Tnns; CSF; Spch A; Yth Fel; Mentally Gifted Minors; *Christian Heritage Col; Biblical Psych.*

VOGT, Kim Marie
Chappell HS; Chappell, NE (2-20) Ed, Ann; Band; Chor; Drama; Ensm; S-T, FHA; NHS; SC; Bkbl; Golf; Alg A; Most Out; Sal; Piano Guild As; Pep C; Mus Groups; Tres, Church Yth Group; *U of Wyo; Statistics.*

VOGT, Mary Lynn
John Burroughs HS; Burbank, CA; Drill Tm; Service As; Dance A; Drill Tm As; *LA Valley Col.*

VOIGT, Bradford William
Warwick Veterans Mem HS; Warwick, RI; Band; French NHS; Order/Arrow; Tnns; God & Country A; Hon Prog; Order/Arrow A; Eagle Sct; All-St Bands.

VOIGT, Cynthia Ann
Yates Center HS; Yates Center, KS; 4H; JV, Bkbl; 4H A; *Allen Co Jr Col; Ed.*

VOIGT, Gregory Alan
Warwick Veterans HS; Warwick, RI; Band; BS; Ensm; Order/Arrow; Soccer; Tnns; God & Country A; Hon Prog; Order/Arrow A; Eagle Sct; Fr Hon Soc; *US Military Acad; Biological Sci.*

VOIGT, Karen Sue
Heritage Christian Sch; Indianapolis, IN (5-61) 4H; Rptr, Sch P; Hon Prog; *Olivet Nazarene Col; Elem Ed.*

VOIGT, Mary Christine
Bartow Sr HS; Bartow, FL (70-270) Drama; Pres, Fr C; Secy, FHA; 4H; Hmrm; InterClub Coun; Ed, Sch P; SC; Yth Fair; FHA Encounter; *Fla Sou Col; Yth Ministries.*

VOIROL, Paul Joseph
Eastside HS; Butler, IN (25-125) Bsbl; Ftbl; Tr; Basic Elec A's; *Mech.*

VOITIK, Katherine Marie
Glenbrook S HS; Glenview, IL (39-600) Band; CYO; Chor; NHS; Ski C; Mgr, Vlbl; *Western Ill U; Mus Theory and Composition.*

VOLAND, Peggy Anne
Brown Co HS; Nashville, IN (8-170) F-Ed, Ann; NHS; Phi Beta Kappa; St Scholar; Cummins Engine Co; Hon Schol, Olivet; *Olivet Nazarene Col; Social Welfare.*

VOLDEN, Douglas John
Taft HS; Chicago, IL (160-800) Bsbl; Bkbl; COM; Hon Prog; Yth Fel; Asst, Drivers Ed; Tres, Luther League; *Valparaiso U; Engr.*

VOLGENAU, Lisa
Herndon HS; Herndon, VA; AFS; Chor; Lat C; NHS; Ski C; Tres, Jr Cl; Tres, Lat NHS; Bkbl; Tr; Athletic Letters; Mus A's; Phys Phys Fitness; *VPI.*

VOLKEL, Karen Elizabeth
Westchester HS; Houston, TX (26-523) Tres, JETS; Secy, Lit Mag; Secy, Mu Alpha Theta; NHS; God & Country A; Hist A; Hon Prog; Magna Cum Laude; Type A; Schlumberger Schol; *Tex A&M U; Chem.*

VOLKOFF, Jon Brian
Bethel Christian Sch; Garden Grove, CA (1-30) Chess C; Dbte Tm; Sci C; Bkbl; Ftbl; Highest Acad Grade Point Avg; 1st Pl, Chess; Accelerated Christian Ed Calif Conv; *Santa Ana Col; Elec Engr.*

VOLL, Thomas James
Toronto HS; Toronto, OH; Band; BS; Chess C; Rptr, Sch P; Amer Leg A; Bkbl Statistician; Davis A; *Milligan Col; Hist.*

VOLLE, Julie Ann
Garfield Sr HS; Hamilton, OH (24-496) Chem C; Chor; Pres, Ger C; NHS; Span C; Span C; Secy, SC; Y-Tns; Amer Leg A; 1st Cl Sct; *Hist.*

VOLLER, Bernadette Elizabeth
Elmira HS; Elmira, OR (1-192) *Animal Sci.*

VOLLMER, Daniel Lee
Althoff Cath HS; Belleville, IL (113-301) BS; CYO; Hon Prog; *Trade Sch; Mech.*

VOLNER, Lori Ann
Highland HS; Highland, IN (285-530) Ensm; Secy, FHA; Span C; Health Careers C; WW; *Ind U; Dental Asst.*

VOMHOF, Allen Steven
Henry HS; Minneapolis, MN (31-440) Ger C; Bkbl; Sftbl; Hon Prog; BSct A; *Concordia Col; Hist.*

VON, Terri Lynn
Yosemite Union HS; Oakhurst, CA; Cpt, Chldr; Chor; Hmrm; Bkbl; Sftbl; Swtht; Most Inspirational, Vlbl; Valentine Qn.

VonAHNEN, Matthew Todd
Dixon HS; Dixon, IL (80-440) Band; Swim; Lifesaving; Church Yth Committee; *Oral Roberts U; Pre-Law.*

VONDELL, Jeffrey Roy
Lakeview HS; Battle Creek, MI (14-450) NHS; Order/Arrow; Span C; Bsbl; Cpt, Bkbl; Soccer; JV, Swim; Amer Leg A; Hon Prog; Bkbl Tr; Yth Fel; Rookie Umpire o-t Yr A; Rep, LLA; Sr Patrol Ldr, BSA; Life Sct; *US Naval Acad; Marine Biol.*

VONDERLAGE, Lori Gay
Paris HS; Paris, IL (50-250) Band; 4H; Golf; 4H A;
HCt; Type A.

VonESCHEN, Deborah Kay
Cresbard HS; Cresbard, SD (6-31) Ann; Pres,
Band; Chldr; Chor; Monogram; Ed, Sch P; Secy,
SC; Secy, Jr Cl; HQn; Hon Prog; Type A; N St Col;
Elem Ed.

VonESCHEN, Susan Rae
Cresbard HS; Cresbard, SD; Ann; Band; Chor; Sch
P; Bkbl; Journ A; Pres A; Type A; N St Col; Ed.

**VON FRIELING,
Dorothea Maria**
Prospect HS; Saratoga, CA (10%-400) InterAct C;
Math C; Spch C; COM; Hon Prog; Opt A; St
Scholar; Art A; S-T, Art C; Ecology C; Ger A; San
Jose St U; Bio.

Von HATTEN, Nancy Jane
Southside HS; Ft Smith, AR (11-430) Tres, CYO;
Chor; Fr C; NHS; U of Ark; Art.

VonLANKEN, Brett W
Dundee Comm HS; Dundee, IL (180-300) Ftbl;
Sftbl; Tr; Wrest; St Champ Bible Quiz Tm; St Top
Bible Quizzer; Drama Presentation; Central Bible
Col; Bible.

VonLANKEN, Brian Donald
Dundee Sr HS; E Dundee, IL (50%-350) Hmrm;
Win, N League Bible Quiz; Pres, Yth Group; Cen-
tral Bible Col; Bible.

VON PELT, Wesley Herman
Kelly Walsh HS; Casper, WY; A Cap Choir; Chess
C; Chor; 4H; Bsbl; Bkbl; Ftbl; Tr; Wrest; Gym
Medal; NW Bible Col; Mus & Voice.

VOORHEES, Donald Lee Jr
Hitchcock HS; Hitchcock, SD (2-22) Ed, Ann; BS;
Chor; Drama; NHS; Var C; Pres, Sr Cl; Pres, Jr Cl;
Co-Cpt, Ftbl; Amer Leg A; B Crocker A; HCt;
NMF; NMS; Val; VFW A; SD Sch of Mines &
Tech; Geol.

VOORHEES, Michael Lee
Roxana HS; Roxana, IL; Var C; Bsbl; Wrest; Yth
Fel.

VOORHEES, Mitchell Leon
Roxana HS; Roxana, IL; Rptr, Sch P; Var C; Bsbl;
Ftbl; Wrest; Yth Fel.

VOORHEIS, Michael John
Bath HS; Bath, MI (13-90) NHS; Bsbl; JV, Bkbl;
Cpt, Ftbl; JV, Swim; Cpt, Tr; Cpt, Wrest; Cl Fav;
HKg; Cl Clown; Cl Rep; All-St, Tr; All-League,
Ftbl; Mich St U; Bus Adm.

VORACEK, Teresa Pearl
Gov John Rogers HS; Puallup, WA (13-360) NHS;
Top Jr Ntl Math Test; JV, Vlbl; Brigham Young U;
Interior Design.

VOREK, Lorita Rae
Terre Haute S Vigo HS; Terre Haute, IN (105-626)
Ger C; Y-Tns; Lincoln Christian Col; Christian Ed.

VORICK, Robert Lewis
Glenbard W HS; Glen Ellyn, IL; Mu Alpha Theta;
Ftbl; Tr; JA A; Col of DuPage; Math and Sci.

VORIS, Judy Elaine
Southport HS; Indianapolis, IN; Chor; VP, FHA;
Rainbow.

VORTHMANN, Jill Janelle
Treynor Comm HS; Treynor, IA (11-56) Ann;
Band; Chor; Drama; Secy, FHA; VP, 4H; Spch C;
Tres, Sr Cl; Golf; Swim; Tr; COM; Citz A; 4H A;
JA A; Most Out; Sci A; Spch A; Better Grooming
A Co Level; Miss 4-H; Candystriper o-t Month;
Miss Potawattamie Pork Countess; Iowa St U; Spe-
cial Ed.

VORTHMANN, Lynette Edna
Treynor Comm HS; Treynor, IA (4-52) FHA; 4H;
NHS; Tres, Soph Cl; Bkbl; Tr; 4H A; Hon Prog;
Piano A's.

VORTHMANN, Scott Allan
Freeport Sr HS; Freeport, IL (1-575) JETS; Math
C; Math A.

VORWERK, Lauren Lorraine
Summerville HS; Summerville, SC (25%-500)
Drama; FTA; Swim; Mus Schol; Super, 1st Alt, Ntl
Fed of Mus; Converse Col; Piano.

VOSS, Brenda Ann
Independence HS; Independence, MS (10%-106)
Secy, BC; FBLA.

VOSS, Diane Marie
Northeast Comm HS; Goose Lake, IA (31-104)
Band; Mgr, Bsbl; Spch A; Type A; Sch Plays And
Musicals; Luther League; Pom Pom Girls; AIC;
Acct.

VOSS, Lorraine Jean
Owatonna HS; Owatonna, MN (6-423) Band; VP,
Chor; Ensm; Pres, 4H; NHS; Orch; Spch C; Swim;
COM; 4H A; Spch A; Thon Outst Young Musician
A; Wheaton Col; Pre-Med.

VOSS, Marilyn Joan
Arlington HS; Arlington, NE (15-77) Co-Ed, Ann;
Band; Chor; Ger C; Pres, 4H; NHS; Y-Tns; COM;
Citz A; 4H A; Hon Prog; Pep C Coun; U of Nebr-
Lincoln; Pre-Med.

VOSTAD, Bradley Dale
Brookings HS; Brookings, SD (150-216) A Cap
Choir; Band; Chor; Ensm; Monogram; Orch; Thes;
Citz A; SD St U; Nurs.

VOTAW, Jennifer
Victoria HS; Victoria, TX (20%-600) Chor; Ensm;
Fin, GS; Madrigal; NHS; COM; Citz A; Opt A; St
Choir; Oral Roberts U; Mus.

VOTH, Sharon Rose
Lindsay Public HS; Lindsay, TX (8-37) CYO;
FHA; Pres, 4H; 4H A; Hon Prog; Spch A; N Tex St
U; Home Ec.

VOTIPKA, Anna Louise
Geneva Pub HS; Geneva, NE (11-59) Chldr; Chor;
COM; Masonic A; Math A; Star Student; Outst
Bookkeeping Stu; U of Nebr; Bus Adm.

VOUDOURIS, Demetris
Buckley HS; Sherman Oaks, CA; JV, Ftbl; Math A;
NEDT; Top 90% Entrance Exam; Harvard U;
Med.

VOYTEK, Andrew Joseph
The Fannie A Smith Prep Sch; Bridgeport, CT; Ed,
Sch P; Pres, Jr Cl; Bsbl; Ftbl; Swim; MLS.

VOZNIK, Patricia Ellen
Adlai E Stevenson HS; Bronx, NY (52-788) Hon
Prog; Arista; Katherine Gibbs Sch; Secretarial.

VRANA, Kalena Gail
St John HS; Ennis, TX (2-42) NHS; Pres, SC; Sftbl;
Amer Leg A; Chem A; SMU; Chem.

VRANICAR, David William
Stanton Comm Sch; Stanton, NE (1-55) All Amer
Yth; Ann; VP, CYO; Drama; VP, Ger C; NHS; SC;
Var C; Bkbl; Cr-Ctry; Ftbl; Golf; COM; Hon Prog;
Spch A; Star Student; Val; VofDEM; Creighton U;
Pre-Law.

VRH, Lori Ann
Turlock HS; Turlock, CA (20-400) CSF; Hon Prog;
Ed.

VRIELINK, Joan Marguerite
Maine Township HS N; Des Plaines, IL (82%-405)
A Cap Choir; Band; Chor; Ensm; Hmrm; Mod Mus
Mas; Ski C; SC; Var C; Golf; JV, Sftbl; Tr; Bio A;
Citz A; Hon Prog; Pres A; Sci A; Sct A.

VROMAN, Gary James
E Peoria Comm HS; E Peoria, IL (5-515) Band;
Ensm; Ger C; Orch; F-Ed, Sch P; SC; MVP, Golf;
Tnns; NMS; Naval Acad; Math.

VROMAN, Rex Warner
Mayville HS; Mayville, MI (9-90) Band; Ensm;
NHS; Cr-Ctry; Maranatha Baptist Bible Col; Ed.

VROOMAN, Susan Mary
Union Springs Acad; Union Springs, NY (6-45)
Band; Chor; NHS; SC; COM; NEDT; Girls C; Cl
Offices; Atlantic Union Col; Nurs.

VROSH, Darlene Lynn
Caledonia HS; Caledonia, MI (7-170) Bus C; Chor;
Ensm; NHS; COM; Hon Prog; Type A; Shorthand,
Theory & Transcipition; Choir, Pins; Bus.

W

WAAGEN, Jerry Lynn
Valley City Sr HS; Valley City, ND (13-150) JV,
Ftbl; JV, Wrest; ND St U; Biol.

WACHOB, Joellen
Arthur HS; Arthur, IL (10-44) Ann; Band; Chor;
Ensm; Tres, FHA; Rptr, FNA; GS; Mjrte; Math C;
Sch Achieve Tm; Sch P; Spch C; Beauty; MLS; Ill
Wesleyan U; Med.

WACHS, Lisa Janelle
Topeka W HS; Topeka, KS; Band; Ger C; Orch;
Dist & St Hon Bands; Med Tech.

WACHSMUTH, Kim Marie
Bayfield HS; Bayfield, WI (3-45) All Amer Yth;
F-Ed, Ann; NHS; Ski C; Cpt, Bkbl; Cpt, Sftbl; B
Crocker A; Hon Prog; Type A; Cpt, Vlbl; HS All
Amer Vlbl; U of Wis; Phys Ed.

WACKER, Thomas Dale
Battle Creek HS; Battle Creek, NE (25%-54) VP,
CYO; Drama; Ger C; Spch C; Var C; Mgr, Bkbl;
Mgr, Ftbl; Tr; COM; Stu Trnr A; N Tech Sch of
Bus; Court Rptr.

WACKERMAN, Sharon Kay
Miami R-1 HS; Amoret, MO (3-45) AFS; Band;
Chldr; FHA; Hmrm; NHS; Sch P; NC; NHS Hon
Prog; Journ A; Most Out; All Conf Band; Band Ltr.

WACKLER, John Edmond
Ardmore HS; Ardmore, OK (72-285) A Cap Choir;
Band; Chor; Hmrm; SC; Masonic A; Murray State
Col; Mus.

WACLAWSKI, Annette Louise
Springdale HS; Springdale, AR (87%-427) Secy,
CYO.

WACLAWSKI, Julianne
Rossford HS; Rossford, OH (2-150) Chor; Pres,
NHS; ARC; SC; Pres, Y-Tns; Hon Prog; I Dare
You; ARC A; Sal; Outst Fr Stut; WW; Michael J
Owens Tech Col; Radiologic Tech.

WADDELL, Dale Edward
Newton Falls HS; Newton Falls, OH (38-170)
Band; Chem C; Sci C; Span C; Var C; Cr-Ctry; Tr;
Youngstown St U; Micro Bio.

WADDELL, David Joseph
Ironton HS; Ironton, OH (2-181) Bus Mgr, Lat C;
Model UN; NHS; Sci C; Pres, Jr Cl; Pres, Soph Cl;
Cr-Ctry; JV, Ftbl; Tr; Bio A; Chem A; Sci A; Ani-
mal Psych.

WADDELL, Diana Kay
Wichita HS N; Wichita, KS; Fin, Chldr; GS;
Hmrm; MVP, Orch; Sch Achieve Tm; Secy, Span
C; Secy, SC; Var C; Mgr, Bkbl; Tr; Hist A; Hon
Prog; Math A; Most Out; Type A; Pom-Pon; Vlbl;
Emporia St Col.

WADDELL, Tammy Ann
Manchester HS; Manchester, GA (7-140) F-Ed,
Ann; BC; Rptr, FHA; NHS; Algebra Commenda-
tion; Essay Win; Hon Group; Actress, Sr Play; Ga
SW Col; Nurs.

WADDELL, Terrance Franklin
H V Jenkins HS; Savannah, GA; Cpt, Bkbl; Ftbl;
4H A; Opt A; UCLA; Hist.

WADDELOW, Kelli Annette
Tara HS; Baton Rouge, LA (8-377) Secy, Band;
BC; Mu Alpha Theta; NHS; Sci C; NEDT; Pres A;
Stu Conductor, Band; All-Parish Band; Outst
Bandsman A; LSU Fresh Hon Schol.

WADDILL, Shirley Jean
Belton HS; Belton, TX (200-280) Band; French
NHS; Span C.

WADDINGTON, Todd Michael
Pennsville Mem HS; Pennsville, NJ; Band; BS;
Chor; Drama; Hmrm; InterAct C; SC; Soloist,
Madrigal; Best Section A; Alt, BS; Band Section
Ldr; Most Talented; Directors Vocal A; U of
Bridgeport; Cinema.

WADDLE, Catherine Lee
Ballard HS; Louisville, KY (210-435) Ensm; Fr C;
Mjrte; SC; Mgr, Cr-Ctry; Mgr, Tr; Stu Dir, Madri-
gal; Stu Dir Chor; Sch Choir Ldrship As; Stu Direc-
tor, Chor; Pres, Secy & Coun Mem, Chrch Choir;
Samford U; Mus.

WADDLE, Elizabeth Anne
New Monroe Comm Sch; Monroe, IA (30-62)
Ann; Band; Secy, Chor; Fr C; FHA; Madrigal;
Golf; Sci A; Mus Contest A's; Church Pianist; *Area
XI Col; Elem Ed.*

WADDLE, Geraldine
Superior HS; Superior, NE (11-87) Band; Chldr;
FHA; Y-Tns; HR.

WADDLE, Mary Catherine
Superior HS; Superior, NE (14-81) Chor; FHA;
Mjrte; SC; HQn; Snowball & Church Swtht, Qn;
HR.

WADDLE, Ralph Richard Jr
Franklin Co HS; Frankfort, KY; FBLA; Ftbl; Golf;
Aeronautics.

WADDLE, Sharon Elaine
Heritage HS; Conyers, GA (5%-200) Band; BC;
Chldr; Chor; Drama; 4H; Hmrm; Mjrte; Math C;
Pres, Span C; SC; Tr; Hon Prog; Gym; 1st Pl, Re-
gional Lit; All St Chor; *U of Ga; Early Childhood
Ed.*

WADDOUPS, Gwen Jolene
Douglas HS; Douglas, AZ (13-325) Band; Cpt,
Chldr; Drama; GS; Key C; NHS; Thes; Tri-HiY;
Var C; Tr; Beauty; COM; HCt; Miss Ntl Tnager
Pageant; *U of Ariz; Pre-Med.*

WADE, Ann Kay
Temple Baptist Acad; Denver, CO (5-47) Cpt,
Chldr; Chor; Ensm; Secy, NHS; Sftbl; All-Star Vlbl;
Airline Stewardess.

WADE, Anthony Drake
Alain LeRoy Locke HS; Los Angeles, CA (3-30)
Band; Hmrm; Ch, NHS; Span C; SC; JV, Bsbl; JV,
Ftbl; Tnns; Math A; PA; Boys League; Bowl; *USC;
Med.*

WADE, Catherine Ann
John F Kennedy Sr HS; Bloomington, MN
(40-686) Chor; NHS; Chor Accompanist; Th Missions; Church Singing Group; Sch Dance Line;
Sterling Col; Phys Therapy.

WADE, Clayton Ernest
Mendenhall HS; Mendenhall, MS; MIP, Band; *Ole
Miss; Mus.*

WADE, Constance Lynn
Big Sandy HS; Big Sandy, TN (2-28) Bus Mgr,
Ann; Tres, BC; Rptr, FHA; Tres, Sr Cl; Tres, Jr Cl;
Bkbl; Sftbl; Sal; Type A; Ath A's; Poetry Published;
Drama Productions; *Union U; Creative Writing.*

WADE, Deana Sue
R L Turner HS; Farmers Branch, TX (99-800)
Chor; Ensm; Sftbl; Tr; Yth Fel; Women Select;
Kent St U; Interior Design.

WADE, Deborah Lee
Stoneham HS; Stoneham, MA (36-400) Drama;
NHS; Cl Fav; Yth Fel; 1st Cl, GSct; *U of Mass; Bio.*

WADE, Debra Helen
Montpelier HS; Montpelier, OH (13-98) Chor;
FHA; Co-Cpt, Wrest; Alg A; Academic Achv C;
Vlbl; Drill Tm A; *Mt Vernon Nazarene Col; Acct.*

WADE, Donna Anne
Miami Killian Sr HS; Miami, FL (34-1200) Chor;
Drama; Ensm; Hmrm; Pres, Sci C; SC; Thes; Secy,
Soph Cl; Bio A; HCt; Dade Co Honor Choir; Semi-
Fin, Bst Grl Thespian Pledge; *Fla St U; Mus Ed.*

WADE, Donna Lynn
Muskogee HS; Muskogee, OK (20%-800) Chldr;
Chor; ARC; Span C; Pres, Y-Tns; Cl Fav; Church
Ensm; Friendliest; *MW Christian Col; Social
Worker.*

WADE, Doris Ruth
Harrison Central HS; Harrison, MS; BC; Chldr;
Ensm; Rainbow; SC; B Crocker A; Yth Fel; Yth
Foundation A.

WADE, Gregory Eugene
Phil Campbell HS; Phil Campbell, AL; Rptr, FFA;
4H; Secy, NHS; Sch P; Pres, Sr Cl; Cpt, Ftbl; 4H A;
FHA Beau; Best Offensive Lineman; MS All Star
Tm; *Northwest Jr Col; Bus Mgt.*

WADE, Jackie Lynn
Calhoun HS; Calhoun, GA (10%-250) Band; Math
C; NHS; Span C; Tri-HiY; Band Letter; Acct A; *U
of Ga; Sociology.*

WADE, Jeffrey Brooks
Fort Osage HS; Independence, MO (40-450) Band;
Sci C; Mgr, Cr-Ctry; *Mo U; Mus.*

WADE, John Wilkinson III
Cartersville HS; Cartersville, GA (4-150) BC; HiY;
Hmrm; Pres, Key C; Math C; Mu Alpha Theta;
Order/Arrow; Sci C; Span C; SC; Cpt, Ftbl; Tr;
COM; Cl Fav; NMS; Rotary A; Star Student;
MVP, Ftbl; Eagle Sct; *Ga Inst of Tech; Civil Engr.*

WADE, Karen Louise
Parkersburg South HS; Parkersburg, WV; MVP,
Vlbl; Sr Ath A; *PCC; Acct.*

WADE, Karen Lynia
Broken Bow HS; Broken Bow, OK (10%-148)
Chor; FHA; St Hon Soc; *Okla St U; Chem.*

WADE, Kathy Lynn
Highland HS; Sparta, OH (80-108) VP, Bus C;
Chess C; FHA; Tres, 4H; 4H A.

WADE, Mark Allen
Copeland HS; Copeland, KS (1-12) Chor; 4H;
NHS; VP, SC; Bkbl; Ftbl; Tr; Wrest; Citz A; Most
Out; *Vet Medicine.*

WADE, Mark Evan
Coronado HS; El Paso, TX; Band; Community Yth
Symph; Ensm; Hmrm; Orch; Co-Cpt, Bkbl; Sftbl;
COM; Citz A; Kiwanis A; Yth Fel; Ntl Jr Hon Soc;
Outst Soloist NMSU Jr Festival; *Rice U; Archt.*

WADE, Mark Irving
Stoneham HS; Stoneham, MA (48-419) Band;
Drama; Ensm; Math C; Orch; V-Ch, Sci C.

WADE, Merrill Douglas
Starkville HS; Starkville, MS; Band; Chem C; Pres,
SC; Tr; Most Out; *U of Sou Miss; Psych.*

WADE, Regina Ranee
Community HS; Houston, TX (10%-98) Band;
Chor; SC.

WADE, Rhonda Cheryl
Lee Co HS; Beattyville, KY; Co-Ed, Ann; Band;
Pres, FHA; 4H; F-Ed, Sch P; SC; Tres, Soph Cl;
HCt; Swtht; Band Front A.

WADE, Rhonda Harolynn
Fredrick Douglass HS; Atlanta, GA (107-346) All
Amer Yth; CYO; Commercial C; Dbte Tm; Drama;
FHA; 4H; Hmrm; Mjrte; Ntl Yth Conf; ARC; Sch
P; Sci C; Y-Tns; Tnns; Tr; Hon Prog; Mjrte A;
Sigma Gama Rho Schol A; *Bennett Col; Pre-Med.*

WADE, Robert Alfred Jr
Briggs Sr HS; Columbus, OH (29-300) Band; BS; Fr
C; Sch P; Hon Prog; *Ohio St U; Law.*

WADE, Sharon Kaye
N Shore HS; W Palm Beach, FL (45-266) Secy,
Band; Hmrm; Parl, Key C; Mjrte; NHS; Rptr, Sch
P; SC; Secy, Sr Cl; Secy, Jr Cl; Secy, Soph Cl; HCt;
Pres, Human Relations; Runner Up, Miss Fa-
shionette; *Clark Col; Psych.*

WADELL, Thomas Mark
Kickapoo Sr HS; Springfield, MO (37-300) Chor;
Tres, Dbte Tm; Tres, Drama; Ensm; Madrigal;
NFL; SC; Thes; VP, Jr Cl; Rotary A; Spch A; Yth
Leg; Outst Sr Vocalist; *SW Mo St U; Mus.*

WADSWORTH, Dacia Melisse
Acad o-t Holy Names; Tampa, FL (24-68) Ann;
CYO; NHS; Sodality; Tr; Hon Prog; *Auburn U.*

WAECHTER, David Bradley
Pacifica HS; Garden Grove, CA; Band; Ensm;
Hmrm; Math C; Order/Arrow; Span C; Alg A;
CSF; COM; Citz A; Hon Prog; Math A; Order/
Arrow A; Pres A; *Religion.*

WAELTZ, Kelley Ann
Steeleville Comm Unit HS; Steeleville, IL (9-45)
Ann; FBLA; NHS; Tres, Span C; Golf; Sftbl.

WAGE, Micki Lea
Bethel Baptist Sch; Memphis, TN (4-26) Chldr;
Chor; Ensm; Sftbl; Swim; Tnns; COM; Cl Fav; H of
F; HCt; Miss Total Christian Young Lady A; *Sci.*

WAGENER, Peter Willy
Montville HS; Oakdale, CT (9-253) Chess C; JETS;
NHS; Span C; Tnns; WW; NML; *Chem Engr.*

WAGENKNECHT, Terri Renee
Benton Co R-1 Sch; Cole Camp, MO (10-51) A-
Ed, Ann; Chor; Dbte Tm; Sch P; B Crocker A; Citz
A; Hon Prog; Swtht; Type A; *U of Kans; Occupa-
tional Therapy.*

WAGERS, Ira Lynn
Vandalia Butler Sr HS; Vandalia, OH; Chor; Secy,
Drama; Ensm; Rainbow; Sch P; SC; HR; Drill Tm;
Best Supporting Actress; *Eckerd Col; Ed.*

WAGES, Deborah Denise
Independence HS; Independence, MS (10%-72)
BC; FBLA; FHA; Sch P; Beauty; COM; Cl Fav;
HCt; Miss IHS.

WAGES, Janice Suzzette
Eau Claire HS; Columbia, SC; Chldr; Chor; Hmrm;
NHS; SC; Pres, Jr Cl; Beauty; COM; Citz A; Hon
Prog; Jr Civinettes; Jr NHS; WW; Chor A; *U of
Mich; Meteorology.*

WAGES, Laurie Ann
Westwood HS; Palestine, TX; F-Ed, Ann; Band;
BC; Chor; Drama; Secy, FHA; Swtht; Top 10,
Fresh & Soph; *E Tex Baptist Col; Bus.*

WAGES, Mary Beth
Dothan HS; Dothan, AL (14-551) FBLA; FTA;
NHS; Span C; COM; Hon Prog; Type A; Top 20 Sr
Schol; WW; *Troy St U; Sci.*

WAGES, Staci Eilene
Rider HS; Wichita Falls, TX (350-500) Chldr; Fr C;
Lat C; Tri-HiY; Beauty; Cl Fav; Yth Fel; Goal Post
A; Tnns Asst; *Baylor U.*

WAGGONER, Eileen Marie
London HS; London, OH (4-165) 4H; NHS; Span
C; 4H A; Kiwanis A; Sci A; Tri-L; *Ohio U; Sci.*

WAGGONER, Mark Gaylon
A J Terrell HS; Blanchard, OK; A Cap Choir; F-Ed,
Ann; VP, BC; Chor; Ensm; Math C; NHS; Sch P;
Span C; Var C; Pres, Soph Cl; Co-Cpt, Bsbl; Bkbl;
Co-Cpt, Ftbl; Sftbl; COM; Citz A; Gov Honor
Prog; Hist A; Hon Prog; Magna Cum Laude; St
Scholar; Swtht; Yth Fel; Secy of St A; Pres, Church
Yth Coun; Hon Men, All Dist Ftbl; All Conf, Bsbl;
Okla U.

WAGGONER, Steven Richard
London HS; London, OH (5-93) Ann; Tres, Chess
C; 4H; NHS; 4H A; Kiwanis A; *Ohio U; Elec Engr.*

WAGLER, Marcia Dee
Burlington Comm HS; Burlington, IA (13-537)
Sftbl; Hon Prog; March of Dimes Tn Comm; Tres,
Soph Cl Cabinet; *Social Service.*

WAGLEY, Janice Lynn
Adrian Sr HS; Adrian, MI (19-382) Secy, Chor;
Secy, Ensm; GS; Hmrm; NHS; Pres, SC; VP, Var
C; Cpt, Sftbl; Cpt, Tnns; H of F; Kiwanis A; Distin-
guished Service A; Top 20; Co-Cpt MVP, Vlbl;
Mich St U; Phys Therapy.

WAGLEY, Joseph Lafayette
Adrian Sr HS; Adrian, MI (21-390) Band; BS;
Chor; Rptr, Hmrm; Pres, NHS; Orch; Order/
Arrow; Phys C; SC; Y-Tns; Swim; Tnns; COM;
God & Country A; Order/Arrow A; Rotary A; Ex-
change C A; Eagle Sct A; *Northwestern U; Med.*

WAGNER, Alice Karen
The Fannie A Smith Prep Sch; Bridgeport, CT; Ed,
Sch P; Pres, Sr Cl; VP, Jr Cl; Swim; Hist A; Hon
Prog; MLS; Intramural Vlbl; *Bridgeport Hospital
Sch of Nurs; Nurs.*

WAGNER, Beth Alison
Santa Monica HS; Santa Monica, CA; Chor;
Drama; Fr C; NHS; SC; *UCLA; Mus.*

WAGNER, Blake Douglas
Malabar HS; Mansfield, OH (27-245) Math C; Mu
Alpha Theta; Cr-Ctry; Tr; Amer Leg A; Citz A;
God & Country A; Hon Prog; Journ A; Opt A;
Spch A; Eagle Sct; Pres, Yth Fel.

WAGNER, Brian Richard
Wapsig Valley HS; Fairbank, IA (2-85) Sch P; Gov
Honor Prog; Sal; St Scholar; *U of Northern Iowa;
Pol Sci.*

WAGNER, Cathy Elizabeth
Katella HS; Anaheim, CA (33%-600) Chor; Inter-
Club Coun; Mjrte; Swim; Type A; *Calif St U.*

WAGNER, Christopher Anthony
Arlington Heights HS; Ft Worth, TX (100-500)
Bsbl; Golf; Soccer; *Stephen F Austin St U; Acct.*

WAGNER, Cindy Sue
West HS; Columbus, OH (50%-577) Yth Fel;
Teachers Aide, Day Care.

WAGNER, Connie Sue
Belvidere HS; Belvidere, IL (39-363) A Cap Choir; AFS; Tres, Chor; Fr C; French NHS; *Rock Valley Col; Earth Sci.*

WAGNER, Cynthia Lee
Elyria W HS; Elyria, OH; A Cap Choir; *Ohio St U; Phys Therapist.*

WAGNER, Denise Kay
Norris HS; Firth, NE (22-84) Chor; Fr C; FNA; Pres, 4H; Tr; 4H A; VP, Tres, Rptr, 4 H C; *Bryan Sch of Nurs; Nurs.*

WAGNER, Elizabeth Ann
Mercy HS; Albany, NY (2-108) Chldr; Drama; Fr C; Hmrm; NHS; SC; VP, Jr Cl; COM; NEDT; *Siena Col; Math.*

WAGNER, Gwendolyn Dawn
S Park Sr HS; Library, PA (20-180) CYO; GS; NHS; F-Ed, Sch P; Y-Tns; Tr; JV, Vlbl; *Carnegie Art Inst; Ed.*

WAGNER, J Kent Lynwood
Annville-Cleona HS; Annville, PA (30-156) Chor; Math C; Model UN; NHS; Ed, Sch P; Tr; Hon Prog; Journ A; Math A; *Harrisburg Area Comm Col; Math.*

WAGNER, Janette
Northside HS; Muncie, IN (10-289) Band; Ger C; NHS; Hon Prog; Kiwanis A; Opt A; Sci A; *Purdue U; Biochem.*

WAGNER, Jennifer Lynn
N Torrance HS; Torrance, CA (50%-650) Chor; Drama; Hmrm; Thes; *Pacific Christian Col; Early Childhood Ed.*

WAGNER, John Martin
Livermore HS; Livermore, CA; Chor; Drama; Fr C; Lat C; NHS; JV, Swim; Amer Leg A; CSF; *Lang.*

WAGNER, Keith Dwayne
Annville-Cleona HS; Annville, PA (25-183) Chor; NHS; JV, Ftbl; Tr; *Pa St U; Pre-Med.*

WAGNER, Kelly Nan
Phoenixville Area HS; Phoenixville, PA; NHS; Var C; Hockey; COM; LaCrosse.

WAGNER, Kenneth Edward
H L Richards HS; Oak Lawn, IL (20-800) Math C; NHS; Bkbl; Cr-Ctry; Golf; *Hope Col; Bus.*

WAGNER, Lisa Diane
Attica Central HS; Attica, NY (38-194) AFS; JV, Chldr; Chor; Drama; Hmrm; NHS; Ski C; VP, Sr Cl; Tres, Jr Cl; Tres, Soph Cl; Soccer; Swim; COM; Yth Fel; Secy, GSct; *Genesee Comm Col; Liberal Arts.*

WAGNER, Lisa Renee
Cedar Crest HS; Lebanon, PA (75-374) Band; Bus C; Chor; FBLA; NHS; Rptr, Sch P; Type A; Win, FSA Schol; *Central Pa Bus Sch; Para Legal Secy.*

WAGNER, Mary Beth
Mexico HS; Mexico, MO; Pres, Chor; 4H; Hmrm; Lat C; ARC; SC; JV, Tnns; JV; Tr; Citz A; *Sci.*

WAGNER, Naketa Elaine
Lemuel A Penn Career Center; Washington, DC; Band; *U of Maryland; Art.*

WAGNER, Nevin Wendell
Conrad Weiser HS; Robesonia, PA (16-200) Band; NHS; JV, Bkbl; Pres, Yth Fel.

WAGNER, Pamela Sue
Arlington Heights HS; Fort Worth, TX; Fin, Hmrm; Span C; SC; Bkbl; Soccer; JV, Tnns; Tr; *Tex Tech; Interior Dec.*

WAGNER, Paul Robert
Westessex Sr HS; N Caldwell, NJ; Tr; Citz A; Tulip Leaf, BSct; Sct Lifeguard, BScts.

WAGNER, Paula Sue
Col Crawford HS; N Robinson, OH (19-115) Band; FHA; S-T, 4H; NHS; Ski C; Tr; B Crocker A; Yth Fel; Dairy Princess; *Ohio St U; Social Work.*

WAGNER, Robert Jan
Harold L Richards HS; Oaklawn, IL (30-630) Golf; *Hope Col; Bus Adm.*

WAGNER, Robyn Rae
Lindbergh HS; St Louis, MO (35-910) Co-Ed, Ann; Jr Miss Pagent; Lit Mag; NHS; Span C; SC; Swim; COM; HCt; Hon Prog; Journ A; Q&S A; Co-Piolets; Pep C; Bible C; Sch Store; *U of Mo; Nurs.*

WAGNER, Roger Allan
Dominguez HS; Compton, CA; *Pepperdine U; Computer Sci.*

WAGNER, Rosalyn Morelle
Huntington HS; Shreveport, LA (3-390) Chldr; Parl, Fr C; Lit Ral; Math C; Mu Alpha Theta; PTA A; Safety A; Jr NHS; 1st, Literary Rally; *Sou U.*

WAGNER, Rosemarie Marta
Cissna Park HS; Cissna Park, IL (2-42) FHA; Ger C; Sal; *Eastern Ill U; Zoology.*

WAGNER, Stephen Vincent
Fairhope HS; Fairhope, AL; Band; Tnns; Yth Fel; Pres, Church Yth Fel; Church Ensm; *U of Ala; Med.*

WAGNER, Tyrania Wagner
Lexington Sr HS; Lexington, NC (128-279) Band; CYO; FNA; VP, 4H; Hmrm; Mjrte; SC; Tres, Jr Cl; Sftbl; Tr; Beauty; COM; Citz A; Cl Fav; 4H A; HQn; HCt; JA A; Most Out; Yth Fel; Sport A; *U of Greensboro; Nurs.*

WAGNER, Vallerie Denise
Huntington HS; Shreveport, LA (5-310) Chem C; GS; Hmrm; Lit Ral; Math C; Mu Alpha Theta; NHS; Phys C; Sci C; Span C; Parl; SC; VP, Sr Cl; Alg A; COM; Delta Sigma Theta A; Hon Prog; Math A; Pres A; Safety A; *Sou La U; Mech Engr.*

WAGNER, Vincent Anthony
Bellevue Sr HS; Bellevue, NE (177-777) Ntl Yth Conf; COM; *U of Nebr; Bus.*

WAGNER, Wesley Jay
Warsaw Comm HS; Warsaw, IN (82-420) A Cap Choir; Fin, Ensm; *Grace Col; Mus.*

WAGNER, William Henry III
Phoenixville Area HS; Phoenixville, PA (40-260) NHS; Span NHS; Var C; Bkbl; WW; *Juniata Col; Pre-Law.*

WAGNON, Loretta Ann
Jacksonville HS; Jacksonville, AR (46-520) Secy, BC; FBLA; GS; Hmrm; Fin, Jr Miss Pagent; Mu Alpha Theta; NHS; VP, SC; Tnns; VP, Nike C; Drill Tm; Yth Leadership A; *Ark St U; Bus.*

WAGONER, Barbara Jean
Maumee HS; Maumee, OH; Y-Tns; Bowl Tm.

WAGONER, Crystalyn Kay
Frankfort HS; Ridgeley, WV (10%-151) Hmrm; VP, NHS; Rptr, Sch P; SC; Fr A; Eng A; *W Va Wesleyan Col; Christian Ed.*

WAGONER, Debbie Ruth
Kenmore HS; Akron, OH; Bkbl; Tr; CC, Vlbl; *Akron U; Acct.*

WAGONER, Loretta Denise
E Rowan HS; Salisbury, NC (48-200) Citz A; Camera C; Christian Action C; *Sweet Briar Col; Nurs.*

WAGONER, Lynne Elizabeth
Eastern Guilford HS; Gibsonville, NC (1-164) Co-Ed, Ann; VP, Fr C; French NHS; GS; Pres, 4H; Hmrm; Monogram; VP, NHS; Sci C; SC; Co-Cpt, Bkbl; Gr Marshal; 4H A; NMS; Summa Cum Laude; Vlbl; WW; Fr A; *U of NC; Phar.*

WAGSTAFF, W Reed
Cokeville HS; Cokeville, WY (3-12) S-T, Band; Chor; Drama; 4H; NHS; Ed, Sch P; Rptr, Sr Cl; Rptr, Jr Cl; Journ A; Type A; NMSQT Commended Stu; *Utah St U.*

WAGUESPACK, Cathy Marie
St Charles Borromeo HS; Destrehan, LA (7-79) BC; Bus C; Lit Ral; Span C; Tres, Spch C; Alg A; Hon Prog; Shorthand, Bookkeeping, Hon Certs; Span, Eng, Econ & Civics, Hon Certs; *Nicholls St Col; Secy.*

WAGUESPACK, Lynnette Ann
St Charles Borromeo HS; Destrehan, LA (4-79) Tres, BC; 4H; Lit Ral; Pres, Span C; S-T, Spch C; Amer Leg A; Chem A; Hist A; Math A; Spch A; Most Intelligent; *Charity Hospital Sch of Nurs; Nurs.*

WAGUESPACK,
Timothy Michael
St Charles Borromeo HS; Destrehan, LA (25-79) BC; BS; Pres, Key C; Math C; MVP, Bsbl; Bkbl; Cpt, Ftbl; Most Out; BS A; *SE La U; Wildlife Mgr.*

WAHL, Robert Kent
Highland HS; Albuquerque, NM (102-656) Pres, A Cap Choir; Pres, Chldr; Pres, Chor, Secy, Fr C; Hmrm; Key C; Orch; SC; Pres, Soph Cl; JV, Tnns; King, Twerp Wk; *U of NM.*

WAHL, Stephen Lawrence
Western HS; Las Vegas, NV (145-768) NHS; Sci C; Ski C; JV, Wrest; *Ariz St U; Elec Engr.*

WAHLSTROM, Marjo Ruth
Kerkhoven HS; Kerkhaven, MN (10-60) Band; Chldr; FHA; Pres, 4H; Mu Alpha Theta; NHS; Span C; Var C; Tr; COM; 4H A; Hon Prog; Spch A; 4-Star A; Tr A's; *Willmar Comm Col; Elem Ed.*

WAHRER, Marty
Fairmont W HS; Kettering, OH (120-610) Drama; Fr C; Orch; Cpt, Bsbl; Cpt, Bkbl; Yth Fel; Pres, Yth Fel; Dragon Bell A; Amateur Bsbl Commission Umpire; MVP, Bsbl & Bkbl; Bowl Singles Champion; *Math.*

WAIBEL, Marvin John
Jesuit HS; Portland, OR (50%-123) V-Ch, CYO; Bkbl; Ftbl; Sftbl; *Port Comm Col; Cook.*

WAID, Christopher John
Adrian HS; Adrian, MI (50%-450) A Cap Choir; Band; Chor; Ensm; Madrigal; Yth Fel; WW; All Co Band; All Co Hon Choir; HS Mus; *Adrian Col; Vocal & Instrumental Mus.*

WAID, Danny Robert
Crestwood HS; Cresco, IA (62-209) Bsbl; Ftbl; Tr; Wrest; St Wrest Champion; NE Iowa Conf Champ; *Engr.*

WAID, William Mark
Northside HS; Roanoke, VA (128-415) Monogram; Var C; Ftbl; *Va Tech Col; Engr.*

WAINWRIGHT, Irene Desiree
Bradford HS; Starke, FL (10%-315) Pres, NHS; Span C; SC; COM; Citz A; Hon Prog; Sci A; Yth Fel; *Sewanee; Psych.*

WAIT, Suzanne Kay
Sandusky HS; Sandusky, MI (2-140) Chor; NHS; NMS; *Adrian Col; Math.*

WAITE, Barry Mitchell
Adolfo Camarillo HS; Camarillo, CA (10%-650) VP, Band; Fr C; Orch; Hon Prog; Band, Most Valuable Service A; *Meteorology.*

WAITE, Dan Roland
Rancho HS; North Las Vegas, NV (37-578) Band; City Conf; Key C; NHS; Orch; Order/ Arrow; VP, SC; Tnns; DARGCA; Elk A; Duty to God A; Eagle Sct; NSP Engr A; *Brigham Young U; Chem Engr.*

WAITE, Tamre Suzanne
W Columbus HS; Cerro Gordo, NC (10%-285) BC; Fr C; Pres, Hmrm; Order/Arrow; SC; Bsbl; JV, Bkbl; Ftbl; Sct o-t Mo; Life Sct; *NC U; Phar.*

WAITE, Tamre Suzanne
Watkins Glen HS; Watkins Glen, NY; Band; Chldr; Chor; Ensm; Rptr, Hmrm; Mjrte; Span NHS; Rptr, SC; Var C; Swim; Tr; Yth Fel; Tr As; *U of NM; Mus Therapy.*

WAITS, Barry Lewis
Sumrall Attendance Center; Sumrall, MS; Mgr, Band; Chem C; Mod Mus Mas; Sci C; Tres, SC; MVP, Band; *Miss Sou Col; Dentistry.*

WAITS, Shirley Caramia
Beebe HS; Beebe, AR; BC; FBLA; FHA; GS; Pres, 4H; Math C; Sci C; DARGCA; 4H A; Historian, SC; *ASU at Beebe; Nurs.*

WAJER, Cheryl Ann
Putnam Catholic Acad; Putnam, CT (9-44) F-Ed, Ann; JV, Chldr; Thes; Secy, Sr Cl; Secy, Jr Cl; Secy, Soph Cl; NEDT; Type A; *Utica Col; Occupational Therapy.*

WAKEFIELD, Deborah Marlene
East HS; Columbus, OH (23-350) Drama A; Vlbl A; *Urbana Col; Acct.*

WAKEFIELD, Helen Elizabeth
George Henry Corliss HS; Chicago, IL (35-726) Band; NHS; COM; Citz A; Hon Prog; Spch A; Art C; Pep Sq; PSP; PSP A; Flag Tm; GAA; *Northwestern U; Journ.*

WAKEFIELD, Joel Zobrist
Freedom HS; Morganton, NC (200-444) VP; Hmrm; Sci C; Span C; Semi-Fin, Arch; Bsbl; Bkbl; JV, Ftbl; Fin, Tnns; Tnn A; Bus Driver A; Western Piedmont Comm Col; Engr.

WAKEFIELD, Lori Linn
Robert E Lee HS; Tyler, TX; FHA; SC; Homemaking A; Drill Tm; Stephen F Austin St U; Special Ed.

WAKEFIELD, Wendy K
Robt E Lee HS; Tyler, TX; Pol Sci C; F-Ed, Sch P; SC; Pres Phys Fitness A; Drill Tm; Rptr, Sch Paper; Govt C; Chem A; Tyler Jr Col; Special Ed.

WALASEK, June Monique
Peachtree HS; Chamblee, GA (20%-341) BC; Fr C; Mjrte; Math C; Sftbl; Bus.

WALBORN, Glen Aldrich
Grand Haven HS; Grand Haven, MI (50-500) VP, Band; Ski C; JV, Bsbl; Ftbl; Swim; Hon Prog; Sailing Tm.

WALCOTT, Donna Sue
Switzerland Co Jr Sr HS; Vevay, IN (17-108) Band; Chor; Tres, 4H; Sci C; Span C; COM; 4H A; Sullivan Jr Col of Bus; Data Processing.

WALD, Lori Ann
Bishop Ryan HS; Minot, ND (25-92) Chor; Pres, 4H; COM; 4H A; Gov Coun on Human Resources Essay; Minot St Col; Clerical.

WALD, Peggy Lynn
Bishop Ryan HS; Minot, ND (11-73) F-Ed, Ann; Tres, 4H; Hmrm; VP, NHS; Sodality; SC; Sftbl; COM; 4H A; K of C A; Type A; VFW A; VofDEM; Art Schol; Yth Essay A; St & Local Legal Secy Schol; Minot St Col; Bus Adm.

WALD, Timothy James
Hobart HS; Hobart, OK; Cpt, CYO; Cpt, Chor; Fin, FFA; Fin, FTA; Pres, Key C; SC; Var C; Bsbl; Bkbl; Cpt, Ftbl; Tr; Citz A; Cl Fav; HKg; All-Conf, All-Dist, Ftbl; All-St HON Men, Ftbl.

WALDEN, Gilbert Lee
Canton Pub HS; Canton, MS (11-216) Ann; NHS; ARC; Sci C; Span C; COM; HCt; Phi Beta Kappa; ROTC A; Pres, Stu Adv Committee; U of Miss; Acct.

WALDEN, Greg Tyrone
Jellico HS; Jellico, TN (21-66) VP, FFA; SC; Var C; Bkbl; Ftbl; Cl Fav; HKg; Cumberland Col; Hist.

WALDEN, Robert Brian
Staunton HS; Staunton, VA (25%-60) Secy, Key C; Tres, Monogram; Bsbl; Cpt, Bkbl; Co-Cpt, Bkbl; Bsbl Ltr & Trophy; Ind St U; Archt.

WALDEN, Sandra Lynn
Preble HS; Green Bay, WI (5%-600) A Cap Choir; Band; Chor; Dbte Tm; Drama; Fr C; Hmrm; Madrigal; Sch P; Ski C; SC; Soccer; Sftbl; Tnns; Tr; Bio A; Rotary A; Mus.

WALDORPH, Joanne Sue
Hobart Sr HS; Hobart, IN; Ger C; Organ A.

WALDREP, Philip Lee
W Morgan HS; Trinity, AL (10%-63) Rptr, Hmrm; SC; Mgr, Bsbl; Mgr, Bkbl; Mgr, Ftbl; Yth Fel; WW; Samford U; Religion.

WALDREP, Stephen A
Goodrich HS; Goodrich, TX; Pres, FFA; Bsbl; Ftbl; Sam Houston St Col; Law Enforcement.

WALDRON, Cathy Lou
New Haven HS; New Haven, IN (20%-222) Band; Ger C; Hmrm; NHS; SC; Y-Tns; Sftbl; Swim; Hon Prog; Pres A; Gym; WW Foreign Lang; WW; Purdue U; Nurs.

WALDRON, Danette Lynn
Timberline HS; Weippe, ID (3-70) Ed, Ann; Band; JV, Chldr; Chem C; Secy, 4H; JETS; NHS; Bkbl; Tr; 4H A; HCt; Hon Prog; Journ A; JA A; Intermountain Jr Sci Symp.

WALDRON, Nadine Andrea
Gilbert Sch; Brooklyn, NY (1-35) Pres, Chem C; Hmrm; F-Ed, Lit Mag; Secy, Math C; SC; Tres, Jr Cl; Co-Cpt, Tr; COM; Chem A; Hon Prog; MLS; Sci A; HR; Service A; Fordham U; Phys Sci.

WALDRON, Rebecca Ann
Fort Myers HS; Fort Myers, FL (150-400) Ann; Drama; Hmrm; Thes; COM; NEDT; VP, Civinettes; Journ.

WALDRON, Todd Jay
Middle Park HS; Granby, CO (27-78) SC; Pres, Jr Cl; Pres, Soph Cl; Cpt, Bkbl; Ftbl; Tr; U of Hawaii; Biol.

WALDRON, Vanessa Kaye
Dunedin HS; Dunedin, FL (57-900) Hmrm; SC; Concord Col; Social Work.

WALDRUP, David Alan
El Dorado HS; El Dorado, AR; BS; Pres, Chor; NHS; Bkbl; Tr; La Tech U; Elec.

WALES, Donna Lynn
University HS; Baton Rouge, LA; Band; FHA; Mjrte; Span C; Most Out; LSU.

WALES, Lafayette Eugene
Canton Pub HS; Canton, MS (5-222) Fr C; NHS; Bus Mgr, Sci C; Parl, Sr Cl; Pres, Soph Cl; Bio A; Phi Beta Kappa; ROTC A; Tougaloo Col; Biol.

WALES, Lisa Kaye
S Rapides HS; Lecompte, LA (5-24) Chldr; Secy, Hmrm; NHS; Bkbl; Sftbl; Cl Fav; HQn; HCt; Most Talented; Best Dressed; Most Ath.

WALES, Lydia Diane
University HS; Baton Rouge, LA (1-60) Band; Chldr; FHA; Hmrm; Key C; Fin, Lit Ral; NHS; Span C; VP, SC; Cl Fav; Most Out; PTA A; Swtht; Val; WW; Winter Formal Court; Ed, Uniteens; LSU; Pre-Med.

WALGAMUTH, Randy Marion
Brown HS; Sturgis, SD (275-350) Rptr, 4H; Pres, Jr Cl; 4H A; Black Hills St Col; Bus.

WALGREN, Sue Elizabeth
Columbus Sr HS; Columbus, NE (30%-266) F-Ed, Ann; Band; Fin, Chor; Fin, Ensm; 4H; Span C; Thes; Tr; HCt; Journ A; Q&S A; Yth Fel; Hon Qn, Job's Daughters; VP, Booster C; Design As; U of Nebr; Arts & Sci.

WALKENFELD, Caryn Mariam
Bruriah HS; Elizabeth, NJ (9-26) Tres, Jr Cl; Hon Prog; Ed.

WALKER, Alan Eugene
Ralston HS; Ralston, NE; Sci.

WALKER, Andrea Dorris
Lutheran HS; Los Angeles, CA; CSF; USC; Sci.

WALKER, Andrea Jean
Cathedral HS; Boston, MA (14-91) SC; Livingstone Col.

WALKER, Angela Kay
Altavista HS; Altavista, VA (15-180) Chldr; FTA; Sci C; Secy, SC; Var C; Swim; Tnns; HCt; Nom, NHS; Secy, SG Coun; Duke U; Phys Therapy.

WALKER, Anita LaRae
Redlands Sr HS; Redlands, CA (50-778) AFS; Fr C; Orch; CSF; Daughter o-t Yr; Hon Girl; SB Valley Col; Home Ec.

WALKER, Ava Ann
Irving HS; Irving, TX; Chor; Ensm; A-Ed, Lit Mag; NHS; ARC; Citz A; Interlochen Ntl Mus; Poet A; Q&S A; ARC A; U of Tex at Arlington; Bio.

WALKER, Barbara McCoy
Albemarle HS; Charlottesville, VA (10%-700) Fr C; Tres, French NHS; Hmrm; NHS; F-Ed, Sch P; NEDT; 6th in St, Ntl Fr Contest.

WALKER, Benny Patrick
Belton-Honea Path HS; Honea Path, SC; Secy, FFA; Hmrm; SC; JV, Ftbl; Tr; Star Student; Tri-County Tech Col; Textile Mgt.

WALKER, Bernice Marguerite
Asbury Park HS; Asbury Park, NJ; Band; 4H; NHS; Tr.

WALKER, Calvin
Goodrich HS; Goodrich, TX (5-30) BC; FFA; Bkbl; Cl Fav; Tex A&M Col; Elec.

WALKER, Carol Elaine
Redlands HS; Redlands, CA; Band; Sftbl; Pres A.

WALKER, Charles Burtran
South Side HS; Memphis, TN (10%-370) Bus Mgr, Span C; SC; Cpt, Ftbl; Sci A; 2nd Pl, Sci Fair; Purdue U; Engr.

WALKER, Charles Mark
Pickens HS; Jasper, GA; Fr C; 4H; Sci C; Var C; Mgr, Bkbl; Ftbl; Hon Prog; Best Personality; Mercer Col; Art.

WALKER, Cindy Cherise
Hobbs HS; Hobbs, NM (84-440) Secy, A Cap Choir; Band; Chor; Type A; WW; St Win, Baldwin Achievement A; NM All-St Choir; Co Tnager; 1st Theory, Mus Teachers Assn; Tex Tech U; Mus.

WALKER, Cledius Shea
John Ehret HS; Marrero, LA; Mu Alpha Theta; Bkbl; Co-Cpt, Sftbl; MVP; WW; Nicholls St U; Bus Ed.

WALKER, Coleen
Bullock Co HS; Union Springs, AL (3-148) Dbte Tm; 4H; VP, Hmrm; Secy, NHS; SC; Bio A; COM; Chem A; 4H A; HCt; Hon Prog; I Dare You; Math A; Sci A; Val; Ala St Col; Optometry.

WALKER, Crystal Ann
Eastmont Sr HS; E Wenatchee, WA (3-225) Chor; Dbte Tm; Drama; Ensm; Hmrm; NHS; Orch; Sci C; Ch, SC; Elk A; NMF; NMS; Spch A; Yth Leg; VICA; Harvey Mudd Col; Physics.

WALKER, Darrell Emil
Middletown HS; Middletown, OH (50%-710) Band; Orch; SC; Bsbl; Bkbl; MLS; Mus A; Mus.

WALKER, Daryl Jerome
South HS; Denver, CO (126-438) Pres, A Cap Choir; Chor; Sachs Found Grant; Omega Fraternity A; Omar D Blair Yth Achv A; U of Colo; Communications.

WALKER, David Kent
Hastings HS; Hastings, NE (1-304) Fin, AFS; Chor; Dbte Tm; Hmrm; Ch, Madrigal; NFL; Cr-Ctry; COM; Citz A; Hon Prog; Regent Schol; Spch A; Val; Bicycle Racing; NML; WW; Hastings Col; Sci.

WALKER, Deborah Ann
Pewaukee HS; Pewaukee, WI (37-128) Tres, Bus C; Span C; Var C; Tr; Type A; U of Wisc; Ed.

WALKER, Deborah Ann
Jackson HS; Jackson, LA (3-92) Bus Mgr, Ann; Pres, BC; Cpt, Chldr; Tres, FBLA; Hmrm; Lit Ral; Math C; SC; S-T, Sr Cl; S-T, Jr Cl; Alg A; HCt; WW; Distinguished Young Amer; SE La U; Ed.

WALKER, Deborah Ann
Los Angeles HS; Los Angeles, CA; Chor; Ed, Bsbl; Bkbl; Sftbl; Citz A; Choir; Glee C; Cpt, Drill Tm; Pepperdine U; Math.

WALKER, Deborah Deanne
Reidsville Sr HS; Reidsville, NC (7-324) Fr C; Math C; Marshal; U of NC at Greensboro; Acct.

WALKER, Deborah Ellen
Panhandle HS; Panhandle, TX (7-61) Ann; Band; Dbte Tm; Ensm; Secy, FHA; FTA; NHS; Spch C; Thes; Bkbl; Tnns; Tr; MLS; Eng A; Regional UIL Spelling; All Region Band; Tex A&M U; Acct.

WALKER, Debra Jean
Bloomington HS; Bloomington, CA (15-217) Bank of Amer A; CSF; Chem A; Yth Fel; Badminton; Pres, VP, Home Ec C; Pres, Church Group; Nurs.

WALKER, Delores Louise
East HS; Cleveland, OH (7-350) NHS; Parl, SC; JA A; Martha Holden Jennings A; NHS A; Book of Golden Deeds; HR; Merit Roll; Cleveland St U; Acct.

WALKER, Donald Dale
Flint Christian HS; Flint, MI (1-16) NHS; Rptr, Sch P; SC; Var C; VP, Soph Cl; Bsbl; Cpt, Bkbl; Cpt, Soccer; Tr; Hon Prog; MVP, Bkbl; Schol Athl-Sportsmanship A; Engr.

WALKER, Dwight Edgar
Harlingen HS; Harlingen, TX (25%-400) A Cap Choir; Chess C; Demolay; Ensm; Madrigal; Tr; God & Country A; Church Yth Coun; W Tex St U; Mus Ed.

WALKER, Edward James
Riverside HS; Taylor, PA (1-195) Ger C; Hmrm; VP, NHS; Cpt, Sch Achieve Tm; SC; COM; Hon Prog; NMS; NEDT; St Scholar; Val; Penn St Sci Sym; WW; Astronomy.

WALKER, Elizabeth Tamer
Acad of Our Lady; Chicago, IL; CYO; Hmrm; Orch; Service A; Cert of Appreciation; Humorous A; McCormac Col; Med Secy.

WALKER, Elvis
W Monroe HS; W Monroe, LA (5-31) Band; NHS; Cpt, Bsbl; MVP, Sftbl; Hist A; Hon Prog; Sci A; Yth Fel; Yth Foundation; DECA C; PA; *Bradley U; Bus.*

WALKER, Ethel Lorinda
Detroit HS; Detroit, TX (9-36) Ann; VP, BC; S-T, Chor; FHA; Sch P; Cpt, Bkbl; Tr; MVP, Bkbl; *Paris Jr Col; Data Processing.*

WALKER, Fatima Darlice
Union HS; Leslie, GA; Drama; FHA; 4H; Sci C; Span C; Cpt, Bkbl; Hon Prog; Type A; Bkbl A; Shorthand A; Home Ec A; *Fort Valley St Col; Bus Adm.*

WALKER, Gary Thomas
Tishomingo HS; Tishomingo, MS (2-55) Ann; Pres, BC; Pres, Jr Cl; Alg A; Citz A; Hist A; Math A; Driver Ed A; Alg A; *U of Miss; Bio.*

WALKER, George Edmund
Robinson Secondary HS; Fairfax, VA (50%-584) Demolay; *Auto Mech.*

WALKER, Glenda Kay
Los Angeles HS; Los Angeles, CA (35-700) Candystriper; Pep C; Church Choir; *US Air Force; Bus.*

WALKER, Gwynnita Kae
Paris HS; Paris, TX (68-236) Chldr; FTA; Span C; Tri-HiY; Tres, Sr Cl; Tres, Soph Cl; Ftbl Swtht; Pres, Keywanettes; *Interior Design.*

WALKER, Harlan Ray
Metamora HS; Metamor, IL (32-193) Ger C; Span C; Var C; Bsbl; JV, Bkbl; Ftbl; *U of Ill; Bus Adm.*

WALKER, Jacqueline Delphine
Havana HS; Havana, FL (4-125) Chldr; FBLA; NHS; SC; Cpt, Bsbl; Most Out; Type A; *Tallahassee Comm Col; Bus.*

WALKER, James C
Arroyo HS; El Monte, CA (240-388) Sci C; Ftbl; B Crocker A; *Pasadena City Col; Engr.*

WALKER, James Michael
Jones Valley HS; Birmingham, AL (3-178) Fin, A Cap Choir; Chor; Ensm; Math C; Secy, NHS; Var C; Ftbl; Tr; Alg A; Math A; A For Excellence; Cert of Achv; Exchange C Schol A; Outst Choir; *U of Ala; Elec Engr.*

WALKER, James Scott
Brookfield Central HS; Brookfield, WI (1-500) AFS; Pres, Ger C; Hmrm; NHS; Order/Arrow; SC; Mgr, Ftbl; Elk A; Math A; Order/Arrow A; Yth Fel; Eagle Sct; *U of Wis; Bus Adm.*

WALKER, Janice Ruth
W Monroe HS; W Monroe, LA (4-26) Chldr; Chor; Ntl Yth Conf; Sftbl; Math A; Yth Fel; Yth Foundation; Yth Foundation A; Mus A; Vocalist; PA; *Bradley U; Mus.*

WALKER, Jennifer Ruth
Coconino HS; Flagstaff, AZ (20%-500) Band; Chor; Madrigal; Band A's; *N Ariz U; Mus.*

WALKER, John Hudson
Vernon HS; Vernon, TX; Drama; Pres, SC; Ftbl; Golf; *Colo St U; Forestry.*

WALKER, John Michael
Scott HS; Madison, WV; Chess C; Cpt, Cr-Crty; Mgr, Ftbl; Tr; Art C; Gifted Cl; *Missionary Work.*

WALKER, Joyce Annette
Crenshaw HS; Los Angeles, CA (3-1100) Pres, Hmrm; Pres, Sch Achieve Tm; Up Bound; Bkbl; Sftbl; CSF; Citz A; Type A; Cpt, Badminton; Bkbl & Badminton Trophies; *UCLA; Bus Adm.*

WALKER, Julia Gwen
Industry HS; Industry, IL (1-33) Band; Chor; Drama; Fr C; Rptr, Sch P; Sci C; SC; Pres, Soph Cl; DARGCA; I Dare You; NEDT; St Scholar; Val; WW; *Blackburn Col; Mus Ed.*

WALKER, Karen Ann
Jonathan Alder HS; Plain City, OH; Chor; Drama; Ensm; FTA; Span C; Y-Tns; Bkbl; Swim; *Bowling Green Col; Teachers.*

WALKER, Katherine Lee
Paris HS; Paris, TX (3-266) Band; FTA; NHS; Tres, Span C; Tri-HiY; COM; Hon Prog; WW, Foreign Lang; *Austin Col; Music.*

WALKER, Kathleen Ann
South HS; Pueblo, CO; Band; Chor; NFL; Spch C; Thes; Church Chor; *Ed.*

WALKER, Kendall Lee
Classical HS; Springfield, MA (196-576) MVP, Bsbl; MVP, Bkbl; MVP, Ftbl; Sftbl; MVP, Tr; Alg A; Cl Fav; MLS; Spch A; Yth Fel; Yth Foundation; Yth Foundation A; Yth Leg; Karate; *Philadelphia Col o-t Bible; Evangelism.*

WALKER, Kent Alan
Rolling Meadows HS; Rolling Meadows, IL (10%-800) NHS; Var C; Bkbl; Tnns; Church Chor; Sr Tuxis; All Conf Bkbl; *Acct.*

WALKER, Kerri Elaine
Natrona Co HS; Casper, WY (122-644) Band; Ensm; Lat C; *Psych.*

WALKER, Kevin Keith
Whitney Ind HS; Whitney, TX (11-52) Ann; Bus C; FFA; FHA; Spch C; Math A; Attendance A; *Howard Payne Col; Mus.*

WALKER, Kevin Schofield
McDonogh HS; McDonogh, MD (79-91) Chor; Drama; SC; Tr; COM; Yth Fel; WW; Big Brothers Assc; *Morehouse Col; Mass Communications.*

WALKER, Laura Lea
Center HS; Center, TX (6-150) Ann; Secy, 4H; VP, NHS; Secy, Jr Cl; Sftbl; Tr; 4H A; Hon Prog; I Dare You; Rodeo Qn; Gold Star Girl; WW; High Point Horseman, Dist; *Elem Ed.*

WALKER, Laurrie Anne
Lawrence Central HS; Indianapolis, IN; Chor; Community Yth Symph; Drama; Orch; Sch P; COM; Hon Prog; Math A; NEDT; Yth Fel; Drill Tm; All St Orch; *Purdue U; Math.*

WALKER, Lawrence Glenn
River Oaks Sch; Monroe, LA (5-44) Band; Key C; Fin, Lit Ral; Span C; COM; MLS; NMF; Engr o-t Day; Yth Choir; Karate C; Built, Flown Hang Glider; Built Model Aircraft; Pres, MYF; Theater Productions; *Ga Inst of Tech; Aeronautical Engr.*

WALKER, Leanne Elizabeth
Hickman Mills HS; Kansas City, MO (66-577) Ensm; Sftbl; Math A; *Mo U; Ed.*

WALKER, Leonard Anderson III
McMinn Co HS; Athens, TN (13-278) Fr C; Hmrm; Math C; Mu Alpha Theta; Pres, NHS; Bkbl; Elk A; Hon Prog; Kiwanis A; MLS; NMF; NMS; NEDT; ROTC A; Star Student; Alt, BS; Cert Lifeguard & Swim Instructor; WW; *U of Tenn; Bio.*

WALKER, Linda Lee
McKeesport Sr HS; McKeesport, PA (84-635) A Cap Choir; Tres, Band; Chor; Ensm; Hmrm; Orch; Span C; SC; Y-Tns; JV, Swim; JV, Tnns; Sch Hon Soc; Dist Band A; Dist Orch A; *Ind U of Pa; Elem Ed.*

WALKER, Lori LaVonne
Bozeman Sr HS; Bozeman, MT; A Cap Choir; All Amer Yth; Chor; Ensm; FHA; Lat C; Lat NHS; JV, Bkbl; *Okla Christian U; Special Ed.*

WALKER, Louretha Louise
Adult Learning Center; Buffalo, NY;

WALKER, Lucreacia Venita
A H Parker HS; Birmingham, AL (15-296) Band; Community Yth Symph; Dbte Tm; Drama; Hmrm; Math C; NHS; Orch; Ed, Sch P; Sci C; Span C; Spch C; SC; Secy, Sr Cl; Tnns; COM; Citz A; HQn; Hon Prog; Journ A; Spch A; Church Choir; St SC; Pres, St SG A; *U of Ala; Lib Arts.*

WALKER, Lucreacia Venita
A H Parker HS; Birmingham, AL (15-496) Band; Chem C; Secy, City Conf; Community Yth Symph; Dbte Tm; Drama; Parl, Hmrm; Math C; Mu Alpha Theta; NHS; Orch; Ed, Sch P; Span C; Spch C; Pres, St Stu Congres; SC; VP, Jr Cl; Pres, Soph Cl; Tnns; Alg A; COM; Gov Honor Prog; HQn; Hon Prog; Journ A; Math A; Poet A; Pres A; Sanctuary Soc; Sci A; Spch A; Type A; Church Choir; Pres, Tnettes; *U of Ala; Law.*

WALKER, Marcus C
Paris HS; Paris, TX; Band; Key C; *Paris Jr Col; Bus.*

WALKER, Margaret Lynne
Fern Creek HS; Louisville, KY (20-264) BC; Hmrm; Span C; Ch, SC; COM; Schol Art A; *U of Louisville; Art.*

WALKER, Mark Anthony
Susquehanna Comm HS; Susquehanna, PA (14-119) Sch P; Ski C; Tr; Ed, Yrbk; *Penn St U; Surveying.*

WALKER, Mark Erwin
Huntington Beach HS; Huntington Beach, CA (42-866) Bsbl; Wrest.

WALKER, Martin Douglass
Woodrow Wilson HS; Dallas, TX; Chor; FFA; Ftbl; Sftbl; Tnns; COM; Tnns C; *Baylor U; Law.*

WALKER, Marty Thomas
Daviess Co HS; Owensboro, KY; All Amer Yth; JV, AFS; Ann; Young Hist; *U of Ky; Engr.*

WALKER, Mary Jo
Lew Wallace HS; Gary, IN; Ger C; Y-Tns; Bkbl; Sftbl; Tr; *NW Ind U; Bus.*

WALKER, Mary Kathleen
Ritenour Sr HS; St John, MO;

WALKER, Mayna Louise
Nederland HS; Nederland, TX (33%-500) Band; CYO; COM; Hon Prog; Historian, OEA; Band Ensm; Tres, CFG; Shorthand Merit; PA; *Lamar U; Secretarial.*

WALKER, Merry Gail
Welch HS; Welch, WV (13-153) Pres, FBLA; GS; Secy, NHS.

WALKER, Michael Anthony
Clarkrange HS; Clarkrange, TN (1-51) BC; Pres, FFA; FHA; 4H; Sci C; Pres, Soph Cl; Bsbl; Cpt, Bkbl; Bio A; Chem A; Cl Fav; MLS; Val; All Conf, Bkbl; *U of Tenn; Law.*

WALKER, Michael Blake
McMinn Co HS; Athens, TN; Tres, HiY; Key C; Var C; Co-Cpt, Bkbl; Golf; Star Student; Yth Leg.

WALKER, Nelson Edward III
Los Angeles HS; Los Angeles, CA (4-77) Band; CSF; Tres, Yth Group; Yth Church Jr Choir; Sci Hon C; *U of Sou Calif; Dental Surgeon.*

WALKER, Nina Frances
Leroy HS; Leroy, AL (10%-68) Ann; Band; BC; Cpt, Chldr; VP, FHA; Tres, Jr Cl; *Livingston U.*

WALKER, Pamela Jo
Pewaukee HS; Pewaukee, WI (17-128) Bus C; NHS; Tres, Span C; Var C; Secy, Jr Cl; JV, Bkbl; JV, Tr; HCt; Hon Prog; Type A; Outst Bus A; *UW-Whitewater; Bus Adm.*

WALKER, Pamela Rena
Hancock Central HS; Sparta, GA; FBLA; 4H; Pres, Hmrm; Math C; NHS; Sci C; JV, Bkbl; COM; 4H A; Math A; Eng A; Spelling A; *Savannah St Col.*

WALKER, Philip Merle
Choctaw HS; Choctaw, OK; SC; NHS; Bsbl; Bkbl; Ftbl; Tr; Math A; Sci A; Most Faithful A; Church; *Okla City SW Jr Col; Minister.*

WALKER, Rebecca Dawn
Bethel Christian Sch; Ruston, LA (10%-15) Ed, Ann; 4H; Lit Ral; SC; Pres, Jr Cl; Pres, Soph Cl; Bkbl; Sftbl; B Crocker A; COM; Citz A; Cl Fav; DARGCA; HCt; Yth Fel; Most Schol; All Dist, Sftbl & Bkbl; *NE La U; Bus.*

WALKER, Rhonda June
Wakulla HS; Crawfordville, FL (20%-150) Ann; Lit Mag; *FSU; Social Stu.*

WALKER, Richard Bruce
Eastmont Sr HS; E Wenatchee, WA (100-285) Chor; Ensm; Hmrm; SC; Var C; Co-Cpt, Ftbl; Tr; Cpt, Wrest; Most Pins Trophy, Wrest; Player o-t Wk, Ftbl; *Wash St U; Phys Ed.*

WALKER, Rita Carol
Rufus King HS; Milwaukee, WI; City Conf; Drama; Math C; NHS; Span C; Semi-Fin, Tr; Math A; DECA A; *U of Wisc; Bus Adm.*

WALKER, Rob
Bremen HS; Bremen, GA; Hmrm; Tres, InterAct C; Pres, SC; Pres, Jr Cl; Cpt, Bkbl; Cpt, Ftbl; Stan Slaughter A; Mr BHS; *LaGrange Col; Criminal Justice.*

WALKER, Robert Alan
N Hollywood HS; N Hollywood, CA; Drama; Rptr, Hmrm; JV, Ftbl; JV, Tr; Pres A; *Eng.*

WALKER, Robert Allen
Ketron HS; Kingsport, TN (1-144) BC; SC; Math A; MLS; Phy A; Val; Eagle Sct; *Tenn Tech U; Elec Engr.*

WALKER, Ronald Scott
Flint Christian Sch; Flint, MI (10%-10) Co-Ed, Ann; Chor; Ensm; NHS; Rptr, Sch P; Var C; Pres, Jr Cl; Bsbl; MVP, Bkbl; Cpt, Soccer; Citz A; Cl Fav; Hon Prog; Mus A's; *Bus Adm.*

WALKER, Scott Elton
Lubbock Christian HS; Lubbock, TX (28-50) Band; Chess C; Chor; FFA; Ger C; Ed A; Sch P; Bsbl; Co-Cpt, Ftbl; JV, Golf; Sftbl; Tr; Hist A; *Lubbock Christian Col; Bible.*

WALKER, Sharon Ruth
Newton Co Comprehensive HS; Covington, GA (15%-249) Ch, Chor; Drama; Ensm; GS; 4H; Jr Miss Pagent; Lat C; Lit Ral; Span C; Ch, Tri-HiY; All St Chor; *Queens Col; Fine-Arts.*

WALKER, Shelia DeLois
Moultrie Sr HS; Moultrie, GA; FHA; Rptr, Hmrm; Cpt, Jr Miss Pagent; Cpt, Sftbl; Cpt, Swim; Cpt, Tnns; Beauty; COM; JA A; FHA As; *Valdosta St Col; Mus.*

WALKER, Sidney Allen
Bryan HS; Bryan, TX; VP, 4H; Citz A; God & Country A; *Tex A&M U; Agr.*

WALKER, Sondria Kay
Independence HS; Independence, MS (10-106) BC; FBLA; Bkbl; MVP, Sftbl; Tr; *Bus.*

WALKER, Sonja Maria
Texas HS; Texarkana, TX (80-475) A Cap Choir; Ann; Chldr; Cl Fav; *Texarkana Col; Photography.*

WALKER, Stephen Edward
Landrum HS; Landrum, SC (25%-56) BC; Key C; Var C; Bkbl; Co-Cpt, Ftbl; MVP, Tr; Pres, Bus Drivers C; All Conf, Ftbl; Ath Schol A; Graduation Usher; WW; *Greenville Tech Col; Engr Graphics.*

WALKER, Susan Diane
Clearfield HS; Clearfield, UT (21-547) Band; FHA; NHS; Orch; *Stevens Henager Col; Secy.*

WALKER, Susan Jeanne
Auburn HS; Auburn, NY (27-608) Band; Math C; NHS; Orch; COM; Hon Prog; VFW A; Yth Fel; WW; *Potsdam St U; Lib Arts.*

WALKER, Suzanne Clara
Brethren HS; Paramount, CA (50%-100) Pres, A Cap Choir; Dbte Tm; Co-Ed, Lit Mag; SC; HCt; Spch A; Most Considerate; *LBCC; Nurs.*

WALKER, Tamara Lucille
Monticello Ind HS; Monticello, KY (25%-41) Fr C; FHA; FTA; 4H; 4H A; Kiwanis A; Spch A; Yth Fel; Dyslexia Aid; MYF; *Somerset Comm Col; Social Work.*

WALKER, Tammie Frances
Oroville HS; Oroville, CA; AFS; Rptr, FFA; 4H; NHS; Bank Of Amer A; CSF; Spch A; Star Chapter Farmer; *UC Davis; Animal Sci.*

WALKER, Teresa
Asher HS; Asher, OK (5%-29) Band; Chldr; Dbte Tm; VP, Drama; Pres, FHA; Rptr, Sch P; VP, Spch C; SC; Secy, Soph Cl; B Crocker A; Spch A; Debate A; *East Central U; Spch.*

WALKER, Terri M
Northern HS; Baltimore, MD (40%-750) ARC; Mus Schol; Cert of Achv; *Towson St U; Mus.*

WALKER, Terry Steven
Spencer HS; Spencer, WV (3-147) Arch; BS; Chess C; Pres, NHS; Amer Leg A; Bio A; Chem A; Phy A; *W Va U; Engr.*

WALKER, Therese Florrette
Acad of Our Lady; Chicago, IL; CYO; Vlbl; Service A; Dance Contest A; *Journ.*

WALKER, Tim Allen
LaFarge Pub HS; LaFarge, WI (5-45) FFA; Bkbl; Citz A; BSct A; *Western Wis Tech Col; Mech.*

WALKER, Timothy Scott
New Monroe Comm HS; Monroe, IA (10-48) Band; NHS; Wrest; *Hawkeye Inst of Tech; Tool & Die Design.*

WALKER, Varron Giselle
John Ehret HS; Marrero, LA; *U of Southwestern La; Spch & Hearing Therapy.*

WALKER, Venita Deenii
Charles Bayne Ghent HS; Birmingham, AL (9-114) FHA; Pres, Hmrm; NHS; Co-Ed, Sch P; SC; Pres, Sr Cl; Cr-Ctry; Soccer; Tr; COM; Yth Fel; *Birmingham Sou Col; Pol Sci.*

WALKER, William Darryl
University City HS; Philadelphia, PA (19-587) JETS; Math C; NHS; Phys C; Sci C; Bsbl; Bkbl; Ftbl; Tnns; Tr; COM; Citz A; Hon Prog; Math A; *Ind U of Pa; Physics.*

WALKER, William Earney
Vandalia Christian Sch; Greensboro, NC (2-14) Ann; Chem C; Drama; Hmrm; Model UN; Monogram; Sch P; Parl, Span C; SC; Cpt, Var C; Pres, Sr Cl; Cpt, Bkbl; Cpt, Soccer; Sal; Jr Marshal; Sportsmanship A; *UNCG; Psych.*

WALKER, William Gordon
Carroll HS; Ozark, AL; Band; Alg A; Bio C; Band A; Piano A; *Mus.*

WALKER, William Hazen
Thomas Stone HS; Waldorf, MD (18-365) Drama; NHS; Thes; Hon Thespian; *Ball St U; Theatre.*

WALKER, William Paul
Brookfield Central HS; Brookfield, WI (10%-500) Band; Secy, Ger C; Key C; Ski C; SC; Mgr, Ftbl; JV, Golf; Tnns; Tr; Math A; Sci A; Yth Fel; Eagle Sct; *U of Wis; Med.*

WALKINE, Darlene Rebbecca
John I Leonard HS; Lake Worth, FL; Chor; Ensm; Citz A; Hon Prog; Most Out; Hon C; *Ed.*

WALKLEY, Patricia Mae
Cheyenne Central HS; Cheyenne, WY (26-400) A Cap Choir; Band; Chor; Ensm; FBLA; Jr Miss Pagent; NFL; NHS; Orch; Sch P; Tnns; VofDEM; Yth Fel; Qn, Job's Daughters; All NW, Choir; Mus As; Pep C; Big Sisters; HR; Color Guard; Jr Mus C; All St Choir; Yth Fellowship; *U of Wyo; Mus Ed.*

WALKLING, Karla Glee
Dakota Christain HS; New Holland, SD (2-38) Ensm; Tres, Hmrm; NHS; Rptr, Sch P; JV, Bkbl; Val; *Math.*

WALKLING, Victor Alyn
Valentine HS; Valentine, NE; Bsbl; Bkbl; Ftbl; Golf; Yth Fel; Steering Committee, Church Yth Fel; Church Coun of Minstries; *Sci.*

WALKOVIAK, Sharon Denise
Sam Houston Sr HS; Houston, TX (50-660) Bus C; NHS; VOE; OEA.

WALKUP, Beverly Jane
Ashland Sr HS; Ashland, MA (5-153) Fr C; NHS; Sch P; JV, Tr; Alg A; Hon Prog; Fr A; Soph Associate, NHS; *U of Maine; Fr.*

WALKUP, David Leverett
Venice HS; Venice, FL (32-380) Chor; Ensm; Key C; Madrigal; NHS; Hon Prog; Madrigal A; Ensm A; St Chor Festival; *U of Fla; Architecture.*

WALL, Allan Ephraim
Perkins-Tryon HS; Perkins, OK (5-77) Band; Ensm; Pres, 4H; VP, SC; Bkbl; Ftbl; Tr; Bio A; 4H A; I Dare You; Eng Lit A; Preaching Contest Win; Conservation Fair; Hon Soc.

WALL, Brian James
Shaker Sr HS; Latham, NY;

WALL, Colleen Fay
Immanuel HS; Reedley, CA (1-92) Band; Ensm; Amer Leg A; CSF; COM; Chamber of Comm A; Citz A; Hon Prog; Interlochen Ntl Mus; Most Out; Star Student; Drama A; *Fresno St U; Mus.*

WALL, Eva Jeanette
Jupiter Christian Sch; Jupiter, FL (2-25) Chor; Secy, Soph Cl; Bkbl; Sftbl; HCt; Type A; *Miss U; Mus.*

WALL, Glenna Rene
Farragut HS; Concord, TN; AFS; Chor; Ensm; FHA; Tri-HiY; Sftbl; News E, Church Paper; *U of Tenn; Interior Design.*

WALL, Karen Malinda
Reidsville Sr HS; Reidsville, NC (2-324) AFS; Chldr; Fr C; Hmrm; InterClub Coun; Math C; Ed, Sch P; VP, SC; Cpt, Bkbl; Sftbl; Tnns; NEDT; Sci A; Yth Fel; St Sci Symp; NC Writing A; Marshal; *Pre-Med.*

WALL, Karla Stephanie
Alfred E Beach HS; Savannah, GA; BC; Lat C; Lat NHS; Mu Alpha Theta; Tres, NHS; COM; Hist A; 7th Pl, Hist Contest; Lat A; Eng A; Achieve Cert, Orginality Plus Lit; *Armstrong St Col; Pre-Math.*

WALL, Karren Marie
Sebastopol Attendance Center; Sebastopol, MS; BC; FHA; SC; Var C; VP, Jr Cl; S-T, Soph Cl; Bkbl; Bio A; HCt; Eng, Home Ec, A's; *E Central Jr Col; Cosmetology.*

WALL, Rama Lorraine
Great Bridge HS; Chesapeake, VA (95-575) Chor; Ensm; Yth Fel; Chor Cert; *Tidewater Comm Col.*

WALL, Rebecca Lee
Plano Sr HS; Plano, TX (25%-1300) Bus C; FBLA; SC; Pres A; Type A; Drill Tm; OEA; *Abilene Christian U; Bus.*

WALL, Royce Womble
Farmerville HS; Farmerville, LA; BS; F-Ed, Sch P; Cr-Ctry; Co-Cpt, Ftbl; Tr; *LSU; Mech Engr.*

WALL, Samuel Leigh
Eastern Guilford HS; Gibsonville, NC (1-175) Band; S-T, Chess C; Fr C; French NHS; NHS; Sci C; WW; *Duke U; Med.*

WALL, Teresa Ann
W Mid-High Sch; Norman, OK (5%-420) Chor; Ensm; VP, Fr C; NHS; Rainbow; Amer Leg A; Math A; Most Out; Jr NHS; Church Choir A; Handbell Choir; *U of Okla; Law.*

WALL, Teresa Lynn
Baker HS; Baker, LA; BC; Fr C; Rptr, Sch P; Tri-HiY; Hist A; *LSU; Psych.*

WALL, Terry Michelle
Central HS; Macon, GA (1-500) Band; BC; Ensm; French NHS; COM; Chor Pianist; Solo Twirler, Mjrte.

WALL, Timothy O'Dell
Palmer HS; Palmer, TX (1-40) Bus Mgr, Ann; FFA; Tres, Soph Cl; Bsbl; Ftbl; Tr; Alg A; Citz A; Math A; Sliderule Quarter Fin; *U of Tex; Computer Sci.*

WALL, Woodrow Anderson
Reidsville Sr HS; Reidsville, NC (19-344) BS; Monogram; Order/Arrow; Sch P; Span C; Pres, Jr Cl; Bsbl; Bkbl; Ftbl; God & Country A; Hon Prog; Most Out; Order/Arrow A; Rotary A; *Elon Col; Phys Ed.*

WALLACE, Anne Louise
Moline Sr HS; Moline, IL; Chor; Community Yth Symph; Fr C; NFL; Orch; Sci C; VP, Soph Cl; Bsbl; H of F; Spch A; Orch A; *Western Ill Col; Special Ed.*

WALLACE, Carol Ann
Dawson Co HS; Dawsonville, GA; Ann; Drama; Rptr, FBLA; 4H; Secy, SC; Mgr, Bkbl; Cl Fav; HCt; Ath C; *N Ga Col.*

WALLACE, Carolyn Marie
James Ford Rhodes HS; Cleveland, OH; Hon Prog; Outdoors C; *Lang.*

WALLACE, Charles Lee
Ross S Sterling HS; Baytown, TX (50-500) NHS; *Lamar U; Civil Engr.*

WALLACE, Colleen Anne
Napa HS; Napa, CA (150-500) F-Ed, Ann; Community Yth Symph; Ensm; HiY; InterAct C; Key C; Orch; *Pacific Union Col; Mus.*

WALLACE, Cynthia Jean
Princess Anne HS; Virginia Beach, VA (55-500) Ann; FBLA; Ger C; COM; Type A; Piano A; *Old Dominion U; Ger.*

WALLACE, Cynthia Rogene
Chapman HS; Inman, SC (25-140) FHA; Sch P; Beauty; VICA C; Young Life C; Church Jr Choir; *Spartanburg Methodist Col; Social Worker.*

WALLACE, Daniel Brian
Uniontown HS; Uniontown, PA; *Auto Mech.*

WALLACE, David Michael
R B Stall HS; Charleston, SC; Band; Fr C; Bsbl; Co-Cpt, Ftbl; Tr; Royal Ambassadors; *NC St U; Sci.*

WALLACE, Deborah Lynn
Pompano Beach Sr HS; Pompano Beach, FL; Band; Shorthand A; *Broward Comm Col; Fashion & Design.*

WALLACE, Donna Elizabeth
York Comp HS; York, SC (17-240) Band; S-T, Fr C; Ch, Hmrm; Cpt, Mjrte; Secy, NHS; SC; S-T, Soph Cl; HCt; Hon Prog; Outst Mjrte As; Sr Twirling A; Jr Marshal; WW; *Winthrop Col; Sociology.*

WALLACE, Eric Charles
Columbus E HS; Columbus, OH (75-300) Band; Orch; Cpt; Golf; COM; MVP, Cpt, Golf.

WALLACE, Frank Nelson
Bowman HS; Wadesboro, NC; Band; Ftbl; Yth Fel; *Elon Col; Phys Ed.*

WALLACE, Freda Gail
Gosnell HS; Blytheville, AR (6-94) Pres, A Cap Choir; Secy, BC; Chor; Ensm; Secy, Fr C; Madrigal; NHS, Secy, SC; Secy, Sr Cl; Secy, Jr Cl; Secy, Soph Cl; Hon Prog; *Union U; Mus Ed.*

WALLACE, Glenda Victoria
Manual HS; Denver, CO; FBLA; *Colo St U; Mus Therapy.*

WALLACE, Jack Lorence
Bryan Adams HS; Dallas, TX; Co-Cpt, Band; Chor; Mgr, Sch P; Bsbl; Bkbl; Soccer; Dallas Mus Ed Assn Gold Pin; Section Ldr Pin, Band; Dist 1st Pl Project, VICA; St 2nd Pl Project, VICA; *Plastics.*

WALLACE, Jackie Denise
Monroe HS; Albany, GA (25-329) Band; Secy, Chldr; Hmrm; Mjrte; SC; Tri-HiY; Tr; COM; Citz A; 4H A; *U of Ga; Med.*

WALLACE, Joseph Daniel Jr
Shelby Sr HS; Shelby, NC (115-324) A-Ed, Sch P; *U of NC; Bus.*

WALLACE, Julie Duerson
Jonesboro Sr HS; Jonesboro, GA (10%-350) Band; Fr C; *U of Ga; Journ.*

WALLACE, Karen Kay
Adolpho Camarillo HS; Camarillo, CA (5-600) AFS; Community Yth Symph; Ger C; NHS; Sci C; JV, Sftbl; Amer Leg A; CSF; COM; Ntl Sci Found; VP, Explorers; Vlbl; *Central Col; Pre-Med.*

WALLACE, Kristi Ann
Spirit Lake Comm HS; Spirit Lake, IA (16-110) Chldr; Pres, 4H; Span C; Mgr, Tr; 4H A; Yth Fel; Rptr, 4-H C; *Iowa St U; Home Ec.*

WALLACE, Lee Anne
Springville HS; Springville, AL (10%-55) Ann; BC; Co-Cpt, Chldr; Chor; NHS; Rainbow; Co-Ed, Sch P; Spch C; Var C; Beauty; Hon Prog; Math A; Yth Fel; *Sou Inst; Interior Design.*

WALLACE, Lisa Anne
Franklin Co HS; Frankfort, KY (20%-300) Ann; BC; Lat C; Secy, Lat NHS; Mu Alpha Theta; Co-Ed, Sch P; Sci C; Span C; Span NHS; SC; Swim; COM; Elk A; Journ A; Rep, Soph, Jr, Sr Cl; Cert of Merit, Span Semi Finals; Head Writer, Sch TV Show; Asst Producer, Sch TV Show; *E Ky U; Pol Sci.*

WALLACE, Lisa Kaye
Columbine HS; Littleton, CO (35-500) A Cap Choir; Chor; Fr C; Ski C; Sftbl; Mission Preparation; Yth Leader; *Lubbock Christian Col; Med.*

WALLACE, Mary Ellen
Robert A Taft Sr HS; Cincinnati, OH (5-192) Ann; Hmrm; NHS; SC; Var C; Tres, Sr Cl; Tres, Jr Cl; Tnns; Citz A; Cl Fav; Delta Sigma Theta A; HQrn; MLS; Women Alliance A; Acct-A; Tres A; McCall's Schol; *Xavier U; Acct.*

WALLACE, Michael Wayne
Lincoln HS; Dallas, TX; Span C; Pres A; ROTC A; Pres, Woods & Waters.

WALLACE, Nancy Jo
East HS; Columbus, OH (7-300) Band; Co-Cpt, Chldr; GS; Orch; COM; WW; *Drama.*

WALLACE, O'Neal Richard
Chapman HS; Inman, SC (4-127) Ann; BC; Fr C; French NHS; Span C; Span NHS; COM; Hon Prog; Presbyterian Schol; Benjamin Wofford Schol; Newberry Schol; Span-F A.

WALLACE, Renee Elizabeth
Warren Co Sr HS; McMinnville, TN (13-412) Co-Cpt, Band; Fr C; GS; InterAct C; Lat C; Sci C; Sftbl; Pom Pom Girl; 1st Pl, Freedom Documents Essay.

WALLACE, Richard Darrell
Hillside HS; Durham, NC (11-375) Arch; Lat C; Lat NHS; NHS; Cpt; Cr-Ctry; Cpt; Tnns; Alg A; COM; Math A; Sci A; Star Student; Lat A; *Duke U; Law.*

WALLACE, Richard Neil
Mt Vernon Township HS; Mt Vernon, IL (41-417) Band; BS; NHS; WW; *Kaskaskia Col; Data Processing.*

WALLACE, Rita Jane
Waverly HS; Waverly, OH (10-165) Pres, Band; Fr C; 4H; NHS; Rptr, Sch P; Tr; 4H A; Most Out; Mus As; WW; All-Ohio St Fair Band.

WALLACE, Sheryl Ann
Kent-Meridian HS; Kent, WA (33%-540) Span C; Citz A; Most Out; ARC A; Wrest Swthts; Ral Board; Soph Steering Comm; *Northwest Col.*

WALLACE, Stanley Thomas
Tuscaloosa HS; Tuscaloosa, AL (200-350) Mgr, Bkbl; Mgr, Ftbl; Sftbl; *Shelton St Tech Col; Commercial Art.*

WALLACE, Stephanie Lynn
Pompano Beach HS; Pompano Beach, FL;

WALLACE, Steven Lee
Bangor Area Sr HS; Bangor, PA; SC; Var C; Ftbl; Mgr, Tr; JV, Wrest; Type A; *Sports.*

WALLACE, Tammy Sue
Kubasaki HS; Okinawa, JAPAN (15-271) BC; Mjrte; NHS; A-Ed, Sch P; Secy, SC; Secy, Soph Cl; Journ A; Cert of Merit, Home Ec; Cert of Merit, Phys Ed; HR; *U of Va; Elem Ed.*

WALLACE, Tara Tamara
East HS; Columbus, OH (5-350) NHS; Span NHS; Hon Prog; Fresh Found Schol; *Ohio St U; Elec Eng.*

WALLACE, Theodore
Harding HS; Charlotte, NC; Band; Tr; *UNC-CH; Med.*

WALLACE, Timothy Ford
Chickasaw Acad; Prichard, AL; Ensm; Key C; Pres, SC; COM; HCt; Math A; Yth Appreciation.

WALLACE, Vicki Sue
Springhill HS; Springhill, LA; Band; *La Tech U; Interior Decorator.*

WALLACH, Cooper Bentley
Mission HS; Mission, TX (67-375) Pres, Key C; Co-Cpt, Golf; Cl Fav; *U of Tex; Bus.*

WALLAR, Mark Wayne
Munster HS; Munster, IN (182-410) Var C; Bsbl; Hockey; Tnns; *Edison Comm Col; Bus.*

WALLENHORST, Linda Lee
Our Lady of Angels; St Bernard, OH (8-136) Bus C; NHS; COM; Hon Prog; Highest Scholastic Avg.

WALLENMEYER, Patricia Loreen
McMinnville HS; McMinnville, OR (5-235) Ed, Ann; Band; Ensm; Ger C; Semi-Fin, GS; Key C; NHS; JV, Bkbl; JV, Tnns; Amer Leg A; Kiwanis A; Poet A; WW Among Mus Stu in Amer HS; Rotana Schol; Pres Hon at Entrance, Pacific U.

WALLER, David Anthony
Saint Augustine HS; New Orleans, LA (10-35) Server, Religion, A's; *Xaiver U; Bus Adm.*

WALLER, David Richard
Chicopee HS; Chicopee, MA (25-400) Hmrm; NHS; Tnns; *Holyoke Comm Col; Acct.*

WALLER, Gwendolyn Rae
Post Falls HS; Post Falls, ID (7-154) Dbte Tm; FHA; Pres, 4H; Hmrm; SC; COM; 4H A; Hon Prog; Yth Fel; *N Idaho Col; Math.*

WALLER, Laura Diane
George Wythe HS; Wytheville, VA (72-137) Chor; Tr; *Wythe Comm Col.*

WALLER, Lori Marcella
Grand Blanc HS; Grand Blanc, MI (60-600) Band; NHS; Sci C; COM; GSct; Church Bkbl; Mich Schol; *Anderson Col; Nurs.*

WALLER, Mark Wayne
Munster HS; Munster, IN (185-410) Var C; Bsbl; Hockey; Tnns; *Edison Comm Col; Bus.*

WALLER, Mary Ester
E Atlanta HS; Atlanta, GA (14-142) BC; Chor; Hmrm; SC; HCt; Chor A; *Atlanta Area Tech Sch; Computer Data Process.*

WALLER, Rachel Lynn
Emerson HS; Emerson, AR (4-30) Pres, FBLA; VP, FHA; GS; Mgr, Bkbl; Tr; COM; Citz A; Most Courteous; Most Stu; Eng, Bus, A's; *Sou Ark U; Bus.*

WALLER, Rickey James
Zwolle HS; Zwolle, LA; Band; MVP, Bsbl; MVP, Tr; Bands A; *Northwestern U; Mus.*

WALLER, Wendelyn Faye
Joelton HS; Joelton, TN; Ann; Secy, BC; Cpt, Chldr; S-T, SC; VP, Jr Cl; VP, Soph Cl; HCt.

WALLIN, John Edward
Tishomingo HS; Tishomingo, MS (5-52) Rptr, BC; Chor; Pres, 4H; Ed, Sch P; Bkbl; Ftbl; Most Outst 4-Her; Drivers Ed A; *US Air Force Acad; Law.*

WALLIN, Julie Kay
Lyons Township HS; LaGrange, IL (93%-1100) A Cap Choir; Chor; Ensm; COM; Citz A; *St Olaf Col; Biol.*

WALLIN, William Robert
Stillwater HS; Stillwater, MN (330-612) A Cap Choir; Chor; Ensm; Madrigal; Hockey; *Berkley Col of Mus; Piano.*

WALLINTIN, James Michael
Randolph HS; Randolph, WI (49-54) CYO; FFA; NHS; Alt, Badger Boy; *U of Wis; Engr.*

WALLISCH, Mary Ellen
Incarnate Word HS; Normandy, MO (17-91) CYO; Drama; Lat C; SC; Pres, Jr Cl; Sftbl; Amer Leg Orator A; NEDT; *Cardinal Newman Col; Bus.*

WALLS, Andrew Dale
North HS; Bakersfield, CA (8-500) Band; Chess C; Pres, Dbte Tm; Math C; Model UN; Pres, NFL; Pres, Spch C; JV, Bsbl; Bank Of Amer A; CSF; Spch A; VFW Orator Win; VofDEM; Mus As; Pres Hon Attendance; *U of Calif at Santa Barbara; Engr.*

WALLS, Barbara Kay
Ulysses HS; Ulysses, KS; Band; Y-Tns.

WALLS, Cynthia Peterson
Clinton HS; Clinton, NC (3-180) F-Ed, Ann; Band; BC; Chor; Monogram; Bio A; Gov Honor Prog; Math A; NMS; Most Outst Chor Stu; WW; Exec Comm, Beta C; Mistress, Band Concert; *Johnson C Smith Col; Psych.*

WALLS, Deborah Faye
Wade Hampton HS; Greenville, SC; NHS; Span C; Span NHS; Var C; Co-Cpt, Tnns; Gr Marshal; *U of Ga; Banking.*

WALLS, Greg Glenn
Wade Hampton HS; Greenville, SC (8-373) Pres, Hmrm; NHS; Order/Arrow; Span C; Bkbl; God & Country A; Hist A; Eagle Sct A; *Clemson U; Bus Adm.*

WALLS, Laura Elizabeth
Glenbrook N HS; Northbrook, IL; A Cap Choir; Band; Chor; Hmrm; Key C; Lit Mag; Sch P; Ski C; Swim; Beauty; COM; Hon Prog; Most Out; Pres A; Yth Fel.

WALLS, Sylvia Lynn
Franklin Co HS; Winchester, TN; FHA; Bronze & Silver A, Marketing.

WALLUS, Lisa Anne
Kalamazoo Central HS; Kalamazoo, MI (20-532) Band; Dbte Tm; FNA; NFL; ARC; Co-Ed, Sch P; SC; Band A; Coun On Missions; HR; Radio Contest A; Choir; Coun of Ministries; Adm Board Yth Rep; *Psych.*

WALLUS, Susan Ellyn
Kalamazoo Christian HS; Kalamazoo, MI (20-320) A Cap Choir; Chor; ARC; Sch P; Ski C; SC; Concert Choir; ESAA Comm; Hmrm Rep, SAC Comm; Worship Comm; St Solo Ensm; Yth Ldrship Camp; Art C; UN & Wash Seminars; *Ministry.*

WALMA, Catherine Elizabeth
Spring Lake Sr HS; Springlake, MI (1-200) Ann; GS; VP, NHS; Tres, Ski C; VP, Jr Cl; Tres, Soph Cl; Tnns; Tr; Amer Leg A; COM; DARGCA; HCt; MLS; Pres A; Regent Schol; Sci A; Val; Outst Sr, Piano, Tr, A's; Conf Tnns Champ; *Mich Tech U; Engr.*

WALPOLE, Nancy Elizabeth
Gainesville HS; Gainesville, GA (4-203) Ann; BC; Span C; Tres, Thes; Secy, Sr Cl; COM; Col Trustee Merit Schol; Acad Letter; *Converse Col.*

**WALRATH,
Catherine O Donnell**
Wellsboro Area Sr HS; Wellsboro, PA (15-205)
AFS; CYO; Fr C; NHS; SC; Var C; Cpt, Bkbl;
COM; NEDT; ARC A; VofDEM; Eng A; Ntl A for
Excellence; WW; *Dickinson Col; Eng.*

WALRATH, Eva Lynn
Wylie Sr HS; Wylie, TX; FHA; Span C.

WALRATH, Lorrie Dawn
Orofino HS; Orofino, ID (18-97) Ed, Ann; VP,
CYO; Pres, Chor; Dbte Tm; Ensm; GS; Secy, 4H;
Sch P; Spch C; SC; Bkbl; Golf; Swim; 4H A; Vof-
DEM; Past Hon Qn, Jobs Daughters; Best of Festi-
val Mus A; Win, Elks Hoop Shoot; *Mus.*

WALSDORF, Kimberly Ruth
Haines City Sr HS; Haines City, FL; Lat C; NHS;
VP, Rainbow; COM; *U of S Fla; Commercial Art.*

WALSER, Cheryl Marie
Enid HS; Enid, OK (33-540) Rptr, Band; Ensm;
Secy, FHA; Rptr, FTA; NHS; Orch; Span C; Secy,
SC; COM; NHS Schol; St Hon Soc; Outst Bandsman
A; *Westminster Col; Ed.*

WALSH, Edward Stephen
Archmere Acad; Claymont, DE; Ger C; Sci C;
Drexel U; Math.

WALSH, Eileen Marie
Mercy HS; Albany, NY (18-108) Pres, CYO;
Chldr; Fr C; Tres, 4H; Hmrm; NHS; Bkbl; Swim;
4H A; *Hudson Valley Comm Col; Sci.*

WALSH, James Francis
N Shore Sr HS; W Palm Beach, FL (9-266) Ann;
Band; Drama; Fr C; Hmrm; InterClub Coun; Secy,
NHS; Sch P; Tnns; COM; Journ A; Acad Letter;
Photography.

WALSH, James Harold
Thomas L Grace HS; Fridley, MN (93-230) Fr C;
Lit Mag; VP, SC; VP, Sr Cl; Ch, Jr Cl; Ch, Soph Cl;
Bsbl; Golf; COM; VFW A; Outst Service A; 'Un-
sung Sr' A; *Col of St Thomas; Theology.*

WALSH, Kathleen Dawn
Burnt Hills-Ballston Lake Sr HS; Ballston Lake,
NY (35-400) Chor; Hmrm; Co-Ed, Sch P; Tres, Sr
Cl; Tres, Jr Cl; High Avg Medals; *Washington Bible
Col; Missions.*

WALSH, Kevin John
Marianapolis Prep Sch; Thompson, CT (14-28)
CYO; Secy, SC; Bsbl; Bkbl; Cr-Ctry; Soccer; *U of
RI; Oceanography.*

WALSH, Maureen L
N Shore HS; W Palm Beach, FL (13-336) Band;
Ensm; Fr C.

WALSH, Michael Lloyd
Gaylord HS; Gaylord, MN; Order/Arrow; Var C;
Bsbl; Ftbl; Tr; FCA; Most Improved Ftbl; Bob
Bandmir A, Mst Devoted Player; *Carpenter.*

WALSH, Scott Russell
Boro Hall Acad; Brooklyn, NY (3-17) CYO; Y-
Tns; Bsbl; NEDT; *City Col; Meteorology.*

WALSH, Susan Marie
Mount Mercy Acad; Buffalo, NY (9-220) Pres, Fr
C; Math C; NFL; NHS; F-Ed, Sch P; Bio A; Jr
Chamber of Com A; K of C A; NEDT; Q&S A;
Regent Schol; Sci A; NML; Fr, Lat, A's; 'It's Aca-
demic' Tm; Oceanography Summer Prog; *Hist.*

WALSH, Wendy Lee
Kingsway Regional HS; Swedesboro, NJ (21-166)
NHS; Tnns; Statistician, Bsbl; *Gloucester Co Col;
Legal Secy.*

WALSMAN, Emily Ann
Heritage Christian Sch; Indianapolis, IN (7-38)
Band; Co-Cpt, Chldr; Chor; Fr C; Ger C; Co-Ed,
Lit Mag; Secy, Sr Cl; Hockey; Math A; Ed, Yrbk;
Cpt, Vlbl; *Purdue U; Pre-Med.*

WALSTON, Sharon Louise
Lutheran HS; Burbank, CA; FBLA; Span C; CSF;
W Los Angeles Col; Dental Hygiene.

WALSTON, Trenia Carol
Rossville HS; Rossville, GA (7-212) COM; Star
Student; HS Schol; *Tenn Temple Col; Bible.*

WALTEMATH, Ross Edward
Bishop Luers HS; Fort Wayne, IN (25%-220)
Drama; Ftbl; St Scholar; Coach, CYO; Amateur
Pro, Soccer; Prom Court; *St Francis Col; Bus.*

WALTENBAUGH, Bonnie Carol
Freeport Area HS; Freeport, PA (33%-200) Chor;
Ensm; Fr C; Pres, Hmrm; SC; Candystriper; Blue &
Gold; Co Chor.

WALTER, Charles Dale
Harrisburg HS; Harrisburg, IL (5-195) Chess C;
Chor; Pres, 4H; Key C; Var C; Cr-Ctry; Tr; Wrest;
4H A; I Dare You; *Engr.*

WALTER, Cindy Ann
Attica HS; Attica, IN (75-98) Chor; Drama; Fr C;
FTA; 4H; Swim; Tr; Citz A; *Ind St Col; Nurs.*

WALTER, Gwendolyne Delorise
Fores And Brook Sr HS; Houston, TX (30-600)
Anchor C; Band; Chem C; Cum Laude Soc; Drama;
FBLA; Pres, FTA; Hmrm; Math C; NHS; Tres, Sci
C; Span C; SC; Up Bound; Pres, Sr Cl; Pres, Jr Cl;
VP, Soph Cl; Sftbl; Tnns; Bio A; COM; Cl Fav; H of
F; HCt; Hon Prog; Magna Cum Laude; MLS; Most
Out; PTA A; Pres A; Sci A; Type A; *Tex Sou Col;
Phar.*

WALTER, Herman David
Waynesboro Are Sr HS; Waynesboro, PA (5-342)
NHS; Ftbl; Tr; Citz A; *Penn St U; Mech Engr.*

WALTER, James Brett
Keokuk Sr HS; Keokuk, IA (10%-350) Bsbl; JV,
Bkbl; Ftbl; Tnns; COM; Citz A; Pres A; 3 Yr Hon's
A; Stu o-t Mo; *Med.*

WALTER, Jeffery George
S Central HS; Union Mills, IN (35-72) F-Ed, Ann;
Drama; Pres, Ger C; Ed, Sch P; Ski C; Spch C;
Thes; Secy, Soph Cl; Cl Fav; 4H A; HKg; HCt;
Spch A; Swthrt; Type A; VofDEM; Yth Fel; Valen-
tine Kg; Win, Oratorical; *Purdue U; Horticulture.*

WALTER, Jodi Evonne
Harrisburg HS; Harrisburg, IL (6-238) Chess C;
Chor; Ensm; FHA; Pres, 4H; Thes; JV, Bkbl; Sftbl;
Amer Leg A; DARGCA; 4H A; I Dare You.

WALTER, John A
Grove City HS; Grove City, PA (40%-240) Monogram; Sci C; Bsbl; Ftbl; Sftbl; Wrest; Sports A's.

WALTER, Linda Marie
McHenry Comm HS; McHenry, IL (4-557) Chor;
Fr C; Lit Mag; Amer Leg A; NHS; *Health Careers.*

WALTER, Mark Curtis
Salina HS S; Salina, KS (50-350) Chor; Drama;
Ensm; 4H; Hmrm; Lat C; ARC; Sci C; SC; Var C;
Ftbl; Swim; Tr; COM; 4H A; Yth Fel; Gym; Fed
Mus Hon; Driving Safety A; HR; Athletic As;
Horsemanship As; *US Air Force Acad; Sci.*

WALTER, Sandra Kay
Burke HS; Omaha, NE; JV, Chldr; Chor; Orch;
Pres A; Gym Tm; *UNO.*

WALTER, Sarah Louise
Guttenberg Comm HS; Guttenberg, IA (3-95) Ed,
Ann; Chor; Pres, FHA; Madrigal; Pres, NHS; Secy,
Jr Cl; HCt; Spch A; *St Lukes Col; Nurs.*

WALTER, Thomas Edward
Upper Merion Area HS; King of Prussia, PA
(104-540) Soccer; COM; Hon Prog; Cpt, Intramural Bkbl & Vlbl Tms; Academic A; HR; *Ursinus
Col; Math.*

WALTERS, Ann Barbara
Columbus Sr HS; Columbus, NE (25-250) Chldr;
Chor; Orch; Ed, Sch P; Bkbl; Tr; God & Country A;
Pres A; Job's Daughters; Vlbl; *U of Nebr; Bus.*

WALTERS, Brenda Sue
Keyes HS; Keyes, OK (4-14) Band; Chldr; VP,
NHS; Pres, SC; Bkbl; Tr; Cl Fav; I Dare You; Ma-
sonic A; Most Courteous; Most Talented; Home-
coming Princess; NRECA Essay Win; *Panhandle
St U; Med Tech.*

WALTERS, Carrie Ruth
Yorkwood Jr-Sr HS; Monmouth, IL; Band; Chldr;
Chor; Drama; FHA; Madrigal; Span C; Spch C; SC;
Bkbl; Tr; *Graham Nurs Col; Nurs.*

WALTERS, Cherie Marie
Delphos Jefferson HS; Delphos, OH (25-118)
Chor; Y-Tns; *Central Bible Col; Child Care.*

WALTERS, Douglas Dean
O'Neill Pub HS; O'Neill, NE (10-80) Ann; Chor;
NHS; Var C; Ftbl; JV, Golf; JV, Wrest.

WALTERS, Fred Siedleburg
Chamblee HS; Atlanta, GA; Order/Arrow; *Ga St
U; Bus Mgt.*

WALTERS, Gloria Agatha
Southview Acad; Wadesboro, NC (2-16) Chldr;
Drama; 4H; Pres, Hmrm; Monogram; SC; S-T,
Soph Cl; Sftbl; Alg A; Beauty; 4H A; HCt; Math A;
NEDT; Fin, Miss Interntl Tn USA Pageant; *Mere-
dith Col; Bio.*

WALTERS, Gregory Alan
Eldorado HS; Albuquerque, NM (67-818) CYO;
Ger C; Hmrm; Key C; NHS; Order/Arrow; Ski C;
Tr; Order/Arrow A; W Point Ldrship A; USAF
Acad Seminar Graduate; *US Air Force Acad;
Aerospace Engr.*

WALTERS, Gussie Mae
C O P E Center HS; Miami, FL; FHA; Sch P; Cl
Fav; Hist A.

WALTERS, Jon Regan
Mansfield Christian HS; Mansfield, OH (23-46)
Ensm; Bkbl; Ftbl; Mgr, Soccer; *N Central Tech
Col; Archt.*

WALTERS, Judith Ann
Marian HS; Tamaqua, PA (94-175) FNA; Hockey;
Tr; Hon Prog; *Allentown Col; Nurs.*

WALTERS, Lynda Berg
Patrick Henry Acad; Estill, SC (13-18) Ann; Cpt,
Chldr; Chor; GS; SC; Pres, Jr Cl; Cl Fav; HQn;
HCt; HQn Miss Patrick Henry Acad; *Lander Col;
Nurs.*

WALTERS, Melinda Hinton
Brookville HS; Brookville, OH (18-195) Band; Cpt,
Chldr; Chor; Drama; NHS; Var C; Pres A.

WALTERS, Peter Hudson
Webster Co HS; Providence, KY (33%-125) Var C;
Cpt, Ftbl; Cpt, Wrest; Most Out; MVP, Ftbl, Wrest;
Western Ky U; Religion.

WALTERS, Sandra Renee
Asheboro HS; Asheboro, NC (49-310) Chor;
Ensm; Monogram; Span C; Mgr, Bkbl; *W Carolina
U.*

WALTERS, Sylvia Jene
Ahrens HS; Louisville, KY; Ed, Ann; Hmrm; NHS;
SC; *U of Louisville; Bio.*

WALTERS, Tracy Jane
Arlington HS; Riverside, CA; Ann; Chldr; Campos
Crusade for Christ; Social Sci Achv A; *Social Stu.*

WALTERS, Virginia Anne
Garinger HS; Charlotte, NC (4-626) Chor; Ensm;
Ed, Lit Mag; Tres, NHS; Co-Ed, Sch P; COM;
Coun of Teach A; Gr Marshal; Hon Prog; Journ A;
Col Schol; *Wake Forest U; Eng.*

WALTHALL, Bonnie Rushell
El Dorado HS; El Dorado, AR; *Ouachita Baptist U;
Mus.*

WALTHER, Marcia Lynn
Monte Vista HS; Danville, CA (42-368) Pres,
Chor; VP, SC; CSF; *Calif Polytech St U; Construc-
tion Engr.*

WALTKE, Barbara Jean
Crestwood HS; Mountaintop, PA (6-215) Chor;
Secy, NHS; SC; Bsbl; Bkbl; Sftbl; *Houghton Col;
Math.*

WALTKE, Christa Lydia
Wallkill Sr HS; Wallkill, NY; *Sci.*

WALTKE, Cindy Lee
Wallkill Sr HS; Wallkill, NY; *Bus.*

WALTMAN, Michael Scott
Fayetteville HS; Fayetteville, AR (78-352) Dbte
Tm; NFL; NHS; Spch C; Tnns; Spch A; Athletic
Cert; *U of Ark; Law.*

WALTON, Barbara Jane
Salem HS; Salem, IN (25%-180) All Amer Yth;
MVP, Band; Bus C; Chor; Drama; FHA; Pres, 4H;
NHS; Ntl Yth Conf; Spch C; VP, Tri-HiY; Beauty;
4H A; Hon Prog; JA A; Kiwanis A; Lion A; Yth
Fel; 4-H St Choir; *Ivy Tech; Data Processing.*

WALTON, Brenda Joyce
Horace Mann HS; Gary, IN; Band; Fr C; GS; NHS;
SC; Tres, Jr Cl; COM; Eng A; Cl Offices; *Ind
Northwest U; Bus Adm.*

WALTON, Cheryl Anita
Williamson HS; Mobile, AL; Ann; Chor; Sch P;
PA.

WALTON, Cindy Claire
DeForest HS; DeForest, WI; Rptr, Fr C; Co-Cpt, Math C; Co-Cpt, Swim; Fin, MVP, Swim.

WALTON, Cindy Jean
St Francis HS; St Francis, MN (22-165) Ann; Bus C; Chor; Ensm; 4H; NHS; Sch P; Secy, SC; Mgr, Bsbl; Mgr, Bkbl; Type A; Steno A; Bus A; *Anoka Ramsey Col; Secy.*

WALTON, David Brian
St Francis HS; St Francis, MN; MVP, Bsbl; MVP, Ftbl; Co-Cpt, Ftbl.

WALTON, Debra Lynell
John F Kennedy HS; Richmond, VA (40-114) Drama; Fr C; Rptr, Hmrm; Math C; ARC; SC; Citz A; ARC A; Sci A; Chaplain, Sr Cl; Source of Life Mission; March of Dimes; Service Aid; *Madison Col; Med.*

WALTON, Endia Patrice
Our Lady of Victory Acad; Dobbs Ferry, NY (124-176) Bus C; CYO; Chem C; Chor; Dbte Tm; Drama; Lit Mag; Sci C; Span C; SC; Bkbl; Sftbl; Tnns; Tr; COM; Sci A; 1st Cl GSct; *Drew U; Social Sci.*

WALTON, Erica Regina
Haynesville HS; Haynesville, LA; Bus C; Chor; FBLA; Rptr, FHA; Hmrm; F-Ed, Sch P; SC; Cl Fav; HCt; Hon Prog; *Tex Sou U; Data Processing.*

WALTON, Gary Dale Jr
Harrison HS; Colorado Springs, CO; Var C; VP, Jr Cl; Bkbl; Ftbl; Amer Leg A; Pres A.

WALTON, Joan Oline
Scott Preparatory HS; Opelika, AL (10%-29) Anchor C; Secy, BC; Pres, 4H; Pres, SC; S-T, Jr Cl; Bkbl; 4H A; NEDT; VofDEM; *Auburn U; Agr Journ.*

WALTON, Joel Price
Dupont Sr HS; Hermitage, TN; FTA; Hist A; *Cumberland Comm St Col; Hist.*

WALTON, Joy Romette
Walnut Hills HS; Cincinnati, OH; Pep C; Drill Tm; *Art.*

WALTON, Judith Marie
John Bowne HS; Flushing, NY (20%-900) Chor; Drama; FFA; Span C; SC; Tr; Hon Prog; Type A; Speedwriting A; Church School Fund; Benjmn S Chancey Cit of Hon, Mus; *Bennett Col; Mus.*

WALTON, Kevin Craig
Oscoda Area HS; Oscoda, MI; Chor; VP, Soph Cl; Ftbl; Cpt, Wrest; Wrest Ltr; Ftbl Ltr; Dist & Regional Qualifier, Wrest; *Central Mich U; Elem Ed.*

WALTON, Lillian Ann
Mineral Wells HS; Mineral Wells, TX (90-225) Drama; FHA; FTA; Tres, Church Yth Group; *Oral Roberts U; Sci.*

WALTON, Martha Frances
Crossett HS; Crossett, AR (6-248) BC; Lit Mag; Mu Alpha Theta; NHS; Rptr, Sch P; Mgr, Bkbl; NEDT; Girl's Service C; GSct; *U of Ark; Nurs.*

WALTON, Mary Zealy Willingham
Thornwell HS; Clinton, SC; Ann; BC; Cpt, Chldr; GS; Jr Miss Pagent; Cpt, Bkbl; Sftbl; HCt; Yth Fel; Co-Cpt, Chldr; MVP, Bkbl; *W Carolina U; Phys Ed.*

WALTON, Myra Gail
Lincoln HS; Jersey City, NJ (176-287) Mjrte; Bsbl; Tr; *Rutgers Col; Nurs.*

WALTON, Penelope Debree
Woodlawn HS; Birmingham, AL; *UAB; Dental Asst.*

WALTON, Robert Bruce
Oscoda HS; Oscoda, MI; Chor; ARC; Cr-Cctry; Cpt, Swim; COM; ARC A; MVP, Swim; Record Holder, Swim; St Qualifier, Swim; *Mich St U; Chem.*

WALTON, Skip Mark
Lynnwood Sr HS; Lynnwood, WA (18-400) Dbte Tm; Hmrm; NHS; Spch C; Most Out; 1st Pl, Reg & Ntl Vocal Comp; *Moody Bible Inst; Christian Ed.*

WALTON, Susan Leigh
Upper Merion Sr HS; King of Prussia, PA (32-520) Chor; Hmrm; NHS; Var C; Hon Prog; Gym; Most Improved Player; Acad A; *Drew U; Bus.*

WALTON, Theresa Gayle
Union HS; Union, MS (10%-50) F-Ed, Ann; S-T, BC; S-T, Drama; FHA; GS; Hmrm; Jr Miss Pagent; S-T, SC; VP, Jr Cl; COM; MLS; Most Courteous; *E Central Jr Col.*

WALTON, Veronica Ann
Martin Luther King HS; Philadelphia, PA (245-698) Bus C; Commercial C; Dbte Tm; Hmrm; Sch P; Hockey; Soccer; Tnns; *Cheyney St Col; Bus Ed.*

WALTON, Yevonne Faye
W A Berry HS; Birmingham, AL; Band; Ensm; Mjrte; Thes; COM; Sci A; Art A.

WALTRIP, Elizabeth Ann
Plano Sr HS; Plano, TX (30-850) Band; FBLA; Secy, Ger C; NHS; Type A; *N Tex St U; Bus.*

WALTRIP, Melissa LeAnn
Plano Sr HS; Plano, TX (5%-1000) Band; FBLA; NHS; COM; St Shorthand C; *N Tex St U; Bus.*

WALTZ, Debra Marie
Morton W HS; Berwyn, IL (23-732) A Cap Choir; Chldr; Chor; Fin, Jr Miss Pagent; Mjrte; NHS; Span C; Bkbl; Pres A; Trophies & Ribbons, Baton Twirling; 1st Pl, Chldr Competition; Golden HR & Scroll Cards; *Triton Col; Radiology.*

WALTZ, Kent Arliss
Bedford N Lawrence HS; Bedford, IN (48-409) BC; Semi-Fin, BS; Chess C; Math C; NHS; Order/Arrow; Soccer; Swim; Math A; *Elec.*

WALTZ, Randall Robert
Sierra Joint Union HS; Tollhouse, CA (86-250) Pres, Band; Ensm; Math C; NHS; Mgr, Wrest; CSF; Math A; *Fresno City Col; Elec Engr.*

WALTZ, Steven Layne
Little Rock Central HS; Little Rock, AR (2-576) BC; Chess C; Cum Laude Soc; Key C; Mu Alpha Theta; NHS; Tnns; Alg A; Bausch & Lomb A; Hon Prog; Math A; NEDT; Poet A; Lang A; KLRA Outst Yth; *Computer Sci.*

WALTZ, Susan Mary
Arlington Sr HS; Poughkeepsie, NY (80-750) Chor; Drama; Span C; Soccer; Sftbl; Yth Fel; Pres, VP, Secy, Church Yth; Mid-Hudson Opera Company; *Lang.*

WALTZ, Theresa Grace
Heritage Christian HS; Indianapolis, IN; Secy, Band; Chor; Lit Mag; Orch; Bkbl; Tr; Bkbl As; *Grace Bible Col; Elem Ed.*

WALVOORD, Kyla Kay
Norris District 160 HS; Firth, NE (2-91) Band; Tres, Bus C; Chor; Tres, FBLA; FNA; GS; Pres, 4H; NHS; Ed, Sch P; Sftbl; COM; DARGCA; 4H A; Math A; Pres A; Sal; Type A; *Med.*

WALZ, Donna Rae
Wakonda HS; Wakonda, SD (6-17) Ann; Band; Cpt, Chldr; Ensm; Pres, FHA; Secy, GS; NHS; Orch; SC; 4H A; Mus A; *SD St U; Home Ec.*

WAMACK, James Howell Jr
Vestavia Hills HS; Vestavia Hills, AL (1-280) Band; Ensm; VP, Key C; Math C; NHS; All-St Jazz Ensm; *Harding Col; Engr.*

WAMBO, Barbara Jane
Richmond Sr HS; Richmond, IN (25-731) Band; Rainbow; Sci A; Jr NHS; Spelling A; *Phar.*

WAMBOLDT, Carol Anne
Normal Comm HS; Normal, IL (1-484) F-Ed, Ann; Band; Secy, Mu Alpha Theta; Q&S A; ROTC A; Hon Prog; Spch A; Stu Ambsdr, People to People Prgm; Pep Band; Marching Band; Alpha Delta Tau Hon Soc; Drill Tm.

WAMPLER, Katherine Jean
Canencro HS; Lafayette, LA (5%-180) VP, Math C; NHS; JV, Bkbl; Key C Swtht; *Tex A&M U; Corrective Therapy.*

WANDLING, William Edward II
Sissonville HS; Charleston, WV (25%-202) MVP, Band; VP, Chess C; Chor; Fr C; Rptr, Sch P; Thes; Golf; Tnns; Most Out; Bible C; Drum Major; Boy Twirler; Bowl Tm; All Co Chor & Band; Pres, Audio-Visuals; Best Supporting Actor; *Alderson-Broaddus Col; Mus Ed.*

WANDTKE, Mary Patricia
Little Wolf HS; Mawawa, WI (23-83) Band; CYO; JV, Chldr; Drama; Ensm; FHA; Hmrm; NFL; Rptr, Sch P; Span C; SC; Secy, Jr Cl; Tres, Soph Cl; Sftbl; Tnns; Journ A; Band As; Forensics A; Pep C A; *Univ of Wisc; Fashion Design.*

WANER, Terry Ann
Permian HS; Odessa, TX (169-618) NHS; *Ed.*

WANG, Andy
John F Kennedy HS; Tumon, GUAM; NHS; Alg A; Hist A; Math A; *Rice U; Biochemistry.*

WANG, Annie
John F Kennedy HS; Tumuning, GUAM (1-511) Chor; NHS; Rainbow; Pres, Chinese C; Chor A; HR; Hon Choir; *Pepperdine U; Engr.*

WANG, Lucy Hsiao Tsing
David Douglas HS; Portland, OR; Ger C; COM; *U of Oreg; Med.*

WANG, Margaret Ming-Sen
Saint Mary's HS; Stockton, CA (2-204) CYO; FTA; A-Ed, Lit Mag; Model UN; NHS; CSF; Hon Prog; Math A; Ntl Sci Found; NEDT; Fr, Bank of Amer Cert, A's; 1st Pl, Math Field Day; NML; *Stanford U; Med.*

WANN, Kathy Jane
Howe HS; Howe, OK; Ed, Ann; VP, FHA; Pres, Sr Cl; VP, Jr Cl; VP, Soph Cl; Cpt, Bkbl; Sftbl; Cl Fav; HCt; FFA Swtht; *Carl Albert Jr Col.*

WANNER, William Leo
Regis HS; Stayton, OR (18-56) BS; Chem C; Drama; Math C; NHS; Sci C; Pres, SC; Var C; Pres, Jr Cl; Ftbl; Tr; *U of Portland; Ed.*

WANSLEY, Timmie Metoyer
Flint Sw HS; Flint, MI; Chor; Hon Prog; Yth Fel; *UCLA; Computer Tech.*

WANTZ, Greg Scott
Temple Christian Sch; Ventura, CA; A-Ed, Ann; F-Ed, Sch P; Co-Cpt, Bkbl; Cpt, Soccer; *U of Calif; Aviation.*

WARBINGTON, James Doby Jr
Vienna HS; Vienna, GA; Dbte Tm; Rptr, FFA; 4H; Sci C; Bsbl; Ftbl; COM; HCt; Hon Prog; NEDT; Yth Foundation; Yth Foundation A; FFA A'S; Hugh O'Brien Yth Found; Natural Resources Conserv Workshop; Ntl FFA Convention; *Agr.*

WARD, Andrea Gayle
Lutheran HS; Burbank, CA; Band; Chor; Key C; NHS; Orch; Span C; Tres, Jr Cl; Secy, Soph Cl; Bkbl; Cpt, Cr-Cctry; Cpt, Tr; Sr Rep, SC; *Sci.*

WARD, Angela Gayle
Monticello HS; Monticello, MS; Secy, Bus C; Secy, FHA; A-Ed, Sch P; Sftbl; Hon Prog; *Co-Lin Jr Col; Acct.*

WARD, Barbara Carol
Centerville HS; Centerville, OH (196-616) Pres, Chor; Span C; World Affairs C; Cinders, Statistician, Tr Tm; Outst Acct A; *Cumberland Col; Acct.*

WARD, Carole Verlita
E Atlanta HS; Atlanta, GA (7-175) BC; Hmrm; Sch P; SC; ROTC A; C Qn; HR; *Clarks Col; Mass Communication.*

WARD, Charles Galloway
Eupora HS; Eupora, MS (12-120) BC; Dbte Tm; VP, SC; Bsbl; Tr; COM; Cl Fav; Yth Fel; *Miss St U; Acct.*

WARD, Cynthia Jo
Washington HS; Cedar Rapids, IA (205-533) Band; ARC; JV, Bkbl; JV, Tr; Hon Prog; ARC A; Yth Fel; *U of Iowa; Ed.*

WARD, Dale Brian
Lutheran HS S; St Louis, MO (70-182) Band; Chor; Drama; VP, Jr Cl; JV, Bsbl; JV, Bkbl; JV, Ftbl; Sftbl; Cert of Participation; *Southern California Col; Film.*

WARD, David Benjamin
Independence HS; Independence, MS (15%-106) BC; Bsbl; *U of Miss; Communication.*

WARD, Debbie Faye
Adairsville HS; Adairsville, GA (2-100) Ann; Band; FHA; JA A; *U of Ga; Interior Decorating.*

WARD, Debra Kay
Mesa Verde HS; Citrus Heights, CA (3-228) Hmrm; Secy, SC; Sftbl; COM; Elk A; Hist A; Hon Prog; Most Out; Stu o-t Mon A; Recreation Entertainment A; *Psych.*

WARD, Desiree Rose
W Columbus HS; Cerro Gordo, NC (10-209) BC; Fr C; FHA; *Mars Hill Col; Psych.*

WARD, Diane Marie
William A Wirt HS; Gary, IN (10%-225) Chess C; Math C; NHS; Pres, Sci C; Span C; Sftbl; Hon Prog; *NW Ind U; Microbiol.*

WARD, Dodie Ann
John Ehret HS; Marrero, LA; Lit Ral; Mu Alpha Theta; NHS; Chem A; Hon Prog; Art A; Scholastic A; *Our Lady of Holy Cross Col; Elem Ed.*

WARD, Heidi Leigh
S Miami Sr HS; Miami, FL; Band; Ensm; Sftbl; Alg A; Crown-Sceptor-Cape A; Barefoot Mailman; Phys Fitness A.

WARD, Jane Ellen
Russell HS; Russell, KY; Ann; BC; Chor; Fr C; Madrigal; Sch P; Tnns; COM; Hon Prog; Opt Out Tn; Shorthand A; *Transylvania U; Elem Ed.*

WARD, Janet Lynn
Pathway HS; Savannah, GA; Chldr; Drama; Sftbl.

WARD, Jeannine Alisa
Columbus HS; Columbus, GA (10%-379) Drama; Hmrm; Sch P; Hon Prog; Jr Civitan; Pres, ST, Church Yth; Pep C; *Journ.*

WARD, Julie Ann
La Grande HS; La Grande, OR (16-200) A Cap Choir; Secy, Chor; Ensm; Ntl Yth Conf; Ch, SC; Tres, Sr Cl; VP, Bible C; Pres, Yth Group; Hon Choir; Fin, May Mus Wk; *Columbia Christian Col; Missions.*

WARD, Kristie Leigh
Bowman HS; Wadesboro, NC (20%-400) Band; Sci C; Sftbl; HCt; Pres, FCA; Hist C; VP, Church Yth Coun; Pres, Acteens; Co Acteens Coun; Bio C; Church Yth & Handbell Choir; *Montreat Anderson Col; Recreation.*

WARD, Lenisa Gaye
Salem HS; Salem, AR; S-T, FHA; Sci C; Tres, SC; Rptr, Soph Cl; Bkbl; Hist A; Yth Fel; *Ark St U; Sci.*

WARD, Leroy Edward
Pathway HS; Savannah, GA (1-15) Dbte Tm; Ger C; Hmrm; Pres, SC; Bsbl; Ftbl; Tnns; Tr; Alg A; Hon Prog; Journ A; Most Out; Opt A; Type A; *Armstrong St Col; Zoology.*

WARD, Margie Beatrice
Clovis HS; Clovis, NM (17-800) Mu Alpha Theta; NHS; Type A; *Los Cruses Col; Vet Med.*

WARD, Marianne
Stratford Sr HS; Houston, TX (100-465) Fr C; FHA; Key C; Mjrte; Orch; COM; Yth Fel; S-T, Church Yth Fel; Achv A; Drill Tm; Phys Ed A; Service A; Comp A; *Baylor U; Registered Nurs.*

WARD, Mario Heinz
Andress HS; El Paso, TX (3-624) Pres, Ger C; NHS; Order/Arrow; Var C; Cpt, Ftbl; Tr; Order/Arrow A; *Ed.*

WARD, Mark Cunningham
Washington Co HS; Springfield, KY (7-186) Band; Chor; Ensm; Hmrm; Orch; Ftbl; Wrest; Chem A; Sci A; *U of Va; Archt.*

WARD, Mary Ann
Cradock HS; Portsmouth, VA (29-250) A Cap Choir; BC; Chor; Dbte Tm; Fr C; GS; Hmrm; Fin, Jr Miss Pagent; Madrigal; Math C; Monogram; Ntl Yth Conf; Secy, Sci C; Tri-HiY; Beauty; COM; MLS; Ldrship A; Chor A; VP, Church Yth; *Old Dominion U; General Stu.*

WARD, Michael Arden
Martinsville HS; Martinsville, IN (40%-300) Mgr, Bkbl; FCA; *Bible Col; Bible.*

WARD, Mike Allen
Fairfield HS; Fairfield, OH (10-560) Band; Community Yth Symph; Mod Mus Mas; NHS; Orch; Tres, Span C; Stu Conductor, Band; Church Bkbl & Sftbl; John Phillip Sousa Band A; *E Ky U; Acct.*

WARD, Nancy Ann
Greeley Central HS; Greeley, CO (79-323) Band; Cpt, Chldr; Chor; Fr C; Ski C; SC; Bkbl; Co-Cpt, Tnns; HQn; Prom Qn; FCA; *UNC; Dental Hygiene.*

WARD, Norman
Heritage Baptist Sch; Sand Springs, OK;

WARD, Rita Margaret
Cradock HS; Portsmouth, VA (10-222) Band; Chor; Tres, Drama; Fr C; French NHS; Ed, Sch P; SC; Thes; Swim; *William & Mary Col; Lit.*

WARD, Roy Eugene
Crenshaw HS; Los Angeles, CA (10-40) *U of Sou Calif; Mus.*

WARD, Sarah Wendelyn
Antioch HS; Antioch, CA; A Cap Choir; AFS; Drama; Hmrm; Mod Mus Mas; 4H A; Yth Fel; Church Choir; Church Comms; *Los Medanas Jr Col.*

WARD, Tammy Beth
Russell HS; Russell, KY; Band; BC; GS; Cpt, Bkbl; 110% Bkbl A; Region & Dist All-Tourney; Best Defensive Player.

WARD, Tammy June
Athens HS; Athens, AL; Band; Ensm; FBLA; *Calhoun Comm Col; Secy Sci.*

WARD, Tammy LuVenia
Albany HS; Albany, GA (21-278) F-Ed, Ann; Cpt, Chldr; HiY; Hmrm; Lat C; Spch C; SC; Var C; Secy, Sr Cl; Sftbl; COM; Cl Fav; Spch A; *Albany Jr Col; Cosmetology.*

WARD, Theodore Tyronne
Glenn HS; Birmingham, AL; Ftbl; Cl Fav.

WARD, Thomas John
Marian HS; Tamaqua, PA (99-143) Band; Chor.

WARD, Timmy Eugene
Dothan HS; Dothan, AL (235-632) Hmrm; SC; JV, Ftbl; Tr; ROTC A.

WARD, Valencia Lavada
Burke HS; Charleston, SC (6-28) ARC; ARC A.

WARD, Vernett Casandra
St Mark HS; Kingstree, SC (2-46) Drama; NHS; Sci C; SC; Pres, Jr Cl; Alg A; Bio A; Math A; Sci A; *Clemson U; Phar.*

WARD, Veronica Ann
Scotland HS; Laurinburg, NC; Band; *Bus Adm.*

WARD, Viveca Lane
Smiths Station HS; Smiths, AL (10%-180) Ann; BC; Drama; FHA; 4H; Hmrm; Lit Mag; Mu Alpha Theta; Sch P; Sci C; VP, SC; Tres, Jr Cl; Beauty; COM; HCt; Yth Fitness A; Photographer, Sch P & Annual; *Auburn U; Biol.*

WARD, William Griffin Jr
Daviess Co HS; Owensboro, KY; Bkbl; Young Hist.

WARD, Yolanda Lynn
Greenville Sr HS; Greenville, TX (5-350) Band; Dbte Tm; JETS; Pres, Math C; NHS; Hon Prog; MLS; NML; Acad Excel A; Tex Schol; *U of Dallas; Math.*

WARDEN, Diane Frances
Hazlewood E HS; St Louis, MO (80-455) A Cap Choir; Pres, Chor; Pres A; Pres, Yth Fel; Choir Ltr; Church Coun; *Florrisant Valley Comm Col; Human Relations.*

WARDEN, Kevin Doyle
Centralia HS; Centralia, MO (50%-118) Ftbl; JV, Tr; Citz A; Young Lutherans Alive; 1st Aid, Conservation, A's; Phys Fitness, A; *Mo U; Elem Ed.*

WARDEN, Krystal Denise
Wethersfield HS; Kewanee, IL; Chor; NHS; SC; Tr; Cpt, Pom Pon Sq.

WARDLAW, Emily Ann
Okolona HS; Okolona, MS (20%-78) Ed, Ann; Span C; Y-Tns; Yth Fel; Cl Fav; Friendliest Campus Favorite; WW; Most Dependable; Spell A; *Miss St U; Lib Arts.*

WARDLAW, Kimberly Ann
DeSoto HS; De Soto, TX (25%-320) Ann; Band; Chldr; FHA; FTA; Mgr, Bkbl; Tnns; Crisco A; Type A: *Okla Christian Col; Bus.*

WARE, Anita Carol
Bovina HS; Bovina, TX (4-50) Band; Chldr; FHA; NHS; VP, SC; Tres, Soph Cl; Bkbl; Homemaking A; Reading A; *Tex Tech U; Hist.*

WARE, Arlene
F O Alexander HS; Starkville, MS (10-59) Y-Tns; Pres, Soph Cl; Bkbl; Hon Prog; Yth Fel; *Miss U For Women; Nurs.*

WARE, Don Jesse
Sumner HS; Sumner, WA (42-300) Band; *Phys Sci.*

WARE, Johnnie Ann
Claiborne Acad; Haynesville, LA (11-30) Band; Fr C; HS Band Directors A; *La Tech U.*

WARE, Johnny Anthony
Cushing HS; Cushing, OK (1-120) Pres, Band; Demolay; S-T, Fr C; NHS; Lion A; Masonic A; MLS; Val; Drum Major; Best Personality; WW; Explorers; Band A; Varsity Schol; St Hon Soc; All-Dist Band; *OSU; Engr.*

WARE, Kathryn Marie
Owego Free Acad; Owego, NY (50-350) A Cap Choir; AFS; Chor; Drama; Ensm; 4H; Hmrm; SC; Tnns; Tr; *Grove City Col; Acct.*

WARE, Kent Dean
Estes Park HS; Estes Park, CO (29-79) Chess C; Chor; Drama; VP, Fr C; Hmrm; InterClub Coun; Monogram; Ski C; Pres, Spch C; Pres, SC; Parl, Thes; Co-Cpt, Ftbl; Amer Leg Orator A; COM; Opt A; Opt Out Tn; Spch A; Yth Fel; *U of Colo; Religion.*

WARE, Lois Denice
S Beloit HS; S Beloit, IL; Bkbl; Pep C; Vlbl; Tres, Black Hist.

WARE, Lorrie Ann
Hillcrest HS; Jamaica, NY; Chldr; VP, Chor; FNA; Pres, Hmrm; Sftbl; Tnns; Ntl Achv Schol; NMS; Sci A; *St U of NY; Nurs.*

WARE, Mary Lisa
Claiborne Acad; Haynesville, LA (3-37) S-T, Band; Secy, Chor; Ensm; GS; Lit Ral; Mjrte; NHS; Secy, Jr Cl; 3rd Hon Graduate; Col Schol; *La Tech U; Special Ed.*

WARE, Melodie Lynn
Arts Magnet HS; Dallas, TX (3-100) A Cap Choir; Chor; Drama; Ensm; Madrigal; Secy, NHS; Orch; Span C; Span NHS; Secy, SC; JV, Golf; Tnns; Chamber of Comm A; Citz A; Hon Prog; Kiwanis A; Yth Fel; *Baylor Col; Mus.*

WARE, Penelope Elizabeth
Washington and Lee HS; Montross, VA (22-147) Semi-Fin, Jr Miss Pa; NHSt; Span C; Arch; Bkbl; Swim; Tnns; Wrest; Water Skiing; Motorcycling; Art As; *VCU; Interior Design.*

WARE, Terry Diane
Union HS; Union, MS (10%-58) Band; BC; Chor; FHA; Hmrm; Sci C; SC; Tri-HiY; *E Central Jr Col.*

WARE, Zana Marie
Continued Ed Project; St Louis, MO (10-46) Chldr; Pres, Hmrm; SC; Hockey; Tr; PA; Sports A; *Harris Teacher Col; Ed.*

WAREHAM, Jeffrey Charles
Penn Hills Sr HS; Penn Hills, PA (20%-1300) Key C; Order/Arrow; Span C; JV, Tr; Amer Leg A; Yth Fel; Pres, Explorers; Jr Toastmaster; Eagle Sct; Church Choir; *Engr.*

WARF, Mark Edward
Jones HS; Lynnville, TN (6-22) Ann; BC; BS; Chor; FFA; FTA; F-Ed, Sch P; Pres, SC; Var C; MVP, Bkbl; Ftbl; Tr; HCt; WW; Exchange C Yth o-t Mo; Gen Mills Ldrship A.

WARFIELD, Russell Byron
Middletown Sr HS; Middletown, OH; Band; Community Yth Symph; Thes; Tr; Sci A; YMCA Ldrs C; Gym; Ntl Qualifier, Gym; AAU Jr Dist Olympics Champion.

WARFIELD, Scott Kevin
Ysleta HS; El Paso, TX (2-648) Ann; Pres, Chess C; Cpt, Dbte Tm; Drama; Pres, NFL; NHS; Phys C; Spch C; VP, Thes; Swim; Tnns; Hon Prog; Journ A; Masque & Gavel A; Math A; Most Out; Opt A; Phy A; Sal; Sci A; Spch A; *Lubbock Christian Col; Bus.*

WARFORD, Clinton Micheal
Jersey Comm HS; Jerseyville, IL; Chor; JV, Bkbl; JV, Ftbl.

WARHURST, Cynthia Louise
Western Hills HS; Fort Worth, TX (269-600) VP,
FTA; Orch; Span C; 1st Cl, GSct; *Mus.*

WARING, Bruce James
Greely Central HS; Greeley, CO (5-364) Band;
Chor; VP, Ger C; Key C; SC; VP, Jr Cl; Ftbl; Sch
Mus; *Med.*

WARING, Deborah Ann
Burke HS; Charleston, SC (8-210) Band; Bus C;
FBLA; *SCSU; Bus Adm.*

WARINNER, Barbara Ann
Walnut Hills HS; Cincinnati, OH; Band; Chor;
Tres, NHS; SC; Sftbl; COM; Citz A; Yth Fel; Hosp
Vol; Church Yth Coun; Academic A.

WARLICK, Dawn
S Macklenburg HS; Charlotte, NC; Drama; Ger C;
Ski C; Girls C, Sabres Out to Serve; *UNC; Law.*

WARMAN, Peggy Sue
Canton S HS; Canton, OH; A Cap Choir.

WARNER, Beverly Denise
Middlesex HS; Saluda, VA (25-100) FTA; Hmrm;
ARC; *Ntl Bus Col; Secy Sci.*

WARNER, Cheryl Denise
Robert Lee Paschal HS; Fort Worth, TX (108-596)
Band; Cum Laude Soc; Rptr, Hmrm; SC; Ftbl;
Beauty; COM; Citz A; Hon Prog; Most Out; Sci A;
Cum Laude; *N Tex St U; Psych.*

WARNER, Darlene
Dunedin HS; Dunedin, FL (20-830) Chor; Drama;
Pres, Ensm; GS; NHS; Thes; Kiwanis A; St Solo &
Ensm Medals; Chaplain, GS; *Child Developement.*

WARNER, Elaine
Independence HS; Charlotte, NC; Band; Ensm;
Key C; NHS; ARC; Span C; Hon Prog; ARC A;
Sewing, Choir; A's; Child Tutor; Modern Dance;
Appalachian St Col.

WARNER, Jack Randall
Allen Cons Sch; Allen, NE (9-35) A Cap Choir;
Band; Chor; Pres, FFA; Pres, 4H; NHS; Sch P; SC;
Var C; Tres, Soph Cl; Cpt, Ftbl; Tr; 4H A; JA A;
Star Student; Swtht; Pep, Stage, Bands; Ntl Ayr-
shire; Swing Choir; Boys Glee C; Brass Quartet;
Western Iowa Tech Col; Diesel Mech.

WARNER, Kathy Lynne
Pendleton HS; Pendleton, OR (9-238) Tres, Chor;
Fr C; NHS; SC; Citz A; HCt; St Scholar; Swtht;
Blue Mountain Comm Col.

WARNER, Kheva Renee
Mangum HS; Mangum, OK (1-63) Chor; Ensm;
FHA; NHS; Eng A.

WARNER, Larami Lee
Johnstown HS; Johnstown, OH (50%-130) Band;
Chor; VP, 4H; NHS; Tres, Span C; HR; *Elem Ed.*

WARNER, Linda Deane
Bennington Pub HS; Bennington, NE (15-38) Co-
Ed, Ann; Chldr; Chor; Dbte Tm; Drama; Ensm;
4H; Sch P; Spch C; Bkbl; Sftbl; Tr; COM; Most
Out; Spch A; Yth Fel; All Conf, Spch & Mus; WW;
Super Ratngs, Mus, Spch, Drama; Outst Chldr; *U
of Nebr; Spch.*

WARNER, Lisa Therese
S Plantation HS; Plantation, FL; Pres, Exchange
Service C; *Broward Comm Col; Art.*

WARNER, Lori Ann
Springfield HS; Bergholz, OH; A Cap Choir; Band.

WARNER, Martha Leigh
Alto HS; Alto, TX (1-41) Bus Mgr, Ann; Band;
Drama; Lit Ral; Span C; COM; Hon Prog; Yth Fel;
Most Scholastic; *Texas A&M U; Med.*

WARNER, Nancy Jean
Sterling HS; Sterling, KS (2-55) Ed, Ann; Chor;
Drama; Ensm; FHA; Secy, 4H; Madrigal; NHS;
SC; Hon Prog; Sal; St Scholar; Yth Fel; Yrbk A's;
Guitarist, Crossfire Singers; *Sch o-t Ozarks; Photo
Journ.*

WARNER, Phillip Irl
Sterling HS; Sterling, KS (2-50) Band; Chor;
Drama; Ensm; Madrigal; Thes; COM; 4H A; Type
A; Church Choir; KAYS; I Rating, St Mus Contest;
BSct; Interntl Lion's Band; *Math.*

WARNER, Rosemary Ellen
Norman HS; Norman, OK (1-704) Community
Yth Symph; Drama; FHA; Pres, 4H; Key C; NHS;
Orch; Span C; Spch C; Span NHS; JV, Bkbl; Sftbl;
Citz A; 4H A; H of F; I Dare You; Lion A; Spch A;
WW; NRA Rifle C; Church Puppet Ministry; Lung
Assn Yth Worker A; HS Musical.

WARNHOFF, Lisa Beth
Pineville HS; Pineville, LA (15%-250) Lit Ral;
NHS; Hon Prog; *La Col; Phys Therapy.*

WARNICK, Christopher Robin
Union HS; Union, MS; Pres, BC; VP, Sci C; Var C;
Pres, Sr Cl; Pres, Jr Cl; Pres, Soph Cl; Ftbl; Cl Fav;
Mr UHS; Beau.

WARNING, Diane Marie
Highland HS; Ewing, MO; Band; Secy, FBLA;
NHS; Sch Achieve Tm; Type A.

WARNOCK, Jeri Lynn
Rex Putnam HS; Milwaukie, OR (20-350) A Cap
Choir; BC; Mgr, Cr-Ctry; COM; Citz A; Sci A;
Oreg St U; Pre-Vet.

WARNOCK, Teresa Ann
Vicksburg HS; Vicksburg, MS (6-244) AFS; Rptr,
FHA; Ch, NHS; Span C; WW; *Delta St Col; Phys
Therapy.*

WARR, Charlotte Lee
C E Murray HS; Greeleyville, SC; FHA; 4H; PA
Cert; *Eng.*

WARR, Christina LaNora
Smiths Station HS; Smiths, AL (15%-188) F-Ed,
Ann; BC; Co-Cpt, Chldr; Chor; FHA; 4H; Hmrm;
NHS; Co-Ed, Sch P; Sci C; Pres, SC; COM; 4H A;
Hon Prog; Yth Fel; Cpt, Chldr; Ms Al Tn Qn; Miss
Citz; Miss Congeniality; Best Writn Essay; Cpt,
Pom Pom; Gayfer Girl; Stu Adv Committee; *U of
Ala; Biol.*

WARREN, Ann Marie
Lincoln HS; Jersey City, NJ (52-300) Chldr;
Hmrm; Sch P; SC; WW; *Seton Hall Col; Bus.*

WARREN, Beth Christine
E Hartford HS; E Hartford, CT; Hmrm; Span C;
Tres, Soph Cl; Hon Prog; Drill Tm; Yth Coun; Sun-
day Sch Teacher.

WARREN, Cynthia Denise
Ensley HS; Birmingham, AL; Y-Tns; Reach Out C;
BOE; *Legal Secy.*

WARREN, David Lee
Dexter HS; Dexter, KS; A-Ed, Ann; Band; Chor;
Ensm; NHS; Ed, Sch P; SC; Cpt, Bkbl; Citz A; Cl
Fav; DARGCA; Journ A; Sal; Type A; Rebounder
o-t Yr; Outst, Bookkeeping; Friendliest; Best
Dressed; *Deseil Mech.*

WARREN, Dorna Camille
Lew Wallace HS; Gary, IN; Mu Alpha Theta;
Modern Dance C; GAA; Booster C; *Howard U;
Pre-Med.*

WARREN, Gilbert Brian
Cherokee HS; Marlton, NJ (10%-350) Bowl Tm;
Math.

WARREN, Jennifer Seale
Jefferson Davis HS; Montgomery, AL; Fr C;
Hmrm; Tres, Lat C; Lat NHS; Math C; Parl, NHS;
MVP, Tnns; Alg A; Math A; NEDT; A of Hon; Lat
A; Most Intelligent; Librarian A; *Med.*

WARREN, Jerry Lee
James B Dudley HS; Greensboro, NC; Var C; Bsbl;
Ftbl; Wrest; Most Out; *NC A&T U; Sociology.*

WARREN, Karen Leigh
Ensley HS; Birmingham, AL (125-339) VP, Hmrm;
Secy, Lat C; Rainbow; SC; Y-Tns; Citz A; *U of Ala;
Nurs.*

WARREN, Katherine Keeter
Winter Haven HS; Winter Haven, FL (59-650)
NHS; Span C; Tnns; COM; Type A; God & Comm
A; Ntl Fed of Mus C; Ntl Piano Playing Auditions;
*Randolph-Macon Woman's Col; Span-Latin Amer
Stu.*

WARREN, Lisa Denise
Pathway Day Sch; Savannah, GA (2-15) Drama; Fr
C; FHA; SC; HCt; Hon Prog; *Armstrong St Col;
Med.*

WARREN, Michael Dwight
Edwin Stanton Sr HS; Jacksonville, FL; Pres,
Hmrm; SC.

WARREN, Nancy Kay
Quartz Hill HS; Lancaster, CA (15%-467) Key C;
Pres, Ski C; Span C; Tnns; CSF; Ind Schol; *Pepper-
dine U; Eng.*

WARREN, Nora Lois
Round Rock HS; Round Rock, TX (89-300) Parl,
FFA; Pres, 4H; 4H A; Star Student; FFA A's;
Church Yth Coun & Chor.

WARREN, Phillip Grant
N Co HS; Desloge, MO (50-188) Golf.

WARREN, Scott Courtney
Victoria HS; Victoria, TX (80-700) Demolay; Ger
C; *Sci.*

WARREN, Sheila Lenesse
Clements HS; Athens, AL (50%-50) BC; VP, FHA;
GS; VP, Sr Cl; 4H A; HCt; Miss FHA; *Ala A&M U;
Home Ec.*

WARREN, Shirley Ann
Hancock Central HS; Sparta, GA; Chor; Dbte Tm;
Drama; FNA; VP, 4H; VP, Hmrm; NHS; Ed, Sch
P; SC; Up Bound; Cl Fav; 4H A; *Fort Valley St Col;
Child Development.*

WARREN, Steve Lamar
Cass HS; Cassville, GA (20%-200) Cpt, Band;
Math C; COM; All St Band; Sr Superlative; *Jack-
sonville St U; Mus.*

WARREN, Susan Elizabeth
Carrollton HS; Carrollton, MO (14-98) Band;
Chor; S-T, Drama; Ensm; Madrigal; NHS; Sci C;
VP, Span C; S-T, Thes; Tnns; COM; Hon Prog;
Pres A; WW; *Southwest Baptist Col; Church Rec-
reation.*

WARREN, Terri Lynn
Union Hill HS; Gilmer, TX (1-16) Ed, Ann; BC;
Chldr; FHA; Cl Fav; MLS; Val; Yth Fel; Bus Ed A;
WW; WW, Chldr; *Kilgore Jr Col; Elem Ed.*

WARREN, William Charles
Northland HS; Columbus, OH; Band; Fr C; SC;
Capitol Ohio State; Law.

WARRENBURG, Duane Thomas
Delavan-Darien HS; Delavan, WI (43-157) Band;
Ensm; FFA; Bsbl; Mgr, Bkbl; Co-Cpt, Ftbl; Tr; Solo
Medals; Jr NHS; *Le Tourneau Col; Missions.*

WARRENDER, Doreen Kay
Columbus Sr HS; Columbus, NE; Fin, AFS; Span
C; SC; Exchange Stu; *Platte Tech Comm Col; Span.*

WARRICK, Glenn Scott
Newark Sr HS; Newark, OH (10%-780) Chor;
Drama; Ensm; Lat C; NFL; NHS; Spch C; Thes;
Ftbl; Tr; Wrest; COM; Citz A; Opt A; Spch A; Yth
Fel; Wilson Mus A; Dramatist o-t Yr; All Star Cast;
Med.

WARRINER, Mark McIver
Powell HS; Knoxville, TN (20%-250) Bkbl; Out-
door C; TVA Golfer Assn; VP, Church Yth Fel;
Tenn Travelers; Math Achv Cert; *Va Tech U; Engr.*

WARRINGTON, Jill Diane
Palestine HS; Palestine, TX (20%-350) Chor; VP,
Hmrm; Ed, Sch P; Span C; Church Yth Group &
Choir; Drill Tm; Radio Announcer; *Howard Payne
Col; Radio Broadcasting.*

WARTHMAN, Kendra Ann
Logan HS; Logan, OH (55-310) Pres, FHA; Lat C;
Pres, Rainbow; Span C; Tres, Y-Tns; Yth Fel; WW;
GAA; Powder-Puff Ftbl; Pep C; Yth Choir; Red Cr
Tn-Aide.

WARTMAN, Jane Marie
Chaska Sr HS; Chaska, MN; Band; Chldr; Ger C;
4H; Hmrm; VP, Jr Cl; Cpt, Wrest; HCt; Hon Prog;
Most Out; Pres A; Cpt & MVP, Gym; Vlbl; *U of
Wisc at La Crosse; Phy Therapy.*

WARWICK, Harvey Hodgen
Keswick Christian HS; Saint Petersburg, FL
(33%-20) Pres, Chess C; Pres, SC; Bkbl; Soccer;
Cert of Hon, Span; Fin, Scripps Howard Ntl Spell
Bee; Win, St Ptrsburg Tms Suncoast Spell; *LeTour-
neau Col; Math.*

WARWICK, Steven James
John T Hoggard HS; Wilmington, NC (15%-750)
Key C; Bsbl; JV, Bkbl; Ftbl; Bio A; VP, FCA; *U of
NC at Chapel Hill; Bus Adm.*

WARYE, Deborah Jo
Fraser HS; Fraser, MI; Hmrm; Ski C; SC; Co-Cpt, Bkbl; MVP, Sftbl; COM; Sci A; MVP, Bkbl; JV Vlbl; All Star, Summer Sftbl League; Math.

WASE, Millie
Marshall Islands HS; Majuro, MARSHALL ISLANDS; Math A.

WASH, Mary Lee
Stone HS; Wiggins, MS; VP, Band; VP, Chor; VP, Drama; VP, Fr C; VP, 4H; Spch C; VP, Sftbl; VP, Tnns; VP, Tr; Sal; Flag Corp Band; Phillis Col; Paper Work.

WASHBURN, Martha Alice
Milton HS; Milton, MA (10%-350) Chor; FHA; Lat C; Y-Tns; MVP, Bkbl; Odd Fellow Fin; Yth Fel; Fr, Eng, A's.

WASHBURN, Terry Lynn
Berea HS; Greenville, SC (23-243) A Cap Choir; Tres, Mod Mus Mas.

WASHEK, Richard C
S Kitsap HS; Port Orchard, WA (238-460) Band; Chor; Tres, Dbte Tm; Dram; JV, Tr; Most Out; Spch A; Western Wash St; Mus.

WASHER, Kimberly Ann
Homewood HS; Birmingham, AL; Chldr; Chor; Cl Fav; Pres A; Most Sch Spirit; Most Improved Gymnast.

WASHER, Mitchell Lee
Lakeshore HS; St Clair Shores, MI (33%-750) A Cap Choir; Chor; Drama; Hon Prog; Cancer Foundation; Mich Christian Col; Lib Arts.

WASHER, Susan Beth
Kearsarge Regional HS; Sutton, NH (2-144) Band; Chor; Drama; Ensm; Math C; Ch, Model UN; Rainbow; Yth Fel; VP, GSct; Chamber Chor; Vet Med.

WASHINGTON, Antonio Rene
Rantoul Township HS; Rantoul, IL; Secy, A Cap Choir; Band; Tr; Art Merit; Pepperdine U; Mus.

WASHINGTON, Beverly Ann
Kenwood HS; Chicago, IL (10%-443) Hmrm; NHS; Sch P; Span C; COM; Hon Prog; ARC A; Sal; Sci A; Hospital Vol; Health Co-Op; Pres, CYF; Stu C; Bowl A; Pres Yth Choir; TAC; Lit Work Published in Book; Med.

WASHINGTON, Blondell Marie
Burke HS; Charleston, SC (11-24) Nurs.

WASHINGTON, Brenda Joyce
Beloit Mem HS; Beloit, WI (349-520) Band; Hmrm; Bsbl; JA A.

WASHINGTON, Candiff Camielle
Rantoul Twp HS; Rantoul, IL (118-359) Chor; Hmrm; Bkbl; Tr; Morehouse Col; Mus.

WASHINGTON, Carl
Bell HS; Bell, CA; Bkbl; Ftbl; Tr; Pepperdine U; Eng.

WASHINGTON, Carla Marcelle
Wando HS; Mt Pleasant, SC (11-383) Ann; 4H; Hmrm; Lit Mag; NHS; Sch P; Span C; SC; Mgr, Bkbl; Mgr, Tr; Civitan A; Math.

WASHINGTON, Cassandra Faye
Rayne HS; Rayne, LA; A Cap Choir; U of Southwestern La; Mus.

WASHINGTON, Charles Linwood
King William HS; King William, VA; BS; Hmrm; Sci C; JV, Bsbl; Bkbl; Ftbl; Tr; Bkbl, Ftbl, A's; Army; Commercial Art.

WASHINGTON, Cordelia Vonette
E E Smith Sr HS; Fayetteville, NC (17-278) JV, Chldr; Tres, FHA; Fin, Jr Miss Pageant; NHS; SC; Tri-HiY; Secy, Jr Cl; Secy, Soph Cl; Gr Marshal; HCt; WW; FHA A; Outst Sr; Cpt, Pom Pom Sq; NC St U; Med Technology.

WASHINGTON, Cynthia LaVerne
Tuskegee Inst HS; Tuskegee Inst, AL; Chem C; Chor; Drama; FHA; 4H; Pres, NHS; A-Ed, Sch P; Sci C; Span C; SC; Pres, Sr Cl; COM; 4H A; Hon Prog; NEDT; Wake Forest U; Bio.

WASHINGTON, Darryl Wayne
Maplewood HS; Nashville, TN; Band; NHS; Hon Prog.

WASHINGTON, Debra Leigh
Booker T Washington HS; Tulsa, OK; Band; Ensm; FBLA; Span C; SC; COM; Spch A; Dance Ensm A; Tex Sou Col; Acct.

WASHINGTON, Dena Marie
East HS; Columbus, OH (22-331) Chor; NHS; Span C; Sftbl; Central State U; Mus.

WASHINGTON, Earl Jerome
Miami Beach HS; Miami Beach, FL (58%-689) Ftbl; Tr; Pres A; Miami Dade S Col.

WASHINGTON, Greta Olivia
Holy Family HS; Birmingham, AL (7-35) Cpt, Chldr; Tres, NHS; SC; Pres, Jr Cl; Pres, Soph Cl; COM; Hon Prog; Type A; Fr A; Eng A; WW; Adya WW Chldr; Fisk U; X-Ray Tech.

WASHINGTON, James Anthony
Roxborough HS; Philadelphia, PA; Bkbl; Ftbl; Bkbl.

WASHINGTON, Jeffrey
Petersburg HS; Petersburg, VA (55-555) BS; Hmrm; Span C; SC; Pres, Sr Cl; Amer Leg A; COM; Citz A; MLS; Most Out; Opt A; Opt Out Tn; SCA Ldrship Schol; U of Va; Pol Sci.

WASHINGTON, Joilynn
Gardena HS; Gardena, CA; F-Ed, Ann; InterAct C; Bkbl; Sftbl; Calif St U; Psych.

WASHINGTON, Kathleen Verna
James Island HS; Charleston, SC (29-164) Ann; Pres, Band; Ensm; Hmrm; Lit Mag; Orch; Span C; SC; Tr; COM; Hon Prog; Most Out; Vlbl; All-Co Hon Band A; WW; Tr A; Most Improved Band Member A; SC St U; Mus.

WASHINGTON, Kimberley Marie
Central HS; Minneapolis, MN (40%-350) Chldr; Hmrm; Bus Mgr, Sch P; SC; Tnns; Type A; Journ.

WASHINGTON, Madeleine Jeanette
Forest Brook HS; Houston, TX (10%-500) Band; Cum Laude Soc; Type A; Mus Achv; Outst Band Member; Cum Laude; U of Houston; Bus Law.

WASHINGTON, Madlene Denise
Lake Clifton HS; Baltimore, MD (10%-500) Chor; 4H; Hmrm; NHS; Bkbl; Cpt, Tnns; Cpt, Badminton; Catonville Col; Bus.

WASHINGTON, Margaret Elizabeth
Bayon Acad; Boyle, MS (90%-60) BC; Fr C; Pres, FHA; GS; Hmrm; Sch P; SC; Pres, Sr Cl; Pres, Jr Cl; S-T, Soph Cl; JV, Bkbl; Beauty; Cl Fav; Hon Prog; Yth Fel; Church Swtht; Secy, Church Yth Fel; Delta St U; Home Ec.

WASHINGTON, Monee Yvonne
Compton Sr HS; Compton, CA (50%-800) Cpt, Chldr; Chor; FHA; SC; Swim; Beauty; CSF; Cl Fav; HCt; Most Out; Choir, Sewing, Modern Dance, A's; Mary Mount Palos Verdes Col; Psych.

WASHINGTON, Pamela Denise
Carver HS; Chicago, IL; Band; NHS; Pres, Ski C; Tr; COM; MLS; Cpt, Pom-Pon; Phys Therapy.

WASHINGTON, Renee Karen
Lutheran HS; Burbank, CA; FBLA; Semi-Fin, GS; Hmrm; SC; CSF; Hon Prog; Keyettes; Co-Cpt, Drill Tm; USC; Pre-Med.

WASHINGTON, Richard
HS of Charleston; Charleston, SC; Hmrm; Key C; SC; Wrest; Hon Prog; The Citadel; Bio.

WASHINGTON, Rita LaGail
Banning HS; Banning, CA (50-218) Band; Fr C; Var C; Mgr, Bkbl; Sftbl; CSF; Citz A; Vlbl; Church Choir; Rally C; Afro-Amer Yth Assn; U of Calif; Dental Asst.

WASHINGTON, Robert Jr
Lynwood HS; Lynwood, CA; Cpt, Bkbl; Cpt, Ftbl; Pepperdine U; Bus.

WASHINGTON, Robin Kara
Springville HS; Springville, AL (1-80) FHA; Alg A; Bio A; Hon Prog; Math A; Sci A; Eng A; Geom A; Geography A; Spelling Bee Champion; Math.

WASHINGTON, Sandra Kay
Pontiac N HS; Pontiac, MI (70-450) Cpt, Band; Bus C; Ensm; Cpt, Hmrm; Hon Prog; Y-Tns; Beauty; COM; JA A; Negro Bus & Professional Women's A; Central Mich U; Bus Adm.

WASHINGTON, Shelbert Curtis
Skyline C D C HS; Dallas, TX; Chor; Dbte Tm; Drama; Ensm; VP, French NHS; FTA; NHS; Fin, Ntl Yth Conf; ARC; Sch Achieve Tm; Spch C; Pres, Var C; Bsbl; Bkbl; Tr; Bank OF Amer A; Gov Honor Prog; Hon Prog; Math A; MLS; Most Out; Ntl Achv Schol; ROTC A; Spch A; Yth Fel; U of Tex; Data Processing.

WASHINGTON, Tamara Leah
Fairdale HS; Fairdale, KY; JA A; Safety Coun; Exploratory Bus; Bus.

WASHINGTON, Terri Lynn
Skyline HS; Dallas, TX (10%-890) Chor; Drama; Fr C; Hmrm; ARC; Hon Prog; Life Ldrship Pride & Unity A; Pres, Tx As of Health Occup Stu; Health Occup Cooperative Training; U of Tex at Arlington; Bio.

WASHINGTON, Thurman Jr
Santa Clara HS; Santa Clara, CA (120-436) Soccer; Tr.

WASHINGTON, Toye Michelle
Emerson HS; Gary, IN; Chldr; Tr; HQn; JA A; Pres A; Accountant.

WASHINGTON, Vanessa Clarise
DeLand Sr HS; DeLand, FL (25%-800) Fr C; Home Ec, Comm Service, A's; Fla A&M U; Phar.

WASIELEWSKI, Patricia Ellen
Oak Lawn Comm HS; Oak Lawn, IL (274-780) Chldr; Sftbl; COM; Safty, Sftbl, Chldr, A's; Bradley U; Psych.

WASIELEWSKI, Philip Gerald
St Mary's Prep; Orchard Lake, MI (5-36) Dbte Tm; NHS; Spch C; Tr; Spch A; First Hon; US Naval Acad; Russian.

WASINGER, Manny Lee
Arvada Sr HS; Arvada, CO (88-600) Var C; Ftbl; Tr; Wrest; COM; Most Out; Pres A; FCA; Adams St Col; Bus.

WASKO, Eugene Richard Jr
Lincoln HS; Sioux Falls, SD; Cr-Ctry; Brookings St Col.

WASLEY, David Milton
Dodgeville HS; Dodgeville, WI (5-130) Fin, AFS; Bus Mgr, Ann; Model UN; Order/Arrow; A-Ed, Sch P; SC; Mgr, Bkbl; Mgr, Ftbl; Eagle Sct; Law.

WASS, Jeffrey Carl
Central Dauphin HS; Harrisburg, PA; Chess C; NHS; JV, Bkbl; Ftbl; Soccer; Yth Fel; Juniata Col; Sci.

WASS, Warren Roger
Worthington Sr HS; Waithington, MN; Band; Chor; Madrigal; NHS; Tr; NHS; Waithington Comm Col; Agr.

WASSER, Cynthia Jane
Brownstown HS; Brownstown, IL (5-39) Ann; Chldr; HQn.

WASSILCHALK, Daniel Mark
Belle Vernon Area HS; Belle Vernon, PA (25-371) Bsbl; Bkbl; Ftbl; MLS; Star Student; Ath As; Dancer; HR; U of Pittsburgh; Bus Adm.

WASSON, Frances Carol
Arkadelphia Sr HS; Arkadelphia, AR (23-163) A Cap Choir; Ann; Chldr; Chor; GS; Pres, 4H; NHS; HCt; Journ A; Pres, United Methodist Yth; U of Ark.

WASSON, Laurie Lynne
Honolulu Jr Acad; Honolulu, HI;

WASSON, Susan J
Honolulu Jr Acad; Honolulu, HI; Cr-Ctry; Scripps Col; Art.

WASTLICK, John Michael
Weston HS; Cazenovia, WI (2-56) Bus Mgr, Ann; 4H; NFL; Pres, NHS; Span C; Tres, SC; Var C; Tr; U of Wisc; Physics.

WASZAK, Barbara Kazimiera
Franklin HS; Los Angeles, CA (75-681) CYO; JV, Chldr; Pres, Fr C; VP, FTA; A-Ed, Lit Mag; Cpt, Golf; USC; Med.

WATANABE, Melanie Ann
The Cecilian Acad; Philadelphia, PA (2-43) Chldr; Chor; Fr C; World Affairs C; Hon Prog; Lat A; *Chestnut Hill Col; Biol.*

WATCHORN, Crystal Jeanne
Big Bay de Noc HS; Cooks, MI; Band; Chldr; Chor; Drama; Sch P; Secy; Sr Cl; JV, Tr; HCt; Journ A; *Bay de Comm Col.*

WATERBURY, Patti Denise
Perryton HS; Perryton, TX (25%-152) Band; Chor; Madrigal; SC; Tr; COM; Vlbl; Most Consistent Spiker.

WATERFALL, Danita Kay
John F Kennedy Mem HS; Seattle, WA (1-333) Chldr; Ensm; Lat C; Rptr, Sch P; Bkbl; Sftbl; Tnns; Tr; Citz A; Hon Prog; JA A; Sci A; Val; Piano Playing Recognition.

WATERMAN, Donna Ruth
W Charlotte HS; Charlotte, NC (40-601) AFS; A-Ed, Ann; Band; Chor; Drama; Secy, Ger C; NHS; Sftbl; Hon Prog; Vlbl; *Va Tech Col; Forestry.*

WATERMAN, Lawrence Alan
Cassadaga Valley Central Sch; Sinclairville, NY (15-120) Band; BS; Pres, Chor; Ensm; Hmrm; Madrigal; Orch; Order/Arrow; Ski C; SC; Var C; Ftbl; Tr; JV, Wrest; God & Country A; HCt; Regent Schol; Yth Leg; WW; *St U of NY; Physics.*

WATERMAN, Sharon Elizabeth
Southwick HS; Southwick, MA (10-160) Ann; Drama; Semi-Fin, GS; Math C; Hon Prog; Ntl Radio C; Square Dance C; Teach, Span; *Communications.*

WATERMAN, Vicki Kay
Highland HS; Ewing, MO (4-135) Secy, FBLA; Rptr, FHA; NHS; Sci C; SC; Co-Cpt, Bkbl; Sftbl; Mgr, Tr; COM; Citz A; Hon Prog; Pres A; Regent Schol; WW; *NE Mo St U; Acct.*

WATERS, Brenda Lee
S Broward HS; Hollywood, FL; Secy, Chor; FHA; Madrigal; NHS; ARC; Swim; ARC A; Chor, Phys Ed, Jr NHS, Mus, A's; *Eckerd Col; Special Ed.*

WATERS, Carla Jean
Zanesville HS; Zanesville, OH (3-400) Chor; Ensm; ARC; Magna Cum Laude; ARC A; Yth Fel; *Ohio U; Registered Nurs.*

WATERS, Carol Ann
Ensley HS; Birmingham, AL; Chor; Sftbl; Clerical.

WATERS, Carolyn Elizabeth
New Bern Sr HS; New Bern, NC (75-450) Anchor C; Chor; Drama; Ensm; 4H; Hmrm; Sci C; Span C; Tri-HiY; Tri-Chi; *E Carolina U; Special Ed.*

WATERS, Cheryl Downing
Bayside HS; Virginia Beach, VA (200-525) Anchor C; Chor; Drama; Atlantic Ecology C; S-T, Christian Yth Fel; Yth Cong Plan Com & Brd of Dir; Worship Comm & Board of Directors;; *ODU; Vet Med.*

WATERS, Chris David
Topeka HS; Topeka, KS; Rptr, Sch P; Bkbl; Tr; Pres A; *Kans U; Bus.*

WATERS, David Burnham
S Hadley HS; South Hadley, MA (15-300) Bus Mgr, Ann; Dbte Tm; Drama; Hmrm; Lat C; NHS; Thes; COM; Hon Prog; MLS; Yth Fel; Pro Merito; Pres, Yth Group; *Middlebury Col; Eng.*

WATERS, George Arthur
Claremont HS; Claremont, CA; Ann; Drama; Cr-Ctry; Tr; Pres A; Best Actor of Yr.

WATERS, Jacquelyn Dawn
Temple Heights Christian Sch; Tampa, FL; NHS; MVP, Sftbl; Vlbl; *Phys Therapy.*

WATERS, Kathy Gail
Benton Acad; Benton, MS; Ann; BC; Chor; Community Yth Symph; Ensm; 4H; Key C; Orch; VP, Soph Cl; Bkbl; Sftbl; Tr; Hist A; UDC Essay Win; Most Intellectual; Social Sci, Eng, A's; Math, St Hist, A's.

WATERS, Kimberly Jane
Menchville HS; Newport News, VA (50-600) Ann; Drama; NHS; JV, Hockey; Sci A; Geog C; Hockey Ltr; *William and Mary Col; Psych.*

WATERS, Larry R
LaSalle Sr HS; Niagara Falls, NY (10%-535) Band; NHS; *Mech Engr.*

WATERS, Lori Michelle
Floyd Co HS; Floyd, VA (22-160) BC; Chor; Tri-HiY; Cpt, Tr; *Roanoke Mem Sch of Nurs; Nurs.*

WATERS, Mary Elizabeth
Carroll HS; Monroe, LA; Orch; SC; Chaplain, Span C; *NE La U; Nurs.*

WATERS, Ray Allen
Hall HS; Little Rock, AR; Chess C; VP, Dbte Tm; Cpt, Arch; Soccer.

WATERS, Sandra Elaine
E Central HS; Tulsa, OK; Chor; Soph Board; Soph Rep of Evangelistic Activ; *OSU; Med.*

WATERS, Sherre Ann
Hokes Bluff HS; Gadsden, AL (45-90) FTA; Pres, HiY; Tri-HiY; *Elem Ed.*

WATERS, Terri Lynn
S Range HS; North Lima, OH (15-80) Ger C; Sch P; Bsbl; Tr; Alg A; COM; Math A; Sci A; Eng, Foreign Lang, Spelling A's.

WATERS, Vickie Lane
Clayton HS; Clayton, NC (9-118) Ann; BC; Pres, FHA; GS; Hmrm; Bio A; Jr Marshal; Jr Eng A; Dist Tres, E Central NC Beta; Del, FHA Ntl Convention; Essay Contest Regional Win; *E Carolina U; Nurs.*

WATHEN, Edith Marie
Chopticon HS; Morganza, MD (10-300) Drama; Hmrm; F-Ed, Lit Mag; Secy, NHS; COM; Math A.

WATKIN, Martha Alice
Girls' Preparatory Sch; Chattanooga, TN (22-88) Band; BC; Drama; Hmrm; S-T, Lat C; Orch; Secy, ARC; Sch P; Span C; SC; Tr; DARGCA; Most Out; Star Student; Church Bkbl; Outst Mus A; Most Stu; Yth Coun, Church; Jr Classical League; *Pol Sci.*

WATKIN, Mary Kathryn
S Central HS; Union Mills, IN; Drama; FHA; Ger C; Tr; *Purdue U.*

WATKINS, Alvin Lee
Lanier HS; Jackson, MS; Band; YWCA Mus C; *Jackson St Col; Mus.*

WATKINS, Billy Ray
Carthage HS; Carthage, MS (1-71) BC; Rptr, FFA; Hmrm; VP, Sr Cl; Pres, Jr Cl; *Miss St U; Civil Engr.*

WATKINS, Bryan Joseph
Newburgh Free Acad; Newburgh, NY (350-800) Chor; Wrest; Yth Fel; Boys Glee C; Red Cross Swim Prog; *Gordon Col; Religion.*

WATKINS, Carol Ann
Corliss HS; Chicago, IL (33-215) COM; *Roosevelt Col; Bus Adm.*

WATKINS, Carolyn Denise
Hendersonville HS; Hendersonville, NC (55-204) FHA; FTA; *U of Cincinnati; Communication.*

WATKINS, Celeste Karen
Springbrook HS; Silver Spring, MD; *Law.*

WATKINS, Charlene Denise
Woodrow Wilson HS; Washington, DC (226-501) Lit Mag; Journ A; VofDEM; Inaugural Comm Press Credentials; Outst Journ Stu, Urban Journ Wrkshp; *Va Commonwealth U; Mass Communications.*

WATKINS, Chrystal Renee
Archbishop Keough HS; Baltimore, MD; Tres, Yth Fel; SG; Alcolytes; *Interior Decorating.*

WATKINS, Dana Linn
Newburgh Free Acad; Newburgh, NY (50%-700) Chor; Hockey; Soccer; Swim; Yth Fel; Vlbl; Mixed & All St Chor; UMYF; Dist Coun On Yth Fel; *Occupational Therapy.*

WATKINS, Debra Janelle
Citronelle HS; Citronelle, AL; F-Ed, Ann; BC; FHA; 4H; Jr Miss Pageant; Math C; Secy, NHS; Sch P; Sci C; Rptr, SC; Sftbl; 4H A; Type A; *Mobile Col; Mus Ed.*

WATKINS, Debra Renae
Sebastopol HS; Sebastopol, MS (5%-32) Ed, Ann; BC; Cpt, Chldr; Chor; S-T, Drama; VP, FHA; Jr Miss Pageant; SC; Sftbl; Cl Fav; Hist A; HCt; Hon Prog; Type A; Bus Mgr, Drama C; Civics A; *Hinds Jr Col; Data Processing.*

WATKINS, James Edwards
Harlem HS; Rockford, IL (8-628) BS; NHS; Var C; Ftbl; Tr; MLS; All Conf, Tr; *Chem.*

WATKINS, Jerry Dail
Red Bank HS; Red Bank, TN (86-336) Band; Demolay; Lat C; Lat NHS; Order/Arrow; Sci C; Cr-Ctry; Sftbl; Eagle Sct; Sr Talent; MYF; Lat A; Jr Capers; *UTC; Med Tech.*

WATKINS, JoAnn Marie
Rapid City Central HS; Rapid City, SD (18-700) Band; Fr C; Hmrm; Rptr, Sch P; SC; Cpt, Sftbl; Hon Prog; Star Student; Pep C; *Elem Ed.*

WATKINS, Kevin Darnell
Edward Tilden HS; Chicago, IL (6-408) Cpt, Chess C; Chor; Drama; Math C; NHS; Ed, Sch P; VP, Sci C; SC; Bio A; Math A; ROTC A; Sci A; Yth Foundation; *U of Chicago; Pre-Med.*

WATKINS, Larrie Ellen
Falls Church HS; Falls Church, VA (63-400) NHS; Mgr, Tr; MVP, Gym; *Med Col of Va; Phys Therapy.*

WATKINS, Margie Lea
Mount Ida HS; Mount Ida, AR (10-36) Ed, Ann; Pres, BC; Ch, GS; Hmrm; Sch P; SC; Cpt, Bkbl; Amer Leg A; COM; Hon Prog; Historian, FHA; WW; Best Dressed; Pres, Lib C; *Henderson Col; Spch Pathology.*

WATKINS, Mary Ruth
Hart HS; Hart, MI (7-129) Band; Secy, Drama; NFL; NHS; ARC; Ed, Sch P; Ski C; Pres, SC; Bus Mgr, Thes; Journ A; Spch A; Summa Cum Laude; Powder Puff Ftbl; Fine Arts Schol; Mich Comp Schol; Journ School; Pep Band; *Mich St U; Journ.*

WATKINS, Mecletus Tremelle
Carthage HS; Carthage, AR; BC; FBLA; FHA; *Special Ed.*

WATKINS, Melba Anita
Groveton HS; Alexandria, VA; French NHS; NFL; COM; Spch A; Drama A; *Biol.*

WATKINS, Myra Lynn
Sebastopol Attendance Center; Sebastopol, MS (5%-32) F-Ed, Ann; Secy, BC; Chor; Drama; Tres, FHA; SC; Pres, Soph C; Beauty; Hon Prog; Home Ec, Best Talent, A's; *E Central Jr Col; Intensive Business.*

WATKINS, Nadine
Sky View HS; Smithfield, UT (63-573) All Amer Yth; VP, Band; Community Yth Symph; Pres, Ensm; 4H; Model UN; Orch; COM; Most Out; Band, Symph Band, A's; Outst, Soloist & Mus; *Utah St U; Mus.*

WATKINS, Nancy Kaye
Central HS; Newnan, GA; Chor; Span C; Sftbl; 1st Cl, GSct; *Emory U; Yth Ministry.*

WATKINS, Rebecca Sue
Bena Sr HS; Bend, OR (107-520) Chldr; Chor; Drama; Ensm; Thes; Rotary A; Up With People; Girl o-t Mo; *George Fox Col; Mus.*

WATKINS, Robbie Marion
Millbrook HS; Raleigh, NC (15%-500) Bsbl; Ftbl; Jr NHS; S-T, FCA; *U of NC; Phys Ed.*

WATKINS, Robert Franklin
Abbeville HS; Abbeville, LA (4-260) Band; Ensm; Lit Ral; Bsbl; Bkbl; *U S Air Force Acad; Engr.*

WATKINS, Tamulia Raniece
Karns HS; Knoxville, TN (5-250) AFS; Chor; Drama; GS; NHS; Secy, Jr Cl; Alg A; Ntl Sci Symposium; Opt A; Sci A; Spch A; Lat A; *Vanderbilt U; Psych.*

WATKINS, Teresa Lynn
Washington HS; Washington, IN (27-240) BC; Bus C; *Ind Bus Col; Bookkeeping.*

WATKINS, Timothy Lee
Tulsa Christian Acad; Tulsa, OK (20%-23) Chldr; Chor; Dbte Tm; Bsbl; Ftbl; JV, Tr; Citz A; Sci A; PA; HR; *Oral Roberts U; Bus Adm.*

WATLINGTON, Janis Marie
Reidsville Sr HS; Reidsville, NC (11-344) Hmrm; Tres, NHS; Cpt, Bkbl; HCt; Ltr A; *UNC at Chapel Hill.*

WATMORE, Mark Steven
Geneva HS; Geneva, NE (8-49) Ann; Band; Chess C; Drama; Tres, FFA; 4H; Sch P; Thes; Bsbl; Ftbl; Golf; COM; Hon Prog; Journ A; Photography A; *U of Nebr; Biol Research.*

WATROUS, John Jacob
Whitewater HS; Whitewater, WI (8-170) Pres, Band; Chor; Pres, Drama; VP, Fr C; Madrigal; NFL; NHS; VP, Thes; Pres, Sr Cl; JV, Golf; B Crocker A; WSMA St Hons Choir; *Rose Hulman Inst of Tech; Phys Sci.*

WATSABAUGH, Dawn Marie
Wayne Comm HS; Corydon, IA (10-64) Band; Chldr; Chor; Pres, FHA; 4H; NHS; Rainbow; *NE Mo St U; Mus.*

WATSON, Alan Wayne
Central HS; Woodstock, VA; Band; Orch; Order/ Arrow; Ski C; SC; Cr-Ctry; Tr; COM; Order/ Arrow A; ARC A; Eagle Sct; Sr Patrol Ldr; Den Chief; *Lord Fairfax Comm Col.*

WATSON, Alice Clare
Jefferson Forest HS; Bedford County, VA (10-173) Lat C; Tr; NEDT; *VPI; Horticulture.*

WATSON, Alice Faye
Fairfield Comm HS; Fairfield, IL (69-155) Rptr, 4H; Lat C; Span C; *SW Assembly of God Col; Missions.*

WATSON, Ann Katherine
Northgate HS; Walnut Creek, CA (20-425) AFS; Chor; Hmrm; Madrigal; Model UN; ARC; Span C; Bsbl; Swim; CSF; Secy, Jobs Daughters; Rep, Amigos de las Amer; *U of Calif; Zoology.*

WATSON, Barbara Ann
F O Alexander HS; Starkville, MS (5-59) Pres, Jr Cl; *Jackson St U; Social Work.*

WATSON, Becky Gayle
Sooner HS; Bartlesville, OK; Bus C; FBLA; Pep C; Vocal Ensm; *Claremore Jr Col; Bus.*

WATSON, Becky Lynn
Frost HS; Frost, TX (3-27) Ann; VP, FHA; Secy, SC; Pres, Soph Cl; Bkbl; *Navarro Col; Journ.*

WATSON, Bruce Craig
Stivers-Patterson Co-Op HS; Dayton, OH (91-400) SC; Mgr, Bkbl; JV, Ftbl; Tr; VICA; Best Actor A; Med Arts Stu o-t Yr; Beau of 1977; *Ohio St U; Pre-Med.*

WATSON, Bryna Alwyn
Westminster Sch; Atlanta, GA (33%-100) Chor; Fr C; Lat C; Rptr, Lit Mag; Swim; Tnns; Chem A.

WATSON, Carmen Alecia
Central HS; Tulsa, OK; *Pepperdine Col.*

WATSON, Carolyn Ann
Harry D Jacobs HS; Algonquin, IL (54-184) COM; Sci A; Art A; *Judson Col; Ed.*

WATSON, Carolyn Louise
Red Springs HS; Red Springs, NC (6-130) Secy, BC; Chldr; FTA.

WATSON, Carolyn Sue
Livingston Central HS; Burna, KY; A Cap Choir; Co-Ed, Ann; Band; BC; Chor; Ensm; 4H; Madrigal; Mod Mus Mas; Secy, SC; Bkbl; A; 4H A; Hist A; MLS; Sci A; WW; Lib C; All St Choir; Pep C; Acteens; *Murray St U; Pre-Med.*

WATSON, Cindy Jo
Gila Bend HS; Gila Bend, AZ (3-52) S-T, Band; VP, Chor; Drama; Ensm; Pres, FHA; Semi-Fin, GS; VP, NHS; Co-Ed, Sch P; Rptr, SC; COM; Math A; Fin, Hugh O'Brien Outst Soph A; *Biola Col; Home Ec.*

WATSON, Craig Dennis
Cumberland Valley HS; Mechanicsburg, PA (27-585) Band; Secy, Chess C; NHS; VP, Orch; Soccer; *Carnegie-Mellon U; Math.*

WATSON, Craig William
Sherman HS; Sherman, TX (30-460) Fr C; Pres, Hmrm; NHS; Order/Arrow; SC; Mgr, Ftbl; Swim; NEDT; Eagle A; *Austin Col; Pre-Law.*

WATSON, David Lynn
Mt Vernon HS; Mt Vernon, MO (8-100) Band; Chor; Ensm; Mgr, Bkbl; Tr; Most Outst, Band A; *Mus.*

WATSON, Deborah Karen
Santa Teresa HS; San Jose, CA; Fr C; CSF.

WATSON, Dian LaVerne
Burke HS; Charleston, SC (6-177) NHS; Secy, SC; Secy, Jr Cl; WW; Hon Graduate; OSA; *SCSU; Ed.*

WATSON, Donald Carlyle
Astoria HS; Astoria, IL (25%-28) Band; Span C; Spch A; *State Park Adm.*

WATSON, Elaine
Eastside HS; Paterson, NJ (10%-615) Hmrm; SC; COM; Citz A; Cl Fav; Coun of Teach A; Hist A; Hon Prog; MLS; Ntl Achv Schol; NMF; NMS; Star Student; Yth Fel; *Wash U; Criminal Justice.*

WATSON, Elizabeth Anne
Herbert Hoover HS; San Diego, CA (132-421) Chor; Fr C; NHS; ARC; Art C; *San Diego St U; Art.*

WATSON, Ferrell Kent
Christian Sch; Dallas, TX (2-43) Chor; NHS; Bsbl; Ftbl; Tr; Citz A; Hon Prog; Most Out; Bible A; 2nd Pl, Bible Bowl A; *Harding Col; Bible.*

WATSON, George Stuart Jr
Deerfield Sch; Albany, GA (13-57) MVP, Band; BC; BS; Dbte Tm; Tres, Key C; ARC; Pres, SC; VP, Jr Cl; DARGCA; Lieutenant, BS; *Vanderbilt U; Pre-Med.*

WATSON, Glenn Edwin
Tallulah HS; Tallutah, LA; Band; 4H; Bsbl; Ftbl.

WATSON, Gregory Eugene
Eldorado HS; Eldorado, IL (15-122) Span C; JV, Tr; *Math.*

WATSON, James William
St Joseph HS; St Joseph, MI (74-350) Arch; Band; VP, Chor; Ensm; Math C; NHS; Orch; Rptr, Sch P; MVP, Arch; MVP, Sftbl; NMF; NMS; Order/ Arrow A; Vigil, Order o-t Arrow; Eagle Sct; Church Usher; HS Musical Med Explorer Post; Variety Show; *Mich St U; Med.*

WATSON, Jane Harward
Saint Mary's Col; Raleigh, NC (2-103) VP, Lat C; Sci C; COM; St Mary's Hon Soc; Outst Service Cert; Latin Contest; *Duke U; Math.*

WATSON, Janet Marie
Alliance Sr HS; Alliance, NE (1-150) Drama; Semi-Fin, GS; Pres, 4H; Spch C; Thes; Y-Tns; JV, Golf; 4H A; Hist A; Spch A; *U of Nebr; Animal Sci.*

WATSON, Jerita Sue
Marked Tree HS; Marked Tree, AR (1-75) A Cap Choir; Ed, Ann; Band; Pres, BC; Chem C; Chor; Pres, Drama; Ensm; Secy, FHA; FTA; GS; Fin, Jr Miss Pagent; A-Ed, Lit Mag; Madrigal; Mjrte; NHS; S-T, Span C; Spch C; Beauty; COM; Citz A; Cl Fav; DARGCA; H of F; Hist A; HCt; Hon Prog; JA A; Most Out; Type A; Best Actress, Thespians; Highest GPA; Eng A; *Ark St U; Spch.*

WATSON, Jim Todd
Piggott HS; Piggott, AR (20-97) FFA; Sci C; Bsbl; MVP, Bkbl; Ftbl; Golf; Fin, Tr; Cl Fav; HCt; Cpt, Bkbl; Best Defensive, Bkbl; Sadie Hawkins Kg.

WATSON, Kathryn Dawn
Wm C Overfelt HS; San Jose, CA (1-304) NHS; Spch C; Var C; Swim; Tr; Bank Of Amer A; CSF; COM; Lion A; MLS; Val; Magna Cum Laude; GAA; *San Jose St U; Social Sci.*

WATSON, Kenneth LeGrand
Purcell HS; Cincinnati, OH (20%-171) Cpt, Tnns; Ftbl; JA A; *Bowling Green St U; Adm Mgr.*

WATSON, Kevin Mark
Wheaton HS; Wheaton, MO (3-31) BS; Ch, FFA; NHS; Bsbl; Bkbl; Tr; Regent Schol; General Mills A; *SW Mo St U; Engr.*

WATSON, Laura Bernot
George Walton Acad; Monroe, GA (10-26) Ann; Chldr; VP, Hmrm; Co-Ch, InterAct C; Span C; SC; HCt; Literary C; Miss Tnage Welton C, 1977-78; *Health.*

WATSON, Laura Lee
Stephens Co HS; Toccoa, GA; InterAct C; NHS; Tri-HiY; *N Ga Col; Phys Therapy.*

WATSON, Linda Diane
Kountze HS; Kountze, TX (2-84) Secy, Band; Parl, FTA; Cpt, Mjrte; Pres, NHS; SC; Beauty; DARGCA; H of F; HCt; Hon Prog; Sal; Yth Foundation A; *Lamar U; Math.*

WATSON, Lori Lynn
Greenland HS; Greenland, AR (10-44) Ann; Chldr; FHA; GS; Tres, Hmrm; Ed, Sch P; Tres, Sr Cl; Tres, Jr Cl; Alg A; Home Ec, Eng, A's; *U of Ark; Nurs.*

WATSON, Lynetta Marie
Apollo HS; Simi Valley, CA; Ann; Bus C; Cpt, Chldr; Dbte Tm; Tres, Hmrm; VP, InterClub Coun; Math C; Sch Achieve Tm; Tres, Sch P; Spch C; SC; I Dare You; Spch A; Swtht; Yth Fel; *Cosmetology.*

WATSON, Margaret Crittenden
Hoopeston-E Lynn HS; Hoopeston, IL (1-170) NHS; Color Guard; Accompanist, Chor; Swing Choir.

WATSON, Margaret Dean
Madison Acad HS; Huntsville, AL (1-42) BC; Math C; NHS; Spch C; Alg A; Bio A; COM; Hist A; Hon Prog; Math A; NEDT; Opt A; Sci A; Spch A; Star Student; Fr A; Eng A; Bible A; PE A; *UA; Med.*

WATSON, Martha Marie
New Castle Sr HS; New Castle, PA; Band; Chor; Ensm; Pres A; Yth Fel; Fr A; 2nd Runnerup, Bicentennial Qn; *Mus.*

WATSON, Mary Elizabeth
Central HS; Woodstock, VA; Bus Mgr, Ann; Chor; FBLA; Hmrm; InterAct C; Mjrte; NHS; Ski C; Var C; Secy, Soph Cl; Tr; COM; ARC A.

WATSON, Michael Lee
Lefors HS; Lefors, TX; Pres, Chor; Drama; Pres, Jr Cl; Co-Cpt, Bkbl; Co-Cpt, Ftbl; Tnns; Tr; FHA Beau; Outst Boy Choir; Best-All-Around; Popularity; Hon Men Ftbl; *Clarendon Jr Col; Ranch Mgt.*

WATSON, Nancy Louise
Elkhart Central HS; Elkhart, IN; Band; 4H; Secy, Ski C; Tr; 4H A; Pres A; Yth Fel; *Acct.*

WATSON, Nora Beth
Zion-Benton Township HS; Zion, IL; AFS; Drama; Fr C; NHS; Tnns; Hist A; Eng A; *Col of Lake Co; Hist.*

WATSON, Pamela Louise
Antelope Valley HS; Lancaster, CA (84-600) Hmrm; Tres, Ski C; Tres, SC; Cr-Ctry; Tr; CSF; Hon Prog; Yth Fel; 'Z' C; WW; *San Jose St Col; Occupational Therapy.*

WATSON, Patrick Michael
Baker HS; Baker, FL (2-75) Tres, BC; Mu Alpha Theta; Sch P; Sci C; Swim; Ntl Sci Found; WW; Inst of Math; *Auburn U; Engr.*

WATSON, Randall Dean
Field Kindley HS; Coffeyville, KS (25%-265) Chess C; VP, Fr C; Hmrm; Span C; SC; Bkbl; Ftbl; *Kans St U; Hist.*

WATSON, Rebecca Gayle
Sooner HS; Bartlesville, OK; Bus C; Ensm; FBLA; Pres, Church Yth Group; Pep C; *Claremore Jr Col; Bus.*

WATSON, Robert Alan
Westminster Christian HS; Miami,. FL (39-112) Hmrm; Co-Ed, Sch P; SC; Soccer; Tr; COM; Best Christian Witness.

WATSON, Robert Donald
Ayden-Grifton HS; Ayden, NC (14-196) NHS; VICA; Design C; *U of NC; Marine Bio.*

WATSON, Rose Marie
Norview Sr HS; Norfolk, VA (72-600) Pres, All Amer Yth; Chor; Fr C; FBLA; Hmrm; Monogram; Ntl Yth Conf; Var C; Bkbl; Sftbl; Cpt, Tr; Alg A; Bio A; Cl Fav; MLS; Pres A; Yth Fel; *Va Commonwealth U; Elem Ed.*

WATSON, Sharon Gay
Coleman HS; Coleman, TX; FHA; Latin I Scholastic A; *McMurry Col; Fine Arts-Drama.*

WATSON, Sheila
Halter HS; Wellston, MO (5-110) Chldr; Pres, Chor; FHA; Mjrte; NHS; Sch P; Tres, Soph Cl; Hon Prog; Type A; *Bus Off Ed.*

WATSON, Sheri Ann
Atherton HS; Burton, MI; Chor; Tr; Type A; Shorthand A; *Secy.*

WATSON, Steve Jon
Bonneville HS; Ogden, UT (10%-500) Dbte Tm; Ftbl; Ftbl Ltrman; *Weber St Col; Police Sci.*

WATSON, Susan Camille
Fayetteville HS; Fayetteville, AR; Chldr; Chor; Ch, FHA; Sch P; Drill Tm; Civics A.

WATSON, Tina Louise
Miramar HS; Miramar, FL (190-657) *Broward Co Sch of Practical Nurs; Nurs.*

WATSON, Tonya Renee
Wheaton HS; Wheaton, MO (7-34) JV; Chldr; Chor; Rptr; FHA; 4H; Hmrm; Bkbl; Sftbl; Tr; *SMS U; Farming.*

WATSON, Valerie Lynn
St Mary's Col; Raleigh, NC (13-103) Ann; BC; Drama; Ger C; Lat C; NHS; Pol Sci C; ARC; COM; ARC A; WW; *Wake Forest U; Law.*

WATT, John C
Crawford HS; San Diego, CA (90-600) AFS; Math C; NHS; Phys C; CSF; Math A; *U of Cal San Diego; Math.*

WATTENBARGER, Mark Steven
Narrows HS; Narrows, VA; Demolay; Span C; SC; Swim; Tnns; Pres, UMYF; Good Citz A; *U of Tenn; Law.*

WATTENBARGER, Richard Ernest
Putnam Co Sr HS; Cookeville, TN (10%-340) BC; Community Ym Symph; Fr C; NFL; Orch; Sch P; Spch C; St Stu Congress; Amer Leg Orator A; All St Orch; *Col-Conservatory at Cincinat; Mus.*

WATTERS, Anthony Marice
Kokomo HS; Kokomo, IN; Bus C; Chor; Drama; Hmrm; Order/ Arrow; Spch C; Tri-HiY; Bsbl; Ftbl; Sftbl; Amer Leg A; Most Out; Opt A; Order/ Arrow A; Spch A.

WATTERS, Joanne
Bethlehem Central Sr HS; Delmar, NY (300-377) FBLA; Yth Fel; Shorthand A; *St Margaret's Sch; Nurs.*

WATTERSON, Sheri Jan
David W Carter HS; Dallas, TX; Chor; Drama; Fr C; NHS; Spch C; NHS A; *Tex Tech U; Eng.*

WATTERUD, Lynn Eugene
Columbus HS; Columbus, ND (8-21) Drama; Rptr, Sch P; Var C; Bkbl; Ftbl; Tr; Yth Foundation; Sports Ltrs; *Glasgow Col; Plumbing.*

WATTS, Avis Drusilla
Compton Sr HS; Compton, CA (25%-850) Band; Orch; Span C; CSF; Hon Prog; Kiwanis A; Type A; *UCLA; Psych.*

WATTS, David Edward
Butler R-V HS; Butler, MO (13-96) Bus C; Chess C; Chor; FBLA; Parl, FFA; VP, 4H; Math C; Var C; Bsbl; Ftbl; Sftbl; Tr; Alg A; Math A; Sci A; Yth Fel; FFA St Chor; Nom, USNA; USMA; *U of Mo; Engr.*

WATTS, Debbie Lynn
Asheville HS; Asheville, NC (100-400) Crown & Scepter; Fr C; FHA; Hmrm; Ski C; SC; Sftbl; Tnns; Cl Fav; MLS; Yth Fel; Gamma Zeta Delta; Sigma Alpha Kai; *U of NC; Primary Ed.*

WATTS, Diana Lee
Wheelersburg HS; Wheelersburg, OH (23-131) Band; Chor; FHA; 4H; Sch Achieve Tm; Sch P; Sci C; Bkbl; Mgr, Sftbl; Tr; COM; NEDT; 'A' HR; Tr Ltr; 1st Pl Bkbl Tm; *Shawnee St Col; Med Tech.*

WATTS, Frank Byrd
Loris HS; Loris, SC (6-123) BS; 4H; Pres, Hmrm; NHS; Sci C; Bsbl; JV, Ftbl; Amer Leg A; Hon Prog; Most Out; Class Marshal; WW; Allied Yth; PC Jr Fel; *Clemson U.*

WATTS, Katherine Baldwin
Handley HS; Winchester, VA (53-265) JV; Chldr; Pres, Hmrm; Monogram; Sci C; SC; Jr Hist Soc; Gym; *Mary Washington Col; Dance.*

WATTS, Kathi Ann
Coronado HS; Colorado Springs, CO (90-400) A Cap Choir; Chor; SC; Arch; Swim; Young Life; *Westmont Col; Phys Therapist.*

WATTS, Mark Wadsworth
Hargrave Military Acad; Chatham, VA; Chess C; Fr C; Hmrm; SC; MVP, Bsbl; Bkbl; Ftbl; Cpt, Golf; Swim; *Wake Forest U; Engr.*

WATTS, Michael James
Maumee HS; Maumee, OH (91-354) Var C; Cpt, Bkbl; Cr-Ctry; Tr; *Owens Tech Col; Fire Sci.*

WATTS, Ora Bestella
W Charlotte HS; Charlotte, NC (417-594) Upward Bound JCSU Outst Stu; *NC Central U; Bus Adm.*

WATTS, Pamela Kay
Farmington Sr HS; Farmington, MO (5-275) A Cap Choir; Band; Madrigal; Span C; SC; Math A; Pom-Pon; A-Ed, Sch Paper; *William Jewell Col; Elem Ed.*

WATTS, Sheila Ann
McCurtain HS; McCurtain, OK (5-14) Bus C; Chldr; FHA; Secy, 4H; NHS; SC; Bkbl; Tr; Hist A; HQn; *Eastern Okla St Col; Nurs.*

WATTS, Stephen Franklin
James W Robinson Secondary Sch; Fairfax, VA; FTA; Citz A; Yth Fel; Patrol; *Asbury Col; Psych.*

WATTS, Timothy Morton
Lansdowne Sr HS; Baltimore, MD; NHS; Math A; Yth Fel; Art A; *Catonsville Comm Col; Bus.*

WATTS, Tommie Lynn
Picayune Mem HS; Picayune, MS (50-200) Chor; Drama; Ensm; NHS; Span C; COM; Hon Prog; Yth Fel; *SW Baptist Col; Eng.*

WAUGH, Carolyn Jane
Twin Lakes HS; W Palm Beach, FL (35-400) Co-Cpt, Chldr; Dbte Tm; Pres, Fr C; Pres, Key C; NFL; St Stu Congress; SC; JV, Cr-Ctry; JV, Tnns; Spch A; Parl, Key C; Kick-Off Qn; *Fla St U.*

WAUGH, Delia Kay
Tipton HS; Tipton, OK (3-63) Band; Chldr; Chor; FHA; 4H; NHS; Spch C; Bkbl; Sftbl; Citz A; 4H A; HCt; Interlochen Ntl Mus; Spch A; *PE.*

WAUGH, Douglas Allen
Pathfinder Regional Voc Tech HS; Three Rivers, MA (15-110) 4H; Bsbl; Bkbl; 4H A; Grange; *Carpentry.*

WAUGH, Micki Kay
College Park HS; Pleasant Hill, CA (5%-300) Tres, Band; Co-Ch, Chldr; Chor; Drama; Hmrm; Inter-Act C; InterClub Coun; Madrigal; Cpt, Mjrte; NHS; Spch C; SC; VP, Jr Cl; Bkbl; Sftbl; Swim; Tnns; Amer Leg A; Beauty; CSF; COM; Math A; Opt A; Most Outst Gym A; Most Outst Girl Ath; Highest Schol Average; *Cal St-Fullerton; Drama.*

WAUGHTAL, Elizabeth Anne
Bemidji HS; Bemidji, MN (9-405) Ger C; Pres, 4H; Sci C; Spch C; 4H A; N Minn Math Contest A; Sons of Norway; ISE Participant, Germany; *Lit.*

WAUN, Deborah Anne
Goshen HS; Goshen, IN; Band; Bus C; Chldr; Chor; Ensm; Orch; Sch P; Shorthand, Choir, Band, A's; *Marion Col; Ed.*

WAY, David Orelious
Crestview Sr HS; Crestview, FL (132-252) Bsbl; Mgr, Ftbl.

WAY, Hubert Andrew
Sullivan Central HS; Blountville, TN (96-379) Bkbl; Coach A, Bkbl; *U of Tenn; Law.*

WAY, Pamela Kay
Escanaba Area Pub HS; Escanaba, MI; JV, Band; 4H; Ski C; SC; Arch; Sftbl; JV, Tnns; 4H A; HCt; *Northland Col; Social Worker.*

WAYCHOFF, Patricia Lynn
Ripon HS; Ripon, CA (15-105) Band; Drama; FFA; FHA; 4H; Co-Cpt, Bkbl; Sftbl; Swim; Tr; *Pepperdine U; Life Sci.*

WEAD, Cindy Jean
Science Hill HS; Johnson City, TN; BC; Chor; Pres, Ger C; Orch; SC; MVP, Cr-Ctry; Tr; *Milligan Col.*

WEAK, Lannie Lee Jr
Burke HS; Omaha, NE (50-875) Chor; Ensm; Pres, HiY; Secy, SC; Bkbl; Co-Cpt, Ftbl; Hon Prog; Rotary A; Awana Ldr; *Dentistry.*

WEALE, Richard Dean
Campbell Central Sch; Campbell, NY (9-60) Band; Hmrm; NHS; Var C; Cpt, Soccer; Prom Kg; *Corning Comm Col; Math.*

WEATHERALL, James Thomas
Frost HS; Frost, TX (3-15) Drama; 4H; Spch P; Pres, SC; Bkbl; Ftbl; Tr; MLS; Most Rep; *Navarro Col; Computer Tech.*

WEATHERFORD, Karen Renee
Antioch HS; Antioch, TN (9-400) Band; VP, Bus C; VP, Hmrm; NHS; Span C; SC; Y-Tns; Bkbl; Sftbl; Art A; *Middle Tenn St U; Art.*

WEATHERFORD, Kenneth Gregory
Columbia Acad; Columbia, MS; Bkbl; Ftbl; Sftbl; Cl Fav; Mr Jr HS; *Pearl River Jr Col; Engr.*

WEATHERFORD, Sidney E I III
Rowan Center Hattiesburg HS; Hattiesburg, MS (125-525) *U of Sou Miss; TV-RADIO Production.*

WEATHERHEAD, Gwyneth Mary
Glenbard E HS; Lombard, IL (19-634) Chor; COM; Hon Prog; Home Ec A; *Northern Ill U; Special Ed.*

WEATHERHOLT, Otis Victor
Moorefield HS; Moorefield, WV (4-89) NHS; Pres, Sr Cl; *West Va U; Bio.*

WEATHERLY, Tammy Sue
Heritage HS; Littleton, CO (15%-399) Band; Cpt, Bkbl; Sftbl; Tnns; Hon Prog; Magna Cum Laude; Cpt, Vlbl; All-St Bkbl; All-St Sftbl; All League Bkbl; Outst Soph, Marching Band; All-League & All-St Vlbl; *U of Denver; Phys Ed.*

WEATHEROAD, Janice Yvonne
Briarcrest HS; Memphis, TN (25-370) Chldr; FHA; Secy, Hmrm; Y-Tns; Co-Cpt, Bkbl; Golf; Sftbl; COM; Hist A; Hon Prog; Magna Cum Laude; Math A; Sci A; Type A; Yth Fel; S-T, Yth Fel; All Star, Sftb; Vlbl; GSct; Eng A; Lat A; Span A; FCA; Jaycees.

WEATHERS, Deborah Lynn
Chinle HS; Chinle, AZ (4-145) Band; Drama; FHA; Model UN; Pres, NHS; Tres, Ski C; Tres, Span C; SC; Thes; 4H A; *Cochise Col; Med.*

WEATHERS, Mark Tracy
Jones Co HS; Gray, GA; Ann; Chess C; Drama; NHS; Order/ Arrow; Rptr, Sch P; Span C; SC; Y-Tns; Mgr, Ftbl; COM; *Brigham Young U; Communications.*

WEATHERS, Robert D Jr
Lakeside HS; Atlanta, GA; Key C; Var C; Tr; Cpt, MVP, Ftbl; Viking A; Cpt, MVP, Tr; Tr As; Atlanta Tr C; Man o-t Yr; *Presbyterian Col; Bus.*

WEATHERSBY, Donna
G W Carver Sr HS; New Orleans, LA; Pres, NHS; ARC; Tri-HiY; Semi, Ciz A; Semi-Fin, Phi Beta Kappa; Semi-Fin, Homecom Ct; Semi-Fin, Hon; *UCLA; Program Computers.*

WEATHERSPOON, Illinois
R E Lindblom; Chicago, IL (300-500) Chem C; Cpt, Dbte Tm; Drama; Fr C; Math C; Tnns; COM; Hon Prog; NMS; WW; *Trinity Col; Pre-Med.*

WEAVER, Amy Marie
Midwest City HS; Midwest City, OK; Band; NHS; Secy, Sci C; SC.

WEAVER, Beth
Northeast HS; N Little Rock, AR; Band; Orch; COM; *UCA; Special Ed.*

WEAVER, Carol Ann
Penns Grove HS; Penns Grove, NJ (13-277) Band; Chem C; Swim; COM; VFW A; VofDEM; GSct; Hon A.

WEAVER, Dauna Jean
Eufaula HS; Eufaula, OK; Chor; Ensm; 4H; NHS; Span C; Bkbl; Sftbl; 4H A; HCt; Hon Prog; Sal; Yth Fel; Runnerup, FFA Swtht; *Bethany Nazarene Col; Social Work.*

WEAVER, David Lee
N Gwinnett HS; Suwanee, GA (10-120) BC; Var C; Bkbl; Ftbl; Tnns; COM; Hon Prog; Math A; Most Intellectual; *Ga Tech U; Archt.*

WEAVER, Dick Richard Allen
Central Mid HS; Norman, OK; Chor; Ensm; Orch; Amer Leg A; Midwestern Mus Camp Schols; Mus Ltrs; Sup, Voc Mus Ensm & Solo Orch As; *Kans U; Mus.*

WEAVER, Don Stannard Jr
Southwestern Central HS; Jamestown, NY; Band; Ger C; Order/ Arrow; Ski C; Pres, Soph Cl; JV, Bkbl; Golf; HCt; Opt A; Ski Tm; Camper o-t Wk; *Alfred U; Engr.*

WEAVER, Donna Elaine
Granby HS; Norfolk, VA; Span C; Alg A; Math A; Sci A; Yth Fel; Jr NHS; Pres, Yth Fel; Span A; Jr Adv, Yth Group; Social Stu A; Sunday Sch Teacher; Eng A; *Old Deminion U; Elem Teaching.*

WEAVER, Evalin Claire
Vicksburg HS; Vicksburg, MS (5-244) A-Ed, Ann; JV, Chldr; Chor; Secy, Drama; GS; Key C; Lat C; Math C; NHS; Bkbl; Tnns; Bio A; HCt; Swtht; *Millsaps Col; Nurs.*

WEAVER, Gregory Allen
Tuscola HS; Tuscola, IL (16-118) Pres, Chor; FTA; VP, Lat C; Var C; Bkbl; Cpt, Cr-Ctry; Tr; *Eastern Ill U; Engr.*

WEAVER, Julius Andrews
Williamston HS; Williamston, NC (6-170) Band; Demolay; VP, Fr C; NHS; *NC St U; Archt.*

WEAVER, Karl Winter
Fairhope HS; Fairhope, AL (37-356) Parl, Band; Chess C; NHS; Order/Arrow; Tres, Sci C; Ch, Span C; Order/Arrow A; HS Bowl; Solo & Ensm Medals; Red Cross Sr Lifesaving; *U of S Ala; Engr.*

WEAVER, Leslie Ann
Abraham Lincoln HS; Denver, CO (197-728) A Cap Choir; Chor; Rptr, Sch P; Span C; Citz A; Eng A; *Bus.*

WEAVER, Linda Fay
San Diego HS; San Diego, CA; MVP, Bkbl; MVP, Golf; MVP, Sftbl; Type A; *San Diego St Col.*

WEAVER, Lori Lee
West HS; Billings, MT; Chor; Ensm; Sch P; Pres, Jobs Daughters; *E Mo Col.*

WEAVER, Lu Anne
Liberty Christian Sch; Durham, NC (2-9) Cpt, CYO; Chldr; Chor; Hmrm; SC; Bkbl; Sch Spirit A; Ath A; Cpt, Vlbl; *Watts Hospital Sch of Nurs; Nurs.*

WEAVER, Lydia Jane
Clarke Central HS; Athens, GA; Chor; Drama; Thes; *Oral Roberts U; Religion.*

WEAVER, Marjorie Koch
Walt Whitman HS; Bethesda, MD (599-753) A Cap Choir; Hmrm; ARC; SC; Hockey; I Dare You; ARC A; *Pa St U; Recreation.*

WEAVER, Marsha Wyllene
Maplewood HS; Nashville, TN (78-387) Band; Chor; SC; *Tenn St U; Psych.*

WEAVER, Mary Kay
Cotter HS; Winona, MN (21-96) Band; Chldr; Fr C; Hmrm; Sch P; Sodality; SC; Y-Tns; Tnns; Sunday Sch Teacher; Drill Tm; Candystriper; *St Cloud St Col; Bus.*

WEAVER, Micheal Todd
W Monroe HS; W Monroe, LA; Drama; Secy, Key C; Thes; Sftbl; Key C'Er o-t Yr; *NE La U; Bus Mgt.*

WEAVER, Millie Rose
Colchester HS; Colchester, IL (15-55) Ann; Tres, Band; Tres, Chor; Secy, Drama; Ensm; Secy, 4H; Pres, Hmrm; Math C; NHS; Pres, Jr Cl; Cpt, Bkbl; Sftbl; Tr; COM; 4H A; Swtht; Type A; S-T, FSA; Prom Qn; *Robert Morris Col; Bus.*

WEAVER, Pamela Gail
Derby Senior HS; Wichita, KS; JV, Chldr; Fr C; Tr; Hon Prog; Gym; *Oral Roberts U; Sci.*

WEAVER, Rita Arlene
Hiawatha HS; Hiawatha, KS (1-86) Chor; GS; Parl, 4H; Fin, Jr Miss Pageant; VP, NHS; Spch C; Citz A; Hon Prog; Val; *Kan St U; Social Work.*

WEAVER, Robert Thomas
Billings W HS; Billings, MT; Chor; Demolay; Key C; Math C; JV, Ftbl; JV, Swim; JV, Tnns; Mgr, Wrest; *Mont St U.*

WEAVER, Roger L
Potomac Sr HS; Oxon Hill, MD;

WEAVER, Rose Ellen
Walter E Stebbins HS; Dayton, OH; GS; Y-Tns; Vlbl, Tr, Ath, A's; Drill Tm.

WEAVER, Royal Worth III
W Columbus HS; Cerro Gordo, NC (15-204) BC; Span C; SC; Co-Cpt, Bkbl; Sci A; JC; *U of NC; Chem.*

WEAVER, Sharon Marie
Fairmont Sr HS; Fairmont, WV (12-300) Chor; VP, Mu Alpha Theta; Span C; Span NHS; Math A; *Fairmont St Col; Early Childhood Ed.*

WEAVER, Tami Lynn
Fairland HS; Fairland, OK (5-30) Co-Cpt, Chldr; Chor; Dbte Tm; Drama; FHA; 4H; Cl Fav; Gov Honor Prog; Hist A; HCt; *NE Okla A&M Col; Bus.*

WEAVER, Terri Kay
Burnside HS; Burnside, KY (2-40) Mgr, Ann; BC; Rptr, Sch P; DARGCA; Math A; Star Student; *Somerset Comm Col; Nurs.*

WEBB, Barry L
W Chester Christian Sch; W Chester, PA (8-25) Chor; Bkbl; MVP, Soccer; COM; Hon Prog; Pres A; Cpt, Soccer; *Bob Jones U; Religion.*

WEBB, Burnetta
Plymouth HS; Plymouth, NC (24-204) Hmrm; Math C; NHS; Span C; Tr; Marshal; *NC St U; Engr.*

WEBB, Cathi Ann
Huntington E HS; Huntington, WV (11-330) Secy, A Cap Choir; F-Ed, Ann; Fr C; Rptr, Hmrm; Key C; Mu Alpha Theta; NHS; Swtht; Zone & Regional Bible Quiz Tm; Sch Spirit A; *Marshall U; Sci.*

WEBB, Deborah Lynn
Durrett HS; Louisville, KY (32-250) A Cap Choir; BC; Chor; Ensm; FBLA; Mod Mus Mas; All-St Chor; *U of Louisville; Bus.*

WEBB, Janet Carole
Huntington HS; Shreveport, LA; FBLA; FHA; InterClub Coun; Span C; Mgr, Ftbl; Sftbl; Bkkeeping Proficiency A; Candy Striper; 4th Pl, Dist Lit Rally-Bkbl; Christian Ath o-t Yr; *La Tech U.*

WEBB, Jennifer Lynn
Westmont HS; Westmont, IL (1-160) Tres, NHS; Secy, ARC; Sch P; Soccer; Hon Prog; Math A; NEDT; *Bradley U; Bio.*

WEBB, Joanne Louise
Santa Rita HS; Tucson, AZ (16-576) A Cap Choir; Band; Chem C; Mgr, Chor; Ensm; Fr C; Hmrm; NHS; Orch; Sci C; SC; Bkbl; Hon Prog; Journ A; WW; Sup, Solo Ensm Festival; Regional Choir; *Los Angeles Baptist Col; Natural Sci.*

WEBB, John Douglas
Denver Christian HS; Denver, CO (20-70) JV, Bkbl; Tnns; Tr; *Baylor U; Dentistry.*

WEBB, John Edwin
Carriage Hills Christian Sch; Lawton, OK; Hmrm; Span C; Secy, SC; Pres, Sr Cl; Pres, Jr Cl; Citz A; Cl Fav; Hist A; MLS; Most Out; Sal; Val; Founders A; Okla St Citation; *Midwest Christian Col; Ministry.*

WEBB, Julia Leigh
Elbert Co Comp HS; Elberton, GA (27-260) BC; Span C; Co-Cpt, Bkbl; WW; *U of Ga; Elem Ed.*

WEBB, Katheryn Inez
McMinn Co HS; Athens, TN; FBLA; FHA; Tenn Off Ed C.

WEBB, Kathy Ann
Juanita HS; Kirkland, WA; FBLA; Hmrm; NHS.

WEBB, Kerry Scott
Center HS; Center, TX; Span C; Tnns; Sci.

WEBB, Laurie Ladene
Morrison HS; Morrison, OK (12-30) Ann; Bus C; FBLA; FHA; Hmrm; Sch P; SC; Tres, Sr Cl; Bkbl; Sftbl; COM; Citz A; HCt; Hon Prog; Type A; Val; Eng A; Okla Hon Soc; Okla Mus Teacher Assn A; St House of Rep Citation; *Okla St U; Computer Sci.*

WEBB, Leroy Gilbert
Maple Shade HS; Maple Shade, NJ (15-241) BS; Pres, Key C; NHS; Ftbl; Soccer; Tr; Cpt, Wrest; 1st Pl, St Craftsmen Show; *U of Del; Marine Biol.*

WEBB, Lori Ruth
Cloverdale HS; Cloverdale, IN (23-72) Sci C; Thes; WW; *DePauw U; Elem Ed.*

WEBB, Lynn Alexis
Slaton HS; Slaton, TX; All Amer Yth; Secy, Band; FHA; NHS; SC; Bkbl; Sftbl; Tnns; Beauty; 4H A; Lion A; Most Out; All St, All Dist, Bkbl; *Tex Tech U; Home and Family Relations.*

WEBB, Lynne Caroline
Osborne HS; Marietta, GA; Chldr; Chor; Hmrm; Sch P; Pres, Y-Tns; Beauty; HCt; *W Ga Col; Elem Ed.*

WEBB, Marjo Christine
Ouachita Parish HS; Monroe, LA (330-350) Anchor C; Spch C; Bkbl; Sftbl; COM; *Louisiana Col; Therapy.*

WEBB, Mark Foutch
Battle Ground Acad; Franklin, TN (5-76) Fr C; Key C; SC; Secy, Jr Cl; Tres, Soph Cl; Cr-Ctry; Tr; Plato Soc Off; Fr A; *Tenn Tech U; Pre-Law.*

WEBB, Renee Kathleen
Peru HS; Peru, IN; Chldr; Chor; *Fort Wayne Bus Col; Secy.*

WEBB, Richard Dean
Blanchet HS; Seattle, WA (76-285) BS; Tnns; *U of Wash; Engr.*

WEBB, Wanda Jean
John Barteam HS; Philadelphia, PA (5-36) Chor; COM; Drama A; *Data Processing.*

WEBBER, Benjamin James
Princeton HS; Princeton, IL (1-186) Band; St Scholar; NMS Win; Cpt, Scholastic Bowl Tm; *U of Mich; Lib Arts.*

WEBBER, Douglas Elliot
Homewood-Flossmoor HS; Flossmoor, IL (211-903) Orch; ARC; COM; *Elem Ed.*

WEBBER, James Clifford
Castleberry HS; Fort Worth, TX; Pres, Chor; Ensm; Key C; *Howard Payne U; Mus.*

WEBBER, Janet Lynne
Sparland HS; Sparland, IL (2-30) Co-Ed, Ann; Band; Chor; VP, FHA; Pres, 4H; NHS; Spch C; SC; 4H A; I Dare You; Vlbl; Pom Pon Squad; *Acct.*

WEBBER, Karen Louise
Shamrock HS; Decatur, GA (5-400) Chor; Span C; Yth Foundation A; *Dekalb Col; Nurs.*

WEBBER, Linda Christine
Motley HS; Columbus, MS (1-70) Arch; VP, BC; 4H; Hmrm; F-Ed, Sch P; Sci C; VP, SC; Tri-HiY; Secy, Jr Cl; Secy, Soph Cl; Bio A; Hist A; Math A; MLS; Sci A; Val; Eng A; Span A; DECA; *Miss St U; Acct.*

WEBBER, Stephen Edward
Castleberry HS; Ft Worth, TX (5-216) Rptr, A Cap Choir; Ensm; FTA; Ch, Key C; NHS; Sci C; Kiwanis A; *Sou Methodist Col; Bus.*

WEBBERT, David Gerard
Loyola HS; Baltimore, MD; Lit Mag; NHS; Cpt, Soccer; NEDT.

WEBER, Ann Lysbeth
Merrill Sr HS; Merrill, WI (10-379) A Cap Choir; Band; Chor; Ger C; Hmrm; Madrigal; Ski C; SC; Citz A; Opt A; Yth Fel; Vlbl; SC Pres A; WSMA Mus Contest A; *Mus.*

WEBER, Anthony Russell
Newton Comm HS; Newton, IL (15-260) Tres, Band; Ch, InterClub Coun; NHS; Orch; St Stu Congress; Parl, SC; Bkbl; Co-Cpt, Golf; COM; Type A; *E Ill U; Math.*

WEBER, Darlene Dee
Paulsboro HS; Paulsboro, NJ; All Amer Yth; Band; Ch, Hmrm; Cert of Appreciation; *Social Work.*

WEBER, Darren Christopher
Watkins Memorial HS; Pataskala, OH (70-210) VP, Hmrm; Monogram; Var C; Co-Cpt, Bsbl; Bkbl; JV, Ftbl; COM; HCt; *Dentistry.*

WEBER, David Philip
Dondero HS; Royal Oak, MI; MVP, Dbte Tm; Ger C; VP, Pol Sci C; Swim; Spch A; Star Spangled Banner A; Swim; *Law.*

WEBER, Elizabeth Ann
Arsenal Tech HS; Indianapolis, IN (20%-925) Secy, Ger C; Hmrm; NFL; ARC; Spch C; Sftbl; Cpt, Swim; Tnns; Hon Prog; ARC A; Spch A; Yth Fel; Swim A's; *Aquatics.*

WEBER, JoAnn Kay
Hilbert HS; Hilbert, WI (4-66) Ann; Tres, Band; Co-Cpt, Chldr; Ensm; NHS; Secy, Sr Cl; Secy, Soph Cl; Trees For Tomorrow Camp; *U of Wis; Acct.*

WEBER, Julie Anne
Valley HS; Gilcrest, CO (28-109) A Cap Choir; Bus C; Tres, Chor; FBLA; 4H; Hmrm; Madrigal; SC; District FBLA; 4th Conf, Econ; *Highland Hills Beauty Acad; Cosmetology.*

WEBER, Kandyce Lea
Parkway W HS; Ballwin, MO (21-630) NHS; ARC; Bio A; Chem A; Hon Prog; Ntl Conf Chr & Jews; Vlbl; *Carleton Col; Hist.*

WEBER, Kathleen Marie
Valmeyer HS; Valmeyer, IL (4-45) Chor; FHA; Rptr, Sch P; Sftbl; Math A; Pres Phys Fitness A; *SIU-Carbondale.*

WEBER, Kathy Jo
Newton Comm HS; Newton, IL (150-250) Bus C; Chor; FTA; Madrigal; Spch C; Sftbl; Tnns; Spch A; Type A; *MacMurray Col; Special Ed.*

WEBER, Kathy Marie
Valmeyer HS; Valmeyer, IL (4-45) Chor; FHA; Sch P; Sftbl; Math A; Pres A.

WEBER, Kevin Dale
Dover HS; Dover, OK (1-25) FFA; NHS; Var C; Bsbl; Bkbl; Val; Acct A; Most Scholarly; *Okla St U.*

WEBER, Kevin Matthew
Cary Grove HS; Cary, IL; Bsbl; Hon Prog; *Law.*

WEBER, Laurrie Louise
Randolph Pub HS; Randolph, NE (17-68) Chor; VP, Drama; Ensm; Madrigal; VP, Thes; Spch A; Yth Fel; Prom Court; *Nebr NE Tech Comm Col; Nurs.*

WEBER, Linda Lea
Arroyo HS; San Lorenzo, CA (4-350) A Cap Choir; Rptr, Ann; Chldr; Chor; Hmrm; Madrigal; Ch, Span C; Tres, SC; Var C; Cpt, Sr Cl; Cpt, Jr Cl; Secy, Soph Cl; CSF; Cl Fav; Elk A; JA A; MLS; Spch A; Job's Daughters; Fin, Gemco Schol; Trampoline; Ca Savngs & Loan Stu; Vlbl; Badminton; St Mus Ed Assn Excellent Ratng Solo; *Cal St Hayward; Bus.*

WEBER, Patricia Carol
Chester F Awalt HS; Mountain View, CA (40-368) Ann; Chldr; SC; Secy, Sr Cl; Hockey; Badminton; CASC Reg Secy, Publ Chairperson; *Foothill Col; Architecture.*

WEBER, Rebecca Lynnette
Richmond Sr HS; Richmond, IN (85-540) Chor; NHS; Pres, Rainbow; DARGCA; Ntl Achv Schol; *Ind U East; Ed.*

WEBER, Richard H
Grove City HS; Grove City, PA; Parl, FFA; Pres, 4H; Pres Phys Fitness As.

WEBER, Robert Daniel
Plant City HS; Plant City, FL (2-600) BS; Chess C; Demolay; Key C; Ch, Model UN; Tres, NHS; Ch, UN Council; Tnns; Amer Leg A; Bio A; DARGCA; Hist A; Math A; ROTC A; Sal; Army ROTC, Ntl ROTC Schol's; *U of Tampa; Civil Engr.*

WEBER, Roslyn Laurel
Richmond Sr HS; Richmond, IN; Fr C; VP, Rainbow; Sch P.

WEBER, Susan Jane
Westboro HS; Westboro, MA; AFS; Band; Secy, Chor; Dbte Tm; Rptr, Hmrm; ARC; Spch C; SC; Bkbl; Color Guard; Ice Skating; Secy & Ch, 1st Cl GSct; VP & Tres, Yth Fel; *Interior Decorator.*

WEBER, Susan Lillian
St Angela Hall Acad; Brooklyn, NY (1-90) Chldr; Chor; Drama; Hmrm; Math C; VP, NHS; COM; Hon Prog; Ntl Achv Schol; Phi Beta Kappa; Regent Schol; Val; *Adelphi U; Earth Sci Ed.*

WEBER, Timothy Edward
Montrose HS; Montrose, MO (4-26) Bus Mgr, Ann; NHS; VP, Jr Cl; Bkbl; Tr; Bio A; Heath A; Mech Drawing A; *CMSU-Warrensburg.*

WEBER, Tony Russell
Newton Community HS; Newton, IL (15-260) Tres, Band; NHS; Orch; St Stu Congress; Parl, SC; Bkbl; Golf; COM; Hon Prog; Type A; *Eastern Ill U; Math.*

WEBER, Vicki Sue
Freeburg Comm HS; Freeburg, IL (25%-150) Chldr; Pres, Sci C; Var C; Mgr, Cr-Ctry; Swim; JA A; Sci A; Yth Fel; *Belleville Area Col; Phys Therapy.*

WEBSTER, Christopher Lynn
E Tenn St U Sch; Johnson City, TN (30-64) Band; Order/Arrow; God & Country A; Eagle Sct; Coun On Ministries; *Draftsman.*

WEBSTER, Craig Alan
Dublin HS; Dublin, GA (24-225) Dbte Tm; Key C; Lit Ral; Var C; MVP, Ftbl; *Mercer Col; Pol Sci.*

WEBSTER, David Fitch
La Jolla HS; La Jolla, CA (250-550) Hmrm; Ski C; Order/Arrow A; Pres A; Sr Patrol Ldr, BSct.

WEBSTER, Deborah Jean
Griswold HS; Jewett City, CT (6-168) FNA; 4H; NHS; SC; UN Council; 4H A; Most Out; UN Rep; *Mohegan Comm Col; Nurs.*

WEBSTER, Florence Amelia
Harpeth HS; Nashville, TN (5%-90) Chor; Pres, Cum Laude Soc; Lat C; Math C; Mu Alpha Theta; Hon Prog; Math A; Yth Fel; Coun on Yth Ministries; Steering Committee; Handbell Choir; Church Adm Board; Ed, Church Yth Directory.

WEBSTER, Holly Ann
Highland HS; Ewing, MO; NHS; *Culver-Stockton Col; Art.*

WEBSTER, Iris Elaine
Highland HS; Ewing, MO (14-121) Chor; Drama; NHS; NHS A; *Burlington Beauty Acad; Beautician.*

WEBSTER, James Alan
Rossville Comp HS; Rossville, GA; Tres, Key C; SC; Wrest; Drama; Pres, VOCA; VOCA Spelling & Math As; Cand, St Pres VOCA.

WEBSTER, James Lance
Fayette Co HS; Fayette, AL (6-151) NHS; SC; Var C; Pres, Sr Cl; Bsbl; Cpt, Ftbl; COM; NEDT; Sportsmanship A, Ftbl; *U of Ala; Pre-Law.*

WEBSTER, Judith Lee
E Aurora HS; Aurora, IL (85-600) Band; Chor; VP, FTA; Mgr, Swim; Hon Prog; Co-Cpt, Swim; Pres, Church Yth Fel; Art A's; *Bethel Col; Art.*

WEBSTER, Laura Claire
Glencliff HS; Nashville, TN; Ed, Ann; Cpt, Chldr; GS; Rainbow; VP, SC; S-T, Jr Cl; Bkbl; Tnns; Citz A; Ann Staff A; *Middle Tenn St U; Mass Communications.*

WEBSTER, Mark David
Waukegan W HS; Waukegan, IL (31-529) Lit Mag; NFL; NHS; Orch; Spch C; Thes; JA A; NEDT; Spch A; *Lib Arts.*

WEBSTER, Melanie Anne
Homestead HS; Cupertino, CA; A Cap Choir; Chor; Swim; *De Anza Jr Col.*

WEBSTER, Phillip Steven
Central HS; Memphis, TN (100-260) Pres, Hmrm; Key C; Lit Mag; VP, Monogram; Order/Arrow; ARC; Sch Achieve Tm; Bsbl; Cr-Ctry; Cpt, Ftbl; COM; Cl Fav; H of F; Hon Prog; All-Memphis, All Conf Ftbl; *Memphis St U; Communications.*

WEBSTER, Tegree Allipa
Compton HS; Compton, CA; Chor; FHA; Hmrm; Lat NHS; Math C; Sch P; Ch, Bsbl; Bkbl; Ch, Sftbl; Swim; B Crocker A; Citz A; Cl Fav; DARGCA; Math A; MLS; Most Out; *UCLA; Fashion Designer.*

WECKERLY, Alan Guy Jr
Monroe HS; Monroe, WI (50%-268) Band; 4H; Cr-Ctry; Tr; 4H A; Most Improved A, Cr-Ctry; *UW at Platteville; Light Building Constr.*

WECKERLY, Scott Byron
Monroe HS; Monroe, WI (75-200) Band; Ensm; Ger C; Secy, 4H; Bkbl; MVP, Ftbl; *U of Wis; Mus.*

WEDDING, Karen Ann
Vanguard HS; Ocala, FL (16-350) Key C; Mu Alpha Theta; NHS; Span C; Swtht; Span, Phys Fitness, A's; *Sci.*

WEDDLE, Kathy Lynn
Northeast HS; Pasadena, MD (9-653) Tres, Mjrte; NHS; SC; Mjrte Ltr.

WEDDLE, Melissa Carol
John D Bassett HS; Bassett, VA (5-150) VP, AFS; Band; Ensm; S-T, NHS; Alg A; Gov Honor Prog; NML; Math Tm; Asst Church Pianist; All Region, All Co, Bands; Dist & Regional Forensics; Ed, Folklife Magazine; *Salem Col; Psych.*

WEDEMEYER, David Alvin
Steeleville Comm Unit HS; Steeleville, IL; Band; Chor; FBLA; SC; VP, Soph Cl; Bkbl; Sftbl; Swim; Amer Leg A; Cl Fav; MLS; Free Throw A; All Tourney Tm.

WEDEMEYER, Sally Ann
Exira Comm HS; Exira, IA (4-54) Ann; FHA; NHS; Var C; Pres, Sr Cl; VP, Jr Cl; Co-Cpt, Bkbl; Tr; COM; Hon Prog; *Iowa W Comm Col; Computor Prog.*

WEDEN, Paul Frederick
Borger HS; Borger, TX (15%-280) Span C; Yth Fel; *Frank Phillips Jr Col; Math.*

WEDGE, Tracey Ann
Chardon HS; Chardon, OH; All Amer Yth; AFS; Chor; Ensm; HiY; Rainbow; *Sawyer Col of Bus; Secy.*

WEDOW, Juli Anne
Rogers HS; Michigan City, IN (40-560) Drama; NHS; Orch; ARC; Span C; Var C; Swim; Amer Leg A; ARC A; Exchange Stu; Schol; *DePauw U; Nurs.*

WEED, Jerry Loyd Jr
James Island HS; Charleston, SC (3-200) BC; BS; Mu Alpha Theta; VP, NHS; JV, Bkbl; Ftbl; Tr; Wrest; Hon Prog; Math A; Most Out; Pres A; Sci A; All-Conf Ftbl Tm Center; *Clemson U; Computer Sci.*

WEED, Nancy Sue
Fairfield HS; Fairfield, AL (1-160) Ed, Ann; Cpt, Band; Tres, BC; InterClub Coun; Orch; Sch P; SC; Y-Tns; Beauty; Hist A; HCt; Stu o-t Mo, Exchange C; Top 5% School Acv, U of Al Alumni A; *U of Ala; Acct.*

WEEKES, Monica Ann
Moreau HS; Hayward, CA (24-383) CYO; 4H; Hmrm; Secy, Soph Cl; Bkbl; Mgr, Cr-Ctry; Fin, Tr; Amer Leg A; COM; Citz A; 4H A; Hon Prog; Star Student; Fr Francis Kladnik Schol; *U of Santa Clara; Hist.*

WEEKLEY, Anne Lynn
Hardaway HS; Columbus, GA (28-379) NHS; Cpt, Bkbl; Sftbl; Tr; Female Ath o-t Yr A; Bsbl, Bkbl, Tr A; *Auburn U.*

WEEKLEY, William Michael
Washington HS; Massillon, OH; Chor; S-T, Ger C; Parl, Hmrm; Ftbl; Yth Fel; *Bethany Col; Ministry.*

WEEKLY, Cindy Ann
Wilmot Pub Sch; Wilmot, SD (2-28) Rptr, FHA; GS; Pres, 4H; S-T, NHS; Tr; Amer Leg A; B Crocker A; 4H A; NMS; Secy & VP, 4-H C; Del, Gov Schol; 4-H Judgng Tm; Stu o-t Mo; Tres & Secy, Rough Riders Horse C; Jr-Sr Dramatic Play; *Northern St Col; Acct.*

WEEKLY, Steven Lane
Grand Blanc HS; Grand Blanc, MI (210-680) Ftbl; Opt A; *U of Mich.*

WEEKS, Ernest George
Lakewood Sr HS; St Petersburg, FL (23-454) NHS; Span C; Tres, SC; Golf; Soccer; Hon Prog; High-Q Tm; *U of Fla; Aeronautical Engr.*

WEEKS, Judy Faye
Southern HS; Durham, NC; *NC St U; Phys Ed.*

WEEKS, Louis David
Hanahan HS; Hanahan, SC; *TEC; Air Conditioning & Ref.*

WEEKS, Susan Claire
Leesburg HS; Leesburg, FL (10%-400) Secy, Sci C; DARGCA; *Marine Bio.*

WEGENER, Cindy Ann
Kewanee HS; Kewanee, IL (6-180) AFS; Fr C; SC; Tr; Hon Prog; Pres, VP, Tres, Hmrm; *Kewanee Pub Hospital; Radiological Tech.*

WEGER, Edward Victor
John F Kennedy Sr HS; Tumon, GUAM (1-511) Chess C; NHS; Sch P; JV, Cr-Ctry; JV, Ftbl; Journ A; Math A; NMS; *U of Calif; Law.*

WEGNER, Cynthia Lynn
Bellevue HS; Bellevue, WA (40-450) A-Ed, Ann; NHS; Rptr, Sch P; Cpt, Bkbl; Vlbl; Badminton; *WSU; Communications.*

WEGNER, Dale Allen
Westfield HS; Westfield, WI (7-100) Band; BS; Chess C; Ensm; Math C; VP, NHS; Order/Arrow; Var C; JV, Bkbl; JV, Ftbl; Golf; Amer Leg A; Math A; Order/Arrow A; *UW-Platteville; Civil Engr.*

WEGNER, Mark A
Stanton HS; Stanton, NE (8-54) Secy, FFA; Ger C; Pres, 4H; Tres, Soph Cl; 4H A.

WEGNER, Nancy Jean
Luverne HS; Luverne, MN (10-140) Band; Chor; Pres, FHA; Madrigal; *Moorhead St U; Med Tech.*

WEGSMAN, Deborah Lea
Hebrew Acad HS; Yonkers, NY (3-15) Drama; COM; Cpt, Vlbl.

WEHMHOEFER, Tara Beth Cornelia
Jamaica HS; Jamaica, NY (2-1102) A Cap Choir; Band; Chor; Lit Mag; Math C; NHS; Orch; Var C; JV, Bkbl; JV, Sftbl; Bio A; Gov Honor Prog; Hist A; Hon Prog; Math A; Regent Schol; Sal; Val; Fr A; Mus A; Fin, AAL Schol; Semi- fin, NHS Schol; *Queens Col; Theology.*

WEHNER, Sherry Lee
Bishop Watterson HS; Columbus, OH (85-256) Ski C; Tr; COM; *Med.*

WEHNER, Tim Jay
Oak Harbor HS; Oak Harbor, OH; Secy, 4H; Bkbl.

WEHRHAN, Tracy Dean
Waverly-Shell Rock HS; Waverly, IA (70-206) Chor; Var C; Bkbl; Ftbl; Swim; Tr; Eagle Sct; *Iowa St U; Engr.*

WEHUNT, Gary Ronald
Northside HS; Fort Smith, AR; Mu Alpha Theta; NHS; Bkbl; *U of Ark; Acct.*

WEIBERT, Kim Renee
Hillsboro HS; Hillsboro, KS; Band; Chldr; Chor; 4H; Span C; SC; *Kans St U; Fashion Merchandising.*

WEIBLE, Jerry Lynn
Mossyrock HS; Mossyrock, WA (5%-34) CYO; Chor; FBLA; FFA; VP, NHS; Ed, Sch P; Pres, Sci C; Pres, SC; Var C; Pres, Soph Cl; Ftbl; Tr; NEDT; *U of Wash.*

WEIBY, Michael Richard
St Patrick HS; Chicago, IL (48-342) Chor; NHS; Order/Arrow; Rptr, Sch P; SC; Ch, Sr Cl; Swim; Tr; Life Sct; *Northwestern U; Engr.*

WEICHERS, Stacey
Willows HS; Willows, CA (11-130).

WEICHERT, Cindy Sue
Assumption HS; Assumption, IL (1-35) Ann; Drama; NHS; F-Ed, Sch P; VP, SC; Thes; Hon Prog; Journ A; St Scholar; Val; SAA.

WEIDEL, Cheryl Anne
Newfane Sr HS; Newfane, NY (27-192) Bus C; Chor; NHS; Co-Ed, Sch P; Hon Prog; *Bryant & Stratton Bus Inst; Court Rptr.*

WEIDEMAN, Randy Scott
Beloit HS Mem Campus; Beloit, WI (15%-600) Band; Bsbl; Sftbl; Tnns; Band Solo As; Sftbl As; Tnns Letters; *U of Madison; Computer Sci.*

WEIDLER, Janet Lynn
Gainesville HS; Gainesville, FL (35-483) Mu Alpha Theta; NHS; Tres, Span C; Span NHS; Yth Choir; Span A; Schol A; Yth Church Coun; NHS As; FCA; Jr Humane Soc; *U of F; Phych.*

WEIDLER, Scott Clifford
Lutheran HS; Burbank, CA; A Cap Choir; A-Ed, Ann; Pres, Band; Pres, SC; Pres, Jr Cl; Tres, Soph Cl; Mgr, Bkbl; Mgr, Sftbl; Concordia A of Excellence; Synodical Grant; *Concordia Col; Mus.*

WEIDLER, Susan Denise
Gainesville HS; Gainesville, FL (25-500) Band; Ger C; NHS; Span C; Citz A; *U of Fla.*

WEIDLICH, Jonathan Andrew
Stephen Decatur HS; Decatur, IL (15-290) Lit Mag; NHS; Ed, Sch P; COM; Journ A; Q&S A; *Richland Comm Col; Journ.*

WEIDNER, Amy Phyllis
Fargo S HS; Fargo, ND (50-200) GS; NHS; Sch P; Swim; Alg A; Journ A; Yth Fel; Pom Pon; *Minn St Col; Journ.*

WEIDNER, David Lee
Octavia HS; Colfax, IL (10-50) Chor; Ensm; Hmrm; NHS; Co-Ed, Sch P; Sci C; Pres, SC; Ftbl; St Scholar; *Harding Col; Bible.*

WEIDNER, James David
William Allen HS; Allentown, PA (69-777) Band; NHS; Order/Arrow; ARC; Var C; Swim; God & Country A; Hon Prog; Order/Arrow A; *Shippensburg St; Bus Adm.*

WEIDNER, Nancy Jean
Downers Grove S HS; Downers Grove, IL (75%-550) Young Adult Art Talent Contest; Secy.

WEIER, Jaime Sue
Freeport Sr HS; Freeport, IL (120-558) Chor; Ger C; Math C; Sci C; Cr-Ctry; Tr; Bio A; COM; Cl Fav; Hist A; Math A; MLS; Most Out; Poet A; Sci A; Spch A; Star Student; Yth Fel; Essay A; Ice Skating A; Poetry A; Reading A; Ballet A; *Doctor of Sports Med.*

WEIGEL, Dulce Anne
Rhinebeck Central HS; Rhinebeck, NY (10%-150) Band; Ensm; NHS; COM; Hon Prog; Pres, Bell Choir; Vol, Co Fair; Acolyte; Sr Choir; Social Ch, Church Yth Group.

WEIGEL, John Michael
Columbia HS; Columbia, PA (13-109) Pres, NHS; Co-Ed, Sch P; SC; Pres, Var C; Bsbl; Cpt, Bkbl; *DARGCA; Sociology.*

WEIGEL, Timothy Christian
Rhinebeck Central HS; Rhinebeck, NY (4-110) Band; Chor; Ensm; NHS; NEDT; Regent Schol; ROTC A; NY All-St Choir; Ltr of Commendation, NMS; Pres, Church Yth Group; *U of R; Math.*

WEIGELT, Lynette Ann
Logan-Magnolia Comm HS; Logan, IA (4-66) Bus Mgr, Ann; Pres, Band; VP, Chor; Ensm; VP, 4H; Madrigal; Pres, NHS; SC; Secy, Jr Cl; JV, Bkbl; Sftbl; 4H A; *Grand View Col; Nurs.*

WEIHS, Randall Francis
Manasquan HS; Manasquan, NJ; Kiwanis A; Board of Ed Academic A.

WEIKEL, Jan Ellen
Hershey Sr HS; Hershey, PA (39-264) FBLA; Ger C; Bkbl; ARC A; Gregg Filing A; Off Procedures; 3rd Pl, Region, FBLA Conf; *Harrisburg Area Comm Col; Retailing.*

WEIKERT, Douglas Ray
Springs Valley HS; French Lick, IN (1-95) Band; Fr C; SC; Bsbl; Bkbl; Ftbl; Golf; Fr As; Highest GPA.

WEILAND, Pamela Lee
Kirkwood HS; St Louis, MO (81-592) A Cap Choir; Chor; Ensm; Sftbl; COM; Yth Foundation; Fresh Schol A; *Central Methodist Col; Mus Ed.*

WEILER, Jeffrey Keith
Blacksburg HS; Blacksburg, VA (95-298) Order/Arrow A; All Region Band; *Va Tech U; Archt.*

WEILER, Lynda Mary
Oregon City HS; Oregon City, OR; *Willamette U; Legal Secy.*

WEILER, Mark Steven
Lyon Pub Sch; Lyons, NE (7-39) Band; FFA; Orch; Var C; Ftbl; Tr; Wrest.

WEIMAN, Larry Alan
Quincy Notre Dame HS; Quincy, IL (15-160) CYO; NHS; SC; Var C; VP, Jr Cl; Bsbl; Co-Cpt, Ftbl; *Bus.*

WEIMER, Sandra Jo
David Starr Jordan HS; Long Beach, CA; Band; Orch; Leo C; *U of Calif; Vet Sci.*

WEINBERG, Melinda Candace
Vicksburg HS; Vicksburg, MI; Band; 4H; Mjrte; Sci C; SC; Sftbl; COM; 4H A; *Grand Rapids Baptist Col; Commercial Art.*

WEINBERG, Mortimer Meyer III
Wilson Hall Acad; Sumter, SC (10%-55) Order/Arrow; Ed, Sch P; Tnns; God & Country A; Hist A; Order/Arrow A; Yth Fel; Photographer, Ann; Tres, Octagon C; Hist C; Eagle Sct; Tres, Photography C; Pres, Sunday Sch Cl; *Wofford Col; Pre-Law.*

WEINDORFF, Janice LaVerne
Stonewall HS; Stonewall, LA (6-21) VP, FBLA; VP, FHA; 4H; Fin, Lit Ral; Sch P; 4H A; Type A; *La Tech; Secy.*

WEINDORFF, Marvin Timothy
Stonewall HS; Stonewall, LA (3-34) Parl, FBLA; 4H; Fin, Lit Ral; Sch P; Alg A; Bio A; Math A; Phy A; Sci A; Spch A; Pres, VP, Rep, FFA; Pres, Treas, Stu Coun; Most Intelligent; *La Tech; Agr.*

WEINGARTNER, Linda Elly
Amos Alonzo Stagg HS; Palos Hills, IL (96-532) Chldr; Chor; Ger C; InterClub Coun; Mjrte; Hon Prog; Ntl Yth Phys Fitness A; *U of Ill; Lang.*

WEINGARTZ, Carol Marie
Holy Cross HS; Marine City, MI; NHS; Tr; Hon Prog.

WEINGARTZ, Cynthia Frances
Holy Cross HS; Marine City, MI; Chldr; FTA; VP, NHS; Sch P; Pres, Soph Cl; *Mich St U; Horticulture.*

WEINHOLD, Lisa Faith
East HS; Pueblo, CO (30-550) A Cap Choir; Chor; Drama; Pres, Fr C; Pres, FBLA; NHS; Thes; Rotary A; *U of Sou Colo; Nutrition.*

WEINKAUF, Suzanne Marie
Topeka HS; Topeka, KS (1%-490) Chor; Bkbl; Sftbl; COM; JV, Vlbl; Top 1%; Drill Tm; *Concordia Col at Seward; Ed.*

WEINMAN, Gary Michael
S San Antonio W Campus HS; San Antonio, TX (20-160) Chor; Ger C; Hmrm; SC; Var C; Cpt, Ftbl; Sftbl; Cpt, Tr; Hon Prog; Yth Fel; All Dist Ftbl; 300 C, Weightlifting; *Howard Payne U; Bus.*

WEINMAN, Melissa Elizabeth
Luverne HS; Luverne, MN (4-130) AFS; Co-Ed, Ann; Band; Chldr; Pres, FHA; Ger C; VP, 4H; NFL; NHS; Rptr, Sch P; Spch C; Thes; Golf; Spch A; WW; 4th Pl, St Declam; *Carleton Col; Studio Art.*

WEINREICH, Lawrie Stevens
Lake Highlands HS; Dallas, TX; CYO; Chor; Model UN; Mod Mus Mas; Orch; Order/Arrow; Ski C; Golf; Soccer; Swim; God & Country A; ARC A; Eagle Sct; Best of Show, St Fair; *Tex A&M U; Engr.*

WEINTRAUB, Samuel Isaac
George Washington Carver Sr HS; Montgomery, AL (6-400) Ann; Band; Ger C; Math C; Tres, Mu Alpha Theta; Tres, NHS; Order/Arrow; ARC; Sci C; Order/Arrow A; ARC A; Pres, SE Found of Temple Yth; Eagle Sct; *Brandeis U; Pol Sci.*

WEIR, Alexandra Lee
Brazoswood HS; Clute, TX (15%-490) Ann; Rptr, Bus C; Rptr, FBLA; FHA; 4H; NHS; Span C; COM; God & Country A; 4H A; VP, JA; Drill Tm; *Tex A&M U; Acct.*

WEIR, Deborah Jo
Toms River N S; Toms River, NJ (56-435) Tres, Band; Hmrm; Secy, Key C; Model UN; NHS; SC; Pres, Sr Cl; Tr; Hon Prog; Yth Fel; Prom Ch; Executive Committee; *U of Md; Computer Sci.*

WEIR, Donna Mae
Searcy HS; Searcy, AR (15-215) A Cap Choir; Band; BC; Chor; Community Yth Symph; Drama; Co-Cpt, Ensm; FTA; 4H; Co-Cpt, Madrigal; Co-Cpt, Mjrte; Mod Mus Mas; NHS; Orch; Rainbow; ARC; Golf; Sftbl; Swim; Tr; Pres A; ARC A; Pres, 1st Cl, GSct; *Neurology.*

WEIR, Eric Wayne
North Co HS; Desloge, MO (48-188) Band; Bus C; Chess C; Chor; FBLA; Hmrm; Pres, NHS; SC; Var C; Pres, Jr Cl; VP, Soph Cl; Bkbl; Ftbl; Tnns; Hon Prog; *MAC.*

WEIR, Teresa Jan
Mt Carmel HS; Mt Carmel, IL (23-187) Chldr; Chem C; Chor; Drama; Lat C; Math C; Secy, Jr Cl; Secy, Soph Cl; Sr GSct; *Phys Therapy.*

WEIR, Thomas Daniel
Morgan City HS; Morgan City, LA; Chor; Drama; K of C; Lit Ral; Pres, Spch C; Bkbl; JV, Ftbl; JV, Soccer; Tnns; VFW A; VFW Orator Win; VofDEM; Swtht Court; *La Tech U; Pre Law.*

WEIS, Larry Wayne
Ulysses HS; Ulysses, KS (15-110) CYO; NHS; Var C; Bkbl; Ftbl; Swim; Tnns; *Pittsburg St U; Construction Technology.*

WEISBERG, Bradley Eugene
Redlands HS; Redlands, CA; A Cap Choir; Chor; Drama; NFL; Ftbl; Bank Of Amer A; *Crafton Hills Col; Drama.*

WEISBERG, Gary Codworth
Redlands HS; Redlands, CA; A Cap Choir; Chor; Drama; Model UN; Thes; Bsbl; Bkbl; Sftbl; Ch, Security Coun; *Ed.*

WEISENBECK, Denise Jude
Durand HS; Durand, WI; Band; Drama; 4H; NHS; Sodality; WW; Waseca Col; Animal Tech.

WEISENBERGER, Terri Carol
Liberty HS Unit 2; Liberty, IL (19-46) F-Ed, Ann; JV, Chldr; Chor; Ensm; FHA; Pres, 4H; Sci C; SC; Var C; Tr; 4H A; Most Out; Tres, Pep C; Sr Choir; Cpt, Vlbl; Chrch Yth Fel; Tumbling; 4-H C; Church Organist; Sunday Sch Pianist; Quincy Col; Art.

WEISENFELS, John Charles
Subiaco Acad; Subiaco, AR; CYO; Chor; Order/Arrow; Span C; Ftbl; Bio A; Hist A; Hon Prog; Order/Arrow A; Eagle Sct; U of Ark; Sci.

WEISENSEL, Jeffery Dean
Beaver Dam HS; Beaver Dam, WI (17-310) BS; Chess C; Dbte Tm; Demolay; Pres, 4H; Hmrm; Pres, Order/Arrow; Sch P; Spch C; SC; Var C; Tres, Bsbl; Tres, Bkbl; Tres, Ftbl; Tres, Tr; Tres, Wrest; Citz A; God & Country A; 4H A; Hon Prog; Spch A; Eagle Sct; DeMolay Rep; Ntl Sojourners, Ntl Bicen Yth; U of Wis; Civil Engr.

WEISER, Mary Christine
Fairview HS; Fairview, MT (12-40) Band; CYO; Chldr; Chor; Ensm; Jr Miss Pagent; Madrigal; Mjrte; Rainbow; S-T; SC; Bkbl; Tr; Masonic A; Hon Choir; Rainbow Grand Choir; I-Rating, Solo; Carroll Col; Med.

WEISER, Tammy Darlene
Chamberlain HS; Tampa, FL; Anchor C; Chiefette, Band; Bus Asst; Hillsborough Comm Col.

WEISER, William Harold
Hershey Sr HS; Hershey, PA (75-250) Band; Chor; Ensm; Pres, Hmrm; NHS; Mgr, Bkbl; Mgr, Tr; Hon Prog; Susquehanna U; Religion.

WEISS, Bryan Duane
Pflugerville HS; Pflugerville, TX (1-76) VP, BC; Tres, FFA; Pres, NHS; SC; Ftbl; Alg A; COM; Hon Prog; Math A; Tex A&M U; Agr Econ.

WEISS, Daniel George
Center HS; Center, ND (10-42) Drama; Rptr, FFA; Ger C.

WEISS, Georganne
Laguna Beach HS; Laguna Beach, CA; Chor; Fr C; Ski C; Bkbl; Ftbl; Tr; DARGCA; Badminton; U of Calif; Early Childhood.

WEISS, Jackie Rose
Pflugerville HS; Pflugerville, TX (10%-107) Pres, BC; VP, FHA; Ger C; NHS; Span C; SC; VP, Soph Cl; Bkbl; Tr; Chamber of Comm A; Hist A; Concordia Lutheran Col; Bus.

WEISS, Kathy Sue
Gilbert HS; Gilbert, MN (25-67) Ann; Band; CYO; Chor; Sci C; Bkbl; Tnns; Tr; HCt; Hon Prog; Mesabi Comm Col.

WEISS, Ron
Hebrew Acad of Nassau Co; Uniondale, NY (1-50) Sal; Summa Cum Laude; Princeton U; Med.

WEISS, Ted Bernard
Doane Stuart HS; Albany, NY (33%-40) Chor; Ski C; Bkbl; Tnns; VASSAR Col; Med.

WEISS, Theodore Bernard
Doane Stuart HS; Albany, NY (33%-38) Ski C; Tnns; Vassar Col; Med.

WEISS, Victoria Dawn
Centerville HS; Centerville, OH; Fr C; Swim; Tr; 4H A; Pres A; Yth Fel; Gym; Fr C; Sweet Briar Col; Sci.

WEISS, Walt Michael
Post Falls HS; Post Falls, ID (1-154) Tr; Val; NML; WW; Oreg St U; Chem Engr.

WEISSE, Cindy Ann
Mona Shores HS; Muskegon, MI; Band; Orch; Swim; Tr; Mus.

WEISSER, Chad Stanley
Foley HS; Foley, MN (33%-200) Chor; Ensm; Var C; Ftbl; Golf; JV, Wrest.

WEISSHAAR, Janet Lee
Santa Monica HS; Santa Monica, CA (45-840) Cpt, Band; Ger C; Model UN; Orch; CSF; COM; WW; United Methodist Women A; Calif St Northridge; Bus.

WEITZEL, Ken Edward
Manchester HS; Akron, OH (60-250) Akron U; Mech.

WEITZEN, Steven Howard
Hightstown HS; Hightstown, NJ (1-253) AFS; Ed, Ann; Fr C; Pres, NHS; MLS; St Jr Double Champ, Table Tnns; Dickinson Col; Pol Sci.

WELBER, Kevin Amit
Canarsie HS; Brooklyn, NY (14-945) NHS; Tr; Hist A; Hon Prog; Regent Schol; Co-Cpt, Math Tm; SUNY; Pol Sci.

WELBORN, David Neil
Phil Campbell HS; Phil Campbell, AL (7-95) F-Ed, Ann; FTA; NHS; F-Ed, Sch P; Bkbl; Rptr, Ftbl; Amer Leg Orator A; COM; 4H A; I Dare You; Rptr, Phil Campbell Sr 4-H C; Pres, Franklin Co 4-H Coun; UAB; Premed.

WELBURN, William Drummond IV
John Jay HS; Hopewell Junction, NY (61-551) Band; Chess C; Chor; Drama; Ensm; Hmrm; NHS; Thes; JV, Ftbl; Co-Cpt, Soccer; Regent Schol; Auburn U; Math.

WELCH, Becky Lynette
Warren HS; Monmouth, IL (16-45) Bus Mgr, Ann; Bus C; Tr; Amer Leg A; Pres Clrm for Young Amer.

WELCH, Benny David
Ringgold HS; Ringgold, GA (1-230) Tres, BC; Pres, Chor; Dbte Tm; Drama; Pres, FBLA; Rptr, Hmrm; Key C; Lit Ral; SC; COM; Gov Honor Prog; Hon Prog; Opt A; Spch A; Type A; Val; Yth Fel; Acct A; GA Power Schol; Chor A; Pres, Bible C; Pres, PTSA; Dalton Jr Col; Bus Adm.

WELCH, David Duane
Callaway HS; Callaway, NE (7-24) All Amer Yth; Band; Cpt, Chldr; 4H; St Stu Congress; SC; Pres, Var C; Bsbl; Cpt, Ftbl; Tr; HCt; Hon Prog; Fin, Homecoming Kg; Cradon St U; Agr.

WELCH, David Lynn
Crestview HS; Crestview, FL; Auburn U; Wild Life Mgt.

WELCH, Elizabeth Louise
Williamsburg Acad; Kingstree, SC (12-50) Chor; Semi-Fin, Jr Miss Pa; Sch P; Pres, SC; Co-Cpt, Bkbl; Tnns; Beauty; Most Out; Columbia Col; Pub Relations.

WELCH, James Earl
Edward H White HS; Jacksonville, FL; Demolay; Sftbl; Berklee Sch of Mus; Guitar.

WELCH, Jed JoeEd
Vega HS; Vega, TX; Drama; Parl, FFA; Key C; SC; Bkbl; Ftbl; Best Actor, UIL; Dist One Act Plays; Hon Men, Bi-Dist Plays.

WELCH, John Walter
Swain HS; Bryson City, NC (30-115) FTA; Pres, 4H; Pres, Hmrm; Bus Mgr, Monogram; ARC; Sci C; SC; COM; Citz A; 4H A; ARC A; Heartfund, Founder's, A's; Pres, United Heartfund; Health C; Head Stu Trnr; Ntl Ath Trnr Assn; E Carolina U; Med.

WELCH, Karen Sue
Palmdale HS; Palmdale, CA (26-497) Chldr; Chor; Rainbow; Hon Prog; 2nd Pl, Tnns Trophy; Dodger A Tickets; Azusa Pacific Col; Bus.

WELCH, Lee Andrew
Marvell HS; Marvell, AR (4-151) BC; Rptr, Sch P; U of Ark; Math.

WELCH, Leonard Alfonso
Food And Maritime Trade HS; NY, NY;

WELCH, Linda Rene
Moses Lake HS; Moses Lake, WA (30-345) Hmrm; NHS; Ed, Sch P; SC P; VP, Jr Cl; JV, Tr; Powder Puff Ftbl; Stu o-t Week; Vennard Col; Christian Ed.

WELCH, Margaret Mary
Acad of Our Lady of Mercy; Milford, CT (13-93) Chor; Fr C; VP, NHS; Ski C; Mgr, Swim; NEDT; Col at Holy Cross; Ec.

WELCH, Mary Frances Ellen
St Mary's Acad; Alexandria, VA; Ann; CYO; Chldr; Secy, Fr C; Secy, French NHS; Key C; Math C; Mu Alpha Theta; ARC; Swim; COM; Gov Honor Prog; HCt; Hon Prog; NEDT; ARC A; Type A; Fr A; Health A; Phys Ed A; First Hons; Vanderbilt U; Phar.

WELCH, Mary Janelle
McGavock HS; Nashville, TN (7-970) BC; Pres, Fr C; FFA; GS; Hmrm; Mu Alpha Theta; NFL; SC; Hon Prog; Spch A; U of Tenn; Vet Med.

WELCH, Michelle Irene
John Marshall Fundamental HS; Pasadena, CA; Cpt, Bkbl; CSF; Anderson Col.

WELCH, Nancy Wynette
Orangefield HS; Orangefield, TX (6-76) Ann; Band; Drama; FHA; Tres, FTA; Pres, Lit Mag; Mjrte; VP, NHS; Sch P; Pres, Jr Cl; HR; WW; FTA' ER of Yr; Big O' As; Lamar U; Secretarial.

WELCH, Patricia Lee
W Union Attendance Center; Pinola, MS (1-50) Ann; BC; FBLA; FHA; Ed, Sch P; Secy, Sr Cl; Hist A; Math A; MLS; Star Student; Val; Most Intellectual; Co-Lin Jr Col; Secy Sci.

WELCH, Reba Jean
Lake Co HS; Leadville, CO (41-135) Ann; Secy, Band; Bus C; Co-Cpt, Chldr; FBLA; Ger C; Ski C; SC; Var C; Hon Band A; 1st Chair A; Western St Col; Bus.

WELCH, Ronald Buck
Coronado HS; Lubbock, TX; Orch; Mgr, Bsbl; Tex Tech U; Military Sci.

WELCH, Susan Ducote
Cottonport HS; Cottonport, LA (6-60) Band; BC; NHS; Co-Ed, Sch P; Co-Cpt, Bkbl; HCt; Hon Prog; Woodman o-t World; LSUA; Math Ed.

WELCH, Terri Elaine
du Pont Manual HS; Louisville, KY (1-362) Chor; Pres, Dbte Tm; Ensm; 4H; Lit Mag; Madrigal; NHS; Sci C; VP, Span C; Pres, Spch C; Amer Leg Orator A; COM; 4H A; Hon Prog; Journ A; Math A; NEDT; Sci A; Spch A; Type A; Val; VFW Orator Win; VofDEM; Hannah Mem A; High-Q Tm; Elvy Curtain Smith A; Schol A; Advanced Placement Graduate; Ky Wesleyan Col; Pre-Law.

WELCHER, Mark Andrew
Ballou HS; Washington, DC (3-30) Md U; Computering.

WELDON, Christine Ann
Plainview HS; Ardmore, OK (33%-50) Band; Chldr; Chor; Rptr, FHA; 4H; Swim; Tr.

WELDON, David Gerard
Owensboro Cath HS; Owensboro, KY (15-230) Pres, CYO; Hmrm; NHS; Pres, SC; Mgr, Bsbl; Bkbl; Ftbl; Tnns; Citz A; Most Out; Opt A; Civitan A; U of Ky; Engr.

WELDON, David Reams
Warren Acad; Warrenton, NC (33%-27) Drama; Fr C; NC St U; Entertainment.

WELDON, JoAnn Kay
Detroit Lakes Sr HS; Detroit Lakes, MN (28-290) Chor; Amer Leg A; Citz A; Yth Fel; Vlbl; Moorhead St Col; Hist.

WELDON, Michael Wayne
Rancho Cotate HS; Rohnert Park, CA;

WELDON, Sherrill Anne
The Bolles Sch; Jacksonville, FL; VP, Drama; Ed, Lit Mag; Pres, Lit Soc; Jacksonville U; Drama.

WELDY, Robert Stan
Mt Healthy HS; Cincinnati, OH; Bus Mgr, A Cap Choir; Chess C; Bus Mgr, Chor; Pres, Drama; Ensm; InterClub Coun; Sch P; Thes; Var C; Cr-Ctry; Tr; Wrest; COM; God & Country A; HCt; Interlochen Ntl Mus; Marion Col; Drama.

WELK, Glenn Eugene
Anacortes HS; Anacortes, WA (1-195) Pres, Chor; Ensm; Key C; Model UN; NHS; Pres, SC; Var C; Pres, Jr Cl; Bsbl; Bkbl; Cr-Ctry; Elk A; Kiwanis A; Most Out; Val; Top 10 Acad A; Outst 10; Bus Adm.

WELK, William Alan
Lowpoint-Washburn HS; Washburn, IL (11-51) Math C; Var C; Bsbl; Bkbl; Cr-Ctry; Tr; Hon Prog; Yth Fel; 1st Pl A, Cr-Ctry; Sou Ill U; Radio-tV.

WELKER, Darlene Ellen
Eastern Regional HS; Gibbsboro, NJ; Band; Chldr; Chor; Span C; Hon Prog; Most Artistic; Gym Tm; EYC; Choir A; Art Staff; Ed, Yrbk; Teacher of Special Children.

WELKER, David Mitchell
Frankfort HS; Ridgeley, WV (10%-151) NHS; SC; Tres, Sr Cl; Tres, Jr Cl; VP, Soph Cl; JV, Bkbl; Cr-Ctry; Tr; Bio A; Hist A; MLS; NEDT; Wm Randolph Hearst Sen Yth Del; Potomac St Col; Secondary Ed.

WELKER, Keith Bernhardt
Neshannock HS; New Castle, PA (22-150) Band; Drama; Hmrm; Lat C; Math C; NHS; Sci C; Bkbl; Cr-Ctry; Sftbl; Tr; Bio A; HCt; Hon Prog; MLS; Houghton Col; Pre-Med.

WELKER, Vicki Anne
Southwest HS; St Louis, MO; A Cap Choir; Sftbl.

WELKIE, Katherine Ann
Logan Sr HS; Logan, UT (20-235) Community Yth Symph; NHS; Orch; VP, Sci C; Citz A; U of Utah; Hist.

WELLBORN, Charles Daniel
Clinton Sr HS; Clinton, TN; Chor; Demolay; Sftbl; Pres, RA'S; Comm Chor; Carson Newman Col; Minister of Mus.

WELLER, Ellen Jane
Perry Meridian HS; Indianapolis, IN (53-564) Band; NHS; St Scholar; Drum Major; Ind U; Optomistrist Tech.

WELLER, Ellen Jane
Perry Meridian HS; Indianapolis, IN (44-550) Band; NHS; St Scholar; Drum Major; Ind U; Optometric Tech.

WELLER, John Robert
Coatesville Area Sr HS; Coatesville, PA (22-630) Chor; Fr C; Ger C; NHS; NEDT; Dist & Region Chor; Gifted Stu Prog; Ind U of Pa; Geog.

WELLINGHOFF, Deborah Ann
Landmark Christian HS; Cincinnati, OH (10-37) Band; Chor; Drama; Ensm; FHA; ARC; Semi-Fin, Sch P; Span C; Var C; Bsbl; Sftbl; Tnns; Tr; ARC A; Hosp A; Dance A; Camping A; Choir A; Home Ec A; '100' C A; Tutoring A; Office Asst A; Tr & Tn Var Ltrs; Cedarville Col; Bio.

WELLINGTON, Haruko Katherine
Kailua HS; Kailua, HI; AFS; Chor; Community Yth Symph; Drama; Orch; Thes; Art A; U of Hawaii; Social Sci.

WELLIVER, Monica Joy
Amanda-Clearcreek HS; Amanda, OH (71-112) Band; Chor; 4H; Sci C; Sftbl; Tr; 4H A; Sci A; Bus.

WELLS, Alan Lee
Normal Comm HS; Normal, IL (82-500) Ann; Drama; A-Ed, Sch P; Thes; Mgr, Bkbl; St Scholar; Spch Tm; Baylor U; Computer Sci.

WELLS, Bambi Lynn
Baker HS; Baker, LA (4-425) BC; VP, FHA; FTA; Secy, Tri-HiY; Alg A; Bio A; Rptr, Pepsters; Geom A; Eng A; LSU; Med.

WELLS, Bradley Dean
John Marshall HS; Okla City, OK (150-400) Drama; SC; Thes; Rptr, Soph Cl; Okla City U; Pre-Law.

WELLS, Brenda Ann
The Cecilian Acad; Philadelphia, PA (11-43) Chor; Lat C; Sci C; Hon Prog; Math A; Lat A; Presidential Phys Fitness A; Nurs.

WELLS, Brenda Kay
Wenatchee HS; Wenatchee, WA; Chor; Interior Design.

WELLS, Brenda Kaye
Bainbridge HS; Bainbridge, GA; Pres, FBLA; Bainbridge Jr Col; Bus Adm.

WELLS, Carolyn Dianne
Wingfield HS; Jackson, MS; Chor; Tr; Pres, Yth Fel; WW; Secy, Church Sch; VP, Church Yth Choir; Jackson St U; Mus.

WELLS, Carolyn Marie
Maxwell HS; Maxwell, CA (4-25) Band; Cpt, Chldr; Chor; Tres, FFA; FHA; GS; 4H; Parl, Span C; SC; Var C; Pres, Soph Cl; Bsbl; Bkbl; Sftbl; Tr; CSF; COM; HCt; Hon Prog; Lion A; Spch A; Swtht; Yth Fel; Rptr, FFA; Gold HR; FFA Calif St Swtht; Ch, Maxwell Rodeo Parade; Church Pianist.

WELLS, Christina Lynne
Central Baptist HS; Cincinnati, OH; Citz A.

WELLS, Cindy J
Pocatello HS; Pocatello, ID (103-500) A Cap Choir; Fr C; NHS; Pres, Rainbow; 4H A; Masonic A; Yth Fel; Girls Coun; Pep C; Whitworth Col; Eng.

WELLS, Craig Mark
Tift Co HS; Tifton, GA (30-350) Ed, Ann; Drama; Fr C; Math C; Sci C; WW; Abraham Baldwin Col; Journ.

WELLS, Damon Ray
Bridgeport HS; Bridgeport, NE (2-60) Chor; JV, Bkbl; Tr; Alg A; Sci A; U of Iowa; Astronomy.

WELLS, Donella Renise
Garden City HS; Garden City, KS; HCt; Yth Fel; Mid-Amer Nazarene Col; Missionary Nurs.

WELLS, Enid Patricia
Bishop Noll Inst; Hammond, IN; Chldr; Chor; Drama; Ensm; Hmrm; ARC; Sch P; SC; GSct; Fin, NISBOVA; Ind U; Mus.

WELLS, Gay Caroline
The Heritage Sch; Newman, GA (2-13) Ed, Ann; Chldr; Drama; Pres, Fr C; Pres, InterAct C; SC; Cpt, Bkbl; Soccer; Tnns; COM; NEDT; Vet Med.

WELLS, Gregory Dale
St Joseph Ogden HS; St Joseph, IL; Band; Spch C; SC; Thes; Var C; Cpt, Bkbl; Cpt, Ftbl; Sftbl; MVP, Tr.

WELLS, James Paul
Northwest HS; Cincinnati, OH; Band; Bkbl; JV, Ftbl; Sftbl; COM; Yth Fel; Bible Bowl; Yth Orch; U of Cincinnati; Archt.

WELLS, James William
N Iredell HS; Olin, NC (2-375) Fr C; FFA; FTA; Sci C; Citz A; Sci A; Yth Fel; Gov Page Prog; Hugh O'Brian Ldrship Nom; Pres, Church Yth Fel; Humanities C.

WELLS, Julie Ann
Springfield HS; Springfield, IL (68-478) A Cap Choir; Chor; Drama; Ensm; Span C; Ill Wesleyan Col; Mus.

WELLS, Karen Ann
Crystal Lake Comm HS; Crystal Lake, IL (6-540) AFS; Cpt, Chldr; NHS; Ski C; Span NHS; Bausch & Lomb A; U of Ill; Sci.

WELLS, Kathryn Gay
Butler HS; Butler, MO; VP, AFS; Ann; Cpt, Chldr; Rptr, Chor; FBLA; FHA; GS; 4H; Pres, Rainbow; Co-Ed, Sch P; Secy, Span C; Tres, SC; Pres, Soph Cl; Tr; HCt; Hon Prog; Central Mo St U; Legal Secy.

WELLS, Kathy Ann
Burlington Co Vo-tech HS; Mt Holly, NJ (1-207) Chor; Hmrm; MLS; Val; Fin, VICA; Women's Am ORT; Bus.

WELLS, Keith Alonzo
Kashmere Sr HS; Houston, TX (20-475) Chem C; JETS; NHS; Rptr, Sch P; Ftbl; Hon Prog; Pres, Cpt, Taxidermy; Pres, Cpt, Kamera; Tex A&M U; Engr.

WELLS, Kenneth Dale
Greenfield-Central HS; Greenfield, IN (13-275) Band; Chess C; Chor; Drama; Madrigal; NHS; Sci C; Thes; Hon Prog; NEDT; Bible C; Hancock Co Bank As; Gold Watch, Hancock Co Bank; Ind Central U; Sci.

WELLS, Lawrence
Skyline HS; Oakland, CA (5%-714) Chess C; Dbte Tm; JV, Bkbl; JV, Tr; CSF; Chem A; Hon Prog; MLS; Eng A; Span A; Stanford Col; Engr.

WELLS, Pamela Denise
Halter HS; Wellston, MO (3-58) Tres, Chor; FNA; Sch P; SC; Tnns; Journ A; JA A; Bowl; Forest Park Comm Col; Pediatric Nurs.

WELLS, Patricia Anne
Winchester HS; Winchester, MA (35-300) Chor; Drama; Outst Performance Choir; Tufts Col; Mus.

WELLS, Peter
Evander Childs HS; Bronx, NY (121-1936) Chor; Drama; Orch; ARC; Swim; Tr; Med.

WELLS, Richard Aaron
John Marshall HS; Oklahoma City, OK; Bsbl; U of Okla; Aviation.

WELLS, Robert Lee
Pleasant Hill HS; Pleasant Hill, MO (5-116) NHS; Var C; Pres, Jr Cl; Ftbl; MVP, Tr; MVP, Wrest; Schol A; Cleveland Chiropractic Col; Chiropractic Med.

WELLS, Robin Kim
NW HS; Cincinnati, OH (35-400) Band; Community Yth Symph; Orch; Spch C; JV, Bkbl; Tr; Bio A; Citz A; Cl Fav; U of Cincinnati; Special Ed.

WELLS, Ronald Douglas
Trinity Christian HS; Chattanooga, TN (1-14) VP, SC; Pres, Sr Cl; Pres, Jr Cl; Pres, Soph Cl; Co-Cpt, Bkbl; Co-Cpt, Ftbl; Sftbl; Alg A; Hkg; Math A; Most Out; Sci A; Val; Most Ath; Chattanooga Bar Assn A; U of Tenn; Law.

WELLS, Russell David
Southmoreland Sr HS; Alverton, PA (70-291) Demolay; Fr C; World Affairs C; Video Personnel, Wrest; Elec.

WELLS, Sarah Frances
Plano Sr HS; Plano, TX (450-900) Sci C; Bkbl; Tr; Sr Rep, All Region, Band; St Solo & Ensm; Tex Tech U; Biol.

WELLS, Sherri Vanessa
Charles D Owen HS; Swannanoa, NC (144-267) JV, Chldr; Chor; 4H; SC; Bkbl; Sftbl; Tnns; A, B HR; Mus.

WELLS, Sherry L
Bridgeport HS; Bridgeport, NE (6%-66) Chor; Drama; Tres, FBLA; Secy, FHA; NHS; Amer Leg Orator A; Spch A; Type A; Home Ec A; Bio, Eng As; All St Chor; Chadron St Col; Spec Ed.

WELLS, Shirley Diane
East Central HS; Hurley, MS; BC; Rptr, Bus C; Chldr; Rptr, FBLA; Parl, 4H; SC; Mgr, Bkbl; Tr; 4H A; HCt; ROTC A; Sci A; Yth Fel; U of Sou Miss; Personnel Mgt.

WELLS, Virginia Denise
The HS For Health Professions; Houston, TX (7-140) Band; Cpt, Chldr; Chess C; Drama; Bus Mgr, Hmrm; Math C; NHS; VP, Jr Cl; Sftbl; Cpt, Tnns; COM; Citz A; Math A; Sci A; Val; Med Explorers; Bowl Tm; Freedom & Fine Arts, Bowl, A's; Win, Span Contest; Outst Mus; U of Tex; Pre-Med.

WELLSKOPF, Tamara Ellen
Nathan Hale HS; W Allis, WI; Orch; Swim.

WELP, Mary Beth
S Hamilton Jr-Sr HS; Jewell, IA (2-92) Band; Chor; GS; Secy, 4H; Madrigal; NHS; SC; Pres, Soph Cl; Co-Cpt, Bkbl; Sftbl; Tr; St Scholar.

WELSCH, Gail Sue
Pinckneyville Comm HS; Pinckneyville, IL (5-164) FHA; NHS; Spch C; Hon Prog; Rend Lake Col; Secy.

WELSCHER, Marilyn Anne
Mabel-Canton HS; Mabel, MN (13-52) Ensm; Cpt, FHA; Sch P; Solo Mus A; Ensm Mus A; Winona St U; Mus.

WELSH, Judy Lynn
Holy Rosary Acad; Louisville, KY (8-89) Chldr; Hmrm; NHS; SC; H of F; U of Ky; Bus.

WELSH, Justine Ann
Bucyrus Sr HS; Bucyrus, OH (10-220) Band; Chor; Drama; 4H; Spch C; Pres, SC; COM; 4H A; Interlochen Ntl Mus; Pres, Yth Fel; Solo A; Acad A; Mus.

WELSH, Marcella Elaine
Parkview HS; Springfield, MO; A Cap Choir; FHA; Lat C; Madrigal; Rating, Vocal Solo-St Mus Festival; SW Mo St U; Vocal Mus.

WELSH, Patricia Anne
N Augusta Sr HS; N Augusta, SC (40%-530) F-Ed, Ann; Band; Chor; Ensm; Rptr, Sch P; Beauty; Hon Prog; Excel, Band Contests; U of SC; Ed.

WELTE, Letha Jane
Larimore HS; Larimore, ND (10%-75) Band; Chldr; Chor; Drama; Ensm; 4H; Lit Mag; Span C; Spch C; SC; Var C; COM; 4H A; Spch A.

WELTMAN, Wende Oreste
Sheffield HS; Memphis, TN (10%-214) Band; Fr C; NHS; Rainbow; Band Ltr; Best Player; UT at Knoxville; Computer Sci.

WELTY, Diane Louise
Woodrow Wilson HS; Portland, OR (4-419) Chor; NHS; Bus Mgr, Sch P; COM; Q&S A; *Whitworth Col; Mus.*

WENDELL, Stephen Nicholas
Imperial HS; Imperial, CA (36-92) Band; FFA; Orch; ARC; Sr Cl; Jr Cl; Soph Cl; JV, Ftbl; JV, Wrest; VP, VICA; FFA, Safety A; FFA Showmanship A; *Imperial Valley Col; Diesel and Industrial Mech.*

WENDLAND, Beth Louise
Helena HS; Helena, MT (25-269) Secy, Bus C; Hmrm; NHS; COM; Citz A; Pres, Church Yth; *Mont St U; Acct.*

WENDLAND, Karen Yvonne
Helena HS; Helena, MT (20%-375) Chldr; Chor; Hmrm; Mjrte; Sch P; SC; Sftbl; Tr; JA A; Secy, Yth Fel; Valentine Qn.

WENDLAND, Scott Alan
Champaign Centennial HS; Champaign, IL; JV, Swim; JV, Tr; *U of Ill; Vet Med.*

WENDLAND, Wanda Kay
Pflugerville HS; Pflugerville, TX (5-76) Ed, Ann; VP, Band; BC; JV, Chldr; Ensm; 4H; Mjrte; NHS; Sch P; SC; Pres, Jr Cl; Tres, Soph Cl; Bkbl; Sftbl; Tr; Alg A; Math A; Most Out; MVP, Band; Adv Bus A; Band, Ensm As; Drummajor A; Highest Ranking Girl; Eng As; *Durham's Bus Col; Computer Operator.*

WENDLING, Kathy Marie
Warren Central HS; Indianapolis, IN (92-950) VP, Chor; Lat C; Cpt, Sftbl; *Ind U; Psychiatry.*

WENDLING, Tammy Lenice
Belmont HS; Dayton, OH; Bus C; IOE Clerical A; *Circleville Bible Col; Missionary.*

WENDT, David Ronald
Starpoint HS; Lockport, NY (50-210) Band; Ensm; Spch C; Var C; Bkbl; Ftbl; Co-Cpt, Tr; Pres A; Col Orch; *Law.*

WENDT, Judith Ann
Lynnwood Sr HS; Lynnwood, WA; Ensm; NHS; Amer Leg A; Sci A; Illuminati Hon Soc; Illuminati Cert Hghst Grade Point; *Sci.*

WENDT, Michelle Linda
Suring HS; Suring, WI (8-65) NHS; Quiz Tm; Prom Court; Vlbl.

WENDTLAND, Glenn Robert
Taft HS; Chicago, IL (50%-250) Band; Tr; Sci A; Awana C; Outst Bible A; *Forestry.*

WENGER, Carole Lynn
Central HS; Chambersburg, PA; Chldr; Chor; Ensm; Lat C; ARC; Bkbl; Lat V'S; Lib A's; *Lit.*

WENGER, Dennis Russell
Calvary Christian Acad; Ridgeland, SC (1-3) Cpt, Ftbl; Sftbl; Co-Cpt, Tr; HCt; VP, HS Cl; Member, Pace Bowl Tm; VP, HS Cl; *Annapolis Naval Acad; Hist.*

WENGER, Katrena Lee
Chambersburg Area Sr HS; Chambersburg, PA (1-725) Chldr; Chor; Secy, Ensm; Lat C; NHS; Bkbl; St Scholar; Lat V'S; Spelling A; Lib A's; *Shippensburg Col; Ed.*

WENGER, Kay Leslie
Larkin HS; Elgin, IL (15%-800) Chor; Ensm; Fr C; *Conservation.*

WENGER, Margot Eileen
Larkin HS; Elgin, IL; Fr C; Orch; Tnns; District Orch; *Cornell U; Theology.*

WENGLOSKI, Philip Isidore
Lyman Mem HS; Lebanon, CT (15-84) Chess C; *Hartford St Tech Col; Nuclear Engr.*

WENIG, Elizabeth Marie
Chilton Public HS; Chilton, WI (9-140) FHA; NHS; SC; Tres, Sr Cl; Tres, Jr Cl; Chamber of Comm A; Type A; Cath Knights A; *Marian Col; Ed.*

WENNER, Clare Ann
Wellsboro Sr HS; Wellsboro, PA (19-204) Band; Chor; Drama; Fr C; Hmrm; NHS; VP, Sci C; SC; Var C; Mgr, Bkbl; Mgr, Tr; Mgr, Wrest; *Mansfield Col.*

WENNERHOLM, Scott Edward
Westminster HS; Atlanta, GA (70-100) Secy, Band; Orch; Span C; Golf; *Furman U; Mus.*

WENNLUND, Ruthanne
Twin Lakes HS; Monticello, IN (51-261) Band; Chor; FTA; NFL; Orch; Rainbow; Span C; Spch C; Masonic A; Gold Medals, St Band Contests; *Mus.*

WENTE, Brent Rae
Effingham HS; Effingham, IL (12-178) Bsbl; Bkbl.

WENTHE, Anne Virginia
Cumberland Valley HS; Mechanicsburg, PA (15-630) Chor; Ger C; Math C; NHS; Sch P; Var C; Swim; COM; Hon Prog; NEDT; Water Polo; *Gettysburg Col; Biol.*

WENTINK, Francyse Wynn
MecKraberg HS; Charlotte, NC (82-600) Chldr; Chor; Fr C; SC; Swim; Alg A; Sci A; Type A; Med Explorers; Glee C; Ntl Mus Fed; Sounds of Amer; SOS; Candystriper; PA A; Homecoming Comm; Tres, Lettergirls; *NG St U; Med.*

WENTINK, Michael Guy
South Mecklenburg HS; Pineville, NC; Mgr, Bsbl; Swim; Art Cert of A; *NC St U; Fish & Wildlife Mgt.*

WENTWORTH, Laura Jean
Lakota Cons Sch; Lakota, IA (3-21) Band; Chor; FTA; Rptr, Sch P; Secy, SC; Bkbl; Sftbl; Tr; Fr A.

WENTWORTH, Roger Blair
McMinn HS; Athens, TN; Band; Orch; Sch P; Sci C; SC; Bsbl; Cpt, Bkbl; Most Sch Spirit; *Mus.*

WENTWORTH, Steven A
South HS; Minneapolis, MN (10%-350) F-Ed, Ann; NHS.

WENTZ, Sally Janine
Adrian HS; Adrian, MI (20-395) Band; Chor; Dbte Tm; 4H; VP, Lat C; Orch; SC; Thes; Pres, Jr Cl; Lat, Debate Tm, A's; *U of Mich; Med.*

WENTZEL, Deborah Kay
Stevens HS; Rapid City, SD (45-463) Band; Fr C; NHS; Orch; ARC; ARC A; All St Orch; Superior, Solo-Ensm Contest; *Wisc U; Mus Therapy.*

WENTZEL, Susan Lee
Leland HS; San Jose, CA;

WENTZKY, John Darin
Thomas Lucas Hanna HS; Anderson, SC (10%-428) Chess C; Community Yth Symph; Ger C; NHS; Orch; Alg A; Math A; NEDT; All St Orch; Schol A; Driver's A; *Oral Roberts U; Med.*

WENZEL, Cindy Rae
Port Washington HS; Port Washington, WI (67-300) Chor; GS; Tr; Hon Prog; Lion A; *Law Enforcement.*

WENZEL, Douglas Mark
Mineral Wells HS; Mineral Wells, TX (28-208) Band; Tres, Lat C; NHS; Tnns; Sweepstakes Band; Tres, Yth for Christ; *Tex A&M U; Engr.*

WENZEL, Julie Anne
W Fargo HS; West Fargo, ND (10%-300) Band; Ensm; NHS; ND St Mus Festival; *ND St U; Bio.*

WENZEL, Lori Lynn
Roseville HS; Roseville, MI; Band.

WENZEL, Robinette Jane
New London-Spicer Jr Sr HS; New London, MN (10-110) Band; Chldr; Ensm; Tres, FHA; NHS; Sch P; S-T, SC; Star Student; VP, FHA; Superior, Solo & Ensm; *Psych.*

WENZEL, Vicki Lynn
Port Washington HS; Port Washington, WI (39-360) Chor; Tr; Hon Prog; *Architecture.*

WENZELL, Stuart Brush
St James Sch; St James, MD (4-30) Ann; Band; Chess C; Chor; Dbte Tm; Lit Rral; Spch C; Golf; Mgr, Soccer; Sci A; Fr A; *Lehigh Col; Engr.*

WENZL, Frederick Louis
Loyola HS; Towson, MD (18-134) Drama; NHS; Thes; Cpt, Tnns; COM; Hon Prog; NEDT; *Towson St Col; Drama.*

WENZL, Joseph Andrew
Lourdes Central HS; Nebraska City, NE (3-41) Band; Chem C; Ensm; Mu Alpha Theta; NHS; Pres, Jr Cl; Tres, Soph Cl; Ftbl; *Creighton U; Phar.*

WERBACH, Lisa Lorraine
Lone Tree Comm HS; Lone Tree, IA (6-44) A Cap Choir; Ed, Ann; Band; Chor; VP, FFA; Yth Fel; *Iowa St U; Agr.*

WERCHAN, Judy Lynn
Pflugerville HS; Pflugerville, TX (10%-107) Ann; BC; FHA; NHS; Sch P; Span C; Mgr, Bkbl; Mgr, Tr; Alg A; Chamber of Comm A; Chem A; Homemaking A; Span A.

WERCKLE, Curtis David
Stillman Valley HS; Stillman Valley, IL (54-100) Band; Chor; Drama; Ski C; Span C; Spch C; Var C; Mgr, Ftbl; Mgr, Wrest; Cit A; Pres, Church Yth; *Rock Valley Jr Col; Elec Tech.*

WERHAN, Candy
Robert H Goddard HS; Roswell, NM (3-310) FHA; InterClub Coun; Fin, Jr Miss Pagent; NHS; Rptr, Sch P; Tres, Ski C; Span C; Span NHS; Secy, SC; Cl Fav; DARGCA; HQn; HCt; AAUW Girl For Oct; *Baylor U; Home Ec.*

WERKMEISTER, Mark William
Century HS; Bismarck, ND (1-170) Chess C; Lat C; Bkbl; Ftbl; Tr; Amer Leg A; NMS; Val; Mem A; *U of ND; Acct.*

WERNECKE, Debbie Kay
Guide Rock Public Sch; Guide Rock, NE (6-13) JV, Chldr; Chor; Rptr, 4H; F-Ed, Sch P; Bkbl; Sftbl; 4H A; Amer Leg Auxiliary A; *Hastings Tech Sch; Nurs.*

WERNER, Anita Laverne
Gideon HS; Gideon, MO (4-60) Band; CYO; Chldr; Ensm; VP, FHA; Rptr, SC; Var C; Sftbl; Beauty; COM; Sci A; Type A; Drum Mjrte; Band A; Superintendent's List; *Phys Therapy.*

WERNER, Anne Marie
Harding HS; St Paul, MN (6-742) Band; Ensm; NHS; Span C; Co-Cpt, Bkbl; Tr; Hon Prog; Co-Cpt, Vlbl; NHS; Natl Merit Commended Stu; *Luther Col; Bilingual Elem Ed.*

WERNER, Catherine Pauline
Anderson HS; Anderson, IN; Band; Ger C; NHS; Alg A; Hist A; Sal; Eng A; Band A; Piano A; *Anderson Col; Ministry.*

WERNING, John Walter
Boardman HS; Youngstown, OH (66-602) Ger C; HiY; Bsbl; Bkbl; *Pre-Med.*

WERNING, Linda Fay
Boardman Sr HS; Boardman, OH; Ski C; Sftbl; ARC A.

WERRE, Wanda Kay
Underwood Pub HS; Underwood, ND (4-27) Band; Chldr; Chor; FHA; Mjrte; Bkbl; Tr; Hon Prog; Masonic A; *Minot St Col; Legal Secy.*

WERTH, David Eugene
Niagara Wheatfield HS; Sanborn, NY (7-458) Ger C; Math C; NHS; F-Ed, Sch P; Amer Leg A; Bio A; COM; Citz A; Hist A; Hon Prog; Journ A; Math A; NEDT; Regent Schol; Trustee Schol, Eisenhower Col; Competitive Schol, Niagara U; *Niagara U; Math.*

WERY, Amy Ann
East HS; Green Bay, WI; CYO; Chor; Fr C; Bkbl; Cpt, Soccer; Cpt, Vlbl; Bowl Tm; Gym Hons; Mus A; *Mus.*

WESCHE, Barbara Ann
Capital HS; Boise, ID (84-550) Rptr, Ann; Band; Ensm; Cpt, Tr; H of F; *Northwest Nazarene Col.*

WESELOH, David Melvin
Moline Sr HS; Moline, IL (20%-900) Drama; Ger C; Bkbl; God & Country A; Eagle Sct.

WESLAGER, Sandra Lee
Belle Vernon Area HS; Belle Vernon, PA; Tres, FBLA; Tres, Hmrm; Ski C; Tr; Pres A; *ICM Bus Sch; Court Reporting.*

WESLEY, Daemone Howard
Chester HS; Chester, PA (11-680) Ann; Band; Order/Arrow; SC; Distinguished Stu A; *Swarthmore Col; Med.*

WESLEY, Laurie Diane
Kemper Acad; DeKalb, MS (2-31) A-Ed, Ann; BC; Chor; COM; Chem A; Sci A; HR; *U of Miss; Lab Tech.*

WESLEY, Sonja Marie
Walker HS; Walker, LA (1-90) Band; BC; Chor; Ensm; Rptr, 4H; VP, Soph Cl; 4H A; Ed, Yth Baptist Paper; Outst Soph Band A; *Northeast Col; Phar.*

WESLEY, Stevie Larnell
Killeen HS; Killeen, TX; *Phys Ed.*

WESLEY, Thomas A
PaloDuro HS; Amarillo, TX (160-285) Hmrm; Key C; NHS; SC; Cr-Cxtry; Cpt, Tr; Yth Fel; SC Fav; Escort, Tr & Field Qn; Young Life C; *Amarillo Col; X-Ray Tech.*

WESLEY, Ylana Monique
Chester HS; Chester, of Pa; Med. Ann; Band; Mjrte; NHS; VP, SC; *U of Pa; Med.*

WESNER, Ronald Ernest
Lakeshore HS; Stevensville, MI; Band; Pres, FFA; NHS; Spch A; Agr A; Dekalb A; *Mich St U; Agr Tech.*

WESOLEK, Timothy Joseph
Lansing Christian HS; Lansing, MI (12-26) Band; Ensm; Orch; Sch P; Mgr, Ftbl; JV, Swim; Mgr, Tr; *Taylor U; Pre-Med.*

WESOLIK, Carol Angela
New Athens Comm HS; New Athens, IL (6-65) Ed, Ann; Band; Ch, CYO; Chldr; FHA; NHS; Q&S A; ARC A; Type A; *Ill St U; Spch Pathology.*

WESSEL, Steven Mark
Old Mill Sr HS; Millersville, MD (5%-500) Band; Ensm; Ger C; NHS; Bkbl; Sci A; Band A; *Air Force Acad; Computers.*

WESSELY, Michael Jerold
Bay City W HS; Bay City, MI (40-600) Band; Chem C; Chor; Dbte Tm; Ger C; NHS; Sch P; Pres, Soph Cl; JV, Ftbl; COM; Cl Fav; Hon Prog; Pres A; Band A; *U of Mich; Bus.*

WESSIES, Debbie Lynn
Mt Whitney HS; Visalia, CA (78-500) Band; Ger C; GS; Model UN; Swim; *Humbolt Col; Wildlife Mgt.*

WESSON, Jimmy Delane
S San Antonio HS; San Antonio, TX (14-430) NHS; Ftbl; Tr; Hon Prog; WW; *Ouachita Baptist U; Pre-Med.*

WESSON, Joel Cutler
R J Reynolds HS; Winston-Salem, NC (4-820) Tres, Chess C; Order/Arrow; Sci C; Span C; Tnns; Gov Honor Prog; Hon Prog; Math A; Rensselaer A; St Jr Sci Symposium; Wake Forest Chem Symposium; *Swarthmore Col; Sci.*

WEST, Amy Kay
Wichita Falls HS; Wichita Falls, TX (30-475) VP, FTA; GS; MN; NHS; ARC; Rptr, Sch P; SC; Tri-HiY; Pres, Jr Cl; Rptr, Soph Cl; Rotary A; *Baylor U; Social Work.*

WEST, Arthur Jr
Inglewood HS; Inglewood, CA (28-325) Band; Hmrm; Math C; Opt A; Spch A; WW; *U of Calif; Oceanography.*

WEST, Ben David
Hatley HS; Amory, MS; BC; VP, FFA; SC; FFA Chapter Farmer; FFA A; *Freed-Hardeman Col; Bible.*

WEST, Caleb Dwight
Hampton Roads Acad; Newport News, VA (11-63) Key C; Lat C; Pres, Span C; SC; Var C; Bsbl; JV, Bkbl; Ftbl; JV, Soccer; HR; *Wake Forest U; Econ.*

WEST, Christa Mae
Adairsville HS; Adairsville, GA; Fr C; Rptr, FHA; Hmrm; Lit Ral; Rptr, Sci C; SC; Bkbl; Sftbl; Tr; HCt.

WEST, Deborah Janine
Auburn Christian Sch; Auburn, NY (3-5) Chldr; A-Ed, Sch P; SC; Bsbl; Bkbl; Sftbl; *New Tribes Bible Inst; Bible.*

WEST, Deborah Lynn
Fairfax HS; Los Angeles, CA; CSF; Black Stu Union; Pep C; *Special Ed.*

WEST, Denise Renee
Auburn Christian Sch; Auburn, NY (3-6) Chldr; Sch P; Bsbl; Bkbl; Sftbl; *New Tribes Bible Inst; Bible.*

WEST, Diana
The Buckley Sch; Sherman Oaks, CA;

WEST, Donna Jo
Aragon HS; San Mateo, CA; Yth Fel; *Col of San Mateo; Ed.*

WEST, Franklin Eugene Jr
Palmetto HS; Palmetto, GA (20%-137) Ann; BC; Chor; Drama; JV, Bkbl; Cr-Cxtry; Ftbl; Sftbl; Tr; JV, Wrest; COM; Yth Fel; *Chem.*

WEST, Gordon Dean
El Camino HS; Sacramento, CA (1-321) Ann; Arch; Pres, Bus C; Chor; Drama; Ensm; Parl, Ger C; Pres, Hmrm; InterClub Coun; Secy, Key C; Rptr, Lit Mag; Madrigal; Math C; V-Ch, ARC; Var C; Bank Of Amer A; CSF; COM; Citz A; DARGCA; Hon Prog; Kiwanis A; Math A; Type A; Val; JV Water Polo; Cpt, Rifle Tm; St Cadet Corps Brigade Commander; Soroptomist Schol; St Teachers Assn Schol; *UCLA; Communication Stu.*

WEST, Harold Oscar
Duquesne HS; Duquesne, PA (10-150) Band; Chess C; Tres, NHS; Order/Arrow; JV, Bkbl; Wrest; DARGCA; H of F; Most Intelligent; *Penn St U; Elec Engr.*

WEST, Harvey John
Marion Franklin HS; Columbus, OH; Cpt, Band; NHS; Orch; Wrest; COM; JA A; Head Drummer; Stage Band; *Columbus Tech Inst; Elec.*

WEST, Janice Carol
Piner HS; Santa Rosa, CA (10%-350) A Cap Choir; Chor; Community Yth Symph; Jr Miss Pagent; NHS; Orch; ARC; SC; Bkbl; CSF; Most Out; Yth Fel; GSA; Santa Rosa Jr Miss; Vlbl; Rose Festival Qn; Badminton; Outst Ldrship, GSA; Young Life; *Santa Rosa Jr Col; Recreation.*

WEST, Jeffrey Edward
Franklin HS; Seattle, WA; NHS; Sch P; Ftbl; Soccer; VFW Orator Win; VofDEM; Fin NCTE; *Mus.*

WEST, Jimmie Lynn
Groveton HS; Groveton, TX (4-54) BC; Dbte Tm; FHA; Secy, SC; VP, Soph Cl; Bkbl; Mgr, Tr; HCt; *Sam Houston St U; Acct.*

WEST, Jonathan Crowe
Hampton Roads Acad; Newport News, VA (8-55) BS; Fr C; Tres, Key C; VP, Jr Cl; Bkbl; MVP, Ftbl; JV, Soccer; HR; V Ltrs; Hon Men, Ntl Merit; *Econ.*

WEST, Karen Sue
Brazil Sr HS; Brazil, IN (26-192) Band; FHA; FTA; NHS; SC; Thes; Tres, Tri-HiY; Rptr, Tnns; WW; *Ind St U; Elem Ed.*

WEST, Kendal Dean Jr
Plano Sr HS; Plano, TX (20-1100) A Cap Choir; Chor; Drama; 2nd, Pl, St Art A; Bible Schol; Art Schol; *Lubbock Christian Col; Bible.*

WEST, Kerry Lloyd
Center HS; Center, TX (42-160) FFA; Span C; Cpt, Radeo; *Sul Ross Col; Farm and Ranch Mgt.*

WEST, Lisa Lynn
Sunset HS; Portland, OR (38-502) Marshal, Guide, Job's Daughters; Sch Plays; Entrance Hon, Willamette U; *Willamette U.*

WEST, Lisa Marie
Naperville N HS; Naperville, IL (132-525) Band; Chor; Ski C; Swim; Tr; *U of Ill; Nurs.*

WEST, Lora Jo
Fort Myers HS; Fort Myers, FL (4-378) Bus C; FBLA; NHS; Rainbow; *X-Ray Tech.*

WEST, Mara Kren
Eula HS; Clyde, TX (3-32) Ann; Pres, FHA; Secy, SC; Secy, Jr Cl; Mgr, Bkbl; Tr; Cl Fav; *Hardin-Simmons Col; Nurs.*

WEST, Margaretha Dean
Covington HS; Covington, TN (3-228) FHA; NHS; B Crocker A; *Union U; Chem.*

WEST, Mary Lue
Wilcox Co HS; Rochelle, GA (10-97) Ann; Rptr, BC; Pres, FHA; Pres, FTA; Mjrte; NHS; VP, SC; Pres, Var C; Rptr, Rainbow; VP, Soph Cl; MVP, Bkbl; COM; Cl Fav; HQn; Hon Prog; Cpt, Bkbl; FHA A; Miss Wilcox Co HS; *Mercer U; Pol Sci.*

WEST, Paula Denette
Marysville HS; Marysville, MI (50-160) Chor; 4H; *St Clair Co Comm Col; X-Ray Tech.*

WEST, Ralph Douglas
Forest Brook Sr HS; Houston, TX (20%-486) NHS; Spch C; JV, Bkbl; Mgr, Ftbl; Most Out; VOE A; *Morehouse Col; Eng.*

WEST, Robert Royce
Ridgeview HS; Atlanta, GA (50-180) Ann; BC; Lit Mag; Var C; Soccer; Tr; Hon Prog; Journ A; Tres, FCA; HR; Super HR; *Valdosta St Col; Commercial Art.*

WEST, Robin Evon
Camden HS; Camden, NC (29-92) Community Yth Symph; FHA; 4H; Hmrm; Hon Prog; Most Out; Type A; Ecology C; Hist C; *Harbarger Bus Col; Secy.*

WEST, Robyne Rene
Fox Sr HS; Arnold, MO (3-785) Band; Dbte Tm; Fr C; Pres, FTA; GS; Hmrm; Math C; NFL; Pres, NHS; Orch; A-Ed, Sch P; Rptr, SC; Pres, Jr Cl; COM; Citz A; DARGCA; Elk A; Math A; Q&S A; Rotary C A; Super Sr; MAMTA Win; Stage Band; *Northeast Mo St U; Mus Ed.*

WEST, Ron Leroy
Wichita W HS; Wichita, KS; Orch; *Kansas City Med Center; Med.*

WEST, Sally Ann
Charlotte HS; Charlotte, MI; FTA; SC; Swim; Phys Fitness A; Goodale Mothers C; *Nurs.*

WEST, Tammy Ann
Shawnee Mission NW HS; Shawnee, KS (50%-700) VP, CYO; Secy, Fr C; 4H; Sch P; SC; Y-Tns; Bkbl; Sftbl; Tnns; Tr; Cl Fav; Most Out; Sunday Sch Teacher; Best Personality A.

WEST, Teri DeAnn
Travelers Rest HS; Travelers Rest, SC; Bkbl; Tr; Vlbl; *Furman U; Phys Ed.*

WEST, Timothy Guy
Robert E Lee Inst; Thomaston, GA; SC; Mgr, Bsbl; Ftbl; Sftbl; Tr; ROTC A; *U of Ga; Criminology.*

WEST, Timothy Steven
W Craven HS; Vanceboro, NC (13-160) Co-Ed, Lit Mag; Monogram; NHS; Bkbl; Tr; VFW A; Vof-DEM; *E Carolina U.*

WEST, Troy Curtis
Center HS; Center, TX; Pres, FFA; COM; Pres, FFA Chapter; Rptr, FFA Dist; FFA Shop Mech A; *Tex St Tech Inst; Saddle Making-Leathercraft.*

WEST, Vivian Lynn
Abe Lincoln HS; Port Arthur, TX; Bus C; Drama; FHA; FTA; Hmrm; NHS; ARC; Sci C; Span C; Spch C; SC; Mgr, Bkbl; Mgr, Tnns; COM; Citz A; Hon Prog; Type A; Bus A; FHA A; *Lamar U; Off Adm.*

WEST, Yvonne Lynn
Edward H White Sr HS; Jacksonville, FL (30%-600) Band; Yth Fel; *Huntington Col; Mus.*

WESTALL, William Edward
Red Springs HS; Red Springs, NC (12-120) CYO; Co-Cpt, Ftbl; Tr.

WESTBERG, Laura Christine
Royal Oak HS; Covina, CA (174-322) Chor; Dbte Tm; Drill Tm; Modern Dance Tm; *Mount Sac Jr Col; Early Childhood Ed.*

WESTBROOK, Barbara Dorothea
Colo HS; Colo City, TX (2-126) FHA; Span C; Math A; WW; Span, Eng, Hist, Homemaking As; *Tex Tech U; Pre-Med.*

WESTBROOK, Cheryle Jean
Woodlawn Sr HS; Baton Rouge, LA; Chor; Fr C; FBLA; Y-Tns; Type A.

WESTBROOK, Deborah Kay
W Memphis Sr HS; W Memphis, AR; Ann; Band; BC; Ensm; FHA; Hmrm; Lat C; Sch P; VP, SC; COM; Hist A; Math A; Summa Cum Laude; Home Ec A; SC A; Grand A, Sci Fair; Eng A.

WESTBROOK, Gladys Marie
Justin F Kimball HS; Dallas, TX; A Cap Choir; F-Ed, Ann; Chor; Math C; Span C; Span NHS; SC; *LIFE Bible Col; Missions.*

WESTBROOK, Tamara Lynn
W Monroe; La, U; Anchor C; JV, Chldr; Semi-Fin, Jr Miss Pa; Parl, NHS; SC; Y-Tns; Bkbl; Sftbl; Hon Prog; Dance Tm; Nurs Off Aide; UMYF; Church Pianist; Rep, Soph Cl; *NE La U 0280002813c.*

WESTEEN, Lesa Mae
Leesville HS; Leesville, LA; Chldr; Secy, Chess C; Drama; 4H; ARC; Span C; Spch C; Tr.

WESTENDORF, Glenda Jane
Wapsie Valley HS; Fairbank, IA; Co-Ed, Ann; Chor; Madrigal; NHS; JV, Bkbl; Golf; Type A; VP, Pep C; *Hawkeye Inst of Tech; Acct.*

WESTER, Kelly Ann
Thomas A Edison HS; Elmira Heights, NY; Band; Orch; VP, Yth Fel; Co Band; Hist C.

WESTER, Virginia Lee
Lumberton Sr HS; Lumberton, NC (10%-315) Lat C; NHS; Sci C; Tri-HiY; *Math.*

WESTERDAHL, Elaine Elizabeth
Bemidji HS; Bemidji, MN (14-384) A-Ed, Ann; VP, Chor; Ensm; Pres, 4H; NHS; Ski C; 4H A; Q&S A; GSct Ldr; *Nurs.*

WESTERDALE, Edward Paul
Amer Christian Acad; Pomona, CA (5-21) Chor; VP, SC; Var C; Bsbl; Bkbl; Ftbl; Citz A; Sal; Essay A.

WESTERMANN, David John
Escanaba Area HS; Escanaba, MI; Bsbl; *Archt.*

WESTFALL, Ann Marie
Susquehanna Comm HS; Susquehanna, PA (4-110) Ski C; VP, Soph Cl; Mgr, Bsbl; JV, Bkbl; *Rochester Inst; Photography.*

WESTFALL, Cindy Sue
Estherville HS; Estherville, IA (24-154) Chor; Tres, FHA; JV, Bkbl; Vlbl; Camp Ldrship A; Camp Drama A; Vol, Campaign for Christ; Camp Bible A; Camp Sportsmanship A; ACT Schol; Danforth Found A; *Lubbock Christian Col; Psych.*

WESTFALL, Kimberly Kay
Piqua Central HS; Piqua, OH (12-400) Band; NHS; COM; Hon Prog; PTA A; Home Ec; Top 100; *Math.*

WESTFALL, Kurt Gerald
Northeast R-IV HS; Cairo, MO (5-25) Chor; NHS; SC; Pres, Var C; Pres, Soph Cl; Bsbl; Bkbl; Tr; *U of Mo; Conservation.*

WESTFALL, Mary Jane
Beulah HS; Riverview, AL (9-29) Ann; BC; FHA; 4H; Rptr, Sch P; 4H A; ARC A; *Auburn U.*

WESTGATE, Cherry Lynn
Kenmore W Sr HS; Kenmore, NY (481-943) Band; Chor; FNA; ARC; Sftbl; Guidance Off Secy A; Mus Band-Chor; 1st Pl, Social Stu Project; *St U Col; Nurs.*

WESTLAKE, Leslie Mark
DeLand Sr HS; DeLand, FL (10%-700) FFA; NHS; Ch, Order/Arrow; Cr-Ctry; Soccer; Tr; Order/Arrow A; Yth Fel; *Machinist.*

WESTMAN, James Lee
N Platte Sr HS; N Platte, NE (28-450) Drama; Order/Arrow; Span C; Order/Arrow A; *Nebr U; Archt.*

WESTMAN, Julie Marie
Douglas Co HS; Castle Rock, CO (190-451) *CSU-Ft Collins; Dental Asst.*

WESTMORELAND, Barney Wayne
Brandon Sr HS; Brandon, FL; Band; Ensm; Ski C; SC; Bsbl; Ftbl; NATO Cup; *U of S Fla; Law.*

WESTMORELAND, Cheridan Michelle
Warren Western Reserve HS; Warren, OH; A Cap Choir; Band; Chor; Pres, Drama; Ensm; Hmrm; Madrigal; Orch; SC; Thes; JA A; Jr Women League A; *Kent St U; Theatre.*

WESTMORELAND, Frank Eugene
Warren Western Reserve HS; Warren, OH; Bsbl; Ftbl; *Elec Engr.*

WESTMORELAND, Jacqueline Renee
W Charlotte Sr HS; Charlotte, NC; Mgr, Bkbl; Sch Service A; *Modeling.*

WESTON, Cheryl Marie
Thomas Jefferson HS; San Antonio, TX (10%-550) Secy, A Cap Choir; Ger C; Hmrm; SC; *Trinity U; Mus.*

WESTON, Debra Marie
Clatskanie HS; Clatskanie, OR (2-100) AFS; Band; Chor; Co-Ed, Sch P; Tr; Alg A; Journ A; Math A; Q&S A; Sal; Sci A; Gen Bus A; *Portland Comm Col; Computer Prog.*

WESTON, Eric Clayton
New Hartford HS; New Hartford, NY (46-425) A Cap Choir; Drama; Mod Mus Mas; NHS; Ski C; JV, Cr-Ctry; JV, Soccer; Tr; COM; *Regent Schol; Hamilton Col; Pre-Med.*

WESTON, James William
Sherman E Burroughs HS; Ridgecrest, CA (40-500).

WESTON, Larry Dean
Clatskanie HS; Clatskanie, OR; Band; Chor; NHS; Power Mech A.

WESTON, Marain Louise
Compton Sr HS; Compton, CA (12-500) Chor; *Long Beach St Col.*

WESTON, Maria Gabriella
Immanuel Christian Sch; Ridgecrest, CA (20-40) Chor; Bkbl; Ftbl; Sftbl; Vlbl; *Sci.*

WESTON, Mark Anthony
W Memphis Christian Sch; W Memphis, AR; Bsbl; Bkbl; Cpt, Ftbl; Tr; Alg A; COM; Chem A; God & Country A; HCt; Math A; MLS; Yth Fel; *Harding Col; Math.*

WESTON, Regina Ann
Claskanie HS; Claskanie, OR (25%-100) Band; Chor; 4H; Math A.

WESTON, Susan Lee
Holbrook HS; Holbrook, MA; Lib Aide; *Berkshire Christian Col; Theology.*

WESTON, Wayde Mitchell
Neshaminy Maple Point HS; Langhorne, PA; Band; Chor; Drama; Math C; NHS; Order/Arrow; NMF; WW; *Bio.*

WESTOVER, Debra Lynne
Pasadena HS; Pasadena, CA (131-700) Bank of Amer A; MVP, Orchesis C; *Pasadena City Col.*

WESTRICK, Bruce Michael
Tigard HS; Tigard, OR; Span C; Var C; Ftbl.

WESTROPE, Jeffrey Clayton
Huntsville HS; Huntsville, AL; Ch, Hmrm; Ski C; SC; Var C; Ftbl; Wrest; Hon Prog; Most Out; Pres, Fresh Cl; *Marine Biol.*

WETHERBY, Larry Dean
Napoleon HS; Napoleon, MI (4-120) Chess C; Dbte Tm; VP, NHS; SC; Cpt, Bkbl; Golf; Sftbl; COM; Hist A; Hon Prog; Math A; Yth Fel; Art A; Pres, MYF; Yth Choir; Drama A; Yth Coun; VP, Dist Yth Co; St Indust Ed A; Del, UN-WASH Sem; Church Adm Board; *Western Mich U; Bus Adm.*

WETHERHOLT, Paul D
Aurora W HS; Aurora, IL (203-810) A Cap Choir; Dbte Tm; NFL; Bkbl; Ftbl; Spch A; Vocal Mus Schol Win; Swing Choir; St Fin, Male Vocal Comp; 1st Pl, Col Talent Ral; Lead, Gilb; Bert & Sullivan Productions; *Lincoln Christian Col; Mus.*

WETHERINGTON, Charles Thomas
Delavan Comm HS; Delavan, IL (4-68) A Cap Choir; Secy, Band; Chess C; Chor; VP, Drama; Ensm; 4H; Madrigal; Spch C; VP, Thes; Cr-Ctry; MVP, Golf; Tr; JV, Wrest; Hon Prog; NMS; NEDT; Special HR A; *Northwestern Ill U; Engr.*

WETHERINGTON, Melanie
Buchholz HS; Gainesville, FL (82%-340) Ensm; Hmrm; NHS; Rainbow; Span C; COM; Masonic A; VIA A; Hospital Vol A; Sch Patrol A; *U of Fla; Ed.*

WETZ, Cynthia Lea
St John Lutheran HS; Ocala, FL (25%-30) Tres, NHS; Tres, SC; Hon Prog; Opt A; Spch A; Star Student; *Central Fla Comm Col; Radiological Health Technology.*

WETZEL, Michael Neal
Antioch Sr HS; Antioch, TN (27-398) Ann; Band; BC; Chor; Madrigal; NHS; Associate Pastor, Yth Wk; Band A; *Middle Tenn St U; Mus Ed.*

WEWER, Jean Ellen
Nordonia HS; Macedonia, OH (26-518) Hmrm; Sci C; Hon Prog; VofDEM; Eng A; 3rd Pl, OCTM Math; Hon Mention, Ohio Scholastic; *Math.*

WEYGANDT, Kathryn Diane
S Albany HS; Albany, OR; AFS; FBLA; GAA; Gym; MVP, Vlbl; *Lynn Benton Comm Col; Bus.*

WEYGANDT, Lauren
Henderson Sr HS; W Chester, PA (120-425) Hmrm; SC; *Philadelphia Col of Art; Art.*

WEYGANDT, Roxanne DaVee
Reynolds HS; Greenville, PA (15-212) Band; Chor; FTA; Tres, Ger C; Lat C; Math C; NHS; S-T, Sci C; Tri-HiY; *Westminster Col; Sci.*

WEYGANDT, Victor Warren
S Albany HS; Albany, OR (30-300) A Cap Choir; Band; BS; Chess C; Fr C; NHS; *Reed Col; Particle-Plasma Physics.*

WEYGANDT, Victoria Lynn
Reynolds HS; Greenville, PA (5-207) Band; Chor; VP, 4H; Math C; 4H A; Pres A; Gym; *Theil U; Sci.*

WEYLAND, Pamela Suzanne
The Immaculata HS; Chicago, IL (7-150) Cpt, Chldr; Chor; Ger C; NHS; Sch P; Span NHS; Secy, Sr Cl; St Scholar; Co, Lit Magazine; *De Paul U; Chem.*

WEZENSKI, John Eric
Notre Dame HS; W Haven, CT; NHS; Ski C; Var C; Golf; *U of Conn.*

WHALEN, Mary Margaret
Acad of Holy Names; Tampa, FL (25-68) CYO; Secy, NHS; Span NHS; Tres, Sr Cl; Secy, Jr Cl; Secy, Soph Cl; Cpt, Swim; Hon Prog; *St Mary's Col; Bus Adm.*

WHALEY, Darwin Tansey
Chisago Lakes Sr HS; Lindstrom, MN (10-177) Band; Ensm; FBLA; Ger C; Orch; Most Out; *Wartburg Col; Ger.*

WHALEY, Donald Victor
Tyner HS; Chattanooga, TN (43-261) BC; Hmrm; Var C; Bsbl; Bkbl; Citz A; *U of Tenn; Engr.*

WHALEY, Donna Kay
W Craven HS; Vanceboro, NC (10%-212) A-Ed, Ann; Band; Secy, BC; FBLA; FHA; Hmrm; NHS; F-Ed, Sch P; Type A; Stu Gov Assn; 2nd Pl, Sci Fair; PA; Secy, Fresh Cl; Principal's A; Pres, Pep C; HR Cert; Secy, DECA; *William & Mary Col.*

WHALEY, Erin Eileen
Chisago Lakes Sr HS; Lindstrom, MN (65-165) Bus C; Chor; *Minn Sch of Bus; Fashion Merchandising.*

WHALEY, James William
Swifton HS; Swifton, AR (3-19) Band; BC; 4H; SC; Mgr, Var C; Mgr, Bkbl; Citz A; Gr Marshal; 4H A; Hon Prog; Stu Trainer; Mus A; *Vanderbilt U; Med Technology.*

WHALEY, Karen Cindy
DeSoto Sr HS; De Soto, MO (15-270) Ann; Band; Chor; Drama; NHS; SC; Jr Rotarian; *U of Mo; Pre-Med.*

WHALEY, Lori Jean
Tyner HS; Chattanooga, TN (22-261) BC; Drama; Model UN; NHS; Sch P; SC; Tr; VP, Sigma Phi Omega; Christmas Court; *U of Tenn.*

WHALEY, Ronald James
Huntington HS; Huntington, NY (33%-600) Band; InterAct C; Key C; Soccer.

WHALEY, Steve Patrick
Cleveland HS; Cleveland, OK (3-115) NHS; Phys C; Sci C; Var C; Bsbl; MVP, Bkbl; MVP, Ftbl; MVP, Tr; HCt; Math A; Most Out; All-St Ftbl; All-St Bkbl; *Okla U; Acct.*

WHALEY, Susan Marie
Pleasant Hill Jr Acad; Pleasant Hill, CA (3-10) Chor; 4H; Hockey; Sftbl; Tutor Prog; *Oakwood Col; Nurs.*

WHALEY, Timothy Joe
Ulysses HS; Ulysses, KS (10-100) Chess C; NHS; Var C; JV, Golf; *Engr.*

WHARTON, Charles
Titusville HS; Titusville, FL; Fr C; Bsbl; JV, Ftbl; *Abilene Christian Col; Counciling.*

WHARTON, Heather PerCharlie
St Josephs HS; Camden, NJ; Hmrm; JV, Bkbl; *Rutgers U; Law.*

WHARTON, James Robert
Sandy Valley HS; Magnolia, OH; Arch; Band; 4H A; Elec Engr.

WHARTON, Rebecca Ladon
Mt Ida HS; Mt Ida, AR (6-36) Ann; BC; Chor; Rptr, FHA; Rptr, Hmrm; Lit Mag; F-Ed, Sch P; Hon Prog; WW; Garland Co Comm Col; Nurs.

WHATLEY, Debbie Jean
East HS; Columbus, OH (21-350) Tres, COE; IOE Most Outst Stu; Lib Helper; Capital U; Acct.

WHATLEY, Donna Elisa
Pineville HS; Pineville, LA (10%-350) A-Ed, Ann; InterAct C; InterClub Coun; NFL; Rainbow; Spch C; Pres, Y-Tns; Spch A; LSU; Spch & Drama.

WHATLEY, Robert Frank
Alexander Galt Regional HS; Lennoxville, CANADA (20-539).

WHEAT, Lawrence Reagan
Big Spring HS; Big Spring, TX (25%-525) Band; Lat C; Order/Arrow; Ntl Piano Guild Auditions; Church Pianist; Yth Choir; Stage Band; Featured Pianist, Campus Revue; Theater.

WHEAT, Susan Kay
Roswell HS; Roswell, NM (1-325) A-Ed, Ann; Community Yth Symph; Drama; Ensm; GS; VP, NHS; Orch; Parl, SC; Bkbl; COM; H of F; Val; VofDEM; AAUW Girl o-t Mo; Outst Young Musician; Acct A; JHS Service A; Ozark Bible Col; Christian Ed.

WHEATCRAFT, Loree Jeanne
Greeley W HS; Greeley, CO (42-364) Secy, Drama; FHA; Semi-Fin, GS; VP, 4H, VP, ARC; Secy, Span C; Spch C; 4H A; Spch A; Hospiteen; Explorers; U of N Colo; Biol.

WHEATER, Richard Charles
Fremont HS; Fremont, MI (42-147) Band; Dbte Tm; ACT Hon School; Grand Rapids Sch of Bible & Mus; Bible.

WHEATLEY, Chris Edmund
Shawnee Mission N HS; Overland Park, KS (40-400) Band; BS; Dbte Tm; Drama; NFL; ARC; Spch C; SC; Tri-HiY; Golf; ARC A; Spch A; Yth Leg; Hon Band; NFL Congress; Tri St Mus Fest; Church Spkr; Communications.

WHEATLEY, Debra Lynn
S R Butler HS; Huntsville, AL; JV, Swim; Sci.

WHEATLEY, Sammie Adrean
Creative Arts Acad; Dallas, TX; Pres, FHA; Hmrm; Secy, NHS; ARC; Sch P; SC; Bkbl; Soccer; Citz A; Hon Prog; Secy, Church Choir; NHS A; Dance.

WHEATLEY, Susan Marie
Fremont Ross HS; Fremont, OH (15-500) 4H; NHS; Bkbl; Tr; Alg A; COM; 4H A; Math A; Sci A; Yth Fel; Pom-Pom; Cheerblock; Bowling Green St U; Eng.

WHEATON, Kevin M
Nash N HS; Nashville, TN (10%-202) Cpt, Ftbl; MVP, Tr; Math A; FCA; Christian Ath o-t Yr HS; Tenn St U; Elec Engr.

WHEATON, Rise Lynn
North HS; Nashville, TN; Chldr; GS; Hmrm; NHS; Span C; SC; Tnns; Hon Prog; Span As; Tenn St U; Pre-Med.

WHEEKER, Joanne Donna
Churchill HS; Livonia, MI (10%-850) Henry Ford Comm Col; Nurs.

WHEELAND, Cynthia Elaine
Patterson HS; Patterson, CA (25-175) Ann; Band; Bus C; Chldr; Drama; 4H; Jr Miss Pageant; Mjrte; Sch P; Ski C; Span C; SC; Cpt, Sftbl; Co-Cpt, Swim; Tr; Citz A; 4H A; HQn; Hon Prog; Phy A; MVP, Co-Cpt, Cpt, Bkbl; MVP, Vlbl; UCLA; Recreation Director.

WHEELAND, Bryan James
Centralia HS; Centralia, WA; Chor; JV, Bkbl; JV, Golf; Soccer; Swim; Wrest; Math.

WHEELER, Catherine Jeanne
Chariho Regional HS; Wood River Jct, RI (1-228) NHS; COM; Rensselaer A; Type A; Val; Nom, NCTE Achv Writing; Lion's C Exchange Stu; Gregg Shorthand A; NEA 'My Am' Stu Bicen Comp Sch Win; Colo St U; Vet Med.

WHEELER, Curtis Lyle
Southland HS; Southland, TX (3-9) A-Ed, Ann; VP, Band; VP, 4H; VP, NHS; A-Ed, Sch P; Secy, Soph Cl; Bsbl; Cpt, Bkbl; Co-Cpt, Ftbl; Tr; Cl Fav; 4H A; Journ A; Math A; MLS; Val; Yth Fel; Spelling, Tr, Essay, A's; Tex Tech U; Agr.

WHEELER, Cynthia Bernice
Sherwood HS; Creighton, MO (10-87) VP, FHA; NHS; Warrensburg Col; Ed.

WHEELER, Cynthia Gale
Marvell HS; Marvell, AR (5-151) BC; FHA.

WHEELER, David Alan
Dupont Sr HS; Hermitage, TN; SC; Bsbl; Ftbl; JV, Wrest; All Star, St Champs, Bsbl; U of Tenn; Law.

WHEELER, Debra O'Neil
Cal Comm Sch; Latimer, IA; Ann; Band; Cpt, Chldr; Chor; Drama; NHS; Secy, Jr Cl; Secy, Soph Cl.

WHEELER, Dennis Alan
Klamath Union HS; Klamath Falls, OR; A Cap Choir; Band; Pres, Chess C; Chor; Community Yth Symph; Ensm; 4H; Hmrm; SC; Mgr, Bkbl; Mgr, Tr; Comm Orch; Oral Roberts U; Mus.

WHEELER, Donna Jean
John Graham Sr HS; Warrenton, NC (20-165) Fr C; VP, FBLA; Hmrm; SC; Amer Leg A; Amer Leg Orator A; Spch A; Peace Col; Elem Ed.

WHEELER, Gary Keith
Piqua Central HS; Piqua, OH (100-600) Chor; Drama; NHS; Orch; Opt A; Accomodores; Asbury Col; Ministry.

WHEELER, Jo Ann
McMullen Co HS; Tilden, TX; Ann; Chldr; FFA; Secy, 4H; NHS; Parl, SC; Bkbl; Tnns; Tr; COM; 4H A; FFA Swtht; Schreiner Col; Phys Ed.

WHEELER, Karen S
La Crosse HS; LaCrosse, KS (4-50) Band; Chor; Drama; Pres, FHA; Madrigal; Spch C; SC; Ch, Jr Cl; Hon Prog; Spch A; St Scholar; Type A; Tr Off; NML; Wichita St U; Eng.

WHEELER, Kimberly Ann
Menchville HS; Newport News, VA; A Cap Choir; Chor; Ensm; Madrigal; COM; Madison Col; Special Ed.

WHEELER, Kirk Woodford
Independence HS; Charlotte, NC (135-600) Key C; Ski C; JV, Ftbl; Order/Arrow A; Eagle Sct; U of Mont; Bio.

WHEELER, Kyle Allen
Big Spring HS; Big Spring, TX; Pres, Chor; VP, Key C; All Region, All Area Choir; WW; Tex Tech U; Bus.

WHEELER, Lori Sue
Joliet E HS; Joliet, IL (33-356) Secy, A Cap Choir; Ed, Ann; Chor; Madrigal; NHS; Amer Leg A; Q&S A; Type A; Yth Fel; Pres, Office Occupations C; Pom-Pom; Lion's C Stu o-t Mo; St, Yth Fel; Joliet Jr Col; Biol.

WHEELER, Martha Hope
Walnut Hills HS; Cincinnati, OH; A Cap Choir; Chor; Drama; Sftbl; COM; Yth Fel; Big Brothers & Sisters; Pre-Sch Ed.

**WHEELER,
Mary Beth Elizabeth**
Clark Co R-1 HS; Kahoka, MO (6-96) CYO; Rptr, FHA; 4H; Rptr, NHS; Mgr, Bkbl; Mgr, Tr; 4H A; I Dare You; Northeast Mo U; Dental Hygienist.

WHEELER, Michelle Dawn
Woodlake Union HS; Woodlake, CA (11-120) Chem C; FHA; Tr; CSF; Chamber of Comm A; Bus.

WHEELER, Nathan Vincent
Southland HS; Southland, TX (1-5) Band; NHS; Bkbl; Ftbl; Tr; Tex Tech U; Agr.

WHEELER, Patricia Ann
N Shore HS; W Palm Beach, FL (7-336) VP, Fr C; Hmrm; NFL; Spch C; SC; Alg A; Hist A; Hon Prog; Math A; Spch A.

WHEELER, Patricia Dianne
Memphis HS; Memphis, TX (10-45) Ann; Band; Ensm; Rptr, FHA; Clarendon Jr Col; Bus Adm.

WHEELER, Robin Denise
Union Springs Acad; Union Springs, NY (33%-32) VP, A Cap Choir; VP, Band; Chor; Pres, Jr Cl; Hon Prog; Most Out; Tumbling Tm; Touring Choir, Soloist; Stu Missionary Activities Group; MVP, Mus; Andrews U; Nurs.

WHEELER, Scott Mitchell
Sehome HS; Bellingham, WA; Band; Cpt, Bkbl; U of Wash; Bus Adm.

WHEELER, Vera Joanne
Penns Manor Area HS; Clymer, PA (15-160) Chor; Gov Intern; Altoona Sch of Nurs; Nurs.

WHEELER, Vince Pendleton
Caney Valley HS; Caney, KS (8-66) Co-Ed, Ann; VP, Band; BS; Chor; FHA; NHS; VP, Span C; SC; Var C; Bsbl; Cpt, Bkbl; Cpt, Ftbl; Cpt, Golf; Journ A; 3rd, Mr Future Bus Employee; Mr FHA; Kans St U; Creative Writing.

WHEELER, Warren Philip
McMullen Co HS; Tilden, TX (4-6) VP, FFA; VP, 4H; Math C; Tres, NHS; VP, SC; Bkbl; Tnns; COM; 4H A; WW; Tex A&M U; Agr Engr.

WHEELER, William Alvin
Hume-Fogg Comprehensive HS; Nashville, TN (3-221) NHS; VP, SC; Tnns; Civitan A.

WHEELESS, Bruce Dale
Woodrow Wilson HS; Dallas, TX (10-300) Key C; VP, NHS; SC; Bsbl; MVP, Bkbl; Cpt, Ftbl; Cl Fav; Yth o-t Month; Talented & Gifted Program; Tex A&M U; Acct.

WHEELINGS, Debra Elaine
Chicora HS; Charleston, SC; Chldr; Ensm; Fr C; Pres, Hmrm; ARC; SC; Bkbl; Vlbl; Nurs.

WHEELIS, Roger Dale
Valdosta HS; Valdosta, GA; Yth Fel; Bible Lit.

WHEELOCK, Rebecca Marie
Stillman Valley HS; Stillman Valley, IL (33%-125) Band; Chor; Drama; Ensm; FHA; Yth Fel; Church Handbell Choir; Area & Ntl Handbell Festivals.

WHELAN, Edward Lee
Owensboro Cath HS; Owensboro, KY (95-210) CYO; JV, Bsbl; Ftbl; Tnns; JA A; CCD Teacher; VP, Jr Crime Coun; JDC; E Ky U; Law Enforcement.

WHELCHEL, Martha Ann
Cartersville HS; Cartersville, GA (13-152) Tres, BC; Chor; Ensm; Fr C; FTA; Sch P; VP, Tri-HiY; N Ga Col; Eng.

WHELCHEL, Sherri Lynne
Canoga Park HS; Canoga Park, CA; A Cap Choir; Chor; Ensm; ARC; Rptr, Sch P; Secy, SC; Sftbl; Semi-Fin, Swim; Beauty; COM; Citz A; Cl Fav; MLS; ARC A; Yth Fel; California Baptist Col.

WHELESS, Sharon Kay
Edward Best HS; Louisburg, NC (2-53) BC; Chor; NHS; Co-Cpt, Bkbl; Sports C; All Conf Bkbl; Marshall, Fresh & Sopho Cl; Sch Pianist; Arts & Craft C; U of NC at Chapel Hill; Phys Ed.

WHERRY, Elise Wall
Chester Sr HS; Chester, SC; Hmrm; SC; York Tech Col; Nurs.

WHERRY, Rickey Dale
Central HS; Memphis, TN (8-275) Fr C; Mu Alpha Theta; COM; Citz A; Hon Prog; Southwestern at Memphis; Acct.

WHERRY, Russell Martin
Briarcrest HS; Memphis, TN (72-323) Pres, Hmrm; Key C; VP, SC; Bkbl; MVP, Ftbl; Cpt, Tr; Memphis St U; Pol Sci.

WHETRO, Suzette Jeanne
Montpelier HS; Montpelier, OH (2-110) Chor; GS; NHS; Yth Fel; Cert of Schol Achv A; Ohio St U; Phys Terapy.

WHETSTONE, Deborah May
W Holmes HS; Millersburg, OH (35-173) Band; Chor; Drama; Ensm; GS; Sci C; Span C; Spch C; Thes; Tri-HiY; H of F; Rotary A; Acct A; Dramatics A; N Central Tech; Acct.

WHETZEL, Mary Beth
St Elizabeth HS; Pittsburgh, PA (38-102) Drama; Hmrm; VP, SC; Wheeler's Bus Sch; Secy.

WHICKER, Beverly Grey
East Forsyth Sr HS; Kernersville, NC (47-687) Anchor C; Pres, FNA; ARC; ARC A; *Forsyth Tech Inst; Nurs.*

WHICKER, Gary Lee
Ottumwa HS; Ottumwa, IA (7-491) Band; Order/ Arrow; JV, Cr-Crtry; Wrest; B Crocker A; St Scholar; Eagle Sct; *Iowa St U; Engr.*

WHICKER, Sandra Renee
Ragsdale HS; Greensboro, NC (26-385) BC; Fr C; FBLA; French NHS; NHS; Tnns; *UNC-Chapel Hill.*

WHIDBY, Lisa Lynn
Franklin HS; Franklin, TN; Band; Pres, FHA; Var C; Bkbl; Yth Fel; Church Yth Choir & Sftbl; Pres, Sunday Sch Cl; All Region Bkbl; *Belmont Col; Bus.*

WHIDDON, Deborah Kay
Carthage HS; Carthage, TX; NHS; Type A.

WHIDDON, Jill Ann
Edmond Mem HS; Edmond, OK; A Cap Choir; Chor; VP, Drama; Ensm; Lat C; Spch C; VP, Thes; Tr; Outst Vocalist; *Mus Theatre.*

WHIGHAM, Greg Lee
S Page Comm Sch; College Springs, IA (25%-43) Band; VP, FFA; 4H; SC; Var C; Bsbl; Bkbl; Ftbl; Tr; COM.

WhirlwindHORSE, Kevin Lee
Crazy Horse Sch; Wanblee, SD (2-14) 4H; Hmrm; NHS; Sch P; Spch C; SC; Var C; Pres, Sr Cl; Parl, Jr Cl; Bsbl; Co-Cpt, Bkbl; Cpt, Ftbl; Cpt, Golf; Swim; Tr; Citz A; 4H A; Sal; Spch A; *SD Sch of Mines & Tech; Civil Engr.*

WHISLER, Bryce Gerald III
Douglas MacArthur HS; San Antonio, TX (12-630) A Cap Choir; Band; Math C; NHS; Span C; Span NHS; Hon Prog; Fin, Piper Schol; Span C A's; *Baylor U; Pre-Dental.*

WHISLER, William Scott
Indian Springs HS; Indian Springs, NE (2-25) Band; Chor; Drama; Ensm; NHS; Ed, Sch P; Ski C; Pres, SC; Pres, Sr Cl; Tr; COM; Journ A; Math A; NMS; NEDT; Sci A; *Mus.*

WHISMAN, William Bourne
Schoolcraft HS; Schoolcraft, MI (5-64) Band; NHS; JV, Bkbl; Ftbl; Tr.

WHISNANT, John Mullins
Brookstone HS; Columbus, GA (15%-45) Chess C; French NHS; Hmrm; Semi-Fin, Lit Ral; Tres, SC; Tres, Sr Cl; Tres, Jr Cl; Tres, Soph Cl; JV, Ftbl; NEDT; *U of Ga; Corporate Law.*

WHISNANT, Patricia Ann
Freedom HS; Morganton, NC (38-458) Bio A; *Western Peidmont Comm Col; Engr.*

WHISNANT, Richard Byron
R J Reynolds Sr HS; Winston-Salem, NC (1-822) VP, BS; Cpt, Dbte Tm; Hmrm; InterClub Coun; Parl, Key C; Monogram; NFL; NHS; Order/ Arrow; Spch C; Span NHS; Pres, SC; Ch, Jr Cl; Tnns; Amer Leg A; Gov Honor Prog; Gr Marshal; Hon Prog; Masque & Gavel A; NMF; Opt A; Order/Arrow A; Spch A; Val; Senator, Boy's Nation; St Debate Champ; *U of NC; Lib Arts.*

WHISNANT, Sandra Lea
Hunter Huss HS; Gastonia, NC (40-550).

WHISTANCE, Cathy Renee
Stockton R-1 HS; Stockton, MO (30-89) FFA; Rptr, FHA; Secy, 4H; Rptr, Sch P; Tr; 4H A; 4-H Qn; Washington DC Trip, FFA Tm A.

WHISTANCE, Jan Gale
Stockton R-1 HS; Stockton, MO; Bus C; Chor; Pres, FHA; Bkbl; Tr; FHA A.

WHISTANCE, Janice Gale
Stockton HS; Stockton, MO (40-76) Chor; Pres, FHA; VP, 4H; Bkbl; Tr; *Bus.*

WHITAKER, Angela Monica
Marshall Sr HS; Marshall, TX (5%-560) Band; FTA; Tr; Beauty; Opt A; Poet A; Art A; Semi Fin, Beauty; Fin, Optimist A; Fin, Poetry Assn A; *Stephen F Austin Col; Elem Ed.*

WHITAKER, Betsy Ann
Windber Area HS; Windber, PA (11-135) Ann; Band; Drama; Mjrte; Tres, NFL; NHS; Rainbow; Spch A; Ntl VP, Eastern Region, CAR; Sr Cl Coun; St SAR Good Citz A; Yth Rep, Coun of Ministry; Grand Cr of Colors, Rainbow Girls; *Duquesne U; Mus Therapy.*

WHITAKER, Carrie Lu
Dixon HS; Dixon, MO (10-100) Ann; Band; BC; Chor; Drama; Pres, FHA; Rptr, FTA; Mod Mus Mas; SC; Mgr, Bkbl; Sci A; Shorthand A; PA; HR; Home Ec A; *Mo U; Interior Design.*

WHITAKER, Christopher Thomas
Goodlettsville HS; Goodlettsville, TN (78-155) VP, Chor; Tres, FFA; Pres, Hmrm; VP, InterClub Coun; VP, SC; Cpt, Ftbl; Tr; Cpt, Wrest; FCA; *Journ.*

WHITAKER, Crystal Ann
Jacksonville HS; Jacksonville, IL; Chor; Ensm; Ed, Sch P; Pres, SC; Tr, JA A; Pres A; Lib Asst; Stu Govt; Group Auto Safety; *Cosmetology.*

WHITAKER, Edward Scott
E Davidson HS; Thomasville, NC (30-135) Chor; Order/Arrow; Span C; God & Country A; Eagle Sct A; *Davidson Co Comm Col; Acct.*

WHITAKER, Jeffrey A
Wheatland-Chili Central HS; Scottsville, NY (45-108) Band; Chor; Ensm; Sci C; Var C; Bsbl; JV, Bkbl; Tnns; Tr; Wrest; MLS; Sci A; Yth Fel; Most Improved Stu A; *Conservation.*

WHITAKER, Joe Lewis
M B Smiley HS; Houston, TX (8-461) Band; FTA; Hmrm; Orch; Pres, SC; Bsbl; Cpt, Bkbl; Ftbl; Bio A; Citz A; Cl Fav; Sci A; *N Tex St U; Ed.*

WHITAKER, Katrina Yvonne
Jacksonville HS; Jacksonville, IL (200-323) Band; Secy, 4H; *Ill Col; Bus.*

WHITAKER, Les Alan
Muskogee HS; Muskogee, OK (18-575) VP, Band; Ensm; Pres, NHS; Orch; Order/Arrow; Ski C; Bio A; COM; Cl Fav; Hon Prog; Opt A; Opt Out Tn; Order/Arrow A; St Scholar; Eagle Sct; Okla Hon Soc; *U of Okla; Engr.*

WHITAKER, Linda Diane
Second Ward HS; Gloster, LA; Bus C; FBLA; FHA; Mod Mus Mas; SC; *Sou U; Phys Ed.*

WHITAKER, Lynn
W S Creecy HS; Rich Square, NC; BC; WW.

WHITAKER, Lynn Guy
Schleicher Co I S D HS; Eldorado, TX (10-40) Dbte Tm; NHS; Orch; Spch C; Var C; Pres, Sr Cl; Bkbl; Ftbl; Golf; Tr; Sr Prom King; All Dist Bkbl & Ftbl; *Baylor U.*

WHITAKER, Mabel
W S Creecy HS; Rich Square, NC (8-42) FFA; Bkbl; Hon Prog; *Saint Augustine Col; Bus Ed.*

WHITAKER, Peggy Lynn
Montgomery Co HS; Mt Sterling, KY (15-215) Ann; Cpt, Chldr; Chor; Dbte Tm; Drama; FBLA; FHA; Hmrm; NHS; Spch C; SC; Y-Tns; Ftbl; Golf; COM; HCt; Hon Prog; Spch A; HR; *E Ky U; Communications.*

WHITAKER, Sharon Jean
Dilce Combs Mem Sch; Jeff, KY (1-113) Tres, BC; COM; Hon Prog; Most Out; Heartfund Qn; VP, Bible C; *Cumberland Col; Nurs.*

WHITAKER, Warren Lee
Monterey HS; Lubbock, TX; Pres, Order/Arrow; SC; Bsbl; Bkbl; Ftbl; Sftbl; Order/Arrow A; Eagle Sct; *Tex Tech U; Parks Adm.*

WHITBY, Racheal Dean
W Carteret HS; Morehead City, NC; Band; Fr C; 4H; Hmrm; Swim; *E Carolina U; Math.*

WHITCOMB, Reatha Gayle
Siloam Springs Pub HS; Siloam Springs, AR (7-140) A Cap Choir; Band; BC; Chor; Drama; FTA; GS; Pres, 4H; Mjrte; Orch; 4HA; Hon Prog; Star Student; 4-H Swtht; *NW Okla St U; Eng.*

WHITE, Alan C
Indian River HS; Chesapeake, VA; French NHS; NHS; Bkbl; Alg A; Outst Achv Fr; Gifted, Talented Program; *Duke U; Med Tech.*

WHITE, Alan Wayne
Clarke Comm HS; Osceola, IA (20-118) AFS; Band; Bkbl; Cr-Crtry; Tr.

WHITE, Angela Faye
Madison HS; Richmond, KY; Band; Secy, BC; Drama; Pres, Fr C; Sch P; Sci C; Bio A; Highest Score, Achv Test; *Bio.*

WHITE, Anne Leslie
University HS; San Diego, CA (54-311) Chor; Tres, Jr Cl; Co-ordinator, Religious Activ; *U of San Diego; Ed.*

WHITE, Anthony Patrick
Murray Wright HS; Detroit, MI; Bkbl; Citz A; *U of Mich; Math.*

WHITE, Beverly Jean
Lanphier HS; Springfield, IL; Type A; Choir A; Chldr A; *Lincolnland Col; Nurs.*

WHITE, Bobby Earl
Crenshaw HS; Los Angeles, CA; Mgr, Ftbl; Ltrman A; *W Los Angeles Col; Commercial Art.*

WHITE, Bonnie Raye
Sunnyside HS; Sunnyside, WA; Tres, Bus C; FTA; Monogram; Var C; Tr; Yth Fel; Pres, Church Yth.

WHITE, Brenda Gale
Rankin Acad; Star, MS (9-30) Chor; FHA; Sftbl; Patriotic Amer Yth.

WHITE, Bruce Allen
Broad Ripple HS; Indianapolis, IN; Chor; Tres, Drama; Ntl Yth Conf; Sch P; Cr-Crtry; Ftbl; Yth Fel; YAD General Assembly; Yth Taskforce; Deacon of Church.

WHITE, Carol Ann
Dillon HS; Dillon, SC (25%-250) Anchor C; BC; Crown & Scepter; NEDT; Regent Schol; Christian Ldrship A; *Baptist Col at Charleston.*

WHITE, Chen Ming
Chester HS; Chester, PA (7-680) A-Ed, Ann; Monogram; Var C; Mgr, Ftbl; Wrest; Alg A; Hon Prog; Math A; Star Student; *Widener Col; Engr.*

WHITE, Christina June
Springfield HS; Springfield, OR; NHS; *Oreg St U; Tech Engr.*

WHITE, Christopher Richard
Hopewell Area HS; Aliquippa, PA (75-489) Hmrm; Lat C; F-Ed, Sch P; SC; Pres, Sr Cl; Pres, Jr Cl; VP, Soph Cl; HCt; *Duquesne U; Bus.*

WHITE, Daniel Jo
Ross Sr HS; Hamilton, OH (10-180) NHS; Sch P; Bsbl; Fin, Tnns; Bio A; Math A; Sci A; *Miami U; Zoology.*

WHITE, Danna June
Blackwell HS; Blackwell, OK (15%-160) FHA; Outst Soph, FHA; Secy, Yth Coun; *Math.*

WHITE, David Glenn
Holston HS; Knoxville, TN; Band; NHS; Order/ Arrow; Amer Leg A; ROTC A; *Vanderbilt Col; Med.*

WHITE, David Scott
Alvin HS; Alvin, TX (180-464) Ann; *Photography.*

WHITE, David Wayne
Robert E Lee HS; Jacksonville, FL (340-489) Drama; Ensm; Hmrm; Madrigal; NFL; SC; COM; Cl Fav; JA A; Yth Fel; Historian, Chor; Spirit Ldr; Chaplain, Soph Cl; Most Sch Spirit; Young Life; *Fla Jr Col; Drama.*

WHITE, Deborah Ann
Norview HS; Norfolk, VA (1-650) NHS; Span C; JNHS; WW; Civitan C; Vol Pin; Brothers & Sisters in Christ; Omega Tri-Hi-Y; Oceana Yth Grp; Office Asst; Acolyte.

WHITE, Deborah Duke
Beech Hill HS; Pulaski, TN (5-26) Rptr, Ann; VP, BC; Chor; FHA; Hmrm; Tres, SC; Pres, Sr Cl; VP, Jr Cl; VP, Soph Cl; Sftbl; B Crocker A; COM; Cl Fav; VP, Stu Body; 1st Runner-up, DREC Essay; *Columbia St Comm Col; Med Sci.*

WHITE, Deborah Jo
Rock Hill HS; Rock Hill, SC; Monogram; Var C; Yth Fel; Vlbl; Gym; *Winthrop Col; Child Development.*

WHITE, Deborah Sue
Brown HS; Sturgis, SD (50-200) Band; FHA; Ger C; Band A; Bowl A; *Black Hills St Col; Elem Ed.*

WHITE, Debra Lynn
Kemper Acad; DeKalb, MS (3-42) Ed, Ann; VP, BC; Chldr; 4H; Fin, Jr Miss Pagent; SC; Var C; S-T, Sr Cl; S-T, Jr Cl; Bkbl; Beauty; B Crocker A; 4H A; HCt; Sci A; Sr o+ Mo; Cutest; Judges' A; Engr Soc; Most Congenial; *U of Miss; Pre-Med.*

WHITE, Debra Ruth
Robert A Long HS; Longview, WA (115-275) ARC; Rptr, Sch P; Art C; Outst Art Stu; *Seattle Pacific U; Nurs.*

WHITE, Donald Wayne
Wossman HS; Monroe, LA; Ntl Yth Conf; Sci C; Var C; Cpt, Bkbl; Cpt, Ftbl; Cpt, Tr; COM; Citz A; H of F; Most Out; Ntl Soci Found; Pres A; VP, Fresh Cl; Sports A; *Northeast La U; Archt.*

WHITE, Douglas Richard
Porter HS; Marryville, TN (5-80) Ann; BC; VP, Key C; Math C; Var C; VP, Jr Cl; Bkbl; Co-Cpt, Ftbl; Tres, Pep C; *US Air Force Acad; Aeronautics.*

WHITE, Earnest Terry
Wilcox Co HS; Rochelle, GA (4-116) BC; Chem C; Lit Ral; Lit Mag; Math C; Phys C; Sch P; Sci C; Span C; COM; Hist A; Hon Prog; *Mercer U; Journ.*

WHITE, Edgar Dwaine
Timberline HS; Weippe, ID (6-47) Bus C; Chor; Fr C; 4H; Ski C; Spch C; Pres, St Stu Congres; Pres, SC; Var C; Bkbl; Cpt, Ftbl; Sftbl; Elk A; Gov Honor Prog; Hon Prog; Yth Leg; *U of Idaho; Bus.*

WHITE, Elizabeth Jean
S Charleston HS; S Charleston, WV (22-291) All Amer Yth; Band; Chor; Co-Ed, Lit Mag; NHS; Span C; Span NHS; Tri-HiY; Citz A; DAR Hist A; *Marshall U; Spch Therapy.*

WHITE, Ella Louise
Howard HS; Georgetown, SC (15-150) Ensm; Hmrm; Sci C; SC; Math A; MLS; Hon Guard; *Morgan St Col; Nurs.*

WHITE, Emerson Bennington
Indian River HS; Chesapeake, VA (10%-499) Dbte Tm; Pres, Fr C; NHS; SC; Co-Cpt, Bkbl; Alg A; COM; Hon Prog; Ntl Achv Schol; NMS; WW; *General Motors Inst; Elec Engr.*

WHITE, Ernest Terral
Motley HS; Columbus, MS (3-81) BC; SC; *MSU; Elec.*

WHITE, Eula Mae
G W Carver Sr HS; New Orleans, LA (35-400) Chor; FNA; Sftbl; Hon Prog; Nurs Asst A; *Sou U; Nurs.*

WHITE, Florrie Anne
Central HS; Louisville, KY (60-300) Band; Chor; Community Yth Symph; Ensm; Ger C; Orch; All St Orch; *Ind U; Mus.*

WHITE, Gail Anita
Bishop Hartley HS; Columbus, OH (20-200) Drama; Semi-Fin, GS; Mjrte; NHS; A-Ed, Sch P; Span C; Mgr, Bkbl; Tr; Journ A; *Journ.*

WHITE, Gary
Harlingen HS; Harlingen, TX; Arch; Arch; JV, Bsbl; Sftbl; *Tex A&M U; Bus.*

WHITE, Genevieve Alice
N Hollywood HS; N Hollywood, CA (10%-800) Secy, AFS; Secy, Chor; Drama; Madrigal; Thes; COM; Hon Prog; Math A; CSF; Fresh Graduation Speaker; Drama A; Art A; Bk Festival A; *UCLA; Creative Arts.*

WHITE, Gilbert William
Crenshaw HS; Los Angeles, CA; *W Los Angeles Col; Law.*

WHITE, Gloria Joyce
Nanih Waiya HS; Louisville, MS (1-32) Ed, Ann; BC; Pres, FHA; COM; H of F; Val; St Contestant A; *Miss U; Nurs.*

WHITE, Gordon Delano
Barberton HS; Barberton, OH (164-605) Hmrm; VP, Key C; NHS; SC; JV, Bsbl; JV, Ftbl; Wrest; Amer Leg A; HCt; *Florida Col; Teacher.*

WHITE, Greg Alan
Spring Hill HS; Springhill, KS; A Cap Choir; Chor; Ensm; 4H; Madrigal; NHS; Span C; 4H A; Yth Fel; St Chor; St Piano Contest; WW; *Mus.*

WHITE, Gregory Allen
Sprague HS; Salem, OR (36-400) Band; Ensm; Ftbl; Tr; COM; *Oreg St U; Agronomy.*

WHITE, Gregory Otis
Cottage Grove HS; Cottage Grove, OR; Chor; Pres, Demolay; Ensm; Hmrm; Spch C; SC; JV, Ftbl; JV, Swim; Wrest; Masonic A; Spch A; VFW A; VFW Orator Win; VofDEM; *Bus Mgt.*

WHITE, Harold Naylor
St Albans HS; St Albans, WV; Hmrm; Tres, Inter-Act C; Sch P; Pres, Ski C; SC; Ftbl; Co-Cpt, Swim; Tnns; Cl Fav; *Archt.*

WHITE, Helen Renee
Eastside HS; Paterson, NJ; Pres, Sr Cl; *William Paterson Col; Special Ed.*

WHITE, Huel Alvin III
Hardaway HS; Columbus, GA (60-425) Hmrm; InterAct C; Key C; NHS; Var C; Golf; Cl Fav; *U of Ga; Pre-Dentistry.*

WHITE, Iris Odell
Dunbar HS; Lubbock, TX; FHA; Hmrm; NHS; Hist A; *Tex Tech U; Nurs.*

WHITE, Jackie Kay
Plainfield HS; Plainfield, IL (20%-310) Band; JV, Chldr; FTA; Span C; Sftbl; Wrest; COM; Citz A; HR; Most Rep; Metetorius; Timothy A; *Eng.*

WHITE, James Blakely
Glenbrook S HS; Glenview, IL; Bsbl; Ftbl; Pres A; ARC A; *U of Ill; Archt.*

WHITE, James Keith
Farmerville HS; Farmerville, LA; 4H; Co-Ed, Sch P; Ftbl; Tr; 4H A; FCA; *La Tech U; Journ.*

WHITE, James Ocleto
Merced Union HS; Merced, CA; Band; Ftbl; Pres, Usher Board; Pres, Yth Church; *Elec.*

WHITE, Jason
Hamilton HS; Los Angeles, CA (11-600) Bus C; Chess C; Dbte Tm; Ch, FBLA; Ftbl; Wrest; Alg A; Bio A; *Harvard U; Law.*

WHITE, Jennifer Ann
Mullens HS; Mullens, WV (8-105) Ann; Tres, BC; VP, FBLA; FHA; HiY; Hmrm; Secy, NHS; SC; Sci A; Type A; *Beckley Col; Secy Stu.*

WHITE, Jennifer Ruth
Richwoods HS; Peoria, IL (150-500) Chor; *Western Ill U; Spch & Hearing.*

WHITE, Joan Carol
Virgie HS; Virgie, KY; BC; Chor; FHA; FTA; 4H; Sftbl; Tr; Bio A; 4H A; Swtht; *Pikeville Col; Art.*

WHITE, Joanne Kay
Castro Valley HS; Castro Valley, CA (10%-400) A Cap Choir; Madrigal; CSF; St Mus Ed Assn; *Calif St U.*

WHITE, John Wesley
Marvell HS; Marvell, AR (6-120) BC; Hmrm; Sch Achieve Tm; Pres, SC; Co-Cpt, Ftbl; Tr; Alg A; Hon Prog; *U of Ark; Pol Sci.*

WHITE, Joseph Leonard III
Concord HS; Concord, NC (25%-230) Band; Key C; Pres, SC; JV, Bsbl; JV, Bkbl; Ftbl; *U of NC at Chapel Hill; Radio-tV Broadcasting.*

WHITE, Judith Dawn
Franklin HS; Franklin, IL (7-43) 4H; Ed, Sch P; Tres, Jr Cl; Vlbl; Prom Court.

WHITE, Judy Ann
Simon Gratz HS; Philadelphia, PA (10-1000) Attendance & Punctuality As; *Penn U.*

WHITE, Julie
Robert E Lee HS; Tyler, TX; Chem C; Beauty; Hon Prog; *Baylor U; Phys Therapy.*

WHITE, Julie Patricia
Calvary Christian Acad; Midland, MI; Co-Cpt, Chldr; Chor; Ski C; Vlbl; *Nurs.*

WHITE, Kameron Kay
MacArthur HS; San Antonio, TX; Secy, Band; Ensm; 4H; Mjrte; Orch; Co-Cpt, Band; Pres, Secy, Yth Choir; All St & Dist Band; *Baylor U; Mus.*

WHITE, Karen Joyce
Hempstead HS; Hempstead, NY (4-300) Band; Community Yth Symph; Dbte Tm; Drama; Ensm; Fr C; Hmrm; Lat C; Rptr, Lit Mag; Math C; Orch; Phys C; F-Ed, Sch P; Mgr, Bsbl; Mgr, Soccer; Tnns; Alg A; Delta Sigma Theta A; Hon Prog; Regent Schol; Sci A; Yth Leg; HR; *Hematology.*

WHITE, Karen Lee
Hillsborough HS; Tampa, FL (96-640) Bus C; FBLA; NHS; *Hillsborough Comm Col; Secretarial.*

WHITE, Kenneth Carnail
Soldan HS; St Louis, MO (90-300) Hon Men, Art; Schol Art A; *Forest Park Col; Art.*

WHITE, Kimberlee Cass
N Iredell HS; Olin, NC (4-280) BC; Model UN; Span C; Citz A; Candystriper; Gov Page; Tres, Tnage Republican C; Humanities C; Win, Sci Fair; Fel of Christian Stu; *Med.*

WHITE, Kimberly Ann
George Washington HS; Los Angeles, CA; Sch P; Journ A; Pep C; *LACC; Interior Design.*

WHITE, Kimberly Sue
R L Osborne HS; Marietta, GA (10%-365) BC; Chor; FTA; Hmrm; Span C; COM; Hon Prog; Star Student; Yth Fel; *Data Processing.*

WHITE, Kimily Dawn
Gainesville HS; Gainesville, GA (92-270) All Amer Yth; Cpt, Chldr; Chem C; Chor; Drama; Ensm; HiY; Jr Miss Pagent; Lit Ral; NHS; Sci C; Spch C; SC; Thes; Tri-HiY; Bkbl; Tr; Wrest; Beauty; HCt; Hon Prog; Kiwanis A; Ntl Conf Chr & Jews; Spch A; Yth Fel; Cl Fav; Key C Swtht; Jr Drama Hon A; WW; Drill Tm; Sch Plays; Church Choir; FCA; Mis GHS; WW, Mus Stus; Pep C; All St Chor; *Wesleyan Col; Mus.*

WHITE, Kris Eddy
Caprock HS; Amarillo, TX; Secy, A Cap Choir; Secy, Chor; Ensm; Madrigal; Tnns; Amer Leg A; COM; Curator A; Sci A; HS Musical; Outst Musician; Most Improved, Tnns; *Mus Ministry.*

WHITE, Larry Dale
Tascosa HS; Amarillo, TX (108-445) Co-Ch, Key C; NFL; Ch, Spch C; SC; VP, Soph Cl; JV, Tnns; COM; 1st Pl, Area, & Ntl OEA Contest; 3rd Pl, St OEA Contest; *Amarillo Col; Acct.*

WHITE, Laura Lee
Manchester HS; Manchester, OH (2-100) Band; Chldr; Chor; VP, 4H; NHS; Sch Achieve Tm; Span C; SC; Tr; 4H A; Yth Fel; Eng II A; Sch Snowball Princess.

WHITE, Lauri Lea
Lasalle-Peru Township HS; LaSalle, IL (162-434) Band; Rptr, Hmrm; Span C; Swim; St Mus Ensm; St Symphonic Band; *IVCC; Ed.*

WHITE, Leeann K
Lyons Township HS; LaGrange, IL (77%-1255) Chor; JV, Dbte Tm; Hon Prog; Yth Fel; *Bradley U; Ed.*

WHITE, Leonard Everick
Rock Hill HS; Rock Hill, SC (167-540) BS; Chor; Drama; Pres, Hmrm; InterClub Coun; Span C; SC; Var C; Pres, Sr Cl; VP, Jr Cl; Wrest; *Clemson U; Pol Sci.*

WHITE, Linda Diane
New Bloomfield R III HS; New Bloomfield, MO; Band; Chldr; Chor; Ensm; Sch P; Mgr, Bkbl; JV, Sftbl; Citz A; *Mus.*

WHITE, Lois Irene
Orleans Pub HS; Orleans, NE (1-28) Hmrm; Cpt, Chldr; Chor; Fin, Jr Miss Pagent; Mjrte; Pres, NHS; SC; Pres, Sr Cl; VP, Jr Cl; VP, Soph Cl; B Crocker A; HQn; Regent Schol; Val; *Kearney St U; Mus.*

WHITE, Lori Ann
Motley Pub Sch; Motley, MN (15-65) Band; Chldr; Chor; Ensm; Secy, 4H; Mgr, Bsbl; Mgr, Bkbl; COM; PA; Schol A; *Brainerd Voc Sch; Secy.*

WHITE, Lori Ann
East HS; Columbus, OH; Pres, A Cap Choir; Chess C; Chor; Drama; Pres, Ensm; ARC; Rptr, Sch P; Span C; Span NHS; Cpt, Bkbl; Sftbl; Tr; Mgr, Wrest; Chem A; ARC A; Sci A; Sport As; Off Helper; Cpt, Vlbl; WW; *Annhurst Col; Pre-Med.*

WHITE, Lori Jeanine
Holton HS; Holton, KS (5-100) Pres, Band; Chor; 4H; NHS; SC; Tres, Soph Cl; Co-Cpt, Bkbl; Sftbl; Hon Prog; Eng A; Arion A; Church Pianst; Band Qn; Twirler; *Emporia Kans St Col; Counseling.*

WHITE, Lynda Jane
Stamford HS; Stamford, TX (1-65) Ann; Band; Chor; FHA; NHS; Alg A; Type A.

WHITE, Lynnae Annette
Westminster HS; Atlanta, GA (29-96) Chor; Drama; Ensm; Ed, Lit Mag; Tr; Alg A; Chem A; Hon Prog; Math A; Sci A; Yth Fel; *Bio.*

WHITE, Lynne Vera
Upper Darby HS; Upper Darby, PA (51-947) Band; Ski C; Hon Prog; Yth Fel; *Interior Design.*

WHITE, Margaret Ann
Borger HS; Borger, TX; Chor; Ensm; Madrigal; Bkbl; *Tex Tech; Psych.*

WHITE, Marilyn Kaye
Dugway HS; Dugway, UT (7-50) Band; Chor; Drama; GS; 4H; Model UN; 4H A; HR; *Brigham Young U.*

WHITE, Marjorie Johnson
W Charlotte Open HS; Charlotte, NC; Chldr; Chor; Drama; Ensm; Most Talented, Sr Cl; *Drama.*

WHITE, Mark William
Clements HS; Athens, AL (8-53) Pres, BC; Chor; FFA; FTA; 4H; Pres, Sr Cl; Tres, Jr Cl; Mgr, Bkbl; COM; Citz A; DARGCA; 4H A; Hist A; MLS; *U of N Ala; Social Studies.*

WHITE, Marty DeWayne
Tallulah HS; Tallulah, LA (9-56) Band; Chem C; 4H; Var C; Bsbl; Ftbl; Tr; FHA Beau; 'T' C; Mr THS; All St Bsbl & Ftbl.

WHITE, Mary Beth
Elkins HS; Elkins, WV (4-215) Ed, Ann; GS; NHS; Ski C; Tres, SC; Secy, Var C; Tres, Jr Cl; VP, Soph Cl; Tnns; Type A; Yth Fel; *W Va U; Pre-Dental.*

WHITE, Mary Kay
Schleicher Co HS; Eldorado, TX; Band; FHA; SC; Bkbl; Tnns; Tr; *Baylor U.*

WHITE, Michael Loren
Newbury Park Adventist Acad; Newbury Park, CA (30-62) A Cap Choir; Band; Chor; Cr-Ctry; *UCSB; Philosophy.*

WHITE, Neva Darlene
Denham Springs HS; Denham Springs, LA (25-250) Cpt, Chldr; Secy, FHA; FTA; NHS; HCt; Key C Swtht; Dist Rally, Home Ec; WW; Cl Tres; *LSU; Fashion Merchandising.*

WHITE, Nina Sue
Traditional HS; Louisville, KY (1-60) Pres, BC; Tres, SC; Pres, Soph Cl; *Freed-Hardeman Col; Elem Ed.*

WHITE, Patricia Jean
Whitewater HS; Whitewater, WI (32-170) Co-Ed, Ann; Band; Chldr; Chor; Ensm; Hmrm; NHS; Ski C; Secy, Var C; Tr; DARGCA; *La Crosse Col; Phys Therapy.*

WHITE, Patricia Joyce
Westborough HS; Westborough, MA; AFS; Chor; Orch; Rainbow; Grand Cross of Color; *Occupational Therapy.*

WHITE, Peachie Elaine
Crispus Attucks HS; Indianapolis, IN (4-255) Band; Cpt, Chldr; GS; Pres, Lat C; Lat NHS; Math C; NHS; Orch; Span C; Pres, SC; Bausch & Lomb A; Citz A; DARGCA; HQn; Sci A; St Scholar; Type A; Yth Fel; Attousa A; AC Cox Sci A; Upper Decile of Cl; *U of Notre Dame; Pre-Med.*

WHITE, Peggi Jean
Abingdon HS; Abingdon, IL (1-120) Band; Chldr; Chor; Ensm; VP, 4H; Hmrm; Span C; Ch, SC; Secy, Var C; JV, Bkbl; JV, Sftbl; Tr; 4H A; Star Student; *Health.*

WHITE, Penni Jo
Abingdon Sr HS; Abingdon, IL (4-120) Band; Chldr; Chor; Ensm; VP, 4H; Hmrm; Span C; Var C; Bkbl; Sftbl; Tr; Amer Leg C; 4H A; Star Student; S-T, Rptr, 4-H C; *U of Ill; Phys Therapy.*

WHITE, Preston Raynard
Buena HS; Seirra Vista, AZ; Pres, Hmrm; Var C; JV, Bkbl; JV, Ftbl; Tr; Most Out; Type A; *Ariz St U; Data Computer Processing.*

WHITE, Ramona Lynn
Valhalla HS; El Cajon, CA (40-525) Chor; 4H; Hmrm; Pol Sci C; Span C; St Stu Congress; MVP, Sftbl; Tr; Bio A; CSF; COM; Citz A; Cl Fav; 4H A; Most Out; Ath Service A; *Med.*

WHITE, Randall David
Hardin-Central HS; Hardin, MO (20%-40) Band; Chor; Dbte Tm; FFA; Ftbl; Tr; Amer Leg A; Citz A; Phi Beta Kappa; Escort; Homecoming; Tres, SS; Asst Song Leader; BSct; *U of Mo; Agr.*

WHITE, Regina Michelle
Cass Tech HS; Detroit, MI (25%-1300) Chor; NHS; Val; *Wayne St U; Nurs.*

WHITE, Rhonda Dell
Duncan HS; Duncan, OK (2-319) A Cap Choir; Band; Ensm; Fr C; Orch; COM; Masonic A; *Okla U; Lang.*

WHITE, Richard Kent Jr
Rocky Mt Sr HS; Rocky Mt, NC; Wrest; Tres, Homerm; Wrestler o-t Wk; *NC St U; Engr.*

WHITE, Richard Lee
Loyalton HS; Loyalton, CA (5%-50) Fin, Arch; S-T, Band; Chess C; Ensm; 4H; Order/Arrow; Ski C; Var C; Fin, Arch; Bsbl; JV, Ftbl; Swim; 4H A; Archery A; *Hardin-Simmons U; Bio Stu.*

WHITE, Rosamond Elizabeth
Southwest Complex McEvoy B HS; Macon, GA (30-950) VP, 4H; COM; Gov Honor Prog; Best of Show A; *Wesleyan Col; Art Ed.*

WHITE, Royal Lynn
Bradley-Bourbonnais Comm HS; Bradley, IL (50-364) NHS; Span C; Span HS; Tr, Tnns; St Scholar; St Schol; *Olivet Nazarene Col; Bio.*

WHITE, Russell Todd
Karlsruhe Amer HS; Karlsruhe, GERMANY; Ger C; NHS; Ftbl; Tr; Wrest; *U of Tex; Military Sci.*

WHITE, Samuel Garland Jr
Flatonia HS; Flatonia, TX (9-39) Band; Ensm; Hmrm; Sch P; SC; Var C; Mgr, Bkbl; Mgr, Ftbl; Golf; *Tex A&M U; Bus Adm.*

WHITE, Shelia Dian
Motley HS; Columbus, MS (10-101) 4H; Lit Mag; COM; Hist A; Sci A; Lib C; Deca C; *Miss St U; Math.*

WHITE, Shirley Ann
Crenshaw HS; Los Angeles, CA; Tnns; *W Los Angeles Col; Bus Adm.*

WHITE, Stacey Ann
Robert W Groves HS; Garden City, GA; JV, Chldr; Crown & Scepter; FHA; Pres, Hmrm; SC; Var C; MVP, Bkbl; Sftbl; Swim; COM; HCt; Sci A; Yth Fel; *Armstrong St Col; Phys Ed.*

WHITE, Stacie Ann
Pickens HS; Jasper, GA (3-109) Ed, Ann; Parl, BC; Pres, Drama; VP, Ensm; FTA; Ed, Sch P; Pres, Span C; Var C; Pres, Sr Cl; Bkbl; MVP, Tnns; COM; Hist A; Girl's Essay Region & St A's; Best Ldrship; Mr & Miss PHS Court; *Shorter Col; Communications.*

WHITE, Stephen Jerry
Colorado Springs Christian Sch; Colorado Springs, CO (1-13) Ann; Chess C; Chor; Drama; Ed, Sch P; Spch C; Pres, SC; Bsbl; Bkbl; Sftbl; Citz A; Regent Schol; Val; VofDEM; Tres, SC; *U of Colo; Pol Sci.*

WHITE, Steve Elliott
Sussex Central HS; Sussex Co, VA (5-200) VP, BC; Rptr, Jr Cl; Bkbl; Ftbl; Tr; Alg A; Citz A; HCt; Most Out; Sci A; *Va St Col.*

WHITE, Steven Curtis
Sw HS; Kansas City, MO (100-483) Chor; Hmrm; ARC; VP, Sci C; *U of Mo; Bus Adm.*

WHITE, Steven Michael
Trinity Christian Sch; Williston, VT (1-3) Chor; Pres, Span C; Bkbl; JV, Soccer; JV, Sftbl; JV, Tr; *Bob Jones U; Elec.*

WHITE, Sue Ann
Jena HS; Jena, LA (1-130) Band; Pres, Drama; FTA; Secy, 4H; Lit Ral; NHS; 4H A; Hon Prog; *La Col; Pre-Sch Ed.*

WHITE, Susan Ellen
T L Hanna HS; Anderson, SC (10%-750) Ann; Chess C; NHS; Sch P; COM; Hist A; *Med Tech.*

WHITE, Susan Gerthea
Smiths Station HS; Smiths, AL (11-148) BC; Drama; FHA; 4H; Mu Alpha Theta; A-Ed, Sch P; Sci C; Span C; *Auburn U; Psych.*

WHITE, Susan Jane
Dearborn HS; Dearborn, MI (30%-400) Chor; Sch P; SC; Thes; Var C; Bsbl; Bkbl; Hockey; Soccer; Cpt, Swim; Most Out; Spch A; Yth Fel; Badminton; Vlbl; *Central Mich U; Ed.*

WHITE, Suzanne
Clay Co HS; Ashland, AL (10%-72) BC; Chldr; Ensm; FHA; FTA; 4H; Hmrm; Secy, Sci C; SC; Swim; *Samford U; Ed.*

WHITE, Suzanne Lynn
Motley Public HS; Motley, MN (10-42) Co-Ed, Ann; Secy, Band; Chem C; Tres, Chor; Drama; FHA; Tres, 4H; Math C; Tres, Jr Cl; Mgr, Bkbl; Mgr, Ftbl; COM; 4H A; Best Actress; Schol A; FHA A; *Anoka-Ramsey Comm Col; Occupational Therapy.*

WHITE, Teddy Ann
Grand Junction HS; Grand Junction, CO; Chor; Sftbl; Math A; Tres, Job's Daughters; St Rep,BYF; Vlbl; Pres, Amerbaptist Guild Girls; Tres, BYF; *Mesa Col; Child Care.*

WHITE, Teddy Wayne
Tipton HS; Tipton, OK; Band; Chor; FFA; 4H; Spch C; Bsbl; Bkbl; Ftbl; Cl Fav; 4H A; HCt; Spch A; *OCC; PE.*

WHITE, Teresa Denise
John A Holmes HS; Edenton, NC (11-134) Co-Cpt, Chldr; Pres, Chor; Pres, Mod Mus Mas; NHS; VP, Sci C; SC; HCt; Mus A; All St Chor; *Meredith Col; Mus Ed.*

WHITE, Teresa Jeralyn
Washington Co HS; Springfield, KY (5-177) Band; BC; Cpt, Chldr; Pres, FTA; Semi-Fin, Jr Miss Pa; Key C; NHS; ARC; Sch P; Rptr, SC; Var C; Tres, Sr Cl; Tres, Jr Cl; Tres, Soph Cl; Swim; Tr; COM; Cl Fav; 4H A; HQn; HCt; Hon Prog; ARC A; Swtht; A & S Schol; WW; *U of Louisville; Acct.*

WHITE, Teresa Kay
S D Lee HS; Columbus, MS; Rptr, Sch P; SC; Citz A; HCt; Math A; Sci A; Eng A; *Harding Col; Psych.*

WHITE, Theresa Serena
Reid Ross HS; Fayetteville, NC; Ann; Chldr; Chor; Drama; FBLA; 4H; Hmrm; InterClub Coun; Lat C; Sci C; Span C; Tri-HiY; COM; Most Out; Star Student; Tres & Secy, SC; Chldr A; *Pol Sci.*

WHITE, Toni Elizabeth
Calvary Christian Acad; Midland, MI; Band; Cpt, Chldr; 4H; F-Ed, Sch P; Ski C; Secy, SC; Bkbl; HQn; HCt; Vlbl; Stamp C; *Saginaw Valley Col; Computer Processing.*

WHITE, Tracinda Louise
Chippewa Falls Sr HS; Chippewa Falls, WI (28-439) JV, Dbte Tm; Model UN; NFL; Span C; Spch A; Church Yth Elder; *U of Wis; Nurs.*

WHITE, Valerie Regina
Norview Sr HS; Norfolk, VA (11-249) Chor; FHA; JA A; Yth Fel; Modern Dance A; *Hampton Inst; Lab Tech.*

WHITE, VanLauwn
Martin Luther King Jr HS; Chicago, IL (26-583) JETS; Sftbl; COM; Citz A; Hon Prog; MLS; Elec A; Eng A; *Ill Inst of Tech; Elec Engr.*

WHITE, Vicki Ann
Hickman Mills HS; Kansas City, MO (56-490) Hmrm; Math C; NHS; Secy, Pol Sci C; Sci C; Ch, Job's Daughters; Med Careers C; Orient of Eastern Star; *Rockhurst Col; Respiratory Therapy.*

WHITE, Vicki Lynne
Coldwater HS; Coldwater, MI (5-320) Band; Ensm; Semi-Fin, GS; VP, 4H; Secy, NHS; Span C; VP, Soph Cl; Alg A; Bio A; COM; 4H A; Hon Prog; Math A; NMS; *Math.*

WHITE, Vicki Sue
Berkeley HS; Moncks Corner, SC (27-340) Chldr; Fr C; FTA; Hmrm; Secy, Sr Cl; HQn; Best Looking; WW; *Trident Tech Col; Med Secy.*

WHITE, Vickie Lynn
Bowman HS; Wadesboro, NC; Chldr; Rptr, Drama; Hmrm; HCt; Homecoming Sponsor; Miss NC Jr Civitan; Homecoming Sponsor; Civitan Yth Co; Chldr Championship Sq; *U of NC; Special Ed.*

WHITE, Virginia Ann
Tamalpais HS; Mill Valley, CA; Chldr; Chor; Secy, Hmrm; NHS; Phys C; Sch Achieve Tm; Span C; Secy, SC; JV, Bkbl; JV, Soccer; JV, Sftbl; JV, Tnns; JV, Tr; Citz A; Cl Fav; Math A; Most Out; ARC A; Yth Fel; *Heald's Col; Clerical Work.*

WHITE, Wanda Kay
Rock Hill HS; Rock Hill, SC (156-545) Chor; SC; VP, Soph Cl; Tr.

WHITE, Wanda Louise
Ensley HS; Birmingham, AL; Y-Tns; Sftbl.

WHITEAKER, Frankie
Roy Miller HS; Corpus Christi, TX; Order/ Arrow; Rptr, Sch P; Sci C; Secy, SC; Mgr, Bsbl; Bkbl; Mgr, Ftbl; Sftbl; Tnns; COM; God & Country A; Spch A; S-T, HS Westerners; BScts; *E Tex Baptist Col; Ministry.*

WHITEFIELD, Elizabeth
Bryan Adams HS; Dallas, TX (51-750) Secy, Band; Community Yth Symph; Drama; Ensm; HiY; Secy, Hmrm; NHS; Orch; ARC; Co-Ed, Sch P; Span C; Hon Prog; Chamber Ensm; All City Band; Bible A; Superior Ratings, UIL Solo & Ensm; *Abilene Christian U; Mus Therapy.*

WHITEFORD, Frances Renee
Thornwell HS; Clinton, SC (2-20) Ann; S-T, BC; Pres, Fr C; FHA; Fin, GS; SC; COM; DARGCA; *Clemson U; Acct.*

WHITEHAIR, Thelma
Chinle HS; Chinle, AZ; Rptr, FFA; FHA; NHS; MVP, Tr; Pub Info A, FFA; Best Field Events, Tr; *Eastfield Col; Phys Therapist.*

WHITEHEAD, Donna Marie
Notre Dame Acad HS; Staten Island, NY; Chor; Drama; Math C; Bowl Tm; Pres, Church Yth Group; Tutor; Vol, Hospital; *Houghton Col; Med.*

WHITEHEAD, Gail Denise
Chester HS; Chester, PA (20-670) Co-Ed, Ann; NHS; Secy, Prom Committee; *Secy.*

WHITEHEAD, James Thomas
Midwest HS; Midwest, WY (5-22) NHS; Bkbl; Ftbl; JV, Tr; Wrest; *U of Wyom; Geology.*

WHITEHEAD, Robert James
Oak Ridge HS; Orlando, FL; Civitan C; *Math.*

WHITEHEAD, Teresa Christine
S Kitsap HS; Port Orchard, WA (75-555) A Cap Choir; Chor; Hon Prog; *Mus.*

WHITEHEAD, Valencia Yvonne
Terrell HS; Dawson, GA (10%-112) Fr C; FBLA; FHA; Hmrm; SC; Sci A; Fr, Home Ec, A's; *Fla Jr Col; Nurs.*

**WHITEHURST,
Burke Gibson Jr**
Jones Co HS; Gray, GA (10%-200) FFA; *Mercer U; Bus Adm.*

WHITELAW, Mary Ellen
Seekonk HS; Seekonk, MA (12-224) Fr C; VP, NHS; Tnns; Co-Ed, Yrbk Lit; GAA; *Pol Sci.*

**WHITELOW,
Deborah Ann Renee**
Collinwood HS; Cleveland, OH (20%-342) Ensm; Fr C; Ger C; Alg A; Citz A; Fr A; Growth A; Black Unity C; *Howard U; Med.*

WHITEMAN, Alice Renee
Moon Sr HS; Coraopolis, PA (100-428) Ger C; Hmrm; SC; Var C; Mgr, Bkbl; JV, Sftbl; Co-Cpt, Vlbl; Jr NHS; MEEP; *Mount Union Col; Spch And Drama.*

WHITEMAN, Kimberly
R J Reynolds Sr HS; Winston-Salem, NC;

WHITENER, Russell Edward
Bethel HS; Hampton, VA (67-500) Pres, Drama; Thes; Eagle Sct; Outst Tn Citizen; Sr Patrol Ldr, BSct; St Flag Carrier, Gov Conf.

WHITESELL, Anne Marie
St Mary's Acad; Alexandria, VA (1-70) Bus Mgr, Ann; Drama; French NHS; Key C; Math C; Mu Alpha Theta; NHS; Tres, SC; Secy, Sr Cl; Tr; Alg A; Bausch & Lomb A; COM; Citz A; Hon Prog; Math A; NMS; NEDT; Opt A; Phy A; Sci A; Fr, Eng, A's; Ntl Guild of Piano Playrs Aud A; *Amherst Col; International Law.*

WHITESELL, Beverly Ann
Eaton HS; Eaton, OH (6-187) Chor; Ensm; 4H; Mjrte; Tres, Soph Cl; Tr; 4H A; 2nd Pl, 4-H Talent Contest; Phys Fitness A; I Rating, St Vocal Solo; *U of Cincinnati; Legal Secy.*

WHITESIDE, Arthur Lemont
Chapman HS; Inman, SC (50-268) *U of SC; Govt.*

WHITESIDE, Linda Darnell
Lincoln HS; Dallas, TX; Band; Math C; NHS; *Biol.*

WHITESIDE, Stephanie Jean
Chapman HS; Inman, SC (69-268) *U of SC; Nurs.*

WHITESIDE, Tami Anne
New Bern Sr HS; New Bern, NC (18-500) Chldr; Chor; Fr C; NHS; Sci C; Gr Marshal; HCt; Rptr, Jr Civitan C; Jr-Sr Prom Pageant; Schol Nom; F-Ed, Sch Yrbk; *E Carolina U; Bio.*

WHITESIDES, Mary Lynn
York Comp HS; York, SC (1-240) Ed, Ann; BC; Cpt, Chldr; Drama; Fr C; GS; 4H; Ch, Hmrm; InterClub Coun; Jr Miss Pagent; VP, NHS; Sch P; Sci C; SC; Secy, Soph Cl; Alg A; Amer Leg A; Beauty; Cl Fav; Coun of Teach A; 4H A; HCt; Type A; Eng Achievement A; PC Jr Fel; Newberry Schol; Winthrop Col; Commercial Art.

WHITESIDES, Michael Lee
Tift Co HS; Tifton, GA; InterClub Coun; Pres, Key C; Tnns; *Abraham Baldwin Col; Engr.*

WHITFIELD, Daniel Wayne
Arvada Sr HS; Arvada, CO (118-560) Key C; Lat C; NHS; Co-Cpt, Ftbl; Wrest; FCA; *Adams St Col.*

WHITFIELD, Joseph Matthew
Wewahitchka HS; Wewahitchka, FL (1-59) Band; Chor; Drama; FFA; Hmrm; Math C; Pres, NHS; Sci C; SC; Pres, Jr Cl; JV, Ftbl; Amer Leg A; Bio A; I Dare You; Magna Cum Laude; Val; Most Intelligent; Gulf Coast Comm Col Schol; Sr Hall of Fame; *Gulf Coast Comm Col; Engr.*

WHITFIELD, Margaret Ann
Litchfield HS; E Gadsden, AL (29-149) Band; Chor; Tri-HiY; Miss Congeniality; *Jacksonville St U; Psych.*

WHITFIELD, Neva Gayle
Assumption HS; E St Louis, IL (50%-118) Bus C; Drama; Jr Miss Pagent; ARC; Sci A; Spch A; Yth Foundation; Cpt, Bowl Tm; Miss Birthday; *W Ill U; Pre-Med.*

WHITFIELD, Teresa Diane
Pendleton HS; Pendleton, SC; BC; *Anderson Col.*

WHITFIELD, Tina Louise
Takoma Acad; Takoma Park, MD; *Psych.*

WHITFIELD, Wanda Elayne
Louisville HS; Louisville, GA (15-120) Ann; Secy, Drama; Secy, Fr C; Secy, 4H; Fin, Lit Ral; Lit Mag; Co-Ed, Sch P; COM; 4H A; Hon Prog; Literary A; *Ga Southwestern U; Pol Sci.*

WHITFORD, Marjorie Jeanne
Meridian HS; Meridian, TX (3-36) Ann; Band; BC; Chor; Drama; Ensm; VP, FHA; Ed, Sch P; Bkbl; Tnns; Tr; Sal; Yth Fel; Drum Major; WW; Jr Hist; Band Swtht; UIL Reg Qual, Typng, Poet, Writng; *SW Tex St U; Secondary Ed.*

WHITFORD, Patricia Sue
Meridian HS; Meridian, TX; Band; BC; FHA; Rptr, Sch P; JV, Bkbl; Tr; Beauty; *UCLA; Vocal Performance.*

WHITING, Deanna Renee
Ruthven Cons Sch; Ruthven, IA (5-28) Band; Chor; Ensm; FHA; VP, 4H; Var C; Bkbl; Golf; Sftbl; Tr; COM; 4H A; HCt; Type A; Yth Fel; St Mus Contest; All Conf Bkbl; *Bus.*

WHITING, Kayla Irene
Carterville HS; Carterville, IL (5-113) Ann; Band; Bus C; Chor; Drama; Ensm; Fr C; FBLA; FHA; Rainbow; Rptr, Sch P; HCt; Hon Prog; Fresh Paddleball Champ; Mus Medals; Eng A; Schol Plaques; PA Cert; *John A Logan Col; Secy.*

WHITING, Vanessa Louise
John Marshall HS; Richmond, VA; VP, Drama; VP, Fr C; Orch; F-Ed, Sch P; Pres, SC; Bus Mgr, Tri-HiY; VP, Jr Cl; Mgr, Bkbl; MVP, Hockey; Co-Cpt, Tr; Metro-Ath Schol Fund; *Law.*

WHITINGER, Susann Elaine
Elyria Christain Acad; Elyria, OH; Orch; Span C; Candystriper; Detroit Yth Orch; Choir Accompanist; Piano Stu; *Nurs.*

WHITIS, Donald Phillip
Burgard Voc HS; Buffalo, NY; COM; *Aviation.*

WHITIS, Michael Eugene
Belen HS; Belen, NM (7-315) Span C; Tr; Alg A; Bio A; *NM St U.*

WHITIS, Scherrie Lyn
Burnside HS; Burnside, KY (4-40) Secy, BC; ARC; F-Ed, Sch P; Pres, Jr Cl; Pres, Soph Cl; Cpt, Bkbl; ARC A; Sci A; Yth Fel; GSct; Eng A; *Somerset Comm Col; Special Ed.*

WHITLEY, Christopher Lee
T Wingate Andrews HS; High Point, NC (21-327) BC; Wrest; Pittsburgh Plate Glass A; *Davidson Ctry Comm Col; Construction.*

WHITLEY, Franklin Dallas
Stamford HS; Stamford, TX; Ann; Pres, Band; Drama; JV, Bkbl; JV, Ftbl; Cl Fav; All Star Cast Dist & Area; Band A; *Howard Payne U; Radio and TV.*

WHITLEY, James Craig
S Point HS; Belmont, NC (10-220) F-Ed, Ann; BC; InterClub Coun; Key C; Pres, SC; Bkbl; I Dare You; Journ A; Kiwanis A; MLS; Q&S A; *Davidson Col; Pre-Med.*

WHITLEY, James Mark
Monroe Area HS; Monroe, GA (22-300) 4H; Ftbl; Golf; Pres A; Phys Ed A; Most Dependable; *U of Ga; Dentistry.*

WHITLEY, Janet Marie
Monroe Area Comprehensive HS; Monroe, GA; Anchor C; FBLA; Hmrm; InterAct C; SC; Tri-HiY; *Athens Tech Col; Bus.*

WHITLEY, Lou Ann
Goodwater HS; Goodwater, AL (1-38) Ann; VP, BC; Chor; VP, FHA; FNA; 4H; Math C; Phys C; VP, Jr Cl; HCt; Lion A; Val; Coosa Co Bicentennial Hostess; *Alexander St Jr Col; X-Ray Technician.*

WHITLEY, Mattie Ann
Winnfield Sr HS; Winnfield, LA (5-128) Anchor C; FBLA; FHA; 4H; Lit Ral; Spch C; B Crocker A; HCt; *U of NE La; Med Tech.*

WHITLEY, Michelle Leigh
W Rome HS; Rome, GA (5%-233) Chor; Fr C; Secy, Sci C; SC; Horseback Riding; *Auburn U; Vet Med.*

WHITLEY, Susan Claire
Smithfield-Selma Sr HS; Smithfield, NC (5-355) VP, CYO; NHS; Span C; *U of NC; Art.*

WHITLOCK, David Mark
Bosse HS; Evansville, IN; Hmrm; Lat C; SC; Citz A; VP, Secy, Jr Elec Cl; Secy, Sr Sunday Sch Cl; Church Usher Board; Schol 'B'.

WHITLOCK, Denise Lucille
Campbell HS; Fairburn, GA (8-124) Secy, BC; Chor; FBLA; FTA; Math C; NHS; SC; Hon Prog; NEDT; Drill Tm; Jr Civitan; Cert of A; *Auburn U; Bus Adm.*

WHITLOCK, Karla Rachelle
Reidsville Sr HS; Reidsville, NC (31-344) Hmrm; NHS; Span C; *UNC-Chapel Hill; Psych.*

WHITLOCK, Leigh Anne
Paul M Dorman HS; Spartanburg, SC (25%-500) Ch, Hmrm; SC; Drill Tm; Pres, Sunday Sch Cl; Jr Civitan C; Adv Lifesaving Red Cross; VP, Yth Group; *Clemson U; News Media.*

WHITLOCK, Steve Alexander
Carroll HS; Monroe, LA; Band; Lat C; SC; Hist A; Math A; Eng A; Opt Yth Appreciation; *U of Tenn; Acct.*

WHITLOW, Diane Elaine
Glasgow HS; Glasgow, KY (20%-130) Band; BC; Chor; VP, FHA; Sci C; SC; VP, Tri-HiY; Handbell Choir; JA; Yth Del, A; Yng Singrs; Mus A; Pres, UMYF; Ann Conf, United Methodist Church; VP, Sub Dist UMYF; Jr Chptr St Dg; *Ky Wesleyan Col; Acct.*

WHITLOW, Laurie Ann
Northside HS; Roanoke, VA (69-415) WW; Pres, Acteens; Chorale; Women's Glee C; Flag Corps; *Carson-Newman Col; Religion.*

WHITMAN, Clara Gertrude
Orono HS; Orono, ME (65-110) VP, Dbte Tm; GS; Hmrm; Ed, Sch P; St Yth Congress; Tr; COM; Spch A; Rptr, Sch P; Church Yth Ministries Commision; Philosphy.

WHITMAN, Curtis Dale
Metro HS; St Louis, MO; Pres, Chor; Drama; Sch P; Citz A; JA A; Morehouse Col; Bus Adm.

WHITMAN, Kelly Lee
Titusville HS; Titusville, PA (34-270) Band; Fr C; Lat C; NHS; WW; Geneva Col; Nurs.

WHITMAN, Mary Ann
Philipsburg-Osceola HS; Philipsburg, PA (45-231) Co-Ed, Ann; Chldr; FTA; Fin, Jr Miss Pagent; JV, Bkbl; Clarion St Col; Early Childhood Ed.

WHITMAN, Victoria Lea
Graham HS; Bluefield, VA (27-151) FBLA; Lat C; Sodality; Secy, Span C; WW; Bluefield Col; Elem Ed.

WHITMIRE, Marjorie Anita
Spartanburg HS; Spartanburg, SC; Band; Pres, Hmrm; Jr Miss Pagent; SC; U of SC; Acct.

WHITMIRE, Rosanne
Wingfield HS; Jackson, MS (10%-355) Ed, Ann; Pres, Lat C; Pres, Lat NHS; Mu Alpha Theta; NHS; SC; Secy, Soph Cl; DARGCA; H of F; Hon Prog; I Dare You; MLS; Miss St U; Fashion Merchandising.

WHITMORE, Margy Lynn
Grace M Davis HS; Modesto, CA; Chor; 4H; 4H A; Yth Advisory Board; Yth Service.

WHITMORE, Paula Rae
Siloam Springs HS; Siloam Springs, AR (2-150) Band; BC; Chor; Ensm; NHS; All Region, All St Band; John Brown U; Mus.

WHITMORE, Robin Rene
Rancho Cotate HS; Rohnert Park, CA; A Cap Choir; Band; NHS; F-Ed, Sch P; CSF; Ch, Yth Commission; VP, Church Yth.

WHITNEY, Barbara Jean
Barrington Comm HS; Barrington, IL; A Cap Choir; Ger C; Christian Science Col; Nurs.

WHITNEY, Cheryl Ann
Manheim Township HS; Neffsville, PA; Chor; Ensm; HCt; Binkley Choir A; Semi-Fin, Homecoming Court; Co, Dist & Reg Chor; Most Outst Mus Stu.

WHITNEY, David Paul
Arsenal Tech HS; Indianapolis, IN; Lat C; Sftbl; Tr; Hon Prog; Math A; Hon Soc; Art.

WHITNEY, Deborah Lea
Buffalo HS; Buffalo, MO (15-150) A Cap Choir; Chor; Madrigal; COM; Spch A; Star Student; 'I' Ratings, Mus Festival; Ariz St Essay; SW Mo St U; Vocal Mus.

WHITNEY, Derek Lee
Sol C Johnson HS; Savannah, GA (140-240) Ann; Chor; Up Bound; Savannah St Col; Hist.

WHITNEY, Dorothy Ruth
Euclid Sr HS; Euclid, OH; Mjrte; Coun of Teach A; Yth Fel; Sawyer Bus Col; Secy.

WHITNEY, Duncan Harrower
Mount Anthony Union HS; Bennington, VT (20%-375) Bkbl; Co-Cpt, Cr-Crty; Co-Cpt, Tr; Hon Prog; Art A; Duke U; Studio Arts.

WHITNEY, Jennifer Lynn
Barrington Consolidated HS; Barrington, IL; A Cap Choir; Chor; Fr C; Ski C; Arch; Bsbl; Bkbl; Soccer; Sftbl; Swim; Tnns; Church Usher; Sunday Sch Presenter; Child Development.

WHITNEY, Joseph Sylvester
Wakefield HS; Arlington, VA (14-475) Mu Alpha Theta; NHS; SC; Citz A; Foreign Lang A; Hofstra U; Pre-Dental.

WHITNEY, Judith Michelle
Concord Christian Sch; Concord, NH; A Cap Choir; Chldr; Chor; GS; Pres, 4H; Lat C; ARC; F-Ed, Sch P; Cpt, Bkbl; Swim; COM; 4H A; JA A; Math A; ARC A; Summa Cum Laude; 4H Dress Revue; MIP, Christian Attitude; VP, Tres, 4-H C.

WHITNEY, Kathy Rosemary
Northmor HS; Galion, OH; JV, Chldr; Span C; 4H; Sch P; Span C; God & Country A; 4H A; Spch A; Type A; Gym; Ohio St Branch Col; Bus.

WHITNEY, Maureen Jeanne
Saint Joseph HS; Hammonton, NJ (5-62) Bus C; Chor; Drama; Secy, 4H; NFL; Tres, Spch C; JV, Bkbl; 4H A; Hon Prog; Spch A; General Excellence A; Saint Joseph Col; Med.

WHITNEY, Wayne B
Milford Sr HS; Milford, DE; VP, FFA.

WHITSITT, Cheryl Annette
Southside HS; Fort Smith, AR (30-435) Co-Ed, Ann; Secy, Lat C; NHS; DARGCA; Hon Prog; Journ A; Q & S; Journ.

WHITSON, Deborah Kay
David Lipscomb HS; Nashville, TN; David Lipscomb Col; Home-Ec.

WHITSON, Robbie Jane
Bryan Adams HS; Dallas, TX (85-750) Chor; NHS; Secy, Sr Cl; MVP, Bkbl; Sftbl; Tr; Outst Stu; Most Dedicated, Drill Tm; Cpt, Vlbl; MVP, Bkbl; E Tex St U; Phys Ed.

WHITSON, Susan Lethell
Jefferson Moore HS; Waco, TX (30-300) Parl, A Cap Choir; Chor; Ensm; Cpt, Drill Tm; One Act Play; McMurry Col; Mus.

WHITT, Jimmy Dale Jr
Woodland HS; Woodland, MS; Ann; FFA; Sch P; Bsbl; Bkbl; Cl Fav; MLS; FHA Beau; Dignified Sr; Itawamba Jr Col; Phys Ed.

WHITT, Jimmy Ted Jr
Duncan HS; Duncan, OK; FFA; Okla St U; Agr.

WHITT, Melissa Grace
Morristown-Hamblen E HS; Morristown, TN (29-290) A Cap Choir; Anchor C; Rptr, Band; BC; Chess C; Chor; Community Yth Symph; VP, Drama; Fr C; Orch; ARC; Rptr, Sch P; VP, Thes; Co-Cpt, Sftbl; Swim; Tnns; All St Band Clinic; Stephens Col; Radio-Film-TV Production.

WHITT, Tracy Hugh
Houston HS; Houston, MS; Var C; Bkbl; Ftbl; Cl Fav; HCt; Yth Fel; Most Handsome; Ole Miss.

WHITTAKER, Andrew Robert
N Penn HS; Lansdale, PA; Hmrm; Key C; Hockey; Tr; Wrest; Yth Fel; Sch Board Proclamation.

WHITTAKER, Lydia Darlene
Norview Sr HS; Norfolk, VA; Chor; 4H; NHS; Bkbl; Tr; Hon Prog; Ath, Cerebral Palsy, A's; Chor, Attendance, A's; Howard U; Special Ed.

WHITTAKER, Paula Marie
Central HS; Columbia, TN (23-376) BC; VP, Drama; GS; 4H; Sch P; Span C; SC; 4H A; I Dare You; MLS; People-To-People Stu Ambas to Europ; Miss U for Women; Journ.

WHITTAKER, Robin Denise
McClymonds HS; Oakland, CA; NHS; Span C; UCLA; Special Ed.

WHITTEN, Joy Lynn
Alvin HS; Alvin, TX (140-360) Band; Drama; Spch C; Pres, Thes; COM; Spch A; Gym; Band A; Tex A&M U; Vet.

WHITTEN, Kimberly Kay
Telstar Regional HS; Bethel, ME (2-75) GS; Math C; Pres, NHS; Secy, SC; Bkbl; Sftbl; Citz A; Hon Prog; Math A; WW; U of Maine; Criminal Justice.

WHITTEN, Kimberly Sue
Bryan Adams HS; Dallas, TX; Chor; Ensm; Rainbow; Hon Prog; Mus A; Drill Tm; FCA; Baylor U; Bus.

WHITTENTON, Gary Dean
Warner Christian Acad; Daytona Beach, FL (4-24) Ann; Band; Chess C; Chor; F-Ed, Sch P; Sci C; Most Christian; PA; Special Band, A's; U of Fla; Sci.

WHITTIER, Nancy Ellen
Middleton HS; Charleston, SC (10%-350) Chor; NHS; Span A; Hons All-St Chor; U of Fl; Hist.

WHITTINGTON, Daniel Mark
Staunton HS; Staunton, IN (20-60) Band; Yth Fel.

WHITTINGTON, John Scott
Wilkes Central HS; N Wilkesboro, NC; FFA; Monogram; Mgr, Ftbl; Mgr, Tr; Co-Cpt, Wrest; Wilkes Comm Col; Bus.

WHITTINGTON, Jon Hammon Jr
Jackson Prep Sch; Jackson, MS (15%-150) Ann; Band; BC; Sci C; Sci A; Pres, LAMPS; Belhaven Col; Psych.

WHITTINGTON, Rebecca Ann
Union HS; Union Grove, WI (3-300) AFS; Band; Dbte Tm; Drama; Hmrm; NFL; NHS; Sch P; Thes; Tr; Citz A; Journ A; Spch A; Type A; Baylor U; Law.

WHITTLE, Janet Kathryn
Moultrie Sr HS; Moultrie, GA; A Cap Choir; BC; Drama; FHA; HiY; Span C; Tri-HiY; Bsbl; Kiwanis A; Spch A; WW Among Mus Stu in Amer HS; Shorter Col; Mus Ed.

WHITTOM, Norris Eugene
Bueno HS; Sierra Vista, AZ; Band; Bsbl; Band A; Ariz St; ROTC Scholar.

WHITTY, Nettie Ozella
Carroll HS; Monroe, LA; Band; Fr C; Hmrm; Math C; F-Ed, Sch P; SC; Bkbl; Sftbl; Tnns; Cl Fav; Hist A; HCt; Hon Prog; Journ A; Sci A; Band A; PA A; HR; Academic Ath A; Ldrship A; Math.

WHITTY, Rosalind
Carroll HS; Monroe, LA (10%-205) Co-Cpt, Band; Co-Cpt, BC; Dbte Tm; Math C; Pres, NHS; VP, Phys C; Citz A; Cl Fav; Hist A; Hon Prog; Math A; MLS; Most Out; Pres A; YES A; Band A; Jazz Band; Civil Engr.

WHITVEN, Joel Lee
Ephrata HS; Ephrata, WA (53-130) Pol Sci C; Var C; Pres, Sr Cl; Pres, Jr Cl; Span C; Bsbl; Mgr, Ftbl; Swim; Cl Fav; Yth Fel; Bsbl St Champs; Best Personality; Boise St Col; Criminal Sci.

WHITWORTH, Barbara Sue
Independence HS; Independence, MS (10%-106) BC.

WHITWORTH, Belinda Kay
Cowan HS; Muncie, IN (6-70) Band; CYO; Chldr; Chem C; Tres, NHS; Var C; Co-Cpt, Bkbl; Tr; Bio A; COM; Chem A; Hon Prog; Vlbl; Ball St U; Acct.

WHITWORTH, Nannette
Cleburne HS; Cleburne, TX; Ann; Band; FTA; Sch P; Sci C; Ski C; Span C; Mgr, Bkbl; Tr; PA; Abilene Christian U; Amer Hist.

WHITWORTH, Stephanie Gwin
Coosa HS; Rome, GA; Band; Tres, JA; Zoology.

WHYTE, Julie A
Celina Sr HS; Celina, OH (36-275) Ann; Band; Fr C; FBLA; FTA; NHS; Jr Candy Ch; Prom Invitation Ch; Prom Decoration Committee; Sr Commencement Committee; Bowling Green St U; Marketing.

WHYTE, Sharon Toshi
Madison HS; San Diego, CA (93-1060) Chor; Ensm; Tnns; CSF; Most Out; Modeling; Most Outst; Explorer Sct; Dance; Vlbl; UC at Davis; Vet.

WHYTE, Wilhelmina Ann
Gilbert Sch; Brooklyn, NY (5-35) Co-Cpt, Chldr; Cpt, Dbte Tm; Drama; Hmrm; Rptr, Lit Mag; SC; Secy, Jr Cl; Tnns; Co-Cpt, Tr; COM; Citz A; Hon Prog; PTA A; Service A; Jr Marshal; Fordham U; Eng.

WIATER, Mary Rose
Willibrord Catholic HS; Chicago, IL (10%-80) Fr C; French NHS; Math C; Monogram; Secy, NHS; Co-Ed, Sch P; Pres, Sci C; Pres, SC; Bkbl; Cpt, Soccer; Cpt, Sftbl; Tnns; Alg A; Beauty; Bio A; COM; Chem A; Hist A; Hon Prog; Journ A; Math A; Sci A; St Scholar; Val; WW; Intra-Mural Bkbl; U of I-Champaign-Urbana Col; Chem.

WIBERT, Paula June
Howland HS; Warren, OH; Ensm; Bus.

WICHLAJEW, Brigitta
Hightstown HS; Hightstown, NJ (43-253) Chor; Drama; VP, Ger C; Mjrte; ARC; Ski C; Ursinus Col; Ger.

WICHMAN, Michael James
Centennial HS; Utica, NE (3-70) Band; Chem C; Ensm; Phys C; Pres, SC; Hon Prog; Mech.

WICHT, Julie Ann
Osseo Sr HS; Osseo, MN (6-516) Band; Ensm; Fr C; Pres, 4H; NHS; Orch; COM; St Band Ensm; Evangel Col; Eng.

WICK, Barbara Janet
Valley City HS; Valley City, ND (5%-163) A Cap Choir; Drama; 4H; Hmrm; Sci C; Ski C; Span C; Bus Mgr, Bkbl; Foreign Stu C.

WICK, Dave Iver
N Beach Sr HS; Moclips, WA; Ann; Band; BS; Key C; NHS; Sch P; Secy, Ski C; SC; JV, Bkbl; Cr-Ctry; Golf; Tr; Journ A; Type A; Sup Crt Judg; BS; Art A; Rocket C; Head Photographer, Sch P; Ltrmen C; Pub Mgr, SC; St Cr; Ctry Meet Most Improved, Cr; Ctry & Tr, Bkbl *Pacific Lutheran U; Biol.*

WICK, Diane Elaine
N Beach Jr-Sr HS; Moclips, WA (2-80) F-Ed, Ann; Band; Chor; FHA; NHS; A-Ed, Sch P; Ski C; SC; Tr; COM; Citz A; Journ A; Type A; Hon Pin; Annual A; *Grays Harbor Comm Col; Med.*

WICKEM, Lela Beth
John Glenn HS; New Concord, OH (25-200) Band; Chor; Orch; Hon Prog; HR; Missionette Hon Star, Church; *Central Bible Col; Sacred Mus.*

WICKEM, Teresa Jane
John Glenn HS; New Concord, OH (13-160) Chor; Hon Prog; 4 Yrs HR; Missionette Hon Star Church; *Central Bible Col; Religious Ed.*

WICKENS, Corrine Cecilia
St Pius X HS; Albuquerque, NM (50%-186) All Amer Yth; CYO; Chor; Pres, Mod Mus Mas; Var C; Cpt, Bkbl; Cpt, Sftbl; Most Out; GAP; All Amer; Ath o-t Yr; Vlbl A's; Regional & St Mus A's; MVP, Sftbl & Bkbl; All City; Med Self Help A; *U of NM; Phys Ed.*

WICKER, Janis Elaine
Chanute HS; Chanute, KS (5%-200) Band; JV, Chldr; Lit Mag; Mjrte; Tr; Pres A; Type A; *Kans St Col; Secy Work.*

WICKER, Patricia Ann
Morristown Jr-Sr HS; Morristown, IN (2-80) Lat C; Pres, NHS; Var C; Tr; Bausch & Lomb A; Bio A; Magna Cum Laude; Sal; St Scholar; Gym; DAHSS; Lat As; Eng A; WW; *Purdue U; Pre-Vet Med.*

WICKER, Veronica Ann
John Ehret HS; Marrero, LA; SC; *U of New Orleans; Communications.*

WICKERHAM, Dave Milton II
Bellefontaine Sr HS; Bellefontaine, OH (13-235) Band; BS; NHS; Orch; Sch Achieve Tm; Cl Fav; Kiwanis A; Rotary A; *Ohio St U; Bio.*

WICKERSHAM, Deanna Jean
Columbia HS; Richland, WA (70%-450) Tr; Exec Coun, Columbia League; Drill Tm; Vlbl; SERVE, Working with Handicapped; *Whitworth Col; Phys Therapy.*

WICKERT, Dorothy Johnson
Falls Church HS; Falls Church, VA; Band; Drama; Fr C; FBLA; Ski C; Tri-HiY; JV, Hockey; Secy, Fresh Cl; *Col of Wooster; Religion.*

WICKES, Melissa Anne
Rockdale HS; Rockdale, TX (13-133) AFS; Band; Chor; Ensm; NHS; Orch; ARC; B Crocker A; Alcoa Found Schol A; Outst Sr Bandsman; *SW Tex U; Applied Mus.*

WICKES, Michael Howard
Sparks HS; Sparks, NV (6-290) Band; Chess C; Fr C; Pres, NHS; SC; JV, Ftbl; Fr A; WW; *Oreg St U; Marine Biol.*

WICKHAM, Brent Allen
Cory Rawson HS; Rawson, OH; Band; Fr C; SC; JV, Bkbl; Ftbl; Math A; *Bowling Green U; Communications.*

WICKLINE, Jane Henderson
James River HS; Buchanan, VA (25%-145) Tres, 4H; Monogram; Bkbl; Sftbl; Tr; 4H A; Secy, FCA; Presidential Phys Fitness A.

WICKS, Kevin James
Liberty Central HS; Swan Lake, NY; Hmrm; Sch P; SC; Pres, Jr Cl; Bsbl; Bkbl; Cr-Ctry; Citz A.

WICKS, Steven Charles
Laville Jr Sr HS; Lakeville, IN (47-165) Chor; FFA; Span C; Bkbl; Yth Fel; *Construction.*

WIDDER, Kerry Robert
Menomonee Falls HS; Menomonee Falls, WI (1-300) Math C; Mu Alpha Theta; NHS; Orch; Math A; *Elec.*

WIDEMAN, Mark Luther
Koshkonong HS; Koshkonong, MO (3-27) Ann; Chor; Lit Mag; Rptr, Sch P; SC; Type A; VofDEM.

WIDEMON, Willie Henry
Skyline HS; Dallas, TX (20-800) Chor; NHS; ARC; Tnns; God & Country A; Math A; Most Out; Sci A; Spch A; Eagle Sct; Med Lab, Eagle Sct, A's; *Howard U; Chem.*

WIDENER, Darla Kay
R L Turner HS; Carrollton, TX (10-900) Chor; Span C; JV, Soccer; Hon Prog; Pres A; Win, Bicentennial Poetry Contest; *Bob Jones U; Elem Ed.*

WIDICK, Timothy D
St Joseph-Ogden HS; St Joseph, IL (50-125) FFA; VP, 4H; SC; Bkbl; Tr; 4H A; Most Improved Tr A; *Parkland Jr Col.*

WIDMER, Kelly Cae
John F Kennedy HS; Cedar Rapids, IA (3-547) A Cap Choir; Band; Ch, Chor; Drama; Ch, Ensm; Thes; Hon Prog; *U of Iowa; Mus.*

WIEBE, Julie Kay
Hobart HS; Hobart, OK (1-77) Band; FTA; Secy, 4H; Mjrte; NHS; Bkbl; Sftbl; Tr; 4H A; *Altus Jr Col; Art.*

WIEBESIEK, Claudia Rose
Thomas Jefferson HS; Council Bluffs, IA (95-450) AFS; Hmrm; NHS; Orch; Span C; Golf; Opt A; Library A's; *Mid-Amer Nazarene Col.*

WIECHMANN, Robert Jerome
Hastings Sr HS; Hastings, MN (10-550) NHS; Bsbl; JV, Bkbl; Cr-Ctry; Hon Prog; *U of Minn; Biol.*

WIECZOREK, Joseph Augustus
Cathedral HS; Springfield, MA (14-655) Pres, Band; Drama; NHS; Orch; Hon Prog; Trustee Schol; Stu Band Conductor; Minstrel; *Eisenhower Col; Fr.*

WIECZOREK, Robert Clayton
Fitzgerald HS; Fitzgerald, GA (10%-190) BC; 4H; HiY; Sch P; COM; Hon Prog; Ltr C; HR; Stu Trnr; WW; PA; *Columbus Col; Pre-Med.*

WIEDEMAN, James Alvin
Gilroy HS; Gilroy, CA (10%-250) Fin, AFS; Band; Chor; Orch; SC; VP, Soph Cl; CSF; *Gavilan Col; Aviation.*

WIEDEMAN, Tracy Lynn
Lake Worth HS; Fort Worth, TX (40-110) FHA; Span C; Cpt, Bkbl; Sftbl; Tr; Co-Cpt, Vlbl; All Dist, All Tourn, Bkbl; Tr A; *Phys Ed.*

WIEDENBECK, Thomas John
Waunakee HS; Waunakee, WI (12-158) AFS; Ed, Ann; Drama; Math C; NHS; Pres, Phys C; F-Ed, Sch P; Pres, Sci C; Pres, Ski C; Ftbl; Tr; COM; Math A; Photography C; Graduation Hon Cards; Yrbk A; 4 0 High Hons; Teacher Lab Asst Hons; *UW at Madison; Elec Engr.*

WIEDENFELD, Kenneth Ray
Nederland HS; Nederland, TX (28-495) AFS; Chem C; JETS; Lat A; NHS; Phys C; JV, Bsbl; Ftbl; 'A' HR; Sci Fair, Chem Div; Adv Math Prog; *Tex A&M Col; Pre-Dentistry.*

WIEDERIEN, Cindy Lou
Midwest HS; Midwest, WY (1-21) Ann; Band; Chess C; Chor; Community Yth Symph; VP, Drama; Pres, FHA; GS; Tres, Hmrm; Math C; NHS; Sch P; VP, Ski C; S-T, SC; Thes; Tres, Jr Cl; Tres, Soph Cl; Bkbl; Swim; Tr; Citz A; Cl Fav; HCt; Type A; All St Band; Wyo Bicentennial HS Band; Band Director's A; VP, Future Secy of Amer; *Black Hills St Col; Elem Ed.*

WIEDERKEHR, Patricia Ann
Southside HS; Fort Smith, AR (9-435) Bus Mgr, Ann; VP, CYO; NHS; Sch P; Bkbl; Sftbl; Tnns; Tr; B Crocker A; Citz A; Journ A; MLS; Q&S A; Tres, Cath Yth; S-T, VP, Service C; Cath Yth Singers; Search Tm; Campaigners; Col Schol; Young Life; *U of Dallas; Pre-Vet.*

WIEDL, Kathryn Ann
Coon Rapids Sr HS; Coon Rapids, MN (88-654) CYO; Jr Miss Pagent; NHS; *Anoka Voc Tech Col; Child Development.*

WIEDNER, John Francis
Glenbard W HS; Glen Ellyn, IL (25%-488) CYO; Rptr, Sch P; Ski C; Tnns; Bus Mgr, Radio Station; *U of Mich; Med.*

WIEGLEY, Scott James
University Sch; Fort Lauderdale, FL; Fr C; Inter-Act C; Lat C; Pres, SC; Var C; Pres, Soph Cl; JV, Bkbl; Co-Cpt, Ftbl; Swim; Wrest; HKg; Yth Fel; *Wake Forest U; Med.*

WIELAND, Alexis Paul
University HS; Los Angeles, CA (5%-900) Ger C; Madrigal; Pres, Math C; Order/Arrow; Spch C; Tr; COM; Hon Prog; Math A; Ntl Conf Chr & Jews; Order/Arrow A; *U of Calif at San Diego; Physics.*

WIELAND, Sharon Marie
Lancaster Sr HS; Lancaster, WI (4-131) AFS; Ann; Band; Chldr; Chor; Hmrm; Madrigal; Mjrte; Model UN; NHS; Orch; Sch P; Tres, Span C; SC; Bkbl; Pres A; Spch A; DAHSS; *UW-WHITEWATER; Bus.*

WIEMANN, Laura Ann
John F Hodge HS; St James, MO (94%-130) Band; Fr C; Mod Mus Mas; SC; Sftbl; Tnns; Tr; Cpt, MVP, Vlbl; Red Cross Lifesaving Cert; *Stephens Col; Phys Therapy.*

WIERINGA, Dirk Kevin
Bloom HS; Chicago Hts, IL (67-661) Band; Chess C; NHS; SC; Co-Cpt, Wrest; Hon Prog; NMS; Pres A; *U of Ill; Elec Engr.*

WIERSBE, Judy L
Taft HS; Chicago, IL (109-830) NHS; Rptr, Sch P; Span C; Span NHS; COM; Citz A; Type A; Ath A; *NE Col; Early Childhood Ed.*

WIERSEMA, Daniel F
Thomson HS; Thomson, IL (16-52) Chor; Ensm; Madrigal; Ch, Model UN; Pres, NHS; Var C; Bkbl; Golf; Hon Prog; John Philip Sousa Band A; Ntl Chor A; *Blackhawk Col; Mus.*

WIERSEMA, Steven Lee
Milledgeville HS; Milledgeville, IL (12-60) Commercial C; SC; Var C; Pres, Sr Cl; Bsbl; Ftbl; HKg; HCt; Hon Prog; Ftbl A's Golden Hammer A; HR; Dick Kendall A; All Conf Ftbl; *Elec.*

WIESE, Craig William
Washington HS; Cherokee, IA (33%-175) Tnns.

WIESE, Gina Lee
Gainesville HS; Gainesville, TX (8-240) Co-Ed, Ann; VP, CYO; Chem C; Rptr, Drama; FTA; Tres, NHS; Spch C; VP, Jr Cl; COM; Opt A; Spch A; VFW Orator Win; VofDEM; Ceramic A's; Dist Spch Medal; Hon Men, Dist UIL Play; *N Tex St U; Recreation Adm.*

WIESE, Lynda Marie
Washington HS; Sioux Falls, SD (14-633) Chor; Fr C; NHS; Rptr, Sch P; JV, Tnns; Q&S A; *Doane Col; Environmental Stu.*

WIESE, Michael David
Haworth HS; Kokomo, IN (30-400) Pres, Bus C; Dbte Tm; FBLA; NFL; NHS; Spch C; Hon Prog; Spch A; Yth Fel; Debate, Church Conf, A's; *Olivet Nazarene Col; Bus Adm.*

WIESE, Thomas James
Marcus Comm Sch; Marcus, IA; Band; Chor; Community Yth Symph; Madrigal; Orch; Span C; Spch C; Yth Fel; All NW Iowa Chor & Band; Male Lead, Sch Mus & All Sch Play; *Morningside Col; Mus.*

WIESMAN, John Michael
Horicon HS; Horicon, WI (6-124) NFL; Pres, Span C; Tnns; Hon Prog; Stu o-t Mo; Tnns Ltr; *U of Wis; Med.*

WIETSTOCK, Steven Milo
Crestwood-Dearborn Heights HS; Dearborn Heights, MI (1-425) Band; Chor; Ensm; God & Country A; Yth Fel; Computer C; Cl Wizard; Eagle Sct; Chapel Organist; Handbell Choir; Ntl Piano Playing Auditions; Asst to Minister, Easter Services.

WIGAND, Lois Marie
Grand Rapids Sr HS; Grand Rapids, MN (48-375) Band; Cr-Ctry; Tr; Most Dedicated; *Benidji St U.*

WIGFALL, Joycelyn
Cainhoy HS; Huger, SC (4-45) Bus C; Commercial C; Drama; FHA; FNA; 4H; NHS; ARC; Bsbl; Bkbl; Bio A; 4H A; Hist A; HQn; Math A; ARC A; Type A; *US Armed Forces; Nurs.*

WIGGIN, Donna Kathleen
Loyalton HS; Loyalton, CA; A Cap Choir; Chor; Tres, 4H; 4H A; Hon Prog; ARC A; Yth Fel.

WIGGIN, Julie Annette
Loyalton HS; Loyalton, CA; FBLA; Secy, 4H; Ski C; CSF; COM; 4H A; Pres A; Rotary A; Type A; YMCA Conf; *Reading A.*

WIGGINGTON, Tammie Jo
Hobart HS; Hobart, OK (6-52) Band; Var C; Mgr, Bkbl; Sftbl; Hon Prog; *Western Okla St Col; Acct.*

WIGGINS, Debra Marie
Hillside HS; Durham, NC; Band; Lat C; Tr; Tr Ribbons; *Duke U; Med.*

WIGGINS, Donna Leigh
Columbia HS; Columbia, MS; Ann; Ensm; FHA; NHS; Hon Prog.

WIGGINS, Erin Elizabeth
Santa Monica HS; Santa Monica, CA (90-1000) Pres, Hmrm; Secy, Lat C; Lat NHS; SC; NMS; Spch A; Yth Fel; *Pre-Law.*

WIGGINS, Jeanne Paige
Lakeshore HS; College Park, GA (40-139) Anchor C; Chor; Drama; Ensm; Fr C; FHA; COM; *Ga Sou U.*

WIGGINS, Jennifer Darlene
London Christian Acad; London, KY (2-10) Dbte Tm; *Sue Bennet Jr Col; Legal Secy.*

WIGGINS, Lewis Charles II
W Anchorage HS; Anchorage, AK; Band; BS; Ger C; Hmrm; Ftbl; Tr; ROTC A; Pres, Ebony Culture C; *LSU; Med.*

WIGGINS, Pamela Beatrice
Columbus HS; Columbus, GA; Community Yth Symph; NHS; Orch; COM; Hon Prog; *Young Harris Col.*

WIGGINS, Raphael Lennard
Christian Co HS; Hopkinsville, KY (29-300) Band; BC; Chor; Fin, Jr Miss Pageant; SC.

WIGGINS, Robert Linton
Williamston HS; Williamston, NC (41-179) Band; BC; Drama; Hmrm; Monogram; Tr.

WIGGINS, Robin Jill
Rockdale HS; Rockdale, TX (25-126) Band; SC; Tres, Jr Cl; Tnns; Yth Fel; 1st Pl, Dist Tnns; Comm Yth Choir; *Sam Houston St U; Elem Ed.*

WIGGINS, Ruth Ann
Harlingen HS; Harligen, TX (1-850) A Cap Choir; Chor; NHS; Hist A; Journ A; Math A; Eng A; *Oral Roberts U; Eng.*

WIGGINS, Sylvia
Cecilian Acad HS; Philadelphia, PA; Bus C; Secy, SC; Beauty; Yth Fel; Glee C; Phys Ed, Bible Sch, Church, A's; Self-Improvement Course; *Morehouse Col; Ed.*

WIGGINS, Yvonne
Smith HS; Atlanta, GA; Band; MVP, Chldr; Hmrm; SC; Tr; HQn; Hon Prog; Ed, Yrbk; *Albany St Col; Pol Sci.*

WIGGS, Susan Elizabeth
Cave Spring HS; Roanoke, VA (75-500) Band; Tres, Span C; Sci A; VP, Explorers; *Phys Therapy.*

WIGHT, Barry Leroy
Livermore Falls HS; Livermore Falls, ME (5-94) A-Ed, Ann; BS; Math C; VP, NHS; ARC; Sci C; SC; Var C; Pres, Jr Cl; Bsbl; Ftbl; HKg; MLS; *U of Maine; Bus Adm.*

WIGHT, Scott Fredrick
Telstar Regional HS; Bethel, ME (10-83) Chor; Drama; Math C; SC; VP, Soph Cl; Cr-Ctry; Tr; Alg A; Balfour A; Bio A; COM; Hon Prog; Math A; Phy A; Sci A; *Engr.*

WIGHT, Thomas Lowell
Telstar Regional HS; Bethel, ME (1-77) VP, Band; BS; Chor; Drama; VP, InterAct C; Cpt, Math C; Tres, NHS; Co-Ed, Sch P; VP, SC; Tr; Balfour A; Bausch & Lomb A; Bio A; Chem A; Math A; NMS; Phy A; Sci A; Val.

WIGHTMAN, Gregory John
Kent Meridian Sr HS; Kent, WA; Band; Key C; NHS; Ski C; NML; *U of Wash; Bus Adm.*

WIGINGTON, Judy Mae
Wilburton HS; Wilburton, OK (15-62) Ann; Band; FHA; PTA; 4H; Jr Miss Pageant; SC; Cl Fav; HCt; Yth Fel; St Hon Soc; Band Duet; *Eastern Okla St Col; Mus.*

WIGLEY, Clara Elizabeth
Columbus HS; Columbus, GA; Chor.

WIGTON, Marcy Lee
Northwood Jr-Sr HS; Shreveport, LA (3-136) Lit Ral; NHS; Rptr, Sch P; Bkbl; Sftbl; Tr; COM; Hon Prog; Yth Fel; *LSU; Phys Ed.*

WIKEL, Andrea
Ralph C Mahar Reginal HS; Orange, MA; Band; Chor; Community Yth Symph; Drama; Fr C; Thes; GS Alt; *Interior Decorating.*

WIKEL, Spencer Henry
Ralph C Mahar Regional HS; Orange, MA; Band; Chor; Orch; Ftbl.

WIKLUND, Craig Lloyd
John F Kennedy Sr HS; Bloomington, MN (1-700) Ann; VP, Ger C; NHS; Wrest; HCt; *US Air Force Acad; Aeronautical Engr.*

WILBANKS, Deborah Francis
First Assembly Christian Sch; Memphis, TN (1-32) Chor; Sch P; HCt; Hon Prog; Spirit A; Bk A.

WILBANKS, Lisa Rae
Gasconade Co R III HS; Bland, MO (3-14) Chldr; Chor; VP, FHA; Secy, FTA; Sch P; Pres, SC; Bkbl; Sftbl; Tr; Hist A; HCt; Hon Prog; Health A; Art A; PA; *Barnes Hospital; Nurs.*

WILBANKS, Sheryl Lynn
Walnut HS; Walnut, MS (2-50) BC; Chor; FFA; Alg A; COM; Cl Fav; Hist A.

WILBER, Ann Elizabeth
Marion Co HS; Lebanon, KY (22-298) Chldr; Chor; Pres, Drama; FHA; Fin, Jr Miss Pageant; NHS; Pres, Spch C; SC; Var C; Swim; MVP, Tr; HCt; Hon Prog; NMS; Spch A; Yth Fel; Gym; Phys Ed, Chor, A's; Co Jr Miss; *E Ky U; Broadcasting.*

WILBERT, Patricia Lynne
Halter HS; Wellston, MO (2-58) FNA; NHS; Sch P; Swim; Cl Fav; Hon Prog; Journ A; MLS; Ntl Achv Schol; Sal; *Pediatric Nurs.*

WILBORN, Colleen Rachelle
San Gabriel HS; Alhambra, CA (125-500) VP, A Cap Choir; AFS; Arch; Chor; Drama; VP, Madrigal; ARC; SC; Tres, Thes; Arch; Bank Of Amer A; PTA A; Yth Fel; *Azusa Pacific Col; Mus.*

WILBORN, Ivan Marchand
S-W HS; Atlanta, GA (11%-271) Band; Chor; Ensm; Bsbl; Soccer; Hon Prog; *Mus.*

WILBORN, Ron Wheat
San Gabriel HS; San Gabriel, CA; A Cap Choir; Band; Drama; Madrigal; ARC; Thes; Var C; Ftbl; JV, Tr; Ftbl A; Wrest A; NRA Pro-Marksman.

WILBOURN, Dan
Searcy HS; Searcy, AR; BC; BS; Key C; Tnns; *U of Ark; Law.*

WILBOURN, Robert Lamar
W Point HS; W Point, MS; Royal Ambassador; BSct; Church Choir.

WILBUR, Deborah Ellen
Penns Grove HS; Penns Grove, NJ (55-200) Band; ARC; Yth Fel; *Pittsburg Art Inst; Interior Design.*

WILBUR, Heidi Maria
Will C Crawford HS; San Diego, CA (100-594) Drama; Hmrm; Y-Tns; Sftbl; Swim; COM; Cl Fav; *Pepperdine U; Journ.*

WILBUR, Mary Catherine
Miami Springs Sr HS; Miami Springs, FL (25-816) Secy, Anchor C; VP, Band; A-Ed, Lit Mag; Type A; Marching Band Ltr; Concert Band Ltr; Schol Ltr; *Fla St U; Mus.*

WILBUR, Richard George
Penns Grove HS; Penns Grove, NJ; Chem C; Mgr, Bsbl; Mgr, Bkbl; Cr-Ctry; Co-Cpt, Sftbl; JV, Swim; JV, Tnns; JV, Tr; *US Navy; Elec.*

WILBURN, Ella Mae
W Carter HS; Olive Hill, KY (4-128) Bus C; FBLA; FHA; Cl Fav; HQn; Library C; Home Ec A; Cl Swtht; *Bus.*

WILBURN, Terri Lynn
Bethel Baptist Sch; Memphis, TN (3-27) Chor; COM; *Memphis St U; Nurs.*

WILBURN, Walter Ross III
Calhoun HS; Calhoun, GA (10%-327) Band; Chess C; Fr C; Ch, HiY; Hmrm; NHS; *Pepperdine U; Sci.*

WILCK, James Henry
Lyons Jr-Sr HS; Lyons, NY (9-132) Band; 4H; Lat C; Order/Arrow; JV, Bsbl; Ftbl; Wrest; God & Country A; Most Out.

WILCOX, Brenda Gail
Woodham HS; Pensacola, FL (18-530) BC; Bio A; *Pensacola Jr Col; Dental Hygiene.*

WILCOX, Brian Kenneth
Jeff Davis HS; Hazlehurst, GA; Bkbl; Tr; Pres, Bible C; *Bible & Psych.*

WILCOX, Lorraine Ann
Lakewood HS; Lake Odessa, MI (3-175) Band; Chor; NHS; SC; Pres, Soph Cl; Bkbl; Sftbl; Hardest Worker, Bkbl; Best Attitude, Bkbl; Most Improved, Sftbl; Most Dedicated, Bkbl; *Guidance.*

WILCOX, Peggie Lynn
S Hamilton HS; Jewell, IA (28-86) Band; Chldr; Chor; 4H; SC; Bkbl; Tr; HR; Twirler; *Hawkeye Col; Commercial Art.*

WILCOX, Rita Diane
Wilkes Central HS; N Wilkesboro, NC (82-300) Band; Hmrm; InterAct C; NHS; SC; HCt; *Liberal Arts.*

WILCOX, Sherie Helen
Rule HS; Knoxville, TN; VP, Band; Chldr; Chor; Y-Tns; JA A; ROTC A; Awa-Nita; All City Choir; Drum Majorette; *Eckerd Col; Psych.*

WILCOX, Timothy E
Upper Lake HS; Upper Lake, CA; Tr; Judo and Karate; *LaTourneau Col; Mech.*

WILD, Dorothy Ruth
St Mary's Acad; Alexandria, VA (6-70) Pres, Math C; Pres, Mu Alpha Theta; Mgr, Tr; Hon Prog; Math A; *U of Pa; Elem Ed.*

WILD, Laura Allison
Fort Myers HS; Fort Myers, FL (4-450) Hmrm; Secy, NHS; Rptr, Sch P; Swim; Beauty; COM; NEDT; Pres A; Swim Tm Var Ltr; Jr Olymp; Diving T; AAU Sprtsmnshp Trophy; Gym Tm; Chapln, Omega Serv C; VP, Chrch Y; Secy, Forestry Explorer Post; *Eastern Ky Col; Wildlife Mgt.*

WILDBERGER, Sueanne Marie
Holy Family HS; Huntington, NY (87-365) Chor; Drama; Lit Mag; Sch P; SC; Swim; *Mary Wood Col; Communications.*

WILDE, Clay Thomas
Manila HS; Manila, UT; Ann; Band; BS; 4H; Hmrm; Math C; Ntl Yth Conf; Sch P; Bsbl; Bkbl; Tr; Bio A; COM; God & Country A; 4H A; *Brigham Young U; Ath Statistician.*

WILDE, Dan Eugene
North East HS; Ft Lauderdale, FL (29-600) Chor; Key C; NHS; Hon Prog; Yth Fel; Yth Leg; *U of Fla; Engr.*

WILDER, Audrey Lee
James Island HS; Charleston, SC; Hmrm; NHS; Span C; SC; Hon Prog; Type A; *Winston-Salem St U; Nurs.*

WILDER, Cynthia Dawn
Cary Sr HS; Cary, NC (1-600) Band; BC; Secy, Chor; Secy, Drama; Fr C; Hmrm; Fin, Jr Miss Pageant; Beauty; COM; Gov Honor Prog; Gr Marshal; Hon Prog; Ballet; Color Guard; Creative & Performing Arts Jr Ms; *Dance-Drama.*

WILDER, Helen Kay
Campbell HS; Fairburn, GA (2-200) Band; Drama; NHS; Span NHS; Parl, Y-Tns; Gov Honor Prog; Hon Prog; Math A; NMF; NEDT; Yth Fel; *Emory U; Special Ed.*

WILDER, Karen Louise
E Providence Sr HS; E Providence, RI; Ann; Mgr, Bkbl; Sftbl; Presidential Phys Ed A; 3rd, St Archt Drafting; Worthy Adviser, Rainbow Girls; VICA; *Engr.*

WILDER, Kenneth Kyle
Clarke Comm HS; Osceola, IA (11-109) Pres, Band; NHS; WW, Mus.

WILDER, Luana Lou
Coldwater HS; Coldwater, MI; Pres, 4H; JV, Tnns; 4H A; Best Attendance in Church.

WILDER, Sterly Lebey
Durham Acad; Durham, NC (6-70) Fr C; Bkbl; JV, Hockey; Sftbl; Cpt, Vlbl; *Duke U; Law.*

WILDER, Steve Ernest
Montpelier HS; Montpelier, OH; Fr C; JV, Bkbl; Tr; Acad Achv C.

WILDHIRT, Sandra Ann
Paradise HS; Paradise, CA (79-236) Chor; Hockey; San Francisco Art Inst; Commercial Art.

WILDING, Denise Marie
duPont Manual HS; Louisville, KY (2-390) Secy, BC; Chor; Ensm; Hmrm; Mod Mus Mas; NHS; Secy, Soph Cl; Cl Fav; HQn; PTA A; Pres A; Yth Fel; U of Louisville; Nurs.

WILDMAN, Kathleen Ann
Dixon HS; Dixon, IL; Chor; NHS; Evangel Bible Col; Sociology.

WILDMAN, Linda Lea
Fountain Central HS; Veedersburg, IN (1-150) Band; Drama; FHA; 4H; Lat C; SC; Hon Prog; Latine Cum Laude; Ind U; Psych.

WILDMAN, Lorrie Lynn
Fountain Central Jr-Sr HS; Veedersburg, IN (10-135) F-Ed, Ann; Secy, Band; Drama; FHA; 4H; NHS; Sch P; SC; Tres, Jr Cl; Bkbl; Hon Prog; Drill Tm; JV Vlbl; Ind U; Nurs.

WILDMAN, Tamara Sue
Dixon HS; Dixon, IL (60-398) Bus C; Chor; NHS; Sftbl; Tr; Central Bible Col; Missions.

WILDROM, Jerry A
Grand Haven Sr HS; Grand Haven, MI; A Cap Choir; Band; Chor; VP, Drama; Fr C; Hmrm; NHS; VP, Thes; Bkbl; Musk Comm Col; Phar.

WILEMAN, Jennifer Lynn
Hoover HS; North Canton, OH (89-433) A Cap Choir; Chor; Ensm; Stark Tech Col; Acct.

WILEMON, Kathy Lynne
Fairfield HS; Fairfield, AL (25%-186) Chor; Ensm; Pres, Y-Tns; COM; Hon Prog; U of Ala; Home Ec.

WILEMON, Robin Michelle
Greenville HS; Greenville, TX (10-275) Chor; SC; Citz A; Schol A; Med.

WILES, Betty Lou
Southeast HS; Bradenton, FL (123-246) Bus C; Chess C; Chor; Hmrm; Fin, DECCA; Muscular Dystrify Telethon A; March of Dimes Walkathon Cert; Manatee Jr Col; Social.

WILES, Dennis Ray
Ensley HS; Birmingham, AL (5-395) Math C; NHS; SC; Cpt, Bsbl; Bkbl; Ftbl; Cl Fav; Best Freshman; Ten Outst Srs; Sr Best All Around; Acad Schol; U of Ala Birmingham; Systems Mgt.

WILES, Michele Diane
Saks HS; Anniston, AL (1-173) PHS; NHS; Alg A; Citz A; Hist A; Hon Prog; Math A; MLS; Val; Art A; Jacksonville St U; Acct.

WILES, Patricia Ellen
Marvell HS; Marvell, AR (6-151) Ann; Rptr, FHA; Cl Fav; HCt; Eng, World Geography, A's.

WILES, Robert Kevin
Aurora HS; Aurora, WV; Chess C; Tres, FFA; Sftbl.

WILES, Susan Lynn
Sullivan Central HS; Blountville, TN (15-450) BC; Secy, Fr C; GS; Lat C; NHS; Mgr, Tr; Most Dependable; Ballet.

WILEY, Brian Rapheal
Luther Burbank HS; Sacramento, CA (344-624) Band; Chor; Bkbl; Tr; UC at Berkley; Sociology.

WILEY, Don Carlin
Glenbard E HS; Lombard, IL (24-635) Mu Alpha Theta; NHS; Var C; Ftbl; Wrest; St Scholar; NML; U of Ill; Elec Engr.

WILEY, Donna Maria
Waterproof HS; Waterproof, LA (1-62) Secy, Band; Secy, BC; Chldr; Chor; Pres, FBLA; LSU; Med.

WILEY, Eddie Lee Jr
Stivers-Patterson Cooperative HS; Dayton, OH (171-396) Parl, Bus C; Pres, Chor; VP, Drama; Ensm; Hmrm; Ftbl; Type A; Beautillion Militaire; Debutante Escort; Omega Psi Phi Talent Search Contest.

WILEY, Gary Leroy
Jack Yates Sr HS; Houston, TX; NHS; SC; Tres, Jr Cl; Co-Cpt, Bkbl; COM; U of Tex; Computer Prog.

WILEY, James Conrad
Charles Henderson HS; Troy, AL (20%-180) BC; Dbte Tm; Hmrm; InterClub Coun; Key C; SC; Pres, Jr Cl; Tnns; Law.

WILEY, Janet Lee
Maple Hts Sr HS; Maple Hts, OH (25-481) Cpt, Chldr; NHS; SC; Qn, Key C; DCT; Voc Distinction A; Cuyohoga Comm Col; Health.

WILEY, Joy Ellen
S Allegheny HS; Liberty Boro, PA (69-300) Band; Y-Tns; Color Guard; Robert Morris Col; Secy.

WILEY, Katherine Elaine
Rutherford HS; Rutherford, NJ (5-239) Band; Chor; Ensm; Fr C; Hmrm; Key C; NHS; Tnns; Hon Prog; NEDT; Board of Ed Schol Keys; Bio.

WILEY, Kathryn Anne
Decatur HS; Decatur, AL; Chem C; Lat C; Math C; Mu Alpha Theta; Sci C; Bkbl; NEDT; Auburn U; Vet.

WILEY, Kathryn Joan
Marion HS; Marion, IN (3-600) Ger C; Orch; Hon Prog; Faith, Life A; Ind All St Orch; NISBOVA As, Cello; Mus.

WILEY, Kevin James
Kashmere Sr HS; Houston, TX (184-607) JV, Bkbl; San Jacinto Jr Col; Mech Engr.

WILEY, Malcolm Gordon
Gladewater HS; Gladewater, TX; FFA; FTA; SC; Ftbl; Tr.

WILEY, Milton Jr
Smith HS; Atlanta, GA (7-140) VP, Band; Hmrm; Tres, SC; Var C; Cpt, Bsbl; Tr; Alg A; Cl Fav; Hon Prog; Math A.

WILEY, Sara Gray
Washington HS; Washington, NC (6-307) Mgr, Chldr; InterAct C; Span NHS; Most Out; Col of William & Mary; Journ.

WILEY, Sylvia Jean
George Henry Corliss HS; Chicago, IL; Secy, 4H; Hon Prog; Type A; Moser Bus Sch; Bus.

WILEY, Tammy Lynn
McNary HS; Salem, OR (10-350) Secy, FBLA; Hmrm; Tnns; Westmont Col; Bus Adm.

WILEY, Woodrow Wilson III
Waterproof HS; Waterproof, LA (1-55) Pres, Band; BC; Chor; Pres, SC; Pres, Soph Cl; LSU; Med.

WILF, Debra Carol
Searcy HS; Searcy, AR (22-178) Co-Ed, Ann; Tres, BC; Co-Cpt, Chldr; Drama; FBLA; GS; NHS; Co-Ed, Sch P; Span C; Thes; Beauty; U of Central Ark; Bus.

WILHARM, Daniel Jay
Shawano HS; Shawano, WI (25%-250) Chor; Madrigal; SC; Var C; Mgr, Bkbl; Mgr, Ftbl; Mgr, Tr; Mgr, Wrest; Amer Leg A.

WILHELM, Bethany Ann
Starmount HS; Boonville, NC (6-150) Chor; FHA; Fin, Jr Miss Pagent; Monogram; Mu Alpha Theta; NHS; Span C; SC; Gov Honor Prog; HCt; Scholastic Art As; U of NC at Greensboro; Art.

WILHELM, Karen Joyce
Nashwauk-Keewatin HS; Nashwauk, MN (10-95) AFS; Ed, Ann; Chor; FHA; Madrigal; Sch P; Spch C; Tr; Crisco A; Journ A; Spch A; Vlbl; All St Choir; Oral Roberts U; Communication.

WILHELM, Nancy Ann
Stevens HS; Rapid City, SD (10-473) Band; Dbte Tm; Ensm; NFL; NHS; Spch A; Band A; Debate Ctr; Social Work.

WILHELM, Patti Lee
LuVerne Comm Sch; LuVerne, IA (1-16) Band; Chor; Secy, Soph Cl; Mgr, Bkbl; Sftbl; VofDEM; Instrumental Solo A; Secretarial.

WILHELM, Paula Rae
Luverne Comm Sch; LuVerne, IA (2-18) Band; Chor; SC; Pres, Soph Cl; Bkbl; Sftbl; Type A; VofDEM; Vocal Solo A; Math.

WILHELM, Tina Marie
William Penn HS; York, PA (1-425) Band; Secy, Drama; InterClub Coun; Mu Alpha Theta; NHS; Orch; SC; Thes; Pres, Soph Cl; Sftbl; Amer Leg A; Pres A; St Scholar; Val; Elmira Key A; Pa St U; Pre-Med.

WILHELMI, Camille Ann
Nekoma Pub Sch; Nekoma, ND (2-6) Ann; Band; Chldr; Chor; Drama; 4H; A-Ed, Sch P; Bkbl; Tr; 4H A; Sci A.

WILHELMSON, Curt Scott
Hudson Sr HS; Hudson, WI; Band; Ensm; Order/Arrow; Forestry.

WILHITE, Cathy Lynn
Gulf Comprehensive HS; New Port Richey, FL; Chor; Hon Prog; Vlbl; Secy, Yth Group; Bus.

WILHITE, Lori Ann
John F Kennedy HS; Tumon, GUAM; Chldr; Hmrm; NHS; SC; JV, Cr-Ctry; Sftbl; Tnns; Sacramento St Col; Computer Sci.

WILHITE, Scott Gene
Gulf Comprehensive HS; New Port Richey, FL; Hmrm; NHS; SC; Var C; MVP, Bsbl; Cpt, Bkbl; Co-Cpt, Ftbl; Amer Leg A; Hon Prog; Co-Cpt, MVP, Bkbl; WW; 2nd St, Recreation Cntr Bkbl Coach; VP, Sou Christian Yth; Pres, Yth Group; Milligan Col; Law.

WILHITE, Timothy Ray
Abraham Lincoln HS; Council Bluffs, IA (15%-500) Band; Chor; COM; DARGCA; Hon Prog; Band Letters; Elec C; Mid Amer Nazarene Col; Elec Engr.

WILK, Joyce Elaine
Union-Scioto HS; Chillicothe, OH (1-130) Band; FTA; Span C; Span NHS; SC; COM; Bell Choir; Explorer Post; Journ.

WILK, Pamela Henzel
Doane Stuart HS; Albany, NY (33%-39) Ed, Lit Mag; Ed, Sch P; Ski C; Religion Prize; Faculty Price; Deane Stuart A; Wheelock Col; Special Ed.

WILK, Raymond Richard
Harold L Richards HS; Oak Lawn, IL (33%-1100) Band; Wrest; Outst Chorister; Musichorale Choral Group; Concordia Teachers Col; Psych.

WILKE, Nathan Paul
Horicon Sr HS; Horicon, WI (2-130) Band; Madrigal; Order/Arrow; Ski C; Span C; Var C; JV, Ftbl; JV, Golf; Wrest; Order/Arrow A; Life BSct; Carleton Col; Aeronautics.

WILKENING, Jerri Jean
Ralston HS; Ralston, NE (13-360) AFS; Chor; NHS; Ski C; Tres, SC; JV, Tr; Hon Prog; St Secy, SC; Kearney U; Psych.

WILKENING, Lori Renee
Milford Township HS; Milford, IL (10-55) Ann; FHA; Sch P; Swim; Amer Leg A; HCt; Sunday Sch Teacher; Eastern Col; Bus.

WILKENS, Randy Philip
Clifton Rural HS; Clifton, KS (1-25) Band; Ensm; 4H; Blue Valley League Piano Festival; Kan St U; Mus.

WILKER, Joel David
Tustin HS; Tustin, CA (29-650) Ann; NHS; Var C; Ftbl; Tr; MVP, Wrest; CSF; Wrest Coach A.

WILKERSON, Chip
Tex Sr HS; Texarkana, TX (10%-650) Bkbl; Sftbl; Church Yth Coun; Ouachita Bapt U; Religion.

WILKERSON, Cindy Lynn
St Albans HS; St Albans, WV; Anchor C; Lat C; SC; Secy, Soph Cl; Bkbl; Swim; Tnns; Amer Leg A; Marshall U; Med.

WILKERSON, David Bruce Jr
Western Grove HS; Western Grove, AR (3-15) Co-Ed, Ann; VP, CYO; NHS; Sch P; Span C; Span NHS; SC; HCt; MLS; N Ark Comm Col.

WILKERSON, Elizabeth Ann
Muskogee HS; Muskogee, OK; Band; Chor; Orch; DARGCA; Sci A; Eng A; Vocal Mus A; Band A; Okla City U.

WILKERSON, James Mark
Muskogee HS; Muskogee, OK (192-575) Ann; Span C; Bsbl; Co-Cpt, Ftbl; Tr; Opt A; Yth Fel; All Sch Play; Outst Athlete; Optimist A; Yth in Religion; Okla St U.

WILKERSON, James Steve
Coffee HS; Douglas, GA (5%-300) BC; Key C; MVP, Cr-Ctry; Tr; 280000800c; Emory U; Med.

WILKERSON, Johnnie Lea
Waterproof HS; Waterproof, LA (25%-54) BC; Tres, FBLA; NE La U; Acct.

WILKERSON, Keith Bernard
NW HS; Flint, MI; Cpt, Swim; Tr; Beauty; H of F; Ntl Conf Chr & Jews; Star Student; Swtht; VofDEM; Yth Fel; *Jackson St U; Acting.*

WILKERSON, Lisa Lynn
Dallas Christian HS; Dallas, TX (19-53) A Cap Choir; A-Ed, Ann; Drama; FHA; Spch C; SC; Homemaking A; *Okla Christian Col; Retarded Children Ed.*

WILKERSON, Peter Lee
Woodward Acad; College Park, GA (30-200) Chess C; Dbte Tm; Hmrm; NFL; Hon Prog; NEDT; Spch A.

WILKERSON, Samuel O'Neal
Block HS; Jonesville, LA (20%-100) Drama; *Sou U; Acct.*

WILKERSON, Samuel Stephen
George Washington Carver HS; Birmingham, AL (17-237) NHS; *U of Ala; Hist.*

WILKERSON, Suzanne
Couch HS; Myrtle, MO (1-34) Ed, Ann; VP, Band; Chldr; Pres, Chor; Drama; VP, FHA; GS; Fin, Jr Miss Pagent; Tres, NHS; VP, Soph Cl; Citz A; I Dare You; Journ A; MLS; Val; VofDEM; St Off, FHA; Home Ec A; Drama A; 4th Runner-Up, Mo Jr Miss; Eng A; Band A; Chor A; *William Woods Col; Mus.*

WILKERSON, Tony Dale
Block High; Jonesville, LA (20-90).

WILKES, Cordelia Prudence
Parkland Sr HS; Winston Salem, NC (250-600) Chor; Drama; FBLA; Ntl Yth Conf; Bkbl; Sftbl; ROTC A; Vlbl; Presidential Phys Fitness A; *Computer Sci.*

WILKES, Diane Kay
Shelton HS; Shelton, CT; Bus C; Fr C; Rptr, FFA; Ger C; Shorthand A; Ger C A; *Quinnipiac Col; Adm Asst.*

WILKES, Pamela Lena
Miami Norland HS; Miami, FL; Band; Mod Mus Mas; Tri-HiY; Acteens; Qn Regent in Service; Creative Writing A; Band Ltr; *Phar.*

WILKES, William Floyd
Jesse Lanier HS; Bessemer, AL; HCt; Soc Stu A; Alpha Zeta Gamma; Pres, Usher Board; *Tuskegee Inst; Med.*

WILKEY, Janice Darlene
Fillmore, CA (3-294) Tres, FBLA; GS; SC; Var C; VP, Jr Cl; Co-Cpt, Bkbl; Sftbl; Tr; CSF; Most Out; Okla Christian Col; Ed.

WILKIN, Laura Jean
Arkansas City HS; Arkansas City, KS (3-221) AFS; Band; JV, Chldr; Chor; Drama; Ensm; FTA; Hmrm; Orch; Sci C; Span C; SC; Amer Leg A; Hon Prog; St Scholar; Presidential Phy Fitness A; Gym; 1st Rating in St Piano Contest; Schol WSU; Pep C; Church Choir; Soroptimist Grl; Sundy Sch Tchr; *Wichita St U; Mus Ed.*

WILKIN, Philip Lloyd
Bowling Green Sr HS; Bowling Green, OH; NHS; JV, Tnns; 1st Pl, IPS; 3rd Pl, Beg Woods; Hon E; *BGSU; Computer Sci.*

WILKINS, Bret Allen
Helix HS; Lamesa, CA; Bus Mgr, Chor; Bus Mgr, Ensm; Sci C; JV, Cr-Ctry; JV, Tr; VP, Christian Yth Organization; *Grossmont Col; Bus.*

WILKINS, Cindy Sue
Allen HS; Lafayette, OH (5-101) Ed, Ann; Band; Secy, Chor; Ensm; FHA; Semi-Fin, GS; Pres, 4H; Ch, Lat C; NHS; 4H A; OARBC St Win.

WILKINS, Elizabeth Price
Springfield Sr HS; Springfield, PA; Mgr, Band; Chor; Mgr, Orch; COM; LMC Aid; Band A; *Photography.*

WILKINS, Harold Quincy
Frayser HS; Memphis, TN (80%-160) Chess C; Chor; Ensm; Ftbl; Sftbl; Tnns; Choir Contest A; All-St Chor; Regional A; *Bradley U; Mus.*

WILKINS, John Carl Jr
Hanson Mem HS; Franklin, LA; Band; NHS; Order/Arrow; Swim; Eagle Sct.

WILKINS, Karen Yvette
Spackenkill HS; Poughkeepsie, NY (74-241) Band; Monogram; Sftbl; Swim; Tr; COM; Pres A; 1st Cl GSct; *Bus Adm.*

WILKINS, Lisha Jolene
Crestview Sr HS; Crestview, FL (6-247) A Cap Choir; Anchor C; BC; Chor; Ensm; FTA; Hmrm; Madrigal; NHS; SC; COM; Fla All St Mus A; *Troy St U; Mus.*

WILKINS, Mark Arnold
Central Bucks HS; Buckingham, PA; Anchor C; Band; Drama; Order/Arrow; Ski C; Order/Arrow A; *US Coast Guard Acad; Oceanography.*

WILKINS, Nancy Brown
Brebeuf HS; Indianapolis, IN (10-165) Hmrm; Tr; Pres, Euvola C; *Bio.*

WILKINS, R Michael
Central Acad; Macon, MS; Bkbl; Ftbl; Sci A; Span A; *Orthodontist.*

WILKINS, Rochelle Thomasyne
Carver Area HS; Chicago, IL; Chor; Drama; Ensm; Up Bound; Tnns; HCt; Spch A; Yth Fel; *Moody Bible Inst; Religion.*

WILKINSON, Carlton Frederick
Father Ryan HS; Nashville, TN; Rptr, Sch P; JV, Tnns; Tr; Sci A; *Washington U; Commercial Art.*

WILKINSON, Carol Ann
Brazosport HS; Freeport, TX (3-220) A Cap Choir; VP, NHS; SC; COM; Vlbl; Admiral, Drill Tm; Vocational Office Ed; WW; *Brazosport U; Acct.*

WILKINSON, David Dawson
Hephzibah HS; Hephzibah, GA (35%-210) Dbte Tm; Drama; DARGCA; God & Country A; PTA A; Eagle Sct; Augusta Yth Players; Best Actor A; *Ga Sou Col; Communications.*

WILKINSON, Eric Eugene
Tuscola Sr HS; Waynesville, NC (25%-327) Tres, Key C; Tnns; Yth Fel; Yth Choir; *Brevard Col; Pre Engr.*

WILKINSON, Pam Jean
Karlsruhe Amer HS; Karlsruhe, GERMANY; Band; Chldr; Chor; FHA; NHS; Alg A; Math A; Most Out; Sci A; Soc Stu, Eng, Home Ec, A's.

WILKINSON, Tammy Jo
Central HS; Martinsburg, PA (90-240) Band; VP, FNA; 4H; Fin, Jr Miss Pagent; Mjrte; Var C; Tr; COM; Hon Prog; NEDT; Pres A; *Lancaster Sch of Nurs; Nurs.*

WILKS, Barry Henry
Morgan City HS; Morgan City, LA; *LSU; Archt.*

WILKS, Jeffery Bruce
Tulia HS; Tulia, TX (86-142) Band; Sci C; Bkbl; Ftbl; Tr; Yth Fel; WW.

WILKS, Vicki Lynn
Romulus HS; Romulus, MI; Band; Sftbl; Mjrte; Band, A's; *Arlington Baptist Bible Col; Mus.*

WILKS, Victoria Lynn
Romulus HS; Romulus, MI; Band; Ensm; Sftbl; Band A; *Arlington Baptist Bible Col; Mus.*

WILKS, Winifred Ruth
Rufus King HS; Milwaukee, WI; Chldr; City Conf; FBLA; Math C; Orch; Sci C; Span C; Ch, Y-Tns; Semi-Fin, Tr; COM; Math A; Span A; Scholastic Pin; Orch A; GAA; Tr A; *UWM-Milwaukee; Acct.*

WILL, Brian Lee
Lindbergh HS; St Louis, MO (128-1392) 4H; Lat C; Orch; Secy, Order/Arrow; Sci C; Cr-Ctry; Tr; Bio A; 4H A; Order/Arrow A; PTA A; Pres A; Sci A; Yth Fel; Ntl Federation of Mus C'S; *U of Mo; Vet.*

WILL, Daniel Joseph
Whitehall HS; Whitehall, MI (25%-170) Chor; Drama; Ski C; Span C; Tres, SC; Thes; Tr; Blue Lake Fine Arts Camp Schol; *Hope Col; Theatre.*

WILL, Jeff Gordon
Lindbergh Sr HS; St Louis, MO (145-903) Chem C; NHS; Order/Arrow; Var C; JV, Cr-Ctry; Tr; Order/Arrow A; Yth Fel; Eagle Sct; *U of Mo; Sci.*

WILL, Mary Cassandra
Rosenwald HS; New Roads, LA (1-100) BC; Drama; FBLA; Pres, Jr Cl; Hon Prog; *Sou U; Interior Design.*

WILL, Michael Joseph
Collegiate Sch; Passaic, NJ (5-21) Demolay; NHS; ARC; Ski C; Bsbl; Cpt, Bkbl; Ftbl; Golf; Soccer; Bio A; Hist A; Span A; Most Outst; Gym; *Bio-Chem.*

WILL, Rodney Lee
Spirit Lake HS; Spirit Lake, IA (25-110) 4H; Span C; Ftbl; JV, Tr; 4H A; *Westmar Col; Physics.*

WILLAIMS, Taller
East Tech HS; Cleveland, OH; *Cosmotology.*

WILLARD, Bruce Conrad
Charlottesville HS; Charlottesville, VA (10%-400) Chess C; Hmrm; NHS; Ski C; Span C; SC; Var C; Bsbl; Ftbl; Pres A; Lacrosse; Span A; Var Ltr; *U of Va; Archt.*

WILLARD, Carla Marjorie
North HS; Omaha, NE (1-455) Band; VP, Dbte Tm; Ed, Lat C; NFL; Orch; Chamber of Comm A; NEDT; Pres A; Star Student; Stu Writer, Local Newspaper; Sr GSct; GSct Opportunity A; S-T, U Meth Yth Fel; 1st Cl, GSct; *Social Work.*

WILLARD, Christopher Jon
Arapahoe HS; Littleton, CO (240-569) Band; Chor; Drama; Hmrm; Best Actor; Theatre Achv; *Hastings Col; Dentistry.*

WILLARD, Kerrilee Ann
Hannibal Central HS; Hannibal, NY (25%-120) AFS; Band; Tres, Chor; 4H; Hmrm; SC; Tres, Jr Cl; Bkbl; Golf; *Broome Col; Bus.*

WILLARD, Richard Todd
Port Huron Cetnral HS; Port Horon, MI (25-200) A Cap Choir; Band; Chor; City Conf; Dbte Tm; Drama; Ensm; Ger C; Hmrm; Madrigal; Bus Mgr, Sch P; Ski C; Pres, Sr Cl; Pres, Jr Cl; COM; Citz A; Interlochen Ntl Mus; Most Out; 1st Pl, Solo Ensm A; Outst Tenor; Pres, Church Yth Group; Sch Play Lead; *Olivet Col; Mus.*

WILLARD, Susan Angela
Patrick Henry HS; Roanoke, VA; Ann; Fr C; FHA; VP, Hmrm; ARC; Hist A; *Emory & Henry Col; Biol.*

WILLARD, Tim Owen
Royalton Hartland HS; Middleport, NY (10-172) NHS; Order/Arrow; Var C; Cpt, Cr-Ctry; Tr; Order/Arrow A; Eagle Sct; BOCES Acad A; *Niagara Comm Col; Building Trades.*

WILLARD, Valerie Lynn
Wheelersburg HS; Wheelersburg, OH (1-143) Band; Chldr; Chor; Fr C; NHS; Rainbow; Tr; HCt; WW; *Nurs.*

WILLBANKS, Laura Ann
Long Beach Poly Tech HS; Long Beach, CA (16-650) AFS; NHS; Ski C; JV, Tnns; Dar Hist A; Medallion Diploma; *U Cal.*

WILLCOX, Julie Ann
Gainesville HS; Gainesville, FL; Tres, 4H; 4H A; Church Chor; Keyettes; Batgirl; Church Sftbl Tm; NJHS; VP, MYF.

WILLCOX, Margaret Ann
Harlem HS; Harlem, GA; Chor; COM; Hon Prog; Gifted Prog.

WILLE, Elizabeth Grace
Silver HS; Silver City, NM (8-208) Pres, Band; NHS; Rainbow; SC; Opt A; Sci A; Grand Cross of Color; John Philip Sousa Band A; Grant Co Tnagers Salute; *U of NM; Dietetics.*

WILLEN, Howard Douglas
Eastern HS; Middletown, KY (50-900) BC; Pres, 4H; Hmrm; ARC; Span C; Bsbl; Ftbl; Cpt, Wrest; COM; Cl Fav; Hon Prog; *U of Ky; Bus Adm.*

WILLER, Victoria Kay
Northgate HS; Walnut Creek, CA (1-413) Band; Fr C; Lit Mag; Model UN; Cr-Ctry; Ftbl; CSF; Hon Prog; Val; Cert of Achv, Engr Wk; *U of Calif; Chem Engr.*

WILLERT, Marcene L
Elkton Pub HS; Elkton, SD (13-34) Ann; Band; Chor; Dbte Tm; FHA; Ed, Sch P; Spch C; Sftbl; Tr; Secy, Drill Tm; *U of SD; Special Ed.*

WILLET, Stephen Scott
Hamburg HS; Hamburg, NY (3-514) Bus Mgr, Band; Community Yth Symph; NHS; Orch; Var C; Bsbl; Cpt, Soccer; Rensselaer A; MVP, Championship Bsbl League Tm; Player-Coach, Jr Soccer League; *Va Tech U; Civil Engr.*

WILLETT, Carla Frances
Tioga HS; Tioga, LA; BC; Lit Ral; Q&S; *LSUA; Bus.*

WILLETT, Carol Jo
Mott HS; Warren, MI (32-700) Band; NHS; Span C; Sftbl.

WILLETTE, Steven Francis
Blanchet HS; Seattle, WA (8-285) Chess C; Bkbl; Cr-Ctry; Ftbl; Soccer; Tr; Wrest; COM; Hon Prog; Math A; Nuclear Power Sem; Superior Workshops; Most Inspirational, Cr-Ctry; *U of Chicago; Math.*

WILLEY, Jeffrey Bryan
King Sr HS; Tampa, FL (10-35) Octogan C; *U of Fla; Elec.*

WILLEY, Rebecca Jane
Springfield HS; Springfield, OR; A Cap Choir; Drama; Ensm; FHA; ARC; *U of Oreg; Mus.*

WILLHITE, Juanita Darlene
Sulphur Springs HS; Sulphur Springs, TX (35-200) FTA; VP, Hmrm; Parl, Lat C; NHS; SC; Hist A; Future Teachers A.

WILLHITE, Judy Denise
Dan River HS; Ringgold, VA (7-238) Ann; BC; FHA; Sch P; Alg A; Hon Prog; Geog A.

WILLHOUR, Alice Jane
Heritage HS; Littleton, CO (22-436) Band; Chldr; Chor; Hmrm; SC; Soccer; VP, Christian Yth Fel; Ed.

WILLIAMS, Alicia Elizabeth
Franklin Co HS; Carnesville, GA; Chor; Drama; Fr C; Ch, FHA; FTA; Lit Mag; F-Ed, Sch P; Thes; Tri-HiY; 4H A; JA A; Pep C; GSct Ldr; WW; *Erskine Col; Elem Ed.*

WILLIAMS, Allison Montgomery
Newton Co Comprehensive HS; Covington, GA (10%-325) Band; BC; Ensm; Pres, 4H; HiY; Tres, InterAct C; InterClub Coun; Span C; COM; Citz A; DARGCA; 4H A; JA A; Most Out; *Ga Tech; Archt.*

WILLIAMS, Alvin Douglas
Bartram Motivation Center; Philadelphia, PA (23-749) NHS; Ntl Yth Conf; COM; Sci A; Lit, Span, A's; *NC St U; Dentistry.*

WILLIAMS, Alvin LaBrone
Washington HS; Kans City, KS; Drafting Field.

WILLIAMS, Amy Elizabeth
Williamston HS; Williamston, NC (1-221) Co-Ed, Ann; Band; Fr C; Hmrm; VP, Key C; Pres A; Secy, Christian Yth Rally; Flagteam; Pres, Fresh Cl; *E Carolina U; Early Childhood Ed.*

WILLIAMS, Andrea Melvnia
Eau Claire HS; Columbia, SC (28-359) Bus C; S-T, Chor; Hmrm; NHS; SC; Parl, Chor; JV Vlbl; Chor, NHS, A's; *Airports Tech Col; Phys Ther.*

WILLIAMS, Anita Lynne
Woodrow Wilson HS; Dallas, TX; Ann; Sci C; Span C; *N Tex U; Psych.*

WILLIAMS, Anthony Carl
Western Hills HS; Ft Worth, TX (120-360) Ann; Order/Arrow; Cr-Ctry; Ftbl; Pres, Explorer Post; Pres, Camera C; *Stephen F Austin Col; Forestry.*

WILLIAMS, Anthony Ervin
University Sch of Nashville; Nashville, TN; Chor; Madrigal; Span C; Mus Schol; *Mus.*

WILLIAMS, Ardeth Leah
Pendleton HS; Pendleton, SC (14-130) F-Ed, Ann; Secy, BC; Cpt, Chldr; GS; InterClub Coun; Scholastic Banquet; *Erskine Col; Hist.*

WILLIAMS, Audrey Rence
Eugene J Butler HS; Jacksonville, FL; Chor; Math C; Phys C; Bsbl; Bkbl; Ftbl; Tr; Hon Prog; Masonic A; Math A; Phy A; *Bethune Cookman Col; Math.*

WILLIAMS, Avon Nyanza III
University Sch of Nashville; Nashville, TN; Chess C; Chor; Drama; Hmrm; Co-Ed, Lit Mag; Math C; ARC; Ed, Sch P; Span C; Pres, SC; Mgr, Golf; Soccer; Ntl Achv Schol; NMF; NMS; NEDT; ARC A; Newspaper Most Valuable Staffer A; VP, Law Explorers; 1st Pl, Talent Show; Cpt, Scholastic Bowl Tm; *Williams Col; Philosophy.*

WILLIAMS, Barbara Ann
Terrell Co HS; Dawson, GA (10%-112) BC; NHS; Sch P; Tres, Sr Cl; COM; *Tuskegee Inst; Ed.*

WILLIAMS, Barbara Elaine
Richland HS; Ft Worth, TX (29-570) Fr C; NHS; Magna Cum Laude; *Harding Col; Hist.*

WILLIAMS, Barbara Lynne
Eisenhower HS; Hopkins, MN (96-414) Chor; Bkbl; Sftbl; MVP, Vlbl; Hon Qn, Jobs Daughters; GSct; *St Olaf Col; Dental Hygienist.*

WILLIAMS, Beth Ann
Claremore HS; Claremore, OK (42-217) AFS; Band; Chess C; Ensm; VP, FBLA; FHA; NHS; Hon Prog; Superior, Dist Band Contest; St Hon Soc; Acad Achv, A; Muscular Dystrophy VIP Stu, A's; *Claremore Jr Col; Bus.*

WILLIAMS, Beth Ellen
Shaler Area HS; Glenshaw, PA (10-950) A-Ed, Ann; MVP, Sftbl; Art C; Gym; *Allegheny Comm Col; Bus Mgt.*

WILLIAMS, Beverly
IS 117 J HS; Brooklyn, NY (26-116) Band; Chor; Orch; Bkbl; Tr; Yth Fel; Sunday Sch HR; *NYCCC; Fashion.*

WILLIAMS, Billy Dewayne
Southside HS; Counce, TN (5-34) Ann; BS; FFA; 4H; Hmrm; SC; Amer Leg A; 4H A; Hist A; *NE Miss Jr Col; Machine Shop.*

WILLIAMS, Billy Garrid
Simpson Acad; Mendenhall, MS; BS; Bkbl; Ftbl; Swim; Cl Fav; WW; *Ole Miss; Law.*

WILLIAMS, Brenda
Marvell HS; Marvell, AR (3-118) Secy, BC; FBLA; Bio A; Home Ec A; *Ark St U; Med Tech.*

WILLIAMS, Brenda Gail
Metter HS; Metter, GA; FHA.

WILLIAMS, Brenda Nadine
Jones HS; Lynnville, TN (2-22) Co-Ed, Ann; Secy, BC; Bus C; Chor; Drama; FHA; FTA; Rptr, Sch P; Spch C; Var C; Secy, Sr Cl; Mgr, Bkbl; Sftbl; Tr; Alg A; COM; Citz A; Hon Prog; Math A; MLS; Sal; Exchange C Yth o-t Mo; *Volunteer St Comm Col; Computer Prog.*

WILLIAMS, Brenda Patricia
Germantown HS; Philadelphia, PA (130-665) All Amer Yth; Chor; Bkbl; Sftbl; Bank Of Amer A; Citz A; Health A; *Temple Col; Nurs.*

WILLIAMS, Brenda Rheuanell
Leland HS; San Jose, CA; Chldr; Community Yth Symph; Orch; Sch P; Alg A; CSF; Church Choir; Missionary, Tm, Baja Caravan; Schol A; Church HS Core Grp, Visit Group; *San Jose St Col; Clinical Psych.*

WILLIAMS, Brian David
Warsaw Comm HS; Warsaw, IN (6-410) Band; A-Ed, Sch P; Ski C; COM; Yth Fel; *Butler U; Mus Performance.*

WILLIAMS, Bruce Gordon
W fulton HS; Atlanta, GA (12-25) MVP, Band; ARC; Sch P; MVP, Bkbl; Bio A; Hon Prog; Journ A; Math A; ROTC A; Sci A; Health A; *Air Force.*

WILLIAMS, Byron
W Fulton HS; Atlanta, GA (9-32) Band; Chor; Fireman.

WILLIAMS, C Bradley
St Edward HS; Saint Edward, NE (10-27) Band; Chor; Monogram; Pres, SC; Var C; Bsbl; Co-Cpt, Bkbl; Ftbl; Tr; HCt; All-Conf Ftbl & Bkbl; Saxaphone Solo; *Yankton Col; Coaching.*

WILLIAMS, Camille Selene
Hampton HS; Hampton, VA (83-550) Band; Ensm; Math C; COM; Yth Fel; *Ind Inst of Tech; Computer Sci.*

WILLIAMS, Candyce Yvonne
Father Ryan HS; Nashville, TN (25-244) Hmrm; NHS; SC; Hist A; Eng A; Secy, Keyettes C; *Premed.*

WILLIAMS, Carla Louise
Whetstone HS; Columbus, OH; Bus C; JA A; PTA A; Type A; Tr Judge; Off Helper; PTA A; *Journ.*

WILLIAMS, Carol Ann
Wheelersburg HS; Wheelersburg, OH (29-150) Band; Chor; Orch; Span C; Festival of Sacred Arts; Acad Excel Cert of Achv; *Mount Vernon Nazarene Col; Mus Ed.*

WILLIAMS, Carol Sue
Eufaula HS; Eufaula, OK (6-95) Band; Chor; Ensm; Mjrte; NHS; Secy, Sr Cl; Secy, Jr Cl; Bkbl; Hist A; HCt; Drum Mjrte; Most Popular; Band Attendant; Hon Band; *NE Okla St U; Elem Ed.*

WILLIAMS, Carolyn
Laurens Dist 55 HS; Laurens, SC; Chem C; Drama; Fr C; Pres, FHA; FTA; Tres, SC; *U of SC; Biol.*

WILLIAMS, Carolyn Elaine
Whetstone HS; Columbus, OH; Bus C; JA A; PTA A; Type A; Tr Judge; Nurs Helper; PTA A; *Nurs.*

WILLIAMS, Cassandra Renee
E Atlanta HS; Atlanta, GA (5-175) BC; Hmrm; Sftbl; Hon Prog; ROTC A; *Emory Col; Nurs.*

WILLIAMS, Catherine Ann
W Monroe HS; W Monroe, LA (25%-500) Anchor C; Chldr; Chor; InterAct C; Key C; NHS; SC; Thes; Tres, Y-Tns; *La Tech U; Interior Design.*

WILLIAMS, Cathy Raye
Hobbs HS; Hobbs, NM (87-440) Drama; Rainbow; Thes; Worthy Adviser, Rainbow Girls; *Cisco Jr Col; Secy.*

WILLIAMS, Cheryl Kay
Panhandle HS; Panhandle, TX; Chldr; Chor; Drama; FHA; FTA; NFL; Span C; Thes; Bkbl; Tr; HCt; Lair Personality.

WILLIAMS, Cheryl Lane
Dan River HS; Ringgold, VA; Tres, BC; JV, Chldr; Dbte Tm; Hmrm; Span C; Tri-HiY; DARGCA; Spch A; *NC St U; Computer Sci.*

WILLIAMS, Cheryl Lynn
Peebles HS; Peebles, OH (4-109) Ann; Band; Chor; Secy, Drama; Fr C; FTA; Hmrm; Lat C; Co-Ed, Sch P; Journ A; Q&S A; Spch A; *Sou St Col; Ed.*

WILLIAMS, Cheryl Lynn
Uniondale HS; Uniondale, NY (40-563) Bus C; Chor; Dbte Tm; Fr C; Pres, FHA; Pres, 4H; NHS; Secy, Jr Cl; Secy, Soph Cl; Citz A; 4H A; Best Sch Spirit; *Bus Mgr.*

WILLIAMS, Cheryl Rae
Montclair HS; Montclair, NJ; SC; Citz A; Spch A; Spch Pathology.

WILLIAMS, Cheryl Renee
William Penn HS; Philadelphia, PA (87-675) Pol Sci C; Sci C; SC; Vlbl; Motivation A; *W Chester St Col.*

WILLIAMS, Chiquita Yvette
Van Nuys HS; Van Nuys, CA; JV, Bkbl; Human Relations C; Black Awareness C.

WILLIAMS, Christopher Theodore
Jupiter Christian Sch; Jupiter, FL (1-29) F-Ed, Sch P; Sci C; Journ.

WILLIAMS, Cindy Caye
Hastings HS; Hastings, MN (20%-500) Tres, Bus C; Chor; FHA; Ski C; Golf; Med.

WILLIAMS, Clency DeWayne
Sumner Hill HS; Clinton, MS (5-33) BC; FFA; Hmrm; Ftbl; Hon Stu; *Jackson St U; Elec Engr.*

WILLIAMS, Connie Jean
Forest Hills Central HS; Grand Rapids, MI (15-250) Band; Ski C; Var C; Tnns; COM; Gold Tassel A; *Grand Rapids Jr Col; Med.*

WILLIAMS, Consetta
A H Parker HS; Birmingham, AL (12-35) Modeling.

WILLIAMS, Constance Lanear
Saint Vincent Acad; Newark, NJ (1-74) Chor; Pres, NHS; Sftbl; Val; Commend Stu o-t Ntl Achv Schol Prog; *Pratt Inst; Chem Engr.*

WILLIAMS, Crystal Hope
Scioto Co Joint Voc Sch; Lucasville, OH; Ann; Hmrm; Sch P; Pres, SC; Pres, Jr Cl; *Computer Programmer.*

WILLIAMS, Cynthia Lori
Theodore Roosevelt HS; Washington, DC; *Ohio St U; Architecture.*

WILLIAMS, Cynthia Louise
Riverdale HS; Ft Myers, FL; Band; SC; Edison Comm Col; Mus.

WILLIAMS, Cynthia Lynn
Sprayberry HS; Marietta, GA; Bkbl; Sftbl; Tnns; Tr; COM; Ga St U; Phys Ed.

WILLIAMS, Cynthia Mae
Parkersburg South HS; Parkersburg, WV (2%-550) Bus C; Pres, 4H; Secy, SC; Y-Tns; COM; 4H A; Acct Proficiency Cert; 4-H Qn Cand; Co 4-H A.

WILLIAMS, Cynthia Susan
Saluda HS; Saluda, SC (30%-125) BC; COM; Gardner Webb Col; Religious Ed.

WILLIAMS, Cynthia Yvonne
Marion L Steele HS; Amherst, OH (52-350) Pres, Chor; NHS; Sftbl; Church, Sch Choir, Soloist; 3rd Girl's Voice, Talents; Inst of Computer Mgt; Computer Mgt.

WILLIAMS, Dale Roger
Newton Co Comprehensive HS; Covington, GA (10-500) Band; BC; Chess C; HiY; Key C; Lat C; Gov Honor Prog; Hon Prog; Kiwanis A; Sci A; Vanderbilt U; Sci.

WILLIAMS, Daniel Paul
Tabernacle Christian Acad; San Diego, CA (3-8) Chess C; Cpt, Dbte Tm; Drama; Sci C; Spch C; Spch A; Piano A; Rocketry C; San Diego U.

WILLIAMS, Daniel Willie
Hebert HS; Beaumont, TX (2-260) Pres, NHS; Span C; St Stu Congress; Pres, SC; Tri-HiY; Ftbl; Tr; Amer Leg A; COM; Cl Fav; Magna Cum Laude; Sou Methodist U; Elec Engr.

WILLIAMS, Danielle Denise
Eleanor McMain HS; New Orleans, LA; CYO; Drama; Hmrm; NHS; ARC; SC; Tres, Soph Cl; COM; Citz A; Hon Prog; PTA A; ARC A; Tulane U; Med.

WILLIAMS, Darryl K
Horace Mann HS; Gary, IN (92-288) Band; Bus Mgt.

WILLIAMS, Darwin
Simon Gratz HS; Philadelphia, PA; Chem C; FTA; Hmrm; JETS; Bkbl; Tr; Math A; Spch A; Drexel U; Acct.

WILLIAMS, David Edward
William Byrd HS; Vinton, VA (18-240) Band; Parl, BC; BS; Chess C; Chor; Drama; Hmrm; Order/Arrow; Sch P; Tres, SC; Var C; Pres, Sr Cl; VP, Jr Cl; JV, Ftbl; Wrest; Amer Leg A; COM; Citz A; DARGCA; NMS; NEDT; Pres A; WW; Carson-Newman Col; Religion.

WILLIAMS, David Lawrence
Bowman Sr HS; Wadesboro, NC; Anson Tech Inst; Diesel Mech.

WILLIAMS, David M
Superior HS; Superior, NE (23-85) Chem C; Chor; Key C; Rptr, Sch P; Span C; SC; Pres, Jr Cl; Bsbl; Bkbl; Golf; Hastings Col; Mortuary Sci.

WILLIAMS, David Ray
Clinton Co HS; Albany, KY; BC; Chess C; Chor; Drama; FFA; FHA; Ger C; Pres, 4H; Mgr, Bsbl; Mgr, Cr-Ctry; Mgr, Ftbl; COM; Eastern Ky U.

WILLIAMS, David Ronnell
Glenn Hills HS; Augusta, GA (22-100) Chor; Dbte Tm; ARC; ROTC A; BSct, ROTC Promotion, A's; Morehouse Col; Religion.

WILLIAMS, David Thomas
Reidsville Sr HS; Reidsville, NC (5-324) BS; Fr C; Math C; V-Ch, Order/Arrow; JV, Tr; Order/Arrow A; Var A; Eagle Sct; NC St U; Bus Adm.

WILLIAMS, Dawn Marie
Tomahawk HS; Tomahawk, WI (108-199) Bkbl; Soccer; Sftbl; Tnns; Cl Fav; God & Country A; Yth Fel; Pres Phys Fitness A; Vlbl Trophy; Tr Trophy; Gym Trophy.

WILLIAMS, Debbie Estille
Plano HS; Plano, TX; Secy, A Cap Choir; Secy, Chor; Madrigal; NHS; Thes; Hon Prog; I Ratings, UIL Contest; Harding Col; Mus.

WILLIAMS, Debbie Lynn
North East HS; Oakland Park, FL (30%-750) A Cap Choir; Anchor C; Chor; Drama; Fr C; Hmrm; SC; Thes; Lion A; Spch A; Stetson U; Bus.

WILLIAMS, Deborah Ann
Xenia HS; Xenia, OH; Chor; Secy, 4H; Span C; Tr; Tr A; Drill Tm; Morehead U; Teacher of Deaf & Blind.

WILLIAMS, Deborah Anne
Karlsruhe Amer HS; Karlsruhe, GERMANY; S-T, A Cap Choir; Ann; Band; Drama; Tres, SC; Cr-Ctry; Tnns; Fla U; Med.

WILLIAMS, Debra Ann
Compton Sr HS; Compton, CA (14-800) Band; Pres, Ger C; Ch, Sci C; Tres, Sr Cl; Tres, Soph Cl; Bank Of Amer A; CSF; Flag Girl; Psych C; U of Sou Calif; Dental Sci.

WILLIAMS, Debra Ann
East Saint Louis Sr HS; E Saint Louis, IL (1-720) Chem C; Drama; Hmrm; Lit Mag; Secy, Math C; Secy, Mu Alpha Theta; NHS; SC; Alg A; Amer Leg A; Bausch & Lomb A; COM; DARGCA; Delta Sigma Theta A; Hon Prog; Math A; Ntl Achv Schol; Ntl Sci Symposium; Sci A; Val; Northwestern U; Engr.

WILLIAMS, Delanna Marie
Baker Sr HS; Baker, LA (27-374) Band; BC; Bus C; Chor; Ensm; FHA; 4H; Orch; ARC; SC; Tri-HiY; Bkbl; Sftbl; COM; Cl Fav; 4H A; Hist A; Hon Prog; Most Out; Sci A; Vlbl; Ensm A; LSU; Chem Engr.

WILLIAMS, Delmar Onetha
Zwolle HS; Zwolle, LA (5-43) Band; Tres, FBLA; FHA; Lit Ral; SC; Sftbl; Grambling St U; Early Childhood Ed.

WILLIAMS, Delores Marie
Williamston HS; Williamston, NC (102-179) Co-Ed, Ann; Bus C; Chldr; FHA; FTA; Monogram; Hardbarger Bus Col; Fashion Merchandising.

WILLIAMS, Denise
McAdams HS; McAdams, MS; Bus Mgr, Band; FFA; FHA; Tres, Tri-HiY; Most Dependable; Nurs.

WILLIAMS, Denise Marie
W Middlesex HS; W Middlesex, PA (16-146) Tres, Band; Bus C; Chor; FTA; NHS; Co-Ed, Sch P; Tres, SC; Secy, Soph Cl; HCt; Journ A; Q&S A; Type A; Hon Band; Band A; Most Talented; Youngstown Bus Col; Acct.

WILLIAMS, Derek
MacKenzie HS; Detroit, MI (22-352) NHS; Bkbl; Ftbl; Cpt, Tr; Hon Prog.

WILLIAMS, Dexter Lemuel
O D Wyatt HS; Fort Worth, TX (27-435) A Cap Choir; Pres, Band; Chor; NHS; Citz A; Hon Prog; Magna Cum Laude; Opt A; Head Drum Major; U of Tex; Pub Relations.

WILLIAMS, Diane
Terrell Co HS; Dawson, GA (2-200).

WILLIAMS, Diane Katherine
Okeechobee HS; Okeechobee, FL (4-189) Pres, FHA; NHS; B Crocker A; Hist A; Sci A; Spch A; Type A; Cpt, Drill Tm; Cpt's A; FHA-HERO Pub Speaking St Win; Cosmetology Diploma; FHA' ER o-t Yr; U of W Fla; Bus Adm.

**WILLIAMS,
Dianjunese Jameshia**
Westwood HS; Memphis, TN (14-212) Hmrm; NHS; ARC; Span C; SC; Citz A; Hist A; ARC A; Sci A; Cl Rank A; Miss Jr; Memphis St U; Bus Acct.

WILLIAMS, Diann Sue
Kalamazoo Central HS; Kalamazoo, MI (25-450) 4H; Var C; Bkbl; Co-Cpt, Golf; Yth Fel; Yth Foundation; Western Mich Col; Elem Art Teacher.

WILLIAMS, Don Jeffery
Clint HS; Clint, TX (12-40) Tres, FFA; Tnns; Tex Tech Col; Pre-Dental.

WILLIAMS, Donald Chip
Whitney M Young HS; Chicago, IL (25%-400) A Cap Choir; Semi-Fin, Order/Arrow; Ski C; Bsbl; Tr; COM; Type A; Yth Fel; Yth Ministries Steering Comm; Bowling; Black Ethnic Group; Feat-Writer Yth Ministries Newslet; Journ.

WILLIAMS, Donald Everett
Warwick HS; Lititz, PA (28-273) BS; Chor; Ensm; Hmrm; NHS; Order/Arrow; Var C; Co-Cpt, Cr-Ctry; Co-Cpt, Tr; Rotary A; Eagle Sct; Millerville St Col; Pol Sci.

WILLIAMS, Donald Ray
Baker HS; Baker, LA; BC; Mu Alpha Theta; NHS; LSU; Lab Tech.

WILLIAMS, Donald Toy
York Comprehensive HS; York, SC (25-300) Chem C; Pres, FFA; Phys C; Sci C; Var C; Ftbl; Rptr, FFA; FFA A's; Win, FFA Quiz Contest; Clemson U; Agr Ed.

WILLIAMS, Donna Joyce
Franklin Co HS; Carnesville, GA (10%-200) BC; Fr C; FHA; FTA; Tri-HiY; COM; 4H A; Hon Prog; Yth Fel; Alpha Scroll; HR; Sct, Art, Handiworks, A's; Erskine Col; Med.

WILLIAMS, Donna Kaye
Kountze HS; Kountze, TX; Band; VP, FHA; Math C; Sci C; Span C; SC; Pres, Soph Cl; Beauty; Cl Fav; Lamar U; Home Ec.

WILLIAMS, Donnie R
Westside HS; Newark, NJ (79-280) FBLA; Cr-Ctry; Ftbl; Tr; Amer Leg A; COM; Star Student; Yth Fel; Montclair St Col; Computer Tech.

WILLIAMS, Doreen Beatrice
Simon Gratz HS; Philadelphia, PA (15-1000) Pres, Hmrm; InterAct C; NHS; World Affairs C; Mgr, Tr; COM; Hist A; Attendance A; Thomas Jefferson U; Radiology.

WILLIAMS, Doris Marie
Bullock Co HS; Union Springs, AL (10-200) All Amer Yth; Band; Chldr; Chem C; Drama; FBLA; 4H; NHS; Ntl Yth Conf; ARC; SC; Up Bound; Bsbl; Bkbl; Swim; Alg A; Bio A; COM; Chem A; Citz A; 4H A; Hist A; Hon Prog; Math A; MLS; Most Out; Ntl Achv Schol; Ntl Sci Found; ARC A; Sci A; Spch A; Star Student; Type A; NAACP; Phys Ed, A's; U of Ala; Med.

WILLIAMS, Dudley Carroll
St Helena HS; Greensburg, LA (6-54) Bus C; Chor; Pres, FBLA; Sci C; Pres, SC; Pres, Sr Cl; VP, Jr Cl; VP, Soph Cl; Co-Cpt, Ftbl; Pres A; Mus, SC, A's; Sou U; Bus.

WILLIAMS, Dudley Leigh
William T Sutherlin Acad; Danville, VA (1-6) Ann; Chor; Tres, Drama; Fr C; Hmrm; Lit Mag; F-Ed, Sch P; Sci C; Soph Cl; Sftbl; Alg A; Bio A; Gr Marshal; Hist A; Math A; Spch A; Val; Judge AM Aiken Schol A; Col of William and Mary; Chem.

WILLIAMS, Earl
Cotton Plant HS; Cotton Plant, AR (3-46) Drama; Fr C; FFA; SC; VP, Jr Cl; VP, Soph Cl; Bkbl; Tr; COM; Mich St U; Engr.

WILLIAMS, Easter Denise
Northeastern HS; Detroit, MI (10%-250) Wayne St U; Lib Arts.

WILLIAMS, Eddie Ermon
Harry Ells HS; Richmond, CA (17-276) Chor; Ger C; CSF; Citz A; Type A; Phys Fitness A; US Military Acad; Chem Engr.

WILLIAMS, Edith Alice
Petersburg HS; Petersburg, VA (50%-585) Span C; Va Commonwealth U; Bus Adm.

WILLIAMS, Elaine
Spring Valley HS; Pontiac, SC; JV, Chldr; Hmrm; SC; Bkbl; Sftbl; U of SC.

WILLIAMS, Elisa Adele
Boro Hall Acad; Brooklyn, NY (1-17) DA Citz A; Service A; Schol As; Long Island U; Respiratory Therapy.

WILLIAMS, Elizabeth Ann
Booker T Washington HS; New Orleans, LA; VP, Hmrm; NHS; SC; Cosmotology A; Stu Vol; Dillard U; Ed.

WILLIAMS, Emily Hereford
Crenshaw Christian Acad; Luverne, AL (4-24) Band; Bus C; Chldr; Chor; Fin, Jr Miss Pagent; Math C; Bkbl; NEDT; Hon Soc; Auburn U; Bus.

WILLIAMS, Emma Jean
Spartanburg HS; Spartanburg, SC (419-827) Cpt, Chldr; VP, Drama; Pres, FHA; VP, 4H; Pres, Hmrm; InterClub Coun; Cpt, Sftbl; Limestone Col; Dramatics.

WILLIAMS, Eric Allen
Newton Conover HS; Newton, NC (40-213) Band; Ensm; Order/Arrow; Tnns; Order/Arrow A; Band Ltr; HR; Heywood Tech Col; Forestry.

WILLIAMS, Eric Curtis
Gainesville HS; Gainesville, TX (20-208) Drama; Secy, FFA; NEDT; FFA Star Chapter Farmer A; FFA Beef Proficiency A; *Cooke Co Col; Law.*

WILLIAMS, Eric Pinson
Scotland HS; Laurinburg, NC (10-650) Band; Fr C; Bsbl; Ftbl; *Law.*

WILLIAMS, Eunice Adiisa
Boothbay Region HS; Boothbay Region, ME; FHA.

WILLIAMS, Felita Thynette
Tuscaloosa HS; Tuscaloosa, AL; Band; SC; *Eng.*

WILLIAMS, Florine
O H Wingfield HS; Jackson, MS; Chor; NHS; Var C; JV, Tr; *Miss St Col; Law.*

WILLIAMS, Frances Greer II
DuVal Sr HS; Glenn Dale, MD; Hmrm; ARC; Ed, Sch P; SC; Pres, Jr Cl; Pres, Soph Cl; Sftbl; COM; Citz A; 1st Chair, Band; *Law.*

WILLIAMS, Franklin Jerome
Moultrie Sr HS; Moultrie, GA (10%-350) Co-Cpt, Band; Hmrm; Orch; SC; Sftbl; Swim; COM; Cl Fav; Delta Sigma Theta A; Hon Prog; MLS; Hon Graduate; Distin Serv A & Spirit A, Band; *Valdosta St Col; Bus Adm.*

WILLIAMS, Freddie Jr
Frederick Douglass HS; Atlanta, GA; Chor; ROTC A; Drill Tm; Gym Tm; Sch Service A; *Military.*

WILLIAMS, Frederick
Jess Lanier HS; Bessemer, AL (39-270) *Journ.*

WILLIAMS, Gail Renee
Charleston HS; Charleston, SC (34-64) FTA; Pres, Hmrm; Lit Ral; ARC; Sch P; SC; Beauty; COM; Delta Sigma Theta A; I Dare You; ARC A; Type A; *Albany St Col; Nurs.*

WILLIAMS, Gary David
Oswego Sr HS; Oswego, IL (3-340) Pres, Chess C; Fr C; NHS; Hon Prog; JA A; Math A; *U of Chicago; Natural Sci.*

WILLIAMS, Gay Lynn
Penncrest HS; Media, PA (16-450) Chor; Drama; NHS; Hon Prog; Dist, Regional, Chor; WW; *Cincinnati Bible Col; Mus.*

WILLIAMS, Gerri LeAnne
Southern Wayne Sr HS; Dudley, NC (2-420) AFS; Pres, BC; Chldr; Secy, Fr C; FHA; Semi-Fin, GS; NHS; SC; Golf; COM; Gov Honor Prog; Hon Prog; MLS; Gov's Sch; Eng C; Church Choir; Marshal; Acteens; Church Organist; Secy, Hist C; *Meredith Col; Pre-Med.*

WILLIAMS, Gibson Mark
Burke HS; Charleston, SC (47-210) All Amer Yth; Band; Cpt, Bkbl; *U of Va; Bus.*

WILLIAMS, Gino Warren
Floyd Co HS; Floyd, VA (12-150) Band; BC; Ensm; Fr C; Pres, 4H; Hmrm; Rptr, Sci C; SC; Secy, Var C; Bsbl; Bkbl; Co-Cpt, Golf; 4H A; I Dare You; PTA A; VFW A; VofDEM; Yth Foundation; *Anthropology.*

WILLIAMS, Gloria Dean
Claxton HS; Claxton, GA (25%-110) Band; FHA; Hmrm; SC; Secy, Jr Cl; Rptr, Soph Cl; Bio A; HCt; Tres & Parl, Sci C; Art Medal; WW; Miss Tiger; *Atlanta Col of Bus; Executive Secy.*

WILLIAMS, Gloria Denise
Williamston HS; Williamston, NC; FBLA; FFA; Tr; Art A; *Winston Salem Col; Art Instruction.*

WILLIAMS, Gloria Jean
Plymouth HS; Plymouth, NC (25-200) Secy, FHA; Pres, 4H; Sch P; 4H A; *Beaufort Tech; Early Childhood.*

WILLIAMS, Gregory Denton
Oscoda HS; Oscoda, MI (13-250) Math C; NHS; Order/Arrow; Ftbl; Tnns; Eagle Sct, 3 Palms; *Carson-Newman Col; Phys Sci.*

WILLIAMS, Gregory George
Dadeland Ctry Day Sch; Miami, FL (2-11) Tres, Ann; Sch P; Arch; Ftbl; Alg A; Bio A; Hon Prog; Journ A; NEDT; Sportsmanship A; *U of Ala at Hunstville; Pre-Law.*

WILLIAMS, Harold Doc
Niles McKinley HS; Niles, OH (66-423) Ch, A Cap Choir; AFS; Chess C; Chor; Demolay; Drama; NHS; ARC, Pres, Sci C; Masonic A.

WILLIAMS, Henry Clifford
Wade Hampton HS; Greenville, SC (20%-490) Chor; Ensm; Bkbl; Cr-Ctry; Ftbl; Tnns; Tr; Amer Leg A; *Clemson U; Archt.*

WILLIAMS, Henry Clifford II
Wade Hampton HS; Greenville, SC (80-500) Cr-Ctry; Ftbl; Tr; Amer Leg A; *Clemson U; Engr.*

WILLIAMS, Henry Warren
Palm Springs HS; Palm Springs, CA; Co-Cpt, Bkbl; Ftbl; Ashanti C; *San Jose St U.*

WILLIAMS, Izola Mae
Banning HS; Banning, CA (13-218) Band; Chor; Fin, GS; Span C; Bsbl; Sftbl; CSF; Yth Fel; Block B; Afro-Amer Yth Assn; Vlbl; Rally C; Church Usher Board; Red Circle; *Med.*

WILLIAMS, James Cecil
E Hills HS; Fort Worth, TX (50%-450) JV, Ftbl; Tr; Opt A; Vlbl King; *Tarrant Co Jr Col; Bus Mgt.*

WILLIAMS, James Michael
Rebecca Comer HS; Eufaula, AL (4-64) Drama; FFA; 4H; NHS; SC; Bkbl; 4H A; Hist A; Sci A; Spch A; Art C; *Bio.*

WILLIAMS, Janet Carolyn
J Frank Dobie HS; Houston, TX (10%-400) Ann; Hmrm; Span C; SC; Bkbl; Sftbl; Type A; Yth Foundation; Woodmen o-t World.

WILLIAMS, Janet Ellen
Livermore Falls HS; Livermore Falls, ME (9-94) JV, Bkbl; Hockey; Sftbl; *Springfield Col; Recreation.*

WILLIAMS, Jayme Lee
Ole Main HS; N Little Rock, AR; S-T, Drama; VP, FBLA; Tres, Rainbow; Sci C; Spch A; Ch, FBLA; *U of Ark; Bus Adm.*

WILLIAMS, Jeanette Marie
Weldon HS; Weldon, NC (7-121) VP, AFS; Ann; Chor; Tres, FBLA; Hmrm; Math C; NHS; Sch P; VP, Sci C; Secy, SC; Var C; Secy, Jr Cl; Secy, Soph Cl; Bsbl; Co-Cpt, Bkbl; Citz A; Cl Fav; HCt; Journ A; Sci A; Type A; WW; Eng A; Miss Fresh; *U of NC; Psych.*

WILLIAMS, Jeffrey Paul
Alliance HS; Alliance, NE; Band; Demolay; SC; Var C; JV, Ftbl; Tr; Wrest; HCt; Yth Fel; 'A' C; City Govt Day; St Qualifier, Wrest.

WILLIAMS, Jennifer Lee
Lincoln HS; Portland, OR (25%-250) Chldr; Ger C; Orch; Soccer; COM.

WILLIAMS, Jerry Willis Jr
Winn Acad; Winnfield, LA (2-9) VP, Chem C; 4H; Lit Ral; VP, Sci C; Pres, Spch C; Bsbl; Bkbl; Cpt, Ftbl; Cl Fav; MLS; Sal; Yth Fel; Mr Winn Acad; Tres, FCA; *La Tech U; Pre-Med.*

WILLIAMS, Jill Alyson
Melbourne HS; Melbourne, FL (20%-800) Ed, Ann; Chldr; Chor; Ensm; 4H; Madrigal; Ed, Sch P; Cr-Ctry; NEDT; Sal; Dean's A; Pres Phys Fitness A; DAR A; Mus A; *Psych.*

WILLIAMS, Jim James
Central Jersey Christian Sch; Asbury Park, NJ (5-16) Drama; Fr C; VP, Lit Ral; NEDT; Director, Movie C; *Sci.*

WILLIAMS, Jo Ann
Music and Art HS; New York, NY (81-580) Chor; Orch; Ed, Sch P; COM; Citz A; Hon Prog; Journ A; Math A; Sci A; Mus A; *NYU; Mus.*

WILLIAMS, Joan Anita
Weldon HS; Weldon, NC (14-156) Chor; Drama; Math C; Sch P; Sci C; Span C; SC; Bsbl; Bkbl; Sftbl; Miss Jr; *St Augustine Col; Early Childhood.*

WILLIAMS, Joann
Northwestern HS; Flint, MI (12-470) A Cap Choir; Chor; Pres, Drama; Ensm; Hmrm; SC; Pres, Thes; Beauty; Interlochen Ntl Mus; Most Out; Pres A; Solo, Ensm; Vlbl; Tr; Law Day; *Ky St U; Mus.*

WILLIAMS, Joanne Sue
Ritenour Sr HS; Overland, MO (2-664) Secy, A Cap Choir; Drama; NHS; Secy, Orch; Curator A; Sal; Ntl Sch Orch Assn A; *Harding Col.*

WILLIAMS, Joannie Alicia
Miami Sr HS; Miami, FL; *Miami Dade Jr Col; Professional Nurs.*

WILLIAMS, Jodie Lynn
New Caney HS; Porter, TX (4-269) Chem C; FHA; Hmrm; NHS; Sci C; Span C; Cpt, Bkbl; Cr-Ctry; Sftbl; Tr; COM; Hist A; Hon Prog; *Tex Tech U; Biological Sci.*

WILLIAMS, Joel Ray
Berea HS; Greenville, SC;

WILLIAMS, John David
Nw Classen HS; Okla City, OK; Demolay; Hmrm; Pres, Key C; Order/Arrow; MVP, Bkbl; Ftbl; Sftbl; Citz A; Cl Fav; Order/Arrow A; Yth Fel; Eagle Sct; *Okla St U; Communications.*

WILLIAMS, John Neal
Jones HS; Lynnville, TN; Ann; BC; Bus C; Chor; FFA; Bus Mgr, Sch P; SC; Var C; Mgr, Bkbl; Tr; Citz A; Cl Fav; HCt; *Columbia St Comm Col; Liberal Arts.*

WILLIAMS, Joni Sue
Glenwood HS; Chatham, IL (21-250) A Cap Choir; Band; Chor; Ensm; Fr C; FHA; GS; 4H; Sci C; VP, Spch C; SC; Bkbl; Ftbl; 4H A; MLS; Sal; *U of Tenn; Ed.*

WILLIAMS, Jonna Beth
Red Bank HS; Chattanooga, TN (28-336) Chor; Drama; S-T, FBLA; Bus Mgr, Lit Mag; NHS; Sci C; FHA; Journ A; Star Student; Vlbl; *Tenn Wesleyan Col; Arts.*

WILLIAMS, Jonna Schirl
Southern HS; Graham, NC (5-260) FHA; NHS; Gr Marshal; Art C; *Bob Jones U; Art.*

WILLIAMS, Judi Marlene
Horace Maynard HS; Maynardville, TN (2-127) Ann; VP, BC; Chor; FHA; GS; 4H; Sci C; VP, Spch C; SC; Bkbl; Ftbl; 4H A; MLS; Sal; *U of Tenn; Ed.*

WILLIAMS, Judith Ann
River Forest HS; Lake Station, IN (2-100) NHS; Crisco A; Hist A; Most Out; Sal; Type A.

WILLIAMS, Julie Lea
Ottumwa HS; Ottumwa, IA (50%-476) Band; Y-Tns; Sftbl; *Ottumwa Heights Col; Social Work.*

WILLIAMS, Julie Rose
Vandalia Christian Sch; Greensboro, NC (2-13) Chldr; Pres, Hmrm; Math C; Monogram; Sci C; SC; Pres, Soph Cl; Bkbl; COM; *UNC at Greensboro; Nurs.*

WILLIAMS, Karen Denyse
John Tyler HS; Tyler, TX (10%-300) Bus C; Pres, Chor; FHA; NHS; Tr; Hon Prog; Phi Beta Kappa; Vlbl; *Tyler Jr Col; Bus.*

WILLIAMS, Karen Elaine
Douglas S Freeman HS; Richmond, VA (50%-600) 1st Pl Vica Health Asst Comp Dist; *VCU-MCV; Nurs.*

WILLIAMS, Karla Sue
Kountze HS; Kountze, TX (7-84) Band; FFA; Pres, FHA; Pres, FHA; Hmrm; Math C; Sci C; Span C; Pres, SC; Beauty; Cl Fav; H of F; HCt; Pres A; Color Guard; *Lamar U; Nurs.*

WILLIAMS, Kathe M
Ulysses HS; Ulysses, KS (4-126) Chldr; FHA; 4H; NHS; Tres, Y-Tns; VP, Soph Cl; 4H A; Yth Fel; *Abilene Christian U; Architecture.*

WILLIAMS, Katherine Anne
Mountain Brook HS; Birmingham, AL; AFS; Ann; Fr C; Bkbl; Cr-Ctry; Tr; Sch Bank Teller; Young Life; Secy, Birmingham Presbyter Yth Coun; *U of Colo; Forestry.*

WILLIAMS, Kathia Lynn
James H Bowen HS; Chicago, IL; Semi-Fin, Ntl Teache; Bkbloun; Vlbl; Secy, JA; *Bradley U; Child Psych.*

WILLIAMS, Kathleen Marie
Oroville HS; Oroville, CA (4-200) AFS; Fr C; S-T, NHS; CSF; Chem A; Hon Prog; Yth Fel; GAA; Christmas Formal Qn; S-T, GAA; Service C; Fellows C; *Calif St U; Bio.*

WILLIAMS, Kathleen Renee
Alliance HS; Alliance, NE (30-152) Tres, Band; S-T, Chor; Pres, 4H; Thes; VP, Y-Tns; Pres, Jr Cl; Citz A; 4H A; HQn; Yth Fel; Swing Choir; WW; Hon Qn, Job's Daughters; Hastings Col Hon Choir; Co Attorney, Gov Day; *Chadron St Col; Bus.*

WILLIAMS, Kathryn Ann
University Christian Sch; Jacksonville, FL; COM; Most Intellectual; *Fla Jr Col.*

WILLIAMS, Kathy Ann
Guthrie HS; Guthrie, OK; Chldr; Chor; Ensm; GS; 4H; Madrigal; NHS; Cr-Ctry; Sftbl; Tr; Amer Leg A; 4H A; *Okla St U; Bus.*

WILLIAMS, Kathy Faye
Alain Leroy Locke HS; Los Angeles, CA; Rptr; Sch P; SC; Co-Cpt, Bkbl; Sftbl; COM; Citz A; Cl Fav; Hon Prog; Eng A; PA; Ladies A; Leadership A; *U of Calif; Bus.*

WILLIAMS, Kathy Lynn
Central HS; Little Rock, AR (44-666) BC; FBLA; Mu Alpha Theta; Math A; *U of Ark; Med.*

WILLIAMS, Katie Mae
Tompkins HS; Savannah, GA (6-30) FBLA; *Savannah St Col; Bus Adm.*

WILLIAMS, Kay Lorraine
New Rochelle HS; New Rochelle, NY; Chor; Drama; NHS; Span NHS; Hon Prog; *Drama.*

WILLIAMS, Kay Lynette
St Elmo Jr-Sr HS; St Elmo, IL (5-50) Pres, Band; Pres, Chor; Ensm; Pres, FHA; NHS; Orch; SC; Tres, Sr Cl; Tres, Jr Cl; Tres, Soph Cl; COM; Citz A; DARGCA; HQn; HCt; Hon Prog; I Dare You; Swtht; Yth Fel; Nettie Bingham A; Semi-Fin, Miss Sr; Most Mus Talent; *Anderson Col; Elem Ed.*

WILLIAMS, Kenneth John
Homewood-Flossmoor HS; Flossmoor, IL (61-920) Band; Orch; WW, Mus Stu; Dist, All St IMEA; 1st Chair, Band, Orch, Jazz Band.

WILLIAMS, Kenneth Lyell
Kenmore HS; Akron, OH; Tr; NHS; Sch P; Golf; Amer Leg A; N Ohio Scho Press Assn.

WILLIAMS, Kevin
McDonogh 35 Sr HS; New Orleans, LA; Band; *U of Sou Calif; Archt.*

WILLIAMS, Kevin Curtis
Mt Carmel HS; Mt Carmel, IL (23-196) Chess C; VP, Key C; Ed, Sch P; Sci C; Pres, SC; Mgr, Bkbl; Journ A; Kiwanis A; St Scholar; Yth Fel; NASA Viking Stu Project; Lt Gov, Key C; Dist Tres, Key C; Sons of Union Veterns o-t Civl War; 2nd, Key C Dist Talent Contest; *U of Ill; Pol Sci.*

WILLIAMS, Kevin Edwin
Vidalia HS; Vidalia, GA (26-139) Pres, Chor; HiY; Semi-Fin, Lit Ral; Model UN; Sch P; Bsbl; Ftbl; Most Talented; *Mus.*

WILLIAMS, Kimberly Kay
Trinity Christian HS; Chattanooga, TN; Co-Ed, Ann; FBLA; Hmrm; NHS; SC; Sftbl; Beauty; HCt; Hon Prog; Journ A; Star Student; Acct A; *Chattanooga St U; Dental Asst.*

WILLIAMS, Kurt Oliver
Woodward HS; Woodward, OK (28-177) Band; Hmrm; Order/Arrow; Var C; Bkbl; Ftbl; Tr; All Dist, Ftbl; Eagle Sct; WW; *Okla U; Law.*

WILLIAMS, LaVerne Dianne
Withrow HS; Cincinnati, OH (38-650) Chldr; Hmrm; NHS; SC; Sftbl; Tr; COM; *U of Cincinnati; Med.*

WILLIAMS, LaVerne Velmora
Potomac Sr HS; Oxon Hill, MD; Bkbl; Tres, Drill Tm.

WILLIAMS, LaWanda
Woodward HS; Cincinnati, OH;

WILLIAMS, Lane Hadley
Suffield Acad; Suffield, CT (13-130) Bus Mgr, Bus C; Chess C; Cum Laude Soc; FBLA; Pres, Lat C; Lat NHS; Lit Mag; NHS; Rptr, Sch P; Ski C; Secy, Var C; S-T, Jr Cl; Bsbl; Soccer; Alg A; Aux Lat; Chamber of Comm A; Delta Sigma Theta A; Gov Honor Prog; H of F; Hon Prog; Journ A; Magna Cum Laude; Math A; MLS; Opt A; Q&S A; *Georgetown U; Bus.*

WILLIAMS, Larry Dean
Plainfield HS; Plainfield, IL (100-300) Sch P; COM; *Art.*

WILLIAMS, Laura Carol
Holy Cross HS; Delran, NJ (1%-373) CYO; Cr-Ctry; Tr; Hon Prog; Full Academic Schol, Cath Acad; GS Wider Opportunity; *Drexel U; Math.*

WILLIAMS, Laurel Ruth
Chowchilla HS; Chowchilla, CA; VP, Dbte Tm; FBLA; VP, FFA; Pres, 4H; Hmrm; Ntl Teachers Coun; Secy, Jr Cl; CSF; 4H A; FFA St Farmer; Star Greenhand; Livestock A; Star Chapter Farmer; *Merced Jr Col; Bus.*

WILLIAMS, Lauri Ann
Tompkins HS; Savannah, GA (4-30) Tr; *Armstrong St Col; Acct.*

WILLIAMS, LeRoy Patrick
Carolina HS; Greenville, SC (23-249) CYO; Pres, Hmrm; St Stu Congress; VP, SC; Bsbl; Mgr, Bkbl; Amer Leg A; COM; Citz A; MLS; PTA A; Furman Schol; Bus Driver o-t Yr; PTSA Service A; *Clemson U; Bio.*

WILLIAMS, Leadon Denise
Bogalusa HS W; Bogalusa, LA; BC; NHS; Bkbl; Hon Prog; Yth Fel; PKT Service C; Yth Choir; Yth Coun; Church Organist; Golden 'B' Hon Soc; Pres, Acteens; *LSU; Sci.*

WILLIAMS, Lee Alan
E Jordan HS; E Jordan, MI; Band; Chor; Tr; *Bethel Col; Pastor.*

WILLIAMS, Lee Ann
John F Kennedy HS; Denver, CO (6-500) Band; Chor; Fr C; Semi-Fin, GS; NHS; Ntl Yth Conf; ARC; Ed, Sch P; Hon Prog; Journ A; Yth Fel; Pres, Church Yth Fel; Hon Cadet, ROTC; Couns On Yth Ministries; *U of Denver; Creative Writing.*

WILLIAMS, Leila Sue
Newton Co Comprehensive HS; Covington, GA (25-375) Band; BC; Pres, 4H; Hmrm; Span C; Secy, SC; Bkbl; COM; 4H A; Hon Prog; JA A; Kiwanis A; Pres A; Rookie A; *U of Ga; Math.*

WILLIAMS, Lettye Ann
Canton Acad; Canton, MS (5%-80) Ann; Band; BC; JV, Chldr; Orch; SC; Y-Tns; Secy, Jr Cl; HCt; Yth Fel; Drum Mjrte; *Miss St U; Elem Ed.*

WILLIAMS, Linda Ann
Franklin Rd Christian Sch; Murfreesboro, TN; Band; Cpt, Chldr; Chor; Dbte Tm; Drama; 4H; Lat C; Mjrte; Span C; 4H A; Col Schol; *Bus.*

WILLIAMS, Linda Marie
Ferriday HS N; Ferriday, LA (1-220) Tres, BC; Rptr, FBLA; Drama As; *Grambling St U; Pol Sci.*

WILLIAMS, Lisa Aline
Claiborne Acad; Haynesville, LA (2-37) Chor; 4H; Lit Ral; Rptr, NHS; SC; VP, Sr Cl; Tres, Jr Cl; Cpt, Bkbl; Sftbl; HCt; MLS; Sal; VP, Bkbl; WW; *NE La U; Computer Sci.*

WILLIAMS, Lisa Gaye
New Braunfels HS; New Braunfels, TX; Chor; Fr C; *Bethany Col; Ed.*

WILLIAMS, Lloyd
Chicago Voc HS; Chicago, IL (121-1768) Chor; Drama; Math C; NHS; Order/Arrow; ARC; Sci C; SC; Bkbl; Bio A; God & Country A; Ntl Achv Schol; Phy A; ARC A; Sci A; Ltrman's C; Drama A; *Bradley U; Med.*

WILLIAMS, Lloyd Anthony
John C Fremont HS; Los Angeles, CA; *Tuskegee Inst; Mus.*

WILLIAMS, Lola Ann
F O Alexander HS; Starkville, MS (5-59) Cpt, Chldr; Secy, Hmrm; Pres, SC; *Miss St U; Journ.*

WILLIAMS, Lola Elizabeth
Humboldt HS; Humboldt, TN (46-188) BC; Chldr; Chor; Secy, FHA; 4H; Sch P; Span C; SC; Secy, Jr Cl; Cpt, Bkbl; Tr; COM; DARGCA; 4H A; Yth Fel; Bkbl A; WW; *U of Tenn; Home Ec.*

WILLIAMS, Lorrie Lyn
Kearney Sr HS; Kearney, NE; Chor; Ed, Sch P; Hon Prog; *Okla Baptist U; Religious Journ.*

WILLIAMS, Lou Ann
Crystal City HS; Crystal City, MO (6-103) A Cap Choir; Chor; Dbte Tm; Ensm; NHS; Bkbl; Nurs.

WILLIAMS, Loyd Dane
Caprock HS; Amarillo, TX (38-400) Co-Ed, Ann; Pres, Band; NHS; Orch; A-Ed, Sch P; Journ A; All Reg Band; Serv A, Band; John Philip Sousa A; Medal, Newswriting Contes; Solo & Ensm A's; *Amarillo Col; Bus.*

WILLIAMS, Lucinda Sue
Johnston City HS; Johnston City, IL (45-102) Band; Bus C; FHA; *Airline Hosting.*

WILLIAMS, Madelyn LaVerne
John Tyler HS; Tyler, TX; Chor; FHA; Cr-Ctry; Tr; Citz A.

WILLIAMS, Marcia Ann
John Tyler HS; Tyler, TX (3-472) A Cap Choir; Secy, Chor; FHA; Secy, AFLCIO Yth Coun; NAACP; Church Choir; Win, UIL Solo; *Pepperdine U; Mus.*

WILLIAMS, Margie Lee
Edison Sr HS; Lake Station, IN (12-136) Chor; Ensm; Fr C; FTA; Fin, GS; Hmrm; Madrigal; NHS; Sci C; SC; Amer Leg A; HCt; PTA A; Sci A; Choir Accompanist.

WILLIAMS, Marilyn
Mount Olive HS; Seale, AL; Chor; FHA; 4H; Cpt, Mjrte; Sch P; SC; 4H A; Hist A; Sci A; *Ala St U; Phys Therapist.*

WILLIAMS, Marisa Lynne
Gibbs Sr HS; St Petersburg, FL; Chor; Thes; Y-Tns; Yth Fel; *Med.*

WILLIAMS, Marjorie
Notre Dame HS; Crowley, LA (5-120) BC; Rptr, CYO; Fr C; Rptr, 4H; InterAct C; 4H A; Superior, Foreign Lang Festival; *NE La U; Med.*

WILLIAMS, Mark James
Spring Hill HS; Spring Hill, KS (12-96) NHS; Span C; Rptr, SC; Pres, Jr Cl; *Moody Bible Inst; Missionary Aviation.*

WILLIAMS, Marshall Gerard
Sumner & O'Fallon Tech S; St Louis, MO (100-560) Drama; Soccer; Citz A; JA A; Most Out; Barbizon Mod; VP, Dist YPD.

WILLIAMS, Marvin John
Libbey HS; Toledo, OH (10%-300) Pres, Demolay; Fr C; Pres, FFA; Bus Mgr, Sch P; JA A; *U of Toledo; Teaching.*

WILLIAMS, Mary Elizabeth
Gainesville HS; Gainesville, GA (2-250) Anchor C; Pres, BC; Span C; Span NHS; Eng, Span A's; Highest Avg A; *Berea Col; Art.*

WILLIAMS, Mary Etta
Forest Brook Sr HS; Houston, TX; Sch P; *Interior Decorator.*

WILLIAMS, Mary Rochelle
Columbus N HS; Columbus, IN (154-464) Tri-HiY; Spch Tm; VP, Jr Humane Soc; Mgr, Intramural Bkbl; Bible C.

WILLIAMS, Mary Susan
New Bern Sr HS; New Bern, NC; Ann; Co-Ch, Chor; Drama; Fr C; FTA; Co-Ch, Rainbow; Sch P; Sci C; Swim; COM; Hist A; Hon Prog; NEDT; *U of NC.*

WILLIAMS, Mary Yvonne
Clyde HS; Clyde, TX; *Bible Baptist Col; Missions.*

WILLIAMS, Mashella Wanda
Hayti HS; Hayti, MO (1-88) Chor; NHS; VP, Span C; SC; Eng, Span, A's; *Draughon Bus Col; Bus Ed.*

WILLIAMS, Melanie Rose
Chillicothe HS; Chillicothe, OH (53-390) Chor; Dbte Tm; Semi-Fin, Jr Miss Pa; NHSt; Span C; Bkbl; Tr; COM; Spch A; Fresh Found, Ohio St U; *Ohio St U; Pre-Med.*

WILLIAMS, Melinda Ann
Harlingen HS; Harlingen, TX; A Cap Choir; Chor; Ensm; Rainbow; COM; Hon Prog; Superior Dance; 1st Div, Solo Mus; *Tex A&M U; Vet.*

WILLIAMS, Melinda Kay
Lancaster HS; Lancaster, TX; S-T, Drama; Secy, FHA; Secy, FTA; S-T, Spch C; Teach Asst, Kindergarten, 1st Gr; *TCU; Spec Ed.*

WILLIAMS, Melissa Denise
Plano Sr HS; Plano, TX; Chor; Span C; *Bethany Nazerene Col; Elem Ed.*

WILLIAMS, Melnee Lee
Brookhaven Acad; Brookhaven, MS; Ann; Rptr, BC; Fr C; FHA; Semi-Fin, Jr Miss Pa; Ed,tSch P; VP, Soph Cl; Bkbl; Sftbl; Tr; Beauty; HCt; Journ A; Jr Chamber of Com A; Lion A; *U of Miss; Pol Sci.*

WILLIAMS, Michael Robert
Arkadelphia HS; Arkadelphia, AR (26-170) BS; Key C; NHS; Bus Mgr, Sch P; SC; Pres, Sr Cl; Pres, Jr Cl; Ftbl; MVP, Tnns; All District, Ftbl; *Ouachita Baptist U; Pre-Law.*

WILLIAMS, Michele Maureen
Northwestern Sr HS; Hyattsville, MD; Hon Prog; BSO; Gospel Choir; Pom Pom; Outst Kickette, Pep Sq; *Harvard U; Journ.*

WILLIAMS, Michelle Rae
Henderson Co Sr HS; Henderson, KY (10%-650) A Cap Choir; Band; BC; Chor; Ensm; FHA; NHS; Sftbl.

WILLIAMS, Mygleetus Therese
Peach Co HS; Fort Valley, GA (1-189) Ann; S-T, BC; Dbte Tm; Pres, FHA; 4H; Hmrm; Fin, Jr Miss Pagent; Ed, Lit Mag; Model UN; Pres, Sci C; Pres, Sr Cl; Amer Leg Orator A; Bio A; COM; Citz A; Cl Fav; DARGCA; Gov Honor Prog; Hon Prog; I Dare You; Poet A; Spch A; Type A; Val; COPE A; AKA A; Sr Superlative; *Emory U; Pre-Med.*

WILLIAMS, Nancy Derinda
Boswell HS; Fort Worth, TX (35-202) Band; Dbte Tm; Rptr, Fr C; FTA; Pres, NHS; Secy, SC; Thes; *U of Houston; Social Work.*

WILLIAMS, Nathel
Manual HS; Peoria, IL (93-318) Var C; Ftbl; *ICC; Engr.*

WILLIAMS, Noel Denise
Mary Star o-t Sea HS; San Pedro, CA; Ed, Ann; CYO; Pres, Hmrm; NHS; Ed, Sch P; SC; JV, Bkbl; Sftbl; CSF; COM; NEDT; Poet A; NHS A; GAA A; *Creighton U; Bio.*

WILLIAMS,
   Norman Washington
Aviation HS; New York, NY (336-658) Band; Chor; VP, Hmrm; Orch; JV, Bkbl; Soccer; Tr; COM; Citz A; Hist A; JA A; *Engr.*

WILLIAMS, Pamela Gail
Kinston HS; Kinston, NC (127-331) A Cap Choir; Chor; Hmrm; SC; Tri-HiY; *U of NC; Criminal Justice.*

WILLIAMS, Pamela Lynn
Englewood HS; Jacksonville, FL (3-466) FBLA; InterClub Coun; NHS; SC; Tri-HiY; Pres, Sr Cl; Pres, Jr Cl; Cl Fav; H of F; HCt; MLS; Outst Bus Stu; *U of Fla.*

WILLIAMS, Pamela Marcelette
Reading Sr HS; Reading, PA (204-907) Secy, Commercial C; Pres, Hmrm; COM; Type A; HR; School Pin; *Bus.*

WILLIAMS, Pamela Susette
George Washington HS; Denver, CO; Cpt, Tr; JA A; Gym A; Tr A; Pep C; *Metropolitan St Col; Early Childhood Ed.*

WILLIAMS, Patrice
McDonogh 35 Sr HS; New Orleans, LA; 4H A; JA A; PA; Special, Schol, A's; *Sou U; Social Worker.*

WILLIAMS, Patricia
Paterson Cath HS; Paterson, NJ (60-168) Chor; SC; Sch Spirit; *Registor Nurs.*

WILLIAMS, Patricia Ann
Flemington HS; Flemington, WV (3-50) Band; Cpt, Chldr; Drama; Ensm; Fr C; Tres, FHA; VP, FTA; GS; Pres, 4H; NHS; Orch; A-Ed, Sch P; Secy, Sr Cl; Secy, Jr Cl; Secy, Soph Cl; Cl Fav; 4H A; Most Out; All-St Bands; *W Va U; Mus.*

WILLIAMS, Patricia Jean
River Forest HS; Hobart, IN; GAA Cert; Vlbl.

WILLIAMS, Patricia Lee
Sardis HS; Sardis, TN (4-29) FHA; S-T, Jr Cl; Cl Fav; *W Tenn Bus Col; Secretarial Sci.*

WILLIAMS, Patricia Marie
Saint Mary's Acad; Alexandria, VA (2-70) VP, Chor; Lit Mag; Pres, Span NHS; NMF; NMS; *Saint Mary's Col; Theatre Arts.*

WILLIAMS, Patricia Renee
Fairview Alpha HS; Coushatta, LA (4-26) Bus Mgr, Ann; FHA; SC; Cpt, Bkbl; 4H A; H of F; HCt; Swtht; Defensive A; *Northwestern St U; Acct.*

WILLIAMS, Paul Gamaliel
Fremont HS; Oakland, CA (33%-500) Band; F-Ed, Sch P; Ftbl; Cpt, Tr; HCt; Most Out; Ldrship A; *San Jose St Col; Phys Ed.*

WILLIAMS, Philip Michael
Purcell HS; Cincinnati, OH; Cpt, K of C; Bkbl; JA A; K of C A; *U of Cincinnati; Broadcasting.*

WILLIAMS, Pocahontas Nikita
Henry Grady HS; Atlanta, GA; Band; Cpt, Chldr; Drama; Fr C; Mu Alpha Theta; Sch P; Sci C; SC; Pres, Jr Cl; VP, Soph Cl; Hist A; Hon Prog; Sci A; *Ga Tech U; Math.*

WILLIAMS, Randall Earl
Hobart Sr HS; Hobart, IN; AFS; Tres, Ger C; Ed, Sch P; Bkbl; JV, Tnns; Fin, Most Outst; Straight 'A' A; Fin, Sci A; PA; President's Phys Fitness A; Asst Church Organist; *Ind U; Med.*

WILLIAMS, Rebecca Lynne
Florence HS; Florence, MS (5-189) BC; FHA; COM; *Math.*

WILLIAMS, Regina Ann
Slaton HS; Slaton, TX (75%-98) Ann; Band; JV, Chldr; Mjrte; Bkbl; Golf; JV, Tr.

WILLIAMS, Regina Faye
Baker HS; Baker, LA (23-374) Chldr; SC; Tri-HiY; *Southeastern U; Nurs.*

WILLIAMS, Regina Joyce
Raines Sr HS; Jacksonville, FL; Chor; PA; *U of Fla; Nurs.*

WILLIAMS, Reginald
Buena Vista HS; Saginaw, MI; Mgr, Ftbl; Tr; 4H A; *Mich Col; Math.*

WILLIAMS, Renee Denise
Evans HS; Evans, GA; Secy, Fr C; Tnns; Best Leadership; Nom, Hon Govt; Game Coach A; Stu Coun; *Bio.*

WILLIAMS, Rhonda Renee
Fairfield HS; Fairfield, AL; BC; Chor; Drama; FHA; Pres, SC; *U of Ala; Law.*

WILLIAMS, Rhonette Caren
Beaumont HS; St Louis, MO (45-655) Band; Bsbl; Bkbl; Citz A; JA A.

WILLIAMS, Richard Allen
George Washington HS; Denver, CO (300-750) A Cap Choir; AFS; Chor; Fin, Hmrm; NFL; Pol Sci C; ARC; Spch C; SC; JV, Cr-Ctry; Sftbl; Swim; Mgr, Tr; COM; Citz A; Cl Fav; JA A; Spch A; Yth Leg; *Wilberforce U.*

WILLIAMS, Rita Lyn
Duncan HS; Duncan, OK (1-324) A Cap Choir; Chem C; VP, Chor; Ensm; FHA; GS; Hmrm; NHS; Sch Achieve Tm; SC; S-T, Soph Cl; Bkbl; Bio A; COM; Citz A; Hon Prog; JA A; Most Out; Sci A; St Hon Soc; Chor Qn; Dist Hon Chor; Mus A's; *Okla Christian Col; Engr.*

WILLIAMS, Robert Eddie
York Comp HS; York, SC (11-272) Band; Ensm; NHS; Bkbl; Cr-Crtry; JV, Ftbl; Cpt, Tnns; Cl Fav; MVP, Tnns; Marshal; *USC; Bus Adm.*

WILLIAMS, Robert Edward
Aberdeen Sr HS; Aberdeen, MD (8-368) A Cap Choir; Chess C; Chor; Dbte; Co-Cpt, Ftbl; NMS; Outst Ath Schol; *Abilene Christian U; Mus Composition.*

WILLIAMS, Robert Lyndon
H B Plant HS; Tampa, FL (15-600) VP, NHS; VP, Span C; Hon Prog; JA A; Rensselaer A; I Dare You; *Morehouse Col; Elec Engr.*

WILLIAMS, Rosalind Denise
Washington HS; Lake Charles, LA; JV, Chldr; FHA; Hmrm; Parl, NHS; Span C; Spch C; Secy, SC; Parl, Tri-HiY; Hon Prog; Spch A; Yth Fel; GSct A; *Tex Sou U; Law.*

WILLIAMS, Roxie Lynne
Stanzel Christian HS; Greenfield, IA (2-4) Ed, Ann; Band; Chor; FHA; Pres, SC; S-T, Jr Cl; Pres, Soph Cl; Tr; Spch A; *Grace Col o-t Bible; Psych.*

WILLIAMS, Rubie Francyne
Corliss HS; Chicago, IL; Band; COM; Sal; *Bradley U; Ed.*

WILLIAMS, Sandra Ann
Christiansburg HS; Christiansburg, VA; FHA; Hmrm; SC; Secy & Rptr, Chor; Bible Sch Cert; FHA Cert; Sch Ltr; Chor Off Pin; Mus A; Most Active Cl Member A; *Radford Col; Secretarial Work.*

WILLIAMS, Sandra Faye
Mt Olive HS; Ft Mitchell, AL (3-52) DARGCA; 4H A; Hon Prog; MLS; *Acct.*

WILLIAMS, Sandra Gail
Benjamin Franklin HS; New Orleans, LA; Acteens, Qn; Ballet; Attendance A; *UNO.*

WILLIAMS, Sandra Kay
Star-Spencer HS; Spencer, OK (3%-375) Rptr, Ann; VP, FHA; Secy, GS; NHS; COM; WW; Church Yth o-t Yr; Del, GS; Acad A, Okla St U; *Okla St U; Communications.*

WILLIAMS, Sandra Marie
Terrell Co HS; Dawson, GA (10%-147) Bio A; Hist A; HCt; Hon Prog; Sci A; Type A; Eng A.

WILLIAMS, Sarah Louise
Wheeler Co HS; Alamo, GA (3-50) Chor; FBLA; Pres, 4H; NHS; Pres, SC; Pres, Tri-HiY; 4H A; *Brewton Parker Col; Mus.*

WILLIAMS, Saundra Sherrell
Clinton HS; Clinton, NC (10%-275) Citz A; Drama, Lang Arts, A's; *Pepperdine U.*

WILLIAMS, Sharon
Northeastern HS; Detroit, MI (10-202) Citz A; Hons A; *Wayne St U; Nurs.*

WILLIAMS, Sharon Ann
Southampton Acad; Courtland, VA (3-35) Ann; BC; Lit Mag; NFL; Co-Ed, Sch P; Span C; Var C; Bsbl; Bkbl; Ftbl; Sftbl; COM; Citz A; Hon Prog; Yth Fel; Coun On Ministries; *Lynchburg Col; Mus.*

WILLIAMS, Sharon Lois
John L McClellan HS; Little Rock, AR (1-500) Band; FBLA; Span C; Type A; Flagline; Span A; 1st Pl, Ntl Span Exams; *Ouachita Baptist U; Foreign Lang.*

WILLIAMS, Sherry Ann
Monroe Area Comprehensive HS; Monroe, GA; Chor; SC; Hist A; Hon Prog; Drill Tm; Paramed C; *Med.*

WILLIAMS, Sherwin O Jr
Arkadelphia HS; Arkadelphia, AR (20%-200) Band; Chess C; MVP, Golf; Stage Band; Fire Marshal; *Ouachita Baptist U; Pre-Law.*

WILLIAMS, Shirley Ann
Williamstown HS; Williamstown, WV (3-116) NHS; Rainbow; JA A; MLS; *Glenville St Col; Secondary Ed.*

WILLIAMS, Shon Loretta
Miami Northwestern Sr HS; Miami, FL; S-T, Mjrte; Alg A; Citz A; Math A; Sci A; Alice B Stephens Sci A; Principal's HR A; Statistician, Bkbl & Tr; *Ga Inst of Tech; Engr.*

WILLIAMS, Stanley Michael
Traverse City Sr HS; Traverse City, MI (137-734) A Cap Choir; Band; Chess C; Chor; Madrigal; NMF; Band & Choir Ltrs & Pins; Jazz Band; *Alma Col; Mus.*

WILLIAMS, Stephanie
Abington Friends Sch; Jenkintown, PA; Chor; *Penn St U; Ed.*

WILLIAMS, Stephen Trumane
Cape Fear HS; Fayetteville, NC; Dbte Tm; FFA; Sci C; VP, SC; Bkbl; Cpt, Sftbl; Tr; *Sweet Briar Col.*

WILLIAMS, Steve Alan
Eastern Randolph HS; Ramseur, NC (39-223) BC; FFA; Key C; JV, Ftbl; Special Achv Cert; *Appalachian St U; Computers.*

WILLIAMS, Steve Carl
Western Hills HS; Cincinnati, OH (485-905) HiY; SC; Soccer; Tr; Wrest; Citz A; *Cincinnati Bible Col; Ministry.*

WILLIAMS, Steve Richard
Fern Creek HS; Louisville, KY; Ger C; JV, Soccer; Yth Fel; *U of Ky; Meteorology.*

WILLIAMS, Steve Wright
Cleburne HS; Cleburne, TX (5-644) Dbte Tm; NFL; Span C; Spch C; COM; Spch A; Yth Leg; *U of Tex; Law.*

WILLIAMS, Steven
Johnstown-Monroe HS; Johnstown, OH (1-142) Chess C; NHS; Rptr, Sch P; Pres, Sci C; Span C; VP, Jr Cl; VP, Soph Cl; Var C; JV, Bsbl; Bkbl; Tr; Alg A; Hist A; NEDT.

WILLIAMS, Steven Andrew
Cedar Shoals HS; Athens, GA (140-400) Band; Tres, Lat C; Order/ Arrow; Order/ Arrow A; Eagle Sct; U of Ga; Mus.

WILLIAMS, Sue Sawatzky
Cushing HS; Cushing, OK (13-129) Fr C; Pres, FHA; NHS; Span C; Var C; FHA Qn.

WILLIAMS, Susan Elaine
Glendale HS; Springfield, MO (7-411) AFS; Anchor C; Ger C; NMS; Regent Schol; Pres, TYM; SW Mo St U.

WILLIAMS, Susan Ellen
Lumberton Sr HS; Lumberton, NC (2-400) S-T, Lat C; Pres, Church Yth; Vlbl; Col Bowl.

WILLIAMS, Susan Frances
Dan River HS; Ringgold, VA (5-238) Ed, Ann; BC; Lit Mag; Span C; SC; Tri-HiY; Bkbl; Chem A; Hon Prog; William & Mary Col.

WILLIAMS, Susan Kay
Gilmer Co HS; Glenville, WV (8-94) Band; Chldr; Drama; 4H; Secy, NHS; Sch P; Secy, SC; Var C; Secy, Sr Cl; Secy, Jr Cl; Secy, Soph Cl; Bkbl; Tr; Type A; Yth Fel; Fairmont St Col.

WILLIAMS, Susan Kay
Russell HS; Russell, KY; BC; Chor; Drama; GS; Madrigal; Model UN; Tri-HiY; HQn; Prom Court.

WILLIAMS, Tamberlin Jean
Washington HS; Washington, NC (20%-350) Parl, Drama; Span C; Sftbl; Drama A; Oral Roberts U; Yth Ministry.

WILLIAMS, Tammi Gae
N Denver HS; Denver, CO (45-433) Chor; NHS; JA A; Pres A; Awana C A; Metropolitan St Col; Commercial Art.

WILLIAMS, Tammy Sue
Shawnee Mission S HS; Overland Park, KS; Ensm; Type A; Johnson Co Comm Col; Bus.

WILLIAMS, Teresa Elaine
Booker T Washington Sr HS; Tulsa, OK (25%-309) Ensm; Fr C; Hmrm; Ntl Yth Conf; Bkbl; COM; Citz A; Hist A; Hon Prog; Masonic A; Math A; Phys Fitness, Secy of St, A's; Bkbl Ltr, Ldrship, A's; Loma Linda U; Med.

WILLIAMS, Teresa Francine
T Wingate Andrews HS; High Point, NC (123-327) Span C; Essay A; Biol.

WILLIAMS, Teresa Lynn
Rocky Mt Sr HS; Rocky Mount, NC (21-553) JV, Chldr; Fr C; French NHS; NHS; Ballet A; HR; Piano As; U of NC.

WILLIAMS, Terri Lee
New London-Spicer HS; New London, MN (40-97) Chor; Ensm; FHA; Madrigal; Rptr, Sch P; N Central BC Col; Mus.

WILLIAMS, Terry Wayne
A H Parker HS; Birmingham, AL; Fla A&M U; Elec.

WILLIAMS, Theresa Maria
The Mary Inst; St Louis, MO (10-60) Chor; Cum Laude Soc; COM; Math A; Ntl Achv Schol; Playworkers; Pres, Lib C; Stanford U; Chem.

WILLIAMS, Timmy Owen
Isabella HS; Maplesville, AL (2-25) Co-Ed, Ann; Pres, BC; BS; Drama; Pres, 4H; Ed, Sch P; Var C; MVP, Bsbl; Cpt, Bkbl; Cpt, Ftbl; Semi-Fin, Tr; Amer Leg A; COM; 4H A; Kiwanis A; Lion A; NEDT; Sal; Spch A; Star Student; Yth Fel; U of Montevallo; Bus.

WILLIAMS, Timothy Earl
Smith HS; Atlanta, GA (1-293) Band; Hmrm; Orch; Tres, SC; Cr-Ctry; Cpt, Tnns; Gov Honor Prog; Math A; ROTC A; Sci A; Wood Tech No 1; Computer Engr.

WILLIAMS, Timothy Kevin
Shaker Heights HS; Shaker Heights, OH (30-515) Ger C; Ntl Achv Schol; NMF; Note A; Greek Stu A; Ger A; Northwestern U; Pre-Med.

WILLIAMS, Tony Dwayne
Kensington HS; Buffalo, NY; Chor; Bkbl; Tnns; Chamber of Comm A; Ntl Achv Schol; ROTC A; Morehouse Col; Marketing Research.

WILLIAMS, Tony K
Berkeley HS; Berkeley, CA; Band; JV, Ftbl; JV, Tr; Wrest; Mus, Outst Mus, A's; UCLA; Audio Engr.

WILLIAMS, Tracy Ann
Amador HS; Pleasanton, CA (2-400) Band; Pres, CYO; Chldr; Pres, Chor; Pres, Ensm; Sci C; Bkbl; Sftbl; Citz A; Sci A; Yth Leg; GSct; Chabot Col; Oceanography.

WILLIAMS, Trinna Lou
Buckeye Valley HS; Delaware, OH; A Cap Choir; Ann; Band; Chldr; Fr C; A-Ed, Sch P; Var C; S-T, Soph Cl; JV, Bkbl; Tr.

WILLIAMS, Vanessa
C E Byrd HS; Shreveport, LA; Band; Chor; Drama; FTA; 4H; Hmrm; Sch P; VP, SC; Var C; Cpt, Bkbl; Cpt, Sftbl; Cpt, Swim; Tr; Bkbl Ltr; Swim A; Phys Ed A; Band A; Miss St U; Phys Ed.

WILLIAMS, Vanessa Annette
Glenn HS; Birmingham, AL; S-T, FBLA; Sci C; HR.

WILLIAMS, Velda Denise
Eastwood HS; El Paso, TX; SC; Eastwood in Elegance Court; Nurs.

WILLIAMS, Veralisa Ann
Callaway HS; Jackson, MS; Chor; Bkbl; Vlbl; BTU; Pres, YWA; Delta St Col; Food Service.

WILLIAMS, Vernadine
Fortier HS; New Orleans, LA (8-280) NHS; Orch; Pres, Sr Cl; Dillard U; Acct.

WILLIAMS, Vickey Lorene
Alexander HS; Starkville, MS (10-59) Chor; Y-Tns; Tres, Soph Cl; Hon Prog; Miss Alexander; Miss St U; Social Work.

WILLIAMS, Vickie Gail
Atwood HS; Atwood, TN (5-26) Arch; BC; FHA; 4H; Hmrm; Sci C; SC; Arch; Cl Fav; 4H A; Hist A; Spch A; Principal's A; Eng A; Med.

WILLIAMS, Victoria Lynn
The Hockaday Sch; Dallas, TX (25%-95) Fin, AFS; Ann; Drama; Fr C; French NHS; Lat C; Lat NHS; Lit Mag; Math C; Mu Alpha Theta; A-Ed, Sch P; Thes; Sftbl; Hon Prog; S-T, Photography C; VP, Church Yth Group; Interntl C; Mgr, Vlbl; Cornell U; Archeology.

WILLIAMS, Victoria Regina
Sidney Lanier HS; Montgomery, AL (230-438) Chldr; Drama; Hmrm; Span C; Tri-HiY; Cl Fav; HCt; Most Outst Chldr; U of Ala; Pre-Sch.

WILLIAMS, Viola Ellease
John Muir HS; Pasadena, CA (132-527) Fin, Chldr; Chor; Ensm; Hmrm; SC; CSF; U of Calif; Law.

WILLIAMS, Walter Lewis
John F Kennedy HS; Denver, CO (10-600) Band; Chor; Tres, Jr Cl; Citz A; Hon Prog; JA A; Math A; Sci A; Yth Fel; VP, JA; Handbell Choir; Denver U; Bio.

WILLIAMS, Wanda Jean
W Craven HS; Vanceboro, NC; BC; Chldr; Hmrm; Secy, Span C; SC; Mgr, Bkbl; COM; Co- cpt, Bkbl; E Carolina Col; Bus.

WILLIAMS, Wayne Edward
Union HS; Union, NJ; Alg A.

WILLIAMS, Wayne Rene
Rocky Mount Sr HS; Rocky Mount, NC (95-700) Band; Chor; Pres, Hmrm; Hampton Inst; Pol Sci.

WILLIAMS, William Benson
Wichita N HS; Wichita, KS (20%-485) Drama; Fr C; Math C; Pres, Sr Cl; JV, Bkbl; Ftbl; Golf; Pres, Med Careers C; MYF; St Yth Ch, March of Dimes; Sch Plays; Wichita St Col; Med.

WILLIAMS, William Dean
Clyde A Erwin HS; Asheville, NC (100-300) FFA; Bkbl; Ftbl.

WILLIAMS, William Edward
North HS; Phoenix, AZ (20%-1500) Band; Spch C; Spch A; Northern Ariz U; Engr.

WILLIAMS, Wilma Fryn
Fairfield HS; Fairfield, CA; Band; Chor; Sch P; Tr; Citz A; Most Outst; Type A; Band A; Tr A; Trackett A.

WILLIAMS, Yvonnee Denisa
Darby Township HS; Sharon Hill, PA (35-165) Bus C; Chor; Drama; Math C.

WILLIAMSON, Alice Kay
Goddard HS; Roswell, NM (31-310) Ann; Chor; Secy, Fr C; Hmrm; Sch P; Ski C; SC; Tres, Sr Cl; Ftbl; Beauty; COM; Cl Fav; Mistletoe Jr Princess; Tex Tech U; Fashion Merchandising.

WILLIAMSON, Anne Elizabeth
John F Kennedy Sr HS; New Orleans, LA (7-368) Band; Co-Ch, FBLA; Hmrm; Lit Ral; Mu Alpha Theta; NHS; ARC; F-Ed, Sch P; COM; DARGCA; Hon Prog; Journ A; Q&S A; Tres, Future Mus Ldrs of Amer; FBLA 1st Pl Dist Meet, Acct I; U of New Orleans; Acct.

WILLIAMSON, Barbara
Fayette-Ware N HS; Somerville, TN (10-315) BC; Secy, FHA; 4H; Hmrm; SC; Eng A; Fayette-Ware Vo-tech Facility; Bus.

WILLIAMSON, Clark Eugene
Crestview HS; Crestview, FL; Troy U; Bus.

WILLIAMSON, Cynthia Ann
Springfield HS; Springfield, OR; Rptr, Ann; Dbte Tm; Ch, Ger C; NHS; Ed, Sch P; Spch C; Cpt, Bkbl; Sftbl; Tr; Hon Prog; Journ A; Most Outst; Spch A; VofDEM; Cpt, MVP, Vlbl; Oreg Col of Ed; Secondary Ed.

WILLIAMSON, Dana Lynn
Cherry Creek HS; Englewood, CO; Chor; Ski C; Symp Debs; Industrial Arts A; Math A; Becon Center Vol; Law.

WILLIAMSON, David Alan
Celina Sr HS; Celina, OH (31-275) Bus C; Chor; FBLA; FTA; Lat C; VP, NHS; Rptr, Sch P; Tres, SC; Bsbl; Mgr, Ftbl; Wrest; COM; 2nd St, Mr FBLA; 2nd Dist, Acct; Drake U; Acct.

WILLIAMSON, Dawn Beth
Santa Teresa HS; San Jose, CA (13-472) CSF; Magna Cum Laude; U Ca Santa Cruz.

WILLIAMSON, Deborah Ann
Crescent HS; Starr, SC; Band; Block 'C' C.

WILLIAMSON, Debra Ruth
Roy J Wasson HS; Colorado Springs, CO (73-548) Bus C; Drama; Parl, FBLA; NHS; John Brown U; General Clerical.

WILLIAMSON, Diane Julie
E B Erwin HS; Birmingham, AL (6-320) Band; Ger C; NHS; Citz A; Hon Prog; U of Ala; Nurs.

WILLIAMSON, Donna Antoinette
Westside HS; Anderson, SC (25-305) Tres, Bus C; NHS; WW; Church Yth Choir; Sun Sch Teacher; Yth Girl o-t Yr; Tri-Co Tech Sch; Secy Sci.

WILLIAMSON, Douglas Lanier
Columbia HS; W Columbia, TX; Parl, AFS; Chem C; Chor; Parl, Drama; SC; Parl, Thes; Var C; Pres, Jr Cl; Bsbl; Ftbl; Stephen F Austin Col; Communications.

WILLIAMSON, Edward Secord
Lee's Summit Sr HS; Lee's Summit, MO; Chor; 4H; Bkbl; JV, Cr-Ctry; Golf; Hockey; Soccer; Eckerd Col; Psych.

WILLIAMSON, Evelyn Jeanette
James B Dudley Sr HS; Greensboro, NC; Band; Bus C; Ensm; FBLA; Thes; COM; Hon Prog; JA A; Dance A; U of NC; Med.

WILLIAMSON, George Taylor Brodnax
The Webb Sch; Bell Buckle, TN (8-42) F-Ed, Ann; BC; Dbte Tm; Drama; InterAct C; Lit Mag; Sch P; Spch C; Pres, SC; Co-Cpt, Ftbl; Hist A; Magna Cum Laude; Summa Cum Laude; Pres, Hon Coun; Eng.

WILLIAMSON, James Leon
Brookville HS; Brookville, OH (16-130) Band; Bus C; NHS; Orch; Order/ Arrow; Var C; Sftbl; Co-Cpt, Wrest; Most Outst; Order/ Arrow A; Yth Fel; WW; Eagle Sct; Wright St U; Computer Sci.

WILLIAMSON, Jeffrey White
Towering Oaks Baptist Sch; Memphis, TN (20%-95) Key C; JV, Bkbl; Cr-Ctry; Tr; U of Tenn; Sci.

WILLIAMSON, Karen Anne
Spring Woods Sr HS; Houston, TX; JETS; Lat C; Math C; Mu Alpha Theta; Chem A; JA A; Treas, JA; Mgr, Vlbl; Rice U; Engr.

WILLIAMSON, Kelly Gene
Stamps HS; Stamps, AR (3-100) BS; Rptr, Mu Alpha Theta; NHS; SC; Amer Leg A; Trade & Industry A; *Camden Tech Col; Aviation Maintenance.*

WILLIAMSON, Keva Sue
Scott Comm HS; Scott City, KS (19-120) Band; Chldr; Ensm; Var C; JV, Bkbl; Golf; Sftbl; JV, Tr; Type A; Yth Fel; Golf, Band, Chldr, A's; *U of Kans; Occupational Therapy.*

WILLIAMSON, Leila Christine
N Forrest Attendance Center; Hattiesburg, MS (5-53) Band; Rptr, BC; JV, Chldr; Sch P; Pres, Y-Tns; Sftbl; Beauty; *Nurs.*

WILLIAMSON, Leslie Roseanna
Central Private HS; Baker, LA; Chor; Crown & Scepter; Rptr, Sch P; Sci C; Cpt, Bkbl; Sftbl; Fin, Tr; COM; Citz A; Cl Fav; Coun of Teach A; MVP, Bkbl; *Phys Ed.*

WILLIAMSON, Mary Carol
Redwood HS; Visalia, CA (10%-450) AFS; Band; S-T, FHA; Ger C; Hon Prog; Kiwanis A; *Ark Col; Bus Math.*

WILLIAMSON, Maryjo Donnell
Burbank HS; Burbank, CA; A Cap Choir; Chor; Drama; Madrigal; SC; Sftbl; Yth Fel; Yth Leg; *Calif Arts Col; Fine Arts.*

WILLIAMSON, Melissa Ann
Bellaire Sr HS; Bellaire, TX; A Cap Choir; FFA; Mgr, Tr; COM; Acteen Service Aide; Head Trnr, Vlbl; Chapter Farmer, FFA; *Stephen F Austin St U; Agr-Bus.*

WILLIAMSON, Melissa Anne
Nanih Waiya HS; Louisville, MS (3-33) Pres, BC; FHA; Ed, Sch P; Pres, Sr Cl; Cpt, Bkbl; Star Student; *Miss St U; Vet Sci.*

WILLIAMSON, Pamela Joyce
McCluer N HS; Florissant, MO (198-764) Nom, NHS.

WILLIAMSON, Patricia Ann
Westford Acad; Westford, MA (12-204) Fin, GS; Pres, Lat C; VP, NHS; *Middlesex Comm Col; Dental Hygiene.*

WILLIAMSON, Retha June
N Forrest HS; Hattiesburg, MS; Band; Pres, Y-Tns; Bkbl; Sftbl; Ntl Federation of Mus C Hon.

WILLIAMSON, Rick Eugene
N Union HS; Richwood, OH (24-127) Band; Lat C; Ed, Lit Mag; Sch Achieve Tm; Alg A; Yth Fel; *Tenn Temple Col; Bible.*

WILLIAMSON, Robert Wheeler
Pineville HS; Pineville, LA (102-230) Key C; Bsbl; Bkbl; Ftbl; Sftbl; Tr; Bsbl, Bkbl, Ftbl, Sftbl, Tr, Trnr; Royal Ambassador o-t Yr; AN Star Trnr; WW.

WILLIAMSON, Russell Gordon
Towering Oaks Baptist Sch; Memphis, TN (10%-70) Pres, Hmrm; VP, NHS; Order/Arrow; Pres, Sci C; SC; Bsbl; Bkbl; Cr-Ctry; Mgr, Ftbl; Tnns; Tr; Wrest; Alg A; Amer Leg A; Bio A; COM; Math A; MLS; Order/Arrow A; Sci A; Yth Fel; Lions C Outst Achv A; Drivers Ed Hon A; Industrial Arts Cert of A; Cert of A, W Tenn Ind Arts Assn; *Christian Brothers Col; Engr.*

WILLIAMSON, Stephen Wayne
Sanford Acad; Sanford, MS; Ann; BC; Chor; Pres, Hmrm; Sch P; Pres, Sr Cl; VP, Jr Cl; Bkbl; Ftbl; Sftbl; H of F; MLS.

WILLIAMSON, Susan Bringle
Covington HS; Covington, TN; Tn C; Lib C; Acappella Choir; Chor; *Sweet Briar Col; Interior Design.*

WILLIAMSON, Tabitha Layne
Jackson HS; Jackson, GA (1-152) Chldr; FHA; 4H; HiY; Parl, Tri-HiY; Bkbl; Tr; HCt; Sr Superlative, Best Personality; *Macon Jr Col; Social Work.*

WILLIAMSON, Ted Secord
Lee's Summit Sr HS; Lee's Summit, MO; Chor; 4H; Ntl Yth Conf; SC; JV, Bkbl; JV, Cr-Ctry; Golf; JV, Hockey; Pres, Yth of Unity; *Eckerd Col; Psych.*

WILLIAMSON, Teresa Fay
New Hanover HS; Wilmington, NC (39-537) Ed, Ann; Chor; Ensm; Hmrm; Madrigal; NHS; Q&S A; Yth Fel; *Computer Sci.*

WILLIAMSON, Valerie Jean
Redlands Sr HS; Redlands, CA (7-778) Ch, Band; Fr C; Ch, Orch; CSF; Math A; Secy, Assisteens; Kimberly Jr's; Mus Tchr's Assn of Calif A; 1st Cl GSct; Co Hon Band; Summer Mus Clinic Schol; *Math.*

WILLIAMSON, Wendy Lee
Destrehan HS; Destrehan, LA; Co-Ed, Ann; Pres, Drama; Fr C; FTA; Pres, SC; Pres, Soph Cl; *Theater Arts.*

WILLIAN, Deborah Jean
Pacific Christian HS; Los Angeles, CA (10-45) A Cap Choir; Drama; Ensm; Hmrm; Orch; Rptr, Sch P; SC; Var C; Bkbl; Sftbl; Service, Perfect Merit, A's; *Biola Col; Nurs.*

WILLIFORD, Angela Denise
Portal HS; Portal, GA (4-43) Ann; Bus C; Chor; FBLA; Tres, FHA; 4H; Hmrm; Sch P; Pres, SC; Alg A; DARGCA; 4H A; Hist A; Math A; *Ga Sou Col; Phys Therapy.*

WILLIMON, Lori Ann
Wren HS; Piedmont, SC (10-180) Chldr; Chor; Ensm; Fr C; *Furman Col; Mus.*

WILLIS, Carol Ann
Ritenour Sr HS; Overland, MO (65-904) A Cap Choir; Tr; Ringwald A; Top Ten A; *Nurs.*

WILLIS, Cynthia
Ritenour Sr HS; Overland, MO (8-889) NHS; Tr; Citz A; Hon Prog; JA A; Ringwalk A; *Med.*

WILLIS, David Vincent
Ithaca HS; Ithaca, WI; FFA; Pres, 4H; JV, Bsbl; JV, Ftbl; 4H A; *U of Wis; Agr.*

WILLIS, Donna Denise
Phineas Banning HS; Wilmington, CA; FBLA; *CSULB; Bus.*

WILLIS, Dorothy Ray
Burkeville HS; Burkeville, TX (3-36) Chor; FHA; SC; Tnns; *UCLA; Psych.*

WILLIS, Gina Maria
Live Oak HS; Morgan Hill, CA (100-550) AFS; FBLA; Rainbow; Candystriper; *Calif Baptist Col; Sociology.*

WILLIS, Gregg Allen
Mooreville HS; Mooreville, MS (3%-82) Band; Pres, BC; FFA; FTA; VP, Hmrm; SC; VP, Soph Cl; Ftbl; Hist A; Highest Acad A; Greenhand A, FFA; *U of Miss; Med.*

WILLIS, Jeffrey Collins
Marysville-Pilchuck HS; Marysville, WA; Ed, Ann; Band; Chor; Ensm; Key C; NHS; Sch Achieve Tm; Ed, Sch P; Jr Chamber of Com A; *Everett Comm Col; Art.*

WILLIS, Jody Allan
Crestview Sr HS; Crestview, FL (45-260) Var C; MVP, Bsbl; MVP, Ftbl; COM; Most Out; Pres A; Yth Fel; Schol Merit A; *Fla St U; Phys Ed.*

WILLIS, Joseph Velau
Sooner HS; Bartlesville, OK (11-280) AFS; Band; Chor; Drama; NHS; Co-Cpt, Soccer; JV, Tnns; Elk A.

WILLIS, Kathy Ellen
Clay Co HS; Ashland, AL (5-57) Bus Mgr, Ann; BC; Chldr; Chor; Dbte Tm; FHA; NHS; Pres, Jr Cl; Cl Fav; Phi Theta Kappa; Outst Stu A; *Sou Union St U; Nurs.*

WILLIS, Kim Renee
Provine HS; Jackson, MS; Ann; Lit Mag; NHS; *Hinds Jr Col; X-Ray Tech.*

WILLIS, Leaslee Anne
Robert H Goddard HS; Roswell, NM (9-310) Chldr; NHS; Sci C; SC; Tr; Hon Prog; Silver Bell A; *NMSU; Elem Ed.*

WILLIS, Linda Denise
Sterling HS; Sterling, KS (7-50) Band; Chor; Drama; Ensm; Fr C; Spch A; St Scholar; *Wichita St U; Mus.*

WILLIS, Mary Lu
Walla Walla HS; Walla Walla, WA (20%-455) Pres, Drama; FHA; Hmrm; Most Out; Tres, Theta Rho Assem; Narcissa Rebekah Lodge; *NW Nazarene Col; Social Work.*

WILLIS, Melvin Douglas
Hayti HS; Hayti, MO (7-83) Chor; Math C; NHS; Span C; Pres, SC; Pres, Thes; Pres, Sr Cl; Bkbl; Mgr, Ftbl; Tr; Hist A; Math A; Type A; Drama A; Best All Around; *U of Mo; Engr.*

WILLIS, Mila Laine
E Carteret HS; Beaufort, NC (10%-250) Chldr; GS; Hmrm; Monogram; NHS; Tr; Phys Ed A; Home Ec A; Eng Cert; *E Carolina U; Bus.*

WILLIS, Miriam Michelle
Chester HS; Chester, PA; Ed, Ann; Chor; NHS; Amer Leg A; Hon Prog; *Pa St U; Nurs.*

WILLIS, Netta Renae
E Carteret HS; Beaufort, NC; Ann; Bus C; Chldr; Chor; Drama; FBLA; FHA; FNA; 4H; Hmrm; SC; Tres, Jr Cl; Bkbl; Hockey; Soccer; Sftbl; Tr; Cl Fav; HCt; Hon Prog; Most Out; Spch A; Eng A; Cert, Sem; Pres, Laurel C; Pres, APYW Activity Night; *Bus.*

WILLIS, Patricia Gay
Montpelier HS; Montpelier, OH (25-75) Band; Mjrte; Rainbow; Swim; Vlbl; *Cosmetology.*

WILLIS, Paul Andrew
Abilene HS; Abilene, TX (50-500) A Cap Choir; Ensm; Pres, Hmrm; NHS; SC; Hon Prog; UIL Solo As; UIL Ensm; UIL St Solo; All-Area, All-Reg & Zone Choirs; *Abilene Christian U; Bio.*

WILLIS, Paula Denise
Stone Mountain HS; Stone Mountain, GA; Chor; FTA; Madrigal; *Mercer Col; Mus.*

WILLIS, Rod Stephen
Tulare Union HS; Tulare, CA (20-350) Co-Cpt, Wrest; Pres A; Art A; Wrest Medals; HR; *Col of Sequoias; Bus.*

WILLIS, Rosalyn Lovett
Green B Trimble Tech HS; Fort Worth, TX; Chor; FHA; VP, Soph Cl; Citz A; Cl Fav; Hon Prog; Poet A; ROTC A; ESSA Advisery Committee; Comm C'S; Stu Film Fest, Spell Bee, A's; *Oral Roberts U; Psych.*

WILLIS, Saundra Renee
Mooreville HS; Mooreville, MS; BC; FHA; FTA; Ntl Teachers Coun; SC; Pres, Var C; Y-Tns; MVP, Bkbl; Sftbl; Swim; MVP, Tr; Bio A; Cl Fav; 4H A; Hist A; *Miss St Col; Med.*

WILLIS, Sharon Beth
Normandy Sr HS; St Louis, MO (52-565) Chor; Citz A; *SW Baptist Col; Phys Therapy.*

WILLIS, Sharon Jill
York Acad; Shacklefords, VA (2-45) BC; Chldr; VP, Lat C; VP, SC.

WILLIS, Sharon Marie
Hayti HS; Hayti, MO; Chor; NHS; Secy, Span C; Hist A; Mus, Span, Lib, A's.

WILLIS, Shelia Renee
Shaw HS; E Cleveland, OH; Bus C; COM; Citz A; Hon Prog; Sci A; Art A; *U of Sou Calif; Court Rptr.*

WILLIS, Tamara Jean
Boyd HS; Boyd, TX (20-80) Ann; Band; Chldr; VP, FHA; VP, 4H; Hmrm; Semi-Fin, Jr Miss Pa; JV, tBkbl; Tr; Beauty; Swtht; *Homemaking.*

WILLIS, Ted Scott
Amarillo HS; Amarillo, TX (5-720) VP, Lat C; Lat NHS; NHS; Sci C; JV, Tnns; Tex Nuclear Sci Symp; *Tex A&M U; Chem.*

WILLIS, Teri Raleighn
Marysville-Pilchuck HS; Marysville, WA; Ann; Chor; Sch P; Span C.

WILLIS, Theresa Jean
Grove City HS; Grove City, OH; Chor; Jr Miss Pagent; Cpt, Tr; *Wittenberg Col.*

WILLIS, Thomas Stephen
Amite HS; Amite, LA (2-150) Rptr, Key C; Fin, Lit Ral; Alg A; NMF; *LSU; Computer Sci.*

WILLIS, Timothy Mark
Abilene HS; Abilene, TX (5-500) VP, A Cap Choir; Chldr; VP, Math C; VP, NHS; VP, Sci C; Bsbl; Exchange Sports A; Hugh O'Brien Ldrship A; *Abilene Christian U; Bible.*

WILLIS, Tommy Bernard
Bethel Christian Sch; Ruston, LA (10%-18) Lit Ral; Bsbl; JV, Bkbl; PA; *La Tech U; Bus Mgr.*

WILLIS, Traci Lynette
Central Union HS; El Centro, CA (200-340) Band; Chldr; Chor; Sftbl; Tr; *Imperial Valley Col; Bus.*

WILLISON, Jana Kay
Castleberry HS; Fort Worth, TX (10%-290) Chor; NHS; ARC; JV Vlbl; *Bethany Nazarene Col; Mus.*

WILLITS, Marty Dean
Northbrook Sr HS; Houston, TX; Bkbl; Fin, Tr; *Houston Baptist U; Religion.*

WILLMAN, Laura Kay
Apollo HS; Simi Valley, CA (4-90) Secy, Ann; Bus C; Chess C; Drama; FTA; VP, Ger C; Hmrm; A-Ed, Sch P; Spch C; SC; Var C; Coun of Teach A; Elk A; Hon Prog; MLS; Spch A; Type A; Yth Fel; Gym; *Moorpark Col; Ed.*

WILLMAN, Mindy Lee
R L Turner HS; Carrollton, TX (228-727) Band; Rptr, Hmrm; SC; Mascot; *Tex Col; Med.*

WILLOUGHBY, Brenda Lee
Farmville Central HS; Farmville, NC (102-195) FHA; Pol Sci C; Sci C; Yth Fel; PA A; *Bus.*

WILLOUGHBY, Deborah Mae
Bertie Sr HS; Windsor, NC (5-340) Pres, BC; Drama; FHA; COM; Gr Marshal; Hon Prog; *Bus.*

WILLOUGHBY, Mark Thomas
Fairdale HS; Fairdale, KY (10%-350) Fr C; Hmrm; Ftbl.

WILLOUGHBY,
Morton Edward
Dewey HS; Dewey, OK (25-100) Bsbl; Bkbl; Cpt, Ftbl; Tr; HCt; Type A; *Okla St U; Acct.*

WILLS, Barry Edward
Bellwood Antis HS; Bellwood, PA (9-113) Ann; Band; Chor; NHS; Alg A; Hist A; Math A; NMS; Sci A; Band A; *Washington Bible Col; Religion.*

WILLS, Deborah Lorraine
Haywood HS; Brownsville, TN; FHA; Sci C; Spch A; *U Tenn; Elem Ed.*

WILLS, Denise Jean
Fairmont HS; Fairmont, MN (80-199) Cpt, Chldr; Chor; FHA; ARC; Parl, Health C; Hon Qn, Job's Daughters; Nurse Aide; Skills Olympics; *Augustana Col; Nurs.*

WILLS, Garry Laurence
Loyola HS; Baltimore, MD (1-180) Lat C; Bsbl; Bkbl; Tnns; NEDT.

WILLS, Meredith Louise
Harpeth Hall Sch; Nashville, TN (60-85) AFS; Chor; Hon Prog; UMYF; Sch Plays, Musicals; Glee C; Coun On Yth Ministries; Triad C; Yth Rep, Commission On Worship; Mountain TOP; Arch Intramurals; *Math.*

WILLSON, Joel Ray
Denham Springs HS; Denham Springs, LA (10-300) VP, Key C; VP, NHS; Pres, Soph Cl; Bkbl; Ftbl; Cl Fav; WW; St Most Outst Male Ar Stu; *Baylor Univ; Architecture.*

WILMES, Audrey Marie
Penns Manor HS; Clymer, PA (16-106) Ed, Ann; VP, Chldr; Chor; FTA; Hmrm; NHS; Pres, Soph Cl; HCt; Yth Fel; Cl Brownie; Spkr, FFA Banquet; *Ind U; Psych.*

WILMORE, Jacquelynne Renee
Overbrook HS; Philadelphia, PA; Orch; *Med.*

WILMOTH, Renaldo Buswart
Northeastern Acad; New York, NY (12-34) Ann; Bus C; Chem C; Chor; Cpt, Bkbl; Tr; Cpt, Gym; *Oakwood Col; Drafting.*

WILRIDGE, Darla Fay
Rayne HS; Rayne, LA (65-106) A Cap Choir; Band; Chor; 4H; Key C; Bsbl; Bkbl; Tr; Lib A; *Grambling St U; Mus.*

WILSDORF, Patricia Kay
Madison C-3 HS; Madison, MO (1-29) Ed, Ann; Pres, BC; Secy, FHA; Pres, 4H; Key C; Ed, Sch P; SC; Secy, Var C; Secy, Sr Cl; Secy, Soph Cl; Sftbl; Alg A; Amer Leg A; B Crocker A; 4H A; Hist A; HCt; Math A; NMS; Type A; Cpt, Schol Quiz Tm; *Northeast Mo St U; Home Ec.*

WILSIE, John Thomas
Tecumseh HS; Tecumseh, OK (8-103) FTA; NHS; Pres, Sr Cl; MVP, Bsbl; Cpt, Bkbl; Cpt, Ftbl; Pres, FCA; Outst Boy Athlete; All Co Bkbl; Co All Star Bsbl; Player o-t Yr, Ftbl; *Okla St U; Bus Adm.*

WILSON, Alisa Renee
Chastain Jr HS; Jackson, MS (10%-280) Hmrm; SC; Cl Fav; HR; *Fisk U; Med.*

WILSON, Amy Jobes
Cumberland Valley HS; Mechanicsburg, PA (23-585) Band; Secy, Chor; Ch, 4H; NHS; Pres, Orch; Pres, Span C; Hon Prog; NEDT; *U of Vt.*

WILSON, Amy Susan
Mena HS; Mena, AR (24-134) Band; FHA; Rptr, Sch P; Sci C; COM; *Med Career.*

WILSON, Anita Ann
Montrose Hill-McCloy HS; Montrose, MI (33%-170) Band; Chldr; Hmrm; Colorguard; Tres, Christ Ambassadors; *Social Work.*

WILSON, Ann Marie
Kewanna HS; Kewanna, IN (2-20) Band; Chor; Fr C; Pres, 4H; Tres, Soph Cl; JV, Bkbl; 4H A; Outst Underclassman, Band; *Med.*

WILSON, Antoinette Daphaine
C E Byrd HS; Shreveport, LA; *Southern U; Elem Ed.*

WILSON, Arianne
St Joesph Acad; New Orleans, LA; Band; Chor; Drama; MVP, Bsbl; MVP, Sftbl; MVP, Swim; Tr; Band, Service, A's; *Xavier U; Phar.*

WILSON, Audre Leigh
Fairhope HS; Fairhope, AL (11-305) Chor; Ensm; Tres, Hmrm; NHS; ARC; DARGCA; Opt Out Tn; Yth Fel; Outst Service A; All St Chor; Pres, UMYF; S-T, Girl's Service C; *Auburn U; Pre-Sch Ed.*

WILSON, Barbara Jean
Glenbrook S HS; Glenview, IL (457-626) Chor; Alg A; *Lincoln Col; Early Childhood Ed.*

WILSON, Baron M
Bishop M Wilson HS; Harrisburg, PA (5-379) Marine Corp Fitness Test A; *Va St U; Bus Adm.*

WILSON, Beth Dawn
N Harford HS; Pylesville, MD; AFS; Ger C; S-T, Mjrte; Rptr, Sch P; Job's Daughters; *U of Md; Phys Therapy.*

WILSON, Beth Lori
Sandy Valley HS; Magnolia, OH (30-160) A Cap Choir; Band; Chor; Fin, GS; NHS; Ski C; Tr; Amer Leg A; COM; HCt; Interlochen Ntl Mus; Yth Fel; *Mus.*

WILSON, Blair Anthony
Simon Gratz HS; Philadelphia, PA (21-450) FTA; Hmrm; InterAct C; Sci C; Var C; Ftbl; *Drexel U; Bus Adm.*

WILSON, Bonnie Denise
Miami Killian Sr HS; Miami, FL (75%-1140) *Morehouse Col; Tech Engr.*

WILSON, Bonnie Sue
Oakdale HS; Oakdale, LA (3-146) Tres, Ann; FBLA; NHS; Secy, Sch P; H of F; Hon Prog; Type A; Social Stu C; Fresh & Soph Scholastic Avg As; *Northeast La U; Bus Adm.*

WILSON, Bradley Jay
Culver City HS; Culver City, CA (277-489) Cpt, Swim; Cpt, Water Polo; *Santa Monica City Col; Life Sci.*

WILSON, Brenda Jo
Fike Sr HS; Wilson, NC (10-30) Band; Co-Cpt, Chldr; Fr C; Secy, Hmrm; Cpt, Mjrte; Beauty; HCt; Feature Twirler; *Appalchian St Col; Gym.*

WILSON, Bruce Ray
Clarkston Sr HS; Clarkston, MI (52-507) Span C.

WILSON, Charles Kenneth
St John's HS; Darlington, SC (9-132) BS; Chess C; Drama; Pres, Hmrm; Key C; Pres, NHS; SC; Most Polite; Marshall; *Francis Marion Col; Math.*

WILSON, Charles Thomas Jr
Lord Berkeley Acad; Moncks Corner, SC; Bkbl; WW; *Fish and Wildlife.*

WILSON, Christine Lynn
Oak Hills HS; Cincinnati, OH (105-857) Var C; Bkbl; Sftbl; *Miami of Ohio U; Phys Ed.*

WILSON, Christopher Alan
Notre Dame HS; Sherman Oaks, CA; Demolay; Drama; Key C; VP, Soph Cl; Golf; Chem A; HKg; Sci A; Swtht; Water Polo; 1st, Co Sci Fair; Hon Men, St Fair; *USC; Med.*

WILSON, Christopher Eric
Schenley HS; Pittsburgh, PA; Chor; Up Bound; Bkbl; Ftbl; Sftbl; Swim; Tr; COM; Hon Prog; Most Out; *Pa St U; Archt.*

WILSON, Clarke Christian
Kensington HS; Buffalo, NY; Chor; Ftbl; Tr; *Morehouse Col; Law.*

WILSON, Craig Simpson
Battle Ground Acad; Franklin, TN (12-76) 4H; Key C; Lat C; NHS; Bsbl; Tr; NEDT; *Western Ky U; Agr.*

WILSON, Cynthia Ann
Hillsborough Sr HS; Tampa, FL; Anchor C; Hmrm; Dance A; Piano A; Principal's HR; *U of S Fla; Bus Adm.*

WILSON, Cynthia Gay
Eisenhower Sr HS; Lawton, OK; FHA; NHS; Span C; *Ed.*

WILSON, Cynthia Lynn
Richland HS; Fort Worth, TX (15%-675) Band; Fr C; FHA; NHS; Orch; Hon Prog; Magna Cum Laude; *UT at Arlington; Med Sci.*

WILSON, Cynthia Marie
R L Turner HS; Dallas, TX (77-636) Band; Chldr; Ensm; Hmrm; Bus Mgr, Sch P; Hon Prog; *Harding Col; Nurs.*

WILSON, Daniel Alan
Thomas Jefferson HS; Pittsburgh, PA (1-400) Band; Chor; Drama; Lat C; NHS; Thes; Alg A; Hon Prog; Kiwanis A; Math A; Yth Fel; Interntl Thespians; Church Elder; Tutor; Pres, Handbell Choir; *Chem.*

WILSON, Daniel Jeffrey
Shawnee HS; Lima, OH; Band; Chess C; Demolay; Key C; Lit Mag; NHS; Sch P; JV, Tnns; Hon Prog; Journ A; Math A; Yth Fel; *Ohio St U; Pre-Med.*

WILSON, Daniel Mark
Skyline HS; Oakland, CA (78-700) A Cap Choir; S-T, Band; Chor; Drama; Ger C; Hmrm; Key C; Madrigal; Mod Mus Mas; Co-Ch, Orch; Thes; Pres, Sr Cl; Bkbl; Swim; Tr; Yth Fel; Best Supporting Actor As; Marcus A; Foster Schol *Bishop Col; Ministry.*

WILSON, Dawn
Sky View Baptist Acad; Memphis, TN (10%-113) Co-Ed, Ann; Pres, BC; FTA; Sci C; SC; Commissioner, Stu Actv, Stu Coun; *Memphis St U; Law.*

WILSON, Dawn Renee
Robert E Lee HS; Tyler, TX (94-620) Cpt, Chldr; Chem C; NHS; Span C; Y-Tns; *Tyler Jr Col.*

WILSON, Dean Alan
Griswold HS; Jewett City, CT (38-169) CYO; Bsbl; Bkbl; Cr-Ctry; Sftbl; Tr; Amer Leg A; Sci A; *U of RI; Oceanography.*

WILSON, Debbie Kathleen
Marion Sr HS; Marion, AR (6-103) A Cap Choir; Ann; Chor; FHA; Secy, Math C; NHS; Sch P; Hon Prog; Faithfulness A; Secy, Yth Coun; Sch Off Worker; Vacation Bible Sch Teacher; *St Joseph Hospital; Nurs.*

WILSON, Debbie Kay
Vinson HS; Huntington, WV; Ann; Band; FHA; HiY; Y-Tns; *Marshall Col; Med.*

WILSON, Debra Ann
S Shore HS; Chicago, IL (36-554) Chor; Ensm; COM; Citz A; Hon Prog; *U of Ill; Elem Ed.*

WILSON, Debra Raye
Beebe HS; Beebe, AR (20-92) Ann; BC; Pres, Fr C; VP, FBLA; Math C; Sch P; Bkbl; Tr; VP, FCA; *Ark St U at Beebe; Phys Ed.*

WILSON, Denise Marie
Holmer L Ferguson HS; Newport News, VA (38-497) Ensm; VP, Lat C; Secy, Math C; Mu Alpha Theta; NHS; Sci C; Chem A; WW; *Christopher Newport Col; Sci.*

WILSON, Derma Cantell
Starkville HS; Starkville, MS; Chldr; Chor; FBLA; Sci C; Y-Tns; Alg A; Bio A; *Nurs.*

WILSON, Diana Kaye
Beebe HS; Beebe, AR (9-92) Ann; BC; Fr C; Secy, FBLA; Math C; Sch P; Bkbl; Tr; *Ark St U at Beebe; Phys Ed.*

WILSON, Diane Elizabeth
Nova HS; Ft Lauderdale, FL (25%-460) Chor; City Conf; Drama; Key C; Madrigal; Rptr, Sch P; SC; Beauty; Spch A; Pep C; Jr Hospital Aide; Tn Board; Co-Ch, Prom Comm; Yth Group; Drill Tm; Dance Group; U of Fla; Sociology.

WILSON, Donald Mark
Rosemark Acad; Millington, TN (25-52) Var C; Bsbl; Ftbl; Pol Sci.

WILSON, Donna Lynn
Jeannette HS; Jeannette, PA (18-225) AFS; Band; Fr C; Hmrm; Lat C; NHS; Rainbow; Ski C; SC; Color Guard; Computers.

WILSON, Donny Lee
Hobbs HS; Hobbs, NM (7-400) NHS; JV, Bsbl; Ftbl; Hon Prog; Math & Sci Stu o-t Yr; Hon Graduate; U of NM; Engr.

WILSON, Doris Little
Roanoke Rbsonville, NC (2-175) Ann; BC; Chldr; Fr C; FBLA; Pres, InterClub Coun; Math C; Pres, SC; Alg A; HQn; HCt; Sal; Marshal; Semi-Fin John Motley Morehead Schol; Salem Col; Fashion Merchandising.

WILSON, Dorothy Annette
N Gaston HS; Dallas, NC (20-210) BC; FHA; Hmrm; Secy, InterClub Coun; Span C; Beauty; HQn; HCt; VP, Civinettes; Most Charming; Appalachian St Col; Psych.

WILSON, Dorothy FlaVilla
Central HS; Martinsburg, PA (20%-255) COM; NEDT; Yth Fel; Lib C; Penn St U.

WILSON, Douglas Eugene
Marion HS; Marion, IN (10%-800) Ensm; Model UN; Orch; UN Council; COM; Chem A; Chem.

WILSON, Ernestine Benita
Carol W Hayes HS; Birmingham, AL (2-222) Ann; Chor; Community Yth Symph; Drama; NHS; Orch; SC; Citz A; Hon Prog; Special Ed.

WILSON, Ethel
Simon Gratz HS; Philadelphia, PA (18-450) FTA; JETS; Co-Ch, Jr Miss Pagent; Math C; Model UN; NHS; Bus Mgr, SC; World Affairs C; Math A; Eng Hon A; Plant Identification A; Kirkland-Hamilton Col; Engr.

WILSON, Eugenia Lynn
Powell Valley HS; Speedwell, TN; BC; 4H; Mu Alpha Theta; VP, Tri-HiY; St Mary's Sch of Nurs; Nurs.

WILSON, Felicia Ann
Neal F Simeon HS; Chicago, IL; Sch P; COM; Citz A; Hon Prog; Math A; Bradley U; Data Processing.

WILSON, Frances McKee
Tishomingo HS; Tishomingo, MS (5-33) Bus Mgr, Ann; Band; BC; FHA; Pres, 4H; Cl Fav; WW; NE Miss Jr Col; Drafting & Design Tech.

WILSON, Freddy Bernard
E Atlanta HS; Atlanta, GA (15-142) BC; Chor; Hmrm; NHS; Span C; Cpt, Ftbl; Cpt, Soccer; Cpt, Tnns; Alg A; COM; Hon Prog; Math A; Most Out; ROTC A; Span, Attendance, ROTC, A's; US Air Force Acad; Engr.

WILSON, Gary Don
McNeil HS; McNeil, AR (6-27) GS; Hmrm; Star Student.

WILSON, George
Blair HS; Pasadena, CA; Bkbl; Ftbl; Tr.

WILSON, George Dale
Lafayette High; Lafayette, GA (11-200) Var C; Bsbl; Sftbl; Wrest; Morehouse Col; Yth Director.

WILSON, Greg Stuart
Palisades HS; Pacific Palisades, CA; Math C; Tnns; God & Country A; Oreg St U; Computer Sci.

WILSON, Gregg T
Maumee HS; Maumee, OH; Band; Ski C; Mgr, Bkbl; Swim; Tres, A-V C; Owens Tech Col; Marketing Mgt.

WILSON, Gregory Dean
Tupelo HS; Tupelo, MS (219-438) Bsbl; Ftbl; Yth Fel.

WILSON, Gregory James
Hanna HS; Anderson, SC (10%-400) Chem C; Pres, Chess C; Dbte Tm; Hmrm; Pres, Lat C; Lat NHS; Ed, Sch P; NEDT; Q&S A; ARC A; Anderson Col; Mus.

WILSON, Gregory Roger
Clintonville Sr HS; Clintonville, WI (20%-175) AFS; Band; BS; Math C; NHS; Tres, SC; Var C; JV, Tr; Wrest; Rotary A; Forensics Tm; Eau Claire St U; Pre-Optometry.

WILSON, Gregory Scott
Lodi Unified HS; Lodi, CA (40%-480) Pres, Key C; Ftbl; Co-Cpt, Tr; Delta Comm Col; Bus.

WILSON, Isadore Cassevetts
Saint Peter And Paul HS; Saginaw, MI; Chor; Var C; Bsbl; Bkbl; COM; Citz A; Hon Prog; Math A; Most Out; MVP, Bkbl; Spell A; W Mich U; Math.

WILSON, Isadore Melvin
Hillsbrough HS; Tampa, FL; Band; FHA; FTA; Spch C; Citz A; Interlochen Ntl Mus; Most Out; ARC A; ROTC A; Spch A; Type A; Drum Major; Solo, Bible Sch, A's; Mus.

WILSON, Isaiah
DuSable HS; Chicago, IL (184-300) Bkbl; Ill St U; Bus.

WILSON, Jack Edward
Clark Co R-1 HS; Kahoka, MO (11-92) Tr.

WILSON, James Myron
Bokchito HS; Bokchito, OK; Band; Pres, FFA; 4H; SC; Cl Fav; 4H A; Hon Prog.

WILSON, James Russell
Marist Sch; Atlanta, GA (3-92) Rptr, Hmrm; NHS; S-T, Jr Cl; S-T, Soph Cl; JV, Bkbl; Cpt, Ftbl; Tr; COM; Hon Prog; NEDT; MVP, Ftbl; Dean's List; Ath Schol; Ga Tech; Bio.

WILSON, James Smiley
P S 25 HS; Staten Island, NY; Drama; Math C; Sch Achieve Tm; Sch P; Bsbl; Bkbl; Ftbl; Hockey; Sftbl; Swim; Math A; Type A; Wagner Col; Acct.

WILSON, Janet LaWanda
Piggott HS; Piggott, AR (4-81) Ann; Band; BC; FHA; GS; Math C; S-T, Sci C; H of F; HCt; Math A; MLS; Teenager o-t Wk; WW; Ouachita Baptist U; Acct.

WILSON, Jean Ann
Eastside HS; Greenville, SC; Chor; Ensm; Pres, Hmrm; God & Country A; Yth Fel; Jr NHS; Clemson U.

WILSON, Jeanita Michelle
Westland HS; Galloway, OH (396-576) Spch C; JV, Bkbl; Beauty; Bkbl A; Most Quiet; Merits; Franklin U; Writing.

WILSON, Jeffrey Parker
Lee HS; Huntsville, AL (60-375) Hmrm; Key C; SC; VP, Jr Cl; VP, Soph Cl; Bkbl; Ftbl; Tr; MVP, Wrest; Cl Fav; Auburn U; Law.

WILSON, Jennifer Ann
Estancia HS; Estancia, NM (7-68) Band; Chor; Drama; FHA; Soccer; Spelling, Band, Lit, A's; Legislature Page; E NM U; Elem Ed.

WILSON, Jimmie II
Toulminville HS; Mobile, AL (75-358) Band; Chor; Ensm; NHS; Orch; Span C; Concordia Col; Bio.

WILSON, John Herman
Williamsburg HS; Andrews, SC; U of SC; Engr.

WILSON, Joseph Paul
Tuscumbia R III HS; Tuscumbia, MO (2-27) Ntl Teachers Coun; Pres, Sr Cl; Bsbl; Co-Cpt, Bkbl; Alg A; Hon Prog; Math A; Industrial Arts A; US Marine Corps; Elec.

WILSON, Judy Ann
Warren Central HS; Vicksburg, MS (20-210) AFS; Math C; Mu Alpha Theta; Span C; Span A; WW; Hinds Jr Col; Linguistics.

WILSON, Judy Kay
Center Grove HS; Greenwood, IN; FHA; GS; Model UN; NHS; SC; Yth Fel; Ind Bus Col; Acct.

WILSON, June Alice
San Bernardino HS; San Bernardino, CA; 1st Cl GSct; Most Authentic Bicen Costume; Calif Poly Tech Col; Home Ec.

WILSON, Karen Ann
Joppatowne Jr-Sr HS; Joppa, MD (1-271) Band; Chor; Ensm; Tres, 4H; Secy, Span C; SC; Alg A; 4H A; Spch A; Cpt, Bowl; Eng, Art, Mus, A's; Stu o-t Mo; Eng.

WILSON, Karen Denise
Orangeburg-Wilkinson HS; Orangeburg, SC (3-400) Fr C; Hmrm; Secy, NHS; SC; Cpt, Tnns; COM; Citz A; Hist A; Yth Fel; MVP, Tnns; Lang Arts; Clemson U; Wood Utilization.

WILSON, Karen Gwynn
August Martin HS; Jamaica, NY (3-36) Band; Chor; Citz A; Yth Fel; Arista; Cert of Merit; Soc Stu Cert.

WILSON, Karen Louise
Northgate HS; Walnut Creek, CA (1-450) Band; Lit Mag; Bank of Amer A; CSF; Hon Prog; Pres A; Sacramento St Col; Nurs.

WILSON, Kathy Jean
Rockville Jr-Sr HS; Rockville, IN (50%-83) Chor; Jr Miss Pagent; NHS; Sch P; Sftbl; Tr; Pres A; Yth Foundation; 1st Pl, Singing Solo & Ensm; Ind Central Col; Bus.

WILSON, Kathy Lynn
Uniontown Area Sr HS; Uniontown, PA (3%-510) Band; Fr C; Secy, 4H; Tres, Hmrm; Rainbow; Ski C.

WILSON, Kathy Sue
Breckinridge Co HS; Harned, KY; Band; Pres, Chor; Ensm; FTA; H of F; All St Band; All St Chor; U of Ky; Mus.

WILSON, Kevin Carl
Lincoln HS; E St Louis, IL (11-38) 4H; 4H A; JA A; Shilite Chor; Ill St U; Voice.

WILSON, Kevin R
Clinton Sr HS; Clinton, MO (10-175) 4H A; Elec Engr.

WILSON, Kim Denise
Leland HS; San Jose, CA (64-580) COM; Hon Prog; Square Dancing C; Luther League; Cert of Achv, Soc Stu; Pepperdine U; Fine Arts.

WILSON, Kimberly Kaye
North HS; Wichita, KS; Q&S A; People's Awareness C; Oral Roberts U; Psych.

WILSON, Kristal Renee
A Stockton HS; Fort Stockton, TX; Band; Tex A&M U; Marine Bio.

WILSON, Kyle Steven
Parkersburg HS; Parkersburg, WV; Band; Order/ Arrow; Bsbl; Bkbl; Ftbl; Tr; Wrest; COM; God & Country A; Order/Arrow A; Yth Fel; Eagle Sct; CPR Instructor; Ath Tr, Bsbl, Bkbl, Ftbl, & Wrest; W Va U; Phys Therapy.

WILSON, Larry Joseph
Jacksonville HS; Jacksonville, IL; Bkbl; Ftbl; Tr; Phys Ed.

WILSON, Larry Nelson
Kemper Acad; DeKalb, MS (4-37) Band; BC; Chor; Rptr, SC; Tr; Cl Fav; Meridian Jr Col; Med.

WILSON, Laurie Jo
Alsea HS; Alsea, OR (1-20) Ed, Ann; Chess C; VP, NHS; Rptr, Sch P; Pres, SC; Secy, Soph Cl; Cpt, Bkbl; Tr; Journ A; Math A; Most Out; Val; Cpt, Vlbl; Oreg Col of Ed; Math.

WILSON, Lera Marie
Jupiter Christian Sch; Jupiter, FL (1-18) Ann; Ed, Sch P; Val; Span A.

WILSON, Linda Kay
Flint SW HS; Flint, MI; SC; U of Mich.

WILSON, Lynn Ann
Glenbrook S HS; Glenview, IL (74-611) Chldr; NHS; Y-Tns; HCt; Hon Prog; Sci A; Foreign Lang A; Home Ec.

WILSON, Margaret Elizabeth
Notre Dame HS; Clarksburg, WV; Bus Mgr, Ann; Dbte Tm; FBLA; FTA; GS; Bus Mgr, Lit Mag; NHS; Bus Mgr, Sch P; Secy, Spch C; Bkbl; Swim; Tr; Hist A; Sci A; Spch A; Ariz St U; Hist.

WILSON, Margaret Elizabeth
Franklin Co HS; Frankfort, KY (115-500) BC; Hmrm; Math C; Mu Alpha Theta; Span C; Span NHS; Bkbl; Sftbl; Tr; Alg A; 4H A; Tr Medal; All Star Tm; Bkbl Trophy; Eathenu Ky U; Math.

WILSON, Maria Theresa
Newton Falls HS; Newton Falls, OH (45-197) Band; Chem C; Sch P; Sci C; Span C; Sftbl; Yth Fel; Youngstown U; Mus.

WILSON, Mark James
Bangor Pub HS; Bangor, MI; Band; Chor; Key C; JV, Bsbl; JV, Bkbl; JV, Ftbl; JV, Tr; COM; Hon Prog; PTA A; *Mich St U; Sci.*

WILSON, Mary E
Pinole Valley HS; Pinole, CA (15-457) A Cap Choir; Band; Bus Mgr, Drama; Fr C; Lit Mag; Madrigal; SC; Thes; Tnns; Bank Of Amer A; CSF; Bel Canto Mus A; *Biola Col; Pol Sci.*

WILSON, Mary Ellen
North Community HS; Minneapolis, MN (1-496) *St Mary's Dominican Col; Bus.*

WILSON, Mary Marceline
New Caney HS; Porter, TX (20-225) Chldr; Hmrm; NHS; Rptr, Sch P; VP, SC; Cpt, Bkbl; Beauty; Cl Fav; HCt; Ftbl Swtht; *Angelina Jr Col; Phys Ed.*

WILSON, Matthew Thomas
San Bernardino HS; San Bernardino, Ca (100-456) Chess C; Chor; Key C; Var C; Swim; Tr; COM; Citz A; Kiwanis A; ROTC A; *Howard U; Med.*

WILSON, Mavis Annette
Palos Verdes HS; Palos Verdes Estates, CA (35%-580) Rptr, FHA; Key C; SC; *UC Santa Barbara; Phar.*

WILSON, Melissa Lee
Peachtree HS; Chamblee, GA; BC; Fr C; Math C; NHS; Mgr, Bkbl; Cpt, Cr-Ctry; Tr; Hon Prog; *Hist.*

WILSON, Melody Anne
Lawrence Central HS; Indianapolis, IN; Tri-HiY; Pres, VP, Secy, Church Yth Fel; *Central Col; Home Ec.*

WILSON, Michael Stephen
Medina HS; Medina, TN (3-23) Co-Ed, Ann; BC; Tres, FFA; 4H; Hmrm; Mgr, Var C; Pres, Jr Cl; Mgr, Bkbl; Cl Fav; MLS; Most Out; *Jackson St Comm Col; Acct.*

WILSON, Michael Todd
Rosemark Acad; Millington, TN (1-54) BC; Fr C; SC; Var C; Bsbl; Ftbl; NEDT; Yth Fel; St Math Contest; *Tenn Tech U; Med.*

WILSON, Michael Vernon
Malta Comm HS; Malta, IL (6-30) FFA; Arch; Hockey; Soccer; Swim; Tr; USMC Ntl Yth Phys Fit Cert of Exce; *Kishwaukee Jr Col; Ag Mech.*

WILSON, Miriam Pamela
York Comp HS; York, SC (2-461) Fr C; FTA; COM; 4H A; *Winthrop Col; Bus.*

WILSON, Monica Luann
O D Wyatt HS; Fort Worth, TX (10%-500) Ed, Ann; SC; Type A; People A; Sextet Singing Group; Bible C.

WILSON, Myron Glenn
San Antonio HS Campus S; San Antonio, TX (122-185) Tres, Band; Chor; Ensm; Bio A; Church Choir; Royal Ambassadors; All Dist UIL Band; Bank Bicentennial Band; *Mus Ed.*

WILSON, Nanci Carol
Piggott HS; Piggott, AR (20-88) BC; Fr C; FHA; Hmrm; Sci C; SC; Tr.

WILSON, Nancy Jane
Columbiana HS; Columbiana, OH (14-101) A Cap Choir; Chldr; Fr C; Madrigal; NHS; Tres, SC; Tri-HiY; Ch, Sr Cl; Secy, Jr Cl; Cl Fav; HQn; Pep C; Safe Driver's A; *Grove City Col; Elem Ed.*

WILSON, Odell Wayne
Bowling Green Sr HS; Bowling Green, KY; Band; Chor; 4H; Hmrm; Rptr, Sch P; Mgr, Bkbl; Ftbl; Wrest; 4H A; Hist A; ARC A; *Mass Communication.*

WILSON, Pamela Jo
Prestonsburg HS; Prestonsburg, KY; Band; BC; Chor; Tres, Hmrm; Mjrte; NHS; Mjrte A; *Morehead St U.*

WILSON, Paul Anthony
Tallulah HS; Tallulah, LA; Chor; 4H; NHS; Sch P; SC; Ftbl; Cpt, Tnns; Bio A; 4H A; Hist A; Hon Prog; Math A; Sci A; *NE La U.*

WILSON, Randy Vern
Hobbs HS; Hobbs, NM; A Cap Choir; Chor; Ensm; Bsbl; Sftbl; *Mus.*

WILSON, Raymond
Arsenal Tech HS; Indianapolis, IN; A Cap Choir; Chor; Ensm; Ger C; Pres, Hmrm; Key C; Madrigal; Sch Achieve Tm; Sch P; VP, SC; VP, Jr Cl; COM; Citz A; Cl Fav; Journ A; Kiwanis A; Opt A; *Ball St U; Med.*

WILSON, Rebecca Neile
Trenton HS; Trenton, FL (3-80) Band; Secy, BC; Secy, FBLA; FHA; Tres, Jr Cl; Amer Leg A; NMS; Sci A; Hist A; Math A; Top 5%, Ntl Merit Schol Corp; Outst Stu A; 1st Pl, Dist Acct Contest; *Stetson U; Acct.*

WILSON, Renee Ellen
Suring Pub HS; Suring, WI (1-60) Band; Chor; Drama; FHA; 4H; S-T, NHS; Rptr, Sch P; Pres, Jr Cl; Cl Fav; 4H A; Journ A; Val; *Mus.*

WILSON, Renee R
Wakefield Comm HS; Wakefield, NE (4-55) Chldr; Chor; Ensm; FBLA; 4H; NHS; Tres, Jr Cl; Tr; 4H A; Hon Prog; Star Student; Vlbl; *Northeast Tech Comm Col; Computer Programming.*

WILSON, Richard Allen
Clearwater HS; Clearwater, FL (2-725) BS; NHS; Var C; MVP, Cr-Ctry; Tr; Sci.

WILSON, Rita Marie
Simon Gratz HS; Philadelphia, PA (259-703) *Fla A&M U; Bus.*

WILSON, Robert Jeffrey
Uniontown Area Sr HS; Uniontown, PA; Span C; Bsbl; MVP, Bkbl; Ftbl; *Penn St; Mining Eng.*

WILSON, Robert Karl
Midland HS; Midland, TX (33%-500) Ger C; VP, Key C; Order/Arrow; SC; Var C; Cr-Ctry; Cpt, Tr; Industrial Arts A; *Tex Tech U; Mech Engr.*

WILSON, Roberta Ellen
Fort Hayes Career Center; Columbus, OH (11-24) Bkbl; Sftbl; *Med Lab.*

WILSON, Robin Elaine
Miffin HS; Columbus, OH; *Ohio St U; Bus.*

WILSON, Ruth Denise
Princess Anne HS; Virginia Beach, VA (20%-650) Ann; NHS; Sch P; Drill Tm; Q&S; Church Choir; *E Carolina U; Journ.*

WILSON, Sandra Faye
Bradleyville HS; Bradleyville, MO (5-28) Pres, Chor; Rptr, FHA; Ed, Sch P; Journ A; Shorthand, Child Development, A's.

WILSON, Sandra Lee
Clintonville HS; Clintonville, WI (21-200) Pres, AFS; Chldr; Secy, Ger C; NHS; SC; Var C; Tr; Yth Fel; Rookie o-t Yr, Tr; Most Improved, Gym; Handicapped.

WILSON, Sandra Louise
United Township HS; E Moline, IL (95-590) *Brewer St Jr Col; Elem Ed.*

WILSON, Sarah Jane
Rockville Jr-Sr HS; Rockville, IN (50%-96) Tres, Chor; Span C; Tr; Pres A; Best Personality; GAA; Tres; MYF; Cpt, Vlbl; Tres, FCA; Pep C; *Sue Bennett Col; Rec Ldr.*

WILSON, Shannon Hunt
Marion Sr HS; Marion, VA (53-250) Pres, Chess C; Lit Mag; SC; Hist A; Semi-Fin, Forensics; Ch, Sr Cl Prophecy; Sr Play; *Berea Col; Chem.*

WILSON, Sharon Catherine
Robert E Lee HS; Houston, TX (200-616) Chor; Drama; FHA; NHS; Var C; Pres, Missionettes; Librarian, Yth Choir; Church Choir; Historian, Drama Group.

WILSON, Shaun Dean
Chatsworth HS; Chatsworth, CA (160-1100) Band; Hmrm; Order/Arrow; Ed, Sch P; JV, Wrest; Hon Prog; Order/Arrow A; Eagle Sct; *CSUSLO; Design Arts.*

WILSON, Shelia Ann
Marion-Franklin HS; Columbus, OH (20-350) Secy, Chor; NHS; SC; COM; Delta Sigma Theta A; Hon Prog; PTA A; Cpt, Vlbl; Law Enforcement Cert of Ldrship; *Ohio St U; Psych.*

WILSON, Steven Charles
Trinity Christian Sch; Chattanooga, TN; Ann; Chor; Ensm; Ger C; Hmrm; SC; VP, Soph Cl; Bsbl; Ftbl; Sftbl; COM; Hon Prog; Spch A; Mr Trinity; Most Religious; *Tennessee Temple Col; Bible.*

WILSON, Steven Curtis
Sooner HS; Bartlesville, OK (100-300) Fr C; Ch, Order/Arrow; Rptr, Sch P; Hon Prog; Order/Arrow A; Band Photographer; *U of Mo; Photo Journ and Advertising.*

WILSON, Steven Lee
Manchester HS; Manchester, GA (25-150) Key C; Ftbl; *Ga U; Communications.*

WILSON, Sue Ann
Newton Falls HS; Newton Falls, OH (45-195) Secy, Chem C; Pres, FNA; Secy, Sci C; Bio A; Yth Fel; *Kent St U; Med Tech.*

WILSON, Susan Anita
Sharpstown HS; Houston, TX (80-700) AFS; Anchor C; A-Ed, Ann; Fr C; FHA; Hmrm; NHS; SC; Hon Prog; Journ A; Most Out; *Tex A&M U; Bus.*

WILSON, Susan Ann
Reid Ross HS; Fayetteville, NC (20-250) Chor; Tres, Ensm; Tres, FHA; FTA; Lat C; ARC; COM; Citz A; Lang Arts A; Most Dependable; Tres, Harmony C; Stu Director, Mus; *U of NC; Spch Pathology.*

WILSON, Susan Lynn
Columbia HS; Columbia, IL (21-127) Arch; Drama; FHA; Pres, FTA; NHS; Tres, SC; Var C; Arch; Tr; HCt; Opt A; Pres A; Vlbl; Pom Pom; Prom Attendent; *SE Mo St U; Sci.*

WILSON, Susan Mary
Santa Curz HS; Santa Cruz, CA; AFS; Ski C; SC; Cr-Ctry; Tnns; CSF; Inter-Sch C; Vlbl; *Humbolt Col; Natural Sci.*

WILSON, Suzanne Marie
Mercy HS; San Francisco, CA (50-240) CYO; GS; Pres, Hmrm; ARC; VP, Sr Cl; Co-Cpt, Swim; Amer Leg A; *Oreg St U; Phar.*

WILSON, Tammy Kay
Mission HS; San Fernando, CA; Ed, Ann; Chess C; Sch Achieve Tm; Sci C; Pres, Jr Cl; Cl Fav; Star Student; *Art.*

WILSON, Tana Lynn
Springfield HS; Springfield, OR; Band; Drama; Hmrm; Cl Fav; Pres A; GSct; Christian Endeavor; Pres, Church Yth; Substitute Sunday Sch Teacher; *Med.*

WILSON, Tarita Ann
Haworth HS; Kokomo, IN; Band; *Nurs.*

WILSON, Teri Lynn
S Range HS; N Lima, OH; Co-Cpt, Chldr; Sftbl; Tnns; *Youngstown St Col; Ed.*

WILSON, Terri Lynn
Bangor HS; Bangor, MI (8-118) Band; Cpt, Chldr; Orch; Sch P; Pres, Span C; Var C; Sftbl; Bsbl; Beauty; Citz A; Hon Prog; Kiwanis A; MLS; Most Out; PTA A; *Western Mich U; Bus Adm and Public Relations.*

WILSON, Terry Allene
Richland HS; N Richland Hills, TX; Chor; Tres, FHA; NHS; Sftbl; Citz A; *Mus.*

WILSON, Theresa Ann
Pike Central HS; Petersburg, IN; Band; Pres, 4H; Swim; Band, Piano, Fr, A's; *Purdue U; Phar.*

WILSON, Thomas Alan
Port Huron Northern HS; Port Huron, MI (20%-500) Parl, SC; Golf; *Pre-Med.*

WILSON, Thomas Angelo
N Charleston HS; N Charleston, SC; Hmrm; ARC; ARC A; Yth Fel; *Columbia Commercial Col; Fashion.*

WILSON, Thomas Brooks
Palisades HS; Pacific Palisades, CA (230-760) Hmrm; Order/Arrow; ARC; Var C; Cr-Ctry; Tr; COM; God & Country A; Order/Arrow A; Yth Fel; Stu A; United Methodist Women; *U of Wash; Bus.*

WILSON, Thomas Gilbert
United Township HS; E Moline, IL (50-1000) Bsbl; Golf; Yth Fel; *Math.*

WILSON, Timothy Ralph
Perry Hall HS; Baltimore, MD; Bsbl; Soccer; *Essex & Towsen Col; Air Force-ROTC.*

WILSON, Timothy Ray
Richland HS; Fort Worth, TX; VP, Chess C.

WILSON, Tina Louise
Graham HS; Graham, NC; Church Choir; Tn Chorale; VP, Sunday Sch; Early Childhood Ed.

WILSON, Tony Alexander
Chardon HS; Chardon, OH (1-260) AFS; Ed, Ann; BS; Drama; Key C; NHS; Sch Achieve Tm; F-Ed, Sch P; Thes; Cr-Ctry; Tnns; Wrest; Bausch & Lomb A; COM; Journ A; Q&S A; ROTC A; Val; Drama A; MIT; Physics.

WILSON, Tyrone Kenneth
Port Chester HS; Port Chester, NY (130-362) A Cap Choir; All Amer Yth; Pres; Chor; Drama; Lit Mag; Thes; Pres, Sr Cl; Cpt, Bkbl; Cpt, Ftbl; Citz A; Cl Fav; Sci A; Cl Dramatist; Most Versatile; Middlebury Col; Psych.

WILSON, Vernita Mashell
Westland HS; Galloway, OH; Cpt, Bkbl; Beauty; Schol Meritorious Bkbl; Columbus Tech Inst; Cosmetology.

WILSON, Veronica L
Dorsey HS; Los Angeles, CA; Hmrm; CSF; Hon Prog; Drill Tm; UCLA; Bus.

WILSON, Vickie Renae
E E Byrd HS; Shreveport, LA (232-400) Band; Sou U; Social Worker.

WILSON, Wendy Lynn
Arlington HS; Arlington, TX (1-479) AFS; Tres, InterAct C; Pres, NHS; Span C; Bkbl; Tr; Amer Leg A; Hon Prog; Most Out; Val; Cpt, MVP, Vlbl; Athenian o-t Mo; Sr o-t Mo; Tex A&M U; Acct.

WILSON, Wendy Marie
Cottage Grove HS; Cottage Grove, OR (1-290) Band; Thes; S-T, Soph Cl; Tr; MLS; Most Out; Pres A; Outst, Schol & Ldr; US Air Force; Math.

WILSON, William Andrew
Concord Sr HS; Concord, NC; AFS; Demolay; Hmrm; InterAct C; Lat C; ARC; JV, Bkbl; Ftbl; Citz A; Central Piedmont Comm Col; Bus Adm.

WILSON, William Gregory
Newton Co Comprehensive HS; Covington, GA (10%-487) Band; Lat C; Thes; Tri-HiY; Golf; Tnns; Band A; Ga Inst of Tech; Aeronautics.

WILSON, William Morgan
Mathiston HS; Mathiston, MS (4-35) BC; Rptr, FFA; Rptr, Sch P; VP, Jr Cl; Ftbl; Tr; Hon Prog; Jolliest Jr; Miss St U; Social Stu.

WILSON, William Wayne
Charlotte HS; Charlotte, TX (1-33) Band; Ensm; FFA; Pres, NHS; Sch P; Thes; Pres, Sr Cl; Pres, Jr Cl; VP, Soph Cl; JV, Bkbl; Co-Cpt, Ftbl; JV, Tr; Citz A; Cl Fav; Math A; Opt A; Highest Ranking Boy; Swtht, Band, FHA; All Region, Band; Campus Favorite; Tex A&M U; Elec Engr.

WILT, Judith Lynn
Wilmington HS; Wilmington, OH (55-301) Band; BS; Chldr; Chor; Drama; Ensm; Secy, FTA; Tres, 4H; Semi-Fin, Jr Miss Pa; Orch; A-Ed, Sch P; Span C; Thes; Secy, Jr Cl; VP, Soph Cl; 4H A; Phi Delta Sigma; Davis & Elkins Col; Theatre Arts.

WILT, Roger L
Northern Chester Co Tech Sch; Phoenixville, PA (10%-200) NHS; Tr.

WILTSEY, Melody Layne
Centralia HS; Centralia, WA; Chor; The Navigator; Cosmetology.

WILTSHIRE, Robert Warren
Port Richmond HS; Staten Island, NY (18-618) Chem C; Fr C; NHS; Orch; Hon Prog; Kiwanis A; Sci A; HR; Arista; Church A's; Brooklyn Col; Marine Bio.

WILUSH, Kevin Edward
Struthers HS; Struthers, OH (150-298) Lat C; Sci.

WIMAN, Leslie Jeanne
James I O'Neill; Highland Falls, NY (17-200) Band; NHS; Soccer; Amer Leg A; Hon Prog; Sci A; Ch, Prom Committee; Ski Tm; Marine Bio.

WIMBERLEY, Earlceline Marie
Pass Christian HS; Pass Christian, MS; BC; CYO; Fr C; Hist A; Hon Prog; U of Sou Miss; Computer Programer.

WIMBERLEY, James Roderick
Church Point HS; Church Point, LA (6-122) Ann; BS; Pres, FFA; Lit Ral; NHS; Bkbl; Ftbl; Golf; Cl Fav; K of C A; U of SW La; Civil Engr.

WIMBERLEY, Rhonda Maria
Church Point HS; Church Point, LA; CYO; FBLA; Parl, FHA; Rptr, NHS; Cpt, Sftbl; Pep Squad; L'Ours Staff; McNeese St U; Phys Ed.

WIMBERLY, Cathy Lynn
Meridian HS; Meridian, TX (10-30) Band; BC; Chor; FHA; Mjrte; Co-Ed, Sch P; Var C; Bkbl; Golf; Sftbl; Cl Fav; HCt; Sam Houston St U; Med.

WIMBERLY, Mendy Lee
Coronado HS; Lubbock, TX (127-632) NHS; Sci C; Tri-HiY; Prom Qn; Tex Tech; Park Adm.

WIMBLEY, Birdie Lee
Northrop HS; Fort Wayne, IN (329-630) Ind U.

WIMMER, Kenton Louis
Northside HS; Muncie, IN (35-220) Lat C; Orch; JV, Cr-Ctry; Tr; JA A; Ball St U; Sci.

WIMPFHEIMER, Robert Arthur
Hempstead HS; Hempstead, NY (2-280) NHS; Sch P; Bausch & Lomb A; NMS; Ntl Sci Found; Sal; St U of Stony Brook; Computer Sci.

WIMPY, Christi Gayle
Thrifthaven Baptist Sch; Memphis, TN (6-17) Cpt, Chldr; Chor; VP, Hmrm; Tenn Temple Col; Bible.

WINANS, Carol Anne
Harrison HS; Colorado Springs, CO; Chor; FHA; Lat C; Home Ec.

WINANS, Gayle Dawn
Jenks HS; Jenks, OK (57-256) Secy, Bus C; Chldr; NHS; Pres, Jr Cl; Bkbl; Tnns; HCt; 2nd Pl St Win, DECA; FFA Swtht; Semi-Fin, Miss Teenage Tulsa; Okla St U; Phys Therapy.

WINANS, Pamela Marshell
Carson HS; Carson, CA; Hmrm; Citz A; El Camingno Jr Col; Bus Ed.

WINBURN, Glenn Carroll
Aynor HS; Aynor, SC (15%-85) FFA; St Farmer A; Clemson U; Agri.

WINBUSH, Janice DiaVette
Pershing HS; Detroit, MI; U of Mich; Journ.

WINCHESTER, Marie Ann
Prosser Voc HS; Chicago, IL; Chor; Drama; COM; Hon Prog.

WINCHESTER, Mary Robin
Temple Christian HS; Anderson, SC (1-9) Chor; SC; Pres, Soph Cl; Cpt, Bkbl; Clemson U; Phys Ed.

WINCHESTER, Terry Eugene
Plant City HS; Plant City, FL (150-1000) Leo C; Camera C; Sou Col; Airline Travel.

WINDHAGER, Anne Lisa
Ross S Sterling HS; Baytown, TX (25-575) Band; Fr C; NHS; Yth Fel; Ch, Jr Rotary Anns; 1st Div, UIL Flute Solo; Flute Trio; SW Tex St U; Behavioral Sci.

WINDHAM, Jane Huntley
Aiken HS; Aiken, SC (52-652) BC; Pres, Fr C; Pres, Hmrm; Semi-Fin, Jr Miss Pa; Key C; Pol Sci C; SC; VP, Soph Cl; Hon Prog; U of SC; International Stu.

WINDHAM, Joyce Ann
Leander HS; Leander, TX (1-120) FTA; VP, NHS; VP, Sr Cl; Alg A; Chem A; Hist A; MLS; Most Out; Val; WW A; Cpt, Vlbl; All Dist Player; Operation Roar; U of Tex; Law.

WINDHAM, Lori Ann
Parkview HS; Springfield, MO; AFS; Baylor U; Art.

WINDHORST, James Daniel
Dunlap HS; Dunlap, IL (25%-100) Band; Mod Mus Mas; Var C; Bsbl; Bkbl; Ftbl; Data Programming.

WINDOM, Cheryl Dian
Inglewood HS; Inglewood, CA; Orch; SC; JV, Tnns; CSF; Hon Prog; Stu A; UCLA; Surgical Tech.

WINDOM, Ruby
McAdams HS; McAdams, MS (25%-60) Band; Chldr; FHA; Mjrte; Alg A; Miss Valley St U; Phys Ed.

WINDOM, Ruth
McAdams HS; McAdams, MS (4-60) Band; FHA; Mjrte; Miss Valley St Col; Social Worker.

WINDSCHITL, Martha Mary
Kuemper HS; Carroll, IA (36-282) Band; Fr C; Orch; Sch P; Bkbl; Ftbl; Tr; COM; Journ A; NMS; Poet A; Band Qn; Iowa St U; Horticulture.

WINDSOR, Kenneth Allen
Crestview Sr HS; Crestview, FL; SC; Pres, Span Cl; JV, Ftbl; Tr; Cl Fav; 4H A; US Marine Corps.

WINDSOR, Mary Benton
Hardaway HS; Columbus, GA (20%-400) A Cap Choir; Secy, Fr C; Gym.

WINE, Kerry Esther
King's Temple Sch; Seattle, WA; Band; Chor; Orch; Bkbl; COM; Gov Honor Prog; Hon Prog; Pres A; Yth Fel; Harvard U; Theology.

WINE, Marlene Marie
King's Temple Christian Sch; Seattle, WA; Band; Chor; Hmrm; Orch; SC; Bkbl; COM; Hon Prog; Journ A; NEDT; Pres A; Yth Fel.

WINE, Martha Cheryl
Riverside HS; Greenville, SC (25-135) BC; Fr C; VP, Hmrm; Clemson U; Pol Sci.

WINE, Teresa Carol
Riverside HS; Greer, SC (20-135) BC; VP, Fr C; Clemson U; Bus Mgr.

WINEBARGER, Diana Lynne
Post Falls HS; Post Falls, ID (5-155) F-Ed, Ann; Drama; NFL; NHS; Ntl Yth Conf; Spch C; S-T, SC; Citz A; Spch A; Miss Congeniality; Sportsmanship A, Bsbl; Semi-Fin, Miss Idaho Tn Pageant; N Idaho Jr Col; Fashion Merchandising & Design.

WINEBRENNER, Lynn Marie
Highland HS; Highland, IN (50-536) Band; Hon Prog; Purdue U; Elem Ed.

WINEGAR, Karen Elisabeth
West HS; Bakersfield, CA; Band; Ger C; Lit Mag.

WINEGARDNER, Kim Annette
North HS; Sioux City, IA (67-343) Ann; Hmrm; Orch; Rainbow; SC; Hon Prog; Star Student; Iowa St U; Acct.

WINEGARTNER, Becky Jane
Robert E Lee HS; Baytown, TX (5%-500) AFS; Anchor C; Band; Ger C; Opt A; Tex A&M U; Math.

WINEMAN, Richard Lee II
Claymont HS; Uhrichsville, OH (50-200) Sergeant, Police Cadets; Kent St U; Sci.

WINFIELD, Aleen Marie
Wood River Valley HS; Hood River, OR (1-249) Band; Model UN; NHS; Pres, Rainbow; Span C; Type A; Schol; Lions Yth Exchange; Oregon St Col; Computer Sci.

WINFIELD, Tonyia Elaine
Van-Cove HS; Cove, AR (4-26) Chor; FHA; SC; Sou Ark U; Bus.

WINFORD, Janet Sue
Hillsboro R-3 HS; Hillsboro, MO; Fin, Crown & Scepter; Dbte Tm; Math C; Var C; Bkbl; Sftbl; Tr; Balfour A; COM; HCt; Interlochen Ntl Mus; Math A; Pres A; Regent Schol; Yth Fel; Yth Leg; VBS A; Sports A; Statistician, Ftbl; Honor Recruiter, US Marine Corps; Emergency Med.

WINFORD, Laurie Leigh
Borah Sr HS; Boise, ID (10%-400) A Cap Choir; Pres, BC; Fin, Chldr; Chor; Ensm; Fin, Hmrm; Madrigal; NHS; VP, SC; VP, Jr Cl; VP, Soph Cl; CSF; H of F; Pres A; Biola Col; Christian Ed.

WINFORD, Linda Ruth
U S Grant HS; Oklahoma City, OK; Chor; FBLA; S Okla City Jr Col; Computer Sci.

WINFORD, Richard Earl
U S Grant HS; Oklahoma City, OK (5-400) Band; BS; Chess C; FBLA; Math C; Mu Alpha Theta; Pres, NHS; Order/Arrow; Ed, Sch P; Bkbl; JV, Tr; Alg A; Bio A; Journ A; Math A; Sal; Anderson Col; Religion.

WINFREE, Crystal Paulette
Eastwood HS; El Paso, TX; JV, Chldr; Key C; Tr; COM; Citz A; WW; All-Dist Tr; U Tex at Austin; Architecture.

WINFREE, Trina Lynn
Amherst Co HS; Amherst, VA (120-326) Chldr; Fr C; 4H; ARC; VP, Var C; Swim; Tnns; Tr; Pres A; ARC A; WW; Radford Col; Recreation.

WINFREE, William Russell
Eastwood HS; El Paso, TX; Dbte Tm; Wrest; *US Air Force Acad.*

WINFREY, Dana Machelle
Melrose Sr HS; Memphis, TN (167-340) *Shelby St Col; Vocal Mus.*

WING, Barbara Carol
Elk Grove HS; Elk Grove Village, IL; Band; Fr C; Lit Mag; Campus Life; 2nd Pl, Creative Writing Contest; *Eng.*

WING, Susanne Linda
Crestview Sr HS; Crestview, FL (10%-214) Anchor C; Chldr; Ch, FHA; *Okaloosa-Walton Jr Col; Archt Drafting.*

WINGATE, Debbie Marie
Abramson HS; New Orleans, LA (12-30) FHA; VP, Hmrm; JA A; *Pepperdine U; Acct.*

WINGATE, Marjorie Leisa
Wayne Co HS; Jesup, GA (50%-425) Band; Hmrm; SC; Rptr, Soph Cl; Tnns; *Phar.*

WINGATE, Tommy Dawson
Franklin Co HS; Frankfort, KY (20%-350) Mu Alpha Theta; Sftbl; VP, Church Yth Group; Church Board; Ch, Jr Deacons; *U of Ky; Humanities.*

WINGEIER, Lisa Jean
Thornapple Kellogg HS; Middleville, MI (10%-160) Band; Ensm; Pres, 4H; Hmrm; SC; Pres, Soph Cl; MVP, Sftbl; Co-Cpt, Tnns; 4H A; HCt; Co-Cpt, Vlbl; *Secy.*

WINGERT, Dennis Roy
DuBois Area Sr HS; DuBois, PA (20-340) Band; Chor; Ensm; NHS; Sci A; V-Ch, Miss Teenage Pageant; *Penn St U; Agr.*

WINGERT, Joan Adele
Atkins HS; Winston-Salem, NC (53-683) Fin, Tnns; MVP, Tr; Jr Lifesaving; Presidential Phys Fitness A.

WINGERT, John Louis
Spencer Pub Sch; Spencer, WI (10-65) CYO; Pres, Drama; FFA; VP, 4H; NFL; Thes; Var C; VP, Jr Cl; Bkbl; Ftbl; Tr; Wrest; Cl Fav; 4H A; Spch A; Prom Ct; Forensics St Win; 4-H Spch A.

WINGERT, Steven Harry
E Richland HS; Olney, IL (37-272) Band; Chor; Madrigal; *Greenville Col; Mus.*

WINKELMANN, Anne
Saint Bede Acad; Peru, IL (34-101) Chor; Tr; Meritorius A's; *Ill U.*

WINKELMANN, Luke Edward
St Bede Acad; Peru, IL (5-130) Band; Orch; Tr; Rotary A; St Scholar; *IVCC; Physics.*

WINKLE, Anita Perilyn
Lewiston Sr HS; Lewiston, ID (32-550) Band; NHS; Hist A; Pres A; Dist Ntl Mus Guild; *NW Nazarene Col; Nurs.*

WINKLE, Christi Anne
Ind St Laboratory HS; Terre Haute, IN (5-63) Cpt, Chldr; Hmrm; Model UN; NHS; SC; VP, Jr Cl; HCt; St Scholar; Mus A; Art A; Tri Kappa Fin; *Ind St U; Art.*

WINKLE, Jerry Myrl
Henrico HS; Richmond, VA (25-600) Chor; Madrigal; Bkbl; Ftbl; Hon Prog; Ftbl Defensive Player o-t Yr; *Northwest Nazarene Col; Math.*

WINKLER, Becky Sue
Abingdon HS; Abingdon, IL (5-90) Band; Chldr; Chor; Ensm; NHS; Span C; HCt; Hon Prog; *Fla Sou Col; Elem Ed.*

WINKLER, Carrie Lanette
Hobart HS; Hobart, OK (16-51) Pres, FHA; Secy, FTA; GS; Span C; S-T, Jr Cl; S-T, Swthl; Swthl; FFA Swthl; Semi-Fin, Miss Tnage Pageant; Pres, Pep C; *Southwestern Ok U; Phar.*

WINKLER, Gigi Ann
Jewish Educational Center HS; Elizabeth, NJ (11-26) Chldr; Dbte Tm; VP, Hmrm; Rptr, Sch P; VP, World Affairs C; Ch, Y-Tns; Hon Prog; Type A; VP, Jewish Yth Organization; Ed, Lit Yrbk; *Phys Therapy.*

WINKLER, Rodney Gerard
South Shelby HS; Shelbina, MO (12-100) CYO; VP, FFA; Tres, 4H; K of C; NHS; Pres, Sr Cl; Ftbl; WW; *Mo U at Columbia; Vet Sci.*

WINKLEY, Stan Wesley
Hughson Union HS; Hughson, CA; Lit Mag; JV, Bkbl; MVP, Tr; CSF; Cl Fav; Cpt, Tnns; Stat, Ftbl & Bkbl; *Sacramento St Col; Acct.*

WINN, Benjie C
Haynesville HS; Haynesville, LA (3-83) A-Ed, Ann; Band; Dbte Tm; FFA; Hmrm; Lit Ral; SC; VP, Soph Cl; Fin, Bkbl; Bkbl; Ftbl; Alg A; Cl Fav; Law Tm A; Ltrman A; *La Tech U; Engr.*

WINN, Beverly Jo
Wilson Hall HS; Sumter, SC (3-57) Ann; Lat C; Rptr, Lit Mag; Pres, NHS; F-Ed, Sch P; COM; Gov Honor Prog; Gr Marshal; Hon Prog; Journ A; NMS; NEDT; Pres A; Yth Fel; Yth Leg; Most Intellectual; Black Rvr Elec Co- op Wash Yth; *Wofford Col; Math.*

WINN, Carol Ann
Elbert Co Comprehensive HS; Elberton, GA (6-250) Pres, Anchor C; BC; Pres, FBLA; NHS; COM; DARGCA; Hon Prog; Math A; NEDT; Sci A; Spch A; Type A; Miss FBLA; Shorthand A; Bus & Professional Women's A; FBLA A; *La Grange Col; Pre-Phar.*

WINN, Cynthia Jean
Crenshaw HS; Los Angeles, CA; Beauty; HCt; 1st Pl, Hair Styling Contest; *Cosmetologist.*

WINN, Debran Elise
Aiken HS; Aiken, SC (5-750) Pres, BC; Fr C; VP, 4H; Mu Alpha Theta; NHS; COM; 4H A; Math A; Augusta Col Cert of Achv; Soc Stu A; Woodmn o-t Wrld Hist A; Math Tm; SC Walk Horse As; Gov's Sch Nom; Tn Walk Horse As; Fr & Eng A's; *U of SC-AIKEN; Computer Sci.*

WINN, Karen Anne
Brazil Sr HS; Brazil, IN (6-196) Band; Drama; Secy, Fr C; FHA; COM; Math A; Top Ten A; GAA A; Fr A; Pep C; Straight 'A' A; Drama C A; Band A.

WINNING, Robin Jill
Montclair Prep Sch; Van Nuys, CA; Secy, Fr C; French NHS; VP, Lat C; NHS; VP, Soph Cl; Aux Lat; COM; Hist A; Hon Prog; Most Out; NEDT; Star Student; Eng A; Fr A; *Stanford U; Lang.*

WINQUIST, Colleen Ardith
Denison Comm HS; Denison, IA (45-165) Pres, Band; Chor; Drama; Ensm; Madrigal; Tres, Sr Cl; Type A; Pres, Church Yth; Band Qn; Dist Band Qn; Superior Mus A's; *Wm Jewell Col; Mus.*

WINSKI, Mark Jerome
Uniontown Sr HS; Uniontown, PA (5-450) Math C; NHS; Phys C; Pres, Sci C; Var C; Tnns; Chamber of Comm A; Math A; Rotary A; Sci A; Ntl Math Assn A; World Affairs Just; *Carneige Mellon U; Elec Engr.*

WINSLOW, James Carey
Arcadia HS; Arcadia, CA; Band; MVP, Cr-Ctry; Tr.

WINSLOW, Sarah Elizabeth
Cold Spring Harbor HS; Cold Spring Harbor, NY (50%-220) Ann; Chldr; Key C; SC; Tr; HCt; Pep C; 3rd Pl, Co Cheering Competition; *U of Tenn; Nurs.*

WINSLOW, Virginia Joan
Chopticon HS; Morganza, MD (2-289) A Cap Choir; Band; Fr C; Madrigal; NHS; Tr; Alg A; COM; Hon Prog; Math A; Rotary A; Sal; Sci A; Chor Accompanist; Co Chor; Comm Band; Math Assn of Am A; Ensm Jazz; Most Talented Girl; St Chor; *Prince George's Comm Col; Med Technology.*

WINSTANLEY, Carol Alexandra
A Crawford Mosley HS; Panama City, FL (25%-510) Anchor C; Band; VP, BC; VP, Fr C.

WINSTEAD, Marcia Jane
Webster Co HS; Dixon, KY (21-151) BC; Tres, Chor; VP, Drama; Spch C; Sci A; Recreation Ldr, FHA; Biol Stu in Action; Best Mus A; FHA Jr & Chapter Degrees; *Mus.*

WINSTEAD, Perry Glenn
Union HS; Union, MS (10%-50) BC; VP, Sci C; Var C; Bsbl; Bkbl; Amer Leg A; Star Student; Yth Fel; Most Intellectual; WW; Ath A; *E Central Jr Col; Acct.*

WINSTEAD, Rochelle Lynn
Worth Co R-3 HS; Grant City, MO (1-54) Chldr; FTA; GS; 4H; NHS; SC; Var C; Bkbl; Sftbl; Tr; Alg A; Bio A; Citz A; Hist A; Sci A; Type A; Librarian A; All-Conf Bkbl; *Northwest Mo St U; Spch Therapy.*

WINSTEAD, Sherry Lynne
Union HS; Union, MS (10%-47) Ann; Band; Tres, BC; FHA; S-T, Jr Cl; COM; Drum Major; Band Coun; Dist Band Clinic; 1st Chair Player; *Miss St U; Mus.*

WINSTEAD, Terrell Elton
Union HS; Union, MS (10%-58) Band; BC; V-Ch, HiY; Bsbl; Bkbl; Yth Fel; *Miss St U.*

WINSTON, Colleen Elizabeth
Notre Dame HS; Crowley, LA (2-99) Rptr, Anchor C; BC; GS; Semi-Fin, K of C; Lit Ral; SC; Thes; Alg A; Bio A; DARGCA; NEDT; Sal; Fr II A; Eng A; Cath Action A; *St Mary's Dominican Col; Eng Ed.*

WINSTON, Karen Denise
Northwest HS; St Louis, MO (41-550) NHS; Citz A; *Data Processing.*

WINSTON, Katherine
Benhaven Sch; Olivia, NC; Pres, Band; BC; SC; Eng, Span, Band Service, A's; *Bennett Col; Special Ed.*

WINSTON, Stephanie
Northwest HS; St Louis, MO; SC.

WINTER, Brice Robert
Cordova Sr HS; Rancho Cordova, CA; CYO; Y-Tns; Cr-Ctry; Swim; Cr-Ctry A; *UOP; Law.*

WINTER, Cindy Frieda
Otsego HS; Otsego, MI (9-247) Cpt, Chldr; Secy, Chor; Tres, Lat C; NHS; Var C; Sftbl; Citz A; Hon Prog; Choreographer, Sch Mus; Church Organist; Secy, Church Yth; Accompanist, Sch Chor; *Bronson Methodist Hosp Sch of Nurs; Nurs.*

WINTER, Jonathan David
Bridgman HS; Bridgman, MI (25-91) JV, Bsbl; Bkbl; JV, Golf.

WINTER, Joyce Lynn
Newton Comm HS; Newton, IL (33%-200) Band; Chor; 4H; 4H A; Interlochen Ntl Mus; Yth Fel; *Carthage Col; Elem Ed.*

WINTER, Paul William
Orofino HS; Orofiro, ID (8-97) CYO; NHS; Var C; JV, Bkbl; Cr-Ctry; Tr; VFW A; VofDEM; Yth Leg.

WINTER, Rebecca Lyn
Arlington Heights, IL (240-550) AFS; Band; Social Work.

WINTER, Scott William
Newbury Park Acad; Newbury Park, CA; Bsbl; Bkbl; Golf; Hockey; *Ventura Col.*

WINTERS, Rose Ann
Lomega HS; Omega, OK; Co-Ed, Ann; Pres, 4H; Tres, Sr Cl; Pres, Soph Cl; Cpt, Bkbl; Lion A; Most Out; *Okla St U; Phys Ed.*

WINTERS, Tina Joy
Pritchett HS; Pritchett, CO (5-10) Chor; VP, FHA; VP, Soph Cl; Cl Fav; HCt; Type A; *W Tex St U; Phar.*

WINTERSOLE, Mark Steven
Enid HS; Enid, OK (50-568) Band; Bus Mgr, Ensm; NHS; Hist A; NMS; S-T, Amateur Radio C; Okla Hon Soc; Army Radio Opr o-t Mo; *Westminister Col; Hist.*

WINTON, Tammy Gail
Lexington Sr HS; Lexington, NC; All Amer Yth; *Bennett Col; Bus.*

WINTON, Vickie Lynn
Piggott HS; Piggott, AR; Band; FHA; Sci C; SC; MVP, Bkbl; Beauty; Cl Fav; HCt; Pres, Fresh Cl; Miss Tr; Rep, Alpha C; Bkbl Tm Mate A; Bkbl Most Valuable Player; *Ark Col; Math.*

WINWOOD, Robin Cenene
Star Spencer HS; Spencer, OK (3-425) Key C; NHS; Secy, Sci C; SC; MVP, Sftbl; Tnns; Alg A; Bio A; *Okla U; Bio Sci.*

WINZ, Mark William
Holdrege Sr HS; Holdrege, NE (30-130) Ann; Sch P; JV, Ftbl; Chem A; Citz A; *U of Nebr; Photo-Journ.*

WINZELER, Megan Elizabeth
Montpelier HS; Montpelier, OH; Chldr; Sch Achieve Tm; Var C; Bus Adm.

WIPPERMAN, Duane Lindsay
Elston Sr HS; Michigan City, IN; A Cap Choir; Band; Chor; Drama; NHS; Cpt, Swim; Interlochen Ntl Mus; VICA Carpenter Contest; Sch Mus Recognition A; Voc Building Trades C; Carpentry.

WIREMAN, Janice Lorran
Amer Sch; Chicago, IL; Val; Church Organist; Covenant Found Col; Mus.

WIRHUN, Paul William
St Basil's Prep Sch; Stamford, CT (5-41) Chor; NHS; Hon Prog; Prin A; Vlbl Tm; St Basil's Col; Theology.

WIRTANEN, Scott Michael
Gilbert Sr HS; Gilbert, MN (5-77) Band; Pres, CYO; Chor; SC; Bkbl; Cr-Ctry; Tnns; Tr; Math A; Computer A; Notre Dame U; Math.

WIRTH, Angela Kay
Mt Carmel HS; Mt Carmel, IL; Cpt, Chldr.

WIRTH, Tami F
Pinole Valley HS; Pinole, CA; A Cap Choir; Ger C; Contra Costa Col.

WISCOVICH, Eric
Luis Munoz Marin HS; Cabo Rojo, PR (9-200) Chem C; SC; Sftbl; CAAM; Ingenieria Electrica.

WISCOVITCH, Adanette
Luis Munoz Marin HS; Cabo Rojo, PR (1-150) Band; Chldr; Chor; Beauty; COM; Hon Prog; Masonic A; Recinto Universitario de Mayaguez; Bio.

WISDOM, Beth Ann
Skyline HS; Dallas, TX; Lat C; NJHS; Southwestern Col; Sci.

WISE, Barbara Jeane
Grove City HS; Grove City, PA (18-241) AFS; Secy, 4H; Sci C; Span C; Sftbl; Tr.

WISE, Cathy Marie
Holy Rosary Acad; Louisville, KY (9-89) NHS; Tres, SC; Co-Cpt, Bkbl; Hockey; Tnns; Tr; WW; Phar.

WISE, Demaris Jo
McCurtain HS; McCurtain, OK (4-14) Bus C; FHA; Secy, 4H; Math C; NHS; 4H A; Hist A

WISE, Diana Lee
Queen City HS; Queen City, TX (1%-44) Bus Mgr, Ann; FHA; VP, NHS; Sch P; Rptr, Span C; Bkbl; Tr; Cl Fav; MLS.

WISE, Elizabeth Ruth
Skyline HS; Dallas, TX; Mu Alpha Theta; NHS; WW; Sou Methodist U; Math Ed.

WISE, James Hunter
Mathiston HS; Mathiston, MS (1-29) Ann; Secy, BC; F-Ed, Sch P; Bsbl; Bkbl; Ftbl; Alg A; Cl Fav; Hist A; Math A; MLS; NMS; Sci A; Star Student; Val; U of Miss; Phar.

WISE, Laura Jane
Skyline HS; Salt Lake City, UT (12%-700) Chor; Hmrm; Mjrte; NHS; SC; VP, Jr Cl; Hon Prog; Yth Leg; Young Life; WW; Utah Jr Yth Symph; Gym; Dance; U of Utah; Law.

WISE, Lori Ann
Hilton Central HS; Hilton, NY; Chor; Hmrm; Tres, SC; Mgr, Bkbl; JV, Soccer; Mgr, Sftbl; Mgr, Tr; Hon Prog; Bus Stu o-t Mo; Specialized Nurs.

WISE, Lori Lynn
Mt Carmel HS; San Diego, CA (20-456) A Cap Choir; Chor; Ensm; Most Out; Chapman Col; Mus.

WISE, Natalie Gay
Staples HS; Staples, MN (6-150) Band; Chor; Ensm; Madrigal; Cpt, Mjrte; NHS; ARC; Ski C; MVP, Spch C; SC; HCt; Hon Prog; Spch A; Mus Schol; Sno-Daze Qn Court; Mus.

WISE, Paula Lynn
Guymon Sr HS; Guymon, OK; Chor; Dbte Tm; Drama; FHA; Sci C; Spch C; Citz A; Med Careers C; Outst Art A; Panhandle St U.

WISE, Randy Ray
Wichita Falls HS; Wichita Falls, TX (39-440) NHS; Cr-Ctry; JV, Ftbl; Tr; Tex A&M U; Engr.

WISE, Roger Lee
Leigh HS; San Jose, CA (15-550) Lat C; Sci C; CSF; COM; Hon Prog; Hon Soc; N Calif Bible Col; Theology.

WISE, Sharon Ann
Tulpehocken HS; Bernville, PA; Chor; 4H; Tr; Albright Col; Acct.

WISE, Stephen Craig
Dothan HS; Dothan, AL; Ger C; Neatest Cadet, Best Drilled, ROTC.

WISE, Stephen Scott
North Hills HS; Pittsburgh, PA (99-842) Community Yth Symph; Orch; A-Ed, Sch P; Sci C; Phy A; PMEA Region & St Orch; Newspaper A; Elec Engr.

WISE, Susan Kathleen
Mississinewa HS; Gas City, IN (15-230) Pres, Chor; VP, Drama; Ensm; S-T, Fr C; GS; Fin, Jr Miss Pagent; NHS; VP, Thes; Tri-HiY; Ball St U; Nurs.

WISEHART, Linda Gayle
Thayer HS; Thayer, MO (6-65) Co-Ed, Ann; Band; BC; Drama; Parl, FHA; SC; Ftbl; Spch A; St FHA Officer; Eng, Drama, A's; SW Mo St U; Broadcasting.

WISEMAN, Amy Lynne
Seven Hills HS; Cincinnati, OH; Chor; Hmrm; Bsbl; Bkbl; Sftbl; Ath Assn; Sewing A; Ed.

WISEMAN, Andrew William
Walnut Hills HS; Cincinnati, OH; A-Ed, Ann; Band; Chor; Lat C; SC; Sftbl; Sci A; Jazz Pep Marching Band; Gym; Ohio Wesleyan Col; Mus.

WISEMAN, Douglas Allen
Elston Sr HS; Michigan City, IN; Pres, A Cap Choir; Ann; Ch, Band; NHS; SC; Pres, Sr Cl; Pres, Jr Cl; Tnns; COM; H of F; JA A; Rotary A; Bronze Schol; Band Hall of Fame; Horizon, Hoosier Rep; Vocal, Instrumental, A's; Ball St U; Special Ed.

WISEMAN, Gary Harold
Elkhart Mem HS; Elkhart, IN (3-417) Secy, Band; Ensm; 4H; NHS; Orch; SC; Q&S A; Northwestern U; Sci.

WISEMAN, Kelly Ann
John Marshall HS; Indianapolis, IN (40-623) Chor; 4H; Hmrm; A-Ed, Sch P; Pres, Span C; SC; 4H A; Govt.

WISEMAN, Kimberly Ann
Phillips HS; Phillips, TX; Chldr; Pres, FHA; Bkbl; Tnns; Amer Leg A; Cl Fav; U of Kans; Elem Teacher.

WISEMAN, Patricia Jo
Paul G Blazer HS; Ashland, KY (33%-400) Band; GS; Span C; Tr; WW; Sergeant-At-Arms, Theta C; Armco Self-Reliant A; Pep C; Georgetown Col; Dentistry.

WISEMAN, Rebecca Anne
Holy Cross HS; Marine City, MI (4-41) Chor; NHS; Rptr, Sch P; Ski C; SC; Hon Prog; Religion A; St Clair Co Comm Col; General Stu.

WISEMAN, Wendy Mary
Holy Cross HS; Marine City, MI; Chor; NHS; Rptr, Sch P; VP, SC; Tr; Citz A; DARGCA; Hist A; Hon Prog; Religion A; Choral A; Eastern Mich U; Special Ed.

WISHON, Lois Anne
Pattonville Sr HS; Creve Coeur, MO (4-895) Pres, Chor; Ensm; Madrigal; VP, NHS; SC; Sftbl; Tr; COM; Citz A; Mus A; Art Show A; Math.

WISKA, Janice Christine
Cabrini HS; Allen Park, MI (1-160) Hmrm; Pres, NHS; Sch P; Ski C; SC; Var C; Bkbl; Amer Leg A; COM; Hon Prog; Kiwanis A; MLS; Phi Beta Kappa; Val; Eng A; Prom Court; HR; Mich St Col; Pre-Nurs.

WISNIEWSKI, Diana Marie
Rosary HS; Aurora, IL (7-94) F-Ed, Lit Mag; Pres, NHS; Co-Ed, Sch P; SC; St Scholar; Women's C of Aurora Schol; Waubonsee Comm Col; Geol.

WISNIEWSKI, Jeffery Scott
Alexander Hamilton HS; Milwaukee, WI (30-650) Tres, CYO; Var C; Co-Cpt, Soccer; Tr; Hon Prog; U of Wis-Madison; Vet Tech.

WISS, Debra Jeanne
Saint Mary's HS; Stockton, CA (10%-200) Pres, Band; NHS; Bkbl; Sftbl; Tr; Bank Of Amer A; Vlbl; Most Outst, Phys Ed; U o-t Pacific; Mus.

WISSER, Jeffrey John
Elgin HS; Elgin, IL (61-753) Co-Ed, Sch P; Bkbl; Mac Murray Col; Journ.

WISSWELL, Keith Robert
Kearny HS; San Diego, CA (267-796) Order/Arrow; God & Country A; Jr Asst Scoutmaster; Eagle Sct; Newspaper Carrier A; Mesa Jr Col; Archt.

WISTHUFF, Mark Albert
Lyons Township HS; LaGrange, IL (99%-1203) Pres, Band; Ensm; Math C; Mu Alpha Theta; NHS; Orch; Thes; Ftbl; COM; Hon Prog; NEDT; St Scholar; Hon Men, St Arts Fair; NML; U of Ill; Archt.

WITCHER, Nancy Annette
Westside HS; Jonesboro, AR (4-101) BC; FBLA; FTA; Ntl Teachers Coun; Sci C; Sftbl; Tr; Ark St U; Phys Ed.

WITEK, Susan Lynn
St Hedwig HS; Detroit, MI (6-71) NHS; Span C; Pres, Soph Cl; HCt; VofDEM; Henry Ford Comm Col; Acct.

WITHEE, Lori Louise
Gallia Acad; Gallipolis, OH (15-150) Band; Chor; Ensm; FHA; FTA; Sci C; Span C; Tri-HiY; Sftbl; Job's Daughters; Sr GSct; Schol Tm; Ohio St U.

WITHERINGTON, Annie Laurie
Hatley HS; Hatley, MS; All Amer Yth; FHA; Cpt, Bkbl; Tr; Star Student.

WITHERS, Linda Ann
Independence Sr HS; Charlotte, NC (420-740) FTA; Key C; Lat C; ROTC A; ROTC; Spirit of '77; Tutoring C; Bible Sch A; Central Peidmont Comm Col; Secy Sci.

WITHERS, Michael Aaron
Spring Brook HS; Silver Spring, MD; Span C; Bkbl; Tr; Ath Ltr; Archt.

WITHERS, Susan Marie
Colonial Heights HS; Colonial Heights, VA (25-350) Chor; Drama; Fr C; FHA; Eastern Mennonite Col.

WITHERSPOON, Debbie Lynn
Daviess Co HS; Owensboro, KY; Chldr; Hmrm; Secy, SC; Sftbl.

WITHERSPOON, Deborah Jean
W H Taft HS; Bronx, NY (74-500) Chldr; Chor; Ed, Sch P; Pres, Sr Cl; Citz A; Journ A; Regent Schol; NY City Col; Journ.

WITHERSPOON, Demetta Lenee
A L Brown HS; Kannapolis, NC (4-380) A Cap Choir; BC; Chor; Ensm; FTA; Hmrm; NHS; Sci C; Span C; Citz A; Ldrship Conf; Graduation Marshal; U of NC; Law.

WITHERSPOON, Marvin
Paul Laurence Dunbar HS; Baltimore, MD (10-515) NHS; Cr-Ctry; Tr; COM; HEW Summer Employee A; U of Mich; Biol.

WITHERSPOON, Willette Cassandra
Parkway Prog Beta HS; Philadelphia, PA; Dbte Tm; Drama; Ed, Yrbk; Registered Nurs.

WITHERSPOON, Yvette Quintine
Compton Sr HS; Compton, CA (34-800) Fr C; NHS; Up Bound; CSF; COM; Hon Prog; ESSA A; Rockwell Schol; Outst Service to Sr Cl; U of Sou Calif; Psych.

WITHINGTON, Dennis Lee
Youngsville HS; Youngsville, PA; Key C; SC; Bkbl; Ftbl; Tr; Gym.

WITHROW, Kathy Ann
Burkburnett HS; Burkburnett, TX (23-281) Bus C; NHS; COM; Hist A; Math A; Sci A; Type A; Lang Arts A.

WITHROW, Pamela Jo
Pike HS; Indianapolis, IN (150-800) FBLA; GS; Hist A.

WOLF, Daniel A
Morrison Comm HS; Morrison, IL (6-153) BS; NHS; Var C; Pres, Soph Cl; Ftbl; Hon Prog; St Scholar; Summa Cum Laude; *Hope Col; Bio.*

WOLF, David Ray
New Albany HS; New Albany, IN; Arch; Tr.

WOLF, Deborah Lynn
Lutheran HS S; Affton, MO (45-155) Cpt, Band; Cpt, Bowl Tm; *Elem Ed.*

WOLF, Diane Marie
Aurora Central HS; Aurora, CO; VP, 4H; Ski C; Tr; Sci A; 4 H A; Hon Prog; Math A; Pres A; Pres Phys Fitness A; *Sci.*

WOLF, Donice Marie
El Reno HS; El Reno, OK; Band; Fr C; Tres, Hmrm; NHS; Secy, Sr Cl; Alg A; COM; HQn; PTA A; Type A; T&I Ltr; Social Stu A; Eng A; Fr A; *Southwestern Col; Secretarial.*

WOLF, Elaine Mary
Rosary HS; St Louis, MO (3-400) Ann; CYO; NHS; Sci C; Bio A; COM; Hon Prog; Top 15%; Amer HS Stu; *St Louis U; Pre-Med.*

WOLF, Julie
Napoleon HS; Napoleon, ND (10-86) Band; Chldr; Chor; Mjrte; NHS; SC; Tr; Hon Prog; Gym; Letterette Tres; Stage Band; Swing Choir; *UND; Coaching.*

WOLF, Laurie Dawn
Blacksburg HS; Blacksburg, VA (54-300) Band; VP, 4H; 4H A; Sci A; Regional Band; Art Show A; *VPI.*

WOLF, Lori Lynne
Spring Woods Sr HS; Houston, TX; Chor; JETS; Math C; Mu Alpha Theta; Sci C; Thes; Alg A; Math A; *Rice U; Engr.*

WOLF, Nancy L
Mason HS; Mason, TX; Band; Ensm; FHA; FNA; FTA; NHS; Co-Ed, Sch P; Arch; Co-Cpt, Tr; B Crocker A; *Hardin Simmons U; Pre Nurs.*

WOLF, Tracey Marie
Shawano HS; Shawano, WI (24-275) Band; NHS; Var C; Golf; *Marquette U; Med Tech.*

WOLFE, Betty Jean
Cleveland Heights HS; Cleveland Heights, OH (25%-850) AFS; Pres, City Conf; Hmrm; Secy, Orch; Ski C; Ch, SC; S-T, Sr Cl; Mgr, Bsbl; Tr; COM; Citz A; Gov Honor Prog; Hon Prog; Sci A; Cert of Participation, Orch; *Case Western Reserve U; Bus.*

WOLFE, Bruce Lynn
Elmhurst HS; Fort Wayne, IN (50-390) Chor; Mgr, Bkbl; Mgr, Ftbl; Audio-Visual A; Drafting A; HR; *Central Christian Col; Bible.*

WOLFE, Carol Jean
Herbert Hoover HS; Glendale, CA (20-500) A Cap Choir; AFS; Lat C; CSF; Hon Prog; NEDT; Ntl Merit Commended Stu; *Pol Sci.*

WOLFE, Cathy Marie
E J Wilson HS; Spencerport, NY (100-350) Ann; Chor; Secy, Drama; JV, Bkbl; JV, Tnns; Yth Fel; *Archt.*

WOLFE, Charles Jr
Sterling HS; Sterling, KS; Band; S-T, Chor; Drama; Order/Arrow; Pres, Jr Cl; Lion A; Order/Arrow A; Type A; *Kans St U; Instrumental Mus Ed.*

WOLFE, Cheryl Diane
Reseda HS; Reseda, CA; A Cap Choir; NHS; Ski C; Hon Prog; Drill Tm; *Calif St Col; Eng.*

WOLFE, Edward Arthur Jr
Newburgh Free Acad; Newburgh, NY (136-850) Band; Ensm; Orch; Hon Prog; Regent Schol; Pres, Yth Fel; Pres, Stage Band; Mus Coun; NYSSMA Solo; *SUNY Albany; Pre-Med.*

WOLFE, Grace Louise
Lebanon Sr HS; Lebanon, PA (180-355) Band; Bus C; FBLA; Hmrm; Tri-HiY; Math A; *Empire Beauty Sch; Cosmetology.*

WOLFE, James Lawton
Broken Bow HS; Broken Bow, OK (28-188) Chor; Drama; Ensm; NHS; All Dist & All St Choir; *Okla St U; Mus.*

WOLFE, Jane Ann
Cleveland Heights HS; Cleveland Heights, OH (50%-850) Chor; City Conf; Hmrm; SC; COM; Bowling Green St U; *Early Childhood Ed.*

WOLFE, Janeen Kay
Winfield Sr HS; Winfield, KS; Band; NFL; Rainbow; Var C; Mgr, Bkbl; Golf; Swim; *Kans U; Pre-Med.*

WOLFE, Julie Lynne
Attica HS; Attica, IN (8-115) Band; Tres, Hmrm; Tr; Vlbl; *Bus.*

WOLFE, Lori Ann
Mayfield HS; Mayfield, KY; Band; BC; Pres, Tri-HiY; Tnns; *Murray St U; Criminology.*

WOLFE, Mark Leonard
Elmhurst HS; Fort Wayne, IN (14-334) Chor; Ensm; Bio A; Chamber of Comm A; Hist A; Hon Prog; Choral A; Scholastic Achv A; HR; Principal's List; Audio-Visual A; *Central Christian Col; Bible.*

WOLFE, Martin Eugene
Asheville HS; Asheville, NC (100-450) Drama; Hmrm; ARC; Thes; Var C; Ftbl; Wrest; *U of NC; Math.*

WOLFE, Nancy Ellen
Tallmadge HS; Tallmadge, OH (125-322) Lat C; *U of Akron; Transportation.*

WOLFE, Natalie Helen
Norco Sr HS; Norco, CA; *Bus Course.*

WOLFE, Renee June
Austin HS; Austin, MN; Chor; Span C; DECA; Bible Bowl Trophies; Minn Bible Col Schol; *Minn Bible Col; Radio Ministry.*

WOLFE, Richard Alan
Mayfield HS; Mayfield, KY (10-154) A-Ed, Ann; Pres, BC; Pres, Chess C; Fr C; Rptr, Hmrm; VP, Key C; Phys C; Spch C; SC; Var C; Golf; Chem A; Kiwanis A; MLS; *U of Louisville; Elec Engr.*

WOLFE, Tanya Marie
S Fork Comm HS; Kincaid, IL (10-39) Drama; Span C; B Crocker A; Cpt, Vlbl; Jr-Sr Prom Qn; *Lincoln Land Comm Col; Vet Med.*

WOLFF, Abigail Marie
The Doane Stuart HS; Albany, NY (3-32) Chldr; Chor; Lit Mag; Sch P; SC; JV, Soccer; JV, Sftbl; COM; Sacristan; Ed, Yrbk; Ntl Merit Schol; Hon Doane Stuart HS; Silver Cross A; *Bio.*

WOLFF, Lauri Sue
Stanton Pub HS; Stanton, NE (5-46) Band; Chor; Ensm; FHA; Pres, 4H; NHS; Orch.

WOLFF, Lisa Marie
Penns Manor HS; Clymer, PA; Band; Chor; Mjrte.

WOLFGANG, Cheryl Ann
Kelly Walsh HS; Casper, WY (13-411) Ann; Chor; S-T, FBLA; Tres, 4H; Hmrm; Lat NHS; Ntl Yth Conf; Var C; Bkbl; Tr; 4H A; Hon Prog; Yth Fel; Yth Leg; Vlbl; Key C Swtht; MVP, Vlbl; Bkbl; *U of Wyo; Computer Programming.*

WOLFGANG, Cheryl Lynn
E A Johnson HS; Mt Morris, MI (31-248) Chor; Drama; Ensm; FNA; NHS; COM; Hon Prog; Sewing A; Billy Milne A; Choir Festival Medals; Health Careers; Vol, Candystriper; *Olivet Nazarene Col; Registered Nurs.*

WOLFGANG, Robert Allen
Poland Seminary HS; Poland, OH (45-320) Semi-Fin, BS; Chess C; Dbte Tm; Hmrm; Lat C; NFL; NHS; Bkbl; Ftbl; COM; God & Country A; Eagle Sct; *Youngstown St U; Engr.*

WOLFORD, Donald Raymond
Frankfort HS; Ridgeley, WV (10%-139) Band; BS; NHS; VP, SC; Var C; Tres, Jr Cl; Bkbl; Ftbl; Tr; Hist A; Math A; Summa Cum Laude; *WVU; Engr.*

WOLFORD, Tamera Lee
W Albany HS; Albany, OR (128-280) Rainbow; Sftbl; Masonic A; Grand Choir; *Oreg St U.*

WOLINSKI, Jeffrey Paul
Ewing HS; Trenton, NJ (5%-450) Math C; Amer Leg A; Chem A; Math A; Bible C; Lat A; Ancient World Cultures A; *Physics.*

WOLKOWICZ, Joseph Anthony
St Hedwig HS; Detroit, MI (3-71) Chess C; NHS; Sci C; Bio A; Hist A; Math A; VFW A; VofDEM; *Sci.*

WOLKOWSKI, John Alonzo
Bishop Guertin HS; Nashua, NH (12-127) BS; Cpt, Dbte Tm; NHS; Ed, Sch P; Mgr, Bsbl; Golf; Cl Fav; H of F; Hon Prog; Journ A; Type A; Rptr, Sch Paper; Most Valuable Debator; *Boston Col; Pre-Law.*

WOLLAM, Perry Gene
Anacortes HS; Anacortes, WA (36-187) Pres, Band; Chor; Pres, Ensm; HiY; Key C; Orch; Tr; Amer Yth Concert; Outst Musician As; Hon Band NW; *Western Wash St Col; Mus.*

WOLLAN, Mark Byron
Thomas Jefferson Sr HS; Bloomington, MN (20%-500) Chor; Dbte Tm; Fr C; Spch C; Spch A; Fr A; *Bethel Col; Theology.*

WOLLBRINK, Ellen Beth
Warsaw HS; Warsaw, IN (2-53) Pres, AFS; Chor; Drama; FBLA; FHA; Pres, 4H; Secy, NHS; Tres, SC; 4H A; Kiwanis A; Type A; Chor A; FHA A; *Danville Jr Col; Commercial Floriculture.*

WOLLENHAUPT, Thomas Lee
Delphos Jefferson HS; Delphos, OH (15-100) Var C; JV, Golf; Tr; Amer Leg A; Hist A; HR; Assn Sr Patrol Ldr, BSct; *Bowling Green U; Communications Tech.*

WOLLMUTH, Lonnie Paul
Garrison HS; Garrison, ND (5%-76) Ann; Band; Chor; Sci C; Var C; Pres, Soph Cl; Bkbl; Co-Cpt, Ftbl; Tr; 4H A; Sci A; Swtht; Drama A; *UND-Grand; Med.*

WOLTER, Christine Barbara
Taft HS; Chicago, IL (57-850) Chor; Lit Mag; Rptr, Sch P; COM; Chamber of Comm A; Hon Prog; Ntl Sci Symposium; Sci A; Hon C; Usherettes; Fin, Sci Fair; Fin, Talent Show; Sch Play; *Mus Ed.*

WOLTER, Donna Louise
Taft HS; Chicago, IL (38-850) Chor; Lit Mag; COM; Hon Prog; Hon C; Sci Fair; Talent Show; *Mus Ed.*

WOLTERS, Lari Ann
Steeleville Comm Unit HS; Steeleville, IL (29-70) Bus C; Cpt, Chldr; Chor; FBLA; FHA; Hmrm; Cl Fav; *Belleville Area Jr Col; Cosmetology.*

WOLTERS, Leland Alan
Steeleville HS; Steeleville, IL (50%-56).

WOLTHOFF, Paula Rae
Layton HS; Layton, UT; Band; Chor; NHS; Citz A; Hon Prog; 1st Cl Sct; Bicentennial Essay A; *U of Utah; Elem Ed.*

WOLVEN, Kent Elbert
Reeds Spring HS; Reed Spring, MO (25%-90) AFS; VP, Band; Ensm; H of F; Hon Prog; *Southwest Baptist Col; Mus.*

WOLVERTON, Daucy William
Stephen Decatur HS; Decatur, IL; AFS; Band; Arch; COM; Citz A; First Aid; *Bradley U; Law.*

WOLVERTON, Lisa Anne
London HS; London, OH (1-165) NHS; Span C; SC; Tr; Jr Chamber of Com A; Kiwanis A; TriL; Show A; *Nurs.*

WOLVERTON, Robert Keith
Jackson Prep Sch; Jackson, MS (1-176) Pres, Mu Alpha Theta; NHS; Alg A; COM; Chem A; Hist A; Math A; Phy A; Lat A; *Pre-Med.*

WOLVERTON, Tina Kaye
McGavock HS; Nashville, TN (27-973) Pres, BC; Chor; FHA; Ger C; Hmrm; Madrigal; Math C; Mu Alpha Theta; NFL; NHS; ARC; Sch P; Span C; Spch C; SC; Sftbl; COM; Citz A; DARGCA; PTA A; Spch A; Most Christlike A; *Belmont Col; Elem Ed.*

WOLZ, Karla Ingrid
All Saints Cathedral Sch; St Thomas, VI (3-21) Chldr; Span C; SC; Bkbl; Sftbl; Tnns; Hon Prog.

WOMACK, Brenda Jean
Parkwood HS; Joplin, MO; Pres, A Cap Choir; Bus C; Pres, Chor; Drama; Ensm; Madrigal; NHS; Thes; Shorthand A; Snowball Sr Princess.

WOMACK, Stephanie Jean
Chester HS; Chester, PA (80-680) Band; Chor; Drama; Hmrm; Up Bound; Bkbl; Swim; Tr; *Julliard Col; Mus.*

WOMACK, Susan Janine
Parkwood HS; Joplin, MO; A Cap Choir; Bus C; Chor; Drama; Ensm; Thes; 1st Run-Up, Ms Merry Christmas; *Mid Amer Nazarene Col.*

WOMACK, Timothy Bruce
Denison HS; Denison, TX (5-387) Band; NHS; Symph Orch; All Region, Orch, Band; SMU Hon Choir; Outst Mus A; WW; *SMU; Mus.*

WOMELDORPH, David Michael
Niskayuna HS; Schenectady, NY (50%-400) Key C; Bsbl; Ftbl; Tr; Wrest.

WOMICK, Donald Lee Jr
Swain Co HS; Bryson City, NC (7-110) Band; Chess C; Fr C; FTA; NHS; A-Ed, Sch P; Sci C; Alg A; Bio A; NMF; All St Band; *Wake Forest U; Psych.*

WOMMACK, Clay Carter
Suffolk HS; Suffolk, VA (17-135) BS; Chem C; Drama; Fr C; HiY; VP, InterAct C; InterClub Coun; Pres, Lat C; Monogram; NHS; ARC; Thes; Var C; Tres, Soph Cl; Ftbl; Cpt, Tnns; Amer Leg Orator A; Chem A; God & Country A; ARC A; Sci A; Yth Fel; *VMI; Bio.*

WOMMACK, Timothy Loren
Jefferson City HS; Jefferson City, MO (250-500) Var C; Cpt, Wrest; Rotary A; All Conf, All Dist, Wrest; *Lincoln U; Horticulture.*

WONG, Alvin Wilmer
Adlai E Stevenson HS; New York, NY; Chess C; Wrest; COM; Hon Prog; *Med.*

WONG, Brian Walter
Red Bank Regional HS; Red Bank, NJ (9-260) Chess C; NHS; Sftbl; Tnns; Bio A; COM; Elk A; Hon Prog; Appalachia Service Project; Methodist Yth Fel; MYU Midwest Prog; *Yale U; Liberal Arts.*

WONG, Gladys Ying
Eagle Rock HS; Los Angeles, CA; AFS; Hmrm; CSF; Home Ec A; Silver Thimble A; Young Author's Conference A; *Home Ec.*

WONG, Harry Thomas
N Central HS; Manly, IA (5-66) Bus Mgr, Ann; Band; Ensm; Fr C; VP, Hmrm; Pres, NHS; Var C; VP, Sr Cl; VP, Jr Cl; VP, Soph Cl; Bsbl; Golf; Hines Mem Schol; *Iowa St U; Engr.*

WONG, Henry Lee
N Central HS; Manly, IA (5-58) NHS; SC; Golf; Amer Leg A; *Engr.*

WONG, Joe
Woodrow Wilson HS; Los Angeles, CA (9-550) VP, Chess C; Bkbl; Tnns; CSF; *U of Sou Calif; Computer Sci.*

WONG, John Check Wah
Vicent Massey Secondary Sch; Windsor, CANADA; Math C; Cr-Ctry; Tr; Wrest; Engr A; *U of Toronto; Engr.*

WONG, Lanny Wayne
Woodrow Wilson HS; Los Angeles, CA (20-550) *Pepperdine U; Bio.*

WONG, Linda Jean
Rockford E HS; Rockford, IL (36-607) NHS.

WONG, Lisa Yuen
Belmont HS; Los Angeles, CA; NFL; Bkbl; CSF; Hon Prog; Spch A; Mgr, Vlbl; Gym.

WONG, Patti Sue
Belmont HS; Los Angeles, CA; Chor; Semi-Fin, GS; NFL; NHS; Spch C; Tnns; CSF; COM; Citz A; Hon Prog; Spch A; Gold Seal Bearer; Chinese Composition; *U of Sou Calif.*

WONG, Randall Craig
Sunny Hills HS; Fullerton, CA; FFA; JV, Wrest; *USC; Law.*

WONG, Simeon Siu Mo
Belmont HS; Los Angeles, CA (170-800) K of C; Var C; Bkbl; Tnns; CSF; Citz A; Hon Prog; K of C A; Art A; *UCSD; Bio.*

WOO CHING, Sililo
Marist Brothers' HS; Pago Pago, AMERICAN SAMOA (3-50) Bus C; CYO; Pres, Hmrm; Sch P; SC; Pres, Jr Cl; Hon Prog; *Bradford Col; Physics.*

WOOD, Arthur Clarence
Bossier HS; Bossier City, LA (20%-340) *LSU; Naval ROTC.*

WOOD, Becky Jane
Pickwick South Side HS; Counce, TN (6-33) Ann; BC; Secy, FHA; WW; *Memphis St U; Mus.*

WOOD, Bradley Thomas
Harry A Burke Sch; Omaha, NE; ARC; Rptr, Sch P; Sacristan; Provost, Order of St John; Cert Swim Instructor; *U of Nebr; Journ.*

WOOD, Brian Robert
Tower Hill HS; Tower Hill, IL (2-30) VP, Sci C; Pres, Jr Cl; Bsbl; Bkbl; HCt; Industrial Arts A.

WOOD, Carol Katherin
Benson Union HS; Benson, AZ (50-84) Band; Drama; Model UN; Orch; ARC; Span C; Spch C; Thes; UN Council; Var C; Tnns; Chem A; ARC A; Type A; Mgr, Vlbl; WW; *Cochise Col; Nurs.*

WOOD, Carol Margaret
A E Beach HS; Savannah, GA; Ann; Band; Pres, BC; Lat C; Mu Alpha Theta; NHS; Pres, Jr Cl; COM; Citz A; Hon Prog; NEDT; WW; Most Intellectual; Nom, Magna Cum Laude; Nom, Salutatorian; *Journ.*

WOOD, Catherine Arnett
Northeastern HS; Detroit, MI; NHS; Tnns; Automation Acad; Keypunch.

WOOD, Cindy Renee
Knob Noster HS; Knob Noster, MO; Secy, Drama; Tres, SC; Tr; Best Actress A; Drama Contest A; Secy, Stu Coun; 'B' HR; *Central Mo St U; Drama.*

WOOD, Connie Gena
Warren HS; Warren, AR (20-146) Cpt, Chor; Chor; FHA; 4H; Off Worker; *U of Ark; Acct.*

WOOD, Cynthia Jane
Mountain View HS; Mtn View, OK (1-32) Band; Chor; Ensm; FHA; 4H; S-T, Soph Cl; Bkbl; Alg A; 4H A; HCt; Masonic A; Sci A; Okla Hon Soc; Piano A; Voice A; Band A; *Okla St U; Math.*

WOOD, Cynthia Ruth
Montgomery Blair HS; Silver Spring, MD; Chldr; Yth Fel; Yrbk Staff.

WOOD, D Lisa Lou
Hobbs HS; Hobbs, NM (25-425) Band; Chldr; FTA; Rainbow; SC; Secy, Jr Cl; Cl Fav; HCt; *NM St U; Nurs.*

WOOD, Darryl Allen
Northeastern HS; Detroit, MI; Chess C; Sci C; Golf; Alg A; Citz A; Hon Prog; Most Out; *Mich St U; Eng.*

WOOD, David Allen
Dos Pueblos HS; Goleta, CA (14-650) A Cap Choir; BS; Drama; Ensm; Madrigal; Pol Sci C; VP, Sci C; Thes; Bank Of Amer A; CSF; HCt; Hon Prog; Math A; Most Out; NMF; NMS; NEDT; Vlbl; UCSB Engr Schol; Nominated Rotary A; Nominated MLS; *U of Calif at Santa Barbara; Computer Sci.*

WOOD, David Brian
McCluer N HS; Florissant, MO; Band; Ftbl; Sftbl; *U of Mo; Engr.*

WOOD, David E
Pleasant Hill HS; Pleasant Hill, MO; Ann; NHS; Sch P; Pres, SC; JV, Bkbl; Cr-Ctry; Tr; Journ A; Eagle Sct; *Mo U; Art.*

WOOD, David Lee II
Woodrow Wilson HS; Beckley, WV; Order/Arrow; God & Country A; Sci A; Yth Fel; Eagle Sct; *Wildlife Mgt.*

WOOD, David Russell
Lee Davis HS; Mechanicsville, VA; BC; Fr C; Most Stu; Alpha Delta Kappa; Fellowship A; St, Astronomy C; *VPI; Elec Engr.*

WOOD, Debra Evelyn
Wellington HS; Wellington, TX; Band; Pres, BC; JV, Chldr; Pres, FHA; Sch P; SC; VP, Soph Cl; Bkbl; Beauty; Swtht; Swtht, Key C; Flag Corps; Semi-Fin, Miss Irish Rose; Semi-Fin, Miss Wellington; Semi-Fin Miss Spirit '76; *Texas Tech U; Speech Therapy.*

WOOD, Denise Ann
Ainsworth Sr HS; Flint, MI (25-250) NHS; Ftbl; *Baker Jr Col; Bus.*

WOOD, Donna Gene
Melbourne HS; Melbourne, FL; Chldr; Secy, Chor; Jr Civitan; Yth for Christ; Bake Off Contest Cert; Nurs.

WOOD, Donna Merrill
Eastwood HS; Tuscaloosa, AL; President's Phys Fitness A; Bicentennial Art Contest Win; Ntl Piano Playing Auditions; *U of Ala; Art.*

WOOD, Donna Sue
Pickwick Southside HS; Counce, TN (3-32) Ann; Secy, BC; Cpt, Chldr; Parl, FHA; Secy, 4H; Hmrm; Sci C; Var C; Rptr, Soph Cl; Bkbl; Beauty; 4H A; Hon Prog; MLS; Sci A; Star Student; Yth Fel; FHA Sub-Region Off; Stu For Christ; Art C; *Martin Col; Home Ec.*

WOOD, Doris Elizabeth
S R Butler HS; Huntsville, AL (25-570) Chor; City Conf; Ensm; Hmrm; Lat C; Math C; VP, Mu Alpha Theta; NHS; F-Ed, Sch P; VP, Sci C; SC; COM; Citz A; Hon Prog; NEDT; Sci A; Alpha Lambda Delta; Lat A; Sch & Comm A; *U of Tenn; Engr.*

WOOD, Eddie Vaughn III
Wilcox Co HS; Rochelle, GA (5-110) FFA; 4H; Hmrm; SC; Bkbl; Ftbl; Alg A; Hist A; Hon Prog; Math A; Eng A; *U of Ga; Phys Ed.*

WOOD, Elaine Ann
Jonesboro HS; Jonesboro, GA (100-450) Drama; Fr C; S-T, Tri-HiY; 4H A; NEDT; Yth Fel; *Clayton Jr Col.*

WOOD, Emmett Grant
Bardstown HS; Bardstown, KY (20%-159) Band; Fr C; Hmrm; Sch P; SC; Bsbl; JV, Bkbl; Cr-Ctry; Ftbl; Tr; *Eastern Ky U; Elec.*

WOOD, Gary Lynn
Borch HS; Boise, ID; AFS; Ger C; Var C; JV, Bkbl; Ftbl; Church Bell Choir; *NW Nazarene Col.*

WOOD, Harry Michael
Mechanicville HS; Mechanicville, NY (50-159) Chor; Drama; Ed, Sch P; Span C; DARGCA; MLS; Type A; *Piedmont Col; Social Work.*

WOOD, James Waldo
Oak Hall Private Sch; Gainesville, FL (6-40) Chor; Ensm; Secy, Fr C; Math C; Order/Arrow; Sci C; Amer Leg A; COM; Citz A; Order/Arrow A; Art C, Art A; Sr Patrol Leader; PA; Ch, Yth Board of Deacons; Mile Swim, BSA.

WOOD, Janice Ruth
McNary Sr HS; Salem, OR; A Cap Choir; Pres, CYO; Chem C; ARC; Med.

WOOD, Jeffrey Allen
Pike HS; Indianapolis, IN (19-295) Band; Ensm; Math C; Mu Alpha Theta; NHS; Orch; Span C; Hon Prog; *Greenville Col; Math.*

WOOD, Jodie Anne
Franklinton HS; Franklinton, LA; Ann; BC; Chor; Ensm; S-T, FBLA; Lit Ral; Rainbow; Sch P; SC; Gov Honor Prog; Miss FHS; Most Talented; *SE La U; Acct.*

WOOD, Johnny Dalton
Dell City HS; Dell City, TX (1-23) Pres, FFA; NHS; Pres, SC; Pres, Jr Cl; Cpt, Ftbl; Tnns; Tr; Math A; Sci A; *Human Chem.*

WOOD, Karen Renee
New Albany HS; New Albany, IN; Ger C; Hmrm; NAHS Letter; Vlbl A; *Prossure LPN Sch; Nurs.*

WOOD, Kendall Lee
Anderson HS; Anderson, IN; Band; 4H; Madrigal; 4H A; Type A; Val; *Anderson Col; Mus.*

WOOD, Larry Allen
Macon Co HS; Macon, MO (5-120) Var C; Chor; Golf; Math A; Yth Fel; Bowl A; Pitch, Hit & Throw A; Punt, Pass & Kick A; Phys Fitness A; *Kirksville Col; Math.*

WOOD, LeAnn Marie
Allen Cons HS; Allen, NE (4-32) Ann; Band; VP; 4H; Sch P; JV, Bkbl; 4H A; Mgr, Vlbl; *Vet Sci.*

WOOD, Mark Cole
Jonesboro HS; Jonesboro, AR (10%-300) A Cap Choir; BC; Ensm; Mu Alpha Theta; NHS; Order/Arrow; Sch P; Eagle Sct; *Ark St U; Bus.*

WOOD, Mary Elizabeth
Emma Sansom HS; Gadsden, AL (10%-235) FTA; Sci C; Span C; Span NHS; COM; WW; *Gadsden S Jr Col; Primary Ed.*

WOOD, Michelle Denise
Marshall HS; Marshall, MO (15-209) FBLA; FHA; Orch; Pom Pon; WW; Courtwarming; *Central M St U; Acct.*

WOOD, Miriam Elizabeth
Oak Hall Private Sch; Gainesville, FL (1-20) Ann; Chor; Ensm; Span C; Span NHS; Secy, SC; Mgr, Bkbl; COM; Citz A; Coun of Teach A; Hist A; Vlbl; Schol A; Elem Ed.

WOOD, Nathaniel Jeffrey
William Penn S HS; York, PA (50-400) Chor; Pres, Dbte Tm; Drama; Pres, Ensm; Ger C; Thes; Bsbl; MVP, Bkbl; Ftbl; Tnns; Tr; Manna Bible Inst; Theology.

WOOD, Patty Joy
Duncan HS; Duncan, OK (50%-325) Band; Chor; Span C; Tr; Okla Christian Col.

WOOD, Rebecca Leigh
Jonesboro HS; Jonesboro, AR (3-300) A Cap Choir; BC; FBLA; Lit Mag; Mu Alpha Theta; NHS; Sch P; Secy, SC; Secy, Jr Cl; Bkbl; Tr; Jr & Sr Cl Plays; Hon Graduate; Ark St U; Bus.

WOOD, Richard Alan
Battle Ground Acad; Franklin, TN (1-64) A-Ed, Ann; BS; Dbte Tm; Secy, Key C; Lat C; NFL; Pres, NHS; Spch C; SC; Pres, Soph Cl; Cpt, Cr-Ctry; Co-Cpt, Tr; COM; NEDT; Schol A; Most Studious; Furman U; Chem.

WOOD, Robert Glenn
Burnside HS; Burnside, KY (1-40) Pres, BC; Bus C; Fr C; FBLA; Tres, FTA; Math C; Order/Arrow; Ed, Sch P; Bkbl; Cr-Ctry; Tr; COM; HCt; Order/Arrow A; Tres, Beta C; Eng A; Schol Ath; US Military Acad; Humanities.

WOOD, Sandra Lea
Yosemite HS; Oakhurst, CA (10-96) Chldr; Secy, FBLA; FNA; JV, Bkbl; Sftbl; Citz A; Fresno City Col; Bus.

WOOD, Sharon Lori
Woodham HS; Pensacola, FL (13-530) FBLA; NHS; Gym; HS All Amer; Pensacola Jr Col; Phys Therapy.

WOOD, Sherrie Lynn
Centralia Sr HS; Centralia, WA; Interntl Social Ch, Nazarene Yth; Concessions Ch, Girls League; NW Nazarene Col; Early Childhood Ed.

WOOD, Stephanie Lynne
Caney Valley HS; Caney, KS (3-66) F-Ed, Ann; Chldr; Chor, Tres, FBLA; FHA; GS; NHS; Sch P; Pres, Span C; S-T, SC; Var C; HCt; Yth Fel; Yth Leg; Coffeyville Comm Jr Col; Bus.

WOOD, Steve Alton
Itawamba HS; Fulton, MS (20%-150) A Cap Choir; Band; Chor; Ensm; Spch C; NMS; Spch A; U of Miss; Engr.

WOOD, Steven Michael
Fort Scott Sr HS; Fort Scott, KS (27-150) Dbte Tm; NFL; St Stu Congress; VP, Sr Cl; Ftbl; Sftbl; Wrest; Spch A; Coffeyville Comm Col; Spch.

WOOD, Susan Marie
Estill HS; Estill, SC (1-50) Ed, Ann; BC; GS; Cl Fav; Hon Prog; Cpt, Vlbl; TAPS; Statistician, Bkbl; Miss Estill High; Clemson U; Horticulture.

WOOD, Susanna Lee
Bossier HS; Bossier City, LA (15%-327) A Cap Choir; Tres, Bus C; Chor; Drama; Span C; Y-Tns; JV, Sftbl; Swim; Tnns; Hon Prog; JA A; Yth Fel; Pepperdine U; Drama.

WOOD, Teena Marie
South HS; Columbus, OH; Chldr; Orch; Cpt, Tnns; Tr; Ohio St U.

WOOD, Teresa Ann
Macon R 1 HS; Macon, MO; Chor; Drama; Madrigal; Rainbow; Sch Achieve Tm; SC; JV, Bkbl; Tr; Hist A; HCt; Yth Fel; Yth Leg.

WOOD, Timothy Clark
Knob Noster HS; Knob Noster, MO; Wrest; Bio; B HR; CMSU; Bio.

WOOD, Timothy Lee
Pomona HS; Arvada, CO (10-550) Bsbl; Bkbl; Tnns.

WOOD, Virginia Carol
Trinity Christian Sch; Chattanooga, TN (2-17) NHS; ARC; SC.

WOOD, William Dayton
Mossyrock HS; Mossyrock, WA (8-35) NHS; Sci C; Cpt, Wrest; Wash St U; Elec.

WOODALL, Daniel Thomas
Glendale HS; Springfield, MO (75-400) AFS; Pres, Chor; Ensm; Madrigal; SC; Thes; Sch Mus; Comm Theatre; Wichita St U; Vocal Mus.

WOODALL, Gaila Jannine
McClellan HS; Little Rock, AR; A Cap Choir; BC; Bus C; Chor; FBLA; FHA; Tres, GS; Hmrm; Inter-Act C; InterClub Coun; NHS; ARC; Y-Tns; Tres, Sr Cl; Citz A; HCt; Hon Prog; All-St Choir; Ouachita Baptist Col; Interior Design.

WOODALL, Michael Ernest
Capital HS; Boise, ID (130-536) A Cap Choir; Band; Chor; Ensm; Madrigal; JV, Bkbl; JV, Tnns; Northwest Nazarene Col; Bus.

WOODALL, Randall Eugene
D W Daniel HS; Central, SC; BC; Sci C; Art, Mus, C'S; PA; Clemson U; Industrial Mgr.

WOODARD, Ann Elizabeth
London HS; London, OH (11-98) Band; Chor; Ensm; Tres, Fr C; 4H; Lit Mag; NHS; Kiwanis A; Type A; Purdue U; Elem Ed.

WOODARD, Celia Marieh
Baker Sr HS; Baker, LA (2-374) Bus C; Drama; Spch C; Bio A; COM; Eng A; Art A; Phys Fitness A.

WOODARD, Charlotte Renee
W Charlotte Sr HS; Charlotte, NC (123-594) BC; Chor; Orch; Ski C; Span C; Violin; Piano; U of NC; Mus.

WOODARD, Cynthia Renee
W Laurens Sr HS; Dublin, GA (20-186) Ann; BC; Ch, FBLA; FHA; 4H; Hmrm; Ed, Sch P; Pres, SC; VP, Jr Cl; HQn; HCt; Journ A; Art C; Jr-Sr Prom Qn; Primary Sunday Sch Teacher; Outst FHA; Ga Sou Col; Early Childhood Ed.

WOODARD, David Dixon
Greenville Christian Acad; Greenville, NC (2-8) Drama; Ensm; Bkbl; Bus Adm.

WOODARD, Greg Alan
Chillicothe HS; Chillicothe, OH; BS; Orch; Bsbl; Bkbl; Ftbl; Tr; Med.

WOODARD, Gregory Keith
Medford Sr HS; Medford, OR (50-500) NHS; ARC; Ftbl; COM; 4H A; Pepperdine U; Pre-Med.

WOODARD, James Emanuel
Glenbrook HS; Minden, LA (3-32) BS; 4H; Hmrm; Fin, Lit Ral; NHS; SC; Pres, Jr Cl; Pres, Soph Cl; Bsbl; Bkbl; Cr-Ctry; Ftbl; Tnns; Tr; Cl Fav; Hon Prog; NEDT; Type A; LSU; Vet Med.

WOODARD, Jerry Eugene Jr
Lincoln Comm HS; Lincoln, IL (16-340) Fr C; Bsbl; U of Ill; Computer Sci.

WOODARD, Kevin Lee
Lee HS; Midland, TX (40-700) NHS; Rptr, Sch P; Fin, Thes; Southwestern Area Art Exhibit A; 3rd Pl, Big Spring Art Show; Merit A, Snyder Art Assn; 2nd, Postern, TFA San Ant Spch Fes; Abilene Christian U; Art.

WOODARD, Lea Ann
Dodge Co HS; Eastman, GA (20%-209) Anchor C; Ann; Ensm; Fr C; 4H; Sch P; Sci C; Bkbl; Tr; Cl Fav; Hist A; Rotary Stu; Coach's Trophy, Bkbl; Fr Cert; Ga Sou Col.

WOODARD, Linda Louise
Marion Sr HS; Marion, IL (100-280) Span NHS; Friends in Christ; Span A; Shorthand A; Rotary A Nom; John A Logan Col; Bus.

WOODARD, Nicol Lloyd
A E Beach HS; Savannah, GA; Pres, Chem C; Pres, Chess C; Ch, Dbte Tm; Key C; Order/Arrow; Sci C; SC; Ftbl; Tnns; Bio A; Chem A; Hon Prog; NMS; Pre-Med.

WOODARD, Richard Wayne
Medford Sr HS; Medford, OR (250-500) ARC; Tr; Rptr, Explorers; Tr Ltr; Crime Prevention.

WOODBECK, Carol Lynn
Edward H White HS; Jacksonville, FL (63-800) Chor; NHS; COM; Citz A; Eckerd Col; Nurs.

WOODBECK, Michael Scott
Gordon HS; Gordon, NE (77-88) FFA; JV, Bkbl; Citz A; ARC A; Yth Fel; Tres, Church Yth Group.

WOODBURN, Karen Ena
St Angela Hall Acad; Brooklyn, NY (6-89) Chor; Fr C; NHS; Y-Tns; Swim; Tnns; COM; Pres A; 2nd Hon, Fr Contest; St Joseph's Col; Biol.

WOODBURN, Shari Ann
La Canada HS; La Canada, CA (2%-447) Drama; Math C; Mu Alpha Theta; Thes; Swim; CSF; Hon Prog; Yth Fel; Job's Daughters; Board of Deacons; Young Life; Bus Adm.

WOODBURY, Lori Kay
Kent-Meridian Sr HS; Kent, WA (20-564) Bus Mgr, Ann; Band; Chor; Drama; NHS; ARC; Ed, Sch P; Ski C; SC; COM; Hon Prog; Most Out; Semi-Fin, Miss Tnage Seattle; Ed.

WOODBURY, Steven Anthony
Albuquerque HS; Albuquerque, NM (6-66) CYO; Secy, Chor; Hmrm; NHS; SC; Citz A; Cl Fav; Ntl Cath Mus Ed Asn; Pres A; Mus A; SC Pres A; U of NM; Mus.

WOODCOCK, Janice Marie
Weedsport Central HS; Weedsport, NY (10-89) Band; Chor; FHA; French NHS; Fin, Jr Miss Pagent; Ski C; VP, Jr Cl; Sftbl; MVP, Tr; COM; Cl Fav; HCt; Hon Prog; NEDT; Regent Schol; Cpt, Vlbl; MVP, Cpt, Field Hockey; MVP, Cpt, Bkbl; St Lawrence U; Liberal Arts.

WOODEN, Monica Lynn
Lincoln HS; Lincoln, CA (1-209) Band; Drama; Ensm; Bsbl; Hon Prog; Tr & Wrest Statistician.

WOODEN, Tracey Ann
Del Campo HS; Fair Oaks, CA; Span C; CSF; Yth Fel; Psych.

WOODHOUSE, Lauri Maureen
C-P P West HS; Painted Post, NY; Band; Drama; Hmrm; Ski C; Var C; Bkbl; Sftbl; COM.

WOODKE, Catherine
Batavia HS; Batavia, IL; AFS; NHS; Ill St Schol; U of Iowa; Liberal Stu.

WOODLAND, Kathy Patrice
Forest Park HS; Baltimore, MD (10-300) COM; Hon Prog; Morgan St U; Pre-Med.

WOODLEY, Debra Dianne
N Mercer R-3 Sch; Mercer, MO (3-19) Ann; Chor; 4H; JV, Bkbl; Sftbl; Tr; Secy.

WOODMANSEE, Michael Asbury
S Miami Jr HS; S Miami, FL (15-350) Chess C; Hmrm; Ch, NHS; Tr; Co-Cpt, Wrest; Citz A; God & Country A; Masonic A; Eagle Sct.

WOODNORTH, Donna Jean
Westmont Hilltop HS; Johnstown, PA (15-196) Tres, Arch; Chor; Ski C; Hon Prog; Yth Ed Assn; Church Yth Group; Church Bell Choir; Duquesne U; Phar.

WOODRIDGE, Calvin Jerome
Central HS; W Helena, AR; Drama; Fr C; Ed, Sch P; SC; Var C; Bkbl; Cr-Ctry; Tr; Journ A; Q&S A; Miss St U; Journ.

WOODRING, Rose Ellen Marie
Williamsburg HS; Williamsburg, PA (2-65) Band; Drama; FNA; FTA; 4H; Jr Miss Pagent; Rptr, Sch P; COM; HCt; NEDT; Sal; VofDEM; BPW C Schol; Blair Co Women's Med Soc Schol; Ind U of Penn; Nurs.

WOODRING, Sandra Penny
Adairsville HS; Adairsville, GA (20%-200) A-Ed, Ann; Band; Dbte Tm; FHA; Rptr, Sch P; Sci C; Band A's; Mus.

WOODROOF, Susan Jane
Spring Woods HS; Houston, TX (10%-510) JETS; Mjrte; Secy, Math C; Secy, Mu Alpha Theta; NHS; Sci C; Tres, Span C; Alg A; Chem A; Hon Prog; Math A; Span A; Texas A&M U; Chem Engr.

WOODROOF, Susan Marie
Woodway Sr HS; Edmonds, WA; NHS; Orch; Sftbl; NW Nazarene Col; Elem Ed.

WOODRUFF, Charlotte Ann
Captain Shreve HS; Shreveport, LA (64-518) Dbte Tm; VP, Drama; Rptr, 4H; Hmrm; InterClub Coun; NHS; SC; Secy, Thes; 4H A; PTA A; Spch A; Rodeo Tm; Rodeo A; Hon Thespian & Best Thespian; Best Supporting Actress; Forensic A; Centenary Col; Spch Pathology.

WOODRUFF, Dennis Scott
Wachusett Regional HS; Holden, MA (60-500) Sci C; Tr; NMS; Pres, Church Yth; Ldr, Bible Stu; Win, Sci Fair; Church Bkbl; *Barrington Col; Yth Ministry.*

WOODRUFF, Iris Anne
Upland HS; Upland, CA (1-597) A Cap Choir; AFS; NHS; Orch; Tnns; CSF; MLS; Most Out; Spch A; Chaffey Trust Fund Schol; General Dynamics Mgt C Schol; Fin, Soroptimist C; *Wheaton Col; Pre-Law.*

WOODRUFF, Marjorie Starr
Van Buren Comm HS; Keosauqua, IA (30-96) A Cap Choir; Band; Cpt, Chldr; Chor; Ensm; Rptr, 4H; Madrigal; Rptr, Sch P; Mus A's; *Iowa Weslyan Col; Med.*

WOODS, Anita Lynne
Henry McNeal Turner HS; Atlanta, GA; Band; Ensm; Hmrm; Citz A; Dance A; *Clark Col; Ed.*

WOODS, Annette
Robert A Millikan HS; Long Beach, CA; *Calif St U; Bus Adm.*

WOODS, Bonnie Jean
Chester HS; Chester, PA; Hon Prog; Sci A; *Law Enforcement.*

WOODS, Brenda Cheryl
Jones Valley HS; Birmingham, AL; Chor; Y-Tns; Math A; Lang Arts A; *U of Ala; Law.*

WOODS, Byron Eugene
Reidsville Sr HS; Reidsville, NC (9-324) Band; Drama; Fr C; Hmrm; Rptr, Sch P; NEDT; NC Gov Sch; *Fine Arts.*

WOODS, Calvin
Nettie Lee Roth HS; Dayton, OH; *Bus Math.*

WOODS, Cynthia Adele
Thornton Township HS; Harvey, IL (50-750) Ed, Ann; Hmrm; NHS; Span C; Spch C; SC; Secy, Tri-HiY; Tnns; Ch, Girls V; High Hon As; Ch, Prom Comm; Varsity Tnns Ltr; JV Badminton; May Qn Court; *Ecology.*

WOODS, David John
Brookwood HS; Ontario, WI (7-46) Co-Ed, Ann; Band; Chor; Drama; Spch C; SC; Bsbl; Bkbl; Golf; Spch A; Brightest Ideas; Stu o-t Mo; Band A; *Marian Col; Mus.*

WOODS, Deborah Elane
Tillamook HS; Tillamook, OR (97-182) Band; Chor; FBLA; 4H; Rainbow; 4H A; Grand Choir, Rainbow Girls.

WOODS, Gerald Alan
Northport HS; Northport, MI (10-29) Co-Cpt, Bkbl; Soccer; Tr; *Elec Engr.*

WOODS, Holly Kathleen
Ross S Sterling HS; Baytown, TX (15-649) Chor; Parl, FTA; Key C; SC; Cl Fav; Drill Tm Duchess; *U of Houston; Med.*

WOODS, Inez Royal
Hueytown HS; Hueytown, AL (2-30) Hmrm; Cl Fav; HQn; *Ala A&M U; Special Ed.*

WOODS, Jeffrey Don
Abilene HS; Abilene, TX (16-541) A Cap Choir; Ensm; Lat C; Pres, Math C; Mu Alpha Theta; NHS; Pres, Sci C; JV, Ftbl; COM; Hon Prog; Math A; NMF; NMS; Sci A; *Abilene Christian U; Physics.*

WOODS, Jimmy Carl
Powell Valley HS; Speedwell, TN; BC; FFA; Ftbl; *U of Tenn.*

WOODS, Karen Patricia
Petersburg HS; Petersburg, VA (10%-600) Band; Chor; Span C; Cl Fav; Most Out; Choir Pianist; Regional Choir; Alt, Regional Band; *Mich St U; Mus.*

WOODS, Karen Venessa
Myrtle Beach HS; Myrtle Beach, SC (5-30) Band; Chldr; Chor; Pres, Hmrm; Pres, SC; Bkbl; Sftbl; Tr; COM; HCt; Pres A; Yth Fel; Gym Tm; Ballet Sq; Sunday Sch Teacher; *SC St U; Psych.*

WOODS, Kenneth
Mill Valley Tamalpais HS; Mill Valley, CA; Bsbl; Ftbl; Tr; Most Out; Sci A; *Col of Marin; Phys Ed.*

WOODS, Lauren Marie
Patten Acad of Christian Ed; Oakland, CA (2-14) A Cap Choir; Band; Chor; Community Yth Symph; Cpt, Dbte Tm; Drama; Orch; Rptr, Sch P; VP, SC; VP, Sr Cl; Bsbl; Sftbl; B Crocker A; Citz A; St Scholar; Model Stu; *Patten Bible Col; Theology.*

WOODS, Laurie Ellen
Cascade HS; Turner, OR; Band; Chor; FFA; Hmrm; JV, Sftbl; Mgr, Tr; Festival Ct; Most Improved; *Biola Bible Col; Missions.*

WOODS, LeRoyce Donnell
Benedictine HS; Cleveland, OH (48-125) Drama; Hmrm; Sch P; SC; Yth Fel; *Bishop Col; Theology.*

WOODS, Louetta Mildred
Lackawanna Sr HS; Lackawanna, NY; *Drew U; Cosmetology.*

WOODS, Marvell Collins
Mendel Cath HS; Chicago, IL (75-255) Band; Orch; Ski C; MVP, Ftbl; Jazz, Section Ldr, Band; *Burkley U; Mus.*

WOODS, Mary Marjorie
Reynolds HS; Greenville, PA (8-183) Pres, AFS; FTA; Ger C; Tri-HiY; Tres, Jr Cl; *Penn St U; Bio.*

WOODS, Mary Samuel
Harrodsburg HS; Harrodsburg, KY (3-78) F-Ed, Ann; BC; Dbte Tm; Ch, NFL; NHS; Pres, Spch C; St Stu Congress; Tnns; Amer Leg Orator A; B Crocker A; MLS; VofDEM; Pres, St Jr Hist Soc; St Ldr, Century III; *Purdue U; Vet Sci.*

WOODS, Miriam Elizabeth
Wm J Woodham HS; Pensacola, FL (9-530) Math C; Mu Alpha Theta; NHS; Span C; NMF; NMS; Spch A; Pensacola Jr Col Found Schol; *Pensacola Jr Col; Pre-Vet Med.*

WOODS, Patricia Ann
George Henry Corliss HS; Chicago, IL (35-485) Secy, Chor; NHS; VP, Span C; COM; Hon Prog; Principal Schol A; *Pepperdine Col; Nurs.*

WOODS, Paula Lee
Flora HS; Flora, IL (25-165) Bus C; FBLA; 4H; Span C; JV, Bkbl; Sftbl.

WOODS, Phyllis Yvonne
N Nashville HS; Nashville, TN; Rptr, Hmrm; SC; Secy, Xinos Sorority.

WOODS, Rhonda Darselle
Lincoln HS; Dallas, TX; Cpt, Band; Pres, Cum Laude Soc; Pres, Hmrm; Secy, Math C; Pres, NHS; VP, Sci C; SC; Y-Tns; Hon Prog; Band, Foreign Lang, A's; *Tex Sou U; Phar.*

WOODS, Richard Mark
Groveton HS; Groveton, TX (3-48) Pres, BC; Pres, 4H; Pres, SC; Ftbl; Tr; 4H A; HKg; Best All Around; *Tex A&M U; Building Construction.*

WOODS, Ruth Elaine
Haverford Sr HS; Havertown, PA (10-666) Band; Lat C; Lat NHS; NHS; Sci C; Aux Lat; NMS; *Houghton Col; Bio.*

WOODS, Sandra Jean
Lyons Sr HS; Lyons, GA (30-100) Chor; FBLA; JV, Bkbl; Tr; VICA C; Bkbl, PA, Bible C, A's; *Trinity Col; Bible Stu.*

WOODS, Teresa Ann
Gravette HS; Gravette, AR (13-80) Ann; Band; Chor; VP, FHA; GS; 4H; A-Ed, Sch P; Sci C; Sftbl; Swim; Buss Cpt and Evanglism Comm Ch; *Lynchburg Baptist Col; Religion.*

WOODS, Teresea Gayle
Permian HS; Odessa, TX (150-850) Lat C; Rainbow; *Odessa Col; Art.*

WOODS, Velma Jean
Breckinridge Co HS; Harned, KY (10-200) Math C; Mu Alpha Theta; Bio C; *Joseph Holt Hist C.*

WOODS, Yolanda Maurie
Woodlawn Sr HS; Baltimore, MD; Cpt, Chldr; Chor; Fr C; FHA; Fin, Jr Miss Pagent; Mjrte; Swim; Beauty; Cl Fav; Delta Sigma Theta A; Pres A; Model; 4th Pl, Miss Tn of Amer; *U of Md; Criminal Justice.*

WOODSIDES, Karla Denise
DuQuoin HS; Du Quoin, IL; FHA; Key C; Pres, Spch C; Amer Leg A; Citz A; Hist A; Opt A; Rotary A; Spch A; *Spch Communications.*

WOODSON, Cheryl Lynn
Cass Tech HS; Detroit, MI (33%-987) HR; '78' C; Black Stu Assn; Pre-Med Career Coun Prog; Stu Alliance; Pre-Law C; *Wayne St U; Chem.*

WOODSON, Eva Maria
Monterey HS; Monterey, CA; Chor; Ger C; Bkbl; Hockey; Sftbl; Tr; Debutant; Vlbl; Most Inspirational; GSct; Ldrship A; FCA; Yth Coun; *Monterey Penninsula Col; Nurs.*

WOODSON, Michele
St Mary's HS; Jersey City, NJ (3-66) Chldr; Hist A; Math A; NEDT; Religion, Geom, Eng, A's; *Bus Adm.*

WOODSON, Robert Athel
Wayne Co HS; Jesup, GA; Band; Tri-HiY; MVP, Golf; MVP, Soccer; MVP, Sftbl.

WOODWARD, Anne Fraser
Robert F Munroe Sch; Quincy, FL (9-33) Ann; BC; Co-Cpt, Chldr; Drama; Bkbl; Sftbl; 4H A; *Weslyan Col; Communications.*

WOODWARD, Arlene Frances
Morrison HS; Morrison, IL (1-153) NHS; Hon Prog; Math A; Val; Ill St Sch; *Augustana Col; Bus.*

WOODWARD, Charles Edward
Grissom HS; Huntsville, AL; A Cap Choir; Bus Mgr, Band; Chor; Ensm; Hmrm; Key C; JV, Bsbl; JV, Bkbl; JV, Ftbl; Cl Fav; Yth Fel; All City Chor.

WOODWARD, Diane Lynn
N Montgomery HS; Crawfordsville, IN (20-189) Band; Hmrm; Span C; HCt; Math A; Pres A; ARC A; *Purdue U; Phar.*

WOODWARD, Helen Eva
Niagara Wheatfield Sr HS; Sanborn, NY (60-475) Chor; Drama; Lat C; Co-Cpt, Mjrte; Bsbl; Bkbl; Cl Fav; Spelling A; 90% Cl Avg A; Play Festival A; *Navy; Photography.*

WOODWARD, Joanne Mary
Alexander Galt Regional HS; Lennoxville, CANADA (16-539) Ger C; S-T, Hmrm; *Math.*

WOODWARD, Kathryn
Arapahoe HS; Littleton, CO (3-600) Ensm; Alg A; Bio A; COM; Hon Prog; Math A; Sci A; Pep C; *Oral Roberts U; Nurs.*

WOODWARD, Kimberly Joyce
Rockdale HS; Rockdale, TX (70-140) Bus C; Pres, FBLA; SC; HCt; Swtht; Yth Fel; Secy, FBLA; WW; OEA, VOE, A's; Best Looking, Sr Cl; *Secy.*

WOODWARD, Mark Allen
Texhoma HS; Texhoma, OK; FFA; Mgr, Bkbl; 4H A; Pres Clrm For Young Amer; *Okla St U; Animal Sci.*

WOODWARD, Victoria Lynn
Manual HS; Denver, CO (75-400) VP, FBLA; NHS; Soccer; *Bethany Col.*

WOODWELL, Renee Ruth
Martin Co HS; Stuart, FL (84-500) F-Ed, Ann; Pres, FBLA; HCt; Tigerettes; Q&S; Sigma Phi; *Indian River Comm Col; Secy Sci.*

WOODWORTH, Steve Edward
North Love Christian Sch; Rockford, IL (1-20) Chor; Bsbl; Bkbl; Cr-Ctry; Soccer; *Hist.*

WOODY, Sally Lynn
Herndon HS; Herndon, WV (5-58) Chldr; FHA; Pres, Hmrm; NHS; SC; Pres, Jr Cl; Cpt, Bkbl; Sftbl; MVP, Bkbl; Chldr A; Sports As; Bkbl Trophy; *Concord Col; Bio.*

WOODY, Yvonne
Eli Whitney Voc HS; Brooklyn, NY (126-600) Secy, CYO; ARC; Tnns; Bus Eng Off Training; *Laguardia Comm Col; Data Processing.*

WOODYARD, Georgianne
Leroy HS; Leroy, AL (10-50) Pres, Band; 4H; NHS; Tres, Jr Cl; 4H A; Yth Fel; *Mobile Col; Mus.*

WOODYARD, Michael Olin
Glenwood Springs HS; Glenwood Springs, CO; Band; Ensm; JV, Golf; JV, Wrest; Yth Fel; *Colo S; U; Bus.*

WOOLARD, Dora Elizabeth
Chatsworth HS; Chatsworth, CA (600-1500) Vlb Art Textiles.

WOOLBRIGHT, Pamela Ann
Abbeville HS; Abbeville, SC (20-167) Chldr; Chess C; FTA; Hmrm; SC; Var C; Beauty; HCt; U of SC; Med.

WOOLDRIDGE, Sue Ellen
Willows HS; Willows, CA (2-148) Bkbl; Ftbl; Hockey; Sftbl; Swim; Tnns; Tr; CSF; Pres A.

WOOLERY, Mark William
Sparks HS; Sparks, NV (3-290) Chess C; Pres, Ger C; Pres, NHS; SC; St Parl, VICA; 2nd Pl, VICA St Skill Olympics; U of Nev; Elec Engr.

WOOLEVER, Susan Louise
Fairfax HS; Fairfax, VA (158-448) Band; Chor; Thes; Aux Lat; Ger Hon Soc; Outst Musician A; Cum Laude Lat A; Metropolitan Edison Art A; George Mason U; Bus.

WOOLEY, Genetra
Hammond HS; Hammond, IN (213-353) Chldr; 4H; Hmrm; Secy, Sun Sch; Dress Designer.

WOOLFOLK, Roberta Lee
Huntington HS; Huntington, WV; Pres, Tri-HiY; Home Ec A.

WOOLHISER, Kenten Darrell
Canby Union HS; Canby, OR (55-300) Chess C; Drama; Span C; Swim; Oreg Math HR; Humboldt St Col; Oceanography.

WOOLHISER, Vicki A
Canby Union HS; Canby, OR (22-220) Chor; Ensm; NHS; Thes; May Court Princess; VP, Girl's League Coun; Most Talented A; Mus.

WOOLSEY, Brady Lynn
Jacksboro HS; Jacksboro, TX (50%-61) Bus C; FBLA; Ftbl; Type A; All Dist Ftbl; Member o-t Yr, FBLA; Machine A'S, VOE; Midwestern St U; Bus.

WOOLSON, Clinton Joel
Kingsway Regional HS; Swedesboro, NJ (20-160) NHS; Drexel U; Mech Engr.

WOOLSON, Mary Anne
Archmere Acad; Claymont, DE; Drama; Fr C; A-Ed, Sch P; NEDT; Archmere School.

WOOLVERTON, Katherine Jo
Coahoma HS; Coahoma, TX (4-72) Band; Bus C; Ensm; NHS; Pres, Sci C; Span C; Spch C; SC; MLS; WW; Girl of Month; Abilene Christian U; Bus.

WOOLWORTH, Richard Alan
Brookings HS; Brookings, SD (50%-190) Band; Ensm; VP, 4H; Orch; Rptr, Sch P; Sci C; 4H A; Journ A; Mus Contest A; BScts; SD St U; Journ.

WOOTEN, Claudia Lynne
N Iredell HS; Olin, NC (2%-340) Secy, BC; FHA; Sci C; JV, Bkbl; Pres A; Sci A; Schol A.

WOOTEN, David Allen
N Iredell HS; Olin, NC (20%-340) AFS; Secy, FFA; Hmrm; Secy, Key C; Sci C; SC; Mgr, Bkbl; Mgr, Ftbl; HCt; Hon Prog; Sci A; Spch A; NC St U; Conservation.

WOOTEN, Linda Jean
Pendleton HS; Pendleton, SC (5-133) BC; Fr C; FHA; 4H; Pres, Hmrm; NHS; Sci C; Hon Prog; Allied Yth; Ch, Foreign Stu C; Fr A; WW; Clemson U; Fr.

WOOTEN, Mary Allison
Starmount HS; Boonville, NC (24-150) FHA; 4H; Secy, Sr Cl; Tnns; Pep C; Health Careers C; Secy, VICA; GAA; U of NC; Nurs.

WOOTEN, Paula Ruth
Lanse Creuse HS; Mount Clemens, MI; Band; Drama; NHS; Thes; Nurs.

WOOTEN, RoRene
E St Louis Sr HS; E St Louis, IL (119-824) A Cap Choir; Band; Chor; Commercial C; Ensm; Hmrm; Rainbow; SC; Var C; Cl Fav; Interlochen Ntl Mus; Yth Fel; HS St A; Ill St U; Bus Adm.

WOOTSON, Letitia Dora
Nether Providence HS; Wallingford, PA (164-264) Band; Cpt, Chldr; Mgr, Tr; Phys Therapy.

WOOTTON, Steven Bryon
Manatee HS; Bradenton, FL (20-570) Band; Ensm; NHS; Order/Arrow; JV, Bsbl; Order/Arrow A; Evangel Col; Pre-Chiropractic.

WORD, Debra Jean
Steeleville HS; Steeleville, IL (14-68) Ann; Band; Chem C; Chor; Rptr, FBLA; Tres, FHA; Tres, Hmrm; SC; Amer Leg A; Cl Fav; Pep C; Mascot; Librarian; St Luke's Sch of Nurs; Nurs.

WORD, Kerry
Gilbert HS; Gilbert, LA (4-29) Bus Mgr, Ann; Secy, BC; Bus C; Chldr; FBLA; FHA; Lit Ral; Sch P; Span C; Bkbl; HCt; La Tech U; Psych.

WORD, William Emerson
David Starr Jordan HS; Long Beach, CA (5%-500) Drama; Cr-Ctry; JV, Ftbl; Tr; CSF; Math A; Most Out; St Scholar; Best Bit Actor, Thespians; All League, Most Inspir, Cr-Ctry; Long Beach City Col; Math.

WORDEN, Floyd Lee
Mount Ida HS; Mount Ida, AR (5-50) Ann; Band; BC; FFA; Lit Mag; Mgr, Bkbl; Most Out; Hist, Beta C; All Region Band; Most Spirited; Merit A, Bookkeeping; Horticulture.

WORDEN, Meredith R
Coronado HS; El Paso, TX (60-581) Secy, Band; Pres, Ensm; A-Ed, Sch P; Cr-Ctry; Tr; God & Country A; Journ A; Q&S A; Phillips U; Physics.

WORK, William Whyte
John Muir HS; Pasadena, CA (35-525) Pres, Key C; A-Ed, Sch P; SC; Swim; CSF; COM; God & Country A; Water Polo; NESA; Eagle Sct; Bus A; WSI; Pomona Col; Hist.

WORKENTINE, Robert James
William J Brown HS; Sturgis, SD (40-224) F-Ed, Ann; SC; MVP, Bsbl; Bkbl; Golf; Tr; 2nd St, Art Contest; Black Hill St Col; Sci.

WORKMAN, Julie Marie
Franklin HS; Franklin, WI (70-200) A Cap Choir; Chor; Ensm; Fr C; Lat C; Cpt, Bkbl; Sftbl; Yth Fel; Secy, Yth Fel; Stage Crew; Vlbl; U of Wis; Sci.

WORKMAN, Kimberly Sue
Shawnee HS; Louisville, KY (1-250) Band; Hmrm; VP, NHS; Cr-Ctry; Co-Cpt, Tr; Bio A; COM; Hist A; U of Louisville; Biomed Engr.

WORKMAN, Leslie Anne
Hartshorne HS; Hartshorne, OK (2-81) FHA; NHS; Bkbl; Tr; DARGCA; Sci A; Yth Hon Soc; E Central U; Acct.

WORKMAN, Mary Joyce
Charlotte HS; Charlotte, MI; MSU; Microbio.

WORKMAN, Randy Lee
Sylvania Northview HS; Sylvania, OH (43-350) A Cap Choir; Community Yth Symph; Ensm; NHS; MVP, Orch; Ntl Arion A; St Orchestra; U of Toledo; Violin Performance.

WORKS, Cynthia Jo
Oakland Comm HS; Oakland, IA (10%-61) Band; Chldr; Chor; FHA; Rptr, 4H; NHS; S-T, SC; Pres, Jr Cl; Bkbl; Tr; Cl Fav; 4H A; Hon Prog; Ed.

WORLEY, Carla Kay
McKinney HS; McKinney, TX; Band; FHA; FTA; Co-Ed, Sch P; Hardin Simmons U; Piano.

WORLEY, Gregory Jay
Stevenson HS; Stevenson, AL (10%-63) Pres, BC; FFA; Bkbl; Most Stu; Auburn U; Vet Med.

WORLEY, Judith Lynn
Franklin HS; Somerset, NJ; Chor; Hmrm; Middlesex Co Col; Nurs.

WORLEY, LeAnn Kay
Braman HS; Braman, OK (1-14) F-Ed, Ann; Chor; Ensm; 4H; S-T, Jr Cl; S-T, Soph Cl; Bkbl; HCt; Swtht; Pres, Pep C; Hon Chor, Tri St; Vlbl; All-Around Girl; Superintendents HR; Oral Roberts U; Med.

WORLEY, Mark Judson II
Marion Military Inst; Marion, AL; Sci C; Tres, Span C; Spch C; Golf; Outst Span Stu A; Citz Medal; Dean's List; Staff Sgt; 3rd Regional Sci Fair; Samford U.

WORLEY, Phillip David
Douglas Co Comp HS; Douglasville, GA (8-326) Dbte Tm; Pres, NHS; Phys C; Pres, SC; COM; HKg; Hon Prog; Spch A; PC Jr Fellow; Ga Tech; Architecture.

WORLEY, Vikki Dawn
Mullens HS; Mullens, WV (2-103) Ch, Ann; VP, BC; Cpt, Chldr; Chor; FBLA; FHA; HiY; VP, Hmrm; NHS; Pres, Rainbow; ARC; A-Ed, Sch P; VP, SC; Tri-HiY; Tres, Soph Cl; Tnns; HCt; Yth Fel; Hon Guard; W Va U; Med Tech.

WORMACK, Maxine Lorraine
Overbrook HS; Philadelphia, PA; Chor; Orch; World Affairs C; Hon Prog; Star Student; Cabrini Col; Med.

WORMELY, Yolanda
Rogers HS; Toledo, OH (3-300) FHA; Bkbl; Cpt, Tnns; Child Care Cert; Owens Tech Col; Nurs.

WORMLEY, Lettie Leverne
Welch HS; Welch, WV (52-152) Chor; Lit Mag; HCt; Most Popular; Best Looking; McDowell Vocational Center; Bus.

WORONOWYCZ, Roman Michael
Immaculate Conception HS; Hamtramck, MI (8-31) Chor; Pres, Hmrm; VP, SC; Pres, Sr Cl; Bkbl; Ftbl; HCt; NMS; U of Mich; Pre-Law.

WORRELL, L Suzanne
Atlantic HS; Delray Beach, FL (33%-420) Ed, Ann; Chor; Drama; Hmrm; ARC; Co-Ed, Sch P; VP, SC; Thes; JV, Bkbl; JV, Sftbl; JV, Tnns; Star Student; Miss Christian Acad; Vet Med.

WORRELL, Mark Joseph
Cathedral HS; Indianapolis, IN (28-100) Tres, CYO; Var C; Cr-Ctry; Tr; Hon Prog; Wabash Col; Eng.

WORRELL, Todd Roland
Maranatha HS; Arcadia, CA (20-60) MVP, Bsbl; MVP, Bkbl; Ftbl; CSF; Biola Col; Christian Ed.

WORRELLIA, Annette Marie
Ursuline HS; Youngstown, OH (109-378) Fr C; NHS; PTA A; Cert of Appreciation; Gym A; Ohio St U; Phys Therapy.

WORSHAM, Donna Lynn
Pisgah HS; Canton, NC (12-337) Band; Chor; Ensm; Lat C; Secy, SC; Secy, Soph Cl; Cr-Ctry; Tr; COM; Citz A; FCA; Most Studious; VP, Yth Coun; May Court; Band A; Nurs.

WORSLEY, Catherine
Bronx HS of Sci; Bronx, NY; Chor; Secy, Hmrm; NHS; Rptr, Sch P; Sci C; SC; Up Bound; Bkbl; COM; Hon Prog; Harvard Col; Bio.

WORSLEY, Tammy Melisa
Early Co HS; Blakely, GA (9-143) BC; 4H; Ch, Span C; COM; Valdosta St Col; Ed.

WORTHAM, Vivian
Troup HS; LaGrange, GA; FHA; Bkbl; Sftbl; W Ga Col; Home Ec.

WORTHEY, Merry Jane
W Charlotte HS; Charlotte, NC; Chess C; Chor; Lat C.

WORTHINGTON, Mary Anne
Guilderland HS; Guilderland Center, NY (19-485) Chor; NHS; Rptr, Sch P; Tres, Sci C; Bkbl; Alg A; Bio A; Chem A; Regent Schol; Sci A; Fr A; Sch of Envir Sci & Forestry; Landscape Archt.

WORTHINGTON, Rebekah Dianne
Kimball HS; Royal Oak, MI (60-600) Band; BC; Chor; Ensm; Fr C; Rptr, 4H; Ntl Yth Conf; Y-Tns; COM; 4H A; Hon Prog; NEDT; Principal's List; Bob Jones U; Mus.

WORTHY, Mary Eunice
Bentonia HS; Bentonia, MS; Chldr; Secy, FBLA; Pres, FFA; 4H; Cl Fav; Swtht; Holmes Jr Col.

WOTT, Pamela Cheryl
Clyde Sr HS; Clyde, OH (20-207) A Cap Choir; Band; Chldr; Ensm; Secy, Y-Tns; COM; Hon Prog; Band A; FFA Ct; Fireman's Qn; U of Mich; Mus.

WOYAKOWSKI, Dorothy
St Anthony HS; Jersey City, NJ; A Cap Choir; Chor; Cum Laude Soc; NHS; Alg A; COM; Hon Prog; Sci A; Religion A; World Culture A; Span A; Montclair St Col; Aviation.

WOYTKO, Lori Kae
Cambridge Sr HS; Cambridge, OH (1-273) A Cap Choir; Band; Secy, Chor; VP, Drama; Tres, Fr C; Hmrm; Co-Cpt, Mjrte; NHS; Sch P; Thes; COM; Communications.

WRAIGHT, Christopher Laney
Wethersfield HS; Wethersfield, CT (40-400) Demolay; 4H; Hmrm; Ski C; JV, Ftbl; JV, Tr; *Mech Engr.*

WRAPE, Theresa Marie
Mount St Mary's Academy; Little Rock, AR (10-149) CYO; GS; Tres, NHS; Amer Leg A; Citz A; Hon Prog; NEDT; Spch A; Val; Drill Tm; *Gonzaga U; Med Engr.*

WRAY, Cynthia Arlene
Ashbrook HS; Gastonia, NC (25%-450) Sftbl; Sci A; *Nurs.*

WRAY, David Combs
Choctaw Co HS; Butler, AL (16-110) Ensm; FFA; FHA; Sci C; Span C; Var C; Mgr, Bsbl; Mgr, Ftbl; B Crocker A; Chem A; Sci A; *Samford U; Phys Ed.*

WRAY, Trena Darlene
Ashbrook HS; Gastonia, NC (200-450) *Wingate Col; Bus.*

WREEDE, Dina Marie
Delphos Jefferson Sr HS; Delphos, OH (1-130) Band; Pres, Fr C; Orch; Y-Tns; Alg A; Amer Leg A; Math A; Sci A; Statistician, Bsbl; Top Academic A; *Cincinnati U; Math.*

WREN, John Carlos
Gilmer HS; Gilmer, TX (10%-156) Pres, Soph Cl; JV, Ftbl; *U of Tex; Sci.*

WREN, Karla DeAnn
Port Neches-Groves HS; Port Neches, TX; AFS; Band; Drama; Spch A; UIL Twirling; UIL Mus Ensm; *Lamar U; Spch & Drama.*

WREN, Kathryn Ann
Hillsboro Sr HS; Hillsboro, OR (30-580) Chor; Pres, 4H; Citz A; Pres A; *Portland Comm Col; Graphic & Commercial Art.*

WRENN, Yvonne Marie
Bishop Byrne HS; Memphis, TN (36-187) Chor; Span C; Tr; *Memphis St U; Ed.*

WRIGHT, Alberta
Hunter Col HS; Ny, NY; *Math.*

WRIGHT, Ann Marie
Cowan HS; Muncie, IN (2-70) Pres, FHA; GS; Pres, 4H; VP, NHS; Secy, Sr Cl; Secy, Soph Cl; Tr; DARGCA; 4H A; Hist A; Math A; Sal; Secy, 4-H C; *Purdue U; Nurs.*

WRIGHT, Annette Valencia
Glynn Acad; Brunswick, GA; Span C; Tnns; Citz A; Type A; Span, Art, A's; *Brunswick Jr Col; Nurs.*

WRIGHT, Annie Kathleen
Hogansville HS; Hogansville, GA (2-65) Ed, Ann; VP, BC; Ch, FHA; Rptr, FTA; S-T, Span C; Secy, SC; Pres, Jr Cl; VP, Soph Cl; COM; Hist A; Journ A; Math A; Type A; PC Jr Fel A; *Auburn U; Journ.*

WRIGHT, Annie Marie
Marvell HS; Marvell, AR (3-118) Ann; Pres, BC; Secy, FBLA; VP, FHA; Secy, Ger C; Spch C; SC; Spch A; *U of Pine Bluff; Secy Sci.*

WRIGHT, Barbara Ann
Williamsburg HS; Andrews, SC (5-105) Drama; FHA; Secy, 4H; Tres, Hmrm; Math C; Rptr, Sch P; VP, Soph Cl; Bkbl; Bio A; Cl Fav; 4H A; HCt; 4-H Dress Revue A; *Howard U; Bus Adm.*

WRIGHT, Becky Sue
Oil City HS; Oil City, PA; Band.

WRIGHT, Brad Wayne
Midland HS; Midland, MI (10%-500) Bsbl; Ftbl; Wrest; *U of Mich; Wildlife and Fisheries.*

WRIGHT, Brenda Sue
Heritage HS; Littleton, CO (15%-438) Chor; MVP, Tr; Yth Fel; *Wildlife.*

WRIGHT, Bruce Timothy
Cape Henry Collegiate HS; Virginia Beach, VA (1-9) Ann; Monogram; Ed, Sch P; Pres, SC; Co-Cpt, Bkbl; COM; Chem A; Pres A; Val; *Randolph Macon Col; Pre-Med.*

WRIGHT, Cara Jo
Arkadelphia HS; Arkadelphia, AR (10%-196) Band; Chor; Ensm; Thes; Hon Prog; Yth Fel; *Henderson St U.*

WRIGHT, Carmela Judy
Lincoln Sr HS; E Saint Louis, IL (9-200) All Amer Yth; Secy, Bus C; Chor; Dbte Tm; 4H; MLS; Spch A; Yth Leg; Choir A; Talent A; *SIU Edwardsville; Special Ed.*

WRIGHT, Carolyn Esther
Putnam Co Sr HS; Cookeville, TN (13-363) Band; BC; Chor; Community Yth Symph; Ensm; Lit Mag; Orch; Sch P; Mgr, Tnns; Journ A; Q&S A; Mus Schol; WW; Pres, MYF; Photojourn A; *Tenn Tech U; Mus Ed.*

WRIGHT, Carolyn Marie
George Washington HS; Los Angeles, CA (5-700) Ensm; NHS; Bio A; CSF; COM; Hon Prog; NMS; Ntl Gdwill Comm; Aerospace Engr A; Page Service C; Sftbl Scorekeeper; Ladies Hon Soc; Summer Schol; Pep C; VP, Altores Jr Hon Soc; *UCLA; Med.*

WRIGHT, Cheryl Lynn
Clarkrange HS; Clarkrange, TN; Bus Mgr, Ann; BC; Chor; FHA; Pres, 4H; Pol Sci C; F-Ed, Sch P; Sci C; Spch C; Bkbl; Cl Fav; 4H A; Yth Fel; Most Charming; Most Dependable; Ranger Attendant; *Voc Sch; Bus.*

WRIGHT, Clifton Herbert
Carver Voc Tech HS; Baltimore, MD (40%-499) A Cap Choir; Chor; Bsbl; Cr-Ctry; Swim; Cpt, Tr; HKg; Oldtimers, Sports, A's; Social Stu, Coaches, A's; *U of Md; Phys Ed.*

WRIGHT, Crystal Laurita
St Frances de Sales HS; Chicago, IL (84-416) Chor; Citz A; Ntl Cath Mus Ed Asn; *Nurs.*

WRIGHT, Crystal Lynn
S Gwinnett HS; Snellville, GA; Band; Drama; Jr Miss Pagent; Hon Prog; Yth Fel; Gym.

WRIGHT, Cynthia Jean
Northwood HS; Silver Spring, MD (10%-457) Drama; Math C; NHS; ARC; Y-Tns; Swim; Hon Prog; Math A; ARC A; Yth Fel; Drama A; Church Board of Christian Ed; *Nurs.*

WRIGHT, Cynthia Jo
Dunedin HS; Dunedin, FL (117-750) A Cap Choir; Band; Chor; Ensm; Lat C; Ntl VP, Span C; SC; Yth Leg; Pres, Yth Fel; *U of S Fla; Nurs.*

WRIGHT, Cynthia Leverne
Miami Killian Sr HS; Miami, FL (327-1102) Hmrm; Civinettes Service C; PA Trophy; *U of Miami; Dental Hygiene.*

WRIGHT, Cynthia Lynn
Vinson HS; Huntington, WV (23-130) Ann; Band; Chor; Drama; Jr Miss Pagent; Cpt, Mjrte; NHS; Orch; Co-Ed, Sch P; Y-Tns; Tres, Sr Cl; Beauty; Hon Prog; Opt A; TAG Prog; Most Talented; Ntl Cand, Miss Tnage Amer; *Marshall U; Ed.*

WRIGHT, Cynthia Sue
Tecumseh HS; Tecumseh, MI (79-263) Var C; Bkbl; Tr; HQn; HCt; Hon Prog; Pres, Yth Group; Pres, Church Yth Singers; Jr Play; Mst Improv Plyr, St Run-Up, Bkbl; *Hope Col; Bus Adm.*

WRIGHT, D Andrea Denese
St Mary's Acad; Inglewood, CA (40-133) Sewing A; *UCLA.*

WRIGHT, Darlene Eloise
Warsaw HS; Warsaw, IL (4-55) Tres, AFS; S-T, Chor; S-T, Drama; FBLA; Pres, 4H; NHS; Pres, Span C; SC; Sftbl; 4H A; I Dare You; Kiwanis A; VP, Yth Fel; Vlbl; Chor A; *Southeastern Comm Col; Math.*

WRIGHT, DeAnna Elizabeth
Gulf Comprehensive HS; New Port Richey, FL (50-450) SC; Excel, Geom; A-B HR; Cpt, Powderpuff Ftbl; *Math.*

WRIGHT, Deanna Lynn
Snohomish HS; Snohomish, WA; FFA; Secy, FHA.

WRIGHT, Deborah Lynn
Lakewood HS; Lakewood, CA (1-789) A Cap Choir; Chor; Co-Ch, Ensm; Hmrm; InterClub Coun; Pres, Madrigal; NHS; Tnns; Amer Leg A; CSF; COM; Type A; Nom, NHS Schol; Runner-up, Bank of Amer A; *U of Sou Calif; Lib Sci.*

WRIGHT, Debra Louise
Vanguard HS; Ocala, FL (19-370) Bus C; Fr C; Pres, FBLA; NHS; SC; Swim; Acct A; Outst Bus Stu; *Central Fla Comm Col; Acct.*

WRIGHT, Delores Yvonne
Chester HS; Chester, PA (1-680) Band; Chor; Tres, SC; Up Bound; Bkbl; Sftbl; Swim; COM; Chem A; *Biol.*

WRIGHT, Denise Mosell
Jean Ribault Sr HS; Jacksonville, FL (11-650) Band; VP, Hmrm; NHS; SC; Hon Prog; *U of Miami; Exceptional Child Ed.*

WRIGHT, Douglas Edwards
Mossyrock HS; Mossyrock, WA (3-25) CYO; VP, FFA; S-T, 4H; Pres, NHS; Sci C; Tres, SC; Bkbl; Ftbl; Cl Fav; 4H A; Sci A; *Oreg St U; Nuclear Engr.*

WRIGHT, Eugenia
Oak Ridge Acad; Oak Ridge, NC (4-31) Ed, Ann; Cpt, Chldr; Chor; Ensm; Monogram; Rainbow; Ski C; Var C; Pres, Jr Cl; Sftbl; Swim; MVP, Tnns; Gr Marshal; Greensboro Yth Coun Rep; *Converse Col; Law.*

WRIGHT, Evvie LaReece
Pecos HS; Pecos, TX (100-201) Pres, FHA; Tnns; Secy, Church Chor; *Angelo St U; Home Ec.*

WRIGHT, Greg John
Foster HS; Seattle, WA (7-190) Ann; Band; Drama; Math C; Sci C; JV, Ftbl; Math A; *Highline Comm Col; Computer Sci.*

WRIGHT, Gregory Lance
Putnam City HS; Oklahoma City, OK (7-850) BS; Dbte Tm; Pres, JETS; Lat C; Math C; Model UN; Mu Alpha Theta; Tres, NFL; NHS; Order/Arrow; F-Ed, Sch P; Spch C; Pres, SC; World Affairs C; Pres, Jr Cl; Pres, Soph Cl; Amer Leg Orator A; God & Country A; Hon Prog; MLS; NMF; NMS; Rotary A; Spch A; VFW Orator Win; VofDEM; Ch, Ntl Assn Stu Coun Adv Comm; WW; Pres, St Assn Stu Coun; Eagle Sct; Church Jr Deacon; Golden Scroll A; Yale A; Exchange C Yth o-t Mo; *Princeton U; Econ.*

WRIGHT, Gregory Ronald
Eureka HS; Eureka, IL (25%-125) Band; Ensm; Order/Arrow; Bsbl; Bkbl; Ftbl; Mgr, Tr; Elk A; Order/Arrow A; Eagle Sct.

WRIGHT, Gwendolyn Delores
North HS; Nashville, TN; Co-Cpt, Chldr; NFL; St Stu Congress; Bank Of Amer A; B Crocker A; COM; Citz A; HQn; Hon Prog; I Dare You; Opt Out Tn; Poet A; Pres A; ARC A; Spch A; Type A; Most Spirited A; Best Dancer; *Nashville Tech Inst; Computer Prog.*

WRIGHT, Hilda
Hancock Central HS; Sparta, GA; Chem C; Ensm; Fr C; FHA; 4H; NHS; Sci C; Up Bound; Hon Prog; *Albany St Col; Special Ed.*

WRIGHT, Ian Paul
Evander Childs HS; New York, NY (233-1036) *Fordham U; Engr.*

WRIGHT, Inge Helene
Josephinum HS; Chicago, IL (45-124) A Cap Choir; Chor; Drama; Bkbl; Sftbl; Tnns; *Briar Cliff Col; Nurs.*

WRIGHT, James Doyle
Hall HS; Little Rock, AR (20-430) BC; BS; Math C; Mu Alpha Theta; NHS; Cr-Ctry; Tr; Math A; *Vanderbilt U; Med.*

WRIGHT, Jan Allison
Star Spencer HS; Spencer, OK (23-425) Chor; NHS; SC; Sftbl; Tnns.

WRIGHT, Jeffrey Hostetter
Oak Ridge Acad; Oak Ridge, NC (1-31) A-Ed, Ann; Band; Drama; Monogram; Var C; Bsbl; Bkbl; Ftbl; Soccer; Gov Honor Prog; Gr Marshal; Hon Prog; ROTC A; Sup Cadet A; Marksman A; *Vanderbilt U; Engr.*

WRIGHT, Jeffrey Mark
Minnehaha Acad; Minneapolis, MN (69-153) A Cap Choir; Band; Chor; Ensm; Orch; Pres, SC; Var C; Tnns; Biggest Flirt; Most Involved; Spiritual Ldr A; *Bethel Col; Mus Ed.*

WRIGHT, Joanna Lynne
Queen City HS; Queen City, TX (20%-41) Ann; Chldr; FHA; Rptr, NHS; Rainbow; Sch P; Sci C; VP, SC; S-T, Jr Cl; UIL; *Stephen F Austin U; Guidance.*

WRIGHT, Jonathon Keith
Aloha HS; Beaverton, OR; Ski C; Bsbl; Ftbl; Pres A; *NW Nazarene Col.*

WRIGHT, Judi Lauren
Parkway Prog-Beta HS; Philadelphia, PA; *Bus Adm.*

WRIGHT, Keith L
Thornton HS; Harvey, IL (430-878) Cpt, Bkbl.

WRIGHT, Kelli Lynn
Cleburne HS; Cleburne, TX (50%-265) Ed, Ann; FHA; FTA; Span C; FCA; Tres, Exchangettes; Lt Col, Drill Tm; *Harding Col; Elem Ed.*

WRIGHT, Kimm Lorett
Central HS; Flint, MI; A Cap Choir; Band; Drama; Madrigal; Thes; JV, Swim; Interlochen Ntl Mus; *Taylor U; Fine Arts.*

WRIGHT, Kyle Ann
Scott Comm HS; Scott City, KS (11-104) Band; Chldr; Chor; Ensm; Tr; Type A; Secy, FCA; MYF Rep; Kayettes; Pep A; St Mus Medals; *Fort Hays St Col; Elem Ed.*

WRIGHT, Larry Dean
R L Turner HS; Carrollton, TX (162-850) Band; Tnns; Drum Major; Pres, FCA; Church Yth Group; *Tex Tech U; Forestry.*

WRIGHT, Laurelyn Jean
Whitman-Hanson Regional HS; Whitman, MA (11-324) VP, Bus C; S-T, CYO; Drama; VP, FBLA; FTA; Hmrm; Key C; NHS; Sch P; Ski C; Sftbl; COM; Citz A; Hon Prog; Poet A; Type A; VFW A; DECA Stu o-t Yr; 1st Pl, St Essay Exam; Fin, Spellman Essay; *Katharine Gibbs Col; Bus.*

WRIGHT, Laurie Ann
MacDuffie Sch for Girls; Springfield, MA; Drama; Sch P; Ski C; SC; Pres, Soph Cl.

WRIGHT, Linda Suzanne
Western Albemarle HS; Crozet, VA (25%-700) Drama; Ensm; 4H; Lat C; Thes; 4H A; Sci A; DAR A; Hon Thespian; Rep, Church Yth Coun; *Roanoke Col; Math.*

WRIGHT, Lisa Anne
Cushing HS; Cushing, OK (88-129) Secy, FFA; FHA; Secy, 4H; Rptr; SC; Rptr, Sr Cl; Bkbl; Sftbl; Amer Leg A; Swtht; Yth Fel; WW; St Farmer; *Miami Jr Col; Agr.*

WRIGHT, Lisa Marie
Coon Rapids Sr HS; Coon Rapids, MN (54-654) CYO; Hon Prog; Salesmanship A; HR.

WRIGHT, Lisa Renee
Bishop O'Dowd HS; Oakland, CA (33%-247) Ann; Chor; Hmrm; Orch; Bkbl; Citz A; Hon Prog; Q&S A; Yth Fel; Mus & Religion A's; *Los Angeles St Col; Acct.*

WRIGHT, Lon Shane
North Toole County HS; Sunburst, MT (1-33) Band; Chor; Drama; Math C; ARC; Sci C; Secy, SC; Var C; S-T, Jr Cl; S-T, Soph Cl; Mgr, Bkbl; Tr; Amer Leg A; COM; Citz A; HC; Most Out; NEDT; Star Student; Life Sct; Most Outst Band Member; 4th Interntl Sci & Engr Fair; PA; NASA A; Arrow of Light in Webelos; Air Force A; Scholastic As; *Engr.*

WRIGHT, Marcia Elizabeth
N Tonawanda Sr HS; North Tonawanda, NY; Band; Rptr, Sch P; COM; Yth Fel; Bell Choir; Church Yth Choir; NJHS.

WRIGHT, Margaret Georgiana
Burns Sr HS; Lawndale, NC; Band; FBLA; *Mus.*

WRIGHT, Marsha Gayle
Raytown S HS; Raytown, MO (122-583) Dbte Tm; Nom, Schol A; Nom, Outst Citz A; *U of Mo; Ed.*

WRIGHT, Mary Jane
Big Spring HS; Big Spring, TX (50-350) A Cap Choir; Bus Mgr, Chor; Drama; Ensm; Madrigal; Pres, Rainbow; Tnns; *Baylor U; Marketing.*

WRIGHT, Matthew Leigh
Aiken Sr HS; Aiken, SC (5%-890) Band; Hmrm; SC; Cr-Ctry; Swim; Tnns; Tr; Star Student; Yth Fel; *U of Ga; Law.*

WRIGHT, Michael Leon
Hillcrest HS; Country Club Hills, IL (60%-451) Band; Orch; Var C; Cr-Ctry; Tr; Wrest; COM; Var Ltr; Band Letterman; *Ill St U; Acct.*

WRIGHT, Michelle Elizabeth
John Bartram HS; Philadelphia, PA; Chor; Drama; Sci A; Schol Achv A; *Jefferson Col; X-Ray Tech.*

WRIGHT, Monte Dean
Snohomish HS; Snohomish, WA; All Amer Yth; Var C; Cpt, Cr-Ctry; Tr; Hon Prog; Yth Fel; HS All Amer, Cross Ctry; Inspirational, Cross Ctry; *Mech Engr.*

WRIGHT, Monte Shane
Briarwood Christian HS; Birmingham, AL (5-52) Band; BC; Pres, Chor; City Conf; Pres, SC; Ch, Y-Tns; JV, Bkbl; Co-Cpt, Ftbl; Cpt, Golf; Hon Prog; Magna Cum Laude; Yth Fel; Social Ldrship A; Best All Around Sr; All St Ftbl; *Samford U.*

WRIGHT, Nancy Anne
Greencastle Sr HS; Greencastle, IN (61-155) Community Yth Symph; Drama; Ensm; Pres, Lat C; Orch; ARC; Sci C; Swim; God & Country A; ARC A; GAA; WW; Outst Orch Member; *Millsaps Col; Ed.*

WRIGHT, Neil Cecil
Burns HS; Lawndale, NC (25-220) Band; Ensm; Fr C; Hmrm; Secy, Key C; Monogram; SC; Pres, Sr Cl; Bsbl; Golf; HCt; Dedicated Drummer; Key C A; Band Above Self; Best Multiple Percussionist; *UNC Chapel Hill; Radio.*

WRIGHT, Rebecca Joyce
Parkside HS; Jackson, MI; Band; Community Yth Symph; Hmrm; Orch; Span C; SC; Mgr, Bsbl; *Lansing Comm Col; Dental Hygienist.*

WRIGHT, Renee Sue
Shawnee HS; Lima, OH (16-277) A Cap Choir; Secy, FHA; Fin, Jr Miss Pageant; NHS; Ski C; Y-Tns; Hon Prog; *U of Cincinnati; Marketing.*

WRIGHT, Rex Alan
Cherry Hill E HS; Cherry Hill, NJ (450-850) SC; WW; *U of Mo; Mech Engr.*

WRIGHT, Rhonda Gayle
Springdale HS; Springdale, AR; Band; *ORU; Secretarial.*

WRIGHT, Richard Norman
Interboro Sr HS; Prospect Park, PA (40-420) Band; Ger C; Bsbl; Mgr, Ftbl; Wrest; *U of Md; Mus.*

WRIGHT, Richard Stephen
Washington Col Acad; Washington Col, TN; Ed, Ann; Tres, BC; Drama; Sch P; Sci C; Span C; Spch C; VP, Jr Cl; Cl Fav; HCt; Hon Prog; Spch A; VofDEM; Pres, Fresh Cl; Phys Ed Pin; Acad Singers; Eng A; Chamber Singer; Dist Win, Mens Original Oratory; *E Tenn St U; Radio & TV.*

WRIGHT, Rickey Don
Judsonia HS; Judsonia, AR (3-35) Ann; BC; Chor; Drama; Tres, FBLA; Pres, FFA; Spch C; SC; Pres, Jr Cl; Cpt, Bkbl; Tr; COM; Citz A; MLS; 1st, Cl B Discus; FFA St Farmer; Dekalb A; *Harding Col; Pre-Vet Med.*

WRIGHT, Robby Alan
Paradise HS; Paradise, CA (76-225) Ftbl; *Washington Col; Forestry.*

WRIGHT, Robert Charles
Foster HS; Seattle, WA (9-130) Chem C; NHS; Phys C; ARC; A-Ed, Sch P; Sci C; Ski C; Span C; Var C; Cpt, Ftbl; JV, Tr; Bio A; COM; Hon Prog; Span A; Math Tr Meet; *Washington St U; Life Sci.*

WRIGHT, Robert Worth
Wilbrahame Monson Acad; Wilbraham, MA; *Early Childhood Ed.*

WRIGHT, Roshelle Kimber
Detroit Central HS; Detroit, MI; Chor; Ensm; FNA; FTA; Phys C; Cpt, Bkbl; Cpt, Tnns; Cl Fav; Yth Fel; *Mary Groove Col; Nurs.*

WRIGHT, Samuel Eugene
N Union HS; Richwood, OH; Fr C; F-Ed, Lit Mag; Mgr, Bkbl; *Drafting.*

WRIGHT, Sandra Lanette
Commodore Perry HS; Hadley, PA; NHS; Gifted Stu Prog; *Architecture.*

WRIGHT, Sara Elaine
Alfred Eli Beach HS; Savannah, GA; Chor; 4H; Lat C; Lat NHS; Math A; Sci A; *Phys Therapy.*

WRIGHT, Scott Noel
Lee's Summit Sr HS; Lee's Summit, MO (4-479) Band; Chem C; Chess C; Hmrm; JETS; Order/Arrow; Phys C; World Affairs C; JV, Bsbl; JV, Bkbl; Alg A; COM; Curator A; Order/Arrow A; Eagle Sct; *U of Mo; Engr.*

WRIGHT, Sharon Ann
Richard Gahr HS; Artesia, CA; Drill Tm; *Pepperdine Col; Child Care.*

WRIGHT, Shellee Layo
Greece Arcadia HS; Rochester, NY; Secy, Band; CYO; Drama; Lat C; Sch P; COM; Regent Schol; Howard Hanson Piano; *Houghton Col; Nurs.*

WRIGHT, Stacey Lynn
Pompano Bch HS; Pompano Beach, FL; Pres A; *Photography.*

WRIGHT, Stephen Ray
Wooster HS; Wooster, OH (20%-280) Band; Fr C; Cr-Ctry; Swim; Tr; COM; Most Improved, Swim Tm; Var Ltr, Swim; *Ohio St U; Engr.*

WRIGHT, Steven Burgers
Princeton HS; Princeton, NJ (90-275) AFS; Band; Chor; InterAct C; Orch; Order/Arrow; Ski C; SC; JV, Soccer.

WRIGHT, Susan Leigh
Sheridan HS; Englewood, CO; Cpt, Chldr; FHA; Var C; Bkbl; MVP, Swim; Tr; HCt; Graduation Escort; Sportsmanship A; *UNC-Greeley; Phys Ed.*

WRIGHT, Tamara Nell
Sissonville Sr HS; Charleston, WV (2-195) Chor; Drama; Math C; Mu Alpha Theta; NHS; Thes; Cpt, Bkbl; Cpt, Tr; COM; Fr A; Phys Ed; *WV Tech Col; Math.*

WRIGHT, Tanya Jo
Middletown HS; Middletown, OH (33%-700) A Cap Choir; Chldr; Chor; FHA; Sci C; SC; Arch; Bkbl; Sftbl; Tnns; Tr; Cl Fav; Hon Prog; Opt A; Sci A; Spch A; VFW A; VFW Orator Win; Talent A; *Ohio St U; Sci.*

WRIGHT, Terry Dean
Elmira HS; Elmira, OR (60-200) Bsbl; JV, Bkbl; Ftbl; Citz A; Pres, Sr High Yth Conf; *Williamette U; Psych.*

WRIGHT, Timothy Lee
Washington Col Acad; Washington Col, TN; BC; Bkbl; Sftbl; Cl Fav; Hon Prog; Acad Singers; Phys Ed Pin; VP, Fresh Cl; Eng A; Industrial Arts A; *E Tenn St U; Industrial Arts.*

WRIGHT, Todd Earl
Clovis HS; Clovis, NM; VP, Hmrm; JV, Tr; I Dare You; Spch A; Kg, Church Swtht Banquet; VP, Sr Cl; Tn o-t Week; BS Del to NM; *Med.*

WRIGHT, Tracy Campbell
Martin Co HS; Stuart, FL (33-500) Pres, FBLA; Most Out; Type A; Cl Offices; Sigma Phi; *Indian River Comm Col; Nurs.*

WRIGHT, Valerie Gae
Alexander Central HS; Taylorsville, NC (16-275) BC; HCt; Hon Prog; Yth Fel; Jr Marshall; Gov Page; School Search; WW; *U of NC; Acct.*

WRIGHT, Veronica Lynn
Greece Olympia HS; Rochester, NY; COM; High HR; *Roberts Wesleyan U; Nurs.*

WRIGHT, Warren Keith
Saint Pius X HS; Atlanta, GA (20%-220) Chor; Bkbl; Citz A; Hon Prog; School Excel A; *Engr.*

WRIGHT, William Alan
Scott HS; Scott City, KS (30-103) Chor; SC; Ftbl; Tr; *Fort Hays Kans St Col; Pol Sci.*

WRIGHT, William Clay
Dulles HS; Stafford, TX (15-750) Band; Secy, Bus C; Ensm; Ger C; Mu Alpha Theta; NHS; Sci C; Hon Prog; JA A; Ensm A; 100% Att; Ger A; Band Sweepstakes A; *Baylor U; Med.*

WRIGHT, William Henry II
Lake Taylor HS; Norfolk, VA (6-700) Ed, Ann; Fin, BS; Hmrm; Key C; NFL; S-T, NHS; SC; Bus Mgr, Jr Cl; Pres, Soph Cl; Citz A; Cl Fav; Hon Prog; Opt A; Spch A; Yth Fel; Yth Foundation; Yth Foundation A; Yth Leg; Page, US House of Rep; WW; *Harvard U; Med.*

WRIGHT, William Warren
Loyola HS; Baltimore, MD; Hmrm; SC; JV, Bsbl; JV, Bkbl; COM; Math A; Opt A; *Notre Dame U; Math.*

WRIGHT, Yvonne
Bronx HS of Sci; Bronx, NY; Cpt, Bkbl; Sftbl; Handball; Vlbl; *Bio-Med.*

WRIGHT, Yvonne Beth
Greece Olympia HS; Rochester, NY; FBLA; Hmrm; SC; Mgr, Tnns.

WRIGHTSMAN, Sandra Elaine
Quincy Sr HS; Quincy, IL (7%-750) Orch; Span C; SC; Soc of Acad Achv; *Oral Roberts U; Ed.*

WRING, Carolyn Sue
Hobart HS; Hobart, IN (27-423) Span C; COM; Hon Prog; Industrial Arts A.

WRITER, Jamila Thoha
Doane-Stuart Sch HS; Albany, NY (6-35) VP; Chldr; Drama; Fr C; Lat C; Ed, Lit Mag; SC; JV, Soccer; JV, Sftbl; COM; Citz A; Hist A; Spch A.

WRITZ, Jeanne Marie
Abbotsford HS; Abbotsford, WI (1-60) CYO; VP, FBLA; Hmrm; FHA; GS; Pres, NHS; Ed, Sch P; Secy, SC; Secy, Sr Cl; Tr; DARGCA; Elk A; Lion A; MLS; Sci A; Val; VFW A; Laird Yth Ldrship; *St Joseph's Sch of Nurs; Nurs.*

WROBLEWSKI, Celeste Judine
Hinsdale Township HS Central; Hinsdale, IL (28-601) AFS; CYO; Fr C; Co-Ed, Lit Mag; NHS; S-T, Orch; Rptr, Sch P; Ski C; SC; Pres, Soph Cl; COM; NEDT; Poet A; St Scholar; Exchange Stu; NML; Runnerup, Century III Ldrs; Solo & Ensm Mus A; Polish Arts C Essay; *U of Ill; Lib Arts.*

WRONA, Ramona
Thomas Kelly HS; Chicago, IL (15-485) Co-Ed, Lit Mag; Math C; NHS; ARC; Sci C; Alg A; COM; Hon Prog; Comm Coun Court; *IIT; Computer Sci.*

WROTEN, J Max
Kenton HS; Kenton, OH; Ann; Pres, SC; Var C; Bsbl; JV, Bkbl; Ftbl; Yth Fel; Bible Sch Teacher; Lib Helper; HR.

WROTEN, Vanessa Ann
Washington HS; Milwaukee, WI; FHA; Hero C; Jr Opt C; Jr Opt A; *U of Wis-Stout; Home Ec.*

WRUCK, Dwayne Allan
Mott Lincoln HS; Mott, ND (6-52) A Cap Choir; Ann; Chor; Ensm; FFA; Pres, 4H; Sch P; Sci C; Var C; JV, Bsbl; JV, Bkbl; Tr; Amer Leg A; *U of ND; Med.*

WRUCKE, Tammie Lynn
Horicon HS; Horicon, WI (50-114) Chldr; Chor; Var C; Bkbl; Sftbl; Tr; HCt; Yth Fel; *Concordia River Forest Col; Teacher.*

WU, Esther Un-Wah
Alhambra HS; Alhambra, CA (5%-756) CSF; Chaplain, Service C; Ntl Yth Consulting Committee; Nom, NML; *U of Sou Calif; Bio.*

WUERPEL, Carla Christina
Jackson Central Merry HS; Jackson, TN (152-495) Chor; Ensm; FHA; Hmrm; Span C; Sftbl; *Wildlife Conservation.*

WUERTZ, Carla Marie
Beaufort Acad; Beaufort, SC (3-42) Hmrm; NHS; SC; Mgr, Bkbl; Hon Prog; *Environmental Design.*

WUFLESTAD, Jane Marie
Cooperstown HS; Cooperstown, ND (2-40) Band; Chldr; Chor; Rptr, Sch P; Type A; Mus A.

WUFLESTAD, Marsha
Cooperstown HS; Cooperstown, ND (1-30) Tres, Band; Chldr; Chor; FHA; Tres, 4H; NHS; Rptr, Sch P; SC; 4H A; Type A; Mus A; *Valley City St Col.*

WULF, John Paul
Clarence Central HS; Clarence, NY (100-417) A Cap Choir; Chem C; Chess C; Chor; Ensm; Madrigal; Math C; Orch; Sci C; Sftbl; *Chem.*

WULLER, Robin Ann
St Mary's Acad; Englewood, CO (5-50) CYO; Chor; Fr C; NHS; Swim; Ch, Spirit C; Swim; *Aviation.*

WUNDERLICH, Catherine Sue
Ferndale Union HS; Ferndale, CA (1-75) A-Ed, Ann; Band; CYO; Chldr; Pres, 4H; Sch P; Tres, Soph Cl; JV, Bkbl; Tr; CSF; 4H A; Math A; JV Vlbl; Win, St Wool Contest; *Stanford U; Med.*

WUNDERLICH, Cindi Ann
Ferndale Union HS; Ferndale, CA (10-54) Ann; CYO; GS; Pres, 4H; Sch P; Span C; Tres, SC; Tr; CSF; 4H A; Math A; *Col o-t Redwoods; Acct.*

WURTELE, Carrie Lynn
Lourdes Central HS; Nebraska City, NE (3-29) A-Ed, Ann; Pres, 4H; Math C; NHS; 4H A; Hon Prog; Opt A; *NCE Sch of Commerce; Acct.*

WURTH, Laurie Ann
Winston Churchill HS; San Antonio, TX (75%-800) Band; *Bookkeeping.*

WURTZ, Jean Ann
Perry HS; Perry, OK (1-84) Band; CYO; Ensm; FHA; FTA; GS; Mjrte; Secy, NHS; Secy, Sr Cl; Amer Leg A; Citz A; Hist A; HCt; MLS; Val; Feature Twirler; Okla Hon Soc; Stage Band; All-Sch Revue Dancer; Stu Librarian Assn; Jr Rotarian; Mat-Maid; OSU Alumni Hon Banquet; *Oklahoma State Univ; Computer Science.*

WUTHNOW, Mark Steven
Coronado HS; El Paso, TX (80-575) Chess C; Chor; Pres, Math C; SC; Mgr, Swim; Hon Prog; *U of Tex; Engr.*

WYATT, Barbara Ann
Hydro HS; Hydro, OK (2-24) Ed, Ann; Chldr; Pres, FHA; FNA; GS; Secy, 4H; NHS; Spch C; Pres, SC; Pres, Jr Cl; Pres, Soph Cl; Bkbl; Sftbl; Amer Leg A; Citz A; Cl Fav; 4H A; Most Out; Clothing A; Ldrship A; *Southwestern Okla St U; Nurs.*

WYATT, Barbara Lee
Helix HS; La Mesa, CA; Chor; Drama; Spch C; Outst, Choir; *Sou Calif Col; Mus.*

WYATT, Cheryl Denise
William Marion Raines HS; Jacksonville, FL (20-488) Secy, Band; Rptr, Hmrm; NHS; Ntl Yth Conf; Span C; SC; Swim; COM; Citz A; Delta Sigma Theta A; Hon Prog; Kiwanis A; Sci A; Star Student; Yth Fel; Yth Leg; Band A; Span A; *U of Fla; Med.*

WYATT, Connie Faye
E Laurens HS; Dublin, GA; Secy, Drama; Secy, Span C; Secy, Spch C; Alg A; Bio A; COM; Chem A; Hist A; Math A; Sci A; Type A; Eng, Span, Mus, Home Ec, A's.

WYATT, Connie Jo
Mercer R-III Sch; Mercer, MO (1-19) Co-Ed, Ann; Band; Chldr; SC; Band Carnival Qn.

WYATT, Debra Jean
Concord HS; Concord, NC (18-243) AFS; Band; Hmrm; Mjrte; Math C; Span C; *UNC Chapel Hill; Sci.*

WYATT, Denise Rene
Matoaca HS; Ettrick, VA (12-150) Ann; Cpt, Chldr; Fr C; FHA; Key C; NHS; SC; WW; Jr Marshall; *Richard Bland Col; Math.*

WYATT, Dina Gaye
Levelland HS; Levelland, TX (10%-250) Ed, Ann; Rptr, Band; Pres, Chor; FHA; GS; NHS; SC; Tnns; Citz A; Cl Fav; UIL Band & Choir Solo & Ensm; HR; *Tex Tech U; Psych.*

WYATT, Gary Allan
John F Hodge HS; St James, MO; Band; Mod Mus Mas; Sch P.

WYATT, James Michael
E Central HS; Tulsa, OK (40-600) Chem C; Math C; Mu Alpha Theta; NHS; Phys C; Span C; Co-Cpt, Swim; Co-Cpt, Tnns; Hon Prog; Magna Cum Laude; *Abilene Christian U; Bus.*

WYATT, Rebecca Ellen
N Wilkes HS; Hays, NC (2-150) Co-Ed, Ann; BC; Chor; FHA; Hmrm; Span C; Hon Prog; Marshal; Interpreter's A; Advanced Math A; *Wilkes Comm Col; Special Ed.*

WYATT, Rhonda Gail
Franklin Road Christian Sch; Murfreesboro, TN (1-12) F-Ed, Ann; BC; Chldr; Chor; Ensm; VP, Hmrm; Secy, SC; Var C; Y-Tns; COM; Citz A; Hist A; Interlochen Ntl Mus; Sci A; Yth Fel; Pres, Bible C; 2nd Pl, Girls Duet; *Pensacola Christian Col; Ed.*

WYATT, Rudolph Byrd Jr
Jackson HS; Jackson, GA (15%-175) Pres, Math C; Wrest; NEDT; *Ga Tech; Textile Engr.*

WYATT, Sheila Jane
Rossville Camp HS; Rossville, GA (23-211) Ann; BC; Y-Tns; Tres, Sr Cl; VP, Jr Cl; Bkbl; Most Improved, Bkbl.

WYATT, Vicki Kay
Marshalltown HS; Marshalltown, IA; Band; Chor; Y-Tns; Pep Band; Kindergarden Cl Helper; Band Ltr; *Marshalltown Comm Col; Dental Asst.*

WYATT, Victoria Ann
Marshall HS; Marshall, TX (179-424) A Cap Choir; Cpt, Band; FTA; COM; Most Out; Choir; Christians in Action; Cpt, Show Flags; Summer Camp, Mus Stu; *E Tex Baptist Col; Elem Ed.*

WYATT, Wanita Jane
Southwestern HS; Hanover, PA (13-180) AFS; Drama; Fr C; A-Ed, Sch P; *Hood-Fredrick Col; Early Childhood Development.*

WYBLE, Mark Lane
Belmont Acad; Opelousas, LA (10-29) CYO; 4H; Key C; JV, Bkbl; COM; 4H A; Hon Prog; Pres, La Jr Angus Assn; 4-H As; Agr Bus Achv A; *LSU; Vet Med.*

WYCHOR, James John II
Worthington Sr HS; Worthington, MN; Chor; Ensm; Key C; Ftbl; MVP, Tr; Co-Cpt, Wrest; All Conf, St, Wrest Tourn; Merit A; *Worthington Comm Col; Pre-Law Enforcement.*

WYDA, James
Loyola HS; Towson, MD (8-134) CYO; NHS; JV, Bsbl; Ftbl; *Amherst Col; Amer Stu.*

WYDA, Juanita Theresa
Norfolk Cath HS; Norfolk, VA; Chldr; Drama; 4H; Key C; MVP, Bkbl; Swim; Gen Excel A; *Old Dominion U; Psych.*

**WYDRONEK,
Mary Ann Elizabeth**
St Angela Hall Acad; Brooklyn, NY (2-82) Math C; NHS; Sodality; Bio A; COM; Citz A; Math A; Sci A; Essay A's; *St John's U; Bus Adm.*

WYGANT, Theodore Maxwell
Harding HS; Marion, OH (87-446) FTA; Hmrm; Ski C; Span C; Cr-Ctry; COM; Yth Fel; Tutor; *Ohio St U-Marion; Dentistry.*

WYLAM, Ben Evan
Old Forge HS; Old Forge, PA (10-146) CYO; Sci C; Ski C; Marksmanship A; *Pa St U; Pre-Law.*

WYLE, Patrick Laurel
Marshall HS; Marshall, MO (20%-200) Order/ Arrow; JV, Golf; God & Country A; Yth Fel; St Yth Cab Rep; Del Intrntl Affairs; VICA; Eagle Sct; Jr Deacon; Asst, Sch Office; Finance Dept; Asst, Sch Office; *Culver Stockon Col; Aviation Mech.*

WYLIE, Carol Sue
Peru HS; Peru, IN (27-246) Band; NHS; *Interntl Jr Col; Secretarial.*

WYLIE, Debbie Lynne
Blacksburg HS; Blacksburg, SC (10%-130) Drama; FHA; FTA; 4H; Bkbl; Sftbl; *U of SC; Eng.*

WYLIE, Paula Lea
Monterey HS; Lubbock, TX (150-750) A Cap Choir; Chor; Fr C; Rptr, FHA; Madrigal; NHS; Tri-HiY; Bkbl; Sftbl; COM; Hon Prog; Yth Fel; Yth Leg; *Tex Tech U; Communication.*

WYLONG, Dawn Christine
Yonkers HS; Yonkers, NY (14-450) A Cap Choir; Chor; Ensm; Hmrm; NHS; Sch P; Ski C; SC; Var C; Hon Prog; Co-Cpt, Twirling; Vlbl; *Vet Med.*

WYMAN, David Snow
Oakmont Regional HS; S Ashburnham, MA (3-145) Band; BS; Chor; Ensm; NHS; MVP, Bkbl; MVP, Ftbl; Co-Cpt, Tr; Balfour A; Hist A; Most Out; *U of Maine; Computer Sci.*

WYMAN, Mark Donald
Maranatha Christian Acad; New Hartford, NY; Cpt, Chess C; Chor; Ensm; Ed, Sch P; Pres, SC; Soccer; Tr; 1st Pl, Pub Spkg, Talen for Christ; *Baptist Bible Col of Pa; Theology.*

WYMAN, Nina Joy
Theodore HS; Theodore, AL; *U of S Ala; Ed.*

WYNIA, Carol Faye
Luverne Jr-Sr HS; Luverne, MN (20-160) Chor.

WYNIA, Marla Joy
Luverne Jr Sr HS; Luverne, MN (5-134) Co-Ed, Ann; Chor; NHS; Sal; *Willmar Voc Sch; Med Secy.*

WYNN, Audrey Faye
Northern HS; Flint, MI; Chor; Bsbl; Type Lamda Kappa Mu A; Secy Cert; *Bus Adm.*

WYNN, David Jeffery
Lithia Springs HS; Lithia Springs, GA (1-345) A Cap Choir; Chor; Ensm; Pres, NHS; Tnns; COM; Val; Choral Solo & Ensm A; Ga Tech Distinguished Sci Schol; *Shorter Col; Microbio.*

WYNN, Debra
Alexander HS; Starkville, MS (10-59) A Cap Choir; Chldr; Fin, Hmrm; Secy, Sr Cl; Pres, Jr Cl; HCt; *Golden Triangle Vo-tech Col; Nurs.*

WYNN, Harold Henderson Jr
Marianna HS; Marianna, FL; Pres, 4H; Tr; 4H A; ROTC A; Spch a; WW; *Chipola Jr Col; Ed.*

WYNN, Jeffery Ray
Copeland HS; Copeland, KS (6-11) 4H; Bkbl; Bio A; 4H A; *Wildlife Mgt.*

WYNN, Michael
Alexander HS; Starkville, MS (3-59) Fr C; Hon Prog; Ntl Sci Found; *Miss St U; Elec.*

WYNN, Stephen William
Albia Community HS; Albia, IA (12-165) CYO; Chor; Pres, 4H; Hmrm; Span C; Pres, SC; Var Cl; Pres, Jr Cl; Pres, Soph Cl; JV, Bkbl; Co-Cpt, Ftbl; Tr; Citz A; 4H A; Hon Prog; I Dare You; 4-H Ldrship & Achv As; *U of Iowa; Pre-Med.*

WYNNE, Gary Alan
Permian HS; Odessa, TX (48-798) NHS; JV, Bkbl; UIL Solo, Ensm Medals; Choir Beau; *Odessa Col; Law.*

WYRICK, Charles Lynn
Eastern Guilford HS; Gibsonville, NC (8-164) Ann; Pres, Fr C; French NHS; NHS; COM; Math A; Fr A; *NC St U; Chem Engr.*

WYRICK, Kathy Lynne
Eastern Guilford HS; Gibsonville, NC (12-164) Drama; Fr C; French NHS; NHS; Sci C; COM; Fr A; Jr Marshal; *U of NC; Pre-Med.*

WYSCARVER, Sandra Marie
NW HS; Omaha, NE (90-590) A Cap Choir; Band; Chor; Madrigal; *Yankton Col; Mus.*

WYSCHARVER, Andy Jay
Northwest HS; Omaha, NE (180-450) Pres, Band; Hmrm; JV, Wrest; COM; Drum Major; Band Schol; Best Woodwind A; *Grace Col of the Bible.*

WYSE, Carla Rae
Northridge HS; Middlebury, IN (6-147) Chldr; Chor; Fin, Jr Miss Pagent; NHS; Tres, Jr Cl; Type A; Drill Tm; *Ball St Col.*

WYSE, Theresa Alice
Monsignor Ryan Mem HS; Dorchester, MA; Pres, Fr C; Sch P; St Stu Congress; SC; VP; Sr Cl; VP, Soph Cl; Bkbl; Sftbl; Swim; Hon Prog; GSct Ldr; *Providence Col; Health Service Adm.*

WYSKIVER, Sue Ann
Chillicothe HS; Chillicothe, OH; Band; Chor; Ensm; Hmrm; NHS; Orch; Span C; Co-Ch, SC; Cpt, Bkbl; JV, Tnns; Tr; Amer Leg A; COM; Hon Prog; Pres A; Sci A; Yth Fel; *Ed.*

WYSOCKI, Edmund J
G A R Mem HS; Wilkes-Barre, PA (7-190) Drama; NHS; Co-Cpt, Bsbl; Co-Cpt, Bkbl; Co-Cpt, Ftbl; Rotary A; *Biol.*

WYSONG, Chad Leif
Delaware Acad; Delhi, NY (10-120) AFS; Chor; Hmrm; Pres, NHS; *Regent Schol; Cornell U.*

WYSOR, Elizabeth Jane
George Wythe HS; Wytheville, VA (9-120) Key C; Math C; Mu Alpha Theta; NHS; Sci C; Bkbl; Tnns; *Archt.*

WYSS, Brenda Ann
Warrensburg HS; Warrensburg, MO (10-213) A Cap Choir; Co-Ed, Ann; Band; Chldr; Sci C; VP, Span C; Math A; Opt A; Opt Out Tn; Sci A; Spch A; Type A; *Med.*

WYSZKOWSKI, Patricia Ann
Whitney Point Sr HS; Whitney Point, NY (10-150) Chldr; FTA; Hmrm; NHS; Ski C; Tnns; COM; Runner-Up, Outst Tn Young Woman; *Marywood Col; Ed.*

VYTOSKI, Carol Dianne
Springfield Sr HS; Springfield, OH; Ch, Ger C; 4H; ARC; COM; JA A; *California Baptist Col; Mus.*

WYZARD, Lorraine Antoinette
Gould Academy; Bethel, ME (15-70) Bkbl; Hockey; Cpt, Tr; Co-Cpt & MVP, Tr; *Bradford Col; Hist.*

Y

YACCARINO, Rosemarie Libera
Secaucus HS; Secaucus, NJ (19-164) CYO; Cpt, Chldr; Chor; Hmrm; NHS; SC; Secy, Sr Cl; Beauty; Most Sch Spirit; Best Personality; WW; *Fairleigh Dickinson U; Nurs.*

YACOVINO, Thomas Michael
Saint Joseph HS; Toms River, NJ (20-174) BS; CYO; VP, Drama; VP, NHS; VP, SC; Thes; Mgr, Ftbl; Hon Prog; *U of Notre Dame; Engr.*

YAGER, Denise Lynn
Woodruff HS; Peoria, IL (44-216) AFS; Tres, Fr C; Hmrm; NHS; VP, SC; VP, Jr Cl; DARGCA; WW; *ICC; Med Tech.*

YALE, David Eric
Claremont HS; Claremont, CA (20%-500) Sci C; CSF; Hon Prog; Encampment for Citz; Sch Board Advisory Comm; Principal's Advisory Comm; *U of Calif; Pol Sci.*

YAMADA, Ann Miye
McKinley HS; Honolulu, HI (28-819) NHS; Co-Ed, Sch P; *U of Hawaii; Bus.*

YAMAGUCHI, Dexter Makoto
Kubasaki HS; Okinawa, JAPAN (7-271) Mu Alpha Theta; Pres, NHS; Wrest; Citz A; NMS; Elec A; Soc Stu A; Photo C; Radio C; *U of Calif; Engr.*

YAMAMOTO, Leah Tamie
Kohala HS; Kapaau, HI (5-78) AFS; Hmrm; NHS; SC; VP, Jr Cl; Bsbl; DARGCA; *U of Hawaii; Acct.*

YAMANOUCHI, Daryl Takeo
Laupahoehoe HS; Laupahoehoe, HI (1-39) VP, FHA; Pres, NHS; Sci C; Pres, Sr Cl; Bsbl; Bkbl; Lettermen C; PAAC; Vlbl; Bowl; *U of Hawaii.*

YAMASHITA, Lori Kazuko
Laupahoehoe HS; Laupahoehoe, HI (1-39) FHA; NHS; Sci C; *U of Hawaii; Engr.*

YAMATE, Janet Lynn
Castle Park HS; Chula Vista, CA (1-425) JV, Chldr; Hmrm; Bus Mgr, SC; Pres, Sr Cl; Alg A; Chem A; Citz A; MLS; Val; Pres, CSF; Drill Tm; Secy; AJB Ldrship A; *San Diego St U; Health Sci.*

YANAGI, Gail Masue
Henry Perrine Baldwin HS; Wailuku, HI; Pres, FTA; Pres, 4H; Hmrm; NHS; Spch C; V-Ch, SC; VP, Soph Cl; 4H A; Sci A; *Ed.*

YANCEY, Albert Lee
Woodlawn Sr HS; Baltimore, MD (20%-675) Bus C; VP, Chor; Madrigal; *UMBC; Math.*

YANCEY, Ronald Christopher
Eastern Sr HS; Washington, DC (3-750) NHS; Bio A; Citz A; Hon Prog; Math A; Sci A; Type A; HR A's; Art A; PA; Superintendent's Accomodation Ltr; *Computers.*

YANCEY, Timothy Robert
Eastern HS; Washington, DC; Bkbl; Ftbl; Swim; Citz A; Eng A; HR A; *American U; Journ.*

YANCEY, Tyrone Felix
Eastern HS; Washington, DC; Ftbl; ARC A; Art Asst; *Art.*

YANCY, Angela LaNorris
Smith HS; Atlanta, GA (2-145) Cpt, Chldr; Dbte Tm; Hmrm; NHS; SC; Var C; Tnns; Tr; COM; Chem A; MLS; Sal; Sci A.

YANCY, David Joe
Hugh Manley HS; Chicago, IL (5-219) City Conf; Model UN; Tres, NHS; Up Bound; Co-Cpt, Bkbl; Ftbl; Tr; Alg A; COM; Hon Prog; Math A; *Western Mich U; Graphic Designs.*

YANCY, Karen Regina
Smith HS; Atlanta, GA; Band; Chem C; Fr C; Hmrm; Math C; NHS; Sci C; SC; Var C; Cr-Ctry; Tr; Alg A; Bio A; COM; Gov Honor Prog; Math A; Sci A; YCC A; Close-Up A; *Ga St Col; Math.*

YANDA, Richard Eric
Hampton HS; Allison Park, PA (20-292) Band; Ensm; NHS; Orch; Order/Arrow; Phys C; *Grove City Col; Acct.*

YANDELL, Kevin Scott
Richwoods HS; Peoria, IL (20-460) A Cap Choir; Chor; Drama; Ensm; Fr C; Madrigal; NHS; COM; Hon Prog; NMS; St Scholar; All St Choir; *Lincoln Christian Col; Ministry.*

YANG, Helen Hsien
Kubasaki HS; Okinawa, JAPAN (5-424) Ann; Tres, Chor; Citz A; Hist A; Math A; Eng A; Span A; Vlbl C; VP, Chinese Culture C; *UCLA; Math.*

YANG, Stanley K
Kubasaki HS; Okinawa, JAPAN (8-355) Tres, Chess C; Lit Mag; NHS; Sch P; JV, Bsbl; JV, Bkbl; Cl Fav; Hon Prog; Most Out; Span A; Tres, Tnns C; Philsophers C; Vlbl; *Stanford U; Sci.*

YANKELITIS, Janet Anne
Bishop Klonowski HS; Scranton, PA (10-106) Chor; NHS; Amer Leg A; *Mercy Hospital Sch of Nurs; Nursing.*

YANOSICH, Debra Lynn
Western Bearver Sr-Sr HS; Industry, PA (5-165) Co-Cpt, Chldr; Chor; Lat C; NHS; Rptr, Sch P; Tr; Amer Leg A; Hon Prog; *Penn St U; Bus Adm.*

YANTKO, Regina Marie
Uniontown Sr HS; Uniontown, PA (1-435) F-Ed, Ann; Fr C; NHS; Sci C; Ski C; *Seton Hill Col; Bio.*

YANTZER, John Owen
Center HS; Center, ND (10%-52) Band; CYO; FFA; Ger C; Bsbl; Bkbl; Ftbl; Type A; Attendance As; *ND St Sch of Sci; Mech.*

YANTZER, Joletta Marie
Center HS; Center, ND (1-36) Band; CYO; Chldr; Chor; VP, FHA; Ger C; SC; Tr; B Crocker A; Val; WW; *Mary Col; Nurs.*

YARBOR, Joseph Edward
Winsor Forest HS; Savannah, GA; Co-Cpt, Band; *Clark Col; Mass Communications.*

YARBOROUGH, Lisa Ann
Princeton HS; Cincinnati, OH; Lat C; *X-Ray Tech.*

YARBOROUGH, Lona Susan
Colonial HS; Orlando, FL; A Cap Choir; Ensm; Hmrm; Key C; ARC; Sftbl; Jr NHS; Valentine Banquet Qn.

YARBOROUGH, Rene Rochelle
Ursuline Acad; Cincinnati, OH (80-140) CYO; Chldr; Chess C; Pres, Ger C; K of C; Lit Ral; Spch C; Sftbl; Swim; Tnns; COM; Citz A; Yth Fel; *Dennison U; Med.*

YARBOROUGH, Vickie Gail
Thompson HS; Alabaster, AL; Band; BC; Chor; Ensm; Fr C; VP, SC; Bio A; Hon Prog; Star Student; Drum Major; Chor Accompanist; Eng, Fr, All A'S, A's; *Samford U; Mus.*

YARBROUGH, Caren Denise
Panhandle HS; Panhandle, TX; Ann; Chldr; Drama; FHA; FTA; Jr Miss Pagent; Bkbl; Tr; Home Ec A.

YARBROUGH, Carol Elaine
Tuscaloosa HS; Tuscaloosa, AL (26-561) Chor; Pres, Ensm; NHS; Cl Fav; HCt; Most Out; Swtht; Yth Fel; All-St Chor; Outst Accompanist; *U of Ala.*

YARBROUGH, Judith Hazel
Vanguard HS; Ocala, FL (24-350) Fr C; Secy, FBLA; Rptr, Mu Alpha Theta; NHS; Fr, Ger, A's; *Central Fla Comm Col.*

YARBROUGH, Martin Landers
Tupelo HS; Tupelo, MS; Order/Arrow; Thes; Bkbl; Ftbl; Sftbl; *Miss St Col; Agr.*

YARBROUGH, Rhonda Sabrina
Humboldt HS; Humboldt, TN; BC; FHA; Bkbl; Tr; *Martin Col; Sci.*

YARBROUGH, Ruth Ann
Milo Adventist Acad; Days Creek, OR (10-66) Pres, SC; Citz A; *Umpqua Comm Col; Secy.*

YARBROUGH, Terri Louise
DeSoto HS; DeSoto, MO; Art, Poetry, Creative Writing, A's; Commercial Art.

YARBROUGH, Vanessa Renay
Regina Caeli HS; Compton, CA; Bus C; Chor; Tres, Hmrm; VP, Lit Mag; HCt; Most Inspirational; Calif St Col; Psych.

YARD, James William
Taylorville Sr HS; Taylorville, IL (74-275) SC; Span A; Lincoln Land Comm Col; Math.

YARDLEY, Louis Leon
Deerborne HS; Coral Gables, FL (6-80) Golf; Soccer; Tnns; Psych.

YARLEY, Luann
Northmont Sr HS; Clayton, OH (10%-500) Band; Chor; Sch Achieve Tm; Yth Rep; Wittenburg U; Mus.

YASSA, Nadia Ann
Dover-Sherborn Regional HS; Dover, MA (6-200) AFS; Chor; Lat Cum Laude Soc; Lit Mag; NHS; Bio A; Yth Fel; Fr, Chor, A's.

YATES, David Martin
Woodrow Wilson HS; Dallas, TX (25%-280) Bus C; Pres, Key C; Ftbl; JA A; MLS; Escort for MTA Pageant; Zale Corp Intern Mgr; Baylor U; Bus Adm.

YATES, Deborah Ann
Tri-County Christian HS; Mechanicsburg, PA (10%-20) Chldr; Tres, Chor; Ensm; Sftbl; COM; HCt; Sal; Bible Quiz A; Christian Testimony; Wm Port Sch of Nurs; Nurs.

YATES, Denise Elizabeth
Kenwood HS; Chicago, IL (5%-475) Dbte Tm; Ger C; NHS; Pres, SC; Alg A; Hist A; Hon Prog; Pres A; Sci A; Star Student; Morehouse Col; Law.

YATES, Elizabeth Catherine
Sky View HS; Smithfield, UT; Band; Chor; FHA; Span C; Outst Span Stu A; Cert of Completion; Nurse's Aid; Paducah Comm Col; Nurs.

YATES, James Carlton
Richland HS; Ft Worth, TX (300-700) Chem C; Drama; Lit Ral; Math C; Sci C; Thes; ROTC A; Tex A&M U; Elec Engr.

YATES, Jeffrey Gerald
Park Center HS; Brooklyn Park, MN (50%-500) JV, Ftbl; Tr; Wrest; Yth Fel; Most Valuable Defense, Ftbl; AAU Wrest Medals; 1st Pl, USKWF; N Hennepin Comm Col; Law Enforcement.

YATES, Joyce Elaine
Kingsbury HS; Memphis, TN (28-30) Shelby St; Home Ec.

YATES, Julianne
Willis HS; Willis, TX (3-150) Band; Chor; Ensm; VP, FHA; VP, FTA; Madrigal; SC; COM; 1st Div, UIL Voice Ensm; 2nd Div, UIL Piano Solo; 2nd Pl, Dist Miss FTA; Mus.

YATES, Karon Lynne
Travelers Rest HS; Travelers Rest, SC (10%-300) Ann; Chor; Mod Mus Mas; NHS; F-Ed, Sch P; Hon Prog; HR; PA; Clemson U; Nurs.

YATES, Lisa Gale
Trion HS; Trion, GA (1-51) Pres, BC; Chldr; Dbte Tm; Pres, SC; Tnns; COM; Gov Honor Prog; HCt; Math A; MLS; NEDT; Star Student; Val; W Ga Col.

YATES, Mary Louise
Hillside HS; Durham, NC; Sunday Sch A; Ministry Sch; Ministry.

YATES, Robert Donald
Montgomery HS; San Diego, CA (2-490) InterClub Coun; Tres, Key C; SC; B Crocker A; DARGCA; Elk A; MLS; NMS; Opt A; Point Loma Col; Ministry.

YATES, Sharon Dee
Wingfield HS; Jackson, MS (10%-280) F-Ed, Ann; Chor; Lat NHS; Miss St U.

YATES, Sheryl Lynn
Bossier Acad; Haughton, LA (1-13) Ed, Ann; Cpt, Chldr; Lit Ral; Co-Ed, Sch P; Pres, SC; Parl, Sr Cl; Pres, Soph Cl; Alg A; Bio A; Hist A; HCt; Math A; MLS; Sci A; Type A; Val; Most Sch Spirit; Outst Stu Coun Member; Mardi Gras Qn; La Tech U; Med Technology.

YATES, William Anthony
Sullivan Central HS; Blountville, TN (10%-600) Ann; BC; Lat C; Lat NHS; NHS; VP, SC; Mgr, Bsbl; Cr-Ctry; Ftbl; Voice o-t Cougars; Mgr; 2nd Pl Certamen Tm, Lat A; Eng A; Latin Magna Cum Laude A; Sch Service A.

YATES, William Derois
Kenwood HS; Chicago, IL (10%-500) Band; Ensm; SC; Pres, Sr Cl; Pres, Jr Cl; Pres, Soph Cl; Hist A; Hon Prog; General Motors; Bus Adm.

YATKO, Doreen Maria
John S Fine Sr HS; Nanticoke, PA (1-300) Mgr, Ann; Arch; Co-Cpt, Chldr; Chor; Drama; Hmrm; Spch C; SC; Var C; Amer Leg A; COM; Lion A; NEDT; VFW A; Juniata Col; Bio-Chem.

YATOR, Charles Henry
Springfield HS; Bergholz, OH (50%-85) JV, Ftbl; JV, Wrest.

YAU, Grace Choi Hing
Inglewood HS; Inglewood, CA; El Camino Col.

YAWN, Barbara Fay
Indian Springs Acad; Jackson, GA; Sch P; Bkbl; Sftbl; Tr; Bus Sch; Bus Adm.

YAWN, Brenda Kay
Indian Springs Acad; Jackson, GA; Sch P; Bkbl; Sftbl; Tr; HCt; Bus Sch; Bus Adm.

YAWN, Donna Luan
Brunswick HS; Brunswick, GA (11-416) FBLA; Hmrm; Lit Mag; NHS; Pres, Rainbow; Span C; COM; Type A; Hon Grad; NCTE, Semi-Fin; Grand Cross of Colo; Poetry Contest Win; St Outer Observ, Rainbow Girls; Brunswick Jr Col; Bus.

YAWORSKY, Jean Louise
Port Byron Central HS; Port Byron, NY (7-100) Chldr; Dbte Tm; FTA; NHS; Sch P; Span C; Spch C; NEDT.

YAZZIE, Robert Franklin
Chinle HS; Chinle, AZ (9-130) FFA; NHS; Cpt, Cr-Ctry; JV, Ftbl; Cpt, Tr; Cpt, Wrest; MVP, Tr; Northern Ariz U.

YBARRA, Cindy
David Crockett HS; Austin, TX; CYO; Ger C; Span C; Sftbl; COM; Order Clerk Cert; Personnel Clerk Cert; St Edwards U.

YEADON, Timothy Raymond
John Glenn HS; Huntington, NY (4-365) Chess C; Drama; 4H; NHS; Golf; Cpt, Soccer; Tr; COM; Hon Prog; NMS; Regent Schol; All Col Schol; Cornell U; Biol.

YEAGER, Denise Ann
Dodgeville HS; Dodgeville, WI (3-150) Ch, AFS; Band; Chor; Community Yth Symph; Ensm; 4H; Lit Mag; Model UN; NFL; Orch; Span C; Spch C; God & Country A; Hist A; JA A; Most Out; Spch A; Type A; Mus A; Berea Col; Mus.

YEAGER, Douglas Paul
Parkland HS; Orefield, PA (46-540) Band; Demolay; NHS; Orch; COM; Yth Fel; Rochester Inst of Tech; Printing.

YEAGER, Gregory Scott
Lakeview HS; Battle Creek, MI (350-400) Hon Prog; Kellogg Comm Col; Bus Adm.

YEAGER, Jeffrey Dean
Lakeview HS; Battle Creek, MI (200-400) Hon Prog; Kellogg Comm Col; Ed.

YEAGER, Victor Raymond
McCluer N HS; Florissant, MO (107-700) Bkbl; MVP, Cr-Ctry; Tr; Ntl Merit Schol Recognition.

YEAGLE, Donald Paul
Muhlenberg HS; Reading, PA (130-350) HiY; Pol Sci C; UN Council; Ftbl; Wrest; Audio-Visual C; Pepperdine U; Theology.

YEAKLEY, Cheryl Jean
Hoisington HS; Hoisington, KS (25%-95) Band; JV, Chldr; Chor; Pres, 4H; SC; Pres, Var C; Co-Cpt, Bkbl; Tr; 4H A; Hon Prog; Secy, Rptr; 4-H C; Co-Cpt, Vlbl; Barton Co Comm Col; Fashion Design.

YEAKLEY, Steven Wayne
E Central HS; Tulsa, OK (10-600) A Cap Choir; Chem C; Chor; Ensm; Hmrm; NHS; Bkbl; Tr; I Dare You; Danforth A; Most Talented; Pres, Church Yth Comm; Okla Christian Col; Med.

YEATER, Gregory Scott
Michigan City Elston HS; Michigan City, IN; A Cap Choir; Band; Chor; Order/Arrow; Ftbl; Cpt, Swim; Radio-tV-Film Communications; Ind St U; Radio-tV-FILM Communications.

YEAZEL, James Robert
National Trail HS; New Paris, OH (5-140) Chor; Pres, FFA; Pres, 4H; Tres, NHS; Sci C; 4H A; Star Student; Ohio St ATI U; Agr.

YEAZEL, Mark Thomas
National Trail HS; New Paris, OH (8-160) Band; Secy, FFA; Sci C; Cr-Ctry; Tr; 4H A; Math A; Star Student; Outward Bound; Ohio St U; Vet.

YEE, Catherine
Lutheran HS; Burbank, CA; Chor; Rptr, Sch P; Tr; CSF; Drill Tm; Pep C.

YEE, Julie Diane
John F Kennedy Sr HS; Sacramento, CA (94-673) Ann; Sch P; CSF; Citz A; Span A; San Jose St Col; Bus Adm.

YEE, Steven S
Interlochen Arts Acad; Interlochen, MI (1-165) Ensm; Orch; Regent Schol; Val; Schol, Baldwin Piano; Hon A, Boston U Trustees; Semi-Fin, Mi Compet School Prog; Northwestern U; Pre-Med.

YEE, Tracy
Westminster HS; Westminster, CA (18-812) Band; Chor; Swim; CSF; Hon Prog; Pianist, 11 Yrs; Cpt, Color-Guard; Ed.

YEE, William W
St Agnes HS; NY, NY (65-120) Bus Mgr.

YELM, Brenda Lee
Mesa Verde HS; Citrus Heights, CA (34-400) Tres, AFS; Secy, Chess C; Chor; Math C; Orch; SC; Cpt, Var C; Pres, Sr Cl; VP, Jr Cl; Bkbl; Bio A; CSF; COM; ARC A; Stu Advocate; Cpt, Badminton; Heart & Lung Assn A; American River Jr Col; Acct.

YENCHO, Mary Ann
Bentworth Sr HS; Bentleyville, PA (24-170) Band; Chess C; Drama; Ski C; Thes; COM; Hon Cert's; Mus Ability A; W Va U; Engr.

YEOMANS, Cynthia LaNeve
Cohasset HS; Cohasset, MA (4-178) Ann; Drama; NHS; Hon Prog; MLS; Yth Fel; Math Tutor; Campus Coordinator; Carved Art Cl Rings; U of Mass; Finance.

YERKS, Laurie Ann
Hutchinson Jr-Sr HS; Hutchinson, MN; Tres, AFS; Band; Chldr; Hmrm; Spch C; Tres, Thes; Amer Leg A; COM; Hon Prog; Opt A; Spch A; Yth Fel; Cert of Excellence For Art; Cert of Appreciation; Candystriper; Gustavus Adolphus Col; Nurs.

YESSAK, Rebecca Lynn
Sheffield HS; Memphis, TN; Pres, FBLA; Math C; Rep, Stu Coun; Toe C; Memphis St; Acct.

YETSKO, Sandra Joann
Hobart Sr HS; Nobart, IN (296-393) A Cap Choir; Chor; Drama; FHA; Jr Miss Pagent; ARC; Sci C; Spch C; Ftbl; Interlochen Ntl Mus; Pom Pon.

YETTER, Elizabeth Marie
Aldine Sr HS; Houston, TX (5%-750) Band; Crown & Scepter; Dbte Tm; Drama; Ensm; FTA; NHS; Span C; Spch C; Hon Prog; Tex A&M U; Elem Ed.

YETTER, Larry Wilson Jr
Bangor Area HS; Bangor, PA (35-250) NHS; Order/Arrow; VP, SC; Var C; Ftbl; Tr; Amer Leg A; Elk A; God & Country A; Order/Arrow A Type A; Eagle Sct; Lehigh U; Engr.

YIANNAKOS, Andrew Evangelos
Stuyvesant HS; New York, NY (65%-750) Ger C; Hmrm; NHS; Order/Arrow; Bsbl; Co-Cpt, Bkbl; COM; Order/Arrow A; Alpha Omega A; Hellenic Amer Soc; Ntl Fed Stu Ger; New York U; Dentistry.

YOAKUM, Pamela Celeste
Sebastopol Attendance Center; Sebastopol, M (1-32) Ann; Pres, Band; VP, BC; Chldr; Chess C Chor; Dbte Tm; Drama; VP, Fr C; Hmrm; Sch I Sci C; Pres, SC; JV, Bkbl; COM; Cl Fav; Hist A HCt; MLS; Star Student; Eng A; Millsaps Co Law.

YOCOM, Sherri
Hope HS; Hope, AR; Band; Pres, BC; Secy, SC; Ouachita Baptist U.

YOCUM, David Michael
Brawley Union HS; Brawley, CA (6-450) Chess C; Key C; Ftbl; JV, Tnns; CSF; Annapolis-Naval Acad; Oceanography.

YODER, Cathy Diane
Goshen HS; Goshen, IN (42-250) Band; Community Yth Symph; Hmrm; ARC; Span C; JV, Bkbl; Sftbl; JV, Swim; Mgr, Tr; Kiwanis A; St Mary's Col; Law.

YODER, Katherine Lynn
Northwood HS; Nappanee, IN (119-184) 4H; JA A; Bethel Col; Ed.

YODER, Kay Annette
Goshen HS; Goshen, IN (57-268) Chor; Ensm; Hmrm; Ntl Yth Conf; Secy, Orch; Tr; Professional Symph; Chamber Orch; VP, Yth Group; Secy, Sunshine Soc; Social Work.

YODER, Kristine Joy
Concord HS; Elkhart, IN (84-252) Band; Mjrte; Cheer Block; Baton Twirling; Ribbons, Medals, Camp; Band Medals; Secy.

YODER, Richard Kent
Lake Clifton Sr HS; Baltimore, MD (10-315) JETS; Key C; Tres, Lit Mag; Math C; NHS; Alg A; Amer Leg A; Hist A; Hon Prog; Math A; Yth Fel; La-Crosse; Gym A; Service As; Schol As; Eng A; U of Md at Baltimore Co; Chem.

YODSNUKIS, Diane Elizabeth
John W Hallahan Cath HS; Philadelphia, PA (1-432) CYO; Chor; VP, Math C; NHS; Rptr, Sch P; Secy, Span NHS; Bkbl; Chem A; Hon Prog; Math A; Sci A; Lang A; Eng A; Saint Joseph's Col; Chem.

YOHE, Linda Marian
Wapello Comm Sch; Wapello, IA (40-80) Band; Co-Cpt, Chldr; Chor; Drama; Ensm; S-T, 4H; Madrigal; NFL; Spch C; Thes; VP, Jr Cl; Bkbl; Sftbl; Tr; Beauty; Yth Fel; Cpt, Chldr; Jr Church Elder; Prom Qn; Band Dance Girl; People to People Ambassador; Indian Hills Comm Col; Computer Prog.

YOHN, Karen Lynn
Steubenville HS; Steubenville, OH (9-290) Band; Pres, FTA; Hmrm; Mjrte; Orch; Sch P; Sci C; Pres, Span C; Secy, SC; Y-Tns; Secy, Sci C; Secy, Jr Cl; Secy, Soph Cl; Alt, GS; Secy, Fresh Cl; Pres, Secy, MYF; Pres, Pep C; Church Stu Adv Comm; Ch, Prom Comm; Fresh Cl Steuben Qn; Kent St U; Special Ed.

YOKEM, Cathy Ann
Southeast HS; Springfield, IL (254-557) Drama; Fr C; Rptr, Sch P; SC; Co-Cpt, Bkbl; COM; HR; Newspaper Staff; Home Ec A; Phys Ed A; Ray Vogue Col; Fashion Design.

YONCK, Richard Thomas
Inglemoor HS; Bothell, WA (8-359) NHS; Wrest; U of Wash.

YONGUE, Michal Grace
Clarke Central HS; Athens, GA (29-288) BC; Hmrm; Sch P; SC; Co-Cpt, Flag Corp; Young Life; Most Sincere; Young Harris Col; Pol Sci.

YOO, Kil Won Linda
Alameda Sr HS; Lakewood, CO (80-700) Ann; Chor; Fr C; Hmrm; NHS; SC; Type A; U of Colo; Med.

YOOS, Laura Jean
West HS; Denver, CO (10-365) Band; NHS; Doane Col; Art.

YOOS, Lynda Marie
West HS; Denver, CO (5-350) Chor; Madrigal; NFL; Rptr, Sch P; Spch C; COM; Citz A; Most Out; Spch A; Art As.

YORK, Andrea Gay
NE HS; Oklahoma City, OK (36-300) GS; NHS; Ch, Span C; Thes; Tres, Jr Cl; Cl Fav; Secy, Pep C; Sch Bible Stu; Okla St U; Interior Design.

YORK, Brenda Joy
Williams Bay HS; Williams Bay, WI (5-36) Band; Chldr; Chor; Span C; Pres, Jr Cl; Citz A; HQn; Girls Glee C; Pianst Chor; Rep, Church Yth Officer Comm; Wheaton Col; Med.

YORK, DeVee Sue
Karlsruhe Amer HS; Karlsruhe, GERMANY; Ann; Drama; Ger C; Hmrm; SC; Bkbl; Pres A; Vlbl.

YORK, Diana Claire
Pomona HS; Pomona, CA (20-600) All Amer Yth; AFS; Cpt, Chldr; Drama; Fr C; Rptr, Lat C; Phys C; CSF; COM; Keywanettes; Comm Theatre A; Foreign Lang C; Pres, VCTEENS; Ed, VCTEENEWS.

YORK, Karen Lynn
Bath Co HS; Owingsville, KY; Band; Cpt, Chldr; Chor; Secy, Y-Tns; Tr; Drum Mjrte; Ldrship A; Morhead Col; Ed.

YORK, Laura Kelly
Ballard HS; Louisville, KY; A Cap Choir; BC; Chor; Drama; Ensm; Fr C; Madrigal; SC; Bkbl; Sftbl; Tr; Cl Fav; Hon Prog; Math A; Sci A; Best Personality; Sargeant- at-Arms, Soph Cl; Med.

YORK, Lydia Elizabeth
Peabody HS; Pittsburgh, PA (16-479) Pres, Hmrm; Parl, NHS; Orch; SC; Thes; World Affairs C; Mgr, Swim; COM; Hon Prog; NMF; NMS; Pa Gov's Sch for The Arts; Fla A&M U; Acct.

YORK, Marsha Renee
Maysville HS; Maysville, OK (6-50) Ann; Chldr; Drama; Pres, FHA; GS; S-T, NHS; Sch P; Spch C; Pres, SC; Mgr, Bkbl; Bio A; HCt; Spch A; Type A; Home Ec Medals; Eng A; Okla U; Elem Ed.

YORK, Phillip Mark
J J Pearce HS; Dallas, TX (55-812) Pres, Chor; VP, HiY; Order/Arrow; COM; Hon Prog; Order/ Arrow A; Sci A; Spch A; Eagle Sct; Pres, Ntl Jr Hon Soc; Baylor U; Psych.

YOSHIDA, Marilyn Eiko
Faith Baptist Sch; Canoga Park, CA (7%-28) Cpt, Chldr; ARC; Var C; Tres, Jr Cl; Tres, Soph Cl; Bkbl; Sftbl; COM; Yth Fel; MVP, Chldr; Vlbl; Camper o-t Wk; Bus Cpt; HR; Newspaper 'A' HR; Jr Church Pianist; Tres, Fresh Cl.

YOSHIDA, Suzanne Natsue
Kailua HS; Kailua, HI (28-668) Hmrm; NHS; Ch, SC; Yth Leg; Outst Soph Fr A.

YOST, Marjorie Ann
Sandusky HS; Sandusky, OH (27-461) Bus C; 4th Pl Region, Records Mgr Clerk; Firelands Col; Bus.

YOST, Scott Dayvault
Grimsley Sr HS; Greensboro, NC; Band; Fr C; NHS; Tnns; Hon Prog; Meth Conf Yth Coun Rep; VP, MYF; Special HR; WW; Duke U; Med.

YOTTER, Craig Bradley
Annandale HS; Annandale, MN; Band; Ensm; Pres, 4H; NHS; JV, Bkbl; U of Minn; Acct.

YOUDELL, Pamela Susan
Lakeshore HS; Stevensville, MI; A Cap Choir; Chor; Pres, JA; Med Careers; Future Secretaries; Church Yth Group; Western Mich U; Elem Ed.

YOUENS, Sheryl Kay
N Shore HS; Houston, TX (96-500) VP, Fr C; Tres, MYF; Hon Soc; Christian Stu Union.

YOUMANS, Barbara Ann
Claxton HS; Claxton, GA (50%-115) Yth For Christ; Ga Sou Col; Bus.

YOUMANS, Michael Lee
Dover Sr HS; Dover, OH (1-273) Tres, Chess C; NHS; Span C; Alg A; Bio A; Chem A; Math A; Span A.

YOUMANS, Sharon Lynn
Millville Sr HS; Millville, NJ (46-580) A Cap Choir; Drama; Fr C; FNA; Lat C; A-Ed, Lit Mag; Orch; Bio A; Drama, Acad Achv, A's; UCLA; Nurs.

YOUMANS, Theresa Estelle
Secaucus HS; Secaucus, NJ (2-206) Band; Secy, Soph Cl; Cr-Crtry; JV, Tnns; JV, Tr; PTO; Jr NHS; Secy, Fresh Cl; Cpt, JV Bowl; Math.

YOUNG, Albert
Wadley HS; Wadley, GA (10-82) Band; BC; Chor; FFA; 4H; JA; Sci A; Eng, PA, Mech, A's; Swainsboro Tech Col; Auto Mech.

YOUNG, Amanda Krise
Roland Park Ctry Sch; Baltimore, MD (5-34) Pres, A Cap Choir; Ed, Ann; Pres, Chor; Cum Laude Soc; Dbte Tm; 4H; Madrigal; NMF; Badminton; Princeton U; Pol Econ.

YOUNG, Amy Dawson
Batavia HS; Batavia, IL (15-195) Fr C; Rptr, Lit Mag; Ed, Sch P; Ski C; Spch C; SC; Hon Prog; Journ A; Q&S A; St Scholar; Sou Ill U; Journ.

YOUNG, Amy Joy
South Hills HS; Pittsburgh, PA; Chldr; Chor; Dbte Tm; Secy, Hmrm; Fin, Jr Miss Pagent; Rptr, Sch P; SC; Mgr, Cr-Ctry; Mgr, Tr; COM; Citz A; Hon Prog; JA A; VP, JA; Drill Tm; Gym; Lib C; Social C; Dance Stu; Church Choirs; Air Force; Nurs.

YOUNG, Anita Jo
Central HS; San Angelo, TX; Chor; Drama; FHA; Pres, SC; Bkbl; Tr; Pres Phys Fitness A; Pres, Stu Body; Sports As; Abilene Christian Col; Psych.

YOUNG, Bart Bernard
Gulf Comprehensive HS; New Port Richey, FL; Band; Ensm; Key C; Var C; Co-Cpt, Ftbl; Co-Cpt, Soccer; St Pete Jr Col; Bio.

YOUNG, Belinda Ella
Acad of St Aloysius; Jersey City, NJ (5-104) Math C; VP, NHS; Pres, Span C; COM; Hon Prog; Bowl Trophies; St Peter's Col; Math.

YOUNG, Benita Audrey
Ahrens HS; Louisville, KY; FBLA; Hmrm; NHS; SC; JV, Bkbl; Co-Cpt, Tr; HCt; Type A; PA; Span A; Western Ky U; Elem Ed.

YOUNG, Bessie Mae
Lake Clifton Sr HS; Baltimore, MD; All Amer Yth; City Conf; Ntl Yth Conf; Social Work.

YOUNG, Beth Ann
Marion HS; Marion, IN; Taylor U; Bio.

YOUNG, Beth Lorene
Arvin HS; Arvin, CA (3-265) Pres, Band; Drama; Model UN; NHS; Pres, SC; S-T, Jr Cl; Tres, Soph Cl; Swim; CSF; Ntl Sci Found; Bakersfield Jr Col; Counseling.

YOUNG, Beverly Jo
New Lexington HS; New Lexington, OH; Span C; COM; Church Choir; MVP, Bible Quiz Tm; Apostolic Bible Inst; Secy.

YOUNG, Bryan Earl
Tahlequah Sr HS; Tahlequah, OK (50-285) A Cap Choir; Chor; Drama; FBLA; FTA; VP, NHS; Var C; Bsbl; Co-Cpt, Ftbl; Tr; HCt; All Conf Def Back; Golden Glove A, Bsbl; Alumni Schol; Northeastern Ok St U; Phys Ed.

YOUNG, Candis Love
Oakhaven HS; Memphis, TN (2-100) Pres, A Cap Choir; Ann; Chor; Pres, Drama; Secy, Math C; Pres, Mod Mus Mas; Secy, NHS; Ed, Sch P; Pres, Spch C; SC; VP, Thes; Pres, Soph Cl; Cpt, Sftbl; Alg A; Beauty; Bio A; COM; Cl Fav; H of F; HCt; Math A; Sal; Spch A; Type A; Yth Fel; Teenager of Week; Modern Mus Masters Top-Notcher A; Yth of Yr; Southwestern Col; Pre-Law.

YOUNG, Carlton Joseph
Central HS; Philadelphia, PA; Chess C; World Affairs C; Tr; Math A; HR; Penn St; Med.

YOUNG, Carma Ann
Meadowdale HS; Dayton, OH (5-400) Co-Ed, Lit Mag; NHS; I Dare You; NEDT; WW; U of Dayton; Acct.

YOUNG, Carol Ann
Passaic HS; Passaic, NJ; Chor; Drama; FTA; Hmrm; Fin, Jr Miss Pagent; Ski C; Tres, SC; Beauty; Opt A; Dancing Sch, PA A; Fashion Inst of Tech; Fashion Design.

YOUNG, Charles Dale
Berea HS; Greenville, SC (167-243) Hmrm; ARC; Var C; Bsbl; Bkbl; Ftbl; PTA A; Pres A; ARC A; Yth Fel; Ath o-t Yr; Explorer; Spartanburg Methodist Col; Criminal Justice.

YOUNG, Charles Samuel Jr
Myers Park HS; Charlotte, NC (10%-700) Band; BC; Fr C; Orch; Order/Arrow; Sci C; COM; Order/Arrow A; Yth Fel; AAU Swim; Young American's Abroad; Eagle Sct; U of NC; Art.

YOUNG, Cheri Lynn
Momence HS; Momence, IL; CYO; Drama; Math C; Span C; Thes; HCt; Spch A; U of Ill; Drama.

YOUNG, Cheryl Ann
Hobbs HS; Hobbs, NM (19-640) Ann; Pres, Bus C; NHS; Tr; Hon Prog; MLS; Outst Off Ed Stu; Am U of Women As, Girl o-t Month; NM Jr Col; Data Processing.

YOUNG, David Michael
Williamsville HS; Williamsville, IL (9-86) CYO; Helpers of Christ.

YOUNG, Dawn Elizabeth
Oppenheim Ephratah Central Sch; St Johnsville, NY (28-38).

YOUNG, Debbie Marie
Robert E Lee HS; Midland, TX (45-670) Pres, FHA; NHS; Tres, SC; Hon Prog; Lion A; Opt A; Miss Integrity; St Officer, FHA; Key C Calendar Girl; *Abilene Christian U; Ed.*

YOUNG, Deborah Ann
Susquehanna Comm HS; Susquehanna, PA (1-100) Band; Chess C; Chor; 4H; Bkbl; Tr; 4H A; Pres, Explorer; Sch Ltr; *Sociology.*

YOUNG, Deborah Sue
Andress HS; El Paso, TX; Cpt, Sftbl; Librarian Band; All-Dist, Golf; Drum Major; MV Pitcher, Golf; Cpt, Golf; Swtht, Golf; Band Prin; Ltr, Golf; Ltr Band; Symphonic Bnd; *NM St U; Math.*

YOUNG, Denise
Alain Leroy Locke HS; Los Angeles, CA; Band; GS; JA A; Math A; Eng A; PA; *Calif St U; Math.*

YOUNG, Diane Kay
Wheaton HS; Wheaton, MO (4-36) Chldr; Ch, FHA; Pres, Rainbow; Mgr, Bkbl; Sftbl; Type A; St Fin, Miss Ntl Tnager Pageant; Grand Religion, St Rainbow; *Mo Sou St Col; Hist.*

YOUNG, Douglas Koons
John Motley Morehead Sr HS; Eden, NC (1-300) VP, Band; Pres, NHS; Order/Arrow; Pres, Sci C; SC; Cr-Ctry; Gov Honor Prog; *U of NC.*

YOUNG, Elaine K
Pilgrim HS; Los Angeles, CA (7-11) V-Ch, Hmrm; SC; VP, Soph Cl; COM; Citz A.

YOUNG, Frederick William III
Columbus HS; Columbus, GA (5%-360) Bus Mgr, Ann; VP, NHS; Tnns; COM; Citz A; Hon Prog; Q&S A; Star Student; *Columbus Col; Math.*

YOUNG, Gregg Allen
Williamsville HS; Williamsville, IL (31-81) CYO; ARC; Ski C; Var C; Bsbl; JV, Bkbl; ARC A; Helpers of Christ; *Meteorology.*

YOUNG, Helen Dianne
Tyronza HS; Tyronza, AR; Chem C; Chor; FHA; GS; VP, Hmrm; S-T, NHS; VP, Jr Cl; Family Living A; Most Studious; *Med.*

YOUNG, Jana Lea
Greenport HS; Greenport, NY (3-80) Chldr; Chor; Fr C; Math C; NHS; Mgr, Tr; All Star Cheering A; WW in HS Cheering.

YOUNG, Janice Denise
Percy L Julian HS; Chicago, IL (40-350) Hmrm; Sch Achieve Tm; Sci C; Mgr, Bkbl; Yth Fel; GSct, Service, A's; *Bradley U; Engr.*

YOUNG, Jeannean Althea
Savannah HS; Savannah, GA; *Savannah St Col; Math.*

YOUNG, Jeffrey Eugene
Montpelier HS; Montpelier, OH (13-100) BS; Pres, Chess C; VP, Sci C; JV, Bsbl; JV, Ftbl; *U of Toledo; Pharmacy.*

YOUNG, Jennifer Lynn
Highstown HS; Hightstown, NJ; AFS; Band; Hmrm; Ski C; SC; Secy, Jr Cl; Mgr, Bkbl; Hockey; Sftbl; Hon Prog; Yth Fel; *Duke U; Elem Ed.*

YOUNG, Jill Suzanne
Jefferson HS; Rockford, IL (59-583) Orch; Cpt, Bkbl; Sftbl; Kiwanis A; *Nurs.*

YOUNG, John Gregory
Southwest HS; Kansas City, MO (130-560) Chor; InterClub Coun; Order/Arrow; SC; Var C; VP, Sr Cl; Bkbl; Golf; *U of Mo; Bus.*

YOUNG, John Harold
Belvidere HS; Belvidere, IL (10-370) Dbte Tm; Drama; Thes; JV, Bsbl; Bkbl; Hon Prog; Pres A; Spch A; *Bus.*

YOUNG, John William
Shamrock HS; Shamrock, TX; VP, NHS; Span C; JV, Bkbl; Ftbl; Golf; WW; *Tex Tech U; Sci.*

YOUNG, Joyce Laverne
Martin Luther King HS; Philadelphia, PA; Tr; Gym; Stenography.

YOUNG, Joyce Louise
Glenbard W HS; Glen Ellyn, IL (72-488) Band; Ger C; Hmrm; Sch P; Mgr, Cr-Ctry; Mgr, Tr; Deacon, Church; Young Life C; G-Tns Coun; Teach, Sun Sch; *Valporasio Col; Pre-Med.*

YOUNG, Julia Diane
Clyde A Erwin HS; Asheville, NC (20%-210) Chldr; FHA; FTA; Lit Mag; F-Ed, Sch P; Span C; Tr; Vlbl; Mus Cert; Essay A; *Western Carolina Col; Journ.*

YOUNG, Julianna Eva
Grace Baptist HS; South Bend, IN (1-14) *SW Mich U; Secy Sci.*

YOUNG, Karen Beth
Willard HS; Willard, MO (27-190) Band; Chor; Ensm; Model UN; NHS; Bkbl; Sftbl; Tr; *SW Mo St U; Bus.*

YOUNG, Katherine Anne
Eisenhower HS; Decatur, IL (1-366) Band; Fr C; Pres, 4H; Lat C; Tres, NHS; Secy, Soph Cl; 4H A; Math A; St Health A; NHS A; Pub Speaking A; Consumer Ed A; *Bus.*

YOUNG, Kaylene
Sky View HS; Smithfield, UT (85-573) A Cap Choir; Chor; Drama; Hmrm; InterClub Coun; Madrigal; Spch C; SC; Secy, Jr Cl; Spch A; *Ricks Col.*

YOUNG, Kelly Richard
Manchester HS; Manchester, OH (2-100) A Cap Choir; Band; Chor; Community Yth Symph; Dbte Tm; Ensm; Rptr, 4H; Lit Mag; Madrigal; NHS; Orch; Sch P; Pres, Soph Cl; 4H A; H of F; Interlochen Ntl Mus; MLS; Most Out; Sci A; Yth Fel; Schol Tm; World Yth Symph; *U of Cincinnati; Mus.*

YOUNG, Kimberly Trenise
Phineas Banning HS; Wilmington, CA; FBLA; Hmrm; SC; Flag Twirler; *Calif St U; Bus.*

YOUNG, Linda Ann
Bethel Christian Sch; Garden Grove, CA (1-6) Ann; Co-Cpt, Chldr; Ensm; S-T, Hmrm; NHS; S-T, SC; Y-Tns; Bkbl; Chldr A; *Christian Hertiage Col; Home Ec.*

YOUNG, Linda Darnell
Lindblom Tech HS; Chicago, IL (25-433) Hmrm; NHS; Sch P; Tr; Hist A; Hon Prog; Yth Fel; GSct, GAA, A's; *U of Ill; Chem.*

YOUNG, Lisa A
Christian Co HS; Hopkinsville, KY; BC; FHA; Tres, Hmrm; NHS; B Crocker A; Blue Ribbon, Drill Tm; *Maryville Col; Spec Ed.*

YOUNG, Lola
Hammond HS; Hammond, IN; *Ind U.*

YOUNG, Mark Alan
Leavenworth HS; Leavenworth, KS (81-400) Chess C; Drama; Ensm; Pres, SC; Thes; Tr; Wrest; Spch A; Stu Director, Band; Sch Plays; Pep Band; Concert Band; Director, Stage Band; *Kans City Jr Col; Mus.*

YOUNG, Martha Rose
Oppenheim-Ephratah Central Sch; St Johnsville, NY (9-38) AFS; Fr C; NHS; SC; Pres, Soph Cl; Bkbl; Soccer; Sftbl; Tr; *Phys Ed.*

YOUNG, Mary Janice
Putnam City HS; Oklahoma City, OK (117-845) Band; Chor; Dbte Tm; Hmrm; Fin, Jr Miss Pagent; S-T, Lat C; Cpt, Mjrte; Math C; Mu Alpha Theta; NHS; Orch; Citz A; Gov Honor Prog; Hist A; Hon Prog; *Okla St U; Chem.*

YOUNG, Melanie Dawn
William Byrd HS; Vinton, VA (22-268) BC; Hmrm; Lit Mag; Span C; Tr; Hon Prog; Pres, New Life C; VP, Church Yth Coun; S-T, FCA; Stu Organ for Develop Attitudes; *Va W Comm Col; Psych.*

YOUNG, Melba Dianne
Washington Sr HS; Cedar Rapids, IA (8-500) Community Yth Symph; NHS; Orch; COM; Hon Prog; Yth Fel; *Med.*

YOUNG, Michael
Northeastern HS; Detroit, MI (4-202) NHS; Bkbl; Cr-Ctry; Safety Patrol; *Western Mich Col; Phys Ed.*

YOUNG, Michael DeWayne
Hamilton HS; Memphis, TN (141-400) Co-Ch, Hmrm; Cr-Ctry; Ftbl; Co-Cpt, Tr; COM; C Swtht; Pres, Social C; VP, Soc Organ, Outst Runner; *U of Tenn at Knoxville; Draftsmen.*

YOUNG, Nancy Carol
Galva Comm Sch; Galva, IA (5-23) Band; Chldr; Rptr, Chor; Bkbl; Sftbl; Tr; Type A; *Morningside Col; Art.*

YOUNG, Nancy Jeanne
Penncrest HS; Media, PA (59-432) Band; NHS; Tr; Citz A; GSct; *Juniata Col; Bus.*

YOUNG, Pamela Lorraine
Hammond HS; Hammond, IN;

YOUNG, Patricia Elaine
Mt Ida HS; Mt Ida, AR (8-76) F-Ed, Ann; Tres, BC; VP, FHA; Lit Mag; Tres, SC; Secy, Soph Cl; Bkbl; B Crocker A; COM; Hon Prog; WW; *Bus Adm.*

YOUNG, Paulette Lorraine
Chapman HS; Inman, SC (79-128) JV, Chldr; FHA; Secy, SC; Up Bound; Tr; Service A; Best Sch Spirit; *N Greenville Col; Social Sci.*

YOUNG, Peggy Ann
Galva Comm HS; Galva, IA (6-16) Ann; Band; SC; S-T, Jr Cl; JV, Bkbl; Sftbl; Mgr, Tr; HCt; Type A.

YOUNG, Phillip Edward
Webster Groves HS; Webster Groves, MO (301-439) *Meramec Comm Col; Acct.*

YOUNG, Richard Randall
London HS; London, OH (7-165) JV, Bsbl; JV, Golf; Kiwanis A; Sci A.

YOUNG, Rickey Renay
Ocean Spring HS; Ocean Springs, MS; Ann; BC; Drama; Ch, 4H; Co-Ch, JETS; Key C; Co-Ed, Sch P; VP, SC; JV, Bsbl; Bkbl; Ftbl; JV, Tr; Afro-Amer C; *Jackson St U; World Hist.*

YOUNG, Robert Brian
Bay Village HS; Bay Village, OH (33%-350) Band; Community Yth Symph; Orch; Tnns; Outst Mus; Attitude A; *Okla St U; Bus.*

YOUNG, Robert Francis
St Joseph HS; Hammonton, NJ; Pres, CYO; Chess C; Chor; Hmrm; Pres, Sci C; VP, Sr Cl; Parl, Jr Cl; Cr-Ctry; Hon Prog; *NEDT; Rutgers U; Biochem.*

YOUNG, Roger Blake
Eunice HS; Eunice, LA (3-160) BS; Chess C; Fr C; Key C; Fin, Lit Ral; Math C; Pres, NHS; Sch Achieve Tm; Sci C; Tres, SC; Pres, Sr Cl; Pres, Soph Cl; Mgr, Ftbl; Citz A; Elk A; H of F; Hon Prog; Jr Chamber of Com A; Phy A; Pres, Lib C; Jaycee A; Dist Econ Ral; Excellence, Sup, Foreign Lang Ral; Math C Beau; *LSU Eunice; Sci.*

YOUNG, Sandra Dale
J S Abrams HS; Bessemer, AL (2-87) FHA; NHS; Rptr, Sch P; Cpt, Arch; B Crocker A; Hist A; Math A; Sci A; Val; Eng A; Social Studies A; *Miss U for Women; Pol Sci.*

YOUNG, Sandra Denise
Albany HS; Albany, NY (427-471) Chor; 4H; *Albany Bus Col; Legal Secy.*

YOUNG, Sandra Kwock
Pilgrim HS; Los Angeles, CA (2-8) Chor; Hmrm; CSF; Citz A; DARGCA; HCt; Hon Prog; *UCLA; Pre-Health.*

YOUNG, Sandra Lois
Seaside HS; Seaside, CA; Chor; Dbte Tm; Drama; ARC; Spch C; COM; ARC A; *Monterey Peninsula Col; Occupational Therapy.*

YOUNG, Scott MacGregor
Hinsdale Township HS Central; Hinsdale, IL (1-730) VP, Key C; Math C; NHS; Ski C; JV, Soccer; Hon Prog; Yth Fel; Tnns A; Sportsmanship A; Swim; *Med.*

YOUNG, Sheila Carlene
N Miami HS; Denver, IN (6-114) Band; Chor; Secy, Drama; Fin, Jr Miss Pagent; Mjrte; Secy; Mod Mus Mas; NFL; Orch; Sci C; VP, SC; HCt; Scholar; March of Dimes Schol; Dollars for Scho A; Citizens Schol Found; *Goshen Col; Nurs.*

YOUNG, Shelly Renee
Vian HS; Vian, OK (10-105) Band; Yth Fel; N; *Okla St U; Sociology.*

YOUNG, Slade Charles
Northside HS; Atlanta, GA (20%-150) Chor; Drama; Sci C; Span C; Mus A; *U of Ga; Bus Adm.*

YOUNG, Stephania Lynette
Emerson HS; Emerson, AR (11-31) Chor; FHA; 4H; Arch; Ftbl; Golf; Soccer; Sftbl; Swim; Tnns; Fin, Tr; COM; JA A; *Henderson St U; Nurs.*

YOUNG, Stephen Douglas
El Dorado Springs HS; El Dorado Springs, MO (9-103) NHS; Tres, DECA; Heart-Throb King; *Radio Broadcasting.*

YOUNG, Steve Michael
Hughes Springs HS; Hughes Springs, TX (23-68) Demolay; Tres, FFA; Co-Cpt, Bsbl; Ftbl; Karate.

YOUNG, Susan Faye
Oppenheim Ephratah Central Sch; St Johnsville, NY (3-49) AFS; Band; Fr C; 4H; Tres, Hmrm; NHS; Soccer; Sftbl; 4H A; Hist A; *Bob Jones U.*

YOUNG, Susan Kay
Wapakoneta Sr HS; Wapakoneta, OH (16-325) Chem C; Chor; FNA; Tres, 4H; NHS; Sch Achieve Tm; SC; Y-Tns; COM; God & Country A; NEDT; Yth Fel; Chem Bowl; Future Med Careers C; *Ohio Northern U; Pharmacy.*

YOUNG, Susanne
Bowling Green HS; Bowling Green, KY (34-371) Band; FHA; Hmrm; NHS.

YOUNG, Theda Joyce
Clarkrange HS; Clarkrange, TN (9-42) BC; FHA; 4H; F-Ed, Sch P; Sci C; Spch C; Mgr, Bkbl; *Ft Sanders Nurs Sch; Nurs.*

YOUNG, Timothy Craft
Lower Richland HS; Hopkins, SC (210-501) Chess C; Chor; Ed, Lit Mag; SC; *U of SC; Math.*

YOUNG, Travis Keith
Douglass HS; Oklahoma City, OK (10%-400) Math C; NHS; Order/Arrow; ARC; JA A; Order/Arrow A; *Acct.*

YOUNG, Trisha Ann
Mission HS; Mission, TX (27-365) Band; Ensm; Mjrte; Math C; Mu Alpha Theta; Orch; ARC; SC; Y-Tns; COM; H of F; Rotary A; Type A; *Baylor U; Med Tech.*

YOUNG, Valerie Christine
Calvin Coolidge Sr HS; Washington, DC; Mgr, Chldr; Drama; FHA; Hmrm; NHS; SC; COM; Citz A; Hon Prog; JA A; Yth Fel; *Morgan St U; Acct.*

YOUNG, Valerie Diane
Girls' HS; Philadelphia, PA; Tr; Citz A; Cl Fav; MLS; Poet A; Q&S A; *Drexel U; Bus Ec.*

YOUNG, Victoria Nicolette
Burbank Sr HS; Burbank, CA; A Cap Choir; Ch, Band; Chor; Community Yth Symph; Drama; Hmrm; Madrigal; Pres, Orch; Spch C; Pres, SC; Pres, Jr Cl; Directors A; Orch Most Outst Contribution; *Cal St Northridge; Lib Sci.*

YOUNG, William Conn
Jonathan Dayton Regional HS; Springfield, NJ (10%-400) French NHS; Var C; Bsbl; Ftbl; Tr; NHS; Sch Bsbl Ltr; Play Piano; Fr Horn; Talent Show; Church Choir; *Med.*

YOUNG, William Robert
Northeast Sr HS; Kansas City, MO (9-325) BS; NHS; Bus Mgr, Spch C; SC; Thes; Pres, Var C; Sr Cl; Jr Cl; Ftbl; JV, Tr; JV, Wrest; Regent Schol; *U of Mo; Civil Engr.*

YOUNG, William Staurt
Notre Dame-Bishop Gibbons HS; Schenectady, NY (18-176) Cr-Ctry; Tr; NEDT.

YOUNGBERG, David Rowland
Shenandoah Valley Acad; New Market, VA (5%-77) A Cap Choir; Band; BC; Drama; NHS; Ski C; Bkbl; Ftbl; Sftbl; Tnns; Hon Prog; Soph Pastor; *Sou Missionary Col; Med.*

YOUNGBERG, Lisha Martin
Bonneville HS; Ogden, UT; Community Yth Symph; Secy, Dbte Tm; Drama; FBLA; 4H; NFL; Thes; Cpt, Swim; Horse Possie; Jobs Daughters; Swim Ltr, Region Drama, A's; *Acting.*

YOUNGBLOOD, Barbara Yvonne
Independence HS; Independence, MS (1-72) Ann; Band; Tres, BC; Chldr; Chor; Ensm; FBLA; F-Ed, Sch P; COM; Cl Fav; NMS; Ntl Sci Found; Star Student; Val; Cpt, Math-Sci Tm; Cpt, Flag Corps; 1st Cl GSct; Mid-South Hon Band; *Math.*

YOUNGBLOOD, Carey James Jr
Northbrook Sr HS; Houston, TX; Ann; Chor; Fr C; Sftbl; Academic HR; Sportsmanship A, Bsbl; *Sam Houston St U; Criminology.*

YOUNGBLOOD, Cynthia Denise
Lennox HS; Lennox, CA; Bkbl; Soccer; Sftbl; Hon Prog; *Pepperdine U; Nurs.*

YOUNGBLOOD, David Wayne
Newellton HS; Newellton, LA (1-50) Ed, Ann; Semi-Fin, Lit Ral; Pres, NHS; Ftbl; Hon Prog; Math A; MLS; Val; 3 5 A; *Tulane U; Engr.*

YOUNGBLOOD, Edna Lee
Bullock Co HS; Union Springs, AL (3-145) Secy, FHA; 4H; Hmrm; Tres, NHS; Sch P; SC; Pres, Jr Cl; Val; *Auburn U; Engr.*

YOUNGBLOOD, Laurie Carole
Burkeville HS; Burkeville, TX (2-47) Ann; Tres, FHA; Hmrm; NHS; Rptr, Sch P; Cl Fav; Hon Prog; Most Attractive; Best Dressed; Jr Play; Dogwood Festival Duchess; *Tyler Commercial Col; Executive Secy.*

YOUNGBLOOD, Peggy Lee
Carter G Woodson HS; Tullahassee, OK; Chor; Sftbl; HQn; *Northeastern Col; Acct.*

YOUNGBLOOD, Trelawney Liani
Reynolds HS; Greenville, PA (13-212) Band; Chor; Ensm; FTA; Ger C; Pres, 4H; HiY; Hmrm; Lat C; NHS; Secy, Thes; COM; 4H A; Hon Prog; NEDT; VP, Piano, Organ C; PSAT Cert; HR; *Thiel Col; Psych.*

YOUNGDALE, Eric Paul
Beaver Dam Sr HS; Beaver Dam, WI (10%-322) BS; Ensm; Orch; Order/Arrow; Ski C; Tr; JV, Wrest; Hon Prog; Order/Arrow A; *U of Wis; Sci.*

YOUNGER, Marion Veronica
Ballou Sr HS; Washington, DC; Chor; Secy, Hmrm; NHS; Citz A; Hist A; Hon Prog; Math A; Sci A; Type A; *Secy.*

YOUNGER, Teena Kaye
Sooner HS; Bartlesville, OK; Chor; Cpt, Mjrte; Orch; Span C; Sftbl; Tr; Citz A; Hon Star A; Pres Fitness A; Indian C; *NE Okla U; Bus.*

YOUNGMAN, Althea Marie
Alliance HS; Alliance, NE (7-152) AFS; Ed, Ann; Chor; Dbte Tm; GS; NHS; Pres, Thes; Y-Tns; Elk A; Q&S A; Pres, Pep C; Best Actress A, Thespians; Lead, All Sch Mus; District, St, One Act Contest; *U of Nebr; Special Ed.*

YOUNGQUIST, Jill Marie
Robert A Long HS; Longview, WA (5%-350) Chor; Fr C; VP, 4H; Hmrm; NHS; Amer Leg A; Citz A; 4H A; Hon Prog; *Wash St U; Hotel Mgt.*

YOUNGQUIST, Susan Lorraine
Edgewood HS; W Covina, CA (15%-450) Chor; COM; Citz A; Type A; Principal's, NHS, HR'S; Stenoscript A; *Mt San Antonio Col; Lib Arts.*

YOUNGSTROM, Michael Steven
Central HS; Davenport, IA (45-622) A Cap Choir; AFS; Band; Chor; Community Yth Symph; Drama; Ensm; Fr C; Lit Mag; Madrigal; Orch; Ski C; SC; JV, Tnns; COM; Hon Prog; I Rating, St Solo & Ensm; COM, Ntl Fr Contest; All St Band; *Bradley U; Bus Adm.*

YOUNT, Carolyn
Rockdale HS; Rockdale, TX (30-135) Secy, Band; FTA; NHS; Tres, SC; Bkbl; Tnns; Cl Fav; HCt; Drum Major; RHS WW; *TSTI; Mental Health.*

YOUNT, Lori Lee
Sharpstown HS; Houston, TX (1-686) Ensm; Fr C; NHS; Beauty; *Tex A&M U; Finance.*

YOUNT, Mary Stowe
S Point HS; Belmont, NC (12-214) F-Ed; Ann; BC; Journ A; Future Teacher Schol; *Appalachian St U; Elem Ed.*

YOUNT, Susie Janine
W Monroe HS; W Monroe, LA;

YOUNT, Tracey Orren
Reidsville Sr HS; Reidsville, NC (5%-375) Band; Drama; Fr C; Hmrm; NEDT; *Math.*

YOUNTS, Tammy Dawn
Allen Jay HS; High Point, NC (3-96) BC; Chldr; Fr C; Jr Miss Pagent; Monogram; Pres, SC; Tr; Math A; MLS; Most Out; Jr Marshal; *Appalachian St U; Home Ec.*

YOUSSI, Cathy Lynn
Batavia HS; Batavia, IL; Community Yth Symph; Drama; Ensm; Orch; Hon Prog; Off Ed Contest; Mus A, Orch; *Aurora Col; Pre-Law.*

YOUST, Rhonda Michelle
Landmark Christian HS; Cincinnati, OH (5-48) Ann; Cpt, Chldr; Chor; Sftbl; *Wheaton Col; Elem Ed.*

YSBRAND, Pamella Diane
Blackwell HS; Blackwell, OK; Band; Chor; Ensm; Madrigal; Orch; Citz A; Cl Fav; Hon Prog; ARC A; Yth Fel; Outst Ensm; *Mus.*

YTTERBERG, Alan Victor
Richardson HS; Richardson, TX (1%-1000) NHS; JV, Bsbl; Cpt, Bkbl; Ftbl; COM; FCA; *Bus.*

YU, Clarissa
Lowell HS; San Francisco, CA; Vlbl; Bridgeclub; *Berkely Col; Psych.*

YU, Peter Shin En
John Adams HS; Ozone Park, NY (25-1077) Math C; NHS; Sci C; NY Regent Schol Alt; WW; *Brown U; Biological Sci.*

YULDUZIAN, Joan Marie
Ursuline Acad; Wilmington, DE (50%-43) Ann; Band; Chldr; Drama; Phys C; Sch P; Span C; Span NHS; JV, Bsbl; JV, Hockey; JV, Tnns; COM; Pres A; Pres, Lib Coun; Vol, Self Help; Opera Soc; *U of Del; Drama Therapy.*

YULE, Larry George Jr
Ed W Clark HS; Las Vegas, NV (648-781) God & Country A; *Drafting.*

YUN, Steven Ki
Bronx HS of Sci; New York, NY (7-40) Band; Chor; InterClub Coun; Orch; Ski C; Var C; MVP, Soccer; Sftbl; Hon Prog; Most Out; Cpt, Soccer; Chancy Mus A; Industrial Arts A; Hon Soc; Rookie o-t Yr, Soccer; *Harvard U; Med.*

YUNG, William Martin
Canyon HS; Canyon, TX (50%-385) Drama; Pres, Jr Cl; Ftbl; *Baylor U; Law.*

YURCAK, Lisa Jo
Parma Sr HS; Parma, OH (364-836) Chor; Span C; Yth Fel; Pres, Yth Organization; *Cuyahoga Comm Col; Child Care.*

YUSK, Timothy Gerard
St Patrick HS; Oak Park, IL (37-350) Chor; Pres, Ger C; NHS; Sch P; Sci C; Mgr, Bsbl; COM; Hon Prog; NMS; Sanctuary Soc; WW; Ill St Schol; *De Paul U; Med.*

YUTZY, Teresa Lynn
Arthur HS; Arthur, IL (35-70) Band; Chor; FHA; FNA; Jr Miss Pagent; Mjrte; Arch; Bkbl; Swim; Tr; Beauty; Pres A; Vlbl; Secy.

Z

ZABEL, John
Junipero Serra HS; Gardena, CA (1-90) F-Ed, Ann; CYO; Pres, Ger C; Pres, Hmrm; Monogram; NHS; Sch Achieve Tm; F-Ed, Sch P; Ski C; SC; Pres, Var C; Pres, Sr Cl; Cpt, Bkbl; MVP, Ftbl; Alg A; Bank Of Amer A; CSF; COM; Citz A; Coun of Teach A; DARGCA; H of F; Hon Prog; Lion A; Most Out; NMS; Star Student; Val; VFW A; Stu Ath; Outst Stu; Eng A; Ftbl A; *LA Valley Col; Acct.*

ZABINSKI, Marianne
Mercy HS; Albany, NY (6-108) Band; Dbte Tm; InterAct C; NHS; Sftbl; Bio A; Hon Prog; Vlbl; *Siena Col; Pre-Med.*

ZABLE, Judy Catherine
Prairie du Chien HS; Prairie du Chien, WI (26-123) Band; Ensm; Lat C; Lat NHS; Var C; Co-Cpt, Bkbl; Sftbl; Tr; Hon Prog; Rescue Squad; Co-Cpt, Vlbl; *Med.*

ZABLOCKI, Theresa Marie
John S Fine Sr HS; Nanticoke, PA (9-347) Hon Prog; *Ed.*

ZABRISKIE, Linda Jane
Ridgewood HS; Ridgewood, NJ; Ann; SC; Tnns; HR; *Richmond U; Fashion Merchandising.*

ZABRISKIE, Mark William
Lakewood HS; Lakewood, CO (22-500) *U of Colo; Engr.*

ZABRISKIE, Rhoda Evangeline
Hunterdon Central HS; Flemington, NJ; *Citton Court Reporting Col; Stenographer.*

ZABRUCKY, Theresa Lynn
Ambridge Area HS; Ambridge, PA (33%-476) AFS; Band; FBLA; FTA; Hmrm; NHS; Orch; Sch P; SC; Thes; Var C; Amer Leg A.

ZACHARIAH, Gail Ellen
Ed W Clark HS; Las Vegas, NV (45-830) Ann; City Conf; Fr C; Pres, 4H; NHS; Sch P; Ski C; Span C; Swim; COM; Citz A; 4H A; Hon Prog; I Dare You; Pres A; Type A; *Scripps Col; Eng.*

ZACHARIAH, Tracey Lea
Belaire HS; Baton Rouge, LA (100-450) S-T, A Cap Choir; Co-Cpt, Chldr; S-T, Chor; S-T, Ensm; HiY; Hmrm; SC; Cpt, Bkbl; Cpt, Ftbl; Co-Cpt, Sftbl; Beauty; Cl Fav; HCt; Hon Prog; Yth Fel; Miss Belaire; WW; WW Amer HS Chldr; Baton Rouge Bicentennial Mus Show; *Delta Sch of Bus; Legal Secy.*

ZACHARISEN, Mark Howe
Glenwood Springs HS; Glenwood Springs, CO (10%-125) Band; S-T, Key C; NHS; Order/Arrow; JV, Tr; Wrest; God & Country A; *US Military Acad; Sci.*

ZACHARY, Cherie Yvonne
Breck HS; Minneapolis, MN (33%-45) Chor; JV, Bkbl; Mgr, Tr; Hon Prog; Masters A; Span Schol; *Pre-Med.*

ZACHARY, Marla Marie
Allen Jay HS; High Point, NC (10-96) Co-Ed, Ann; Secy, BC; Cpt, Chldr; Chor; Tres, Fr C; Semi-Fin, Jr Miss Pa; Monogram; SC; Secy, Sr Cl; Tr; HCt; Jr Marshal; Jr-Sr Qn; Outst Sr; *Appalachian St U; Sociology.*

ZACHARY, Ronald Wayne
Webster Co HS; Dixon, KY (10-109) FFA; Hon Prog; Math A; Health A; Act A; *U of Ky; Metallurgical Engr.*

ZACHRICH, Edward Dean
Holgate HS; Holgate, OH (50%-72) Pres, Band; Chess C; Chor; Community Yth Symph; Ensm; Orch; Alg A; H of F; Math A; *Bowling Green St U; Mus.*

ZACHRY, Karl Scott
Grand Junction HS; Grand Junction, CO (10%-400) Band; Chor; Community Yth Symph; Ensm; Ger C; NHS; Orch; Math A; *Math.*

ZAGREDA, Age
Aquinas HS; Bronx, NY (32-231) Math C; Hon Prog; PA & Punctuality; *Fordham U; Computer Tech.*

ZAGREDA, Sander
Cardinal Hayes HS; Bronx, NY (90-400) Hon Prog; Math A; *Columbia Col; Engr.*

ZAHN, Paul Frederick
Lutheran HS S; Afton, MO (82-164) A Cap Choir; Chor; Ensm; Mgr, Cr-Ctry; Mgr, Tr; *Meremac Comm Col; Mus.*

ZAHN, Vivian Joy
Brandon HS; Brandon, FL; Ensm; Tres, Brandon Area Musicale; Accompianist, Chor; Mus B A; Chrch Yth Coun; Sup Ratng, Voc Solo; Ed, Chrch Yth Nwsp; Sup Ratng Duet; *Carson-Newman Col; Journ.*

ZAHND, Jeff Robert
Martinsville HS; Martinsville, IN (93-439) Bus C; *Math.*

ZAHNOW, Karen Louise
Auburn Sr HS; Auburn, WA (60-480) Chor; 4H; Hmrm; Orch; *Green River Comm Col; Phys Therapy.*

ZAIMAN, Nicole
Hillel HS; Lawrence, NY; Chldr; Drama; Pres, Hmrm; NHS; Co-Ed, Sch P; Span C; Pres, Soph Cl; Tr; Keter Hon Soc; Span HR; *Queens Col; Communications.*

ZAISER, Mark Alan
Laurel Highlands Sr HS; Uniontown, PA (31-418) Chor; Drama; Math C; Span C; *Eastern Col; Foreign Lang.*

ZAMBOROWSKI, John William
Holy Cross HS; Marine City, MI (7-41) Chor; K of C; NHS; Sch P; Hon Prog; K of C A; Math A; Pres, Bowling; *St Clair Co Comm Col; Mech.*

ZAMORA, Rodolfo R
Gladys Porter HS; Brownsville, TX; Hmrm; JETS; Key C; Lit Mag; Co-Ed, Sch P; Sci C; St Stu Congress; SC; Tres, Soph Cl; Mgr, Bkbl; Citz A; DARGCA; BS Alt; Dist Pres, SC; Wittiest, Sr Cl; Sch Photographer; *Tex Southmost Col; Bus Mgt.*

ZANG, David Scott
Kewanee HS; Kewanee, IL (33-175) Ger C; Oddfellow Attendance A; *Black Hawk Col; Bus Adm.*

ZANKER, Paula Marie
Philipsburg-Osceola Area HS; Philipsburg, PA (20%-140) Ann; Drama; Fr C; NHS; Fr A.

ZANNI, Timothy James
York Central Sch; Retsof, NY; NHS; Bsbl; MVP, Bkbl; Hon Prog; *Bus.*

ZANTOW, Alfred Robert
Leola Ind HS; Leola, SD (12-32) *Sci.*

ZAPACH, Thomas Steve
Uniontown Area Sr HS; Uniontown, PA (3%-510) Secy, Hmrm; NHS; Span C; JV, Bkbl; JV, Ftbl; Tr; Amer Leg A; COM; Citz A; Hon Prog; Math A; Pres A; Sal; Sci A; Explorers C; Rifle C.

ZAPATA, Melvin
Adlai E Stevenson HS; New York, NY (43-788) Anchor C; Chess C; FTA; Alg A; COM; Citz A; Hon Prog; Co-Cpt, Gym; Haney Medal, Art.

ZAPPULLA, Josephine Ann
Union HS; Union, NJ; Mus A; *Mus.*

ZARAGOZA, Dorca Milagros
Notre Dame HS; Caguas, PR (9-128) *Bio.*

ZARDUS, Heidi
Woodlake Union HS; Woodlake, CA (7-155) Band; Pres, Fr C; Ski C; SC; Bkbl; CSF; Vlbl; Mentally Gifted Minors; Pres, LDS; Directors A, Band; *Ricks Col; Bio.*

ZAREMBA, Patricia
St Pius X HS; Piscataway, NJ (5-222) Hon Prog; NEDT; Candystriper; CYO Mass Tutor; CCD Teacher; Principal's HR; *Nurs.*

ZARGARIAN, Jacklin
Watertown HS; Watertown, MA (1-200) Band; Math C; Orch; Ski C; JV, Bkbl; MVP, Sftbl; JV, Tnns; MLS; JV, Field Hockey; *Math.*

ZARRIELLO, Lynette Denise
Carl Schurz HS; Chicago, IL (64-1100) Chor; SC; COM; VP, Yth Fel; Guard o-t Mo, Awana; *Moody Bible Inst; Christian Ed.*

ZARRILLI, Jean
Moore Cath HS; Staten Island, NY (25-149) Cpt, Chldr; VP, NHS; Sftbl; Amer Leg A; *Syracuse U; Wildlife.*

ZARZYCKI, Ann Marie
St Hedwig HS; Detroit, MI (3-70) Band; JV, Chldr; Chor; Dbte Tm; Mjrte; NHS; Journ A; Opt A; Vof-DEM; Cert of Recog; St of Mich Comp School Prog Semi; *Mercy Col of Detroit; Nurs.*

ZASTROW, Donald Claude
Oconomowoc Sr HS; Oconomowoc, WI; Bkbl; Ftbl; Sftbl; JV, Tr; Wrest; Hon Roll; *Waukesha Co Tech Inst; Carpentry.*

ZASTROW, Susan Kay
Kennedy HS; Cedar Rapids, IA; Chor; Bkbl; COM; *Med.*

ZAVALA, Michelle Irene
Del Rio HS; Del Rio, TX (10-450) Chldr; NHS; SC; VP, Jr Cl; Secy, Soph Cl; Tnns; Cl Fav; Sci A; Yth Fel; Extracurricular Activities A; Individual Achv A; *U of Tex; Photojourn.*

ZAVERTNIK, Thomas Gerard
Christopher Columbus HS; Miami, FL (5-200) Lat C; Var C; Cr-Ctry; Tr; Dean's List; *Duke U; Bus.*

ZAWESKI, John David
Mercy HS; Riverhead, NY; Var C; Bsbl; Ftbl; Wrest; *Agr-Bus.*

ZEBROWSKI, Linda Helen
The Cecilian Acad; Philadelphia, PA; Fr C; Sodality; Sftbl; Hon Prog; K of C A; Lat A; *Chesnut Hill Col.*

ZEBROWSKI, Susan Marie
Cecilian Acad; Philadelphia, PA; Hon Prog; Secy.

ZEBROWSKI, Tami Ann
Binghamton North Sr HS; Binghamton, NY (2-230) Band; Mgr, Ann; VP, Fr C; Hmrm; Secy, NHS; Sal; Civic A; Honorary Teachers Sorority A; Ladies of Lebanon Fr A; *Broome Comm Col; Math.*

ZEDICK, Mary Frances
Dillon HS; Dillon, SC; Ann; Chor; 4H; Lat C; Rptr, Sch P; 1st St, DAR Essay; JAC A; *Col of Charleston; Sci.*

ZEHR, Kathy Jean
Lowville Acad Central Sch; Louville, NY (3-140) Fin, AFS; VP, Chor; Dbte Tm; Fr C; S-T, NHS; COM; Kiwanis A; Regent Schol; Delta Kappa Gamma Interntl Soc A; *Goshen Col; Fr.*

ZEHR, Lisa Renae
Ogallala HS; Ogallala, NE (1-160) Chor; Pres, 4H; NHS; Span NHS; Tres, SC; Sftbl; Tr; COM; 4H A; Star Student; Vlbl; *Hastings Col; Pub Relations.*

ZEHRER, Michele Kay
Brooten HS; Brooten, MN (3-53) Band; Chldr; Chor; Drama; Ensm; 4H; NHS; SC; Thes; Tr; 4H A; Spch A; Most Improved Player; Best Server, Vlbl; *U of Minn; Sci.*

ZEIGLER, Jane Claire
N Augusta Sr HS; N Augusta, SC; Ann; Fr C; Hmrm; *Anderson Col; Bus.*

ZEIGLER, Lori Jo
Bellevue Sr HS; Bellevue, NE (94-851) HR; Phys Fitness A; *Central Col; Legal Secy.*

ZEINER, Sherri Lynn
Greencastle HS; Greencastle, IN (10%-250) Fr C; 4H; NHS; ARC; Var C; Bkbl; Swim; Tr; 4H A; Hon Prog; ARC A; Yth Fel; GAA; Cpt, Judges & Timers; Cpt, Co Qn; *Purdue U; Design.*

ZEIT, Ralph Carl
Greenfield HS; Greenfield, WI (67-400) Band; *St U.*

ZELAZNY, Lisa Marie
Garfield Heights HS; Garfield Heights, OH;

ZELINKA, Scott D
Morton West HS; Berwyn, IL; Sch Achieve Tm; COM; Hon Prog; Blue Rib A, N II U Mach Shop Comp; *Mech Engr.*

ZELLE, Janine Marie
Whitewater HS; Whitewater, WI (15-200) Chor; Madrigal; ARC; Ski C; Spch C; Bkbl; Sftbl; Tnns; Tr; COM; Spch A; Type A; Vlbl; Pres, Lutheran Yth Organization; Solo & Ensm A; *Cathage Col; Special Ed.*

ZELLER, Dawn Marie
East HS; Green Bay, WI; Chor; Vlbl; *Mus.*

ZELLER, Rodney Walter
Ionia Sr HS; Ionia, MI; Tres, Tite Group; *Concordia Col; Ed.*

ZEMAITIS, Carol Elizabeth
Jacksonville Sr HS; Jacksonville, NC (150-490) Bus C; CYO; Chem C; Chor; Dbte Tm; Pres, FNA; InterClub Coun; Pol Sci C; Sch P; Sci C; Ch, Span C; Span NHS; Var C; Sftbl; MVP, Tnns; Tr; MLS; Type A; Co-Cpt, Drill Tm; Best Dressed; *Coastal Carolina Col; Nurs.*

ZEMKE, Thomas Leonard
Armstrong HS; Minneapolis, MN; Ski C; Bkbl; Cr-Ctry; Tr; Cr-Ctry Skiing; *U of Minn; Archt.*

ZEMMER, Deborah Rose
Lapeer E HS; Lapeer, MI (21-250) Band; Ensm; Fr C; NHS; Solo Ensm Blue Medals; Awana; Distinguished Musician Cert; All Star Band; *Grand Rapids Baptist Col; Elem Teacher.*

ZENDER, Frances Allene
Lawrence HS; Lawrence, KS; Band; Hmrm; Orch; SC; JA A; *Kansas U; Math.*

ZENDER, Marjorie Lucille
Celina Sr HS; Celina, OH (1-275) Pres, A Cap Choir; Chor; FTA; Lat C; NHS; Sch Achieve Tm; Pres, SC; Ch, Sr Cl; Sci A; WW; *Miami U of Ohio; Biol.*

ZENDER, Patricia Diane
Sandia HS; Albuquerque, NM (259-703) Chor; Community Yth Symph; Ensm; Orch; Albuq Yth Sym; NM All-St Solo & Ensm Festival; *Eastern NM U; Mus Therapy.*

ZENI, Barbara Ann
Saint Angela Hall Acad; Brooklyn, NY (3-90) Chor; Drama; Pres, Hmrm; Math C; NHS; Sch P; Co-Ch, SC; Var C; Co-Ch, Sr Cl; COM; Hon Prog; Math A; Ntl Achv Schol; Regent Schol; Pres, Sr Cl; Vlbl; WW; All Amer A; *Molloy Col; Nurs.*

ZENO, Carmen Sotera
Dra Maria Cadilla HS; Arecibo, PR (78-636) Sftbl; Tr; *Universidad Catolica; Jecnologa Medica.*

ZEPF, David Paul
University of San Diego HS; San Diego, CA (6-374) Band; CYO; Drama; Hmrm; NHS; Rptr, Sch P; Sci C; CSF; COM; Citz A; Hon Prog; Math A; Most Out; Sci A; Spelling, Art, A's; *San Diego St U; Art.*

ZEPF, Susan Mary
University of San Diego HS; San Diego, CA (1-315) CYO; Hmrm; NHS; CSF; Hon Prog; Most Out; Star Student; *San Diego St U; Ed.*

ZEPKA, Diane P
St Cecilia HS; Kearny, NJ (3-29) F-Ed, Ann; Chldr; Drama; GS; Ed, Lit Mag; Pres, NHS; F-Ed, Sch P; Ski C; VP, SC; Mgr, Bkbl; Mgr, Soccer; Mgr, Sftbl; B Crocker A; COM; WW; Ntl HS A for Excellence; Eng A; Drama A; Newspaper A; *Fordham U; Marketing.*

ZERBI, Nohemi
Wesleyan Acad; Guaynabo, PR (1-29) Bus Mgr, Ann; Chldr; Chor; VP, NHS; SC; Sftbl; Swim; Hon Prog; NEDT; Sch HR; DAHSS; *Baylor U; Sci.*

ZERBINOPOULOS, Elaine Leslie
Dover HS; Dover, NH (20-396) Band; Secy, Mu Alpha Theta; Secy, Rainbow; Secy, Span C; Tr; *U of NH; Lib Arts.*

ZERCHER, Vickie Lynne
Warwick HS; Lititz, PA (25%-300) Band; Chor; Ensm; Tnns; HCt; Yth Fel; Outst, Band; *Elizabethtown Col; Med Secy.*

ZERHUSEN, Jeffrey Scott
Loyola HS; Towson, MD (30-180) A Cap Choir; Chldr; VP, Chess C; Chor; Drama; Fr C; NHS; Thes; JV, Tnns; *Bucknel U; Engr.*

ZERKLE, Belinda Lou
Wahama HS; Mason, WV; FHA; NHS; Val; Home Ec A; Robert Byrd Scholastic Recogn A.

ZERLER, Barbara Jean
Dodgeville HS; Dodgeville, WI (30-150) Ann; VP, Bus C; JV, Chldr; Chor; Ensm; VP, FBLA; Hmrm; Sch P; Ski C; SC; Var C; Cpt, Bkbl; Hon Prog; MVP, Bkbl; Mus & Phys Ed A's; *Scientific Sch of Beauty; Cosmotology.*

ZERN, Cathy Ann
Beaman-Conrad-Liscomb Comm HS; Conrad, IA; Band; Chor; Pres, 4H; Secy, Soph Cl; Bkbl; Golf; Co-Cpt, Sftbl; 4H A; HQn; *Iowa St U; Home Ec.*

ZESCH, Scott Kelly
Mason HS; Mason, TX (1-58) Dbte Tm; Rptr, FFA; FTA; SC; Tr; Outst Tr.

ZETTERSTRAND, Sylvia Johanna
Universitary Col o-t Sacred Heart; San Juan, PR (1-25) Alg A; COM; Chem A; Hon Prog; Most Out; NEDT; Phy A; Sci A; Summa Cum Laude; Val; *U of Puerto Rico; Sci.*

ZETTS, Frederick William
Lutheran HS W; Rocky River, OH (65-103) COM.

ZETZER, Heidi Anne
Shaker Heights HS; Shaker Heights, OH (10%-500) Band; Chldr; Ensm; Orch; Sch P; Bkbl; Hon Prog; Pres, Girl's Cabinet; Gym Tm; Church Cabinet & Committees; *Eng Ed.*

ZGABAY, Terry Wayne
Waco HS; Waco, TX (5%-200) Ger C; Pres, Key C; NHS; Co-Cpt, Ftbl; Tr; Citz A; DARGCA; Hist A; Math A; Sci A; *Princeton U; Engr.*

ZIBROWSKI, Bart Layne
Onalaska Luther HS; Onalaska, WI (70-80) A Cap Choir; Band; Chor; Ger C; Lat C; Madrigal; Math C; Orch; Phys C; SC; Bkbl; Ftbl; Golf; Tnns; Golf Ltr; Tnn Ltr; Band Ltr; *U of Wis; Sci.*

ZICKERT, Caren Lyn
Hinsdale Central HS; Hinsdale, IL (32-626) Var C; *Purdue U.*

ZICKRICK, Mark S
T F Riggs HS; Pierre, SD; Ann; Fin, BS; Monogram; NHS; Co-Ed, Sch P; SC; Golf; Q&S A; *U of SD; Computer Sci.*

ZIEBARTH, Robin Paul
Mankato W HS; Mankato, MN (10-299) Dbte Tm; NFL; NHS; Spch C; Tnns; Rensselaer A; Rotary A; *Mankato St U; Math.*

ZIEGLER, Cheryl Lynn
Princeton HS; Sharonville, OH (13-800) Co-Cpt, Chldr; Secy, Chor; Drama; Lat C; Lat NHS; SC; Thes; COM; Hon Prog; Most Out.

ZIEGLER, Lori Ann
Alamosa HS; Alamosa, CO (10-186) GS; Pres, 4H; Model UN; NHS; World Affairs C; 4H A; Yth Advisory Del, Gen Assb Pres Ch; Hon Men, Sci Fair; *Colo St U; Agr.*

ZIEGLER, Peggy Diane
Fruitland Sr HS; Fruitland, ID (7-78) Ed, Ann; Tres, Band; Tres, Chor; Drama; NHS; Type A; *Willamette Col; Mus Therapy.*

ZIEGLER, Robbie Ann
Powell Valley HS; Speedwell, TN; BC; Mu Alpha Theta; Tri-HiY.

ZIEGLER, Susan Kay
Tulpehocken HS; Bernville, PA (3-140) Band; Chor; NHS; JV, Hockey; NEDT; *Grace Col; Hist.*

ZIELIN, Sandra A
Westminster Christian Sch; Miami, FL (2-120) Co-Cpt, Chldr; NHS; ARC; Span NHS; Secy, SC; Secy, Jr Cl; WW; *Home Ec.*

ZIELINSKI, Betsy
MacDuffie Sch; Springfield, MA (2-45) Chor; NEDT; *Math.*

ZIELINSKI, Rebecca
MacDuffie Sch; Springfield, MA (10%-50) Chor; Cum Laude Soc; Pres, Math C; SC; COM; Magna Cum Laude; *Williams Col; Math.*

ZIELS, Cathy Ann
Bellingham HS; Bellingham, WA (5%-350) Ann; Secy, CYO; NHS; A-Ed, Sch P; Ski C; JV, Swim; Serving People in Need C; *Seattle U; Phys Therapy.*

ZIELSDORF, Lani June
Littleton HS; Littleton, CO; Secy, Chor; Drama; Ensm; Ger C; Semi-Fin, GS; VP, 4H; Hmrm; Secy, Lit Mag; NHS; Spch C; Y-Tns; JV, Bkbl; 4H A; Hon Prog; Most Out; NMS; Poet A; Spch A; Vlbl; *Linguistic-Translator.*

ZIEMAN, Zandra Kay
Bennette Co HS; Martin, SD (1-70) Band; Chor; Drama; Ensm; GS; 4H; NHS; SC; Pres, Jr Cl; Bkbl; Tr.

ZIER, Judith Lynn
Kewanee HS; Kewanee, IL (5%-180) AFS; Dbte Tm; Drama; FHA; Ger C; Tres, Sci C; Spch C; Secy, SC; Math A; Spch A; *Vet Med.*

ZILBERT, Bonnie Sue
San Angelo Central HS; San Angelo, TX (173-650) Ch, Chor; FHA; Lib, A Cappella Choir, Ensm; Chorale; U Interschol A; St Solo & Ensm Contest; *Angelo St Col; Nurs.*

ZIMBELMAN, Laurie Louise
Yreka Union HS; Yreka, CA; Cpt, Chldr; Chor; Ensm; Ger C; S-T, GS; 4H; Co-Cpt, Mjrte; CSF; 4H A; Hon Prog; Rotary A; *Healds Col; Bus.*

ZIMDARS, Terry Wayne
Ripon Sr HS; Ripon, WI (12-170) BS; Pres, FFA; Pres, 4H; JV, Bkbl; Elk A; 4H A; Hon Prog; Rotary A; *U of Wisc; Dairy Sci.*

ZIMMANN, Robyn Lee
Springfield S HS; Springfield, OH (75-450) Band; Chor; Community Yth Symph; Ensm; NHS; Orch; Sftbl; Amer Leg A; Hon Prog; PTA A; OMEA A; *Wittenberg U; Mus.*

ZIMMER, Shelli Jean
Delavan HS; Delavan, IL (50%-70) Co-Cpt, Chldr; Chor; Drama; Ensm; SC; Secy, Var C; Bkbl; Sftbl; MVP, Tr; Citz A; Most Out; Secy, Art C; Secy, Yth Fel; Hall Cadet; Fin, Carnival Court; Fin, Stu o-t Month; Fin, Hon Prog; Vlbl; *Eastern Ill U; Journ.*

ZIMMERER, Robert
Henry P Becton Regional HS; E Rutherford, NJ (18-195) Lit Mag; NHS; JV, Bkbl; Q&S A; Vof-DEM; *Seton Hall Col; Pol Sci.*

ZIMMERER, Susie Marie
Lindsay Public HS; Lindsay, TX (3-38) Ann; Chldr; FHA; Tres, SC; Tres, Jr Cl; Bkbl; Tr; Cl Fav; Sci A; Swtht; Pep C; Eng II A; Ntl Meril Ltr; VP, Fresh Cl; HR; Home Ec A; General Bus A; *Cooke Co Col; Floriculture.*

ZIMMERMAN, Alan Paul
Northglenn Sr HS; Northglenn, CO (80-650) BS; Pres, Chem C; Dbte Tm; Model UN; NFL; NHS; Spch C; SC; World Affairs C; Cpt, Soccer; COM; Elk A; HCt; Spch A; Most Spirited; Superintendents Ldrship Conf; *Colo U.*

ZIMMERMAN, Brenda Kay
Chamberlain HS; Tampa, FL (41-671) BC; Fr C; NHS; Hon Prog; *Bob Jones U.*

ZIMMERMAN, Brian Reese
Hightstown HS; Hightstown, NJ; VP, Band; Chor; Ch, Sr Cl; Region Band & Jazz Band; *U of Ala; Engr.*

ZIMMERMAN, David Charles
N Tonawanda Sr HS; N Tonawanda, NY (12-649) Band; Sch Achieve Tm; Hon Prog; Sch Hon Letter; Math.

ZIMMERMAN, Demaris Jean
Paynesville HS; Paynesville, MN; Band; *N Central Bible Col; Christian Ed.*

ZIMMERMAN, Diane Elizabeth
Meadville Area Sr HS; Meadville, PA (157-377) FHA; Var C; Cpt, Bkbl; DARGCA; Type A; Yth Fel; Pres, UMY; Vlbl; Yth Against Cancer; Pres, UMY Conf; Sewing A; *Ind U of Penn; Home Ec.*

ZIMMERMAN, Don Michael
Paynesville HS; Paynesville, MN (20-145) Ann; Rptr, Bus C; FFA; NHS; Sch P; Cabinet Making A; Soil Judging A; *Bus.*

ZIMMERMAN, Gary Edmund
Central HS; Martinsburg, PA; Ski C; Var C; Tnns; God & Country A; *La St U; Engr.*

ZIMMERMAN, Gary Paul
York Comm HS; Elmhurst, IL (150-973) Chor; Mu Alpha Theta; Tnns; *U of Ill; Elec Engr.*

ZIMMERMAN, Jane Ann
Grinnell-Newburg Comm HS; Grinnell, IA (8-180) NHS; Ed, Sch P; VP, SC; MVP, Tnns; COM; Journ A; Q&S A; Star Student; *Carlton Col; Eng.*

ZIMMERMAN, Kendra Lenora
Notre Dame Acad; Toledo, OH; CYO; Chor; 4H; Hmrm; ARC; Rptr, Sch P; Bkbl; Sftbl; *Jackson St U; Pre-Med.*

ZIMMERMAN, Lee Ann
Snider HS; Fort Wayne, IN (140-500) Chor; Mus Theory A; *Mus.*

ZIMMERMAN, Mark Stowe
Salem Sr HS; Salem, OH (48-326) Ed, Ann; Band; BS; Chor; VP, Drama; Ensm; Secy, Ger C; Thes; Sci A; Pres, Mus Stu C; Marie Burns Mus A; Ntl Act Co; Tnager o-t Mo Comp; CYF; Dist & St Comp, Solo & Ensm; Plays & Musical Productions; *Baldwin-Wallace Col; Mus.*

ZIMMERMAN, Nancy Ann
Salisbury HS; Salisbury, NC (1-231) AFS; Co-Ed, Ann; Ch, Fr C; Secy, Lat C; Secy, NHS; Sch P; Thes; COM; Citz A; Hon Prog; Journ A; Q&S A; Yth Fel; Marshal; Accompanist, Church Choir; GScts; Sgt at Arms, Jr Civitan; Jr Classical League; *Davidson Col; Hist.*

ZIMMERMAN, Paula Kay
Fremont Ross HS; Fremont, OH; Sch P; Bkbl; *Secretarial Work.*

ZIMMERMAN, Ronda Faye
Alisal HS; Salinas, CA; S-T, A Cap Choir; S-T, Chor; S-T, Ensm; Tnns.

ZIMMERMAN, Scott James
Iroquois Central Sch; Elma, NY (63-350) Pres, Band; Community Yth Symph; Drama; Ensm; Hmrm; NHS; VP, Orch; Bsbl; Bkbl; Mgr, Sftbl; Bio A; Sci A; All St Ensm; JC Outst Tn; *Houghton Col; Biol.*

ZIMMERMAN, Susan Joan
Litchfield Comm HS; Litchfield, IL (1-150) Co-Ed, Ann; BC; NHS; Rptr, Sch P; Span C; Pres, SC; Pres A; Val; *Murray St U; Recreation.*

ZIMMERMAN, Terian Marie
Lake Brantley HS; Forest City, FL (12-422) Chor; S-T, FBLA; Semi-Fin, GS; Key C; NHS; Var C; Bkbl; Mgr, Golf; Beauty; JA A; Type A; Off & Lib Asst; Pres, JA Bank; Pep C; Vlbl; McDonald's All-Amer Crew Tm; *U of S Fla; Bus Adm.*

ZIMMERMAN, William
Cedar Crest HS; Lebanon, PA (60-250) Fr C; *Messiah Col; Sci.*

ZIMMERMANN, James Victor
Henry P Becton Regional HS; E Rutherford, NJ (10-195) Lit Mag; Math C; NHS; Rptr, Sch P; Hon Prog; *Montclair St Col; Acct.*

ZIMMERMANN, Joan Kay
Kirkwood HS; Kirkwood, MO (17-592) Orch; Co-Ed, Sch P; SC; Tri-HiY; COM; Curator A; Hon Prog; Journ A; Q&S A; Type A; Co-Cpt, Pom Pon Squad; YMCA Yth in Gov; Gold 'K' Schol A; Gold 'K' Schol A; Pep C; *U of Mo; Journ.*

ZIMMERMANN, Jonathan David
Prosser HS; Prosser, WA (53-156) Demolay; Tr; *W Wash Col; Computer Prog.*

ZIMMERMANN, Robert Louis
Lawrence Central HS; Lawrence, IN (3%-500) Band; Order/Arrow; Hon Prog; NEDT; Eagle Sct; Pres, Sci Fiction C; *Valparaiso U; Broadcasting.*

ZINCK, Laura Ann
Clarkstown Sr HS S; W Nyack, NY (800-900) Bus C; FBLA; Rainbow; Sftbl; Swim; *St Petersburg Jr Col; Data Processing.*

ZINICOLA, Tony John
Highline HS; Burien, WA (72-416) VP, Band; NHS; *Big Bend Comm Col; Airline Pilot.*

ZINK, Sydney Lou
Wilburton HS; Wilburton, OK (15-62) CYO; Cpt, Chldr; Chor; Ensm; FHA; 4H; Hmrm; Sch C; Pres, SC; Tr; Citz A; HQn; *Okla St U; Interior Decorating.*

ZINK, Terrance Leo
Carrington Pub HS; Carrington, ND (5-101) A Cap Choir; Co-Ed, Ann; Band; Chor; Drama; Ensm; VP, FFA; Pres, 4H; Sch P; Star Student; St Prof; European Goodwill Tour; Win, FFA Poultry Production; European Tour Choir; Interntl Peace Gardens.

ZINKEL, Russell Charles Jr
Colonial Christian HS; Homestead, FL (6-32) Chor; Sch P; Yth Fel; Yth Church Organist; *Optometry.*

ZINN, Harry Alexander
El Camino Real HS; Woodland Hills, CA (12-1100) Semi-Fin, BS; Hmrm; Pres, Math C; Pres, Model UN; Spch C; Tres, SC; JV, Tnns; Bank Of Amer A; B Crocker A; CSF; Hist A; Hon Prog; Regent Schol; VP & Tres, Calif Jr St; Eng A; CSF Seymour A; UCLA Alumni Schol; Century III A; *UCLA; Pol Sci.*

ZINN, Tracy Ann
Kickapoo HS; Springfield, MO; Chor; Ensm; Madrigal; VP, SC; Bkbl; Tnns; Tr; COM; *Evangel Col; Phys Ed.*

ZINNECKER, Karen Elaine
Warren Co R III HS; Warrenton, MO (7-115) A Cap Choir; Chor; Drama; Ensm; NHS; Tnns; COM; Secy, Yth Fel; Tr A; *SE Mo St U; Nurs.*

ZINNECKER, Timothy Robert
Warren Co R-III HS; Warrenton, MO (4-111) A Cap Choir; Chor; Drama; Ensm; S-T, FTA; Madrigal; NHS; SC; Tres, Soph Cl; Mgr, Bkbl; Mgr, Ftbl; COM; Chamber of Comm A; Most Out; Regent Schol; Yth Fel; Cpt, MVP, Schol Quiz Tm; Statis, Ftbl; All Conf Pianist; Church Rep, Winter Olympics; Outst St Mus Contest; *Central Mo St U; Acct.*

ZIPAY, Juli Marguerite
Whitney Point Sr HS; Whitney Point, NY (19-150) Secy, Band; Chldr; Chor; VP, 4H; Co-Cpt, Mjrte; VP, NHS; COM; 4H A; HCt; WW; Outst Tn Young Woman; *Broome Comm Col; Radiology Tech.*

ZIPP, Dina Marie
Seguin HS; Seguin, TX (25%-450) Band; Drama; Ch, FHA; Secy, Ger C; Rptr, NHS; Cl Fav; HCt; Hon Prog; Pres A; Luther Charity Coronation; 7th Pl UIL Typing; Fair Qn Contestant; VP And Secy, Luther League; *Tex Lutheran Col; Med.*

ZIPP, Lisa Anne
New Braunfels HS; New Braunfels, TX (6-290) Band; Ensm; FTA; VP, Ger C; Fin, Jr Miss Pagent; Math C; Mu Alpha Theta; Tres, NHS; Sci C; Tres, SC; Parl, Jr Cl; Tr; Amer Leg A; Citz A; Elk A; Rotary A; WW; *U of Tex; Bio.*

ZIPPERER, Dana Ross
A E Beach HS; Savannah, GA (1-325) BC; Math C; Secy, NHS; Sci C; Bsbl; Alg A; Bio A; Citz A; Hist A; Math A; NEDT; Sci A; HR Medal; Sci Fair A; Eng A; Semi-Fin, Govn Hons; *Chem.*

ZIRPEL, David Norbert
Parkston Pub Sch; Parkston, SD (27-86) Band; Chor; VP, Dbte Tm; Drama; Ensm; NFL; Spch C; St Stu Congress; Var C; COM; Spch A; Type A; Declam; Declam A; PA; Band Solo A; Debate Trophys; Farmers Union A; *Augustana Sioux Falls Col; Eng.*

ZIRPS, Nora Ann
Fort Hunt HS; Alexandria, VA (1-446) Fr C; French NHS; Lat C; A-Ed, Lit Mag; Math C; NHS; Bkbl; JV, Hockey; Sunday Sch Teacher; Church Yth Group; GSct; Bkbl Statistician; Cpt, Lat Bowl Tm; *MIT; Math.*

ZITTROWER, Teresa Lynne
Paxon Sr HS; Jacksonville, FL; Anchor C; Band; Rainbow; Sftbl; Hon Band.

ZLOTNICK, Lynn Sue
Eastside HS; Paterson, NJ; Secy, Drama; A-Ed, Lit Mag; NHS; Thes; Zonta C; Horseback Riding C; *Journ.*

ZMUDA, Clara Celeste
St Mary's Acad; Alexandria, VA; Ann; Band; Ensm; S-T, Span NHS; Dance C; Health A; Mus Ed Ntl Conf; *Med.*

ZOBRIST, Keith Harold
Metamora Township HS; Metamora, IL (70-215) BS; NHS; Var C; Bkbl; Co-Cpt, Cr-Ctry; Golf; Co-Cpt, Tr; I Dare You; MVP, Cr-Ctry; *N Central Col; Acct.*

ZOCCOLI, Maria Christina
The Mary Louis Acad; Jamaica Estates, NY (124-307) S-T, All Amer Yth; Drama; Thes; Sftbl; Tnns; COM; Hon Prog; Math A; Italian C; Rap Group; Service & Hon Cert of Hon; MVP, Bowl; JV Vlbl; *Queens Col; Biol Chem.*

ZOCH, Gary Ray
Westbury HS; Houston, TX; Chor; Co-Cpt, Bkbl; Cpt, Ftbl; Cpt, Sftbl; Church Usher; Sr Patrol Ldr & Star Sct; *Tex A&M; Marine Bio.*

ZOELLE, Melissa Lee
Spring Branch HS; Houston, TX (120-549) Cpt, Chldr; FHA; GS; Cpt, Tnns; Beauty; WW; Phys Ed A; *Phys Ed.*

ZOELLICK, Kimberly Lynn
Crystal Lake Comm HS; Crystal Lake, IL (16-484) A Cap Choir; Fr C; FTA; NHS; Bkbl; Tr; Pres A; Cpt, FCA; Gym; Outst Female Ath of; *Elem Ed.*

ZOGLMANN, Sharon Marie
Owensboro Cath HS; Owensboro, KY (9-240) Band; 4H; NHS; Sftbl; COM; 4H A; Hon Prog; NEDT; Opt A; Spch A; *Western Ky U; Vet Med.*

ZOLL, Bonnie Kay
Tinora HS; Defiance, OH; Chor; 4H; ARC; F-Ed, Sch P; Arch; 4H A; Co Jr Fair Board; Jr Ldrship; Campus Life; Co Historical Soc; *Manchester Col; Eng.*

ZOLTON, Cynthia Ann
S River HS; S River, NJ (8-365) Tres, Fr C; Ger C; Math C; NHS; Ski C; Mgr, Bkbl; Mgr, Ftbl; *U of Del; Computer Sci.*

ZONE, Terri Jean
St Joseph Acad; Cleveland, OH (150-232) Secy, CYO; Chor; Bsbl; CYO Off A; *TRI-C Col; Pre-Sch Ed.*

ZOSS, Lisa Marie
Valparaiso Sr HS; Valparaiso, IN; Band; Drama; 4H; NHS; Spch C; Thes; *Purdue U; Phar.*

ZOTTNICK, Diane Lynn
Sentinel HS; Missoula, MT (10%-375) NFL; Spch C; Spch A; *U of Mont; Med.*

ZRUBEK, Julie Ann
Clear Creek HS; League City, TX (1-518) GS; Secy, JETS; Ch, Model UN; Pres, Mu Alpha Theta; NHS; Hon Prog; Rensselaer A; Drill Tm; *Rice U; Engr.*

ZUBEK, Mary Therese
Cleveland Central Cath HS; Cleveland, OH (33-176) Ann; Chor; Drama; NHS; Hon Prog; Drill Tm; Hospital Vol A; Schol, Ntl Col of Ed; *Ntl Col of Ed; Ed.*

ZUCH, Carolyn Lisbeth
Richardson HS; Richardson, TX (21-888) NHS; SC; Tres, Tri-HiY; VP, Soph Cl; Tr; Cpt, Drill Tm; Girls Service League; *U of Tex at Austin; Med.*

ZUEHL, Lori Ann
S St Paul Sr HS; S St Paul, MN; Drama; Ger C; Tr; Vlbl.

ZUERCHER, James Warren
Triway HS; Wooster, OH (33%-183) Dbte Tm; Rptr, Sch P; Cr-Ctry; God & Country A; *Akron U; Mus.*

ZULAK, Rosemary Nadine
Chester HS; Chester, PA; NHS; Hon Prog; Secy.

ZUNIGA, Chris J
E Central HS; Tulsa, OK (1-41) Span C; Citz A; Bowl; *Okla Christian Col; Bible.*

ZUPKE, Cheryl Ann
Saint Joseph HS; Saint Joseph, MI (100-320) VP, Thes; Manassa Cutler Schol; *Ohio U.*

ZURCHER, Janita Ruth
S Adams HS; Berne, IN; A Cap Choir; Chor; Ensm; *Ft Wayne Bible Col; Biblical Stu.*

ZURLIENE, Elizabeth Joan
Central HS; Breese, IL (7-157) Pres, CYO; Drama; Fr C; Pres, Ger C; Model UN; VP, SC; 4H A; St Scholar; WW; *Saint Louis U; Med Technology.*

ZUROWSKI, Thomas Arthur
Tisdale Unit Composite Sch; Tisdale, CANADA (2-97) Hist A.

ZUVAT, Maximilian Steven
Pine Grove Area HS; Pine Grove, PA (20-150) Chor; Drama; *Messiah Col; Religion.*

ZUZUL, Marcia Ann
Orange Park HS; Orange Park, FL; Lat C; Math C; NHS; Sci C; Var C; Drama; Swim; Tr; Bio A; God & Country A; Hon Prog; Sci A; Lat A; Tr A; *U of Fla; Nurs.*

ZWANZIGER, Karl David
Weed HS; Weed, CA (1-65) Band; VP, 4H; Ski C; SC; Pres, Jr Cl; JV, Bkbl; JV, Ftbl; Semi-Fin, Tr; Amer Leg A; CSF; 4H A; Sci A; 4-H Co All Star.

ZWENG, Frederick John
Holy Cross HS; Marine City, MI (2-41) 4H; NHS; Var C; Bsbl; Bkbl; *Archt.*

ZWERNEMAN, Mark David
Pflugerville HS; Pflugerville, TX (10%-110) BC; Rptr, FFA; NHS; Secy, Jr Cl; Citz A; Sci A; Eng A; *U of Tex.*

ZWICK, Maureen Marie
Immaculata Acad; Hamburg, NY (6-79) VP, CYO; Pres, 4H; ARC; *Med.*

ZWICKE, Noreen Elizabeth
Waukegan E HS; Waukegan, IL (46-629) Ger C; JV, Tnns; Outst Ger Stu.

ZWIERS, Gail Susan
Kaukauna HS; Kaukauna, WI (13-366) A Cap Choir; Ann; Band; Chor; Ensm; Ch, FHA; 4H; NHS; Orch; JV, Tnns; 4H A; Q&S A; *U Wis Stevens Point; Fashion Merchandising.*

ZYCH, Leonard John Jr
Weber HS; Chicago, IL (3-231) Chess C; Lat C; NHS; Sci C; JV, Ftbl; Hon Prog; NEDT; Sci A; Stu Ch, Regional Jr Acad of Sci; *U of Loyola; Pathology.*

ZYLBERMINC, Viviana Marcela
Reseda HS; Reseda, CA; Hmrm; InterAct C; VP, NHS; SC; Thes; CSF; *Claremont Men's Col; Pre-Law.*

ZYLKS, Mary Jean
Brazoswood HS; Clute, TX (25%-467) AFS; Lat C; NHS; VP, Orch; God & Country A; Cpt, Drill Tm; WW; Vlbl; Best Dancer; Runner- up, Belle o-t Ball; *Tex A&M U; Acct.*

ZYLSTRA, Donna Jean
Oak Harbor HS; Oak Harbor, WA (7-350) Chor; Madrigal; Secy, NHS; VP, Sr Cl; *Seattle Pacific U; Mus Ed.*

ZYLSTRA, Sylvia Mae
Hiram Johnson Sr HS; Sacramento, CA (9-600) Chor; Co-Ed, Lit Mag; SC; Hon Prog; PTA A; *Seattle Pacific U; Eng Communications.*

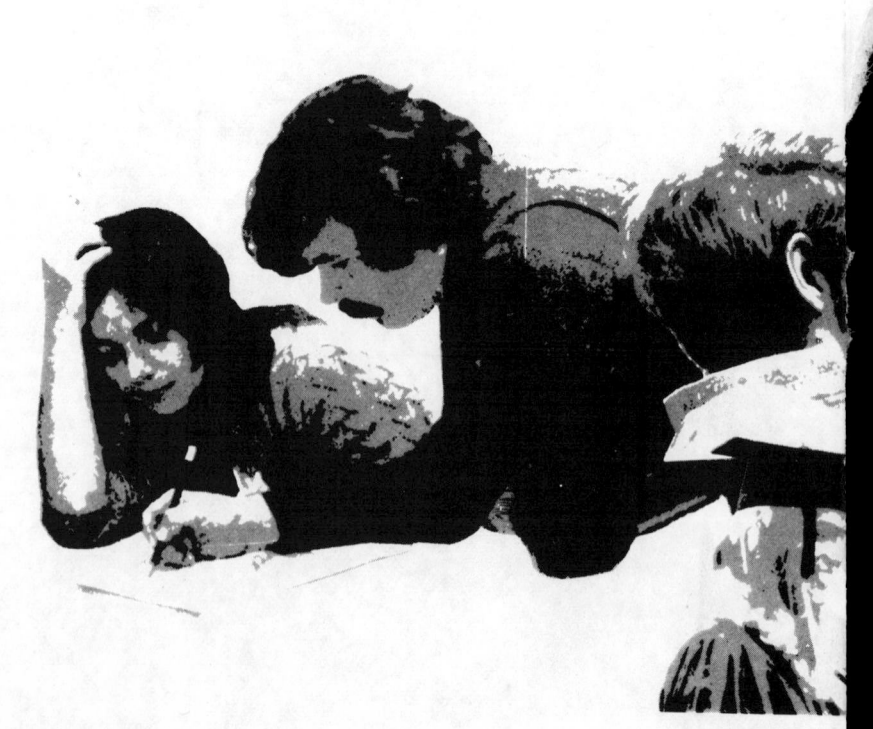